TABLE OF CONTENTS—Continued

Page No.

GENERAL SERVICE

The data reported herein has been compiled from authoritative sources. While every effort is made by the editors to attain accuracy, manufacturing changes as well as typographical errors and omissions may occur. The publisher then cannot be responsible nor does it assume responsibility for such omissions, errors or changes.

MOTOR
AUTO REPAIR MANUAL

GENERAL MOTORS CORPORATION

54th Edition, Volume 1

First Printing

Michael J. Kromida, SAE
Editor

John R. Lypen, SAE
Managing Editor

Warren Schildknecht, SAE
Senior Editor

Christopher P. Jakubowski
Associate Editor

Mark L. Kaufman
Assistant Editor

Timothy P. Kedzior
Assistant Editor

Rick Metcalf
Assistant Editor

Timothey L. Martin
Assistant Editor

Andy Brian
Assistant Editor

Marian A. Merriman
Assistant Editor

Richard F. Cahoon
Assistant Editor

Richard G. Glover
Assistant Editor

Donald R. Cobb
Assistant Editor

Charles R. Burstall
Assistant Editor

Daniel C. Rock
Assistant Editor

Bruce W. Clippert
Assistant Editor

Authorized Publisher Representative

Mark C. Ferrand
Technical Assistance Editor

Lynda Slater
Production Assistant

Vita Green
Editorial Assistant

Published by

MOTOR

Hearst Books/Business Publishing Group,
A Division of The Hearst Corp.

5600 Crooks Road, Troy, MI 48098

Printed in the U.S.A.
© Copyright 1990 by The Hearst Corporation
ISBN 0-87851-691-3

Frank A. Bennack, Jr.
President

Gilbert C. Maurer
Executive Vice-President

Philip D. Shalala
*Group Vice-President
Business Publishing*

Kevin F. Carr
*Publisher
Motor Books*

Randolph A. Hearst
Chairman

Gordon L. Jones
*Vice-President
Hearst Books/Business
Publishing Group*

Nelson J. Maione
*Vice-President &
Resident Controller*

Louis C. Forier, SAE
*Vice-President
Editorial Director
Motor Books*

SERVICE REMINDER & WARNING LAMP RESET PROCEDURES

TABLE OF CONTENTS

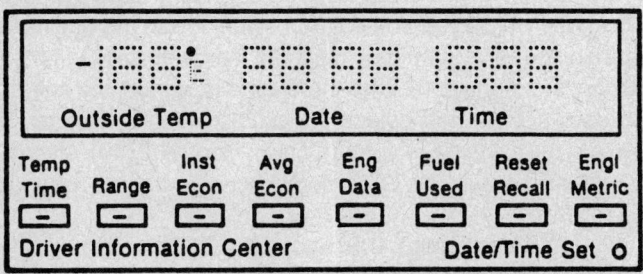

Fig. 1 Driver Information Center. 1986–90 Cadillac Eldorado & Seville

ANTI-LOCK WARNING LAMP

This lamp will be illuminated when the ignition switch is placed in the On position. The lamp may be illuminated for as long as 30 seconds as a bulb and system check. If lamp remains illuminated or comes on while operating the vehicle, a problem in the anti-lock brake system is indicated. When lamp is illuminated, place ignition switch in Off position, then restart engine. If lamp still remains illuminated, the anti-lock brake system should be serviced. The brake system will remain functional, but without the anti-lock function. After servicing the anti-lock brake system the lamp will automatically reset. On some models it may be necessary to operate vehicle at a speed over 18 MPH to reset lamp.

CHANGE OIL OR CHANGE OIL NOW MESSAGE

CADILLAC

1989–90 Eldorado & Seville

When the engine oil life index has reached 0, the Change Engine Oil message will be indicated on the Driver Information Display. After performing the engine oil change, the engine Oil Life Index may be reset by depressing and holding the Engine Data and Range buttons for at least 5 seconds, **Fig. 1.**

OLDSMOBILE

1988–91 Cutlass Calais, Cutlass Ciera, Cutlass Cruiser, Cutlass Supreme, 88 & 98

When the engine oil life index has reached 10 or less, the Driver Information System display will indicate distance to oil change and sound a beep, when ignition switch is placed in the Run or Accessory position for the first time each day. When the engine oil life index has reached 0, the Driver Information System display will indicate Change Oil Now and sound a beep, when ignition switch is placed in the Run or Accessory position for the first time each day. After engine oil change has been performed, the oil life index may be reset by depressing and holding the Oil and Reset buttons for approximately 5 seconds, **Fig. 2.**

1986–90 Toronado

When the engine oil life index has reached 0, the Informa-

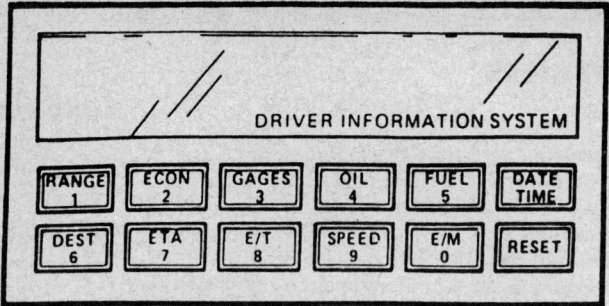

Fig. 2   Driver Information Center. 1988–91 Oldsmobile Cutlass Calais, Cutlass Cutlass Ciera, Cutlass Cruiser, Cutlass Supreme, 88 & 98

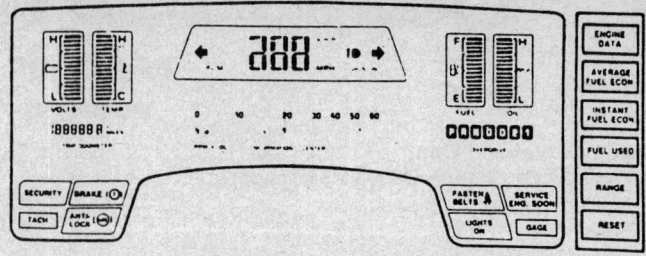

Fig. 3   Information Center. 1986–90 Oldsmobile Toronado

tion System display will indicate Change Oil. After engine oil change has been performed, the oil life index may be reset by depressing and holding the Engine Data and Gauge buttons until Oil Index 100 message appears in Information Display panel, **Fig. 3.**

PONTIAC
6000 STE & BONNEVILLE SSE

After changing engine oil and filter, if necessary, reset service interval indicator by depressing and releasing the service reminder button until the desired item is displayed. When the desired item is displayed, do not release service reminder button. After button has been depressed for approximately 10 seconds, the service interval mileage display will begin to count down in 500 mile intervals. When desired service interval mileage is reached, release button. The service interval reminder indicates miles to service, not miles from last service.

CHECK ENGINE INDICATOR LAMP (DIESEL ENGINE)

MODELS w/DIESEL ELECTRONIC CONTROL SYSTEM

The check engine lamp will be illuminated when the ignition switch is placed in the On position. When the engine is started, the lamp should go off. If the lamp remains On after the engine is started, the self diagnosis system has detected a problem and has stored a code in the system Electronic Control Module (ECM). After diagnosis and repair, the ECM memory can be cleared of codes when the ignition switch has been placed in the Off position. To clear codes, disconnect battery ground cable for approximately 30 seconds. It should be noted, when battery ground cable is disconnected to clear codes, components such as clocks, electronically tuned radios etc., will have to be reset.

CHECK ENGINE OR SERVICE NOW/SOON ENGINE INDICATOR LAMPS (GASOLINE ENGINES w/ELECTRONIC ENGINE CONTROLS OR EFI)

EXCEPT CHEVROLET SPECTRUM & SPRINT, GEO & PONTIAC LEMANS

The check engine lamp will be illuminated when the ignition switch is placed in the On position. When the engine is started, the lamp should go off. If the lamp remains On for 10 seconds or constantly after the engine is started, the self diagnosis system has detected a problem and has stored a code in the system Electronic Control Module (ECM). After diagnosis and repair, the ECM memory can be cleared of codes as follows:

On models except Cadillac with DEFI and 1986-90 Buick Riviera and Toronado, remove the ECM fuse or disconnect the battery ground cable for approximately 30 seconds, with ignition switch in the Off position. It should be noted, if battery ground cable is disconnected to clear codes, components such as clocks, electronically tuned radios etc., will have to be reset.

On vehicle that are equipped as such, the ECM power feed is connected by a pigtail, inline fuse holder, at the positive battery terminal. To clear codes within the ECM system and protect the components that need resetting, disconnect the inline fuse.

On 1980-85 Cadillac models with DEFI engines, depress Electronic Climate Control Off and Hi buttons to clear codes. On 1986-90 Cadillac Deville and Fleetwood models, depress Off and Lo button on the Electronic Climate Control to clear stored BCM codes. Depress Off and Hi to clear stored ECM codes.

On 1986-90 Buick Riviera, Cadillac Eldorado and Seville and Oldsmobile Toronado models, the stored codes are cleared during the self-diagnostic procedure.

CHEVROLET SPECTRUM

The check engine lamp will be illuminated when the ignition switch is in the On position with engine not operating. When engine is started, the Check Engine lamp should go off. If lamp remains on, a code has been stored by the Electronic

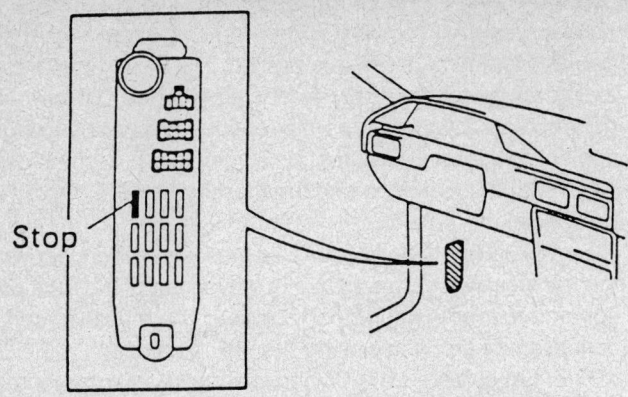

Fig. 4 Stop fuse location. Geo Prizm

When engine is started, the Check Engine lamp should go off. If lamp remains on, a code has been stored by the Electronic Control Unit (ECU) memory. After diagnosis and repair, place ignition switch in Off position, then clear codes stored in the ECU memory by removing the Stop Fuse. The Stop fuse is located in a fuse panel, in the passenger compartment, on driver's side, behind kick panel, **Fig. 4.** The fuse must be removed for 10 seconds or longer, depending on ambient temperature. The lower the ambient temperature, the longer the fuse will have to be removed.

GEO STORM

The check engine lamp will be illuminated when the ignition switch is in the On position with engine not operating. When engine is started, the Check Engine lamp should go off. If lamp remains on, a code has been stored by the Electronic Control Module (ECM) memory. After diagnosis and repair, place ignition switch in Off position, then clear codes stored in the ECM memory by disconnecting the battery ground cable for approximately 30 seconds.

GEO SPECTRUM

The check engine lamp will be illuminated when the ignition switch is in the On position with engine not operating. When engine is started, the Check Engine lamp should go off. If lamp remains on, a code has been stored by the Electronic Control Module (ECM) memory. After diagnosis and repair, place ignition switch in Off position, then clear codes stored in the ECM memory by disconnecting the battery ground cable for approximately 30 seconds.

PONTIAC LEMANS

The check engine lamp will be illuminated when the ignition switch is placed in the On position. When the engine is started, them should go off. If the lamp remains On for 10 seconds or constantly after the engine is started, the self diagnosis system has detected a problem and has stored a code in the system Electronic Control Module (ECM). After diagnosis and repair, the ECM memory can be cleared of codes, by disconnecting battery ground cable for 10 seconds, with ignition switch in the off position.

CHECK INFO CENTER WARNING LAMP

1986–90 CADILLAC ELDORADO & SEVILLE

This lamp will be illuminated for a few seconds when the ignition switch is placed in the On position as a bulb check. If lamp remains illuminated, a message is store in the Driver Information Center. Refer to "Driver Information Center."

CHOKE OR OIL/CHOKE WARNING LAMP

MODELS WITH CARBURETED ENGINE

On models less gauges, the oil/choke warning indicator lamp should be illuminated when the ignition switch is in the

Control Module (ECM). After diagnosis and repair, place ignition switch in Off position, then clear codes stored in the ECM memory by removing the Emission or ECM fuse, located in the fuse box under the instrument panel on the left hand side, for approximately 10 seconds.

CHEVROLET SPRINT

1987–88 Models Less Turbo Engine

The check engine lamp will be illuminated when the ignition switch is in the On position with engine not operating. When engine is started, the Check Engine lamp should go off. If lamp remains on, a code has been stored by the Electronic Control Module (ECM) memory. After diagnosis and repair, with diagnosis switch in Off position, start engine and allow to reach operating temperature. After engine has reached operating temperature, the Check Engine lamp should be off while engine is operating.

1987–88 Models w/Turbo Engine

The check engine lamp will be illuminated when the ignition switch is in the On position with engine not operating. When engine is started, the Check Engine lamp should go off. If lamp remains on, a code has been stored by the Electronic Control Module (ECM) memory. After diagnosis and repair, place ignition switch in Off position, then clear codes stored in the ECM memory by disconnecting the battery ground cable, for approximately 20 seconds.

GEO METRO

The check engine lamp will be illuminated when the ignition switch is in the On position with engine not operating. When engine is started, the Check Engine lamp should go off. If lamp remains on, a code has been stored by the Electronic Control Module (ECM) memory. After diagnosis and repair, place ignition switch in Off position, then clear codes stored in the ECM memory by disconnecting the battery ground cable, for approximately 20 seconds.

GEO PRIZM

The check engine lamp will be illuminated when the ignition switch is in the On position with engine not operating.

Run or Start position. When the engine is started, the choke warning indicator lamp should go off. If the lamp fails to illuminate with ignition switch in Run or Start position with engine not operating, a burnt out bulb or fuse or defect in choke electrical system is indicated. If lamp remains on after engine has been started, a problem in the engine oil pressure system or electrical choke system exist.

On models equipped with gauges, the choke warning indicator lamp should be illuminated when the ignition switch is in the Run or Start position. When the engine is started, the choke warning indicator lamp should go off. If fails to illuminate with ignition switch in Run or Start position with engine not operating, a burnt out bulb or fuse or defect in choke electrical system is indicated. If lamp remains on after engine has been started, a problem in the alternator circuit is indicated.

After service has been completed, the lamp operation should return to normal.

DRIVER INFORMATION CENTER
CADILLAC

1986–88 Cadillac Eldorado & Seville

This system, **Fig. 1,** incorporates a warning lamp, located on the instrument cluster, that is illuminated when the ignition switch is in the On position. After a few seconds the lamp should go off, unless a message in The Driver Information System is present. The driver information center will display the following messages:

A/C Overheated—A/C Compressor Off—This message is displayed when excessive pressure in the refrigerant system is encountered. When this condition is encountered, the A/C compressor clutch will be de-energized and cool air will not be delivered to the vehicle interior. The message will continue to appear and the A/C compressor clutch will continue to be de-energized until the system pressure returns to normal range. If this message frequently appears, the A/C system should be serviced.

A/C Sensor Fault—This message will be displayed when the sensor controlling A/C compressor clutch cycling has failed. When this sensor has failed, the A/C compressor will not operate and the A/C system will emit warmer air. After servicing system and replacing sensor, the display message will be cancelled.

Battery Volts High—This message will appear when the charging system is overcharging the battery. After completing charging system diagnosis and repair, the message will be cancelled when battery voltage returns to 11.5 to 15.5 volts with engine operating. Battery voltage can be displayed on the Drive Information Center Display by depressing the Eng-Data button three times.

Battery Volts Low—If this message is displayed while driving the vehicle or after vehicle has been started, a problem in the charging system is present or battery has been drained. After diagnosing charging system or electrical system for cause of battery drain, the message will be cancelled when engine is operating and battery voltage is between 11.5 to 15.5 volts. Battery voltage can be displayed on the Drive Information Center Display by depressing the Eng-Data button three times.

Engine Hot—A/C Compressor Off—This message will appear when A/C system is on Auto or Defrost and engine coolant temperature is excessive. The A/C compressor clutch will be automatically de-energized when excessive engine coolant temperatures are encountered. When engine coolant temperature returns to normal, the A/C compressor clutch will be energized and the message on the display will be cancelled.

Front Or Rear Door Ajar—This message will appear when the transmission selector lever is moved out of the Park position and a door is not properly closed. The message can be cancelled by properly closing the indicated door.

Fuel Level Very Low—When low fuel level conditions are encountered this message will appear. To cancel message, add fuel.

Headlamps Or Parking Lamps On—This message will be displayed when the headlamp switch is On, vehicle is moving and the sensed level of outside light indicates that headlamps should not be illuminated. This message may be cancelled by placing the headlamp switch in the Off position.

Low A/C Refrigerant—A/C Compressor Off—This message will be displayed when the A/C system detects a refrigerant charge low enough to cause compressor damage. When this condition is encountered, the A/C compressor clutch is de-energized and the A/C system is switched from Auto to Econ. The system will remain in Econ until necessary repairs are made and system is recharged. After completing necessary repairs and recharging the system, A/C system operation will return to normal and the message on the display will be cancelled.

Low A/C Refrigerant—Service A/C Soon—This message will be displayed when the A/C system detects that refrigerant charge is low enough to cause a reduction in cooling capacity. This message will be displayed until system has been recharged.

Low Washer Fluid—This message will appear when windshield washer fluid level is low. To cancel message, refill windshield washer fluid reservoir.

Service Electrical System—This message will appear when a problem in the charging system is present. After repairing charging system, the message will be automatically cancelled.

Service Now Or Service Soon—This message will be displayed when a problem in one the engine monitored systems is present. After diagnosis and repair the message will be automatically cancelled.

System Problem—Service Car Soon—This message will be displayed when one or more of the vehicle computers supplying information to the Driver Information Center become defective. After diagnosis and repair of the defective computer, the message will be automatically cancelled.

Theft System Problem/Car May Not Start—This message will appear when the vehicle security system senses an improper ignition key has been placed in the ignition switch. After removal of key from ignition switch, the Driver Information Center display will indicate "Wait 3 Minutes", "Wait 2 Minutes", Wait 1 Minute" and then "Start Car." When the "Start Car" message appears, insert ignition key and attempt to start vehicle. If message appears again, check ignition key for damage and replace as necessary. If key appears to be satisfactory, clean pellet contacts with a soft cloth and attempt to restart vehicle.

Trunk Open—This message will appear when the ignition switch is the Run position and the trunk is not properly closed. The message can be cancelled by properly closing the trunk.

1989–90 Cadillac Eldorado & Seville

This system incorporates a warning lamp, located on the instrument cluster, that is illuminated when the ignition switch is in the On position. After a few seconds the lamp should go off, unless a message in The Driver Information System is present. The driver information center will display the following messages:

A/C Overheated—A/C Compressor Off—This message is displayed when excessive pressure in the refrigerant system is encountered. When this condition is encountered, the A/C Compressor clutch will be de-energized and cool air will not be delivered to the vehicle interior. The message will continue to appear and the A/C compressor clutch will continue to be de-energized until the system pressure returns to normal range. If this message frequently appears, the A/C system should be serviced.

A/C Sensor Fault—This message will be displayed when the sensor controlling A/C compressor clutch cycling has failed. When this sensor has failed, the A/C compressor will not operate and the A/C system will emit warmer air. After servicing system and replacing sensor, the display message will be cancelled.

Battery Volts High—This message will appear when the charging sys tem is overcharging the battery. After completing charging system diagnosis and repair, the message will be cancelled when battery voltage returns to 11.5 to 15.5 volts with engine operating. Battery voltage can be displayed on the Drive Information Center Display by depressing the Eng-Data button three times.

Battery Volts Low—If this message is displayed while driving the vehicle or after vehicle has been started, a problem in the charging system is present or battery has been drained. After diagnosing charging system or electrical system for cause of battery drain, the message will be cancelled when engine is operating and battery voltage is between 11.5 to 15.5 volts. Battery voltage can be displayed on the Drive Information Center Display by depressing the Eng-Data button three times.

Change Engine Oil—When the engine oil life index has reached 0, the Change Engine Oil message will be indicated. After performing the engine oil change, the engine Oil Life Index may be reset by depressing and holding the Engine Data and Range buttons for at least 5 seconds

Cooling Fan Fault—This message will appear when the engine cooling fan system inoperative. After repairing cooling fan system the message will be automatically cancelled.

Engine Hot—A/C Compressor Off—This message will appear when A/C system is Auto or Defrost and engine coolant temperature is excessive. The A/C compressor clutch will be automatically de-energized when excessive engine coolant temperatures are encountered. When engine coolant temperature returns to normal, the A/C compressor clutch will be energized and the message on the display will be cancelled.

Front Or Rear Door Ajar—This message will appear when the transmission selector lever is moved out of the Park position and a door is not properly closed. The message can be cancelled by properly closing the indicated door.

Fuel Level Very Low—When low fuel level conditions are encountered this message will appear. To cancel message, add fuel.

Gear Select Problem—This message will appear if a problem in the transaxle gear select system is encountered while operating vehicle. After performing necessary service, the message will automatically be cancelled.

Headlamps Or Parking Lamps On—This message will be displayed when the headlamp switch is On, vehicle is moving and the sensed level of outside light indicates that headlamps should not be illuminated. This message may be cancelled by placing the headlamp switch in the Off position.

Headlamps Suggested—This message will be displayed when the Twilight Sentinel is in the Off position, vehicle is moving and the sensed level of outside light indicates that headlamps should be illuminated. This message may be cancelled by activating the Twilight Sentinel System.

Low A/C Refrigerant—A/C Compressor Off—This message will be displayed when the A/C system detects a refrigerant charge low enough to cause compressor damage. When this condition is encountered, the A/C compressor clutch is de-energized and the A/C system is switched from Auto to Econ. The system will remain in Econ until necessary repairs are made and system is recharged. After completing necessary repairs and recharging the system, A/C system operation will return to normal and the message on the display will be cancelled.

Low A/C Refrigerant—Service A/C Soon—This message will be displayed when the A/C system detects that refrigerant charge is low enough to cause a reduction in cooling capacity. This message will be displayed until system has been recharged.

Low Washer Fluid—This message will appear when windshield washer fluid level is low. To cancel message, refill windshield washer fluid reservoir.

Oil Life Index—The oil life index is a series of numerals ranging from 0 to 100. The 100 is indicated when engine oil has been drained and replacement engine oil has been installed. The 0 is an indication that the engine oil should be changed. The oil life index is accessed by depressing the Engine Data button four times.

Service Electrical System—This message will appear when a problem in the charging system is present. After repairing charging system, the message will be automatically cancelled.

Set Timing Mode—This message will appear if ignition timing is improperly set. After performing necessary service, the message will be automatically cancelled.

Starting Disabled/Due to Theft System/Remove Ignition Key—This message is an indication of a problem in the vehicle security system that may prohibit the vehicle from being restarted after the ignition switch has been placed in the Off position. After servicing the vehicle security system the message will be automatically cancelled.

System Ok—This message will be displayed for approximately 5 seconds after ignition switch has been placed in the On position, unless a problem in the system has been detected. After approximately 5 seconds the display will return to the last display function selected.

System Problem—Service Car Soon—This message will be displayed when one or more of the vehicle computers supplying information to the Driver Information Center become defective. After diagnosis and repair of the defective computer, the message will be automatically cancelled.

Theft System Problem/Car May Not Start—This message will appear when the vehicle security system senses an improper ignition key has been placed in the ignition switch. After remove key from ignition switch, the Driver Information Center display will indicate "Wait 3 Minutes", "Wait 2 Minutes", Wait 1 Minute" and then "Start Car." When the "Start Car" message appears, insert ignition key and attempt to start vehicle. If message appears again, check ignition key for damage and replace as necessary. If key appears to be satisfactory, clean pellet contacts with a soft cloth and attempt to restart vehicle.

Trunk Open—This message will appear when the ignition switch is the Run position and the trunk is not properly closed. The message can be cancelled by properly closing the trunk.

PONTIAC 6000 STE & BONNEVILLE SSE

The Driver Information Center Display, **Fig. 5**, is located on the instrument panel. When the ignition switch is placed in the On position, the display will go through a bulb check, in which the vehicle graph and message title will be displayed in sequence. After the sequence has been completed, all messages and vehicle graph will remain illuminated for approximately 2 seconds. After approximately 2 seconds, if all monitored systems are functioning properly, the message titles should go off and only the vehicle outline should be illuminated. If a problem in any of the monitored systems is present, the particular title for the monitored system will be illuminated and its approximate location on the vehicle graphic display will be illuminated. The following messages will be displayed:

1. **Function Monitor**—The coolant level, fuel level and windshield washer levels are monitored when ignition switch is the On position.
   a. **Coolant Level**—This message will be indicated when engine coolant level in the radiator drops below a pre-determined level. To cancel message, check cooling system, then add coolant to bring system to proper level.
   b. **Fuel Level**—This message will be indicated when fuel level is 5 gallons or less. To cancel message add fuel to fuel tank.
   c. **Washer Fluid**—This message will be indicated when windshield washer fluid is at about 40% of capacity. To cancel message, add washer fluid to reservoir.

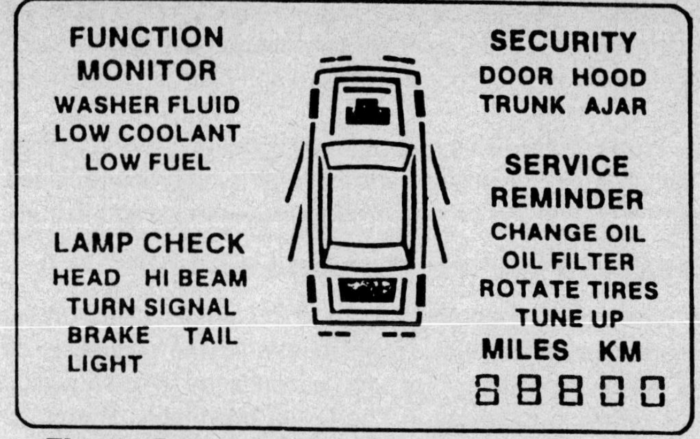

Fig. 5 Driver Information Center. Pontiac 6000 STE & Bonneville SSE

2. **Lamp Check**—The headlamps, tail lamps, brake lamps and turn signal lamps will be checked whenever the lamp system is activated. To cancel this message, replace bulb or check and repair electrical system as necessary for lamp system indicated.

3. **Security**—Door, Hood Or Trunk Ajar are monitored. This message will appear when the indicated component is open or improperly closed. To cancel message, properly close indicated component.

4. **Service Reminder**—Oil change, oil filter change, engine tune-up and tire rotation intervals are monitored.
   a. After the bulb check sequence has been completed, the service interval can be checked by depressing the service reminder button. Depressing the button once will display the Change Oil indication and mileage remaining to service interval. Depressing the button a second time, will display the Change Oil Filter indication and mileage remaining to service interval. Depressing the button a third time will display the Rotate Tires and mileage to service interval. Depressing the button a fourth time will display Tune-Up indication and mileage to service interval.
   b. After completing the required service, reset service interval indicator by depressing and releasing the service reminder button until the desired item is displayed. When the desired item is displayed, do not release service reminder button. After button has been depressed for approximately 10 seconds, the service interval mileage display will begin to count down in 500 mile intervals. When desired service interval mileage is reached, release button. The service interval reminder indicates miles to service, not miles from last service.

EMISSION OR SENSOR MAINTENANCE REMINDER FLAG 1980 MODELS & 1981–83 CADILLAC LIMOUSINE & COMMERCIAL CHASSIS

At 30,000 mile intervals, a Emission or Sensor reminder flag, if equipped, will appear across the odometer to indicate the need for oxygen sensor replacement. After performing the required service, the flag must be reset for the next 30,000 mile interval.

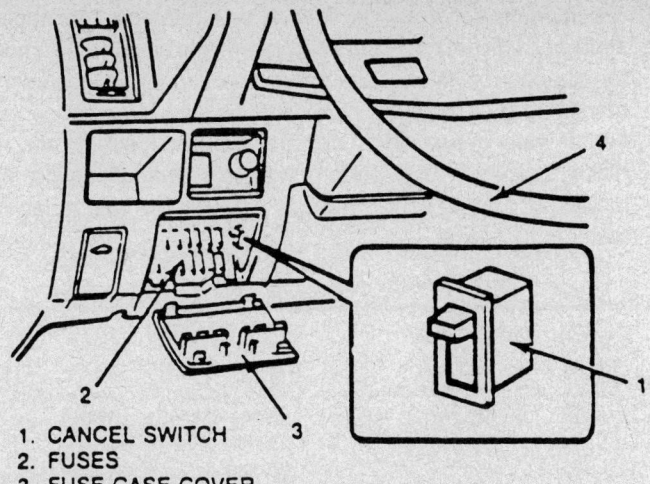

1. CANCEL SWITCH
2. FUSES
3. FUSE CASE COVER
4. STEERING WHEEL

Fig. 6   Oxygen sensor indicator lamp cancel switch. 1985–86 Chevrolet Sprint

On models except Cadillac, this is accomplished by gaining access to the speedometer head and removing the speedometer lens. Using a suitable pointed tool, rotate edge of flag wheel detents downward, until flag wheel can no longer be rotated. Flag wheel alignment mark should center in odometer.

On Cadillac models, remove lower steering column cover, then lightly pull sensor reset cable to reset flag. The sensor reset cable is located to the left of the speedometer cluster.

ENGINE CONTROL SYSTEM WARNING LAMP

1986–90 CADILLAC ELDORADO & SEVILLE

This lamp will be illuminated for a few seconds when the ignition switch is placed in On position as a bulb check. If lamp remains on, a problem in one of the emission control systems is indicated. The Driver Information Center should indicate a Service Soon or Service Now message. Refer to "Driver Information Center."

LOW COOLANT LAMP

This lamp will be illuminated when engine coolant level in the radiator drops below a pre-determined level. To turn lamp off, check cooling system, then add coolant to bring system to proper level.

OXYGEN SENSOR MAINTENANCE REMINDER LAMP

1985–86 CHEVROLET SPRINT

A Sensor lamp is located on the instrument panel to indicate proper operation of the oxygen sensor feedback circuit. Every 30,000 miles of vehicle operation, the lamp will begin to flash. When the lamp begins to flash, the feedback circuit should be checked and the lamp reset using the following procedure.

1. Ensure that ignition switch is off, remove fuse panel cover and move cancel switch to on position, **Fig. 6.**
2. Turn ignition switch to On position and observe Sensor lamp. If lamp does not light (without flashing), check for defective bulb or open feed circuit and repair as needed.
3. After illumination of lamp is confirmed, start engine and run until it reaches normal operating temperature.
4. Run engine at 1500-2000 RPM while observing lamp.
5. If lamp flashes, system is operating properly. If lamp does not flash, a problem in the Computer Controlled Emission Control System may be indicated.
6. After proper system operation has been verified, place cancel switch in off position to reset automatic indicator system.

SERVICE AIR COND LAMP

CADILLAC

This lamp will be illuminated when the A/C system detects a low refrigerant charge. The lamp will be illuminated for approximately 2 seconds after ignition switch has been placed in the On position as a bulb check.

If while operating vehicle, the lamp illuminates for approximately 60 seconds and then goes off, the refrigerant level is low enough to cause reduced cooling capacity. At this point the blower motor will increase speed to try to offset the loss in cooling capacity. The lamp will be automatically reset after system has been checked and refrigerant charge has been brought to proper level.

If lamp is illuminated for approximately 60 seconds after engine start up, the refrigerant charge may be low enough to cause A/C compressor damage. When this condition is encountered, the A/C compressor clutch is de-energized and the A/C system is switched from Auto to Econ. The system will remain in Econ until necessary repairs are made and system is recharged. After completing necessary repairs and recharging the system, A/C system operation will return to normal and the lamp will be automatically reset.

SERVICE ELECTRICAL SYSTEM LAMP

CADILLAC

This lamp will be illuminated when a problem in the charging system is present. The lamp will be illuminated during engine starting as a bulb check. If lamp is illuminated while engine is operating, the charging system should be checked. After repairing charging system, the lamp will be automatically reset.

WATER IN FUEL OR DRAIN FUEL FILTER WARNING LAMP

MODELS w/DIESEL ENGINE

The water in fuel indicator will be illuminated when excessive water has entered the fuel system. As the fuel filter becomes plugged, a low pressure sensor activates the lamp. The lamp will be illuminated during engine starting as a bulb check. Once the engine has started, the lamp should go off. If the lamp is illuminated intermittently, drain fuel filter. If lamp remains illuminated, drain fuel filter. If the lamp still remains on after fuel filter has been drained, replace fuel filter. If lamp is illuminated during high speed operation or during heavy acceleration, replace fuel filter. If after starting, the engine stalls and will not restart and lamp remains illuminated, check for plugged fuel filter or fuel lines. If this condition occurs immediately after refueling, check fuel tank for large concentration of water in fuel, and if necessary purge fuel tank and replace fuel filter. After performing the required service, the increased fuel pressure through the fuel filter will reset the water in fuel lamp.

VEHICLE LIFT POINTS

INDEX

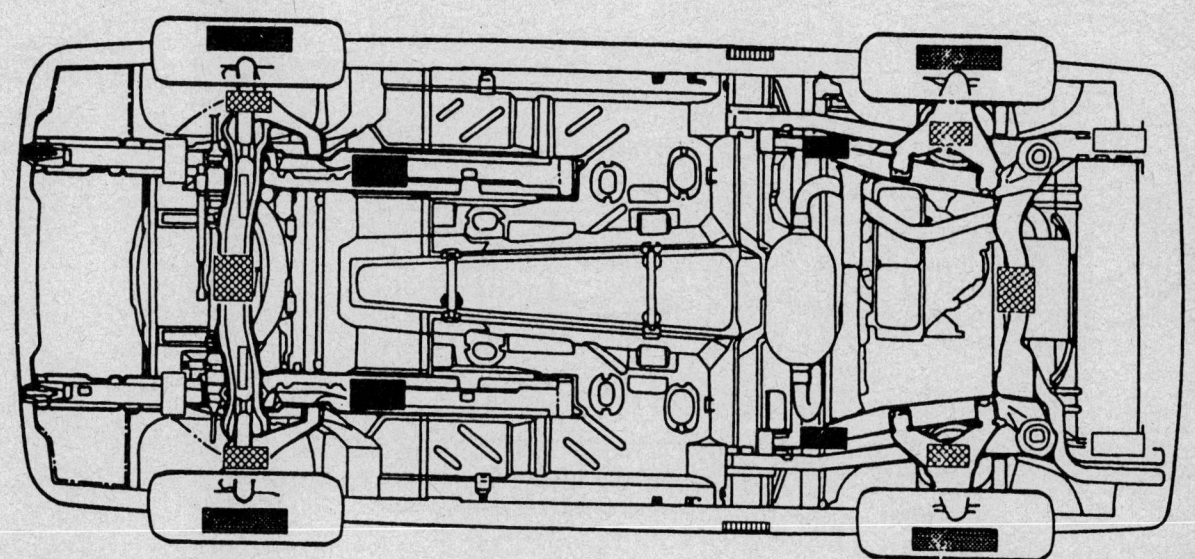

FRAME/BODY
CONTACT HOIST

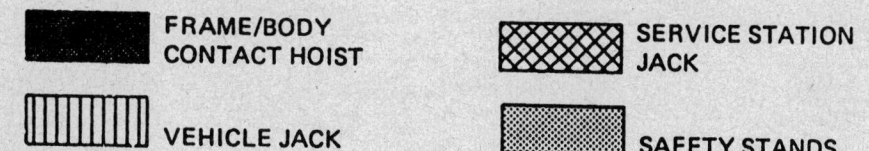

SERVICE STATION
JACK

WHEEL LIFT
HOIST

VEHICLE JACK

SAFETY STANDS

Fig. 1 Fiero

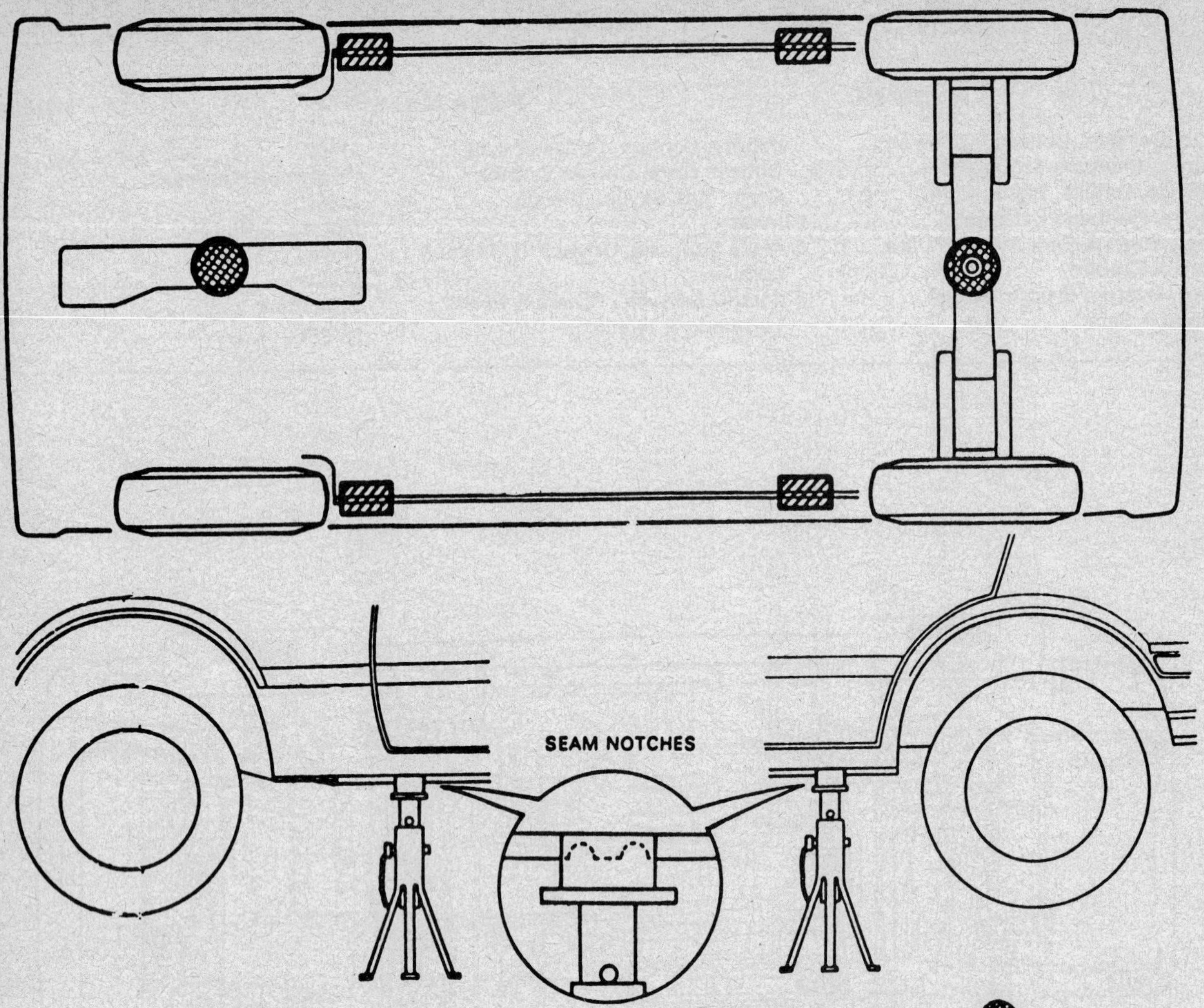

VEHICLE LIFT POINTS

SEAM NOTCHES

JACK POSITION

Front .... Center of engine mounting center member

Rear .... Jack up support of rear floor pan

SUPPORT POSITION

Safety stand ....

Fig. 2   Nova

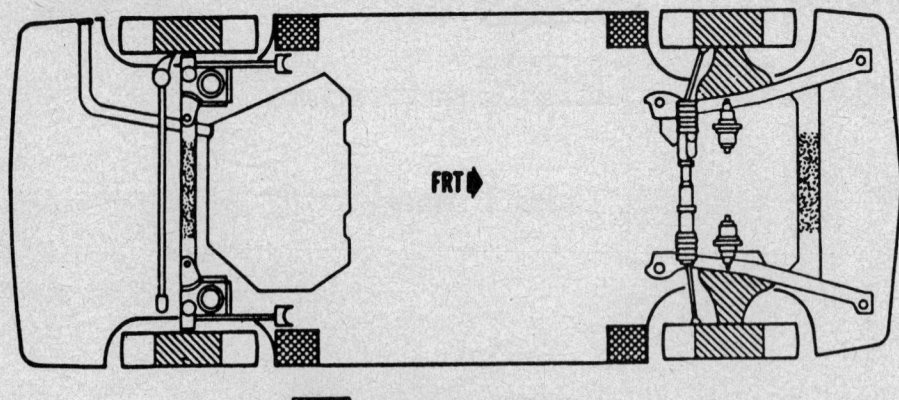

FRT

FRAME CONTACT HOIST

FLOOR JACK

SUSPENSION CONTACT HOIST

Fig. 3   Celebrity, Century, Cutlass Calais, Cutlass Ciera, Cutlass Cruiser, Grand Am, Skylark & 6000

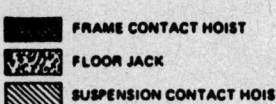

FRT

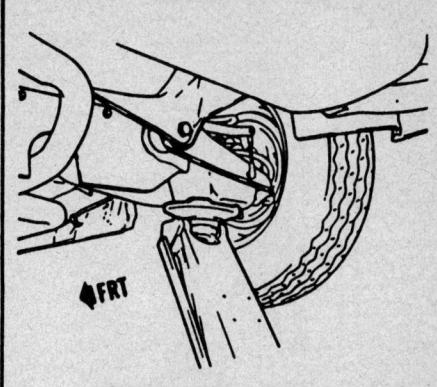

FRAME CONTACT HOIST

FLOOR JACK

SUSPENSION CONTACT HOIST

USING FLOOR JACK UNDER
REAR CONTROL ARM

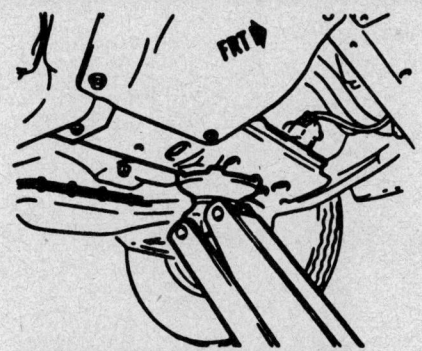

WHEN USING FLOOR JACK, LIFT
ON CENTER OF FRONT CROSSMEMBER

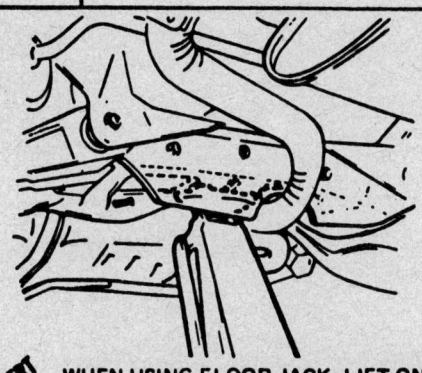

WHEN USING FLOOR JACK, LIFT ON
REAR SUSPENSION CENTER SUPPORT

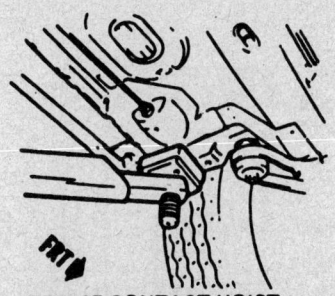

FRAME CONTACT HOIST
(REARWARD OF FRONT TIRE)

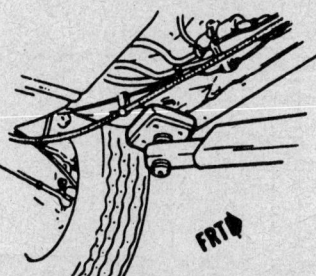

FRAME CONTACT HOIST
(FORWARD OF REAR TIRE)

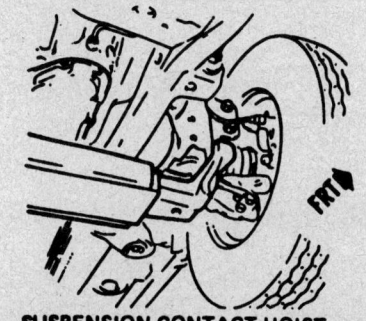

SUSPENSION CONTACT HOIST
(UNDER FRONT LOWER CONTROL ARM)

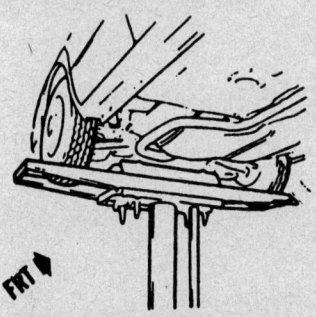

SUSPENSION CONTACT HOIST
(LIFTING ON REAR TIRES)

Fig. 4 Bonneville, DeVille, Eighty-Eight, Electra, Fleetwood, LeSabre, Nintey-Eight & Park Avenue/Ultra

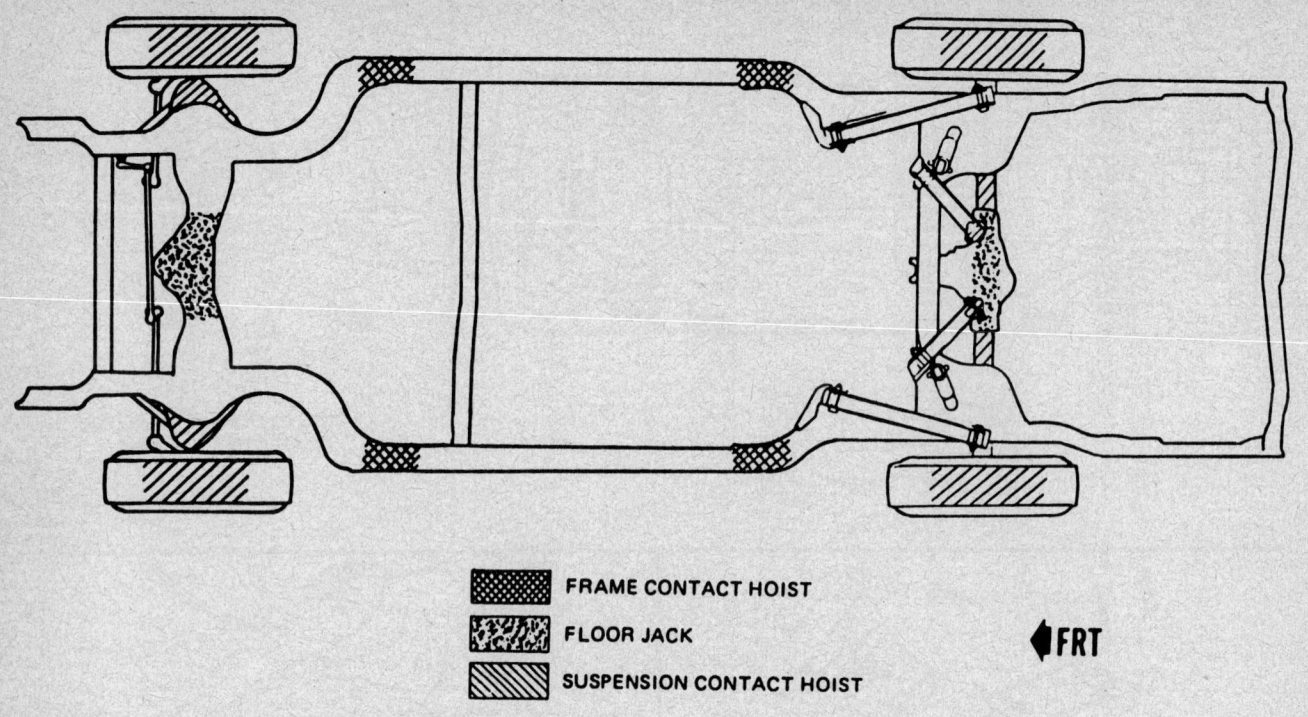

FRAME CONTACT HOIST
FLOOR JACK
SUSPENSION CONTACT HOIST

◀ FRT

Fig. 5   Caprice, Custom Cruiser, Estate Wagon & Safari

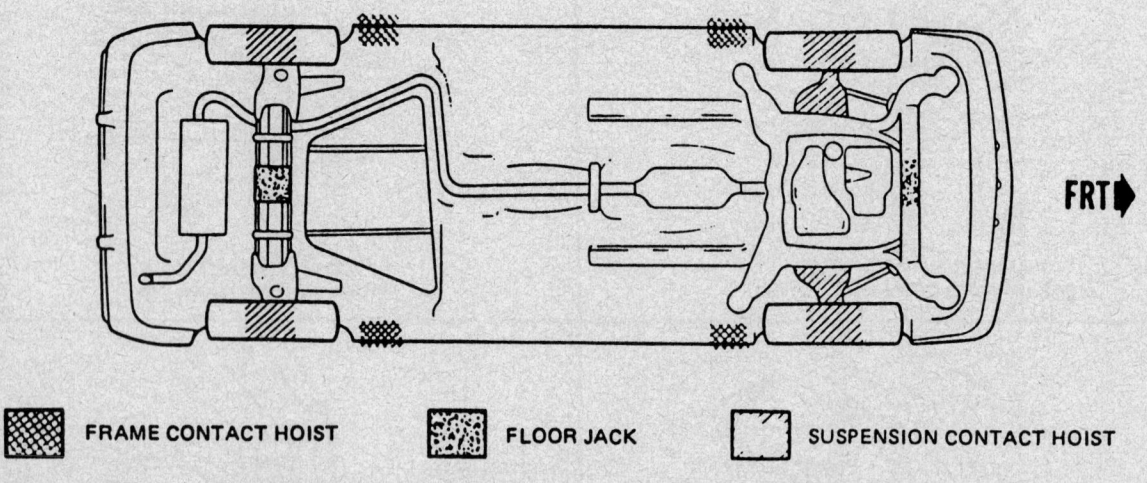

FRT ▶

FRAME CONTACT HOIST   FLOOR JACK   SUSPENSION CONTACT HOIST

Fig. 6   Eldorado & Seville, Riviera & Reatta, Toronado & Trofeo

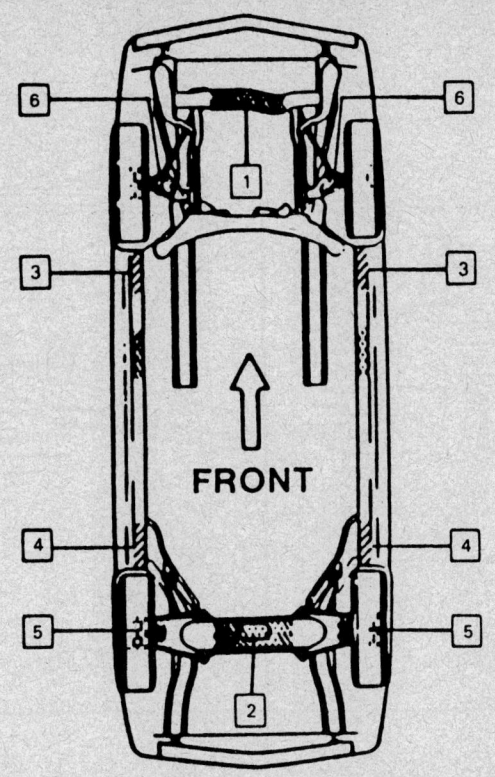

CAUTION: Use jacking pad only for raising the vehicle with a floor jack. Do not use lateral links, trailing arm or jacking pad for pulling or towing the vehicle.

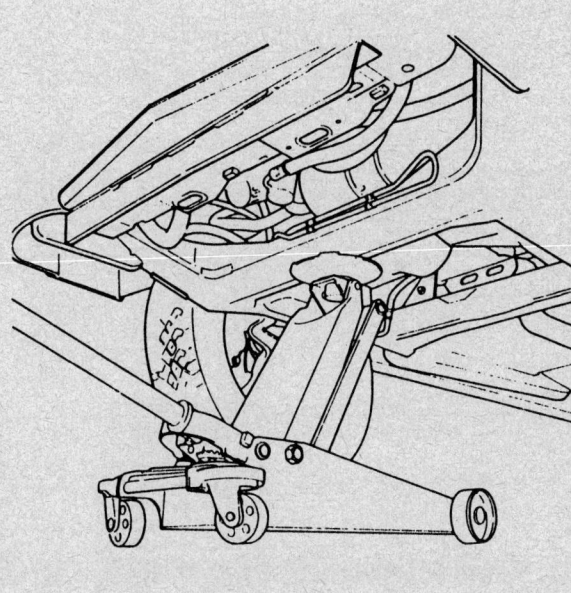

1 WHEN USING FLOOR JACK, LIFT ON CENTER OF FRONT CROSSMEMBER

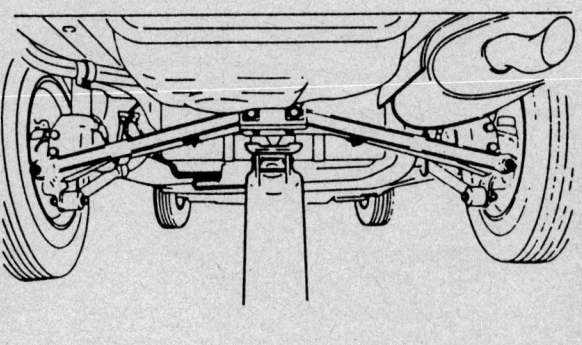

2 WHEN USING FLOOR JACK, LIFT ON REAR JACK PAD

Fig. 7 Cutlass Supreme, Grand Prix, Regal & Lumina (Part 1 Of 2)

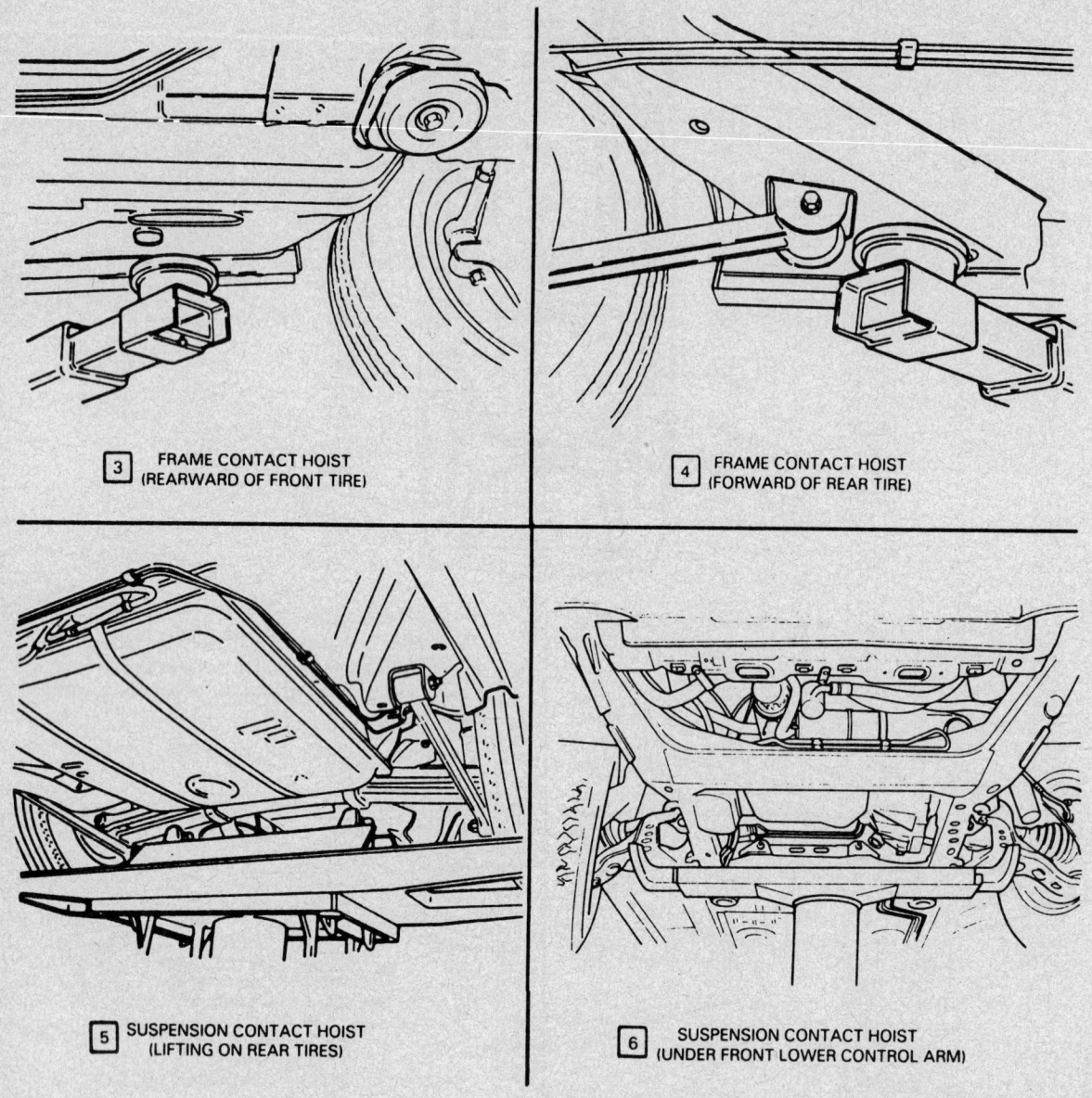

3 FRAME CONTACT HOIST
(REARWARD OF FRONT TIRE)

4 FRAME CONTACT HOIST
(FORWARD OF REAR TIRE)

5 SUSPENSION CONTACT HOIST
(LIFTING ON REAR TIRES)

6 SUSPENSION CONTACT HOIST
(UNDER FRONT LOWER CONTROL ARM)

Fig. 7 Cutlass Supreme, Grand Prix, Regal & Lumina (Part 2 Of 2)

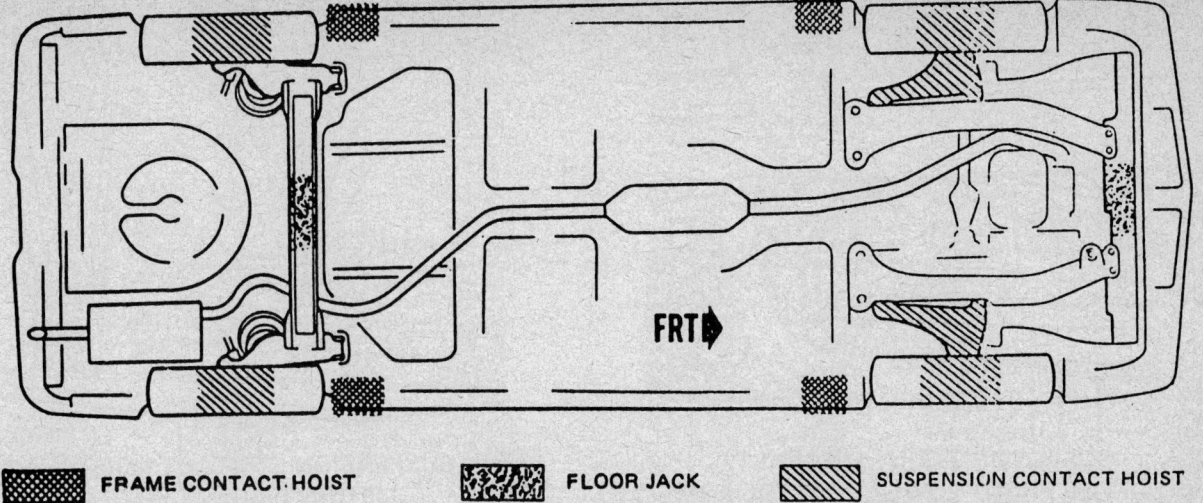

▓ FRAME CONTACT HOIST	▓ FLOOR JACK	▨ SUSPENSION CONTACT HOIST

Fig. 8   Beretta, Cavalier, Cimarron, Corsica, Firenza, Skyhawk & Sunbird

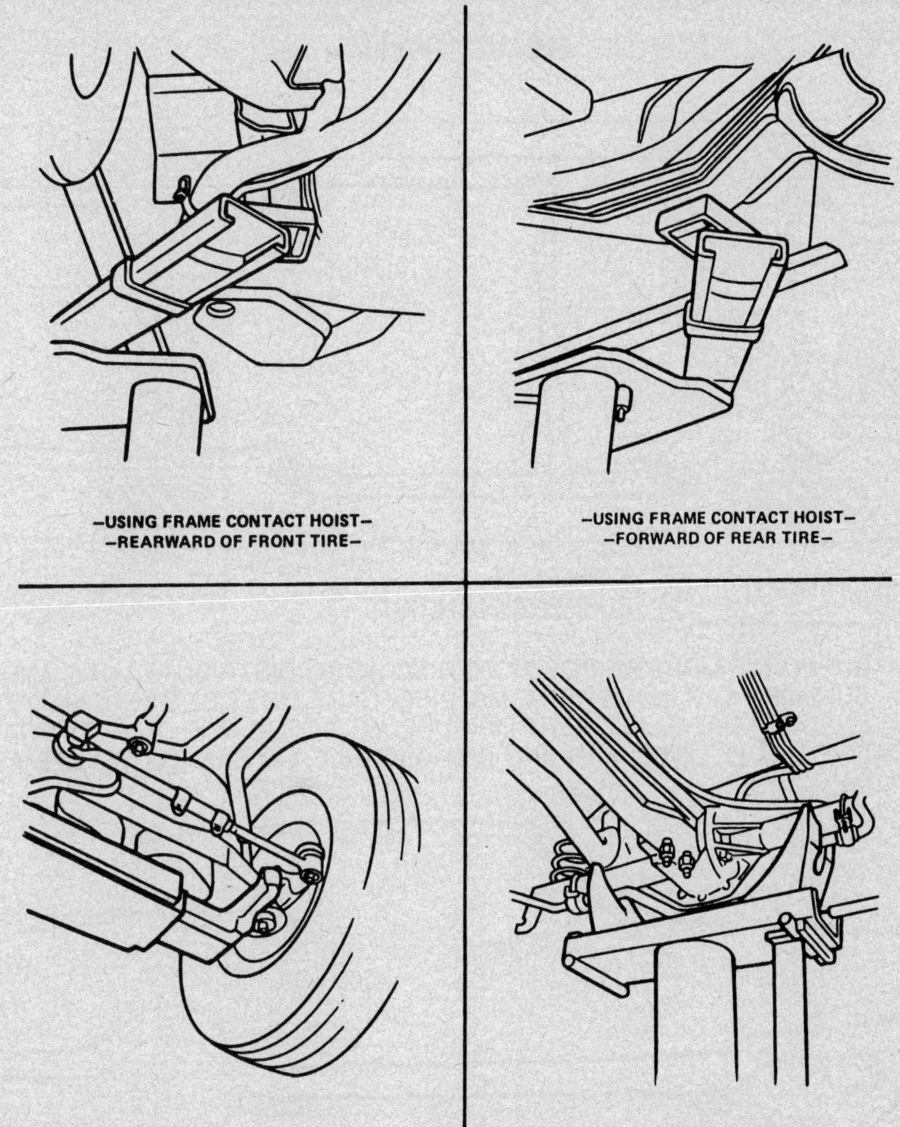

—USING FRAME CONTACT HOIST—
—REARWARD OF FRONT TIRE—

—USING FRAME CONTACT HOIST—
—FORWARD OF REAR TIRE—

—USING SUSPENSION CONTACT HOIST—
—UNDER FRONT LOWER CONTROL ARM—

—USING SUSPENSION CONTACT HOIST—
—LIFTING ON REAR AXLE—

Fig. 9   Camaro & Firebird

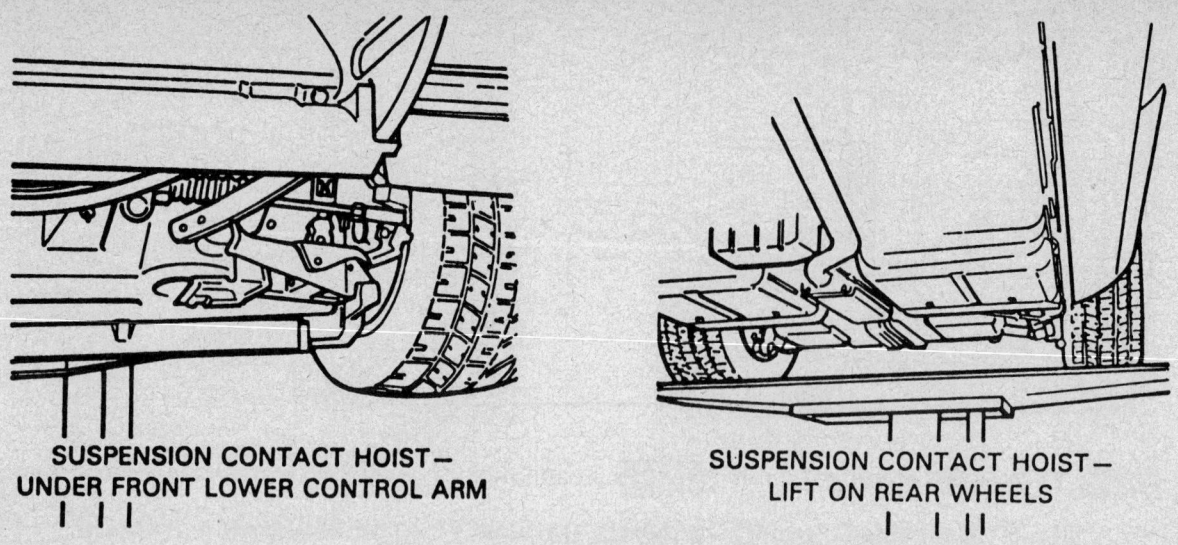

SUSPENSION CONTACT HOIST—
UNDER FRONT LOWER CONTROL ARM

SUSPENSION CONTACT HOIST—
LIFT ON REAR WHEELS

Fig. 10   Corvette

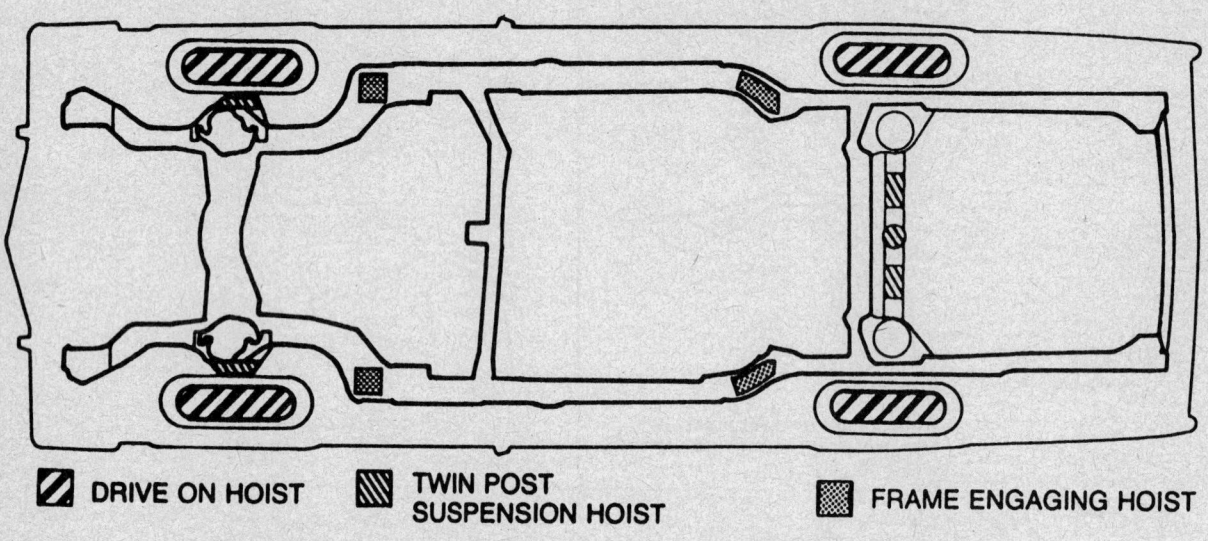

▧ DRIVE ON HOIST   ▨ TWIN POST SUSPENSION HOIST   ▦ FRAME ENGAGING HOIST

SUPPORTS MUST BE POSITIONED SO AS TO DISTRIBUTE LOAD AND
SUPPORT CAR IN A STABLE MANNER. CARE MUST BE EXERCISED TO
ENSURE THAT PLACEMENT OF SUPPORTS DOES NOT DAMAGE BRAKE
LINES, FUEL LINES, PARKING BRAKE CABLE, OR EXHAUST SYSTEM.

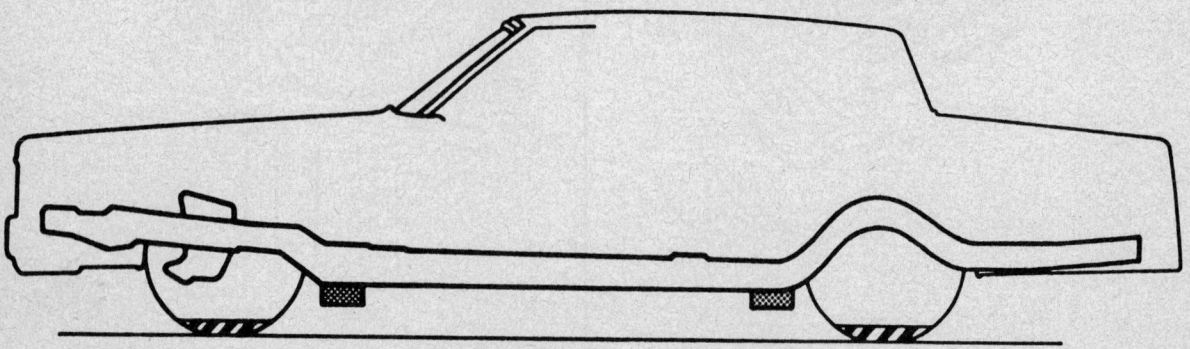

Fig. 11   Fleetwood Brougham

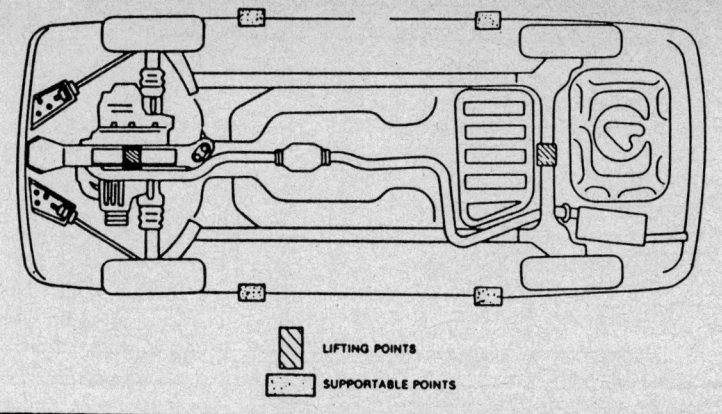

LIFTING POINTS

SUPPORTABLE POINTS

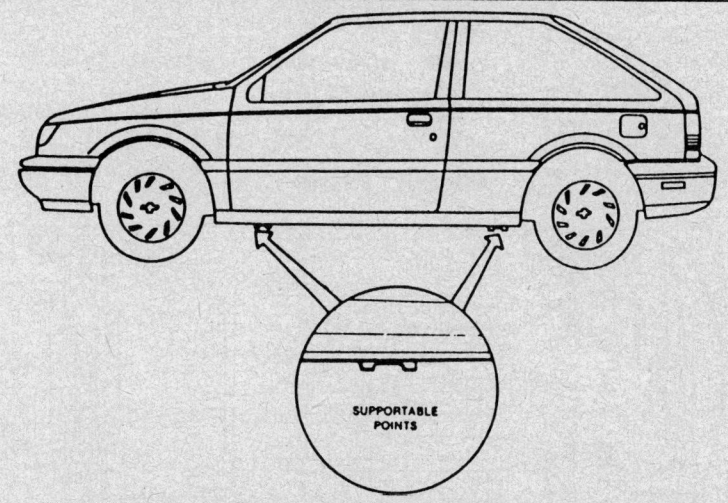

SUPPORTABLE POINTS

Fig. 12   Spectrum

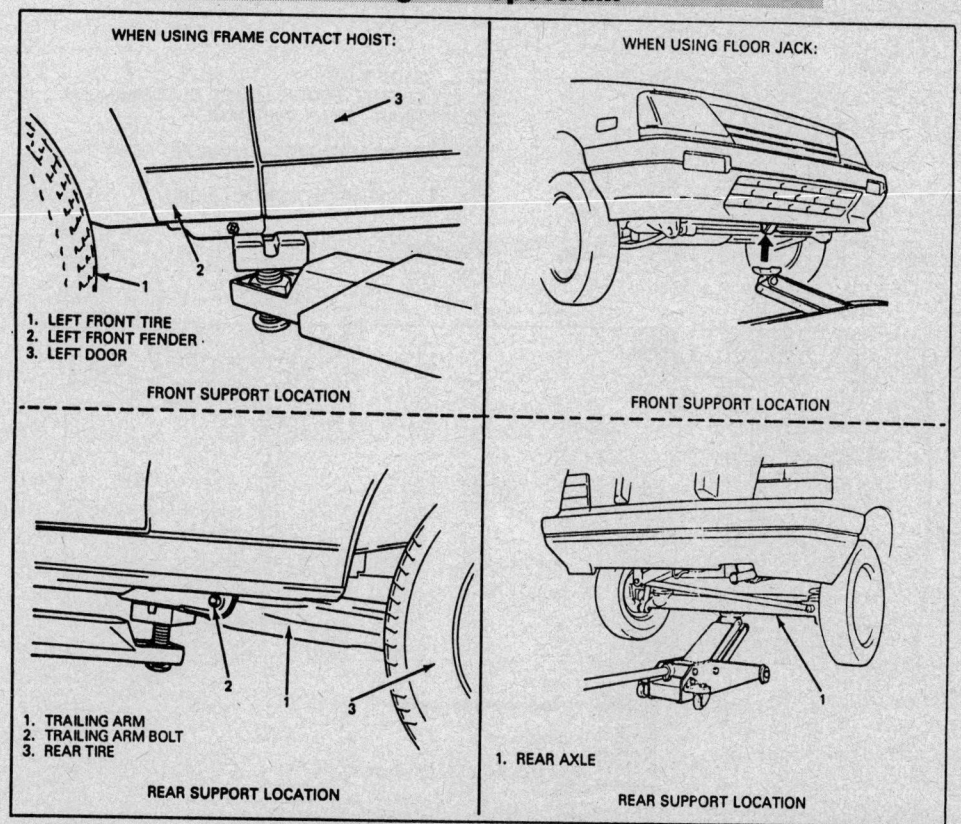

WHEN USING FRAME CONTACT HOIST:

3

2

1

1. LEFT FRONT TIRE
2. LEFT FRONT FENDER
3. LEFT DOOR

FRONT SUPPORT LOCATION

WHEN USING FLOOR JACK:

FRONT SUPPORT LOCATION

2

1

3

1. TRAILING ARM
2. TRAILING ARM BOLT
3. REAR TIRE

REAR SUPPORT LOCATION

1

1. REAR AXLE

REAR SUPPORT LOCATION

Fig. 13   Metro & Sprint

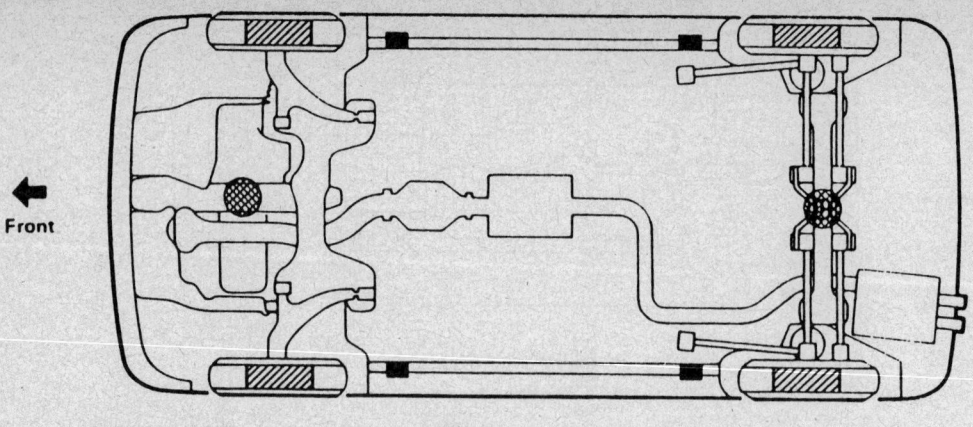

SUSPENSION CONTACT HOIST

FRAME CONTACT HOIST/SAFETY STAND

FLOOR JACK
FRONT . . .ENGINE LOWER CROSSMEMBER
REAR . . .REAR SUBFRAME

Fig. 14   Prizm

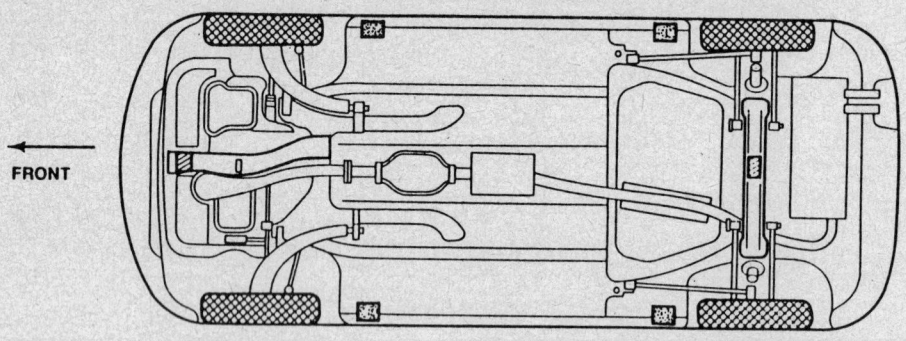

FLOOR JACK
FRONT... ENGINE LOWER CROSSMEMBER
REAR... REAR SUBFRAME

FRAME CONTACT HOIST/SAFETY STAND

SUSPENSION CONTACT HOIST

Fig. 15   Storm

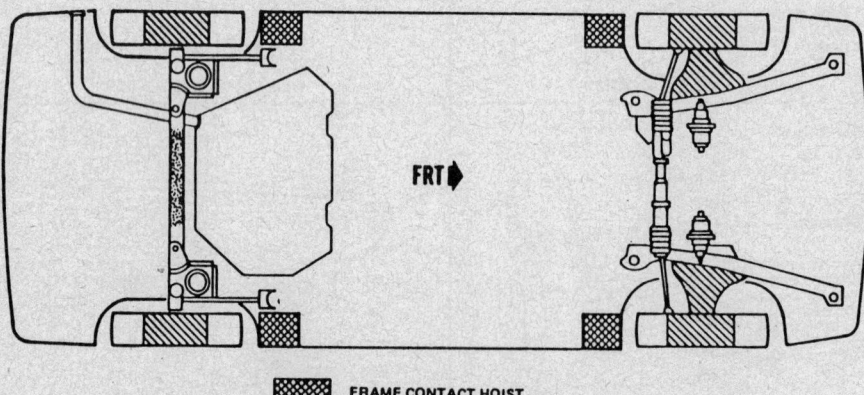

FRAME CONTACT HOIST

FLOOR JACK

SUSPENSION CONTACT HOIST

Fig. 16   LeMans

VEHICLE IDENTIFICATION

TABLE OF CONTENTS

BUICK
V.I.N. DEFINED

1st POSITION
COUNTRY
- 1 = United States
- 2 = Canada

2nd POSITION
MANUFACTURER
- G = General Motors

3rd POSITION
DIVISION
- 4 = Buick
- 7 = GM of Canada

4th POSITION
CARLINE CODE
- A = Century
- B = LeSabre, Electra (RWD)
- B = Estate Wagon (RWD)
- C = Electra (FWD)
- D = Electra (RWD)
- E = Riviera/Reatta
- G = Regal
- H = LeSabre (FWD)
- J = Skyhawk
- N = Somerset Regal/Skylark
- W = Regal
- X = Skylark

5th POSITION, 1985-88
CARLINE SERIES
- B = Skylark Custom
- C = Skylark Limited
- D = Skylark Sport
- E = Skylark T-Type
- F = Electra T-Type
- G = Century Sport
- H = Century Custom
- J = Regal/Somerset
- K = Regal/Somerset
- L = Century Limited
- M = Regal/Somerset Limited
- N = LeSabre Custom
- P = Lesabre Limited
- R = Electra Limited
- S = Skyhawk Custom
- T = Skyhawk Limited
- U = Park Avenue (RWD)
- V = Electra Estate
- W = Park Avenue (FWD)
- X = Electra Limited (FWD)
- Y = Riviera T-TYPE
- Z = Riviera Luxury

5th POSITION, 1989-91
CARLINE SERIES
- B = Regal Custom
- C = Reatta/Skylark
- D = Regal/Skylark Limited
- E = Skyhawk Sport
- F = Electra T-Type
- H = Century Custom
- J = Skylark Custom 2 Door
- K = Regal / Somerset
- L = Century Limited
- L = Estate Wagon

5th POSITION (CONTINUED)
- M = Skylark Limited
- M = Skylark Grand Sport
- P = Lesabre Custom
- R = LeSabre Limited
- R = LeSabre Estate Wagon
- S = Skyhawk Custom
- U = Elect Park Ave (Ultra)
- V = Electra Estate (RWD)
- V = Skylark
- W = Electra Park Avenue
- X = Electra Limited (FWD)
- Z = Riviera Luxury

6th & 7th POSITION, 1985-86
BODY TYPE
- 19 = 4 Door Sedan
- 27 = 2 Door Coupe
- 35 = 4 Door Wagon
- 37 = 2 Door Coupe
- 47 = 2 Door Coupe
- 57 = 2 Door Coupe
- 67 = 2 Door Convertible
- 69 = 4 Door Sedan
- 77 = 2 Door Hatchback
- 87 = 2 Door Coupe

6th POSITION, 1987-91
BODY TYPE
- 1 = 2 Door Coupe
- 2 = 2 Door Hatchback
- 3 = 2 Door Convertible
- 5 = 4 Door Sedan
- 6 = 4 Door Sedan
- 8 = 4 Door Wagon

7th POSITION, 1987-91
RESTRAINT SYSTEM
- 1 = Manual Belts
- 2 = Manual Belts (Built in Safety)
- 3 = Manual Belts (Driver Inflatable)
- 4 = Automatic Belts

8th POSITION, 1985-88
ENGINE CODE
- A = 3.8-V6, 2 barrel
- B = 3.8-V6, 2 barrel
- D = 2.3-L4, Fuel Injected
- E = 3.0-V6, 2 barrel
- H = 5.0-V8, 4 barrel
- J = 1.8-L4, MFI
- M = 3.0-V6, Fuel Injected
- N = 5.7-V8, Diesel
- P = 2.0-L4, EFI
- R = 2.5-L4, TBI
- T = 4.3-V6, Diesel
- U = 2.5-L4, TBI
- V = 4.3-V6, Diesel
- W = 2.8-V6, MFI
- X = 2.8-V6, 2 barrel
- Y = 5.0-V8, 4 barrel
- Z = 4.3-V6, TBI
- 0 = 1.8-L4, TBI
- 1 = 2.0-L4, EFI
- 3 = 3.8-V6, MFI
- 7 = 3.8-V6, SFI
- 9 = 3.8-V6, SFI

8th POSITION, 1989-91
ENGINE CODE
- C = 3.8-V6, MFI
- D = 2.3-L4, MFI
- E = 5.0-V8, TBI
- G = 2.2-L4, TBI
- L = 3.8-V6, MFI
- N = 3.3-V6, MFI
- R = 2.5-L4, TBI
- T = 3.1-V6, MFI
- U = 2.5-L4, TBI
- W = 2.8-V6, Fuel Injected
- Y = 5.0-V8, 4 barrel
- Z = 4.3-V6, TBI
- 1 = 2.0-L4, Fuel Injected

9th POSITION
CHECK DIGIT

10th POSITION
MODEL YEAR
- F = 1985
- G = 1986
- H = 1987
- J = 1988
- K = 1989
- L = 1990
- M = 1991

11th POSITION
ASSEMBLY PLANT
- A = Lakewood, GA
- B = Lansing, MI
- C = Lansing, MI
- D = Doraville, GA
- H = Flint, MI
- K = Leeds, MO
- M = Lansing, MI
- P = Pontiac, MI
- R = Arlington, TX
- S = Ramos Arizpe, Mexico
- T = Tarrytown, NY
- U = Hamtramck, MI
- X = Fairfax, KS
- Z = Fremont, Ca
- 1 = Oshawa # 2, Canada
- 1 = Wentzville, MO
- 2 = Ste. Therese, Canada
- 4 = Orion, MI
- 6 = Oklahoma City, OK
- 7 = Lordstown, OH
- 9 = Oshawa # 1, Canada

12th Thru 17th POSITION
PRODUCTION SEQUENCE NUMBER

CADILLAC
V.I.N. DEFINED

1st POSITION
COUNTRY
- 1 = United States
- 2 = Canada
- J = Japan

2nd POSITION
MANUFACTURER
- G = General Motors

3rd POSITION
DIVISION
- 6 = Cadillac
- 7 = GM of Canada

4th POSITION
CARLINE CODE
- C = Fleetwood/DeVille (FWD)
- C = Commercial Chassis
- D = Fleetwood/DeVille (RWD)
- D = Brougham
- E = Eldorado
- J = Cimarron
- K = Seville
- K = Seville Touring
- V = Allante'

5th POSITION
CARLINE SERIES
- B = Fleetwood (FWD)
- D = DeVille (FWD)
- F = Fleetwood Limo
- G = Cimarron
- G = Fleetwood 60 Special
- H = Fleetwood Limo
- L = Eldorado
- M = Deville (RWD)
- R = Allante'
- S = Seville
- S = Convertible
- S = Fleetwood 60 Special
- W = Fleetwood Brougham
- Y = Seville Touring Sedan
- Z = Commercial Chassis

6th & 7th POSITION, 1985-86
BODY TYPE
- 19 = 4 Door Sedan
- 27 = 2 Door Coupe
- 35 = 4 Door Wagon
- 37 = 2 Door Coupe
- 47 = 2 Door Coupe
- 57 = 2 Door Coupe
- 67 = 2 Door Convertable
- 69 = 4 Door Sedan
- 77 = 2 Door Hatchback
- 87 = 2 Door Coupe

6th POSITION, 1987-91
BODY TYPE
- 1 = 2 Door Coupe
- 3 = 2 Door Convertible
- 5 = 4 Door Sedan

7th POSITION, 1987-91
RESTRAINT SYSTEM
- 1 = Manual Belts
- 2 = Manual Belts (Built in Safety)
- 3 = Manual Belts (Driver Air Bag)
- 4 = Automatic Belts

8th POSITION
ENGINE CODE
- B = 4.9-V8, MFI
- E = 5.0-V8, TBI
- N = 5.7-V8, Diesel
- P = 2.0-L4, EFI
- W = 2.8-V6, MFI
- Y = 5.0-V8, 4 Barrel
- 3 = 4.5-V8, MFI
- 5 = 4.5-V8, Fuel Injected
- 6 = 4.5-V8, Fuel Injected
- 7 = 4.1-V8, Fuel Injected
- 7 = 5.7-V8, TBI
- 8 = 4.1-V8, DFI
- 8 = 4.5-V8, MFI
- 9 = 5.0-V8, 4 Barrel

9th POSITION
CHECK DIGIT

10th POSITION
MODEL YEAR
- F = 1985
- G = 1986
- H = 1987
- J = 1988
- K = 1989
- L = 1990
- M = 1991

11th POSITION
ASSEMBLY PLANT
- J = GMAD Janesville, WI
- R = Arlington, TX
- U = Hamtramck, MI
- 4 = Lake Orion, MI
- 9 = Detroit, MI

12th Thru 17th POSITION
PRODUCTION SEQUENCE NUMBER

VEHICLE IDENTIFICATION

CHEVROLET

V.I.N. DEFINED

1st POSITION
COUNTRY
- 1 = United States
- 2 = Canada
- J = Japan

2nd POSITION
MANUFACTURER
- G = General Motors
- Y = N.U.M.M.I.
- 8 = General Motors

3rd POSITION
DIVISION
- 1 = Chevrolet
- 7 = GM of Canada

4th POSITION
CARLINE CODE
- A = Celebrity
- B = Impala, Caprice
- F = Camaro
- G = El Camino, Monte Carlo
- J = Cavalier
- L = Corsica, Beretta
- M = Sprint
- R = Spectrum
- S = Nova, TVS, Venture
- T = Chevette
- W = Lumina
- X = Citation
- Y = Corvette

5th POSITION
CARLINE SERIES
- B = Chevette
- C = Cavalier Cadet
- D = Cavalier CS
- E = Cavalier Hatchback, Type 10
- F = Cavalier Convertible (1989-91)
- F = Cavalier Z24 (1989-91)
- F = Spectrum Level I
- G = Spectrum Level II
- H = Citation
- J = Chevette Scooter
- K = Nova, TVX
- L = Impala, Caprice
- L = Lumina
- L = Nova Twin Cam
- N = Caprice Classic
- N = Lumina Eurosport
- P = Camaro Convertible
- P = Camaro Sport Coupe
- P = Lumina Z34
- R = Sprint
- S = Camaro Berlinetta
- S = Sprint E/R
- T = Corsica
- T = Corsica LT
- T = Sprint
- U = Caprice Classic Brougham & LS
- V = Beretta
- W = Celebrity
- W = Beretta GT
- X = Citation
- Y = Corvette
- Z = Beretta GTZ
- Z = Corsica LTZ
- Z = Corvette ZR1
- Z = Monte Carlo

6th & 7th POSITION, 1985-86
BODY TYPE
- 08 = 2 Door Hatchback
- 19 = 4 Door Sedan
- 27 = 2 Door Coupe
- 35 = 4 Door Wagon
- 37 = 2 Door Coupe
- 47 = 2 Door Coupe
- 57 = 2 Door Coupe
- 67 = 2 Door Convertible
- 68 = 4 Door Hatchback
- 69 = 4 Door Sedan
- 77 = 2 Door Hatchback
- 87 = 2 Door Coupe

6th POSITION, 1987-91
BODY TYPE
- 1 = 2 Door Coupe
- 2 = 2 Door Coupe
- 2 = 2 Door Hatchback
- 3 = 2 Door Convertible
- 5 = 4 Door Sedan
- 6 = 4 Door Hatchback
- 6 = 4 Door Sedan
- 8 = 4 Door Wagon

7th POSITION, 1987-91
RESTRAINT SYSTEM
- 1 = Manual Belts
- 2 = Manual Belts (Built in Safety)
- 3 = Manual Belts (Driver Inflatable)
- 4 = Automatic Belts

8th POSITION, 1985-88
ENGINE CODE
- A = 3.8-V6, 2 barrel
- B = 3.8-V6, 2 barrel
- C = 1.6-L4, 2 barrel
- D = 1.8-L4, Diesel
- E = 5.0-V8, Fuel Injected
- F = 5.0-V8, Fuel Injected
- G = 5.0-V8, 4 barrel
- H = 5.0-V8, 4 barrel
- K = 1.5-L4, 2 barrel
- K = 2.0-L4, EFI
- M = 1.3-L3, 2 barrel
- M = 2.0-L4, MFI
- N = 5.7-V8, Diesel
- P = 2.0-L4, EFI
- R = 2.5-L4, TBI
- S = 2.8-V6, MFI
- T = 4.3-V6, Diesel
- V = 4.3-V6, Diesel
- W = 2.8-V6, MFI
- X = 2.8-V6, 2 barrel
- Z = 4.3-V6, TBI
- 1 = 2.0-L4, EFI
- 2 = 1.0-L3, EFI
- 2 = 1.0-L3, Turbo
- 2 = 2.5-L4, TBI
- 4 = 1.6-L4, 2 barrel
- 5 = 1.0-L3, 2 barrel
- 5 = 1.5-L4, Diesel
- 5 = 1.6-L4, EFI
- 6 = 1.0-L3, TBI
- 6 = 5.7-V8, 4 barrel
- 7 = 1.5-L4, 2 barrel
- 8 = 5.7-V8, MFI
- 9 = 1.5-L4, Fuel Injected
- 9 = 1.5-L4, Turbocharged

8th POSITION, 1989-91
ENGINE CODE
- A = 2.3-L4, MFI
- E = 5.0-V8, TBI
- F = 5.0-V8, MFI
- G = 2.2-L4, TBI
- J = 5.7-V8, MFI
- R = 2.5-L4, TBI
- S = 2.8-V6, Fuel Injected
- T = 3.1-V6, MFI
- W = 2.8-V6, Fuel Injected
- X = 3.4-V6, MFI
- Y = 5.0-V8, 4 barrel
- Z = 4.3-V6, TBI
- 1 = 2.0-L4, Fuel Injected
- 2 = 1.0-L3, MFI
- 5 = 1.6-L4, MFI
- 6 = 1.0-L3, TBI
- 6 = 1.6-L4, MFI
- 7 = 5.7 V8, TBI
- 8 = 5.7 V8, MFI

9th POSITION
CHECK DIGIT

10th POSITION
MODEL YEAR
- F = 1985
- G = 1986
- H = 1987
- J = 1988
- K = 1989
- L = 1990
- M = 1991

11th POSITION
ASSEMBLY PLANT
- A = Lakewood, GA
- D = Doraville, Ga
- E = Linden, NJ
- G = Framingham, Ma
- H = Flint, MI
- J = Janesville, WI
- K = Kosia, Japan
- K = Leeds, MO
- L = Van Nuys, CA
- N = Norwood, OH
- R = Arlington, TX
- S = Ramos Arizpe, Mexico
- T = Tarrytown, NY
- W = Willow Run, MI
- X = Fairfax, KS
- Y = Wilmington, DE
- Z = Fremont, Ca
- 1 = Oshawa # 2, Canada
- 2 = Ste. Therese, Canada
- 5 = Bowling Green, KY
- 6 = Oklahoma City, OK
- 7 = Fugisawa, Japan (1987)
- 7 = Lordstown, OH
- 8 = Fugisawa, Japan (1988)
- 9 = Oshawa # 1, Canada

12th Thru 17th POSITION
PRODUCTION SEQUENCE NUMBER

GEO
V.I.N. DEFINED

1st POSITION
COUNTRY
1 = United States
2 = Canada
J = Japan

2nd POSITION
MANUFACTURER
G = General Motors
Y = N.U.M.M.I.
8 = General Motors

3rd POSITION
DIVISION
1 = Chevrolet
7 = GM of Canada

4th POSITION
CARLINE CODE
M = Metro
R = Spectrum
R = Storm
S = Prizm

5th POSITION
CARLINE SERIES
F = Spectrum Level I
F = Storm Level I
G = Spectrum Level II
G = Storm Level II
K = Prizm
L = Prizm Twin Cam
R = Metro LSI
S = Metro

6th POSITION
BODY TYPE
1 = 2 Door Coupe Sedan
2 = 2 Door Hatchback
3 = 2 Door Convertible
5 = 4 Door Sedan
6 = 4 Door Hatchback
7 = 4 Door Liftback
8 = 4 Door Wagon

7th POSITION
RESTRAINT SYSTEM
1 = Manual Belts
2 = Manual Belts (Built in Safety)
3 = Manual Belts (Driver Inflatable)
4 = Automatic Belts

8th POSITION
ENGINE CODE
K = 1.5-L4, 2 Barrel
2 = 1.0-L3, Turbo
5 = 1.6-L4, EFI
6 = 1.0-L3, TBI
6 = 1.6-L4, EFI
7 = 1.5-L4, 2 Barrel
9 = 1.5-L4, Turbo

9th POSITION
CHECK DIGIT

10th POSITION
MODEL YEAR
K = 1989
L = 1990
M = 1991

11th POSITION
ASSEMBLY PLANT
K = Kosia, Japan
Z = Fremont, Ca
8 = Fujisawa, Japan

12th Thru 17th POSITION
PRODUCTION SEQUENCE NUMBER

OLDSMOBILE

V.I.N. DEFINED

1st POSITION COUNTRY
1 = United States
2 = Canada
3 = Japan

2nd POSITION MANUFACTURER
G = General Motors

3rd POSITION DIVISION
3 = Oldsmobile
7 = GM of Canada
Z = Isuzu

4th POSITION CARLINE CODE
A = Cutlass Ciera
B = 88 Custom Cruiser (RWD)
C = Toronado Trofe'o
C = 98 Regency/Brougham (FWD)
D = 98 Regency Elite (RWD)
E = Toronado
E = Toronado Trofe'o
G = Cutlass
H = Delta 88 (FWD)
H = 88 Royale (FWD)
J = Firenza
N = Cutlass International
W = Cutlass

5th POSITION, 1985-88 CARLINE SERIES
C = Firenza
D = Firenza
F = Calais
G = 98 Regency (RWD)
H = 98 Regency Brougham (RWD)
J = Cutlass Ciera
K = Cutlass International
L = Cutlass Calais
L = Cutlass Ciera
M = Cutlass Ciera SL & Cruiser SL Wagon
N = Delta 88
P = Custom Cruiser
R = Cutlass Supreme
W = 98 Regency Brougham
X = 98 Regency
Y = Delta 88 Brougham
Z = Toronado Brougham

5th POSITION, 1989-91 CARLINE SERIES
C = Calais
F = Calais S
H = Cutlass Supreme
J = Cutlass Ciera/Wagon
K = Cutlass International
L = Cutlass Calais
L = Cutlass Ciera
M = Cutlass Ciera SL & Cruiser SL Wagon
N = Delta 88
N = 88 Royale
P = Custom Cruiser
R = Cutlass Supreme Int'l
S = Cutlass Ciera Int'l
S = Cutlass Supreme SL

5th POSITION, 89-91(CONT'D) CARLINE SERIES
T = Calais SL
T = Cutlass Convertible
V = Toronado Trofe'o
V = Touring Sedan
W = 98 Regency Brougham
W = 98 Regency Elite
X = 98 Regency (FWD)
Y = Delta 88 Brougham
Y = 88 Royale Brougham (FWD)
Z = Toronado

6th & 7th POSITION, 1985-86 BODY TYPE
19 = 4 Door Sedan
27 = 2 Door Coupe
35 = 4 Door Wagon
37 = 2 Door Coupe
47 = 2 Door Coupe
57 = 2 Door Coupe
67 = 2 Door Convertible
69 = 4 Door Sedan
77 = 2 Door Hatchback
87 = 2 Door Coupe

6th POSITION, 1987-91 BODY TYPE
1 = 2 Door Coupe
1 = 2 Door Sedan
2 = 2 Door Sedan
3 = 2 Door Convertible
5 = 4 Door Sedan
6 = 4 Door Sedan
8 = 4 Door Wagon

7th POSITION, 1987-91 RESTRAINT SYSTEM
1 = Manual Belts
2 = Manual Belts (Built in Safety)
3 = Manual Belts (Driver Inflatable)
4 = Automatic Belts

8th POSITION, 1985-88 ENGINE CODE
A = 3.8-V6, 2 barrel
B = 3.8-V6, 2 barrel
D = 2.3-L4, Fuel Injected
E = 3.0-V6, 2 barrel
H = 3.0-V6, 2 barrel
L = 1.8-L4, TBI
M = 3.0-V6, MFI
N = 5.7-V8, Diesel
P = 2.0-L4, EFI
R = 2.5-L4, TBI
U = 4.3-V6, Diesel
V = 4.3-V6, Diesel
W = 2.8-V6, MFI
X = 2.8-V6, 2 barrel
Y = 5.0-V8, 4 barrel
0 = 1.8-L4, TBI
1 = 2.0-L4, MFI
3 = 3.8-V6, MBI
7 = 4.3-V6, Diesel
9 = 5.0-V8, 4 barrel

8th POSITION, 1989-91 ENGINE CODE
A = 2.3-L4, MFI
C = 3.8-V6, MFI
D = 2.3-L4, MFI
E = 5.0-V8, TBI
N = 3.3-V6, MFI
R = 2.5-L4, TBI
T = 3.1-V6, MFI
U = 2.5-L4, TBI
W = 2.8-V6, MFI
X = 3.4-V6, MFI
7 = 3.8-V6, TBI

9th POSITION CHECK DIGIT

10th POSITION MODEL YEAR
F = 1985
G = 1986
H = 1987
J = 1988
K = 1989
L = 1990
M = 1991

11th POSITION ASSEMBLY PLANT
B = Lansing, MI
C = Lansing, MI
D = Doraville, GA
D = Linden, NJ
F = Flint, MI
G = Framingham, MA
K = Leeds, MO
M = Lansing, MI
R = Arlington, TX
U = Hamtramck, MI
W = Willow Run, MI
X = Fairfax, KS
Y = Wilmington, DE
Z = Fremont, Ca
1 = Wentzville, MO
2 = Ste. Therese, Canada
4 = Orion, MI
7 = Lordstown, OH
9 = Oshawa # 1, Canada

12th Thru 17th POSITION PRODUCTION SEQUENCE NUMBER

PONTIAC

V.I.N. DEFINED

1st POSITION COUNTRY
1 = United States
2 = Canada
J = Japan
K = Korea

2nd POSITION MANUFACTURER
G = General Motors
L = Daewoo Motors

3rd POSITION DIVISION
2 = Pontiac
7 = GM of Canada
Z = Isuzu

4th POSITION CARLINE CODE
A = 6000
B = Parisienne/Safari
F = Firebird
G = Grand Prix Brougham
H = Bonneville
J = Sunbird 2000
M = Firefly
N = Grand Am
P = Fiero
T = T-1000/Lemans
W = Grand Prix

5th POSITION CARLINE SERIES
B = Sunbird J2000
C = Sunbird LE
D = Sunbird J2000 LE
D = Sunbird J2000 SE
E = Fiero/Grand Am/6000 SE
F = Fiero SE/6000 LE
G = Grand Am LE
G = 6000 LE/Fiero GT
H = 6000 STE
J = Grand Prix LE
J = 6000 SE
K = Grand Prix LJ
L = T1000/Parisienne
M = Bonneville/Parisienne
N = Bonneville/Parisienne Brougham
N = Lemans
P = Grand Prix Brougham & SE
R = Bonneville Brougham
R = Firefly
R = Lemans SE
S = Firebird/Bonneville
S = Lemans GSE
T = Grand Prix STE
T = Parisienne Brougham
V = Sunbird GT/Parisienne export
V = Grand Am LE
W = Firebird Trans Am
W = Grand Am SE
X = Firebird SE/Bonneville LE
Y = Lemans GSE
Z = Bonneville SSE
Z = Bonneville LE & SE

6th & 7th POSITION, 1985-86 BODY TYPE
19 = 4 Door Sedan
27 = 2 Door Coupe
35 = 4 Door Wagon
37 = 2 Door Coupe
47 = 2 Door Coupe
57 = 2 Door Coupe
67 = 2 Door Convertible
69 = 4 Door Sedan
77 = 2 Door Hatchback
87 = 2 Door Coupe

6th POSITION, 1987-91 BODY TYPE
1 = 2 Door Coupe
2 = 2 Door Coupe
2 = 2 Door Hatchback
3 = 2 Door Convertible
5 = 4 Door Sedan
6 = 4 Door Sedan
8 = 4 Door Hatchback
8 = 4 Door Wagon

7th POSITION, 1987-91 RESTRAINT SYSTEM
1 = Manual Belts
2 = Manual Belts (Built in Safety)
4 = Automatic Belts

8th POSITION, 1985-88 ENGINE CODE
B = 3.8-V6, 2 barrel
C = 3.8-V6, 2 barrel
D = 1.8-L4, Diesel
E = 5.0-V8, Fuel Injected
F = 5.0-V8, Fuel Injected
G = 5.0-V8, 4 barrel
J = 1.8-L4, MFI
L = 3.0-V6, MFI
N = 5.7-V8, Diesel
P = 2.0-L4, EFI
R = 2.5-L4, TBI
S = 2.8-V6, MFI
U = 2.5-L4, TBI
V = 4.3-V6, Diesel
W = 2.8-V6, MFI
Z = 2.8-V6, 2 barrel
0 = 1.8-L4, TBI
2 = 2.5-L4, TBI
6 = 1.6-L4, 2 barrel
6 = 1.6-L4, TBI
9 = 2.8-V6, MFI

8th POSITION, 1989-91 ENGINE CODE
A = 2.3-L4, MFI
C = 3.8-V6, MFI
D = 2.3-L4, MFI
E = 5.0-V8, MFI
K = 5.0-V8, TBI
M = 2.0-L4, TBI
R = 2.5-L4, TBI
S = 2.8-V6, MFI
U = 2.5-L4, MFI
W = 2.8-V6, MFI
X = 3.4-V6, MFI
Z = 5.0-V8, 4 barrel
6 = 1.6-L4, TBI
7 = 3.8-V6, MFI
8 = 5.7-V8, MFI

9th POSITION CHECK DIGIT

10th POSITION MODEL YEAR
F = 1985
G = 1986
H = 1987
J = 1988
K = 1989
L = 1990
M = 1991

11th POSITION ASSEMBLY PLANT
A = Lakewood, GA
B = Lansing, MI
C = Korea
C = Lansing, MI
F = Flint, MI
L = Van Nuys, CA
M = Lansing, MI
N = Norwood, OH
P = Pontiac, MI
U = Hamtramck, MI
W = Willow Run, MI
X = Fairfax, KS
Y = Wilmington, DE
1 = Oshawa # 2, Canada
5 = Bowling Green, KY
6 = Oklahoma City, OK
7 = Lordstown, OH
9 = Oshawa # 1, Canada

12th Thru 17th POSITION PRODUCTION SEQUENCE NUMBER

VEHICLE MAINTENANCE SCHEDULES
Cadillac 1988–89 All & 1990–91 Brougham

SCHEDULE I

Follow Schedule I if your car is MAINLY operated under one or more of the following conditions:

- When most trips are less than 4 miles (6 kilometers).
- When most trips are less than 10 miles (16 kilometers) and outside temperatures remain below freezing.
- Idling and/or low-speed operation in stop-and-go traffic.[1]
- Towing a trailer.[***]
- Operating in dusty areas.

Item No.	To Be Serviced	When to Perform Miles (Kilometers) or Months Whichever Occurs First	The services shown in this schedule up to 40,000 miles (80 000 km) are to be performed after 40,000 miles at the same intervals.														
		Miles (000) Kilometers (000)	3 5	6 10	9 15	12 20	15 25	18 30	21 35	24 40	27 45	30 50	33 55	36 60	39 65	42 70	45 75	48 80
1	Engine Oil & Oil Filter Change*	Every 3,000 mi. (5 000 km) or 3 mos.	●	●	●	●	●	●	●	●	●	●	●	●	●	●	●	●
2	Chassis Lubrication	Every other oil change		●		●		●		●		●		●		●		●
3	Carburetor Choke and Hose Inspection (Brougham only)	At 6,000 mi. (10 000 km) and then every 30,000 mi. (50 000 km)		●								●**						
4	Fuel Injection or Carburetor Mounting Bolt Torque*	At 6,000 mi. (10 000 km) only		●**														
5	Engine Idle Speed Adjustment* (Brougham Only)	At 6,000 mi. (10 000 km) only		●**														
6	Tire & Wheel Inspection and Rotation	At 6,000 mi. (10 000 km) and then every 15,000 mi. (25 000 km)		●				●						●				
7	Vacuum or A.I.R. Pump Drive Belt Inspection*	Every 30,000 mi. (50 000 km) or 24 mos.										●**						
8	Cooling System Service*											●						
9	Wheel Bearing Repack (Brougham Only)	See explanation for service on on page 7.																
10	Transmission/Transaxle Service																	
11	Spark Plug Replacement*	Every 30,000 mi. (50 000 km)										●**						
12	PCV Valve Inspection*											●						
13	EGR System Service*											●						
14	Air Cleaner, PCV Filter & A.I.R. Filter Replacement*	Every 30,000 mi. (50 000 km) or 36 mos.										●**						
15	Engine Timing Check*											●						
16	Fuel Tank, Cap & Lines Inspection*	Every 30,000 mi. (50 000 km)										●						
17	Thermostatically Controlled Air Cleaner Inspection*											●						

SCHEDULE II

Follow Schedule II ONLY IF NONE of the driving conditions specified in Schedule I apply.

Item No.	To Be Serviced	When to Perform Miles (kilometers) or Months, Whichever Occurs First	The services shown in this schedule up to 45,000 miles (75 000 km) are to be performed after 45,000 miles at the same intervals.					
		Miles (000) Kilometers (000)	7.5 12.5	15 25	22.5 37.5	30 50	37.5 62.5	45 75
1	Engine Oil Change*	Every 7,500 mi. (12 500 km) or 12 mos.	●	●	●	●	●	●
	Oil Filter Change*	At first and then every other oil change or 12 mos.	●		●		●	
2	Chassis Lubrication	Every 7,500 mi. (12 500 km) or 12 mos.	●	●	●	●	●	●
3	Carburetor Choke and Hose Inspection* (If Equipped)	At 7,500 mi. (12 500 km) and then every 30,000 mi. (50 000 km)	●			●**		
4	Fuel Injection or Carburetor Mounting Bolt Torque*	At 7,500 mi. (12 500 km) Only	●**					
5	Engine Idle Speed Adjustment* (Brougham Only)	At 7,500 mi. (12 500 km) Only	●**					
6	Tire & Wheel Inspection and Rotation	At 7,500 mi. (12 500 km) and then every 15,000 mi. (25 000 km)	●		●		●	
7	Vacuum or A.I.R. Pump Drive Belt Inspection*	Every 30,000 mi. (50 000 km) or 24 mos.				●**		
8	Cooling System Service*					●		
9	Wheel Bearing Repack (Brougham Only)	Every 30,000 mi. (50 000 km)				●		
10	Transmission/Transaxle Service	See explanation for service on page 7.						
11	Spark Plug Replacement*	Every 30,000 mi. (50 000 km)				●**		
12	PCV Valve Inspection*					●		
13	EGR System Service*					●		
14	Air Cleaners, PCV Filter & A.I.R. Filter Replacement*	Every 30,000 mi. (50 000 km) or 36 mos.				●**		
15	Engine Timing Check*					●		
16	Fuel Tank, Cap & Lines Inspection*	Every 30,000 mi. (50 000 km)				●		
17	Thermostatically Controlled Air Cleaner Inspection*					●		

*An Emission Control Service.

**In California, these are the minimum Emission Control Maintenance Services an owner must perform according to the California Air Resources Board. General Motors, however, urges that all Emission Control Maintenance Services shown be performed. To maintain your other new car warranties, all services shown in this booklet should be performed.

[1]Schedule 1 should also be followed if the car is used for livery service or commercial application

***Trailer pulling is not recommended for some models. See Owner's Manual for details.

VEHICLE MAINTENANCE SCHEDULES
Cadillac Except Brougham 1990-91

Follow Schedule I if the car is mainly operated under one or more of the following conditions:
- When most trips are less than 4 miles (6 kilometers).
- When most trips are less than 10 miles (16 kilometers) and outside temperatures remain below freezing.
- When most trips include extended idling and/or frequent low-speed operation as in stop-and-go traffic.
- Towing a trailer**
- Operating in dusty areas.

Schedule I should also be followed if the car is used for delivery service, police, taxi or other commercial applications.

The services shown in this schedule up to 48,000 miles (80 000 km) are to be performed after 48,000 miles at the same intervals

ITEM NO.	TO BE SERVICED	WHEN TO PERFORM Miles (Kilometers) or Months, Whichever Occurs First	3 / 5	6 / 10	9 / 15	12 / 20	15 / 25	18 / 30	21 / 35	24 / 40	27 / 45	30 / 50	33 / 55	36 / 60	39 / 65	42 / 70	45 / 75	48 / 80
1	Engine Oil & Oil Filter Change*	Every 3,000 (5 000 km) or 3 mos.	●	●	●	●	●	●	●	●	●	●	●	●	●	●	●	●
2	Chassis Lubrication	Every other oil change		●		●		●		●		●		●		●		●
3	Throttle Body Mount Bolt Torque (Some Models)*	At 6,000 mi. (10 000 km) only		●														
4	Tire & Wheel Insp. and Rotation	At 6,000 mi. (10 000 km) and then every 15,000 mi. (25 000 km)		●					●					●				
5	Engine Accessory Drive Belt(s) Insp.*	Every 30,000 mi. (50 000 km) or 24 mos.										●						
6	Cooling System Service*											●						
7	Transmission/Transaxle Service	See explanation for service interval																
8	Spark Plug Replacement*											●						
9	Spark Plug Wire Insp. (Some Models)*	Every 30,000 mi. (50 000 km)										●						
10	PCV Valve Insp. (Some Models)*††											●						
11	EGR System Insp.*††	Every 30,000 mi. (50 000 km) or 36 mos.										●						
12	Air Cleaner & PCV Filter Repl.*											●						
13	Eng. Timing Check (Some Models)*											●						
14	Fuel Tank, Cap & Lines Insp.*††	Every 30,000 mi. (50 000 km)										●						
15	Thermostatically Controlled Air Cleaner Insp. (Some Models)*											●						

FOOTNOTES:
- * An Emission Control Service
- †† The U.S. Environmental Protection Agency has determined that the failure to perform this maintenance item will not nullify the emission warranty or limit recall liability prior to the completion of vehicle useful life. General Motors, however, urges that all recommended maintenance services be performed at the indicated intervals and the maintenance be recorded in Section C of the Owner's Maintenance Schedule.
- ** Trailering is not recommended for some models. See the Owner's Manual for details.

Cadillac Except Brougham
1990–91

Follow Schedule II only if none of the driving conditions specified in Schedule I apply.

The services shown in this schedule up to 45,000 miles (75 000 km) are to be performed after 45,000 miles at the same intervals.

ITEM NO.	TO BE SERVICED	WHEN TO PERFORM Miles (Kilometers) or Months, Whichever Occurs First	MILES (000) 7.5 / KILOMETERS (000) 12.5	15 / 25	22.5 / 37.5	30 / 50	37.5 / 62.5	45 / 75
1	Engine Oil Change*	Every 7,500 mi. (12 500 km) or 12 mos.	●	●	●	●	●	●
	Filter Change*	At first and every other oil change or 12 mos.	●		●		●	
2	Chassis Lubrication	Every 7,500 mi. (12 500 km) or 12 mos.	●	●	●	●	●	●
3	Throttle Body Mount Bolt Torque (Some Models)*	At 7,500 mi. (12 500 km) only	●					
4	Tire & Wheel Insp. and Rotation	At 7,500 mi. (12 500 km) and then every 15,000 mi. (25 000 km)	●		●		●	
5	Engine Accessory Drive Belt(s) Insp.*	Every 30,000 mi. (50 000 km) or 24 mos.				●		
6	Cooling System Service*					●		
7	Transmission/Transaxle Service	See explanation for service interval						
8	Spark Plug Replacement*	Every 30,000 mi. (50 000 km)				●		
9	Spark Plug Wire Insp. (Some Models)*					●		
10	PCV Valve Insp. (Some Models)* ††					●		
11	EGR System Insp.* ††	Every 30,000 mi. (50 000 km) or 36 mos.				●		
12	Air Cleaner & PCV Filter Repl.*					●		
13	Eng. Timing Check (Some Models)*	Every 30,000 mi. (50 000 km)				●		
14	Fuel Tank, Cap & Lines Insp.* ††					●		
15	Thermostatically Controlled Air Cleaner Insp. (Some Models)*					●		

FOOTNOTES:
* An Emission Control Service
†† The U.S. Environmental Protection Agency has determined that the failure to perform this maintenance item will not nullify the emission warranty or limit recall liability prior to the completion of vehicle useful life. General Motors, however, urges that all recommded maintenance services be performed at the indicated intervals and the maintenance be recorded in Section C of the owner's Maintenance Schedule.

All Except Cadillac, Lemans, Sprint & Spectrum
1988

Follow Schedule I if the the car is mainly operated under one or more of the following conditions:

- When most trips are less than 4 miles (6 kilometers).
- When most trips are less than 10 miles (16 kilometers) and outside temperatures remain below freezing.
- • • Idling and/or low-speed operation in stop-and-go traffic.
- • • • Towing a trailer
- • • • • Operating in dusty areas.

Schedule I should also be followed if the car is used for delivery service, police, taxi or other commercial applications.

The services shown in this schedule up to 48,000 miles (80 000 km) are to be performed after 48,000 miles at the same intervals

ITEM NO.	TO BE SERVICED	WHEN TO PERFORM — Miles (Kilometers) or Months, Whichever Occurs First	MILES (000) 3 / KM 5	6 / 10	9 / 15	12 / 20	15 / 25	18 / 30	21 / 35	24 / 40	27 / 45	30 / 50	33 / 55	36 / 60	39 / 65	42 / 70	45 / 75	48 / 80
1	Engine Oil & Oil Filter Change*	Every 3,000 (5 000 km) or 3 mos.	•	•	•	•	•	•	•	•	•	•	•	•	•	•	•	•
2	Chassis Lubrication	Every other oil change		•		•		•		•		•		•		•		•
3	Carb. Choke & Hose Insp.* (If Equipped)††	At 6,000 mi. (10 000 km) and then every 30,000 mi. (50 000 km)		•										•				
4	Carb. or Throttle Body Mount Bolt Torque (Some Models)*	At 6,000 mi. (10 000 km) only		•														
5	Eng. Idle Speed Adj. (Some Models)*			•														
6	Tire & Wheel Insp. and Rotation	At 6,000 mi. (10,000 km) and then every 15,000 mi. (25,000 km)		•					•					•				
7	Vac. or Air Pump Drive Belt Insp.*	Every 30,000 mi. (50 000 km) or 24 mos.										•						
8	Cooling System Service*											•						
9	Wheel Brg. Repack (Rear-Wheel-Drive Cars Only)											•						
10	Transmission/Transaxle Service	See explanation for service interval																
11	Spark Plug Service*											•						
12	Spark Plug Wire Insp. (Some Models)*	Every 30,000 mi. (50 000 km)										•						
13	PCV Valve Insp. (Some Models)*††											•						
14	EGR System Insp.*††											•						
15	Air Cleaner & PCV Filter Repl.*	Every 30,000 mi. (50 000 km) or 36 mos.										•						
16	Eng. Timing Check (Some Models)*											•						
17	Fuel Tank, Cap & Lines Insp.*††	Every 30,000 mi. (50 000 km)										•						
18	Thermostatically Controlled Air Cleaner Insp. (Some Models)*											•						

FOOTNOTES:

* An Emission Control Service

†† The U.S. Environmental Protection Agency has determined that the failure to perform this maintenance item will not nullify the emission warranty or limit recall liability prior to the completion of vehicle useful life. General Motors, however, urges that all recommended maintenance services be performed at the indicated intervals and the maintenance be recorded in section C of the owner's maintenance schedule.

All Except Cadillac, Lemans, Sprint & Spectrum
1988

Follow Schedule II if, as a general rule, the car is driven on a daily basis for several miles (km) and none of the above conditions apply.

The services shown in this schedule up to 45,000 miles (75,000 km) are to be performed after 45,000 miles at the same intervals

ITEM NO.	TO BE SERVICED	WHEN TO PERFORM Miles (Kilometers) or Months, Whichever Occurs First	7.5 / 12.5	15 / 25	22.5 / 37.5	30 / 50	37.5 / 62.5	45 / 75
1	Engine Oil Change*	Every 7,500 mi. (12 500 km) or 12 mos.	●	●	●	●	●	●
	Filter Change*	At first and every other oil change or 12 mos.	●		●		●	●
2	Chassis Lubrication	Every 7,500 mi. (12 500 km) or 12 mos.	●	●	●	●	●	●
3	Carb. Choke & Hose Insp.* (If Equipped)††	At 7,500 mi. (12 500 km) and then at each 30,000 mi. (50 000 km) interval	●					
4	Carb. or Throttle Body Mount Bolt Torque (Some Models)	At 7,500 mi. (12 500 km) only	●					
5	Eng. Idle Speed Adj. (Some Models)*		●					
6	Tire & Wheel Insp. and Rotation	At 7,500 mi. (23,500 km) and then every 15,000 mi. (25,000 km)			●			●
7	Vac. or Air Pump Drive Belt Insp.*	Every 30,000 mi. (50 000 km) or 24 mos.				●		
8	Cooling System Service*					●		
9	Wheel Brg. Repack (Rear Wheel-Drive Cars Only)	Every 30,000 mi. (50 000 km)				●		
10	Transmission/Transaxle Service	See explanation for service interval				●		
11	Spark Plug Service*	Every 30,000 mi. (50 000 km)				●		
12	Spark Plug Wire Insp. (Some Models)*					●		
13	PCV Valve Insp. (Some Models)*††					●		
14	EGR System Insp.*††	Every 30,000 mi. (50 000 km) or 36 mos.				●		
15	Air Cleaner & PCV Filter Repl.*					●		
16	Eng. Timing Check (Some Models)*	Every 30,000 mi. (50 000 km)				●		
17	Fuel Tank, Cap & Lines Insp.††					●		
18	Thermostatically Controlled Air Cleaner Insp. (Some Models)					●		

MILES (000)
KILOMETERS (000)

FOOTNOTES: * An Emission Control Service

†† The U.S. Environmental Protection Agency has determined that the failure to perform this maintenance item will not nullify the emission warranty or limit recall liability prior to the completion of vehicle useful life. General Motors, however, urges that all recommended maintenance services be performed at the indicated intervals and the maintenance be recorded in section C of the owner's maintenance schedule.

All Except Cadillac, Lemans, Metro & Spectrum 1989

Follow Schedule I if the the car is mainly operated under one or more of the following conditions:
- When most trips are less than 4 miles (6 kilometers).
- When most trips are less than 10 miles (16 kilometers) and outside temperatures remain below freezing.
- When most trips include extended idling and/or frequent low-speed operation as in stop-and-go traffic.
- Towing a trailer**
- Operating in dusty areas.

Schedule I should also be followed if the car is used for delivery service, police, taxi or other commercial applications.

The services shown in this schedule up to 48,000 miles (80 000 km) are to be performed after 48,000 miles at the same intervals.

ITEM NO.	TO BE SERVICED	WHEN TO PERFORM Miles (Kilometers) or Months, Whichever Occurs First	MILES (000) 3 / KM 5	6 / 10	9 / 15	12 / 20	15 / 25	18 / 30	21 / 35	24 / 40	27 / 45	30 / 50	33 / 55	36 / 60	39 / 65	42 / 70	45 / 75	48 / 80
1	Engine Oil & Oil Filter Change*	Every 3,000 (5 000 km) or 3 mos.	•	•	•	•	•	•	•	•	•	•	•	•	•	•	•	•
2	Chassis Lubrication	Every other oil change		•		•		•		•		•		•		•		•
3	Carb. Choke & Hose Insp.* (If Equipped)††	At 6,000 mi. (10 000 km) and then every 30,000 mi. (50 000 km)		•										•				
4	Carb. or Throttle Body Mount Bolt Torque (Some Models)*	At 6,000 mi. (10 000 km) only		•														
5	Eng. Idle Speed Adj. (Some Models)*			•														
6	Tire & Wheel Insp. and Rotation	At 6,000 mi. (10 000 km) and then every 15,000 mi. (25 000 km)		•					•					•				
7	Vac. or Air Pump Drive Belt Insp.*	Every 30,000 mi. (50 000 km) or 24 mos.								•		•						
8	Cooling System Service*									•		•						
9	Wheel Brg. Repack (Rear-Wheel-Drive Cars Only)											•						
10	Transmission/Transaxle Service	See explanation for service interval																
11	Spark Plug Replacement*											•						
12	Spark Plug Wire Insp. (Some Models)*	Every 30,000 mi. (50 000 km)										•						
13	PCV Valve Insp. (Some Models)*††											•						
14	EGR System Insp.*††											•						
15	Air Cleaner & PCV Filter Repl.*	Every 30,000 mi. (50 000 km) or 36 mos.										•						
16	Eng. Timing Check (Some Models)*											•						
17	Fuel Tank, Cap & Lines Insp.*††	Every 30,000 mi. (50 000 km)										•						
18	Thermostatically Controlled Air Cleaner Insp.*††											•						

FOOTNOTES: * An Emission Control Service

†† The U.S. Environmental Protection Agency has determined that the failure to perform this maintenance item will not nullify the emission warranty or limit recall liability prior to the completion of vehicle useful life. General Motors, however, urges that all recommended maintenance services be performed at the indicated intervals and the maintenance be recorded in section C of the owner's maintenance schedule.

**Trailoring is not recommended for some models. See the Owner's Manual for details.

All Except Cadillac, Lemans, Metro & Spectrum
1989

Follow Schedule II only if none of the driving conditions specified in Schedule I apply.

The services shown in this schedule up to 45,000 miles (75,000 km) are to be performed after 45,000 miles at the same intervals

ITEM NO.	TO BE SERVICED	WHEN TO PERFORM Miles (Kilometers) or Months, Whichever Occurs First	MILES (000) 7.5 / KM 12.5	15 / 25	22.5 / 37.5	30 / 50	37.5 / 62.5	45 / 75
1	Engine Oil Change*	Every 7,500 mi. (12 500 km) or 12 mos.	•	•	•	•	•	•
	Filter Change*	At first and every other oil change or 12 mos.	•		•		•	•
2	Chassis Lubrication	Every 7,500 mi. (12 500 km) or 12 mos.	•	•	•	•	•	•
3	Carb, Choke & Hose Insp.* (If Equipped)††	At 7,500 mi. (12 500 km) and then at each 30,000 mi. (50 000 km) interval	•				•	
4	Carb or Throttle Body Mount Bolt Torque (Some Models)	At 7,500 mi. (12 500 km) only	•					
5	Eng. Idle Speed Adj. (Some Models)*	At 7,500 mi. (12 500 km) and then every 15,000 mi. (25 000 km)	•		•		•	
6	Tire & Wheel Insp. and Rotation	At 7,500 mi. (12 500 km) and then every 15,000 mi. (25 000 km)	•		•		•	
7	Vac. or Air Pump Drive Belt Insp.*	Every 30,000 mi. (50 000 km) or 24 mos.				•		
8	Cooling System Service*	Every 30,000 mi. (50 000 km)				•		
9	Wheel Brg. Repack (Rear Wheel-Drive Cars Only)	Every 30,000 mi. (50 000 km)				•		
10	Transmission/Transaxle Service	See explanation for service interval				•		
11	Spark Plug Replacement*	Every 30,000 mi. (50 000 km)				•		
12	Spark Plug Wire Insp. (Some Models)*	Every 30,000 mi. (50 000 km)				•		
13	PCV Valve Insp. (Some Models)*††	Every 30,000 mi. (50 000 km) or 36 mos.				•		
14	EGR System Insp.*††	Every 30,000 mi. (50 000 km)				•		
15	Air Cleaner & PCV Filter Repl.*	Every 30,000 mi. (50 000 km)				•		
16	Eng. Timing Check (Some Models)*††	Every 30,000 mi. (50 000 km)				•		
17	Fuel Tank, Cap & Lines Insp.*††	Every 30,000 mi. (50 000 km)				•		
18	Thermostatically Controlled Air Cleaner Insp. (Some Models)*					•		

FOOTNOTES: * An Emission Control Service

†† The U.S. Environmental Protection Agency has determined that the failure to perform this maintenance item will not nullify the emission warranty or limit recall liability prior to the completion of vehicle useful life. General Motors, however, urges that all recommended maintenance services be performed at the indicated intervals and the maintenance be recorded in section C of the owner's maintenance schedule.

LeMans

Select and follow Schedule I or Schedule II based on how you use your car:

SCHEDULE I

Follow Schedule I if your car is mainly operated under one or more of the following conditions:

- When most trips are less than 4 miles (6 kilometers).
- When most trips are less than 10 miles (16 kilometers) and outside temperatures remain below freezing.
- Idling and/or low speed operation in stop-and-go traffic.
- Operating in dusty areas.

Schedule I should also be followed if the car is used for delivery service, police, taxi or other commercial applications.

ITEM NO.	TO BE SERVICED	WHEN TO PERFORM Miles (kilometers) or Months, Whichever Occurs First	The services shown in this schedule up to 48,000 miles (80 000 km) are to be performed after 48,000 miles at the same intervals.															
		MILES (000)	3	6	9	12	15	18	21	24	27	30	33	36	39	42	45	48
		KILOMETERS (000)	5	10	15	20	25	30	35	40	45	50	55	60	65	70	75	80
1	Engine Oil & Oil Filter Change*	Every 3,000 miles (5 000 km) or 3 months	●	●	●	●	●	●	●	●	●	●	●	●	●	●	●	●
2	Throttle Body Mounting Bolt Torque*	At 6,000 miles (10 000 km) only		●														
3	Tire & Wheel Rotation	At 6,000 miles (10 000 km), and then every 15,000 miles (25 000 km)		●					●					●				
4	Drive Belt Inspection*	Every 30,000 miles (50 000 km) or 24 months																
5	Cooling System Service*	Every 30,000 miles (50 000 km) or 24 months										●						
6	Brake System Service											●						
7	Transaxle Service	See Explanation on Page 1																
8	Spark Plug Service*																	
9	Spark Plug Wire Inspection*	Every 30,000 miles (50 000 km)										●						
10	Fuel Micro-Filter Replacement*											●						
11	Air Cleaner Element Replacement*	Every 30,000 miles (50 000 km) or 36 months										●						
12	Engine Timing Check*											●						
13	Fuel Tank, Cap & Lines Inspection*	Every 30,000 miles (50 000 km)										●						
14	Thermostatically Controlled Air Cleaner Inspection*											●						

SCHEDULE II

Follow Schedule II **only** if none of the driving conditions specified in Schedule I apply.

ITEM NO.	TO BE SERVICED	WHEN TO PERFORM Miles (kilometers) or Months, Whichever Occurs First	The services shown in this schedule up to 45,000 miles (75 000 km) are to be performed after 45,000 miles at the same intervals					
		MILES (000)	7.5	15	22.5	30	37.5	45
		KILOMETERS (000)	12.5	25	37.5	50	62.5	75
1	Engine Oil & Oil Filter Change*	Every 7,500 miles (12 500 km) or 12 months	●	●	●	●	●	●
2	Throttle Body Mounting Bolt Torque*	At 7,500 miles (12 500 km) only	●					
3	Tire & Wheel Rotation	At 7,500 miles (12 500 km) and then every 15,000 miles (25 000 km)	●		●		●	
4	Drive Belt Inspection*	Every 30,000 miles (50 000 km) or 24 months						
5	Cooling System Service*	Every 30,000 miles (50 000 km) or 24 months				●		
6	Brake System Service					●		
7	Transaxle Service	See Explanation on Page 1						
8	Spark Plug Service*							
9	Spark Plug Wire Inspection*	Every 30,000 miles (50 000 km)				●		
10	Fuel Micro-Filter Replacement*					●		
11	Air Cleaner Element Replacement*	Every 30,000 miles (50 000 km) or 36 months				●		
12	Engine Timing Check*					●		
13	Fuel Tank, Cap & Lines Inspection*	Every 30,000 miles (50 000 km)				●		
14	Thermostatically Controlled Air Cleaner Inspection*					●		

FOOTNOTES:

* An Emission Control Service.

Metro & Spectrum 1988–89

Follow Schedule I if your car is MAINLY operated under one or more of the following conditions:

- When most trips are less than 4 miles (6 kilometers).
- When most trips are less than 10 miles (16 kilometers) and outside temperatures remain below freezing.
- When most trips include extended idling and/or frequent low-speed operation as in stop-and-go traffic.‡
- Towing a trailer.‡
- Operating in dusty areas.
- Schedule I should also be followed if the car is used for delivery service, police, taxi or other commercial applications.

The services shown in this schedule up to 60 000 miles (96 000 km) are to be performed after 60 000 miles at the same intervals.

ITEM NO.	TO BE SERVICED	WHEN TO PERFORM (Miles (kilometers) or Months, Whichever Occurs First)	MILES(000) 3 / KM 5	6 / 10	9 / 15	12 / 20	15 / 25	18 / 30	21 / 35	24 / 40	27 / 45	30 / 50	33 / 55	36 / 60	39 / 65	42 / 70	45 / 75	48 / 80	51 / 85	54 / 90	57 / 95	60 / 100
1	Engine Oil Replacement*	Every 3 000 Miles (5 000 km) or 3 Months	•	•	•	•	•	•	•	•	•	•	•	•	•	•	•	•	•	•	•	•
2	Oil Filter Replacement*	At First and Then Every Other Oil Change	•		•		•		•		•		•		•		•		•		•	
3	Chassis and Body Lubrication	Every Other Oil Change		•		•		•		•		•		•		•		•		•		•
4	Carburetor Choke Inspection*‡	Every 30 000 Miles (50 000 km)										•										•
5	Valve Clearance Adjustment*	Every 15 000 Miles (25 000 km)					•					•					•					•
6	Timing Belt Replacement	Every 60 000 Miles (96 000 km)																				•
7	Engine Idle Speed Adjustment*	At 3 000 Miles (5 000 km) Only	•																			
8	Tire and Wheel Inspection and Rotation	At 6 000 Miles (10 000 km) and Then Every 15 000 Miles (25 000 km)		•					•					•					•			
9	Drive Belt Inspection*	Every 30 000 Miles (50 000 km)										•										•
10	Cooling System Inspection*	Every 15 000 Miles (25 000 km)					•					•					•					•
11	Cooling System Refill*	Every 30 000 Miles (50 000 km)										•										•
12	Rear Wheel Bearing Repack	See Explanation of Scheduled Maintenance Services																				
13	Manual Transaxle Fluid Replacement	Every 15 000 Miles (25 000 km)					•					•					•					•
14	Automatic Transaxle Fluid Replacement	Every 15 000 Miles (25 000 km)					•					•					•					•
15	Spark Plug Replacement*	Every 30 000 Miles (50 000 km)										•										•
16	Power Steering Fluid Replacement	Every 21 000 Miles (35 000 km) or 24 Months							•							•						
17	Power Steering Rubber Hose Inspection	Every 42 000 Miles (70 000 km)														•						
18	Air Cleaner Element Replacement*	See Explanation of Scheduled Maintenance Services																				
19	Fuel Cap, Lines and Tank Inspection*‡	Every 15 000 Miles (25 000 km)					•					•					•					•
20	PCV Valve Inspection*‡	Every 30 000 Miles (50 000 km)										•										•

* An Emission Control Service.

‡The U.S. Environmental Protection Agency has determined that the failure to perform this maintenance item will not nullify the emission warranty or limit recall liability prior to the completion of vehicle useful life. General Motors, however, urges that all recommended maintenance services be performed at the indicated intervals and the maintenance be recorded in Section C.

‡ Trailering is not recommended for some models. See your Owner's Manual for details.

Metro & Spectrum
1988–89

Follow Schedule II only if none of the driving conditions specified in Schedule I apply.

The services shown in this schedule up to 60 000 miles (96 000 km) are to be performed after 60 000 miles at the same intervals.

ITEM NO.	TO BE SERVICED	WHEN TO PERFORM — Miles (kilometers) or Months, Whichever Occurs First	3	6	7.5	9	12	15	18	21	22.5	24	27	30	33	36	37.5	39	42	45	48	51	52.5	54	57	60
	MILES (000) → / KILOMETERS (000) →		5	10	12.5	15	20	25	30	35	37.5	40	45	50	55	60	62.5	65	70	75	80	85	87.5	90	95	100
1	Engine Oil Replacement*	Every 7 500 Miles (12 500 km) or 12 Months			•			•			•			•			•			•			•			•
	Oil Filter Replacement*	At First and Then Every Other Oil Change			•						•						•						•			
2	Chassis and Body Lubrication	Every 7 500 Miles (12 500 km) or 12 Months			•			•			•			•			•			•			•			•
3	Carburetor Choke Inspection*‡	Every 30 000 Miles (50 000 km)												•												•
4	Valve Clearance Adjustment*	Every 15 000 Miles (25 000 km)						•						•						•						•
5	Timing Belt Replacement	Every 60 000 Miles (96 000 km)																								•
6	Engine Idle Speed Adjustment*	At 5 000 Miles (8 000 km) Only	•																							
7	Tire and Wheel Inspection and Rotation	At 7 500 Miles (12 500 km) and Then Every 15 000 Miles (25 000 km)			•						•						•						•			
8	Drive Belt Inspection*	Every 30 000 Miles (50 000 km)												•												•
9	Cooling System Inspection*	Every 15 000 Miles (25 000 km)						•						•						•						•
	Cooling System Refill*	Every 30 000 Miles (50 000 km)												•												•
10	Rear Wheel Bearing Repack	Every 30 000 Miles (50 000 km)												•												•
11	Manual Transaxle Fluid Replacement	Every 30 000 Miles (50 000 km)												•												•
	Automatic Transaxle Fluid Replacement	Every 30 000 Miles (50 000 km)												•												•
12	Spark Plug Replacement*	Every 30 000 Miles (50 000 km)												•												•
13	Power Steering Fluid Replacement	Every 22 500 Miles (37 500 km) or 24 Months									•									•						
14	Power Steering Rubber Hose Replacement	Every 45 000 Miles (75 000 km)																		•						
15	Air Cleaner Element Replacement*	Every 30 000 Miles (50 000 km)												•												•
16	Fuel Cap, Lines and Tank Inspection*‡	Every 15 000 Miles (25 000 km)						•						•						•						•
17	PCV Valve Inspection*‡	Every 30 000 Miles (50 000 km)												•												•

* An Emission Control Service.

‡ The U.S. Environmental Protection Agency has determined that the failure to perform this maintenance item will not nullify the emission warranty or limit recall liability prior to the completion of vehicle useful life. General Motors, however, urges that all recommended maintenance services be performed at the indicated intervals and the maintenance be recorded in Section C.

All Except Cadillac, LeMans, Metro, Prizm & Storm
1990–91

Follow Schedule I if the car is mainly operated under one or more of the following conditions:
When most trips are less than 4 miles (6 kilometers).
When most trips are less than 10 miles (16 kilometers) and outside temperatures remain below freezing.
When most trips include extended idling and/or frequent low-speed operation as in stop-and-go traffic.
Towing a trailer**
Operating in dusty areas.

Schedule I should also be followed if the car is used for delivery service, police, taxi or other commercial applications.

The services shown in this schedule up to 48,000 miles (80 000 km) are to be performed after 48,000 miles at the same intervals

ITEM NO.	TO BE SERVICED	WHEN TO PERFORM Miles (Kilometers) or Months, Whichever Occurs First	3/5	6/10	9/15	12/20	15/25	18/30	21/35	24/40	27/45	30/50	33/55	36/60	39/65	42/70	45/75	48/80
1	Engine Oil & Oil Filter Change*	Every 3,000 mi. (5 000 km) or 3 mos.	•	•	•	•	•	•	•	•	•	•	•	•	•	•	•	•
2	Chassis Lubrication	Every other oil change		•		•		•		•		•		•		•		•
3	Throttle Body Bolt Torque (Some Models)*	At 6,000 mi. (10 000 km) only		•														
4	Tire & Wheel Insp. and Rotation	At 6,000 mi. (10 000 km) and then every 15,000 mi. (25 000 km)		•					•					•				
5	Engine Accessory Drive Belt(s) Insp.*	Every 30,000 mi. (50 000 km) or 24 mos.										•						
6	Cooling System Service*	Every 30,000 mi. (50 000 km) or 24 mos.										•						
7	Wheel Brg. Repack (Rear-Wheel-Drive Cars Only)	See explanation for service interval																
8	Transmission/Transaxle Service	See explanation for service interval																
9	Spark Plug Replacement*	Every 30,000 mi. (50 000 km)										•						
10	Spark Plug Wire Insp. (Some Models)*	Every 30,000 mi. (50 000 km)										•						
11	PCV Valve Insp. (Some Models)*††	Every 30,000 mi. (50 000 km)										•						
12	EGR System Insp.*††	Every 30,000 mi. (50 000 km) or 36 mos.										•						
13	Air Cleaner & PCV Filter Repl.*	Every 30,000 mi. (50 000 km) or 36 mos.										•						
14	Eng. Timing Check (Some Models)*	Every 30,000 mi. (50 000 km)										•						
15	Fuel Tank, Cap & Lines Insp.*††	Every 30,000 mi. (50 000 km)										•						
16	Thermostatically Controlled Air Cleaner Insp.* (Some Models)	Every 30,000 mi. (50 000 km)										•						

FOOTNOTES:
* An Emission Control Service
†† The U.S. Environmental Protection Agency has determined that the failure to perform this maintenance item will not nullify the emission warranty or limit recall liability prior to the completion of vehicle useful life. General Motors, however, urges that all recommended maintenance services be performed at the indicated intervals and the maintenance be recorded in Section C of the Owner's Maintenance Schedule.
** Trailering is not recommended for some models. See the Owner's Manual for details.

All Except Cadillac, LeMans, Metro, Prizm & Storm 1990–91

Follow Schedule II only if none of the driving conditions specified in Schedule I apply.

The services shown in this schedule up to 45,000 miles (75 000 km) are to be performed after 45,000 miles at the same intervals

ITEM NO.	TO BE SERVICED	WHEN TO PERFORM — Miles (Kilometers) or Months, Whichever Occurs First	MILES (000): 7.5 / KM: 12.5	15 / 25	22.5 / 37.5	30 / 50	37.5 / 62.5	45 / 75
1	Engine Oil Change*	Every 7,500 mi. (12 500 km) or 12 mos.	●	●	●	●	●	●
	Filter Change*	At first and every other oil change or 12 mos.	●		●		●	
2	Chassis Lubrication	Every 7,500 mi. (12 500 km) or 12 mos.	●	●	●	●	●	●
3	Throttle Body Mount Bolt Torque (Some Models)*	At 7,500 mi. (12 500 km) only	●					
4	Tire & Wheel Insp. and Rotation	At 7,500 mi. (12 500 km) and then every 15,000 mi. (25 000 km)	●		●		●	
5	Engine Accessory Drive Belt(s) Insp.*	Every 30,000 mi. (50 000 km) or 24 mos.				●		
6	Cooling System Service*	Every 30,000 mi. (50 000 km) or 24 mos.				●		
7	Wheel Brg. Repack (Rear-Wheel-Drive Cars Only)	Every 30,000 mi. (50 000 km)				●		
8	Transmission/Transaxle Service	See explanation for service interval						
9	Spark Plug Replacement*	Every 30,000 mi. (50 000 km)				●		
10	Spark Plug Wire Insp. (Some Models)*	Every 30,000 mi. (50 000 km)				●		
11	PCV Valve Insp. (Some Models)* ††	Every 30,000 mi. (50 000 km)				●		
12	EGR System Insp.* ††	Every 30,000 mi. (50 000 km) or 36 mos.				●		
13	Air Cleaner & PCV Filter Repl.*	Every 30,000 mi. (50 000 km) or 36 mos.				●		
14	Eng. Timing Check (Some Models)*	Every 30,000 mi. (50 000 km)				●		
15	Fuel Tank, Cap & Lines Insp.* ††	Every 30,000 mi. (50 000 km)				●		
16	Thermostatically Controlled Air Cleaner Insp. (Some Models)*	Every 30,000 mi. (50 000 km)				●		

FOOTNOTES:
* An Emission Control Service
†† The U.S. Environmental Protection Agency has determined that the failure to perform this maintenance item will not nullify the emission warranty or limit recall liability prior to the completion of vehicle useful life. General Motors, however, urges that all recommded maintenance services be performed at the indicated intervals and the maintenance be recorded in Section C of the owner's Maintenance Schedule.

Metro
1990–91

SCHEDULED MAINTENANCE SERVICES
SCHEDULE I

Follow Schedule I if your vehicle is MAINLY operated under one or more of the following conditions:
- When most trips are less than 4 miles (6 kilometers).
- When most trips are less than 10 miles (16 kilometers) and outside temperatures remain below freezing.
- When most trips include extended idling and/or frequent low-speed operation as in stop-and-go traffic.
- Operating in dusty areas.
- Schedule I should also be followed if the vehicle is used for delivery service, police, taxi or other commercial applications.

The services shown in this schedule up to 60 000 miles (100 000 km) are to be performed after 60 000 miles at the same intervals.

#	TO BE SERVICED	WHEN TO PERFORM — Miles (Kilometers) or Months, Whichever Occurs First (Also, See Explanation of Services Pages 6–7)	MILES (000) → 3	6	9	12	15	18	21	24	27	30	33	36	39	42	45	48	51	54	57	60
		KILOMETERS (000) →	5	10	15	20	25	30	35	40	45	50	55	60	65	70	75	80	85	90	95	100
1	Engine Oil and Oil Filter Change*	Every 3 000 Miles (5 000 km) or 3 Months	•	•	•	•	•	•	•	•	•	•	•	•	•	•	•	•	•	•	•	•
2	Chassis Lubrication	Every Other Oil Change		•		•		•		•		•		•		•		•		•		•
3	Tire and Wheel Inspection and Rotation	Every 6 000 Miles (10 000 km)		•		•		•		•		•		•		•		•		•		•
4	Water Pump Belt Inspection*	Every 30 000 Miles (50 000 km) or 30 Months										•										•
5	Cooling System Service*	See Explanation of Scheduled Maintenance Services																				•
6	Brake Fluid Inspection	Every 15 000 Miles (25 000 km) or 15 Months					•					•					•					•
7	Transaxle Service	See Explanation of Scheduled Maintenance Services															•					
8	Spark Plug Replacement*	Every 30 000 Miles (50 000 km)										•										•
9	Spark Plug Wires, Replacement*	Every 60 000 Miles (100 000 km) or 60 Months																				•
10	Air Cleaner Element Replacement*	Every 30 000 Miles (50 000 km) or 30 Months										•										•
11	Fuel Tank, Cap and Lines—Inspection‡	Every 15 000 Miles (25 000 km) or 15 Months					•					•					•					•

* An Emission Control Service.

‡ The U.S. Environmental Protection Agency has determined that the failure to perform this maintenance item will not nullify the emission warranty or limit recall liability prior to the completion of vehicle useful life. General Motors, however, urges that all recommended maintenance services be performed at the indicated intervals and the maintenance be recorded in the Maintenance Schedule Booklet.

Metro
1990–91

SCHEDULED MAINTENANCE SERVICES
SCHEDULE II

Follow Schedule II only if none of the driving conditions specified in Schedule I apply.

The services shown in this schedule up to 60 000 miles (100 000 km) are to be performed after 60 000 miles at the same intervals.

To Be Serviced	When to Perform — Miles (kilometers) or Months, Whichever Occurs First (Also, See Explanation of Services Pages 6–7)	7.5	15	22.5	30	37.5	45	52.5	60
	MILES (000) → / KILOMETERS (000) ↓	12.5	25	37.5	50	62.5	75	87.5	100
1 Engine Oil and Oil Filter Change*	Every 7 500 Miles (12 500 km) or 7.5 Months	●	●	●	●	●	●	●	●
2 Chassis Lubrication	Every 7 500 Miles (12 500 km) or 7.5 Months	●	●	●	●	●	●	●	●
3 Tire and Wheel Inspection and Rotation	At 7 500 Miles (12 500 km) and Then Every 15 000 Miles (25 000 km)	●		●		●		●	
4 Water Pump Belt Inspection*	Every 30 000 Miles (50 000 km) or 30 Months				●				●
5 Cooling System Service*	See Explanation of Scheduled Maintenance Services		●		●		●		●
6 Brake Fluid Inspection	Every 15 000 Miles (25 000 km) or 15 Months		●		●		●		●
7 Transaxle Service	See Explanation of Scheduled Maintenance Services								
8 Spark Plug Replacement*	Every 30 000 Miles (50 000 km)				●				●
9 Spark Plug Wires, Replacement*	Every 60 000 Miles (100 000 km) or 60 Months								●
10 Air Cleaner Element Replacement*	Every 30 000 Miles (50 000 km) or 30 Months				●				●
11 Fuel Tank, Cap and Lines—Inspection‡	Every 15 000 Miles (25 000 km) or 15 Months		●		●		●		●

* An Emission Control Service

‡ The U.S. Environmental Protection Agency has determined that the failure to perform this maintenance item will not nullify the emission warranty or limit recall liability prior to the completion of vehicle useful life. General Motors, however, urges that all recommended maintenance services be performed at the indicated intervals and the maintenance be recorded in the Maintenance Schedule Booklet.

Prizm
1990–91

SCHEDULED MAINTENANCE SERVICES
SCHEDULE I (VIN ENGINE CODE 6)

Follow Schedule I if the car is MAINLY operated under one or more of the following conditions:

- When most trips are less than 4 miles (6 kilometers).
- When most trips are less than 10 miles (16 kilometers) and outside temperatures remain below freezing.
- When most trips include extended idling and/or frequent low-speed operation as in stop-and-go traffic.
- Towing a trailer.‡
- Operating in dusty areas.

Schedule I should also be followed if the car is used for delivery service, police, taxi or other commercial applications.

The services shown in this schedule up to 50 000 miles (83 500 km) are to be performed after 50 000 miles at the same intervals unless specified otherwise.

ITEM NO.	TO BE SERVICED	WHEN TO PERFORM — Miles (kilometers) or Months, Whichever Occurs First	MILES (000) 5	10	15	20	25	30	35	40	45	50
			KILOMETERS (000) 8.3	16.7	25	33.5	41.5	50	58.3	66.7	75	83.5
1	Engine Oil and Oil Filter Change*	Every 5 000 Miles (8 300 km) or 6 Months	•	•	•	•	•	•	•	•	•	•
2	Chassis, Body and Lubrication	See Explanation of Scheduled Maintenance Services										
3	Engine Idle Speed Adjustment*	At 10 000 Miles (16 700 km) and Every 30 000 Miles (50 000 km)		•				•				
4	Engine Coolant Replacement	See Explanation of Scheduled Maintenance Services										
5	Spark Plug Replacement	Every 30 000 Miles (50 000 km) or 36 Months						•†				
6	Air Filter Service* ¹	Every 5 000 Miles (8 300 km) or 6 Months	•	•	•	•	•	•	•	•	•	•
7	Valve Clearance Adjustment*	Every 60 000 Miles (100 000 km) or 72 Months						•†				
8	Engine Drive Belt Service	See Explanation of Scheduled Maintenance Services										
9	Charcoal Canister Inspection	See Explanation of Scheduled Maintenance Services										
10	Exhaust Pipes System Inspection	Every 15 000 Miles (25 000 km) or 18 Months			•			•			•	
11	Fuel Lines and Connection Inspection Ø	Every 30 000 Miles (50 000 km) or 36 Months						•				
12	Fuel Tank Cap Gasket Replacement Ø	See Explanation of Scheduled Maintenance Services										
13	Engine Timing Belt Replacement	See Explanation of Scheduled Maintenance Services										

* An Emission Control Service.

Ø The U.S. Environmental Protection Agency has determined that the failure to perform this maintenance item will not nullify the emission warranty or limit recall liability prior to the completion of vehicle useful life. General Motors, however, urges that all recommended maintenance services be performed at the indicated intervals and the maintenance be recorded in Section C.

¹ Applicable only when operating the vehicle mainly on dusty roads. If not, use interval in Schedule II.

‡ Trailering is not recommended for some models. See the Owner's Manual for details.

† In California, these are the minimum Emission Control Maintenance Services an owner must perform according to the California Air Resources Board. General Motors, however, urges that all Emission Control Maintenance Services shown be performed. To maintain other new car warranties, all services shown in this booklet should be performed.

Prizm
1990–91

SCHEDULED MAINTENANCE SERVICES
SCHEDULE II (VIN ENGINE CODE 6)

Follow Schedule II only if none of the driving conditions specified in Schedule I apply.

ITEM NO.	TO BE SERVICED	WHEN TO PERFORM — Miles (kilometers) or Months, Whichever Occurs First	MILES (000) 10 / KM 16.7	20 / 33.5	30 / 50	40 / 66.7	50 / 83.5	60 / 100	70 / 116.7	80 / 133.5	90 / 150	100 / 166.7
1	Engine Oil and Oil Filter Change*	Every 10 000 Miles (16 700 km) or 12 Months	•	•	•	•	•	•	•	•	•	•
2	Chassis, Body and Lubrication	See Explanation of Scheduled Maintenance Services		•		•		•		•		•
3	Engine Idle Speed Adjustment*	At 10 000 Miles (16 700 km) and Every 30 000 Miles (50 000 km)	•			•			•			•
4	Engine Coolant Replacement	At 60 000 Miles (100 000 km) or 72 Months, Every 30 000 Miles (50 000 km) or 36 Months Thereafter						•			•	
5	Spark Plug Replacement*	Every 30 000 Miles (50 000 km) or 36 Months			†			•†			†	
6	Air Filter Service*	Every 30 000 Miles (50 000 km) or 36 Months			†			•†			†	
7	Valve Clearance Adjustment*	Every 60 000 Miles (100 000 km) or 72 Months						•				
8	Engine Drive Belt Service	See Explanation of Scheduled Maintenance Services						•				
9	Charcoal Canister Inspection	See Explanation of Scheduled Maintenance Services										
10	Exhaust Pipes System Inspection Ø	Every 30 000 Miles (50 000 km) or 36 Months			•			•			•	
11	Fuel Lines and Connection Inspection Ø	Every 30 000 Miles (50 000 km) or 36 Months			•			•			•	
12	Fuel Tank Cap Gasket Replacement Ø	See Explanation of Scheduled Maintenance Services										

* An Emission Control Service.

Ø The U.S. Environmental Protection Agency has determined that the failure to perform this maintenance item will not nullify the emission warranty or limit recall liability prior to the completion of vehicle useful life. General Motors, however, urges that all recommended maintenance services be performed at the indicated intervals and the maintenance be recorded in Section C.

† In California, these are the minimum Emission Control Maintenance Services an owner must perform according to the California Air Resources Board. General Motors, however, urges that all Emission control Maintenance Services shown be performed. To maintain other new car warranties, all services shown in this booklet should be performed.

Storm
1990–91

SCHEDULED MAINTENANCE SERVICES
SCHEDULE I

Follow Schedule I if your car is MAINLY operated under one or more of the following conditions:

- When most trips are less than 4 miles (6 kilometers).
- When most trips are less than 10 miles (16 kilometers) and outside temperatures remain below freezing.
- When most trips include extended idling and/or frequent low-speed operation as in stop-and-go traffic.
- Towing a trailer.#
- Operating in dusty areas.

Schedule I should also be followed if the car is used for delivery service, police, taxi or other commercial applications.

The services shown in this schedule up to 60 000 miles (100 000 km) are to be performed after 60 000 miles at the same intervals.

#	TO BE SERVICED	WHEN TO PERFORM (Miles (kilometers) or Months, Whichever Occurs First)	MILES (000): 3 / 6 / 9 / 12 / 15 / 18 / 21 / 24 / 27 / 30 / 33 / 36 / 39 / 42 / 45 / 48 / 51 / 54 / 57 / 60 — KILOMETERS (000): 5 / 10 / 15 / 20 / 25 / 30 / 35 / 40 / 45 / 50 / 55 / 60 / 65 / 70 / 75 / 80 / 85 / 90 / 95 / 100
1	Engine Oil Replacement*	Every 3 000 Miles (5 000 km) or 3 Months	3, 6, 9, 12, 15, 18, 21, 24, 27, 30, 33, 36, 39, 42, 45, 48, 51, 54, 57, 60
2	Oil Filter Replacement*	At First and Then Every Other Oil Change	3, 9, 15, 21, 27, 33, 39, 45, 51, 57
3	Chassis and Body Lubrication	Every Other Oil Change	6, 12, 18, 24, 30, 36, 42, 48, 54, 60
	Valve Clearance Adjustment* VIN 6	Every 15 000 Miles (25 000 km)	15, 30, 45, 60
	Valve Clearance Adjustment* VIN 5	Every 60 000 Miles (100 000 km)	60
4	Timing Belt Replacement	Every 60 000 Miles (100 000 km)	60
5	Tire and Wheel Inspection and Rotation	At 6 000 Miles (10 000 km) and Then Every 15 000 Miles (25 000 km)	6, 21, 36, 51
6	Drive Belt Inspection*	Every 30 000 Miles (50 000 km)	30, 60
7	Cooling System Inspection*	Every 15 000 Miles (25 000 km)	15, 30, 45, 60
	Cooling System Refill*	Every 30 000 Miles (50 000 km)	30, 60
8	Manual Transaxle Fluid Replacement	Every 15 000 Miles (25 000 km)	15, 30, 45, 60
	Automatic Transaxle Fluid Replacement	Every 15 000 Miles (25 000 km)	15, 30, 45, 60
9	Spark Plug Replacement*	Every 30 000 Miles (50 000 km)	30, 60
10	Power Steering Fluid Replacement	Every 21 000 Miles (35 000 km) or 24 Months	21, 42
11	Power Steering Hose Inspection	Every 42 000 Miles (70 000 km)	42
12	Air Cleaner Element Replacement*	See Explanation of Scheduled Maintenance Services	—
13	Fuel Cap, Lines and Tank Inspection*‡	Every 15 000 Miles (25 000 km)	15, 30, 45, 60
14	PCV Valve Inspection*‡	Every 30 000 Miles (50 000 km)	30, 60

* An Emission Control Service.

‡ The U.S. Environmental Protection Agency has determined that the failure to perform this maintenance item will not nullify the emission warranty or limit recall liability prior to the completion of vehicle useful life. General Motors, however, urges that all recommended maintenance services be performed at the indicated intervals and the maintenance be recorded in Section C of the Owner's Maintenance Schedule.

Trailering is not recommended for some models. See your Owner's Manual for details.

Storm
1990–91

SCHEDULED MAINTENANCE SERVICES
SCHEDULE II

Follow Schedule II only if none of the driving conditions specified in Schedule I apply.

The services shown in this schedule up to 60 000 miles (96 000 km) are to be performed after 60 000 miles at the same intervals.

#	TO BE SERVICED	WHEN TO PERFORM (Miles (kilometers) or Months, Whichever Occurs First)	3	6	7.5	9	12	15	18	21	22.5	24	27	30	33	36	37.5	39	42	45	48	51	52.5	54	57	60
		MILES (000) / KILOMETERS (000)	5	10	12.5	15	20	25	30	35	37.5	40	45	50	55	60	62.5	65	70	75	80	85	87.5	90	95	100
1	Engine Oil Replacement*	Every 7 500 Miles (12 500 km) or 12 Months			•			•			•			•			•			•			•			•
	Oil Filter Replacement*	At First and Then Every Other Oil Change			•						•						•						•			
2	Chassis and Body Lubrication	Every 7 500 Miles (12 500 km) or 12 Months			•			•			•			•			•			•			•			•
3	Valve Clearance Adjustment* VIN 6	Every 15 000 Miles (25 000 km)						•						•						•						•
	VIN 5	Every 60 000 Miles (100 000 km)																								•
4	Timing Belt Replacement	Every 60 000 Miles (100 000 km)																								•
5	Tire and Wheel Inspection and Rotation	At 7 500 Miles (12 500 km) and Then Every 15 000 Miles (25 000 km)			•			•						•						•						•
6	Drive Belt Inspection*	Every 30 000 Miles (50 000 km)												•												•
7	Cooling System Inspection*	Every 15 000 Miles (25 000 km)						•						•						•						•
	Cooling System Refill*	Every 30 000 Miles (50 000 km)												•												•
8	Manual Transaxle Fluid Replacement	Every 30 000 Miles (50 000 km)												•												•
	Automatic Transaxle Fluid Replacement	Every 30 000 Miles (50 000 km)												•												•
9	Spark Plug Replacement*	Every 30 000 Miles (50 000 km)												•												•
10	Power Steering Fluid Replacement	Every 22 500 Miles (37 500 km) or 24 Months									•									•						
11	Power Steering Hose Inspection	Every 45 000 Miles (75 000 km)																		•						
12	Air Cleaner Element Replacement*	Every 30 000 Miles (50 000 km)												•												•
13	Fuel Cap, Lines and Tank Inspection*‡	Every 15 000 Miles (25 000 km)						•						•						•						•
14	PCV Valve Inspection*‡	Every 30 000 Miles (50 000 km)												•												•

* An Emission Control Service.

‡ The U.S. Environmental Protection Agency has determined that the failure to perform this maintenance item will not nullify the emission warranty or limit recall liability prior to the completion of vehicle useful life. General Motors, however, urges that all recommended maintenance services be performed at the indicated intervals and the maintenance be recorded in Section C of the Owner's Maintenance Schedule.

ELECTRICAL SYMBOL IDENTIFICATION

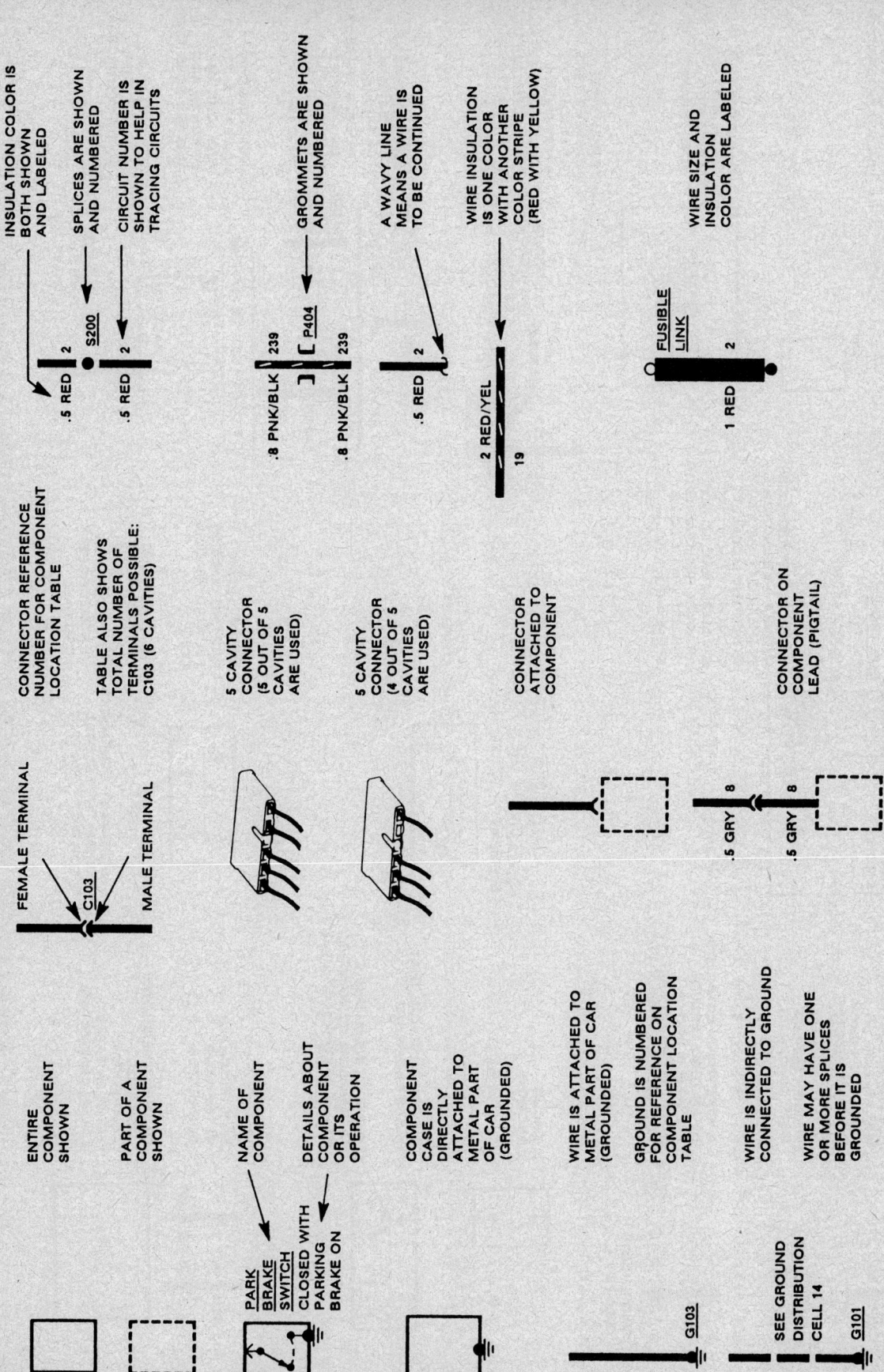

Fig. 1 Symbol Identification (Part 1 of 2). 1988 All Except LeMans & Spectrum

INSULATION COLOR IS BOTH SHOWN AND LABELED

SPLICES ARE SHOWN AND NUMBERED

CIRCUIT NUMBER IS SHOWN TO HELP IN TRACING CIRCUITS

GROMMETS ARE SHOWN AND NUMBERED

A WAVY LINE MEANS A WIRE IS TO BE CONTINUED

WIRE INSULATION IS ONE COLOR WITH ANOTHER COLOR STRIPE (RED WITH YELLOW)

WIRE SIZE AND INSULATION COLOR ARE LABELED

FUSIBLE LINK

.5 RED 2 S200

.5 RED 2

.8 PNK/BLK 239   P404   .8 PNK/BLK 239

.5 RED 2

2 RED/YEL 19

1 RED 2

CONNECTOR REFERENCE NUMBER FOR COMPONENT LOCATION TABLE

TABLE ALSO SHOWS TOTAL NUMBER OF TERMINALS POSSIBLE: C103 (6 CAVITIES)

5 CAVITY CONNECTOR (5 OUT OF 5 CAVITIES ARE USED)

5 CAVITY CONNECTOR (4 OUT OF 5 CAVITIES ARE USED)

CONNECTOR ATTACHED TO COMPONENT

CONNECTOR ON COMPONENT LEAD (PIGTAIL)

FEMALE TERMINAL

C103

MALE TERMINAL

.5 GRY 8   .5 GRY 8

ENTIRE COMPONENT SHOWN

PART OF A COMPONENT SHOWN

NAME OF COMPONENT

DETAILS ABOUT COMPONENT OR ITS OPERATION

COMPONENT CASE IS DIRECTLY ATTACHED TO METAL PART OF CAR (GROUNDED)

WIRE IS ATTACHED TO METAL PART OF CAR (GROUNDED)

GROUND IS NUMBERED FOR REFERENCE ON COMPONENT LOCATION TABLE

WIRE IS INDIRECTLY CONNECTED TO GROUND

WIRE MAY HAVE ONE OR MORE SPLICES BEFORE IT IS GROUNDED

PARK BRAKE SWITCH

CLOSED WITH PARKING BRAKE ON

G103

SEE GROUND DISTRIBUTION CELL 14

G101

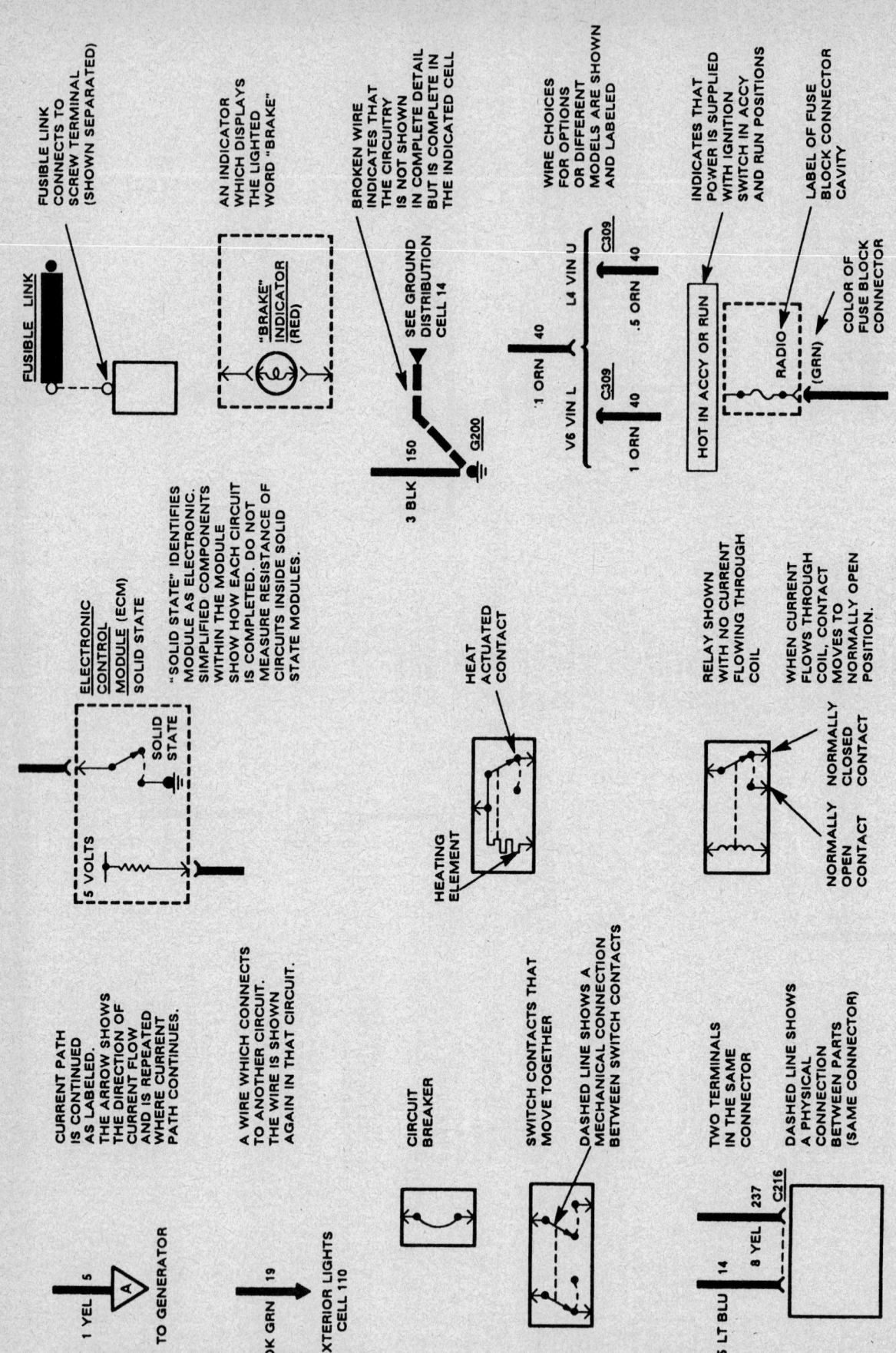

Fig. 1 Symbol Identification (Part 2 of 2), 1988 All Except LeMans & Spectrum

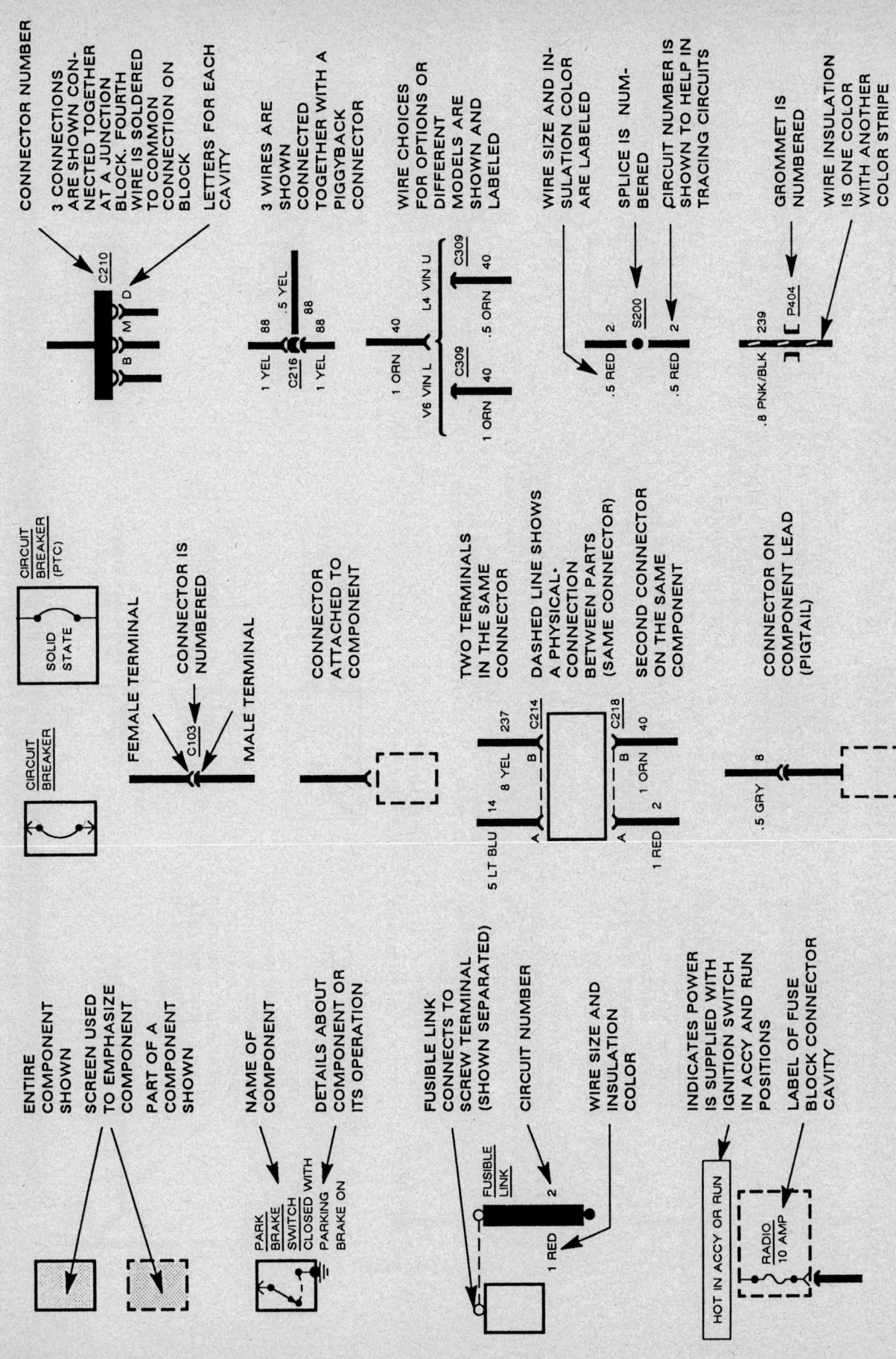

Fig. 2 Symbol Identification (Part 1 Of 3), 1989–91 All Except Geo, LeMans, Electra, LeSabre & 1991 Park Avenue/Ultra

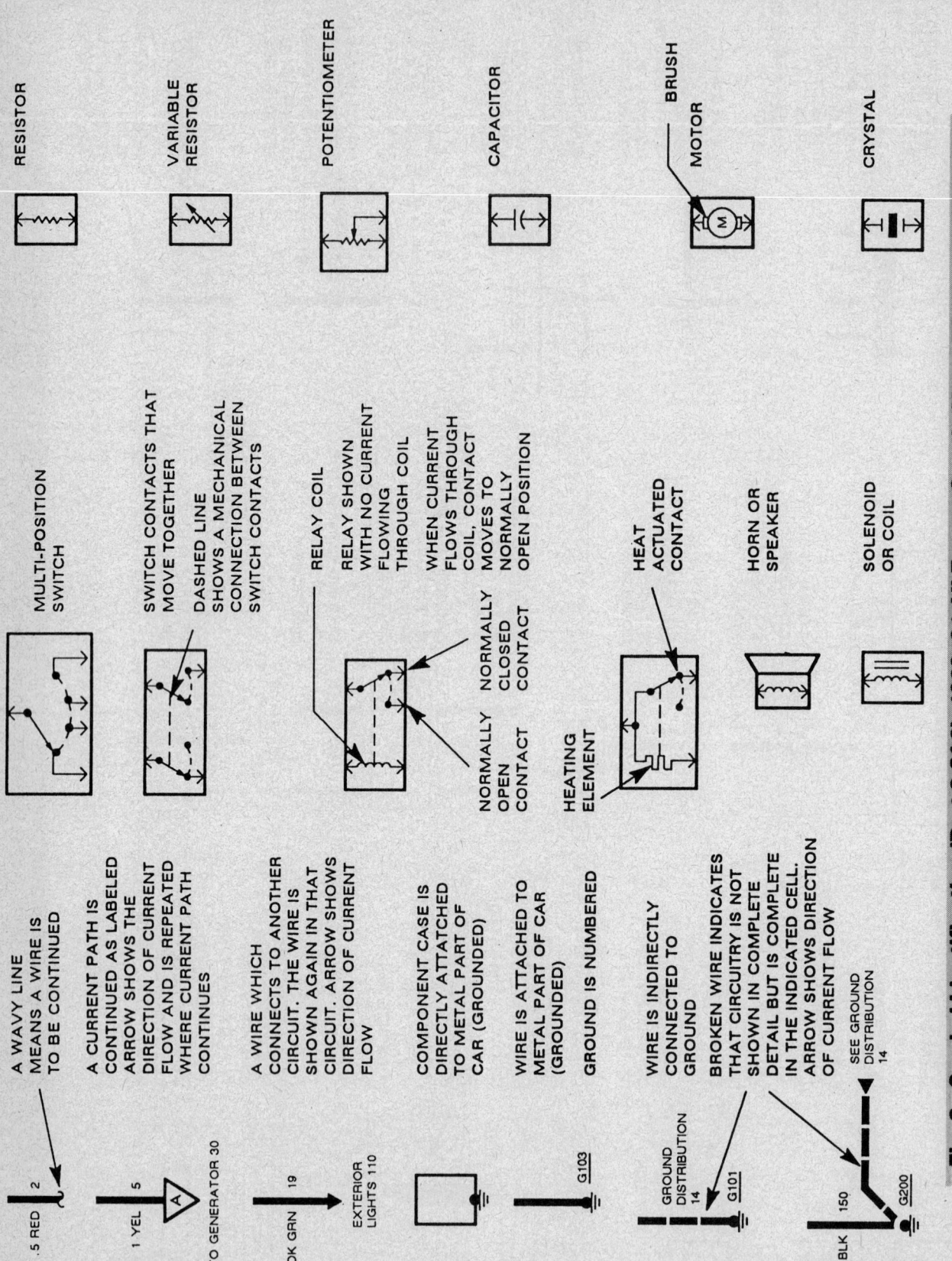

RESISTOR

VARIABLE RESISTOR

POTENTIOMETER

CAPACITOR

MOTOR
BRUSH

CRYSTAL

MULTI-POSITION SWITCH

SWITCH CONTACTS THAT MOVE TOGETHER

DASHED LINE SHOWS A MECHANICAL CONNECTION BETWEEN SWITCH CONTACTS

RELAY COIL

RELAY SHOWN WITH NO CURRENT FLOWING THROUGH COIL

WHEN CURRENT FLOWS THROUGH COIL, CONTACT MOVES TO NORMALLY OPEN POSITION

NORMALLY CLOSED CONTACT

NORMALLY OPEN CONTACT

HEATING ELEMENT

HEAT ACTUATED CONTACT

HORN OR SPEAKER

SOLENOID OR COIL

A WAVY LINE MEANS A WIRE IS TO BE CONTINUED

.5 RED 2

A CURRENT PATH IS CONTINUED AS LABELED ARROW SHOWS THE DIRECTION OF CURRENT FLOW AND IS REPEATED WHERE CURRENT PATH CONTINUES

1 YEL 5
A

A WIRE WHICH CONNECTS TO ANOTHER CIRCUIT. THE WIRE IS SHOWN AGAIN IN THAT CIRCUIT. ARROW SHOWS DIRECTION OF CURRENT FLOW

1 DK GRN 19
TO GENERATOR 30

EXTERIOR LIGHTS 110

COMPONENT CASE IS DIRECTLY ATTACHED TO METAL PART OF CAR (GROUNDED)

WIRE IS ATTACHED TO METAL PART OF CAR (GROUNDED)

GROUND IS NUMBERED

G103

WIRE IS INDIRECTLY CONNECTED TO GROUND

GROUND DISTRIBUTION 14
G101

BROKEN WIRE INDICATES THAT CIRCUITRY IS NOT SHOWN IN COMPLETE DETAIL BUT IS COMPLETE IN THE INDICATED CELL. ARROW SHOWS DIRECTION OF CURRENT FLOW

3 BLK 150

SEE GROUND DISTRIBUTION 14
G200

Fig. 2 Symbol Identification (Part 2 Of 3), 1989–91 All Except Geo, LeMans, Electra, LeSabre & 1991 Park Avenue/Ultra

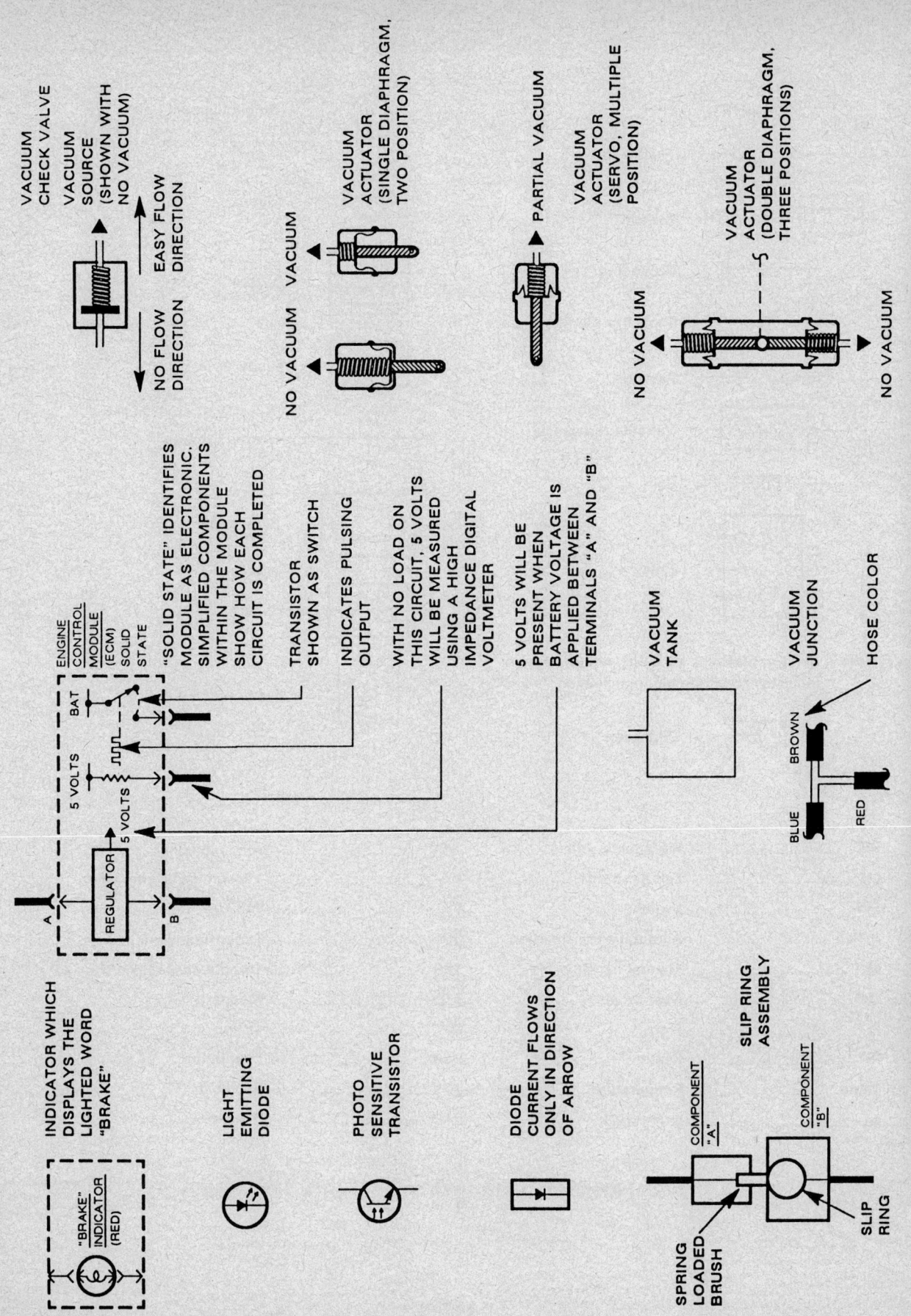

Fig. 2 Symbol Identification (Part 3 of 3). 1989-91 All Except Geo, LeMans, Electra/LeSabre & 1991 Park Avenue/Ultra

VACUUM CHECK VALVE

VACUUM SOURCE (SHOWN WITH NO VACUUM)

EASY FLOW DIRECTION

NO FLOW DIRECTION

VACUUM ACTUATOR (SINGLE DIAPHRAGM, TWO POSITION)

NO VACUUM   VACUUM

PARTIAL VACUUM

VACUUM ACTUATOR (SERVO, MULTIPLE POSITION)

VACUUM ACTUATOR (DOUBLE DIAPHRAGM, THREE POSITIONS)

NO VACUUM   NO VACUUM

ENGINE CONTROL MODULE (ECM) SOLID STATE

BAT

5 VOLTS

REGULATOR

5 VOLTS

5 VOLTS

A

B

"SOLID STATE" IDENTIFIES MODULE AS ELECTRONIC. SIMPLIFIED COMPONENTS WITHIN THE MODULE SHOW HOW EACH CIRCUIT IS COMPLETED

TRANSISTOR SHOWN AS SWITCH

INDICATES PULSING OUTPUT

WITH NO LOAD ON THIS CIRCUIT, 5 VOLTS WILL BE MEASURED USING A HIGH IMPEDANCE DIGITAL VOLTMETER

5 VOLTS WILL BE PRESENT WHEN BATTERY VOLTAGE IS APPLIED BETWEEN TERMINALS "A" AND "B"

VACUUM TANK

VACUUM JUNCTION

HOSE COLOR

BROWN

BLUE

RED

INDICATOR WHICH DISPLAYS THE LIGHTED WORD "BRAKE"

"BRAKE" INDICATOR (RED)

LIGHT EMITTING DIODE

PHOTO SENSITIVE TRANSISTOR

DIODE CURRENT FLOWS ONLY IN DIRECTION OF ARROW

SLIP RING ASSEMBLY

COMPONENT "A"

COMPONENT "B"

SPRING LOADED BRUSH

SLIP RING

ELECTRICAL SYMBOL IDENTIFICATION

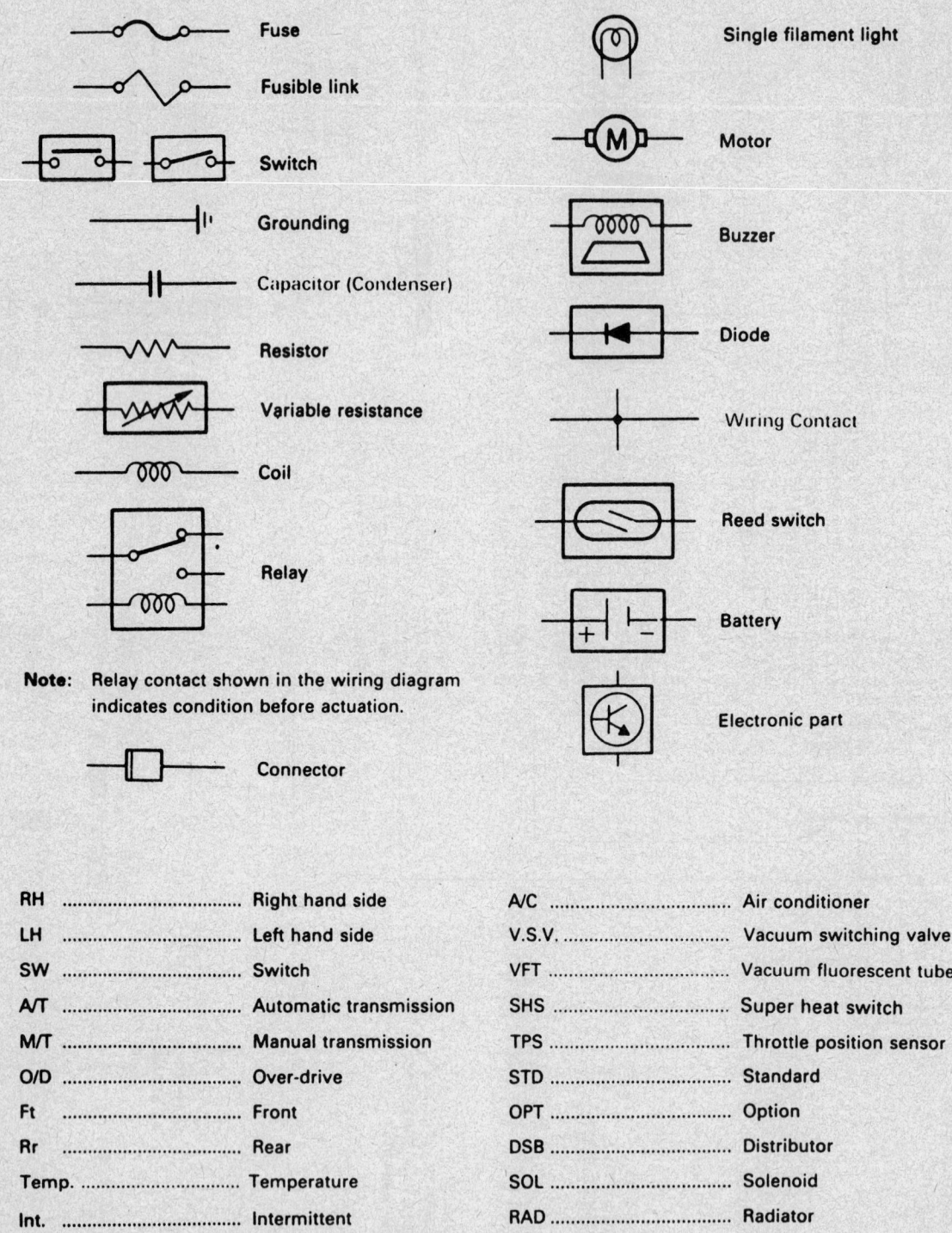

	Fuse			Single filament light
	Fusible link			Motor
	Switch			Buzzer
	Grounding			Diode
	Capacitor (Condenser)			Wiring Contact
	Resistor			Reed switch
	Variable resistance			Battery
	Coil			Electronic part
	Relay			

Note: Relay contact shown in the wiring diagram indicates condition before actuation.

Connector

RH	Right hand side		A/C	Air conditioner
LH	Left hand side		V.S.V.	Vacuum switching valve
SW	Switch		VFT	Vacuum fluorescent tube
A/T	Automatic transmission		SHS	Super heat switch
M/T	Manual transmission		TPS	Throttle position sensor
O/D	Over-drive		STD	Standard
Ft	Front		OPT	Option
Rr	Rear		DSB	Distributor
Temp.	Temperature		SOL	Solenoid
Int.	Intermittent		RAD	Radiator

Fig. 3   Symbol Identification. 1988 Spectrum & 1989 Geo

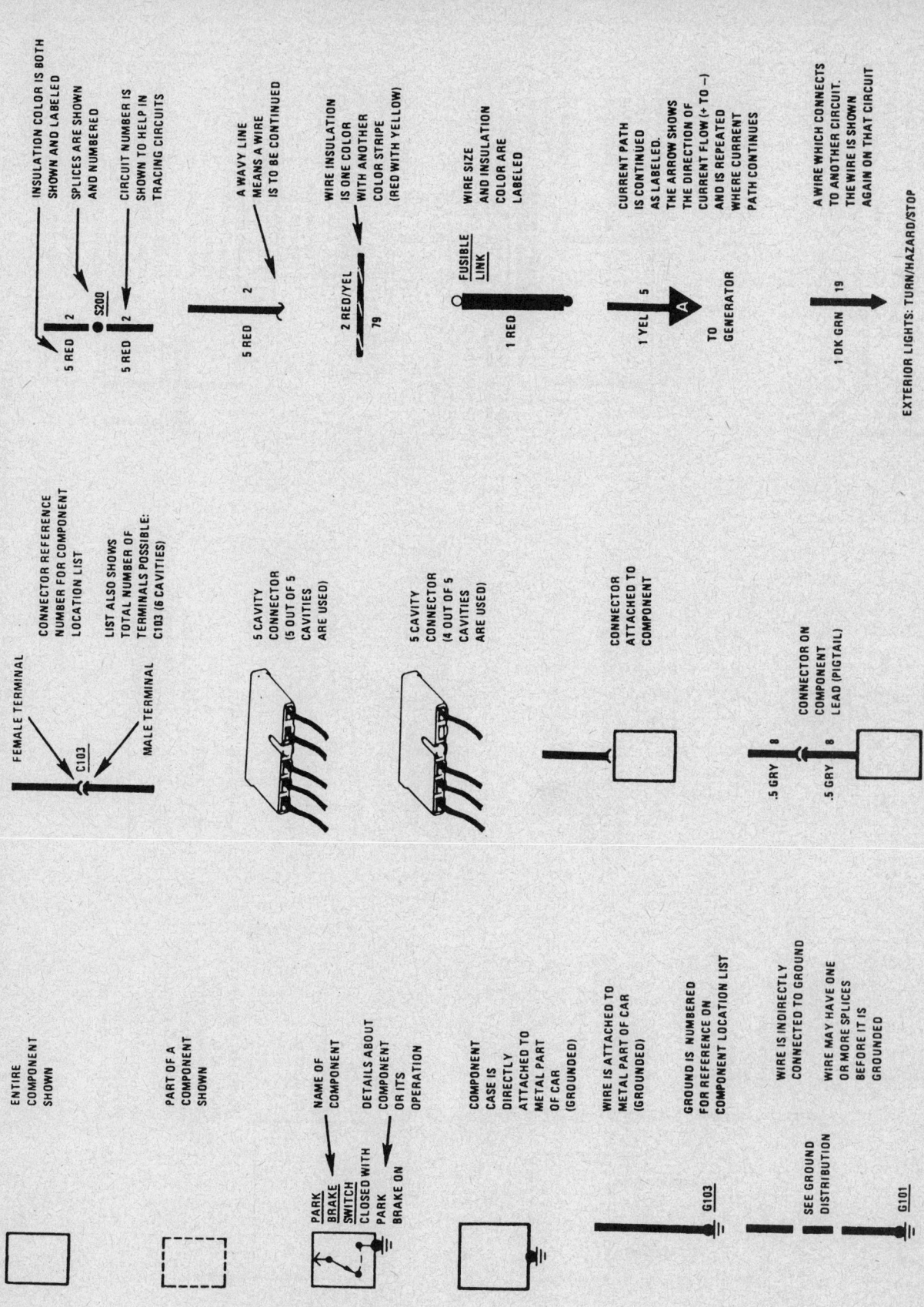

Fig. 4 Symbol Identification (Part 1 of 2). 1988-90 LeMans & 1990 Geo

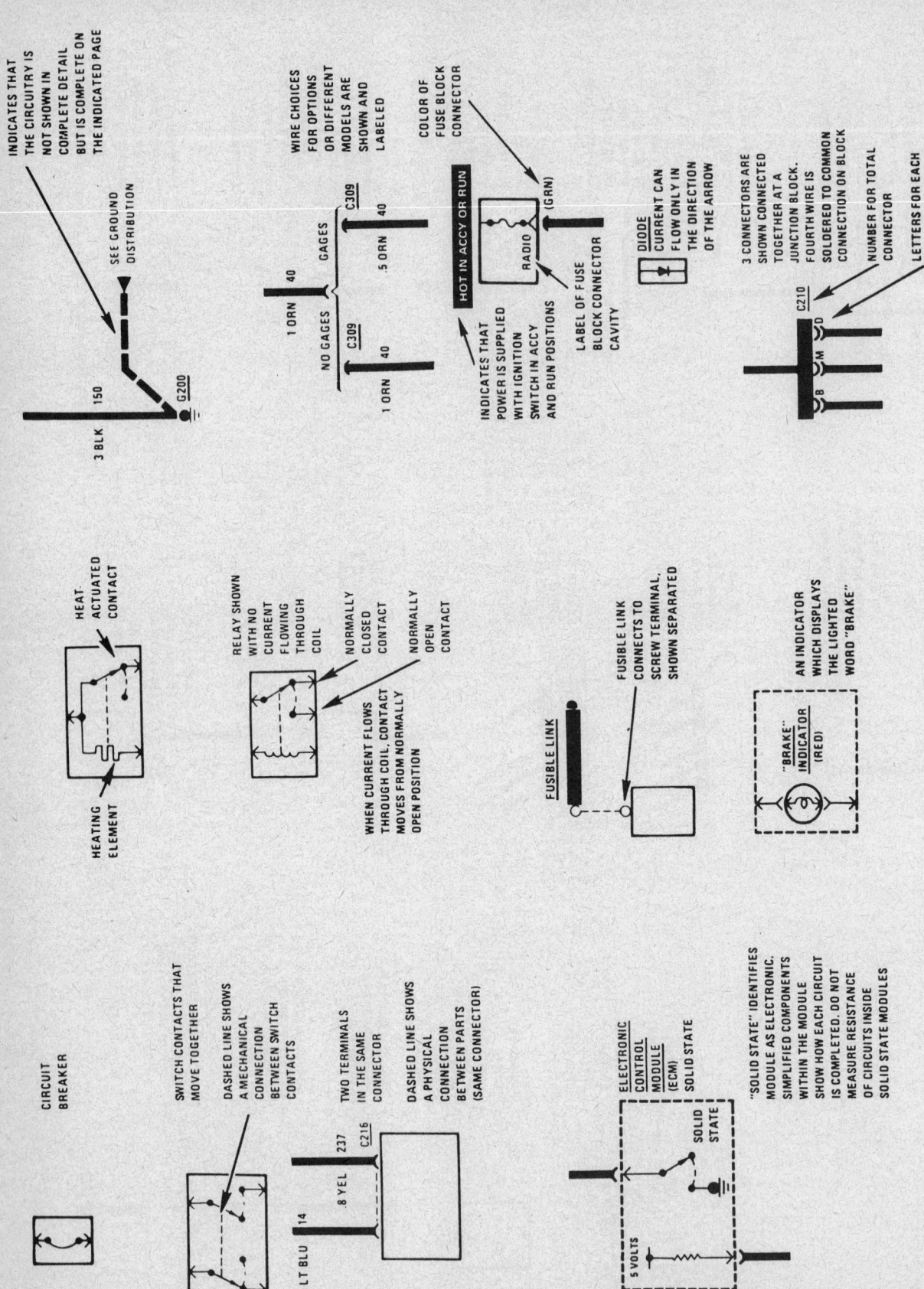

INDICATES THAT THE CIRCUITRY IS NOT SHOWN IN COMPLETE DETAIL BUT IS COMPLETE ON THE INDICATED PAGE

SEE GROUND DISTRIBUTION

G200

150

3 BLK

WIRE CHOICES FOR OPTIONS OR DIFFERENT MODELS ARE SHOWN AND LABELED

COLOR OF FUSE BLOCK CONNECTOR

C309

40

.5 ORN

GAGES

1 ORN

40

NO GAGES

C309

40

1 ORN

HOT IN ACCY OR RUN

(GRN)

RADIO

INDICATES THAT POWER IS SUPPLIED WITH IGNITION SWITCH IN ACCY AND RUN POSITIONS

LABEL OF FUSE BLOCK CONNECTOR CAVITY

DIODE CURRENT CAN FLOW ONLY IN THE DIRECTION OF THE ARROW

3 CONNECTORS ARE SHOWN CONNECTED TOGETHER AT A JUNCTION BLOCK. FOURTH WIRE IS SOLDERED TO COMMON CONNECTION ON BLOCK

NUMBER FOR TOTAL CONNECTOR

LETTERS FOR EACH CONNECTOR

C210

D

M

B

HEAT ACTUATED CONTACT

HEATING ELEMENT

RELAY SHOWN WITH NO CURRENT FLOWING THROUGH COIL

NORMALLY CLOSED CONTACT

NORMALLY OPEN CONTACT

WHEN CURRENT FLOWS THROUGH COIL, CONTACT MOVES FROM NORMALLY OPEN POSITION

FUSIBLE LINK CONNECTS TO SCREW TERMINAL, SHOWN SEPARATED

FUSIBLE LINK

AN INDICATOR WHICH DISPLAYS THE LIGHTED WORD "BRAKE"

"BRAKE" INDICATOR (RED)

CIRCUIT BREAKER

SWITCH CONTACTS THAT MOVE TOGETHER

DASHED LINE SHOWS A MECHANICAL CONNECTION BETWEEN SWITCH CONTACTS

TWO TERMINALS IN THE SAME CONNECTOR

DASHED LINE SHOWS A PHYSICAL CONNECTION BETWEEN PARTS (SAME CONNECTOR)

237

C216

.8 YEL

14

.5 LT BLU

ELECTRONIC CONTROL MODULE (ECM) SOLID STATE

"SOLID STATE" IDENTIFIES MODULE AS ELECTRONIC. SIMPLIFIED COMPONENTS WITHIN THE MODULE SHOW HOW EACH CIRCUIT IS COMPLETED. DO NOT MEASURE RESISTANCE OF CIRCUITS INSIDE SOLID STATE MODULES

SOLID STATE

5 VOLTS

Fig. 4 Symbol Identification (Part 2 of 2). 1988-90 LeMans & 1990 Geo

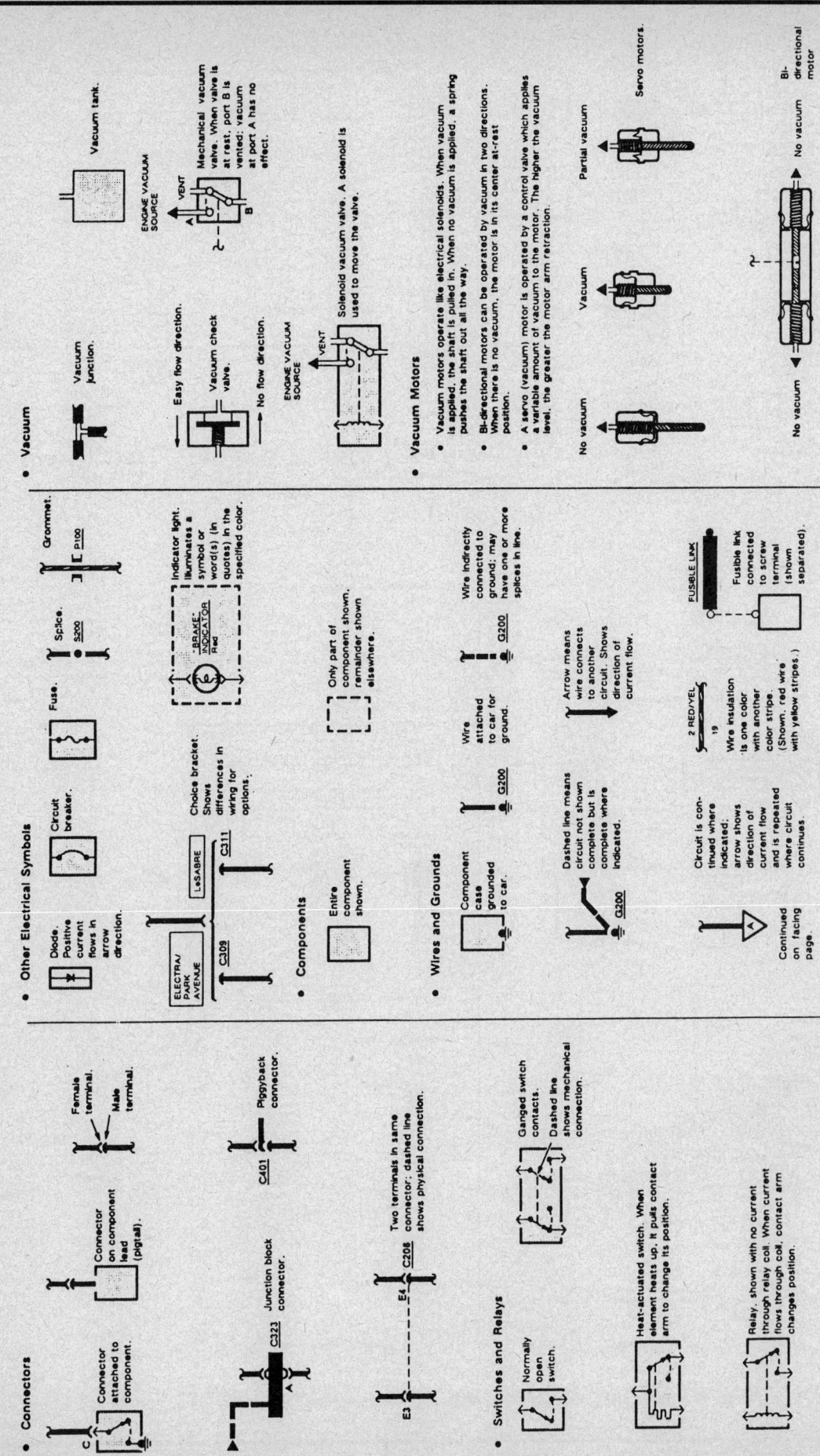

- **Connectors**

Connector attached to component.

Connector on component lead (pigtail).

Female terminal. Male terminal.

Piggyback connector. C401

Junction block connector. C323

Two terminals in same connector; dashed line shows physical connection. E4 C206

E3

- **Switches and Relays**

Normally open switch.

Ganged switch contacts. Dashed line shows mechanical connection.

Heat-actuated switch. When element heats up, it puts contact arm to change its position.

Relay, shown with no current through relay coil. When current flows through coil, contact arm changes position.

- **Other Electrical Symbols**

Diode. Positive current flows in arrow direction.

Circuit breaker.

Choice bracket. Shows differences in wiring for options.

LeSabre C311

ELECTRA/PARK AVENUE C309

- **Components**

Entire component shown.

Only part of component shown; remainder shown elsewhere.

- **Wires and Grounds**

Component case grounded to car. G200

Dashed line means circuit not shown complete but is complete where indicated. G200

Circuit is continued where indicated; arrow shows direction of current flow and is repeated where circuit continues.

Continued on facing page.

Fuse.

Circuit breaker.

Indicator light. Illuminates a symbol or word(s) (in quotes) in the specified color.

BRAKE INDICATOR Red

Wire attached to car for ground. G200

Wire indirectly connected to ground; may have one or more splices in line. G200

Arrow means wire connects to another circuit. Shows direction of current flow.

FUSIBLE LINK

Fusible link connected to screw terminal (shown separated).

2 RED/YEL 19

Wire insulation is one color with another color stripe. (Shown, red wire with yellow stripes.)

Splice. S200

Grommet. P100

- **Vacuum**

Vacuum junction.

Easy flow direction.

Vacuum check valve.

No flow direction.

ENGINE VACUUM SOURCE

VENT

Solenoid vacuum valve. A solenoid is used to move the valve.

Vacuum tank.

ENGINE VACUUM SOURCE

VENT

A

B

Mechanical vacuum valve. When valve is at rest, port B is vented; vacuum at port A has no effect.

- **Vacuum Motors**

- Vacuum motors operate like electrical solenoids. When vacuum is applied, the shaft is pulled in. When no vacuum is applied, a spring pushes the shaft out all the way.
- Bi-directional motors can be operated by vacuum in two directions. When there is no vacuum, the motor is in its center at-rest position.
- A servo (vacuum) motor is operated by a control valve which applies a variable amount of vacuum to the motor. The higher the vacuum level, the greater the motor arm retraction.

No vacuum

Vacuum

Partial vacuum

Servo motors.

No vacuum

No vacuum

Bi-directional motor

Fig. 5 Symbol Identification. 1989–90 Electra & 1989–91 LeSabre

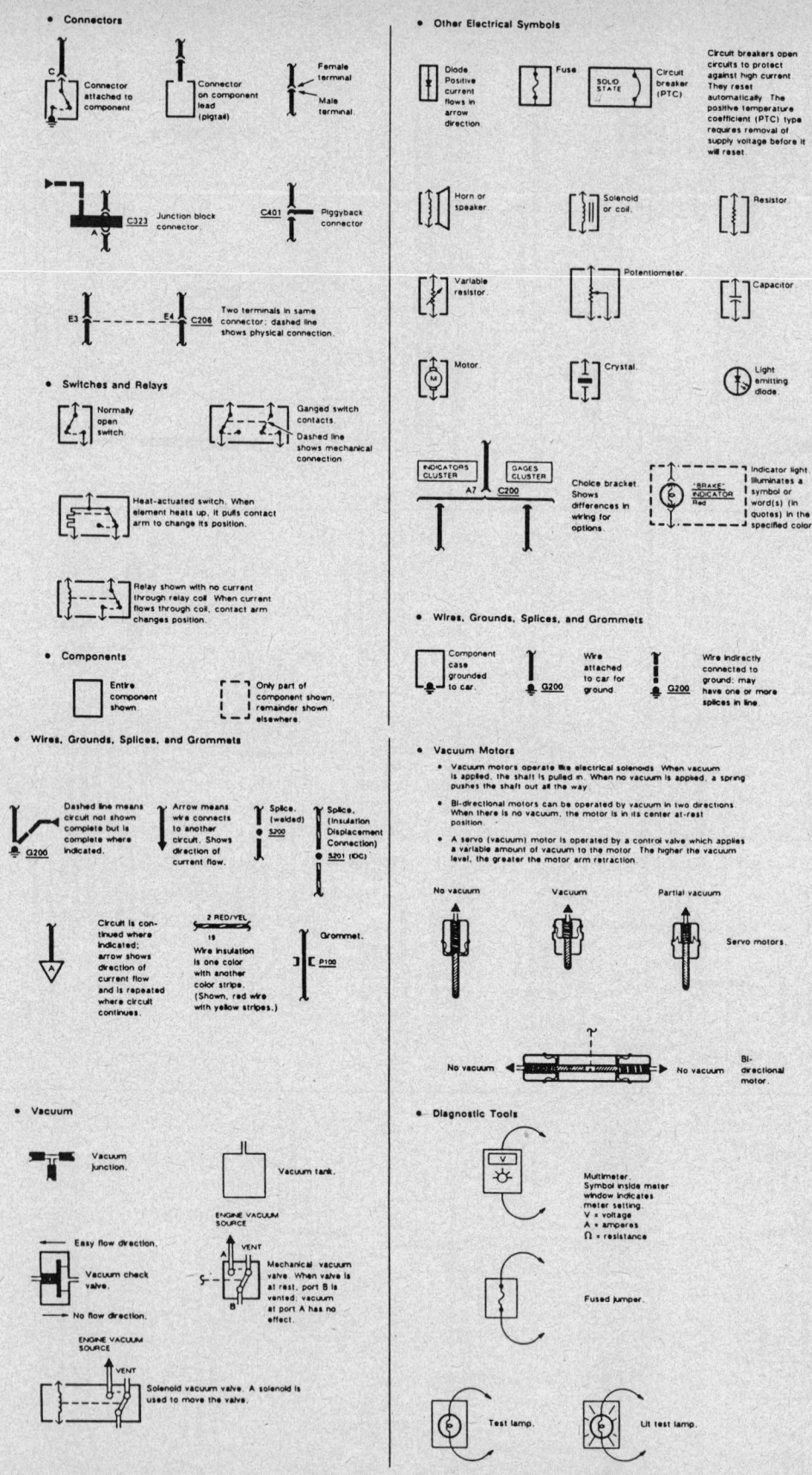

Fig. 6   Symbol Identification. 1991 Park Avenue/Ultra

BUICK ESTATE WAGON, CADILLAC BROUGHAM, CHEVROLET CAPRICE & MONTE CARLO, OLDSMOBILE CUSTOM CRUISER & CUTLASS SUPREME CLASSIC & PONTIAC SAFARI

(B/D/G Cars)

INDEX OF SERVICE OPERATIONS

NOTE: Refer To Rear Of This Manual For Vehicle Manufacturer's Special Tool Suppliers.

Continued

BUICK ESTATE WAGON, CADILLAC BROUGHAM, CHEVROLET CAPRICE & MONTE CARLO, OLDSMOBILE CUSTOM CRUISER & CUTLASS SUPREME CLASSIC & PONTIAC SAFARI

1-1

INDEX OF SERVICE OPERATIONS—Continued

Specifications

GENERAL ENGINE SPECIFICATIONS

Year	Engine Liter/CID	VIN Code ①	Fuel System	Bore & Stroke	Compression Ratio	Net Brake H.P. @ RPM②	Maximum Torque	Normal Oil Pressure Psi.
1988	4.3L/V6-262	Z	EFI	4.00 x 3.48	9.3	145 @ 4200	225 @ 2000	③
	5.0L/V8-305④	H	4 Bbl.	3.74 x 3.48	9.3	150 @ 4000	240 @ 2000	③
	5.0L/V8-305⑤	H	4 Bbl.	3.74 x 3.48	9.3	170 @ 3200	250 @ 2800	③
	5.0L/V8-305 HO	G	4 Bbl.	3.74 x 3.48	9.3	180 @ 4800	225 @ 3200	③
	5.0L/V8-307	Y	4 Bbl.	3.800 x 3.385	8.0	140 @ 3200	255 @ 2000	30⑥
1989	5.0L/V8-305⑤	E	TBI	3.74 x 3.48	9.3	170 @ 4000	255 @ 2400	③
	5.0L/V8-307	Y	4 Bbl.	3.800 x 3.385	8.0	140 @ 3200	255 @ 2000	30⑥
1990	5.0L/V8-305⑤	E	TBI	3.74 x 3.48	9.3	170 @ 4400	255 @ 2400	③
	5.0L/V8-307	Y	4 Bbl.	3.800 x 3.385	8.0	140 @ 3200	255 @ 2000	30⑥
	5.7L/V8-350	7	TBI	4.00 x 3.48	9.3	175 @ 4200	295 @ 2000	③
1991	5.0L/V8-305⑤	E	TBI	3.74 x 3.48	9.3	170 @ 4200	255 @ 2400	③
	5.7L/V8-350	7	TBI	4.00 x 3.48	9.8	185 @ 3800	300 @ 2400	③

TBI—Throttle Body Fuel Injection.
4 Bbl.—4 barrel carburetor.
①—The eighth digit of the VIN denotes engine code.

②—Ratings are net, as installed in vehicle.
③—Minimum with engine hot, 6 psi. @ 1000 RPM; 18 psi. @ 2000 RPM; 24

psi. @ 4000 RPM.
④—Monte Carlo.
⑤—Caprice.
⑥—Minimum with engine hot @ 1500 RPM.

TUNE UP SPECIFICATIONS

Year & Engine/VIN Code ①	Spark Plug Gap	Ignition Timing			Curb Idle Speed ④	Fast Idle Speed ④	Fuel Pump Pressure Psi.
		Firing Order Fig. ②	Degrees BTDC ③	Mark Fig.			
1988							
4.3L/V6-262/Z	.035	A	TDC ⑤	B	⑥	⑥	9–13 ⑦
5.0L/V8-305/H	.035	C	TDC ⑧	D	500D	2200 ⑨	7.5–9
5.0L/V8-305/G HO	.035	C	6 ⑧	D	500D	2200 ⑨	6.5–9
5.0L/V8-307/Y	.060	E	20 ⑩	F	⑪	550D ⑫	5.5–6.5
5.0L/V8-307/9 HO	.060	E	20 ⑩	F	600D ⑪	750D ⑫	5.5- —6.5
1989							
5.0L/V8-305/E	.035	C	6 ⑤	D	⑥	⑥	9–13 ⑦
5.0L/V8-307/Y	.060	E	20 ⑩	F	⑪	550D ⑫	5.5–6.5
1990							
5.0L/V8-305/E	.035	C	6 ⑤	D	⑥	⑥	9–13 ⑦
5.0L/V8-307/Y	.060	E	20 ⑩	F	⑪	550D ⑫	5.5–6.5
5.7L/V8-350/7	.035	C	6 ⑤	D	⑥	⑥	9–13 ⑦
1991							
5.0L/V8-305/E	.035	C	6 ⑤	D	⑥	⑥	9–13 ⑦
5.7L/V8-350/7	.035	C	6 ⑤	D	⑥	⑥	9–13 ⑦

①—The eighth digit of the VIN denotes engine code.

②—Before removing wires from distributor cap, determine location of No. 1 wire in cap, as distributor position may have been altered from that shown at the end of this chart.

③—BTDC: Before Top Dead Center.

④—D: Drive. When adjusting idle speed set parking brake & block drive wheels.

⑤—Disconnect set timing by-pass connector (tan/black wire) when adjusting ignition timing. The timing by-pass connector breaks out of the engine wiring harness on the right hand side of the engine compartment. After completing adjustment, reconnect set timing connector. With engine off, clear trouble code from ECM memory by removing battery voltage to the ECM for 30 seconds.

⑥—Controlled by IAC (Idle Air Control) valve.

⑦—Wrap shop towel around fuel hose to steel line connection in engine compartment to prevent fuel spillage. Disconnect hose from steel line & install suitable fuel pressure gauge between hose & line. Ensure gauge connections are tight, then start engine & check fuel pressure readings.

⑧—Disconnect distributor 4 wire connector when adjusting ignition timing. After completing adjustment, reconnect distributor 4 wire connector. With engine off, clear trouble code from ECM memory by removing battery voltage from ECM for 30 seconds.

⑨—On high step of fast idle cam.

⑩—At 1100 RPM.

⑪—Connect jumper wire between ALCL connector terminals A & B. The ALCL connector is located under the instrument panel to the right of the steering column. After completing adjustment, disconnect jumper wire from ALCL terminals. With engine off, clear trouble code form ECM memory by removing battery voltage from ECM for 30 seconds.

⑫—On low step of fast idle cam.

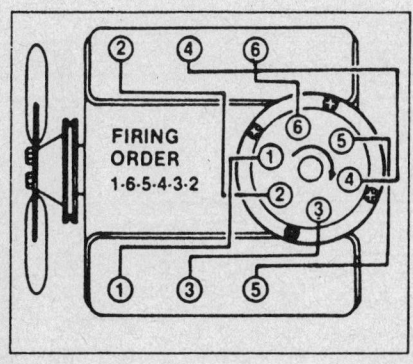

Fig. A

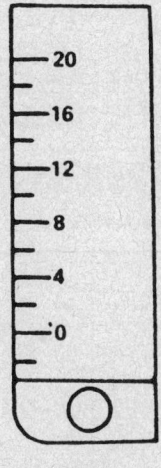

Fig. B

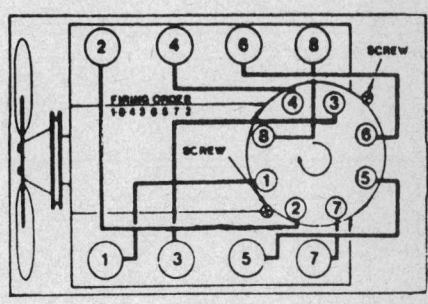

Fig. C

SPECIFICATIONS—Continued

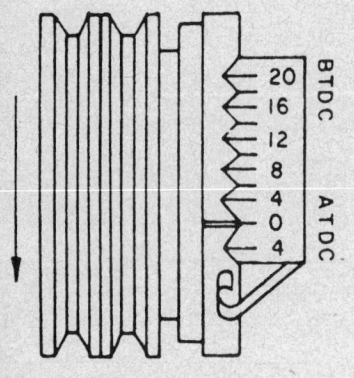

Fig. D

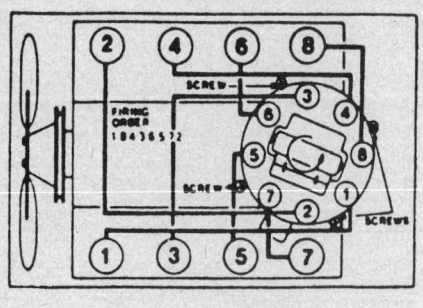

Fig. E

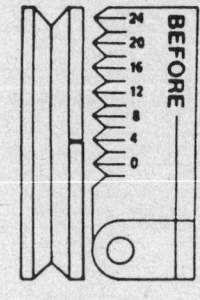

Fig. F

ALTERNATOR SPECIFICATIONS

Year	Ident. No.	Model	Series	Rated Hot Output Amps
1988	1101137	Delco Remy	CS-130	85
	1101138	Delco Remy	CS130	100
	1101213	Delco Remy	CS144	120
	1101214	Delco Remy	CS130	108
	1101229	Delco Remy	CS130	85
	1101275	Delco Remy	CS130	105
	1101299	Delco Remy	12SI	94
	1101300	Delco Remy	12SI	78
	1101302	Delco Remy	CS130	94
	1101304	Delco Remy	12SI	94
	1105565	Delco Remy	12SI	78
1989–90	1101229	Delco Remy	CS130	85
	1101253	Delco Remy	CS130	85
	1101254	Delco Remy	CS130	100
	1101275	Delco Remy	CS130	105
	1101292.	Delco Remy	CS130	100
	1101454	Delco Remy	CS144	120
1991	1101599	Delco Remy	CS130	100
	1101454	Delco Remy	CS144	120

STARTER MOTOR APPLICATIONS

Refer To "Starter Motors" For Starter Specifications.

Year	Engine/VIN ①	Ident. No.	Model
1988	4.3L/V6-262/Z	1998591	Delco Remy SD300 (10MT)
	5.0L/V8-305/H	1998591	Delco Remy SD300 (10MT)
	5.0L/V8-305/G HO	1998580	Delco Remy SD300 (10MT)
	5.0L/V8-307/Y	1999536	Delco Remy SD300 (10MT)
	5.0L/V8-307/Y, 9	10455007	Delco Remy SD200 (5MT)
1989	5.0L/V8-305/E	1998591	Delco Remy SD300
	5.0L/V8-307/Y	10455007	Delco Remy SD200
	5.0L/V8-307/Y	10455016	Delco Remy SD200
	5.0L/V8-307/Y	1999548	Delco Remy SD200

Continued

STARTER MOTOR APPLICATIONS—Continued

Refer To "Starter Motors" For Starter Specifications.

Year	Engine/VIN ①	Ident. No.	Model
1990	5.0L/V8-305/E	1998579	Delco Remy SD300
	5.0L/V8-305/Y	1998591	Delco Remy SD200
	5.0L/V8-307/Y	10455007	Delco Remy SD200
	5.7L/V8-350/7	10455301	Delco Remy SD300
	5.7L/V8-350/7	1998579	Delco Remy SD300
1991	5.0L/V8-305/E	10455012	Delco Remy SD260
	5.7L/V8-350/7	1998579	Delco Remy SD300

REAR AXLE SPECIFICATIONS

Year	Model	Ring Gear Back Lash, Inch	Pinion Bearing Preload, Inch Lbs. ① New Bearings	Pinion Bearing Preload, Inch Lbs. ① Used Bearings	Differential Assembly Preload, Inch Lbs. ① New Bearings	Differential Assembly Preload, Inch Lbs. ① Used Bearings
1988–90	All	.005–.009	20 to 25	10 to 15	35 to 40	20 to 25
1991	All	.005–.009	②	10 to 15	35 to 40	20 to 25

①—Rotating torque with new seal.
②—7½ ring gear, 15 to 30 inch lbs., 8½ ring gear 18 to 36 inch lbs.

WHEEL ALIGNMENT SPECIFICATIONS

Model	Year	Caster Angle, Degrees Limits	Caster Angle, Degrees Desired	Camber Angle, Degrees Limits	Camber Angle, Degrees Desired	Toe, Degrees
Buick Estate Wagon	1988	+1.8 to +3.8	+2.8	0 to +1.6	+.8	+.1 ①
	1989–90	+2.5 to +3.5	+3	+.3 to +1.3	+.8	+.05 ②
Cadillac Brougham	1988–90	+2 to +4	+3	−.5 to +.5	0	0 ①
Chevrolet Caprice	1988	+1.8 to +3.8	+2.8	0 to +1.6	+.8	+.1 ①
	1989–90	+2.5 to +3.5	+3	+.3 to +1.3	+.8	+.05 ②
	1991	+2.5 to +4.5	+3.5	0 to +1.6	+.8	+.16
Chevrolet Monte Carlo	1988	+1.8 to +3.8	+2.8	−.3 to +1.3	+.5	+.05 ②
Oldsmobile Custom Cruiser	1988	+1.8 to +3.8	+2.8	0 to +1.6	+.8	+.1 ①
	1989–90	+2.5 to +3.5	+3	+.3 to +1.3	+.8	+.05 ②
Oldsmobile Cutlass Supreme Classic	1988	−.2 to +1.8	+.8	−.3 to +1.3	+.5	+.05 ②
Pontiac Safari	1988	+1.8 to +3.8	+2.8	0 to +1.6	+.8	+.1 ①
	1989	+2.5 to +3.5	+3	+.3 to +1.3	+.8	+.05 ②

①—Total toe.
②—Toe per wheel.

COOLING SYSTEM & CAPACITY DATA

Make & Year	Model	Engine Liter /CID ①	Cooling System Capacity, Qts.	Radiator Cap Relief Pressure, Psi.	Thermo. Opening Temp.	Fuel Tank, Gals.	Engine Oil, Qts. ②	Auto. Trans. Qts. ③	Rear Axle, Pts.
BUICK									
1988	Estate Wagon	5.0L/V8-307	15	15	195	22	4④⑤	⑥	4.25⑦
1989	Estate Wagon	5.0L/V8-307	15.6	15	195	22	4④⑤	⑥	4.25⑦
1990	Estate Wagon	5.0L/V8-307	15.9	15	195	22	4④⑧	⑥	4.25⑦
1991	Estate Wagon	5.0L/V8-305	16.9	15	195	22	4④⑧	⑩	4.25⑦

Continued

COOLING SYSTEM & CAPACITY DATA—Continued

Make & Year	Model	Engine Liter /CID ①	Cooling System Capacity, Qts.	Radiator Cap Relief Pressure, Psi.	Thermo. Opening Temp.	Fuel Tank, Gals.	Engine Oil, Qts. ②	Auto. Trans. Qts. ③	Rear Axle, Pts.
CADILLAC									
1988–89	Brougham	5.0L/V8-307	15.2	15	195	25	4④⑤	⑥	4.25⑦
1990	Brougham	5.0L/V8-307	15.2	15	195	25	4④⑧	⑥	⑦⑨
	Brougham	5.7L/V8-350	16.5	15	195	25	4④⑧	⑩	⑦⑨
1991	Brougham	5.0L/V8-305	17.6	15	195	25	4④⑧	⑩	4.2⑦
	Brougham	5.7L/V8-350	16.5	15	195	25	4④⑧	⑩	⑦⑨
CHEVROLET									
1988	Caprice Sedan	4.3L/V6-262	12.2	15	195	25	4⑤⑪	⑫	⑦⑬
		5.0L/V8-305	16.8	15	195	25	4④⑤	⑭	⑦⑬
	Caprice Wagon	5.0L/V8-307	17.1	15	195	22	4④⑤	⑥	4.25⑦
	Monte Carlo	4.3L/V6-262	13.1	15	195	17.6	4⑤⑪	⑥	3.5⑦
		5.0L/V8-305	⑮	15	195	18.1	4④⑤	⑥	3.5⑦
1989	Caprice Sedan	5.0L/V8-305	16.8	15	195	25	4④⑤	⑥	⑦⑬
	Caprice Wagon	5.0L/V8-307	17.1	15	195	22	4④⑤	⑥	4.25⑦
1990	Caprice Sedan	5.0L/V8-305	16.9	15	195	24.5	4④⑧	⑥	⑦⑬
	Caprice Wagon	5.0L/V8-307	16.1	15	195	22	4④⑧	⑥	4.25⑦
1991	Caprice Sedan	5.0L/V8-305	16.9	14.6	195	23	4④⑧	⑩	4.2⑦
	Caprice Wagon	5.7L/V8-350	16.7	15	195	23	4④⑧	⑩	4.25⑦
OLDSMOBILE									
1988	Custom Cruiser	5.0L/V8-307	15.3	15	195	22	4④⑤	⑥	4.25⑦
	Cutlass Supreme Classic	5.0L/V8-307	⑯	15	195	18.2	4④⑤	⑥	3.5⑦
1989	Custom Cruiser	5.0L/V8-307	15.6	15	195	22	4④⑤	⑥	4.25⑦
1990	Custom Cruiser	5.0L/V8-307	15.9	15	195	22	4④⑧	⑥	4.25⑦
1991	Custom Cruiser	5.0L/V8-305	16.9	15	195	22	4④⑧	⑩	4.25⑦
PONTIAC									
1988	Safari	5.0L/V8-307	15	15	195	22	4④⑤	⑥	4.25⑦
1989	Safari	5.0L/V8-307	17.1	15	195	22	4④⑤	⑥	4.25⑦

①—CID: Cubic Inch Displacement.
②—Approximate, additional oil may be required.
③—Approximate, make final check with dipstick.
④—Add 1 qt. with filter change.
⑤—Recommended engine oil, SAE 5W–30 API service SG Or SF/CC, CD.
⑥—THM 200-4R, drain & refill, 3.5 qts.; total capacity, 11 qts. Use Dexron II type automatic transmission fluid.

⑦—Recommended gear lubricant, SAE 80W–90 GL-5.
⑧—Recommended engine oil, SAE 5W–30 API service SG.
⑨—Rear axle ratios 2.73 & 2.93, 3.5 pts.; rear axle ratio 3.08, 4.2 pts.
⑩—THM 4L60, drain & refill, 4.5 qts.; total capacity, 10 qts. Use Dexron II type automatic transmission fluid.
⑪—With or without filter change.
⑫—THM 700, drain & refill, 5 qts.; total capacity, 11.5 qts. Use Dexron II type

automatic transmission fluid.
⑬—7.5 inch ring gear, 3.5 pts.; 8.5 inch ring gear, 4.25 pts.
⑭—THM 200-4R, drain & refill, 3.5 qts.; total capacity, 11 qts. THM 700, drain & refill, 5 qts.; total capacity, 11.5 qts. Use Dexron II type automatic transmission fluid.
⑮—V8-305 except HO engine, 16.5 qts.; V8-305 HO engine, 16.7 qts.
⑯—Less A/C, 14.8 Qts.; with A/C, 15.6 qts.

Electrical
INDEX

FUSE PANEL & FLASHER LOCATIONS

The fuse panel is located behind behind the left hand side of the instrument panel near the shroud.

On all models except 1991 Caprice, the hazard warning flasher is located on the fuse panel. On 1991 Caprice the hazard warning flasher is located on the convenience center next to the auxiliary fuse panel.

On 1988 Buick Estate Wagon, the turn signal flasher is located lower right hand side of the steering column. On 1989–91 Buick Estate Wagon, the turn signal flasher is located on the fuse panel. On Cadillac Brougham, the turn signal flasher is located on a bracket behind the instrument panel to the right of the steering column. On Pontiac Safari and 1988–90 Chevrolet Caprice, the turn signal flasher is located on the fuse panel. On 1991 Chevrolet Caprice, the turn signal flasher is located on the convenience center next to the auxiliary fuse block. On Chevrolet Monte Carlo behind left hand side of instrument panel on convenience panel. On Oldsmobile Custom Cruiser, the turn signal flasher is located behind the instrument panel at the base of the steering column. On Oldsmobile Cutlass Supreme Classic, the turn signal flasher is located under the instrument panel on right hand side of the steering column.

AIRBAG RESTRAINT SYSTEM, DISABLE
EXCEPT 1991 MODELS

On models with airbag restraint system, battery ground cable must be disconnected and isolated before performing this procedure. Failure to do so may result in accidental deployment and personal injury.

1991 MODELS

On models equipped with Supplemental Inflatable Restraint (SIR) System, the system must disabled prior to preforming any service on or around SIR components, failure to disable system may result in accidental deployment and personal injury.
1. **Position steering wheel that front wheels point straight ahead.**
2. Turn ignition switch to "Lock" position.
3. Remove SIR fuse from fuse block, (12).
4. Disconnect yellow two-way SIR harness and clip at base of steering wheel.
5. Reverse to enable system, then turn ignition switch to "Run" position ensuring inflatable restraint indicator flashes 7 to 9 times then goes off.

STARTER
REPLACE

If shims are used between starter and engine block, they should be placed in their original location during installation.
1. Disconnect battery ground cable.
2. Raise and support vehicle.
3. Remove starter to engine brace and starter heat shields, if equipped.
4. Remove flywheel housing cover.
5. Remove starter mounting bolts and lower starter. Note position of shims, if used.
5. Disconnect solenoid wires and the battery cable.
6. Remove starter from vehicle.
7. Reverse procedure to install.

DISTRIBUTOR
REPLACE
REMOVAL

1. Disconnect battery ground cable.
2. Disconnect ignition switch feed and tachometer leads from distributor cap. Screwdriver or other tools should not be used to release lead connector locking tab.
3. Remove distributor cap attaching screws, then position cap out of way.
4. Disconnect four terminal ECM electrical connector from distributor electrical connector.
5. Remove distributor hold down clamp and bolt. Mark position of distributor rotor to distributor housing and position of distributor housing to engine for use during installation.
6. Lift distributor upward until rotor stops rotating and mark position of rotor to distributor housing for use during installation.
7. Remove distributor from engine.

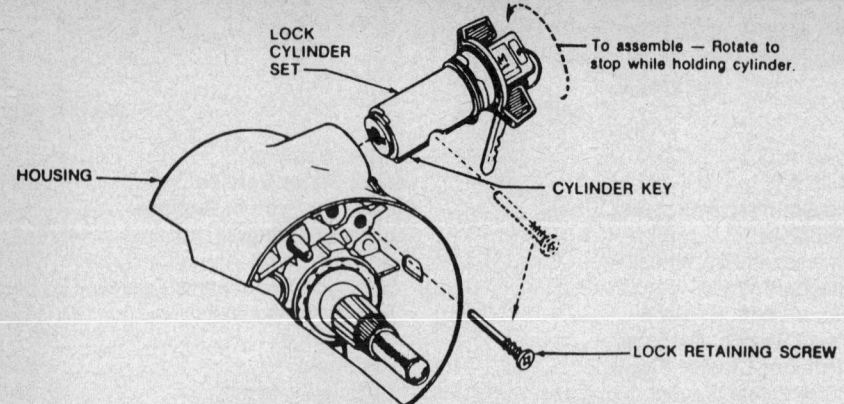

Fig. 1   Ignition lock installation

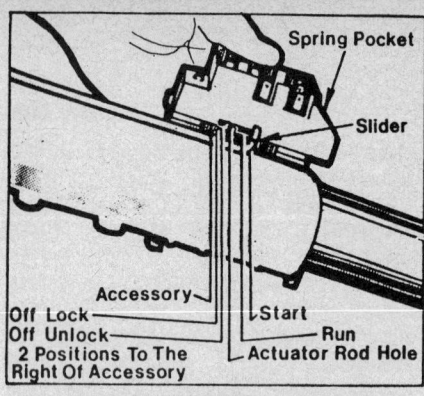

Fig. 2   Ignition switch

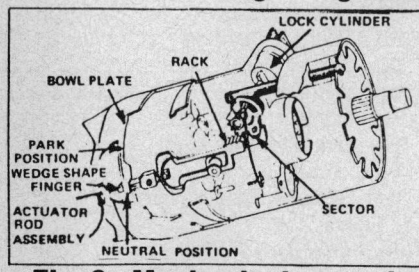

Fig. 3   Mechanical neutral safety system. Models with tilt column

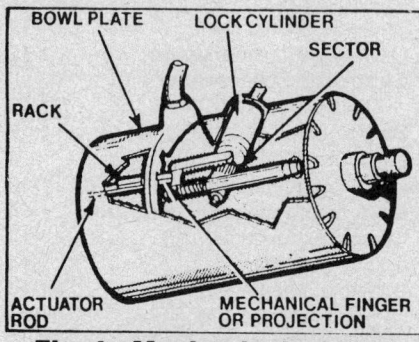

Fig. 4   Mechanical neutral safety system. Models with standard column

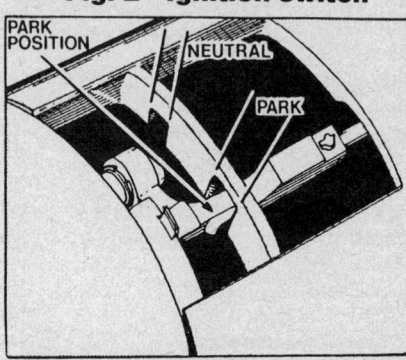

Fig. 5   Mechanical neutral safety system in Park position

INSTALLATION

1. Position rotor to mark on distributor housing, then insert distributor into engine aligning rotor to housing and housing to engine marks made during removal.
2. If engine was was disturbed while distributor was removed, proceed as follows:
   a. Remove spark plug from No. 1 cylinder.
   b. With transmission in Neutral or Park and parking brake applied, position finger over spark plug opening in cylinder head, then slowly crank engine until compression is felt.
   c. Align crankshaft pulley with TDC (0) mark on timing indicator.
   d. Locate distributor rotor contact between No. 1 and 8 spark plug firing positions on distributor.
   c. Insert distributor into engine.
3. Install distributor hold clamp and bolt. Hand tighten bolt.
4. Connect ECM four terminal electrical connector to distributor.
5. Install distributor cap, then connect ignition switch and tachometer lead connector to cap.
6. Connect battery ground cable, then check and adjust ignition timing as necessary. Torque distributor hold down bolt to 27 ft. lbs.

IGNITION LOCK
REPLACE

Disable airbag system as outlined under "Airbag Restraint System, Disable."
1. Remove steering wheel as described under Horn Sounder and Steering Wheel.
2. Remove turn signal switch as de-

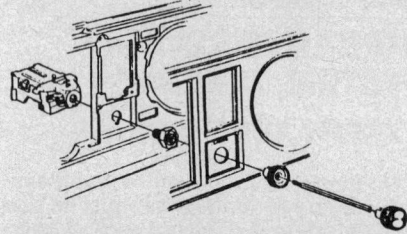

Fig. 6   Headlamp switch replace. Buick Estate Wagon

scribed under Turn Signal Switch, Replace, then remove buzzer switch.
3. Place ignition switch in Run position, then remove lock cylinder retaining screw and lock cylinder.
4. Install by rotating lock cylinder to stop while holding housing, **Fig. 1.** Align cylinder key with keyway in housing, then push lock cylinder assembly into housing until fully seated.
5. Install lock cylinder retaining screw.
6. Install buzzer switch, turn signal switch and steering wheel.

IGNITION SWITCH
REPLACE

Disable airbag system as outlined under "Airbag Restraint System, Disable."
The ignition switch is mounted on top of the mast jacket inside the brake pedal support and is actuated by a rod and rack assembly.
1. Disconnect battery cable.
2. Disconnect and lower steering column. **It may be necessary, on some models, to remove the upper column mounting bracket if it hinders

servicing of switch. Use extreme care when lowering steering column to prevent damage to column assembly. Only lower steering column a sufficient distance to perform ignition switch service.
3. Rotate ignition lock to Off unlocked position.
4. If lock cylinder has been removed, pull switch actuator rod up to stop, then push rod down to second detent to place switch in Off unlocked position, **Fig. 2.**
5. Remove column mounted dimmer switch, if equipped, then remove switch retaining screws and switch.
6. Reverse procedure to install, noting the following:
   a. Place gear shift lever in neutral.
   b. Place lock cylinder and switch in Off locked position, **Fig. 2.**
   c. Fit actuator rod into hole in switch slider and secure switch with retaining screws, ensuring switch does not move out of detent.
   d. Install and adjust dimmer switch, if removed, as outlined in "Dimmer Switch, Replace."

NEUTRAL START SWITCH

Actuation of the ignition switch is prevented by a mechanical lockout system, **Figs. 3 and 4,** which prevents the lock cylinder from rotating when the selector lever is out of Park or Neutral. When the selector lever is in Park or Neutral, the slots in the bowl plate and the finger on the actuator rod align, allowing the finger to pass through the bowl plate in turn actuating the ignition switch, **Fig. 5.** If the selector lever

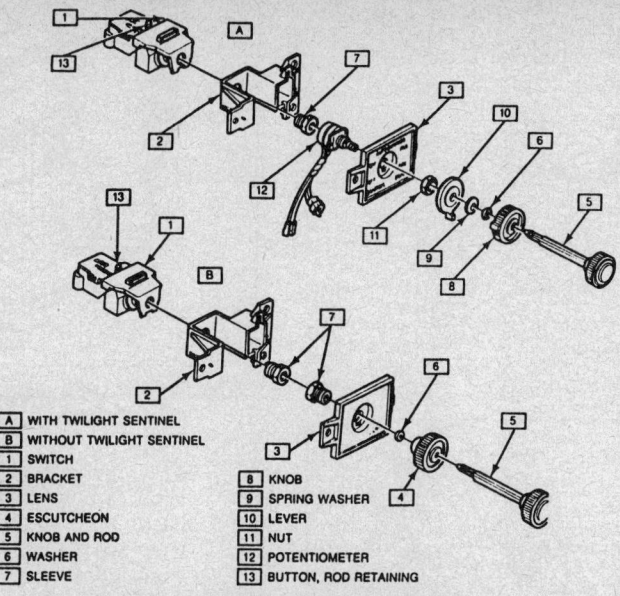

A	WITH TWILIGHT SENTINEL
B	WITHOUT TWILIGHT SENTINEL
1	SWITCH
2	BRACKET
3	LENS
4	ESCUTCHEON
5	KNOB AND ROD
6	WASHER
7	SLEEVE
8	KNOB
9	SPRING WASHER
10	LEVER
11	NUT
12	POTENTIOMETER
13	BUTTON, ROD RETAINING

Fig. 7 Headlamp switch replace. Cadillac Brougham

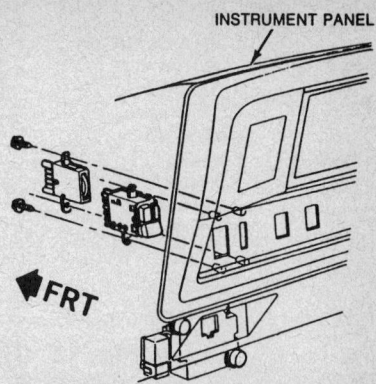

Fig. 8 Headlamp switch replace. Chevrolet Caprice

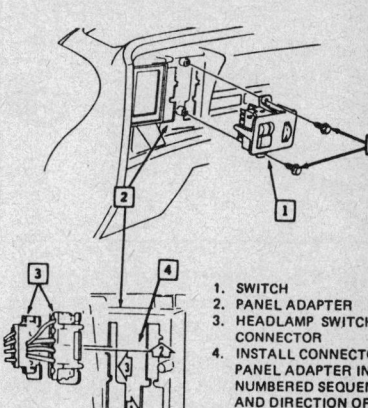

1. SWITCH
2. PANEL ADAPTER
3. HEADLAMP SWITCH CONNECTOR
4. INSTALL CONNECTOR TO PANEL ADAPTER IN NUMBERED SEQUENCE AND DIRECTION OF ARROWS
5. FULLY DRIVEN, SEATED AND NOT STRIPPED

Fig. 10 Headlamp switch replace. Oldsmobile Cutlass Supreme Classic

1. CLUSTER CARRIER
2. HEADLAMP SWITCH
3. MOUNTING PLATE
4. 4.7 N•m (42 LBS. IN.)
5. SWITCH KNOB ASSEMBLY
6. FULLY DRIVEN, SEATED AND NOT STRIPPED

Fig. 9 Headlamp switch replace. Oldsmobile Custom Cruiser

is in any position other than Park or Neutral, the finger contacts the bowl plate when the lock cylinder is rotated, thereby preventing full travel of the lock cylinder.

On all models incorporating an electric neutral start switch, the start switch, back-up light switch and parking brake vacuum release valve are combined into one unit. This unit is mounted on the steering column under the instrument panel.

HEADLAMP SWITCH REPLACE

Disable airbag system as outlined under "Airbag Restraint System, Disable."

BUICK ESTATE WAGON

1. Disconnect battery ground cable.
2. Remove left lower instrument panel trim, then A/C ducts as required.
3. Pull headlamp switch to full on position, then depress retainer through slot in rear of knob and pull knob from stem, as applicable, **Fig. 6.**
4. Remove switch stem escutcheon and instrument cluster bezel.
5. Remove nut securing switch, lower switch from rear of instrument panel,

then disconnect electrical connector from switch.
6. Reverse procedure to install.

CADILLAC BROUGHAM

1. Disconnect battery ground cable.
2. Remove left hand instrument panel insert.
3. Remove three screws attaching light switch to instrument panel, **Fig. 7.**
4. On vehicles equipped with Cruise Control and Twilight Sentinel, remove two screws retaining Cruise Control switch to instrument panel.
5. Slide Cruise Control switch forward to remove headlamp switch.
6. Disconnect electrical connector from headlamp switch.
7. While depressing rod retaining button, pull switch knob and rod from switch, **Fig. 7.**
8. Remove nut from switch lens housing, then remove switch.
9. Reverse procedure to install.

CHEVROLET CAPRICE

1. Disconnect battery ground cable.
2. Remove left hand sound insulator panel.
3. Remove steering column trim plate, then disconnect electrical connector from headlamp switch.
4. Remove headlamp switch to instrument panel attaching screws, then remove switch, **Fig. 8.**
5. Reverse procedure to install.

CHEVROLET MONTE CARLO

1. Disconnect battery ground cable.
2. Remove instrument panel bezel.
3. Pull switch knob to On position.
4. Remove three screws attaching windshield wiper/light switch mounting plate to cluster and pull assembly rearward.

5. Depress shaft retainer button on switch and pull knob and shaft assembly from switch.
6. Remove ferrule nut and switch assembly from mounting plate.
7. Reverse procedure to install.

OLDSMOBILE CUSTOM CRUISER

1. Disconnect battery ground cable.
2. Remove left hand sound insulator, steering column trim cover and headlamp switch knob.
3. Remove two screws attaching left side trim cover to cluster carrier, then remove trim cover by pulling rearward.
4. Remove two screws attaching mounting plate to cluster carrier, **Fig. 9.**
5. Pull switch and mounting plate rearward and disconnect electrical connector.
6. Remove nut and separate mounting plate from switch.
7. Reverse procedure to install.

OLDSMOBILE CUTLASS SUPREME CLASSIC

1. Disconnect battery ground cable.
2. Remove cluster pad assembly.

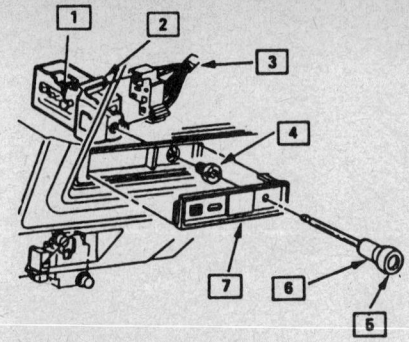

1—RELEASE BUTTON
2—SWITCH ASM.
3—HARNESS
4—2 NUT ASM.
5—KNOB ASM.
6—SHAFT
7—WINDSHIELD WIPER
    SWITCH
8—FUSE PANEL

Fig. 11 Headlamp switch replace. Pontiac Safari

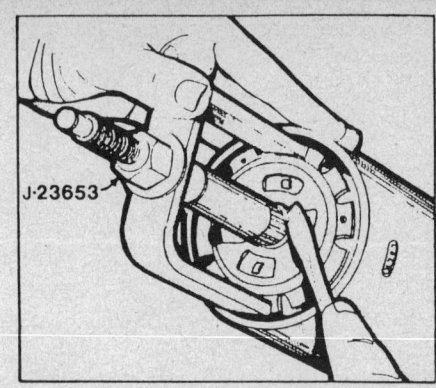

Fig. 12 Lock plate retaining ring removal

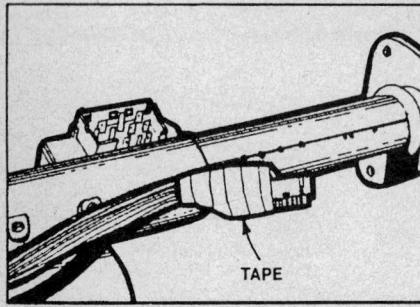

TAPE

Fig. 13 Taping turn signal electrical connector & wiring

3. Remove two headlight switch mounting screws, then pull switch away from panel adapter.
4. Disconnect wire connector. Pull connector out, then slide to left and push forward to remove.
5. Reverse procedure to install. Refer to **Fig. 10**, to install wire connector.

PONTIAC SAFARI

1. Disconnect battery ground cable.
2. Pull headlight knob to "On" position, then reach under instrument panel, depress switch shaft release button and pull knob and shaft assembly from switch, **Fig. 11**.
3. Remove windshield wiper switch.
4. Remove switch retaining nut, wire connector and switch.
5. Reverse procedure to install.

STOP LIGHT SWITCH REPLACE

The stop light switch has a slip fit in the mounting sleeve which permits positive adjustment by pulling the brake pedal up firmly against the stop. The pedal arm forces the switch body to slip in the mounting sleeve bushing to position the switch properly.

1. Disconnect wires from switch and remove switch from bracket.
2. Position replacement switch in bracket and push inward until fully seated. Brake pedal arm moves switch to correct distance on rebound. Check if pedal is in full return position by lifting slightly by hand.
3. Connect switch electrical connector.

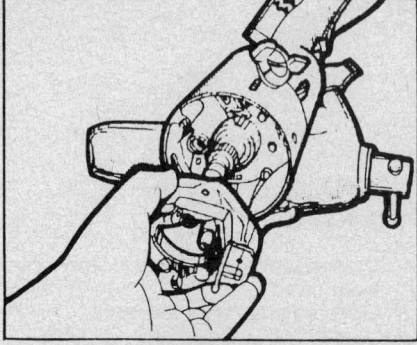

Fig. 14 Lifting turn signal switch assembly from column bowl

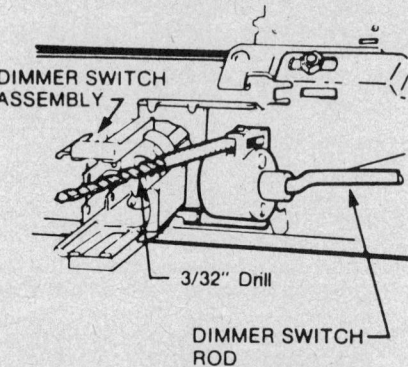

DIMMER SWITCH ASSEMBLY

3/32" Drill

DIMMER SWITCH ROD

Fig. 16 Column mounted dimmer switch installation

TURN SIGNAL SWITCH REPLACE

Disable airbag system as outlined under "Airbag Restraint System, Disable."

1. Disconnect battery cable, then remove steering wheel and column to instrument panel trim cover.
2. **On models with telescoping column,** remove bumper spacer and snap ring retainer. On all other models, remove cover from lock plate.
3. Using a suitable tool, compress lock plate (horn contact carrier on tilt models) and remove snap ring (C-ring on tilt models), **Fig. 12**.
4. Remove lock plate, cancelling cam, upper bearing preload spring, thrust washer and signal lever.
5. Remove turn signal lever or actuating

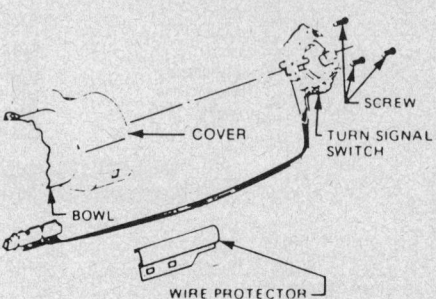

SCREW
COVER
TURN SIGNAL SWITCH
BOWL
WIRE PROTECTOR

Fig. 15 Turn signal switch assembly replace

arm screw, if equipped, or on models with column mounted wiper switch, pull lever straight out of detent. Depress hazard warning button, then unscrew button.

6. Pull connector from bracket and wrap upper part of connector with tape to prevent snagging the wires during removal, **Fig. 13**. On Tilt models, position shifter housing in Low position. Remove harness cover.
7. Remove retaining screws and remove switch, **Figs. 14 and 15**.
8. Reverse procedure to install.

COLUMN-MOUNTED DIMMER SWITCH REPLACE

Disable airbag system as outlined under "Airbag Restraint System, Disable."

1. Disconnect battery ground cable.
2. Remove instrument panel lower trim and on models with A/C, remove A/C duct extension at column.
3. Disconnect shift indicator from column and remove toe-plate cover screws.
4. Remove two nuts from instrument panel support bracket studs and lower steering column, resting steering wheel on front seat.
5. Remove dimmer switch retaining screws and the switch. Tape actuator rod to column and separate switch from rod.
6. Reverse procedure to install. To adjust switch, depress dimmer switch slightly and install a 3/32 inch twist drill to lock the switch to the body, **Fig. 16**.

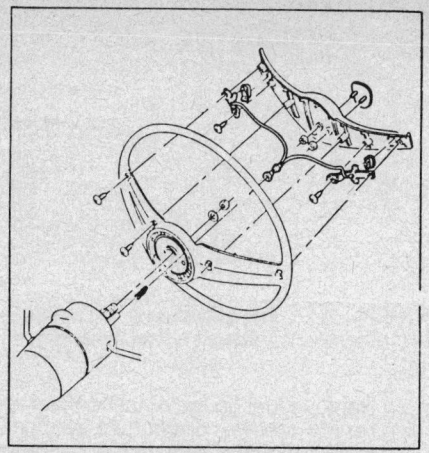

Fig. 17   Steering wheel & horn contact (Typical). Standard wheel

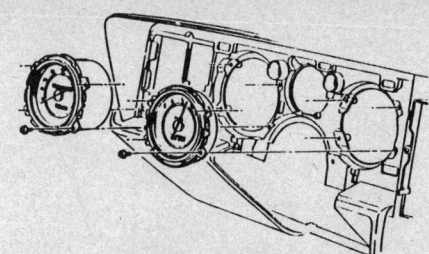

Fig. 18   Speedometer & fuel gauge replace. Buick Estate Wagon

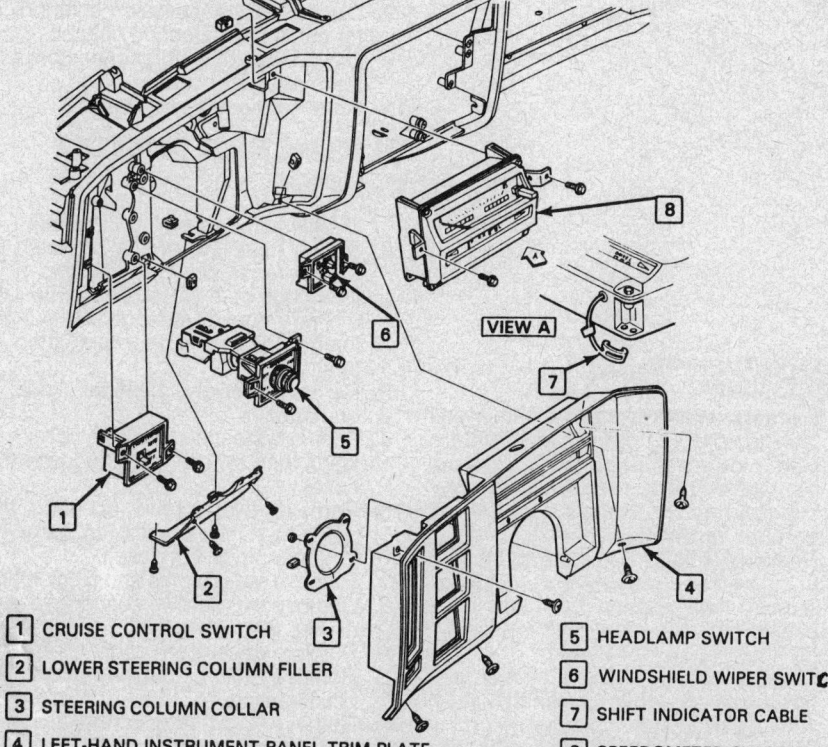

1	CRUISE CONTROL SWITCH	5	HEADLAMP SWITCH
2	LOWER STEERING COLUMN FILLER	6	WINDSHIELD WIPER SWITCH
3	STEERING COLUMN COLLAR	7	SHIFT INDICATOR CABLE
4	LEFT-HAND INSTRUMENT PANEL TRIM PLATE	8	SPEEDOMETER CLUSTER

Fig. 19   Instrument cluster replace. Cadillac Brougham

Force switch upward to remove lash between switch and pivot, then remove tape from actuator rod. Remove twist drill and check for proper operation.

HORN SOUNDER & STEERING WHEEL REPLACE

Disable airbag system as outlined under "Airbag Restraint System, Disable."

Mark position of steering wheel in relation to shaft prior to removal to ensure correct installation.

CUSHIONED RIM WHEEL
1. Disconnect battery ground cable.
2. Pry off horn button cap.
3. Remove three spacer screws, spacer, plate and belleville spring.
4. Remove steering wheel nut, washer and snap ring.
5. Using a suitable puller, remove steering wheel.
6. Reverse procedure to install.

STANDARD WHEEL
1. Disconnect battery ground cable.
2. Remove attaching screws on underside of the steering wheel, **Fig. 17.**
3. Lift steering wheel shroud and pull horn wires from cancelling cam tower.
4. Remove steering wheel nut, washer

and snap ring.
5. Using a suitable puller, remove steering wheel.
6. Reverse procedure to install.

INSTRUMENT CLUSTER REPLACE

Disable airbag system as outlined under "Airbag Restraint System, Disable."

BUICK ESTATE WAGON

On these models, the speedometer and fuel gauge are removed from the instrument panel carrier as separate assemblies.
1. Disconnect battery ground cable.
2. If speedometer is to be removed, disconnect speedometer cable from transmission, cruise control transducer or union in engine compartment.
3. Pull steering column filler forward, then remove headlamp switch knob as outlined previously.
4. Remove left (cluster) trim bezel, grasping bezel on both sides and pulling straight away from instrument panel.
5. Remove fuel gauge, **Fig. 18**, as follows:
   a. Remove 4 screws securing gauge.
   b. Withdraw gauge assembly from carrier, remove bulb sockets, then disconnect electrical connector from gauge.
6. Remove speedometer, **Fig. 18**, as follows:
   a. Remove 4 screws securing speedometer.
   b. Withdraw speedometer just far enough to gain access to cable and electrical connections.
   c. Remove bulb sockets, then disconnect cable from speedometer.
   d. Remove screws securing speed sensor optic head, then disconnect sensor from speedometer.
   e. Remove speedometer.
7. Reverse procedure to install.

CADILLAC BROUGHAM

1. Disconnect battery ground cable.
2. Remove cluster bezel, then with shift lever in the Park position, remove the screw securing shift indicator cable to steering column.
3. Remove four screws securing cluster to instrument horizontal support, **Fig. 19.** On vehicles equipped with speed control sensor, disconnect sensor from cluster before completely removing cluster assembly. This will prevent connector from damaging cluster during removal.
4. Disengage speedometer cable at neck by pulling cluster straight out and depressing retaining spring. **To remove cluster, place shift lever in Low range and on models with tilt wheel, place wheel in lowest position.**
5. Rotate cluster downward, disconnect printed circuit connector, then remove cluster.
6. Reverse procedure to install.

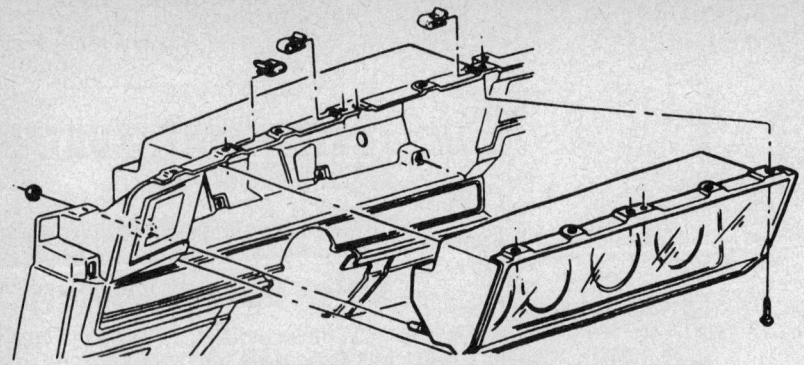

Fig. 20 Instrument cluster replace. Chevrolet Caprice & Pontiac Safari

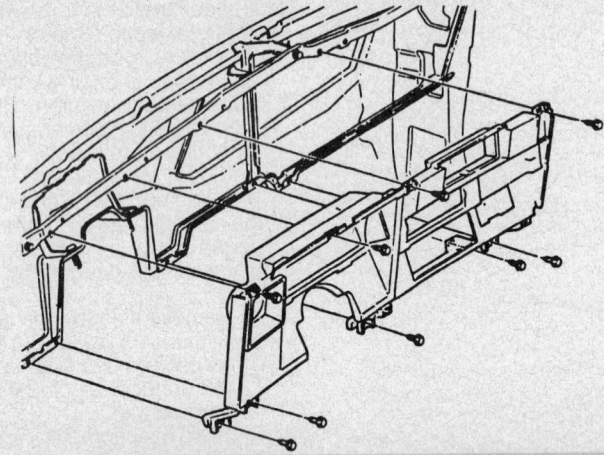

Fig. 22 Instrument cluster replace. Oldsmobile Custom Cruiser

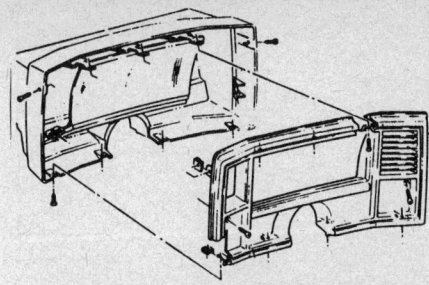

Fig. 21 Instrument cluster replace. Chevrolet Monte Carlo

7. Remove fuel gauge or tachometer retaining screws, disconnect electrical connectors and remove fuel gauge or tachometer.
8. Remove clock or voltmeter retaining screws, disconnect electrical connectors and remove clock or voltmeter.
9. Disconnect transmission shift indicator cable from steering column.
10. Disconnect all wiring connectors and remove cluster case.
11. Reverse procedure to install.

OLDSMOBILE CUSTOM CRUISER

1. Disconnect battery ground cable.
2. Rotate headlight switch so notch on switch faces downward. Bend a 1/8 inch hook on a piece of stiff wire. Use the wire hook in the notch to pull the knob retainer clip, then pull knob off shaft.
3. Remove twilight sentinel knob, if equipped
4. Position steering column collar upward, then remove column lower trim cover.
5. Remove two screws securing trim cover to cluster carrier, **Fig. 22.**
6. Pull trim cover from clips.
7. Remove radio knobs and cigar lighter.
8. Remove two screws securing to panel, **Fig. 22.**
9. Pull trim cover from panel clips.
10. Remove radio as outlined under "Radio, Replace."
11. Remove A/C-heater control attaching screws, pull control outward, then disconnect control cables and electrical connectors.
12. Remove switches, clock, then disconnect ashtray lamp.
13. Remove right hand outside remote mirror control screws.
14. Disconnect shift indicator cable clip.
15. Remove steering column bolts at floor pan and the nuts from the steering column bracket. Lower the steering column, resting steering wheel on seat.
16. Disconnect speedometer cable.
17. Remove instrument panel cluster carrier bolts and the two instrument panel screws, **Fig. 22.**
18. Remove center air duct screws.
19. Pull cluster outward to disconnect electrical connectors.
20. Remove cluster carrier, **Fig. 22.**
21. Reverse procedure to install.

CHEVROLET CAPRICE

1988–90 Models

1. Disconnect battery ground cable.
2. Remove four steering column lower cover screws and the cover.
3. If equipped with automatic transmission, disconnect shift indicator cable from steering column.
4. Remove two steering column to instrument panel screws and lower steering column. **Use extreme care when lowering steering to prevent damage to column assembly.**
5. Remove six screws and the three snap-in fasteners from perimeter of instrument cluster lens, **Fig. 20.**
6. Remove two screws from upper surface of metal trim plate.
7. Remove two stud nuts from lower corner of cluster.
8. Disconnect speedometer cable and pull cluster from instrument panel.
9. Disconnect electrical connectors from cluster and remove from vehicle.
10. Reverse procedure to install.

1991 Models

1. Disconnect battery ground cable.
2. Remove steering column lower trim panel attaching screws, then remove trim panel.
3. Through glove compartment, unsnap righthand moulding.
4. Loosen steering column support bracket to instrument panel carrier attaching bolts. **Do not remove bolts.**
5. Gently lower steering column assembly. **Use extreme care when lowering steering to prevent damage to column assembly.**
6. Remove lefthand trim plate to instrument carrier assembly six attaching screws, then unsnap left hand trim panel from instrument carrier assembly.
7. Remove five instrument cluster attaching screws, then unclip shift indicator cable at steering column.
8. Disconnect instrument cluster electrical connectors, then remove instrument cluster assembly.
9. Reverse procedure to install.

CHEVROLET MONTE CARLO

1. Disconnect battery ground cable.
2. Remove radio knobs and clock set stem knob.
3. Remove instrument bezel retaining screws, **Fig. 21.**
4. Pull bezel rearward slightly and disconnect the rear defogger switch and remote control mirror control, if equipped.
5. Remove bezel, **Fig. 21.**
6. Remove speedometer retaining screws, pull speedometer from cluster slightly, disconnect speedometer cable and remove speedometer.

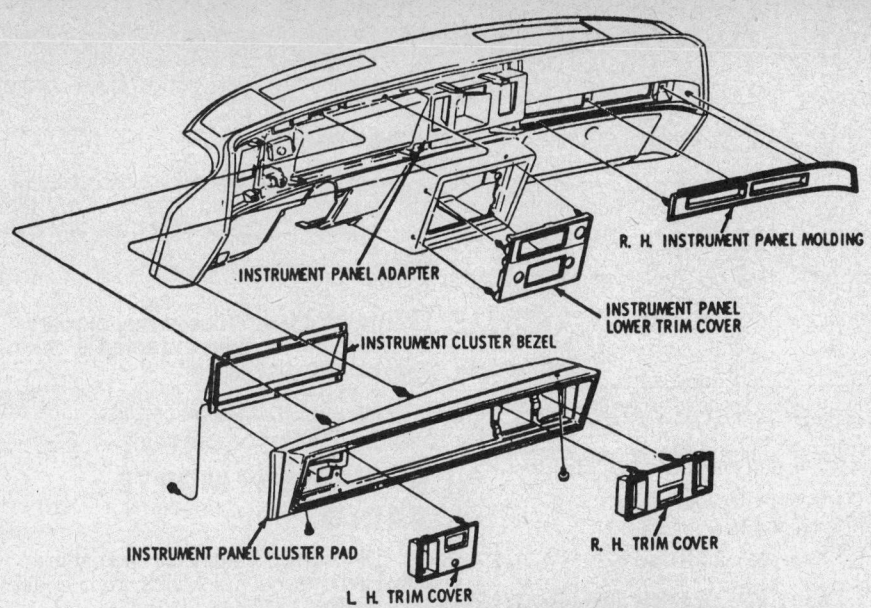

Fig. 23 Instrument cluster replace. Oldsmobile Cutlass Supreme Classic

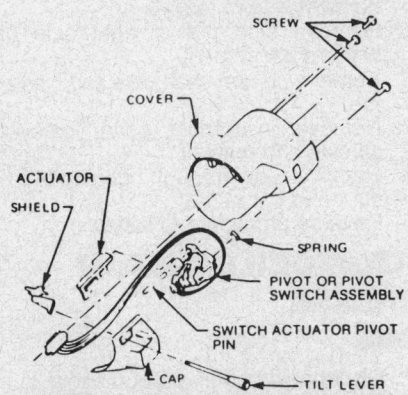

Fig. 25 Windshield wiper switch. Tilt steering column

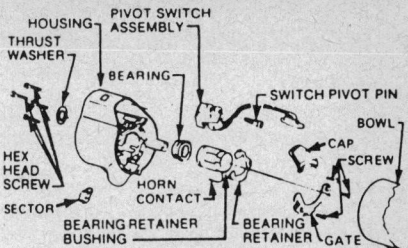

Fig. 24 Windshield wiper switch. Standard steering column

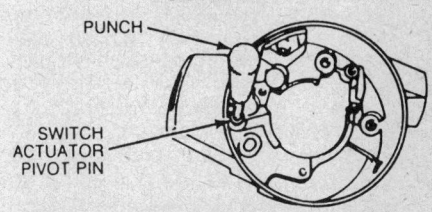

Fig. 26 Windshield wiper switch actuator pivot pin replace

OLDSMOBILE CUTLASS SUPREME CLASSIC

1. Disconnect battery ground cable.
2. Remove right hand and left hand trim panels, **Fig. 23.**
3. Remove the 7 screws retaining cluster pad to panel adapter.
4. Pull panel pad to disengage it from retaining clips, then remove pad assembly, **Fig. 23.**
5. Remove steering column trim cover, then disconnect shift indicator clip from shift bowl.
6. Remove the four screws retaining cluster assembly, disconnect speedometer cable and electrical connectors, then remove cluster assembly.
7. Reverse procedure to install.

PONTIAC SAFARI

1. Disconnect battery ground cable.
2. Remove four steering column lower cover screws and cover.
3. If equipped with automatic transmission, disconnect shift indicator cable from steering column.
4. Remove two steering column to instrument panel screws and lower steering column. **Use extreme care when lowering steering to prevent damage to column assembly.**
5. Remove six screws and three snap-in fasteners from perimeter of instrument cluster lens, **Fig. 20.**
6. Remove two screws from upper surface of gray sheet metal trim plate.
7. Remove two stud nuts from lower corner of cluster.
8. Disconnect speedometer cable and pull cluster from instrument panel.
9. Disconnect electrical connectors from cluster and remove from vehicle.
10. Reverse procedure to install.

WINDSHIELD WIPER MOTOR
REPLACE

1. Raise hood and remove cowl screen or grille.
2. Disconnect wiring and washer hoses.
3. Reaching through cowl opening, loosen transmission drive link attaching nuts to motor crankarm.
4. Disconnect drive link from motor crankarm.
5. Remove motor attaching screws.
6. Remove motor while guiding crankarm through hole.
7. Reverse procedure to install.

WINDSHIELD WIPER TRANSMISSION
REPLACE

1. Raise hood and remove wiper arm assemblies.
2. Remove lower windshield reveal molding and cowl vent screen.
3. Place suitable lever between drive link and motor crankarm, then pry drive link from crankarm.

4. Remove screws securing transmission pivot retainers to body, then withdraw transmission assembly through plenum opening.
5. Reverse procedure to install.

WINDSHIELD WIPER SWITCH
REPLACE

Disable airbag system as outlined under "Airbag Restraint System, Disable."

EXCEPT CADILLAC BROUGHAM

1. Disconnect battery ground cable and remove turn signal switch as outlined.
2. Remove ignition lock, ignition switch and dimmer switch as outlined.
3. Remove ignition lock housing retaining screws and housing, **Figs. 24 and 25.**
4. Remove pivot bolt and wiper switch from lock housing, **Fig. 26.**
5. Reverse procedure to install.

CADILLAC BROUGHAM

1. Disconnect battery ground cable.
2. Remove left hand climate control outlet grille.
3. Remove screw securing switch to instrument panel.
4. Pull control switch and electrical connector out, then disconnect from panel.
5. Reverse procedure to install.

RADIO
REPLACE

Disable airbag system as outlined under "Airbag Restraint System, Disable."

When installing radio, be sure to adjust antenna trimmer for peak reception. Also, be sure to connect speaker before applying power to radio.

BUICK ESTATE WAGON

1. Disconnect battery ground cable.
2. Pull steering column filler collar forward.
3. Position a suitable screwdriver into slot on headlamp switch knob, then push forward on clip and remove knob.
4. Remove headlamp switch bezel, then carefully pull left hand trim cover from instrument panel.
5. Carefully pull right hand trim cover from instrument panel. If vehicle is equipped with electro-luminescent trim plate, disconnect electrical connector after carefully pulling right hand trim cover from instrument panel.
6. Remove radio knobs, escutcheons, then remove rear defogger knob.
7. Remove center trim plate attaching screws, then carefully pull trim plate from instrument panel. Carefully open retaining tabs and pull end of rear defogger control fiber optic from socket.
8. Remove screws from front of radio bracket, then carefully pull radio and bracket from instrument panel.
9. Disconnect radio harness connectors and antenna lead, then remove radio and bracket.
10. Reverse procedure to install.

CADILLAC BROUGHAM
1988–89

1. Disconnect battery ground cable.
2. Remove radio knobs and clips, then remove two nuts retaining radio to trim plate.
3. Using tool No. J-24612-01 or equivalent, remove A/C grilles.
4. Remove center trim plate lower left and right hand retaining screws, then remove trim plate.
5. Remove three screws attaching radio to to lower instrument panel.
6. Disconnect radio electrical connectors and antenna lead, then remove radio.
7. Reverse procedure to install.

1990–91
Radio Control Head

1. Disconnect battery ground cable.
2. Remove set screws at bottom of each A/C vent on/off lever heads, then pull lever heads forward and off.
3. Remove two screws from lower portion of instrument panel trim plate, then remove trim plate from instrument panel.
4. Remove center 7 mm black screw from upper center radio control head upper bracket.
5. Remove two screws from lower ends of bottom radio control bracket.
6. Carefully pull radio control forward.
7. Disconnect electrical connectors from radio control, then remove radio control and bracket.
8. Reverse procedure to install.

Radio Receiver

The radio receiver is located behind the left hand side of the instrument panel.

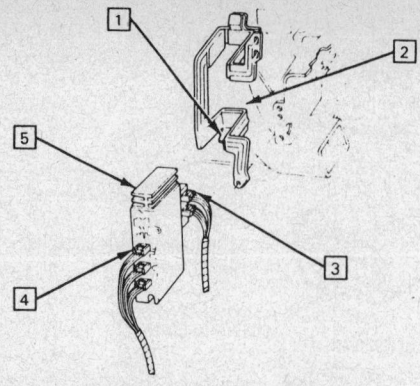

1	BRACKET LEDGE FOR FULLY SEATED REMOTE CHASSIS
2	REAR CONNECTOR (2) HARNESS ROUTES THROUGH SIDE SLOT IN BRACKET
3	REAR CONNECTORS (2)
4	FRONT CONNECTORS (3)
5	REMOTE RADIO CHASSIS

Fig. 27 Radio receiver replace. 1990–91 Cadillac Brougham

1. Disconnect battery ground cable.
2. Remove 4 screws and one wing nut from left hand side hush panel, then remove panel.
3. Remove attaching screw from left hand A/C duct, then pull duct down and outward.
4. Remove attaching screw from right hand A/C duct, then pull duct down and outward.
5. Remove two mounting bolts and ground strap from chime module mounting bracket.
6. Remove nut from bottom of radio receiver.
7. Position chime module, bracket and wiring downward and out of way.
8. Disconnect antenna lead from radio receiver.
9. Carefully pull radio receiver downward and toward front of vehicle, then disconnect gray and black electrical connectors from rear of receiver, Fig. 27.
10. Carefully pull radio receiver from behind instrument panel, then disconnect blue, white and black electrical connectors from front radio receiver.
11. Remove radio receiver.
12. Reverse procedure to install.

CHEVROLET CAPRICE
1988–90 Models

1. Disconnect battery ground cable.
2. Remove glove compartment, then through glove compartment opening, disconnect temperature control cable(s) at temperature door(s).
3. Remove radio and heater and A/C control panel to instrument panel attaching screws.
4. Carefully pull radio and heater and A/C control assembly from instrument panel. Disconnect electrical connectors and vacuum hoses from radio and heater and A/C control.
5. Remove knobs and trim plate from

heater and A/C control.
6. Remove radio from mounting bracket.
7. Reverse procedure to install. Adjust heater and A/C temperature control cable(s).

1991 Models

1. Disconnect battery ground cable.
2. Remove steering column lower trim panel, then remove left hand trim panel.
3. Remove radio bracket to instrument carrier attaching screws, then pull radio and bracket assembly outward.
4. Disconnect radio and antenna electrical connectors.
5. Remove radio to bracket attaching nuts, then remove radio.
6. Reverse procedure to install.

CHEVROLET MONTE CARLO

1. Disconnect battery ground cable.
2. Remove control knobs from control shafts.
3. Remove trim plate attaching screws and trim plate.
4. Disconnect antenna lead and wire connector from radio.
5. Remove stud nut at right side of bracket attachment.
6. Remove control shaft nuts and washers.
7. Remove instrument panel bracket screws and bracket.
8. Remove radio through opening in instrument panel.
9. Reverse procedure to install.

OLDSMOBILE CUSTOM CRUISER
1988

1. Disconnect battery ground cable.
2. Remove radio knobs, cigar lighter and right hand trim panel cover.
3. Remove radio mounting plate attaching screws and nuts, then the plate.
4. Remove ashtray, then the left hand sound absorber, if equipped.
5. Remove lower center air duct attaching screw and the duct.
6. Remove radio support bracket attaching nut.
7. Pull radio rearward, then disconnect antenna lead and electrical connectors, then remove radio assembly.
8. Reverse procedure to install.

1989–91

1. Disconnect battery ground cable.
2. Pull steering column filler collar forward.
3. Position a suitable screwdriver into slot on headlamp switch knob, then push forward on clip and remove knob.
4. Remove headlamp switch bezel, then carefully pull left hand trim cover from instrument panel.
5. Carefully pull right hand trim cover from instrument panel. If vehicle is equipped with electro-luminescent trim plate, disconnect electrical connector after carefully pulling right

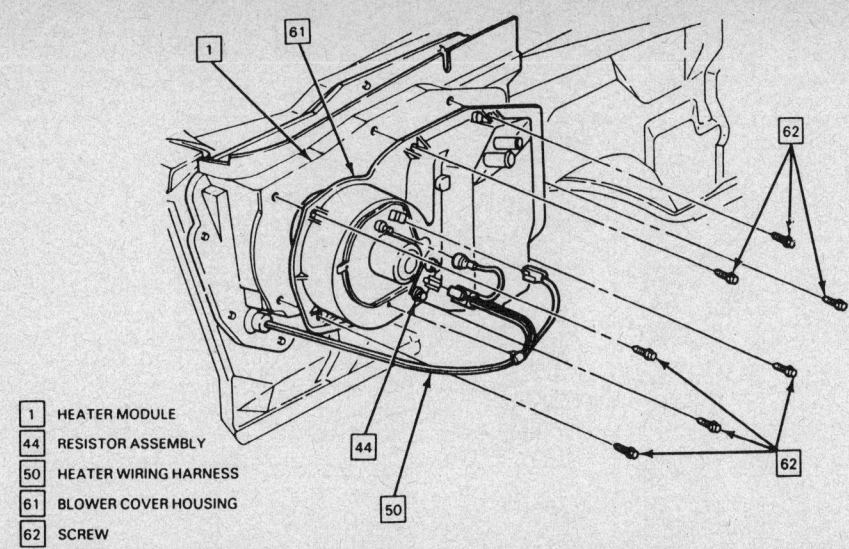

1 HEATER MODULE
44 RESISTOR ASSEMBLY
50 HEATER WIRING HARNESS
61 BLOWER COVER HOUSING
62 SCREW

Fig. 28 Blower motor & heater core. Less A/C except Monte Carlo & Cutlass Supreme Classic

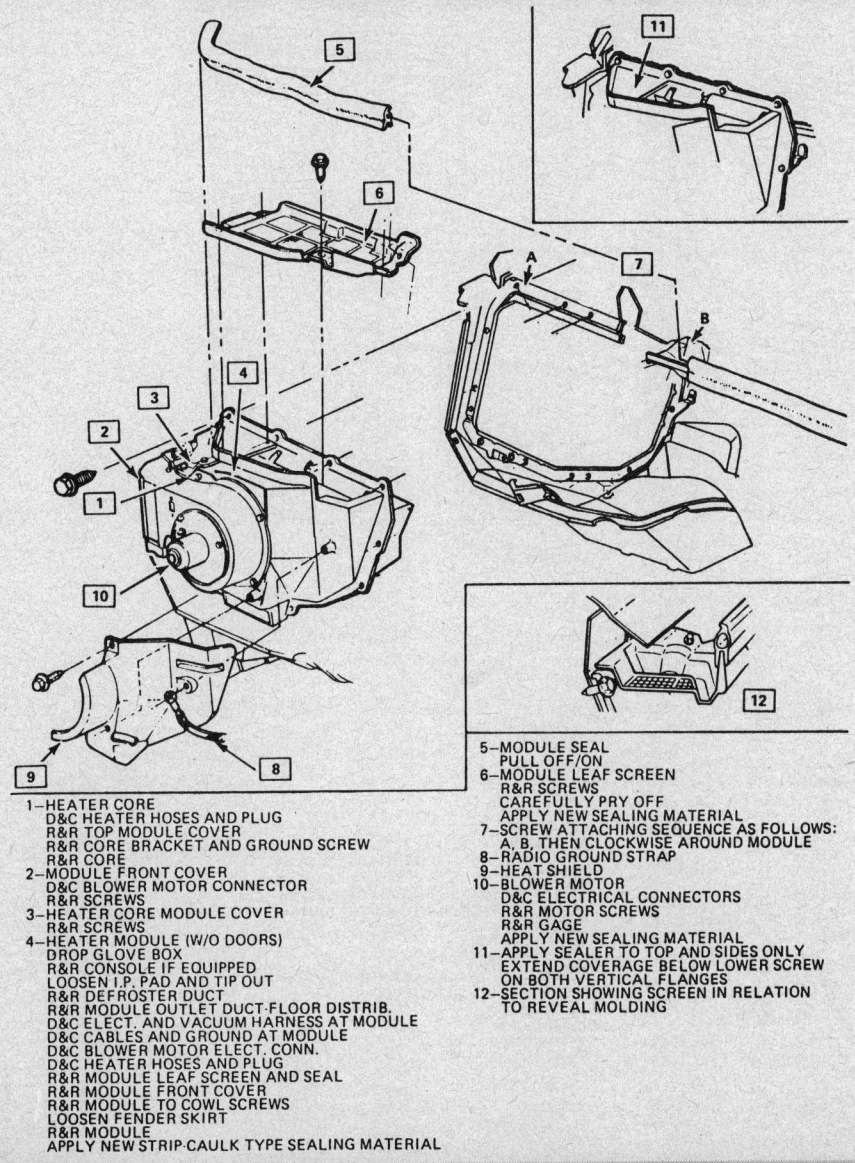

5—MODULE SEAL
    PULL OFF/ON
6—MODULE LEAF SCREEN
    R&R SCREWS
    CAREFULLY PRY OFF
    APPLY NEW SEALING MATERIAL
7—SCREW ATTACHING SEQUENCE AS FOLLOWS:
    A, B, THEN CLOCKWISE AROUND MODULE
8—RADIO GROUND STRAP
9—HEAT SHIELD
10—BLOWER MOTOR
    D&C ELECTRICAL CONNECTORS
    R&R MOTOR SCREWS
    R&R GAGE
    APPLY NEW SEALING MATERIAL
11—APPLY SEALER TO TOP AND SIDES ONLY
    EXTEND COVERAGE BELOW LOWER SCREW
    ON BOTH VERTICAL FLANGES
12—SECTION SHOWING SCREEN IN RELATION
    TO REVEAL MOLDING

1—HEATER CORE
    D&C HEATER HOSES AND PLUG
    R&R TOP MODULE COVER
    R&R CORE BRACKET AND GROUND SCREW
    R&R CORE
2—MODULE FRONT COVER
    D&C BLOWER MOTOR CONNECTOR
    R&R SCREWS
3—HEATER CORE MODULE COVER
    R&R SCREWS
4—HEATER MODULE (W/O DOORS)
    DROP GLOVE BOX
    R&R CONSOLE IF EQUIPPED
    LOOSEN I.P. PAD AND TIP OUT
    R&R DEFROSTER DUCT
    R&R MODULE OUTLET DUCT-FLOOR DISTRIB.
    D&C ELECT. AND VACUUM HARNESS AT MODULE
    D&C CABLES AND GROUND AT MODULE
    D&C BLOWER MOTOR ELECT. CONN.
    D&C HEATER HOSES AND PLUG
    R&R MODULE LEAF SCREEN AND SEAL
    R&R MODULE FRONT COVER
    R&R MODULE TO COWL SCREWS
    LOOSEN FENDER SKIRT
    R&R MODULE
    APPLY NEW STRIP-CAULK TYPE SEALING MATERIAL

Fig. 29 Blower motor & heater core. Less A/C Monte Carlo & Cutlass Supreme Classic

hand trim cover from instrument panel.
6. Remove radio knobs, escutcheons, then remove rear defogger knob.
7. Remove center trim plate attaching screws, then carefully pull trim plate from instrument panel. Carefully open retaining tabs and pull end of rear defogger control fiber optic from socket.
8. Remove screws from front of radio, then carefully pull radio from instrument panel.
9. Disconnect radio harness connectors and antenna lead, then remove radio.
10. Reverse procedure to install.

OLDSMOBILE CUTLASS SUPREME CLASSIC

1. Disconnect battery ground cable.
2. Remove instrument panel lower trim cover.
3. Remove the four radio mounting plate screws, and the screw from radio support bracket on lower instrument panel tie bar.
4. Pull radio outward, then disconnect antenna and electrical connectors, then remove radio.
5. Reverse procedure to install.

PONTIAC SAFARI

1. Disconnect battery ground cable.
2. Remove control knobs from radio control shafts.
3. Remove three trim plate attaching screws, then remove trim plate.
4. Remove two screws and one nut attaching radio mounting bracket to instrument panel.
5. Disconnect electrical connectors and antenna lead from rear of radio.
6. Remove radio and mounting bracket from instrument panel.
7. Reverse procedure to install.

BLOWER MOTOR
REPLACE
EXCEPT 1991 CAPRICE

1. Disconnect battery ground cable.
2. Disconnect blower motor lead wire, then the cooling tube, if equipped.
3. Remove blower motor to case attaching screws, then remove blower motor, **Fig. 28 through 31.**
4. Reverse procedure to install.

1991 CAPRICE

1. Disconnect battery ground cable.
2. Remove righthand instrument panel sound insulator attaching screws, then pull panel rearward disengaging attaching studs.
3. Disconnect blower assembly electrical connector.
4. Remove righthand hinge pillar trim finish panel.
5. Remove secondary ECM bracket attaching screw, then position secondary ECM and bracket aside.
6. Support blower motor assembly, then remove blower motor assembly attaching screws.
7. Remove blower motor assembly.
8. Reverse procedure to install.

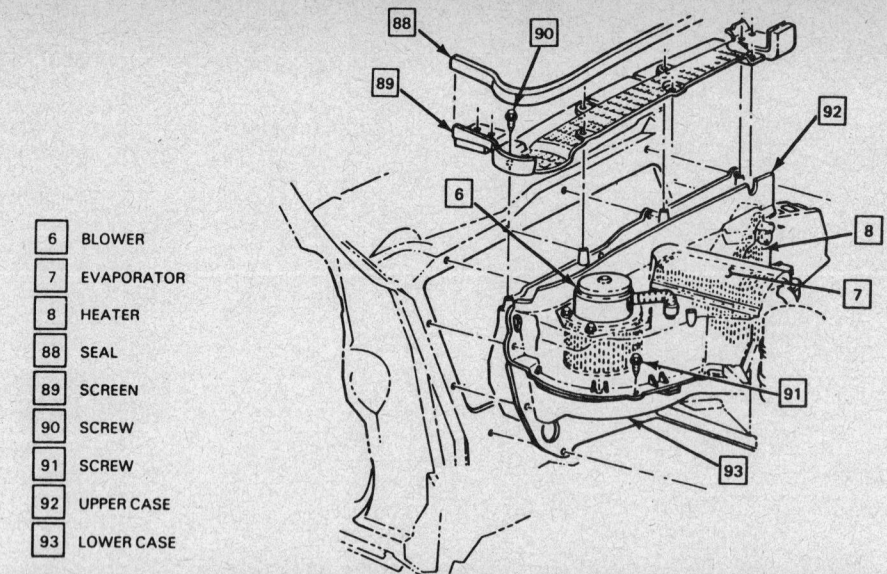

6	BLOWER
7	EVAPORATOR
8	HEATER
88	SEAL
89	SCREEN
90	SCREW
91	SCREW
92	UPPER CASE
93	LOWER CASE

Fig. 30 Blower motor, heater core & evaporator core. With A/C except Monte Carlo & Cutlass Supreme Classic

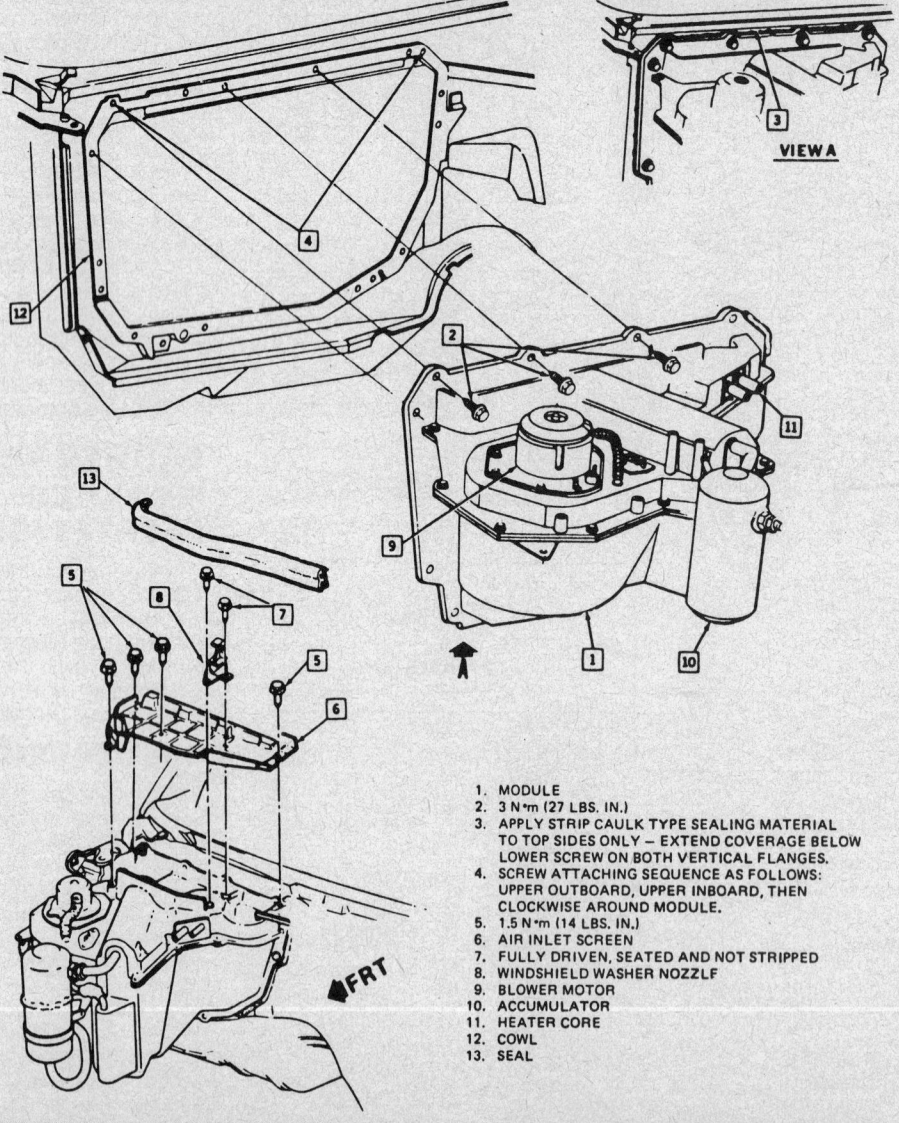

VIEW A

1. MODULE
2. 3 N·m (27 LBS. IN.)
3. APPLY STRIP CAULK TYPE SEALING MATERIAL TO TOP SIDES ONLY — EXTEND COVERAGE BELOW LOWER SCREW ON BOTH VERTICAL FLANGES.
4. SCREW ATTACHING SEQUENCE AS FOLLOWS: UPPER OUTBOARD, UPPER INBOARD, THEN CLOCKWISE AROUND MODULE.
5. 1.5 N·m (14 LBS. IN.)
6. AIR INLET SCREEN
7. FULLY DRIVEN, SEATED AND NOT STRIPPED
8. WINDSHIELD WASHER NOZZLE
9. BLOWER MOTOR
10. ACCUMULATOR
11. HEATER CORE
12. COWL
13. SEAL

Fig. 31 Blower motor, heater core & evaporator core. With A/C Monte Carlo & Cutlass Supreme Classic

HEATER CORE
REPLACE

LESS A/C

1. Disconnect battery ground cable and drain cooling system.
2. Disconnect heater hoses from heater core. Plug core outlets to prevent coolant spillage.
3. Disconnect electrical connections at blower motor and resistor.
4. Detach heater wiring from clip at blower housing cover.
5. Remove blower housing cover attaching screws, then remove blower housing cover, **Figs. 28 and 29.**
6. Remove heater core.
7. Reverse procedure to install.

WITH A/C

Except Cutlass Supreme Classic & Monte Carlo & 1991 Caprice

1. Disconnect battery ground cable and drain cooling system.
2. Disconnect heater hoses at heater core. Cap core outlets to prevent coolant spillage.
3. Pull hood seal from A/C module flange and area above air screen.
4. Remove air inlet screen attaching screws and air inlet screen.
5. Remove right hand windshield wiper arm.
6. Detach A/C module ground strap from dash panel.
7. Disconnect electrical connectors from A/C module upper case components.
8. Remove upper A/C module attaching screws, then remove A/C module upper case, **Fig. 30.**
9. Remove heater core tube seal, then remove heater core retaining clamp and lift heater core from case.
10. Reverse procedure to install.

Cutlass Supreme Classic & Monte Carlo

1. Disconnect battery ground cable and drain cooling system.
2. Disconnect heater hoses at heater core.

3. Remove retaining bracket and ground strap.
4. Remove module rubber seal and module screen, **Fig. 21.**
5. Remove right hand windshield wiper arm.
6. Remove high blower relay and thermostatic switch mounting screws.
7. Disconnect wire connector at top of module, then remove module top cover, **Fig. 31.**
8. Remove heater core from module.
9. Reverse procedure to install.

1991 Caprice

1. Disconnect battery ground cable, then drain cooling system.
2. Remove heater outlet attaching screw.
3. Disconnect heater core pipe fittings, then disengage pipe from fitting.
4. Remove righthand instrument insulator panel attaching screws, then pull panel rearward to disconnect.
5. Remove instrument panel lower reinforcement attaching nut and screw.
6. Disconnect lower evaporator case vacuum electrical connectors.
7. Remove righthand pillar trim finish panel, then roll carpet back to gain access.
8. Remove seven lower evaporator case attaching screws, then remove lower evaporator case.
9. Remove heater core attaching straps and screws, then pull heater core rearward working heater tubes out of seal.
10. Reverse procedure to install.

EVAPORATOR CORE
REPLACE

EXCEPT 1991 CAPRICE

1. Disconnect battery ground cable and discharge refrigerant from A/C system.
2. Disconnect evaporator core inlet and outlet refrigerant lines. Cap lines and outlets.

3. Remove expansion tube from evaporator inlet pipe using tool No. J26549-D or equivalent.
4. Pull hood seal from A/C module flange and area above air screen.
5. Remove air inlet screen attaching screws and air inlet screen.
6. Remove right hand windshield wiper arm.
7. Detach A/C module ground strap from dash panel.
8. Disconnect electrical connectors from A/C module upper case components.
9. Remove upper A/C module attaching screws, then remove A/C module upper case, **Figs. 30 and 31. On Cutlass Supreme Classic and Monte Carlo,** remove accumulator bracket screws.
10. Remove evaporator core clamp, then lift evaporator core from case.
11. Reverse procedure to install. When installing, ensure evaporator core seal remain properly positioned. After completing installation, add three ounces of refrigerant oil and recharge A/C system, refer to "Air Conditioning" section.

1991 CAPRICE

1. Disconnect battery ground cable and discharge refrigerant from A/C system.
2. Disconnect evaporator core inlet and outlet refrigerant lines. Cap lines and outlets.
3. Remove righthand instrument insulator panel attaching screws, then pull panel rearward to disconnect.
4. Remove instrument panel lower reinforcement attaching nut and screw.
5. Disconnect lower evaporator case vacuum electrical connectors.
6. Remove righthand pillar trim finish panel, then roll carpet back to gain access.
7. Remove seven lower evaporator case attaching screws, then remove lower evaporator case.
8. Remove evaporator core attaching screw and bracket.
9. Pull heater core rearward and down to remove.
10. Reverse procedure to install.

4.3L/V6-262, 5.0L/V8-305 & 5.7L/V8-350

INDEX

ENGINE MOUNTS
REPLACE

1. Remove mount retaining bolt from below frame mounting bracket, **Fig. 1.**
2. Raise front of engine and remove mount to engine bolts and mount. On models equipped with 4.3L/V6-262 engines, the right hand mount may be removed by loosening the through bolt. **Raise engine only enough to provide sufficient clearance for mount removal. Check for interference between rear of engine and cowl panel which could result in distributor damage.**
3. Reverse procedure to install.

ENGINE
REPLACE
4.3L/V6-262 ENGINE

1. Disconnect battery ground cable.
2. Raise and support front of vehicle, then disconnect exhaust pipe at exhaust manifold.
3. Remove flywheel cover, then disconnect transmission oil cooler lines at oil pan.
4. Remove left hand engine mount through bolt, then loosen right hand bolt.
5. Remove flywheel to torque converter attaching bolts.
6. Remove flywheel housing to engine attaching bolts.
7. Disconnect converter clutch control wiring harness at transmission.
8. Disconnect knock sensor electrical connector.
9. Wrap shop towel around fuel hose to steel line connection to prevent fuel spillage, then disconnect fuel hoses from lines at frame.
10. Remove lower fan shroud.
11. Disconnect electrical wiring from starter motor.
12. **On Monte Carlo models, remove starter motor.**

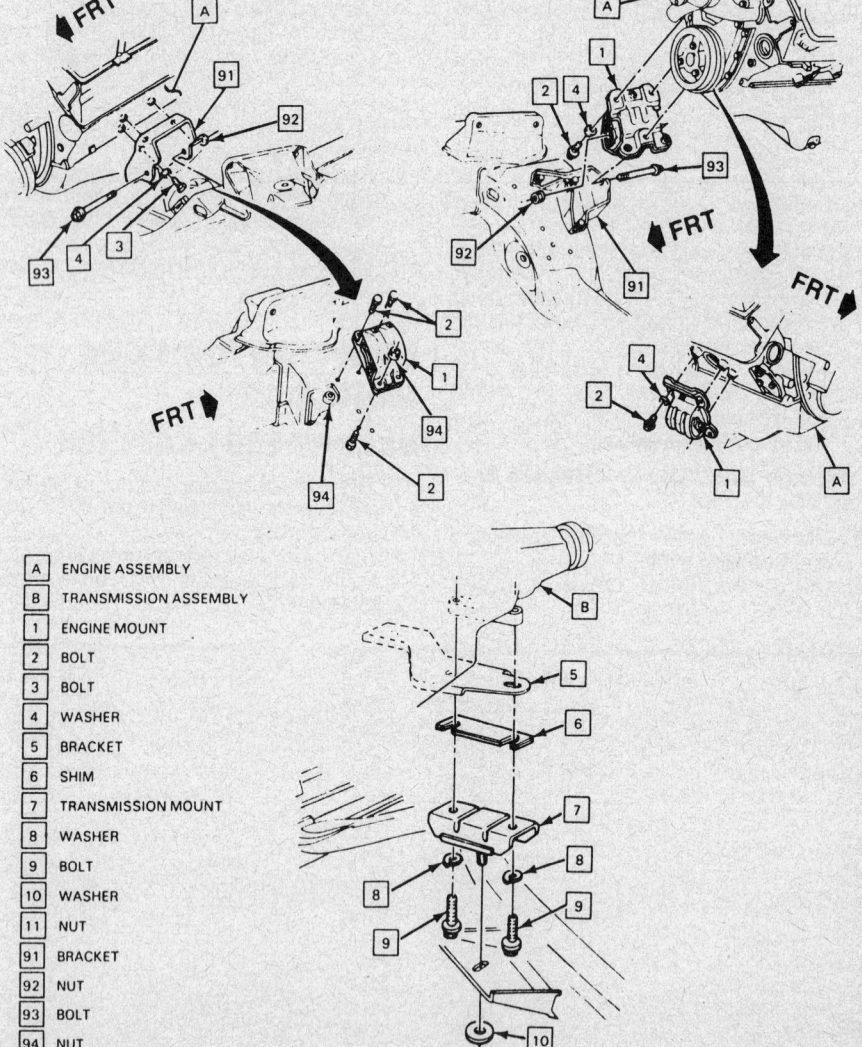

A	ENGINE ASSEMBLY
B	TRANSMISSION ASSEMBLY
1	ENGINE MOUNT
2	BOLT
3	BOLT
4	WASHER
5	BRACKET
6	SHIM
7	TRANSMISSION MOUNT
8	WASHER
9	BOLT
10	WASHER
11	NUT
91	BRACKET
92	NUT
93	BOLT
94	NUT

Fig. 1 Engine & transmission mounting

13. **On all models,** lower vehicle, then disconnect ECM wiring harness at engine.
14. On Caprice models, remove windshield washer bottle.
15. **On all models,** disconnect electrical wiring and vacuum hoses as necessary to permit engine removal. Tag electrical wiring and vacuum hoses so the may be installed at the same locations.
16. Remove air cleaner, then remove upper fan shroud.
17. Disconnect throttle and T.V. cables at throttle body.
18. Drain cooling system, then disconnect radiator and heater hoses.
19. Remove A/C compressor from mounting and position aside with refrigerant hoses attached.
20. Remove power steering pump from mounting and position aside with refrigerant hoses attached.
21. Disconnect transmission oil cooler lines from radiator.
22. **On Caprice models,** perform the following:
    a. Remove coolant recovery system bottle.
    b. Remove radiator.
    c. Remove alternator adjusting bracket.
    d. Disconnect heater hoses from intake manifold bracket.
23. **On all models,** disconnect battery cable from frame.
24. **On Monte Carlo models,** remove fan and pulley.
25. **On all models,** scribe alignment marks on hinges, then remove hood.
26. **On Caprice models, disconnect battery ground cable from left hand cylinder head. On Monte Carlo models,** disconnect battery ground straps from both cylinder heads.
27. **On all models,** disconnect AIR pipe at exhaust manifold.
28. Disconnect AIR hose from AIR pipe at converter.
29. Support transmission using a suitable jack.
30. Attach suitable engine lifting fixture to engine, then remove engine from vehicle.
31. Reverse procedure to install.

5.0L/V8-305 & 5.7L/V8-350 ENGINES

1. Disconnect battery cable from battery.
2. Remove air cleaner assembly.
3. Drain cooling system, then disconnect radiator and heater hoses.
4. Remove upper fan shroud, then remove engine cooling fan.
5. Remove power steering pump from bracket and position aside with hoses attached.
6. Remove A/C compressor from mounting and position aside with hoses attached.
7. Disconnect accelerator and T.V. cables from throttle body.
8. Remove radiator from vehicle.
9. Disconnect electrical wiring and vacuum hoses as necessary to permit engine removal. Tag electrical wiring

and vacuum hoses so they may be installed at the same locations.
10. Disconnect AIR hose at pipe to converter.
11. Disconnect ground strap at engine bulkhead.
12. Scribe alignment marks on hinges, then remove hood.
13. **On 1988-90 models,** remove distributor cap.
14. **On 1991 models,** remove distributor, wiper motor and MAP sensor.
15. **On all models,** disconnect cruise control cable, if equipped.
16. Disconnect battery ground cable from cylinder head.
17. Raise and support vehicle, then drain crankcase.
18. Disconnect electrical wiring from starter motor.
19. Disconnect exhaust cross over pipe from exhaust manifold.
20. Remove flywheel cover, then remove flywheel to converter attaching bolts.
21. Remove engine mount through bolts.
22. **On TBI models,** wrap shop towel around fuel hose to steel line connection to prevent fuel spillage, then disconnect fuel hoses from fuel lines. On carbureted engines, disconnect fuel line from fuel pump.
23. **On all models,** disconnect converter clutch wiring at transmission.
24. Detach transmission oil cooler lines from clip at oil pan.
25. Remove transmission to engine attaching bolts.
26. Lower vehicle, then support transmission using a suitable jack.
27. Install a suitable engine lifting fixture to engine, then remove engine from vehicle.
28. Reverse procedure to install.

INTAKE MANIFOLD
REPLACE

1. Disconnect battery ground cable, drain cooling system and remove air cleaner.
2. Disconnect accelerator, transmission and cruise control linkages, as equipped.
3. Disconnect fuel line from carburetor or TBI unit and remove fuel line clips as needed.
4. Remove carburetor or throttle body from intake manifold.
5. Disconnect necessary vacuum hoses and electrical connectors, noting position for installation.
6. Disconnect upper radiator and heater hoses from manifold.
7. Remove distributor as described in "Electrical" section under "Distributor, Replace."
8. Remove ignition coil, AIR pump, cruise control servo and brackets, as needed.
9. Remove alternator upper mounting bracket and EGR solenoids.
10. Remove manifold retaining bolts and the manifold.
11. Reverse procedure to install, noting

the following:
a. Ensure surfaces are clean and dry, then apply 3/16 bead of RTV sealer on each block ridge and apply suitable sealer around water outlets, install gaskets and secure gasket position by extending bead of sealer approximately 1/2 inch onto gasket ends.
b. Install manifold and retaining bolts, ensuring areas between case ridges and manifold are completely sealed.
c. Torque manifold bolts to specifications in sequence shown in **Figs. 2 and 3.**
d. After installing carburetor or TBI unit, check to ensure no fuel leakage is present.

EXHAUST MANIFOLD
REPLACE

1. Disconnect battery ground cable.
2. Raise and support vehicle.
3. Disconnect cross-over pipe from exhaust manifold.
4. Lower vehicle, then remove air cleaner, if necessary.
5. Disconnect spark plug wires, if necessary.
6. Remove hoses, brackets and pipes as necessary to permit exhaust manifold removal. Tag hoses so they can be installed in the same locations.
7. Remove exhaust manifold attaching bolts and studs, then remove exhaust manifold and gasket, **Fig. 4.**
8. Reverse procedure to install.

CYLINDER HEAD
REPLACE

1. Disconnect battery ground cable, then drain cooling system and engine block.
2. Remove intake manifold and exhaust manifolds.
3. **On 1991 models,** remove rocker arm covers.
4. Remove alternator lower mounting bolt and position alternator aside.
5. Remove dipstick tube and bracket.
6. If equipped with A/C, remove compressor and forward mounting bracket and position aside.
7. Remove power steering pump and bracket, position aside.
8. Remove rocker arm cover, rocker arms and push rods. **Keep rocker arm, rocker arm balls and push rods in order so they can be installed in the same position.**
9. Remove diverter valve, if equipped.
10. Remove cylinder head bolts and cylinder head.
11. Reverse procedure to install. Apply suitable sealer to cylinder head bolts and gradually torque bolts to specifications in sequence shown in **Figs. 5 and 6.**

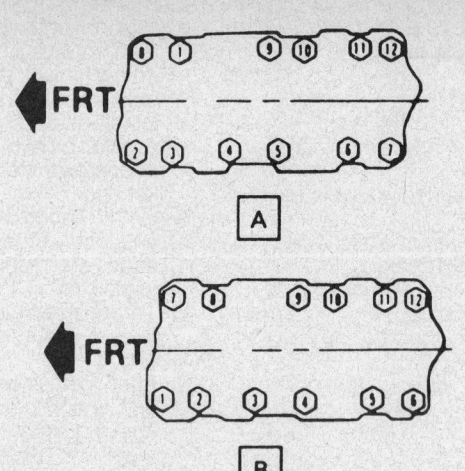

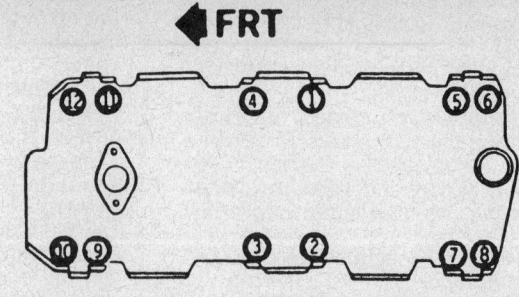

A — INITIAL TIGHTENING SEQUENCE

B — FINAL TIGHTENING SEQUENCE

Fig. 2   Intake manifold bolt tightening sequence. 4.3L/V6-262

Fig. 3   Intake manifold bolt tightening sequence. 5.0L/V8-305 & 5.7L/V8-350

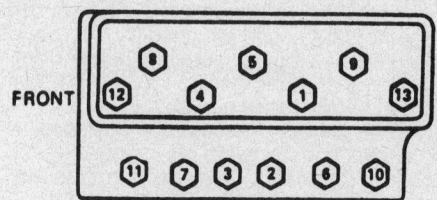

Fig. 5   Cylinder head bolt tightening sequence. 4.3L/V6-262

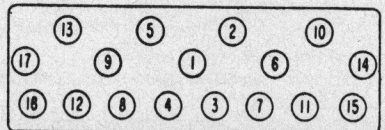

Fig. 6   Cylinder head bolt tightening sequence. 5.0L/V8-305 & 5.7L/V8-350

VALVE LASH SPECIFICATIONS

Year	Engine/VIN	Valve Lash
1988	4.3L/V6-262/Z	1 Turn①
	5.0L/V8-305/G & H	1 Turn①
1989–91	5.0L/V8-305/E	1 Turn①
1991	5.7L/V8-350/7	1 Turn①

①—Turn rocker arm stud nut until all lash is eliminated, then tighten nut the additional turn listed in ¼ turn increments. Refer to "Valve Lash, Adjust" procedure.

VALVE LASH
ADJUST

After the engine has been thoroughly warmed up the valves may be adjusted, **Fig. 7,** with the engine shut off as follows: With engine in position to fire No. 1 cylinder the following valves may be adjusted: V6-262, Exhaust 1-5-6, intake 1-2-3. V8's, Exhaust 1-3-4-8, intake 1-2-5-7. Then crank the engine one more complete revolution which will bring No. 4 cylinder on V6-262, engine and No. 6 cylinder on V8 engines, to the firing position at which time the following valves may be adjusted: V6-262, Exhaust 2-3-4, intake 4-5-6. V8's, Exhaust 2-5-6-7, intake 3-4-6-8.

The following procedure, performed with the engine running, should be done only in case readjustment is required.
1. After engine has been warmed up to operating temperature, remove valve cover and install a new valve cover gasket.
2. With engine running at idle speed, back off valve rocker arm nut until rocker arm starts to clatter.
3. Turn rocker arm nut down slowly until

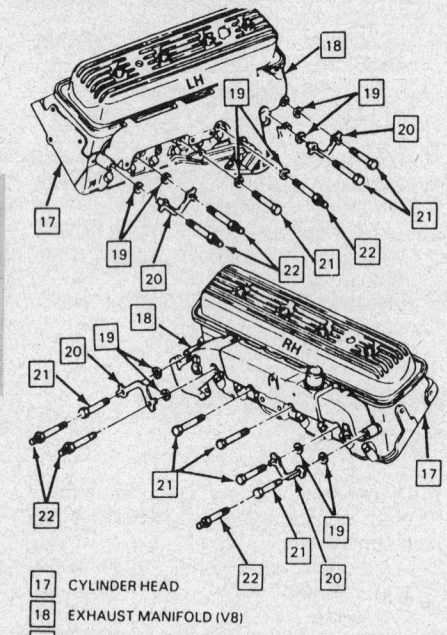

17	CYLINDER HEAD
18	EXHAUST MANIFOLD (V8)
19	WASHER
20	LOCK
21	BOLTS
22	STUDS

Fig. 4   Exhaust manifold installation

the clatter just stops. This is the zero lash position.
4. Turn nut down ¼ additional turn and pause 10 seconds until engine runs smoothly. Repeat additional ¼ turns, pausing 10 seconds each time, until nut has been turned down the number of turns listed in the "Valve Lash Specifications" chart from the zero lash position. **This preload adjustment must be done slowly to allow**

the lifter to adjust itself to prevent the possibility of interference between the valve head and top of piston, which might result in internal damage and/or bent push rods. Noisy lifters should be replaced.

ROCKER ARMS & BALLS

When replacing rocker arms or rocker arm balls, bearing surfaces of rocker arms and balls should be coated with pre-lube 3755008 or equivalent.

ROCKER ARM STUDS
REPLACE

If studs are loose in cylinder head, .003 inch or .013 inch oversize studs may be installed after reaming holes with a proper size reamer.
1. Remove the old stud by placing a suitable spacer, **Fig. 8,** over stud. Install nut and flat washer and remove stud by turning nut.
2. Ream hole for oversize stud.
3. Coat press-fit area of stud with rear axle lube. Then install new stud, **Fig. 9.** If tool shown is used, it should bottom on the head.

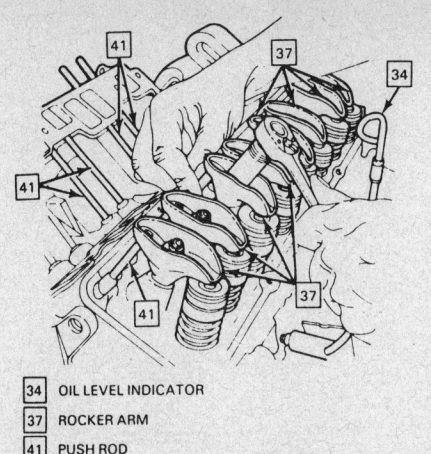

34 OIL LEVEL INDICATOR
37 ROCKER ARM
41 PUSH ROD

Fig. 7   Adjusting valve lash

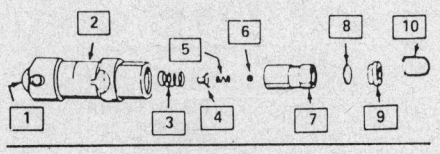

1—ROLLER
2—LIFTER BODY
3—PLUNGER SPRING
4—BALL CHECK RETAINER
5—BALL CHECK SPRING
6—BALL CHECK
7—PLUNGER
8—OIL METERING VALVE
9—PUSH ROD SEAT
10—RETAINER RING

Fig. 10   Exploded view of hydraulic valve lifter

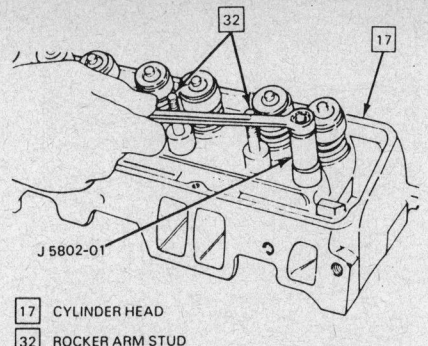

17 CYLINDER HEAD
32 ROCKER ARM STUD

Fig. 8   Removing rocker arm stud

Fig. 9   Installing rocker arm stud

VALVE LIFT SPECIFICATIONS

Engine/VIN	Year	Int.	Exh.
4.3L/V6-262/Z	1988	.350	.385
5.0L/V8-305/H	1988	.350	.385
5.0L/V8-305/G	1988	.385	.404
5.0L/V8-305/E	1989–91	.350	.385
5.7L/V8-350/7	1990	.385	.404
5.7L/V8-350/7	1991	.413	.428

CAMSHAFT LOBE LIFT SPECIFICATIONS

Engine/VIN	Year	Int.	Exh.
4.3L/V6-262/Z	1988	.234	.257
5.0L/V8-305/H	1988	.234	.257
5.0L/V8-305/G	1988	.269	.276
5.0L/V8-305/E	1989–91	.234	.257
5.7L/V8-350/7	1991	.257	.269

A TIMING MARKS
38 CYLINDER BLOCK
58 TIMING CHAIN
59 CRANKSHAFT SPROCKET
101 CAMSHAFT SPROCKET

Fig. 11   Valve timing marks

PUSH RODS

On engines that use push rods with a hardened insert at one end, the hardened end is identified by a color stripe and should always be installed toward the rocker arm during assembly.

VALVE GUIDES

On all engines valves operate in guide holes bored in the head. If clearance becomes excessive, use the next oversize valve and ream the bore to fit. Valves with oversize stems are available in .003, .015 and .030 inch.

VALVE ARRANGEMENT

FRONT TO REAR

4.3L/V6-262

Right.........................E-I-I-E-I-E
Left...........................E-I-E-I-I-E

5.0L/V8-305 & 5.7L/V8-350

All..............................E-I-I-E-I-I-E

HYDRAULIC LIFTERS
REPLACE

Valve lifters can be lifted from their bores after removing rocker arms and push rods and intake manifold. Adjustable pliers with protected jaws may be used to remove lifters which are stuck due to carbon or varnish deposits. **Fig. 10** illustrates the type of valve lifter used.

ENGINE FRONT COVER
REPLACE

On all engines the cover oil seal may be replaced without taking off the timing gear cover. After removing the vibration damper, pry out the old seal with a screwdriver. Install the new seal with the lip or open end toward inside of cover and drive it into position.
1. Disconnect battery ground cable and drain cooling system.
2. Remove vibration damper and water pump.
3. Remove oil pan and gasket as outlined.
4. Remove timing cover retaining screws and the timing cover.
5. Reverse procedure to install.

TIMING CHAIN
REPLACE

1. Remove engine front cover as outlined previously.
2. Remove crankshaft oil slinger.
3. Crank engine until timing marks on sprockets are in alignment, **Fig. 11.**
4. Remove three camshaft to sprocket bolts.
5. Remove camshaft sprocket and timing chain together. Sprocket is a light press fit on camshaft for approximately 1/8 inch. If sprocket does not come off easily, a light blow with a plastic hammer on the lower edge of the sprocket should dislodge it.
6. If crankshaft sprocket is to be replaced, remove it with a suitable gear puller. Install new sprocket, aligning key and keyway.
7. Install chain on camshaft sprocket. Hold sprocket vertical with chain hanging below and shift around to align the timing marks on sprockets.
8. Align dowel in camshaft with dowel hole in sprocket and install sprocket on camshaft. Do not attempt to drive sprocket on camshaft as welch plug at rear of engine can be dislodged.

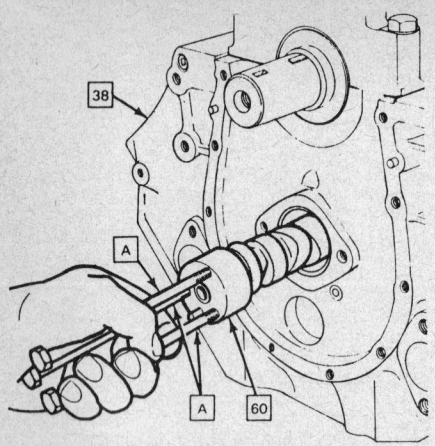

A	5/16 INCH 18 x 4 INCH BOLTS
38	CYLINDER BLOCK
60	CAMSHAFT

Fig. 12   Removing camshaft from cylinder block

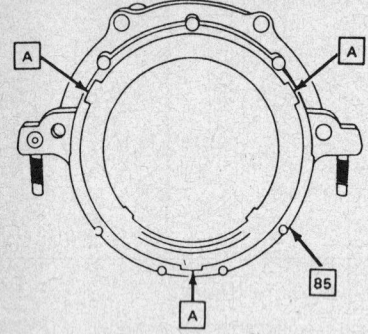

A	SEAL REMOVAL NOTCHES
85	REAR CRANKSHAFT SEAL RETAINER

Fig. 15   Crankshaft rear oil seal retainer notch locations

9. Draw sprocket onto camshaft, using the three mounting bolts. Tighten to specifications.
10. Lubricate timing chain with engine oil and install cover.

CAMSHAFT
REPLACE

1. Remove intake manifold as described under "Intake Manifold, Replace."
2. Remove valve covers, rocker arms and push rods. Keep rocker arms and push rods in order so they can be installed in the same locations.
3. Remove accessory drive belt(s), then remove upper fan shroud.
4. **On 1991 models,** disconnect oil cooler lines.
5. **On all modeles,** remove radiator. **On models equipped with A/C,** discharge refrigerant system and remove condenser
6. Remove timing chain as described under "Timing Chain, Replace."
7. **On carbureted engine,** remove fuel pump.
8. **On TBI engines,** disconnect fuel hose from front fuel line. Position shop

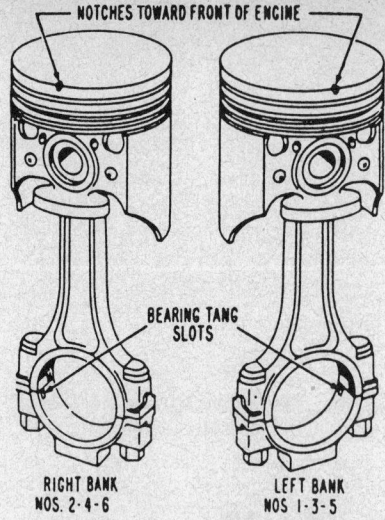

Fig. 13   Piston & rod assembly. 4.3L/V6-262

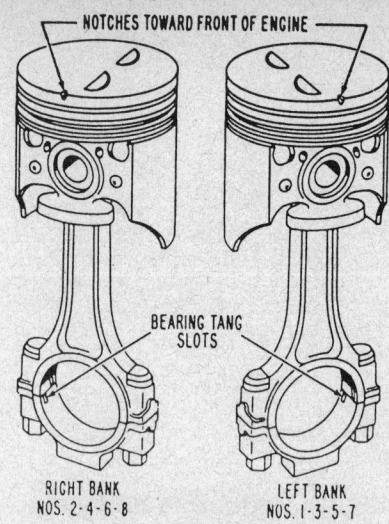

Fig. 14   Piston & rod assembly. 5.0L/V8-305 & 5.7L/V8-350

towel around fuel hose to fuel line connection to prevent fuel spillage.
9. **On all models,** remove grille.
10. Remove valve lifters. Keep valve lifters in order so they can be installed in the same locations.
11. Install two 5/16-18 x 4 bolts in camshaft bolt holes, then carefully remove camshaft, **Fig. 12.**
12. Reverse procedure to install.

PISTONS & RODS, ASSEMBLE

Assemble pistons to connecting rods as shown in **Figs. 13 and 14.**
Upon installation, measure the connecting rod side clearance using a suitable feeler gauge. Refer to "Engine Rebuilding Specifications" for connecting rod side clearance.

PISTONS, PINS & RINGS

Pistons are available in standard and oversizes of .010 and .030 inch.
Piston rings are available in standard and oversizes of .030 inch.

MAIN & ROD BEARINGS

Connecting rod bearings are available in standard and undersizes of .001, .002, .010 and .020 inch.
Main bearings are available in standard and undersizes of .001, .002, .009, .010 and .020 inch.

CRANKSHAFT REAR OIL SEAL
REPLACE

These engines are equipped with a one-piece, lip type seal mounted in a separate seal retainer. Seal replacement requires removal of the transmission.
1. Raise and support vehicle, then remove transmission and flywheel.

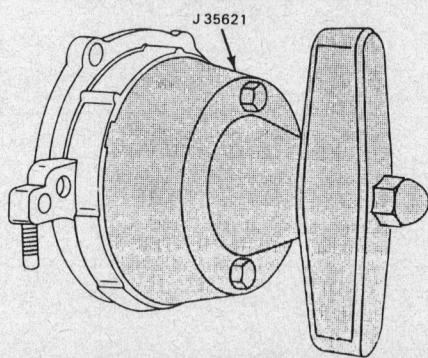

Fig. 16   Crankshaft rear oil seal installation

2. Pry seal from retainer, inserting screwdriver in notches provided in seal retainer, **Fig. 15.**
3. Lubricate inner and outer diameters of replacement seal with engine oil, then mount seal on tool J-35621 or equivalent, **Fig. 16.**
4. Mount tool on rear of crankshaft, tightening screws snugly to ensure seal will be installed squarely on crankshaft.
5. Tighten wing nut on tool until it bottoms, then remove tool from crankshaft.
6. Reverse remaining procedure to complete installation.

OIL PAN
REPLACE

1. Disconnect battery ground cable.
2. Remove air cleaner.
3. **On 1991 models with 5.0L/V8-305 and 5.7L/V8-350 engines,** remove distributor cap and wires.
4. **On all models,** remove upper fan shroud.
5. Raise and support vehicle, then disconnect AIR pipe at exhaust manifold.
6. Disconnect AIR hose at converter pipe.

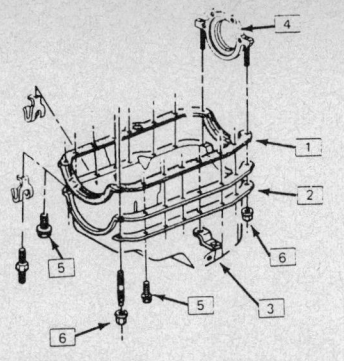

ENGINE OIL PRESSURE 10 LBS. MINIMUM AT 500 RPM AND 30-55 LBS. AT 2000 RPM. OIL FILTER BY-PASS VALVE OPERATES AT 9- TO 11 LBS. PRESSURE.

1. GASKET
2. REINFORCEMENT
3. OIL PAN
4. RETAINER
5. 72-130 IN. LBS. (13)
6. 150-250 IN. LBS.

Fig. 17   Oil pan & gasket assembly. 4.3L/V6-262

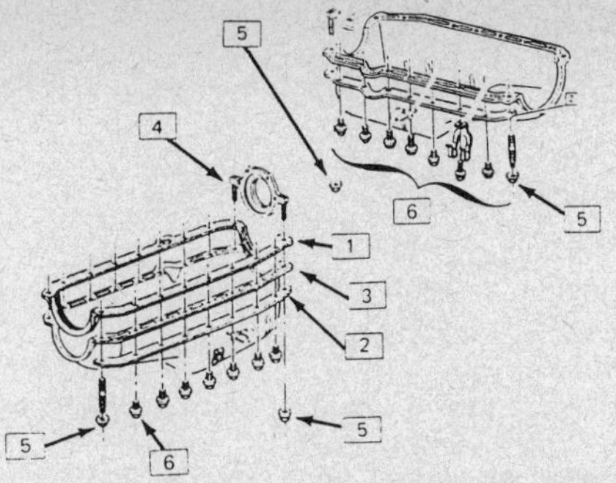

ENGINE OIL PRESSURE 10 LBS. MINIMUM AT 500 RPM AND 30-55 LBS. AT 2000 RPM. OIL FILTER BY-PASS VALVE OPERATES AT 9- TO 11 LBS. PRESSURE.

1. GASKET
2. REINFORCEMENT
3. OIL PAN
4. RETAINER
5. 150-250 IN. LBS.
6. 72-130 (14)

Fig. 18   Oil pan & gasket assembly. 5.0L/V8-305 & 5.7L/V8-350

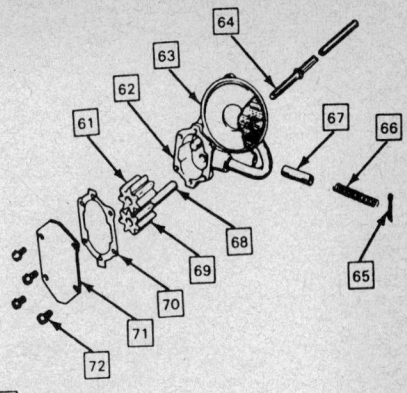

61. IDLER GEAR
62. PUMP BODY
63. PICKUP SCREEN AND PIPE ASSEMBLY
64. DRIVE SHAFT EXTENSION
65. RETAINING PIN
66. SPRING
67. PRESSURE REGULATOR VALVE
68. DRIVE SHAFT
69. DRIVE GEAR
70. GASKET
71. COVER
72. COVER SCREW

Fig. 19   Exploded view of oil pump

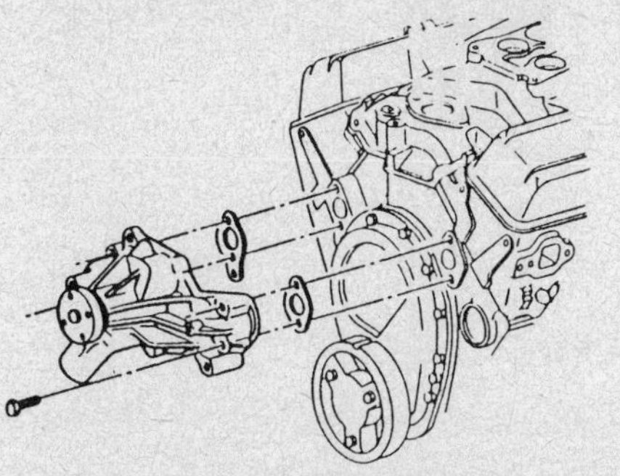

Fig. 20   Water pump replacement

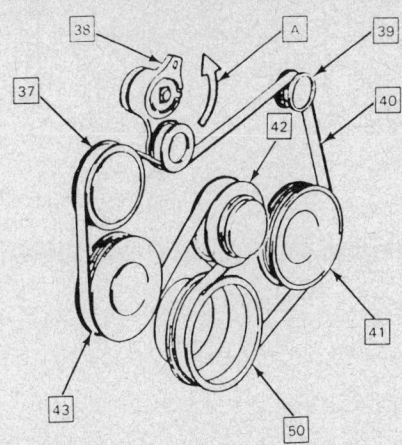

A   ROTATE TENSIONER IN DIRECTION SHOWN TO INSTALL OR REMOVE BELT
37   A C COMPRESSOR OR BELT IDLER PULLEY
38   BELT TENSIONER
39   GENERATOR ASSEMBLY PULLEY
40   SERPENTINE BELT
41   P S PUMP PULLEY
42   WATER PUMP PULLEY
43   AIR PUMP PULLEY
50   CRANKSHAFT PULLEY

Fig. 21   Serpentine drive belt routing

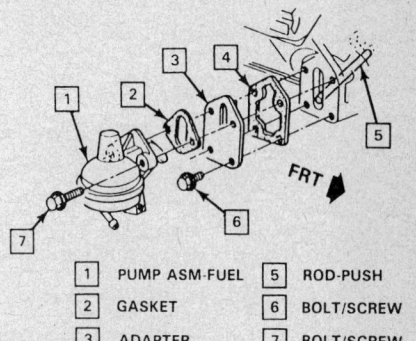

1. PUMP ASM-FUEL
2. GASKET
3. ADAPTER
4. GASKET
5. ROD-PUSH
6. BOLT/SCREW
7. BOLT/SCREW

Fig. 22   Engine mounted mechanical fuel pump.

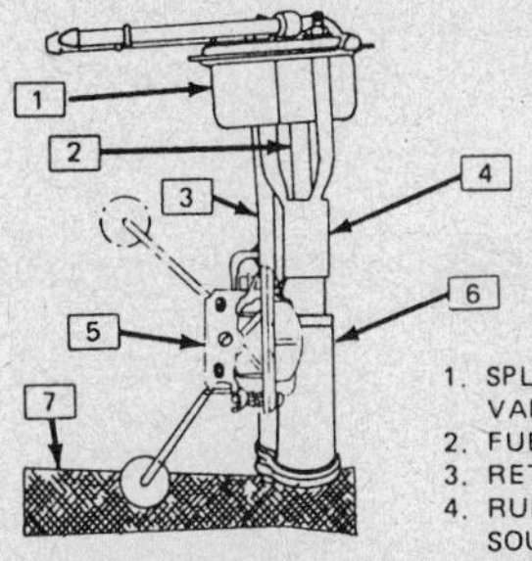

1. SPLASH CUP LIQUID VAPOR SEPARATOR
2. FUEL TUBE
3. RETURN TUBE
4. RUBBER COUPLER AND SOUND ISOLATOR
5. FUEL LEVEL SENDER
6. ELECTRIC FUEL PUMP
7. FUEL FILTER

FUEL GAGE SENDING UNIT WITH FUEL PUMP

Fig. 23   Intake electric fuel pump & fuel gauge sending unit

7. Drain crankcase.
8. Disconnect exhaust pipe at exhaust manifold.
9. Remove flywheel cover.
10. Detach transmission oil cooler lines from oil pan clips.
11. Remove attaching bolts, then remove starter motor.
12. On 1991 models with 5.0L/V8-305 and 5.7L/V8-350 engines, remove oil level sensor electrical connector, then remove oil level sensor.
13. On models with 4.3L/V6-262 engine, remove left hand engine mount through bolt and loosen right hand engine mount through bolt.

14. On models with 5.0L/V8-305 and 5.7L/V8-350 engine, remove both left and right hand engine mount through bolts.
15. On all models, remove oil pan attaching nuts and bolts, then lower oil pan, Fig. 17 and 18.
16. Position forward crankshaft counterbalance weight and throw to permit oil pan removal.
17. Raise engine slightly to permit oil pan removal.
18. Remove oil pan and gasket.
19. Reverse procedure to install. Apply a small quantity of sealer 1052914 or equivalent to front cover and engine

block junction and rear seal retainer and engine block junction.

OIL PUMP
REPLACE

1. Remove oil pan as described previously.
2. Remove pump to rear main bearing cap bolt and remove pump and extension shaft.
3. Reverse procedure to install. Make sure that installed position of oil pump screen is with bottom edge parallel to oil pan rails.

OIL PUMP SERVICE

1. Remove oil pump as described previously.
2. Remove pump cover screws and pump cover, Fig. 19.

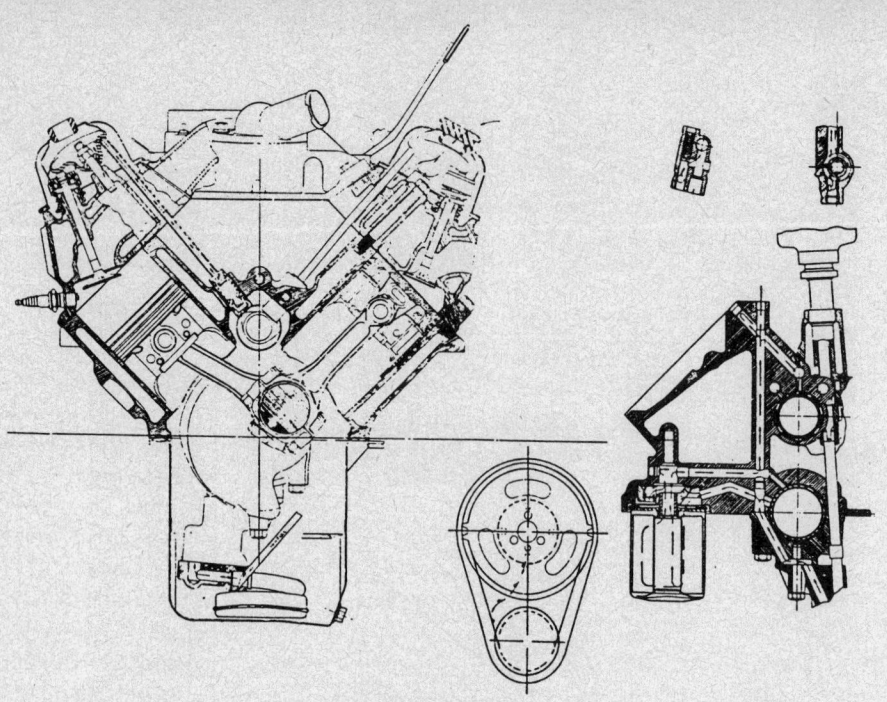

Engine oil system (front view)

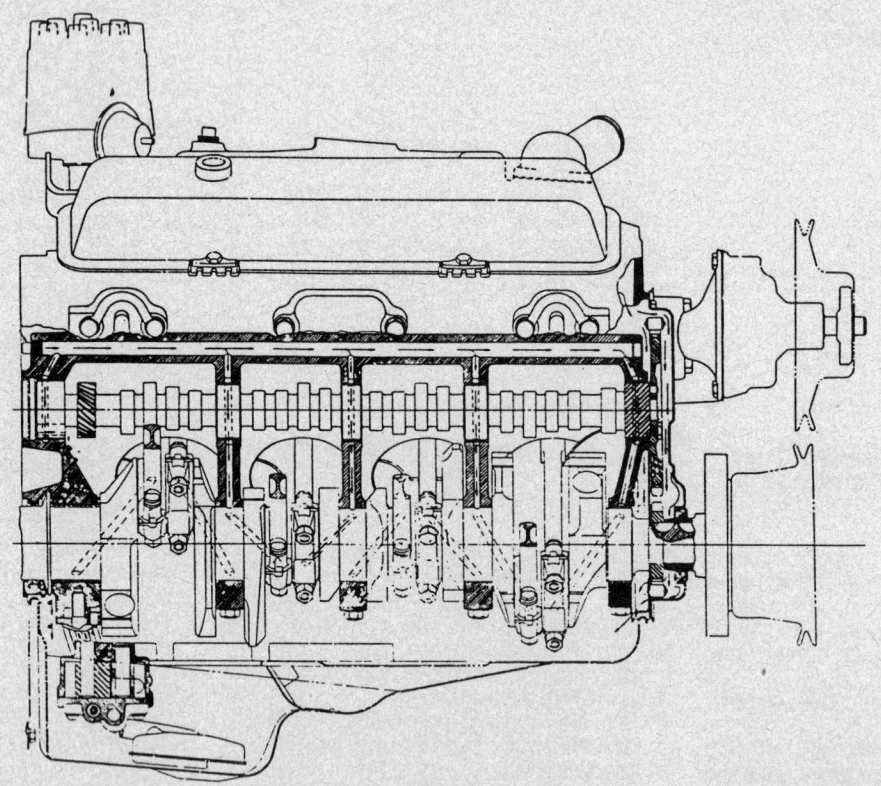

Engine oil system (side view)

3. Mark gear teeth so they can be reassembled with same teeth indexing, then remove drive gear, idler gear and shaft.
4. Remove pressure regulator valve retaining pin, pressure regulator valve and related parts.
5. If pickup screen and pipe require replacement, mount pump in a soft-jawed vise and extract pipe from pump.
6. Wash all parts in cleaning solvent and dry with compressed air.
7. Inspect pump body and cover for cracks and excessive wear.
8. Inspect pump gears for damage or excessive wear.
9. Check drive gear shaft for looseness in pump body.
10. Inspect inside of pump cover for wear that would allow oil to leak past the ends of the gears.
11. Inspect pickup screen and pipe assembly for damage to screen, pipe or relief grommet.
12. Check pressure regulator valve for fit in pump housing.
13. Reverse procedure to assemble. Turn drive shaft by hand to check for smooth operation. **The pump gears and body are not serviced separately. If the pump gears or body are damaged or worn, the pump assembly should be replaced. Also, if the pick-up screen and pump assembly was removed, it should be replaced with a new one as loss of the press fit condition could result in an air leak and loss of oil pressure.**

WATER PUMP REPLACE

1. Disconnect battery ground cable and drain cooling system.
2. Remove upper fan shroud, then remove accessory drive belts.
3. Remove fan and pulley from water pump hub.
4. Remove power steering pump, A/C compressor and AIR pump brackets.
5. Remove radiator lower hose and heater hose from water pump.
6. Remove radiator lower hose and heater hose from water pump.
7. Remove water pump attaching bolts and the pump, **Fig. 20.** Note position of bolts for assembly reference.
8. Reverse procedure to install.

BELT TENSION DATA

Year	New Lbs.	Used Lbs.
A/C Compressor		
1988	169	90
AIR Pump, Alternator & Steering Pump		
1988	146	67
Serpentine Drive Belt		
1989–90	99–121	99–121
1991	105–125	105–125

SERPENTINE DRIVE BELT ROUTING

Refer to **Fig. 21** for serpentine belt routing diagrams.

COOLING SYSTEM BLEED

These engines do not require a specific bleed procedure. After filling cooling system, start engine and allow to reach operating temperature with radiator cap removed. Air in system will then be automatically bled through cap opening.

FUEL PUMP REPLACE
CARBURETED ENGINES

1. Disconnect fuel lines from pump.
2. Disconnect vapor return line, if so equipped.
3. Remove fuel pump attaching bolts and pump, **Fig. 22.**
4. Reverse procedure to install.

FUEL INJECTED ENGINES

1. Remove fuel tank filler cap, then disconnect battery ground cable.
2. Drain fuel tank.
3. Remove fuel tank as follows:
   a. Raise and support vehicle.
   b. Disconnect electrical connectors.
   c. Disconnect hoses from sending unit.
   d. Support fuel tank, then disconnect retaining straps.
   e. Lower tank and remove from vehicle.
4. Remove fuel level sending unit and pump assembly by turning cam lock ring counterclockwise.
5. Remove fuel pump from level sending unit by pulling fuel pump up and outward, away from bottom support, **Fig. 23.**
6. Reverse procedure to install.

TIGHTENING SPECIFICATIONS
4.3L/V6-262 ENGINE

Year	Component	Torque/Ft. Lbs.
1988	Camshaft Sprocket	13–23
	Connecting Rod Cap Bolt	42–47
	Coolant Outlet	18–23
	Cylinder Head Bolt	60–75
	Engine Front Cover	69–130①
	Exhaust Manifold Bolt	20
	Flywheel To Crankshaft	50–70
	Flywheel Housing To Engine	25–40
	Flywheel Housing Cover	72–90①
	Ignition Distributor Clamp	20–35
	Intake Manifold Bolt	25–45
	Main Bearing Cap Bolt	70–85
	Oil Pan	②
	Oil Pump	60–70
	Oil Pump Cover	80①
	Rear Seal Retainer	120–150①

Continued

TIGHTENING SPECIFICATIONS—Continued

Year	Component	Torque/Ft. Lbs.
	Rocker Arm Cover	50–65 ①
	Spark Plug	22
	Thermostat Housing	19
	Throttle Body To Intake Manifold	12
	Vibration Damper	65–75
	Water Pump	25–35

①—Inch lbs.
②—Torque oil pan attaching screws to 72 to 130 inch Lbs.; torque oil pan attaching nuts to 150 to 250 inch Lbs.

5.0L/V8-305 & 5.7L/V8-350 ENGINES

Year	Component	Torque/Ft. Lbs.
1988	Camshaft Sprocket	13–23
	Carburetor To Intake Manifold	12
	Connecting Rod Cap Bolt	42–47
	Cylinder Head Bolt	60–75
	Engine Front Cover	69–130 ①
	Engine Front Mount Bolts	50
	Exhaust Manifold Bolt	20
	Flywheel To Crankshaft	50–70
	Flywheel Housing Cover	53 ①
	Ignition Distributor Clamp	20–35
	Intake Manifold Bolt	25–45
	Main Bearing Cap Bolt	70–85
	Oil Pan Attaching Bolts	72–130 ①
	Oil Pan Attaching Nuts	150–250 ①
	Oil Pump	60–70
	Oil Pump Cover	80 ①
	Rear Seal Retainer	120–150 ①
	Rocker Arm Cover	50–65 ①
	Spark Plug	22
	Thermostat Housing	18–23
	Torque Converter To Flywheel Bolts	46
	Transmission To Engine	35
	Vibration Damper	65–75
	Water Pump	25–35
1989–91	Camshaft Retainer Bolt	105 ①
	Camshaft Sprocket	21
	Connecting Rod Cap Bolt	44
	Crankshaft Pulley Bolt	43
	Cylinder Head Bolt	68
	Engine Block Coolant Drain Plug	③
	Engine Cooling Fan Bolts	18
	Engine Front Cover	100 ①
	Engine Front Mount Bolts	④
	Exhaust Manifold Bolt	②
	Flywheel To Crankshaft	74
	Flywheel Housing Cover	89 ①
	Ignition Distributor Clamp	27
	Intake Manifold Bolt	35
	Main Bearing Cap Bolt	77

Continued

TIGHTENING SPECIFICATIONS—Continued

Year	Component	Torque/Ft. Lbs.
	Oil Filter Adapter Bolt	18
	Oil Gallery Plug	⑤
	Oil Pan Attaching Bolts	101①
	Oil Pan Attaching Nuts	17
	Oil Pump	77
	Oil Pump Cover	80①
	Rear Seal Retainer	⑥
	Rocker Arm Cover	⑦
	Spark Plug	22
	Thermostat Housing	21
	Throttle Body To Intake Manifold	16
	Torque Converter To Flywheel Bolts	35
	Transmission To Engine	35
	Valve Lifter Retainer Bolt	12
	Vibration Damper	70
	Water Pump	30

①—Inch lbs.
②—Bolt 26 ft. lbs.; stud, 20 ft. lbs.
③—1989–90, 16 ft. lbs.; 1991, 15 ft. lbs.
④—1989–90, 47 ft. lbs.; 1991, 33 ft. lbs.
⑤—1989–90, 113 inch lbs.; 1991, 25 ft. lbs.
⑥—1989, 135 inch lbs.; 1990–91, 11 ft. lbs.
⑦—1989–90, 75 inch lbs.; 1991, 95 inch lbs.

5.0L/V8-307 Engine
INDEX

ENGINE MOUNTS
REPLACE

1. Disconnect battery ground cable.
2. Raise and support vehicle, then remove mount to bracket through bolts.
3. Using a suitable engine lifting fixture, raise engine slightly so that mount clears bracket.
4. Remove mount to engine attaching bolts, then remove mount, **Fig. 1.**
5. Reverse procedure to install.

ENGINE
REPLACE

1. Mark hood hinge before removing to aid in proper alignment upon reassembly.
2. Disconnect battery, then drain radiator.
3. Disconnect radiator hoses, heater hoses, vacuum hoses, power steering pump hoses (if necessary), starter cable at junction block, engine-to-body ground strap, fuel hose from fuel line, wiring and accelerator linkage.
4. Disconnect AIR pipe, if equipped, from catalytic converter.
5. Remove fan blade and pulley, coil, upper radiator support and radiator, as necessary.

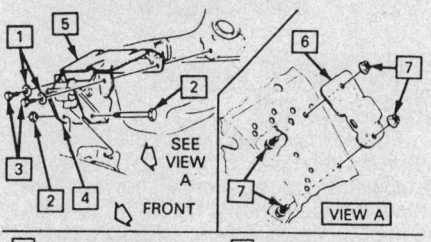

1	FLAT WASHER (4)	5	SHIELD
2	73 N·m (55 LBS. FT.)	6	BRACKET
3	100 N·m (75 LBS. FT.)	7	48 N·m (35 LBS. FT.)
4	MOUNT ASM.		

Fig. 1   Front engine mount

6. Raise vehicle.
7. Disconnect exhaust pipes at manifolds.
8. Remove torque converter cover, then the three bolts securing converter to flywheel.
9. Remove engine mount bolts, then three transmission to engine bolts on right side.
10. Remove starter with wiring attached, then position aside.
11. Lower vehicle, then support engine with lifting equipment.
12. Support transmission with a jack, then remove three left hand transmission to engine bolts.
13. Remove engine from vehicle.

INTAKE MANIFOLD
REPLACE

1. Disconnect battery ground cable, then drain cooling system.
2. Remove air cleaner assembly.
3. Disconnect all hoses and electrical connectors that will interfere with

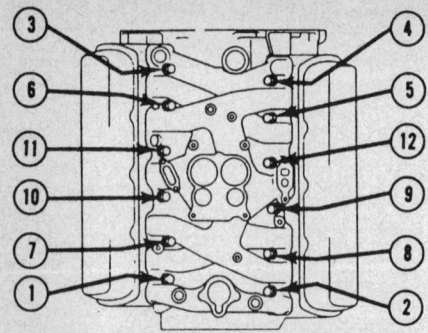

Fig. 2   Intake manifold bolt tightening sequence

Fig. 5   Cylinder head bolt tightening sequence

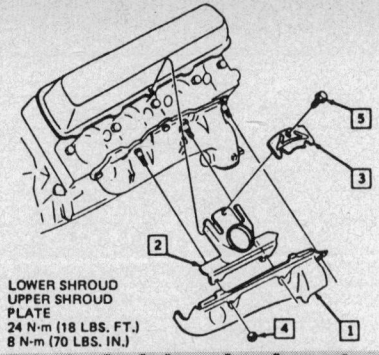

1. LOWER SHROUD
2. UPPER SHROUD
3. PLATE
4. 24 N·m (18 LBS. FT.)
5. 8 N·m (70 LBS. IN.)

Fig. 3   Left hand exhaust manifold replacement

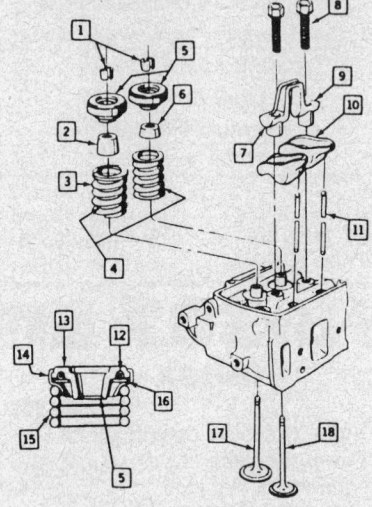

1. VALVE KEYS
2. INTAKE VALVE SEAL
3. SPRING
4. DAMPENER SPRING
5. VALVE ROTATOR
6. EXHAUST VALVE SEAL
7. IDENTIFICATION PAD
8. 28 N·m (22 LBS. FT.)
9. ROCKER ARM PIVOT
10. ROCKER ARMS
11. PUSH RODS
12. COIL SPRING
13. BODY
14. COLLAR
15. VALVE SPRING
16. FLAT WASHER
17. INTAKE VALVE
18. EXHAUST VALVE

Fig. 6   Valve & rocker arm components

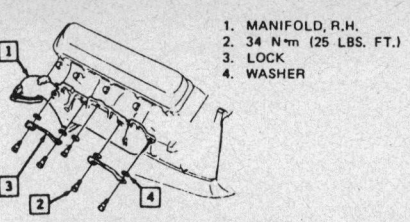

1. MANIFOLD, R.H.
2. 34 N·m (25 LBS. FT.)
3. LOCK
4. WASHER

Fig. 4   Right hand exhaust manifold replacement

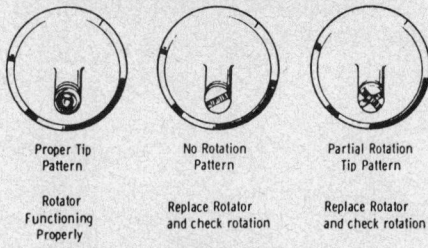

AFTER BOLTS ARE TORQUED TO SPECIFICATION, BEND LOCK TAB AROUND BOLT HEADS

Proper Tip Pattern — Rotator Functioning Properly

No Rotation Pattern — Replace Rotator and check rotation

Partial Rotation Tip Pattern — Replace Rotator and check rotation

Fig. 7   Valve stem wear patterns

manifold removal.

4. Disconnect throttle and T.V. cables from throttle linkage.
5. Remove alternator rear mounting bracket.
6. Remove A/C compressor rear brace, if equipped.
7. Remove EGR solenoid, idle load compensator and bracket assembly as applicable.
8. Remove EGR valve.
9. Remove intake manifold attaching bolts, then the intake manifold.
10. Reverse procedure to install. Torque attaching bolts to specification in sequence shown in **Fig. 2**.

EXHAUST MANIFOLD
REPLACE
LEFT SIDE

1. Disconnect battery ground cable.
2. Remove air cleaner.
3. Raise and support vehicle.
4. Straighten exhaust manifold bolt locking tabs.
5. Disconnect exhaust cross-over pipe from exhaust manifold.
6. Lower vehicle, then remove exhaust manifold heat shrouds, **Fig. 3**.
7. Remove lower alternator bracket, then remove exhaust manifold and gasket.
8. Reverse procedure to install.

RIGHT SIDE

1. Disconnect battery ground cable.
2. Disconnect oxygen sensor electrical connector.
3. Raise and support vehicle.
4. Disconnect exhaust cross-over pipe from exhaust manifold.
5. Remove oil filter adapter and gasket, then remove front right hand wheel and tire assembly.
6. Straighten exhaust manifold bolt locking tabs, then remove bolts, **Fig. 4**.
7. Remove exhaust manifold and gasket.
8. Reverse procedure to install.

CYLINDER HEAD
REPLACE

Prior to installation, clean the head bolts, then dip in engine oil. Tighten head bolts in steps and in the sequence shown in **Fig. 5**. Final torquing should be to the specifications listed in "Tightening Specifications."

1. Disconnect battery ground cable.
2. Drain radiator and cylinder block.
3. Remove intake and exhaust manifolds.
4. Remove ground strap from left cylinder head, if applicable.
5. Remove rocker arm bolts, pivots, rocker arms and push rods. Keep rocker arms, pivots and push rods in order so they can be installed in the same position.
6. Remove cylinder head attaching bolts, then remove cylinder head.
7. Reverse procedure to install. Torque cylinder head bolts in sequence shown in **Fig. 5**.

ROCKER ARMS
REPLACE

These engines use valve rotators, **Fig. 6**. The rotator operates on a sprag clutch principle utilizing the collapsing action of a coil spring to give rotation to the rotor body which turns the valve.

1. Remove valve cover.
2. Remove flanged bolts, rocker arm pivot and rocker arms, **Fig. 6**.
3. When installing rocker arm assemblies, lubricate wear surfaces with specified lubricant. **Torque** flanged bolts to 25 ft. lbs.

VALVE ROTATORS

The rotator operates on a Sprag clutch principle utilizing the collapsing action of coil spring to give rotation to the rotor body which turns the valve, **Fig. 6**.

To check rotator action, draw a line across rotator body and down the collar. Operate engine at 1500 RPM, rotator body should move around collar. Rotator action can be in either direction. Replace rotator if no movement is noted.

When servicing valves, valve stem tips should be checked for improper wear pattern which could indicate a defective valve rotator, **Fig. 7**.

VALVES

Whenever a new valve is installed or after grinding valves, it will be necessary to measure valve stem height using the Special Tool shown in **Figs. 8 and 9**.

There should be a minimum clearance of .015 inch between gauge surface and the valve stem, **Fig. 8**.

Check valve rotator height, **Fig. 9**. If valve stem tip extends less than .005 inch above rotator, replace rotator.

Lacking this tool the only alternative is to lay flat feeler gauges on the retainer and check the distance between the retainer and valve stem tip.

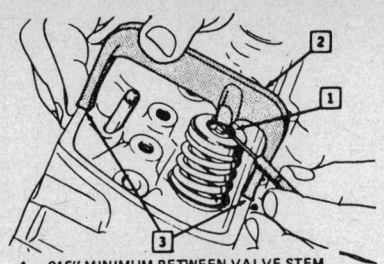

1. .015" MINIMUM BETWEEN VALVE STEM AND GAGE (.015" GAGE INCLUDED IN CARBURETOR KIT BT-3005)
2. BT-6428 OR J 25289
3. AREA WHERE GAGE SEATS MUST BE CLEAN AND SMOOTH

Fig. 8 Measuring valve stem height

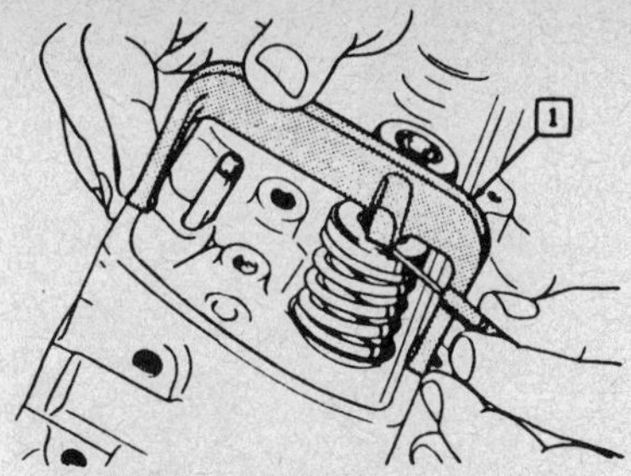

1. BT-6428 OR J 25289

IF VALVE STEM TIP IS LESS THAN .005" ABOVE ROTATOR AFTER GRINDING STEM INSTALL NEW VALVE

Fig. 9 Measuring valve rotator height

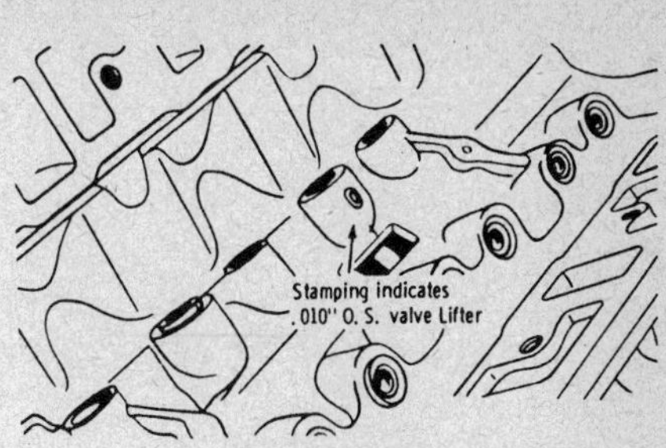

Stamping indicates .010" O. S. valve lifter

Fig. 10 Valve guide bore marking

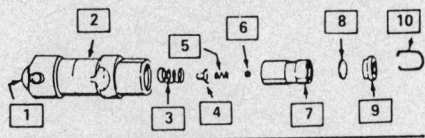

1—ROLLER
2—LIFTER BODY
3—PLUNGER SPRING
4—BALL CHECK RETAINER
5—BALL CHECK SPRING
6—BALL CHECK
7—PLUNGER
8—OIL METERING VALVE
9—PUSH ROD SEAT
10—RETAINER RING

Fig. 11 Hydraulic valve lifter

1. CAMSHAFT
2. CAMSHAFT FLANGE ADAPTER
3. CAMSHAFT SPROCKET
4. 88 N·m (65 LBS. FT.)
5. CHAIN
6. CRANKSHAFT SPROCKET
7. KEY
8. PLUG
9. PLATE
10. PLUG – L.H.
11. PLUG – R.H.
12. SPRING
13. BUTTON
14. FUEL PUMP ECCENTRIC
15. GASKET
16. FRONT COVER
17. 30 N·m (22 LBS. FT.)
18. 47 N·m (35 LBS. FT.)

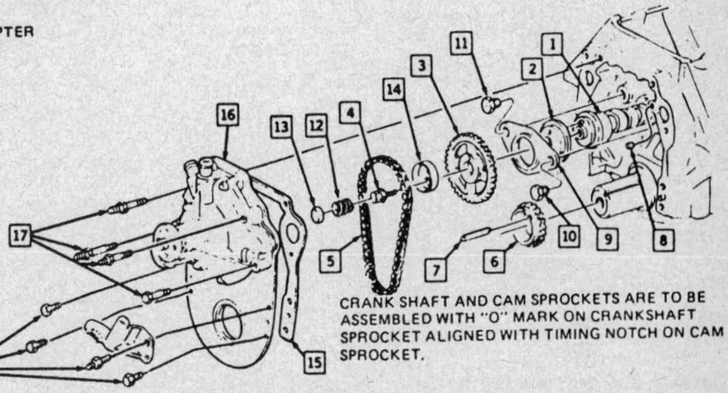

CRANK SHAFT AND CAM SPROCKETS ARE TO BE ASSEMBLED WITH "O" MARK ON CRANKSHAFT SPROCKET ALIGNED WITH TIMING NOTCH ON CAM SPROCKET.

Fig. 12 Engine front cover, timing chain, sprocket & camshaft

VALVES
ADJUST

These engines are equipped with hydraulic valve lifters. No provision for adjustment is provided.

VALVE GUIDES

Valve stem guides are not replaceable, due to being cast in place. If valve guide bores are worn excessively, they can be reamed oversize.

If a standard valve guide bore is being reamed, use a .003 inch or .005 inch oversize reamer. For the .010 inch oversize valve guide bore, use a .013 inch oversize reamer. If too large a reamer is used and the spiraling is removed, it is possible that the valve will not receive the proper lubrication.

Occasionally a valve guide will be oversize as manufactured. These are marked on the cylinder head. If no markings are present, the guide bores are standard. If oversize markings are present, any valve replacement will require an oversize valve. Service valves are available in standard diameters as well as .003 inch, .005 inch, .010 inch and .013 inch oversize.

VALVE LIFTERS

Valve lifters are available in standard size and an oversize of .010 inch. An "O" is etched on the side of the .010 inch oversize lifter for identification. Also, the cylinder block near the valve lifter bore is marked with an "O", **Fig. 10**. Ensure valve lifters are reinstalled in original bores.

Plungers are not interchangeable because they are fitted to the bodies at the factory.

If plunger and body appear satisfactory blow off with air to remove all particles of dirt. Install the plunger in the body without other parts and check for free movement. A simple test is to be sure that the plunger will drop of its own weight in the body, **Fig. 11**.

VALVE ARRANGEMENT
FRONT TO REAR

5.0L/V8-307 . . . . I-E-I-E-I-E-I

CAMSHAFT LOBE LIFT SPECIFICATIONS

Engine	Year	Intake	Exhaust
5.0L/V8-307	1988–90	.247	.251

TIMING CASE COVER
REPLACE

When it becomes necessary to replace the cover oil seal, the cover need not be removed.
1. Disconnect battery ground cable.
2. Drain cooling system, then disconnect radiator hoses and bypass hose.
3. Remove all drive belts, fan, pulley, crankshaft pulley, harmonic balancer, and accessory brackets.
4. Remove timing indicator and water pump, **Fig. 12**.
5. Remove remaining front cover attaching bolts, then the front cover. Also, remove the dowel pins. It may be necessary to grind a flat on the dowel pin to provide a rough surface for gripping.
6. Grind a chamfer on one end of each dowel pin.
7. Cut excess material from front end of oil pan gasket on each side of cylinder block.
8. Trim approximately 1/8 inch from each end of new front pan seal.
9. Install new front cover gasket and apply sealer to gasket around coolant holes.
10. Apply RTV sealer to mating surfaces of cylinder block, oil pan and front cover.
11. Place front cover on cylinder block and press downward to compress seal. Rotate cover right and left, then guide oil pan seal into cavity with a small screwdriver.
12. Apply engine oil to bolts.
13. Install two bolts finger tight to retain cover.
14. Install the two dowel pins, chamfered end first.
15. Install timing indicator and water pump.
16. Install harmonic balancer and crankshaft pulley.
17. Install accessory brackets.
18. Install fan, pulley and drive belts.
19. Connect radiator hoses and bypass hose.
20. Connect battery ground cable.

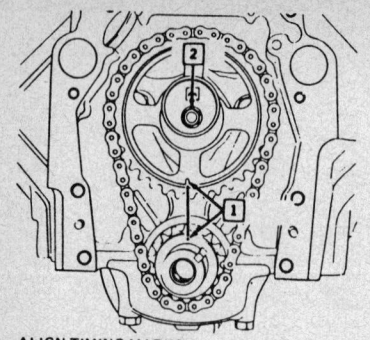

1. ALIGN TIMING MARKS
2. 88 N·m (65 LBS. FT.)

Fig. 13   Valve timing marks

NOTCH TOWARD
FRONT OF ENGINE

Fig. 14   Piston & rod assembly

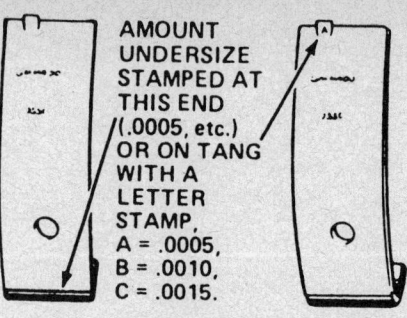

AMOUNT UNDERSIZE STAMPED AT THIS END (.0005, etc.) OR ON TANG WITH A LETTER STAMP,
A = .0005,
B = .0010,
C = .0015.

Fig. 15   Main bearing size location

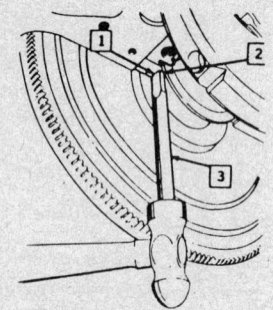

1. REAR MAIN OIL SEAL GROOVE
2. PACK SEAL INTO GROOVE
3. TOOL, BT-6433 OR J 29368

Fig. 16   Packing upper rear main bearing oil seal

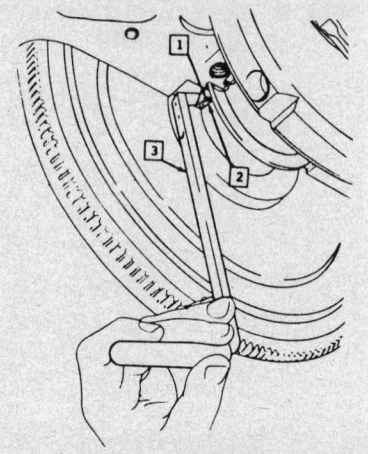

1. REAR MAIN BEARING UPPER OIL SEAL
2. CUT SEAL FLUSH WITH BLOCK
3. TOOL BT-6436

Fig. 17   Trimming upper rear main bearing oil seal

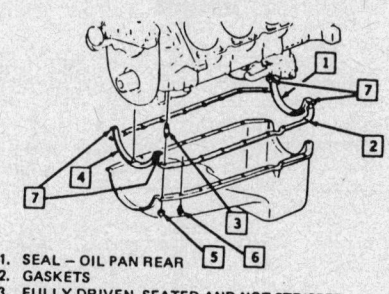

1. SEAL – OIL PAN REAR
2. GASKETS
3. FULLY DRIVEN, SEATED AND NOT STRIPPED
4. SEAL – OIL PAN FRONT
5. 24 N·m (17 LBS. FT.)
6. 14 N·m (10 LBS. FT.)
7. APPLY 1052915, GE 1673 OR EQUIVALENT RTV.

Fig. 18   Oil pan & gasket

TIMING CHAIN REPLACE

1. After removing front cover, remove fuel pump eccentric, oil slinger, crankshaft sprocket, chain and camshaft sprocket, **Fig. 12.**
2. Install camshaft sprocket, crankshaft sprocket and timing chain together, aligning timing marks as shown in **Fig. 13.**
3. Install fuel pump eccentric with flat side rearward, then install oil slinger and replace front cover. The valve timing marks, **Fig. 12,** do not indicate TDC compression stroke for No. 1 cylinder, which is used for distributor installation. If distributor was removed, install timing chain and sprockets, aligning timing marks, **Fig. 13,** then rotate engine until No. 1 cylinder is on compression stroke and camshaft timing mark is 180° from valve timing position shown in illustrations, then install distributor.

CAMSHAFT REPLACE

1. Disconnect battery ground cable, then drain radiator.
2. Remove upper radiator baffle and disconnect upper radiator hose from water outlet.
3. Disconnect transmission oil cooler lines at radiator.

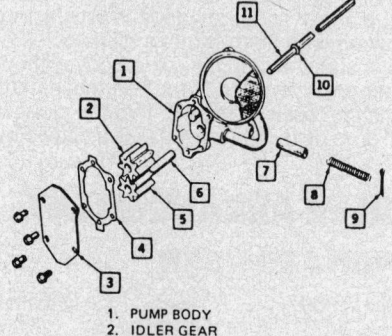

1. PUMP BODY
2. IDLER GEAR
3. COVER
4. GASKET
5. DRIVE GEAR
6. DRIVE SHAFT
7. VALVE
8. SPRING
9. RETAINING PIN
10. WASHER
11. DRIVE SHAFT EXTENSION

Fig. 19   Oil pump disassembled view

4. Remove radiator fan shroud, then the radiator.
5. Disconnect fuel lines from fuel pump.
6. Remove air cleaner, then disconnect throttle cable.
7. Remove all drive belts, then position alternator, power steering pump and air conditioning compressor aside.
8. Disconnect bypass hose from water

pump, all electrical and vacuum connections from engine.
9. Remove distributor.
10. Raise vehicle, then drain oil pan.
11. Remove exhaust crossover pipe, then the starter.
12. Disconnect exhaust pipe from manifold.
13. Install engine support bar.
14. Remove engine mount to bracket bolts, raise engine, then remove engine mounts.
15. Remove flywheel cover and engine oil pan.
16. Place wood blocks between exhaust manifolds and crossmember to support engine, then remove engine support bar.
17. Remove crankshaft pulley and balancer, then the engine front cover.
18. Lower vehicle, then remove valve covers, intake manifold, rocker arms, push rods and valve lifters. **Note position of the valve train components to ensure installation in original location.**
19. If equipped with A/C, discharge refrigerant, then remove condenser.
20. Remove fuel pump eccentric, camshaft sprocket, oil slinger and timing chain, **Fig. 12.**
21. Slide camshaft from front of engine.
22. Reverse procedure to install. **To insure proper camshaft installation, and to provide initial lubrication, it is extremely important that the camshaft be coated with GM Concentrate (Part No. 1051396).**

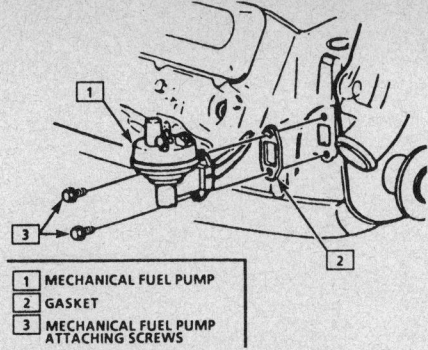

1. MECHANICAL FUEL PUMP
2. GASKET
3. MECHANICAL FUEL PUMP ATTACHING SCREWS

Fig. 20 Fuel pump replacement

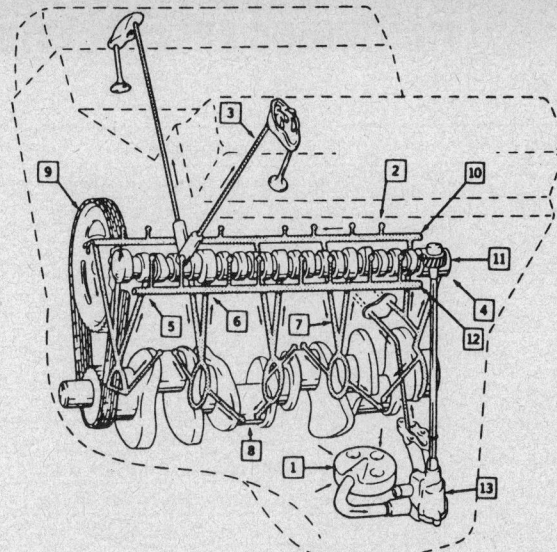

1. OIL PICK-UP
2. LIFTER FEED
3. ROCKER ARM VALVE TIP FEED
4. SPLASH LUBE TO DISTRIBUTOR AND OIL PUMP DRIVE
5. LEFT MAIN GALLERY FEED
6. CAM BEARING FEED
7. MAIN BEARING FEED
8. ROD BEARING FEED
9. SPLASH LUBE TO TIMING CHAIN AND FUEL PUMP CAM
10. RIGHT MAIN GALLERY
11. DISTRIBUTOR AND OIL PUMP DRIVE
12. LEFT MAIN GALLERY
13. OIL PUMP

Engine oiling system

PISTON & ROD ASSEMBLE

Lubricate the piston pin hole and piston pin to facilitate installation of pin, then position the connecting rod with its respective piston as shown in **Fig. 14.** Measure connecting rod side clearance using a feeler gauge, clearance should be .006-.020 inch.

PISTONS, RINGS & PINS

Pistons are available in standard sizes and oversizes of .010 and .030 inch. Rings are available in standard sizes and oversizes of .010 and .030 inch.

MAIN & ROD BEARINGS

Main bearings are available in standard sizes and undersizes of .0005, .001, .0015, .002, .010 and .020 inch.

Rod bearings are available in standard sizes and undersizes of .001, .002, .005, .010, .012 and .020 inch.

Main bearing clearances not within specifications must be corrected by the use of selective upper and lower shells. **Fig. 15** illustrates the undersize identification marking on the bearing tang.

REAR CRANKSHAFT SEAL SERVICE

Since the braided fabric seal used on these engines can be replaced only when the crankshaft is removed, the following repair procedure is recommended.

1. Remove oil pan, then the bearing cap.
2. Drive end of old seal gently into groove, until packed tight. This may vary between 1/4 and 3/4 inch depending on amount of pack required.
3. Repeat previous step for other end of seal.
4. Measure and note amount that seal was driven up on one side. Using the old seal removed from bearing cap, cut a length of seal the amount previously noted plus 1/16 inch.
5. Repeat previous step for other side of seal.
6. Pack cut lengths of seal into appropriate side of seal groove. A packing tool,

BT-6433, **Fig. 16,** may be used since the tool has been machined to provide a built-in stop. Use tool BT-6436 to trim the seal flush with block, **Fig. 17.**
7. Install new seal in lower bearing cap.

OIL PAN
REPLACE

1. Remove distributor cap and align rotor with No. 1 firing position.
2. Disconnect ground cable, remove dip stick and drain oil pan.
3. Remove upper radiator support and fan shroud attaching screws.
4. Remove flywheel cover and starter.
5. Disconnect exhaust pipes and crossover pipe on single exhaust models.
6. Disconnect engine mounts, then raise engine.
7. Remove oil pan bolts and oil pan, **Fig. 18.**
8. Reverse procedure to install. Torque oil pan bolts to specifications. Drain engine oil, then remove oil pan.

OIL PUMP REPAIRS

1. Remove oil pan and pump baffle. Remove attaching screws, then the pump and driveshaft extension.
2. To service the pump, refer to **Fig. 19.**
3. To install, insert the driveshaft extension through the opening in the block until the shaft mates into the distributor drive gear. Position pump onto rear main bearing cap and torque the attaching bolts to specifications.
4. Install oil pump baffle and pan.

WATER PUMP
REPLACE

1. Drain cooling system, then remove heater and lower hoses from pump.
2. Loosen pulley belts, then remove fan and pulley. On air conditioned cars, re-

move clutch fan assembly and pulley.
3. Remove pump from front cover, **Fig. 12.**
4. Reverse procedure to install.

BELT TENSION DATA

Belt	New Lbs.	Used Lbs.
Air Conditioning	170	110
A.I.R. Pump	80①	55①
Alternator	160②	110②
Power Steering	170	110

① —3/8 inch belts; new, 145 Lbs.; used, 90 Lbs.
② —Cogged belts; new, 145 Lbs.; used, 90 Lbs.

COOLING SYSTEM BLEED

These engines do not require a specific bleed procedure. After filling cooling system, start engine and allow to reach operating temperature with radiator cap removed. Air in system will then be automatically bled through cap opening.

FUEL PUMP
REPLACE

1. Disconnect fuel line from fuel pump.
2. Remove fuel pump mounting bolts, then the fuel pump, **Fig. 20.**
3. Remove all gasket material from the pump and block gasket surfaces. Apply sealer to both sides of new gasket.
4. Position gasket on pump flange and hold pump in position against its mounting surface. Make sure rocker arm is riding on camshaft eccentric.
5. Press pump tight against its mounting. Install retaining screws and tighten them alternately.
6. Connect fuel lines. Then operate engine and check for leaks.

TIGHTENING SPECIFICATIONS

Year	Component	Torque/Ft. Lbs.
1988-90	Carburetor To Intake Manifold	12
	Coolant Outlet To Manifold	20
	Connecting Rod Nuts	①
	Crankshaft Damper	200–310
	Cylinder Head Bolts	130③
	EGR Valve To Intake Manifold	20
	Engine Mount To Cylinder Block	75
	Engine Mount To Frame	55
	ESC Knock Sensor	13
	Exhaust Manifold To Cylinder Head	25
	Fan To Fan Clutch Or Water Pump	20
	Flywheel To Crankshaft	60
	Flywheel To Torque Converter	46
	Front Cover To Engine	35
	Front Cover & Water Pump To Engine	22
	Fuel Pump Eccentric To Camshaft	65
	Fuel Pump To Engine	25
	Ignition Distributor Clamp Bolt	26
	Intake Manifold To Cylinder Head	40③
	Main Bearing Cap Bolts	②
	Oil Filter Adapter To Engine	35
	Oil Pan Bolts	10
	Oil Pan Drain Plug	30
	Oil Pan Nuts	17
	Oil Pump Cover To Body	97④
	Oil Pump To Main Bearing Cap	35
	Rocker Arm Cover	90④
	Rocker Arm Pivot Bolt	22
	Spark Plug	22
	Starter Motor To Engine	32
	Transmission To Engine	35
	Valve Lifter Guide Retainer Bolt	82④
	Water Pump To Front Cover	11
	Water Pump To Front Cover & Engine	22

① —Torque to 18 ft. lbs., then tighten an additional 70°.
② —Nos. 1, 2, 3 & 4, 80 ft. lbs.; No. 5, 120 ft. lbs.
③ —Clean and dip entire bolt into SAE 5W-30 engine oil prior to installation.
④ —Inch lbs.

Rear Axle, Rear Suspension & Propeller Shaft

INDEX

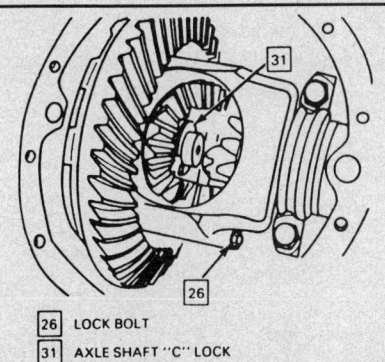

26 LOCK BOLT
31 AXLE SHAFT "C" LOCK

Fig. 1   Pinion shaft lock bolt & C-lock removal

DESCRIPTION

In these rear axles, the rear axle housing and differential carrier are cast into an integral housing assembly. The drive pinion assembly is mounted in two opposed tapered roller bearings. The pinion bearings are preloaded by a spacer behind the front bearing. The pinion is positioned by a washer between the head of the pinion and the rear bearing. The differential is supported in the carrier by two tapered roller side bearings. These bearings are preloaded by spacers located between the bearings and carrier housing. The differential assembly is positioned for proper ring gear and pinion backlash by varying these spacers. The differential case houses two side gears in mesh with two pinions mounted on a pinion shaft which is held in place by a lock pin. The side gears and pinions are backed by thrust washers. A limited slip rear axle, available on most models, uses disc or cone type clutches which are splined to the side gears to lock the axle shafts to the case or in effect to each other. Therefore, if one drive wheel is on a slippery surface, the other wheel must develop more torque than on a standard type differential before the differential case will allow wheel spin. However, axle shaft torques produced during cornering are sufficient to overcome the clutch action, allowing axles to rotate at different speeds.

REAR AXLE
REPLACE

Construction of the axle assembly is such that service operations may be performed with the housing installed in the vehicle or with the housing removed and installed in a holding fixture. The following

procedure is necessary only when the housing requires replacement.
1. Raise and support vehicle, then support rear axle with a suitable jack.
2. **On models equipped with anti-lock brake systems,** remove rear axle speed sensor as follows:
   a. Disconnect speed sensor electrical harness.
   b. Remove speed sensor harness bracket attaching bolt.
   c. Remove speed sensor to rear axle attaching bolt, then remove speed sensor and bracket assembly and position aside.
   d. Reverse procedure to install. Wheel speed sensors are to installed by hand. **Do not hammer sensors into position, as damage may result.**
3. Disconnect shock absorbers from lower mountings.
4. Remove propeller shaft.
5. Disconnect upper control arms from axle housing attachments.
6. Disconnect brake line from axle housing junction block and the parking brake cable.
7. Disconnect lower control arms from axle housing attachments.
8. Lower axle slowly until springs can be moved. Roll axle assembly out from under vehicle.
9. Reverse procedure to install.

AXLE SHAFT
REPLACE

1. Raise vehicle and remove wheel and brake drum or rotor.
2. Drain lube from carrier and remove cover.
3. Remove differential pinion shaft lock bolt and remove differential pinion shaft, **Fig. 1.**
4. Pull flanged end of axle shaft toward center of vehicle and remove C-lock from button end of shaft.
5. Remove axle shaft from housing, being careful not to damage seal.
6. Reverse procedure to install the axle shaft.

PROPELLER SHAFT
REPLACE

1. Raise and support vehicle.
2. Mark position of shaft in relation to pinion flange for reassembly.
3. Remove straps securing universal joint to pinion flange, then disconnect shaft from flange. **Tape bearing cups**

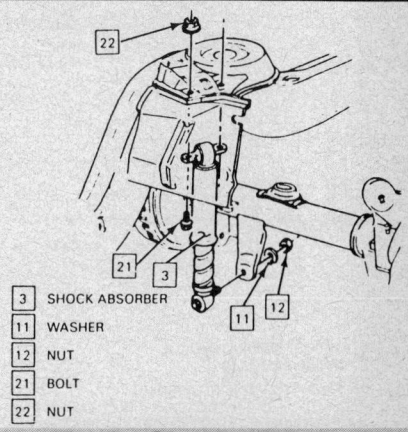

3 SHOCK ABSORBER
11 WASHER
12 NUT
21 BOLT
22 NUT

Fig. 2   Shock absorber replacement

to universal joint to prevent loss of needle bearings.
4. Slide yoke out of transmission and remove propeller shaft. Insert suitable plug in transmission to prevent fluid loss.
5. Reverse procedure to install.

SHOCK ABSORBER
REPLACE

1. If equipped with Superlift shock absorbers, disconnect air lines from shock absorber fittings.
2. With rear axle properly supported, disconnect shock absorber from upper and lower mountings, **Fig. 2.**
3. Reverse procedure to install.

COIL SPRINGS
REPLACE

If more than one coil spring is being replaced, remove and install one spring at a time to prevent axle assembly from slipping or twisting out of position.
1. Support vehicle at frame and rear axle.
2. **On models equipped with anti-lock brake systems,** remove rear axle speed sensor as follows:
   a. Disconnect speed sensor electrical harness.
   b. Remove speed sensor harness bracket attaching bolt.
   c. Remove speed sensor to rear axle attaching bolt, then remove speed sensor and bracket assembly and position aside.
   d. Reverse procedure to install. Wheel speed sensors are to installed by hand. **Do not hammer**

A	5 DEGREES MAXIMUM REARWARD
B	15 DEGREES MAXIMUM FORWARD
C	ARROW POINTING TO LEFT SIDE OF CAR, PERPENDICULAR TO CENTERLINE OF CHASSIS
D	COIL LEG
1	REAR SPRING
3	SHOCK ABSORBER
11	WASHER
12	NUT
13	INSULATOR

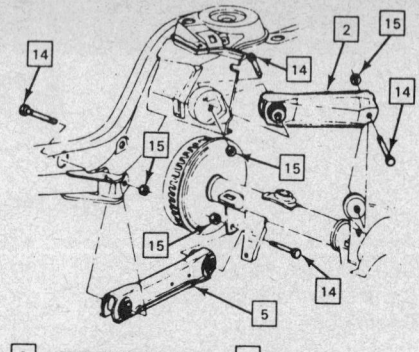

2	UPPER CONTROL ARM	14	BOLT
5	LOWER CONTROL ARM	15	NUT

Fig. 4   Control arm replacement

Fig. 3   Coil spring installation

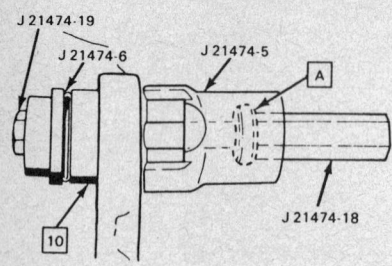

A	THRUST BEARING (HIDDEN INSIDE J 21474-5)
10	REAR AXLE HOUSING BUSHING

Fig. 5   Upper control arm rear bushing (differential carrier bushing) removal

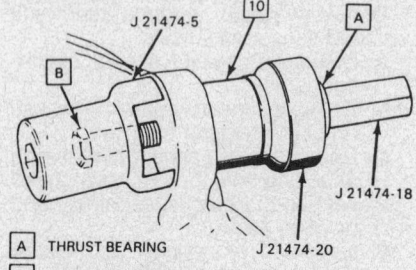

A	THRUST BEARING
B	J 21474-19 (HIDDEN INSIDE J 21474-5)
10	REAR AXLE HOUSING BUSHING

Fig. 6   Upper control arm rear bushing (differential carrier bushing) installation

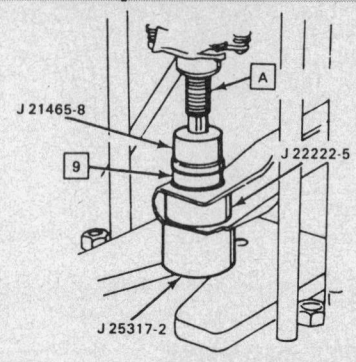

A	PRESS
9	CONTROL ARM BUSHING

Fig. 7   Control arm bushing removal

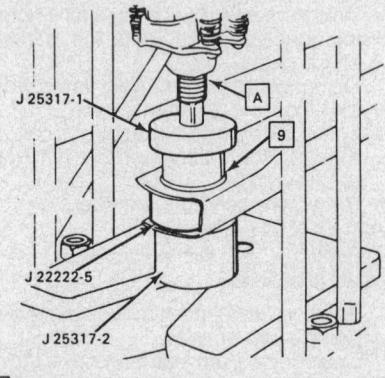

A	PRESS
9	CONTROL ARM BUSHING

Fig. 8   Control arm bushing installation

sensors into position, as damage may result.

3. Disconnect shock absorbers at lower mountings.
4. Disconnect upper control arms from axle housing.
5. If equipped with a stabilizer bar, disconnect bar from either right or left hand side of control arm.
6. **On all models,** remove brake hose support bolt and support without disconnecting the brake lines.
7. Lower axle until spring can be removed, then remove spring and insulator.
8. Reverse procedure to install. Springs must be installed with an insulator between upper seat and spring and positioned properly, **Fig. 3.**

CONTROL ARMS & BUSHINGS
REPLACE

If more than one control arm is being replaced, remove and install one arm at a time to prevent axle assembly from slipping or twisting out of position.

CONTROL ARMS, REPLACE

1. Raise vehicle and support at frame pads. Support nose of axle housing to prevent assembly from twisting when control arm is removed.
2. **On models equipped with anti-lock brake systems,** remove rear axle speed sensor as follows:
   a. Disconnect speed sensor electrical harness.

b. Remove speed sensor harness bracket attaching bolt.
c. Remove speed sensor to rear axle attaching bolt, then remove speed sensor and bracket assembly and position aside.
d. Reverse procedure to install. Wheel speed sensors are to installed by hand. **Do not hammer sensors into position, as damage may result.**
3. If lower control arm is being replaced, remove bolts securing stabilizer bar to control arm, if equipped.
4. Remove bolts securing control arm to

chassis and rear axle, and the control arm, **Fig. 4.**
5. Reverse procedure to install, lower vehicle and torque control arm bolts to specifications, with vehicle at normal ride height. **All torque prevailing type fasteners must be torqued at the nut, not at the bolt, to ensure proper clamping force.**

BUSHING REPLACEMENT
Differential Carrier Bushings (Upper Control Arm Rear Bushing)

The upper control arm rear bushing, which is pressed into the differential carrier, can be replaced using the following procedure:

1. Raise vehicle and support at frame pads, and support nose of axle housing to prevent assembly from twisting.
2. Lower rear axle to obtain clearance, disconnect upper control arm from axle and position aside.
3. Install suitable bushing removal tool as shown in **Fig. 5,** tighten puller screw and press bushing out of housing.
4. To install replacement bushing, reverse position of removal tool and pull bushing into position by tightening screw, **Fig. 6.**

Control Arm Bushings

1. Raise and support vehicle and remove control arm as outlined previ-

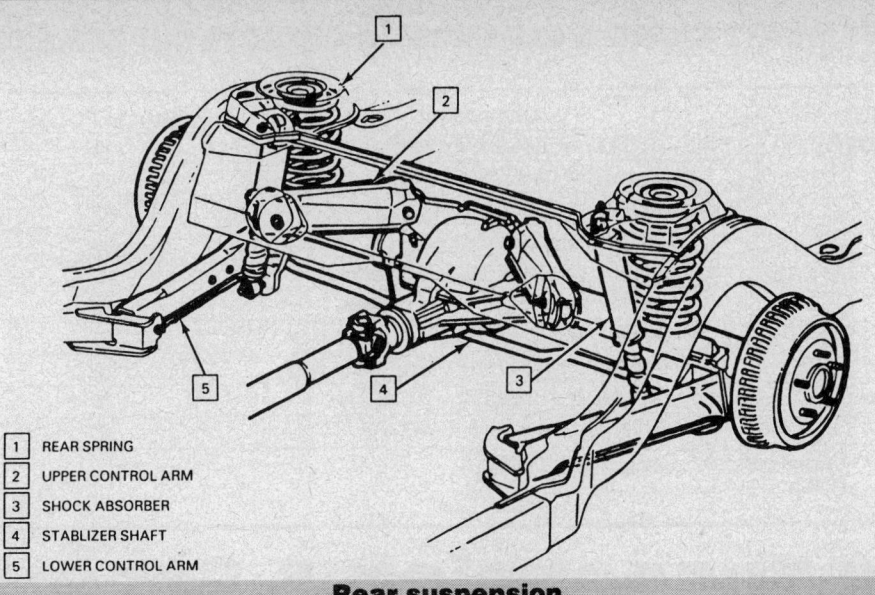

1. REAR SPRING
2. UPPER CONTROL ARM
3. SHOCK ABSORBER
4. STABLIZER SHAFT
5. LOWER CONTROL ARM

Rear suspension

ously.
2. Press bushings out of control arm using suitable tools as shown in **Fig. 7**.
3. Reverse procedure to install, ensuring bushing is properly seated in control arm, **Fig. 8**. If replacement bushing fits loosely in control arm, or if mounting areas are damaged or deformed, control arm must be replaced.

STABILIZER BAR REPLACE
1. Support vehicle at rear axle.
2. Remove bolts securing stabilizer bar to lower control arms.
3. Reverse procedure to install. Use spacer shims, if needed, placed equally on each side of stabilizer bar. Tighten attaching bolts with vehicle at curb height.

TIGHTENING SPECIFICATIONS
BUICK ESTATE WAGON, CADILLAC BROUGHAM, CHEVROLET CAPRICE, OLDSMOBILE CUSTOM CRUISER & PONTIAC SAFARI

Year	Component	Torque/Ft. Lbs.
1988	Lower Control Arm Bushing Bolt	125
	Lower Control Arm Bushing Nut	92
	Propeller Shaft Rear Universal Joint To Pinion Yoke	15
	Shock Absorber Lower Attachment	65
	Shock Absorber Upper Attachment	20
	Stabilizer Bar To Mounting Bracket	52
	Stabilizer Mounting Bracket To Control Arm	21
	Upper Control Arm Front Bushing Nut	92
	Upper Control Arm Rear Bushing Bolt	80
	Upper Control Arm Rear Bushing Nut	70
	Wheel & Tire Assembly	②
1989–91	Lower Control Arm Bushing Bolt	122
	Lower Control Arm Bushing Nut	92
	Propeller Shaft Rear Universal Joint To Pinion Yoke	15
	Shock Absorber Lower Attachment	48
	Shock Absorber Upper Attachment	①
	Stabilizer Bar To Mounting Bracket	52
	Stabilizer Mounting Bracket To Control Arm	21
	Upper Control Arm Front Bushing Bolt	122
	Upper Control Arm Front Bushing Nut	92
	Upper Control Arm Rear Bushing Bolt	80
	Upper Control Arm Rear Bushing Nut	70
	Wheel & Tire Assembly	③

①—Upper bolt, 20 ft. lbs.; upper nut, 12 ft. lbs..
②—Sedan, 80 ft. lbs.; wagon, 100 ft. lbs.
③—Sedan, 81 ft. lbs.; wagon, 103 ft. lbs.

CHEVROLET MONTE CARLO & OLDSMOBILE CUTLASS SUPREME CLASSIC

Year	Component	Torque/Ft. Lbs.
1988	Lower Control Arm To Axle	79
	Lower Control Arm To Frame	70
	Propeller Shaft Rear Universal Joint To Pinion Yoke	16
	Shock Absorber Lower Attachment	65
	Shock Absorber Upper Attachment	①
	Stabilizer To Control Arm	35
	Upper Control Arm To Axle Pivot Bolt	79
	Upper Control Arm To Axle Pivot Nut	70
	Upper Control Arm To Frame	70
	Wheel & Tire Assembly	80

①—Upper bolt, 20 ft. lbs.; upper nut, 12 ft. lbs.

Front Suspension & Steering

INDEX

DESCRIPTION

All models use a Short-Long Arm (SLA) type front suspension with independent coil springs riding on lower control arms, **Fig. 1.** Ball joints link upper and lower control arms to a spindle assembly, and tubular shock absorbers are used to dampen spring action. On some models, a spring steel stabilizer shaft is connected between the chassis and lower control arms to control side roll.

WHEEL BEARINGS
ADJUST

1. While rotating wheel forward, torque spindle nut to 12 ft. lbs. **Fig. 2**
2. Back off nut until just loose then hand tighten nut and back it off again until either hole in spindle lines up with hole in nut. **Do not back off nut more than ½ flat.**
3. Install new cotter pin. With wheel bearing properly adjusted, there will be .001-.005 inch end play.

WHEEL BEARINGS
REPLACE

1. Raise car and remove front wheels.
2. **On models equipped with anti-lock brake systems,** remove right and left wheel speed sensors as follows:
   a. Under vehicle hood, disconnect speed sensor electrical harness.
   b. Raise and support vehicle, then remove speed sensor harness bracket attaching bolt.
   c. Remove speed sensor to steering knuckle attaching bolt, then remove speed sensor and bracket assembly and position aside.
   d. Reverse procedure to install. Wheel speed sensors are to be installed by hand. **Do not hammer sensors into position, as damage may result.**
3. Remove bolts holding brake caliper to its mounting and insert a fabricated block (1¹/₁₆ x 1¹/₁₆ x 2 inches in length) between the brake pads as the caliper is being removed. Once removed, the caliper can be wired or secured in some manner away from the disc.
4. Remove spindle nut and hub and disc

assembly. Grease retainer and inner wheel bearing can now be removed, **Fig. 3.**
5. Reverse procedure to install.

CHECKING BALL JOINTS FOR WEAR

UPPER BALL JOINT

1. Raise and support vehicle. Position jack stands under lower control arm as close to lower ball joint as possible.
2. Position a suitable dial indicator against wheel rim, **Fig. 4.**
3. Grasp wheel at top and bottom, then pull top of wheel outward, while pushing inward on bottom of wheel. Note dial indicator reading.
4. Pull bottom of wheel outward, while pushing inward on top of wheel. Note dial indicator reading.
5. Deflection reading on dial indicator should not exceed .125 inch.
6. If reading exceeds .125 inch replace upper ball joint.

LOWER BALL JOINT

All models have a wear indicator built into the lower ball joint, **Fig. 5.** When inspecting wear indicator, vehicle must be

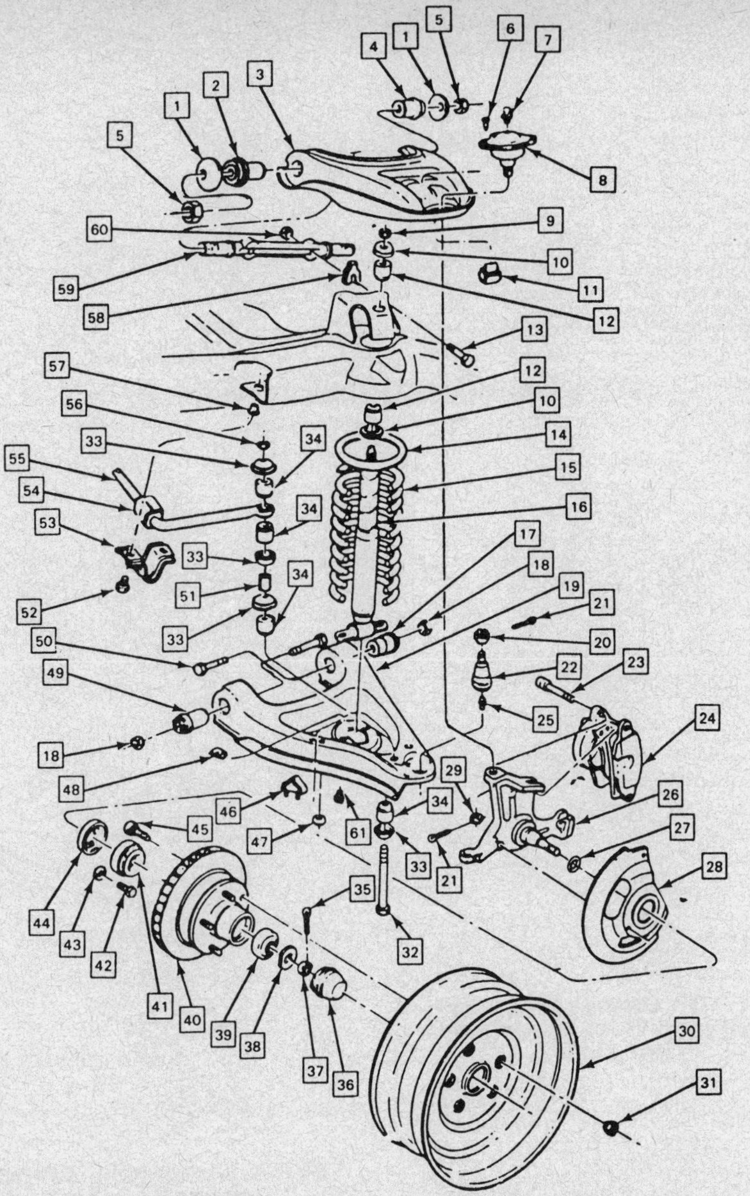

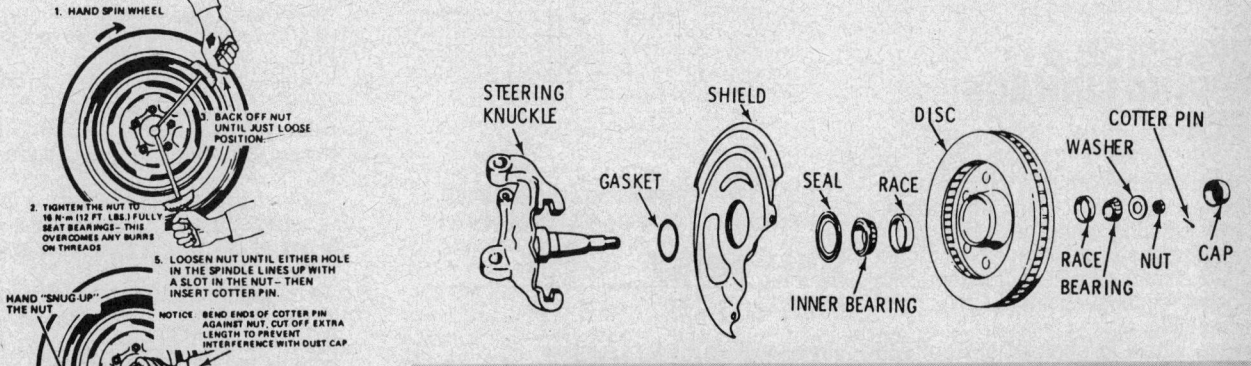

1. RETAINER, Upper Cont Arm Bush
2. BUSHING, Upper Cont Arm
3. ARM, Frt Suspension Upper Cont Arm
4. BUSHING, Front
5. NUT, Hex (5/8"-18)
6. RIVET, Strg Knu Upr Cont Arm Ball Stud
7. FITTING, Lubrication
8. BALL JOINT KIT, Upper Cont Arm
9. NUT, Hex (3/8"-16)
10. RETAINER, Frt Shk Abs to Upr Arm Brkt
11. BUMPER, Upper Strg Knu Upr Cont Arm
12. GROMMET, Frt Shk Abs to Upr Arm Brkt
13. BOLT, Upr Arm Shaft to Frame Brkt
14. INSULATOR, Frt Spring
15. SPRING, Frt Coil
16. SHOCK ABSORBER, Frt
17. BUSHING, Lower Cont Arm Rear
18. NUT, Hex (1/2"-13)
19. ARM, Frt Suspension Lwr Cont Arm
20. NUT, Strg Knu Cont Arm Ball Stud
21. PIN, Cotter (1/8" x 1-1/4")
22. BALL JOINT KIT, Lwr Cont Arm
23. BOLT, Caliper Asm
24. CALIPER, Frt Brake
25. FITTINGS, Ball Joint
26. KNUCKLE, Steering
27. GASKET, Frt Brake Supt to Knu
28. SHIELD, Frt Disc Brake
29. NUT, Ball Joint to Strg Knu
30. WHEEL, Frt Suspension
31. NUT, Wheel Bolt (1/2"-20)
32. LINK KIT, Frt Stablizer
33. RETAINER, Frt Stab Link Grommet
34. GROMMET, Frt Stab Link
35. PIN, Cotter (1/4" x 1-1/4")
36. CAP, Wheel Bearing Grease
37. NUT, Steering Knuckle (3/4"-20)
38. WASHER, Strg Knu Spindle
39. BEARING, Hub & Disc
40. HUB, W/Disc Frt Wheel
41. BEARING, Frt Wheel Inner
42. BOLT, Shield to Knuckle
43. WASHER, Flat (9/16")
44. SEAL, Frt Wheel Hub Oil
45. BOLT, Frt Wheel Hub
46. BUMPER, Strg Knu Lwr Cont Arm
47. NUT, Bumper Asm (3/8"-16)
48. NUT, Frt Shk Abs to Lwr Cont Arm
49. BUSHING, Strg Knu Lwr Cont Arm
50. BOLT, Frt Susp Lwr Cont Arm to Frm (M12 x 1.75 x 110)
51. SPACER, Frt Stab Link Bolt Grommet
52. SCREW, Frt Stab Shaft Brkt
53. BRACKET, Frt Stab Shaft
54. BUSHING, Frt Stab to Frame
55. SHAFT, Frt Stab
56. NUT, Frt Stab Link (5/16"-18)
57. NUT, Stab Brkt to Frame (3/8"-16)
58. SHIM, Upper Cont Arm Shaft
59. SHAFT KIT, Upper Cont Arm
60. NUT, Upper Cont Arm to Frame Brkt (1/2"-13)
61. BOLT, Frt Shk Abs to Lwr Cont Arm Nut

Fig. 1 Front suspension

Fig. 2 Front wheel bearing adjustment

Fig. 3 Hub & wheel bearing replacement

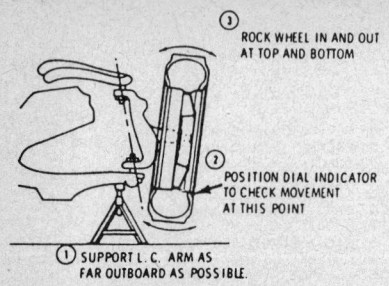

Fig. 4   Checking upper ball joint for wear

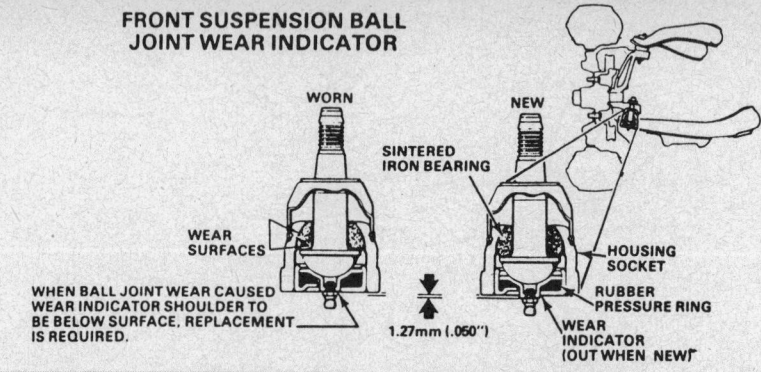

Fig. 5   Lower ball joint wear indicator

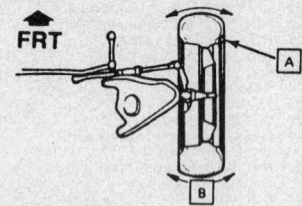

A — POSITION DIAL INDICATOR TO CHECK MOVEMENT AT THIS POINT

B — MOVE WHEEL IN AND OUT AT FRONT AND BACK

Fig. 6   Suspension & steering linkage check

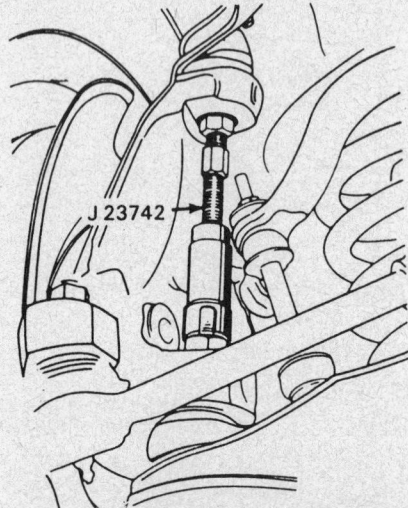

Fig. 7   Disconnecting upper ball joint from steering knuckle

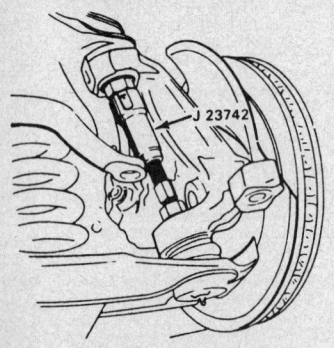

Fig. 9   Disconnecting lower ball joint from steering knuckle

supported in a normal manner on wheels to properly load ball joint.

SUSPENSION & STEERING LINKAGE CHECK

1. Raise vehicle with jack placed under frame torque box behind front wheel.
2. Lock steering wheel with wheels in straight ahead position, then mount dial indicator on a suitable stand with pointer bearing against outer rim of wheel, **Fig. 6.**
3. Move wheel in and out at front and rear, without moving steering wheel, while observing gauge.
4. If gauge reading exceeds .108 inches, check steering linkage and suspension for excessive wear or damage and wheel bearings for proper adjustment.

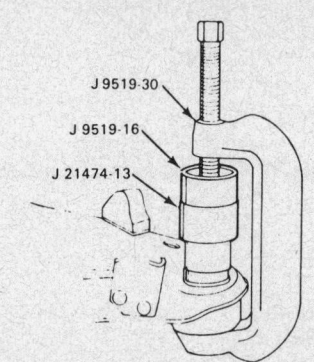

Fig. 10   Pressing lower ball joint from lower control arm

BALL JOINT REPLACE

UPPER BALL JOINT

1. Raise vehicle and support with stands at outer ends of lower control arms.
2. Remove wheel and tire.
3. Remove cotter pin and retaining nut, then separate ball joint stud from knuckle using a suitable tool, **Fig. 7.**

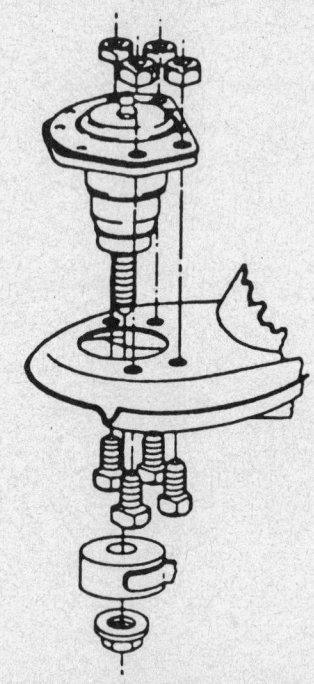

Fig. 8.   Installing service upper ball joint

4. Support upper control arm in a raised position.
5. Remove heads of rivets securing joint to arm, then drive out rivets to remove joint.
6. Position replacement joint on top of control arm, insert retaining bolts supplied with joint from under arm, install nuts and torque to specifications, **Fig. 8.**
7. Remove upper control arm support, assemble ball joint to steering knuckle, install washer, if equipped, and retaining nut.
8. Torque retaining nut to specifications.
9. Tighten retaining nut up to an additional $1/16$ turn, if necessary, to align hole in ball stud with nut, then install cotter pin.

LOWER BALL JOINT

1. Raise vehicle and support at frame, and remove wheel and tire.
2. Position a suitable jack under lower

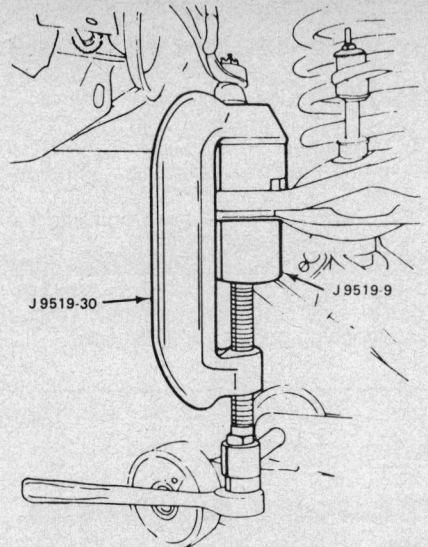

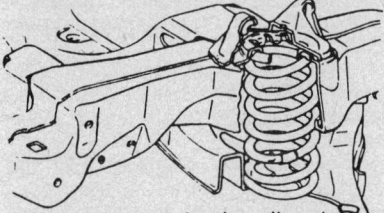

Spring to be installed with tape at lowest position. Bottom of spring is coiled helical, and the top is coiled flat with a gripper notch near end of wire.

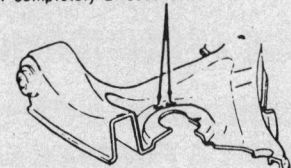

After assembly, end of spring coil must cover all or part of one inspection drain hole. The other hole must be partly exposed or completely uncovered.

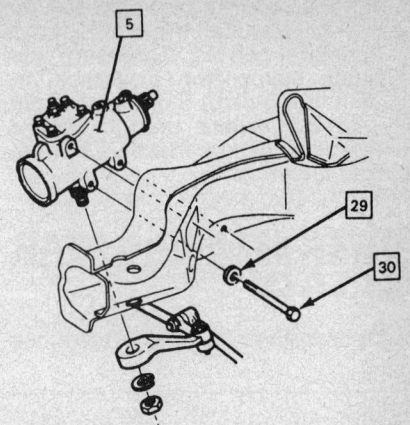

5	POWER STEERING GEAR
29	WASHER
30	BOLT

Fig. 13   Power steering gear mounting

Fig. 11   Pressing lower ball joint into lower control arm

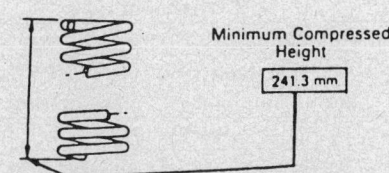

Minimum Compressed Height

241.3 mm

Fig. 12   Positioning coil spring

SHOCK ABSORBER
REPLACE

1. Raise and support vehicle as needed, and remove wheel and tire.
2. Hold shock absorber shaft with a suitable wrench and remove upper retaining nut, washer and bushing.
3. Remove lower retaining bolts and shock absorber.
4. Reverse procedure to install. Torque upper retaining nut and lower mounting bolts to specifications.

COIL SPRING
REPLACE

1. Raise and support front of vehicle, then remove wheel and tire assembly. Support vehicle by frame so control arms hang free.
2. **On models equipped with anti-lock brake systems**, remove right and left wheel speed sensors as follows:
   a. Under vehicle hood, disconnect speed sensor electrical harness.
   b. Raise and support vehicle, then remove speed sensor harness bracket attaching bolt.
   c. Remove speed sensor to steering knuckle attaching bolt, then remove speed sensor and bracket assembly and position aside.
   d. Reverse procedure to install. Wheel speed sensors are to be installed by hand. **Do not hammer sensors into position, as damage may result.**

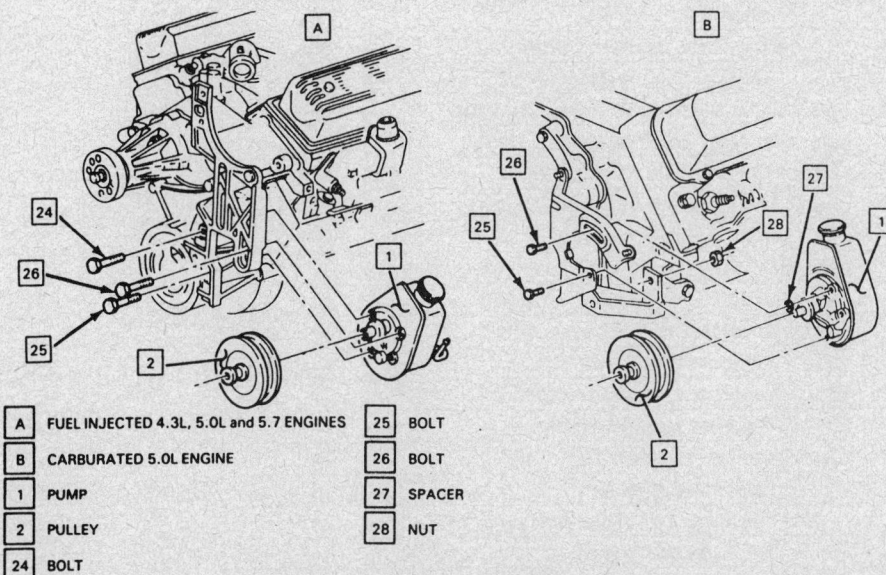

A	FUEL INJECTED 4.3L, 5.0L and 5.7 ENGINES	25	BOLT
B	CARBURATED 5.0L ENGINE	26	BOLT
1	PUMP	27	SPACER
2	PULLEY	28	NUT
24	BOLT		

Fig. 14   Power steering pump mounting

control arm spring seat, and raise jack to compress coil spring. **Jack must remain in place during ball joint replacement to hold spring and lower control arm in position.**

3. Remove cotter pin and nut securing ball joint stud to steering knuckle, then disconnect joint from knuckle using a suitable tool, **Fig. 9.**
4. Lift knuckle assembly from ball stud, guiding control arm out of splash shield, then support knuckle aside to

allow clearance for joint removal.
5. Remove grease fitting, then press ball joint assembly out of lower control arm using a suitable tool, **Fig. 10.**
6. Press replacement joint into arm using suitable tools, **Fig. 11.** Fit spindle over ball stud, install washer, if equipped, and retaining nut.
7. Torque retaining nut to specifications.
8. Tighten nut up to an additional 1/16 turn, if necessary, to align hole in ball stud with nut, then install cotter pin.

3. Remove stabilizer to lower control arm attachment.
4. Disconnect tie rod end from from steering knuckle.
5. Install a suitable coil spring compressor, then compress coil spring.
6. Remove lower control arm to frame bolts, then pivot lower control arm rearward.
7. Carefully loosen coil spring compressor and remove coil spring from vehicle.

8. Reverse procedure to install. Position coil spring as shown in **Fig. 12.** Install front pivot bolt first. **To ensure adequate suspension clearance, install front pivot bolt from front, with nut toward rear of vehicle. Rear bolt can be installed from either direction.**
9. Torque pivot bolts to specifications.

POWER STEERING GEAR REPLACE

1. Disconnect pressure and return hoses from power steering gear. Position hoses in upward direction to prevent fluid drainage. Cap lines and fittings.
2. Disconnect intermediate steering shaft from steering gear stub shaft.
3. Disconnect Pitman arm from steering gear.
4. **On models equipped with ABS brake systems,** remove ABS modulator bracket attaching nut from steering gear.
5. Remove steering attaching bolts and washers, then remove steering gear, **Fig. 13.**
6. Reverse procedure to install. Torque attaching bolts to specifications.

POWER STEERING PUMP REPLACE

1. Disconnect hoses at power steering pump, then plug pump parts and hoses.
2. Loosen pump adjusting bolt and remove pump drive belt.
3. Remove pump to support bracket attaching bolts and the pump, **Fig. 14.**
4. Reverse procedure to install. Torque attaching bolts to specifications.

TIGHTENING SPECIFICATIONS

BUICK ESTATE WAGON, CADILLAC BROUGHAM, CHEVROLET CAPRICE, OLDSMOBILE CUSTOM CRUISER & PONTIAC SAFARI

Year	Component	Torque/Ft. Lbs.
1988	Intermediate Shaft Coupling Flange Bolt	35
	Lower Ball Joint To Knuckle Stud Nut	83
	Lower Control Arm To Frame Nuts	92
	Pitman Shaft Nut	185
	Service Ball Joint To Control Arm	13
	Shock Absorber Lower Attachment	20
	Shock Absorber Upper Attachment	8
	Stabilizer Bar Bracket To Frame	24
	Stabilizer Link Nut	13
	Steering Gear To Frame Bolts	80
	Tie Rod Clamp Nuts	14
	Tie Rod End To Steering Knuckle Stud Nut	35
	Upper Ball Joint To Knuckle Stud Nut	61
	Upper Control Arm Bushing Nuts	85
	Upper Control Arm To Frame Nuts	72
	Wheel & Tire Assembly	①
1989–91	Intermediate Shaft Coupling Flange Bolt	52
	Lower Ball Joint To Knuckle Stud Nut	83
	Lower Control Arm To Frame Nuts	92
	Pitman Shaft Nut	184
	Shock Absorber Lower Attachment	20
	Shock Absorber Upper Attachment	97③
	Stabilizer Bar Bracket To Frame	24
	Stabilizer Link Nut	13
	Steering Gear To Frame Bolts	70
	Tie Rod Clamp Nuts	14
	Tie Rod End To Steering Knuckle Stud Nut	35
	Upper Ball Joint To Knuckle Stud Nut	60
	Upper Control Arm Bushing Nuts	85
	Upper Control Arm To Frame Nuts	72
	Wheel & Tire Assembly	②

①—Sedan, 80 ft. lbs.; wagon, 100 ft. lbs.
②—Sedan, 81 ft. lbs.; wagon, 103 ft. lbs.
③—Inch lbs.

CHEVROLET MONTE CARLO & OLDSMOBILE CUTLASS SUPREME CLASSIC

Year	Component	Torque/Ft. Lbs.
1988	Intermediate shaft Coupling Flange Bolt	35
	Lower Ball Joint To Knuckle Stud Nut	83
	Lower Control Arm To Frame Nuts	65
	Pitman Shaft Nut	185
	Service Ball Joint To Control Arm	13
	Shock Absorber Lower Attachment	20
	Shock Absorber Upper Attachment	8
	Stabilizer Bar Bracket To Frame	24
	Stabilizer Link Nut	13
	Steering Gear To Frame Bolts	80
	Tie Rod Clamp Nuts	14
	Tie Rod End To Steering Knuckle Stud Nut	30
	Upper Ball Joint To Knuckle Stud Nut	61
	Upper Control Arm Bushing Nuts	85
	Upper Control Arm To Frame Nuts	48
	Wheel & Tire Assembly	80

Wheel Alignment
INDEX

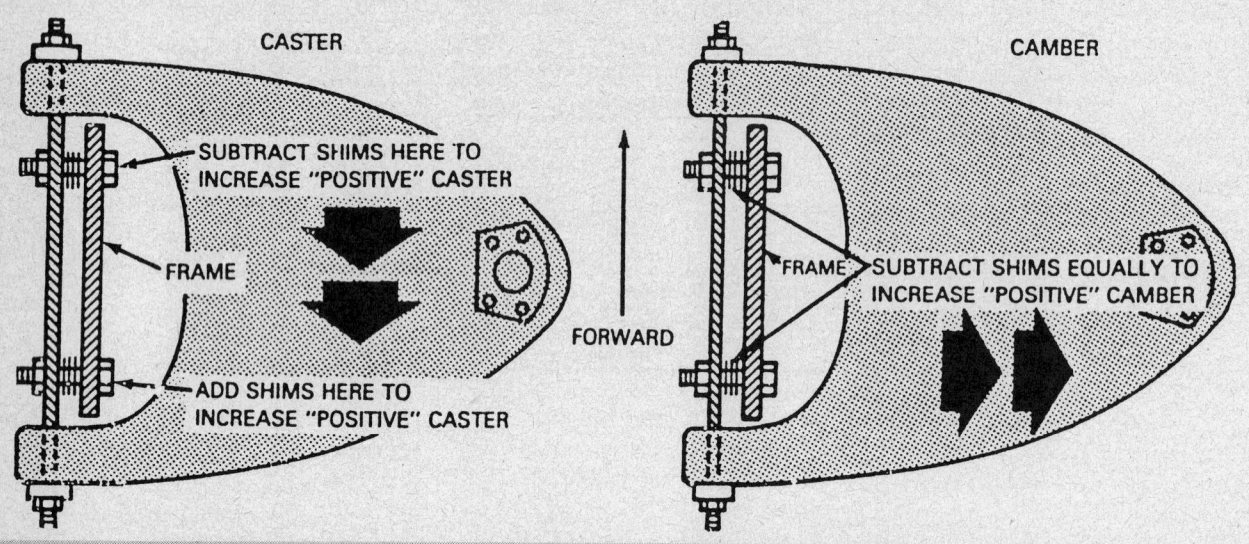

Fig. 1   Caster & camber adjustments

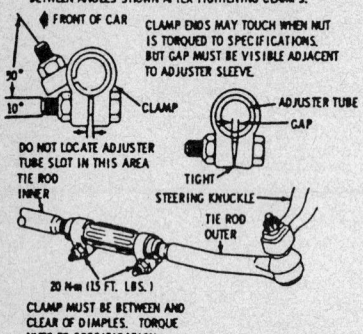

Fig. 2   Toe-in adjustment

FRONT WHEEL ALIGNMENT

Prior to checking or adjusting front suspension alignment, inspect suspension components for damage or excessive wear, and replace as needed. Ensure tire pressures and wheel bearings are properly adjusted, then raise and release front bumper several times to allow vehicle to assume normal ride height.

CASTER, ADJUST

Caster adjustments are made by means of shims between the upper control arm inner support shaft and the support bracket attached to the frame, **Fig. 1**. Shims may be added, subtracted or transferred to change the readings.

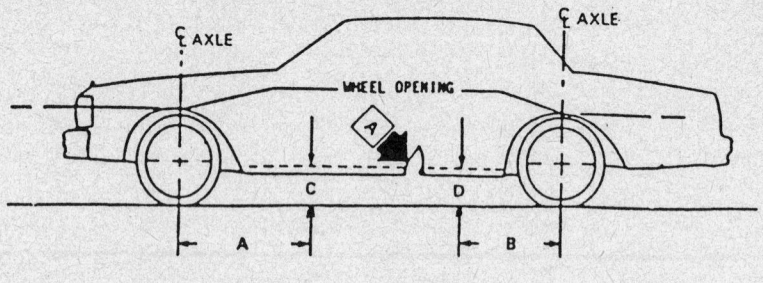

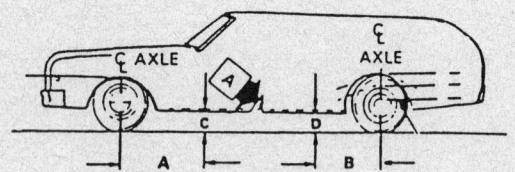

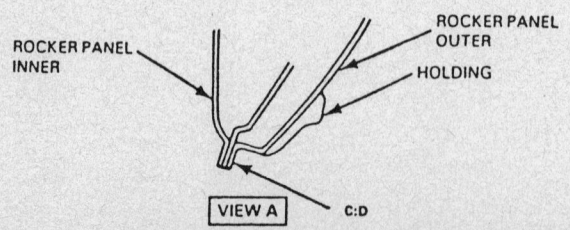

Fig. 3   Vehicle riding height measurement locations & specifications (Part 1 of 2). Buick, Chevrolet, Oldsmobile & Pontiac

VEHICLE RIDE HEIGHT SPECIFICATIONS

Make & Model	Year	Riding Height Measurements In Inches [1]			
		Dimension A	Dimension B	Dimension C	Dimension D
BUICK					
Estate Wagon	1988–91	$31\frac{1}{2}$	$24\frac{39}{64}$	$10\frac{7}{16}$	$10\frac{9}{16}$
CHEVROLET					
Caprice Sedan	1988	$31\frac{1}{2}$	$24\frac{39}{64}$	$10\frac{1}{2}$	$10\frac{5}{8}$
	1989	$31\frac{1}{2}$	$24\frac{39}{64}$	[2]	[3]
	1990	$31\frac{1}{2}$	$24\frac{39}{64}$	[4]	[5]
	1991	$31\frac{57}{64}$	$24\frac{13}{64}$	$9\frac{59}{64}$	$10\frac{25}{64}$
Caprice Wagon	1988	$31\frac{1}{2}$	$24\frac{39}{64}$	$10\frac{9}{16}$	$10\frac{5}{8}$
	1989–90	$31\frac{1}{2}$	$24\frac{39}{64}$	$10\frac{33}{64}$	$10\frac{9}{16}$
	1991	$31\frac{57}{64}$	$24\frac{13}{64}$	$9\frac{59}{64}$	$10\frac{25}{64}$
Monte Carlo	1988	$24\frac{33}{64}$	$20\frac{15}{16}$	[6]	[7]
OLDSMOBILE					
Custom Cruiser	1988	$29\frac{21}{64}$	$18\frac{11}{16}$	$10\frac{1}{2}$	$10\frac{5}{8}$
	1989–91	$31\frac{1}{2}$	$24\frac{39}{64}$	$10\frac{1}{2}$	$10\frac{5}{8}$
Cutlass Supreme Classic	1988	$24\frac{17}{32}$	$20\frac{15}{16}$	10	10
PONTIAC					
Safari	1988–89	$31\frac{1}{2}$	$24\frac{39}{64}$	$10\frac{9}{16}$	$10\frac{5}{8}$

[1] —Plus or minus $\frac{13}{32}$ inch.
[2] —Models with P205-75 or P225-70 tires, $10\frac{23}{64}$ inches; models with P215-75 tires, $10\frac{47}{64}$ inches.
[3] —Models with P205-75 or P225-70 tires, $10\frac{19}{32}$ inches; models with P215-75 tires, $10\frac{55}{64}$ inches.
[4] —Models with V6 engine & P225-70 tires, $10\frac{23}{64}$ inches; other models, $10\frac{7}{16}$ inches.
[5] —Models with V6 engine & P225-70 tires, $10\frac{19}{32}$ inches; other models, $10\frac{23}{64}$ inches.

Fig. 3 Vehicle riding height measurement locations & specifications (Part 2 of 2). Buick, Chevrolet, Oldsmobile & Pontiac

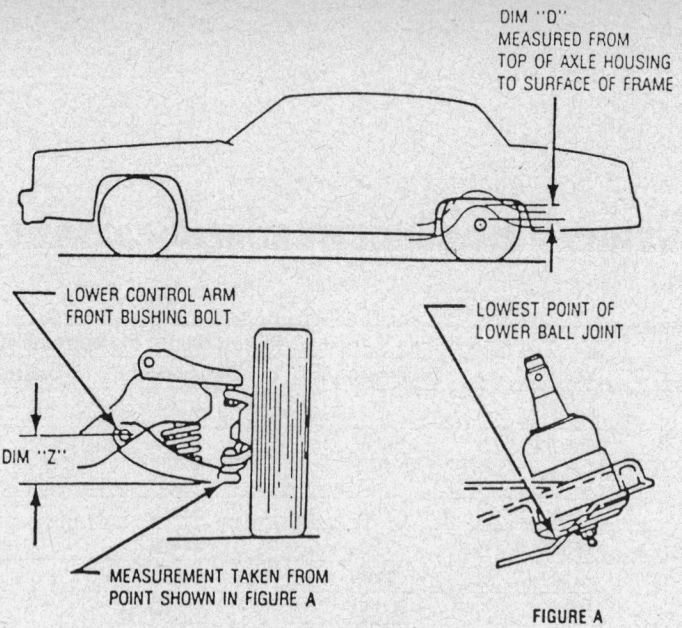

DIMENSIONS IN MILLIMETERS

MODEL	FRONT-DIM "Z" (MM)			REAR-DIM "D" (MM)			
	MIN.	CURB TARGET	MAX.	MIN.	CURB TARGET	MAX.	
W/O ELC	46 (1.81")	56 (2.21")	66 (2.60")	130 (5.11")	140 (5.51")	150 (5.91")	MAX. VARIATION IN TRIM HEIGHT FROM SIDE TO SIDE IS 9 MM (.35")
WITH ELC	44 (1.73")	54 (2.13")	64 (2.52")	121 (4.76")	131 (5.16")	141 (5.55")	
WITH HEAVY DUTY RIDE	44 (1.73")	54 (2.13")	64 (2.54")	121 (4.76")	131 (5.16")	141 (5.55")	
WITH TRAILER TOWING	35 (1.38")	45 (1.77")	55 (2.17")	112 (4.41")	122 (4.80")	132 (5.20")	

Fig. 4   Ride height measurement. Cadillac Brougham

Transfer shims from front to rear or rear to front. The transfer of one shim to the front bolt from the rear bolt will decrease positive caster. One shim (1/32 inch) transferred from the rear bolt to the front bolt will change caster about 1/2 degree.

CAMBER, ADJUST

Camber adjustments are made by means of shims between the upper control arm inner support shaft and the support bracket attached to the frame, **Fig. 1.** Shims may be added, subtracted or transferred to change the readings.

Change shims at both the front and rear of the shaft. Adding an equal number of shims at both front and rear of the support shaft will decrease positive camber. One shim (1/32 inch) at each location will move camber approximately 1/6 degree.

TOE-IN, ADJUST

Toe-in can be adjusted by loosening the clamp bolts at each end of each tie rod and turning each tie rod to increase or decrease its length as necessary until proper toe-in is secured and the steering gear is

on the high point for straight-ahead driving, **Fig. 2.**

RIDE HEIGHT

EXCEPT CADILLAC

Refer to **Fig. 3** for ride height measurements and specifications.

CADILLAC

Refer to **Fig. 4** for ride height measurements and specifications.

CHEVROLET CAMARO & PONTIAC FIREBIRD
(F Cars)
INDEX OF SERVICE OPERATIONS

NOTE: Refer To The Rear Of This Manual For Vehicle Manufacturer's Special Tool Suppliers.

INDEX OF SERVICE OPERATIONS—Continued

Specifications
GENERAL ENGINE SPECIFICATIONS

Year	Engine CID/Liter	VIN Code ①	Fuel System	Bore & Stroke	Compression Ratio	Net Brake H.P. @ RPM ②	Maximum Torque	Normal Oil Pressure Psi.
1988	2.8L/V6-173	S	MFI	3.50 x 2.99	8.9	135 @ 4900	160 @ 3900	⑦
	5.0L/V8-305	E	EFI	3.74 x 3.48	9.3	170 @ 4000	255 @ 2400	⑧
	5.0L/V8-305 ③	F	TPI	3.74 x 3.48	9.3	195 @ 4000	295 @ 2800	⑧
	5.0L/V8-305 ④	F	TPI	3.74 x 3.48	9.3	220 @ 4400	290 @ 3200	⑧
	5.7L/V8-350	8	TPI	4.00 x 3.48	9.3	230 @ 4400	330 @ 3200	⑧
1989	2.8L/V6-173	S	MFI	3.50 x 2.99	8.9	135 @ 4900	160 @ 3900	⑦
	3.8L/V6-231 Turbo	7	SFI	3.80 x 3.40	8.0	245 @ 4400	340 @ 2800	37⑨
	5.0L/V8-305	E	EFI	3.74 x 3.48	9.3	170 @ 4000	255 @ 2400	⑧
	5.0L/V8-305 ③	F	TPI	3.74 x 3.48	9.3	195 @ 4000	295 @ 2800	⑧
	5.0L/V8-305 ④ ⑤	F	TPI	3.74 x 3.48	9.3	220 @ 4400	290 @ 3200	⑧
	5.0L/V8-305 ④ ⑥	F	TPI	3.74 x 3.48	9.3	230 @ 4400	300 @ 3200	⑧
	5.7L/V8-350 ⑤	8	TPI	4.00 x 3.48	9.3	230 @ 4400	330 @ 3200	⑧
	5.7L/V8-350 ⑥	8	TPI	4.00 x 3.48	9.3	240 @ 4400	345 @ 3200	⑧
1990	3.1L/V6-191	T	MFI	3.50 x 3.31	8.5	140 @ 4400	180 @ 3600	⑦
	5.0L/V8-305	E	TBI	3.74 x 3.48	9.3	170 @ 4000	255 @ 2400	⑧
	5.0L/V8-305 ③	F	TPI	3.74 x 3.48	9.3	205 @ 4400	285 @ 3200	⑧
	5.0L/V8-305 ④	F	TPI	3.74 x 3.48	9.3	225 @ 4400	295 @ 3200	⑧
	5.7L/V8-350	8	TPI	4.00 x 3.48	9.3	240 @ 4400	340 @ 2800	⑨
1991	3.1L/V6-191	T	MFI	3.50 x 3.31	8.5	140 @ 4400	180 @ 3600	⑦
	5.0L/V8-305	E	EFI	3.74 x 3.48	9.3	170 @ 4000	255 @ 2400	⑧
	5.0L/V8-305 ③	F	TPI	3.74 x 3.48	9.3	205 @ 4200	285 @ 3200	⑧
	5.0L/V8-305 ④	F	TPI	3.74 x 3.48	9.3	230 @ 4200	300 @ 3200	⑧
	5.7L/V8-350	8	TPI	4.00 x 3.48	9.3	245 @ 4400	345 @ 3200	⑨

Continued

GENERAL ENGINE SPECIFICATIONS—Continued

① —The eighth digit of the VIN denotes engine code.
② —Ratings are net-as installed in vehicle.
③ —Auto. trans.

④ —Man. trans.
⑤ —Single exhaust.
⑥ —Dual exhaust.
⑦ —10 psi. @ 500 RPM minimum; 51 to 55 psi. @ 2000 RPM.

⑧ —Minimum, 6 psi. @ 1000 RPM; 18 psi. @ 2000 RPM; 24 psi. @ 4000 RPM.
⑨ —At 2400 RPM.

TUNE UP SPECIFICATIONS

| Year & Engine/VIN code ① | Spark Plug Gap | Firing Order Fig. ③ | Ignition Timing BTDC ② | | | Curb Idle Speed ④ | | Fast Idle Speed | | Fuel Pump Pressure Psi. |
			Man. Trans.	Auto. Trans.	Mark Fig.	Man. Trans.	Auto. Trans.	Man. Trans.	Auto. Trans.	
1988										
V6-173(2.8L)/S	.045	A	10⑤	10⑤	B	⑥	⑥	⑥	⑥	34–47⑦
V8-305(5.0L)/E	.035	C	—	6⑤	B	—	⑥	—	⑥	9–13⑧
V8-305(5.0L)/F	.035	C	6⑤	6⑤	B	⑥	⑥	⑥	⑥	34–47⑦
V8-350(5.7L)/8	.035	C	—	6⑤	D	—	⑥	—	⑥	34–47⑦
1989										
V6-173(2.8L)/S	.045	A	10⑤	10⑤	B	⑥	⑥	⑥	⑥	34–47⑦
V6-231(3.8L)/7	.035	⑨	—	⑩	⑪	—	⑥	—	⑥	40–47⑦
V8-305(5.0L)/E	.035	C	—	6⑤	B	—	⑥	—	⑥	9–13⑧
V8-305(5.0L)/F	.035	C	6⑤	6⑤	B	⑥	⑥	⑥	⑥	34–47⑦
V8-350(5.7L)/8	.035	C	—	6⑤	D	—	⑥	—	⑥	34–47⑦
1990–91										
V6-191(3.1L)/T	.045	A	10⑤	10⑤	B	⑥	⑥	⑥	⑥	34–47⑦
V8-305(5.0L)/E	.035	C	—	6⑤	B	—	⑥	—	⑥	9–13⑧
V8-305(5.0L)/F	.035	C	6⑤	6⑤	B	⑥	⑥	⑥	⑥	34–47⑦
V8-350(5.7L)/8	.035	C	—	6⑤	D	—	⑥	—	⑥	34–47⑦

① —The eighth digit of VIN denotes engine code.
② —BTDC: Before Top Dead Center.
③ —Before removing wires from distributor cap, determine location of No. 1 wire in cap, as distributor position may have been altered from that shown at the end of this chart.
④ —D: Drive.
⑤ —With set timing connector (tan/black wire located near blower motor) disconnected. After completing adjustment, reconnect timing connector. With engine off clear trouble code from ECM

memory by removing battery voltage to ECM for 30 seconds.
⑥ —Idle speed is controlled by an idle air control (IAC) valve.
⑦ —With shop towel around fuel pressure valve to prevent fuel spillage, connect a suitable fuel pressure gauge to fuel pressure valve. Check fuel pressure with ignition switch On, engine not running.
⑧ —Wrap shop towel around fuel hose to steel line connection in engine compartment to prevent fuel spillage. Disconnect hose from steel

line & install a suitable fuel pressure gauge between hose & line. Ensure gauge connections are tight, then start engine & check fuel pressure readings.
⑨ —Cylinder numbering front to rear, left bank 1, 3, 5; right bank 2, 4, 6. Firing order 1-6-5-4-3-2. Refer to Fig. E for spark plug wire connections at coil unit.
⑩ —Electronically controlled, no adjustment.
⑪ —Equipped with a crankshaft position sensor.

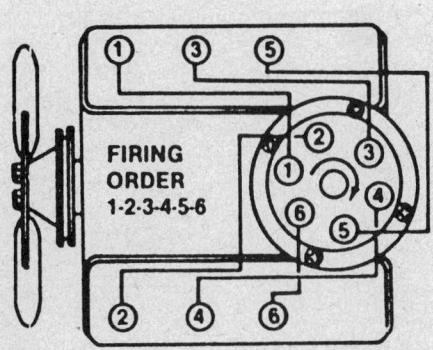

Fig. A

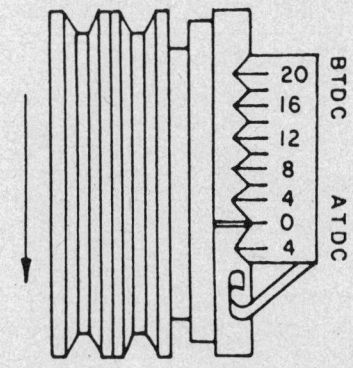

Fig. B

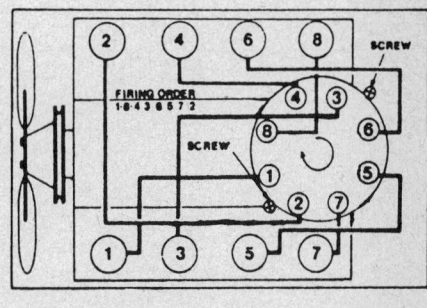

Fig. C

Continued

TUNE UP SPECIFICATIONS—Continued

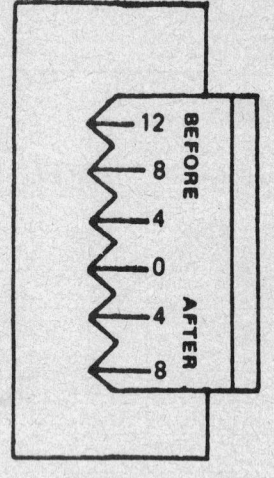

Fig. D

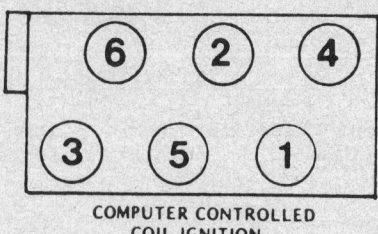

COMPUTER CONTROLLED
COIL IGNITION

Fig. E

ALTERNATOR SPECIFICATIONS

Year	Model	Series	Rated Hot Output Amps
1988–89	1101139	CS130	85
	1101140	CS130	100
	1101253	CS130	85
	1101254	CS130	100
	1101255	CS130	105
1989	1101349	CS144	120
1990	1101140	CS130	100
	1101646	CS130	100
	1101647	CS130	105
1991	1101593	CS130	100
	1101600	CS130	105
	1101645	CS130	100

STARTER MOTOR APPLICATIONS

Refer To "Starter Motors" For Starter Specifications.

Year	Engine/VIN ①	Ident. No.
1988	V6-173(2.8L)/S ②	1998524
	V6-173(2.8L)/S ③	10455016
	V8-305(5.0L)/E & F ② ④	1998527
	V8-305(5.0L)/E ③ ④	1998548
	V8-305(5.0L)/E ⑤	1998591
	V8-305(5.0L)/F ⑤	1998580
	V8-350(5.7L)/8	1998591
1989	V6-173(2.8L)/S	10455016
	V6-231(3.8L)/7	—
	V8-305(5.0L)/E & F ④	1998548
	V8-305(5.0L)/E ⑤	1998591
	V8-305(5.0L)/F ⑤	1998580
	V8-350(5.7L)/8	1998591

Continued

STARTER MOTOR APPLICATIONS—Continued

Year	Engine/VIN①	Ident. No.
1990	V6-191(3.1L)T	10455016
	V8-305(5.0L)/E & F④	1998548
	V8-305(5.0L)/E & F⑤	1998591
	V8-305(5.0L)/E & F⑥	10455300
	V8-350(5.7L)/8	10455300
1991	V6-191(3.1L)T	10455011
	V8-305(5.0L)/E & F	10455012
	V8-350(5.7L)/8	10455300

①—The eighth digit of VIN denotes engine code.
②—1st design.
③—2nd design.
④—Man. trans.
⑤—Auto. trans.

REAR AXLE SPECIFICATIONS

Year	Axle Model	Ring Gear Diameter, Inch	Ring Gear Backlash, Inch	Pinion Bearing Preload, Inch Lbs.		Total Assembly Preload, Inch Lbs.		Side Bearing Preload, Inch Lbs.		Differential Bearings, Inch Lbs.	
				New	Used	New	Used	New	Used	Used	New
1988	GM①	7.62	.006–.008	20–25	10–15	35–40	20–25	—	—	—	—
1988–89	Borg Warner②	7.75	.004–.007	12–25	6–12	—	—	10–25	6–12	10–25	5–12
1989–91	GM①	7.62	.005–.009	24–32	9–12	35–40	20–25	—	—	—	—
1990–91	Borg Warner②	7.75	.004–.007	12–25	5–12	—	—	10–25	5–12	10–25	5–12

①—Models with rear drum brakes.
②—Models with rear disc brakes.

WHEEL ALIGNMENT SPECIFICATIONS

Year	Model	Caster Angle, Degrees		Camber Angle, Degrees		Total Toe, Degrees
		Limits	Desired	Limits	Desired	
1988–90	All	+4.2 to +5.2	+4.7	–.2 to +.8	+.3	0
1991	All	+4.5 to +5.5	+5	–.2 to +.8	+.3	0

COOLING SYSTEM & CAPACITY DATA

Year	Model Or Engine/VIN ①	Cooling System Capacity, Qts.		Radiator Cap Relief Pressure, Psi.	Thermo. Opening Temp.	Fuel Tank, Gals.	Engine Oil, Qts.②		Transmission Oil		Rear Axle Pts.
		Less A/C	With A/C				Less Filter Change	With Filter Change	Man Trans. Pts.	Auto. Trans. Qts.②	
1988	V6-172(2.8L)/S	12.5	12.5	15	195	15.9	4③	4③	④⑤	2.9⑤	1.8⑥
	V8-305(5.0L)/E	15.3	15.6	15	195	15.9	4③	5③	④⑤	2.9⑤	1.8⑥
	V8-305(5.0L)/F	17	17	15	195	15.9	4③	5③	④⑤	2.9⑤	1.8⑥
	V8-350(5.7L)/F	17	17	15	195	15.9	4③	5③	④⑤	2.9⑤	1.8⑥
1989	V6-172(2.8L)/S	12.4	12.4	15	195	15.5	4③	4③	④⑤	2.96⑤	1.8⑥
	V6-231(3.8L)/7 Turbo	13	13	15	195	15.5	5⑦	5⑦	⑧⑨	—	1.8⑥
	V8-305(5.0L)/E	15.6	15.6	15	195	15.5	4③	5③	④⑤	2.96⑤	1.8⑥
	V8-305(5.0L)/F	17	17	15	195	15.5	4③	5③	④⑤	2.96⑤	1.8⑥
	V8-350(5.7L)/F	17	17	15	195	15.5	4③	5③	④⑤	2.96⑤	1.8⑥
1990	V6-191(3.1L)/T	14.5	14.5	15	195	15.5	4③	5③	⑤⑩	2.96⑤	1.8⑥
	V8-305(5.0L)/E	17.5	18	15	195	15.5	4③	5③	⑤⑪	2.96⑧	1.8⑥
	V8-305(5.0L)/F	17.2	17.4	15	195	15.5	4③	5③	⑤⑪	2.96⑤	1.8⑥
	V8-350(5.7L)/F	16.1	16.3	15	195	15.5	4③	5③	⑤⑪	2.96⑤	1.8⑥
1991	V6-191(3.1L)/T	14.66	14.66	15	195	15.5	4⑨	5⑨	⑤⑩	2.95⑧	1.8⑥
	V8-305(5.0L)/E	17.33	17.97	15	195	15.5	4⑨	5⑨	⑤⑪	2.95⑤	1.8⑥
	V8-305(5.0L)/F	17.11	17.26	15	195	15.5	4⑨	5⑨	⑤⑪	2.95⑤	1.8⑥
	V8-350(5.7L)/F	16.43	16.43	15	195	15.5	4⑨	5⑨	⑤⑪	2.95⑤	1.8⑥

Continued

COOLING SYSTEM & CAPACITY DATA—Continued

①—The eighth digit of the VIN denotes engine code.

②—Approximate, make final check with dipstick.

③—Recommended engine oil API Service SG or SF/CC, CD SAE 5W-30.

④—Drain & refill, 5 qts,.; total capacity, 11.5 qts.

⑤—Use Dexron II type transmission fluid.

⑥—Use 80W-90 GL-5 gear oil. Limited slip differentials require 4 oz. of

additive lubricant 1052358 or equivalent.

⑦—Recommended engine oil API Service SG or SF/CC, CD SAE 10W-30. When changing engine oil, prime oil filter with engine oil prior to installation. Disconnect electrical connectors at computer controlled coil ignition unit and fuel pump relay, then crank engine until a steady oil pressure is observed. After a steady oil pressure reading has been observed, reconnect

computer controlled coil ignition unit and fuel pump relay electrical connects and start engine.

⑧—Drain & refill, 3.5 qts,.; total capacity, 11 qts.

⑨—Recommended engine oil API Service SG SAE 5W-30.

⑩—Drain & refill, 5 qts,.; total capacity, 8.35 qts.

⑪—Drain & refill, 5 qts,.; total capacity, 11.2 qts.

Electrical
INDEX

FUSE PANEL & FLASHER LOCATION

The fuse panel is located behind the left hand side of the instrument panel. The hazard warning flasher is located behind the instrument panel to the right of the steering column, in the convenience center. The turn signal flasher on 1988-89 models is located behind the instrument panel, clipped to the right hand side of the steering column bracket. On 1990-91 models, then turn signal flasher is located behind the left hand side of the instrument panel, clipped to the fuse block bracket.

STARTER
REPLACE

If shims are used between starter and engine block, they should be placed in their original location during installation. If starter is noisy during cranking, remove

one .015 inch double shim or add one .015 single shim to the outer bolt. If starter makes a high pitched whine after firing, add .015 inch double shims until noise ceases.

1. Disconnect battery ground cable.
2. Raise and support vehicle. Remove starter wiring.
3. Remove starter to engine brace and starter heat shields, if equipped.
4. Remove starter mounting bolts and lower starter. Note position of shims, if used.
5. Disconnect solenoid wires and the battery cable.
6. Remove starter from vehicle.
7. Reverse procedure to install.

DISTRIBUTOR
REPLACE
REMOVAL

1. Disconnect battery ground cable.

2. Disconnect ignition switch feed and tachometer leads from distributor cap. Screwdriver or other tools should not be used to release lead connector locking tab.
3. Remove distributor cap attaching screws, then position cap out of way.
4. Disconnect four terminal ECM electrical connector from distributor electrical connector.
5. Remove distributor hold down clamp and bolt. Mark position of distributor rotor to distributor housing and position of distributor housing to engine for use during installation.
6. Lift distributor upward until rotor stops rotating in counterclockwise direction and mark position of rotor to distributor housing for use during installation.
7. Remove distributor from engine.

INSTALLATION

1. Position rotor to mark on distributor housing, then insert distributor into

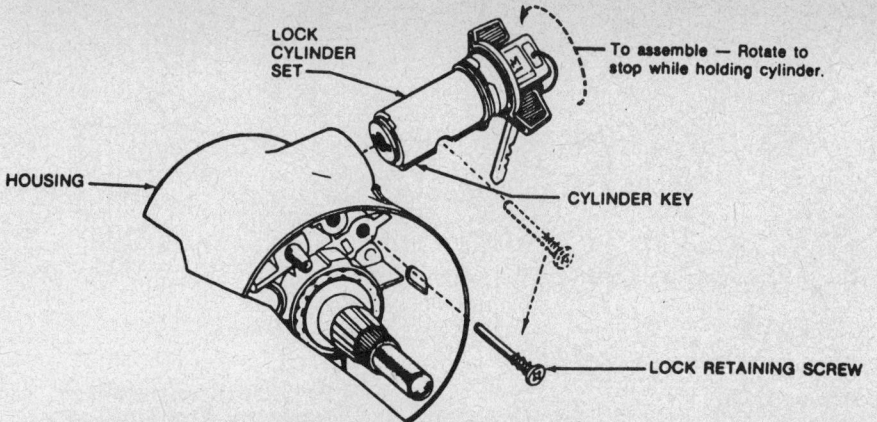

Fig. 1 Ignition lock installation. Models less supplemental inflatable restraint system

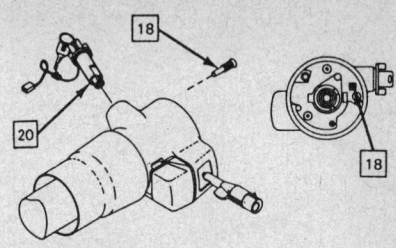

18 LOCK RETAINING SCREW
20 VATS LOCK CYLINDER SET

Fig. 2 Ignition lock installation. Models with supplemental inflatable restraint system

engine aligning rotor to housing and housing to engine marks made during removal.
2. If engine was was disturbed while distributor was removed, proceed as follows:
   a. Remove spark plug from No. 1 cylinder.
   b. With transmission in Neutral or Park and parking brake applied, position finger over spark plug opening in cylinder head, then slowly crank engine until compression is felt.
   c. Align crankshaft pulley with TDC (0) mark on timing indicator.
   d. Locate distributor rotor contact between No. 1 and 8 spark plug firing positions on distributor.
   c. Insert distributor into engine.
3. Install distributor hold clamp and bolt. Hand tighten bolt.
4. Connect ECM four terminal electrical connector to distributor.
5. Install distributor cap, then connect ignition switch and tachometer lead connector to cap.
6. Connect battery ground cable, then check and adjust ignition timing as necessary. Torque distributor hold down bolt to 25 ft. lbs.

IGNITION LOCK
REPLACE
MODELS LESS SUPPLEMENTAL INFLATABLE RESTRAINT SYSTEM

1. Remove steering wheel as described under "Horn Sounder and Steering Wheel."
2. Remove turn signal switch as described under Turn Signal Switch, Replace, then remove buzzer switch.
3. Place ignition switch in Run position, then remove lock cylinder retaining screw and lock cylinder.
4. Install by rotating lock cylinder to stop while holding housing, **Fig. 1.** Align cylinder key with keyway in housing, then push lock cylinder assembly into

housing until fully seated.
5. Install lock cylinder retaining screw.
6. Install buzzer switch, turn signal switch and steering wheel.

MODELS WITH SUPPLEMENTAL INFLATABLE RESTRAINT SYSTEM

1. **To avoid personal injury when servicing models equipped with Supplemental Inflatable Restraint (Airbag) System, temporarily disable system as follows:**
   a. Place ignition switch in off position.
   b. Disconnect battery ground cable and tape cable end.
   c. Remove SIR fuse from fuse panel.
   d. Remove lower left hand trim panel, then disconnect connector position assurance and yellow two way SIR connector at base of steering column.
2. Remove steering wheel as described under "Horn Sounder and Steering Wheel, Replace."
3. Remove turn signal switch as described under "Turn Signal Switch, Replace."
4. Place ignition switch in Lock position.
5. Remove lock cylinder retaining screw, **Fig. 2.**
6. Disconnect terminal electrical connector at bulkhead connection to provide slack.
7. Remove wiring connector from steering column.
8. Attach a suitable length of mechanic wire to ignition lock electrical connector for use during installation. Detach wire retaining clip, then carefully pull ignition lock wiring through housing shroud, steering column and lock housing cover.
9. Remove lock cylinder.
10. Reverse procedure to install. Ensure lock cylinder wiring is properly routed through steering column. Torque lock cylinder retaining screw to 22 inch lbs.
11. **After completing service procedure activate Supplemental Inflatable Restraint (SIR) system as follows:**

   a. Ensure ignition switch is in Off position.
   b. Connect yellow SIR two way electrical connector and connector position assurance at base of steering column.
   c. Install lower left hand trim panel.
   d. Install SIR fuse into fuse panel.
   e. Connect battery ground cable.
   f. Place ignition switch in Run position and note operation of "Inflatable Restraint" warning lamp. Warning lamp should flash 7 to 9 times and then turn off. If not, refer to "Passive Restraint" section for diagnostic system check.

IGNITION SWITCH
REPLACE

The ignition switch is mounted on top of the mast jacket inside the brake pedal support and is actuated by a rod and rack assembly.

1. **To avoid personal injury when servicing models equipped with Supplemental Inflatable Restraint (Airbag) System, temporarily disable system as follows:**
   a. Place ignition switch in off position.
   b. Disconnect battery ground cable and tape cable end.
   c. Remove SIR fuse from fuse panel.
   d. Remove lower left hand trim panel, then disconnect connector position assurance and yellow two way SIR connector at base of steering column.
2. On all models, disconnect battery cable if performed previously.
3. Disconnect and lower steering column. **It may be necessary, on some models, to remove the upper column mounting bracket if it hinders servicing of switch. Use extreme care when lowering steering column to prevent damage to column assembly. Only lower steering column a sufficient distance to perform ignition switch service.**
4. Rotate ignition lock to Off unlocked position.
5. If lock cylinder has been removed, pull switch actuator rod up to stop, then push rod down to second detent to

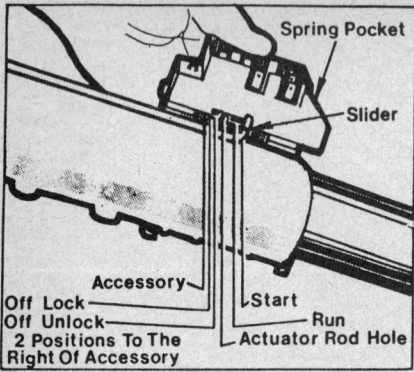

Fig. 3   Ignition switch

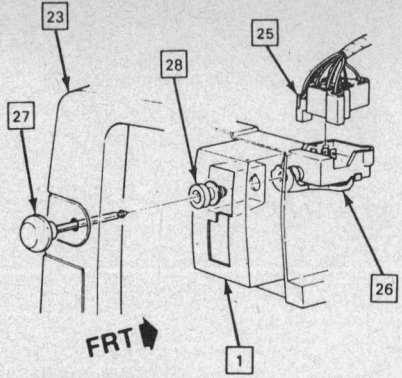

1	INSTRUMENT PANEL
23	CLUSTER TRIM PLATE
25	ELECTRICAL CONNECTOR
26	SWITCH
27	SWITCH KNOB
28	NUT

Fig. 4   Headlamp switch replace. Camaro

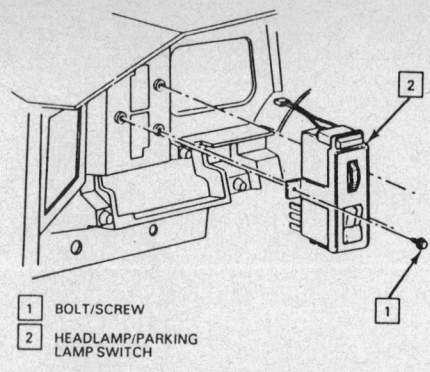

1	BOLT/SCREW
2	HEADLAMP/PARKING LAMP SWITCH

Fig. 5   Headlamp switch replace. Firebird

place switch in Off unlocked position, **Fig. 3.**

6. Remove column mounted dimmer switch, if equipped, then remove switch retaining screws and switch.
7. Reverse procedure to install, noting the following:
   a. Place gear shift lever in neutral.
   b. Place lock cylinder and switch in Off unlocked position, **Fig. 3.**
   c. Fit actuator rod into hole in switch slider and secure switch with retaining screws, ensuring switch does not move out of detent.
   d. Install and adjust dimmer switch, if removed, as outlined in "Dimmer Switch, Replace."
8. **After completing service procedure activate Supplemental Inflatable Restraint (SIR) system as follows:**
   a. Ensure ignition switch is in Off position.
   b. Connect yellow SIR two way electrical connector and connector position assurance at base of steering column.
   c. Install lower left hand trim panel.
   d. Install SIR fuse into fuse panel.
   e. Connect battery ground cable.
   f. Place ignition switch in Run position and note operation of "Inflatable Restraint" warning lamp. Warning lamp should flash 7 to 9 times and then turn off. If not, refer to "Passive Restraint" section for diagnostic system check.

LIGHT SWITCH REPLACE

To avoid personal injury when servicing models equipped with Supplemental Inflatable Restraint (Airbag) System, temporarily disable system as follows:

1. Place ignition switch in off position.
2. Disconnect battery ground cable and tape cable end.
3. Remove SIR fuse from fuse panel.
4. Remove lower left hand trim panel, then disconnect connector position assurance and yellow two way SIR connector at base of steering column.

After completing service procedure activate Supplemental Inflatable Restraint (SIR) system as follows:

1. Ensure ignition switch is in Off position.
2. Connect yellow SIR two way electrical connector and connector position assurance at base of steering column.
3. Install lower left hand trim panel.
4. Install SIR fuse into fuse panel.
5. Connect battery ground cable.
6. Place ignition switch in Run position and note operation of "Inflatable Restraint" warning lamp. Warning lamp should flash 7 to 9 times and then turn off. If not, refer to "Passive Restraint" section for diagnostic system check.

CAMARO

1. Disconnect battery ground cable.
2. Open screw covers, then remove knee bolster attaching screws and knee bolster.
3. From under instrument panel, depress release button on light switch, then remove switch knob and shaft assembly from switch, **Fig. 4.**
4. Remove instrument cluster trim plate, then remove switch retaining nut.
5. Lower switch and disconnect electrical connector, then remove switch.
6. Reverse procedure to install.

FIREBIRD

1. Disconnect battery ground cable.
2. Remove left and right hand lower instrument panel trim covers.
3. Remove instrument cluster trim plate.
4. Remove switch attaching screws, then depress switch side tangs and pull switch from instrument panel, **Fig. 5.**
5. Disconnect electrical connector and remove switch.
6. Reverse procedure to install.

STOP LIGHT SWITCH REPLACE

1. **To avoid personal injury when servicing models equipped with Supplemental Inflatable Restraint (Airbag) System, temporarily disable system as follows:**
   a. Place ignition switch in off position.
   b. Disconnect battery ground cable and tape cable end.
   c. Remove SIR fuse from fuse panel.
   d. Remove lower left hand trim panel, then disconnect connector position assurance and yellow two way SIR connector at base of steering column.
2. Remove left hand side hush panel.
3. Working from underneath instrument panel, disconnect wire connector from switch at brake pedal support.
4. Remove switch from mounting bracket, **Fig. 6.**
5. Depress brake pedal and install new switch into clip, until shoulder on switch bottoms out against clip.
6. If adjustment of the switch is necessary, the switch may be rotated or pulled in the clip. Electrical contact should be made when brake pedal is depressed .053 inch from its fully released position.
7. **After completing service procedure activate Supplemental Inflatable Restraint (SIR) system as follows:**
   a. Ensure ignition switch is in Off position.
   b. Connect yellow SIR two way electrical connector and connector position assurance at base of steering column.
   c. Install lower left hand trim panel.
   d. Install SIR fuse into fuse panel.
   e. Connect battery ground cable.
   f. Place ignition switch in Run position and note operation of "Inflatable Restraint" warning lamp. Warning lamp should flash 7 to 9 times and then turn off. If not, refer to "Passive Restraint" section for diagnostic system check.

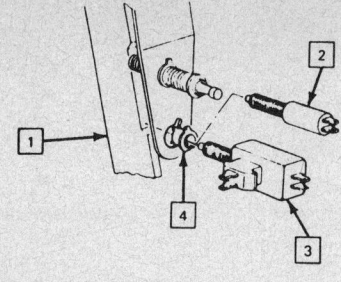

1	BRAKE PEDAL
2	SWITCH – WITHOUT CRUISE CONTROL
3	SWITCH – WITH CRUISE CONTROL
4	CLIP

Fig. 6 Stop lamp switch replace

CLUTCH START SWITCH REPLACE

1. **To avoid personal injury when servicing models equipped with Supplemental Inflatable Restraint (Airbag) System, temporarily disable system as follows:**
   a. Place ignition switch in off position.
   b. Disconnect battery ground cable and tape cable end.
   c. Remove SIR fuse from fuse panel.
   d. Remove lower left hand trim panel, then disconnect connector position assurance and yellow two way SIR connector at base of steering column.
2. Disconnect wire connector at switch.
3. Remove retaining nut, if so equipped and unscrew switch from bracket.
4. To install: depress clutch pedal, then insert and push switch into clip until shoulder bottoms out.
5. Plug connector on switch and check for proper operation.
6. **After completing service procedure activate Supplemental Inflatable Restraint (SIR) system as follows:**
   a. Ensure ignition switch is in Off position.
   b. Connect yellow SIR two way electrical connector and connector position assurance at base of steering column.
   c. Install lower left hand trim panel.
   d. Install SIR fuse into fuse panel.
   e. Connect battery ground cable.
   f. Place ignition switch in Run position and note operation of "Inflatable Restraint" warning lamp. Warning lamp should flash 7 to 9 times and then turn off. If not, refer to "Passive Restraint" section for diagnostic system check.

NEUTRAL SAFETY SWITCH REPLACE

1. Remove floor console cover, then disconnect electrical connectors from switch.

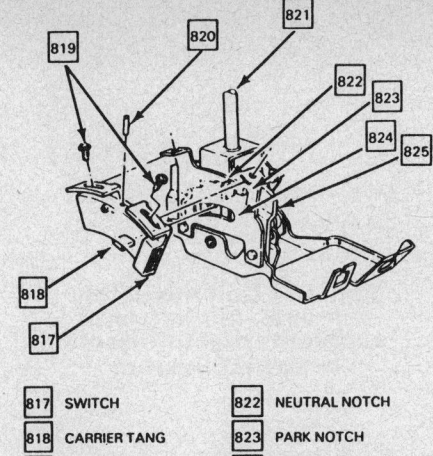

817	SWITCH	822	NEUTRAL NOTCH
818	CARRIER TANG	823	PARK NOTCH
819	BOLTS	824	TANG SLOT
820	GAGE PIN	825	DETENT PLATE
821	SHIFT CONTROL LEVER		

Fig. 7 Neutral safety switch replace

2. Place shift lever in Neutral position of detent plate, then remove switch attaching screws and switch, **Fig. 7.**
3. To install, ensure the shift lever is in Neutral, then position switch on shift lever making sure pin on shaft is in slot of switch.
4. Move shift lever out of Neutral to shear pin which is part of new switch.
5. Reconnect electrical connectors to switch, then apply parking brake and start engine. Check back-up lights and seat belt warning system for proper operation and ensure engine will start only in Park or Neutral.
6. Turn ignition off and install floor console.
7 Position connector side of switch into lower jacket cut out.
8. Push down front of switch, ensuring switch tangs snap into holes in steering column jacket.
9. Adjust switch by placing gear selector in "Park" position. Switch main housing and housing back should ratchet, providing proper adjustment.

TURN SIGNAL SWITCH REPLACE

MODELS LESS SUPPLEMENTAL INFLATABLE RESTRAINT SYSTEM

On tilt column, the column must first be lowered from panel.
1. Disconnect battery ground cable, then remove steering wheel using puller. **Do not hammer on end of shaft as hammering could collapse shaft or loosen plastic injections which maintain column rigidity.**
2. Remove cover by prying out with a screwdriver at slots provided in cover for this purpose.
3. Depress lock plate and pry round wire lock ring out of shaft groove, **Fig. 8.**

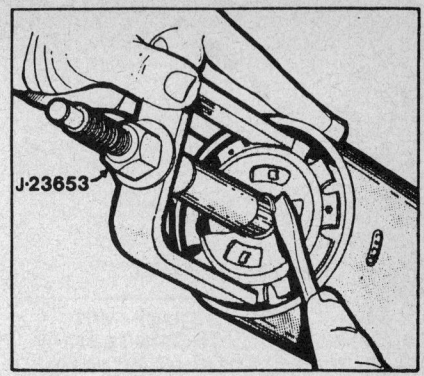

J·23653

Fig. 8 Lock plate retaining ring removal

Remove lock plate.
4. Slide upper bearing preload spring and turn signal cancelling cam off shaft.
5. Remove actuator arm screw and actuator arm, then turn signal lever.
6. Push hazard warning switch in and unscrew knob.
7. Pull turn signal wiring connector out of bracket on jacket and disconnect.
8. Remove three turn signal switch screws.
9. Remove shift indicator cable, if equipped.
10. Lower steering column from instrument panel and remove wire protector, then pull switch straight up with wire protector and remove housing. **Place tape around upper part of connector and wires to prevent snagging when switch is being removed, Fig. 9.**

MODELS WITH SUPPLEMENTAL INFLATABLE RESTRAINT SYSTEM

1. **To avoid personal injury when servicing models equipped with Supplemental Inflatable Restraint (Airbag) System, temporarily disable system as follows:**
   a. Place ignition switch in off position.
   b. Disconnect battery ground cable and tape cable end.
   c. Remove SIR fuse from fuse panel.
   d. Remove lower left hand trim panel, then disconnect connector position assurance and yellow two way SIR connector at base of steering column.
2. Remove steering wheel as described under "Horn Sounder and Steering Wheel, Replace."
3. Place ignition switch in Lock position to retain coil assembly in the centered position.
4. Disconnect battery ground cable.
5. Remove coil assembly retaining ring, **Fig. 10.**
6. Lift coil assembly from from steering shaft and allow to hang from wire.
7. Using a suitable tool, compress lock plate and remove snap ring (C-ring on tilt models), **Fig. 8.**

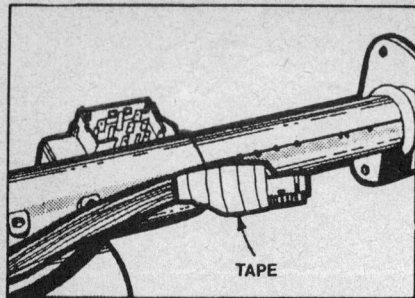

Fig. 9 Turn signal switch removal. Models less supplemental inflatable restraint system

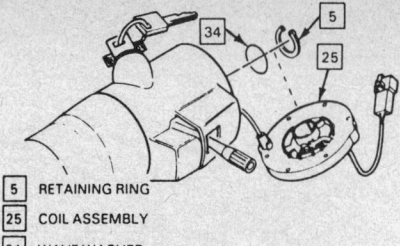

5	RETAINING RING
25	COIL ASSEMBLY
34	WAVE WASHER

Fig. 10 Coil assembly removal. Models with supplemental inflatable restraint system

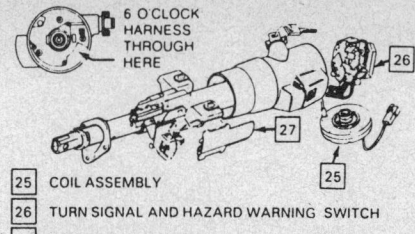

25	COIL ASSEMBLY
26	TURN SIGNAL AND HAZARD WARNING SWITCH
27	WIRING PROTECTOR

Fig. 11 Turn signal switch removal. Models with supplemental inflatable restraint system

8. Remove lock plate, turn signal canceling cam and upper bearing spring, inner race seat and inner race.
9. Place turn signal lever in right hand turn position, then remove multi-function lever and hazard warning flasher knob.
10. Remove turn signal switch lever attaching screw, then remove lever.
11. Remove turn signal switch attaching screws.
12. Disconnect turn signal switch electrical connector at lower portion of steering column.
13. Remove turn signal switch wiring protector cover from steering column, **Fig. 11.**
14. Carefully pull turn signal switch wiring up and out of steering column, Fig. 11.
15. Reverse procedure to install.
16. **After completing service procedure activate Supplemental Inflatable Restraint (SIR) system as follows:**
    a. Ensure ignition switch is in Off position.
    b. Connect yellow SIR two way electrical connector and connector position assurance at base of steering column.
    c. Install lower left hand trim panel.
    d. Install SIR fuse into fuse panel.
    e. Connect battery ground cable.
    f. Place ignition switch in Run position and note operation of "Inflatable Restraint" warning lamp. Warning lamp should flash 7 to 9 times and then turn off. If not, refer to "Passive Restraint" section for diagnostic system check.

COLUMN-MOUNTED DIMMER SWITCH
REPLACE

1. **To avoid personal injury when servicing models equipped with Supplemental Inflatable Restraint (Airbag) System, temporarily disable system as follows:**
    a. Place ignition switch in off position.
    b. Disconnect battery ground cable and tape cable end.
    c. Remove SIR fuse from fuse panel.
    d. Remove lower left hand trim panel, then disconnect connector position assurance and yellow two way SIR connector at base of steering column.

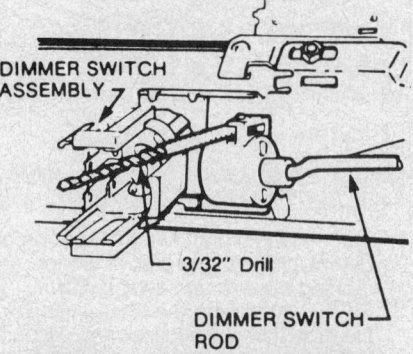

Fig. 12 Column mounted dimmer switch installation

2. Disconnect battery ground cable.
3. Remove instrument panel lower trim and on models with A/C, remove A/C duct extension at column.
4. Remove toe-plate cover screws.
5. Remove two nuts from instrument panel support bracket studs and lower steering column, resting steering wheel on front seat.
6. Remove dimmer switch retaining screw(s) and the switch. Tape actuator rod to column and separate switch from rod.
7. Reverse procedure to install. To adjust switch, depress dimmer switch slightly and install a 3/32 inch twist drill to lock the switch to the body, **Fig. 12.** Force switch upward to remove lash. Torque retaining screws to 35 inch lbs. and remove tape from actuator rod. Remove twist drill and check for proper operation.
8. **After completing service procedure activate Supplemental Inflatable Restraint (SIR) system as follows:**
    a. Ensure ignition switch is in Off position.
    b. Connect yellow SIR two way electrical connector and connector position assurance at base of steering column.
    c. Install lower left hand trim panel.
    d. Install SIR fuse into fuse panel.
    e. Connect battery ground cable.
    f. Place ignition switch in Run position and note operation of "Inflatable Restraint" warning lamp. Warning lamp should flash 7 to 9 times and then turn off. If not, refer to "Passive Restraint" section for diagnostic system check.

HORN SOUNDER & STEERING WHEEL
REPLACE

MODELS LESS SUPPLEMENTAL INFLATABLE RESTRAINT SYSTEM

1. Disconnect battery ground cable.
2. Remove steering wheel shroud screws on underside of steering wheel.
3. Remove steering wheel shroud and horn contact lead assembly from the steering wheel.
4. Remove snap ring and steering wheel nut.
5. Using steering wheel puller, remove steering wheel. Note position of steering wheel to shaft.
6. Reverse procedure to install.

MODELS WITH SUPPLEMENTAL INFLATABLE RESTRAINT SYSTEM
Removal

1. Place ignition switch in off position.
2. Disconnect battery ground cable and tape cable end.
3. Remove SIR fuse from fuse panel.
4. Remove lower left hand trim panel, then disconnect connector position assurance and yellow two way SIR connector at base of steering column.
5. Remove inflator module attaching screws from rear of steering wheel.
6. Lift inflator module from steering wheel, then disconnect electrical connectors from inflator module.
7. Remove steering wheel retaining nut.
8. Using puller J-1859-03 or equivalent, pull steering wheel from steering shaft.
9. Disconnect horn electrical connect and remove steering wheel.

Installation

1. Connect horn electrical connector.
2. Position steering wheel spline alignment marks to alignment marks of steering shaft splines, then install

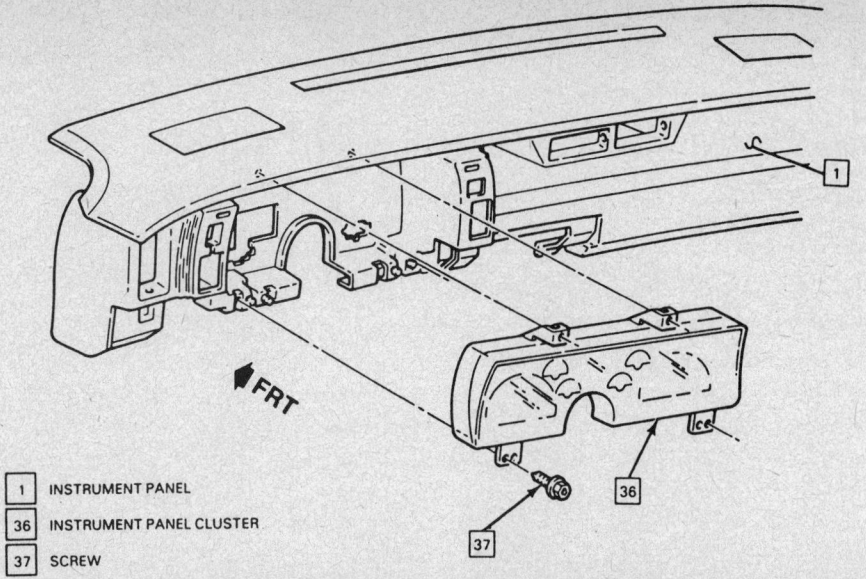

1 INSTRUMENT PANEL
36 INSTRUMENT PANEL CLUSTER
37 SCREW

Fig. 13   Instrument cluster. Camaro

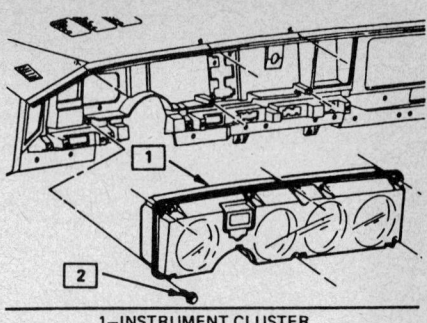

1—INSTRUMENT CLUSTER

2—SCREW

Fig. 14   Instrument cluster. Firebird

steering wheel.
3. Install steering wheel retaining nut and torque to 30 ft. lbs.
4. Connect SIR coil electrical connector to inflator module, then install connector position assurance.
5. Position inflator module to steering wheel, then install new mounting screws. **Torque** mounting screws to 25 inch lbs.
6. Ensure ignition switch is in Off position.
7. Connect yellow SIR two way electrical connector and connector position assurance at base of steering column.
8. Install lower left hand trim panel.
9. Install SIR fuse into fuse panel.
10. Connect battery ground cable.
11. Place ignition switch in Run position and note operation of "Inflatable Restraint" warning lamp. Warning lamp should flash 7 to 9 times and then turn off. If not, refer to "Passive Restraint" section for diagnostic system check.

INSTRUMENT CLUSTER
REPLACE

To avoid personal injury when servicing models equipped with Supplemental Inflatable Restraint (Airbag) System, temporarily disable system as follows:
1. Place ignition switch in off position.
2. Disconnect battery ground cable and tape cable end.
3. Remove SIR fuse from fuse panel.
4. Remove lower left hand trim panel, then disconnect connector position assurance and yellow two way SIR connector at base of steering column.

After completing service procedure activate Supplemental Inflatable Restraint (SIR) system as follows:
1. Ensure ignition switch is in Off position.
2. Connect yellow SIR two way electrical connector and connector position assurance at base of steer-

ing column.
3. Install lower left hand trim panel.
4. Install SIR fuse into fuse panel.
5. Connect battery ground cable.
6. Place ignition switch in Run position and note operation of "Inflatable Restraint" warning lamp. Warning lamp should flash 7 to 9 times and then turn off. If not, refer to "Passive Restraint" section for diagnostic system check.

CAMARO

1. Disconnect battery ground cable.
2. Remove instrument cluster trim panel.
3. Remove cluster retaining screws, then pull cluster back and disconnect speedometer cable and electrical connectors, **Fig. 13.**
4. Reverse procedure to install.

FIREBIRD

1. Disconnect battery ground cable, then remove right and left lower trim plates.
2. Remove instrument cluster trim plate.
3. Remove six cluster attachment screws, pull cluster back and disconnect speedometer cable, **Fig. 14.**
4. Disconnect necessary electrical connections.
5. Remove trip odometer reset knob, if equipped, then cluster lens.
6. Reverse procedure to install.

WIPER MOTOR
REPLACE

FRONT

1. Raise hood, then remove wiper arms and cowl cover.
2. Disconnect wiring and washer hoses.
3. Reaching through cowl opening, loosen transmission drive link attaching nuts to motor crankarm.
4. Disconnect drive link from motor crankarm.
5. Remove motor attaching screws.

6. Remove motor while guiding crankarm through hole.
7. Reverse procedure to install.

REAR

1. Remove wiper arm using tool No. J-8966 or equivalent.
2. Remove nut and spacer from wiper motor shaft, then raise lid and remove lift window trim panel.
3. Disconnect wire connectors from motor, then remove rivets securing motor support to trim panel and remove assembly from vehicle.
4. Remove motor attaching screws and motor.
5. Reverse procedure to install.

WIPER TRANSMISSION
REPLACE

FRONT

1. Ensure motor is in park position.
2. Raise hood and remove wiper arm assemblies.
3. Remove cowl vent screen.
4. Loosen nuts securing pivot at motor crankarm, then disconnect transmission rod from crankarm.
5. Remove retaining nuts or screws securing transmission to body, then withdraw transmission assembly through cowl opening.
6. Reverse procedure to install.

REAR

1. Remove three mounting grommets from transmission housing cover and cover.
2. Remove drive link retainer, then disengage drive link from cam drive pin and position so that cam retainer is accessible. **When reassembling drive link to cam, a new retainer must be used.**
3. Remove cam retainer and washer, then cam from shaft. **During assembly, if cam does not seat fully when pushed onto drive shaft, rotate cam 180 degrees.**
4. Drill out three rivets attaching housing to wiper gearbox, and remove transmission.

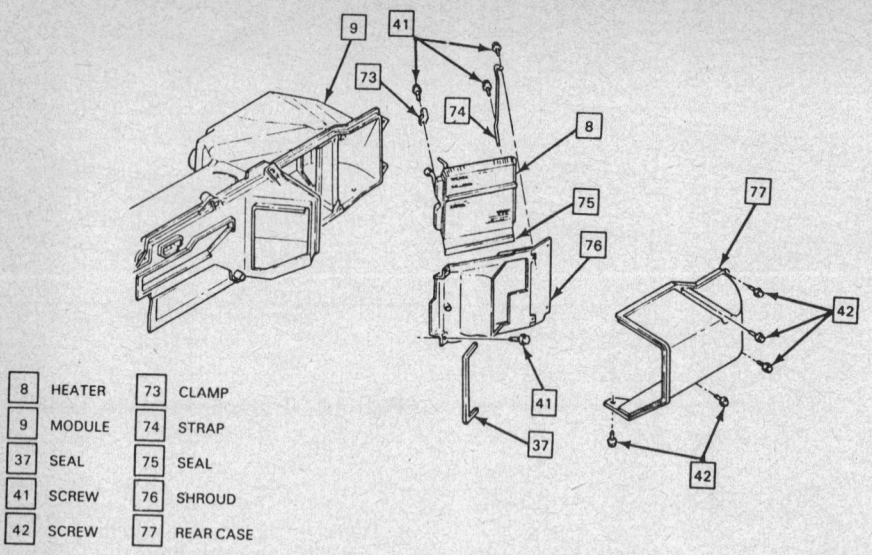

8	HEATER	73	CLAMP	
9	MODULE	74	STRAP	
37	SEAL	75	SEAL	
41	SCREW	76	SHROUD	
42	SCREW	77	REAR CASE	

Fig. 15 Heater core replace

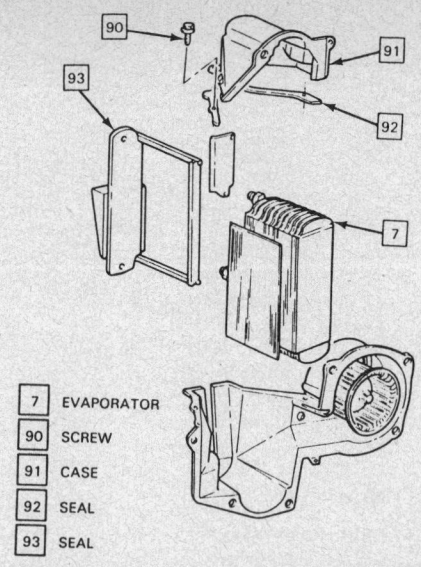

7	EVAPORATOR
90	SCREW
91	CASE
92	SEAL
93	SEAL

Fig. 16 Evaporator core replace

5. Reverse procedure to install. **A service kit is available for installation of the transmission. The kit includes screw, nuts and washers to replace the rivets.**

WINDSHIELD WIPER SWITCH
REPLACE

1. **To avoid personal injury when servicing models equipped with Supplemental Inflatable Restraint (Airbag) System, temporarily disable system as follows:**
   a. Place ignition switch in off position.
   b. Disconnect battery ground cable and tape cable end.
   c. Remove SIR fuse from fuse panel.
   d. Remove lower left hand trim panel, then disconnect connector position assurance and yellow two way SIR connector at base of steering column.
2. Disconnect battery ground cable and remove turn signal switch as outlined.
3. Remove ignition lock, ignition switch and dimmer switch as outlined.
4. Remove ignition lock housing retaining screws and housing.
5. Remove pivot bolt and wiper switch from lock housing.
6. Reverse procedure to install.
7. **After completing service procedure activate Supplemental Inflatable Restraint (SIR) system as follows:**
   a. Ensure ignition switch is in Off position.
   b. Connect yellow SIR two way electrical connector and connector position assurance at base of steering column.
   c. Install lower left hand trim panel.
   d. Install SIR fuse into fuse panel.
   e. Connect battery ground cable.
   f. Place ignition switch in Run position and note operation of "Inflatable Restraint" warning lamp.

Warning lamp should flash 7 to 9 times and then turn off. If not, refer to "Passive Restraint" section for diagnostic system check.

RADIO
REPLACE

1. **To avoid personal injury when servicing models equipped with Supplemental Inflatable Restraint (Airbag) System, temporarily disable system as follows:**
   a. Place ignition switch in off position.
   b. Disconnect battery ground cable and tape cable end.
   c. Remove SIR fuse from fuse panel.
   d. Remove lower left hand trim panel, then disconnect connector position assurance and yellow two way SIR connector at base of steering column.

When installing radio, be sure to adjust antenna trimmer for peak reception. Also, be sure to connect speaker before applying power to radio.
2. Disconnect battery ground cable.
3. Remove three console bezel and four radio to console attaching screws.
4. Pull radio outward and disconnect electrical connector, then remove radio.
5. Reverse procedure to install.
6. **After completing service procedure activate Supplemental Inflatable Restraint (SIR) system as follows:**
   a. Ensure ignition switch is in Off position.
   b. Connect yellow SIR two way electrical connector and connector position assurance at base of steering column.
   c. Install lower left hand trim panel.
   d. Install SIR fuse into fuse panel.
   e. Connect battery ground cable.
   f. Place ignition switch in Run position and note operation of "Inflatable Restraint" warning lamp. Warning lamp should flash 7 to 9

times and then turn off. If not, refer to "Passive Restraint" section for diagnostic system check.

BLOWER MOTOR
REPLACE

1. Disconnect battery ground cable.
2. Disconnect blower motor and resistor wires.
3. Disconnect cooling tube, if equipped.
4. Remove blower motor retaining screws and motor/cage assembly from case.
5. While holding blower motor cage, remove cage retaining screw and slide cage from motor shaft.
6. Reverse procedure to install.

HEATER CORE
REPLACE

To avoid personal injury when servicing models equipped with Supplemental Inflatable Restraint (Airbag) System, temporarily disable system as follows:
   a. Place ignition switch in off position.
   b. Disconnect battery ground cable and tape cable end.
   c. Remove SIR fuse from fuse panel.
   d. Remove lower left hand trim panel, then disconnect connector position assurance and yellow two way SIR connector at base of steering column.

After completing service procedure activate Supplemental Inflatable Restraint (SIR) system as follows:
   a. Ensure ignition switch is in Off position.
   b. Connect yellow SIR two way electrical connector and connector position assurance at base of steering column.
   c. Install lower left hand trim panel.
   d. Install SIR fuse into fuse panel.
   e. Connect battery ground cable.

f. Place ignition switch in Run position and note operation of "Inflatable Restraint" warning lamp. Warning lamp should flash 7 to 9 times and then turn off. If not, refer to "Passive Restraint" section for diagnostic system check.

1988

1. Disconnect battery ground cable and drain cooling system.
2. Remove right lower hush panel and instrument panel trim panel.
3. Remove ESC module, if equipped.
4. Remove lower right instrument panel carrier to cowl screw.
5. Remove heater case cover attaching screws and cover. To gain access to the upper left screw, position a long 3/8 inch socket extension through the opening exposed by removal of the trim panel. Carefully lift lower right corner of instrument panel to align socket extension.
6. Remove support plate and baffle screws, then heater core, support plate and baffle from case.

1989–91

1. Disconnect battery ground cable and drain cooling system.
2. Remove instrument panel and center console.
3. Remove heater case, Fig. 15.
4. Remove heater core shroud screws, then separate heater case assembly.
5. Remove core mounting strap, then the core.
6. Reverse procedure to install.

EVAPORATOR CORE
REPLACE

1. To avoid personal injury when servicing models equipped with Supplemental Inflatable Restraint (Airbag) System, temporarily disable system as follows:
   a. Place ignition switch in off position.
   b. Disconnect battery ground cable and tape cable end.
   c. Remove SIR fuse from fuse panel.
   d. Remove lower left hand trim panel, then disconnect connector position assurance and yellow two way SIR connector at base of steering column.
2. On all models, disconnect battery ground cable, if not previously performed.
3. Discharge A/C refrigerant system, then remove pressure cycling switch and accumulator.
4. Remove blower motor resistor assembly.
5. Remove blower motor relay and bracket.
6. Remove upper evaporator case attaching screws, then remove upper evaporator case and seal, Fig. 16.
7. Disconnect refrigerant line from lower fitting of evaporator. Cap refrigerant line and evaporator fitting.
8. Remove evaporator and seal.
9. Reverse procedure to install.
10. After completing service procedure activate Supplemental Inflatable Restraint (SIR) system as follows:
    a. Ensure ignition switch is in Off position.
    b. Connect yellow SIR two way electrical connector and connector position assurance at base of steering column.
    c. Install lower left hand trim panel.
    d. Install SIR fuse into fuse panel.
    e. Connect battery ground cable.
    f. Place ignition switch in Run position and note operation of "Inflatable Restraint" warning lamp. Warning lamp should flash 7 to 9 times and then turn off. If not, refer to "Passive Restraint" section for diagnostic system check.

2.8L/V6-173, 3.1L/V6-191, 5.0L/V8-305 & 5.7L/V8-356 Engines

INDEX

ENGINE MOUNTS
REPLACE

2.8L/V6-173 & 3.1L/V6-191

1. Disconnect battery ground cable.
2. Remove upper half of fan shroud, if necessary.
3. Raise and support vehicle.
4. Remove engine mount through bolt, then raise front of engine to release weight from mount.
5. Remove mount to engine bolts and mount, Fig. 1. Raise engine only enough to provide sufficient clearance for mount removal. Check for interference between rear of engine and cowl panel which could result in distributor damage.
6. Reverse procedure to install.

5.0L/V8-305 & 5.7L/V8-350

1. Remove mount retaining bolt from below frame mounting bracket, Fig. 2.
2. Raise front of engine and remove mount to engine bolts and mount.
3. Reverse procedure to install.

ENGINE
REPLACE

1. Disconnect battery ground cable and

remove air cleaner and fresh air hoses.

2. Disconnect electrical connectors from hood lamp or air door, if equipped, mark position of hood hinges for reassembly, and remove hood.

3. Drain cooling system, remove radiator hoses, and disconnect heater hoses from engine.

4. If equipped with A/C, disconnect electrical connector from compressor clutch and ground wire from bracket, remove compressor and secure aside.

5. Disconnect and plug transmission cooler lines at radiator, if equipped, then remove fan blade, shroud and radiator. On 4-151 engines with manual transmission, only fan blade and upper shroud should be removed.

6. **On V6 and V8 engines,** remove power steering pump retaining bolts and secure pump aside.

7. Disconnect accelerator and cruise control linkage at throttle and brackets, then the vacuum hoses from all body mounted accessories, and secure cables and hoses.

8. Disconnect and plug fuel supply and return hoses. On models with port fuel injection, relieve fuel system pressure before disconnecting hoses. Connect pressure gauge J-34370-1 or equivalent to pressure tap on fuel rail, position bleed hose in suitable container and slowly relieve fuel system pressure. **Failure to relieve system pressure prior to disconnecting fuel system components may cause fire or personal injury.**

9. Remove distributor cap and lay wiring aside.

10. Disconnect electrical connectors to alternator, distributor and all other engine mounted switches and accessories.

11. Release engine harness from retaining clips and secure harness aside.

12. Disconnect battery and chassis ground straps from engine, then raise and support vehicle.

13. Disconnect exhaust pipes from manifolds.

14. Disconnect electrical connectors and battery cable from starter and remove wiring shields.

15. Remove flywheel shield and bolts securing converter to flex plate, if equipped. Mark position of converter in relation to flex plate for reassembly.

16. **On models with manual transmission,** remove clutch linkage.

17. **On all models,** remove motor mount through bolts and bolts securing bellhousing to engine.

18. Lower vehicle and support transmission with suitable floor jack.

19. Attach suitable lifting equipment to engine lifting brackets, remove bracket securing AIR injection pipe, then raise engine and transmission assembly.

20. Separate engine and transmission, and lift engine from vehicle after removing bracket from rear of left cylinder head. On automatic transmission models, ensure converter remains

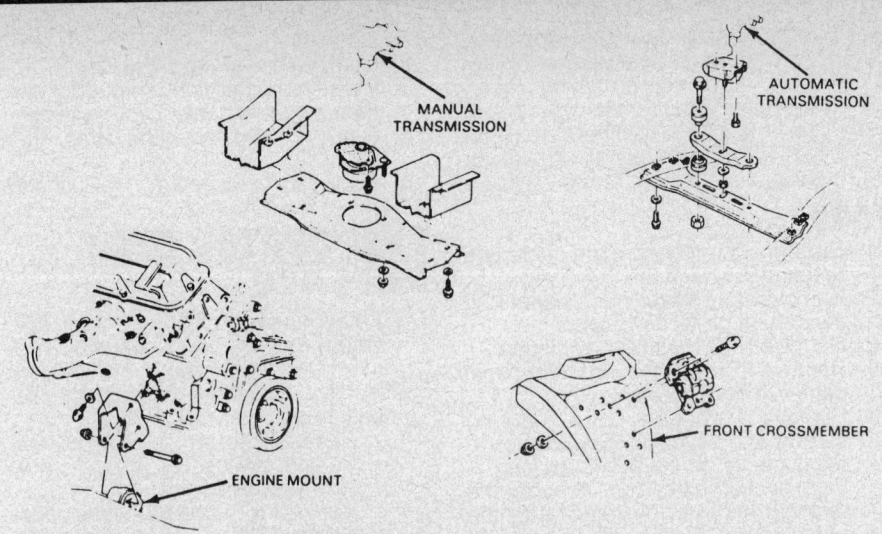

Fig. 1   Engine mounting. 2.8L/V6-173 & 3.1L/V6-191

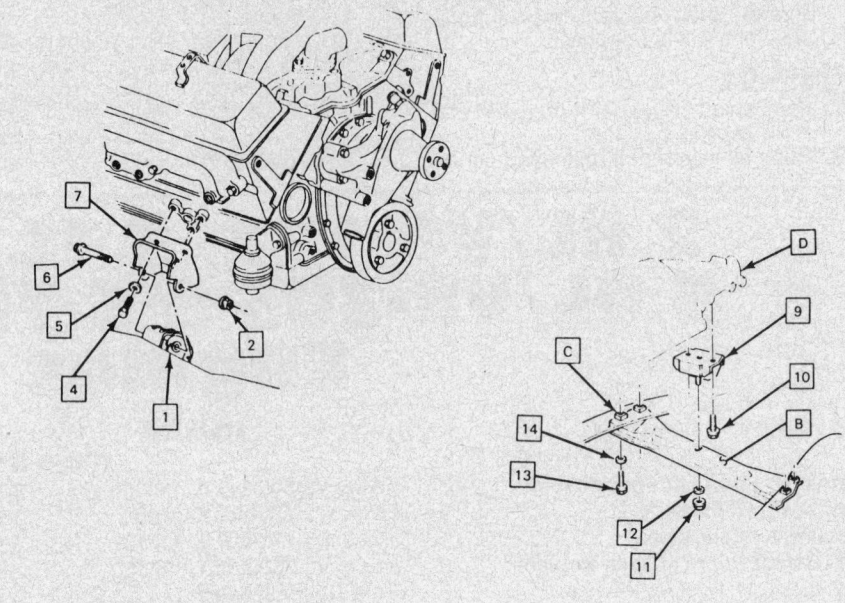

A	FRONT CROSSMEMBER
B	REAR CROSSMEMBER
C	WELD NUT
D	TRANSMISSION ASSEMBLY
1	MOUNT
2	NUT
4	BOLT
5	WASHER
6	THROUGH-BOLT
7	BRACKET
8	NUT
9	REAR MOUNT
10	BOLT
11	NUT
12	WASHER
13	BOLT
14	WASHER

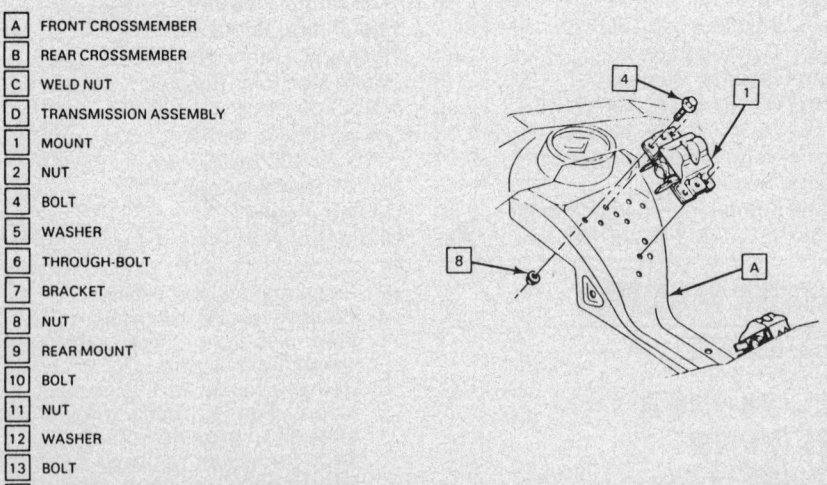

Fig. 2   Engine mounting. 5.0L/V8-305 & 5.7L/V8-350

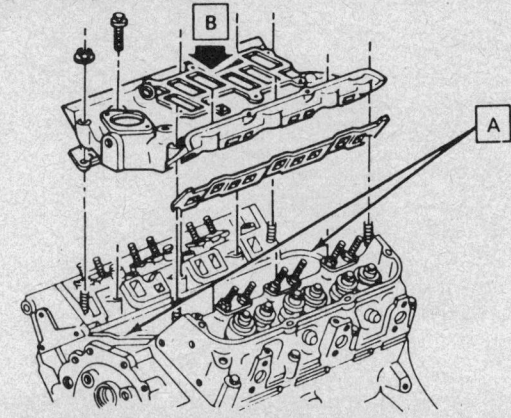

A APPLY A SMOOTH CONTINUOUS BEAD APPROX 2.0-3.0 MM (0.08-0.12-INCH) WIDE AND 3.0-5.0 MM (0.12-INCH·0.2-INCH) THICK ON BOTH SURFACES. BEAD CONFIGURATION MUST INSURE COMPLETE SEALING OF WATER AND OIL. SURFACE MUST BE FREE OF OIL AND DIRT TO INSURE ADEQUATE SEAL.

TORQUE INTAKE MANIFOLD BOLTS TO 26 N·m (19 FT. LBS.)

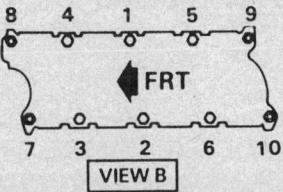

Fig. 3 Intake manifold replace & bolt tightening sequence. 2.8L/V6-173 & 3.1L/V6-191

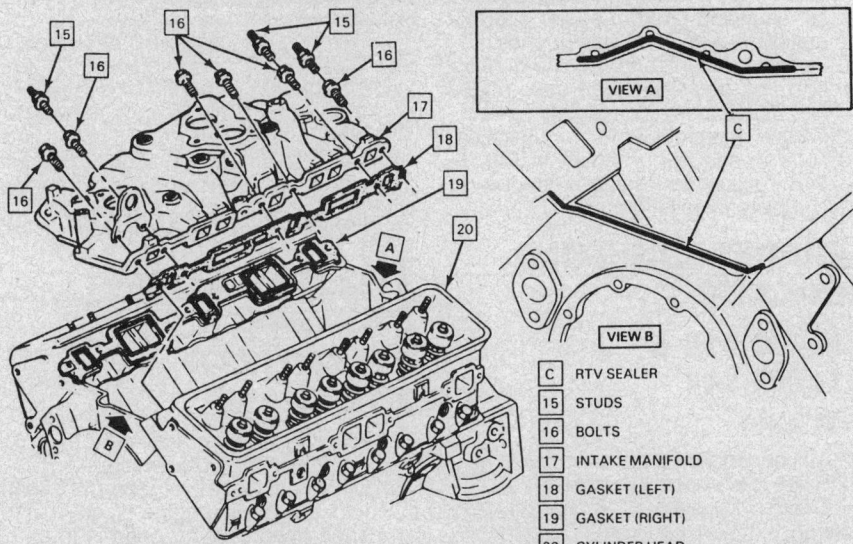

C	RTV SEALER
15	STUDS
16	BOLTS
17	INTAKE MANIFOLD
18	GASKET (LEFT)
19	GASKET (RIGHT)
20	CYLINDER HEAD

Fig. 4 Intake manifold replace. 5.0L/V8-305 & 5.7L/V8-350

INTAKE MANIFOLD
REPLACE

2.8L/V6-173 & 3.1L/V6-191

1. Disconnect battery ground cable, re-

with transmission during engine removal, and that it is properly seated prior to engine installation.
21. Reverse procedure to install.

move air cleaner and drain cooling system.
2. Connect pressure gauge J-34730-1 or equivalent to fuel rail pressure valve, position bleed hose in suitable container and relieve fuel system pressure. **Failure to relieve fuel pressure prior to disconnecting fuel system connections may cause fire or personal injury.**
3. Disconnect air inlet duct, electrical connectors, coolant hoses and vacuum hoses from throttle body, noting

position for installation.
4. Disconnect accelerator, cruise control and transmission cables, as equipped.
5. Remove throttle body retaining bolts and the throttle body.
6. Remove EGR pipe retaining bolts and throttle cable bracket.
7. Remove bolts securing plenum to manifold and the plenum, **Fig. 3.**
8. Disconnect fuel lines from fuel rail and remove cold start valve.
9. Disconnect vacuum hose from pressure regulator and remove fuel rail retaining bolts.
10. Disconnect injector harness connectors and remove fuel rail assembly, **Fig. 3.**
11. Disconnect high tension leads from spark plugs and disconnect wiring from coil.
12. Remove distributor cap and plug wire assembly.
13. Rotate crankshaft until No. 1 cylinder is at TDC on compression stroke, mark position of distributor rotor and remove distributor.
14. Remove air injection hose, if equipped, disconnect canister hoses and remove pipe bracket from front of left valve cover.
15. Remove left valve cover and air management bracket, then remove right valve cover.
16. Disconnect upper radiator and heater hoses from manifold.
17. Disconnect coolant switches and remove manifold retaining bolts.
18. Remove manifold and thoroughly clean old gasket and sealer from mating surfaces.
19. Ensure surfaces are clean and dry, then apply 3/16 bead of RTV sealer on each block ridge, install gaskets and secure gasket position by extending bead of sealer approximately 1/4 inch onto gasket ends. **New gaskets must be cut to fit behind push rods. When installing gaskets, note left and right side markings.**
20. Install manifold and retaining bolts, ensuring areas between case ridges and manifold are completely sealed.
21. Torque manifold bolts to specifications in sequence shown in **Fig. 3,** then reverse remaining procedure to complete installation.

5.0L/V8-305 W/TBI

1. Disconnect battery ground cable, drain cooling system and remove air cleaner.
2. Disconnect accelerator, transmission and cruise control linkages, as equipped.
3. Disconnect fuel line from TBI unit and remove fuel line clips as needed.
4. Disconnect necessary vacuum hoses and electrical connectors, noting position for installation.
5. Disconnect upper radiator and heater hoses from manifold.
6. Disconnect high tension leads from spark plugs in right side of engine and remove distributor cap, rotate crankshaft until No. 1 cylinder is at TDC on compression stroke, mark position of

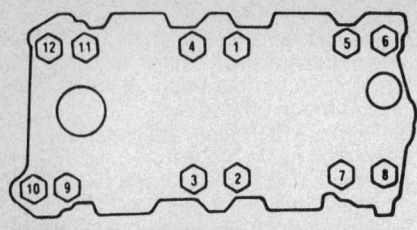

Fig. 5   Intake manifold bolt tightening sequence. 5.0L/V8-305 & 5.7L/V8-350

distributor rotor, then remove distributor.

7. Remove ignition coil, AIR pump, cruise control servo and brackets, as needed.
8. Remove alternator upper mounting bracket and EGR solenoids.
9. Remove manifold retaining bolts and the manifold, **Fig. 4.**
10. Ensure surfaces are clean and dry, then apply ³/₁₆ bead of RTV sealer on each block ridge and apply suitable sealer around water outlets, install gaskets and secure gasket position by extending bead of sealer approximately ½ inch onto gasket ends.
11. Install manifold and retaining bolts, ensuring areas between case ridges and manifold are completely sealed.
12. Torque manifold bolts to specifications in sequence shown in **Fig. 5,** then reverse remaining procedure to complete installation.

5.0L/V8-305 W/TPI & 5.7L/V8-350

1. Disconnect battery ground cable, drain cooling system and remove air intake duct.
2. Disconnect accelerator, cruise control and transmission cables, as equipped.
3. Disconnect coolant hoses, electrical connectors, and the vacuum and breather hoses from throttle body, noting position for installation.
4. Remove throttle body from plenum, then remove distributor shield.
5. Disconnect brake booster and vacuum hoses from plenum, noting position for installation.
6. On engines with port fuel injection, connect pressure gauge J-34370-1 or equivalent to pressure tap on fuel rail, position bleed hose in suitable container and slowly relieve fuel system pressure. **Failure to relieve system pressure prior to disconnecting fuel system components may cause fire or personal injury.**
7. Disconnect canister control valve pipe, remove right side runners and plenum bolt, then remove plenum.
8. Disconnect fuel line to cold start valve and remove valve.
9. Disconnect fuel lines from fuel rail and electrical connectors from injectors.
10. Loosen fuel rail retaining bolts and raise rail assembly.
11. Remove remaining manifold runners and the fuel rail assembly.
12. Rotate crankshaft until No. 1 cylinder

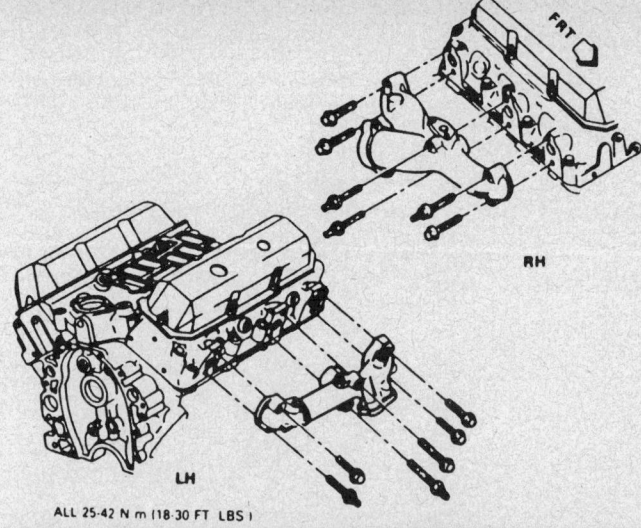

Fig. 6   Exhaust manifold replace. 2.8L/V6-173 & 3.1L/V6-191

is at TDC on compression stroke, remove distributor cap and mark position of distributor rotor, then remove distributor.

13. Disconnect EGR solenoid and all necessary electrical connectors, then remove manifold retaining bolts and the manifold, **Fig. 4.**
14. Ensure surfaces are clean and dry, then apply ³/₁₆ bead of RTV sealer on each block ridge and apply suitable sealer around water outlets, install gaskets and secure gasket position by extending bead of sealer approximately ½ inch onto gasket ends.
15. Install manifold and retaining bolts, ensuring areas between case ridges and manifold are completely sealed.
16. Torque manifold bolts to specifications in sequence shown in **Fig. 5,** then reverse remaining procedure to complete installation.

EXHAUST MANIFOLD REPLACE

2.8L/V6-173 & 3.1L/V6-191

Left Side

1. Disconnect battery ground cable.
2. Raise and support vehicle.
3. Disconnect exhaust crossover pipe from exhaust manifold, then lower vehicle.
4. Remove power steering pump rear bracket.
5. Remove exhaust manifold attaching bolts and nut, then remove exhaust manifold and gasket, **Fig. 6.**
6. Reverse procedure to install.

Right Side

1. Disconnect battery ground cable.
2. Raise and support vehicle.
3. Disconnect exhaust crossover pipe from exhaust manifold, then lower vehicle.
4. Remove EGR adapter from manifold.
5. Remove alternator rear bracket.

6. Remove EGR transfer tube.
7. Disconnect AIR pipe from exhaust manifold.
8. Remove exhaust manifold attaching bolts, then remove exhaust manifold and gasket, **Fig. 6.**
9. Reverse procedure to install.

5.0L/V8-305 & 5.7L/V8-350

1. Disconnect battery ground cable.
2. If necessary, disconnect spark plug wires from spark plugs.
3. Remove AIR pipes and AIR valve.
4. Raise and support vehicle.
5. Disconnect exhaust crossover pipe from exhaust manifold, then lower vehicle.
6. Remove exhaust manifold attaching bolts, then remove exhaust manifold and gasket, **Fig. 7.**
7. Reverse procedure to install.

CYLINDER HEAD REPLACE

2.8L/V6-173 & 3.1L/V6-191

1. Remove intake manifold.
2. Raise and support vehicle.
3. Disconnect exhaust pipe from manifold, then drain engine block.
4. If left hand cylinder head is to be removed, remove dipstick tube attachment.
5. Lower vehicle, then remove serpentine belt, as required.
6. Loosen rocker arms until push rods can be removed.
7. If right hand cylinder head is to be removed, remove alternator bracket and AIR bracket. If left hand cylinder head is to be removed, remove A/C compressor and power steering pump brackets.
8. Remove cylinder head bolts and cylinder head, **Fig. 8.**
9. Reverse procedure to install. Coat cylinder head bolts with sealer. Torque

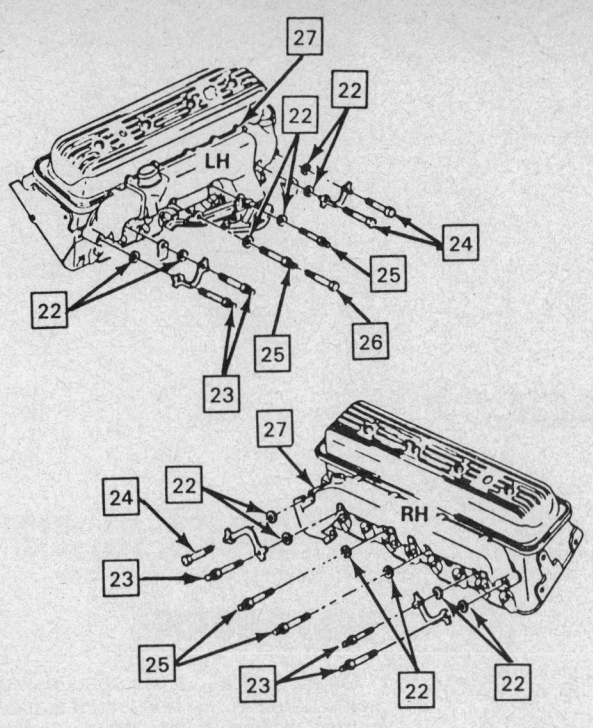

22 WASHER
23 STUD
24 BOLT
25 STUD
26 BOLT (L03 ENGINE)
27 EXHAUST MANIFOLD

Fig. 7 Exhaust manifold replace. 5.0L/V8-305 & 5.7L/V8-350

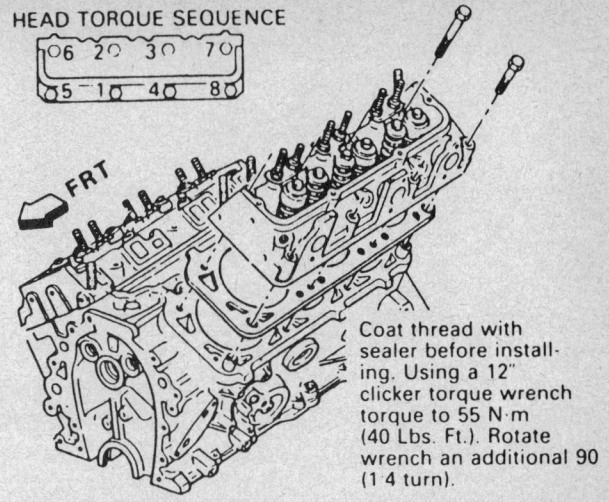

HEAD TORQUE SEQUENCE

Coat thread with sealer before installing. Using a 12" clicker torque wrench torque to 55 N·m (40 Lbs. Ft.). Rotate wrench an additional 90 (1 4 turn).

Fig. 8 Cylinder head replace & bolt tightening sequence. 2.8L/V6-173 & 3.1L/V6-191

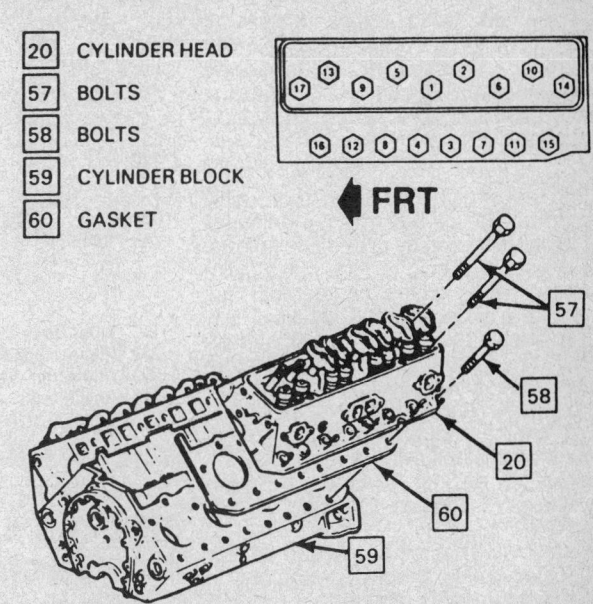

20 CYLINDER HEAD
57 BOLTS
58 BOLTS
59 CYLINDER BLOCK
60 GASKET

Fig. 9 Cylinder head replace & bolt tightening sequence. 5.0L/V8-305 & 5.7L/V8-350

cylinder bolts in sequence shown in **Fig. 8.**

5.0L/V8-305 & 5.7L/V8-350

1. Disconnect battery ground cable, then drain cooling system and engine block.
2. Remove intake manifold and exhaust manifolds.
3. Remove alternator lower mounting bolt and position alternator aside.
4. Remove dipstick tube and bracket.
5. If equipped with A/C, remove compressor and forward mounting bracket and position aside.
6. Remove power steering pump and bracket, position aside.
7. Remove rocker arm cover, rocker arms and push rods. **Keep rocker arm, rocker arm balls and push rods in order so they can be installed in the same position.**
8. Remove diverter valve, if equipped.
9. Remove cylinder head bolts and cylinder head, **Fig. 9.**
10. Reverse procedure to install. Apply suitable sealer to cylinder head bolts

and gradually torque bolts to specifications in sequence shown in **Fig. 9.**

VALVE LASH SPECIFICATIONS

Year	Engine/VIN	Valve Lash
1988–89	V6-173/S	1½ Turns ①
	V8-305/E & F	1 Turn ①
	V8-350/8	1 Turn ①
1990–91	V6-191/T	1½ Turns ①
	V8-305/E & F	1 Turn ①
	V8-350/8	1 Turn ①

①—Turn rocker arm stud nut until all lash is eliminated, then tighten nut the additional turn listed.

VALVE ARRANGEMENT
FRONT TO REAR
V6-173 & 191

Right . . . . E-I-E-I-E
Left . . . . E-I-I-E-I-E

V8-305 & 350

All . . . . E-I-I-E-E-I-I-E

CAMSHAFT LOBE LIFT SPECIFICATIONS

Engine/VIN	Int.	Exh.
V6-173/S	.2626	.2732
V6-191/T	.2626	.2732
V8-305/E	.2340	.2570
V8-305/F	.2690	.2760
V8-350/8	.2730	.2820

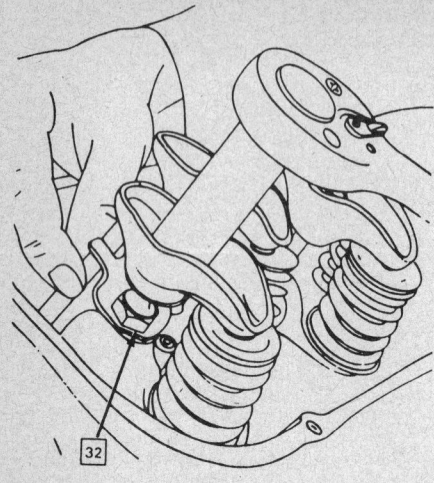

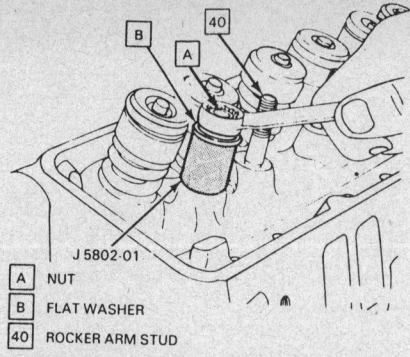

[A] NUT
[B] FLAT WASHER
[40] ROCKER ARM STUD

Fig. 11 Removing pressed-in type rocker arm stud

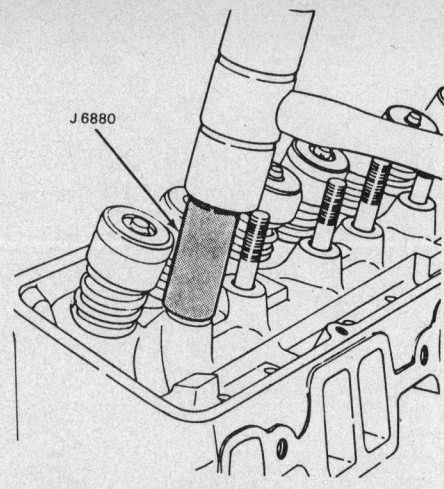

Fig. 12 Installing pressed-in type rocker arm stud

[32] ROCKER ARM NUT

Fig. 10 Adjusting valve lash

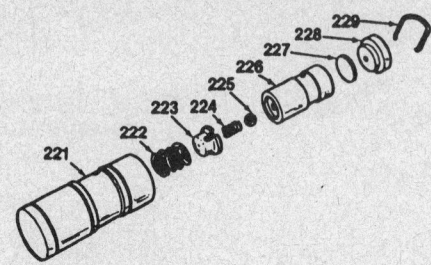

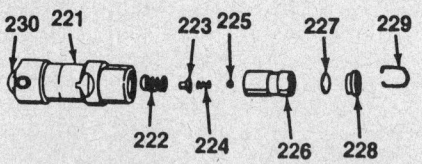

221. Lifter Body
222. Plunger Spring
223. Check Ball Retainer
224. Check Ball Spring
225. Check Ball
226. Plunger
227. Metering Valve
228. Pushrod Seat
229. Retainer
230. Roller

Fig. 13 Hydraulic valve lifters

VALVES
ADJUST

After the engine has been thoroughly warmed up the valves may be adjusted, **Fig. 10**, with the engine shut off as follows: With engine in position to fire No. 1 cylinder the following valves may be adjusted: V6 engines, exhaust 1-2-3, intake 1-5-6. V8 engines, exhaust 1-3-4-8, intake 1-2-5-7. Then crank the engine one more complete revolution which will bring No. 4 cylinder on V6 engines and No. 6 cylinder on V8 engines, to the firing position at which time the following valves may be adjusted: V6 engines, Exhaust 4-5-6, intake 2-3-4. V8 engines, Exhaust 2-5-6-7, intake 3-4-6-8.

The following procedure, performed with the engine running, should be done only in case readjustment is required.

1. After engine has been warmed up to operating temperature, remove valve cover and install a new valve cover gasket.
2. With engine running at idle speed, back off valve rocker arm nut until rocker arm starts to clatter.
3. Turn rocker arm nut down slowly until the clatter just stops. This is the zero lash position.
4. Turn nut down 1/4 additional turn and pause 10 seconds until engine runs smoothly. Repeat additional 1/4 turns, pausing 10 seconds each time, until nut has been turned down the number of turns listed in the Valve Lash Specifications Chart from the zero lash position. **This preload adjustment must be done slowly to allow the lifter to adjust itself to prevent the possibility of interference between the intake valve head and top of piston, which might result in internal damage and/or bent push rods. Noisy lifters should be replaced.**

ROCKER ARM STUDS
REPLACE

If studs are loose in cylinder head, .003 inch or .013 inch oversize studs may be installed on all engines with pressed-in type studs, after reaming holes with a proper size reamer. On engines with threaded rocker studs, looseness can be corrected by installing the proper size Heli-Coil insert, or by replacing cylinder head. Replace damaged pressed-in rocker arm studs using the following procedure:

1. Remove the old stud by placing a suitable spacer, **Fig. 11**, over stud. Install nut and flat washer and remove stud by turning nut.
2. Ream hole for oversize stud.
3. Coat press-fit area of stud with rear axle lube. Then install new stud, **Fig. 12**. If tool shown is used, it should bottom on the head.

PUSH RODS

On engines that use push rods with a hardened insert at one end, the hardened end is identified by a color stripe and should always be installed toward the rocker arm during assembly.

VALVE GUIDES

On all engines valves operate in guide holes bored in the head. If clearance becomes excessive, use the next oversize valve and ream the bore to fit. Valves with oversize stems are available in .003, .015 and .030 inch.

HYDRAULIC LIFTERS
REPLACE

Valve lifters can be lifted from their bores after removing rocker arms and push rods and intake manifold. Adjustable pliers with protected jaws may be used to remove lifters which are stuck due to carbon or varnish deposits. **Fig. 13** illustrate types of valve lifters used.

FRONT COVER
REPLACE

On all engines the cover oil seal may be replaced without taking off the timing gear cover. After removing the vibration damper, pry out the old seal with a screwdriver. Install the new seal with the lip or open end toward inside of cover and drive it into position.

2.8L/V6-173 & 3.1L/V6-191

1. Remove oil pan as described under "Oil Pan, Replace."
2. **On models with 3.1L/V6-191 engine,** remove power steering pump and bracket.
3. Remove water pump as described under Water Pump, Replace".
4. **On models with 2.8L/V6-173 engine,** if equipped with A/C, remove compressor and mounting bracket and position aside.
5. **On all models,** Remove vibration damper, then disconnect lower radiator hose from cover and heater hose from water pump.

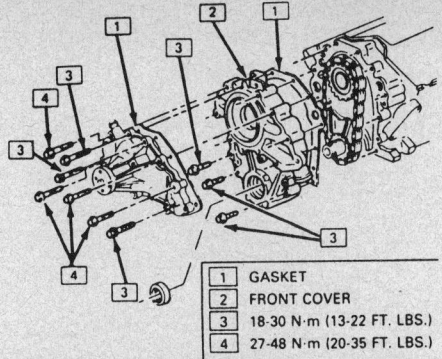

1	GASKET
2	FRONT COVER
3	18-30 N·m (13-22 FT. LBS.)
4	27-48 N·m (20-35 FT. LBS.)

Fig. 14 Front cover & water pump bolt tightening specifications. 1988 2.8L/V6-173

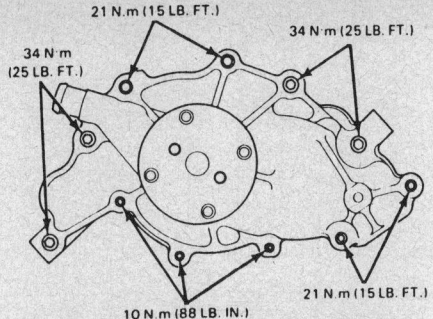

Fig. 15 Water pump bolt tightening specifications. 1989 2.8L/V6-173 & 1990–91 3.1L/V6-191

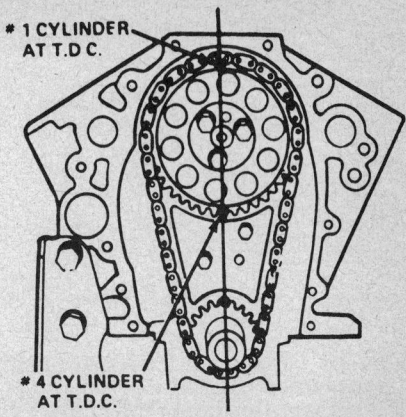

Fig. 16 Valve timing marks. 2.8L/V6-173 & 3.1L/V6-191

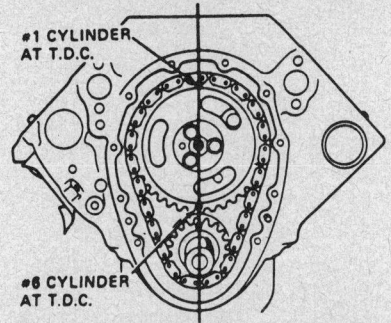

Fig. 17 Valve timing marks. 5.0L/V8-305 & 5.7L/V8-350

6. Remove cover retaining bolts and cover.
7. Thoroughly clean sealing surfaces of front cover and engine block, then apply a continuous thin bead of anerobic sealant 1052357 or equivalent to front cover sealing surface.
8. Install front cover and water pump on engine. On 1988 engines install retaining bolts and nut and torque to specifications shown in **Fig. 14.** On 1989-91 engines; install retaining bolts and nut and torque the three front cover attaching bolts to 15 ft. lbs. and water pump attaching bolts to specifications shown in **Fig. 15. Final torquing of bolts must be completed within five minutes of installing the cover.**
9. Reconnect hoses and install vibration damper.
10. Install A/C compressor and mounting bracket.
11. Service cooling system as required.

5.0L/V8-305 & 5.7L/V8-350

1. Disconnect battery ground cable and drain cooling system.
2. Remove vibration damper and water pump.
3. Remove oil pan and gasket as outlined.
4. Remove timing cover retaining screws and the timing cover.
5. Reverse procedure to install.

TIMING CHAIN
REPLACE

1. Remove timing chain cover as outlined previously.
2. Remove crankshaft oil slinger.
3. Crank engine until timing marks on sprockets are in alignment, **Figs. 16 and 17.**
4. Remove three camshaft-to-sprocket bolts.
5. Remove camshaft sprocket and timing chain together. Sprocket is a light press fit on camshaft for approximately 1/8 inch. If sprocket does not come off easily, a light blow with a plastic hammer on the lower edge of the sprocket should dislodge it.
6. If crankshaft sprocket is to be replaced, remove it with a suitable gear puller. Install new sprocket, aligning key and keyway.
7. Install chain on camshaft sprocket. Hold sprocket vertical with chain hanging below and shift around to align the timing marks on sprockets.
8. Align dowel in camshaft with dowel hole in sprocket and install sprocket on camshaft. Do not attempt to drive sprocket on camshaft as welch plug at rear of engine can be dislodged.
9. Draw sprocket onto camshaft, using the three mounting bolts. Tighten to specifications.
10. Lubricate timing chain and install cover.

CAMSHAFT
REPLACE

1. Remove valve lifters and engine front cover.
2. Remove grille, radiator and condenser.
3. Remove timing chain as outlined previously.
4. On models with 5.0L/V8-305 and 5.7L/V8-350 engines, install two 5/16-18x4 bolts in camshaft bolt holes, **Fig. 18.**
5. On all models, remove camshaft from engine using care not to damage camshaft bearings.
6. Reverse procedure to install.

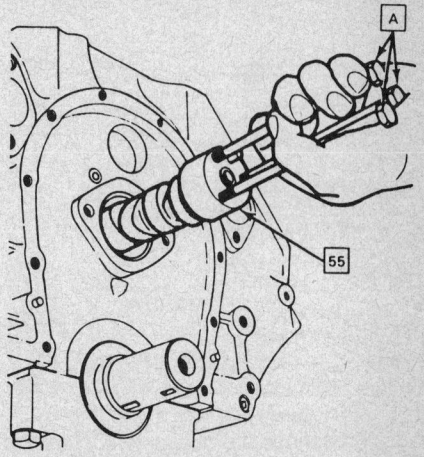

A	BOLTS
55	CAMSHAFT

Fig. 18 Removing camshaft. 5.0L/V8-305 & 5.7L/V8-350

PISTON & ROD ASSEMBLE

Assemble pistons to connecting rods as shown in **Figs. 19 and 20.**

Upon installation, measure the connecting rod side clearance using a suitable feeler gauge. Refer to "Engine Rebuilding Specifications" for connecting rod side clearance.

PISTONS, PINS & RINGS

Pistons are available in standard and oversizes of .010 and .030 inch.

Piston rings are available in standard and oversizes of .030 inch.

MAIN & ROD BEARINGS

Connecting rod bearings are available in standard and undersizes of .001, .002, .010 and .020 inch.

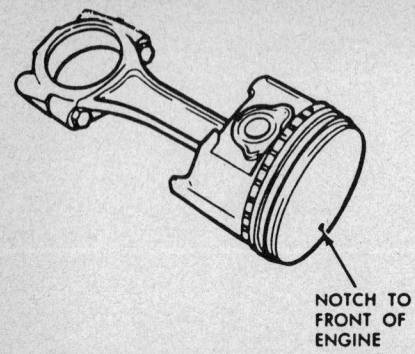

Fig. 19 Piston & rod assemble (numbers on rod & cap must be on same side). 2.8L/V6-173 & 3.1L/V6-191

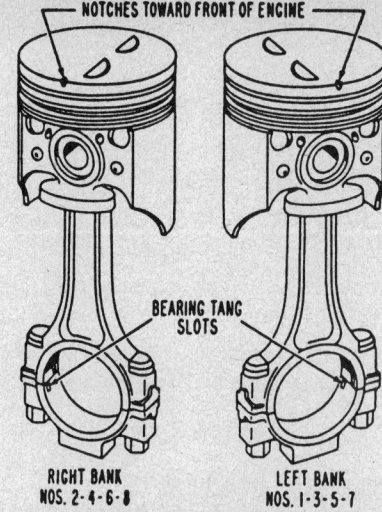

Fig. 20 Piston & rod assemble. 5.0L/V8-305 & 5.7L/V8-350

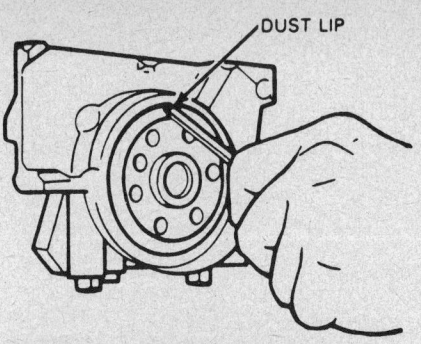

Fig. 21 Crankshaft rear oil seal removal. 2.8L/V6-173 & 3.1L/V6-191

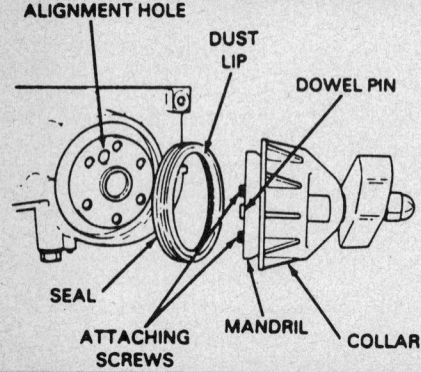

Fig. 22 Crankshaft rear oil seal installation. 2.8L/V6-173 & 3.1L/V6-191

Main bearings are available in standard and undersizes of .001, .002, .009, .010 and .020 inch.

CRANKSHAFT REAR OIL SEAL
REPLACE

2.8L/V6-173 & 3.1L/V6-191

1. Raise and support vehicle.
2. Support engine as needed, then remove transmission.
3. Remove clutch and pressure plate, if equipped, then remove flywheel or flex plate.
4. Insert screwdriver through seal lip and pry seal from bore, taking care not to damage crankshaft, **Fig. 21.**
5. Clean seal bore and crankshaft, then inspect for burrs, nicks and wear, and repair as needed.
6. Lightly lubricate replacement seal lip with engine oil, mount seal on installer J-34686 or equivalent and seat dust lip of seal squarely against collar.
7. Lubricate outer diameter of seal with engine oil, align dowel pin of tool with dowel pin hole in crankshaft, mount tool on crankshaft and torque to 24 to 60 inch lbs., **Fig. 22.**
8. Rotate T handle of tool clockwise, pressing seal into bore until collar is tight against engine case to ensure seal is fully seated.

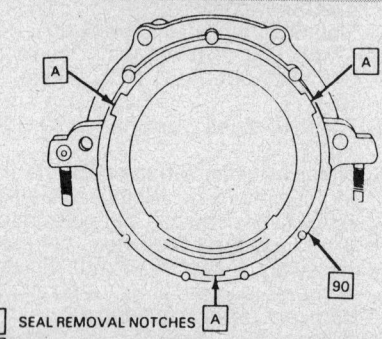

Fig. 23 Crankshaft rear oil seal removal. 5.0L/V8-305 & 5.7L/V8-350

9. Rotate T handle of tool counterclockwise to stop, then remove tool and ensure seal is seated squarely in bore.
10. Reverse remaining procedure to complete installation.

5.0L/V8-305 & 5.7L/V8-350

These engines are equipped with a one-piece, lip type seal mounted in a separate seal retainer. Seal replacement requires removal of the transmission.

1. Raise and support vehicle, then remove transmission, clutch assembly and flywheel, as equipped.
2. Pry seal from retainer, inserting screwdriver in notches provided in seal retainer, **Fig. 23.**
3. Lubricate inner and outer diameters of replacement seal with engine oil, then mount seal on tool J-35621 or equivalent.
4. Mount tool on rear of crankshaft, tightening screws snugly to ensure seal will be installed squarely on crankshaft.
5. Tighten wing nut on tool until it bottoms, then remove tool from crankshaft.
6. Reverse remaining procedure to complete installation.

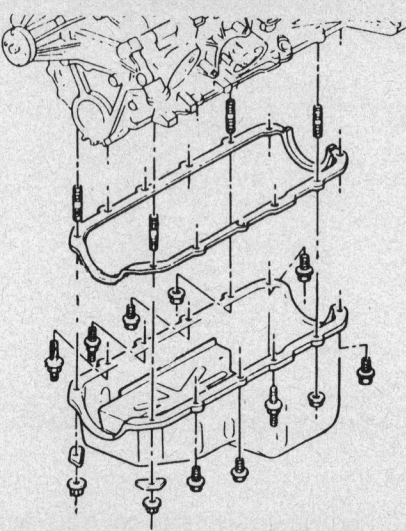

Fig. 24 Oil pan replace. 2.8L/V6-173 & 3.1L/V6-191

OIL PAN
REPLACE

1. Disconnect battery ground cable, then remove fan shroud.
2. Raise and support vehicle, then drain crankcase.
3. Remove AIR pipe, if equipped, and hanger bolts from catalytic converter. On some models it may be necessary to disconnect exhaust crossover pipe at exhaust manifolds.
4. Remove starter motor attaching bolts and position starter motor aside.
5. Remove engine mount through bolts, then raise engine.
6. Remove oil pan attaching bolts and oil pan, **Figs. 24 and 25.** If oil pan removal is hampered by the forward crankshaft throw and/or counterweight extending downward, turn crankshaft as needed to put throw in a horizontal position.
7. Reverse procedure to install, using a new gasket and seals.

OIL PUMP
OIL PUMP, REPLACE

1. Remove oil pan as described previously.

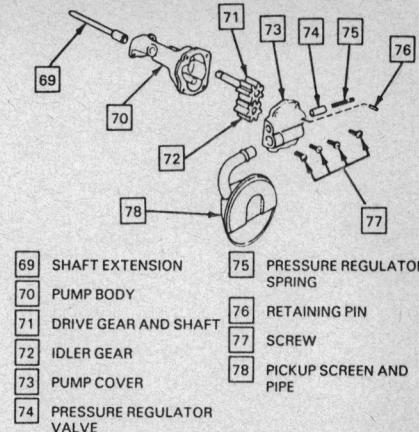

69	SHAFT EXTENSION	75	PRESSURE REGULATOR SPRING
70	PUMP BODY	76	RETAINING PIN
71	DRIVE GEAR AND SHAFT	77	SCREW
72	IDLER GEAR	78	PICKUP SCREEN AND PIPE
73	PUMP COVER		
74	PRESSURE REGULATOR VALVE		

Fig. 26   Exploded view of oil pump

cracks and excessive wear.

8. Inspect pump gears for damage or excessive wear.
9. Check drive gear shaft for looseness in pump body.
10. Inspect inside of pump cover for wear that would allow oil to leak past the ends of the gears.
11. Inspect pickup screen and pipe assembly for damage to screen, pipe or relief grommet.
12. Check pressure regulator valve for fit in pump housing.
13. Reverse procedure to assemble. Turn drive shaft by hand to check for smooth operation. **The pump gears and body are not serviced separately. If the pump gears or body are damaged or worn, the pump assembly should be replaced. Also, if the pick-up screen and pump assembly was removed, it should be replaced with a new one as loss of the press fit condition could result in an air leak and loss of oil pressure.**

SERPENTINE DRIVE BELT ROUTING

Refer to **Figs. 27 through 30** for serpentine belt routing diagram.

COOLING SYSTEM BLEED

After filling cooling system, start engine and allow to reach operating temperature with radiator cap removed. Air in system is bleed through radiator cap opening. Add coolant as necessary to bring to proper level, then install radiator cap and check coolant level in recovery reservoir.

WATER PUMP REPLACE

1. Disconnect battery ground cable and drain cooling system.
2. Remove fan shroud or upper radiator support, as applicable, then remove accessory drive belts.
3. Remove fan and pulley from water pump hub.

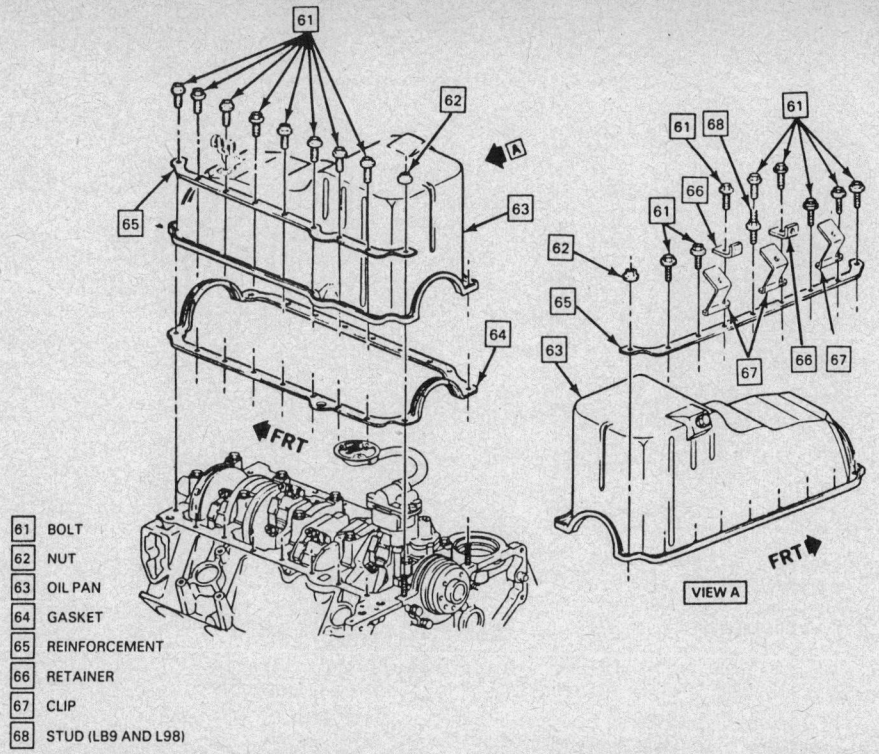

61	BOLT		
62	NUT		
63	OIL PAN		
64	GASKET		
65	REINFORCEMENT		
66	RETAINER		
67	CLIP		
68	STUD (LB9 AND L98)		

Fig. 25   Oil pan replace. 5.0L/V8-305 & 5.7L/V8-350

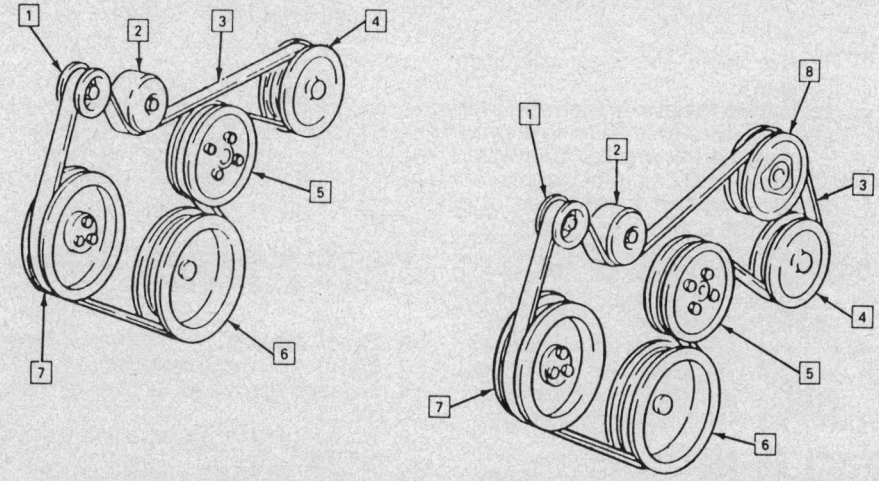

1. GENERATOR	5. WATER PUMP	
2. TENSIONER	6. CRANKSHAFT	
3. BELT	7. A.I.R. PUMP	
4. P/S PUMP	8. A/C COMPRESSOR	

Fig. 27   Serpentine drive belt routing. 2.8L/V6-173 & 3.1L/V6-191 w/man. trans.

2. Remove pump to rear main bearing cap bolt and remove pump and extension shaft.
3. Reverse procedure to install. Make sure that installed position of oil pump screen is with bottom edge parallel to oil pan rails.

OIL PUMP SERVICE

1. Remove oil pump as described previously.
2. Remove pump cover screws and pump cover, **Fig. 26**.
3. Mark gear teeth so they can be reassembled with same teeth indexing, then remove drive gear, idler gear and shaft.
4. Remove pressure regulator valve retaining pin, pressure regulator valve and related parts.
5. If pickup screen and pipe require replacement, mount pump in a soft-jawed vise and extract pipe from pump.
6. Wash all parts in cleaning solvent and dry with compressed air.
7. Inspect pump body and cover for

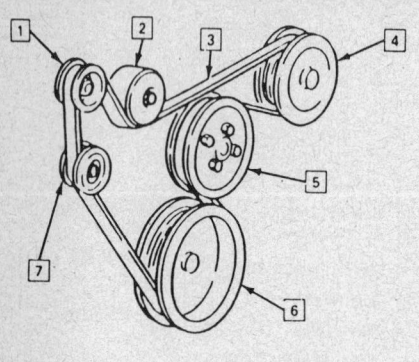
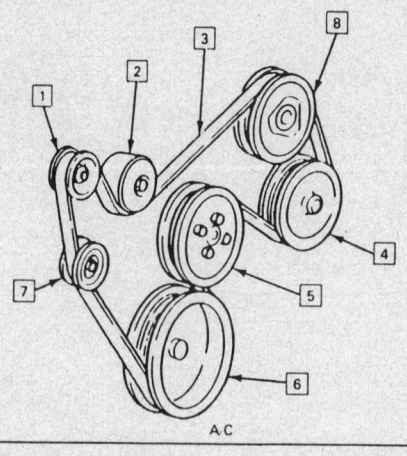

W/O A C

A.C

1. GENERATOR
2. TENSIONER
3. BELT
4. P/S PUMP
5. WATER PUMP
6. CRANKSHAFT
7. BELT IDLER
8. A/C COMPRESSOR

Fig. 28   Serpentine drive belt routing. 2.8L/V6-173 & 3.1L/V6-191 w/auto. trans.

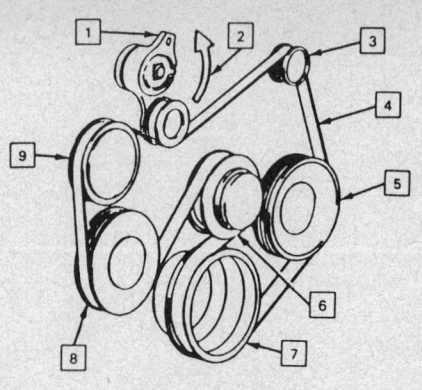

1	TENSIONER ASSEMBLY
2	ROTATE TENSIONER IN DIRECTION SHOWN TO INSTALL OR REMOVE BELT
3	GENERATOR ASSEMBLY
4	ACCESSORY DRIVE BELT
5	P/S PUMP
6	WATER PUMP
7	CRANKSHAFT
8	AIR PUMP
9	A/C COMPRESSOR OR BELT IDLER

Fig. 29   Serpentine drive belt routing. 1988—89 5.0L/V8-305 & 5.7L/V8-350

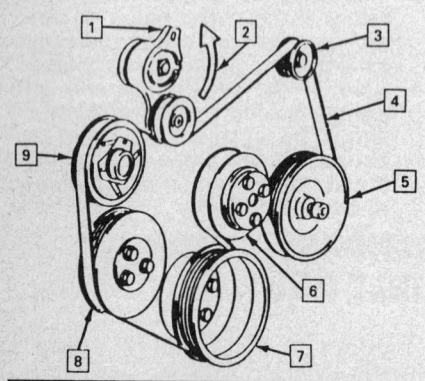

1. TENSIONER ASSEMBLY
2. ROTATE TENSIONER IN DIRECTION SHOWN TO INSTALL OR REMOVE BELT
3. GENERATOR ASSEMBLY
4. ACCESSORY DRIVE BELT
5. P/S PUMP
6. WATER PUMP
7. CRANKSHAFT
8. A.I.R. PUMP
9. A/C COMPRESSOR OR BELT IDLER

Fig. 30   Serpentine drive belt routing. 1990—91 5.0L/V8-305 & 5.7L/V8-350

4. Remove upper and lower alternator brackets.
5. If equipped, remove A/C compressor brace and bracket, then remove power steering lower bracket from water pump and position out of way.
6. Remove radiator lower hose and heater hose from water pump.
7. Remove water pump attaching bolts and the pump, **Figs. 14, 15 and 31,** noting position of bolts for assembly reference.
8. Reverse procedure to install. On 2.8L/V6-173 and 3.1L/V6-191 engines, refer to **Figs. 14 and 15 for bolt tightening specifications.**

FUEL PUMP REPLACE

1. Disconnect battery ground cable, then disconnect engine harness connector at ignition distributor.
2. **On models with port fuel injection,** relieve fuel system pressure as follows:
   a. Loosen fuel tank filler cap.
   b. Wrap shop towel around fuel press valve to prevent fuel spillage, then connect fuel pressure gauge J-34730-1 or equivalent to fuel pressure valve.
   c. Position bleed hose into an approved container, then open bleed valve and allow system pressure to bleed down.

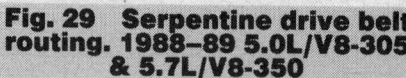
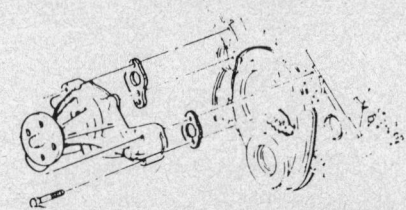

Fig. 31   Water pump replace. 5.0L/V8-305 & 5.7L/V8-350

3. **On all models,** drain fuel tank. Place fuel in an approved container.
4. Remove gas cap and filler neck shield.
5. Remove tires, then raise and support vehicle.
6. Remove track bar and brace.
7. Support axle, then disconnect lower shock mount.
8. Remove exhaust from converter back, then the heat shield.
9. Disconnect brake cables from S clips, then from retainers on frame rails.
10. Remove stabilizer bar links.
11. Lower axle, then remove rear springs.
12. Disconnect fuel lines and wires.
13. Support fuel tank and remove straps.
14. Remove fuel tank from vehicle.
15. Remove fuel level sending unit and pump assembly by turning cam lock ring counterclockwise.
16. Remove fuel pump from level sending unit by pulling fuel pump up and outward, away from bottom support.
17. Reverse procedure to install.

TIGHTENING SPECIFICATIONS

2.8L/V6-173 & 3.1L/V6-191 ENGINES

Year	Component	Torque/Ft. Lbs.
1988	Bell Housing To Engine (Man. Trans.)	55
	Camshaft Rear Cover	6–9
	Camshaft Sprocket	15–25
	Connecting Rod Caps	34–45
	Crankshaft Damper	67–85
	Cylinder Head	①
	Engine Mount Nut	30
	Engine Mount Through Bolt	50
	Exhaust Manifold	19–31
	Flywheel To Crankshaft	50
	Front Cover	③
	Ignition Distributor Hold Down Bolt	20–31
	Intake Manifold (Center)	15–22
	Intake Manifold (Lower)	13–25
	Main Bearing Caps	63–83
	Oil Pan	③
	Oil Pump	25–35
	Rocker Arm Nut	5–11
	Spark Plugs	7–15
	Thermostat Housing	13–18
	Timing Chain Damper	14–19
	Torque Converter To Flywheel	35
	Transmission To Engine (Auto. Trans.)	35
	Valve Cover	7–15
	Water Pump	③
1989	Bell Housing To Engine (Man. Trans.)	35
	Camshaft Rear Cover	71–106 ②
	Camshaft Sprocket	15–26
	Connecting Rod Caps	34–44
	Crankshaft Damper	66–85
	Cylinder Head	①
	Engine Mount Nut	30
	Engine Mount Through Bolt	50
	Exhaust Manifold	18–31
	Flywheel To Crankshaft	49–59
	Front Cover	③
	Ignition Distributor Hold Down Bolt	20–30
	Intake Manifold (Center)	13–18
	Intake Manifold (Lower)	13–25
	Main Bearing Caps	63–83
	Oil Pan	③
	Oil Pump	26–36
	Rocker Arm Nut	53–124 ②
	Spark Plugs	17–33
	Thermostat Housing	97–124 ②
	Timing Chain Damper	13–18
	Torque Converter To Flywheel	46
	Transmission To Engine (Auto. Trans.)	35
	Valve Cover	6–15
	Water Pump	③

Continued

TIGHTENING SPECIFICATIONS—Continued
2.8L/V6-173 & 3.1L/V6-191 ENGINES

Year	Component	Torque/Ft. Lbs.
1990	Bell Housing To Engine (Man. Trans.)	35
	Camshaft Rear Cover	89②
	Camshaft Sprocket	21
	Connecting Rod Caps	39
	Crankshaft Damper	76
	Cylinder Head	①
	Engine Mount Nut	30
	Engine Mount Through Bolt	50
	Exhaust Manifold	25
	Flywheel To Crankshaft	52
	Front Cover	③
	Ignition Distributor Hold Down Bolt	25
	Intake Manifold (Center)	15
	Intake Manifold (Lower)	19
	Main Bearing Caps	73
	Oil Pan	③
	Oil Pump	30
	Rocker Arm Nut	89②
	Spark Plugs	25
	Thermostat Housing	18
	Timing Chain Damper	15
	Torque Converter To Flywheel	46
	Transmission To Engine (Auto. Trans.)	35
	Valve Cover	10
	Water Pump	③

①—Coat bolt threads with a suitable sealer prior to installation. Torque bolts to 40 ft. lbs., then tighten each bolt and additional ¼ turn.
②—Inch Lbs.
③—Refer to text.

5.0L/V8-305 & 5.7L/V8-350 ENGINES

Year	Component	Torque/Ft. Lbs.
	Bell Housing To Engine (Man. Trans.)	68
	Camshaft Sprocket	13–23
	Connecting Rod Caps	42–47
	Crankshaft Damper To Crankshaft Bolt	70
	Crankshaft Pulley To Damper Bolt	43
	Cylinder Head Bolts	60–75
	Engine Mount Bracket	38
	Engine Mount Through Bolts	50
	Exhaust Manifold	②
	Flywheel To Crankshaft	63–85
	Front Cover	69–130①
	Intake Manifold	25–45
	Main Bearing Caps	63–85
	Oil Pan Bolts	101①
	Oil Pan Nuts	17
	Oil Pump To Rear Main Bearing Cap	60–70
	Rear Crankshaft Seal Retainer	11
	Spark Plug	22
	Torque Converter To Flywheel	35
	Transmission To Engine (Auto. Trans.)	35
	Valve Covers	62–115①
	Valve Lifter Retainer	12
	Water Pump	25–35

Continued

Year	Component	Torque/Ft. Lbs.
1990	Bell Housing To Engine (Man. Trans.)	70
	Camshaft Sprocket	21
	Connecting Rod Caps	44
	Crankshaft Damper To Crankshaft Bolt	70
	Crankshaft Pulley To Damper Bolt	43
	Cylinder Head Bolts	68
	Engine Mount Bracket	38
	Engine Mount Through Bolts	50
	Exhaust Manifold	②
	Flywheel To Crankshaft	74
	Front Cover	100①
	Intake Manifold	35
	Main Bearing Caps	77
	Oil Pan Bolts	101①
	Oil Pan Nuts	17
	Oil Pump To Rear Main Bearing Cap	65
	Rear Crankshaft Seal Retainer	11
	Spark Plug	22
	Torque Converter To Flywheel	46
	Transmission To Engine (Auto. Trans.)	35
	Valve Covers	89①
	Valve Lifter Retainer	12
	Water Pump	30

①—Inch Lbs.
②—Center bolts & studs, 20 ft. lbs.;
 outer bolts & studs, 26 ft. lbs.

3.8L/V6-231 Engine

INDEX

ENGINE MOUNTS
REPLACE

1. Raise and support vehicle.
2. Support weight of engine at forward edge of pan.
3. Remove engine mount through bolts.
4. Raise engine slightly, then remove mount to mount bracket bolt and nut, **Fig. 1.**
5. Remove mount.
6. Reverse procedure to install.

ENGINE
REPLACE

1. Remove hood from vehicle.
2. Disconnect battery ground cable.
3. Disconnect air inlet tube from turbocharger.
4. Discharge A/C refrigerant system, then disconnect refrigerant lines from compressor, accumulator and condenser.
5. Drain cooling system, then disconnect radiator inlet and outlet hoses.
6. Disconnect coolant reservoir hose.
7. Disconnect cooling fan electrical connectors, then remove fan shroud with cooling fans attached.
8. Disconnect transmission oil cooler lines at radiator.
9. Remove radiator from vehicle.
10. Disconnect power steering pressure hose from pump and return hose from reservoir.
11. Relieve fuel system pressure as follows:
    a. Loosen fuel tank filler cap.
    b. Wrap shop towel around fuel press valve to prevent fuel spillage, then connect fuel pressure gauge

J-34730-1 or equivalent to fuel pressure valve.

   c. Position pressure gauge bleed hose into an approved container, then open bleed valve and allow system pressure to bleed down.

12. Disconnect fuel lines at intake manifold, then remove fuel line valve cover brackets.
13. Disconnect fuel vapor canister hose at engine.
14. Disconnect heater hoses at fire wall.
15. Disconnect cables at throttle body.
16. Disconnect engine to body ground strap.
17. Disconnect power brake unit vacuum hose.
18. Disconnect and tag all vacuum hoses and electrical wiring at upper portion of engine which would interfere with engine removal.
19. Disconnect exhaust pipe from turbocharger.
20. Raise and support vehicle, then disconnect wiring from starter motor.
21. Remove clips attaching transmission oil cooler lines to engine and intercooler.
22. Disconnect exhaust crossover pipe.
23. Remove torque converter cover, then remove torque converter to flywheel attaching bolts. Mark position of torque converter to flywheel so they can be installed in the same position.
24. Remove lower and side bellhousing to engine attaching bolts.
25. Remove engine mount through bolts.
26. Disconnect and tag all vacuum hoses and electrical wiring at lower portion of engine which would interfere with engine removal.
27. Lower vehicle, then disconnect battery ground cable from engine.
28. Remove upper bellhousing to engine attaching bolts.
29. Remove windshield wiper motor.
30. Remove transmission fluid filler tube.
31. Support transmission using a suitable transmission jack.
32. Install a suitable engine lifting device to engine, then remove engine from vehicle.
33. Reverse procedure to install.

INTAKE MANIFOLD
REPLACE

1. Disconnect battery ground cable.
2. Drain cooling system.
3. Remove throttle body to intercooler intermediate cooler pipe.
4. Disconnect radiator and coolant by-pass hoses at intake manifold.
5. Disconnect coolant inlet and outlet hoses at throttle body.
6. Disconnect and tag electrical connectors form intake manifold mounted components.
7. Remove EGR valve and EGR vacuum control and bracket.
8. Disconnect power brake unit vacuum hose.
9. Disconnect and tag intake manifold vacuum hoses.
10. Disconnect control cables from throttle body.

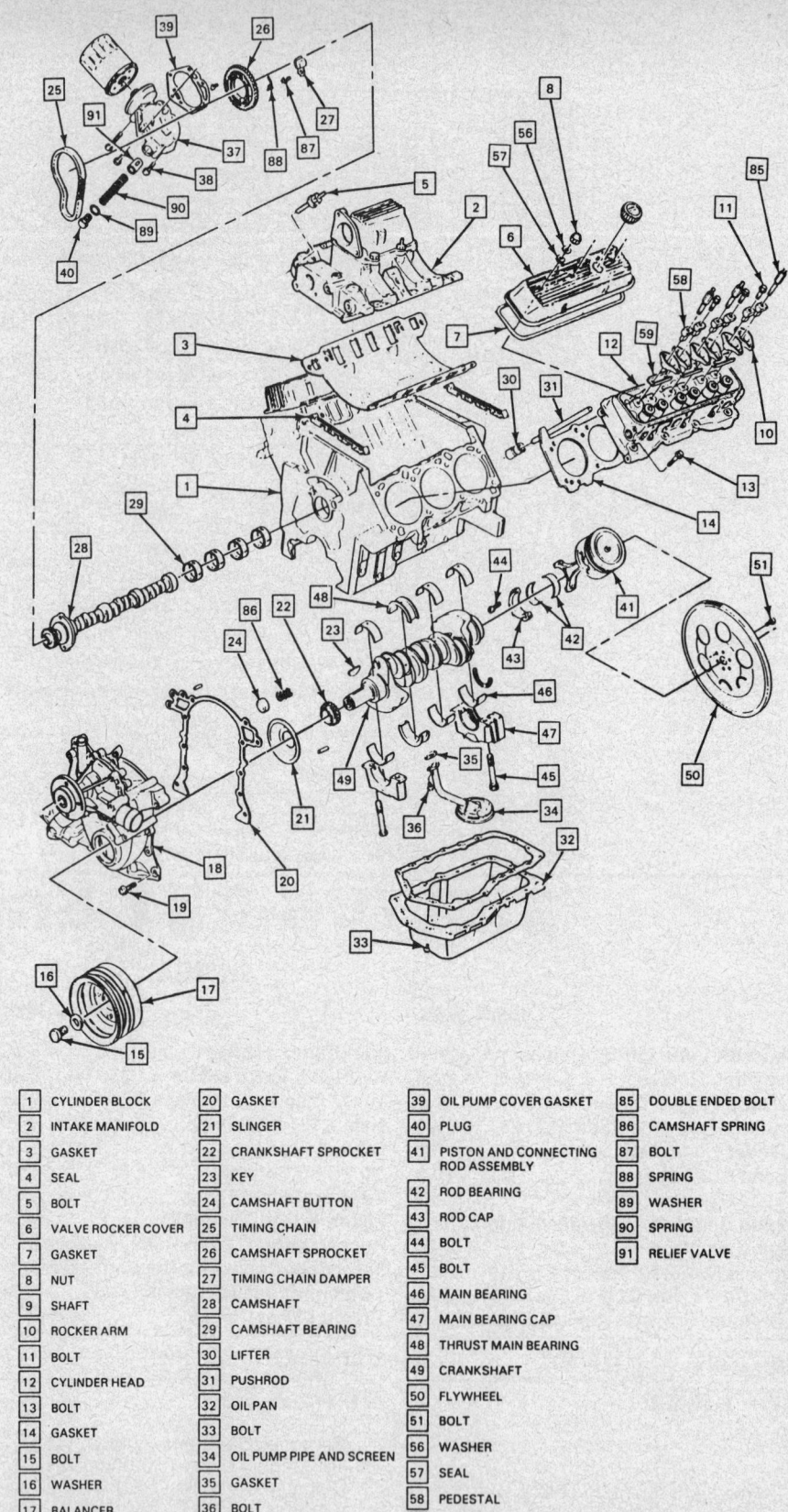

1	CYLINDER BLOCK	20	GASKET
2	INTAKE MANIFOLD	21	SLINGER
3	GASKET	22	CRANKSHAFT SPROCKET
4	SEAL	23	KEY
5	BOLT	24	CAMSHAFT BUTTON
6	VALVE ROCKER COVER	25	TIMING CHAIN
7	GASKET	26	CAMSHAFT SPROCKET
8	NUT	27	TIMING CHAIN DAMPER
9	SHAFT	28	CAMSHAFT
10	ROCKER ARM	29	CAMSHAFT BEARING
11	BOLT	30	LIFTER
12	CYLINDER HEAD	31	PUSHROD
13	BOLT	32	OIL PAN
14	GASKET	33	BOLT
15	BOLT	34	OIL PUMP PIPE AND SCREEN
16	WASHER	35	GASKET
17	BALANCER	36	BOLT
18	FRONT COVER	37	OIL PUMP COVER
19	BOLT	38	BOLT

39	OIL PUMP COVER GASKET	85	DOUBLE ENDED BOLT
40	PLUG	86	CAMSHAFT SPRING
41	PISTON AND CONNECTING ROD ASSEMBLY	87	BOLT
42	ROD BEARING	88	SPRING
43	ROD CAP	89	WASHER
44	BOLT	90	SPRING
45	BOLT	91	RELIEF VALVE
46	MAIN BEARING		
47	MAIN BEARING CAP		
48	THRUST MAIN BEARING		
49	CRANKSHAFT		
50	FLYWHEEL		
51	BOLT		
56	WASHER		
57	SEAL		
58	PEDESTAL		
59	PEDESTAL RETAINER		

Exploded view of engine

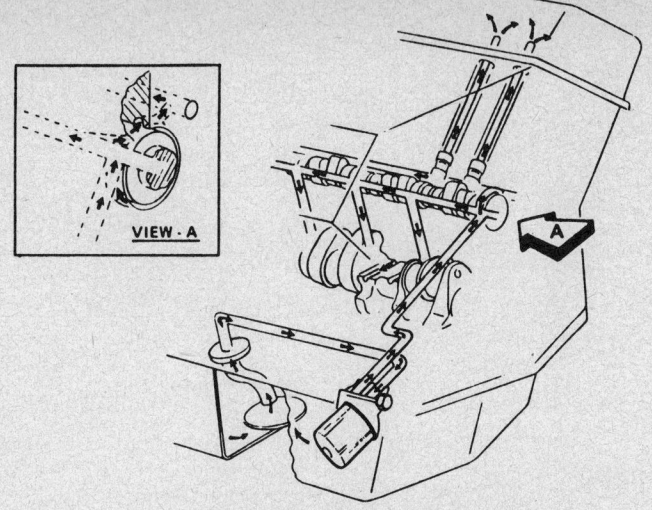

Engine Oiling system

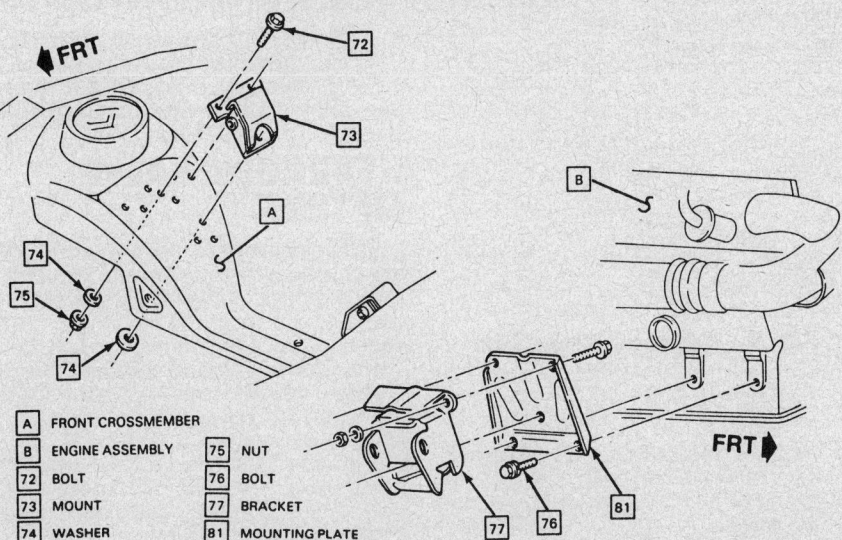

A	FRONT CROSSMEMBER		
B	ENGINE ASSEMBLY	**75**	NUT
72	BOLT	**76**	BOLT
73	MOUNT	**77**	BRACKET
74	WASHER	**81**	MOUNTING PLATE

Fig. 1   Engine mounting

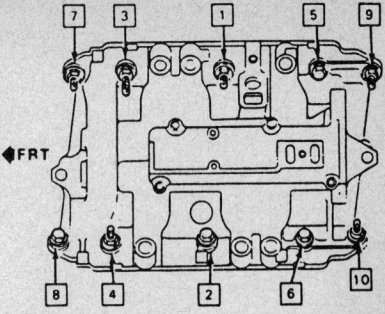

Fig. 2   Intake manifold bolt tightening sequence

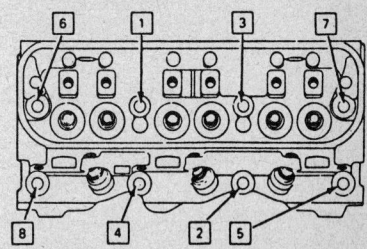

Fig. 3   Cylinder head bolt tightening sequence

11. Disconnect heater inlet and outlet pipes.
12. Disconnect ignition wires from coil unit, then remove coil unit.
13. Relieve fuel system pressure as follows:
    a. Loosen fuel tank filler cap.
    b. Wrap shop towel around fuel press valve to prevent fuel spillage, then connect fuel pressure gauge J-34730-1 or equivalent to fuel pressure valve.
    c. Position bleed hose into an approved container, then open bleed valve and allow system pressure to bleed down.
14. Disconnect fuel lines at fuel rail and pressure regulator.
15. Remove intake manifold attaching bolts and intake manifold.
16. Reverse procedure to install. apply sealer 12345336 or equivalent to ends of intake manifold seal. When installing intake manifold attaching bolts, tighten bolts, **Fig. 2**, positions 1 and 2 until snug, then tighten all bolts in sequence shown in **Fig. 2**.

EXHAUST MANIFOLD REPLACE

1. If right hand exhaust manifold is to be replaced, remove exhaust pipe and exhaust manifold to turbocharger attaching nuts.
2. If right hand exhaust manifold is to be replaced, remove oxygen sensor from exhaust manifold.
3. If left hand exhaust manifold is to be replaced, loosen alternator and A/C compressor brace nuts.
4. Disconnect spark plug wires from spark plugs.
5. Raise and support vehicle.
6. Remove turbocharger exhaust pipe and clamp from exhaust flex coupling.
7. Disconnect exhaust crossover pipe from exhaust manifold.
8. If left hand exhaust manifold is to be replaced, remove engine oil level dipstick and tube.
9. Remove exhaust manifold to cylinder head attaching bolts, then remove exhaust manifold. If left hand exhaust manifold is to be replaced, position alternator and A/C compressor to permit exhaust manifold removal.
10. Reverse procedure to install.

CYLINDER HEAD REPLACE

Prior to reinstalling cylinder head bolts, coat the head bolts with thread sealer. This is to prevent coolant leakage, as the head bolt holes extend into the water jacket.

An accurate torque wrench should be used when installing head bolts. Uneven tightening of the head bolts can distort the cylinder bores, causing compression loss and excessive oil consumption.

1. Disconnect battery ground cable.
2. Remove serpentine drive belt.
3. If left hand cylinder head is to be replaced proceed as follows:
    a. Remove alternator and position aside with wiring attached.
    b. Remove A/C compressor and position aside with refrigerant lines attached.
    c. Remove power steering pump and bracket and position aside with hoses attached.
4. If right hand cylinder head is to be replaced, remove turbocharger.
5. Remove valve covers, rocker arms and push rods. Tag rocker arms and push rods so they can be installed in the same positions.
6. Remove intake manifold as described under "Intake Manifold, Replace."

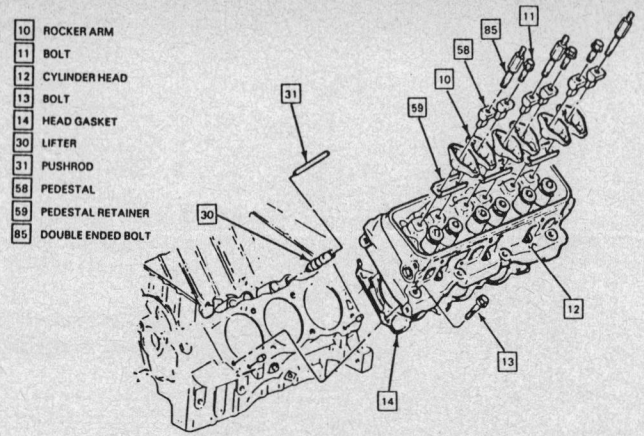

10	ROCKER ARM
11	BOLT
12	CYLINDER HEAD
13	BOLT
14	HEAD GASKET
30	LIFTER
31	PUSHROD
58	PEDESTAL
59	PEDESTAL RETAINER
85	DOUBLE ENDED BOLT

Fig. 4 Valve train components

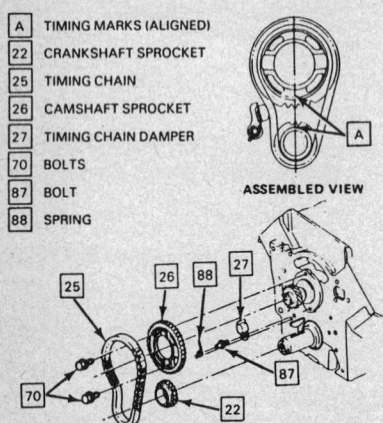

A	TIMING MARKS (ALIGNED)
22	CRANKSHAFT SPROCKET
25	TIMING CHAIN
26	CAMSHAFT SPROCKET
27	TIMING CHAIN DAMPER
70	BOLTS
87	BOLT
88	SPRING

ASSEMBLED VIEW

Fig. 6 Timing chain replace

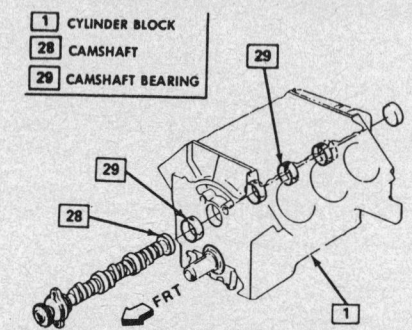

1	CYLINDER BLOCK
28	CAMSHAFT
29	CAMSHAFT BEARING

Fig. 7 Camshaft replace

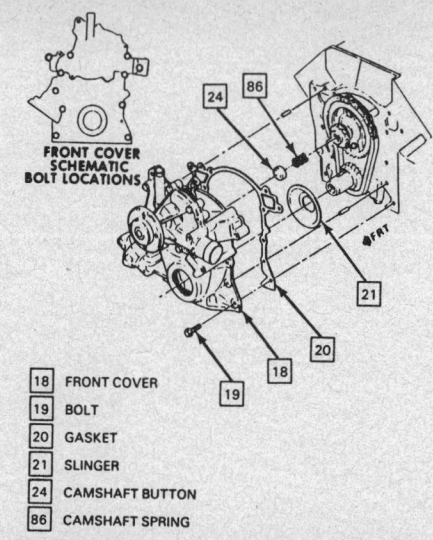

FRONT COVER SCHEMATIC BOLT LOCATIONS

18	FRONT COVER
19	BOLT
20	GASKET
21	SLINGER
24	CAMSHAFT BUTTON
86	CAMSHAFT SPRING

Fig. 5 Front cover replace

7. Remove exhaust manifold as described under "Exhaust Manifold, Replace."
8. Remove cylinder head attaching bolts, then remove cylinder head.
9. Reverse procedure to install, noting the following:
   a. Install cylinder head, then apply a sealant to bolt threads.
   b. Insert cylinder head bolts, then **torque** to 35 ft. lbs., in sequence shown, **Fig. 3**.
   c. Tighten each bolt an additional ¼ turn in tightening sequence. **If 65 ft. lbs. of torque is obtained, stop, do not complete ¼ turn.**
   d. Again tighten each bolt an additional ¼ turn in tightening sequence. **If 65 ft. lbs. of torque is obtained, do not complete ¼ turn.**

ROCKER ARMS & PUSH RODS
REPLACE

1. Remove valve covers.
2. Remove rocker arm pedestal bolts, **Fig. 4**. Note location of pedestal bolts for use during installation.

3. Remove pedestals, rocker arms pedestal retainers and push rods. Note location of components for use during installation.
4. Reverse procedure to install.

VALVE ARRANGEMENT
FRONT TO REAR

3.8L/V6-231
   Right . . . . E-I-I-E-I-E
   Left . . . . E-I-E-I-I-E

CAMSHAFT LOBE LIFT SPECIFICATIONS

	Lift, Inch	
Engine	Int.	Exh.
3.8L/V6-231	.397	.397

VALVES
ADJUST

These engines are equipped with hydraulic valve lifters, which have zero lash clearance. No provision for adjustment is provided.

VALVE GUIDES

The valve guides are an integral part of

the cylinder head and cannot be replaced.

If valve stem clearance is excessive, the valve guide must be reamed and an oversize valve installed. Valves are available in the oversize of .010 inch.

HYDRAULIC VALVE LIFTERS

Failure of hydraulic valve lifters is generally caused by an inadequate oil supply or dirt. An air leak at the intake side of the oil pump or too much oil in the engine will cause air bubbles in the oil supply to the lifters, causing them to collapse. This is a probable cause of trouble if several lifters fail to function, but air in the oil is an unlikely cause of failure of a single unit.

The valve lifters may be lifted out of their bores after removing the rocker arms, push rods and intake manifold. Adjustable pliers with taped jaws may be used to remove lifters that are stuck due to varnish, carbon or dirt.

FRONT COVER
REPLACE

1. Disconnect battery ground cable.
2. Drain cooling system and crankcase.
3. Remove oil cooler and adapter.
4. Remove water pump as described under "Water Pump, Replace."
5. Disconnect radiator inlet hose from intake manifold.
6. Remove front clamp from coolant by-pass hose.
7. Remove serpentine drive belt.
8. Remove intercooler duct.
9. Remove crankshaft hub pulley bolts, then remove pulley and hub as an assembly.
10. Remove crankshaft damper bolt and washer, then remove crankshaft damper.
12. Disconnect crankshaft speed sensor electrical connector.
13. Remove oil pan to front cover and oil pan to engine block attaching bolts.
14. Remove crankshaft speed sensor.
15. Remove front cover and gasket, **Fig. 5.**

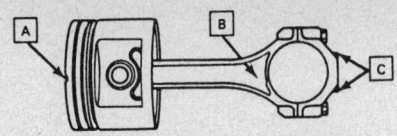

A NOTCH ON PISTON TOWARDS FRONT OF ENGINE

B LEFT BANK: NO. 1, 3 & 5 TWO BOSSES ON ROD TOWARDS REAR OF ENGINE (NOT SHOWN)

RIGHT BANK: NO. 2, 4 & 6 TWO BOSSES ON ROD TOWARDS FRONT OF ENGINE (NOT SHOWN)

C LEFT BANK: CHAMFERED CORNERS ON ROD CAP TOWARDS FRONT OF ENGINE

RIGHT BANK: CHAMFERED CORNERS ON ROD CAP TOWARDS REAR OF ENGINE

Fig. 8   Piston & connecting rod assemble

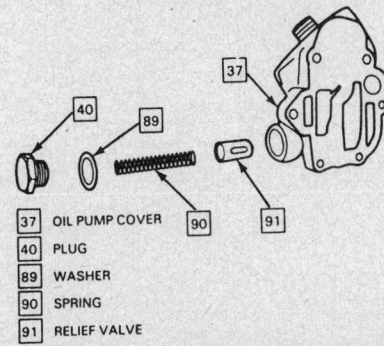

37 OIL PUMP COVER

40 PLUG

89 WASHER

90 SPRING

91 RELIEF VALVE

Fig. 11   Oil pump relief valve installation

16. Reverse procedure to install, noting the following:
   a. Remove the oil pump cover and pack the space around the oil pump gears completely full of petroleum jelly. There must be no air space left inside the pump.
   b. Reinstall the cover using a new gasket. This step is very important as the oil pump may lose its prime whenever the pump, pump cover or timing chain cover is disturbed. If the pump is not packed it may not begin to pump oil as soon as the engine is started.
   c. Prior to installation, apply suitable sealer to threads of front cover to engine block attaching bolts.

TIMING CHAIN REPLACE

1. With the timing case cover removed as outlined above, temporarily install the vibration damper bolt and washer in end of crankshaft.
2. Turn crankshaft so sprockets are positioned as shown in **Fig. 6**. Use a sharp rap on a wrench handle to start the vibration damper bolt out without disturbing the position of the sprockets.
3. Remove oil slinger.
4. Remove distributor drive gear, fuel pump eccentric, and chain dampener, if applicable.
5. Use two large screwdrivers to alternately pry the camshaft sprocket then

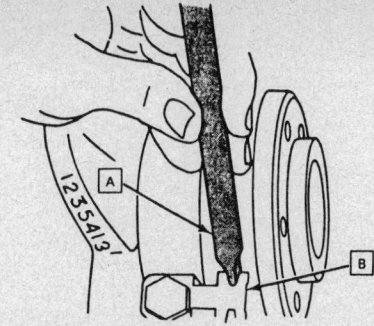

A PART OF J 21526

B PART OF J 21526

Fig. 9   Repairing crankshaft rear seal

the crankshaft sprocket forward until the camshaft sprocket is free. Remove camshaft sprocket and chain, then pull crankshaft sprocket off crankshaft.
6. To install, assemble chain on sprockets, then slide sprockets on their respective shafts with the marks on the sprockets lined up as shown, **Fig. 6**.
7. Reverse procedure to install.

CAMSHAFT REPLACE

1. Disconnect battery ground cable.
2. Remove intake manifold as described under "Intake Manifold, Replace."
3. Remove valve covers, rocker arms, push rods and valve lifters.
4. Remove radiator and A/C condenser from vehicle.
5. Remove timing chain and sprocket as described under "Timing Chain, Replace."
6. Remove camshaft retainer bolts, then remove camshaft, **Fig. 7**.
7. Reverse procedure to install. Lubricate camshaft lobes and bearing journals with lubricant 1052365 or equivalent prior to installation. If a replacement camshaft is being installed, add lubricant 1052367 to engine crankcase.

PISTON & ROD ASSEMBLE

Rods and pistons should be assembled and installed as shown in **Fig. 8**.
Measure connecting rod side clearance using a feeler gauge. Clearance obtained should be .004–.015 inch.

PISTONS, PINS & RINGS

Pistons are available in standard size and oversizes of .010 and .030 inch.
Rings are furnished in standard sizes and oversizes of .010 and .030 inch.
Piston pins are supplied with piston.

MAIN & ROD BEARINGS

Main bearings are available in standard

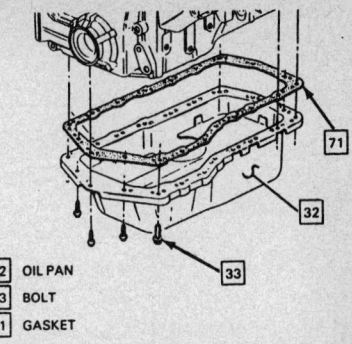

71
32

32 OIL PAN

33 BOLT

71 GASKET

Fig. 10   Oil pan replace

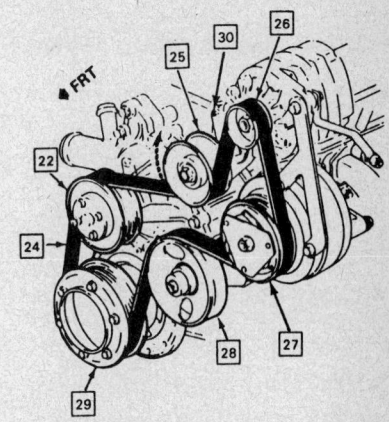

◄ FRT

22 COOLANT PUMP PULLEY

24 BELT

25 TENSIONER PULLEY

26 GENERATOR PULLEY

27 AIR CONDITIONING COMPRESSOR PULLEY

28 POWER STEERING PUMP PULLEY

29 CRANKSHAFT PULLEY

30 TENSIONER

Fig. 12   Serpentine drive belt routing

size and undersize of .001 inch.
Rod bearings are furnished in standard size only.

CRANKSHAFT REAR OIL SEAL REPAIR

Since the braided fabric seal used on these engines can be replaced only when the crankshaft is removed, the following repair procedure is recommended.
1. Remove oil pan and bearing cap.
2. Drive end of old seal gently into groove, using a tool, until packed tight. This may vary between 1/4 and 3/4 inch depending on amount of pack required.
3. Repeat previous step for other end of seal.
4. Measure and note amount that seal was driven up on one side. Using the old seal removed from bearing cap, cut a length of seal the amount previously noted plus 1/16 inch.
5. Repeat previous step for other side of seal.

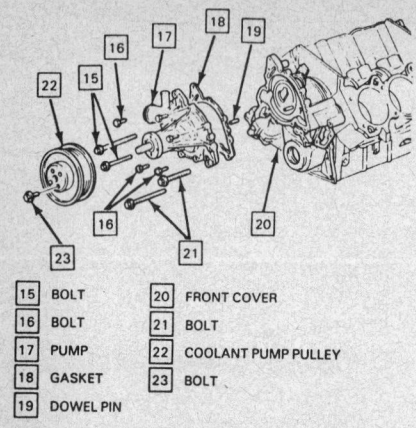

15	BOLT	20	FRONT COVER
16	BOLT	21	BOLT
17	PUMP	22	COOLANT PUMP PULLEY
18	GASKET	23	BOLT
19	DOWEL PIN		

Fig. 13 Water pump replace

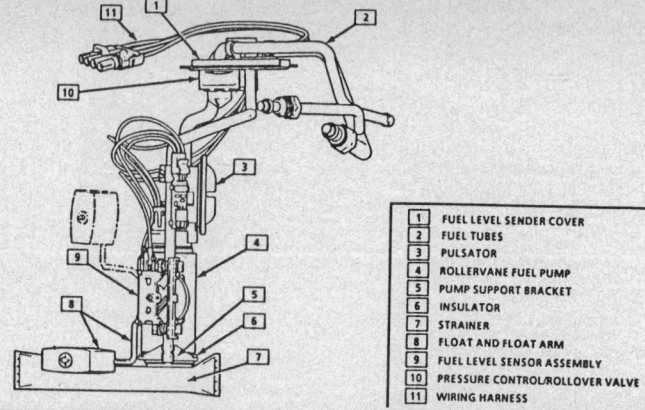

1	FUEL LEVEL SENDER COVER
2	FUEL TUBES
3	PULSATOR
4	ROLLERVANE FUEL PUMP
5	PUMP SUPPORT BRACKET
6	INSULATOR
7	STRAINER
8	FLOAT AND FLOAT ARM
9	FUEL LEVEL SENSOR ASSEMBLY
10	PRESSURE CONTROL/ROLLOVER VALVE
11	WIRING HARNESS

Fig. 14 Electric fuel pump assembly

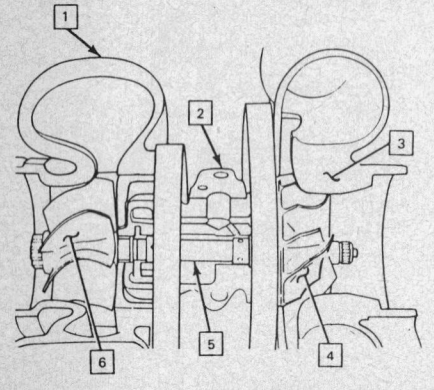

1	TURBINE HOUSING	4	COMPRESSOR WHEEL
2	CENTER HOUSING	5	SHAFT
3	COMPRESSOR HOUSING	6	TURBINE WHEEL

Fig. 15 Turbocharger assembly

6. Pack cut lengths of seal into appropriate side of seal groove. A guide tool, J-21526-1, and packing tool, J-21526-2, may be used since these tools have been machined to provide a built-in stop, **Fig. 9**
7. Install new seal in bearing cap.
8. Apply thin coat of sealer to block contact surfaces of bearing cap, install cap, then torque bolts to specifications.

OIL PAN
REPLACE

1. Disconnect battery ground cable.
2. Remove windshield wiper motor.
3. Remove ignition module.
4. Raise and support front of vehicle, then drain engine oil from crankcase.
5. Remove exhaust crossover pipe.
6. Remove torque converter cover.
7. Remove engine mount through bolts, then raise and support engine.
8. Remove transmission oil cooler line bracket from oil pan stud.
9. Remove nut retaining electrical wiring harness bracket to oil pan stud.
10. Remove oil pan attaching bolts, then remove oil pan and gasket, **Fig. 10**.
11. Reverse procedure to install. Prime

turbocharger with engine oil prior to operating vehicle, refer to "Turbocharger" for procedure.

OIL PUMP SERVICE

1. Remove front cover as described under "Front Cover, Replace."
2. Remove screws retaining oil pump cover to front cover. Remove cover and slide out pump gears. Replace any parts not serviceable.
3. Check relief valve in its bore in cover, **Fig. 11.** Valve should have no more clearance than an easy slip fit. If any perceptible side shake can be felt, the valve and/or cover should be replaced.
4. The filter bypass valve should be flat and free of nicks and scratches.
5. Pack gear pocket with petroleum jelly.
6. Reinstall gears so petroleum jelly is forced into every cavity of gear pocket and between teeth of gears. Unless pump is properly packed, it may not prime when engine is started.
7. Install cover, then tighten screws alternately and evenly.
8. Install front cover.
9. Prior to operating vehicle, prime turbocharger, refer to "Turbocharger" for procedure.

SERPENTINE DRIVE BELT ROUTING

Refer to **Fig. 12** for serpentine belt routing diagram.

COOLING SYSTEM BLEED

After filling cooling system, start engine and allow to reach operating temperature with radiator cap removed. Air in system is bleed through radiator cap opening. Add coolant as necessary to bring to proper level, then install radiator cap and check coolant level in recovery reservoir.

WATER PUMP
REPLACE

1. Disconnect battery ground cable.

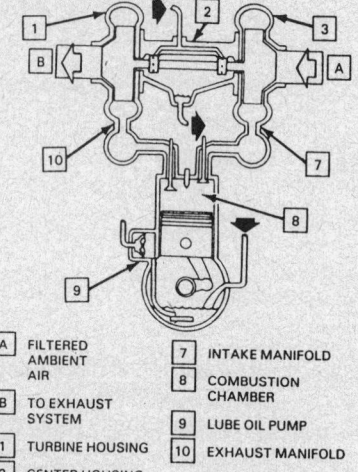

A	FILTERED AMBIENT AIR	7	INTAKE MANIFOLD
B	TO EXHAUST SYSTEM	8	COMBUSTION CHAMBER
1	TURBINE HOUSING	9	LUBE OIL PUMP
2	CENTER HOUSING	10	EXHAUST MANIFOLD
3	COMPRESSOR HOUSING		

Fig. 16 Turbocharger system schematic

2. Drain cooling system.
3. Remove clamps, then remove intermediate hose.
4. Remove air cleaner duct.
5. Remove serpentine drive belt.
6. Remove water pump pulley attaching bolts, then remove pulley.
7. Disconnect radiator and heater hoses from water pump.
8. Remove water pump attaching bolts, then remove water pump, **Fig. 13**.
9. Reverse procedure to install.

FUEL PUMP
REPLACE

1. Disconnect battery ground cable, then disconnect engine harness connector at ignition distributor.
2. Relieve fuel system pressure as follows:
   a. Loosen fuel tank filler cap.
   b. Wrap shop towel around fuel press valve to prevent fuel spillage, then connect fuel pressure gauge J-34730-1 or equivalent to fuel pressure valve.

c. Position bleed hose into an approved container, then open bleed valve and allow system pressure to bleed down.
3. Drain fuel tank. Place fuel in an approved container.
4. Remove gas cap and filler neck shield.
5. Remove tires, then raise and support vehicle.
6. Remove track bar and brace.
7. Support axle, then disconnect lower shock mount.
8. Remove exhaust from converter back, then the heat shield.
9. Disconnect brake cables from S clips, then from retainers on frame rails.
10. Remove stabilizer bar links.
11. Lower axle, then remove rear springs.
12. Disconnect fuel lines and wires.
13. Support fuel tank and remove straps.
14. Remove fuel tank from vehicle.
15. Remove fuel level sending unit and pump assembly by turning cam lock ring counterclockwise.
16. Remove fuel pump from level sending unit by pulling fuel pump up and outward, away from bottom support, **Fig. 14.**
17. Reverse procedure to install.

TURBOCHARGER
DESCRIPTION

The turbocharger, **Fig. 15**, is used to increase engine power on a demand basis, therefore allowing a smaller, more economical engine to be used. The turbocharged 3.8L/V6-231 engine is equipped with sequential port fuel injection.

As engine load increases and the throttle opens, more air-fuel mixture is drawn into the combustion chambers. As the increased volume is burned, a larger volume of high energy exhaust gasses enters the engine exhaust system and is directed through the turbocharger turbine housing, **Fig. 16.** Some of the exhaust gas energy is used to increase the speed of the turbine wheel which is connected to the compressor wheel. The increased speed of the compressor wheel compresses the air-fuel mixture and delivers the compressed air-fuel mixture to the intake manifold. The high pressure in the intake manifold allows a denser charge to enter the combustion chambers, in turn developing more engine power during the combustion cycle.

The intake manifold pressure (Boost) is controlled to a maximum value by an exhaust gas bypass valve (Wastegate). The wastegate allows a portion of the exhaust gas to bypass the turbine wheel, thereby not increasing turbine speed. An electronic wastegate is used. In this system, a pulse width modulated solenoid has been positioned between the manifold and wastegate diaphragm. Information regarding air flow, engine RPM, transmission gear and detonation is collected and analyzed by the Electronic Control Module. If the engine will tolerate additional boost, the solenoid signals the wastegate accordingly. Inside the wastegate, the exhaust divert valve is normally closed, allowing boost pressure to rise until the mass air flow called for by the ECM is satisfied. When air flow reaches this level, the exhaust divert valve opens, allowing the exhaust gas to divert around the turbine and flow directly into the exhaust system.

PRIMING TURBOCHARGER WITH ENGINE OIL

Oil pressure and flow lag can damage turbocharger bearings. This will occur most often when engine oil has been changed, engine has not been operated for a long period of time or when cold weather has caused the oil to congeal.

When changing engine oil, prime oil filter with engine oil prior to installation. Disconnect electrical connectors at computer controlled coil ignition unit and fuel pump relay, then crank engine until a steady oil pressure is observed. After a steady oil pressure reading has been observed, reconnect computer controlled coil ignition unit and fuel pump relay electrical connects and start engine.

TIGHTENING SPECIFICATIONS

Year	Component	Torque/Ft. lbs.
1989	A/C Compressor Brace Nut	11
	Alternator Brace Nut	37
	Bellhousing To Engine Bolts	35
	Camshaft Sprocket Bolt	31
	Crankshaft Main Bearing Caps	100
	Connecting Rod Caps	40
	Crankshaft Damper Bolt	219
	Crankshaft Hub To Damper	26
	Crankshaft Pulley To Hub	21
	Cylinder Head Attaching Bolts	②
	Engine Mount Bracket To Engine Bolt	33
	Engine Mount Through Bolt	50
	Exhaust Crossover Pipe Bolts	23
	Exhaust Manifold To Cylinder Head Bolts	37
	Exhaust Manifold to Turbocharger Nuts.	20
	Flywheel To Crankshaft	60
	Front Cover Bolts	22
	Intake Manifold Bolts	32
	Intercooler Fan Bolt	21
	Oil Pan Bolts	89①
	Oil Pressure Relief Valve Plug	35
	Oil Pump Cover	12
	Oil Pump Tube & Screen Bolt	97①
	Rocker Arm Pedestal Bolt	44
	Spark Plug	20
	Timing Chain Damper Bolt	14

Continued

TIGHTENING SPECIFICATIONS—Continued

Year	Component	Torque/Ft. lbs.
	Torque Converter Cover Bolts	53①
	Torque Converter To Flywheel Bolts	46
	Turbocharger Exhaust Pipe Bolt	22
	Valve Cover Nut	13
	Water Long Attaching Bolts	22
	Water Pump Pulley Attaching Bolts	89①
	Water Short Attaching Bolts	115①

①—Inch lbs.
②—Prior to installation, apply a suitable sealant to bolt threads. Torque to 35 ft. lbs. then tighten each bolt an additional ½ turn in ¼ turn increments. If 65 ft. lbs. of torque is obtained, do not complete the additional ¼ turns.

Clutch & Manual Transmission

INDEX

HYDRAULIC CLUTCH SYSTEM BLEEDING

1. Clean area around clutch fluid reservoir, then remove cap and add DOT 3 type brake fluid as necessary to bring to proper level, **Fig. 1.**
2. At clutch slave cylinder, fully loosen bleeder screw located near fluid inlet line connection.
3. Allow system to gravity bleed until a steady stream of fluid is expelled from bleeder valve. Maintain reservoir level during gravity bleeding operation.
4. After air has been expelled from slave cylinder, tighten bleeder screw.
5. Push clutch fork lightly toward actuator, then open bleeder screw. While maintaining light force on clutch fork, tighten bleeder screw.
6. Push clutch fork lightly toward actuator with bleeder screw closed. This will force any remaining air into reservoir.
7. Check clutch system by starting vehicle, then select reverse gear with clutch pedal fully depressed. If gears do not grate, system is satisfactory. If gears do grate, repeat bleeding procedure.
8. Check actuator output rod travel. Minimum travel should be .43 inch for V6 engines, .57 inch for V8 engines.

CLUTCH
REPLACE

1. Support engine and remove transmission as outlined further on.
2. Remove slave cylinder heat shield and cylinder from flywheel housing. Prior to removing slave cylinder, disconnect push rod from clutch master cylinder.
3. Remove flywheel housing, **Fig. 2.**
4. Slide clutch fork from ball stud and remove fork from dust boot. **Look for X**

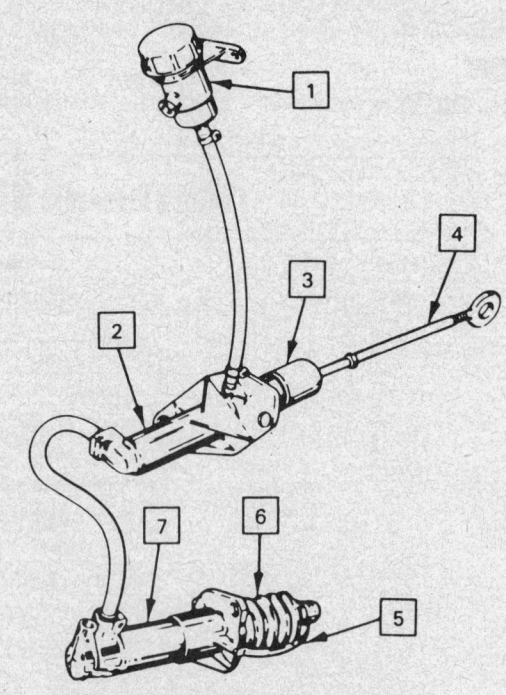

1	FLUID RESERVOIR
2	CLUTCH MASTER CYLINDER
3	BOOT
4	CLUTCH MASTER CYLINDER INPUT ROD
5	SHIPPING STRAP
6	BOOT
7	ACTUATOR

Fig. 1   Clutch hydraulic system

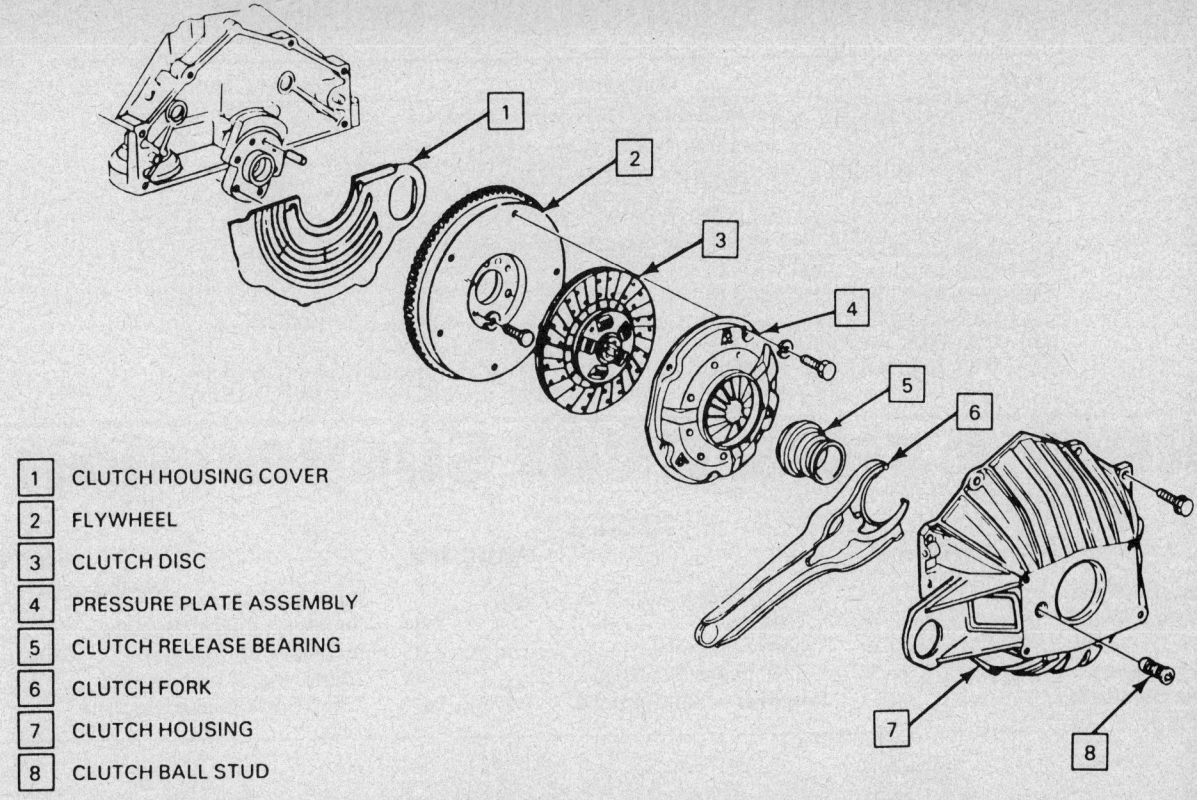

1. CLUTCH HOUSING COVER
2. FLYWHEEL
3. CLUTCH DISC
4. PRESSURE PLATE ASSEMBLY
5. CLUTCH RELEASE BEARING
6. CLUTCH FORK
7. CLUTCH HOUSING
8. CLUTCH BALL STUD

Fig. 2 Clutch disc, pressure plate & housing

mark on flywheel and on clutch cover. If X mark is not evident, prick punch marks on flywheel and clutch cover for indexing purposes during installation.
5. Loosen clutch-to-flywheel attaching bolts evenly one turn at a time until spring pressure is released. Then remove bolts and clutch assembly.
6. Reverse procedure to install. Prior to installation, lubricate pilot bearing sparingly with machine oil. Also apply wheel bearing lubricant 1051344 or equivalent to clutch fork ball socket and fingers and release bearing collar recesses. Use a suitable pilot tool to center clutch disc. Tighten clutch cover bolts evenly and gradually to avoid distorting cover.

MANUAL TRANSMISSION REPLACE

It may be necessary to remove the catalytic converter and its support bracket to facilitate transmission removal.
1. Disconnect battery ground cable, remove shifter boot retaining screws and slide boot up lever.
2. Remove shift lever retaining bolts and lever, then raise and support vehicle.
3. Remove torque arm and propeller shaft.
4. Disconnect speedometer cable and electrical connectors from transmission.
5. Support transmission and remove transmission mount retaining bolts and catalytic converter bracket.
6. Remove crossmember retaining bolts, crossmember and bolts securing flywheel cover.
7. Remove bolts securing transmission to engine, transmission and flywheel cover.
8. Reverse procedure to install.

TIGHTENING SPECIFICATIONS

Year	Component	Torque/Ft. Lbs.
1989–91	Actuator (Slave Cylinder) To Housing	15
	Clutch Housing To Engine (V6)	①
	Clutch Housing To Engine (V8)	②
	Clutch Pedal Mounting Bracket	③
	Extension Housing Bolt	22
	Flywheel To Crankshaft (V6)	④
	Flywheel To Crankshaft (V8)	⑤
	Heat Shield To Clutch Housing	15
	Master Cylinder To Cowl	⑥
	Neutral Safety Switch	⑦
	Pressure Plate To Flywheel (V6)	15

Continued

TIGHTENING SPECIFICATIONS—Continued

Year	Component	Torque/Ft. Lbs.
	Pressure Plate To Flywheel (V8)	30
	Reservoir To Mounting Bracket	⑧
	Shift Control Lever Bolt	13
	Transmission Drain & Fill Plugs	20
	Transmission To Flywheel Housing Bolt	55

① —1988, 55 ft. lbs.; 1989–91, 35 ft. lbs.
② —1988, 68 ft. lbs.; 1989–91, 70 ft. lbs.
③ —1988–89, 25 ft. lbs.; 1990–91, 26 ft. lbs.
④ —1988, 50 ft. lbs.; 1989–91, 52 ft. lbs.
⑤ —1988, 75 ft. lbs.; 1989–91, 74 ft. lbs.

⑥ —1989, 113 inch lbs.; 1990–91, 115 inch lbs.
⑦ —1988–89, 27 inch lbs.; 1990–91, 19 inch lbs.
⑧ —1988, 30 inch lbs.; 1989–91, 53 inch lbs.

Rear Axle & Rear Suspension

INDEX

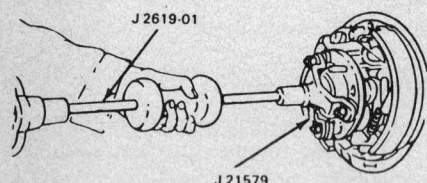

Fig. 1 Removing axle shaft. Borg Warner axle

REAR AXLE
REPLACE

Construction of the axle assembly is such that service operations may be performed with the housing installed in the vehicle or with the housing removed and installed in a holding fixture. The following procedure is necessary only when the housing requires replacement.

1. Raise and support vehicle, then support rear axle with a suitable jack.
2. Disconnect shock absorbers from lower mountings.
3. Remove track bar.
4. Disconnect brake line from axle housing junction block and the parking brake cable.
5. Disconnect lower control arms from axle housing attachments, if equipped with coil springs.
6. Remove propeller shaft.
7. Lower axle slowly until springs can be moved. Roll axle assembly out from under vehicle.
8. Reverse procedure to install.

AXLE SHAFT
REPLACE
BORG WARNER AXLE

1. Raise and support rear of vehicle, then remove wheel and tire assembly.

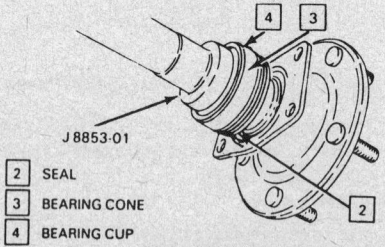

2	SEAL
3	BEARING CONE
4	BEARING CUP

Fig. 2 Removing axle shaft bearing retainer nuts. Borg Warner axle

2. Remove brake caliper, then remove brake rotor.
3. Remove four nuts attaching axle shaft bearing retainer to axle housing.
4. Using puller and adapter J-21579 and J-2619-01 or equivalent, pull axle shaft from housing, **Fig. 1.**
5. To replace axle shaft bearing, split inner retainer with a suitable chisel, then remove retainer from axle shaft, **Fig. 2.** Using Tool No. J-22912-01 or equivalent, press bearing and seal from axle shaft.
6. Reverse procedure to install. When replacing oil seals, it should be noted right hand seal is identified by black bands, while left hand seal is identified by gold bands. Prior to installation, seal lips should be lightly coated with a suitable grease. When pressing bearing and seal onto axle shaft, use tool No. J-8853-01 or equivalent. Position chamfer on outer diameter of bearing retainer toward bearing. On models with limited slip, both axle shaft splines should be fully engaged before axle shaft is rotated to maintain spline alignment.

GM AXLE

1. Raise vehicle and support vehicle,

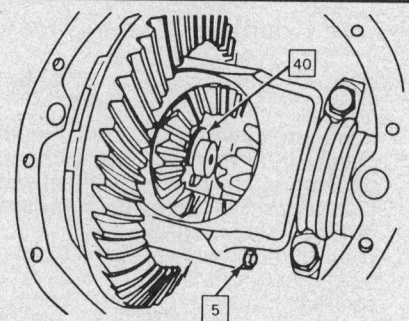

| 5 | LOCK SCREW |
| 40 | C-LOCK |

Fig. 3 Pinion shaft lock screw & axle shaft C-lock. GM axle

then remove wheel and brake drum or rotor.
2. Drain lube from carrier and remove cover.
3. Remove differential pinion shaft lock screw and remove differential pinion shaft, **Fig. 3.**
4. Pull flange end of axle shaft toward center of vehicle and remove C-lock from button end of shaft, **Fig. 3.**
5. Remove axle shaft from housing, being careful not to damage seal.
6. Reverse procedure to install the axle shaft.

PROPELLER SHAFT
REPLACE

1. Raise and support vehicle.
2. Mark position of shaft in relation to pinion flange for reassembly.
3. Remove straps securing universal joint to pinion flange, then disconnect shaft from flange. **Tape bearing cups to universal joint to prevent loss of needle bearings.**
4. Slide yoke out of transmission and re-

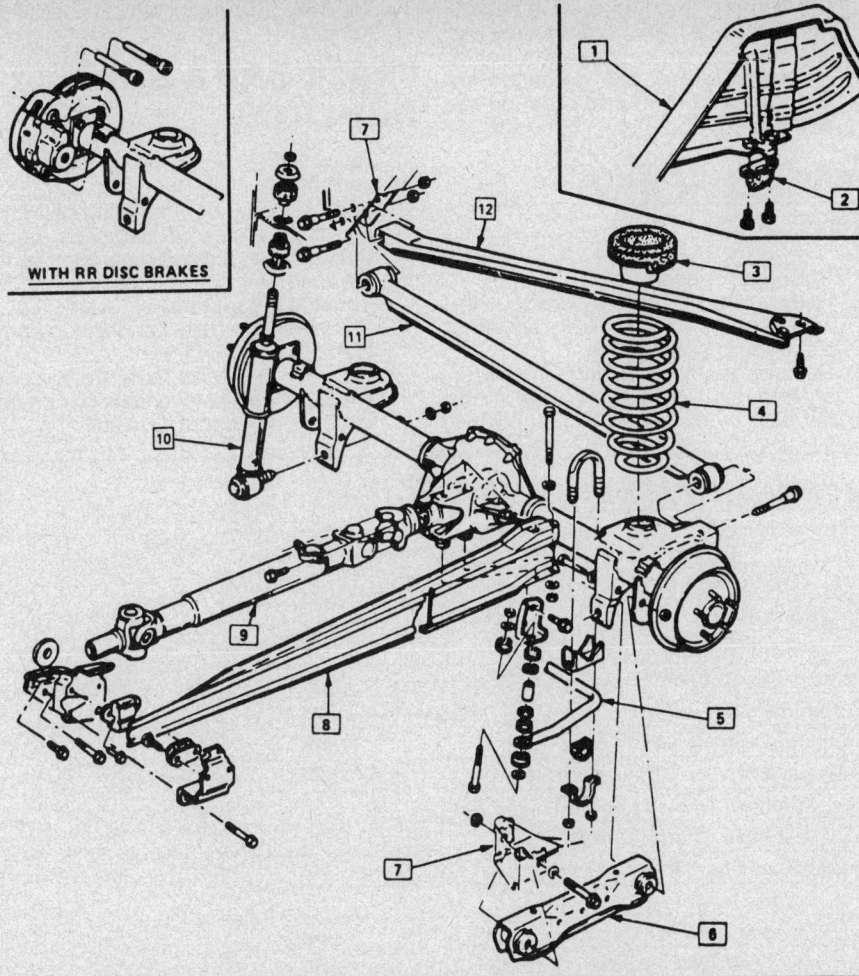

WITH RR DISC BRAKES

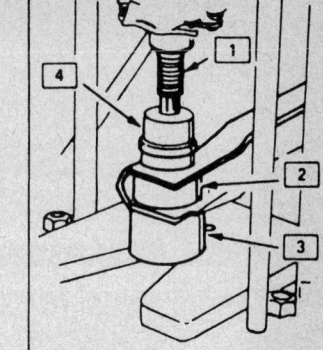

Fig. 5   Control arm bushing removal

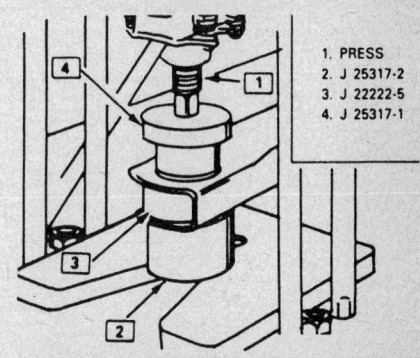

Fig. 6   Control arm bushing installation

1. RAIL	7. UNDERBODY
2. JOUNCE BUMPER	8. TORQUE ARM
3. SPRING INSULATOR ASSEMBLY	9. PROP SHAFT
4. COIL SPRING	10. SHOCK ABSORBER
5. OPTIONAL STABILIZER BAR	11. TRACK BAR
6. LOWER CONTROL ARM	12. TRACK BAR BRACE

Fig. 4   Exploded view of rear suspension

move propeller shaft. Insert suitable plug in transmission to prevent fluid loss.

5. Reverse procedure to install.

SHOCK ABSORBER
REPLACE

1. Raise vehicle and support rear axle.
2. Pull back carpeting, then remove shock absorber upper mounting nut.
3. Remove shock absorber lower mounting nut, then remove shock absorber, **Fig. 4.**
4. Reverse procedure to install.

COIL SPRINGS
REPLACE

1. Raise and support vehicle and support rear axle with a suitable adjustable jack.
2. Remove track bar mounting bolt from axle and loosen track bar bolt at body brace, **Fig. 4.**
3. Disconnect rear brake hose clip at underbody, then disconnect shock absorbers at lower mountings.
4. Carefully lower rear axle and remove springs and insulators.
5. Reverse procedure to install.

LOWER CONTROL ARM & BUSHINGS
REPLACE
LOWER CONTROL ARM

If both control arms are to be removed,

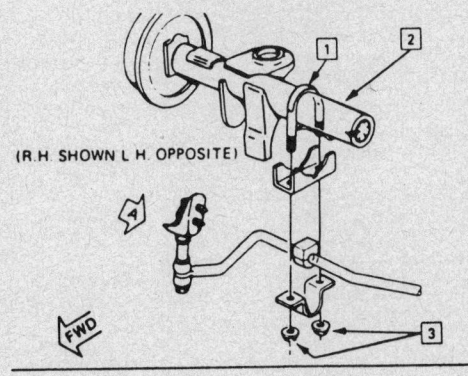

(R.H. SHOWN L.H. OPPOSITE)

FWD

Fig. 7   Stabilizer bar installation

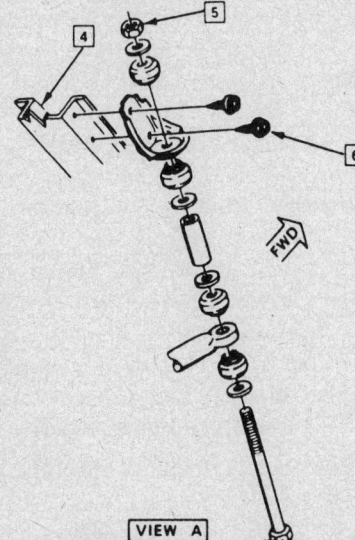

FWD

VIEW A

remove one control arm at a time to prevent axle from slipping or rolling.

1. Raise vehicle and support at frame pads. Support nose of axle housing to prevent assembly from twisting when control arm is removed.
2. Remove bolts securing control arm to chassis and rear axle, and the control arm, **Fig. 4.**
3. Reverse procedure to install.

CONTROL ARM BUSHINGS

1. Raise and support vehicle and remove control arm as outlined previously.
2. Press bushings out of control arm using suitable tools as shown in **Fig. 5.**
3. Reverse procedure to install, ensuring

bushing is properly seated in control arm, **Fig. 6.** If replacement bushing fits loosely in control arm, or if mounting areas are damaged or deformed, control arm must be replaced.

STABILIZER BAR
REPLACE

1. Raise and support vehicle.
2. Remove link bolt nuts, washers, bushings, spacers and link bolts securing stabilizer to chassis, **Fig. 7.**
3. Remove clamps securing stabilizer shaft to rear axle and stabilizer shaft.
4. Reverse procedure to install. Torque

link bolts and U-bolt nuts to specifications.

TRACK BAR & BRACE
REPLACE

1. Raise vehicle and support rear axle at curb height.
2. Remove track bar mounting bolt and nut from rear axle and from body bracket, then remove track bar, **Fig. 4.**
3. Remove heat shield attaching screws from track bar brace.
4. Remove three track bar brace to body brace screws.
5. Remove nut and bolt from body bracket, then remove track bar brace.
6. Reverse procedure to install.

TIGHTENING SPECIFICATIONS

Year	Component	Torque/Ft. lbs.
1988	Control Arm To Rear Axle	80
	Control Arm To Underbody	80
	Rear Axle Housing Cover To Axle	20
	Rear Axle Pinion Shaft Lock Screw (GM)	20
	Rear Axle Shaft Bearing Retainer Nuts (Borg Warner)	35
	Shock Absorber Lower Mounting	70
	Shock Absorber Upper Mounting	150①
	Stabilizer Bracket To Body	35
	Stabilizer Clamp To U-Bolt	20
	Stabilizer Shaft To Body Bracket	16
	Torque Arm Outer Bracket	31
	Torque Arm To Rear Axle	100
	Track Bar To Axle	59
	Track Bar To Body Bracket	78
	Track Bar Brace To Body Bracket Nut	78
	Track Bar Brace To Body Bracket Screw	34
	Universal Joint Strap Bolt	16
	Wheel & Tire Assembly Lug Nuts	80
1989-90	Control Arm To Rear Axle	85
	Control Arm To Underbody	85
	Rear Axle Housing Cover To Axle	20
	Rear Axle Pinion Shaft Lock Screw (GM)	20
	Rear Axle Shaft Bearing Retainer Nuts (Borg Warner)	35
	Shock Absorber Lower Mounting	70
	Shock Absorber Upper Mounting	13
	Stabilizer Bracket To Body	35
	Stabilizer Clamp To U-Bolt	20
	Stabilizer Shaft To Body Bracket	16
	Torque Arm Outer Bracket	30
	Torque Arm To Rear Axle	98
	Track Bar To Axle	61
	Track Bar To Body Bracket	80
	Track Bar Brace To Body Bracket Nut	80
	Track Bar Brace To Body Bracket Screw	35
	Universal Joint Strap Bolt	16
	Wheel & Tire Assembly Lug Nuts	81

①—Inch Lbs.

Front Suspension & Steering

INDEX

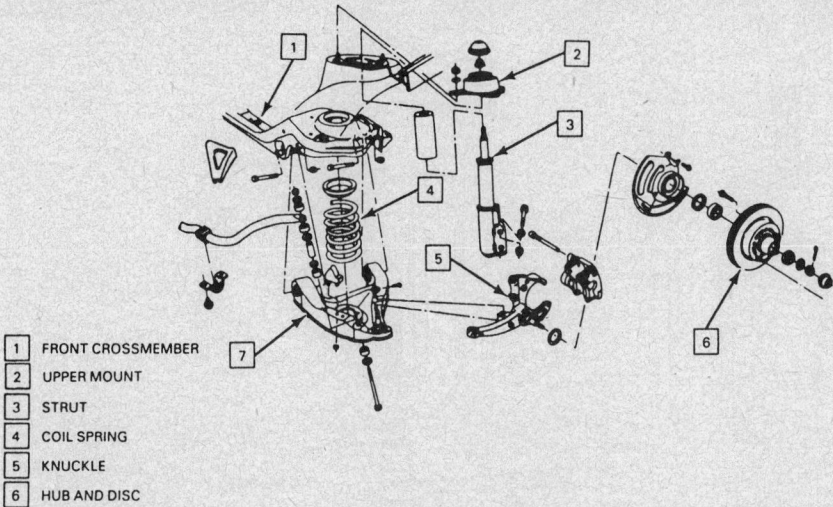

1. FRONT CROSSMEMBER
2. UPPER MOUNT
3. STRUT
4. COIL SPRING
5. KNUCKLE
6. HUB AND DISC
7. LOWER CONTROL ARM

Fig. 1   Front suspension exploded view

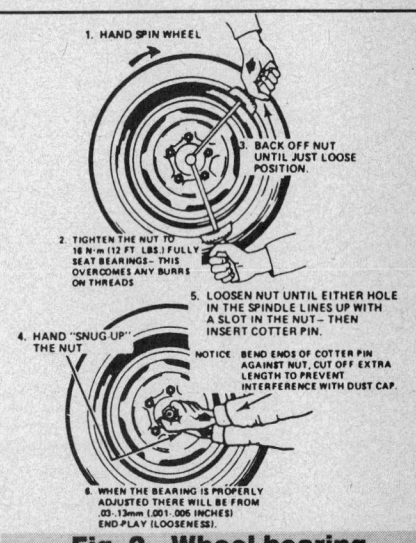

Fig. 2   Wheel bearing adjustment

DESCRIPTION

A modified strut type suspension is used on Camaro and Firebird, **Fig. 1.** Each wheel is independently connected to the chassis by a lower control arm, spindle and a strut assembly which locates the spindle and controls ride by dampening spring action. Coil springs are mounted between the lower control arm and crossmember, and a stabilizer shaft is connected between the chassis and control arms to control side roll.

WHEEL BEARINGS
ADJUST

1. While rotating wheel forward, torque spindle nut to 12 ft. lbs., **Fig. 2.**
2. Back off nut until just loose then hand tighten nut and back it off again until either hole in spindle lines up with hole in nut. **Do not back off nut more than ½ flat.**
3. Install new cotter pin. With wheel bearing properly adjusted, there will be .001-.005 inch end play.

WHEEL BEARINGS
REPLACE

1. Raise and support vehicle, then remove wheel and tire assembly.
2. Remove bolts holding brake caliper to its mounting and insert a fabricated

block (1¹/₁₆ x 1¹/₁₆ x 2 inches in length) between the brake pads as the caliper is being removed. Once removed, the caliper can be wired or secured in some manner away from the disc.
3. Remove spindle nut and hub and disc assembly. Grease retainer and inner wheel bearing can now be removed.
4. Reverse procedure to install.

SUSPENSION & STEERING LINKAGE CHECK

1. Raise vehicle with jack placed under frame torque box behind front wheel.
2. Lock steering wheel with wheels in straight ahead position, then mount dial indicator on a suitable stand with pointer bearing against outer rim of wheel, **Fig. 3.**
3. Move wheel in and out at front and rear, without moving steering wheel, while observing gauge.
4. If gauge reading exceeds .108 inches, check steering linkage and suspension for excessive wear or damage.

LOWER BALL JOINT INSPECTION

Ball joint seals should be checked for cuts and tears. If cuts and tears are present, replace ball joint.

LOWER BALL JOINT
REPLACE

1. Raise vehicle and support at frame, and remove wheel and tire.
2. Position a suitable jack under lower control arm spring seat, and raise jack to compress coil spring. **Jack must remain in place during ball joint replacement to hold spring and lower control arm in position.**
3. Remove cotter pin and nut securing ball joint stud to steering knuckle, then disconnect joint from knuckle using a suitable tool.
4. Lift knuckle assembly from ball stud, guiding control arm out of splash shield, then support knuckle aside to allow clearance for joint removal.
5. Remove grease fitting, then press ball joint assembly out of lower control arm using a suitable tool, **Fig. 4.**
6. Press replacement joint into arm by reversing removal tools, fit spindle over ball stud, install washer, if equipped, and retaining nut.
7. Torque retaining nut to specifications.
8. Tighten nut up to an additional ¹/₁₆ turn, if necessary, to align hole in ball stud with nut, then install cotter pin.

STRUT
REPLACE

1. Raise and support vehicle.
2. Remove wheel and support lower control arm with a suitable jack.

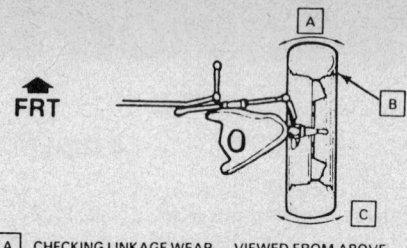

A CHECKING LINKAGE WEAR – VIEWED FROM ABOVE.

B POSITION DIAL INDICATOR TO CHECK
   MOVEMENT AT THIS POINT

C MOVE WHEEL IN AND OUT AT
   FRONT AND BACK

**Fig. 3   Suspension & steering
linkage check**

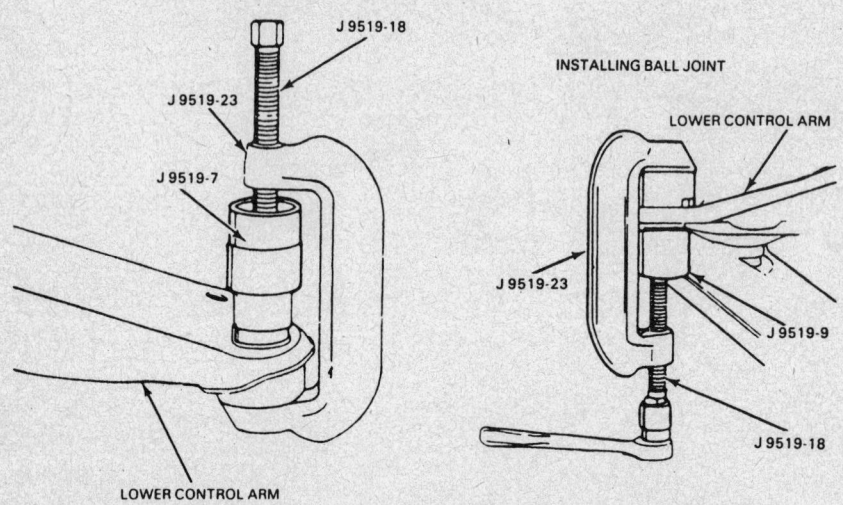

REMOVING BALL JOINT

J 9519-18

J 9519-23

J 9519-7

LOWER CONTROL ARM

INSTALLING BALL JOINT

LOWER CONTROL ARM

J 9519-23

J 9519-9

J 9519-18

Fig. 4   Lower ball joint replace

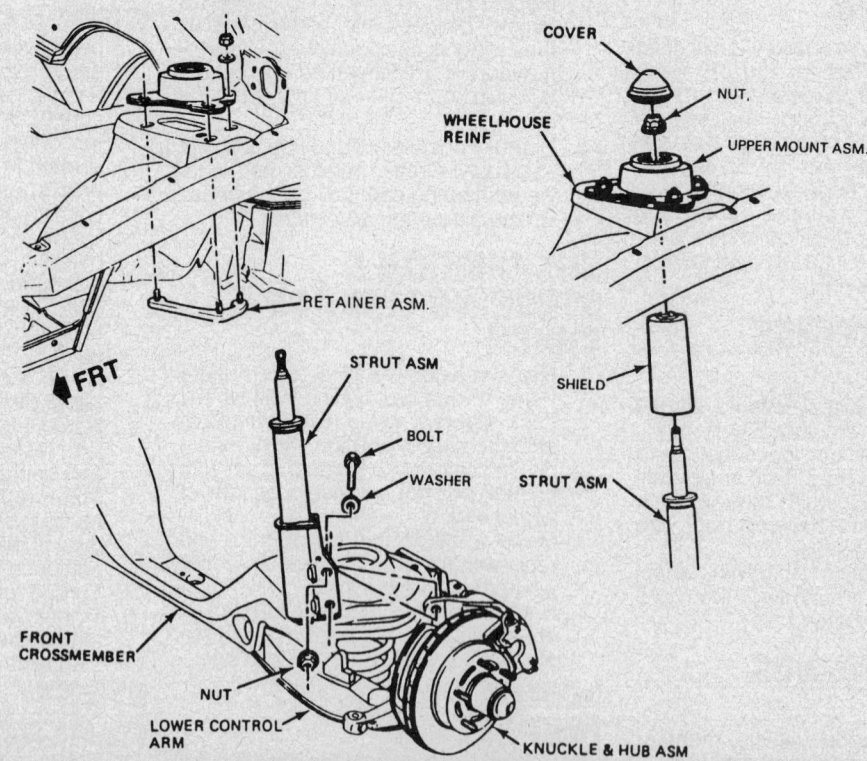

RETAINER ASM.

FRT

STRUT ASM

BOLT

WASHER

FRONT
CROSSMEMBER

NUT

LOWER CONTROL
ARM

COVER

NUT.

WHEELHOUSE
REINF

UPPER MOUNT ASM.

SHIELD

STRUT ASM

KNUCKLE & HUB ASM

Fig. 5   Front suspension strut replace

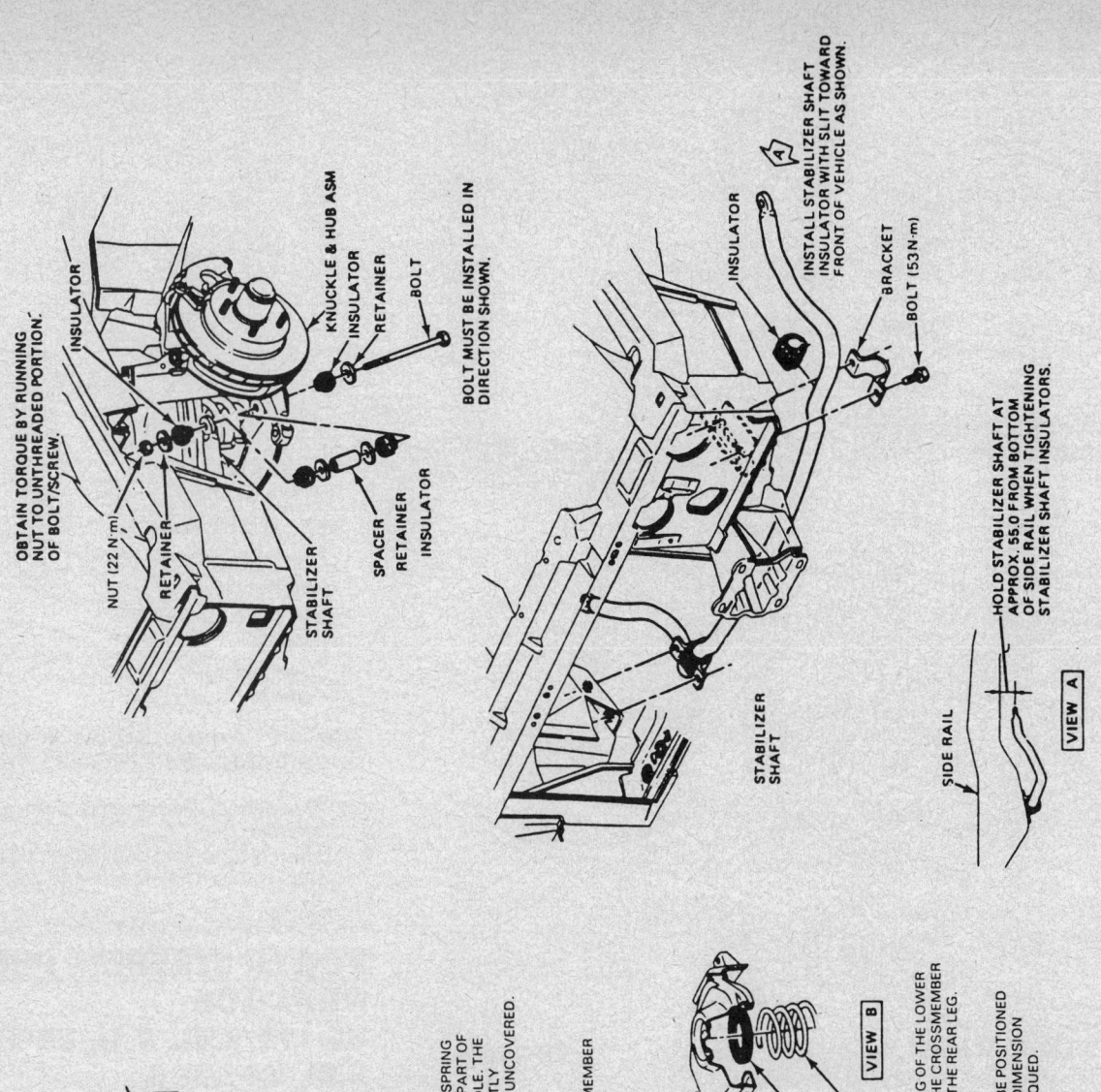

OBTAIN TORQUE BY RUNNING NUT TO UNTHREADED PORTION OF BOLT/SCREW.

INSULATOR

KNUCKLE & HUB ASM

INSULATOR

RETAINER

BOLT

BOLT MUST BE INSTALLED IN DIRECTION SHOWN.

NUT (22 N·m)

RETAINER

STABILIZER SHAFT

SPACER

RETAINER

INSULATOR

INSTALL STABILIZER SHAFT INSULATOR WITH SLIT TOWARD FRONT OF VEHICLE AS SHOWN.

INSULATOR

BRACKET

BOLT (53N·m)

STABILIZER SHAFT

HOLD STABILIZER SHAFT AT APPROX. 55.0 FROM BOTTOM OF SIDE RAIL WHEN TIGHTENING STABILIZER SHAFT INSULATORS.

SIDE RAIL

VIEW A

Fig. 7 Stabilizer shaft replace

FRONT CROSSMEMBER

INSULATOR

SPRING

VIEW B

LOWER CONTROL ARM

INSTALL THE FRONT LEG OF THE LOWER CONTROL ARM INTO THE CROSSMEMBER PRIOR TO INSTALLING THE REAR LEG.

CONTROL ARM MUST BE POSITIONED TO "Z" CURB HEIGHT DIMENSION WHEN BOLTS ARE TORQUED.

BOLT MUST BE INSTALLED IN DIRECTION SHOWN.

NUT 90 N·m (66 LB. FT.)

VIEW A

SPRING TO BE INSTALLED WITH TAPE AT LOWEST POSITION. BOTTOM OF SPRING IS COILED HELICAL, AND THE TOP IS COILED FLAT WITH A GRIPPER NOTCH NEAR END OF WIRE.

AFTER ASSEMBLY, END OF SPRING COIL MUST COVER ALL OR PART OF ONE INSPECTION DRAIN HOLE. THE OTHER HOLE MUST BE PARTLY EXPOSED OR COMPLETELY UNCOVERED.

FRONT CROSSMEMBER

SPRING

LOWER CONTROL ARM

NUT 90 N·m (66 LB. FT.)

FRONT CROSSMEMBER

BOLT MUST BE INSTALLED IN DIRECTION SHOWN.

BUMPER

NUT 28 N·m (21 LB. FT.)

A UNIVERSAL SPRING INSTALLER
1 FRONT COIL SPRING
2 LOWER CONTROL ARM

Fig. 6 Coil spring replace

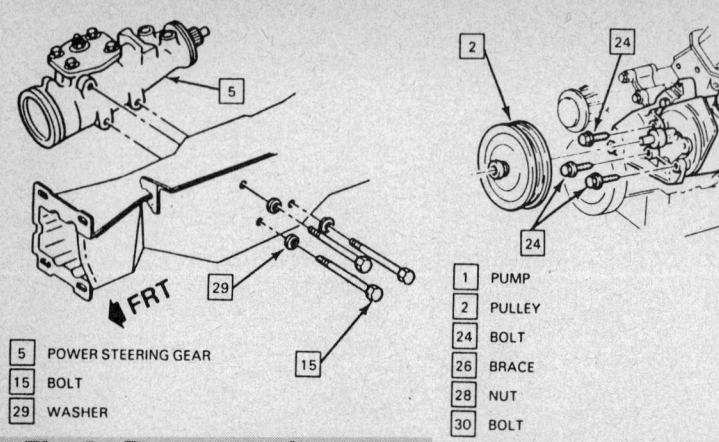

5	POWER STEERING GEAR
15	BOLT
29	WASHER

Fig. 8   Power steering gear installation

1	PUMP
2	PULLEY
24	BOLT
26	BRACE
28	NUT
30	BOLT

Fig. 9   Power Steering pump installation. 2.8L/V6-173 & 3.1L/V6-191

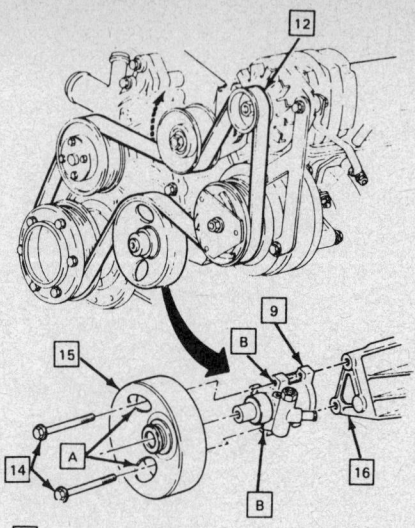

A	PULLEY ACCESS HOLES
B	PUMP MOUNTING HOLES
9	POWER STEERING PUMP
12	DRIVE BELT
14	BOLT
15	PULLEY
16	MOUNTING BRACKET

Fig. 11   Power Steering pump installation. 3.8L/V6-231 Turbo

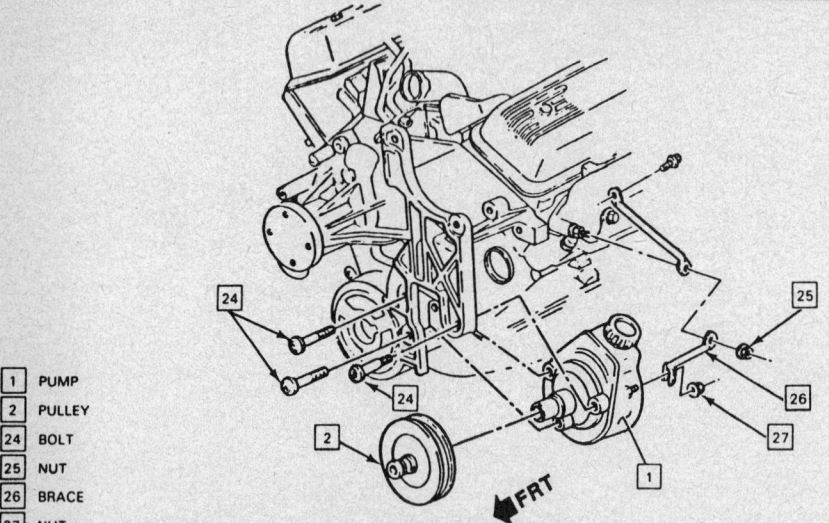

1	PUMP
2	PULLEY
24	BOLT
25	NUT
26	BRACE
27	NUT

Fig. 10   Power Steering pump installation. 5.0L/V8-305 & 5.7L/V8-350

3. Remove brake hose bracket and two strut to knuckle bolts, **Fig. 5**.
4. Remove upper mounting assembly cover.
5. Remove nut from upper end of strut, then the strut and shield.
6. Reverse procedure to install.

COIL SPRING
REPLACE

1. Raise and support vehicle, then remove wheel and tire assembly.
2. Remove stabilizer link and bushings from lower control arm.
3. Remove cotter pin and nut from tie rod end.
4. Using tool J-24292-B or equivalent, disconnect tie rod end from steering knuckle.
5. Using a suitable spring compressor, compress coil spring, **Fig. 6**.
6. Remove lower control arm pivot bolt, then pivot control arm rearward.
7. Remove spring compressor and coil spring.

8. Reverse procedure to install. When installing, position coil spring as shown in **Fig. 6**.

STABILIZER SHAFT
REPLACE

1. Raise and support vehicle.
2. Remove nut from link bolt located at each side, then remove bolt, grommets and bushings, **Fig. 7**.
3. Remove stabilizer shaft to body bolts, then remove stabilizer bar.
4. Reverse procedure to install.

POWER STEERING GEAR
REPLACE

1. Disconnect pressure hose and cooling pipe from power steering gear. Position pressure hose in upward position to prevent fluid drainage.
2. Disconnect intermediate steering shaft from power steering gear stub shaft.

3. Disconnect Pitman arm from power steering gear.
4. Remove steering gear attaching bolts, then remove power steering gear, **Fig. 8**.
5. Reverse procedure to install.

POWER STEERING PUMP
REPLACE
V6-172/2.8L, 3.1L/V6-191, 5.0L/V8-305 & 5.7L/V8-350

1. Disconnect hoses at power steering pump, then plug pump ports and hoses.
2. Loosen pump adjusting bolt and remove pump drive belt.
3. Remove pulley from power steering pump shaft, **Figs. 9 and 10**.
4. Remove pump to support bracket attaching bolts and the pump.
5. Reverse procedure to install. Torque attaching bolts to specifications.

3.8L/V6-231 TURBO

1. Place steering wheel in full left turn position.
2. Disconnect battery ground cable.
3. Remove serpentine drive belt, then remove left hand intercooler bracket.
4. Raise and support vehicle.
5. Disconnect pressure and return hoses from power steering pump.
6. Align holes in pump pulley with mounting bolt holes on pump, then remove mounting bolts.
7. Remove power steering pump, **Fig. 11**.
8. Reverse procedure to install.

TIGHTENING SPECIFICATIONS

Year	Component	Torque/ft. lbs.
1988	Lower Control Arm Ball Joint Stud	78
	Lower Control Arm Pivot Bolt	63
	Pitman Arm Nut	185
	Power Steering Gear Mounting Bolts	70
	Stabilizer Bracket Bolt	37
	Stabilizer Link Nut	13
	Strut To Steering knuckle	202
	Strut Bottom Upper Nut	44
	Strut Upper Mount To Wheel Housing Tower	19
	Tie Rod End To Steering Knuckle	35
1989-91	Lower Control Arm Ball Joint Stud	83
	Lower Control Arm Pivot Bolt	66
	Pitman Arm Nut	185
	Power Steering Gear Mounting Bolts	①
	Stabilizer Bracket Bolt	39
	Stabilizer Link Nut	16
	Strut To Steering knuckle	203
	Strut Bottom Upper Nut	46
	Strut Upper Mount To Wheel Housing Tower	18
	Tie Rod End To Steering Knuckle	35

①—1989, 66 ft. lbs.; 1990-91, 60 ft. lbs.

Wheel Alignment

INDEX

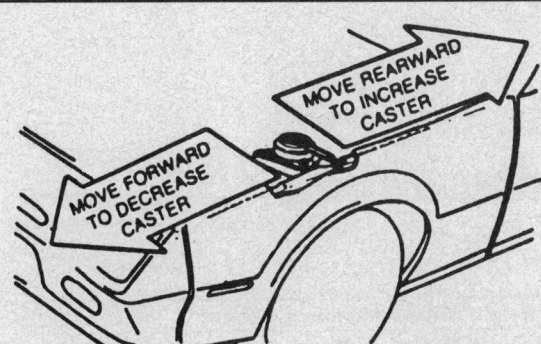

Fig. 1 Caster adjustment

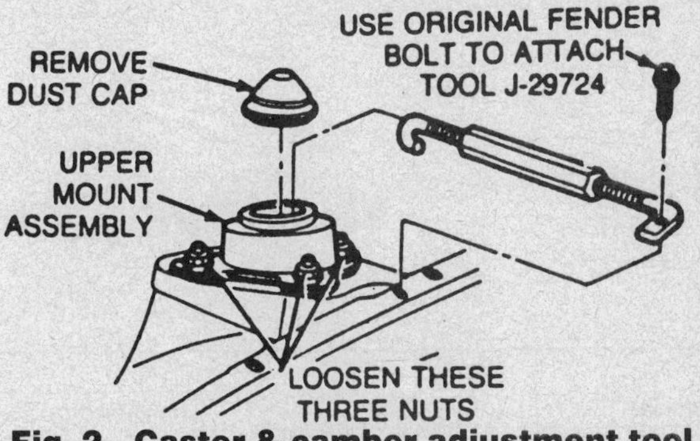

Fig. 2 Caster & camber adjustment tool installation

FRONT WHEEL ALIGNMENT

Prior to checking or adjusting front suspension alignment, inspect suspension components for damage or excessive wear, and replace as needed. Ensure tire pressures and wheel bearings are properly adjusted, then raise and release front bumper several times to allow vehicle to assume normal ride height.

CASTER

Caster adjustments are made by moving the position of the upper strut mount assembly, **Fig. 1.** To make adjustment, remove dust cap and fender bolt and attach tool J-29724 to original fender bolt, **Fig. 2.** Tighten the turnbuckle and loosen the three strut mount attaching nuts.

Adjust caster by lightly tapping the mount assembly forward or rearward. Move mount forward to decrease caster, or rearward to increase caster, **Fig. 1.**

CAMBER

Camber adjustments are made by moving the position of the upper strut mount assembly, **Fig. 3.** To make adjustment, remove dust cap and fender bolt and attach tool J-29724 to original fender bolt, **Fig. 2.** Tighten the turnbuckle and loosen the three strut mount attaching nuts.

Adjust camber by rotating the turnbuckle to move mount assembly inward or outward. Move mount inboard to decrease camber, or outboard to increase camber, **Fig. 3.**

CHEVROLET CAMARO & PONTIAC FIREBIRD

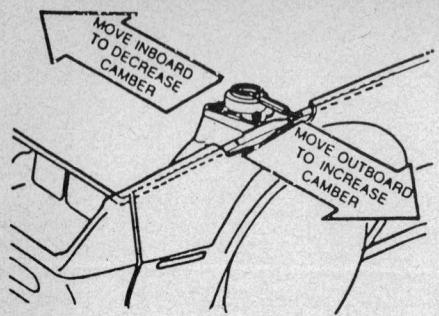

Fig. 3   Camber adjustment

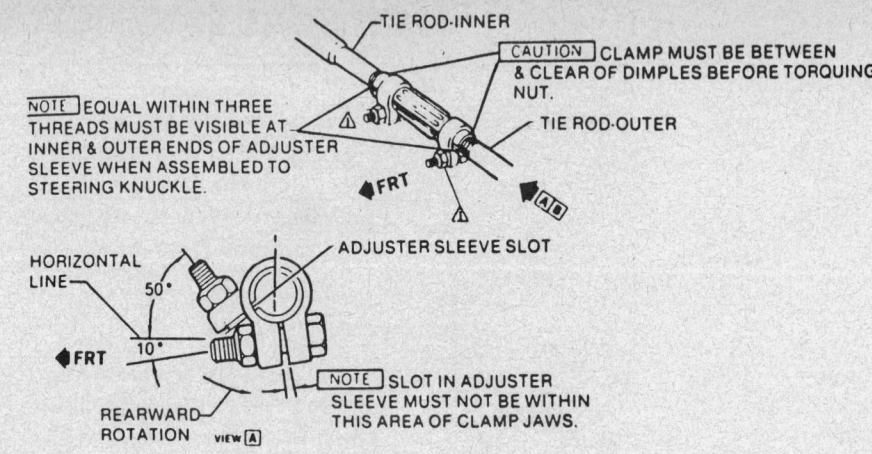

Fig. 4   Tie rod clamp & sleeve positioning

TOE-IN

1. Loosen clamp bolts at each end of tie rod adjustable sleeves.
2. Set steering wheel in straight-ahead position, then turn tie rods as necessary until toe-in is within specifications.
3. After adjustment is complete, ensure threads exposed on each end of sleeve are equal and tie rod end housings are at right angles to steering arm.
4. Position tie rod clamps and sleeves as shown, **Fig. 4**, then tighten nuts.

RIDE HEIGHT

Refer to **Fig. 5** for ride height measurements and specifications.

Fig. 5   Vehicle riding height measurement locations & specifications (Part 1 of 2)

VEHICLE RIDE HEIGHT SPECIFICATION

Make & Model	Year	Riding Height Measurements In Inches ①			
		Dimension A	Dimension B	Dimension C	Dimension D
Camaro	1988	32 19/32	17 15/64	②	③
	1989–91	32 19/32	17 15/64	②	④
Firebird	1988–91	32 19/32	17 15/64	8 15/64	8 17/64

① —Plus or minus 13/32 inch.
② —Except models with P245-50VR16 tires, 8 11/32 inches; models with P245-50VR16 tires, 8 1/32 inches.
③ —Except models with P245-50VR16 tires, 8 19/64 inches; models with P245-50VR16 tires, 8 1/32 inches.
④ —Except models with P245-50VR16 tires, 8 19/64 inches; models with P245-50VR16 tires, 8 7/64 inches.

Fig. 5   Vehicle riding height measurement locations & specifications (Part 2 of 2)

CHEVROLET CORVETTE
(Y Car)

INDEX OF SERVICE OPERATIONS

NOTE: Refer To The Rear Of This Manual For Vehicle Manufacturer's Special Tool Suppliers.

Continued

INDEX OF SERVICE OPERATIONS — Continued

Specifications

GENERAL ENGINE SPECIFICATIONS

Year	Engine Liter/CID	Engine VIN Code ①	Fuel System	Bore & Stroke	Compression Ratio	Net Brake H.P. @ RPM ②	Maximum Torque	Normal Oil Pressure Psi.
1988–89	5.7L/V8-350③	8	TPI	4.00 x 3.48	9.5	240 @ 4000	335 @ 3200	④
	5.7L/V8-350⑤	8	TPI	4.00 x 3.48	9.5	245 @ 4300	340 @ 3200	④
1990–91	5.7L/V8-350③⑧	8	TPI	4.00 x 3.48	9.5	245 @ 4000	340 @ 3200	④
	5.7L/V8-350⑤	8	TPI	4.00 x 3.48	9.5	250 @ 4400	345 @ 3200	④
	5.7L/V8-350⑥	J	TPI	3.90 x 3.66	11.0	375 @ 5800	370 @ 4800	⑦

CID—Cubic Inch Displacement.
TPI—Tune Port Injection.
①—The eighth digit of the VIN denotes engine code.
②—Ratings are net, as installed in vehicle.

③—Models with single outlet mufflers.
④—With engine hot, minimum oil pressure at 1000 RPM, 6 psi.; at 2000 RPM, 18 psi.; at 4000 RPM, 24 psi.
⑤—Models with dual outlet sport mufflers.

⑥—4 Cam 32 valve engine (ZR-1).
⑦—With engine hot, minimum oil pressure, at idle speed, 12 psi.; above 3000 RPM, 40 psi.
⑧—Single cam 16 valve engine.

TUNE UP SPECIFICATIONS

| Year & Engine/VIN code ① | Spark Plug Gap | Firing Order Fig. ③ | Ignition Timing BTDC ② | | | Curb Idle Speed ④ | | Fast Idle Speed | | Fuel Pump Pressure, Psi |
			Man. Trans.	Auto. Trans.	Mark Fig.	Man. Trans.	Auto. Trans.	Man. Trans.	Auto. Trans.	
1988–89										
5.7L/V8-350/8	.035	A	6⑤	6⑤	B	⑥	⑥	⑥		40.5–47⑦
1990–91										
5.7L/V8-350/8⑩	.035	A	6⑤	6⑤	B	⑥	⑥	⑥	⑥	40.5–47⑦
5.7L/V8-350/J⑧	.035	C	6⑨	—	D	⑥	⑥	⑥		48–55⑦

① —The eighth digit of the VIN denotes engine code.
② —BTDC: Before Top Dead Center.
③ —Before removing from distributor cap, determine location of No. 1 wire in cap, as distributor position may have been altered from that shown at the end of this chart.
④ —When checking idle speed, set parking brake & block drive wheels.

⑤ —Disconnect set timing by-pass connector (tan/black wire), which breaks out of the engine wiring harness conduit. After completing ignition timing check, reconnect timing by pass connector. With engine Off, clear ECM memory by removing battery voltage to ECM for 30 seconds.
⑥ —Idle speed is controlled by an idle

speed control motor.
⑦ —With shop towel wrapped around fuel pressure fitting to prevent fuel spillage, connect a suitable fuel pressure gauge. Check fuel pressure with ignition switch in On position, engine not running.
⑧ —4 Cam 32 valve engine (ZR-1).
⑨ —ECM controlled, no adjustment.
⑩ —Single cam 16 valve engine.

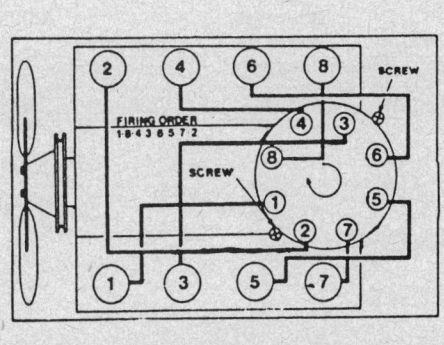

Fig. A

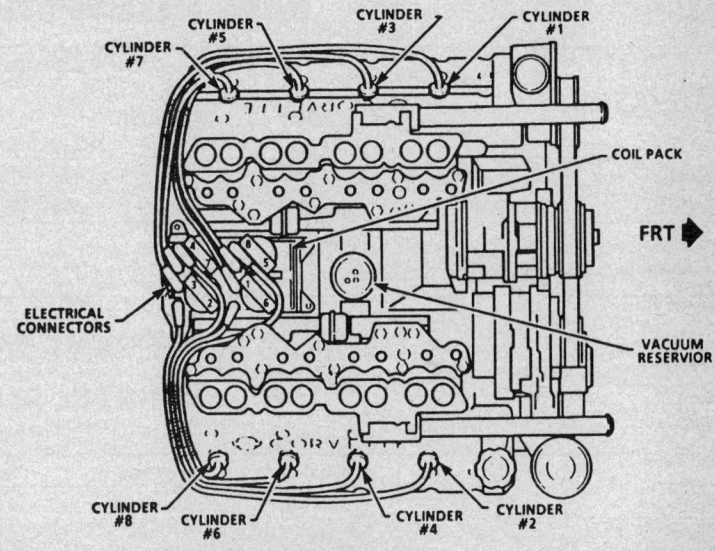

Fig. C

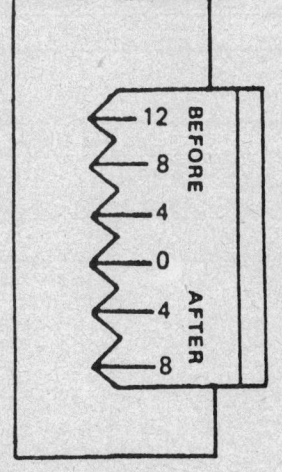

Fig. B

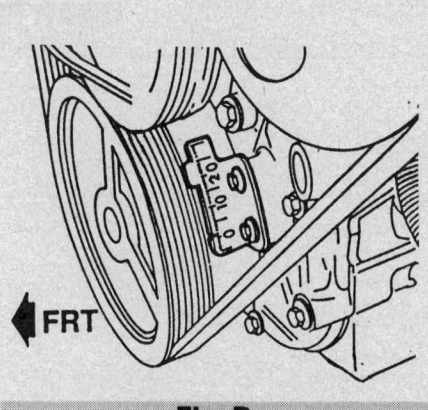

Fig. D

ALTERNATOR SPECIFICATIONS

Year	Ident. No.	Model	Series	Rated Hot Output Amps	Rotor Field Current @ 70°F
1988–90	1101264	Delco Remy	CS-130	105	—
1989–90	1101238	Delco Remy	CS-144	120	—
1990	1101849	Delco Remy	CS-144	120	1.7–2.1
1991	1101597	Delco Remy	CS-144	124	2.2–2.3
	1101601	Delco Remy	CS-130	105	1.7–2.0

STARTER MOTOR APPLICATIONS

Refer to "Starter Motors" for starter specifications.

Year	Engine/VIN ①	Ident. No.	Model
1988	5.7L/V8-350/8	1998578	Delco Remy
1988–91	5.7L/V8-350/8 ①	10455702	Delco Remy
1990–91	5.7L/V8-350/J ②	10455704	Nippondenso

①—Single cam 16 valve engine.
②—4 cam 32 valve engine (ZR-1).

REAR AXLE SPECIFICATIONS

Year	Axle Model	Carrier Type	Ring Gear Backlash		Pinion Bearing Preload		Side Gear Preload	
			Method	Adjustment	Method	New Bearings, Inch Lbs.	Method	Adjustment, Inch
1988–91	Dana Model 36 ①	Integral	Shims	.006–.009	Shims	15–35	Shims	.015–.020
	Dana Model 44 ②	Integral	Shims	.006–.009	Shims	20–40	Shims	.008–.012

①—Models with auto. trans.
②—Models with man. trans.

WHEEL ALIGNMENT SPECIFICATIONS
FRONT WHEEL ALIGNMENT

Year	Model	Caster Angle, Degrees		Camber Angle, Degrees		Toe Per Wheel, Degrees	
		Limits	Desired	Limits	Desired	Limits	Desired
1988	All	+5.5 to +6.5	+6	+.3 to +1.3	+.8	−.15 to +.15	0
1989	All	+5.3 to +6.3	+5.8	0 to +1	+.5	−.10 to +.10	0
1990–91	All	+5.5 to +6.5	+6	0 to +1	+.5	−.10 to +.10	0

REAR WHEEL ALIGNMENT

Year	Model	Camber Angle, Degrees		Toe Per Wheel, Degrees	
		Limits	Desired	Limits	Desired
1988–91	All	−.5 to +.5	0	−.1 to +.1	0

COOLING SYSTEM & CAPACITY DATA SPECIFICATIONS

Year	Model Or Engine/VIN ①	Cooling System Capacity, Qts.	Radiator Cap Relief Pressure, Psi	Thermo. Opening Temp., °F	Fuel Tank, Gals.	Engine Oil, Qts. ②		Transmission Oil			Rear Axle, Pts.
						Less Filter Change	With Filter Change	Man Trans., Pts.	Auto. Trans., Qts. ③		
									Drain & Refill	Total Capacity	
1988	5.7L/V8-350/8	14	18	195	20	4④	5④	⑤	5⑥	11.5⑥	3.75⑦
1989	5.7L/V8-350/8	14	18	195	20	4④	5④	4.4⑧	5⑥	11.5⑥	3.75⑦
1990	5.7L/V8-350/8 ⑪	14.7	18	195	20	4⑨	5⑨	4.4⑧	5⑥	11.5⑥	3.75⑦
	5.7L/V8-350/J ⑫	16.7	17	180	20	⑩	⑩	4.4⑧	5⑥	11.5⑥	3.75⑦
1991	5.7L/V8-350/8 ⑪	17.8	15	195	20	4⑨	5⑨	4.4⑧	5⑥	11.2⑥	3.75⑦
	5.7L/V8-350/J ⑫	14.7	15	180	20	⑩	⑩	4.4⑧	5⑥	11.2⑥	3.75⑦

①—The eighth digit of the VIN denotes engine code.
②—After refilling, recheck oil level.
③—Approximate, make final check with dipstick.
④—Recommended engine oil SG, SF/CC or SF/CD SAE 5W-30.
⑤—Transmission, 2.1 pts. 80W GL-5 gear lubricant; overdrive unit, 3.45 pts. Dexron II automatic transmission fluid.
⑥—Use Dexron II type automatic transmission fluid.
⑦—Use 80W-90 GL-5 gear lubricant & lubricant additive (GM part No. 1052358 or equivalent).
⑧—Use manual transmission fluid SAE 5W-30.
⑨—Recommended engine oil SG SAE 5W-30.
⑩—Recommended engine oil SG SAE 10W-30. Less filter change, 7.6 qts.; with filter change 8.6 qts. With oil cooler drain & flush, less filter change, 9.6 qts.; with filter change, 10.6 qts. Total system capacity with filter removed & oil pan dry, 11.6 qts.
⑪—Single cam 16 valve engine.
⑫—4 cam 32 valve engine (ZR-1).

Electrical
INDEX

FUSE PANEL & FLASHER LOCATION
1988-89

The fuse panel is located behind the right hand side of the instrument panel. The hazard warning flasher is located behind the center of the instrument panel in the multi-use center. The turn signal flasher is located behind the right hand side of the instrument panel near the fuse panel.

1990-91

The fuse panel is located behind the far right hand corner of the instrument panel. The hazard warning flasher is located behind the right hand side of the instrument panel near radio receiver. The turn signal flasher is located behind the below left hand side of the instrument panel to the left of the steering column.

STARTER REPLACE

If shims are used between starter and engine block, they should be placed in their original location during installation. If starter is noisy during cranking, remove one .015 inch double shim or add one .015 single shim to the outer bolt. If starter makes a high pitched whine after firing,

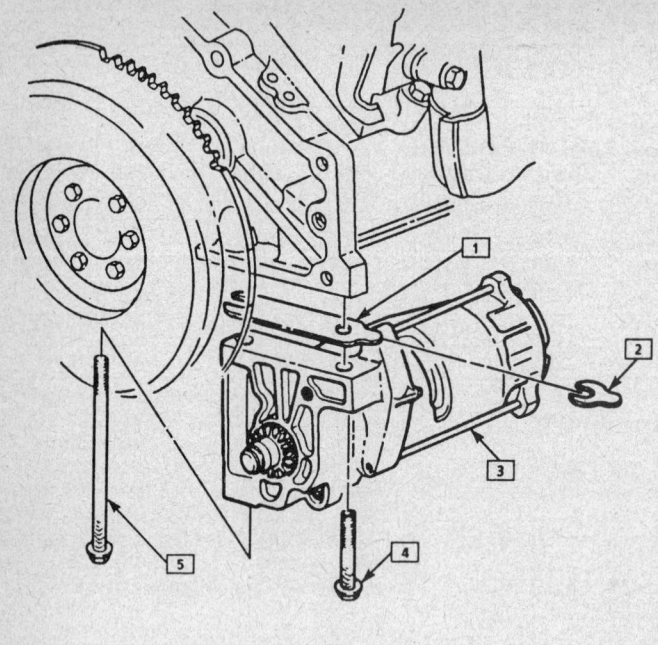

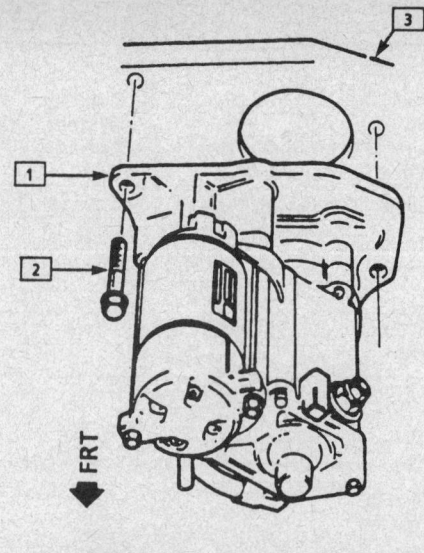

1	LONG SHIM
2	SHORT SHIM
3	STARTER MOTOR
4	OUTBOARD BOLT
5	INBOARD BOLT

Fig. 1   Starter motor replacement. 5.7L/V8-350 single cam 16 valve engine

1	MOTOR, STARTER
2	BOLT, STARTER MOTOR MOUNTING
3	CASE, CYLINDER

Fig. 2   Starter motor replacement. 5.7L/V8-350 4 cam 32 valve (ZR-1) engine

add .015 inch double shims until noise ceases.

1988–91 5.7L/V8-350 SINGLE CAM 16 VALVE ENGINE

1. Disconnect battery ground cable.
2. Raise and support vehicle, then disconnect starter wiring.
3. Remove starter to engine brace and starter heat shields, if equipped.
4. Remove starter mounting bolts and lower starter, **Fig. 1.** Note position of shims, if used.
5. Disconnect solenoid wires and the battery cable.
6. Remove starter from vehicle.
7. Reverse procedure to install. **Torque** starter mounting bolts to 35 ft. lbs.

1990–91 5.7L/V8-350 4 CAM 32 VALVE (ZR-1) ENGINE

1. Disconnect battery ground cable, then drain cooling system.
2. Remove intake plenum assembly. Refer to the "5.7L/V8-350 4 Cam 32 Valve Engine" section, "Intake Plenum Assembly, Replace" procedure.
3. Remove ignition coil pack described under "Ignition Coil Pack, Replace."
4. Disconnect battery positive cable and electrical leads from starter motor.
5. Remove starter motor to engine block attaching bolts, then remove starter motor, **Fig. 2.**
6. Reverse procedure to install. Prior to installation, coat threads of starter mounting bolts with Loctite 262 or equivalent. Torque starter mounting bolts to 38 ft. lbs.

DISTRIBUTOR REPLACE

1988–91 5.7L/V8-350 SINGLE CAM 16 VALVE ENGINE

Removal

1. Disconnect battery ground cable.
2. Remove intake manifold plenum extension.
3. Disconnect ignition switch feed and tachometer leads from distributor cap. Screwdriver or other tools should not be used to release lead connector locking tab.
4. Remove distributor cap attaching screws, then position cap out of way.
5. Disconnect four terminal ECM electrical connector from distributor electrical connector.
6. Remove distributor hold down clamp and bolt. Mark position of distributor rotor to distributor housing and position of distributor housing to engine for use during installation.
7. Lift distributor upward until rotor stops rotating in counterclockwise direction and mark position of rotor to distributor housing for use during installation.
8. Remove distributor from engine.

Installation

1. Position rotor to mark on distributor housing, then insert distributor into engine aligning rotor to housing and housing to engine marks made during removal.
2. If engine was was disturbed while distributor was removed, proceed as follows:
   a. Remove spark plug from No. 1 cyl-

inder.
   b. With transmission in Neutral or Park and parking brake applied, position finger over spark plug opening in cylinder head, then slowly crank engine until compression is felt.
   c. Align crankshaft pulley with TDC (0) mark on timing indicator.
   d. Locate distributor rotor contact between No. 1 and 8 spark plug firing positions on distributor.
   c. Insert distributor into engine.
3. Install distributor hold clamp and bolt. Hand tighten bolt.
4. Connect ECM four terminal electrical connector to distributor.
5. Install distributor cap, then connect ignition switch and tachometer lead connector to cap.
6. Connect battery ground cable, then check and adjust ignition timing as necessary. Torque distributor hold down bolt to 25 ft. lbs.

IGNITION COIL PACK REPLACE

1990–91 5.7L/V8-350 4 CAM 32 VALVE (ZR-1) ENGINE

1. Disconnect battery ground cable.
2. Remove intake plenum assembly. Refer to the "5.7L/V8-350 4 Cam 32 Valve Engine" section, "Intake Plenum Assembly, Replace" procedure.
3. Note position of spark plug wires to coils, **Fig. 3.**
4. Disconnect spark plug wires from coils.
5. Disconnect electrical connectors from ignition coil pack terminals.

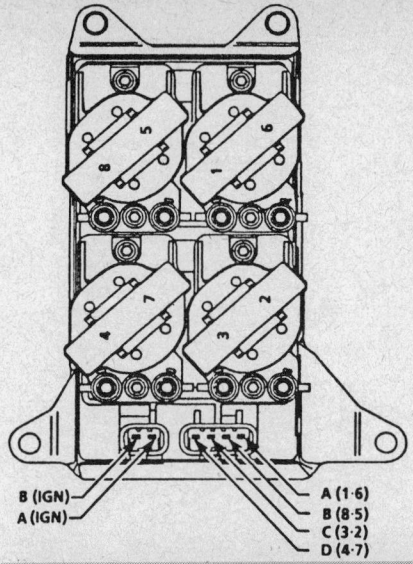

B (IGN)
A (IGN)

A (1-6)
B (8-5)
C (3-2)
D (4-7)

Fig. 3   Coil pack electrical & spark plug wire connections. 5.7L/V8-350 4 cam 32 valve (ZR-1) engine

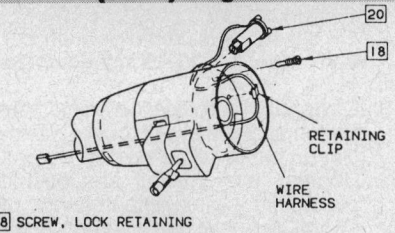

RETAINING CLIP

WIRE HARNESS

18 SCREW, LOCK RETAINING
20 LOCK CYLINDER SET, STRG COL PASS KEY

Fig. 5   Ignition lock replacement. 1990-91

6. Remove four coil pack retaining bolts, then remove coil pack.
7. Reverse procedure to install. Torque coil pack M6-16 retaining bolts to 89 inch lbs. and M8-20 retaining bolts to 19 ft. lbs.

IGNITION LOCK
REPLACE

1988-89

1. Disconnect battery ground cable.
2. Remove steering wheel as described under "Horn Sounder and Steering Wheel, Replace."
3. Remove turn signal switch as described under Turn Signal Switch, Replace, then remove buzzer switch.
4. Place ignition switch in Run position, then remove lock cylinder retaining screw and lock cylinder.
5. Cut wire at lock cylinder assembly, then attach remaining wire extending from steering column cover to back of connector body of new lock cylinder. Pull original wire through column while feeding through new wire.
6. Install by rotating lock cylinder to stop while holding housing, **Fig. 4**. Align cylinder key with keyway in housing, then push lock cylinder assembly into housing until fully seated.

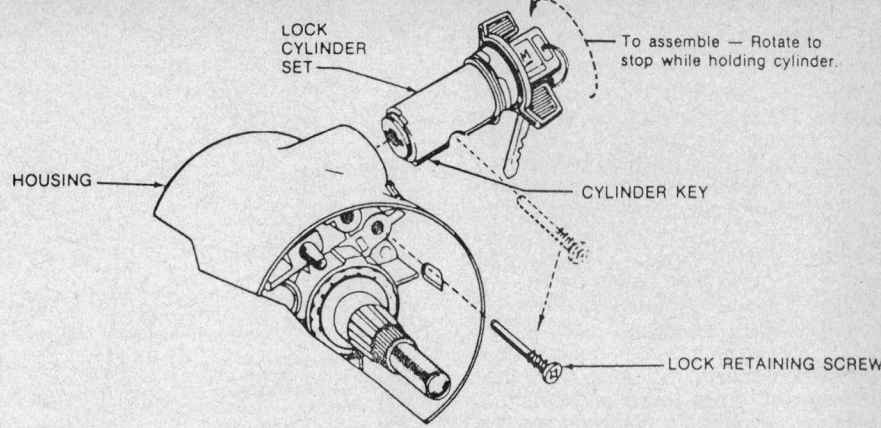

LOCK CYLINDER SET

To assemble — Rotate to stop while holding cylinder.

HOUSING

CYLINDER KEY

LOCK RETAINING SCREW

Fig. 4   Ignition lock replacement. 1988-89

7. Install lock cylinder retaining screw.
8. Install buzzer switch, turn signal switch and steering wheel.

1990-91

1. **To avoid personal injury when servicing models equipped with Supplemental Inflatable Restraint (Airbag) System, temporarily disable system as follows:**
   a. Place ignition switch in off position.
   b. Remove Airbag fuse from fuse panel.
   c. Remove lower left hand trim panel, remove connector position assurance and disconnect yellow two way Supplemental Inflatable Restraint connector at base of steering column.
2. Disconnect battery ground cable.
3. Remove steering wheel as described under "Horn Sounder and Steering Wheel, Replace."
4. Remove turn signal switch as described under "Turn Signal Switch, Replace."
5. Place ignition switch in Lock position.
6. Remove lock cylinder retaining screw.
7. Disconnect terminal electrical connector at bulkhead connection to provide slack.
8. Remove wiring connector from steering column.
9. Attach a suitable length of mechanic wire to ignition lock electrical connector for use during installation. Detach wire retaining clip, then carefully pull ignition lock wiring through housing shroud, steering column and lock housing cover, **Fig. 5**.
10. Remove lock cylinder.
11. Reverse procedure to install. Ensure lock cylinder wiring is properly routed through steering column. Torque lock cylinder retaining screw to 22 inch lbs.
12. **After completing service procedure activate Supplemental Inflatable Restraint (SIR) system as follows:**
    a. Ensure ignition switch is in Off position.
    b. Connect yellow SIR two way electrical connector and install position

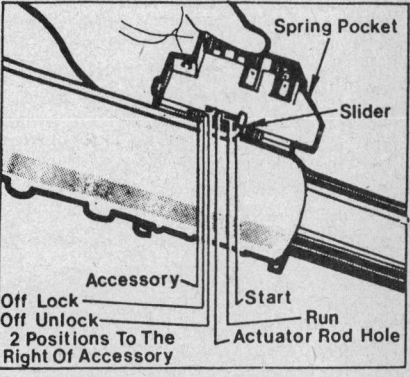

Spring Pocket

Slider

Accessory

Off Lock
Off Unlock
2 Positions To The
Right Of Accessory

Start

Run

Actuator Rod Hole

Fig. 6   Ignition switch

assurance at base of steering column.
c. Install Airbag fuse into fuse panel.
d. Install lower left hand trim panel.
e. Place ignition switch in Run position and note operation of "Infl Rest" warning lamp. Warning lamp should flash 7 to 9 times and then turn off. If not, refer to "Passive Restraint" section for diagnostic system check.

IGNITION SWITCH
REPLACE

The ignition switch is mounted on top of the mast jacket inside the brake pedal support and is actuated by a rod and rack assembly.

1. **To avoid personal injury when servicing models equipped with Supplemental Inflatable Restraint (Airbag) System, temporarily disable system as follows:**
   a. Place ignition switch in off position.
   b. Remove Airbag fuse from fuse panel.
   c. Remove lower left hand trim panel, remove connector position assurance and disconnect yellow two way Supplemental Inflatable Restraint connector at base of steering column.

2. **On all models,** disconnect battery cable.

3. **On models less Supplemental Inflatable Restraint System,** disconnect and lower steering column. It may be necessary, on some models, to remove the upper column mounting bracket if it hinders servicing of switch. Use extreme care when lowering steering column to prevent damage to column assembly. Only lower steering column a sufficient distance to perform ignition switch service.

4. **On all models,** rotate ignition lock to Off unlocked position.

5. If lock cylinder has been removed, pull switch actuator rod up to stop, then push rod down to second detent to place switch in Off unlocked position, **Fig. 6.**

6. Remove column mounted dimmer switch, then remove switch retaining screws and switch.

7. Reverse procedure to install, noting the following:
   a. Place lock cylinder and switch in Off unlocked position, **Fig. 6.**
   b. Fit actuator rod into hole in switch slider and secure switch with retaining screws, ensuring switch does not move out of detent.
   c. Install and adjust dimmer switch, if removed, as outlined in "Dimmer Switch, Replace."

8. **On models equipped with Supplemental Inflatable Restraint (SIR) system,** after completing service procedure activate system as follows:
   a. Ensure ignition switch is in Off position.
   b. Connect yellow SIR two way electrical connector and install position assurance at base of steering column.
   c. Install Airbag fuse into fuse panel.
   d. Install lower left hand trim panel.
   e. Place ignition switch in Run position and note operation of "Infl Rest" warning lamp. Warning lamp should flash 7 to 9 times and then turn off. If not, refer to "Passive Restraint" section for diagnostic system check.

HEADLAMP SWITCH
REPLACE
1988–89

1. Disconnect battery ground cable.
2. Remove hush panel from under left side of instrument panel.
3. Pull switch knob to On position, reach up under dash and depress release button on switch, and remove shaft and knob assembly.
4. Remove cluster bezel and nut securing switch to instrument panel and lower switch.
5. Disconnect electrical connectors and remove switch.
6. Reverse procedure to install.

1990–91

1. To avoid personal injury when servicing models equipped with Supplemental Inflatable Restraint

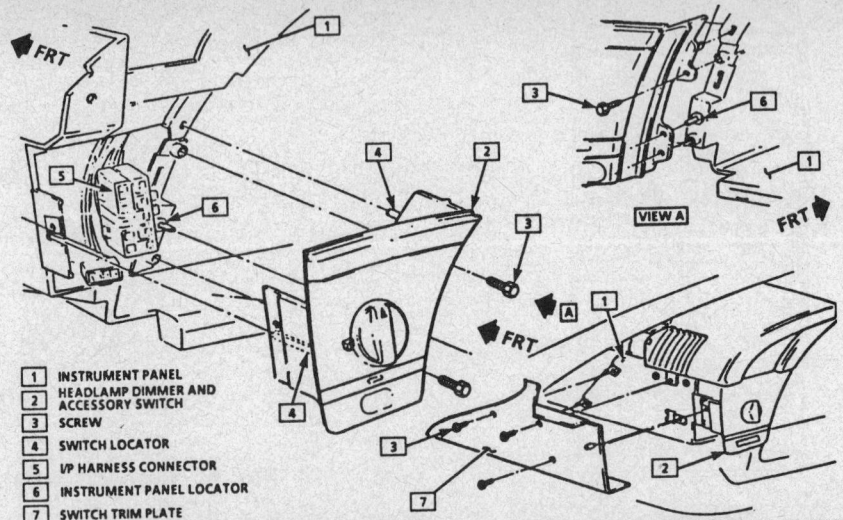

1 INSTRUMENT PANEL
2 HEADLAMP DIMMER AND ACCESSORY SWITCH
3 SCREW
4 SWITCH LOCATOR
5 I/P HARNESS CONNECTOR
6 INSTRUMENT PANEL LOCATOR
7 SWITCH TRIM PLATE

Fig. 7 Headlamp switch replacement. 1990–91

(Airbag) System, temporarily disable system as follows:
   a. Place ignition switch in off position.
   b. Remove Airbag fuse from fuse panel.
   c. Remove lower left hand trim panel, remove connector position assurance and disconnect yellow two way Supplemental Inflatable Restraint connector at base of steering column.

2. Disconnect battery ground cable.
3. Remove instrument cluster as described under "Instrument Cluster, Replace."
4. Remove attaching screws from right hand side of switch, **Fig. 7.**
5. Remove switch trim plate attaching screws.
6. Disconnect electrical connectors, then remove switch.
7. Reverse procedure to install.
8. **After completing service procedure activate system as follows:**
   a. Ensure ignition switch is in Off position.
   b. Connect yellow SIR two way electrical connector and install position assurance at base of steering column.
   c. Install Airbag fuse into fuse panel.
   d. Install lower left hand trim panel.
   e. Place ignition switch in Run position and note operation of "Infl Rest" warning lamp. Warning lamp should flash 7 to 9 times and then turn off. If not, refer to "Passive Restraint" section for diagnostic system check.

STOP LIGHT SWITCH
REPLACE

1. **To avoid personal injury when servicing models equipped with Supplemental Inflatable Restraint (SIR) System,** temporarily disable system as follows:
   a. Place ignition switch in off position.
   b. Remove Airbag fuse from fuse panel.
   c. Remove lower left hand trim panel,

remove connector position assurance and disconnect yellow two way Supplemental Inflatable Restraint connector at base of steering column.

2. **On all models,** remove hush panel from under left side of instrument panel.
3. Disconnect electrical connectors from switch and pull switch out of retaining clip on brake pedal support.
4. Depress brake pedal and push replacement switch into retainer until switch shoulder is bottomed against bracket.
5. Adjust switch by pulling brake pedal back against stop.
6. Ensure switch has continuity when pedal is depressed .53 inch from normal rest position, and pedal fully returns to rest position.
7. Reconnect electrical connectors and install hush panel.
8. **On models equipped with Supplemental Inflatable Restraint (SIR) system,** after completing service procedure activate system as follows:
   a. Ensure ignition switch is in Off position.
   b. Connect yellow SIR two way electrical connector and install position assurance at base of steering column.
   c. Install Airbag fuse into fuse panel.
   d. Install lower left hand trim panel.
   e. Place ignition switch in Run position and note operation of "Infl Rest" warning lamp. Warning lamp should flash 7 to 9 times and then turn off. If not, refer to "Passive Restraint" section for diagnostic system check.

CLUTCH START SWITCH
REPLACE

1. **To avoid personal injury when servicing models equipped with Supplemental Inflatable Restraint**

(Airbag) System, temporarily disable system as follows:
  a. Place ignition switch in off position.
  b. Remove Airbag fuse from fuse panel.
  c. Remove lower left hand trim panel, remove connector position assurance and disconnect yellow two way Supplemental Inflatable Restraint connector at base of steering column.

2. Disconnect battery ground cable and set parking brake.
3. Remove retaining screw and switch from clutch pedal bracket, rotate switch slightly, and pull switch actuating lever from hole in pedal arm.
4. Disconnect electrical connector and remove switch.
5. Position replacement switch with actuating lever installed in hole in pedal arm, then secure switch to bracket with retaining screw.
6. Connect electrical connector to switch and adjust by fully depressing clutch pedal. **If readjustment is necessary, depress detent on switch adjusting block and slide block fully forward on switch rod. Fully depress clutch pedal to complete adjustment.**
7. **On models equipped with Supplemental Inflatable Restraint (SIR) system, after completing service procedure activate system as follows:**
  a. Ensure ignition switch is in Off position.
  b. Connect yellow SIR two way electrical connector and install position assurance at base of steering column.
  c. Install Airbag fuse into fuse panel.
  d. Install lower left hand trim panel.
  e. Place ignition switch in Run position and note operation of "Infl Rest" warning lamp. Warning lamp should flash 7 to 9 times and then turn off. If not, refer to "Passive Restraint" section for diagnostic system check.

NEUTRAL SAFETY SWITCH
REPLACE

1. **To avoid personal injury when servicing models equipped with Supplemental Inflatable Restraint (Airbag) System, temporarily disable system as follows:**
  a. Place ignition switch in off position.
  b. Remove Airbag fuse from fuse panel.
  c. Remove lower left hand trim panel, remove connector position assurance and disconnect yellow two way Supplemental Inflatable Restraint connector at base of steering column.
2. **On all models,** remove floor console cover, then disconnect electrical connectors from switch.
3. Place shift lever in Neutral position of detent plate, then remove switch attaching screws and switch.

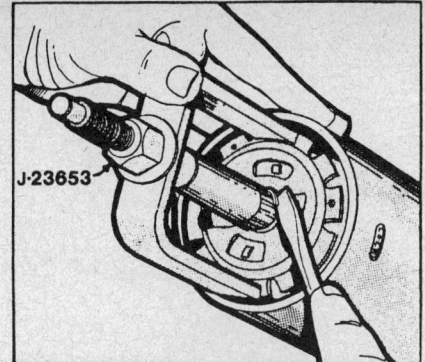

Fig. 8 Lock plate retaining ring removal

4. To install, ensure the shift lever is in Neutral, then position switch on shift lever making sure pin on shaft is in slot of switch.
5. Move shift lever out of Neutral to shear pin which is part of new switch.
6. Reconnect electrical connectors to switch, then apply parking brake and start engine. Check back-up lights and seat belt warning system for proper operation and ensure engine will start only in Park or Neutral.
7. Turn ignition off and install floor console.
8. **On models equipped with Supplemental Inflatable Restraint (SIR) system, after completing service procedure activate system as follows:**
  a. Ensure ignition switch is in Off position.
  b. Connect yellow SIR two way electrical connector and install position assurance at base of steering column.
  c. Install Airbag fuse into fuse panel.
  d. Install lower left hand trim panel.
  e. Place ignition switch in Run position and note operation of "Infl Rest" warning lamp. Warning lamp should flash 7 to 9 times and then turn off. If not, refer to "Passive Restraint" section for diagnostic system check.

TURN SIGNAL SWITCH
REPLACE

1988–89

1. Disconnect battery cable, then remove steering wheel and column to instrument panel trim cover.
2. **On models with telescoping column,** remove bumper spacer and snap ring retainer. **On all other models,** remove cover from lock plate.
3. Using a suitable tool, compress lock plate (horn contact carrier on tilt models) and remove snap ring (C-ring on tilt models), **Fig. 8.**
4. Remove lock plate, cancelling cam, upper bearing preload spring, thrust washer and signal lever.
5. Remove turn signal lever or actuating arm screw, if equipped, or on models with column mounted wiper switch, pull lever straight out of detent. Depress hazard warning button, then un-

screw button.
6. Pull connector from bracket and wrap upper part of connector with tape to prevent snagging the wires during removal. **On Tilt models,** position shifter housing in Low position. Remove harness cover.
7. Remove retaining screws and remove switch, **Figs. 9 and 10.**
8. Reverse procedure to install.

1990–91

1. **To avoid personal injury when servicing models equipped with Supplemental Inflatable Restraint (Airbag) System, temporarily disable system as follows:**
  a. Place ignition switch in off position.
  b. Remove Airbag fuse from fuse panel.
  c. Remove lower left hand trim panel, remove connector position assurance and disconnect yellow two way Supplemental Inflatable Restraint connector at base of steering column.
2. Remove steering wheel as described under "Horn Sounder and Steering Wheel, Replace."
3. Place ignition switch in Lock position to retain coil assembly in the centered position.
4. Disconnect battery ground cable.
5. Remove coil assembly retaining ring, **Fig. 11.**
6. Lift coil assembly from from steering shaft and allow to hang from wire.
7. Using a suitable tool, compress lock plate and remove snap ring (C-ring on tilt models), **Fig. 8.**
8. Remove lock plate, turn signal canceling cam and upper bearing spring, inner race seat and inner race.
9. Place turn signal lever in right hand turn position, then remove multi-function lever and hazard warning flasher knob.
10. Remove turn signal switch lever attaching screw, then remove lever.
11. Remove turn signal switch attaching screws.
12. Disconnect turn signal switch electrical connector at lower portion of steering column.
13. Remove turn signal switch wiring protector cover from steering column, **Fig. 9.**
14. Carefully pull turn signal switch wiring up and out of steering column, **Fig. 10.**
15. Reverse procedure to install. If coil assembly has become uncentered, refer to **Fig. 12** for centering procedure.
16. **After completing service procedure activate system as follows:**
  a. Ensure ignition switch is in Off position.
  b. Connect yellow SIR two way electrical connector and install position assurance at base of steering column.
  c. Install Airbag fuse into fuse panel.
  d. Install lower left hand trim panel.
  e. Place ignition switch in Run position and note operation of "Infl Rest" warning lamp. Warning lamp

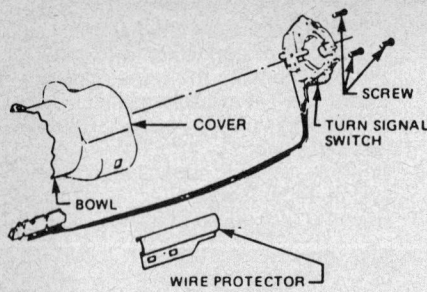

Fig. 9   Turn signal switch assembly

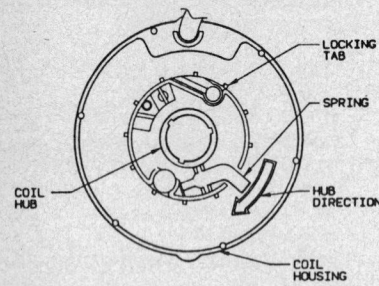

Perform the following steps to center coil assembly:
A. Remove coil assembly.
B. Hold coil assembly with clear bottom up to see coil ribbon.
C. While holding coil assembly, push down spring lock to rotate hub in direction of arrow until it stops.
D. The coil ribbon should be wound up snug against center hub.
E. Rotate coil hub in opposite direction approximately three (3) turns. Release spring lock between locking tabs in front of arrow.

Fig. 12   Centering coil assembly. 1990–91

should flash 7 to 9 times and then turn off. If not, refer to "Passive Restraint" section for diagnostic system check.

COLUMN-MOUNTED DIMMER SWITCH REPLACE

1988–89

1. Disconnect battery ground cable.
2. Remove instrument panel lower trim and on models with A/C, remove A/C duct extension at column.
3. Disconnect shift indicator from column and remove toe-plate cover screws.
4. Remove two nuts from instrument panel support bracket studs and lower steering column, resting steering wheel on front seat.
5. Remove dimmer switch retaining screws and the switch. Tape actuator rod to column and separate switch from rod.
6. Reverse procedure to install. To adjust switch, depress dimmer switch slightly and install a 3/32 inch twist drill to lock the switch to the body, **Fig. 7**. Force switch upward to remove lash between switch and pivot, then remove tape from actuator rod. Remove twist drill and check for proper operation.

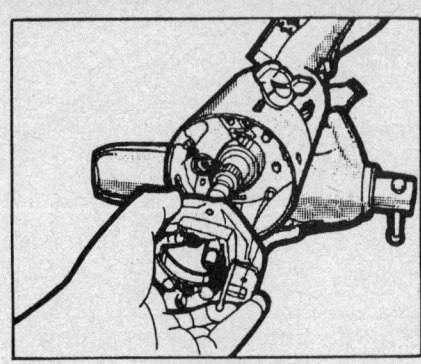

Fig. 10   Turn signal switch removal

1990–91

1. To avoid personal injury when servicing models equipped with Supplemental Inflatable Restraint (Airbag) System, temporarily disable system as follows:
   a. Place ignition switch in off position.
   b. Remove Airbag fuse from fuse panel.
   c. Remove lower left hand trim panel, remove connector position assurance and disconnect yellow two way Supplemental Inflatable Restraint connector at base of steering column.
2. Disconnect battery ground cable.
3. Remove screw and nut attaching dimmer switch to steering column.
4. Remove horn pad ground wire from dimmer and ignition switch mounting stud.
5. Remove cable retaining bracket.
6. Remove dimmer switch from mounting bracket, then disconnect electrical connector.
7. Reverse procedure to install. Adjust dimmer switch as follows:
   a. Depress dimmer switch slightly and install a 3/32 inch twist drill to lock the switch to the body, **Fig. 13**.
   b. Force switch upward to remove lash between switch and pivot.
   c. Remove drill bit and check for proper operation.
8. After completing service procedure activate system as follows:
   a. Ensure ignition switch is in Off position.
   b. Connect yellow SIR two way electrical connector and install position assurance at base of steering column.
   c. Install Airbag fuse into fuse panel.
   d. Install lower left hand trim panel.
   e. Place ignition switch in Run position and note operation of "Infl Rest" warning lamp. Warning lamp should flash 7 to 9 times and then turn off. If not, refer to "Passive Restraint" section for diagnostic system check.

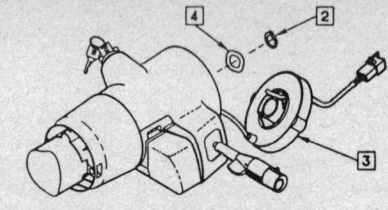

2 RING, RETAINING
3 COIL ASM, INFL RESTRAINT
4 WASHER, WAVE

Fig. 11   Coil assembly removal. 1990–91

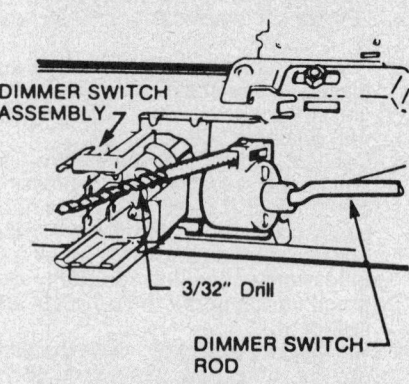

Fig. 13   Column mounted dimmer switch installation

HORN SOUNDER & STEERING WHEEL REPLACE

Mark position of steering wheel in relation to shaft prior to removal to ensure correct installation.

1988–89

1. Disconnect battery ground cable.
2. Squeeze horn button cap to disengage locks, then disconnect contact from steering wheel and remove cap, **Fig. 14**.
3. Remove screws securing center star screw, star screw, and adjusting lever.
4. Remove snap ring and nut from steering shaft.
5. Remove steering wheel using a suitable puller.
6. Reverse procedure to install.

1990–91

Removal

1. Place ignition switch in off position.
2. Remove Airbag fuse from fuse panel.
3. Remove lower left hand trim panel, then disconnect connector position assurance and yellow two way SIR connector at base of steering column.
4. Disconnect battery ground cable.
5. Remove inflator module attaching screws from rear of steering wheel, **Fig. 15**.
6. Lift inflator module from steering wheel, then disconnect electrical connectors from inflator module.

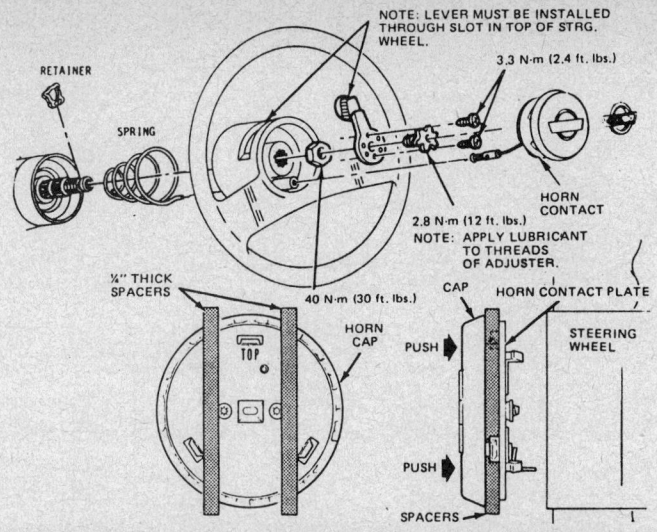

Fig. 14 Horn sounder & steering wheel. 1988–89

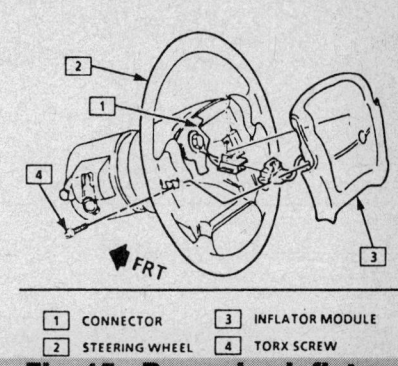

| 1 | CONNECTOR | 3 | INFLATOR MODULE |
| 2 | STEERING WHEEL | 4 | TORX SCREW |

Fig. 15 Removing inflator module from steering wheel. 1990–91

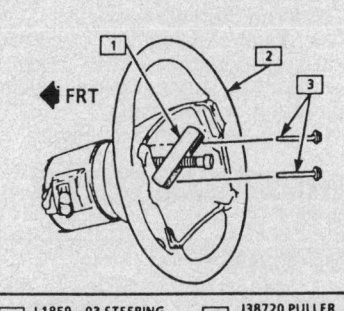

| 1 | J 1859–03 STEERING WHEEL PULLER | 3 | J38720 PULLER SIDE SCREWS |
| 2 | STEERING WHEEL | | |

Fig. 16 Steering wheel removal. 1990–91

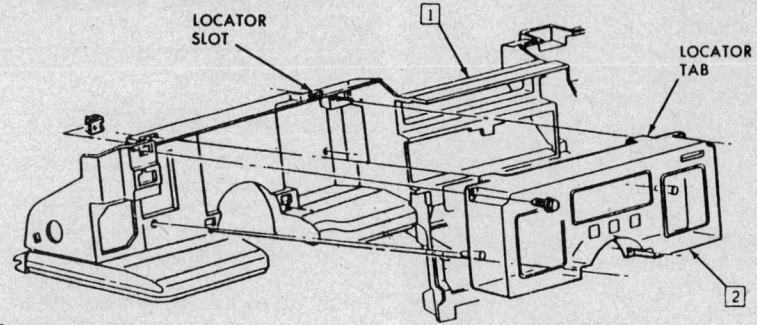

| 1 | CARRIER I/P |
| 2 | CLUSTER ASM-I/P |

Fig. 18 Instrument cluster replacement. 1988–89

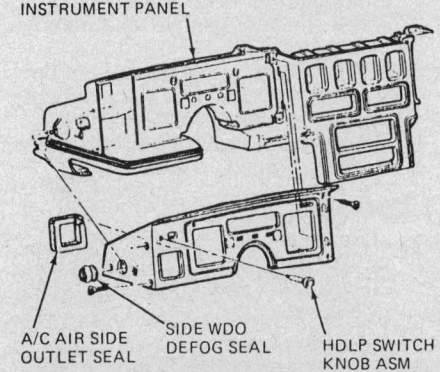

Fig. 17 Instrument cluster bezel replacement. 1988–89

7. Remove steering wheel retaining nut.
8. Then using puller J-1859-03 or equivalent, pull steering wheel from steering shaft, **Fig. 16.**
9. Disconnect horn electrical connect and remove steering wheel.

Installation

1. Connect horn electrical connector.
2. Position steering wheel spline alignment marks to alignment marks of steering shaft splines, then install steering wheel.
3. Install steering wheel retaining nut and torque to 30 ft. lbs.
4. Connect SIR coil electrical connector to inflator module, then install connector position assurance.
5. Position inflator module to steering wheel, then install new mounting screws, **Fig. 15. Torque** mounting screws to 87 inch lbs.
6. Ensure ignition switch is in Off position, then connect battery ground cable.
7. Connect yellow SIR two way electrical connector and connector position assurance at base of steering column.
8. Install Airbag fuse into fuse panel.
9. Install lower left hand trim panel.
10. Place ignition switch in Run position and note operation of "Infl Rest" warning lamp. Warning lamp should flash 7 to 9 times and then turn off. If not, refer to "Passive Restraint" section for diagnostic system check.

INSTRUMENT CLUSTER REPLACE

1988–89

1. Disconnect battery ground cable.
2. Remove left hush panel, lower instrument panel pad, and steering column cover.
3. Remove light switch knob and shaft, and bezel nut securing switch
4. Remove nuts securing steering column to instrument panel brace and lower column.
5. Remove cluster bezel retaining screws and bezel, **Fig. 17.**
6. Remove cluster retaining screws and pull cluster away from dash, **Fig. 18.**
7. Release metal retainers securing electrical connectors, disconnect electrical connectors from cluster, and remove cluster assembly.
8. Reverse procedure to install.

1990–91

1. To avoid personal injury when servicing models equipped with Supplemental Inflatable Restraint (Airbag) System, temporarily disable system as follows:
   a. Place ignition switch in off position.
   b. Remove Airbag fuse from fuse

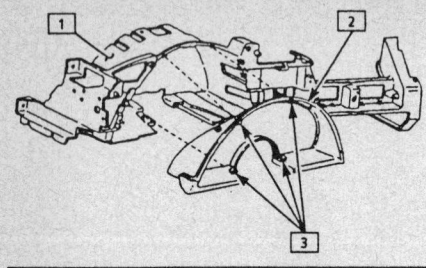

1 INSTRUMENT PANEL CARRIER
2 INSTRUMENT PANEL CLUSTER BEZEL
3 SCREWS

Fig. 19 Instrument cluster bezel replacement. 1990–91

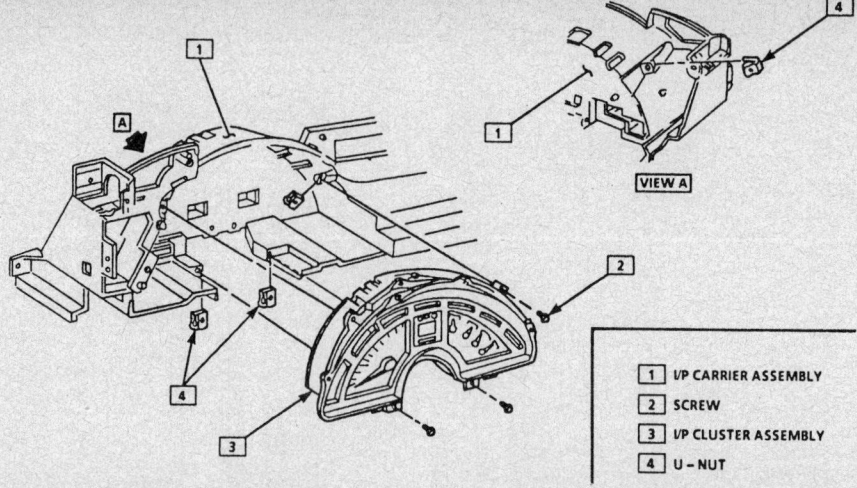

1 I/P CARRIER ASSEMBLY
2 SCREW
3 I/P CLUSTER ASSEMBLY
4 U-NUT

Fig. 20 Instrument cluster replacement. 1990–91

panel.
c. Remove lower left hand trim panel, remove connector position assurance and disconnect yellow two way Supplemental Inflatable Restraint connector at base of steering column.
2. Disconnect battery ground cable.
3. Remove transmission shift lever knob.
4. Remove console trim plate attaching screws, then disconnect electrical connectors and remove trim plate.
5. Remove center air duct attaching screws.
6. Remove accessory trim plate attaching screws, clips and trim plate.
7. Remove left hand lower trim plate attaching screws and retainers. Remove screw attaching ALDL connector to trim panel, then disconnect courtesy lamp electrical connector and remove trim panel.
8. Remove drivers side knee booster attaching screws.
9. Remove steering column tilt lever.
10. Remove steering column upper attaching bolts, then carefully lower steering column.
11. Remove instrument cluster bezel attaching screws, then remove bezel, **Fig. 19.**
12. Remove instrument cluster attaching screws, then disconnect electrical connectors and remove instrument cluster, **Fig. 20.**
13. Reverse procedure to install.
14. After completing service procedure activate system as follows:
    a. Ensure ignition switch is in Off position.
    b. Connect yellow SIR two way electrical connector and install position assurance at base of steering column.
    c. Install Airbag fuse into fuse panel.
    d. Install lower left hand trim panel.
    e. Place ignition switch in Run position and note operation of "Infl Rest" warning lamp. Warning lamp should flash 7 to 9 times and then turn off. If not, refer to "Passive Restraint" section for diagnostic system check.

WINDSHIELD WIPER MOTOR
REPLACE

1988–90 EXCEPT ZR-1

1. Open hood, then remove wiper arms and air inlet screen.
2. Turn ignition on and operate motor. Stop motor with crank arm pointing to a position between 4 and 5 o'clock (viewed from passenger compartment) by turning ignition off.
3. Disconnect battery ground cable.
4. Disconnect upper electrical connector from wiper motor.
5. Remove motor retaining bolts, and remove motor after disconnecting lower electrical connector and linkage.
6. Reverse procedure to install.

1990 ZR-1 & 1991 ALL

1. Disconnect battery ground cable.
2. Remove wiper arms, if necessary.
3. Disconnect wiper motor upper electrical connectors.
4. Remove left hand plenum screen.
5. Remove left and right hand wiper transmission attaching nuts.
6. Remove left and right hand wiper transmission sockets.
7. **On ZR1 models**, disconnect vacuum booster supply hose at plenum.
8. **On all models**, remove wiper motor attaching bolts, then carefully lift wiper motor from mounting.
9. Disconnect wiper motor lower electrical connectors and remove wiper motor.
10. Reverse procedure to install.

WINDSHIELD WIPER TRANSMISSION
REPLACE

1. Ensure motor is in park position.
2. Raise hood and remove wiper arm assemblies.

3. Remove left hand cowl vent screen.
4. Loosen nuts securing pivot at motor crankarm, then disconnect transmission rod from crankarm.
5. Remove retaining nuts or screws securing transmission to body, then withdraw transmission assembly through cowl opening.
6. Reverse procedure to install.

WINDSHIELD WIPER SWITCH
REPLACE

1988–89

1. Disconnect battery ground cable.
2. Remove 2 screws securing left armrest, push inward to release armrest from door trim and remove armrest.
3. Remove screws securing accessory trim plate to door panel, including screw behind handle, and remove lock button.
4. Pull accessory plate away from door panel and disconnect electrical connectors to panel switches.
5. Remove wiper switch from trim plate.
6. Reverse procedure to install.

1990–91

1. **To avoid personal injury when servicing models equipped with Supplemental Inflatable Restraint (Airbag) System, temporarily disable system as follows:**
   a. Place ignition switch in off position.
   b. Remove Airbag fuse from fuse panel.
   c. Remove lower left hand trim panel, remove connector position assurance and disconnect yellow two way Supplemental Inflatable Restraint connector at base of steering column.
2. Pull column housing end toward from of vehicle and remove cover, **Fig. 21.**
3. Disconnect electrical connector and grommet.
4. Pull outward on multi-function lever to release from detent.

5. Reverse procedure to install. When installing, position lever in off position, then align lever tab with mounting slot.
6. **After completing service procedure activate system as follows:**
   a. Ensure ignition switch is in Off position.
   b. Connect yellow SIR two way electrical connector and install position assurance at base of steering column.
   c. Install Airbag fuse into fuse panel.
   d. Install lower left hand trim panel.
   e. Place ignition switch in Run position and note operation of "Infl Rest" warning lamp. Warning lamp should flash 7 to 9 times and then turn off. If not, refer to "Passive Restraint" section for diagnostic system check.

RADIO
REPLACE

When installing radio, be sure to adjust antenna trimmer for peak reception. Also, be sure to connect speaker before applying power to radio.

1988–89

1. Disconnect battery ground cable and remove instrument cluster as outlined.
2. Remove accessory trim plate retaining screws and trim plate.
3. Remove screws securing radio and bracket, and pull radio away from dash.
4. Disconnect electrical connectors and antenna lead, then remove radio.
5. Reverse procedure to install, ensuring A/C center outlet seal is properly positioned.

1990–91
Radio Control

1. **To avoid personal injury when servicing models equipped with Supplemental Inflatable Restraint (Airbag) System, temporarily disable system as follows:**
   a. Place ignition switch in off position.
   b. Remove Airbag fuse from fuse panel.
   c. Remove lower left hand trim panel, remove connector position assurance and disconnect yellow two way Supplemental Inflatable Restraint connector at base of steering column.
2. Disconnect battery ground cable.
3. Remove transmission gear selector knob.
4. Remove console trim plate attaching screws from under ash tray.
5. Disconnect electrical connectors from console trim plate components, then remove trim plate.
6. Remove screw attaching center air outlet to instrument panel carrier, then remove outlet.
7. Remove screws attaching accessory trim plate to instrument panel.

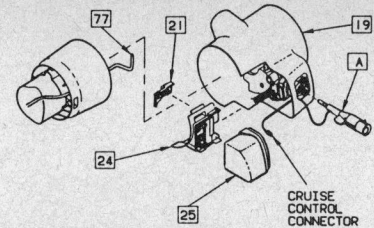

A MULTI-FUNCTION LEVER
19 COVER ASM. LOCK HOUSING
21 ACTUATOR, DIMMER SWITCH ROD
24 BASE PLATE, COL HSG COVER END
25 CAP, COL HSG COVER END
77 ROD, DIMMER SWITCH

Fig. 21 Multi-function lever replacement. 1990–91

8. Disconnect electrical connector to engine power switch, then remove accessory trim plate.
9. Remove console door.
10. Remove screws attaching console right hand side trim panel to instrument panel and console. Remove passenger seat from vehicle to gain access to screws at side of trim panel. After all attaching screws have been removed, remove side trim panel.
11. Remove screws attaching radio control to instrument panel.
12. Pull radio control outward, then disconnect electrical connectors and remove radio control.
13. Reverse procedure to install.
14. **After completing service procedure activate system as follows:**
    a. Ensure ignition switch is in Off position.
    b. Connect yellow SIR two way electrical connector and install position assurance at base of steering column.
    c. Install Airbag fuse into fuse panel.
    d. Install lower left hand trim panel.
    e. Place ignition switch in Run position and note operation of "Infl Rest" warning lamp. Warning lamp should flash 7 to 9 times and then turn off. If not, refer to "Passive Restraint" section for diagnostic system check.

Radio Receiver

1. **To avoid personal injury when servicing models equipped with Supplemental Inflatable Restraint (Airbag) System, temporarily disable system as follows:**
   a. Place ignition switch in off position.
   b. Remove Airbag fuse from fuse panel.
   c. Remove lower left hand trim panel, remove connector position assurance and disconnect yellow two way Supplemental Inflatable Restraint connector at base of steering column.
2. Disconnect battery ground cable.
3. Remove screws attaching lower right hand trim panel to instrument panel and support.
4. Disconnect courtesy lamp electrical connector and air dust, then remove lower right hand trim panel.
5. Remove radio receiver front attaching nut and loosen side mounting nuts.

6. Slide radio receiver forward to release tab, then disconnect electrical connectors and antenna lead.
7. Remove radio receiver.
8. Reverse procedure to install.
9. **After completing service procedure activate system as follows:**
   a. Ensure ignition switch is in Off position.
   b. Connect yellow SIR two way electrical connector and install position assurance at base of steering column.
   c. Install Airbag fuse into fuse panel.
   d. Install lower left hand trim panel.
   e. Place ignition switch in Run position and note operation of "Infl Rest" warning lamp. Warning lamp should flash 7 to 9 times and then turn off. If not, refer to "Passive Restraint" section for diagnostic system check.

BLOWER MOTOR
REPLACE

1. Disconnect battery ground cable.
2. Remove right front wheel housing rear panel, and push housing aside.
3. Remove motor cooling tube and screws securing relay, and set relay aside.
4. Remove motor retaining screws, motor and impeller.
5. Reverse procedure to install.

HEATER CORE
REPLACE

1988–89

1. Disconnect battery ground cable, place heater control in warm position, and drain cooling system.
2. Remove instrument cluster bezel and tilt wheel control lever.
3. Remove instrument panel upper trim pad retaining screws and trim pad, then remove A/C distribution ducts and disconnect flex hoses.
4. Remove right lower hush panel and side defroster flex hose.
5. Remove screws securing side defroster outlet to heater cover, and disconnect extension.
6. Remove temperature control cable and bracket from heater cover and disconnect heater door control shaft.
7. Remove electronic control module and disconnect electrical connectors to module.
8. Remove support brace between door pillar and instrument panel reinforcement brace.
9. Remove screws securing heater core cover, heater pipe bracket and water control valve bracket.
10. Cut heater hoses at core pipes and remove heater core. **Measure and install replacement heater hose links during reassembly.**
11. Reverse procedure to install. Refill cooling system and check for leaks.

1990-91

1. **To avoid personal injury when servicing models equipped with Supplemental Inflatable Restraint (Airbag) System, temporarily disable system as follows:**
   a. Place ignition switch in off position.
   b. Remove Airbag fuse from fuse panel.
   c. Remove lower left hand trim panel, remove connector position assurance and disconnect yellow two way Supplemental Inflatable Restraint connector at base of steering column.
2. Disconnect battery ground cable, then drain cooling system.
3. Remove transmission gear selector knob.
4. Remove console trim plate attaching screws from under ash tray.
5. Disconnect electrical connectors from console trim plate components, then remove trim plate.
6. Remove screw attaching center air outlet to instrument panel carrier, then remove outlet.
7. Remove screws attaching accessory trim plate to instrument panel.
8. Disconnect electrical connector to engine power switch, then remove accessory trim plate.
9. Remove left and right hand side window defogger ducts.
10. Remove screws attaching instrument panel storage compartment to instrument panel, then remove compartment.
11. Remove windshield defogger nozzle grille from instrument panel.
12. Remove screws attaching instrument panel upper trim panel to instrument panel and bulkhead.
13. Disconnect in-vehicle temperature sensor aspirator hose and electrical connector.
14. Remove heat deflector and right hand knee bolster brace trim.
15. Remove relays from relay bracket.
16. Remove wiring harness retainer from radio receiver.
17. Remove instrument panel carrier to right hand pillar attaching nuts.
18. Remove relay bracket attaching screws.
19. Remove right hand knee booster brace attachments.
20. Remove side window defogger duct clip, then detach defogger hose from knee bolster brace.

21. Pull instrument panel carrier rearward and remove knee bolster brace.
22. Disconnect electrical connector from radio.
23. Disconnect electrical connectors from cruise control module and relay bracket.
24. Remove screws attaching side window defroster duct to rear of heater housing.
25. Remove fuse panel from instrument panel carrier.
26. Disconnect vacuum hose from actuator.
27. Detach vacuum hoses from heater housing.
28. Remove wiring harness retainer from rear of heater housing.
29. Remove side window defogger center extension from heater housing.
30. Remove heater housing screw and rear heater housing half.
31. Remove high fill reservoir.
32. Disconnect heater hoses from heater core, then remove heater core.
33. Reverse procedure to install.
34. **After completing service procedure activate system as follows:**
    a. Ensure ignition switch is in Off position.
    b. Connect yellow SIR two way electrical connector and install position assurance at base of steering column.

    c. Install Airbag fuse into fuse panel.
    d. Install lower left hand trim panel.
    e. Place ignition switch in Run position and note operation of "Infl Rest" warning lamp. Warning lamp should flash 7 to 9 times and then turn off. If not, refer to "Passive Restraint" section for diagnostic system check.

EVAPORATOR CORE
REPLACE

1. Disconnect battery ground cable.
2. Discharge A/C refrigerant system
3. Drain cooling system.
4. Remove front wheel house rear panel and seal.
5. Disconnect electrical connectors from blower motor.
6. Disconnect evaporator outlet hose.
7. Remove pressure cycling switch.
8. Disconnect heater hoses and evaporator inlet hose, then expansion tube.
9. Disconnect vapor pipe bracket from evaporator case.
10. Remove attaching bolt from upper right hand fender apron.
11. Remove nuts and bolts attaching evaporator core and blower housing to dash panel, **Fig. 22.**
12. Remove evaporator housing from vehicle, then separate housing and remove evaporator core.
13. Reverse procedure to install.

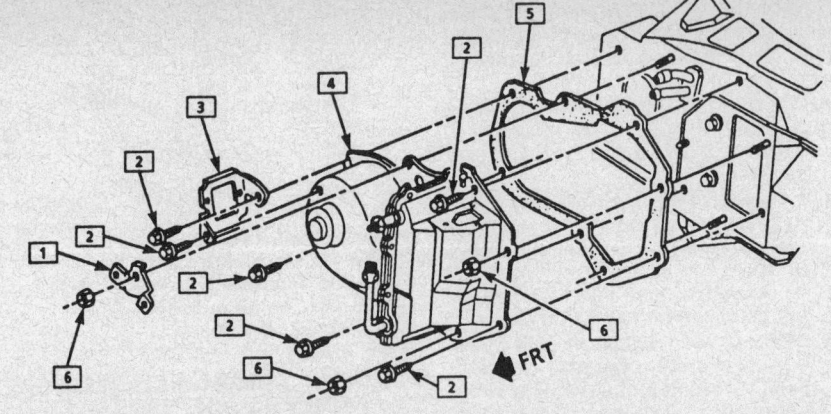

1 AIR CONDITIONING WIRING HARNESS BRACKET	4 AIR CONDITIONING EVAPORATOR AND BLOWER MOTOR MODULE
2 BLOWER MOTOR AND EVAPORATOR MODULE BOLT	5 AIR CONDITIONING EVAPORATOR AND BLOWER MOTOR MODULE GASKET
3 ELECTRONIC SPARK CONTROL BRACKET	6 BLOWER MOTOR AND EVAPORATOR MODULE NUT

Fig. 22 Evaporator core housing

5.7L/V8-350 Single Cam 16 Valve Engine

INDEX

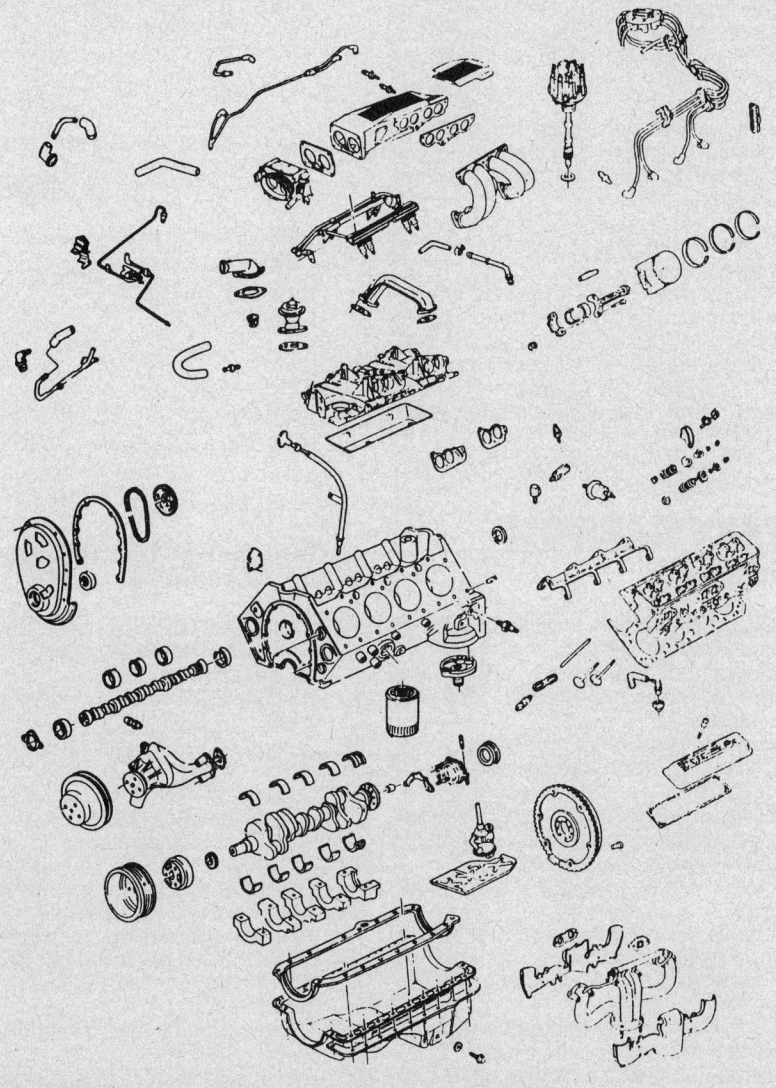

Exploded view of engine

ENGINE MOUNT
REPLACE

1. Disconnect battery ground cable, then disconnect air intake duct from air cleaner.
2. Raise and support vehicle, then remove Electronic Spark Control sensor shield.
3. Support engine and remove mount through bolt, **Fig. 1.**
4. Raise engine sufficiently to provide clearance for mount bolt removal.
5. Remove bolts securing engine mount to block and the mount.
6. Position replacement mount on engine, lower engine into position and install retaining bolts.
7. Reverse procedure to install.

ENGINE
REPLACE

1. Disconnect battery ground cable, then drain cooling system.
2. Disconnect throttle, cruise control and TV cables.
3. Remove plenum extension from plenum.
4. Disconnect EGR pipe from intake and exhaust manifolds.
5. Remove ignition distributor from engine. Refer to "Distributor, Replace" procedure in the "Electrical" section.
6. Disconnect electrical connector from oil pressure switch.
7. Disconnect windshield wiper motor electrical connector, then remove wiper motor cover.
8. Remove air intake duct.
9. Disconnect power brake unit vacuum hose.
10. Disconnect fuel vapor canister hoses.
11. Disconnect electrical connectors from cooling fan control switch, alternator, EGR solenoid, coolant temperature sensor, AIR switch and control valve,

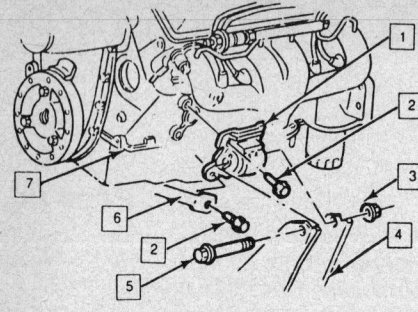

1	MOUNT, ENGINE
2	BOLT
3	NUT, ENGINE MOUNT BOLT
4	FRAME, DRIVETRAIN AND FRONT SUSPENSION
5	BOLT, ENGINE MOUNT
6	BRACE, SUPPORT
7	BLOCK, ENGINE

Fig. 1 Engine mounts

throttle position sensor, idle air control valve, A/C compressor and manifold air temperature sensor. Also disconnect fuel injector wiring harness from left and right hand sides.
12. Disconnect vapor hose from intake manifold. Also disconnect cruise control and A/C vacuum connectors.
13. Disconnect heater hose at throttle body.
14. Disconnect upper radiator hose at thermostat housing.
15. Remove water pump damper, then remove serpentine drive belt and water pump pulley.
16. Remove AIR switch, control and mounting bracket.
17. Connect pressure gauge J-34370-1 or equivalent to pressure tap on fuel rail, position bleed hose in suitable container and slowly relieve fuel system pressure. **Failure to relieve system pressure prior to disconnecting fuel system components may cause fire or personal injury.**
18. Disconnect and cap fuel lines at fuel rail.
19. Remove A/C accumulator clamping bolt.
20. Remove lower right hand side wheel housing center panel.
21. Remove A/C compressor brace, then remove A/C compressor and accumulator from mounting brackets and position aside with refrigerant hoses attached.
22. Remove A/C compressor front mounting brace, then remove belt tensioner.
23. Disconnect heater hose from water pump.
24. Remove A/C compressor lower brace and fuel line clamp.
25. Remove alternator, then remove AIR pump with mounting brackets and pipe as an assembly.
26. Remove A/C compressor mounting bracket and AIR system muffler.
27. Disconnect lower radiator hose from water pump, then disconnect hose from engine oil cooler pipe.

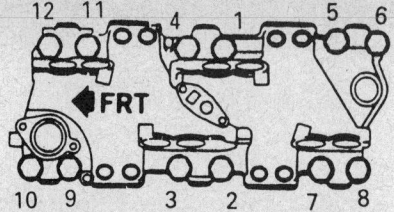

Fig. 2 Intake manifold bolt tightening sequence

28. Remove crankshaft pulley.
29. Remove power steering pump with bracket and position aside with hoses attached.
30. Raise and support vehicle.
31. Disconnect AIR pipe from right hand exhaust manifold.
32. Disconnect exhaust cross-over pipe at exhaust manifolds.
33. Disconnect electrical connectors from oil temperature sensor, starter motor, ESC sensor and right hand side coolant temperature sensor. Also disconnect battery ground cable at engine block.
34. Remove flywheel cover, then remove starter motor.
35. Drain crankcase, then remove oil filter.
36. **On models with manual transmission,** remove transmission and clutch assembly.
37. **On models with automatic transmission,** remove transmission to engine and torque converter to flywheel attaching bolts.
38. **On all models,** remove engine mount through bolts and nuts.
39. Lower vehicle.
40. **On models with automatic transmission,** use suitable transmission jack to support transmission.
41. **On all models,** install suitable engine lifting fixture, then ensure all wiring and hoses that would interfere with engine removal are disconnected.
42. Carefully lift engine from vehicle.
43. Reverse procedure to install.

INTAKE MANIFOLD REPLACE

1. Disconnect battery ground cable, then drain cooling system.
2. Disconnect throttle, TV and cruise control cables from throttle body and brackets.
3. Remove bracket from plenum.
4. Disconnect electrical connectors from coolant temperature sensor, throttle position sensor, manifold air temperature sensor, idle air control and manifold absolute pressure sensor.
5. Disconnect air inlet duct from throttle body.
6. Disconnect and tag vacuum hoses from plenum and throttle body.
7. Disconnect heater hoses from throttle body.
8. Disconnect power brake unit vacuum hose from plenum fitting.
9. Remove plenum to runner attaching bolts, then remove plenum from engine.

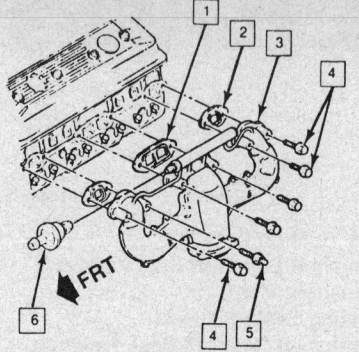

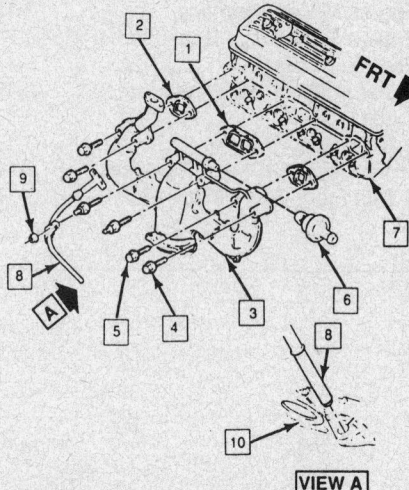

1	GASKET, EXHAUST MANIFOLD CENTER
2	GASKET, EXHAUST MANIFOLD
3	MANIFOLD, EXHAUST
4	BOLT
5	STUD
6	VALVE, CHECK
7	HEAD, CYLINDER
8	TUBE, OIL LEVEL INDICATOR
9	NUT
10	BLOCK, ENGINE

Fig. 3 Exhaust manifold replacement

10. Disconnect vacuum hose, then remove EGR solenoid from thermostat housing.
11. Remove EGR valve from intake manifold.
12. Remove injector wiring harness attaching bolts.
13. Connect pressure gauge J-34370-1 or equivalent to pressure tap on fuel rail, position bleed hose in suitable container and slowly relieve fuel system pressure. **Failure to relieve system pressure prior to disconnecting fuel system components may cause fire or personal injury.**
14. Disconnect fuel lines at fuel rail connections.
15. Remove fuel rail and injector assemblies.
16. Remove ignition distributor, refer to "Distributor, Replace" procedure in the "Electrical" section.

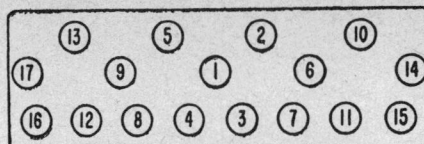

Fig. 4 Cylinder head tightening sequence

17. Disconnect upper radiator hose from thermostat housing.
18. Remove AIR pump brace.
19. Disconnect EGR valve pipe and position aside.
20. Disconnect hose from PCV valve and crankcase vent tube from intake manifold.
21. Remove intake manifold attaching bolts and intake manifold.
22. Ensure gasket surfaces are clean and dry, then install gaskets on cylinder head with blocked openings toward rear of engine.
23. Bend gasket tabs flush with rear face with cylinder head, then apply a .2 inch bead of RTV sealer to front and rear ridges of cylinder block.
24. Apply sealant 1052624 or equivalent to manifold bolts.
25. Install manifold and torque bolts to specifications in sequence shown in **Fig. 2**, then reverse remaining procedure to complete installation.

EXHAUST MANIFOLD
REPLACE

LEFT SIDE

1. Disconnect battery ground cable.
2. Disconnect AIR hose at check valve, then remove alternator brace.
3. Disconnect spark plug wires from spark plugs and brackets and position aside, then remove spark plugs after engine has cooled.
4. Raise and support vehicle.
5. Disconnect exhaust cross-over pipe at exhaust manifolds.
6. Lower vehicle, then remove exhaust manifold attaching bolts and remove exhaust manifold, **Fig. 3**.
7. Reverse procedure to install.

RIGHT SIDE

1. Disconnect battery ground cable.
2. Disconnect EGR valve pipe and position aside.
3. Remove A/C compressor brace, then remove oil level dipstick and tube.
4. Disconnect AIR hose at check valve.
5. Disconnect temperature sending unit electrical connector.
6. Disconnect spark plug wire from spark plugs and brackets, then remove spark plugs after engine has cooled.
7. Raise and support vehicle.
8. Remove AIR pipe clamp at manifold.
9. Disconnect exhaust cross-over pipe at exhaust manifolds.
10. Lower vehicle.
11. Remove exhaust manifold attaching bolts, then remove exhaust manifold, **Fig. 3**.
12. Reverse procedure to install.

CYLINDER HEAD
REPLACE

1. Disconnect battery ground cable and remove air cleaner.
2. Drain cooling system and engine block, then remove intake manifold.
3. Disconnect AIR hose from exhaust manifold check valve, and if right cylinder head is to be removed, disconnect AIR hose from converter pipe.
4. If right cylinder head is to be removed, remove A/C compressor as follows:
   a. Remove lower compressor mounting bolt and nuts securing bracket to water pump.
   b. Move compressor assembly forward, remove upper mounting bolt and disconnect electrical connector, and secure compressor aside.
   c. Disconnect electrical connectors to high pressure switch, then remove high pressure switch and EGR solenoid.
   d. Disconnect EFI harness from rocker cover clamp.
5. If left cylinder head is to be removed, remove alternator and brace.
6. Remove valve cover retaining bolts, bend plug wire bracket away from cover for clearance, and remove cover.
7. Remove spark plugs and temperature sending unit from cylinder head.
8. Raise and support vehicle, and disconnect exhaust pipe from manifold. If right cylinder head is to be replaced, remove 2 rear manifold bolts and dipstick tube bolt.
9. Lower vehicle and remove exhaust manifold.
10. If left cylinder head is to be removed, remove AIR pump upper bracket and power steering reservoir, and set aside.
11. Remove spark plug wire bracket and bolts securing ground straps to cylinder head.
12. Loosen rocker arm nuts and remove push rods.
13. Remove head bolts and cylinder head.
14. Reverse procedure to install, noting the following:
    a. Ensure gasket surfaces are clean and free of nicks or deep scratches, and bolt and block threads are clean.
    b. Coat both sides of head gasket with a thin even coat of sealer, and ensure gasket is properly positioned over dowel pins.
    c. Coat cylinder head bolt threads with GM sealer No. 1052080 or equivalent, then install all bolts finger tight.
    d. Torque cylinder head bolts to specifications in sequence shown in **Fig. 4**.
    e. Install intake manifold gaskets on head with blocked openings toward rear, bend gasket tabs flush with rear face of cylinder head, and apply a .2 inch bead of RTV sealer on front and rear cylinder block ridges.

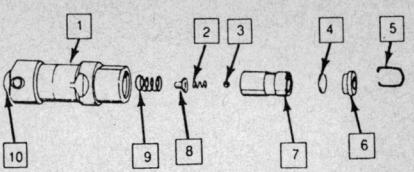

1	BODY, LIFTER	6	SEAT, PUSHROD
2	SPRING, BALL CHECK	7	PLUNGER
3	CHECK, BALL	8	RETAINER, BALL CHECK
4	VALVE, OIL METERING	9	SPRING, PLUNGER
5	RING, RETAINER	10	ROLLER

Fig. 5 Roller type hydraulic lifter

f. Install manifold, apply sealant 1052624 or equivalent to manifold bolts, and torque bolts to specifications in sequence shown in **Fig. 2**.

VALVE LASH SPECIFICATIONS

Year	Engine/VIN	Valve Lash
1988–91	V8-350/8	1 Turn ①

①—Turn rocker arm stud nut until all lash is eliminated, then tighten nut the additional turn listed.

VALVE ARRANGEMENT
FRONT TO REAR

All . . . . E-I-I-E-E-I-I-E

CAMSHAFT LOBE LIFT SPECIFICATIONS

Engine	Year	Int.	Exh.
5.7L/V8-350	1988–89	.2733	.2820
	1990–91	.2750	.2856

VALVE LASH
ADJUST

After the engine has been thoroughly warmed up the valves may be adjusted with the engine shut off as follows: With engine in position to fire No. 1 cylinder the following valves may be adjusted: Exhaust 1-3-4-8, intake 1-2-5-7. Then crank the engine one more complete revolution which will bring No. 6 cylinder to the firing position at which time the following valves may be adjusted: Exhaust 2-5-6-7, intake 3-4-6-8.

The following procedure, performed with the engine running, should be done only in case readjustment is required.

1. After engine has been warmed up to operating temperature, remove valve cover and install a new valve cover gasket.
2. With engine running at idle speed, back off valve rocker arm nut until rocker arm starts to clatter.
3. Turn rocker arm nut down slowly until the clatter just stops. This is the zero lash position.

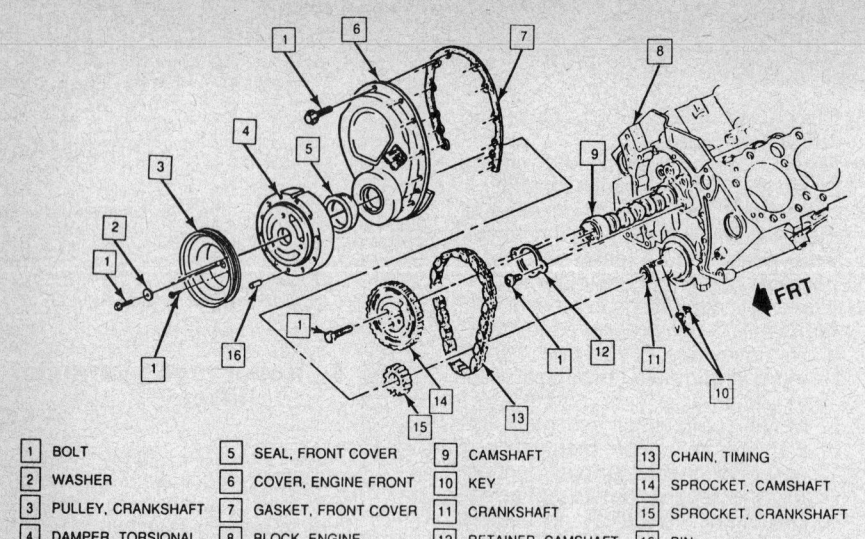

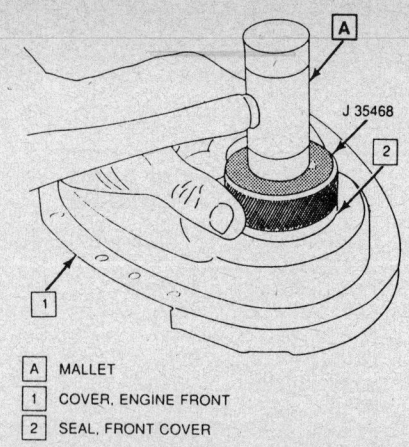

1	BOLT	5	SEAL, FRONT COVER	9	CAMSHAFT	13	CHAIN, TIMING
2	WASHER	6	COVER, ENGINE FRONT	10	KEY	14	SPROCKET, CAMSHAFT
3	PULLEY, CRANKSHAFT	7	GASKET, FRONT COVER	11	CRANKSHAFT	15	SPROCKET, CRANKSHAFT
4	DAMPER, TORSIONAL	8	BLOCK, ENGINE	12	RETAINER, CAMSHAFT	16	PIN

Fig. 6   Front cover & timing chain components

A	MALLET
1	COVER, ENGINE FRONT
2	SEAL, FRONT COVER

Fig. 7   Engine front cover seal installation

4. Turn nut down 1/4 additional turn and pause 10 seconds until engine runs smoothly. Repeat additional 1/4 turns, pausing 10 seconds each time, until nut has been turned down the number of turns listed in the Valve Clearance Specifications Chart from the zero lash position. **This preload adjustment must be done slowly to allow the lifter to adjust itself to prevent the possibility of interference between the intake valve head and top of piston, which might result in internal damage and/or bent push rods. Noisy lifters should be replaced.**

ROCKER ARMS & BALLS

When replacing rocker arms or rocker arm balls, bearing surfaces of rocker arms and balls should be coated with pre-lube 3755008 or equivalent.

ROCKER ARM STUDS

Rocker arm studs with damaged threads should be replaced. Threads of replacement rocker arms studs should be coated with sealing compound 1052080 or equivalent prior to installation. Looseness can be corrected by installing the proper size Heli-Coil insert, or by replacing cylinder head.

PUSH RODS

On engines that use push rods with a hardened insert at one end, the hardened end is identified by a color stripe and should always be installed toward the rocker arm during assembly.

VALVE GUIDES

Valves operate in guide holes bored in the head. If clearance becomes excessive, use the next oversize valve and ream the

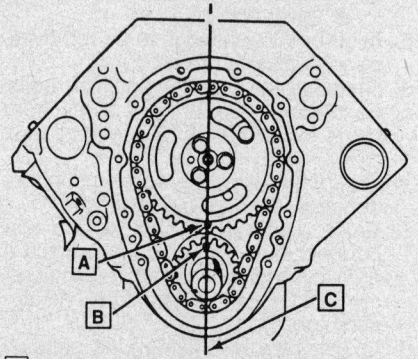

A	TIMING MARK, CAMSHAFT SPROCKET
B	TIMING MARK, CRANKSHAFT SPROCKET
C	SPROCKET CENTER LINE

Fig. 8   Aligning timing chain sprocket timing marks

bore to fit. Valves with oversize stems are available in .003, .015 and .030 inch.

HYDRAULIC LIFTERS
REPLACE

Valve lifters, **Fig. 5** can be lifted from their bores after removing rocker arms, push rods, intake manifold and valve lifter retainer. When removing, position valve lifters in rack so they may be installed at the same location. Adjustable pliers with protected jaws may be used to remove lifters which are stuck due to carbon or varnish deposits. When installing replacement valve lifters, coat roller with pre-lube 3755008 or equivalent.

FRONT COVER
REPLACE

1. Disconnect battery ground cable and drain cooling system.
2. Remove vibration damper and water pump.
3. Remove oil pan and gasket as outlined.

4. Remove AIR control valve, check valve pipe and silencer as an assembly.
5. Remove fuel inlet and return lines.
6. Remove A/C compressor mounting bracket.
7. Remove water pump as described under "Water Pump, Replace."
8. Remove front cover retaining screws and the front cover, **Fig. 6.**
9. Reverse procedure to install. Apply sealant 1052080 or equivalent approximately 1 inch in either direction at front cover to engine junction and at point where rear seal retainer meets case prior to installation of oil pan.

FRONT COVER OIL SEAL
REPLACE

WITH FRONT COVER INSTALLED

1. Disconnect battery ground cable.
2. Remove serpentine drive belt.
3. Remove water pump damper and crankshaft pulley.
4. Disconnect power steering gear line, if necessary.
5. Remove attaching bolts, then using puller J-23523 or equivalent, remove crankshaft damper.
6. Carefully pry oil seal from front cover.
7. Using tool No. J-35468, position oil to front cover with open side of seal toward inside of front cover.
8. Tap seal into front cover until properly seated.
9. Using puller J-23523 or equivalent, install crankshaft damper and install attaching bolt.
10. Connect power steering line, if removed. After completing installation check power steering fluid lever in reservoir.
11. Install crankshaft pulley and water pump damper.
12. Install serpentine drive belt and connect battery ground cable.

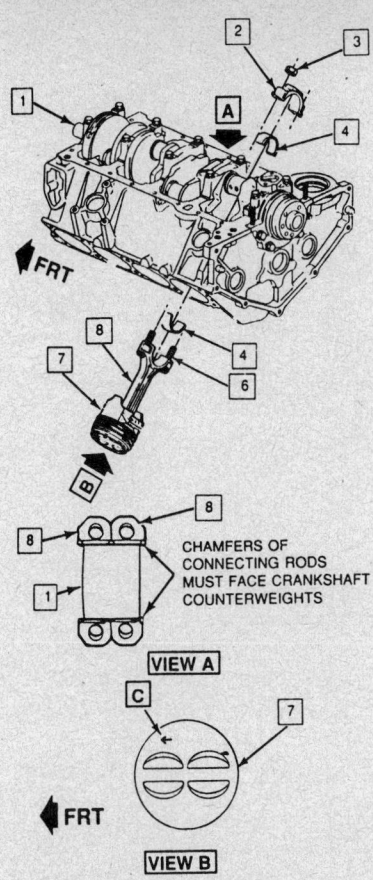

C ARROW, TO BE ORIENTED TO FRONT OF ENGINE
1 CRANKSHAFT
2 CAP, CONNECTING ROD
3 NUT, CONNECTING ROD
4 INSERT, BEARING
5 BLOCK, CYLINDER
6 BOLT, CONNECTING ROD
7 PISTON
8 ROD, CONNECTING

Fig. 9 Piston & rod assembly

WITH FRONT COVER REMOVED

1. Remove front cover as described under "Front Cover, Replace."
2. From rear of front cover, tap out oil seal.
3. Properly support front cover in seal area.
4. Using tool No. J-35468 or equivalent, install oil seal. Position open end of oil seal toward inside of front cover, **Fig. 7.**
5. Install engine front cover.

TIMING CHAIN
REPLACE

1. Remove front cover as outlined previously.
2. Remove crankshaft oil slinger.
3. Crank engine until timing marks on

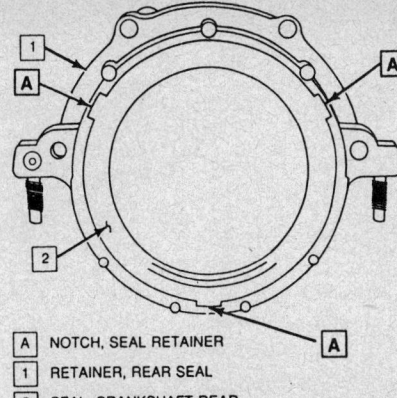

A NOTCH, SEAL RETAINER
1 RETAINER, REAR SEAL
2 SEAL, CRANKSHAFT REAR

Fig. 10 Crankshaft rear seal retainer notch locations

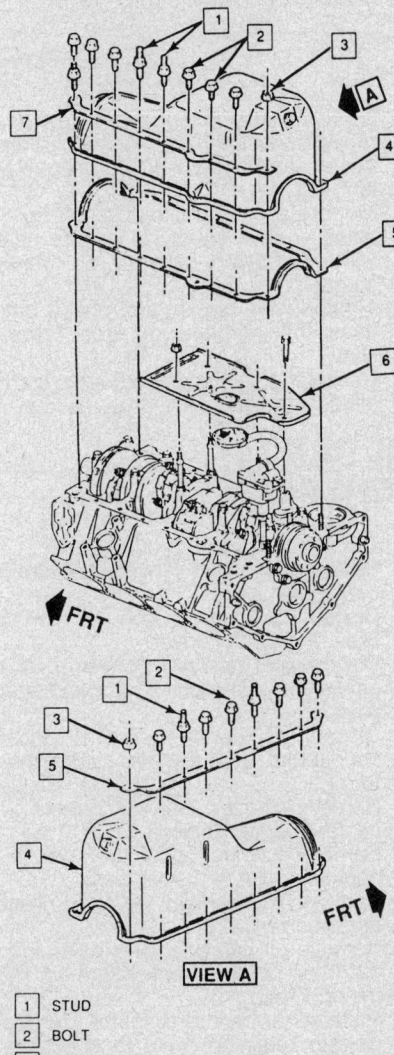

1 STUD
2 BOLT
3 NUT
4 PAN, OIL
5 GASKET, OIL PAN
6 BAFFLE
7 REINFORCEMENT, OIL PAN

Fig. 12 Oil pan replacement

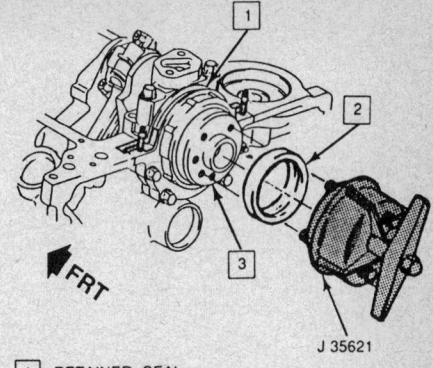

J 35621

1 RETAINER, SEAL
2 SEAL, CRANKSHAFT REAR
3 CRANKSHAFT

Fig. 11 Crankshaft rear seal installation

sprockets are in alignment, **Fig. 8.**
4. Remove three camshaft-to-sprocket bolts, **Fig. 6.**
5. Remove camshaft sprocket and timing chain together. Sprocket is a light press fit on camshaft for approximately 1/8 inch. If sprocket does not come off easily, a light blow with a plastic hammer on the lower edge of the sprocket should dislodge it.
6. If crankshaft sprocket is to be replaced, remove it with a suitable gear puller. Install new sprocket, aligning key and keyway.
7. Install chain on camshaft sprocket. Hold sprocket vertical with chain hanging below and shift around to align the timing marks on sprockets.
8. Align dowel in camshaft with dowel hole in sprocket and install sprocket on camshaft. Do not attempt to drive sprocket on camshaft as welch plug at rear of engine can be dislodged.
9. Draw sprocket onto camshaft, using the three mounting bolts. Tighten to specifications.
10. Lubricate timing chain with engine oil, then install cover.

CAMSHAFT
REPLACE

1. Remove valve lifters and engine front cover.
2. Remove grille, radiator and A/C condenser.
3. Remove timing chain as outlined previously.
4. Remove camshaft retainer bolts and retainer, **Fig. 6.**
5. Install two 5/16-18x4 bolts in camshaft bolt holes, then remove camshaft.
6. Reverse procedure to install. Prior to installing camshaft, coat lobes and distributor drive gear with pre-lube 3755008 or equivalent.

PISTONS & ROD ASSEMBLY

Assemble pistons to connecting rods as shown in **Fig. 9.**

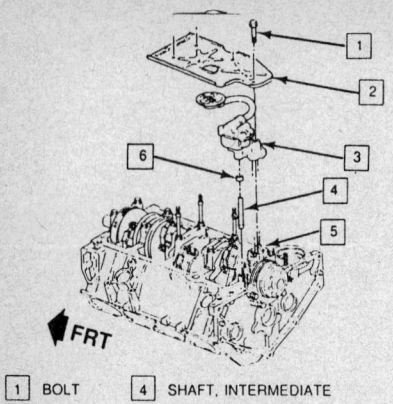

1 BOLT	**4** SHAFT, INTERMEDIATE
2 BAFFLE	**5** CAP, MAIN BEARING
3 PUMP, OIL	**6** RETAINER, SHAFT

Fig. 13 Oil pump & baffle replacement

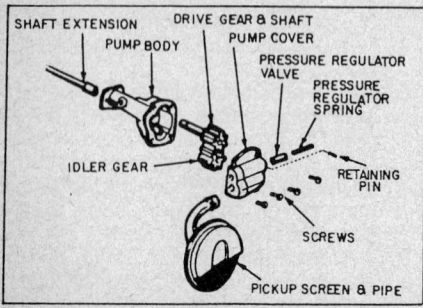

Fig. 14 Oil pump exploded view

Upon installation, measure the connecting rod side clearance using a suitable feeler gauge. Refer to "Engine Rebuilding Specifications" for connecting rod side clearance.

PISTONS, PINS & RINGS

Pistons are available in standard and oversizes of .010 and .030 inch.

Piston rings are available in standard and oversizes of .030 inch.

MAIN & ROD BEARINGS

Connecting rod bearings are available in standard and undersizes of .001, .002, .010 and .020 inch.

Main bearings are available in standard and undersizes of .001, .002, .009, .010 and .020 inch.

CRANKSHAFT REAR OIL SEAL

REPLACE

These engines are equipped with a one-piece, lip type seal mounted in a separate seal retainer. Seal replacement requires removal of the transmission.

1. Raise and support vehicle, then remove transmission, clutch assembly and flywheel, as equipped.
2. Pry seal from retainer, inserting screwdriver in notches provided in seal retainer, **Fig. 10.**

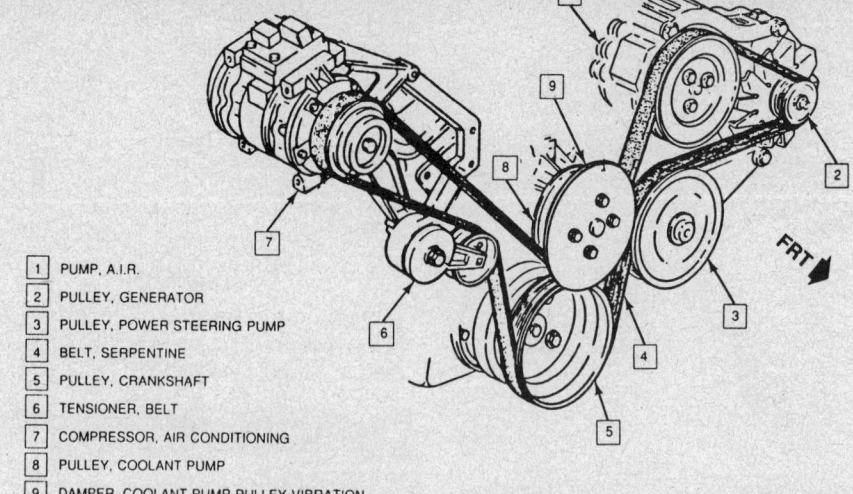

1	PUMP, A.I.R.
2	PULLEY, GENERATOR
3	PULLEY, POWER STEERING PUMP
4	BELT, SERPENTINE
5	PULLEY, CRANKSHAFT
6	TENSIONER, BELT
7	COMPRESSOR, AIR CONDITIONING
8	PULLEY, COOLANT PUMP
9	DAMPER, COOLANT PUMP PULLEY VIBRATION

Fig. 15 Serpentine drive belt routing

3. Lubricate inner and outer diameters of replacement seal with engine oil, then mount seal on tool J-35621 or equivalent, **Fig. 11.**
4. Mount tool on rear of crankshaft, tightening screws snugly to ensure seal will be installed squarely on crankshaft.
5. Tighten wing nut on tool until it bottoms, then remove tool from crankshaft.
6. Reverse remaining procedure to complete installation.

OIL PAN
REPLACE

1. Disconnect battery ground cable.
2. Raise and support vehicle, then drain crankcase.
3. Disconnect transmission oil cooler lines at flywheel cover.
4. Disconnect catalytic converter AIR pipe clamps at manifold and exhaust pipe.
5. Disconnect starter motor electrical connectors, then remove starter motor.
6. Remove oil filter, then disconnect oil cooler adapter at block.
7. Remove flywheel cover, then disconnect oil cooler line at oil pan.
8. Remove ESC shield, then the front crossmember braces.
9. Remove oil pan attaching bolts, **Fig. 12,** then rotate crankshaft and remove oil pan.
10. Reverse procedure to install. Torque oil pan retaining bolts to specifications.

OIL PUMP
OIL PUMP, REPLACE

1. Remove oil pan as described previously.
2. Remove oil pan baffle nuts, then remove baffle.
3. Remove pump to rear main bearing

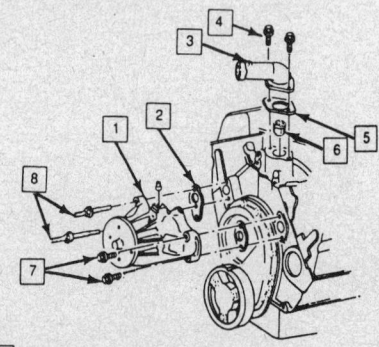

1	PUMP, COOLANT
2	GASKET, COOLANT PUMP
3	HOUSING, THERMOSTAT
4	BOLT, THERMOSAT HOUSING
5	GASKET, THERMOSTAT HOUSING
6	THERMOSTAT
7	BOLT, COOLANT PUMP
8	STUD, COOLANT PUMP

Fig. 16 Water pump replacement

cap bolt and remove pump and extension shaft, **Fig. 13.**

4. Reverse procedure to install. Prime oil pump with clean engine oil prior to installation. Make sure that installed position of oil pump screen is with bottom edge parallel to oil pan rails.

OIL PUMP SERVICE

1. Remove oil pump as described previously.
2. Remove pump cover screws and pump cover, **Fig. 14.**
3. Mark gear teeth so they can be reassembled with same teeth indexing, then remove drive gear, idler gear and shaft.
4. Remove pressure regulator valve retaining pin, pressure regulator valve and related parts.
5. If pickup screen and pipe require replacement, mount pump in a

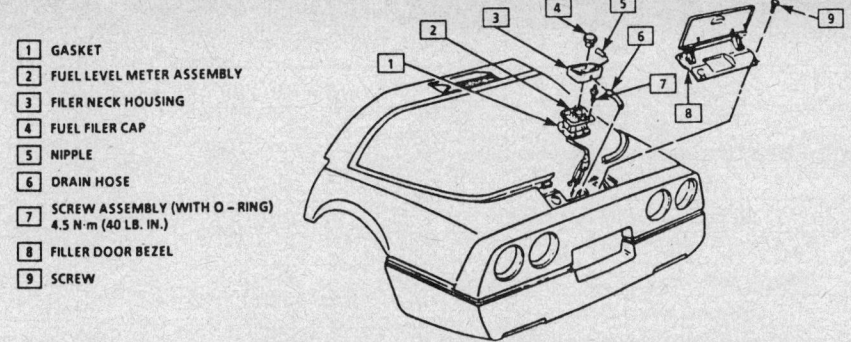

1. GASKET
2. FUEL LEVEL METER ASSEMBLY
3. FILER NECK HOUSING
4. FUEL FILER CAP
5. NIPPLE
6. DRAIN HOSE
7. SCREW ASSEMBLY (WITH O – RING) 4.5 N·m (40 LB. IN.)
8. FILLER DOOR BEZEL
9. SCREW

Fig. 17 Fuel meter & pump assembly replacement

soft-jawed vise and extract pipe from pump.
6. Wash all parts in cleaning solvent and dry with compressed air.
7. Inspect pump body and cover for cracks and excessive wear.
8. Inspect pump gears for damage or excessive wear.
9. Check drive gear shaft for looseness in pump body.
10. Inspect inside of pump cover for wear that would allow oil to leak past the ends of the gears.
11. Inspect pickup screen and pipe assembly for damage to screen, pipe or relief grommet.
12. Check pressure regulator valve for fit in pump housing.
13. Reverse procedure to assemble. Turn drive shaft by hand to check for smooth operation. **The pump gears and body are not serviced separately. If the pump gears or body are damaged or worn, the pump assembly should be replaced. Also, if the pick-up screen and pump assembly was removed, it should be replaced with a new one as loss of the press fit condition could result in an air leak and loss of oil pressure.**

BELT TENSION DATA

Engine/VIN	Year	New Lbs. ①	Used Lbs. ①
V8-350/8	1988–89	120–140	120–140
	1990–91	60–90	60–90

①—Checked between alternator & AIR pump.

SERPENTINE DRIVE BELT ROUTINGS

Refer to **Fig. 15** for serpentine belt routing diagrams.

COOLING SYSTEM BLEED

After filling cooling system, start engine and allow to reach operating temperature with radiator cap removed. Air in system will be bled through radiator cap opening. Add coolant as necessary to bring level to bottom of high fill reservoir neck, then install radiator cap and check coolant level in recovery reservoir.

WATER PUMP
REPLACE

1. Disconnect battery ground cable, and drain cooling system.
2. Remove air cleaner and duct assembly.
3. Rotate belt tensioner counterclockwise to release tension, and remove drive belt.
4. Remove water pump and AIR pump pulleys, and disconnect air management valve adapter from AIR pump.
5. Remove AIR pump, then disconnect

fuel supply and return lines. **Relieve fuel system pressure before disconnecting fuel hoses.**
6. Remove A/C compressor rear braces and lower mounting bolt.
7. Remove nuts securing A/C compressor and idler pulley bracket to water pump and disconnect electrical connector from compressor.
8. Move compressor bracket forward, remove upper mounting bolt and compressor, and secure aside.
9. Disconnect AIR hoses at check valves and AIR pipe at intake manifold and power steering bracket.
10. Remove power steering reservoir bracket and upper alternator mounting bolt.
11. Remove lower AIR pump bracket, then disconnect hoses from water pump.
12. Remove mounting bolts, then the water pump, **Fig. 16**.
13. Reverse procedure to install.

FUEL PUMP
REPLACE

The fuel pump is an electric in tank design attached to the fuel level sending unit. Replace fuel pump as follows:
1. Disconnect battery ground cable.
2. Connect pressure gauge J-34370-1 or equivalent to pressure tap on fuel rail, position bleed hose in suitable container and slowly relieve fuel system pressure. **Failure to relieve system pressure prior to disconnecting fuel system components may cause fire or personal injury.**
3. Drain fuel tank. Drain fuel into an approved fuel storage container.
4. Remove fuel filler door bezel attaching screws, then remove bezel, **Fig. 17.**
5. Remove fuel filler cap, then lift fuel filler neck housing and disconnect drain hose.
6. Remove fuel meter and pump attaching screws.
7. Disconnect fuel lines, hoses and electrical connectors from fuel meter and pump assembly. Tag hoses and electrical connectors so they may be installed at the same location.
8. Carefully remove fuel meter and pump assembly.
9. Reverse procedure to install.

TIGHTENING SPECIFICATIONS

Year	Component	Torque/Ft. Lbs.
1988–89	Camshaft Gear	20
	Clutch Pressure Plate To Flywheel Bolts	30
	Connecting Rod	45
	Crankshaft Pulley	③
	Crankshaft Rear Seal Retainer	11
	Crankshaft Vibration Damper	④
	Cylinder Head Bolts	⑤
	Distributor Clamp Bolt	25
	Engine Front Cover	80②
	Engine Mount To Engine	⑥
	Engine Mount Through Bolt	⑦
	Exhaust Manifold	⑧
	Flywheel Attaching Bolts	74
	Intake Manifold Runner	18
	Intake Manifold	35
	Main Bearings	80
	Oil Cooler	⑨
	Oil Pan Baffle Nuts	25
	Oil Pan Bolts (Front & Rear Corners)	16
	Oil Pan Bolts (Side Rails)	8
	Oil Pan Drain Plug	20
	Oil Pump Bolt	65
	Rocker Arm Cover	80②
	Rocker Arm Stud	50
	Spark Plugs	22
	Thermostat Housing	⑩
	Torque Converter To Flywheel Bolts	46
	Transmission To Engine Bolts (Auto. Trans.)	35
	Transmission To Flywheel Housing Bolts (Man. Trans.)	⑪
	Valve Lifter Retainer	12
	Water Pump	30
1990–91	Camshaft Gear	15
	Clutch Pressure Plate To Flywheel Bolts	30
	Connecting Rod	45
	Crankshaft Pulley	32
	Crankshaft Rear Seal Retainer	11
	Crankshaft Vibration Damper	70
	Cylinder Head Bolts	67
	Distributor Clamp Bolt	25
	Engine Front Cover	98②
	Engine Mount To Engine	41
	Engine Mount Through Bolt	40
	Exhaust Manifold	19
	Flywheel Attaching Bolts	74
	Intake Manifold Runner	25
	Intake Manifold	①
	Main Bearings	80
	Oil Cooler	13
	Oil Pan Baffle Nuts	25

Continued

TIGHTENING SPECIFICATIONS—Continued

Year	Component	Torque/Ft. Lbs.
1990-91 Cont'd.	Oil Pan Bolts (Front & Rear Corners)	16
	Oil Pan Bolts (Side Rails)	8
	Oil Pan Drain Plug	16
	Oil Pump Bolt	65
	Rocker Arm Cover	90②
	Rocker Arm Stud	50
	Spark Plugs	22
	Thermostat Housing	25
	Torque Converter To Flywheel Bolts	46
	Transmission To Engine Bolts (Auto. Trans.)	35
	Transmission To Flywheel Housing Bolts (Man. Trans.)	37
	Valve Lifter Retainer	12
	Water Pump	30

①—Except tightening sequence positions 1 & 4, 35 ft. lbs.; tightening sequence positions 1 & 4, 45 ft. lbs.
②—Inch lbs.
③—1988, 26-37 ft. lbs.; 1989, 32 ft. lbs.
④—1988, 60 ft. lbs.; 1989, 70 ft. lbs.
⑤—1988, 65 ft. lbs.; 1989, 67 ft. lbs.

⑥—1988, 33-49 ft. lbs.; 1989, 41 ft. lbs.
⑦—1988, 70-85 ft. lbs.; 1989, 40 ft. lbs.
⑧—1988, 20 ft. lbs.; 1989, 19 ft. lbs.
⑨—1988, 15 ft. lbs.; 1989, 13 ft. lbs.
⑩—1988, 18-23 ft. lbs.; 1989, 25 ft. lbs.
⑪—1988, 45-60 ft. lbs.; 1989, 37 ft. lbs.

5.7L/V8-350 4 CAM 32 Valve (ZR-1) Engine

INDEX

ENGINE MOUNTS
REPLACE

1. Disconnect battery ground cable.
2. Remove exhaust manifold from side on engine mount is to be replaced. Refer to "Exhaust Manifold, Replace."
3. Remove nut attaching engine mount to engine and frame, Fig. 1.
4. Support engine.
5. Raise engine slightly to permit removal of engine mount to bracket nut and bolt, then remove nut and bolt.
6. Remove engine mount and heat shield from vehicle.
7. If necessary, remove bolt attaching mount bracket to engine, then remove bracket.
8. Reverse procedure to install.

ENGINE
REPLACE

1. Disconnect battery ground cable.
2. Raise and support vehicle.
3. Drain cooling system and crankcase.
4. Remove exhaust system from vehicle.
5. Remove drive shaft from vehicle.
6. Position suitable support under transmission.
7. Remove drive line support member from vehicle.
8. Remove transmission from vehicle, refer to "Transmission, Replace."
9. Remove clutch assembly, refer to "Clutch, Replace."

10. Install engine lifting hook J-37307 or equivalent, to rear of engine.
11. Detach AIR tube center section from AIR hose and oil pan.
12. Remove oxygen sensors.
13. Detach lower power steering hose from oil cooler.
14. Disconnect battery ground cable from engine.
15. Remove engine mount to engine and frame attaching nut.
16. Lower vehicle, then remove air cleaner assembly and duct.
17. Disconnect oil cooler lines from oil filter housing.
18. Raise rear of engine.
19. Remove fuel tank filler cap.
20. Connect pressure gauge J-34370-1 or equivalent to pressure tap on fuel rail, position bleed hose in suitable container and slowly relieve fuel system pressure. **Failure to relieve system pressure prior to disconnecting fuel system components may cause fire or personal injury.**
21. Disconnect fuel lines at fuel rail.
22. Remove evaporator housing panel and restrictor.
23. Remove right hand firewall wiring harness connector retaining bolts.
24. Disconnect engine right hand wiring harness connector.
25. Remove right hand lower instrument panel sound insulator, then disconnect right firewall connector wiring harness from under instrument.
26. Disconnect air bleed hose from at plenum.
27. Disconnect radiator upper and lower hoses.
28. Disconnect vacuum lines from power steering pump.
29. Discharge A/C refrigerant system.
30. Disconnect A/C suction and discharge line flange from A/C compressor.
31. Disconnect A/C compressor to accumulator line at accumulator.
32. Remove A/C accumulator from bracket and position aside, then remove accumulator bracket from vehicle.
33. Disconnect power steering pressure line at power steering gear.
34. Disconnect accelerator and cruise control cables from throttle body and plenum retainers.
35. Install lifting hook J-37307-1 or equivalent, to front of engine.
36. Disconnect electrical connectors from ECM.
37. Remove left front fender from vehicle.
38. Disconnect battery positive cable and remove battery hold-down, then remove battery from vehicle.
39. Disconnect engine left hand firewall electrical connector.
40. Disconnect engine wiring harness fusible links at junction block.
41. Disconnect electrical connectors from secondary injector modules, battery positive cable junction block, differential pressure switch, A/C cut-out relay, A/C high blower relay, transmission shift solenoid relay, fuel pump fuse and forward lamp link.
42. Disconnect battery positive lead, then

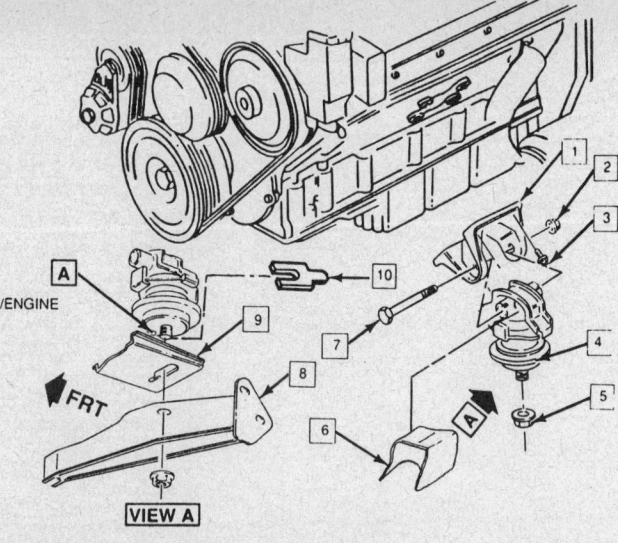

A	LOCATION PEG
1	BRACKET, ENGINE MOUNT
2	NUT, ENGINE MOUNT/BRACKET
3	BOLT, ENGINE MOUNT BRACKET/ENGINE
4	MOUNT, ENGINE HYDRAULIC
5	NUT, ENGINE MOUNT/FRAME
6	HEAT SHIELD, ENGINE MOUNT
7	BOLT, ENGINE MOUNT/BRACKET
8	SIDE MEMBER, FRONT
9	FRAME, DRIVETRAIN AND FRONT SUSPENSION
10	SPACER, ENGINE MOUNT

Fig. 1 Engine mount replacement

disconnect electrical connectors at blower motor resistor, blower motor, A/C pressure sensors, A/C cooling fan switch, W/S washer pump, low coolant sensor and ESC knock sensor and sensor relay.
43. Disconnect vacuum pump hose.
44. Disconnect front and rear vacuum connectors.
45. Position engine wiring harness out of way.
46. Disconnect engine ground strap from left hand frame rail.
47. Position battery positive out of way.
48. Remove left hand plenum screen.
49. Disconnect vacuum hose from power brake unit.
50. Remove W/S wiper motor.
51. Remove MAP sensor and bracket from plenum.
52. Disconnect AIR hose from left hand exhaust manifold.
53. Ensure all electrical connector and vacuum hoses that would interfere with engine removal are disconnected.
54. Attach suitable engine lifting fixture and remove engine from vehicle.
55. Reverse procedure to install.

PLENUM ASSEMBLY REPLACE

1. Disconnect battery ground cable.
2. Drain cooling system, then remove air intake duct.
3. Remove cable shield, then disconnect throttle and cruise control cables at throttle body.
4. Remove cable hold-down clamps from plenum.
5. Disconnect fresh air hoses from throttle body extension.
6. Disconnect electrical connectors from TPS, IAC and MAT.
7. Disconnect air bleed hose from plenum.
8. Disconnect power brake unit vacuum hose at plenum.

9. Disconnect vacuum hose located between plenum and fuel pressure regulator.
10. Disconnect vacuum hoses at mid-plenum.
11. Disconnect vacuum hose from MAP sensor and plenum, then disconnect electrical connector from MAP sensor.
12. Remove bolts attaching plenum assembly to injector housing.
13. Disconnect electrical connectors from ignition module.
14. Disconnect PCV and purge canister vacuum hoses from plenum.
15. Disconnect vacuum hose from lower portion of throttle body extension.
16. Remove plenum assembly. Cover injector housing openings.
17. Reverse procedure to install. Tighten plenum assembly attaching bolts in sequence shown in **Fig. 2.**

INJECTOR HOUSING REPLACE

1. Disconnect battery ground cable, then drain cooling system.
2. Remove plenum assembly as described under "Plenum Assembly, Replace."
3. Remove fuel tank filler cap.
4. Connect pressure gauge J-34370-1 or equivalent to pressure tap on fuel rail, position bleed hose in suitable container and slowly relieve fuel system pressure. **Failure to relieve system pressure prior to disconnecting fuel system components may cause fire or personal injury.**
5. Disconnect fuel lines at right hand fuel rail.
6. Disconnect electrical connectors from injectors.
7. Remove bolts attaching fuel rail to injector housing, then remove injectors from housing and remove fuel rail.
8. Disconnect coolant outlet pipe from injector housing being removed.
9. If left hand injector housing is to be re-

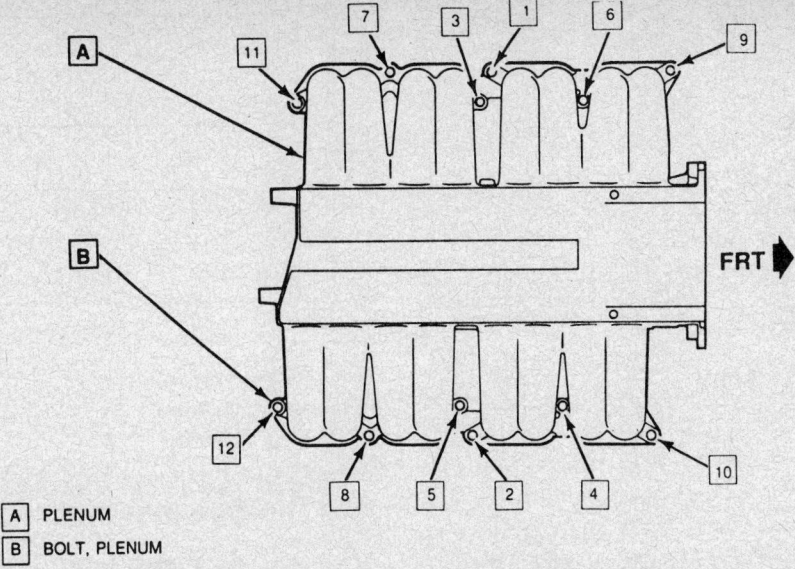

A PLENUM
B BOLT, PLENUM

Fig. 2 Plenum assembly bolt tightening sequence

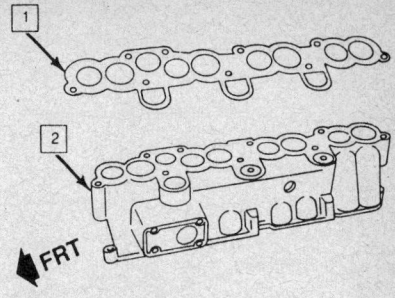

1 GASKET, PLENUM
2 HOUSING, INJECTOR

Fig. 3 Injector housing & gasket

moved, remove bolt retaining outlet pipe bracket to power steering pump bracket.
10. If right hand injector housing is to be removed, remove oil pressure sensor from oil filter housing, then remove bolt attaching outlet pipe to alternator bracket.
11. Remove PCV grommet from injector housing, then disconnect ventilation hose.
12. If left hand injector housing is to be removed, disconnect electrical connectors from coolant temperature and cooling fan switches.
13. If right hand injector housing is to be replaced, remove bolt attaching alternator rear support bracket and ventilation pipe bracket to injector housing, then remove ventilation pipe and bracket.
14. Remove injector housing to cylinder head attaching bolts, then remove injector housing and gasket, **Fig. 3**.
15. Reverse procedure to install.

EXHAUST MANIFOLD
REPLACE

LEFT SIDE

1. Disconnect battery ground cable.
2. Remove wheel housing lower rear and center panels.
3. Disconnect AIR hose from exhaust manifold, then remove exhaust manifold to cylinder head attaching bolts and nut.
4. Remove gasket from exhaust manifold.
5. Raise and support vehicle.
6. Disconnect catalytic converter oxygen sensor electrical connector.
7. Remove catalytic converter heat shield attaching screws, then remove heat shields.
8. Remove bolts attaching exhaust pipe

to converter, then remove exhaust manifold and converter assembly, **Fig. 4**.
9. Reverse procedure to install. If exhaust stud was removed or is loose, apply Loctite 620 or equivalent to stud threads.

RIGHT SIDE

1. Disconnect battery ground cable.
2. Remove wheel housing lower rear and center panels.
3. Remove engine level dipstick and tube.
4. Remove front exhaust manifold to cylinder head attaching bolts, then remove center stud nut.
5. Raise and support vehicle.
6. Disconnect oxygen sensor electrical connector. It may be necessary to remove ignition timing and oxygen sensor electrical connector bracket attaching bolts to gain access to connector.
7. Disconnect AIR hose from exhaust manifold.
8. Remove converter heat shield attaching screws, then remove heat shield.
9. Remove exhaust pipe to converter attaching bolts.
10. Remove exhaust manifold to cylinder head rear attaching bolts, then remove gasket and manifold and converter assembly, **Fig. 4**.
11. Reverse procedure to install. If exhaust stud was removed or is loose, apply Loctite 620 or equivalent to stud threads.

CYLINDER HEAD
REPLACE

LEFT SIDE

1. Disconnect battery ground cable.
2. Remove left hand injector housing as described under "Injector Housing,

Replace."
3. Disconnect vacuum hose from throttle valve actuator secondary port.
4. Remove power brake unit.
5. Remove valve lash adjusters from left hand side as described under "Hydraulic Valve Lash Adjusters, Replace."
6. Disconnect AIR control valve hoses and electrical connectors.
7. Remove camshaft position sensor.
8. Remove left hand exhaust manifold to cylinder head attaching bolts. Refer to "Exhaust Manifold, Replace" procedure. It is not necessary to remove exhaust manifold from vehicle.
9. Remove access plug from front of cylinder head, then remove upper bolt attaching secondary timing chain fixed guide.
10. Remove cylinder head attaching bolts, then remove cylinder head and gasket.
11. Reverse procedure to install. Prior to installation of cylinder head bolts, coat threads and washers with engine oil. Tighten cylinder head attaching bolts in sequence shown in **Fig. 5**. Prior to installation of secondary timing chain fixed guide upper attaching bolt, apply Loctite 262 or equivalent to bolt threads.

RIGHT SIDE

1. Disconnect battery ground cable.
2. Remove right hand injector housing as described under "Injector Housing, Replace."
3. Remove valve lash adjusters from right hand side as described under "Hydraulic Valve Lash Adjusters, Replace."
4. Remove alternator.
5. Remove right hand exhaust manifold to cylinder head attaching bolts. Refer to "Exhaust Manifold, Replace" procedure. It is not necessary to remove exhaust manifold from vehicle.
6. Remove fuel filter heat shield.
7. Disconnect vacuum hose from throttle valve actuator secondary port.
8. Remove access plug from front of cylinder head, then remove upper bolt attaching secondary timing chain fixed guide.
9. Remove cylinder head attaching bolts, then remove cylinder head and

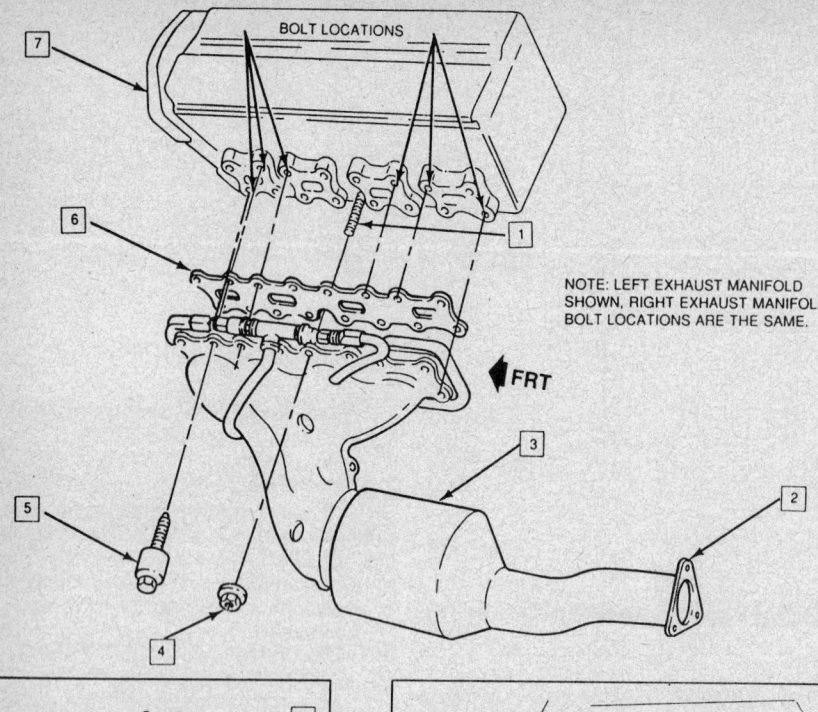

BOLT LOCATIONS

NOTE: LEFT EXHAUST MANIFOLD SHOWN, RIGHT EXHAUST MANIFOLD BOLT LOCATIONS ARE THE SAME.

←FRT

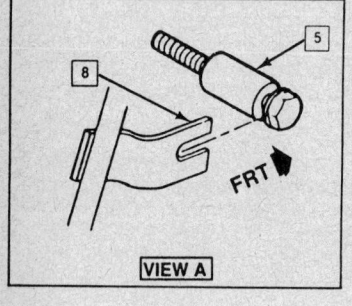

VIEW A

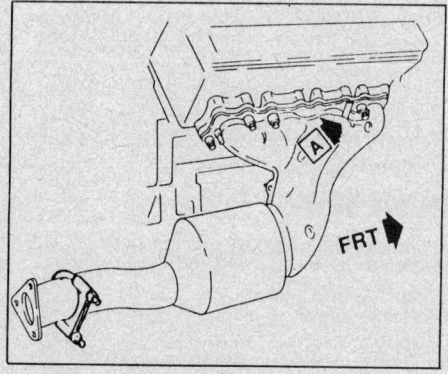

FRT

1	STUD, EXHAUST MANIFOLD	5	BOLT W/SPACER, EXHAUST MANIFOLD/CONVERTER
2	FLANGE, EXHAUST	6	GASKET, EXHAUST MANIFOLD/CONVERTER
3	MANIFOLD/CONVERTER, EXHAUST	7	HEAD, CYLINDER
4	NUT, EXHAUST MANIFOLD STUD	8	BRACKET, BOLT

Fig. 4 Exhaust manifold & converter assembly

gasket.

10. Reverse procedure to install. Prior to installation of cylinder head bolts, coat threads and washers with engine oil. Tighten cylinder head attaching bolts in sequence shown in **Fig. 5**. Prior to installation of secondary timing chain fixed guide upper attaching bolt, apply Loctite 262 or equivalent to bolt threads.

VALVE LASH SPECIFICATIONS

Year	Engine/VIN	Valve Lash
1990–91	V8-350/J	①

①—Equipped with hydraulic valve lash adjusters, no adjustment.

VALVE ARRANGEMENT

Exhaust valve are located on the exhaust manifold side of the cylinder head. Intake valve are located on the plenum side of the cylinder head.

CAMSHAFT LOBE LIFT SPECIFICATIONS

Engine/VIN	Year	Int. ①	Exh. ①
V8-350/J	1990–91	.3898	.3898

①—Plus or minus .002 inch.

VALVE LASH ADJUST

This engine is equipped with hydraulic

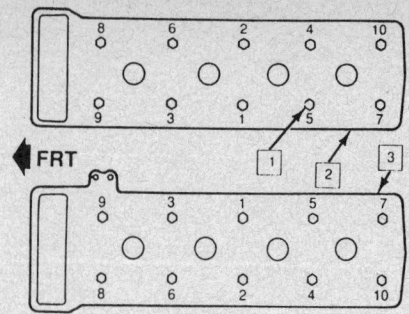

←FRT

1	BOLT, CYLINDER HEAD
2	HEAD, CYLINDER-RH
3	HEAD, CYLINDER-LH

Fig. 5 Cylinder head bolt tightening sequence

valve lash adjusters, which require no adjustment.

HYDRAULIC VALVE LASH ADJUSTERS
REPLACE

1. Disconnect battery ground cable.
2. Remove camshaft(s) as described under "Camshaft, Replace."
3. Remove valve lash adjusters from cylinder head, **Fig. 6.**. Note position of lash adjusters during removal so they may be reinstalled into the same bore.
4. Check lash adjuster contact surfaces for concave wear using a straight edge and replace as necessary. If camshaft lobe is worn, replace lash adjusters and camshaft as an assembly.
5. Reverse procedure to install. Apply engine oil to lash adjusters and bores prior to installation.

CAMSHAFT COVER
REPLACE

LEFT SIDE

1. Disconnect battery ground cable.
2. Remove power steering pump.
3. Discharge A/C refrigerant system, then disconnect suction and discharge hoses from A/C compressor. Cap refrigerant lines and A/C compressor openings.
4. Disconnect spark plug wires from spark plugs.
5. Disconnect ventilation hose from camshaft cover.
6. Remove hold down clamps retaining throttle and cruise control cables to plenum.
7. Disconnect vacuum hose from power brake unit.
8. Remove bolts attaching camshaft cover to cylinder head, then remove cover.
9. Reverse procedure to install. Apply Permabond A136 or equivalent to camshaft cover prior to installation.

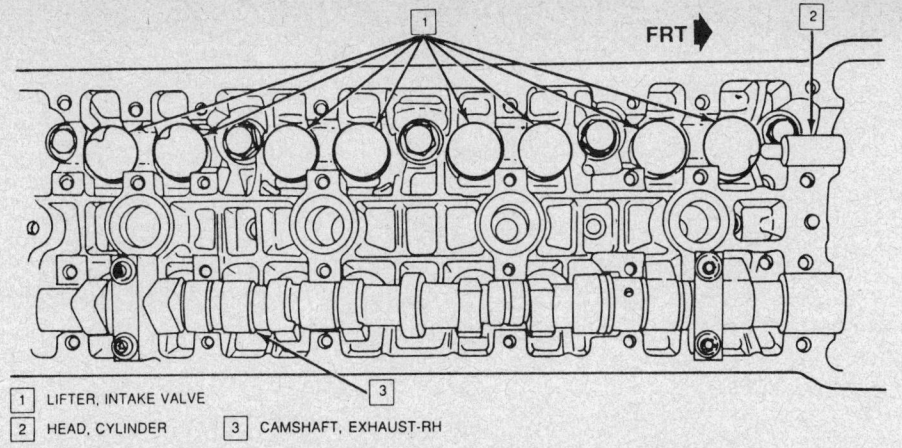

1 LIFTER, INTAKE VALVE
2 HEAD, CYLINDER
3 CAMSHAFT, EXHAUST-RH

Fig. 6   Hydraulic valve lifter installation

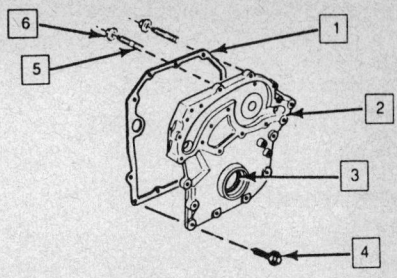

1 GASKET, ENGINE FRONT COVER
2 COVER, ENGINE FRONT
3 SEAL, ENGINE FRONT COVER
4 BOLT, ENGINE FRONT COVER
5 STUD, ENGINE FRONT COVER
6 NUT, ENGINE FRONT COVER STUD

Fig. 8   Engine front cover & gasket

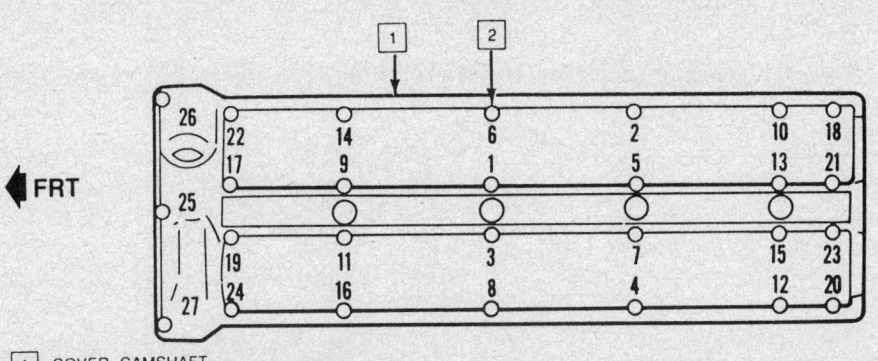

1 COVER, CAMSHAFT
2 BOLT, CAMSHAFT COVER

Fig. 7   Camshaft cover bolt tightening sequence

Prior to installation, ensure camshaft end plugs and spark plug bore O-rings are properly position. Also insert the two rear lower camshaft cover bolts prior to placing cover on cylinder head. Tighten camshaft cover attaching bolts in sequence shown in **Fig. 7.**

camshaft cover prior to installation. Prior to installation, ensure camshaft end plugs and spark plug bore O-rings are properly position. Tighten camshaft cover attaching bolts in sequence shown in **Fig. 7.** When installing coolant outlet pipe bracket bolt and oil pressure sensor, apply Loctite 565 or equivalent to threads.

RIGHT SIDE

1. Disconnect battery ground cable, then drain cooling system.
2. Disconnect spark plug wires from spark plugs.
3. Disconnect blower motor resistor electrical connectors.
4. Remove evaporator housing panel attaching screws, then remove panel.
5. Remove oil pressure sensor from oil filter housing.
6. Remove bolt attaching coolant outlet pipe to alternator bracket.
7. Remove screws attaching coolant outlet to injector housing, then position coolant outlet aside.
8. Remove bolt attaching fresh air pipe bracket to injector housing.
9. Remove camshaft cover to cylinder head attaching bolts, then remove cover.
10. Reverse procedure to install. Apply Permabond A136 or equivalent to

ENGINE FRONT COVER & SEAL
REPLACE
REMOVAL

1. Disconnect battery ground cable.
2. Remove water pump as described under "Water Pump, Replace."
3. Discharge A/C refrigerant system, then remove A/C compressor.
4. Remove steering gear, if necessary.
5. Remove serpentine drive belt.
6. Remove crankshaft damper to crankshaft retaining bolt and washer, then remove damper using puller J-24420-C or equivalent.
7. Remove key from crankshaft keyway.
8. Remove front cover attaching screws and nuts, then remove front cover, **Fig. 8.**
9. Using tool No. J-29077-A, remove seal from front cover.

INSTALLATION

1. Apply Loctite 262 or equivalent to front cover stud threads. Apply Loctite 565 or equivalent to front cover bolt threads.
2. Position front cover and gasket to engine, then install attaching bolts and nuts finger tight.
3. Lubricate front cover seal with engine oil, then install seal using installation tool No. J-37309 or equivalent, **Fig. 9.** Torque front cover attaching bolts and nuts to specification, then remove seal installation tool.
4. Install water pump and A/C compressor.
5. Apply engine oil to seal surface of crankshaft damper, then position damper to crankshaft.
6. Apply Loctite 262 or equivalent to crankshaft damper attaching bolt, then install bolt and tighten to specification.
7. Install serpentine drive belt and connect battery ground cable.

TIMING CHAIN
REPLACE
PRIMARY TIMING CHAIN

1. Disconnect battery ground cable.
2. Remove engine front cover as described under "Engine Front Cover, Replace."
3. Remove left and right hand intake camshafts as described under "Camshaft, Replace."
4. Remove bolts attaching primary timing chain guide to oil pump, then remove chain guide.
5. Remove idler sprocket assembly attaching bolts, **Fig. 10.**
6. Detach primary timing chain from idler sprocket and crankshaft sprocket, then remove timing chain from engine.
7. Reverse procedure to install. Apply Loctite 262 or equivalent to idle sprocket attaching and primary timing

guide bolt threads prior to installation. When installing primary timing chain guide, use only finger pressure to remove slack from chain.

SECONDARY TIMING CHAINS

Removal

1. Disconnect battery ground cable.
2. Remove camshafts as described under "Camshaft, Replace."
3. Remove primary timing chain as described previously.
4. Disengage left and right hand secondary timing chains from idler sprocket.
5. Remove idler sprocket attaching bolts, then remove idle sprocket, **Fig. 10.**
6. Remove left and right hand secondary timing chains.

Installation

1. Install longer outer secondary timing chain through left hand cylinder head and hold in position with retainer J-38099 or equivalent, then place chain on inner idler sprocket.
2. Install shorter inner secondary timing chain through right hand cylinder head and hold in position with retainer J-38099 or equivalent, then place chain on outer idler sprocket.
3. Install primary timing chain as described previously.
4. Install camshafts as described under "Camshaft, Replace."
5. Connect battery ground cable.

CRANKSHAFT SPROCKET

REPLACE

1. Disconnect battery ground cable.
2. Remove primary timing chain as described under "Timing Chain, Replace."
3. Using tool No. J-38211 and J-24420-C, remove crankshaft sprocket from crankshaft.
4. Remove key and oil pump seal seat from crankshaft.
5. Reverse procedure to install. Position sprocket to crankshaft with short shoulder toward front, **Fig. 11.** Use tool No. J-38132 or equivalent to install crankshaft sprocket.

CAMSHAFT

REPLACE

REMOVAL

1. Disconnect battery ground cable.
2. If camshaft(s) is to be removed from left hand cylinder head, remove A/C compressor.
3. If camshaft(s) is to be removed from right hand cylinder head, remove oil filter housing.
4. Remove camshaft cover as described under "Camshaft Cover, Replace."
5. Raise and support vehicle.
6. Disconnect electrical connector from

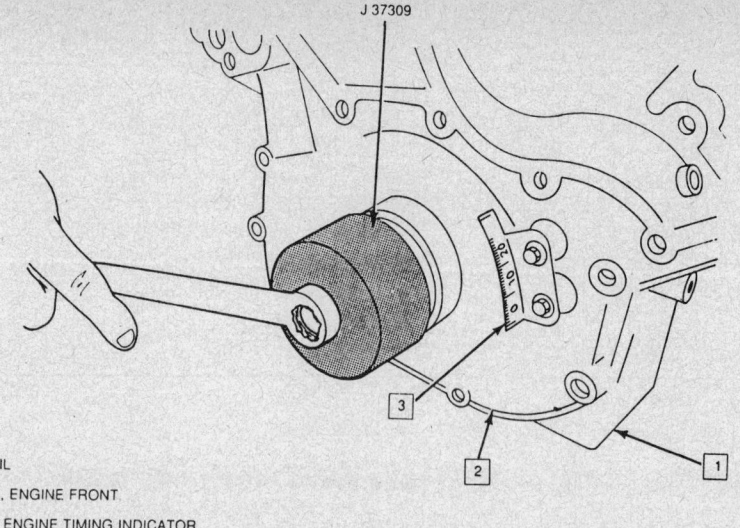

J 37309

1	PAN, OIL
2	COVER, ENGINE FRONT
3	PLATE, ENGINE TIMING INDICATOR

Fig. 9   Engine front cover seal installation

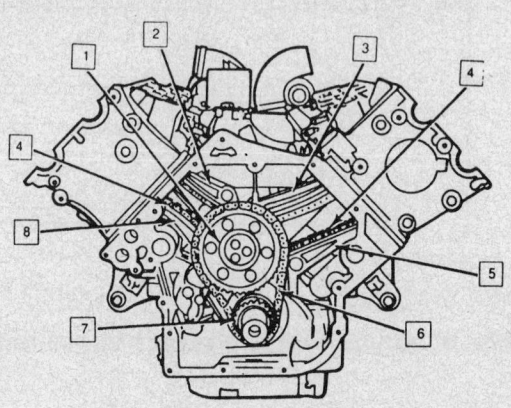

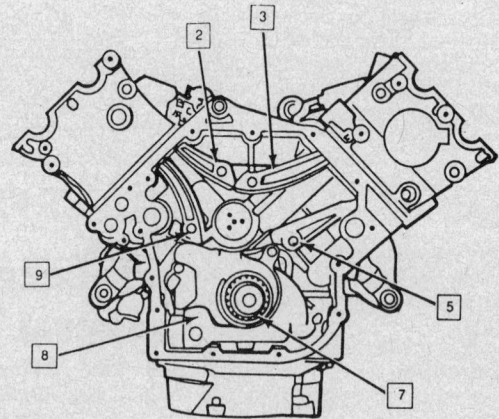

1	SPROCKET ASSEMBLY, CAMSHAFT TIMING CHAIN IDLER
2	GUIDE, CAMSHAFT SECONDARY TIMING CHAIN FIXED - RH
3	GUIDE, CAMSHAFT SECONDARY TIMING CHAIN PIVOT - LH
4	CHAIN, CAMSHAFT SECONDARY TIMING
5	GUIDE, CAMSHAFT SECONDARY TIMING CHAIN FIXED - LH
6	CHAIN, CAMSHAFT PRIMARY TIMING
7	SPROCKET, CRANKSHAFT
8	PUMP, OIL
9	GUIDE, CAMSHAFT TIMING CHAIN PIVOT - RH

Fig. 10   Primary & secondary timing chains & guides

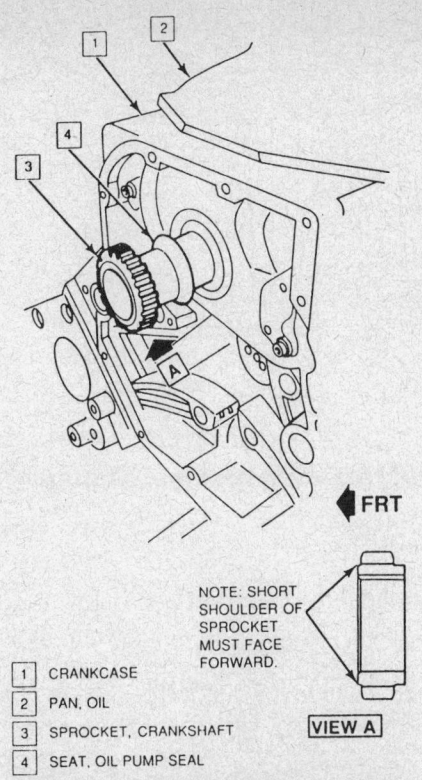

NOTE: SHORT SHOULDER OF SPROCKET MUST FACE FORWARD.

VIEW A

1	CRANKCASE
2	PAN, OIL
3	SPROCKET, CRANKSHAFT
4	SEAT, OIL PUMP SEAL

Fig. 11 Crankshaft sprocket installation

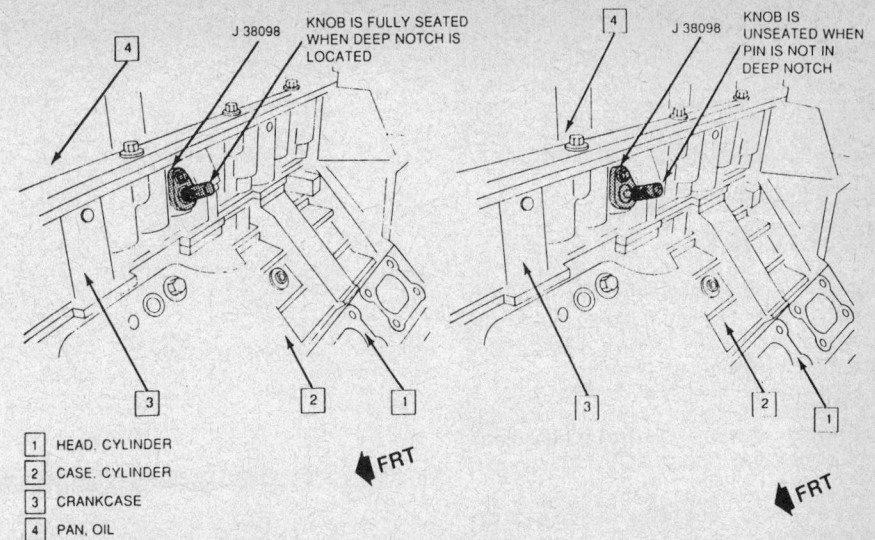

1	HEAD, CYLINDER
2	CASE, CYLINDER
3	CRANKCASE
4	PAN, OIL

Fig. 12 Installing tool No. J-38098 into crankshaft position sensor opening

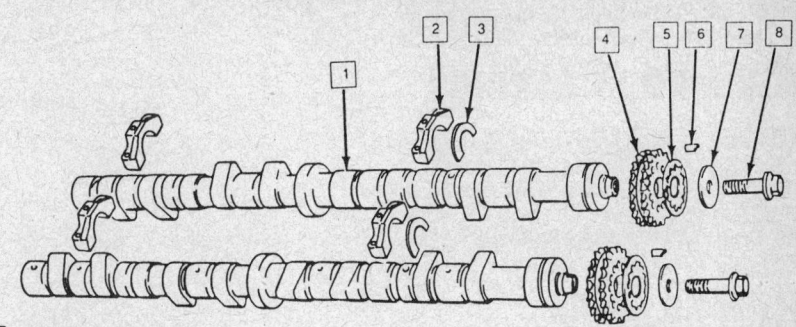

1	CAMSHAFT
2	RETAINER, CAMSHAFT
3	WASHER, CAMSHAFT THRUST
4	SPROCKET, CAMSHAFT
5	PLATE, CAMSHAFT SPROCKET TIMING
6	PIN, CAMSHAFT SPROCKET
7	WASHER, CAMSHAFT SPROCKET
8	BOLT, CAMSHAFT SPROCKET

Fig. 13 Camshafts, sprocket & retainers

crankshaft position sensor, then remove crankshaft position sensor from engine.

7. Install tool No. J-38098 or equivalent into crankshaft position sensor opening. Ensure tool properly positioned in sensor opening, **Fig. 12.**
8. Lower vehicle, then remove secondary timing chain tensioner housing to cylinder head attaching bolts.
9. Remove secondary timing chain tensioner housing, O-ring and tensioner.
10. Position a suitable wrench at rear of camshaft on hex, then remove camshaft sprocket attaching bolt(s) and washer(s), **Fig. 13.**
11. Remove camshaft timing plates and pins, then remove camshaft retainers and thrust washers.
12. Remove camshaft and sprocket. Use tool No. J-38099 or equivalent to retain secondary timing chain, **Fig. 14.**

INSTALLATION

If a replacement camshaft is to be installed, the hydraulic valve lash adjusters should also be replaced to aid in preventing premature camshaft wear.

1. Position camshaft sprocket to secondary timing chain while removing retaining tool(s).
2. Note position of alignment hole for timing pin tool, then slide camshaft into camshaft sprocket. Position camshaft so that no valves are open.
3. Lubricate camshaft lobes, journals, thrust washers and retainers with engine oil.
4. Install camshaft retainers, thrust washers and bolts, **Fig. 13.**
5. If both camshafts where removed, repeat steps 1 through 4 for other camshaft.
6. Install timing pin(s) J-37326 or equivalent into camshaft retainers and alignment hole on camshaft. Use a suitable wrench on hex at rear of camshaft to position camshaft alignment holes, **Fig. 15.**
7. Install secondary timing chain pre-tensioning tool No. J-37305 or equivalent, then tighten tool until slack is removed from timing chain, **Fig. 16.**
8. Install timing plate and pin. If holes are not aligned on timing plate, reverse plate.
9. Apply Loctite 262 or equivalent to a new camshaft sprocket retaining bolt threads. Apply engine oil to camshaft sprocket washer.
10. Position a suitable wrench on hex at rear of camshaft to prevent rotation, then install camshaft sprocket bolt and washer and torque to 19 ft. lbs. Using tool No. J-36660 or equivalent, tighten bolt an additional 80 to 85 degrees.
11. Remove timing pins from camshaft retainer(s) and alignment hole(s).
12. Remove pre-tensioning tool from secondary timing chain.
13. Lubricate a new secondary timing chain tensioner exterior with engine oil.
14. Install secondary timing chain tensioner, housing, O-ring and bolts. Ensure oil hole in tensioner piston is in vertical position and fork at end of tensioner is properly engaged on chain guide.
15. Raise and support vehicle.
16. Remove tool from crankshaft position sensor opening, then install crankshaft position sensor and connect electrical connector.

17. Lower vehicle, then install camshaft cover.
18. If camshaft was removed left hand cylinder head, install A/C compressor.
19. If camshaft was removed right hand cylinder head, install oil filter housing.
20. Connect battery ground cable.

PISTONS & ROD ASSEMBLY

Assemble pistons to connecting rods as shown in **Fig. 17**. When install piston and rod assembly, arrow on piston head must face front of engine.

Upon installation, measure the connecting rod side clearance using a suitable feeler gauge. Connecting rod side clearance should be .008 to .028 inch.

PISTONS, PINS, RINGS & LINERS

Pistons, pins, rings and cylinder liners are replaced in matched sets as an assembly.

MAIN & ROD BEARINGS

Main and rod bearing are of the precision insert type and must be replaced in a complete set of upper and lower halves. If main or rod bearing are found to be worn or out of round, the crankshaft must be replaced.

CYLINDER LINER REPLACE

REMOVAL

1. Disconnect battery ground cable.
2. Remove engine from vehicle as described under "Engine, Replace."
3. Remove flywheel attaching bolts, then remove flywheel from crankshaft.
4. Remove crankshaft rear oil seal housing.
5. Remove cylinder heads from engine.
6. Remove oil pump from engine.
7. Install cylinder liner retainers J-37330 or equivalent, **Fig. 18**.
8. Invert engine, then remove oil pan.
9. Rotate crankshaft until piston is located at bottom of cylinder liner bore.
10. Remove connecting rod bearing cap bolts, then remove cap and bearing. Mark side of rod cap so they can be installed in the same position.
11. Remove piston and rod assemblies from cylinder liner.
12. Remove bolts and washers attaching crankcase at main bearing journals.
13. Remove bolts attaching crankcase to cylinder case, then remove crankcase from cylinder case.
14. Remove crankshaft, then remove main bearing inserts. Tag bearing insert so they can be installed in the same locations.
15. Remove cylinder liner retaining tool, then remove cylinder liner using tool Nos. J-38124 and J-8092 or equivalent, **Fig. 19**.

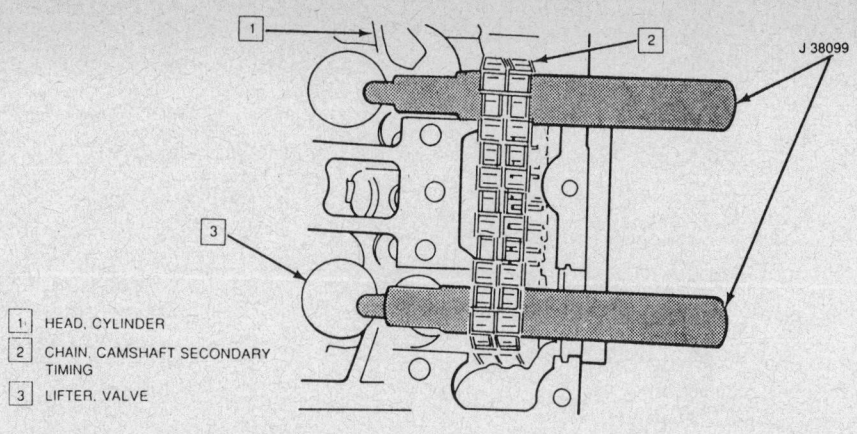

1	HEAD, CYLINDER
2	CHAIN, CAMSHAFT SECONDARY TIMING
3	LIFTER, VALVE

Fig. 14   Secondary timing chain retaining tool installation

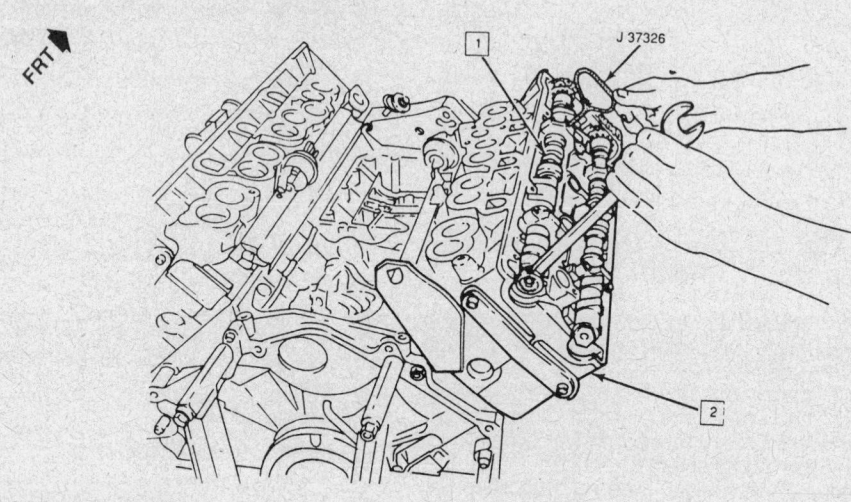

| 1 | CAMSHAFT, INTAKE RH |
| 2 | HEAD, CYLINDER |

Fig. 15   Camshaft timing pin installation

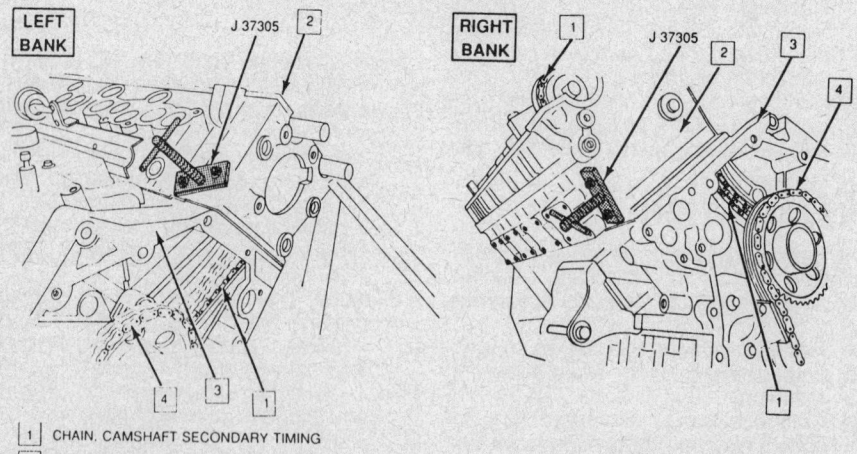

1	CHAIN, CAMSHAFT SECONDARY TIMING
2	HEAD, CYLINDER
3	CASE, CYLINDER
4	CHAIN, CAMSHAFT PRIMARY TIMING

Fig. 16   Secondary timing chain tension tool installation

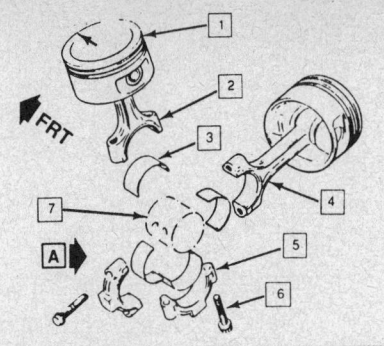

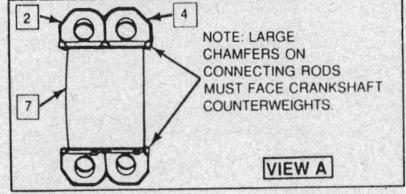

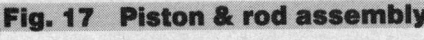

1. PISTON
2. ROD, CONNECTING - LH
3. BEARING, CONNECTING ROD
4. ROD, CONNECTING - RH
5. CAP, CONNECTING ROD BEARING
6. BOLT, CONNECTING ROD BEARING CAP
7. CRANKSHAFT

Fig. 17 Piston & rod assembly

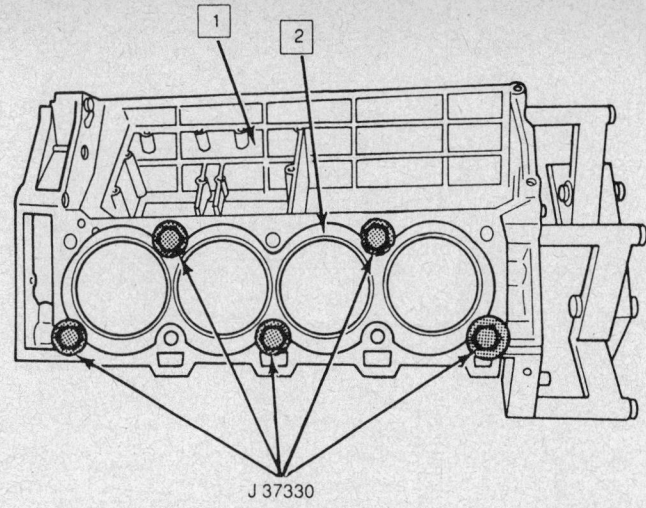

1. CASE, CYLINDER
2. LINER, CYLINDER

Fig. 18 Cylinder liner retainer installation

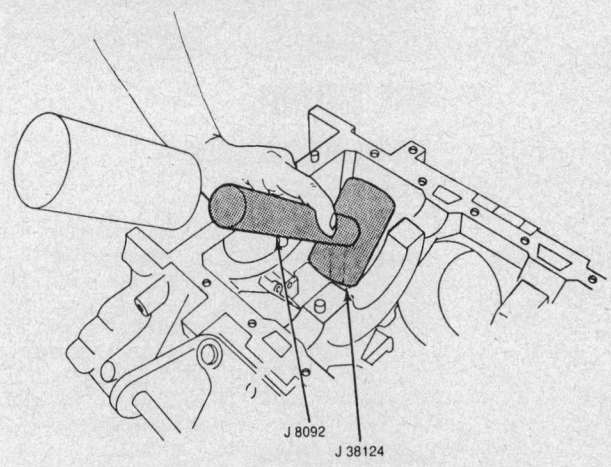

Fig. 19 Cylinder liner removal

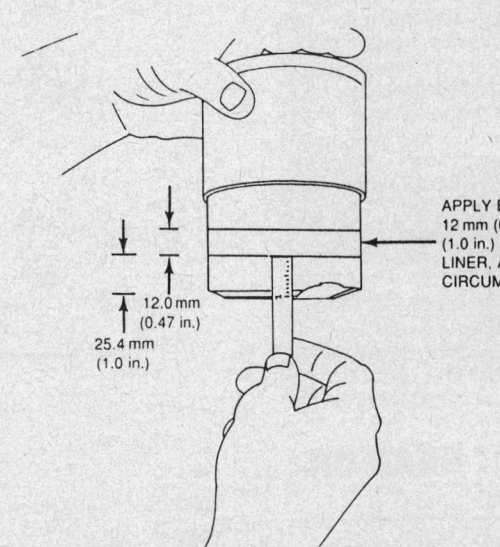

APPLY BAND OF SEALER 12 mm (0.47 in.) WIDE AND 25.4 mm (1.0 in.) FROM BASE OF CYLINDER LINER, AROUND ENTIRE CIRCUMFERENCE.

12.0 mm (0.47 in.)
25.4 mm (1.0 in.)

Fig. 20 Applying sealer to cylinder liner outer surface

INSTALLATION

1. Position cylinder liners into cylinder case. Flats on liners should face front and rear of cylinder case.
2. Check cylinder liner protrusion. Distance between cylinder case deck and lower ridge at top of liner should be .001 to .003 inch. If protrusion is not within limits, check liner ridge and cylinder case seat for burrs, damage or debris and clean as necessary. If protrusion is still not within limits, replace cylinder liner.
3. After proper cylinder liner protrusion has been obtained, remove liner. Apply a bead approximately .47 inch wide, around circumference of liner, 1 inch from liner bottom edge, **Fig. 20**.
4. Position liner into cylinder case and install liner retainer J37330 or equivalent, **Fig. 18**.
5. Lubricate main bearing insert with engine oil. Insert upper main bearing insert into cylinder case bores. Insert lower main bearing inserts into crankcase bores.
6. Position crankshaft on cylinder case.
7. Apply Permabond A136 or equivalent to crankcase on cylinder case sealing surfaces. Be sure to route sealant around bolt holes.
8. Install crankcase on cylinder case.
9. Coat new bolts and washers located at main bearing journals with engine oil. Do not coat other crankcase to cylinder case attaching bolts.
10. Install all crankcase to cylinder case bolts finger tight. Do not rotate crankshaft until bolts have been tighten to final torque reading.
11. Torque crankcase to cylinder case attaching bolts to specified torque in sequence shown in **Fig. 21**. Torque bolts listed in numbered sequence first, then tighten bolts listed in lettered sequence.
12. Lubricate pistons, connecting rod bearings, cylinder liner bores and crank pin journals with engine oil.
13. Using a suitable ring compressor install piston and rod assemblies into cylinder liner bores and locate rod and

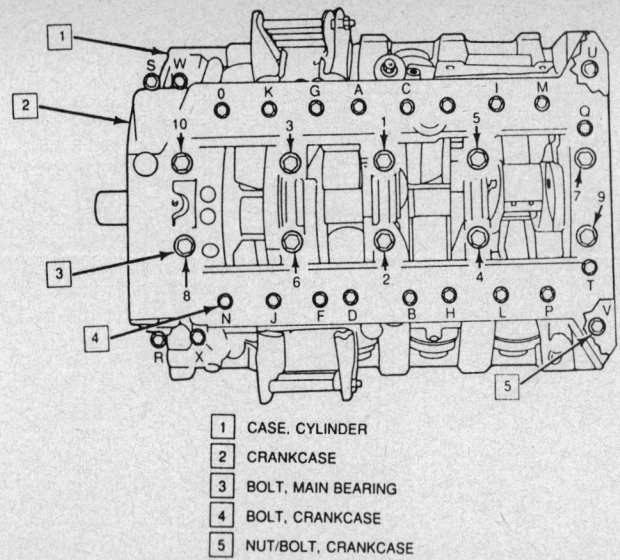

1	CASE, CYLINDER
2	CRANKCASE
3	BOLT, MAIN BEARING
4	BOLT, CRANKCASE
5	NUT/BOLT, CRANKCASE

Fig. 21 Crankcase to cylinder case bolt tightening sequence

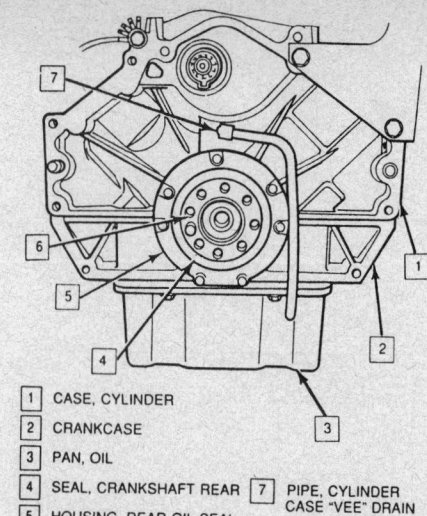

1	CASE, CYLINDER		
2	CRANKCASE		
3	PAN, OIL		
4	SEAL, CRANKSHAFT REAR	7	PIPE, CYLINDER CASE "VEE" DRAIN
5	HOUSING, REAR OIL SEAL		
6	CRANKSHAFT		

Fig. 22 Crankshaft rear seal & housing

bearing on crankshaft.
14. Install connecting rod bearings and caps. Torque new connecting bolts to 22 ft. lbs., then tighten bolts an additional 80 to 85 degrees using tool No. J-36660 or equivalent. Rotate crankshaft as necessary to install piston and connecting rod assemblies.
15. Install oil pan and gasket, then invert engine. Apply Loctite 565 or equivalent to oil pan front center bolt threads.
16. Remove cylinder liner retainers, then install oil pump.
17. Install cylinder heads.
18. Install crankshaft rear oil seal housing.
19. Apply Loctite 262 or equivalent to flywheel attaching bolt threads, then install flywheel. Flywheel must be installed with crankshaft dowel pin at the 6 o'clock position.
20. Install engine in vehicle.

CRANKSHAFT REAR OIL SEAL
REPLACE

1. Disconnect battery ground cable.
2. Remove transmission and clutch assembly.
3. Remove flywheel from crankshaft.
4. Remove oil seal housing to cylinder block attaching screws.
5. Remove seal housing assembly from crankshaft, then remove seal from housing, **Fig. 22.**
6. Reverse procedure to install. Using tool J-37312 or equivalent, install seal into housing until it is 1 to 1.5 mm below housing surface. Lubricate seal lip with engine oil prior to installation.

OIL PAN
REPLACE

1. Disconnect battery ground cable.

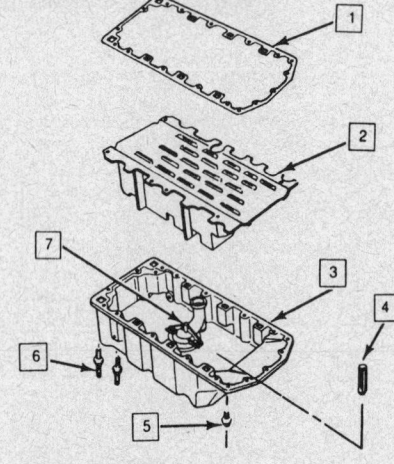

1	GASKET, OIL PAN
2	BAFFLE, OIL PAN
3	PAN, OIL
4	SPACER, OIL PAN PICKUP
5	BOLT, OIL PAN
6	BOLT, OIL PAN STUD
7	PIPE AND SCREEN ASSEMBLY, OIL PICKUP

Fig. 23 Oil pan, baffle & gasket

2. Remove oil level dipstick from tube.
3. Raise and support vehicle, then drain oil from crankcase.
4. Remove flywheel housing cover attaching bolts, then remove cover.
5. Remove bolts attaching AIR pipe bracket to oil pan.
6. Remove converter heat shield attaching screws, then remove heat shields.
7. Remove engine mount retaining nuts at front crossmember rear brace from left and right hand sides.
8. Remove bolts attaching front crossmember rear braces to front

crossmember and side crossmembers, then remove braces.
9. Remove bolts attaching oil pan to engine block, then remove oil pan, **Fig. 23.**
10. Reverse procedure to install. Apply Loctite 565 or equivalent to center screw at front of oil pan.

OIL PUMP
REPLACEMENT
Removal

1. Disconnect battery ground cable.
2. Remove crankshaft sprocket as described under "Crankshaft Sprocket, Replace."
3. Remove bolts attaching oil pump to engine block, then remove oil pump.
4. Remove O-ring from crankshaft.
5. Remove oil pump shaft seal using tool No. J-29077-A or equivalent.

Installation

1. Position O-ring on crankshaft.
2. Apply Loctite 262 or equivalent to oil pump attaching bolt threads.
3. Position oil pump to engine, aligning flats on oil pump drive gear with flats on crankshaft.
4. Install oil pump to engine block attaching bolts and finger tighten.
5. Using tool No. J-38383 or equivalent, align oil pump on crankshaft, then tighten oil pump to engine block attaching bolts.
6. Install oil pump shaft seal using tool Nos. J-38135 and J-38463 or equivalent.
7. Install crankshaft sprocket.

SERVICE
Disassemble

1. Remove oil pump plate to pump housing attaching screws, then remove plate, **Fig. 24.**

5.7L/V8-350 4 CAM 32 VALVE (ZR-1) ENGINE

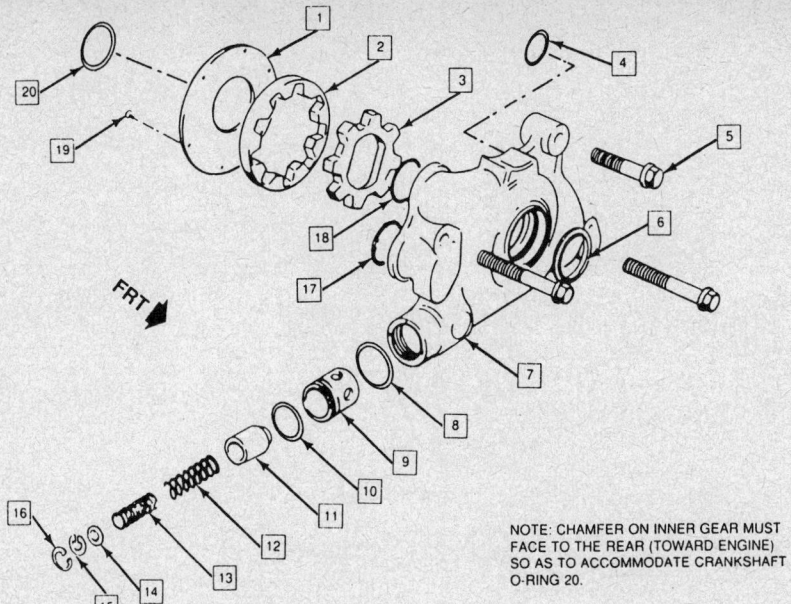

NOTE: CHAMFER ON INNER GEAR MUST FACE TO THE REAR (TOWARD ENGINE) SO AS TO ACCOMMODATE CRANKSHAFT O-RING 20.

1	PLATE, OIL PUMP	11	VALVE, OIL PRESSURE REGULATION
2	GEAR, OUTER	12	SPRING, OIL PRESSURE REGULATION VALVE OUTER
3	GEAR, INNER	13	SPRING, OIL PRESSURE REGULATION VALVE INNER
4	O-RING, OIL PUMP BODY	14	STOP, OIL PRESSURE REGULATION VALVE
5	BOLT, OIL PUMP	15	RETAINER, OIL PRESSURE REGULATION VALVE
6	SEAL, OIL PUMP CRANKSHAFT	16	RETAINER, OIL PRESSURE REGULATION VALVE
7	BODY, OIL PUMP	17	O-RING, OIL FILTER FEED RETURN
8	O-RING, OIL PRESSURE REGULATION VALVE	18	O-RING, OIL FILTER FEED RETURN
9	HOUSING, OIL PRESSURE REGULATION VALVE	19	SCREW, OIL PUMP PLATE
10	O-RING, OIL PRESSURE REGULATION VALVE	20	O-RING, OIL PUMP CRANKSHAFT

Fig. 24 Exploded view of oil pump

2. Remove inner and outer gears from pump housing.
3. Remove snap ring retaining pressure regulator valve to pump housing, then remove pressure regulator valve.
4. Remove snap ring from pressure regulator valve and disassembly valve, if necessary.
5. Remove oil pump shaft seal using tool No. J-29077-A or equivalent, if not removed during disassembly.
6. Remove O-rings from pump housing.

Assemble

1. Install O-rings into pump housing, **Fig. 24.**
2. Assemble pressure regulator valve and install snap ring.
3. Position pressure regulator valve into pump housing, then install snap ring.
4. Position inner and outer gears into pump housing. Place inner gear into pump housing with chamfer facing rear of pump housing (toward engine). Place outer pump gear in housing with chamfer facing toward recess in pump housing.
5. Position pump plate to pump housing, then install attaching screws.

OIL FILTER HOUSING
REPLACE

1. Disconnect battery ground cable.
2. Drain cooling system.
3. Remove air intake duct.
4. Disconnect hoses from coolant outlets and radiator inlet.
5. Remove clamps from inlet pipe, then remove inlet pipe and hose assembly.
6. Rotate serpentine belt tensioner, then slip belt behind water pump pulley.
7. Release belt tensioner, then remove belt from pulleys.
8. Remove serpentine drive belt tensioner attaching bolt and tensioner.
9. Remove oil filter.
10. Disconnect electrical connectors from oil pressure, oil temperature and low oil pressure switches.
11. Remove oil pressure sensor from filter housing.
12. Remove bolt attaching outlet pipe to alternator bracket.
13. Disconnect oil cooler lines from oil filter housing.
14. Remove oil filter housing to engine block attaching bolts, then remove oil

filter housing, **Fig. 25.**
15. Reverse procedure to install. Apply Loctite 565 or equivalent to threads of oil pressure sensor and outlet pipe bracket to alternator bracket bolt.

OIL COOLER
REPLACE

1. Disconnect battery ground cable.
2. Drain cooling system.
3. Remove air cleaner assembly.
4. Remove radiator upper air deflector.
5. Disconnect electrical connectors from cooling fan relays.
6. Remove accumulator bracket to upper radiator support attaching bolts.
7. Remove fan shroud to upper radiator attaching screws.
8. Remove rubber access plug from upper part of radiator, then disconnect radiator air bleed hose.
9. Remove bolts and nuts attaching upper radiator support to frame side member.
10. Remove oil cooler line to oil cooler attaching bolts, then remove seal retainers and seals from oil cooler and A/C lines.
11. Remove AIR pump.
12. Remove AIR rear bracket bolt and loosen front bracket bolt.
13. Remove AIR pump intake duct, then remove bolt attaching upper radiator support to lower radiator.
14. Remove upper radiator support from vehicle.
15. Disconnect upper and lower radiator hoses from radiator, then remove radiator from vehicle.
16. Disconnect oil cooler lines from oil cooler. Cap oil cooler lines and fittings.
17. Remove oil cooler to condenser attaching screws, then remove oil cooler, **Fig. 26.**
18. Reverse procedure to install. Ensure oil cooler O-rings are properly positioned prior to installation.

CYLINDER CASE VENTILATION COVER & BAFFLE
REPLACE

1. Disconnect battery ground cable.
2. Remove plenum as described under "Plenum Assembly, Replace."
3. Discharge A/C system, then remove A/C compressor.
4. Disconnect spark plug wires from coil pack, then remove bolts attaching ignition coil pack to ventilation cover and cylinder case.
5. Disconnect electrical connectors, then remove ignition coil pack assembly.
6. Disconnect vacuum hoses from vacuum reservoir, then remove reservoir attaching nuts and reservoir.
7. Disconnect vacuum hoses and electrical connector from vacuum solenoid, then remove vacuum solenoid attaching screw and vacuum solenoid.

8. Disconnect vacuum hoses from secondary port throttle actuators, then remove actuator to bracket attaching nuts and retaining clips and remove actuators.
9. Remove actuator bracket to control cover attaching screws, then remove covers.
10. Disconnect links from lever assemblies.
11. Disconnect electrical connectors from coolant temperature sensor and cooling fan switch, then remove sensor and switch from injector housing.
12. Disconnect hoses from ventilation cover, then remove ventilation cover attaching screws and ventilation cover, **Fig. 27.**
13. Remove cylinder case ventilation baffle attaching screws, then remove baffle, **Fig. 28.**
14. Reverse procedure to install. Prior to installing coolant sensor and cooling fan switch, apply Loctite 565 or equivalent to threads.

BELT TENSION DATA

Engine/VIN	Year	New Lbs.	Used Lbs.
V8-350/J	1990–91	①	①

①—Controlled by belt tensioner.

SERPENTINE DRIVE BELT ROUTINGS

Refer to **Fig. 29.** for serpentine belt routing diagrams.

COOLING SYSTEM BLEED

After filling cooling system, start engine and allow to reach operating temperature with radiator cap removed. Air in system will be bled through radiator cap opening. Add coolant as necessary to bring level to bottom of high fill reservoir neck, then install radiator cap and check coolant level in recovery reservoir.

WATER PUMP
REPLACE

1. Disconnect battery ground cable.
2. Drain cooling system.
3. Remove air intake duct.
4. Remove throttle body extension attaching screws, then remove extension from throttle body.
5. Disconnect hoses from coolant inlets and outlet and radiator upper hose.
6. Remove hose and inlet pipe assembly from vehicle.
7. Remove serpentine drive belt.
8. Remove bolt attaching serpentine drive belt tensioner to water pump, then remove tensioner.
9. Disconnect engine to water pump hose.
10. Remove bolts attaching lower alternator mounting bracket, then remove bracket. Note length and location of bolts for installation.
11. Remove water pump to front cover attaching bolts, **Fig. 30.**

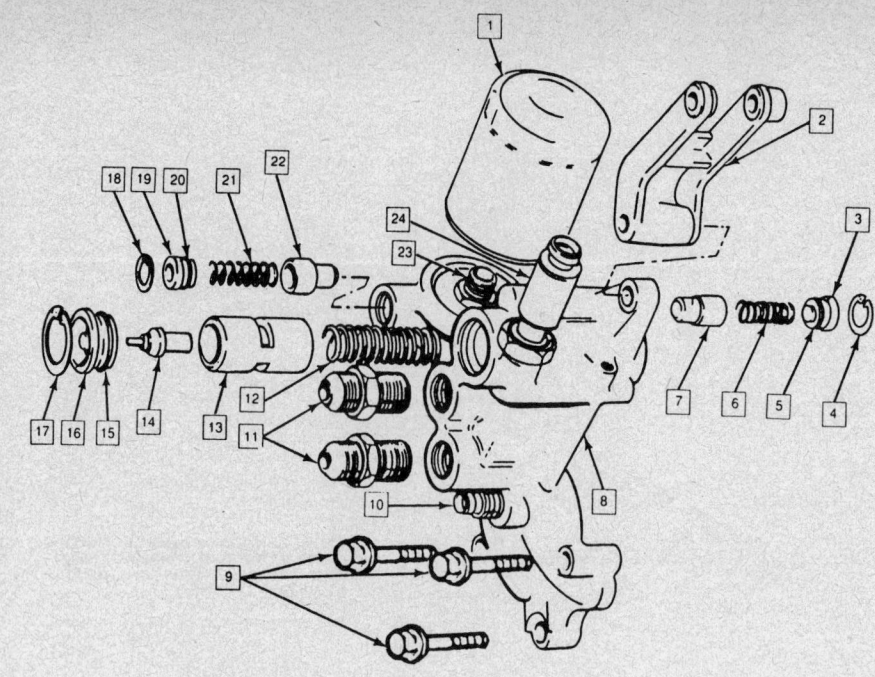

1 FILTER, OIL	14 VALVE, OIL TEMPERATURE CONTROL
2 BRACKET, OIL FILTER HOUSING	15 O-RING, OIL TEMPERATURE CONTROL VALVE
3 CAP, OIL COOLER BYPASS SEAL	16 DISC, OIL TEMPERATURE CONTROL VALVE SEAL
4 RETAINER, OIL COOLER BYPASS VALVE	17 RETAINER, OIL TEMPERATURE CONTROL VALVE
5 O-RING, OIL COOLER BYPASS VALVE	18 RETAINER, OIL FILTER BYPASS VALVE
6 SPRING, OIL COOLER BYPASS VALVE	19 CAP, OIL FILTER BYPASS VALVE SEAL
7 VALVE, OIL COOLER BYPASS	20 O-RING, OIL FILTER BYPASS VALVE
8 HOUSING, OIL FILTER	21 SPRING, OIL FILTER BYPASS VALVE
9 BOLT, OIL FILTER HOUSING	22 VALVE, OIL FILTER BYPASS
10 SENSOR, OIL TEMPERATURE	23 ADAPTER, OIL FILTER
11 ADAPTER, OIL COOLER	24 SENSOR, OIL PRESSURE
12 SPRING, OIL TEMPERATURE CONTROL VALVE	
13 SLEEVE, OIL TEMPERATURE CONTROL VALVE	

Fig. 25   Oil filter housing assembly

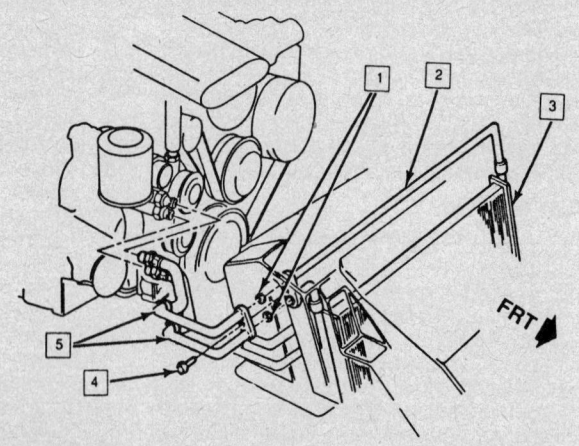

1 O-RING, ENGINE OIL COOLER
2 PIPE, ENGINE OIL COOLER
3 COOLER, ENGINE OIL
4 BOLT, ENGINE OIL COOLER
5 HOSE, ENGINE OIL COOLER

Fig. 26   Oil cooler assembly replacement

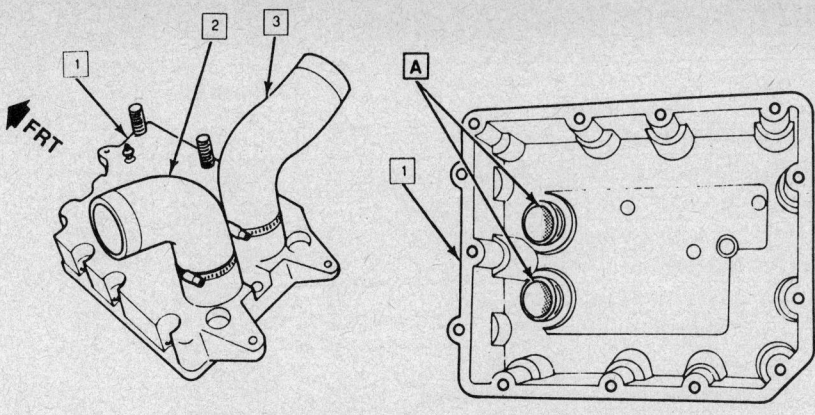

A — PASSAGE. CYLINDER CASE VENTILATION COVER
1 — COVER. CYLINDER CASE VENTILATION
2 — HOSE, CYLINDER CASE VENTILATION - LEFT HAND
3 — HOSE, CYLINDER CASE VENTILATION - RIGHT HAND

Fig. 27 Cylinder case ventilation cover

1 — CASE, CYLINDER
2 — BAFFLE, CYLINDER CASE VENTILATION
3 — HEAD, CYLINDER
4 — RAIL, FUEL

**Fig. 28 Cylinder case
ventilation baffle**

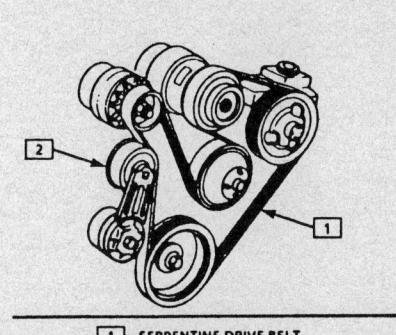

1 — SERPENTINE DRIVE BELT
2 — BELT TENSIONER

**Fig. 29 Serpentine drive belt
routing**

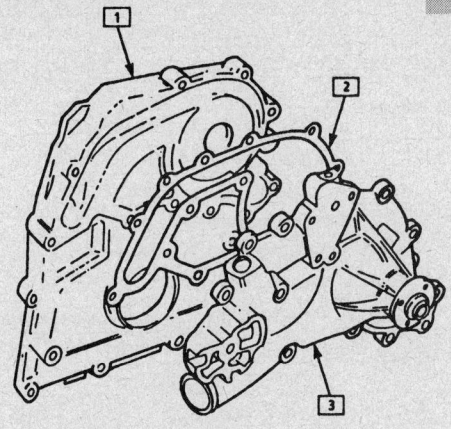

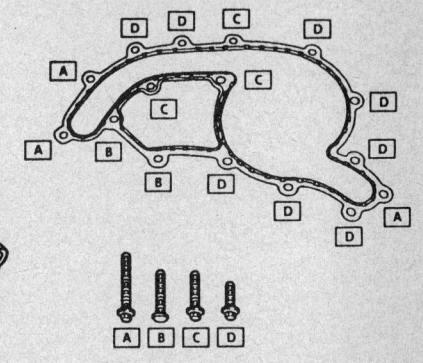

1 — ENGINE FRONT COVER   2 — COOLANT PUMP GASKET   3 — COOLANT PUMP

Fig. 30 Water pump installation & bolt locations

1 — GASKET
2 — FUEL LEVEL METER ASSEMBLY
3 — FILLER NECK HOUSING
4 — FUEL FILLER CAP
5 — NIPPLE
6 — DRAIN HOSE
7 — SCREW ASSEMBLY (WITH O - RING)
    4.5 N·m (40 LB. IN.)
8 — FILLER DOOR BEZEL
9 — SCREW

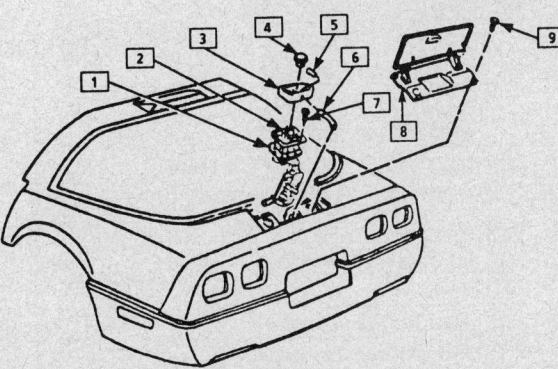

Fig. 31 Fuel pump replacement

12. Remove bolt attaching A/C compressor to water pump.
13. Remove water pump from engine.
14. Reverse procedure to install. Apply Loctite 565 or equivalent to alternator lower bracket attaching bolt threads prior to installation.

FUEL PUMP
REPLACE

The fuel is an electric in tank design attached to the fuel level sending unit. Replace fuel pump as follows:
1. Disconnect battery ground cable.

2. Connect pressure gauge J-34370-1 or equivalent to pressure tap on fuel rail, position bleed hose in suitable container and slowly relieve fuel system pressure. **Failure to relieve system pressure prior to disconnecting fuel system components may cause fire or personal injury.**
3. Drain fuel tank. Drain fuel into an approved fuel storage container.
4. Remove fuel filler door bezel attaching screws, then remove bezel, **Fig. 17.**
5. Remove fuel filler cap, then lift fuel filler neck housing and disconnect drain hose.
6. Remove fuel meter and pump attaching screws.
7. Disconnect fuel lines, hoses and electrical connectors from fuel meter and pump assembly. Tag hoses and electrical connectors so they may be installed at the same location.
8. Carefully remove fuel meter and pump assembly.
9. Reverse procedure to install.

TIGHTENING SPECIFICATIONS

Year	Component	Torque/Ft. Lbs.
1990-91	AIR Pipe Bracket To Oil Pan	20
	Belt Tensioner To Water Pump	45
	Camshaft Cover To Cylinder Head Bolt (M6)	89 ①
	Camshaft Cover To Cylinder Head Bolt (M8)	15
	Camshaft Position Sensor	71 ①
	Camshaft Retainer Bolt	89 ①
	Camshaft Sprocket Bolt	②
	Connecting Rod Cap Bolts	③
	Coolant Outlet Cover To Injector Housing	53 ①
	Coolant Outlet Cover Pipe Bracket To Alternator Bracket	38
	Coolant Outlet Cover Pipe Bracket To Power Steering Pump Bracket	20
	Crankcase To Cylinder Case Bolts	④
	Crankshaft Damper Bolt	148
	Crankshaft Position Sensor	71 ①
	Crankshaft Rear Seal Housing To Cylinder Case	89 ①
	Cylinder Case Ventilation Baffle To Cylinder Case	89 ①
	Cylinder Case Ventilation Cover To Cylinder Case	89 ①
	Cylinder Head Bolts	118
	Engine Front Cover Bolt	20
	Engine Front Cover Stud Nut	21
	Engine Front Cover Stud	97 ①
	Engine Mount To Engine Bolts	38
	Engine Mount To Drivetrain & Frame Nut	40
	Engine Mount To Front Crossmember Nut	40
	Engine Timing Plate To Front Cover Bolts	89 ①
	Exhaust Manifold To Cylinder Head Bolt & Stud Nut	11
	Exhaust Manifold To Stud	22
	Engine Mount Bracket To Cylinder Case Bolt	38
	Exhaust Pipe To Converter Flange	15
	Flywheel To Crankshaft	74
	Front Crossmember Rear Brace To Crossmember Bolt	59
	Front Crossmember Rear Brace To Side Member	46
	Fuel Rail To Injector Housing Bolt	20
	Ignition Coil Pack Bracket To Cylinder Case Ventilation Cover	89 ①
	Injector Housing To Cylinder Head	20
	Low Oil Pressure Switch	9
	MAP Sensor Bracket	89 ①
	Oil Dipstick Tube To Exhaust Manifold	11
	Oil Filter Housing To Cylinder Case	20
	Oil Pan Baffle To Oil Pan Bolt	89 ①
	Oil Pan To Crankcase	20
	Oil Pick-up Tube To Oil Pan Bolt	89 ①
	Oil Pressure Sensor	9
	Oil Pump Plate To Housing	27 ①
	Oil Pump To Cylinder Case	20
	Plenum To Injector Housing	20
	Secondary Timing Chain Pivot Guide To Cylinder Case	20
	Spark Plug	15
	Thermostat Housing Bolt	18
	Throttle Body Extension To Throttle Body	53 ①
	Throttle Body To Plenum	11
	Timing Chain Idler Sprocket Bolts	20

Continued

5.7L/ V8-350 4 CAM 32 VALVE (ZR-1) ENGINE

TIGHTENING SPECIFICATIONS — Continued

Year	Component	Torque/Ft. Lbs.
1990-91 Cont'd.	Timing Chain Tensioner	89①
	Transmission To Clutch Housing Bolts	37
	Water Pump Pulley To Hub	89①
	Water Pump To Cylinder Case	20

①—Inch Lbs.
②—Torque to 19 ft. lbs., then tighten an additional 80 to 85 degrees.
③—Torque to 22 ft. lbs., then tighten an additional 80 to 85 degrees.
④—Torque M12 bolts (at main bearing journal Nos. 1, 3 & 5) to 30 ft. lbs.

then tighten an additional 45 to 50 degrees. Torque M10 bolts (at main bearing journal Nos. 2 & 4) to 15 ft. lbs., then tighten an additional 77.5 to 82.5 degrees. Torque remaining crankcase to cylinder case bolts to 20 ft. lbs.

Clutch & Manual Transmission

INDEX

CLUTCH PEDAL
ADJUST

The clutch release mechanism on these models is hydraulically operated, and is not adjustable. When the clutch pedal is depressed, the pedal push rod contacts a plunger in the clutch master cylinder bore. The plunger first closes off the master cylinder fluid return port, then when moved further, forces fluid under pressure into the clutch actuating cylinder. As pressure is applied to the actuating cylinder, the actuating cylinder piston is forced outward activating the clutch release fork. To diagnose malfunctions in the clutch release system, proceed as follows:

1988
Inspection

1. With engine running at normal operating temperature and brakes applied, hold clutch pedal approximately 1/2 inch from fully depressed position and move transmission selector between 1st and reverse several times.
2. If transmission selector can be moved without binding or gear clash, clutch is releasing properly.
3. If shifter cannot be moved or if gear clash is evident, inspect linkage, fork and ball stud for damage and wear, and replace as needed.
4. If linkage is satisfactory, check clutch pedal and actuating cylinder travel.
5. Clutch pedal travel should be 7³/₈ inch, and actuating cylinder plunger travel should be .70 inch, measured at the clutch fork.

6. If pedal travel is not within specifications, repair as needed. If plunger travel is not as specified, bleed or repair hydraulic system.

Bleeding

1. Fill clutch master cylinder reservoir with DOT 3 brake fluid.
2. Raise and support vehicle.
3. Remove actuating cylinder attaching bolts and secure cylinder at 45° angle with bleeder screw at highest point.
4. Fully depress and hold clutch pedal, then open bleeder.
5. Close bleeder then release clutch pedal.
6. Repeat steps 4 and 5 until all air has been purged from system, remount actuating cylinder and repeat inspection. **Check and fill master cylinder reservoir, as needed, to ensure no air is drawn into system during bleeding.**

1989—91
Inspection

1. With engine running at normal operating temperature and brakes applied, hold clutch pedal in fully depressed position and move transmission selector between 1st and reverse several times.
2. If transmission selector can be moved without binding or gear clash, clutch is releasing properly.
3. If shifter cannot be moved or if gear clash is evident, inspect clutch pedal

bushings for damage and wear, and replace as needed.
4. If bushings are satisfactory, check clutch pedal travel.
5. Clutch pedal travel should be 6.25 inch.

Bleeding

1. Fill clutch master cylinder reservoir with clutch hydraulic fluid 12345347 or DOT 3 brake fluid. It may be necessary to remove ECM from mounting bracket to gain access to reservoir. If a squeaking noise is present in clutch master cylinder, drain DOT 3 brake fluid from clutch hydraulic system and fill with clutch hydraulic fluid 12345347 or equivalent.
2. Raise and support vehicle.
3. Remove actuating cylinder attaching bolts and lower cylinder to a point below the catalytic converter, then remove bleeder screw cap.
4. Hold cylinder in horizontal position with bleeder screw vertical.
5. Fully depress and hold clutch pedal, then open bleeder screw.
6. Close bleeder screw, then release clutch pedal.
7. Repeat steps 4 and 5 until all air has been purged from system, remount actuating cylinder and repeat inspection. **Check and fill master cylinder reservoir, as needed, to ensure no air is drawn into system during bleeding.**

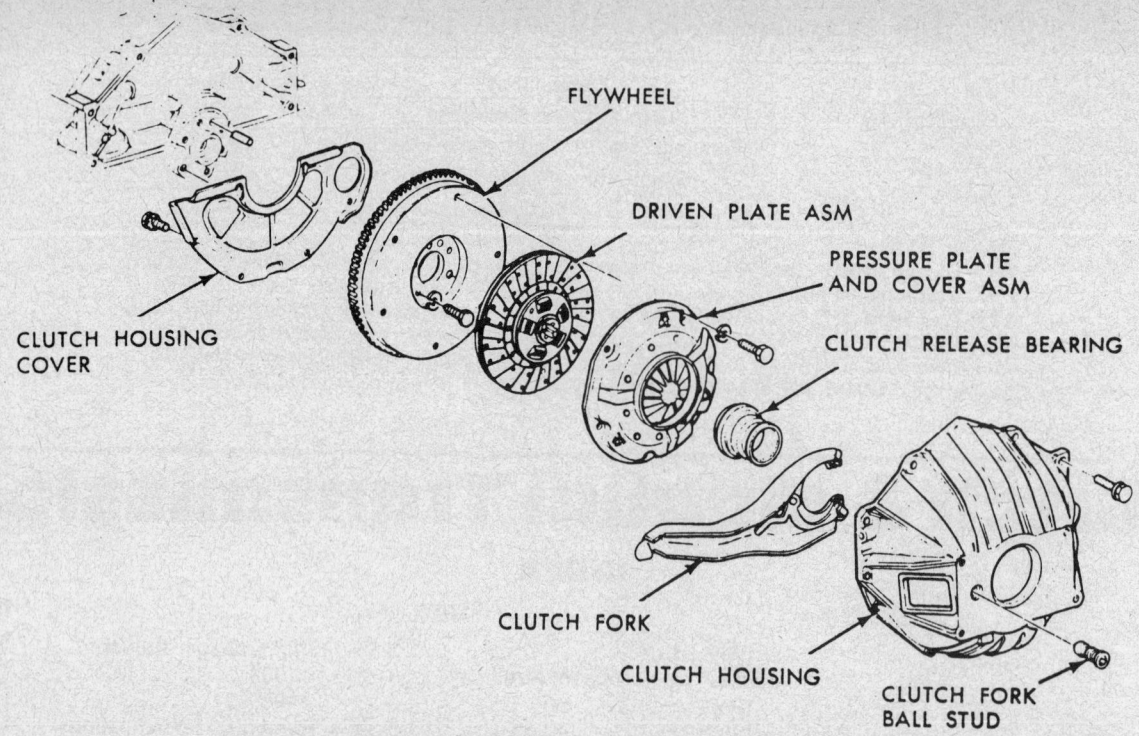

Fig. 1 Exploded view of clutch assembly. 1988

CLUTCH REPLACE

1988

1. Support engine and remove transmission as outlined further on.
2. Remove actuating cylinder heat shield and cylinder from flywheel housing. Prior to removing actuating cylinder, disconnect push rod from clutch master cylinder.
3. **On all models,** remove flywheel housing.
4. Slide clutch fork from ball stud and remove fork from dust boot. **Look for X mark on flywheel and on clutch cover. If X mark is not evident, prick punch marks on flywheel and clutch cover for indexing purposes during installation.**
5. Loosen clutch to flywheel attaching bolts evenly one turn at a time until spring pressure is released. Then remove bolts and clutch assembly, **Fig. 1.**
6. Reverse procedure to install, using suitable pilot tool to center clutch disc. Tighten clutch cover bolts evenly and gradually to avoid distorting cover. Lubricate clutch fork ball socket, fork fingers, recesses on inside of release bearing and clutch fork groove with graphite grease.

1989–91

1. Disconnect battery ground cable.
2. Remove exhaust system from vehicle.

3. Remove transmission from vehicle as described under "Transmission, Replace."
4. **On models except ZR-1,** disconnect ground connection at left hand side of clutch housing.
5. **On all models,** remove nuts attaching actuating cylinder to clutch housing, then position actuating cylinder aside. Support actuating cylinder so that hydraulic hose does not become damaged.
6. Remove starter motor from vehicle.
7. **On ZR-1 models,** remove nut attaching left hand side catalytic converter shield to converter housing.
8. **On all models,** remove clutch cover from clutch housing.
9. Remove bolts attaching clutch housing to engine. **On ZR-1 models,** also remove bolt attaching right hand catalytic converter heat shield to clutch housing.
10. Remove clutch housing. Align fork with two flats on release bearing, push fork away from bearing. **On some models,** it may be necessary to loosen ball stud locking screw and ball stud to remove housing.
11. Place align marks on clutch cover and flywheel for use during installation.
12. Alternately and evenly loosen clutch cover to flywheel attaching bolts one turn at a time until spring tension is relieved.
13. Remove clutch cover and clutch disc, **Fig. 2.**
14. Reverse procedure to install. When installing clutch cover to flywheel, align marks made during removal. When installing clutch cover attaching bolts, tighten alternately and evenly in a side

to side-cross pattern. Lubricate clutch fork ball and release bearing inner and outer circumference with lubricant 1052356 or equivalent.

MANUAL TRANSMISSION REPLACE

It may be necessary to remove the catalytic converter and its support bracket to facilitate transmission removal.

1988

1. Disconnect battery ground cable and remove air cleaner assembly.
2. Disconnect overdrive throttle valve cable from throttle linkage.
3. Remove distributor cap to prevent damage and lay cap aside, leaving plug wires connected.
4. Raise and support vehicle.
5. Remove complete exhaust system as follows:
   a. Disconnect AIR pipe from converter and remove AIR pipe clamps from manifold.
   b. Disconnect electrical connector to oxygen sensor.
   c. Remove bolts securing exhaust hangers to mufflers and hanger bracket from converter.
   d. Disconnect exhaust system from manifolds and remove system as an assembly.
   e. Remove exhaust hanger from transmission.
6. Support transmission with suitable jack.

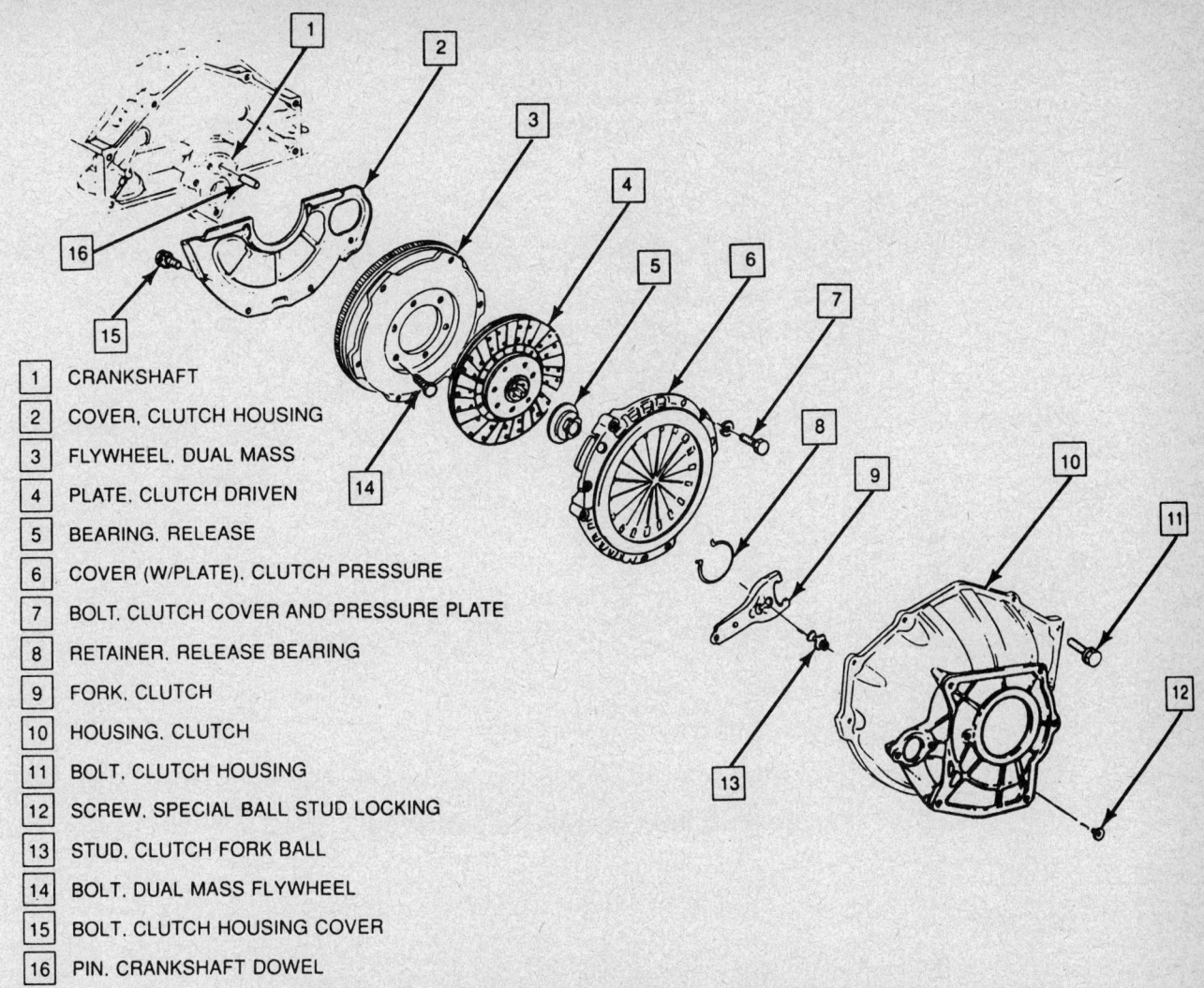

1 CRANKSHAFT
2 COVER, CLUTCH HOUSING
3 FLYWHEEL, DUAL MASS
4 PLATE, CLUTCH DRIVEN
5 BEARING, RELEASE
6 COVER (W/PLATE), CLUTCH PRESSURE
7 BOLT, CLUTCH COVER AND PRESSURE PLATE
8 RETAINER, RELEASE BEARING
9 FORK, CLUTCH
10 HOUSING, CLUTCH
11 BOLT, CLUTCH HOUSING
12 SCREW, SPECIAL BALL STUD LOCKING
13 STUD, CLUTCH FORK BALL
14 BOLT, DUAL MASS FLYWHEEL
15 BOLT, CLUTCH HOUSING COVER
16 PIN, CRANKSHAFT DOWEL

Fig. 2 Exploded view of clutch assembly. 1989–91

7. Remove bolts securing driveline beam to transmission and axle housings, then the driveline beam.
8. Mark installation position of propeller shaft, then remove shaft assembly. **Tape bearing cups to universal joints to prevent loss of needle bearings.**
9. Disconnect oil cooler lines and throttle valve cable from overdrive unit.
10. Disconnect shift linkage at transmission side cover, noting position for installation.
11. Disconnect electrical connectors from transmission and overdrive unit.
12. Lower transmission and support engine.
13. Remove bolts securing transmission to bellhousing, slide transmission rearward until input shaft clears housing, then lower transmission from vehicle.

1989–91

1. Disconnect battery ground cable.

2. Remove shift lever.
3. Remove complete exhaust system.
4. Remove front cross over hanger from transmission.
5. Remove propeller shaft.
6. Support transmission with a suitable jack, then remove driveline support beam.
7. Disconnect electrical connectors.
8. Remove transmission to clutch housing attaching bolts, then the transmission from vehicle.
9. Reverse procedure to install.

SHIFT LINKAGE
ADJUST
1988

1. Disconnect battery ground cable.
2. Remove left seat, disconnecting electrical connectors as needed.
3. Remove shift knob, console cover

and glove box lock.
4. Remove left console side panel and shifter cover.
5. Loosen front and rear adjuster nut on each shift rod.
6. Ensure transmission is in neutral, align shifter levers in neutral position, then insert gauge pin through lever alignment holes, **Fig. 3.**
7. Equalize swivels on each shift rod, hand tightening front and rear adjuster nuts simultaneously.
8. Simultaneously tighten front and rear adjuster nuts on each shift rod.
9. Remove gauge pin and check shifter operation.
10. Reinstall components removed to gain access to shifter.

1989–91

The gear shift lever assembly is floor mounted and located on top of extension housing. The shift assembly does not require adjustment.

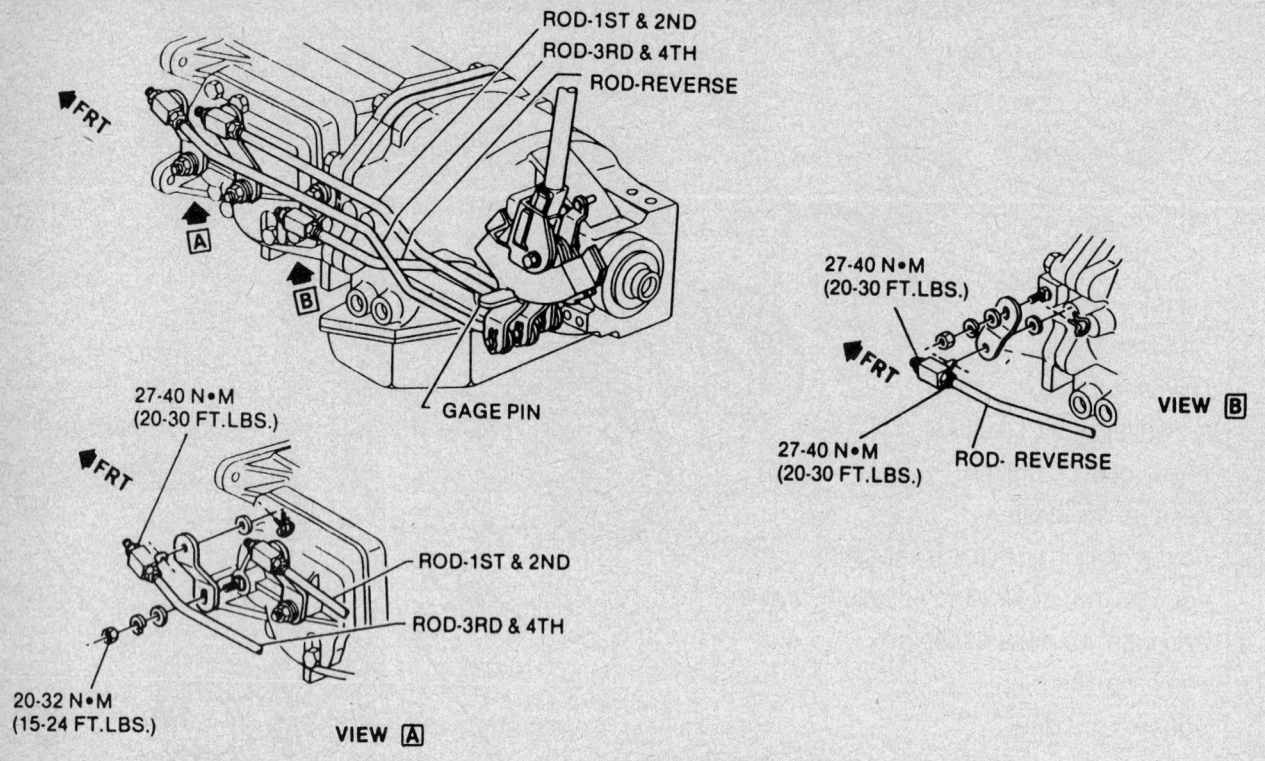

ROD-1ST & 2ND
ROD-3RD & 4TH
ROD-REVERSE

FRT

A

B

GAGE PIN

27-40 N•M
(20-30 FT.LBS.)

FRT

VIEW B

27-40 N•M
(20-30 FT.LBS.)

ROD- REVERSE

27-40 N•M
(20-30 FT.LBS.)

FRT

ROD-1ST & 2ND

ROD-3RD & 4TH

20-32 N•M
(15-24 FT.LBS.)

VIEW A

Fig. 3   Shift linkage adjustment. 1988

TIGHTENING SPECIFICATIONS

Year	Component	Torque/Ft. Lbs.
1988	Clutch Actuating Cylinder Bolts Or Nuts	30–44
	Clutch Cover To Flywheel	25–35
	Clutch Fork Ball Stud Nut	—
	Clutch Fork Ball Stud Locking Screw	—
	Clutch Housing To Engine	37
	Clutch Master Cylinder Bolts	20–29
	Clutch Pedal Pivot Bolt Or Nut	22–30
	Flywheel Bolt To Crankshaft	63–85
	Hydraulic Hose Fittings At Clutch Actuating Cylinder	25–40
	Hydraulic Hose Fittings At Clutch Master Cylinder	15–19
	Oil Cooler Lines To Overdrive Unit	8–12
	Support Beam To Differential Carrier Bolt	59
	Support Beam To Transmission Bolt	37
	Transmission Drain Plug	15–25
	Transmission Fill Plug	25–35
	Transmission To Clutch Housing Bolt	45–60
1989–91	Clutch Actuating Cylinder Bolts Or Nuts	19
	Clutch Cover To Flywheel	30
	Clutch Fork Ball Stud Nut	33
	Clutch Fork Ball Stud Locking Screw	20
	Clutch Housing To Engine	37
	Clutch Master Cylinder Bolts	①
	Clutch Pedal Pivot Bolt Or Nut	②
	Flywheel Bolt To Crankshaft	74
	Hydraulic Hose Fittings At Clutch Actuating Cylinder	13
	Hydraulic Hose Fittings At Clutch Master Cylinder	13
	Support Beam To Differential Carrier Bolt	60
	Support Beam To Transmission Bolt	37
	Transmission Drain Plug	34
	Transmission Fill Plug	34
	Transmission To Clutch Housing Bolt	37

①—1989, 25 ft. lbs.; 1990–91, 12 ft. lbs.
②—1989, 26 ft. lbs.; 1990–91, 13 ft. lbs.

Rear Axle, Rear Suspension & Propeller Shaft

INDEX

REAR AXLE
REPLACE

1. Raise and support vehicle, and remove spare tire, tire cover and under body braces, as required.

2. Remove exhaust system assembly as follows:
   a. Disconnect AIR pipe at converter and AIR pipe clamps at manifold.
   b. Disconnect electrical connector from oxygen sensor.
   c. Support exhaust system, remove bolts securing mufflers to hangers,

   and remove converter bracket.
   d. Disconnect exhaust pipes at manifolds and remove exhaust system.

3. Disconnect leaf spring from spindle support knuckles, then remove bolts securing spring to differential carrier and spring as outlined under "Leaf Springs & Bushings Replace."

4. Scribe mark between cam bolts and brackets, then remove cam bolts and mounting bracket from carrier.
5. Disconnect tie rods from left and right spindle support knuckles.
6. Remove straps securing driveshaft universal joints to differential side yokes, push wheel and tire assemblies outward, and disconnect drive shafts from side yokes. **Tape bearing cups to universal joint yokes to prevent loss of needle bearings.**
7. Remove straps securing propeller shaft universal joint to pinion flange, push propeller shaft forward into transmission and tie shaft to support beam.
8. Support transmission and remove bolts securing differential carrier beam to frame brackets, **Fig. 1.**
9. Remove mounting bolts at front of differential carrier and carrier assembly.
10. Reverse procedure to install, then check rear suspension alignment.

REAR WHEEL SHAFT REPLACE

1. Remove center cap from wheel.
2. Remove cotter pin, spindle nut and washer from spindle, **Fig. 2.**
3. Raise and support vehicle, and remove wheel and tire.
4. Disconnect tie rod and spring from spindle support knuckle.
5. Scribe a reference mark between cam bolt and bracket, remove cam bolt and separate spindle support rod from bracket.
6. Remove straps securing inner universal joint to drive yoke, pull knuckle assembly outward, and disconnect shaft from yoke. **Tape bearing cups to universal joint yoke to prevent loss of needle bearings.**
7. Pull spindle out of hub and remove rear wheel shaft.
8. Reverse procedure to install, torquing cam bolt and spindle nut to specifications.

REAR HUB & BEARING REPLACE

1. Remove rear wheel shaft assembly as outlined in "Rear Wheel Shaft, Replace."
2. Remove wheel speed sensor.
3. Remove 2 bolts securing brake caliper bracket to support knuckle, secure caliper aside, then remove brake rotor.
4. Remove hub and bearing retaining bolts, **Fig. 2.**
5. Remove cotter pin, wheel nut retainer, nut and washer from spindle.
6. Remove hub and bearing assembly.
7. Reverse procedure to install. Install spindle washer with flat portion against should of wheel spindle and with lip of washer facing spindle splines. Do not allow vehicle to rest on tires until after wheel spindle nut has been tightened to the specified torque.

REAR WHEEL SPINDLE REPLACE

1. Raise and support vehicle, then remove wheel and tire assembly.
2. Remove wheel speed sensor.
3. Detach rear spring from knuckle.
4. Remove axle outer socket from knuckle.
5. Remove spindle rod from spindle bracket.
6. Remove cotter pin, wheel nut retainer, nut and washer from spindle.
7. Remove rear wheel shaft.
8. Remove spindle from hub and bearing, then remove washer from spindle.
9. Reverse procedure to install. Install spindle washer with flat portion against should of wheel spindle and with lip of washer facing spindle splines. Do not allow vehicle to rest on tires until after wheel spindle nut has been tightened to the specified torque.

PROPELLER SHAFT REPLACE

1. With transmission in neutral and parking brake released, raise and support vehicle, then remove under body braces, as required.
2. Remove exhaust system as follows:
   a. Disconnect AIR pipe from catalytic converter and exhaust pipe.
   b. Disconnect electrical connector to oxygen sensor.
   c. Remove bolts securing muffler to hangers, disconnect exhaust pipes from manifolds and remove exhaust system as an assembly.
3. Support transmission, remove support beam retaining bolts and support beam.
4. Mark position of shaft in relation to pinion flange for installation.

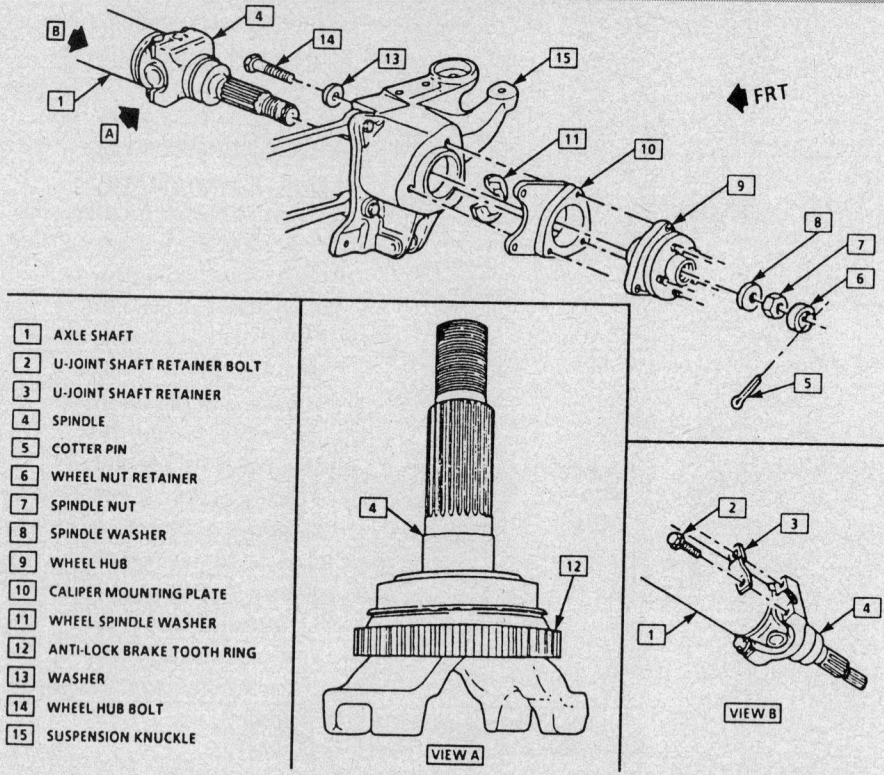

Fig. 1 Differential carrier attachment

| A | COVER TO BODY ATTACHMENT |
| B | CARRIER TO SUPPORT BEAM |

1	AXLE SHAFT
2	U-JOINT SHAFT RETAINER BOLT
3	U-JOINT SHAFT RETAINER
4	SPINDLE
5	COTTER PIN
6	WHEEL NUT RETAINER
7	SPINDLE NUT
8	SPINDLE WASHER
9	WHEEL HUB
10	CALIPER MOUNTING PLATE
11	WHEEL SPINDLE WASHER
12	ANTI-LOCK BRAKE TOOTH RING
13	WASHER
14	WHEEL HUB BOLT
15	SUSPENSION KNUCKLE

Fig. 2 Rear wheel hub, bearing & spindle

CHEVROLET CORVETTE

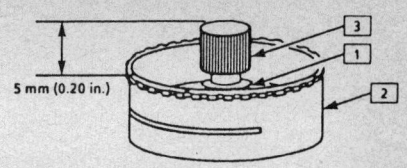

5 mm (0.20 in.)

1	HEX PREVAILING TORQUE NUT
2	CUP ASSEMBLY RETAINER
3	SELECTOR GEAR

Fig. 6 Positioning selector gear. Models with Selective Ride Control

to .60 inch from bottom of shock absorber and drill a .20 inch hole to release gas pressure from shock absorber. Measure 5.5 to 6 inches from gas pressure release drill hole and drill another .20 inch hole to drain oil from shock absorber.

MODELS LESS SELECTIVE RIDE CONTROL

1. Raise and support vehicle.
2. Using a suitable jack stand, support knuckle.
3. Disconnect shock absorber from upper and lower mountings, **Fig. 3**.
4. Reverse procedure to install.

MODELS WITH SELECTIVE RIDE CONTROL
Removal

1. Disconnect battery ground cable.
2. Raise and support vehicle.
3. Using a suitable jack stand, support knuckle.
4. Disconnect shock absorber from upper and lower mountings, **Fig. 4**. Do not allow shock absorber to hang from wiring harness.
5. Remove retaining clip, then remove electrical actuator from shock absorber.
6. Remove shock absorber from vehicle.

Installation

1. Install retaining clip onto cup assembly retainer, **Fig. 5**.
2. Install electrical actuator into cup retainer with electrical lead facing toward front of vehicle. A click should be noted when actuator is properly seated. Selector gear should be located a minimum of .20 inch top of retainer, **Fig. 6**.
3. Ensure actuator is properly seated in cup retainer, then position shock absorber to lower mounting.
4. Position shock absorber to upper mounting.
5. Position vehicle at proper trim height using jack stands, then tighten upper shock absorber attaching bolts.
6. Install shock absorber lower attaching nut and washer.
7. Lower vehicle and connect battery ground cable.

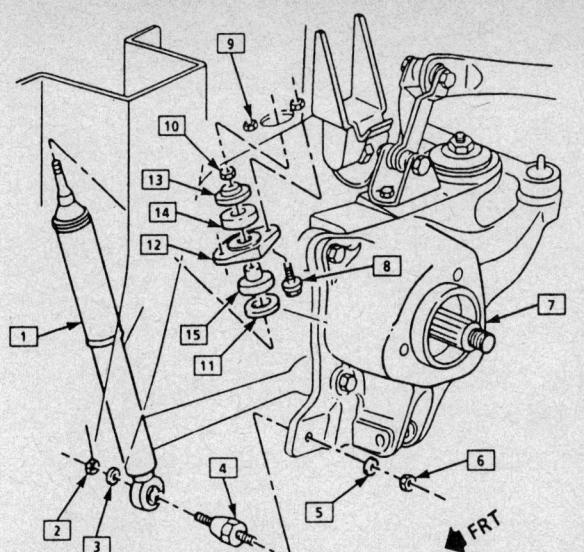

1	SHOCK ABSORBER
2	HEX NUT
3	SHOCK ABSORBER WASHER
4	SHOCK ABSORBER STUD
5	SHOCK ABSORBER WASHER
6	HEX NUT
7	SUSPENSION KNUCKLE
8	SHOCK ABSORBER BRACKET BOLT
9	WELD NUT
10	HEX NUT
11	SHOCK ABSORBER INSULATION RETAINER
12	SHOCK ABSORBER UPPER BRACKET
13	SHOCK ABSORBER INSULATION RETAINER
14	SHOCK ABSORBER UPPER GROMMET
15	SHOCK ABSORBER UPPER INSULATOR

Fig. 3 Shock absorber replacement. Models less Selective Ride Control

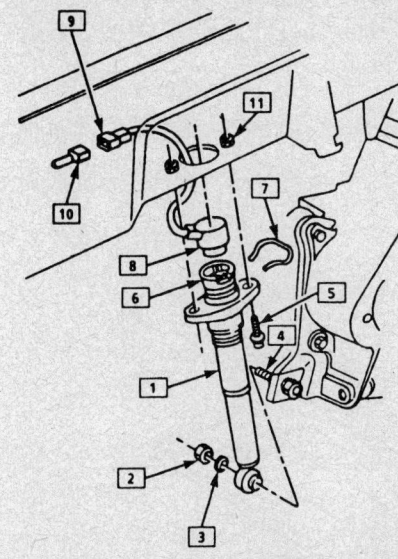

1	SELECTIVE RIDE CONTROL SHOCK ABSORBER
2	HEX NUT
3	SHOCK ABSORBER WASHER
4	SHOCK ABSORBER STUD
5	SHOCK ABSORBER BRACKET BOLT
6	CUP ASSEMBLY RETAINER
7	ACTUATOR RETAINING CLIP
8	SHOCK ABSORBER ELECTRICAL ACTUATOR
9	ACTUATOR ELECTRICAL CONNECTOR
10	WIRING HARNESS CONNECTOR
11	WELD NUT

Fig. 4 Shock absorber replacement. Models with Selective Ride Control

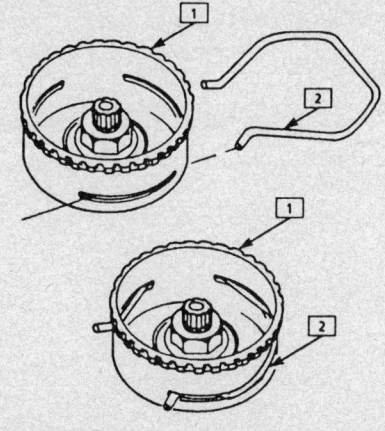

| 1 | CUP ASSEMBLY RETAINER |
| 2 | ACTUATOR RETAINING CLIP |

Fig. 5 Installing actuator clip. Models with Selective Ride Control

5. Remove straps securing universal joint to pinion flange, then disconnect shaft from flange. **Tape bearing cups to universal joint to prevent loss of needle bearings.**
6. Slide yoke out of transmission and remove propeller shaft. Insert suitable plug in transmission to prevent fluid loss.
7. Reverse procedure to install.

SHOCK ABSORBER REPLACE

If shock absorber is to be discarded, position shock absorber in a suitable vise with piston facing downward. Measure .40

LEAF SPRING & BUSHINGS
REPLACE

When servicing, use care not to scratch the fiber glass leaf spring. Also do not use any cleaning solvent on spring.
1. Raise and support vehicle and remove wheel and tire assembly.
2. **On 1990-91 models,** use tool No. J-33432 or equivalent to compress spring.
3. **On all models,** remove cotter pin, retaining nuts, bushings and link bolts securing spring to spindle support knuckles, **Fig. 7.**
4. **On 1990-91 models,** release spring and remove compressing tool J-33432 or equivalent.
5. **On all models,** remove bolts securing spring anchor plate to rear axle carrier, **Fig. 8.**
6. Reverse procedure to install.

CONTROL ARMS
REPLACE

1. Raise and support vehicle, and remove wheel and tire assembly.
2. Remove bolts securing control arm to spindle support knuckle, **Fig. 9.**
3. Remove control arm bolt at mounting bracket and control arm.
4. Reverse procedure to install. Torque control arm to bracket bolt and control arm to knuckle bolt to specifications.

STABILIZER BAR
REPLACE

1. Raise and support vehicle, then remove wheel and tire assemblies.
2. Remove spare tire and carrier.
3. Disconnect stabilizer links from spindle support knuckles, **Fig. 10.**
4. Remove retainers securing shaft bushings to crossmember, bushings and stabilizer shaft.
5. Reverse procedure to install. Torque bushing retaining nuts and bolts securing stabilizer links to knuckles to specifications, and bolts securing links to stabilizer bar to specifications.

SPINDLE SUPPORT ROD
REPLACE

1. Raise and support vehicle, and remove wheel and tire.
2. Scribe mark between cam bolt and bracket for reassembly.
3. Remove cam bolt and disconnect support rod from bracket, **Fig. 9.**
4. Remove bolt securing spindle support rod to knuckle and rod.
5. Reverse procedure to install, then check rear suspension alignment. Torque retaining bolt at knuckle and cam bolt to specifications.

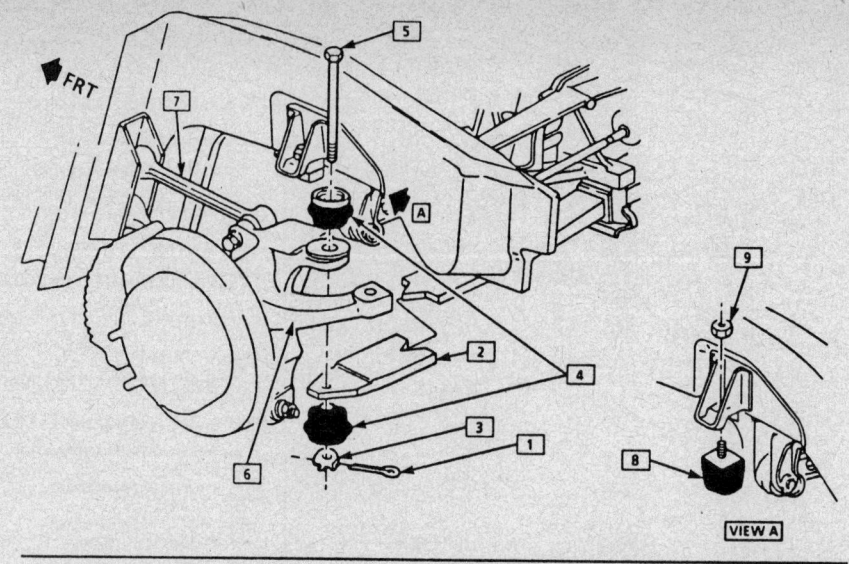

1 COTTER PIN	6 SUSPENSION KNUCKLE
2 REAR SPRING	7 WHEEL SPINDLE UPPER CONTROL ROD
3 SLOTTED SPRING NUT	8 SUSPENSION BUMPER
4 SPRING INSULATOR	9 HEX NUT
5 SPRING BOLT	

Fig. 7 Leaf spring to knuckle attachment

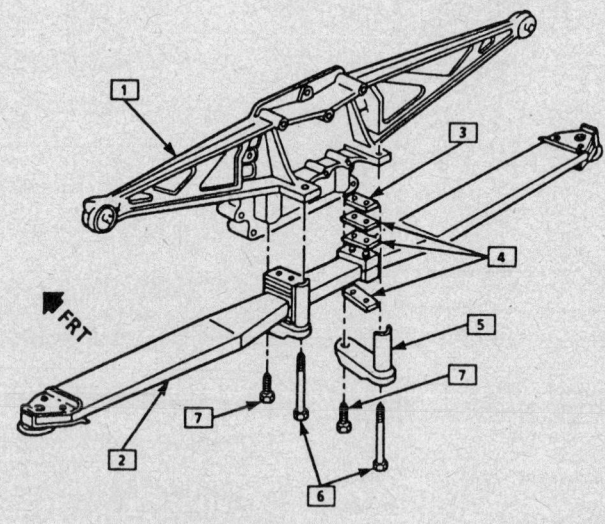

1 DIFFERENTIAL CARRIER	5 SPRING ANCHOR PLATE
2 REAR SPRING	6 HEX FLANGED HEAD BOLT
3 SPRING INSULATOR	7 HEX FLANGED HEAD BOLT
4 SPRING SPACER	

Fig. 8 Leaf spring to differential carrier attachment

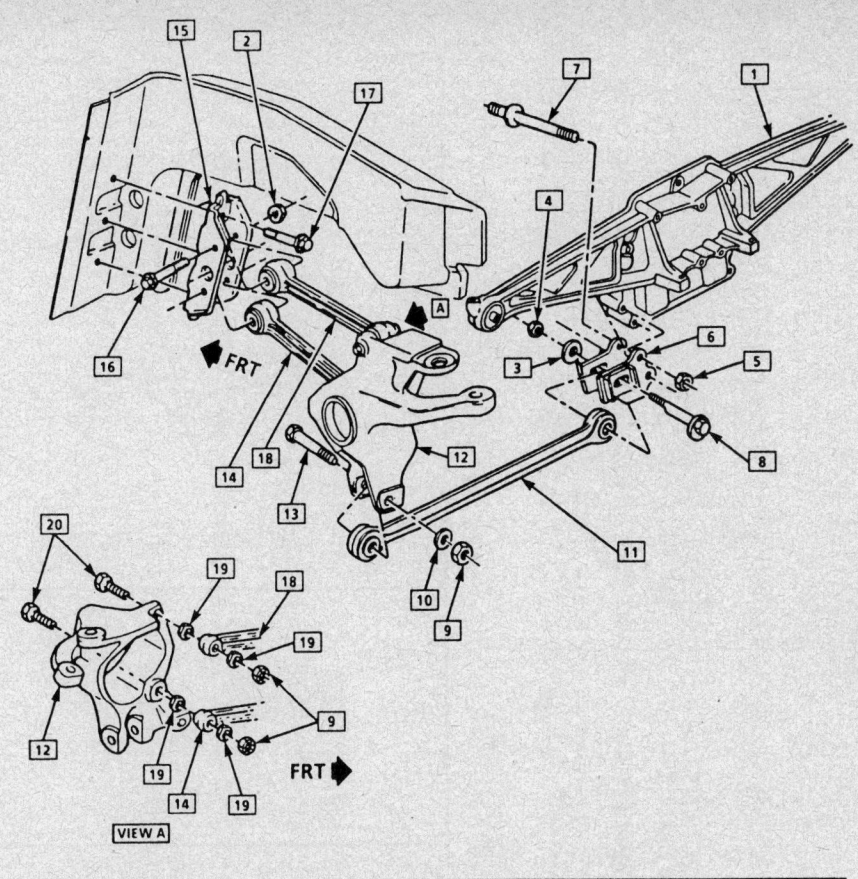

1	DIFFERENTIAL CARRIER	11	SPINDLE ROD
2	HEX NUT	12	SUSPENSION KNUCKLE
3	SPINDLE ROD ADJUSTMENT CAM	13	HEX BOLT
4	SPINDLE ROD ADJUSTMENT NUT	14	WHEEL SPINDLE LOWER CONTROL ROD
5	HEX NUT	15	SPINDLE CONTROL ROD BRACKET
6	SPINDLE ROD BRACKET	16	WHEEL SPINDLE ROD BOLT
7	SPINDLE ROD BRACKET STUD	17	HEX BOLT
8	WHEEL SPINDLE ROD ADJUSTMENT BOLT	18	WHEEL SPINDLE UPPER CONTROL ROD
9	HEX NUT	19	SPINDLE ROD WASHER
10	SPINDLE ROD WASHER	20	SPINDLE ROD BOLT

Fig. 9   Knuckle & control arm

TIE ROD
REPLACE

1. Raise and support vehicle, then remove wheel and tire.
2. Loosen outer tie rod jam nuts, then remove cotter pin and nut securing tie rod to spindle support knuckle, **Fig. 11.**
3. Press tie rod from knuckle using tool J-24319-01 or equivalent.
4. Remove tie rod from adjusting sleeve, counting number of turns necessary.
5. Reverse procedure to install, then check rear suspension alignment. Torque tie rod nut specifications.

SPINDLE SUPPORT KNUCKLE
REPLACE

1. Remove center cap from wheel, cotter pin and spindle nut.
2. Raise and support vehicle, and remove wheel and tire.
3. Remove 2 bolts securing brake caliper to knuckle, brake caliper assembly and brake rotor.
4. Disconnect tie rod, leaf spring and stabilizer shaft from knuckle as outlined previously.

5. Disconnect parking brake cable from backing plate and bracket.
6. Disconnect shock absorber and support rod from knuckle, using a back-up wrench on shock mounting stud.
7. Remove bolts securing control arms to knuckle, lower knuckle assembly and slide spindle out of hub and bearing.
8. Remove hub and bearing and parking brake assembly from knuckle, using a No. 45 Torx bit to remove hub retaining bolts, then remove splash shield.
9. Reverse procedure to install, then check rear suspension alignment. Torque all bolts to specifications.

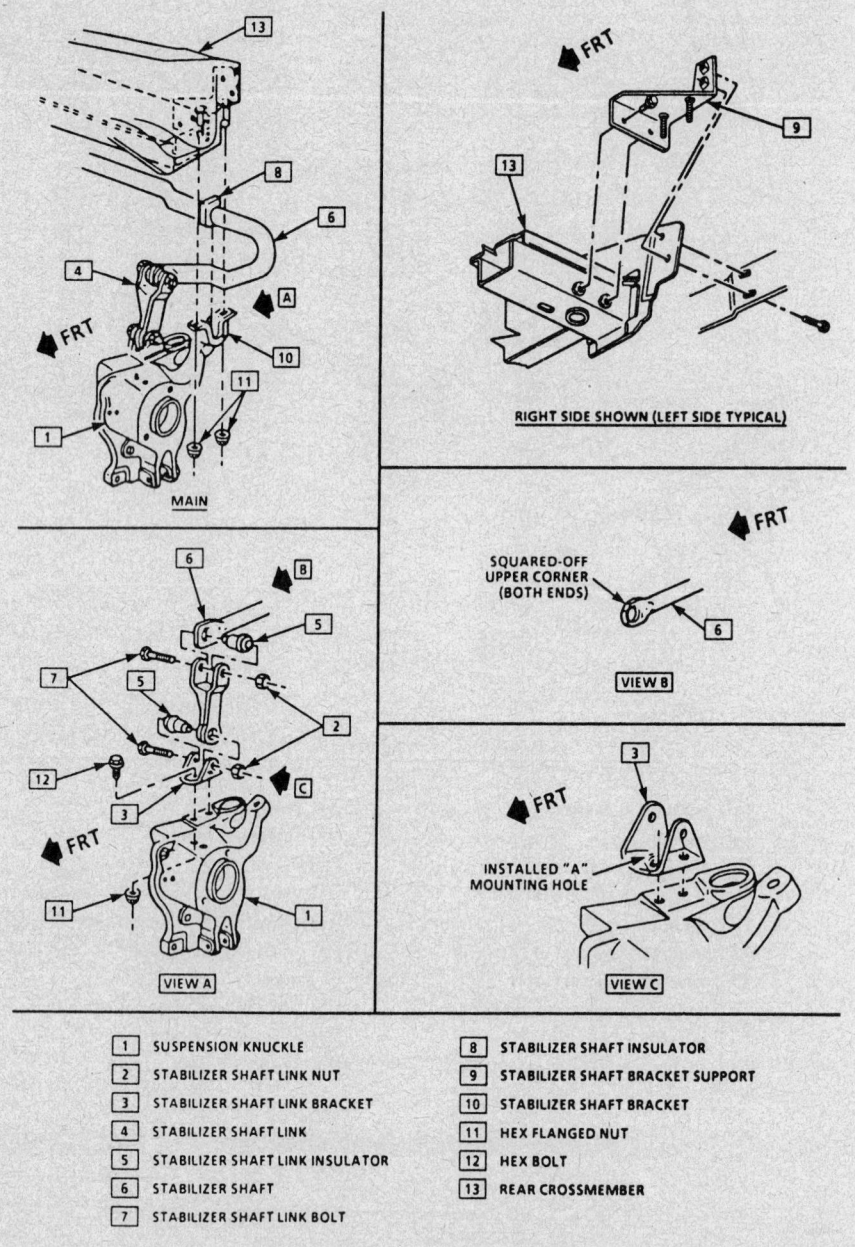

RIGHT SIDE SHOWN (LEFT SIDE TYPICAL)

SQUARED-OFF
UPPER CORNER
(BOTH ENDS)

VIEW B

INSTALLED "A"
MOUNTING HOLE

VIEW C

MAIN

VIEW A

1	SUSPENSION KNUCKLE	8	STABILIZER SHAFT INSULATOR
2	STABILIZER SHAFT LINK NUT	9	STABILIZER SHAFT BRACKET SUPPORT
3	STABILIZER SHAFT LINK BRACKET	10	STABILIZER SHAFT BRACKET
4	STABILIZER SHAFT LINK	11	HEX FLANGED NUT
5	STABILIZER SHAFT LINK INSULATOR	12	HEX BOLT
6	STABILIZER SHAFT	13	REAR CROSSMEMBER
7	STABILIZER SHAFT LINK BOLT		

Fig. 10 Stabilizer bar replacement

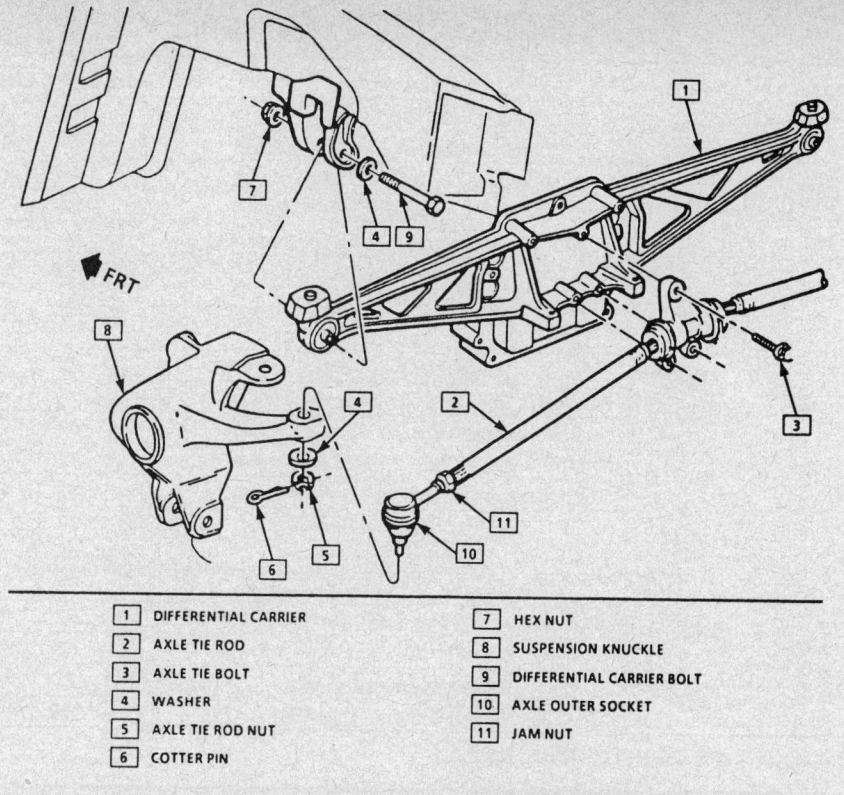

1	DIFFERENTIAL CARRIER		7	HEX NUT
2	AXLE TIE ROD		8	SUSPENSION KNUCKLE
3	AXLE TIE BOLT		9	DIFFERENTIAL CARRIER BOLT
4	WASHER		10	AXLE OUTER SOCKET
5	AXLE TIE ROD NUT		11	JAM NUT
6	COTTER PIN			

Fig. 11   Tie rod replacement

TIGHTENING SPECIFICATIONS

Year	Component	Torque/Ft. Lbs.
1988-89	Cam Bolt To Spindle Rod	186
	Control Rods To Knuckle	140
	Control Rods To Spindle Control Rod	63
	Differential Carrier To Body	100
	Hub & Bearing To Knuckle	66
	Shock Absorber To Body Bolt	22
	Shock Absorber To Knuckle	65
	Shock Absorber Stud To Knuckle Nut	80
	Spindle Nut	164
	Spindle Rod To Differential Carrier	60
	Spindle Rod To Knuckle	107
	Stabilizer Bar To Body	18
	Stabilizer Bar To Link Bracket To Knuckle	18
	Stabilizer Link To Bracket & Bar	35
	Support Beam To Differential Carrier Bolt	60
	Support Beam To Transmission	37
	Tie Rod End To Knuckle	33
	Tie Rod Jam Nut	46
	Tie Rod To Differential Carrier	55
	Transverse Spring To Differential Carrier	37
	Trunnion Strap (Pinion)	26
	Trunnion Strap (Yoke)	26
	Wheel & Tire Assembly	100
1990-91	Cam Bolt To Spindle Rod	①
	Control Rods To Knuckle	140
	Control Rods To Spindle Control Rod	63

Continued

TIGHTENING SPECIFICATIONS

Year	Component	Torque/Ft. Lbs.
1990-91 Cont'd.	Differential Carrier To Body	89
	Hub & Bearing To Knuckle	66
	Shock Absorber To Body Bolt	22
	Shock Absorber To Knuckle	61
	Shock Absorber Stud To Knuckle Nut	89
	Spindle Nut	164①
	Spindle Rod To Differential Carrier	60
	Spindle Rod To Knuckle	107
	Stabilizer Bar To Body	18
	Stabilizer Bar To Link Bracket To Knuckle	18
	Stabilizer Link To Bracket & Bar	39
	Support Beam To Differential Carrier Bolt	59
	Support Beam To Transmission	37
	Tie Rod End To Knuckle	37
	Tie Rod Jam Nut	46
	Tie Rod To Differential Carrier	55
	Transverse Spring To Differential Carrier	37
	Trunnion Strap (Pinion)	17
	Trunnion Strap (Yoke)	26
	Wheel & Tire Assembly	100

① —1990, 186 ft. lbs.; 1991, 187 ft. lbs.

Front Suspension & Steering

INDEX

WHEEL BEARING
REPLACE

The wheel bearing and hub assembly is a sealed unit. If end play exceeds .005 inch, or if noise or roughness is detected, the unit must be replaced as an assembly.

1. Raise and support vehicle, and remove wheel and tire. Prior to raising vehicle, remove tie offs and grommets to provide ABS sensor wire to lower control arm clearance.
2. Remove bolts securing brake caliper bracket to steering knuckle and secure caliper assembly aside, then remove brake rotor.
3. Disconnect electrical connector from speed sensor, then remove speed sensor cable bracket.
4. Remove bolts securing hub to knuckle and hub assembly, **Fig. 1.**
5. Reverse procedure to install.

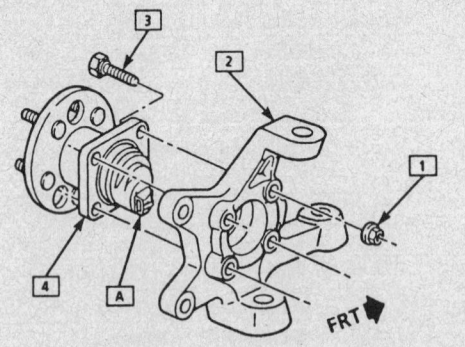

1	HEX FLANGE TORQUE NUT
2	STEERING KNUCKLE
3	WHEEL HUB BOLT
4	WHEEL HUB
A	SPEED SENSOR CONNECTOR MUST BE FACING THE REAR OF THE VEHICLE

Fig. 1 Hub & bearing assembly replacement

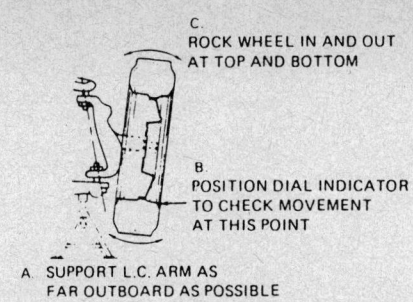

Fig. 2 Upper ball joint inspection

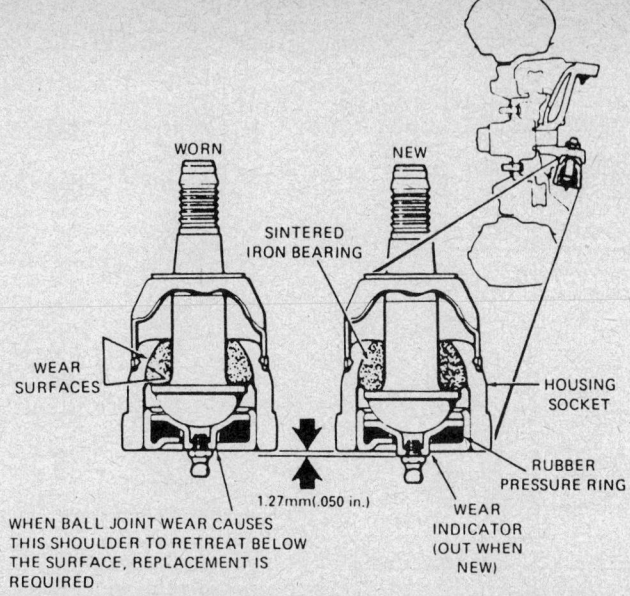

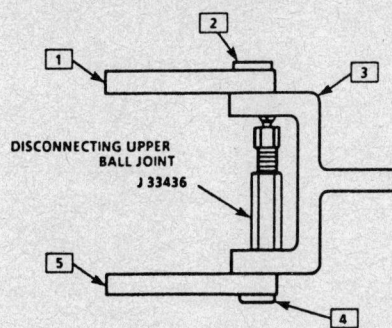

Fig. 3 Lower ball joint inspection

2. Position a suitable dial indicator against wheel rim, **Fig. 2**.
3. Move wheel inward and outward, while observing dial indicator reading. Indicator reading should not exceed .125 inch.
4. Replace upper ball joint if looseness is indicated.

LOWER BALL JOINT

Lower ball joints are equipped with with visual wear indicators. When checking, vehicle must be supported by wheel and tire assemblies to maintain load on ball joints. Refer to **Fig. 3**.

BALL JOINT
REPLACE

UPPER BALL JOINT

1. Raise vehicle and support with stands at outer ends of lower control arms.
2. Remove wheel and tire assembly.
3. Remove cotter pin and retaining nut, then separate ball joint stud from knuckle using a suitable tool, **Fig. 4**.
4. Support upper control arm in a raised position.
5. Remove heads of rivets securing joint to arm, then drive out rivets to remove joint, **Fig. 4**.
6. Position replacement joint on top of control arm, insert retaining bolts supplied with joint from under arm, install nuts and torque to specifications, **Fig. 5**.
7. Remove upper control arm support, assemble ball joint to steering knuckle, install washer, if equipped, and retaining nut.
8. Torque retaining nut to specifications.
9. Tighten retaining nut up to an additional ¹/₁₆ turn, if necessary, to align hole in ball stud with nut, then install cotter pin.

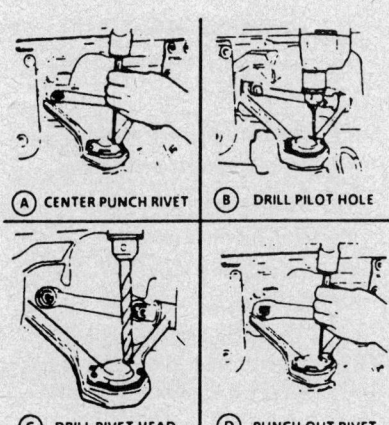

1 UPPER CONTROL ARM
2 UPPER CONTROL ARM BALL STUD
3 STEERING KNUCKLE
4 LOWER CONTROL ARM BALL STUD
5 LOWER CONTROL ARM

Fig. 4 Upper ball joint removal

CHECKING BALL JOINTS FOR WEAR

UPPER BALL JOINT

1. Raise and support front of vehicle, then position jack stands under lower control arms.

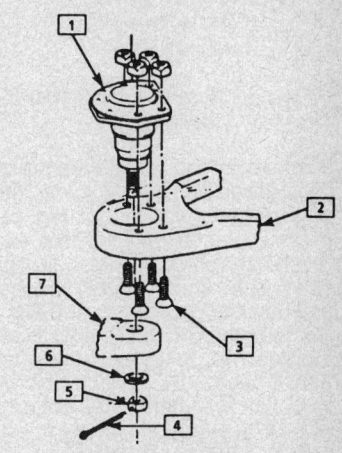

1 UPPER CONTROL ARM BALL STUD
2 UPPER CONTROL ARM
3 BOLTS MUST BE MOUNTED IN THE DIRECTION SHOWN
4 COTTER PIN
5 UPPER CONTROL ARM BALL STUD NUT
6 UPPER CONTROL ARM BALL STUD MUST BE REPLACED WASHER
7 STEERING KNUCKLE

Fig. 5 Upper ball joint installation

LOWER BALL JOINT

1. Raise vehicle and support front of vehicle.
2. Support lower control using a suitable jack stand, then remove wheel and tire assembly.
3. Remove cotter pin and nut securing ball joint stud to steering knuckle, then disconnect joint from knuckle using a suitable tool, **Fig. 6**.
4. Lift knuckle assembly from ball stud, guiding control arm out of splash shield, then support knuckle aside to allow clearance for joint removal.

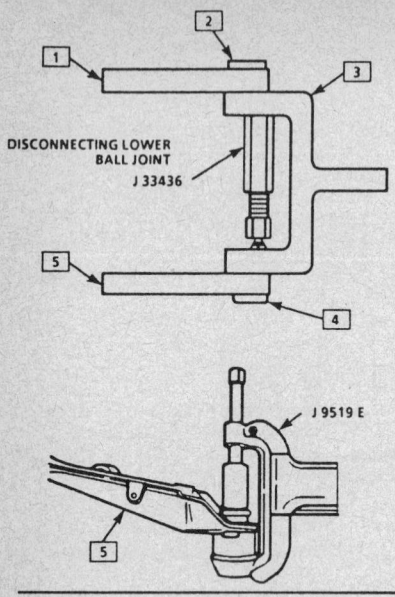

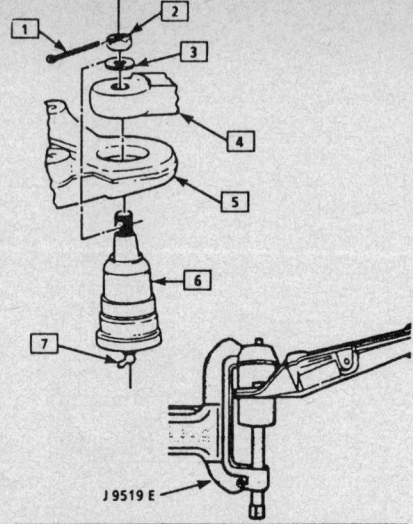

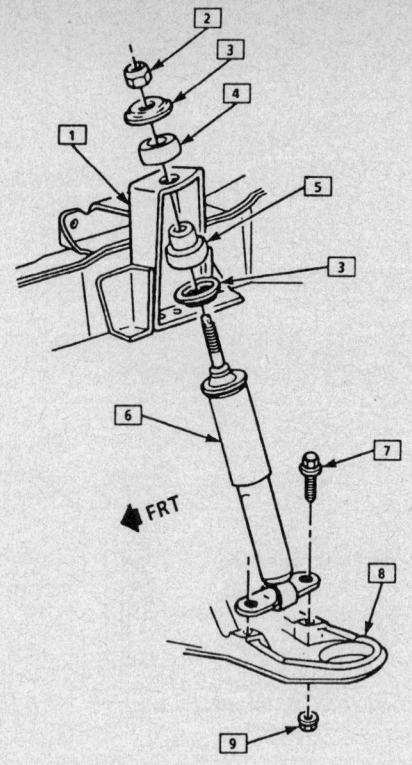

1 UPPER CONTROL ARM
2 UPPER CONTROL ARM BALL STUD
3 STEERING KNUCKLE
4 LOWER CONTROL ARM BALL STUD
5 LOWER CONTROL ARM

Fig. 6 Lower ball joint removal

1 COTTER PIN
2 HEX SLOTTED NUT
3 LOWER CONTROL ARM BALL STUD MUST BE REPLACED WASHER
4 STEERING KNUCKLE
5 LOWER CONTROL ARM
6 LOWER CONTROL ARM BALL STUD
7 INSTALL ZERK FITTING AS SHOWN

Fig. 7 Lower ball joint installation

1 SHOCK ABSORBER TOWER
2 HEX PREVAILING TORQUE NUT
3 SHOCK ABSORBER INSULATOR RETAINER
4 SHOCK ABSORBER UPPER INSULATOR
5 SHOCK ABSORBER LOWER INSULATOR
6 SHOCK ABSORBER
7 HEX FLANGE HEAD BOLT
8 LOWER CONTROL ARM
9 HEX FLANGE NUT

Fig. 8 Shock absorber replacement. Models less Selective Ride Control

5. Remove grease fitting, then press ball joint assembly out of lower control arm using a suitable tool, **Fig. 6.**
6. Press replacement joint into arm by reversing removal tools, fit spindle over ball stud, install washer, if equipped, and retaining nut, **Fig. 7.**
7. Torque retaining nut to specifications.
8. Tighten nut up to an additional 1/16 turn, if necessary, to align hole in ball stud with nut, then install cotter pin.

SHOCK ABSORBER
REPLACE

If shock absorber is to be discarded, position shock absorber in a suitable vise with piston facing downward. Measure .40 to .60 inch from bottom of shock absorber and drill a .20 inch hole to release gas pressure from shock absorber. Measure 5.5 to 6 inches from gas pressure release drill hole and drill another .20 inch hole to drain oil from shock absorber.

MODELS LESS SELECTIVE RIDE CONTROL

1. Raise and support vehicle as needed, and remove wheel and tire.
2. Remove shock absorber from upper and lower attachments, **Fig. 8.** If upper retaining nut is difficult to remove, remove wheel housing lower center panel to gain access to nut.
3. Reverse procedure to install.

MODELS WITH SELECTIVE RIDE CONTROL

1. Disconnect battery ground cable.
2. Raise and support front of vehicle, then remove wheel and tire assembly.

3. Support lower control arm with suitable jack stand.
4. Remove actuator retaining clip, then remove actuator from cup retainer. Note position of electrical connector for use during installation.
5. Remove shock absorber upper retaining nut, then remove cup retainer, **Fig. 9.**
6. Remove shock absorber retainer and upper insulator.
7. Remove shock absorber lower attaching nuts and bolts, then compress shock absorber and remove from vehicle.
8. Reverse procedure to install. When installing actuator, a click should be noted when actuator is properly seated. Selector gear should be located a minimum of .20 inch top of retainer, **Fig. 10.** A minimum clearance of .315 inch should be maintained between wheel housing lower center panel and actuator electrical lead, **Fig. 9.** Electrical connector should be positioned as noted during removal.

LEAF SPRING
REPLACE

When servicing, use care not to scratch the fiber glass leaf spring. Also do not use any cleaning solvent on spring.
1. Disconnect battery ground cable.
2. Raise and support vehicle, and remove front wheel and tire assembly.
3. Remove shock absorber to lower control arm attachments.
4. Remove bolts and nuts attaching stabilizer shaft links to lower control arms.

5. **On models with Selective Ride Control,** disconnect electrical connector and detach sensor cable from bracket.
6. **On all models,** remove both spring protectors, **Fig. 11.**
7. Install spring compressor J-33432 or equivalent, **Fig. 12.**
8. Disconnect lower ball joints from steering knuckles.
9. Compress spring by rotating turnbuckle on spring compressor.
10. Remove bolts securing shock brackets to lower control arms and spring mounting bolts.
11. Release tension on spring compressor and remove compressor.
12. Remove spring and retainer shims, if equipped. Note number of shims removed.
13. Reverse procedure to install. Prior to installation, lubricate spring pads with a suitable rubber lubricant. If equipped, install spring retainer shims.

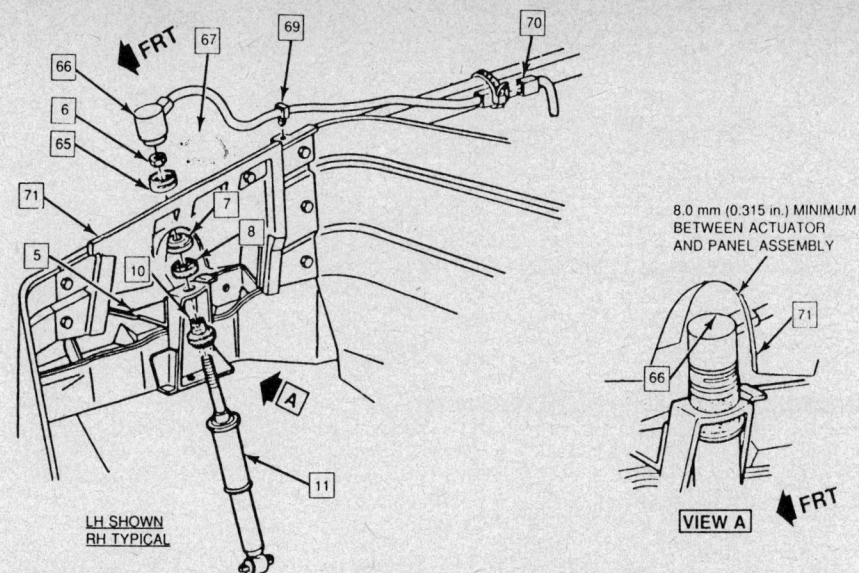

5	TOWER, SHOCK ABSORBER
6	NUT, HEX PREVAILING TORQUE
7	RETAINER, SHOCK ABSORBER INSULATOR
8	INSULATOR, SHOCK ABSORBER UPPER
10	INSULATOR, SHOCK ABSORBER LOWER
11	ABSORBER, SHOCK (SELECTIVE RIDE)
65	RETAINER, CUP ASSEMBLY
66	ACTUATOR, SHOCK ABSORBER ELECTRICAL
67	CLIP, ACTUATOR RETAINING
69	CLIP, ROSEBUD
70	CONNECTOR, ACTUATOR ELECTRICAL
71	PANEL, FRONT WHEELHOUSE LOWER CENTER

Fig. 9   Shock absorber replacement. Models with Selective Ride Control

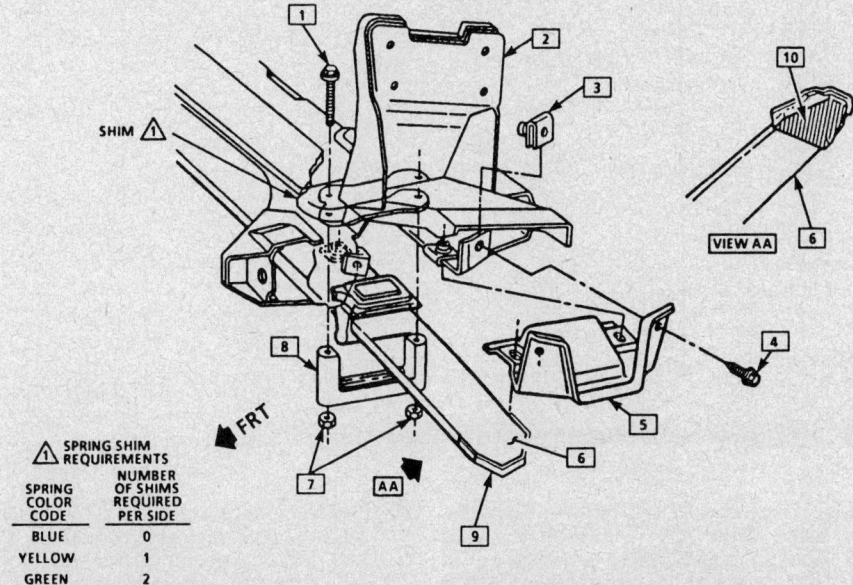

SPRING COLOR CODE	NUMBER OF SHIMS REQUIRED PER SIDE
BLUE	0
YELLOW	1
GREEN	2

⚠ SPRING SHIM REQUIREMENTS

1	SPRING RETAINING BOLT
2	DRIVETRAIN AND SUSPENSION FRAME
3	MULTI-THREAD "U" NUT
4	SPRING PROTECTOR TO FRAME BOLT 25 N·m (18 lb. ft.)
5	SPRING PROTECTOR
6	FRONT TRANSVERSE SPRING
7	SPRING RETAINER NUT
8	FRONT SPRING RETAINER
9	SPRING PAD
10	APPLY RUBBER LUBRICANT

Fig. 11   Front leaf spring replacement

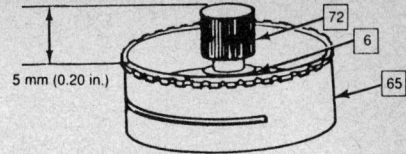

5 mm (0.20 in.)

6	NUT, HEX PREVAILING TORQUE
65	RETAINER, CUP ASSEMBLY
72	GEAR, SELECTOR

Fig. 10   Positioning selector gear

The number of spring retaining shims can be determined by the color code located on the spring. If color code is blue, no shims are required; yellow or white, 1 shim; green, 2 shims. Torque spring mounting bolts to specifications, with vehicle on ground.

CONTROL ARM REPLACE

UPPER CONTROL ARM

1. Disconnect battery ground cable.
2. Raise and support vehicle, then remove wheel and tire assembly.
3. Remove wheel housing seal and lower center panel.
4. **On models equipped with Selective Ride Control,** disconnect shock absorber actuator electrical connector.
5. **On all models,** using a suitable jack stand, support lower control arm.
6. Disconnect wheel speed sensor electrical connector and detach speed sensor cable from bracket.
7. Using tool No. J-33436 or equivalent, detach upper ball joint from steering knuckle.
8. Remove upper control arm to frame member attaching bolts and shims, **Fig. 13.** Note location and number of shims for installation.
9. Remove upper control arm from vehicle.
10. Reverse procedure to install. Install shims in same location as removed. Install upper ball joint stud cotter pin from rear to front of vehicle. After completing installation, check wheel alignment and adjust as necessary.

LOWER CONTROL ARM

1. Disconnect battery ground cable.
2. Raise and support vehicle, then remove wheel and tire assembly.
3. Remove both spring protectors, then install spring compressor J-33432 or equivalent.
4. Compress front spring with tool, then support lower control arm with suitable jack stand.
5. Disconnect shock absorber and stabilizer shaft link from lower control arm.
6. Disconnect front wheel speed sensor electrical connector, then detach speed sensor cable from bracket.
7. Disconnect lower ball joint from steering knuckle.
8. Remove lower control arm to frame

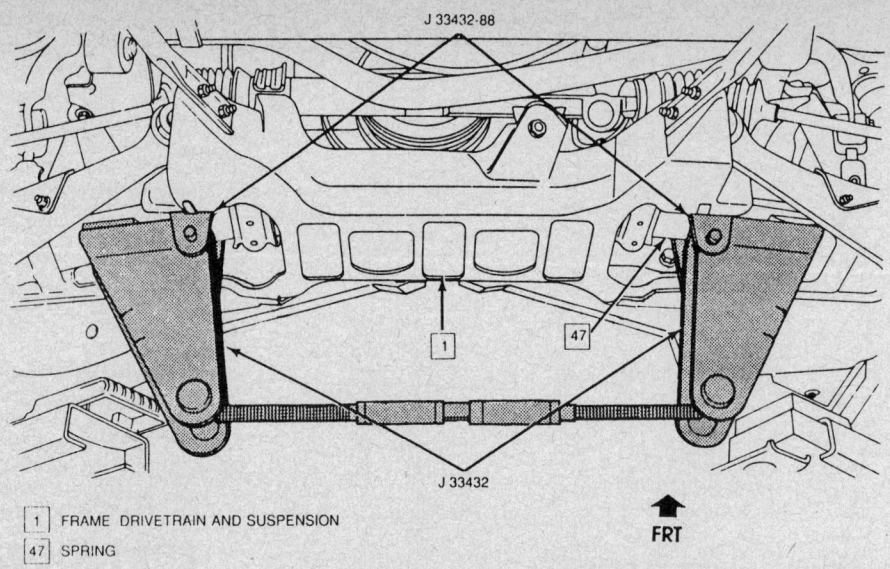

1	FRAME DRIVETRAIN AND SUSPENSION
47	SPRING

FRT

Fig. 12   Compressing front leaf spring

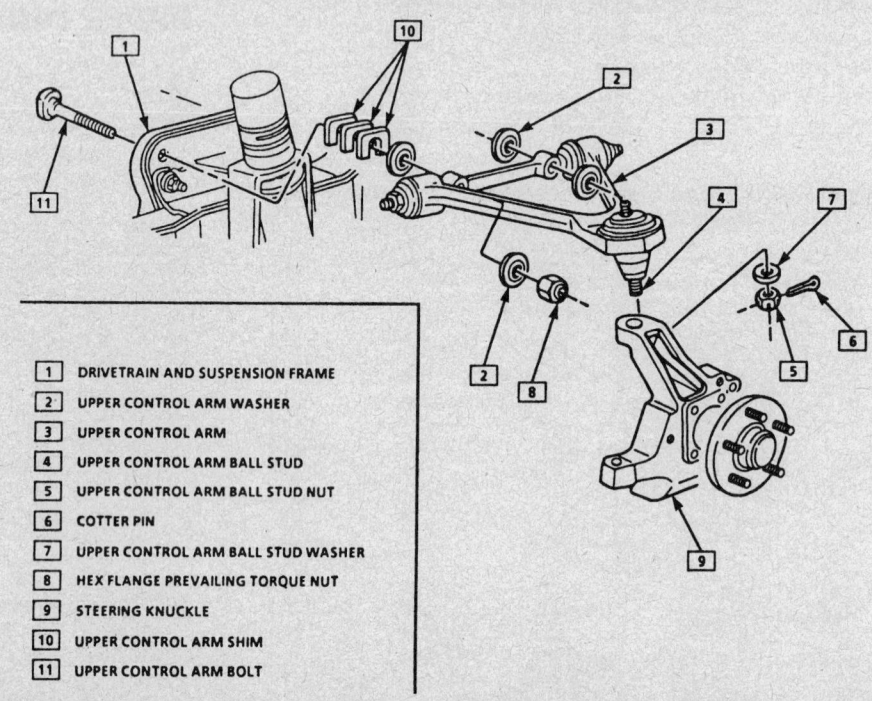

1	DRIVETRAIN AND SUSPENSION FRAME
2	UPPER CONTROL ARM WASHER
3	UPPER CONTROL ARM
4	UPPER CONTROL ARM BALL STUD
5	UPPER CONTROL ARM BALL STUD NUT
6	COTTER PIN
7	UPPER CONTROL ARM BALL STUD WASHER
8	HEX FLANGE PREVAILING TORQUE NUT
9	STEERING KNUCKLE
10	UPPER CONTROL ARM SHIM
11	UPPER CONTROL ARM BOLT

Fig. 13   Upper control arm replacement

member attaching bolts, then remove lower control arm, **Fig. 14.**
9. Reverse procedure to install. When installing, position lower ball joint stud so that cotter pin can be installed from rear to front of vehicle. When tightening stabilizer shaft link, lower control arm and shock absorber lower attaching bolts and nuts, use jack stands to hold suspension at proper trim height.

STEERING KNUCKLE REPLACE

1. Disconnect battery ground cable.

2. Raise and support vehicle, then remove wheel and tire assembly.
3. Remove brake caliper and rotor.
4. Disconnect wheel speed sensor electrical connector, then detach speed sensor cable from bracket.
5. Remove hub assembly attaching bolts and nuts, then remove hub assembly.
6. Support lower control arm using a suitable jack stand.
7. Disconnect upper and lower control arms from steering knuckle, **Fig. 15.**
8. Disconnect tie rod end from steering knuckle.
9. Remove steering knuckle.

10. Reverse procedure to install. When installing, position ball joint studs so that cotter pins can be installed from rear to front of vehicle. When installing wheel hub, speed sensor cable should be facing rearward.

STABILIZER SHAFT REPLACE

1. Raise and support vehicle, then re-

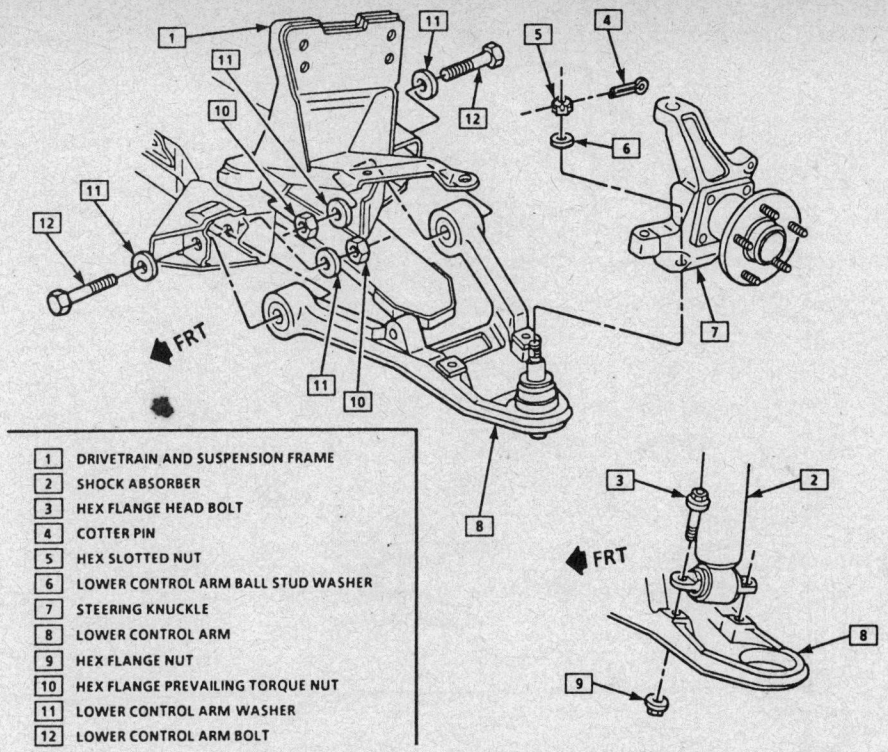

1	DRIVETRAIN AND SUSPENSION FRAME
2	SHOCK ABSORBER
3	HEX FLANGE HEAD BOLT
4	COTTER PIN
5	HEX SLOTTED NUT
6	LOWER CONTROL ARM BALL STUD WASHER
7	STEERING KNUCKLE
8	LOWER CONTROL ARM
9	HEX FLANGE NUT
10	HEX FLANGE PREVAILING TORQUE NUT
11	LOWER CONTROL ARM WASHER
12	LOWER CONTROL ARM BOLT

Fig. 14   Lower control arm replacement

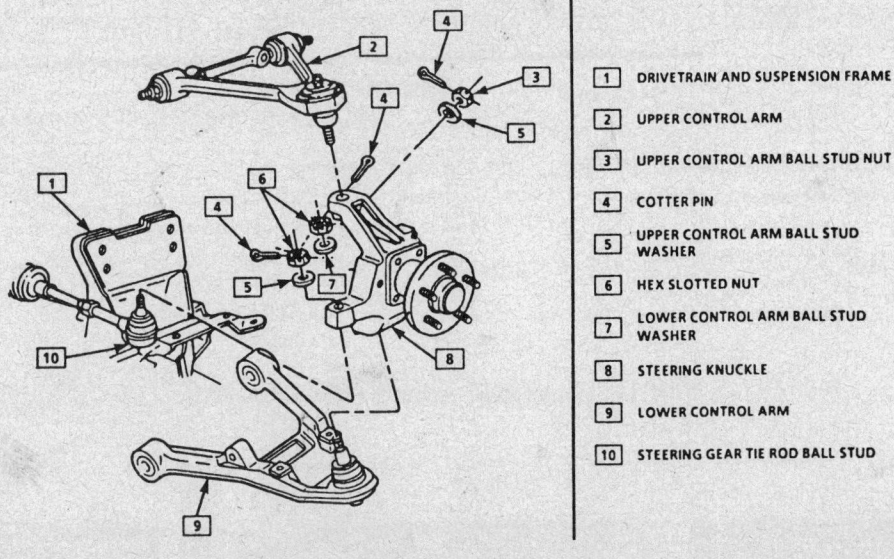

1	DRIVETRAIN AND SUSPENSION FRAME
2	UPPER CONTROL ARM
3	UPPER CONTROL ARM BALL STUD NUT
4	COTTER PIN
5	UPPER CONTROL ARM BALL STUD WASHER
6	HEX SLOTTED NUT
7	LOWER CONTROL ARM BALL STUD WASHER
8	STEERING KNUCKLE
9	LOWER CONTROL ARM
10	STEERING GEAR TIE ROD BALL STUD

Fig. 15   Steering knuckle replacement

move wheel and tire assembly.
2. Support lower control arm with a suitable jack stand.
3. Remove stabilizer shaft attaching bolts, insulator clamps and brackets from frame, **Fig. 16.**
4. Remove stabilizer shaft from vehicle.
5. Reverse procedure to install. When tightening stabilizer shaft link attaching bolts and nuts, use jack stands to hold suspension at proper trim height. Refer to **Fig. 16,** for bolt installation direction.

RACK & PINION STEERING GEAR REPLACE

1. Disconnect battery ground cable.
2. Position drain pan under vehicle, then disconnect inlet and outlet hoses from steering gear.
3. Disconnect power steering fluid cooling pipes, if equipped.
4. Disconnect intermediate steering

shaft from power steering gear.
5. Raise and support vehicle, and remove wheel and tire assemblies.
6. Disconnect outer tie rods from steering knuckles, **Fig. 17.**
7. Remove power steering fluid oil cooler, if equipped.
8. Remove stabilizer shaft from vehicle as describe under "Stabilizer Shaft, Replace."
9. Remove steering gear to frame attaching bolts and nuts, then remove steering gear.

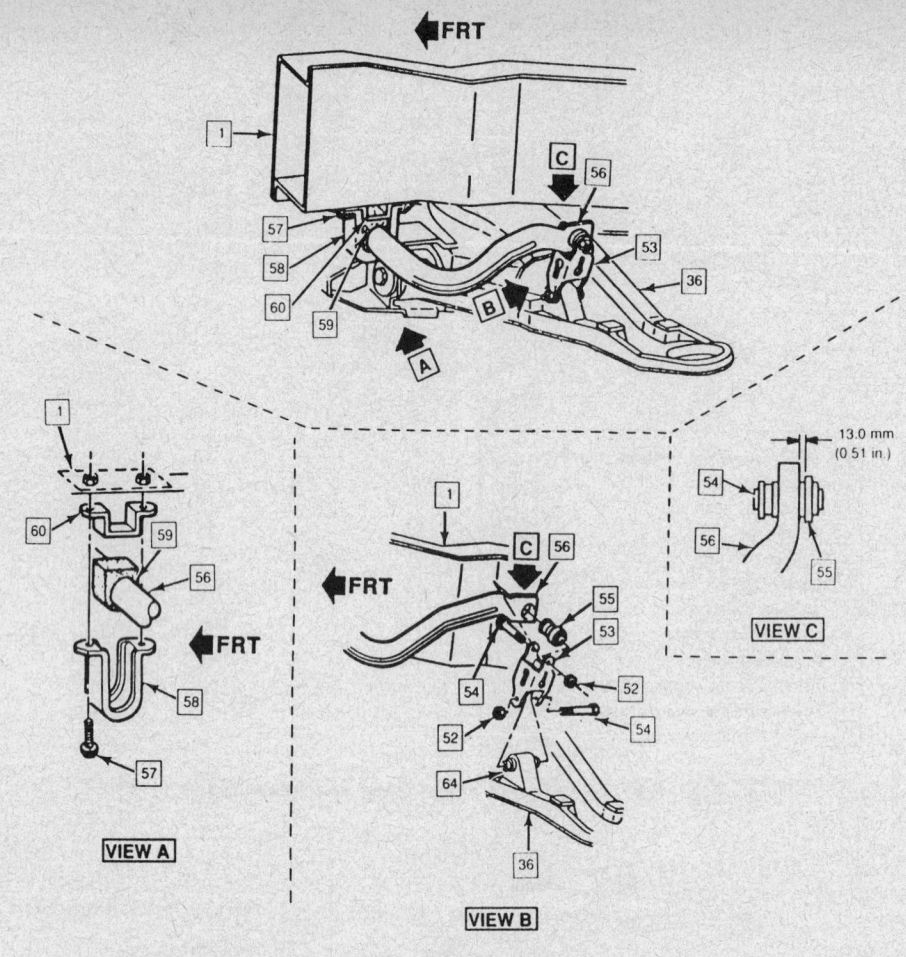

1	FRAME, DRIVETRAIN AND SUSPENSION	56	SHAFT, STABILIZER
36	ARM, LOWER CONTROL	57	BOLT
52	NUT, HEX	58	CLAMP, STABILIZER SHAFT INSULATOR
53	LINK, STABILIZER SHAFT	59	INSULATOR, STABILIZER SHAFT
54	BOLT, HEX	60	BRACKET, STABILIZER SHAFT
55	INSULATOR, STABILIZER SHAFT LINK UPPER	64	INSULATOR, STABILIZER SHAFT LINK LOWER

Fig. 16 Stabilizer shaft replacement

10. Reverse procedure to install. Top off fluid reservoir, bleed system and check for leaks. After completing installation, check front toe setting.

POWER STEERING PUMP
REPLACE
EXCEPT ZR-1

1. Disconnect battery ground cable.
2. Position suitable drain pan under vehicle.
3. Remove serpentine drive belt.
4. **On models with automatic transmission,** remove water pump damper.
5. Loosen power steering reservoir and bracket attaching bolts, then position reservoir and bracket to permit power steering pump pulley removal.
6. Remove cap from power steering pump pulley, then remove pulley using a suitable puller.
7. Disconnect hoses from power steering pump.
8. Remove bolts attaching power steering pump rear bracket to brace, **Fig. 18.**
9. Remove engine mount bolt, then remove power steering pump rear brace.
10. Remove power steering pump attaching bolts, then remove power steering pump and rear bracket.
11. Reverse procedure to install.

ZR-1

1. Disconnect battery ground cable.
2. Drain cooling system, then remove air intake duct.
3. Drain power steering fluid.
4. Remove vacuum hose retainer from power steering fluid reservoir, then disconnect and position hoses aside.
5. Remove left hand coolant outlet housing and hose.
6. Remove serpentine drive belt.
7. Remove power steering pump to cylinder head bracket attaching bolts, **Fig. 19.**
8. Remove power steering pump to A/C compressor bracket bolt.
9. Disconnect power steering fluid cooler hose from reservoir.
10. Disconnect power steering gear inlet hose from power steering pump.
11. Remove power steering pump from vehicle.
12. Reverse procedure to install.

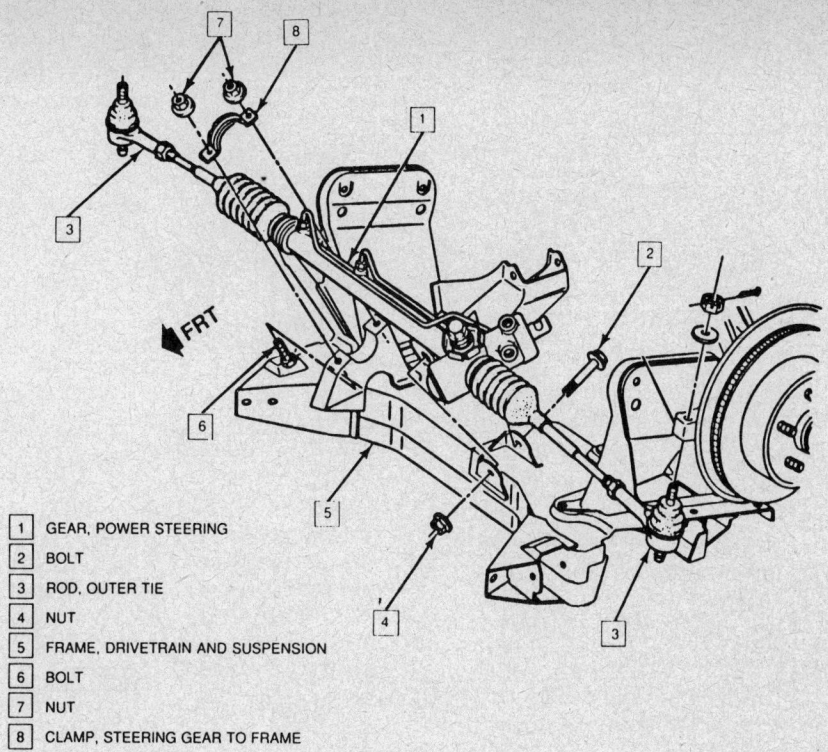

1 GEAR, POWER STEERING
2 BOLT
3 ROD, OUTER TIE
4 NUT
5 FRAME, DRIVETRAIN AND SUSPENSION
6 BOLT
7 NUT
8 CLAMP, STEERING GEAR TO FRAME

Fig. 17   Steering gear attachment

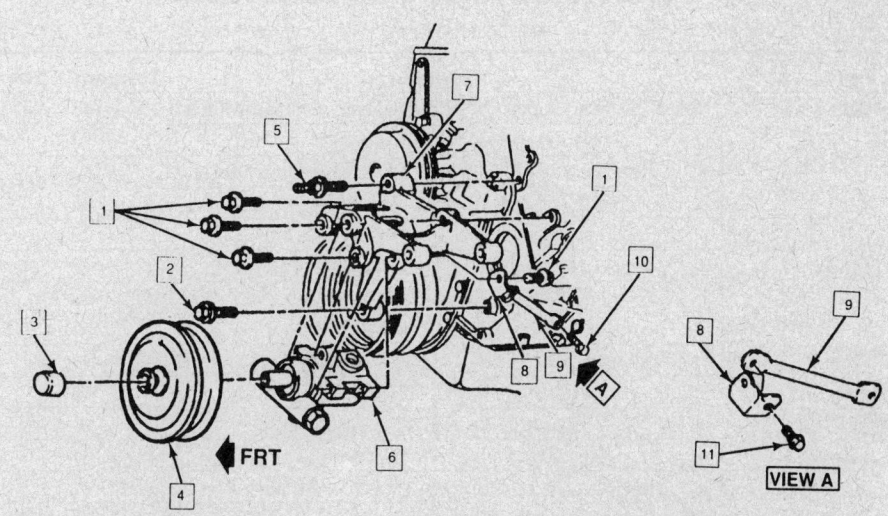

1	BOLTS, POWER STEERING PUMP MOUNTING	7	BRACKET, GENERATOR/POWER STEERING PUMP
2	BOLT, BRACKET MOUNTING	8	BRACKET, POWER STEERING PUMP REAR
3	CAP, POWER STEERING PUMP PULLEY HUB	9	BRACE, POWER STEERING PUMP REAR
4	PULLEY, POWER STEERING PUMP	10	BOLT, ENGINE MOUNT
5	STUD, AIR INJECTION BRACKET	11	BOLT, REAR BRACE MOUNTING
6	PUMP. POWER STEERING		

Fig. 18   Power steering pump installation. Except ZR-1

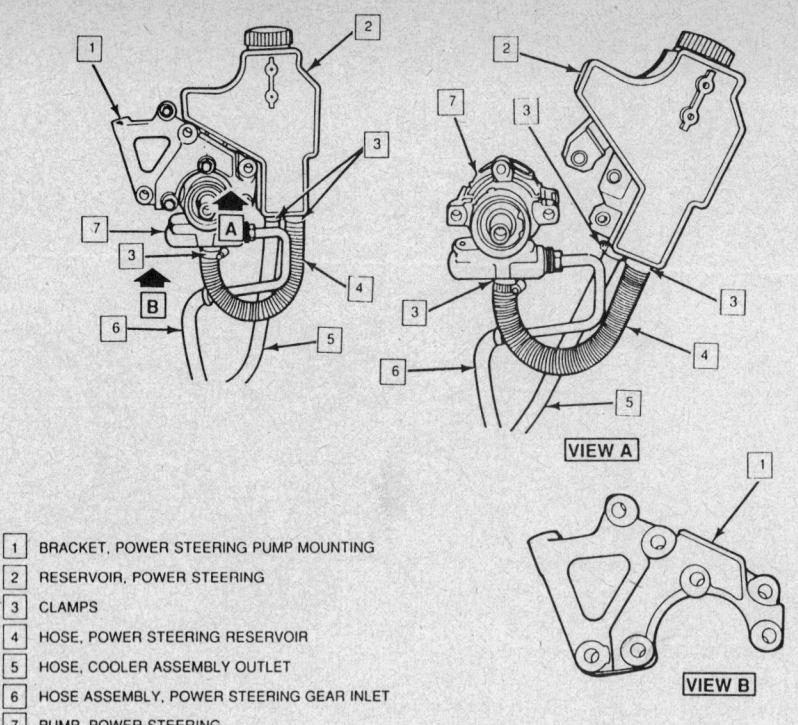

1. BRACKET, POWER STEERING PUMP MOUNTING
2. RESERVOIR, POWER STEERING
3. CLAMPS
4. HOSE, POWER STEERING RESERVOIR
5. HOSE, COOLER ASSEMBLY OUTLET
6. HOSE ASSEMBLY, POWER STEERING GEAR INLET
7. PUMP, POWER STEERING

Fig. 19   Power steering pump installation. ZR-1

TIGHTENING SPECIFICATIONS

Year	Component	Torque/Ft. Lbs.
1988-91	Hub & Bearing Assembly To Steering Knuckle Bolts	46
	Lower Ball Joint Stud Nut	50
	Lower Control Arm Shaft To Frame Member	82
	Shock Absorber Lower Attaching Bolt	19
	Shock Absorber Upper Attaching Nut	①
	Spring Protector To Crossmember Bolt	18
	Spring Retainer Bolts	48
	Stabilizer Shaft Clamp Bolts	40
	Stabilizer Shaft Link To Lower Control Arm Bolt	35
	Stabilizer Shaft To Link Bolt	35
	Steering Gear Clamp Bolts	18
	Steering Gear To Crossmember	②
	Tie Rod End To Steering Knuckle Stud Nut	③
	Tie Rod Jam Nut	50
	Upper Ball Joint Stud Nut	④
	Upper Ball Joint To Control Arm Bolts	⑤
	Upper Control Arm Shaft To Frame Member	37

①—Except 1991 models, 19 ft. lbs.; 1991 models less Selective Ride Control, 19 ft. lbs.; with Selective Ride Control, 31 ft. lbs.

②—1988, 25 ft. lbs.; except 1988, 30 ft. lbs.

③—1988-89, 32 ft. lbs.; 1990-91, 33 ft. lbs.

④—1988, 37 ft. lbs.; except 1988, 33 ft. lbs.

⑤—Except 1991, 19 ft. lbs.; 1991, 18 ft. lbs.

Wheel Alignment

INDEX

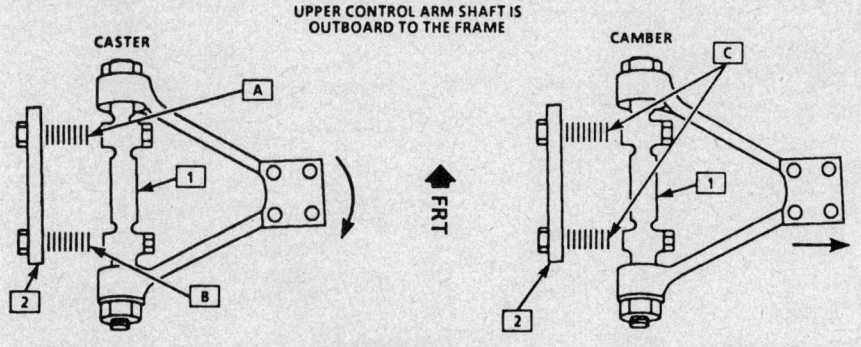
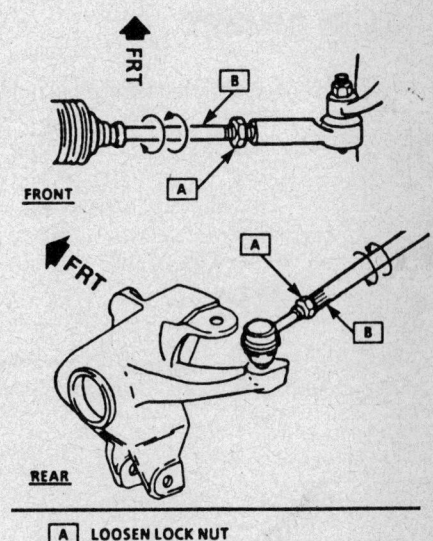

A ADD SHIMS HERE TO INCREASE POSITIVE CASTER

B SUBTRACT SHIMS HERE TO INCREASE POSITIVE CASTER

C ADD SHIMS EQUALLY TO INCREASE POSITIVE CAMBER

1 UPPER CONTROL ARM SHAFT

2 DRIVETRAIN AND FRONT SUSPENSION FRAME

Fig. 1   Front caster & camber adjustments

A LOOSEN LOCK NUT

B ADJUST TOE BY ROTATING TIE ROD

Fig. 2   Toe-in adjustment

FRONT WHEEL ALIGNMENT

Prior to checking or adjusting front suspension alignment, inspect suspension components and wheel bearings for damage or excessive wear, and replace as needed. Ensure tire pressure is properly adjusted, then raise and release front bumper several times to allow vehicle to assume normal ride height.

CASTER, ADJUST

Caster adjustments are made by means of shims between the upper control arm shaft and the support bracket attached to the frame. Shims may be added, subtracted or transferred to change the readings. Transfer shims from front to rear or rear to front. The transfer of one shim to the front bolt from the rear bolt will decrease positive caster. One shim transferred from the rear bolt to the front bolt will change caster about .36 degree. Refer to **Fig. 1**, and note the effect of shim placement.

CAMBER, ADJUST

Camber adjustments are made by means of shims between the upper control arm shaft and the support bracket attached to the frame, **Fig. 1**. Shims may be added, subtracted or transferred to change the readings.

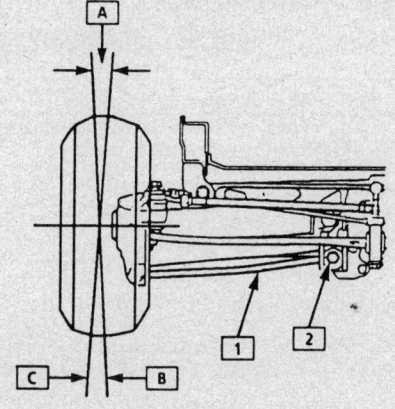

A NEGATIVE CAMBER ANGLE

B VERTICAL

C CENTERLINE OF WHEEL

1 SPINDLE ROD

2 WHEEL SPINDLE ROD ADJUSTMENT BOLT

Fig. 3   Rear camber adjustment

Change shims at both the front and rear of the shaft. Adding an equal number of shims at both front and rear of the support shaft will decrease positive camber.

TOE-IN, ADJUST

Toe-in can be adjusted by loosening the clamp bolts at each end of each tie rod and turning each tie rod to increase or decrease its length as necessary until proper toe-in is secured and the steering gear is on the high point for straight-ahead driving, **Fig. 2**.

REAR WHEEL ALIGNMENT

Rear wheel alignment should be checked and adjusted periodically, when rear tires indicate abnormal wear, or when suspension components are replaced. Prior to rear wheel alignment, check suspension components for damage or excessive wear and repair as needed. Also ensure tires are properly inflated, and wheel bearing end play is within specifications.

CAMBER, ADJUST

Camber is adjusted by rotating the eccentric cam and bolt located at the inboard end of the spindle support rod, **Fig. 3**. To check and adjust camber, proceed as follows:

1. Place rear wheels of vehicle on suitable alignment equipment following manufacturer's instructions, then check camber reading.
2. If wheel camber is not within specifications, loosen cam bolt retaining nut.
3. Rotate cam bolt, **Fig. 3**, until camber reading is within specifications listed at the front of this chapter.

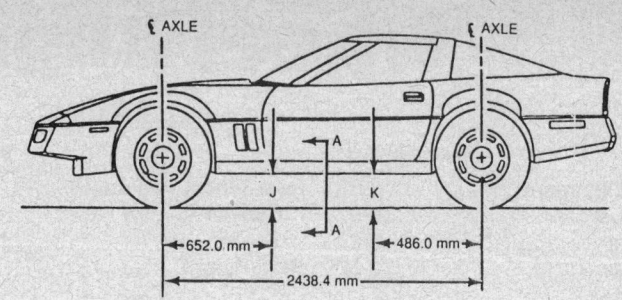

TOE-IN ADJUST

Toe-in is adjusted by loosening locknuts on tie rod ends and rotating adjuster sleeves until desired setting is obtained, **Fig. 2**.

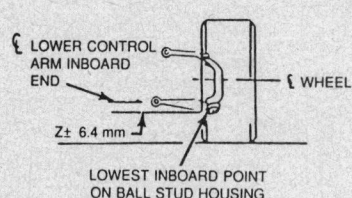

FRONT SUSPENSION

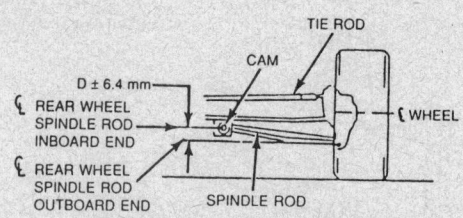

REAR SUSPENSION

RIDE HEIGHT

Refer to **Figs. 4 through 7** for ride height measurements and specifications.

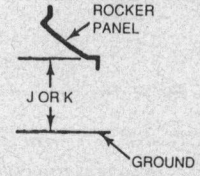

Vertical heights: "Z" and "J" dimensions-lift front bumper of vehicle up approximately 38.0 mm. Gently remove hands and let vehicle settle on its own. Repeat twice for a total of 3 times. Measure "Z" and "J" dimensions. Push front bumper of vehicle down approximately 38.0 mm. Gently remove hands and let vehicle rise on its own. Repeat twice for a total of 3 times. Measure "Z" and "J" dimensions. True heights are the average of the high and low measurements.

"D" and "K" dimensions - same procedure as "Z" and "J" dimensions using rear bumper.

Recommended tire pressure: Trim height. Set tire pressure to agree with vehicle's tire pressure sticker for loading "up to vehicle capacity."

NOTE: Load Conditions:
Shipping Weight-Vehicle is built to parts list specifications including coolant to capacity and 20.8 liters (5.5 gallons) of gasoline.

Curb Weight-Vehicle is built to parts list specifications including coolant to capacity and full tank of gasoline.

Fig. 4   Ride height measurement locations

MODEL			Z		D		J		K	
VIN	TIRE	SUSP	SHIPPED	CURB	SHIPPED	CURB	SHIPPED	CURB	SHIPPED	CURB
YA00	P255-50VR16	STD	46.4	49.2	92.7	80.2	191.7	190.3	205.0	194.6
YA00	P255-50VR16	FE7	52.2	54.6	87.3	77.6	194.5	193.5	201.8	193.6
YA67	P255-50VR16	STD	55.9	58.8	100.6	88.1	200.3	199.0	212.8	202.4

NOTE: All dimensions in mm.
Dimension "Z", "J", "K" and "D" . . . Vertical to ground and apply to all vehicles.

Fig. 5   Ride height specifications. 1988 (FE7=Heavy Duty Suspension; YA00=Hatchback; YA67=Convertible)

MODEL			Z		D		J		K	
VIN	TIRE	SUSP	SHIPPED	CURB	SHIPPED	CURB	SHIPPED	CURB	SHIPPED	CURB
YY07	P275-40ZR17	FE1	57.7	59.4	63.3	56.1	198.8	198.0	206.5	200.6
YY07	P275-40ZR17	FE7	52.7	54.2	56.2	50.8	193.0	192.6	199.6	195.2
YY67	P275-40ZR17	FE1	64.5	66.2	70.1	62.9	204.5	203.8	212.3	206.3

NOTE: All dimensions in mm.
Dimension "Z", "J", "K" and "D" . . . Vertical to ground and apply to all vehicles.

Fig. 6   Ride height specifications. 1989 (FE1=Soft Ride Suspension; FE7=Heavy Duty Suspension; YY07=Hatchback; YY67=Convertible)

MODEL	SUSP.	ENG.	Z		D		J		K	
			SHIPPED	CURB	SHIPPED	CURB	SHIPPED	CURB	SHIPPED	CURB
1YY07	FE1	L98	55.5	57.2	62.8	55.6	197.0	196.2	205.7	199.7
1YY07	FE7	L98	52.7	54.2	56.2	50.8	193.0	192.6	199.6	195.2
1YY07	FE1	LT5	43.7	45.4	62.8	55.6	187.9	187.1	203.2	197.3
1YY07	FE7	LT5	41.5	43.0	57.1	51.7	184.6	184.2	198.1	193.6
1YY67	FE1	L98	64.5	66.2	70.1	62.9	204.5	203.8	212.3	206.3
1YY67	FE1	LT5	52.5	54.2	70.4	63.2	195.3	194.5	210.0	204.1
1YZ07	FE7	LT5	42.1	43.6	57.4	52.0	185.2	184.7	198.4	193.9

NOTE: All dimensions in mm.
Dimension "Z", "J", "K" and "D" . . . Vertical to ground and apply to all vehicles.

Fig. 7   Ride height specifications. 1990-91 (FE1=Soft Ride Suspension; FE7=Heavy Duty Suspension; L98=V8-250/5.7L Single Cam Engine; LT5=V8-350/5.7L 4 Cam Engine; 1YY07=Hatchback; 1YY67=Convertible; 1YZ07=ZR-1 Hatchback)

CHEVROLET CELEBRITY, BUICK CENTURY, OLDS CUTLASS CIERA & CUTLASS CRUISER & PONTIAC 6000
(A Cars)
INDEX OF SERVICE OPERATIONS

NOTE: Refer To The Rear Of This Manual For Vehicle Manufacturer's Special Service Tool Suppliers.

Continued

INDEX OF SERVICE OPERATIONS—Continued

Specifications

GENERAL ENGINE SPECIFICATIONS

Year	Engine Liter/CID ①	Engine VIN Code ②	Fuel System	Bore & Stroke	Compression Ratio	Net H.P. @ RPM ③	Maximum Torque Ft. Lbs. @ RPM	Normal Oil Pressure Pounds
1988	2.5L/4-151	R	T.B.I. ⑤	4.00 x 3.00	8.3	98 @ 4800	135 @ 3200	50 ⑦
	2.8L/V6-173	W	M.P.F.I. ⑥	3.50 x 2.99	8.9	125 @ 4500	160 @ 3600	50–65 ⑧
	3.1L/V6-189	T	M.P.F.I. ⑥	3.50 x 3.31	8.9	140 @ 4800	185 @ 3200	⑪
	3.8L/V6-231	3	S.F.I. ④	3.80 x 3.40	8.5	150 @ 4400	200 @ 2000	37 ⑨
1989	2.5L/4-151	R	T.B.I. ⑤	4.00 x 3.00	8.3	98 @ 4800	135 @ 3200	50 ⑦
	2.8L/V6-173	W	M.P.F.I. ⑥	3.50 x 2.99	8.9	125 @ 4500	160 @ 3600	50–65 ⑧
	3.1L/V6-189	T	M.P.F.I. ⑥	3.50 x 3.31	8.9	140 @ 4800	185 @ 3200	⑪
	3.3L/V6-204	N	S.F.I. ④	3.70 x 3.16	9.0	160 @ 5200	185 @ 2000	45 ⑦
1990	2.5L/4-151	R	T.B.I. ⑤	4.00 x 3.00	8.3	110 @ 5200	135 @ 3200	⑩
	3.1L/V6-189	T	M.P.F.I. ⑥	3.50 x 3.31	8.8	135 @ 4400	180 @ 3600	⑪
	3.3L/V6-204	N	S.F.I. ④	3.70 x 3.16	9.0	160 @ 5200	185 @ 2000	45 ⑦
1991	2.5L/4-151	R	T.B.I. ⑤	4.00 x 3.00	8.3	110 @ 5200	135 @ 3200	50
	3.1L/V6-189	T	M.P.F.I. ⑥	3.50 x 3.31	8.8	135 @ 4400	180 @ 3600	⑪
	3.3L/V6-204	N	S.F.I. ④	3.70 x 3.16	9.0	160 @ 5200	185 @ 2000	45 ⑦

① —CID-cubic inch displacement.
② —The eighth digit denotes engine code.
③ —Ratings are net-as installed in vehicle.
④ —Sequential-port fuel injection.
⑤ —Throttle body injection.
⑥ —Multi-port fuel injection
⑦ —@ 2000 RPM.
⑧ —@ 1200 RPM.
⑨ —@ 2400 RPM
⑩ —50 psi @ 2000 RPM or 26 psi @ 800 RPM.
⑪ —15 psi @ 1100 RPM or 50–65 @ 2400 RPM.

TUNE UP SPECIFICATIONS

Engine Liter/CID	Engine VIN Code ①	Spark Plug Gap	Ignition Timing BTDC Firing Order Fig.	Ignition Timing BTDC Man. Trans.	Ignition Timing BTDC Auto. Trans.	Ignition Timing BTDC Mark Fig.	Curb Idle Speed Man. Trans.	Curb Idle Speed Auto Trans.	Fast Idle Speed Man. Trans.	Fast Idle Speed Auto. Trans.	Fuel Pump Pressure
1988											
2.5L/4-151	R	.060	⑦	③	③	④	⑤	⑤	⑤	⑤	4–13 ⑥
2.8L/V6-173	W	.045	⑧	③	③	④	⑤	⑤	⑤	⑤	34–47 ⑨
3.1L/V6-189	T	.045	⑧	—	③	④	—	⑤	—	⑤	34–47 ⑨
3.8L/V6-231	3	.045	②	—	③	④	—	⑤	—	⑤	37–43 ⑨
1989											
2.5L/4-151	R	.060	⑦	③	③	④	—	⑤	—	⑤	9–13 ⑥
2.8L/V6-173	W	.045	⑧	③	③	④	—	⑤	—	⑤	34–47 ⑨
3.1L/V6-189	T	.045	⑧	—	③	④	—	⑤	—	⑤	34–47 ⑨
3.3L/V6-204	N	.060	②	—	③	④	—	⑤	—	⑤	37–43 ⑨
1990											
2.5L/4-151	R	.060	⑦	③	③	④	—	600D ⑤	—	⑤	9–13 ⑥
3.1L/V6-189	T	.045	⑧	—	③	④	—	600D ⑤	—	⑤	40.5–47 ⑨
3.3L/V6-204	N	.060	②	—	③	④	—	600D ⑤	—	⑤	41–47 ⑨
1991											
2.5L/4-151	R	.060	⑦	③	③	④	—	⑤	—	⑧	9–13 ⑥
3.1L/V6-189	T	.045	⑧	—	③	④	—	⑤	—	⑤	40.5–47 ⑨
3.3L/V6-204	N	.060	②	—	③	④	—	⑤	—	⑤	41–47 ⑨

① —The eighth digit of the Vehicle identification Number (V.I.N.) denotes engine code.
② —Cylinder numbering left to right as viewed from front of vehicle, front bank 1, 3, 5; rear bank 2, 4, 6. Firing order 1-6-5-4-3-2. Refer to Figs. A & B for spark plug wire connections at coil unit.
③ —No adjustment.
④ —Equipped with crankshaft position sensor.
⑤ —Idle speeds are controlled by the idle air control (IAC) valve or idle speed control (ISC) motor.

Continued

TUNE UP SPECIFICATIONS—Continued

⑥—Wrap shop towel around fuel hose to steel line connection to prevent fuel spillage. Disconnect fuel hose from steel line & connect suitable fuel pressure gauge. Ensure pressure gauge connections are tight, then start engine & note fuel pressure reading.

⑦—Cylinder numbering from front of engine 1, 2, 3, 4. Firing order 1-3-4-2. Refer to Fig. C for spark plug wire connections at coil unit.

⑧—Cylinder numbering left to right as viewed from front of vehicle, front bank 2, 4, 6; rear bank 1, 3, 5. Firing order 1-2-3-4-5-6. Refer to Fig. D for

spark plug wire connections at coil unit.

⑨—With shop towel wrapped around fuel pressure valve to prevent fuel spillage, connect a suitable fuel pressure gauge to fuel pressure valve. Check fuel pressure with ignition switch On, engine not running.

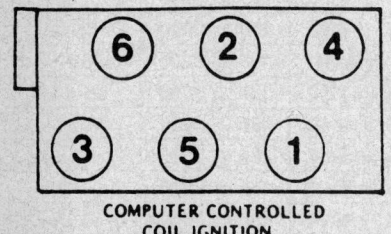

COMPUTER CONTROLLED COIL IGNITION

Fig. A

COMPUTER CONTROLLED COIL IGNITION

Fig. B

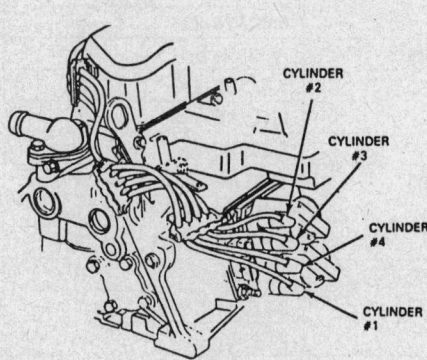

Fig. C

Fig. D

STARTING MOTOR APPLICATIONS

Refer to "Starter Motor" section for starter specifications.

| Year | Engine | | Starter Ident. No. |
	Liter/CID	VIN ①	
1988	2.5L/4-151	R	10455017
	2.8L/V6-173	W	10455019
	3.1L/V6-189	T	③
	3.8L/V6-231	3	10455006
1989	2.5L/4-151	R	10455017
	2.8L/V6-173	W	10455019
	3.1L/V6-189	T	10455019
	3.3L/V6-204	N	10455006
1990	2.5L/4-151	R	10455004
	3.1L/V6-189	T	10455019
	3.3L/V6-204	N	10455006
1991	2.5L/4-151	R	②
	3.1L/V6-189	T	10455019
	3.3L/V6-204	N	10455006

①—For VIN code, refer to the "General Engine Specifications" at the beginning of chapter.

②—Buick models, 10455004; Pontiac models, 10455017.

③—First design, 01998533; second design, 10455014 and 10455023.

ALTERNATOR SPECIFICATIONS

Year	Model	Rated Hot Output Amps.
1988	1101142	85
	1101143	100
	1101273	105
	1101344	105
	1105694	100
	1105698	85
1989	1101142	85
	1101273	105
	1105694	100
	1105698	85
1990	1101142	85
	1101344	105
	1101475	105
	1105694	100
1991	1101142	85
	1101475	105
	1101603	105
	1101810	85

FRONT WHEEL ALIGNMENT SPECIFICATIONS

Year	Model	Caster Angle, Degrees		Camber Angle, Degrees				Toe-In Inch
		Limits	Desired	Limits		Desired		
				Left	Right	Left	Right	
1988-91	All	+.7 to +2.7①	+1.7①	−.5 to +.5	−.5 to +.5	0	0	0

①—Non-adjustable.

REAR WHEEL ALIGNMENT SPECIFICATIONS

Year	Model	Camber Angle, Degrees				Toe-In Inch
		Limits		Desired		
		Left	Right	Left	Right	
1988	All	−.25 to +.25①	−.25 to +.25①	0①	0①	0①
1989	All except 6000 STE AWD	−.25 to +.25①	−.25 to +.25①	0①	0①	0①
	6000 STE AWD	—	—	−.5	−.5	.15
1990	All except 6000 STE AWD	−.25 to +.25①	−.25 to +.25①	0①	0①	0①
	6000 STE AWD	−1.0 to 0	1.0 to 0	−.25	−.25	.2
1991	All	−.3 to +.3①	−.3 to +.3①	0①	0①	0①

①—Non-adjustable.

COOLING SYSTEM & CAPACITY DATA

Year	Engine Liter/CID	VIN	Cooling Capacity, Qts. Less A/C	With A/C	Radiator Cap Relief Pressure, Lbs.	Thermo. Opening Temp.	Fuel Tank Gals.	Engine Oil Refill Qts.	Transaxle Oil Manual Transaxle Pts.	Auto. Transaxle Qts. ①
1988	2.5L/4-151	R	9.4②	9.7②	15	195	15.7	4.0⑧	4.1	⑦
	2.8L/V6-173	W	13	13.2	15	195	15.7	4.0⑧	4.1	⑦
	3.1L/V6-189	T	12.6	12.6	15	195	15.7	4.0⑧	—	⑦
	3.8L/V6-231	3	12	12.7	15	195	15.7	4.0⑧	—	⑦
1989	2.5L/4-151	R	9.4	9.7	15	195	15.7	4.0⑧	—	⑦
	2.8L/V6-173	W	13	13.2	15	195	15.7	4.0⑧	—	⑦
	3.1L/V6-189	T	12.6	12.6	15	195	16	4.0⑧	—	⑦
	3.3L/V6-204	N	12	12.7	15	195	15.7	4.0⑧	—	⑦
1990	2.5L/4-151	R	9.7	9.9	15	195	15.7	4.0⑧	—	③
	3.1L/V6-189	T	④	④	15	195	15.7⑤	4.0⑧	—	③
	3.3L/V6-204	N	12.9	13.2	15	195	15.7	4.0⑧	—	③
1991	2.5L/4-151	R	9.7	9.9	15	195	15.7	4.0⑧	—	⑥
	3.1L/V6-189	T	④	④	15	195	15.7	4.0⑧	—	⑥
	3.3L/V6-204	N	12.9	13.2	15	195	15.7	4.0⑧	—	⑥

①—Approximate, make final check with dipstick.
②—w/heavy duty cooling system, 12 qts.
③—Oil pan only, 7 qts. w/3T40 trans. or 6 qts. w/4T60 trans.; total capacity, 9 qts. w/3T40 trans. or 8 qts. w/4T60 trans.
④—w/three speed trans., 13.1 qts; w/four speed trans., 12.8 qts.
⑤—6000 STE AWD, 14.3 gal.
⑥—Oil pan only, 7 qts. w/3T40 trans. or 6 qts. w/4T60 trans.; total capacity, 9 qts. w/3T40 trans. or 6 qts. w/4T60 trans.
⑦—Oil pan only, 4 qts. w/125C trans. or 6 qts. w/440 trans.; total capacity, 6 qts. w/125C trans. or 10 qts. w/440 trans.
⑧—Additional oil may be required to bring oil level to full mark when changing oil filter.

Electrical

INDEX

FUSE PANEL & FLASHER LOCATION
CELEBRITY
1988

The fuse panel is located behind the lefthand side of the instrument panel to the right side of the steering column.

The hazard and turn signal flashers are located in the convenience center, near the glove box.

1989

The fuse panel is located behind the lefthand side of the instrument panel to the right side of the steering column.

The hazard flasher is located in the convenience center behind the righthand side of the instrument panel and the turn signal flasher is located on the instrument panel brace to the left of the steering column.

CENTURY

The fuse panel is located behind the righthand side of the instrument panel, in or near the glove box.

The hazard flasher is located in the convenience center behind the instrument panel, to the left of the steering column and the turn signal flasher is located on the accelerator pedal bracket.

CUTLASS CIERA, CUTLASS CRUISER, 6000 & 1990 CELEBRITY

The fuse panel is located behind the righthand side of the instrument panel, in or near the glove box.

The hazard flasher is located in the convenience center behind the righthand side of instrument panel and the turn signal flasher is located on the instrument panel brace to the right side of the steering column.

STARTER
REPLACE

Upon removal of starter, note if any shims are used. If shims are used, they should be reinstalled in their original location during installation.

If starter is noisy during cranking, remove one .015 inch double shim or add one .015 inch single shim to the outer bolt. If starter makes a high pitched whine after firing, add .015 inch double shims until noise ceases.

2.5L/4-151 & 2.8L/V6-173 ENGINES

1. Disconnect battery ground cable.
2. Raise and support vehicle.
3. Remove all electrical wiring from starter.
4. Remove dust cover attaching bolts, then dust cover.
5. Remove starter motor attaching bolts. On 2.5L/4-151 engine, remove nut securing starter bracket to rear of starter.
6. Remove starter from vehicle. **If starter needs additional room, remove engine brace and roll engine rearward.**
7. Reverse procedure to install.

3.1L/V6-189 ENGINE

1. Disconnect battery negative cable, then remove air cleaner.
2. Raise and support vehicle, then remove nut from brace at A/C compressor.
3. Remove nut from brace at engine and brace, then electrical connector from oil pressure sending unit.
4. Remove oil pressure sending unit, then oil filter.
5. Remove dust cover attaching bolts, then dust cover.
6. Remove starter attaching bolts, then lower starter.
7. Remove all electrical wiring from starter, then remove starter from vehicle.
8. Reverse procedure to install.

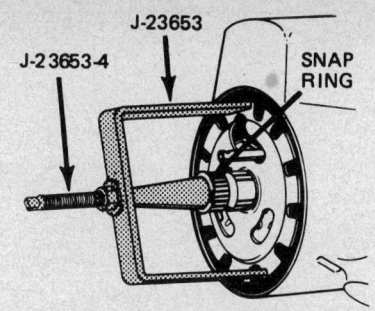

Tighten nut until tool slightly depresses lock plate

Fig. 1   Compressing lock plate

3.3L/V6-204 ENGINE

1. Disconnect battery ground cable, then discharge A/C system.
2. Remove cooling fan, then front exhaust manifold.
3. Raise and support vehicle.
4. Remove dust cover attaching bolts, then dust cover.
5. Disconnect A/C condenser hose from compressor and position aside.
6. Remove all electrical wires from starter.
7. Remove starter motor attaching bolts, then starter motor and shims, if equipped.
8. Reverse procedure to install. **Torque** starter attaching bolts to 30 ft. lbs. and inspection cover bolts to 89 inch lbs.

3.8L/V6-231 ENGINE

1. Disconnect battery ground cable.
2. Remove engine side torque strut bolt, then upper radiator panel and engine side strut bracket.
3. Discharge A/C system, then raise and support vehicle.
4. Remove fan lower attaching bolts, then disconnect fan electrical connector.
5. Lower vehicle, then remove fan upper attaching bolts.
6. Remove dipstick tube, then three front plug wires from exhaust manifold.
7. Remove bolt that holds A/C compressor to the manifold, then A/C line retaining bolt.
8. Remove all electrical wiring from starter.
9. Raise and support vehicle, then remove flywheel inspection cover.
10. Remove starter from vehicle.
11. Reverse procedure to install, **torquing** starter attaching bolts to 30 ft. lbs.

STEERING WHEEL
REPLACE

1. Disconnect battery ground cable.
2. Remove horn button or pad.
3. Disconnect horn pad and lead by pushing down and turning counterclockwise.
4. Remove retainer and steering wheel retaining nut.
5. Using steering wheel puller No. J-1859-03 or equivalent, remove

steering wheel. **On 1990-91 models with steering wheel controls, puller bolts should not be turned in more than five complete turns.**
6. Reverse procedure to install.

TURN SIGNAL SWITCH
REPLACE

1. Disconnect battery ground cable.
2. Remove steering wheel as outlined under "Steering Wheel, Replace" procedure.
3. Using a screwdriver, pry cover from housing.
4. Using lock plate compressing No. J-23653 or equivalent, compress lock plate, and pry snap ring from groove on shaft, **Fig. 1.** Slowly release lock plate compressing tool, then remove tool and lock plate from shaft end.
5. Slide canceling cam and upper bearing preload spring from end of shaft.
6. Remove turn signal (multi-function) lever.
7. Remove hazard warning knob retaining screw, button, spring and knob.
8. Remove pivot arm.
9. Wrap upper part of electrical connector with tape to prevent snagging of wires during switch removal.
10. Remove switch retaining screws and pull switch up from column, guiding wire harness through column.
11. Reverse procedure to install.

IGNITION LOCK
REPLACE

1. Remove turn signal switch as outlined under "Turn Signal Switch, Replace."
2. Remove buzzer switch and spring clip. On 1990-91 models, ignition key must be removed from lock to remove buzzer switch. On 1991 models, switch and spring clip are one assembly.
3. Turn lock cylinder to Run position on 1988-89 models or Lock position on 1990-91 models, then remove lock cylinder retaining screw and the lock cylinder.
4. To install, rotate lock cylinder to the stop while holding housing. Align cylinder key with keyway in housing, then push lock cylinder into housing until fully seated. Lock cylinder must be in Run position to install buzzer switch.
5. Install lock cylinder retaining screw, then the buzzer switch, turn signal switch and steering wheel.

IGNITION & DIMMER SWITCHES
REPLACE

FIXED COLUMN

1. Remove ignition lock as outlined under "Ignition Lock, Replace."
2. Refer to **Fig. 2,** for ignition and dimmer switch replacement procedures.

TILT COLUMN

1. Remove ignition lock as outlined under "Ignition Lock, Replace."
2. Remove housing as follows:
   a. Reinstall tilt lever and place column in full Up position.
   b. Pull upward on tilt lever and pull housing upward until it stops.
   c. Move housing to right to disengage rack from actuator, then remove housing from steering column.
3. Refer to **Fig. 3**, for ignition and dimmer switch replacement procedures.
4. Install housing as follows:
   a. While holding up on tilt lever to disengage lock shoes install over steering shaft.
   b. Move rack downward and hold. Tip housing to the left until rack engages pin on actuator rod.
   c. Push housing down until pivot pin holes are in alignment.

WIPER SWITCH REPLACE

FRONT WIPER

Fixed Column

1. Remove ignition and dimmer switches as outlined under "Ignition & Dimmer Switches, Replace."
2. Refer to **Fig. 4**, for wiper switch replacement.

Tilt Column

1. Remove ignition lock as outlined under "Ignition Lock, Replace."
2. Refer to **Fig. 5**, for wiper switch replacement.

REAR WIPER

1. Disconnect battery ground cable.
2. Remove lefthand trim panel, then right side switch trim cover.
3. Remove switch attaching screws, then switch.
4. Reverse procedure to install.

STOP LAMP SWITCH
ADJUST

Insert switch into tubular clip until the switch body seats on the tube clip. Pull the brake pedal rearward against internal pedal stop. This will properly position switch in tubular clip.

HEADLAMP SWITCH
REPLACE

1988–89 CELEBRITY

1. Disconnect battery ground cable, then remove accessory trim plate.
2. Remove headlamp switch knob by pushing release on switch.
3. Remove switch mounting plate attaching screws, then disconnect switch electrical conncecter.

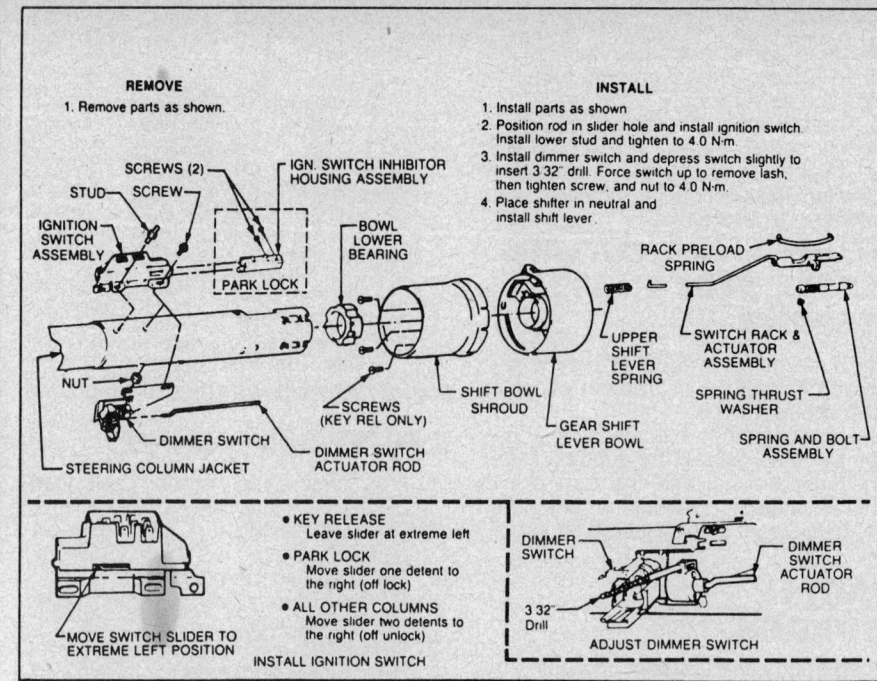

Fig. 2   Replacing ignition & dimmer switch. Fixed column.

4. Remove switch assembly from vehicle, then separate switch from mounting plate.
5. Reverse procedure to install.

CENTURY

1. Disconnect battery ground cable.
2. Remove left instrument panel trim plate as follows:
   a. Remove screws holding ALDL connector, then lower connector.
   b. Remove filler panel attaching screws, then lap vent hose.
   c. Remove filler panel by swinging down and pulling out.
   d. Remove steering column opening filler attaching screws, then opening filler.
   e. Remove left trim plate attaching screw, then trim plate. On vehicles with column shift, shift transaxle to First gear.
3. Remove switch trim plate attaching screws, then trim plate.
4. Remove switch attaching screws, then switch.
5. Reverse procedure to install.

6000 & 1990 CELEBRITY

1. Disconnect battery ground cable.
2. Remove headlight rod and knob assembly, then left trim plate.
3. Remove switch/bracket assembly attaching screws, then disconnect electrical connector.
4. Remove switch/bracket assembly. Loosen bezel and remove switch from bracket.
5. Reverse procedure to install.

CUTLASS CIERA & CRUISER

1. Disconnect battery ground cable, then

remove upper console, if equipped.
2. Remove accessory trim plate as follows:
   a. Pry steering column collar rearward, using a suitable tool, and remove.
   b. Remove outer air deflectors, then the two screws behind the deflector openings.
   c. Remove screw from behind steering column collar.
   d. **On models less console,** open ashtray and remove trim plate attaching screws.
   e. **On models with console,** remove four screws from ashtray trim cover, then ashtray trim cover. Remove trim plate attaching screws.
   f. **On all models,** pull trim plate rearward to release clips, then remove trim plate.
3. Remove 3 switch to panel attaching screws.
4. Pull switch rearward and remove from panel.
5. Reverse procedure to install.

INSTRUMENT CLUSTER
REPLACE

CELEBRITY

1. Disconnect battery ground cable.
2. Remove glove compartment, then ten screws holding trim pad to instrument panel.
3. Remove four nuts from under instrument panel, pull trim pad forward.
4. Remove headlamp switch knob, then trim pad, **Fig. 6**.
5. Disconnect shift indicator clip from steering column shift bowl.
6. Remove six cluster attaching screws, **Fig. 7**.

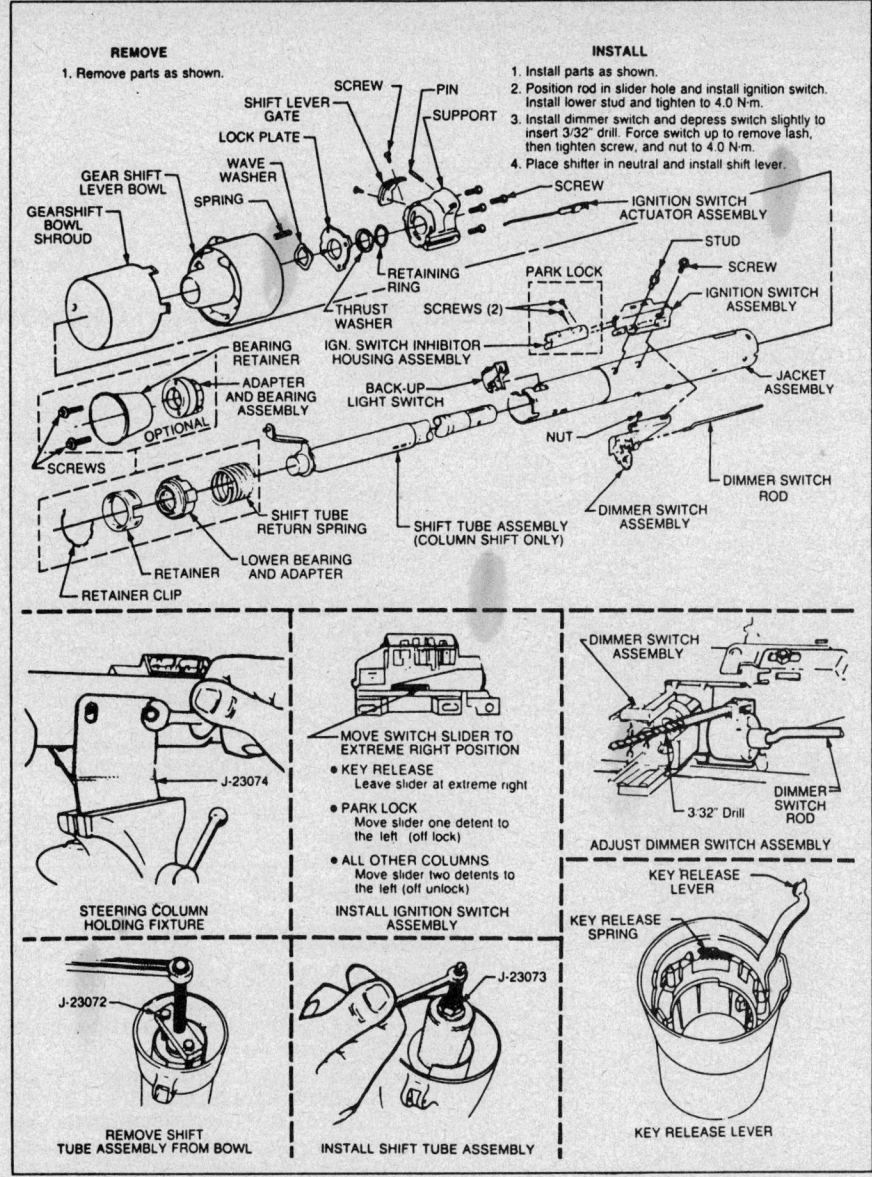

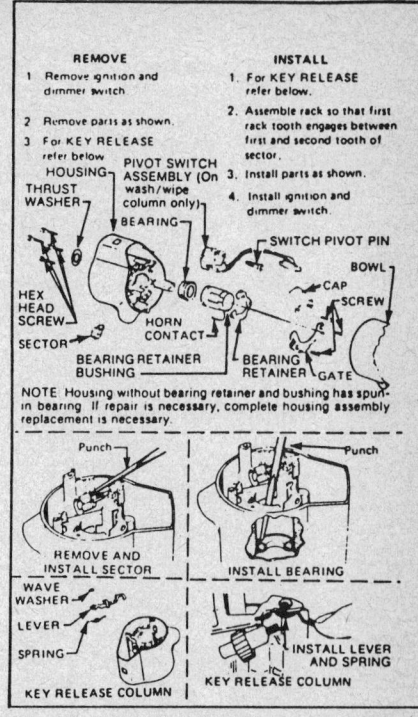

Fig. 4   Replacing housing and wiper switch. Fixed column

Fig. 3   Replacing ignition & dimmer switch. Tilt column

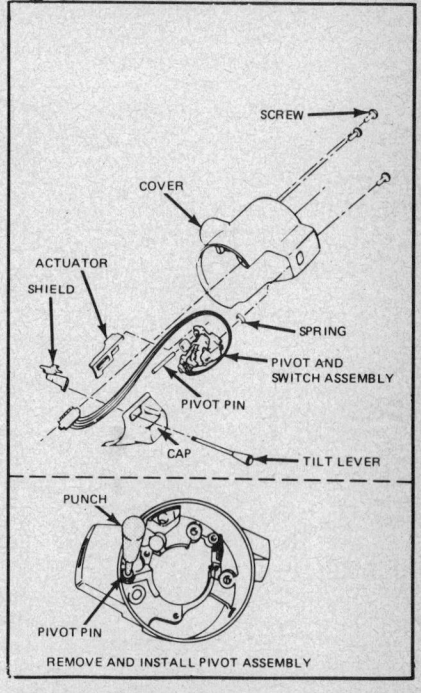

Fig. 5   Replacing cover and wiper switch. Tilt column

7. Tilt cluster rearward slightly and disconnect all electrical connectors and speedometer cable. Remove cluster.
8. Reverse procedure to install.

CENTURY

1. Disconnect battery ground cable.
2. Remove steering column filler panel as follows:
   a. Remove ALDL connector attaching screws, then lower ALDL connector.
   b. Remove filler panel attaching screws, then lap vent hose.
   c. Remove filler panel by swinging down and pulling out.
3. Remove left trim plate as follows:
   a. Remove steering column opening filler attaching screws, then opening filler.
   b. Remove ashtray, then trim plate attaching screws, **Fig. 8.**
   c. Pull trim panel straight forward to

release two retaining clips in center of panel, then remove panel.
4. Disconnect speedometer cable from transmission. If two piece cable is used, disconnect in engine compartment to ensure there is cable slack.
5. Remove shift indicator clip from steering column shift bowl, then cluster attaching screws, **Fig. 9.**
6. Pull cluster assembly out far enough to reach behind and disconnect speedometer cable.
7. Remove cluster.
8. Reverse procedure to install.

CUTLASS CIERA & CRUISER

1. Disconnect battery ground cable, then remove upper console, if equipped.
2. Remove accessory trim plate as follows:

a. Pry steering column collar rearward, using a suitable tool, and remove.
b. Remove outer air deflectors, then the two screws behind the deflector openings.
c. Remove screw from behind steering column collar.
d. **On models less console,** open ashtray and remove trim plate attaching screws.

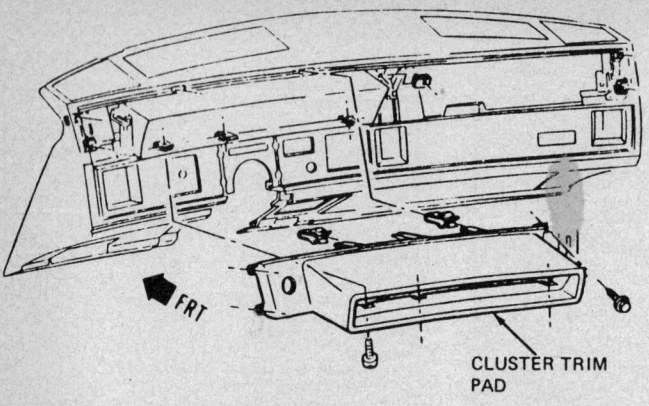

Fig. 6 Removing instrument cluster trim pad. Celebrity

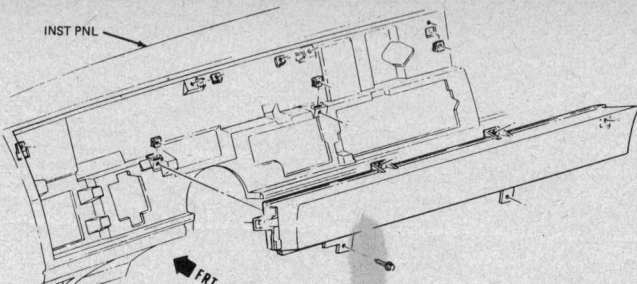

Fig. 7 Replacing instrument cluster. Celebrity

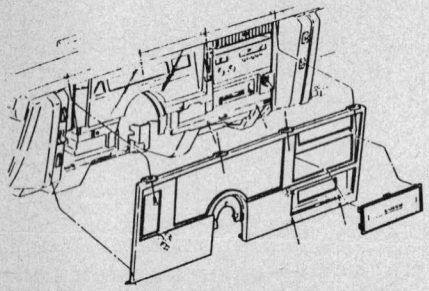

Fig. 8 Removing left trim plate. Century

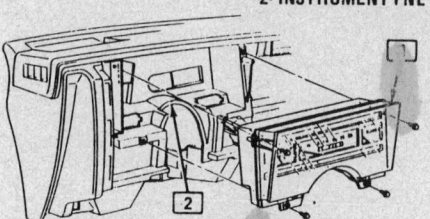

1- CLUSTER ASM
2- INSTRUMENT PNL

Fig. 9 Removing instrument cluster. Century

6000

1. Call up and record maintenance reminder mileage, if equipped w/driver information center (DIC).
2. Disconnect battery ground cable.
3. Remove center and lefthand lower instrument panel trim plates.
4. Remove cluster pad, **Fig. 13,** then air duct.
5. Remove cluster attaching screws, then pull cluster rearward, this will disengage two cluster connectors.
6. Disconnect DIC connector, located in a cable about one foot from cluster, if equipped.
7. Remove cluster from vehicle.
8. Reverse procedure to install.

RADIO
REPLACE
CELEBRITY

1. Disconnect battery ground cable, then remove sound insulator.
2. Remove steering column trim cover as follows:
   a. **On models less A/C,** remove vent control housing.
   b. **On all models,** remove trim cover attaching bolts, then lower cover.
   c. Disconnect trunk/tailgate release switch electrical connector, then remove trim cover.
3. Remove ashtray and ashtray retainer assembly attaching bolts, then ashtray retainer assembly.
4. Remove fuse block attaching bolts and electrical connectors, then fuse block.
5. Disconnect lighter and rear defogger switch electrical connectors, then remove lighter assembly.
6. Remove accessory trim plate attaching screws, pull trim plate to release clips.
7. Remove headlight and rear wiper/washer switch knobs, then accessory trim plate.
8. Remove radio attaching screws, then pull out radio.
9. Disconnect all electrical connectors from radio, then remove radio.
10. Reverse procedure to install.

CENTURY

1. Disconnect battery ground cable.
2. Remove steering column filler panel

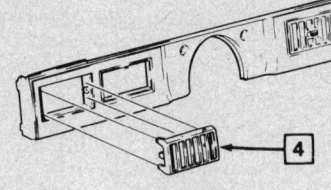

1. TRIM PLATE
2. I.P.
3. SPEAKER OPENING
4. DUCT

VIEW A

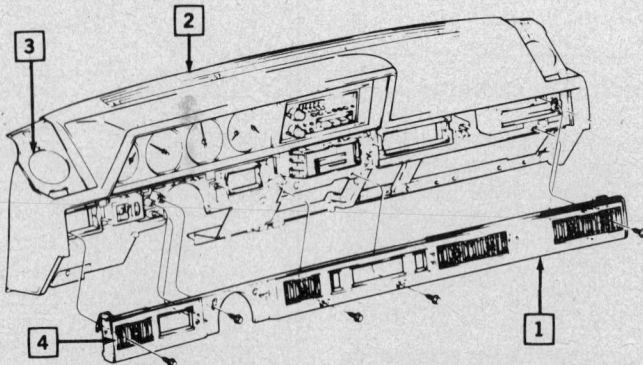

Fig. 10 Removing accessory trim plate. Cutlass Ciera & Cruiser

e. **On models with console,** remove four screws from ashtray trim cover, then ashtray trim cover. Remove trim plate attaching screws.
f. **On all models,** pull trim plate rearward to release clips, then remove accessory trim plate, **Fig. 10.**
3. Remove screws attaching cluster trim plate, then trim plate, **Fig. 11.**
4. Remove steering column trim collar and trim plate.
5. Disconnect shift indicator clip from steering column shift bowl.
6. Remove cluster assembly attaching bolts, **Fig. 12,** then pull cluster rearward.
7. Disconnect speedometer cable from cluster.
8. Remove cluster assembly.
9. Reverse procedure to install.

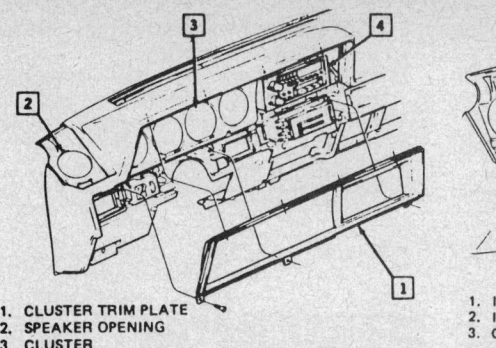

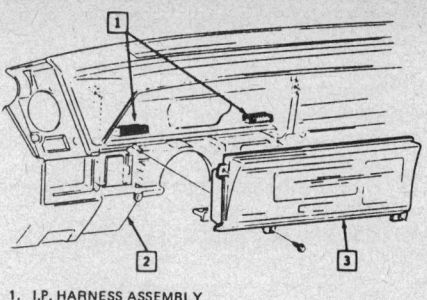

1. CLUSTER TRIM PLATE
2. SPEAKER OPENING
3. CLUSTER
4. RADIO

Fig. 11 Removing cluster tim plate. Cutlass Ciera & Cruiser

1. I.P. HARNESS ASSEMBLY
2. INSTRUMENT PANEL
3. CLUSTER ASSEMBLY

Fig. 12 Removing instrument cluster. Cutlass Ciera & Cruiser

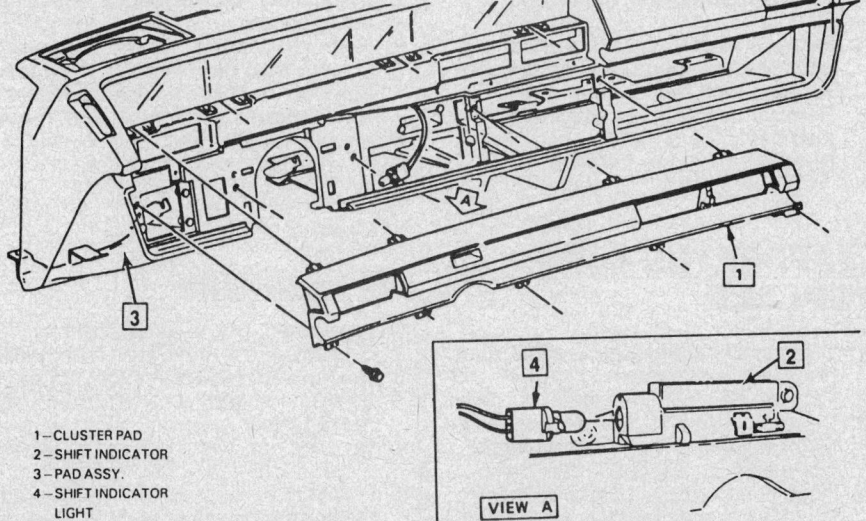

1—CLUSTER PAD
2—SHIFT INDICATOR
3—PAD ASSY.
4—SHIFT INDICATOR LIGHT

Fig. 13 Removing Cluster pad. 6000

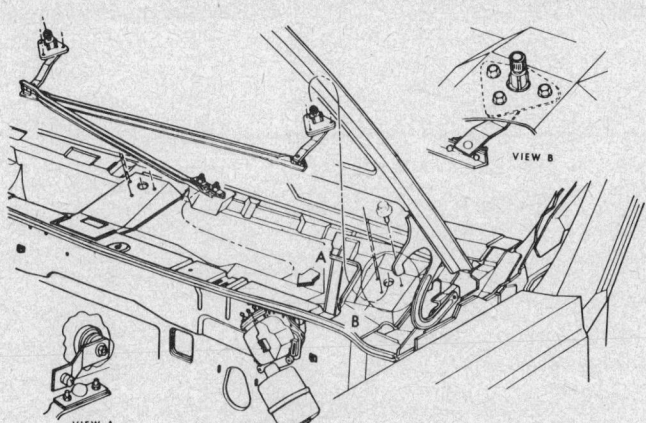

Fig. 14 Windshield wiper transmission removal

as follows:
  a. Remove ALDL connector attaching screws, then lower ALDL connector.
  b. Remove filler panel attaching screws, then lap vent hose.
  c. Remove filler panel by swinging down and pulling out.

3. Remove left trim plate as follows:
  a. Remove steering column opening filler attaching screws, then opening filler.
  b. Remove ashtray, then trim plate attaching screws, **Fig. 8.**
  c. Pull trim panel straight forward to release two retaining clips in cen-

ter of panel, then remove panel.
4. Remove right cluster trim plate attaching screws, then trim plate.
5. Remove radio assembly attaching screws, then pull out radio.
6. Disconnect all electrical connectors from radio, then remove radio.
7. Reverse procedure to install.

CUTLASS CIERA & CRUISER

1. Disconnect battery ground cable, then remove upper console, if equipped.
2. Remove accessory trim plate as follows:
  a. Pry steering column collar rearward, using a suitable tool, and remove.
  b. Remove outer air deflectors, then the two screws behind the deflector openings.
  c. Remove screw from behind steering column collar.
  d. **On models less console,** open ashtray and remove trim plate attaching screws.
  e. **On models with console,** remove four screws from ashtray trim cover, then ashtray trim cover. Remove trim plate attaching screws.
  f. **On all models,** pull trim plate rearward to release clips, then remove accessory trim plate, **Fig. 10.**
3. Remove screws attaching cluster trim plate, then trim plate, **Fig. 11.**
4. Remove radio attaching bolts, then pull out radio.
5. Disconnect all electrical connectors from radio, then remove radio.
6. Reverse procedure to install.

6000

1. Disconnect battery ground cable.
2. Remove right side instrument panel trim plate.
3. Remove four radio attaching screws, then disconnect electrical and antenna connections.
4. Remove radio from vehicle.
5. Reverse procedure to install.

WINDSHIELD WIPER MOTOR REPLACE

1. Raise hood, then remove right and left wiper arm and blade assemblies.
2. Remove shroud grille to body attaching screws, then shroud grille.
3. Loosen, but do not remove nuts securing transmission drive link to motor crank arm, then disconnect drive link.
4. Disconnect wiring connectors and washer hoses.
5. Remove 3 screws attaching wiper motor to firewall.
6. Remove motor while guiding crank arm through hole.
7. Reverse procedure to install. Motor must be in "Park" position before assembling transmission drive link to crank arm. **Torque** transmission drive link to 48-75 inch lbs.

REAR WIPER MOTOR
REPLACE

1. Remove wiper arm, then nut on transmission shaft.
2. Remove liftgate glass opening upper finishing molding, the disconnect electrical connector from motor.
3. Remove upper mounting screw (second screw is a dowell).
4. Rotate motor assembly to 12 o'clock position, guide motor pivot out of tailgate assembly.
5. Reverse procedure to install.

WINDSHIELD WIPER TRANSMISSION
REPLACE

1. Raise hood, then remove right and left wiper arm and blade assemblies.
2. Loosen, but do not remove nuts securing transmission drive link to motor crank arm.
3. Remove air inlet panel attaching screw, then panel.
4. Disconnect transmission drive link from motor crank arm, **Fig. 14.**
5. Remove wiper transmission to body attaching screw, **Fig. 14.**
6. Carefully guide transmission assembly through access hole in upper shroud panel to remove.
7. Reverse procedure to install. **Torque** transmission drive link nuts to 53-75 inch lbs.

HEATER CORE
REPLACE

LESS A/C

1. Drain cooling system.
2. Disconnect heater inlet and outlet hoses.
3. Remove lower instrument panel sound insulator, then radio noise suppression strap.
4. Remove cover retaining screws and cover.
5. Remove heater core strap, then heater core.
6. Reverse procedure to install.

WITH A/C

1. Drain cooling system.
2. Disconnect heater inlet and outlet hoses.
3. Remove lower instrument panel sound insulator, then heater floor outlet duct.
4. Remove heater core cover screws and clips securing cover to air valve housing, then heater core cover.
5. Remove heater core retaining straps, then heater core.
6. Reverse procedure to install.

EVAPORATOR CORE
REPLACE

1. Disconnect battery ground cable, then discharge A/C system.
2. Remove air cleaner assembly.
3. Disconnect A/C heater module electrical connectors, then harness straps. Move harness aside.
4. If equipped, remove heater hose routing bracket and resistor from cover, then vacuum tank.
5. Disconnect liquid line at evaporator inlet and low pressure line at evaporator outlet.
6. Dismount alternator and move away from module, if necessary.
7. Remove evaporator core cover retaining screws (loosen bottom screws only), then remove evaporator core cover.
8. Remove evaporator core.
9. Reverse procedure to install.

BLOWER MOTOR
REPLACE

EXCEPT 1991 CENTURY

1. Disconnect battery ground cable.
2. Disconnect blower motor electrical connections.
3. Remove blower motor attaching screws, then blower motor. **On models with A/C it may be necessary to dismount alternator and move away from module.**
4. Reverse procedure to install.

1991 CENTURY

1. Disconnect battery ground cable.
2. Remove wiper arms, then cowl panel.
3. Disconnect blower motor electrical connectors and vent tube, then remove blower motor attaching screws.
4. Remove fan retaining nut from blower motor shaft.
5. Holding fan securely, remove fan from blower motor while removing blower motor from vehicle. **Failure to hold fan securely can cause fan to fall into heater A/C module.**
6. Reverse procedure to install.

4-151/2.5L Engine
INDEX

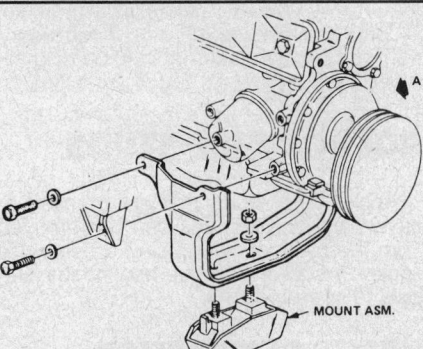

Fig. 1   Engine mounts. 1988

FUEL SYSTEM PRESSURE RELIEF

Whenever the fuel lines are to be disconnected for engine service on fuel injected engines, relieve fuel system pressure following the procedures outlined below. Failure to follow these procedures exactly, may result in personal injury.

1. Place transmission in Park or Neutral.
2. Disconnect fuel pump at rear body connector or remove fuel pump inline fuse located in the engine compartment, behind righthand headlights.
3. Start engine and allow to run until engine stalls.
4. After engine stalls, engage starter for approximately three seconds to relieve any residual pressure remaining in system.
5. Turn ignition switch off, then reconnect fuel pump connector or replace fuel pump inline fuse.

ENGINE MOUNTS
REPLACE

1. Raise and support front of vehicle,

then remove chassis to mount attaching nuts, **Figs. 1 and 2.**
2. Remove forward torque rod attaching bolts at radiator support panel.
3. Raise engine slightly using a suitable engine lifting device. Raise engine only enough to provide clearance for mount removal.
4. Remove two upper mount to engine support bracket attaching nuts and remove engine mount.
5. Reverse procedure to install.

ENGINE
REPLACE

1. Disconnect cables from battery, then drain cooling system.
2. Remove air cleaner assembly, then disconnect engine electrical harness connector.
3. Remove hood support, then prop hood up.
4. Disconnect all external vacuum hose connections, then remove radiator and heater hoses.
5. **On models equipped with A/C,** disconnect compressor and position aside. Do not disconnect refrigerant lines from compressor.
6. **On all models,** remove alternator and alternator bracket, then engine torque strut.
7. Remove throttle and transaxle linkages at the throttle body assembly and intake manifold.
8. Remove all transaxle-to-engine attaching bolts except the top two bolts.
9. Remove front engine mount-to-cradle nuts, then front exhaust pipe.
10. Remove flywheel inspection cover, then torque converter-to-flywheel attaching bolts.
11. Remove starter motor.
12. **On models equipped with power steering,** remove power steering pump and bracket and position aside.

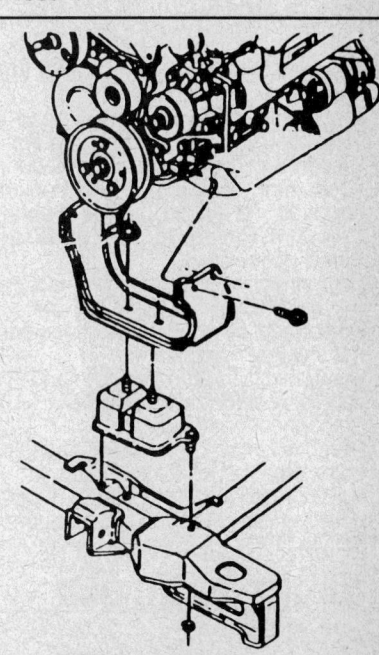

Fig. 2   Engine mounts. 1989–91

13. **On all models,** disconnect fuel feed line. Refer to "Fuel System Pressure Relief" for fuel pressure bleed procedure.
14. Remove 2 rear transaxle support bracket bolts.
15. Using a suitable jack and a block of wood placed under transaxle, raise engine and transaxle until engine front mount studs clear cradle bracket.
16. Attaching suitable lifting equipment to engine. Put tension on engine and remove 2 remaining transaxle to engine attaching bolts.
17. Slide engine assembly forward and lift from vehicle.
18. Reverse procedure to install.

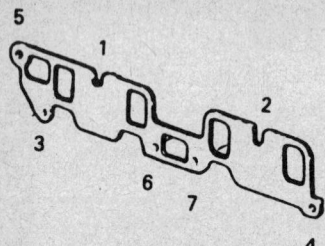

Fig. 3 Intake manifold tightening sequence

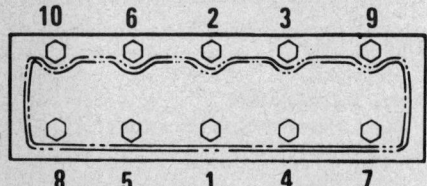

Fig. 5 Cylinder head tightening sequence

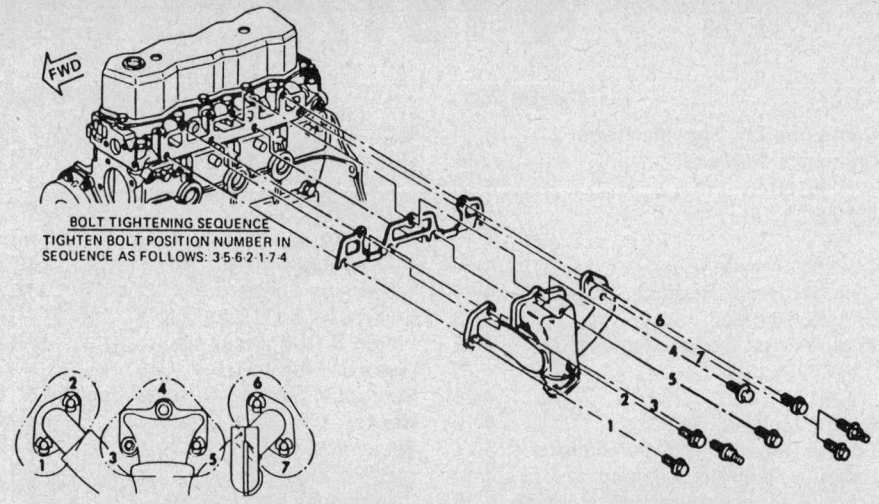

BOLT TIGHTENING SEQUENCE
TIGHTEN BOLT POSITION NUMBER IN
SEQUENCE AS FOLLOWS: 3-5-6-2-1-7-4

Fig. 4 Exhaust manifold tightening sequence

INTAKE MANIFOLD
REPLACE

1. Disconnect battery ground cable, then remove air cleaner.
2. Disconnect PCV valve and hose at TBI unit, then drain cooling system.
3. Disconnect fuel line and all vacuum hoses that will interfere with manifold removal. **Refer to "Fuel System Pressure Relief" for fuel pressure bleed procedure.**
4. Disconnect all electrical connections and throttle linkage from TBI unit.
5. Disconnect downshift and cruise control linkage, if applicable.
6. Disconnect throttle linkage and TV cables, position cables aside.
7. Disconnect heater hose.
8. Remove intake manifold attaching bolts, then the intake manifold.
9. Reverse procedure to install. Torque bolts to specification in sequence shown in **Fig. 3.**

EXHAUST MANIFOLD
REPLACE

1. Remove air cleaner, then torque rod strut.
2. Remove oxygen sensor connector, then dipstick tube.
3. Raise and support vehicle, then remove exhaust pipe from manifold.
4. Lower vehicle, then remove exhaust manifold attaching bolts and washers.
5. Remove exhaust manifold and gasket.
6. Reverse procedure to install, **torquing** exhaust manifold bolts 1,2,6 and 7 to 28 ft. lbs. and bolts 3,4 and 5 to 37 ft. lbs. in sequence shown in **Fig. 4.**

CYLINDER HEAD
REPLACE

1. Disconnect battery ground cable, then

drain cooling system.
2. Raise and support vehicle, then disconnect exhaust pipe from exhaust manifold.
3. Disconnect oxygen sensor connector, then lower vehicle.
4. Remove battery (auxiliary) ground cable, then oil dipstick tube and air cleaner.
5. Disconnect wire connectors, throttle linkage and fuel lines from TBI unit. **Refer to "Fuel System Pressure Relief" for fuel pressure bleed procedure.**
6. Disconnect heater hose from intake manifold, then all wiring connections from intake manifold and cylinder head.
7. Remove all vacuum lines that will interfere with manifold or cylinder head removal.
8. Remove engine torque strut rod bolts from upper support, then serpentine drive belt.
9. Remove alternator brackets and position alternator aside.
10. **On vehicles equipped w/top mounted A/C compressor,** remove compressor brackets and position compressor aside.
11. **On vehicles equipped w/top mounted power steering pump,** remove pump upper bracket.
12. **On all models,** remove radiator hoses, then rocker arm and push rod covers.
13. Remove rocker arms, push rods, then cylinder head attaching bolts.
14. Lift cylinder head with intake and exhaust manifolds as an assembly from cylinder block.
15. Reverse procedure to install. Coat heads and threads of cylinder bolts with a suitable sealing compound, then install bolts finger tight.
16. Tighten cylinder head bolts in sequence shown in **Fig. 5** as follows:
    a. **Torque** all bolts to 18 ft. lbs.
    b. **Torque** all bolts except No. 9 to 26 ft. lbs. **Torque** No. 9 bolt to 18 ft. lbs.

c. Repeat sequence again, turning all bolts an additional 90 degrees ($1/4$ turn).
17. Tighten intake manifold bolts in sequence shown in **Fig. 3,** if necessary.
18. Tighten exhaust manifold bolts in sequence shown in **Fig. 4,** if necessary.

ROCKER ARM STUDS

Rocker arm studs that are cracked or have damaged threads can be removed from the cylinder head using a deep well socket. Install and torque new rocker arm stud to specifications.

VALVE CLEARANCE
SPECIFICATIONS

4-151 engines are equipped with hydraulic lifters, no provision for adjustment is provided.

VALVE ARRANGEMENT
FRONT TO REAR

2.5L/4-151 . . . . I-E-I-E-E-I-E-I

CAM LOBE LIFT
SPECIFICATIONS

Engine	Year	Int.	Exh.
2.5L/4-151	1988–89	.232	.232
	1990–91	.248	.248

VALVE TIMING
INTAKE OPENS BEFORE TDC

Engine	Year	Degrees
2.5L/4-151	1988	33

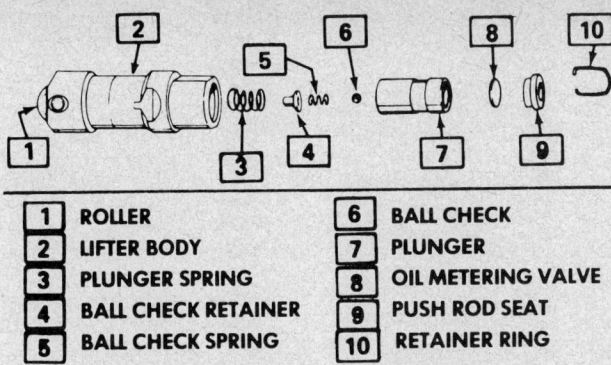

Fig. 6 Exploded view of roller type hydraulic lifter

1	ROLLER	6	BALL CHECK
2	LIFTER BODY	7	PLUNGER
3	PLUNGER SPRING	8	OIL METERING VALVE
4	BALL CHECK RETAINER	9	PUSH ROD SEAT
5	BALL CHECK SPRING	10	RETAINER RING

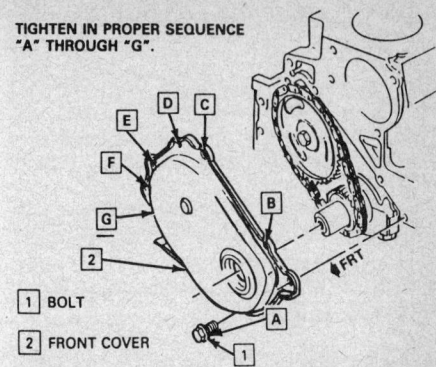

Fig. 7 Front cover tightening sequence. 1991 models

TIGHTEN IN PROPER SEQUENCE "A" THROUGH "G".

1 BOLT
2 FRONT COVER

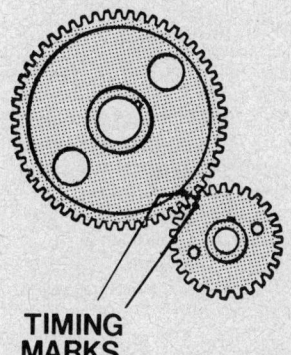

Fig. 8 Valve timing marks

TIMING MARKS

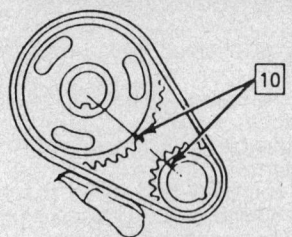

10 TIMING MARKS TO BE ALIGNED AS SHOWN WHEN ENGINE IS ROTATED TO T.D.C.

Fig. 9 Aligning timing marks. 1991 models

VALVE GUIDES

Valve guides are an integral part of the cylinder head and are not removable. If valve stem clearance becomes excessive, the valve guide should be reamed to the next oversize and the appropriate oversize valves installed. Valves are available in .003 and .005 inch oversizes.

VALVE LIFTERS

Failure of a hydraulic valve lifter, **Fig. 6**, is generally caused by an inadequate oil supply or dirt. An air leak at the intake side of the oil pump or too much oil in the engine will cause air bubbles in the oil supply to the lifters, causing them to collapse. This is a probable cause of trouble if several lifters fail to function, but air in oil is an unlikely cause of failure of a single unit.

Valve lifters can be removed after removing rocker arm cover, intake manifold, pushrod cover and pushrod retainer and guide, if applicable. Loosen rocker arm stud nut and rotate rocker arm so that pushrod can be removed, then remove valve lifter. It may be necessary to use lifter remover No. J-3049 or equivalent to facilitate lifter removal.

ENGINE FRONT COVER REPLACE

1988-90

1. Disconnect battery ground cable, then remove torque strut rod bolt from cylinder head bracket.
2. Remove serpentine drive belt, then raise and support vehicle.
3. Remove right side wheel assembly, then right fender splash shield.
4. Remove lower alternator bracket, then install engine support fixture No. J-28467 or equivalent.
5. Remove engine mount bracket to cylinder block attaching bolts, then mount and bracket as an assembly.
6. Remove flywheel cover, then install suitable tool to prevent flywheel from rotating.
7. Remove crankshaft harmonic balancer attaching bolt, then balancer and key.
8. Remove front cover attaching screws, then front cover.
9. Using flathead screwdriver, remove oil seal. Do not distort cover.
10. Reverse procedure to install, noting the following:
    a. Position centering tool No. J-34995 or equivalent, into cover, then install and partially tighten two opposing cover screws.
    b. Torque bolts to specifications.

1991

1. Disconnect battery ground cable, then remove serpentine drive belt tensioner and drive belt.
2. Raise and support vehicle, then remove right hand wheel assembly.
3. Remove right fender splash shield, then flywheel cover. Install suitable tool to prevent flywheel from rotating.
4. Remove crankshaft harmonic balancer attaching bolt, then balancer and key.
5. Remove front cover attaching screws, then front cover.
6. Using flathead screwdriver, remove oil seal. Do not distort cover.
7. Reverse procedure to install, noting the following:
    a. Position centering tool No. J-34995 or equivalent, into cover, then install and partially tighten two opposing cover screws.
    b. Torque bolts to specifications in sequence shown in **Fig. 7**.

TIMING GEARS

1988-90

When necessary to install a new camshaft gear, the camshaft will have to be removed as the gear is a pressed fit on the camshaft. The camshaft is held in place by a thrust plate which is retained to the engine by two capscrews which are accessible through the two holes in the gear web.

To remove gear, use an arbor press and a suitable sleeve to properly support gear on its steel hub.

Before installing gear, assemble thrust plate and gear spacer ring, then press gear onto shaft until it bottoms against spacer ring. The thrust plate end clearance should be .0015-.0050 inch. If clearance is less than .0015 inch, the spacer ring should be replaced. If clearance is greater than .0050 inch, the thrust plate should be replaced.

The crankshaft gear can be removed using a puller and two bolts in the tapped holes of the gear.

When installing timing gears, make sure that the marks on the gears are properly aligned, **Fig. 8**. The valve timing marks do not indicate TDC, compression stroke for No.1 cylinder.

TIMING CHAIN REPLACE

1991

1. Remove front cover as outlined under "Engine Front Cover, Replace."

2. Loosen but do not remove camshaft bolt.
3. Align timing marks on camshaft and crankshaft gears, then remove camshaft bolt.
4. Remove timing chain and sprocket.
5. Reverse procedure to install, noting the following:
   a. Align timing marks as shown in **Fig. 9**.

CAMSHAFT REPLACE

1988–89

1. Remove engine from vehicle as outlined under "Engine, Replace."
2. Remove rocker arm cover, then push rods.
3. Remove pushrod cover, then valve lifters.
4. Remove crankshaft harmonic balancer, then front cover.
5. Remove camshaft thrust plate retaining screws.
6. Pull camshaft and gear assembly from engine block. Use care not to damage camshaft bearings.
7. Reverse procedure to install. When installing camshaft, align crankshaft and camshaft valve timing marks on gear teeth, **Fig. 8**.

1990

With Engine In Vehicle

1. Disconnect battery ground cable, then drain cooling system.
2. Remove serpentine drive belt, then bolt securing drive belt idler pulley to tensioner.
3. Remove tensioner to engine attaching bolts, then position tensioner/power steering pump assembly aside.
4. Remove bolt from torque strut at engine bracket, then swing strut aside.
5. Remove both forward hood bumpers, then install engine support fixtures No. J-28467-A and J-36462.
6. Raise and support vehicle, then remove both front wheel assemblies.
7. Drain engine oil, then move steering column intermediate shaft cover aside.
8. Remove steering shaft to steering gear pinch bolt, then right front lower ball joint pinch bolt.
9. Remove right front ball joint from knuckle, then right front wheelhouse engine splash shield.
10. Remove flywheel cover, then crankshaft balancer retaining bolt. **Have an assistant hold flywheel from turning while removing bolt.**
11. Remove lower left front cover attaching bolt, then frame bolts and insulators.
12. Lower vehicle, then remove all remaining front cover attaching bolts.
13. Loosen upper sealing surface of front cover. **Do not distort cover.**
14. Lower frame/powertrain assembly with support fixtures. **Lower passenger side just enough to access camshaft gear area.**

15. Raise and support vehicle. then loosen lower sealing surface of front cover and remove front cover.
16. Align crankshaft to camshaft gear timing marks, then remove front brake line to frame bracket bolt. Move brake line aside.
17. Drive .32 inch (8 mm) hole .5 inch (12.7 mm) deep in center of camshaft end.
18. Tap .32 inch (8 mm) hole with 3/8-16-NC, bottoming tap. **Use proper tapping procedures.**
19. To prepare for drilling, center punch cam gear steel hub in two spots, 180 degrees apart on centerline of shaft.
20. Drill two .12 inch (3 mm) pilot holes .25 inch (6.4 mm) deep at center punched areas in cam gear steel hub.
21. Enlarge pilot holes by drilling with a .22 inch (5.5 mm) drill .25 inch (6.4 mm) deep.
22. Tap .22 inch (5.5 mm) holes with 1/4-28-NF, bottoming tap. **Use proper tapping procedures.**
23. Remove camshaft gear using gear remover No J-24420-B, then shaft key.
24. Remove thrust plate, than spacer ring.
25. Remove camshaft from vehicle.
26. Reverse procedure to install, noting the following:
   a. Ensure crankshaft and camshaft timing marks on gears are aligned, **Fig. 8.**
   b. Torque all bolts/nuts to specifications.

With Engine Removed From Vehicle

Refer to "1988-89" for camshaft replacement procedure.

1991

With Engine In Vehicle

1. Disconnect battery ground cable, then drain cooling system.
2. Remove air cleaner assembly, PCV hose, EGR valve, spark plug wires and clips.
3. Remove fuel line bracket and fuel lines. **Refer to "Fuel System Pressure Relief" for fuel pressure bleed procedure.**
4. Remove vacuum hoses including power brake booster hose.
5. Remove all wiring and throttle linkage from TBI assembly.
6. Remove transaxle downshift bracket, then heater hose from intake manifold.
7. Remove serpentine drive belt, then tensioner to engine attaching bolts. Position tensioner/power steering pump assembly aside.
8. Remove intake manifold, pushrod cover and valve lifters.
9. Disconnect electrical connections from DIS assembly, then remove DIS assembly.
10. Remove bolt from torque strut at engine bracket, then swing strut aside.
11. Install engine lift bracket, then engine support fixtures No. J-28467-A and J-36462.
12. Raise and support vehicle, then remove both front wheel assemblies.

13. Drain engine oil, then move steering column intermediate shaft cover aside.
14. Remove steering shaft to steering gear pinch bolt, then right front lower ball joint pinch bolt.
15. Remove right front ball joint from knuckle, then lower air deflector.
16. Remove right front wheelhouse engine splash shield.
17. Remove flywheel cover, then crankshaft balancer retaining bolt. **Have an assistant hold flywheel from turning while removing bolt.**
18. Remove crankshaft balancer, then front cover.
19. Remove frame bolts and insulators, then brake line to frame bracket and bolt.
20. Remove oil filter, then lower frame/powertrain assembly with support fixtures. **Lower passenger side just enough to access camshaft gear area.**
21. Align timing marks on camshaft and crankshaft sprockets, then remove camshaft sprocket bolt.
22. Remove timing chain and sprockets, then camshaft thrust plate.
23. Remove camshaft. Use care not to damage camshaft bearings.
24. Reverse procedure to install, noting the following:
   a. Ensure crankshaft and camshaft timing marks on gears are aligned, **Fig. 9.**
   b. Torque all bolts/nuts to specifications.

With Engine Removed From Vehicle

1. Remove engine from vehicle as outlined under "Engine, Replace."
2. Remove rocker arm cover, then push rods.
3. Remove pushrod cover, then valve lifters.
4. Remove crankshaft harmonic balancer, then front cover.
5. Remove camshaft sprocket bolt, then timing chain and sprockets.
6. Remove camshaft thrust plate, then pull camshaft from engine block. Use care not to damage camshaft bearings.
7. Reverse procedure to install, noting the following:
   a. Ensure crankshaft and camshaft timing marks on gears are aligned, **Fig. 9.**
   b. Torque all bolts/nuts to specifications.

FORCE BALANCER ASSEMBLY REPLACE

1. Remove oil pan as outlined further on.
2. Remove balancer assembly to crankcase attaching bolts, then balancer assembly.
3. To install, proceed as follows:
   a. Position No. 1 and No. 4 cylinders at TDC (crank counterweights at BDC).

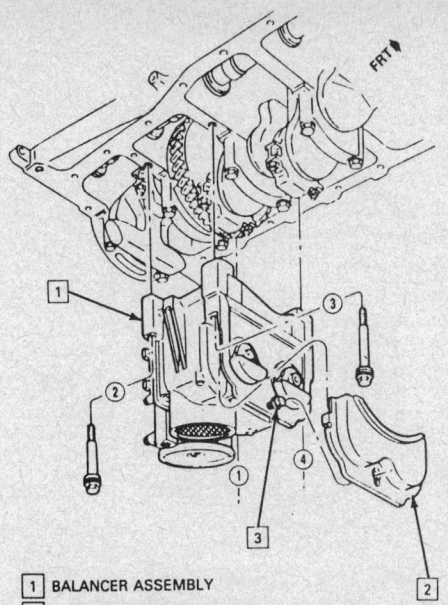

1. BALANCER ASSEMBLY
2. BAFFLE
3. 10 N·m (90 LB. IN.)
* CIRCLED NUMBERS SHOW BOLT POSITION
  (SEE TEXT FOR TIGHTENING SEQUENCE)

Fig. 10 Force balancer tightening sequence

When installing balancer, the end of the housing without dowel pins must remain in contact with block surface. If it loses contact, gear engagement may be lost and permanent damage to either the crank or balancer gears may result.

b. Install balancer onto crankshaft with balance weights at BDC (plus or minus one half gear tooth).
c. Install balancer attaching bolts. **Torque** bolts to 9 ft. lbs. in sequence shown in **Fig. 10.**
d. Following sequence shown in **Fig. 10,** tighten short bolts to 11 ft. lbs. plus 75° and long bolts to 11 ft. lbs. plus 90°.
e. Rotate crankshaft four times and check for clearance between the fourth counterweight and balancer weights.
f. Reinstall oil pan.

PISTON & ROD ASSEMBLE

Assemble piston to rod with mark on piston and rod both facing toward front of engine. Rod may not be marked.

PISTONS, PINS & RINGS

Install rings on pistons as shown in **Fig. 11.**
Pistons, pins and rings are available in standard and oversizes.

MAIN & ROD BEARINGS

Main and rod bearings are available in standard size and undersizes.

OIL PAN
REPLACE

1988

1. Disconnect battery cables, then remove serpentine drive belt.
2. Raise and support vehicle, then drain crankcase.
3. Remove engine front mount to cradle attaching nuts, then disconnect exhaust pipe at manifold and front of converter.
4. Remove A/C compressor, if equipped, and position aside
5. Remove starter motor and flywheel housing cover, then splash shield, if applicable.
6. Remove power steering pump and bracket, then lower vehicle.
7. Support engine with support fixture No. J28467, then remove torque strut.
8. Raise and support vehicle, then remove engine front support bracket.
9. Remove oil pan attaching bolts and oil pan.
10. Clean engine block and oil pan gasket surfaces.
11. Reverse procedure to install, noting the following:
    a. Apply RTV sealant as shown in **Fig. 12.**
    b. Torque all bolts/nuts to specifications.

1989–91

1. Disconnect battery ground cable, then remove coolant reservoir bottle.
2. Remove engine torque strut, then air cleaner assembly.
3. Remove air inlet, then serpentine drive belt.
4. Remove A/C compressor from brackets and set aside, then engine oil level indicator.
5. Support engine using support fixture No. J-28467-A, then raise and support vehicle.
6. Drain engine oil, then remove starter and support bracket. Position starter aside.
7. Remove flywheel covers, then turn front wheels to full right position.
8. Remove engine wiring harness retainer screws under both sides of oil pan.
9. Remove right side engine splash shield, then front engine mount bracket bolts/nuts.
10. Remove transaxle mount nuts.
11. Using support fixture installed in step 5, raise engine approximately two inches, then remove front engine mount and bracket.
12. Loosen frame bolts, then remove oil pan attaching bolts.
13. Remove oil pan.
14. Reverse procedure to install, noting the following:
    a. Apply RTV sealant as shown in **Fig. 12.**
    b. Torque all bolts/nuts to specifications.

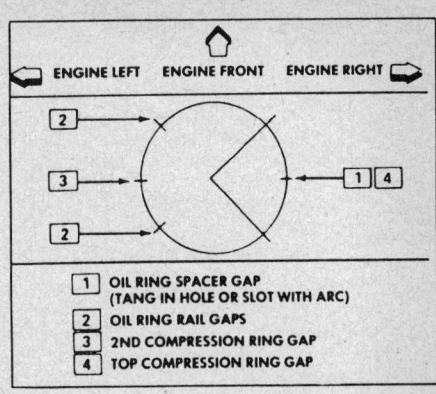

1. OIL RING SPACER GAP (TANG IN HOLE OR SLOT WITH ARC)
2. OIL RING RAIL GAPS
3. 2ND COMPRESSION RING GAP
4. TOP COMPRESSION RING GAP

Fig. 11 Locating pin ring gaps

OIL PUMP SERVICE

REMOVAL & DISASSEMBLY

The oil pump can be serviced without removing the balancer assembly.
1. Remove oil pan as outlined under "Oil Pan, Replace."
2. Remove restrictor, oil filter, oil pump cover assembly and gears, then the pressure regulator plug or pin, spring and valve. **Use caution when removing plug or pin, since spring pressure can cause personal injury.**

CLEANING & INSPECTION

1. Clean all parts in solvent and dry with compressed air.
2. Inspect pump housing, cover assembly, regulator valve and spring and screen assembly for excessive wear or damage.
3. Inspect depth of wear pattern in gear housing pocket and face of oil pump cover assembly, then the gear thickness. Gear pocket depth should be .514-.516 inch, while gear thickness should be .511-.512 inch.

ASSEMBLY & INSTALLATION

1. Lubricate all internal parts with engine oil.
2. Pack all pump cavities with petroleum jelly, then install gears.
3. Install oil pump cover assembly, then the pressure regulator valve, spring and pin or plug. Torque pump cover attaching bolts to specifications.
4. Clean intake screen, then install oil filter and restrictor.

REAR MAIN BEARING OIL SEAL
REPLACE

The rear main oil seal is a one piece unit and is replaced without removing the oil pan or crankshaft.
1. Remove transaxle and flywheel.

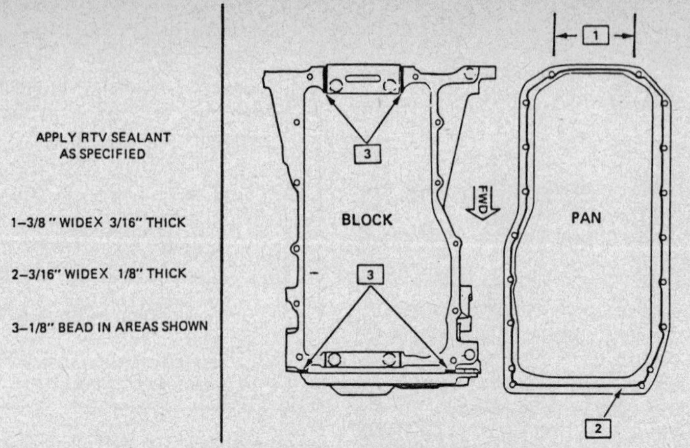

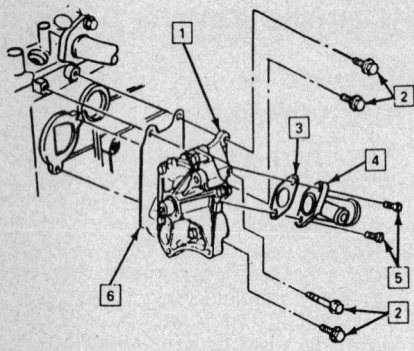

APPLY RTV SEALANT AS SPECIFIED

1—3/8 " WIDE X 3/16 " THICK

2—3/16 " WIDE X 1/8 " THICK

3—1/8 " BEAD IN AREAS SHOWN

Fig. 12 Oil pan sealer application

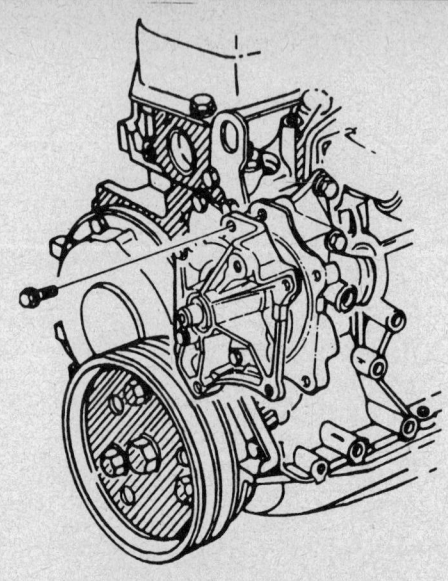

Fig. 13 Removing water pump. 1988 models

SERVICE BULLETIN: On 1988 Cutlass Ciera models, engines may develop a fuel pump noise condition which may be objectionable. To correct this condition, replace original style fuel pump with a turbine style fuel pump. Obtain fuel pump assembly (part No. 25116156).

1	COOLANT PUMP
2	BOLT/SCREW
3	GASKET, COOLANT PUMP INLET
4	INLET, COOLANT PUMP
5	BOLT/SCREW
6	GASKET, COOLANT PUMP

Fig. 14 Removing water pump. 1989–91 models

2. **On models equipped w/manual transaxle,** remove pressure plate and disc.
3. Using a suitable screwdriver, remove rear main bearing oil seal. Use care not to scratch crankshaft.
4. Lubricate inside and outside diameters of replacement seal with engine oil. Install seal using seal installer No. J34924-A onto rear crankshaft flange with helical lip side facing toward engine. Ensure seal is firmly and evenly seated.
5. Install flywheel and transaxle.

FUEL PUMP
REPLACE

1. Relieve fuel pressure as outlined under "Fuel System Pressure Relief," then disconnect battery ground cable.
2. Remove fuel tank.
3. Remove fuel pump assembly by turning cam lock ring counterclockwise. Lift assembly from fuel tank and remove fuel pump from fuel tank sending unit.
4. Reverse procedure to install.

WATER PUMP
REPLACE

1988
Removal

1. Disconnect battery negative cable, then drain cooling system.
2. Remove serpentine drive belt.
3. Using puller No. J-25034, remove pulley.
4. Remove water pump attaching bolts and remove pump, **Fig. 13.**

Installation

1. With sealing surfaces cleaned, place a 1/8 inch bead of sealant, part number 1052289 or equivalent, on water pump sealing surface.
2. With sealing surfaces still wet, install pump and attaching bolts. Coat threaded area of bolts with part number 1052080 sealer or equivalent and torque bolts to specifications.
3. Using pulley installer No. J-25033 or equivalent, install pulley on pump.
4. Install serpentine drive belt and adjust to specifications.
5. Connect battery negative cable.

1989–91

1. Disconnect battery ground cable, then drain cooling system.
2. Remove alternator, then disconnect radiator and heater hoses from inlet.
3. Remove water pump attaching bolts **Fig. 14,** then water pump and pulley assembly.
4. Separate pulley and water pump.
5. Reverse procedure to install, torquing all bolts/nuts to specifications.

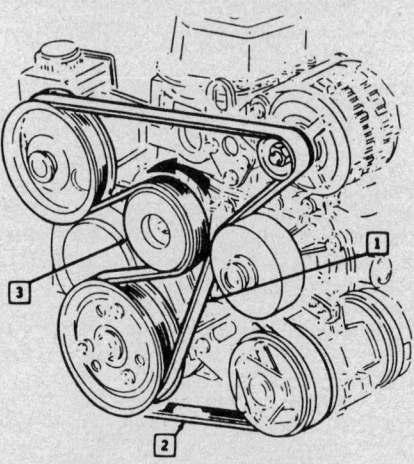

1. ROUTING WITHOUT AIR CONDITIONING
2. ROUTING WITH AIR CONDITIONING
3. TENSIONER – ROTATE DRIVE BELT TENSIONER IN DIRECTION OF ARROW TO INSTALL OR REMOVE DRIVE BELT.

Fig. 15 Serpentine drive belt routing

COOLING SYSTEM BLEED

This engine does not require a specified bleed procedure. After filling cooling system, run engine to operating temperature with radiator/pressure cap off. Air will then be automatically bled through cap opening.

SERPENTINE DRIVE BELT

BELT ROUTING

Refer to **Fig. 15,** for routing of serpentine drive belt.

TENSIONER INSPECTION

1. Run engine, with no accessories on, until normal operating temperature is

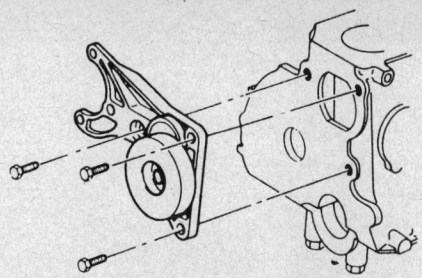

Fig. 16   Removing drive belt tensioner

reached. Shut engine off and read belt tension using belt tension gauge J-23600-B or equivalent. Place gauge halfway between alternator and power steering pump.

2. Start engine, with accessories off, and allow system to stabilize for 15 seconds. Turn engine off. Using a 15 mm socket, apply clockwise force to tensioner pulley bolt. Release force and immediately take a tension reading without disturbing belt tensioner position.

3. Using 15 mm socket, apply counterclockwise force to tensioner pulley bolt, raise pulley to eliminate all tension. Slowly lower pulley to belt and take a tension reading without disturbing belt tensioner position.

4. Average three readings. If average is not between 50-70 lbs. and belt is within tensioner's operating range, replace belt tensioner.

TENSIONER, REPLACE

Refer to "Service Bulletins" for possible tensioner noise condition.
1. Partially drain cooling system, then remove serpentine drive belt.

2. Remove power steering pump bolt from tensioner. Position pump aside.
3. Remove tensioner attaching bolts, then tensioner, Fig. 16.
4. Reverse procedure to install, torquing all bolts/nuts specifications.

SERVICE BULLETINS
INCREASED OIL CONSUMPTION
1988 2.5L/4-151 VIN Code R

Increased oil consumption may be regarded as 200 miles to one quart of oil, or less. If this condition is met, it is recommended the intake valve stem seals be inspected first.

Suspect seals can be identified by a cut-out section on the top portion of the seal Fig. 17. Intake valve stem seals must be replaced with part number 10042875.

FORCE BALANCER REPLACEMENT WHEN CAM GEAR TEETH ARE DAMAGED
1988 2.5L/4-151 VIN R

If one or more of the force balancer cam gear teeth have been damaged or broken off, the force balancer assembly must be replaced. It is not necessary for replacement if gear shows normal wear.

The three components which comprise the force balancer are; the oil pump cover assembly, part number 10038405, force balancer housing assembly, part number 10101422 and oil pump GE rotor, part number 10038402.

It is recommended that all three parts be replaced when a cam gear has failed due to broken or sheered teeth.

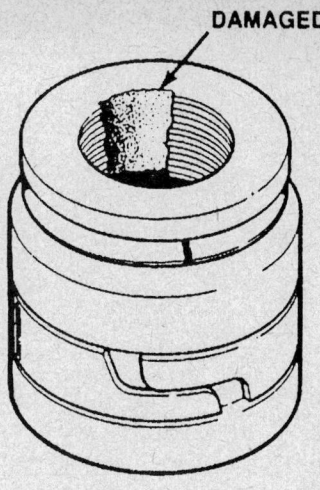

DAMAGED AREA

Fig. 17   Oil seal inspection

VIBRATION, RUMBLE AND/OR SQUEALING SOUND AT OR ABOVE IDLE
1988–89 2.5L/4-151 VIN R

If any of the above stated conditions exist, it may be caused by insufficient drive belt tension and is generally limited to models equipped with A/C.

To correct this condition, obtain improved tensioner assembly (part No. 10101362 for models less A/C) or (part No. 10101898 for models with A/C) and install as outlined under ""Tensioner, Replace."

TIGHTENING SPECIFICATIONS

Year	Component	Torque/Ft. Lbs.
1988–90	Belt Tensioner Bolt	37
	Camshaft Thrust Plate Bolt	7.5
	Connecting Rod Nuts	⑤
	Cylinder Head Bolts	①
	EGR Valve To Manifold Bolt	16
	Engine Bracket To Engine Bolt	40
	Engine Lift Brackets	37
	Engine Mount To Bracket Nut	⑦
	Engine Mount To Frame Nut	⑦
	Engine Torque Strut Bolt/Nut	41
	Engine Torque Strut Bracket Bolt	17
	Exhaust Manifold Bolt	①
	Flywheel To Crankshaft Bolt (Automatic)	55
	Flywheel To Crankshaft Bolt (Manual)	69
	Force Balancer to Block Bolts	①
	Front Cover Bolt	7.5
	Harmonic Balancer Bolt	162
	Intake Manifold Bolt	25③
	Main Bearing To Block Bolt	④
	Oil Filter Access Plug	②

Continued

TIGHTENING SPECIFICATIONS —Continued

Year	Component	Torque/Ft. Lbs.
1988–90	Oil Indicator Fill Tube Nut	17
	Oil Pan Bolt	7.5
	Oil Pan Drain Plug	25
	Oil Pump Cover Bolt	7.5
	Pushrod Cover Nut	7.5
	Rocker Arm Bolt	⑨
	Rocker Arm Cover Bolt	⑧
	Stud Roller Lifter Guide Retainer To Block	7.5
	Thermostat Housing Bolt	20
	Throttle Body Injection Assembly	⑥
	Transaxle Mount To Bracket Nut	33
	Transaxle Mount To Frame Nut	33
	Water Outlet Housing Bolt	20
	Water Pump To Block	25

①—Refer to text.
②—Finger tight, then an additional ¼ turn.
③—Refer to text for tightening sequence.
④—1988–89 70 ft. lbs.; 1990–91 65 ft. lbs.
⑤—1988–89 32 ft. lbs.; 1990–91 29 ft. lbs.
⑥—1988–89 15 ft. lbs.; 1990–91 18 ft. lbs.
⑦—1988–89 33 ft. lbs.; 1990–91 35 ft. lbs.
⑧—1988–89 3.7 ft. lbs.; 1990–91 6.6 ft. lbs.
⑨—1988–89 24 ft. lbs.; 1990–91 20 ft. lbs.

V6-173/2.8L & V6-189/3.1L Engines

INDEX

FUEL SYSTEM PRESSURE RELIEF

Whenever the fuel lines are to be disconnected for engine service on fuel injected engines, relieve fuel system pressure following the procedures outlined below. Failure to follow these procedures exactly, may result in personal injury.

1. Disconnect battery ground cable, then loosen filler cap to relieve tank vapor pressure.
2. Connect fuel pressure gauge No. J-34730-1 or equivalent to fuel pressure valve. Wrap a shop towel around fitting while connecting gauge to avoid spillage.
3. Install bleed hose into an approved container and open valve to bleed system pressure. Fuel connections are now safe for servicing.
4. Drain any fuel remaining in gauge into approved container.

ENGINE MOUNTS
REPLACE
1988

1. Remove mount retaining nuts from below cradle mounting bracket.

2. Raise engine and remove mount to engine attaching nuts, then remove mount, **Fig. 1.** Raise engine only enough to provide clearance for mount removal.
3. Reverse procedure to install, then lower engine into position. Install retaining nuts and torque to specifications. After engine mount is properly installed, check both transaxle mounts for proper alignment. If window "A" is not properly located, **Fig. 2,** loosen mount to frame retaining nuts and allow mount to reposition itself. If transaxle mount is allowed to remain

Fig. 1 Engine mounts

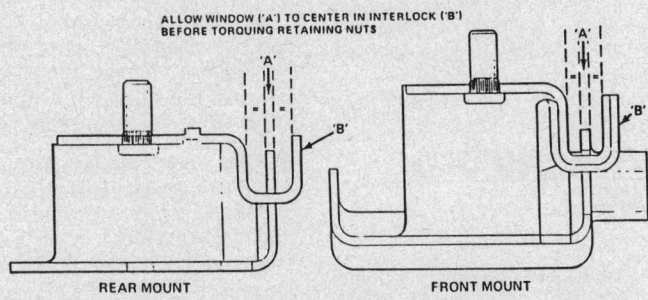

ALLOW WINDOW ('A') TO CENTER IN INTERLOCK ('B') BEFORE TORQUING RETAINING NUTS

REAR MOUNT   FRONT MOUNT

Fig. 2 Transaxle mount alignment. 1988 models

out of position, damage to drive train components may result. Torque retaining nuts to specifications.

1989–91

1. Disconnect battery ground cable, then remove mount retaining nuts from below frame mounting bracket.
2. Remove transaxle mount nuts, then install suitable engine support fixture.
3. Raise engine only enough to provide clearance for mount removal.
4. Remove mount to engine bracket nuts, then mount **Fig. 1**.
5. Reverse procedure to install, torquing bolts/nuts to specifications.

ENGINE
REPLACE

1. Disconnect battery cables, then drain cooling system.
2. Remove air cleaner assembly, including air flow duct from throttle body, then all necessary wiring.
3. Remove hood, then disconnect throttle, T.V. and cruise control cables.
4. Remove fuel lines. Refer to "Fuel System Pressure Relief" for fuel pressure bleed procedure.
5. Remove crossover pipe from manifolds, then serpentine drive belt.
6. Remove radiator and heater hoses from engine, then A/C bolts at front bracket.

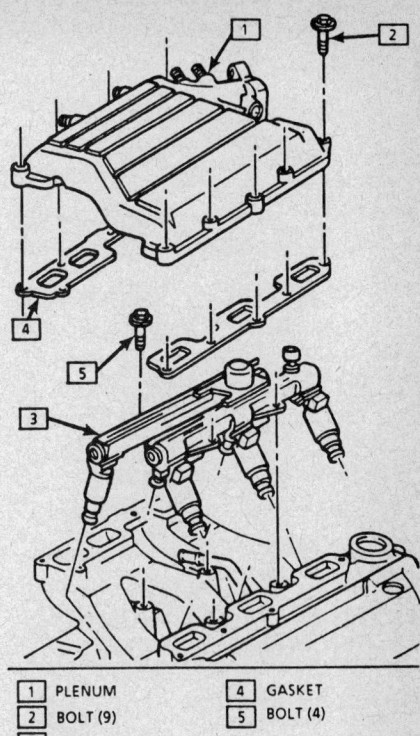

1	PLENUM	4	GASKET
2	BOLT (9)	5	BOLT (4)
3	FUEL RAIL ASM		

Fig. 3 Removing plenum and fuel rail

7. Remove power steering pump and position aside, then remove alternator, if necessary.
8. Remove brake booster vacuum supply line, then EGR at exhaust, if equipped.
9. Raise and support vehicle, then remove A/C compressor bolts at rear bracket. Position compressor aside.
10. Remove A.I.R. pump, if equipped, then flywheel cover.
11. Remove starter, then torque converter bolts.
12. Remove transaxle bracket. then exhaust pipe from manifold.
13. Remove engine front mount retaining nuts, then lower vehicle.
14. Remove engine torque strut(s), then bulkhead connector.
15. Support transaxle, then remove transaxle attaching bolts.
16. Attach suitable lifting device to engine, then remove engine from vehicle.
17. Reverse procedure to install, torquing all bolts/nuts to specifications.

INTAKE MANIFOLD
REPLACE

1. Remove air cleaner assembly, including air flow duct from throttle body, then disconnect battery ground cable.
2. Remove all cables at throttle body, then disconnect brake vacuum pipe at plenum.
3. Remove cable bracket at plenum, then all necessary vacuum lines.
4. Remove EGR valve, throttle body and ignition wire plastic shield bolts from plenum.

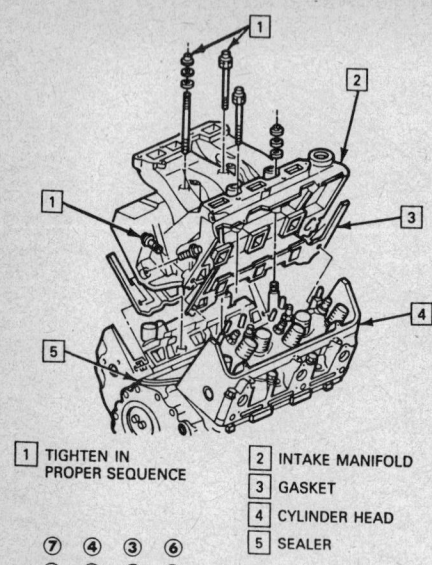

1 TIGHTEN IN PROPER SEQUENCE	2 INTAKE MANIFOLD
	3 GASKET
	4 CYLINDER HEAD
	5 SEALER

⑦ ④ ③ ⑥
⑧ ① ② ⑤

Fig. 4 Intake manifold tightening sequence

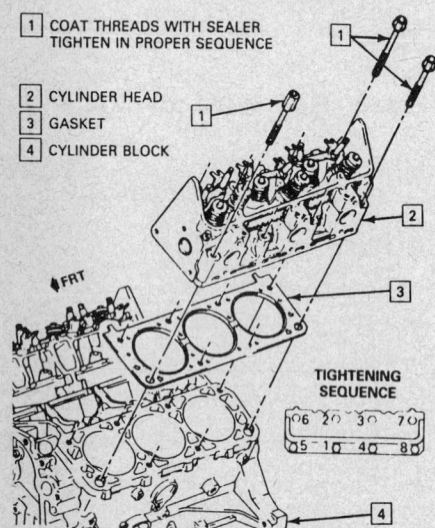

1 COAT THREADS WITH SEALER TIGHTEN IN PROPER SEQUENCE	
2 CYLINDER HEAD	
3 GASKET	
4 CYLINDER BLOCK	

◄FRT

TIGHTENING SEQUENCE

⑥ ② ③ ⑦
⑤ ① ④ ⑧

Fig. 6 Cylinder head tightening sequence

5. Remove plenum attaching bolts, then plenum, **Fig. 3.**
6. Remove fuel lines at fuel rail. Refer to "Fuel System Pressure Relief" for fuel pressure bleed procedure.
7. Remove serpentine drive belt, then alternator. Position alternator aside.
8. Remove power steering lines at alternator bracket, then power steering pump mounting bolts. Position pump aside.
9. Remove wiring from fuel injectors, then drain cooling system.
10. Remove bypass hose at water pump and cylinder head.
11. Remove PCV hose, then front valve cover.
12. Remove alternator brace and bracket, then rear valve cover.
13. Remove upper radiator hose, then all necessary wiring.

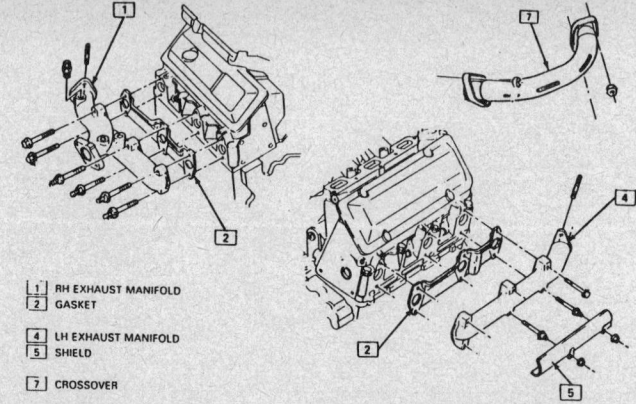

1 RH EXHAUST MANIFOLD	
2 GASKET	
4 LH EXHAUST MANIFOLD	
5 SHIELD	
7 CROSSOVER	

Fig. 5 Removing exhaust manifolds

14. Remove coolant sensor, then fuel lines at bracket.
15. Remove throttle body heater hose, then heater pipe at intake.
16. Remove intake manifold attaching bolts, then intake manifold. **Retain Belleville washers in same orientation on four center bolts.**
17. Loosen rocker arms, then remove pushrods. **Intake and exhaust pushrods are different lengths with exhaust pushrods being longer of the two.**
18. Reverse procedure to install, noting the following:
    a. Place 3 mm bead of suitable RTV sealer on each ridge where front and rear of intake manifold contacts the block.
    b. **Torque** intake manifold attaching bolts to 15 ft. lbs. in sequence shown in **Fig. 4**, then retighten to 24 ft. lbs. in sequence shown in **Fig. 4.**
    c. Torque all bolts/nuts to specifications.

EXHAUST MANIFOLD
REPLACE
LEFT

1. Remove battery ground cable, then air cleaner assembly.
2. Remove coolant recovery bottle, then serpentine drive belt.
3. Remove A/C compressor. Position compressor aside.
4. Remove right side torque strut, then strut mounting bracket.
5. Remove heat shield, then crossover pipe at manifolds.
6. Remove exhaust manifold attaching bolts, then manifold, **Fig. 5.**
7. Reverse procedure to install, torquing all bolts/nuts to specifications.

RIGHT

1. Remove battery ground cable, then air cleaner assembly.
2. Raise and support vehicle, then remove exhaust pipe from manifold.
3. Lower vehicle, then remove breather and mass air flow sensor.
4. Remove heat shield, then crossover at manifold.
5. Remove throttle and T.V. cables from

throttle body, then throttle and T.V. cable bracket at plenum.
6. Remove oxygen sensor, then exhaust manifold attaching bolts.
7. Remove exhaust manifold, **Fig. 5.**
8. Reverse procedure to install, torquing all bolts/nuts to specifications.

CYLINDER HEAD
REPLACE
LEFT

1. Remove intake manifold as outlined under "Intake Manifold, Replace."
2. Remove left exhaust manifold as outlined under "Exhaust Manifold, Replace."
3. Remove oil level indicator, then plug wires from left cylinder head.
4. Loosen rocker arms, then remove pushrods. **Intake and exhaust pushrods are different lengths with exhaust pushrods being longer of the two.**
5. Remove cylinder head attaching bolts, then cylinder head, **Fig. 6.**
6. Reverse procedure to install, noting the following:
    a. Coat cylinder head bolt threads with a suitable sealing compound.
    b. **Torque** cylinder head attaching bolts to 33 ft. lbs. in sequence shown in **Fig. 6.**
    c. Turn bolts and additional ¼ turn in sequence shown in **Fig. 6.**
    d. Torque all bolts/nuts to specifications.

RIGHT

1. Remove intake manifold as outlined under "Intake Manifold, Replace."
2. Remove right exhaust manifold as outlined under "Exhaust Manifold, Replace."
3. Remove plug wires from right cylinder head.
4. Loosen rocker arms, then remove pushrods. **Intake and exhaust pushrods are different lengths with exhaust pushrods being longer of the two.**
5. Remove cylinder head attaching bolts, then cylinder head, **Fig. 6.**

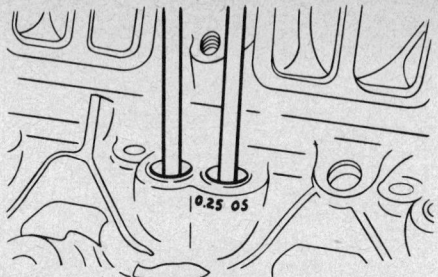

Fig. 7 Oversize valve lifter marking

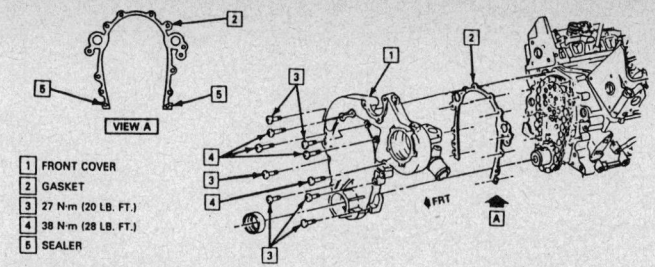

1	FRONT COVER
2	GASKET
3	27 N·m (20 LB. FT.)
4	38 N·m (28 LB. FT.)
5	SEALER

Fig. 8 Removing front cover assembly

6. Reverse procedure to install, noting the following:
   a. Coat cylinder head bolt threads with a suitable sealing compound.
   b. **Torque** cylinder head attaching bolts to 33 ft. lbs. in sequence shown in **Fig. 6.**
   c. Turn bolts and additional ¼ turn in sequence shown in **Fig. 6.**
   d. Torque all bolts/nuts to specifications.

ROCKER ARM STUDS

Rocker arm studs that are cracked or have damaged threads can be replaced. If threads in cylinder head are damaged or stripped, the head can be retapped and a helical type insert added. When installing a new rocker arm stud, torque stud to specifications.

VALVES
ADJUST

1. Crank engine until mark on torsional damper is aligned with TDC mark on timing tab. Check to ensure engine is in the No. 1 cylinder firing position by placing fingers on No. 1 cylinder rocker arms as mark on damper comes near TDC mark on timing tab. If valves are not moving, the engine is in the No. 1 firing position. If valves move as damper mark nears TDC mark on timing tab, engine is in the No. 4 cylinder firing position and should be rotated one revolution to reach the No. 1 cylinder firing position.
2. With engine in the No. 1 cylinder firing position, adjust the following valves: Exhaust-1, 2,3; Intake-1, 5, 6. To adjust valves, back off adjusting nut until lash is felt at push rod, then tighten adjusting nut until all lash is removed. This can be determined by rotating the push rod while tightening the adjusting nut. When all lash has been eliminated, turn adjusting nut an additional 1 ½ turns.
3. Crank engine one revolution until mark on torsional damper and TDC mark are again aligned. This is the No. 4 cylinder firing position. With engine in this position, the following valves can be adjusted: Exhaust-4, 5 & 6; Intake-2, 3 & 4.

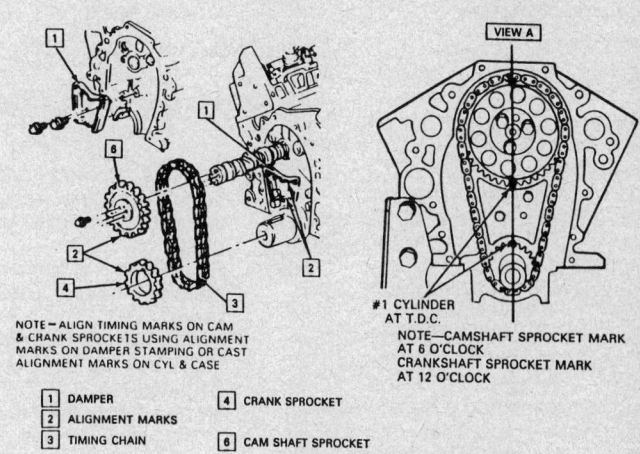

NOTE – ALIGN TIMING MARKS ON CAM & CRANK SPROCKETS USING ALIGNMENT MARKS ON DAMPER STAMPING OR CAST ALIGNMENT MARKS ON CYL & CASE

#1 CYLINDER AT T.D.C.

NOTE—CAMSHAFT SPROCKET MARK AT 6 O'CLOCK
CRANKSHAFT SPROCKET MARK AT 12 O'CLOCK

1	DAMPER	4	CRANK SPROCKET
2	ALIGNMENT MARKS	5	
3	TIMING CHAIN	6	CAM SHAFT SPROCKET

Fig. 9 Replacing timing chain

4. Install rocker arm covers, then start engine and check timing and idle speed.

VALVE ARRANGEMENT
FRONT TO REAR

Left . . . . E-I-I-E-I-E
Right . . . . E-I-E-I-I-E

CAM LOBE LIFT SPECIFICATIONS

Engine	Year	Int.	Exh.
2.8L/V6-173	1988–89	.262	.273

VALVE TIMING
INTAKE OPENS BEFORE TDC

Engine	Year	Degrees
2.8L/V6-173	1988	31

VALVE GUIDES

Valve guides are an integral part of the cylinder head and are not removable. If valve stem clearance becomes excessive, the valve guide should be reamed to the next oversize and the appropriate oversize valves installed. Valves are available in oversizes of .003, .015 and .030 inch.

VALVE LIFTERS

Some engines will be equipped with both standard and .010 inch oversize valve lifters. The cylinder case will be marked where the oversize valve lifters are installed with a dab of white paint and .25 mm. O.S. will be stamped on the valve lifter boss, **Fig. 7.**

Failure of a hydraulic valve lifter is generally caused by an inadequate oil supply or dirt. An air leak at the intake side of the oil pump or too much oil in the engine will cause air bubbles in the oil supply to the lifters, causing them to collapse. This is a probable cause of trouble if several lifters fail to function, but air in oil is an unlikely cause of failure of a single unit.

Valve lifters can be removed after removing rocker arm covers, intake manifold, rocker stud nuts, rocker arm balls, rocker arms and pushrods.

ENGINE FRONT COVER
REPLACE

1. Disconnect battery ground cable, then drain cooling system.
2. Remove serpentine drive belt, then drive belt tensioner.
3. Remove alternator and power steering pump. Position pump aside.
4. Raise and support vehicle, then remove inner splash shield.
5. Remove flywheel cover at transaxle, then starter.
6. Remove harmonic balancer as follows:

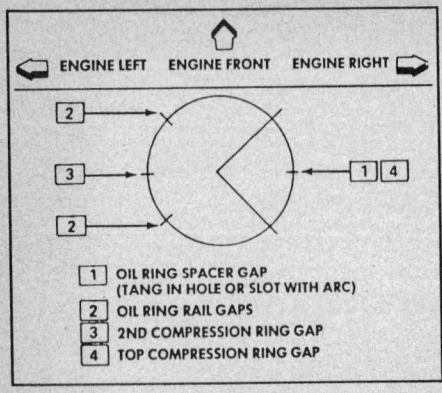

Fig. 10   Locating pin ring gaps

a. Remove balancer retaining bolt. Have an assistant keep flywheel from turning.
b. Using harmonic balancer puller No. J-24420-B, remove balancer.
7. Remove serpentine belt idler pulley, then lower oil pan.
8. Remove lower cover bolts, then lower vehicle.
9. Remove radiator hose at water pump, then heater hose at cooling system fill pipe.
10. Remove bypass and overflow hoses, then canister purge hose.
11. Remove upper cover bolts, then front cover, **Fig. 8**.
12. Reverse procedure to install, torquing all bolts/nuts to specifications.

TIMING CHAIN
REPLACE

1. Remove front cover as outlined under "Engine Front Cover, Replace."
2. Place No. 1 piston at top dead center with marks on camshaft and crankshaft sprockets aligned, **Fig. 9**.
3. Remove camshaft sprocket bolts, then remove sprocket and timing chain. If sprocket does not come off easily, tap lower edge of sprocket with a plastic mallet.
4. If crankshaft sprocket is to be replaced, remove sprocket using a suitable puller. Install new sprocket, aligning key and keyway.
5. Install timing chain on camshaft sprocket. Hold sprocket vertically with chain hanging down and align marks on camshaft and crankshaft sprockets.
6. Align dowel pin hole in sprocket with dowel pin on camshaft, then install sprocket on camshaft.
7. Using camshaft sprocket attaching bolts, draw sprocket on camshaft. Torque bolts to specifications.
8. Lubricate timing chain with engine oil, then install front cover as outlined previously.

CAMSHAFT
REPLACE

1. Remove engine from vehicle as described under "Engine, Replace."

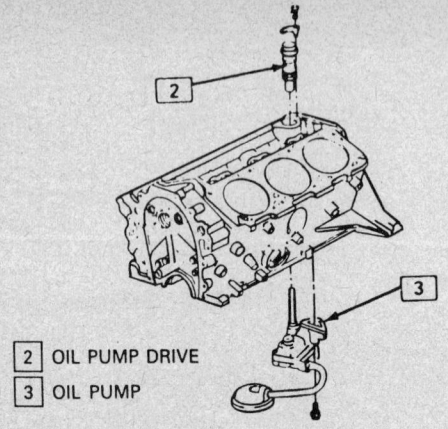

2 OIL PUMP DRIVE

3 OIL PUMP

Fig. 11   Remove oil pump

2. Remove pushrods and valve lifters.
3. Remove engine front cover as outlined under "Engine Front Cover, Replace."
4. Remove timing chain and sprocket as outlined under "Timing Chain, Replace."
5. Withdraw camshaft from engine, using care not to damage camshaft bearings.
6. Reverse procedure to install. When installing timing chain, align valve timing marks as shown in **Fig. 9**.

PISTON & ROD
ASSEMBLE

Assemble piston to rod with mark on piston and rod both facing toward front of engine. Rod may not be marked.

PISTONS, PINS & RINGS

Install rings on pistons as shown in **Fig. 10**.

Pistons, pins and rings are available in standard and oversizes.

MAIN & ROD BEARINGS

Main and rod bearings are available in standard size and undersizes.

OIL PAN
REPLACE
1988

1. Disconnect battery ground cable.
2. Remove serpentine belt and tensioner.
3. Raise and support vehicle.
4. Drain engine oil from crankcase.
5. Remove flywheel housing shield or clutch housing cover as applicable.
6. Remove starter motor and air bracket, as required.
7. Attach suitable lifting equipment to engine. Remove engine mount bracket-to-engine attaching bolts and raise engine slightly.
8. Remove oil pan attaching bolts and the oil pan.

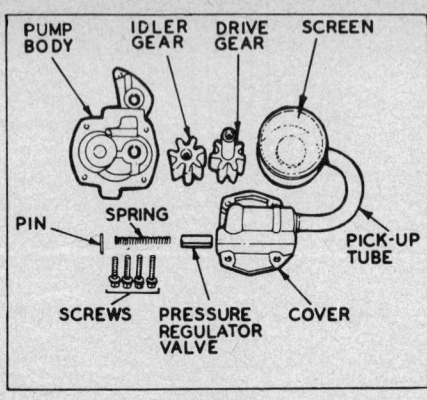

Fig. 12   Oil pump exploded view

9. Reverse procedure to install. Apply a 1/8 inch bead of RTV sealer to oil pan sealing flange.

1989–91

1. Remove battery ground cable, then serpentine drive belt and tensioner.
2. Support vehicle using support fixtures No. J-28467-A and J-36462 or equivalent.
3. Raise and support vehicle, then drain engine oil from crankcase.
4. Remove right side wheel assembly, then right side splash shield.
5. Remove steering gear pinch bolt. **Failure to disconnect intermediate shaft from rack and pinion stub shaft can result in damage to steering gear and/or intermediate shaft.**
6. Remove transaxle mount retaining nut, then engine to frame mount nuts.
7. Remove front engine mount bracket from block, then outboard flywheel/starter plastic shield.
8. Remove inboard flywheel metal shield, then start.
9. Place jack stand under frame front center crossmember, then loosen rear frame bolts. **Do not remove rear frame bolts.**
10. Remove front frame bolts, then lower front of frame.
11. Disconnect DIS sensor wire, then remove oil pan retaining bolts.
12. Remove oil pan retaining nuts, then oil pan.
13. Reverse procedure to install, torquing all bolts/nuts to specifications.

OIL PUMP SERVICE
REMOVAL

1. Remove oil pan as described under "Oil Pan, Replace."
2. Remove pump to rear main bearing cap bolt and remove pump and extension shaft, **Fig. 11**.

DISASSEMBLY

1. Remove pump cover attaching bolts and pump cover, **Fig. 12**.
2. Mark drive and idler gear teeth so they can be installed in the same position, then remove idler and drive gear and shaft from pump body.

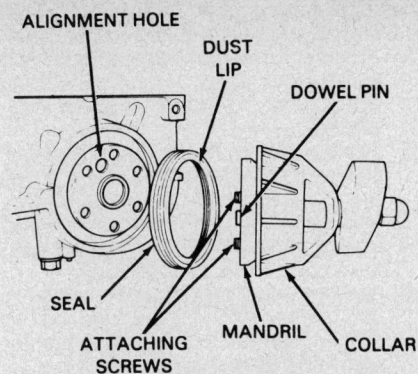

Fig. 13 Installing rear main bearing oil seal

3. Remove pin, spring and pressure regulator valve from pump cover.
4. If pickup tube and screen assembly are to be replaced, mount pump cover in a soft jawed vise and remove pickup tube from cover. Do not remove screen from pickup tube, these components are serviced as an assembly.

INSPECTION

1. Inspect pump body and cover for excessive wear and cracks.
2. Inspect pump gear for damage or excessive wear. If pump gears are damaged or worn, the entire pump assembly must be replaced.
3. Check drive gear shaft for looseness in pump body.
4. Inspect pump cover for wear that would allow oil to leak past gear teeth.
5. Inspect pickup tube and screen assembly for damage.
6. Check pressure regulator valve for fit in pump cover.

ASSEMBLY

1. If pickup tube and screen were removed, apply sealer to end of pickup tube, then mount pump cover in a soft jawed vise and using mounting tool No. J-8369 or equivalent, tap pickup tube into position using a plastic mallet. **Whenever the pickup tube and screen assembly has been removed, a new pickup tube and screen assembly should be installed. Use care when installing pickup tube and screen assembly so that tube does not twist, shear or collapse. Loss of a press fit condition could result in an air leak and a loss of oil pressure.**
2. Install pressure regulator valve, spring and pin, **Fig. 12.**
3. Install drive gear and shaft in pump body.
4. Align marks made during disassembly, then install idler gear.
5. Install pump cover gasket, cover and attaching bolts. Torque bolts to specifications. Rotate pump drive shaft by hand and check pump for smooth operation.

INSTALLATION

1. Assemble pump and extension shaft

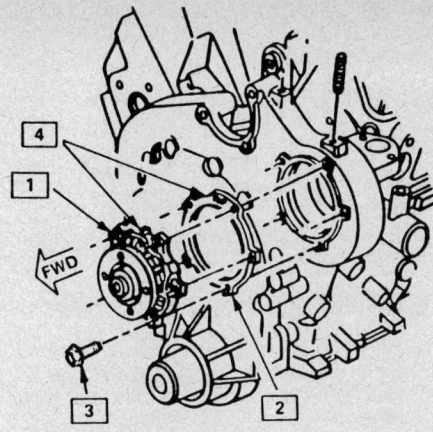

1—WATER PUMP
2—GASKET
3—BOLTS
4—LOCATOR - MUST BE VERTICAL

Fig. 14 Replacing water pump assembly

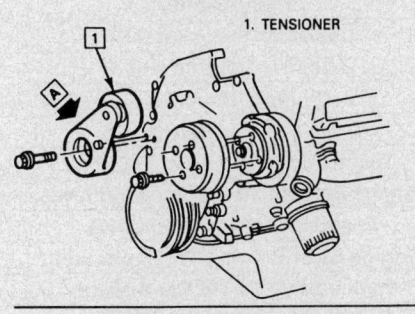

1. TENSIONER

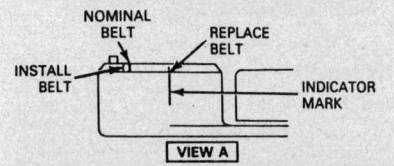

NOMINAL BELT
REPLACE BELT
INSTALL BELT
INDICATOR MARK

VIEW A

THE INDICATOR MARK ON THE MOVEABLE PORTION OF THE TENSIONER MUST BE WITHIN THE LIMITS OF THE SLOTTED AREA ON THE STATIONARY PORTION OF THE TENSIONER. ANY READING OUTSIDE THESE LIMITS INDICATES EITHER A DEFECTIVE BELT OR TENSIONER.

Fig. 16 Replacing belt tensioner.

with retainer to rear main bearing cap, aligning extension shaft with drive gear.
2. Install pump to rear main bearing cap bolt.
3. Install oil pan as described under "Oil Pan, Replace."

REAR MAIN BEARING OIL SEAL
REPLACE

1. Remove transaxle and flywheel.
2. Using a screwdriver, pry out old seal. Use care to avoid damaging crankshaft. File all burrs or nicks as required.
3. Install new seal using seal installer No. J34686 or equivalent, as follows:

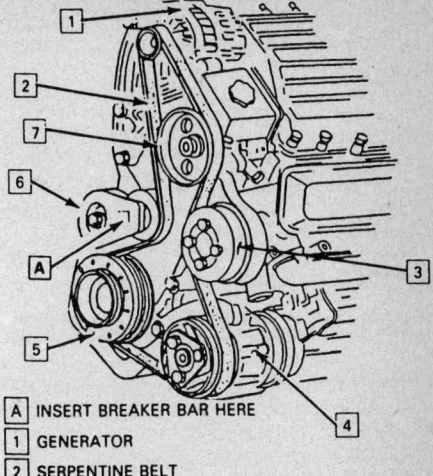

A	INSERT BREAKER BAR HERE
1	GENERATOR
2	SERPENTINE BELT
3	WATER PUMP
4	AIR CONDITIONING COMPRESSOR
5	CRANKSHAFT
6	BELT TENSIONER
7	POWER STEERING PUMP

Fig. 15 Serpentine drive belt routing

a. Apply a light coat of engine oil to I.D. and O.D. of oil seal.
b. Slide seal over tool mandrel until dust lip bottoms squarely against collar of tool.
c. Align dowel pin of tool with dowel pin hole in crankshaft, **Fig. 13**, then attach tool to crankshaft with screw provided.
d. Turn handle of tool until seal is pushed into bore and collar is positioned firmly against case. Remove tool.
4. Install flywheel and transmission, then start engine and check for leaks.

FUEL PUMP
REPLACE

1. Relieve fuel pressure as outlined under "Fuel System Pressure Relief," then disconnect battery ground cable.
2. Remove fuel tank.
3. Remove fuel pump assembly by turning cam lock ring counterclockwise. Lift assembly from fuel tank and remove fuel pump from fuel tank sending unit.
4. Reverse procedure to install.

SERVICE BULLETIN: On 1988 Cutlass Ciera models, engines may develop a fuel pump noise condition which may be objectionable. To correct this condition, replace original style fuel pump with a turbine style fuel pump. Obtain fuel pump assembly (part No. 25116156).

WATER PUMP
REPLACE

1. Disconnect battery ground cable, then drain cooling system.

2. **On 3.1L/V6-189 engine,** remove vacuum line from top of coolant pump.
3. **On all models,** remove serpentine drive belt, then water pump pulley.
4. Remove water pump attaching bolts, then water pump **Fig. 14.**
5. Reverse procedure to install, noting the following:
   a. **On 2.8L/V6-173 engine,** coat bolt thread with sealant No. 1052080 or equivalent.
   b. **On all models,** torque all bolts/nuts to specifications.

COOLING SYSTEM BLEED

These engines do not require a specified bleed procedure. After filling cooling system, run engine to operating temperature with radiator/pressure cap off. Air will then be automatically bled through cap opening.

On 3.1L/V6-189 engine, open air bleed vent on bypass pipe three turns when draining system. The 3.1L/V6-189 engine has two engine drain plug.

SERPENTINE DRIVE BELT

BELT ROUTING

Refer to **Fig. 15,** for routing of serpentine drive belt.

TENSIONER INSPECTION

1. Run engine, with no accessories on, until normal operating temperature is reached. Turn engine off and read belt tension using belt tension gauge J-23600-B or equivalent. Place gauge halfway between alternator and power steering pump.
2. Start engine, with accessories off, and allow system to stabilize for 15 seconds. Turn engine off. Using a 15 mm socket, apply clockwise force to tensioner pulley bolt. Release force and immediately take a tension reading without disturbing belt tensioner position.
3. Using a 15 mm socket, apply counterclockwise force to tensioner pulley bolt, raise pulley to eliminate all tension. Slowly lower pulley to belt and take a tension reading without disturbing belt tensioner position.
4. Average three readings. If average is not between 50-70 lbs. and belt is within tensioner's operating range, replace belt tensioner.

TENSIONER, REPLACE

1. Remove serpentine drive belt.
2. Remove tensioner attaching bolts, then tensioner, **Fig. 16.**
3. Reverse procedure to install, torquing all bolts/nuts specifications.

TIGHTENING SPECIFICATIONS

Year	Component	Torque/ft. lbs.
1988–90	Camshaft Sprocket Bolt	21
	Connecting Rod Nut	39
	Cylinder Head Bolt	②
	Drive Belt Tensioner Bolt	④
	Engine Bracket To Engine Bolt	81
	Engine Bracket To Engine Mount Nut	34
	Engine Mount To Frame Nut	34
	Engine Strut Bracket To Engine Bolt	17
	Engine Strut To Tie Bar Bracket	41
	Engine Strut To Upper Tie Bar	17
	Exhaust Crossover Nut	18
	Exhaust Manifold Heat Shield Nut	89①
	Exhaust Manifold To Cylinder Head Bolt	18
	Flywheel Bolt	52
	Front Cover Bolt	③
	Intake Manifold Bolt	②
	Main Bearing Cap Bolt	73
	Oil Filter	11
	Oil Filter Adaptor Connector	50
	Oil Level Indicator Retaining Nut	18
	Oil Pan Bolt	89①
	Oil Pan Nut	89①
	Oil Pan Rear Bolts (2)	18
	Oil Pan Stud To Cylinder Block	89①
	Oil Pump Drive Bolt	25
	Oil Pump Mounting Bolt	30
	Oxygen Sensor	31
	Rocker Arm Cover Bolt	89①
	Rocker Arm Nut	18
	Spark Plug	10-25
	Thermostat Housing	15-23
	Timing Chain Dampener Bolt	15
	Torsional Dampener (Harmonic Balancer)	76
	Water Pump	89①

①—Inch lbs.
②—Refer to text.
③—Refer to Fig. 8.
④—1988–90 40 ft. lbs.; 1991 37 ft. lbs.

3.3L/V6-204 & 3.8L/V6-231 Engines

INDEX

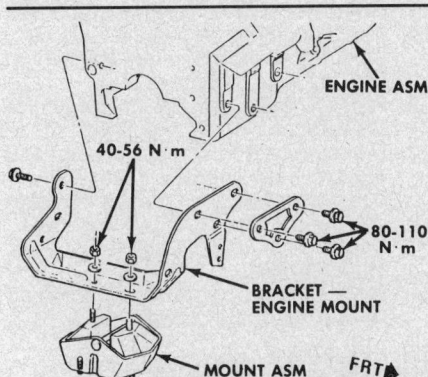

Fig. 1 Removing engine mount. 3.8L/V6-231 engine

FUEL SYSTEM PRESSURE RELIEF

Whenever the fuel lines are to be disconnected for engine service on fuel injected engines, relieve fuel system pressure following the procedures outlined below. Failure to follow these procedures exactly, may result in personal injury.

3.3L/V6-204

1. Disconnect battery ground cable, then loosen filler cap to relieve tank vapor pressure.
2. Connect fuel pressure gauge No. J-34730-1 or equivalent to fuel pressure valve. Wrap a shop towel around fitting while connecting gauge to avoid spillage.
3. Install bleed hose into an approved container and open valve to bleed system pressure. Fuel connections are now safe for servicing.
4. Drain any fuel remaining in gauge into approved container.

3.8L/V6-231

1. Disconnect fuel tank harness connector.
2. Start engine and allow to run until engine stalls.
3. After engine stalls, engage starter for approximately three seconds to relieve any residual pressure remaining in system.
4. With ignition off, reconnect fuel tank harness connector.

ENGINE MOUNTS
REPLACE

1. Attach suitable engine lifting fixture to engine.
2. Raise and support front of vehicle.
3. Remove mount to engine mount bracket nuts. Raise engine slightly and remove mount to frame nuts. Remove mount, **Figs. 1 and 2**.
4. Reverse procedure to install, torquing all bolts/nuts to specifications.

ENGINE
REPLACE

1. Remove hood, then disconnect battery ground cable.
2. Drain cooling system, then remove radiator and heater hoses.
3. Remove upper engine torque strut, then engine cooling fan.
4. Remove air intake duct from throttle body, then vacuum hosing to all non-engine mounted components.
5. Remove fuel lines. Refer to "Fuel System Pressure Relief" for fuel pressure bleed procedure.
6. Remove all cables from throttle body, then cable bracket.
7. Remove serpentine drive belt, then disconnect all necessary electrical connections.

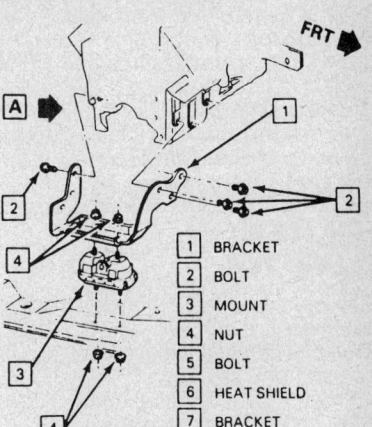

1	BRACKET
2	BOLT
3	MOUNT
4	NUT
5	BOLT
6	HEAT SHIELD
7	BRACKET

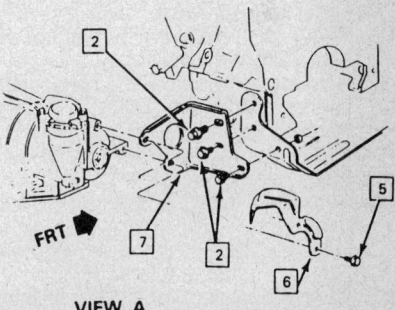

VIEW A

Fig. 2 Removing engine mount. 3.3L/V6-204 engine

8. **On 3.8L/V6-231 engine,** remove alternator and power steering lines at steering gear.
9. **On 3.3L/V6-204 engine,** remove power steering pump from mounting bracket. Position pump aside.
10. **On all models,** remove upper transaxle to engine bolts, then raise and support vehicle.
11. Remove A/C compressor. Position

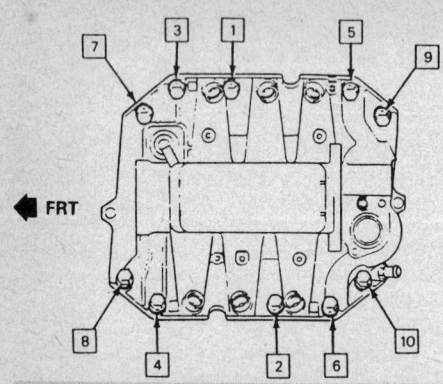

Fig. 3 Intake manifold tightening sequence. 3.3L/V6-204 engine

compressor aside.
12. Remove engine mount to frame nuts, then exhaust pipe from exhaust manifold.
13. Remove flywheel dust cover, then flywheel to converter bolts. Mark torque converter and flywheel to assure proper assembly.
14. Remove lower engine to transaxle bolts. **One bolt is located between transaxle case and engine block and is installed in the opposite direction.**
15. Lower car, then install engine lift fixture.
16. Remove engine.
17. Reverse procedure to install, torquing all bolts/nuts to specifications.

INTAKE MANIFOLD
REPLACE
3.3L/V6-204

1. Disconnect battery ground cable, then drain cooling system.
2. Remove serpentine drive belt, then alternator and bracket.
3. Remove power steering pump braces, then coolant bypass hose.
4. Remove air inlet duct, heater pipe and upper radiator hose.
5. Remove throttle cable bracket and cables from throttle body.
6. Remove vacuum lines and wiring connectors as necessary.
7. Remove fuel lines. Refer to "Fuel System Pressure Relief" for fuel pressure bleed procedure.
8. Remove heater hose from throttle body.
9. Remove intake manifold attaching bolts, then intake manifold.
10. Reverse procedure to install, noting the following:
    a. Apply suitable sealer to ends of manifold seals.
    b. Apply thread lock compound No. 12345493 or equivalent, to intake manifold bolt threads before assembly.
    c. **Torque** intake manifold bolts **twice** to 89 inch lbs., in sequence shown in **Fig. 3.**

3.8L/V6-231

1. Remove battery ground cable, mass air flow sensor and air intake duct.

2. Remove serpentine drive belt, then alternator and bracket.
3. Remove C3 ignition module and wiring.
4. Remove vacuum lines and wiring connectors as necessary.
5. Remove throttle, cruise control and T.V. cables from throttle body, then drain cooling system.
6. Remove heater hoses from throttle body, then upper radiator hose.
7. Remove fuel lines. Refer to "Fuel System Pressure Relief" for fuel pressure bleed procedure.
8. Remove intake manifold attaching bolts, then intake manifold.
9. Reverse procedure to install, noting the following:
    a. Apply suitable sealer to ends of manifold seals.
    b. Apply sealant No. 1052080 or equivalent, to all pipe thread fittings.
    c. **Torque** intake manifold bolts to 32 ft. lbs., in sequence shown in **Fig. 4.**

EXHAUST MANIFOLD
REPLACE
3.3L/V6-204
Left

1. Disconnect battery ground cable, then remove air cleaner inlet duct.
2. Remove spark plug wires, then exhaust crossover pipe to manifold attaching bolts.
3. Remove engine lift hook, then manifold heat shield.
4. Remove oil level indicator tube, then manifold studs.
5. Remove exhaust manifold.
6. Reverse procedure to install, torquing all studs/nuts to specifications.

Right

1. Disconnect battery ground cable, then remove spark plug wires.
2. Disconnect oxygen sensor lead, then remove throttle cable bracket and cables from throttle body.
3. Remove brake booster hose from manifold, then exhaust crossover pipe to manifold attaching bolts.
4. Remove exhaust pipe from manifold, then engine lift hook.
5. Remove transaxle oil level indicator tube, then manifold heat shield.
6. Remove manifold studs, then exhaust manifold.
7. Reverse procedure to install, torquing all studs/nuts to specifications.

3.8L/V6-231
Left

1. Remove upper engine torque strut, then exhaust crossover pipe to manifold attaching bolts.
2. Remove manifold attaching bolts, then manifold.
3. Reverse procedure to install, torquing all bolts to specifications.

Right

1. Disconnect battery ground cable.

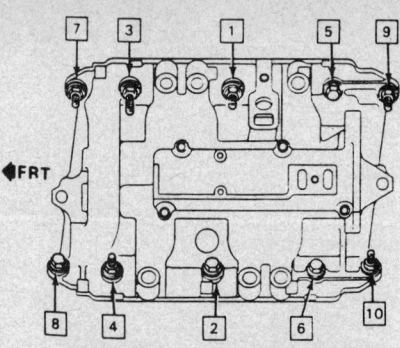

Fig. 4 Intake manifold tightening sequence. 3.8L/V6-231 engine

2. Remove pinch bolt at intermediate shaft, then separate intermediate shaft from rack and pinion stub shaft.
3. Raise and support vehicle, then remove exhaust pipe from manifold.
4. Lower vehicle, then remove upper engine torque strut.
5. Place jack under front crossmember of cradle and raise jack until vehicle starts to rise.
6. Remove two front body mount bolts.
7. With cushions removed, thread body mount bolts and retainers a minimum of three turns into cage nuts.
8. Release jack slowly. Do not lower cradle without it being restrained.
9. Remove power steering pump and bracket from cylinder head and exhaust manifold, then disconnect oxygen sensor wire.
10. Remove manifold attaching bolts, then manifold.
11. Reverse procedure to install, torquing all bolts to specifications.

CYLINDER HEAD
REPLACE
3.3L/V6-204

1. Remove intake manifold as outlined under "Intake Manifold, Replace."
2. Remove exhaust manifolds as outlined under "Exhaust Manifold, Replace."
3. Remove valve covers.
4. **For left cylinder head removal,** remove alternator bracket with ignition module and coils attached.
5. Remove A/C compressor bracket bolt, then power steering pump. Position pump aside.
6. **For right cylinder head removal,** remove serpentine drive belt, then tensioner assembly.
7. **For either cylinder head removal,** remove spark plug wires, rocker arm assemblies, guide plate and pushrods.
8. Remove cylinder head attaching bolts, then cylinder head.
9. Reverse procedure to install, noting the following:
    a. Apply sealant No. 1052080 or equivalent to underside of cylinder head bolt heads.

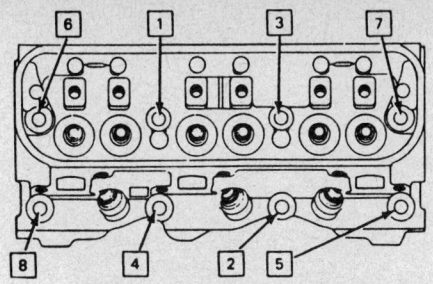

Fig. 5 Cylinder head tightening sequence

b. Apply thread locker No. 12345382 or equivalent to bolt threads.
c. **Torque** cylinder head bolts to 35 ft. lbs. in sequence shown in **Fig. 5**.
d. Rotate each bolt 130° in sequence shown in **Fig. 5**.
e. Rotate center four bolts an additional 30° in sequence shown in **Fig. 5**.
f. Apply thread locker No. 12345493 or equivalent to rocker arm pedestal bolts before assembly.
g. Torque all bolts/nuts to specifications.

3.8L/V6-231

1. Disconnect battery ground cable, the remove serpentine drive belt.
2. Remove exhaust manifolds as outlined under "Exhaust Manifold, Replace."
3. **For left cylinder head removal**, remove oil dipstick.
4. **For right cylinder head removal**, remove alternator, then power steering pump and mounting bracket. Position pump aside.
5. **For either cylinder head removal**, remove spark plug wires, then C3 ignition unit.
6. Remove intake manifold as outlined under "Intake Manifold, Replace."
7. Remove valve covers then rocker arm assemblies, guide plate and pushrods.
8. Remove cylinder head attaching bolts, then cylinder head.
9. Reverse procedure to install, noting the following:
   a. Apply sealant No. 1052080 or equivalent to cylinder head bolt threads.
   b. **Torque** head bolts to 25 ft. lbs. in sequence shown in **Fig. 5**. Should 60 ft. lbs. be obtained during steps c or d, stop at that point. Do not complete balance of tightening procedure.
   c. Tighten each bolt ¼ turn in sequence shown in **Fig. 5**.
   d. Tighten each bolt an additional ¼ turn in sequence shown in **Fig. 5**.

ROCKER ARMS

Rocker arms are mounted to the cylinder head via individual iron pedestals and are retained by hardened steel bolts.

To install rocker arms, position pedestal retainer, rocker arm and pedestal onto cyl-

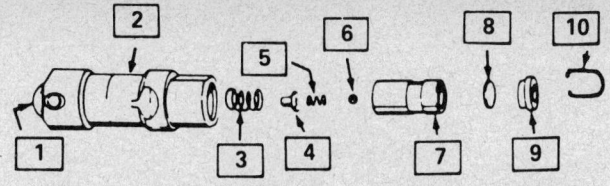

1—ROLLER
2—LIFTER BODY
3—PLUNGER SPRING
4—BALL CHECK RETAINER
5—BALL CHECK SPRING
6—BALL CHECK
7—PLUNGER
8—OIL METERING VALVE
9—PUSH ROD SEAT
10—RETAINER RING

Fig. 6 Exploded view of roller type hydraulic valve lifter

inder head. Install retaining bolts and torque to specification.

VALVE ARRANGEMENT

FRONT TO REAR

Left side.....................E-I-E-I-I-E
Right side...................E-I-I-E-I-E

VALVE CLEARANCE SPECIFICATIONS

These engines are equipped with hydraulic lifters. No provision for adjustment is provided.

VALVE GUIDES

The valve guides are an integral part of the cylinder head and cannot be replaced.

If valve stem clearance is excessive, the valve guide must be reamed and an oversize valve installed. Valves are available in oversize of .010 inch.

VALVE LIFTERS

Failure of an hydraulic valve lifter, **Fig. 6**, is generally caused by dirt or an inadequate oil supply. An air leak at the intake side of the oil pump or too much oil in the engine will cause air bubbles in the oil supply to the lifters, causing them to collapse. This is a probable cause of trouble if several lifters fail to function, but air in the oil is an unlikely cause of failure of a single unit.

The valve lifters may be lifted out of their bores after removing the rocker arms, pushrods and intake manifold. Adjustable pliers with taped jaws may be used to remove lifters that are stuck due to varnish, carbon, etc. Roller type lifters are used to reduce friction and improve performance. The lifters are cylindrical with the exception of two parallel flats milled into the upper part of the body. Slotted guides which hold the lifters in pairs fit over the milled area to keep the lifters from turning in their bores.

ENGINE FRONT COVER REPLACE

3.3L/V6-204

1. Disconnect battery ground cable and drain cooling system.
2. Remove serpentine drive belt, then heater hoses.
3. Disconnect lower radiator and coolant bypass hoses from cover.
4. Raise and support vehicle, then remove right front wheel.
5. Remove right inner fender splash shield.
6. Remove torque converter cover, then prevent flywheel from turning using suitable tool.
7. Remove balancer bolt and washer, then remove balancer assembly.
8. Disconnect electrical connections at camshaft, crankshaft and oil pressure sensors.
9. Remove bolts attaching engine front cover to cylinder block, then oil pan to engine front cover bolts.
10. Remove engine front cover assembly and gasket.
11. Reverse procedure to install, noting the following:
    a. Adjust crankshaft sensor using tool shown in **Fig. 7**.
    b. When reinstalling engine front cover bolts, apply a suitable sealer to the threads to prevent leakage.
    c. Torque all bolts/nuts to specifications.

3.8L/V6-231

1. Drain engine coolant and engine oil.
2. Disconnect upper and lower radiator hoses, then heater return hose at water pump.
3. Remove nuts securing front engine mount to cradle, raise engine using suitable lifting device.
4. Remove serpentine drive belt, then water pump pulley.
5. Remove alternator bracket and alternator.

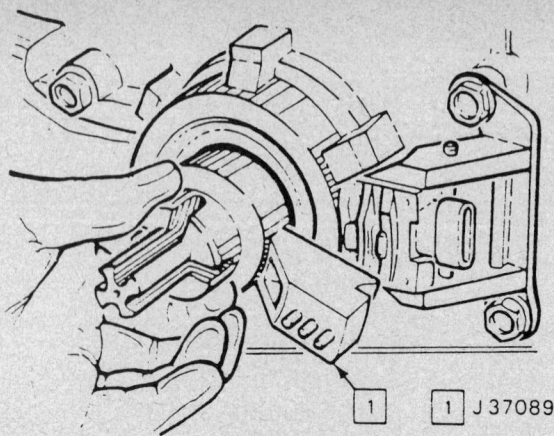

Fig. 7   Adjusting crankshaft sensor

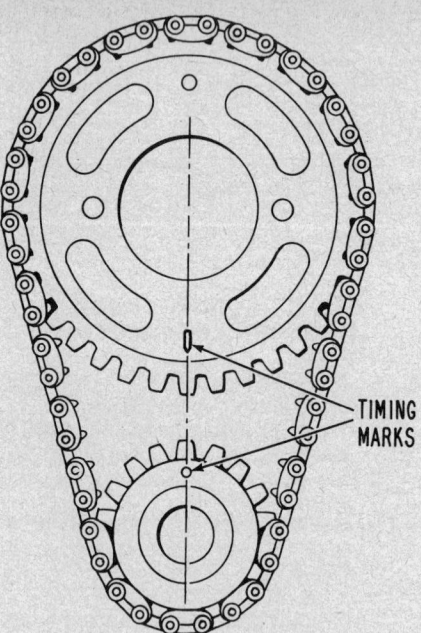

Fig. 8   Valve timing marks

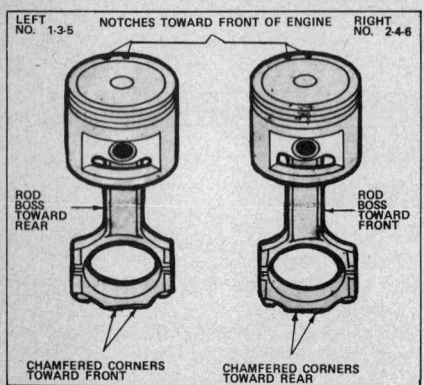

Fig. 9   Piston and rod assembly. 3.8L/V6-231 engine

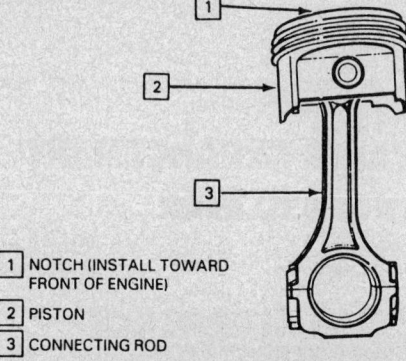

1 NOTCH (INSTALL TOWARD FRONT OF ENGINE)
2 PISTON
3 CONNECTING ROD

Fig. 10   Piston and rod assembly. 1989 3.3L/V6-204 engine

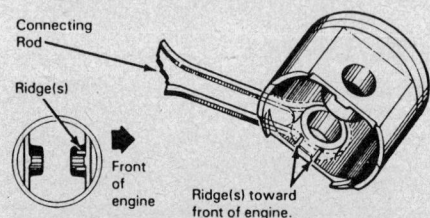

Fig. 11   Piston and rod assembly. 1990–91 3.3L/V6-204 engine

6. Remove harmonic balancer bolt and washer, then remove harmonic balancer assembly.
7. Remove bolts attaching engine front cover to cylinder block, then two oil pan to engine front cover bolts.
8. Remove engine front cover assembly and gasket.
9. Reverse procedure to install, noting the following:
   a. Prior to reinstalling the engine front cover, remove the oil pump cover and pack the space around the oil pump drive gears completely full of petroleum jelly. Failure to do this may result in the pump losing its prime, causing a "dry" engine start. When reinstalling engine front cover bolts, apply a suitable sealer to the threads to prevent leakage.
   b. Torque all bolts/nuts to specifications.

TIMING CHAIN
REPLACE

1. Remove engine front cover as outlined under "Engine Front Cover, Replace."
2. Temporarily install balancer bolt and washer in end of crankshaft. Turn crankshaft so timing marks on sprockets are as close together as possible.

Remove balancer bolt and washer using a sharp blow on wrench handle, so bolt can be removed without changing position of sprockets.
3. Remove timing chain dampener, then and camshaft sprocket bolts.
4. **On 3.8L/V6-231 engines**, remove cam sensor magnet assembly, if necessary.
5. Using two large screwdrivers, alternately pry off sprockets and chain.
6. Reverse procedure to install, noting the following:
   a. Assemble timing chain on sprockets and slide sprockets and chain assembly onto camshaft and crankshaft with timing marks aligned as shown in **Fig. 8**.
6. Torque all bolts/nuts to specifications.

CAMSHAFT
REPLACE

1. Remove engine as outlined under "Engine, Replace."
2. Remove intake manifold as outlined under "Intake Manifold, Replace."
3. Remove rocker arm covers.
4. Remove rocker arms, pushrods and valve lifters.
5. Remove engine front cover as outlined under "Engine Front Cover, Replace."

6. Align timing marks of camshaft and crankshaft sprocket. Remove timing chain and sprockets.
7. Remove cam sensor magnet assembly and camshaft thrust plate if applicable.
8. Slide camshaft forward out of bearing bores, using care so as not to damage bearing surfaces.
9. Reverse procedure to install, noting the following:
   a. Ensure crankshaft and camshaft timing marks as shown in **Fig. 8**.
   b. Torque all bolts/nuts to specifications.

PISTON & ROD ASSEMBLE
3.8L/V6-231

Rods and pistons should be assembled and installed as shown in **Fig. 9**.

3.3L/V6-204
1989

Rods and pistons should be assembled and install as shown in **Fig. 10**.

1990—91

Pistons can be installed on connecting rod in either direction.

Piston/connecting rod assembly must be installed in engine as shown in **Fig. 11**.

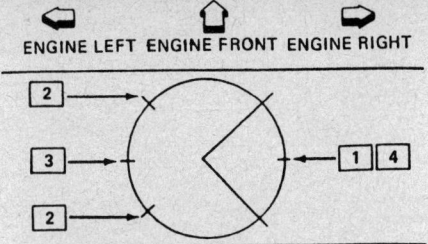

1–OIL RING SPACER GAP
(TANG IN HOLE OR SLOT WITH ARC)
2–OIL RING RAIL GAPS
3–2ND COMPRESSION RING GAP
4–TOP COMPRESSION RING GAP

**Fig. 12   Piston ring end gap
locations**

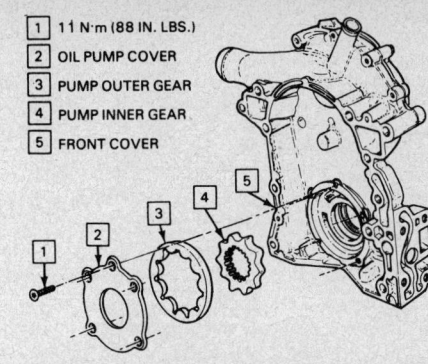

**Fig. 13   Oil pump and housing
assembly**

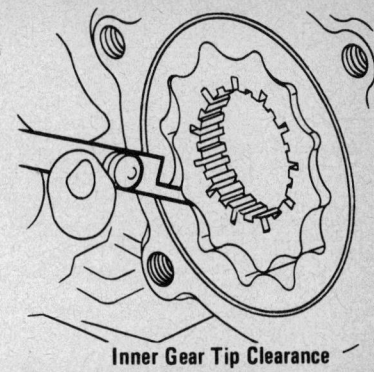

Inner Gear Tip Clearance

**Fig. 14   Checking inner gear
tip clearance**

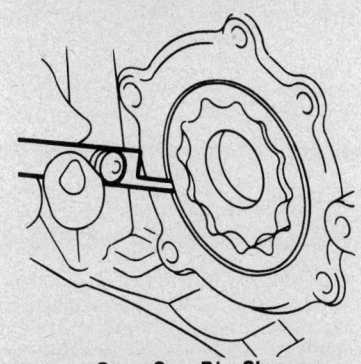

Outer Gear Dia. Clearance

**Fig. 15   Checking outer gear
diameter clearance**

PISTONS, PINS & RINGS

Install rings on piston as shown in **Fig. 12.**

Pistons are available in standard sizes and oversize of .010 inch. Rings are available in standard sizes and oversize of .010 inch. Piston pins are supplied with piston and available only in standard sizes.

MAIN & ROD BEARINGS

Main and connecting rod bearings are available in standard sizes and undersizes of .0005, .0010 and .0015 inch.

OIL PAN
REPLACE

1. Disconnect battery ground cable, then raise and support vehicle.
2. Drain engine oil, then remove flywheel cover.
3. Remove starter, then oil filter.
4. Remove oil pan attaching bolts, then oil pan.
5. Remove and discard old oil pan gasket.
6. Reverse procedure to install, torquing all bolts/nuts to specifications.

OIL PUMP SERVICE
REMOVAL & INSPECTION

1. Remove engine front cover, then the oil filter adapter, pressure regulator valve and valve spring.
2. Remove oil pump cover attaching screws, cover and gears, **Fig. 13.**
3. Inspect pump cover and housing for cracks, scoring, porosity and damaged threads, pressure regulator valve and spring for sticking, scoring or tension loss and gears for chipping, galling or excessive wear. Replace as necessary.
4. Check gear clearance as follows:
   a. Check inner gear tip clearance with feeler gauge as shown in **Fig. 14.** Maximum clearance should not exceed .006 inch.
   b. Check outer gear diameter clearance with feeler gauge as shown in **Fig. 15.** Clearance should be .008-.015 inch.
   c. Check gear end clearance (gear drop in housing) as shown in **Fig. 16.** Clearance should be .001-.0035 inch.
5. Replace parts as necessary.

ASSEMBLY & INSTALLATION

1. Lubricate gears with petroleum jelly, then install into oil pump housing.
2. Pack gear cavity with petroleum jelly, then install pump cover and attaching screws. Torque attaching screws to specifications.
3. Install pressure regulator valve spring and valve.
4. Install oil filter adapter using new gasket. Torque adapter bolts to specifications.
5. Reinstall front cover onto engine.

REAR MAIN BEARING OIL SEAL REPAIR

3.8L/V6-231 & 1988–90 3.3L/V6-204

1. Raise and support vehicle, then drain engine oil.

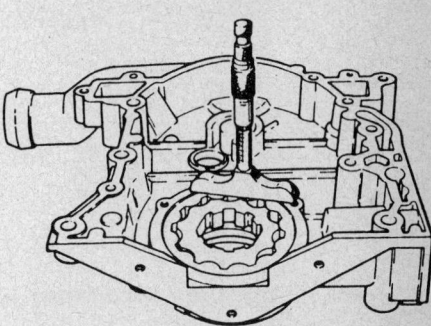

**Fig. 16   Checking gear end
clearance**

2. Remove oil pan as outlined under "Oil Pan, Replace."
3. Remove rear main bearing cap, then oil seal from bearing cap.
4. Using suitable tool, gently pack upper seal into groove until tight.
5. Repeat step 3 for other end of seal.
6. Measure the amount that was driven in on one side and add 1/16 inch. Using a suitable cutting tool, cut this length from the old rear main bearing cap lower seal using the main bearing cap as a guide. Repeat this step for the other end of seal.
7. Place piece of cut seal into groove of seal installer tool guide and install tool guide onto engine block.
8. Using seal packing tool, drive piece of seal into block. Drive seal in until packing tool contacts machined stop.
9. Remove tool guide and repeat steps 6 and 7 for other end of seal.
10. Install new seal in bearing cap.
11. Install rear main bearing cap. Apply a thin film of sealant No. 1052357 or equivalent to rear main bearing cap and case interface. Use care not to allow sealant to contact crankshaft journal or main bearing.

1991 3.3L/V6-204

1. Remove transaxle and flywheel.
2. Using a screwdriver, pry out old seal. Use care to avoid damaging crankshaft. File all burrs or nicks as required.

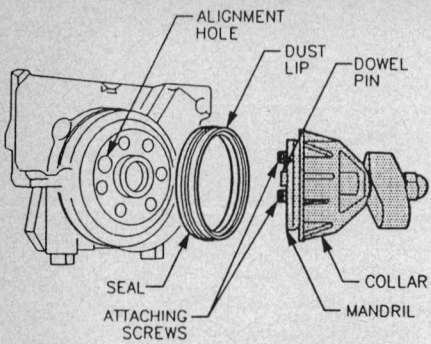

Fig. 17 Installing rear main seal. 1991 3.3L/V6-204

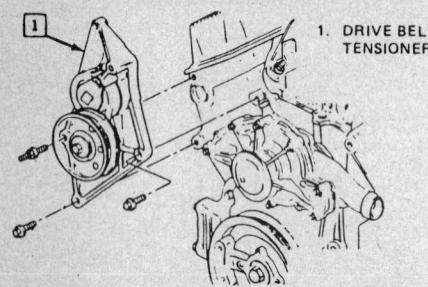

Fig. 20 Replacing tensioner

3. Install new seal using seal installer No. J38196 or equivalent, as follows:
   a. Apply a light coat of engine oil to I.D. and O.D. of oil seal.
   b. Slide seal over tool mandrel until dust lip bottoms squarely against collar of tool.
   c. Align dowel pin of tool with dowel pin hole in crankshaft, **Fig. 17**, then attach tool to crankshaft with screw provided.
   d. Turn handle of tool until seal is pushed into bore and collar is positioned firmly against case. Remove tool.
4. Install flywheel and transmission, then start engine and check for leaks.

FUEL PUMP
REPLACE

1. Relieve fuel pressure as outlined under "Fuel System Pressure Relief," then disconnect battery ground cable.
2. Remove fuel tank.
3. Remove fuel pump assembly by turning cam lock ring counterclockwise. Lift assembly from fuel tank and remove fuel pump from fuel tank sending unit.
4. Reverse procedure to install.

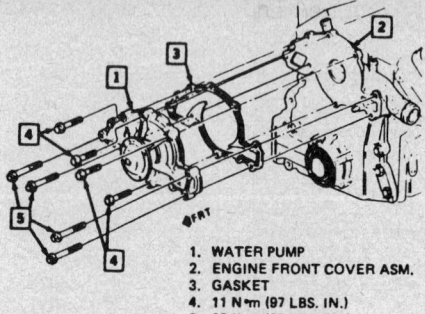

1. WATER PUMP
2. ENGINE FRONT COVER ASM.
3. GASKET
4. 11 N·m (97 LBS. IN.)
5. 39 N·m (29 LBS. FT.)

Fig. 18 Water pump removal & installation

SERVICE BULLETIN: On 1988 Cutlass Ciera models, engines may develop a fuel pump noise condition which may be objectionable. To correct this condition, replace original style fuel pump with a turbine style fuel pump. Obtain fuel pump assembly (part No. 25116156).

WATER PUMP
REPLACE

1. Disconnect battery ground cable.
2. Drain cooling system, then remove serpentine drive belt.
3. Remove lower radiator hose and heater hose at pump.
4. Remove water pump pulley attaching bolts. Long bolt is removed through access hole located in the body side rail.
5. Remove water pump pulley.
6. Remove water pump attaching bolts, then the water pump, **Fig. 18**.
7. Reverse procedure to install, torquing bolts to specifications.

COOLING SYSTEM BLEED

These engines do not require a specified bleed procedure. After filling cooling system, run engine to operating temperature with radiator/pressure cap off. Air will then be automatically bled through cap opening.

SERPENTINE DRIVE BELT

BELT ROUTING

Refer to **Fig. 19**, for routing of serpentine drive belt.

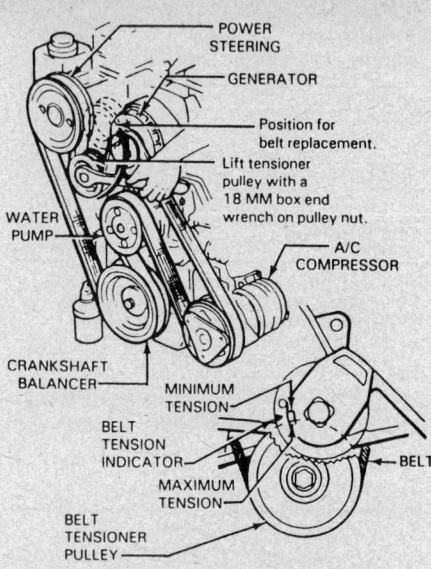

Fig. 19 Serpentine drive belt routing

TENSIONER INSPECTION

1. Run engine, with no accessories on, until normal operating temperature is reached. Turn engine off and read belt tension using belt tension gauge J-23600-B or equivalent. On models equipped with A/C, place gauge halfway between alternator and A/C compressor. On models less A/C, place gauge halfway between power steering pump and crankshaft pulley.
2. Start engine, with accessories off, and allow system to stabilize for 15 seconds. Turn engine off. Using a 18 mm socket, apply clockwise force to tensioner pulley bolt. Release force and immediately take a tension reading without disturbing belt tensioner position.
3. Using a 18 mm socket, apply counterclockwise force to tensioner pulley bolt, raise pulley to eliminate all tension. Slowly lower pulley to belt and take a tension reading without disturbing belt tensioner position.
4. Average three readings. If average is lower than 67 lbs. and belt is within tensioner's operating range, replace belt tensioner.

TENSIONER, REPLACE

1. Remove serpentine drive belt.
2. Remove tensioner attaching bolts, then tensioner, **Fig. 20**.
3. Reverse procedure to install, torquing all bolts/nuts specifications.

TIGHTENING SPECIFICATIONS
3.3L/V6-204 ENGINE

Year	Component	Torque/ft. lbs.
1989–90	Alternator Support To Cylinder Head	⑦
	Alternator Support Through Generator	⑧
	Balancer Assembly To Crankshaft	219
	Camshaft Sensor To Front Cover	80 ⑤
	Camshaft Sprocket Bolt	26
	Camshaft Thrust Plate Bolt	11 ⑤
	Connecting Rod Bolts	①
	Coolant Temperature Sensor To Intake	15
	Crankshaft Bearing Caps To Cylinder Block	90
	Crankshaft Sensor To Front Cover	22
	Crankshaft Sensor Clamp Bolt	3.3
	Cylinder Block Drain Plug	④
	Cylinder Head To Block	②
	Engine Mount Bracket To Cylinder Block	44
	Engine Mount To Cylinder Block	70
	Engine Mount To Frame	33
	Engine Mount To Engine Mount Bracket	33
	ESC Knock Sensor To Cylinder Block	13
	Exhaust Manifold To Cylinder Head	30
	Flywheel Cover To Transaxle	4
	Flywheel To Crankshaft	61
	Front Cover To Block	22
	Fuel Feed & Return Pipes TO Fuel Rail	22
	Fuel Rail To Intake Manifold	⑥
	Heater Hose Pipe To Throttle Body	20
	Ignition Module To Alternator Support	18
	Intake Manifold To Cylinder Head	7.4 ③
	Oil Filter Adapter To Front Cover	24
	Oil Filter Assembly To Filter Adapter	⑨
	Oil Galley Plugs	25
	Oil Pan Drain Plug	⑩
	Oil Pan To Cylinder Block	10.3
	Oil Pan To Front Cover	10.3
	Oil Pressure Switch To Oil Filter Adapter	24
	Oil Pump Cover To Timing Chain Cover	8
	Oil Screen Housing To Cylinder Block	9.5
	Oxygen Sensor To Exhaust Manifold	31
	Rocker Arm Cover To Cylinder Head	7.3
	Rocker Arm Pedestal To Cylinder Head	28
	Serpentine Belt Tensioner To Cylinder Head	⑦
	Spark Plug	20
	Starting Motor To Cylinder Block	35
	Strut Bracket To Manifold Studs	24
	Strut Bracket To Cylinder Head	37
	Thermostat Housing To Intake Manifold	20
	Throttle Body To Intake Manifold	⑪
	Throttle Cable Bracket To Throttle Body	3
	Timing Chain Dampener	⑫
	Torque Converter To Flywheel	46
	Transaxle To Cylinder Block	⑬
	Vacuum Harness To Intake Manifold	9.5

Continued

TIGHTENING SPECIFICATIONS—Continued

Year	Component	Torque/ft. lbs.
1989–90	Valve Lifter Guide Retainer Bolts	⑭
	Water Pump To Front Cover	7
	Water Pump Pulley To Hub	⑮

① —20 ft. lbs., plus an additional 50°.
② —Refer to text.
③ —Refer to text for tightening sequence.
④ —1989–90 32 ft. lbs.; 1991 25 ft. lbs.
⑤ —Inch lbs.
⑥ —1989–90 21 ft. lbs.; 1991 11 ft. lbs.
⑦ —1989–90 33 ft. lbs.; 1991 37 ft. lbs.

⑧ —1989–90 36 ft. lbs.; 1991 37 ft. lbs.
⑨ —1989–90 21 ft. lbs.; 1991 18 ft. lbs.
⑩ —1989–90 18 ft. lbs.; 1991 30 ft. lbs.
⑪ —1989–90 21 ft. lbs.; 1991 20 ft. lbs.
⑫ —1989–90 16 ft. lbs.; 1991 14 ft. lbs.
⑬ —1989–90 55 ft. lbs.; 1991 46 ft. lbs.
⑭ —1989–90 22 ft. lbs.; 1991 27 ft. lbs.
⑮ —1989–90 11.8 ft. lbs.; 1991 9.5 ft. lbs.

3.8L/V6-231 ENGINE

Year	Component	Torque/Ft. Lbs.
1988	Accelerator Cable Bracket To Cylinder Head	37
	Alternator Support To Cylinder Head	35
	Alternator Support Through Generator	36
	Balance Assembly To Crankshaft	219
	Camshaft Sensor To Front Cover	6.25
	Camshaft Sprocket To Camshaft	29
	Connecting Rods	45
	Crankshaft Bearing Caps To Cylinder Block	100
	Crankshaft Sensor To Front Cover	22
	Crankshaft Block Drain Plug	32
	Cylinder Head To Block	①
	EGR Valve To Intake Manifold	13
	Engine Mount To Cylinder Block	70
	ESC Knock Sensor To Block	13
	Exhaust Crossover Pipe To Manifold	15
	Exhaust Manifold To Cylinder Head	37
	Filter Assembly To Filter Adapter	18
	Flywheel Cover To Transaxle	4
	Flywheel To Crankshaft	60
	Front Cover To Block	22
	Fuel Rail To Intake Manifold	10
	Intake Manifold To Cylinder Head	32②
	Oil Filter Adapter To Timing Chain Cover	24
	Oil Galley Plugs	25
	Oil Pan Drain Plug	30
	Oil Pan To Cylinder Block	7.3
	Oil Pressure Switch To Oil Filter Adapter	24
	Oil Pump Cover To Front Cover	8
	Rocker Arm Cover To Cylinder Head	7.3
	Rocker Arm To Cylinder Head	45
	Spark Plug	20
	Starting Motor To Cylinder Block	35
	Thermostat Housing To Intake Manifold	13
	Throttle Body To Intake Manifold	20
	Timing Chain Dampener	14②
	Torque Converter To Flywheel	46
	Transaxle To Cylinder Block	55
	Valve Lifter Guide Retainer Bolts	25
	Water Pump Cover To Timing Chain Cover	7
	Water Pump Pulley To Hub	8.8

① —Refer to text. ② —Refer to text for tightening sequence.

Clutch & Manual Transaxle
INDEX
Page No.

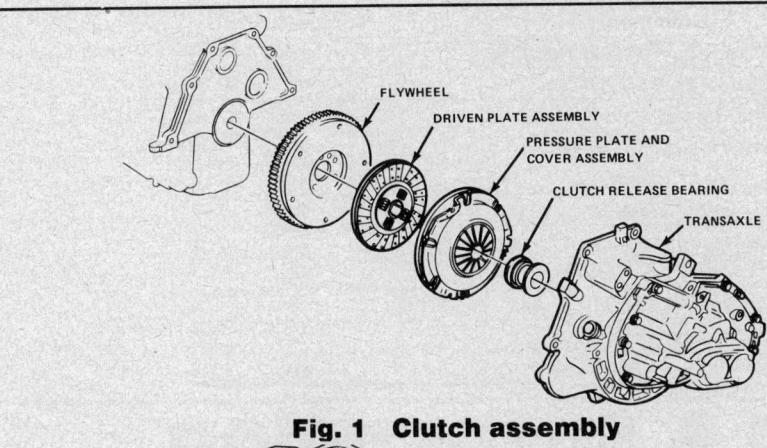

Fig. 1   Clutch assembly

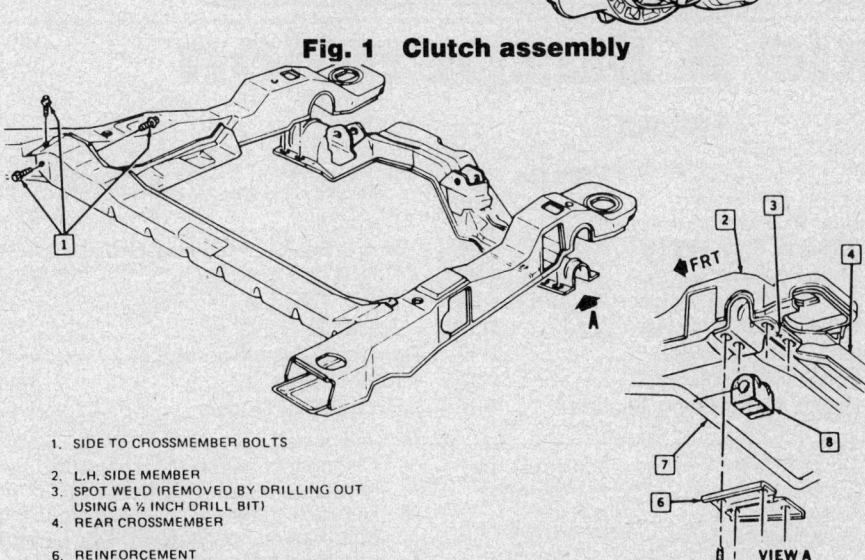

1. SIDE TO CROSSMEMBER BOLTS

2. L.H. SIDE MEMBER

3. SPOT WELD (REMOVED BY DRILLING OUT USING A ½ INCH DRILL BIT)

4. REAR CROSSMEMBER

6. REINFORCEMENT

7. STABILIZER SHAFT

8. INSULATOR

Fig. 2   Removing left side frame and crossmember assembly

CLUTCH HYDRAULIC SYSTEM BLEED PROCEDURE

1. Remove cap and diaphragm, then fill reservoir to the top with approved hydraulic clutch fluid.
2. Fully loosen bleed screw. Located on slave cylinder body next to inlet connection.
3. Let fluid flow from slave cylinder until all bubbles are expelled. Reservoir must be kept full at all times.
4. Torque bleed screw to specifications, then replace cap and diaphragm.

CLUTCH REPLACE

1. Disconnect battery ground cable, then remove hush panel from inside of vehicle.
2. Disconnect clutch master cylinder push rod from clutch pedal.
3. Remove transaxle as described under "Manual Transaxle, Replace."
4. Mark position of pressure plate to flywheel to aid reassembly.
5. Gradually loosen pressure plate attaching bolts until spring pressure is relieved.
6. Support pressure plate and remove mounting bolts. Remove pressure plate and driven disc, **Fig. 1.**
7. Clean pressure and flywheel mounting surfaces. Inspect bearing retainer outer surface of transaxle.
8. Place driven disc in relative installed position and support with a dummy shaft. **The driven disc is installed with the damper springs offset to-**
ward the transaxle. Stamped letters found on the driven disc identify the "Flywheel Side."
9. Install and gradually tighten the pressure plate to flywheel bolts. Remove dummy shaft.
10. Lubricate the release bearing outside diameter groove and the inside diameter recess.
11. Install transaxle.

MANUAL TRANSAXLE REPLACE

1. Disconnect battery ground cable, then remove air cleaner assembly.
2. Remove sound insulator from passenger compartment, then disconnect clutch master cylinder push rod from clutch pedal.
3. Disconnect hydraulic clutch slave cylinder and bracket from transaxle. Use caution not to allow manual clutch shaft to move while removing or installing clutch lever.
4. Remove exhaust crossover pipe, then disconnect shift cables at transaxle.
5. Install suitable engine support fixture, then remove top transaxle to engine attaching bolts.
6. Raise and support vehicle, then install suitable drive axle boot seal protectors on both inner and outer seals.
7. Remove left front wheel assembly, then lower vehicle.
8. Remove left side frame and crossmember assembly as follows:
   a. Install necessary engine support fixtures.
   b. Disconnect intermediate shaft assembly from rack and pinion gear stub shaft. Position attaching bolt in up position before removal.
   c. Raise and support vehicle, then remove power steering line brackets.
   d. Remove steering gear mounting bolts. Position steering aside.
   e. Disconnect front stabilizer bar from left lower control arm, then left lower ball joint at knuckle.
   f. Remove both front stabilizer bar reinforcements and bushings from right and left side members.
   g. Using a ½ inch drill, drill through spotweld located between rear holes of left front stabilizer bar mounting, **Fig. 2.**
   h. Remove engine and transaxle mounts from frame, then side to crossmember bolts, **Fig. 2.**
   i. Remove bolts from left frame mounts, then left side and front

crossmember assembly. If necessary gently pry crossmember loose.
9. Drain transaxle, then disengage lefthand drive axle from transaxle.
10. Remove clutch housing cover bolts, then speedometer cable.
11. Attach suitable jack to transaxle case,

then remove remaining transaxle to engine bolts.
12. Slide transaxle away from engine. Carefully lower jack guiding righthand drive axle out of transaxle.
13. Reverse procedure to install, noting the following:
    a. When installing transaxle, position

right side drive axle shaft into its bore, as driveshaft cannot be installed after transaxle is attached to engine.
    b. After transaxle is attached to engine and lefthand drive axle shaft is installed, immediately install frame and attaching bolts.

TIGHTENING SPECIFICATIONS

Year	Component	Torque/ft. lbs.
1988	Clutch Housing To Gear Housing	15
	Clutch Slave Cylinder	15
	Electronic Speed Sensor Retainer	7
	Engine Mount Nuts	30
	Fluid Drain Plug	18
	Flywheel	52
	Front Crossmember Lower And Upper Bolts	76
	Oil Level Check/Fill Plug	18
	Pressure Plate To Flywheel	16
	Stabilizer Link	12
	Steering Gear Stub Shaft	40

Rear Axle & Suspension

INDEX

EXCEPT AWD MODELS

DESCRIPTION

The rear suspension, **Fig. 1,** consists of a rear axle assembly, control arms, coil springs, shock absorbers, track bar and a track bar brace. The rear axle is trailing arm type design. A non-serviceable stabilizer bar is welded to the inside of the axle housing and is an integral part of the axle assembly. A single unit hub and bearing assembly is bolted to each end of the axle assembly. The hub and bearing assembly is a sealed unit and must be replaced as an assembly.

REAR AXLE, REPLACE

When removing rear axle assembly, do not use twin-post type hoist. The swing arc tendency of this axle may cause it to slip from hoist. Perform axle removal on floor if necessary.
1. Raise rear of vehicle and support rear axle using a jack.
2. Remove rear wheel assembly and brake drum. **Do not hammer on**

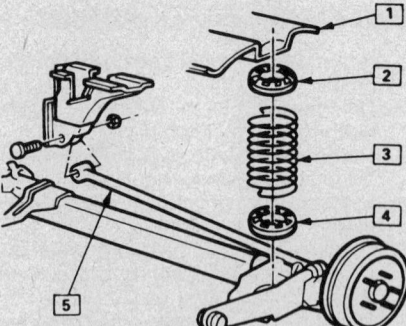

1	UNDERBODY
2	INSULATOR UPPER
3	SPRING
4	LOWER INSULATOR ON A SERIES ONLY
5	TRACK BAR

Fig. 1   Rear axle and suspension. Except AWD models

brake drum since damage to bearings may result.
3. Disconnect parking brake cable from equalizer, then remove brake line brackets from frame.

4. Disconnect shock absorber from lower mountings on axle housing.
5. Remove track bar attaching nut and bolt, then disconnect track bar. **Do not suspend rear axle by brake hoses, otherwise damage to hoses may result.**
6. Carefully lower rear axle assembly, then remove coil spring and insulators.
7. Disconnect brake lines from control arm attachments.
8. Remove parking brake cable from rear axle attachments.
9. Remove hub attaching bolts, then the hub and bearing assembly. Position backing plate out of way.
10. Remove control arm bracket to underbody attaching bolts (four each side), then lower axle assembly and remove from vehicle.
11. Reverse procedure to install, noting the following:
    a. If control arm brackets were removed from control arms, install control arm bracket at a 40-44° angle as shown in **Fig. 2.**
    b. Torque all bolts/nuts to specifications.

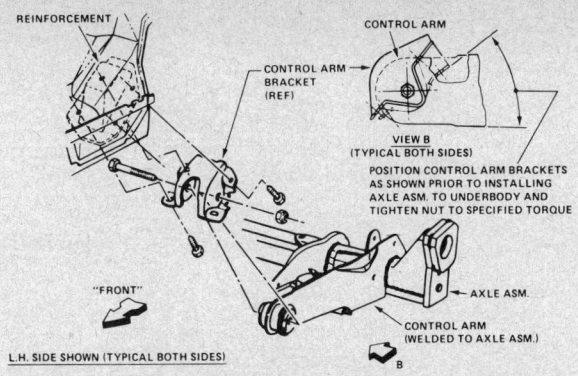

Fig. 2   Control arm bracket installation. Except AWD models

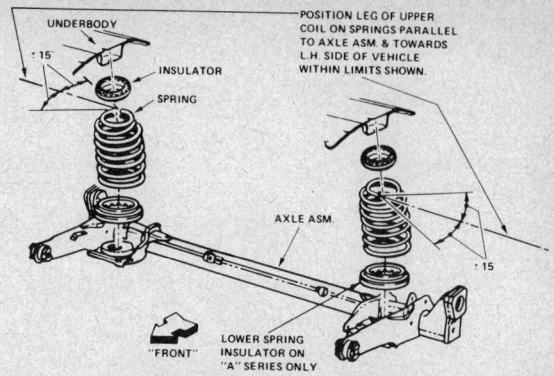

Fig. 3   Coil spring & insulator installation. Except AWD models

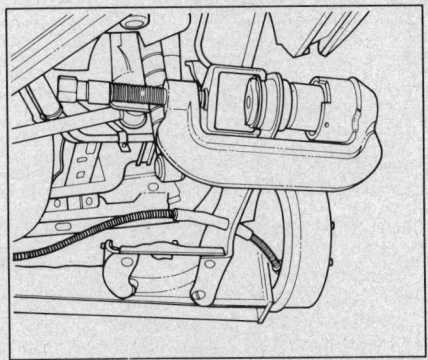

Fig. 4   Control arm bushing removal. Except AWD models

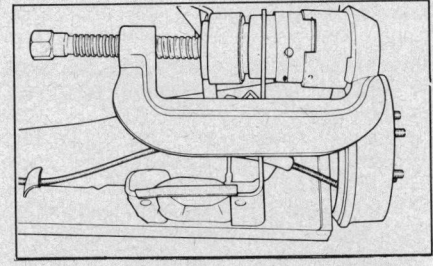

Fig. 5   Control arm bushing installation. Except AWD models

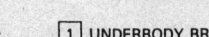

	UNDERBODY BRACKET
3	TRACK BAR
4	AXLE ASM.

6 TRACK BAR BRACE (WAGON ONLY)

Fig. 6   Track bar installation. Except AWD models

HUB & BEARING ASSEMBLY, REPLACE

1. Raise and support rear of vehicle, then remove wheel and tire assembly and brake drum. **Do not hammer on brake drum since damage to bearing may result.**
2. Remove hub and bearing assembly attaching bolts, then hub and bearing assembly. Do not support brake assembly by brake line.
3. Reverse procedure to install, torquing bolts/nuts to specifications.

COIL SPRING, REPLACE

1. Raise rear of vehicle and support rear axle using a jack.
2. Remove right and left brake line bracket attaching bolts from frame and allow brake lines to hang freely.
3. Remove track bar attaching nut and bolt at rear axle, then disconnect track bar.
4. Disconnect shock absorbers at lower mountings. **Do not suspend rear axle by brake hoses since damage to hoses may result.**
5. Carefully lower rear axle assembly, then remove springs and insulators.
6. Reverse procedure to install, **Fig. 3.**

CONTROL ARM BUSHING, REPLACE

1. Raise rear of vehicle and support rear

axle under front side of spring seat using a jack.
2. If right hand side bushing is to be replaced, disconnect parking brake cable from equalizer.
3. Remove parking brake cables from bracket attachment, then position out of way.
4. Disconnect brake line bracket from frame.
5. Disconnect shock absorber from lower mounting, then pull spring out of way.
6. Remove four control arm to underbody attaching bolts, then allow control arm to rotate downward.
7. Remove nut and bolt from bracket attachment, then remove bracket.
8. The bushing can now be replaced using tools shown in **Figs. 4 and 5.** When installing bushing, cut-outs on rubber portion of bushing must face front and rear of vehicle. Press bushing in until end of bushing is aligned with scribed line on tool No. J-28685-2, **Fig. 5.**
9. Reverse procedure to install control arm. Install bracket to control arm as shown in **Fig. 2.**

TRACK BAR, REPLACE

1. Raise rear of vehicle and support rear axle using a jack.
2. Remove nut and bolt attaching track bar to axle housing and underbody, then remove track bar, **Fig. 6.**
3. Reverse procedure to install, torquing bolts/nuts to specifications.

SHOCK ABSORBER, REPLACE

1. Open deck lid and remove trim cover, then remove shock absorber upper attaching nut.
2. Raise rear of vehicle and support rear axle using a jack.
3. Disconnect shock absorber from lower attachment and remove shock absorber from vehicle.
4. Reverse procedure to install, torquing bolts/nuts to specifications.

AWD MODELS
UPPER STRUT MOUNT, REPLACE

1. Open rear compartment lid, then raise and support vehicle.
2. Install spring compressor No. J-33432 on leaf spring to support control arm.
3. Insert Torx wrench into upper end of mount, then remove nut and washer.
4. Hand-compress strut until stud clears mount. Remove air from ELC system to facilitate hand compression, if necessary.

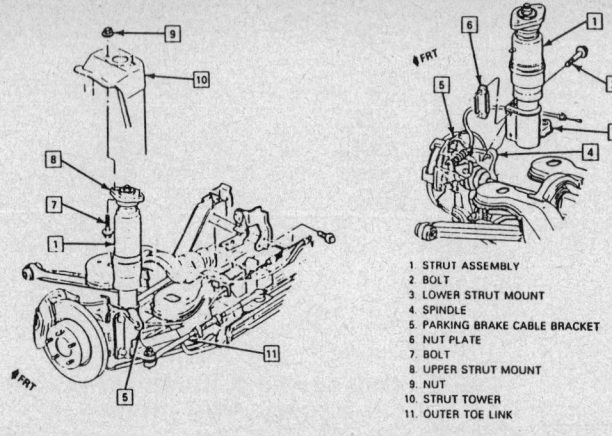

1 STRUT ASSEMBLY
2 BOLT
3 LOWER STRUT MOUNT
4 SPINDLE
5 PARKING BRAKE CABLE BRACKET
6 NUT PLATE
7 BOLT
8 UPPER STRUT MOUNT
9 NUT
10 STRUT TOWER
11 OUTER TOE LINK

Fig. 7   Replacing strut. AWD models

1. J 28733-A
2. TURN FORCING SCREW UNTIL AXLE SPLINES ARE JUST LOOSE

Fig. 9   Separating hub from drive axle. AWD models

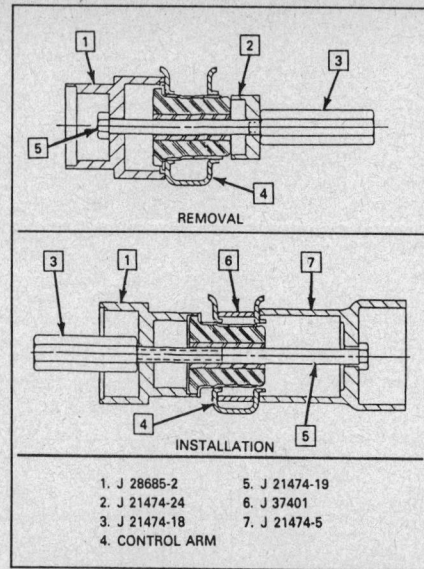

1. J 28685-2	5. J 21474-19
2. J 21474-24	6. J 37401
3. J 21474-18	7. J 21474-5
4. CONTROL ARM	

Fig. 8   Replacing control arm bushing. . AWD models

5. Remove upper mount attaching bolts/nuts, then mount.
6. Reverse procedure to install, torquing bolts/nuts to specifications.

STRUT, REPLACE

1. Open rear compartment lid, then raise and support vehicle.
2. Remove wheel assembly, then install spring compressor No. J-33432 on leaf spring to support control arm.
3. Remove outer toe link end from lower strut mount assembly, then parking brake cable from strut mount bracket.
4. Remove parking brake cable bracket, then bolts from lower strut mount to knuckle assembly.
5. Remove ELC air hose, then upper strut attaching nut.
6. Release spring tension at spring compressor, then remove strut, **Fig. 7**.
7. Reverse procedure to install, torquing bolts/nuts to specifications.

LOWER CONTROL ARM, REPLACE

1. Raise and support vehicle.
2. Remove wheel assembly, then install spring compressor No. J-33432 on leaf spring to support control arm.
3. Remove outer stabilizer shaft bracket to control arm attaching bolts/nuts.
4. **On left side control arm,** remove bolt securing brake line/ELC sensor bracket to control arm. Move bracket aside.

5. **On either control arms,** remove control arm to knuckle attaching bolt/nut.
6. Lower control arm by loosening spring compressor, then remove control arm to frame bolts/nuts.
7. Remove control arm from leaf spring.
8. Reverse procedure to install, noting the following:
   a. Ensure leaf spring is in correct position.
   b. Torque all bolts/nuts to specifications.

LOWER CONTROL ARM BUSHING, REPLACE

1. Remove control arm as outlined under "Lower Control Arm, Replace."
2. Refer to **Fig. 8**, for bushing replacement procedure.

HUB & BEARING ASSEMBLY, REPLACE

Hub and bearing are replaced as an assembly.
1. Raise and support vehicle, then remove wheel assembly.
2. Remove and discard hub nut, then brake caliper. Suspend caliper with wire.
3. Install drive axle seal protectors. **These protectors should be used any time service is performed on or near drive axle. Failure to use them may result in interior joint or seal damage.**
4. Remove brake rotor, then Torx bolts mounting hub and bearing assembly to knuckle.
5. Remove hub and bearing assembly from axle using puller shown in **Fig. 9**.
6. Reverse procedure to install, torquing bolts/nuts to specifications.

KNUCKLE, REPLACE

1. Remove hub and bearing assembly as outlined under "Hub & Bearing Assembly, Replace."
2. Remove speed sensor and bracket from knuckle, then outer toe link castle nut.
3. Install spring compressor No. J-33432 on leaf spring to support control arm.

4. Scribe position of strut to knuckle bolts, then remove strut to knuckle bolts.
5. Remove outer control arm bolt/nut, then knuckle from vehicle.
6. Reverse procedure to install, torquing bolts/nuts to specifications.

LEAF SPRING, REPLACE

1. Raise and support vehicle.
2. Remove wheel assembly, then install spring compressor No. J-33432 on leaf spring to support control arm.
3. Remove bolt securing brake line/ELC sensor bracket to lefthand control arm. Move bracket aside.
4. Remove control arm outer bolts/nuts at knuckles, then outer stabilizer shaft brackets from control arms.
5. Loosen spring compressor to allow control arms to drop. Remove spring compressor.
6. Remove bolts from spring to frame brackets, then brackets.
7. Remove leaf spring by sliding outward.
8. Reverse procedure to install, torquing bolts/nuts to specifications.

REAR AXLE MODULE, REPLACE

1. Open rear compartment lid, then raise and support vehicle.
2. Remove both wheel assemblies, then loosen parking brake cable at tensioner.
3. Remove parking brake cable ends at spindle brackets, then parking brake springs, bracket bolts and brackets.
4. Separate parking brake cable at tensioner, then remove calipers. Suspend caliper with wire.
5. Remove anti-lock sensor bolts, then position sensors aside, if equipped.
6. Disconnect ELC electrical connections and air lines, then height sensor arm from bracket stud.

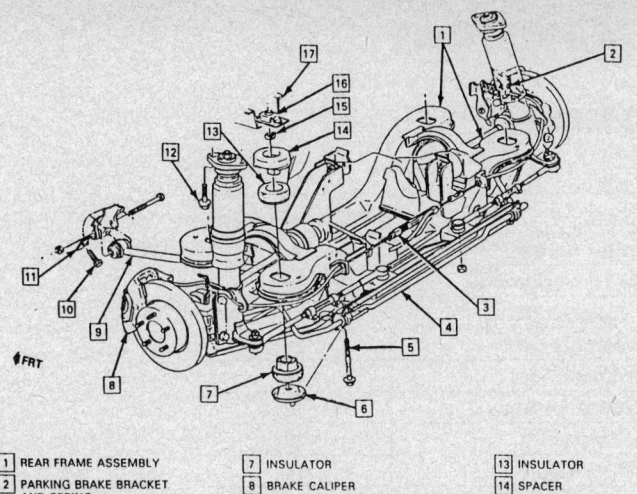

1	REAR FRAME ASSEMBLY	7	INSULATOR	13	INSULATOR
2	PARKING BRAKE BRACKET AND SPRING	8	BRAKE CALIPER	14	SPACER
3	PARKING BRAKE TENSIONER	9	FRAME BRACE	15	RETAINER
4	STABILIZER SHAFT	10	UNDERBODY BRACKET BOLT	16	CAGE NUT
5	FRAME MOUNT BOLT	11	UNDERBODY BRACKET	17	BODY RAIL
6	RETAINER	12	BOLT		

Fig. 10   Replacing rear module. AWD models

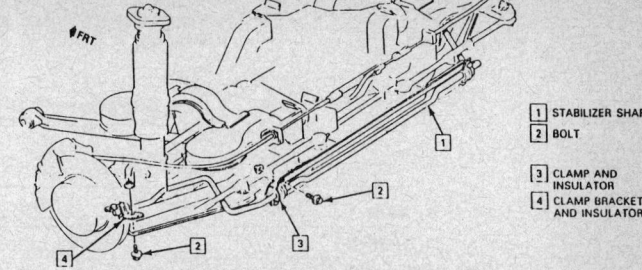

1	STABILIZER SHAFT
2	BOLT
3	CLAMP AND INSULATOR
4	CLAMP BRACKET AND INSULATOR

Fig. 11   Replacing stabilizer shaft. AWD models

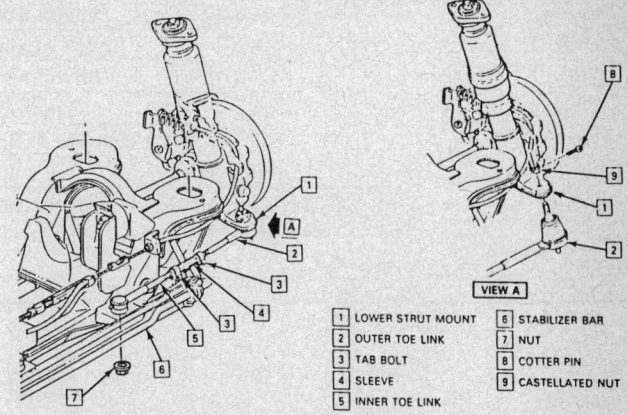

1	LOWER STRUT MOUNT	6	STABILIZER BAR
2	OUTER TOE LINK	7	NUT
3	TAB BOLT	8	COTTER PIN
4	SLEEVE	9	CASTELLATED NUT
5	INNER TOE LINK		

Fig. 12   Replacing toe link assembly. AWD models

7. Remove bolts securing brake line/ELC sensor bracket to lefthand control arm, then exhaust support bolt (above frame).
8. Scribe propeller shaft and rear axle pinion flange, then remove propeller shaft from rear axle pinion flange.
9. Remove frame brace to underbody bracket bolts, then install spring compressor No. J-33432 on leaf spring to support control arm.
10. Place transmission jack under rear module, then install bolts into existing jacking plate bores.
11. Lower vehicle, then remove strut upper mount bolts.
12. Raise and support vehicle, then loosen spring compressor to release spring tension. Remove spring compressor.
13. Remove four frame mounting bolts, then lower module assembly slightly to disconnect differential vent tube.
14. Remove rear module from vehicle, **Fig. 10.**
15. Reverse procedure to install, noting the following:
    a. Ensure scribe marks are align on propeller shaft and rear axle pinion flange.
    b. Torque all bolts/nuts to specifications.

STABILIZER SHAFT, REPLACE

1. Raise and support vehicle, then remove wheel assemblies.
2. Remove outer stabilizer shaft bracket to control arm attaching bolts/nuts.

3. Remove inner stabilizer shaft bracket to frame bracket attaching bolts.
4. Remove stabilizer shaft from vehicle, **Fig. 11.**
5. Reverse procedure to install, torquing bolt/nuts to specifications.

OUTER TOE LINK, REPLACE

1. Raise and support vehicle, then loosen toe link sleeve outer tab bolt/nut.
2. Remove castle nut from outer toe link end, then parking brake cable from bracket.
3. Remove outer toe link end from lower strut mount assembly, **Fig. 12.**
4. Unscrew outer toe link from toe link sleeve.
5. Reverse procedure to install, noting the following:
    a. Torque bolt/nuts to specification.
    b. Adjust rear wheel toe as necessary.

INNER TOE LINK, REPLACE

1. Raise and support vehicle, then loosen toe link sleeve inner tab bolt/nut.
2. Remove castle nut from inner toe link end, then inner toe link end from rear crossmember, **Fig. 12.**
4. Unscrew outer toe link from toe link sleeve.
5. Reverse procedure to install, noting the following:
    a. Torque bolt/nuts to specification.
    b. Adjust rear wheel toe as necessary.

TOE LINK SLEEVE, REPLACE

1. Remove outer toe link as outlined under "Outer Toe Link, Replace."
2. Loosen sleeve inner tab bolt/nut, then unscrew sleeve from inner toe link, **Fig. 12.**
3. Reverse procedure to install, noting the following:
    a. Torque bolt/nuts to specification.
    b. Adjust rear wheel toe as necessary.

TIGHTENING SPECIFICATIONS

EXCEPT AWD MODELS

Year	Component	Torque/Ft. Lbs.
1988–91	Brake Line Bracket Screw	8
	Control Arm Bracket To Underbody	28
	Control Arm To Bracket Nut	84
	Hub & Bearing Assembly Bolts	44
	Shock Absorber Lower Nut	44
	Shock Absorber Mount To Body	16
	Shock Absorber Upper Nut	16
	Track Bar Bolt At Axle	44
	Track Bar Nut At Brace Or Underbody Bracket	35
	Wheel Nuts	①

① —1988–89 100 ft. lbs.; 1990 103 ft. lbs.;
1991 92 ft. lbs.

AWD MODELS

Year	Component	Torque/Ft. Lbs.
1988–90	ABS Speed Sensor Bracket Bolt	7.4
	Axle Hub Nut	192
	Control Arm Bolts/Nuts At Frame	61
	Control Arm Outer Nut At Knuckle	125
	ELC/Brake Line Bracket Bolt	18
	Frame Brace To Underbody Bracket Bolt	28
	Hub And Bearing Assembly Bolts	44
	Inner Toe Link Nut	61
	Jacking Plate Bolt	35
	Leaf Spring To Frame Bracket Bolt	61
	Lower Strut Mounting Bolt	148
	Outer Toe Link Castle Nut	46
	Propeller Shaft To Differential Bolt	40
	Rear Frame Mounting Bolt	103
	Stabilizer Bracket Bolt	26
	Toe Link Sleeve Tab Nut	14
	Upper Strut Attaching Bolt	40
	Upper Strut Mount Nut	20
	Wheel Nuts	①

① —1988–89 100 ft. lbs.; 1990 103 ft. lbs.;
1991 92 ft. lbs.

Front Suspension & Steering

INDEX

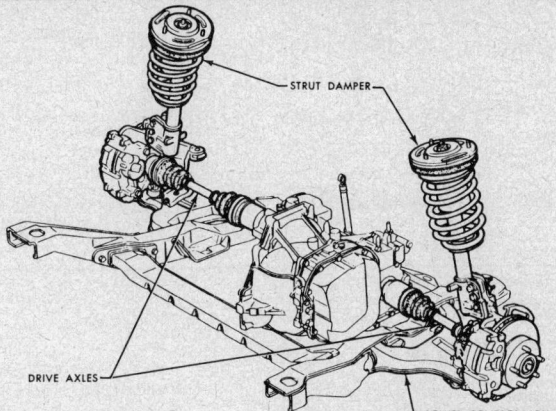

Fig. 1   Front suspension

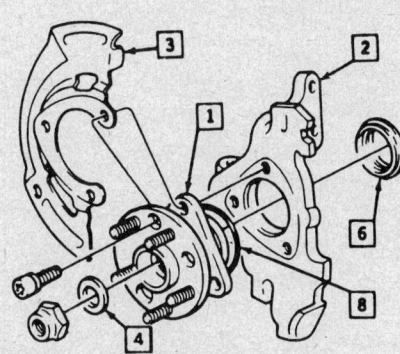

1. HUB AND BEARING ASSEMBLY
2. STEERING KNUCKLE
3. SHIELD
4. WASHER
6. SEAL
8. O-RING

Fig. 3   Exploded view of hub, bearing and seal assembly

DESCRIPTION

The front suspension, **Fig. 1,** on these vehicles is a MacPherson strut design. The lower control arms pivot from the engine cradle. This engine cradle has isolation mounts to the body and conventional rubber bushings are used for the lower control arm pivots. The upper end of the strut is isolated by a rubber mount incorporating a bearing for wheel turning. The lower end of the steering knuckle pivots on a ball stud which is retained in the lower control arm with rivets and is clamped to the steering knuckle. Sealed wheel bearings are used and are bolted to the steering knuckle.

HUB, BEARING & SEAL REPLACE

Hub and bearing are replaced as an assembly.
1. Loosen hub nut with vehicle on ground.
2. Raise and support vehicle, then remove front wheel.
3. Install drive axle seal protectors. **These protectors should be used any time service is performed on or near drive axle. Failure to use them may result in interior joint or seal damage.**
4. Remove, then discard hub nut and washer.
5. Remove brake caliper from support and suspend caliper from frame with a length of wire. **Do not suspend caliper by the brake hose.** Remove rotor.
6. Using tool No. J-28733, or equivalent, separate hub and drive axle, **Fig. 2.**
7. Remove hub and bearing attaching bolts, then shield, hub and bearing assembly and O-ring, **Fig. 3.**
8. To remove factory seal, tap seal toward engine. When seal is removed from steering knuckle, cut it off drive axle using side cutters. **Factory seal**

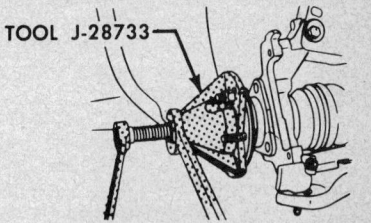

TOOL J-28733

REMOVING FRONT SPINDLE

Fig. 2   Removing front wheel bearing & hub assembly

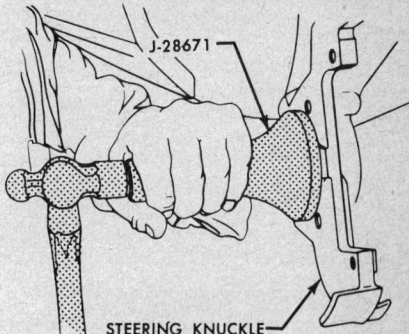

J-28671

STEERING KNUCKLE

Fig. 4   Installing front wheel bearing seal

is installed from engine side of steering knuckle. Replacement seal is installed from wheel side of steering knuckle.
9. Reverse procedure to install, noting the following:
   a. Lubricate seal, then install using seal installer No. J-28671 or equivalent, **Fig. 4.**
   b. Torque bolts/nuts to specifications.

LOWER BALL JOINT REPLACE

1. Raise and support vehicle, then place jack stands under suspension.
2. Lower vehicle slightly so weight of vehicle rests on jack stands, then remove wheel assembly.
3. Install drive axle seal protectors. **These protectors should be used any time service is performed on or near drive axle. Failure to use them may result in interior joint or seal damage.**
4. Remove pinch bolt, then ball joint from steering knuckle.

5. Drill out three rivets retaining ball joint. Use a 1/8 inch drill to make a pilot hole through rivets. Finish drilling rivets with 1/2 inch drill bit.
6. Loosen stabilizer shaft bushing assembly nut, then remove ball joint from control arm.
7. Reverse procedure to install, torquing bolts/nuts to specifications.

LOWER CONTROL ARM & BUSHINGS
REPLACE

1. Raise and support vehicle, then place jack stands under suspension.
2. Lower vehicle slightly so weight of vehicle rests on jack stands, then remove wheel assembly.
3. Install drive axle seal protectors. **These protectors should be used any time service is performed on or near drive axle. Failure to use them may result in interior joint or seal damage.**
4. Remove pinch bolt holding ball joint to steering knuckle, then control arm mounting bolts.
5. Remove control arm from vehicle, **Fig. 5.**
6. Refer to **Fig. 6,** for bushing replacement procedure.
7. Reverse procedure to install, noting the following:
   a. Weight of vehicle must be supported by control arms when tightening control arm mounting nuts.
   b. Torque bolts/nuts to specifications.

STEERING KNUCKLE
REPLACE

For removal and installation procedures, refer to **Fig. 7.**

STABILIZER BAR & BUSHINGS
REPLACE

1. Raise and support vehicle.
2. Remove stabilizer shaft insulator clamp and insulator at control arms. Do not remove studs from control arms.
3. Remove plates from frame, then stabilizer bar and insulator bushings, **Fig. 8.**
4. Reverse procedure to install, torquing bolts/nuts to specifications.

STRUT ASSEMBLY
REPLACE

1. Remove strut top attaching nuts, then raise and support vehicle.
2. Place jack stands under suspension support, the lower vehicle slightly so weight of vehicle rests on jack stands.
3. Remove wheel assemblies, then install drive axle seal protectors.

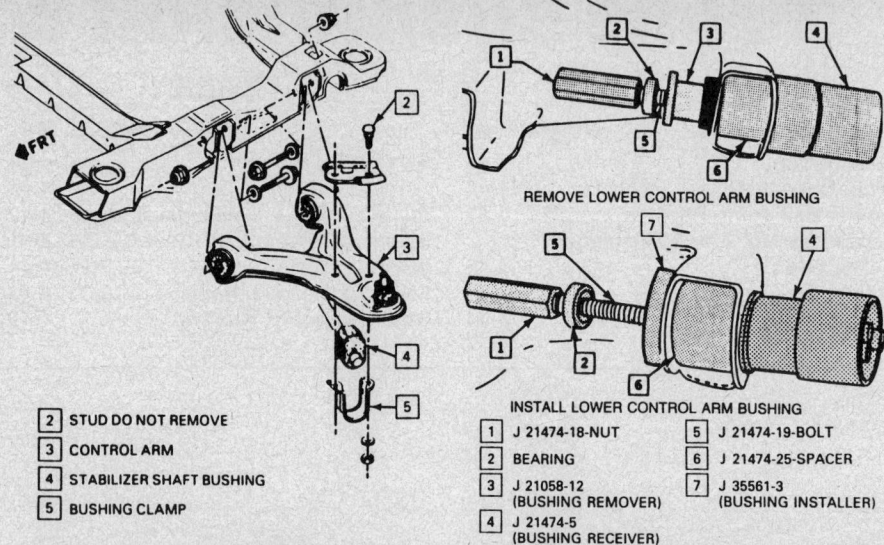

REMOVE LOWER CONTROL ARM BUSHING

INSTALL LOWER CONTROL ARM BUSHING

2	STUD DO NOT REMOVE
3	CONTROL ARM
4	STABILIZER SHAFT BUSHING
5	BUSHING CLAMP

1	J 21474-18-NUT	5	J 21474-19-BOLT
2	BEARING	6	J 21474-25-SPACER
3	J 21058-12 (BUSHING REMOVER)	7	J 35561-3 (BUSHING INSTALLER)
4	J 21474-5 (BUSHING RECEIVER)		

Fig. 5 Replacing control arm   **Fig. 6 Replacing control arm bushings**

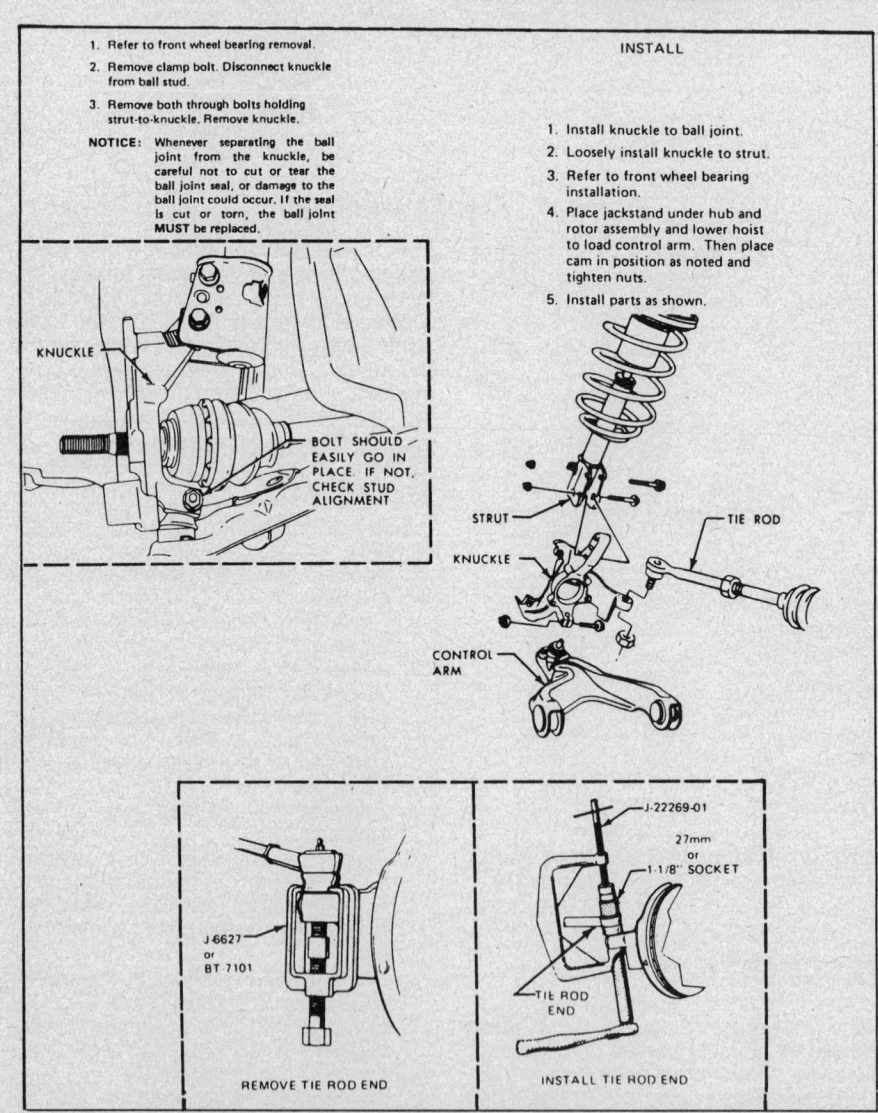

1. Refer to front wheel bearing removal.
2. Remove clamp bolt. Disconnect knuckle from ball stud.
3. Remove both through bolts holding strut-to-knuckle. Remove knuckle.

NOTICE: Whenever separating the ball joint from the knuckle, be careful not to cut or tear the ball joint seal, or damage to the ball joint could occur. If the seal is cut or torn, the ball joint MUST be replaced.

INSTALL

1. Install knuckle to ball joint.
2. Loosely install knuckle to strut.
3. Refer to front wheel bearing installation.
4. Place jackstand under hub and rotor assembly and lower hoist to load control arm. Then place cam in position as noted and tighten nuts.
5. Install parts as shown.

BOLT SHOULD EASILY GO IN PLACE. IF NOT, CHECK STUD ALIGNMENT

REMOVE TIE ROD END   INSTALL TIE ROD END

Fig. 7 Replacing steering knuckle

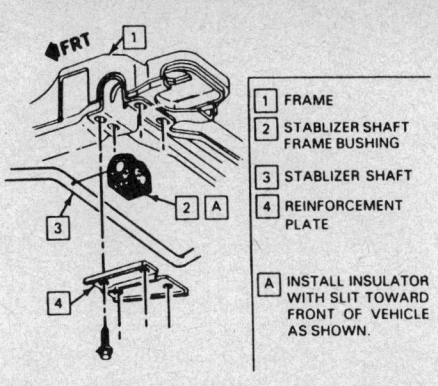

1. FRAME
2. STABLIZER SHAFT FRAME BUSHING
3. STABLIZER SHAFT
4. REINFORCEMENT PLATE

A. INSTALL INSULATOR WITH SLIT TOWARD FRONT OF VEHICLE AS SHOWN.

Fig. 8   Replacing stabilizer bar

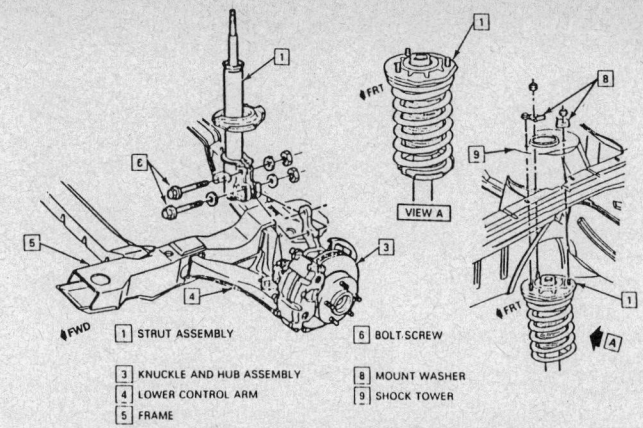

1. STRUT ASSEMBLY
3. KNUCKLE AND HUB ASSEMBLY
4. LOWER CONTROL ARM
5. FRAME
6. BOLT·SCREW
8. MOUNT WASHER
9. SHOCK TOWER

Fig. 9   Replacing strut assembly

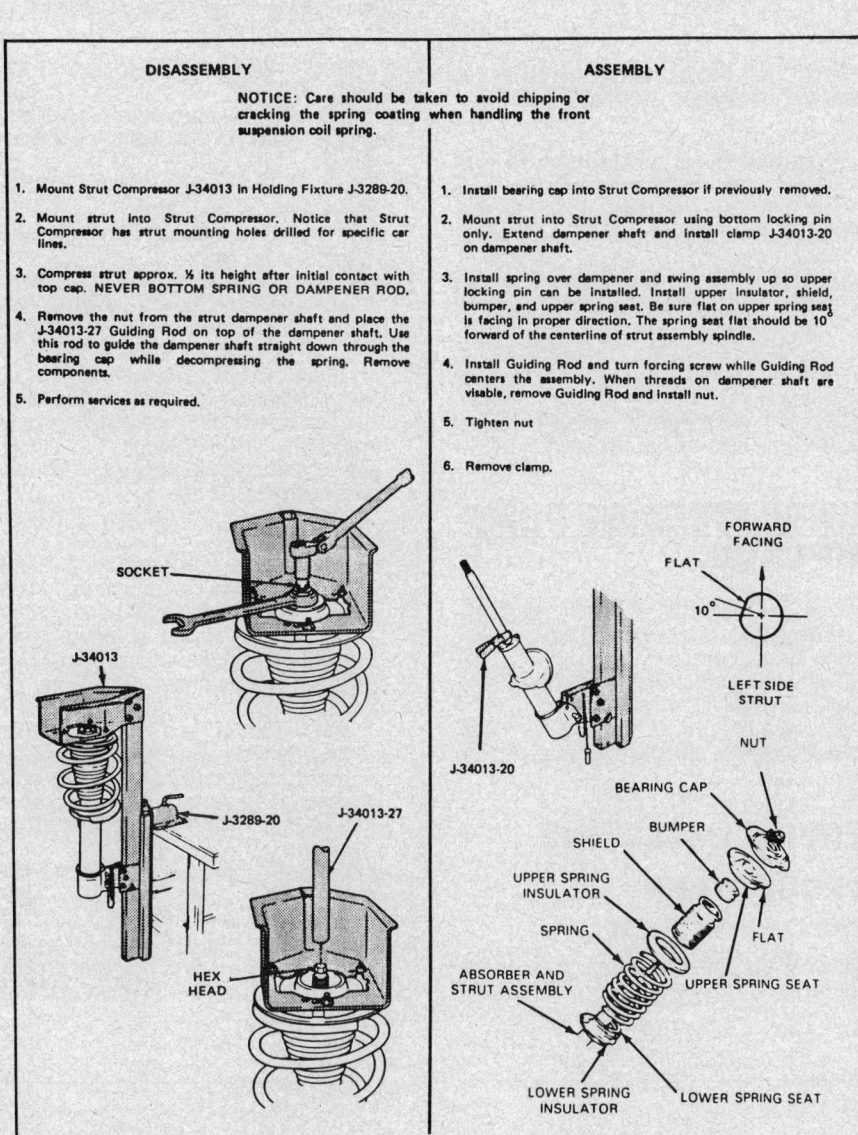

DISASSEMBLY	ASSEMBLY
NOTICE: Care should be taken to avoid chipping or cracking the spring coating when handling the front suspension coil spring.	
1. Mount Strut Compressor J-34013 in Holding Fixture J-3289-20.	1. Install bearing cap into Strut Compressor if previously removed.
2. Mount strut into Strut Compressor. Notice that Strut Compressor has strut mounting holes drilled for specific car lines.	2. Mount strut into Strut Compressor using bottom locking pin only. Extend dampener shaft and install clamp J-34013-20 on dampener shaft.
3. Compress strut approx. ½ its height after initial contact with top cap. NEVER BOTTOM SPRING OR DAMPENER ROD.	3. Install spring over dampener and swing assembly up so upper locking pin can be installed. Install upper insulator, shield, bumper, and upper spring seat. Be sure flat on upper spring seat is facing in proper direction. The spring seat flat should be 10° forward of the centerline of strut assembly spindle.
4. Remove the nut from the strut dampener shaft and place the J-34013-27 Guiding Rod on top of the dampener shaft. Use this rod to guide the dampener shaft straight down through the bearing cap while decompressing the spring. Remove components.	4. Install Guiding Rod and turn forcing screw while Guiding Rod centers the assembly. When threads on dampener shaft are visable, remove Guiding Rod and install nut.
5. Perform services as required.	5. Tighten nut.
	6. Remove clamp.

Fig. 10   Disassembly and assembly of strut

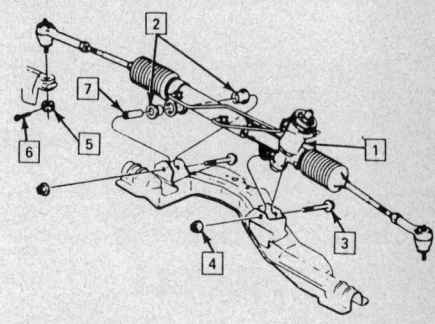

1. STERING GEAR
2. BUSHING
3. BOLT
4. NUT –
5. NUT –
6. COTTER PIN
7. SLEEVE

Fig. 11   Replacing steering gear

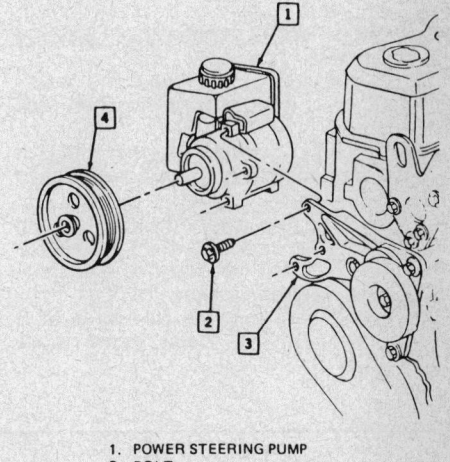

1. POWER STEERING PUMP
2. BOLT
3. TENSIONER ASSY.
4. PULLEY

Fig. 12   Replacing power steering pump. 2.5L/4-151

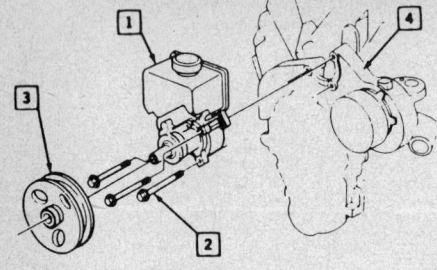

1. POWER STEERING PUMP
2. BOLT
3. PULLEY
4. COVER

Fig. 13   Replacing power steering pump. 2.8L/V6-173 & 3.1L/V6-189

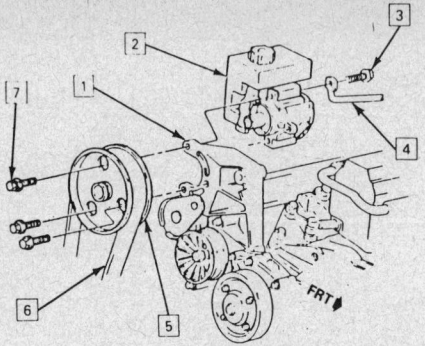

1	BELT TENSIONER ASM.
2	POWER STEERING PUMP
3	BOLT.SCREW
4	BELT TENSIONER BRACE
5	PULLEY
6	ACCESSORY DRIVE BELT
7	BOLT

Fig. 14   Replacing power steering pump. 3.3L/V6-204

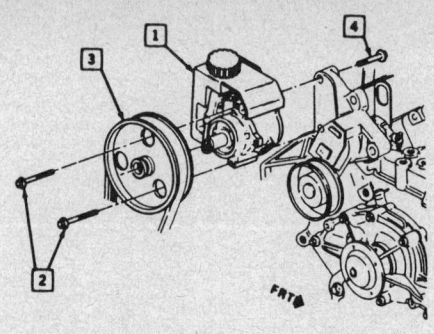

1. POWER STEERING PUMP
2. BOLT
3. PULLEY
4. BOLT

Fig. 15   Replacing power steering pump. 3.8L/V6-231

4. Disconnect front wheel sensor, if equipped w/anti-lock brakes.
5. Remove brake line bracket from strut assembly, then strut to steering knuckle attaching bolts.
6. Remove strut from vehicle, **Fig. 9.**
7. Reverse procedure to install, torquing bolts/nuts to specifications.

STRUT ASSEMBLY SERVICE

Refer to **Fig. 10**, for strut assembly service.

STEERING GEAR REPLACE

1. Install engine support fixture No. J-28467-A or equivalent.
2. Raise and support vehicle, then remove both front wheel assemblies.
3. Remove intermediate shaft lower pinch bolt, then intermediate shaft from stub shaft.
4. Disconnect tie rod ends from steering knuckles.
5. If equipped, remove brake line retaining bolts from heat shield, then heat shield.
6. Support engine frame at rear with jack stand, then remove engine mounts to frame attaching bolts.
7. Remove rear engine frame retaining bolts, then loosen front engine retaining bolts. **Do not remove front engine retaining bolts.**
8. Lower engine frame at rear 4 to 5 inches. **Do not lower frame more**

than specified, as damage to engine components may result.
9. Remove steering gear heat shield, then line retaining clip from steering gear.
10. Disconnect and cap pump lines at steering gear.
11. Remove steering gear assembly mounting bolts, **Fig. 11**, then steering gear assembly through left wheel opening.
12. Reverse procedure to install, torquing all bolts/nuts to specifications.

POWER STEERING PUMP REPLACE

1. Remove serpentine drive belt from pulley, then disconnect power steering lines at pump.
2. Remove pump retaining bolts, then pump, **Figs. 12 through 15.**
3. Reverse procedure to install, torquing bolts/nuts to specifications.

SERVICE BULLETINS

TORQUE STEER

1988 Cutlass Ciera

This vehicle has a tendency to steer left or right while driving straight. To ensure torque steer is the problem, proceed as follows:

1. Check tires for correct pressure and ensure alignment is within specifications.
2. Check all suspension components to ensure proper operation.
3. Drive vehicle on straight and flat road surface at 40 mph.
4. Shift transaxle to neutral and allow vehicle to coast. Momentarily release steering wheel and note if vehicle varies from straight ahead. If no variance is noticed, proceed to step 5.
5. Place transaxle in drive while proceeding at 40 mph, momentarily apply maximum acceleration. If vehicle shows a change in steering direction, torque steer is present.
6. To repair a torque steer condition, proceed as follows:
   a. **On models equipped with automatic transaxle,** a difference in drive axle angles will be indicated by measuring the difference between transaxle left and right pan rail height as shown.
   b. **On models equipped with manual transaxle,** a difference in drive axle angles will be indicated by measuring the difference in height of axles as measured at the largest diameter of inboard axle joint as shown.
   c. **On all models,** to correct this difference, replace sagged engine/transaxle mounts and/or shim as necessary to raise the side with lower reading, using appropriate wheel alignment shim stock.

TIGHTENING SPECIFICATIONS

Year	Component	Torque/Ft. Lbs.
1988–91	Ball Joint Pinch Bolt Nut	33
	Brake Line Bracket Bolt	13
	Control Arm Pivot Bolt Nut	61
	Caliper Bolt	38
	Hub & Bearing Retaining Bolt	①
	Hub Nut	②
	Insulator Clamp Nut	33
	Reinforcement Plate To Frame Bolt	40
	Stabilizer Shaft Bushing Clamp Nut	33
	Steering Knuckle To Strut Assembly Bolt	140
	Strut Assembly To Body Nut	18
	Strut Dampener Shaft Nut	65
	Wheel Nut	③

① —w/standard brakes, 63 ft. lbs.,
　w/heavy duty brakes, 70 ft. lbs.
② —1988–89 185 ft. lbs.; 1990–91 192 ft.
　lbs.
③ —1988–89 100 ft. lbs.; 1990 103 ft. lbs.;
　1991 92 ft. lbs.

Wheel Alignment

INDEX

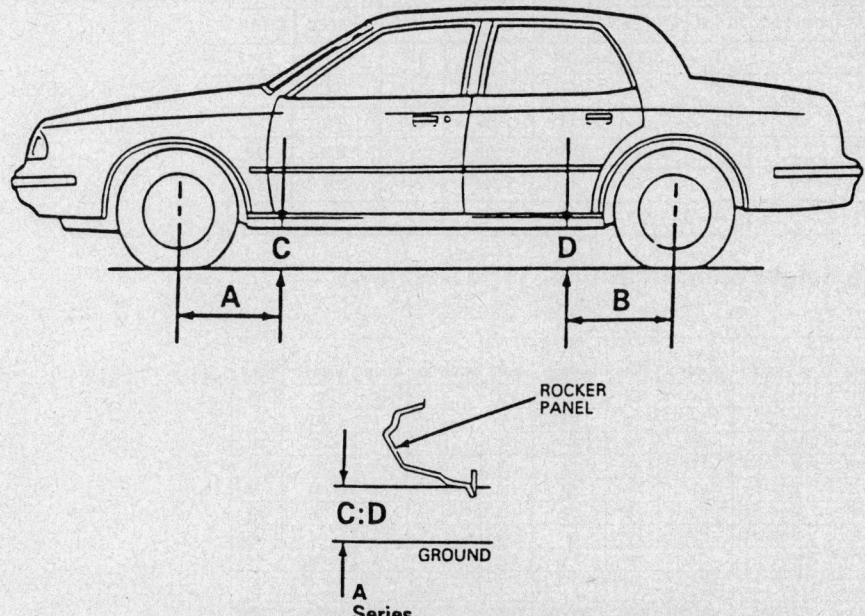

Fig. 1 Measurement location points. 1988 Cutlass Ciera, Cruiser and Century

MAXIMUM VARIATION SIDE TO SIDE AND FRONT TO REAR IS 19 mm (3/4")

		A	B	C	D
A	Series Coupe - Sedan Wagon	505 (19 7 8)	459 (18 1 16)	231 (9 3 32) 233 (9 11 64)	233 (9 11 64) 238 (9 3 8)

Specifications are in millimeters & (inches)

Fig. 2. Ride height specifications. 1988 Century

Camber and toe-in are the only adjustments that can be performed on these vehicles.

CAMBER

The camber angle is adjusted by loosening the strut cam bolt and the through bolt, then rotating the cam bolt to move the upper portion of the steering knuckle inward or outward. When correct camber angle is obtained, **torque** cam and through bolts to 140 ft. lbs.

When performing this adjustment, the top through bolt must be loosened to prevent damage to the outer cam guide.

TOE-IN

Toe-in is controlled by tie rod position. Adjustment is made by loosening the nuts at the steering knuckle end of the tie rods and rotating the rods to obtain proper toe-in setting. When adjusting toe-in, the tie rod boot clamps must be removed. After correct toe-in setting is obtained, **torque** tie rod nuts to 45 ft. lbs.

RIDE HEIGHT

Refer to **Figs. 1 through 16**, for ride height specifications and measurement location points.

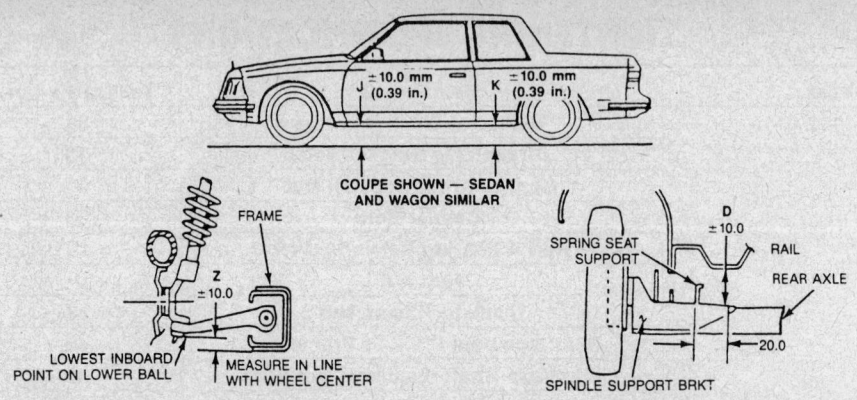

Fig. 3 Measurement location points. All models except 1988 Cutlass Ciera, Cruiser and Century

COUPE/SEDAN			Z		D		J		K	
SUSP	TRANS	TIRE SIZE	SHIPPED	CURB	SHIPPED	CURB	SHIPPED	CURB	SHIPPED	CURB
STD	AUTO	P185-75 R14	1	-1	204	191	240	236	254	242
STD	AUTO	P195-75 R14	1	-1	204	191	247	243	261	249
F40	ALL	P185-75 R14	0	-1	200	191	239	236	250	242
F40	ALL	P195-75 R14	0	-1	200	191	246	243	257	249
ZV8	AUTO	P195-75 R14	1	-1	204	191	246	242	260	248
ZV8	AUTO	P195-70 R14	1	-1	204	191	237	232	251	239
ZV8	MAN	P195-75 R14	-7	-8	204	191	240	236	258	247
ZV8	MAN	P195-70 R14	-7	-8	204	191	231	227	250	238

WAGON			Z		D		J		K	
SUSP	TRANS	TIRE SIZE	SHIPPED	CURB	SHIPPED	CURB	SHIPPED	CURB	SHIPPED	CURB
STD	AUTO	P185-75 R14	1	-1	198	191	239	236	247	241
STD	AUTO	P195-75 R14	1	-1	198	191	246	243	254	248
F40	ALL	P185-75 R14	0	-1	197	191	238	236	246	241
F40	ALL	P195-75 R14	0	-1	197	191	245	243	253	248
ZV8	AUTO	P195-75 R14	1	-1	198	191	244	241	253	246
ZV8	AUTO	P195-70 R14	1	-1	198	191	236	232	244	237

Fig. 4 Ride height specifications. 1988 Celebrity

COUPE/SEDAN					J		K		Z		D	
ENG	BUMPER CODE	SUSP	TRANS	TIRE SIZE	SHIPPED	CURB	SHIPPED	CURB	SHIPPED	CURB	SHIPPED	CURB
ALL	AAE/ABE	FE1	AUTO	P185-75 R14	240	236	251	242	1	-1	201	191
ALL	AAF/ABF	FE1	AUTO	P195-75 R14	247	243	258	249	1	-1	201	191
ALL	AAG/ABG	F40	AUTO	P185-75 R14	239	236	248	242	0	-1	198	191
ALL	AAH/ABH	F40	AUTO	P195-75 R14	246	243	255	249	0	-1	198	191
LR8	AAJ/ABJ	F41	AUTO	P195-75 R14	239	235	251	242	-6	-8	196	186
LR8	AAK/ABK	F41	AUTO	P195-70 R14	230	226	242	233	-6	-8	196	186
LB6	AAN/ABN	F41	AUTO	P195-75 R14	239	235	251	242	-6	-8	196	186
LB6	AAP/ABP	F41	AUTO	P195-70 R14	230	226	242	233	-6	-8	196	186
WAGON					J		K		Z		D	
ENG	BUMPER CODE	SUSP	TRANS	TIRE SIZE	SHIPPED	CURB	SHIPPED	CURB	SHIPPED	CURB	SHIPPED	CURB
LR8	ACA	FE1	AUTO	P185-75 R14	239	236	247	240	1	-1	198	191
LR8	ACB	FE1	AUTO	P195-75 R14	246	243	254	247	1	-1	198	191
LB6	ACC	FE1	AUTO	P185-75 R14	239	236	247	240	0	-1	198	191
LB6	ACD	FE1	AUTO	P195-75 R14	246	243	253	247	0	-1	198	191
ALL	ACG	F40	AUTO	P185-75 R14	238	236	246	240	0	-1	197	191
ALL	ACH	F40	AUTO	P195-75 R14	245	243	253	247	0	-1	197	191
LR8	ACU	F41	AUTO	P195-75 R14	239	236	248	242	-5	-7	195	188
LR8	ACK	F41	AUTO	P195-70 R14	230	227	239	233	-5	-7	195	188
LB6	ACN	F41	AUTO	P195-75 R14	239	236	248	242	-6	-7	195	188
LB6	ACP	F41	AUTO	P195-70 R14	230	227	230	233	-6	-7	195	188

Fig. 5 Ride height specifications. 1989 Celebrity

Cutlass Ciera
Exc. GT		236 mm (9-9/32")	238 mm (9-3/8")	238 mm (9-3/8")
4-Dr. GT	505 mm (19-7/8")	459 mm (18-1/16")	234 mm (9-3/16")	231 mm (9-3/32")
2-Dr. GT			226 mm (8-7/8")	228 mm (9")

Fig. 6   Ride height specifications. 1988 Cutlass Ciera & Cruiser

SUSPENSION	TIRE SIZE	Z (CURB)	D (CURB)	J (CURB)	K (CURB)
FE1	P185-75R14	−1mm (−.04 IN.)	191mm (7.52 IN.)	236mm (9.29 IN.)	240mm (9.45 IN.)
FE1	P195-75R14	−1mm (−.04 IN.)	191mm (7.52 IN.)	243mm (9.57 IN.)	247mm (9.72 IN.)
F41	P195-75R14	−1mm (−.04 IN.)	191mm (7.52 IN.)	241mm (9.49 IN.)	247mm (9.72 IN.)
F41	P195-70R14	−1mm (−.04 IN.)	191mm (7.52 IN.)	232mm (9.13 IN.)	238mm (9.37 IN.)

Fig. 7   Ride height specifications. 1990 Celebrity

SEDAN				Z		D		J		K	
ENGINE	SUSP	TRANS	TIRE SIZE	SHIPPED	CURB	SHIPPED	CURB	SHIPPED	CURB	SHIPPED	CURB
ALL	ALL	ALL	P185-75 R14	-9	-8	198	185	233	232	248	237
	ALL	ALL	P195-70 R14	-9	-8	198	185	233	233	248	237
	FE2	ALL	P195-70 R15	-6	-8	195	185	242	239	254	245

WAGON				Z		D		J		K	
ENGINE	SUSP	TRANS	TIRE SIZE	SHIPPED	CURB	SHIPPED	CURB	SHIPPED	CURB	SHIPPED	CURB
ALL	ALL	ALL	P185-75 R14	-9	-8	196	185	233	232	246	237

Fig. 8   Ride height specifications. 1988 6000

MODEL	SUSPENSION	TIRE SIZE	Z (CURB)	D (CURB)	J (CURB)	K (CURB)
WAGON	FE1	P185-75R14	−8mm (−.31 IN.)	185mm (7.28 IN.)	228mm (8.98 IN.)	233mm (9.17 IN.)
WAGON	FE2	P195-70R15	−8mm (−.31 IN.)	185mm (7.28 IN.)	240mm (9.45 IN.)	243mm (9.57 IN.)
WAGON	F40	P185-75R14	−8mm (−.31 IN.)	185mm (7.28 IN.)	230mm (9.06 IN.)	233mm (9.17 IN.)
SEDAN	FE1	P185-75R14	−8mm (−.31 IN.)	185mm (7.28 IN.)	231mm (9.09 IN.)	234mm (9.21 IN.)
SEDAN	FE2	P195-70R15	−8mm (−.31 IN.)	185mm (7.28 IN.)	239mm (9.41 IN.)	242mm (9.53 IN.)
SEDAN	FE2	P195-70R15	−8mm (−.31 IN.)	185mm (7.28 IN.)	241mm (9.49 IN.)	244mm (9.61 IN.)
SEDAN	F40	P185-75R14	−8mm (−.31 IN.)	185mm (7.28 IN.)	230mm (9.06 IN.)	234mm (9.21 IN.)

Fig. 9   Ride height specifications. 1989–90 6000

MODEL	SUSPENSION	TIRE SIZE	Z (CURB)	D (CURB)	J (CURB)	K (CURB)
WAGON	FE1-F40	P185-75R14	−8mm (−.31 IN.)	185mm (7.28 IN.)	228mm (8.98 IN.)	234mm (9.21 IN.)
WAGON	FE1-F40	P195-75R14	−8mm (−.31 IN.)	185mm (7.28 IN.)	239mm (9.40 IN.)	244mm (9.60 IN.)
SEDAN	FE1	P185-75R14	−8mm (−.31 IN.)	185mm (7.28 IN.)	228mm (8.97 IN.)	234mm (9.21 IN.)
SEDAN	FE2	P195-70R15	−8mm (−.31 IN.)	185mm (7.28 IN.)	239mm (9.41 IN.)	245mm (9.64 IN.)
SEDAN	FE2	P195-70R15	−8mm (−.31 IN.)	185mm (7.28 IN.)	238mm (9.37 IN.)	245mm (9.64 IN.)
SEDAN	F40	P185-75R14	−8mm (−.31 IN.)	185mm (7.28 IN.)	229mm (9.01 IN.)	234mm (9.21 IN.)

Fig. 10   Ride height specifications. 1991 6000

ALL DIMENSIONS IN MM

VEHICLE CONFIGURATION				Z		D		J		K	
MODEL	ENG	SUSP	TIRE SIZE	SHIPPED	CURB	SHIPPED	CURB	SHIPPED	CURB	SHIPPED	CURB
4AH35	LR8 LB6	FE1	P185-75 R14	−1	−5	197	190	236	233	244	238
4AH35	LR8 LB6	FE1	P195-75 R14	−8	−11	189	183	236	233	244	238
4AH35	ALL	F40	P185-75 R14	−2	−3	196	190	236	233	243	238
4AH35	ALL	F40	P195-75 R14	−9	−11	189	183	236	233	243	238
4AH37/69	LR8	FE1	P185-75 R14	−2	−4	191	181	235	231	242	233
4AH37/69	LR8	F41	P195-75 R14	−9	−11	183	174	235	231	242	233
4AH37/69	LB6	FE1	P185-75 R14	−2	−4	191	181	235	231	242	233
4AH37/69	LB6	F41	P195-75 R14	−9	−12	183	174	235	231	241	233
A4H37/69	LG7	F41	P195-75 R14	−9	−12	182	174	235	231	240	233
4AH37/69	ALL	FE2	P215-60 R14	5	3	197	190	235	231	240	233

Fig. 11   Ride height specifications. 1989 Century

MODEL	SUSPENSION	TIRE SIZE	Z (CURB)	D (CURB)	J (CURB)	K (CURB)
WAGON	FE1	P185-75R14	−1mm (−.04 IN.)	191mm (7.52 IN.)	235mm (9.25 IN.)	239mm (9.41 IN.)
WAGON	FE1	P195-75R14	−1mm (−.04 IN.)	191mm (7.52 IN.)	242mm (9.53 IN.)	246mm (9.69 IN.)
COUPE	FE1	P185-75R14	−1mm (−.04 IN.)	191mm (7.52 IN.)	236mm (9.29 IN.)	242mm (9.53 IN.)
COUPE	F41	P195-75R14	−1mm (−.04 IN.)	191mm (7.52 IN.)	243mm (9.57 IN.)	249mm (9.80 IN.)
SEDAN	FE1	P185-75R14	−1mm (−.04 IN.)	191mm (7.52 IN.)	236mm (9.29 IN.)	242mm (9.53 IN.)
SEDAN	F41	P195-75R14	−1mm (−.04 IN.)	191mm (7.52 IN.)	243mm (9.57 IN.)	249mm (9.80 IN.)

Fig. 12   Ride height specifications. 1990 Century

MODEL	SUSPENSION	TIRE SIZE	Z (CURB)	D (CURB)	J (CURB)	K (CURB)
WAGON	FE1	P185-75R14	−1mm (−.04 IN.)	191mm (7.52 IN.)	236mm (9.29 IN.)	240mm (9.44 IN.)
WAGON	FE1	P195-75R14	−1mm (−.04 IN.)	191mm (7.52 IN.)	242mm (9.53 IN.)	246mm (9.69 IN.)
COUPE	FE1	P185-75R14	−1mm (−.04 IN.)	191mm (7.52 IN.)	236mm (9.29 IN.)	242mm (9.53 IN.)
SEDAN	FE1	P185-75R14	−1mm (−.04 IN.)	191mm (7.52 IN.)	236mm (9.29 IN.)	242mm (9.53 IN.)
SEDAN	F41	P195-75R14	−1mm (−.04 IN.)	191mm (7.52 IN.)	243mm (9.57 IN.)	249mm (9.80 IN.)

Fig. 13   Ride height specifications. 1991 Century

ALL DIMENSIONS IN MM

MODEL	ENG	SUSP	PKG.	TIRE SIZE	Z SHIPPED	Z CURB	D SHIPPED	D CURB	J SHIPPED	J CURB	K SHIPPED	K CURB
3AA35	ALL	FE1	BASE	P185-75 R14	3	1	202	195	241	238	250	243
3AA35	ALL	FE1	BASE	P195-70 R14	4	2	203	196	241	238	250	243
3AA35	ALL	FE2	BASE	P185-75 R14	2	0	201	195	241	238	249	243
3AA35	ALL	FE2	BASE	P195-70 R14	3	2	202	196	241	238	249	243
3AA37/69	LR8 LB6	FE1	BASE	P185-75 R14	2	0	197	187	240	236	247	238
3AA37/69	LR8 LB6	FE1	BASE	P195-70-R14	4	2	198	188	240	236	247	238
3AA37/69	LR8 LB6	FE2	BASE	P185-75 R14	2	0	195	187	239	236	246	238
3AA37/69	LR8 LB6	FE2	BASE	P195-70-R14	3	1	197	189	239	236	246	238
3AA37/69	LR8 LB6	FE2 FE3	BASE	P215-60 R14	9	8	204	195	239	236	246	238
3AA37/69	LG7	FE1	BASE	P185-75 R14	2	0	195	187	239	236	246	238
3AA37/69	LG7	FE1	BASE	P195-70 R14	4	2	197	189	239	236	246	238
3AA37/69	LG7	FE2	BASE	P185-75 R14	2	0	195	187	239	236	246	238
3AA37/69	LG7	FE2	BASE	P195-70 R14	4	2	197	189	239	236	246	238
3AA37/69	LG7	FE2 FE3	BASE	P215-60 R14	10	8	204	195	240	236	246	238
3AJ37	L67	FE3	W45	P215-60 R14	-1	-3	194	185	229	226	236	228
3AJ69	LG7	FE3	W49	P215-60 R14	4	2	200	191	234	231	242	234

Fig. 14   Ride height specifications. 1989 Cutlass Ciera & Cruiser

MODEL	SUSPENSION	TIRE SIZE	Z (CURB)	D (CURB)	J (CURB)	K (CURB)
WAGON	FE1	P185-75R14	−1mm (−.04 IN.)	191mm (7.52 IN.)	236mm (9.29 IN.)	240mm (9.45 IN.)
WAGON	FE1	P195-75R14	−1mm (−.04 IN.)	191mm (7.52 IN.)	243mm (9.57 IN.)	247mm (9.72 IN.)
WAGON	FE1	P195-70R14	−1mm (−.04 IN.)	191mm (7.52 IN.)	234mm (9.21 IN.)	238mm (9.37 IN.)
COUPE/SEDAN	FE1	P185-75R14	−1mm (−.04 IN.)	191mm (7.52 IN.)	236mm (9.29 IN.)	240mm (9.45 IN.)
COUPE/SEDAN	FE1	P195-75R14	−1mm (−.04 IN.)	191mm (7.52 IN.)	243mm (9.57 IN.)	247mm (9.72 IN.)
COUPE/SEDAN	FE1	P195-70R14	−1mm (−.04 IN.)	191mm (7.52 IN.)	234mm (9.21 IN.)	239mm (9.41 IN.)
COUPE/SEDAN	FE3	P215-60R14	−1mm (−.04 IN.)	191mm (7.52 IN.)	227mm (8.94 IN.)	232mm (9.13 IN.)
COUPE	FE3	P215-60R14	−1mm (−.04 IN.)	191mm (7.52 IN.)	227mm (8.94 IN.)	232mm (9.13 IN.)
SEDAN	FE3	P215-60R14	−1mm (−.04 IN.)	191mm (7.52 IN.)	227mm (8.94 IN.)	232mm (9.13 IN.)

Fig. 15   Ride height specifications. 1990 Cutlass Ciera & Cruiser

MODEL	SUSPENSION	TIRE SIZE	Z (CURB)	D (CURB)	J (CURB)	K (CURB)
WAGON	FE1	P185-75R14	−1mm (−.04 IN.)	191mm (7.52 IN.)	234mm (9.21 IN.)	238mm (9.37 IN.)
WAGON	FE1	P195-75R14	−1mm (−.04 IN.)	191mm (7.52 IN.)	234mm (9.21 IN.)	246mm (9.68 IN.)
WAGON	FE1	P195-70R14	−1mm (−.04 IN.)	191mm (7.52 IN.)	232mm (9.13 IN.)	237mm (9.33 IN.)
COUPE/SEDAN	FE1	P185-75R14	−1mm (−.04 IN.)	191mm (7.52 IN.)	234mm (9.21 IN.)	240mm (9.45 IN.)
COUPE/SEDAN	FE1	P195-75R14	−1mm (−.04 IN.)	191mm (7.52 IN.)	241mm (9.48 IN.)	247mm (9.72 IN.)
COUPE/SEDAN	FE1	P195-70R14	−1mm (−.04 IN.)	191mm (7.52 IN.)	232mm (9.13 IN.)	238mm (9.68 IN.)
SEDAN	FE3	P195-75R14	−1mm (−.04 IN.)	191mm (7.52 IN.)	241mm (9.48 IN.)	248mm (9.76 IN.)

Fig. 16   Ride height specifications. 1991 Cutlass Ciera & Cruiser

FRONT WHEEL DRIVE BUICK ELECTRA, LESABRE & PARK AVE., CADILLAC DEVILLE & FLEETWOOD, OLDSMOBILE EIGHTY EIGHT & NINETY EIGHT & PONTIAC BONNEVILLE
(C & H Cars)

INDEX OF SERVICE OPERATIONS

NOTE: Refer To The Rear Of This Manual For Vehicle Manufacturer's Special Service Tool Suppliers.

*FRONT WHEEL DRIVE BUICK ELECTRA, LESABRE & PARK AVE., CADILLAC DEVILLE &
FLEETWOOD, OLDSMOBILE EIGHTY EIGHT & NINETY EIGHT & PONTIAC BONNEVILLE (C & H CARS)*

5-1

INDEX OF SERVICE OPERATIONS—Continued

Specifications

GENERAL ENGINE SPECIFICATIONS

Year	Engine		Carburetor	Bore and Stroke	Compression Ratio	Net H.P. @ RPM [2]	Maximum Torque Ft. Lbs. @ RPM	Normal Oil Pressure Pounds
	Liter/CID	VIN Code [1]						
1988	3.8L/V6-231	3	Fuel Injection	3.80 x 3.40	8.50	150 @ 4400	200 @ 2000	37
	3800/V6-231	C	Fuel Injection	3.80 x 3.40	8.50	165 @ 5200	210 @ 2000	37
	4.5/V8-273L	5	Fuel Injection	3.62 x 3.31	9.0	155 @ 4000	240 @ 2600	30
1989	3800/V6-231	C	Fuel Injection	3.80 x 3.40	8.50	165 @ 5200	210 @ 2000	37
	4.5L/V8-273	5	Fuel Injection	3.62 x 3.31	9.0	155 @ 4000	240 @ 2800	30
1990	3800/V6-231	C	Fuel Injection	3.80 x 3.40	8.50	165 @ 5200	210 @ 2000	37
	4.5L/V8-273	—	Fuel Injection	3.62 x 3.31	9.5	180 @ 4300	245 @ 3000	—
1991	3800/V6-231	C	Fuel Injection	3.80 x 3.40	8.50	165 @ 5200	210 @ 2000	37
	3800/V6-231	L	Fuel Injection	3.80 x 3.40	8.50	170 @ 5200	220 @ 3200	37
	4.9L/V8-300	—	Fuel Injection	3.62 x 3.62	9.5	200 @ 4100	275 @ 3000	—

①—The eighth digit denotes engine code.

②—Ratings are net-as installed in vehicle.

TUNE UP SPECIFICATIONS

Year & Engine/V. I.N. Code ①	Spark Plug Gap	Firing Order Fig. ②	Ignition Timing BTDC			Curb Idle Speed		Fast Idle Speed		Fuel Pump Pressure
			Man. Trans.	Auto. Trans.	Mark Fig.	Man. Trans.	Auto Trans.	Man. Trans.	Auto. Trans.	
1988										
3.8L/V6-231/3	.045	⑥	—	⑦	⑧	—	③	—	③	40–47⑤
3800/V6-231/C	.045	⑥	—	⑦	⑧	—	③	—	③	40–47⑤
4.5L/V8-273/5	.060	A	—	10⑧	B	—	④	—	④	9–12⑦
1989										
3800/V6-231/C	.045	⑥	—	⑦	⑧	—	③	—	③	40–47⑤
4.5L/V8-273/5	.060	A	—	10⑧	B	—	④	—	④	9–12⑦
1990										
3800/V6-231/C	.045	⑥	—	⑦	⑧	—	③	—	③	40–47⑤
4.5L/V8-273/3	—	—	—	—	—	—	—	—	—	—
1991										
3800/V6-231/C	.045	⑥	—	⑦	⑧	—	③	—	③	40–47⑤
3800/V6-231/L	.045	⑥	—	⑦	⑧	—	③	—	③	40–47⑤
4.9L/V8-300/—	—	—	—	—	—	—	—	—	—	—

①—The eighth digit of the Vehicle Identification Number (V.I.N.) denotes engine code.

②—Before removing wires from distributor cap, determine location of No. 1 wire in cap, as distributor position may have been altered from that shown at the end of this chart.

③—Idle speed is controlled by an idle speed control (ISC) motor or an idle air control (IAC) valve.

④—Connect jumper wire between ALCL connector terminals A & B. The ALCL connector is located under the instrument panel to the right of the steering column. After completing adjustment, disconnect jumper wire from between terminals A & B. With engine off, clear trouble code from Electronic Control Module (ECM) memory by removing battery voltage from ECM for 30 seconds.

⑤—With shop towel wrapped around fuel pressure valve to prevent fuel spillage, connect a suitable fuel pressure gauge to fuel pressure valve. Check fuel pressure with ignition switch in the On position, engine not running.

⑥—Cylinder numbering left to right as viewed from front of vehicle, front bank, 1, 3, 5; rear bank, 2, 4, 6. Firing order 1-6-5-4-3-2. Two different types computer controlled coil ignition systems are used. Refer to Figs. C & D for spark plug wire connections at coil unit.

⑦—Computer controlled, no adjustment.

⑧—Equipped with crankshaft position sensor.

FIRING ORDER 1-8-4-3-6-5-7-2

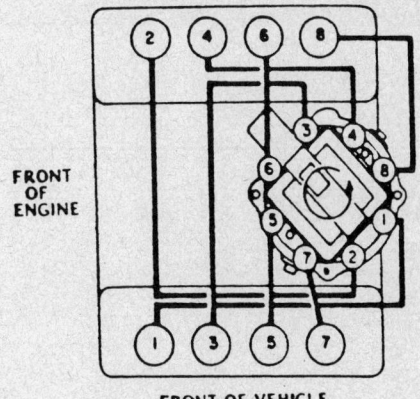

Fig. A

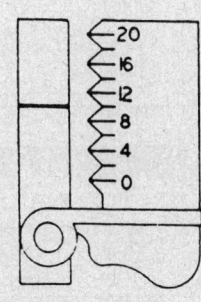

Fig. B

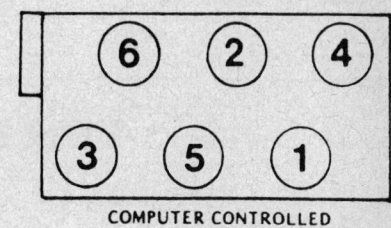

COMPUTER CONTROLLED COIL IGNITION

Fig. C

SPECIFICATIONS—Continued

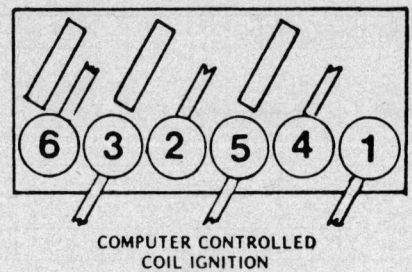

COMPUTER CONTROLLED
COIL IGNITION

Fig. D

FRONT WHEEL ALIGNMENT SPECIFICATIONS

Year	Model	Caster Angle, Degrees		Camber Angle, Degrees				Toe-In Inch
		Limits	Desired	Limits		Desired		
				Left	Right	Left	Right	
1988	Bonneville	+2 to +3	+2.5	−.3 to +.7	−.3 to +.7	+.2	+.2	①
	DeVille & Fleetwood	+2.5 to +3.5	+3	−1 to 0	0 to +1	−.5	+.5	①
	Electra & LeSabre	+2.5 to +3.5	+3	−.3 to +.7	−.3 to +.7	+.2	+.2	①
	88 & 98	+2.5 to +3.5	+3	−.3 to +.7	−.3 to +.7	+.2	+.2	①
1989	Bonneville	+2.5 to +3.5	+3	−.3 to +.7	−.3 to +.7	+.2	+.2	①
	DeVille & Fleetwood	+2.5 to +3.5	+3	−1 to 0	0 to +1	−.5	+.5	②
	Electra & LeSabre	+2.5 to +3.5	+3	−.3 to +.7	−.3 to +.7	+.2	+.2	①
	88 & 98	+2.5 to +3.5	+3	−.3 to +.7	−.3 to +.7	+.2	+.2	①
1990	Bonneville	+2.5 to +3.5	+3	−.3 to +.7	−.3 to +.7	+.2	+.2	①
	DeVille & Fleetwood	+2.5 to +3.5	+3	−1 to 0	0 to +1	−.5	+.5	②
	Electra & LeSabre	+2.5 to +3.5	+3	−.3 to +.7	−.3 to +.7	+.2	+.2	①
	88 & 98	+2.5 to +3.5	+3	−.3 to +.7	−.3 to +.7	+.2	+.2	①
1991	Bonneville	+2.5 to +3.5	+3	−.3 to +.7	−.3 to +.7	.0	.0	②
	DeVille & Fleetwood	+2.5 to +3.5	+3	−1 to 0	0 to +1	−.5	+.5	②
	LeSabre	+2.5 to +3.5	+3	−.3 to +.7	−.3 to +.7	.0	.0	②
	Park Avenue	+2.5 to +3.5	+3	−.3 to +.7	−.3 to +.7	.0	.0	①
	88 & 98	+2.5 to +3.5	+3	−.3 to +.7	−.3 to +.7	.0	.0	②

①—Total toe, −.3° to +.3°.
②—Total toe; −2° to +.2°.

REAR WHEEL ALIGNMENT SPECIFICATIONS

Year	Model	Camber Angle, Degrees		Toe-In, Inches
		Limits	Desired	
1988	Bonneville	−.8 to +.2	−.3	②
	DeVille & Fleetwood	−.8 to +.2	−.3	②
	Electra & LeSabre	−.8 to +.2	−.3	②
	88 & 98	−.8 to +.2	−.3	①
1989	Bonneville	−.8 to +.2	−.3	②
	DeVille & Fleetwood	−.8 to +.2	−.3	②
	Electra & LeSabre	−.8 to +.2	−.3	②
	88 & 98	−.8 to +.2	−.3	②

Continued

REAR WHEEL ALIGNMENT SPECIFICATIONS —Continued

Year	Model	Camber Angle, Degrees		Toe-In, Inches
		Limits	Desired	
1990	Bonneville	−.8 to +.2	−.3	②
	DeVille & Fleetwood	−.8 to +.2	−.3	②
	Electra & LeSabre	−.8 to +.2	−.3	②
	88 & 98	−.8 to +.2	−.3	②
1991	Bonneville	−.8 to +.2	−.3	②
	DeVille & Fleetwood	−.8 to +.2	−.3	②
	LeSabre	−.8 to +.2	−.3	②
	Park Avenue	−.8 to +.2	−.3	②
	88 & 98	−.8 to +.2	−.3	②

①—Toe-in. 1° per wheel.
②—Total toe, −.1° to +.3°.

ALTERNATOR SPECIFICATIONS

Year	Model	Rated Hot Output Amps.
1988	1101310	105
	1101316	120
1989-90	1101310	105
	1101316	120
	1101519	120
1991	1101577	105
	1101580	140

STARTING MOTOR APPLICATIONS

Year	Engine/VIN	Starter Ident. No.
1988	3.8L/V6-231/3	1998544
	3800/V6-231/C	1998544
	4.5L/V8-273/5	—
1989	3800/V6-231/C	1998544
	4.5L/V8-273/5	10455024
1990	3800/V6-231/C	10455024
	4.5L/V8-273/	10455024
1991	3800/V6-231/C	10455024
	3800/V6-231/L	10455024
	3800/V6-231/L	10455706

COOLING SYSTEM & CAPACITY DATA

Year	Model	Engine/VIN	Cooling Capacity, Qts.	Radiator Cap Relief Pressure, Lbs.	Thermo. Opening Temp.	Fuel Tank Gals.	Engine Oil Refill Qts.	Auto. Transaxle Qts. ①
1988	Bonneville	3800/V6-231/C	13	15	195	18	4②	③
		3.8L/V6-231/3	13	15	195	18	4②	③
	Electra/Park Avenue	3800/V6-231/C	13	15	195	18	4②	③
	DeVille/Fleetwood	4.5L/V8-273/5	13.2	15	195	18	5②	③
	LeSabre	3.8L/V6-231/3	13	15	195	18	4②	③
	88	3.8L/V6-231/3	13	15	195	18	4②	③
	98	3800/V6-231/C	13	15	195	18	4②	③
1989	Bonneville	3800/V6-231/C	13	15	195	18	4②	③
	Electra/Park Avenue	3800/V6-231/C	13	15	195	18	4②	③
	Deville/Fleetwood	4.5L/V8-273/5	13.2	15	195	18	5②	③
	LeSabre	3800/V6-231/C	13	15	195	18	4②	③
	88 & 98	3800/V6-231/C	13	15	195	18	4②	③
1990	Bonneville	3800/V6-231/C	13	15	195	18	4②	③
	DeVille/Fleetwood	V8-273/5	13.2	15	195	18	5②	③
	Electra/Park Avenue	3800/V6-231/C	13	15	195	18	4②	③
	LeSabre	3800/V6-231/C	13	15	195	18	4②	③
	88 Royale & 98 Regency	3800/V6-231/C	13	15	195	18	4②	③
1991	Bonneville	3800/V6-231/C	13	15	195	18	4②	③
	DeVille/Fleetwood	4.9L/V8-300/—	13.2	15	195	18	5②	③
	LeSabre	3800/V6-231/C	13	15	195	18	4②	③
	Park Avenue/Park Avenue Ultra	3800/V6-231/L	13	15	195	18	4②	③
	88 Royale	3800/V6-231/C	13	15	195	18	4②	③
	98 Regency	3800/V6-231/L	13	15	195	18	4②	③

①—Approximate, make final check with dipstick.
②—Additional oil may be required to bring oil level to full mark when changing oil filter.
③—Oil pan capacity, 6 qts.; total capacity, 11 qts.

Electrical
INDEX

FUSE PANEL & FLASHER LOCATION

The fuse panel is located under the left-hand side of the instrument panel.

The hazard flasher is located on the fuse panel and the turn signal flasher is located on the underside of the steering column.

STARTER
REPLACE

When removing starter, note if any shims are used between the starter and mounting surface. If shims are found, reinstall in original locations.

If starter is noisy during cranking, remove one .015 inch double shim or add one .015 inch single shim to the outer bolt. If starter makes a high pitched whine after engine start, add .015 inch double shims until noise ceases.

1. Disconnect battery ground cable and raise and support vehicle.
2. Remove starter braces, shields or other components that may hinder starter removal.
3. Support starter and remove mounting bolts.
4. Lower starter and disconnect solenoid wires and battery cable.
5. Remove starter from vehicle.
6. Reverse procedure to install. Refer to previous note.

DISABLING SUPPLEMENTAL INFLATABLE RESTRAINT (SIR) SYSTEM

EXCEPT CADILLAC, 1991 OLDS 98 & 1991 PARK AVENUE

1. Turn ignition switch to "Lock" position.
2. Disconnect and tape end of battery ground cable. **Wait 15 seconds before continuing to step 3.**
3. Remove three of four module to steering wheel attaching screws from backside of steering wheel.
4. Support module with one hand and carefully remove fourth screw, then disconnect and tape module connector.

CADILLAC, 1991 OLDS 98 & 1991 PARK AVENUE

The following procedure must be followed in order listed to temporarily disable the SIR system and prevent false diagnostic codes from setting. Failure to follow this procedure could result in possible air bag deployment, personal injury, or unneeded SIR system repairs.
1. Turn ignition switch off, then disconnect and tape end of battery ground cable.

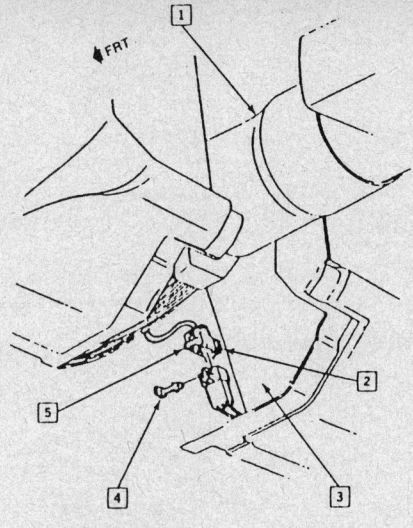

1. STEERING COLUMN ASSEMBLY
2. EDGE METAL CLIP
3. IP LOWER TIE BAR ASSEMBLY
4. CONNECTOR POSITION ASSURANCE (CPA)
5. SIR HARNESS CONNECTOR

Fig. 1   Removing connector position assurance

2. Remove inflatable restraint fuse No. 3 on Buick and Cadillac, No. 7 on Olds 98.
3. Remove lefthand side sound insulator.
4. Remove Connector Position Assurance (CPA), **Fig. 1.**
5. Disconnect yellow two-way SIR harness connector located at base of steering column.

STEERING WHEEL
REPLACE
EXCEPT MODELS W/INFLATABLE RESTRAINT SYSTEM
STANDARD & TILT WHEEL

1. Disconnect battery ground cable.
2. **On models with control pad assembly,** pry out control pad using a thin bladed tool.
3. **On models less control pad assembly,** remove two steering wheel pad retaining screws.
4. **On all models,** disconnect horn wire from cam tower.
5. **On models with control pad assembly,** pry rocker button and push button from control pad.
6. **On all models,** remove steering wheel nut retainer.
7. Remove steering wheel retaining nut.
8. Using a suitable puller, remove steering wheel.
9. Reverse procedure to install.

TELESCOPING WHEEL
Except Cadillac

1. Disconnect battery ground cable.

2. Remove two steering wheel pad retaining screws.
3. Disconnect horn wire from steering wheel pad.
4. Remove steering shaft lock knob bolt positioning screws, then the lock knob bolt from steering shaft.
5. Remove steering wheel nut retainer and the steering wheel nut. Using a suitable puller, remove steering wheel.
6. Reverse procedure to install.

Cadillac

1. Disconnect battery ground cable.
2. Remove two steering wheel pad retaining screws.
3. Disconnect horn wire from steering wheel pad.
4. Remove three screws from telescoping adjusting lever.
5. Remove steering shaft lock knob from steering shaft.
6. Remove steering wheel nut.
7. Using a suitable puller, remove steering wheel.
8. Reverse procedure to install.

MODELS w/INFLATABLE RESTRAINT SYSTEM
Except Cadillac, 1991 Olds 98 & 1991 Park Avenue

1. Turn ignition switch to "Lock" position.
2. Disconnect and tape end of battery ground cable. **Wait 15 seconds before continuing to step 3.**
3. Remove three of four module to steering wheel attaching screws from backside of steering wheel.
4. Support module with one hand and carefully remove fourth screw, then disconnect and tape module connector.
5. Disconnect horn lead.
6. Remove retaining and nut.
7. Using a suitable puller, remove steering wheel.
8. Reverse procedure to install.

Cadillac, 1991 Olds 98 & 1991 Park Avenue

1. Turn ignition switch to "Lock" position.
2. Disconnect and tape end of battery ground cable.
3. Remove inflatable restraint fuse No. 3 on Buick and Cadillac, No. 7 on Olds 98.
4. Remove left sound insulator.
5. Remove connector position assurance, then disconnect yellow two-way SIR harness connector, **Fig. 1.**
6. Remove module retaining screws from back of steering wheel.
7. Remove module from steering wheel, then disconnect horn contact, by pushing slightly and twisting counterclockwise.
8. Remove connector position assurance, then disconnect coil assembly connector, **Fig. 2.**
9. Remove steering wheel retaining nut.
10. Using puller tool No. J1859-03 or equivalent, remove steering wheel.
11. Reverse procedure to install, noting the following:

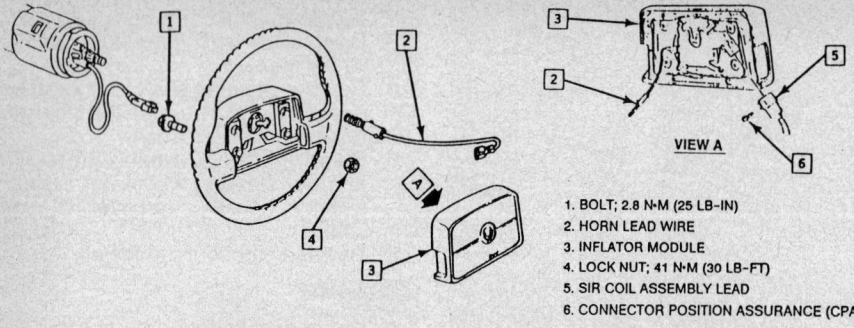

1. BOLT; 2.8 N·M (25 LB-IN)
2. HORN LEAD WIRE
3. INFLATOR MODULE
4. LOCK NUT; 41 N·M (30 LB-FT)
5. SIR COIL ASSEMBLY LEAD
6. CONNECTOR POSITION ASSURANCE (CPA)

VIEW A

Fig. 2   Inflator module assembly

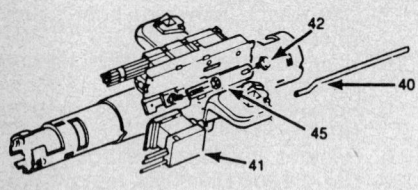

40. ROD, DIMMER SWITCH ACTUATOR
41. SWITCH ASSY, DIMMER
42. SCREW, WASHER HEAD
45. NUT, HEXAGON

Fig. 4   Ignition switch removal. Standard column

43. STUD, DIMMER & IGNITION SWITCH MOUNTING
44. SWITCH ASSY, IGNITION

Fig. 5   Dimmer switch removal. Standard column

TO ASSEMBLE, ROTATE TO STOP WHILE HOLDING CYLINDER.

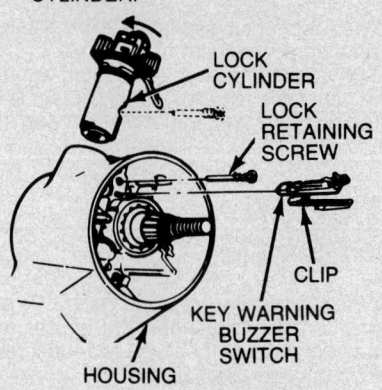

LOCK CYLINDER
LOCK RETAINING SCREW
CLIP
KEY WARNING BUZZER SWITCH
HOUSING

Fig. 3   Lock cylinder removal

64. SCREW, WASH. HD (#10-24 x .25)
65. STUD, DIMR & IGN SW MOUNTING
66. SWITCH ASM, IGN & BEAM CHANGE
68. SWITCH, DIMMER
74. NUT, HEXAGON (#10-24 x .25)

Fig. 6   Ignition & dimmer switch removal. Tilt column & column w/Supplemental Inflatable Restraint (SIR)

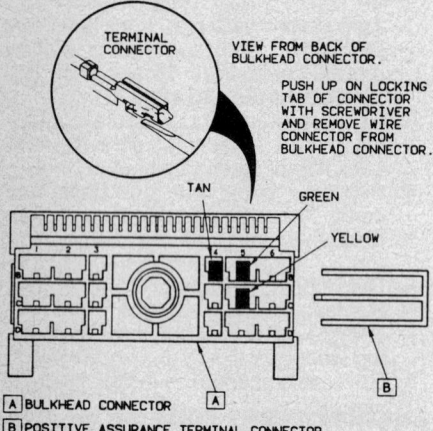

TERMINAL CONNECTOR

VIEW FROM BACK OF BULKHEAD CONNECTOR.

PUSH UP ON LOCKING TAB OF CONNECTOR WITH SCREWDRIVER AND REMOVE WIRE CONNECTOR FROM BULKHEAD CONNECTOR.

TAN   GREEN
YELLOW

Ⓐ BULKHEAD CONNECTOR
Ⓑ POSITIVE ASSURANCE TERMINAL CONNECTOR

Fig. 7   Disconnecting dimmer switch from bulkhead connector

a. **Torque** steering wheel nut to 30 ft. lbs.
b. **Torque** module retaining screws to 25 inch lbs.
c. Turn ignition switch to Run position and ensure "Inflatable Restraint" indicator flashes 7 to 9 times and turns Off.

IGNITION LOCK
REPLACE

Disable the Supplemental Inflatable Restraint (SIR) system as described in "Disabling Supplemental Inflatable Restraint (SIR) System" prior to working on or near the steering column.
1. Remove steering wheel as described in "Steering Wheel, Replace."

2. Remove turn signal switch as described in "Turn Signal Switch, Replace."
3. Remove key from lock cylinder, then remove buzzer switch from column housing.
4. Reinsert key and turn lock cylinder to LOCK position, then remove lock cylinder retaining screw and lock cylinder, **Fig. 3**.
5. To install, rotate lock cylinder to the stop while holding housing. Align cylinder key with keyway in housing, then push lock cylinder into housing until fully seated.
6. Install lock cylinder retaining screw.
7. Install buzzer switch, turn signal switch and steering wheel.

IGNITION & DIMMER SWITCHES
REPLACE

Disable the Supplemental Inflatable Restraint (SIR) system as described in "Disabling Supplemental Inflatable Restraint (SIR) System" prior to working on or near the steering column.
1. Remove turn signal switch as outlined under "Turn Signal Switch, Replace" procedure.
2. Refer to **Figs. 4, 5 and 6** to remove ignition and dimmer switches.
3. Refer to **Fig. 7** to disconnect dimmer switch from bulkhead connector.
4. When installing dimmer switch, depress switch slightly to install a 3/32 inch twist drill. Force switch upward to remove lash and tighten retaining screw.

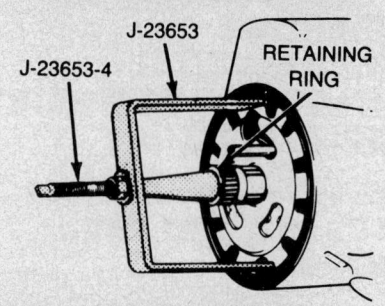

J-23653
J-23653-4
RETAINING RING

TIGHTEN NUT UNTIL TOOL SLIGHTLY DEPRESSES SHAFT LOCK

Fig. 8   Compressing lock plate

TURN SIGNAL SWITCH
REPLACE

Disable the Supplemental Inflatable Restraint (SIR) system as described in "Disabling Supplemental Inflatable Restraint (SIR) System" prior to working on or near the steering column.

1988–90

1. Disconnect battery ground cable.
2. Remove steering wheel as described in "Steering Wheel, Replace."
3. **On models with inflatable restraint,**

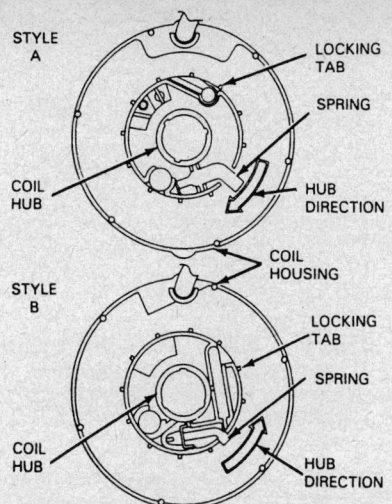

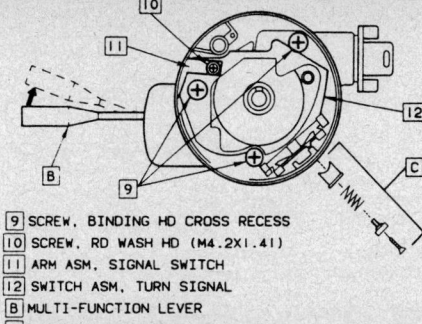

9 SCREW, BINDING HD CROSS RECESS
10 SCREW, RD WASH HD (M4.2X1.41)
11 ARM ASM, SIGNAL SWITCH
12 SWITCH ASM, TURN SIGNAL
B MULTI-FUNCTION LEVER
C HAZARD KNOB ASSEMBLY

Fig. 10   Multi-function lever and hazard knob assembly removal

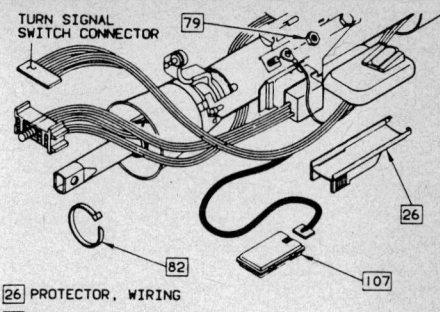

26 PROTECTOR, WIRING
79 NUT, HEXAGON (#10-24)
82 STRAP, WIRE HARNESS
107 MODULE ASM, E & C INTERFACE

Fig. 11   Turn signal switch removal

PERFORM THE FOLLOWING STEPS TO CENTER COIL ASSEMBLY:

A. REMOVE COIL ASSEMBLY.
B. HOLD COIL ASSEMBLY WITH CLEAR BOTTOM UP TO SEE COIL RIBBON.
C. NOTE: THERE ARE TWO DIFFERENT STYLES OF COILS. ONE ROTATES CLOCKWISE AND THE OTHER ROTATES COUNTERCLOCKWISE.
D. WHILE HOLDING COIL ASSEMBLY, DEPRESS SPRING LOCK TO ROTATE HUB IN DIRECTION OF ARROW UNTIL IT STOPS.
E. THE COIL RIBBON SHOULD BE WOUND UP SNUG AGAINST CENTER HUB.
F. ROTATE COIL HUB IN OPPOSITE DIRECTION APPROXIMATELY TWO AND A HALF (2½) TURNS. RELEASE SPRING LOCK BETWEEN LOCKING TABS ADJACENT TO ARROW (AS SHOWN).

Fig. 9   Centering coil assembly

remove coil assembly retaining ring, then the coil assembly from shaft. Allow coil assembly to hang freely.

4. Using lock plate compressing tool J-23653-A, compress lock plate and pry snap ring from shaft groove, **Fig. 8.** Slowly release lock plate compressor and remove tool and lock plate from shaft end.
5. Slide cancelling cam and upper bearing preload spring from end of shaft.
6. Remove turn signal switch lever.
7. Remove hazard warning knob retaining screw, button, spring and knob.
8. Remove pivot arm.
9. Wrap upper portion of electrical connector with tape to prevent snagging of wires during switch removal.
10. Remove switch retaining screws and pull switch up from column, guiding wiring harness through column.
11. Reverse procedure to install. If necessary center coil assembly as shown, **Fig. 9.**

1991

1. Remove steering wheel as described in "Steering Wheel, Replace."
2. Using lock plate compressor tool No. J 23653-C or equivalent, push down shaft lock and remove shaft lock retaining ring.
3. Remove shaft lock, turn signal cancelling cam assembly, upper bearing spring, upper bearing inner race seat and inner race.

4. Set turn signal to RIGHT TURN position, then remove multi-function lever and hazard knob assembly, **Fig. 10.**
5. Remove signal switch arm retaining screw and switch arm.
6. Remove turn signal switch attaching screws, then signal switch as follows:
   a. Disconnect turn signal switch connector from bulkhead connector and wire harness strap, **Fig. 11.**
   b. Disconnect E & C module connector from signal switch harness.
   c. Remove wiring protector, then nut holding ground wire to stud.
   d. Gently pull wire harness through column.
7. Reverse procedure to install.

WIPER SWITCH
REPLACE

Disable the Supplemental Inflatable Restraint (SIR) system as described in "Disabling Supplemental Iflatable Restraint (SIR) System" prior to working on or near the steering column.

1. Remove turn signal switch as outlined under "Turn Signal Switch, Replace" procedure.
2. Refer to **Figs. 12 through 15,** for switch replacement.

PARK/NEUTRAL & BACKUP LAMP SWITCH
REPLACE

1. Disconnect battery ground cable.
2. Disconnect shift cable from transaxle.
3. Disconnect electrical connector from switch.
4. Remove two switch mounting bolts and the switch.
5. Align flats on switch with flats on transaxle shaft and push switch over shaft and fully seat on transaxle.
6. Install and **torque** switch mounting bolts to 20 ft. lbs. **If switch was rotated and the pin broken, the switch will be automatically reset to the neutral position as follows:**
   a. Place transaxle shaft in neutral position.
   b. Install switch on transaxle as outlined previously and loosely install mounting bolts.

c. Insert a ³/₃₂ inch gauge pin into service adjustment hole of switch.
d. Rotate switch until pin drops in detent.
e. **Torque** mounting bolts to 20 ft. lbs.

HEADLAMP SWITCH
REPLACE

BUICK
Refer to **Figs. 16 and 17** for switch replacement.

CADILLAC
Refer to **Fig. 18** for switch replacement.

OLDSMOBILE
Refer to **Figs. 19 and 20,** for switch replacement.

PONTIAC
Refer to **Fig. 21** for switch replacement.

INSTRUMENT CLUSTER
REPLACE

Disable the Supplemental Inflatable Restraint (SIR) system as described in "Disabling Supplemental Iflatable Restraint (SIR) System" prior to working on or near the steering column.

BUICK
Except 1991 Park Avenue

1. Disconnect battery ground cable.
2. Remove upper trim pad, **Fig. 22,** as follows:
   a. Remove defroster grille, then the A/C outlets from upper trim pad.
   b. Remove instrument panel trim plates, then 10 instrument panel pad retaining screws.
   c. **On models equipped with twilight sentinel,** pop up photocell retainer, then remove photocell by turning counterclockwise.
   d. **On all models,** slide panel pad out far enough to disconnect aspirator tube and in-car temperature sensor electrical connector.
   e. Remove pad.

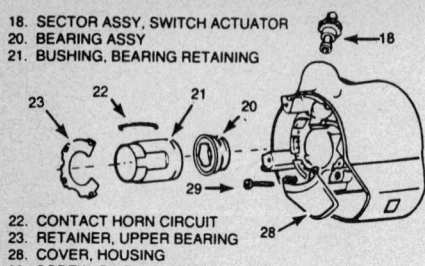

18. SECTOR ASSY, SWITCH ACTUATOR
20. BEARING ASSY
21. BUSHING, BEARING RETAINING

22. CONTACT HORN CIRCUIT
23. RETAINER, UPPER BEARING
28. COVER, HOUSING
29. SCREW, BINDING HEAD

Fig. 12   Lock housing cover removal. Standard column

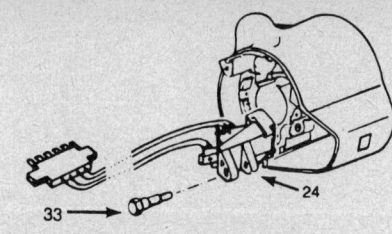

24. SWITCH ASSY, PIVOT &
33. PIN, SWITCH ACTUATOR PIVOT

Fig. 13   Wiper switch removal. Standard column

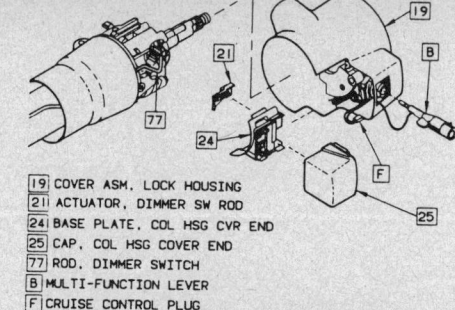

19. COVER ASM, LOCK HOUSING
21. ACTUATOR, DIMMER SW ROD
24. BASE PLATE, COL HSG CVR END
25. CAP, COL HSG COVER END
77. ROD, DIMMER SWITCH
B. MULTI-FUNCTION LEVER
F. CRUISE CONTROL PLUG

Fig. 14   Lock housing cover removal. Tilt column & columns w/Supplemental Inflatable Restraint (SIR)

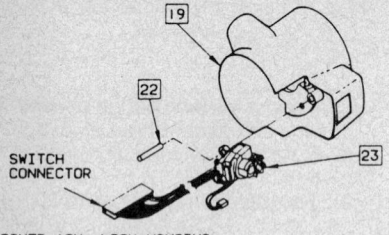

19 COVER ASM, LOCK HOUSING
22 PIN, SWITCH ACTUATOR PIVOT
23 SWITCH ASM, PIVOT & (PULSE)

Fig. 15   Wiper switch removal. Tilt column & columns w/Supplemental Inflatable Restraint (SIR)

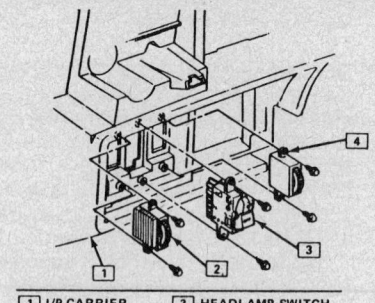

1 I/P CARRIER   3 HEADLAMP SWITCH
2 INTERIOR LIGHT   4 TWILIGHT SENTINEL
  DIMMER   SWITCH

Fig. 16   Headlamp switch removal. Buick except 1991 Park Avenue

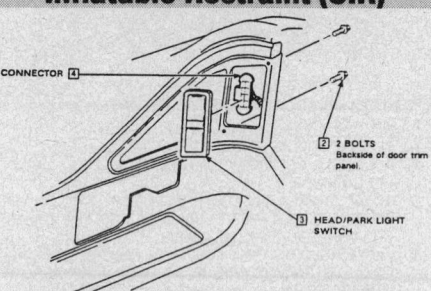

CONNECTOR 4

2 BOLTS
Backside of door trim panel.

3 HEAD/PARK LIGHT SWITCH

Fig. 17   Headlamp switch removal. 1991 Park Avenue

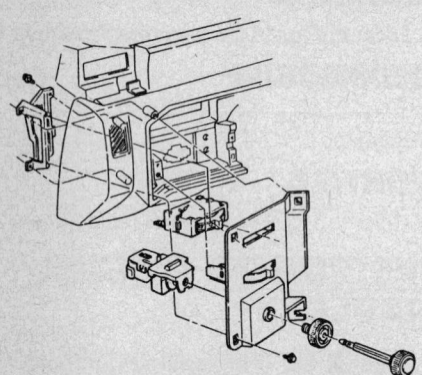

Fig. 18   Headlamp switch removal. DeVille & Fleetwood

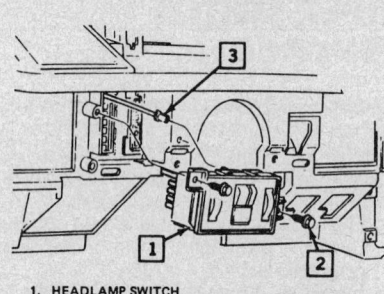

1. HEADLAMP SWITCH
2. FULLY DRIVEN, SEATED AND NOT STRIPPED
3. PLUG FIBER OPTIC INTO REAR OF SWITCH ASM.

Fig. 19   Headlamp switch removal. Oldsmobile except 1991 98

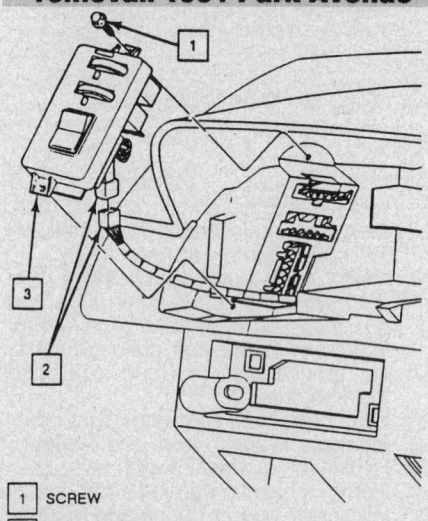

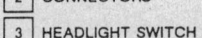

1 SCREW
2 CONNECTORS
3 HEADLIGHT SWITCH

Fig. 20   Headlamp switch removal. 1991 98

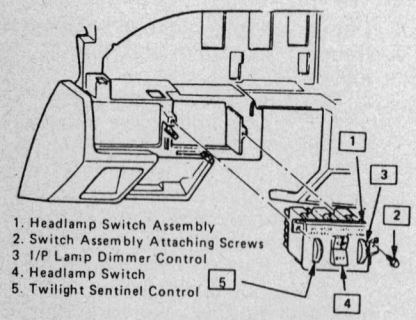

1. Headlamp Switch Assembly
2. Switch Assembly Attaching Screws
3. I/P Lamp Dimmer Control
4. Headlamp Switch
5. Twilight Sentinel Control

Fig. 21   Headlamp switch removal. Bonneville

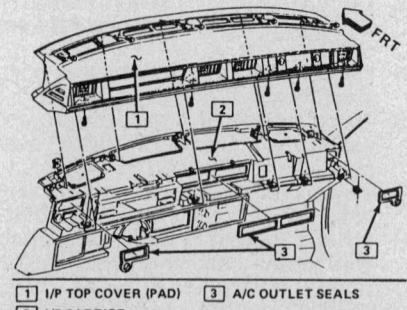

1 I/P TOP COVER (PAD)   3 A/C OUTLET SEALS
2 I/P CARRIER

Fig. 22   Removing instrument panel top cover pad. Buick except 1991 Park Avenue

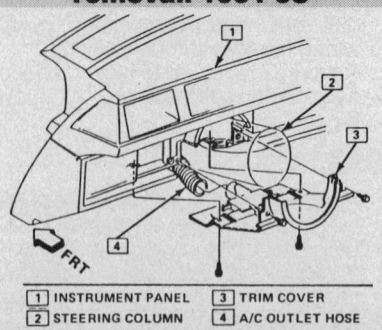

1 INSTRUMENT PANEL   3 TRIM COVER
2 STEERING COLUMN   4 A/C OUTLET HOSE

Fig. 23   Removing steering column cover to disconnect shift cable. Buick except 1991 Park Avenue

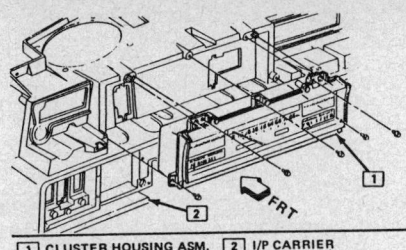

1 CLUSTER HOUSING ASM.   2 I/P CARRIER

Fig. 24   Cluster removal. Buick except 1991 Park Avenue

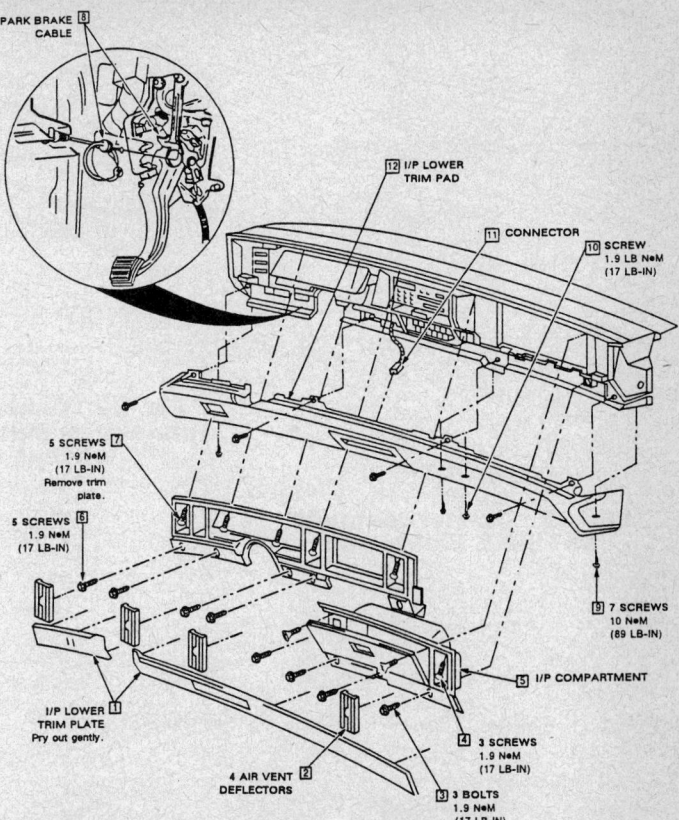

Fig. 25   Removing I/P trim pad & trim panels. 1991 Park Avenue

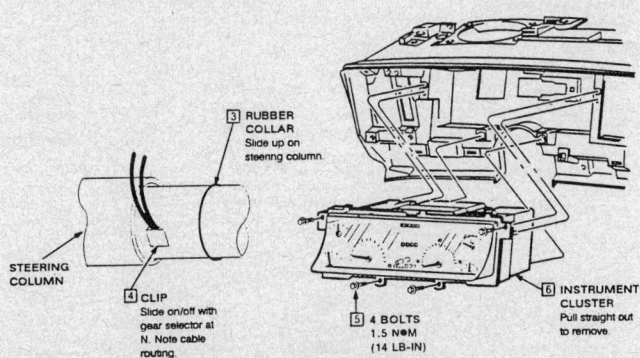

Fig. 26   Removing instrument cluster. 1991 Park Avenue

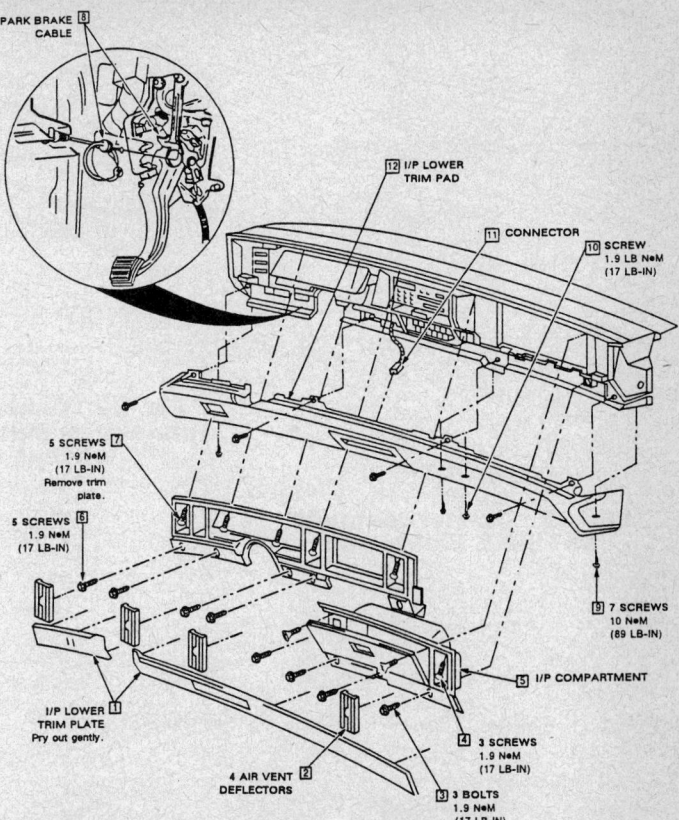

1 CHART – PAD ASSEMBLY
2 SCREW
3 SCREW
4 NUT
5 GRILLE
6 NUT
23 OUTLET

Fig. 27   Upper trim pad assembly. DeVille & Fleetwood

3. **On models with analog cluster,** Remove steering column filler panel, **Fig. 23,** then disconnect shift indicator cable from steering column.
4. **On all models,** remove five instrument cluster attaching screws, then the cluster, **Fig. 24.**

1991 Park Avenue

1. Disconnect battery ground cable.
2. Remove right and left side sound insulators.
3. Remove instrument panel lower trim plates, **Fig. 25.**

4. Remove air vent deflectors, then three glove box attaching bolts.
5. Remove five instrument panel trim plate attaching screws, then trim plate.
6. Remove seven lower instrument panel trim pad to instrument panel attaching screws.
7. Slide rubber collar up steering column, then slide clip off with gear selector as shown in **Fig. 26.**
8. Remove five instrument cluster to instrument panel attaching bolts, then pull cluster straight out.
9. Reverse procedure to install.

CADILLAC

1. Disconnect battery ground cable.
2. Remove upper trim pad as follows:
   a. Remove A/C outlets from upper trim pad.
   b. Remove screws locations 2 and 3 from both side of pad, **Fig. 27.**
   c. Remove upper trim pad.
3. Remove screw (88) and plate (87), **Fig. 28.**
4. Remove cluster attaching screws.
5. Disconnect wiring from rear of cluster and remove cluster from vehicle.
6. Reverse procedure to install.

OLDSMOBILE

Except 1991 98

1. Disconnect battery ground cable.
2. Remove center trim plate, **Fig. 29.**
3. Remove three cluster trim plate attaching screws, then the cluster trim plate, **Fig. 30.**
4. Remove five instrument cluster retaining screws, then disconnect shift indicator cable, if equipped.
5. Disconnect cluster electrical connectors.
6. Remove cluster assembly.
7. Reverse procedure to install.

1991 98

1. Disconnect battery ground cable.
2. Remove cluster trim plate to instrument panel attaching screws, **Fig. 31.**
3. Tilt trim plate rearward and disconnect driver information display and

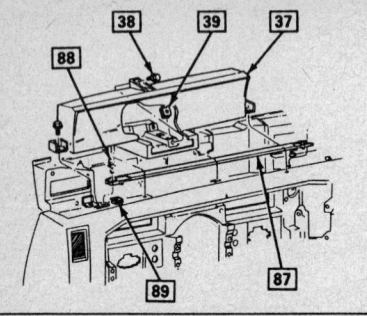

37 CLUSTER ASSEMBLY
38 SCREW
39 NUT
87 PLATE
88 SCREW
89 NUT

**Fig. 28   Cluster removal.
DeVille & Fleetwood**

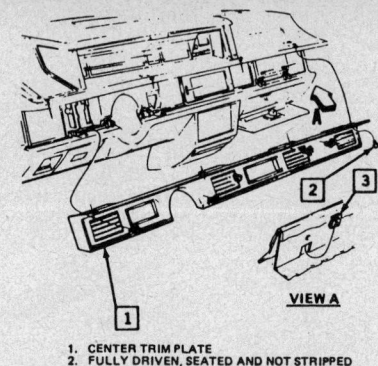

1. CENTER TRIM PLATE
2. FULLY DRIVEN, SEATED AND NOT STRIPPED
3. NUT

**Fig. 29   Center instrument
panel trim plate. Oldsmobile
except 1991 98**

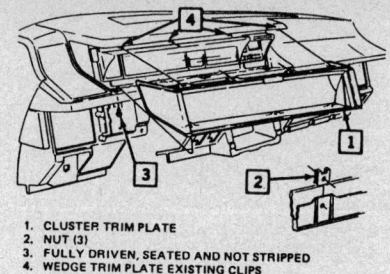

1. CLUSTER TRIM PLATE
2. NUT (3)
3. FULLY DRIVEN, SEATED AND NOT STRIPPED
4. WEDGE TRIM PLATE EXISTING CLIPS
   AND I.P. PAD ASSEMBLY

**Fig. 30   Cluster removal.
Oldsmobile except 1991 98**

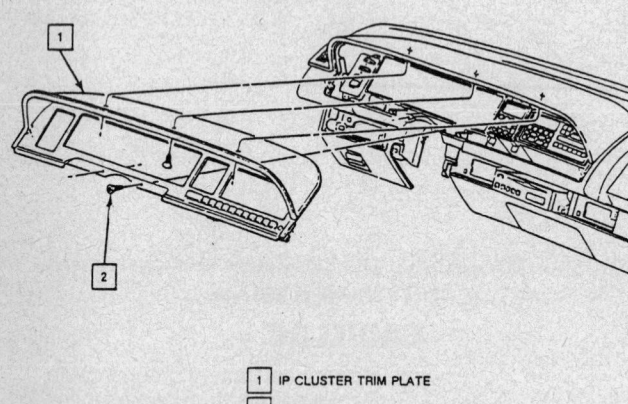

1 IP CLUSTER TRIM PLATE
2 SCREW

Fig. 31   Cluster trim plate removal. 1991 98

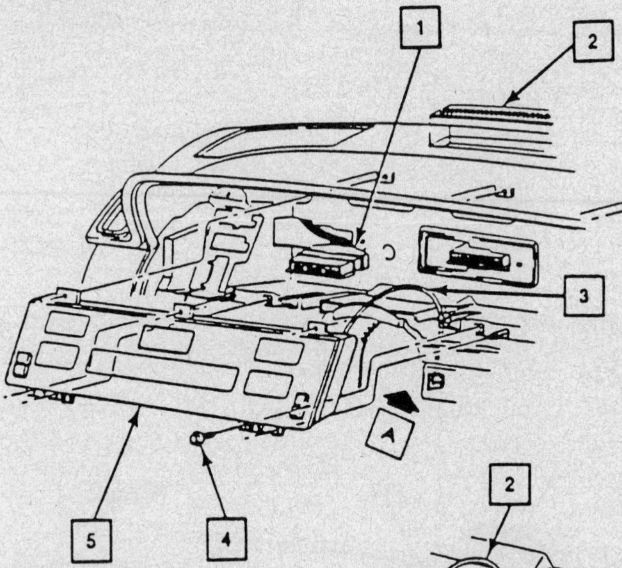

defogger/heated windshield connectors.
4. Remove cluster trim plate, then cluster to instrument panel attaching screws, **Fig. 32.**
5. Pull cluster rearward, then disconnect cluster electrical connector and PRNDL cable.
6. Remove cluster assembly.
7. Reverse procedure to install.

PONTIAC

1. Disconnect battery ground cable.
2. **On models with tilt wheel,** place wheel in lowest position.
3. **On all models,** place selector lever in position "1."
4. lightly pry around perimeter of trim-plate, then remove trimplate.
5. Remove IP trimplate, then the speaker, side defogger and defroster grilles.
6. Remove speaker attaching screws and electrical connectors.
7. Remove I/P pad.
8. Remove 5 attaching screws, **Fig. 33,** then disconnect PRNDL cable from steering column bowl.
9. Remove instrument cluster.
10. Reverse procedure to install.

1 CLUSTER CONNECTOR
2 WINDSHIELD DEFROSTER GRILLE
3 PRNDL CABLE
4 BOLT
5 CLUSTER ASSEMBLY

VIEW A

Fig. 32   Cluster removal. 1991 98

RADIO
REPLACE

Disable the Supplemental Inflatable Restraint (SIR) system as described in "Disabling Supplemental Iflatable Restraint (SIR) System" prior to working on or near the steering column.

BUICK
Except 1991 Park Avenue

1. Remove lower RH trim plate.
2. Remove four radio retaining screws,

then pull radio out of dash and disconnect electrical connectors and antenna lead.
3. Remove radio, **Fig. 34.**
4. Reverse procedure to install.

1991 Park Avenue

1. Disconnect battery ground cable.
2. Remove instrument panel lower trim plates and four air vent deflectors by prying gently.
3. Remove bolts and screws that attach the glove box to the instrument panel, **Fig. 35.**

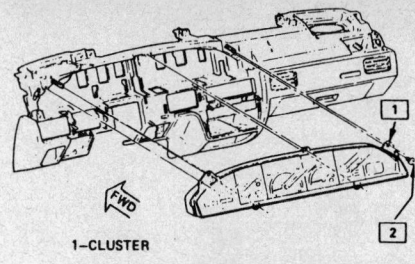

1—CLUSTER

2—FULLY DRIVEN, SEATED, NOT STRIPPED

Fig. 33 Cluster removal. Bonneville

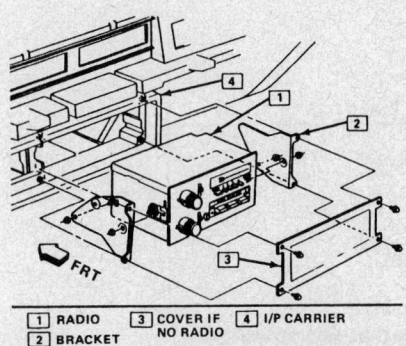

1	RADIO	3	COVER IF NO RADIO
2	BRACKET	4	I/P CARRIER

Fig. 34 Radio installation. Buick except 1991 Park Avenue

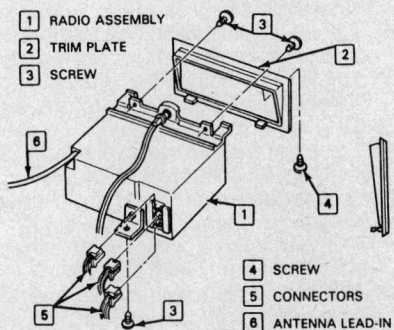

1	RADIO ASSEMBLY
2	TRIM PLATE
3	SCREW
4	SCREW
5	CONNECTORS
6	ANTENNA LEAD-IN

Fig. 36 Radio installation. 1988 DeVille & Fleetwood

4. Remove five instrument panel trim plate attaching screws.
5. Remove five radio to instrument panel attaching bolts and nuts, **Fig. 35.**
6. Pull radio straight back and disconnect electrical connectors and antenna.
7. Reverse procedure to install.

CADILLAC

1988

1. Disconnect battery ground cable.
2. Remove radio trim plate, **Fig. 36.**
3. Remove screws from rear support bracket and front of radio. The ashtray must be opened for access.

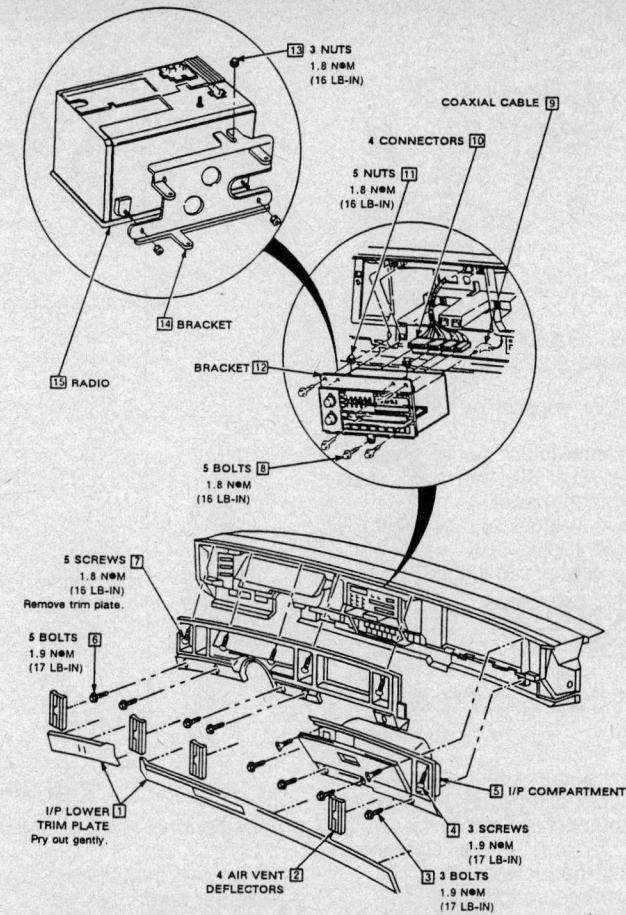

Fig. 35 Radio removal & installation. 1991 Park Avenue

4. Remove light bulb and socket.
5. Disconnect electrical connectors from radio.
6. Disconnect antenna lead from radio.
7. Remove radio from vehicle.
8. Reverse procedure to install.

1989–90

1. Disconnect battery ground cable.
2. Remove radio trim plate, **Fig. 37.**
3. Open ashtray and remove one screw from rear support bracket.
4. Remove two screws from front of radio, then pull radio straight out and disconnect electrical connectors and antenna.
5. Remove four bracket retaining nuts and brackets.
6. Reverse procedure to install.

OLDSMOBILE

Except 1991 98

1. Remove center and lower trim plates.
2. Remove four radio retaining screws, then slide radio rearward and disconnect electrical connectors and antenna lead.
3. Remove radio, **Fig. 38.**
4. Reverse procedure to install.

1991 98

1. Remove instrument cluster trim plate

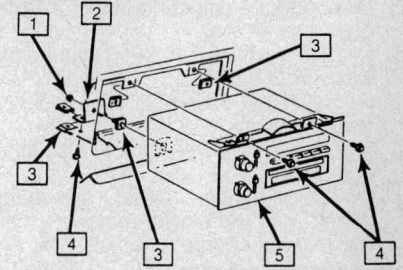

1. NUT; 4N•M (35 LB-IN)	4. BOLT/SCREW 1.9 N•M (17 LB-IN)
2. BRACKET	
3. NUT	5. RADIO

Fig. 37 Radio installation. 1989–90 DeVille & Fleetwood

as described in "Instrument Cluster, Replace."
2. Remove five radio to instrument panel attaching screws.
3. Pulling radio rearward, disconnect electrical connectors and antenna.
4. Remove radio mounting brackets.
5. Reverse procedure to install.

PONTIAC

1. Remove instrument panel trim plate.
2. Disconnect two wires from lighter, then remove ashtray.
3. Remove radio upper mounting bracket retaining screws.

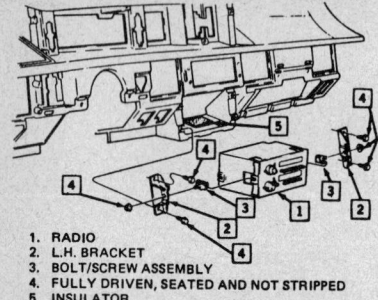

1. RADIO
2. L.H. BRACKET
3. BOLT/SCREW ASSEMBLY
4. FULLY DRIVEN, SEATED AND NOT STRIPPED
5. INSULATOR

Fig. 38 Radio replace. Oldsmobile except 1991 98

4. Remove rear support bracket retaining screw.
5. Press on instrument panel engagement tabs, **Fig. 39**, then pull radio from instrument panel.
6. Disconnect electrical connectors, then remove radio.
7. Reverse procedure to install.

BLOWER MOTOR
REPLACE

EXCEPT 1988 BUICK & PONTIAC

1. Disconnect battery ground cable.
2. Disconnect cooling tube and blower motor electrical connector.
3. Remove blower motor attaching screws and the blower motor.
4. Reverse procedure to install.

1988 BUICK & PONTIAC

1. Disconnect battery ground cable.
2. Disconnect electrical connector from coil.
3. Disconnect Nos. 2, 4 and 6 spark plug wires from coil.
4. Remove coil assembly and position aside.
5. Disconnect blower motor electrical connector.
6. Remove blower motor attaching screws and the blower motor.
7. Reverse procedure to install.

HEATER CORE
REPLACE
EXCEPT CADILLAC

1. Disconnect battery ground cable.
2. Drain cooling system.
3. Remove right sound insulator.
4. Remove center and lower instrument panel trim plates.
5. **On models with automatic climate control**, remove speaker grille and speaker for access to programmer attaching bolt.
6. Disconnect wiring and hoses from programmer.
7. Remove programmer linkage cover and disconnect linkage.
8. Remove programmer attaching bolt and the programmer.
9. **On all models**, remove heater core cover, then the splash cover for access to heater hoses.

10. Disconnect heater hoses from heater core.
11. Remove heater core cover, then the heater core.
12. Reverse procedure to install.

CADILLAC

1. Disconnect battery ground cable.
2. Remove glove box attaching screws, then the glove box.
3. Remove lower sound insulator attaching screws and nuts, then the lower sound insulator.
4. Remove programmer as follows:
   a. Remove programmer shield attaching screws, then the programmer shield.
   b. Disconnect threaded rod from programmer.
   c. Disconnect programmer electrical and vacuum connector, then remove programmer.
5. Disconnect body control module electrical connector, then remove module attaching screws and module.
6. Remove relay panel from module assembly, then the module assembly heater core cover.
7. Disconnect heater hoses from heater core.
8. Remove two heater core attaching screws, then the heater core.
9. Reverse procedure to install.

EVAPORATOR CORE
REPLACE
CADILLAC

1. Disconnect battery ground cable.
2. Drain coolant, then remove front dash cover and vacuum tank.
3. Remove relay pack, EGR solenoid valve and related parts.
4. Loosen wiring harness from front of dash and position aside.
5. Disconnect heater hoses from evaporator module.
6. Remove MAP sensor, sensor bracket and attaching rods from dash panel.
7. Remove wiring harness brackets from lift cover and position out of the way.
8. Discharge A/C system.
9. Remove washer reservoir, then disconnect all accumulator lines.
10. Disconnect upper hose from power steering pump and position aside.
11. Remove blower motor and exhaust manifold heat shield, **Fig. 40**.
12. Disconnect all wiring and connectors attached to evaporator and blower module.
13. Remove all brackets around barrier insulator, then all screws and bolts around insulator.
14. Raise and support vehicle.
15. Cut barrier insulator on mark line, located on right side of barrier insulator.
16. Remove evaporator core.
17. Reverse procedure to install.

1988 OLDSMOBILE, PONTIAC & 1988–89 BUICK

1. Disconnect battery ground cable.
2. Discharge A/C system, then remove engine compartment rear sight shield.
3. Disconnect four electrical connections and remove relay bracket assembly, **Fig. 41**.
4. Disconnect accumulator to condenser hose.

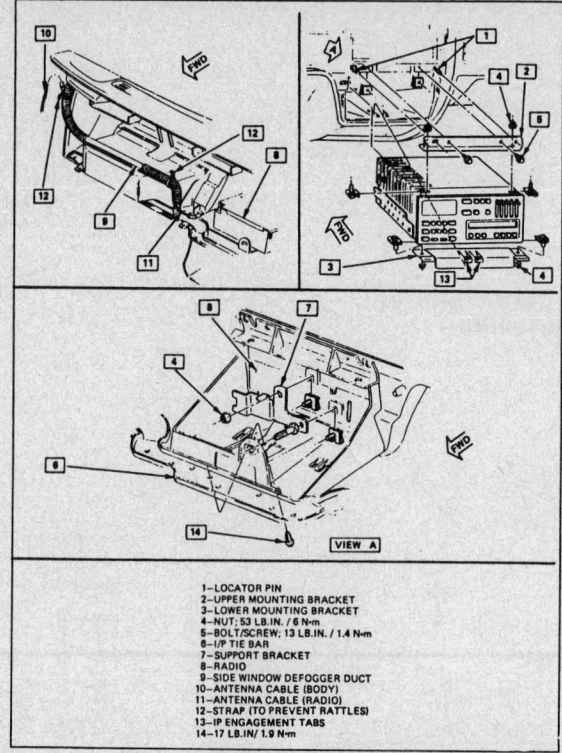

1-LOCATOR PIN
2-UPPER MOUNTING BRACKET
3-LOWER MOUNTING BRACKET
4-NUT; 53 LB.IN. / 6 N-m
5-BOLT/SCREW; 13 LB.IN. / 1.4 N-m
6-I/P TIE BAR
7-SUPPORT BRACKET
8-RADIO
9-SIDE WINDOW DEFOGGER DUCT
10-ANTENNA CABLE (BODY)
11-ANTENNA CABLE (RADIO)
12-STRAP (TO PREVENT RATTLES)
13-IP ENGAGEMENT TABS
14-17 LB.IN./ 1.9 N-m

Fig. 39 Radio replace. Bonneville

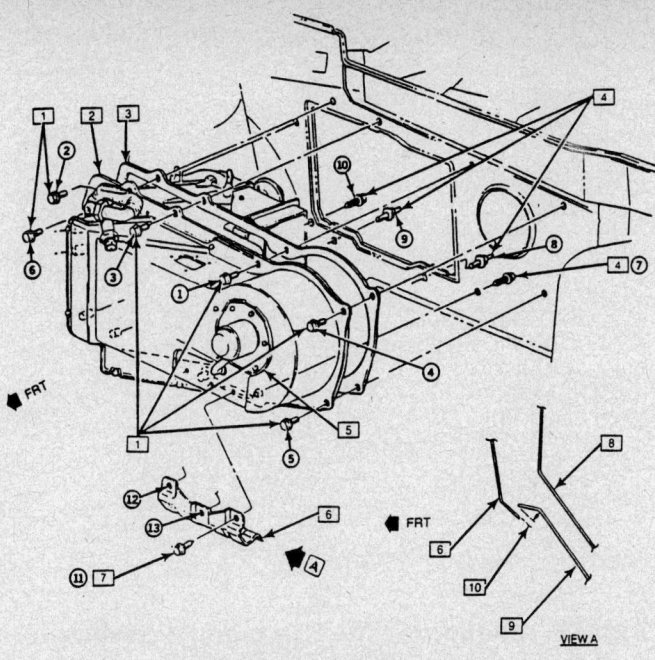

1. BOLT/SCREW; 3 N•M (27 LB-IN)
2. EVAPORATOR AND BLOWER MODULE
3. GASKET
4. BOLT/SCREW; 3.4 N•M (30 LB-IN)
5. BLOWER MOTOR
6. SHIELD
7. BOLT/SCREW: 1.9 N•M (17 LB-IN)
8. DASH PANEL
9. CATALYTIC CONVERTER HEAT SHIELD
10. 13.0 MM (APPROXIMATELY)

Fig. 40   Evaporator removal. DeVille & Fleetwood

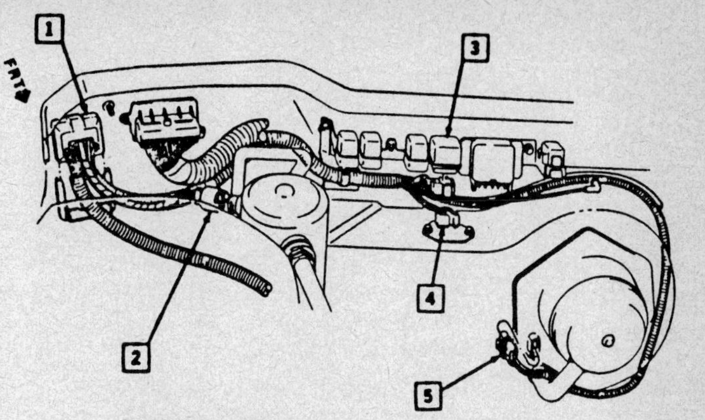

1. HARNESS ASM.
2. CYCLING PRESSURE SWITCH CONNECTOR
3. A/C HIGH BLOWER RELAY
4. RESISTOR CONNECTOR
5. BLOWER MOTOR FEED & GROUND

Fig. 41   Wiring harness & relays. 1988 Oldsmobile, Pontiac & 1988–89 Buick

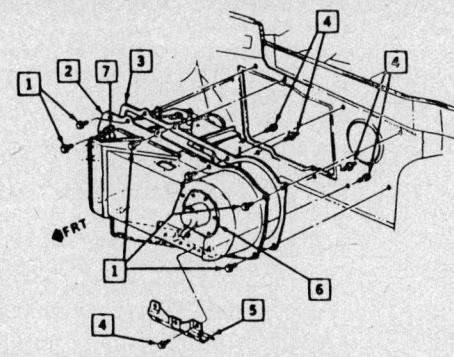

1. 3 N•m (27 LBS. IN.)
2. MODULE
3. GASKET
4. 3.4 N•m (30 LBS. IN.)
5. SHIELD
6. BLOWER MOTOR
7. EVAPORATOR

Fig. 42   Blower module assembly. 1988 Oldsmobile, Pontiac & 1988–89 Buick

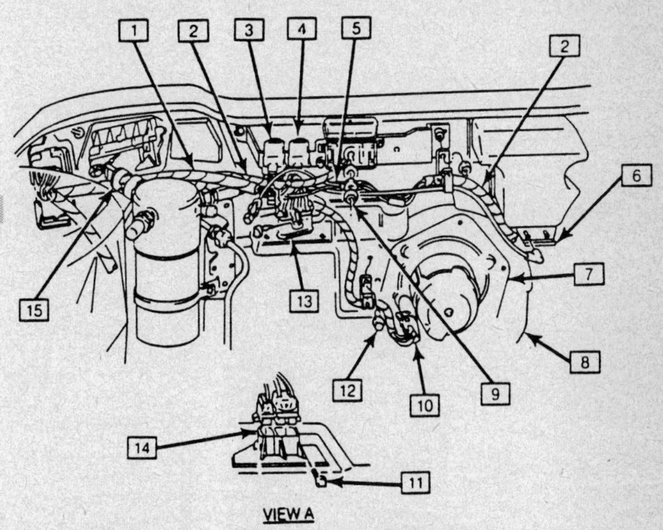

1. DASH HARNESS
2. POSITIVE BATTERY HARNESS
3. BLOWER MOTOR RELAY (C60)
4. A/C CUT OUT RELAY
5. DASH HARNESS
6. VACUUM TANK
7. BLOWER MOTOR
8. HEATER AND A/C MODULE
9. NUT: 17 N•M (150 LB-IN)
10. BLOWER MOTOR CONNECTION
11. RETAINER
12. BOLT/SCREW: 1.5 N•M (13 LB-IN)
13. RESISTOR ASSEMBLY (C60)
14. BLOWER CONTROL MODULE (C68)
15. PRESSURE CYCLING SWITCH CONNECTOR

Fig. 43   Wiring harness & relays. 1989–90 Oldsmobile, Pontiac & 1990 Buick

5. Disconnect electrical connector from pressure cycling switch, then the evaporator outlet line from accumulator.
6. Remove accumulator bracket and accumulator, cap accumulator openings.
7. Disconnect tube from condenser to evaporator, then disconnect power steering pump hose and position aside.
8. Remove vacuum tank and blower motor.
9. Remove exhaust manifold heat shield and blower motor resistor.
10. Remove evaporator outlet line and support bracket.
11. Raise and support vehicle, then remove three lower evaporator module attaching bolts.
12. Cut rubber blower barrier along guide line, then lower vehicle.
13. Remove seven upper evaporator and blower module attaching bolts, **Fig. 42.**
14. Finish cutting rubber barrier along guide lines and remove evaporator core from module.
15. Reverse procedure to install, sealing barrier with strip calk where it had been cut.

1989–90 OLDSMOBILE, PONTIAC & 1990 BUICK

Brazed fittings are used on the condenser and evaporator. These fittings cannot be turned. It is important that the service technician recognize which fitting is to be turned and use backup wrenches. The brazed fitting that should not be turned is always the same color as the pipe it is brazed to.

1. Disconnect battery ground cable.
2. Discharge A/C system, then remove engine compartment rear sight shield.

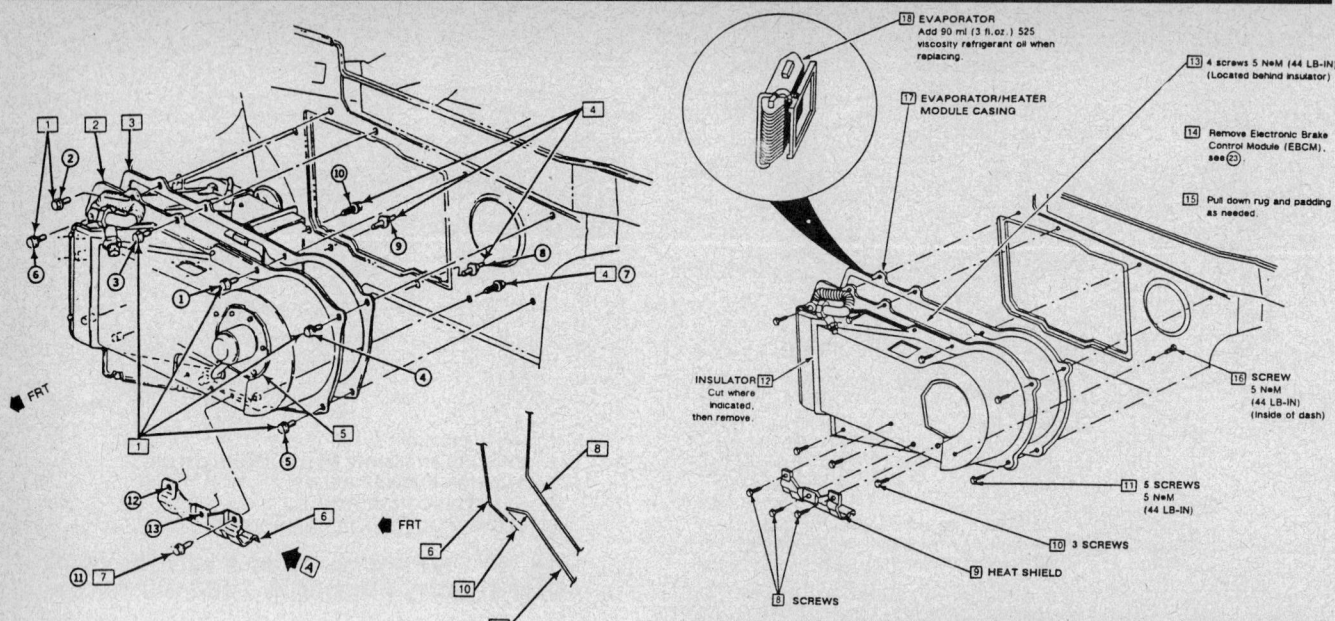

Fig. 45   Evaporator/heater module assembly. 1991 Buick Park Avenue

1. BOLT/SCREW; 3 N•M (27 LB-IN)
2. EVAPORATOR AND BLOWER MODULE
3. GASKET
4. BOLT/SCREW; 3.4 N•M (30 LB-IN)
5. BLOWER MOTOR
6. SHIELD
7. BOLT/SCREW; 1.9 N•M (17 LB-IN)
8. DASH PANEL
9. CATALYTIC CONVERTER HEAT SHIELD
10. 13.0 MM (APPROXIMATELY)

Fig. 44   Blower module assembly. 1989-90 Oldsmobile, Pontiac & 1990 Buick

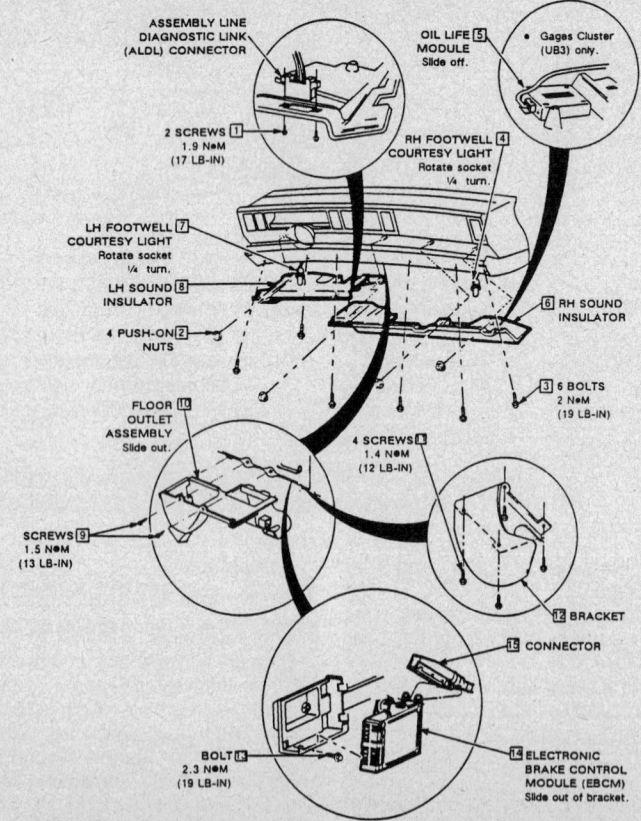

Fig. 46   Electronic Brake Control Module (ECBM) assembly removal. 1991 Buick Park Avenue

3. Disconnect four electrical connections and remove relay bracket assembly, Fig. 43.
4. Disconnect accumulator to condenser hose.
5. Disconnect electrical connector from pressure cycling switch, then the evaporator outlet line from accumulator.
6. Remove accumulator bracket and accumulator, cap accumulator openings.
7. Disconnect tube from condenser to evaporator, then disconnect power steering pump and position aside.
8. Remove vacuum tank and blower motor.
9. Remove exhaust manifold heat shield, then drain engine coolant.
10. Disconnect heater hoses from heater core, then remove blower motor resistor.
11. Disconnect evaporator outlet line and support bracket.
12. Remove right side sound insulator from under instrument panel.
13. Remove floor air outlet duct, then five lower evaporator and blower module attaching bolts, Fig. 44.
14. Raise and support vehicle, then remove three lower evaporator and blower module attaching bolts.
15. Cut rubber blower barrier along guide line, then lower vehicle.
16. Remove seven upper evaporator and blower module attaching bolts.
17. Finish cutting rubber barrier along guide lines.
18. Remove screws from evaporator cover, then evaporator from module.
19. Reverse procedure to install, sealing rubber barrier with strip calk where it had been cut.

1991 BUICK PARK AVENUE

Brazed fittings are used on the condenser and evaporator. These fittings cannot be turned. It is important that the service technician recognize which fitting is to be turned and use backup wrenches. **The brazed fitting that should not be turned is always the same color as the pipe it is brazed to.**

1. Disconnect battery ground cable.
2. Discharge A/C system, then remove vacuum tank.
3. Remove rear sight shield, then disconnect positive battery booster cable from underhood fuse block.
4. Remove underhood fuse block from relay bracket and position aside.
5. Remove relay bracket from dash panel, then the blower resistor from top of evaporator/heater module casing.
6. Disconnect A/C module to accumulator tube from accumulator.
7. Disconnect A/C compressor and condenser hose from the accumulator.
8. Remove clamp from accumulator, then disconnect electrical connector from the pressure cycling switch.
9. Disconnect evaporator to condenser tube from evaporator case and condenser.
10. Disengage tube from clips holding evaporator tube to fender, then remove tube from vehicle.
11. Remove blower motor, the all brackets from evaporator/heater module, **Fig. 45.**
12. Remove heat shield from bottom of evaporator/heater module, then the three screws attaching bottom of module to dash panel.
13. Remove five screws attaching top

and side of module to the dash panel.
14. Cut insulator on module along line indicated, **Fig. 45.**
15. Remove four module to insulator attaching screws, located behind insulator.
16. Remove Electronic Brake Control Module (EBCM) as follows:
    a. Remove two screws attaching the Assembly Line Diagnostic Link (ALDL) connector to the righthand side sound insulator.
    b. Remove push-on nuts and attaching bolts from left and right sound insulators, **Fig. 46.**
    c. Remove righthand footwell courtesy light and oil life module from right side sound insulator, then the insulator from vehicle.
    d. Remove left footwell courtesy light from left side sound insulator, then the insulator from the vehicle.
    e. Remove two floor outlet assembly to instrument panel attaching screws.
    f. Remove four EBCM bracket to instrument panel attaching screws.
    g. Pull bracket away from the instrument panel and remove EBCM to bracket attaching bolt, then slide EBCM out of bracket.
17. Pull down rug and padding, then remove dash panel to evaporator/heater module case attaching screw.
18. Pull module case away from dash panel and remove evaporator.
19. Reverse procedure to install.

1991 BUICK LESABRE, OLDSMOBILE & PONTIAC

Brazed fittings are used on the condenser and evaporator. These fittings cannot be turned. It is important that the service technician recognize which fitting is to be turned and use backup wrenches. **The brazed fitting that should not be turned is always the same color as the pipe it is brazed to.**

1. Disconnect battery ground cable.
2. Discharge A/C system, then remove engine rear sight shield.
3. Disconnect electrical connector from pressure cycling switch.
4. Remove accumulator clamp screw.
5. Disconnect accumulator inlet and outlet connections, then remove accumulator from the vehicle.
6. Remove blower motor resistor, then the vacuum tank.
7. Remove engine coolant reservoir, then the evaporator tube from condenser outlet.
8. Disconnect A/C lines from clamp near the shock tower, then remove evaporator tube from vehicle.
9. Remove blower motor, then the brackets and heat shield from blower module assembly.
10. Cut blower module assembly along indicated line, then remove bolts attaching blower module assembly to front of dash (driver's side only).
11. Remove large piece of blower module assembly insulation.
12. Remove screws from evaporator cover, then the evaporator.
13. Reverse procedure to install.

3.8L/V6-231 & 3800/V6-231 Engines

INDEX

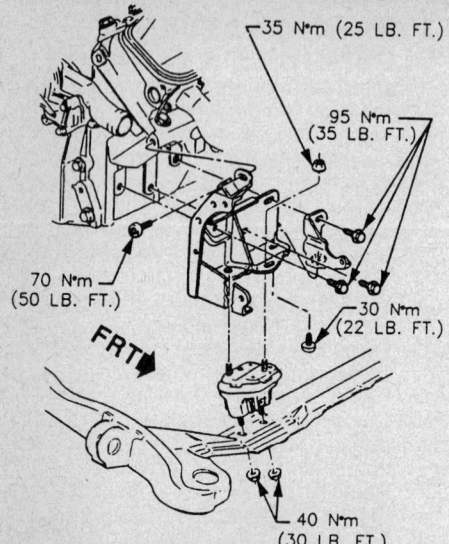

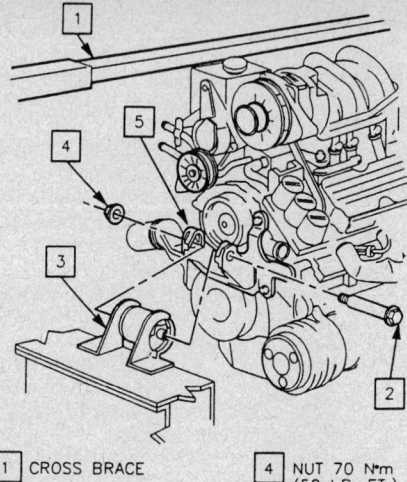

1 CROSS BRACE	4 NUT 70 N·m (52 LB. FT.)
2 BOLT 87 N·m (65 LB. FT.)	5 BRACKET
3 FRONT MOTOR MOUNT (TORQUE AXIS) MOUNTING BRACKET	

Fig. 1 Engine mount removal & installation. 3.8L/V6-231 & 3800/V6-231 Vin C engines

Fig. 2 Engine mount removal & installation. 3800/V6-231 Vin L engine

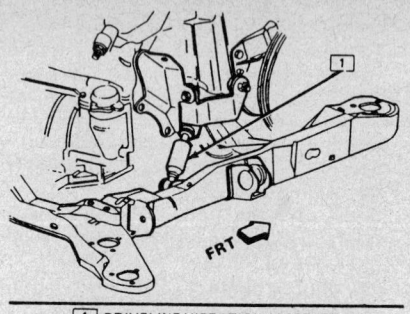

1 DRIVELINE VIBRATION ABSORBER

Fig. 3 Typical drive line vibration absorber

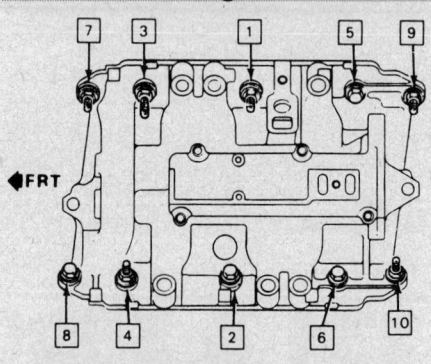

Fig. 4 Intake manifold tightening sequence

ENGINE MOUNTS
REPLACE

3.8L/V6-231 & 3800/V6-231 VIN C

1. **On 1988 models with 3.8L/V6-231 engine,** discharge A/C system.
2. **On all models,** raise and support front of vehicle.
3. Attach suitable engine lifting equipment to engine.
4. **On 1988 models with 3.8L/V6-231 engine,** disconnect and remove A/C compressor.
5. **On all models,** remove mount to engine bracket nuts. Raise engine slightly and remove mount to frame nuts.
6. Remove engine mount, **Fig. 1.**
7. Reverse procedure to install.

3800/V6-231 VIN L

1. Disconnect battery ground cable.
2. Attach suitable lifting equipment to engine, then raise engine slightly to remove weight from engine mounts.
3. Remove accessory drive belt.
4. Remove through bolt from front engine mount, **Fig. 2.**
5. Lift engine until power steering reservoir touches strut tower cross brace, then loosen bottom two bolts on front engine mount.
6. Remove A/C line clip, then the top two bolts from front engine mount and remove mount.
7. Reverse procedure to install.

ENGINE
REPLACE

3.8L/V6-231 ENGINE

1. Depressurize fuel system as follows:
   a. Raise and support vehicle.
   b. Disconnect electrical connector at

fuel tank.
   c. Lower vehicle, then start engine and allow to run until it stalls.
2. Disconnect battery cables.
3. Disconnect mass airflow sensor electrical connector.
4. Remove air intake duct.
5. Drain cooling system.
6. Raise and support vehicle.
7. Disconnect exhaust pipe from exhaust manifolds.
8. Remove engine mount bolts.
9. Remove driveline vibration absorber, **Fig. 3.**
10. Remove starter motor.
11. Remove A/C compressor from bracket and position aside.
12. Disconnect power steering hoses from steering gear.
13. Remove lower transaxle to engine bolts. **One bolt is located between the transaxle case and the engine block and is installed in the opposite direction.**
14. Remove flexplate cover, then the flexplate to torque converter bolts.
15. Remove engine support bracket from transaxle.
16. Lower vehicle.

17. Disconnect radiator and heater hoses from engine.
18. Remove alternator from bracket and position aside.
19. Disconnect engine wiring harness.
20. Remove remaining transaxle to engine bolts.
21. Remove engine from vehicle.
22. Reverse procedure to install.

3800/V6-231 ENGINE

1. Depressurize fuel system as follows:
   a. Raise and support vehicle.
   b. Disconnect electrical connector at fuel tank.
   c. Lower vehicle, then start engine and allow to run until it stalls.
2. Disconnect battery ground cable, then remove air intake duct.
3. Remove throttle cable bracket and the cables from throttle body.
4. Drain coolant, then raise and support vehicle.
5. Disconnect exhaust pipe at rear exhaust manifold, then remove engine mount bolts.
6. Disconnect starter wiring and remove starter, then detach A/C compressor and position out of way.
7. Disconnect power steering hoses at steering gear, then remove lower transaxle to engine attaching bolts. **One bolt is located between transaxle case and engine block and is installed in opposite direction.**
8. Remove flywheel dust cover, then the flywheel to torque converter attaching bolts. **Mark relationship between flywheel and torque converter to ensure proper assembly.**
9. Remove engine support bracket at transaxle, then lower vehicle.
10. Disconnect radiator and heater hoses, vacuum modulator and canister purge lines and the engine wiring harness.
11. Remove remaining engine to transaxle attaching bolts, then the transaxle assembly.
12. Reverse procedure to install.

INTAKE MANIFOLD
REPLACE

3.8L/V6-231 ENGINE

1. Depressurize fuel system as follows:
   a. Raise and support vehicle.

b. Disconnect electrical connector at fuel tank.
c. Lower vehicle, then start engine and allow to run until it stalls.
2. Disconnect battery ground cable.
3. Remove mass air flow sensor and air intake duct.
4. Remove serpentine accessory drive belt, generator and bracket.
5. Disconnect C3 ignition module electrical connector, then remove C3 ignition module.
6. Disconnect vacuum lines and wiring connectors as necessary.
7. Disconnect cruise control, throttle and T.V. cables from throttle body.
8. Drain cooling system, then disconnect heater hoses from throttle body.
9. Disconnect upper radiator hose, then the fuel lines, fuel rail and injectors.
10. Remove intake manifold attaching bolts, then the manifold and gasket.
11. Reverse procedure to install. **Torque manifold bolts to 32 ft. lbs. in sequence shown in Fig. 4.**

3800/V6-231 ENGINE

1988–90

1. Depressurize fuel system as follows:
   a. Raise and support vehicle.
   b. Disconnect electrical connector at fuel tank.
   c. Lower vehicle, then start engine and allow to run until it stalls.
2. Disconnect battery ground cable and drain coolant.
3. Remove serpentine belt, then the alternator and bracket.
4. Remove power steering pump braces, then disconnect coolant bypass hose and remove heater pipe.
5. Disconnect upper radiator hose and air inlet duct.
6. Remove throttle cable bracket from throttle body, then disconnect vacuum hoses at intake manifold.
7. Disconnect electrical connectors as necessary.
8. Remove EGR pipe, then the EGR valve and adapter from throttle body adapter.
9. Remove throttle body coolant pipe, throttle body adapter and throttle body from intake manifold.
10. Disconnect rear spark plug wires, then remove intake manifold attaching bolts and the intake manifold.
11. Reverse procedure to install, noting the following:
    a. Clean cylinder block, heads and intake manifold sealing surface of **all** oil, using a suitable solvent.
    b. Apply suitable sealant to ends of manifold seals.
    c. Clean intake manifold bolts and bolt holes of adhesive compound.
    d. Apply suitable locking compound to intake manifold bolt threads.
    e. Torque intake manifold bolts to specifications **twice** in sequence, **Fig. 4.**
    f. Lubricate throttle body coolant and heater pipe O-ring seals with antifreeze before assembly.

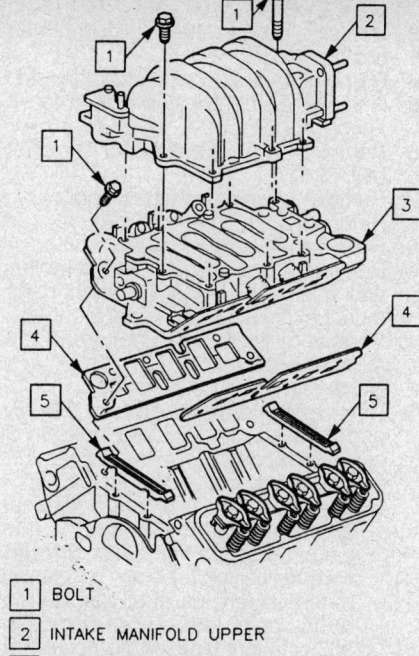

1	BOLT
2	INTAKE MANIFOLD UPPER
3	INTAKE MANIFOLD LOWER
4	INTAKE MANIFOLD GASKET
5	INTAKE MANIFOLD SEAL

Fig. 5 Removing upper intake manifold. 3800/V6-231 Vin L engine.

1991

1. Remove plastic engine cover and air intake duct.
2. Remove fuel rail, then exhaust manifold heat shield.
3. Remove cable bracket to cylinder head mounting bolt, then the power steering pump support bracket.
4. Loosen alternator and move to obtain clearance.
5. Remove alternator bracket, heater pipes and bypass hose.
6. Remove intake manifold attaching bolts, then the manifold.
7. Reverse procedure to install, noting the following:
   a. Clean cylinder block, heads and intake manifold sealing surface of all oil using a suitable solvent.
   b. Remove adhesive compound from intake manifold bolts and bolt holes.
   c. Apply thread lock compound part No. 12345493 or equivalent to intake manifold bolt threads prior to installation.
   d. **Torque** intake manifold bolts in two steps to 88 inch lbs. in sequence shown in **Fig. 4.**

UPPER INTAKE MANIFOLD
REPLACE

3800/V6-231 VIN L

1. Disconnect battery ground cable.
2. Remove spark plug wires on right

(rear) side of engine and position aside.
3. Remove fuel rail, then the exhaust manifold heat shield.
4. Remove cable bracket to cylinder head mounting bolt.
5. Remove upper intake manifold attaching bolts, then the manifold, **Fig. 5.**
6. Reverse procedure to install.

EXHAUST MANIFOLD
REPLACE

3.8L/V6-231 ENGINE

Left Side

1. Disconnect battery ground cable.
2. Remove mass airflow sensor, air intake duct and crankcase ventilation pipe.
3. Remove two bolts attaching exhaust crossover pipe to manifold.
4. Disconnect spark plug wires from spark plugs.
5. Remove exhaust manifold attaching bolts and the exhaust manifold. **The dipstick and tube may be removed to provide additional clearance.**
6. Reverse procedure to install.

Right Side

1. Disconnect battery ground cable.
2. Remove mass airflow sensor, air intake duct and crankcase ventilation pipe.
3. Disconnect IAC wiring connector from throttle body.
4. Remove two bolts attaching exhaust crossover pipe to manifold.
5. Disconnect spark plug wires from spark plugs.
6. Disconnect oxygen sensor electrical lead.
7. Remove heater inlet pipe from manifold studs.
8. Remove alternator support bracket.
9. Remove exhaust manifold bolts.
10. Raise and support vehicle.
11. Remove exhaust pipe to manifold bolts.
12. Remove front exhaust pipe.
13. Remove exhaust manifold.
14. Reverse procedure to install.

3800/V6-231 ENGINE

LEFT SIDE (FRONT)

1. Disconnect battery ground cable.
2. Remove two crossover pipe to manifold attaching bolts.
3. Disconnect spark plug wires at spark plugs.
4. Remove manifold attaching bolts.
5. Remove oil dipstick tube and dipstick.
6. Remove manifold.
7. Reverse procedure to install.

RIGHT SIDE (REAR)
1988–90

1. Disconnect battery ground cable.
2. Disconnect spark plug wires at spark plugs, then the oxygen sensor lead.
3. Remove EGR pipe.
4. Remove two exhaust crossover pipe

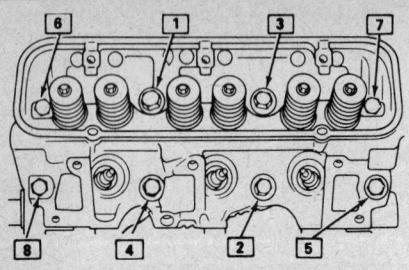

Fig. 6   Cylinder head bolt torque sequence

to manifold attaching bolts, then the manifold attaching bolts.
5. Remove transaxle dipstick tube.
6. Raise and support vehicle, then remove exhaust pipe to manifold attaching bolts and the manifold.
7. Reverse procedure to install.

1991
1. Disconnect battery ground cable.
2. Disconnect spark plug wires from spark plugs and position aside.
3. Remove throttle cable bracket, then the crossover pipe heat shield.
4. Remove transaxle dipstick and dipstick tube.
5. Disconnect oxygen sensor lead, then remove EGR pipe.
6. Remove two exhaust pipe to manifold attaching bolts.
7. Remove plastic vacuum tank mounted on cowl, then raise and support vehicle.
8. Remove catalytic converter heat shield and pipe hanger.
9. Remove front exhaust pipe to manifold attaching nuts, then the pipe from manifold.
10. Lower vehicle, then remove engine lift bracket.
11. Remove exhaust manifold attaching nuts, then the manifold.
12. Reverse procedure to install.

CYLINDER HEAD
REPLACE

3.8L/V6-231 ENGINE
1. Depressurize fuel system as follows:
   a. Raise and support vehicle.
   b. Disconnect electrical connector at fuel tank.
   c. Lower vehicle, then start engine and allow to run until it stalls.
2. Disconnect battery ground cable and drain cooling system.
3. Remove mass airflow sensor and air intake duct.
4. Disconnect accelerator, cruise control and throttle valve cables from throttle body.
5. Remove crankcase ventilation pipe.
6. Disconnect vacuum hoses attached to throttle body and intake manifold.
7. Remove exhaust crossover pipe.
8. Disconnect heater hoses from engine.
9. Disconnect fuel line and electrical connector from throttle body.
10. Disconnect upper radiator hose.
11. Remove fuel rail.

12. Remove alternator and bracket and position aside.
13. Remove power steering pump and position aside.
14. Remove right side exhaust manifold.
15. Remove distributor cap and rotor, if necessary.
16. Remove A/C compressor bracket bolt.
17. Remove left side exhaust manifold.
18. Remove valve covers.
19. Remove intake manifold.
20. Remove rocker arm shaft assemblies and push rods. All valve train parts must be installed in original locations.
21. Remove cylinder head bolts and the cylinder head.
22. Reverse procedure to install.
23. Refer to tightening sequence, **Fig. 6**, and tighten cylinder head bolts in 3 steps as follows:
    a. **Torque** all bolts to 25 ft. lbs.
    b. Tighten each bolt an additional 90°, in sequence, noting torque value as bolt is tightened. **Should torque** on bolt being tightening reached 60 ft. lbs. at any time, stop at this point and do not complete 90° rotation. Uneven tightening of bolts may distort cylinder bores, causing loss of compression and increased oil consumption.
    c. Tighten each bolt an additional 90°, in sequence, noting **torque** value as bolt is tightened.

3800/V6-231 ENGINE
1. Disconnect battery ground cable.
2. Remove intake and exhaust manifolds as described previously.
3. To remove left (front) valve cover, proceed as follows:
   a. Disconnect C³I and spark plug wires.
   b. Remove alternator bracket.
   c. Remove A/C compressor bracket bolt.
4. To remove right (rear) valve cover, proceed as follows:
   a. Remove power steering pump.
   b. Remove belt tensioner assembly.
   c. Remove fuel line heat shield.
5. Remove rocker arm assemblies, guide plate and push rods.
6. **On 1988 models**, reverse procedure to install, noting the following:
   a. Clean all gasket mating surfaces and cylinder head bolt holes in block.
   b. Clean threads in block with appropriate tap.
   c. Apply suitable sealant to bolt threads.
   d. **Torque** cylinder head bolts to 25 ft. lbs. in sequence, **Fig. 6**.
   e. Tighten each bolt an additional 90° in sequence. **Should you reach 60 ft. lbs. in this step or step f, stop. Do not complete balance of turn on this bolt.**
   f. Tighten each bolt an additional 90° in sequence.
7. On 1989-91 models, reverse procedure to install, noting the following:
   a. Clean all gasket mating surfaces and cylinder head bolt holes in block.

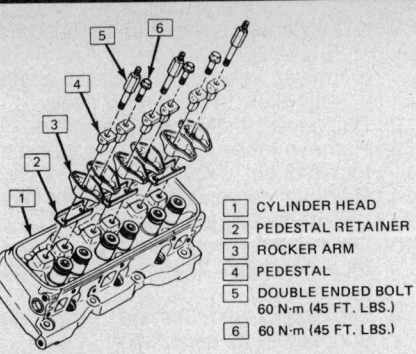

1	CYLINDER HEAD
2	PEDESTAL RETAINER
3	ROCKER ARM
4	PEDESTAL
5	DOUBLE ENDED BOLT 60 N·m (45 FT. LBS.)
6	60 N·m (45 FT. LBS.)

Fig. 7   Rocker arm installation

b. Clean threads in block with appropriate tap.
c. Apply suitable sealant to bolt threads.
d. **Torque** cylinder head bolts to 35 ft. lbs. in sequence, **Fig. 6**.
e. Tighten each bolt an additional 130° in sequence.
f. **On 1989-90 models**, tighten all bolts an additional 30° in sequence.
g. **On 1991 models**, tighten center four bolts an additional 30° in sequence.

ROCKER ARMS

Rocker arms are pedestal mounted, over support plates, **Fig. 7**. To replace rocker arms, remove valve cover, pedestal retaining bolt(s), pedestal and the rocker arm, noting position of double ended bolts, except on 3800/V6-231 engine, for assembly. Replace rocker arms and pedestals as an assembly if they are damaged or excessively worn. If rocker arms are to be reused, they should be installed in original position.

VALVE ARRANGEMENT

FRONT TO REAR
Left Side

3.8L/V6-231 & 3800/V6-231 . . E-I-E-I-I-E

Right Side

3.8L/V6-231 & 3800/V6-231 . . E-I-I-E-I-E

CAM LOBE LIFT SPECIFICATIONS

Engine	Year	Int.	Exh.
3800/V6-231	1988-91	.250	.255

VALVE GUIDES

The valve guides are an integral part of the cylinder head and cannot be replaced. If excessive valve stem clearance is noted, the valve guide must be reamed and an oversize valve guide installed. Valves are available in an oversize of .010 inch.

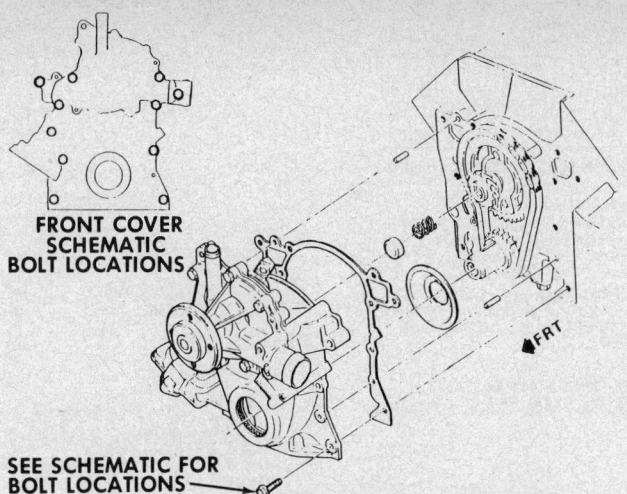

FRONT COVER SCHEMATIC BOLT LOCATIONS

SEE SCHEMATIC FOR BOLT LOCATIONS

Fig. 8 Timing case cover removal & installation

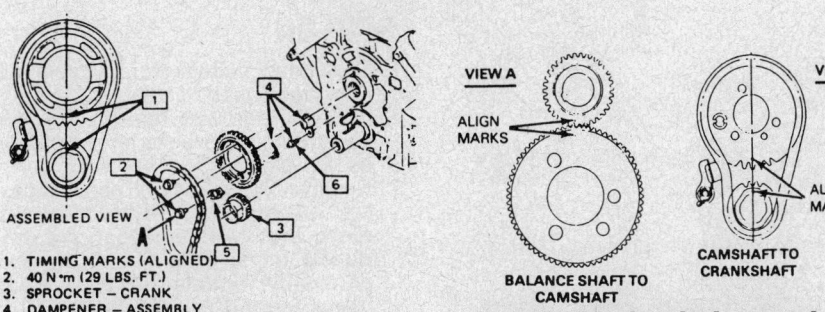

ASSEMBLED VIEW

1. TIMING MARKS (ALIGNED)
2. 40 N·m (29 LBS. FT.)
3. SPROCKET – CRANK
4. DAMPENER – ASSEMBLY
5. CAM POSITION SENSOR MAGNET
6. 19 N·m (14 LBS. FT.)

Fig. 10 Timing chain & sprocket. 3.8L/V6-231 engine

VIEW A
ALIGN MARKS
BALANCE SHAFT TO CAMSHAFT

VIEW B
ALIGN MARKS
CAMSHAFT TO CRANKSHAFT

Fig. 11 Timing balance shaft & camshaft marks. 3800/V6-231 engine

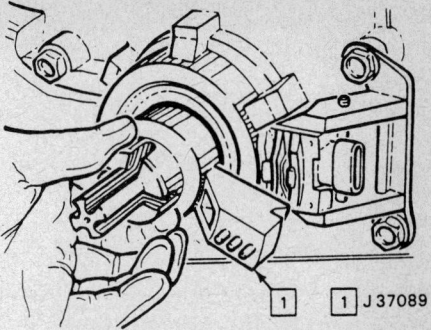

J37089

Fig. 9 Crankshaft sensor adjustment

TIMING CASE COVER REPLACE

3.8L/V6-231 ENGINE

1. Disconnect battery ground cable and drain cooling system and engine oil.
2. Disconnect all hoses from water pump.
3. Remove water pump pulley and drive belts. **It may be necessary to remove two nuts from front engine mount at frame and raise engine to facilitate water pump pulley removal.**
4. Remove alternator and bracket and position aside.
5. Remove distributor, if necessary.
6. Remove crankshaft damper bolt and washer, then the damper.
7. Remove timing case cover to cylinder block attaching bolts.
8. Remove timing case cover to oil pan attaching bolts, then the timing case cover, **Fig. 8.**
9. Reverse procedure to install. **Before installing the case cover, remove oil pump cover and pack oil pump with petroleum jelly. Failure to pack oil pump may result in the pump losing it's "Prime" when the engine is started. Also, apply suitable sealer to case cover bolts.**

3800/V6-231 ENGINE

1988–90

1. Disconnect battery ground cable and drain engine coolant.
2. Remove serpentine drive belt.
3. Disconnect hearer pipes, lower radiator hose and coolant bypass hose.
4. Raise and support vehicle.
5. Remove right front wheel and tire assembly, then the inner fender splash shield.
6. Remove balancer bolt and balancer.
7. Disconnect electrical connectors at camshaft sensor, crankshaft sensor and oil pressure sender.
8. Remove oil pan to front cover bolts.
9. Remove cover attaching bolts and the cover.
10. Reverse procedure to install, applying suitable sealant to bolt threads, and adjust crankshaft sensor.

1991

1. Disconnect battery ground cable.
2. **On Vin L engine,** remove torque axis mount.
3. **On Vin C and Vin L engines,** remove serpentine belt.
4. Using pulling tool No. J38197 or equivalent, remove crankshaft pulley.
5. Remove crankshaft sensor shield, then oil pan to front cover attaching bolts.

6. Remove front cover attaching bolts, then the front cover.
7. Reverse procedure to install, noting the following:
   a. Inspect timing chain for in and out movement, movement should not exceed 1 inch.
   b. Check timing chain sprockets for any signs of wear.
   c. Clean gasket mating surfaces at timing chain cover and cylinder block.
   d. Apply sealant part No. 1052080 or equivalent to bolt threads prior to installation.
   e. Adjust crankshaft sensor using tool No. J37087 or equivalent as shown in **Fig. 9.**

TIMING CHAIN REPLACE

3.8L/V6-231 ENGINE

1. Remove timing case cover as outlined under "Timing Case Cover, Replace" procedure.
2. Reinstall damper bolt and rotate crankshaft until the valve timing marks on camshaft sprocket and crankshaft sprocket are as close together as possible. Remove damper bolt without changing position of valve timing marks.
3. Remove crankshaft oil slinger if equipped, then the camshaft sprocket bolt.
4. Remove cam sensor magnet on V6-231 models, if equipped.
5. Pry off the two sprockets and timing chain assembly.
6. Assemble new chain on sprockets with timing marks aligned and slide assembly onto shafts. Be sure that marks are aligned, **Fig. 10.**
7. Install cam sensor magnet on V6-231 models, if equipped.
8. Install camshaft sprocket bolt and torque to specifications.
9. Install crankshaft oil slinger if equipped and the timing case cover.

3800/V6-231 ENGINE

1. Remove timing case cover as previously described.
2. Remove camshaft thrust button.
3. Align timing marks on sprockets, **Fig. 11,** so that they are as close together

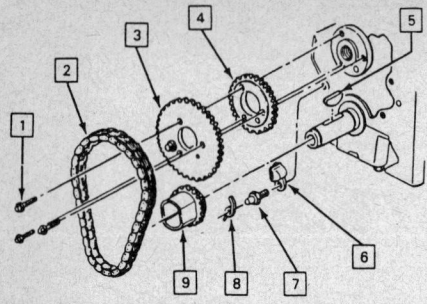

1. 37 N•M (27 LBS. FT.)
2. TIMING CHAIN
3. CAMSHAFT SPROCKET
4. CAMSHAFT GEAR
5. KEY
6. DAMPER
7. BOLT (SPECIAL) 19 N•M (14 LBS. FT.)
8. SPRING
9. CRANKSHAFT SPROCKET

Fig. 12   Timing chain & sprockets. 3800/V6-231 engine

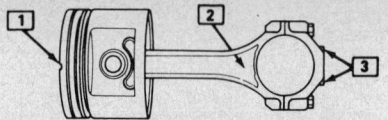

1. NOTCH ON PISTON TOWARDS FRONT OF ENGINE
   LEFT BANK
2. NO. 1, 3 & 5 TWO BOSSES ON ROD TOWARDS REAR OF ENGINE (NOT SHOWN)
3. CHAMFERED CORNERS ON ROD CAP TOWARDS FRONT OF ENGINE
   RIGHT BANK
2. NO. 2, 4 & 6 TWO BOSSES ON ROD TOWARDS FRONT OF ENGINE (NOT SHOWN)
3. CHAMFERED CORNERS ON ROD CAP TOWARDS REAR OF ENGINE

Fig. 13   Piston & rod assembly. 3.8L/V6-231 engine

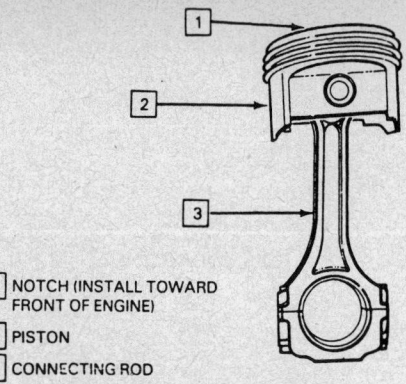

1. NOTCH (INSTALL TOWARD FRONT OF ENGINE)
2. PISTON
3. CONNECTING ROD

Fig. 14   Piston & rod assembly. 1988–90 3800/V6-231 engine

as possible.

4. Remove timing chain dampener.
5. Remove camshaft sprocket bolts, **Fig. 12.**
6. Remove camshaft sprocket and chain, then the crankshaft sprocket.
7. Reverse procedure to install, noting the following:
   a. Ensure No. 1 piston is at TDC.
   b. Ensure camshaft and balance shaft timing marks are straight down, **Fig. 11.**
   c. Assemble timing chain on sprockets with their timing marks in their closest together position.
   d. Torque camshaft sprocket bolts specifications.

CAMSHAFT
REPLACE
1988–90

1. Remove engine as outlined under "Engine, Replace" procedure.
2. Remove intake manifold, rocker arms, valve lifters, timing case cover and timing chain.
3. Slide camshaft out from engine with care not to damage bearings.
4. Reverse procedure to install.

1991

1. Disconnect battery ground cable.
2. Remove intake manifold as described previously.
3. Remove valve cover, rocker arms, push rods and valve lifters.
4. Remove crankshaft pulley and crankshaft sensor cover.
5. Remove front cover, timing chain and sprockets.
6. Remove camshaft thrust plate and camshaft. **When removing or installing camshaft, avoid marring the bearing surface.**
6. Reverse procedure to install, coating

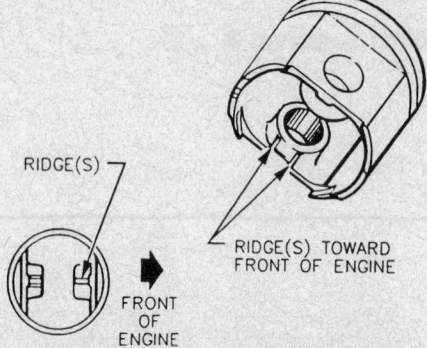

RIDGE(S)

RIDGE(S) TOWARD FRONT OF ENGINE

FRONT OF ENGINE

Fig. 15   Piston installation direction. 1991 3800/V6-231 engine

camshaft and valve lifters with prelube part No. 1052365 or equivalent prior to installation.

PISTON & ROD
ASSEMBLE

Pistons should be assembled to rods and installed as shown in **Figs. 13, 14 and 15.**

After piston and rod installation, measure connecting rod side clearance. Side clearance should be .003-.015 inch.

PISTONS, PINS & RINGS

Pistons and ring are available in standard sizes and oversizes of .010 and .030. Piston pins are supplied with the piston and are available in standard size only.

To check piston fit in bore, measure bore diameter using suitable telescoping gauges and record reading. Measure piston across skirt at a point 3/4 inch below piston pin center line and record reading. Subtract piston diameter from bore diameter and compare to specified clearance.

MAIN & ROD BEARINGS

Main bearings are available in standard sizes and undersizes of .001 and .002 inch. Rod bearings are available in standard size and an undersize of .008 inch.

OIL PAN
REPLACE
1988–90

1. Disconnect battery ground cable and raise and support vehicle.
2. Drain oil pan and remove flexplate cover, then remove starter and oil filter as necessary.
3. Remove oil pan bolts, oil pan and gasket, as equipped. **Production engines with 14 bolt oil pan are produced using RTV sealer to seal pan, while models with 20 bolt pan use a formed rubber gasket. If oil pan must be removed for service, use replacement composition gasket for models with 14 bolt pan and new formed rubber gasket for models with 20 bolt pan.**
4. Position replacement gasket on pan, insert 2 bolts to maintain position, then install pan and gasket assembly.
5. Install remaining bolts, then evenly torque bolts to specifications. **Do not over tighten oil pan retaining bolts as pan may be damaged, resulting in oil leaks.**
6. Reverse remaining procedure to complete installation.

1991

1. Raise and support vehicle, then drain engine oil.
2. Remove oil pan retaining bolts, then the oil pan.
3. Remove old oil pan gasket and discard.
4. Reverse procedure to install.

OIL PUMP SERVICE
REMOVAL & INSPECTION

1. Remove timing case cover, refer to "Timing Case Cover, Replace" procedure.
2. Remove oil filter adapter, pressure regulator valve and spring.
3. Remove oil pump cover attaching screws, then the cover and gears, **Fig. 16.**
4. Check pump cover and housing for cracks, scoring, porous or damaged

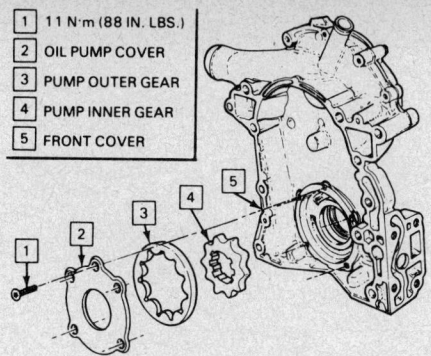

1	11 N·m (88 IN. LBS.)
2	OIL PUMP COVER
3	PUMP OUTER GEAR
4	PUMP INNER GEAR
5	FRONT COVER

Fig. 16   Oil pump

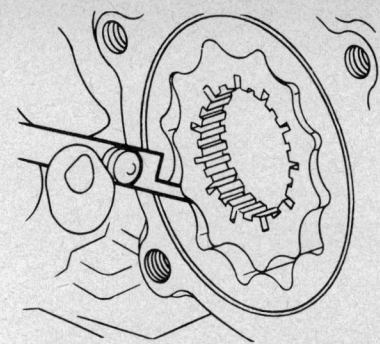

Fig. 17   Measuring oil pump inner gear tip clearance

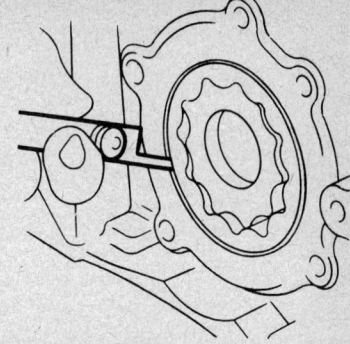

Fig. 18   Measuring oil pump outer gear diameter clearance

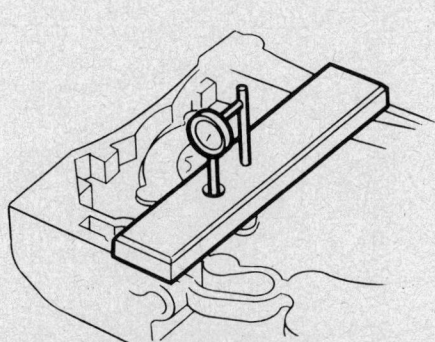

Fig. 19   Measuring oil pump gear end clearance

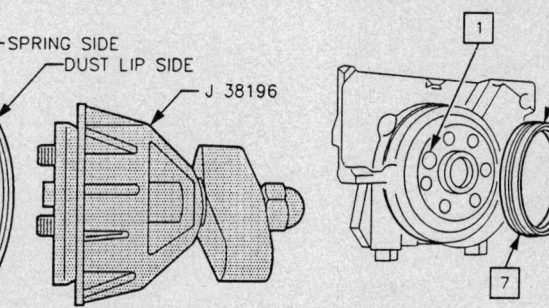

SPRING SIDE
DUST LIP SIDE
— J 38196

SEAL BORE TO SEAL SURFACE TO BE LUBRICATED WITH ENGINE OIL BEFORE ASSEMBLY

Fig. 20   Crankshaft rear oil seal (rear main) & tool. 1991 3800/V6-231 engine

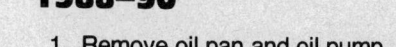

1	ALIGNMENT HOLE
2	DUST LIP
3	DOWEL PIN
4	COLLAR
5	MANDRIL
6	ATTACHING SCREWS
7	SEAL

Fig. 21   Installing crankshaft rear oil seal (rear main). 1991 3800/V6-231 engine

casting, damaged threads or excessive wear or galling. Replace as required.

5. Check pressure regulator valve for scoring, burrs or sticking in valve bore. Replace as required.
6. Check pressure regulator valve spring for tension loss or bending. Replace spring as required.
7. Check gears for chipping galling or excessive wear. Replace as required.

ASSEMBLY & INSTALLATION

1. Measure oil pump inner gear tip clearance, **Fig. 17**. Maximum clearance should be .006 inch.
2. Measure oil pump outer gear diameter clearance, **Fig. 18**. Clearance should be .008-.015 inch.
3. Measure oil pump gear end clearance with gear dropped in housing, **Fig. 19**. Clearance should be .0010-.0035 inch.
4. **On 3800/V6-231 engines**, measure pressure regulator valve for valve to bore clearance of .0015-.003 inch.
5. **On all engines**, lubricate all gears with clean motor oil, then install gears in housing.
6. Pack pump cavity with suitable petroleum jelly.
7. Install pump cover and cover attaching screws. Torque cover attaching screws to specifications.
8. Install pressure regulator valve and spring.

9. Install oil filter adapter using a new gasket. Torque oil filter adapter attaching bolts to specifications.
10. Install timing chain cover on engine. During front cover installation, ensure inner pump gear is properly engaged on crankshaft sprocket.

CRANKSHAFT OIL SEAL REPLACE
1988-90

1. Remove oil pan and oil pump.
2. Remove rear main bearing cap.
3. Using tool J-21526-2, drive upper seal into groove approximately 1/4 inch.
4. Repeat step 3 for other end of seal.
5. Measure the amount that was driven in on one side and add 1/16 inch. Cut this length from lower seal removed from lower cap.
6. Repeat step 5 for other end of seal.
7. Place piece of cut seal into groove of seal installer tool J-21526-1 and install tool guide onto block.
8. Using seal packing tool J-21526-2, drive piece of seal into place. Drive seal in until tool contacts machined stop.
9. Remove tool guide and repeat steps 7 and 8 for other end of seal.
10. Install replacement seal in bearing cap as follows:
    a. Ensure that cap mating surfaces, seal grooves and side seal channels are clean and free from old

seal material.
    b. Soak sealing strips in kerosene or light oil for 5 minutes and apply GM sealer 1052621, Loctite 414 or equivalent to seal groove in cap.
    c. Within 1 minute after applying sealer, roll seal into groove using installer J-28693, pressing seal into groove until seal projects no more than 1/16 inch above each mating surface of cap.
    d. Holding seal in place, cut seal flush with mating surfaces of cap using tool sharp enough to produce clean cut.
    e. Apply thin film of chassis grease to seal surface and thin film of suitable sealer to cap mating surfaces. **Do not allow sealer to contact journal or bearing surfaces.**
11. Install side seals in cap, position bearing cap in block ensuring that cap is properly seated, then torque cap bolts to specifications.
12. Reverse remaining procedure to complete installation.

1991

1. Remove flexplate and confirm rear seal leak.

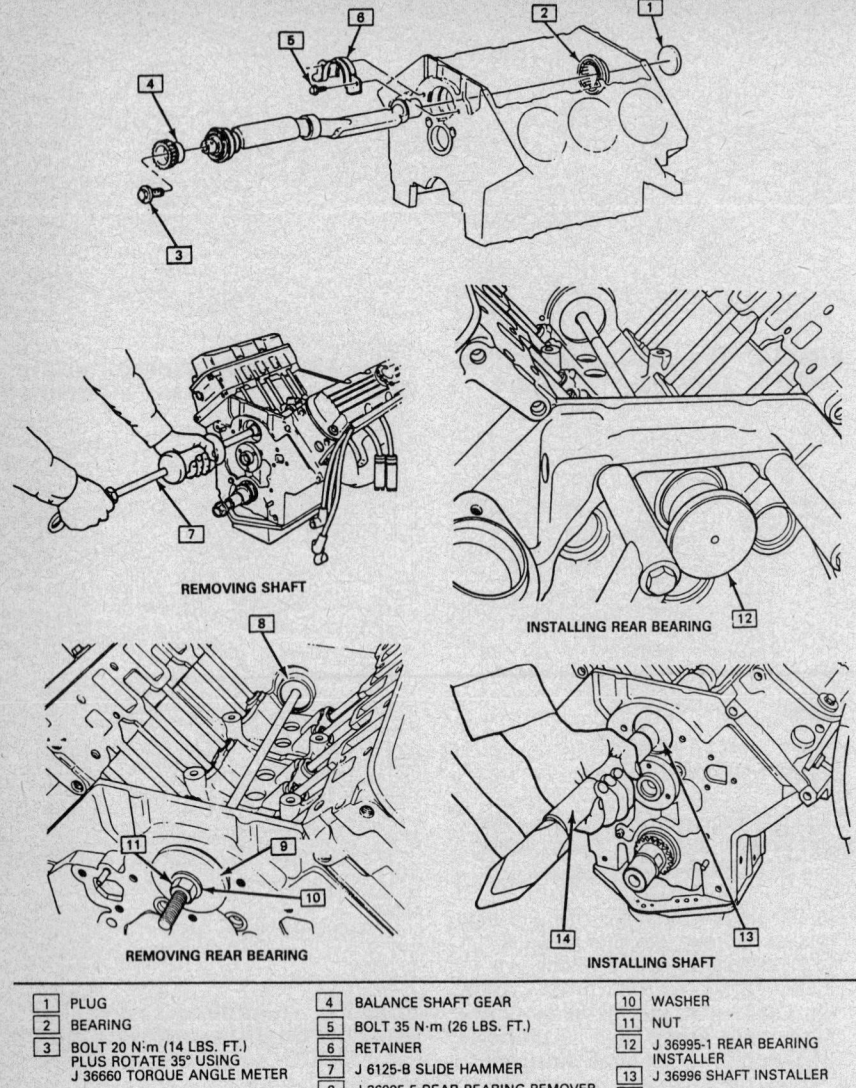

Fig. 22 Balance shaft service

1	PLUG	4	BALANCE SHAFT GEAR	10	WASHER
2	BEARING	5	BOLT 35 N·m (26 LBS. FT.)	11	NUT
3	BOLT 20 N·m (14 LBS. FT.) PLUS ROTATE 35° USING J 36660 TORQUE ANGLE METER	6	RETAINER	12	J 36995-1 REAR BEARING INSTALLER
		7	J 6125-B SLIDE HAMMER	13	J 36996 SHAFT INSTALLER
		8	J 36995-5 REAR BEARING REMOVER	14	J 21465-13 DRIVER HANDLE
		9	J 36995-		

Fig. 23 Measuring balance shaft endplay

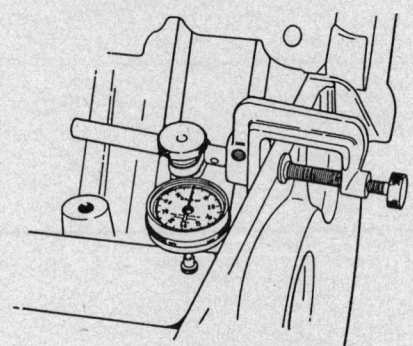

Fig. 24 Measuring balance shaft front radial play

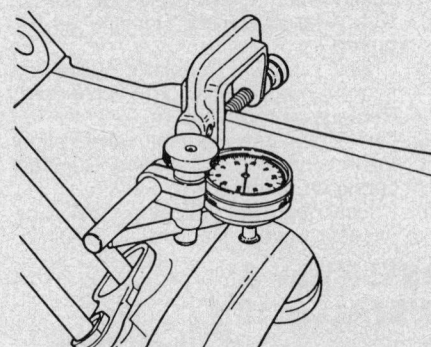

Fig. 25 Measuring balance shaft rear radial play

2. Insert a screwdriver through oil seal dust lip and pry seal out towards end of crankshaft pilot.
3. Reverse procedure to install, noting the following:
   a. Check inside of bore and crankshaft for nicks or burrs. Repair or replace as required.
   b. Apply engine oil to inside and outside surfaces of the new seal, then slide seal over seal installation tool No. J38196 or equivalent as shown in **Fig. 20** until seal bottoms squarely against bottom of tool.
   c. Align dowel pin of tool with dowl pin in crankshaft and attach tool to crankshaft by hand and tighten attaching screws to 60 inch lbs, **Fig. 21.**
   d. Turn T-handle of tool so that collar pushes seal into bore, turn handle until collar is tight against case.
   e. Loosen T-handle, remove attaching screws and the tool.

BALANCE SHAFT
REPLACE
REMOVAL

1. Remove engine as previously described.
2. Remove flywheel, then the intake manifold.
3. Remove lifter guide retainer, then the front cover.
4. Remove balance shaft drive gear bolt, **Fig. 22,** then the camshaft sprocket and timing chain.
5. Remove balance shaft retainer bolts, retainer and gear.
6. Using tool J-6125-B, remove balance shaft. **The balance shaft and both bearings are serviced as a complete package. Use only the correct tools for bearing and shaft removal and installation. Inspect balance shaft drive gear and the camshaft drive gear for nicks and burrs.**

7. Remove balance shaft rear plug.
8. Using tool J-36995-5, remove balance shaft rear bearing.

INSTALLATION

1. Dip balance shaft rear bearing in clean engine oil, then, using tool J-36995-1, install bearing with rolled edge facing into engine and manufacturer's markings facing flywheel side.
2. Dip front balance shaft bearing into clean engine oil, then, using tool J-36996, install balance shaft into block.
3. Temporarily install balance shaft bearing retainer and bolts.
4. Install balance shaft drive gear, then

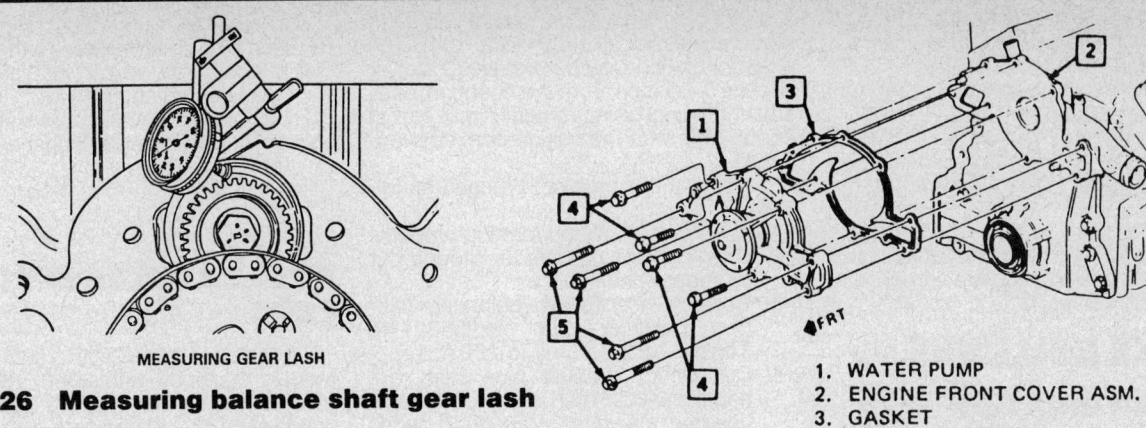

MEASURING GEAR LASH

Fig. 26   Measuring balance shaft gear lash

1. WATER PUMP
2. ENGINE FRONT COVER ASM.
3. GASKET
4. 11 N·m (97 LBS. IN.)
5. 39 N·m (29 LBS. FT.)

Fig. 27   Water pump assembly

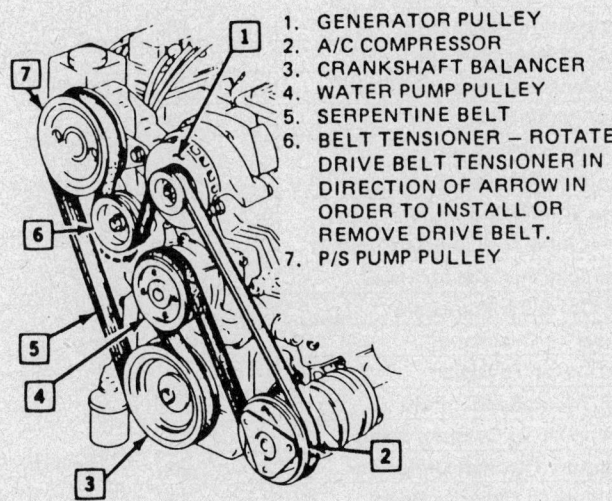

1. GENERATOR PULLEY
2. A/C COMPRESSOR
3. CRANKSHAFT BALANCER
4. WATER PUMP PULLEY
5. SERPENTINE BELT
6. BELT TENSIONER – ROTATE DRIVE BELT TENSIONER IN DIRECTION OF ARROW IN ORDER TO INSTALL OR REMOVE DRIVE BELT.
7. P/S PUMP PULLEY

Fig. 28   Serpentine drive belt routing

apply suitable sealant to and install bolt, **torquing** to 14 ft. lbs. plus an additional 35°.
5. Install balance shaft rear plug.
6. Measure balance shaft endplay, **Fig. 23.**. End play should be 0-.008 inch.
7. Measure balance shaft radial play at both front and rear, **Figs. 24 and 25.** Front radial play should be 0-.0011 inch and rear radial play should be .0005-.0047 inch.
8. Turn camshaft so, with camshaft sprocket temporarily installed, timing mark is straight down.
9. With camshaft sprocket and camshaft gear removed, turn balance shaft so that the timing mark on gear points straight down.
10. Install camshaft gear, aligning marks on balance shaft gear and camshaft gear by turning balance shaft, **Fig. 11.**
11. Turn crankshaft so that No. 1 piston is at TDC.

12. Install timing chain and camshaft sprocket.
13. Measure gear lash, **Fig. 26,** at four places, every 1/4 turn. Lash should be .002-.005 inch.
14. Install balance shaft front bearing retainer and bolts, **torquing** to 26 ft. lbs.
15. Install front cover, then the lifter guide retainer.
16. Install intake manifold, then the flywheel. Torque flywheel bolts to specifications.
17. Install engine in vehicle.

WATER PUMP
REPLACE

1. Disconnect battery ground cable and drain cooling system.
2. Remove drive belts and disconnect radiator hoses and heater hoses from pump.

3. Remove water pump pulley attaching bolts, **Fig. 27.** The long bolt is accessed through hole in body side rail. Remove pump pulley.
4. Remove water pump attaching bolts and the water pump.
5. Reverse procedure to install.

FUEL PUMP
REPLACE

1. Relieve fuel pressure as follows:
   a. Disconnect fuel tank harness connector.
   b. Start engine and run until it stalls, then engage starter for 3 seconds.
2. Disconnect battery ground cable.
3. Drain fuel tank and disconnect tank unit wire from connector in rear compartment.
4. Remove ground wire retaining screw from underbody.
5. Disconnect hoses from tank unit.
6. Support fuel tank and release the two retaining straps. Lower tank from vehicle.
7. Using tool J-24187 or equivalent, release retaining cam and remove sending unit and pump assembly from tank.
8. Remove pump from sending unit.
9. Reverse procedure to install.

BELT TENSION DATA

Belt	New Lbs.	Used Lbs.
Serpentine	①	①

①—Equipped with auto-tensioner.

SERPENTINE DRIVE BELT ROUTING

Refer to **Fig. 28,** for serpentine drive belt routing.

COOLING SYSTEM BLEED

1. Fill cooling system and leave radiator cap off.

2. Turn A/C-heater control to any A/C mode and set temperature to the highest setting.
3. Start engine and allow engine to idle until bottom radiator hose is hot.
4. Cycle engine speed up to 3000 RPM and back to idle five times. This should expel any trapped air in the system.
5. Refill radiator and install pressure cap.
6. Allow engine to return to outside temperature, then fill coolant reservoir to FULL COLD mark.

SERVICE BULLETINS
ENGINE VIBRATION

On some 1988 models equipped with a 3.8L/V6-231 engine, a shake/vibration may be present at 1100-1300 rpm. The shake/vibration may be present at slower speeds 0-15 mph, from the floor pan, seat, steering wheel or instrument panel and at 45-55 mph with the torque converter engaged.

To correct this problem proceed as follows:
1. Ensure engine is performing properly.
2. Check engine mounts for ground out or stress condition.
3. Replace crankshaft balancer with new balancer part No.25532179. **Torque** balancer bolt to 200 ft. lbs.
4. Disconnect exhaust pipe from exhaust manifold, then using a high temperature anti-seize compound, lubricate exhaust seal and reinstall exhaust pipe.
5. Remove intermediate exhaust pipe hanger and rubber insulators, then bend hanger ends upward 1/2 inch. Lubricate rubber insulators with silicone grease, then install hanger and insulators.

BROKEN VALVE SPRING CAPS

On some 1988 Electra and LeSabre models equipped with 3800/V6-231 engines, if broken valve spring caps are encountered, valve spring caps should be replaced with new part No. 25534605.

3.8L/V6-231 TIGHTENING SPECIFICATIONS

Year	Component	Torque/ft. lbs.
1988	Balancer Assembly To Crankshaft	219
	Camshaft Sensor To Front Cover	75 ①
	Connecting Rods	45
	Crankshaft Bearing Caps	100
	Crankshaft Sensor To Front Cover	22
	Cylinder Block Drain Plug	32
	Cylinder Head Bolts	②
	ESC Knock Sensor To Block	13
	EGR Valve To Intake Manifold	13
	Exhaust Crossover Pipe To Exhaust Manifold	15
	Exhaust Manifold To Cylinder Head	37
	Flywheel Cover To Transaxle	48 ①
	Flywheel To Crankshaft	60
	Front Cover To Block	22
	Fuel Rail To Intake Manifold	120 ①
	Generator Support To Cylinder Head	35
	Generator Support Through Generator	20
	Intake Manifold To Cylinder Head	32
	Engine Mount To Block	70
	Oil Filter Adapter To Timing Chain Cover	24
	Oil Galley Plugs	25
	Oil Drain Plug	42
	Oil Pan To Cylinder Block	88 ①
	Oil Pressure Switch To Oil Filter Adapter	115 ①
	Oil Screen Housing To Cylinder Block	97 ①
	Oxygen Sensor	31
	Rocker Arm Cover	115 ①
	Rocker Arm	43
	Spark Plug	20
	Starting Motor	35
	Thermostat Housing	13
	Throttle Body To Intake Manifold	20
	Timing Chain Dampener	14
	Timing Chain Sprocket To Camshaft	31
	Transaxle To Cylinder Block	55
	Valve Lifter Guide Retaining Bolts	25
	Water Pump Cover To Timing Chain Cover	84 ①
	Water Pump Pulley	106 ①

①—Inch lbs.   ②—Refer to text for procedure.

3800/V6-231 TIGHTENING SPECIFICATIONS

Year	Component	Torque/ft. lbs.
1988-91	Balancer Assembly To Crankshaft	219
	Balance Shaft Gear Bolt	14①
	Balance Shaft Retainer	26
	Camshaft Sensor To Front Cover	75②
	Camshaft Sprocket Bolts	26
	Connecting Rod Bolts	43
	Coolant Temperature Sensor To Intake	15
	Crankshaft Bearing Caps	90
	Crankshaft Sensor To Front Cover	22
	Crankshaft Sensor Clamp Bolt	40②
	Cylinder Block Drain Plug	32
	Cylinder Head To Block	③
	EGR Pipe To Exhaust Manifold	15
	EGR Pipe To EGR Valve	20
	EGR Valve To Intake Manifold Adapter	20
	ESC Knock Sensor	13
	Exhaust Manifold To Cylinder Head	41
	Flywheel Cover To Transaxle	48②
	Flywheel To Crankshaft	61
	Front Cover To Block	22
	Fuel Feed & Return Pipes To Fuel Rail	22
	Fuel Rail To Intake Manifold	120②
	Generator Support To Cylinder Head	36
	Generator Support Through Generator	36
	Heater Hose Fitting To Intake	11
	Ignition Module To Generator Support	18
	Intake Manifold To Cylinder Head	88②
	Engine Mount To Cylinder Block	70
	Oil Filter Adapter To Timing Chain Cover	24
	Oil Galley Plugs	25
	Oil Pan Drain Plug	18
	Oil Pan To Block	124②
	Oil Pan To Front Cover	124②
	Oil Pressure Switch	24
	Oil Pump Cover To Timing Chain Cover	97②
	Oil Screen Housing To Cylinder Block	97②
	Oxygen Sensor	31
	Rocker Arm Cover	88②
	Rocker Arm Pedestal	28
	Spark Plug	20
	Starter Motor	35
	Thermostat Housing	20
	Throttle Body Adapter To Intake	20
	Throttle Body To Throttle Body Adapter	20
	Transaxle To Cylinder Block	55
	Water Pump Cover To Timing Chain Cover	84②
	Water Pump Pulley	142②

①—Tighten bolt an additional 35°.
②—Inch lbs.
③—Refer to text for procedure.

4.5L/V8-273 Engines

INDEX

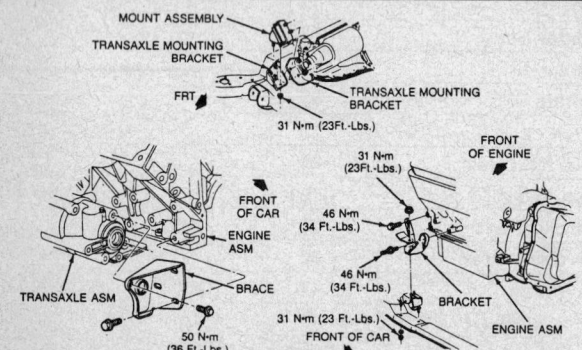

Fig. 1 Right side engine, brace & transaxle mount

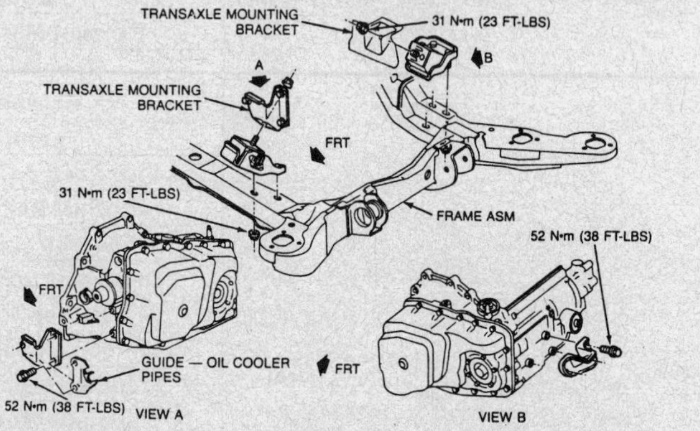

Fig. 2 Left side engine & transaxle assembly mounts

ENGINE MOUNTS
REPLACE
RIGHT SIDE

1. Remove brace from engine bracket to engine, **Fig. 1.**
2. Remove two nuts securing engine bracket to mount.
3. Raise and support vehicle.
4. Remove two nuts securing engine mount to frame.
5. Remove two nuts securing transaxle bracket to frame.
6. Remove two nuts securing transaxle mount to frame bracket.
7. Attach suitable engine lifting equipment to engine and raise engine until bracket is free from engine mount and transaxle mount.
8. Remove stud and two bolts securing bracket to block.
9. Remove mount and bracket by pulling forward.
10. Remove transaxle mount bracket from transaxle.
11. Remove engine mount assembly.
12. Reverse procedure to install.

LEFT SIDE

1. Raise and support vehicle.
2. Remove one nut securing mount to transaxle bracket and two nuts securing mount to frame, **Fig. 2.**

3. Attach suitable engine lifting equipment to engine.
4. Remove three bolts securing bracket to transaxle.
5. Raise engine until brackets are free from mounts.
6. Remove mount and bracket by pulling upward.
7. Reverse procedure to install.

ENGINE
REPLACE

1. Disconnect battery ground cable.
2. Drain cooling system.
3. Remove air cleaner and hood.
4. Disconnect A/C hose strap from right side strut tower.
5. Remove A/C accumulator from bracket and position aside.
6. Remove canister hoses from A/C accumulator bracket.
7. Disconnect ground wire from A/C accumulator bracket.
8. Remove A/C accumulator bracket from wheel house.
9. Remove cooling fans.
10. Remove drive belts and disconnect heater hoses.
11. Disconnect electrical connectors from: oil pressure switch, coolant temperature sensor, distributor, EGR so-

lenoid and engine temperature switch.
12. Disconnect cables from: accelerator, cruise control and transaxle throttle valve.
13. Remove cruise control diaphragm and position aside.
14. Disconnect vacuum supply hose.
15. Remove exhaust crossover pipe.
16. Disconnect oil cooler lines from oil filter adapter.
17. Remove oil cooler line bracket from transaxle and position aside.
18. Remove air cleaner mounting bracket.
19. Disconnect fuel lines from throttle body. **Carefully bleed fuel pressure at fuel line schraeder valve using a suitable tool. Use a container or rag to catch fuel.**
20. Remove fuel line bracket from transaxle and position fuel lines aside.
21. Disconnect small vacuum line from brake booster.
22. Disconnect AIR solenoid electrical and hose connections.
23. Remove AIR valves with bracket.
24. Disconnect electrical connectors from: ISC, TPS, fuel injectors, MAT sensor, oxygen sensor, throttle body base warmer and ground wires from alternator bracket.
25. Remove idler pulley.

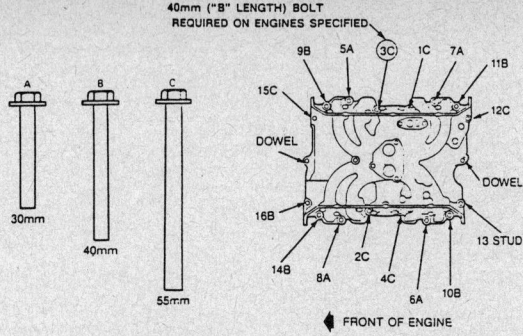

BOLT TIGHTENING SEQUENCE

1. TIGHTEN BOLTS 1, 2, 3, & 4 IN SEQUENCE TO 20.0 N·m (15 FT-LBS).
2. TIGHTEN BOLTS 5 THRU 16 IN SEQUENCE TO 30.0 N·m (22 FT-LBS).
3. RETIGHTEN ALL BOLTS IN SEQUENCE TO 30.0 N·m (22 FT-LBS).
4. REPEAT STEP 3.

Fig. 3   Intake manifold bolt size & bolt torque sequence. V8-273/4.5L engine

26. Remove power steering hose strap from stud-headed bolt in front of right side cylinder head, then the stud-headed bolt.
27. Disconnect AIR pipe clip near number 2 spark plug.
28. Remove power steering pump with bracket and position aside.
29. Raise and support vehicle.
30. Disconnect electrical connectors from starter motor and ground wires from cylinder block.
31. Remove two flexplate covers and the starter motor.
32. Remove three flexplate to torque converter bolts.
33. Remove A/C compressor lower dust shield.
34. Remove right front wheel assembly.
35. Remove outer wheelhouse plastic shield.
36. Remove A/C compressor mounting bolts and position compressor aside.
37. Remove lower radiator hose.
38. Remove driveline dampener with brackets from lower right front of engine and cradle.
39. Remove three right front engine to transaxle bracket bolts.
40. Pull alternator wire with plastic cover down out of way.
41. Remove two exhaust pipe to manifold bolts and springs.
42. Disconnect AIR pipe to converter bracket from exhaust manifold stud.
43. Remove lower right hand transaxle bellhousing to engine bolt.
44. Attach suitable engine lifting equipment to engine and support engine.
45. Remove five upper transaxle bellhousing to engine bolts.
46. Remove three left front engine mount bracket to engine bolts.
47. Remove engine from vehicle.
48. Reverse procedure to install.

INTAKE MANIFOLD
REPLACE

1. Disconnect battery ground cable.
2. Drain cooling system.
3. Remove air cleaner.
4. Remove drive belts.
5. Disconnect spark plug wires from spark plugs.
6. Remove two upper power steering pump bracket bolts and loosen lower nuts.
7. Remove distributor cap, wires and conduit.
8. Disconnect heater hose from thermostat housing.
9. Disconnect electrical connectors from: distributor, oil pressure switch, coolant sensor and EGR solenoid.
10. Remove distributor.
11. Disconnect cables from: accelerator, cruise control and transaxle throttle valve.
12. Disconnect fuel lines from throttle body. **Carefully bleed fuel pressure at fuel line schraeder valve using a suitable tool. Use a container or rag to catch fuel.**
13. Disconnect upper radiator hose from thermostat housing.
14. Remove fuel line brackets from transaxle and position fuel lines aside.
15. Remove cruise control servo bracket from intake manifold.
16. Remove vacuum line bracket from engine lift brackets.
17. Disconnect vacuum supply line from throttle body.
18. Disconnect transaxle modulator vacuum line.
19. Remove belt tensioner and power steering pump and bracket assembly and position aside.
20. Disconnect alternator electrical connectors and remove alternator.
21. Disconnect AIR management solenoid electrical connectors.
22. Remove AIR management valves and bracket assembly.
23. Disconnect electrical connectors from: ISC, TPS, fuel injectors, MAT sensor, oxygen sensor and throttle body base warmer.
24. Disconnect MAP hose.
25. Remove EGR solenoid and bracket assembly.
26. Remove rocker arm covers.
27. Remove rocker arm support assemblies.
28. Remove triangular seals.
29. Remove push rods. **Push rods must** be installed in original locations.
30. Remove idler pulley.
31. Remove power steering pipe and AIR pipe brackets from right side cylinder head.
32. Remove alternator mounting bracket.
33. Remove right front engine lift bracket bolt and position bracket aside.
34. Remove oil filter.
35. Remove right rear engine lift bracket.
36. Remove intake manifold bolts, noting position for installation.
37. Remove intake manifold from vehicle.
38. Reverse procedure to install. Install and torque manifold bolts to specifications in sequence shown in **Fig. 3.**

EXHAUST MANIFOLD
REPLACE

RIGHT SIDE

1. Disconnect battery ground cable.
2. Remove air cleaner and exhaust crossover pipe.
3. Disconnect oxygen sensor and coolant temperature sensor electrical connectors.
4. Remove catalytic converter air pipe to AIR pipe clip bolt.
5. Remove two forward, upper exhaust manifold to cylinder head bolts.
6. Raise and support vehicle.
7. Remove converter air pipe bracket from stud.
8. Remove manifold to converter exhaust pipe.
9. Remove five remaining exhaust manifold to cylinder head attaching bolts.
10. Disconnect AIR pipe from manifold.
11. Remove exhaust manifold from vehicle.
12. Reverse procedure to install.

LEFT SIDE

1. Disconnect ground cable.
2. Remove cooling fans.
3. Remove exhaust crossover pipe.
4. Remove drive belts.
5. Remove AIR pump pivot bolt.
6. Remove belt tensioner and power steering pump brace.
7. Disconnect AIR pipe from manifold.
8. Remove exhaust manifold from vehicle.
9. Reverse procedure to install.

CYLINDER HEAD
REPLACE

1. Disconnect battery ground cable.
2. Drain cooling system.
3. Remove intake manifold as outlined under "Intake Manifold, Replace" procedure.
4. If removing left side cylinder head, remove the two cooling fans.
5. Remove appropriate exhaust manifold as outlined under "Exhaust Manifold, Replace," procedure.
6. Remove ten cylinder head bolts.
7. Reverse procedure to install, referring to **Fig. 4** for bolt tightening sequence. Torque cylinder head bolts in 3 steps

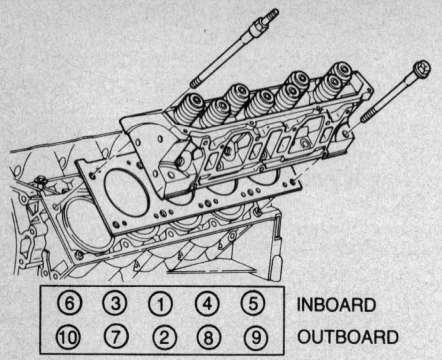

| 6 | 3 | 1 | 4 | 5 | INBOARD |
| 10 | 7 | 2 | 8 | 9 | OUTBOARD |

Fig. 4   Cylinder head bolt torque sequence

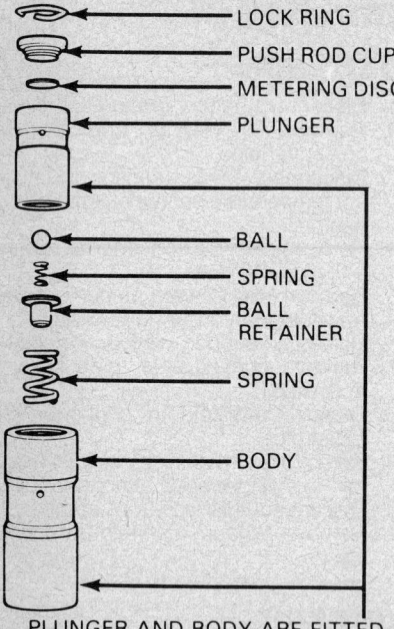

- LOCK RING
- PUSH ROD CUP
- METERING DISC
- PLUNGER
- BALL
- SPRING
- BALL RETAINER
- SPRING
- BODY

PLUNGER AND BODY ARE FITTED PAIRS AND MUST NOT BE MISMATED.

Fig. 6   Hydraulic valve lifter

as follows:
a. **Torque** all bolts to 38 ft. lbs. in specified sequence.
b. **Torque** all bolts to 74 ft. lbs. in specified sequence.
c. **Torque** bolts 1, 3 and 4 to 90 ft. lbs.

VALVE ARRANGEMENT
FRONT TO REAR

4.5L/V8-273 . . . . I-E-I-E-E-I-E-I

VALVE LIFT SPECIFICATIONS

Engine	Year	Int.	Exh.
4.5L/V8-273	1988	.384	.396

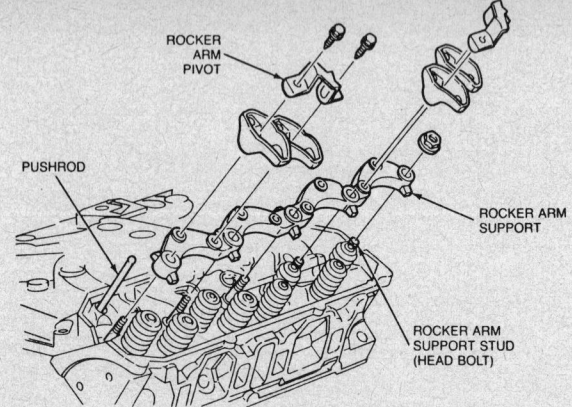

Fig. 5   Rocker arm support, rocker arms & pivots

VALVE TIMING
INTAKE OPENS BEFORE TDC

Engine	Year	Degrees
4.5/V8-273	1988	20

ROCKER ARM SUPPORT, ROCKER ARM & PIVOT REPLACE

1. Remove rocker arm covers.
2. Remove rocker arm support retaining nuts from stud headed cylinder head bolts, **Fig. 5. Removing the rocker arm support with the rocker arms and pivots attached is recommended since the pivot assemblies may be damaged if pivot bolt torque is not removed evenly against valve spring pressure.**
3. Secure support in a suitable vise and remove rocker arms and pivots.
4. Reverse procedure to install. Torque pivot bolts to specifications.

VALVE GUIDES

Check valve stem to valve guide clearance. Clearance should be .005 inch or less. Service valves are available in standard size (.343 inch) or oversizes of .003 and .006 inch. If clearance is excessive, ream valve guide to accommodate next oversize valve. Some engines are factory fitted with .003 inch oversize valve guides and valves and are identified by a "3" stamped on the cylinder head gasket surface in-line with the oversize valve.

HYDRAULIC VALVE LIFTERS
REPLACE

Valve lifters may be removed from their bores after the intake manifold, rocker arms and push rods are removed. Adjust-

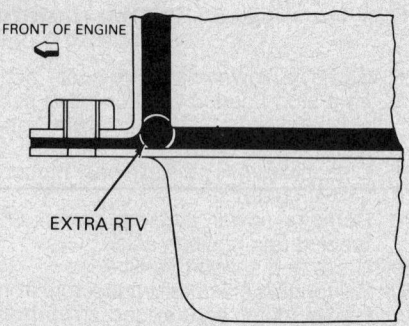

Fig. 7   RTV sealant application

able pliers with taped jaws may be used to remove lifters that are stuck due to varnish, carbon, etc. **Fig. 6** illustrates the type of lifter used.

TIMING CASE COVER
REPLACE

1. Disconnect battery ground cable.
2. Drain cooling system.
3. Remove air cleaner.
4. Remove drive belt.
5. Remove alternator and position aside.
6. Remove A/C accumulator from bracket and position aside.
7. Remove idler pulley, water pump pulley and water pump.
8. Raise and support vehicle.
9. Remove crankshaft puller and hub.
10. Remove cover attaching bolts and the cover.
11. Reverse procedure to install. When installing, place a bead of RTV sealer on the front cover lip on the oil pan sealing surface and a 1/4 inch bead of RTV sealer on the oil pan where the oil pan, cylinder block and cover join together, **Fig. 7.** The 1/4 inch bead is needed because the cover has a rounded corner instead of a square corner. If the extra RTV is not applied an oil leak may occur.

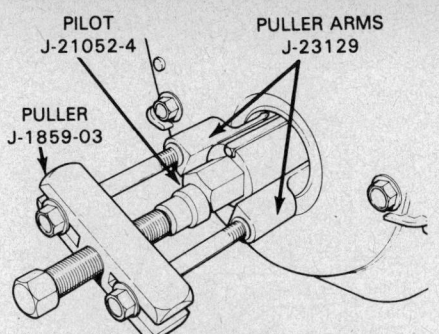

Fig. 8 Timing case oil seal removal

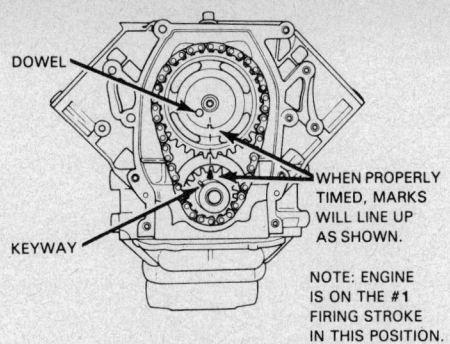

Fig. 9 Camshaft timing marks

Fig. 10 Piston & rod assembly

TIMING CASE OIL SEAL
REPLACE

1. Remove crankshaft pulley and vibration damper.
2. Remove oil seal with tools J-1859-03 and J-23129 or equivalents, **Fig. 8.**
3. Lubricate new oil seal with engine oil and install with tool J-29662 or equivalent.
4. Install crankshaft puller and vibration damper.

TIMING CHAIN
REPLACE

1. Remove timing case cover as outlined under "Timing Case Cover, Replace" procedure.
2. Remove oil slinger from crankshaft.
3. Rotate crankshaft to align camshaft and crankshaft sprocket timing marks, **Fig. 9.**
4. Remove screw attaching camshaft sprocket to camshaft, then the camshaft and crankshaft sprockets with the timing chain attached.
5. Reverse procedure to install. Ensure that timing marks are aligned, **Fig. 9.**

CAMSHAFT
REPLACE

1. Remove engine as outlined under "Engine, Replace" procedure.
2. Remove timing case cover and timing chain.
3. Remove intake manifold and valve lifters.
4. Slide camshaft forward carefully from engine.
5. Reverse procedure to install.

PISTON & ROD
ASSEMBLE

Assemble pistons to rods as shown in **Fig. 10.** Measure c onnecting rod side clearance with a suitable feeler gauge after installation. Clearance should be .008 to .020 inch.

PISTONS

When measuring piston diameter, place

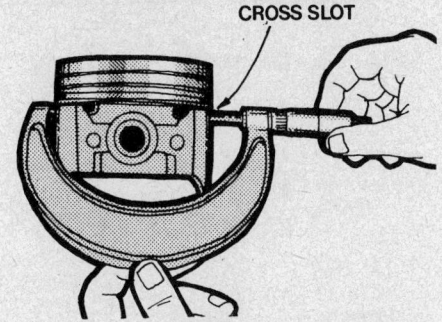

Fig. 11 Measuring piston diameter

micrometer 3/16 inch below cross slot or 3/8 inch below oil ring groove, **Fig. 11.** Cylinder liner diameter is measured two inches down from top of liner and perpendicular to the cylinder centerline. The difference between the two readings should be .0010-.0018 inch. Cylinder bore out-of-round should not exceed .0008 inch on 1988 models. If any reading is not within specifications, the piston and cylinder liner must be replaced. No attempt should be made to rebore or hone the cylinder liner. Refer to "Cylinder Liner, Replace" procedure.

PISTON RINGS

On these engines, replacement rings are available in standard size only. If piston ring clearance is excessive, the piston and cylinder liner must be replaced. Refer to "Cylinder Liner, Replace" procedure.

PISTON PINS

Piston pins are a matched fit with the piston and are not available for separate replacement. Piston pins are pressed into the connecting rods and will not become loose enough to cause a knock or tapping until after very high mileage.

CYLINDER LINER
REPLACE

The cylinder heads, pistons and connecting rods must be removed before replacing cylinder liner. After removing cylinder heads, install tool J-29775 to retain the cylinder liners not being replaced.

1. If original liners are to be reinstalled, mark position of cylinder liner in cylinder block and keep piston with original liner for reference during installation.
2. Pull cylinder liner from cylinder block. Discard O-ring from base of liner.
3. Check cylinder liner and cylinder block mating surfaces.
4. If original cylinder liner is to be installed and engine has not experienced overheating, install new O-ring onto bottom of liner. Align reference marks made during removal and install liner into cylinder block.
5. If new liner is being installed or if original liner is being installed and the engine has experienced overheating, then cylinder liner height must be measured as follows:
   a. Place liner in cylinder block without O-ring.
   b. Place gauge J-29776 or equivalent on cylinder liner. Check that spring-loaded guide pins fit into liner with machined pads resting on edge of liner and dial indicator plunger contacting block deck face. Apply moderate pressure to gauge until dial indicator stops moving. Record this reading. If reading is on the + side of dial indicator, cylinder liner is higher than block face. If reading is on the − side, the liner is lower than the block face.
   c. Repeat step b at two other locations on the liner. Use average of the three readings as actual liner height.
   d. Cylinder liner height should be .0004 liner.
   e. Check liner-to-liner height with tool J-29766 or equivalent. Install adjacent liners with O-ring. Liner-to-liner height should be −.002 to +.002 inch. Mark liners in measured positions.
6. When installing liners into block, check alignment marks. Be sure to install O-ring onto liner.

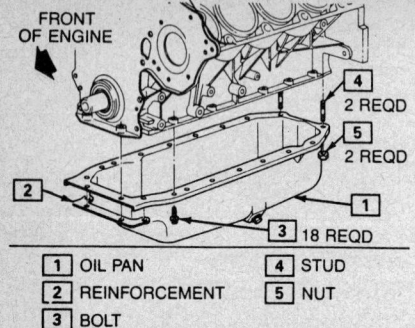

1	OIL PAN	4	STUD
2	REINFORCEMENT	5	NUT
3	BOLT		

Fig. 12   Oil pan removal & installation

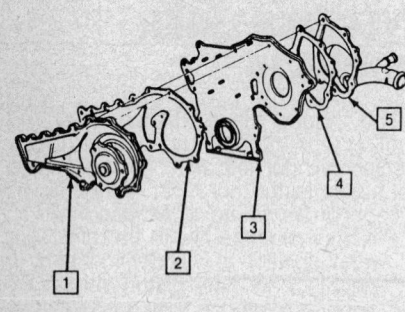

1 WATER PUMP ASSEMBLY
2 WATER PUMP GASKET
3 FRONT COVER
4 WATER PUMP INLET GASKET
5 WATER PUMP INLET

Fig. 15   Water pump assembly

MAIN & ROD BEARINGS

Main and rod bearings are supplied in standard sizes only.

CRANKSHAFT OIL SEAL
REPLACE

Before replacing the crankshaft oil seal, be sure that the apparent oil seal leak is not actually a leak between the sides of the rear main cap and crankcase.
1. Remove transaxle, then the flex plate from crankshaft.
2. Remove old seal with tool J-26868 or equivalent.
3. Lubricate new seal lip with wheel bearing grease and place on crankshaft with spring facing inside of engine.
4. Press seal into position with tool J-34604 or equivalent. Seal is fully installed when flush with block or slightly below. The use of the tool is recommended since the seal must fit squarely on the crankshaft, otherwise an oil leak could result.

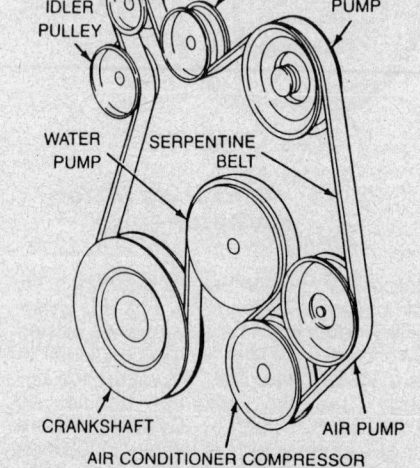

Fig. 13   Oil pump assembly

Fig. 16   Serpentine drive belt routing

OIL PAN
REPLACE

1. Disconnect battery ground cable.
2. Raise and support vehicle.
3. Remove two flexplate covers.
4. Drain oil pan.
5. Remove oil pan attaching bolts and the two nuts from studs.
6. Remove oil pan, **Fig. 12.**
7. Reverse procedure to install. RTV sealer is used to seal the oil pan.

OIL PUMP
REPLACE

1. Remove oil pan as outlined under "Oil Pan, Replace" procedure.
2. Remove bolts securing oil pump to engine, **Fig. 13.**
3. Remove oil pump.
4. Reverse procedure to install.

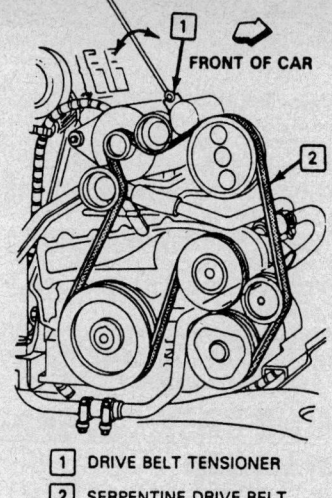

1 DRIVE BELT TENSIONER
2 SERPENTINE DRIVE BELT

Fig. 14   Drive belt removal

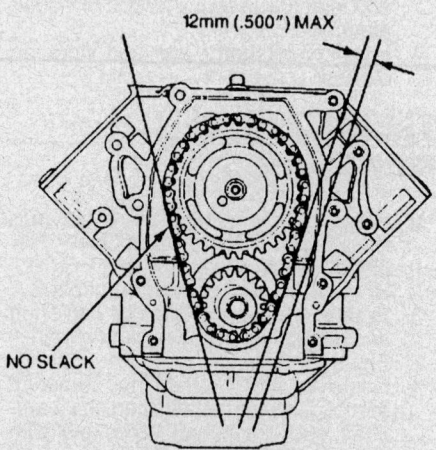

Fig. 17   Checking timing chain

OIL PUMP SERVICE

1. Remove screws securing pump cover to housing, **Fig. 13.**
2. Remove driveshaft, drive gear and driven gear from housing.
3. Remove oil pressure regulator valve and spring from bore in housing. Inspect regulator for nicks and burrs.
4. Check regulator spring free length. Length should be 2.57 inches. Spring compressed length should be 1.46 inches under 9.3-10.5 pound load.
5. Check pump housing for wear and gears for nicks and burrs.
6. Install drive gear over driveshaft so that retaining ring is inside gear. Place drive gear over pump housing shaft closest to pressure regulator bore.
7. Place driven gear over remaining shaft in pump housing, meshing driven gear with drive gear.
8. Install pressure regulator spring and valve in housing bore.
9. Install pump cover over driveshaft. Install and torque retaining screws to specifications.

WATER PUMP
REPLACE

1. Disconnect battery ground cable and drain cooling system.
2. Remove A/C accumulator from bracket and position aside.
3. Remove A/C accumulator bracket from wheel house.
4. Remove right hand cross-car brace.
5. Remove drive belt, **Fig. 14.**
6. Remove drive belt idler puller and bracket.
7. Remove water pump pulley.
8. Remove water pump attaching bolts and the water pump, **Fig 15.**
9. Reverse procedure to install.

FUEL PUMP
REPLACE

1. Remove fuel tank.
2. Remove cam lock with tool J-24187 or equivalent.
3. Remove fuel sending unit and fuel pump assembly from tank.
4. Remove fuel pump from sending unit.
5. Reverse procedure to install.

SERPENTINE DRIVE BELT ROUTING

Refer to **Fig. 16** for routing of serpentine drive belt.

COOLING SYSTEM BLEED

1. Fill cooling system and leave radiator cap off.
2. Start engine, then and push front "DEF" button and increase temperature to 90°.
3. Run engine at 2000 RPM for approximately 10 minutes, then refill radiator until full and install radiator cap with engine running.
4. Fill coolant reservoir to the "FULL" mark.

SERVICE BULLETINS
INTAKE MANIFOLD
Bolts

On some late production 1988 4.5L engines, a different intake manifold was used in production. These manifold use a 40 mm bolt in the No. 3 bolt position instead of a 55 mm bolt as early production models used.

Gaskets

New intake manifold gasket sets are available to increase sealing quality when engine repairs are performed. On 1988 models use part No. 3634746.

VALVE TRAIN NOISE

On 1988 models equipped with 4.5L engines built prior to production No. T10L315315, an abnormal valve train noise may be experienced with the engine at normal operating temperature. This condition may be caused by inconsistencies in valve lifter production. If condition exists, replace lifters with part No. 5235498.

SCREECHING NOISE DURING CRANKING

On some 1988 models. a screeching noise during cranking may be present. If noise is present, replace flywheel with part No. 1648458 to correct condition.

SERPENTINE BELTS

On 1988 models, the serpentine drive belt should be replaced anytime an engine driven accessory becomes seized and prevents rotation of any pulley.

TIMING CHAIN

On 1988 models, timing chain should be checked for excessive wear as shown, **Fig. 17**, and replaced as necessary.

MOANING NOISE AFTER START

On some 1988 models, a low moaning noise after start up may be present. The noise may be caused by vibration of the oil pump pickup. If the pickup is found to be the problem, replace oil pump assembly with part No. 3517753. On 1988 models replacement of the oil pan will also be required due to the installation of a baffle that provides insufficient clearance for the pickup.

TIGHTENING SPECIFICATIONS

Year	Component	Torque/ft. lbs.
1988-90	Air Pipe To Cylinder Head	22
	Connecting Rod Bolts	24 ①
	Coolant Temperature Sensor	22
	Crankshaft Pulley	18
	Cylinder Head	① ②
	Distributor Hold Down	③
	EGR Valve Mounting Screws	15
	Engine Metal Temperature Switch	6
	Exhaust Manifold Bolts	18
	Exhaust Outlet Flange Studs	30
	Flywheel To Crankshaft	70
	Front Cover	15
	Heater Water Valve	22
	Intake Manifold Bolts	②
	Lower Thermostat Housing To Water Pump	④
	Main Bearing Cap Bolts	85
	Oil Filter Adapter To Block	15
	Oil Pan Bolts	11
	Oil Pan Drain Plug	22
	Oil Pan Nuts	11
	Oil Pan Studs	15
	Oil Pressure Switch	10
	Oil Pump Cover Screws	5
	Oil Pump Mounting Bolts	15

Continued

TIGHTENING SPECIFICATIONS—Continued

Year	Component	Torque/ft. lbs.
	Oil Pump Mounting Nut	22
	Oxygen Sensor	30
	Rocker Arm Cover	8
	Rocker Arm Pivot To Support	22
	Rocker Arm Support To Head Bolt Nuts	37
	Rocker Arm Support To Head	7
	Spark Plugs	11
	Thermal Vacuum Switch	15
	Timing Sprocket To Camshaft	37
	Timing Tab To Water Pump Nuts	5
	Upper Thermostat Housing To Lower Thermostat Housing	18
	Water Passage Plug	7

①—Lubricated with engine oil.
②—Refer to text for procedure.
③—Nut, 18 ft. lbs.; Stud, 26 ft. lbs.
④—Bolt, 7 ft. lbs.; Stud, 30 ft. lbs.

Rear Suspension

INDEX

DESCRIPTION

These vehicles use an independent rear suspension consisting of lower control arms, coil springs, toe links, suspension knuckles, superlift struts and stabilizer bar, **Fig. 1.** The hub and wheel bearing is an assembly and does not require periodic lubrication.

HUB & BEARING ASSEMBLY
REPLACE

1. Raise and support rear of vehicle. Remove wheel assembly and brake drum. **Do not hammer on drum since damage to bearing may occur.**
2. Remove four hub and bearing assembly to axle attaching bolts and the assembly from axle, **Fig. 2.**
3. Reverse procedure to install. Torque attaching bolts to specifications.

COIL SPRING
REPLACE

1. Support vehicle so the rear wheel and control arm hang free. Remove rear wheel.
2. Disconnect rear stabilizer bar from knuckle bracket.
3. Disconnect electronic level control height sensor link if removing right control arm.
4. Disconnect parking brake cable clip

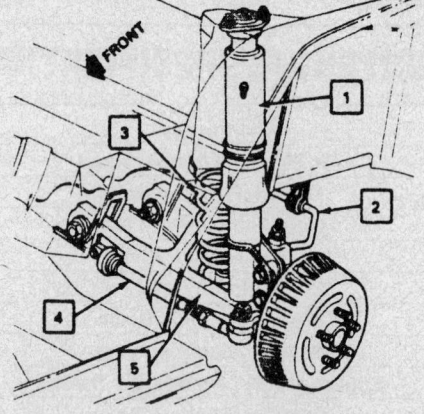

1	SUPERLIFT® STRUT	4	SUSPENSION ADJUSTMENT LINK
2	STABILIZER BAR	5	LOWER CONTROL ARM
3	COIL SPRING		

Fig. 1   Rear suspension

from frame if removing left control arm.
5. Place tool J-23028-01 in position to cradle control arm bushings, **Fig. 3. Tool J-23028-01 should be secured to a suitable jack, otherwise, personal injury could result.**
6. Raise jack to relieve tension from control arm pivot bolts.
7. Place a chain around spring and control for safety.
8. Remove rear control arm pivot bolt and nut, **Fig. 4.**

9. Slowly lower jack until front bolt and nut can be removed.
10. Remove coil spring. **Do not apply force on lower arm and ball joint to remove spring. Maneuver spring to remove.**
11. Reverse procedure to install, noting the following:
    a. Replace spring insulators that are damaged or if vehicle has been in service for more than 50,000 miles
    b. Install springs so that upper pigtail end of left spring faces rear of vehicle, or upper pigtail end of right spring faces front of vehicle when vehicle is at normal ride height.
    c. Tighten suspension fasteners sufficiently to retain position of components, lower vehicle so that it rests on the wheels at normal ride height, then torque fasteners as follows: 1-Torque control arm pivot nuts to specifications 2-Torque control arm pivot bolts to specifications 3-Torque stabilizer support bolt to specifications. **Failure to torque fasteners to specifications in listed sequence may adversely affect ride and handling.**

REAR TIE ROD/ADJUSTMENT LINK
REPLACE

1. Raise and support vehicle.
2. Remove wheel assembly, cotter key and castle nut, **Fig. 5.**
3. Using tool J-24319-01, disconnect

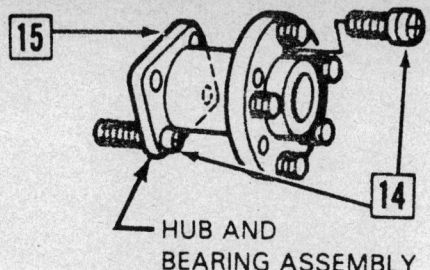

Fig. 2 Hub & bearing assembly

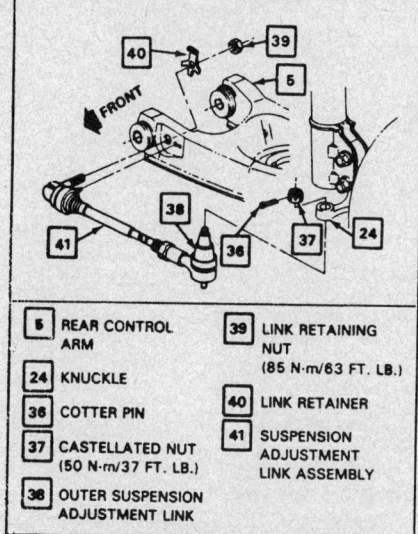

5	REAR CONTROL ARM	**39**	LINK RETAINING NUT (85 N·m/63 FT. LB.)
24	KNUCKLE	**40**	LINK RETAINER
36	COTTER PIN	**41**	SUSPENSION ADJUSTMENT LINK ASSEMBLY
37	CASTELLATED NUT (50 N·m/37 FT. LB.)		
38	OUTER SUSPENSION ADJUSTMENT LINK		

Fig. 5 Tie rod/adjustment link installation

outer tie rod/adjustment from knuckle. **When disconnecting the tie rod/adjustment from knuckle, do not use a wedge since seal damage will occur.**

4. Remove rod/link assembly retaining nut and retainer.
5. Remove rod/link assembly from lower control arm.
6. Reverse procedure to install. **Torque** link retaining nut to specifications and castellated nut securing ball stud to 37 ft. lbs. Install cotter pin retaining castellated nut, tightening nut as needed to insert pin through hole in stud. Do not loosen nut to align slots with hole.

BALL JOINT INSPECTION

The ball joint has a visual wear indicator. Checking the condition of the ball joint is a simple procedure but must be followed accurately to prevent unnecessary ball joint replacement.

The vehicle must be supported by the wheels during inspection to ensure that the vehicle weight is properly loading the ball joints.

The ball joint is inspected for wear by visual observation alone. Wear is indicated by retraction of the 1/2 inch diameter nipple into the ball joint cover (the ball joint grease fitting is threaded into this nipple). The nipple protrudes .050 inch beyond

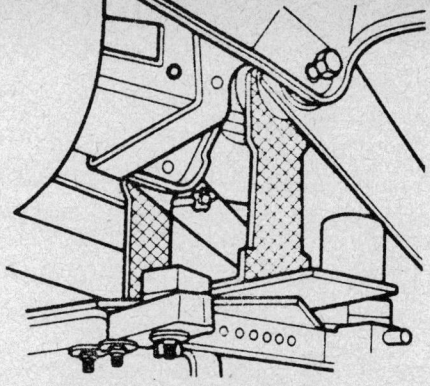

Fig. 3 Installing tool J-23028-01

the surface of the ball joint cover on a new unworn joint. Normal wear will result in the surface of this nipple retracting very slowly inward. The ball joint should be replaced if the nipple is flush or below the cover surface, **Fig. 6.**

Ball stud tightness in the knuckle boss should also be checked when inspecting the ball joint. This may be done by shaking the wheel and feeling for movement of the stud end or castellated nut at the knuckle boss.

Checking the fastener tightness at the castellated nut is an alternative method of inspecting (a loose nut can indicate a bent stud or an "opened up" hole in the knuckle boss). If worn, the ball joint and knuckle must be replaced.

If the ball joint is separated from the knuckle for suspension service, the ball joint seal should be inspected for damage. A damaged seal will cause joint failure. If seal damage is found the ball joint should be replaced.

LOWER CONTROL ARM BALL JOINT
REPLACE

1. Raise and support vehicle.
2. Remove wheel assembly, cotter key and castle nut.
3. Disconnect outer tie rod/adjustment link from knuckle as outlined previously.
4. Disconnect electronic level control height sensor link from right side control arm.
5. Support control arm with a suitable jack.
6. Remove ball joint cotter pin and nut.
7. Using tool J-29330, disconnect ball joint from knuckle, **Fig. 7.**
8. Using tool J-9519-7, remove ball joint from control arm.
9. Reverse procedure to install.

STABILIZER BAR
REPLACE

1. Remove rear wheels and tires.
2. Remove stabilizer shaft support bolt, nut, retainer and insulators from knuckle bracket, **Fig. 8.**

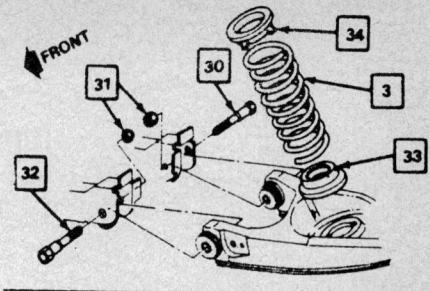

3	COIL SPRING
30	CONTROL ARM PIVOT BOLT-REAR (170 N·m/125 FT. LB.)
31	CONTROL ARM PIVOT NUTS (115 N·m/85 FT. LB.)
32	CONTROL ARM PIVOT BOLT-FRONT (170 N·m/125 FT. LB.)
33	LOWER COIL SPRING INSULATOR
34	UPPER COIL SPRING INSULATOR

Fig. 4 Coil spring replacement

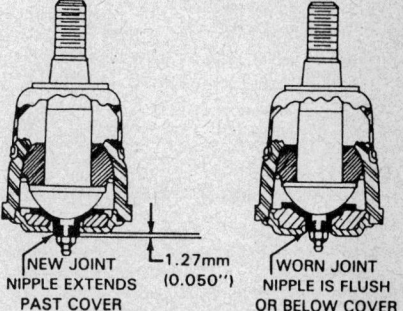

Fig. 6 Ball joint inspection

NEW JOINT NIPPLE EXTENDS PAST COVER — 1.27mm (0.050") — WORN JOINT NIPPLE IS FLUSH OR BELOW COVER

3. Remove bushing clip bolt.
4. Bend open end of support assembly downward.
5. Remove stabilizer shaft and bushings.

LOWER CONTROL ARM
REPLACE

1. Remove coil spring as outlined under "Coil Spring, Replace" procedure.
2. Remove control arm front pivot bolt.
3. Remove control arm from vehicle.
4. Reverse procedure to install.

REAR STRUT
REPLACE

1. Raise and support vehicle.
2. Remove trunk side cover.
3. Remove wheel assembly.
4. Disconnect air tube from superlift strut, **Fig. 9.**
5. Remove two strut tower mount nuts.
6. Remove two strut anchor bolts, washers and nuts from knuckle, then the knuckle bracket.
7. Remove strut from vehicle.
8. Reverse procedure to install.

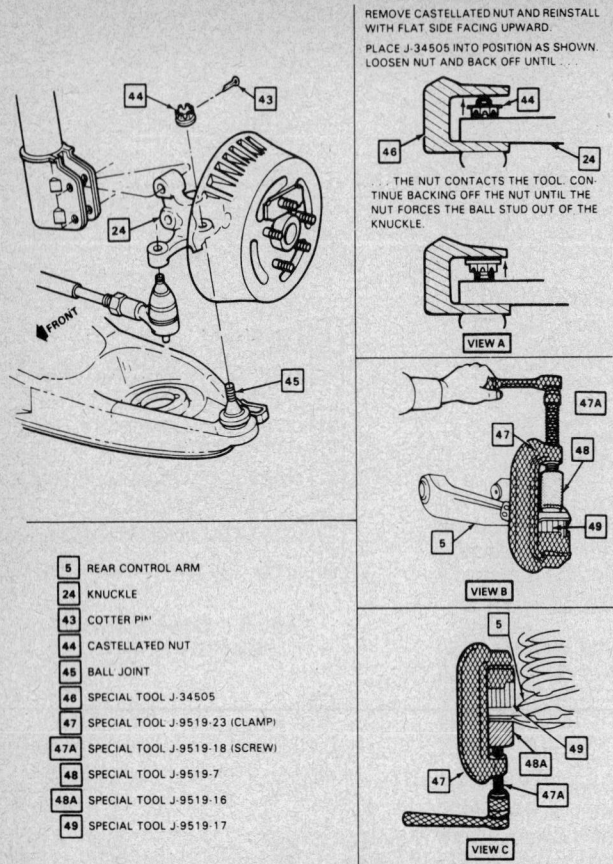

5	REAR CONTROL ARM
24	KNUCKLE
43	COTTER PIN
44	CASTELLATED NUT
45	BALL JOINT
46	SPECIAL TOOL J-34505
47	SPECIAL TOOL J-9519-23 (CLAMP)
47A	SPECIAL TOOL J-9519-18 (SCREW)
48	SPECIAL TOOL J-9519-7
48A	SPECIAL TOOL J-9519-16
49	SPECIAL TOOL J-9519-17

Fig. 7   Ball joint replacement

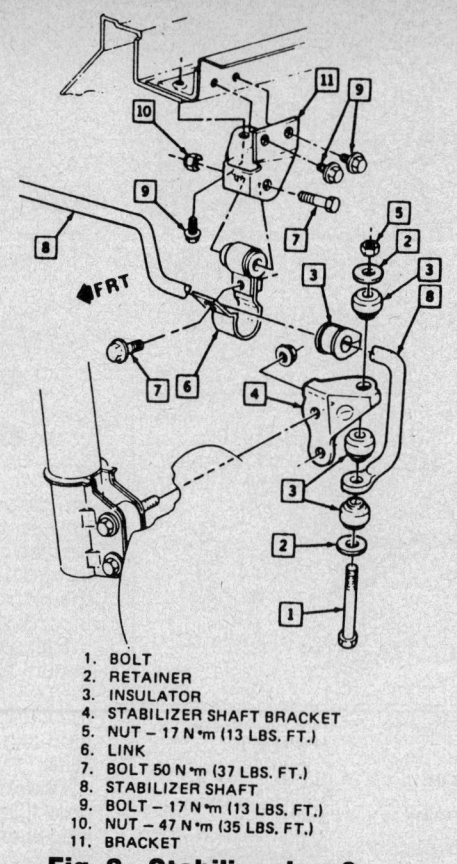

1. BOLT
2. RETAINER
3. INSULATOR
4. STABILIZER SHAFT BRACKET
5. NUT — 17 N·m (13 LBS. FT.)
6. LINK
7. BOLT 50 N·m (37 LBS. FT.)
8. STABILIZER SHAFT
9. BOLT — 17 N·m (13 LBS. FT.)
10. NUT — 47 N·m (35 LBS. FT.)
11. BRACKET

Fig. 8   Stabilizer bar & bushing assembly

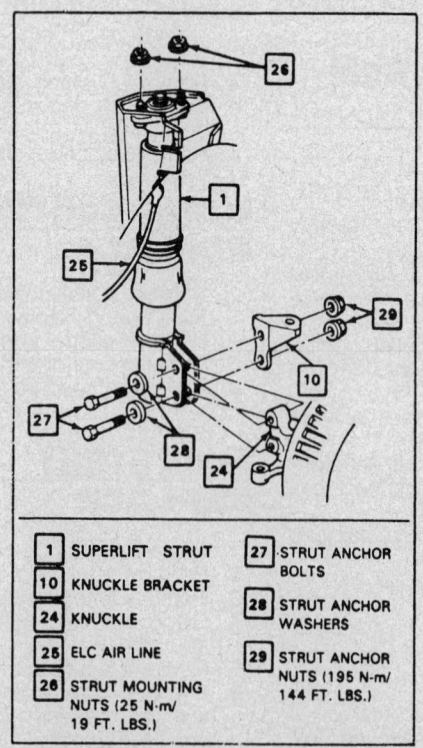

1	SUPERLIFT STRUT	27	STRUT ANCHOR BOLTS
10	KNUCKLE BRACKET	28	STRUT ANCHOR WASHERS
24	KNUCKLE	29	STRUT ANCHOR NUTS (195 N·m/ 144 FT. LBS.)
25	ELC AIR LINE		
26	STRUT MOUNTING NUTS (25 N·m/ 19 FT. LBS.)		

Fig. 9   Strut assembly

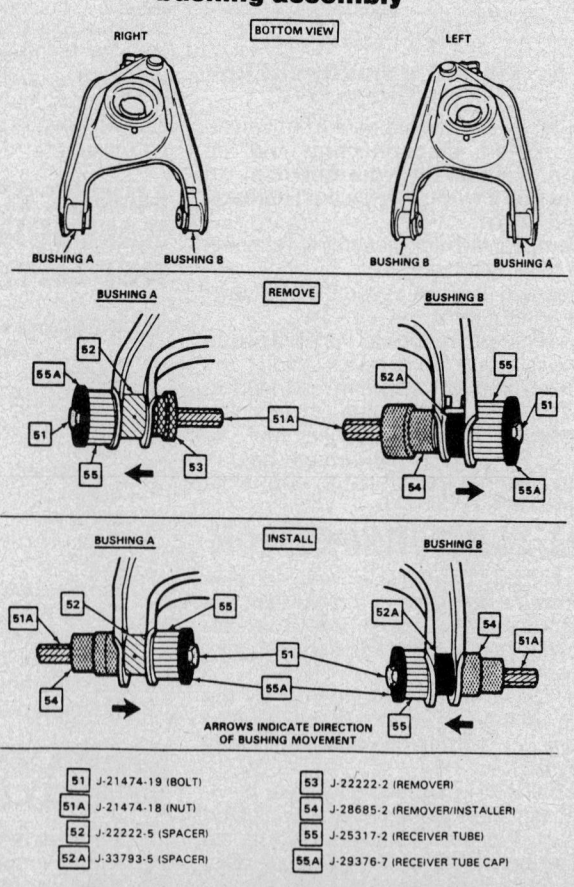

51	J-21474-19 (BOLT)	53	J-22222-2 (REMOVER)
51A	J-21474-18 (NUT)	54	J-28685-2 (REMOVER/INSTALLER)
52	J-22222-5 (SPACER)	55	J-25317-2 (RECEIVER TUBE)
52A	J-33793-5 (SPACER)	55A	J-29376-7 (RECEIVER TUBE CAP)

Fig. 10   Control arm bushing removal/installation

CONTROL ARM BUSHINGS
REPLACE

These vehicles incorporate control arm configuration with two different sized bushings, **Fig. 10**. These bushings are not interchangeable, and require different combinations of special tools for removal and installation. The following service procedure refer to these bushings as A and B.

REMOVAL

1. Remove control arm from vehicle.
2. Place control arm onto a suitable work bench, up side down.
3. For bushing A, install spacer tool J-22222-5, for bushing B, install spacer tool J-33793-5 onto control arm.
4. Position receiver tube J-25317-2 and cap tool J-29376-7 on outer side of control arm. Ensure receiver tube does not contact the bushing flange.
5. Coat threaded area of long bolt J-21474-19 with extreme pressure lubricant J-23444-A, then install bolt through receiver, cap and bushing.
6. Install remover tool J-22222-2 for bushing A or tool J-28685-2 for bushing B onto bolt at inner side of control arm. Position remover so small diameter portion contacts bushing.
7. Place bearing on bolt and install long nut tool J21474-18. Bearing must be installed between nut and remover.
8. Draw bushing out of control arm by tightening the nut.

INSTALLATION

1. With control arm up side down on work bench, position new bushing into control arm. **When installing new bushings, the flanged end of the bushing must face outward when installed in the control arm.**
2. Install spacer tool J-22222-5 for bushing A or tool J-33793-5 for bushing B.
3. Position receiver tube J-25317-2 and cap tool J-29376-7 onto inner side of control arm. Receiver tube should be centered over the hole.
4. Coat threaded area of long bolt with extreme pressure lubricant J-23444-A and install through receiver, cap and bushing.
5. Position installer J-28685-2 onto bolt at outer side of control arm. Installer should be positioned with large diameter end contacting bushing flange.
6. Place bearing on bolt and install long nut J-21474-18. Bearing must be positioned between nut and installer.
7. Draw bushing into control arm by tightening nut. Tighten nut until bushing flange seats firmly against control arm.
8. Install control arm into vehicle, adjust rear wheel alignment, if necessary.

TIGHTENING SPECIFICATIONS

Year	Component	Torque/ft. lbs.
1988-90	**Ball Joint Nut**	88① ②
	Control Arm Pivot Bolts	135
	Control Arm Pivot Nuts	85
	Hub & Bearing Assembly Bolts	52
	Stabilizer Shaft Bushing Assembly Nut	37
	Stabilizer Shaft Bushing Clip Bolt	37
	Stabilizer Shaft Link Nut	160
	Stabilizer Shaft Mounting Bracket Bolt	160
	Strut To Knuckle Bolts	147
	Strut Mount To Underbody	18
	Suspension Adjustment Link At Knuckle	33
	Suspension Adjustment Link At Control Arm	63
	Suspension Adjustment Link Locknut	48
	Top Strut Mount Nut	220

① —Inch lbs.
② —**Tighten nut an additional ⅔ turn after torquing.**

Front Suspension & Steering

INDEX

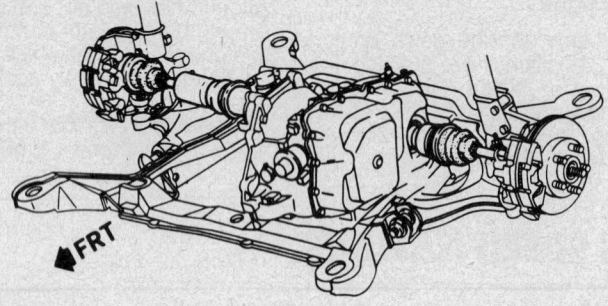

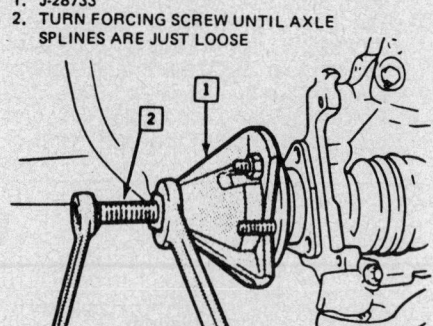

1. J-28733
2. TURN FORCING SCREW UNTIL AXLE SPLINES ARE JUST LOOSE

Fig. 2   Separating drive axle from hub

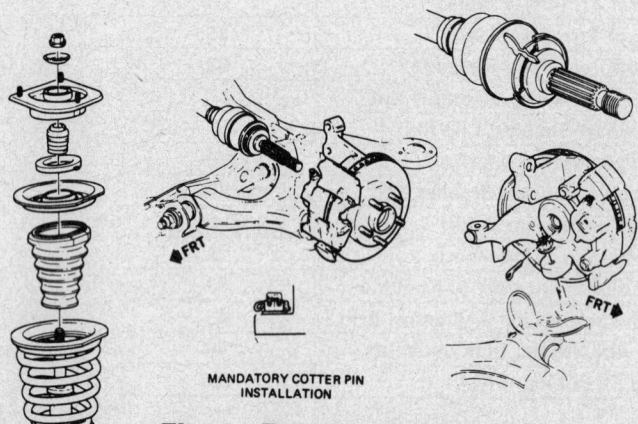

MANDATORY COTTER PIN INSTALLATION

Fig. 1   Front suspension

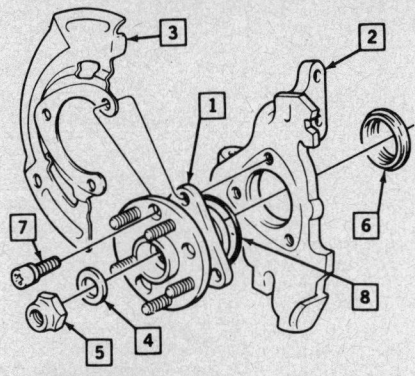

1. HUB AND BEARING ASSEMBLY
2. STEERING KNUCKLE
3. SHIELD
4. WASHER
5. HUB NUT 245 N·m (180 LBS. FT.)
6. SEAL
7. HUB AND BEARING RETAINING BOLT (55 TORX) 95 N·m (70 LBS. FT.)
8. "O" RING

Fig. 3   Hub & bearing assembly

DESCRIPTION

The front suspension is of the MacPhereson design, **Fig. 1**. The control arm pivots from the cradle and is mounted in rubber bushings. The upper end of the strut is isolated by a rubber mount and contains a non-serviceable bearing to allow for rotation. The lower end of the steering knuckle pivots on a ball joint riveted to the control arm. The ball joint is fastened to the steering knuckle with a castle nut and cotter pin.

HUB & BEARING
REPLACE

1. Raise and support vehicle and remove wheel assembly.
2. Install drive axle boot protector tool J-28712 on outer joints and J-34754 on inner joints.
3. Insert a suitable drift through opening in caliper into rotor cooling fins to prevent assembly from rotating, then remove hub nut and washer.
4. Remove caliper bracket mounting bolts and the caliper and bracket assembly, then secure assembly aside taking care not to stretch brake hose. Use care not to damage brake hose.
5. Remove rotor, then press drive axle from hub using J-28733 or equivalent, **Fig. 2**.
6. Remove hub assembly retaining bolts, shield, hub and bearing assembly, and O-ring, **Fig. 3**
7. Reverse procedure to install. Torque hub attaching bolts to specifications, caliper bolts to 38 ft. lbs. and hub nut to specifications.

BALL JOINT
REPLACE

1. Raise and support vehicle and place jackstands under cradle. Vehicle weight should not be placed on the control arms.
2. Remove wheel assembly.
3. Install drive axle boot protectors.
4. Remove cotter key from ball joint nut and, using tool J-34505, separate ball joint from steering knuckle, **Fig. 4**.
5. Drill out ball joint retaining rivets.
6. Remove stabilizer bar bushing to control arm bolt.
7. Pull control arm downward and remove ball joint from steering knuckle and control arm.
8. Reverse procedure to install. **Torque** new ball joint attaching nuts to specifications, **Fig. 5**, and ball joint castle nut to 81 ft. lbs.

1. J 36226 BALL JOINT SEPARATOR

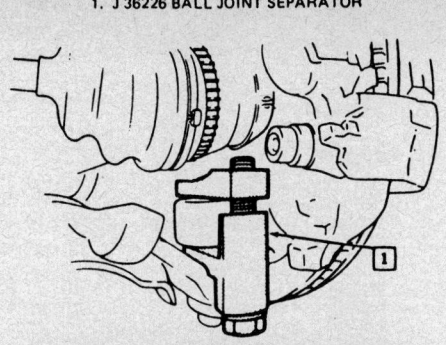

Fig. 4   Separating ball joint from steering knuckle

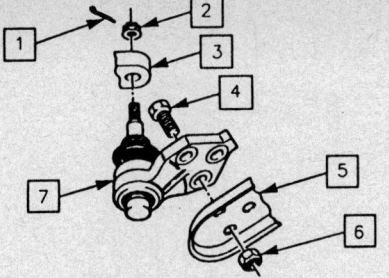

1	COTTER PIN
2	BALL JOINT TO STEERING KNUCKLE NUT 55 N·m (41 LB. FT.) BEFORE COTTER PIN INSTALLATION
3	STEERING KNUCKLE
4	BALL JOINT MOUNTING BOLTS MUST FACE DOWN
5	CONTROL ARM
6	BALL JOINT MOUNTING NUTS 68 N·m (50 LB. FT.)
7	SERVICE BALL JOINT

Fig. 5   Service ball joint attachment

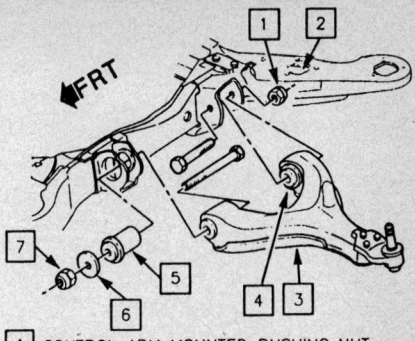

1	CONTROL ARM MOUNTED BUSHING NUT 123 N·m (90 LB. FT.)
2	FRAME
3	CONTROL ARM
4	CONTROL ARM MOUNTED BUSHING
5	FRAME MOUNTED BUSHING
6	WASHER
7	FRAME MOUNTING BUSHING NUT 190 N·m (140 LB. FT.)

Fig. 6   Control arm assembly

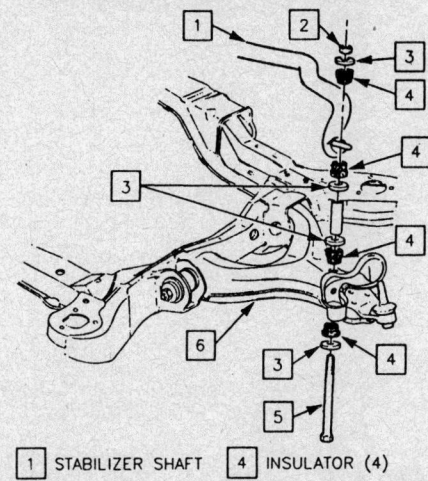

1	STABILIZER SHAFT	4	INSULATOR (4)
2	NUT 17 N·m (13 LB. FT.)	5	BOLT
3	RETAINER (4)	6	CONTROL ARM

Fig. 7   Stabilizer bar bushing assembly

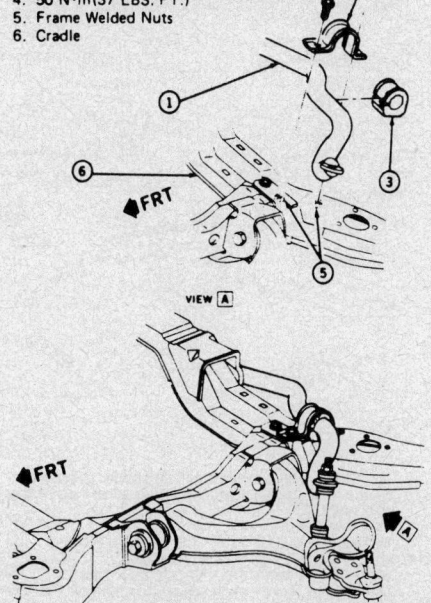

1. Stabilizer Bar
2. Stabilizer Bar Mounting Bracket
3. Stabilizer Bar Mounting Bushing
4. 50 N·m (37 LBS. FT.)
5. Frame Welded Nuts
6. Cradle

VIEW [A]

Fig. 8   Stabilizer bar mounting

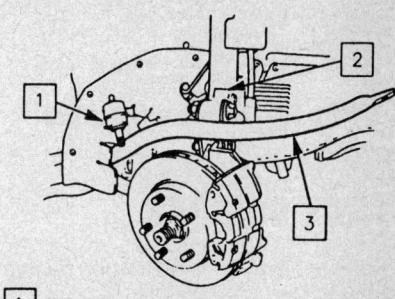

1	TIE ROD
2	STEERING KNUCKLE
3	STABILIZER SHAFT

Fig. 9   Stabilizer bar replacement

CONTROL ARM
REPLACE

1. Raise and support vehicle and place jackstands under cradle. Vehicle weight should not be placed on the control arms.
2. Remove wheel assembly.
3. Install drive axle boot protectors.
4. Remove cotter key from ball joint nut and, using tool J-34505, separate ball joint from steering knuckle.
5. Remove stabilizer bar bushing to control arm bolt.
6. Remove control arm mounting bolts and the control arm, **Fig. 6**.
7. Reverse procedure to install. When installing control arms, install but do not torque control arm mounting bolts. Sufficiently tighten bolts to assure security but final torque is applied when vehicle weight is supported by control arms. Torque rear arm bolt and front bolt to specifications.

STABILIZER BAR
REPLACE

1. Raise and support vehicle and place jackstands under cradle. Vehicle weight should not be placed on the control arms.
2. Remove wheel assembly.
3. Install drive axle boot protectors.
4. Remove nuts, washers, bushings and bolt securing stabilizer shaft to each control arm, **Fig. 7**.
5. Remove stabilizer bar mounting bolts, two bolts from each side, **Fig. 8**.
6. Disconnect tie rods from steering knuckles.
7. Remove exhaust pipe between exhaust manifold and catalytic converter.
8. Rotate right side strut assembly completely to the right.
9. Slide stabilizer bar to the right over the steering knuckle and pull downward on left side until stabilizer bar clears the cradle, **Fig. 9**.
10. Reverse procedure to install.

STRUT ASSEMBLY
REPLACE

1. Remove three nuts attaching top of strut to body, **Fig. 10**.
2. Raise and support vehicle and place jackstands under cradle. Vehicle weight should not be placed on the control arms.
3. Remove wheel assembly.
4. Install drive axle boot protectors.
5. Remove brake line bracket bolt from strut assembly.
6. Remove strut to steering knuckle attaching bolts.
7. Remove strut assembly from vehicle.
8. Reverse procedure to install. Torque strut mounting bolts to specifications.

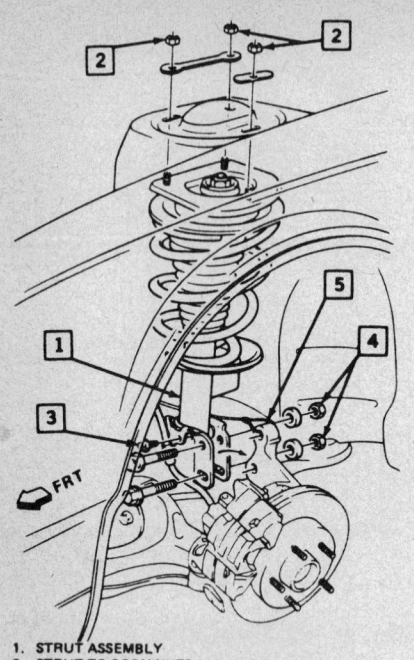

1. STRUT ASSEMBLY
2. STRUT TO BODY NUTS 24 N·m (18 LBS.FT.)
3. BRAKE LINE BRACKET BOLT 17 N·m (13 LBS. FT.)
4. STRUT TO STEERING KNUCKLE NUTS 195 N·m (144 LBS. FT.)
5. RETAIN STEERING KNUCKLE WITH WIRE ONCE STRUT ASSEMBLY IS REMOVED

Fig. 10   Strut assembly

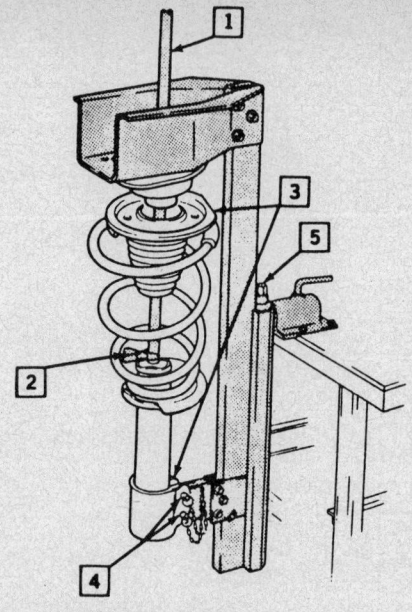

1. ROD J-34013-38 INSTALLED
2. CLAMP J-34013-20 INSTALLED
3. FLAT ON SPRING SEAT MUST FACE SAME DIRECTION AS STEERING KNUCKLE FLANGE
4. BOTH LOCKING PINS INSTALLED
5. COMPRESSOR FORCING SCREW

Fig. 11   Disassembling strut

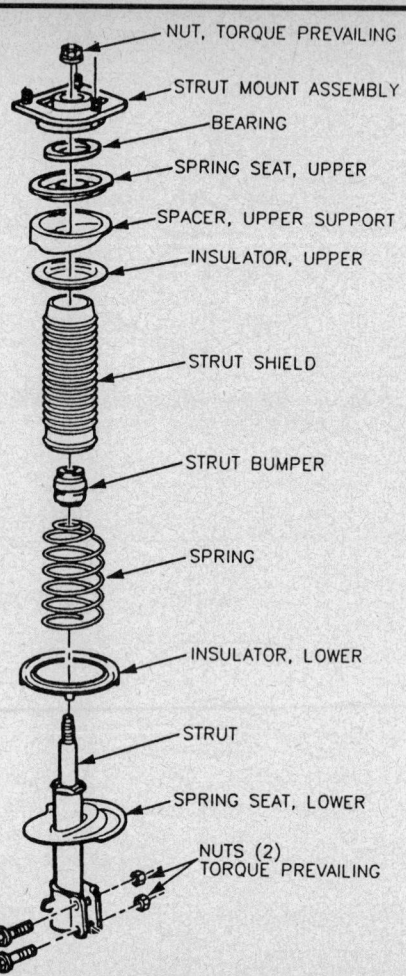

NUT, TORQUE PREVAILING
STRUT MOUNT ASSEMBLY
BEARING
SPRING SEAT, UPPER
SPACER, UPPER SUPPORT
INSULATOR, UPPER
STRUT SHIELD
STRUT BUMPER
SPRING
INSULATOR, LOWER
STRUT
SPRING SEAT, LOWER
NUTS (2) TORQUE PREVAILING

Fig. 12   Exploded view of strut assembly

STRUT SERVICE

Refer to **Figs. 11 and 12** when performing the following procedure.
1. Remove strut as outlined under "Strut Assembly, Replace" procedure.
2. Mount strut in compressor tool J-34013 and holding fixture J-3289-20.
3. Rotate compressor forcing screw until spring compresses slightly.
4. Hold damper shaft from rotating and remove nut from top of strut assembly.
5. Use tool J-34013-30 to guide damper shaft from assembly.
6. Loosen compressor forcing screw while guiding damper shaft from assembly. Continue to loosen nut until strut damper and spring can be removed.
7. Reverse procedure to assemble. When assembling spring, the flat on upper spring seat must face outward 90 degrees from centerline of vehicle or when mounted in the strut compressor, the seat faces in the same direction as the steering knuckle mounting flange.

POWER STEERING GEAR REPLACE

1. Raise and support vehicle with weight resting on suspension.
2. Remove front wheel assemblies.
3. Disconnect intermediate shaft from steering gear stub shaft.
4. Disconnect both tie rod ends from

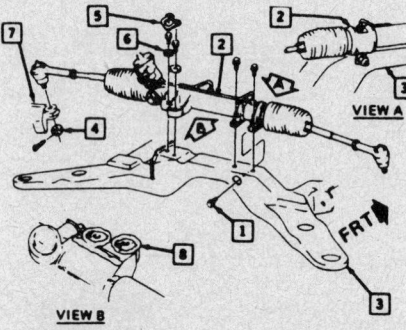

1. BOLT 68 N·m (50 LBS. FT.) AFTER SECOND REUSE OF BOLT, LOCTITE THREAD LOCKING KIT NO. 1052624 MUST BE USED.
2. STEERING GEAR
3. FRAME
4. 40 N·m (30 LBS. FT.), 70 N·m (52 LBS. FT.) MAXIMUM PERMISSIBLE TORQUE TO ALIGN COTTER PIN SLOT. (1/6 TURN MAXIMUM) DO NOT BACK OFF FOR COTTER PIN INSERTION.
5. RETAINER
6. WASHER
7. STEERING KNUCKLE
8. RTV SEALER AROUND INSERTS

Fig. 13   Steering gear replacement

steering knuckles.
5. Remove line retainers and disconnect hydraulic lines from steering gear.
6. Remove five steering gear attaching bolts, **Fig. 13.**
7. Remove steering gear from vehicle by sliding out to the side.
8. Reverse procedure to install. **Torque** steering gear attaching bolts to 50 ft. lbs.

POWER STEERING PUMP REPLACE
3.8L/V6-231 & 3800/V6-231 ENGINES

1. Disconnect battery ground cable.
2. Remove air cleaner, if necessary.
3. Remove alternator drive belt and alternator.
4. Raise and support vehicle.
5. Disconnect hydraulic lines from pump.
6. Remove rear pump adjustment bracket to pump nut.
7. Remove pump drive belt.
8. Lower vehicle.
9. Remove pump rear adjustment bracket.
10. Remove power steering pump from vehicle.
11. Reverse procedure to install.

4.5L/V8-273 ENGINE

1. Disconnect battery ground cable.
2. Remove pump drive belt and the pulley.
3. Disconnect hydraulic lines from pump.
4. Remove two pump mounting bolts.
5. Remove power steering pump from vehicle.
6. Reverse procedure to install.

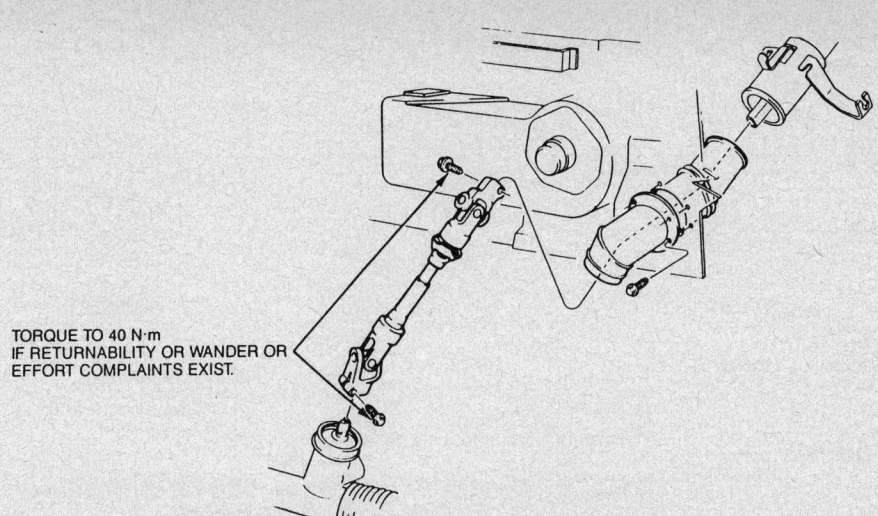

TORQUE TO 40 N·m
IF RETURNABILITY OR WANDER OR
EFFORT COMPLAINTS EXIST.

Fig. 14   Intermediate shaft pinch bolts

SERVICE BULLETINS
INCREASED STEERING EFFORT, SLIGHT WANDER OR POOR RETURNABILITY

On some 1989 Deville and Fleetwood models, a condition of increased steering effort, slight wander and returnability may be experienced.

To correct this condition, loosen pinch bolts at the intermediate shaft, **Fig. 14**, then **torque** pinch bolts to 29.5 ft. lbs.

TIGHTENING SPECIFICATIONS

Year	Component	Torque/ft. lbs.
1988-91	**Ball Joint To Knuckle**	88 ①
	Brake Caliper To Knuckle	38
	Brake Line Bracket To Underbody	13
	Control Arm Mounting Nut (Front)	140
	Control Arm Mounting Nut (Rear)	90
	Drive Axle Shaft Nut	180
	Hub & Bearing To Knuckle	70
	Service Ball Joint To Control Arm	50
	Stabilizer Shaft Bushing Nut	13
	Stabilizer Shaft Mounting Bracket	37
	Steering Knuckle To Strut Bolts	144
	Strut Assembly To Body Nuts	18
	Strut Mount Nut	55
	Tie Rod To Knuckle	35

① —Tighten an additional 120°.

Wheel Alignment

INDEX

FRONT WHEEL ALIGNMENT

Camber and toe are the only adjustments normally required. After checking settings, perform adjustments in the following order: caster, camber and toe in.

CASTER, ADJUST
1988–90

1. Loosen, but do not remove, two of the three top strut mounting nuts covering the slotted mounting holes, **Fig. 1**.
2. Remove the third nut over the oval strut mounting hole and move the washer away from the mounting hole.
3. Raise vehicle by the body to separate the strut from inner wheel house.
4. Drill ¹¹/₃₂ inch holes at front and rear of oval strut mounting hole and file excess metal, **Fig. 1**.
5. Lower body and insert strut into proper position.
6. Set caster to specifications by moving top of strut forward or backward as needed.
7. Install mounting nut and washer. **Torque** all mounting nuts to 18 ft. lbs.
8. Recheck caster.

1991

1. On Bonneville, Eighty Eight and LeSabre models, remove three strut to body attaching nuts, **Fig. 2.**
2. On Ninety Eight and Park Avenue

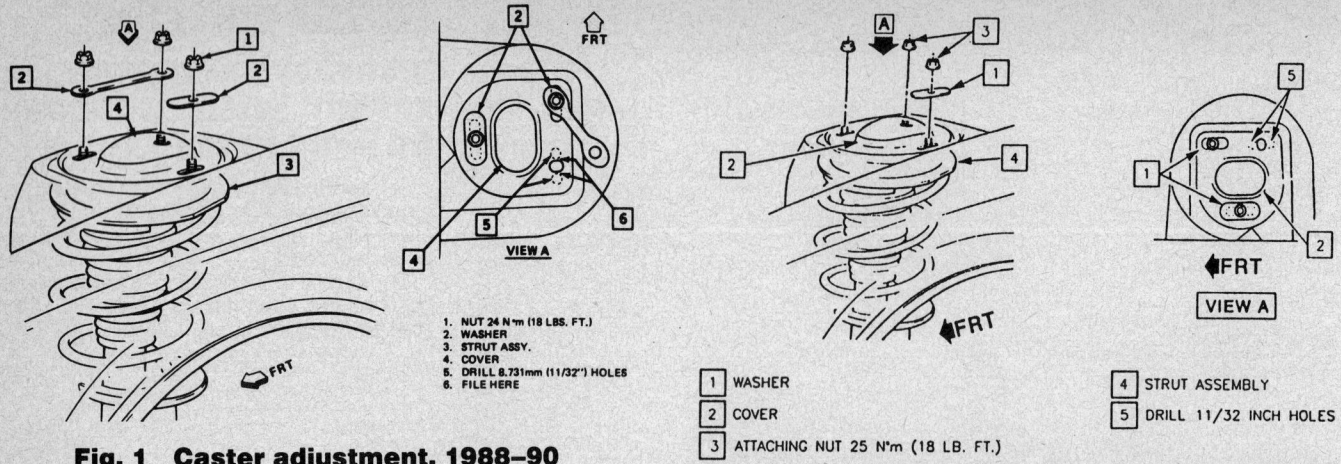

Fig. 1   Caster adjustment. 1988–90

1. NUT 24 N·m (18 LBS. FT.)
2. WASHER
3. STRUT ASSY.
4. COVER
5. DRILL 8.731mm (11/32") HOLES
6. FILE HERE

1	WASHER	4	STRUT ASSEMBLY
2	COVER	5	DRILL 11/32 INCH HOLES
3	ATTACHING NUT 25 N·m (18 LB. FT.)		

Fig. 2   Caster adjustment. 1991 Bonneville, Eighty Eight & LeSabre

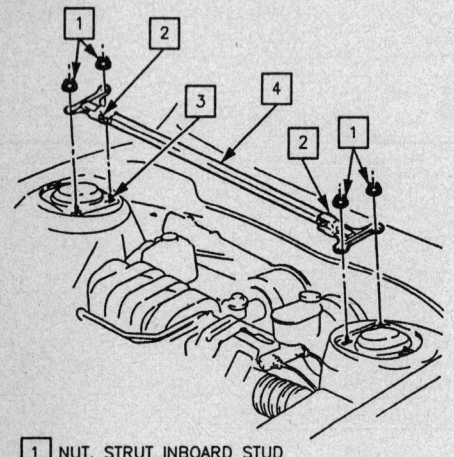

1	NUT, STRUT INBOARD STUD
2	THROUGH–BOLTS
3	STUD, STRUT INBOARD
4	BAR ASM, CROSS BRACE

Fig. 3   Cross brace removal. 1991 Ninety Eight & Park Avenue.

1	WASHER	4	STRUT ASSEMBLY
2	COVER	5	DRILL 11/32 INCH HOLES
3	ATTACHING NUT 24 N·m (18 LB. FT.)		

Fig. 4   Caster adjustment. 1991 Ninety Eight & Park Avenue.

models, proceed as follows:
- a. Loosen cross brace assembly through bolts, **Fig. 3.**
- b. Remove inboard strut nuts, then the brace assembly.
- c. Remove remaining nut over oval strut mounting hole, **Fig. 4.**
3. **On all models,** lift front of vehicle by body to separate strut from inner wheelhouse.
4. Drill two 11/32 inch holes at front and rear of oval strut mounting hole.
5. File excess metal to elongate original holes, then paint exposed metal with primer.
6. Lower front of vehicle.
7. **On Bonneville, Eighty Eight and LeSabre models,** install three strut to body attaching nuts.

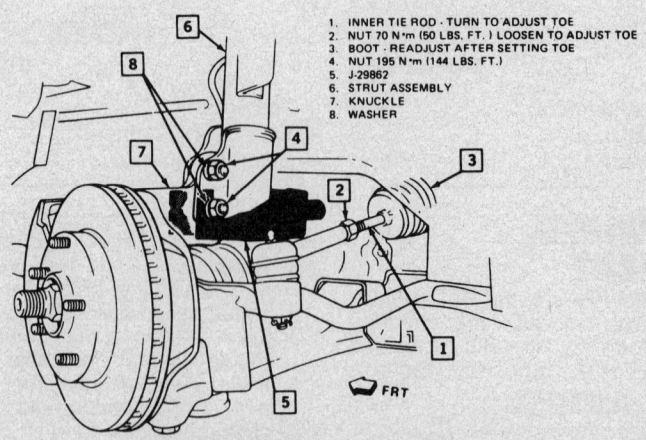

1. INNER TIE ROD - TURN TO ADJUST TOE
2. NUT 70 N·m (50 LBS. FT.) LOOSEN TO ADJUST TOE
3. BOOT - READJUST AFTER SETTING TOE
4. NUT 195 N·m (144 LBS. FT.)
5. J-29862
6. STRUT ASSEMBLY
7. KNUCKLE
8. WASHER

Fig. 5   Camber adjustment

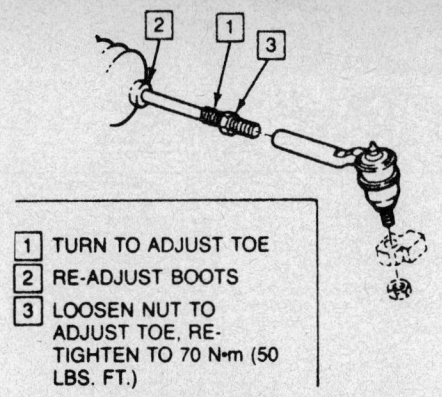

1. TURN TO ADJUST TOE
2. RE-ADJUST BOOTS
3. LOOSEN NUT TO ADJUST TOE, RE-TIGHTEN TO 70 N·m (50 LBS. FT.)

Fig. 6   Rear camber & toe adjustments

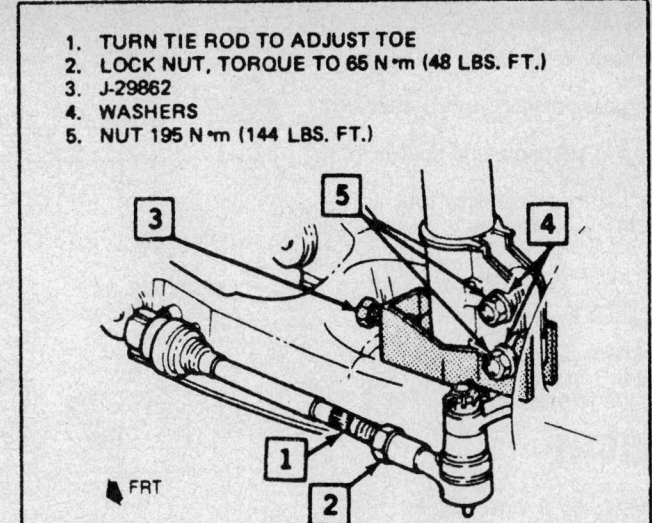

1. TURN TIE ROD TO ADJUST TOE
2. LOCK NUT, TORQUE TO 65 N·m (48 LBS. FT.)
3. J-29862
4. WASHERS
5. NUT 195 N·m (144 LBS. FT.)

Fig. 7   Toe adjustment

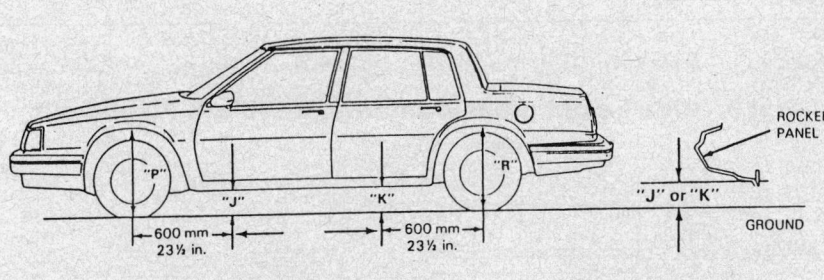

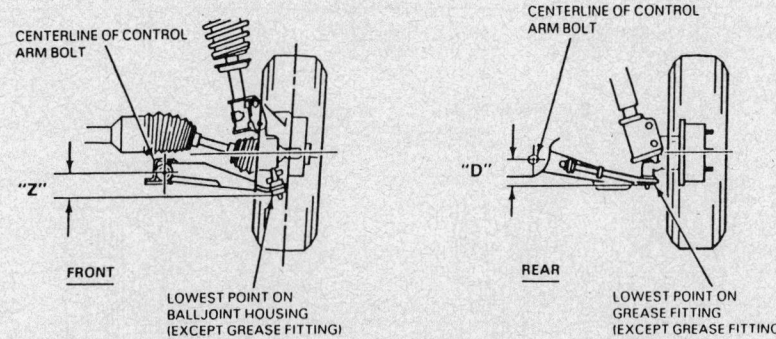

MAXIMUM VARIATION SIDE TO SIDE & FRONT TO REAR IS 19MM (¾ IN)

LOAD CONDITIONS — COOLANT TO CAPACITY AND FULL TANK OF FUEL

	"Z"	"D"	"P"	"R"	"J"	"K"
C	56-76 mm 2¾-3 in.	70-90 mm 2¾-3⁹⁄₁₆ in.	699-719 mm 27½-28⁵⁄₁₆ in.	691-711 mm 27¹³⁄₁₆-28 in.	228-248 mm 8½₃₂-9⁴⁄₁₆ in.	230-250 mm 9³⁄₁₆-9²⁷⁄₃₂ in.
H	50-70 mm 1³¹⁄₃₂-2¾ in.	77-97 mm 3½-3¹³⁄₁₆ in.	699-719 mm 27½-28⁵⁄₁₆ in.	699-719 mm 27½-28⁵⁄₁₆ in.	229-249 mm 9¼-9¹¹⁄₁₆ in.	236-256 mm 9¹³⁄₁₆-10¹⁄₁₆ in.

Fig. 8   Ride height measurements. Electra, LeSabre, Park Ave., 88 & 98

8. **On Ninety Eight and Park Avenue models,** place cross brace assembly on inboard strut studs and install strut attaching nuts.
9. **On all models,** set caster to specifications by moving strut forward or rearward as necessary.
10. **Torque** strut attaching nuts to 18 ft. lbs.
11. **On Ninety Eight and Park Avenue models,** torque cross brace bar through bolts to 21 ft. lbs.

CAMBER, ADJUST

1. Loosen both strut to knuckle attaching nuts, **Fig. 5.**
2. Install camber adjusting tool J-29862.
3. Set camber to specifications.
4. Remove adjusting tool and **torque** strut to knuckle attaching nuts to 144 ft. lbs.
5. Recheck camber.

TOE, ADJUST

1. Loosen locknuts on both inner tie rods, **Fig. 6.**
2. Adjust toe to specifications by rotating inner tie rod.
3. **Torque** locknuts to 50 ft. lbs.
4. Recheck toe setting.

REAR WHEEL ALIGNMENT

When checking rear wheel alignment, the electronic leveling system must have the superlift struts inflated with residual pressure only.

Place a weight in trunk and turn ignition on and move transmission selector from Park to Reverse position and back. This will activate the compressor. Turn ignition off and remove weight from trunk. Wait 30 seconds for the system to exhaust. Roll vehicle forward one complete wheel rotation. Jounce vehicle before checking alignment.

CAMBER, ADJUST

1. Loosen strut to knuckle attaching nuts.
2. Install camber adjusting tool J-29862, **Fig. 7.**
3. Move strut to set camber to specifications.
4. Remove camber adjusting tool and **torque** strut to knuckle nuts to 144 ft. lbs.
5. Recheck camber setting.

TOE, ADJUST

Toe adjustment is made by loosening the locknut at tie rod end and turning inner tie rod to set toe to specifications, **Fig. 7.**

RIDE HEIGHT

Refer to **Figs. 8, 9 and 10,** for ride height specifications and measurement locations. Check ride height as follows:
1. Ensure vehicle is on level ground.
2. Ensure tires are inflated to proper pressures.
3. Fuel tank should be full to obtain accurate readings.
4. Trunk should be empty except for spare tire and jack.
5. Place the front seat in the far rearward position, then turn ignition to On position to activate the electronic level control, if equipped.
6. Bounce the car three times at the front and rear to normalize suspension.
7. Measure from lowest point on the ball joint housing to control arm bolt centerline, "D" and "Z" positions.
8. Measure from level floor to rocker panel at "J" and "K" positions on all models except SSE.
9. Measure from level floor to wheel opening at "P" and "R" positions.

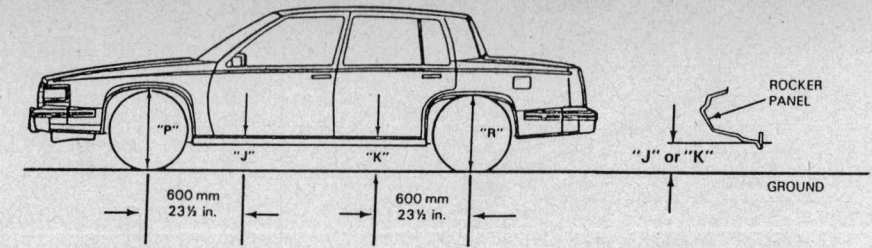

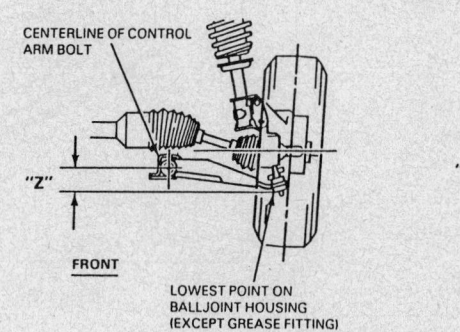
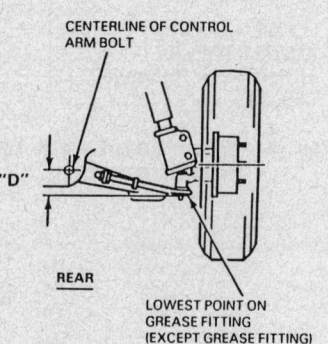

MAXIMUM VARIATION SIDE TO SIDE & FRONT TO REAR IS 19MM (¾ IN)

LOAD CONDITIONS — COOLANT TO CAPACITY AND FULL TANK OF FUEL

"Z"	"D"	"P"	"R"	"J"	"K"
64-84 mm 2¾-3⁵⁄₁₆ in.	71-91 mm 2²¹⁄₆₄-3¹⁹⁄₃₂ in.	706-726 mm 27⁸⁄₆₄-28²⁷⁄₆₄ in.	656-676 mm 25⁹⁄₆₄-26³⁵⁄₆₄ in.	230-250 mm 9¹⁄₆₄-9²⁷⁄₃₂ in.	230-250 mm 9¹⁄₆₄-9²⁷⁄₃₂ in.

Fig. 9   Ride height measurements. DeVille & Fleetwood

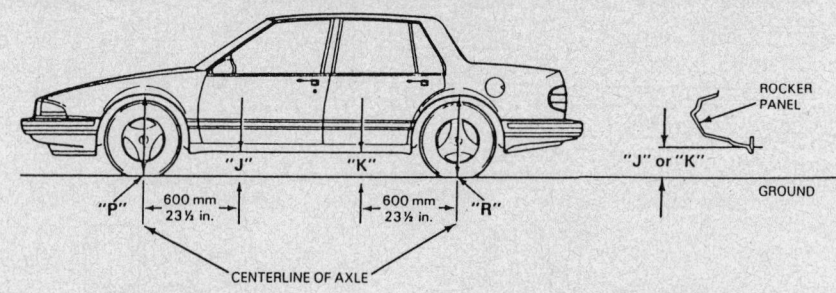

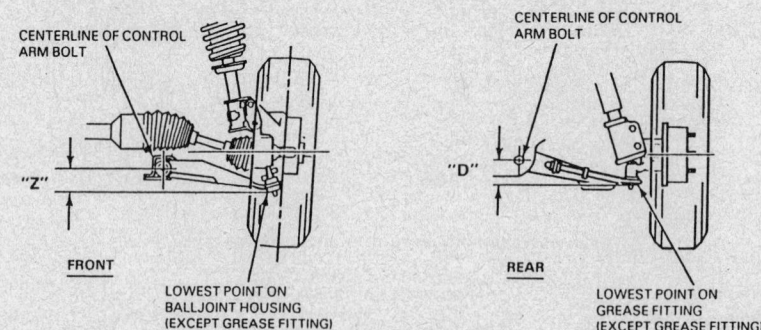

MAXIMUM VARIATION SIDE TO SIDE & FRONT TO REAR IS 19MM (¾ IN)

LOAD CONDITIONS — COOLANT TO CAPACITY AND FULL TANK OF FUEL

"Z"	"D"	"P"	"R"	"J"	"K"
55-75 mm 2⁵⁄₃₂-2¹⁵⁄₁₆ in.	70-90 mm 2¾-3³⁹⁄₆₄ in.	708-728 mm 27⁵⁄₃₂-28¹⁵⁄₃₂ in.	710-730 mm 27⁸⁄₆₄-28¾ in.	231-251 mm 9³⁄₃₂-9⁷⁄₈ in.	231-251 mm 9³⁄₃₂-9⁷⁄₈ in.

Fig. 10   Ride height measurements. Bonneville

BUICK REATTA & RIVIERA, CADILLAC ELDORADO & SEVILLE, OLDSMOBILE TORONADO & TROFEO (E & K Cars)

INDEX OF SERVICE OPERATIONS

NOTE: Refer To Rear Of This Manual For Vehicle Manufacturer's Special Service Tool Suppliers.

Page No.　　　　　Page No.　　　　　Page No.

Continued

INDEX OF SERVICE OPERATIONS—Continued

Specifications

GENERAL ENGINE SPECIFICATIONS

Year	Engine Liter/CID[1]	Engine VIN Code[2]	Fuel Injection System	Bore & Stroke	Compression Ratio	Net H.P. @ RPM[3]	Maximum Torque Ft. Lbs. @ RPM	Normal Oil Pressure Pounds
1988	3.8L/V6-231	C	SPFI[4]	3.80 x 3.40	8.5	165 @ 5200	210 @ 2000	37
	4.5L/V8-273	5	DFI[5]	3.62 x 3.31	9.0	155 @ 4000	240 @ 2600	26
1989	3.8L/V6-231	C	SPFI[4]	3.80 X 3.40	8.5	165 @ 4800	210 @ 2000	37
	4.5L/V8-273	5	DFI[5]	3.62 X 3.31	9.0	155 @ 4000	240 @ 2600	26
1990	3.8L/V6-231	C	SPFI[4]	3.80 X 3.40	8.5	165 @ 4800	210 @ 2000	40[6]
	4.5L/V8-273	3	SPFI[4]	3.62 X 3.31	9.5	180 @ 4300	245 @ 3000	26[7]
1991	3.8L/V6-231	C	SPFI[4]	3.80 X 3.40	8.5	165 @ 4800	210 @ 2000	40[6]
	4.9L/V8-300	—	SPFI[4]	3.62 x 3.62	9.5	200 @ 4400	275 @ 3000	—

[1]—CID-Cubic inch displacement.
[2]—The eighth digit denotes engine code.
[3]—Ratings are net-as installed in vehicle.
[4]—Sequential-Port Fuel Injection.
[5]—Digital Fuel Injection.
[6]—At 1850 RPM, with 5W-30 engine oil.
[7]—At 30 mph and 9 psi at idle.

TUNE UP SPECIFICATIONS

Year & Engine/VIN Code [1]	Spark Plug Gap	Ignition Timing BTDC° — Firing Order Fig. [2]	Ignition Timing BTDC° — Auto. Trans.	Mark Fig.	Curb Idle Speed [3]	Fast Idle Speed	Fuel Pump Pressure psi.
1988–89							
3.8L/V6-231/C	.045	[4]	[5]	[6]	[7]	[7]	40-47[8]
4.5L/V8-273/5	.060	B	10[6]	—	[7]	[7]	9-12[9]
1990							
3.8L/V6-231/C	.045	[4]	[5]	[6]	[7]	[7]	40-47[8]
4.5L/V8-273/3	.060	B	[5]	C	[7]	[7]	9-12[9]
1991							
3.8L/V6-231/C	.045	[4]	[5]	[6]	[7]	[7]	40-47[8]
4.9L/V8-300	.060	B	[5]	—	[7]	[7]	—

[1]—The eighth digit of the Vehicle Identification Number (VIN) denotes engine code.
[2]—Before removing wires from distributor cap, determine location of No. 1 wire in cap, as distributor position may have been altered from that shown at the end of this chart.
[3]—On auto. trans models, idle speed is adjusted in Drive. When adjusting idle speed, set parking brake & block drive wheels.
[4]—Cylinder numbering from left to right as viewed from front of vehicle, front bank, 1, 3, 5; rear bank, 2, 4, 6. Firing order 1-6-5-4-3-2. Refer to Fig. A for spark plug wire connections at coil unit.
[5]—Computer controlled, no adjustment.
[6]—Equipped with crankshaft position sensor.
[7]—Idle speed is controlled by an idle speed control (ISC) motor or an idle air control (IAC) valve.
[8]—With shop towel wrapped around fuel pressure valve to prevent fuel spillage, connect a fuel pressure

Continued

TUNE UP SPECIFICATIONS—Continued

gauge to fuel pressure valve. Check fuel pressure with ignition switch in the On position, engine not running. ⑨—Wrap shop towel around fuel hose to

steel line connection in engine compartment to prevent fuel spillage. Disconnect fuel hose from steel line & connect a fuel pressure

gauge between hose and line. Ensure gauge connections are tight, then start engine & check fuel pressure readings.

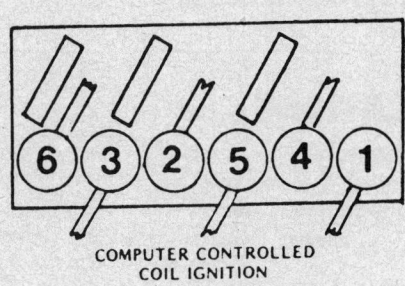

COMPUTER CONTROLLED COIL IGNITION

Fig. A

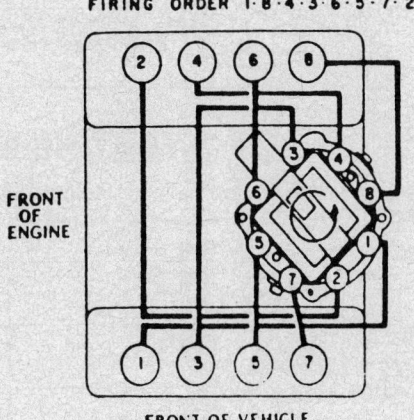

FIRING ORDER 1·8·4·3·6·5·7·2

FRONT OF ENGINE

FRONT OF VEHICLE

Fig. B

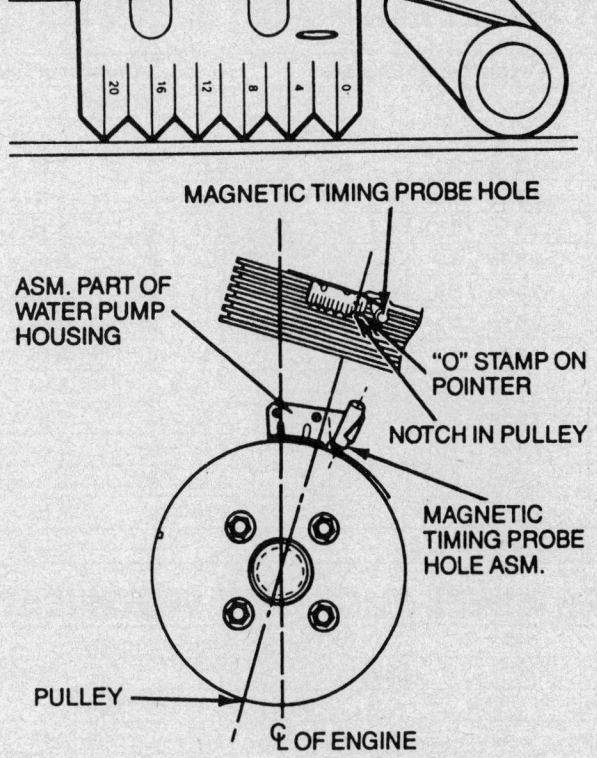

MAGNETIC TIMING PROBE HOLE

ASM. PART OF WATER PUMP HOUSING

"O" STAMP ON POINTER

NOTCH IN PULLEY

MAGNETIC TIMING PROBE HOLE ASM.

PULLEY

℄ OF ENGINE

Fig. C

ALTERNATOR SPECIFICATIONS

Year	Ident. No.	Rated Hot Output Amps.
1988	1101310	105
	1101316	120
1989-90	1101310	105
	1101316	120
	1101519	120
1991	CS 144 Generation II	140

STARTING MOTOR APPLICATIONS

Refer to starter section for specifications.

Year	Engine/VIN	Starter Ident. No.
1988	3.8L/V6-231/C	1998544
	4.5L/V8-273/5	—
1989	3.8L/V6-231/C	1998544
	4.5L/V8-273/5	10455024
1990	3.8L/V6-231/C	10455024
	4.5L/V8-273/3—	10455024
1991	3.8L/V6-231/C	10455024
	4.9L/V8-300/3—	10455024

FRONT WHEEL ALIGNMENT SPECIFICATIONS

Year	Model	Caster Angle, Degrees		Camber Angle, Degrees					Total Toe Degrees
				Limits		Desired			
		Limits	Desired	Left	Right	Left	Right		
1988	Eldorado & Seville	+1.3 to +3.3	+2.3	−.8 to +.8	−.8 to +.8	0	0		0
	Reatta	+1.8 to +3.8	+2.8	−.5 to +.5	−.5 to +.5	0	0		0
	Riviera	+1.5 to +3.5	+2.5	−.8 to +.8	−.8 to +.8	0	0		0
	Toronado	+1.5 to +3.5	+2.5	−.8 to +.8	−.8 to +.8	0	0		0
1989	Eldorado & Seville	+1.3 to +3.3	+2.3	−.8 to +.8	−.8 to +.8	0	0		+.1
	Reatta	+2.0 to +4.0	+3.0	−.8 to +.8	−.8 to +.8	0	0		0
	Riviera	+1.5 to +3.5	+2.5	−.8 to +.8	−.8 to +.8	0	0		0
	Toronado	+1.3 to +3.3	+2.3	−.8 to +.8	−.8 to +.8	0	0		+.1
1990–91	Eldorado & Seville	+1.3 to +3.3	+2.3	−.8 to +.8	−.8 to +.8	0	0		+.1
	Reatta	+2.0 to +4.0	+3.0	−.8 to +.8	−.8 to +.8	0	0		0
	Riviera	+1.5 to +3.5	+2.5	−.8 to +.8	−.8 to +.8	0	0		0
	Toronado & Trofeo	+1.3 to +3.3	+2.3	−.8 to +.8	−.8 to +.8	0	0		+.1

REAR WHEEL ALIGNMENT SPECIFICATIONS

Year	Model	Camber Angle, Degrees				Total Toe Degrees
		Limits		Desired		
		Left	Right	Left	Right	
1988	Eldorado & Seville	−.4 to +.2	−.4 to +.2	−.1	−.1	+.2
	Reatta	−.1 to +.5	−.1 to +.5	+.2	+.2	+.2
	Riviera	−1.3 to −.7	−1.3 to −.7	−1	−1	+.2
	Toronado	−1.3 to −.7	−1.3 to −.7	−1	−1	+.2
1989	Eldorado & Seville	−.4 to +.2	−.4 to +.2	−.1	−.1	+.2
	Reatta	−.1 to +.5	−.1 to +.5	+.2	+.2	+.2

Continued

REAR WHEEL ALIGNMENT SPECIFICATIONS — Continued

| Year | Model | Camber Angle, Degrees | | | | Total Toe Degrees |
| | | Limits | | Desired | | |
		Left	Right	Left	Right	
1989 (Cont'd.)	Riviera	−.4 to +.2	−.4 to +.2	−1	−1	+.2
	Toronado	−.4 to +.2	−.4 to +.2	−.1	−.1	+.2
1990–91	Eldorado & Seville	−.4 to +.1	−.4 to +.1	−.1	−.1	+.2
	Reatta	−1.3 to −.7	−1.3 to −.7	−1	−1	+.2
	Riviera	−1.3 to −.7	−1.3 to −.7	−1	−1	+.2
	Toronado & Trofeo	−.4 to +.1	−.4 to +.1	−.1	−.1	+.2

COOLING SYSTEM & CAPACITY DATA

| Year | Model or Engine/VIN | Cooling Capacity, Qts. | Radiator Cap Relief Pressure, Lbs. | Thermo. Opening Temp. | Fuel Tank Gals | Engine Oil Refill Qts. | Auto Transaxle Qts.① | |
							Drain & Refill	Overhaul
1988-89	3.8L/V6-231/C	12	15	195	18	4②	6.5	11
	4.5L/V8-273/5	12.1	15	195	18.8	5②	6.5	11
1990	3.8L/V6-231/C	13	15	195	18	4②	6.5	11
	4.5L/V8-273/3	12.1	—	—	18.8	5②	6.5	7.9
1991	4.9L/V8-300/3	12.07	—	—	18.8	5②	—	—

①—Approximate. Make final check with dipstick.   ②—Additional oil will be necessary when changing filter.

Electrical
INDEX

FUSE PANEL & FLASHER LOCATION

On Reatta, Riviera, Toronado and Trofeo models, the fuse panel is located inside the glove compartment. On Eldorado and Seville models, the fuse panel is located behind the center of the instrument panel, behind the glove box door.

On Toronado and Trofeo models, the hazard flasher and turn signal flasher are located behind the instrument panel, on the righthand side of the steering column support. On Eldorado, Reatta, Riviera and Seville models, the turn/hazard module is located behind the center of the instrument panel.

STARTER MOTOR REPLACE

If shims are used between starter and engine block, they should be placed in original position during installation. If starter is noisy during cranking, remove double .015 inch shim or add .015 inch shim at outer bolt only. If high pitched whine is observed after engine starts, add double .015 inch shims (to maximum of .045 inch) until noise is corrected.

ELDORADO & SEVILLE

1. Disconnect battery ground cable, then raise and support vehicle.
2. Remove nuts securing starter shield

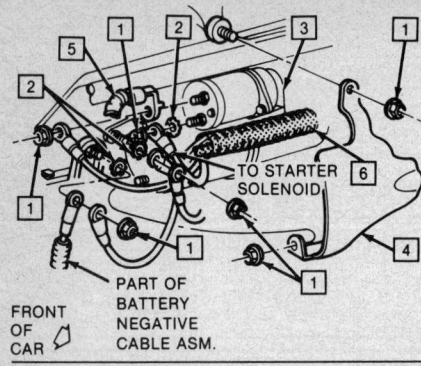

**Fig. 1 Starter wiring.
Eldorado & Seville**

1 RETAINING NUT (6)
2 STAR WASHER (3)
3 STARTER MOTOR SOLENOID
4 SHIELD
5 POSITIVE BATTERY CABLE
6 ENGINE WIRING HARNESS ASM.

and the shield.
3. Remove nuts securing solenoid wires and battery cable, then disconnect wiring, **Fig. 1.**
4. Remove starter brace, mounting bolts and the starter motor.
5. Reverse procedure to install.

REATTA, RIVIERA, TORONADO & TROFEO

1. Disconnect battery ground cable, then raise and support vehicle.
2. Remove starter splash shield, if equipped.
3. Remove 2 bolts securing starter to engine block, then lower starter motor.
4. Remove retaining nuts and disconnect electrical connectors, noting position for installation.
5. Reverse procedure to install.

DISTRIBUTOR
REPLACE

1. Remove distributor appearance cover and retainer.
2. Disconnect ignition switch battery feed wire from distributor cap.
3. Disconnect coil connections from cap. **Do not use a screwdriver or other tool to release locking tabs.**
4. Remove four bolts from distributor cap, note position of cap ignition coil then move cap aside.
5. Disconnect six terminal ECM harness from distributor.
6. Remove distributor clamp nut and hold-down clamp. Use tool No. J29791 or equivalent to remove hold-down nut.
7. Note position of rotor. Pull distributor up until rotor stops turning counterclockwise, then note position of rotor.
8. Remove distributor. **A thrust washer is used between the distributor drive gear and the crankcase. This washer may stick to the bottom of the distributor when removed. Before replacing the distributor, en-**

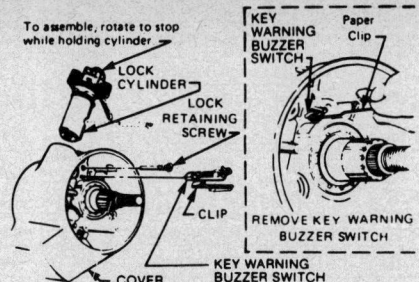

Fig. 2 Ignition lock cylinder & key warning switch

sure thrust washer is located in the crankcase at the bottom of the distributor bore.
9. Reverse procedure to install, noting the following:
   a. If distributor position was lost, or set incorrectly, remove the No. 1 spark plug wire.
   b. Place a finger over the No. 1 spark plug hole while an assistant slowly cranks the engine until compression is felt.
   c. Align the timing mark on the pulley with the 0 on the timing indicator.
   d. Turn rotor to point between the No. 1 and No. 8 spark plug towers on the distributor cap.
   e. Install distributor.

IGNITION LOCK
REPLACE

On 1990-91 models, the Supplemental Inflatable Restraint system (SIR) must be disabled before performing any service procedure near the steering wheel or steering column. Failure to do so may result in accidental deployment of airbag, possibly causing personal injury. To disable SIR system, turn the ignition off, remove No. 3 fuse from SIR fuse panel and disconnect yellow squib connector at base of steering column.
1. Disconnect battery ground cable and remove turn signal switch as outlined.
2. Rotate key to "Run" position, then remove key warning switch, **Fig. 2.**
3. Remove lock retaining screw, then withdraw lock cylinder assembly from column.
4. Reverse procedure to install. **Torque** lock retaining screw to 35 inch lbs.

IGNITION & DIMMER SWITCH
REPLACE

On 1990-91 models, the Supplemental Inflatable Restraint system (SIR) must be disabled before performing any service procedure near the steering wheel or steering column. Failure to do so may result in accidental deployment of airbag, possibly causing personal injury. To disable SIR system, turn the ignition off, remove No. 3 fuse from SIR fuse panel and disconnect yellow squib connector at base of steering column.

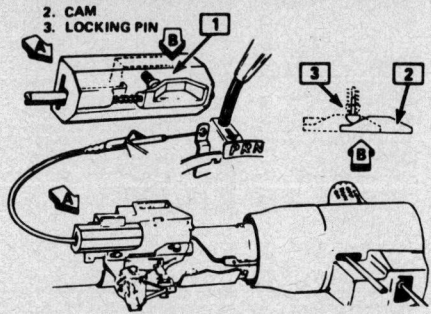

Fig. 3 Park-lock cable. Models w/floor shift

REMOVAL

1. Disconnect battery ground cable.
2. **On models with floor shift,** place transmission selector in park and rotate ignition lock to "Run" position.
3. **On all models,** remove left hush panel, lower steering column cover, insulator at toe plate, and the lower steering column mounting screws.
4. Remove nuts securing upper steering column bracket to instrument panel, then carefully lower column. **Disconnect shift indicator cable and electrical connectors, as needed, prior to lowering column. Do not force column down as it may be damaged.**
5. Remove dimmer switch mounting nut, screw and the dimmer switch, then tape actuator rod to steering column.
6. **On models with floor shift,** insert screwdriver into slot in ignition switch inhibitor, depress park-lock cable latch and disconnect cable from inhibitor, **Fig. 3. Ignition switch must be in "Run" position. Do not attempt to disconnect park-lock cable with switch in any other position.**
7. Rotate ignition key to "Off-Lock" position.
8. **On all models,** remove ignition switch stud bolt, disconnect electrical connector, then remove switch assembly.

INSTALLATION

1. Move ignition switch slider to extreme right, then one detent to the left to place switch in "Off-Lock" position.
2. Connect electrical connector to ignition switch, install switch assembly on column ensuring actuator is properly engaged, and **torque** stud bolt to 35 inch lbs.
3. Install dimmer switch assembly, depress switch against actuator and insert 3/32 inch drill into adjustment slot, **Fig. 4,** then **torque** nut and retaining screw to 35 inch lbs.
4. **On models with floor shift,** rotate ignition lock to "Run" position, then install shift-lock cable on inhibitor.
5. **On all models,** reverse remaining procedure to complete installation. **Torque** upper column bracket bolts to 20 ft. lbs and lower column bolts to 25 ft. lbs.

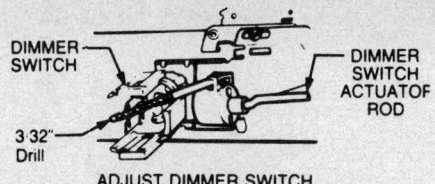

Fig. 4 Dimmer switch installation

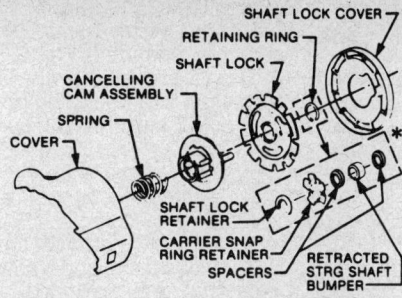

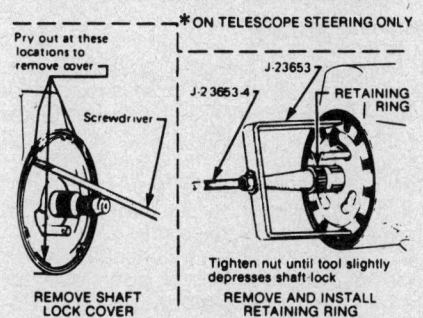

Fig. 5 Lock plate & cancelling cam removal

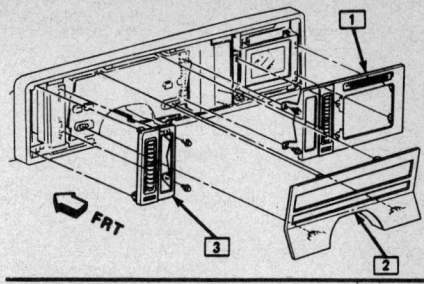

1. I.P. TRIM PLATE - RT
2. I.P. TRIM PLATE - CENTER
3. I.P. TRIM PLATE - LT

Fig. 6 Instrument cluster trim plate removal. Riviera (Reatta similar)

HORN SOUNDER & STEERING WHEEL
REPLACE

1988–89 MODELS
Eldorado & Seville

1. Remove two screws securing pad from rear of steering wheel.
2. Disconnect horn and cruise control electrical connectors, then remove pad.
3. Remove three telescope adjusting lever screws, unscrew telescope adjusting mechanism from steering shaft, then remove adjusting lever.
4. Scribe alignment mark between steering wheel and steering shaft, then remove steering wheel retaining nut.
5. Remove steering wheel using a puller.
6. Reverse procedure to install, noting the following:
   a. Align matching marks between steering wheel and shaft, and **torque** retaining nut to 35 ft. lbs.
   b. Fully extend steering shaft, mount telescope adjusting lever in 5 O'clock position, thread adjuster mechanism onto shaft and hand tighten, then install adjusting lever retaining screws.
   c. Ensure steering wheel moves in and out freely when lever is moved fully to the right, and that lever does not contact shroud in fully locked position.

Reatta, Riviera, Toronado & Trofeo

1. **On models with standard wheel,** remove 2 screws securing pad from rear of steering wheel. On models with sport wheel, carefully pry up center cap.
2. Disconnect horn lead from cam tower, and disconnect cruise control electrical connector, if equipped.
3. Scribe alignment mark between steering wheel and shaft, then remove retainer and nut.
4. Remove steering wheel using a puller.
5. Reverse procedure to install. **Torque** steering wheel nut to 35 ft. lbs.

1990–91 MODELS

When performing service on, or near supplemental inflatable restraint systems, ensure SIR system is disabled. Ensure ignition switch is in the Lock position, then remove SIR fuse.

If the airbag has been deployed, inspect coil for signs of scorching, melting, or other damage. Coil must be replaced if damaged.

1. Turn ignition switch to the Off position, disconnect battery negative cable.
2. Remove SIR fuse from the fuse panel. **Fuse 19 for Eldorado and Seville models, fuse 14 for Reatta and Riviera models and 9 for Toronado and Trofeo models.**
3. Remove left-side sound insulator retaining screws and nuts. **Three screws and two nuts on Eldorado and Seville models. Four screws and two nuts on Reatta and Riviera models. Two nuts and two screws on Toronado and Trofeo models.**
4. Remove the courtesy lamp from the sound insulator, then the lefthand side sound insulator from the vehicle.
5. Disconnect Connector Position Assurance (CPA) and yellow two-way connector from base of the steering column.
6. Remove screws from back of steering wheel pad, then remove module from wheel. **Always carry live inflator modules with the trim cover facing away from you. Never carry module by the wiring. Always place module on a flat surface with the trim cover facing up.**
7. Remove the horn contact by pushing slightly, then twisting counterclockwise.
8. Disconnect CPA and coil assembly connector from inflator module.
9. Remove steering column shaft nut.
10. Remove steering wheel using puller No. J 1859-03 or equivalent.
11. Reverse procedure to install, noting the following:
    a. **Torque** the steering wheel shaft nut to 30 ft. lbs.
    b. **Torque** the SIR module retaining screws to 27 inch lbs.

c. Turn ignition switch to the Run position. Inflatable restraint indicator lamp should flash 7 to 9 times, then remain off.

TURN SIGNAL SWITCH
REPLACE

On 1990-91 models, the Supplemental Inflatable Restraint system (SIR) must be disabled before performing any service procedure near the steering wheel or steering column. Failure to do so may result in accidental deployment of airbag, possibly causing personal injury. To disable SIR system, turn the ignition off, remove appropriate fuse from SIR fuse panel and disconnect yellow double connector at base of steering column.

1. Disconnect battery ground cable and remove steering wheel.
2. Remove left hush panel and lower steering column trim cover.
3. Remove turn signal switch harness cover, then disconnect switch harness connector.
4. Pry off shaft lock cover, then mount a spring compressor on steering shaft, **Fig. 5.**
5. Remove lock plate retaining ring and telescoping wheel components, as equipped, then remove spring compressor.
6. Remove lock plate, canceling cam and shaft spring.
7. Remove turn signal lever, screw securing signal switch actuator arm and the arm, if equipped.
8. Remove turn signal switch retaining screws and the switch assembly.
9. Reverse procedure to install.

WINDSHIELD WIPER SWITCH
REPLACE

ELDORADO & SEVILLE

1. Remove A/C vent and radio trim plate from instrument cluster bezel.
2. Remove seven screws securing instrument cluster bezel and the bezel.
3. Remove two screws securing right switch module and pull module from

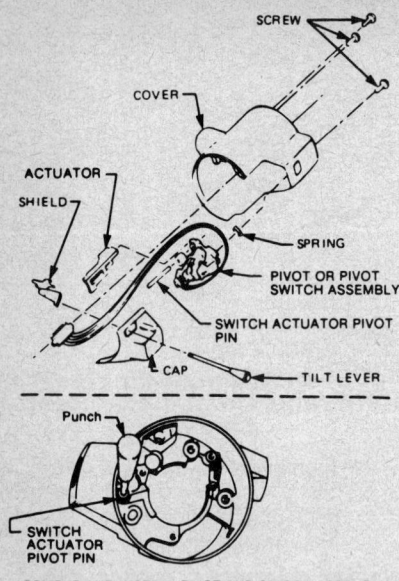

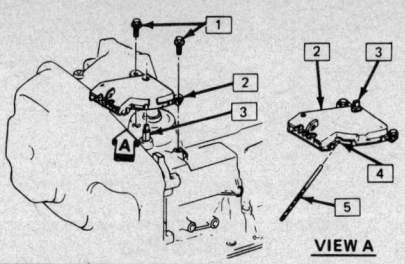

VIEW A

1	BOLT 30N·m (22 FT. LBS.)
2	SWITCH ASM.
3	TRANS. SHAFT
4	SERVICE ADJUSTMENT HOLE
5	3/32 INCH DRILL BIT OR 2.34 DIA. GAGE PIN

Fig. 8 Back up lamp/neutral safety switch installation

Fig. 7 Wiper switch removal. Toronado & Trofeo

instrument panel socket.
4. Reverse procedure to install.

REATTA & RIVIERA

1. Pull center instrument cluster trim plate straight out of instrument panel.
2. Remove screws securing right trim plate and the right trim plate and air outlet assembly, **Fig. 6.**
3. Remove screws securing right switch module and pull switch module out of instrument panel.
4. Disconnect electrical connector and remove switch.
5. Reverse procedure to install.

TORONADO & TROFEO

1. Remove steering wheel, turn signal switch and ignition lock as outlined.
2. Remove screws securing upper mast jacket cover, then the cover assembly.
3. Remove switch and pivot from cover as shown, **Fig. 7.**
4. Reverse procedure to install.

BACK-UP LAMP/NEUTRAL SAFETY SWITCH
REPLACE

REMOVAL

1. Remove nut securing shift lever to transaxle and disconnect lever from shaft.
2. Release "T" latch and disconnect electrical connector from switch.
3. Remove switch mounting bolts and the switch, **Fig. 8.**

INSTALLATION
Used Switch

1. Rotate shift shaft to N.
2. Align flats on switch with flats on shaft, then install switch.

3. Install mounting bolts to case loosely.
4. Insert 3/32 inch drill bit or gauge pin into service adjustment hole, **Fig. 8.**
5. Rotate switch until gauge pin drops to a depth of 9/64, then secure switch position by tightening switch mounting bolts.
6. Remove gauge pin, install shift lever and reconnect electrical connector to switch.
7. Ensure engine will only start with selector in P or N positions and verify proper operation of back up lamps.

New Switch

New switch is pinned in position to provide correct adjustment. If pin is missing or has been broken by rotating switch, follow procedure for installation and adjustment of used switch.
1. Rotate shift shaft to N.
2. Align flats on switch with flats on shaft, then install switch.
3. Install and tighten mounting bolts. **Do not rotate switch if bolts will not align with case mounting boss. Ensure shift shaft is in N. If shaft is properly positioned but bolts still do not line-up with mounting boss, refer to procedure for old switch.**
4. Install shift lever, then reconnect electrical connector to switch.
5. Ensure engine will only start with selector in P and N positions. Verify proper operation of back up lamps.

ADJUSTMENT
1989–91

1. Position transaxle shifter assembly in N notch in detent plate, then loosen switch attaching screws.
2. Rotate switch on shifter assembly until adjustment hole aligns with carrier tang hole.
3. Insert 3/32 inch gauge pin into adjustment hole to a depth of 5/8 inch on Reatta models and 1989-90 Riviera, Toronado and Trofeo models, or 15/32 inch on Eldorado and Seville models.
4. Tighten switch mounting bolts, then remove gauge pin.

LIGHT SWITCH
REPLACE

ELDORADO & SEVILLE

1. Disconnect battery ground cable.
2. Remove A/C vent and radio bezel from instrument cluster bezel.
3. Remove seven screws securing instrument cluster bezel and the bezel.
4. Remove screws securing switch module and pull module from socket in instrument panel.
5. Reverse procedure to install.

REATTA & RIVIERA

1. Disconnect battery ground cable, then place tilt wheel in fully lowered position.
2. Pull center cluster trim panel straight out of dash, then remove screws securing trim panel, **Fig. 6.**

3. Grasp both sides of trim panel and pull panel straight out of dash.
4. Remove screws securing switch module, pull module from instrument panel and disconnect electrical connector.
5. Reverse procedure to install. Ensure trim panel is properly aligned, then secure to instrument panel.

TORONADO & TROFEO

1. Disconnect battery ground cable.
2. Remove screws securing instrument cluster bezel, then pull bezel away from instrument panel to disengage retaining clips.
3. Disconnect electrical connectors to bezel mounted switch.
4. Remove switch from cluster bezel.
5. Reverse procedure to install.

INSTRUMENT CLUSTER
REPLACE

ELDORADO & SEVILLE

1. Disable SIR system as follows:
    a. Turn ignition switch to Off.
    b. Remove SIR fuse No. 19 from fuse panel.
    c. Remove three screws and two nuts from left side sound insulator.
    d. Remove courtesy lamp from sound insulator panel.
    e. Remove sound insulator panel.
    f. Disconnect the yellow two way connector and the Connector Position Assurance (CPA) connector from the base of the steering column.
2. Disconnect battery ground cable.
3. Remove A/C duct and radio trim plate from instrument cluster bezel.
4. Remove seven screws securing instrument panel cluster from housing.
5. Remove digital display and warning lamp lenses, and the trip odometer reset button, **Fig. 9.**
6. Remove two screws securing cluster, then pull cluster from instrument panel socket.
7. Reverse procedure to install. Ensure electrical connector pins are properly aligned when cluster is pressed into instrument panel.

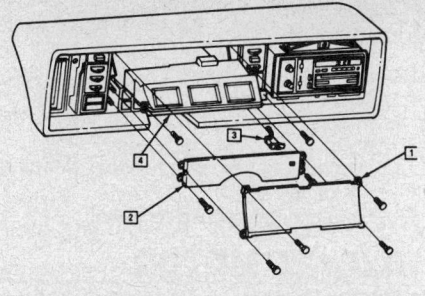

[1] DIGITAL DISPLAY FILTER LENSE   [3] TRIP ODOMETER RESET BUTTON
[2] WARNING LIGHT LENSE   [4] DIGITAL INSTRUMENT CLUSTER ASSEMBLY

Fig. 9 Instrument cluster removal. Eldorado & Seville

REATTA & RIVIERA

1988–89 Models

1. Disconnect battery ground cable.
2. Pull instrument cluster center trim plate straight out of dash, then remove left and right trim plates, Fig. 6.
3. Remove four screws securing cluster, then pull cluster straight out of instrument panel.
4. Reverse procedure to install, ensuring electrical connector pins are properly aligned when cluster is pressed into instrument panel.

1990–91 Models

1. Place the ignition switch in the Off position, then remove SIR fuse No. 14 from fuse panel.
2. Remove left-side sound insulator retaining screws and nuts.
3. Remove the courtesy lamp from the sound insulator, then the lefthand side sound insulator from the vehicle.
4. Disconnect Connector Position Assurance (CPA) and yellow two-way connector from base of the steering column.
5. Disconnect battery ground cable.
6. Remove four trim plate retaining screws, then pull trim plate from lower retaining clips, Fig. 10.
7. Remove center air duct assembly.
8. Remove 13 screws retaining housing to back of instrument panel.
9. Remove two screws from front of instrument panel.
10. Reverse procedure to install.

TORONADO & TROFEO

1988–89

1. Remove body ignition fuse No. 14.
2. Remove left hush panel, lower steering column cover, insulator at toe plate, and the lower steering column mounting screws.
3. Remove nuts securing upper steering column bracket to instrument panel, then carefully lower column. **Disconnect shift indicator cable and electrical connectors, as needed, prior to lowering column. Do not force column down as it may be damaged.**
4. Remove screws securing instrument

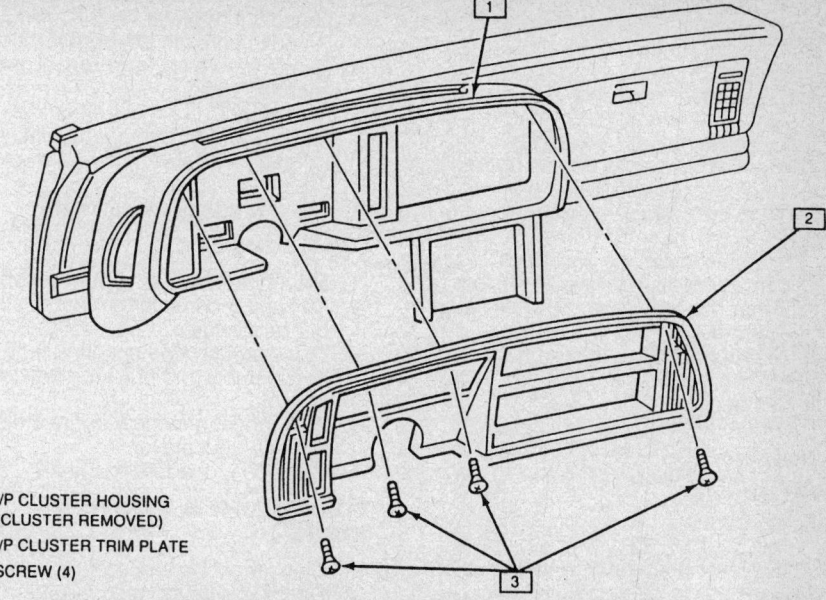

[1] I/P CLUSTER HOUSING (CLUSTER REMOVED)
[2] I/P CLUSTER TRIM PLATE
[3] SCREW (4)

Fig. 10 Trim plate retaining screw locations. 1990–91 Reatta & Riviera.

cluster bezel, then pull bezel away from instrument panel to disengage retaining clips.
5. Disconnect electrical connectors and remove cluster bezel.
6. Remove screws securing instrument cluster, then pull cluster straight out of dash.
7. Reverse procedure to install, ensuring electrical connector pins are properly aligned when cluster is pressed into instrument panel.

1990–91

1. Disable SIR system as follows:
   a. Turn ignition switch to Off.
   b. Remove SIR fuse No. 19 from fuse panel.
   c. Remove two screws and nuts from left side sound insulator.
   d. Remove courtesy lamp from sound insulator panel.
   e. Remove sound insulator panel.
   f. Disconnect the yellow two way connector and the Connector Position Assurance (CPA) connector from the base of the steering column.
2. Disconnect battery negative cable.
3. Remove two front retaining screws, two rear retaining nuts, then the courtesy lamp from lefthand side sound insulator.
4. Remove sound insulator from vehicle.
5. Remove two retaining screws from knee bolster, then the bolster from the vehicle.
6. Remove trim plate retaining screws, then the trim plate from vehicle.
7. Remove screws retaining cluster to instrument panel.
8. Pull cluster forward enough to disconnect electrical connectors, then remove cluster from vehicle.
9. Reverse procedure to install.

CATHODE RAY TUBE (CRT)
REPLACE

CRT's are located in the center of the instrument panel assembly and may also be known as a visual information center (VIC), electronic control center (ECC), or a graphic control center (GCC).

Some of the CRT's have a controller built in. For those which do not, refer to "CRT Controller, Replace."

1. Disconnect battery ground cable.
2. Remove instrument panel trim plate attaching screws, then the trim plate.
3. Remove four attaching bolts securing CRT to instrument panel and mounting bracket assembly.
4. Carefully pull out CRT, then disconnect electrical connector from rear of CRT assembly.
5. Reverse procedure to install.

CRT CONTROLLER
REPLACE

TORONADO & TROFEO
1989

1. Ensure parking brake is applied, or car is properly blocked from rolling.
2. **It may be necessary to place gear selector in N prior to removal of trim plate. Use care as to not break retaining tabs.** Pull shift indicator trim plate up and out slowly.
3. Carefully twist out light bulbs, then pop out lumbar/bolster control switch.
4. Remove outer console trim plate. Pry from glove box end first, then pull upwards.

5. Remove six retaining screws from equalizer and tape mounting plate, then pry up mounting plate similar to outer trim plate.
6. Disconnect equalizer and tape deck electrical connections, then pull tape holder from console bucket.
7. Remove two screws from bottom and one from top of console compartment liner, then remove liner.
8. Remove four 13 mm nuts retaining console to vehicle floor pan. Two nuts are located near the tape deck, the other two are under the console compartment.
9. Pull console upward and out, then disconnect electrical connectors if space is needed.
10. Remove four nuts holding controller to mounting bracket, then two screws holding mounting bracket to console shifter plate.
11. Disconnect controller electrical connector, then the controller.
12. Reverse procedure to install.

1990–91

1. Disconnect battery negative cable.
2. Remove console compartment retaining screws, then the compartment.
3. Gently pry off compact disc trim plate, if equipped.
4. Disconnect console trim plate electrical connectors, then the console trim plate.
5. Remove compact disc player, if equipped.
6. Remove screws and nuts retaining console assembly to the floor.
7. Disconnect electrical connectors, then remove console.
8. Remove four nuts retaining controller to retaining bracket.
9. Disconnect electrical connectors, then remove controller from vehicle.
10. Reverse procedure to install.

RADIO
REPLACE

LESS CRT
ELDORADO & SEVILLE

1. Disconnect battery ground cable.
2. Remove radio trim plate from instrument cluster bezel.
3. Twist lefthand A/C vent to remove.
4. Remove seven screws (six phillips and one Torx) securing instrument panel trim plate.
5. Loosen lower two mounting nuts under radio (top nuts do not have to be loosened), then pull radio away from instrument panel.
6. Disconnect electrical connectors and antenna lead, then remove radio assembly.
7. Reverse procedure to install.

REATTA & RIVIERA
Radio

1. Disconnect battery ground cable.
2. Remove shifter handle and the shift indicator assembly.

3. Remove four screws securing top console trim plate.
4. Remove console left front floor panel.
5. Remove screws from top of bracket securing radio.
6. Disconnect bracket, electrical connectors and antenna lead, noting position for installation, then remove radio.
7. Reverse procedure to install.

Tape Player

1. Disconnect battery ground cable.
2. Pull upper console trim panel straight out of console.
3. Remove 4 screws securing tape player assembly and pull tape player from console.
4. Disconnect electrical connectors and remove tape player.
5. Reverse procedure to install.

TORONADO & TROFEO
Radio

1. Disconnect battery ground cable.
2. Remove screws securing instrument cluster bezel, then pull bezel away from instrument panel to disengage retaining clips.
3. Disconnect electrical connectors and remove cluster bezel.
4. Remove screws securing ECC panel and radio brackets to instrument panel and pull assembly away from panel.
5. Disconnect electrical connectors, noting position for installation, then remove ECC panel and radio assembly.
6. Remove nuts securing Radio to brackets, then the radio.
7. Reverse procedure to install.

Console Mounted Tape Player & Booster

1. Disconnect battery ground cable, then carefully pull trim plate from console.
2. Lift out shift indicator assembly and disconnect bulbs from indicator.
3. Remove screws securing console mounting plate.
4. Disconnect electrical connectors and remove mounting plate assembly.
5. Remove nuts securing tape player or booster to mounting plate and remove components as required.
6. Reverse procedure to install, pressing console trim plate into retaining clip until trim plate is secured.

WITH CRT

1. Disconnect battery ground cable.
2. Pull shift indicator trim plate up and out slowly. Place selector in neutral if necessary.
3. Remove indicator lamp bulbs.
4. Remove lumbar/bolster control switch, if equipped.
5. Remove outer console trim plate.
6. Remove attaching screws securing graphic equalizer and tape mounting plate.
7. Remove mounting plate.
8. Disconnect electrical connector from tape deck and graphic equalizer.
9. Pull tape holder out of console bucket.
10. Remove screws at bottom of console compartment liner and screws at top

of liner, then pull liner out.
11. Remove nuts attaching console to floor pan.
12. Pull console upward and slide back toward rear seat.
13. Pull radio remote chassis out to the right.
14. Disconnect radio chassis electrical connectors.
15. Reverse procedure to install.

BLOWER MOTOR
REPLACE

ELDORADO, SEVILLE, REATTA, RIVIERA & 1990–91 TORONADO & TROFEO

1. Disconnect battery ground cable, then remove strut tower cross brace (two nuts each side).
2. Remove cowl relay center bracket (two nuts), then disconnect electrical connector and cooling hose from blower motor.
3. **On Eldorado and Seville models,** Remove MAP sensor mounting bracket.
4. **On all models,** remove blower motor retaining screws, then tilt blower motor in case to allow fan removal. **Fan must be removed prior to blower motor to prevent fan from being bent.**
4. Remove fan retainer and fan from blower motor, then remove blower motor.
5. Remove blower fan from case.
6. Reverse procedure to install.

1988–89 TORONADO & TROFEO

1. Disconnect battery ground cable and remove front of cowl shield.
2. Remove bulkhead connector screw and disconnect bulkhead connector.
3. Disconnect electrical connector from Electronic Spark Control module, then remove bracket retaining screws and the module.
4. Remove power steering pump bracket support bolts and the support.
5. Remove coil bracket nuts, disconnect high tension leads and electrical connectors from coil, remove wiring conduits and plug wire guides, and position coil aside.
6. Remove shields from blower motor harness, then disconnect cooling tube and electrical connector from blower motor.
7. Remove blower motor mounting screws and the blower motor.
8. Reverse procedure to install.

HEATER CORE
REPLACE
ELDORADO & SEVILLE

1. Disconnect battery ground cable, then drain cooling system.

2. Remove four screws securing glove box module and the glove box, then the righthand lower sound insulator.
3. Remove programmer as follows:
   a. Remove two ECM bracket mounting screws, then position ECM aside to gain access to rear programmer mounting screw.
   b. Remove threaded rod, then the vacuum connector retaining nut from programmer.
   c. Disconnect electrical and vacuum connectors from programmer assembly, then remove three mounting screws and programmer, **Fig. 11.**
4. **On 1990-91 models,** remove electrical connections from BCM, then the BCM and mounting bracket from vehicle.
5. **On all models,** remove electrical connections from ECM, then the ECM and mounting bracket from vehicle.
6. Remove heater core cover, then disconnect heater hoses from heater core.
7. Remove two heater core retaining screws, then the heater core.
8. Reverse procedure to install. Prior to installing glove box module, adjust air mix door link rod as follows:
   a. Set temperature control for 90°F and allow 1-2 minutes for programmer arm to travel to maximum heat position, **Fig. 12.**
   b. Disconnect air mix door link rod from programmer and ensure air mix door operated freely.
   c. Pre-load air mix door in maximum heat position by pulling rod to seat door against seal, then snap rod into connector on programmer arm, taking care not to disturb position of arm or air mix door.
   d. Set control for 60°F and ensure programmer arm and air mix door travel to maximum cooling position.

REATTA & RIVIERA
1988-89

1. Disconnect negative battery cable, then drain the cooling system.
2. Remove hoses from heater core.
3. Remove three screws and two wing nuts, the righthand sound insulator and the courtesy lamp.
4. Remove ten screws retaining glove box, then the programmer electrical connector.
5. Remove one nut and programmer vacuum connector, then the three programmer retaining screws and programmer, **Fig. 11.**
6. Disconnect ECM electrical connectors, ECM, then the ECM bracket.
7. Remove the BCM electrical connectors, BCM, then the BCM bracket.
8. Remove the two heater core cover screws, then cover the carpet to protect against spills.
9. Remove heater core.
10. Reverse procedure to install.

1990-91
When performing service on, or near

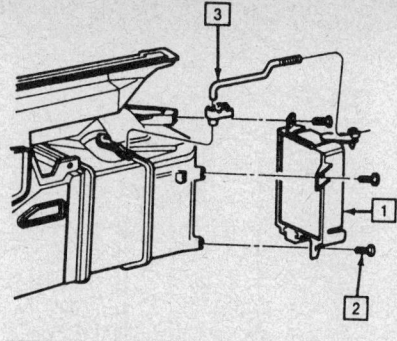

① PROGRAMMER
② PROG. MTG. SCREW (3 REQ'D)
③ THREADED ROD

Fig. 11 Programmer mounting bolt locations.

supplemental inflatable restraint systems, ensure SIR system is disabled. Ensure ignition switch is in the Lock position, then remove SIR fuse.

If the airbag has been deployed, inspect coil for signs of scorching, melting, or other damage. Coil must be replaced if damaged.
1. Disconnect negative battery cable, then drain the cooling system.
2. Remove four upper retaining screws from instrument panel cluster trim plate, then pull trim plate from retaining clips.
3. Remove four cluster retaining screws, disconnect electrical connectors, then remove cluster.
4. Remove two headlamp switch assembly screws, then the switch assembly.
5. Remove four retaining screws, then the electrical connector and climate control head from vehicle.
6. Remove retaining screws, then the radio from vehicle.
7. Remove console trim plate retaining screws, then the trim plates.
8. Remove compact disc player, if equipped.
9. Remove front console storage compartments, then the sound insulators.
10. Remove knee bolster, the steering column reinforcement plate, then the glove box.
11. Remove instrument panel upper trim pad.
12. Remove lower-left retaining bolt, retaining screws, then the hood release assembly.
13. Remove two retaining screws, then the center instrument panel brace.
14. Remove the instrument panel to dash connector.
15. Remove steering column, then the screw above the steering column.
16. Remove the lower-right retaining bolt, three upper retaining screws, electrical connectors, then the instrument panel from vehicle.
17. Remove the electrical connectors, then the programmer from vehicle, **Fig. 11.**

18. Remove the electrical connectors, then the BCM and mounting bracket from vehicle.
19. Remove the electrical connectors, then the ECM and mounting bracket from vehicle.
20. Remove heater core from housing, then the hoses from heater core.
21. Remove two heater retaining screws, then the heater core from vehicle.
22. Reverse procedure to install.

TORONADO & TROFEO
1988-89

1. Disconnect battery ground cable and drain cooling system.
2. Remove left and right hush panels and under dash courtesy lamps.
3. Remove lower steering column cover, insulator at toe plate, and the lower steering column mounting screws.
4. Remove nuts securing upper steering column bracket to instrument panel, then carefully lower column. **Disconnect shift indicator cable and electrical connectors, as needed, prior to lowering column. Do not force column down as it may be damaged.**
5. Remove windshield defroster grille and both deflector housings.
6. Remove 5 screws securing top of instrument panel and 2 bolts securing bottom of instrument panel.
7. Disconnect instrument panel bulkhead connector and pull instrument panel rearward.
8. Remove aspirator duct.
9. Disconnect fuel filler door and deck lid release electrical connectors and the antenna lead.
10. Disconnect fuse panel, then remove instrument panel from vehicle.
11. Disconnect heater hoses from heater core.
12. Remove A/C programmer screws, disconnect electrical and vacuum connectors and remove programmer.
13. Remove A/C power module retaining screws, disconnect electrical connectors and remove module.
14. Remove heater core cover and retaining strap.
15. Remove retaining screws and the heater core.
16. Reverse procedure to install.

1990-91
When performing service on, or near supplemental inflatable restraint systems, ensure SIR system is disabled. Ensure ignition switch is in the Lock position, then remove SIR fuse.

If the airbag has been deployed, inspect coil for signs of scorching, melting, or other damage. Coil must be replaced if damaged.
1. Turn ignition switch to the Off position, then remove fuse No. 9 from the fuse panel.
2. Remove lefthand sound insulator retaining screws, then the insulator.
3. Remove the connector position assurance (CPA) and yellow two-way connector at the base of steering column.

4. Disconnect battery ground cable and drain cooling system, then remove the righthand sound insulator.
5. Remove knee bolster, then the instrument panel column reinforcement plate.
6. Remove instrument panel cluster trim plate, then the lefthand side switch assembly.
7. Remove righthand side switch plate assembly, then the instrument panel cluster.
8. Remove the climate control head, if equipped.
9. Remove four bolts retaining driver information display (DID), then the DID.
10. Remove the center A/C deflectors, then unsnap and remove defroster grille.
11. Remove upper, then lower-left instrument panel mounting screws and bolts.
12. Remove hood release assembly, retaining bolts and center instrument panel brace.
13. Remove the steering column, then the glove box.
14. Remove the lower-right instrument panel retaining bolt, then the retaining screws and fuse box.
15. Remove the consol, instrument panel electrical connectors, then the instrument panel.
16. Remove the programmer electrical connectors, then the programmer, **Fig. 12.**
17. Remove the BCM electrical connections, then the BCM and mounting bracket.
18. Remove the ECM electrical connections, then the ECM and mounting bracket.
19. Remove heater core from the housing, then the hoses from the core.
20. Remove two heater retaining screws, then the heater core from the vehicle.
21. Reverse procedure to install.

EVAPORATOR CORE
REPLACE
ELDORADO & SEVILLE

1. Discharge and recover refrigerant from system. Refer to "A/C Refrigerant Recovery."
2. Drain radiator and cooling system.
3. Remove two bolts from each side of the cross-tower support bracket.
4. Remove two nuts from the cowl relay center bracket, then position relay bracket aside.

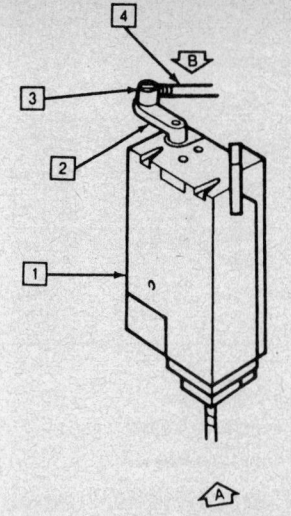

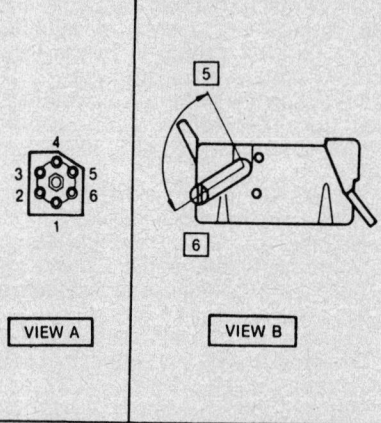

VIEW A	VIEW B

1	PROGRAMMER	4	THREADED ROD
2	OUTPUT ARM	5	MAX. A/C POSITION
3	RETAINER	6	MAX. HEAT POSITION

Fig. 12 Programmer linkage positioning.

5. Disconnect electrical connectors from the power module, blower motor and blower motor resistor.
6. Disconnect both heater core hoses from the heater core.
7. Remove the evaporator line retaining bracket.
8. Remove evaporator core refrigerant

lines. **Cap all open fittings to prevent contamination of system.**
9. Remove heater hose T-connector.
10. Remove two heat shield screws from engine compartment, raise and support vehicle, then the remaining two screws from beneath vehicle. Remove heat shield.
11. Remove two A/C module retaining screws (one 7 mm and one 10 mm).
12. Lower vehicle, then remove the MAP sensor bracket.
13. Remove diverter valve from righthand side valve cover.
14. Remove two harness hold-down brackets from valve cover.
15. Remove power module, blower motor, then the sound insulator.
16. Remove the A/C module cover screws, module cover, sound insulator, then the seal.
17. Remove the evaporator retaining clamp, then pull evaporator core from evaporator case.
18. Reverse procedure to install, noting the following:
    a. **Torque** module cover retaining screws to 27 inch lbs.
    b. **Torque** line fitting bolt to 18 ft. lbs.
    c. Leak test all refrigerant connections.

REATTA, RIVIERA, TORONADO & TROFEO

1. Discharge and recover refrigerant from system. Refer to "A/C Refrigerant Recovery."
2. Disconnect accumulator inlet and outlet fittings. **Cap all open fittings to prevent system contamination.**
3. Remove accumulator retention bolts.
4. Remove accumulator from mounting bracket.
5. Reverse procedure to install. Always use new dual O-rings, coated with refrigerant oil. **Torque** retention bolts to 35 inch lbs.

SERVICE BULLETINS
SCREECHING NOISE DURING CRANKING
1988 Eldorado, & Seville

Some 1988 Eldorado and Seville models may experience a screeching noise during cranking.
To correct this condition, replace flywheel with part No. 1648458.

Engine

NOTE: Refer To Chapter 5 For Service Procedures On 3.8L/V6-231, 4.5L/V8-273 And 4.9L/V8-300 Engines Not Found In This Section.

INDEX

ENGINE MOUNTS
REPLACE

ELDORADO & SEVILLE

RIGHT SIDE ENGINE & TRANSAXLE MOUNT
Removal

Refer to **Fig. 1,** for engine and transaxle mount position.

1. Open hood, then remove brace between engine bracket and engine.
2. Remove two nuts securing mount to engine bracket.
3. Raise vehicle on a hoist and support with stands at each front frame horn.
4. Remove two nuts securing engine mount to frame.
5. Remove two nuts securing transaxle bracket to mount.
6. Remove two nuts securing transaxle mount to frame bracket.
7. Raise engine using support J-28467 or equivalent, lifting engine until bracket is free from engine and transaxle mounts.
8. Remove stud and two bolts securing bracket to block, then the bracket and mount by pulling forward.
9. Remove transaxle mounting bracket from transaxle, then the mount.

Installation

Refer to **Fig. 1,** for engine and transaxle mount position.

1. Position engine mount and bracket between block and frame, then torque bracket bolts and stud to specifications.

2. Position transaxle mount and bracket between transaxle and frame, then torque bracket retaining bolts to specifications.
3. Guide mounts into position while lowering engine and reverse remaining procedure to complete installation, torquing all fasteners to specifications.

LEFT ENGINE MOUNT

Refer to **Fig. 1,** for engine and transaxle mount position.

1. Open hood, disconnect battery ground cable, then remove air cleaner assembly.
2. Remove serpentine drive belt, then discharge A/C system and recover coolant. Refer to "A/C Coolant Recovery."
3. Install engine support tool No. J-28467 or equivalent.
4. Remove lower center exhaust manifold nut and top nut from engine damper.
5. Raise and support vehicle, remove right engine splash shield, then A/C splash shield.
6. Remove engine damper.
7. Remove two A/C compressor brackets, then the A/C compressor.
8. Remove water pipe bracket bolt.
9. Remove bolts securing engine mount bracket to block and cradle.
10. Remove engine mount and bracket assembly through right wheelwell.
11. Remove engine mount from bracket.
12. Reverse procedure to install, torquing engine mount fasteners to specifications.

REATTA, RIVIERA, TORONADO & TROFEO

1. Support engine using tool J-28467 or equivalent.
2. Raise and support vehicle.
3. Remove nuts securing engine mount to bracket, **Figs. 2 and 3,** then raise engine slightly.
4. Remove nuts securing mount to frame and the engine mount.
5. Reverse procedure to install. Torque mount fasteners to specifications as shown in **Figs. 2 and 3.**

ENGINE
REPLACE

ELDORADO & SEVILLE

1. Disconnect battery ground cable, then drain cooling system.
2. Remove air cleaner assembly.
3. Mark position of hood hinges, disconnect necessary electrical connectors, then remove hood hinge bolts and the hood.
4. Remove engine cooling fan and serpentine drive belt.
5. Disconnect upper radiator and heater hoses from thermostat housing.
6. Disconnect electrical connectors from the following components:
   a. Oil pressure switch.
   b. Coolant temperature sensor.
   c. Distributor.
   d. EGR solenoid.
   e. Engine temperature switch.
   f. ISC motor.
   g. Throttle position switch.

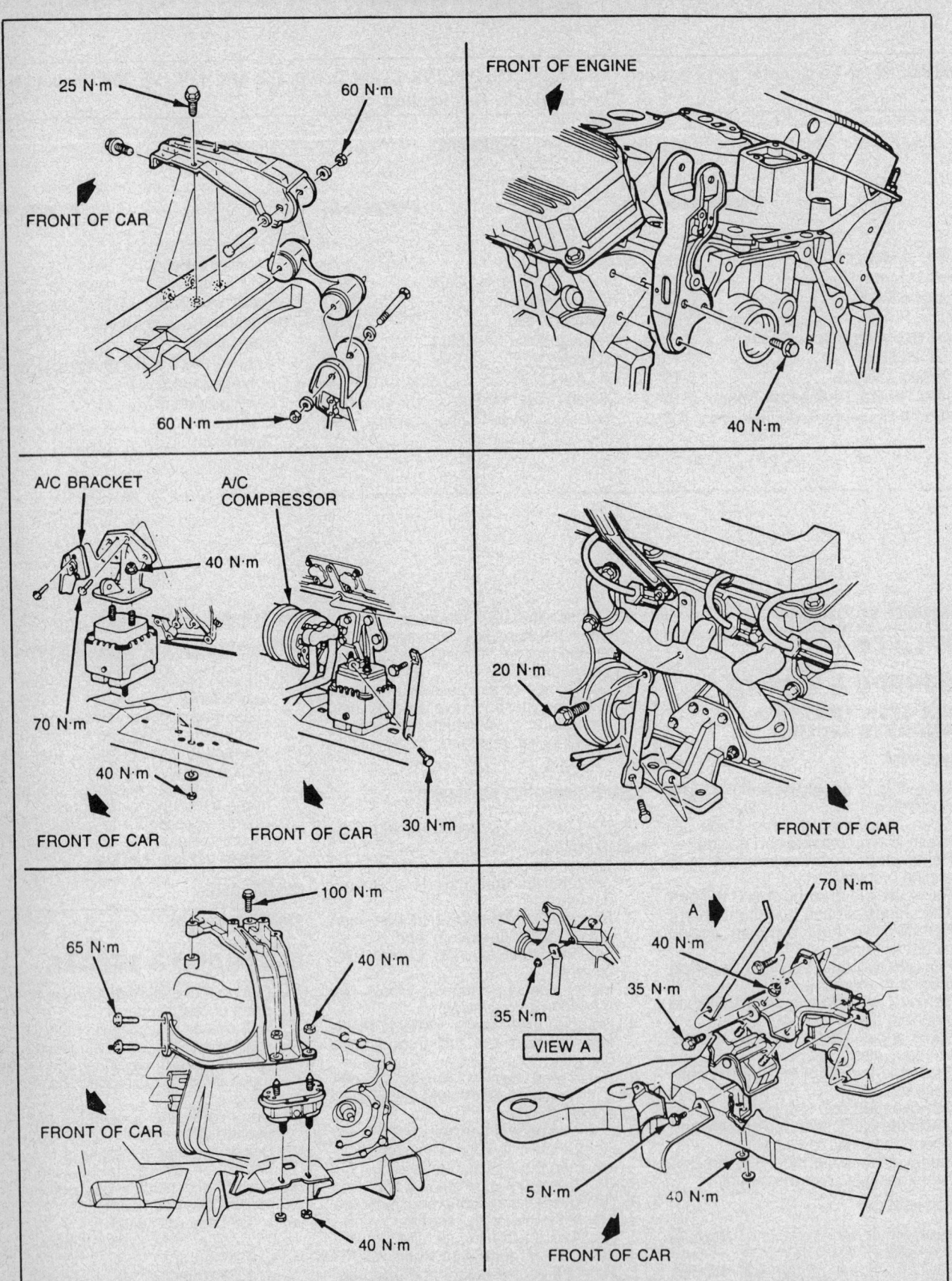

Fig. 1 Engine & transaxle mounts. 1988–90 Eldorado & Seville

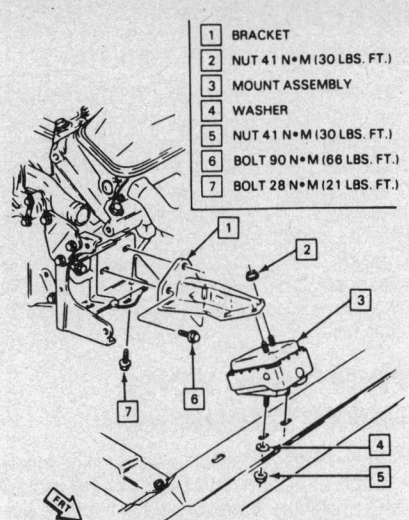

1	BRACKET
2	NUT 41 N·M (30 LBS. FT.)
3	MOUNT ASSEMBLY
4	WASHER
5	NUT 41 N·M (30 LBS. FT.)
6	BOLT 90 N·M (66 LBS. FT.)
7	BOLT 28 N·M (21 LBS. FT.)

Fig. 2 Front engine mount. Reatta, Riviera, Toronado & Trofeo

h. Injectors.
i. MAT sensor.
j. Oxygen sensor.
k. Throttle body base warmer.
l. Alternator and ground wiring at alternator bracket.
m. Electric EFE grid.
7. Release engine harness from retainers and secure aside.
8. Disconnect accelerator, cruise control and transmission cables from throttle body.
9. Remove cruise control diaphragm brackets and secure assembly aside.
10. Disconnect oil and transmission cooler lines from radiator.
11. Disconnect remaining hoses and remove radiator.
12. Disconnect oil cooler lines at filter adapter and remove lines.
13. Remove oil cooler line bracket at transaxle and the air cleaner bracket.
14. Remove oil filter adapter housing.
15. Disconnect AIR tubes from diverter valve, if equipped.
16. Remove front right and rear body cross braces.
17. Disconnect and remove right front heater hose and coolant reservoir.
18. Remove AIR filter box and bracket, if equipped.
19. Disconnect power steering line bracket from right cylinder head, remove power steering pump and tensioner retaining bolts and secure assembly aside.
20. Discharge A/C system, disconnect A/C lines at accumulator and condenser, and plug lines and open fittings.
21. Connect a suitable tool to fuel line Schraeder valve and slowly bleed fuel system pressure into a container.
22. Disconnect fuel lines at throttle body and fuel line bracket from transaxle, then position fuel lines aside.
23. Remove EGR lines and brackets.
24. Disconnect vacuum modulator line, then the power brake vacuum line.
25. Raise and support vehicle, remove starter shield, and disconnect starter wiring and block ground straps.
26. Remove exhaust crossover pipe and the starter motor.
27. Remove both flexplate dust shields, then the three bolts securing torque converter to flexplate.
28. Remove A/C compressor dust shield.
29. Remove right front tire and wheel, then the outer wheel house plastic shield.
30. Remove right rear engine to transaxle mounting bolt and the lower engine damper nut.
31. Remove front (left) engine mount nuts and right rear engine/transaxle mount bolts, **Fig. 1.**
32. Remove alternator and oxygen sensor wiring and the heater bypass bracket from right side of vehicle.
33. Remove right engine brace, then lower vehicle.
34. Remove five top engine to transaxle mounting bolts.
35. Install lift equipment and support transaxle with a jack.
36. Raise engine, separate engine from transaxle, then remove engine from vehicle.
37. Reverse procedure to install.

REATTA, RIVIERA, TORONADO & TROFEO

1. Relieve fuel system pressure as follows:
   a. Disconnect fuel pump electrical connector from fuel tank, then start engine.
   b. After engine stalls, continue to crank for three seconds to ensure relief of any residual pressure.
   c. Turn ignition off and reconnect fuel pump electrical connector.
2. Disconnect battery ground cable, then the air intake duct.
3. Remove throttle cable bracket and throttle cables from throttle body.
4. Drain engine coolant.
5. Raise and support vehicle.
6. Remove exhaust pipe from rear exhaust manifold, then the engine mount bolts.
7. Disconnect starter wiring, then remove starter.
8. Remove A/C compressor and secure aside.
9. Disconnect power steering hoses at steering gear.
10. Remove lower transaxle-to-engine bolts. Note location and direction of bolts for assembly reference.
11. Remove torque converter dust shield, scribe alignment mark between converter and flexplate and remove converter bolts.
12. Remove engine support bracket at transaxle.
13. Lower vehicle, then disconnect radiator hoses and heater hoses at engine.
14. Disconnect vacuum modulator and canister purge lines.
15. Disconnect engine wiring harness, then remove remaining transaxle to engine bolts.

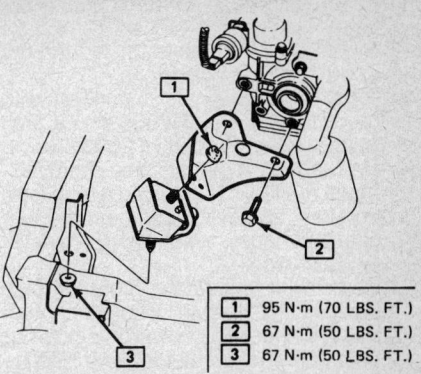

1	95 N·m (70 LBS. FT.)
2	67 N·m (50 LBS. FT.)
3	67 N·m (50 LBS. FT.)

Fig. 3 Rear engine mount. Reatta, Riviera, Toronado & Trofeo

16. Attach lifting equipment to engine and support transaxle.
17. Raise engine, separate engine from transaxle and remove engine from vehicle.
18. Reverse procedure to install.

COOLING SYSTEM BLEED

To be performed after cooling system has been drained, flushed and is ready to be refilled.
1. Fill cooling system with a 50/50 mixture of antifreeze and water, to just below the filler neck.
2. Fill the coolant recovery reservoir to the specified fill mark on the outside of the reservoir.
3. Run engine with the radiator cap removed until normal operating temperature is achieved.
4. With engine running at idle, add coolant to the radiator, until it reaches the bottom of the filler neck.
5. Cycle the engine to 5000 RPM, then back to idle at least five times. This will help expel any air trapped in the system.
6. Replace the radiator cap. **Arrows on the cap must line up with the coolant recovery reservoir hose.**

SERVICE BULLETINS
BROKEN VALVE SPRING CAPS

If broken valve spring caps are encountered on some 1988 models equipped with 3.8L/V6-231 VIN C engine, replace valve spring caps with new part No. GM 25534605.

ENGINE VIBRATION

On some 1988 models equipped with a 3.8L/V6-231 VIN 3 engine, a shake/vibration may be present at 1100–1300 rpm. The shake/vibration may be felt from the floor pan, seat, steering wheel or instrument panel during speeds of 0–15 mph or at 45–55 mph with the torque converter engaged. To correct this condition, proceed as follows:

1. Ensure engine is performing satisfactorily.
2. Check engine mounts for ground-out or other stress conditions.
3. Replace crankshaft balancer with new balancer No. GM 25532179, then **torque** balancer bolt to 200 ft. lbs.
4. Disconnect exhaust pipe from exhaust manifold, then using a high temperature anti-seize compound, lubricate exhaust seal and reinstall exhaust pipe.
5. Remove intermediate exhaust pipe hanger and rubber insulators, then bend hanger ends upward 1/2 inch. Lubricate rubber insulators with silicone grease, then install hanger and insulators.

INTAKE MANIFOLD

Bolts

On some late production 1988 Eldorado and Seville models with 4.5L/V8-273 engines, a different intake manifold was used in production. This manifold uses a 40 mm bolt in the No. 3 bolt position instead of a 55 mm bolt as was used in early production models.

Gaskets

When replacing intake manifold gasket on 1988 Eldorado and Seville models, a new intake manifold gasket set is available to increase sealing quality.

MOANING NOISE AFTER START

On some 1988 Eldorado and Seville models, a low moaning noise after start up may be present. The noise may be caused by vibration of the oil pump pickup. If the pickup is found to be the problem, replace oil pump assembly with part No. GM 3517753. On 1988 models, replacement of the oil pan will also be required, as the old oil pan provides insufficient clearance for the installation of the new pickup.

OIL LEAK DIAGNOSIS

When diagnosing oil leaks from rear of engine, use of a high intensity black light is the recommended procedure. This will

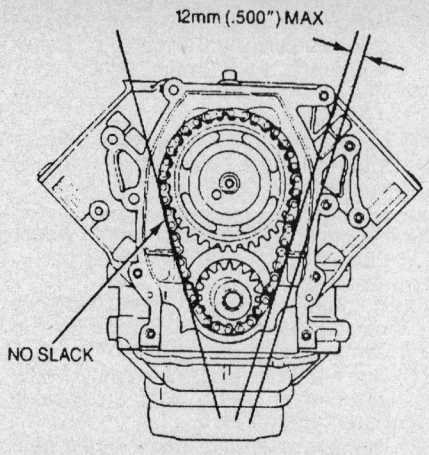

Fig. 4 Checking timing belt for excessive wear. Eldorado & Seville

help eliminate improper diagnosis, as various seals at rear of engine, if leaking, may appear to be a defective rear main seal.

OIL PAN DRAIN PLUG LEAK

1988-89 Eldorado & Seville

On these models, the above condition may be caused by a metal burr around the drain plug hole on the oil pan. This will result in a damaged or torn gasket causing a leak.

To correct this problem, proceed as follows:

1. Remove drain plug and drain oil.
2. Install plug only, without gasket, back into pan. **Torque** to 18 ft. lbs.
3. Remove plug. Replace gasket (part No. 14090908) if necessary.
4. Install plug and gasket, **torquing** to 22 ft. lbs.
5. Refill oil to specification.

OIL LEAKAGE

1989 Eldorado & Seville

These models equipped a 4.5L V8 engine, may experience oil leakage around the oil filter adapter. There are several potential leak points at this location. If diagnosis indicates that the leak is occurring at the junction of the oil filter and oil cooler lines, it is permissible to increase the torque on the oil cooler line nut. Increased **torque** should be limited to 30 ft. lbs. or damage may occur to the adapter or cooler line nut.

SCREECHING NOISE DURING CRANKING

Some 1988 Eldorado and Seville models may experience a screeching noise during cranking. If noise exists, replace flywheel with part No. GM 1648458 to correct condition.

SERPENTINE BELTS

On 1988 Eldorado and Seville models, the serpentine drive belt must be replaced anytime a engine driven accessory becomes seized, preventing rotation of any pulley.

TIMING CHAIN

On 1988 Eldorado and Seville models, once engine reaches high mileage, timing chain should be checked for excessive wear. Rotate camshaft so all slack is on one side of timing chain as shown, **Fig. 4**, then check side-to-side movement. Replace timing chain if slack exceeds .50 inch.

VALVE TRAIN NOISE

On 1988 Eldorado & Seville models equipped with 4.5L engines built prior to production No. T10L315315, an abnormal valve train noise may be experienced with the engine at normal operating temperature. This condition may be caused by inconsistencies in valve lifter production. If condition exists, replace lifters with part No. GM 5235498.

TIGHTENING SPECIFICATIONS*

NOTE: Torque Specifications Are For Clean And Lightly Lubricated Threads Only. Dry Or Dirty Threads Produce Increased Friction Which Prevents Accurate Measurement Of Tightness.

3.8L/V6-231 ENGINE

Year	Component	Torque/ft. lbs.
1988-91	Alternator Support To Cylinder Head	36
	Alternator Support Through Alternator	36
	Balancer Assembly To Crankshaft	219
	Balance Shaft Gear Bolt	14①
	Balance Shaft Retainer	26
	Camshaft Sensor To Front Cover	6.25
	Camshaft Sprocket Bolts	26

Continued

TIGHTENING SPECIFICATIONS—Continued
3.8L/V6-231 ENGINE

Year	Component	Torque/ft. lbs.
	Connecting Rod Bolts	43
	Coolant Temperature Sensor To Intake	15
	Crankshaft Bearing Caps To Cylinder Block	90
	Crankshaft Sensor To Front Cover	22
	Crankshaft Sensor Clamp Bolt	3.3
	Cylinder Block Drain Plug	32
	EGR Pipe To EGR Valve	20
	EGR Pipe To Exhaust Manifold	15
	EGR Valve To Intake Manifold Adapter	20
	Engine Mount To Cylinder Block	70
	ESC Knock Sensor To Cylinder Block	13
	Exhaust Manifold To Cylinder Head	41
	Flywheel Cover To Transaxle	4
	Flywheel To Crankshaft	61
	Front Cover To Block	22
	Fuel Feed & Return Pipes To Fuel Rail	22
	Fuel Rail To Intake Manifold	10
	Heater Hose Fitting To Intake	11
	Ignition Module To Alternator Support	18
	Intake Manifold To Cylinder Head	7.3
	Oil Filter Adapter To Timing Chain Cover	24
	Oil Filter Assembly To Filter Adapter	18
	Oil Galley Plugs	25
	Oil Level Switch To Oil Pan	40
	Oil Pan Drain Plug	18
	Oil Pan To Cylinder Block	10.3
	Oil Pan To Front Cover	10.3
	Oil Pressure Switch To Cylinder Block	24
	Oil Pump Cover To Timing Chain Cover	8
	Oil Screen Housing To Cylinder Block	8
	Oxygen Sensor To Exhaust Manifold	31
	Rocker Arm Cover To Cylinder Head	7.3
	Rocker Arm Pedestal To Cylinder Head	②
	Spark Plug To Cylinder Head	20
	Starter Motor To Cylinder Block	35
	Thermostat Housing To Intake Manifold	20
	Throttle Body Adapter To Intake Manifold	20
	Throttle Body To Throttle Body Adapter	20
	Throttle Cable Bracket To Throttle Body	3
	Timing Chain Dampener	14
	Torque Converter To flywheel	46
	Torque Strut To Bracket	42
	Torque Strut Bracket Nuts To Cylinder Head	20
	Torque Strut Bracket Bolts To Cylinder Head	15
	Torque Strut Bracket To Front Panel	17
	Transaxle To Cylinder Block	55
	Valve Lifter Guide Retainer Bolts	27
	Water Pump Cover To Timing Chain Cover	7
	Water Pump Pulley To Hub	12

①—Rotate an additional 35°   ②—1988, 37 ft. lbs. 1989-91, 28 ft. lbs.

4.5L/V8-273 & 4.9L/V8-300 ENGINES

Year	Component	Torque/ft. lbs.
1988-91	Air Pipe To Cylinder Head	22
	Connecting Rod Bolts	24 ①
	Coolant Temperature Sensor	22
	Crankshaft Pulley To Hub	18
	Damper To Crankshaft	65
	Distributor Hold-Down Nut	18
	Distributor Hold-Down Stud	26
	EGR Valve Mounting Screws	15
	Engine Metal Temperature Switch	6
	Exhaust Manifold Bolts	18
	Exhaust Outlet Flange Studs	30
	Flywheel To Crankshaft	70
	Front Cover Screws	15
	Heater Water Valve	22
	Lift Bracket To Cylinder Head Bolt	37
	Lower Main Oil Galley Plug	18
	Lower Thermostat Housing To Water Pump Bolt	7
	Lower Thermostat Housing To Water Pump Stud	30
	Main Bearing Cap Bolts	85
	MAT Sensor	22
	Oil Filter Adapter To Block Screws	15
	Oil Pan Bolts	11
	Oil Pan Drain Plug	22
	Oil Pan Nuts	11
	Oil Pan Studs	15
	Oil Pressure Switch	10
	Oil Pump Cover Screws	5
	Oil Pump Mounting Nut To Main Bearing Cap	22
	Oil Pump Mounting Screws To Block	15
	Oxygen Sensor	30
	Rocker Arm Cover Screws & Studs	8
	Rocker Arm Pivot To Support Screws	22
	Rocker Arm Support To Head Bolt Nuts	37
	Rocker Arm Support To Head	7
	Spark Plugs	11
	Thermal Vacuum Switch (TVS)	15
	Timing Sprocket To Camshaft	37
	Timing Tab To Water Pump Nuts	5
	Upper Main Oil Galley Plug, Horizontal	22
	Upper Main Oil Galley Plug, Vertical	18
	Upper Thermostat Housing To Lower Thermostat Housing Screws	18
	Water Passage Plug, Lefthand Side Of Block	7

① —Lubricated with engine oil.

Rear Suspension

INDEX

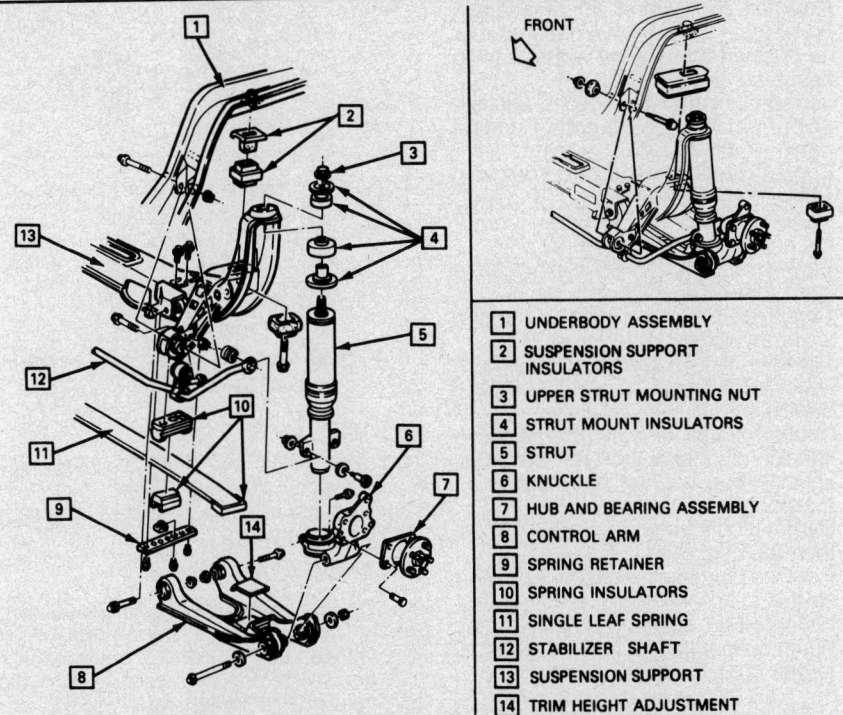

Fig. 1 Rear suspension exploded view. Left side shown

1	UNDERBODY ASSEMBLY
2	SUSPENSION SUPPORT INSULATORS
3	UPPER STRUT MOUNTING NUT
4	STRUT MOUNT INSULATORS
5	STRUT
6	KNUCKLE
7	HUB AND BEARING ASSEMBLY
8	CONTROL ARM
9	SPRING RETAINER
10	SPRING INSULATORS
11	SINGLE LEAF SPRING
12	STABILIZER SHAFT
13	SUSPENSION SUPPORT
14	TRIM HEIGHT ADJUSTMENT SPACER (OPTIONAL)

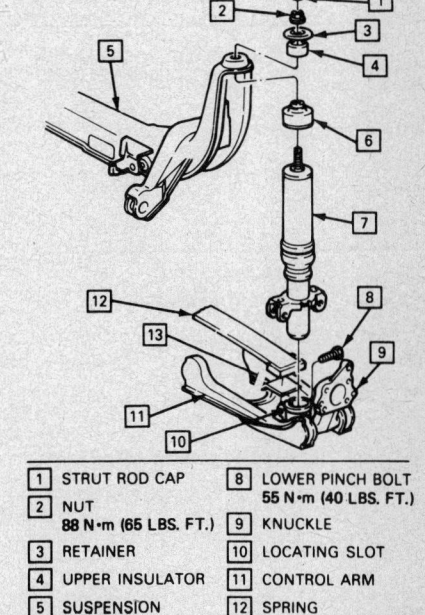

1	STRUT ROD CAP	8	LOWER PINCH BOLT 55 N·m (40 LBS. FT.)
2	NUT 88 N·m (65 LBS. FT.)	9	KNUCKLE
3	RETAINER	10	LOCATING SLOT
4	UPPER INSULATOR	11	CONTROL ARM
5	SUSPENSION SUPPORT	12	SPRING
6	LOWER INSULATOR	13	TRIM HEIGHT ADJUSTMENT SPACER (OPTIONAL)
7	STRUT		

Fig. 2 Rear strut installation

DESCRIPTION

All rear suspension components are mounted on a suspension support assembly, **Fig. 1**, which is attached to the body at four points. The transverse leaf spring is fully isolated from the crossmember and is held in position by left and right retainers and insulators. On their inboard end, the control arms pivot on the suspension support, allowing each end of the leaf spring to act directly on the control arm surface. A suspension knuckle pivots on the outboard end of each control arm, and each knuckle contains a sealed hub and wheel bearing assembly. Each knuckle is located at the top by an air adjustable strut assembly which is connected to the suspension support.

On some models, a stabilizer shaft is used to further locate the knuckle assemblies and provide increased roll stiffness. Strut charging is controlled by an Electronic Level Control (ELC) system, which maintains a standard rear trim height under a variety of load conditions.

HUB & BEARING
REPLACE

1. Raise and support vehicle.

2. Remove tire and wheel assembly.
3. Remove brake caliper attaching bolts and position caliper aside. **Do not suspend caliper by brake line.**
4. Remove rotor retainers, if equipped. Retainers may be discarded after removal.
5. Remove rotor.
6. Remove four hub mounting bolts, then the hub and bearing assembly.
7. Reverse procedure to install, torquing to specifications.

STRUT
REPLACE

1. Raise and support vehicle on frame contact type hoist, then remove wheel and tire assembly.
2. If left strut is to be replaced, disconnect ELC height sensor link.
3. Reinstall two wheel nuts to retain brake rotor, then remove stabilizer shaft mounting bolt at strut, if equipped.
4. Remove brake caliper as outlined, then secure aside leaving hoses connected.

5. Loosen, but do not remove, knuckle pivot bolt at outboard end of control arm. **Support outboard end of control arm with a jackstand to slightly compress spring. Jackstand must be of adequate strength to support vehicle weight and be properly positioned to prevent personal injury.**
6. Remove upper strut rod cap, mounting nut and insulator, **Fig. 2**.
7. Slowly remove jackstand to relieve spring pressure, compress strut by hand, then remove lower insulator.
8. Rotate strut and knuckle assembly outward, remove pinch bolt, then separate strut from knuckle.
9. Reverse procedure to install, ensuring strut is fully seated with tang on strut bottomed in steering knuckle slot. When suspension is fully assembled, torque bolts to specifications.

KNUCKLE
REPLACE

Left and right knuckles are not interchangeable. When replacing knuckles,

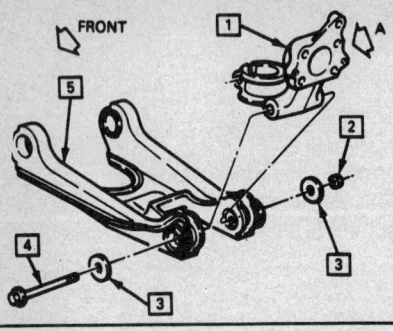

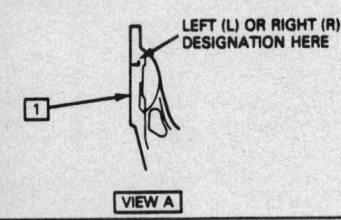

[1] KNUCKLE
[2] NUT (80 N·m/59 FT. LBS.)
[3] RETAINER
[4] PIVOT BOLT
[5] CONTROL ARM

Fig. 3   Knuckle installation

check knuckle for the L or R designation stamped on knuckle.

1. Raise and support vehicle on frame contact type hoist, then remove wheel and tire assembly.
2. If left knuckle is to be replaced, disconnect ELC height sensor link.
3. Remove stabilizer shaft mounting bolt from strut, if equipped.
4. Remove brake caliper as outlined, and secure aside leaving hoses connected.
5. Remove brake rotor, hub retaining bolts and the hub and bearing assembly.
6. Loosen, but do not remove, knuckle pivot bolt at outboard end of control arm.
7. Support outboard end of control arm with a proper jackstand.
8. Remove upper strut rod cap, mounting nut and insulator, **Fig. 2.**
9. Compress strut by hand and remove lower insulator.
10. Rotate strut and knuckle assembly outward, remove pinch bolt, then separate strut from knuckle.
11. Remove speed sensor from knuckle if equipped with anti-lock brakes.
12. Remove knuckle pivot bolt and the knuckle, **Fig. 3.**
13. Reverse procedure to install, ensuring strut is fully seated with tang on strut bottomed in steering knuckle slot. When suspension is fully assembled, torque bolts to specifications.

CONTROL ARM
REPLACE

1. Raise and support vehicle on frame contact type hoist, then remove wheel and tire assembly.
2. If left control arm is to be replaced, disconnect ELC height sensor link.
3. Remove stabilizer shaft mounting bolt from strut, if equipped.
4. Reinstall two wheel nuts to retain brake rotor, then remove brake caliper as outlined and secure aside leaving hoses connected.
5. Loosen, but do not remove, knuckle pivot bolt at outboard end of control arm.
6. Support outboard end of control arm with a proper jackstand.
7. Remove upper strut rod cap, mounting nut and insulator, **Fig. 2.**
8. Slowly remove jackstand to relieve spring pressure.
9. Compress strut by hand and remove lower insulator.
10. Remove wheel speed sensor from knuckle if equipped with anti-lock brakes.
11. Support knuckle assembly, remove knuckle pivot bolt, then remove strut, knuckle, hub, bearing and rotor as an assembly.
12. Remove both inner control arm bolts, then the control arm, **Fig. 4.**
13. Reverse procedure to install, ensuring strut is fully seated with tang on strut bottomed in steering knuckle slot. When suspension is fully assembled, torque bolts to specifications.

CONTROL ARM BUSHINGS
REPLACE
OUTER
Removal

If inner control arm bolts are not loosened, or removed, alignment will not be disturbed and it will not be necessary to perform wheel alignment after outer bushing replacement.

1. Outer control arm bushings can be replaced without removing control arm from vehicle after performing steps 1-12 of "Control Arm, Replace" procedure.
2. Insert spacer between control arm flanges. Special tool No. J-35739-1, is a combination of two spacers. **The wide spacer must be used for outer bushing removal and installation.**
3. Coat the threads of tool No. J-21474-19 bolt with high pressure lubricant J-23444-A, or equivalent, to prevent thread damage.
4. Install tool Nos. J-35739-2 remover, J-21474-5 receiver, bearing,

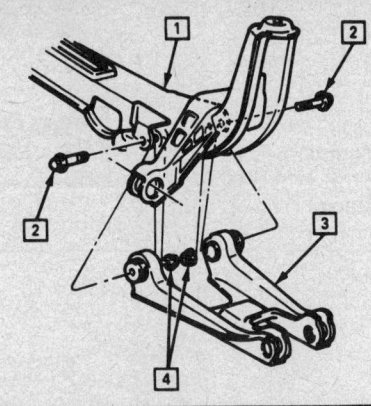

[1] SUSPENSION CROSSMEMBER ASSEMBLY
[2] INNER CONTROL ARM BOLTS
[3] CONTROL ARM
[4] NUTS (90 N·m/66 FT. LBS.)

Fig. 4   Lower control arm installation

J-21474-18 nut and J-21474-19 bolt as shown in **Fig. 5.**
5. Remove bushing from control arm by tightening nut.

Installation

1. Position new bushing for installation on control arm. Bushing must be installed from the outside of the control arm, then drawn inward toward the control arm centerline.
2. Insert wide end of J-35739-1 spacer between control arm flanges.
3. Coat threads of bolt J-21474-19 with high pressure lubricant J-23444-A.
4. Install bushing installer J-28576-1, receiver J-35739-3, bearing, nut J-21474-18 and bolt J-21474-19, **Fig. 5.**
5. Draw bushing into control arm by tightening nut. Tighten nut until bushing flange seats firmly against control arm.
6. Refer to "Control Arm, Replace" for suspension assembly.

INNER

Control arm must be removed from vehicle to replace inner control arm bushings. After replacing inner bushings, check wheel alignment as outlined.

1. Remove control arm as described under "Control Arm, Replace."
2. Insert spacer between control arm flanges. Special tool No. J-35739-1 is a combination of two spacers. **The narrow spacer must be used for inner bushing removal and installation.**
3. Coat the threads of bolt No. J-21474-19 with high pressure lubricant J-23444-A to prevent thread damage.
4. Install remover J-21474, receiver J-21474-5, bearing, nut J-21474-18

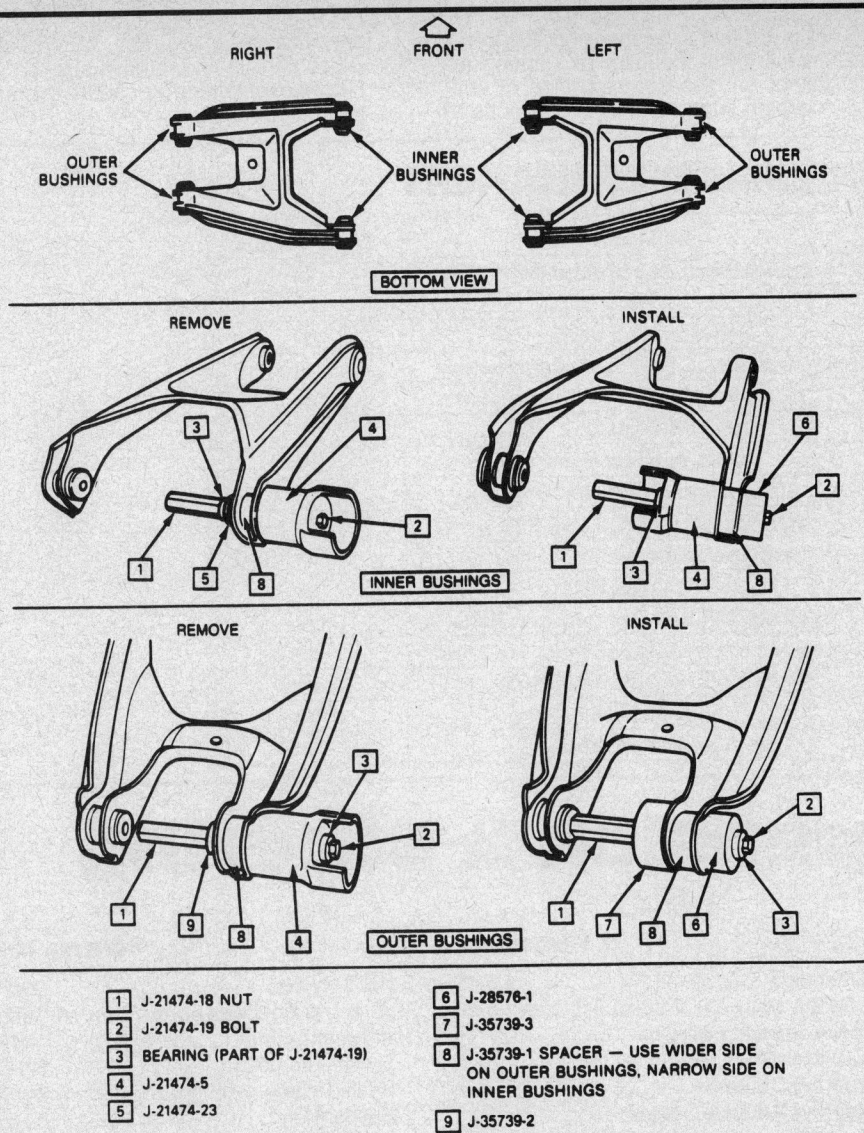

BOTTOM VIEW

INNER BUSHINGS

OUTER BUSHINGS

1	J-21474-18 NUT	
2	J-21474-19 BOLT	
3	BEARING (PART OF J-21474-19)	
4	J-21474-5	
5	J-21474-23	
6	J-28576-1	
7	J-35739-3	
8	J-35739-1 SPACER — USE WIDER SIDE ON OUTER BUSHINGS, NARROW SIDE ON INNER BUSHINGS	
9	J-35739-2	

Fig. 5   Replacing control arm bushings

and bolt J-21474-19, **Fig. 5.**
5. Remove bushing from control arm by tightening nut.

Installation

1. Position new bushing on control arm. **Bushing must be installed from the outside of the control arm, then drawn inward to the control arm centerline.**
2. Insert narrow end of spacer J-35739-1 between control arm flanges, then coat threads of bolt J-21474-19 with high pressure lubricant J-23444-A.
3. Install bushing installer J-28576-1, receiver J-21474-5, bearing, nut J-21474-18 and bolt J-21474-19, **Fig. 5.**
4. Draw bushing into control arm by tightening nut. **Tighten nut until bushing flange seats firmly against control arm.**
5. Refer to "Control Arm, Replace," for suspension assembly.

SPRING & INSULATORS REPLACE

Removal of rear spring requires disassembly of either left or right side of the suspension while leaving opposite side intact. Spring may be removed from either side of vehicle.
1. Remove lower control arm as outlined.
2. Place a support under outboard end of spring as shown in **Fig. 6,** then lower vehicle so weight of vehicle compresses spring. **Ensure jack stand can support weight of vehicle and is properly positioned under spring.**
3. Remove three spring retainer bolts, retainer and lower insulator, **Fig. 7,** from end of spring nearest support stand.
4. Slowly raise vehicle, allowing spring to deflect downward until spring no longer exerts force on stand.
5. Remove retainer bolts, retainer and insulator from opposite end of spring,

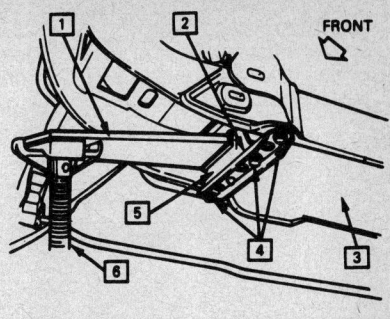

1	SPRING	
2	SPRING RETAINER	
3	SUSPENSION CROSSMEMBER ASSEMBLY	
4	RETAINER BOLTS (28 N·m/21 FT. LBS.)	
5	LOWER OUTBOARD INSULATOR	
6	JACKSTAND	

Fig. 6   Removing & installing spring

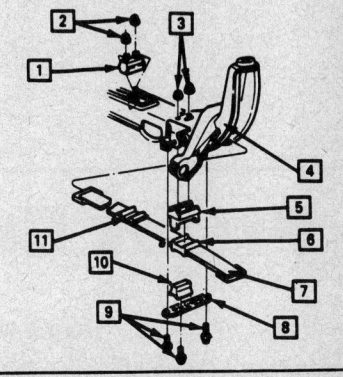

1	CENTER INSULATOR	
2	CENTER INSULATOR NUTS (28 N·m/21 FT. LBS.)	
3	OUTBOARD INSULATOR NUTS (28 N·m/21 FT. LBS.)	
4	SUSPENSION CROSSMEMBER ASSEMBLY	
5	UPPER OUTBOARD INSULATOR	
6	OUTBOARD INSULATOR LOCATING BAND	
7	SPRING	
8	SPRING RETAINER	
9	RETAINER BOLTS (28 N·m/21 FT. LBS.)	
10	LOWER OUTBOARD INSULATOR	
11	CENTER INSULATOR LOCATING BAND	

Fig. 7   Exploded view of spring installation

then withdraw spring from crossmember.
6. Remove upper spring insulators.
7. Inspect spring insulators and retainers and replace as needed.
8. Install center and upper outboard insulators in crossmember, then torque bolts to specifications. **Ensure arrows on upper outboard insulators point toward centerline of vehicle.**
9. Position spring in suspension support by inserting through disassembled side of suspension. Ensure outboard and center insulator bands are centered on spring insulators.
10. Install lower insulator and retainer on side opposite disassembled portion of suspension, torque retaining bolts to

specifications, then place a stand under free end of spring, **Fig. 6.**
11. Lower vehicle, allowing weight to load spring and deflect free end of spring

into position in suspension support.
12. Install lower insulator and spring retainer on disassembled side of suspension support, then torque bolts to

specifications.
13. Raise vehicle and remove stand.
14. Reverse remaining procedure to complete installation.

TIGHTENING SPECIFICATIONS

Year	Component	Torque/ft. lbs.
1988-90	Caliper Mounting Bracket Bolts	83
	Center Insulator Nuts	21
	Hub Mounting Bolts	52
	Inner Control Arm To Suspension Support	66
	Knuckle Pinch Bolt	40
	Knuckle Pivot Bolt	59
	Spring Retainer Bolts	21
	Stabilizer Shaft Bracket Bolt	43
	Stabilizer Shaft Mounting Bolt	43
	Stabilizer Shaft Mounting Nut	43
	Strut Bracket Bolt	43
	Suspension Support Forward Arm Bolts	66
	Suspension Support Upper Mounting Bolts	66
	Upper Outboard Insulator Nuts	21
	Upper Strut Nut	65
	Wheel Lug Nuts	100

Front Suspension & Steering

INDEX

STABILIZER SHAFT
REPLACE

1. Raise vehicle and support with weight of vehicle resting on frame, not the lower control arms.
2. Remove right front wheel and tire.
3. Remove left and right insulators, retainers, spacers and bolts, **Fig. 1.**
4. Remove left and right bracket bolts, brackets and insulators.
5. Disconnect exhaust pipe from rear manifold, raise pipe to gain clearance, then withdraw stabilizer shaft.
6. Reverse procedure to install.

BALL JOINT
REPLACE

1. Raise and support vehicle.
2. Remove tire and wheel assembly.
3. **On 1988-89 models,** remove stabilizer shaft, insulators, retainers, spacer and bolt, **Fig. 1.**
4. **On all models,** remove ball joint from knuckle.
5. Drill out three rivets retaining ball joint.

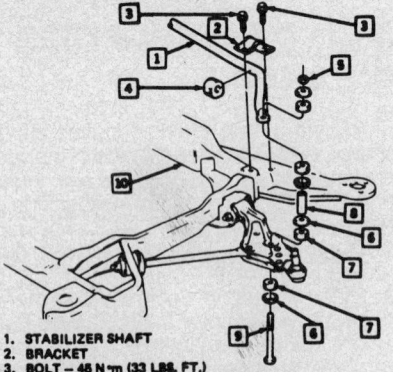

1. STABILIZER SHAFT
2. BRACKET
3. BOLT – 45 N·m (33 LBS. FT.)
4. INSULATOR – INSTALL WITH SLIT TO REAR OF CAR
5. NUT 17 N·m (13 LBS. FT.) OBTAIN TORQUE BY RUNNING NUT TO UNTHREADED PORTION OF BOLT
6. RETAINER
7. INSULATOR
8. SPACER
9. BOLT – INSTALL IN DIRECTION SHOWN
10. FRAME

Fig. 1 Stabilizer shaft installation

Start with a 1/4 inch drill bit, then use a 1/2 inch bit.
6. Remove ball joint.
7. Reverse procedure to install, noting

the following:
a. **Torque** ball joint to control arm nut to 84 inch lbs. using 90° adapter J-35551 or equivalent.
b. Tighten nut an additional 120°, noting torque reading.
c. Tighten nut up to an additional 60° to align holes and install cotter pin. When tightening nut, minimum torque (as listed in "Tightening Specifications") must be obtained. If minimum torque cannot be obtained, check for stripped threads and repair as needed. If threads are satisfactory, replace ball joint and steering knuckle.

CONTROL ARM
REPLACE

Care must be taken not to overextend driveshaft Tri-Pot joints when replacing suspension components. Overextending joint could cause separation of internal joint components, resulting in failure of the joint.

1. Remove ball joint from steering

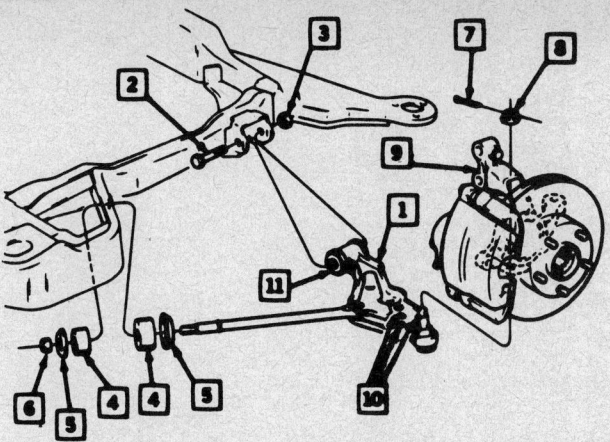

1. CONTROL ARM
2. BOLT – 140 N·m (100 LBS. FT.) TIGHTEN WITH CAR AT PROPER TRIM HEIGHT
3. NUT – 123 N·m (91 LBS. FT.) TIGHTEN WITH CAR AT PROPER TRIM HEIGHT
4. INSULATOR
5. RETAINER
6. NUT – 70 N·m (52 LBS. FT.)
7. PIN
8. NUT – TIGHTEN NUT TO 10 N·m (88 LBS. IN.). CONTINUE TIGHTENING BY ROTATING NUT AN ADDITIONAL 120°, DURING WHICH A MINIMUM TORQUE OF 50 N·m (37 LBS. FT.) MUST BE OBTAINED. INSTALL COTTER PIN
9. KNUCKLE
10. BALL JOINT ATTACHMENT RIVETS
11. BUSHING

Fig. 2 Lower control arm installation

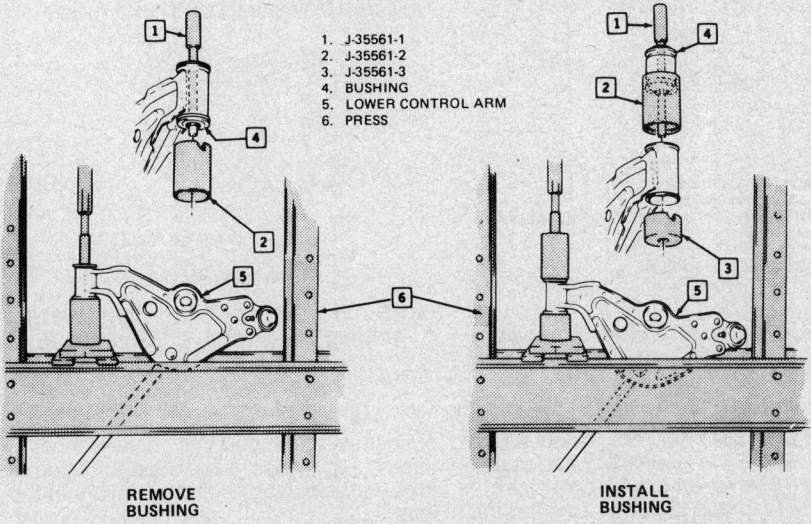

1. J-35561-1
2. J-35561-2
3. J-35561-3
4. BUSHING
5. LOWER CONTROL ARM
6. PRESS

REMOVE BUSHING

INSTALL BUSHING

Fig. 3 Replacing lower control arm bushings

knuckle as outlined in "Ball Joint, Replace."
2. Remove control arm bushing bolt and brake reaction rod nut, retainer and insulator, **Fig. 2.**
3. Remove the control arm from frame.
4. Install control arm on frame.
5. Install control arm bushing bolt and nut, retainer and insulator but do not tighten bolt.
6. Install lower ball joint in steering knuckle as outlined.
7. Reverse remaining procedure to complete installation. Torque bolts to specifications as shown in **Figs. 1 and 2.**

CONTROL ARM BUSHINGS
REPLACE

When replacing lower control arm bushings, refer to **Fig. 3.**
1. Remove lower control arm as outlined in "Control Arm, Replace."
2. Install driver, tool No. J-35561-1, receiver No. J-35561-2 and installing cup No. J-35561-3, or equivalents.
3. Press out bushing.
4. Lubricate new bushing with rubber lube.
5. Install tools, then press in new bushing.
6. Install lower control arm.

HUB & BEARING ASSEMBLY
REPLACE

1. Siphon 2/3 of the brake fluid from master cylinder, then raise vehicle and support frame with stands.
2. Remove wheel and tire assembly.
3. Insert a drift through rotor and remove hub nut and washer.
4. Remove caliper boots, lift caliper off rotor and bracket, then secure caliper aside.
5. Remove bolts securing caliper bracket, bracket and the brake rotor. **Prevailing torque bolts used to secure mounting bracket cannot be reused. If bolts become loose or are removed, bolts must be replaced.**
6. Mount tool J-28733 or equivalent on hub, **Fig. 4**, then tighten screw just enough to separate drive axle from hub.
7. Remove hub retaining bolts and the hub and bearing assembly, **Fig. 5.**
8. If seal is being replaced, drive seal toward engine, then cut seal off drive axle.
9. Lubricate seal lip and install using a driver, install O-ring and fill cavity between seal and bearing with grease.
10. Install hub and bearing assembly over drive axle and torque bolts to specifications.
11. Install rotor and caliper mounting bracket and torque new bracket bolts to specifications.
12. Install caliper ensuring insulators are properly positioned, coat mounting bolt shafts with silicone grease and torque to specifications.
13. Install hub nut and washer, insert drift through rotor and tighten nut securely.
14. Remove drift, install wheel and tire assembly and lower vehicle, then torque hub nut to specifications.

STEERING KNUCKLE
REPLACE

1. Remove hub and bearing assembly as outlined in "Hub & Bearing Assembly, Replace."
2. Remove nut securing tie rod, then separate tie rod from knuckle.

1. J-28733
2. TURN FORCING SCREW UNTIL AXLE SPLINES ARE JUST LOOSE

Fig. 4 Separating drive axle from hub

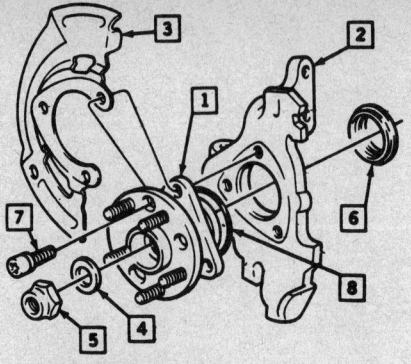

1. HUB AND BEARING ASSEMBLY
2. STEERING KNUCKLE
3. SHIELD
4. WASHER
5. HUB NUT 245 N·m (180 LBS. FT.)
6. SEAL
7. HUB AND BEARING RETAINING BOLT (55 TORX) 95 N·m (70 LBS. FT.)
8. "O" RING

Fig. 5 Hub & bearing assembly installation

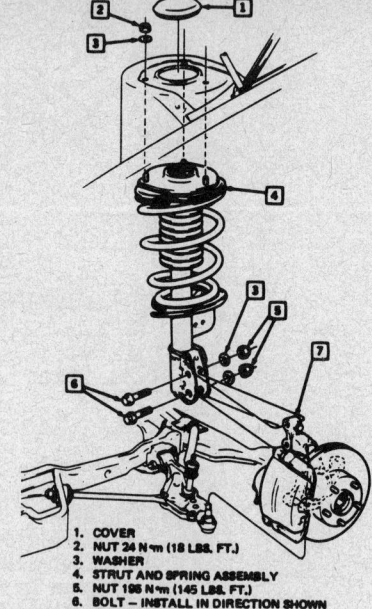

1. COVER
2. NUT 24 N·m (18 LBS. FT.)
3. WASHER
4. STRUT AND SPRING ASSEMBLY
5. NUT 195 N·m (145 LBS. FT.)
6. BOLT – INSTALL IN DIRECTION SHOWN
7. KNUCKLE

Fig. 6 Steering knuckle & strut installation

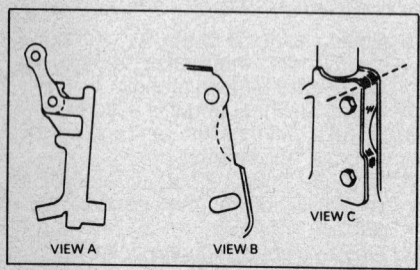

Fig. 7 Marking steering knuckle & strut alignment

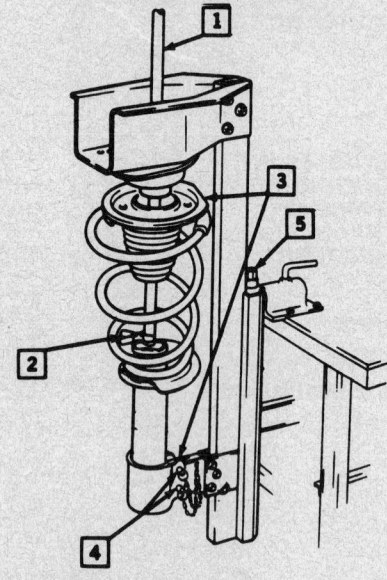

1. ROD J-34013-38 INSTALLED
2. CLAMP J-34013-20 INSTALLED
3. FLAT ON SPRING SEAT MUST FACE SAME DIRECTION AS STEERING KNUCKLE FLANGE
4. BOTH LOCKING PINS INSTALLED
5. COMPRESSOR FORCING SCREW

Fig. 9 Aligning flat on upper spring seat

REMOVE POWER STEERING PUMP PULLEY

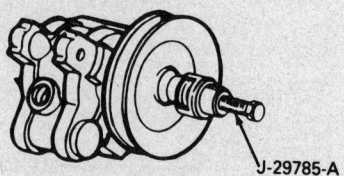

J-29785-A

INSTALL POWER STEERING PUMP PULLEY

J-25033-B

FLAT WASHER MUST BE USED TO POSITION PULLEY FLUSH WITH END OF SHAFT.

Fig. 10 Power steering pump pulley removal. Eldorado & Seville

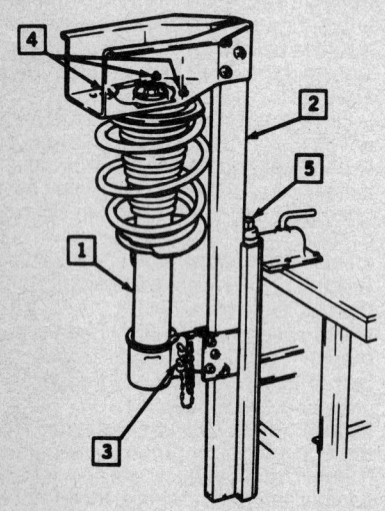

1. STRUT ASSEMBLY
2. STRUT COMPRESSOR J-34013
3. INSTALL LOCKING PINS THROUGH STRUT ASSEMBLY
4. TIGHTEN NUTS TILL FLUSH WITH STRUT COMPRESSOR
5. COMPRESSOR FORCING SCREW

Fig. 8 Installing strut assembly in strut compressor

3. Cut inner tabs from boot protector tool No. J-34754 or equivalent and install protector over drive axle outer joint.
4. Remove cotter pin and nut securing lower ball joint and separate ball stud from steering knuckle.
5. Remove bolts securing strut to steering knuckle, **Fig. 6**, and the steering knuckle.
6. Reverse procedure to install.

STRUT ASSEMBLY REPLACE

Care must be taken not to overextend driveshaft Tri-Pot joints when replacing suspension components. Overextending joint could cause separation of internal joint components, resulting in failure of the joint.

1. Remove nuts securing top of strut assembly to body, **Fig. 6**.
2. Raise vehicle and support frame with stands, then remove wheel and tire.
3. Scribe reference marks between strut and steering knuckle as follows:
   a. Scribe strut along lower outboard strut radius (A), **Fig. 7**.
   b. Scribe strut flange on inboard side along curve of knuckle (B).
   c. Scribe mark along strut/knuckle interface (C).

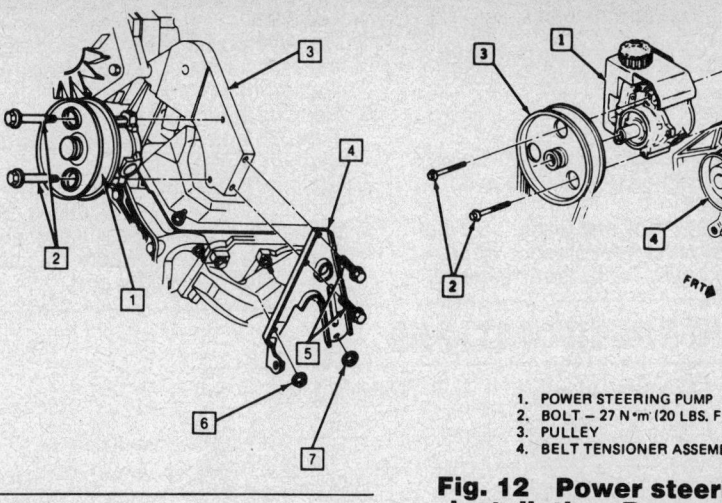

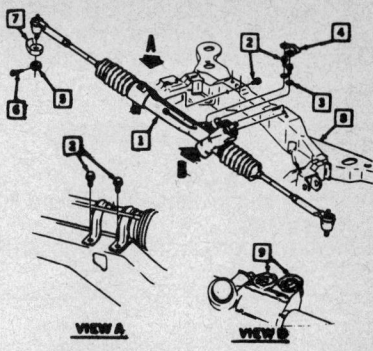

1. POWER STEERING PUMP
2. BOLT – 27 N·m (20 LBS. FT.)
3. PULLEY
4. BELT TENSIONER ASSEMBLY

Fig. 12 Power steering pump installation. Reatta, Riviera, Toronado & Trofeo

1	PUMP
2	PUMP MOUNTING BOLTS (25 N·m/18 FT. LBS.)
3	PUMP AND TENSIONER BRACKET
4	BRACE
5	BOLTS (45 N·m/33 FT. LBS.)
6	NUT (45 N·m/33 FT. LBS.)
7	NUT (25 N·m/18 FT. LBS.)

Fig. 11 Power steering pump installation. Eldorado & Seville

1. STEERING GEAR
2. BOLT – 68 N·m (50 LBS. FT.) AFTER SECOND REUSE OF BOLT, LOCKTITE THREAD LOCKING KIT NO. 1052624 MUST BE USED.
3. WASHER
4. RETAINER
5. NUT – TIGHTEN NUT TO 10 N·m (7 LBS. FT.) THEN TIGHTEN NUT AN ADDITIONAL 120 DEGREES (2 FLATS) DURING WHICH A MINIMUM TORQUE OF 45 N·m (33 LBS. FT.) IS TO BE OBTAINED. IF 45 N·m (33 LBS. FT.) IS NOT OBTAINED, INSPECT FOR STRIPPED THREADS. IF THREADS ARE SATISFACTORY, REPLACE KNUCKLE.
6. PIN
7. KNUCKLE
8. FRAME
9. RTV SEALER AROUND INSERTS

Fig. 13 Power steering gear installation. Reatta, Riviera, Toronado & Trofeo

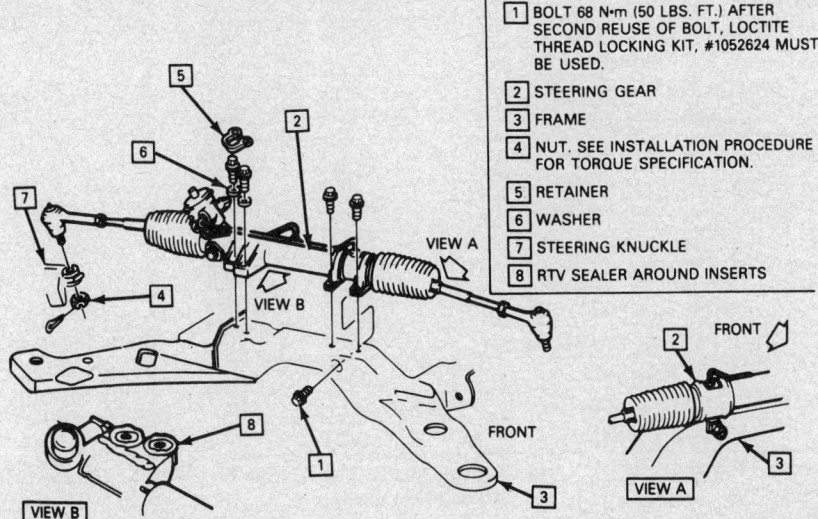

1	BOLT 68 N·m (50 LBS. FT.) AFTER SECOND REUSE OF BOLT, LOCTITE THREAD LOCKING KIT, #1052624 MUST BE USED.
2	STEERING GEAR
3	FRAME
4	NUT. SEE INSTALLATION PROCEDURE FOR TORQUE SPECIFICATION.
5	RETAINER
6	WASHER
7	STEERING KNUCKLE
8	RTV SEALER AROUND INSERTS

Fig. 14 Power steering gear installation. Eldorado & Seville

4. Disconnect brake line bracket from strut.
5. Remove bolt securing strut to stabilizer link, then the stabilizer link.
6. Remove bolts securing strut to steering knuckle, support knuckle with wire and remove strut.
7. Reverse procedure to install, aligning scribe marks made during disassembly. Torque nuts and bolts to specifications, then check alignment.

STRUT SERVICE

1. Place strut assembly in strut compressor J-34013, **Fig. 8.**

2. Turn compressor forcing screw until spring compresses slightly.
3. Keep dampener shaft from turning with a T-50 Torx bit and remove nut from top of dampener shaft.
4. Using tool J-34013-38 or equivalent, guide dampener shaft out of assembly.
5. Loosen compressor screw while guiding dampener shaft out of assembly, continually loosening compressor screw till strut dampener and spring can be removed. **Be careful to avoid chipping or cracking the spring coating when handling the front suspension coil spring.**

6. Install strut dampener in strut compressor J-34013 with clamp J-34013-20 clamped on dampener shaft.
7. Install spring over strut in correct position and move assembly upright in strut compressor and install upper locking pin. **Flat on upper spring seat must face out from centerline of vehicle, Fig. 9, or when mounted in strut compressor spring seat faces same direction as steering knuckle mounting flange.**
8. Install rod J-34013-38 or equivalent into strut assembly to guide dampener shaft on reassembly of strut.
9. Start turning compressor screw clockwise on J-34013 while guiding J-34013-38 which will center dampener shaft in the assembly.
10. Continue turning compressor screw until dampener shaft threads are visible through top of strut assembly.
11. Install washer and nut, then remove J-34013-20 from dampener shaft.
12. Hold dampener shaft with socket, then torque dampener shaft nut to specifications.
13. Remove three nuts securing strut assembly to strut compressor, the two locking pins at bottom of strut compressor and the strut assembly.

POWER STEERING PUMP REPLACE

ELDORADO & SEVILLE

1. Remove serpentine drive belt.
2. Remove pump pulley using a puller, **Fig. 10.**
3. Disconnect pressure and return lines from pump, noting position for installation.

4. Remove two pump mounting bolts, **Fig. 11,** and the pump.
5. Reverse procedure to install.

REATTA, RIVIERA, TORONADO & TROFEO

1. Remove drive belt.
2. Disconnect pressure and return lines from pump.
3. Remove pump mounting bolts, **Fig. 12,** and the pump.

4. Reverse procedure to install.

POWER STEERING GEAR REPLACE

1. Raise vehicle and support vehicle on frame contact hoist, then remove front wheels.
2. Remove pinch bolt and disconnect intermediate shaft from steering gear.
3. Disconnect tie rods from steering knuckles.
4. Remove power steering line retainer, then disconnect pressure and return lines from steering gear.
5. Remove steering gear mounting bolts, **Figs. 13 and 14,** then withdraw gear through wheel opening.
6. Reverse procedure to install. Tighten tie rod nuts to specifications. After tightening nut as specified, continue tightening nut to align cotter pin holes, then install new cotter pins.

TIGHTENING SPECIFICATIONS

Year	Component	Torque/ft. lbs
1988–91	Adjuster Plug Locknut	50
	Ball Joint To Control Arm	50
	Ball Joint To Knuckle	37
	Brake Reaction Rod To Frame	58
	Caliper Attaching Bolts	63
	Caliper Mounting Bracket	83
	Control Arm Bushing Nuts	103
	Cylinder Line Fittings	15
	Dampener Shaft	55
	Hub & Bearing To Knuckle	70
	Hub To Drive Axle	180
	Inner Tie Rod Housing To Rack	70
	Intermediate Shaft Pinch Bolts	35
	Outer Tie Rod Jam Nut	30
	Pinion Locknut	26
	Pinion Pre-load	1.4
	Power Steering Line Fittings	20
	Stabilizer Bracket To Frame	35
	Stabilizer Link Nut	48
	Strut Mount To Body	18
	Strut To Knuckle	136
	Strut To Strut Top Mount	②
	Tie Rod Nuts	③
	Tie Rod Pinch Bolts	41
	Wheel Lug Nuts	100

② —Tighten old design (flanged) nut to 75 ft. lbs. and new design (non-flanged) nut to 55 ft. lbs.

③ —Tighten to 7.5 ft. lbs., then an additional ⅓ turn.

Wheel Alignment
INDEX

FRONT WHEEL ALIGNMENT

Steering and vibration complaints are not always the result of improper alignment. Another possibility is tire "lead" due to worn or improperly manufactured tires.

"Lead" is the vehicles's deviation from a straight path on a level road without pressure on the steering wheel.

Before making any adjustment affecting wheel alignment, make the following checks to ensure correct alignment readings and alignment adjustments.

1. Check all tires for proper inflation pressures and ensure all tires have approximately equal tread wear.
2. Check hub and bearing assemblies for excessive wear, correcting as necessary.
3. Check ball joints and tie rod ends. If they are excessively loose, correct before making adjustment.

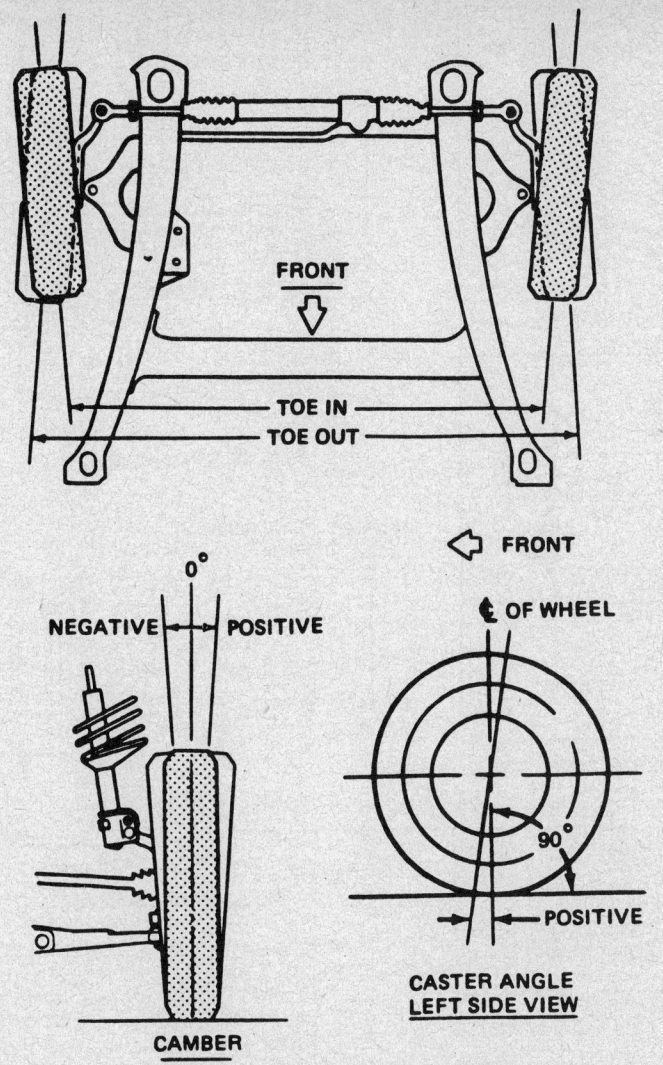

Fig. 1   Front end alignment angles

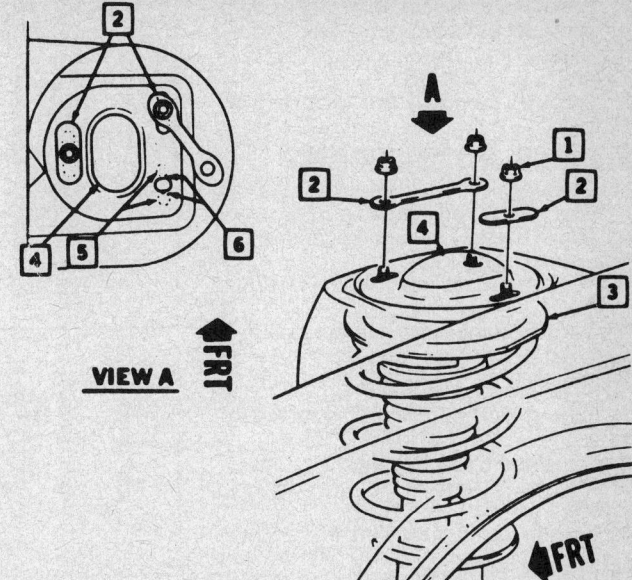

1. NUT 24 N•m (18 LBS. FT.)
2. WASHER
3. STRUT ASSY.
4. COVER
5. DRILL 8.731mm (11/32'') HOLES
6. FILE HERE THEN PAINT WITH PRIMER

Fig. 2   Adjusting front wheel caster

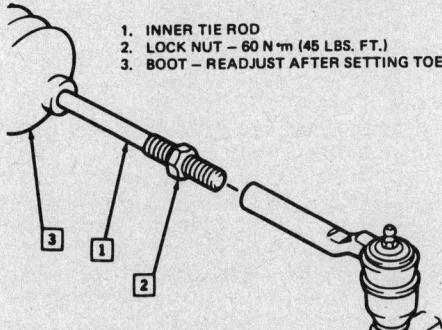

1. INNER TIE ROD
2. LOCK NUT – 60 N•m (45 LBS. FT.)
3. BOOT – READJUST AFTER SETTING TOE

Fig. 4   Adjusting front wheel toe

4. Check runout of wheels and tires.
5. Check vehicle trim height, correcting as necessary before adjusting alignment.
6. Check for proper operation of the Electronic Level Control system.
7. Check strut dampers for proper operation.
8. Check control arms for loose bushings.

9. Check stabilizer bar for loose or missing parts.

Consideration must also be given to excess loads, such as tool boxes or sample cases. If these items are normally carried in the vehicle, they should remain in the vehicle during alignment adjustments. Consideration should be given to condition of equipment being used to adjust alignment. Be sure to follow equipment manufacturer's instructions. Regardless of equipment being used, vehicle must be on level surface, both fore and aft and sideways.

MEASURING FRONT ALIGNMENT ANGLES

Install alignment equipment following equipment manufacturer's instructions. Measure alignment angles, **Fig. 1**, and record the readings. If adjustments are necessary, they must be made in order; caster first, camber second and toe third. Jounce front and rear bumpers three times to normalize suspension prior to measuring angles.

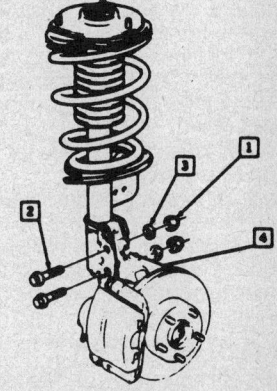

1. NUT 185 N•m (145 LBS. FT.)
2. BOLT
3. WASHER
4. CAMBER ADJUSTMENT BOLT

Fig. 3   Adjusting front wheel camber

CASTER ADJUSTMENT

1. With car supported by its wheels, remove the three top strut mounting nuts and washers, **Fig. 2**.
2. Lift front of car by the body to separate top strut mount from inner wheelhouse. **Do not raise control arms or tires.**
3. Drill two 11/32 inch holes at the front and rear of outboard strut mounting holes. Use a rat-tail file to slot the outboard hole.
4. Paint any bare metal areas with a corrosion protective primer or paint.
5. Reposition strut mount in holes, then lower front of car.

6. Reinstall washers and nuts.
7. Set caster to specifications by moving top of strut forward or rearward as required. 1 mm of movement is equivalent to 0.1° of caster.
8. **Torque** top strut mounting bolts to 18 ft. lbs.

CAMBER ADJUSTMENT

1. Loosen both strut to knuckle bolts just enough to allow movement.
2. Adjust camber by turning camber adjustment bolt, **Fig. 3.**
3. **Torque** strut to knuckle nuts to 136 ft. lbs.
4. **Torque** camber adjustment bolt to 7 ft. lbs.

TOE ADJUSTMENT

1. Loosen locknut on inner tie rods, **Fig. 4.**
2. Adjust toe by turning inner tie rods.
3. Adjust boots so that they are not twisted.
4. **Torque** locknuts to 45 ft. lbs.

REAR WHEEL ALIGNMENT

Rear wheel toe is the only adjustable angle. If camber is not within specifications, inspect for worn or damaged rear suspension components.

Before checking rear trim height or measuring rear alignment angles, the following procedure should be performed to ensure the rear air-adjustable struts are filled with residual pressure only.

1. Place a weight of at least 300 lbs. in vehicle trunk.
2. Turn ignition On, then wait for the Car Is Leveling light to illuminate.
3. Turn ignition Off and remove weight from trunk.
4. Wait at least 30 seconds for ELC system to exhaust.
5. Roll car forward or backward several complete tire rotations to eliminate the effects of tire camber change.
6. Jounce front and rear bumpers 3 times to normalize suspension prior to measuring angles.

TOE ADJUSTMENT

1. Loosen front and rear inside control arm mounting bolts, **Fig. 5.**
2. Insert a screwdriver or pry bar between the inside rear control arm mounting bolt and rear support assembly, then move control arm to set toe to specifications.
3. **Torque** inside front and rear control arm mounting bolt to 66 ft. lbs.

RIDE HEIGHT

Check ride height as follows:
1. Lift center of front bumper up approximately 1½ inches, then gently release and let vehicle settle. Repeat twice.
2. Using your arms, lift center of rear bumper up approximately 1½ inches, then gently release and let vehicle settle. Repeat twice.
3. Measure dimension Z (front ride height) as shown in **Fig. 6** and dimension D (rear ride height) as shown in **Fig. 7.**

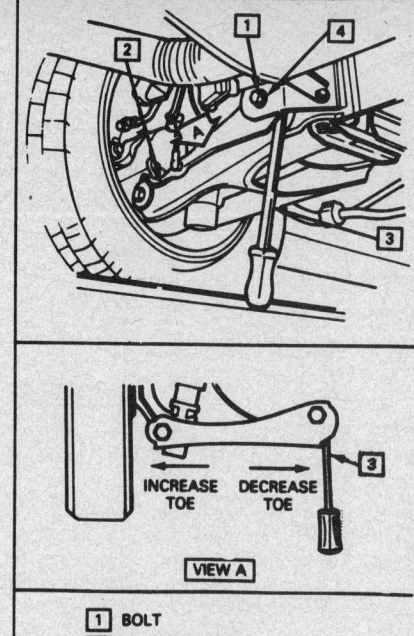

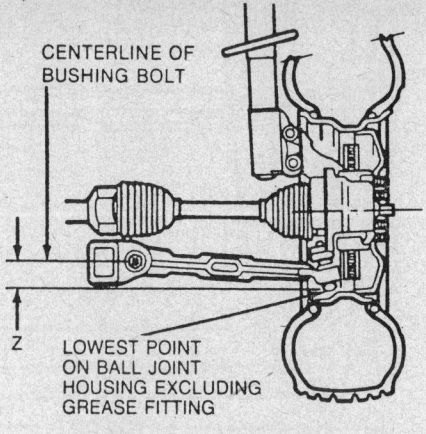

Fig. 6 Front rid

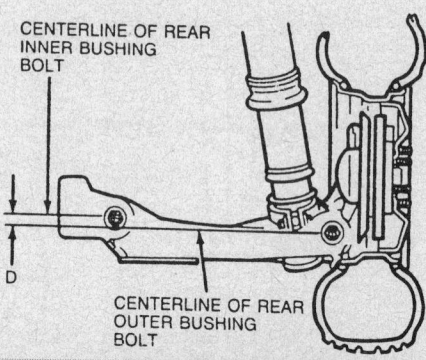

1	BOLT
2	CONTROL ARM
3	SCREW DRIVER OR PRY BAR
4	SLOTTED HOLE

Fig. 5 Adjusting rear toe

Fig. 7 Rear ride height measurement

4. Eldorado and Seville dimension Z measurements are as follows:
   a. 1988-89 Eldorado and Seville should measure 2.09 inches ± .24 inch (53 mm ± 6 mm).
   b. 1990-91 Eldorado should measure 2.05 inches ± .24 inch (52 mm ± 6 mm).
   c. 1990-91 Seville should measure 2.01 inches ± .24 inch (51 mm ± 6 mm).
5. Reatta and Riviera dimension Z measurements are as follows:
   a. 1988 Reatta should measure 1.65 inches ± .24 inch (42 mm ± 6 mm).
   b. 1988 Riviera should measure 2.01 inches ± .24 inch (51 mm ± 6 mm).
   c. 1989 Reatta models should measure 1.70 inches ± .24 inch (43 mm ± 6 mm).
   d. 1989 Riviera models should measure 1.81 inches ± .24 inch (46 mm ± 6 mm).
   e. 1990-91 Reatta should measure 2.17 inches, ± .24 inch (55 mm ± 6 mm).
   f. 1990-91 Riviera should measure 1.85 inches ± .24 inch (47 mm ± 6 mm).
6. Toronado and Trofeo dimension Z measurements are as follows:
   a. 1988-89 models should measure 1.93 inches, with a minimum of 1.69 inches and a maximum of 2.17 inches (49 mm ± 6 mm).
   b. 1990-91 models should measure 1.81 inches, with a minimum of 1.58 inches and a maximum of 2.05 inches (46 mm ± 6 mm).
7. Eldorado and Seville dimension D measurements are as follows:
   a. 1988-89 Eldorado should mea-

sure 1.22 inches ± .28 inch (31 mm ± 7 mm).
   b. 1988-89 Seville models should measure 1.38 inches ± .28 inch (35 mm ± 7 mm).
   c. 1990-91 Eldorado should measure 1.14 inches ± .28 inch (29 mm ± 7 mm).
   d. 1990-91 Seville should measure 1.18 inches ± .28 inch (30 mm ± 7 mm).
8. Reatta and Riviera dimension D measurements are as follows:
   a. 1988 Reatta and Riviera should measure .98 inch ± .28 inch (25 mm ± 7 mm).
   b. 1989 Reatta should measure .98 inch ± .28 inch (25 mm ± 7 mm).
   c. 1989 Riviera should measure 1.18 inches ± .28 inch (30 mm ± 7 mm).
   d. 1990-91 Reatta should measure 1.46 inches, ± .28 inch (37 mm ± 7 mm).
   e. 1990-91 Riviera should measure 1.18 inches, ± .28 inch (30 mm ± 7 mm).
9. Toronado and Trofeo dimension D measurements are as follows:
   a. 1988-89 models should measure .98 inch, with a minimum of .71 inch and a maximum of 1.26 inches (25 mm ± 7 mm).
   b. 1990-91 models should measure .95 inch, with a minimum of .67 inch and a maximum of 1.22 inches (24 mm ± 7 mm).

CHEVROLET CAVALIER, BUICK SKYHAWK, CADILLAC CIMARRON, OLDSMOBILE FIRENZA & PONTIAC SUNBIRD
(J Cars)
INDEX OF SERVICE OPERATIONS

NOTE: Refer To The Rear Of This Manual For Manufacturer's Special Service Tool Suppliers.

INDEX OF SERVICE OPERATIONS—Continued

Specifications

NOTE: All Specifications Given In Inches Unless Otherwise Noted.

GENERAL ENGINE SPECIFICATIONS

Year	Engine Liter/CID ①	VIN Code ②	Fuel System	Bore & Stroke	Compression Ratio	Net H.P. @ RPM ③	Maximum Torque, Ft. Lbs @ RPM	Normal Oil Pressure, Pounds
1988	2.0L/4-121 OHC ⑥	K	EFI	3.39 x 3.39	8.8	96 @ 4800	118 @ 3600	65
	2.0L/4-121 OHC ④ ⑥	M	EFI	3.39 x 3.39	8.0	165 @ 5600	175 @ 4000	—
	2.0L/4-121 OHV ⑤	1	EFI	3.50 x 3.15	9.0	90 @ 5600	108 @ 3200	63-77
	2.8L/V6-173	W	EFI	3.50 x 2.99	8.9	125 @ 4500	160 @ 3600	50-65
1989	2.0L/4-121 OHC ⑥	K	EFI	3.39 x 3.39	8.8	96 @ 4800	118 @ 3600	65
	2.0L/4-121 OHC ④ ⑥	M	EFI	3.39 x 3.39	8.0	165 @ 5600	175 @ 4000	—
	2.0L/4-121 OHV ⑤	1	EFI	3.50 x 3.15	9.0	90 @ 5600	108 @ 3200	63-77
	2.8L/V6-173	W	EFI	3.50 x 2.99	8.9	125 @ 4500	160 @ 3600	50-65
1990	2.0L/4-121 OHC ⑥	K	EFI	3.39 x 3.39	8.8	96 @ 4800	118 @ 3600	65
	2.0L/4-121 OHC ④ ⑥	M	EFI	3.39 x 3.39	8.0	165 @ 5600	175 @ 4000	—
	2.2L/4-134 OHV ⑤	G	EFI	3.50 x 3.46	9.0	95 @ 5200	120 @ 3200	63-77
	3.1L/V6-192	T	EFI	3.50 x 3.31	8.8	140 @ 4500	180 @ 3600	50-65
1991	2.0L/4-121 OHC ⑥	K	EFI	3.39 x 3.39	8.8	96 @ 4800	118 @ 3600	65
	2.2L/4-134 OHV ⑤	G	EFI	3.50 x 3.46	9.0	95 @ 5200	120 @ 3200	63-77
	3.1L/V6-192	T	EFI	3.50 x 3.31	8.8	140 @ 4500	180 @ 3600	50-65

①—CID-cubic inch displacement.
②—The eighth digit denotes engine code.
③—Ratings are net as installed in vehicle.
④—Turbocharged engine.
⑤—Overhead valve engine.
⑥—Overhead cam engine.

TUNE UP SPECIFICATIONS

Year & Engine/ VIN Code ①	Spark Plug Gap	Firing Order Fig. ②	Ignition Timing BTDC Man. Trans.	Auto. Trans.	Mark Fig.	Curb Idle Speed ③ Man. Trans.	Auto Trans.	Fast Idle Speed Man. Trans.	Auto. Trans.	Fuel Pump, Pressure
1988–89										
2.0L/4-121 OHC/K	.060	A	—	—	B	④	④	④	④	9–13 ⑤
2.0L/4-121 Turbo/M	.035	A	—	—	B	④	④	④	④	35–38 ⑥
2.0L/4-121 OHV/1	.035	⑧	⑨	⑨	⑩	④	④	④	④	9–13 ⑦
2.8L/V6-173/W	.045	⑪	⑨	⑨	⑩	④	④	④	④	40.5–47 ⑥
1990										
2.0L/4-121 OHC/K	.045	A	—	—	B	④	④	④	④	9–13 ⑤
2.0L/4-121 Turbo/M	.035	A	—	—	B	④	④	④	④	35–38 ⑥
2.2L/4-134/G	.035	⑧	⑨	⑨	⑩	④	④	④	④	9–13 ⑦
3.1L/V6-192/T	.045	⑪	⑨	⑨	⑩	④	④	④	④	40.5–47 ⑥
1991										
2.0L/4-121 OHC/K	.045	A	—	—	B	④	④	④	④	9–13 ⑤
2.2L/4-134/G	.035	⑧	⑨	⑨	⑩	④	④	④	④	9–13 ⑦
3.1L/V6-192/T	.045	⑪	⑨	⑨	⑩	④	④	④	④	40.5–47 ⑥

Continued

TUNE UP SPECIFICATIONS—Continued

①—The eighth digit of the Vehicle Identification Number (VIN) denotes engine code.

②—Before removing wires from distributor cap, determine location of No. 1 wire in cap, as distributor position may have been altered from that shown at the end of this chart.

③—Not adjustable.

④—Idle speeds are controlled by the idle air control (IAC) valve.

⑤—To relieve fuel pressure, remove fuel pump fuse from fuse panel, then start engine & allow to run until fuel supply is deleted. When engine has stopped, engage starter for 3 seconds to dissipate remaining fuel system pressure. Remove air cleaner & plug Thermac port on throttle body unit. Install a suitable fuel pressure gauge on throttle body side of fuel filter at rear of vehicle near fuel tank. Start engine & note fuel pressure reading. Before removing fuel gauge, relieve fuel system pressure.

⑥—With shop towel wrapped around fuel pressure valve to prevent fuel spillage, connect a suitable fuel pressure gauge to fuel pressure valve. Check fuel pressure with ignition switch in the On position, engine not running.

⑦—Wrap shop towel around fuel hose to steel line connection in engine compartment to prevent fuel spillage. Disconnect fuel hose from steel line and connect a suitable fuel gauge between hose & line. Ensure gauge connections are tight, then start engine & check fuel pressure.

⑧—Cylinder numbering from front of engine to rear of engine, 1, 2, 3, 4. Firing order 1-3-4-2. Refer to Fig. C for spark plug wire connections at coil unit.

⑨—No adjustment.

⑩—Equipped with crankshaft sensor.

⑪—Cylinder numbering left to right as viewed from front of vehicle, front bank, 2, 4, 6; rear bank, 1, 3, 5. Firing order 1-2-3-4-5-6. Refer to Fig. D for spark plug wire connections at coil unit.

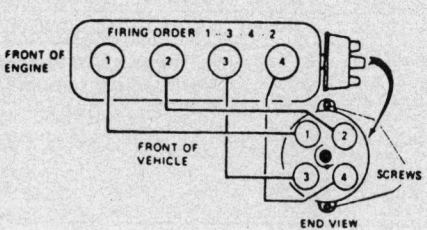

Fig. A

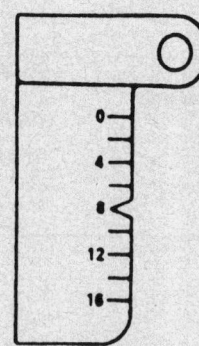

Fig. B

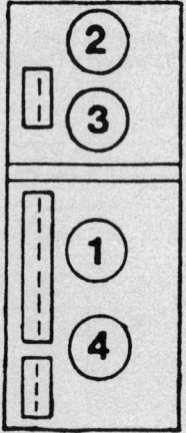

Fig. C

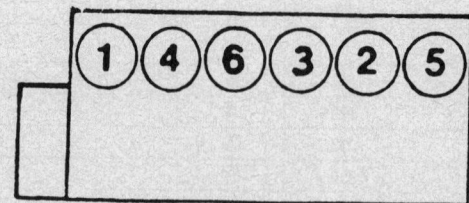

Fig. D

ALTERNATOR SPECIFICATIONS

Year	Model	Rated Hot Output Amps.
1988	1101144 ①	85
	1101145 ①	100
	1101321 ②	74
	1105694 ①	100
	1105697 ②	74
	1105698 ①	85
	1105701 ①	85
1989	1101145 ①	100
	1101319 ②	74
	1101321 ②	74
	1105694 ①	100
	1105697 ②	74
	1105701 ①	85
1990	1101145 ①	100
	1101319 ②	74
	1101321 ②	74
	1102614 ②	80
	1102615 ②	80
	1105694 ①	100
1991	1101319 ②	74
	1102614 ②	80
	1102615 ②	80
	1105694 ①	100

① —CS130.
② —CS121.

STARTING MOTOR APPLICATIONS

Year	Engine/VIN	Starter Ident. No.
1988–89	2.0L/4-121/K, M ②	10455021
	2.0L/4-121/1 ①	10455020
	2.8L/V6-173/W	10455019
1990	2.0L/4-121/K, M ②	10455021
	2.2L/4-134/G ①	10455010
	3.1L/V6-192/T	10455025
1991	2.0L/4-121/K ②	10455021
	2.2L/4-134/G ①	10455010
	3.1L/V6-192/T	10455025

① —Overhead valve engine.
② —Overhead cam engine.

WHEEL ALIGNMENT SPECIFICATIONS

| Year | Model | Caster Angle, Degrees | | Camber Angle, Degrees | | | | Toe-Out Inch |
| | | Limits | Desired | Limits | | Desired | | |
				Left	Right	Left	Right	
1988	Except Cavalier Z24	−.8 to +4.2	+1.7	−.2 to +1.8	−.2 to +1.8	+.8	+.8	①
	Cavalier Z24	+.7 to +2.7	+1.7	−1 to +1	−1 to +1.	0	0	①
1989–90	Except Cavalier Z24	+.7 to +2.7	+1.7	+.1 to +1.5	+.1 to +1.5	+.8	+.8	①
	Cavalier Z24	+.7 to +2.7	+1.7	−1 to +1	−1 to +1.	0	0	①
1991	All	+.7 to +2.7	+1.7	−.7 to +.7	−.7 to +.7	0	0	①

①—Total toe 0 degrees.

COOLING SYSTEM & CAPACITY DATA

| Year | Model or Engine/VIN | Cooling Capacity, Qts. | | Radiator Cap Relief Pressure, Lbs. | Thermo. Opening Temp., °F | Fuel Tank, Gals. | Engine Oil Refill, Qts. | Transaxle Oil | |
		Less A/C	With A/C					Manual Transaxle, Pts.	Auto. Transaxle, Qts. ①
1988–89	Cavalier 2.0L/4-121/1	9.75	9.75	15	195	13.6	4②	④	③
	Cavalier 2.8L/V6-173/W	11	11	15	195	13.6	4②	④	③
	Cimarron 2.8L/V6-173/W	11	11	15	195	13.6	4②	④	③
	Firenza 2.0L/4-121/K	8.5	8.5	15	195	13.6	4②	④	③
	Firenza 2.0L/4-121/1	9.75	9.75	15	195	13.6	4②	④	③
	Skyhawk 2.0L/4-121/K	8.5	8.5	15	195	13.6	4②	④	③
	Skyhawk 2.0L/4-121/1	9.7	9.7	15	195	13.6	4②	④	③
	Sunbird 2.0L/4-121/K, M	8.5	8.5	15	195	13.6	4②	④	③
1990	Cavalier 2.2L/4-134/G	8.5	8.5	15	195	13.6	4②	④	③
	Cavalier 3.1L/V6-192/T	11	11	15	195	13.6	4②	④	③
	Sunbird 2.0L/4-121/K, M	8.5	8.5	15	195	13.6	4②	④	③
1991	Cavalier 2.2L/4-134/G	11.7	11.7	15	195	13.6	4②	④	③
	Cavalier 3.1L/V6-192/T	14.2	14.2	15	195	13.6	4②	④	③
	Sunbird 2.0L/4-121/K	11.7	11.7	15	195	13.6	4②	④	③
	Sunbird 3.1L/V6-192/T	14.2	14.2	15	195	13.6	4②	④	③

①—Approximate, make final check with dipstick.
②—When changing engine oil filter additional oil may be required.
③—Oil pan only, 4 qts. After overhaul, less torque converter drain, 6 qts.; with torque converter drain, 9 qts.
④—Isuzu 5 spd., 5.4 pts.; Muncie 5 spd., 4 pts.

Electrical
INDEX

FUSE PANEL & FLASHER LOCATION

The fuse panel is located on the left side of the instrument panel. To gain access to the panel, pivot access door downward.

The hazard flasher is located under dash panel, left side of steering column.

The turn signal flasher is located under dash panel, right side of steering column.

STARTER
REPLACE
2.0L/4-121 & 2.2L/4-134 OVERHEAD VALVE ENGINES

1. Disconnect battery ground cable.
2. Raise and support vehicle, then remove remove bolts attaching starter motor and bracket to engine.
3. Lower starter motor and disconnect leads at solenoid.
4. Remove starter motor from vehicle. Note position of shims for installation, if used.
5. Reverse procedure to install.

2.0L/4-121 OVERHEAD CAM ENGINE EXCEPT TURBOCHARGED
Manual Transaxle

1. Disconnect battery ground cable.
2. Remove wiring strap from upper starter mounting bolt.
3. Disconnect shifter cables at selector lever.

4. Remove upper and lower transaxle control lever cable bracket and cables.
5. Remove drive axle support brace.
6. Disconnect wiring from starter motor, then remove starter motor mounting bolts and starter motor.
7. Reverse procedure to install.

Automatic Transaxle

1. Disconnect battery ground cable.
2. Remove blower motor as described under "Blower Motor, Replace."
3. Disconnect wiring from starter motor.
4. Remove starter motor bracket, then disconnect wiring loom from upper starter mounting bolt and remove bolt.
5. **On 1988-89 models,** remove transaxle strut.
6. **On all models,** remove starter motor lower mounting bolt, then remove starter motor through blower motor opening.
7. Reverse procedure to install.

2.0L/4-121 OVERHEAD CAM TURBOCHARGED ENGINE

1. Disconnect battery ground cable.
2. Remove intake manifold support brace.
3. Disconnect wire harness clamp at motor mount, then the upper starter to engine block attaching bolt.
4. Raise and support vehicle.
5. **On models equipped with automatic transaxle,** remove transaxle rear strut.
6. **On all models,** remove fuel line to support bracket attaching bolt, then

loosen fuel lines 1/2 turn to gain access to starter. **Place shop towel over fuel line and fitting when disconnecting.**
7. Remove rear starter brace attaching bolts, then the rear starter brace.
8. Remove lower starter to engine block attaching bolt.
9. Disconnect starter motor electrical connectors, then remove starter motor.
10. Reverse procedure to install.

2.8L/V6-173 & 3.1L/V6-192 ENGINES

1. Disconnect battery ground cable, then raise and support vehicle.
2. Remove starter motor to engine attaching bolts.
3. Disconnect starter electrical connectors, then lower starter out of vehicle.
4. Note installation position of starter shim, if equipped.
5. Reverse procedure to install.

DISTRIBUTOR
REPLACE
2.0L/4-121 OVERHEAD CAM ENGINES

1. Disconnect battery ground cable.
2. Remove distributor cap and spark plug wires from distributor.
3. Disconnect coil and EST electrical connectors.
4. Remove distributor to cam carrier nuts, then mark distributor tang drive and camshaft for installation.
5. Remove distributor assembly.
6. Reverse procedure to install. **Torque**

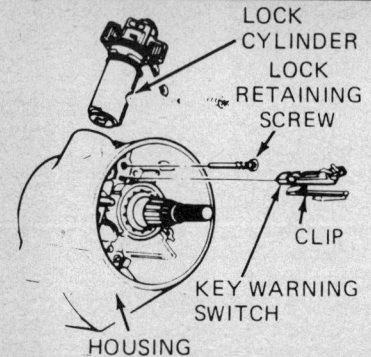

Fig. 1   Lock cylinder removal

distributor to cam carrier nuts to 13 ft. lbs.

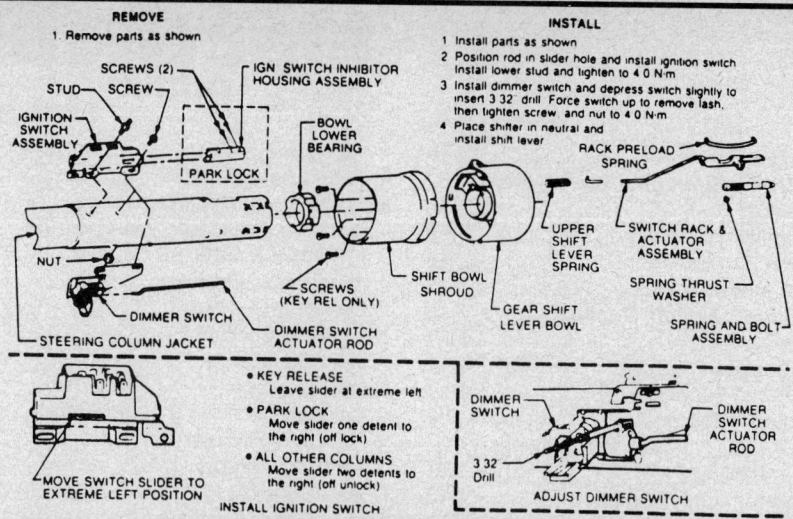

Fig. 2   Ignition & dimmer switch removal. Models less tilt column

IGNITION LOCK
REPLACE

1. Remove steering wheel as outlined under "Steering Wheel, Replace" procedure.
2. Remove turn signal switch as outlined under "Turn Signal Switch, Replace" procedure.
3. Remove buzzer switch.
4. Turn lock cylinder to "Run" position, then remove the lock cylinder retaining screw and lock cylinder, **Fig. 1.**
5. To install, rotate lock cylinder to stop while holding housing. Align cylinder key with keyway in housing, then push cylinder into housing until fully seated.
6. Install lock cylinder retaining screw.
7. Install buzzer switch, turn signal switch and steering wheel.

IGNITION & DIMMER SWITCHES
REPLACE
EXCEPT 1991 CAVALIER

1. Remove steering wheel as outlined under "Steering Wheel, Replace" procedure, then the turn signal switch and lock cylinder as previously described.
2. Refer to **Figs. 2 and 3** to remove ignition and dimmer switches.
3. When installing dimmer switch, depress switch slightly and install a 3/32 drill into switch. Force switch upward to remove lash and tighten retaining screw.

1991 CAVALIER

1. Remove steering wheel as outlined under "Steering Wheel, Replace" procedure.
2. Remove turn signal switch as outlined under "Turn Signal Switch, Replace" procedure.
3. Remove windshield wiper switch as outlined under "Windshield Wiper Switch, Replace" procedure.
4. Remove ignition switch to ignition switch housing attaching screws.
5. Depress ignition switch locking tab, then disconnect switch electrical connectors.
6. Reverse procedure to install, noting the following:
   a. Ensure lock cylinder shaft aligns with slotted opening on ignition switch.

b. **Torque** ignition switch attaching screws to 21 inch lbs.

WINDSHIELD WIPER SWITCH
REPLACE
EXCEPT 1991 CAVALIER

1. Remove turn signal switch as outlined under "Turn Signal Switch, Replace" procedure.
2. Refer to **Figs. 4 and 5** for wiper switch replacement.

1991 CAVALIER

1. Remove steering wheel as outlined under "Steering Wheel, Replace" procedure.
2. Remove turn signal switch as outlined under "Turn Signal Switch, Replace" procedure.
3. Remove windshield wiper switch attaching screws.
4. Depress switch locking tab, then disconnect switch electrical connectors.
5. Reverse procedure to install. **Torque** windshield wiper switch attaching screws to 49 inch lbs.

STOP LIGHT SWITCH
ADJUST

Insert stop lamp switch in retainer until switch body seats on retainer. Pull brake pedal upward against internal pedal stop. Switch will be moved in retainer providing proper adjustment.

Proper switch adjustment is achieved when no audible clicks are heard when the pedal is pulled upward and the brake lights do not remain on without brake aplication.

BACK-UP LIGHT/NEUTRAL START SWITCH
REPLACE

On vehicles equipped with automatic transmission, the neutral start and back-up light switches are combined into one unit and must be replaced as an assembly.

MANUAL TRANSMISSION

For neutral start switch refer to "Clutch Start Switch, Replace." Back-up light switch replacement is as follows:

1. Disconnect battery ground cable.
2. Disconnect back-up lamp electrical connector.
3. Unscrew back-up light switch assembly from transaxle assembly.
4. Reverse procedure to install, noting the following:
   a. Apply pipe sealant GM P/N 1052080 or equivalent to threaded switch.
   b. **On 1988-89 models,** torque back-up lamp switch to 84 inch lbs.
   c. **On 1990-91 models,** torque back-up lamp switch to 24 ft. lbs.

AUTOMATIC TRANSMISSION

1. Disconnect battery ground cable.
2. **On 1988 Cimarron, Firenza and Sunbird and 1988-89 Skyhawk and 1988-90 Cavalier models,** remove console assembly as follows:
   a. Apply parking brake and block wheels, then place gear shift lever in Neutral position.
   b. Remove front ashtray, then remove two console attaching screws through ashtray opening.
   c. Carefully pry button from center of shift lever knob, then remove snap ring retaining knob.
   d. Pull front of console trim cover upward, then lift trim cover from console and disconnect wire connector.
   e. Remove three screws attaching front of console to mounting bracket.
   f. Remove rear ashtray, then remove screw attaching console to rear support.
   g. Remove console assembly. **On models equipped with arm rest, it may be necessary to remove arm rest assembly to provide clearance for console removal.**
3. **On 1989-91 Sunbird models,** remove console assembly as follows:

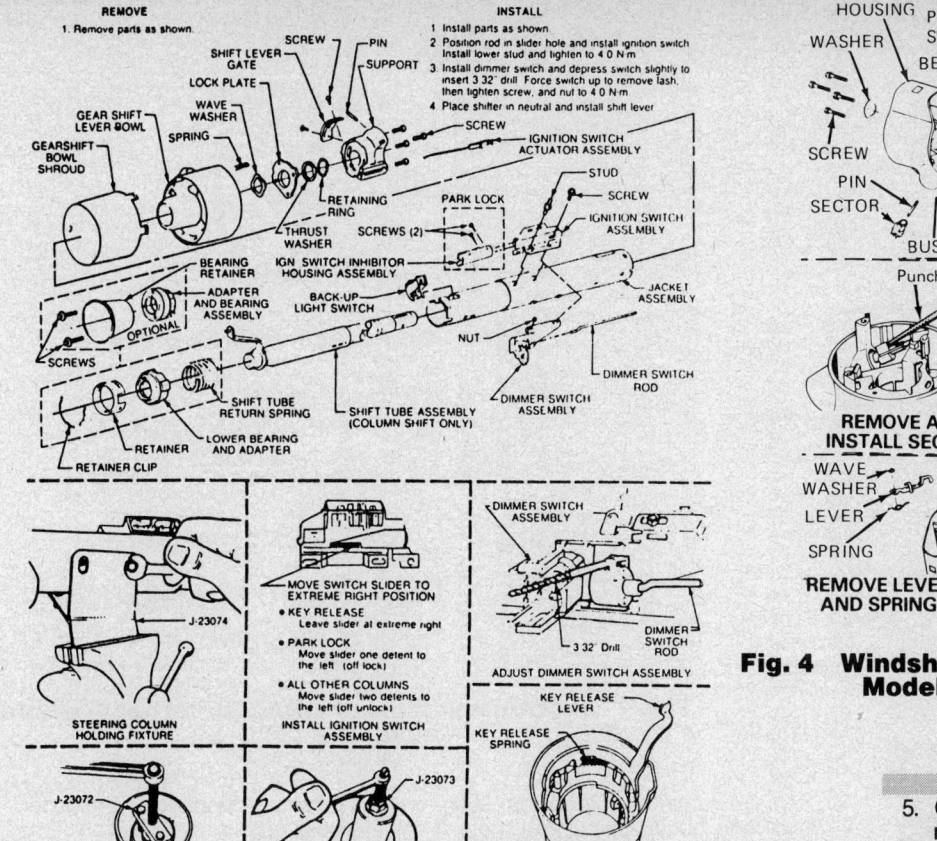

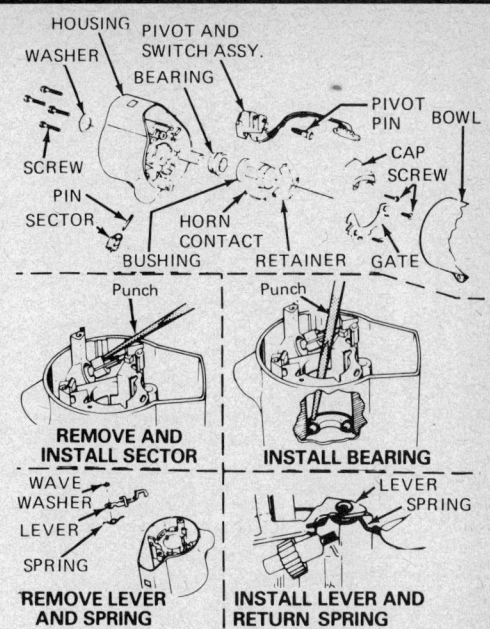

Fig. 4   Windshield wiper switch removal. Models less tilt column

Fig. 3   Ignition & dimmer switch removal. Models with tilt column

a. Position gear selector in Neutral and block wheels. **Do not apply parking brake.**

b. Carefully pry accessory trim panel, right and left side panels outward from console assembly.

c. Remove console to instrument panel attaching nuts.

d. Remove console assembly to console upper bracket attaching screws.

e. Disconnect tape and disc player electrical connectors, then remove upper console bracket.

f. Remove shift lever knob to shift lever attaching setscrew or retainer, then pry shift lever trim plate upward.

g. Remove rear ashtray to console rear trim plate attaching screws, then remove rear ashtray.

h. Remove console rear trim plate to console rear bracket attaching screw.

i. **On models equipped with armrest,** remove armrest inner compartment attaching screw, then remove armrest to console rear bracket attaching screws, then remove armrest assembly.

j. **On all models,** remove parking brake assembly and console from console mounting brackets.

4. **On 1991 Cavalier models,** remove console assembly as follows:

a. Carefully pry accessory trim panel outward.

b. Open ashtray, then remove attaching screw.

c. Remove shift lever knob to shift lever attaching retainer.

d. Disconnect cigar lighter electrical connector, then remove shifter trim plate.

e. Remove upper and lower A/C-Heater control attaching screws.

f. Disconnect radio electrical connector and antenna lead, then remove radio assembly.

g. Disconnect A/C-Heater control electrical connectors and vacuum harness, then remove bowden cable to A/C-Heater control attaching screw, then remove A/C-Heater control assembly.

h. Remove console to instrument panel attaching screws.

i. Remove console rear storage compartment attaching screws.

j. Disconnect remaining console electrical connectors, then remove console assembly.

k. Remove console extension to front console bracket and shift control bracket attaching screws, then re-move console extension.

5. **On all models,** disconnect wire connector from Neutral Safety/Back-up light switch.

6. Remove screws attaching switch to shifter lever, then remove switch.

7. If the same switch is to be reinstalled, proceed as follows:

a. Place shift lever in Neutral position.

b. Position to shift lever and loosely install attaching screws.

c. Rotate switch on shifter to align adjustment hole with carrier tang, then insert a 3/32 inch maximum diameter pin into hole to a depth of 9/64 inch.

d. **On models, except 1991 Cavalier, torque** switch attaching screws to 22 ft. lbs., then remove gauge pin. On 1991 Cavalier models, **torque** switch attaching screw to 18 ft. lbs., then remove gauge pin.

8. If a new replacement switch is to be installed, proceed as follows:

a. Position shift lever in the Neutral position.

b. Align shift shaft flats to switch flats.

c. On all models except 1991 Cavalier, torque switch attaching bolts to 22 ft. lbs. On 1991 Cavalier models, **torque** switch attaching bolts to 18 ft.lbs. If mounting bolts do not align with mounting holes ensure shift shaft is in Neutral position. **Do not rotate switch.**

d. Ensure engine will only start in Park or Neutral.

e. If engine will start in any other position place shift lever in Neutral position.

f. Position switch to shift lever and loosen switch attaching screws.

g. Rotate switch on shifter assembly

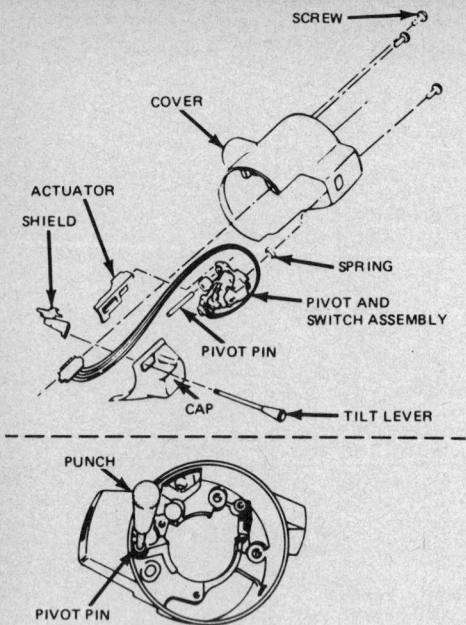

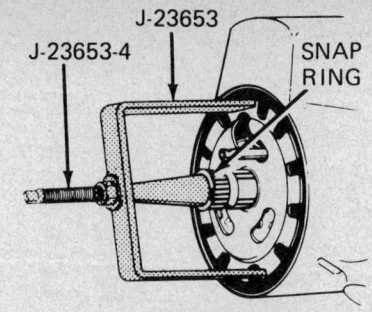

Fig. 6 Compressing lock plate

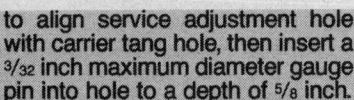

Fig. 5 Windshield wiper switch removal. Models with tilt column

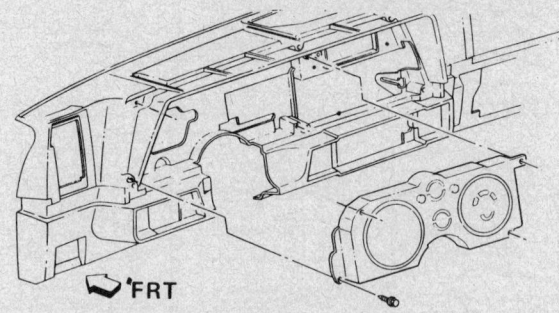

Fig. 7 Instrument cluster. 1988 Cimarron & Sunbird Cavalier & 1988–90

to align service adjustment hole with carrier tang hole, then insert a $3/32$ inch maximum diameter gauge pin into hole to a depth of $5/8$ inch.

h. Torque switch attaching screws to previous specified torque, then remove gauge pin.

9. Install console and connect battery ground cable.
10. Check to ensure that vehicle will not start in any shift lever position except Neutral and Park.

CLUTCH START SWITCH
REPLACE

1. Disconnect clutch switch electrical connector.
2. Remove clutch bracket and switch attaching nuts, then remove switch.
3. Reverse procedure to install. **Torque** switch attaching nuts to 53 inch lbs.

TURN SIGNAL SWITCH
REPLACE

EXCEPT 1991 CAVALIER

1. Disconnect battery ground cable.
2. Remove steering wheel as outlined under "Steering Wheel, Replace" procedure.
3. Using a suitable screwdriver, pry cover from housing.
4. Using lock plate compressing tool J-23653-4, compress lock plate and pry snap ring from groove on steering shaft, **Fig. 6.** Slowly release compressing tool, then remove tool and lock plate from shaft.
5. Slide canceling cam and bearing preload spring from steering shaft.
6. Remove turn signal (multi-function) lever.

7. Remove hazard warning knob retaining screw, button, spring and knob.
8. Remove actuator arm screw and actuator arm.
9. Remove switch retaining screws and pull switch upward from column, guiding wire harness through column.
10. Reverse procedure to install.

1991 CAVALIER

1. Disconnect battery ground cable.
2. Remove steering wheel, refer to "Steering Wheel, Replace" for procedure.
3. Remove lower steering column cover upper and lower attaching bolts, then remove lower steering column cover.
4. Separate rose bud fastener, integral to wiring harness, from jacket assembly.
5. Remove turn signal switch attaching screws, the depress locking tab and remove turn signal switch electrical connectors.
6. Reverse procedure to install. **Torque** turn signal switch attaching screws to 48 inch lbs.

STEERING WHEEL
REPLACE

1. Disconnect battery ground cable.
2. **On 1988 Cavalier and Sunbird models,** remove steering wheel center cap.
3. **On 1988 Firenza and Cimarron and 1989–91 Cavalier and Sunbird models,** remove steering wheel center pad attaching screws.
4. Disconnect horn electrical connector, then remove steering wheel center pad.
5. **On all models,** remove steering wheel retaining nut and retainer.

6. Remove steering dampener, if equipped.
7. Scribe alignment marks on steering wheel and shaft to aid installation.
8. Using tool J-1859-03 or BT-61-9 or equivalent, remove steering wheel from shaft.
9. Reverse procedure to install. **Torque** steering wheel attaching nut to 30 ft. lbs.

INSTRUMENT CLUSTER
REPLACE

CIMARRON (STANDARD CLUSTER) & 1988 SUNBIRD & 1988–90 CAVALIER

1. Disconnect battery ground cable.
2. Remove six screws attaching instrument panel trim plate to instrument panel.
3. Pull top of trim plate outward and remove trim plate from instrument panel.
4. Remove four screws securing instrument cluster to instrument panel, **Fig. 7.**
5. Remove screws attaching steering column cover to instrument panel, then the lower column cover.
6. Remove two steering column retaining bolts and lower steering column to floor.
7. Pull instrument cluster out slightly and disconnect speedometer cable.
8. **On automatic transmission equipped vehicles,** disconnect vehicle speed sensor (VSS) connector from rear of cluster.

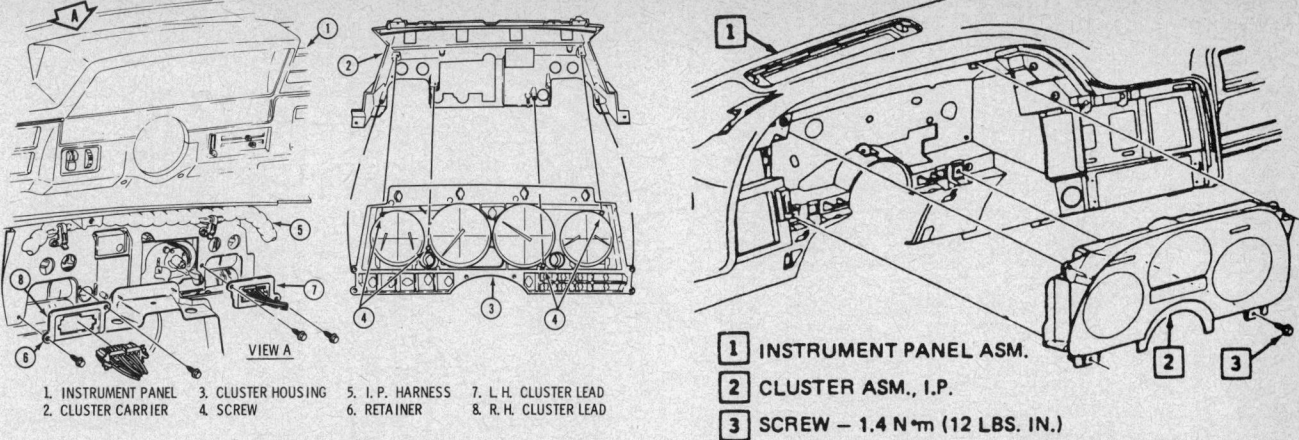

1. INSTRUMENT PANEL   3. CLUSTER HOUSING   5. I. P. HARNESS   7. L. H. CLUSTER LEAD
2. CLUSTER CARRIER   4. SCREW   6. RETAINER   8. R. H. CLUSTER LEAD

Fig. 8 Instrument cluster. Firenza & Skyhawk

1 INSTRUMENT PANEL ASM.
2 CLUSTER ASM., I.P.
3 SCREW — 1.4 N·m (12 LBS. IN.)

Fig. 9 Instrument cluster. 1989–91 Sunbird

9. **On all models,** remove cluster and disconnect instrument panel harness connector from printed circuit located at rear of cluster.
10. Reverse procedure to install. **Torque** instrument cluster attaching bolt to 12 inch lbs.

CIMARRON W/ELECTRONIC CLUSTER

1. Disconnect battery ground cable.
2. Remove six screws attaching instrument cluster trim panel to instrument panel.
3. Remove three screws attaching instrument cluster to instrument panel carrier.
4. Pull cluster slightly outward, then tilt cluster to clear steering column.
5. Disconnect electrical connectors from instrument cluster, then remove cluster.
6. Reverse procedure to install.

FIRENZA & SKYHAWK

1. Disconnect battery ground cable.
2. Remove six screws attaching steering column trim cover to instrument panel and two screws attaching trim cover to left hand instrument panel trim cover, then remove trim cover.
3. Remove screw attaching right end of left hand trim cover to instrument panel, then pull trim cover rearward to disengage retaining clips and remove cover.
4. Remove screw attaching left end of right hand trim cover to instrument panel, then remove two screws from under center trim cover and four screws from front of glove compartment. Pull right hand trim cover rearward to disengage retaining clips, then disconnect wire connectors and remove trim cover.
5. Remove seven screws attaching cluster trim cover to instrument cluster pad, then remove trim cover.
6. Remove five screws attaching bezel and lens to instrument cluster carrier,

then remove bezel and lens.
7. Loosen two upper steering column mounting bolts, then lower steering column slightly to provide clearance for cluster removal.
8. Remove four screws attaching cluster housing to cluster carrier, then pull housing slightly outward and disconnect speedometer cable and remove cluster housing, **Fig. 8.**
9. Reverse procedure to install.

1989–91 SUNBIRD

1. Disconnect battery ground cable.
2. Remove four screws attaching instrument cluster trim plate to instrument panel, then pull trim plate outward to remove.
3. Remove four screws attaching instrument cluster to instrument panel, **Fig. 9.**
4. Remove steering column cover, then remove instrument cluster from instrument panel.
5. Reverse procedure to install. **Torque** instrument cluster attaching bolts to 12 inch lbs.

1991 CAVALIER

1. Disconnect battery ground cable.
2. Remove steering column opening filler attaching screws, then remove steering opening filler.
3. Pull down slightly on steering column cover to remove bottom cluster extension attaching screws, then remove cluster extension.
4. Disconnect instrument panel dimmer and interior lamp control switches electrical connectors.
5. Remove instrument cluster top attaching screws, **Fig. 10.**
6. Pull instrument cluster rearward to remove.
7. Reverse procedure to install. **Torque** instrument cluster attaching bolts to 19 inch lbs.

HEADLIGHT SWITCH REPLACE

CIMARRON & 1988 SUNBIRD & 1988–90 CAVALIER, EXCEPT RS & Z24

1. Disconnect battery ground cable.
2. Remove headlight switch knob by pulling knob to full "On" position, depressing retaining clip behind knob and pulling knob from shaft.
3. Gently pry left hand side trim plate out of instrument panel.
4. Remove switch retaining nut, rotate and tilt switch forward and pull switch from instrument panel.
5. Disconnect wiring connector and remove switch.
6. Reverse procedure to install.

1988–90 CAVALIER RS & Z24

1. Disconnect battery ground cable.
2. Carefully pry left pad trim plate rearward.
3. Remove headlight switch to trim plate attaching screws, then remove switch.
4. Reverse procedure to install.

1991 CAVALIER

The headlamp switch is part of the turn signal lever assembly and is not serviceable. The headlamp switch, turn signal lever and cruise control switch must be replaced as an assembly.

FIRENZA & SKYHAWK

1. Disconnect battery ground cable.
2. Remove six screws attaching steering column lower cover to instrument panel, then remove lower cover.
3. Remove one screw attaching right end of left hand trim cover to instrument panel, then pull cover rearward to detach retaining clips.
4. Remove four screws attaching headlamp switch to instrument panel,

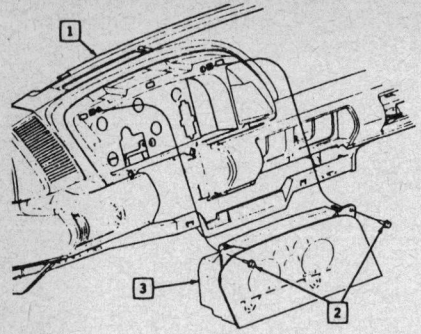

1 INSTRUMENT PANEL
2 SCREW - 2 N.m (19 LBS. IN.)
3 I.P. CLUSTER ASM.

Fig. 10   Instrument cluster. 1991 Cavalier

then pull switch rearward and disconnect wire connector.
5. Reverse procedure to install.

1989–91 SUNBIRD

1. Disconnect battery ground cable.
2. Remove left hand sound insulator.
3. Remove two screws attaching left hand trim panel, then remove trim panel by gently prying from instrument panel.
4. Remove screw attaching headlamp switch to housing, then disconnect electrical connector and remove switch, **Fig. 11**.
5. Reverse procedure to install.

RADIO
REPLACE

CAVALIER, CIMARRON & 1988 SUNBIRD

1. Disconnect battery ground cable.
2. Loosen six instrument panel trim plate to instrument panel attaching screws and remove trim plate.
3. Remove two radio bracket to instrument panel attaching screws.
4. Pull radio forward and disconnect wiring and antenna connections. Remove radio from instrument panel.
5. Reverse procedures to install.

FIRENZA & SKYHAWK

1. Disconnect battery ground cable.
2. Remove six screws attaching steering column trim cover to instrument panel, then lower trim cover.
3. Remove screw attaching left end of right hand trim cover to instrument panel.
4. Remove six screws from under center trim cover and four screws from front of glove compartment, then remove right hand top trim cover attaching screw, then pull trim cover rearward to disengage retaining clips and disconnect wire connectors.

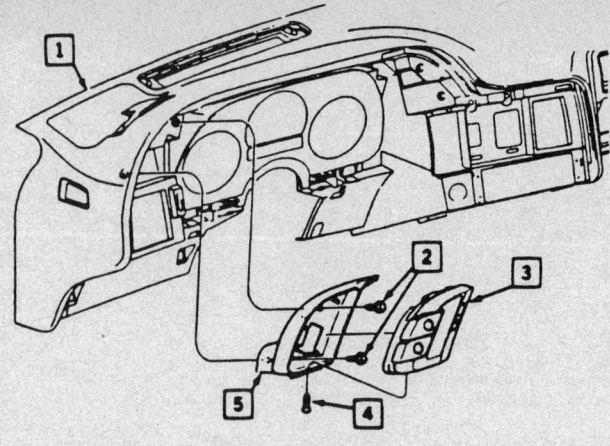

1 INSTRUMENT PANEL ASM.
2 BOLT/SCREW – FULLY DRIVEN, SEATED AND NOT STRIPPED
3 HEADLAMP/FOGLAMP SWITCH ASM.
4 SCREW – FULLY DRIVEN, SEATED AND NOT STRIPPED
5 HEADLAMP SWITCH PANEL HOUSING

Fig. 11   Headlamp/fog lamp switch replacement. 1989–91 Sunbird

5. Remove four screws attaching upper and lower radio mounting brackets to instrument panel.
6. Pull radio out just enough to disconnect wire connector and antenna lead, then remove radio.
7. Reverse procedure to install.

1989–91 SUNBIRD
Radio Control Assembly

1. Disconnect battery ground cable.
2. Remove steering column lower cover.
3. Remove cigar lighter.
4. Remove two screws and one nut, then gently pry right hand trim panel from instrument panel.
5. Remove two screws located at top of radio control.
6. Pull radio control rearward, then disconnect electrical connector and remove from vehicle.
7. Reverse procedure to install.

Radio Receiver

1. Disconnect battery ground cable.
2. Remove two screws and one nut attaching right hand trim panel to instrument panel. Gently pry trim panel from instrument panel to remove.
3. Remove nut attaching radio receiver to duct, then disconnect electrical connector and remove radio receiver.
4. Reverse procedure to install.

WINDSHIELD WIPER MOTOR
REPLACE

1. Disconnect battery ground cable.
2. Remove wiper arms from transmission spindle shafts.
3. Remove shroud top vent grille panel and screen.
4. Loosen, but do not remove, transmission drive link to motor crank arm attaching nuts, then pull drive link out of motor crank arm.
5. Disconnect wiper motor electrical connections and remove wiper motor attaching bolts.
6. Rotate wiper motor upward and outward, and remove from vehicle.
7. Reverse procedure to install. **Torque** wiper motor attaching bolts to 48 inch lbs.

WINDSHIELD WIPER TRANSMISSION ASSEMBLY
REPLACE

1. Remove wiper arms from transmission spindle shafts.
2. Remove shroud top vent grille panel and screen.
3. Loosen, but do not remove, transmission drive link to motor crank arm attaching nuts then pull drive link from motor crank arm.
4. Remove transmission to cowl panel attaching screws and the transmission assembly.

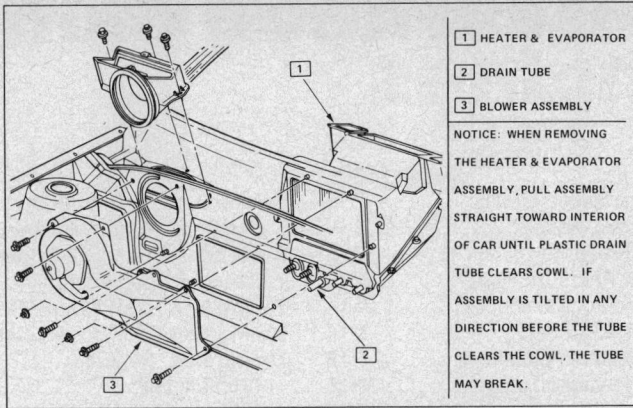

1. HEATER & EVAPORATOR
2. DRAIN TUBE
3. BLOWER ASSEMBLY

NOTICE: WHEN REMOVING THE HEATER & EVAPORATOR ASSEMBLY, PULL ASSEMBLY STRAIGHT TOWARD INTERIOR OF CAR UNTIL PLASTIC DRAIN TUBE CLEARS COWL. IF ASSEMBLY IS TILTED IN ANY DIRECTION BEFORE THE TUBE CLEARS THE COWL, THE TUBE MAY BREAK.

Fig. 12   Heater core & blower motor

5. Reverse procedure to install. **Torque wiper transmission attaching screws and nuts to 64 inch lbs.**

BLOWER MOTOR
REPLACE

1. Disconnect battery ground cable.
2. Disconnect blower motor electrical connections.
3. **On 1988-89 models,** remove plastic water shield from right side of cowl.
4. **On 1990-91 3.1L/V6-192 engines,** remove tower to tower brace assembly.
5. Remove blower motor retaining screws and blower motor.
6. Reverse procedure to install.

HEATER CORE
REPLACE

1. Disconnect battery ground cable and drain cooling system.
2. Raise and support vehicle.
3. Remove rear lateral transaxle strut and mount, if equipped.
4. Disconnect heater case drain tube, then disconnect heater core heater hoses.
5. Lower vehicle and remove right and left hush panels, steering column trim cover and glove compartment.
6. Remove heater duct retaining screw and heater duct.
7. Remove heater core cover attaching screws, then gently pull cover rearward and out of vehicle, **Fig. 12. When removing heater core assembly, pull assembly straight toward interior of vehicle until plastic drain tube clears cowl. If assembly is tilted in any direction before tube clears cowl, the drain tube may break.**
8. Remove heater core retaining clamps and heater core from case.
9. Reverse procedure to install.

EVAPORATOR CORE
REPLACE

1. Disconnect battery ground cable.
2. Discharge air conditioning system, then drain cooling system.
3. Raise and support vehicle.
4. Remove rear lateral transaxle strut and mount, if equipped.
5. Disconnect heater core heater hoses.
6. Disconnect evaporator lines at evaporator core.
7. Disconnect heater and evaporator assembly drain tube.
8. Lower vehicle and remove right and left hush panels, steering column trim cover and glove compartment.
9. Remove heater duct retaining screw and heater duct.
10. Remove heater core cover attaching screws, then gently pull cover rearward and out of vehicle, **Fig. 12. When removing heater core assembly, pull assembly straight toward interior of vehicle until plastic drain tube clears cowl. If assembly is tilted in any direction before tube clears cowl, the drain tube may break.**
11. Remove heater core retaining clamps and heater core from case.
12. Remove defroster vacuum actuator to module case attaching screw.
13. Remove evaporator cover and core.
14. Reverse procedure to install.

2.0L/4-121 Overhead Cam Engines

INDEX

ENGINE MOUNT
REPLACE
FRONT ENGINE MOUNT

1. Disconnect battery ground cable.
2. Support engine using tool No. J28467-A or equivalent, then remove two mount to bracket attaching bolts, **Fig. 1.**
3. Remove two top mount attaching bolts, then raise and support vehicle.
4. Remove lower mount attaching bolt, then the engine mount.
5. Reverse procedure to install. Torque front engine mount attaching bolts to specifications.

REAR ENGINE MOUNT

1. Disconnect battery ground cable.
2. Support engine using tool No. J28467-A or equivalent, then remove two mount to bracket attaching bolts, **Figs. 2 and 3.**
3. Raise and support vehicle.
4. Remove two lower mount attaching nuts and reinforcement, then the engine mount.
5. Reverse procedure to install. Torque rear engine mount attaching bolts to specifications.

FUEL SYSTEM PRESSURE RELIEF
NON-TURBOCHARGED MODELS

1. Remove fuel pump fuse from fuse panel.
2. Start engine and operate until fuel supply remaining in fuel lines is consumed. Engage starter for approximately 3 seconds to ensure fuel pressure has been relieved.

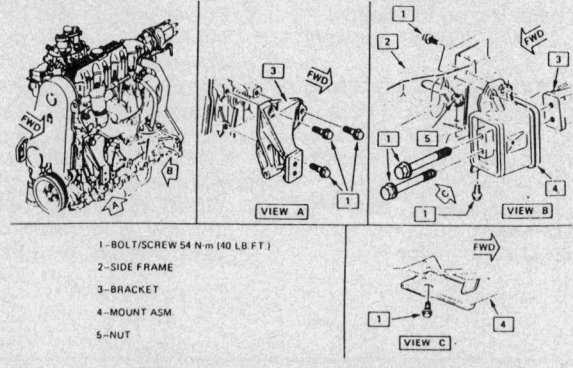

1–BOLT/SCREW 54 N·m (40 LB.FT.)
2–SIDE FRAME
3–BRACKET
4–MOUNT ASM.
5–NUT

Fig. 1 Front engine mounts

3. With the ignition switch in the "Off" position, install fuel pump fuse. **Unless this procedure is followed by servicing fuel system, fuel spray may occur.**

TURBOCHARGED MODELS

1. Disconnect battery ground cable.
2. Loosen fuel filler cap to relieve tank vapor pressure.
3. Install gauge tool No. J34730-1 or equivalent to fuel pressure connection. **Wrap shop towel around fitting while installing gauge.**
4. Install bleed into suitable container, then open valve to bleed system pressure.

ENGINE
REPLACE

1. Relieve fuel system pressure as outlined under "Fuel System Pressure Relief."
2. Disconnect battery cables and engine ground wire, then drain cooling system.
3. **On 1989-91 models,** remove battery assembly.
4. **On all models,** remove air cleaner.
5. Disconnect engine electrical harness connector at bulkhead and electrical connector at brake cylinder. On 1989-91 models, also disconnect wiper motor and cooling fan, relay and ground electrical connections.
6. **On all models,** disconnect throttle cable from bracket and throttle body assembly.
7. Disconnect vacuum hoses from throttle body assembly, then disconnect power steering high pressure hose at cut-off switch.
8. Disconnect vacuum hoses at map sensor and canister, then disconnect air conditioning relay cluster switches.
9. Disconnect power steering return hose at power steering pump.
10. Disconnect ECM electrical connectors, then pull harness through bulkhead and position harness over engine.

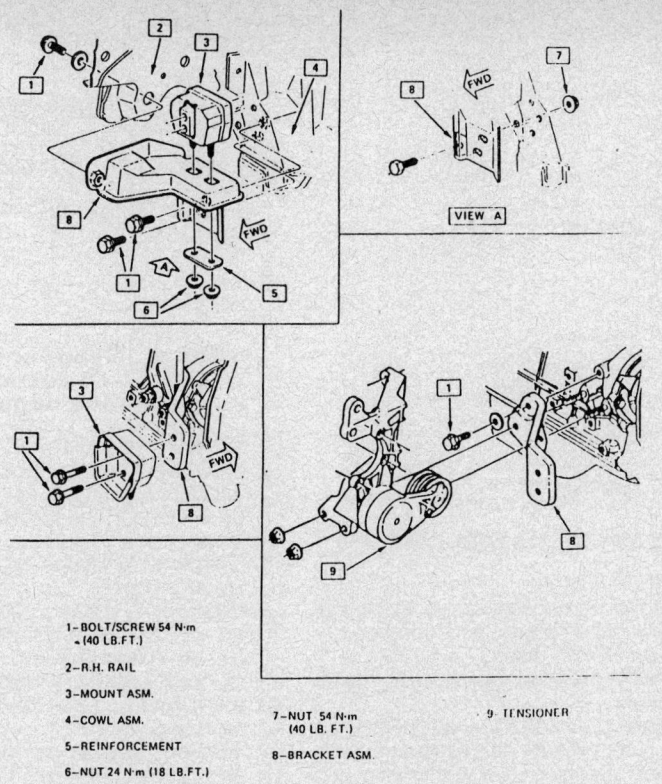

1 – BOLT/SCREW 54 N·m (40 LB.FT.)
2 – R.H. RAIL
3 – MOUNT ASM.
4 – COWL ASM.
5 – REINFORCEMENT
6 – NUT 24 N·m (18 LB.FT.)
7 – NUT 54 N·m (40 LB.FT.)
8 – BRACKET ASM.
9 – TENSIONER

Fig. 2 Rear engine mounts. 1988 models

11. Disconnect upper and lower radiator hoses from engine, then disconnect wire connector at temperature switch on thermostat housing.
12. Disconnect transmission shift cable at transmission, then raise and support vehicle.
13. **On 1988 models,** disconnect speedometer cable at transmission and bracket.
14. **On 1989-91 models,** disconnect vehicle speed sensor electrical connector.
15. **On all models,** disconnect exhaust pipe at exhaust manifold and remove exhaust pipe from converter.
16. Remove heater hoses from heater core, fuel lines at flex hoses and transmission cooler lines at flex hoses. **Place shop towel over fuel line and fitting when disconnecting.**
17. Remove front wheels, right hand spoiler section and splash shield.
18. Remove and support right and left brake calipers.
19. Discharge A/C system, disconnect electrical connectors at A/C compressor, then remove A/C compressor and mounting brackets. Using a piece of wire, support compressor in wheel opening.
20. Remove center front suspension support attachment bolts, then remove one bolt at each end, then loosen remaining bolt.
21. **On automatic transaxle vehicles,** remove rear transaxle lateral strut.
22. **On all models,** remove front transax-

le strut.
23. Lower vehicle and support front end by placing jack stands under core support.
24. Using a suitable hoist, position front post of hoist to rear of cowl.
25. Using a suitable piece of wood (4 inch x 4 inch x 6 ft.), position onto front post of hoist.
26. Raise vehicle slightly and remove jack stands from front end.
27. Position a suitable dolly under engine and transaxle assembly.
28. Position three pieces of wood (4 inch x 4 inch x 12 inch) under engine and transaxle assembly only.
29. Slightly lower vehicle onto dolly and remove right and left front suspension support remaining bolts.
30. Remove transaxle mount to bracket attaching bolt.
31. Remove front and rear engine mount to bracket attaching bolts.
32. Remove right and left steering knuckle to strut attaching bolts.
33. Remove engine and transaxle as an assembly.
34. Position engine and transaxle assembly into vehicle.
35. Loosely install transaxle and left front mounts to side rail bolts.
36. Install right rear mount to body bolts.
37. Position a suitable jack under control arms and raise struts into position, then install retaining nuts.
38. Reverse procedure to complete installation. Torque all nuts, bolts and screws to specifications.

CYLINDER HEAD
REPLACE
1988–89 MODELS

Cylinder head bolts should only be loosened when engine is cold. Do not reuse cylinder head bolts.
1. Relieve fuel system pressure as outlined under "Fuel System Pressure Relief."
2. Disconnect battery ground cable.
3. Remove air cleaner on models equipped with non-turbocharged engines or induction tube on models equipped with turbocharged engines.
4. Remove alternator and bracket from carrier, then the ignition coil.
5. Remove distributor assembly.
6. Remove cables from intake manifold bracket, TBI or throttle body.
7. Remove downshift cable, then the ECM electrical connectors from TBI or throttle body and intake manifold.
8. Remove vacuum brake hose, then the fuel inlet and return lines. **Place shop towel over fuel line and fitting when disconnecting.**
9. Remove coolant and heater hoses.
10. Remove exhaust pipe at manifold on models equipped with non-turbocharged engine or exhaust manifold to turbo connection on models equipped with turbocharged engine.
11. Remove oxygen sensor and thermostat housing electrical connector, if equipped.
12. Remove engine harness, then the timing belt.
13. With engine cold, loosen cam carrier/cylinder head attaching bolts as shown in **Fig. 4.**
14. Remove camshaft carrier, rocker arms and valve lash compensators.
15. Remove cylinder head with intake manifold and exhaust manifold as an assembly.
16. Reverse procedure to install. Torque cylinder head bolts to specifications, in sequence shown in **Fig. 5.**

1990–91 MODELS

Cylinder head bolts should only be loosened when engine is cold. Do not reuse cylinder head bolts.
1. Relieve fuel system pressure as outlined under "Fuel System Pressure Relief."
2. Disconnect battery ground cable and drain coolant.
3. Remove air filter housing assembly.
4. **On turbocharged models,** remove turbo induction tube.
5. **On all models,** remove coolant resevoir tank.
6. Remove fuel vapor pipe assembly. **Place shop towel over fuel line and fitting when disconnecting.**
7. Remove serpentine belt and front timing cover upper attaching bolts.
8. Loosen serpentine belt tensioner and position aside.
9. Raise and support vehicle, then remove righthand inner splash shield

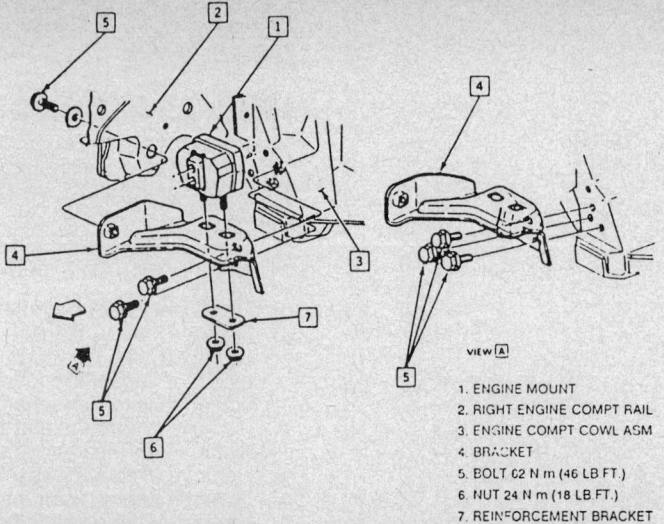

1. ENGINE MOUNT
2. RIGHT ENGINE COMPT RAIL
3. ENGINE COMPT COWL ASM
4. BRACKET
5. BOLT 62 N·m (46 LB.FT.)
6. NUT 24 N·m (18 LB.FT.)
7. REINFORCEMENT BRACKET

Fig. 3   Rear engine mounts. 1989–91 models

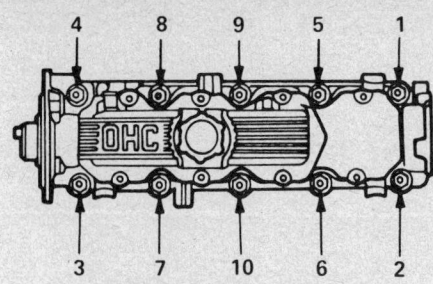

Fig. 4   Cylinder head & camshaft carrier bolt loosening sequence

and lower righthand splash shield.
10. Remove air conditioning belt.
11. Remove crankshaft pulley as outlined under "Crankshaft Pulley, Replace."
12. Remove flywheel inspection cover.
13. Remove front timing belt cover lower attaching bolts, then remove cover, then align timing marks.
14. Loosen water pump attaching bolts and release timing belt tension using tool No. J-33039-A or equivalent, then remove timing belt.
15. **On turbocharged models,** remove exhaust pipe from turbo assembly, then disconnect oil and coolant lines to turbo assembly, then remove lower turbo assembly brace.
16. **On non-turbocharged models,** remove exhaust pipe to manifold.
17. **On all models,** lower vehicle and remove fuel vapor pipe. **Place shop towel over fuel line and fitting when disconnecting.**
18. Remove rear timing cover attaching bolts, then remove rear timing cover.
19. Remove PCV attaching hose.
20. Disconnect intake manifold and cylinder head electrical connectors.
21. Remove exhaust manifold attaching bolts.
22. **On turbocharged models,** remove exhaust manifold and turbo assembly.
23. **On all models,** remove power steering pump pressure and return lines.
24. Remove alternator and alternator bracket with power steering pump.
25. Disconnect front and rear engine lift brackets, then remove coil assembly.
26. **On turbocharged models,** remove turbo boost solenoid.
27. **On all models,** remove breather tube bracket and breather tube.
28. Remove accelerator linkage and bracket, then remove attaching fuel lines. **Place shop towel over fuel line and fitting when disconnecting.**
29. Remove cylinder head and intake manifold electrical connectors and attaching hoses and coolant lines.
30. Remove cylinder head and camshaft carrier attaching bolts in sequence

shown in **Fig. 4.**
31. Remove camshaft carrier, them remove rocker arms, lash compensators and thrust pieces.
32. Remove cylinder head and intake manifold.
33. Reverse procedure to install. Refer to **Fig. 5,** for cylinder head and camshaft carrier attaching bolt tightening sequence. Torque attaching bolts to specifications.

INTAKE MANIFOLD REPLACE

NON-TURBOCHARGED MODELS

1. Relieve fuel system pressure as outlined under "Fuel System Pressure Relief" procedure.
2. Disconnect battery ground cable.
3. Remove air cleaner, then drain cooling system.
4. Remove alternator and bracket at camshaft carrier.
5. Disconnect power steering pump and position aside.
6. Remove power steering bracket at intake manifold.
7. Remove ignition coil and bracket assembly, then the throttle cable from intake manifold bracket.
8. Remove throttle cable and TV cable from TBI unit.
9. Remove TBI unit electrical connector.
10. Remove vacuum brake hose, coolant hoses and fuel lines. **Place shop towel over fuel line and fitting when disconnecting.**
11. Remove ECM harness, then the intake manifold attaching nuts and manifold.
12. Reverse procedure to install. On 1989–91 models, refer to **Fig. 6,** for manifold nut tightening sequence.

TURBOCHARGED MODELS

1. Relieve fuel system pressure as outlined under "Fuel System Pressure

Relief" procedure.
2. Remove induction tube and hoses.
3. Disconnect ignition coil, throttle body, MAP sensor and wastegate electrical connectors.
4. Remove PCV hose and throttle body vacuum hose.
5. Remove throttle cable and cruise control cable, if equipped.
6. Remove fuel line from throttle cable support bracket. **Place shop towel over fuel line and fitting when disconnecting.**
7. Remove ignition coil bracket attaching screws, then remove ignition coil bracket.
8. Remove vacuum hoses at rear of manifold.
9. Remove transmission filler tube bracket.
10. Remove manifold support bracket attaching bolts, then remove bracket.
11. Remove heater tube support bracket on lower side of manifold.
12. Disconnect fuel injector electrical connectors.
13. Remove coolant recovery tank and accessory drive belt.
14. Remove power steering and alternator front adjusting bracket.
15. Remove power steering pump bracket to engine head.
16. Remove fuel line to fuel rail inlet, then remove fuel return line from regulator outlet. **Place shop towel over fuel line and fitting when disconnecting.**
17. Remove intake manifold attaching nuts and washers, then remove manifold.
18. Reverse procedure to install. Torque intake manifold attaching bolts to specifications.

EXHAUST MANIFOLD REPLACE

NON-TURBOCHARGED MODELS

1. Disconnect battery ground cable.
2. Remove air cleaner, then remove spark plug wires and retainers.
3. Remove oil dipstick tube and breather.
4. Disconnect oxygen sensor electrical connectors.

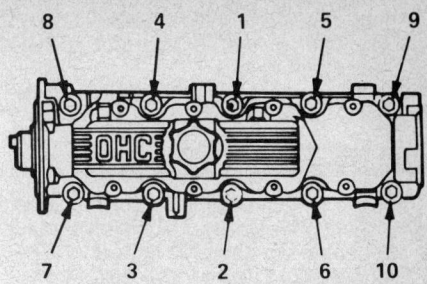

Fig. 5 Cylinder head & camshaft carrier bolt tightening sequence

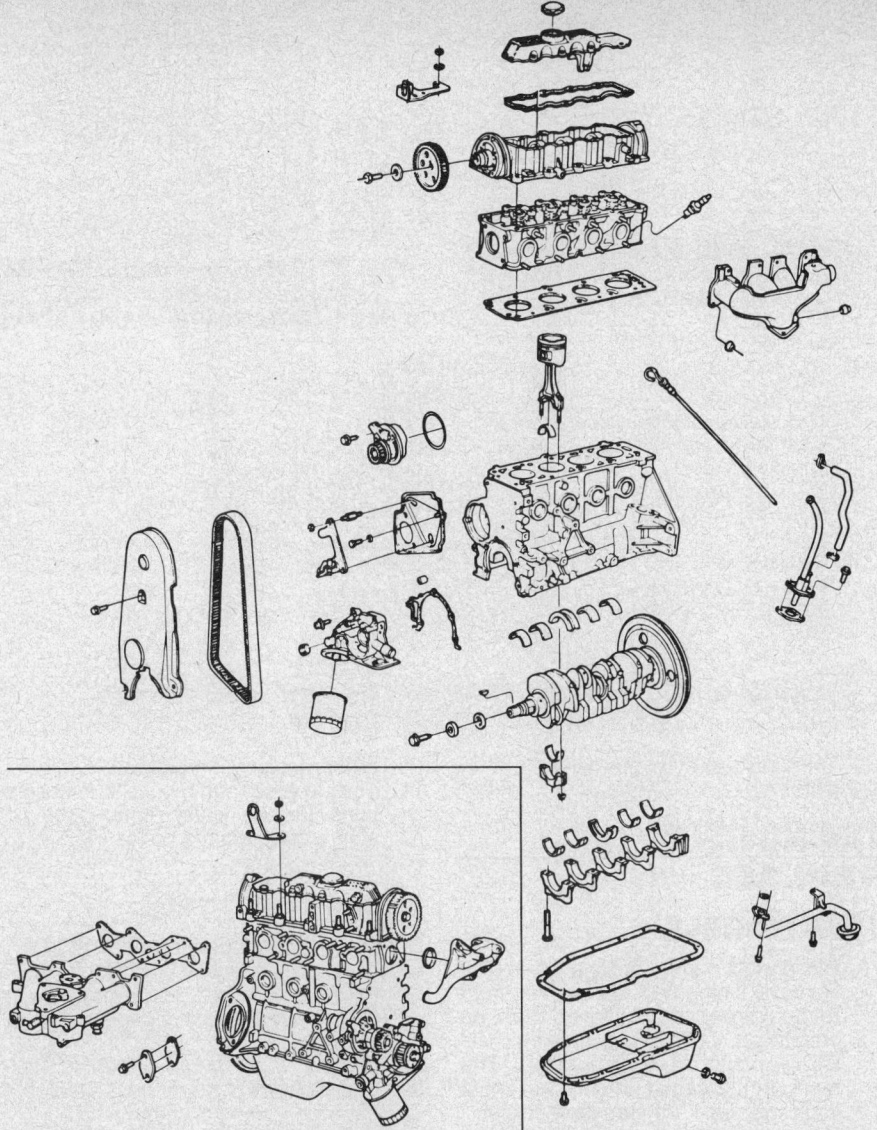

Disassembled view of engine

of hydraulic valve lash compensators. No provision for adjustment is provided.

ROCKER ARM & HYDRAULIC VALVE LASH COMPENSATORS
REPLACE

1. Disconnect battery ground cable.
2. Remove camshaft carrier cover.
3. Using tool No. J-33302-25 or equivalent, **Fig. 9**, compress valve springs and remove rocker arms. Place rocker arms in a suitable rack so they can be installed in the same location.
4. Remove hydraulic lash compensators and place them in a rack so they can be installed in the same location.
5. Reverse procedure to install. **The preload of the hydraulic valve lash compensator is automatic and servicing of the compensator requires only care and cleanliness be exercised in the handling of these components.**

VALVE SPRING & VALVE STEM OIL SEAL
REPLACE

REMOVAL

1. Disconnect battery ground cable.
2. Remove camshaft carrier cover as described under "Camshaft Carrier Cover, Replace."
3. Remove rocker arms and spark plugs.
4. Install air line adapter tool No. J-22794 or equivalent, into spark plug port and apply compressed air to hold valves in place.
5. Using tool No. J-33302-25 or equivalent, **Fig. 9**, compress valve spring and remove rocker guides, valve locks, caps and valve spring.
6. Remove valve stem oil seal.

INSTALLATION

1. Using clean engine oil, lubricate valve stem and install new valve stem oil seal over valve stem and seat onto valve guide.
2. Position valve spring and cap over valve stem. Using tool No. J-33302-25 or equivalent, compress valve spring and install valve locks.

5. Remove exhaust pipe, then remove exhaust manifold attaching nuts.
6. Remove exhaust manifold and gasket.
7. Reverse procedure to install. Refer to **Fig. 7**, for manifold bolt tightening sequence. Torque attaching nuts to specifications.

TURBOCHARGED MODELS

1. Disconnect battery ground cable.
2. Remove spark plug wires.
3. Remove turbocharger as follows:
   a. Raise and support vehicle.
   b. Remove lower fan attaching screw.
   c. Remove exhaust pipe to manifold attaching nuts, then remove exhaust pipe.
   d. Remove rear A/C support bracket attaching bolt, then loosen remaining A/C support bracket bolts.
   e. Remove turbo support bracket to engine attaching bolt.
   f. Remove oil drain hose at turbo, then remove water return pipe.
   g. Lower vehicle, then disconnect coolant recovery pipe and position to one side.
   h. Remove oxygen sensor.
   i. Remove oil and water feed pipes.
   j. Remove air intake duct and vacuum hose at actuator.
   k. Remove exhaust manifold attaching nuts, then remove exhaust manifold and turbocharger assembly.
4. Remove turbocharger to exhaust manifold attaching bolts, then remove exhaust manifold and gasket.
5. Reverse procedure to install. Refer to **Fig. 8**, for exhaust manifold attaching bolt sequence. Torque attaching nuts and bolts to specifications.

VALVE CLEARANCE SPECIFICATIONS

Valve lash is obtained through the use

3. Install rocker guides and rocker arms, then remove tool No. J-33302-25.
4. Remove air line adapter tool and install spark plugs.
5. Install camshaft carrier cover. Torque bolts to specifications.

VALVE SEAT SERVICE

Using a suitable dial indicator measure valve seat concentricity. Valve seat should be concentric to within .002 inch of total indicator reading. Ensure valve guide bores are free from carbon or dirt to allow proper seating of the pilot in the valve guide. When reconditioning the valve seats, use a 45° stone to rough the valve seat and another stone with the same angle to finish the valve seat. On 1988 models, narrow down the valve seats to the proper width, .051-.055 inch for intake valves and .067-.071 for exhaust valves. On 1989-91 models, narrow down the valve seats to the proper width, .0050-.0701 inch for both intake and exhaust.

VALVE GUIDES

Valve guides are an integral part of the cylinder head. If valve stem to guide clearance is excessive, the guide should be reamed to the next oversize and the appropriate oversize valve installed. On 1988 models, valves are available in standard size and oversize of .0075 inch, .015 inch and .030 inch. On 1989-91 models, valves are available in standard sizes and oversizes of .00295 inch, .0059 inch and .00984 inch.

CRANKSHAFT PULLEY REPLACE

1. Disconnect battery ground cable.
2. Remove inner fender shield.
3. Remove air conditioning belt, if equipped, then remove serpentine belt.
4. Remove crankshaft pulley bolts and pulley.
5. Reverse to install, noting the following:
   a. Using a suitable sealer, coat threads of pulley bolts and install onto pulley.
   b. Torque bolts to specifications.

TIMING BELT FRONT COVER
REPLACE

1. Remove serpentine belt.
2. **On 1988 models**, remove belt tensioner attaching nuts, then remove tensioner.
3. **On 1989-91 models**, loosen serpentine belt tensioner attaching bolt, then allow tensioner to swing downward.
4. **On 1988 models**, unsnap and remove upper to lower front timing cover.
5. **On 1989-91 models**, remove timing cover attaching bolts and nut, then remove cover.

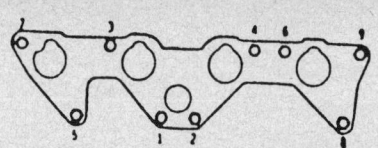

Fig. 6   Intake manifold nut tightening sequence. 1989-91 models

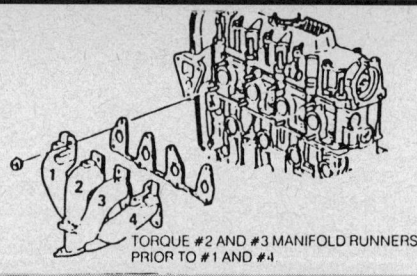

TORQUE #2 AND #3 MANIFOLD RUNNERS PRIOR TO #1 AND #4

Fig. 7   Exhaust manifold bolt tightening sequence. Non-turbocharged models

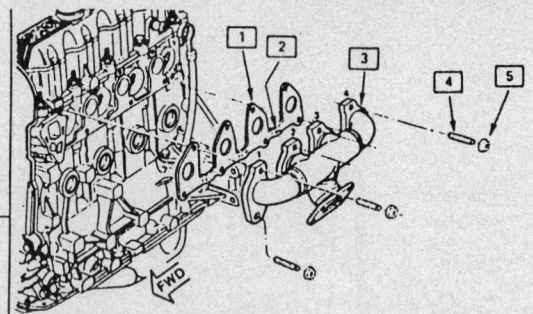

1 GASKET
2 EXPANSION JOINTS FACE OUTWARD
3 MANIFOLD ASM.
4 STUD. 27 N•M (20 LB. FT.)
5 NUT. 22 N•M (16 LB. FT.)

TORQUE NO. 2 & 3 MANIFOLD RUNNERS PRIOR TO NO. 1 & 4 RUNNERS

Fig. 8   Exhaust manifold bolt tightening sequence. Turbocharged models

6. **On all models**, reverse procedure to install.

TIMING BELT
REPLACE
1988 MODELS

1. Disconnect battery ground cable.
2. Remove timing belt front cover, then rotate crankshaft until timing mark on crankshaft pulley aligns with 10° BTDC mark on indicator tab. The mark on the camshaft sprocket must align with mark on camshaft carrier.
3. Raise and support vehicle.
4. Remove crankshaft pulley as previously described.
5. Lower vehicle to just above floor.
6. Remove coolant reservoir.
7. Loosen water pump bolts, then rotate water pump to loosen and remove timing belt.
8. Reverse procedure to install. Note the following information:
   a. Ensure mark on camshaft sprocket aligns with mark on camshaft carrier. The timing mark on the crankshaft pulley should align with the 10° BTDC mark on the indicator tab.
   b. Using tool No. J-33039 or equivalent, **Fig. 10**, rotate water pump clockwise until all slack is removed from timing belt. Install tool No. J-26486 or equivalent, **Fig. 10**, between water pump and camshaft sprockets so pointer is midway between sprockets.
9. Adjust timing belt until tension is within limits indicated on tool J-26486-A.
10. If timing belt tension is incorrect, loosen and using tool No. J-33039 or equivalent, rotate water pump until

proper tension is obtained.
11. Torque water pump bolts to specifications. Ensure water pump does not shift when torquing bolts.

1989-91 MODELS

1. Disconnect battery ground cable.
2. Remove serpentine belt, then remove timing belt cover as outlined under "Timing Belt Front Cover, Replace" procedure.
3. Loosen water pump attaching bolts and release tension with tool No. J33039-A or equivalent.
4. Raise and support vehicle.
5. Lower vehicle, then remove timing belt.
6. Reverse procedure to install, noting the following:
   a. Turn crankshaft and camshaft gears clockwise to align timing marks on gears with timing marks on rear cover.
   b. Install timing belt, ensuring portion between camshaft gear and crankshaft gear is in tension.
   c. Using tool No. J33039-A or equivalent, turn water pump eccentric clockwise until tensioner arm contacts high torque stop, **Fig. 11**. Torque water pump attaching screws slightly.
   d. Turn engine by crankshaft gear bolt 720° clockwise to seat belt to gear teeth.
   e. Turn water pump eccentric counterclockwise until hole in tensioner arm aligns with hole in base. Perform operation with engine at room temperature, approximately 68°F.
   f. Torque water pump attaching bolts to specifications ensuring tensioner holes remain as adjusted.

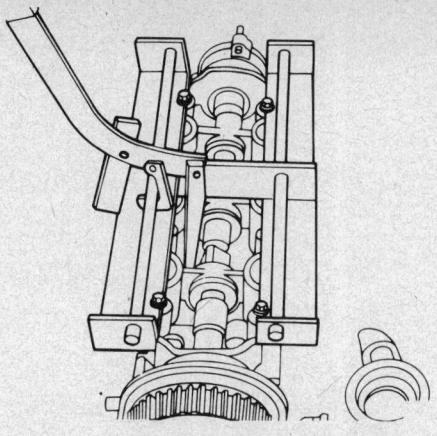

Fig. 9   Using tool No. 33302 to compress valve spring

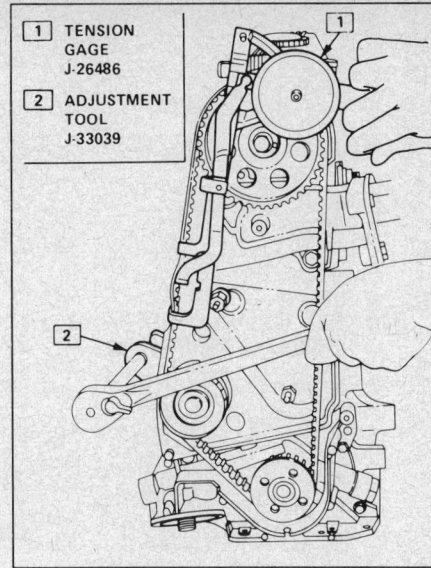

Fig. 10   Timing belt tension adjustment. 1988 models

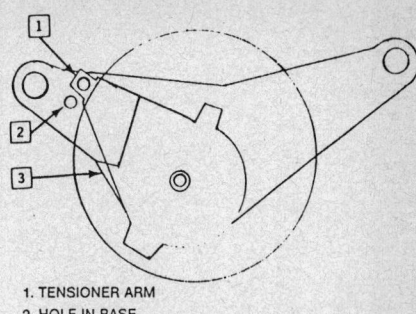

1. TENSIONER ARM
2. HOLE IN BASE
3. HIGH TORQUE STOP

Fig. 11   Timing belt tensioner positions. 1989–91 models

TIMING BELT REAR COVER
REPLACE

1. Disconnect battery ground cable.
2. Remove timing belt as described under "Timing Belt, Replace."
3. **On 1988 models,** remove camshaft sprockets as described under "Camshaft Sprocket, Replace."
4. **On 1989-91 models,** remove camshaft and crankshaft sprockets as described under "Camshaft Sprocket, Replace" and "Crankshaft Sprocket, Replace."
5. Remove timing belt tensioner assembly.
6. **On all models,** remove timing belt rear cover bolts and cover.
7. Reverse procedure to install. Torque bolts to specifications.

CAMSHAFT CARRIER COVER
REPLACE

1. Remove air cleaner and disconnect breather hoses.
2. **On turbocharged models,** remove turbo induction tube.
3. **On all models,** remove cover bolts and cover.
4. Reverse procedure to install. Torque camshaft carrier cover bolts to specification.

CAMSHAFT SPROCKET
REPLACE

1. Disconnect battery ground cable.
2. Remove camshaft carrier cover as outlined under "Camshaft Carrier Cover, Replace."
3. Remove timing belt as outlined under "Timing Belt, Replace."
4. Using a suitable tool, secure camshaft and remove camshaft sprocket bolt, washer and sprocket, **Fig. 12.**
5. Reverse procedure to install. Torque

camshaft sprocket bolt and camshaft carrier cover to specification.

CAMSHAFT
REPLACE
REMOVAL

1. Disconnect battery ground cable.
2. Remove camshaft carrier cover.
3. Using tool No. J-33302-25 or equivalent, **Fig. 9,** compress valve springs and remove rocker arms.
4. Remove camshaft sprocket as described under "Camshaft Sprocket, Replace."
5. **On 1989-91 models,** remove washer fluid container assembly.
6. **On all models,** disconnect spark plug wires from spark plugs, then remove distributor from engine.
7. Remove camshaft thrust plate from rear of camshaft carrier.
8. Slide camshaft rearward and remove camshaft from carrier.

INSTALLATION

1. Install new front oil seal onto camshaft carrier using fingers.
2. Position camshaft into carrier. **Ensure not to damage front oil seal when installing camshaft.**
3. Install camshaft thrust plate and bolts. Torque bolts to specifications.
4. Check camshaft endplay. Endplay should be within .016 to .064 inch.
5. Install distributor, camshaft sprocket, timing belt and timing belt front cover.
6. Using tool No. J-33302-25 or equivalent, **Fig. 9,** compress valve springs and install rocker arms.
7. Install camshaft carrier cover. Torque bolts to specifications.

CRANKSHAFT SPROCKET
REPLACE

1. Disconnect battery ground cable.
2. Remove timing belt as described under "Timing Belt, Replace."
3. Remove crankshaft sprocket bolt, washer and sprocket.
4. Reverse procedure to install.

CRANKSHAFT FRONT OIL SEAL
REPLACE

1. Disconnect battery ground cable.
2. Remove crankshaft sprocket as described under "Crankshaft Sprocket, Replace."
3. Remove key and rear thrust washer from end of crankshaft.
4. **On 1989-91 models,** remove rear timing cover as described under "Timing Belt Rear Cover, Replace."
5. **On all models,** using a suitable tool, remove crankshaft front oil seal.
6. During installation of crankshaft front oil seal, position tool No. J-33083 or equivalent, **Fig. 13,** onto crankshaft. Lubricate front oil seal lip and install onto crankshaft.
7. Reverse procedure to complete installation.

PISTON & ROD ASSEMBLY

Assemble piston to rod, with arrow on piston facing toward front of engine and numbered side toward intake manifold side of engine, **Fig. 14.** Upon installation, measure connecting rod side clearance using a suitable feeler gauge. Side clearance should be .0028 to .0095 inch.

PISTONS, PINS & RINGS

Pistons and rings are available in standard size and oversize of .020 inch (.5 mm). Piston pins are available in standard size only.

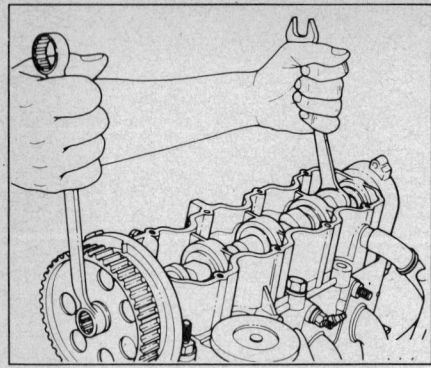

Fig. 12   Camshaft sprocket removal

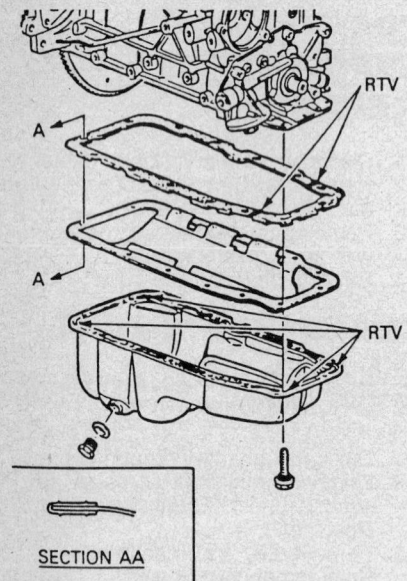

Fig. 15   Oil pan installation

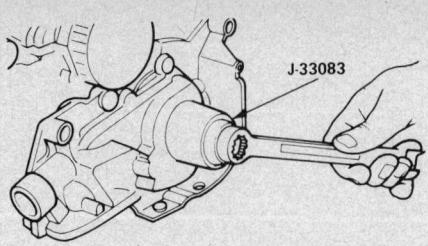

Fig. 13   Crankshaft front oil seal installation

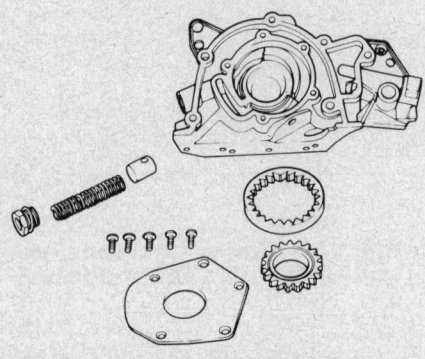

Fig. 16   Disassembled view of oil pump

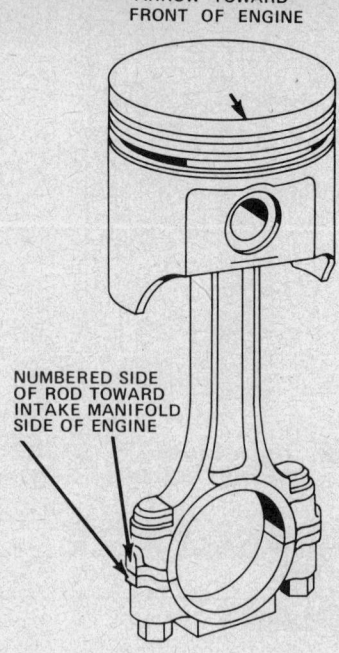

Fig. 14   Piston & rod assembly

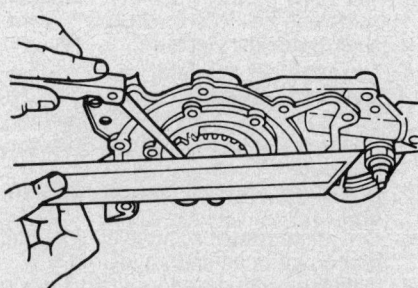

Fig. 17   Checking drive gear to oil pump housing clearance

MAIN & ROD BEARINGS

Main and rod bearings are available in standard sizes and undersizes of .010 inch (.25 mm) and .020 inch (.5 mm).

CRANKSHAFT REAR OIL SEAL
REPLACE

1. Remove transaxle from vehicle as described under "Transaxle, Replace."
2. Remove flywheel attaching bolts and flywheel or flexplate.
3. **On models with manual transaxle,** remove pressure plate and clutch disc.
4. **On all models,** using a suitable tool, pry crankshaft rear oil seal from bore.
5. Clean engine block and crankshaft to seal mating surfaces.
6. Lubricate crankshaft rear oil seal.
7. Use seal installer J-36227 to press seal evenly into position.

8. **On models with manual transaxle,** torque flywheel attaching bolts to specifications.
9. **On models with automatic transaxle,** torque flexplate attaching bolts to specifications.
10. **On models with manual transaxle,** install clutch disc and pressure plate.
11. **On all models,** install transaxle assembly.

OIL PAN
REPLACE

1. Disconnect battery ground cable.
2. Raise and support vehicle.
3. Drain engine oil.
4. **On 1988 models,** remove right front wheel and right hand splash shield.
5. **On all models,** disconnect exhaust pipe from exhaust manifold or waste gate, as required.
6. Remove flywheel cover attaching bolts.
7. Remove oil pan bolts and oil pan.
8. Reverse procedure to install. Apply sealer to oil pan and oil pan gasket as shown in **Fig. 15.** Also coat threads of oil pan bolts with sealer. Torque bolts to specifications.

OIL PUMP SCREEN & PICKUP TUBE
REPLACE

1. Disconnect battery ground cable.

2. Remove oil pan as described under "Oil Pan, Replace."
3. Remove pickup tube support bolts, pickup tube to oil pump bolts, pickup tube and O-ring.
4. Reverse procedure to install. On 1988 models, **torque** pickup tube to oil pump bolts to 5 ft. lbs. On 1989 models, **torque** pickup tube to oil pump bolts to 6 ft. lbs. and pickup tube support to block bolt to 4 ft. lbs. On 1990-91 models, **torque** pickup tube to oil pump bolts to 71 inch lbs. and pickup tube support to block bolt to 53 inch lbs.

OIL PUMP SERVICE
REMOVAL

1. Disconnect battery ground cable and drain engine oil.
2. Remove crankshaft sprocket as outlined under "Crankshaft Sprocket, Replace."
3. Remove timing belt rear cover as outlined under "Timing Belt Rear Cover, Replace."

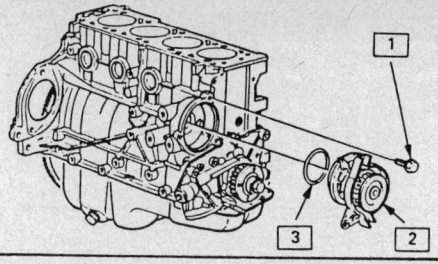

1—BOLT · 28 N·m (21 LB. FT.)

2—WATER PUMP

3—SEAL RING

Fig. 18 Water pump removal & installation

4. Disconnect engine oil pressure switch electrical connector from the switch.
5. Remove oil pan and oil filter.
6. Remove pickup tube to engine block bolts, pickup tube and oil pump.

DISASSEMBLE

1. Remove five screws and rear cover from oil pump, **Fig. 16.**
2. Remove gears, plug, pressure regulator valve plunger and spring.
3. If necessary, remove pickup tube and O-ring from oil pump body.

INSPECTION

After disassembling the oil pump, thoroughly clean all oil pump components and check them for excessive wear and damage.
1. Using a suitable straight edge and feeler gauge, **Fig. 17,** check oil pump clearances.
2. Check clearances for the following oil pump components:
   a. Clearance between idler gear and oil pump body should be .004-.007 inch.
   b. Clearance between drive gear and oil pump body should be .014-.018 inch.
   c. End clearance should be .001-.004 inch.
3. If clearances obtained are not within specified limits, replace worn or damaged oil pump components.

ASSEMBLY

1. Install valve plunger and spring.
2. Using a suitable sealer, coat threads of pressure regulator valve plunger plug and install. Torque plug and attaching bolts to specifications..
3. Install oil pump gears into oil pump body.

INSTALLATION

1. Install gasket and oil pump onto engine. Torque oil pump bolts specifications.
2. Install pickup tube and bolts. Refer to "Oil Pump Screen & Pickup Tube, Replace" for torque specifications.
3. Install oil pan and oil filter.
4. Connect engine oil pressure switch electrical connector to switch.
5. Install timing belt rear covers and crankshaft sprocket.

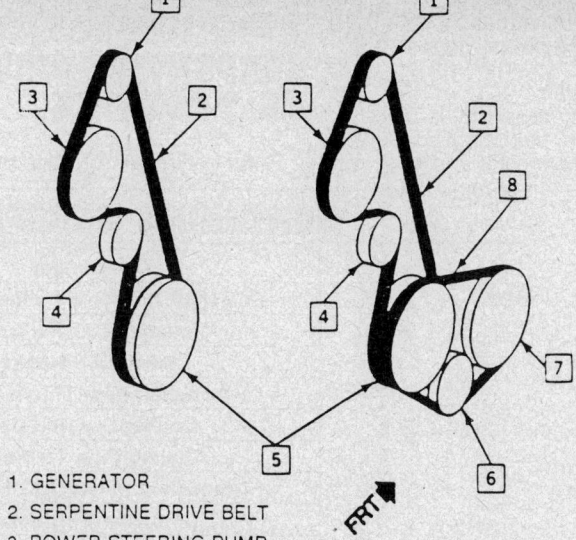

1. GENERATOR
2. SERPENTINE DRIVE BELT
3. POWER STEERING PUMP
4. SERPENTINE TENSIONER
5. CRANKSHAFT PULLEY
6. A/C TENSIONER
7. A/C COMPRESSOR
8. A/C "V" BELT

Fig. 19 Serpentine drive belt routing

WATER PUMP
REPLACE

1. Disconnect battery ground cable.
2. Drain cooling system, then remove timing belt. Refer to "Timing Belt, Replace" for procedure.
3. Remove timing belt rear protective covers, as required.
4. Remove lower radiator hose from water pump.
5. Remove water pump attaching bolts then the water pump and sealing ring, **Fig 18.**
6. Clean engine block and water pump sealing surfaces, then apply a $^3/_{32}$ inch of RTV sealant to sealing surfaces. While RTV sealant is still wet, install water pump. Tighten attaching bolts finger tight.
7. Install lower radiator hose on water pump, then timing belt rear protective covers.
8. Install timing belt. Refer to "Timing Belt, Replace" for procedure.

COOLING SYSTEM BLEED

To ensure sufficient engine cooling, freezing and corrosion protection, maintain the protection level at −34°F or lower. Use a solution of antifreeze and water, ensuring solution is no more than 70 percent antifreeze.
1. Fill surge tank or radiator to base of filler neck, then install pressure cap.
2. Block the drive wheel and apply parking brake.
3. **On models equipped with automatic transaxle,** place shifter in Park position.
4. **On models equipped with manual transaxle,** place transaxle in Neutral position.
5. **On all models,** start engine and allow to run until upper radiator hose is hot.
6. Turn engine Off, check level of coolant in surge tank or radiator.
7. Allow engine to cool, then add coolant as necessary.

ELECTRIC FUEL PUMP
REPLACE

1. Depressurize fuel system as outlined under "Fuel System Pressure Relief."
2. Disconnect battery ground cable.
3. Raise and support vehicle.
4. Remove fuel tank as follows:
   a. Drain fuel tank. **Place shop towel over fuel line and fitting when disconnecting.**
   b. Disconnect tank meter assembly harness from body harness electrical connectors.
   c. Remove tank filler hoses and vent pipes. **Place shop towel over fuel line and fitting when disconnecting.**
   d. Support fuel tank with suitable equipment, then disconnect fuel tank attaching straps.
   e. Carefully lower fuel tank, if required remove fuel tank meter assembly and seal using tool No. J-24187 or equivalent.
5. Remove fuel tank sending unit and pump assembly by turning cam lock ring counterclockwise.
6. Remove fuel meter pump assembly from fuel tank and fuel pump from fuel sending unit.

7. Pull fuel pump upward into fuel hose while pulling outward away from bottom support. **Do not damage rubber insulator and strainer during fuel pump removal.**
8. After fuel pump assembly is clear of bottom support, pull pump assembly out of rubber connector and from vehicle.
9. Reverse procedure to install.

SERPENTINE DRIVE BELT ROUTING

Refer to **Fig. 19**, for drive belt routing.

BELT TENSION DATA

Year	Belt	New Lbs.	Used Lbs.
1988–89	Air Cond.	155	88
1988–89①	—	225	115
1990–91②	—	225–236	112–124

①—Turbocharged.
②—All models.

TIGHTENING SPECIFICATIONS

Year	Component	Torque/Ft. Lbs.
1988	Camshaft Carrier & Cylinder Head	①
	Camshaft Carrier Cover	6
	Camshaft Sprocket	34
	Camshaft Rear Thrust Plate	70⑥
	Connecting Rod Cap	26③
	Coolant Pipe To Block	20②
	Crankshaft Pulley To Sprocket	13
	Crankshaft Sprocket	96③
	Cylinder Head	⑨
	Distributor To Cylinder Head	13②
	Engine Mount (Front)	40
	Engine Mount (Rear)	⑦
	Exhaust Manifold Attaching Nuts	⑧
	Exhaust Manifold Studs	20②
	Exhaust Manifold To Turbocharger	18②
	Exhaust Pipe To Manifold	19
	Exhaust Pipe To Manifold	26②
	Flexplate, Auto. Trans.	48
	Flywheel, Manual Trans.	48⑤
	Fuel Tank Strap Bolt (Front)	25
	Fuel Tank Strap Nut (Rear)	106⑥
	Heater Pipe To Intake	18
	Intake Manifold	18②
	Intake Manifold	16
	Main Bearing Caps	44④
	Oil Pan	4
	Oil Pan Drain Plug	34
	Oil Pump	5
	Oil Pump Cover	124⑥
	Oil Pump Drive	15–22
	Oil Pump Pressure Regulating Valve	177⑥
	Oil Pump Suction Tube Bolts	62⑥
	Pressure Plate To Flywheel	18
	Serpentine Drive Belt Tensioner	35
	Spark Plug	15
	Suspension Support (Front)	65
	Thermostat Housing	20
	Throttle Body Assembly	17②
	Throttle Body Injector Assembly	16
	Timing Belt Rear Cover	54⑥
	Timing Belt Tensioner	18
	Transaxle Mount Bolt	22⑩
	Transaxle To Engine	55⑩
	Transaxle Strut To Body Bolt (Front)	40
	Transaxle Strut To Body Bolt (Rear)	23
	Transaxle Strut To Transaxle (Front	50
	Turbo Injection Tube Clamps	3②
	Water Inlet	15–22

Continued

TIGHTENING SPECIFICATIONS—Continued

Year	Component	Torque/Ft. Lbs.
1988 (Cont'd.)	Water Outlet To Cam Carrier	11
	Water Pump	19
	Wheel And Tire Assembly	100
1989–91	Camshaft Carrier & Cylinder Head	①
	Camshaft Carrier Cover	71⑥
	Camshaft Sprocket	33
	Camshaft Rear Thrust Plate	71⑥
	Connecting Rod Cap	26③
	Coolant Pipe To Block	20②
	Crankshaft Pulley To Sprocket	13
	Crankshaft Sprocket	114
	Cylinder Head	⑨
	Distributor To Cylinder Head	13②
	Engine Mount (Front)	40
	Engine Mount (Rear)	⑦
	Exhaust Manifold Attaching Nuts	⑧
	Exhaust Manifold Studs	20②
	Exhaust Manifold To Turbocharger	18②
	Exhaust Pipe To Manifold	19
	Exhaust Pipe To Manifold	26②
	Flexplate, Auto. Trans.	48
	Flywheel, Manual Trans.	48⑤
	Fuel Tank Strap Bolt (Front)	25
	Fuel Tank Strap Nut (Rear)	106⑥
	Heater Pipe To Intake	18
	Intake Manifold	18②
	Intake Manifold	15–20
	Main Bearing Caps	44④
	Oil Pan	44⑥
	Oil Pan Drain Plug	34
	Oil Pump	62⑥
	Oil Pump Cover	71⑥
	Oil Pump Drive	15–22
	Oil Pump Pressure Regulating Valve	22
	Oil Pump Suction Tube Bolts	71⑥
	Pressure Plate To Flywheel	18
	Serpentine Drive Belt Tensioner	40
	Spark Plug	15
	Suspension Support (Front)	65
	Thermostat Housing	20
	Throttle Body Assembly	17②
	Throttle Body Injector Assembly	16
	Timing Belt Front Cover	89⑥
	Timing Belt Rear Cover	89⑥
	Timing Belt Tensioner	18
	Transaxle Mount Bolt	22⑩
	Transaxle To Engine	55⑩
	Transaxle Strut To Body Bolt (Front)	40
	Transaxle Strut To Body Bolt (Rear)	23
	Transaxle Strut To Transaxle (Front	50
	Turbo Injection Tube Clamps	3②
	Water Inlet	15–22
	Water Outlet To Cam Carrier	11
	Water Pump	18
	Wheel And Tire Assembly	100

Continued

TIGHTENING SPECIFICATIONS—Continued

① —Torque cylinder head & camshaft carrier bolts to 18 ft. lbs., then tighten bolts an additional 180° in 60° increments. Start engine & allow to reach operating temperature, then tighten bolts an additional 30° to 50°.

② —Turbocharged engine.

③ —Plus an additional 40–45°.

④ —Plus an additional 40–50°.

⑤ —Plus an additional 30°.

⑥ —Inch lbs.

⑦ —Refer to Figs. 2 and 3, for specifications.

⑧ —Torque to 16 ft. lbs. for turbocharged and non-turbo models.

⑨ —Torque cylinder head & camshaft

carrier bolts to 18 ft. lbs., then tighten bolts an additional 180° in 60° increments. Start engine & allow to reach operating temperature, then tighten bolts an additional 30° to 50°.

⑩ —Vehicles equipped with automatic transmission.

2.0L/4-121 Overhead Valve Engine

INDEX

ENGINE MOUNT
REPLACE

FRONT

1. Disconnect battery ground cable.
2. Remove upper engine mount to body bracket attaching bolts, then the upper engine mount to engine bracket attaching bolt, **Figs. 1 and 2**.
3. Raise vehicle and support engine, then remove inner fender shield.
4. Remove lower engine mount to body bracket attaching bolt.
5. Remove lower engine mount to engine bracket attaching bolt.
6. Remove engine mount.
7. Reverse procedure to install. Apply suitable locking compound to bolt threads before installation. Refer to **Figs. 1 and 2**, for torque specifications.

REAR

1. Disconnect battery ground cable.
2. Raise and support vehicle.
3. Support engine and remove engine mount nuts, **Figs. 3 and 4**.
4. Remove and discard engine mount to engine attaching bolts.
5. Remove engine mount from vehicle.

6. Reverse procedure to install. Refer to **Figs. 3 and 4**, for torque specifications.

FUEL SYSTEM PRESSURE RELIEF

CHECK TYPE SYSTEM

Some models are equipped with TBI units that hold fuel pump pressure when the engine is not operating. These require a fuel pressure relief procedure prior to servicing the fuel system.

1. Relieve system fuel pressure as follows:
   a. Remove fuel pump fuse from fuse block.
   b. Start engine and allow to run until fuel supply remaining in pipes is consumed, then crank starter an additional 3 seconds to relieve remaining pressure.
   c. With ignition switch in Off position, install fuse.

NON-CHECK TYPE SYSTEM

Some models are equipped with TBI units that are non-checking systems.

1. Relieve system fuel pressure as follows:

a. Disconnect battery ground cable to ensure no attempt is made to start vehicle.
b. Loosen fuel filler cap to relieve tank vapor pressure.
c. The internal constant bleed feature relieves fuel pump system pressure when the engine is in the Off position, ensuring no further fuel pressure relief system is required.

ENGINE
REPLACE

1. Relieve fuel system pressure as outlined under "Fuel System Pressure Relief," disconnect battery and drain cooling system.
2. Remove air intake hose.
3. Disconnect accelerator and TV cables at throttle body.
4. Disconnect ECM wiring on engine.
5. Disconnect any vacuum hoses interfering with engine removal.
6. Disconnect radiator and heater hoses at engine.
7. Remove exhaust heat shield.
8. **On vehicles equipped with A/C**, remove adjustment bolt at engine mount.
9. **On all vehicles**, disconnect engine wiring harness at bulkhead.

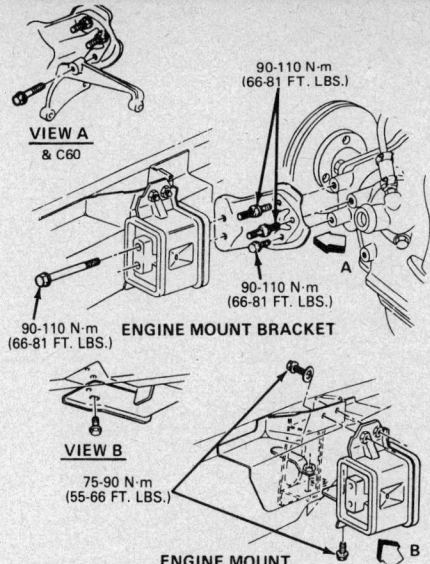

Fig. 1 Engine front mount. 1988

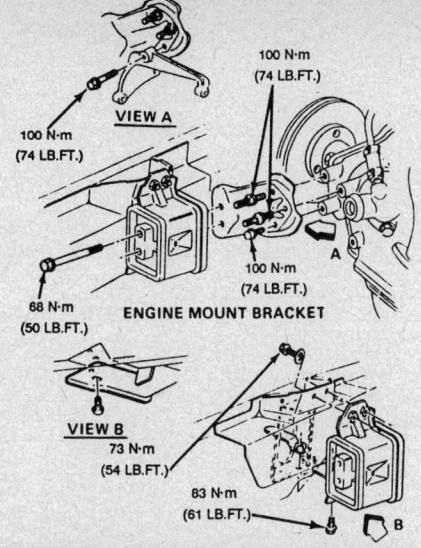

Fig. 2 Engine front mount. 1989

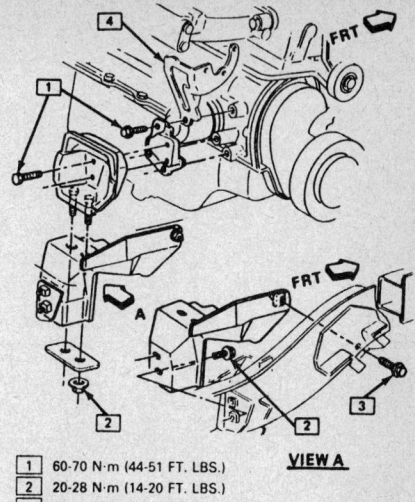

Fig. 3 Engine rear mount. 1988

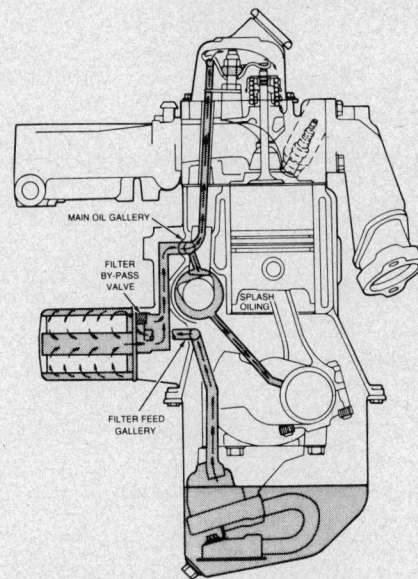

Typical engine oiling system

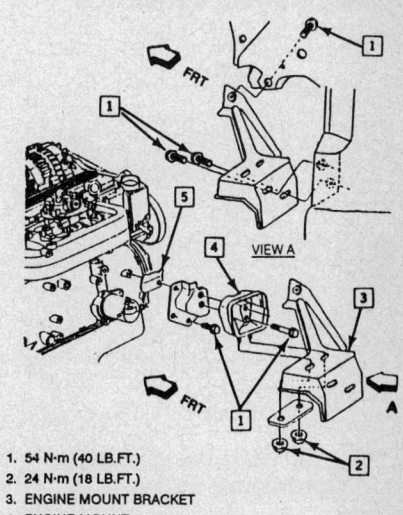

Fig. 4 Engine rear mount. 1989

10. Remove windshield washer reservoir.
11. Remove serpentine belt.
12. Disconnect fuel lines. **Place shop towel over fuel line and fitting when disconnecting.**
13. Raise and support vehicle, then remove inner fender splash shield.
14. **On vehicles equipped with A/C,** remove A/C compressor and position aside.
15. **On all models,** remove flywheel splash shield and disconnect starter wiring.
16. Disconnect front starter brace and remove starter.
17. **On vehicles with automatic transaxles,** remove torque converter bolts.
18. **On all models,** remove crankshaft

pulley using tool No. J-24420, on 1988 models, J-24420-B, on 1989 models,or equivalents.
19. Remove engine oil and oil filter.
20. Disconnect engine to transmission bracket and right rear engine mount.
21. Disconnect exhaust at manifold and center hanger. Loosen muffler hanger.
22. **On vehicles with automatic transaxles,** disconnect TV and shift cable bracket.
23. **On all models,** remove lower bellhousing bolts.
24. Disconnect accelerator and TV cable at intake manifold, then lower vehicle.
25. Remove right front engine mount nuts.
26. Remove alternator and adjusting bracket.
27. Disconnect master cylinder and position aside.
28. Attach suitable lifting device to engine.
29. Remove right front engine mount bracket.
30. Remove upper bellhousing bolts.
31. Lift engine and remove power steering pump, if so equipped.
32. Remove engine.
33. Lower engine into vehicle.
34. Install upper bellhousing bolts and left front engine mount nuts.
35. Reverse removal procedure to install.

CYLINDER HEAD
REPLACE

The cylinder head and the TBI (Throttle Body Injection) unit and the intake and exhaust manifolds are removed as an assembly.
1. Relieve fuel system pressure as outlined under "Fuel System Pressure Relief," then disconnect battery ground cable, then drain cooling system and remove TBI cover.
2. Raise and support vehicle.
3. Disconnect exhaust pipe at exhaust manifold and heater hose at intake manifold.

4. Lower vehicle.
5. Disconnect vacuum lines at intake manifold.
6. Disconnect accelerator linkage at carburetor or TBI unit, then remove accelerator linkage bracket bolt and the bracket.
7. Disconnect all electrical wires that will interfere with cylinder head removal, then remove upper radiator hose from cylinder head.
8. Remove serpentine belt, then remove power steering pump and position aside.
9. Disconnect fuel line from TBI unit. **Place shop towel over fuel line and fitting when disconnecting.**
10. Remove alternator and position aside. Do not remove wires.
11. Remove alternator rear brace.

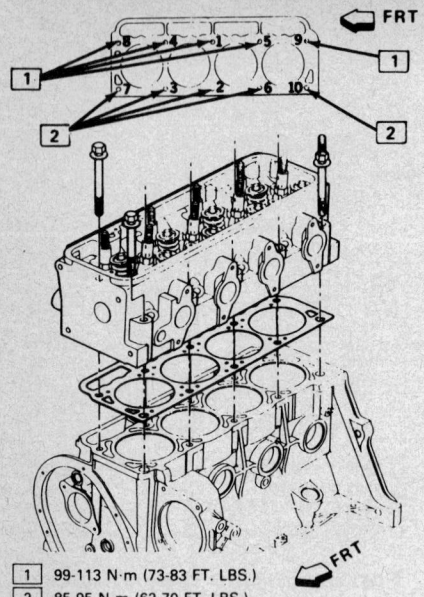

1 99-113 N·m (73-83 FT. LBS.)
2 85-95 N·m (62-70 FT. LBS.)

Fig. 5   Cylinder head bolt tightening sequence

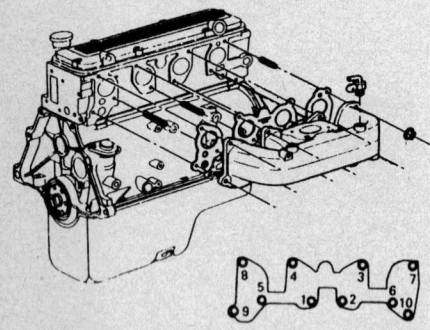

20-30 N·m (15-22 FT. LBS.)

Fig. 6   Intake manifold tightening sequence

12. Remove rocker arm cover and rocker arms, then the pushrods.
13. Remove cylinder head bolts and the cylinder head assembly.
14. Reverse procedure to install. Coat cylinder head and cylinder head bolts with sealer and install bolts finger tight. Torque cylinder head bolts to specification in sequence shown in **Fig. 5**.

INTAKE MANIFOLD
REPLACE

1. Relieve fuel system pressure as outlined under "Fuel System Pressure Relief," then disconnect battery ground cable.
2. Remove TBI cover, then drain engine coolant.
3. Disconnect vacuum lines and electrical connectors, as required.
4. Disconnect fuel lines, then the TBI linkage. **Place shop towel over fuel**

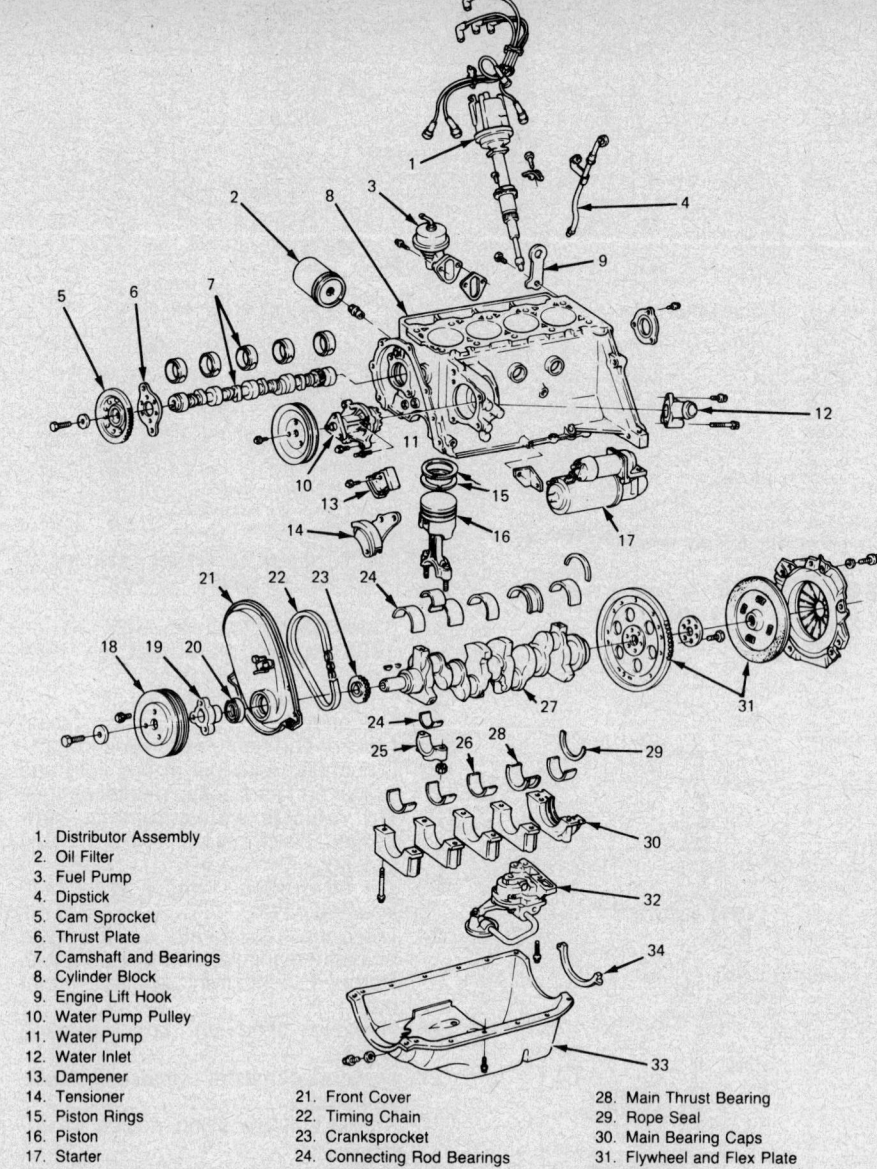

1. Distributor Assembly
2. Oil Filter
3. Fuel Pump
4. Dipstick
5. Cam Sprocket
6. Thrust Plate
7. Camshaft and Bearings
8. Cylinder Block
9. Engine Lift Hook
10. Water Pump Pulley
11. Water Pump
12. Water Inlet
13. Dampener
14. Tensioner
15. Piston Rings
16. Piston
17. Starter
18. Accessory Drive Pulley
19. Hub
20. Seal

21. Front Cover
22. Timing Chain
23. Cranksprocket
24. Connecting Rod Bearings
25. Connecting Rod Bearing Cap
26. Main Bearings
27. Crankshaft

28. Main Thrust Bearing
29. Rope Seal
30. Main Bearing Caps
31. Flywheel and Flex Plate
32. Oil Pump
33. Oil Pan
34. Seal

Cylinder block assembly & components

line and fitting when disconnecting.
5. Remove TBI assembly.
6. Remove power steering pump and position aside.
7. **On 1989 models**, remove intake manifold coolant hose.
8. **On all models**, raise and support vehicle.
9. Remove accelerator and TV cables and bracket.
10. **On 1988 models**, remove hose at bottom of intake manifold.
11. **On 1989 models**, remove lower intake manifold attaching bolts.
12. **On all models**, lower vehicle, then remove intake manifold attaching nuts and bolts, then the intake manifold.
13. Reverse procedure to install. Refer to **Fig. 6**, for nut tightening sequence.

EXHAUST MANIFOLD
REPLACE

1. Disconnect battery ground cable.
2. Disconnect oxygen sensor electrical connector.
3. Remove serpentine belt, then remove alternator and position aside.
4. Raise and support vehicle.
5. Remove exhaust pipe, then lower vehicle.
6. Remove exhaust manifold attaching bolts, then remove oil filler tube.
7. Carefully lift exhaust manifold from exhaust pipe flange, then remove exhaust manifold from cylinder head.
8. Reverse procedure to install.

NOTE: AT TIME OF INSTALLATION, FLANGES MUST BE FREE OF OIL. A 2.0-3.0 BEAD OF SEALANT MUST BE APPLIED TO FLANGES AND SEALANT MUST BE WET TO TOUCH WHEN BOLTS ARE TORQUED.

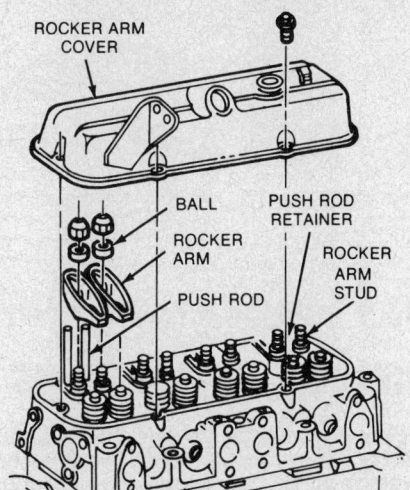

Fig. 7 Rocker arms & rocker arm cover

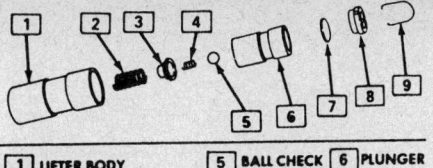

1	LIFTER BODY	5	BALL CHECK	6	PLUNGER
2	PLUNGER SPRING	7	OIL METERING VALVE
3	BALL CHECK RETAINER	8	PUSH ROD SEAT
4	BALL CHECK SPRING	9	RETAINER RING

Fig. 8 Sectional view of hydraulic valve lifter

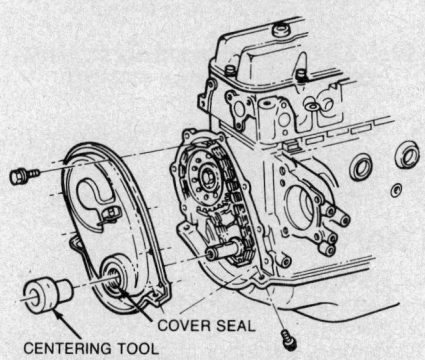

Fig. 10 Installing front cover

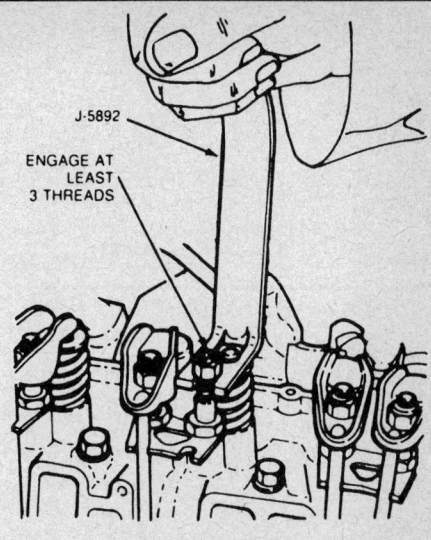

Fig. 9 Valve spring compression

ROCKER ARM COVER
REPLACE

1. Disconnect battery ground cable.
2. Remove TBI and air cleaner air hose.
3. Remove intake to rocker arm cover hose.
4. Remove rocker arm cover attaching bolts, then remove rocker arm cover, **Fig. 7.**
5. Reverse procedure to install.

ROCKER ARM STUDS

Rocker arm studs that have stress cracks or damaged threads can be replaced. If threads in cylinder head are damaged or stripped, the head can be tapped and a helical type insert added. **Torque** replacement rocker arm stud to 33 to 40 ft. lbs.

VALVE CLEARANCE SPECIFICATIONS

Valve lash is obtained through the use of hydraulic valve lash compensators. No provision for adjustment is provided.

VALVE ARRANGEMENT
FRONT TO REAR

2.0L/4-121 . . . . E-I-I-E-E-I-I-E

CAM LIFT SPECIFICATIONS

Engine	Year	Int.	Exh.
2.0L/4-121	1988	.260	.260
2.0L/4-121	1989	.262	.262

VALVE GUIDES

Valve guides are an integral part of the cylinder head and are not removable. If valve stem clearance becomes excessive, the valve guide should be reamed to the next oversize and the appropriate oversize valves installed. Valves are available in .003, .006, and .012 inch oversizes.

VALVE LIFTERS
REPLACE

Some 2.0L/4-121 engines have been manufactured with 0.26 mm oversize lifter bores. An oversize lifter bore can be identified by a vertical stripe of white paint on both sides of the lifter bore inside the lifter cavity. In addition, these engines can also be identified buy a .26 OS stamp on the top right front cylinder block machining pad.
1. Remove rocker arm cover as outlined under "Rocker Arm Cover, Replace."
2. Loosen rocker arm stud nut and rotate rocker arm so that pushrod can be removed. Remove pushrod.
3. Using tool No. J-29834 or equivalent, remove valve lifter from lifter bore.
4. Coat base of new lifter, **Fig. 8**, with Molykote, or equivalent, and install lifter into lifter bore.
5. Reverse procedure to install.

VALVE SPRING & VALVE STEM OIL SEAL
REPLACE

1. Remove rocker arm cover as outlined under "Rocker Arm Cover, Replace."

2. Remove rocker arms and spark plugs.
3. Install air line adapter tool No. J 23590 or equivalent, into spark plug port and apply compressed air to hold valves in place.
4. Using tool No. J 5892-1, on 1988 models, J 5892-B, on 1989 models, or equivalents, compress valve spring, **Fig. 9,** and remove valve locks and cap.
5. Remove spring, valve stem oil seal and shim.
6. Reverse procedure to install, ensuring locks seat properly in upper groove of valve stem, grease may be used to hold locks in place while releasing compressor tool.

ENGINE FRONT COVER
REPLACE

1. Disconnect battery ground cable.
2. Remove serpentine belt and belt tensioner.
3. Raise and support vehicle, then remove oil pan as outlined under "Oil Pan, Replace."
4. Remove crankshaft pulley and hub assembly as follows:
   a. Remove front wheel and tire assembly, then remove inner fender splash shield.
   b. Remove crankshaft pulley attaching bolts, then remove crankshaft pulley and hub attaching bolt, **Fig. 10.**
   c. Remove crankshaft pulley, then install tool No. J 24420, on 1988 models, J 24420-B, on 1989 models, or equivalents to hub, then turn puller screw ans remove hub.
5. **On all models,** remove front cover attaching bolts, then remove front cover.
6. Reverse to install.

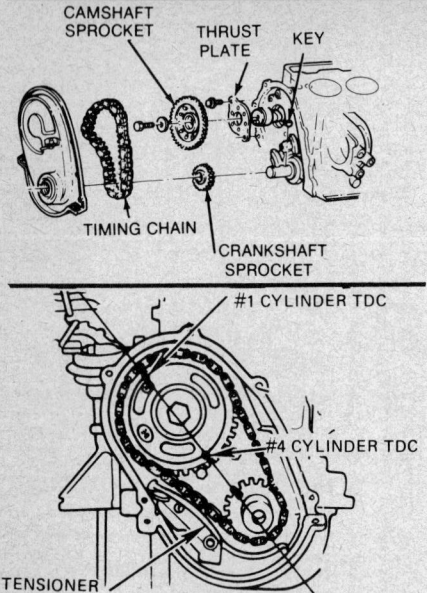

Fig. 11   Valve timing marks

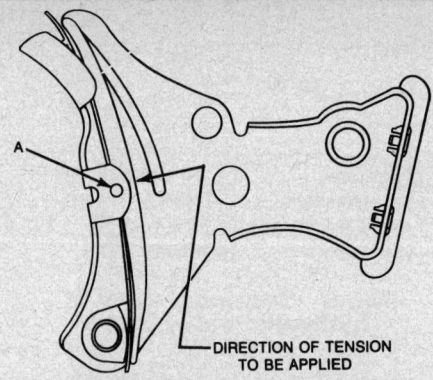

Fig. 12   Compressing timing chain tensioner spring

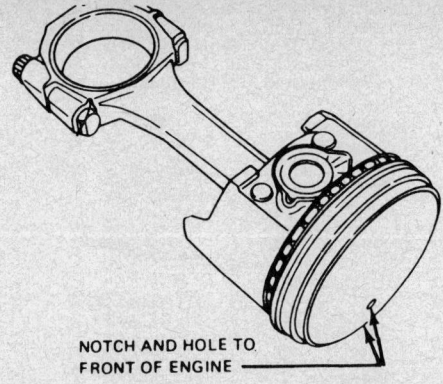

Fig. 13   Piston & rod assembly

TIMING CHAIN
REPLACE

1. Remove engine front cover as previously described.
2. Place No. 1 cylinder at TDC and align timing marks on crankshaft and camshaft sprockets, **Fig. 11.**
3. Remove timing chain tensioner as described under "Timing Chain Tensioner, Replace."
4. Remove camshaft sprocket retaining bolt. Tap lower edge of sprocket with plastic mallet and remove sprocket and timing chain.
5. If crankshaft sprocket is to be replaced, remove sprocket using a suitable puller.
6. To install crankshaft sprocket, align keyway on sprocket with key on crankshaft.
7. Align timing marks, **Fig. 11,** and install timing chain on sprockets.
8. Align dowel on camshaft with dowel hole on camshaft sprocket, then install sprocket to camshaft, using retaining bolt to draw sprocket fully to camshaft. Torque bolt to specification.
9. Lubricate timing chain with engine oil, then install timing chain tensioner.
10. Install engine front cover as outlined previously.

TIMING CHAIN TENSIONER
REPLACE

1988

1. Remove front cover as described previously.
2. Remove attaching bolts.
3. Remove tensioner and damper.
4. Compress spring in direction of arrow, **Fig. 12.**

5. While compressing spring, use a cotter pin and insert into hole A shown.
6. Install chain tensioner.
7. Remove cotter pin from tensioner.

1989

1. Remove engine front cover as outlined under "Engine Front Cover, Replace."
2. Remove tensioner attaching bolt and loosen torx bolt.
3. Remove camshaft sprocket and timing chain.
4. Remove torx bolt and timing belt tensioner assembly.
5. Compress spring in direction of arrow, **Fig. 12.**
6. While compressing spring, use a cotter pin and insert into hole A shown.
7. Install chain tensioner.
8. Remove cotter pin from tensioner.

CAMSHAFT
REPLACE

1. Remove engine from vehicle as previously described.
2. Remove valve lifters and engine front cover as described previously.
3. Mark position of rotor to distributor body, then remove distributor from engine.
4. Remove fuel pump and fuel pump pushrod from engine block.
5. Remove timing chain and camshaft sprocket as previously described.
6. Remove camshaft thrust plate to engine block retaining bolts and the thrust plate, **Fig. 11.**
7. Remove camshaft from engine block.
8. Reverse removal procedure to install. When installing camshaft, align crankshaft and camshaft sprocket timing marks, **Fig. 11.**

PISTON & ROD ASSEMBLY

Install piston to rod with notch or arrow and hole on piston facing toward front of engine and rod bearing tang slot opposite camshaft, **Fig. 13.** Upon installation, measure the connecting rod side clearance using a suitable feeler gauge. Clearance should be .004–.015 inch.

PISTONS, PINS, & RINGS

Pistons and rings are available in standard and oversizes of .020 and .040 inch. Oversize piston pins are not available due to the press fit design.

MAIN & ROD BEARINGS

When removing No. 1 main bearing cap, it will be necessary to remove the timing chain tensioner, refer to Timing Chain Tensioner, Replace.

Main bearings are available in standard size and undersizes of .0013 inch, and connecting rod bearings are available in standard size and undersizes of .0010 inch.

OIL PAN
REPLACE

1. Disconnect battery ground cable.
2. **On 1988 models,** remove exhaust pipe shield.
3. **On 1989 models,** remove exhaust pipe from manifold.
4. **On all models,** raise and support vehicle, then drain crankcase.
5. Remove flywheel cover and starter motor bracket, then remove starter motor and position aside.
6. Remove four right hand suspension support bolts, then lower suspension support slightly to provide clearance for oil pan removal.
7. **On models equipped with automatic transaxle,** remove oil filter adapter.
8. **On all models,** remove oil pan attaching bolts and oil pan.
9. Reverse procedure to install. Before installing oil pan, apply a thin coat of RTV sealer to both ends of oil pan rear seal, then seat seal firmly into rear main bearing cap. Do not allow sealer to extend beyond oil pan rear seal tabs. Apply a continuous 2 mm bead of RTV sealer along oil pan side rails in line with bolt holes, circling inward around each bolt hole location. Also apply RTV sealer to oil pan surface which contacts engine front cover. This bead of sealer must meet the

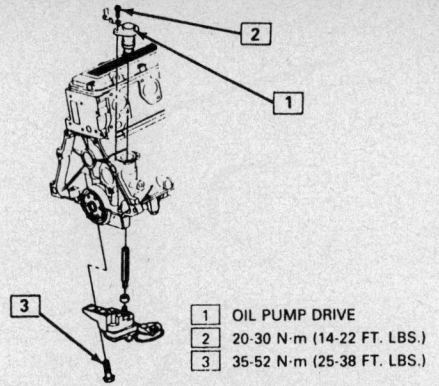

1	OIL PUMP DRIVE
2	20-30 N·m (14-22 FT. LBS.)
3	35-52 N·m (25-38 FT. LBS.)

Fig. 14   Removing oil pump assembly

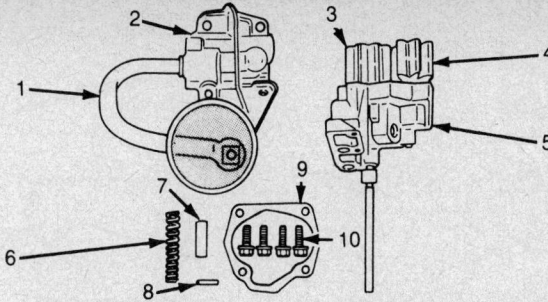

1. PICK UP TUBE AND SCREEN.
2. PUMP COVER.
3. DRIVE GEAR AND SHAFT.
4. IDLER GEAR.
5. PUMP BODY.

6. PRESSURE REGULATOR SPRING.
7. PRESSURE REGULATOR VALVE.
8. RETAINING PIN.
9. GASKET.
10. ATTACHING BOLTS.

Fig. 15   Cross-sectional view of oil pump assembly

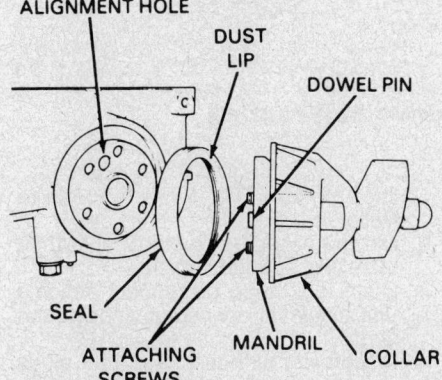

Fig. 16   Installing thick one piece type seal

bead at each oil pan side rail. Do not apply any RTV sealer to oil pan rear seal mating surface. Carefully install oil pan and torque attaching bolts alternately and evenly to specification. Torqing bolts while RTV sealer is still wet to touch.

OIL PUMP SERVICE

REMOVAL

1. Drain crankcase, then remove oil pan as previously described.
2. Remove pump to rear main bearing attaching bolt, then remove pump, extension shaft and retainer, **Fig. 14.**

DISASSEMBLY

1. Remove four pump cover to body attaching bolts, then remove cover, idler and drive gears and shaft, **Fig. 15.** **Place align mark on oil pump drive and idler gear teeth so they can be installed in the same position.**
2. Remove pressure regulator valve retaining pin, spring and the valve from pump body.

INSPECTION

Inspect pump components and should any of the following conditions exist, the oil pump assembly should be replaced.
1. Inspect pump body, gears and cover for cracks or excessive wear.
2. Check drive gear shaft for looseness in housing.
3. Check inside of pump cover for wear that would allow oil to leak past ends of gears.
4. Check oil pickup screen assembly for damage to screen or pickup tube.
5. Check pressure regulator valve for fit in pump body.

ASSEMBLY

1. Install a replacement pickup screen and tube assembly, if removed. Position pump in a soft jawed vise, then apply sealer to end of tube and tap into position using tool No. J 8369 and a plastic hammer. Use care not to damage inlet screen and tube assembly when installing on pump housing.
2. Place pressure regulator valve, spring and retaining pin into pump body, then install drive gear and shaft.
3. Install idler gear into pump body, then the pump cover gasket, **Fig. 15.**
4. Install pump cover and cover retaining bolts, then torque bolts to specification.

INSTALLATION

1. Align oil pump extension shaft to distributor drive gear socket and pump housing with dowels on cap, then install shaft retainer and pump assembly.
2. Install oil pump assembly retaining bolt to rear main bearing cap and torque bolt to specification.
3. Install oil pan as previously described.

REAR MAIN BEARING OIL SEAL
REPLACE

In some cases, rear main seals are being replaced because of a chirping or squealing noise that goes away when oil is sprayed into the area. Improper engine ventilation can produce an internal vacuum depression which draws air past the seal.

If the noise disappears when the dipstick cap is removed, preventing sump depression, check the fresh air feed hole in the air inlet rubber duct for blockage where it connects to the rocker cover. Cut out any blockage to eliminate the noise problem and the need for rear seal replacement.
1. Support engine and remove transaxle.
2. Remove flywheel and check that rear seal is leaking.
3. Remove seal by carefully inserting screwdriver in through dust lip and prying towards end of crankshaft pilot. Repeat as necessary around circumference of seal until seal is removed, taking care not to damage crankshaft circumference.
4. Check inside of seal bore for nicks or burrs and correct as necessary. Inspect crankshaft for burrs or nicks on seal contact surface. Repair or replace crankshaft as necessary.
5. Install new seal using tool J-34686.
6. Place seal on mandrel, making sure that dust lip on seal bottoms squarely against collar of tool, **Fig. 16.**
7. After aligning dowel pin with dowel pin hole in crankshaft, attach tool to crankshaft and on 1988 models, **torque** screws to 2-5 ft. lbs. On 1989 models, **torque** screws to 27-62 inch lbs.
8. **On all models,** turn T-handle of tool until collar is tight against engine block to ensure that seal is seated properly in block.
9. Loosen T-handle of tool until it comes to a stop, then remove attaching screws.
10. Check that seal is seated squarely in bore.
11. Install flywheel and engine.
12. Start engine and check for leaks.

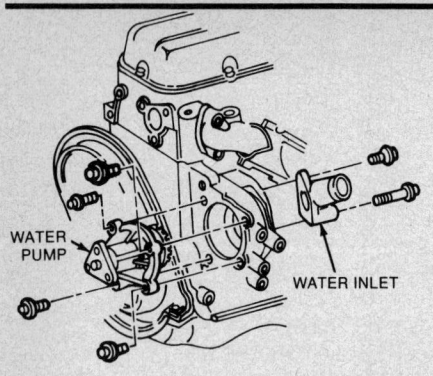

Fig. 17 Replacing water pump assembly

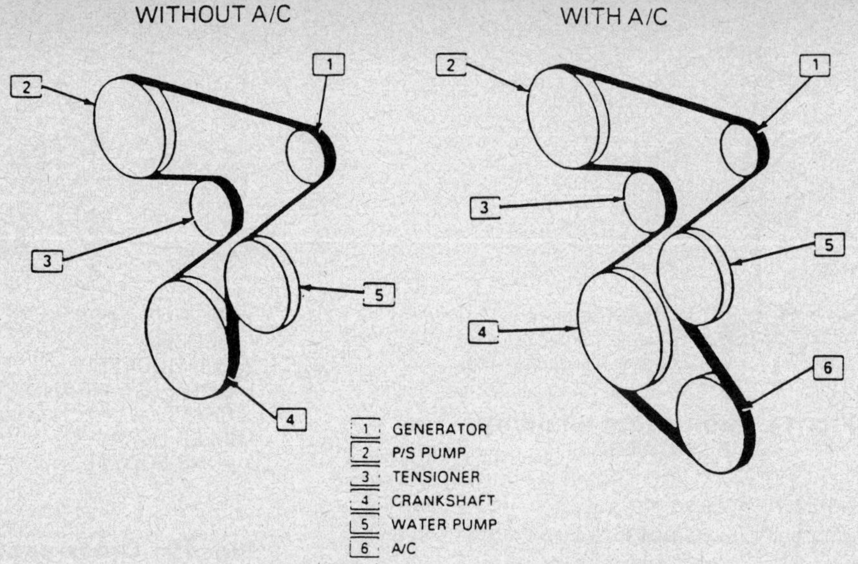

WITHOUT A/C   WITH A/C

1	GENERATOR
2	P/S PUMP
3	TENSIONER
4	CRANKSHAFT
5	WATER PUMP
6	A/C

Fig. 18 Serpentine drive belt routing

WATER PUMP REPLACE

1. Disconnect battery ground cable and drain cooling system.
2. Remove serpentine belt.
3. Remove alternator to alternator bracket retaining bolts and position alternator aside.
4. Remove water pump pulley to water pump attaching bolts, then the pulley from water pump.
5. Remove water pump to block attaching bolts and the water pump, **Fig. 17.**
6. Reverse removal procedures to complete installation.

COOLING SYSTEM BLEED

To ensure sufficient engine cooling, freezing and corrosion protection, maintain the protection level at −34°F or lower. Use a solution of antifreeze and water, ensuring solution is no more than 70 percent antifreeze.

1. Fill surge tank or radiator to base of filler neck, then attach pressure cap.
2. Block the drive wheel and apply parking brake.
3. On models equipped with automatic transaxle, place shifter in Park position.

4. **On models equipped with manual transaxle,** place transaxle in Neutral position.
5. **On all models,** start engine and allow to run until upper radiator hose is hot.
6. Turn engine Off, check level of coolant in surge tank or radiator.
7. Allow engine to cool, then add coolant as necessary.

BELT TENSION DATA

Belt	New Lbs.	Used Lbs.
Air Cond.	168②	90①
Serpentine Drive Belt	③	③

①—Minimum.
②—Maximum.
③—Belt tension is controlled by the belt tensioner.

FUEL PUMP REPLACE

1. Relieve system fuel pressure as outlined under "Fuel System Pressure Relief."
2. Disconnect battery ground cable, then raise and support vehicle.
3. Drain tank, then disconnect sending unit electrical connector and ground strap.
4. Disconnect all hoses and vent pipes at fuel tank.
5. Support fuel tank using a suitable jack, then remove tank retaining straps.
6. Lower fuel tank from vehicle.
7. Remove fuel tank sending unit and pump assembly by turning cam lock ring counterclockwise.
8. Lift assembly from tank, then disconnect pump from sending unit.
9. Reverse procedure to install.

SERPENTINE DRIVE BELT ROUTING

Refer to **Fig. 18,** for drive belt routing.

TIGHTENING SPECIFICATIONS

Year	Component	Torque/Ft. Lbs.
1988-89	Alternator Bracket Bolts (Long)	26-37
	Alternator Bracket Bolts (Short)	19-25
	Camshaft Cover (Rear)	6-9
	Camshaft Sprocket	66-88
	Camshaft Thrust Plate	4-14
	Connecting Rod Cap	34-43
	Crankshaft Pulley Center	66-89
	Crankshaft Pulley To Hub	30
	Cylinder Head (Long Bolts)	73-83
	Cylinder Head (Short Bolts)	62-70
	Drive Belt Tensioner Pulley	30-44
	Exhaust Manifold Nuts	6-13
	Exhaust Manifold Studs	3-11
	Flywheel (Automatic Trans.)	45-59
	Flywheel (Manual Trans.)	47-63
	Front Cover	6-10
	Idler Pulley	19-25
	Intake Manifold	15-22
	Main Bearing Caps	63-77
	Oil Pan	6 ①
	Oil Pump	26-38
	Oil Pump Cover	6-9
	Oil Pump Drive	15-22
	Power Steering Pulley	19-25
	Rocker Arm Cover	8
	Rocker Arm Stud	33-40
	Rocker Nut	11-18
	Spark Plug	7-20
	Timing Chain Tensioner	13-21
	Water Inlet	15-22
	Water Pump Pulley	20-25
	Water Pump To Block	22
	Water Pump To Front Cover	88 ②

2.2L/4-134 Engine

INDEX

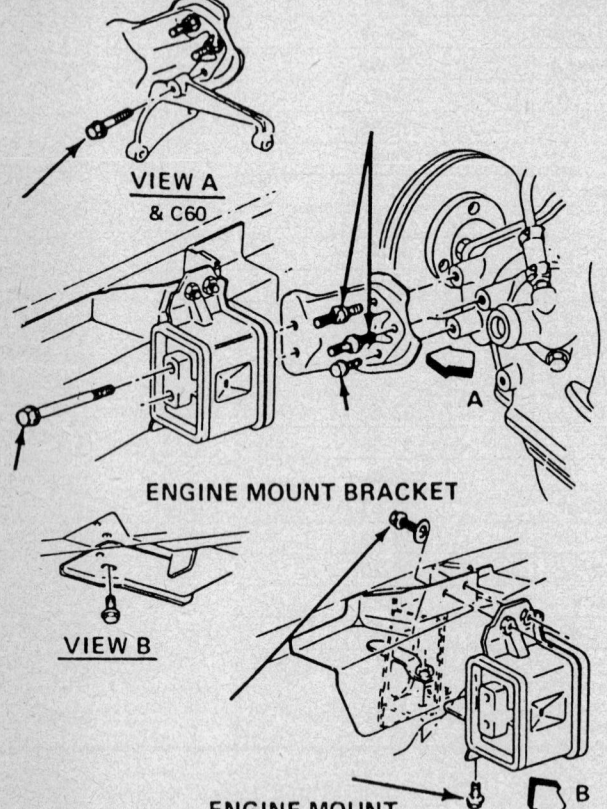

VIEW A
& C60

ENGINE MOUNT BRACKET

VIEW B

ENGINE MOUNT

Fig. 1   Front engine mount

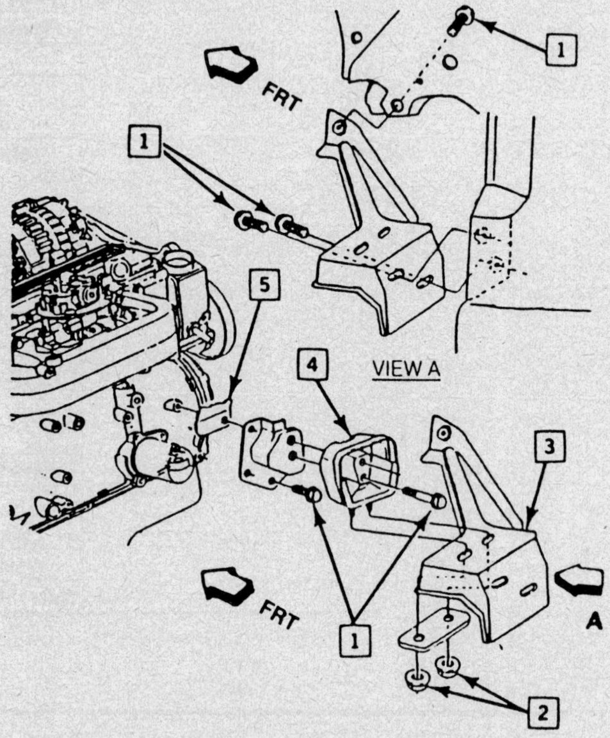

FRT

1

5

4   VIEW A

3

FRT

1

2

A

Fig. 2   Rear engine mount

ENGINE MOUNT
REPLACE
FRONT ENGINE MOUNT

1. Disconnect battery ground cable.
2. Remove upper engine mount to body bolts, **Fig. 1.**
3. Remove upper engine mount to engine bracket bolt.
4. Raise and support vehicle.
5. Using a suitable jack, support engine assembly.

6. Remove inner fender shield.
7. Remove lower engine mount to body bolt.
8. Remove lower engine mount to engine mount bracket bolt, then remove mount.
9. Reverse procedure to install, torque bolts and nuts to specifications.

REAR ENGINE MOUNT

1. Disconnect battery ground cable.
2. Raise and support vehicle.
3. Remove engine mount retaining bolts and nuts, **Fig. 2**, then remove mount.

4. Reverse procedure to install, torque bolts and nuts to specifications.

ENGINE
REPLACE

Refer to **Fig. 3**, when performing the following procedure.
1. Disconnect battery ground cable.
2. Loosen fuel filler cap to relieve tank vapor pressure.
3. Drain engine coolant, then disconnect hood lamp wiring.
4. Mark position of hood for assembly reference, then remove hood retaining bolts and remove hood.

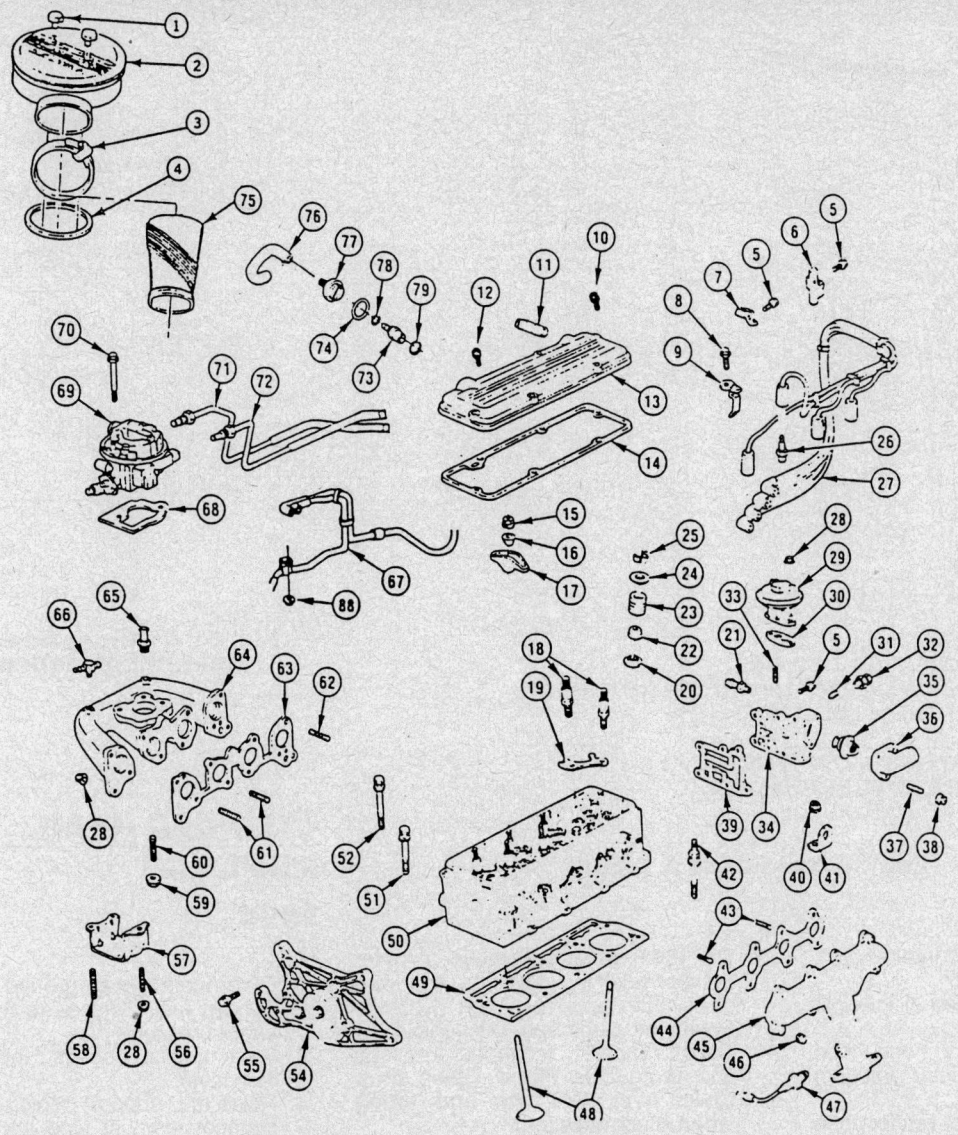

1 NUT, Air Cleaner	21 FITTING, Heater Coolant Hose	40 NUT	61 STUD, Intake Manifold
2 AIR CLEANER ASM.	22 SEAL, Valve Stem Oil	41 BRACKET, Engine Lift	62 STUD, Intake Manifold
3 CLAMP	23 SPRING, Valve	42 BOLT, Cylinder Head	63 GASKET, Intake Manifold
4 SEAL, Throttle Body	24 CAP, Valve Spring	43 STUD, Exhaust Manifold	64 MANIFOLD, Intake
5 BOLT	25 KEY, Valve Stem	44 GASKET, Exhaust Manifold	65 FITTING, Vacuum Power Brake
6 SUPPORT, Spark Plug Wire Front	26 PLUG, Spark	45 MANIFOLD, Exhaust	66 FITTING, Intake Manifold Vacuum
7 SUPPORT, Spark Plug Wire Rear	27 WIRE, Spark Plug	46 NUT	67 TUBE, EGR Vacuum & Evaporator Canister
8 BOLT	28 NUT	47 SENSOR, Oxygen	68 GASKET, TBI
9 SUPPORT, Ignition Wire	29 VALVE, EGR	48 VALVE, Inlet	69 INJECTOR, Throttle Body
10 BOLT, Valve Rocker Cover	30 GASKET, EGR Valve	49 GASKET, Cylinder Head	70 BOLT, TBI
11 TUBE, Crankcase Vent	31 PLUG, Water Outlet	50 HEAD, w Guide and Insert	71 PIPE, Fuel Injection (Return)
12 BOLT, Valve Rocker Cover	32 SENSOR, Coolant Temperature	51 BOLT, Cylinder Head (Short)	72 PIPE, Fuel Injection (Feed)
13 COVER, Valve Rocker	33 STUD, EGR Valve	52 BOLT, Cylinder Head (Long)	73 VALVE, Positive Crankcase Ventilation
14 GASKET, Valve Rocker Cover	34 ADAPTER, Collant Outlet	54 BRACKET, Drive Belt Tensioner	74 SEAL, PCV Cap
15 NUT, Valve Rocker Arm	35 THERMOSTAT, Engine Coolant Outlet	55 BOLT	75 DUCT, Air Cleaner Intake
16 BALL, Rocker Arm	36 OUTLET, Coolant	56 STUD	76 HOSE, PCV
17 ARM, Valve Rocker	37 STUD	57 BRACKET, Accelerator Control Cable	77 CAP, PCV
18 STUD, Valve Rocker Arm Ball	38 NUT	58 STUD	78 SEAL, PCV
19 GUIDE, Push Rod	39 GASKET, Coolant Outlet	59 NUT	79 SEAL, PCV
20 SEAT, Valve Spring		60 STUD	

Fig. 3   Exploded view of cylinder head assembly

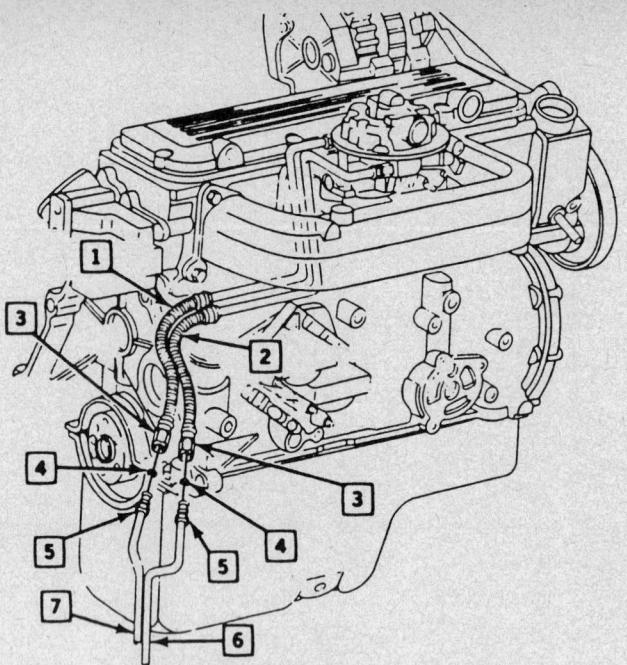

1. HOSE, FUEL FEED
2. HOSE, FUEL RETURN
3. FITTING — BACK-UP WRENCH REQUIRED AT THESE LOCATIONS
4. SEAL — O-RING
5. FITTING — 27 N·m (20 LBS. FT.)
6. PIPE, FUEL RETURN
7. PIPE, FUEL FEED

Fig. 4   Engine fuel hoses & pipes

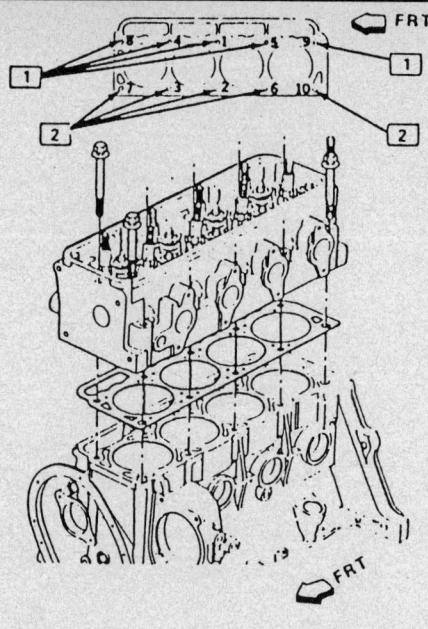

Fig. 5   Cylinder head bolt tightening sequence

CYLINDER HEAD REPLACE

1990

1. Disconnect battery ground cable.
2. Loosen fuel filler cap to relieve tank vapor pressure.
3. Drain engine coolant, then remove TBI cover.
4. Raise and support vehicle, then disconnect exhaust pipe from exhaust manifold.
5. Disconnect heater hose, accelerator and T.V. cable bracket from intake manifold.
6. Lower vehicle, then remove remaining vacuum hoses from the intake.
7. Disconnect accelerator linkage at the TBI any necessary wires.
8. Disconnect upper radiator hose at thermostat, then remove serpentine belt.
9. Remove power steering pump and position aside.
10. Disconnect fuel feed and return lines, **Fig. 4.**
11. Remove alternator with wires and position aside, then remove alternator rear brace.
12. Remove rocker arm cover, then rocker arms and pushrods. Keep valve train components in order. They should be installed in the same locations and with the same mating surfaces as when removed.
13. Remove cylinder head bolts, then remove the cylinder head with manifolds and TBI unit.

5. Remove throttle body intake duct, then rear sight shields.
6. Remove the battery, then air cleaner housing.
7. Remove upper radiator hose, then disconnect brake booster vacuum hose.
8. Remove alternator top brace, then disconnect wiring.
9. Disconnect upper engine wiring harness from engine.
10. Discharge A/C system, then remove compressor to condensor and accumulator lines.
11. Raise and support vehicle.
12. Remove left splash shield, then disconnect exhaust system from the engine.
13. Disconnect lower engine wiring, then remove flywheel inspection cover.
14. Remove front wheels and lower radiator hose.
15. Disconnect heater hoses from the heater core, then remove brake calipers from the steering knuckle. Use wire to support brake calipers.
16. Disconnect tie rod ends from struts, then lower the vehicle.
17. Remove left side sound insulator from under dash panel, then disconnect the clutch master cylinder pushrod from the clutch pedal.
18. Remove clutch slave cylinder retaining nuts at front of dash and disconnect remote reservoir, if equipped.

19. **On 1990 models,** remove actuator cylinder retaining nuts from the transaxle, then remove clutch hydraulic system as a unit from the vehicle.
20. **On all models,** disconnect fuel feed and return lines, **Fig. 4. Place shop towel over fuel line and fitting when disconnecting.**
21. Disconnect transaxle linkage at the transaxle.
22. Disconnect accelerator, cruise control and TV cables from the TBI.
23. **On models equipped with automatic transaxle,** disconnect transmission cooling lines from the transaxle.
24. **On all models,** disconnect power steering hoses from the power steering pump.
25. Remove four center carriage support bolts, then align dolly under frame and lower vehicle to dolly and add support under engine.
26. Support rear of vehicle, then remove upper transaxle mount.
27. Remove upper strut bolts and nuts.
28. Remove front engine mount, then rear engine mount.
29. Remove four rear, then four front carriage retaining bolts.
30. Wire front carriage bolt holes together to prevent axle separation.
31. Raise vehicle and remove engine and transaxle assembly on dolly.
32. Reverse procedure to install.

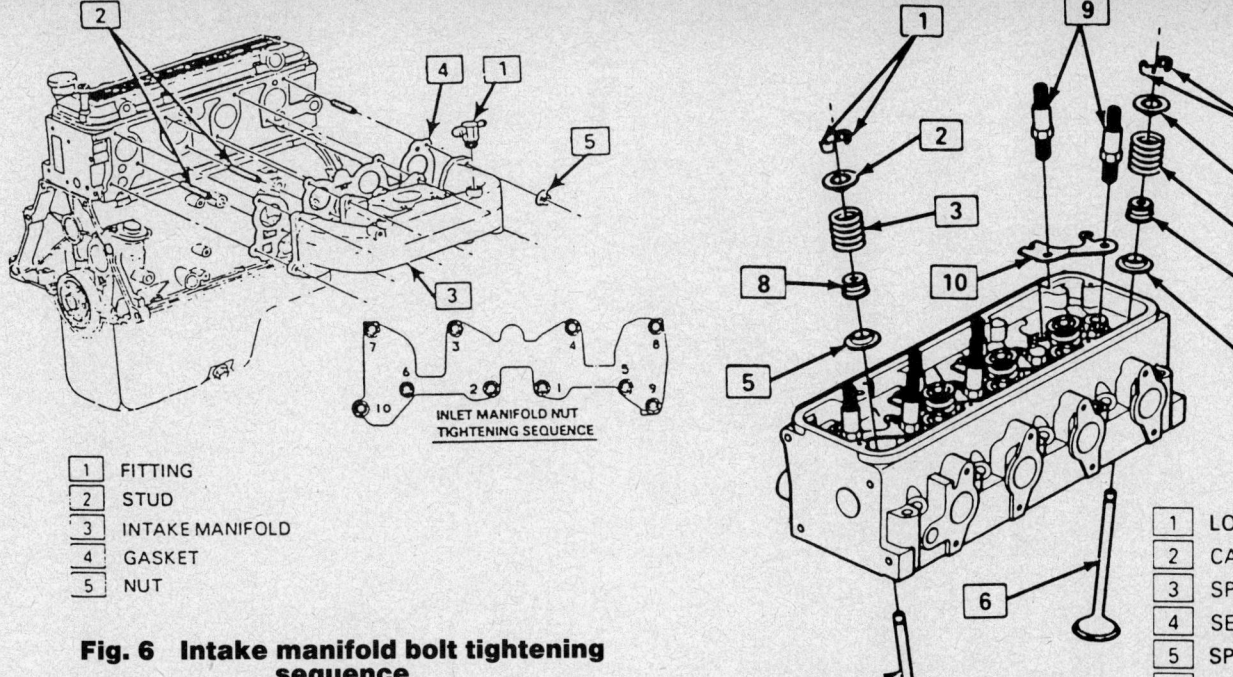

1 FITTING
2 STUD
3 INTAKE MANIFOLD
4 GASKET
5 NUT

INLET MANIFOLD NUT TIGHTENING SEQUENCE

Fig. 6   Intake manifold bolt tightening sequence

1 LOCKS
2 CAP
3 SPRING
4 SEAL (EX)
5 SPRING SEAT
6 VALVE (EX)
7 VALVE (IN)
8 SEAL (IN)
9 STUD
10 GUIDE

Fig. 7   Valves, valve seals & valve springs

14. Reverse procedure to install, torque cylinder head retaining bolts to specifications in sequence shown in **Fig. 5.**

1991

1. Disconnect battery ground cable, then loosen fuel filler cap to relieve tank vapor pressure.
2. Remove air cleaner assembly, then drain cooling system.
3. Disconnect TBI attaching vacuum hoses, electrical connectors and accelerator cable.
4. Remove coolant reservoir tank.
5. Remove serpentine belt, then remove alternator.
6. Loosen power steering pump attaching bolts, then position away.
7. Remove serpentine belt tensioner.
8. Remove ignition wires, then remove canister purge line beneath manifold.
9. Remove upper radiator hose, then remove upper and lower heater hose at manifold.
10. Remove throttle body cables from bracket.
11. Remove cylinder head coolant inlet hose.
12. Remove intake manifold brace to power steering bracket attaching bolts.
13. Remove attaching fuel lines. **Place shop towel over fuel line and fitting when disconnecting.**
14. Remove rocker arm cover attaching bolts, then remove rocker arm cover.
15. Remove rocker arms and pushrods.
16. Remove ignition cable bracket.
17. Remove cylinder head attaching bolts.
18. **On models equipped with automatic transaxle,** remove transaxle fluid level indicator bracket.
19. **On all models,** remove cylinder head assembly.

20. Reverse procedure to install. Refer to **Fig. 5,** for cylinder head bolt tightening sequence. Torque attaching bolts to specifications.

INTAKE MANIFOLD
REPLACE

1. Disconnect battery ground cable, then remove fuel filler cap to relieve fuel tank pressure.
2. Remove air cleaner assembly, then drain engine coolant.
3. Disconnect vacuum lines and wires from the intake as necessary.
4. Disconnect fuel feed and return lines, **Fig. 4.**
5. Disconnect TBI linkage and TBI assembly, then remove the power steering pump and position aside.
6. Disconnect coolant hose to intake manifold.
7. Raise and support vehicle.
8. **On 1990 models,** remove coolant pipe retaining nut, located on top of the D.I.S, and move the pipe rearward.
9. **On all models,** disconnect accelerator and T.V. cables, then remove the bracket.
10. Remove lower intake manifold retaining nuts, then lower the vehicle.
11. Remove upper intake manifold retaining bolts and nuts, then remove intake manifold.

12. Reverse procedure to install, torque bolts to specifications in sequence shown in **Fig. 6.**

EXHAUST MANIFOLD
REPLACE

1. Disconnect battery ground cable.
2. Disconnect oxygen sensor lead, then remove serpentine belt.
3. Remove alternator and position aside.
4. Raise and support vehicle.
5. Disconnect exhaust pipe from the exhaust manifold, then lower the vehicle.
6. Remove exhaust manifold attaching bolts and oil fill tube, then remove exhaust manifold.
7. Reverse procedure to install, torque manifold retaining bolts to specifications.

ROCKER COVER
REPLACE

1. Disconnect battery ground cable.
2. Disconnect air hose at TBI and air cleaner assembly, then disconnect PCV hose.
3. Remove rocker arm cover attaching bolts, then remove cover.
4. Reverse procedure to install, torque attaching bolts to specification.

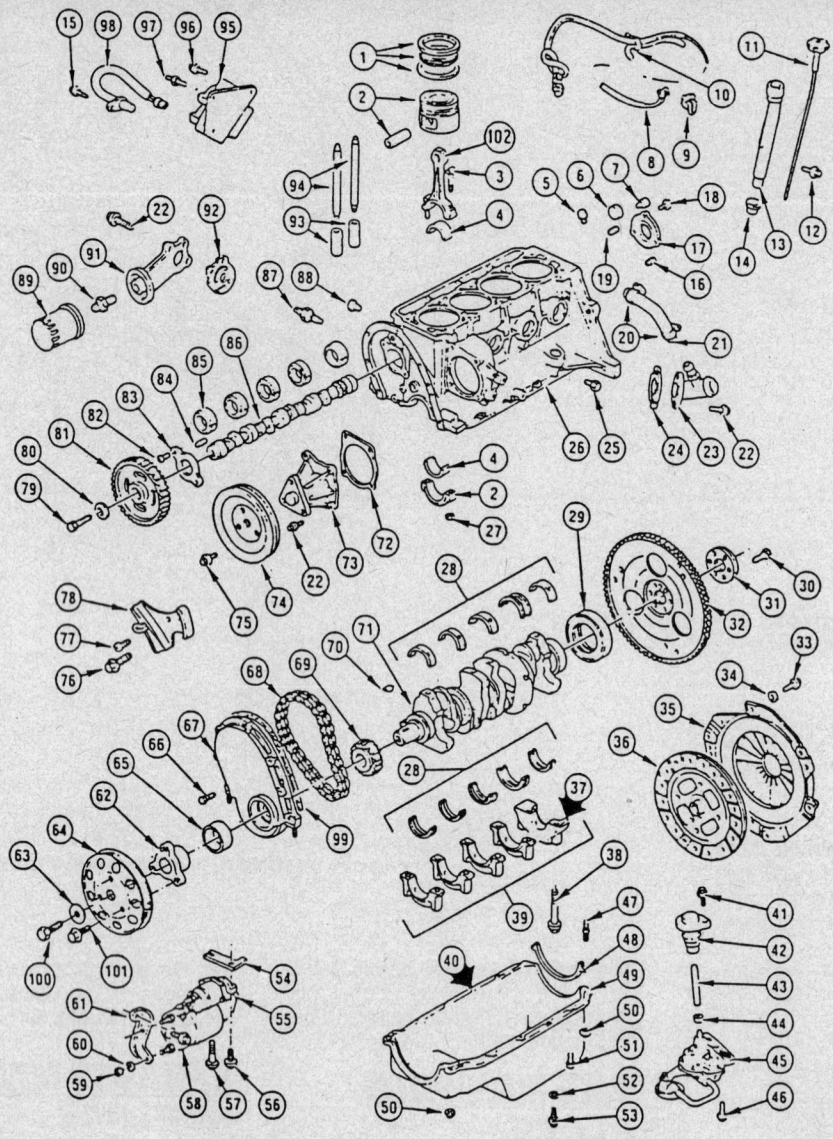

Fig. 8 Exploded view of cylinder block assembly

1. RING, Piston
2. PISTON, w Pin
3. BOLT, Connecting Rod
4. BEARING, Connecting Rod
5. PIN, Cylinder Head Dowel
6. PLUG, Cylinder Water Jacket Hole
7. PIN, Clutch Housing
8. CORD, Engine Block Heater
9. HEATER, Engine Block
10. RETAINER
11. CAP, Oil Fil & Gage
12. BOLT
13. TUBE, Oil Fil
14. SEAL, Oil Fil Tube
15. BOLT
16. PLUG
17. COVER, Camshaft Rear
18. BOLT
19. PLUG
20. CLAMP
21. HOSE, Coolant Inlet
22. BOLT
23. INLET, Coolant
24. GASKET, Coolant Inlet
25. PLUG

26. ENGINE, Partial
27. NUT, Connecting Rod
28. BEARING, Crankshaft
29. SEAL, Crankshaft Rear Oil
30. BOLT, Flywheel
31. RETAINER, Flywheel
32. FLYWHEEL, Crankshaft
33. BOLT, Clutch Cover & Pressure Plate
34. WASHER, Spring Lock
35. COVER, Plate, Clutch Pressure
36. PLATE, Clutch Driven
37. SEALANT
38. BOLT, Crankshaft Bearing Cap
39. CAP, Crankshaft Bearing
40. SEALER
41. BOLT
42. DRIVE, Oil Pump
43. SHAFT, Distributor to Oil Pump
44. RETAINER
45. PUMP, w Screen
46. BOLT, Oil Pump & Screen
47. STUD
48. SEAL, Oil Pan Rear
49. PAN, Oil
50. NUT

51. BOLT
52. GASKET, Oil Pan Drain Screw
53. SCREW, Oil Pan Drain
54. SHIM, Starter Motor
55. MOTOR, Starter
56. BOLT, Starter Motor Outboard
57. BOLT, Starter Motor Inboard
58. BOLT
59. NUT
60. WASHER, Flat
61. BRACKET, Starter Motor
62. HUB, Crankshaft Pulley
63. WASHER
64. PULLEY, Crankshaft
65. SEAL, Crankshaft Front Oil
66. SCREW, Hex
67. COVER, Crankcase Front End
68. CHAIN, Camshaft Timing
69. SPROCKET, Crankshaft
70. KEY
71. CRANKSHAFT, Engine
72. GASKET, Water Pump
73. PUMP, Coolant
74. PULLEY, Water Pump
75. BOLT
76. BOLT

77. BOLT, Tensioner Timing Chain
78. TENSIONER, Timing Chain
79. BOLT, Hex
80. WASHER, Camshaft Sprocket
81. SPROCKET, Camshaft
82. SCREW, Camshaft Thrust Plate
83. PLATE, Camshaft Thrust
84. PIN
85. BEARING, Camshaft
86. CAMSHAFT, Engine
87. SWITCH, Fuel Pump
88. VALVE, Oil Filter By-pass
89. FILTER, Oil (PF52)
90. CONNECTOR, Oil Filter Adapter
91. ADAPTER, Oil Filter
92. GASKET, Oil Filter Adapter
93. LIFTER, Hydraulic Valve
94. ROD, Push
95. COIL, w Module Ignition
96. BOLT
97. STUD, Ignition coil
98. SENSOR, Crankshaft
99. GASKET
100. BOLT, Crankshaft Pulley Hub
101. BOLT, Crankshaft Pulley
102. CONNECTING ROD

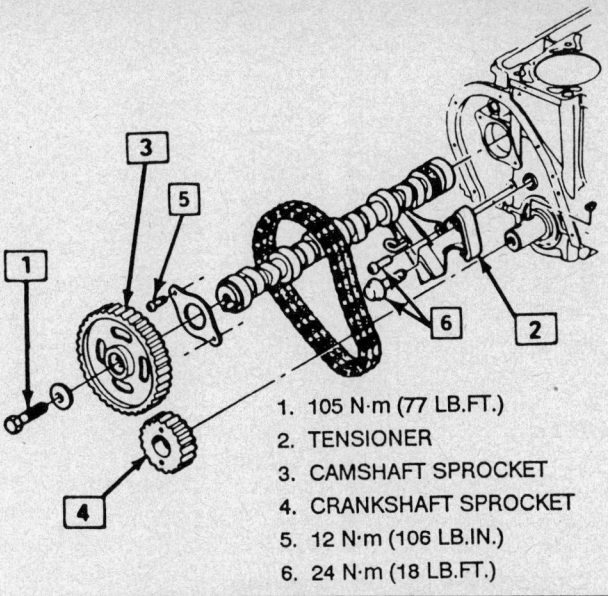

1. 105 N·m (77 LB.FT.)
2. TENSIONER
3. CAMSHAFT SPROCKET
4. CRANKSHAFT SPROCKET
5. 12 N·m (106 LB.IN.)
6. 24 N·m (18 LB.FT.)

NOTE– ALIGN TABS ON TENSIONER WITH MARKS ON CAMSHAFT & CRANKSHAFT SPROCKETS.

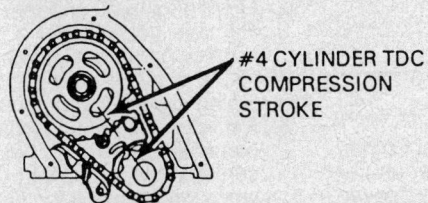

#4 CYLINDER TDC COMPRESSION STROKE

Fig. 9   Timing chain & sprockets

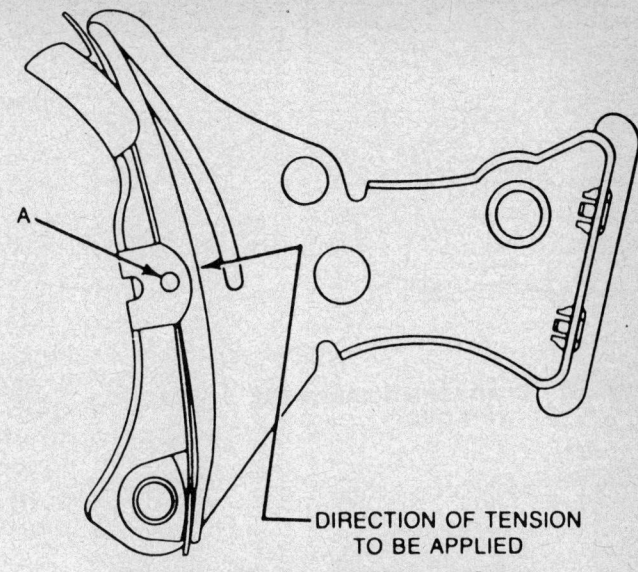

DIRECTION OF TENSION TO BE APPLIED

Fig. 10   Timing chain tensioner

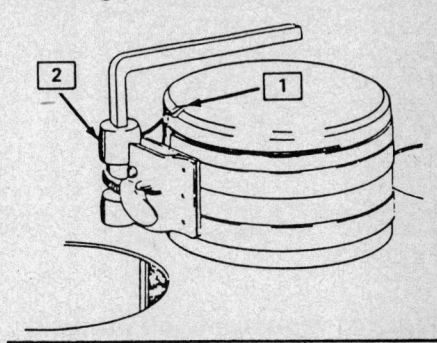

1–NOTCH TOWARDS FRONT OF ENGINE
2–TOOL J-8037

Fig. 11   Installing piston

VALVE GUIDES

Valve guides are an integral part of the cylinder head and are not removable. If valve stem clearance becomes excessive, the valve guide should be reamed to the next oversize and the appropriate oversize valves installed. Valves are available in .00295, .0059 and .00984 inch oversizes.

VALVE LIFTER
REPLACE

1. Remove rocker cover as described previously.
2. Loosen rocker arm nut and swing rocker arm aside.
3. Remove pushrod, then using a flexible magnetic wand remove lifter.
4. Inspect lifter for any signs of damage or wear, replacing as necessary.
5. Reverse procedure to install.

VALVE SPRING & VALVE STEM OIL SEAL
REPLACE
REMOVAL

1. Disconnect battery ground cable, then remove rocker cover.
2. With engine cold, remove spark plug and clean debris from plug recess.
3. Remove rocker arm and pushrod on cylinders to be serviced.
4. Install air line adapter tool No. J 23590 or equivalent in spark plug thread and apply compressed air to hold valves in place.
5. With valve spring compressor tool No. J 5892-B on 1990 models, tool No. J 5892-C on 1991 models or equivalents, compress valve spring and remove valve lock and cap, **Fig. 7.**
6. Remove spring, valve stem oil seal and shim.

INSTALLATION

1. Install shim if required, then new valve stem oil seal.
2. Set valve spring and cap in place.
3. Using valve spring compressor tool No. J 5892-B on 1990 models, tool No. J 5892-C on 1991 models or equivalents, compress valve spring.
4. Install valve locks and release compressor. **Make sure locks seat properly in the upper groove of the valve stem. Grease may be used to hold the locks in place while releasing the compressor tool.**
5. Install spark plug, pushrods, rocker arms and rocker cover.

CRANKSHAFT PULLEY & HUB
REPLACE
REMOVAL

Refer to **Fig. 8,** when performing the following any procedures.
1. Disconnect battery ground cable.
2. Remove serpentine belt, then raise and support vehicle.
3. Remove wheel and tire assembly, then inner fender splash shield.
4. Remove three crankshaft pulley retaining bolts.
5. Remove crankshaft pulley hub bolt, then the crankshaft pulley.
6. Install crankshaft pulley puller tool No. J 24420-B or equivalent on hub.
7. Turn puller screw and remove hub.

INSTALLATION

1. Coat front cover seal contact area with engine oil.

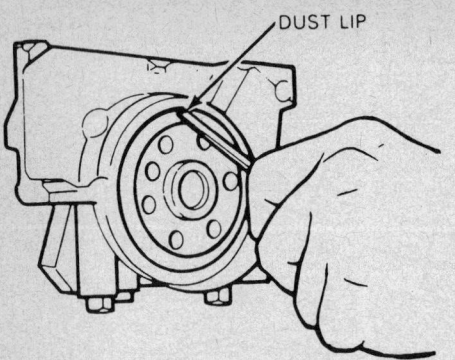

Fig. 12   Crankshaft rear seal removal

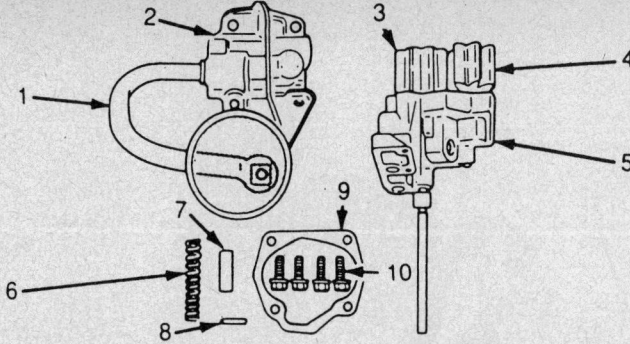

1. PICK UP TUBE AND SCREEN.
2. PUMP COVER.
3. DRIVE GEAR AND SHAFT.
4. IDLER GEAR.
5. PUMP BODY.
6. PRESSURE REGULATOR SPRING.
7. PRESSURE REGULATOR VALVE.
8. RETAINING PIN.
9. GASKET.
10. ATTACHING BOLTS.

Fig. 13   Exploded view of oil pump

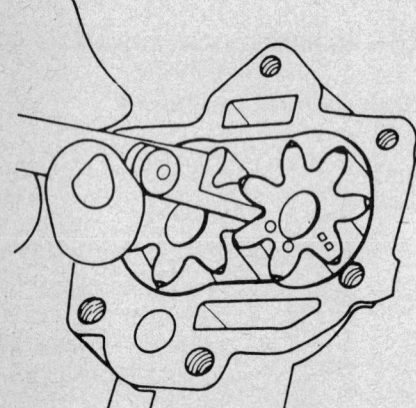

Fig. 14   Measuring oil pump gear lash

2. Apply RTV sealer No. 1052917 or equivalent, to keyway in pulley hub.
3. Place crankshaft pulley hub into position over key on crankshaft.
4. Install crankshaft pulley installer No. J 29113 into crankshaft so that at least 1/4 inch of thread is engaged.
5. Pull pulley hub into position and remove tool from crankshaft.
6. Install crankshaft pulley, then three pulley retaining bolts.
7. Install inner slash shield, then wheel and tire assembly.
8. Lower vehicle and install serpentine belt.
9. Connect battery ground cable.

CRANKCASE FRONT COVER
REPLACE

1. Disconnect battery ground cable.
2. Remove serpentine belt, then the belt tensioner.
3. Raise and support vehicle, then remove oil pan as described in "Oil Pan, Replace."
4. Remove crankshaft pulley and hub as described in "Crankshaft Pulley and Hub, Replace."
5. Remove front cover retaining bolts, then remove front cover.
6. Reverse procedure to install.

TIMING CHAIN & SPROCKETS
REPLACE

1. Disconnect battery ground cable, then remove crankcase front cover as described in "Crankcase Front Cover, Replace."
2. Align marks on crankshaft sprocket and camshaft sprocket, **Fig. 9.**
3. Remove timing chain tensioner upper bolt, then loosen timing chain tensioner torx as far as possible, but do not remove.
4. Remove camshaft sprocket and timing chain.
5. Using puller tool No. J 22888 on 1990 models, tool No. J 22888-20 on 1991 models or equivalents, remove crankshaft sprocket.
6. Reverse procedure to install, noting the following:
   a. Compress tensioner spring, then install a cotter pin or nail into hole A as shown in **Fig. 10.**
   b. Lube timing chain and sprockets with engine oil, lube thrust thrust surface with camshaft assembly lube No. 1052365 or equivalent.
   c. Align marks on camshaft and crankshaft sprockets with tabs on tensioner as shown in **Fig. 10.**
   d. Align dowel in camshaft with dowel hole camshaft sprocket.
   e. Draw camshaft sprocket onto camshaft using the mounting bolt. Torque to specifications.

CAMSHAFT
REPLACE
REMOVAL

1. Remove engine assembly as described in "Engine, Replace."

2. Drain engine oil and remove oil filter.
3. Remove valve lifters and crankcase front cover as described previously.
4. Remove oil pump drive, then remove timing chain and camshaft sprocket.
5. Remove camshaft thrust plate and camshaft. Use care not to damage camshaft bearings with the camshaft when withdrawing the camshaft.
6. Inspect camshaft for wear, galling, wear, gouges and overheating. If any of these problems exist, replace the camshaft.

INSTALLATION

1. Install camshaft and thrust plate. **Coat camshaft lobes and bearings with camshaft lube No. 1051396 or equivalent. Insert camshaft with extreme care to avoid personal injury and gouging of the camshaft bearings.**
2. Torque thrust plate specifications, then install camshaft sprocket and timing chain.
3. Install crankcase front cover.
4. Replace valve lifters. Lifters must be installed in the same bores from which they were removed. **If a new camshaft is installed, replace all valve lifters. Some lifters may be oversized, verify marking near the lifter bore.**
5. Install valve mechanism, parts must be reinstalled in the same position and with the same mating surfaces from which they were removed.
6. Install rocker cover, then the oil pump drive.
7. Replace oil filter, then install engine assembly.

PISTON & ROD ASSEMBLY

Assemble piston to rod, with arrow on piston facing toward front of engine **Fig.**

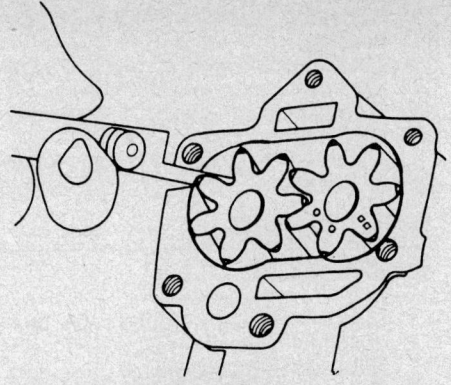

Fig. 15 Measuring gear side clearance

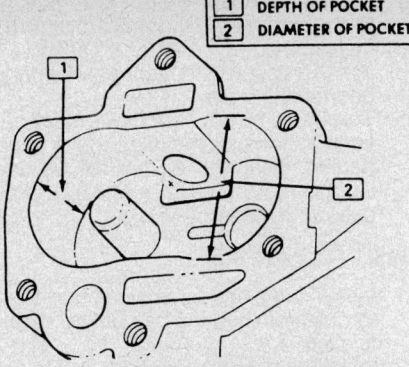

| 1 | DEPTH OF POCKET |
| 2 | DIAMETER OF POCKET |

Fig. 16 Measuring oil pump gear pocket

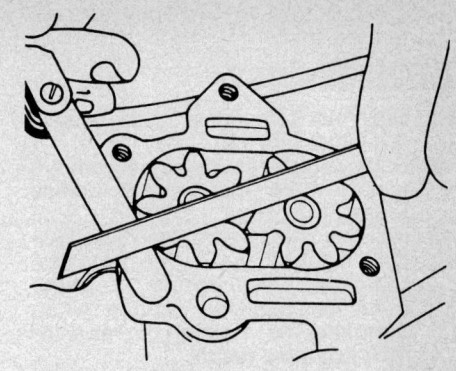

Fig. 17 Measuring oil pump end clearance

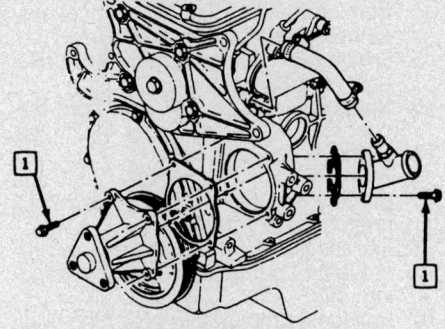

1. BOLT – 25 N·m (18 LBS. FT.)

Fig. 18 Water pump installation

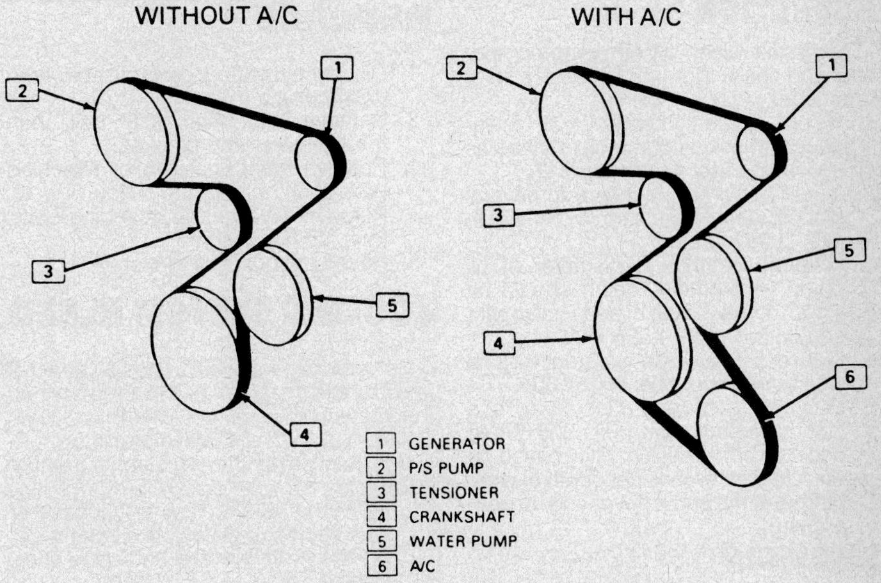

WITHOUT A/C

WITH A/C

1	GENERATOR
2	P/S PUMP
3	TENSIONER
4	CRANKSHAFT
5	WATER PUMP
6	A/C

Fig. 19 Serpentine drive belt routing

11. Upon installation measure connecting rod side clearance using a feeler gauge. Side clearance should be .0039 to .0149 inch.

PISTONS, PINS & RINGS

Pistons are available in standard size and oversize of .020 inch (.5mm). Piston pins are available in standard size only.

CRANKSHAFT REAR OIL SEAL
REPLACE

1. Remove transaxle from vehicle as described in "Transaxle, Replace."
2. **On models with manual transaxle,** remove pressure plate and clutch disc.
3. **On all models,** remove flywheel attaching bolts and flywheel.
4. Insert a screwdriver or similar tool in through the dust lip as shown in **Fig. 12,** pry out seal.
5. Reverse procedure to install, noting the following:
   a. Lubricate seal bore to seal surface with engine oil.
   b. Using seal installation tool No. J 34686 or equivalent, align dowel pin of tool with dowel pin hole in

crankshaft and attach tool to crankshaft.
   c. **Torque** tool attaching screws to 27-62 inch lbs., then tighten tool T handle to push seal into bore. Continue to tighten until tool is flush against block.

OIL PAN
REPLACE

1. Disconnect battery ground cable.
2. Raise and support vehicle, then disconnect exhaust pipe from the exhaust manifold.
3. Drain engine oil, then remove starter bracket at block.
4. Remove starter and position aside, then remove flywheel cover.
5. Remove four right side engine support bolts, then lower support slightly to gain clearance for oil pan removal.
6. **On models with automatic transaxle,** remove oil filter and extension.

7. **On all models,** remove oil pan retaining bolts and oil pan.
8. Reverse procedure to install, noting the following:
   a. Apply a ¹⁄₁₆ inch diameter bead of GM 1052914 RTV or equivalent, on oil pan to block sealing flanges.
   b. Apply RTV sealer or equivalent to oil pan surface which fits to engine front cover.
   c. Using a new oil pan rear seal, apply a thin coat of RTV sealer or equivalent on ends down to ears, install pan against cylinder case and install bolts.
   d. **On models with automatic transaxle,** replace oil filter adapter seal and install oil filter adapter.

OIL PUMP SERVICE
REMOVAL

1. Remove oil pan as described previously.
2. Remove pump to rear main bearing

cap bolt, then remove pump and extension shaft.

DISASSEMBLY

1. Drain oil from pump, then remove driveshaft, **Fig. 13.**
2. Remove pump cover, **Do not remove pickup tube from cover unless loose or broken.**
3. Remove pump gears, then the pressure regulator valve. **The pressure regulator valve spring is under pressure. Exercise caution when removing the retaining pin, as bodily injury may result.**
4. Remove plug, spring and valve. If valve is stuck, soak the pump housing in carburetor cleaning solvent.

INSPECTION

Thoroughly clean all oil pump components and check them for excessive wear or damage.

1. Using a straightedge and feeler gauge, check oil pump clearances as shown in **Figs. 14 through 17.**
2. Install gears and measure in several places, gear lash should be within .004-.008 inch.
3. Measure depth and diameter of oil pump gear pocket, depth should be 1.195-1.198 inch and diameter should be 1.503-1.506 inch.
4. Measure gear side clearance, side clearance should be .0015-.004.
5. Measure gear end clearance, end clearance should be .002-.006. When deciding pump seviceability based on end clearance, consider depth of wear pattern in the pump cover and/or cover plate.

ASSEMBLY

1. Lubricate all internal parts with engine oil during assembly.
2. Install pump gears. **To avoid engine damage, all pump cavities must be** packed with petroleum jelly before installing gears to assure priming.
3. Install oil pump cover and gasket.
4. Install pressure regulator valve, spring and retaining pin.
5. Torque pump cover bolts to specifications. Whenever the oil pump is overhauled, clear the oil pan of oil and sludge, replace oil filter and fill crankcase with clean oil.

INSTALLATION

1. Install pump and extension shaft, then torque main bearing cap bolt to specification.
2. Install oil pan.

WATER PUMP REPLACE

1. Disconnect battery ground cable, then drain cooling system.
2. Remove serpentine drive belt, then the alternator and bracket.
3. Remove water pump pulley attaching bolts, then remove the pulley, **Fig. 18.**
4. Remove water pump attaching bolts, then the water pump.
5. Reverse procedure to install.

COOLING SYSTEM BLEED

To ensure sufficient engine cooling, freezing and corrosion protection, maintain the protection level at −34°F or lower. Use a solution of antifreeze and water, ensuring solution is no more than 70 percent antifreeze.

1. Fill surge tank or radiator to base of filler neck, then attach pressure cap.
2. Block the drive wheel and apply parking brake.
3. **On models equipped with automatic transaxle,** place shifter in Park position.
4. **On models equipped with manual** transaxle, place transaxle in Neutral position.
5. **On all models,** start engine and allow to run until upper radiator hose is hot.
6. Turn engine Off, check level of coolant in surge tank or radiator.
7. Allow engine to cool, then add coolant as necessary.

FUEL PUMP REPLACE

1. Disconnect battery ground cable, then drain fuel tank.
2. Raise and support vehicle.
3. Disconnect tank meter assembly harness from body harness connector.
4. Remove ground wire retaining screw from underbody, then disconnect hoses from fuel meter assembly.
5. Disconnect hoses at tank from filler and vent pipes.
6. Support fuel tank with jack, then disconnect two fuel tank retaining straps.
7. Remove tank assembly.
8. Remove fuel tank sending unit and pump assembly by turning cam lock ring counterclockwise.
9. Lift assembly from fuel tank and remove fuel pump from fuel tank sending unit.
10. Pull fuel pump up into attaching hose while pulling outward away from bottom support. Take care to prevent damage to rubber insulator and strainer during removal. After pump assembly is clear of bottom support, pull pump assembly out of rubber connector for removal.
11. Reverse procedure to install.

SERPENTINE DRIVE BELT ROUTING

Refer to **Fig. 19,** for serpentine drive belt routing.

TIGHTENING SPECIFICATIONS

Year	Component	Torque/ft. lbs.
1990	Brake Booster Vacuum Fitting	10
	Camshaft Pulley	77
	Camshaft Thrust Plate	106 ③
	Coolant Drain Plug (Cylinder Block)	11
	Coolant Outlet To Cylinder Head	8
	Crankcase Front Cover Bolts	97 ③
	Crankshaft Pulley & Hub To Crankshaft	85
	Crankshaft Pulley To Hub	37
	Cylinder Head Bolts	41 ①
	DIS Coil Assembly	18
	Exhaust Manifold Nuts	115 ③
	Exhaust Manifold Studs	9–10
	Exhaust Pipe To Manifold	18
	Engine Mount Bracket, Lower, To Engine, Front	61
	Engine Mount Bracket, Upper, To Engine, Front	54
	Engine Mount, Lower, To Bracket, Rear	18
	Engine Mount To Bracket, Front	74

Continued

TIGHTENING SPECIFICATIONS—Continued

Year	Component	Torque/ft. lbs.
1990 Cont'd	Engine Mount To Bracket, Rear	40
	Flywheel To Crankshaft, Auto. Trans.	52
	Flywheel To Crankshaft, Manual Trans.	55
	Intake Manifold	18
	Main Bearing Cap Bolts	70
	Oil Fill Tube To Cylinder Block	18
	Oil Filter Adapter To Cylinder Block	18
	Oil Pan	89③
	Oil Pump Cover Bolts	89③
	Oil Pump Drive Assembly Bolt	18
	Oil Pump To Bearing Cap	31
	Pressure Plate To Flywheel	15
	Rear Engine Lift Bracket	32
	Rocker Arm Cover	89③
	Rocker Arm Nuts	22
	Rod Bearing Cap Nut	38
	Serpentine Tensioner Assembly	37
	Spark Plugs	11
	Timing Chain Cover	8
	Timing Chain Tensioner	18
	Water Pump	18
	Water Pump Inlet	18
	Wheel And Tire Assembly	100
1991	Brake Booster Vacuum Fitting	10
	Camshaft Pulley	77
	Camshaft Thrust Plate	106③
	Coolant Drain Plug (Cylinder Block)	11
	Coolant Outlet To Cylinder Head	8
	Crankcase Front Cover Bolts	97③
	Crankshaft Pulley & Hub To Crankshaft	77
	Crankshaft Pulley To Hub	37
	Cylinder Head Bolts	②
	DIS Coil Assembly	18
	Exhaust Manifold Nuts	115③
	Exhaust Manifold Studs	9–10
	Exhaust Pipe To Manifold	18
	Engine Mount Bracket To Engine, Front	50
	Engine Mount, Lower, To Bracket, Rear	18
	Engine Mount To Bracket, Front	74
	Engine Mount To Bracket, Rear	50
	Flywheel To Crankshaft, Auto. Trans.	52
	Flywheel To Crankshaft, Manual Trans.	55
	Intake Manifold	18
	Main Bearing Cap Bolts	70
	Negative Battery Cable	13
	Oil Fill Tube To Cylinder Block	18
	Oil Filter Adapter To Cylinder Block	18
	Oil Pan	71③
	Oil Pump Cover Bolts	89③
	Oil Pump Drive Assembly Bolt	18
	Oil Pump To Bearing Cap	32
	Pressure Plate To Flywheel	15
	Rear Engine Lift Bracket	32
	Rocker Arm Cover	89③

Continued

TIGHTENING SPECIFICATIONS —Continued

Year	Component	Torque/ft. lbs.
1991 Cont'd	Rocker Arm Nuts	22
	Rod Bearing Cap Nut	38
	Serpentine Tensioner Assembly	37
	Spark Plugs	11
	Timing Chain Cover	8
	Timing Chain Tensioner	18
	Water Pump	18
	Water Pump Inlet	18
	Wheel And Tire Assembly	100

①—Plus three additional steps; 1st step, all bolts an additional 45°; 2nd step, all bolts an additional 45°; 3rd step, long bolts (8, 4, 1, 5, & 9) an additional 20°, short bolts (7, 3, 2, 6 & 10) an additional 10°.
②—Torque long bolts to 46 ft. lbs. and short bolts to 43 ft. lbs. Tightening all bolts an additional 90° in sequence.
③—Inch lbs.

2.8L/V6-173 & 3.1L/V6-192 Engines

INDEX

IDLE LEARN PROCEDURE

On 1990-91 models with 3.1L/V6-192 port fuel injected (PFI) engine, any time vehicle power has been interrupted the programed position of the IAC valve pintle is lost. The following procedure must be performed to update the ECM memory with the correct IAC valve pintle position for the vehicle and provide a stable idle speed.
1. Restore vehicle power.
2. **On 1991 models,** place transaxle in Park or Neutral position.
3. **On all models,** connect TECH I scan tool to ALDL connector located under the left hand side of the dash panel.
4. Select "IAC System."
5. Select "Idle Learn" in the "Misc. Test" mode.
6. Proceed as directed.

ENGINE MOUNT
REPLACE
FRONT MOUNT
1. Disconnect battery ground cable.
2. Remove engine mount nuts, then raise and support vehicle.
3. Support engine with suitable jack.
4. Remove inner fender shield.
5. Remove and discard engine mount bolts, **Figs. 1 and 2.**
6. Remove engine mount from vehicle.
7. Reverse procedure to install, using new engine mount bolts. Remove alignment bolt. Refer to **Figs. 1 and 2,** for tightening specifications. **If excessive force is required to remove alignment bolt, loosen transaxle adjusting bolts to align power train components.**

REAR MOUNT
1. Disconnect battery ground cable, then raise and support vehicle.
2. Support engine with suitable jack.

3. Remove motor mount nuts and attaching bolts, **Figs. 3 and 4.**
4. Reverse procedure to install. Refer to **Figs. 3 and 4,** for tightening specifications.

ENGINE
REPLACE
1. Disconnect battery ground cable and drain cooling system.
2. **On 1988 models,** remove air cleaner and the mass air flow meter.
3. **On 1989-91 models,** remove air cleaner and duct assembly.
4. **On all models,** remove exhaust crossover heat shield and the exhaust crossover pipe.
5. Remove serpentine belt, tensioner and idler, if equipped.
6. **On 1988 models,** remove power steering pump mounting bracket and disconnect heater pipe at power steering pump mounting bracket.
7. **On all models,** disconnect radiator hose at engine.

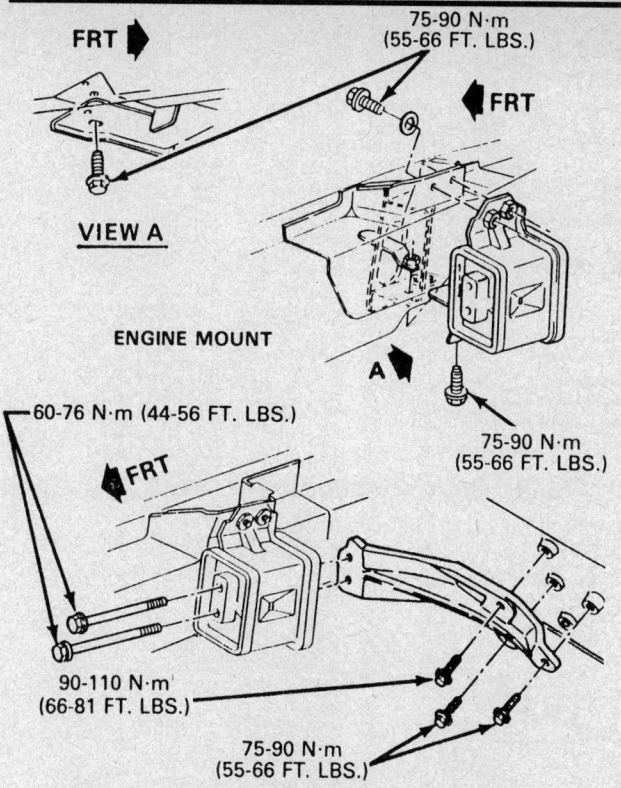

Fig. 1   Front engine mount. 1988

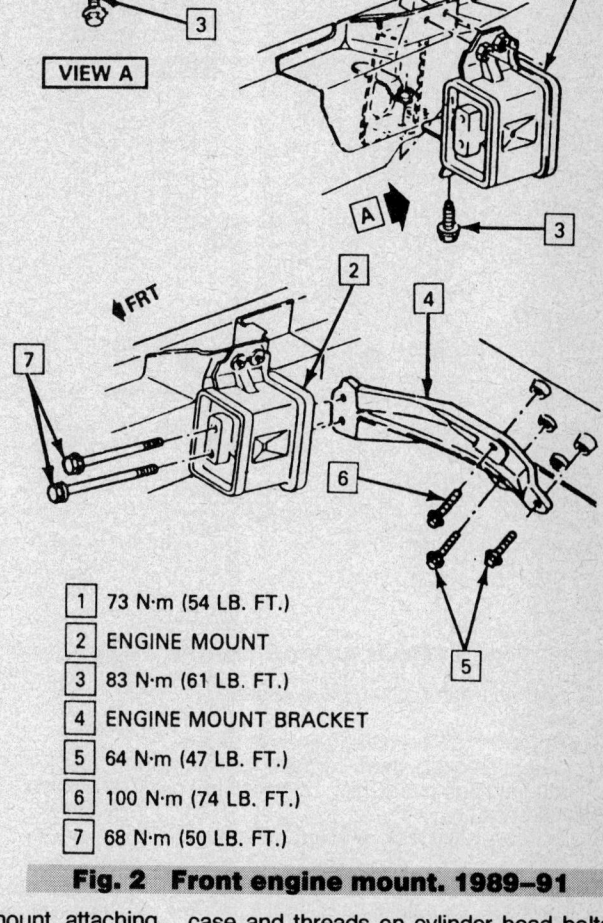

1	73 N·m (54 LB. FT.)
2	ENGINE MOUNT
3	83 N·m (61 LB. FT.)
4	ENGINE MOUNT BRACKET
5	64 N·m (47 LB. FT.)
6	100 N·m (74 LB. FT.)
7	68 N·m (50 LB. FT.)

Fig. 2   Front engine mount. 1989–91

8. Disconnect accelerator and T.V. cables at throttle valve.
9. Remove alternator and disconnect wiring harness at engine.
10. Loosen fuel filler cap to relieve tank vapor pressure, then disconnect fuel hoses and the coolant bypass and overflow hoses at engine.
11. **On 1988 models,** disconnect canister purge hose at canister and remove vacuum hoses as necessary.
12. **On all models,** raise and support vehicle, then remove right inner fender splash shield.
13. Remove harmonic balance and the flywheel cover.
14. Remove starter attaching bolts, disconnect electrical connectors at starter and remove starter.
15. **On 1988 models,** disconnect electrical connector at oil sending unit.
16. **On all models,** remove A/C compressor and its mounting bracket(s).
17. Disconnect exhaust pipe at rear of manifold.
18. Remove flex plate to torque converter attaching bolts and the transaxle to engine brace bolts.
19. **On 1988 models,** remove engine rear mount to frame nuts.
20. **On 1989-91 models,** remove front and rear engine mount to frame attaching bolts.
21. **On all models,** disconnect shift cable bracket at transaxle.
22. Remove lower bellhousing bolts and lower vehicle.
23. Disconnect heater hoses at engine.
24. Install suitable engine lifting device and support transaxle with suitable jack.
25. **On 1988 models,** remove upper bell-

housing and front mount attaching bolts.
26. **On all models,** remove transaxle attaching bolts.
27. Remove engine from vehicle.
28. Reverse procedure to install.

CYLINDER HEAD
REPLACE
REMOVAL

1. Disconnect battery ground cable.
2. Remove intake manifold and plenum assembly as described under "Intake Manifold, Replace."
3. Remove exhaust manifold as described under "Exhaust Manifold, Replace."
4. Disconnect wiring harness at cylinder head.
5. Remove spark plug wires and the spark plugs.
6. Remove rocker arm covers, rocker arm nuts, rocker arm balls, rocker arms and pushrods.
7. Remove cylinder head attaching bolts and the cylinder head.

INSTALLATION

Gasket surfaces on cylinder head and case must be clean and free of nicks or heavy scratches. Cylinder bolt threads in

case and threads on cylinder head bolts must be clean to obtain true torque.

1. Place gasket in position over dowel pins with note "This Side Up" showing and install cylinder head.
2. Coat cylinder head bolt threads with suitable sealant and install bolts.
3. Torque bolts in proper sequence, **Fig. 5.**
4. Install pushrods and loosely retain with rocker arms, ensuring lower ends of pushrods are in lifter seats.
5. Install spark plugs and wires.
6. Install intake and exhaust manifolds, then adjust valves as necessary.

INTAKE MANIFOLD
REPLACE

1. Disconnect battery ground cable.
2. Disconnect accelerator and T.V. cable bracket at plenum.
3. **On 1989-91 models,** disconnect brake vacuum pipe and plug harness at plenum.
4. **On all models,** disconnect throttle body at plenum.
5. Disconnect EGR pipe at EGR valve, then remove plenum.
6. Disconnect fuel inlet and return pipes at fuel rail.
7. Remove serpentine belt, then discon-

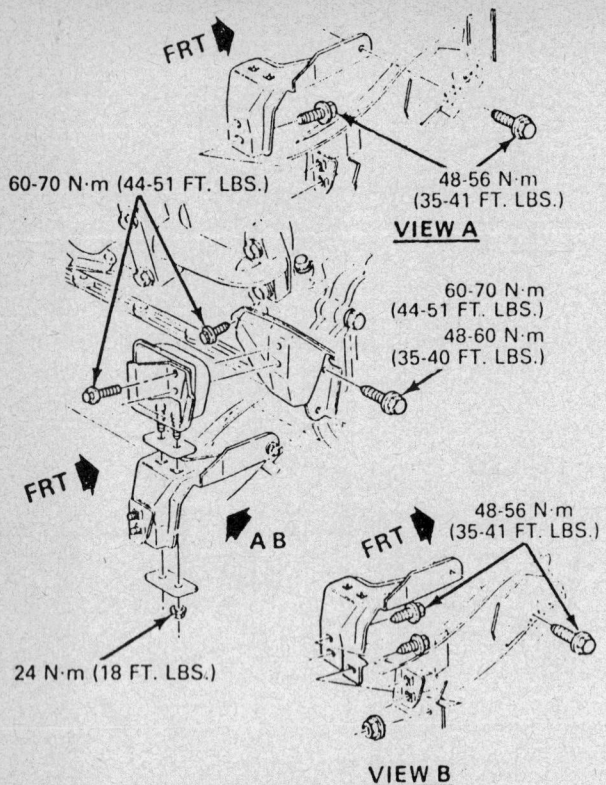

VIEW A

VIEW B

Fig. 3   Rear engine mount. 1988

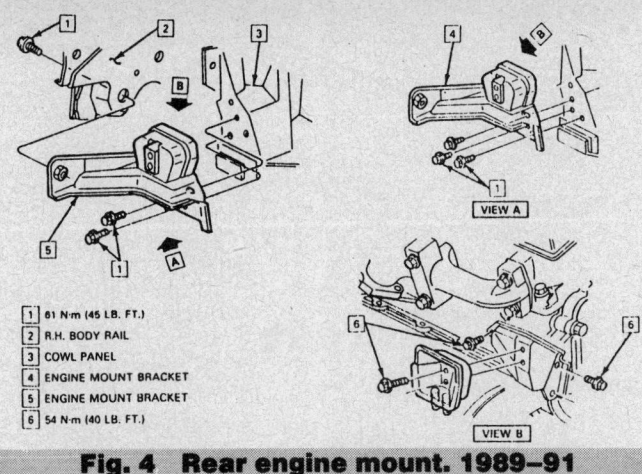

1	61 N·m (45 LB. FT.)
2	R.H. BODY RAIL
3	COWL PANEL
4	ENGINE MOUNT BRACKET
5	ENGINE MOUNT BRACKET
6	54 N·m (40 LB. FT.)

Fig. 4   Rear engine mount. 1989–91

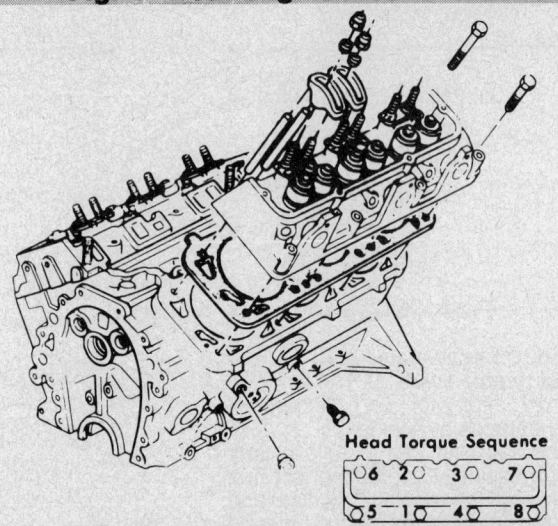

Head Torque Sequence

Fig. 5   Installing cylinder head

nect alternator assembly and position aside.

8. Remove power steering lines at alternator bracket, then remove power steering pump attaching bolts and position aside.
9. Loosen alternator bracket attaching bolts.
10. Remove idle air to throttle body vacuum hose, then disconnect fuel injector electrical connectors.
11. Remove fuel rail and breather tube.
12. **On 1988 models,** remove fuel runner assembly.
13. **On 1989-91 models,** remove plug wires at intake manifold.
14. **On all models,** remove rocker arm covers and drain cooling system.
15. Remove radiator hose at thermostat outlet.
16. Disconnect coolant sensor and oil sending switch electrical connectors, then remove coolant sensor.
17. Remove filler neck to cylinder head bypass hose, then remove heater inlet pipe at manifold.
18. Remove intake manifold attaching bolts, then remove intake manifold.
19. Reverse procedure to install. Refer to **Figs. 6 and 7,** for intake manifold tightening sequence and specifications.

EXHAUST MANIFOLD
REPLACE
LEFT SIDE

1. Disconnect battery ground cable and remove air cleaner and inlet hose.
2. **On 1988 models,** remove mass air flow sensor and the heat shield.

3. **On all models,** drain cooling system, then remove coolant by pass pipe.
4. Disconnect crossover pipe at manifold, then remove manifold attaching bolt s and the manifold.
5. Reverse procedure to install.

RIGHT SIDE

1. Disconnect battery ground cable and remove air cleaner.
2. Raise and support vehicle, then remove heat shield.
3. **On 1988 models,** remove exhaust pipe and crossover pipe.
4. **On 1989-91 models,** remove exhaust pipe at crossover.
5. **On all models,** lower vehicle.
6. **On 1988 models,** remove EGR pipe.
7. **On all models,** disconnect oxygen sensor electrical connector.
8. Remove exhaust manifold attaching bolts, then remove manifold.
9. Reverse to install. Torque attaching nuts, bolts and screws to specifications.

ROCKER ARM COVERS
REPLACE
LEFT SIDE
1988

1. Disconnect battery ground cable.

2. Remove bracket tube at rocker arm cover.
3. Remove plug wire attaching cover.
4. Remove filler neck attaching heater hose.
5. Remove rocker arm cover attaching bolts, then remove rocker arm cover.
6. Reverse procedure to install. Torque rocker arm cover attaching bolts to specifications.

1989–91

1. Disconnect battery ground cable and drain cooling system.
2. Loosen bypass tube at intake, then remove rocker arm cover to air inlet attaching tube.
3. Remove rocker arm cover attaching bolts, then remove rocker arm cover.
4. Reverse procedure to install. Torque rocker arm cover attaching bolts to specifications.

RIGHT SIDE

1. Disconnect battery ground cable.
2. Remove brake booster vacuum line at

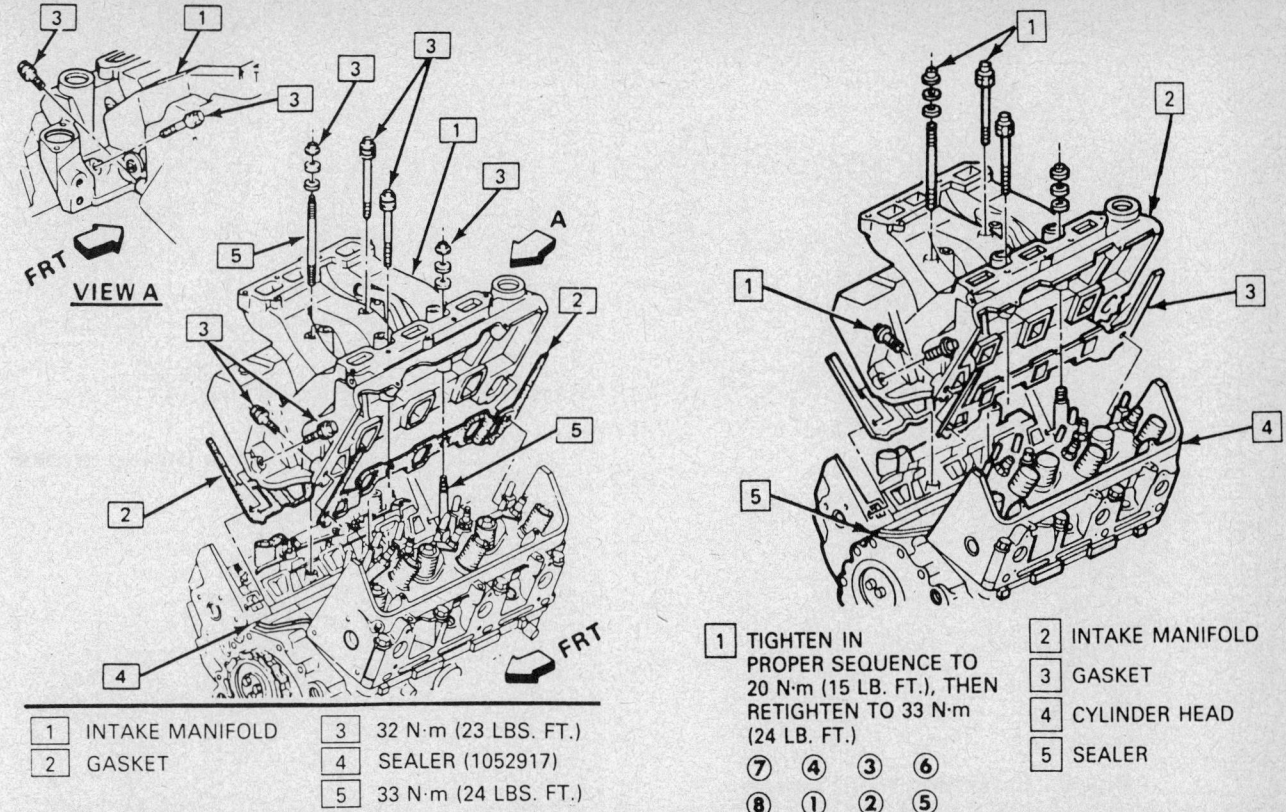

1	INTAKE MANIFOLD	3	32 N·m (23 LBS. FT.)
2	GASKET	4	SEALER (1052917)
		5	33 N·m (24 LBS. FT.)

Fig. 6 Intake manifold installation. 1988

1	TIGHTEN IN PROPER SEQUENCE TO 20 N·m (15 LB. FT.), THEN RETIGHTEN TO 33 N·m (24 LB. FT.)	2	INTAKE MANIFOLD
		3	GASKET
⑦ ④ ③ ⑥		4	CYLINDER HEAD
⑧ ① ② ⑤		5	SEALER

Fig. 7 Intake manifold installation. 1989–91

bracket, then remove cable bracket at plenum.
3. Remove vacuum line bracket at cable bracket, then remove lines at alternator bracket stud.
4. Remove rear alternator attaching brace, then remove serpentine belt.
5. Remove alternator attaching bolts and position alternator aside.
6. Remove PCV valve, then remove rocker arm cover attaching bolts.
7. Remove spark plug wires, then remove rocker arm cover assembly.
8. Reverse procedure to install. Torque attaching bolts to specifications.

VALVE CLEARANCE SPECIFICATIONS

Refer to "Valves, Adjust" procedure.

VALVES
ADJUST

Vehicles are equipped with a non-adjustable rocker arm studs. If valve reconditioning is required, the non-adjustable rocker arm stud must be replaced with an adjustable rocker arm stud and the following procedure must be performed.
1. Remove rocker arm covers.
2. Crank engine until mark on torsional damper lines up with O mark on timing tab. The engine should also be in the No. 1 firing position. This can be determined by placing fingers on No. 1 rocker arms as mark on damper approaches O mark.
3. If valves are not moving, engine is in No. 1 firing position. If valves move as the mark comes up to the timing tab, engine is in No. 4 firing position and should be rotated one revolution to reach No. 1 position.
4. With engine in No. 1 firing position, adjust exhaust valves 1, 2 and 3 and intake valves 1, 5 and 6, as follows:
   a. Back out adjusting nut until lash is felt at pushrod, then turn in adjusting nut until all lash is removed.
   b. When lash has been removed, turn adjusting nut in additional 1 1/2 turns to center lifter plunger.
5. Crank engine one revolution until timing tab O mark and torsional damper mark are again in alignment.
6. With the engine in this, the No. 4 firing position. adjust exhaust valves 4, 5 and 6 and intake valves 2, 3 and 4 as previously described.
7. Install rocker arm covers, then start engine and check timing and idle speed.

VALVE ARRANGEMENT

FRONT TO REAR

Right . . . . E-I-E-I-I-E
Left . . . . E-I-I-E-I-E

CAM LIFT SPECIFICATIONS

Engine	Int.	Exh.
2.8L/V6-173	.262	.273
3.1/V6-192	.2626	.2732

VALVE STEM OIL SEAL & VALVE SPRING
REPLACE

REMOVAL

1. Remove rocker arm cover, then the spark plug, rocker arm and pushrod on cylinder(s) being serviced.
2. Install air line adapter tool J-23590 on 1988 models, J-22794 on 1989-91 models, or equivalents to spark plug port and apply compressed air to hold valves in place.
3. Using tool J-5892 on 1988 models, J-5892-B on 1989 models, J-5892-C on 1990-91 models, or J-26513-A on 1989-91 models, or equivalents to compress valve spring, remove valve locks, valve caps, oil seal and valve spring and damper.
4. Remove valve stem oil seal.

INSTALLATION

1. Set valve spring and damper around valve guide boss.

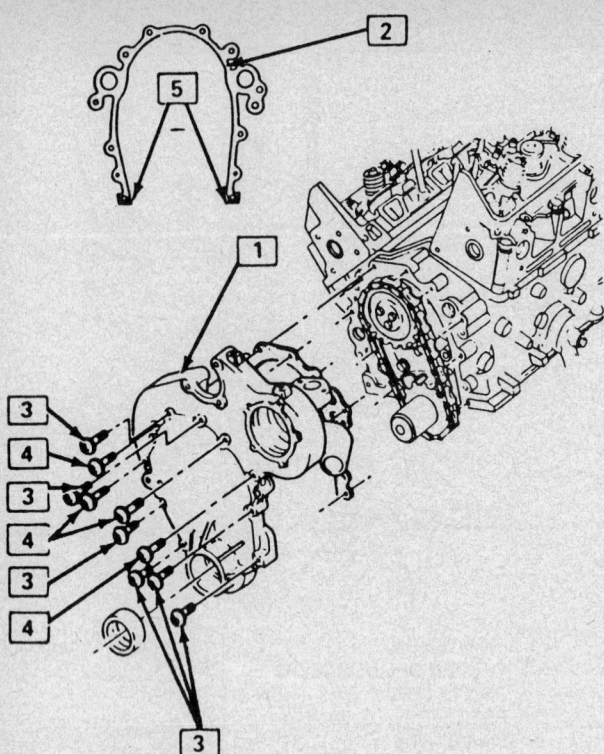

Fig. 8 Installing front cover

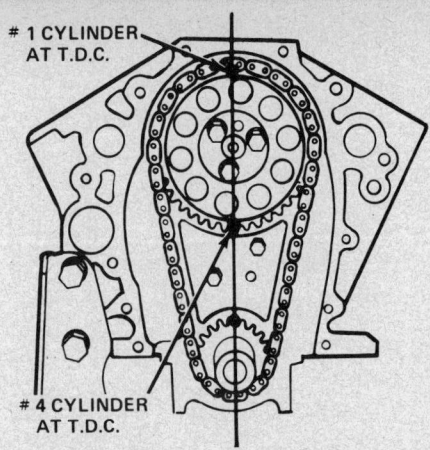

Fig. 9 Valve timing marks

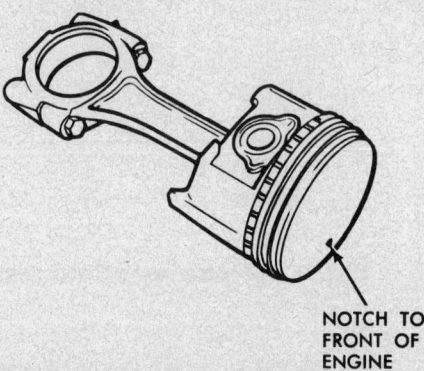

Fig. 10 Piston & rod assembly

2. Install a valve stem seal over the valve stem and valve guide base-inlet only.
3. Drop an oil seal and valve rotator over the exhaust, and a valve spring cap over the valve spring.
4. Compress spring with tool J-5892 on 1988 models, J-5892-B on 1989 models, J-5892-C on 1990-91 models, or J-26513-A on 1989-91 models, or equivalents and install oil seal in lower groove of stem, ensuring seal is flat and not twisted.
5. Install valve locks and release compressor tool, ensuring locks seat properly in upper groove of valve stem. Use suitable grease as necessary to hold locks in place while releasing compressor tool.
6. Using tool J-23994 or equivalent, apply vacuum to valve cap to ensure no air leaks past seal.
7. Install spark plug, torquing to specifications.
8. Install and adjust valve mechanism.

VALVE GUIDES

Valve guides are an integral part of the cylinder head and are not removable. If valve stem clearance becomes excessive, the valve guide should be reamed to the next oversize and the appropriate oversize valves installed. Valves are available in .003, .015 and .030 inch over sizes.

VALVE LIFTERS
REPLACE

1. Remove intake manifold as previously described.
2. Remove valve mechanism, then the valve lifters.
3. Install valve lifters. When installing new lifters, coat foot of valve lifters with Molykote or equivalent, ensuring lifter foot is convex.
4. Install intake manifold as previously described.
5. Install and adjust valve mechanism.

FRONT COVER
REPLACE

1. Disconnect battery ground cable and drain cooling system.
2. Remove serpentine belt and tensioner.
3. Disconnect alternator and position aside.
4. **On 1988 models,** loosen alternator attaching bracket.
5. **On all models,** disconnect power steering pump and position aside.
6. **On 1988 models,** remove serpentine belt idler pulley, if equipped.
7. **On all models,** raise and support vehicle, then remove inner splash shield.
8. Remove flywheel cover attaching bolts at transaxle, then remove flywheel cover.
9. Remove harmonic balancer with tool No. J 24420 on 1988 models, or J 24420-B on 1989-91 models or equivalents.

10. Remove starter assembly.
11. **On 1989-91 models,** remove serpentine belt idler pulley.
12. **On all models,** remove oil pan as outlined under "Oil Pan, Replace."
13. Remove front cover lower attaching bolts.
14. Lower vehicle, then remove water pump attaching radiator hose.
15. Remove heater hose at cooling system fill pipe, then remove bypass and overflow hoses.
16. Remove water pump pulley, the remove spark plug wire shield at water pump.
17. Remove canister purge hose.
18. Remove upper front cover attaching bolts, then remove front cover, Fig. 8.
19. Reverse to install. Torque all attaching nuts, bolts or screws to specifications.

FRONT COVER OIL SEAL
REPLACE

1. Remove front wheel and tire assemblies.
2. Remove inner splash shield and torsional damper, then pry seal from cover using a suitable screwdriver. **Use caution not to damage crankshaft surface during seal removal.**

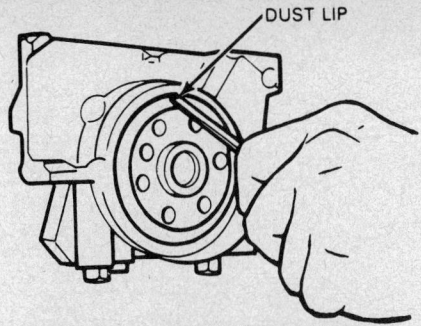

Fig. 11   Removing oil seal

3. Install new seal using tool No. J 35468 or equivalent, so open end faces toward inside of cover, then drive seal into position using suitable tool.

TIMING CHAIN & SPROCKET
REPLACE

1. Remove crankcase front cover, refer to "Front Cover, Replace" procedure.
2. Place No. 1 cylinder at TDC and align timing marks on crankshaft and camshaft sprockets, **Fig. 9.**
3. Remove camshaft sprocket attaching bolts. Tap lower edge of sprocket with plastic mallet and remove sprocket and timing chain.
4. Align timing marks, **Fig. 9,** and install timing chain on sprockets.
5. Align dowel on camshaft with dowel hole on camshaft sprocket, then install sprocket to camshaft, using attaching bolts to to draw sprocket fully to camshaft. Torque attaching bolts to specification.
6. Lubricate timing chain with engine oil, then install front cover.

CAMSHAFT
REPLACE

1. Remove engine from vehicle, refer to "Engine, Replace" procedure.
2. Remove valve lifters, refer to "Valve Lifter, Replace" procedure.
3. Remove crankcase front cover, refer to "Front Cover, Replace" procedure.
4. Remove fuel pump and pushrod, then the timing chain and sprocket. Refer to "Timing Chain & Sprocket, Replace" procedure.
5. Remove camshaft. **Use caution not to damage bearings during camshaft removal.**
6. Reverse procedure to install. Coat camshaft lobes with GM EOS 1052367 or other suitable lubricant before installation.

PISTON & ROD ASSEMBLY

There is a machined hole or cast notch in the top of all pistons. The piston assemblies should always be installed with the hole or notch toward front of engine, **Fig. 10.**

PISTONS, PINS & RINGS

Pistons and rings are available in standard and oversize. Piston pins are available in standard size only.

MAIN & ROD BEARINGS

Main and rod bearing are available in standard sizes and undersizes.

REAR MAIN BEARING OIL SEAL
REPLACE

1. Support engine using tool No. J 28467 on 1988 models, J 28467-A on 1989-91 models, or equivalents then remove transaxle assembly.
2. Remove flywheel assembly.
3. Remove oil seal as shown in **Fig. 11.** Use caution not to damage crankshaft surface with removal tool.
4. Check inside diameter of bore and crankshaft for nicks or burrs. Repair as required.
5. Apply oil to inside diameter of new seal, then install seal on mandrel of tool No. J-34686 until back of seal bottoms squarely against collar of tool, **Fig. 12.**
6. Align dowel pin of tool with dowel pin of crankshaft, then attach tool to crankshaft. On 1988 models, **torque** attaching screws to 2-5 ft. lbs. On 1989-91 models, **torque** attaching screws to 45 inch lbs.
7. Turn "T" handle of tool so collar pushes seal into bore. Ensure seal is properly seated.
8. Loosen "T" handle of tool until it comes to a stop, then remove tool attaching screws. Ensure seal is seated squarely in bore.
9. Install flywheel and transaxle assembly.

OIL PAN
REPLACE
1988

1. Disconnect battery ground cable.
2. Raise and support vehicle, then drain crankcase.
3. Remove flywheel dust cover, then the starter motor.
4. Remove oil pan attaching bolts, then the oil pan.
5. Reverse procedure to install. Apply suitable sealer to oil pan mating surfaces, then torque bolts to specification.

1989–91

1. Disconnect battery ground cable.
2. Remove serpentine belt and belt tensioner.
3. Raise and support vehicle, then drain engine oil.
4. Remove starter assembly, then remove outer plastic flywheel and starter shield.

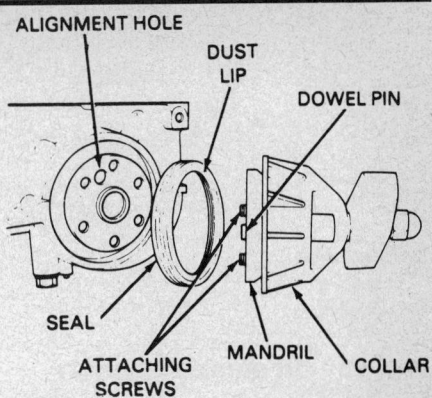

Fig. 12   Installing oil seal

5. Remove inner metal flywheel shield.
6. Remove engine to frame mount attaching nuts as outlined under "Engine Mounts, Replace."
7. Lower vehicle and support engine using tool No. J 28467-A or equivalent.
8. Raise and support vehicle, then remove inner fender splash shield.
9. Remove oil pan attaching nuts and bolts, then remove oil pan.
10. Reverse procedure to install. Torque attaching nuts and bolts to specifications.

OIL PUMP SERVICE
REMOVAL

1. Remove oil pan, refer to "Oil Pan, Replace" procedure.
2. Remove pump to rear main bearing attaching bolt, then the pump and extension shaft.

DISASSEMBLY

1. Remove pump cover attaching bolts (7), **Fig. 13,** and pump cover (3). **Mark gear teeth to ensure correct position during assembly.**
2. Remove idler gear and drive gear (2), then the shaft from pump body (1).
3. Remove pressure regulator valve retaining pin (6), pressure regulator spring (5) and valve (4).
4. If pickup screen and pipe assembly need to be replaced, mount pump in a suitable vise, then remove pipe from pump cover. **Do not remove pickup screen from pipe. This is serviced as an assembly.**

CLEANING & INSPECTION

1. Wash all parts in suitable cleaning solvent, then dry with compressed air.
2. Inspect pump body and cover for cracks or excessive wear.
3. Inspect pump gears for damage or excessive wear. Pump gears and body are not serviced separately. If pump gears are defective, replace entire oil pump assembly.
4. Check drive gear shaft for looseness in the pump body.
5. Inspect inside of pump cover for wear

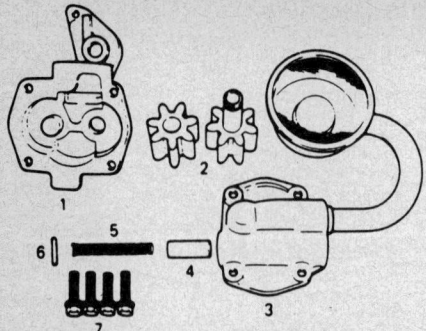

Fig. 13 Oil pump assembly

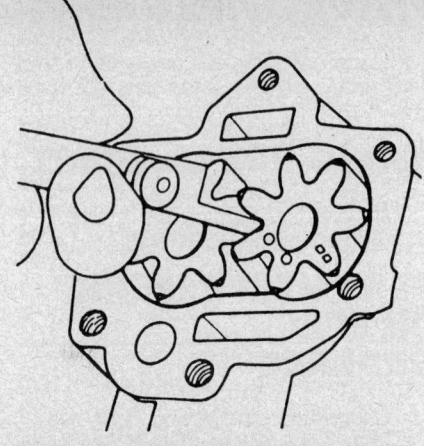

Fig. 14 Measuring oil pump gear lash

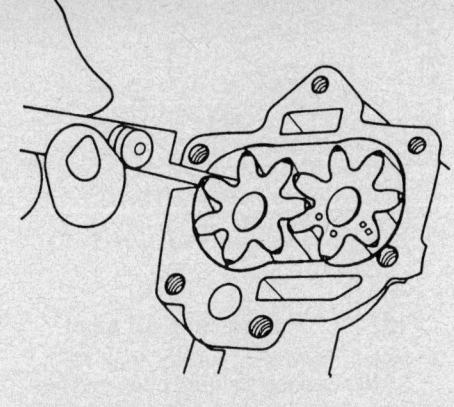

Fig. 15 Measuring gear side clearance

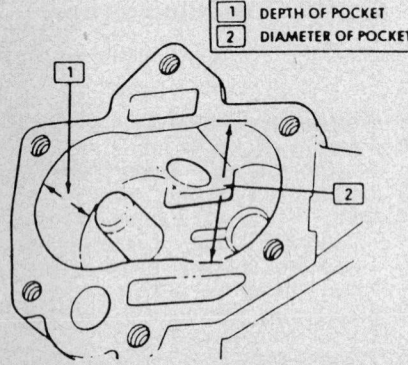

Fig. 16 Measuring oil pump gear pocket

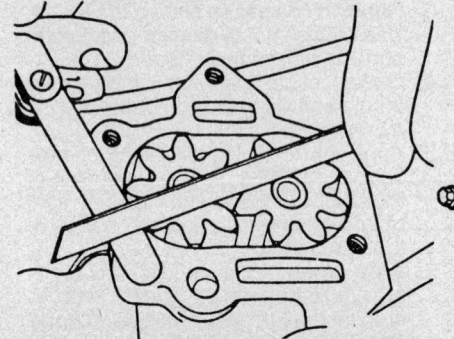

Fig. 17 Measuring oil pump end clearance

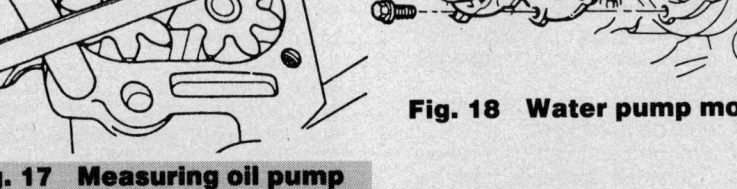

Fig. 18 Water pump mounting

that would permit oil to leak past ends of gears.

6. Inspect pickup screen and pipe assembly for looseness or damage.
7. Check pressure regulator valve for damage and proper fit.
8. Using a straightedge and feeler guage, check clearances as shown in **Figs. 14 through 17.**
9. Install gears and measure in several places, on 1988-89 models, gear lash should be within .009-.015 inch, on 1990-91 models, gear lash should be within .0037-.0077 inch.
10. **On all models,** measure depth and diameter of oil pump gear pocket, on 1988-89 models, depth should be 1.195-1.198 inch and diameter should be 1.498-1.50 inch. On 1990-91 models, depth should be 1.202-1.205 inch and diameter should be 1.504-1.506 inch.
11. **On all models,** measure gear side clearance, gear side clearance should be .003-.004 inch.
12. Measure gear end clearance, on 1988-89 models, gear end clearance should be .002-.005 inch and on 1990-91 models, gear and clearance should be .002-.006 inch. **When determining pump service ability based on end clearance, consider depth of wear pattern in pump cover.**

ASSEMBLY

1. Lubricate all internal parts with engine oil during assembly.

2. Install pump gears.
3. **On 1989-91 models,** prime engine oil galleries by removing engine oil pump drive unit and rotate oil pump using suitable drill motor, socket and extension.
4. **On all models,** install oil pump cover and gasket.
5. Install pressure regulator valve and spring, then install cotter pin or plug, if equipped.
6. If pipe assembly was removed, it should be replaced with a new part. Mount pump in suitable vise and apply suitable sealer to outside diameter of swaged end of pipe, then tap pipe in place using a suitable tool. **Loss of press fit condition could result in an air leak and loss of oil pressure. Also use caution not to twist, shear or collapse pipe during installation.**
7. Turn driveshaft by hand to ensure smooth operation.

INSTALLATION

1. Install pump and extension shaft with retainer to rear main bearing cap, aligning top end of hexagon extension shaft with hexagon socket of distributor drive gear.
2. Install pump to rear bearing cap bolt and torque to specifications.
3. Install oil pan, refer to "Oil Pan, Replace" procedure.

WATER PUMP
REPLACE

1. Disconnect battery ground cable, then drain cooling system.
2. Disconnect serpentine belt at the water pump pulley.
3. Remove water pump pulley, then the water pump, **Fig. 18.**
4. Reverse procedure to install.

COOLING SYSTEM BLEED

To ensure sufficient engine cooling, freezing and corrosion protection, maintain the protection level at −34°F or lower. Use a solution of antifreeze and water, ensuring solution is no more than 70 percent antifreeze.
1. Fill surge tank or radiator to base of filler neck, then attach pressure cap.
2. Block the drive wheel and apply parking brake.
3. **On models equipped with automatic transaxle,** place shifter in Park position.
4. **On models equipped with manual transaxle,** place transaxle in Neutral position.
5. **On all models,** start engine and allow to run until upper radiator hose is hot.
6. Stop engine, check level of coolant in surge tank or radiator.
7. Allow engine to cool, then add coolant as necessary.

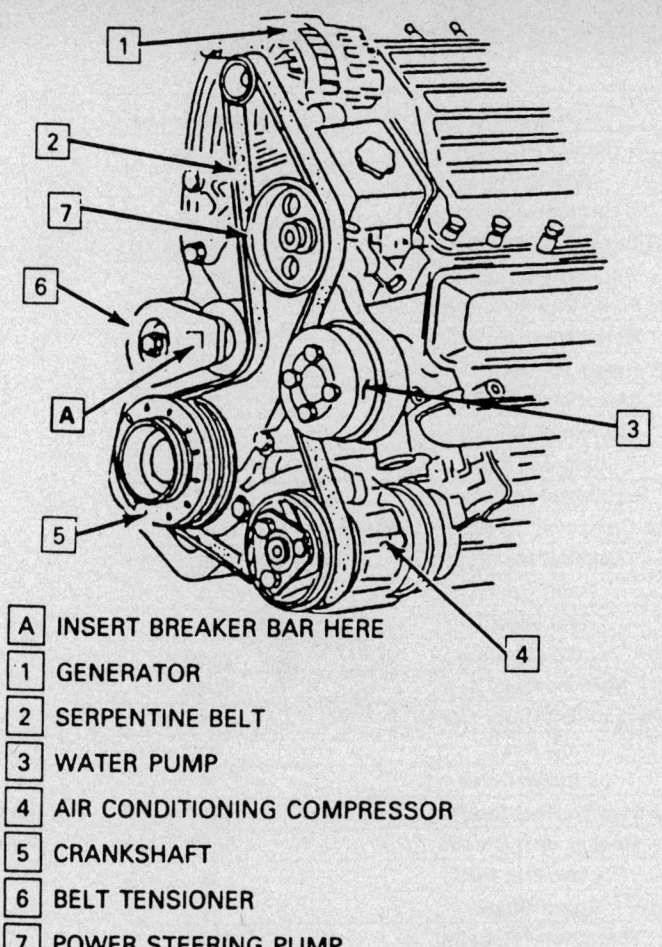

A	INSERT BREAKER BAR HERE
1	GENERATOR
2	SERPENTINE BELT
3	WATER PUMP
4	AIR CONDITIONING COMPRESSOR
5	CRANKSHAFT
6	BELT TENSIONER
7	POWER STEERING PUMP

Fig. 19 Serpentine drive belt routing

vapor pressure, then disconnect battery ground cable.

2. Remove fuel tank as follows:
   a. Drain fuel tank, then raise and support vehicle. **Ensure additional support to the opposite end from which components are being replaced, to avoid personal injury.**
   b. Disconnect fuel tank harness from body harness electrical connectors.
   c. Remove ground wire attaching screw, if equipped.
   d. Remove tank meter assembly, filler and vent pipe hoses.
   e. Support fuel tank with suitable tool, then disconnect fuel tank attaching straps.
   f. Lower fuel tank, then remove fuel tank meter assembly and gasket using tool No. J 24187 or equivalent.
   g. Remove sound insulators.
3. Remove fuel lever sending unit and pump assembly by turning cam lock ring counterclockwise. Lift assembly from fuel tank, then remove fuel pump from fuel lever sending unit.
4. Pull fuel pump up to attaching hose or pulsator while pulling outward away from bottom support. After pump assembly is clear of bottom support, remove assembly from rubber connector or pulsator. **Use caution not to damage rubber insulator and strainer during removal.**
5. Reverse procedure to install.

BELT TENSION DATA

Belt	New Lbs.	Used Lbs.
Air Cond.	160	100
Alternator	①	①
Power Steer.	①	①

①—Serpentine belt.

FUEL PUMP REPLACE

1. Loosen fuel filler cap to relieve tank

SERPENTINE DRIVE BELT ROUTING

Refer to **Fig. 19**, for drive belt routing.

TIGHTENING SPECIFICATIONS

Year	Component	Torque/Ft. Lbs.
1988	Camshaft Rear Cover	6-9
	Camshaft Sprocket	15-20
	Cylinder Head	③
	Distributor Hold Down	20-31
	Engine Mount To Bracket, Front	55-66
	Exhaust Crossover To Right Manifold	22-30
	Exhaust Manifold	15-22
	Front Cover	①
	Intake Manifold	13-25
	Main Bearing Cap	63-83
	Oil Pan	②
	Oil Pump Drive	25-35
	Oil Pump To Rear Bearing Cap	25-35
	Rocker Arm Covers	6-9

Continued

TIGHTENING SPECIFICATIONS—Continued

Year	Component	Torque/Ft. Lbs.
1988 (Cont'd.)	Rocker Arm Nuts	14-20
	Spark Plugs	10-25
	Thermostat Housing	15-23
	Timing Chain Dampener	14-19
	Torsional Dampener	67-85
	Water Pump Pulley To Pump Bolts	15
	Water Pump To Block	18
	Water Pump To Front Cover Bolts	88④
1989–91	Camshaft Rear Cover	6-9
	Camshaft Sprocket	21
	Cylinder Head	③
	Distributor Hold Down	20-31
	Exhaust Crossover To Right Manifold	18
	Exhaust Manifold	18
	Front Cover	①
	Heat Shield	89④
	Intake Manifold	13-25
	Main Bearing Cap	63-83
	Negative Battery Cable	11
	Oil Pan	②
	Oil Pump Drive	25
	Oil Pump To Rear Bearing Cap	30
	Rocker Arm Covers	89④
	Rocker Arm Nuts	18
	Spark Plugs	18
	Thermostat Housing	15-23
	Timing Chain Dampener	15
	Torsional Dampener	67-85
	Water Pump Pulley To Pump Bolts	15
	Water Pump To Block	18
	Water Pump To Front Cover Bolts	90④

① —8 mm bolts, on 1988 models, 13–36 ft. lbs., on 1989–91 models, 20 ft. lbs.; 10 mm bolts, on 1988 models, 20–35 ft. lbs., on 1989–91 models, 28 ft. lbs.

② —6 mm bolts, on 1988 models, 6–15 ft. lbs. on 1989–91 models, 71 inch lbs;

8 mm bolts, on 1988 models, 15–22 ft. lbs. on 1989–91 models, 18 ft.lbs.

③ —Torque bolts in sequence to 33 ft. lbs., then turn an additional 90°.

④ —Inch lbs.

Clutch & Manual Transaxle

INDEX

CLUTCH PEDAL
ADJUST

On these models, a hydraulic clutch system is used, **Fig. 1.** The system consists of a dash mounted master cylinder with integral reservoir, a transmission mounted slave cylinder and high pressure tubing to connect the two components.

The hydraulic clutch system provides automatic clutch adjustment, therefore, there is no provision for adjustment.

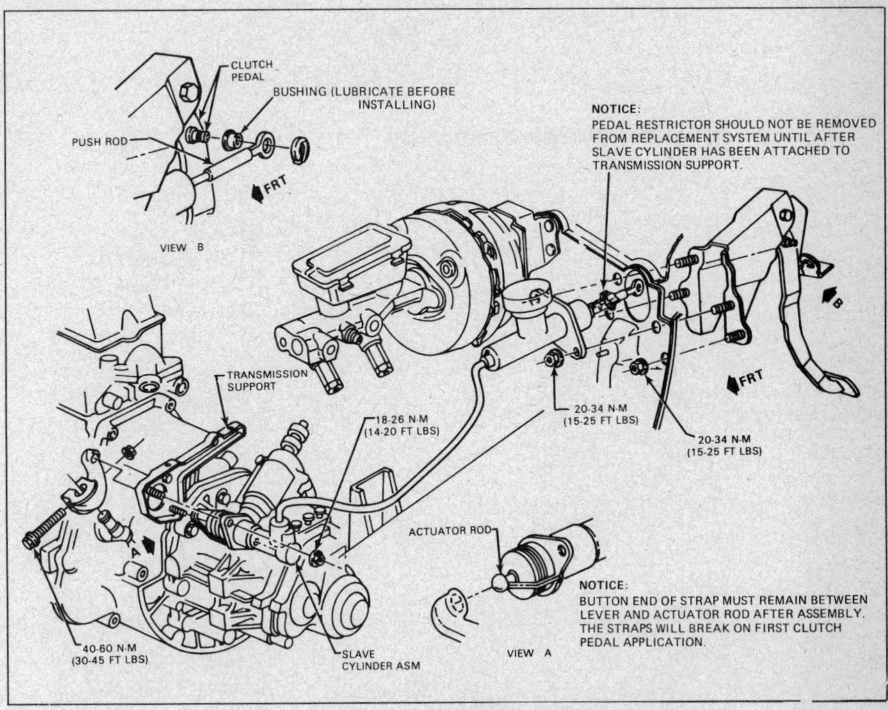

BLEEDING HYDRAULIC SYSTEM

1. Fill reservoir with a suitable DOT 3 type brake fluid.
2. Fully loosen bleeder screw located on slave cylinder near inlet connection.
3. While maintaining reservoir fluid level, allow fluid to flow from bleeder valve until a steady stream of fluid with no air bubbles is present, then tighten bleeder screw.
4. Fill reservoir to proper level, then start engine.
5. Depress clutch for approximately ten seconds, then select reverse gear. If no gear clash is present, system is satisfactory. If gear clash is present, repeat bleeding procedure.

INSPECTION

1. While observing clutch slave cylinder pushrod travel, have an assistant depress clutch pedal.
2. If slave cylinder pushrod moves .433 inch or more, hydraulic system is operating properly.
3. If slave cylinder pushrod did not move .433 inch, proceed as follows:
   a. Check clutch master cylinder fluid level. The clutch slave cylinder must be installed during this operation. Refill as necessary.
   b. If master cylinder requires fluid, check hydraulic system components for leakage. Remove rubber boots from cylinders and check for leakage past pistons. A slight wetting of piston and wall surfaces is acceptable.
   c. If excessive leakage is indicated, entire hydraulic system must be replaced.

CLUTCH
REPLACE

1. Disconnect battery ground cable.
2. Remove hush panel from driver's foot well, as required, then disconnect clutch master cylinder pushrod from clutch pedal.

Fig. 1   Hydraulic clutch assembly

3. Remove transaxle as outlined under "Manual Transaxle, Replace" procedure.
4. Mark position of pressure plate to flywheel to aid reassembly.
5. Gradually loosen pressure plate to flywheel attaching bolts until spring tension is relieved.
6. Support pressure plate and remove attaching bolts, pressure plate and driven disc, **Fig. 2.**
7. Clean pressure plate and flywheel mounting surfaces. Inspect bearing retainer outer surface of the transaxle.
8. Place pressure plate and driven disc in position and support with tool No. J-29074, **Fig. 3. The driven disc is installed with the damper springs offset toward the transaxle. Stamped letters found on the driven disc identify the "Flywheel Side."**
9. Install and gradually tighten the pressure plate to flywheel attaching bolts. Remove support tool.
10. Lubricate the release bearing outside diameter groove and inside diameter recess with lubricant 1051344 or equivalent.
11. Install transaxle.

MANUAL TRANSAXLE SHIFT CABLE
ADJUST
ISUZU

Refer to **Fig. 4,** for exploded view of shifter cables.

MUNCIE

Refer to **Fig. 5** for exploded view of shifter cables.

MANUAL TRANSAXLE
REPLACE
ISUZU

1. Disconnect battery ground cable.
2. Install engine support fixture J-28467, on 1988 models, J-28467-A on 1989-91 models, or equivalents, then raise engine enough to take pressure off motor mounts, **Fig. 6.**
3. Remove left sound insulator.
4. Remove clutch master cylinder pushrod from clutch pedal.
5. Remove wire harness at mount bracket.
6. Remove clutch slave cylinder from

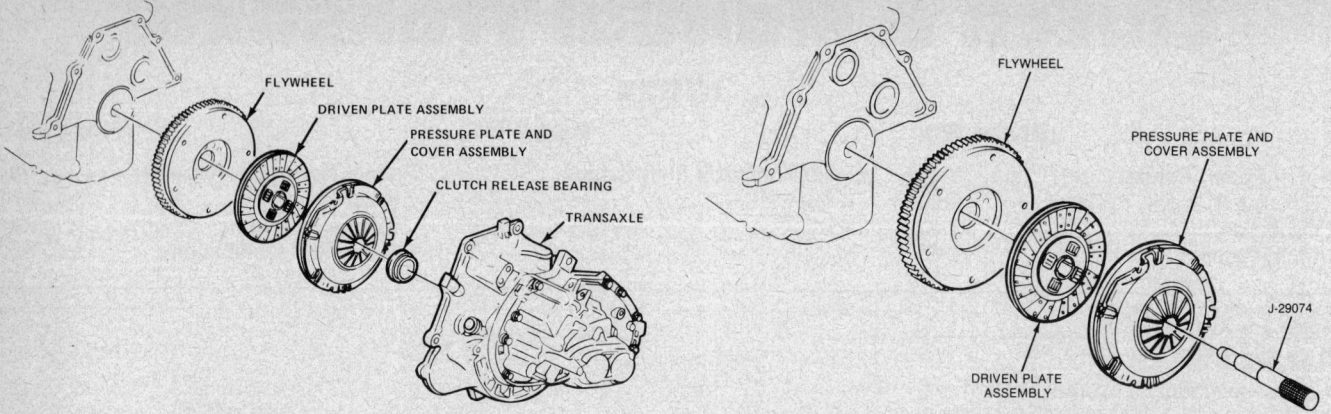

Fig. 2   Clutch assembly

Fig. 3   Aligning clutch disc & pressure plate

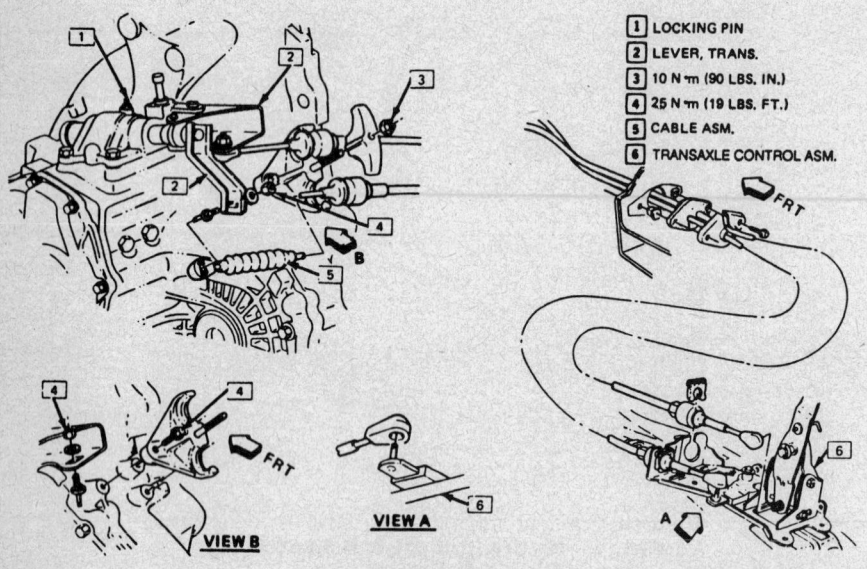

1 LOCKING PIN
2 LEVER, TRANS.
3 10 N·m (90 LBS. IN.)
4 25 N·m (19 LBS. FT.)
5 CABLE ASM.
6 TRANSAXLE CONTROL ASM.

1. TOOL J-28467
2. THREAD ONTO STRUT ATTACHING BOLTS ABOVE NUTS – 3 PER SIDE

Fig. 6   Engine support fixture installation

Fig. 4   Isuzu five speed manual transaxle shift cable adjustment

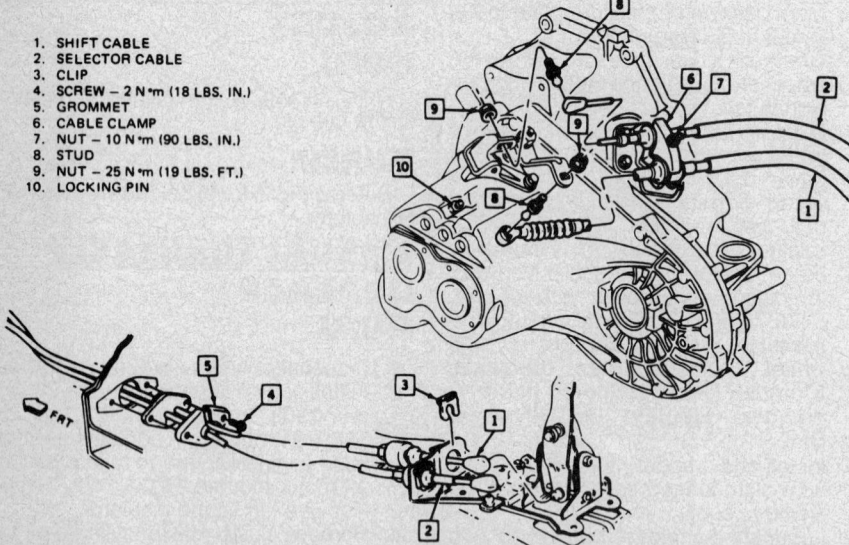

1. SHIFT CABLE
2. SELECTOR CABLE
3. CLIP
4. SCREW – 2 N·m (18 LBS. IN.)
5. GROMMET
6. CABLE CLAMP
7. NUT – 10 N·m (90 LBS. IN.)
8. STUD
9. NUT – 25 N·m (19 LBS. FT.)
10. LOCKING PIN

Fig. 5   Muncie five speed manual transaxle shift cable assembly

transaxle support bracket and position aside.

7. Remove transaxle mount and mount bracket attaching bolts.
8. Remove shift cables and retaining clamp at transaxle.
9. Remove ground cable at transaxle attaching bolts, then disconnect back-up switch electrical connector.
10. Raise and support vehicle, then drain transaxle fluid.
11. Remove left front wheel and inner splash shield.
12. Remove transaxle front strut and front strut bracket.
13. Remove clutch housing cover attaching bolts, then the vehicle speed sensor at transaxle.
14. Remove stabilizer shaft at left suspension support and control arm.
15. Remove left suspension support attaching bolts and swing aside.
16. Remove drive axles and left shaft at transaxle.
17. Position suitable jack under transaxle, then remove transaxle to engine attaching bolts.
18. Slide transaxle towards drivers side, away from engine, then lower transaxle from vehicle while guiding right drive axle out of transaxle.

19. Reverse procedure to install. When installing transaxle, carefully guide right hand drive axle shaft into transaxle bore as transaxle is being raised. The right hand drive axle shaft cannot be installed once the transaxle has been connected to the engine.

MUNCIE

1. Disconnect battery ground cable.
2. Install engine support fixture J-28467, on 1988 models, J-28467-A, on 1989-91 models, or equivalents, then raise engine enough to take pressure off motor mounts, **Fig. 6.**
3. Remove left sound insulator.
4. Remove clutch master cylinder pushrod from clutch pedal.
5. Remove air cleaner and air intake duct assembly.

6. Remove clutch slave cylinder from transaxle support bracket and position aside.
7. Remove transaxle mount through bolt, then raise and support vehicle.
8. Remove exhaust crossover bolts at RH manifold, then lower vehicle.
9. Remove left hand exhaust manifold, then the transaxle mount bracket.
10. Remove transaxle shift cables, then the upper transaxle to engine attaching bolts.
11. **On 1990-91 models,** remove transaxle vent tube
12. **On all models,** raise and support vehicle, then remove left front tire and inner splash shield.
13. Remove transaxle strut and bracket.
14. Drain transaxle, then remove clutch housing cover attaching bolts.
15. Remove speedometer cable, then the stabilizer shaft at left suspension sup-

port and control arm.
16. Remove left hand suspension support attaching bolts and swing aside.
17. Remove left hand drive axle from transaxle.
18. Remove intermediate shaft housing to transaxle attaching bolts, then slide housing away from transaxle. Using a suitable tool, disconnect intermediate shaft from transaxle.
19. Position suitable jack under transaxle, then remove remaining transaxle to engine attaching bolts.
20. Lower transaxle assembly from vehicle.
21. Reverse procedure to install. When installing transaxle, carefully guide right hand drive axle shaft into transaxle bore as transaxle is being raised. The right hand drive axle shaft cannot be installed once the transaxle has been connected to the engine.

TIGHTENING SPECIFICATIONS

Year	Component	Torque/Ft. Lbs.
1988-90	Back-up Switch Assembly To Transaxle	84①
	Clutch Bleed Screw	17①
	Clutch Cover To Flywheel	22
	Clutch Cover To Transaxle	115①
	Clutch Master Cylinder	20
	Clutch Slave Cylinder Nut	16
	Clutch Release Lever (Isuzu)	37
	Front Transaxle Strut To Transaxle	50
	Front Transaxle To Body Bolt	40
	Rear Mount Bracket To Transaxle	40
	Rear Transaxle Mount To Body	23
	Shift Cable Grommet To Shroud	18①
	Shift Control Box To Transaxle (Isuzu)	13
	Shift Control To Floor	18
	Shift Linkage Retainer To Transaxle Case	17
	Shift Retainer To Transaxle Case (Isuzu)	90①
	Shift Shaft Lever Nut	61
	Speedometer/VSS Housing To Transaxle	84①
	Transaxle Mount To Transaxle	37
	Transaxle Shift Cable Bracket To Cables	90①
	Transaxle Shift Lever To Cable Stud	18
	Transaxle To Engine Bolts and Studs (Isuzu)	60
	Transaxle To Engine Nut	55
	Transaxle To Engine Stud	106①
	Transaxle To Engine Stud/Bolts	55
	Wheel & Tire Assembly	100
1991	Back-up Switch Assembly To Transaxle	24
	Clutch Bleed Screw	17①
	Clutch Cover To Flywheel	22
	Clutch Cover To Transaxle	115①
	Clutch Master Cylinder	20
	Clutch Slave Cylinder Nut	16
	Clutch Release Lever (Isuzu)	37
	Front Transaxle Strut To Transaxle	50
	Front Transaxle To Body Bolt	40
	Rear Mount Bracket To Transaxle	40
	Rear Transaxle Mount To Body	23

Continued

TIGHTENING SPECIFICATIONS—Continued

Year	Component	Torque/Ft. Lbs.
1991 (Cont'd.)	Shift Cable Grommet To Shroud	18①
	Shift Control Box To Transaxle (Isuzu)	13
	Shift Control To Floor	18
	Shift Linkage Retainer To Transaxle Case	17
	Shift Retainer To Transaxle Case (Isuzu)	18
	Shift Shaft Lever Nut	61
	Speedometer/VSS Housing To Transaxle	84①
	Transaxle Mount To Transaxle	37
	Transaxle Shift Cable Bracket To Cables	90①
	Transaxle Shift Lever To Cable Stud	18
	Transaxle To Engine Bolts and Studs (Isuzu)	55
	Transaxle To Engine Nut	55
	Transaxle To Engine Stud	106①
	Transaxle To Engine Stud/Bolts	55
	Wheel & Tire Assembly	100

①—Inch lbs.

Rear Axle & Suspension

INDEX

DESCRIPTION

The rear suspension, **Fig. 1,** is a semi-independent type suspension consisting of an axle assembly with trailing arms and twisting cross beam, coil springs and double action shock absorbers. A stabilizer bar is available and is attached to the inside of the axle beam and to the lower end of the control arms. A single unit hub and bearing assembly is bolted to each end of the axle assembly. The hub and bearing assembly is a sealed, non-serviceable unit and must be replaced as an assembly.

REAR AXLE
REPLACE

1. Raise vehicle and support vehicle. Support rear suspension with suitable jack.
2. Disconnect stabilizer bar at axle assembly, if equipped, **Fig. 2.**
3. Remove rear wheel assembly and brake drum. Do not hammer on brake drum since damage to bearings may result.
4. Remove shock absorber to lower mounting bracket attaching bolts, then disconnect shock absorbers from axle assembly, **Fig. 2.**
5. Disconnect parking brake cable and brake lines at axle brackets.
6. Carefully lower rear axle assembly and remove coil springs and insulators.
7. Remove control arm to under body

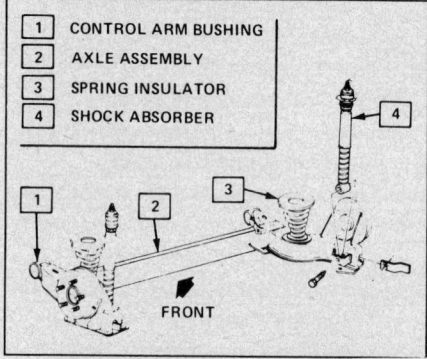

1	CONTROL ARM BUSHING
2	AXLE ASSEMBLY
3	SPRING INSULATOR
4	SHOCK ABSORBER

FRONT

Fig. 1   Rear suspension

bracket bolts, then lower the axle assembly and remove from vehicle.
8. Remove hub to rear axle attaching bolts, then the hubs, bearings and backing plates from rear axle assembly.
9. Reverse procedure to install and bleed brake system.

HUB & BEARING ASSEMBLY
REPLACE

1. Raise and support vehicle, then remove wheel and tire assembly and brake drum. **Do not hammer brake drum since damage to bearing may result.**

2. Remove four hub/bearing assembly to rear axle attaching bolts, then the hub/bearing assembly from axle. **The upper rear hub attaching bolt may not clear brake shoe when removing hub and bearing assembly. Partially remove hub and bearing assembly prior to removing this bolt.**
3. Reverse procedure to install. Torque hub attaching bolts to specification. **Use care not to drop hub/bearing assembly since damage to bearing may result.**

SHOCK ABSORBER
REPLACE

1. Open deck lid, then remove trim cover and shock absorber upper retaining nut.
2. Raise rear of vehicle and support rear axle using a suitable jack.
3. Remove shock absorber lower attaching bolt, then disconnect shock absorber from mounting bracket, **Fig. 2.** Remove shock absorber from vehicle.
4. Reverse procedure to install. Torque attaching bolt to specification.

COIL SPRING
REPLACE

1. Raise and support rear of vehicle. Support rear axle using a suitable jack.
2. Remove wheel and tire assemblies.
3. Remove brake line bracket attaching

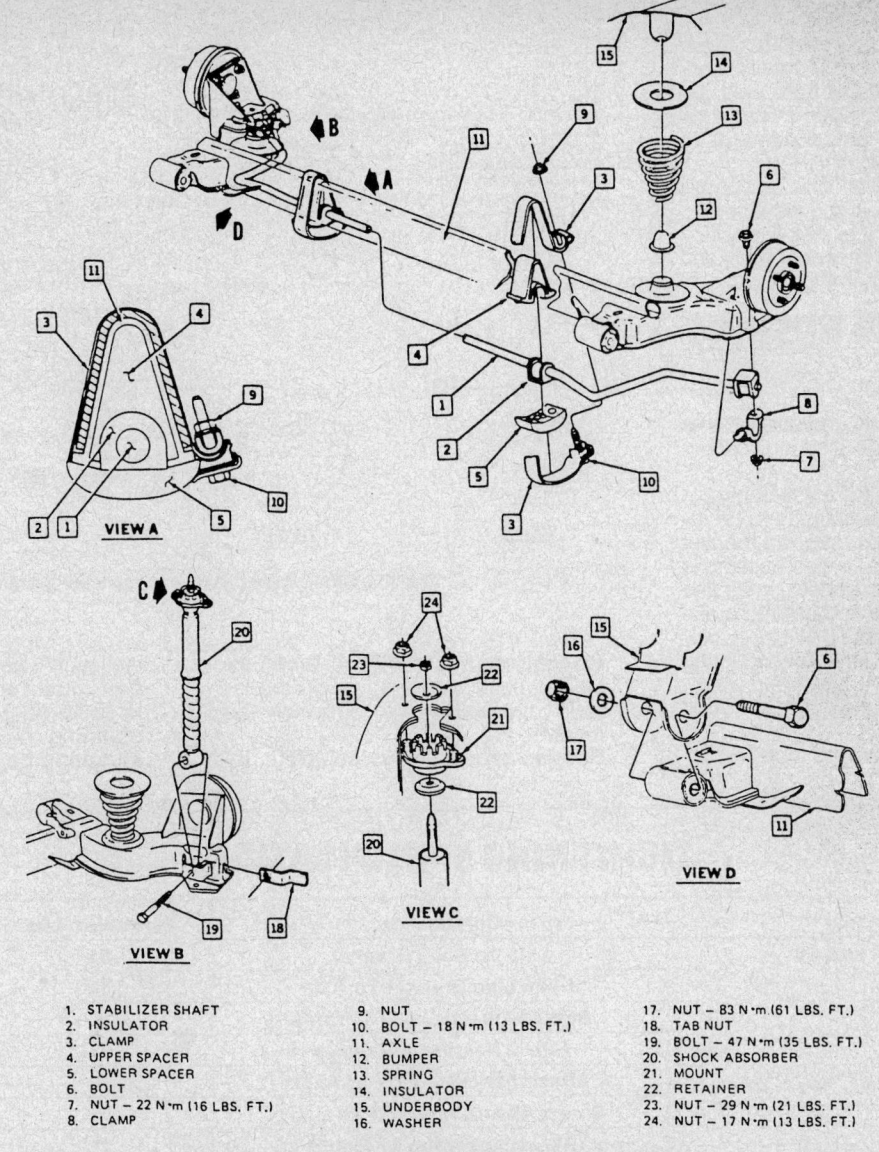

1. STABILIZER SHAFT
2. INSULATOR
3. CLAMP
4. UPPER SPACER
5. LOWER SPACER
6. BOLT
7. NUT – 22 N·m (16 LBS. FT.)
8. CLAMP
9. NUT
10. BOLT – 18 N·m (13 LBS. FT.)
11. AXLE
12. BUMPER
13. SPRING
14. INSULATOR
15. UNDERBODY
16. WASHER
17. NUT – 83 N·m (61 LBS. FT.)
18. TAB NUT
19. BOLT – 47 N·m (35 LBS. FT.)
20. SHOCK ABSORBER
21. MOUNT
22. RETAINER
23. NUT – 29 N·m (21 LBS. FT.)
24. NUT – 17 N·m (13 LBS. FT.)

Fig. 2 Rear suspension exploded view

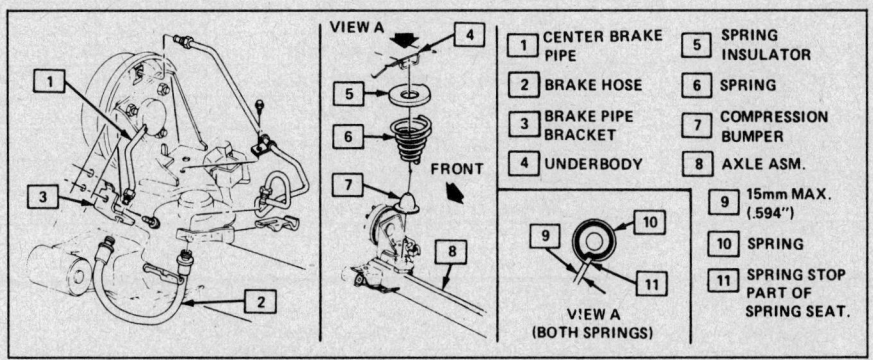

1	CENTER BRAKE PIPE	5	SPRING INSULATOR
2	BRAKE HOSE	6	SPRING
3	BRAKE PIPE BRACKET	7	COMPRESSION BUMPER
4	UNDERBODY	8	AXLE ASM.
		9	15mm MAX. (.594")
		10	SPRING
		11	SPRING STOP PART OF SPRING SEAT.

Fig. 3 Coil spring installation

bolts from frame, **Fig. 2**, and allow brake lines to hang freely.

4. Remove shock absorber to lower mounting bracket bolts, then disconnect shock absorbers from axle assembly. **Do not suspend rear axle by brake hoses since damage to hoses may result.**

5. Carefully lower rear axle assembly and remove springs and insulators.

6. Reverse procedure to install. Position ends of upper coil in seat of body and within limits shown in **Fig. 3**.

CONTROL ARM BUSHING REPLACE

1. Raise rear of vehicle and support rear axle under front side of spring seat using a suitable jack.
2. Remove wheel and tire assembly.
3. If right hand side bushing is to be replaced, disconnect brake line bracket from body. If left hand side bushing is to be replaced, disconnect brake line bracket from frame and parking brake cable at hook guide.
4. Remove control arm to mounting bracket attaching nut, bolt and washer, then allow control arm to rotate downward.
5. The bushing can now be replaced us-

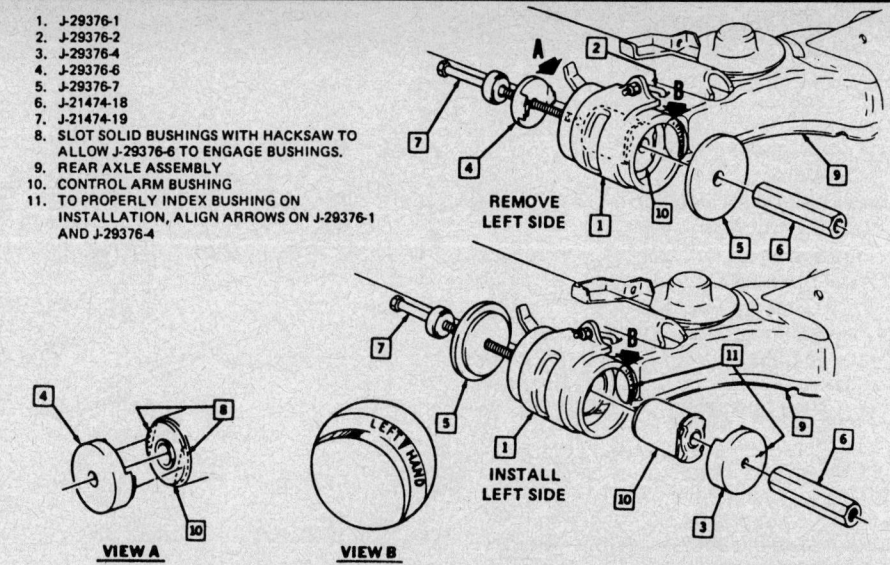

1. J-29376-1
2. J-29376-2
3. J-29376-4
4. J-29376-6
5. J-29376-7
6. J-21474-18
7. J-21474-19
8. SLOT SOLID BUSHINGS WITH HACKSAW TO ALLOW J-29376-6 TO ENGAGE BUSHINGS.
9. REAR AXLE ASSEMBLY
10. CONTROL ARM BUSHING
11. TO PROPERLY INDEX BUSHING ON INSTALLATION, ALIGN ARROWS ON J-29376-1 AND J-29376-4

Fig. 4   Control arm bushing removal and installation

ing tools shown in **Fig. 4**. When installing bushing, the arrow on the installer must align with arrow on the receiver, **Fig. 4**.

6. Reverse procedure to complete installation. **The control arm attaching bolt must be torqued after vehicle is lowered to floor and is in its standing height position. Torque attaching bolt to specifications.**

TIGHTENING SPECIFICATIONS

Year	Component	Torque/Ft. Lbs.
1988-90	Axle To Body Bracket	61
	Brake Line Bracket To Axle	11
	Brake Line Bracket To Frame	8
	Hub & Bearing Assembly	37
	Shock Absorber Bolt At Axle	35
	Shock Absorber Mount To Body	21
	Shock Absorber To Mount	21
	Stabilizer Shaft Clamp Bolts At Axle	13
	Stabilizer Shaft Clamp Nuts	16
	Wheel & Tire Assembly	100
1991	Axle To Body Bracket	68
	Brake Line Bracket To Axle	11
	Brake Line Bracket To Frame	8
	Hub & Bearing Assembly	37
	Shock Absorber Bolt At Axle	35
	Shock Absorber Mount To Body	13
	Shock Absorber To Mount	21
	Stabilizer Shaft Clamp Bolts At Axle	13
	Stabilizer Shaft Clamp Nuts	16
	Wheel & Tire Assembly	100

Front Suspension & Steering
INDEX

DESCRIPTION

The front suspension, **Fig. 1**, on these vehicles is of the MacPherson strut design. The lower control arms pivot from the lower side rails through rubber bushings. The upper end of the strut is isolated by a rubber mount incorporating a non-serviceable bearing for wheel turning. The tie rods connect to the steering arm on the strut, below the spring seat. The lower end of the steering knuckle pivots on a ball stud which is retained to the lower control arm by rivets and is secured to the steering knuckle with a nut and cotter pin. The sealed wheel bearings are integral with the hub and are serviced as an assembly.

WHEEL BEARING
REPLACE
REMOVAL
1988

1. Raise and support vehicle.
2. Remove tire and wheel assembly, then install modified outer seal protector No. J 34754 or equivalent, **Fig. 2.**
3. Insert a drift punch through the rotor, **Fig. 3**, then remove axle shaft nut and washer.
4. Remove brake caliper from support and suspend caliper from flame with a length of wire. Do not suspend caliper by brake hose.
5. Using tool J-28733 or equivalent, remove bearing from steering knuckle, **Fig. 4. If excessive corrosion is present, ensure that bearing is loose in the knuckle before using puller tool.**
6. Remove three hub and bearing attaching bolts. If the old bearing is being reinstalled, mark attaching bolts and corresponding holes for reinstallation, **Fig. 5.**
7. If installing new bearing, replace steering knuckle seal. **Do not move drive axle until hub nut is installed and torqued to specifications.**

1989–91

1. Raise and support vehicle.
2. Remove tire and wheel assembly, then install modified outer seal protector No. J 34754 or equivalent, **Fig. 2.**
3. Insert a drift punch through the rotor, **Fig. 3**, then remove axle shaft nut and washer.

4. **On 1989-90 models,** using a plastic or rubber mallet, strike end of axle shaft to disengage axle from hub and bearing. Shaft nut can be partially installed to protect threads.
5. **On 1991 models,** remove ball joint, then using tool No. J 28733-A or equivalent, disengage axle from hub and bearing assembly.
6. **On all models,** move axle shaft inward, then remove caliper attaching bolts and support caliper.
7. Remove brake rotor, then hub and bearing assembly attaching bolts.
8. Remove hub and bearing assembly.
9. Reverse to install. Torque attaching bolts to specifications.

INSTALLATION
1988

1. Install hub and bearing assembly, torque attaching bolts to specification.
2. Install hub and bearing seal, then the brake rotor.
3. Install caliper, torque attaching bolts to specification.
4. Loosely install shaft nut and washer, then insert drift punch through rotor, **Fig. 3.**
5. Torque shaft nut to specification.
6. Remove drift punch and seal protector.
7. Install tire and wheel assembly, then lower vehicle.

1989–91

1. Install hub and bearing assembly, torque attaching bolts to specification.
2. Install hub and bearing seal, then the brake rotor.
3. Install caliper, torque attaching bolts to specification.
4. Move axle shaft outward, then insert drift punch through rotor, **Fig. 3.**
5. Install washer and new shaft nut, torque shaft nut to specification.
6. **On 1991 models,** install ball joint.
7. **On all models,** remove drift punch and seal protector.
8. Install tire and wheel assembly, then lower vehicle.

BALL JOINT INSPECTION

1. Raise and support vehicle so that suspension is allowed to hang free.
2. Grasp wheel and tire assembly at top and bottom, then rock top of wheel and tire assembly inward and outward.
3. While rocking wheel and tire assem-

bly, observe movement between steering knuckle and control arm. If any horizontal movement is present, replace ball joint.
4. If ball joint is disconnected from steering knuckle, use finger to try to twist ball joint in its socket. If ball joint can be twisted in its socket, replace ball joint.

LOWER BALL JOINT
REPLACE

1. Raise and support vehicle, then remove wheel and tire.
2. Install modified tool No. J 34754 or equivalent, then remove ball joint attaching cotter pin.
3. Remove ball joint stud retaining nut, then, using tool J-29330, on 1988-90 models, or J-38892, on 1991 models, separate ball joint from steering knuckle.
4. Using a 1/8 inch drill, drill pilot holes completely through the rivets. Using a 1/2 inch drill, drill final holes through rivets to ensure fitting of new ball joint.
5. Loosen stabalizer shaft assembly bushing attaching nut.
6. Remove ball joint from steering knuckle and control arm.
7. Assemble new ball joint to lower control arm with bolts provided in service package, **Fig. 6.** Torque bolts to specification.
8. Insert ball joint stud into steering knuckle and torque nut to specifications.
9. Install wheel and tire.

LOWER CONTROL ARM & BUSHING
REPLACE

1. Raise and support vehicle, then remove wheel and tire.
2. Disconnect stabilizer bar at lower control arm and control arm support.
3. Install modified seal protector tool No. J 34754 or equivalent.
4. Using tool J-29330, on 1988-90 models or tool No. J 38892, on 1991 models, separate ball joint from steering knuckle.
5. Remove control arm support to chassis retaining bolts and remove control arm support and control arm as an assembly.
6. Separate control arm from support, then using tool Nos. J29792-1 and

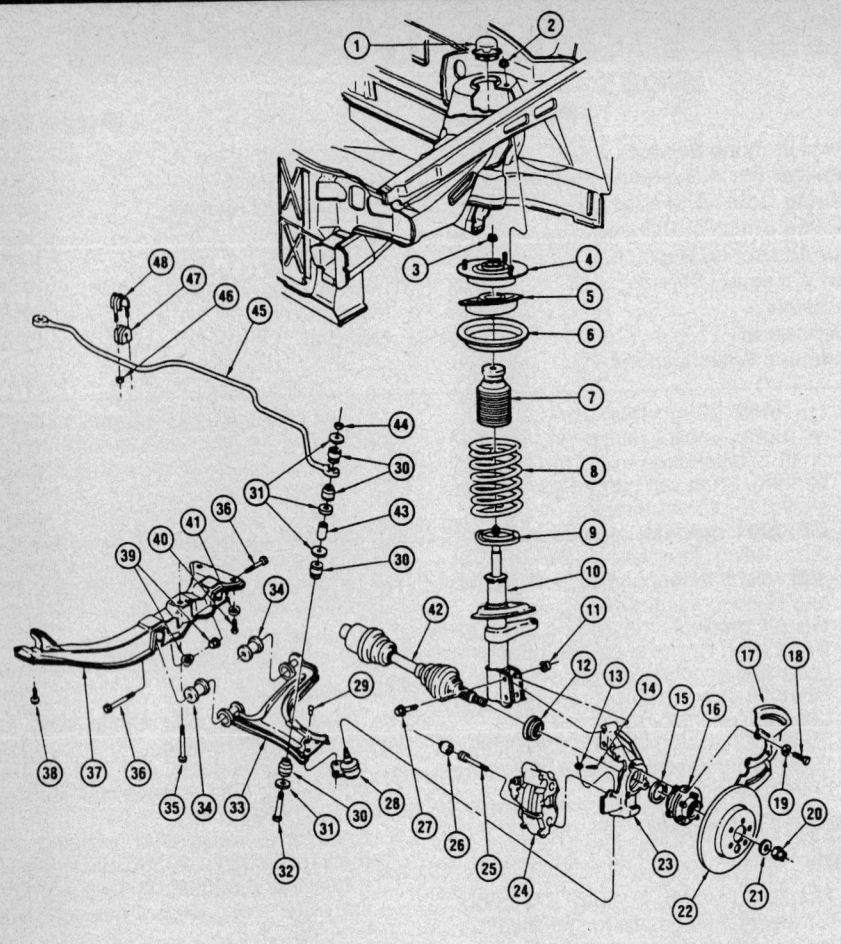

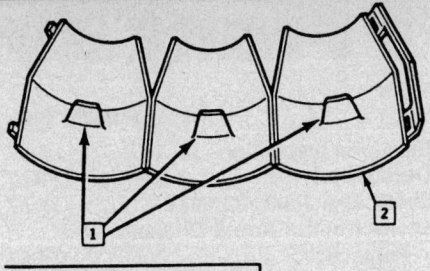

| 1 | REMOVE TABS |
| 2 | J 34754 DRIVE AXLE SEAL PROTECTOR |

Fig. 2   Modified outer seal protector

1. DRIFT PUNCH
2. 6 POINT DEEP WELL SOCKET

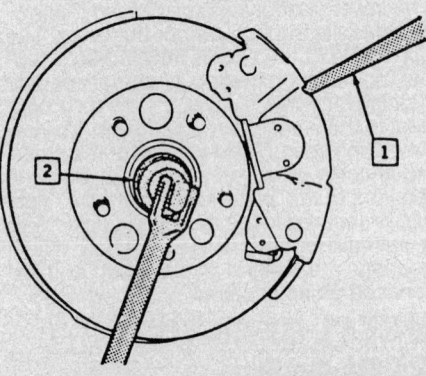

Fig. 3   Removing and installing shaft nut. 1989–90

1. COVER	13. NUT	25. BOLT	37. SUPPORT
2. NUT	14. PIN	26. COVER	38. BOLT
3. NUT	15. SEAL	27. BOLT	39. NUT
4. MOUNT	16. HUB	28. BALL JOINT	40. BOLT
5. SEAT	17. SHIELD	29. RIVET	41. WASHER
6. INSULATOR	18. BOLT	30. GROMMET	42. AXLE
7. BUMPER	19. WASHER	31. WASHER	43. SPACER
8. SPRING	20. NUT	32. BOLT	44. NUT
9. INSULATOR	21. WASHER	33. ARM	45. SHAFT
10. STRUT	22. ROTOR	34. BUSHING	46. NUT
11. NUT	23. KNUCKLE	35. BOLT	47. INSULATOR
12. SEAL	24. CALIPER	36. BOLT	48. CLAMP

Fig. 1   Exploded view of front suspension

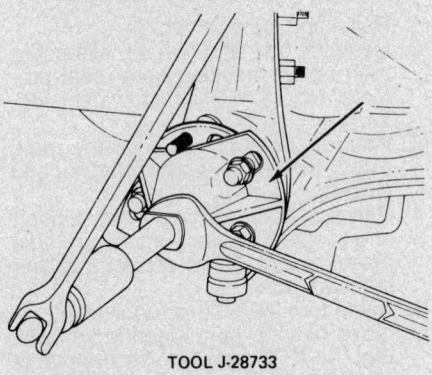

TOOL J-28733

Fig. 4   Front hub & bearing assembly removal

J29792-2 or equivalent, remove bushings from control arm.

7. Lubricate new bushings and install into control arm using tool Nos. J29792-1, J29792-2 and J29792-3 or equivalent.
8. Attach lower control arm to control arm support. **Torque** pivot bolts to 61 ft. lbs.
9. Install control arm support to chassis. Refer to **Fig. 7**, for attaching bolt torques.
10. Reverse procedure to complete installation. Check toe setting and adjust as required.

STEERING KNUCKLE
REPLACE

1. Raise and support vehicle, then remove wheel and tire.
2. Remove front hub and bearing as outlined under "Wheel Bearing, Replace" procedure.

3. Using tool J-29330, on 1988–90 models or J-38892, on 1991 models, separate ball joint from steering knuckle.
4. Remove strut to steering knuckle attaching bolts, then disconnect strut from steering knuckle.
5. Assemble strut to new steering knuckle and install attaching bolts finger tight.
6. Insert ball joint stud into steering knuckle and torque stud nut to specification.
7. Torque strut to steering knuckle bolts to specification.
8. Reverse removal procedure to complete installation.

STABILIZER BAR & BUSHINGS
REPLACE

1. Raise and support vehicle, allowing control arms to hang freely.

2. Remove left front wheel and tire assembly.
3. Disconnect stabilizer bar at control arms and control arm supports.
4. Disconnect stabilizer bar from control arms, **Fig. 8.**
5. Loosen front and remove rear and center bolts from suspension support assembly. Lower support enough to allow stabilizer bar removal.
6. Remove stabilizer bar with insulators.
7. Reverse procedure to install. Torque suspension support assembly in a manner which will allow front suspension to hang free.

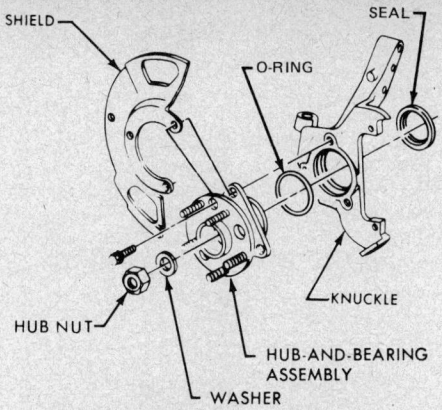

Fig. 5   Front hub & wheel bearing assembly

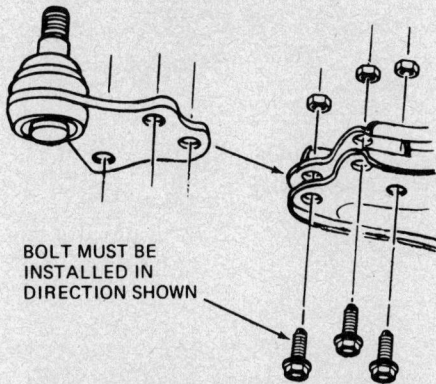

Fig. 6   Assembling lower ball joint to lower control arm

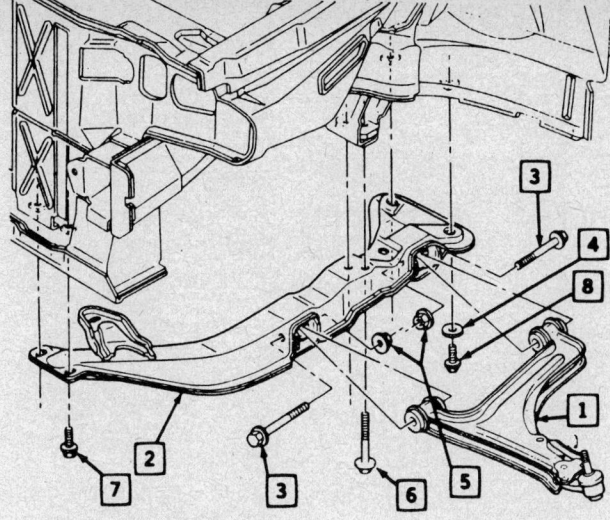

1. CONTROL ARM
2. SUSPENSION SUPPORT
3. BOLT — 83 N·m (61 LBS. FT.)
4. WASHER
5. NUT
6. BOLT — 90 N·m (66 LBS. FT.) TIGHTEN FIRST
7. BOLT — 88 N·m (65 LBS. FT.) TIGHTEN SECOND
8. BOLT — 88 N·m (65 LBS. FT.) TIGHTEN THIRD

Fig. 7   Replacing lower control arm

STRUT ASSEMBLY REPLACE

1. Raise hood and remove strut protective cap and three strut to body attaching nuts.
2. Raise and support vehicle, support suspension using suitable jack stands.
3. Remove wheel and tire assembly, then install modified inner drive joint boot protector tool No. J-34754.
4. **On 1988 models,** remove brake line bracket to strut assembly attaching bolts.
5. **On 1991 models,** using tool J-24319, disconnect tie rod from strut assembly.
6. **On all models,** remove strut to steering knuckle attaching bolts, **Fig. 9,** then remove strut from vehicle.
7. Reverse procedure to install.

STRUT ASSEMBLY SERVICE

Disassembly

1. Position strut compressor J-34013 in holding fixture J-3289-20.
2. Position strut in strut compressor, then compress strut approximately ½ of its height. Use care not to bottom spring or damper rod.
3. Remove nut from strut dampener shaft, then position guide rod J-34013-27 on dampener shaft. Use guide rod J-34013-27 to position dampener shaft down through bearing cap while compressing coil spring.
4. Remove components from coil strut unit.

Assembly

1. Position bearing cap on strut compressor.
2. Position strut to strut compressor and install compressor bottom locking pin.
3. Extend dampener shaft and install clamp J-34013-20 to hold shaft in position, **Fig. 10.**
4. Position spring over dampener, then position strut to strut compressor upper locking pin hole and install pin.
5. Install upper insulator, shield, bumper and upper spring seat. The flat on the upper spring seat should face in the same direction as the centerline of the strut assembly spindle, **Fig. 10.**
6. Install guide rod J-34013-27 onto dampener shaft, the compress strut unit until dampener shaft threads are visible. Remove guide rod and install retaining nut.
7. While holding dampener shaft in position with a suitable wrench, torque retaining nut to specification. After tightening nut, remove clamp from dampener shaft clamp J-34013-20.

MANUAL STEERING GEAR REPLACE

1. Disconnect battery ground cable.
2. Remove left hand sound insulator.
3. From under instrument panel, pull downward on steering column seal, then remove upper pinch bolt from flexible coupling.
4. Raise and support front of vehicle, then remove both front wheel and tire assemblies.
5. Disconnect tie rods from struts using tool No. J24319-01, then lower vehicle.
6. Remove steering gear mounting clamps, **Fig. 11.**
7. Move steering gear assembly slightly forward, then remove lower pinch bolt from flexible coupling and detach coupling from steering gear stub shaft.
8. Remove dash panel seal from steering gear.
9. Raise and support front of vehicle, then remove splash shield from left inner fender.
10. Place left hand knuckle and hub assembly in the full left turn position, then remove steering gear through access hole in left hand inner fender.
11. Reverse procedure to install. Torque attaching nuts, bolts and screws to specifications.

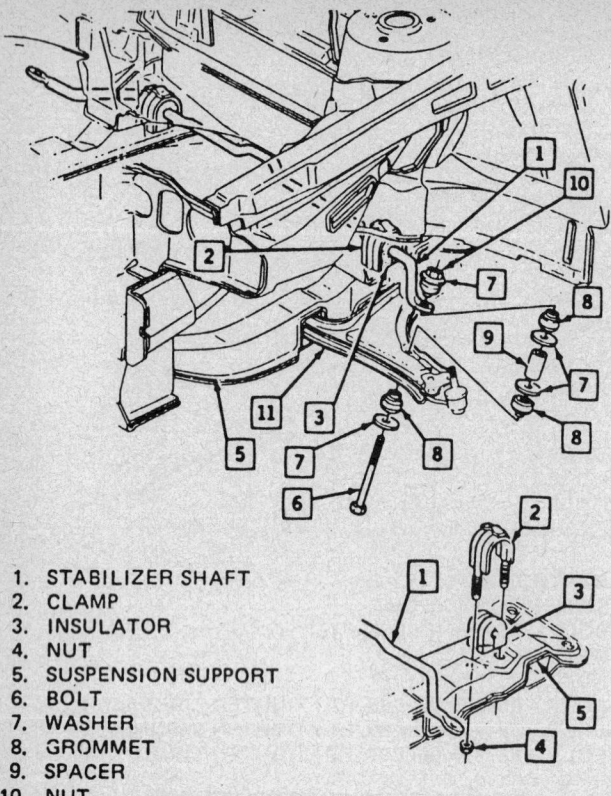

1. STABILIZER SHAFT
2. CLAMP
3. INSULATOR
4. NUT
5. SUSPENSION SUPPORT
6. BOLT
7. WASHER
8. GROMMET
9. SPACER
10. NUT
11. CONTROL ARM

Fig. 8   Stabilizer bar installation

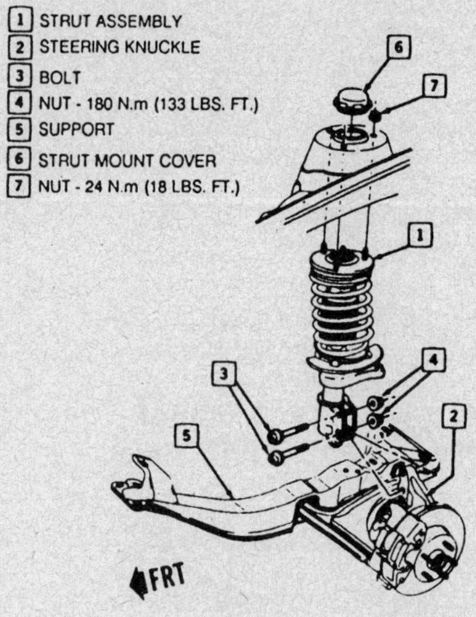

1 STRUT ASSEMBLY
2 STEERING KNUCKLE
3 BOLT
4 NUT - 180 N.m (133 LBS. FT.)
5 SUPPORT
6 STRUT MOUNT COVER
7 NUT - 24 N.m (18 LBS. FT.)

Fig. 9   Installing strut assembly

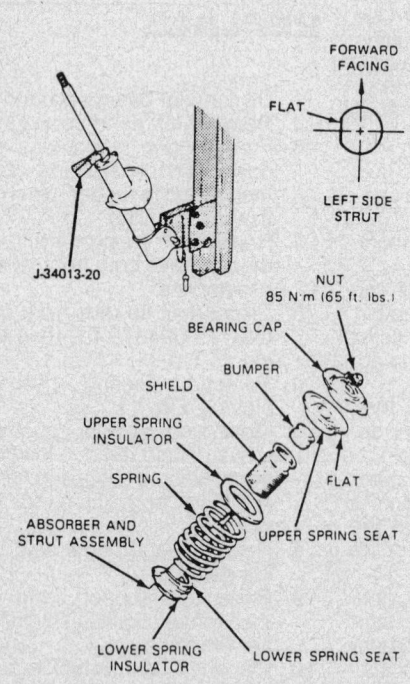

Fig. 10   Assembling strut unit

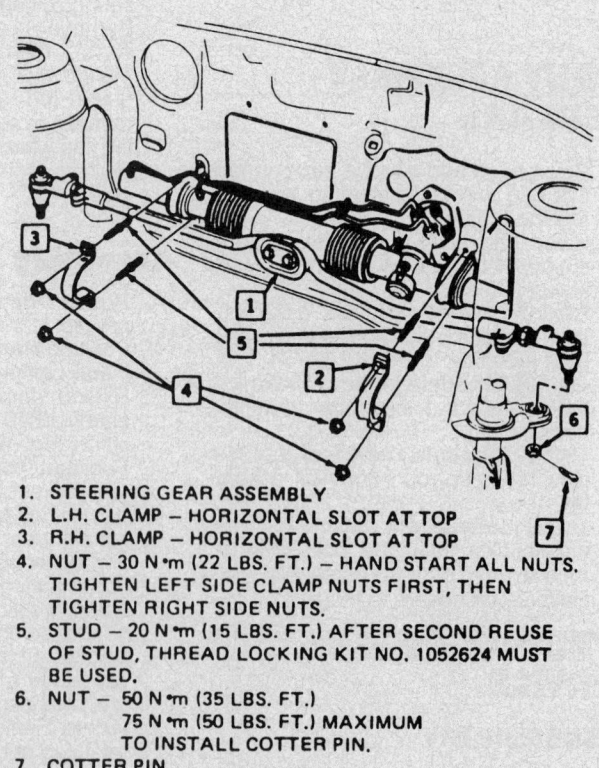

1. STEERING GEAR ASSEMBLY
2. L.H. CLAMP — HORIZONTAL SLOT AT TOP
3. R.H. CLAMP — HORIZONTAL SLOT AT TOP
4. NUT — 30 N·m (22 LBS. FT.) — HAND START ALL NUTS. TIGHTEN LEFT SIDE CLAMP NUTS FIRST, THEN TIGHTEN RIGHT SIDE NUTS.
5. STUD — 20 N·m (15 LBS. FT.) AFTER SECOND REUSE OF STUD, THREAD LOCKING KIT NO. 1052624 MUST BE USED.
6. NUT — 50 N·m (35 LBS. FT.)
   75 N·m (50 LBS. FT.) MAXIMUM TO INSTALL COTTER PIN.
7. COTTER PIN

Fig. 11   Power rack & pinion steering gear removal

POWER STEERING GEAR REPLACE

1. Disconnect battery ground cable.
2. Remove left hand sound insulator.
3. From under instrument panel, pull downward on steering column seal, then remove upper pinch bolt from flexible coupling.
4. Disconnect pressure line from steering gear and remove screw attaching line bracket to cowl.
5. Raise and support front of vehicle, then remove both front wheel and tire assemblies.
6. Disconnect tie rods from struts using tool No. J24319-01, then lower vehicle.
7. Remove steering gear mounting clamps, **Fig. 11.**
8. Move steering gear slightly forward, then disconnect return line from gear and drain power steering fluid.
9. Remove lower pinch bolt from flexible coupling, then detach coupling from steering gear stub shaft and remove dash seal.
10. Raise and support front of vehicle, then remove splash shield from left inner fender.
11. Place steering knuckle and hub assembly into the full left turn position, then remove steering gear through access hole in left hand inner fender.
12. Reverse procedure to install, noting the following:
    a. If steering gear mounting clamps have backed out during removal, install double nuts on stud and torque to 22 ft. lbs.
    b. **Torque** coupling to stub shaft pinch bolt to 30 ft. lbs.
    c. Torque pressure and return line fittings to specifications.

POWER STEERING PUMP REPLACE

1. Disconnect battery ground cable.
2. Remove serpentine belt.
3. Remove power steering pump attaching pressure lines.
4. Remove power steering pump attaching bolts.
5. Remove pump assembly, then transfer power steering pump pulley.
6. Reverse to install. Torque attaching bolts to specifications.

TIGHTENING SPECIFICATIONS

Year	Component	Torque/Ft. Lbs.
1988-90	Ball Joint To Knuckle	37-55
	Brake Line Bracket Bolt	13
	Caliper Bolts	38
	Control Arm Pivot Bolt	61
	Hub & Bearing Assembly	70
	Hub Nut	185
	Inner Tie Rod End Bolts	65
	Manual Coupling To Steering Column	34
	Manual Coupling To Stub Shaft	29
	Manual Rack & Pinion Mounts	22
	Power Coupling To Steering Column	34
	Power Coupling To Stub Shaft	37
	Power Rack & Pinion Mounts	22
	Power Steering Return Lines	20
	Stabilizer Shaft To Control Arm	15
	Stabilizer To Support Assembly	18
	Steering Gear Mounting Clamp	28
	Steering Knuckle To Strut Assembly	133
	Strut Assembly To Body	18
	Strut Cartridge Retaining Nut	65
	Suspension Support Assembly	①
	Tie Rod Pinch Bolts	41
	Tie Rod To Steering Knuckle	37
	Tie Rod To Strut	28
	Wheel & Tire Assembly	100
1991	Ball Joint To Knuckle	41-50
	Caliper Bolts	38
	Control Arm Pivot Bolt	61
	Hub & Bearing Assembly	70
	Hub Nut	185
	Inner Tie Rod End Bolts	65
	Power Coupling To Steering Column	30
	Power Coupling To Stub Shaft	30
	Power Rack & Pinion Mounts	22
	Power Steering Return Lines	19
	Stabilizer Shaft To Control Arm	13
	Stabilizer To Support Assembly	16
	Steering Gear Mounting Clamp	28

Continued

TIGHTENING SPECIFICATIONS—Continued

Year	Component	Torque/Ft. Lbs.
1991 Cont'd	Steering Knuckle To Strut Assembly	133
	Strut Assembly To Body	18
	Strut Cartridge Retaining Nut	65
	Suspension Support Assembly	①
	Tie Rod Pinch Bolts	41
	Tie Rod To Steering Knuckle	37
	Tie Rod To Strut	37
	Wheel & Tire Assembly	100

①—Torque suspension support
assembly center bolts to 66 ft. lbs.;
then front bolts to 65 ft. lbs; then
rear bolts to 65 ft. lbs.

Wheel Alignment

INDEX

Page No.

CAMBER ADJUSTMENT

Toe setting is the only adjustment normally required. However, in special circumstances, such as damage due to road hazard or collision, camber may be adjusted by modifying the strut assembly.

1. Secure bottom of strut assembly in a suitable vise.
2. Enlarge bottom holes in outer flanges with a round file until holes in outer flanges match slots in inner flanges, **Fig. 1.**
3. Connect strut to steering knuckle and install bolts finger tight.
4. Grasp top of tire firmly, then move tire inboard or outboard until correct camber reading is obtained. Tighten re-

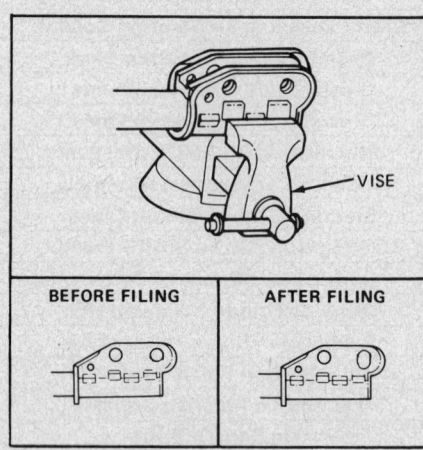

VISE

BEFORE FILING | AFTER FILING

Fig. 1   Modifying strut bracket to adjust camber

taining bolts enough to secure camber setting.
5. Remove wheel and tire and tighten strut to steering knuckle retaining bolts. On 1988-90 models, **torque** strut to steering knuckle retaining bolts to 135 ft. lbs. On 1991 models, **torque** strut to steering knuckle attaching bolt to 133 ft. lbs.

TOE-OUT ADJUSTMENT

Toe-out is controlled by tie rod position. Adjustment is made by loosening the clamp bolts at the steering knuckle end of the tie rods and rotating the rods to obtain proper toe setting. After correct toe setting is obtained, tighten clamp bolts. **Torque** clamp bolts to 41 ft. lbs.

NOTE: Refer To The Rear Of This Manual For Vehicle Manufacturer's Special Service Tool Suppliers.

Continued

INDEX OF SERVICE OPERATIONS—Continued

Specifications

GENERAL ENGINE SPECIFICATIONS

Year	Engine Liter/CID ①	Engine VIN Code ②	Fuel System	Bore & Stroke	Compression Ratio	Net H.P. @ RPM	Maximum Torque Ft. Lbs. @ RPM	Normal Oil Pressure Pounds
1988-89	2.0L/4-121	1	Fuel Injection	3.5 x 3.15	9.0	90 @ 5600	108 @ 3200	63-77 ③
	2.8L/V6-173	W	Fuel Injection	3.5 x 2.99	8.9	125 @ 4500	160 @ 3600	50-65 ③
1990-91	2.2L/4-134	G	Fuel Injection	3.5 x 3.46	9.0	95 @ 5200	120 @ 3200	63-77
	2.3L/4-138	A	Fuel Injection	3.62 x 3.35	10.0	180 @ 6200	160 @ 5000	15-30
	2.3L/4-138	D	Fuel Injection	3.62 x 3.35	10.0	160 @ 6200	155 @ 5200	15-30
	3.1L/V6-192	T	Fuel Injection	3.503 x 3.3122	8.8	135 @ 4200	180 @ 3600	15 @ 1100

①—CID-cubic inch displacement.
②—The eighth digit denotes engine code.
③—At 1200 RPM.

TUNE UP SPECIFICATIONS

Year & Engine/ V.I.N. Code ①	Spark Plug Gap	Ignition Timing BTDC				Curb Idle Speed ③		Fast Idle Speed		Fuel Pump Pressure
		Firing Order Fig. ②	Man. Trans.	Auto. Trans.	Mark Fig.	Man. Trans.	Auto Trans.	Man. Trans.	Auto. Trans.	
1988–89										
2.0L/4-121/1	.035	④	⑤	⑤	⑥	⑦	⑦	⑦	⑦	9-13 ⑧
2.8L/V6-173/W	.045	⑨	⑤	⑤	⑥	⑦	⑦	⑦	⑦	40.5–47 ⑩
1990–91										
2.2L/4-134/G	.035	④	③	③	⑥	⑦	⑦	⑦	⑦	9-13 ⑧
2.3L/4-138/D	.035	④	⑤	⑤	⑥	⑦	⑦	⑦	⑦	40.5–47 ⑩
2.3L/4-138/A	.035	④	⑤	—	⑥	⑦	—	⑦	—	51 ⑩
3.1L/V6-192/T	.045	⑨	③	③	⑥	⑦	⑦	⑦	⑦	40.5–47 ⑩

①—The eighth digit of Vehicle Identification Number (V.I.N.) denotes engine code.

②—Before removing wires from distributor cap, determine location of No. 1 wire in cap, as distributor position may have been altered from that shown at the end of this chart.

③—Not adjustable.

④—Cylinder numbering front to rear, 1, 2, 3, 4. Firing order 1-3-4-2. Refer to Fig. A for spark plug wire connections at coil unit.

⑤—Computer controlled, no adjustment.

⑥—Equipped with a crankshaft position sensor.

⑦—Idle speeds are controlled by the idle air control assembly.

⑧—Wrap shop towel around fuel hose to steel line connection in engine compartment to prevent fuel spillage. Disconnect fuel hose from steel line and connect suitable fuel pressure gauge. Ensure gauge connections are tight, then start engine & check fuel pressure readings.

⑨—Cylinder numbering left to right as viewed from front of vehicle, front bank 2, 4, 6; rear bank 1, 3, 5. Firing order, 1-2-3-4-5-6. Refer to Fig. B for spark plug wire connections at coil unit.

⑩—With shop towel wrapped around fuel pressure valve to prevent fuel spillage, connect a suitable fuel pressure gauge to fuel pressure valve. Check fuel pressure with ignition switch On, engine not running.

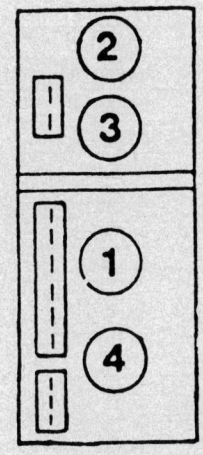

Fig. A

Fig. B

ALTERNATOR SPECIFICATIONS

Year	Model	Rated Hot Output Amps.
1988-89	1105697	74
	1105694	100
	1105698	85
	1105701	85
1990 ①	1105697	74
②	1101461	100
③	1105698	85
④	1105694	100
⑤	1101231	100
1991 ①	1105697	74
②	1101605	100
③	1101612	85
④	1101846	100
⑤	1101231	100

①—VIN G-KGO   ④—VIN T with A/C-K60
②—VIN G with A/C-K60   ⑤—VIN A
③—VIN T-K99

STARTING MOTOR APPLICATIONS

Refer to "Starter Motors" for starter specifications.

Year	Engine/VIN	Starter Ident. No.
1988-89	2.8L/V6-173/W	1109564
	2.8L/V6-173/W	1998511
1990	2.2L/4-134/G	10455010
	2.3L/4-138/D	10455044
	2.3L/4-138/A	10455044
	3.1L/V6-192/T	10455025
1991	2.2L/134/G	10455010
	2.3L/4-138/A	10455049
	3.1L/192/T	10455025

FRONT WHEEL ALIGNMENT SPECIFICATIONS

Year	Model	Caster Angle, Degrees		Camber Angle, Degrees				Toe Degrees
				Limits		Desired		
		Limits	Desired	Left	Right	Left	Right	
1988	All	+.7 to +2.7	+1.7	+.2 to +1.4	+.2 to +1.4	+.8	+.8	0
1989-91	①	+.4 to +1.9	+1.7	+.6 to +.8	+.6 to +.8	.10	.10	0
	②	+.4 to +1.9	+1.7	-.8 to +.4	-.8 to +.4	-.2	-.2	0

①—Standard suspension.
②—Sport suspension.

REAR WHEEL ALIGNMENT SPECIFICATIONS

| Year | Model | Camber Angle, Degrees | | | | Toe, Degrees |
| | | Limits | | Desired | | |
		Left	Right	Left	Right	
1988	Beretta	-.10 to -.40	-.10 to -.40	①	①	0 to .30①
	Corsica	-.17 to -.33	-.17 to -.33	①	①	.12 to .13①
1989-91	Beretta	-.8 to +.3	-.8 to +.3	①	①	.9 to 1.6①
	Corsica	-.9 to +.4	-.9 to +.4	①	①	.1 to .4①

①—Not adjustable.

COOLING SYSTEM & CAPACITY DATA

| Year | Model or Engine/ VIN | Cooling Capacity, Qts. | | Radiator Cap Relief Pressure, Lbs. | Thermo. Opening Temp. °F | Fuel Tank, Gals. | Engine Oil Refill, Qts. | Transaxle Oil | |
		Less A/C	With A/C					Manual Transaxle, Pts.	Auto. Transaxle, Qts. ①
1988-89	2.0L/4-121/1	9.6 Qts. ②	9.6 Qts. ②	15	195	13.6	4③	5.3	④
	2.8L/V6-173/W	11.0 Qts. ②	11.1②	15	195	13.6	4③	4.5	④
1990-91	2.2L/4-134/G	8.5	8.5	15	195	15.6	4⑤	⑥	⑦
	2.3L/4-138/D	8.9	8.9⑧	15	192	15.6	4	4.4	7
	2.3L/4-138/A	9.2	9.2⑨	15	192	15.6	4	4.4	—
	3.1L/V6-192/T	12.5	12.5	15	195	15.6	4	—	6

①—Approximate, make final check with dipstick.
②—Check Owner's Manual for final capacities.
③—With or without filter change.
④—Oil pan only, 4 qts.; after disassembly, 6 qts.
⑤—When changing engine oil filter additional oil may be required.
⑥—Isuzu 5 spd., 5.4 pts.; Muncie 5spd., 4 pts.
⑦—Oil pan only, 4 qts. After overhaul, less torque converter drain, 6 qts.; with torque converter drain, 9 qts.
⑧—With heavy duty radiator, 9.2 qts.
⑨—With heavy duty radiator, 9.4 qts.

Electrical
INDEX

FUSE PANEL & FLASHER LOCATION

The fuse panel is located behind the lefthand side of the instrument panel, near the shroud.

The hazard warning flasher is located behind the lefthand side of the instrument panel in the convenience center. The turn signal flasher is located next to the convenience center.

STARTER
REPLACE
2.0L/4-121 & 2.2L/4-134 ENGINES

1. Disconnect battery ground cable.

2. Raise and support front of vehicle.
3. Disconnect solenoid wires and battery cable at starter motor.
4. **On 2.0L/4-121 engines,** remove rear engine mount support bracket, then the A/C compressor support rod (if equipped).
5. **On 2.2L/4-134 engines,** disconnect wiring clamp at starter support bracket, then remove the support bracket to engine attaching bolt.
6. **On all engines,** remove starter attaching bolts, then carefully lower starter. Note position of shims, if used.
7. Reverse procedure to install.

2.3L/4-138 ENGINE
1990 MODELS

1. Disconnect battery ground cable and electric cooling fan.
2. Remove intake manifold-to-engine bracket.
3. Using a 15mm socket and a six inch extension, remove starter brace bolt.
4. Remove starter attaching bolts. Leave solenoid wires attached at this point.
5. Remove starter as follows:
   a. Lower nose of starter through access hole.
   b. Move rear of starter toward front of vehicle.
   c. Disconnect starter wiring from solenoid, then remove starter.
6. Reverse procedure to install.

1991 MODELS

1. Disconnect battery ground cable, then remove serpentine drive belt.
2. Remove coolant reservoir.
3. Disconnect A/C line rail clip.
4. Remove alternator, then the oil fill tube and dipstick assembly.
5. Remove alternator bracket, then the air cleaner assembly.
6. Place a suitable drain pan under engine oil pan, then remove oil filter.
7. Remove starter as follows:
   a. Remove upper and lower starter mounting bolts.
   b. Position starter for access to solenoid wiring, then disconnect wiring.
   c. Remove starter from near front of engine between intake manifold and engine block.
8. Reverse procedure to install.

2.8L/V6-173 ENGINE

1. Disconnect battery ground cable.
2. Raise and support front of vehicle.
3. Remove engine oil filter.
4. Disconnect solenoid wires and battery cable at starter motor.
5. Remove starter attaching bolts, then carefully lower starter. Note position of shims, if used.
6. Reverse procedure to install.

3.1L/V6-192 ENGINE

1. Remove air cleaner assembly.
2. Disconnect battery ground cable.
3. Raise and support front of vehicle.
4. **On models with engine oil cooler,** remove oil filter, then position oil cooler hose out of the way.
5. Remove A/C compressor brace at-

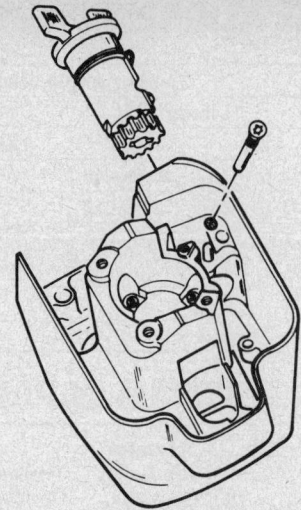

Fig. 1   Lock cylinder set removal

taching nuts, then the starter support brace-to-engine attaching nut.
6. Remove flywheel inspection cover attaching bolts, then the cover.
7. Remove starter attaching bolts, then carefully lower starter. Note position of shims, if used.
8. Disconnect starter wiring at solenoid.
9. Reverse procedure to install. On models with engine oil cooler, check engine oil level after installing filter.

IGNITION LOCK
REPLACE

On models equipped with Supplemental Inflatable Restraint (SIR) system, serious injury can result from unintended airbag deployment.

The SIR system is designed to retain sufficient voltage to deploy the airbag for a short time after power has been disconnected. To avoid serious injury, disarm the SIR as follows:

1. Turn ignition switch to Off position.
2. Remove SIR fuse No. 3 from fuse panel.
3. Disconnect yellow two-way connector at base of steering column, as follows:
   a. Remove lefthand sound insulator retaining screws and nuts.
   b. Remove courtesy lamp from sound insulator, then the sound insulator from vehicle.
   c. Remove Connector Position Assurance (CPA) pin, then disconnect yellow two-way connector at base of steering column.
4. Wait at least 10 minutes before any further work is attempted. Serious injury may result from unintended airbag deployment if service is attempted immediately after SIR fuse is removed.
5. Reverse procedure to arm SIR system, noting the following:
   a. Turn ignition switch to On position.
   b. Observe Inflatable Restraint indi-

cator lamp.
   c. If lamp does not flash 7-9 times then remain Off, refer to "Passive Restraint Systems" for diagnosis.
6. Remove steering wheel as outlined under "Steering Wheel, Replace."
7. Remove turn signal switch as outlined under "Turn Signal Switch, Replace."
8. Position lock cylinder in Run position, then remove turn signal switch housing attaching screws. Remove turn signal switch housing and steering shaft as an assembly.
9. Pry buzzer switch tab with suitable screwdriver, then gently pull on wires to remove buzzer switch.
10. Position lock cylinder in Accessory position, then remove lock retaining screw and the lock cylinder, **Fig. 1.**
11. Reverse procedure to install, noting the following:
   a. **Torque** lock cylinder retaining screw to 22 inch lbs.
   b. **Torque** turn signal switch housing attaching screws to 88 inch lbs.

IGNITION & DIMMER SWITCHES
REPLACE

On models equipped with Supplemental Inflatable Restraint (SIR) system, serious injury can result from unintended airbag deployment.

The SIR system is designed to retain sufficient voltage to deploy the airbag for a short time after power has been disconnected. To avoid serious injury, disarm the SIR as follows:

1. Turn ignition switch to Off position.
2. Remove SIR fuse No. 3 from fuse panel.
3. Disconnect yellow two-way connector at base of steering column, as follows:
   a. Remove lefthand sound insulator retaining screws and nuts.
   b. Remove courtesy lamp from sound insulator, then the sound insulator from vehicle.
   c. Remove Connector Position Assurance (CPA) pin, then disconnect yellow two-way connector at base of steering column.
4. Wait at least 10 minutes any further work is attempted. Serious injury may result from unintended airbag deployment if service is attempted immediately after SIR fuse is removed.
5. Reverse procedure to arm SIR system, noting the following:
   a. Turn ignition switch to On position.
   b. Observe INFLATABLE RESTRAINT indicator lamp.
   c. If lamp does not flash 7-9 times then remain Off, refer to "Passive Restraint Systems" for diagnosis.
6. Disconnect battery ground cable.
7. Position lock cylinder in Accessory position.
8. Remove steering column to instrument panel attaching bolts, then gently lower steering column to drivers seat.

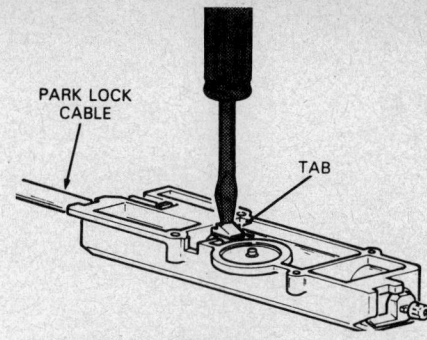

Fig. 2   Park lock cable removal

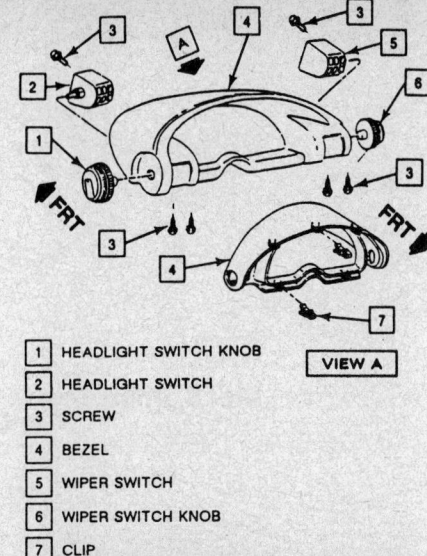

1	HEADLIGHT SWITCH KNOB
2	HEADLIGHT SWITCH
3	SCREW
4	BEZEL
5	WIPER SWITCH
6	WIPER SWITCH KNOB
7	CLIP

VIEW A

Fig. 3   Instrument cluster bezel removal. 1991 Beretta & Corsica

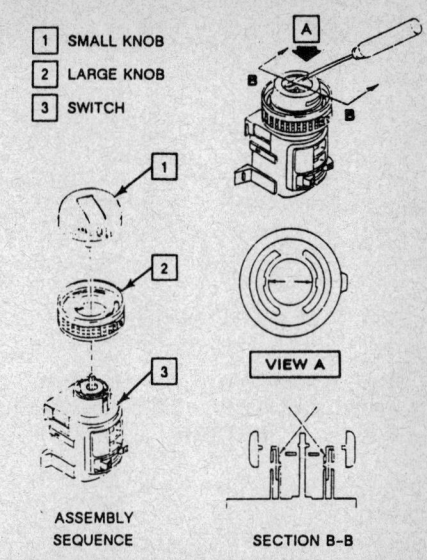

1	SMALL KNOB
2	LARGE KNOB
3	SWITCH

VIEW A

ASSEMBLY SEQUENCE   SECTION B-B

Fig. 4   Headlight & windshield wiper assembly switch. 1991 Beretta & Corsica

9. Remove dimmer and ignition switch mounting stud nut, then the dimmer switch attaching screw and dimmer switch.
10. Remove dimmer switch actuator rod.
11. Remove dimmer and ignition switch mounting stud.
12. Remove ignition switch assembly from ignition switch actuator.
13. Remove inhibitor switch housing to ignition switch assembly attaching screws, then the inhibitor switch housing.
14. On models equipped with park lock steering column, use suitable screwdriver to remove park lock cable from switch inhibitor, **Fig. 2.**
15. Install inhibitor switch housing on ignition switch, then install attaching screws and **torque** to 9 inch lbs.
16. On models equipped with park lock steering column, insert park lock cable into switch inhibitor housing, then push in until locking tabs engage.
17. Ensure lock cylinder is positioned in Accessory position, then place ignition switch slider in far left (accessory) position and install ignition switch over switch actuator.
18. Position ignition switch on steering column, then install dimmer and ignition switch mounting stud. **Torque** stud to 35 inch lbs.
19. Position dimmer switch actuator rod into dimmer switch rod cap hole, then install actuator rod.
20. Install dimmer switch on dimmer and ignition switch mounting stud. Install dimmer switch mounting nut and screw. Do not tighten at this time.
21. Position dimmer switch in such a way so click is heard whenever the turn signal lever is pulled back, then **torque** attaching nut and screw to 35 inch lbs.
22. Install steering column. **Torque** attaching bolts to 29 ft. lbs.

HEADLIGHT, REAR WINDOW DEFOGGER OR WINDSHIELD WIPER/WASHER SWITCH REPLACE

1988–90 MODELS

1. Disconnect battery ground cable.

2. Using suitable tool, pry switch from instrument panel.
3. Disconnect switch wiring, then remove switch.
4. Reverse procedure to install.

1991 MODELS

Refer to **Figs. 3 and 4** when performing the following procedure.
1. Disconnect battery ground cable.
2. Remove instrument cluster bezel.
3. Squeeze small switch knob at side and pull straight out.
4. Insert a suitable flat blade screwdriver into slots adjacent to center of inner knob and disengage knob from switch.
5. Remove switch to bezel screws, then switch.
6. Reverse procedure to install noting the following:
   a. When positioning inner knob to switch, make certain tabs align with slots, then press to secure.
   b. Position outer knob on switch and align "D" shaped hole in knob to shaft on switch, then press to secure.

PULSE WINDSHIELD WIPER MODULE REPLACE

The windshield wiper pulse module circuitry is an integral part of the windshield wiper motor cover.

STOP LAMP SWITCH ADJUST

Insert stop lamp switch into tubular clip above brake pedal until switch body seats fully into clip. Pull brake pedal rearward against internal pedal stop. The switch will be properly positioned in the tubular clip automatically. **Rotate switch** ½ turn

counterclockwise to ensure that switch does not hold brake pedal down after adjustment.

BACK-UP LIGHT/NEUTRAL START SWITCH REPLACE

1. Disconnect battery ground cable.
2. Disconnect shift linkage from transaxle.
3. Disconnect electrical connector from back-up light/neutral start switch.
4. Remove back-up light/neutral start switch attaching screws, then the switch.
5. Ensure transaxle shift shaft is in Neutral position.
6. If installing new switch, align new back-up light/neutral start switch flats with flats of shift shaft, then install switch. **Torque** attaching bolts to 22 ft. lbs.
7. If used switch is being installed, proceed as follows:
   a. Align back-up light/neutral start switch flats with flats of shift shaft, then install switch. Loosely install attaching bolts.
   b. Insert ³/₃₂ inch drill in service adjustment hole, then rotate switch until drill drops to a depth of ⁹/₆₄ inch.
   c. **Torque** attaching bolts to 22 ft. lbs.
8. With either new or used switch, ensure engine will only start in Neutral and Start positions.

CLUTCH START SWITCH REPLACE

1. Disconnect battery ground cable.
2. Disconnect wiring connector from switch located on clutch pedal support above clutch pedal.
3. Disconnect switch link from pedal,

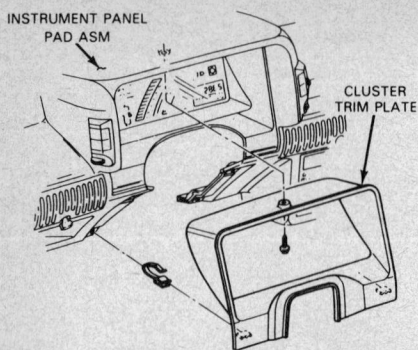

Fig. 5 Instrument cluster removal. 1988–90 Beretta models

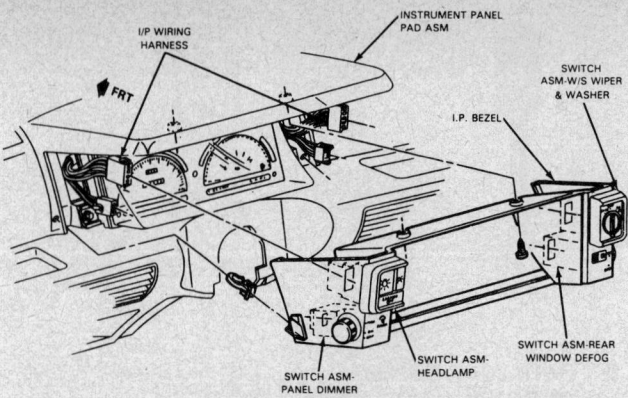

Fig. 6 Instrument cluster removal. 1988–90 Corsica models

then remove switch retaining link and switch.
4. Reverse procedure to install.

TURN SIGNAL SWITCH REPLACE

On models equipped with Supplemental Inflatable Restraint (SIR) system, serious injury can result from unintended airbag deployment.

The SIR system is designed to retain sufficient voltage to deploy the airbag for a short time after power has been disconnected. To avoid serious injury, disarm the SIR as follows:

1. Turn ignition switch to Off position.
2. Remove SIR fuse No. 3 from fuse panel.
3. Disconnect yellow two-way connector at base of steering column, as follows:
   a. Remove lefthand sound insulator retaining screws and nuts.
   b. Remove courtesy lamp from sound insulator, then the sound insulator from vehicle.
   c. Remove Connector Position Assurance (CPA) pin, then disconnect yellow two-way connector at base of steering column.
4. Wait at least 10 minutes before any further work is attempted. Serious injury may result from unintended airbag deployment if service is attempted immediately after SIR fuse is removed.
5. Reverse procedure to arm SIR system, noting the following:
   a. Turn ignition switch to On position.
   b. Observe Inflatable Restraint indicator lamp.
   c. If lamp does not flash 7-9 times then remain Off, refer to "Passive Restraint Systems" for diagnosis.
6. Remove steering wheel, then the turn signal cancel cam assembly.
7. Remove hazard warning knob attaching screw, then the hazard warning knob.
8. Position turn signal switch in such a way so column cover attaching screw and turn signal attaching screws are

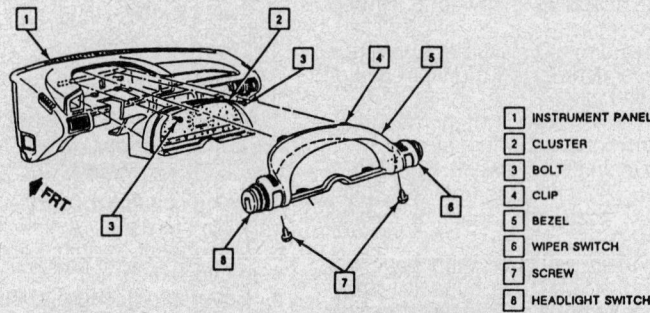

Fig. 7 Instrument cluster removal. 1991 Beretta & Corsica

1	INSTRUMENT PANEL
2	CLUSTER
3	BOLT
4	CLIP
5	BEZEL
6	WIPER SWITCH
7	SCREW
8	HEADLIGHT SWITCH

accessible.
9. Remove column cover attaching screw, then the column cover.
10. Remove dimmer switch actuator upper attaching screw, then the dimmer switch actuator.
11. Remove turn signal lever attaching screw from dimmer switch actuator, then remove lever. **On models equipped with cruise control, disconnect wire connector.**
12. Remove turn signal switch attaching screws.
13. Remove buzzer switch wires (light green and tan/black wires) from turn signal switch wiring connector using terminal remover tool No. J-35689-A or equivalent.
14. Remove turn signal switch.
15. Reverse procedure to install, noting the following:
   a. **Torque** turn signal switch attaching screws to 35 inch lbs.
   b. Attach light green buzzer switch wire to terminal F of turn signal switch wiring connector.
   c. Attach tan/black buzzer switch wire to terminal G of turn signal switch wiring connector.
   d. **Torque** turn signal lever attaching screw to 18 inch lbs.
   e. **Torque** dimmer switch actuator attaching screw to 20 inch lbs.
   f. **Torque** column cover attaching screw to 35 inch lbs.
   g. **Torque** hazard warning switch attaching screw to 7 inch lbs.
   h. **Torque** steering wheel attaching nut to 30 ft. lbs.

STEERING WHEEL REPLACE

On models equipped with Supplemental Inflatable Restraint (SIR) system, serious injury can result from unintended airbag deployment.

The SIR system is designed to retain sufficient voltage to deploy the airbag for a short time after power has been disconnected. To avoid serious injury, disarm the SIR as follows:

1. Turn ignition switch to Off position.
2. Remove SIR fuse No. 3 from fuse panel.
3. Disconnect yellow two-way connector at base of steering column, as follows:
   a. Remove lefthand sound insulator retaining screws and nuts.
   b. Remove courtesy lamp from sound insulator, then the sound insulator from vehicle.
   c. Remove Connector Position Assurance (CPA) pin, then disconnect yellow two-way connector at base of steering column.
4. Wait at least 10 minutes before any further work is attempted. Serious injury may result from unintended airbag deployment if service is attempted immediately after SIR fuse is removed.
5. Reverse procedure to arm SIR system, noting the following:
   a. Turn ignition switch to On position.
   b. Observe Inflatable Restraint indicator lamp.

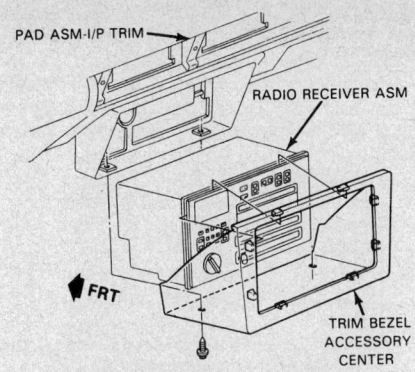

Fig. 8 Radio & A/C-heater control head removal. 1988–90 Beretta models

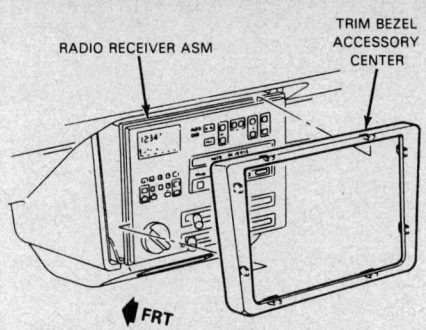

Fig. 9 Radio & A/C-heater control head removal. 1988–90 Corsica models

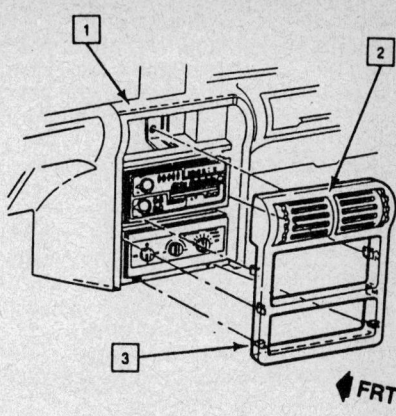

1 INSTRUMENT PANEL PAD
2 TRIM BEZEL
3 RETAINERS

Fig. 10 Radio removal. 1991 Beretta & Corsica

c. If lamp does not flash 7-9 times then remain Off, refer to "Passive Restraint Systems" for diagnosis.
6. Disconnect battery ground cable.
7. Remove horn pad attaching screws from behind steering wheel spokes, then pull horn pad away from steering wheel, disconnect horn wire and remove pad.
8. If necessary, remove horn pad damper.
9. Remove retainer from end of steering column, then remove steering wheel retaining nut.
10. Scribe reference marks on steering wheel hub and steering shaft, then using puller, tool No. J-1859-03, remove steering wheel.
11. Reverse procedure to install. Torque steering wheel retaining nut to 30 ft. lbs.

INSTRUMENT CLUSTER
REPLACE

Refer to **Figs. 5 through 7** for instrument cluster replacement procedures.

DRIVER INFORMATION CENTER KEYPAD
REPLACE

1. Remove instrument cluster trim panel, referring to **Figs. 5 through 7**.
2. Disconnect keypad electrical connector.
3. Remove keypad by pushing it out the back of the trim panel.
4. Reverse procedure to install.

RADIO
REPLACE

1988–90 MODELS

The radio is removed as an assembly with the A/C and heater control head, **Figs. 8 and 9**.

1991 MODELS

Refer to **Fig. 10**, for replacement of radio.

WINDSHIELD WIPER MOTOR
REPLACE

1. Disconnect battery ground cable.
2. Remove left side wiper arm using following procedure:
   a. Remove plastic cap from end of wiper arm shaft.
   b. Remove nut from end of wiper arm shaft.
   c. Using suitable tool, pry wiper arm from wiper arm shaft.
3. Remove wiper drive link from crank arm.
4. Disconnect electrical connectors and washer hoses from wiper motor.
5. Remove wiper motor attaching bolts, then remove wiper motor, guiding crank arm through drive hole.
6. Reverse procedure to install.

WINDSHIELD WIPER TRANSMISSION
REPLACE

1. Disconnect battery ground cable.
2. Remove left and right side wiper arms using following procedure:
   a. Remove plastic cap from end of wiper arm shaft.
   b. Remove nut from end of wiper arm shaft.
   c. Using suitable tool, pry wiper arm from wiper arm shaft.
3. Loosen, but do not remove, transmission drive link(s) to wiper motor crank arm attaching screws.
4. Remove air inlet screen.
5. Disconnect transmission drive link(s) from wiper motor crank arm.
6. Remove wiper transmission to body attaching bolts.
7. Remove wiper transmission by guiding it through shroud upper panel access hole.
8. Reverse procedure to install.

BLOWER MOTOR
REPLACE

LESS A/C

On Models with 3.1L/V6-192 engines it is necessary to remove the serpentine belt and alternator to prior to performing the following procedure.
1. Disconnect battery ground cable.
2. Disconnect blower motor and blower motor resistor electrical connections.
3. Remove plastic water shield from right side of cowl.
4. Remove blower motor attaching screws, then the blower motor.
5. Remove blower motor cage attaching nut, then the cage.
6. Reverse procedure to install.

WITH A/C

On Models with 3.1L/V6-192 engines it is necessary to remove the serpentine belt and alternator to prior to performing the following procedure.
1. Disconnect battery ground cable.
2. Disconnect blower motor electrical connections.
3. Disconnect blower motor attaching screws, then pull blower motor and cage out.
4. Remove plastic water shield from right side of cowl.
5. Remove blower motor.
6. Remove blower cage attaching nut, then the blower cage.
7. Reverse procedure to install.

HEATER CORE
REPLACE

LESS A/C

On models equipped with Supplemental Inflatable Restraint (SIR) sys-

tem, serious injury can result from unintended airbag deployment.

The SIR system is designed to retain
sufficient voltage to deploy the airbag
for a short time after power has been
disconnected. To avoid serious injury,
disarm the SIR as follows:

1. Turn ignition switch to Off position.
2. Remove SIR fuse No. 3 from fuse panel.
3. Disconnect yellow two-way connector at base of steering column, as follows:
   a. Remove lefthand sound insulator retaining screws and nuts.
   b. Remove courtesy lamp from sound insulator, then the sound insulator from vehicle.
   c. Remove Connector Position Assurance (CPA) pin, then disconnect yellow two-way connector at base of steering column.
4. Wait at least 10 minutes before any further work is attempted. Serious injury may result from unintended airbag deployment if service is attempted immediately after SIR fuse is removed.
5. Reverse procedure to arm SIR system, noting the following:
   a. Turn ignition switch to On position.
   b. Observe Inflatable Restraint indicator lamp.
   c. If lamp does not flash 7-9 times then remain Off, refer to "Passive Restraint Systems" for diagnosis.
6. Disconnect battery ground cable.
7. Drain cooling system into suitable container.
8. Disconnect coolant inlet and outlet hoses from heater core.
9. Remove heater outlet deflector from heater assembly.
10. Remove heater core cover from heater assembly.
11. Remove heater core and retaining straps.
12. Reverse procedure to install.

WITH A/C

On models equipped with Supplemental Inflatable Restraint (SIR) system, serious injury can result from unintended airbag deployment.

The SIR system is designed to retain

sufficient voltage to deploy the airbag
for a short time after power has been
disconnected. To avoid serious injury,
disarm the SIR as follows:

1. Turn ignition switch to Off position.
2. Remove SIR fuse No. 3 from fuse panel.
3. Disconnect yellow two-way connector at base of steering column, as follows:
   a. Remove lefthand sound insulator retaining screws and nuts.
   b. Remove courtesy lamp from sound insulator, then the sound insulator from vehicle.
   c. Remove Connector Position Assurance (CPA) pin, then disconnect yellow two-way connector at base of steering column.
4. Wait at least 10 minutes before any further work is attempted. Serious injury may result from unintended airbag deployment if service is attempted immediately after SIR fuse is removed.
5. Reverse procedure to arm SIR system, noting the following:
   a. Turn ignition switch to On position.
   b. Observe Inflatable Restraint indicator lamp.
   c. If lamp does not flash 7-9 times then remain Off, refer to "Passive Restraint Systems" for diagnosis.
6. Disconnect battery ground cable.
7. Drain cooling system into suitable container.
8. Raise and support vehicle.
9. Disconnect drain tube from heater case, then disconnect coolant inlet and outlet hoses from heater core.
10. Lower vehicle, then remove right and left side hush panels and steering column trim covers from under dash.
11. Remove heater outlet duct, then the glove compartment.
12. Pull heater core cover straight back, ensuring not to break drain tube.
13. Remove heater core clamps, then the heater core.
14. Reverse procedure to install.

EVAPORATOR CORE
REPLACE

On models equipped with Supple-

mental Inflatable Restraint (SIR) system, serious injury can result from unintended airbag deployment.

The SIR system is designed to retain
sufficient voltage to deploy the airbag
for a short time after power has been
disconnected. To avoid serious injury,
disarm the SIR as follows:

1. Turn ignition switch to Off position.
2. Remove SIR fuse No. 3 from fuse panel.
3. Disconnect yellow two-way connector at base of steering column, as follows:
   a. Remove lefthand sound insulator retaining screws and nuts.
   b. Remove courtesy lamp from sound insulator, then the sound insulator from vehicle.
   c. Remove Connector Position Assurance (CPA) pin, then disconnect yellow two-way connector at base of steering column.
4. Wait at least 10 minutes before any further work is attempted. Serious injury may result from unintended airbag deployment if service is attempted immediately after SIR fuse is removed.
5. Reverse procedure to arm SIR system, noting the following:
   a. Turn ignition switch to On position.
   b. Observe Inflatable Restraint indicator lamp.
   c. If lamp does not flash 7-9 times then remain Off, refer to "Passive Restraint Systems" for diagnosis.
6. Disconnect battery ground cable.
7. Discharge A/C system.
8. Drain cooling system.
9. Raise and support vehicle.
10. Remove heater hoses at heater, then the evaporator lines at evaporator core.
11. Drain evaporator tube elbow.
12. Remove right and left hush panels, then the steering column trim cover.
13. Remove heater outlet and glove box.
14. Remove the heater core, then the screws holding defroster vacuum actuator to module case.
15. Remove evaporator cover, then the evaporator.
16. Reverse procedure to install.

2.0L/4-121 Engine

INDEX

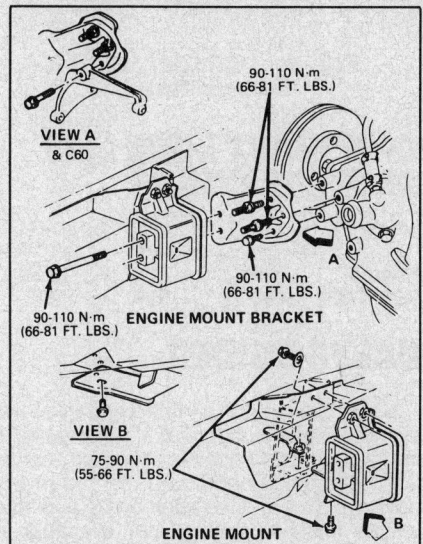

Fig. 1   Engine front mount

ENGINE MOUNT REPLACE

FRONT MOUNT

1. Disconnect battery ground cable.
2. Remove two upper front engine mount to body bracket attaching bolts.
3. Remove upper front engine mount to engine bracket attaching bolt.
4. Raise and support vehicle, then support engine assembly.
5. Remove inner fender shield.
6. Remove lower front engine mount to body bracket attaching bolt.
7. Remove lower front engine mount to engine bracket attaching bolt.
8. Remove front engine mount.
9. Reverse procedure to install. Refer to **Fig. 1,** for torque specifications.
   Prior to installing mount attaching bolts, clean all bolts in suitable cleaning solvent and apply Loctite to threads.

REAR MOUNT

1. Disconnect battery ground cable.
2. Raise and support vehicle, then support engine assembly.
3. Remove rear engine mount attaching nuts.
4. Remove rear engine mount attaching bolt.
5. Remove rear engine mount.
6. If rear engine mount bracket is removed, use the following procedure to ensure proper rear engine mount bracket positioning:
   a. Loosely install engine mount bracket.
   b. Raise engine and transaxle assembly.
   c. Tighten engine mount attaching nuts and bolt.
7. Reverse procedure to install. Refer to **Fig. 2,** for torque specifications. **Prior to installing mount attaching bolts, clean all bolts in suitable cleaning solvent and apply Loctite to threads.**

ENGINE REPLACE

1. Disconnect battery cables.
2. Drain cooling system into suitable container, then remove air intake hose from between air cleaner cover and Throttle Body Injection (TBI) unit.
3. Remove accessory drive belt.
4. Remove air cleaner retainer, then disconnect upper and lower radiator hoses.
5. Remove power steering pump front bolts.
6. Disconnect fuel lines and necessary vacuum hoses.
7. Disconnect shift cables from transaxle, then the throttle cable(s) from TBI unit.
8. Remove wiring shield at bulkhead, then disconnect engine harness at bulkhead.
9. Disconnect wires at Electronic Control Module (ECM), then pull wires

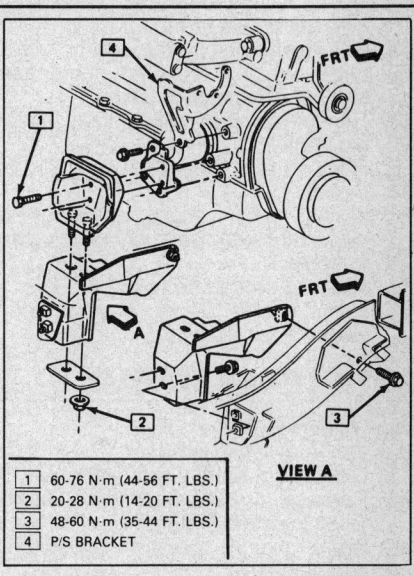

Fig. 2   Engine rear mount

through bulkhead.
10. Remove any wires interfering with engine removal.
11. Remove relay bracket from bulkhead.
12. Raise and support vehicle, then disconnect exhaust system at exhaust manifold and position aside.
13. Disconnect coolant inlet and outlet hoses from heater core.
14. Remove rear power steering pump bolt.
15. Disconnect stabilizer bar at left side lower control arm and support.
16. Remove transaxle strut from lefthand support.
17. Drain transaxle lubricant, then remove front wheels.
18. Disengage drive axles from transaxle.
19. Remove support to body attaching bolts, then swing supports aside.
20. Disconnect A/C compressor mounting bolts (if equipped) and position aside.
21. Remove clutch slave cylinder from transaxle and position aside with hydraulic line connected.

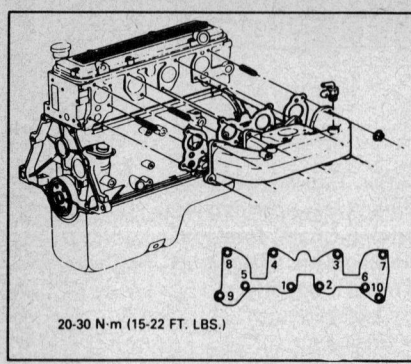

Fig. 3 Intake manifold installation

20-30 N·m (15-22 FT. LBS.)

22. Position engine support table tool No. J-36295 or equivalent under engine/transaxle assembly, then lower vehicle until engine/transaxle assembly is resting on table. Secure engine/transaxle to table.
23. Remove transaxle through bolt, then remove power steering pump from bracket and position aside.
24. Remove front mount to engine attaching bolts.
25. Remove rear mount and bracket assembly.
26. Slowly raise vehicle ensuring engine/transaxle assembly clears components.
27. Reverse procedure to install. Refer to **Figs. 1 and 2**, for engine mount torque specifications.

INTAKE MANIFOLD
REPLACE

1. Disconnect battery ground cable.
2. Remove air inlet duct from Throttle Body Injection (TBI) unit.
3. Drain engine coolant into suitable container.
4. Disconnect necessary vacuum hoses and electrical wiring.
5. Disconnect fuel line, then TBI linkage.
6. Remove power steering pump and position aside.
7. Raise and support front of vehicle.
8. Remove accelerator and T.V. cable bracket.
9. Disconnect heater hose from intake manifold.
10. Lower vehicle.
11. Remove intake manifold attaching nuts and bolts.
12. Remove intake manifold.
13. Reverse procedure to install. Torque intake manifold attaching nuts and bolts to specifications, following sequence given in **Fig. 3**.

EXHAUST MANIFOLD
REPLACE

1. Disconnect battery ground cable.
2. Disconnect oxygen sensor lead.
3. Remove accessory drive belt.
4. Remove alternator and position aside.
5. Raise and support vehicle.

6. Disconnect exhaust pipe from exhaust manifold.
7. Lower vehicle.
8. Remove oil fill tube.
9. Remove exhaust manifold attaching nuts, then the manifold.
10. Reverse procedure to install

CYLINDER HEAD
REPLACE

1. Disconnect battery ground cable.
2. Drain engine coolant into suitable container.
3. Remove air inlet duct from Throttle Body Injection (TBI) unit.
4. Raise and support vehicle.
5. Disconnect exhaust pipe at exhaust manifold, then the heater hose from intake manifold.
6. Remove accelerator and T.V. cable bracket.
7. Lower vehicle.
8. Disconnect any vacuum lines interfering with cylinder head removal from intake manifold and thermostat housing.
9. Disconnect linkage at TBI unit.
10. Disconnect necessary wiring.
11. Disconnect upper radiator from thermostat housing.
12. Remove accessory drive belt.
13. Remove power steering pump and position aside.
14. Disconnect fuel lines.
15. Remove alternator and alternator rear brace, leaving wires attached and position aside.
16. Remove rocker arm cover, then the rocker arms and pushrods. **Keep rocker arms and pushrods in order so they can be reinstalled in position they were removed from.**
17. Remove cylinder head attaching bolts, then the cylinder head, intake and exhaust manifolds as an assembly.
18. Reverse procedure to install. Refer to **Fig. 4**, for bolt tightening sequence and torque values.

ROCKER ARM STUDS
REPLACE

Rocker arm studs that have stress cracks or damaged threads can be replaced. If threads in the cylinder head are damaged or stripped, the head can be retapped and a helical type insert installed. Torque new rocker arm stud(s) to specifications.

VALVES
ADJUST

These engines use hydraulic valve lifters. No provision for adjustment is provided.

VALVE ARRANGEMENT
FRONT TO REAR

2.0L/4-121 . . . . I-E-I-E-I-E-I-E

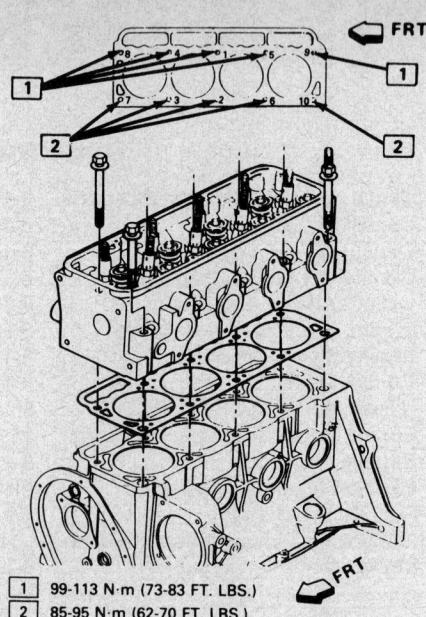

1 99-113 N·m (73-83 FT. LBS.)
2 85-95 N·m (62-70 FT. LBS.)

Fig. 4 Cylinder head installation

CAMSHAFT LOBE LIFT SPECIFICATIONS

Engine	Year	Int.	Exh.
2.0L/4-121	1988-89	.260	.260

VALVE GUIDES

Valve guides are an integral part of the cylinder head and are not removable. If valve stem clearance becomes excessive, the valve guide should be reamed to the next oversize and the appropriate oversize valves installed. Valves are available in .003, .015, and .030 inch oversizes.

On 1988 models with 2.0L/4-121 engine, excessive valve train noise may be caused by two valve spring seats stacked on top of each other during assembly. Any valve spring found to have two seats underneath it will require rocker arm replacement due to the excessive load put on the rocker arm.

VALVE LIFTERS
REPLACE

1. Remove rocker arm cover attaching bolts, then the rocker arm cover.
2. Loosen rocker arm stud nut and rotate rocker arm so that pushrod can be removed. Remove pushrod. **Keep removed parts in order so they can be reinstalled in position removed from.**
3. Using valve lifter removing tool No. J-29834 or equivalent, remove valve lifter from lifter bore.
4. Coat base of replacement with "Moly-kote," or equivalent, and install lifter into lifter bore.
5. Reverse procedure to install.

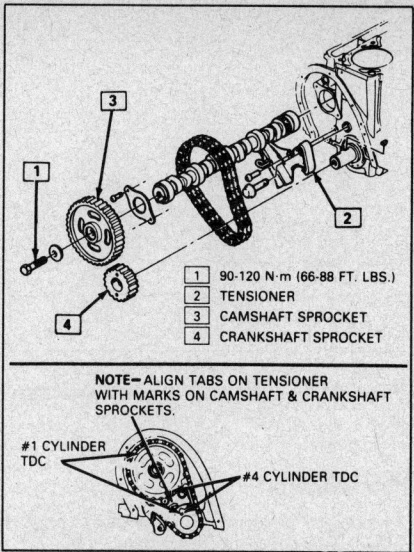

Fig. 5 Timing chain installation

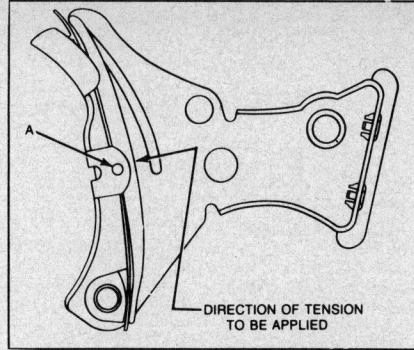

Fig. 6 Compressing timing chain tensioner spring

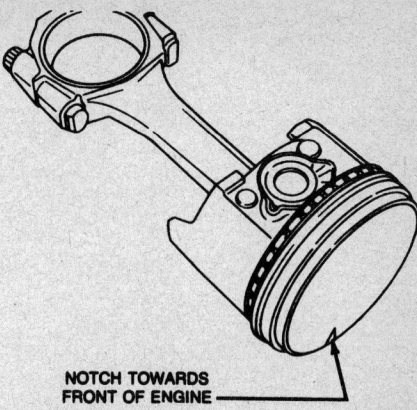

NOTCH TOWARDS FRONT OF ENGINE

Fig. 7 Piston & rod assembly

CRANKSHAFT PULLEY
REPLACE

1. Disconnect battery ground cable.
2. Remove accessory drive belt.
3. Raise and support vehicle, then remove right side tire and wheel assembly.
4. Remove right side inner fender shield, then the crankshaft pulley attaching bolt, 1988 models only.
5. Remove right side inner fender shield, then three crankshaft pulley attaching bolts, then pulley hub bolt.
6. Using puller tool No. J-24420-B or equivalent, remove pulley.
7. Reverse procedure to install. Prior to installing pulley, coat front cover oil seal contact area with engine oil and apply suitable RTV sealer to pulley keyway.

ENGINE FRONT COVER
REPLACE

1. Disconnect battery ground cable.
2. Remove crankshaft pulley as described previously.
3. Raise and support vehicle, then remove oil pan.
4. Lower vehicle, then remove accessory drive belt tensioner.
5. Remove front cover attaching bolts, then the front cover. **If front cover is difficult to remove, loosen with soft faced mallet.**

TIMING CHAIN
REPLACE

1. Remove engine front cover as previously described.
2. Place No. 1 cylinder at TDC and align timing marks on crankshaft and camshaft sprockets, **Fig. 5.**
3. Remove timing chain tensioner upper

attaching bolt, then loosen timing chain tensioner attaching nut as much as possible without removing it.
4. Remove camshaft sprocket attaching bolt, then the sprocket and timing chain.
5. If crankshaft sprocket is to be replaced, remove sprocket using puller tool No. J-5590 or equivalent.
6. To install crankshaft sprocket, align keyway on sprocket with key on crankshaft.
7. Align timing marks, **Fig. 5,** and install timing chain on sprockets.
8. Position sprocket onto camshaft by aligning dowel hole with the dowel pin. Use retaining bolt to seat sprocket fully onto the camshaft. Torque retaining bolt to specifications.
9. Lubricate timing chain with engine oil, then install timing chain tensioner.
10. Install engine front cover as outlined previously.

TIMING CHAIN TENSIONER
REPLACE

1. Remove front cover as described previously.
2. Remove attaching bolts.
3. Remove tensioner and damper.
4. Compress spring in direction of arrow, **Fig. 6.**
5. While compressing spring, use a cotter pin and insert into hole A shown.
6. Install chain tensioner.
7. Remove cotter pin from tensioner.

CAMSHAFT
REPLACE

1. Remove engine from vehicle as previously described.
2. Drain engine oil, then remove oil filter.
3. Remove valve lifters and engine front cover as described previously.
4. Remove oil pump drive.
5. Remove timing chain and camshaft sprocket as previously described.
6. Remove camshaft thrust plate to engine block retaining bolts and the thrust plate, **Fig. 5.**
7. Remove camshaft from engine block. **Use caution when removing cam-**

shaft not to damage bearings.
8. Reverse to install. Prior to installing camshaft, lubricate camshaft bearings with engine oil and camshaft lobes with GM E.O.S. 1051396 lubricant or equivalent. When installing camshaft, align crankshaft and camshaft sprocket timing marks, **Fig. 5.**

PISTON & ROD ASSEMBLY

Install piston to rod with notch or arrow on piston facing toward front of engine and rod bearing tang slot opposite camshaft, **Fig. 7.** Upon installation, measure the connecting rod side clearance using a suitable feeler gauge. Measurement taken should be as follows:

Engine	Year	Clearance In Inch
2.0L/4-121	1988-89	.004-.015

PISTONS, PINS & RINGS

Pistons and rings are available in standard and oversize. Oversize piston pins are not available.

MAIN & ROD BEARINGS

Main and connecting rod bearings are available in standard and various undersizes.

OIL PAN
REPLACE

1. Disconnect battery ground cable, then remove exhaust pipe shield.
2. Raise and support front of vehicle, then drain crankcase.
3. Disconnect exhaust pipe at exhaust manifold.
4. Detach A/C compressor brace at starter motor and A/C compressor bracket.
5. Remove flywheel cover and starter motor bracket, then remove starter motor and position aside.
6. Remove A/C compressor mounting brace.

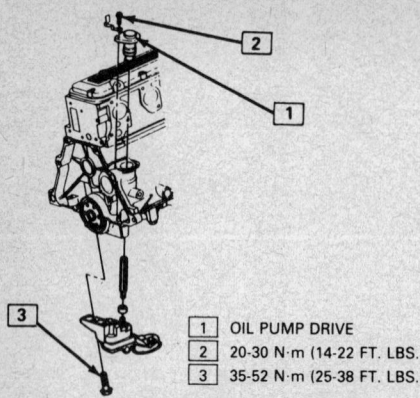

[1] OIL PUMP DRIVE
[2] 20-30 N·m (14-22 FT. LBS.)
[3] 35-52 N·m (25-38 FT. LBS.)

Fig. 8   Oil pump installation

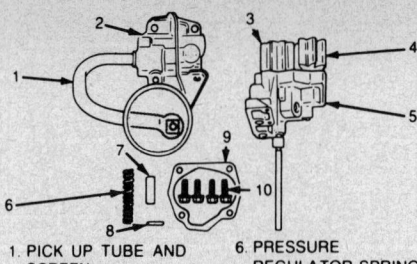

1. PICK UP TUBE AND SCREEN.
2. PUMP COVER.
3. DRIVE GEAR AND SHAFT.
4. IDLER GEAR.
5. PUMP BODY.
6. PRESSURE REGULATOR SPRING.
7. PRESSURE REGULATOR VALVE.
8. RETAINING PIN.
9. GASKET.
10. ATTACHING BOLTS.

Fig. 9   Oil pump assembly

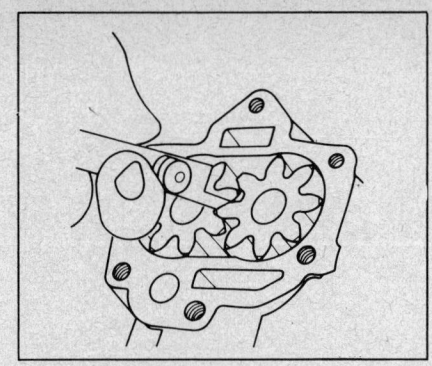

Fig. 10   Measuring oil pump gear lash

7. Remove four righthand suspension support bolts, then lower suspension support slightly to provide clearance for oil pan removal.
8. On models equipped with auto. transaxle, remove oil filter adapter and extension.
9. Remove oil pan attaching bolts and oil pan.
10. Reverse procedure to install. Before installing oil pan, apply a thin coat of RTV sealer to both ends of oil pan rear seal, then seat seal firmly into rear bearing cap. Do not allow sealer to extend beyond oil pan rear seal tabs. Apply a continuous 2 mm bead of RTV sealer along oil pan side rails in line with bolt holes, circling inward around each bolt hole location. Also apply RTV sealer to oil pan surface which contacts engine front cover. This bead of sealer must meet the bead at each oil pan side rail. Do not apply any RTV sealer to oil pan rear seal mating surface. Carefully install oil pan and torque attaching bolts alternately and evenly to specifications. Torque attaching bolts while RTV sealer is still wet to touch.

OIL PUMP
REPLACE
REMOVAL

1. Drain crankcase, then remove oil pan as previously described.
2. Remove pump to rear main bearing attaching bolt, then remove pump and extension shaft, **Fig. 8.**

DISASSEMBLY

1. Drain oil from pump, then remove driveshaft and driveshaft extension.
2. Remove pick up tube and screen.
3. Remove four pump cover to body attaching bolts, then remove cover, idler and drive gears, **Fig. 9. Place alignment mark on oil pump drive and idler gear teeth so they can be installed in the same position.**
4. Remove pressure regulator valve retaining pin, spring and the valve from pump body.

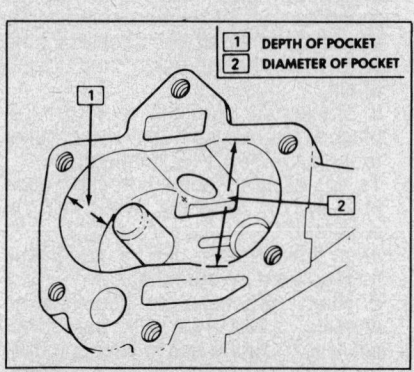

[1] DEPTH OF POCKET
[2] DIAMETER OF POCKET

Fig. 11   Measuring oil pump housing pocket

INSPECTION

1. Inspect pump components and should any of the following conditions exist, the oil pump assembly should be replaced.
   a. Inspect pump body, gears and cover for cracks or excessive wear.
   b. Check drive gear shaft for looseness in housing.
   c. Check inside of pump cover for wear that would allow oil to leak past ends of gears.
   d. Check oil pickup screen assembly for damage to screen or pickup tube.
   e. Check pressure regulator valve for fit in pump body.
2. Install pump gears, then using suitable feeler gauge, measure oil pump gear lash at several locations, **Fig. 10.** Clearance should be .009-.015 inch.
3. Remove pump gears, then measure depth of oil pump housing pocket, **Fig. 11.** Depth should be 1.195-1.198 inch.
4. Measure pump gear length. Length should be 1.199-1.2 inches.
5. Measure pump gear diameters. Diameters should be 1.498-1.5 inch.
6. Install pump gears, then measure side clearance between pump gears and oil pump housing. Side clearance should be .003-.004 inch.
7. If oil pump components are not within specifications, it should be replaced.

ASSEMBLY

Lubricate internal parts with engine oil during assembly.
1. Install replacement pickup screen and tube assembly, if removed. Position pump in a soft jawed vise, then apply sealer to end of tube and tap into position using suction tube installer tool No. J-8369 and a plastic hammer. Use care not to damage inlet screen and tube assembly when installing into pump housing.
2. Place pressure regulator valve, spring and retaining pin into pump body, then install drive gear and shaft.
3. Install idler gear into pump body, then the pump cover gasket. **Fig. 9.**
4. Install pump cover, torque retaining bolts to specifications.

INSTALLATION

1. Align oil pump extension shaft drive gear socket and pump housing, then install pump assembly. Torque pump assembly retaining bolt to specifications.
2. Install oil pan as previously described.

REAR MAIN BEARING OIL SEAL
REPLACE

If rear main seal is being replaced because of a chirping or squealing noise that goes away after oil is sprayed into seal area, first ensure engine is properly ventilated, as improper ventilation may cause an internal depression which draws oil past the seal. Remove engine oil dipstick and run engine. If noise is eliminated, check fresh air feed hole for blockage at rubber duct on rocker cover. If blockage exists, cut away as necessary to eliminate noise problem.
1. Support engine and remove transaxle.
2. Remove flywheel and ensure rear seal is leaking.
3. Remove seal by carefully inserting screwdriver in through dust lip and prying towards end of crankshaft. Repeat as necessary around circumference of seal until seal is removed, taking care not to damage crankshaft circumference.

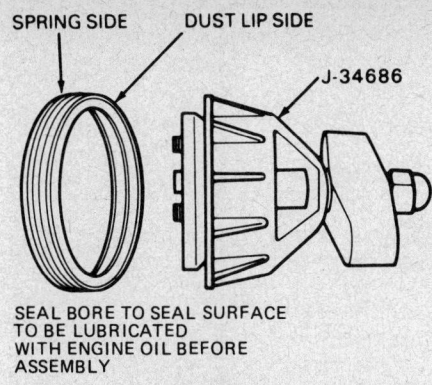

SPRING SIDE   DUST LIP SIDE

J-34686

SEAL BORE TO SEAL SURFACE
TO BE LUBRICATED
WITH ENGINE OIL BEFORE
ASSEMBLY

**Fig. 12   Rear main oil seal
installation**

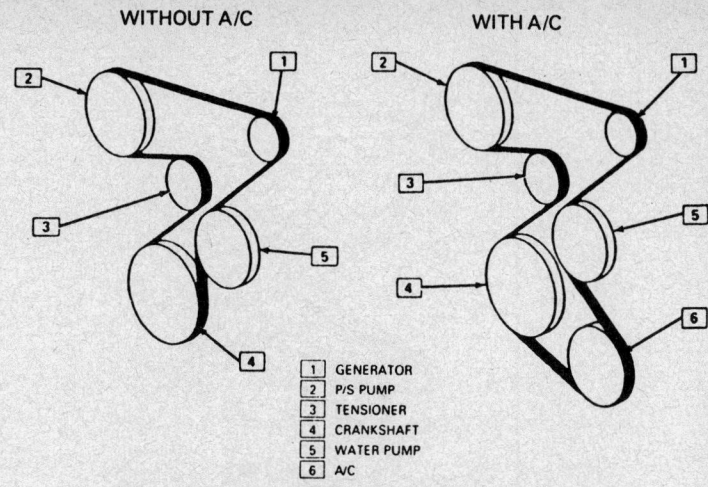

WITHOUT A/C   WITH A/C

1	GENERATOR
2	P/S PUMP
3	TENSIONER
4	CRANKSHAFT
5	WATER PUMP
6	A/C

Fig. 14   Serpentine drive belt routing

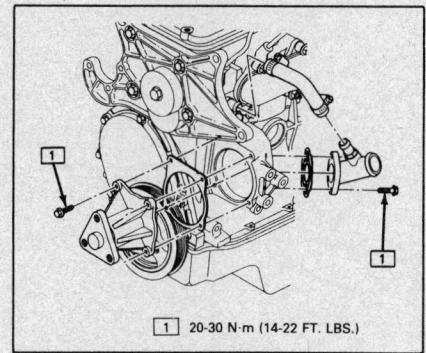

1   20-30 N·m (14-22 FT. LBS.)

**Fig. 13   Water pump
installation**

4. Check inside of seal bore for nicks or burrs and correct as necessary. Inspect crankshaft for burrs or nicks on seal contact surface. Repair or replace crankshaft as necessary.
5. Install new seal using seal installer tool No. J-34686.
6. Place seal on mandrel, making sure that dust lip on seal bottoms squarely against collar of tool, **Fig. 12.**
7. After aligning dowel pin with dowel pin hole in crankshaft, attach tool to crankshaft and **torque** screws to 2-5 ft. lbs.
8. Turn T-handle of tool until collar is tight against engine block to ensure that seal is seated properly in block.
9. Loosen T-handle of tool until it comes to a stop. Remove attaching screws.
10. Check that seal is seated squarely in bore.
11. Install flywheel and transaxle.
12. Start engine and check for leaks.

WATER PUMP
REPLACE

1. Disconnect battery ground cable, then drain cooling system.
2. Remove accessory drive belt.
3. Remove alternator and alternator bracket.
4. Remove water pump pulley to water pump attaching bolts, then the pulley from water pump.

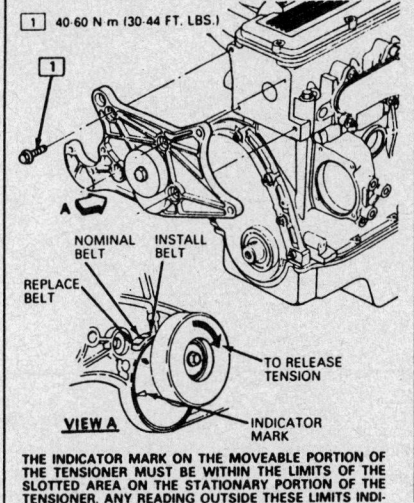

1   40-60 N·m (30-44 FT. LBS.)

NOMINAL   INSTALL
BELT   BELT

REPLACE
BELT

TO RELEASE
TENSION

INDICATOR
MARK

VIEW A

THE INDICATOR MARK ON THE MOVEABLE PORTION OF
THE TENSIONER MUST BE WITHIN THE LIMITS OF THE
SLOTTED AREA ON THE STATIONARY PORTION OF THE
TENSIONER. ANY READING OUTSIDE THESE LIMITS INDI-
CATES EITHER A DEFECTIVE BELT OR TENSIONER.

**Fig. 15   Belt tensioner
operating range**

5. Remove four water pump to block attaching bolts, then the water pump, **Fig. 13.**
6. Clean sealing surfaces of pump and engine block. Install new gasket and pump, torque attaching bolts to specifications.
7. Reverse removal procedures to complete installation.

COOLING SYSTEM BLEED

These engines do not require a specified bleed procedure. After filling cooling system, run engine to operating temperature with radiator/pressure cap off. Air will then be automatically bled through cap opening.

SERPENTINE DRIVE BELTS

BELT ROUTING

Refer to **Fig. 14** for serpentine drive belt routing.

BELT, ADJUST

Belt tension is maintained by a spring loaded belt tensioner. To remove or install drive belt, rotate tensioner with a 15 mm socket. If belt tension is not satisfactory, ensure belt tensioner is within operating limits, **Fig. 15.** If belt tensioner is allowed to operate outside its operating limits, damage to belt tensioner may result.

BELT TENSIONER, REPLACE

1. Disconnect negative battery cable.
2. Remove coolant reservoir.
3. Remove serpentine belt.
4. Remove two alternator bolts, then the belt tension pulley.
5. Disconnect power steering pump and position aside.
6. Remove tensioner bolts, then the tensioner.
7. Reverse procedure to install.

FUEL PUMP
REPLACE

1. Disconnect battery ground cable.
2. Raise and support vehicle.
3. Drain, then remove fuel tank as follows:
   a. Raise and support vehicle.
   b. Remove two rubber exhaust pipe hangers, **Fig. 16.**
   c. Remove two muffler hanger retaining bolts.
   d. Remove three heat shield attaching screws, then the heat shield.
   e. Remove fuel tank filler tube, vent tube, vent hose, and clamps.
   f. Disconnect electrical connector, **Fig. 17.**
   g. Disconnect fuel level meter vapor hose.
   h. Ensure fuel line connections are clean. Disconnect fuel return quick connect fitting by squeezing plastic tab on male end of the fitting. Using Connector Tool Set No. J-37088, disconnect fuel line quick connect fitting. Plug all fittings.

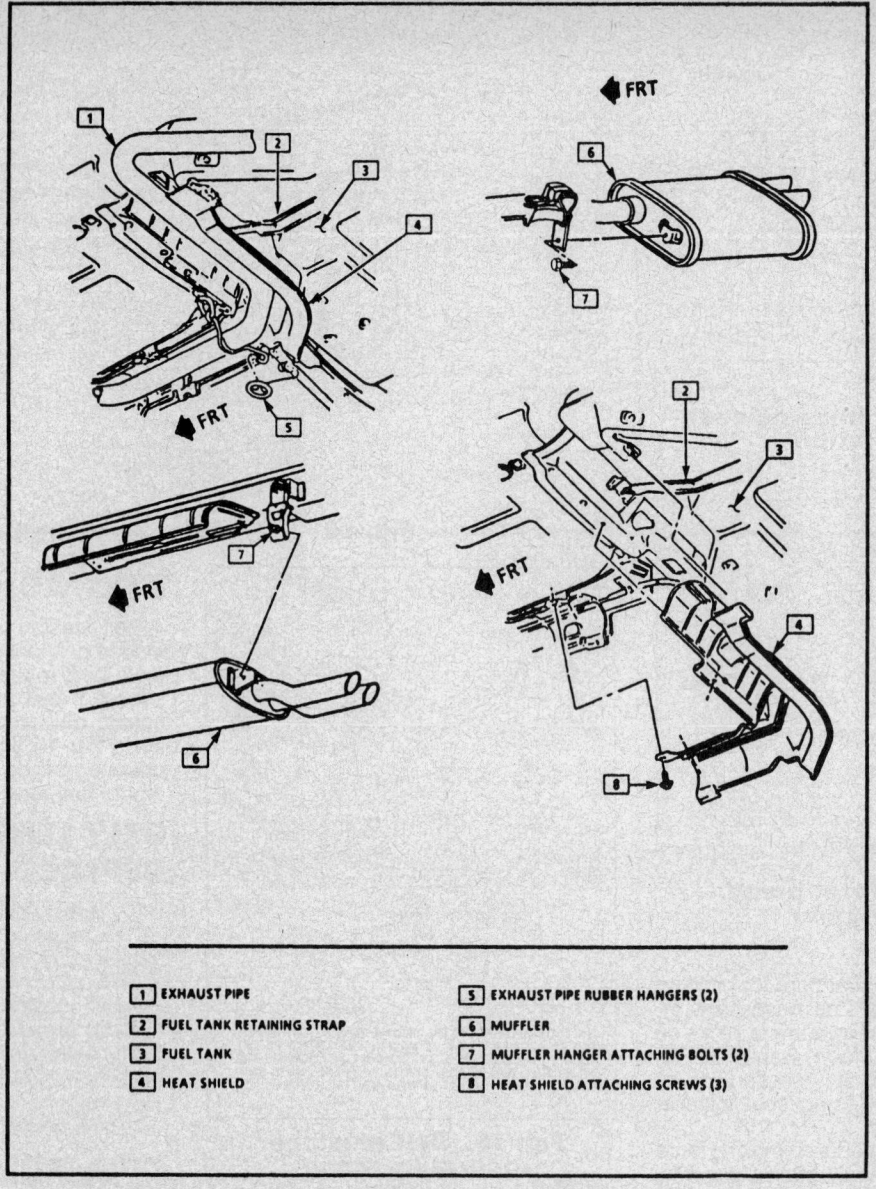

Fig. 16 Exhaust assembly

1	EXHAUST PIPE	5	EXHAUST PIPE RUBBER HANGERS (2)
2	FUEL TANK RETAINING STRAP	6	MUFFLER
3	FUEL TANK	7	MUFFLER HANGER ATTACHING BOLTS (2)
4	HEAT SHIELD	8	HEAT SHIELD ATTACHING SCREWS (3)

i. Properly support tank.
j. Remove two rear retaining strap attaching bolts, then the fuel tank and retaining straps.
4. Rotate fuel sender/pump assembly cam lock ring, then lift out fuel sender/pump assembly.
5. Remove fuel pump from fuel sender by pulling fuel pump up into attaching hose while pulling outwards from lower support.
6. Reverse procedure to install noting the following:
   a. Install new fuel sender/pump assembly O-ring onto fuel tank before installation.
   b. Install new fuel filter.
   c. Do not operate fuel pump unless submerged in fuel.

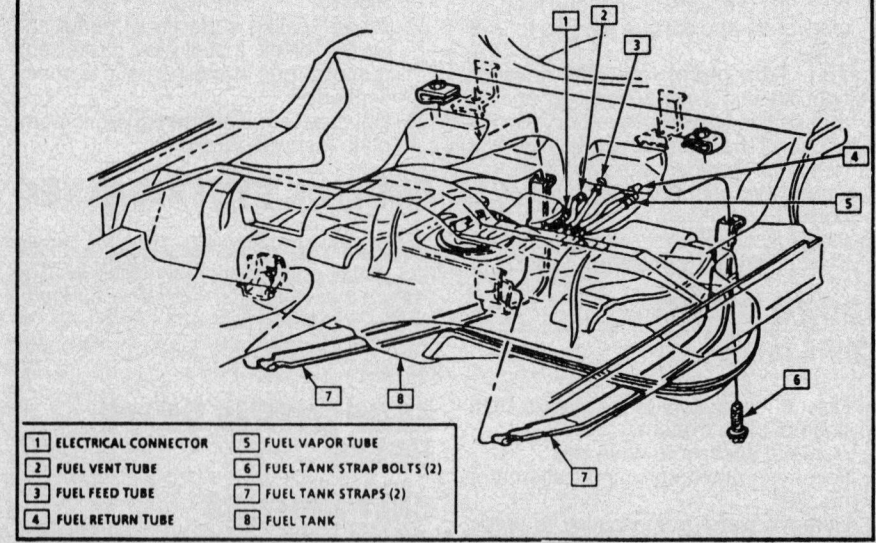

1	ELECTRICAL CONNECTOR	5	FUEL VAPOR TUBE
2	FUEL VENT TUBE	6	FUEL TANK STRAP BOLTS (2)
3	FUEL FEED TUBE	7	FUEL TANK STRAPS (2)
4	FUEL RETURN TUBE	8	FUEL TANK

Fig. 17 Fuel tank removal

TIGHTENING SPECIFICATIONS

NOTE: Torque Specifications Are For Clean And Lightly Lubricated Threads Only.

Year	Component	Torque/ft. lbs.
1988-89	A/C Bracket To Block	62-73
	A/C Compressor To Engine Mount Bracket	63-74
	A/C Compressor To Rear Bracket	19-25
	Camshaft Cover	6-9
	Camshaft Sprocket	66-88
	Camshaft Thrust Plate	4-14
	Connecting Rod Cap Bolts	34-43
	Crankshaft Pulley Center	66-89
	Crankshaft Pulley Outer	29-44
	Cylinder Head Bolts	①
	Drive Belt Tensioner Pulley Assembly	29-44
	EGR Valve	6-13
	Exhaust Manifold	6-13
	Flywheel To Crankshaft	②
	Front Cover	6-10
	Idler Pulley Bolts	19-25
	Intake Manifold	15-22
	Main Bearing Cap	63-77
	Oil Filter	10-13
	Oil Filter Adapter	④
	Oil Level Gage Tube Bracket	15-22
	Oil Pan	6
	Oil Pump	25-38
	Oil Pump Cover	8
	Oil Pump Drive	15-22
	Oxygen Sensor	28-33
	Power Steering Pulley	19-25
	Rocker Arm Cover	4-9
	Rocker Arm Stud	③
	Spark Plugs	7-20
	Starter Motor To Block	26-37
	Starter Motor To Front Bracket	7-10
	Thermostat Adapter	6-10
	Thermostat Outlet	6-9
	Vibration Damper Or Pulley	66-89
	Water Inlet	15-22
	Water Pump	15-22
	Water Pump Pulley	20-25

①—Long bolts, 73–83 ft. lbs.; short bolts, 62–70 ft. lbs.
②—Auto. trans. models, 45–59 ft. lbs.; man. trans. models, 47–63 ft. lbs.
③—Rocker arm stud, 33–40 ft. lbs.; rocker arm stud nut, 11–18 ft. lbs.
④—Auto. trans. models, 10–13 ft. lbs.; man. trans. models, 17–33 ft. lbs.

2.2L/4-134 Engine

NOTE: Refer To 2.2L/4-134 Engine section In Chapter 7 For Service Procedures Not Covered In This Section.

INDEX

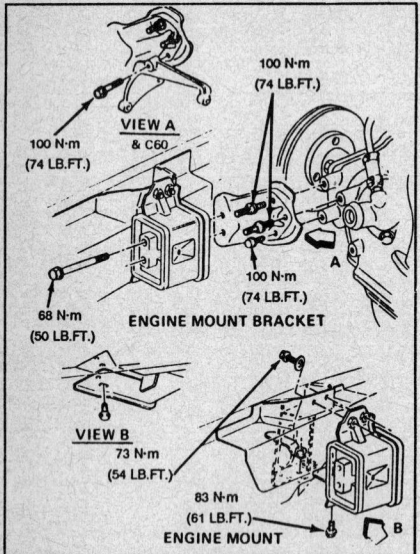

Fig. 1   Front engine mount assembly

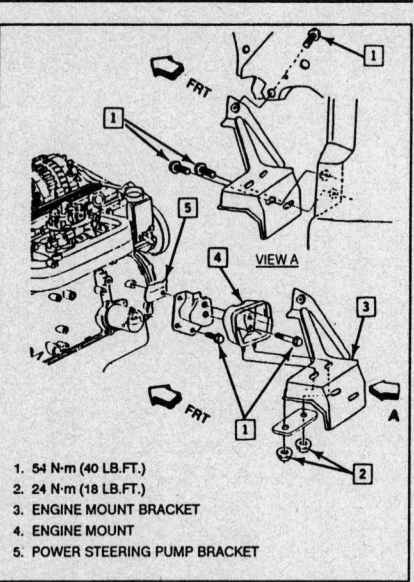

1. 54 N·m (40 LB.FT.)
2. 24 N·m (18 LB.FT.)
3. ENGINE MOUNT BRACKET
4. ENGINE MOUNT
5. POWER STEERING PUMP BRACKET

Fig. 2   Rear engine mount assembly

lock compound to bolt threads.
b. Refer to **Fig. 1** for torque values.

REAR MOUNT

Refer to **Fig. 2** when performing the following procedure.

Removal

1. Disconnect battery ground cable.
2. Raise and support vehicle.
3. Remove engine mount nuts and bolts, then the engine mount.
4. If necessary, remove engine mount bracket.

Installation

1. Clean threads of all bolts removed. Prior to installation apply a suitable lock compound to bolt threads.
2. Install engine mount bracket if removed. Do not tighten bracket bolts at this time.
3. Slightly raise engine and transaxle.
4. Install engine mount. Refer to **Fig. 2** for torque values.
5. Lower vehicle.
6. Install battery ground cable.

ENGINE MOUNT
REPLACE

FRONT MOUNT

Refer to **Fig. 1** when performing the following procedure.
1. Disconnect battery ground cable.
2. Remove two bolts retaining upper engine mount to body.
3. Remove bolt retaining upper engine mount to engine bracket.
4. Raise and support vehicle.
5. Support the engine.
6. Remove inner fender shield.
7. Remove bolt retaining lower engine mount to body.
8. Remove bolt retaining lower engine mount to engine mount bracket, then remove the mount.
9. Reverse procedure to install noting the following:
   a. Clean threads of all bolts removed. Prior to installation apply a suitable

ENGINE
REPLACE

1. Disconnect battery cables, then remove the battery.
2. Relieve fuel tank vapor pressure by loosening the fuel filler cap.
3. Drain cooling system.
4. Disconnect hood lamp wiring. Remove the hood.
5. Remove throttle body intake duct.
6. Remove rear sight shields.
7. Remove air cleaner housing.
8. Remove upper radiator hose.
9. Disconnect vacuum hose from brake booster.
10. Disconnect alternator electrical connector, then remove the top brace, **Fig. 3.**
11. Remove upper engine wiring harness from engine.
12. Properly discharge A/C system. Refer to "Air Conditioning" in the "General Services" section for procedure.

13. Remove compressor-to-condenser, and accumulator refrigerant lines.
14. Raise and support vehicle.
15. Remove left splash shield.
16. Remove exhaust system.
17. Remove lower engine wiring harness.
18. Remove flywheel inspection cover.
19. Remove front wheels.
20. Remove lower radiator hose.
21. Disconnect heater hoses from heater core.
22. Remove calipers from steering knuckle. Properly support calipers.
23. Remove tie rod ends from struts.
24. Lower the vehicle.
25. **On models with manual transaxle,** remove clutch slave cylinder as follows:
   a. Remove slave cylinder to transaxle attaching bolts.
   b. Using Hydraulic Line Separating Tool, No. J-36221, disconnect hydraulic line quick connect fitting.
   c. Remove the slave cylinder.
26. **On all models,** ensure engine com-

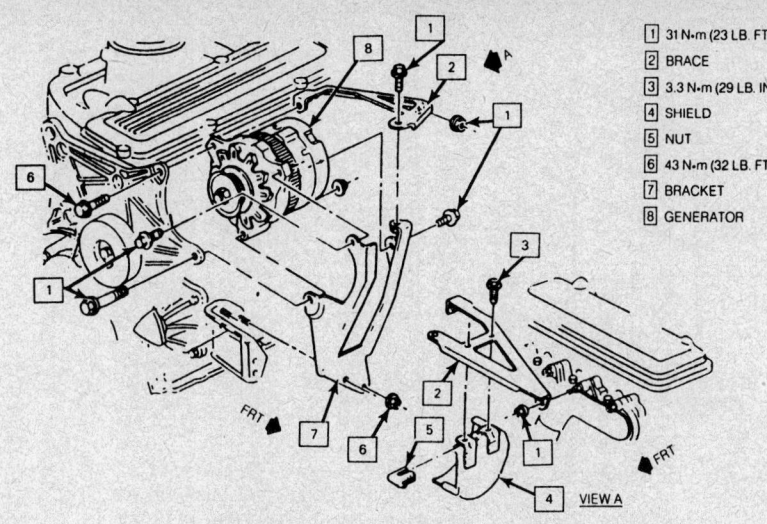

1	31 N·m (23 LB. FT.)
2	BRACE
3	3.3 N·m (29 LB. IN.)
4	SHIELD
5	NUT
6	43 N·m (32 LB. FT.)
7	BRACKET
8	GENERATOR

Fig. 3 Alternator assembly

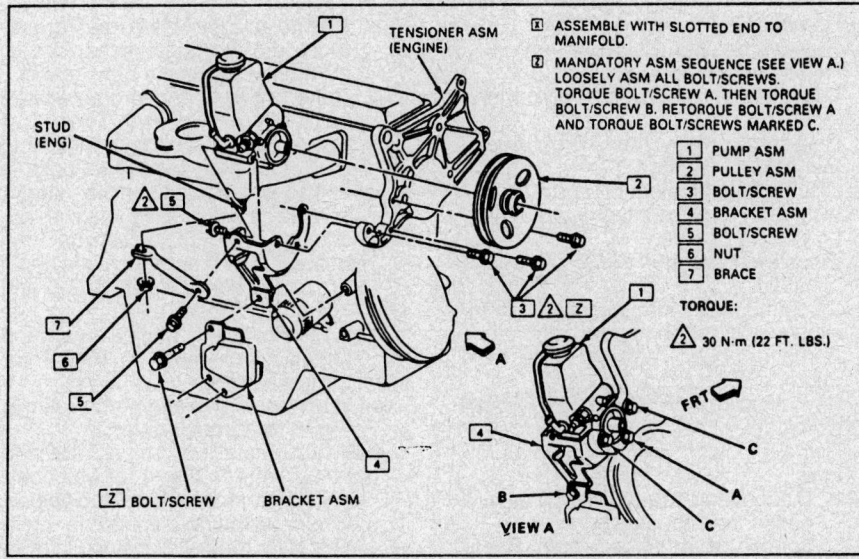

ⓐ ASSEMBLE WITH SLOTTED END TO MANIFOLD.

ⓩ MANDATORY ASM SEQUENCE (SEE VIEW A.) LOOSELY ASM ALL BOLT/SCREWS. TORQUE BOLT/SCREW A. THEN TORQUE BOLT/SCREW B. RETORQUE BOLT/SCREW A AND TORQUE BOLT/SCREWS MARKED C.

1	PUMP ASM
2	PULLEY ASM
3	BOLT/SCREW
4	BRACKET ASM
5	BOLT/SCREW
6	NUT
7	BRACE

TORQUE:

ⓐ 30 N·m (22 FT. LBS.)

Fig. 4 Power steering pump assembly

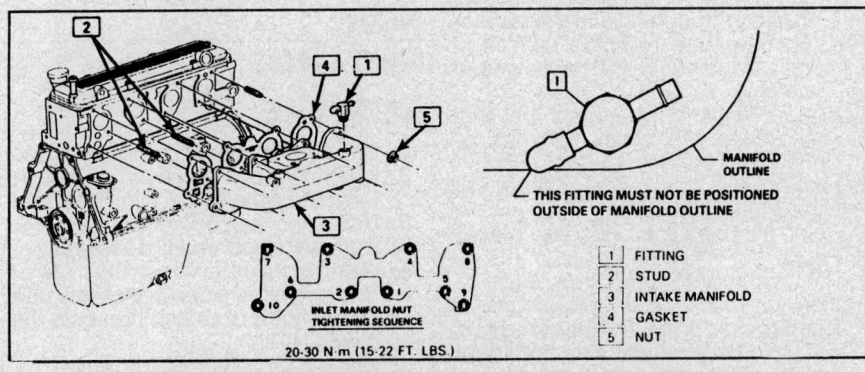

THIS FITTING MUST NOT BE POSITIONED OUTSIDE OF MANIFOLD OUTLINE

1	FITTING
2	STUD
3	INTAKE MANIFOLD
4	GASKET
5	NUT

INLET MANIFOLD NUT TIGHTENING SEQUENCE

20-30 N·m (15-22 FT. LBS.)

Fig. 5 Intake manifold replacement

partment fuel line connections are clean, then using Connector Tool Set No. J-37088 disconnect the fuel line quick connect fittings. Plug all fittings.

27. Disconnect linkage from transaxle.
28. Disconnect accelerator, cruise control, and T.V. cables from the TBI unit.
29. **On models with automatic transax-**

le, disconnect cooling lines from transaxle.
30. **On all models,** disconnect hoses from power steering pump.
31. Remove four center carriage bolts.
32. Position a dolly with added engine support under the vehicle, then lower vehicle onto the dolly.
33. Support rear of vehicle.
34. Remove upper transaxle mount.
35. Remove upper strut mounting nuts and bolts.
36. Remove front and rear engine mounts as described previously.
37. Remove eight front and rear carriage bolts. **To prevent axle separation, wire front carriage bolt holes together.**
38. Raise the vehicle.
39. Remove engine and transaxle assembly on the dolly.
40. Reverse procedure to install noting the following:
    a. **On models with manual transaxle,** bleed the hydraulic clutch system as described in "Clutch And Manual Transaxle" section.
    b. **On all models,** replenish all fluids as needed.
    c. When recharging the A/C system refer to "Air Conditioning" in the "General Services" section for procedure.
    d. Check wheel Alignment, refer to "Wheel Alignment" section in this chapter.

INTAKE MANIFOLD
REPLACE

1. Disconnect battery ground cable.
2. Relieve fuel tank vapor pressure by loosening the fuel filler cap.
3. Remove air cleaner assembly.
4. Drain cooling system.
5. Disconnect all wiring and vacuum lines necessary to facilitate manifold removal.
6. Ensure engine compartment fuel line connections are clean, then using Connector Tool Set No. J-37088 disconnect fuel line quick connect fittings. Plug all fittings.
7. Disconnect TBI linkage, then remove TBI assembly.
8. Remove power steering pump as follows:
    a. Disconnect return and pressure hoses from the pump.
    b. Loosen drive belt tensioner. Separate belt from power steering pulley.
    c. Remove three front pump retaining bolts, **Fig. 4.** Bolts can be accessed through hole in the pulley.
    d. Remove one retaining bolt from rear of the pump, then remove the pump.
9. Remove coolant hose from intake manifold.
10. Raise and support vehicle.
11. Unscrew coolant pipe retaining nut at top of D.I.S. Move the pipe rearward.
12. Disconnect accelerator and T.V. cables, then remove attaching bracket.
13. Remove six lower intake manifold retaining nuts, **Fig. 5.**

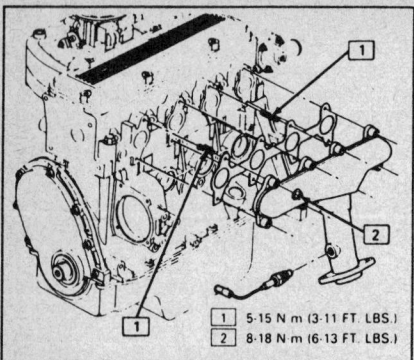

Fig. 6 Exhaust manifold replacement

1	5-15 N·m (3-11 FT. LBS.)
2	8-18 N·m (6-13 FT. LBS.)

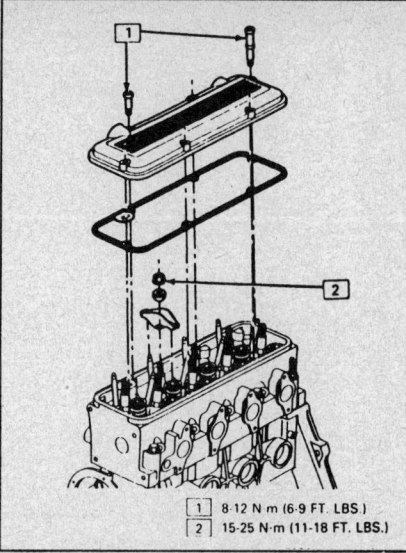

Fig. 7 Rocker cover, rocker arm & pushrod assemblies

1	8-12 N·m (6-9 FT. LBS.)
2	15-25 N·m (11-18 FT. LBS.)

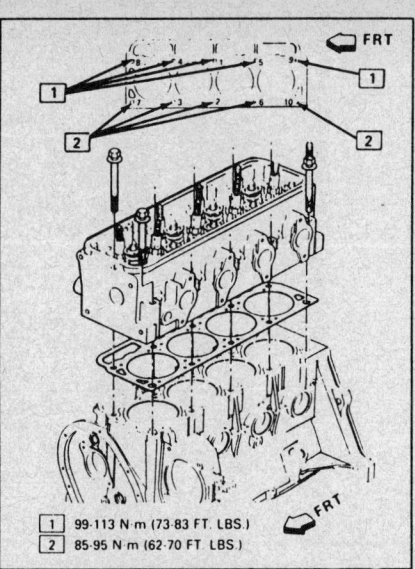

Fig. 8 Cylinder head replacement

1	99-113 N·m (73-83 FT. LBS.)
2	85-95 N·m (62-70 FT. LBS.)

14. Lower the vehicle.
15. Remove the remaining intake manifold retaining bolts and nuts, then the manifold and gasket.
16. Reverse procedure to install noting the following:
    a. Prior to installation, thoroughly clean manifold mating surfaces.
    b. Install intake manifold with new gasket. Refer to **Fig. 5** for tightening sequence and torque values.
    c. When installing power steering pump, refer to **Fig. 4** for bolt tightening sequence and torque values.
    d. When installing serpentine drive belt, refer to "Belt Tension Data" in this section.

EXHAUST MANIFOLD
REPLACE

1. Disconnect battery ground cable.
2. Disconnect oxygen sensor.
3. Loosen drive belt tensioner and remove drive belt.
4. Remove alternator, **Fig. 3**.
5. Raise and support vehicle.
6. Disconnect exhaust pipe from manifold.
7. Lower the vehicle.
8. Remove eight exhaust manifold retaining bolts, **Fig. 6**.
9. Remove oil filler tube.
10. Remove exhaust manifold and gasket.
11. Reverse procedure to install noting the following:
    a. Install exhaust manifold with new gasket. Refer to **Fig. 6** for torque values.
    b. When installing alternator, refer to **Fig. 3** for torque values.
    c. When installing serpentine drive belt, refer to "Belt Tension Data" in this section.

CYLINDER HEAD
REPLACE

1. Disconnect battery ground cable.
2. Remove air cleaner assembly.
3. Relieve fuel tank vapor pressure by loosening the fuel filler cap.
4. Drain cooling system.

5. Remove TBI cover.
6. Remove coolant reservoir.
6. Raise and support vehicle.
7. Disconnect exhaust pipe from manifold.
8. Remove coolant hose from intake manifold.
9. Disconnect accelerator and T.V. cables, then remove attaching bracket.
10. Lower the vehicle.
11. Disconnect vacuum lines at intake manifold.
12. Disconnect all wiring necessary to facilitate cylinder head removal.
13. Remove upper radiator hose from thermostat housing.
14. Remove serpentine belt, then belt tensioner.
15. Remove power steering pump as follows:
    a. Disconnect return and pressure hoses from the pump.
    b. Loosen drive belt tensioner. Separate belt from power steering pulley.
    c. Remove three front pump retaining bolts, **Fig. 4**. Bolts can be accessed through hole in the pulley.
    d. Remove one retaining bolt from rear of the pump, then remove the pump.
16. Ensure engine compartment fuel line connections are clean, then using Connector Tool Set No. J-37088 disconnect fuel line quick connect fittings. Plug all fittings.
17. Remove alternator and rear brace, **Fig. 3**.
18. Remove rocker arm cover, **Fig. 7**, then the rocker arms and pushrods. **Keep rocker arms and pushrods in order so they can be reinstalled in position they were removed from.**
19. Remove cylinder head attaching bolts, then the cylinder head and gasket, intake and exhaust manifolds, and TBI unit as an assembly.
20. Reverse procedure to install noting the following:

a. Ensure cylinder head mating surfaces are thoroughly clean. Install cylinder head with a new gasket.
b. Refer to **Fig. 8,** and torque cylinder head bolts as follows: **Torque** all head bolts in sequence initially to 41 ft. lbs., then **torque** all bolts in sequence an additional 45°. Again, **torque** all bolts in sequence an additional 45°. Finally **torque** long bolts (8, 4, 1, 5 and 9) an additional 20°, and short bolts (7, 3, 2, 6 and 10) an additional 45°.
c. When installing rocker arms, and rocker cover, refer to **Fig. 7** for torque values.
d. When installing alternator, refer to **Fig. 3** for torque values.
e. When installing power steering pump, refer to **Fig. 4** for bolt tightening sequence and torque values.
f. When installing serpentine drive belt, refer to "Belt Tension Data" in this section.

CRANKSHAFT PULLEY & HUB
REPLACE
REMOVAL

1. Disconnect battery ground cable.
2. Loosen drive belt tensioner and remove drive belt.
3. Raise and support vehicle.
4. Remove wheel and tire assembly.
5. Remove inner fender shield.
6. Remove three crankshaft pulley bolts, **Fig. 9**, the pulley and hub bolt, then the pulley.
7. Install Crankshaft Pulley Puller Tool No. J-24420-B to hub. Remove hub by turning the puller screw.

INSTALLATION

1. Apply clean engine oil to contact area of front cover seal.

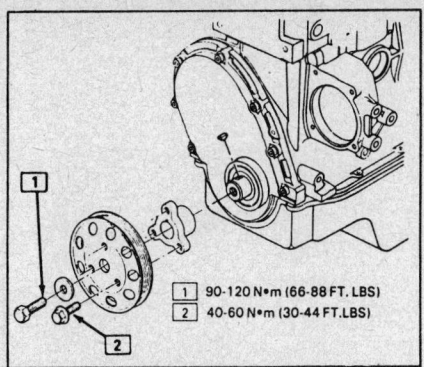

Fig. 9 Crankshaft pulley and hub replacement

| 1 | 90-120 N·m (66-88 FT. LBS) |
| 2 | 40-60 N·m (30-44 FT.LBS) |

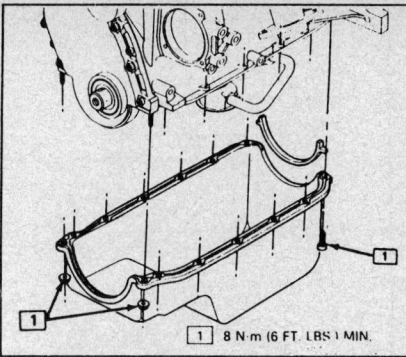

Fig. 10 Oil pan replacement

| 1 | 8 N·m (6 FT. LBS.) MIN. |

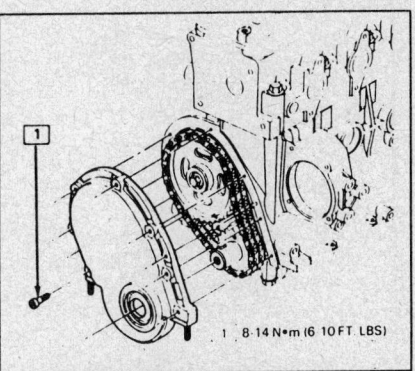

Fig. 12 Front cover replacement

| 1 | 8-14 N·m (6-10 FT. LBS) |

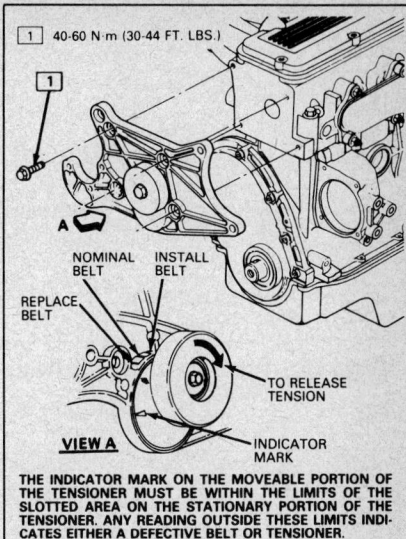

| 1 | 40-60 N·m (30-44 FT. LBS.) |

THE INDICATOR MARK ON THE MOVEABLE PORTION OF THE TENSIONER MUST BE WITHIN THE LIMITS OF THE SLOTTED AREA ON THE STATIONARY PORTION OF THE TENSIONER. ANY READING OUTSIDE THESE LIMITS INDICATES EITHER A DEFECTIVE BELT OR TENSIONER.

Fig. 11 Drive belt tensioner assembly

2. Apply a suitable sealer to pulley hub keyway.
3. Position pulley hub over key on crankshaft.
4. Install Crankshaft Pulley Installer Tool, No. J-29113, to crankshaft. Ensure a minimum of 1/4 inch of threads are engaged. Pull pulley hub into position, then remove the tool.
5. Install crankshaft pulley, then the pulley and hub bolts. Refer to **Fig. 9** for torque values.
6. Install inner fender shield.
7. Install wheel and tire assembly.
8. Lower the vehicle.
9. When installing serpentine drive belt, refer to "Belt Tension Data" in this section.
10. Reconnect battery ground cable.

OIL PAN
REPLACE
REMOVAL

1. Disconnect battery ground cable.
2. Disconnect exhaust pipe from manifold.
3. Raise and support vehicle.
4. Drain the crankcase.
5. Remove starter bracket, and the starter.
6. Remove flywheel inspection cover.
7. Remove four right side support bolts, then slightly lower the support.
8. **On models with automatic transaxle,** remove oil filter and extension.
9. **On all models,** remove twelve bolts and two nuts retaining the oil pan, **Fig. 10.**
10. Remove oil pan and gasket.

INSTALLATION

1. Ensure oil pan mating surfaces are thoroughly clean.
2. Apply a 1/8 inch diameter bead of suitable sealer on the oil pan to engine block sealing flanges.
3. Apply suitable sealer on the oil pan to front cover mating surface.
4. Apply suitable sealer on ends to the ears of a new oil pan rear seal.
5. Install oil pan to engine block. Refer to **Fig. 10** for torque values.
6. **On models with automatic transax-**

le, install oil filter adapter with a new seal, then the oil filter.
7. **On all models,** install exhaust pipe to manifold.
8. Install right side support with attaching bolts.
9. Install starter.
10. Lower the vehicle.
11. Refill crankcase.
12. Connect battery ground cable.

OIL PUMP
REPLACE

1. Remove oil pan as previously described.
2. Remove pump to rear main bearing cap bolt, then the pump and extension shaft.
3. Remove extension shaft and retainer.
4. Reverse procedure noting the following:
   a. Heat retainer in hot water prior to assembling extension shaft.
   b. **Torque oil pump bolt to 32 ft. lbs.**

ENGINE FRONT COVER
REPLACE

1. Disconnect battery ground cable.
2. Loosen drive belt tensioner and remove drive belt.
3. Remove tensioner, **Fig. 11.**
4. Raise and support vehicle.
5. Remove oil pan as described previously.
6. Remove crankshaft pulley and hub as

described previously.
7. Remove eight front cover attaching bolts, **Fig. 12,** then the front cover and gasket.
8. Reverse procedure to install noting the following:
   a. Ensure front cover mating surfaces are thoroughly clean.
   b. Install front cover with new gasket. Refer to **Fig. 12** for torque values.
   c. Clean tensioner bolts and prior to installation apply a suitable lock compound to bolt threads. Refer to **Fig. 11** for torque values.
   d. When installing serpentine drive belt, refer to "Belt Tension Data" in this section.

WATER PUMP
REPLACE

1. Disconnect battery ground cable.
2. Drain cooling system.
3. Loosen drive belt tensioner and remove drive belt.
4. Remove water pump pulley attaching bolts, **Fig. 13,** then the pulley.
5. Remove alternator, **Fig. 3.**
6. Remove alternator side bracket.
7. Remove water pump attaching bolts, **Fig. 14,** then the pump and gasket.
8. Reverse procedure to install noting the following:
   a. Ensure water pump mating surface is thoroughly clean.
   b. Install water pump with new gasket. Refer to **Figs. 13 and 14** for torque values.
   c. When installing alternator, refer to **Fig. 3** for torque values.
   d. When installing serpentine drive belt, refer to "Belt Tension Data" in this section.

COOLING SYSTEM BLEED

These engines do not require a specified bleed procedure. After filling cooling

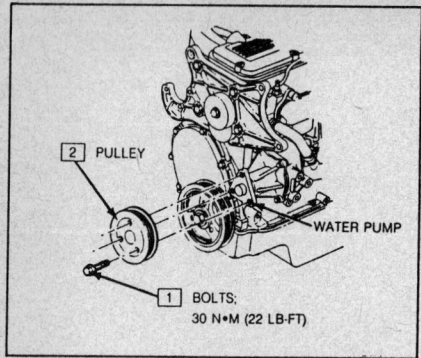

Fig. 13 Water pump pulley installation

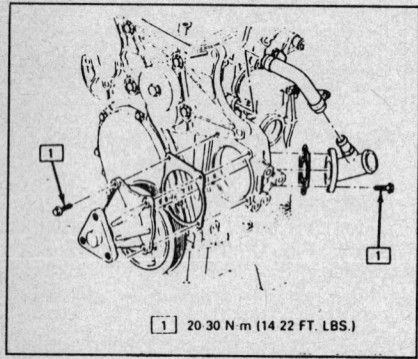

Fig. 14 Water pump replacement

system, run engine to operating temperature with radiator/pressure cap off. Air will then be automatically bled through cap opening.

FUEL PUMP
REPLACE

1. Disconnect battery ground cable.
2. Relieve fuel tank vapor pressure by loosening the fuel filler cap.
3. Using a suitable syphon, drain the fuel tank.
4. Remove fuel tank as follows:
   a. Raise and support vehicle.
   b. Remove two rubber exhaust pipe hangers, **Fig. 15.**
   c. Remove two muffler hanger retaining bolts.
   d. Remove three heat shield attaching screws, then the heat shield.
   e. Remove fuel tank filler tube, vent tube, vent hose, and clamps.
   f. Disconnect electrical connector, **Fig. 16.**
   g. Disconnect fuel level meter vapor hose.
   h. Ensure fuel line connections are clean. Disconnect fuel return quick connect fitting by squeezing plastic tab on male end of the fitting. Using fuel line separator Tool Set No. J-37088, disconnect fuel line quick connect fitting. Plug all fittings.
   i. Properly support tank.
   j. Remove two rear retaining strap attaching bolts, then the fuel tank

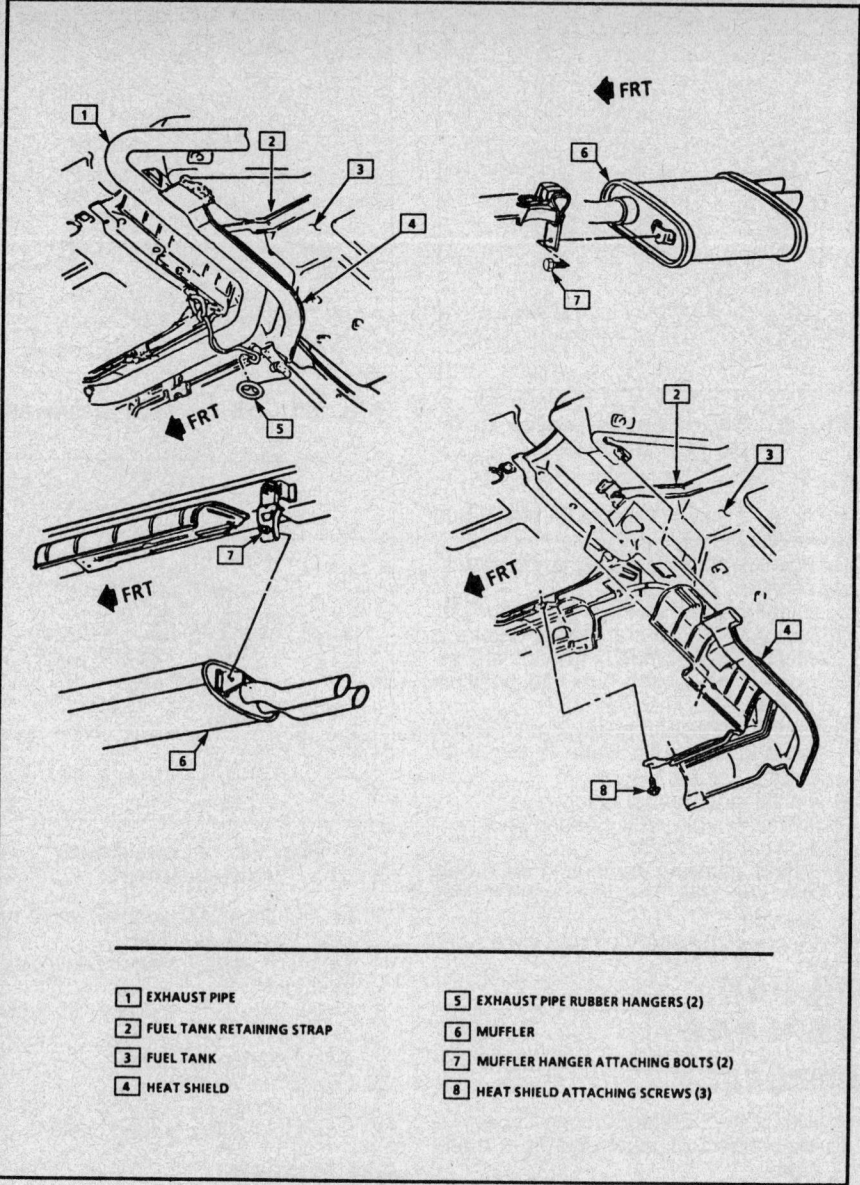

1	EXHAUST PIPE	5	EXHAUST PIPE RUBBER HANGERS (2)
2	FUEL TANK RETAINING STRAP	6	MUFFLER
3	FUEL TANK	7	MUFFLER HANGER ATTACHING BOLTS (2)
4	HEAT SHIELD	8	HEAT SHIELD ATTACHING SCREWS (3)

Fig. 15 Exhaust assembly

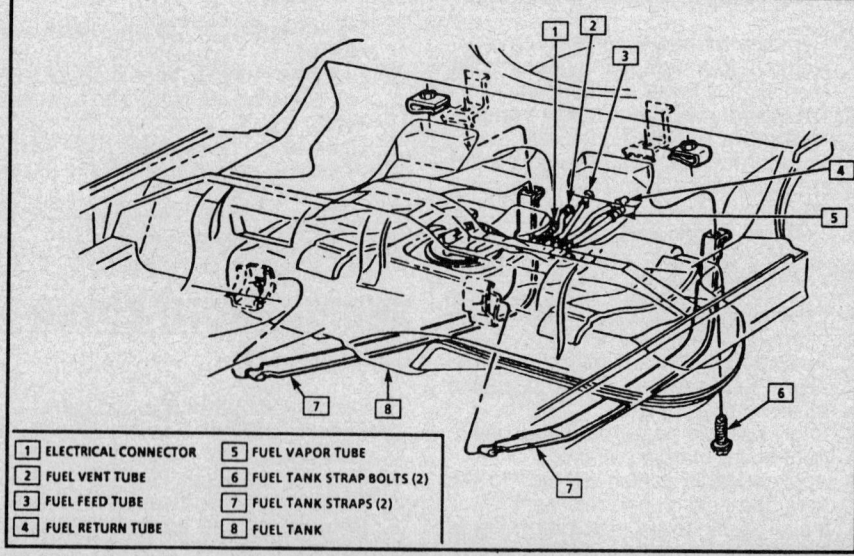

1	ELECTRICAL CONNECTOR	5	FUEL VAPOR TUBE
2	FUEL VENT TUBE	6	FUEL TANK STRAP BOLTS (2)
3	FUEL FEED TUBE	7	FUEL TANK STRAPS (2)
4	FUEL RETURN TUBE	8	FUEL TANK

Fig. 16 Fuel tank removal

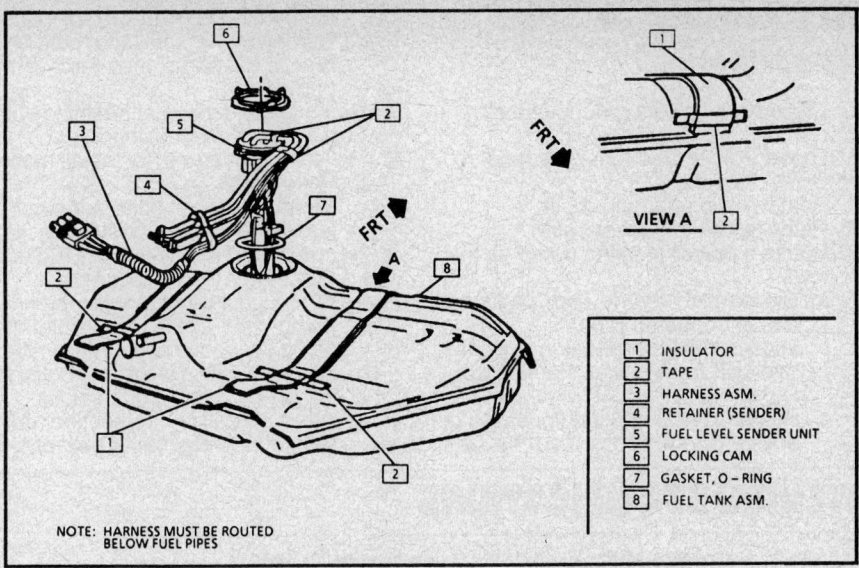

NOTE: HARNESS MUST BE ROUTED BELOW FUEL PIPES

1	INSULATOR
2	TAPE
3	HARNESS ASM.
4	RETAINER (SENDER)
5	FUEL LEVEL SENDER UNIT
6	LOCKING CAM
7	GASKET, O – RING
8	FUEL TANK ASM.

Fig. 17   Fuel tank assembly

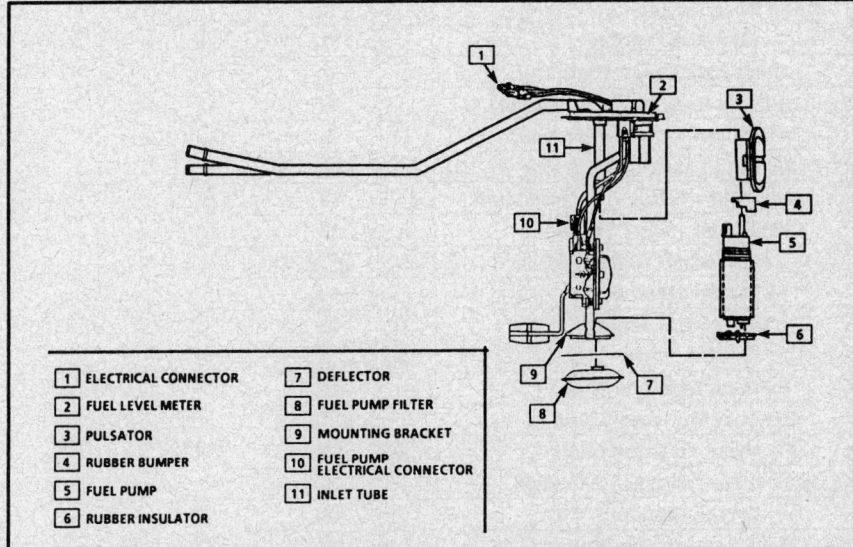

1	ELECTRICAL CONNECTOR	7	DEFLECTOR
2	FUEL LEVEL METER	8	FUEL PUMP FILTER
3	PULSATOR	9	MOUNTING BRACKET
4	RUBBER BUMPER	10	FUEL PUMP ELECTRICAL CONNECTOR
5	FUEL PUMP	11	INLET TUBE
6	RUBBER INSULATOR		

Fig. 18   Fuel level meter assembly

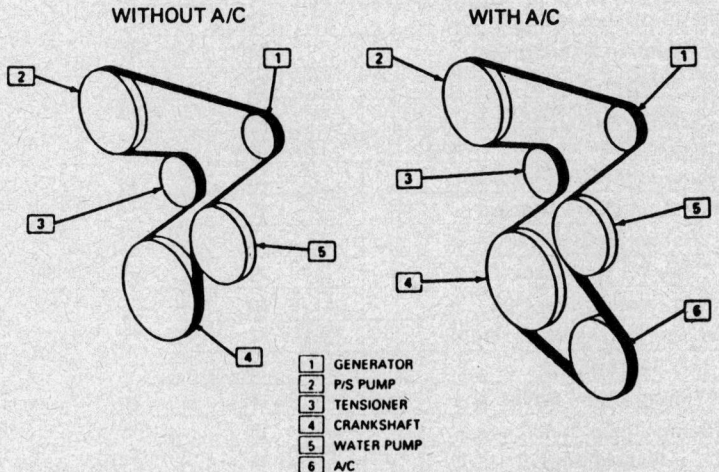

1	GENERATOR
2	P/S PUMP
3	TENSIONER
4	CRANKSHAFT
5	WATER PUMP
6	A/C

Fig. 19   Serpentine drive belt routing

and retaining straps.

5. Thoroughly clean fuel level meter assembly connection and surrounding area, **Fig. 17.**

6. Using fuel sender spanner wrench tool No. J-35731, remove fuel level meter assembly lock ring. Remove assembly from tank, and discard the O-ring.

7. Disassemble fuel level meter assembly as follows:
   a. Note orientation of fuel filter for proper installation.
   b. To remove fuel filter, rotate it while pulling fuel pump in opposite direction, **Fig. 18.**
   c. Disconnect fuel pump electrical connector.
   d. Position fuel level meter assembly upside down on work area.
   e. Pull downward on fuel pump to separate it from mounting bracket. Tilt pump outward and remove it from pulsater.

8. Reverse procedure to install noting the following:
   a. Never run fuel pump unless submerged in fuel.
   b. Always replace fuel filter when installing fuel pump.
   c. Always use new O-ring when installing fuel level meter assembly.

SERPENTINE DRIVE BELT ROUTING

Refer to **Fig. 19** for serpentine drive belt routing.

BELT TENSION DATA

PRECAUTIONS

When installing or removing the drive belt, never exceed 30 ft. lbs. torque on the tensioner center bolt, **Fig. 11.** Care should also be taken to avoid bending or twisting the tensioner. If the belt tensioner or idler assembly produces a whining noise, inspect for bearing failure. If the drive belt becomes frayed, check belt tensioner assembly alignment and ensure belt edge does not contact the tensioner pulley flange.

Serpentine drive belt performance will not be impaired by cracks in the belt ribs. However belt replacement will be required if any of the following conditions occur: Belt ribs are missing, the belt slips or is frayed, or the belt tensioner runs out of travel before adjustment is proper.

CHECKING BELT TENSION

1. Check belt tensioner indicator marks, **Fig. 11**, to ensure belt is in operating range. Replace belt as needed, refer to **Fig. 19** for belt routing.

2. With all accessories Off, run engine until operating temperature is achieved.

3. Turn ignition switch to Off.

4. Position Belt Tensioner Tool, No. J-23600, on the drive belt between power steering pump and alternator.

Note reading, and remove the tool.

5. Run engine for 15 seconds, then turn the ignition switch to Off.

6. Using a 15 mm socket, apply counter-clockwise force to tensioner pulley bolt. Release the pulley, then take a reading as described in step 4.

7. Using a 15 mm socket, apply clockwise force to tensioner pulley bolt until the install position is reached. Slowly release pulley to rest position, then take a reading as described in step 4. Use caution not to disturb the belt tensioner position.

8. If average of the three readings taken is 63–77 lbs., and the belt is in the tensioners operating range, replace the belt tensioner as described in this section.

BELT TENSIONER REPLACEMENT

1. Disconnect battery ground cable.
2. Remove coolant reservoir.
3. Loosen drive belt tensioner and remove drive belt.
4. Remove two alternator bolts.
5. Remove belt tensioner pulley.
6. Remove power steering pump as follows:
   a. Disconnect return and pressure hoses from the pump.
   b. Loosen drive belt tensioner. Separate belt from power steering pulley.
   c. Remove three front pump retaining bolts, **Fig. 4**. Bolts can be accessed through hole in the pulley.
   d. Remove one retaining bolt from rear of the pump, then remove the pump.
7. Remove four tensioner retaining bolts, **Fig. 11**, then the tensioner.
8. Reverse procedure to install noting the following:
   a. Clean tensioner bolts and prior to installation apply a suitable lock compound to bolt threads. Refer to **Fig. 11** for torque values.
   b. When installing power steering pump, refer to **Fig. 4** for bolt tightening sequence and torque values.
   c. When installing alternator bolts, refer to **Fig. 3** for torque values.
   d. When installing serpentine drive belt, refer to **Fig. 19** for belt routing.

TIGHTENING SPECIFICATIONS

Year	Component	Torque/ft. lbs.
1990–91	Accelerator Cable Mounting Bracket	18
	Battery Cables	13
	Brake Booster Vacuum Fitting	10
	Camshaft Pulley	77
	Camshaft Thrust Plate	9
	Coolant Drain Plug (Cylinder Block)	11
	Coolant Outlet To Cylinder Head	8
	Crankcase Front Cover Bolts	97②
	Crankshaft Pulley & Hub To Crankshaft	85
	Crankshaft Pulley To Hub	37
	Crankshaft Sensor	80②
	Cylinder Head Bolts	41①
	DIS Coil Assembly	18
	EGR Valve	16
	Exhaust Manifold Nuts	16
	Exhaust Manifold Studs	9–10
	Flywheel To Crankshaft	52
	Heater Hose To Intake Manifold	24
	Intake Manifold	18
	Main Bearing Cap Bolts	70
	Oil Fill Tube To Cylinder Block	18
	Oil Filter Adapter To Cylinder Block	18
	Oil Pan	7–8
	Oil Pump Drive Assembly Bolt	18
	Oil Pump To Bearing Cap	31
	Oxygen Sensor	31
	PCV Valve Cap	89②
	Power Brake Hose Vacuum Fitting	115②
	Pressure Plate To Flywheel	15
	Rear Engine Lift Bracket	32
	Rocker Arm Cover	7–8
	Rocker Arm Nuts	22
	Rod Bearing Cap Nut	38
	Serpentine Tensioner Assembly	37
	Spark Plugs	11
	Timing Chain Cover	8
	Timing Chain Tensioner	18
	Water Pump	18
	Water Pump Inlet	18
	Wheel Lug Nuts	100

Continued

TIGHTENING SPECIFICATIONS—Continued

①—Plus three additional steps; 1st step, all bolts an additional 45°; 2nd step, all bolts an additional 45°; 3rd step, long bolts (8, 4, 1, 5, & 9) an additional 20°, short bolts (7, 3, 2, 6 & 10) an additional 10°.
②—Inch lbs.

2.3L/4-138 Engine

NOTE: Refer To 2.3L/4-138 Engine Section In Chapter 9 For Service Procedures Not Covered In This Section.

INDEX

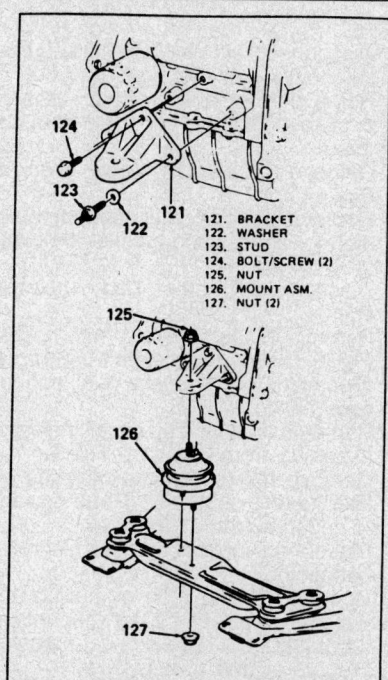

121. BRACKET
122. WASHER
123. STUD
124. BOLT/SCREW (2)
125. NUT
126. MOUNT ASM.
127. NUT (2)

Fig. 1 Front engine mount assembly

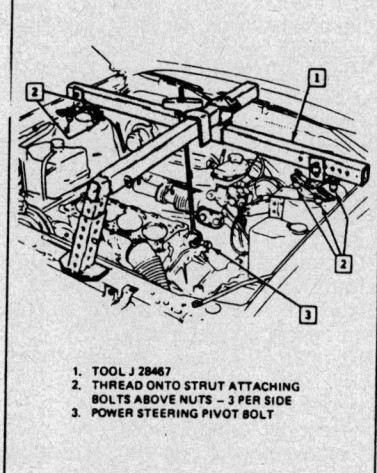

1. TOOL J 28467
2. THREAD ONTO STRUT ATTACHING BOLTS ABOVE NUTS – 3 PER SIDE
3. POWER STEERING PIVOT BOLT

Fig. 2 Engine support tool

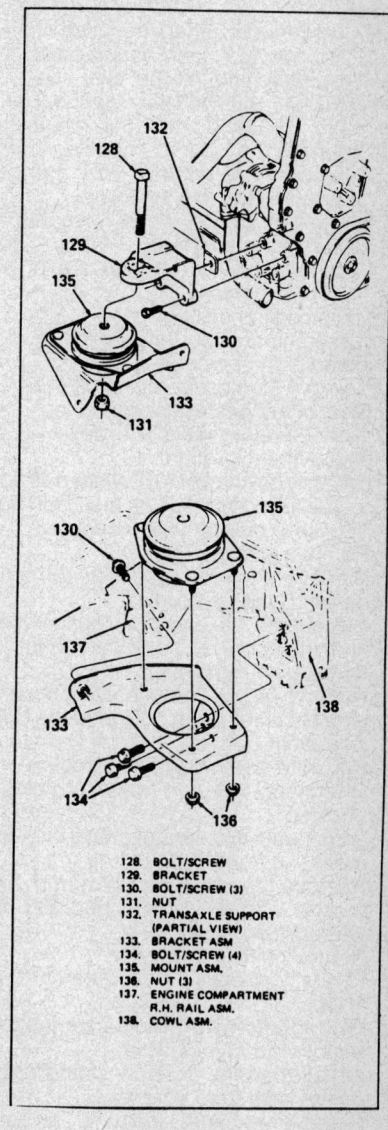

128. BOLT/SCREW
129. BRACKET
130. BOLT/SCREW (3)
131. NUT
132. TRANSAXLE SUPPORT (PARTIAL VIEW)
133. BRACKET ASM.
134. BOLT/SCREW (4)
135. MOUNT ASM.
136. NUT (3)
137. ENGINE COMPARTMENT R.H. RAIL ASM.
138. COWL ASM.

Fig. 3 Rear engine mount assembly

ENGINE MOUNT REPLACE
FRONT MOUNT

Refer to **Fig. 1** when performing the following procedure.
1. Disconnect battery ground cable.
2. Remove upper retaining nut from mount.
3. Using engine support tool, **Fig. 2**, lift engine from mount.
4. Raise and support vehicle.
5. Remove two lower retaining nuts from mount.
6. Lower the vehicle.
7. Remove the mount.
8. Remove nut retaining battery cable clip to mount bracket stud. Separate cable clip from stud.
9. Remove the stud, two retaining bolts, then the mount bracket.
10. Reverse procedure to install. Refer to specifications for torque values.

REAR MOUNT

Refer to **Fig. 3** when performing the following procedure.
1. Disconnect battery ground cable.
2. Disconnect vacuum lines and pull vacuum harness through front lift bracket.
3. Using engine support tool, **Fig. 2**, lift rear of engine slightly.
4. Remove lower right splash shield.
5. Remove nut from engine mount through bolt.
6. Remove four bracket-to-body retaining bolts, then the bracket and mount assembly.
7. Remove three mount-to-bracket retaining nuts. Separate bracket from mount.
8. Reverse procedure to install. Refer to specifications for torque values.

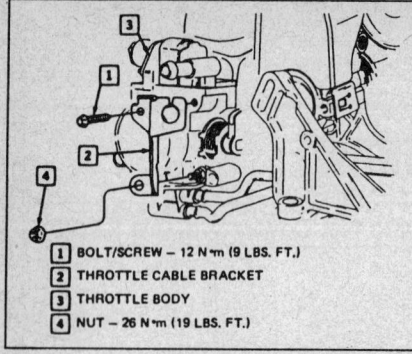

Fig. 4   Accelerator cable bracket

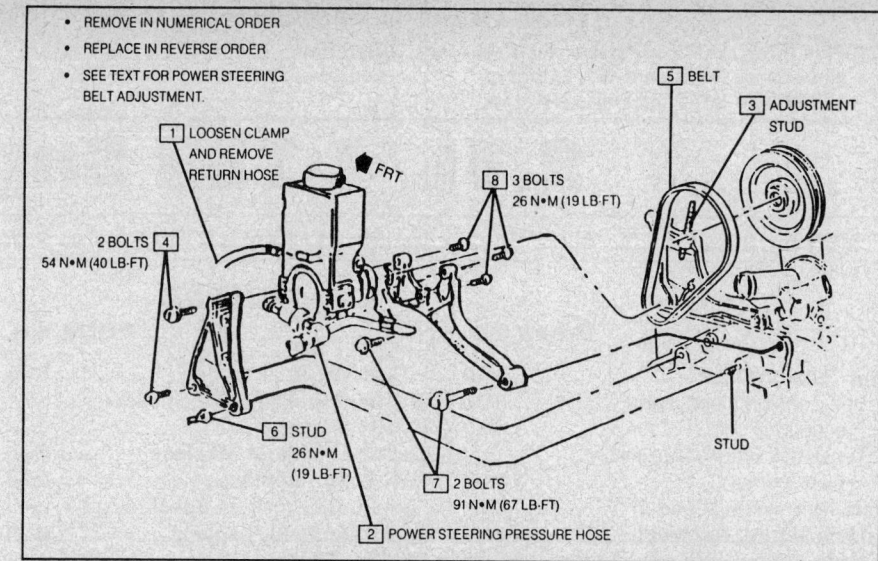

- REMOVE IN NUMERICAL ORDER
- REPLACE IN REVERSE ORDER
- SEE TEXT FOR POWER STEERING BELT ADJUSTMENT.

Fig. 5   Power steering pump assembly

ENGINE
REPLACE

1. Relieve fuel system pressure as follows:
   a. Disconnect battery negative cable.
   b. Relieve fuel tank vapor pressure by loosening the fuel filler cap.
   c. Install Fuel Pressure Gauge Tool, No. J-34730, to fuel pressure valve. **To avoid spilling fuel when connecting the gauge wrap fitting with a towel.**
   d. Position end of bleed hose into a suitable container. Open the bleeder valve until system pressure is gone.
2. Drain cooling system.
3. Raise and support vehicle.
4. Remove front wheels.
5. Remove air cleaner assembly.
6. Disconnect heater hoses.
7. Remove upper radiator hose.
8. Remove coolant fan.
9. Properly discharge A/C system. Refer to "Air Conditioning" in the "General Services" section for procedure.
10. Remove oil filter.
11. Remove A/C compressor to condenser refrigerant line.
12. Disconnect all electrical connectors and vacuum lines necessary to facilitate engine removal.
13. Remove battery ground cable to engine block retaining bolt, then the battery cable.
14. Separate shift cable from bracket.
15. Disconnect vacuum hose from brake booster.
16. Disconnect accelerator cable, then remove the bracket, **Fig. 4.**
17. Remove power steering pump assembly with hoses attached, **Fig. 5,** and position aside.
18. Remove oil/air separator.
19. Disconnect engine compartment fuel lines.
20. **On models with manual transaxle,** remove clutch actuator.
21. **On all models,** disconnect engine oil cooler lines from adapter.
22. Remove exhaust manifold as described later in this section.
23. Remove front engine mount retaining nut, **Fig. 1.**

24. Remove lower radiator hose and heater hose.
25. Install Engine Support Tool No. J-28467, **Fig. 2.**
26. Remove splash shields.
27. Separate ball joints from steering knuckles, then stabilizer shafts from both control arms.
28. Remove drive axles as described in the "Front Wheel Drive" section.
29. Remove suspension support.
30. Remove ground strap from block.
31. Remove rear engine mount assembly as described previously.
32. Remove transaxle mount through bolt.
33. Lower the engine.
34. Disconnect starter wires.
35. Remove engine and transaxle assembly.
36. Reverse procedure to install noting the following:
   a. **On models with manual transaxle,** bleed the hydraulic clutch system as described in "Clutch And Manual Transaxle" section.
   b. Replenish all fluids as needed.
   c. When recharging the A/C system refer to "Air Conditioning" in the "General Services" section for procedure.
   d. Check wheel Alignment, refer to "Wheel Alignment" section in this chapter.

INTAKE MANIFOLD
REPLACE

1. Disconnect battery ground cable.
2. Drain cooling system.
3. Disconnect MAP sensor electrical connector and vacuum hose.
4. Disconnect MAT sensor, purge solenoid, and fuel injector harness electrical connectors.
5. Disconnect intake manifold vacuum hoses.

6. Disconnect fuel regulator, and purge solenoid-to-canister hoses.
7. Remove throttle body-to-air cleaner duct, then separate vent tube from the duct.
8. Remove accelerator cable bracket, **Fig. 4.**
9. Remove brake booster vacuum hose, along with retaining bracket to power steering bracket.
10. Disconnect throttle body coolant lines.
11. Remove oil/air separator with hoses, **Fig. 6.** Disconnect hoses from the oil filler, chain cover, intake duct, and intake manifold.
12. Remove oil filler cap/level indicator assembly from filler tube, **Fig. 6.**
13. Remove bolt/screw retaining the oil filler tube to engine. Pull tube upward to separate it from the block.
14. Disconnect injector harness electrical connector.
15. Remove oil filler tube by pulling upward while rotating it between intake tubes and fuel rail electrical harness. Discard oil filler tube O-ring.
16. Remove intake manifold support brace, **Fig. 7.**
17. Remove five bolts and two nuts retaining the intake manifold, **Fig. 8.**
18. Remove intake manifold and gasket.
19. Reverse procedure to install noting the following:
   a. Install intake manifold with new gasket. Ensure numbers stamped on the gasket face the manifold surface. Refer to **Fig. 8** for tightening sequence, and to specifications for torque values.
   b. Install a new O-ring to oil filler tube. Refer to **Fig. 6** when installing oil filler tube to engine.

EXHAUST MANIFOLD
REPLACE

1. Disconnect battery ground cable.
2. Disconnect oxygen sensor.
3. Raise and support vehicle.

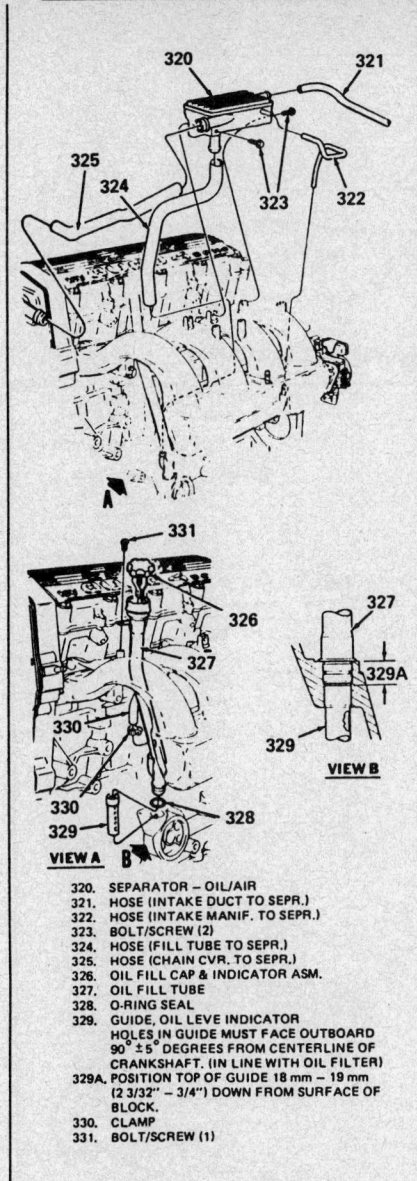

320. SEPARATOR – OIL/AIR
321. HOSE (INTAKE DUCT TO SEPR.)
322. HOSE (INTAKE MANIF. TO SEPR.)
323. BOLT/SCREW (2)
324. HOSE (FILL TUBE TO SEPR.)
325. HOSE (CHAIN CVR. TO SEPR.)
326. OIL FILL CAP & INDICATOR ASM.
327. OIL FILL TUBE
328. O-RING SEAL
329. GUIDE, OIL LEVE INDICATOR
    HOLES IN GUIDE MUST FACE OUTBOARD
    90° ± 5° DEGREES FROM CENTERLINE OF
    CRANKSHAFT. (IN LINE WITH OIL FILTER)
329A. POSITION TOP OF GUIDE 18 mm – 19 mm
    (2 3/32" – 3/4") DOWN FROM SURFACE OF
    BLOCK.
330. CLAMP
331. BOLT/SCREW (1)

Fig. 6 Crankcase ventilation components

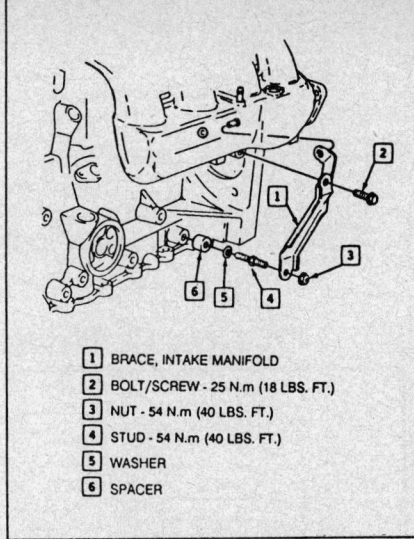

1 BRACE, INTAKE MANIFOLD
2 BOLT/SCREW - 25 N.m (18 LBS. FT.)
3 NUT - 54 N.m (40 LBS. FT.)
4 STUD - 54 N.m (40 LBS. FT.)
5 WASHER
6 SPACER

Fig. 7 Intake manifold support brace

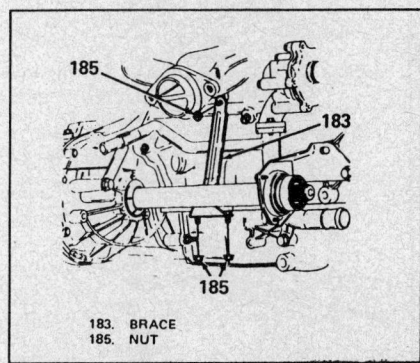

183. BRACE
185. NUT

Fig. 9 Exhaust manifold brace

OIL PAN
REPLACE

1. Disconnect battery ground cable.
2. Drain engine oil.
3. Remove flywheel cover, then the exhaust manifold brace.
4. Disconnect radiator outlet pipe to oil pan bolt, then transaxle to oil pan nut.
5. Remove oil pan to transaxle stud, then the oil pan bolts.
6. Remove oil pan.
7. Reverse procedure to install.

OIL PUMP
REPLACE

1. Remove oil pan as previously described.
2. Remove oil pump assembly bolts.
3. Remove oil pump assembly.
4. Reverse procedure to install.

WATER PUMP
REPLACE

1. Disconnect negative battery cable.

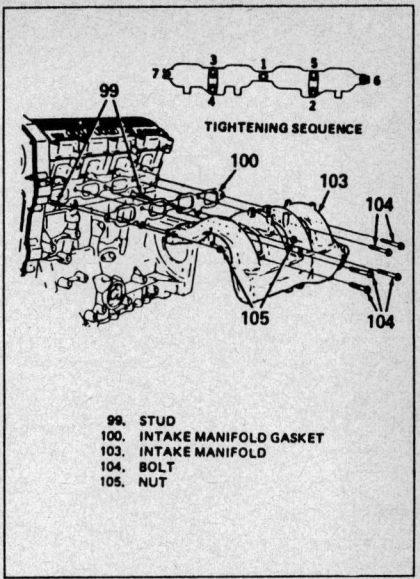

TIGHTENING SEQUENCE

99. STUD
100. INTAKE MANIFOLD GASKET
103. INTAKE MANIFOLD
104. BOLT
105. NUT

Fig. 8 Intake manifold replacement

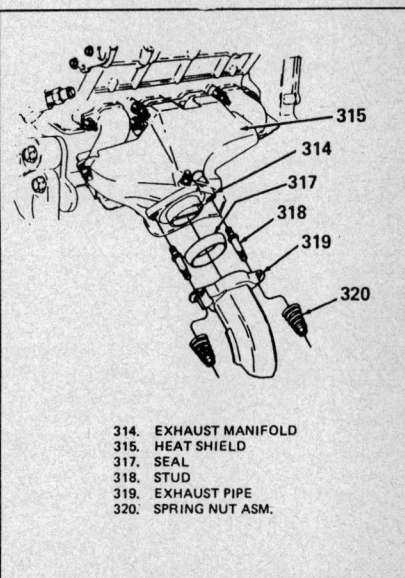

314. EXHAUST MANIFOLD
315. HEAT SHIELD
317. SEAL
318. STUD
319. EXHAUST PIPE
320. SPRING NUT ASM.

Fig. 10 Exhaust pipe installation

2. Drain cooling system.
3. Raise and support vehicle.
4. Disconnect oxygen sensor connector, then the exhaust pipe from exhaust manifold.
5. Remove radiator outlet pipe from oil pan and transaxle.
6. Lower vehicle.
7. Remover upper and lower exhaust manifold heat shields.
8. Remove exhaust manifold to cylinder head retaining nuts, then the exhaust manifold seals and gaskets.
9. Disconnect radiator outlet pipe assembly to coolant pump cover bolts.
10. Remove coolant cover to cylinder block bolts, then coolant pump assembly to timing chain housing nuts, **Fig. 13.**
11. Remove coolant pump and cover assembly.

4. Remove exhaust manifold brace, **Fig. 9.**
5. Remove exhaust pipe from manifold, **Fig. 10.**
6. Lower the vehicle.
7. Remove exhaust manifold heat shields, **Fig. 11.**
8. Remove exhaust manifold and gasket, **Fig. 12.**
9. Reverse procedure to install noting the following:
   a. Install exhaust manifold with new gasket. Refer to specifications for torque values.
   b. Coat threads of Oxygen sensor with suitable anti-seize compound before installing.

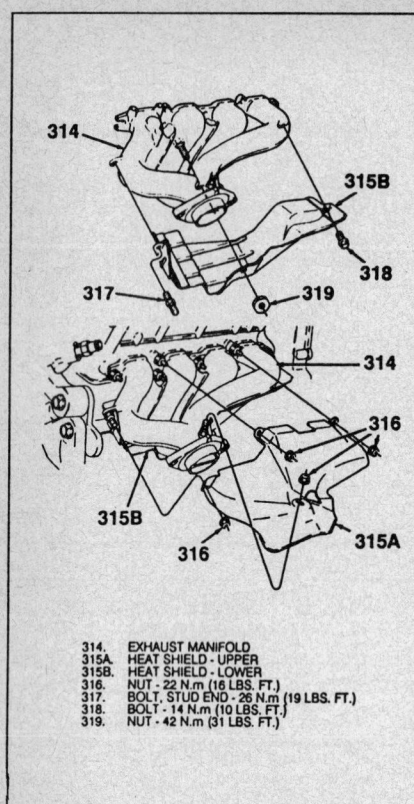

Fig. 11 Exhaust manifold heat shield installation

314. EXHAUST MANIFOLD
315A. HEAT SHIELD - UPPER
315B. HEAT SHIELD - LOWER
316. NUT - 22 N.m (16 LBS. FT.)
317. BOLT, STUD END - 26 N.m (19 LBS. FT.)
318. BOLT - 14 N.m (10 LBS. FT.)
319. NUT - 42 N.m (31 LBS. FT.)

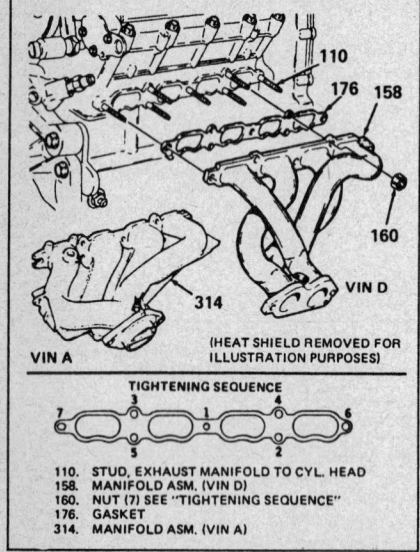

Fig. 12 Exhaust manifold replacement

110. STUD, EXHAUST MANIFOLD TO CYL. HEAD
158. MANIFOLD ASM. (VIN D)
160. NUT (7) SEE "TIGHTENING SEQUENCE"
176. GASKET
314. MANIFOLD ASM. (VIN A)

(HEAT SHIELD REMOVED FOR ILLUSTRATION PURPOSES)

TIGHTENING SEQUENCE

12. Reverse procedure to install noting the following:
   a. Ensure water pump mating surfaces are throughly clean.
   b. Lube O-ring on radiator outlet pipe with coolant prior to installing,

COOLING SYSTEM BLEED

These engines do not require a speci-

fied bleed procedure. After filling cooling system, run engine to operating temperature with radiator/pressure cap off. Air will then be automatically bled through cap opening.

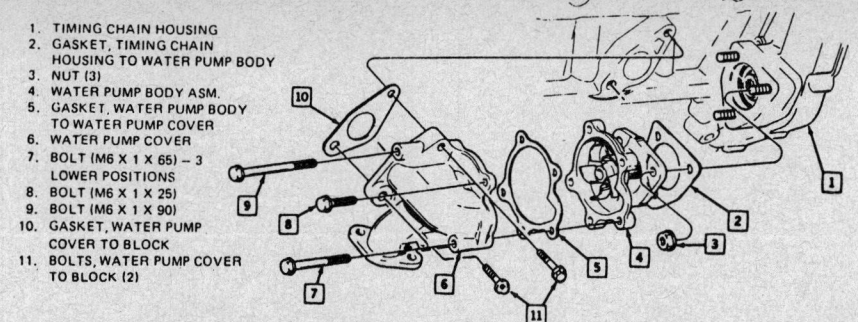

1. TIMING CHAIN HOUSING
2. GASKET, TIMING CHAIN HOUSING TO WATER PUMP BODY
3. NUT (3)
4. WATER PUMP BODY ASM.
5. GASKET, WATER PUMP BODY TO WATER PUMP COVER
6. WATER PUMP COVER
7. BOLT (M6 X 1 X 65) — 3 LOWER POSITIONS
8. BOLT (M6 X 1 X 25)
9. BOLT (M6 X 1 X 90)
10. GASKET, WATER PUMP COVER TO BLOCK
11. BOLTS, WATER PUMP COVER TO BLOCK (2)

Fig. 13 Water pump replacement

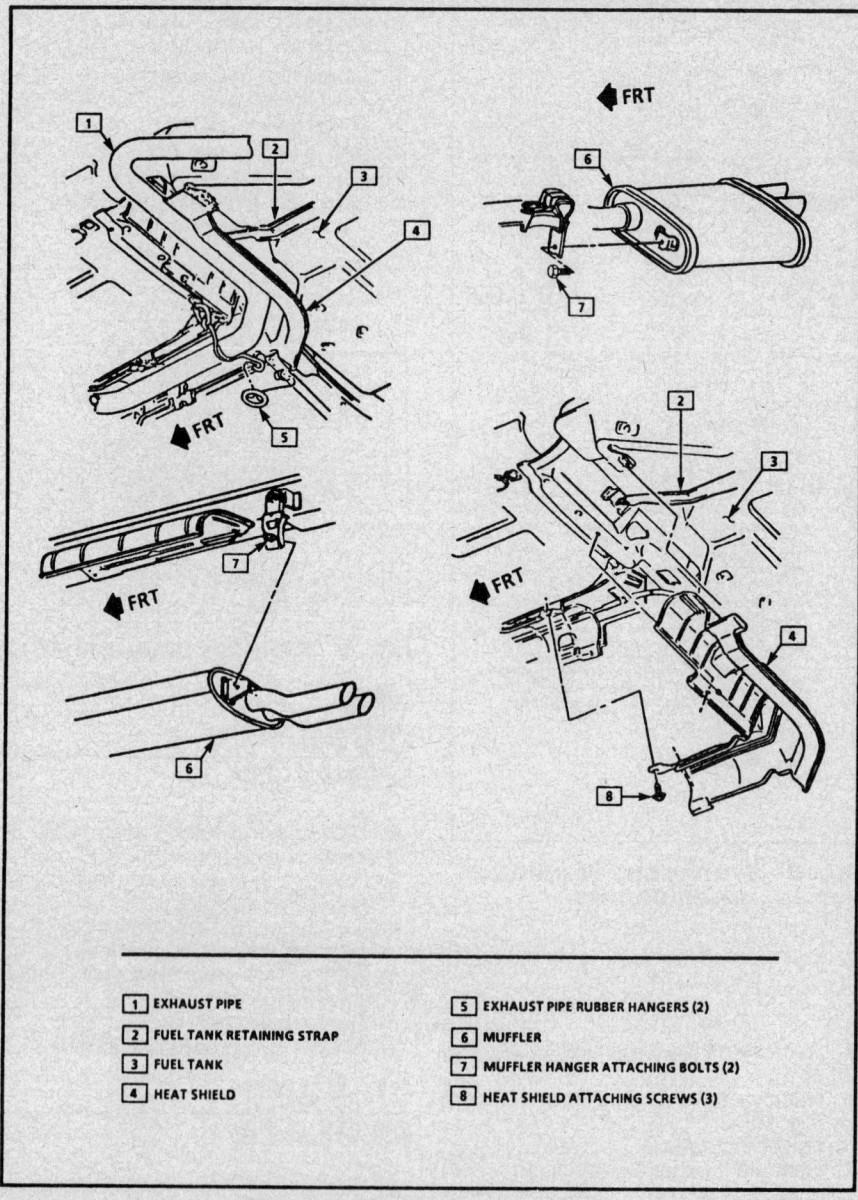

1 EXHAUST PIPE	5 EXHAUST PIPE RUBBER HANGERS (2)
2 FUEL TANK RETAINING STRAP	6 MUFFLER
3 FUEL TANK	7 MUFFLER HANGER ATTACHING BOLTS (2)
4 HEAT SHIELD	8 HEAT SHIELD ATTACHING SCREWS (3)

Fig. 14 Exhaust assembly

FUEL PUMP
REPLACE

1. Disconnect battery ground cable.
2. Relieve fuel tank vapor pressure by

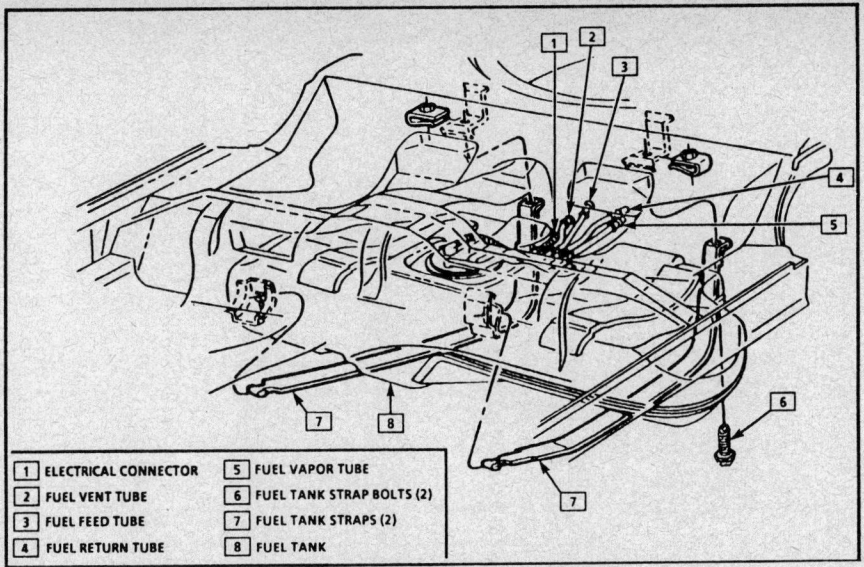

1	ELECTRICAL CONNECTOR	5	FUEL VAPOR TUBE
2	FUEL VENT TUBE	6	FUEL TANK STRAP BOLTS (2)
3	FUEL FEED TUBE	7	FUEL TANK STRAPS (2)
4	FUEL RETURN TUBE	8	FUEL TANK

Fig. 15 Fuel tank removal

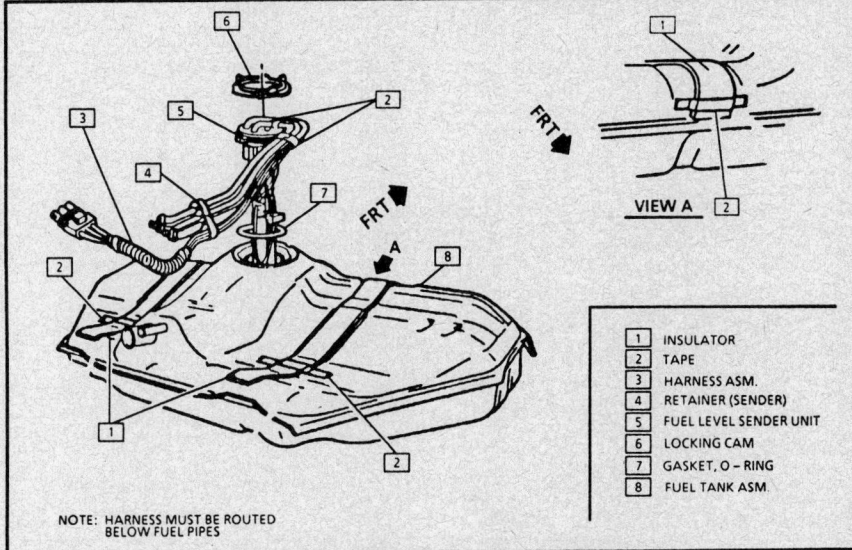

1	INSULATOR
2	TAPE
3	HARNESS ASM.
4	RETAINER (SENDER)
5	FUEL LEVEL SENDER UNIT
6	LOCKING CAM
7	GASKET, O – RING
8	FUEL TANK ASM.

NOTE: HARNESS MUST BE ROUTED BELOW FUEL PIPES

Fig. 16 Fuel tank assembly

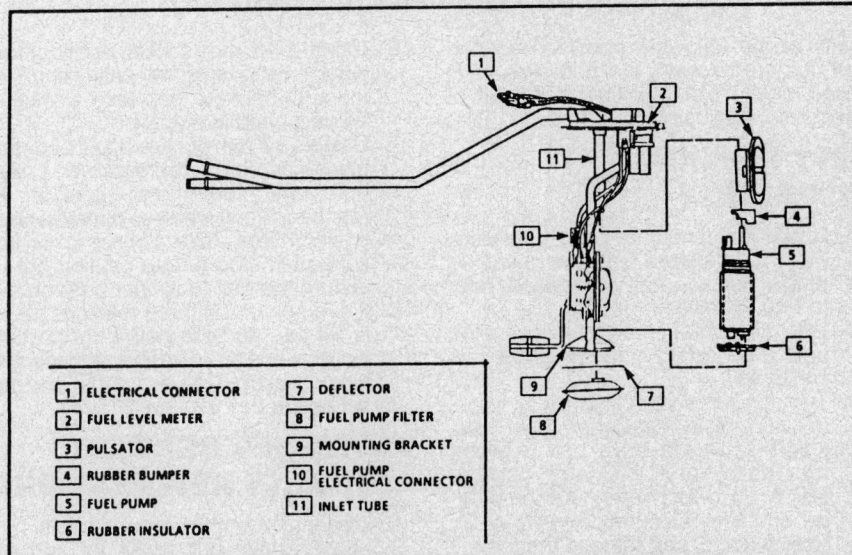

1	ELECTRICAL CONNECTOR	7	DEFLECTOR
2	FUEL LEVEL METER	8	FUEL PUMP FILTER
3	PULSATOR	9	MOUNTING BRACKET
4	RUBBER BUMPER	10	FUEL PUMP ELECTRICAL CONNECTOR
5	FUEL PUMP	11	INLET TUBE
6	RUBBER INSULATOR		

Fig. 17 Fuel level meter assembly

loosening the fuel filler cap.
3. Using a suitable syphon, drain the fuel tank.
4. Remove fuel tank as follows:
   a. Raise and support vehicle.
   b. Remove two rubber exhaust pipe hangers, **Fig. 14.**
   c. Remove two muffler hanger retaining bolts.
   d. Remove three heat shield attaching screws, then the heat shield.
   e. Remove fuel tank filler tube, vent tube, vent hose, and clamps.
   f. Disconnect electrical connector, **Fig. 15.**
   g. Disconnect fuel level meter vapor hose.
   h. Ensure fuel line connections are clean. Disconnect fuel return quick connect fitting by squeezing plastic tab on male end of the fitting. Using fuel line separator Tool Set No. J-37088, disconnect fuel line quick connect fitting. Plug all fittings.
   i. Properly support tank.
   j. Remove two rear retaining strap attaching bolts, then the fuel tank and retaining straps.
5. Thoroughly clean fuel level meter assembly connection and surrounding area, **Fig. 16.**
6. Using fuel sender spanner wrench tool No. J-35731, remove fuel level meter assembly lock ring. Remove assembly from tank, and discard the O-ring.
7. Disassemble fuel level meter assembly as follows:
   a. Note orientation of fuel filter for proper installation.
   b. To remove fuel filter, rotate it while pulling fuel pump in opposite direction, **Fig. 17.**
   c. Disconnect fuel pump electrical connector.
   d. Position fuel level meter assembly upside down on work area.
   e. Pull downward on fuel pump to separate it from mounting bracket. Tilt pump outward and remove it from pulsater.
8. Reverse procedure to install noting the following:
   a. Never run fuel pump unless submerged in fuel.
   b. Always replace fuel filter when installing fuel pump.
   c. Always use new O-ring when installing fuel level meter assembly.

SERPENTINE DRIVE BELT ROUTING

Refer to **Fig. 18** for serpentine drive belt routing.

BELT TENSION DATA
PRECAUTIONS

When installing or removing the drive belt care should be taken to avoid bending or twisting the tensioner. Inspect bearings if belt tensioner or idler assembly produce a whining noise. If the drive belt becomes frayed, check belt tensioner assembly

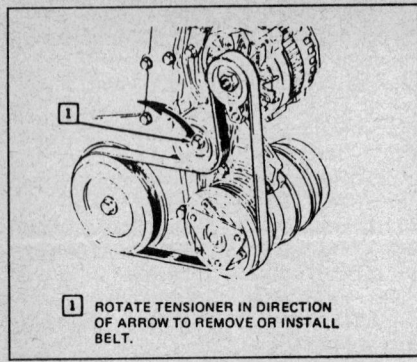

[1] ROTATE TENSIONER IN DIRECTION OF ARROW TO REMOVE OR INSTALL BELT.

Fig. 18 Serpentine drive belt routing

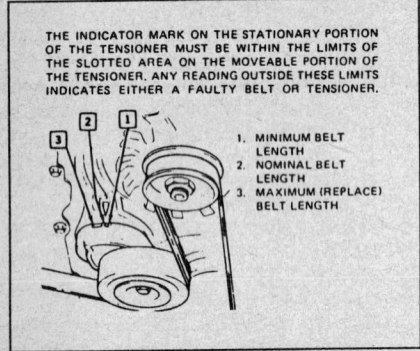

THE INDICATOR MARK ON THE STATIONARY PORTION OF THE TENSIONER MUST BE WITHIN THE LIMITS OF THE SLOTTED AREA ON THE MOVEABLE PORTION OF THE TENSIONER. ANY READING OUTSIDE THESE LIMITS INDICATES EITHER A FAULTY BELT OR TENSIONER.

1. MINIMUM BELT LENGTH
2. NOMINAL BELT LENGTH
3. MAXIMUM (REPLACE) BELT LENGTH

Fig. 19 Drive belt tensioner indicator marks

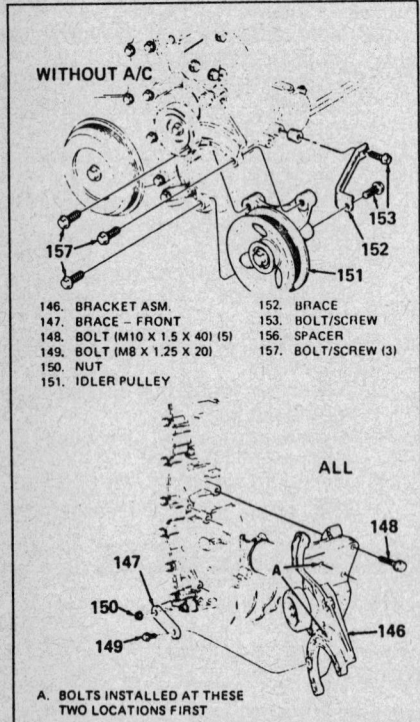

WITHOUT A/C

146. BRACKET ASM.
147. BRACE – FRONT
148. BOLT (M10 X 1.5 X 40) (5)
149. BOLT (M8 X 1.25 X 20)
150. NUT
151. IDLER PULLEY
152. BRACE
153. BOLT/SCREW
156. SPACER
157. BOLT/SCREW (3)

ALL

A. BOLTS INSTALLED AT THESE TWO LOCATIONS FIRST

Fig. 21 Tensioner bracket assembly

alignment and ensure belt edge does not contact the tensioner pulley flange.

Serpentine drive belt performance will not be impaired by cracks in the belt ribs. However belt replacement will be required

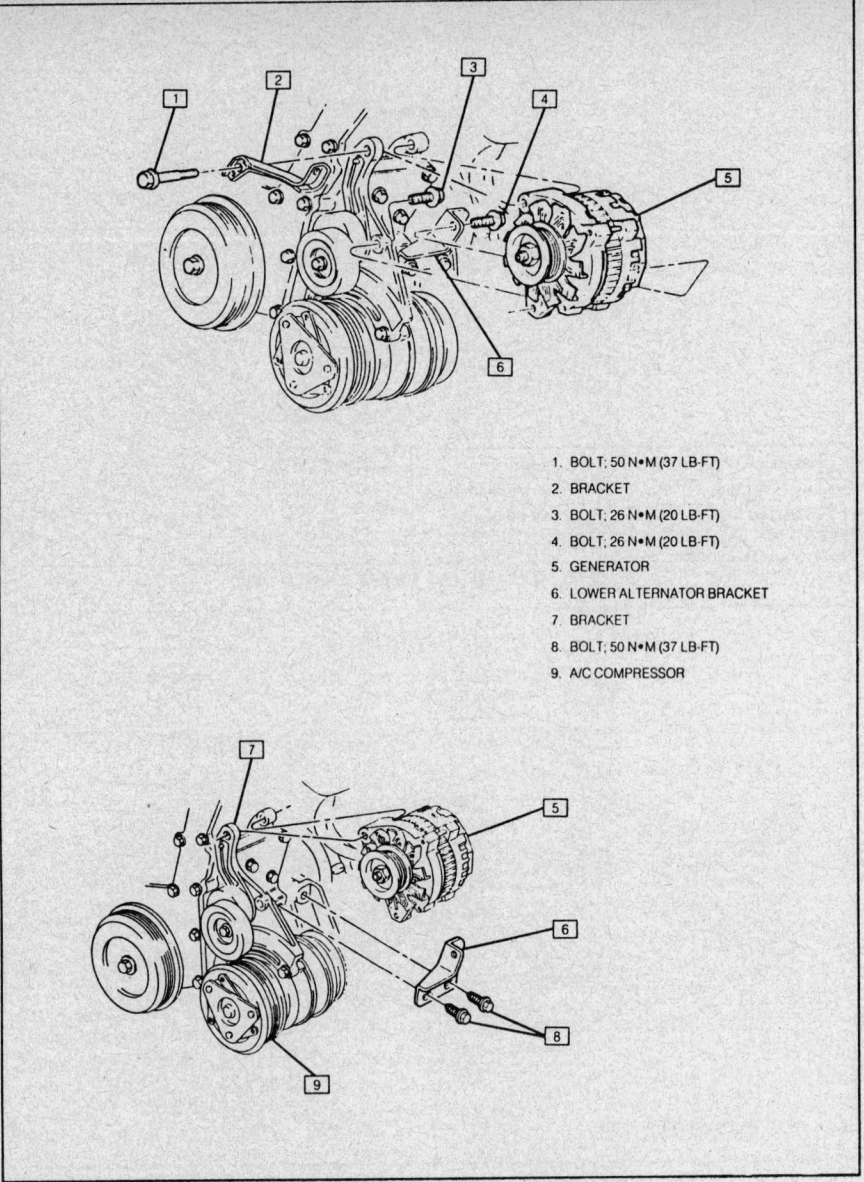

1. BOLT; 50 N•M (37 LB-FT)
2. BRACKET
3. BOLT; 26 N•M (20 LB-FT)
4. BOLT; 26 N•M (20 LB-FT)
5. GENERATOR
6. LOWER ALTERNATOR BRACKET
7. BRACKET
8. BOLT; 50 N•M (37 LB-FT)
9. A/C COMPRESSOR

Fig. 20 Alternator Assembly

if any of the following conditions occur: Belt ribs are missing, the belt slips or is frayed, or the belt tensioner runs out of travel before adjustment is proper.

BELT TENSION INSPECTION

1. Check belt tensioner indicator marks, **Fig. 19**, to ensure belt is in operating range. Replace belt as needed, refer to **Fig. 18** for belt routing.
2. With all accessories Off, run engine until operating temperature is achieved.
3. Turn ignition switch to Off.
4. Position Belt Tensioner Tool, No. J-36018, on the drive belt between idler pulley and alternator (models less A/C), or between A/C compressor and alternator (models with A/C). Note reading, and remove the tool.
5. Run engine for 15 seconds, then turn the ignition switch to Off.
6. Using a 13 mm socket, apply clockwise force to tensioner pulley bolt. Release the pulley, then take a reading as described in step 4.
7. Using a 13 mm socket, apply counterclockwise force to tensioner pulley bolt until the Install position is reached. Slowly release pulley to Rest position, then take a reading as described in step 4. Use caution not to disturb the belt tensioner position.
8. If average of the three readings taken is 50 lbs., and the belt is in the tensioners operating range, replace the tensioner bracket assembly as described in this section.

TENSIONER BRACKET ASSEMBLY REPLACEMENT

1. Disconnect battery ground cable.
2. Loosen drive belt tensioner and remove drive belt.
3. Remove alternator assembly, **Fig. 20**.

4. **On models with A/C,** remove oil filter.
5. **On models with A/C,** remove rear compressor bracket.
6. **On models less A/C,** remove bolts retaining the idle pulley brace. Remove the brace.

7. **On all models,** raise and support vehicle.
8. Remove right splash shield.
9. **On models with A/C,** remove front compressor mounting bolts and position compressor aside.
10. **On all models,** remove chain housing to belt tensioner bracket brace, **Fig. 21.**
11. Remove five bolts retaining bracket to block.
12. Remove bracket from wheel opening.
13. Reverse procedure to install. Refer to specifications for torque values.

TIGHTENING SPECIFICATIONS*

NOTE: Torque Specifications Are For Clean And Lightly Lubricated Threads Only.

Year	Component	Torque/ft. lbs.
1990–91	Camshaft Rear Cover	10
	Camshaft Sprocket To Cam Bolt	40
	Coolant Outlet To Cylinder Head	19
	Crankshaft Position Sensor To Block	80①
	Cylinder Head Threaded Plug	19
	ESC Knock Sensor	15
	Exhaust Manifold To Cylinder Head Nuts	27
	Exhaust Manifold To Cylinder Head Studs	106①
	Exhaust Manifold To Exhaust Pipe	22
	Exhaust Manifold To Oil Pan Brace	19
	Exhaust Manifold Studs To Manifold	22
	Front Cover To Timing Chain Housing	106①
	Front Engine Mount Bracket To Block	40
	Front Engine Mount To Cylinder Block Bracket	55
	Front Engine Mount To Engine Mount Crossmember	30
	Fuel Rail To Camshaft Housing	19
	Ignition Coil And Module Assembly To Camshaft Housing	15
	Intake Manifold Brace Bolts	19
	Intake Manifold To Cylinder Head	18
	Oil/Air Separator To Intake Manifold	71①
	Oil Cooler lines To Oil Cooler Adapter	26
	Oil Filter Connector To Block	21
	Oil Fill Tube Bolt	72①
	Oil Filter To Block	②
	Oil Pan Baffle Bolts	30
	Oil Pan Bolts	17
	Oil Pan Drain Plug	19
	Oil Pump To Block	40
	Oil Pump Cover To Oil Pump Body	106①
	Rear Crankshaft Seal Housing To Block	106①
	Rear Engine Mount Bracket To Body	40
	Rear Engine Mount Bracket To Engine	44
	Rear Engine Mount To Body Bracket	55
	Rear Engine Mount Through Bolt Nut	55
	Spark Pugs To Cylinder Head	17
	Starter To Block Bolt	71
	Tensioner Bracket Assembly Bracket To Block	40
	Tensioner Bracket Assembly Bracket To Front Brace	19
	Tensioner Bracket Assembly Bracket To Idler	40

Continued

TIGHTENING SPECIFICATIONS*—Continued

NOTE: Torque specifications are for clean and lightly lubricated threads only.

Year	Component	Torque/ft. lbs.
1990-91 Cont'd	Tensioner Bracket Assembly Rear Brace To Block Or Idler	40
	Timing Chain Housing To Block	19
	Timing Chain Tensioner To Housing	115①
	Throttle Body To Intake Manifold	19
	Transaxle Mount To Body	40
	Water Pump To Timing Chain Housing	19
	Water Pump To Water Pump Cover	10

①—Inch lbs. ②—¼ to one turn after initial gasket contact.

2.8L/V6-173 & 3.1L/V6-192 Engines

NOTE: Refer To 2.8L/V6-173 & 3.1L/V6-192 Engine Section In Chapter 11 For Service Procedures Not Covered In This Section.

INDEX

IDLE LEARN PROCEDURE

On 1990-91 models with 3.1L/V6-192 engine, any time vehicle power has been interrupted (battery disconnected), the programed position of the IAC valve pintle is lost. The following procedure must be performed to update the ECM memory with the correct IAC valve pintle position, enabling the ECM to provide a stable idle speed.
1. Restore vehicle power.
2. Connect suitable scan tool to ALDL connector, located under the lefthand side of the dash panel.
3. Select "IAC System."
4. Select "Idle Learn" in the "Misc. Test" mode.
5. Proceed as directed by scan tool.

ENGINE MOUNT REPLACE

FRONT MOUNT

1. Disconnect battery ground cable.
2. Remove two engine mount to body bracket bolts, then the upper engine mount to engine bracket bolt. Raise and support vehicle.
3. Support engine with suitable jack.
4. Remove inner fender shield.
5. Remove lower engine mount to body bracket bolt, **Fig. 1.**
6. Remove lower engine mount to engine bracket bolt, then remove mount.
7. Reverse procedure to install. Clean all bolts with suitable solvent and apply suitable locking compound to threads prior to installation. Torque bolts to specifications given in **Fig. 1.**

REAR MOUNT

1. Disconnect battery ground cable, then raise and support vehicle.
2. Support engine with suitable jack.
3. Remove motor mount nuts and attaching bolts, **Fig. 2.**
4. Reverse procedure to install.

ENGINE REPLACE
2.8L/V6-173

1. Disconnect battery ground cable and drain cooling system.
2. Remove air cleaner and the mass air flow meter.
3. Remove exhaust manifold/crossover assembly.
4. Remove accessory drive belt and the tensioner.

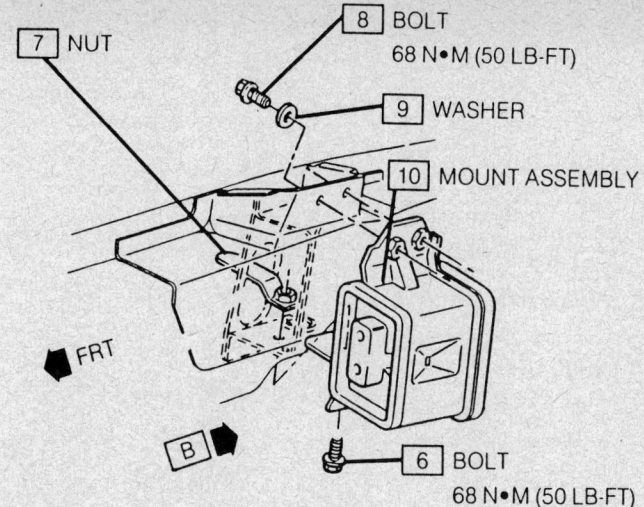

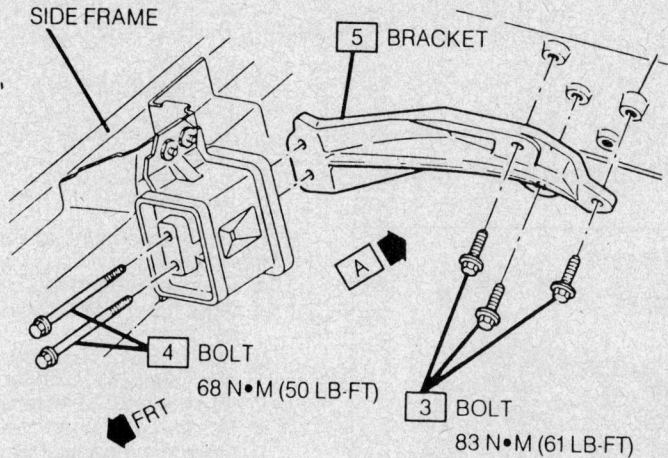

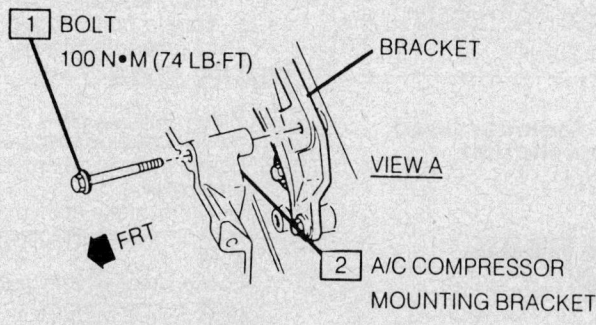

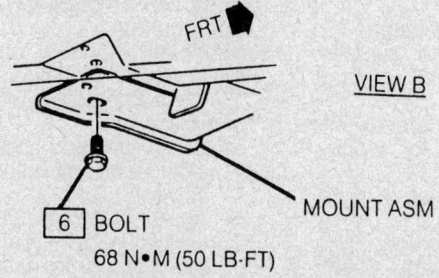

Fig. 1   Engine front mount

5. Remove power steering pump and position aside, then remove idler (if equipped).
6. Disconnect radiator hose at engine.
7. Disconnect accelerator and T.V. cables at throttle valve bracket.
8. Remove alternator and position aside, then disconnect engine wiring harness.
9. Disconnect fuel hoses and the coolant bypass and overflow hoses at engine.
10. Disconnect canister purge hose at canister and remove vacuum hoses as necessary. Support engine with engine holding fixture tool No. J-28467 or equivalent.
11. Raise and support vehicle, then remove right inner fender splash shield.
12. Remove harmonic balance and the flywheel cover.
13. Remove starter attaching bolts, disconnect electrical connectors at starter and remove starter.
14. Disconnect electrical connector at oil sending unit.
15. Remove A/C compressor and its mounting bracket(s).
16. Disconnect exhaust pipe at rear of manifold.
17. Remove flex plate to torque converter attaching bolts.
18. Remove front and rear motor mount bolts and brackets, then the intermediate shaft bracket from engine.
19. Disconnect shift cable bracket at transaxle.
20. Remove lower bellhousing bolts and lower vehicle.
21. Disconnect heater hoses at engine.
22. Install suitable engine lifting device and support transaxle with suitable jack. Remove engine support tool.
23. Remove upper bellhousing and front mount attaching bolts.
24. Remove transaxle mount bracket, then the engine.
25. Reverse procedure to install.

3.1L/V6-192

1. Relieve fuel system pressure as follows:
   a. Disconnect battery ground cable.
   b. Relieve fuel tank vapor pressure by loosening fuel filler cap.
   c. Install fuel pressure gauge tool No. J-34730 or equivalent to fuel pressure valve. **To avoid spilling fuel when connecting the gauge, wrap fitting with a shop towel.**
   d. Position end of bleed hose into a suitable container, then open bleeder valve until system pressure is relieved.
2. Removed air cleaner assembly.
3. Remove battery cables and battery.
4. Drain cooling system, then disconnect transaxle cooler lines at radiator.
5. Disconnect transaxle fluid level indicator.
6. Disconnect upper and lower radiator

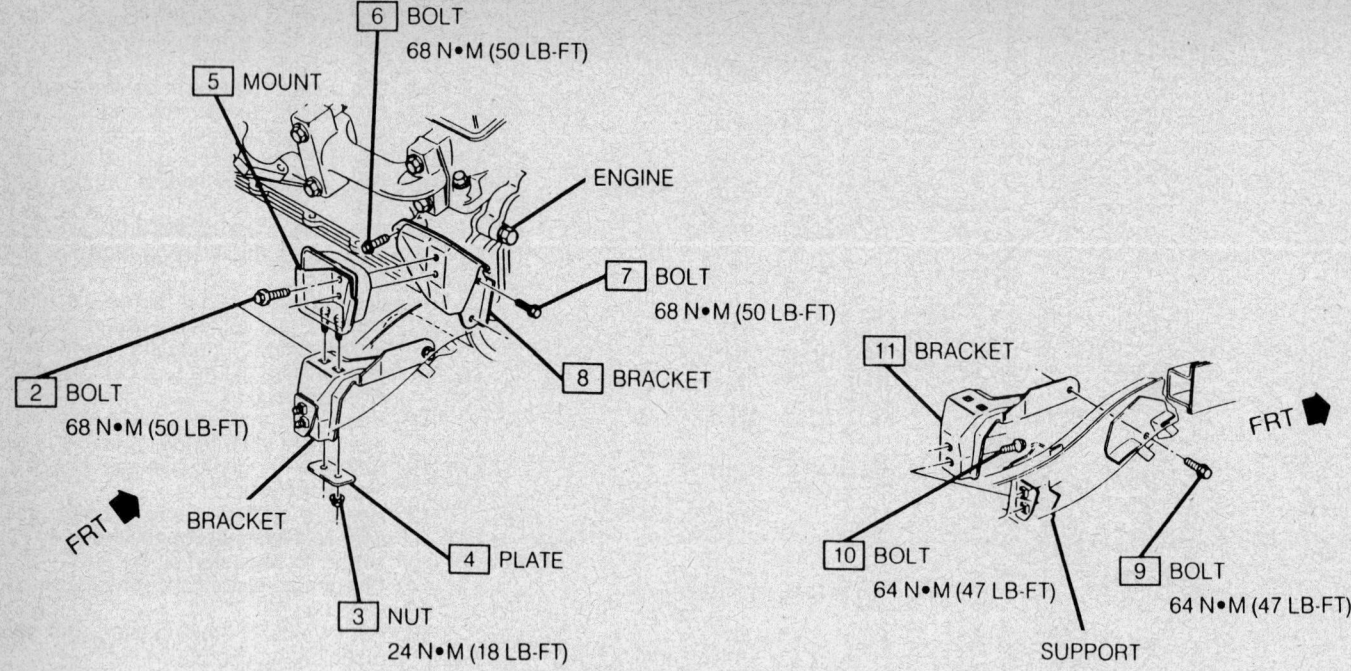

Fig. 2   Engine rear mount

hoses from engine.

7. Disconnect heater outlet hose from water pump, then the heater inlet hose at rear of engine.
8. Remove serpentine belt.
9. Disconnect shift cable linkage and cable from mounting bracket. It may be necessary to place transaxle in low gear.
10. Disconnect accelerator and cruise control cable, if equipped, from throttle linkage.
11. Disconnect A/C pressure switch electrical connector.
12. Disconnect vacuum check valve from power brake booster, then the canister purge vacuum line from the engine.
13. Disconnect upper engine electrical connectors, then the vacuum hose from vacuum reservoir.
14. Raise and support vehicle.
15. Remove front wheel and tire assemblies.
16. Remove righthand splash shield, then the oil filter.
17. Disconnect lower engine electrical connectors.
18. Disconnect A/C compressor, leaving hoses and rear bracket attached, then secure compressor out of the way.
19. Disconnect exhaust pipe from crossover.
20. Disconnect brake hose bracket at strut, then the brake calipers.
21. Disconnect tie rods from strut assemblies.
22. Place suitable engine table under front of vehicle, then lower vehicle enough to place engine and transaxle assembly onto table.
23. Lower table with engine and transaxle assembly, then raise vehicle.
24. Reverse procedure to install.

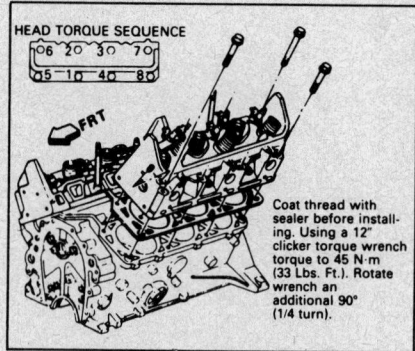

Coat thread with sealer before installing. Using a 12" clicker torque wrench torque to 45 N·m (33 Lbs. Ft.). Rotate wrench an additional 90° (1/4 turn).

Fig. 3   Cylinder head installation

CYLINDER HEAD REPLACE

LEFT SIDE

1. Disconnect battery ground cable.
2. Drain engine coolant into suitable container, then remove rocker arm cover.
3. Remove intake manifold. Refer to "Intake Manifold, Replace" for procedure.
4. Remove exhaust crossover at right side exhaust manifold.
5. Remove oil dipstick tube bracket.
6. Loosen rocker arm nuts until pushrods can be removed. **Keep pushrods in order they are removed so they can be installed in their original position.**
7. Remove cylinder head attaching bolts, then the cylinder head.

8. Reverse procedure to install, noting the following:
   a. Clean cylinder head bolts and cylinder head bolt holes with suitable solvent.
   b. Apply GM 1052080 sealer or equivalent to cylinder head bolt threads prior to installation.
   c. Position new head gasket on deck surface over dowel pins with "This Side Up" facing up, then install cylinder head.
   d. Torque bolts in sequence shown to specifications, **Fig. 3.**

RIGHT SIDE

1. Raise and support vehicle, then remove right side exhaust manifold.
2. Lower vehicle, then remove rocker arm cover.
3. Remove intake manifold. Refer to "Intake Manifold, Replace" for procedure.
4. Loosen rocker arm nuts until pushrods can be removed. **Keep pushrods in order they are removed so they can be installed in their original position.**
5. Remove cylinder head attaching bolts, then the cylinder head.
6. Reverse procedure to install, noting the following:
   a. Clean cylinder head bolts and cylinder head bolt holes with suitable solvent.
   b. Apply GM 1052080 sealer or equivalent to cylinder head bolt threads prior to installation.
   c. Position new head gasket on deck surface over dowel pins with "This Side Up" facing up, then install cylinder head.
   d. Torque bolts in sequence shown to specifications, **Fig. 3.**

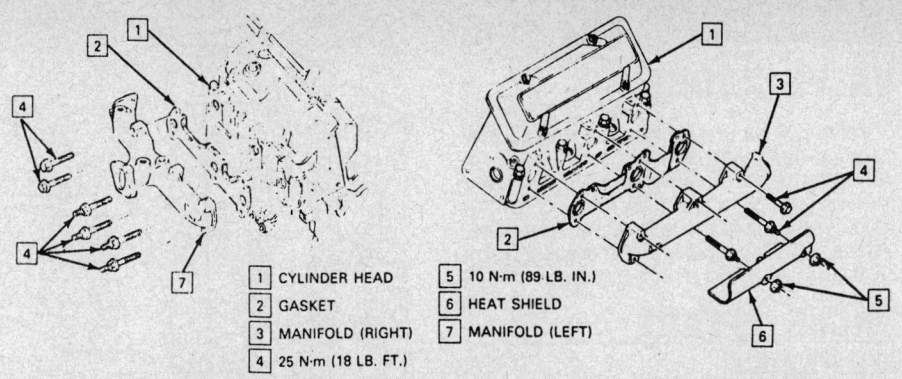

1	CYLINDER HEAD	5	10 N·m (89 LB. IN.)
2	GASKET	6	HEAT SHIELD
3	MANIFOLD (RIGHT)	7	MANIFOLD (LEFT)
4	25 N·m (18 LB. FT.)		

Fig. 4 Exhaust manifold installation. Except 1988 2.8L/V6-173

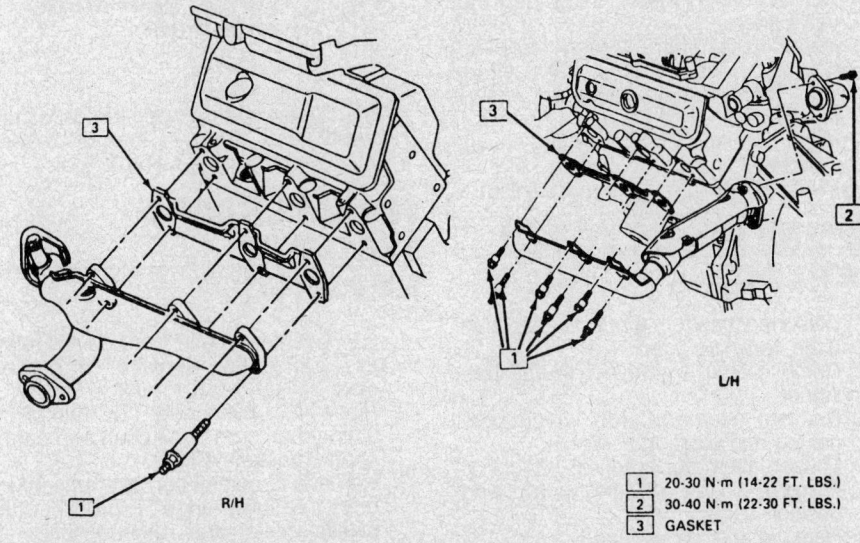

1	20-30 N·m (14-22 FT. LBS.)
2	30-40 N·m (22-30 FT. LBS.)
3	GASKET

Fig. 5 Exhaust manifold installation. 1988 2.8L/V6-173

INTAKE MANIFOLD
REPLACE

1. Disconnect battery ground cable.
2. Disconnect accelerator and T. V. cable bracket at plenum.
3. Disconnect throttle body at plenum.
4. Disconnect E.G.R. pipe at E.G.R. valve, then remove plenum.
5. Disconnect fuel inlet and return pipes at fuel rail.
6. Remove auxiliary drive belt.
7. Remove power steering pump and position aside.
8. Remove alternator with wiring attached and position aside.
9. Loosen alternator bracket.
10. Disconnect idle air vacuum hose at throttle body and the electrical connectors at injectors.
11. Remove fuel rail, breather tube and the runners.
12. Remove both rocker arm covers.
13. Drain cooling system into suitable container.
14. Disconnect radiator hose at thermostat outlet.
15. Disconnect coolant sensor and oil sender switch electrical connectors.
16. Remove coolant sensor, then disconnect cooling system bypass hose and heater inlet pipe at manifold.
17. Remove intake manifold attaching bolts, then the intake manifold.
18. Loosen rocker arm nuts until pushrods can be removed. **Keep pushrods in order they are removed so they can be installed in their original position.**
19. Reverse procedure to install, noting the following:
   a. When installing gaskets, install only on right or left side as marked.
   b. Clean cylinder case sealing surface front and rear ridges and apply a 3/16 inch bead of suitable RTV sealant on each cylinder block ridge.
   c. Install new intake gaskets on cylinder heads, then install pushrods. Torque rocker arm attaching nuts to specifications.
   d. When installing intake manifold, ensure areas between case ridges and manifold are completely sealed.
   e. Install manifold retaining bolts and nuts, torquing to specifications.

EXHAUST MANIFOLD
REPLACE

EXCEPT 1988 2.8L/V6-173 ENGINE
LEFT SIDE

1. Remove air cleaner assembly.
2. Disconnect negative battery cable.
3. Remove coolant fan, then the heat shield.
4. Remove exhaust crossover pipe at manifold.
5. Remove exhaust manifold bolts, then the exhaust manifold, **Fig. 4.**
6. Reverse procedure to install.

RIGHT SIDE

1. Remove air cleaner assembly.
2. Disconnect negative battery cable.
3. Raise and support vehicle.
4. Remove exhaust pipe at crossover, then lower vehicle.
5. Remove heatshield, then the crossover at manifold.
6. Disconnect accelerator and T.V. cables, then remove bracket.
7. Remove oxygen sensor.
8. Remove exhaust manifold bolts, then the exhaust manifold, **Fig. 4.**
9. Reverse procedure to install.

1988 2.8L/V6-173 ENGINE

1. Disconnect battery ground cable, then drain engine coolant into suitable container.
2. Remove air cleaner, inlet hose/mass air flow sensor, coolant bypass hose and the heat shield.
3. Disconnect crossover pipe at right side manifold, then remove manifold attaching bolts and the manifolds, **Fig. 5.**
4. Reverse procedure to install, torquing attaching bolts to specifications.

VALVES
ADJUST

1. Remove rocker arm covers.
2. Crank engine until assembly alignment mark on front face of torsional damper lines up with the arrow on the front cover. The engine should also be in the No. 1 firing position. This can be determined by placing fingers on No. 1 rocker arms as mark on torsional damper approaches arrow on front cover.
3. If valves are not moving, engine is in No. 1 firing position. If valves move as the mark comes up to the arrow on front cover, engine is in No. 4 firing position and should be rotated one revolution to reach No. 1 position.
4. With engine in No. 1 firing position, adjust exhaust valves 1, 2 and 3 and intake valves 1, 5 and 6, as follows:
   a. Back out adjusting nut until lash is felt at pushrod, then turn in adjust-

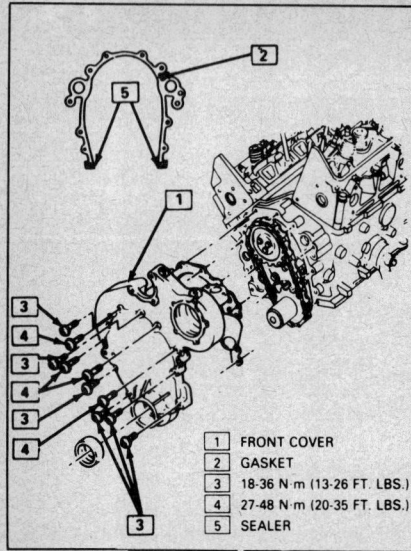

Fig. 6 Engine front cover installation

1	FRONT COVER
2	GASKET
3	18-36 N·m (13-26 FT. LBS.)
4	27-48 N·m (20-35 FT. LBS.)
5	SEALER

ing nut until all lash is removed.

b. When lash has been removed, turn adjusting nut in additional 1 1/2 turns to center lifter plunger.

5. Crank engine one revolution until arrow on front cover and torsional damper mark are again in alignment.
6. With the engine in this, the No. 4 firing position. adjust exhaust valves 4, 5 and 6 and intake valves 2, 3 and 4 as previously described.
7. Install rocker arm covers.

VALVE ARRANGEMENT
FRONT TO REAR

Right . . . . E-I-E-I-E
Left . . . . E-I-I-E-I-E

CAMSHAFT LOBE LIFT SPECIFICATIONS

Engine	Int.	Exh.
2.8L/V6-173	.2626	.2732
3.1L/V6-192	.2626	.2732

VALVE STEM OIL SEAL & VALVE SPRING
REPLACE

1. Remove rocker arm cover, then the spark plug, rocker arm and pushrod on cylinder(s) being serviced. **Keep valve train parts in order they are removed so they can be installed in their original position.**
2. Install air line adapter tool No. J-23590 or equivalent to spark plug port and apply compressed air to hold valves in place.
3. Using valve spring compressor tool No. J-5892 or equivalent to compress valve spring, remove valve locks, valve caps, valve spring and seat.

4. Remove valve stem oil seal.
5. Reverse procedure to install.

VALVE GUIDES

Valve guides are an integral part of the cylinder head and are not removable. If valve stem clearance becomes excessive, the valve guide should be reamed to the next oversize and the appropriate oversize valves installed. Valves are available in .003, .015 and .030 inch oversizes.

VALVE LIFTERS
REPLACE

1. Remove intake manifold as previously described.
2. Remove valve mechanism, then the valve lifters.
3. Install valve lifters. When installing new lifters, coat foot of valve lifters with "Molykote" or equivalent, ensuring lifter foot is convex.
4. Install intake manifold as previously described.
5. Install and adjust valve mechanism.

ENGINE FRONT COVER
REPLACE

1. Disconnect battery ground cable, then drain cooling system.
2. Remove auxiliary drive belt and tensioner.
3. Remove alternator with wiring connected and position aside.
4. Loosen alternator bracket.
5. Remove power steering pump and position aside.
6. Remove idler (if equipped).
7. Raise and support vehicle, then remove inner splash shield.
8. Remove flywheel cover from transaxle, then using torsional dampener tool No. J-24420, remove damper.
9. Remove starter, then the oil pan.
10. Disconnect radiator hose at water pump, then the heater hose from cooling system fill pipe.
11. Disconnect bypass and overflow hoses.
12. Remove water pump pulley.
13. Remove plug wire shield at water pump.
14. Remove canister purge hose.
15. Remove front cover attaching bolts, then the front cover.
16. Reverse procedure to install, noting the following:
    a. Clean all parts in suitable solvent.
    b. Apply sealer, GM 1052080 or equivalent to bolts as shown, **Fig. 6.**

ENGINE FRONT COVER OIL SEAL
REPLACE

1. Remove inner splash shield and torsional damper, then pry seal from cover using a suitable screwdriver. **Use caution not to damage crankshaft surface during seal removal.**

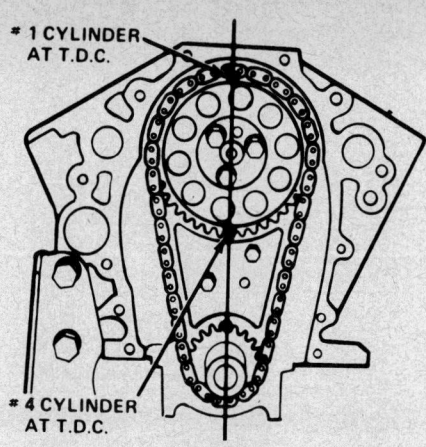

Fig. 7 Timing gear mark alignment

2. Install new seal so open end faces toward inside of cover, then drive seal into position using suitable tool.

TIMING CHAIN & SPROCKET
REPLACE

1. Remove crankcase front cover, refer to "Front Cover, Replace" for procedure.
2. Place No. 1 cylinder at TDC and align timing marks on crankshaft and camshaft sprockets, **Fig. 7.**
3. Remove camshaft sprocket attaching bolts. Tap lower edge of sprocket with plastic mallet and remove sprocket and timing chain.
4. If necessary, replace crankshaft sprocket.
5. Apply Molykote or equivalent to sprocket thrust surface.
6. Align timing marks, **Fig. 7,** and install timing chain on sprockets.
7. Position sprocket onto camshaft by aligning dowel hole with the dowel pin. Use retaining bolt to seat sprocket fully onto the camshaft. Torque retaining bolt to specifications.
8. Lubricate timing chain with engine oil, then install front cover.

CAMSHAFT
REPLACE

1. Remove engine from vehicle, refer to "Engine, Replace" for procedure.
2. Remove valve lifters, refer to "Valve Lifter, Replace" for procedure.
3. Remove engine front cover, refer to "Front Cover, Replace" procedure.
4. Remove timing chain and sprocket. Refer to "Timing Chain & Sprocket, Replace" for procedure.
5. Remove camshaft. **Use caution not to damage bearings during camshaft removal.**
6. Reverse procedure to install. Coat camshaft lobes with GM E.O.S. 1052367 or equivalent prior to installation.

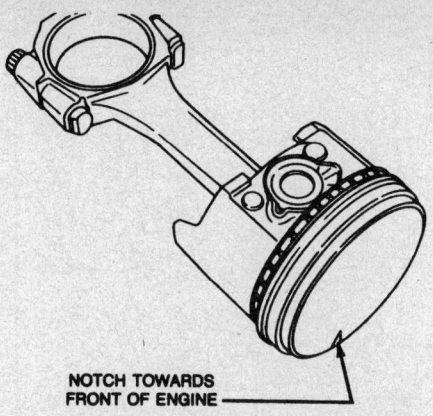

NOTCH TOWARDS FRONT OF ENGINE

Fig. 8   Piston & rod assembly

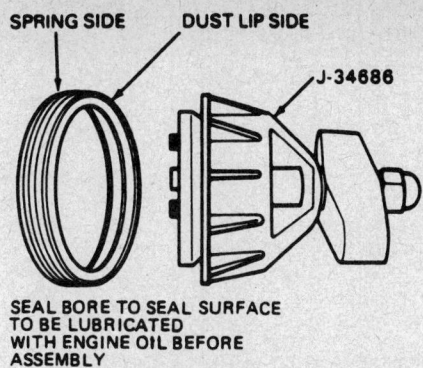

SPRING SIDE   DUST LIP SIDE

J-34686

SEAL BORE TO SEAL SURFACE
TO BE LUBRICATED
WITH ENGINE OIL BEFORE
ASSEMBLY

**Fig. 9   Rear main oil seal
installation**

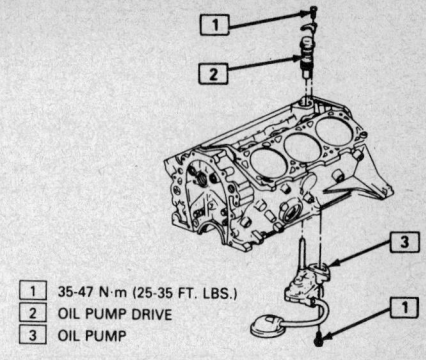

1 35-47 N·m (25-35 FT. LBS.)
2 OIL PUMP DRIVE
3 OIL PUMP

Fig. 10   Oil pump removal

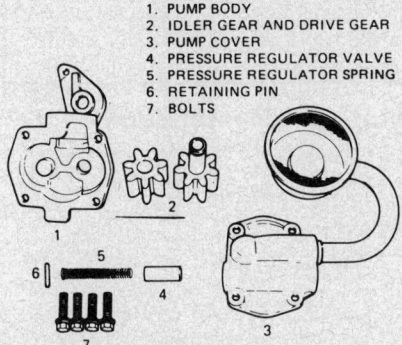

1. PUMP BODY
2. IDLER GEAR AND DRIVE GEAR
3. PUMP COVER
4. PRESSURE REGULATOR VALVE
5. PRESSURE REGULATOR SPRING
6. RETAINING PIN
7. BOLTS

Fig. 11   Oil pump assembly

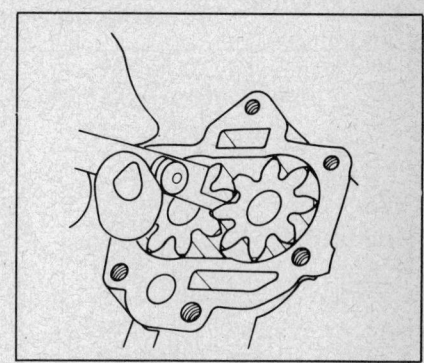

**Fig. 12   Measuring oil pump
gear lash**

4. Check inside of seal bore for nicks or burrs and correct as necessary. Inspect crankshaft for burrs or nicks on seal contact surface. Repair or replace crankshaft as necessary.
5. Install new seal using rear main seal installer tool No. J-34686 or equivalent.
6. Place seal on mandrel, making sure that dust lip on seal bottoms squarely against collar of tool, **Fig. 9.**
7. After aligning dowel pin with dowel pin hole in crankshaft, attach tool to crankshaft and **torque** screws to 2-5 ft. lbs.
8. Turn T-handle of tool until collar is tight against engine block to ensure that seal is seated properly in block.
9. Loosen T-handle of tool until it comes to a stop. Remove attaching screws.
10. Check that seal is seated squarely in bore.
11. Install flywheel and transaxle.
12. Start engine and check for leaks.

OIL PAN
REPLACE

1. Disconnect battery ground cable.
2. Raise and support vehicle, then drain crankcase.
3. Remove flywheel dust cover, then the starter motor.
4. Remove oil pan attaching bolts, then the oil pan.
5. Reverse procedure to install. Apply suitable sealer to oil pan mating surfaces. Torque attaching bolts to specifications.

OIL PUMP
REPLACE

REMOVAL

1. Drain crankcase, then remove oil pan as previously described.
2. Remove pump to rear main bearing attaching bolt, then remove pump, **Fig. 10.**

DISASSEMBLY

1. Drain oil from pump, then remove driveshaft and driveshaft extension.

2. Remove pickup tube and screen.
3. Remove four pump cover to body attaching bolts, then remove cover, idler and drive gears, **Fig. 11. Place alignment mark on oil pump drive and idler gear teeth so they can be installed in the same position.**
4. Remove pressure regulator valve retaining pin, spring and the valve from pump body.

INSPECTION

1. Inspect pump components and should any of the following conditions exist, the oil pump assembly should be replaced.
   a. Inspect pump body, gears and cover for cracks or excessive wear.
   b. Check drive gear shaft for looseness in housing.
   c. Check inside of pump cover for wear that would allow oil to leak past ends of gears.
   d. Check oil pickup screen assembly for damage to screen or pickup tube.
   e. Check pressure regulator valve for fit in pump body.
2. Install pump gears, then using a feeler gauge, measure oil pump gear lash at several locations, **Fig. 12.** Clearance should be .009-.015 inch on 2.8L/V6-173 engines, and .0037-.0077 inch on 3.1L/V6-192 engines.

PISTON & ROD ASSEMBLY

There is a machined hole or cast notch in the top of all pistons. The piston assemblies should always be installed with the hole or notch toward front of engine, **Fig. 8.**

PISTONS, PINS & RINGS

Pistons and rings are available in standard and oversize. Piston pins are available in standard size only.

MAIN & ROD BEARINGS

Main and rod bearing are available in standard sizes and undersizes.

REAR MAIN BEARING OIL SEAL
REPLACE

1. Support engine and remove transaxle.
2. Remove flywheel.
3. Remove seal by carefully inserting screwdriver in through dust lip and prying towards end of crankshaft. Repeat as necessary around circumference of seal until seal is removed, taking care not to damage crankshaft circumference.

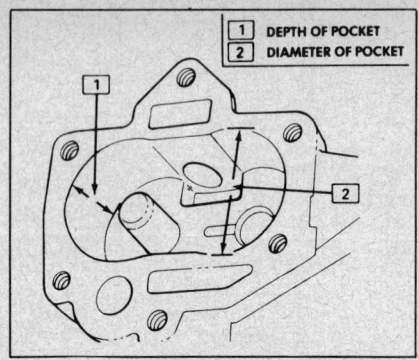

Fig. 13 Measuring oil pump housing pocket

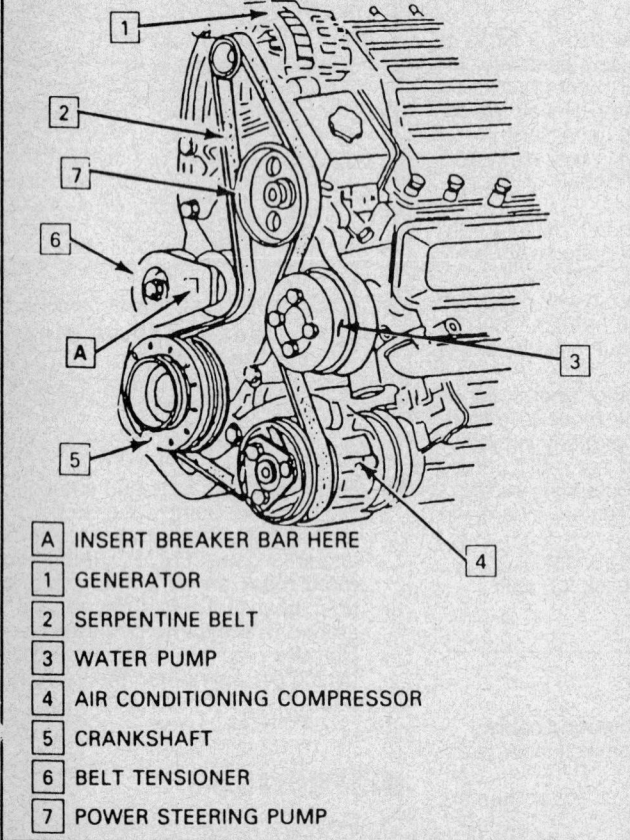

A	INSERT BREAKER BAR HERE
1	GENERATOR
2	SERPENTINE BELT
3	WATER PUMP
4	AIR CONDITIONING COMPRESSOR
5	CRANKSHAFT
6	BELT TENSIONER
7	POWER STEERING PUMP

Fig. 15 Serpentine drive belt routing

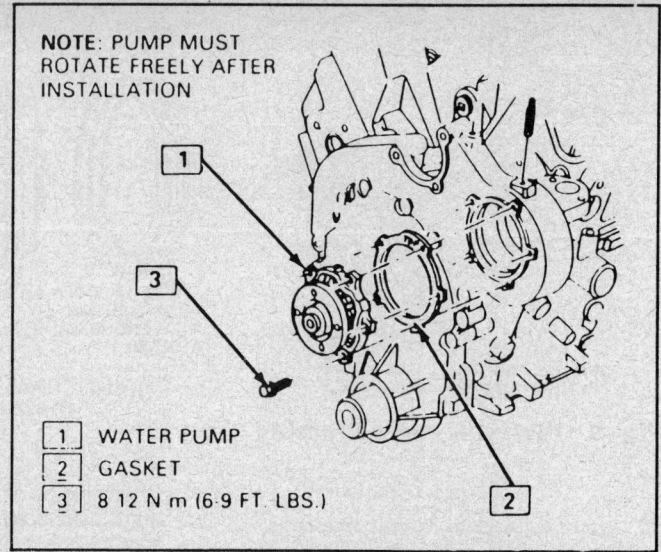

NOTE: PUMP MUST ROTATE FREELY AFTER INSTALLATION

1	WATER PUMP
2	GASKET
3	8-12 N·m (6-9 FT. LBS.)

Fig. 14 Water pump installation

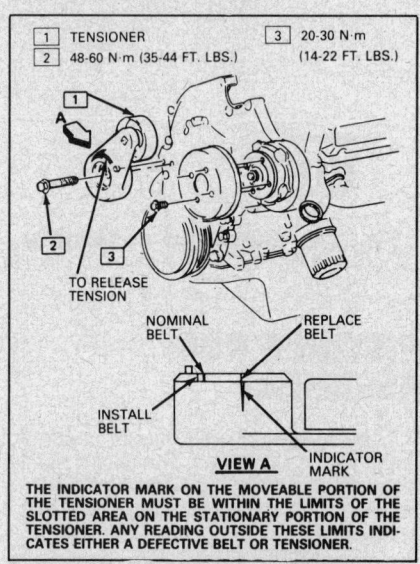

1	TENSIONER	3	20-30 N·m
2	48-60 N·m (35-44 FT. LBS.)		(14-22 FT. LBS.)

TO RELEASE TENSION

NOMINAL BELT   REPLACE BELT

INSTALL BELT   INDICATOR MARK

VIEW A

THE INDICATOR MARK ON THE MOVEABLE PORTION OF THE TENSIONER MUST BE WITHIN THE LIMITS OF THE SLOTTED AREA ON THE STATIONARY PORTION OF THE TENSIONER. ANY READING OUTSIDE THESE LIMITS INDICATES EITHER A DEFECTIVE BELT OR TENSIONER.

Fig. 16 Belt tensioner operating range

3. Remove pump gears, then measure depth of oil pump housing pocket, **Fig. 13**. Depth should be 1.195-1.198 inch on 2.8L/V6-173 and 3.1L/V6-192 engines with aluminum pump bodies, and 1.202-1.205 on 3.1L/V6-192 engine with cast iron pump bodies.
4. Measure pump gear length. Length should be 1.199-1.2 inch.
5. Measure pump gear diameters. Diameters should be 1.498-1.5 inch on 2.8L/V6-173 and 3.1LV6-192 engines with aluminum pump bodies, and 1.504-1.506 on 3.1L/V6-192 engine with cast iron pump bodies.
6. Install pump gears, then measure side clearance between pump gears and oil pump housing. Side clearance should be .003-.004 inch.

7. If oil pump components are not within specifications, it should be replaced.

ASSEMBLY

Lubricate internal parts with engine oil during assembly.
1. Install replacement pickup screen and tube assembly, if removed. Position pump in a soft jawed vise, then apply sealer to end of tube and tap into position using suction tube installer tube tool No. J-8369 or equivalent and a plastic hammer. Use care not to damage inlet screen and tube assembly when installing into pump housing.
2. Place pressure regulator valve, spring and retaining pin into pump body, then install drive gear and shaft.

3. Install idler gear into pump body, then the pump cover gasket. **Fig. 11**.
4. Install pump cover, torque retaining bolts to specifications.

INSTALLATION

1. Align oil pump extension shaft drive gear socket and pump housing, then install pump assembly. Torque pump assembly retaining bolts to specifications.
2. Install oil pan as previously described.

WATER PUMP
REPLACE

1. Disconnect battery ground cable, then drain cooling system.
2. Remove accessory drive belt.
3. Remove water pump pulley, then the water pump, **Fig. 14**.
4. Reverse procedure to install.

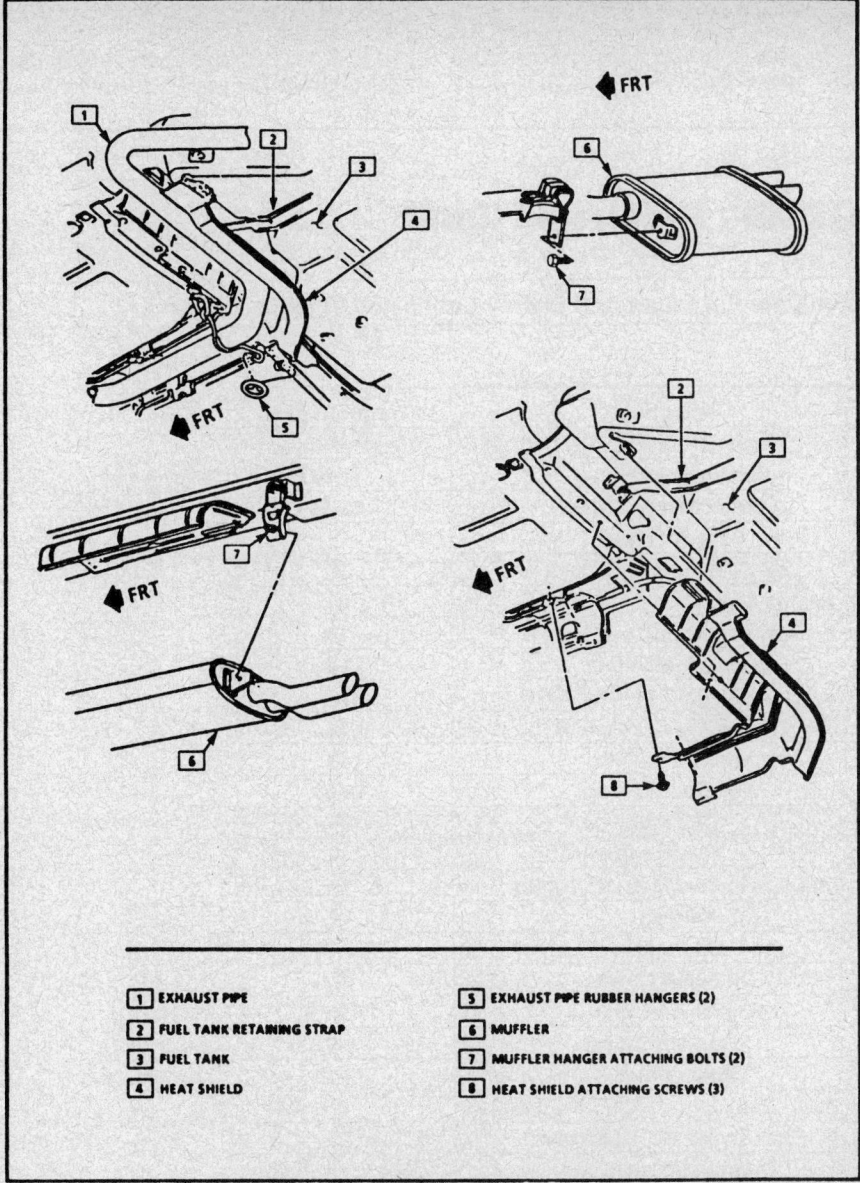

Fig. 17 Exhaust Assembly

1	EXHAUST PIPE	5	EXHAUST PIPE RUBBER HANGERS (2)
2	FUEL TANK RETAINING STRAP	6	MUFFLER
3	FUEL TANK	7	MUFFLER HANGER ATTACHING BOLTS (2)
4	HEAT SHIELD	8	HEAT SHIELD ATTACHING SCREWS (3)

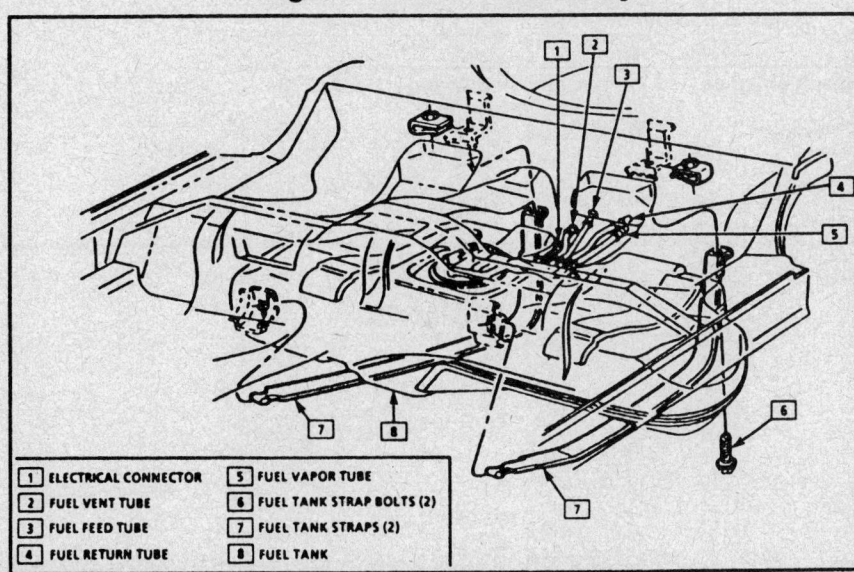

1	ELECTRICAL CONNECTOR	5	FUEL VAPOR TUBE
2	FUEL VENT TUBE	6	FUEL TANK STRAP BOLTS (2)
3	FUEL FEED TUBE	7	FUEL TANK STRAPS (2)
4	FUEL RETURN TUBE	8	FUEL TANK

Fig. 18 Fuel Tank Removal

COOLING SYSTEM BLEED

These engines do not require a specified bleed procedure. After filling cooling system, run engine to operating temperature with radiator/pressure cap off. Air will then be automatically bled through cap opening.

SERPENTINE DRIVE BELTS

BELT ROUTING

Refer to **Fig. 15** for serpentine drive belt routing.

BELT TENSIONER, ADJUST

Belt tension is maintained by a spring loaded belt tensioner. To remove or install drive belt, rotate tensioner with with a 3/4 inch socket. If belt tension is not satisfactory, ensure belt tensioner is within operating limits, **Fig. 16**. If belt tensioner is allowed to operate outside its operating limits, damage to belt tensioner may result.

BELT TENSIONER, REPLACE

1. Remove serpentine belt guard, **Fig. 15.**
2. Lift or rotate tensioner using a 1/2 inch breaker bar.
3. Remove serpentine belt, then the tensioner bolt.
4. Remove tensioner.
5. Reverse procedure to install.

FUEL PUMP
REPLACE

1. Disconnect battery ground cable.
2. Raise and support vehicle.
3. Drain, then remove fuel tank as follows:
   a. Raise and support vehicle.
   b. Remove two rubber exhaust pipe hangers, **Fig. 17.**
   c. Remove two muffler hanger retaining bolts.
   d. Remove three heat shield attaching screws, then the heat shield.
   e. Remove fuel tank filler tube, vent tube, vent hose, and clamps.
   f. Disconnect electrical connector, **Fig. 18.**
   g. Disconnect fuel level meter vapor hose.
   h. Ensure fuel line connections are clean. Disconnect fuel return quick connect fitting by squeezing plastic tab on male end of the fitting. Using Connector Tool Set No. J-37088, disconnect fuel line quick connect fitting. Plug all fittings.
   i. Properly support tank.
   j. Remove two rear retaining strap attaching bolts, then the fuel tank and retaining straps.
4. Rotate fuel sender/pump assembly cam lock ring, then lift out fuel sender/pump assembly.
5. Remove fuel pump from fuel sender

by pulling fuel pump up into attaching hose while pulling outwards from lower support.

6. Reverse procedure to install noting the following:

a. Install new fuel sender/pump assembly O-ring onto fuel tank before installation.

b. Always replace fuel filter when installing new pump.

c. Never run fuel pump unless submerged in fuel.

TIGHTENING SPECIFICATIONS*

NOTE: Torque Specifications Are For Clean And Lightly Lubricated Threads Only.

Year	Component	Torque/ft. lbs.
1988–91	Camshaft Rear Cover	7
	Camshaft Sprocket	15-20
	Connecting Rod Cap	34-44
	Cylinder Head	①
	Drive Belt Tensioner Belt	37
	Engine Strut Bracket To Engine	34
	Exhaust Crossover Nut	18
	Exhaust Manifold	15-23
	Exhaust Manifold To Heat Shield	89 ④
	Flywheel to Crankshaft	52
	Intake Manifold	18
	Main Bearing Cap	63-83
	Oil Filter	11
	Oil Filter Adapter Connector	46
	Oil Level Indicator Retaining Nut	18
	Oil Pan	②
	Oil Pump	25-38
	Oil Pump Cover	8
	Rocker Arm Stud	15-20 ③
	Rocker Arm Cover	6-9
	Spark Plugs	10-25
	Strut Brackets To Upper Tie Bar	16
	Strut To Tie Bar Brackets	32
	Thermostat Housing	19
	Timing Chain Dampener Pulley	15
	Vibration Damper or Pulley	67-85
	Water Pump	7

①—Torque to 33 ft. lbs., then tighten an additional 90°.

②—Torque 6mm bolts to 6-9 ft. lbs., torque 8 mm bolts to 15-23 ft. lbs.

③—Rocker arm nuts.

④—Inch lbs.

Clutch & Manual Transaxle

INDEX

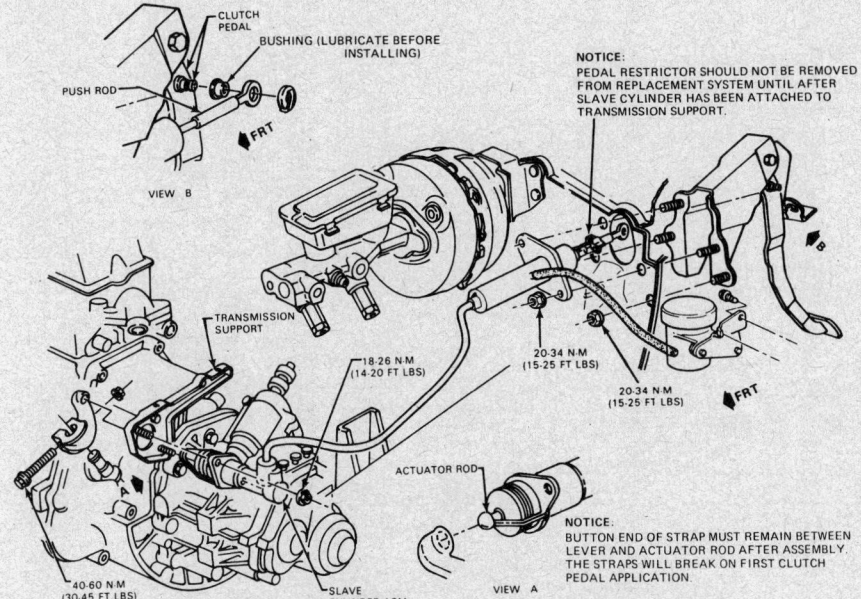

Fig. 1 Hydraulic clutch assembly

3. If slave cylinder pushrod did not move .433 inch, proceed as follows:
   a. Check clutch master cylinder fluid level. The clutch slave cylinder must be installed during this operation. Refill as necessary.
   b. If master cylinder requires fluid, check hydraulic system components for leakage. Remove rubber boots from cylinders and check for leakage past pistons. A slight wetting of piston and wall surfaces is acceptable.
   c. If excessive leakage is indicated, entire hydraulic system must be replaced.

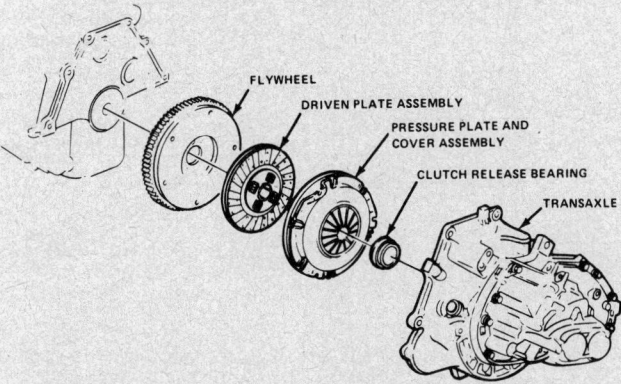

Fig. 2 Clutch assembly

CLUTCH SERVICE

ADJUSTMENT

On these models, a hydraulic clutch system is used, **Fig. 1.** The system consists of a dash mounted master cylinder with integral reservoir, a transmission mounted slave cylinder and high pressure tubing to connect the two components.

The hydraulic clutch system provides automatic clutch adjustment, therefore, there is no provision for adjustment.

INSPECTION

1. While observing clutch slave cylinder pushrod travel, have an assistant depress clutch pedal. Brake pedal should travel approximately 7.4 inches.
2. If slave cylinder pushrod moves .433 inch or more, hydraulic system is operating properly.

REPLACEMENT

1. Disconnect battery ground cable.
2. Remove hush panel from driver's footwell, then disconnect clutch master cylinder pushrod from clutch pedal.
3. Remove transaxle as outlined under "Manual Transaxle, Replace" procedure.
4. Mark position of pressure plate to flywheel to aid reassembly.
5. Gradually loosen pressure plate to flywheel attaching bolts until spring tension is relieved.
6. Support pressure plate and remove attaching bolts, pressure plate and driven disc, **Fig. 2.**
7. Clean pressure plate and flywheel mounting surfaces. Inspect bearing retainer outer surface of the transaxle.
8. Place pressure plate and driven disc in position and support with clutch alignment arbor tool No. J-29074, **Fig. 3. The driven disc is installed with the damper springs offset toward the transaxle. Stamped letters found on the driven disc identify the "Flywheel Side."**
9. Install and gradually **torque** the pressure plate to flywheel attaching bolts to 15 ft. lbs. Remove support tool.
10. Lubricate the clutch throwout fork where it contacts the release bearing and pack the release bearing inside diameter recess with suitable grease.
11. Install transaxle and hush panel, then connect battery ground cable.

BLEEDING CLUTCH HYDRAULIC SYSTEM

1. Clean dirt and grease from the cap to ensure no foreign substances enter the system.
2. Remove cap and diaphragm and fill reservoir to the top with hydraulic clutch fluid No. 12345347 or an equivalent fluid that meets Dot 3 specifications.
3. Loosen bleed screw which is located on the slave cylinder body next to the inlet connection.
4. Fluid will now begin to move from the master cylinder down the tube to the slave. It is important that for efficient gravity fill, the reservoir must be kept full all the time.
5. It will be noticeable at this point, that bubbles will appear at the bleed screw outlet. This means that air is being expelled from the system. When the slave is full, a steady stream of fluid will come from the slave outlet. At this point, tighten bleed screw.
6. Assemble diaphragm and cap to the reservoir, fluid in reservoir should be level with step.
7. The hydraulic system should now be fully bled and should release the clutch. Check vehicle by starting the engine, pushing clutch pedal to the floor and selecting reverse gear. There should be no grating of gears, if there is, the hydraulic system still contains air. If this is the case, repeat bleed procedure.

MANUAL TRANSAXLE SHIFT CABLES
REPLACE

Refer to **Figs. 4 and 5**, when replacing manual shift cables.
1. Disconnect battery ground cable.
2. Remove clamp and nut from each transaxle shift lever.
3. Remove shift knob, console and shift boot.
4. Remove shift cables from shifter control assembly by twisting between cable socket and control lever with suitable screwdriver.
5. Remove spring clips retaining cables to control assembly.
6. Remove right front sill plate, then pull back carpet to gain access to shift cables.
7. Remove shift cable grommet cover attaching screws, then remove cable cover at floor pan and remove shift cables.
8. Reverse procedure to install.

SHIFT CONTROL ASSEMBLY
REPLACE

1. Disconnect battery ground cable.
2. Remove shift knob, console and shift boot.

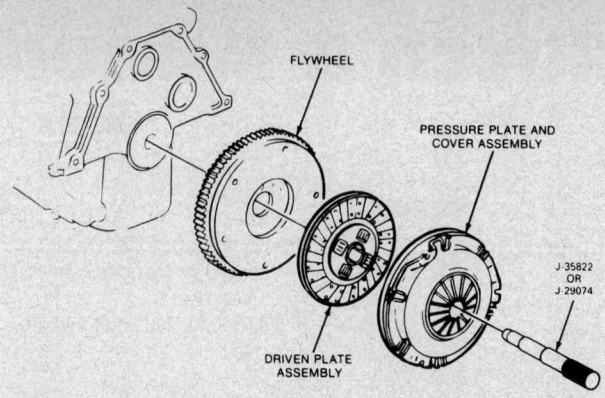

FLYWHEEL

PRESSURE PLATE AND COVER ASSEMBLY

DRIVEN PLATE ASSEMBLY

J-35822 OR J-29074

Fig. 3   Aligning clutch disc & pressure plate

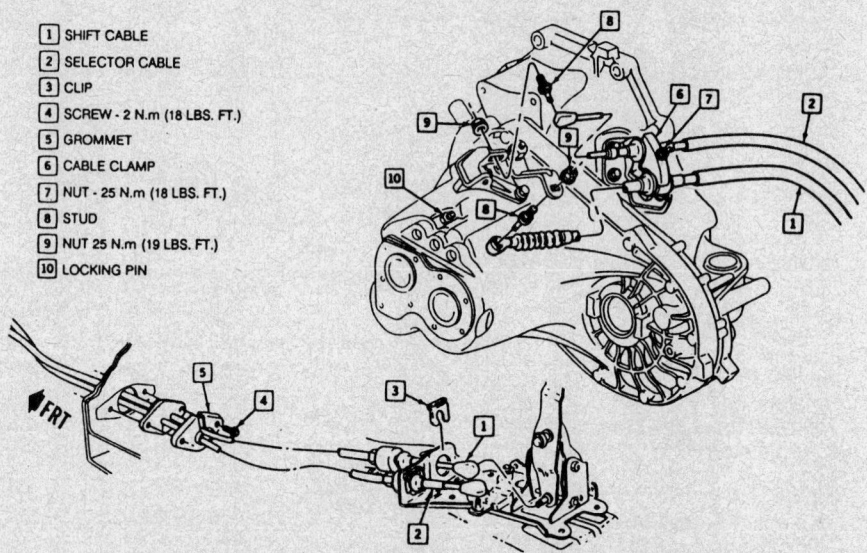

1. SHIFT CABLE
2. SELECTOR CABLE
3. CLIP
4. SCREW - 2 N.m (18 LBS. FT.)
5. GROMMET
6. CABLE CLAMP
7. NUT - 25 N.m (18 LBS. FT.)
8. STUD
9. NUT 25 N.m (19 LBS. FT.)
10. LOCKING PIN

FRT

Fig. 4   Manual shift cable replacement. Muncie

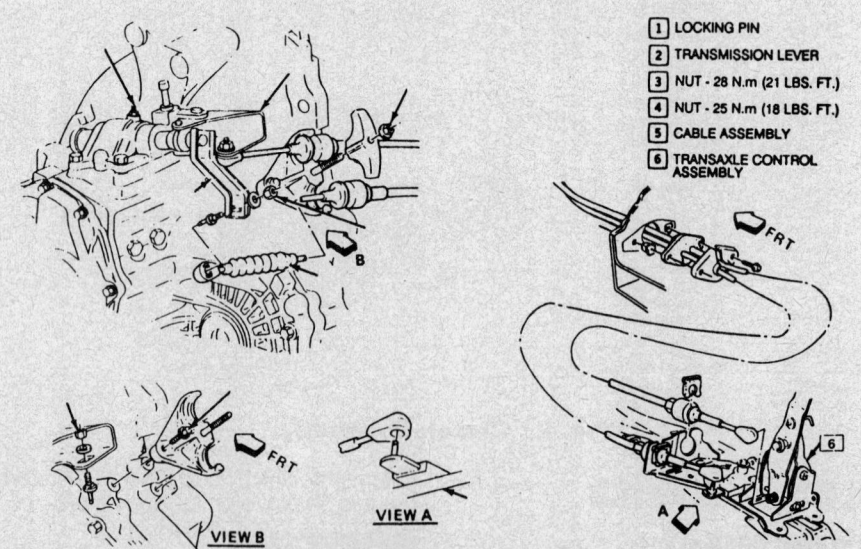

1. LOCKING PIN
2. TRANSMISSION LEVER
3. NUT - 28 N.m (21 LBS. FT.)
4. NUT - 25 N.m (18 LBS. FT.)
5. CABLE ASSEMBLY
6. TRANSAXLE CONTROL ASSEMBLY

VIEW B

VIEW A

FRT

Fig. 5   Manual shift cable replacement. Isuzu

3. Remove shift cables from shifter control assembly by twisting between cable socket and control lever with suitable screwdriver.

4. Remove spring clips retaining cables to control assembly.
5. Remove shift control assembly.
6. Reverse procedure to install.

MANUAL TRANSAXLE REPLACE

MODELS w/ISUZU TRANSAXLE

1. Disconnect battery ground cable.
2. Install engine support fixture, **Fig. 6.** Connect fixture hook to engine lift ring and raise engine enough to relieve weight from engine mounts. The engine support fixture must be positioned in the center of the cowl and the attaching parts properly tightened before supporting engine.
3. Remove left sound insulator from under instrument panel, then disconnect clutch master cylinder pushrod from clutch pedal.
4. Remove clutch slave cylinder from transaxle support and position aside.
5. Remove transaxle mount attaching bolts.
6. Remove transaxle mount bracket attaching bolts and nuts.
7. Disconnect shift cables and remove retaining clips at transaxle.
8. Disconnect ground cable at transaxle mounting stud, then the shift light wiring.
9. Raise and support vehicle, then remove left front wheel.
10. Remove left front inner splash shield retaining screws and the splash shield.
11. Remove transaxle front strut and front strut bracket.
12. Remove clutch housing cover attaching bolts, then disconnect speedometer cable at transaxle.
13. Disconnect stabilizer bar at the left suspension support and control arm.
14. Remove left side support attaching bolts, then swing support aside.
15. Install boot protectors at drive axles, then disengage both drive axles at transaxle. Remove left drive axle from transaxle housing bore.
16. Attach the transaxle case to a suitable jack, then remove transaxle to engine mounting bolts.

1. TOOL J-28467
2. THREAD ONTO STRUT ATTACHING BOLTS, ABOVE NUTS – 3 PER SIDE

Fig. 6 Engine support fixture installation

17. Slide transaxle away from engine, lower jack and guide right drive axle from transaxle housing bore. Remove transaxle from vehicle.
18. Reverse procedure to install. **When installing transaxle, guide the right drive axle into transaxle bore as transaxle is being raised. The right drive axle cannot be installed after the transaxle is connected to engine.**

MODELS w/MUNCIE TRANSAXLE (NEW VENTURE)

1. Disconnect battery ground cable.
2. Install engine support fixture, **Fig. 6.** Connect fixture hook to engine lift ring and raise engine enough to relieve weight from engine mounts. The engine support fixture must be positioned in the center of the cowl and the attaching parts properly tightened before supporting engine.
3. Remove left sound insulator from under instrument panel, then disconnect clutch master cylinder pushrod from clutch pedal.
4. Remove air cleaner and air intake duct assembly.
5. Remove clutch slave cylinder from transaxle brace and position aside.
6. Remove transaxle mount through bolt.
7. Raise and support vehicle, then remove two exhaust crossover bolts from right side manifold.
8. Lower vehicle, then remove left side exhaust manifold.
9. Remove shift cables, then upper transaxle to engine attaching bolts.
10. Raise and support vehicle, then remove left tire and wheel assembly.
11. Remove left front inner splash shield, then the transaxle strut and bracket.
12. Drain transaxle into suitable container, then remove clutch housing cover bolts.
13. Disconnect speedometer wire connector.
14. Remove stabilizer bar from left side suspension support and control arm.
15. Remove left side suspension support attaching bolts, then swing support aside.
16. Install boot protectors at drive axles, then disengage both drive axles at transaxle. Remove left drive axle from transaxle housing bore.
17. Attach the transaxle case to a suitable jack, then remove transaxle to engine mounting bolts.
18. Slide transaxle away from engine, lower jack and guide right drive axle from transaxle housing bore. Remove transaxle from vehicle.
19. Reverse procedure to install. **When installing transaxle, guide the right drive axle into transaxle bore as transaxle is being raised. The right drive axle cannot be installed after the transaxle is connected to engine.**

TIGHTENING SPECIFICATIONS*

NOTE: Torque Specifications Are For Clean And Lightly Lubricated Threads Only.

Year	Component	Torque/ft. lbs.
1988–91	**Actuator Cylinder Support To Transaxle**	37
	Alternate Oil Level Check/Fill Plug	18
	Back-up Light Switch Assembly To Transaxle	①
	Clutch Actuator Cylinder Nut	16
	Clutch Cover To Flywheel Bolt	③
	Clutch Housing Cover To Transaxle	89②
	Clutch Master Cylinder Nut	20
	Clutch Pedal Bracket Nut	20
	Clutch Start Switch Nuts	53②
	Electronic Speed Sensor Retainer	7

Continued

TIGHTENING SPECIFICATIONS* —Continued

Year	Component	Torque/ft. lbs.
1988-91 (Con't.)	Fluid Drain Plug	18
	Fluid Reservoir Bolt	80②
	Fluid Reservoir Bracket Bolt	16
	Front Transaxle Strut To Body Bolt	44
	Front Transaxle Strut To Transaxle	44
	Rear Mount Bracket To Mount	72
	Rear Mount Bracket To Transaxle	44
	Rear Transaxle Mount To Body Bolt	41
	Rear Transaxle Mount To Body Nuts	24
	Shift Cable Grommet To Shroud	12②
	Shift Control To Floor	18
	Shift Control Box To Transaxle	13
	Shift Linkage Retainer To Transaxle Case	17
	Shift Retainer To Transaxle Case	90②
	Shift Shaft To Lever Nut	61
	Speedometer To Vehicle Speed Sensor	84②
	Transaxle Shift Cable Bracket To Cables	18
	Transaxle Shift Lever To Cable Stud	18
	Transaxle To Engine Bolts	55

①—Muncie, 24 ft. lbs.; Isuzu, 7 ft. lbs.
②—Inch lbs.
③—Except 2.3L/4-138, 18 ft. lbs.; 2.3L/4-138, 22 ft. lbs.

Rear Axle & Suspension

INDEX

DESCRIPTION

This rear suspension is a semi-independent type suspension consisting of an axle assembly with trailing arms and twisting cross beam, coil springs and double action shock absorbers. A stabilizer bar is available and is attached to the inside of the axle beam and to the lower end of the control arms. A single unit hub and bearing assembly is bolted to each end of the axle assembly. The hub and bearing assembly is a sealed, nonserviceable unit and must be replaced as an assembly.

REAR AXLE
REPLACE

1. Raise vehicle and support vehicle. Support rear suspension with suitable jack.

2. Disconnect stabilizer bar at axle assembly, if equipped.
3. Remove rear wheel assembly and brake drum. **Do not hammer on brake drum since damage to bearings may result.**
4. Remove shock absorber to lower mounting bracket attaching bolts, then disconnect shock absorbers from axle assembly, **Figs. 1 and 2.**
5. Disconnect parking brake cable and brake lines at axle brackets.
6. Carefully lower rear axle assembly and remove coil springs and insulators.
7. Remove control arm to underbody bracket bolts, then lower the axle assembly and remove from vehicle.
8. Remove hub to rear axle attaching bolts, then the hubs, bearings and backing plates from rear axle assembly.
9. Reverse procedure to install and bleed brake system.

HUB & BEARING ASSEMBLY
REPLACE

1. Raise and support vehicle, then remove wheel and tire assembly and brake drum. **Do not hammer brake drum since damage to bearing may result.**
2. Remove four hub/bearing assembly to rear axle attaching bolts, then the hub/bearing assembly from axle. **The upper rear hub attaching bolt may not clear brake shoe when removing hub and bearing assembly. Partially remove hub and bearing assembly prior to removing this bolt.**
3. Reverse procedure to install. Torque hub to axle attaching bolts to specifications. **Use care not to drop hub/bearing assembly since damage to bearing may result.**

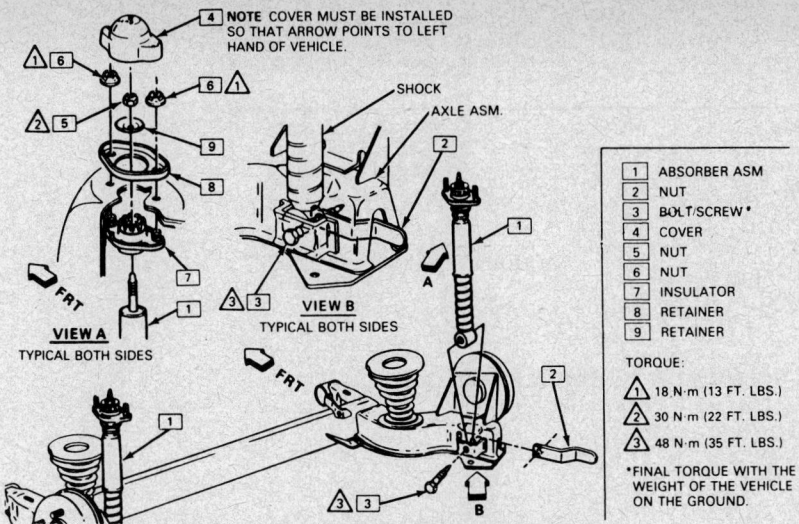

Fig. 1   Rear suspension. Corsica

1	ABSORBER ASM
2	NUT
3	BOLT/SCREW *
4	COVER
5	NUT
6	NUT
7	INSULATOR
8	RETAINER
9	RETAINER

TORQUE:

⚠1 18 N·m (13 FT. LBS.)
⚠2 30 N·m (22 FT. LBS.)
⚠3 48 N·m (35 FT. LBS.)

*FINAL TORQUE WITH THE
WEIGHT OF THE VEHICLE
ON THE GROUND.

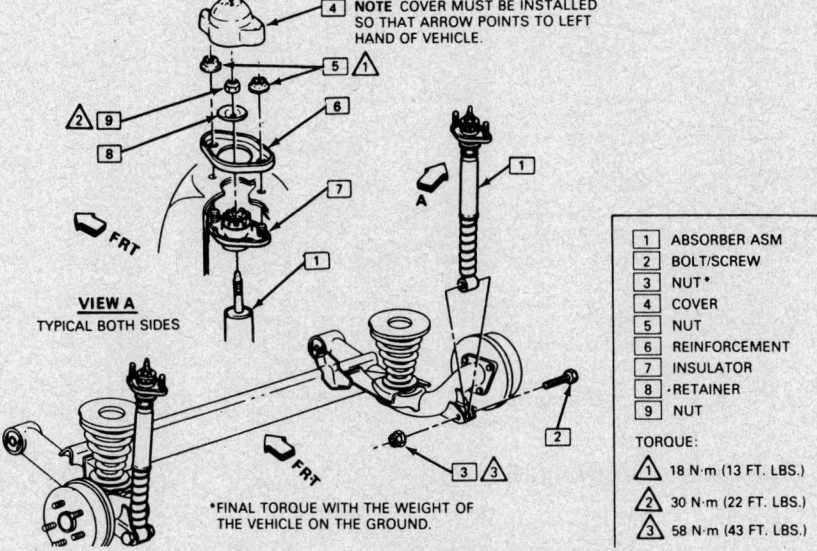

Fig. 2   Rear suspension. Beretta

1	ABSORBER ASM
2	BOLT/SCREW
3	NUT *
4	COVER
5	NUT
6	REINFORCEMENT
7	INSULATOR
8	•RETAINER
9	NUT

TORQUE:

⚠1 18 N·m (13 FT. LBS.)
⚠2 30 N·m (22 FT. LBS.)
⚠3 58 N·m (43 FT. LBS.)

*FINAL TORQUE WITH THE WEIGHT OF
THE VEHICLE ON THE GROUND.

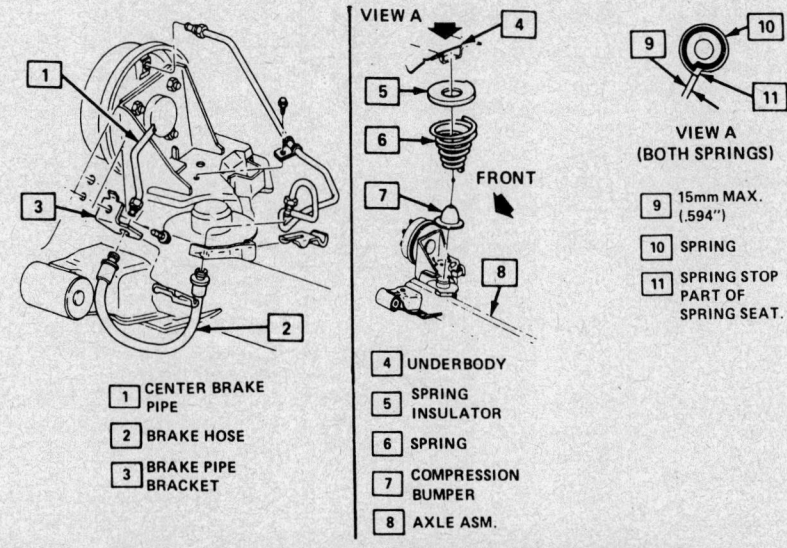

1	CENTER BRAKE PIPE
2	BRAKE HOSE
3	BRAKE PIPE BRACKET

4	UNDERBODY
5	SPRING INSULATOR
6	SPRING
7	COMPRESSION BUMPER
8	AXLE ASM.

VIEW A
(BOTH SPRINGS)

9	15mm MAX. (.594")
10	SPRING
11	SPRING STOP PART OF SPRING SEAT.

Fig. 3   Coil spring and brake line installation

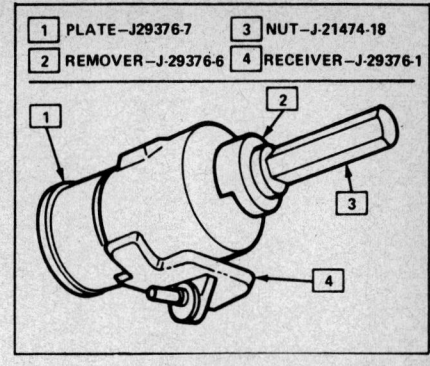

1	PLATE–J29376-7	3	NUT–J-21474-18
2	REMOVER–J-29376-6	4	RECEIVER–J-29376-1

Fig. 4   Control bushing removal

SHOCK ABSORBER
REPLACE

1. Open deck lid, then remove trim cover (if equipped) and shock absorber upper retaining nut.
2. Raise rear of vehicle and support rear axle using a suitable jack.
3. Remove shock absorber lower attaching bolt, then disconnect shock absorber from mounting bracket, **Figs. 1 and 2.** Remove shock absorber from vehicle.
4. Reverse procedure to install. Torque attaching bolts to specifications.

COIL SPRING
REPLACE

1. Raise and support rear of vehicle. Support rear axle using a suitable jack.
2. Remove wheel and tire assemblies.
3. Remove brake line bracket attaching bolts, **Fig. 3,** from frame and allow brake lines to hang freely.
4. Remove shock absorber to lower mounting bracket bolts, then disconnect shock absorbers from axle assembly. **Do not suspend rear axle by brake hoses since damage to hoses may result.**
5. Carefully lower rear axle assembly and remove springs and insulators.
6. Reverse procedure to install. Position ends of upper coil in seat of body and within limits shown in **Fig. 3.**

CONTROL ARM BUSHING
REPLACE

1. Raise and support rear of vehicle.
2. Remove wheel and tire assembly, then support body with suitable jack stands
3. Remove brake line bracket to body attaching screws from both sides.
4. Remove control arm to mounting bracket attaching nut, bolt and washer, then allow control arm to rotate downward.

| 1 | RECEIVER J29376-1 | 3 | NUT J-21474-18 | 5 | BUSHING MUST BE INDEXED IN INSTALLER, AND INSTALLER ARROW MUST ALIGN WITH ARROW ON RECEIVER FOR PROPER BUSHING INSTALLATION. |
| 2 | PLATE J29376-7 | 4 | INSTALLER J29376-4 | | |

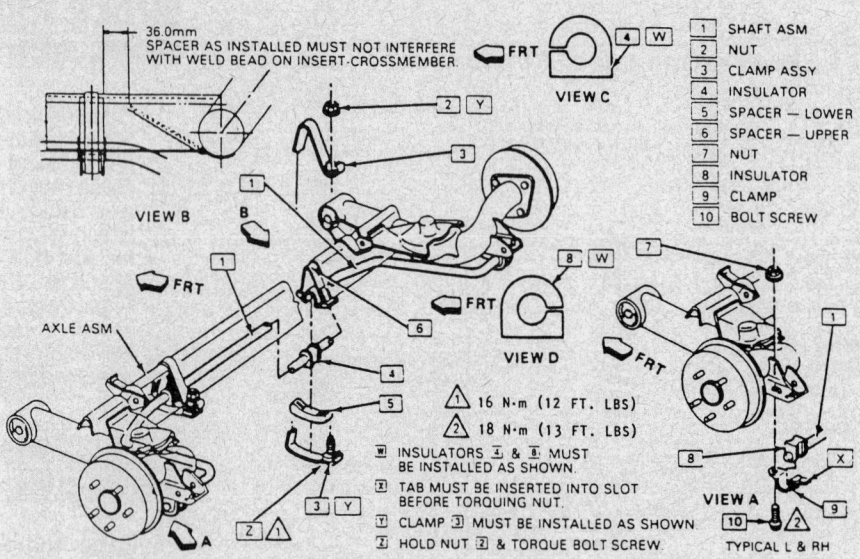

Fig. 5 Control arm bushing installation

Fig. 6 Stabilizer assembly. Beretta

5. The bushing can now be replaced using tools shown in **Figs. 4 and 5.** When installing bushing, the arrow on the installer must align with arrow on the receiver, **Fig. 4.**

6. Reverse procedure to complete installation. **The control arm attaching bolt must be torqued to specifications after vehicle is lowered to floor and is in its standing height position.**

STABILIZER ASSEMBLY
REPLACE

1. Raise vehicle on hoist and support body with jack stands.
2. Remove nuts and bolts at both the axle and control arm attachments and remove bracket, insulator and stabilizer shaft, **Figs. 6 and 7.**
3. Reverse procedure to install.

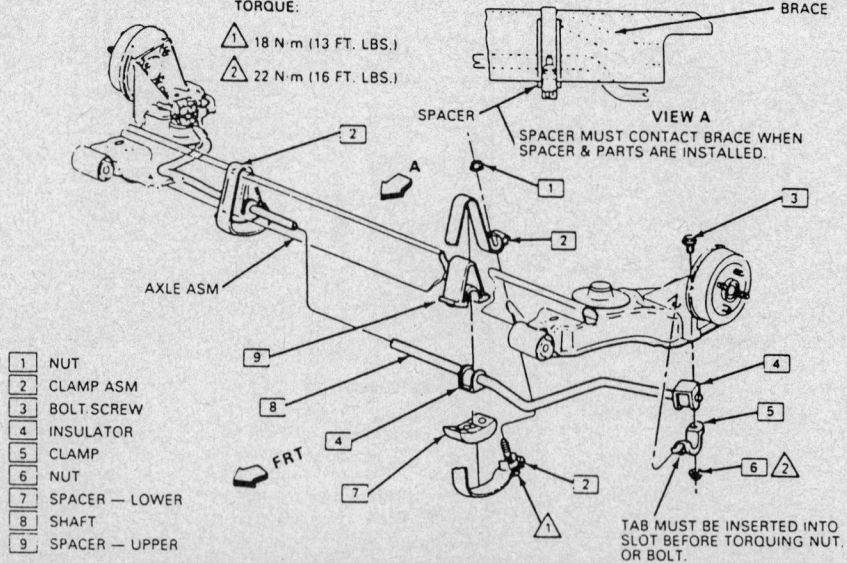

1	NUT
2	CLAMP ASM
3	BOLT SCREW
4	INSULATOR
5	CLAMP
6	NUT
7	SPACER — LOWER
8	SHAFT
9	SPACER — UPPER

Fig. 7 Stabilizer assembly. Corsica

TIGHTENING SPECIFICATIONS

Year	Component	Torque/ft. lbs.
1988-91	Brake Line Bracket To Control Arm	11
	Brake Line Bracket To Frame	8
	Control Arm Pivot Bolts	66 ①
	Control Arm To Underbody Attaching Nut	④
	Hub To Axle	38
	Shock Absorber Lower ②	12
	Shock Absorber Lower ③	12
	Shock Absorber Upper Shaft Nut	22
	Stabilizer Bar To Axle	12
	Stabilizer Bar To Control Arm	13
	Stabilizer Shaft To Rear Axle Assembly Nut ②	103
	Upper Shock Mount	13
	Wheel Lug Nuts	100

① —Torque control arm attaching bolt after vehicle is lowered to floor and is in its' standing height position.
② —Beretta
③ —Corsica
④ —52 ft. lbs., plus 120° rotation.

Front Suspension & Steering

INDEX

DESCRIPTION

The front suspension, **Figs. 1 through 3,** on these vehicles is of the MacPherson strut design. The lower control arms pivot from the lower side rails through rubber bushings. The upper end of the strut is isolated by a rubber mount incorporating a nonserviceable bearing for wheel turning. The tie rods connect to the steering arm on the strut, below the spring seat. The lower end of the steering knuckle pivots on a ball stud which is retained to the lower control arm by rivets and is secured to the steering knuckle with a nut and cotter pin. The sealed wheel bearings are integral with the hub and are serviced as an assembly.

WHEEL BEARING
REPLACE
REMOVAL

1. Loosen hub nut with vehicle on ground.
2. Raise and support vehicle, then remove front wheel.
3. Install drive axle protective boot cover tool No. J-28712 or equivalent.
4. Remove hub nut.
5. Remove brake caliper from support and suspend caliper from flame with a length of wire. Do not suspend caliper by brake hose.
6. Remove brake rotor.
7. Remove three hub and bearing attaching bolts, then the splash shield. If the old bearing is being reinstalled, mark attaching bolts and corresponding holes for reinstallation, **Fig 4.**
8. Using front hub spindle remover tool No. J-28733 or equivalent, remove bearing from steering knuckle, **Fig. 5. If excessive corrosion is present, ensure that bearing is loose in the knuckle before using puller tool.**
9. If installing new bearing, replace steering knuckle seal. **Do not move drive axle until hub nut is installed and torqued to specifications.**

INSTALLATION

1. Clean and inspect bearing mating surfaces and steering knuckle bore for dirt, nicks and burrs.
2. If installing new steering knuckle seal, apply grease to seal and knuckle bore, then press seal into steering knuckle.
3. Push bearing onto axle shaft, then install splash shield and hub to steering knuckle attaching bolts. Torque attaching bolts to specifications. Install hub to axle retaining nut and apply a partial **torque** of 74 ft. lbs., **Fig. 6.**
4. Install rotor, brake caliper and wheel assembly.
5. Lower vehicle and **torque** hub nut to 191 ft. lbs.

LOWER BALL JOINT
REPLACE

1. Raise and support vehicle, then remove wheel and tire.
2. Locate center of rivet body and mark with a center punch.

3. Using a 1/8 inch drill, drill pilot holes completely through the rivets. Using a 1/2 inch drill, drill final holes through rivets to ensure fitting of new ball joint.
4. Remove ball joint stud retaining nut, then, using ball joint separator tool No. J-29330, separate ball joint from steering knuckle. Remove ball joint from lower control arm.
5. Assemble new ball joint to lower control arm with bolts provided in service package, **Fig. 7,** and torque bolts to specifications.
6. Insert ball joint stud into steering knuckle and torque nut to specifications.
7. Install wheel and tire, check toe setting and adjust as required.

LOWER CONTROL ARM & BUSHING
REPLACE

1. Raise and support vehicle, then remove wheel and tire.
2. Disconnect stabilizer bar at lower control arm and control arm support.
3. Using ball joint separator tool No. J-29330, separate ball joint from steering knuckle.
4. Remove control arm support to chassis retaining bolts and remove control arm support and control arm as an assembly.
5. Separate control arm from support, then using tools shown in **Fig. 8,** remove bushings from control arm.
6. Lubricate new bushings and install into control arm using tools shown in **Fig. 8.**
7. Attach lower control arm to control arm support and torque pivot bolts to specifications.
8. Install control arm support to chassis, using attaching bolt tightening sequence shown in **Fig. 9.** Torque bolts to specifications.
9. Reverse procedure to complete installation. Check wheel alignment.

STEERING KNUCKLE
REPLACE

1. Raise and support vehicle, then remove wheel and tire.
2. Remove front hub and bearing as outlined under Wheel Bearing, Replace procedure.
3. Using ball joint separator tool No. J-29330, separate ball joint from steering knuckle.
4. Remove strut to steering knuckle attaching bolts, then disconnect strut from steering knuckle.
5. Assemble strut to new steering knuckle and install attaching bolts finger tight.
6. Insert ball joint stud into steering knuckle and torque stud nut to specifications.
7. Torque strut to steering knuckle attaching bolts to specifications.
8. Reverse removal procedure to complete installation.

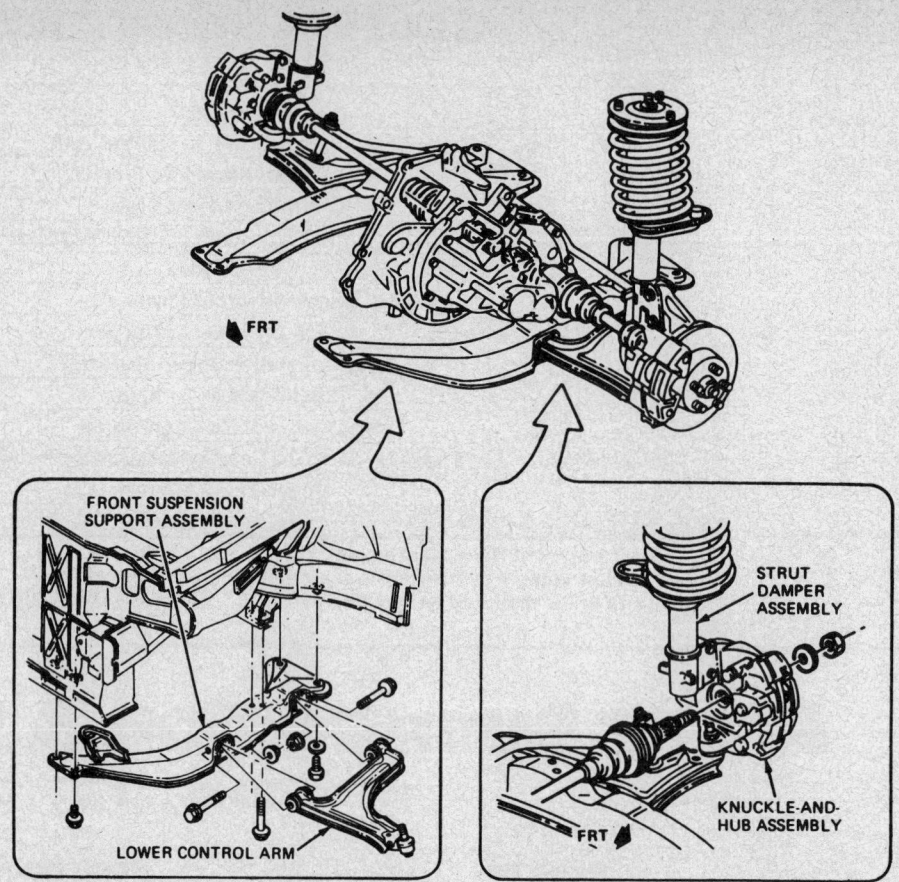

Fig. 1   Front suspension

STABILIZER BAR & BUSHINGS
REPLACE

1. Disconnect battery ground cable.
2. Install engine support tool No. J-28467 or equivalent.
3. Raise and support vehicle, allowing control arms to hang free.
4. Remove left front tire and wheel assembly.
5. Disconnect stabilizer bar from arms, then from support assemblies.
6. Loosen front support attaching bolts, then remove rear and center support bolts. Allow supports to drop down enough to remove stabilizer bar, **Fig. 10.**
7. Reverse procedure to install. Before tightening any attaching bolts, ensure stabilizer bar is centered in chassis. Refer to **Fig. 10,** for torque specifications.

STRUT ASSEMBLY
REPLACE

1. Raise hood and remove strut protective cap and three strut to body attaching nuts **Fig. 11.**
2. Raise and support vehicle, allowing suspension to hang freely.

3. Remove wheel and tire, then install drive axle protective cover, tool No. J-28712 or equivalent.
4. Using steering linkage puller tool No. J-24319 or equivalent, disconnect tie rod from strut assembly.
5. Remove strut to steering knuckle attaching bolts, then remove strut from vehicle.
6. Reverse procedure to install. Position flats of strut mounting bolts as shown in **Fig. 12.** Torque all nuts and bolts to specifications.

STRUT ASSEMBLY SERVICE

DISASSEMBLY

Care must be taken not to damage special coating on coil springs. If special coating is damaged, coil spring damage could occur.

1. Clamp strut compressor tool No. J-26584 in a suitable vise.
2. Place strut assembly in compressor tool and install bottom adapter tool No. J-26584-400, making sure that adapter captures strut and locating pins are fully engaged, **Fig. 13.**
3. Position top adapter tool No. J-26584-430 on strut cap, aligning mounting holes as necessary.
4. Rotate compressor forcing screw clockwise until top support flange contacts top adapter. Continue rotat-

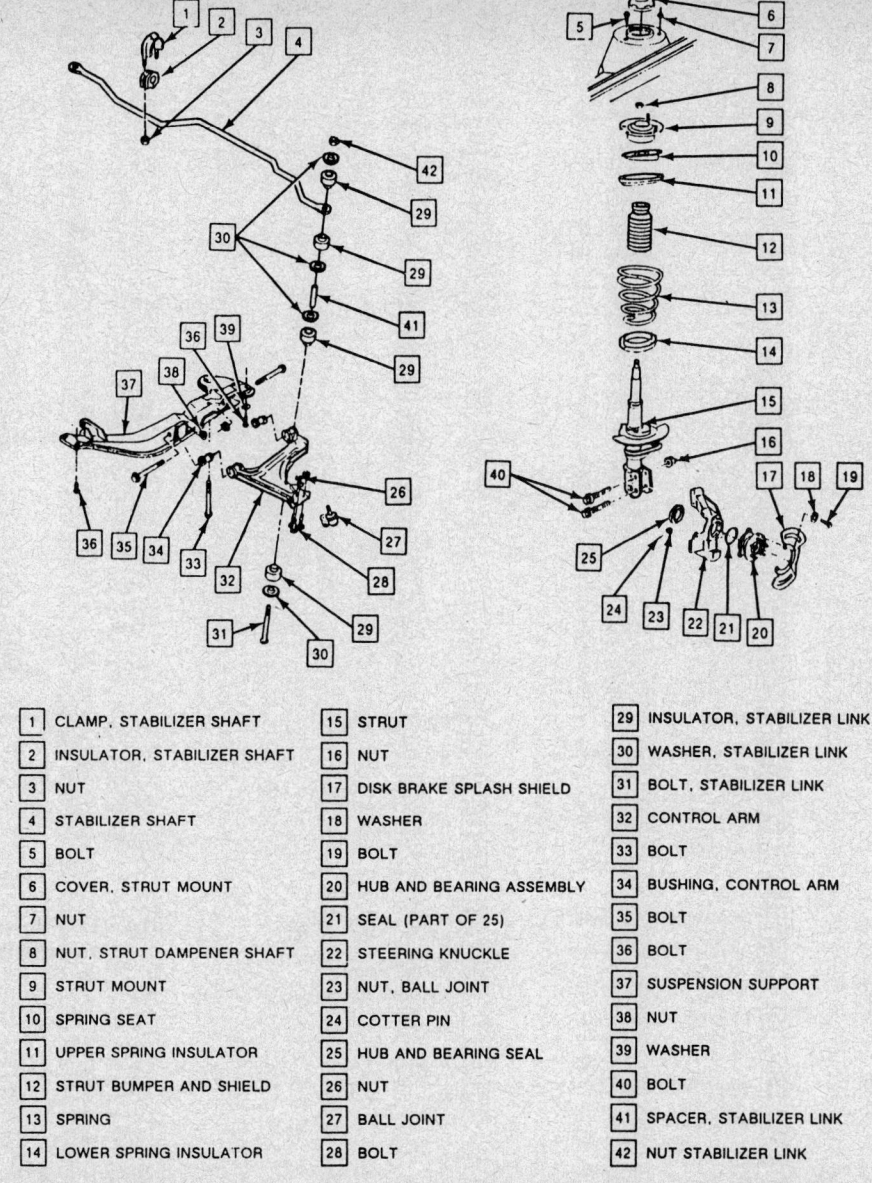

1	CLAMP, STABILIZER SHAFT	15	STRUT	29	INSULATOR, STABILIZER LINK
2	INSULATOR, STABILIZER SHAFT	16	NUT	30	WASHER, STABILIZER LINK
3	NUT	17	DISK BRAKE SPLASH SHIELD	31	BOLT, STABILIZER LINK
4	STABILIZER SHAFT	18	WASHER	32	CONTROL ARM
5	BOLT	19	BOLT	33	BOLT
6	COVER, STRUT MOUNT	20	HUB AND BEARING ASSEMBLY	34	BUSHING, CONTROL ARM
7	NUT	21	SEAL (PART OF 25)	35	BOLT
8	NUT, STRUT DAMPENER SHAFT	22	STEERING KNUCKLE	36	BOLT
9	STRUT MOUNT	23	NUT, BALL JOINT	37	SUSPENSION SUPPORT
10	SPRING SEAT	24	COTTER PIN	38	NUT
11	UPPER SPRING INSULATOR	25	HUB AND BEARING SEAL	39	WASHER
12	STRUT BUMPER AND SHIELD	26	NUT	40	BOLT
13	SPRING	27	BALL JOINT	41	SPACER, STABILIZER LINK
14	LOWER SPRING INSULATOR	28	BOLT	42	NUT STABILIZER LINK

Fig. 2 Exploded view of front suspension. Except GTZ models

ing forcing screws until strut spring is compressed to approximately ½ its height. **Do not bottom the spring or strut damper rod.**
5. Remove damper top nut, then place alignment rod on strut shaft. Use alignment rod to guide shock shaft through spring cap during removal.
6. Remove strut components, then relieve compressor tension.

ASSEMBLY

1. Perform Steps 1 & 2 as outlined in the Disassembly procedure.
2. Position spring on strut, making sure spring is properly seated on bottom spring plate.
3. Install shields, bumpers and insulators on spring seat, then install coil spring seat on top of spring, **Fig. 14**.
4. Install bearing cap on spring seat, ensuring they are centered together and properly aligned.

5. Rotate spring as necessary to have upper end of spring located within 10 mm from end of groove in upper insulator and lower end of spring located 10-15 mm from end of groove in lower insulator.
6. Position top adapter tool No. J-26584-430 on strut cap, then engage compressor slightly. Pull up strut rod to its full extension and clamp in place with clamp tool No. J-34013-20 or equivalent.
7. Insert alignment rod tool No. J-34013-27 or equivalent through bearing and spring cap and position on top of strut rod. Compress spring slowly while guiding strut rod through bearing cap with alignment rod.
8. Continue compressing spring until one inch of strut rod is above bearing cap. Install strut attaching nut and torque to specifications.
9. Remove strut rod clamp, then release

tension on coil spring and remove compressor.

SERVICE BULLETIN: Lead/Pull felt in direction of turn, 1988 Beretta and Corsica models only. On these models, this condition may be caused by front spring wind up. This condition is caused by front strut mounts assembled with bearings exhibiting high frictional characteristics. To correct this condition both front strut mounts must be replaced.

POWER STEERING GEAR
REPLACE

1. Disconnect battery ground cable.
2. Remove lefthand sound insulator.
3. Remove steering column coupling upper pinch bolt.
4. Remove hydraulic line retainer, then disconnect pump pressure and return lines from steering gear.

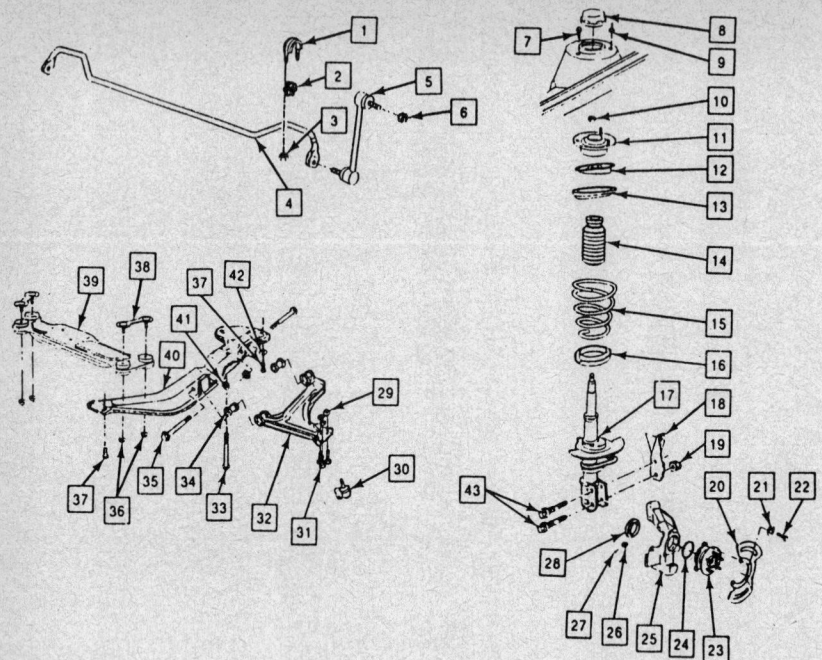

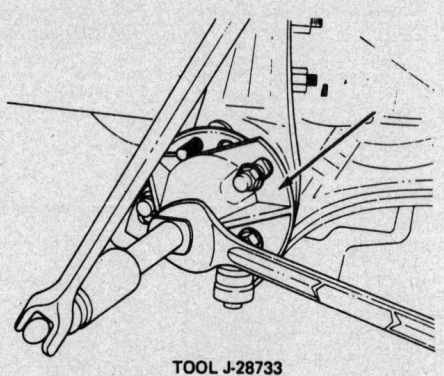

Fig. 4   Front hub & wheel bearing assembly

1 CLAMP, STABLIZER SHAFT	16 LOWER SPRING INSULATOR	31 BOLT
2 INSULATOR, STABILIZER SHAFT	17 STRUT	32 CONTROL ARM
3 NUT	18 BRACKET, STABILIZER LINK	33 BOLT
4 STABILIZER SHAFT	19 NUT	34 BUSHING, CONTROL ARM
5 STABILIZER LINK	20 DISK BRAKE SPLASH SHIELD	35 BOLT
6 NUT	21 WASHER	36 NUT
7 BOLT	22 BOLT	37 BOLT
8 COVER, STRUT MOUNT	23 HUB AND BEARING ASSEMBLY	38 PLATE, FRONT ENGINE MOUNT CROSSMEMBER
9 NUT	24 SEAL (PART OF)	39 CROSSMEMBER, FRONT ENGINE MOUNT
10 NUT, STRUT DAMPENER SHAFT	25 STEERING KNUCKLE	40 SUSPENSION SUPPORT
11 STRUT MOUNT	26 NUT, BALL JOINT	41 NUT
12 SPRING SEAT	27 COTTER PIN	42 WASHER
13 UPPER SPRING INSULATOR	28 HUB AND BEARING SEAL	43 BOLT
14 STRUT BUMPER AND SHIELD	29 NUT	
15 SPRING	30 BALL JOINT	

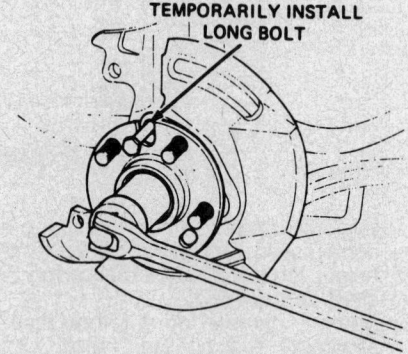

TOOL J-28733

Fig. 5   Front hub & bearing assembly removal

Fig. 3   Exploded view of front suspension. GTZ models

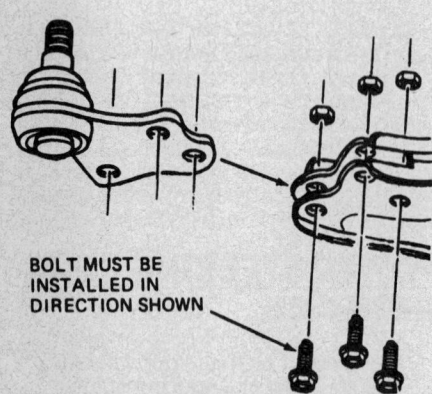

BOLT MUST BE INSTALLED IN DIRECTION SHOWN

Fig. 7   Assembling lower ball joint to lower control arm

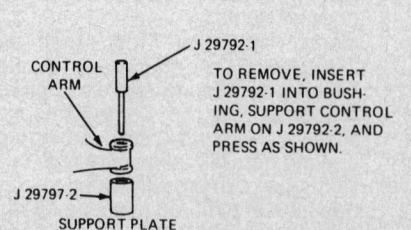

CONTROL ARM

J 29792-1

TO REMOVE, INSERT J 29792-1 INTO BUSHING, SUPPORT CONTROL ARM ON J 29792-2, AND PRESS AS SHOWN.

J 29797-2

SUPPORT PLATE

TEMPORARILY INSTALL LONG BOLT

Fig. 6   Hub nut installation

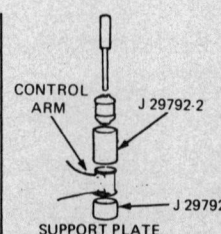

CONTROL ARM

J 29792-2

TO INSTALL, SUPPORT CONTROL ARM ON J 29792-3, PLACE BUSHING INTO J 29792-2, AND PRESS BUSING INTO CONTROL ARM USING J 29792-1. LUBRICATE BUSHING.

J 29792-3

SUPPORT PLATE

Fig. 8   Replacing lower control arm bushing

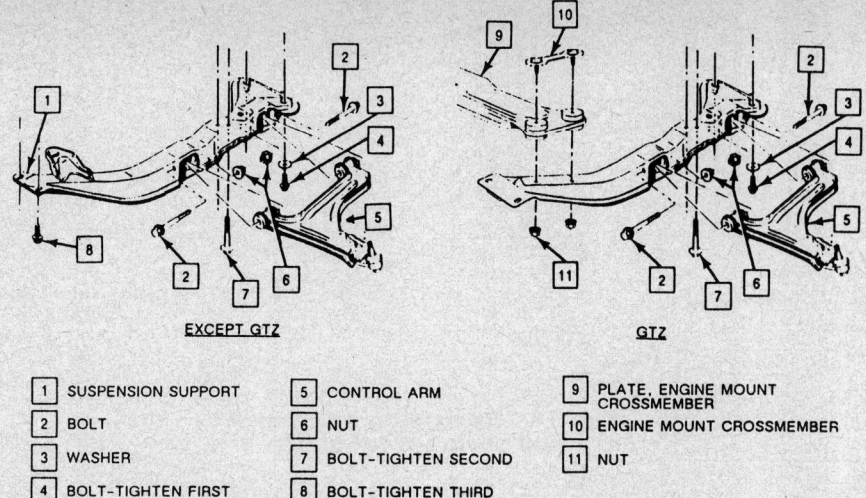

EXCEPT GTZ

GTZ

1	SUSPENSION SUPPORT	5	CONTROL ARM	9	PLATE, ENGINE MOUNT CROSSMEMBER
2	BOLT	6	NUT	10	ENGINE MOUNT CROSSMEMBER
3	WASHER	7	BOLT-TIGHTEN SECOND	11	NUT
4	BOLT-TIGHTEN FIRST	8	BOLT-TIGHTEN THIRD		

Fig. 9 Replacing lower control arm

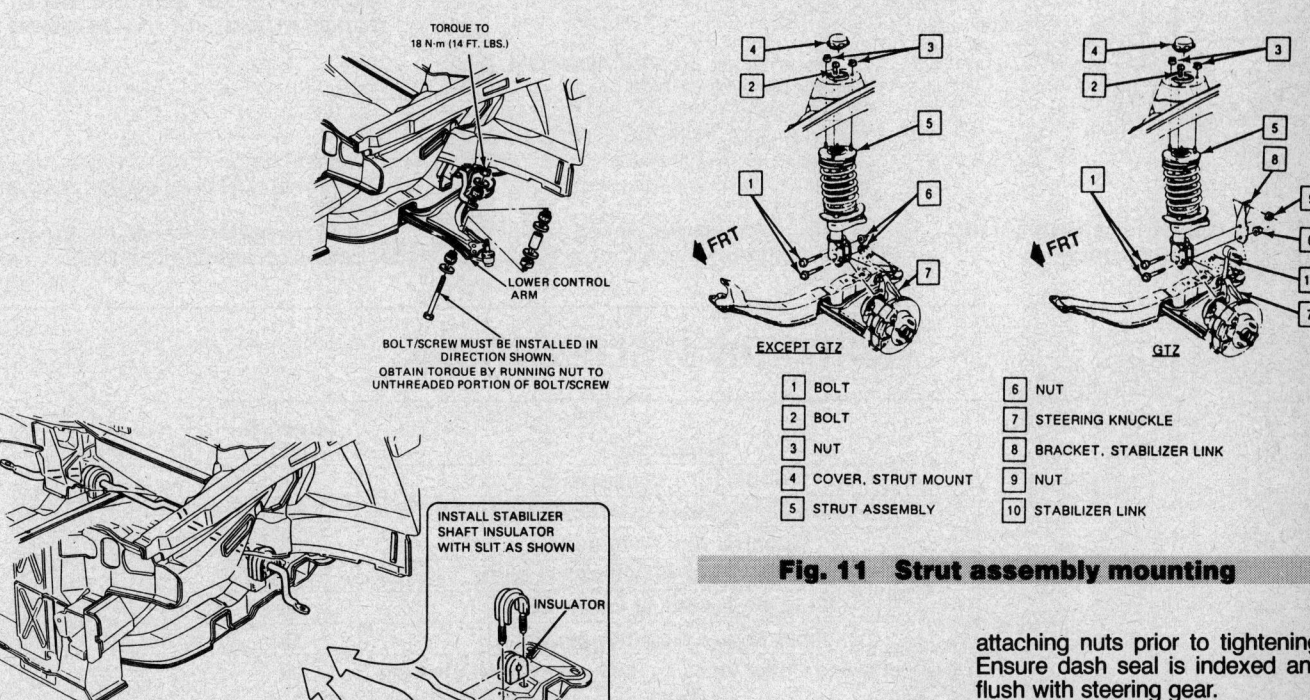

TORQUE TO 18 N·m (14 FT. LBS.)

LOWER CONTROL ARM

BOLT/SCREW MUST BE INSTALLED IN DIRECTION SHOWN.
OBTAIN TORQUE BY RUNNING NUT TO UNTHREADED PORTION OF BOLT/SCREW

EXCEPT GTZ

GTZ

1	BOLT	6	NUT
2	BOLT	7	STEERING KNUCKLE
3	NUT	8	BRACKET, STABILIZER LINK
4	COVER, STRUT MOUNT	9	NUT
5	STRUT ASSEMBLY	10	STABILIZER LINK

Fig. 11 Strut assembly mounting

INSTALL STABILIZER SHAFT INSULATOR WITH SLIT AS SHOWN

INSULATOR

SUPPORT

25 N·m (18 FT. LBS.)

HOLD STABILIZER SHAFT AT APPROX. 55.0mm FROM BOTTOM OF SUPPORT ARM WHEN TIGHTENING STABILIZER SHAFT INSULATORS.

55mm

SUPPORT

Fig. 10 Stabilizer bar installation

5. Raise and support vehicle.
6. Remove front wheel and tire assemblies.
7. Disconnect tie rods from steering knuckles.
8. Lower vehicle, then remove steering gear mounting clamps.
9. Move steering gear forward, then remove steering column coupling lower pinch bolt.

10. Remove steering column coupling and dash seal from steering gear.
11. Raise and support vehicle, then remove steering gear through left front wheel opening.
12. Reverse procedure to install. Torque all bolts to specifications noting the following:
  a. When installing steering gear, attach clamps and finger tighten all

attaching nuts prior to tightening. Ensure dash seal is indexed and flush with steering gear.

POWER STEERING PUMP REPLACE

EXCEPT 2.3L/4-138 ENGINES

1. Disconnect battery ground cable.
2. Place suitable container under pump to catch fluid.
3. Disconnect pressure and return lines at pump, then plug open ends at hoses and pump.
4. Remove auxiliary drive belt.
5. Working through holes in pump pulley, remove pump attaching bolts.
6. Remove power steering pump.
7. Reverse procedure to install.

2.3L/4-138 ENGINES

1. Disconnect negative battery cable.

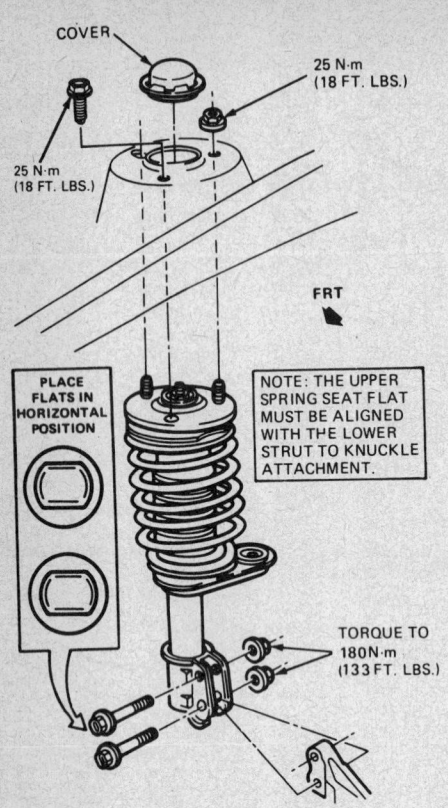

Fig. 12 Installing strut assembly

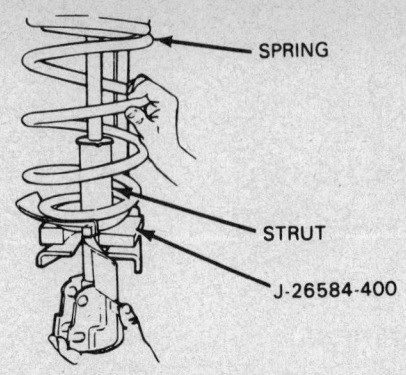

Fig. 13 Removing damper & coil spring from strut

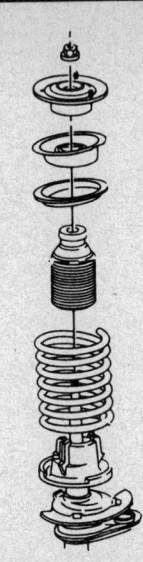

Fig. 14 Strut coil spring & upper mounting installation

2. Remove air cleaner assembly, then the pump drive belt.
3. Disconnect power brake booster vacuum line, then the power steering pressure switch electrical connector.
4. Remove pump bracket bolts and bracket.
5. Disconnect pressure and return lines at pump, then plug open ends at hoses and pump.
6. Remove pump pivot bracket bolts and bracket.
7. Remove power steering pump.
8. Reverse procedure to install.

TIGHTENING SPECIFICATIONS

Year	Component	Torque/ft. lbs.
1988-91	Ball Joint To Control Arm	50
	Ball Joint To Steering Knuckle Nuts	26①
	Control Arm Pivot Bolts	63
	Control To Suspension Support Bolts	44①
	Front Engine Mount Lower Nuts	30
	Front Engine Mount Upper Nut	55
	Gear Inlet And Outlet Pipes To Rack And Pinion Steering Gear	20
	Gear Inlet Pipe To Pump	18
	Hub And Bearing Assembly Bolts	70
	Hub To Axle Nut	192
	Hub To Steering Knuckle	70
	Inner Tie Rod To Rack And Pinion Steering Gear Bolts	66
	Outer Tie Rod End Nuts	55
	Pinion Locknut	26
	Pivot Bracket To Power Steering Pump Bolts ④	23
	Power Steering Pump O-ring Union Fitting	55
	Rack And Pinion Steering Gear Mounting Stud	15
	Stabilizer Link Nuts	③
	Stabilizer Shaft Clamp Nuts	17
	Steering Column Pinch Bolts	②
	Steering Gear Clamps	28
	Strut Assembly To Body Bolts	18
	Strut Rod To Bearing Cap	60

Continued

TIGHTENING SPECIFICATIONS — Continued

Year	Component	Torque/ft. lbs.
1988-91 Cont'd	Strut To Steering Knuckle	129
	Tie Rod To Steering Knuckle	44
	Wheel Lug Nuts	100

①—Plus 60° Rotation.
②—Torque upper pinch bolt to 29 ft. lbs., torque lower pinch bolt to 37 ft. lbs.
③—70 ft. lbs., GTZ models; 13 ft. lbs. except GTZ models.
④—2.3L/4-138 models.

Wheel Alignment

INDEX

FRONT WHEEL ALIGNMENT

Toe setting is the only adjustment normally required. However, in special circumstances, such as damage due to road hazard or collision, camber may be adjusted by modifying the strut assembly. Caster is not adjustable.

CAMBER ADJUSTMENT

1. Secure bottom of strut assembly in a suitable vise.
2. Enlarge bottom holes in outer flanges with a round file until holes in outer flanges match slots in inner flanges, **Fig. 1.**
3. Connect strut to steering knuckle and install bolts finger tight.
4. Grasp top of tire firmly, then move tire inboard or outboard until correct camber reading is obtained. Tighten retaining bolts enough to secure camber setting.
5. Remove wheel and tire and **torque** strut to steering knuckle retaining bolts to 133 ft. lbs.

TOE ADJUSTMENT

Toe is controlled by tie rod position. Ad-

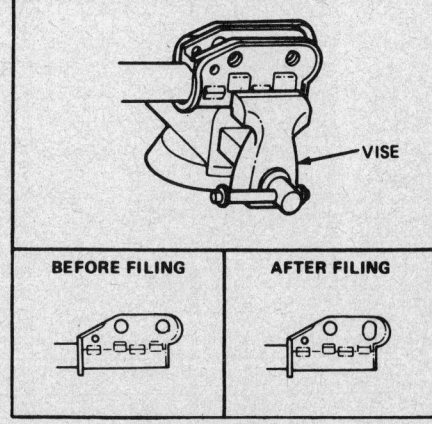

VISE

BEFORE FILING | AFTER FILING

Fig. 1   Modifying strut bracket to adjust camber

justment is made by loosening the clamp bolts at the steering knuckle end of the tie rods and rotating the adjuster to obtain proper toe setting. After correct toe setting is obtained, **torque** clamp bolts to 35 ft. lbs.

REAR WHEEL ALIGNMENT

There are no adjustments to be made on this rear suspension. If alignment is outside specifications, check for broken or bent parts and replace as necessary.

RIDE HEIGHT

Refer to **Fig. 2 and 3,** for ride height specifications and measurement locations. Check ride height as follows:
1. Ensure vehicle is on level ground.
2. Ensure tires are inflated to proper pressures.
3. Fuel tank should be full to obtain accurate readings.
4. Trunk should be empty except for spare tire and jack.
5. Bounce the car three times at the front and rear to normalize suspension.
6. Measure from lowest point on the ball joint housing to control arm bolt centerline, "D" and "Z" positions.
7. Measure from level floor to rocker panel at "J" and "K" positions.

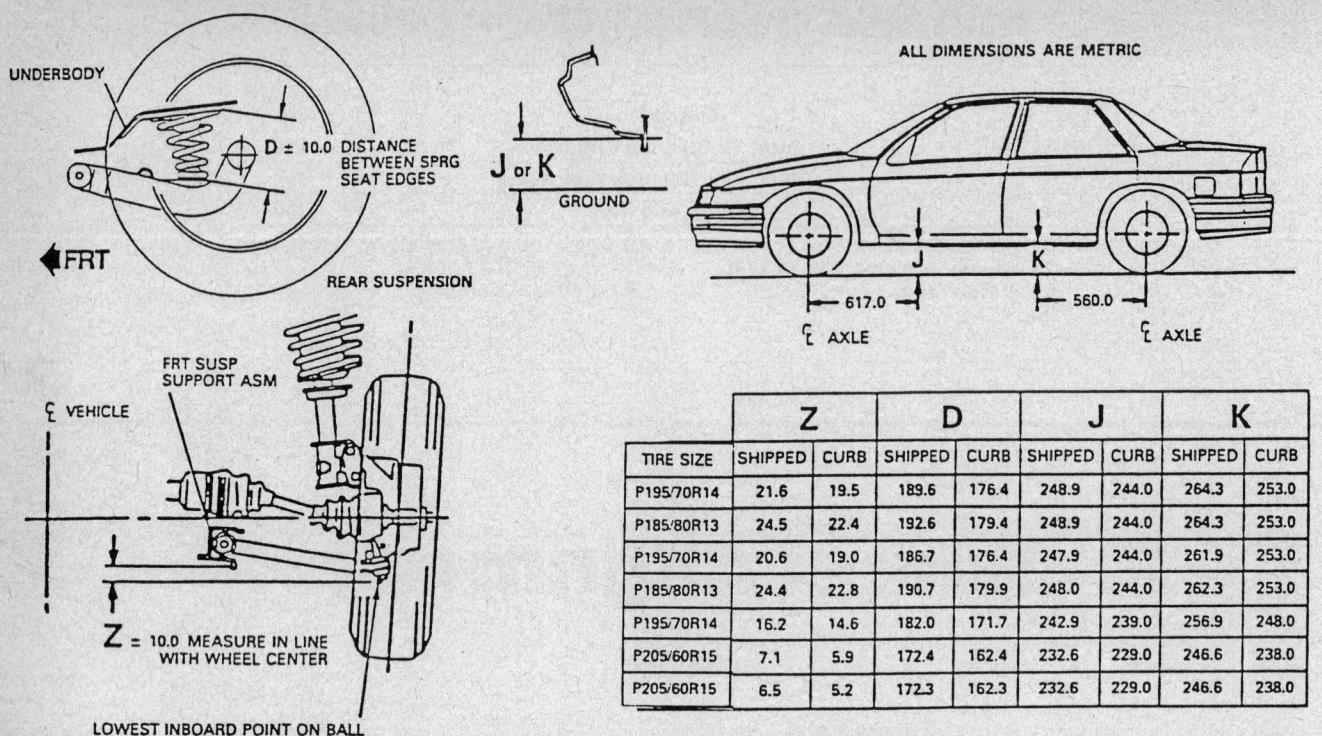

TIRE SIZE	Z		D		J		K	
	SHIPPED	CURB	SHIPPED	CURB	SHIPPED	CURB	SHIPPED	CURB
P195/70R14	21.6	19.5	189.6	176.4	248.9	244.0	264.3	253.0
P185/80R13	24.5	22.4	192.6	179.4	248.9	244.0	264.3	253.0
P195/70R14	20.6	19.0	186.7	176.4	247.9	244.0	261.9	253.0
P185/80R13	24.4	22.8	190.7	179.9	248.0	244.0	262.3	253.0
P195/70R14	16.2	14.6	182.0	171.7	242.9	239.0	256.9	248.0
P205/60R15	7.1	5.9	172.4	162.4	232.6	229.0	246.6	238.0
P205/60R15	6.5	5.2	172.3	162.3	232.6	229.0	246.6	238.0

Fig. 2   Ride height measurements & specifications. 1988–90 models

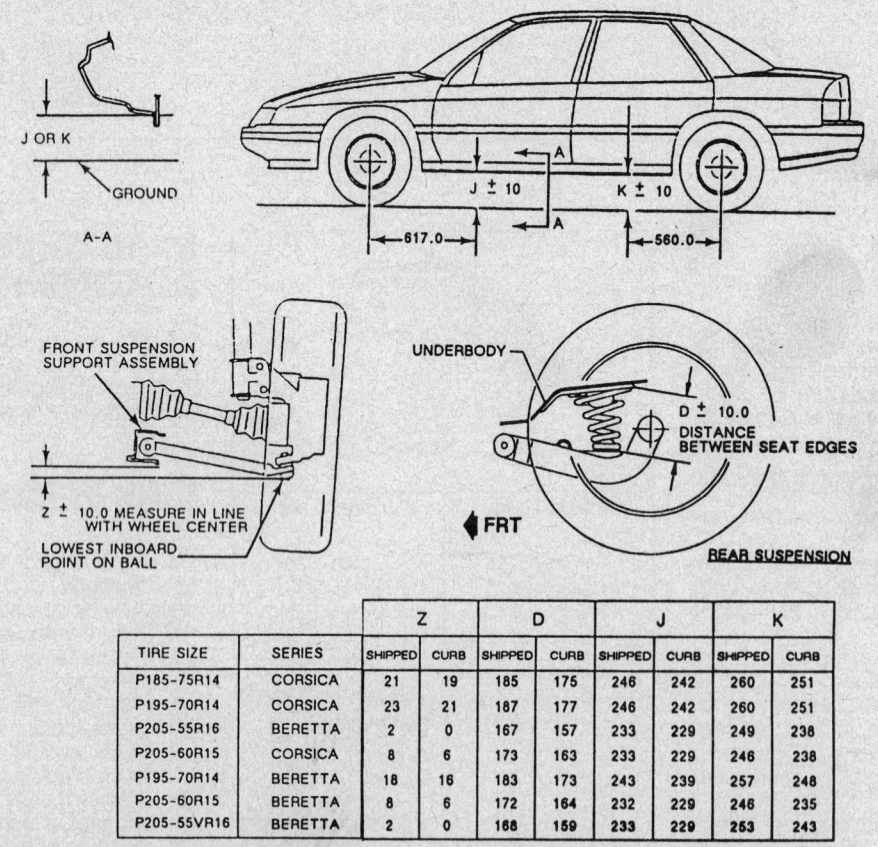

TIRE SIZE	SERIES	Z		D		J		K	
		SHIPPED	CURB	SHIPPED	CURB	SHIPPED	CURB	SHIPPED	CURB
P185-75R14	CORSICA	21	19	185	175	246	242	260	251
P195-70R14	CORSICA	23	21	187	177	246	242	260	251
P205-55R16	BERETTA	2	0	167	157	233	229	249	238
P205-60R15	CORSICA	8	6	173	163	233	229	246	238
P195-70R14	BERETTA	18	16	183	173	243	239	257	248
P205-60R15	BERETTA	8	6	172	164	232	229	246	235
P205-55VR16	BERETTA	2	0	168	159	233	229	253	243

Fig. 3   Ride height measurements & specifications. 1991 models

NOTE: Refer To Rear Of This Manual For Vehicle Manufacturer's Special Service Tool Suppliers.

Continued

INDEX OF SERVICE OPERATIONS—Continued

Specifications
GENERAL ENGINE SPECIFICATIONS

Year	Engine Liter/CID ①	VIN Code ②	Fuel Injection System	Bore and Stroke	Compression Ratio	Net H.P. @ RPM ③	Maximum Torque Ft. Lbs. @ RPM	Normal Oil Pressure Pounds
1988	2.0L/4-121 Turbo	M	M.F.I. ⑤	3.39 x 3.39	8.0	165 @ 5600	175 @ 4000	—
	2.3L/4-138	D	M.F.I. ⑤	3.62 x 3.35	9.5	150 @ 5200	160 @ 4000	30 ⑥
	2.5L/4-151	U	E.F.I. ④	4.00 x 3.00	9.0	98 @ 4800	135 @ 3200	37.5 ⑥
	3.0L/V6-181	L	M.F.I. ⑤	3.80 x 2.70	9.0	125 @ 4900	150 @ 2400	45 ⑥
1989	2.0L/4-121 Turbo	M	M.F.I. ⑤	3.39 x 3.39	8.0	165 @ 5600	175 @ 4000	—
	2.3L/4-138	D	M.F.I. ⑤	3.62 x 3.35	9.5	150 @ 5200	160 @ 4000	30 ⑥
	2.3L/4-138 H.O.	A	M.F.I. ⑤	3.62 x 3.35	10.0	180 @ 6200	160 @ 5200	15-30
	2.5L/4-151	U	E.F.I. ④	4.00 x 3.00	9.0	98 @ 4000	132 @ 2800	37.5 ⑥
	3.3L/V6-204	N	M.F.I. ⑤	3.70 x 3.16	9.0	160 @ 5200	185 @ 2000	45 ⑥
1990	2.3L/4-138	D	M.F.I. ⑤	3.62 x 3.35	9.5	150 @ 5200	160 @ 4000	30 ⑥
	2.3L/4-138 H.O.	A	M.F.I. ⑤	3.62 x 3.35	10.0	180 @ 6200	160 @ 5200	15-30
	2.5L/4-151	U	E.F.I. ④	4.00 x 3.00	9.0	110 @ 5200	135 @ 3200	37.5 ⑥
	3.3L/V6-204	N	M.F.I. ⑤	3.70 x 3.16	9.0	160 @ 5200	185 @ 2000	45 ⑥
1991	2.3L/4-138	D	M.F.I. ⑤	3.62 x 3.35	9.5	160 @ 6200	155 @ 5200	30 ⑥
	2.3L/4-138 H.O.	A	M.F.I. ⑤	3.62 x 3.35	10.0	180 @ 6200	160 @ 5200	30 ⑥
	2.5L/4-151	U	E.F.I. ④	4.00 x 3.00	8.3	110 @ 5200	135 @ 3200	26
	3.3L/V6-204	N	M.F.I. ⑤	3.70 x 3.16	9.0	160 @ 5200	185 @ 2000	60

①—CID-Cubic inch displacement.
②—The eighth digit denotes engine code.
③—Ratings are net-as installed in vehicle.
④—Electronic Fuel Injection.
⑤—Multi-Point Fuel Injection.
⑥—At 2000 RPM.

TUNE UP SPECIFICATIONS

Year & Engine/ V.I.N. Code ①	Spark Plug Gap	Firing Order Fig. ②	Ignition Timing BTDC			Curb Idle Speed ③		Fast Idle Speed		Fuel Pump Pressure
			Man. Trans.	Auto. Trans.	Mark Fig.	Man. Trans.	Auto Trans.	Man. Trans.	Auto. Trans.	
1988										
2.0L/4-121 Turbo/M	.060	C	—	—	D	④	④	④	④	35–38 ⑨
2.3L/4-138/D	.035	F	⑦	⑦	⑧	④	④	④	④	40.5–47 ⑨
2.5L/4-151/U	.060	⑩	⑦	⑦	⑧	④	④	④	④	9–13 ⑤
3.0L/V6-181/L	.045	⑥	—	⑦	⑧	—	④	—	④	40–47 ⑨
1989										
2.0L/4-121 Turbo/M	.060	C	—	—	D	④	④	④	④	35–38 ⑨
2.3L/4-138/D	.035	F	⑦	⑦	⑧	④	④	④	④	40.5–47 ⑨
2.3L/4-138 H.O./A	.035	F	⑦	—	⑧	④	—	④	—	40.5–47 ⑨
2.5L/4-151/U	.060	⑩	⑦	⑦	⑧	④	④	④	④	9–13 ⑤
3.3L/V6-204/N	.045	⑥	—	⑦	⑧	—	④	—	④	41–47 ⑨
1990										
2.3L/4-138/D	.035	F	⑦	⑦	⑧	④	④	④	④	40.5–47 ⑨
2.3L/4-138 H.O./A	.035	F	⑦	—	⑧	④	—	④	—	40.5–47 ⑨
2.5L/4-151/U	.060	⑩	⑦	⑦	⑧	④	④	④	④	9–13 ⑤
3.3L/V6-204/N	.045	⑥	—	⑦	⑧	—	④	—	④	41–47 ⑨
1991										
2.3L/4-138/D	.035	F	⑦	⑦	⑧	④	④	④	④	40.5–47 ⑨
2.3L/4-138 H.O./A	.035	F	⑦	—	⑧	④	—	④	—	40.5–47 ⑨
2.5L/4-151/U	.060	⑩	⑦	⑦	⑧	④	④	④	④	9–13 ⑤
3.3L/V6-204/N	.045	⑥	—	⑦	⑧	—	④	—	④	41–47 ⑨

① —The eighth digit of the Vehicle Identification Number (V.I.N.) denotes engine code.

② —Before removing wires from distributor cap, determine location of No. 1 wire in cap, as distributor position may have been altered from that shown at the end of this chart.

③ —On man. trans. models, idle speed is adjusted in Neutral. On auto. trans. models, idle speed is adjusted in Drive. When adjusting idle speed, set parking brake & block drive wheels.

④ —Idle speed is controlled by an idle air control (IAC) valve or an idle speed control (ISC) motor.

⑤ —Wrap shop towel around around fuel hose to steel line connection in engine compartment to prevent fuel spillage. Disconnect fuel hose from steel line & install a suitable fuel pressure gauge between hose & line. Ensure gauge connections are tight, then start engine & check fuel pressure readings.

⑥ —Cylinder numbering left to right as viewed from front of vehicle, front bank, 1, 3, 5; rear bank, 2, 4, 6. Firing order, 1-6-5-4-3-2. Two different types of coil units are used, refer to Figs. A & B for spark plug wire connections at coil unit.

⑦ —Computer controlled, no adjustment.

⑧ —Equipped with crankshaft position sensor.

⑨ —With shop towel wrapped around fuel pressure valve to prevent fuel spillage, connect a suitable fuel pressure gauge to fuel pressure valve. Check fuel pressure with ignition switch in the On position, engine not running.

⑩ —Cylinder numbering front to rear, 1, 2, 3, 4. Firing order 1-3-4-2. Refer to Fig. E for spark plug wire connections at coil unit.

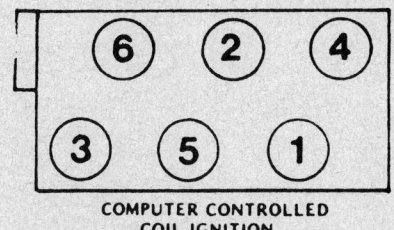

Fig. A

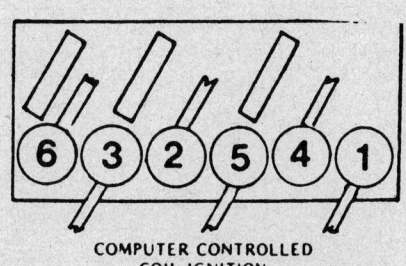

Fig. B

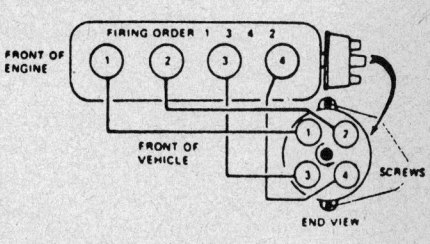

Fig. C

Continued

TUNE UP SPECIFICATIONS—Continued

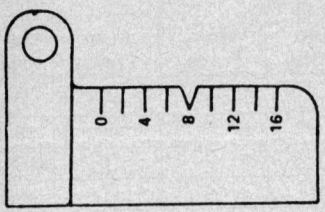

Fig. D

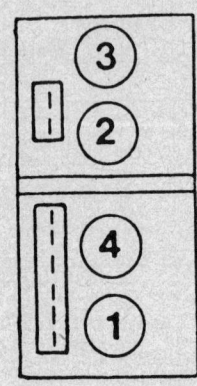

Fig. E

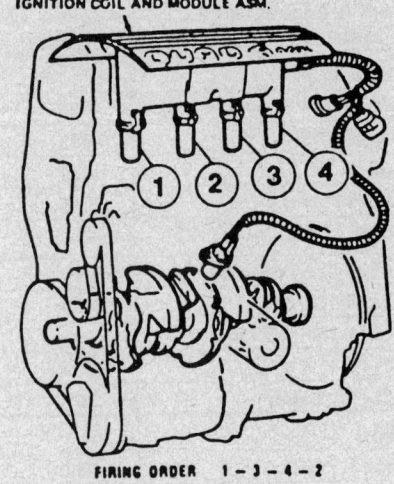

FIRING ORDER 1 — 3 — 4 — 2

Fig. F

ALTERNATOR SPECIFICATIONS

Year	Model	Rated Hot Output Amps.
1988	1101123①	85
	1101124①	100
	1101125①	85
	1101126①	100
	1101144①	85
	1101145①	100
	1101277①	85
	1101278①	100
	1101320②	74
	1101321②	74
	1101483②	74
1989	1101124①	100
	1101126①	100
	1101144①	85
	1101145①	100
	1101277①	85
	1101278①	100
	1101320②	74
1990	1101277①	85
	1101278①	100
	1101320②	74
	1101483②	74
1991	1101124①	100
	1101277①	85
	1101278①	100
	1101320②	74
	1101483②	74

①—CS130.
②—CS121.

STARTING MOTOR APPLICATIONS

Refer to "starter" section for specifications.

Year	Engine/VIN	Starter Ident. No.
1988	2.0L/4-121 Turbo/M	10455021 ①
	2.3L/4-138/D	10455015 ①
	2.5L/4-151/U	10455022 ①
	3.0L/V6-181/L	1998544 ①
1989	2.0L/4-121 Turbo/M	10455021 ①
	2.3L/4-138/D	10455015 ①
	2.3L/4-138 H.O./A	10455044 ①
	2.5L/4-151/U	10455022 ①
	3.3L/V6-204/N	10455024 ①
1990	2.3L/4-138/D	10455044 ①
	2.3L/4-138 H.O./A	10455044 ①
	2.5L/4-151/U	10455022 ①
	3.3L/V6-204/N	10455024 ②
1991	2.3L/4-138/D	10455049 ①
	2.3L/4-138 H.O./A	10455049 ①
	2.5L/4-151/U	10455022 ①
	3.3L/V6-204/N	10455024 ②

① —SD200.
② —SD250.

COOLING SYSTEM & CAPACITY DATA

Year	Model or Engine/VIN	Cooling Capacity, Qts. Less A/C	Cooling Capacity, Qts. With A/C	Radiator Cap Relief Pressure, Lbs.	Thermo. Opening Temp.	Fuel Tank Gals.	Engine Oil Refill Qts.	Transaxle Oil Manual Transaxle Pts.	Transaxle Oil Auto. Transaxle Qts. ①
1988	2.0L/4-121 Turbo/M	8	8	15	195	13.6	4 ②	④	③
	2.3L/4-138/D	7.6	7.6	15	195	13.6	4 ②	④	③
	2.5L/4-151/U	7.8	7.8	15	195	13.6	4 ②	④	③
	3.0L/V6-181/L	10.4	10.4	15	195	13.6	4 ②	④	③
1989	2.0L/4-121 Turbo/M	8	8	15	195	13.6	4 ②	4	③
	2.3L/4-138/D	7.6	7.6	15	195	13.6	4 ②	4	③
	2.3L/4-138 H.O./A	7.6	7.6	15	195	13.6	4 ②	4	③
	2.5L/4-151/U	7.8	7.8	15	195	13.6	4 ②	4	③
	3.3L/V6-204/N	10.8	10.8	15	195	13.6	4 ②	4	③
1990	2.3L/4-138/D	8	8	15	195	13.6	4 ②	4	③
	2.3L/4-138 H.O./A	7.6	7.6	15	195	13.6	4 ②	4	③
	2.5L/4-151/U	7.8	7.8	15	195	13.6	4 ②	4	③
	3.3L/V6-204/N	9.9	10.4	15	195	13.6	4 ②	4	③
1991	2.3L/4-138/D	10.4	10.4	15	195	13.6	4 ②	4	③
	2.3L/4-138 H.O./A	10.4	10.4	15	195	13.6	4 ②	4	③
	2.5L/4-151/U	10.7	10.7	15	195	13.6	4 ②	4	③
	3.3L/V6-204/N	12.7	12.7	15	195	13.6	4 ②	4	③

① —Approximate; make final check with dipstick.
② —When changing filter, additional oil may be required.
③ —Oil pan capacity, 4 qts; total capacity, 6 qts.
④ —Isuzu trans., 5.3 pts.; Muncie trans., 4.1 pts.

FRONT WHEEL ALIGNMENT SPECIFICATIONS

Year	Model	Caster Angle, Degrees		Camber Angle, Degrees				Toe-In Inch
		Limits	Desired	Limits		Desired		
				Left	Right	Left	Right	
1988	All	−.8 to +4.2	+1.7	−.2 to +1.8	−.2 to +1.8	+.8	+.8	①
1989	All	+.7 to +2.7	+1.7	②	②	③	③	④
1990	All	+.7 to +2.7	+1.7	②	②	③	③	①
1991	All	+.7 to +2.7	+1.7	−.7 to +.7	−.7 to +.7	0.0	0.0	④

① —Total toe, −.2° to +.2°.
② —Less 16 inch wheels, +.1 to +1.5; w/16 inch wheels, −.7 to +.7.
③ —Less 16 inch wheels, +.8; w/16 inch wheels, 0.
④ —Total toe, −.1 to +.1°.

REAR WHEEL ALIGNMENT SPECIFICATIONS

Year	Model	Camber Angle, Degrees				Toe-In Inch
		Limits		Desired		
		Left	Right	Left	Right	
1989	All	−.75 to +.25	−.75 to +.25	−.25	−.25	①
1990	All	−.75 to +.25	−.75 to +.25	−.25	−.25	①
1991	All	−.82 to +.32	−.82 to +.32	−.25	−.25	②

① —Total Toe, +.09 to +4.1°.
② —Total Toe, −.1 to +.1°.

Electrical

INDEX

NOTE: Refer To "Electrical" Section In Chapter 7 For Service Procedures Not Covered In This Section.

FUSE PANEL & FLASHER LOCATION

The fuse panel is located behind left side of instrument panel. Flashers are located above the fuse panel.

STARTER
REPLACE

1988–89 2.0L/4-138 TURBO ENGINE
Vehicles w/Manual Transaxle

1. Disconnect battery ground cable.

2. Disconnect wire loom strap from upper starter bolt.
3. Disconnect shift and selector lever cables at external selector lever.
4. Disconnect upper and lower transaxle control lever cable bracket and cables.
5. Disconnect drive axle support brace, starter electrical connectors and remove starter.

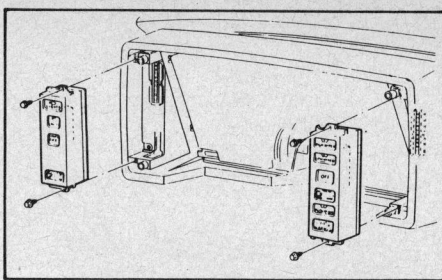

**Fig. 1   Satellite switch
removal. Skylark**

6. Reverse procedure to install.

Vehicles w/Automatic Transaxle

1. Disconnect battery ground cable.
2. Remove blower motor and disconnect starter electrical connectors.
3. Disconnect rear starter brace and wire loom from upper starter bolt.
4. Remove upper starter bolt, transaxle strut and lower starter bolt.
5. Remove starter through blower motor opening.
6. Reverse procedure to install.

1988-89 2.3L/4-138

1. Disconnect battery ground cable, then disconnect throttle body to air cleaner duct.
2. Disconnect electrical connectors from throttle position switch, idle air control valve and manifold absolute pressure sensor.
3. Disconnect vacuum harness from intake manifold.
4. Disconnect manifold absolute pressure sensor vacuum line from intake manifold, then remove cooling fan shroud attaching bolts and shroud.
5. Remove radiator upper support.
6. Disconnect electrical connector from engine cooling fan. Rotate fan attaching bracket until the two lower bracket legs are facing upward, then move fan motor toward driver's side of vehicle and lift from engine compartment.
7. Disconnect wiring harness retaining clip from engine mount bracket stud.
8. Remove starter motor retaining bolts, then tilt starter motor toward radiator and pull outward to gain access to wiring.
9. Disconnect electrical wiring from starter motor and remove starter from vehicle.
10. Reverse procedure to install.

1990-91 2.3L/4-138 ENGINE

1. Disconnect battery ground cable.
2. Disconnect coolant fan connector and remove coolant fan.
3. Remove oil filter and intake manifold brace.
4. **On H.O. (VIN A) engines,** an additional bolt through the starter engine block flange is used.
5. Remove starter bolts and pull starter motor towards the passenger side of vehicle.

6. Disconnect electrical connections and remove starter by lifting out between intake manifold and radiator.
7. Reverse procedure to install.

1988 3.0L/V6-181, 1988-91 2.5L/4-151 & 1989-91 3.3L/V6-204 ENGINE

1. Disconnect battery ground cable.
2. Raise and support vehicle, if necessary.
3. Remove starter motor mounting bolts, then lower the starter motor.
4. **On 2.5L engines,** remove nuts/bolts that hold the starter bracket to the starter and engine.
5. Disconnect starter leads and remove starter from vehicle.
6. Reverse procedure to install.

DISTRIBUTOR
REPLACE

1988-89 2.0L/4-121 TURBO ENGINE

1. Disconnect battery ground cable, then remove coil and spark plug wires from cap.
2. Disconnect coil and EST connectors from cap.
3. Remove distributor to cam carrier nuts.
4. Remove distributor, marking tang drive and camshaft for correct reassembly.
5. Reverse procedure to install, noting the following:
   a. **Torque** distributor to cam carrier nuts to 13 ft. lbs.

SATELLITE SWITCHES
REPLACE

The headlamp, hazard flasher, rear defogger and windshield wiper/washer controls are incorporated into switch modules mounted on either side of the instrument cluster.

1. Disconnect battery ground cable.
2. Remove steering column collar, if equipped, then the steering column filler plate screws and filler plate or lap duct assembly.
3. Remove instrument cluster trim plate attaching screws, then the trim plate.
4. **On Skylark models,** remove switch bezel retaining screws and the bezels.
5. **On all models,** remove switch retaining screws, pull switch assembly away from instrument panel, **Figs. 1 and 2,** and disconnect electrical connectors as needed to complete removal.
6. Reverse procedure to install.

INSTRUMENT CLUSTER
REPLACE

1. Disconnect battery ground cable.

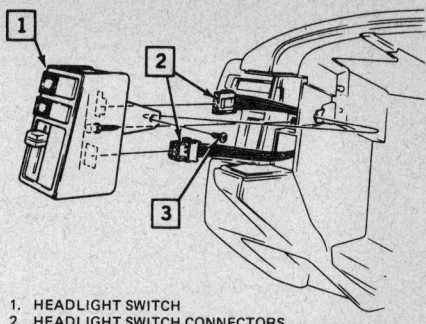

1. HEADLIGHT SWITCH
2. HEADLIGHT SWITCH CONNECTORS
3. FULLY DRIVEN, SEATED AND NOT STRIPPED

**Fig. 2   Satellite switch
removal. Cutlass Calais &
Grand Am**

2. Remove steering column collar, if equipped and the steering column opening filler plate or lap duct assembly.
3. Remove instrument cluster trim plate attaching screws, then the trim plate.
4. Remove screws attaching steering column support to lower steering column assembly.
5. Remove instrument cluster to instrument panel attaching screws, then pull cluster assembly rearward, **Figs. 3, 4 and 5.** On models with electronic instrument cluster, note warning printed on front of cluster and do not touch electronic components as static electricity may damage components. Transfer NVM chip from rear of cluster, **Fig. 6,** and the odometer to replacement cluster.
6. Reverse procedure to install.

STEERING WHEEL
REPLACE

1. Disconnect battery ground cable, then remove the attaching screws for the steering pad.
2. Remove the pad and horn lead, then remove the retainer and nut.
3. **On 1990-91 models,** remove the dampener, if equipped.
4. **On all models,** remove the steering wheel with a suitable steering wheel puller.
5. Reverse procedure to install.

REAR WINDOW
DEFROSTER RELAY
REPLACE

1. Disconnect battery ground cable.
2. Remove glove compartment door and door stop strap.
3. Disconnect electrical connector from relay assembly.
4. Remove relay mounting screw, then the rear window defroster relay.
5. Reverse procedure to install.

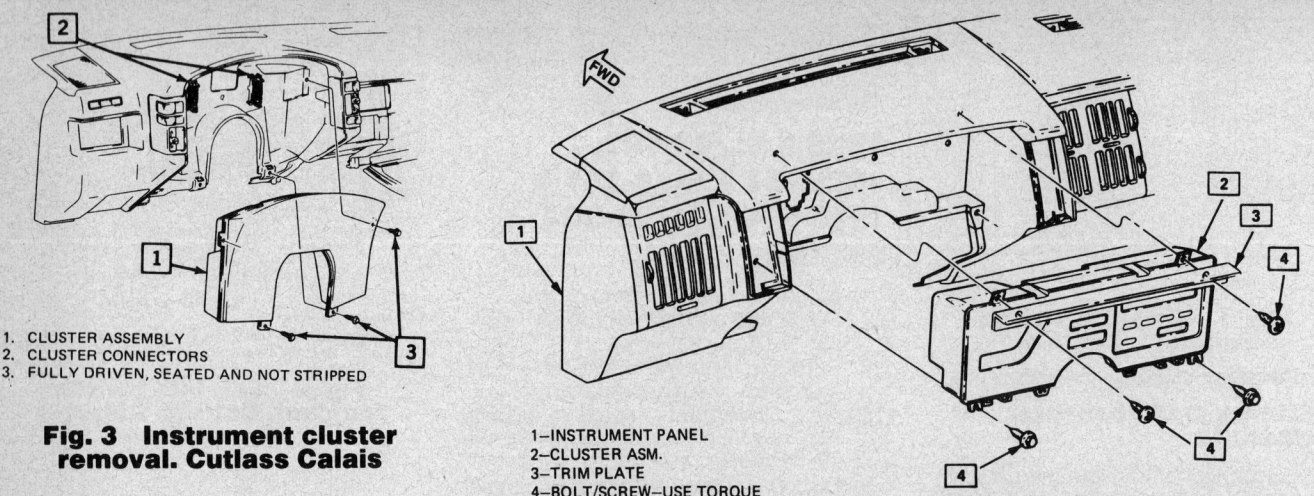

1. CLUSTER ASSEMBLY
2. CLUSTER CONNECTORS
3. FULLY DRIVEN, SEATED AND NOT STRIPPED

Fig. 3   Instrument cluster removal. Cutlass Calais

1—INSTRUMENT PANEL
2—CLUSTER ASM.
3—TRIM PLATE
4—BOLT/SCREW—USE TORQUE CONTROL TOOL 800 RPM MAX.

Fig. 4   Instrument cluster installation. Grand Am

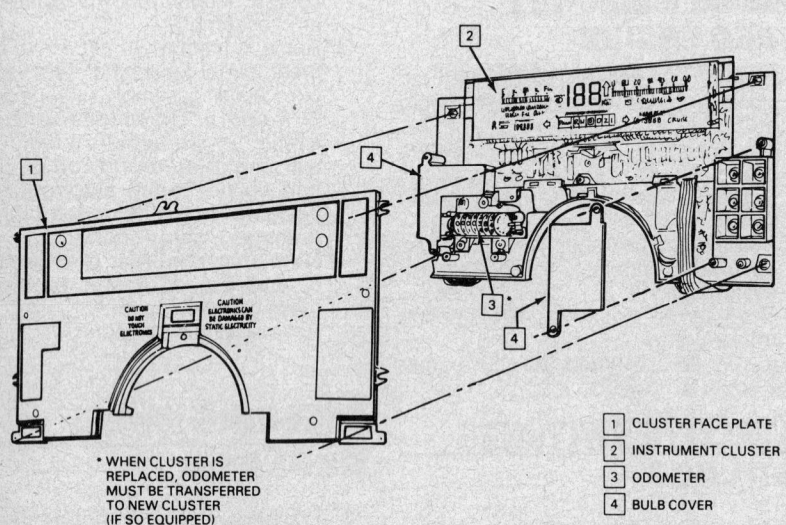

• WHEN CLUSTER IS REPLACED, ODOMETER MUST BE TRANSFERRED TO NEW CLUSTER (IF SO EQUIPPED)

1 CLUSTER FACE PLATE
2 INSTRUMENT CLUSTER
3 ODOMETER
4 BULB COVER

Fig. 5   Instrument cluster installation. Skylark

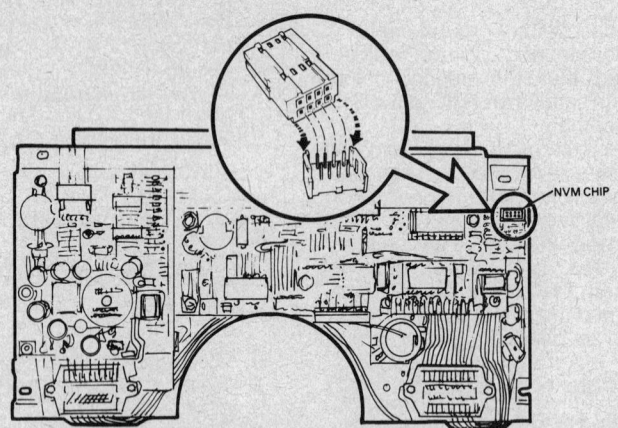

NVM CHIP

Fig. 6   NVM chip installation. Models w/electronic instrument cluster

RADIO
REPLACE
CALAIS & CUTLASS CALAIS
Models w/Auto Calculator

1. Disconnect battery ground cable.
2. Remove radio trim plate attaching screws, then the trim plate.
3. Remove radio mounting bracket attaching screws, then disconnect antenna lead and electrical connector(s) from radio.
4. Remove radio.
5. Reverse procedure to install.

Models Less Auto Calculator

1. Disconnect battery ground cable, then open ashtray and remove insert.
2. Depress tab on each ashtray locking tang, pull ashtray out to second stop, depress tabs again and remove ashtray. **There is a locking tang on each side of ashtray and each tang has a tab on the right side, Fig. 7.**
3. Remove 2 screws securing upper ashtray bracket and the bracket and trim plate assembly.
4. Remove radio mounting screws and withdraw radio.
5. Disconnect antenna lead and electrical connectors, then remove radio.
6. Reverse procedure to install.

GRAND AM

1. Disconnect battery ground cable.
2. Remove right console extension panel and rear main plate.
3. Remove radio mounting screws.
4. Disconnect antenna lead and electrical connectors, then remove radio.
5. Reverse procedure to install.

SKYLARK

1. Disconnect battery ground cable.
2. Remove console extensions, lower instrument panel trim and face plates, as needed, to gain access to components and mounting hardware.
3. Remove necessary screws and nuts,

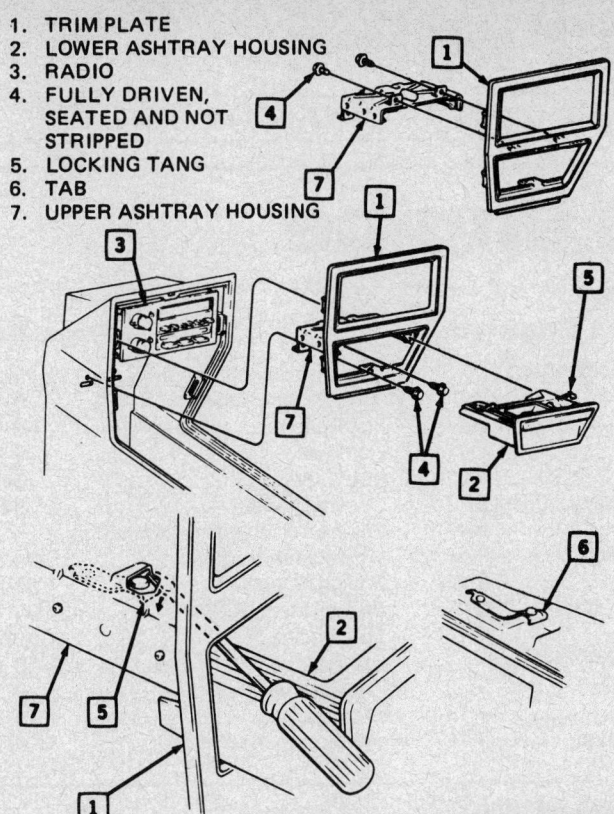

1. TRIM PLATE
2. LOWER ASHTRAY HOUSING
3. RADIO
4. FULLY DRIVEN, SEATED AND NOT STRIPPED
5. LOCKING TANG
6. TAB
7. UPPER ASHTRAY HOUSING

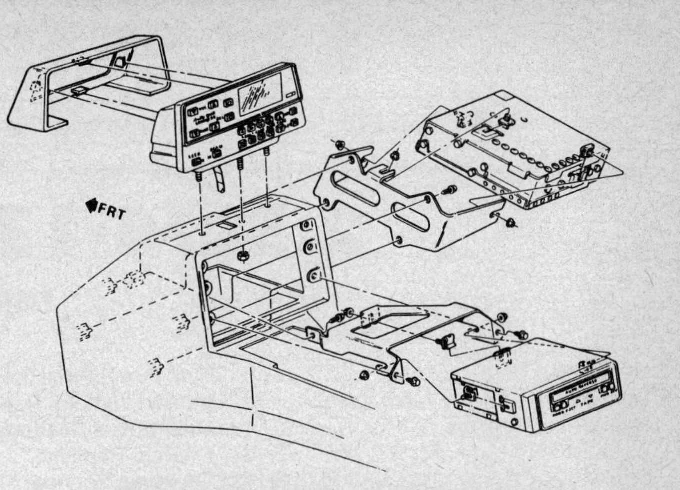

Fig. 8 Radio installation. Skylark

Fig. 7 Radio Installation. Cutlass Calais

Fig. 8, disconnect electrical connectors and antenna lead if necessary, then remove components.
4. Reverse procedure to install.

HEATER CORE
REPLACE

1. Disconnect battery ground cable.
2. Drain cooling system.
3. Raise and support vehicle.
4. Disconnect heater hoses from heater core assembly.
5. Remove drain tube.

6. Lower vehicle.
7. Remove instrument panel sound insulator.
8. Remove heater duct and hose assembly and position aside.
9. Remove 2 heater core cover attaching screws, then the covers.
10. Remove heater core from vehicle.
11. Reverse procedure to install.

EVAPORATOR CORE
REPLACE

1. Disconnect battery ground cable, then discharge A/C system.
2. Drain cooling system, then raise and support vehicle.
3. Remove heater hoses at the heater core, then remove the drain tube.
4. Remove block fitting at the evaporator and discard O-ring seals, then lower vehicle.
5. Remove sound insulators, then the floor air outlet duct and hoses from duct.
6. Remove console assembly, if equipped, then heater core covers.
7. Remove heater core, then evaporator core covers and evaporator core.
8. Reverse procedure to install. Install new O-rings at block fitting and evacuate and recharge system.

BLOWER MOTOR
REPLACE

1. Disconnect battery ground cable.
2. **On 1990-91 models with 2.5L & 3.3L engines,** remove power steering pressure hose from power steering pump.
3. **On all models,** remove blower motor mounting screws.
4. Disconnect electrical connectors from blower motor.
5. Remove blower motor assembly.
6. Reverse procedure to install.

2.0L/4-121 Engine

NOTE: Refer To " 4-121 (2.0L) Overhead Cam Engine" In Chapter 7 For Service Procedures.

2.3L/4-138 Engine

INDEX

ENGINE MOUNTS
REPLACE
FRONT MOUNT

1. Disconnect battery ground cable.
2. Remove front mount upper retaining nut, **Fig. 1.**
3. Using tool No. J-28467 or equivalent, raise engine off mount.
4. Raise and support vehicle, then remove front engine mount lower retaining nuts.
5. Lower vehicle and remove mount assembly.
6. Reverse procedure to install.

REAR MOUNT

1. Disconnect battery ground cable.
2. Using engine support No. J-28467 or equivalent, relieve engine weight from rear mount.
3. Raise and support vehicle, then remove right hand lower splash shield.
4. Remove rear engine mount through bolt and nut, then remove four bracket to body attaching bolts, **Fig. 2.**
5. Remove bracket assembly and mount from vehicle, then remove three mount to bracket attaching nuts and separate mount from bracket.
6. Reverse procedure to install.

ENGINE
REPLACE

1. Disconnect battery ground cable, then drain cooling system.
2. Disconnect heater hose at thermostat housing, then upper radiator hose.
3. Disconnect air cleaner to throttle body duct.
4. **On 1988-89 VIN D model engines,**
   remove engine cooling fan shroud. **On all models,** remove upper radiator support.
5. Remove engine cooling fan.
6. **On models equipped with A/C, proceed as follows:**
  a. **ON 1988 models,** remove oil filter assembly from engine.
  b. Discharge A/C system, then disconnect hoses from A/C compressor and discard O-rings.
7. **On all models,** disconnect two vacuum lines at front of engine.
8. Disconnect electrical connectors from alternator, A/C compressor (if equipped), injector harness, idle air control and throttle position sensor at throttle body and position aside. **On 1989 VIN A and 1990-91 models,** disconnect MAP sensor, MAT sensor and vacuum purge solenoid and position harness aside.
9. Disconnect electrical connections from starter motor solenoid.
10. Disconnect ground connections at engine front mount and battery ground cable at transaxle.
11. **ON 1988-89 models,** disconnect battery lead at junction block.
12. Disconnect electrical connectors at ignition coil and module assembly, both coolant sensors, oil pressure switch, power steering switch, knock sensor, oxygen sensor, crankshaft position sensor, vehicle speed sensor and neutral safety or backup lamp switch. **On 1989-91 models,** disconnect starter solenoid connector.
13. Disconnect power brake unit vacuum hose from throttle body and power brake unit vacuum tube to check valve hose from tube.
14. Disconnect throttle cable and remove

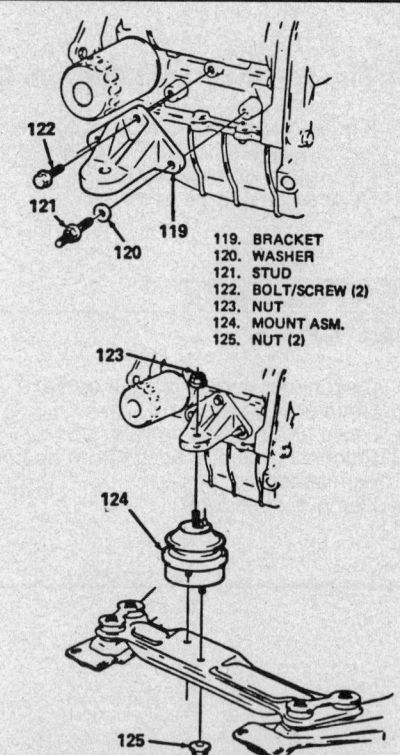

119. BRACKET
120. WASHER
121. STUD
122. BOLT/SCREW (2)
123. NUT
124. MOUNT ASM.
125. NUT (2)

Fig. 1 Engine front mount

throttle cable bracket.
15. Remove power steering pump rear bracket and power brake vacuum tube as an assembly.
16. Remove power steering pivot bolt, pump and drive belt. Position pump aside with lines attached.
17. De-pressurize fuel system, then disconnect fuel lines.
18. **On models with manual transaxle,**

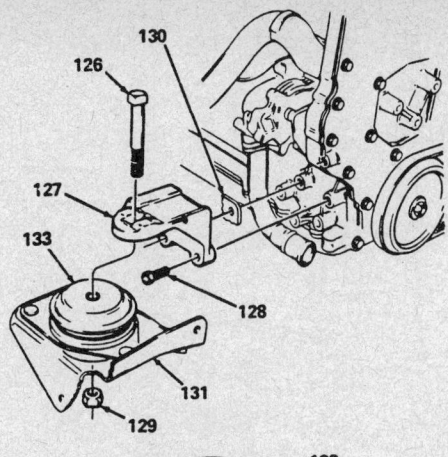

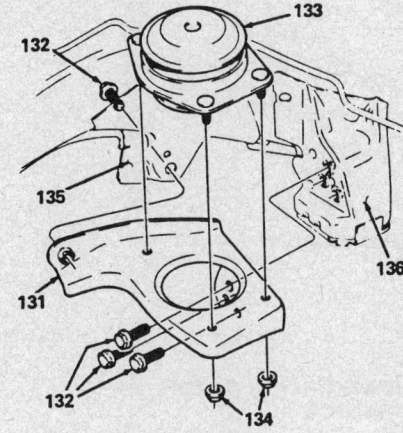

126. BOLT/SCREW
127. BRACKET
128. BOLT/SCREW (3)
129. NUT
130. TRANSAXLE SUPPORT (PARTIAL VIEW)
131. BRACKET ASM.
132. BOLT/SCREW (4)
133. MOUNT ASM.
134. NUT (3)
135. ENGINE COMPARTMENT R.H. RAIL ASM.
136. COWL ASM.

Fig. 2 Engine rear mount

disconnect shift cables, then remove clutch slave cylinder.

19. **On models with automatic transaxle,** disconnect shift cable, throttle valve cables and transaxle oil cooler lines.

20. **On all models,** remove exhaust manifold and heat shield, then lower radiator hose.

21. Remove nut from front engine mount, then install tool J-28467 or other suitable engine lifting fixture.

22. Raise and support vehicle, then remove front wheel and tire assemblies.

23. Remove right hand lower splash shield and radiator air deflector.

24. Separate ball joints from steering knuckles.

25. Using a suitable holding fixture, support front suspension, then remove suspension support attaching bolts. Remove suspension supports, crossmember and stabilizer bar as an assembly. Then remove heater outlet hose from radiator outlet pipe.

26. Position tool J-34754 or equivalent on

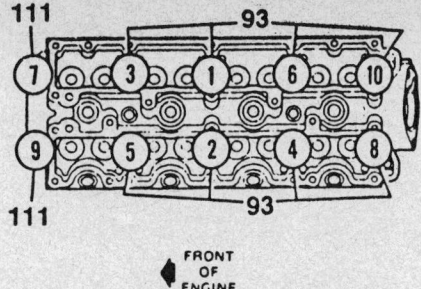

FRONT OF ENGINE

93. 35 Nm (26 LBS. FT.) PLUS 90 DEGREES
111. 35 Nm (26 LBS. FT.) PLUS 80 DEGREES

Fig. 3 1988-89 models, cylinder head bolt tightening sequence

drive axle boots, then remove axle shafts from transaxle and position aside.

27. Remove transaxle rear mount through bolt nut, then remove nut from engine rear mount through bolt.

28. Remove rear engine mount body bracket, then position suitable support under engine and lower vehicle to engine support.

29. Remove transaxle mount through bolt.

30. Mark engine support fixture hook threads so that engine can be returned to this position for installation, then remove engine support fixture.

31. Slowly and carefully raise vehicle off engine and transaxle assembly. It may be necessary to move engine and transaxle assembly slightly rearward to provide for intake manifold clearance.

32. Separate engine from transaxle.

33. Reverse procedure to install.

CYLINDER HEAD REPLACE

1. Disconnect battery ground cable, then drain cooling system.

2. Disconnect upper radiator hose, heater hose and throttle body heater hoses from coolant outlets.

3. Remove exhaust manifold as described under "Exhaust Manifold, Replace."

4. Remove intake camshaft housing as described under "Camshaft, Housing and Valve Lash Adjusters, Replace."

5. Remove exhaust camshaft housing as described under "Camshaft, Housing and Valve Lash Adjusters, Replace."

6. Remove engine oil filler cap and dipstick from engine.

7. Pull oil fill tube upward to unseat from engine.

8. Disconnect injector wiring harness.

9. Remove oil fill tube out top rotating as necessary to gain clearance for oil/air separator nipple, located between intake manifold tubes.

10. Remove air cleaner to throttle body duct.

11. Disconnect power brake unit vacuum hose from throttle body.

12. Remove throttle cable bracket.

13. Remove throttle body from intake

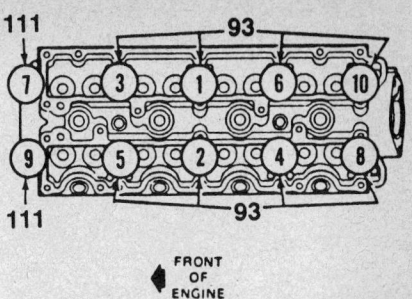

FRONT OF ENGINE

93. BOLT - 35 N.m (26 LBS. FT.) PLUS 110 DEGREES
111. BOLT - 35 N.m (26 LBS. FT.) PLUS 100 DEGREES

Fig. 4 1990-91 models, cylinder head bolt tightening sequence

manifold and position aside with throttle cable, coolant hoses and electrical connectors attached.

14. Disconnect MAP sensor vacuum hose at intake manifold.

15. **On 1988 models,** remove intake manifold bracket to engine block bolt.

16. **On 1989 VIN A and 1990-91 models,** Remove intake manifold brace, then disconnect electrical connectors from the MAP sensor, MAT sensor and purge solenoid.

17. **On all models,** disconnect upper radiator hose from water outlet.

18. Disconnect both coolant temperature sensor electrical connectors.

19. Loosen cylinder head attaching bolts in reverse order of tightening sequence, **Fig. 3.**

20. Remove cylinder head and gasket.

21. Reverse procedure to install. Tighten cylinder head attaching bolts using torque angle meter J-36660 or equivalent, in sequence shown in **Figs. 3 & 4.**

INTAKE MANIFOLD REPLACE

1. Disconnect battery ground cable, then drain coolant to appropriate level.

2. **On 1988 models,** remove cooling fan shroud with vacuum hose and electrical connector from MAP sensor.

3. **On 1989 VIN D and 1990-91 models,** disconnect vacuum hose and electrical connector from MAP sensor.

4. **On 1989 VIN A and 1990-91 models,** disconnect electrical connectors from the MAP sensor, MAT sensor, purge solenoid and fuel injector harness and position aside, then disconnect hoses from intake manifold and hose at fuel regulator and purge solenoid to canister.

5. **On all models,** Disconnect air cleaner to throttle body duct.

6. **ON 1989-91 models,** disconnect vent tube to air cleaner duct.

7. **On all models,** remove throttle cable bracket, then disconnect power brake unit vacuum hose with retaining bracket to power steering bracket and position aside.

8. **On 1988 and 1989 VIN D models,** remove throttle body from intake manifold and position aside with electrical connector, coolant hoses, vacu-

100. STUD, BOLT, INTAKE MANIFOLD TO CYLINDER HEAD
159. BRACE — INTAKE MANIFOLD
160. BOLT/SCREW — BRACE TO BLOCK
161. BOLT SCREW — BRACE TO INTAKE MANIFOLD
162. NUT — BRACE TO INT. MANIFOLD STUD

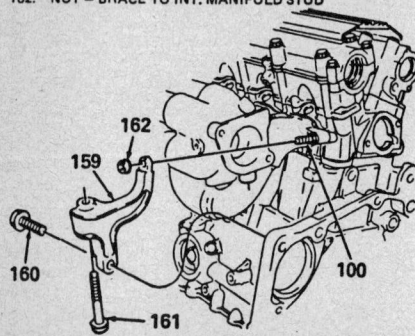

Fig. 5 Intake manifold brace removal

um hoses and throttle cable attached.

9. **On 1989 VIN A and 1990-91 models,** disconnect coolant lines from throttle body.

10. **On 1988 models,** remove oil/air separator, two bolts and four hoses. Leave hoses attached to the separator, then disconnect hoses from oil fill, chain housing and intake manifold. Remove oil/air separator and hoses as an assembly.

11. **On 1989-91 models,** remove oil/air separator, leaving hoses attached to the separator. Disconnect hoses from the oil fill, chain housing, chain cover, intake duct and intake manifold and remove as an assembly.

12. **On all models,** remove oil fill cap and dipstick assembly, then pull oil fill tube upward to unseat from engine block.

13. Disconnect injector wiring harness connector.

14. Remove oil fill tube out top, rotating as necessary to gain clearance for oil/air separator nipple between intake tubes and fuel rail electrical harness.

15. Remove intake manifold support bracket, **Fig. 5.**

16. Remove remaining intake manifold attaching bolts and nuts, then remove intake manifold and gasket.

17. Reverse procedure to install. Tighten intake manifold bolts in sequence shown in **Fig. 6.**

EXHAUST MANIFOLD
REPLACE
1988–89 Models

1. Disconnect battery ground cable.
2. Disconnect electrical connector from oxygen sensor.
3. Remove upper and lower exhaust manifold heat shields.
4. Remove bolt attaching exhaust manifold brace to exhaust manifold.
5. Loosen exhaust manifold to exhaust pipe spring leaded bolts using a 13mm wrench.
6. Raise and support vehicle.
7. Using a 7/32 inch socket, rotate exhaust manifold to exhaust pipe attaching bolts (clockwise) out of exhaust pipe flange . To prevent binding, back one attaching bolt out 4 turns, then remove the other attaching bolt. After removing the other attaching

bolt, remove bolt that was backed out four turns.

8. Disengage exhaust pipe from exhaust manifold, then lower vehicle.

9. Remove exhaust manifold to cylinder head attaching bolts, then remove exhaust manifold and gaskets.

10. Reverse procedure to install. Tighten exhaust manifold attaching bolts in sequence shown in **Fig. 7.** When installing exhaust manifold to exhaust pipe attaching bolts, rotate in a counterclockwise direction to tighten.

1990–91 Models

1. Disconnect battery ground cable.
2. Disconnect electrical connector from oxygen sensor.
3. Remove heat shield, then raise and support vehicle.
4. Remove exhaust manifold brace to manifold bolt.
5. Remove manifold to exhaust pipe spring loaded nuts, then pull down and back on exhaust pipe to disengage from manifold.
6. Lower vehicle and remove exhaust manifold to cylinder head retaining nuts, then manifold seals and gaskets.
7. Reverse procedure to install. Tighten exhaust manifold attaching bolts in sequence shown in **Fig. 7.**

VALVES
ADJUST

These engines are equipped with hydraulic valve lash adjusters, which do not require adjustment.

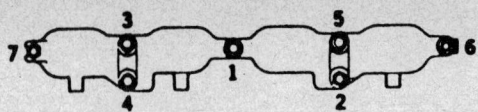

TIGHTENING SEQUENCE

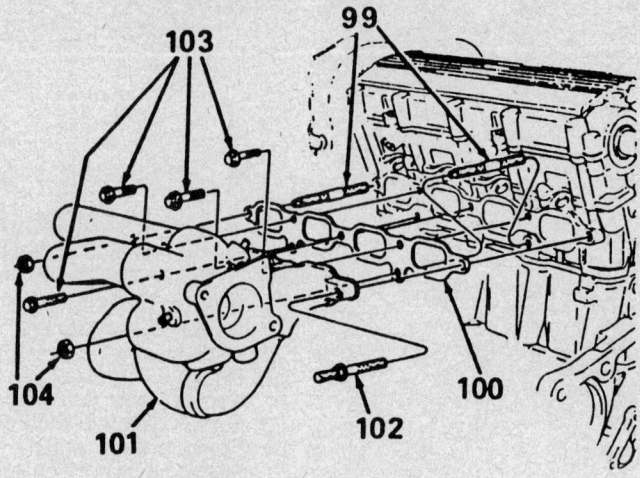

99. STUD
100. INTAKE MANIFOLD GASKET
101. INTAKE MANIFOLD
102. STUD/BOLT
103. BOLT
104. NUT

Fig. 6 Intake manifold installation & bolt tightening sequence

VALVE GUIDES

Valve guides are an integral part of the cylinder head and are not removable. If valve stem clearance becomes excessive, the valve guide should be reamed to the next oversize and the appropriate oversize valves installed. Valves are available in .010 inch oversize.

VALVE LASH ADJUSTERS

These engines use hydraulic valve lash adjusters. The valve lash adjusters can replaced after the intake camshaft and housing or exhaust camshaft and housing are removed. Refer to the appropriate "Camshaft, Housing and Valve Lash Adjusters, Replace" procedure.

ENGINE FRONT COVER
REPLACE

1. Disconnect battery ground cable, then remove coolant reservoir.
2. Remove serpentine drive belt.
3. Remove Remove upper front cover attaching screws.
4. **On 1989-91 models,** remove cover vent hose, then engine lift bracket.
5. Raise and support vehicle, then remove right hand wheel and tire assembly.
6. Remove right hand lower splash shield.
7. Using harmonic balancer tool No. J-37086 to hold crankshaft balancer

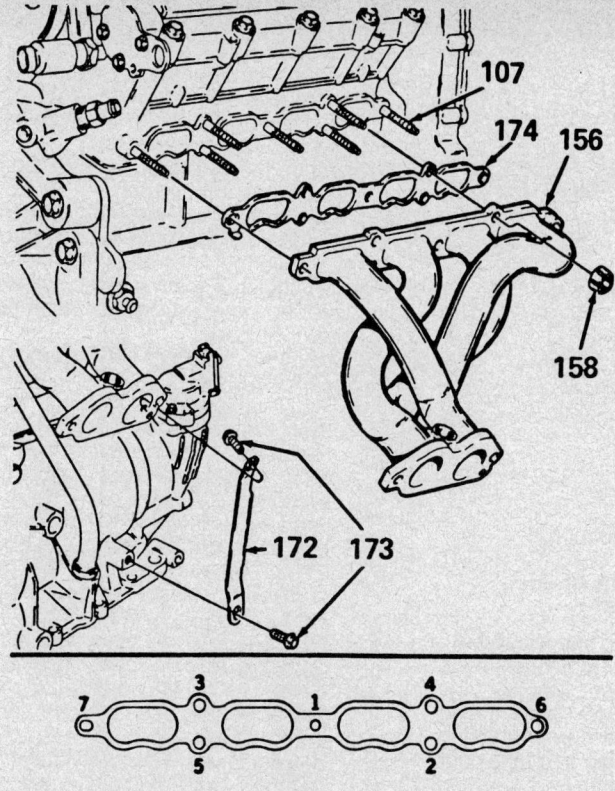

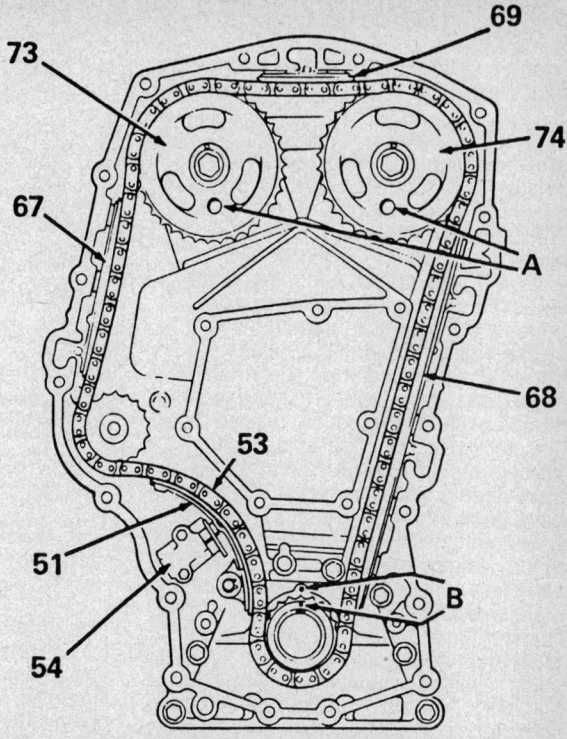

107. STUD, EXHAUST MANIFOLD TO CYL. HEAD
156. MANIFOLD ASM.
158. NUT (7) SEE INSERT FOR TIGHTENING
     SEQUENCE
172. BRACE ASM. – EXHAUST MANIFOLD
173. BOLT/SCREW (2)
174. GASKET

**Fig. 7   Exhaust manifold installation & bolt
tightening sequence**

A.   CAMSHAFT TIMING ALIGNMENT PIN LOCATIONS
B.   CRANKSHAFT GEAR TIMING MARKS
  51.   SHOE ASM. TIMING CHAIN TENSIONER
  53.   TIMING CHAIN
  54.   TENSIONER, TIMING CHAIN
  67.   GUIDE – R.H. TIMING CHAIN
  68.   GUIDE – L.H. TIMING CHAIN
  69.   GUIDE – UPPER TIMING CHAIN
  73.   SPROCKET, EXHAUST CAMSHAFT
  74.   SPROCKET, INTAKE CAMSHAFT

Fig. 8   Valve timing marks

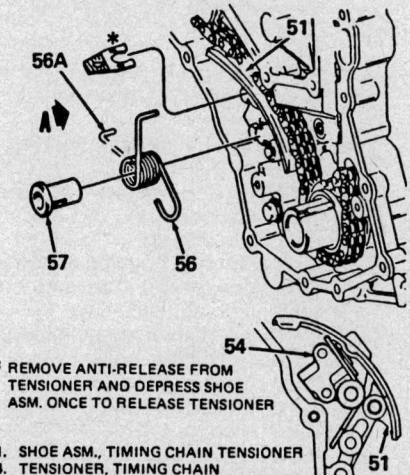

* REMOVE ANTI-RELEASE FROM
  TENSIONER AND DEPRESS SHOE
  ASM. ONCE TO RELEASE TENSIONER

51. SHOE ASM., TIMING CHAIN TENSIONER
54. TENSIONER, TIMING CHAIN
56. SPRING, TIMING CHAIN TENSIONER
    A.   INSTALLED POSITION
57. RETAINER, TIMING CHAIN SPRING TENSIONER

56 AND 57 ARE EARLY PRODUCTION. DO NOT
REINSTALL, NOT NEEDED.

**Fig. 9   Timing chain tensioner
spring & retainer**

in position, remove retaining bolt, then
remove balancer using puller No.
J-24420-B.
8. Remove fasteners attaching lower
portion of front cover, then lower vehicle.
9. Remove front cover and gaskets.
10. Reverse procedure to install.

TIMING CHAIN
REPLACE

On some 1988 models, a light knocking
or rattle noise may occur from the timing
chain housing and water pump area. This
noise is usually noticeable with engine
running at normal operating temperature.
This condition may be the result of low timing chain tension. To correct this problem,
a service kit (part No. 12337084) has been
developed to increase timing chain tension.

REMOVAL

1. Remove front cover as described under "Engine Front Cover, Replace."
2. Remove crankshaft oil slinger.
3. Rotate crankshaft in clockwise direction until camshaft and crankshaft timing marks are aligned, Fig. 8.

4. Remove three timing chain guides.
5. Raise and support vehicle.
6. **On early production engines,** gently pry off timing chain tensioner spring
   retainer and remove spring, **Fig. 9.**
7. **On all models,** removing timing
   chain tensioner shoe retainer.
8. Ensure slack in timing chain is above
   tensioner shoe, then remove chain
   tensioner shoe. The timing chain must
   be disengaged from grooves in tensioner shoe to permit removal of shoe.
   Position a suitable screwdriver under
   timing chain while pulling shoe outward to disengage. If difficulty is encountered in removing tensioner
   shoe, proceed as follows:
   a. Lower vehicle, then while holding
      intake camshaft sprocket in posi-
      tion with camshaft sprocket
      wrench No. J-36013, remove
      sprocket bolt and washer.
   b. Remove washer, then re-install
      bolt into camshaft by hand.
   c. Position a suitable three jaw puller
      into intake camshaft sprocket relief
      holes and remove sprocket. Do not
      pry on camshaft sprocket as dam-
      age to sprocket or timing chain
      housing may result.
9. Remove tensioner assembly attaching bolts and tensioner assembly. Use

care when removing, as tensioner is spring loaded.

10. Remove timing chain tensioner shoe pivot stud, then remove timing chain.

INSTALLATION

1. While holding camshaft sprocket in position with tool No. J-36013, install attaching and washer, if removed. Torque to specifications.

2. Install timing pins J-36008 or equivalent through holes in camshaft sprockets into holes in timing chain housing to position camshafts for proper timing, **Fig. 8.** If camshafts are out of position and must be rotated more that ⅛ turn to insert timing pins, the crankshaft should be rotated in the clockwise direction to a position 90 degrees off TDC. After camshafts have been positioned and timing pins have been installed rotate crankshaft in counterclockwise direction to TDC.

3. Place timing chain cover exhaust camshaft sprocket, idler sprocket and crankshaft sprocket.

4. Remove timing pin from intake camshaft and attach tool J-36013 to camshaft sprocket. Using camshaft sprocket wrench, rotate camshaft sprocket counterclockwise until timing chain can be installed over sprocket. Release tool after timing chain has been installed over sprocket. The timing chain tension between intake and exhaust camshaft sprockets should tighten. The timing pin should easily fit through intake camshaft sprocket timing hole into timing chain housing timing hole. If timing pin does not fit easily, repeat procedure.

5. With timing pins installed, raise and support vehicle.

6. With slack removed from timing chain between intake camshaft sprocket and crankshaft sprocket, timing marks on crankshaft and engine block should be aligned. If crankshaft timing marks are not aligned, move timing chain one tooth forward or rearward to align marks.

7. Install timing chain tensioner shoe pivot.

8. Reset timing chain tensioner, **Fig. 10,** as follows:
   a. Position restraint cylinder, spring and nylon plug into plunger. Align slot in restraint cylinder with peg in plunger. Rotate restraint cylinder in a clockwise direction and push into plunger until it is bottomed. Keep rotating restraint cylinder clockwise, until spring force pushes the restraint cylinder away from the plunger. The plunger peg will lock the restraint cylinder in the loaded position.
   b. Position timing chain tensioner spacer tool J-36589 on plunger assembly.
   c. Position plunger assembly into tensioner body, so that long end of plunger will be toward crankshaft when installed.

9. Install timing chain tensioner assembly with long end of plunger toward

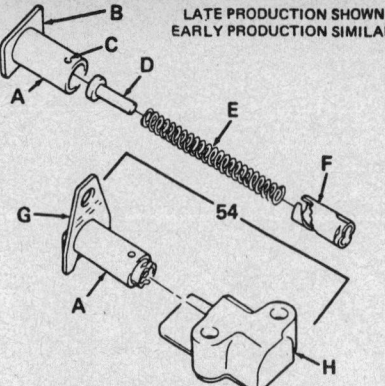

LATE PRODUCTION SHOWN
EARLY PRODUCTION SIMILAR

54. TENSIONER, TIMING CHAIN ASM.
   A. PLUNGER ASM.
   B. LONG END
   C. PEG
   D. NYLON PLUG
   E. SPRING
   F. RESTRAINT CYLINDER
   G. J 36589 ANTI-RELEASE DEVISE
   H. TENSIONER BODY

Fig. 10   Timing chain tensioner

crankshaft. Torque to specifications.

10. Install timing chain tensioner shoe and retainer.

11. Remove tool J-36589 from timing chain tensioner, then press timing chain tensioner plunger into tensioner body to unload plunger.

12. Lower vehicle to point where timing pins can be removed from camshaft sprockets, then rotate crankshaft two revolutions in the clockwise direction. Align crankshaft timing marks, then re-insert timing pins through camshaft sprockets into timing chain housing timing holes. Timing pins should slide easily through timing holes. If timing pins cannot be insert easily, repeat procedure to properly time engine.

13. Install three timing chain guides, then install crankshaft oil slinger.

14. Install engine front cover.

CAMSHAFT, HOUSING & VALVE LASH ADJUSTERS REPLACE

Whenever camshaft housing to cylinder head attaching bolts are loosened, the camshaft housing to cylinder head gasket must be replaced.

INTAKE

1. Disconnect battery ground cable, then disconnect ignition coil and module electrical connectors.

2. Remove four bolts attaching ignition coil and module assembly to camshaft housings, then pull upward on assembly to remove, **Fig. 11.** If connectors are stuck to spark plugs, use spark plug connector remover J-36011 to remove.

3. Disconnect power steering idle speed switch electrical connector.

4. Remove power steering pump and position aside with hoses attached.

5. Using power steering pulley J-36014 and J-29785-A, remove power steer-

ing pump drive pulley from intake camshaft.

6. Remove oil/air separator assembly.

7. Disconnect vacuum line from fuel pressure regulator, then disconnect injector wiring harness.

8. Remove fuel line bracket from top of intake camshaft housing.

9. De-pressurize fuel system, then remove fuel rail retaining bolts and fuel rail. Leave fuel lines attached and position fuel rail over master cylinder. Cover openings in cylinder head and injector nozzles.

10. Disconnect timing chain housing as follows:
   a. Remove coolant recovery tank, then serpentine drive belt.
   b. Raise and support vehicle, then remove right front wheel and tire assembly.
   c. Remove right lower splash shield, then balancer bolt using tool No. J 37086 or equivalent to prevent crankshaft rotation when loosening bolt.
   d. Remove balancer using tool No. J 24420-B or equivalent, then front cover lower bolts and nut.
   e. Lower vehicle, then remove water pump assembly to timing chain housing nuts. If not previously removed.
   f. Remove front cover upper bolts and nuts, then front cover.
   g. Remove timing chain as described under "Timing Chain, Replace."
   h. Remove chain housing to belt tensioner bracket brace.
   i. Remove timing chain housing to block lower fasteners, then four oil pan to front cover bolts.
   j. Remove oil/air separator hose from chain housing.
   k. Remove camshaft sprocket retaining bolts and washers while holding sprockets with tool No. J 36013 or equivalent camshaft sprocket wrench.
   l. Remove camshaft sprockets. Note: sprockets are identical and interchangeable, no marking is necessary.
   m. Remove eight chain housing to camshaft housing bolts, then timing chain housing and gaskets.

11. Remove camshaft housing cover attaching bolts, **Fig. 12.**

12. Loosen camshaft housing to cylinder head attaching bolts in reverse order of tightening sequence, **Fig. 13.**

13. Leave two camshaft housing to cylinder head attaching bolts loosely installed. Thread four of the camshaft housing to cylinder head bolts into tapped holes on camshaft housing cover to separate cover from housing.

14. Remove the two camshaft housing to cylinder head bolts and remove camshaft housing cover.

15. Note position of timing chain sprocket dowel pin for re-assembly, then remove camshaft, using care not to damage journals.

16. Remove oil seal from camshaft. This seal must be replaced any time the

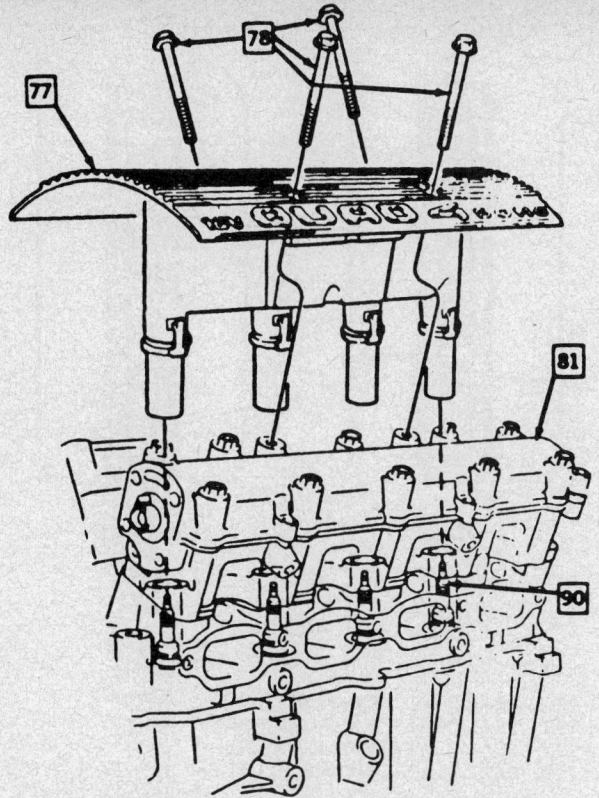

77. IGNITION COIL AND MODULE ASM.
78. BOLTS, IGNITION COIL AND MODULE ASM. TO CAMSHAFT HOUSINGS
81. COVER, CAMSHAFT HOUSING (INTAKE SHOWN)
90. SPARK PLUG

Fig. 11   Ignition coil & module assembly removal

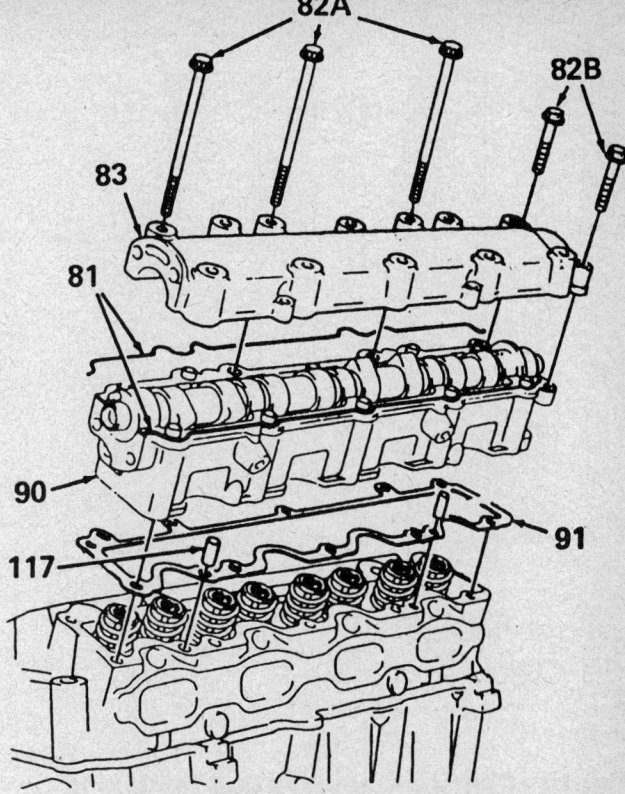

81. SEALS, CAMSHAFT HOUSING TO CAMSHAFT HOUSING COVER (EACH SEAL IS DIFFERENT)
82A. BOLT, CAMSHAFT HOUSING TO CYLINDER HEAD
82B. BOLT, CAMSHAFT HOUSING COVER TO CAMSHAFT HOUSING
83. COVER, CAMSHAFT
90. CAMSHAFT HOUSING (INTAKE SHOWN)
91. GASKET, CAMSHAFT HOUSING TO CYLINDER HEAD
117. DOWEL PIN (2)

Fig. 12   Camshaft housing & cover

cover and camshaft housing are separated.

17. Remove valve lash adjuster. Keep valve lash adjusters in order for re-assembly. Store valve lash adjusters in the upside down position in clean engine oil to prevent lifter bleed down.
18. Remove camshaft housing and gasket from cylinder head.
19. Reverse procedure to install. Prior to installation, lubricate camshaft journals and valve lash adjusters with lubricant No. 1052365 or equivalent. Apply suitable sealant to threads of camshaft housing and cover retaining bolts and ignition coil and module assembly attaching bolts. When installing camshaft housing cover to camshaft housing, refer to **Fig. 14 for seal positioning. Torque camshaft housing and cover bolts in sequence shown in Fig. 13.** Torque bolts in position 1 through 10, **Fig. 13**, to 11 ft. lbs., then tighten an additional 75 degrees. Tighten bolts in positions 11 and 12, **Fig. 13**, to 11 ft. lbs, then tighten an additional 25 degrees. Torque timing chain housing to engine and camshaft housing fasteners to specifications.

EXHAUST

1. Disconnect battery ground cable, then disconnect ignition coil and module electrical connectors.
2. Remove four bolts attaching ignition coil and module assembly to camshaft housings, then pull upward on assembly to remove, **Fig.11.** If connectors are stuck to spark plugs, use tool J-36011 to remove.
3. Disconnect oil pressure switch electrical connector.
4. Remove transaxle dipstick and tube assembly from camshaft cover and position aside.
5. Remove exhaust camshaft cover and gasket.
6. Disconnect timing chain housing as follows:
   a. Remove coolant recovery tank, then serpentine drive belt.
   b. Raise and support vehicle, then remove right front wheel and tire assembly.
   c. Remove right lower splash shield,

then balancer bolt using tool No. J 37086 or equivalent to prevent crankshaft rotation when loosening bolt.
   d. Remove balancer using tool No. J 24420-B or equivalent, then front cover lower bolts and nut.
   e. Lower vehicle, then remove water pump assembly to timing chain housing nuts. If not previously removed.
   f. Remove front cover upper bolts and nuts, then front cover.
   g. Remove timing chain as described under "Timing Chain, Replace."
   h. Remove chain housing to belt tensioner bracket brace.
   i. Remove timing chain housing to block lower fasteners, then four oil pan to front cover bolts.
   j. Remove oil/air separator hose from chain housing.
   k. Remove camshaft sprocket retaining bolts and washers while holding sprockets with tool No. J 36013 or equivalent camshaft sprocket wrench.

11
12
8
9
9
8
4
1
1
4
2
5
5
2
6
3
6
3
10
7
7
10
EXHAUST
INTAKE
FRONT
OF
ENGINE

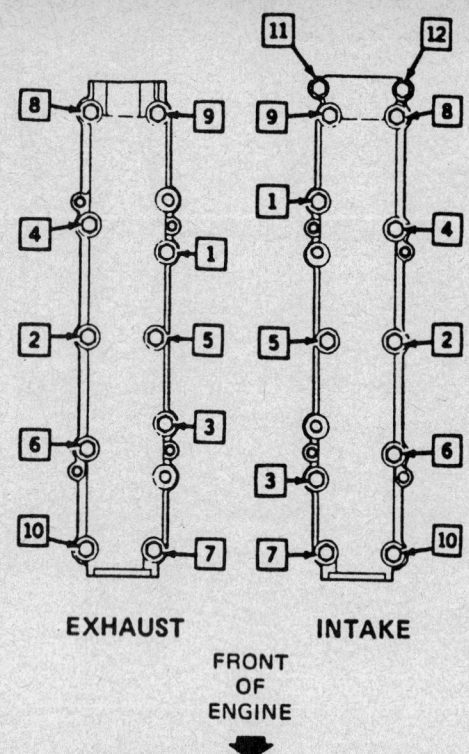

Fig. 13 Camshaft housing bolt tightening sequence

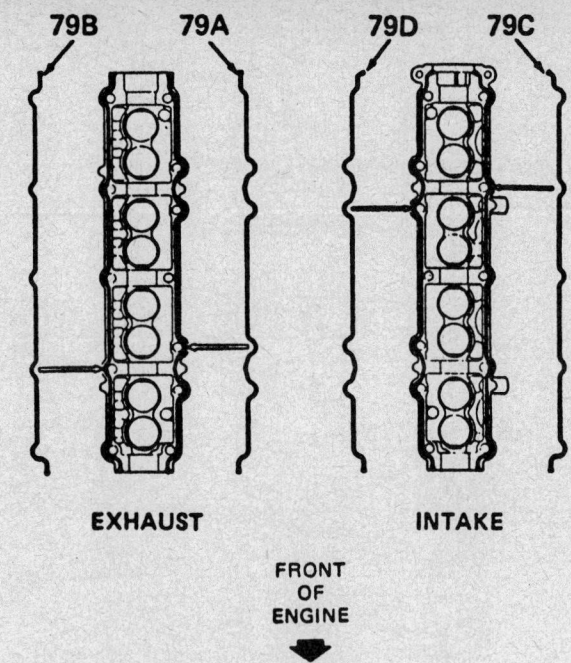

79B
79A
79D
79C
EXHAUST
INTAKE
FRONT
OF
ENGINE
79A. SEAL-INNER (EXHAUST, RED)
79B. SEAL-OUTER (EXHAUST, RED)
79C. SEAL-OUTER (INTAKE, BLUE)
79D. SEAL-INNER (INTAKE, BLUE)

Fig. 14 Camshaft housing cover seal installation & identification

- l. Remove camshaft sprockets. Note: sprockets are identical and interchangeable, no marking is necessary.
- m. Remove eight chain housing to camshaft housing bolts, then timing chain housing and gaskets.

7. Loosen camshaft housing to cylinder head attaching bolts in reverse order of tightening sequence, **Fig. 13.**
8. Leave two camshaft housing to cylinder head attaching bolts loosely installed. Thread four of the camshaft housing to cylinder head bolts into tapped holes on camshaft housing cover to separate cover from housing.
9. Remove the two camshaft housing to cylinder head bolts and remove camshaft housing cover.
10. Note position of timing chain sprocket dowel pin for re-assembly, then remove camshaft, using care not to damage journals.
11. Remove oil seal from camshaft. This seal must be replaced any time the cover and camshaft housing are separated.
12. Remove valve lash adjuster. Keep valve lash adjusters in order for re-assembly. Store valve lash adjusters in the upside down position in clean engine oil to prevent lifter bleed down.
13. Remove camshaft housing and gasket from cylinder head.
14. Reverse procedure to install. Prior to installation, lubricate camshaft journals and valve lash adjusters with lubricant No. 1052365 or equivalent. Apply suitable sealant to threads of camshaft housing and cover retaining bolts and ignition coil and module assembly attaching bolts. When installing camshaft housing cover to camshaft housing, refer to **Fig. 14 for seal positioning. Torque camshaft housing and cover bolts in sequence shown in Fig. 13.** Torque bolts to 11 ft. lbs., then tighten an additional 75 degrees. Torque timing chain housing to engine and camshaft housing fasteners to 19 ft. lbs.

6. PISTON RINGS
A. UPPER COMPRESSION RING (TOP GROOVE)
B. LOWER COMPRESSION RING (MIDDLE GROOVE) MUST BE INSTALLED WITH VENDOR IDENTIFICATION MARK TOWARD TOP OF PISTON.
C. OIL RAIL (2)
D. OIL SPACER (4)
(LOWER GROOVE)
8. PIN
9. RETAINER (2)
10. CONNECTING ROD ASM. (4)
10A. RETAINER GROOVE
10A
6
A
B
C
D
C
9
7
8
9
10

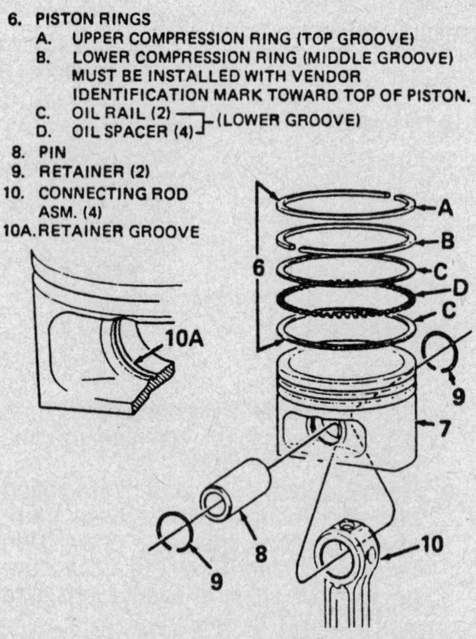

Fig. 15 Piston & rod assembly

PISTON & ROD ASSEMBLE

Assemble piston to rod with arrow on piston toward front of engine and oil squirt hole on rod toward exhaust side of engine, **Fig. 15.**

Upon installation, measure connecting rod side clearance using a suitable feeler gauge. Connecting rod side clearance should be .0059 to .0177 inch.

PISTONS, PINS & RINGS

Pistons and rings are available in standard size and oversize of .010 inch. Piston pins and pistons are serviced as an assembly.

MAIN & ROD BEARINGS

Main and rod bearings are available in standard size only.

CRANKSHAFT REAR OIL SEAL

REPLACE

1. Remove transaxle assembly as described under "Transaxle, Replace."
2. **On models with manual transaxle,** remove clutch as described under "Clutch, Replace."
3. Remove flywheel to crankshaft attaching bolts, then remove flywheel.
4. Remove oil pan to crankshaft rear

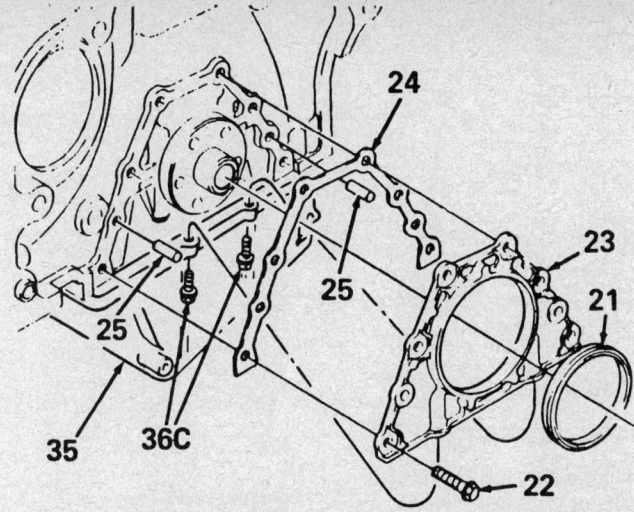

21. SEAL, REAR CRANKSHAFT
22. BOLT, REAR CRANKSHAFT SEAL HOUSING TO BLOCK (6)
23. HOUSING, REAR CRANKSHAFT SEAL
24. GASKET, REAR CRANKSHAFT SEAL HOUSING TO BLOCK
25. DOWEL PIN, REAR CRANKSHAFT SEAL HOUSING TO BLOCK
35. OIL PAN
36C. BOLT, TO SEAL HOUSING

Fig. 16 Crankshaft rear oil seal replacement

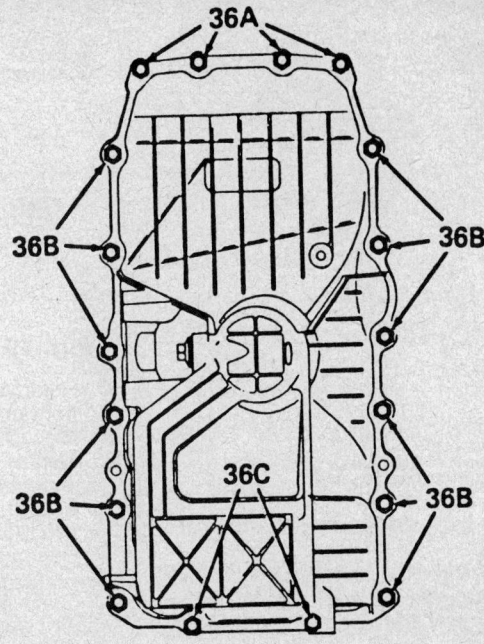

Fig. 17 Oil pan bolt identification & locations

seal housing attaching bolts.
5. Remove crankshaft rear seal housing to engine attaching screws, then remove housing and gasket, **Fig. 16.**
6. Support crankshaft rear seal housing on two wooden blocks of equal thickness with crankshaft side facing upward, then drive seal out through transaxle side of housing.
7. Press replacement seal into housing using rear crankshaft seal installer No. J-36005.
8. Reverse procedure to install. Lubricate seal lips with engine oil prior to installing housing. Torque crankshaft rear seal housing to specifications.

OIL PAN
REPLACE

1. Disconnect battery ground cable, then drain crankcase.
2. Remove flywheel housing inspection cover, then remove splash shield to suspension support bolt.
3. **On models with manual transaxle,** remove exhaust manifold brace.
4. **On all models,** remove radiator outlet pipe to oil pan bolt.
5. Remove transaxle to oil pan nut, then remove stud using a 7mm socket.
6. Carefully pry out spacer located between oil pan and transaxle.
7. Remove oil pan to transaxle stud, then remove oil pan to engine attaching bolts.
8. Remove oil pan and gasket. It may be necessary to rotate crankshaft to provide clearance for oil pan removal.
9. Reverse procedure to install. Install oil

pan attaching bolts as shown in **Fig. 17.** Torque bolts 36A and 36C, **Fig. 17,** to specifications. Torque bolts 36B, **Fig. 17,** to specifications.

OIL PUMP SERVICE
REPLACEMENT

1. Remove oil pan as described under "Oil Pan, Replace."
2. Remove oil pump attaching bolts, then remove oil pump and shims, if equipped, **Fig. 18.**
3. Reverse procedure to install. Torque oil pump to engine attaching bolts to specifications. Torque oil pump screen to engine attaching nut to specifications.

OIL PUMP GEAR BACKLASH ADJUSTMENT

1. Remove oil pump as described under "Oil Pump, Replace."
2. **On 1988 models remove three attaching bolts and on 1989-91 models remove four attaching bolts,** then separate the driven gear cover and screen assembly from the oil pump, **Fig. 19.**
3. Position oil pump housing to engine with original shim(s), then install attaching bolts and torque to specifications.
4. Using dial indicator assembly, measure oil pump driven gear to drive gear backlash, **Fig. 20.** Crankshaft should not move during check. Refer to "Engine Specifications" for proper

clearance. To decrease backlash, remove shims. To increase backlash, add shims.
5. After obtaining proper backlash setting, rotate crankshaft 180 degrees and recheck backlash setting.
6. Remove oil pump from engine.
7. Install oil pump cover and pickup tube to oil pump housing. Torque oil pump cover to oil pump housing attaching screws to specifications.
8. Install oil pump and shims.

WATER PUMP
REPLACE

1. Disconnect battery ground cable, then drain cooling system. Note: disconnect heater hose from thermostat housing for more complete coolant drain.
2. Disconnect electrical connector from oxygen sensor.
3. Remove upper and lower exhaust manifold heat shields.
4. Remove bolt attaching exhaust manifold brace to exhaust manifold.
5. Loosen exhaust manifold to exhaust pipe spring loaded bolts using a 13mm wrench.
6. Remove radiator outlet pipe to water pump cover bolts.
7. Raise and support vehicle.
8. **On 1988-89 models,** Using a 7/32 inch socket, rotate exhaust manifold to exhaust pipe attaching bolts (clockwise) out of exhaust pipe flange. To prevent binding, back one attaching bolt out 4 turns, then re-

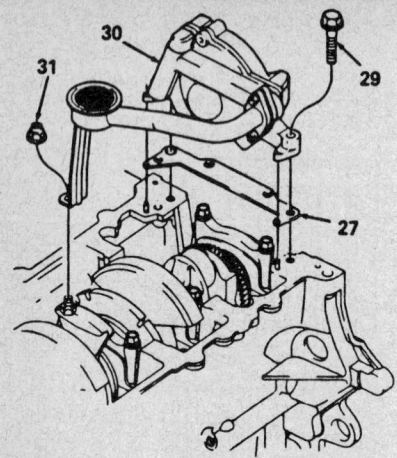

27. SHIM
29. BOLT (2)
30. OIL PUMP AND SCREEN
31. NUT – SCREEN TO BLOCK

Fig. 18 Oil pump removal

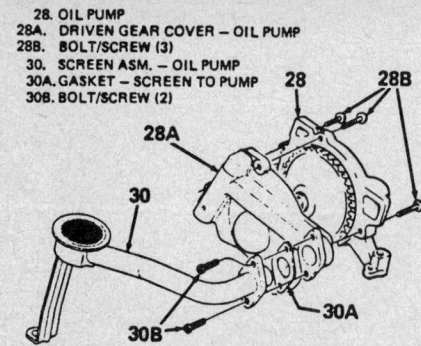

28. OIL PUMP
28A. DRIVEN GEAR COVER – OIL PUMP
28B. BOLT/SCREW (3)
30. SCREEN ASM. – OIL PUMP
30A. GASKET – SCREEN TO PUMP
30B. BOLT/SCREW (2)

Fig. 19 Removing oil cover

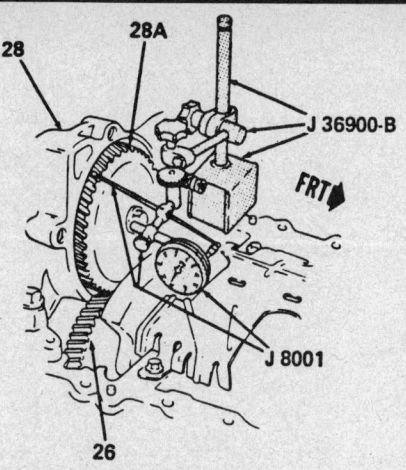

26. OIL PUMP DRIVE GEAR
28. OIL PUMP – COVER REMOVED
28A. OIL PUMP DRIVEN GEAR

Fig. 20 Measuring oil pump gear backlash

move the other attaching bolt. After removing the other attaching bolt, remove bolt that was backed out four turns.

9. **On 1990-91 models,** remove manifold to exhaust pipe spring loaded nuts.

10. **ON all models,** pull down and back on exhaust pipe to disengage from manifold bolts.

11. Remove radiator outlet pipe from oil pan and transaxle. On vehicles equipped with manual transaxle, exhaust manifold brace must be removed.

12. Leave the lower radiator hose attached and pull down gently on the radiator outlet pipe to disengage it from the water pump. Leave outlet pipe to hang.

13. Lower vehicle, then remove exhaust manifold to cylinder head retaining nuts and exhaust manifold, seals and gaskets.

14. Remove water pump cover to cylinder block bolts.

15. Remove water pump assembly to timing chain housing nuts. Note: on early production models it may be necessary to loosen and reposition the rear engine mount, mount to engine block bracket to gain clearance.

16. Remove water pump and cover assembly.

17. Remove water pump cover to water pump assembly, **Fig. 21.**

18. Reverse procedure to install. Torque water pump to water pump cover attaching bolts to specifications. Torque water pump to engine and timing chain cover attaching bolts to specifications.

ELECTRIC FUEL PUMP REPLACE

1. Disconnect battery ground cable, then drain fuel tank.

2. Disconnect tank unit harness connector.

3. Remove ground wire retaining screw from under body.

4. Disconnect hoses from tank meter assembly, then hoses at tank from filler and vent pipes.

5. Support fuel tank and disconnect the two fuel tank retaining straps.

6. Remove fuel tank from vehicle.

7. Remove fuel tank sending unit and pump assembly by turning cam lock ring counterclockwise. Lift assembly from fuel tank and remove pump from sending unit.

8. Pull fuel pump up into attaching hose while pulling outward away from bottom support. Take care to prevent damage to rubber insulator and strainer during removal.

9. After pump assembly is clear of bottom support, pull pump assembly out of rubber connector for removal.

10. Reverse procedure to install.

BELT TENSION DATA

A self-adjusting serpentine drive belt is used to drive accessories in place of the usual V-type belt arrangement.

SERPENTINE DRIVE BELT ROUTING

Refer to **Fig. 22.** for serpentine drive belt routing.

SERVICE BULLETIN

WHISTLE OR HIGH PITCH SOUND

Some 1989 Calais models with a 2.3L Quad 4 engine may exhibit a whistle or high pitch sound with the engine operating at normal temperature. This noise is a result of a high frequency resonance within the oil pump assembly. To correct this condition, replace the oil pump with part No. 22538689.

RATTLE FROM ENGINE MOUNT

Some 1988-89 Calais models with a 2.3L Quad 4 engine may exhibit a rattle in the front engine mount during engine start up and/or shut off. To correct this condition, replace mount with part No.

225638994. The revised mount although identical in appearance, can be identified by a daub of pink paint in the mount top.

ABOVE NORMAL VALVE TRAIN NOISE ON START UP

Some 1988-89 Calais models with a 2.3L Quad 4 engine may exhibit above normal valve train noise during engine start up.

On these models, the engine utilizes an oil flow check valve, located on the top of the cylinder block to the right of number one cylinder, which prevents the engine oil in the cylinder head and camshaft carriers from draining down into the crankcase. A malfunctioning check valve may result in the following conditions:

Above normal valve train noise on start up, but diminishes as engine runs. This condition may be the result of the oil check ball not seating properly. Replacing check valve will correct this condition. **Above normal valve train noise on start up may be the result of oil drain back from the block itself. Prior to replacing the check valve, install a PF47 oil filter.**

Above normal valve train noise and no or low oil pressure. This condition may be due to oil flow restriction caused by the ball check in flow valve being stuck closed. Replacement of the oil flow check valve will correct this condition.

Engine will turn over but will not start. Power steering pump pulley does not turn when engine is turned over. This condition may be due to intake cam, intake cam sprocket or sprocket dowel pin broken due to oil flow restriction caused by the ball check in flow valve being stuck closed. Replacement of the oil flow check valve and any other damaged components will correct this condition.

Engine can not be turned over. This condition may be caused by intake or exhaust camshaft seized in carrier due to oil flow restriction caused by the ball check in flow valve being stuck closed. Replacement of

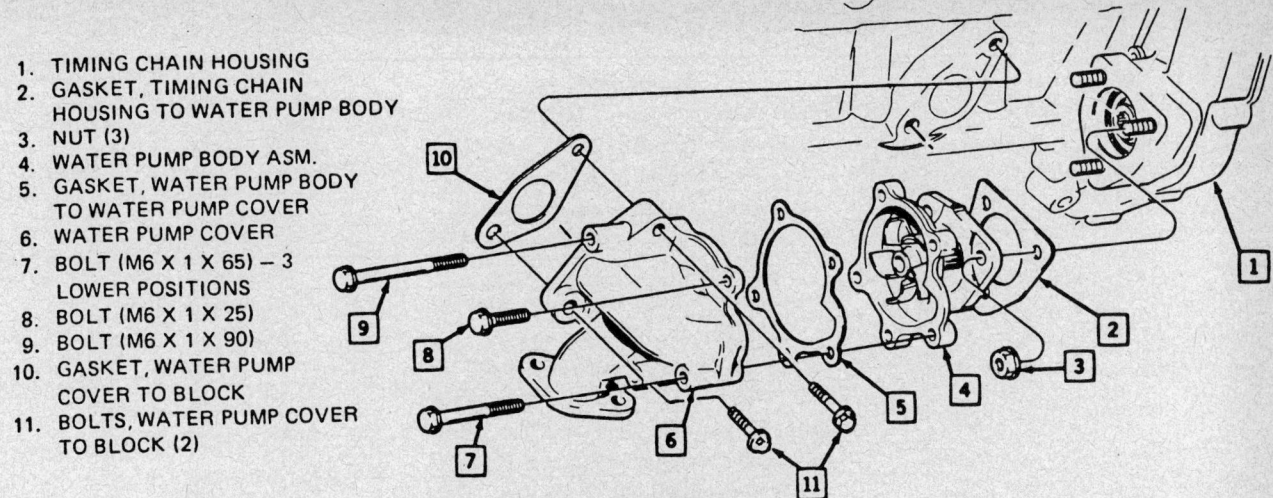

1. TIMING CHAIN HOUSING
2. GASKET, TIMING CHAIN HOUSING TO WATER PUMP BODY
3. NUT (3)
4. WATER PUMP BODY ASM.
5. GASKET, WATER PUMP BODY TO WATER PUMP COVER
6. WATER PUMP COVER
7. BOLT (M6 X 1 X 65) – 3 LOWER POSITIONS
8. BOLT (M6 X 1 X 25)
9. BOLT (M6 X 1 X 90)
10. GASKET, WATER PUMP COVER TO BLOCK
11. BOLTS, WATER PUMP COVER TO BLOCK (2)

Fig. 21 Water pump replacement

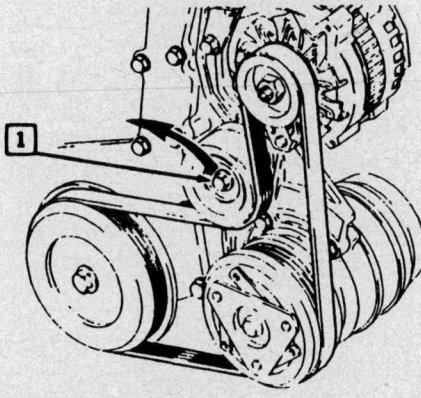

1 ROTATE TENSIONER IN DIRECTION OF ARROW TO REMOVE OR INSTALL BELT.

Fig. 22 Serpentine drive belt routing

the oil flow check valve and any other damaged components will correct this condition.

1. Following are the procedures for correcting each condition listed. All repairs start by checking the oil pressure as follows:
   a. Disconnect cooling fan motor. **To prevent injury, the engine cooling fan must be disconnected when servicing oil filter area.**
   b. Remove oil filter and install oil pressure tester (part No. J25087-C or equivalent) to filter base.
   c. Start engine and observe oil pressure. Minimum pressure for a cold engine is 40 PSI.
   d. Remove pressure tester and install oil filter.
   e. Connect cooling fan and ensure correct oil level.
   f. Remove oil pressure switch/sensor from end of exhaust cam carrier.
   g. Install an accurate engine oil pressure gauge.
   h. Start engine and observe oil pressure. Minimum pressure for a cold engine is 40 PSI.
   i. Remove pressure tester and install switch/sensor.
   j. If pressure is normal at filter base but low or zero at exhaust cam carrier, oil flow check valve is the probable cause.
2. Oil flow valve removal requires tool No. J 38123 or equivalent. If valve removal tool is not available, one can be fabricated as shown.
3. Remove oil flow valve as follows:

   a. Remove cylinder head. Refer to "Cylinder Head, Replace" as previously outlined for head removal procedure.
   b. Carefully soak up any oil remaining in check valve.
   c. Carefully insert valve removal tool. **Impact with the check ball could disengage it from the valve allowing, it to drop into engine oil galleries.**
   d. Pull the valve from its bore. **If ball check is missing from the valve when removed, it must be located and removed from the engine prior to installation of a new valve.**
4. Install oil flow valve as follows:
   a. Place new check valve (part No. 22548701) into valve bore in block.
   b. Use appropriate size socket or flat

nose punch to drive valve lightly seating valve into bore. **A properly seated check valve should not protrude above top of block surface and should be slightly below it.**
5. Remove check valve ball from oil galleries as follows. These procedures should be followed in sequence and stopped when ball is removed.
   a. Insert a narrow magnet into check valve bore.
   b. Remove timing chain housing from engine. Remove front oil gallery plug.
   c. Insert a narrow magnet with flexible handle into front oil gallery. Push magnet to end of gallery.
   d. Drain and remove oil pan.
   e. Insert magnet into front oil gallery plug hole approximately one inch.
   f. Remove number one main bearing cap.
   g. Rotate crankshaft so oil feed hole in number one journal is at the 4 o'clock position as viewed from front of engine.
   h. Ensure oil feed hole in crankshaft journal is lined up with the hole in upper bearing by inserting a small plastic straw thru crankshaft journal and bearing oil feed hole.
   i. Blow compressed air through number one crankshaft main bearing journal oil feed hole to force ball to magnet.
   j. If ball cannot be located, repeat steps 4 through 9 for main journals in sequence of 5, 4, 3, 2 until ball is recovered.

TIGHTENING SPECIFICATIONS

Year	Component	Torque/ft. lbs.
1988-91	Camshaft Housing & Cover To Cylinder Head	11①
	Camshaft Sprocket To Cam Bolt	②
	Connecting Rod Nuts	③
	Coolant Outlet To Cylinder Head	19
	Crankshaft Balancer To Crankshaft	74④
	Crankshaft Bearing Cap Bolts	15④
	Crankshaft Position Sensor To Block	80⑤
	Cylinder Head Bolts	26⑥
	Exhaust Camshaft Housing Cover	10
	Exhaust Manifold To Cylinder Head Nuts	⑦
	Exhaust Manifold To Cylinder Head Studs	106⑤
	Exhaust Manifold To Exhaust Pipe	⑧
	Exhaust Manifold To Oil Pan	19
	Exhaust Manifold Studs To Manifold	22⑨
	Flywheel To Clutch Cover	22
	Flywheel To Converter	46
	Flywheel To Crankshaft	22⑩
	Front Cover To Timing Chain Housing	106⑤
	Fuel Rail To Camshaft Housing	19
	Ignition Coil & Module Assembly To Camshaft Housing	13
	Intake Manifold To Cylinder Head Nuts	18
	Intake Manifold To Cylinder Head Studs	96⑤
	Oil/Air Separator To Intake Manifold	71⑤
	Oil Filter Connector To Block	21
	Oil Filter To Block	⑪
	Oil Pan Bolts	17
	Oil Pan Drain Plug	19
	Oil Pump To Block	⑫
	Oil Pump Cover To Oil Pump Body	106⑤
	Oil Pump Screen To Pump	30
	Rear Crankshaft Seal Housing To Block	106⑤
	Spark Plugs To Cylinder Head	17
	Starter To Block Or Transaxle To Starter	71
	Throttle Body To Intake Manifold	19
	Timing Chain Housing To Block Or Camshaft Housing	19
	Timing Chain Housing To Block Stud	19
	Timing Chain Tensioner To Housing & Block	115⑤
	Transaxle Mount To Body	40
	Water Pump To Timing Chain Housing	19
	Water Pump To Water Pump Cover	⑬
	Water Pump Cover To Block	19

①—Plus an additional 75°.
②—1988-89 models, 37 ft. lbs.; 1990-91 models, 40 ft. lbs.
③—1988 models, 15 ft. lbs. plus an additional 75°; 1989-91 models, 18 ft. lbs. plus an additional 80°.
④—Plus an additional 90°.
⑤—Inch lbs.
⑥—Refer to "Cylinder Head, Replace" for additional procedures.
⑦—1988-90 models, 27 ft. lbs.; 1991 models, 31 ft. lbs.

⑧—1988-90 models, 22 ft. lbs.; 1991 models, 18 ft. lbs.
⑨—H.O.
⑩—Plus an additional 45°.
⑪—1988-90 models, 10 ft. lbs.; 1991 models, ¾ to one turn after initial gasket contact.
⑫—1988-90 models, 33 ft. lbs.; 1991 models, 40 ft. lbs.
⑬—1988-89 models, 106 inch lbs.; 1990-91 models, 10 ft. lbs.

2.5L/4-151 Engine

INDEX

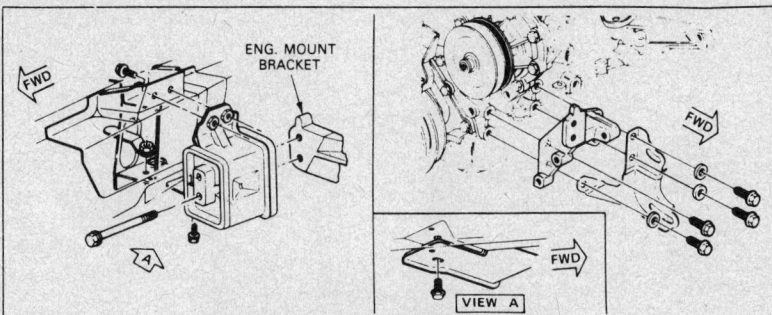

Fig. 1 Front engine mount

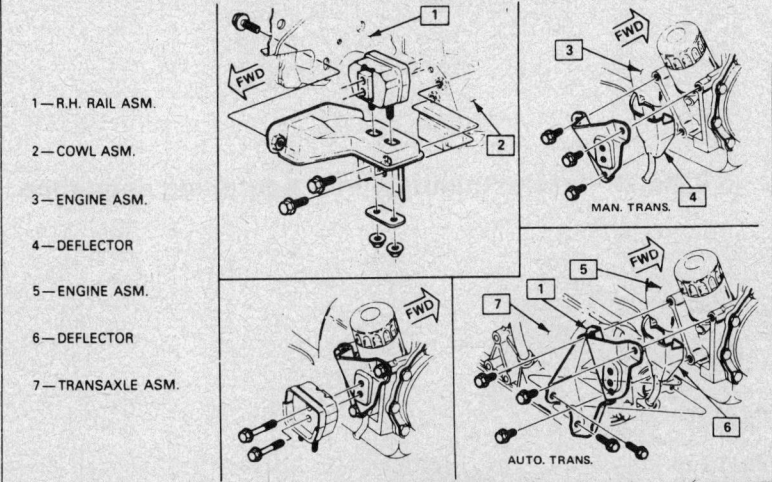

1—R.H. RAIL ASM.

2—COWL ASM.

3—ENGINE ASM.

4—DEFLECTOR

5—ENGINE ASM.

6—DEFLECTOR

7—TRANSAXLE ASM.

Fig. 2 Rear engine mount

ENGINE MOUNTS
REPLACE
FRONT MOUNT

1. Support engine using fixture No. J 28467-A or equivalent.
2. Raise and support vehicle.
3. Remove engine mount to chassis attaching bolts, **Fig. 1.**, then engine mount to bracket nuts from rear mount, **Fig. 2.**
4. Remove engine mount to engine bracket bolts.
5. Remove engine mount.
6. Reverse procedure to install.

REAR MOUNT

1. Support engine using fixture No. J 28467-A or equivalent.
2. Raise and support vehicle.
3. Remove engine mount to chassis bracket nuts, **Fig. 2.**
4. Remove engine mount to engine bracket bolts.
5. Remove engine mount.
6. Reverse procedure to install.

ENGINE
REPLACE

1. Disconnect battery cables, then drain cooling system and remove air cleaner assembly.
2. Disconnect ECM electrical connectors. Route electrical harness through bulkhead and position aside.
3. Disconnect engine wiring harness and position aside.
4. Disconnect all vacuum and coolant hoses necessary for engine removal.
5. **On models equipped with A/C,** unfasten A/C compressor and position aside, leaving refrigerant lines attached.
6. **On models equipped with power steering,** unfasten power steering pump and position aside, leaving hoses attached.
7. **On all models,** remove front and rear transaxle struts.
8. Disconnect fuel lines from throttle body.
9. **On models equipped with automatic transaxle,** disconnect transaxle cooler lines, then the transaxle shift linkage and downshift cable.
10. **On all models,** disconnect throttle cable from throttle body.
11. Disconnect redundant ground wire, then remove multi-relay bracket.
12. Raise and support vehicle.
13. **On models equipped with power steering,** remove power steering line bracket from engine.
14. **On all models,** remove front wheels.
15. Remove brake calipers and rotors.
16. Remove 2 steering knuckle to strut attaching bolts from each side.

17. Disconnect exhaust pipe from exhaust manifold and position aside.
18. Remove 2 body to frame attaching bolts from lower control arm on each side.
19. Loosen 8 remaining body to frame attaching bolts.
20. Remove one bolt from each end of frame side, leaving one bolt per corner.
21. Position suitable jack stands under front of body, then move hoist back to body pan with a 6 foot long 4 x 4 inch block of wood between hoist and vehicle.
22. Raise hoist and remove jack stands, then place dolly under engine with 4 x 4 inch blocks to maintain position on dolly.
23. Lower vehicle, allowing engine to rest on dolly, then remove engine mount bolts and right front bracket.
24. Remove 4 remaining frame to body bolts, then raise vehicle off engine/transaxle assembly.
25. Separate engine from transaxle.
26. Reverse procedure to install.

CYLINDER HEAD
REPLACE

1. Disconnect battery ground cable, then drain cooling system.
2. Remove exhaust manifold as described under "Exhaust Manifold, Replace."
3. Remove oil level indicator tube, then the air cleaner assembly.
4. Disconnect electrical connectors, throttle linkage and fuel lines from throttle body unit, then disconnect heater hose from intake manifold.
5. Disconnect electrical connectors from intake manifold and cylinder head.
6. Disconnect vacuum lines from cylinder head.
7. **On models equipped with A/C,** unfasten A/C compressor and position aside, leaving refrigerant lines attached (if top mounted).
8. **On all models,** position alternator brackets aside, then remove upper power steering pump bracket.
9. Remove upper power steering pump bracket (if top mounted).
10. Remove rocker arm cover, then the rocker arms and push rods.
11. Remove cylinder head attaching bolts, then the cylinder head.
12. Reverse procedure to install. **Torque** cylinder head attaching bolts in the following sequence:
    a. **Torque** all bolts in sequence, **Fig. 3**, to 18 ft. lbs.
    b. Repeat sequence, bringing **torque** to 26 ft. lbs. on all bolts except No. 9. Retorque No. 9 to 18 ft. lbs.
    c. Repeat sequence, turning all bolts 90°.

INTAKE MANIFOLD
REPLACE

1. Disconnect battery ground cable.
2. Remove air cleaner assembly.

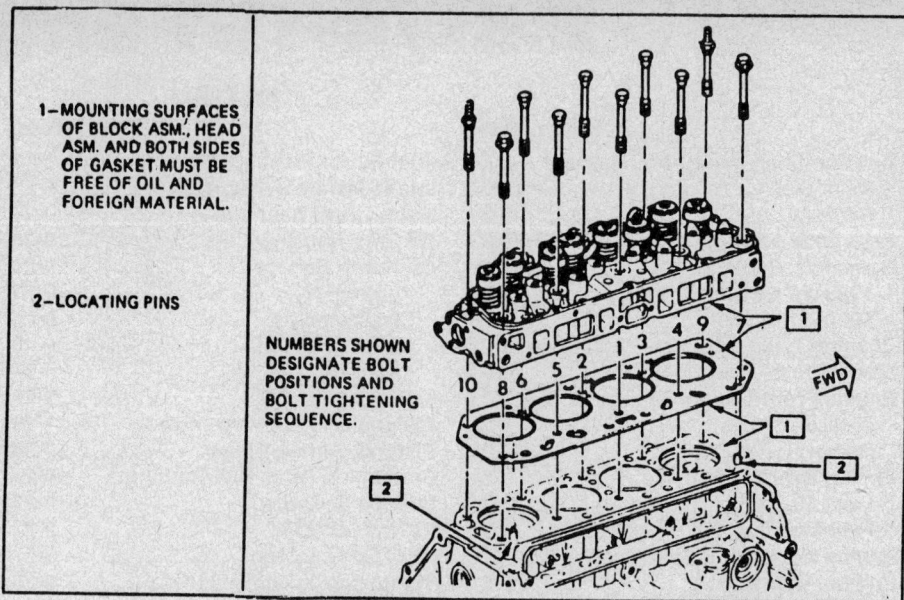

1—MOUNTING SURFACES OF BLOCK ASM., HEAD ASM. AND BOTH SIDES OF GASKET MUST BE FREE OF OIL AND FOREIGN MATERIAL.

2—LOCATING PINS

NUMBERS SHOWN DESIGNATE BOLT POSITIONS AND BOLT TIGHTENING SEQUENCE.

Fig. 3 Cylinder head bolt tightening sequence

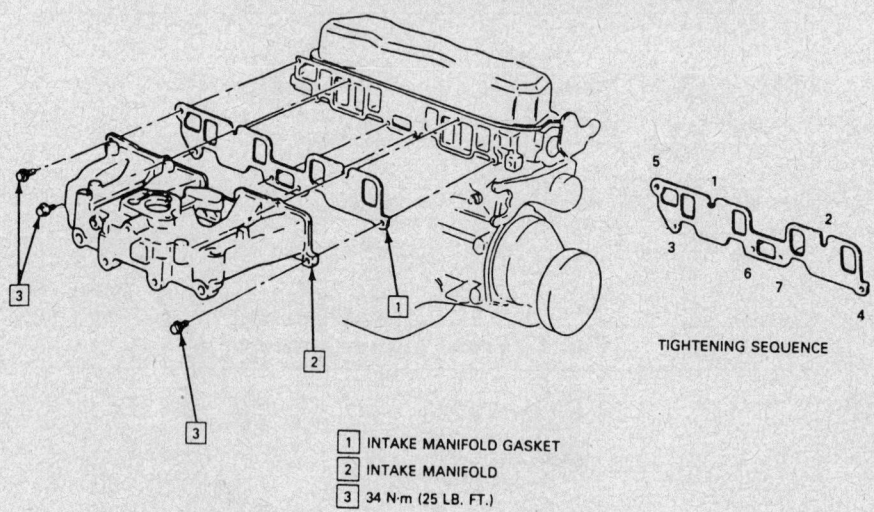

TIGHTENING SEQUENCE

1	INTAKE MANIFOLD GASKET
2	INTAKE MANIFOLD
3	34 N·m (25 LB. FT.)

Fig. 4 Intake manifold bolt tightening sequence.

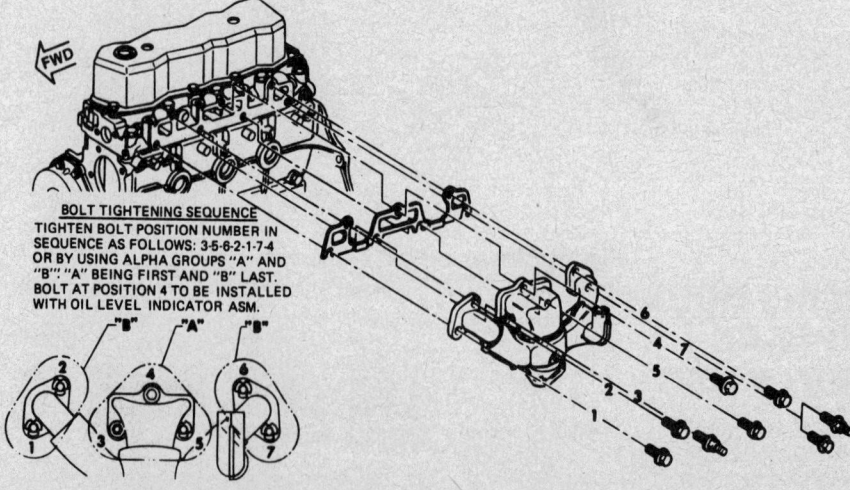

BOLT TIGHTENING SEQUENCE
TIGHTEN BOLT POSITION NUMBER IN SEQUENCE AS FOLLOWS: 3-5-6-2-1-7-4 OR BY USING ALPHA GROUPS "A" AND "B", "A" BEING FIRST AND "B" LAST. BOLT AT POSITION 4 TO BE INSTALLED WITH OIL LEVEL INDICATOR ASM.

"B"   "A"   "B"

Fig. 5 Exhaust manifold bolt tightening sequence

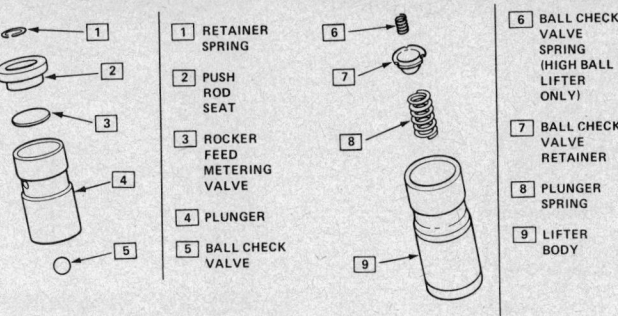

Fig. 6 Hydraulic valve lifter components

1 RETAINER SPRING
2 PUSH ROD SEAT
3 ROCKER FEED METERING VALVE
4 PLUNGER
5 BALL CHECK VALVE
6 BALL CHECK VALVE SPRING (HIGH BALL LIFTER ONLY)
7 BALL CHECK VALVE RETAINER
8 PLUNGER SPRING
9 LIFTER BODY

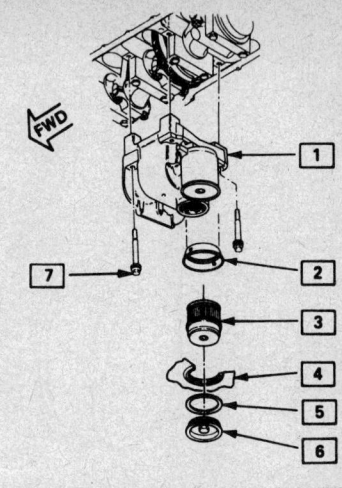

1 – BALANCER ASSEMBLY
2 – RESTRICTOR
3 – FILTER
4 – OIL PAN
5 – GASKET
6 – PLUG
7 – BOLT

Fig. 7 Balance shaft/oil pump assembly removal

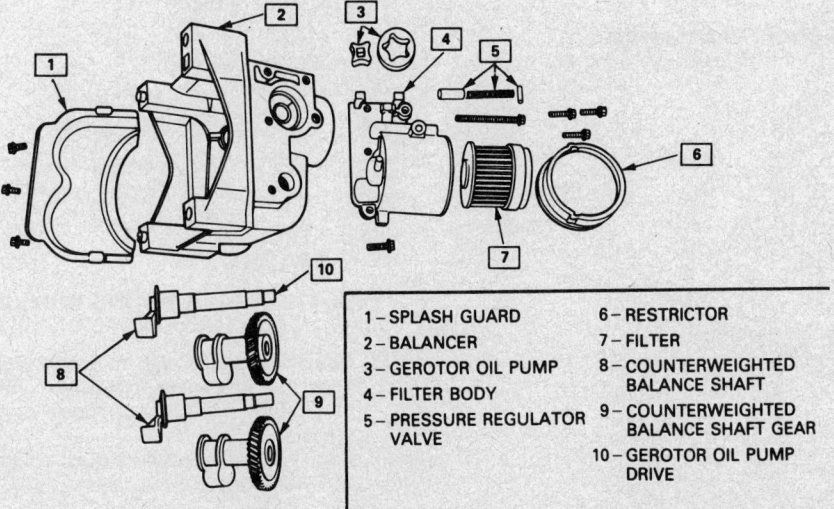

Fig. 8 Exploded view of balance shaft/oil pump assembly

1 – SPLASH GUARD
2 – BALANCER
3 – GEROTOR OIL PUMP
4 – FILTER BODY
5 – PRESSURE REGULATOR VALVE
6 – RESTRICTOR
7 – FILTER
8 – COUNTERWEIGHTED BALANCE SHAFT
9 – COUNTERWEIGHTED BALANCE SHAFT GEAR
10 – GEROTOR OIL PUMP DRIVE

3. Disconnect PCV valve and hose from throttle body unit.
4. Drain engine coolant, then disconnect fuel lines from throttle body.
5. Disconnect vacuum lines, then disconnect electrical connectors and throttle linkage from throttle body unit.
6. Disconnect transaxle downshift cable and cruise control linkage, if equipped.
7. Unfasten throttle linkage and throttle valve cable and position aside.
8. Disconnect heater hose from manifold.
9. Remove intake manifold attaching bolts and the manifold.
10. Reverse procedure to install. Torque attaching bolts to specifications in sequence shown in **Fig. 4.**

EXHAUST MANIFOLD REPLACE

1. Disconnect battery ground cable.
2. Remove air cleaner assembly.
3. Unfasten alternator upper mounting brackets and position aside.
4. Disconnect oxygen sensor electrical connector.
5. Raise and support vehicle.
6. Disconnect exhaust pipe from exhaust manifold, then lower vehicle.

7. Remove exhaust manifold attaching bolts, then the manifold and gasket.
8. Reverse procedure to install. **Torque** attaching bolts in sequence, **Fig. 5. Torque** bolts 1, 2, 6 and 7 to 26 ft. lbs. and bolts 3, 4 and 5 to 37 ft. lbs.

VALVES
ADJUST

These engines are equipped with hydraulic valve lifters. No provision for adjustment is provided.

VALVE ARRANGEMENT

FRONT TO REAR

2.5L/4-151 . . . . I-E-I-E-I-E-I

CAM LOBE LIFT SPECIFICATIONS

Engine	Year	Int.	Exh.
2.5L/4-151	1988	.232	.232
2.5L/4-151	1989-90	.248	.248

VALVE TIMING

INTAKE OPENS BEFORE TDC

Engine	Year	Degrees
2.5L/4-151	1985-90	33

VALVE GUIDES

Valve guides are an integral part of the cylinder head and are not removable. If valve stem clearance becomes excessive, the valve guide should be reamed to the next oversize and the appropriate oversize valves installed. Valves are available in .003 and .005 inch oversizes.

VALVE LIFTERS

Hydraulic roller valve lifters are used on these engines. Lifter retainers and guide plates are used to keep the lifter from rotating on the camshaft. Failure of a hydraulic valve lifter, **Fig. 6,** is generally caused by an inadequate oil supply or dirt. An air leak at the intake side of the oil pump or too much oil in the engine will cause air bubbles in the oil supply to the lifters causing them to collapse. This is a probable cause of trouble if several lifters fail to function, but air in oil is an unlikely cause of failure of a single unit.

Valve lifters can be removed after removing rocker arm cover and push rod cover. Loosen rocker arm bolt and rotate rocker arm so that push rod can be removed, then remove lifter guide, retainer and the valve lifter. It may be necessary to use tool No. J-3049 to facilitate lifter removal.

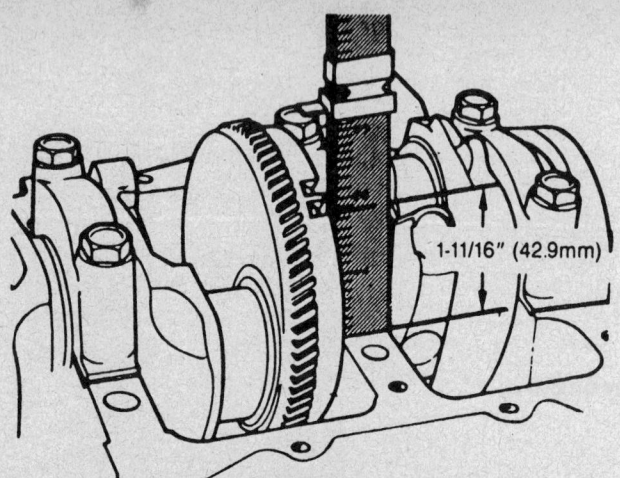

**Fig. 9 Measuring balance shaft clearance.
1988**

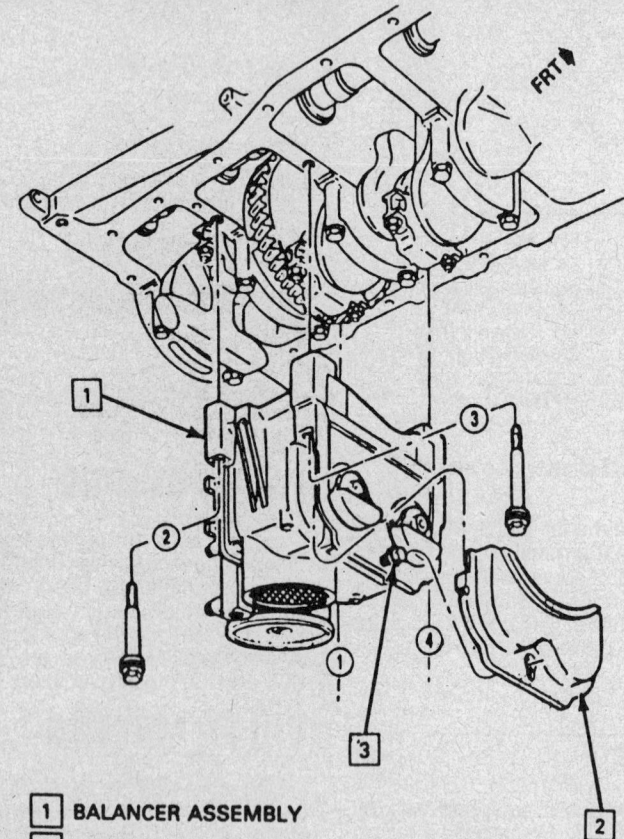

1 BALANCER ASSEMBLY

2 BAFFLE

3 10 N·m (90 LB. IN.)

* CIRCLED NUMBERS SHOW BOLT POSITION
(SEE TEXT FOR TIGHTENING SEQUENCE)

**Fig. 11 Installing balance shaft assembly.
1989-91**

BALANCE SHAFT ASSEMBLY
REPLACE
REMOVAL

1. Remove oil pan attaching bolts and the oil pan.
2. Remove balance shaft assembly at-

taching bolts and the balance shaft assembly, Figs. 7 and 8.

INSTALLATION
1988 Models

1. Rotate engine to T.D.C. on No. 1 and No. 4 cylinders.
2. Measure from block to first cut of double notch on reluctor ring, Fig. 9, dimension should be 1¹¹/₁₆ inch.

**Fig. 10 Mounting balance
shaft assembly. 1988**

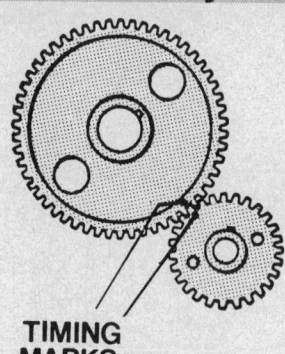

**Fig. 12 Valve timing marks.
1988-89**

3. Mount balancer with counterweights parallel and pointing away from crankshaft, **Fig. 10.** Do not move crankshaft.
4. Install oil pan and **torque** bolts to specifications.

1989–90 Models

When installing the balancer, the end of the housing without dowel pins must remain in contact with the block surface. if it loses contact, gear engagement may be lost and permanent damage to either the crankshaft or the balancer gears may result.
1. Rotate engine to bring No. 1 or No. 4 cylinder to T.D.C. (crankshaft counterweights at B.D.C.)
2. Install balancer onto crankshaft with balance weights at B.D.C. plus or minus ½ gear tooth.
3. Install balancer bolts and **torque** to 107 inch lbs. in sequence, 3-1-2-4 **Fig. 11.**
4. Following the same sequence, **torque** the short bolts to 11 ft. lbs. plus 75° and the long bolts to 11 ft. lbs. plus 90°
5. Install oil pan and **torque** bolts to specifications.

1991 Models

When installing the balancer, the end of the housing without dowel pins must remain in contact with the block surface. if it loses contact, gear engagement may be lost and permanent damage to either the crankshaft or the balancer gears may result.
1. Rotate crankshaft until the fourth counterweight from the front is positioned exactly at B.D.C.

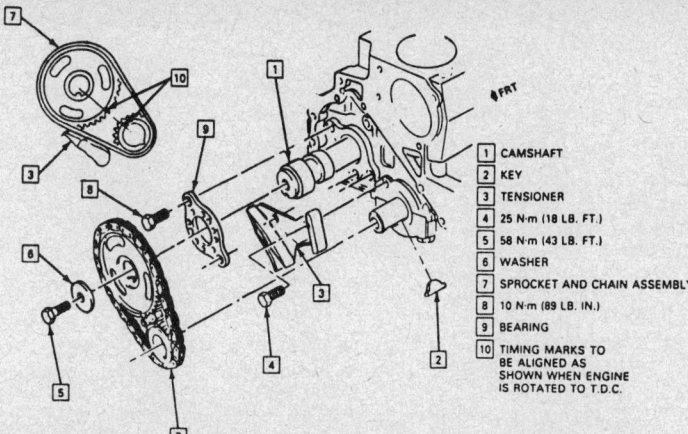

Fig. 13 Valve timing marks. 1990-91

1	CAMSHAFT
2	KEY
3	TENSIONER
4	25 N·m (18 LB. FT.)
5	58 N·m (43 LB. FT.)
6	WASHER
7	SPROCKET AND CHAIN ASSEMBLY
8	10 N·m (89 LB. IN.)
9	BEARING
10	TIMING MARKS TO BE ALIGNED AS SHOWN WHEN ENGINE IS ROTATED TO T.D.C.

Fig. 14 Piston & rod assembly

2. Install balancer onto block with balance weights at exactly B.D.C. plus or minus ½ gear tooth.
3. Install balancer bolts and **torque** to 107 inch lbs. in sequence, 3-1-2-4 **Fig. 11**.
4. Following the same sequence, **torque** the short bolts to 11 ft. lbs. plus 75° and the long bolts to 11 ft. lbs. plus 90°.
5. Rotate crankshaft at least four complete turns while observing for adequate clearance between the fourth crankshaft counterweight and the balancer weights.
6. Install oil pan and **torque** bolts to specifications.

ENGINE FRONT COVER
REPLACE
REMOVAL
1988–89 Models

1. Remove drive belts, then raise and support vehicle.
2. Remove right front tire and wheel assembly, then inner fender splash shield.
3. Remove Crankshaft dampener, then front cover attaching bolts, front cover and oil seal.

1990–91 Models

1. Remove drive belts, then power steering pump bolts and lay pump aside.
2. Raise and support vehicle, then remove right front wheel and tire assembly.
3. Remove inner fender splash shield, then right hand cover.
4. Remove flywheel cover using a suitable tool to prevent flywheel rotation.
5. Remove bolt and washer, then balancer and key.
6. Remove front cover attaching bolts, then front cover and oil seal.

INSTALLATION
1988–89 Models

1. Apply a ³/₈ inch wide by ³/₁₆ inch thick bead of RTV sealant to joint at oil pan and front cover.
2. Apply a ¼ inch wide by ⅛ inch thick bead of RTV sealant to front cover at cylinder block mating surfaces.
3. Install oil seal to front cover using tool No. J-34995 or equivalent and leave installed in front cover oil seal bore.
4. Install front cover and partially tighten 2 opposing front cover screws with tool in place.
5. Install remaining cover to block screws and **torque** to 89 inch lbs., then remove tool.
6. Install crankshaft balancer, bolt and washer and **torque** to 162 ft. lbs.
7. Install inner fender splash shield, then right front tire and wheel assembly.
8. Lower vehicle, then install drive belts.

1990–91 Models

1. Apply a ³/₈ inch wide by ³/₁₆ inch thick bead of RTV sealant to joint at oil pan and front cover.
2. Apply a ¼ inch wide by ⅛ inch thick bead of RTV sealant to front cover at cylinder block mating surfaces.
3. Install oil seal to front cover using tool No. J-34995 or equivalent and leave installed in front cover oil seal bore.
4. Install front cover and partially tighten 2 opposing front cover screws with tool in place.
5. Install remaining cover to block screws and **torque** to 89 inch lbs., then remove tool.
6. Install key, balancer, washer and bolt using a suitable tool to prevent flywheel rotation and **torque** bolt to 162 ft. lbs.
7. Install flywheel cover, then right hand cover.
8. Install inner fender splash shield, then right front wheel and tire assembly.
9. Lower vehicle, then install power steering pump.
10. Install drive belts.

TIMING GEARS
1988–89 MODELS

When necessary to install a new camshaft gear, the camshaft will have to be removed as the gear is a pressed fit on the camshaft. The camshaft is held in place by a thrust plate which is retained to the engine by two capscrews which are accessible through the two holes in the gear web.

To remove gear, use an arbor press and a suitable sleeve to properly support gear on its steel hub.

Before installing gear, assemble thrust plate and gear spacer ring, then press gear onto shaft until it bottoms against spacer ring. The thrust plate end clearance should be .0015-.0050 inch. If clearance is less than .0015 inch, the spacer ring should be replaced. If clearance is greater than .0050 inch, the thrust plate should be replaced.

The crankshaft gear can be removed using a puller and two bolts in the tapped holes of the gear.

When installing timing gears, make sure that the marks on the gears are properly aligned, **Fig. 12**. The valve timing marks, **Fig. 12**, do not indicate TDC, compression stroke for No. 1 cylinder for use during distributor installation. When installing the distributor, rotate engine until No. 1 cylinder is on compression stroke and the camshaft timing mark is 180° from the valve timing position shown in **Fig. 12**.

TIMING CHAIN & GEARS
REPLACE
1990–91 MODELS

1. Remove front cover as described under "Front Cover, Replace."
2. Loosen camshaft bolt, this will aid in preventing camshaft from moving off timing marks.
3. Align cam and crankshaft timing marks, engine at T.D.C. **Fig. 13**.
4. Remove camshaft bolt, then timing chain and sprockets.
5. Reverse procedure to install, **torquing** camshaft bolt to 43 ft. lbs.

CAMSHAFT
REPLACE
1988–89 MODELS

1. Remove engine from vehicle as described under "Engine, Replace."

2. Remove rocker arm cover, push rods, push rod cover and valve lifters.
3. Remove crankshaft balancer, then front cover as described under "Engine Front Cover, Replace."
4. Remove camshaft thrust plate screws, then slide camshaft and gear out through front of block. Use care not to damage camshaft bearings.
5. Remove gear from camshaft using an arbor press and adapter.
6. Reverse procedure to install. When installing camshaft, align crankshaft and camshaft valve timing marks on gear teeth, Fig. 12.

1990–91 MODELS

1. Remove engine from vehicle as described under "Engine, Replace."
2. Remove rocker arm cover, push rods, push rod cover and valve lifters.
3. Remove crankshaft balancer, then front cover as described under "Engine Front Cover, Replace."
4. Align timing marks with engine at T.D.C. Fig. 13.
5. Remove cam sprocket bolt, then timing chain and sprockets.
6. Remove camshaft thrust plate, then slide camshaft out through front of block. Use care not to damage camshaft bearings.
7. Reverse procedure to install aligning marks on cam and crank gears as shown in Fig. 13.

PISTONS & RODS ASSEMBLE

Assemble piston to rod with notch on piston facing toward front of engine and the raised notch side of rod at bearing end facing toward rear of engine, Fig. 14.

Upon installation, measure the connecting rod side clearance using a suitable feeler gauge. Clearance should be .006 to .024 inch.

PISTONS, PINS & RINGS

Pistons and rings are available in standard and oversizes of .010, .020 and .030 inch. Piston pins are available in oversizes of .001 and .003 inch.

MAIN & ROD BEARINGS

Main and rod bearings are available in standard size and undersizes of .001, .002 and .010 inch.

OIL PAN
REPLACE

1. Disconnect battery ground cable, then raise and support vehicle.
2. Drain engine oil, then disconnect exhaust pipe at manifold and hanger and swing out of the way.
3. Remove starter cover, then flywheel cover.
4. Remove starter, then oil pan attaching bolts and the oil pan.
5. Reverse procedure to install.

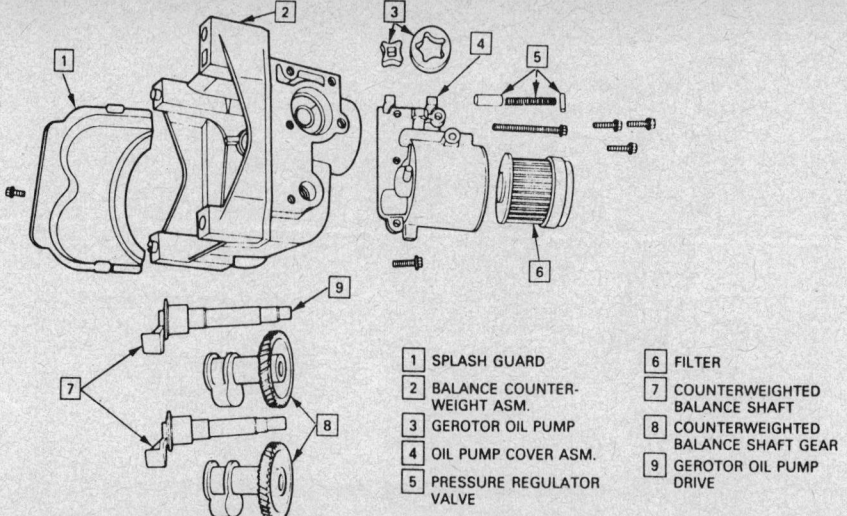

1 SPLASH GUARD	6 FILTER
2 BALANCE COUNTER-WEIGHT ASM.	7 COUNTERWEIGHTED BALANCE SHAFT
3 GEROTOR OIL PUMP	8 COUNTERWEIGHTED BALANCE SHAFT GEAR
4 OIL PUMP COVER ASM.	9 GEROTOR OIL PUMP DRIVE
5 PRESSURE REGULATOR VALVE	

Fig. 15   Exploded view of balance shaft/oil pump assembly 1989-91

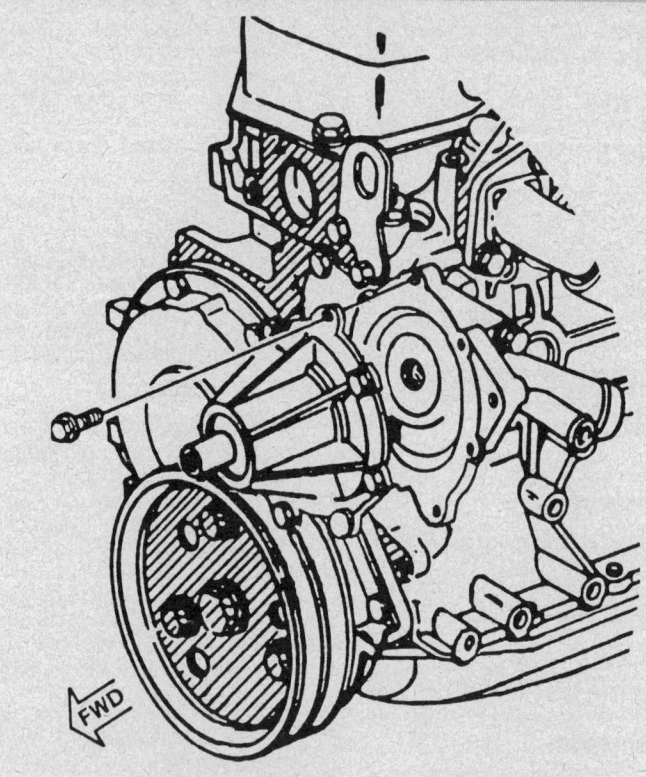

Fig. 16   Water pump assembly

OIL PUMP SERVICE
REMOVAL

It is not necessary to remove the balance shaft assembly to service the oil pump or pressure regulator valve.
1. Drain crankcase, then remove oil pan as described under "Oil Pan, Replace" and oil filter.

DISASSEMBLE

1. On 1988 models, remove restrictor, Fig. 8.

2. On all models, remove oil pump cover assembly, then oil pump gears. Figs. 8 and 15.
3. Remove pressure regulator valve, plug or pin, spring and valve. If valve is stuck, clean valve and pump housing with carburetor cleaner.

INSPECTION

Inspect pump components and should any of the following conditions be found, the oil pump assembly should be replaced.
1. Inspect pump housing and cover assembly for cracks, scoring or casting

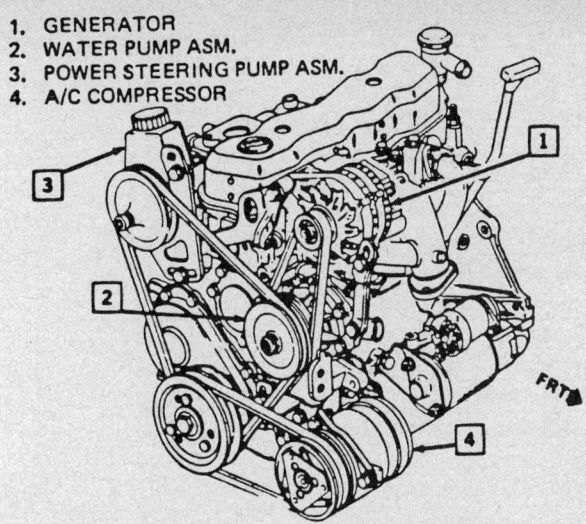

1. GENERATOR
2. WATER PUMP ASM.
3. POWER STEERING PUMP ASM.
4. A/C COMPRESSOR

Fig. 17   Serpentine belt routing

imperfections.
2. Inspect pressure regulator valve for scoring or sticking, burrs may be removed with a fine oil stone.
3. Inspect pressure regulator valve spring for loss of tension or bending, if in doubt replace spring.
4. Inspect screen assembly for looseness or broken wire mesh or screen.
5. Inspect oil pump for chipping, galling or wear.
6. Measure pump housing pocket depth and gear thickness, refer to "Engine Rebuilding Specifications" for specifications.

ASSEMBLY

To avoid engine damage, all pump cavities must be packed with petroleum jelly before installing the gears to assure priming.
1. Lubricate all internal parts with engine oil.
2. Install pump gears, then oil pump cover assembly.
3. Install pressure regulator valve and spring, then plug or pin. Make sure pin is properly secured.
4. **Torque** oil pump cover assembly bolts to 89 inch lbs.

INSTALLATION

1. Clean oil pump screen and oil pan.

2. Install oil filter, then **on 1988 models,** install restrictor.
3. **On all models,** Install oil pan and fill crankcase with clean engine oil.

ELECTRIC FUEL PUMP REPLACE

1. Disconnect battery ground cable, then drain fuel tank.
2. Disconnect tank unit harness connector.
3. Remove ground wire retaining screw from under body.
4. Disconnect hoses from tank meter assembly, then hoses at tank from filler and vent pipes.
5. Support fuel tank and disconnect the two fuel tank retaining straps.
6. Remove fuel tank from vehicle.
7. Remove fuel tank sending unit and pump assembly by turning cam lock ring counterclockwise. Lift assembly from fuel tank and remove pump from sending unit.
8. Pull fuel pump up into attaching hose while pulling outward away from bottom support. Take care to prevent damage to rubber insulator and strainer during removal.
9. After pump assembly is clear of bottom support, pull pump assembly out of rubber connector for removal.
10. Reverse procedure to install.

WATER PUMP REPLACE

REMOVAL

1. Disconnect battery ground cable, then drain cooling system.
2. Remove drive belts.
3. Remove water pump attaching bolts, then remove water pump from cover assembly, **Fig. 16.**
4. If installing a new pump use the pulley from the old unit.

INSTALLATION

1. Apply a 1/8 inch bead of red RTV sealant or equivalent, on the water pump sealing surface.
2. Coat water pump bolts with RTV sealant to avoid coolant leaks.
3. While the sealant is still wet, install the pump and **torque** bolts to 25 ft. lbs.
4. Install drive belts, then fill cooling system and connect battery ground cable.
5. Inspect cooling system for leaks.

SERPENTINE DRIVE BELT ROUTING

Refer to **Fig. 17.** for serpentine drive belt routing.

SERVICE BULLETINS

OIL CONSUMPTION

Some 1988 models may exhibit excessive oil consumption. This condition may be caused by one or more damaged intake valve stem seals. Its recommended the intake valve stem seal be inspected. The damaged seal can be identified by a cutout section on the top portion of the seal. If the seal is damaged, all intake valve stem seals must be replaced.

CAM SERVICING

On some models, when servicing the cam or crank gears, it is recommended that a new gear set kit be used to replace individual gears (part No. 10101789).

TIGHTENING SPECIFICATIONS

Year	Component	Torque/ft. lbs.
1988-91	Balancer To Block Bolts (Short Bolts)	9 ①
	Balancer To Block Bolts (Long Bolts)	9 ②
	Camshaft Sprocket Bolt ④	43
	Camshaft Thrust Plate To Block	90 ③
	Connecting Rod Nut	32
	Crankshaft Dampener Bolt	162
	EFI Assembly To Manifold Bolt	15
	EFI Assembly To Manifold Nut	15
	EGR Valve To Manifold Bolt	16
	Exhaust Manifold (Inner) Bolt	26
	Exhaust Manifold (Outer) Bolt	37
	Flywheel To Crankshaft (Automatic) Bolt	55
	Flywheel To Crankshaft (Manual) Bolt	69
	Intake Manifold Bolt	25
	Main Bearing To Block Bolt	⑤
	Oil Pan Drain Plug Bolt	25
	Oil Pan To Block	⑥
	Push Rod Cover To Block Bolt	90 ③
	Rocker Arm Bolt	24
	Rocker Arm Cover Bolt	⑦
	Spark Plugs	20
	Thermostat Housing Bolt	20
	Timing Gear Cover To Block Bolt	90 ③
	Water Outlet Housing Bolt	20
	Water Pump To Block	25

① —Plus an additional 75°
② —Plus an additional 90°
③ —Inch lbs.
④ —1988-89 models.
⑤ —1988 models, 70 ft. lbs.; 1989-91 models, 65 ft. lbs.
⑥ —1988 models, 20 ft. lbs.; 1989-91 models, 89 inch lbs.
⑦ —1988 models, 45 inch lbs.; 1989-91 models, 80 inch lbs.

3.0L/V6-181 & 3.3L/V6-204 Engine

INDEX

ENGINE MOUNTS
REPLACE
3.0L/V6-181 ENGINE

1. Support engine using fixture No. J-28467 or equivalent.
2. Raise and support vehicle.
3. Remove mount to engine mount bracket nuts.
4. Raise engine slightly, then remove mount to frame attaching nuts and the mount.
5. Reverse procedure to install.

3.3L/V6-204 ENGINE
Front Mount

1. Support engine using fixture No.

J-28467 or equivalent.

2. Load the fixture slightly to remove the weight of the engine from the mount.
3. Remove mount to engine bracket bolts, then raise the engine.
4. Remove mount to engine compartment bolts, then the mount.
5. Reverse procedure to install.

Rear Mount

1. Support engine using fixture No. J-28467 or equivalent.
2. Raise and support vehicle.
3. Remove mount to engine mount bracket nuts.
4. Raise engine slightly, then remove mount to frame bracket nuts and the mount.
5. Reverse procedure to install.

ENGINE
REPLACE

3.0L/V6-181 ENGINE

1. Depressurize and disconnect fuel lines from fuel rail.
2. Disconnect battery ground cable, then raise and support vehicle.
3. Disconnect electrical connectors from starter motor and remove starter.
4. Remove flywheel dust cover, then flywheel to torque converter bolts. Use a scribe to mark flywheel to torque converter relationship to ensure proper reassembly.
5. **On models equipped with A/C**, disconnect A/C electrical connectors, then remove A/C compressor and position aside.
6. **On all models**, drain cooling system, then disconnect lower radiator hose.
7. Remove right front engine mount bolts, then the right side splash guard.
8. Remove lower transaxle to engine bolts. One bolt is located between the transaxle case and engine block and is installed in the opposite direction.
9. Remove right rear engine mount nuts, then the right exhaust pipe at manifold.
10. Disconnect heater hoses from engine, then lower vehicle.
11. Mark hood for proper location and remove.
12. Remove serpentine drive belt, then the alternator.
13. **On models equipped with power steering**, remove power steering and pump.
14. **On all models**, disconnect electrical connectors, then remove the fan.
15. Disconnect upper radiator hose and remove the radiator.
16. Remove Mass Air Flow sensor tubing, then the master cylinder.
17. Remove accelerator and throttle valve cables from throttle body and cable bracket.
18. Install a suitable engine lifting fixture

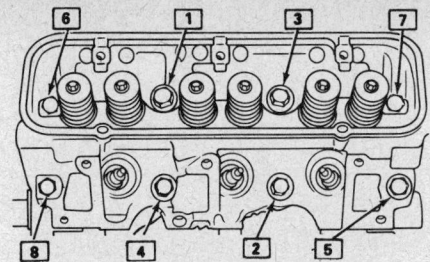

Fig. 1   Cylinder head bolt tightening sequence

and set up engine hoist, then remove left side transaxle support bracket.
19. Remove transaxle mounting bolts, then the engine assembly.
20. Reverse procedure to install.

3.3L/V6-204 ENGINE

1. Remove hood and cover fenders.
2. Depressurize and disconnect fuel lines from fuel rail.
3. Disconnect battery ground cable, then drain engine coolant.
4. Remove radiator and heater hoses, then engine cooling fan.
5. Remove air intake duct from throttle body, then vacuum lines from the brake power booster and evaporative canister purge.
6. Remove cable bracket and cables from throttle body, then the drive belt.
7. Remove power steering pump and position aside, then disconnect electrical connectors.
8. Remove upper transaxle to engine bolts, then raise and support vehicle.
9. **On models with A/C**, remove A/C compressor and position aside.
10. Remove rear engine mount to mount bracket bolts.
11. Remove flywheel dust cover, then flywheel to torque converter bolts. Use a scribe to mark flywheel to torque converter relationship to ensure proper reassembly.
12. Remove lower engine to transaxle bolts. One bolt is located between the transaxle case and engine block and is installed in the opposite direction.
13. Lower vehicle, then remove front engine mount to bracket bolts, then engine assembly.
14. Reverse procedures to install.

CYLINDER HEAD
REPLACE

3.0L/V6-181 ENGINE
Front Head

1. Disconnect battery ground cable.
2. Remove intake manifold as described

under "Intake Manifold, Replace."
3. Remove rocker arms, pedestals, retainers and pushrods. Keep valve train parts in order so they may be installed in their original locations.
4. Remove serpentine belt, then generator and bracket.
5. Remove engine cooling fan, then the radiator.
6. Remove dipstick and tube, then the front exhaust manifold.
7. Remove head bolts, then the cylinder head.
8. Reverse procedure to install noting the following:
   a. Apply G.M. thread sealer No. 1052080 or equivalent, on bolt threads.
   b. **Torque** bolts to specifications in sequence shown in **Fig. 1**: First, **torque** bolts to 25 ft. lbs. Second, tighten each bolt 90 degrees in sequence shown. Third, tighten each bolt an additional 90 degrees in sequence shown. At any time during the second and third tightening steps should you reach 60 ft. lbs., stop immediately and cease the remainder of the 90° turn on that bolt.

Rear Head

1. Disconnect battery ground cable.
2. Remove intake manifold as described under "Intake Manifold, Replace."
3. Remove rocker arms, pedestals, retainers and pushrods. Keep valve train parts in order so they may be installed in their original locations.
4. Remove serpentine belt, then power steering pump and belt tensioner.
5. Remove heater hoses, then rear exhaust manifold as described under "Exhaust Manifold, Replace."
6. Remove head bolts, then the cylinder head.
7. Reverse procedure to install noting the following:
   a. Apply G.M. thread sealer No. 1052080 or equivalent, on bolt threads.
   b. **Torque** bolts to specifications in sequence shown in **Fig. 1**: First, **torque** bolts to 25 ft. lbs. Second, tighten each bolt 90 degrees in sequence shown. Third, tighten each bolt an additional 90 degrees in sequence shown. At any time during the second and third tightening steps should you reach 60 ft. lbs., stop immediately and cease the remainder of the 90° turn on that bolt.

3.3L/V6-204 ENGINE

1. Disconnect battery ground cable.

2. Remove intake manifold as described under "Intake Manifold, Replace."
3. Remove exhaust manifold as described under "Exhaust Manifold, Replace."
4. Remove valve covers, then disconnect spark plug wires.
5. If right hand cylinder is to be removed, proceed as follows:
   a. Remove power steering pump and position aside with hose attached.
   b. Remove belt tensioner assembly.
6. If left hand cylinder head is to be removed, proceed as follows:
   a. Remove alternator bracket with ignition module and coil units attached.
   b. Remove A/C compressor mounting bolt from cylinder head.
7. Remove rocker arm assemblies, guide plate and push rods.
8. Remove cylinder head attaching bolts and cylinder heads.
9. Reverse procedure to install noting the following:
   a. Clean threads in the block using a $7/16$-14 tap, then clean bolt threads.
   b. Apply G.M. sealant No. 1052080 or equivalent, to the underside of the bolt heads.
   c. Apply G.M. thread locker No. 12345382 or equivalent, to the bolt threads.
   d. Install cylinder head bolts and tighten in sequence shown in **Fig. 1. Torque** each cylinder head bolt to 35 ft. lbs., then tighten an additional 130° using torque angle meter No. J-36660. Tighten the center four cylinder head attaching bolts an additional 30 degrees using torque angle meter J-36660.

INTAKE MANIFOLD
REPLACE

3.0L/V6-181 ENGINE

1. Depressurize and disconnect fuel lines from fuel rail, then disconnect battery ground cable.
2. Remove mass air flow sensor and air intake duct.
3. Remove serpentine drive belt, then the alternator and bracket assembly.
4. Remove ignition module and wiring.
5. Disconnect all vacuum lines and electrical connectors as necessary.
6. Disconnect throttle, throttle valve and cruise control cables from throttle body (if equipped).
7. Drain cooling system, then remove heater hoses from the throttle body.
8. Disconnect upper radiator hose, then remove intake manifold attaching bolts and the intake manifold.
9. Reverse procedure to install, noting the following:
   a. Apply G.M. sealant No. 12345336 or equivalent, to the ends of the manifold seals.
   b. Apply G.M. sealant No. 1052080 or equivalent, to all pipe threaded fittings.
   c. **Torque** intake manifold bolts to specifications in sequence shown in **Fig. 2.**

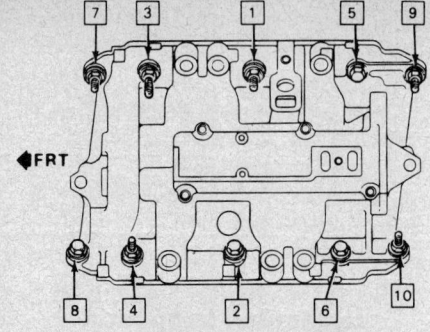

◀FRT

Fig. 2 Intake manifold bolt tightening sequence

3.3L/V6-204 ENGINE

1. Depressurize and disconnect fuel lines from fuel rail, then disconnect battery ground cable.
2. Remove serpentine drive belt, then the alternator and braces.
3. Remove power steering pump and braces and position aside.
4. Remove coolant bypass hose, then the heater pipe.
5. Remove upper radiator hose, then the air inlet duct.
6. Remove throttle cable bracket and cables from throttle body.
7. Disconnect vacuum hoses, then electrical connectors.
8. Remove the fuel rail, then disconnect the vapor canister purge line.
9. Remove heater hose from the throttle body, then disconnect the rear spark plug wires.
10. Remove the intake manifold bolts, then the manifold.
11. Reverse procedure to install noting the following:
    a. Clean the intake manifold bolts and bolt holes of adhesive compound.
    b. Apply G.M. sealant No. 12345336 or equivalent, to the ends of the manifold seals.
    c. Apply G.M. thread lock compound No. 12345493 or equivalent, to the manifold bolt threads.
    d. **Torque** the manifold bolts twice to 88 inch lbs. following the sequence in **Fig. 2.**
    e. Lubricate throttle body coolant and heater pipe O-rings with antifreeze before assembly.

EXHAUST MANIFOLD
REPLACE

3.0L/V6-181 ENGINE
Front

1. Disconnect battery ground cable.
2. Disconnect spark plug wires, then remove manifold to crossover pipe attaching bolts.
3. Remove air cleaner attaching bolts, then the engine cooling fan.
4. Remove exhaust manifold to cylinder head attaching bolts.
5. Remove oil level indicator tube and indicator, then the exhaust manifold.

6. Reverse procedure to install.

Rear

1. Disconnect battery ground cable.
2. Raise and support vehicle.
3. Remove exhaust pipe to manifold attaching bolts, then lower vehicle.
4. Disconnect oxygen sensor electrical connector and spark plug wires.
5. Remove manifold to crossover pipe retaining nuts.
6. Remove serpentine drive belt, then the power steering pump.
7. Disconnect heater hose from tube, then remove manifold heat shield.
8. Remove ignition module bracket attaching nuts.
9. Remove exhaust manifold attaching bolts and the manifold.
10. Reverse procedure to install.

3.3L/V6-204 ENGINE
Front

1. Disconnect battery ground cable.
2. Remove air cleaner inlet duct, then disconnect spark plug wires at spark plugs. Tag spark plug wires so they can be installed at the same location.
3. Disconnect exhaust crossover pipe from exhaust manifold.
4. Remove engine lifting hook.
5. Remove heat shield from exhaust manifold.
6. Remove engine oil dipstick and tube.
7. Remove exhaust manifold attaching studs, then remove exhaust manifold.
8. Reverse procedure to install.

Rear

1. Disconnect battery ground cable.
2. Disconnect spark plug wires at spark plugs. Tag spark plug wires so they can be installed in the same locations.
3. Disconnect electrical connector at oxygen sensor.
4. Disconnect throttle cables at throttle body, then remove throttle cable bracket.
5. Disconnect power brake unit vacuum hose at intake manifold.
6. Disconnect exhaust crossover pipe and exhaust pipe from exhaust manifold.
7. Remove engine lifting hook.
8. Remove transaxle dipstick and tube.
9. Remove heat shield from exhaust manifold.
10. Remove exhaust manifold attaching studs and bolt, then remove exhaust manifold.
11. Reverse procedure to install.

ROCKER ARMS

1. Remove valve cover.
2. Remove rocker arm pedestal retaining bolts. **On 3.0L/V6-181 engines**, note position of double ended bolts for assembly.
3. **On all models**, remove pedestal and rocker arm assembly, **Figs. 3 and 4.** Keep rocker arms and pedestals together and note installation position. Components that are to be reused should be installed in original position.

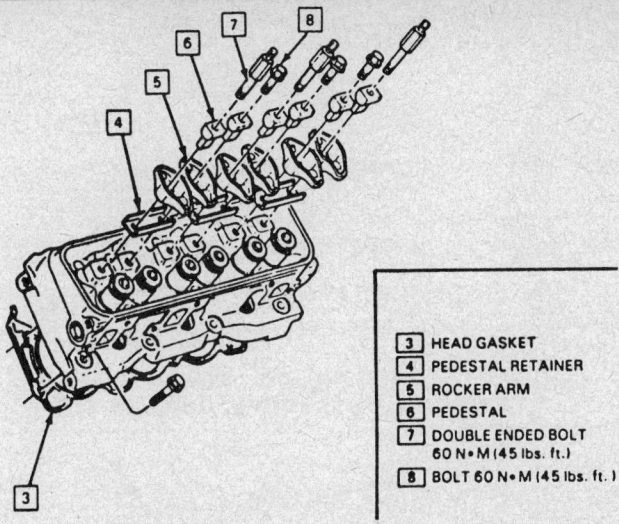

Fig. 3 Rocker arm installation. 3.0L/V6-181

3	HEAD GASKET
4	PEDESTAL RETAINER
5	ROCKER ARM
6	PEDESTAL
7	DOUBLE ENDED BOLT 60 N•M (45 lbs. ft.)
8	BOLT 60 N•M (45 lbs. ft.)

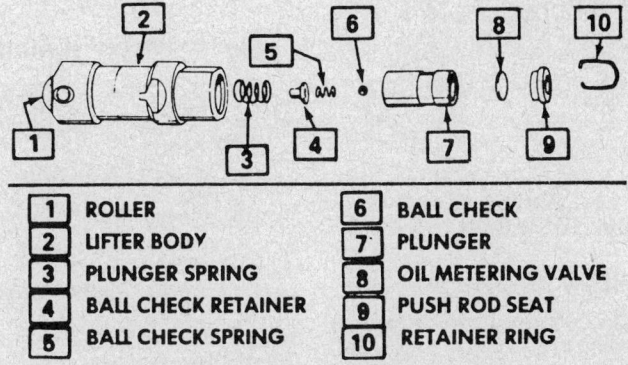

Fig. 4 Rocker arm installation. 3.3L/V6-204

5	PUSHROD GUIDE
6	ROCKER ARM
7	ROCKER ARM PIVOT
8	BOLT 51 N•M (37 LBS. FT.)
9	HEAD GASKET
10	HEAD BOLT

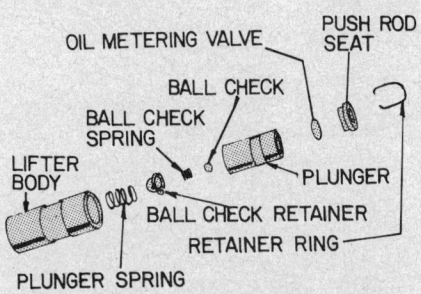

Fig. 5 Hydraulic valve lifter exploded view. 3.0L/V6-181

Fig. 6 Hydraulic roller valve lifter. 3.3L/V6-204

1	ROLLER	6	BALL CHECK
2	LIFTER BODY	7	PLUNGER
3	PLUNGER SPRING	8	OIL METERING VALVE
4	BALL CHECK RETAINER	9	PUSH ROD SEAT
5	BALL CHECK SPRING	10	RETAINER RING

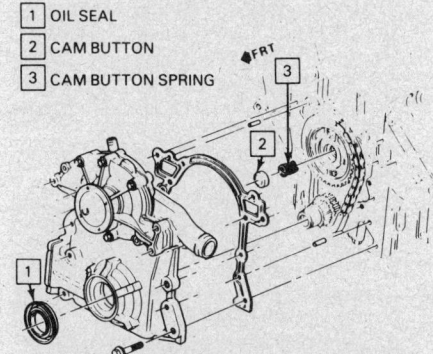

1	OIL SEAL
2	CAM BUTTON
3	CAM BUTTON SPRING

Fig. 7 Engine front cover replacement

4. Reverse procedure to install, **torquing** pedestal retaining bolts to 43 ft. lbs. on 3.0L/V6-181 engines, 28 ft. lbs. on 3.3L/V6-204 engines. On 3.3L/V6-204 engines, clean head bolt threads and apply G.M. sealant No. 1052624 to head bolt threads prior to installation.

VALVES
ADJUST

These engines are equipped with hydraulic valve lifters. No provision for adjustment is provided.

VALVE ARRANGEMENT
FRONT TO REAR

3.0L/V6-181, 3.3L/V6-204 . . . . E-I-I-E-I-E

VALVE GUIDES

The valve guides are an integral part of the cylinder head and cannot be replaced.

If the valve stem clearance is excessive, the valve guide must be reamed and an oversize valve installed. Valves are available in oversize of .010 inch.

VALVE LIFTERS

Failure of an hydraulic valve lifter, **Figs. 5 and 6**, is generally caused by dirt or an inadequate oil supply. An air leak at the intake side of the oil pump or too much oil in the engine will cause air bubbles in the oil supply to the lifters, causing them to collapse. This is a probable cause of trouble if several lifters fail to function, but air in the oil is an unlikely cause of failure of a single unit.

The valve lifters may be lifted out of their bores after removing the rocker arms, push rods and intake manifold. Adjustable pliers with taped jaws may be used to remove lifters that are stuck due to varnish, carbon, etc.

FRONT COVER
REPLACE

3.0L/V6-181 ENGINE

1. Disconnect battery ground cable.
2. Drain cooling system, then remove upper and lower radiator hoses.
3. Remove heater return hose, then serpentine belt.
4. Remove front clamp on coolant bypass hose, then balancer bolt, washer and balancer.
5. Remove front cover to cylinder block bolts, then front cover to oil pan bolts.
6. Remove front cover, **Fig. 7**, then oil pan and gasket.
7. Reverse procedure to install noting the following:
   a. Apply G.M. sealant No. 1052080 or equivalent, to front cover bolt threads and **torque** bolts to 22 ft. lbs. **Torque** oil pan bolts to 88 inch lbs.
   b. Adjust crankshaft sensor using tool No. J-36179 or equivalent.
   c. **Torque** balancer bolt to 219 ft. lbs.

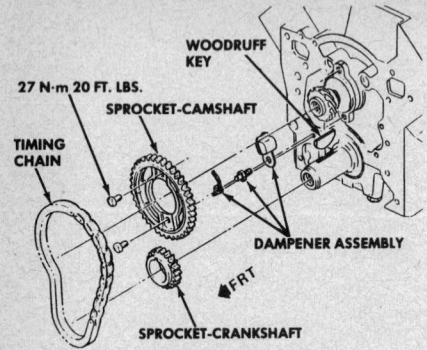

Fig. 8 Timing chain replacement

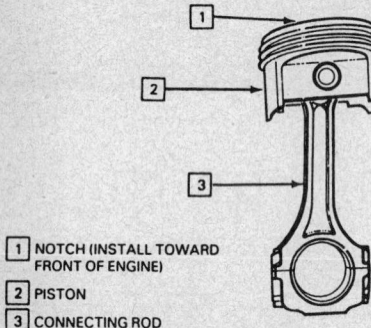

1. NOTCH (INSTALL TOWARD FRONT OF ENGINE)
2. PISTON
3. CONNECTING ROD

Fig. 11 Piston & rod assembly. 1989 3.3L/V6-204

3.3L/V6-204 ENGINE

1. Disconnect battery ground cable, then drain cooling system.
2. Remove serpentine drive belt, then the heater pipes. Remove lower radiator and coolant bypass hoses from front cover.
3. **On 1991 models,** remove alternator and position aside, then the power steering pump.
4. **On all models,** raise and support vehicle.
5. Remove right front wheel and tire assembly, then remove inner fender splash shield.
6. **On 1991 models,** remove right front axle, then support engine using fixture No. J-28467 or equivalent.
7. **On 1991 models,** remove engine mount, then tensioner bracket.
8. **On all models,** remove torque converter cover, then install flywheel holding tool J-37096 or equivalent to hold fly wheel in position.
9. Remove crankshaft balancer bolt, then remove balancer.
10. **On 1991 models,** remove crankshaft sensor shield.
11. **On all models,** disconnect electrical connectors at camshaft and crankshaft sensors and oil pressure sender switch.
12. Remove oil pan to front cover attaching bolts.
13. Remove front cover to engine attaching bolts, then remove front cover, **Fig. 7.**
14. Reverse procedure to install noting the following:

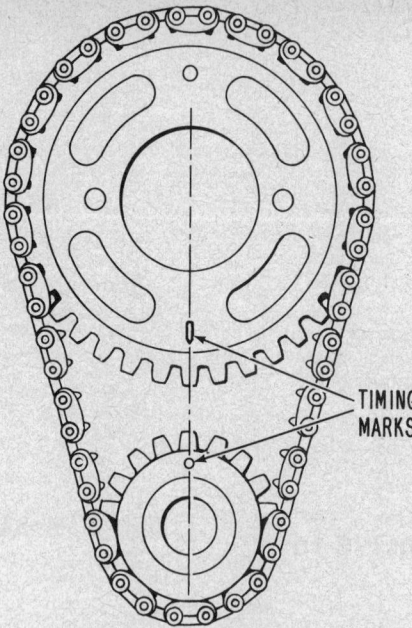

Fig. 9 Valve timing marks

a. Apply G.M. sealant No. 1052080 or equivalent, to front cover bolt threads.
b. **Torque** front cover bolts to 22 ft. lbs.
c. **Torque** oil pan to front cover bolts to 88 inch lbs.
d. Adjust crankshaft sensor using tool No. J-37087 or equivalent.
e. Hold flywheel in place using tool No. J-37096 or equivalent, then **torque** balancer bolt to 219 ft. lbs.

TIMING CHAIN REPLACE

1. Remove front cover as described under "Front Cover, Replace."
2. **On 1989-90 model 3.3L/V6-204 engines,** remove camshaft thrust bearing.
3. **On all models,** align timing marks on sprockets so they are as close together as possible, **Fig. 9.**
4. Remove camshaft sprocket attaching bolts, then the camshaft sprocket, chain and crankshaft sprocket, **Fig. 8.**
5. Reverse procedure to install noting the following:
   a. Install chain with No. 1 piston at TDC, timing mark on camshaft sprocket facing straight down and timing marks on sprockets as close together as possible, **Fig. 9.**
   b. **Torque** camshaft sprocket bolts to 31 ft. lbs. on 3.0L/V6-181 engines and 27 ft. lbs. on 3.3L/V6-204 engines.
   c. **Torque** timing chain dampener to 14 ft. lbs. on 3.0L/V6-181 engines and 16 ft. lbs. on 3.3L/V6-204 engines.

CAMSHAFT REPLACE

1. Disconnect battery ground cable, then

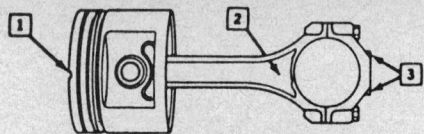

1. NOTCH ON PISTON TOWARDS FRONT OF ENGINE
2. LEFT BANK: NO. 1, 3 & 5 TWO BOSSES ON ROD TOWARDS REAR OF ENGINE (NOT SHOWN)
   RIGHT BANK: NO. 2, 4 & 6 TWO BOSSES ON ROD TOWARDS FRONT OF ENGINE (NOT SHOWN)
3. LEFT BANK: CHAMFERED CORNERS ON ROD CAP TOWARDS FRONT OF ENGINE
   RIGHT BANK: CHAMFERED CORNERS ON ROD CAP TOWARDS REAR OF ENGINE

Fig. 10 Piston & rod assembly. 3.0L/V6-181

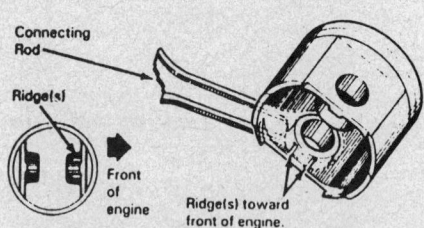

Fig. 12 Piston installation direction. 1990-91 3.3L/V6-204

remove engine as described in "Engine, Replace."
2. Remove intake manifold as described in " Intake Manifold, Replace."
3. Remove valve covers, then rocker arms, push rods and valve lifters.
4. Remove crankshaft balancer assembly, then **on 1991 3.3L/V6-204 engines,** remove crankshaft sensor shield.
5. **On all models,** remove front cover as described in "Front Cover, Replace."
6. Remove timing chain and sprockets.
7. Slide camshaft forward out of bearing bores, using care so as not to damage bearing surfaces.
8. Reverse procedure to install noting the following:
   a. Prior to installation, coat camshaft and dip valve lifters in G.M. lubricant No. 1052365 or equivalent.
   b. When installing camshaft, align crankshaft and camshaft timing marks as shown in Fig. 9.
   c. Dip valve lifters in G.M. prelube No. 12345501 or equivalent.

PISTONS & RODS ASSEMBLE

On 3.0L/V6-181 engines, rods and pistons should be assembled and installed as shown in **Fig. 10.**

On 1989 3.3L/V6-204 engines, when installing piston and connecting rod in cylinder bore, notch on piston must face toward front of engine as shown in **Fig. 11.**

On 1990-91 3.3L/V6-204 engines, when installing piston and connecting rod in cylinder bore, ridge on the outer diameter of the piston pin bore on the inside of the piston must face toward front of engine as shown in **Fig. 12.**

Measure connecting rod side clearance using a suitable feeler gauge. On

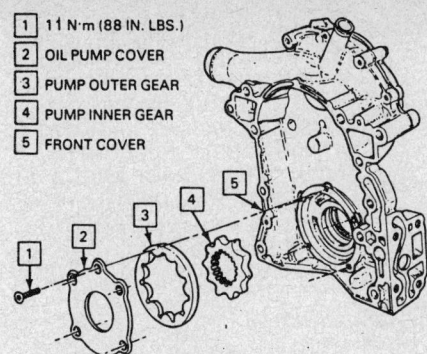

Fig. 13 Oil pump & housing assembly

1. 11 N·m (88 IN. LBS.)
2. OIL PUMP COVER
3. PUMP OUTER GEAR
4. PUMP INNER GEAR
5. FRONT COVER

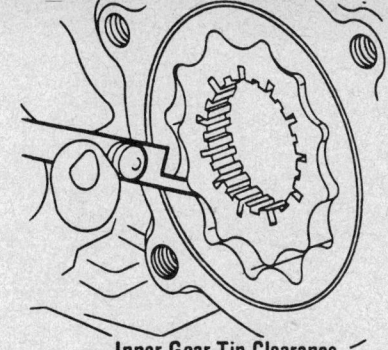

Inner Gear Tip Clearance

Fig. 14 Checking inner gear tip clearance

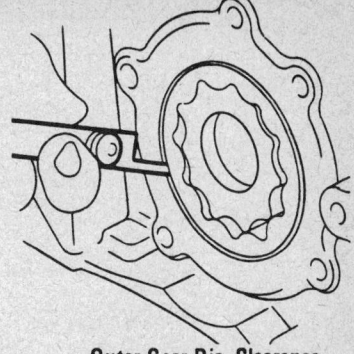

Outer Gear Dia. Clearance

Fig. 15 Checking outer gear diameter clearance

3.0L/V6-181 and 3.3L/V6-204 engines, clearance should be .003 to .015 inch.

PISTONS, PINS & RINGS

Pistons are available in standard sizes and oversizes of .010 and .030 inch. Rings are available in standard sizes and oversizes of .010 and .030 inch. Piston pins are supplied with piston and available only in standard sizes.

MAIN & ROD BEARINGS

Main bearings are available in standard sizes and undersizes of .001 and .002 inch. Rod bearings are available in standard sizes and in undersize of .008.

OIL PAN
REPLACE

3.0L/V6-181 ENGINE

1. Disconnect battery ground cable.
2. Raise and support vehicle.
3. Drain oil and remove flywheel cover.
4. Remove oil filter, then oil pan retaining bolts and oil pan.
5. Reverse procedure to install. **Torque** oil pan bolts to 88 inch lbs.

3.3L/V6-204 ENGINE

1. Disconnect battery ground cable.
2. Raise and support vehicle, then drain oil.
3. Remove transaxle converter cover, then remove starter motor.
4. Remove oil filter, then remove oil pan retaining bolts and oil pan.
5. Reverse procedure to install. **Torque** oil pan attaching bolts to 124 inch lbs.

OIL PUMP SERVICE
REMOVAL & INSPECTION

1. Remove engine front cover as described under "Front Cover, Replace", then the oil filter adapter, pressure regulator valve and valve spring.
2. Remove oil pump cover attaching screws, cover and gears, **Fig. 13.**
3. Inspect pump cover and housing for

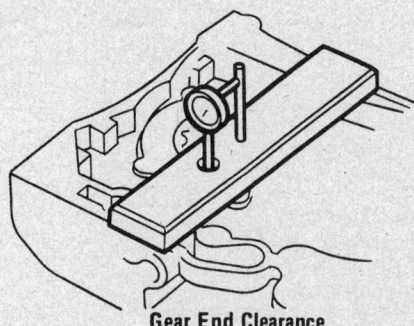

Gear End Clearance

Fig. 16 Checking gear end clearance

cracks, scoring, porosity and damaged threads, pressure regulator valve and spring for sticking, scoring or tension loss and gears for chipping, galling or excessive wear. Replace as necessary.
4. Check gear clearance as follows:
  a. Check inner gear tip clearance with feeler gauge as shown in **Fig. 14.** Maximum clearance should not exceed .006 inch.
  b. Check outer gear diameter clearance with feeler gauge as shown in **Fig. 15.** Clearance should be .008-.015 inch.
  c. Check gear end clearance (gear drop in housing) with suitable dial indicator as shown in **Fig. 16.** Clearance should be .001-.0035 inch.
5. Replace parts as necessary.

ASSEMBLY & INSTALLATION

1. Lubricate gears with petroleum jelly, then install into oil pump housing.
2. Pack pump cavity with petroleum jelly, then install pump cover and attaching screws. **Torque** attaching screws to 97 inch lbs.
3. Install pressure regulator valve spring and valve.
4. Install oil filter adapter using new gasket. **Torque** adapter to 24 ft.lbs.
5. Reinstall front cover onto engine.

REAR MAIN BEARING OIL SEAL
REPLACE

3.0L/V6-181 ENGINE & 1989–90 3.3L/V6-204 ENGINE

1. Remove engine from vehicle as described under "Engine, Replace."
2. Drain engine oil, then remove oil pan as described under "Oil Pan, Replace."
3. Remove crankshaft.
4. Remove old seal and clean remains of sealer and adhesive from upper and lower bearing groove and mating surface of the bearing cap.
5. Apply G.M. adhesive No. 1052621 or equivalent to the seal groove.
6. Within one minute insert rope seal into groove. Roll into place with a suitable tool until seal projects above groove no more than 1/16 inch.
7. Seat the seal with a suitable tool.
8. Cut excess seal material with a sharp knife at the bearing cap parting line using the seal installer to hold the seal in place.
9. Apply a thin film of chassis grease to rope seal.
10. Apply a thin film of G.M. sealer No. 1052942 or equivalent on the bearing cap mating surface around the seal groove. Use sealer sparingly and keep out of bolt threads. Soak sealing strips in light oil or kerosene for about 5 minutes prior to installation.
11. Re-install the rear main bearing cap, then install bearing cap side seals.
12. Install crankshaft, then the oil pan.
13. Install engine into vehicle.

1991 3.3L/V6-204 ENGINE

1. Remove flywheel, then confirm rear seal leak.
2. Insert a screwdriver or similar tool in through the dust lip at any angle and pry seal out by moving the handle of the tool towards the end of the crankshaft pilot. Repeat as required around the seal until seal is removed. Care must be taken not to damage crankshaft OD surface or chamfer with pry tool.

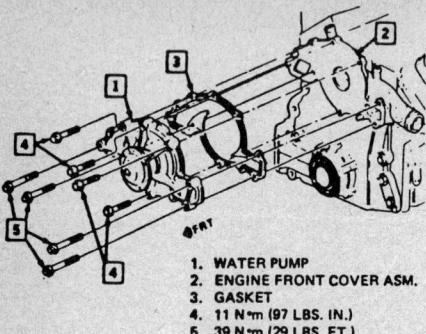

1. WATER PUMP
2. ENGINE FRONT COVER ASM.
3. GASKET
4. 11 N·m (97 LBS. IN.)
5. 39 N·m (29 LBS. FT.)

Fig. 17 Water pump replacement

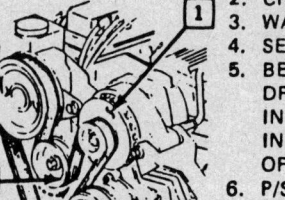

1. GENERATOR PULLEY
2. CRANKSHAFT BALANCER
3. WATER PUMP PULLEY
4. SERPENTINE BELT
5. BELT TENSIONER — ROTATE DRIVE BELT TENSIONER IN DIRECTION OF ARROW IN ORDER TO INSTALL OR REMOVE DRIVE BELT
6. P/S PUMP PULLEY

Fig. 18 Serpentine belt routing. 3.0L/V6-181 less A/C

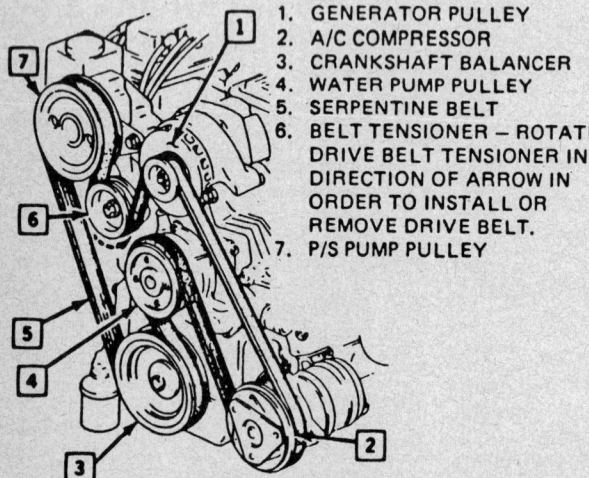

1. GENERATOR PULLEY
2. A/C COMPRESSOR
3. CRANKSHAFT BALANCER
4. WATER PUMP PULLEY
5. SERPENTINE BELT
6. BELT TENSIONER — ROTATE DRIVE BELT TENSIONER IN DIRECTION OF ARROW IN ORDER TO INSTALL OR REMOVE DRIVE BELT.
7. P/S PUMP PULLEY

Fig. 19 Serpentine belt routing. 3.0L/V6-181 with A/C

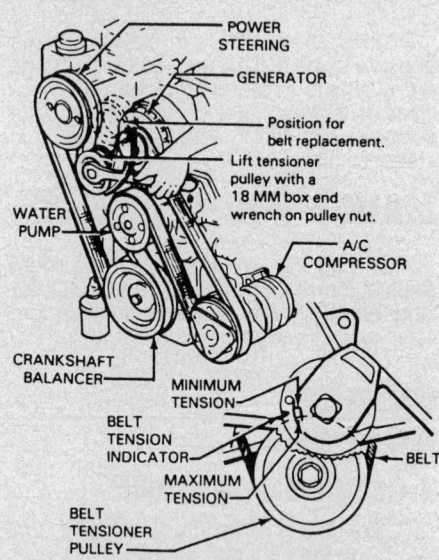

POWER STEERING

GENERATOR

Position for belt replacement.

Lift tensioner pulley with a 18 MM box end wrench on pulley nut.

WATER PUMP

A/C COMPRESSOR

CRANKSHAFT BALANCER

MINIMUM TENSION

BELT TENSION INDICATOR

MAXIMUM TENSION

BELT

BELT TENSIONER PULLEY

Fig. 20 Serpentine belt routing. 3.3L/V6-204

3. Using tool No. J-38196 or equivalent, apply engine oil to the ID and OD of new seal. Slide new seal over mandrel until back of seal bottom squarely fits against collar.
4. Install seal as follows:
   a. Align dowel pin of tool with dowel pin in crankshaft and attach tool to crankshaft by hand, or **torque** attaching screws to 60 inch lbs.
   b. Turn t-handle of tool so that collar pushes seal into bore, turn the handle until the collar is tight against the case. This will ensure the seal is seated properly.
   c. Loosen the T-handle of the tool until it comes to a stop, then remove attaching screws.
5. Install flywheel.

ELECTRIC FUEL PUMP
REPLACE

1. Disconnect battery ground cable, then

drain fuel tank.
2. Disconnect tank unit harness connector.
3. Remove ground wire retaining screw from under body.
4. Disconnect hoses from tank meter assembly, then hoses at tank from filler and vent pipes.
5. Support fuel tank and disconnect the two fuel tank retaining straps.
6. Remove fuel tank from vehicle.
7. Remove fuel tank sending unit and pump assembly by turning cam lock ring counterclockwise. Lift assembly from fuel tank and remove pump from sending unit.
8. Pull fuel pump up into attaching hose while pulling outward away from bottom support. Take care to prevent damage to rubber insulator and strainer during removal.
9. After pump assembly is clear of bottom support, pull pump assembly out of rubber connector for removal.
10. Reverse procedure to install.

WATER PUMP
REPLACE
3.0L/V6-181 ENGINE

1. Disconnect battery ground cable.
2. Drain cooling system, then remove drive belt.
3. Remove lower radiator hose and heater hose at pump.
4. Remove water pump pulley attaching bolts. Long bolt is removed through access hole located in the body side rail.
5. Remove water pump pulley.
6. Remove water pump attaching bolts, then the water pump, **Fig. 17.**
7. Reverse procedure to install. **Torque** bolts to 84 inch lbs.

3.3L/V6-204 ENGINE

1. Disconnect battery ground cable.
2. Drain cooling system, then remove serpentine belt.
3. Remove idler pulley bolt, then water

pump pulley bolts and remove pulley.
4. Remove water pump attaching bolts, then the water pump, **Fig. 17.**
5. Reverse procedure to install. **Torque** bolts to 84 inch lbs.

BELT TENSION DATA

A self-adjusting serpentine drive belt is used to drive accessories in place of the usual v-type belt arrangement.

SERPENTINE DRIVE BELT ROUTING

Refer to **Figs. 18-20.** for serpentine drive belt routing.

TIGHTENING SPECIFICATIONS

3.0L/V6-181 ENGINE

Year	Component	Torque/ft. lbs.
1988	Balance Assembly To Crankshaft	219
	Connecting Rods	45
	Crankshaft Bearing Caps To Cylinder Block	100
	Crankshaft Sensor To Front Cover	22
	Cylinder Block Drain Plug	32
	Cylinder Head To Block	①
	EGR Valve To Intake Manifold	13
	ESC Knock Sensor To Block	13
	Exhaust Cross Over Pipe To Manifold	15
	Exhaust Manifold To Cylinder Head	37
	Flywheel Cover To Transaxle	48②
	Flywheel To Crankshaft	60
	Front Cover To Block	22
	Intake Manifold To Cylinder Head	32
	Mount (Engine) To Cylinder Block	70
	Oil Pan Drain Plug	42
	Oil Pan To Cylinder Block	88②
	Oil Pump Cover To Timing Chain Cover	97②
	Oxygen Sensor To Exhaust Manifold	31
	Rocker Arm Cover To Cylinder Head	10②
	Rocker Arm To Cylinder Head	43
	Spark Plug To Cylinder Head	20
	Starting Motor To Cylinder Block	35
	Torque Converter To Flywheel	46
	Water Pump Cover To Timing Chain Cover	84②
	Water Pump Pulley To Hub	106②

①—See text.
②—Inch lbs.

TIGHTENING SPECIFICATIONS

3.3L/V6-204 ENGINE

Year	Component	Torque/ft. lbs.
1989-90	Balance Assembly To Crankshaft	219
	Camshaft Sprocket Bolts	26
	Connecting Rod Bolts	20①
	Coolant Temperature Sensor To Intake	15
	Crankshaft Bearing Caps To Cylinder Block	90
	Cylinder Block Drain Plug	32
	Cylinder Head To Block	②
	ESC Knock Sensor To Cylinder Block	13
	Exhaust Manifold To Cylinder Head	30
	Flywheel Cover To Transaxle	48③
	Front Cover To Block	22
	Intake Manifold To Cylinder Head	88③
	Mount (Engine) To Cylinder Block	70

Continued

TIGHTENING SPECIFICATIONS —Continued

3.3L/V6-204 ENGINE

Year	Component	Torque/ft. lbs.
1989-90	Oil Pan Drain Plug	18
	Oil Pan To Cylinder Block	124③
	Oil Pan To Front Cover	124③
	Oil Pump Cover To Timing Chain Cover	97③
	Oxygen Sensor To Exhaust Manifold	31
	Rocker Arm Cover To Cylinder Head	88③
	Rocker Arm Pedestal To Cylinder Head	28
	Serpentine Belt Tensioner To Cylinder Head	33
	Spark Plug To Cylinder Head	20
	Starting Motor To Cylinder Block	35
	Timing Chain Dampener	16
	Torque Converter To Flywheel	46
	Transaxle To Cylinder Block	55
	Valve Lifter Guide Retainer Bolts	22
	Water Pump To Front Cover	84③
	Water Pump Pulley To Hub	142③
1991	Balance Assembly To Crankshaft	105④
	Camshaft Sprocket Bolts	52⑤
	Connecting Rod Bolts	20①
	Coolant Temperature Sensor To Intake	15
	Crankshaft Bearing Caps To Cylinder Block	26⑥
	Cylinder Block Drain Plug	25
	Cylinder Head To Block	②
	ESC Knock Sensor To Cylinder Block	13
	Exhaust Manifold To Cylinder Head	41
	Flywheel Cover To Transaxle	53③
	Front Cover To Block	22
	Intake Manifold To Cylinder Head	89③
	Mount (Engine) To Cylinder Block	70
	Oil Pan Drain Plug	30
	Oil Pan To Cylinder Block	124③
	Oil Pan To Front Cover	124③
	Oil Pump Cover To Timing Chain Cover	97③
	Oxygen Sensor To Exhaust Manifold	31
	Rocker Arm Pedestal To Cylinder Head	28
	Serpentine Belt Tensioner To Cylinder Head	38
	Spark Plug To Cylinder Head	20
	Starting Motor To Cylinder Block	35
	Timing Chain Dampener	14
	Torque Converter To Flywheel	46
	Transaxle To Cylinder Block	46
	Valve Lifter Guide Retainer Bolts	27
	Water Pump Pulley To Hub	115③

①—Plus an additional 50°.
②—See text.
③—Inch lbs.

④—Plus an additional 56°
⑤—Plus an additional 110°
⑥—Plus an additional 45°

Clutch & Manual Transaxle

NOTE: Refer To "Clutch & Manual Transaxle" Section In Chapter 7 For Service Procedures.

Rear Axle & Rear Suspension

NOTE: Refer To "Rear Suspension" Section In Chapter 7 For Service Procedures.

Front Suspension & Steering

NOTE: Refer To "Front Suspension & Steering" Section In Chapter 7 For Service Procedures Not Covered In This Section.

INDEX

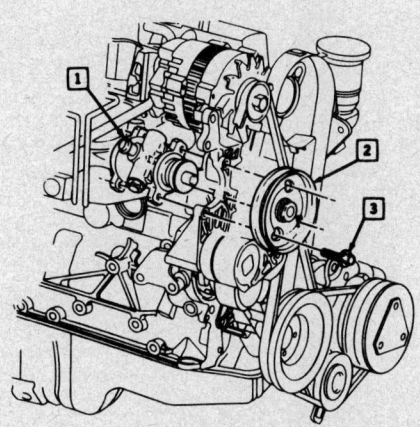

1. POWER STEERING PUMP
2. PULLEY
3. BOLT – 27 N·m (20 LBS. FT.)

Fig. 1 Power steering pump replacement. 2.0L/4-121 engine.

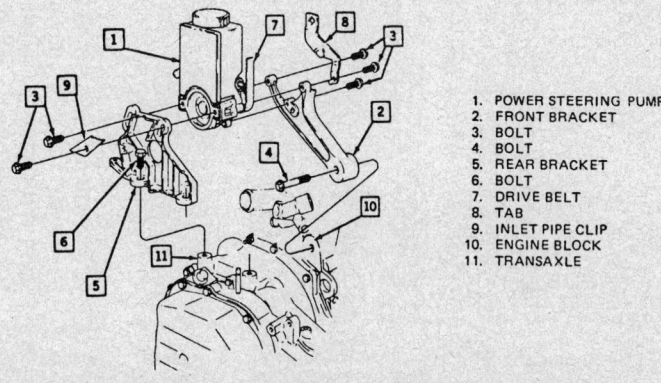

1. POWER STEERING PUMP
2. FRONT BRACKET
3. BOLT
4. BOLT
5. REAR BRACKET
6. BOLT
7. DRIVE BELT
8. TAB
9. INLET PIPE CLIP
10. ENGINE BLOCK
11. TRANSAXLE

Fig. 2 Power steering pump replacement. 1988-89 2.3L/4-138 engine w/automatic transaxle.

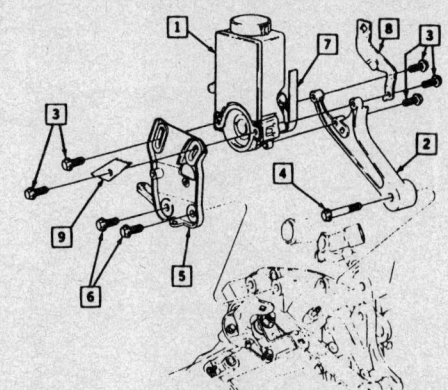

1. POWER STEERING PUMP
2. FRONT BRACKET
3. BOLT – 26 N·m (19 LBS. FT.)
4. BOLT – 96 N·m (71 LBS. FT.)
5. REAR BRACKET
6. BOLT – 54 N·m (39 LBS. FT.)
7. DRIVE BELT
8. TAB
9. CLIP

Fig. 3 Power steering pump replacement. 1988-89 2.3L/4-138 engine w/manual transaxle.

POWER STEERING PUMP
REPLACE

Refer to **Figs. 1 through 11** when replacing the power steering pump.

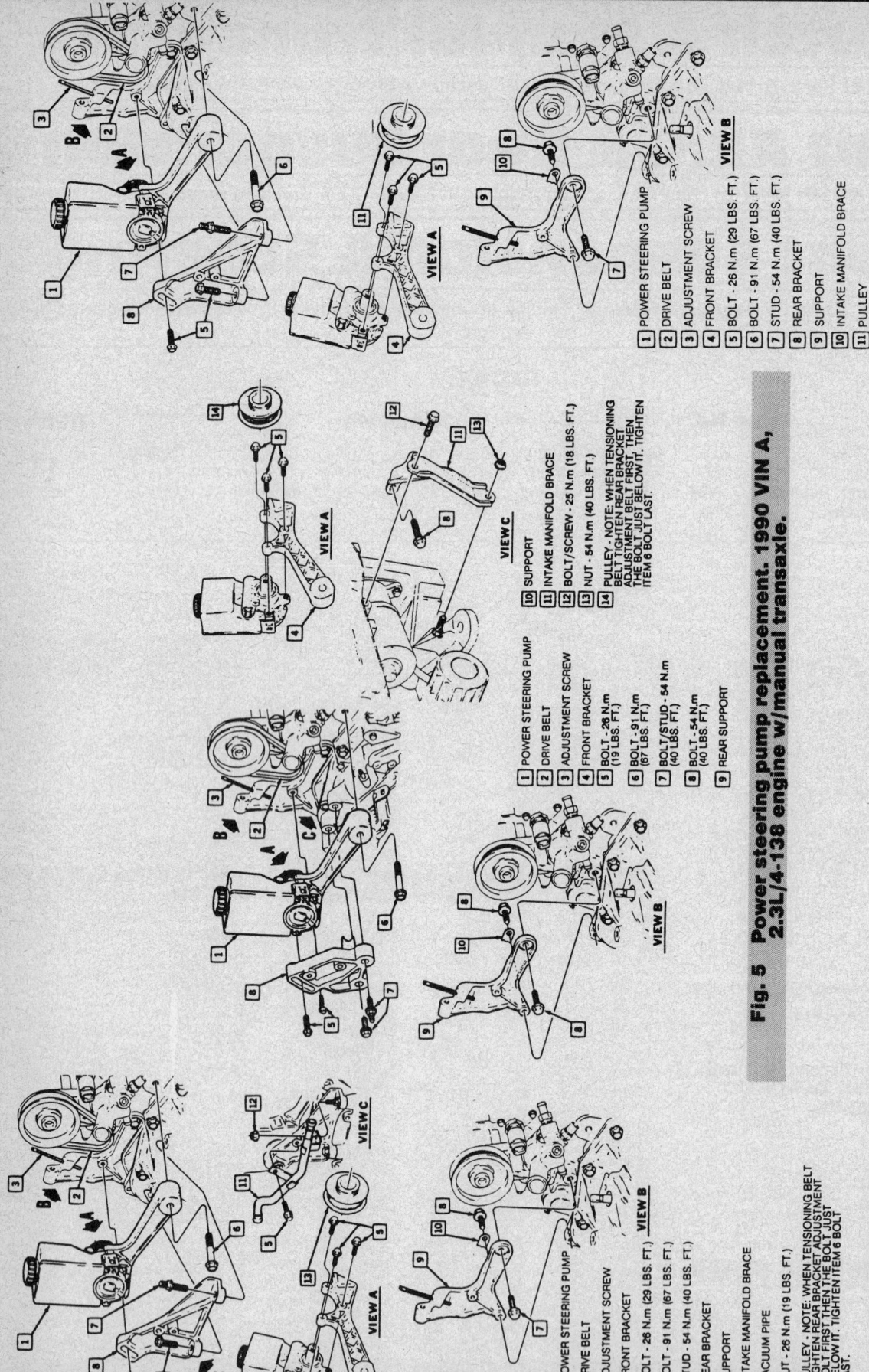

Fig. 6 Power steering pump replacement. 1991 VIN D, 2.3L/4-138 engine.

1. POWER STEERING PUMP
2. DRIVE BELT
3. ADJUSTMENT SCREW
4. FRONT BRACKET
5. BOLT - 26 N.m (29 LBS. FT.)
6. BOLT - 91 N.m (67 LBS. FT.)
7. STUD - 54 N.m (40 LBS. FT.)
8. REAR BRACKET
9. SUPPORT
10. INTAKE MANIFOLD BRACE
11. PULLEY

Fig. 5 Power steering pump replacement. 1990 VIN A, 2.3L/4-138 engine w/manual transaxle.

1. POWER STEERING PUMP
2. DRIVE BELT
3. ADJUSTMENT SCREW
4. FRONT BRACKET
5. BOLT - 26 N.m (19 LBS. FT.)
6. BOLT - 91 N.m (67 LBS. FT.)
7. BOLT/STUD - 54 N.m (40 LBS. FT.)
8. BOLT - 54 N.m (40 LBS. FT.)
9. REAR SUPPORT
10. SUPPORT
11. INTAKE MANIFOLD BRACE
12. BOLT/SCREW - 25 N.m (18 LBS. FT.)
13. NUT - 54 N.m (40 LBS. FT.)
14. PULLEY - NOTE: WHEN TENSIONING BELT TIGHTEN REAR BRACKET ADJUSTMENT BELT FIRST, THEN TIGHTEN THE BOLT JUST BELOW IT. TIGHTEN ITEM 6 BOLT LAST.

Fig. 4 Power steering pump replacement. 1990 VIN D, 2.3L/4-138 engine w/automatic transaxle.

1. POWER STEERING PUMP
2. DRIVE BELT
3. ADJUSTMENT SCREW
4. FRONT BRACKET
5. BOLT - 26 N.m (29 LBS. FT.)
6. BOLT - 91 N.m (67 LBS. FT.)
7. STUD - 54 N.m (40 LBS. FT.)
8. REAR BRACKET
9. SUPPORT
10. INTAKE MANIFOLD BRACE
11. VACUUM PIPE
12. NUT - 26 N.m (19 LBS. FT.)
13. PULLEY - NOTE: WHEN TENSIONING BELT TIGHTEN REAR BRACKET ADJUSTMENT BOLT FIRST, THEN FIX THE BOLT JUST BELOW IT. TIGHTEN ITEM 6 BOLT LAST.

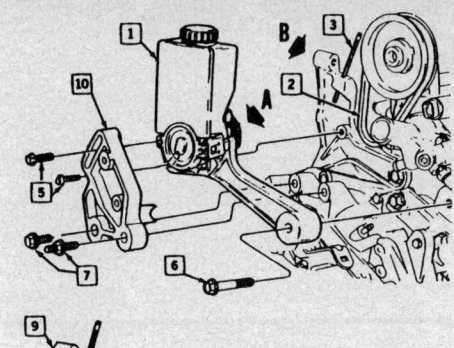

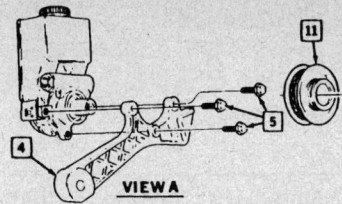

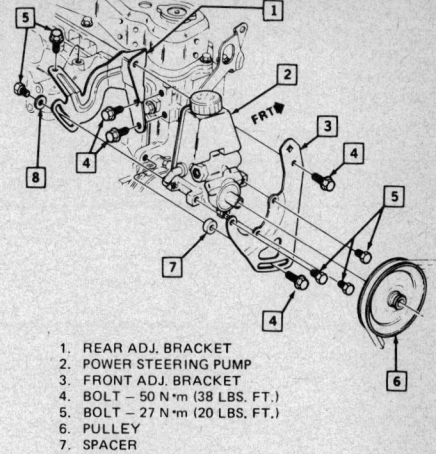

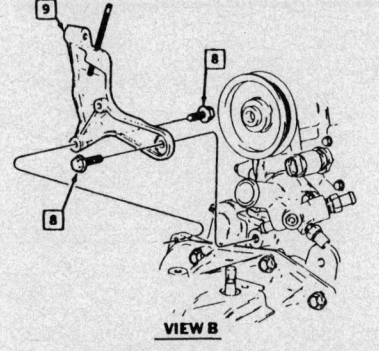

1. POWER STEERING PUMP
2. DRIVE BELT
3. ADJUSTMENT SCREW
4. FRONT BRACKET
5. BOLT - 26 N.m (19 LBS. FT.)
6. BOLT - 91 N.m (67 LBS. FT.)
7. BOLT/STUD - 54 N.m (40 LBS. FT.)
8. BOLT - 54 N.m (40 LBS. FT.)
9. REAR SUPPORT
10. FRONT SUPPORT
11. PULLEY - NOTE: WHEN TENSIONING BELT TIGHTEN REAR BRACKET ADJUSTMENT BELT FIRST, THEN THE BOLT JUST BELOW IT. TIGHTEN BOLT 6 LAST.

1. REAR ADJ. BRACKET
2. POWER STEERING PUMP
3. FRONT ADJ. BRACKET
4. BOLT — 50 N·m (38 LBS. FT.)
5. BOLT — 27 N·m (20 LBS. FT.)
6. PULLEY
7. SPACER
8. WASHER

Fig. 8 Power steering pump replacement. 2.5L/4-151 engine

Fig. 7 Power steering pump replacement. 1991 VIN A, 2.3L/4-138 engine.

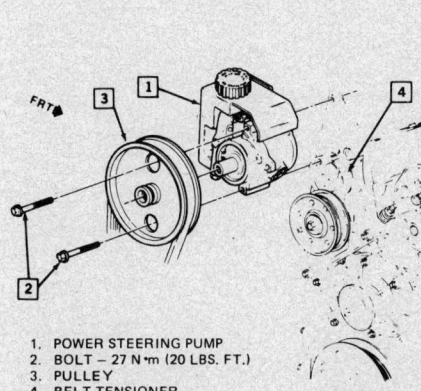

1. POWER STEERING PUMP
2. BOLT — 27 N·m (20 LBS. FT.)
3. PULLEY
4. BELT TENSIONER

Fig. 9 Power steering pump replacement. 3.0L/V6-181 engine

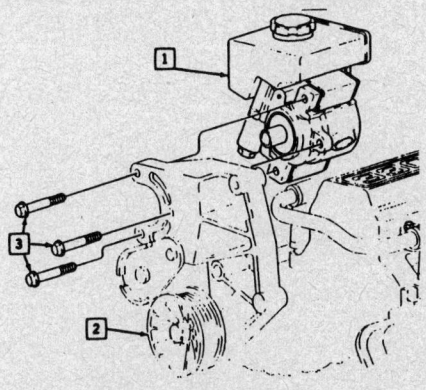

1. POWER STEERING PUMP
2. TENSIONER ASSEMBLY
3. BOLT — 27 N·m (20 LBS. FT.)

Fig. 10 Power steering pump replacement. 1989 3.0L/V6-204 engine

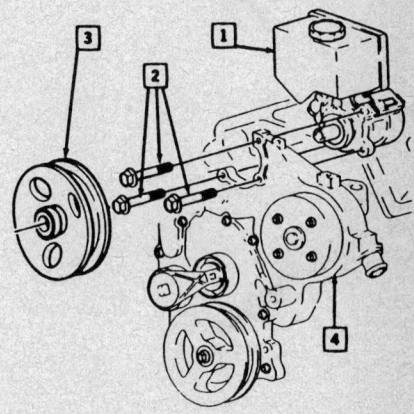

1. POWER STEERING PUMP
2. BOLT - 25 N.m (18 LBS. FT.)
3. PULLEY
4. COVER

Fig. 11 Power steering pump replacement. 1990-91 3.0L/V6-204 engine

Wheel Alignment

NOTE: Refer To "Wheel Alignment" Section In Chapter 7 For Service Procedures.

PONTIAC FIERO
(P Car)

INDEX OF SERVICE OPERATIONS

NOTE: Refer To The Rear Of This Manual For Vehicle Manufacturer's Special Service Tool Suppliers.

INDEX OF SERVICE OPERATIONS—Continued

Specifications
GENERAL ENGINE SPECIFICATIONS

Year	Engine Liter/CID ①	Engine VIN Code	Fuel System	Bore & Stroke	Compression Ratio	Net H.P. @ RPM ②	Maximum Torque Ft. Lbs. @ RPM	Normal Oil Pressure Pounds
1988	2.5L/4-151	R	E.F.I. ③	4.00 x 3.00	9.0	98 @ 4800	135 @ 3200	—
	2.8L/V6-173	9	MPFI ④	3.50 x 2.99	8.5	135 @ 4500	165 @ 3600	—

①—CID-Cubic inch displacement.
②—Ratings are net as installed in vehicle.
③—Electronic fuel injection.
④—Multi-point fuel injection.

TUNE UP SPECIFICATIONS

Year & Engine/ VIN Code ①	Spark Plug Gap	Ignition Timing BTDC ② Firing Order ③	Ignition Timing BTDC ② Man. Trans.	Ignition Timing BTDC ② Auto. Trans.	Ignition Timing BTDC ② Mark Fig.	Curb Idle Speed Man. Trans.	Curb Idle Speed Auto Trans.	Fast Idle Speed Man. Trans.	Fast Idle Speed Auto. Trans.	Fuel Pump Pressure, Psi
1988										
2.5L/4-151/R	.060	⑦	⑧	⑧	⑨	④	④	④	④	9–13 ⑤
2.8L/V6-173/9	.045	⑩	⑧	⑧	⑨	④	④	④	④	40.5–47 ⑥

①—The eighth digit of the Vehicle Identification Number (VIN) denotes engine code.
②—BTDC:Before Top Dead Center.
③—Before disconnecting wires from distributor cap, determine location of No. 1 wire in cap, as distributor position may have been altered from that shown at the end of this chart.
④—Idle speed is controlled by the Idle Air Control (IAC) valve.
⑤—Wrap shop towel around fuel hose to steel line connection to prevent fuel spillage. Disconnect fuel hose from steel line & connect a suitable fuel pressure gauge between hose & steel line. Ensure gauge connections are tight, then start engine & note fuel pressure readings.
⑥—With shop towel wrapped around fuel pressure valve to prevent fuel spillage, connect a suitable fuel pressure gauge to fuel pressure valve. Check fuel pressure with ignition switch ON, engine not running.
⑦—Cylinder numbering from front of engine to rear 1, 2, 3, 4. Firing order 1-3-4-2. Refer to Fig. A for spark plug wire connections at coil unit.
⑧—Electronically controlled, no adjustment.
⑨—Equipped with crankshaft position sensor.
⑩—Cylinder numbering left to right as viewed from front of vehicle, front bank 2, 4, 6; rear bank 1, 3, 5. Firing order 1-2-3-4-5-6. Refer to Fig. B for spark plug wire connections at coil unit.

Continued

TUNE UP SPECIFICATIONS—Continued

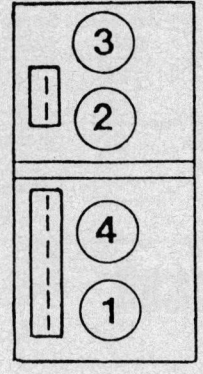

Fig. A

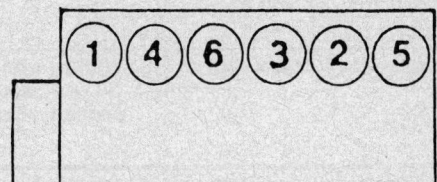

Fig. B

ALTERNATOR SPECIFICATIONS

Year	Model	Rated Hot Output Amps.
1988	1101149	100
	1191465	100

STARTING MOTOR APPLICATIONS

Refer to "Starter Motors" for starter specifications.

Year	Model	Starter Number
1988	All	1998533

WHEEL ALIGNMENT SPECIFICATIONS

Year	Model	Caster Angle, Degrees		Camber Angle, Degrees				Toe-In
		Limits	Desired	Limits		Desired		
				Left	Right	Left	Right	
1988	① ②	+2.5° to +3.5°	+3°	−.5° to +.5°	−.5° to +.5°	0°	0°	−1.7° to +2.3°
	① ③	+4.5° to +5.5°	+5°	−.5° to +.5°	−.5° to +.5°	−.5° to +.5°	−.5° to +.5°	−1.7° to +2.3°
	All ④	—	—	−1.5° to −.5°	−1.5° to −.5°	−1°	−1°	+.05° to +.25°

①—Front wheel alignment.
②—Except GT & Formula.
③—GT & Formula.
④—Rear wheel alignment.

COOLING SYSTEM & CAPACITY DATA

Year	Model or Engine/ VIN	Cooling Capacity, Qts.		Radiator Cap Relief Pressure Lbs.	Thermo. Opening Temp.	Fuel Tank Gals.	Engine Oil Refill Qts.	Transaxle Oil	
		Less A/C	With A/C					Manual Transaxle Pts.	Auto. Transaxle Qts. ①
1988	2.5L/4-151/R	13.8	④	15	195	11.9	4②	⑤	③
	2.8L/V6-173/9	13.8	13.8	15	195	11.9	4②	⑤	③

①—Approximate; make final check with dipstick.

②—With or without filter change.

③—Oil pan capacity, 4 qts.; total capacity, 5 qts.

④—Auto. trans., 13.8 qts.; man. trans., 14.1 qts.

⑤—Isuzu 5 speed, 5.3 pts.; Muncie 5 speed, 4.1 pts.

Electrical
INDEX

FUSE PANEL & FLASHER LOCATION

The fuse panel and flasher are located behind the lefthand side of the instrument panel.

STARTER
REPLACE

1. Disconnect battery ground cable.
2. Disconnect solenoid wires from starter motor.
3. Raise and support vehicle.
4. Remove heat shield, if equipped.
5. **On models with 4-151 engine**, remove rear starter bracket attaching bolts.
6. **On all models**, remove the 2 starter motor motor-to-engine bolts.
7. Remove starter motor through front of converter toward front of engine.
8. Reverse procedure to install.

DISTRIBUTOR
REPLACE
2.8L/V6-173 ENGINE

1. Disconnect ignition switch battery feed and tachometer lead wire from distributor, if equipped.
2. Disconnect distributor cap coil connectors.
3. Remove distributor cap by turning attaching screws counterclockwise. Position cap out of way.
4. Disconnect ECM harness from distributor.
5. If necessary, remove secondary wires from cap, then disconnect wiring harness connectors and remove wiring harness retainers.
6. Remove distributor clamp screw, then the distributor hold-down clamp.
7. Mark position of rotor, then pull distributor up until rotor stops turning counterclockwise and note position of rotor. To ensure proper engine timing the distributor must be installed with rotor correctly positioned.
8. Reverse procedure to install.

STEERING WHEEL
REPLACE
STANDARD STEERING COLUMN

1. Disconnect battery ground cable.
2. Remove steering pad attaching screws, then disconnect horn electrical connector , then remove steering pad assembly.
3. Remove retainer and steering wheel attaching nut.
4. Mark steering wheel and shaft for installation alignment.
5. Remove steering wheel using puller J-1859-03 or equivalent.
6. Reverse procedure to install. **Torque** steering wheel attaching nut to 30 ft. lbs.

TILT STEERING COLUMN

1. Disconnect battery ground cable.
2. Remove steering pad attaching screws, then disconnect horn electrical connectors at steering pad.
3. Remove steering shaft lock bolt positioning screws.
4. Remove steering shaft lock knob bolt at steering shaft.
5. Remove steering wheel nut retainer.
6. Remove steering wheel attaching nut.
7. Mark steering wheel and shaft for installation alignment.
8. Remove steering wheel using puller BT-61-9 or equivalent.
9. Reverse procedure to install. **Torque** steering wheel attaching nut to 30 ft. lbs.

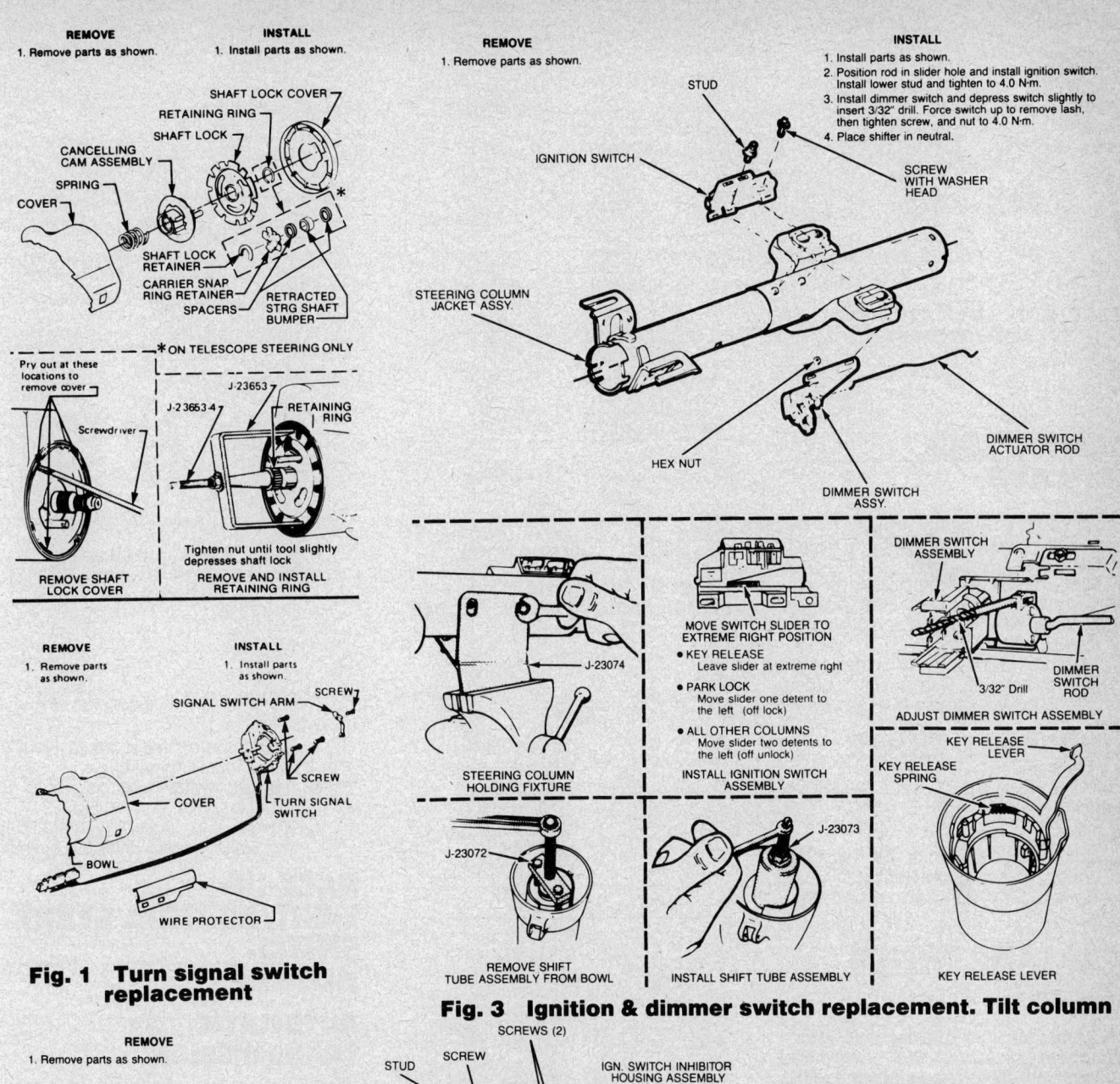

REMOVE
1. Remove parts as shown.

INSTALL
1. Install parts as shown.

SHAFT LOCK COVER
RETAINING RING
SHAFT LOCK
CANCELLING CAM ASSEMBLY
SPRING
COVER
SHAFT LOCK RETAINER
CARRIER SNAP RING RETAINER
SPACERS
RETRACTED STRG SHAFT BUMPER

*ON TELESCOPE STEERING ONLY

Pry out at these locations to remove cover
Screwdriver
J-23653
J-23653-4
RETAINING RING
Tighten nut until tool slightly depresses shaft lock

REMOVE SHAFT LOCK COVER
REMOVE AND INSTALL RETAINING RING

REMOVE
1. Remove parts as shown.

INSTALL
1. Install parts as shown.

SIGNAL SWITCH ARM
SCREW
SCREW
COVER
TURN SIGNAL SWITCH
BOWL
WIRE PROTECTOR

Fig. 1 Turn signal switch replacement

REMOVE
1. Remove parts as shown.

INSTALL
1. Install parts as shown.
2. Position rod in slider hole and install ignition switch. Install lower stud and tighten to 4.0 N·m.
3. Install dimmer switch and depress switch slightly to insert 3/32" drill. Force switch up to remove lash, then tighten screw, and nut to 4.0 N·m.
4. Place shifter in neutral.

STUD
IGNITION SWITCH
SCREW WITH WASHER HEAD
STEERING COLUMN JACKET ASSY.
HEX NUT
DIMMER SWITCH ACTUATOR ROD
DIMMER SWITCH ASSY.

J-23074
STEERING COLUMN HOLDING FIXTURE

MOVE SWITCH SLIDER TO EXTREME RIGHT POSITION
• KEY RELEASE Leave slider at extreme right
• PARK LOCK Move slider one detent to the left (off lock)
• ALL OTHER COLUMNS Move slider two detents to the left (off unlock)
INSTALL IGNITION SWITCH ASSEMBLY

DIMMER SWITCH ASSEMBLY
3/32" Drill
DIMMER SWITCH ROD
ADJUST DIMMER SWITCH ASSEMBLY

J-23072
REMOVE SHIFT TUBE ASSEMBLY FROM BOWL

J-23073
INSTALL SHIFT TUBE ASSEMBLY

KEY RELEASE LEVER
KEY RELEASE SPRING
KEY RELEASE LEVER

Fig. 3 Ignition & dimmer switch replacement. Tilt column

REMOVE
1. Remove parts as shown.

INSTALL
1. Install parts as shown.
2. Position rod in slider hole and install ignition switch. Install lower stud and tighten to 4.0 N·m.
3. Install dimmer switch and depress switch slightly to insert 3/32" drill. Force switch up to remove lash, then tighten screw, and nut to 4.0 N·m.

STUD
SCREW
SCREWS (2)
IGNITION SWITCH ASSEMBLY
IGN. SWITCH INHIBITOR HOUSING ASSEMBLY
PARK LOCK
STEERING COLUMN JACKET
NUT
DIMMER SWITCH
DIMMER SWITCH ACTUATOR ROD

MOVE SWITCH SLIDER TO EXTREME LEFT POSITION
INSTALL IGNITION SWITCH
• KEY RELEASE Leave slider at extreme left
• PARK LOCK Move slider one detent to the right (off lock)
• ALL OTHER COLUMNS Move slider two detents to the right (off unlock)

DIMMER SWITCH
3/32" Drill
DIMMER SWITCH ACTUATOR ROD
ADJUST DIMMER SWITCH

Fig. 2 Ignition & dimmer switch replacement. Except tilt column

TURN SIGNAL SWITCH
REPLACE
1. Disconnect battery ground cable.
2. Remove steering wheel as described under "Steering Wheel, Replace."
3. Refer to **Fig. 1** to replace turn signal switch.

IGNITION & DIMMER SWITCHES
REPLACE
1. Remove turn signal switch as described under "Turn Signal Switch, Replace."
2. Refer to **Figs. 2 and 3** to replace ignition and dimmer switches.

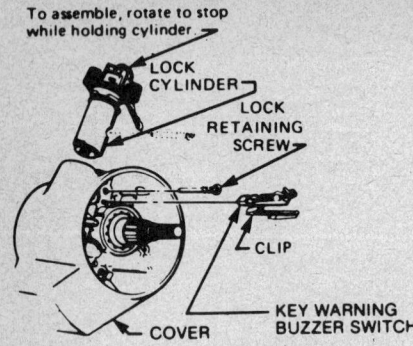

To assemble, rotate to stop while holding cylinder.

LOCK CYLINDER
LOCK RETAINING SCREW
CLIP
COVER
KEY WARNING BUZZER SWITCH

Fig. 4 Lock cylinder replacement

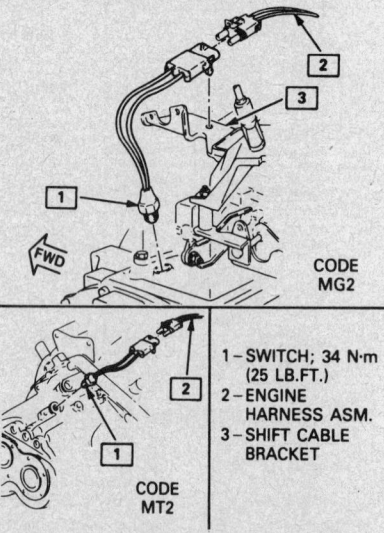

REMOVE
1. Remove ignition and dimmer switch.
2. Remove parts as shown.

INSTALL
1. Assemble rack so that first rack tooth engages between first and second tooth of sector.
2. Install parts as shown.
3. Install ignition and dimmer switch.

HOUSING
WASHER
PIVOT AND SWITCH ASSY.
BEARING
PIVOT PIN
BOWL
CAP SCREW
SCREW
PIN SECTOR
HORN CONTACT
BUSHING
RETAINER
GATE

Punch

REMOVE AND INSTALL SECTOR
INSTALL BEARING

WAVE WASHER
LEVER
SPRING
LEVER SPRING

REMOVE LEVER AND SPRING
INSTALL LEVER AND RETURN SPRING

Fig. 5 Windshield wiper switch replacement. Except tilt column

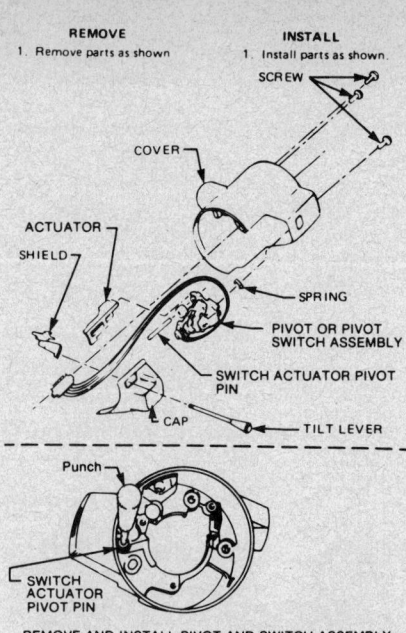

REMOVE
1. Remove parts as shown

INSTALL
1. Install parts as shown.

SCREW
COVER
ACTUATOR
SHIELD
SPRING
PIVOT OR PIVOT SWITCH ASSEMBLY
SWITCH ACTUATOR PIVOT PIN
CAP
TILT LEVER

Punch

SWITCH ACTUATOR PIVOT PIN

REMOVE AND INSTALL PIVOT AND SWITCH ASSEMBLY

Fig. 6 Windshield wiper switch replacement. Tilt column

IGNITION LOCK
REPLACE

1. Remove turn signal switch as described under "Turn Signal Switch, Replace."
2. Remove key warning buzzer switch.
3. Turn lock cylinder to Run position, then remove retaining screw and the lock cylinder, **Fig. 4.**
4. Reverse procedure to install. Turn lock cylinder to Run position before installing key warning buzzer switch.

WINDSHIELD WIPER SWITCH
REPLACE

1. Remove ignition lock as described under "Ignition Lock, Replace."
2. Refer to **Figs. 5 and 6** to replace wiper switch.

STOP LAMP SWITCH
ADJUST

Insert switch into retainer until switch body seats on retainer. Pull brake pedal rearward until clicks are no longer audible.

BACK-UP LIGHT/NEUTRAL START SWITCH
REPLACE

On vehicles equipped with automatic transmission, the neutral start and back-up light switches are combined into one unit and must be replaced as an assembly.

MANUAL TRANSMISSION

1. Disconnect battery ground cable.
2. Remove shift trim plate cover.
3. Disconnect electrical connector from switch, **Fig. 7.**
4. Remove switch retainer and the switch.
5. Reverse procedure to install.

CODE MG2

CODE MT2

1 – SWITCH; 34 N·m (25 LB.FT.)
2 – ENGINE HARNESS ASM.
3 – SHIFT CABLE BRACKET

FWD

Fig. 7 Back-up lamp switch replacement. Manual transmission

AUTOMATIC TRANSMISSION

1. Disconnect battery ground cable.
2. Open deck lid, then open retaining clip and disconnect electrical connector from switch.
3. Pry cable from pivot pin at bottom of shift lever, then remove lever to transmission shaft attaching nut.
4. Remove 2 switch-to-transaxle attaching bolts and the switch, **Fig. 8.**
5. Reverse procedure to install, noting the following:

a. Transmission must be in Neutral when installing switch.
b. **Torque** switch attaching bolts to 20 ft. lbs.
c. **Torque** lever attaching nut to 20 ft. lbs. while holding lever out of Park.

BACK-UP LIGHT/NEUTRAL START SWITCH
ADJUST

AUTOMATIC TRANSMISSION

1. Shift transmission into Neutral.
2. Align flats in switch insert with flats on transmission shaft, and slide switch over shaft.
3. Install attaching bolts hand tight.
4. Insert a 2.34 inch diameter gauge pin into adjustment hole, then rotate switch until pin drops to .354 inch.
5. **Torque** attaching bolts to 20 ft. lbs. and remove gauge pin.

CLUTCH START SWITCH
REPLACE

1. Disconnect battery ground cable.
2. Disconnect electrical connector from switch.
3. Remove switch attaching bolt. Rotate switch to disconnect shaft from clutch pedal hole, then remove switch from vehicle, **Fig. 9.**
4. Reverse procedure to install.

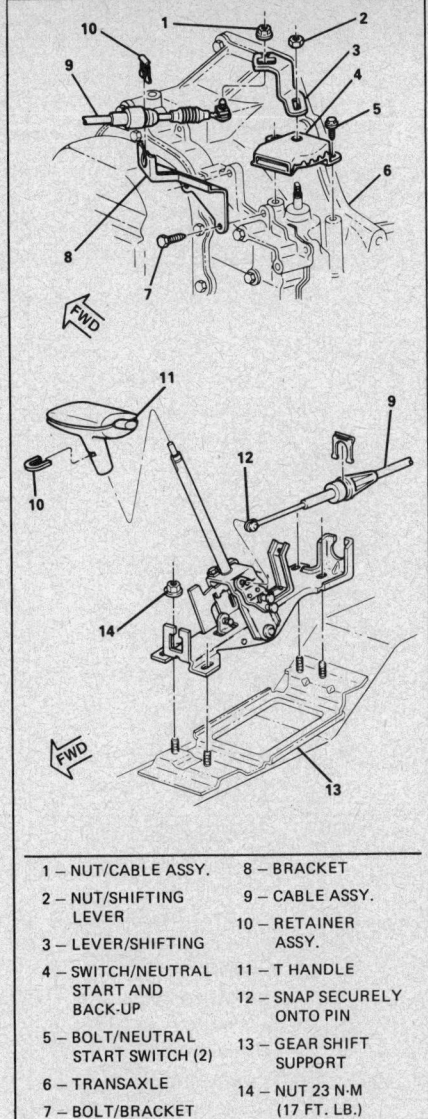

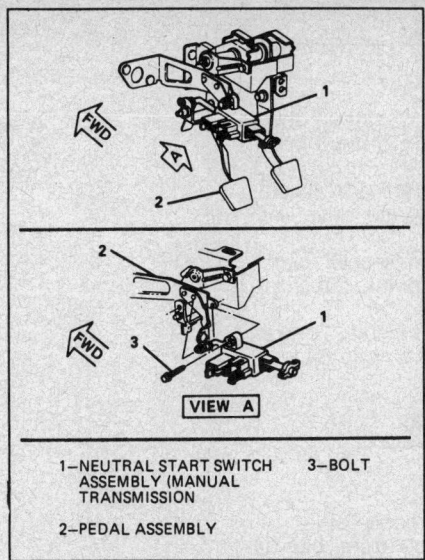

Fig. 9 Clutch start switch replacement

1—NEUTRAL START SWITCH ASSEMBLY (MANUAL TRANSMISSION
2—PEDAL ASSEMBLY
3—BOLT

1 – NUT/CABLE ASSY.	8 – BRACKET
2 – NUT/SHIFTING LEVER	9 – CABLE ASSY.
3 – LEVER/SHIFTING	10 – RETAINER ASSY.
4 – SWITCH/NEUTRAL START AND BACK-UP	11 – T HANDLE
5 – BOLT/NEUTRAL START SWITCH (2)	12 – SNAP SECURELY ONTO PIN
6 – TRANSAXLE	13 – GEAR SHIFT SUPPORT
7 – BOLT/BRACKET	14 – NUT 23 N·M (17 FT. LB.)

Fig. 8 Back-up light/neutral start switch replacement. Automatic transmission

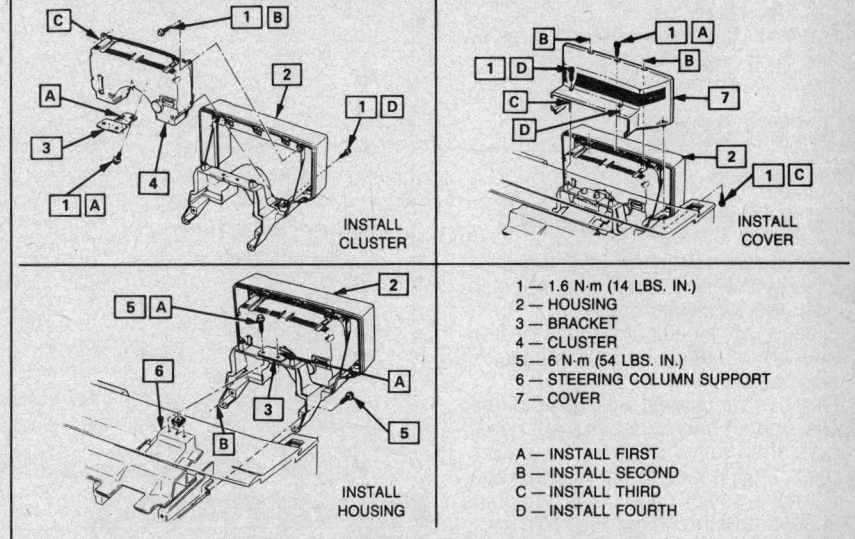

1 — 1.6 N·m (14 LBS. IN.)
2 — HOUSING
3 — BRACKET
4 — CLUSTER
5 — 6 N·m (54 LBS. IN.)
6 — STEERING COLUMN SUPPORT
7 — COVER

A — INSTALL FIRST
B — INSTALL SECOND
C — INSTALL THIRD
D — INSTALL FOURTH

Fig. 10 Instrument cluster

HEADLAMP SWITCH
REPLACE

1. Disconnect battery ground cable.
2. Remove 4 switch attaching screws.
3. Pull switch out of panel and disconnect electrical connectors, then remove switch from vehicle.
4. Reverse procedure to install. **When replacing switch, install lower attaching screws first.**

INSTRUMENT CLUSTER
REPLACE

1. Disconnect battery ground cable.
2. Remove rear cluster cover, front trim plate and steering column cover.
3. Remove instrument cluster attaching screws.

4. Pull cluster rearward and disconnect all electrical connectors, then remove cluster from vehicle, **Fig. 10.**
5. Reverse procedure to install.

RADIO
REPLACE

1. Disconnect battery ground cable.
2. Remove shift knob and both ashtrays.
3. Remove 4 shift plate attaching bolts and the plate.
4. Remove front trim plate, then the front pad attaching screws and front pad.
5. Remove radio attaching screws.
6. Pull radio rearward and disconnect all electrical connectors, then remove radio from vehicle.
7. Reverse procedure to install.

WINDSHIELD WIPER MOTOR
REPLACE

1. Disconnect battery ground cable.
2. Loosen transmission drive link to motor attaching nuts, then disconnect drive link from motor crank arm.
3. Disconnect electrical connectors from wiper motor.
4. Rotate motor up and remove from vehicle.
5. Reverse procedure to install. **Torque** wiper motor attaching nuts to 48 inch lbs.

WINDSHIELD WIPER TRANSMISSION
REPLACE

1. Remove cowl top vent screen, then both wiper arms using tool No. J-8966 or equivalent.
2. Loosen drive link-to-crank arm attaching nuts, then disengage drive link from crank arm.
3. Remove transmission-to-cowl panel attaching screws and the transmission.
4. Reverse procedure to install. **Torque** attaching screws and nuts to 64 inch lbs.

BLOWER MOTOR
REPLACE

1. Disconnect battery ground cable.
2. Remove cooling tube from blower motor.
3. Disconnect blower motor electrical connections.
4. Remove 5 blower motor attaching screws and the blower motor assembly, **Fig. 11.**
5. Remove fan cage attaching screw and slide cage off motor shaft.
6. Reverse procedure to install.

HEATER CORE
REPLACE

LESS AIR CONDITIONING

1. Disconnect battery ground cable.
2. Disconnect all electrical connectors from rear of heater case.
3. Disconnect electrical connector from courtesy lamp bulb socket, if equipped.
4. Remove windshield washer fluid tank.
5. Disconnect heater hoses from heater core, then remove heater core grommets. Plug hoses to prevent spillage.
6. Remove heater case cover attaching screws and the cover, **Fig. 11.**
7. Remove heater core retainer and the heater core.
8. Reverse procedure to install.

WITH AIR CONDITIONING

1. Disconnect battery ground cable.
2. Disconnect heater hoses from heater core. Plug hoses to prevent spillage.
3. Remove speaker grille and the speaker.
4. Remove heater core cover, then the heater core retainers and heater core.
5. Reverse procedure to install.

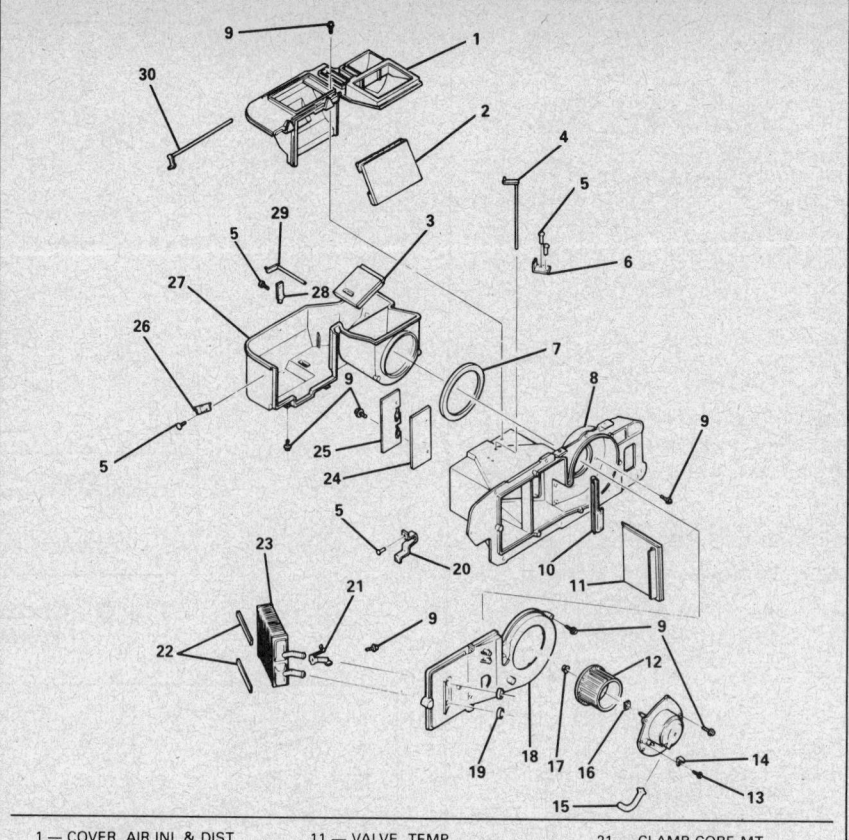

1 — COVER, AIR INL & DIST	11 — VALVE, TEMP	21 — CLAMP, CORE MT
2 — VALVE, VENT	12 — FAN, BLO	22 — SEAL, HTR CORE
3 — VALVE, DEFR	13 — SCREW, HWH TAP (M4.2 x 1.41 x 14)	23 — CORE, HTR
4 — SHAFT, W/LVR, TEMP VLV	14 — TERMINAL, BLO MTR GRD	24 — SEAL, HTR CORE CASE
5 — RIVET, TRUSS HD (9/16" x 1/4")	15 — TUBE, MTR CLG	25 — CLIP, HTR CORE MT
6 — BRACKET, CBL MTG	16 — WASHER, FAN SUPT	26 — BRACKET, CBL MT
7 — SEAL, HTR & BLO CASE	17 — NUT, BLO FAN	27 — CASE, AIR INL & DISTR
8 — CASE, HTR	18 — COVER, BLO	28 — BRACKET, CBL MT
9 — SCREW, HWH TAP (M4.2 x 1.41 x 13)	19 — SEAL, HTR CORE TUBE	29 — SHAFT, W/LVR, DEFR VLV
10 — BAFFLE, AIR	20 — BRACKET, MT	30 — SHAFT, W/LVR, VENT VLV

Fig. 11 Heater core & blower motor. Models less A/C

EVAPORATOR CORE
REPLACE

1. Discharge air conditioning system.
2. Disconnect battery ground cable.
3. Remove air conditioning relay bracket attaching screws.
4. Disconnect electrical connectors at air conditioning module.
5. Disconnect evaporator core tube at accumulator.
6. Disconnect heater hoses at heater core.
7. Remove windshield washer fluid reservoir.
8. Remove blower housing assembly attaching bolts, then remove blower housing assembly.
9. Disconnect evaporator to condensor tube.
10. Remove evaporator core attachments, then remove evaporator core.
11. Reverse to install, noting the following:
    a. Install new O-rings in connections.
    b. **Torque** evaporator to condensor tube connection to 17 ft. lbs.
    c. **Torque** evaporator core tube to accumulator connection to 30 ft. lbs.

2.5L/4-151 Engine
INDEX

ENGINE MOUNT
REPLACE

1. Raise and support vehicle.
2. Remove engine mount-to-chassis attaching nuts, **Fig. 1**.
3. Remove forward torque reaction rod attaching bolts.
4. Raise engine slightly using tool J28467 or equivalent engine lifting device. Raise engine only enough to provide clearance for mount removal.
5. Removal 2 upper mount-to-engine support bracket attaching nuts and the engine mount.
6. Reverse procedure to install, noting the following:
   a. **On models with automatic transmission, torque** engine mount attaching nuts to 35 ft. lbs.
   b. **On models with manual transmission, torque** engine mount attaching nuts to 41 ft. lbs.

ENGINE
REPLACE

1. Release pressure from fuel system as follows:
   a. Remove fuel pump fuse from fuse block, then start and run engine until engine stalls from fuel starvation.
   b. Energize starter for approximately 3 seconds to release any residual pressure from system.
   c. Turn ignition off and replace fuel pump fuse.
2. Disconnect battery cables, then drain cooling system.
3. Remove rear compartment lid. **Do not remove torsion rod retaining bolts.**
4. Remove air cleaner, then disconnect throttle and transaxle cables.
5. Disconnect all necessary vacuum hoses from non-engine components.
6. Disconnect heater hose from intake manifold.
7. Disconnect fuel lines and remove fuel filter.
8. Disconnect fuel pump relay and oxygen sensor electrical connectors.
9. **On models equipped with automatic transaxle,** disconnect transaxle cooler lines.

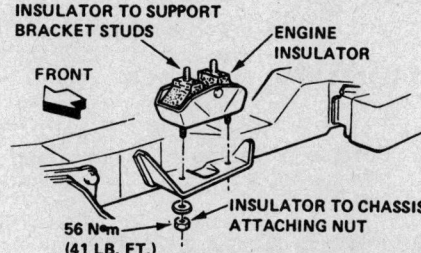

**Fig. 1   Engine mounts.
Manual transmission**

INSULATOR TO SUPPORT BRACKET STUDS
ENGINE INSULATOR
FRONT
INSULATOR TO CHASSIS ATTACHING NUT
56 N·m (41 LB. FT.)

10. **On models equipped with manual transaxle,** remove slave cylinder.
11. **On all models,** disconnect engine ground strap.
12. Disconnect radiator and heater hoses.
13. Disconnect engine harness connector from bulkhead.
14. **On models equipped with A/C,** discharge refrigerant from system, then disconnect and cap lines from A/C compressor.
15. **On all models,** remove rear console.
16. Disconnect electronic control module (ECM) electrical connector through bulkhead panel.
17. Install engine support fixture, tool No. J-28467 or equivalent to engine.
18. Mark the engine strut bracket and attaching bolt for assembly reference, then remove bolt and bracket.
19. Raise and support vehicle.
20. Remove rear wheels.
21. **On models equipped with automatic transaxle,** remove torque converter attaching bolts.
22. **On all models,** disconnect parking brake cable.
23. Remove brake calipers and suspend from frame with a piece of wire. Do not suspend calipers by brake hoses.
24. Mark struts for proper realignment as described under "Strut Assembly, Replace" in the "Drive Axle & Rear Suspension" section, then remove strut attaching bolts.
25. Disconnect any remaining electrical connectors interfering with engine removal.

26. Remove engine cradle attaching bolts.
27. Release parking brake cables from cradle using tool No. J-34065 or equivalent.
28. Support engine, transaxle and cradle assembly with a suitably dolly, then lower vehicle and remove engine support fixture. **When lowering vehicle, ensure outboard ends of lower control arms are properly supported.**
29. Raise vehicle and slide engine, transaxle and cradle assembly out from under vehicle.
30. Separate engine from transaxle.
31. Reverse procedure to install, noting the following:
   a. Finger tighten front cradle bolts.
   b. **Torque** rear cardle bolts to 76 ft. lbs.
   c. **Torque** front cradle bolts to 66 ft. lbs.

CYLINDER HEAD
REPLACE

1. Disconnect battery ground cable.
2. Drain cooling system.
3. Raise and support vehicle.
4. Disconnect exhaust pipe from exhaust manifold, then disconnect oxygen sensor electrical connector, then lower vehicle.
5. Remove oil dipstick tube and air cleaner.
6. Disconnect electrical connectors and throttle linkage from throttle body injection unit.
7. Disconnect heater hose from intake manifold, then remove ignition coil.
8. Disconnect all electrical connectors and vacuum hoses from cylinder head and intake manifold.
9. Remove engine strut attaching bolt from upper engine support.
10. Remove or reposition accessory brackets as necessary.
11. Disconnect upper radiator hose from cylinder head.
12. Remove rocker arm cover, then the rocker arms and pushrods.
13. Remove cylinder head attaching bolts, then lift cylinder head and intake

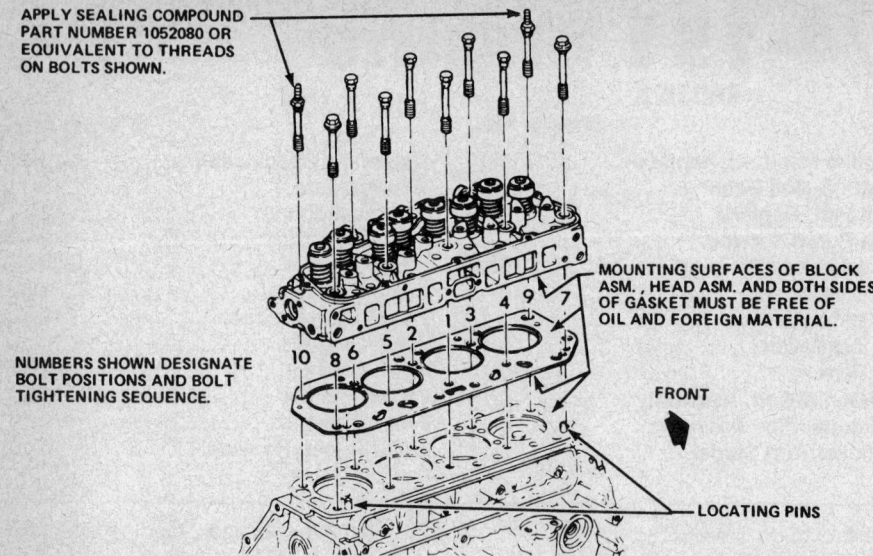

APPLY SEALING COMPOUND PART NUMBER 1052080 OR EQUIVALENT TO THREADS ON BOLTS SHOWN.

NUMBERS SHOWN DESIGNATE BOLT POSITIONS AND BOLT TIGHTENING SEQUENCE.

MOUNTING SURFACES OF BLOCK ASM., HEAD ASM. AND BOTH SIDES OF GASKET MUST BE FREE OF OIL AND FOREIGN MATERIAL.

FRONT

LOCATING PINS

Fig. 2 Cylinder head bolt tightening sequence

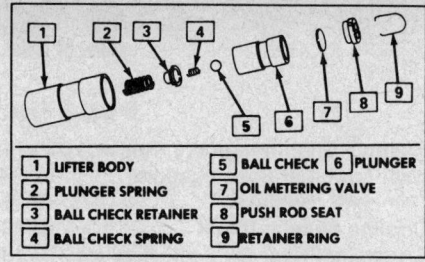

1	LIFTER BODY	5	BALL CHECK	6	PLUNGER
2	PLUNGER SPRING	7	OIL METERING VALVE		
3	BALL CHECK RETAINER	8	PUSH ROD SEAT		
4	BALL CHECK SPRING	9	RETAINER RING		

Fig. 3 Hydraulic valve lifter

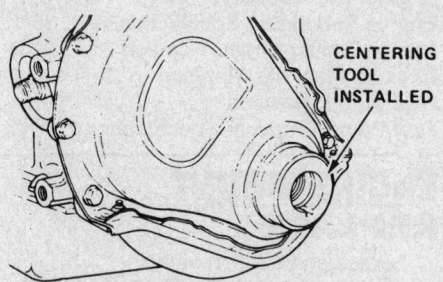

CENTERING TOOL INSTALLED

Fig. 4 Engine front cover installation

and exhaust manifolds as an assembly from cylinder block.

14. Install new head gasket, then the cylinder head assembly, ensuring gasket and head are seated over dowel pins.

15. Tighten bolts in three steps following sequence shown in **Fig. 2**. First, **torque** all bolts to 18 ft. lbs., then **torque** all bolts except bolt No. 9 to 26 ft. lbs. Retorque bolt No. 9 to 18 ft. lbs. Third, tighten all bolts an additional 90°.

16. Reverse remaining procedure to complete installation.

INTAKE MANIFOLD
REPLACE

1. Release pressure from fuel system as follows:
   a. Remove fuel pump fuse from fuse block, then start and run engine until engine stalls from fuel starvation.
   b. Energize starter for approximately 3 seconds to release any residual pressure from system.
   c. Turn ignition off and replace fuel pump fuse.
2. Disconnect battery ground cable and remove air cleaner.
3. Remove PCV valve and disconnect hose at throttle body.
4. Drain coolant.
5. Disconnect related fuel lines and vacuum hoses.
6. Disconnect wiring and throttle linkage at throttle body.
7. Disconnect transaxle downshift linkage and, if equipped, the cruise control and linkage.
8. Disconnect throttle linkage and bell crank, positioning out of way.
9. Disconnect heater hose.
10. Remove intake manifold attaching bolts and the manifold.
11. Clean all gasket surfaces on cylinder head and intake manifold.

12. Reverse procedure to install, using new gasket, then check for vacuum and fluid leaks.

ROCKER ARM STUDS

Rocker arm studs which are cracked or have damaged threads can be removed from the cylinder head using a deep well socket. Install and **torque** new rocker arm stud to 75 ft. lbs.

VALVES
ADJUST

These engines are equipped with hydraulic valve lifters. No provision for adjustment is provided.

VALVE ARRANGEMENT
FRONT TO REAR

All . . . . I-E-I-E-E-I-E-I

CAM LOBE LIFT SPECIFICATIONS

Intake, Inch 398
Exhaust, Inch 398

VALVE TIMING
INTAKE OPENS BEFORE TDC

Degrees 33

VALVE GUIDES

Valve guides are an integral part of the cylinder head and are not removable. If valve stem clearance becomes excessive, the valve guide should be reamed to the next oversize and the appropriate oversize valves installed. Valves are available in oversizes of .003 and .005 inch.

VALVE LIFTERS

Failure of a hydraulic valve lifter, **Fig. 3**, is generally caused by an inadequate oil supply or dirt. An air leak at the intake side of the oil pump or excessive oil in the engine will produce air bubbles in the oil supply to the lifters, causing them to collapse. This is a probable cause of trouble when several lifters fail to function, but air in oil is not likely to cause failure of a single unit.

Valve lifters can be removed after removing rocker arm cover, intake manifold and pushrod cover. Loosen rocker arm stud nut and rotate rocker arm so pushrod can be removed, then remove valve lifter. It may be necessary to use tool No. J-3049 to facilitate lifter removal.

ENGINE TIMING COVER
REPLACE

1. Disconnect battery ground cable.
2. Remove engine compartment lid and side panels.
3. Remove trim panel below battery trim panel.
4. Remove serpentine belt.
5. Raise and support vehicle.
6. Remove righthand rear tire and wheel assembly, then remove inner splash shield.
7. Disconnect starter and allow to hang.
8. Remove flywheel cover attaching bolts, then remove flywheel cover.
9. Remove flywheel pulley and hub.
10. Lower vehicle, then support engine using fixture No. J-34995, then remove engine mount and bracket as an assembly. Remove timing cover attaching screws and the timing cover.
11. Clean cylinder block and front cover

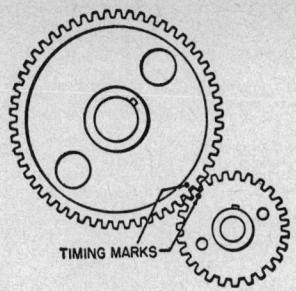

Fig. 5 Valve timing marks

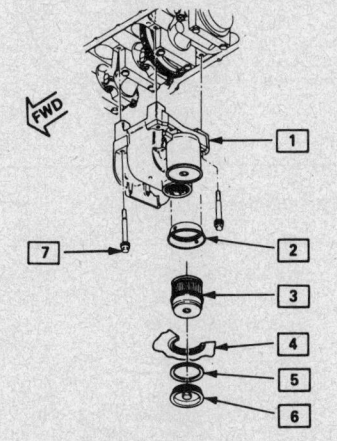

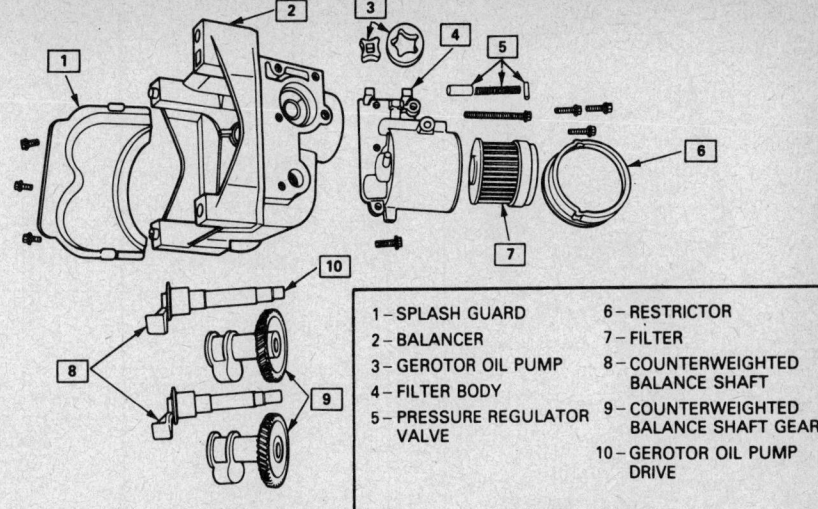

1 – SPLASH GUARD	6 – RESTRICTOR
2 – BALANCER	7 – FILTER
3 – GEROTOR OIL PUMP	8 – COUNTERWEIGHTED BALANCE SHAFT
4 – FILTER BODY	9 – COUNTERWEIGHTED BALANCE SHAFT GEAR
5 – PRESSURE REGULATOR VALVE	10 – GEROTOR OIL PUMP DRIVE

Fig. 7 Exploded view of balance shaft assembly

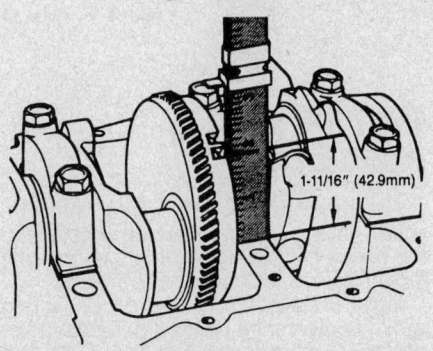

Fig. 8 Positioning crankshaft

Fig. 9 Positioning counterweights

1 – BALANCER ASSEMBLY	5 – GASKET
2 – RESTRICTOR	6 – PLUG
3 – FILTER	7 – BOLT
4 – OIL PAN	

Fig. 6 Balance shaft assembly removal

sealing surfaces, then position oil pan front seal on front cover.

12. Apply a ³/₈ inch wide by ³/₁₆ inch thick bead of RTV sealer to joint formed at oil pan and front cover.
13. Apply a ¹/₄ inch wide by ¹/₈ inch thick bead of RTV sealer on front cover to block mating surface.
14. Install centering tool No. J-23042 in front cover seal, **Fig. 4.**
15. Install front cover. Install 2 attaching screws finger tight, then install remaining screws and torque all screws to specifications.
16. Remove centering tool and install pulley, hub, splash shield and drive belts.

TIMING GEARS

When necessary to install a new camshaft gear, the camshaft will have to be removed as the gear is a pressed fit on the camshaft. The camshaft is held in place by a thrust plate retained to the engine by two capscrews which are accessible through the two holes in the gear web.

To remove gear, use an arbor press and a suitable sleeve to properly support gear on its steel hub.

Before installing gear, assemble thrust plate and gear spacer ring, then press gear onto shaft until it bottoms against spacer ring. The thrust plate end clearance should be .0015-.0050 inch. If clearance is less than .0015 inch, the spacer ring should be replaced. If clearance is greater than .0050 inch, the thrust plate should be replaced.

The crankshaft gear can be replaced using a puller and two bolts in the tapped holes of the gear.

When installing timing gears, ensure marks on gears are properly aligned, **Fig. 5.**

The valve timing marks, **Fig. 5**, do not indicate TDC compression for No. 1 cylinder for use during distributor installation. When installing the distributor, rotate engine until No. 1 cylinder is on compression stroke and the camshaft timing mark is 180° from the valve timing position shown in **Fig. 5.**

CAMSHAFT
REPLACE

1. Remove engine as described under "Engine, Replace." Do not separate engine from transaxle.
2. Remove rocker arm cover, then loosen rocker arm stud nuts. Pivot rocker

arms clear of pushrods and remove the rods.
3. Remove front engine mount and bracket assembly.
4. Remove oil pump driveshaft.
5. Remove front cover as described under "Engine Timing Cover, Replace."
6. Remove camshaft thrust plate attaching screws.
7. Carefully remove camshaft and gear through front of block.
8. Reverse procedure to install. When installing camshaft, align crankshaft and camshaft timing marks on gear teeth, **Fig. 5.**

BALANCE SHAFT ASSEMBLY
REPLACE

1. Remove oil pan as described under "Oil Pan, Replace."
2. Remove balance shaft assembly attaching bolts and the balance shaft assembly, **Figs. 6 and 7.**
3. Install balance shaft assembly, torquing short attaching bolts to 9 ft. lbs. plus an additional 75° turn and long attaching bolts to 9 ft. lbs. plus an additional 90° turn.
4. Rotate engine to TDC on Nos. 1 and 4 cylinders.

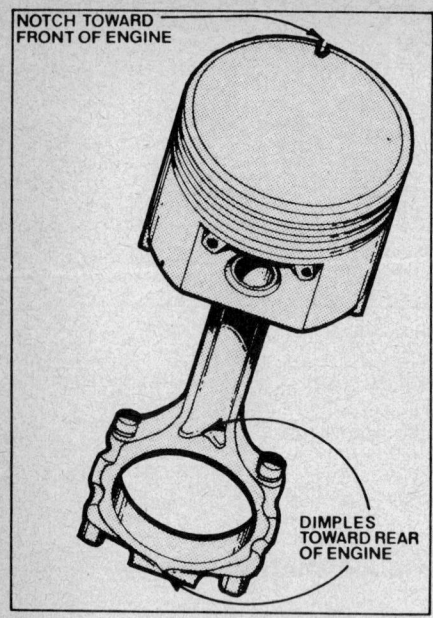

NOTCH TOWARD FRONT OF ENGINE

DIMPLES TOWARD REAR OF ENGINE

Fig. 10   Piston & rod assembly

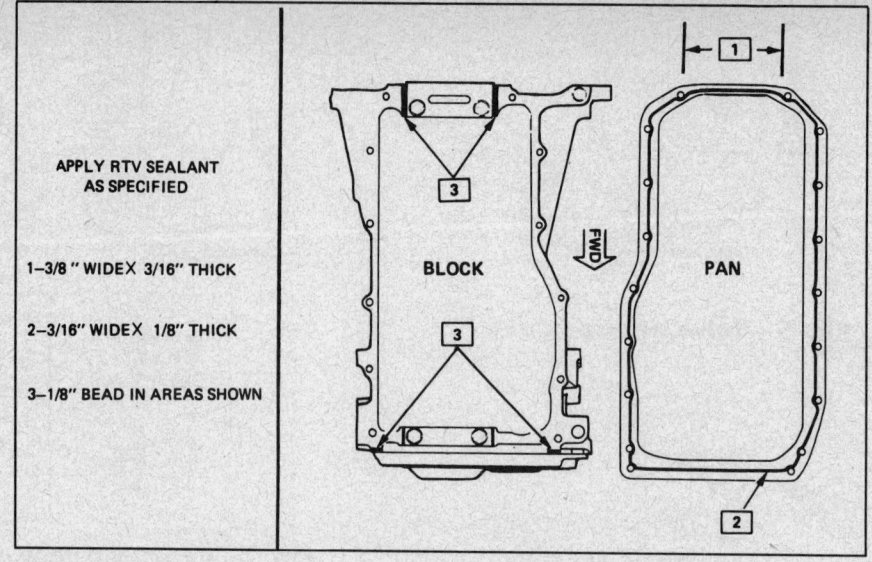

APPLY RTV SEALANT AS SPECIFIED

1–3/8 " WIDE X 3/16" THICK

2–3/16" WIDE X 1/8" THICK

3–1/8" BEAD IN AREAS SHOWN

BLOCK

PAN

FWD

Fig. 11   Oil pan installation

1	PUMP BODY	6	SPRING RETAINER
2	PICKUP TUBE	7	COVER SCREWS
3	PICKUP SCREW ASSEMBLY	8	COVER
4	PRESSURE REGULATOR VALVE	9	IDLER GEAR
5	PRESSURE REGULATOR SPRING	10	DRIVE GEAR AND SHAFT

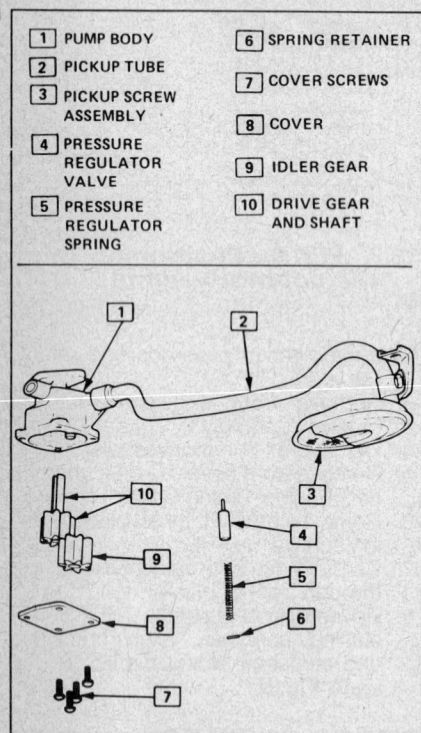

Fig. 12   Exploded view of oil pump

5. Measure from block to first cut of double notch on reluctor ring, **Fig. 8.** Dimension should be 1¹¹/₁₆ inches.
6. Mount balancer with counterweights parallel and pointing away from crankshaft, **Fig. 9. Do not move crankshaft.**
7. Install oil pan.

PISTON & ROD, ASSEMBLY

Assemble piston to rod with notch on piston facing toward front of engine and the raised notch side of rod at bearing end facing toward rear of engine, **Fig. 10.**

Upon installation, measure connecting rod side clearance using a suitable feeler gauge. Clearance should be .006-.022 inch.

PISTONS, PINS & RINGS

Pistons and rings are available in standard size and oversizes of .010, .020 and .030 inch. Piston pins are available in oversizes of .001 and .003 inch.

MAIN & ROD BEARINGS

Main and rod bearings are available in standard size and oversizes of .001, .002 and .010 inch.

OIL PAN
REPLACE

1. Remove battery cables, then the engine compartment lid and side panels. **Scribe alignment marks on engine compartment hinges to facilitate reassembly.**
2. Remove trim at sail panel below below battery side panel.
3. Remove battery side shield, then the serpentine belt.
4. Remove alternator attaching bolts and position alternator out of way.
5. Raise and support vehicle, then drain engine oil and remove oil filter.
6. Remove front engine mount to cradle attaching nuts.
7. Remove starter and flywheel cover, then the starter.

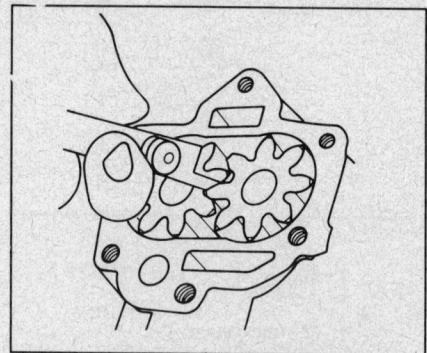

Fig. 13   Measuring oil pump gear backlash

8. Remove right rear wheel, then the splash shield.
9. Loosen lower alternator bracket at mount.
10. Remove A/C compressor heat shield, then remove compressor attaching bolts and position compressor out of way.
11. Lower vehicle and remove engine strut, then, using tool J-28467 or equivalent, support engine.
12. Raise and support vehicle.
13. Remove engine front support and mount, then the oil pan attaching bolts and oil pan.
14. Clean sealing surfaces on oil pan, front cover and cylinder block.
15. Apply suitable sealant as shown, **Fig. 11.**
16. Reverse steps 1 through 13 to complete installation.

OIL PUMP SERVICE
REMOVAL

1. Remove oil pan as described under "Oil Pan, Replace."
2. Remove oil pump attaching bolts and nuts, then the oil pump and screen as an assembly.

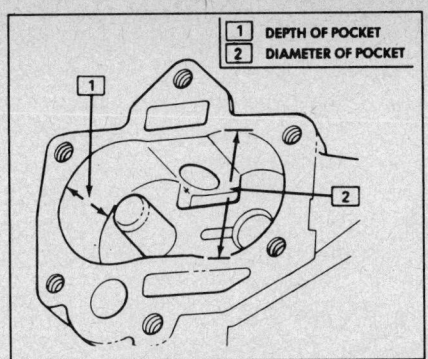

Fig. 14 Measuring oil pump gear pocket

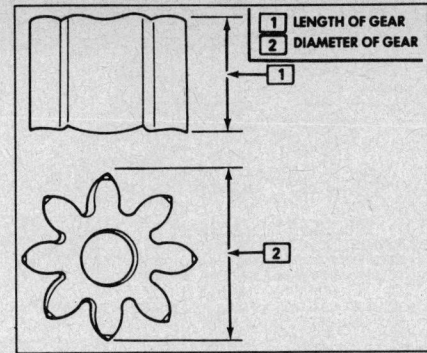

Fig. 15 Measuring oil pump gears

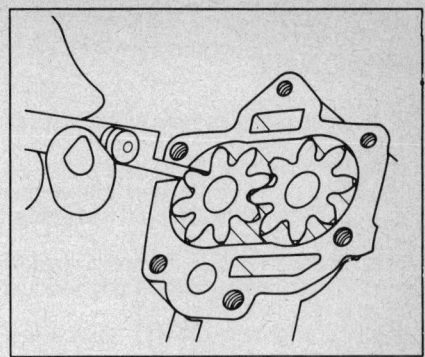

Fig. 16 Measuring oil pump gear side clearance

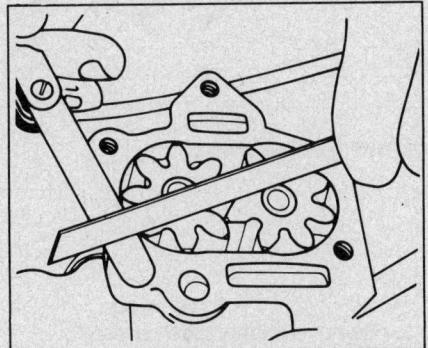

Fig. 17 Measuring oil pump gear end clearance

8. Measure pump housing gear pocket depth and diameter, **Fig. 14**. Depth should measure .995-.998 inch and diameter 1.503-1.506 inches.
9. Measure length and diameter of gears, **Fig. 15**. Length of both gears should be .999-1.002 inch and diameter should be 1.496-1.500 inches.
10. Measure gear side clearance, **Fig. 18**. Side clearance should measure no more than .004 inch.
11. Measure gear end clearance, **Fig. 17**. End clearance should be .002-.005 inch.
12. If any measurements taken in steps 7 through 11 are not within specifications, replace oil pump components as necessary.

ASSEMBLY

1. Lubricate all internal components with clean engine oil and pack all pump cavities with petroleum jelly.
2. Install pump gears into housing.
3. Install pump cover, pressure regulator valve and spring. Torque cover attaching bolts to specifications.
4. Apply suitable sealer to new pipe, then tap pipe into position using a plastic hammer and tool No. J-8369.

INSTALLATION

1. Align oil pump shaft with tang on oil pump driveshaft, then install pump on block, positioning pump flange over oil pump driveshaft lower bushing.
2. Install pump attaching bolts and torque to specifications.
3. Install oil pan.

CRANKSHAFT REAR OIL SEAL
REPLACE

The rear main oil seal is a one-piece seal which can be replaced without removing the oil pan or crankshaft.
1. Remove transaxle and flywheel.
2. **On models equipped with manual transaxle,** remove pressure plate and disc.
3. **On all models,** remove rear main bearing oil seal using a suitable screwdriver. Use care not to scratch crankshaft.

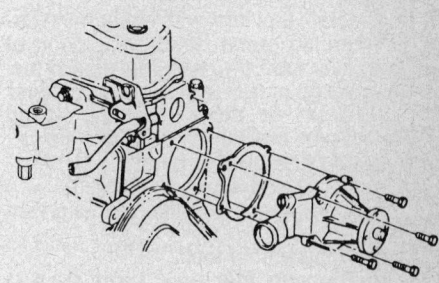

Fig. 18 Water pump installation

4. Reverse procedure to install using tool J34924-A or equivalent. Lubricate outside of seal to ease assembly. Torque flywheel to crankshaft to specifications.

WATER PUMP
REPLACE

1. Disconnect battery ground cable and drain cooling system.
2. Remove accessory drive belts.
3. Disconnect lower radiator hose from water pump.
4. Remove water pump attaching bolts and the pump, **Fig. 18**.
5. Reverse procedure to install. Apply a 1/8 inch bead of sealer to pump sealing surface, then install pump before sealer dries.

COOLING SYSTEM BLEED

These engines doe not require a specific bleed procedure. After filling cooling system, run engine to operating temperature with radiator/pressure cap off. Air will then be automatically bled through cap opening.

DISASSEMBLY

1. Drain residual oil from pump.
2. Remove suction pipe and screen assembly from pump.
3. Remove pump cover attaching screws, then the pump cover and gears, **Fig. 12**.
4. Remove pump regulator valve. Remove plug, spring and ball from valve.

INSPECTION

1. Inspect pump housing and cover for wear or damage, and replace if necessary.
2. Inspect pressure regulator valve for scoring or sticking. Burrs may be removed with a fine oil stone, however more extensive damage requires replacement of valve.
3. Inspect idler gear shaft for wear or damage, and replace if necessary.
4. Inspect pressure regulator spring for lack of tension or distortion, and replace if necessary.
5. Inspect suction pipe and screen, and clean or replace as necessary. **If suction pipe is permanently pressed into the pump body, and if it is loose or has been removed, a new pipe must be installed.**
6. Inspect gears and driveshaft for wear or damage and replace as necessary.
7. Install gears into housing and measure gear backlash, **Fig. 13**. Backlash should measure .009-.015 inch.

FUEL PUMP
REPLACE

1. Release pressure from fuel system as follows:
   a. Remove fuel pump fuse from fuse block, then start and run engine until engine stalls from fuel starvation.
   b. Energize starter for approximately 3 seconds to release any residual pressure from system.
   c. Turn ignition off and replace fuel pump fuse.
2. Disconnect battery ground cable.
3. Raise and support vehicle.
4. Remove fuel tank from vehicle as follows:
   a. Drain fuel tank with either hand operated pump device or siphon at filler tube, the main fuel pipe at fuel pump or fuel tank gage unit. **Never drain or store gasoline in an open container as a fire or explosion could result.**
   b. Raise and support vehicle.
   c. Disconnect fuel filler neck and vent hoses.
   d. Support fuel tank.
   e. Remove fuel tank strap support bolts, then lower tank to disconnect fuel sending unit electrical connectors.
   f. Disconnect fuel line, fuel vapor line and fuel return line.
   g. Remove fuel tank.
5. Remove fuel meter/pump assembly. Turn cam lock ring counterclockwise, then lift assembly from fuel tank and remove pump from meter.
6. Lift pump up into attaching hose while pulling away from bottom support.

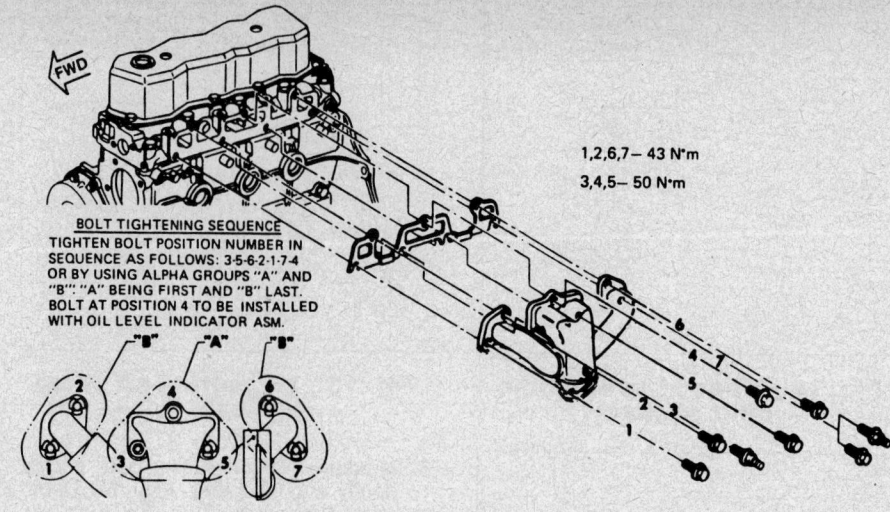

Fig. 19 Exhaust manifold installation

When pump is clear of lower support, remove assembly from rubber connector. **Use care to avoid damage to rubber insulator and strainer during removal.**
7. Reverse procedure to install.

EXHAUST MANIFOLD
REPLACE

1. Disconnect battery ground cable.
2. Remove battery side cover.
3. Disconnect oxygen sensor connector.
4. Disconnect dipstick tube at manifold.
5. Remove exhaust manifold retaining bolts and washers, then the exhaust manifold and gasket.
6. Clean sealing surfaces of cylinder head and manifold and lubricate retaining bolts and threads.
7. Reverse procedure to install, tightening bolts in sequence, **Fig. 19.**

TIGHTENING SPECIFICATIONS

*Torque specifications are for clean and lightly lubricated threads only. Dry or dirty threads produce increased friction which prevents accurate measurement of tightness.

Year	Component	Torque/Ft. Lbs.
1988	Connecting Rod Cap Bolts	32
	Cylinder Head Bolts	①
	Distributor Hold Down Bolt	15
	EGR Valve To Manifold	16
	Exhaust Manifold	①
	Flywheel To Crankshaft	②
	Intake Manifold	25
	Main Bearing Cap Bolts	70
	Oil Drain Plug	25
	Oil Pan To Block	20
	Oil Pump Cover	7
	Oil Pump To Block	20
	Pressure Regulator Valve Plug	15
	Rocker Arm Cover	45③
	Rocker Arm Bolt	24③
	Spark Plug	7-15
	Timing Gear Cover To Block	90③
	Vibration Damper Of Pulley	200
	Water Pump To Block	25

①—Refer to text for procedure.
②—Auto. trans., 55 ft. lbs.; manual trans., 69 ft. lbs.
③—Inch lbs.

2.8L/V6-173 Engine

INDEX

ENGINE MOUNT
REPLACE
ENGINE MOUNT

1. Disconnect battery ground cable.
2. Remove engine compartment lid and side cover panels.
3. Support engine with tools J-28467 and J-35563.
4. Remove torque reaction rod bolt.
5. Raise and support vehicle.
6. Remove engine mount to chassis attaching nuts, **Fig. 1.**
7. Remove engine mount to support bracket upper nuts.
8. Remove engine mount from vehicle.
9. Reverse procedure to install. **Torque** reaction rod bolt to 42 ft. lbs. **Torque** engine mount to support bracket upper nuts to 41 ft. lbs.

TRANSAXLE MOUNT

1. Disconnect battery ground cable.
2. Remove engine compartment lid and side cover panels. Do not remove torsion rod retaining bolts.
3. Support engine and transaxle with tools J-28467 and J-35563.
4. Remove mount to cradle and support bracket attaching nuts, **Fig. 2.**
5. Remove transaxle mount and shield, if equipped.
6. Reverse procedure to install. **Torque** front transaxle mount to cradle and support bracket to 35 ft. lbs. **Torque** rear transaxle mount to cradle to 18 ft. lbs. **Torque** rear transaxle mount to bracket to 35 ft. lbs.

ENGINE
REPLACE

1. Disconnect battery ground cable and drain cooling system.
2. Remove engine compartment lid and side cover panels. **Do not remove torsion rod retaining bolts.**
3. Remove intake flex duct.
4. Disconnect throttle and shift cable.
5. Disconnect heater hoses from engine.
6. Disconnect vacuum hoses to components not engine mounted.
7. Disconnect fuel lines from engine and remove fuel pump relay.
8. **On automatic transaxle models,** disconnect transaxle cooler lines.
9. **On manual transaxle models,** remove slave cylinder and shield from transaxle.
10. **On all models,** disconnect ground strap from engine.
11. Remove radiator hoses.
12. Disconnect engine harness at junction block.
13. Remove rear heat shield.
14. If equipped, discharge air conditioning system. Disconnect A/C lines and wiring from compressor. Plug A/C lines.
15. Remove rear console.
16. Disconnect ECM harness through bulkhead panel.
17. Remove engine strut front bolt.
18. Install engine support fixture tool J28497 and bracket tool J35563 or equivalent.
19. Raise and support vehicle.
20. Remove rear wheels.
21. Remove brake calipers and position aside. **Do not disconnect brake hoses.**
22. Remove two strut bolts on each side. **Scribe alignment marks on bolts to retain camber setting.**
23. Loosen four cradle bolts.
24. Lower vehicle.
25. Support engine and transaxle assembly on a suitable dolly.
26. Remove four cradle bolts.
27. Raise vehicle, leaving engine and transaxle assembly on dolly.
28. Reverse procedure to install. Finger tighten front cradle bolts. **Torque** rear cradle bolts to 76 ft. lbs. and front cradle bolts to 66 ft. lbs.

INTAKE MANIFOLD
REPLACE

1. Disconnect battery ground cable. Drain cooling system.
2. Remove rocker arm covers.
3. Remove intake duct.
4. Remove distributor. Mark location of distributor on engine and rotor on distributor body.
5. Disconnect throttle body from upper plenum.
6. Remove radiator hose and radiator fill inlet.
7. Disconnect heater hoses and the pipe to throttle body.
8. Disconnect wiring harness.

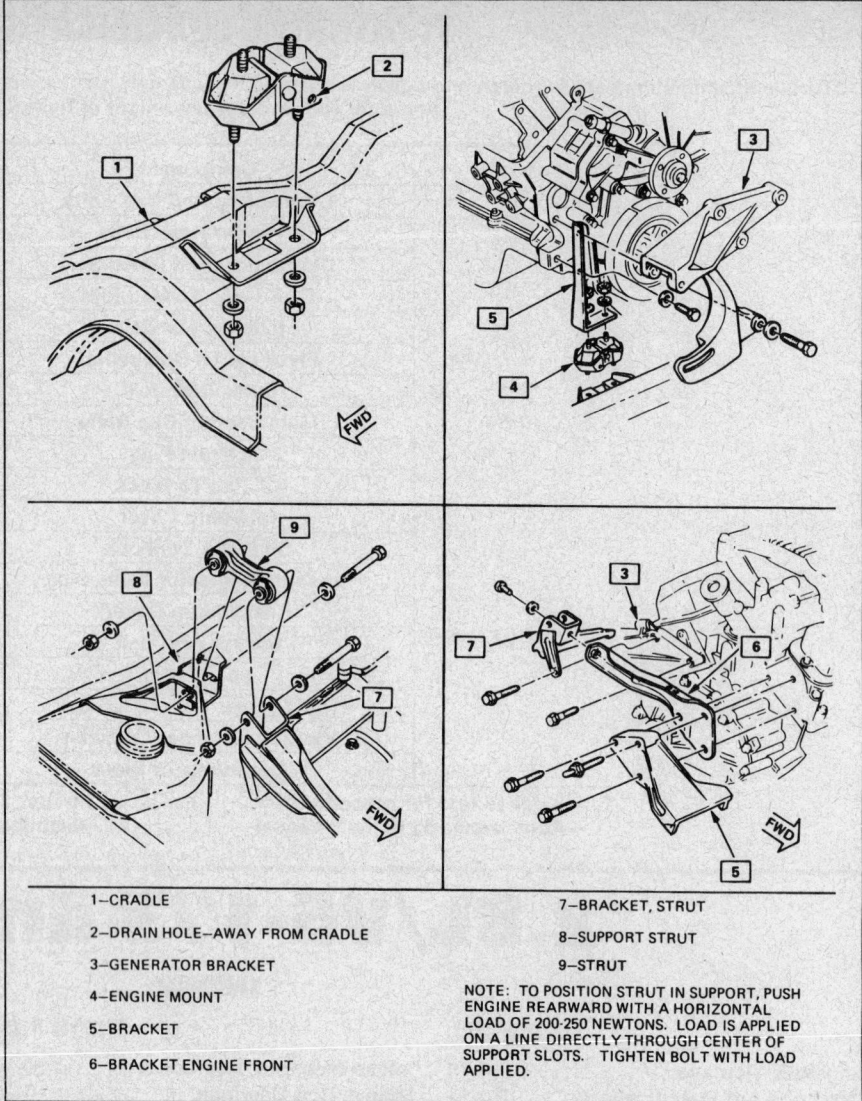

1—CRADLE
2—DRAIN HOLE—AWAY FROM CRADLE
3—GENERATOR BRACKET
4—ENGINE MOUNT
5—BRACKET
6—BRACKET ENGINE FRONT
7—BRACKET, STRUT
8—SUPPORT STRUT
9—STRUT

NOTE: TO POSITION STRUT IN SUPPORT, PUSH ENGINE REARWARD WITH A HORIZONTAL LOAD OF 200-250 NEWTONS. LOAD IS APPLIED ON A LINE DIRECTLY THROUGH CENTER OF SUPPORT SLOTS. TIGHTEN BOLT WITH LOAD APPLIED.

Fig. 1 Engine mount installation

9. Remove heater hoses and disconnect vacuum hoses.
10. Remove brake booster pipe and bracket.
11. Disconnect EGR pipe.
12. Remove upper manifold plenum and gaskets, **Fig. 3.**
13. Remove intermediate intake manifold and gasket.
14. Remove lower intake manifold and gaskets.
15. Reverse procedure to install. Refer to **Fig. 3** for torque sequence. **Torque** lower intake manifold bolts to 19 ft. lbs. **Torque** intermediate intake manifold bolts to 15 ft. lbs. **Torque** upper manifold plenum bolts to 19 ft. lbs.

EXHAUST MANIFOLD
REPLACE

FRONT

1. Disconnect battery ground cable.
2. Remove engine compartment lid. **Do not remove torsion rod retaining bolts.**
3. Disconnect brake vacuum hose.
4. Remove manifold heat shield.
5. Remove front crossover bolts, **Fig. 4.**
6. Raise and support vehicle.
7. Remove front converter heat shield.
8. Remove lower manifold bolts.
9. Lower vehicle.
10. Remove upper manifold bolts and the manifold.
11. Reverse procedure to install. Torque manifold and crossover bolts to specifications.

REAR

1. Remove manifold to crossover bolts, **Fig. 4.**
2. Remove manifold bolts and the manifold.
3. Reverse procedure to install. Torque manifold and crossover bolts to specifications.

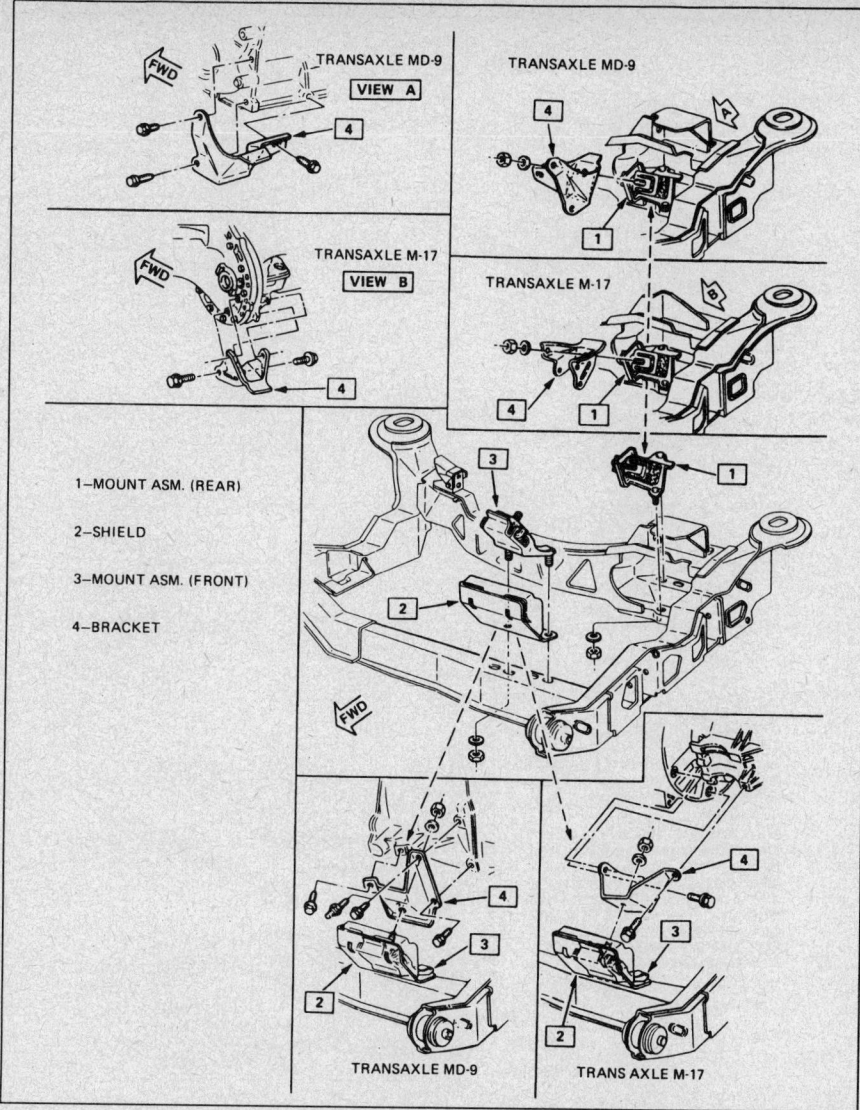

1—MOUNT ASM. (REAR)

2—SHIELD

3—MOUNT ASM. (FRONT)

4—BRACKET

Fig. 2 Transaxle mount installation

5. Disconnect cruise control cable, if equipped.
6. Remove ground cable.
7. Remove PCV valve from rocker arm cover.
8. Remove oil dipstick tube.
9. Disconnect spark plug wires and remove bracket.
10. Remove engine lift hook.
11. Remove rocker arm cover bolts and the cover. **If cover adheres to cylinder head, shear the adhesion by tapping the end of the cover with a rubber mallet. If cover will not release, pry carefully until loose. Do not distort the sealing flange.**
12. Reverse procedure to install. **Torque cover bolts to specifications.**

REAR

1. Disconnect battery ground cable.
2. Remove torque reaction rod attaching bolt from cylinder head.
3. Pivot torque reaction rod upward and remove cylinder head bracket attaching bolt from bracket at front of engine.
4. Loosen lower torque reaction rod bracket attaching bolt at front of engine.
5. Remove upper two torque reaction rod bracket attaching bolts from front of engine.
6. Remove torque reaction rod bracket attaching bolts from cylinder head to exhaust manifold connection.
7. Disconnect wiring harness between rocker arm cover and lower plenum.
8. Remove rocker arm cover attaching bolts and the cover. **If cover adheres to cylinder head, shear the adhesion by tapping the end of the cover with a rubber mallet. If cover will not release, pry carefully until loose. Do not distort the sealing flange.**
9. Reverse procedure to install. **Torque cover attaching bolts to specifications.**

CYLINDER HEAD
REPLACE

LEFT SIDE

1. Disconnect battery ground cable and drain cooling system.
2. Remove intake manifold and exhaust crossover pipe.
3. Remove alternator bracket and oil dipstick tube.
4. Remove rocker arm cover, rocker arms and pushrods.
5. Remove cylinder head bolts and cylinder head.
6. Reverse procedure to install. **Torque cylinder head bolts in sequence, Fig. 5, to 66 ft. lbs.**

RIGHT SIDE

1. Disconnect battery ground cable and drain cooling system.
2. Raise and support vehicle.
3. Disconnect exhaust pipe from manifold.
4. Remove cruise control servo bracket.
5. Remove intake manifold and exhaust crossover pipe.
6. Remove rocker arm cover, rocker arms and pushrods.
7. Remove cylinder head bolts and cylinder head.
8. Reverse procedure to install. **Torque cylinder head bolts in sequence, Fig. 5, to 66 ft. lbs.**

ROCKER ARM COVER
REPLACE

FRONT

1. Disconnect battery ground cable.
2. Remove engine compartment lid. **Do not remove torsion rod retaining bolts.**
3. Remove vacuum boost line and tube.
4. Disconnect throttle and downshift cables and remove bracket.

VALVE ARRANGEMENT
FRONT TO REAR

Right. . . . . E-I-E-I-I-E
Left . . . . E-I-I-E-I-E

CAM LOBE LIFT SPECIFICATIONS

Intake, Inch 246
Exhaust, Inch 267

ROCKER ARM STUDS

Rocker arm studs that are cracked or have damaged threads can be replaced. If threads in cylinder head are damaged or stripped, the head can be re-tapped and a helical type insert added. When installing a new rocker arm stud, torque to specifications.

VALVE CLEARANCE SPECIFICATIONS

Refer to "Valves, Adjust" procedure.

VALVES
ADJUST

1. Crank engine until mark on torsional damper is aligned with TDC mark on timing tab. Check to ensure engine is in the No. 1 cylinder firing position by placing fingers on No. 1 cylinder rocker arms as mark on damper comes near TDC mark on timing tab. If valves are not moving, the engine is in the No. 1 firing position. If valves move as damper mark nears TDC inch mark on timing tab, engine is in the No. 4 cylinder firing position and should be rotated one revolution to reach the No. 1 cylinder firing position.
2. With engine in the No. 1 cylinder firing position, adjust the following valves: Exhaust- 1, 2, 3; Intake- 1, 5, 6. To adjust valves, back off adjusting nut until lash is felt at pushrod, then tighten adjusting nut until all lash is removed, **Fig. 6.** This can be determined by rotating the pushrod while tightening the adjusting nut. When all lash has been eliminated, turn adjusting nut an additional 1½ turns.
3. Crank engine one revolution until mark on torsional damper and TDC mark are again aligned. This is the No. 4 cylinder firing position. With engine in this position, the following valves can be adjusted: Exhaust- 4, 5 & 6; Intake- 2, 3 & 4.
4. Install rocker arm covers, then start engine and check timing and idle speed.

VALVE GUIDES

Valve guides are an integral part of the cylinder head and are not removable. If valve stem clearance becomes excessive, the valve guide should be reamed to the next oversize and the appropriate oversize valves installed. Valves are available in of oversizes .0035, .0155 and .0305 inch.

VALVE LIFTERS

Some engines will be equipped with both standard and .25 mm oversize valve lifters. The cylinder case will be marked where the oversize valve lifters are installed with a dab of white paint and .25 mm O.S. will be stamped on the valve lifter boss, **Fig. 7.**

Failure of a hydraulic valve lifter, **Fig. 8,** is generally caused by an inadequate oil supply or dirt. An air leak at the intake side of the oil pump or too much oil in the engine will cause air bubbles in the oil supply to the lifters causing them to collapse. This is a probable cause of trouble if several lifters fail to function, but air in oil is an unlikely cause of failure of a single unit.

Valve lifters can be removed after removing rocker arm covers, intake manifold, rocker stud nuts, rocker arm balls, rocker arms and pushrods.

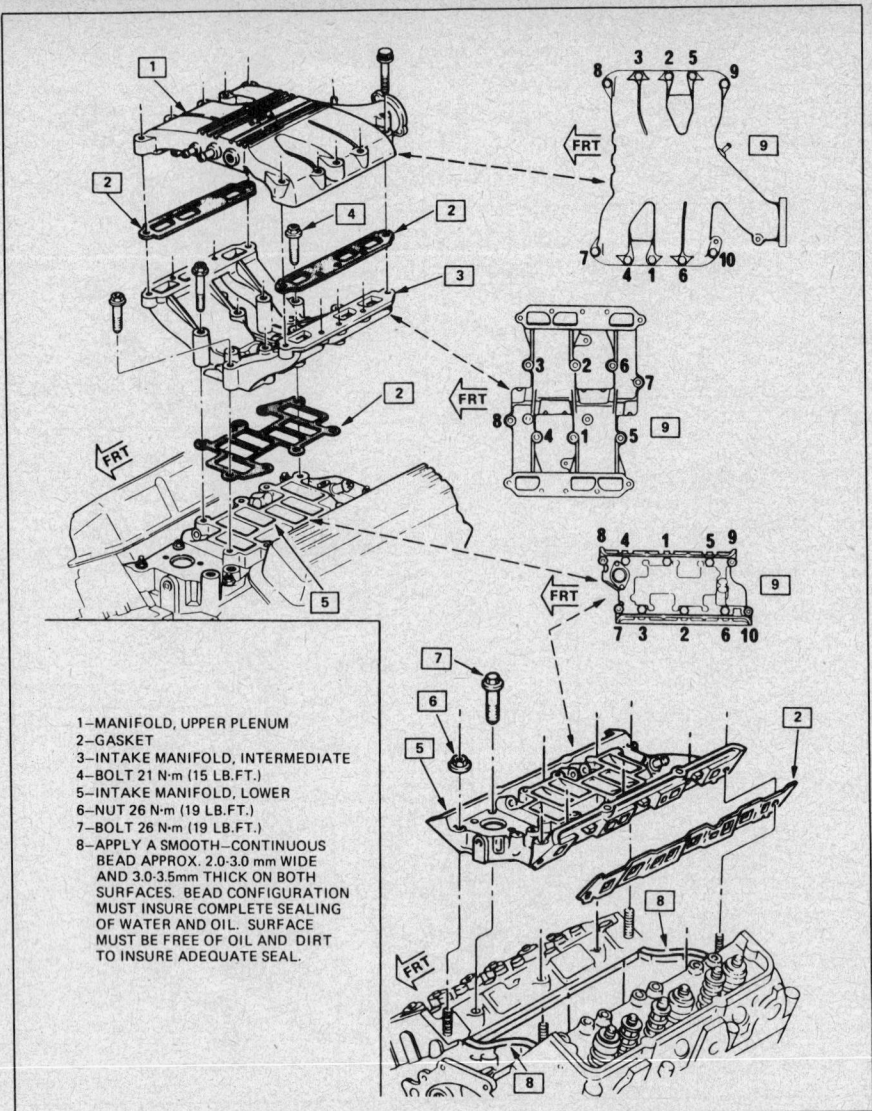

1—MANIFOLD, UPPER PLENUM
2—GASKET
3—INTAKE MANIFOLD, INTERMEDIATE
4—BOLT 21 N·m (15 LB.FT.)
5—INTAKE MANIFOLD, LOWER
6—NUT 26 N·m (19 LB.FT.)
7—BOLT 26 N·m (19 LB.FT.)
8—APPLY A SMOOTH—CONTINUOUS BEAD APPROX. 2.0-3.0 mm WIDE AND 3.0-3.5mm THICK ON BOTH SURFACES. BEAD CONFIGURATION MUST INSURE COMPLETE SEALING OF WATER AND OIL. SURFACE MUST BE FREE OF OIL AND DIRT TO INSURE ADEQUATE SEAL.

Fig. 3   Intake manifold installation

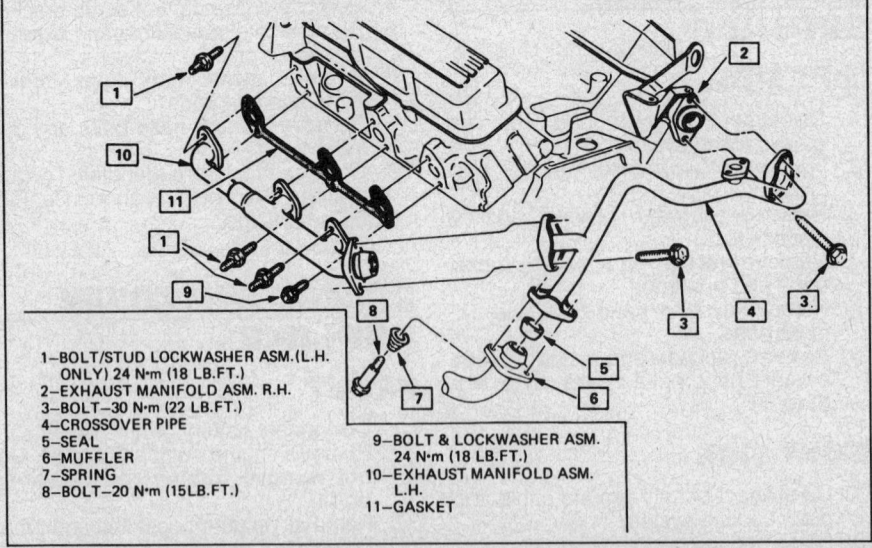

1—BOLT/STUD LOCKWASHER ASM.(L.H. ONLY) 24 N·m (18 LB.FT.)
2—EXHAUST MANIFOLD ASM. R.H.
3—BOLT-30 N·m (22 LB.FT.)
4—CROSSOVER PIPE
5—SEAL
6—MUFFLER
7—SPRING
8—BOLT-20 N·m (15LB.FT.)
9—BOLT & LOCKWASHER ASM. 24 N·m (18 LB.FT.)
10—EXHAUST MANIFOLD ASM. L.H.
11—GASKET

Fig. 4   Exhaust manifold installation

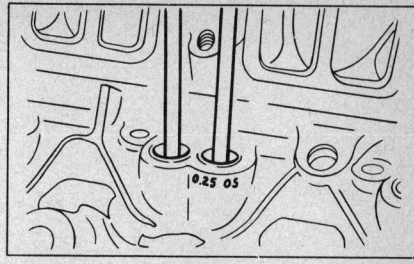

Fig. 7   Oversize valve lifter marking

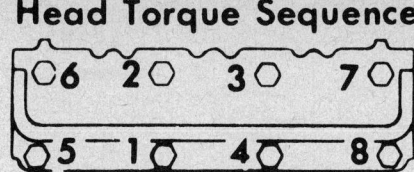

Fig. 5   Cylinder head installation & torque sequence

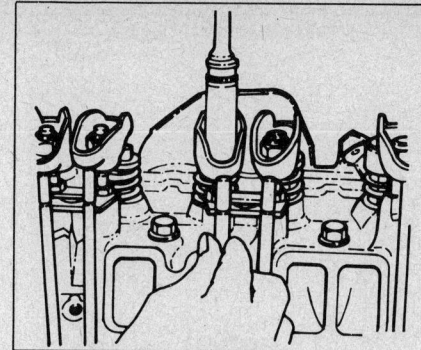

Fig. 6   Adjusting valves

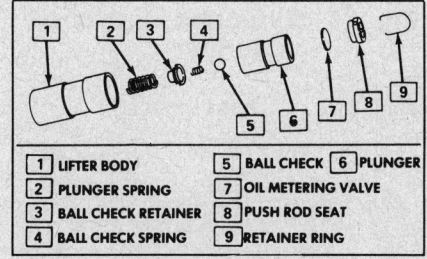

Fig. 8   Exploded view of valve lifter

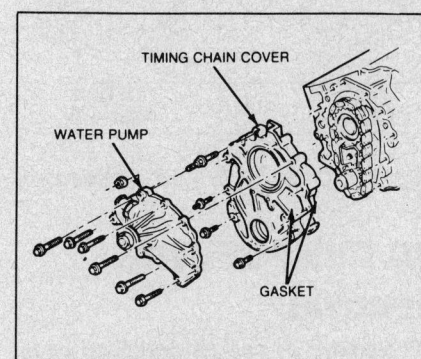

Fig. 9   Engine front cover installation

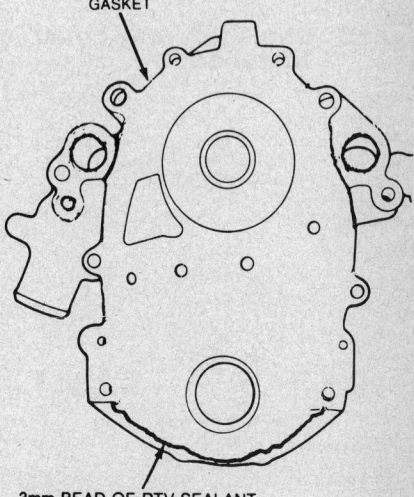

GASKET

3mm BEAD OF RTV SEALANT
#1052366 OR EQUIVALENT

Fig. 10   Engine front cover sealant location

ENGINE FRONT COVER
REPLACE

1. Disconnect battery ground cable.
2. Remove accessory drive belts.
3. **On models equipped with air conditioning,** remove A/C compressor and bracket.
4. **On all models,** remove water pump as described under "Water Pump, Replace."
5. Raise and support vehicle.
6. Remove torsional damper and the oil pan to cover bolts.
7. Lower vehicle.
8. Remove front cover bolts and the cover, **Fig. 9.**
9. Reverse procedure to install. Apply sealant to mating surfaces as shown in **Fig. 10.** It is only necessary to coat oil pan to front cover sealing surfaces since gasket is used in production.

TIMING CHAIN
REPLACE

1. Remove front cover as described under "Engine Front Cover, Replace."
2. Place No. 1 piston at top dead center with marks on camshaft and crankshaft sprockets aligned, **Fig. 11.** The valve timing marks, **Fig. 11,** do not indicate TDC compression stroke for No. 1 cylinder for use during distributor installation. When installing the distributor, rotate engine until No. 1 cylinder is on compression stroke and the camshaft timing mark is 180° from valve timing position shown in **Fig. 11.**
3. Remove camshaft sprocket bolts, then remove sprocket and timing chain. If sprocket does not come off

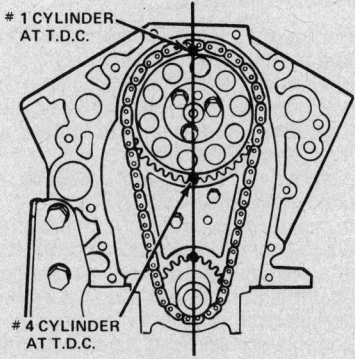

Fig. 11   Valve timing marks

easily, tap lower edge of sprocket with a plastic mallet.
4. If crankshaft sprocket is to be replaced, remove sprocket using a suitable puller or tool J-5825. Install new sprocket, aligning key and keyway.
5. Install timing chain on camshaft sprocket. Hold sprocket vertically with chain hanging down and align marks on camshaft and crankshaft sprockets.
6. Align dowel pin hole in sprocket with dowel pin on camshaft, then install sprocket on camshaft.
7. Using camshaft sprocket attaching bolts, draw sprocket onto camshaft. Torque bolts to specifications.
8. Lubricate timing chain with engine oil, then install front cover as outlined previously.

CAMSHAFT
REPLACE

1. Remove engine from vehicle as described under "Engine, Replace."
2. Remove valve lifters and engine front cover as described previously.
3. Remove timing chain and sprocket as described under "Timing Chain, Replace."
4. Remove camshaft rear cover, **Fig. 12.**
5. Withdraw camshaft from engine, using care not to damage camshaft bearings.
6. Reverse procedure to install. When installing timing chain, align valve timing marks as shown in **Fig. 11.** The valve timing marks, **Fig. 11,** do not indicate TDC compression stroke for No. 1 cylinder for use during distributor installation. When installing the distributor, rotate engine until No. 1 cylinder is on compression stroke and the camshaft timing mark is 180° from valve timing position shown in **Fig. 11.**

PISTON & ROD
ASSEMBLY

Assemble pistons to connecting rods as shown in **Fig. 13.**

2.8L/ V6-173 ENGINE

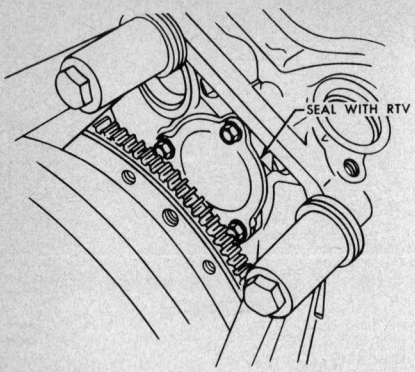

Fig. 12 Camshaft rear cover installation

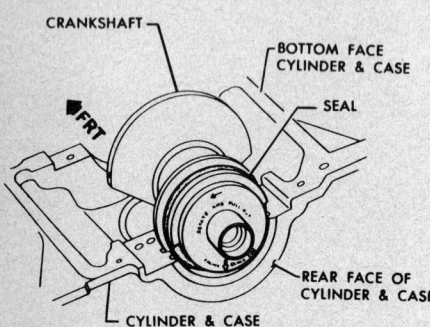

CRANKSHAFT

BOTTOM FACE CYLINDER & CASE

SEAL

FRT

REAR FACE OF CYLINDER & CASE

CYLINDER & CASE

CAUTION RETAINER SPRING SIDE OF SEAL MUST FACE TOWARD FRONT OF CYLINDER & CASE.

Fig. 15 Rear main bearing oil seal installation. Thin seal

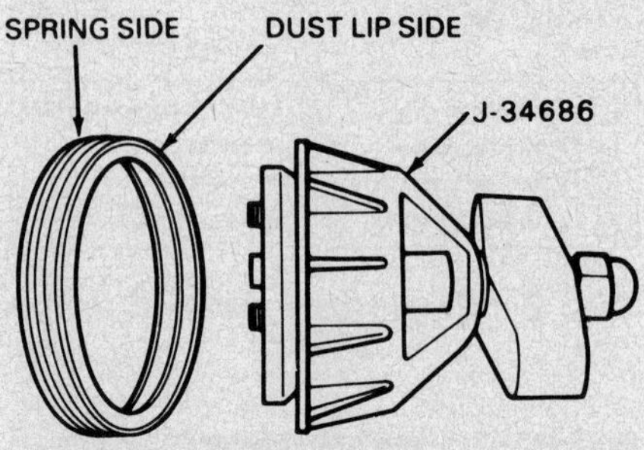

Upon installation, measure the connecting rod side clearance using a suitable feeler gauge. Clearance should be .006 to .017 inch.

PISTONS, PINS & RINGS

Pistons and rings are available in standard size and oversizes of .05 and 1 mm.

MAIN & ROD BEARINGS

Main bearings are available in standard size and undersizes of .013 and .026 mm and connecting rod bearings are available in standard size and undersizes of .016 and .032 mm.

OIL PAN
REPLACE

1. Disconnect battery ground cable.
2. Raise and support vehicle.
3. Drain engine oil from crankcase.
4. Remove flywheel housing shield or clutch housing cover as applicable.
5. Remove starter motor.
6. Remove oil pan attaching bolts and the oil pan.
7. Reverse procedure to install. Apply a ⅛ inch bead of RTV sealer to oil pan sealing flange.

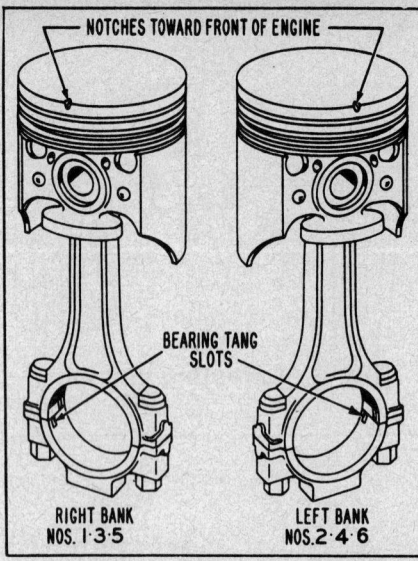

NOTCHES TOWARD FRONT OF ENGINE

BEARING TANG SLOTS

RIGHT BANK NOS. 1·3·5

LEFT BANK NOS. 2·4·6

Fig. 13 Piston & rod assembly

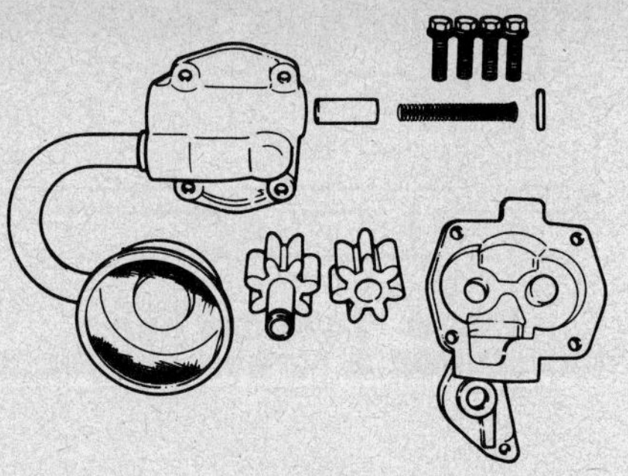

OIL PUMP SERVICE
REMOVAL

1. Remove oil pan as described under "Oil Pan, Replace."
2. Remove pump to rear main bearing cap bolt and remove pump and extension shaft.

DISASSEMBLY

1. Remove pump cover attaching bolts and pump cover, **Fig. 14.**
2. Mark drive and idler gear teeth so they can be installed in the same position, then remove idler and drive gear and shaft from pump body.
3. Remove pin, spring and pressure regulator valve from pump cover.
4. If pickup tube and screen assembly are to be replaced, mount pump cover in a soft jawed vise and remove pickup tube from cover. Do not remove screen from pickup tube, these components are serviced as an assembly.

INSPECTION

1. Inspect pump body and cover for excessive wear and cracks.
2. Inspect pump gear for damage or excessive wear. If pump gears are damaged or worn, the entire pump assembly must be replaced.
3. Check drive gear shaft for looseness in pump body.
4. Inspect pump cover for wear that would allow oil to leak past gear teeth.
5. Inspect pickup tube and screen assembly for damage.
6. Check pressure regulator valve for fit in pump cover.

ASSEMBLY

1. If pickup tube and screen were removed, apply sealer to end of pickup tube, then mount pump cover in a soft jawed vise and using tool No. J-8369,

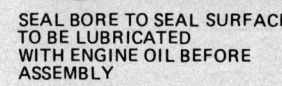

Fig. 14 Exploded view of oil pump

SPRING SIDE   DUST LIP SIDE

J-34686

SEAL BORE TO SEAL SURFACE TO BE LUBRICATED WITH ENGINE OIL BEFORE ASSEMBLY

Fig. 16 Rear main bearing oil seal installation. Thick seal

tap pickup tube into position using a plastic mallet. **Whenever the pickup tube and screen assembly has been removed, a new pickup tube and screen assembly should be installed. Use care when installing pickup tube and screen assembly so that tube does not twist, shear or collapse. Loss of a press fit condition could result in an air leak and a loss of oil pressure.**
2. Install pressure regulator valve, spring and pin, **Fig. 14.**
3. Install drive gear and shaft in pump body.
4. Align marks made during disassembly, then install idler gear.
5. Install pump cover gasket, cover and attaching bolts. Torque bolts to specifications.
6. Rotate pump driveshaft by hand and check pump for smooth operation.

INSTALLATION

1. Assemble pump and extension shaft with retainer to rear main bearing cap, aligning top end of hexagon extension shaft with hexagon socket on lower end of distributor shaft.
2. Install pump to rear main bearing cap bolt.
3. Install oil pan as described under Oil Pan, Replace.

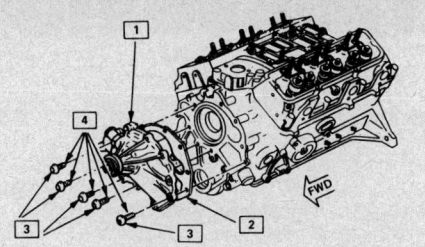

1—WATER PUMP
2—GASKET
3—BOLT - 10 N·m (7 LB. FT.)
4—SEALER

Fig. 17 Water pump installation

REAR MAIN BEARING OIL SEAL REPAIR

THIN SEAL

1. Remove engine as outlined under "Engine, Replace" procedure.
2. Remove oil pan and oil pump assembly.
3. Remove water pump and timing chain.
4. Remove connecting rod and main bearing caps, then the crankshaft and oil seal.
5. Coat outer diameter of new seal with sealant 1052756 or equivalent.
6. Position seal/tool assembly on rear of crankshaft, ensuring arrows on tool face toward cylinder and case assembly, **Fig. 15.**
7. Install crankshaft, discard tool, then coat crankshaft journals with engine oil.
8. Apply a 1 mm bead of anaerobic sealant to bearing cap surface.
9. Reinstall rear main cap, main bearing caps and connecting rod caps and torque to specifications.
10. Reverse removal procedure to complete installation.

THICK SEAL

1. Remove transaxle and flexplate.
2. Using a screwdriver or similar tool, pry out old seal. Use care to avoid damaging crankshaft. File all burrs or nicks as required.
3. Install new seal using tool J-34686, **Fig. 16,** as follows:
   a. Apply a light coat of engine oil to I.D. of oil seal.
   b. Slide seal over tool mandrel until dust lip bottoms squarely against collar of tool.
   c. Align dowel pin of tool with dowel pin hole in crankshaft, **Fig. 16,** then attach tool to crankshaft with screw provided.
   d. Turn handle of tool until seal is pushed into bore and collar is positioned firmly against case. Remove tool.
4. Install flywheel and transmission, then start engine and check for leaks.

WATER PUMP REPLACE

1. Disconnect battery ground cable, then drain cooling system.
2. Remove accessory drive belts, then the radiator and heater hose.
3. Remove water pump attaching bolts and the water pump, **Fig. 17.**
4. Reverse procedure to install. Apply a 2 mm bead of suitable sealer to water pump sealing surface.

COOLING SYSTEM BLEED

These engines doe not require a specific bleed procedure. After filling cooling system, run engine to operating temperature with radiator/pressure cap off. Air will then be automatically bled through cap opening.

TIGHTENING SPECIFICATIONS

*Torque specifications are for clean and lightly lubricated threads only. Dry or dirty threads produce increased friction which prevents accurate measurement of tightness.

Year	Component	Torque/Ft. Lbs.
1988	Camshaft Sprocket	15-20
	Clutch Cover To Flywheel	13-18
	Connecting Rod Cap Bolts	34-40
	Crankshaft Pulley	20-30
	Cylinder Head Bolts	65-90
	Distributor Hold Down Bolt	20-30
	EGR Valve	13-18
	Exhaust Crossover Bolts	22
	Exhaust Manifold	22-28
	Flywheel To Crankshaft	45-55
	Flywheel To Torque Converter	25-35
	Intake Manifold	20-25
	Main Bearing Cap Bolts	63-74
	Oil Pan	6-9
	Oil Pump	26-35
	Rocker Arm Cover	6-9
	Rocker Arm Stud	43-49
	Spark Plug	7-15
	Starter Motor	26-37
	Vibration Damper Of Pulley	66-84

Clutch & Manual Transaxle

INDEX

HYDRAULIC CLUTCH
BLEED

Extreme cleanliness must be maintained while bleeding the clutch system. Do not use linty rags, and ensure no dirt enters the system, particularly at the supply tank. Never add previously used fluid to the supply tank as it may be contaminated or have an excessive moisture content.

1. Fill supply tank with suitable brake fluid.
2. Remove floormat or any other object which may impede full travel of clutch pedal.
3. Back out bleed screw on slave cylinder until fluid can be pumped out (approximately ½ turn).
4. Depress clutch pedal fully, then apply three short, rapid strokes.
5. Release pressure to allow clutch pedal to return quickly to its stop.
6. Repeat steps 2 and 3 until all air has been released from bleed screw.
7. Close bleed screw immediately following last downward stroke of pedal when air bubbles no longer appear.

CLUTCH
REPLACE

1. Remove transaxle as described under "Manual Transaxle, Replace."
2. Mark position of pressure plate to flywheel for assembly reference.
3. Gradually loosen pressure plate attaching bolts until spring pressure is relieved.
4. Support pressure plate and remove mounting bolts, pressure plate and driven disc, **Fig. 1.**
5. Reverse procedure to install. Evenly tighten pressure plate retaining bolts in crossing pattern until pressure plate is seated on flywheel, then **torque** bolts to 15 ft. lbs.

MANUAL TRANSAXLE SHIFT CABLE
ADJUST

W/5 SPEED ISUZU TRANSAXLE

1. Disconnect battery ground cable.
2. Shift transaxle into first gear.
3. Loosen shift cable attaching nuts "E" on transaxle levers "D" and "F," **Fig. 2.**
4. Remove console and trim plates to provide access to shifter.

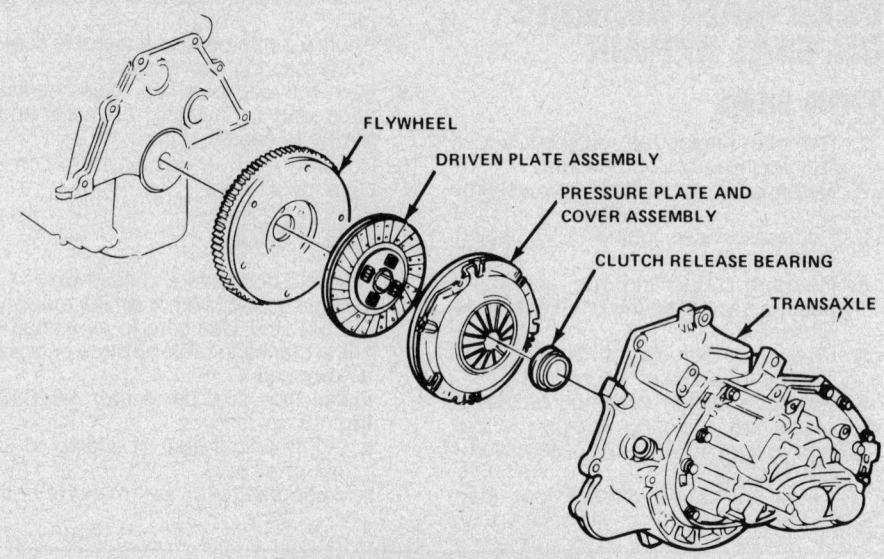

Fig. 1   Clutch assembly

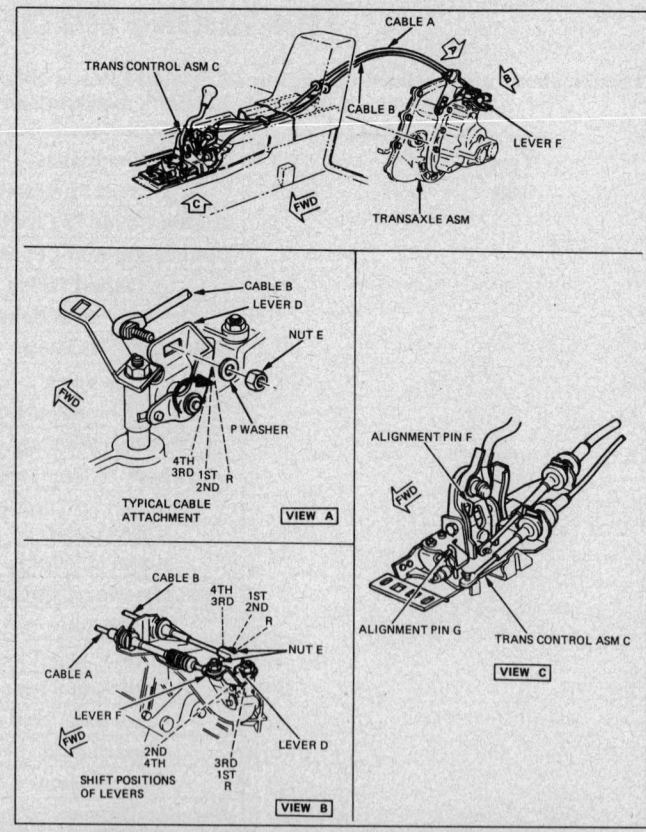

Fig. 2   Manual transaxle shift cable adjustment. w/5 speed Isuzu Transaxle

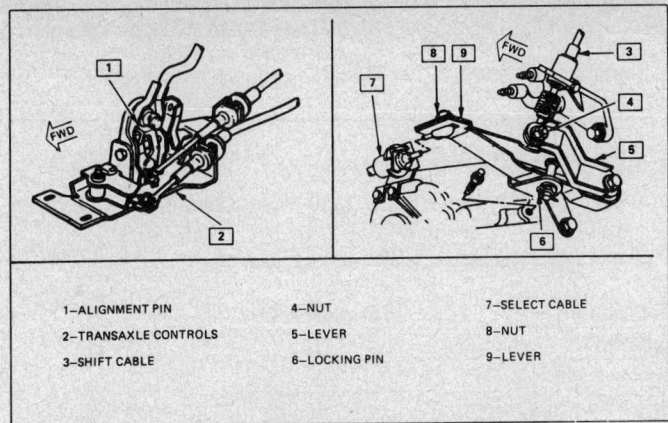

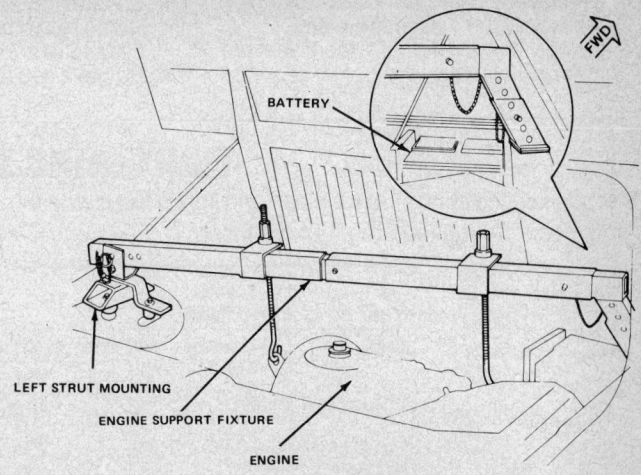

1—ALIGNMENT PIN   4—NUT   7—SELECT CABLE

2—TRANSAXLE CONTROLS   5—LEVER   8—NUT

3—SHIFT CABLE   6—LOCKING PIN   9—LEVER

Fig. 3 Manual transaxle shift cable adjustment. w/5 speed Muncie transaxle

Fig. 4 Engine support fixture. w/5 speed Isuzu transaxle

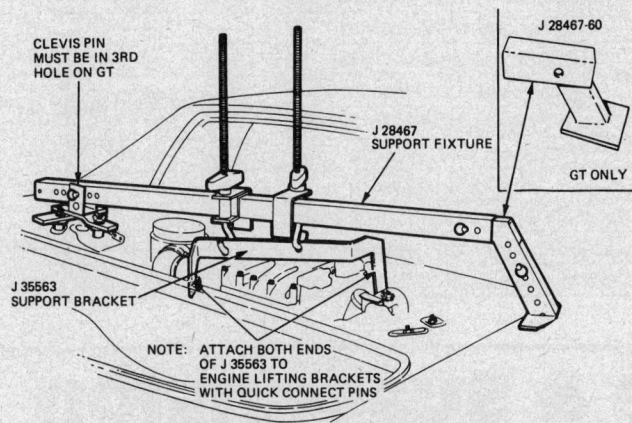

Fig. 5 Engine support fixture. w/5 speed Muncie transaxle

5. With transaxle in first gear, insert alignment pins "F" and "G," view "C," **Fig. 2.**
6. Remove backlash from transaxle by rotating lever "D" in direction of arrow while tightening nut "E" to 20 ft. lbs. Repeat procedure for nut "E" on lever "F." **Levers "D" and "F" must remain stationary while tightening nuts.**
7. Ensure reverse inhibit cam is against roller and align if necessary.
8. Remove alignment pins "F" and "G" from shifter assembly.
9. Install console trim plate and reconnect battery ground cable.

W/5 SPEED MUNCIE TRANSAXLE

1. Loosen nut on transaxle shift lever ball stud on shift cable only, **Fig. 3.**
2. Position transaxle in 3rd gear, then remove shift knob, front trim plate and shifter trim plate.
3. Engage floor shift mechanism in 3rd gear, then **torque** shift cable ball stud nut to 18 ft. lbs.
4. Reinstall trim plates and shift knob.

MANUAL TRANSAXLE REPLACE

W/5 SPEED ISUZU TRANSAXLE

1. Disconnect battery ground cable.
2. Remove deck lid and louvered panels.
3. Remove upper rear engine support bolt.
4. Install engine support fixture tool No. J-28467 or equivalent, **Fig. 4.**
5. Raise and support vehicle.
6. Unfasten slave cylinder from clutch, leaving hydraulic line connected.
7. Disconnect shift cables from transaxle.
8. Disconnect EGR valve output pipe from exhaust manifold.
9. Remove both wheel and tire assemblies.
10. Disconnect parking brake cable from brake calipers and body brackets.
11. Remove lateral control arm/fixed adjusting link through bolts.
12. Remove trailing arms.
13. Remove axle shafts from transaxle.
14. Remove rubber skirts from splash shield cradle retainers.
15. Remove rear transmission bracket mount bolts.
16. Remove motor mount nuts from cradle and front engine mount shock.
17. Remove bolts from crossover pipe to converter.
18. Remove cradle bolts and cradle from engine and support cradle on adjustable stand.
19. Disconnect oxygen sensor wire.
20. Remove crossover pipe heat shields, then the exhaust crossover pipe.
21. Remove upper transmission to engine bolts.
22. Remove clutch inspection plate cover.
23. Remove lower engine bolt studs and the coolant pipe from stud and nut.
24. Reverse procedure to install.

W/5 SPEED MUNCIE TRANSAXLE

1. Disconnect battery ground cable.
2. Remove drain plug and drain transaxle fluid into a suitable container.
3. Disconnect select and shift cables from transaxle brackets.
4. Disconnect back-up light switch electrical connector and remove the switch.
5. Remove shift cables and stud nut securing bracket to transaxle.
6. Remove two select cable mount attaching bolts.
7. Remove two clutch slave cylinder bracket attaching bolts.
8. Remove exhaust crossover pipe.
9. Remove nut, clip and wire from center stud, then the three upper bolts and one stud securing transaxle to engine.
10. Install engine support fixtures as shown in **Fig. 5.**
11. Attach lifting hook to engine lifting ring and raise engine just enough to relieve pressure from mounts.
12. Remove front and rear transaxle mounts.
13. Raise and support vehicle.

14. Remove inspection plate attaching bolts and the inspection plate.
15. Lower frame and tilt, then remove both axle shafts.
16. Support transaxle with a suitable jack.
17. Remove two nuts securing wiring harness to two lower studs.
18. Remove two studs, then carefully lower transaxle from vehicle. **Tilt engine as necessary to provide clearance for transaxle removal.**
19. Reverse procedure to install.

TIGHTENING SPECIFICATIONS

*Torque specifications are for clean and lightly lubricated threads only. Dry or dirty threads produce increased friction which prevents accurate measurement of tightness.

Year	Transaxle Type	Component	Torque/Ft. Lbs.
1988	Isuzu	Clutch Slave Cylinder To Transmission	16
		Clutch Pressure Plate Bolts	15
		Engine Cradle Bolts, Front	67
		Engine Cradle Bolts, Rear	76
		Engine Mount To Bracket	42
		Engine Support, Upper Rear	43
		Transmission Bolts, Upper To Engine	55
		Transmission Bracket Bolts, Rear	40
	Muncie	Back-Up Light Switch	25
		Clutch Inspection Cover	10
		Clutch Pressure Plate Bolts	15
		Clutch Slave Cylinder To Bracket	37
		Engine To Transaxle	55
		Oil Drain Plug	18
		Select & Shift Assembly To Mount	18
		Select & Shift Cables to Mount	89 ①
		Transaxle Control Assembly	13

①–Inch lbs.

Rear Axle & Suspension

INDEX

DESCRIPTION

The drive axles are completely flexible assemblies consisting of an inner Tri-Pot joint and an outer constant velocity joint connected by an axle shaft. The inner joint is completely flexible and has the capability of in and out movement. The outer joint is also flexible, but can not move in and out.

All drive axles except the righthand inboard joint of automatic transaxles incorporate a male spline and interlocks with the transaxle gears through the use of barrel type snap rings. The lefthand inboard shaft attachment on automatic transaxles utilizes a female spline which installs over a stub shaft protruding from the transaxle.

The drive axle spline end mating with the steering knuckle and hub assembly incorporates a slight helix to ensure a tight press fit. This ensures that there is no radial play between hub and drive axle assembly.

The rear suspension, **Fig. 1**, features several improvements over the design used on earlier models. Major changes include the use of a "tri-link" design which allows for specific tuning of each component. In addition, a stabilizer bar is available on some models and the chassis cradle has been revised for suspension attachments.

DRIVE AXLE
REPLACE

It is important that the axle not be over-extended. When one or both ends of the shaft are disconnected, over-extending the joint may cause separation of internal components, which could lead to failure of the joint.

1. Shift transaxle into Neutral position and disconnect battery ground cable, then raise and support vehicle.
2. Remove wheel and tire assemblies.
3. Install drift punch through rotor and remove hub nut and washer, discarding nut.
4. Remove caliper and rotor, then disconnect trailing arm at knuckle.
5. Referring to **Fig. 2**, scribe strut and knuckle assembly as follows:
   a. Using a sharp tool, scribe knuckle along lower outboard strut radius (view A).
   b. Scribe strut flange on inboard side, along curve of knuckle (view B).
   c. Make a chisel mark across the strut/knuckle interface (view C).
6. Remove strut mounting bolts, then the hub from the drive axle.
7. Install tool J-28468 or J-33008 with

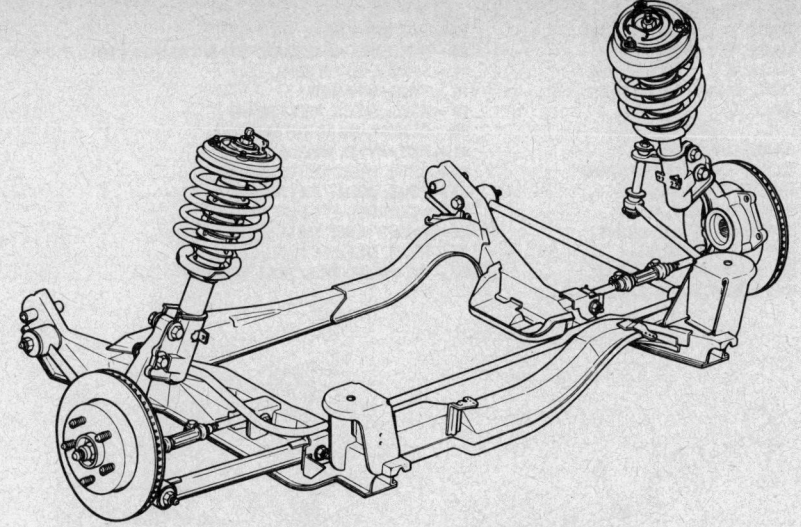

Fig. 1   Rear suspension

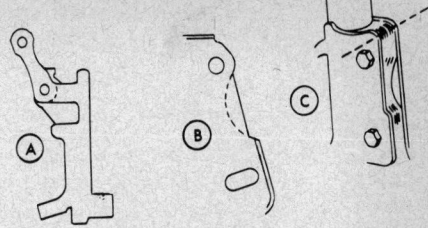

Fig. 2   Scribing strut and knuckle assembly

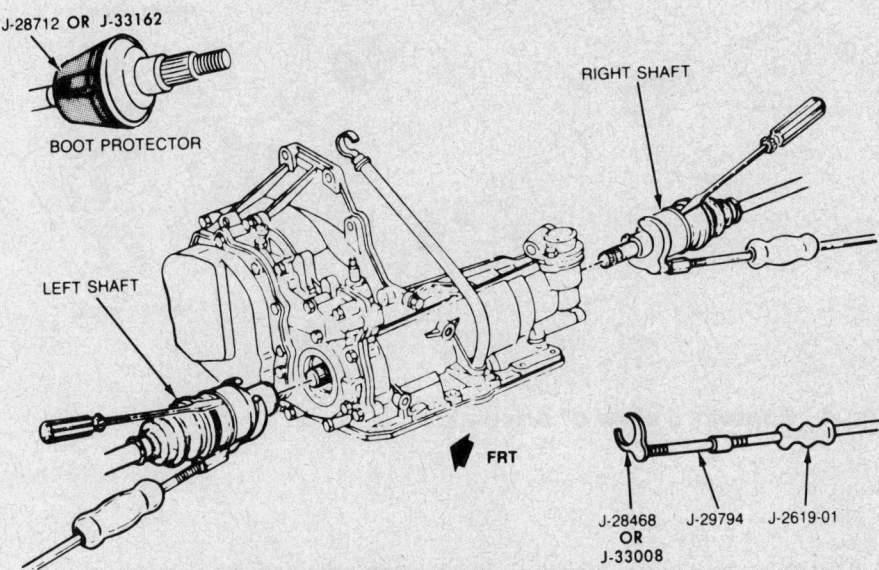

Fig. 3   Drive axle removal

J-29794 and J-2619-01 slide and remove drive axle from transaxle, **Fig. 3.**

8. Install drive axle seal boot protectors J-33162 or equivalent on all Tri-Pot inner joints with silicone (gray) boots.
9. Start splines of drive axle into transaxle and push drive axle until it snaps into place.
10. Align hub assembly with drive axle and install.
11. Loosely install strut mounting bolts with bolt head to rear of vehicle.
12. Install fixed adjusting link, lateral control arm through bolt with bolt head to front of vehicle and **torque** to 37 ft. lbs. plus an additional 90°.
13. Connect trailing arm at knuckle with bolt head inboard and **torque** to 44 ft. lbs. plus an additional 90°.
14. Install strut mounting bolts at knuckle and torque to specification while observing scribe marks.

15. Install caliper and rotor.
16. Insert drift punch through rotor and install washer and new hub nut, **torque** to 183-208 ft. lbs.
17. Remove drive axle seal booster protector, if used.
18. Install tire and wheel assemblies.

DRIVE AXLE SERVICE

Refer to **Figs. 4 and 5** for service procedures on drive axle assembly.

WHEEL BEARING
REPLACE
REMOVAL

1. **On vehicles equipped with steel wheels,** remove hub cap and loosen hub nut, then raise and support vehicle and remove wheel and tire assembly.

2. **On vehicles equipped with 14 inch aluminum wheels,** set parking brake, then raise and support vehicle and remove wheel and tire assembly.
3. **On all models,** install drive axle boot protector J-33162.
4. Remove and discard hub nut.
5. Remove brake caliper and rotor. Suspend caliper from frame with a piece of wire.
6. Remove hub and bearing attaching bolts. **If the old bearing is being reinstalled, mark attaching bolts and corresponding holes for installation reference, Fig. 6.**
7. Remove hub and bearing assembly using tool No. J-28733 or equivalent, **Fig. 7. If assembly is heavily corroded, ensure hub and bearing are loose in knuckle before using puller tool.**
8. Replace knuckle seal if installing new bearing. **Do not move drive axle until hub nut is installed and torqued to specifications.**

INSTALLATION

1. Clean and inspect knuckle bore and bearing mating surfaces for dirt, nicks and burrs.
2. If installing new knuckle seal, apply suitable grease to seal and knuckle bore, then press seal into knuckle using tool No. J-28671 or equivalent.
3. Install hub and bearing assembly onto axle shaft. Torque attaching bolts to specification.
4. Install hub nut and **torque** to 74 ft. lbs.
5. Install brake rotor and caliper.
6. Install wheel and tire assembly, then lower vehicle and **torque** hub nut to 200 ft. lbs.

REAR KNUCKLE
REPLACE
REMOVAL

1. Raise and support vehicle.
2. Install drive axle boot protector.
3. Remove wheel and tire assembly, then remove and discard hub nut.
4. Remove caliper and rotor, then disconnect trailing arm at knuckle.
5. Remove fixed adjusting link/lateral control arm through bolt, then the strut mounting bolts.
6. Remove hub/knuckle assembly from drive axle.

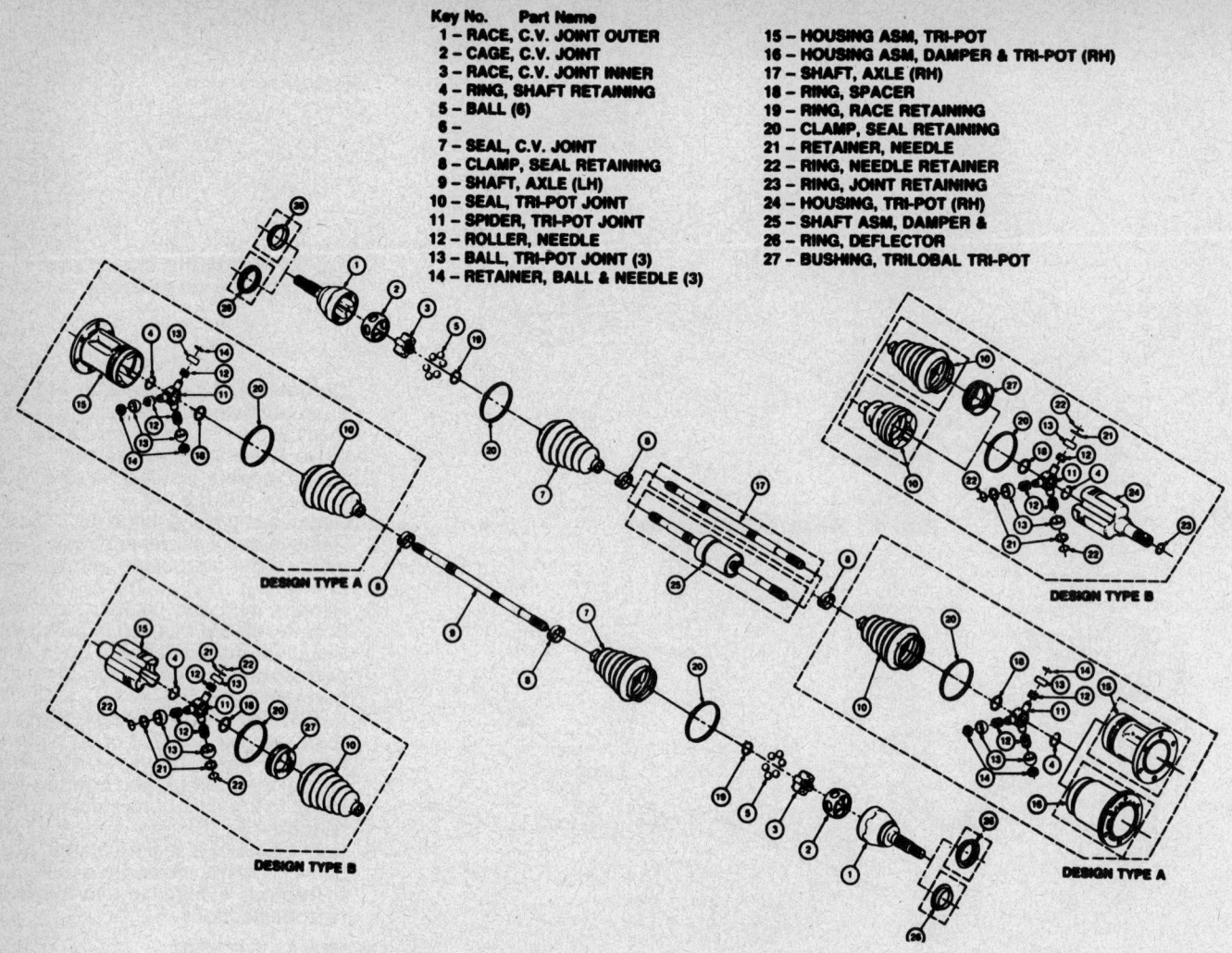

Key No.	Part Name	Key No.	Part Name
1	RACE, C.V. JOINT OUTER	15	HOUSING ASM, TRI-POT
2	CAGE, C.V. JOINT	16	HOUSING ASM, DAMPER & TRI-POT (RH)
3	RACE, C.V. JOINT INNER	17	SHAFT, AXLE (RH)
4	RING, SHAFT RETAINING	18	RING, SPACER
5	BALL (6)	19	RING, RACE RETAINING
6	—	20	CLAMP, SEAL RETAINING
7	SEAL, C.V. JOINT	21	RETAINER, NEEDLE
8	CLAMP, SEAL RETAINING	22	RING, NEEDLE RETAINER
9	SHAFT, AXLE (LH)	23	RING, JOINT RETAINING
10	SEAL, TRI-POT JOINT	24	HOUSING, TRI-POT (RH)
11	SPIDER, TRI-POT JOINT	25	SHAFT ASM, DAMPER &
12	ROLLER, NEEDLE	26	RING, DEFLECTOR
13	BALL, TRI-POT JOINT (3)	27	BUSHING, TRILOBAL TRI-POT
14	RETAINER, BALL & NEEDLE (3)		

Fig. 4   Exploded view of drive axle

INSTALLATION

1. Install hub/knuckle assembly to drive axle.
2. Loosely install strut mounting bolts with bolt head to rear.
3. Install fixed adjusting link/lateral control arm through bolt.
4. Connect trailing arm at knuckle with bolt head inboard.
5. Install strut mounting bolts at knuckle.
6. Install rotor and caliper.
7. **Torque** new hub nut and washer to 74 ft. lbs., then remove drive axle seal boot protector.
8. Install tire and wheel assembly and lower vehicle.
9. **Torque** hub nut and washer to 200 ft. lbs.
10. Adjust camber and toe in as necessary.

STRUT ASSEMBLY REPLACE

1. Remove engine compartment cover.

2. Remove three upper strut nuts and washers.
3. Loosen wheel lug nuts, then raise vehicle and support at rear control arm.
4. Remove wheel and tire assembly, then the brake line retaining clip.
5. Scribe strut and knuckle, **Fig. 2**, for assembly reference. When servicing the jounce bumper, strut mount, strut shield, spring seal or spring insulator, the strut and knuckle must be scribed as shown in **Fig. 2** to maintain the original camber setting. However, it will be necessary to check toe-in setting and adjust as necessary. **When servicing the strut damper, knuckle or rear ride spring, the scribe marks should not be made. However, it will be necessary to check both toe-in and camber settings and correct as necessary.**
6. Remove strut attaching nuts and bolts, then the strut assembly and spacer plate.
7. Reverse procedure to install. Torque knuckle attaching nuts and upper strut attaching nuts to specifications.

STRUT ASSEMBLY SERVICE
DISASSEMBLY

1. Clamp strut compressor, tool No. J-34013 or equivalent, in a suitable vise.
2. Install strut assembly into bottom adapter of compressor and install bottom adapter, **Fig. 8**. Ensure strut and locating pins are fully engaged.
3. Rotate strut assembly until top mounting assembly lip is aligned with compressor support notch.
4. Install upper adapter onto top spring seal, **Fig. 8**, so long stud is at high location to strut flange.
5. Rotate compressor forcing screw clockwise until top support flange contacts top adapter, and continue turning screw to compress strut spring.
6. Install second upper adapter over spring seat assembly, then rotate forcing screw counterclockwise until strut spring tension is relieved.

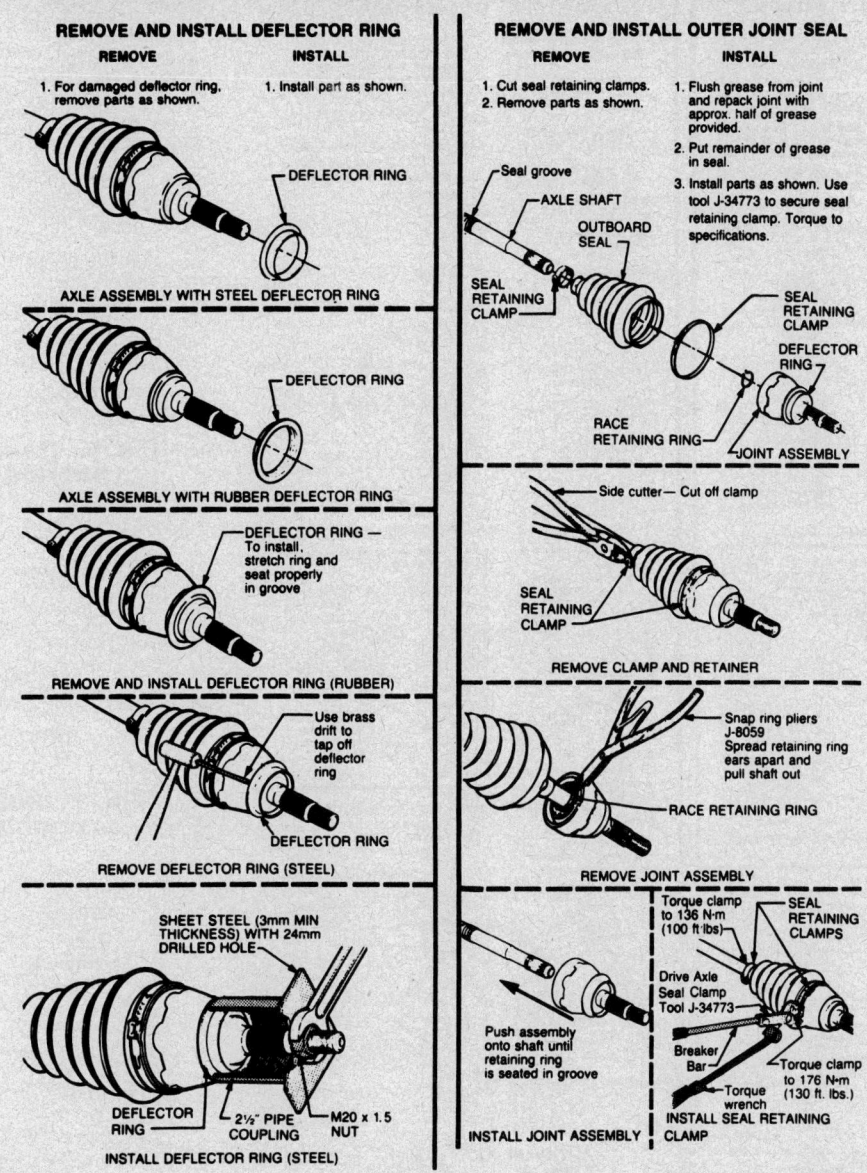

Fig. 5   Drive axle service (Part 1 of 2)

7. Remove top adapters, bottom adapter and strut.

ASSEMBLY

1. Perform steps 1 and 2 as outlined in the "Disassembly" procedure.
2. Rotate strut assembly until mounting flange is facing outward, opposite compressor forcing screw.
3. Install strut components, **Fig. 9.** Ensure spring is properly seated on bottom spring plate.
4. Install strut spring seat assembly on top of spring with long stud positioned 180° from strut mounting flange.
5. Install top adapter over spring seat assembly.
6. Rotate compressor forcing screw until compressor top support just contacts top adapter. Do not compress spring.
7. Install strut alignment rod through top spring seat and thread onto damper shaft hand tight, **Fig. 9.**
8. Rotate compressor forcing screw clockwise to compress spring until damper shaft is exposed enough so nut can be threaded securely, then install the nut. Ensure damper shaft comes through center of spring seat opening to prevent damage. **Do not compress spring until bottomed.**
9. Remove alignment rod, then install mount and **torque** nut to 65 ft. lbs.
10. Rotate compressor forcing screw counterclockwise and remove strut assembly from compressor.

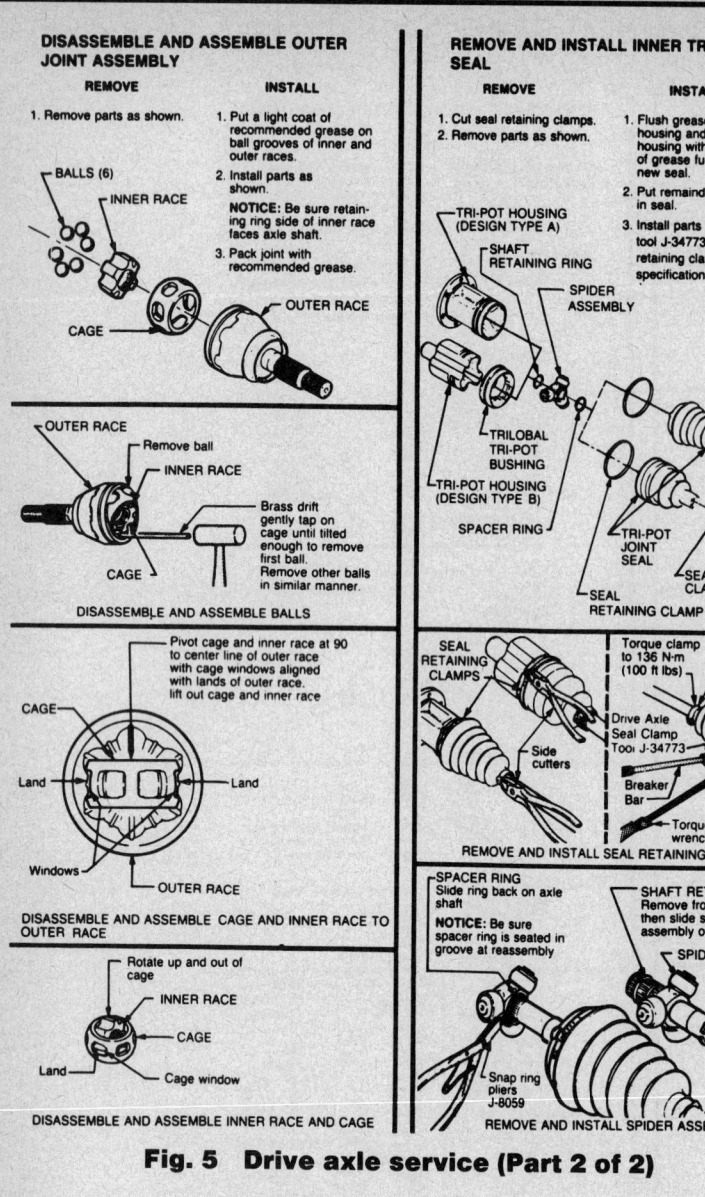

DISASSEMBLE AND ASSEMBLE OUTER JOINT ASSEMBLY

REMOVE

1. Remove parts as shown.

BALLS (6)
INNER RACE
CAGE
OUTER RACE

INSTALL

1. Put a light coat of recommended grease on ball grooves of inner and outer races.
2. Install parts as shown.
NOTICE: Be sure retaining ring side of inner race faces axle shaft.
3. Pack joint with recommended grease.

OUTER RACE
Remove ball
INNER RACE
CAGE
Brass drift gently tap on cage until tilted enough to remove first ball. Remove other balls in similar manner.

DISASSEMBLE AND ASSEMBLE BALLS

Pivot cage and inner race at 90 to center line of outer race with cage windows aligned with lands of outer race. lift out cage and inner race

CAGE
Land
Land
Windows
OUTER RACE

DISASSEMBLE AND ASSEMBLE CAGE AND INNER RACE TO OUTER RACE

Rotate up and out of cage
INNER RACE
CAGE
Land
Cage window

DISASSEMBLE AND ASSEMBLE INNER RACE AND CAGE

REMOVE AND INSTALL INNER TRI-POT SEAL

REMOVE

1. Cut seal retaining clamps.
2. Remove parts as shown.

INSTALL

1. Flush grease from housing and repack housing with approx. half of grease furnished with new seal.
2. Put remainder of grease in seal.
3. Install parts as shown. Use tool J-34773 to secure seal retaining clamp. Torque to specifications.

TRI-POT HOUSING (DESIGN TYPE A)
SHAFT RETAINING RING
SPIDER ASSEMBLY
TRILOBAL TRI-POT BUSHING
TRI-POT HOUSING (DESIGN TYPE B)
SPACER RING
AXLE
TRI-POT JOINT SEAL
Seal groove
SEAL RETAINING CLAMP
SEAL RETAINING CLAMP

SEAL RETAINING CLAMPS
Side cutters
Torque clamp to 136 N·m (100 ft lbs)
SEAL RETAINING CLAMPS
Drive Axle Seal Clamp Tool J-34773
Breaker Bar
Torque clamp to 176 N·m (130 ft. lbs.)
Torque wrench

REMOVE AND INSTALL SEAL RETAINING CLAMP

SPACER RING
Slide ring back on axle shaft
NOTICE: Be sure spacer ring is seated in groove at reassembly
SHAFT RETAINING RING
Remove from axle shaft then slide spider assembly off axle
SPIDER ASSEMBLY
SPACER RING
Snap ring pliers J-8059

REMOVE AND INSTALL SPIDER ASSEMBLY

Fig. 5   Drive axle service (Part 2 of 2)

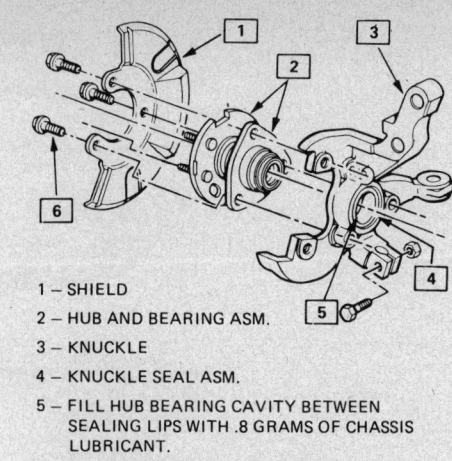

1 – SHIELD
2 – HUB AND BEARING ASM.
3 – KNUCKLE
4 – KNUCKLE SEAL ASM.
5 – FILL HUB BEARING CAVITY BETWEEN SEALING LIPS WITH .8 GRAMS OF CHASSIS LUBRICANT.
6 – BOLT 75-95 N·m (55-70 FT. LB.)

Fig. 6   Rear wheel hub & bearing assembly

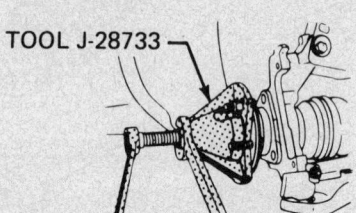

TOOL J-28733

Fig. 7   Hub & bearing assembly removal

SPECIAL TOOL J-26584-430

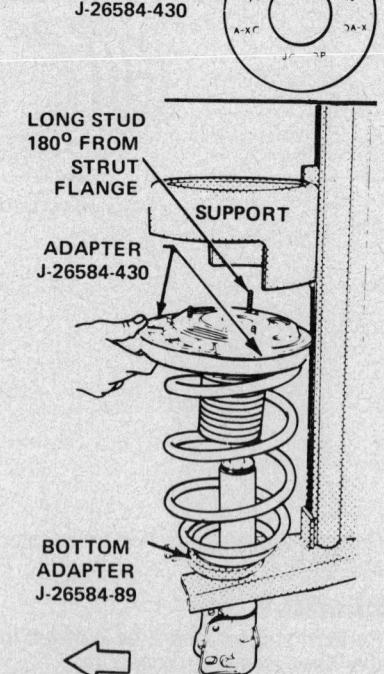

LONG STUD 180° FROM STRUT FLANGE
SUPPORT
ADAPTER J-26584-430
BOTTOM ADAPTER J-26584-89
DIRECTION OF LOWER STRUT FLANGE

Fig. 8   Removing damper & coil spring from strut

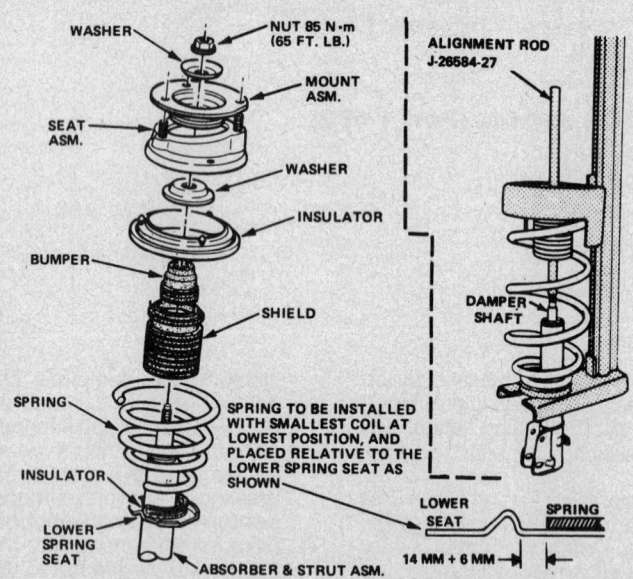

WASHER
NUT 85 N·m (65 FT. LB.)
MOUNT ASM.
SEAT ASM.
WASHER
INSULATOR
BUMPER
SHIELD
SPRING
INSULATOR
LOWER SPRING SEAT
ABSORBER & STRUT ASM.

SPRING TO BE INSTALLED WITH SMALLEST COIL AT LOWEST POSITION, AND PLACED RELATIVE TO THE LOWER SPRING SEAT AS SHOWN

ALIGNMENT ROD J-26584-27
DAMPER SHAFT
LOWER SEAT
SPRING
14 MM + 6 MM

Fig. 9   Strut assembly alignment & components

TIGHTENING SPECIFICATIONS

Year	Component	Torque/ft. lbs.
1988	Hub And Bearing Assembly Attaching Nuts	55-70
	Hub Nut	183-208
	Lower Ball Joint	30-36
	Strut To Knuckle	140
	Upper Strut Attaching Nuts	18
	Wheel Lug Nuts	100

Front Suspension & Steering

INDEX

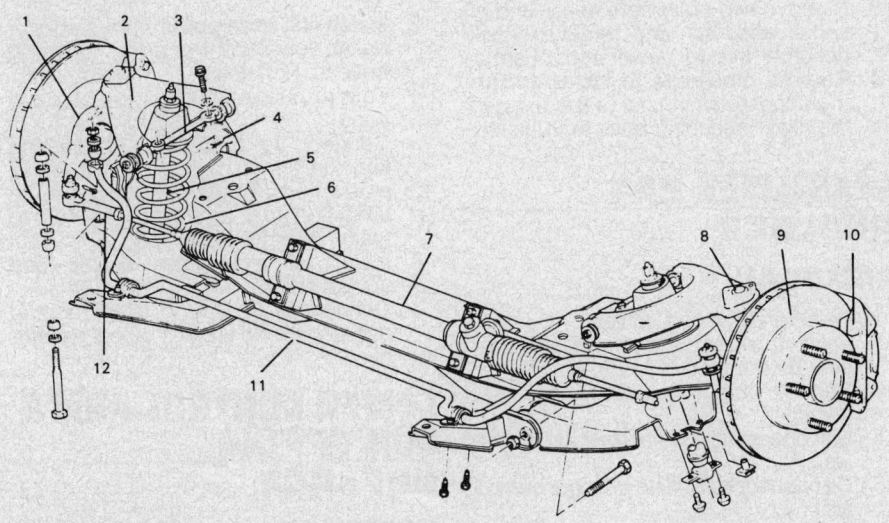

1. STEERING KNUCKLE
2. UPPER CONTROL ARM
3. PIVOT ARM
4. PADDLE NUT ASM.
5. SHOCK ABSORBER
6. SPRING
7. RACK AND PINION ASM.
8. UPPER BALL JOINT
9. ROTOR
10. BRAKE CALIPER
11. STABILIZER BAR
12. TIE ROD END

Fig. 1 Front suspension

DESCRIPTION

The front suspension, **Fig. 1**, features several improvements over the design used on earlier models. In conjunction with the elimination of the steering damper assembly, a larger stabilizer bar is used. Additionally, both the king pin angle and scrub radius have been reduced. Other notable changes include the use of a shorter spindle and an increase in both upper and lower control arm lengths. Besides producing lighter steering effort and a smoother ride, the redesigned suspension also results in a shorter turning radius.

WHEEL HUB & BEARING ASSEMBLY
REPLACE

1. Raise and support vehicle.
2. Remove tire and wheel assembly.
3. Remove brake line clip to upper control arm attaching bolt.
4. Remove caliper and suspend with wire, then remove rotor.
5. Remove hub and bearing assembly attaching bolts.
6. Reverse procedure to install. Torque hub and bearing assembly to specification.

UPPER BALL JOINT
REPLACE

REMOVAL

1. Raise and support vehicle, supporting lower control arm with suitable jack.
2. Remove wheel and tire assembly.
3. Disconnect brake line from upper control arm.
4. Disconnect tie rod end from steering knuckle and swing knuckle outboard.
5. Using tool J-26407 or equivalent, disconnect upper ball joint from steering knuckle.
6. Remove upper ball joint from control arm by drilling out three adjusting rivets, **Fig. 2**.

INSTALLATION

1. Install upper ball joint to control arm with nuts and bolts, torquing to specifications provided in service repair package.
2. Inspect tapered hole in steering knuckle and remove any dirt. If any out of roundness, deformation or damage is noticed, replace knuckle.
3. Install upper ball joint to steering knuckle.

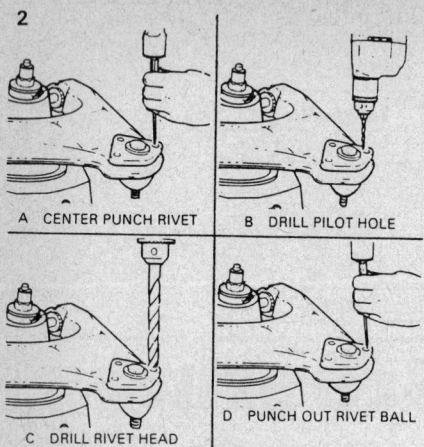

Fig. 2 Upper ball joint removal

4. Torque nut to specifications. Nut may be turned up to an additional 1/6 turn to align cotter pin hole. **Do not exceed torque of 55 ft. lbs.**
5. Attach brake line to control arm and install tire and wheel assembly.

LOWER BALL JOINT
REPLACE

REMOVAL

1. Raise and support vehicle and support lower control arm with suitable jack.
2. Remove tire and wheel assembly and disconnect tie rod end from steering knuckle.
3. Using tool J-26407 or equivalent, disconnect lower ball joint from steering knuckle and swing knuckle with rotor, caliper and bearing out of way.
4. Inspect tapered hole in steering knuckle, removing any dirt.
5. Assemble clamp J-9519-10 and bolt J-9519-18 with removal adapters J-37161-1 and J-37161-3 on lower control arm, Fig. 3.
6. Press ball joint out of lower control arm.

INSTALLATION

1. Assemble clamp J-9519-10 and bolt J-9519-18 with installation adapters J-37161-2 and J-37161-4 on lower control arm, Fig. 4.
2. Press ball joint into lower control arm.
3. Position ball stud into steering knuckle boss and install ball nut.
4. Torque nut to specifications plus an additional 1/2 turn. Nut may be tightened up to an additional 1/6 turn to align cotter pin hole.
5. Connect tie rod to steering knuckle, torquing to specifications plus an additional 1/2 turn. Nut may be tightened up to an additional 1/6 turn to align cotter pin hole.
6. Install tie and wheel assembly.
7. check alignment, adjusting as necessary.

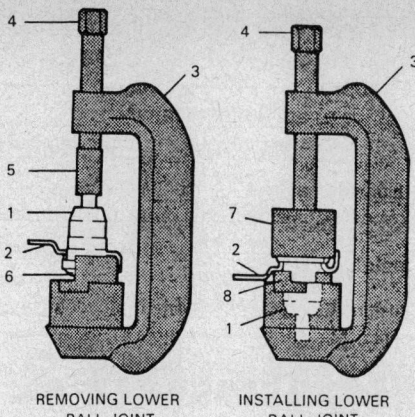

REMOVING LOWER BALL JOINT   INSTALLING LOWER BALL JOINT

1. LOWER BALL JOINT	5. J-37161-3
2. CONTROL ARM	6. J-37161-1
3. J-9519-10	7. J-37161-4
4. J-9519-18	8. J-37161-2

Fig. 3 Lower ball joint replacement

SHOCK ABSORBER
REPLACE

1. Raise and support vehicle.
2. Remove upper retaining nut, washer and shock insulator.
3. Remove two bolts from lower end of shock absorber and remove shock absorber through lower control arm.
4. Reverse procedure to install, **torquing** upper retaining nut to 8 ft. lbs. and the lower attaching bolts to 20 ft. lbs.

STABILIZER BAR
REPLACE

REMOVAL

1. Raise and support vehicle.
2. Mark stabilizer bar on right end to ensure proper installation.
3. Remove both front wheel and tire assemblies.
4. Disconnect tie rods at steering knuckles.
5. Disconnect brake line at upper control arm.
6. Remove left side caliper, rotor and splash shield, suspending caliper out of way.
7. Remove stabilizer bar to lower control arm links.
8. Remove two bolts at each stabilizer bar clamp and bushing assembly.
9. Remove stabilizer bar from underside of vehicle by moving bar toward left side of vehicle until right side clears frame rail.

INSTALLATION

1. Install stabilizer bar from underside of vehicle.
2. Install clamps and bushings and hand tighten bolts to hold stabilizer in place. Slit in stabilizer bushing must be installed toward front of vehicle, Fig. 4.

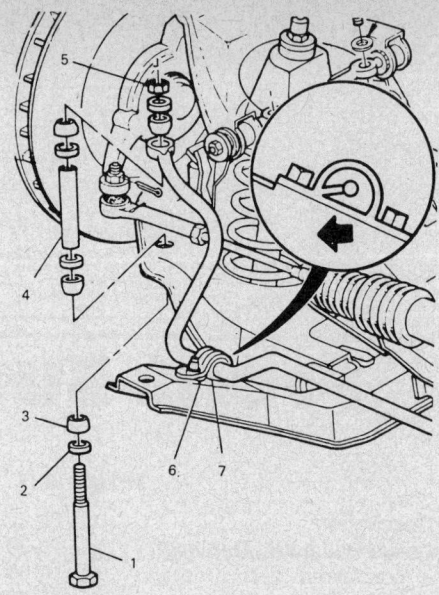

1. BOLT
2. WASHER (4)
3. INSULATOR (4)
4. SPACER
5. NUT
6. CLAMP
7. BUSHING *NOTE SLIT MUST BE TOWARD FRONT OF VEHICLE.

Fig. 4 Installing stabilizer bar

3. Install link assemblies from stabilizer bar to lower control arms, **torquing** bolts to 12 ft. lbs.
4. Torque bushing clamps to specifications.
5. Connect tie rod ends at steering knuckle. Torque nuts to specifications, plus an additional 1/2 turn. Nut may be tightened up to an additional 1/6 turn to align cotter pin hole.
6. Install left side rotor, caliper and splash shield.
7. Connect brake line to upper control arm and install tire and wheel assemblies.

LOWER CONTROL ARM & COIL SPRING
REPLACE

REMOVAL

1. Raise and support vehicle, supporting lower control arm with suitable jack.
2. Remove wheel and tire assembly.
3. Remove shock absorber.
4. Disconnect stabilizer bar from lower control arm.
5. Install suitable chain through spring.
6. Remove lower control arm pivot bolts and **slowly** lower jack, removing safety chain when spring is no longer under load.
7. Remove spring and spring insulator. **Any handling of springs must not cause any damage to the corrosion protection coating on springs. Hard steel contact must be avoided. Springs with a damaged corrosion protection coating should not be used until repaired.**

8. Remove cotter pin from lower ball joint stud and loosen ball stud nut one full turn.
9. Using tool J-26407 or equivalent, loosen lower ball joint from steering knuckle.
10. Remove lower ball stud nut and the lower control arm.
11. Inspect tapered hole in steering knuckle and remove any dirt. If any out of roundness, deformation or damaged is noticed, replace knuckle.

INSTALLATION

1. Place lower control arm with ball joint in position and insert lower ball stud into knuckle boss.
2. Install ball stud nut, torquing to 26 ft. lbs. plus an additional 1/2 turn. Nut may be tightened up to an additional 1/6 turn to align cotter pin hole.
3. Position spring and spring insulator into upper spring seat, then align bottom of spring with lower control arm seat and install.
4. Install a safety chain through spring.
5. Using suitable jack, slowly raise lower control arm and compress spring.
6. Align control arm bushings to crossmember and install pivot bolts, tightening slightly.
7. Remove safety chain.
8. Install shock absorber, then connect stabilizer bar, **torquing** bolt to 12 ft. lbs.
9. Install tire and wheel assembly, then remove jack supporting lower control arm and lower vehicle to ground.
10. With suspension system at its normal standing height, **torque** pivot bolts to 37 ft. lbs. plus an additional 3/4 turn.
11. Check alignment, adjusting as necessary.

UPPER CONTROL ARM
REPLACE

1. Raise and support vehicle and support lower control arm with suitable jack.
2. Remove tire and wheel assembly.
3. Disconnect tie rod end from steering knuckle and swing knuckle outboard.
4. Using tool J-26407 or equivalent, disconnect upper ball joint from steering knuckle.
5. Remove two bolts and paddle nut assembly attaching upper control arm shaft to crossmember and remove control arm assembly.
6. Reverse procedure to install noting the following:
   a. Use new paddle nut assembly and do not torque upper control arm shaft bolts until after alignment is performed.
   b. Inspect tapered hole in steering knuckle, removing any dirt. If out of roundness, deformation or damage is noticed, replace knuckle.
   c. Torque upper ball joint to specifications. Nut may be tightened up to an additional 1/6 turn to align cotter pin hole as long as torque does not exceed 55 ft. lbs.
   d. Check alignment, adjusting as necessary.

STEERING KNUCKLE
REPLACE

1. Raise and support vehicle. Support lower control arm with a suitable jack.
2. Remove wheel and tire assembly, then disconnect brake caliper from steering knuckle and suspend from frame with a piece of wire. Do not let brake lines support weight of caliper. **Install a block of wood between brake shoes to hold piston in caliper bore.**
3. Remove hub, disc and splash shield.
4. Remove both ball joint studs as previously described.
5. Disconnect tie rod end from steering knuckle.

6. Press both ball joint studs from steering knuckle using tool No. J-26407 or equivalent.
7. Remove ball joint stud nuts, then the steering knuckle.
8. Reverse procedure to install. Torque the following to specifications: upper ball joint, plus an additional 1/6 turn to align cotter pin hole as long as torque does not exceed 55 ft. lbs.; lower ball joint, plus an additional 1/2 turn, turning nut up to an additional 1/6 turn to align cotter pin hole; tie rod end to steering knuckle, plus an additional 1/2 turn, turning nut up to an additional 1/6 turn to align cotter pin hole; hub and bearing assembly attaching bolts.

MANUAL STEERING GEAR
REPLACE

1. Raise and support vehicle.
2. Remove flexible coupling to shaft pinch bolt.
3. Remove outer tie rod cotter pins and nuts on both sides.
4. Disconnect tie rods from steering knuckles.
5. Remove four bolts securing steering assembly to crossmember and remove steering assembly.
6. reverse procedure to install, noting the following:
   a. Use new steering assembly to crossmember attaching nuts.
   b. Torque flexible coupling bolt to specifications.
   c. Torque steering assembly attaching bolts to specifications.
   d. Torque tie rod to knuckle attaching nuts to specifications, plus an additional 1/2 turn. Nut may be tightened up to an additional 1/6 turn (39 ft. lbs.) to align cotter pin hole.
   e. Check wheel alignment, adjusting as necessary.

TIGHTENING SPECIFICATIONS

Year	Component	Torque/ft. lbs.
1988	Flex Coupling Bolt	46
	Lower Ball Joint To Steering Knuckle	26
	Stabilizer Bar Bushing Clamps	20
	Steering Assembly Attaching Bolts	20
	Tie Rod To Steering Knuckle	15
	Upper Ball Joint To Steering Knuckle	30-40
	Upper Control Arm Shaft To Steering Knuckle	52
	Wheel Hub & Bearing Assembly To Steering Knuckle	220
	Wheel Lug Nuts	100

Wheel Alignment

INDEX

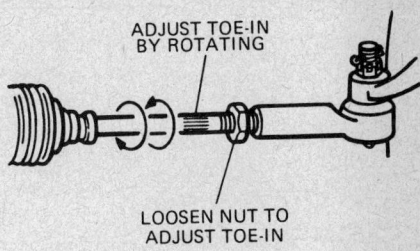

Fig. 2   Toe-in adjustment

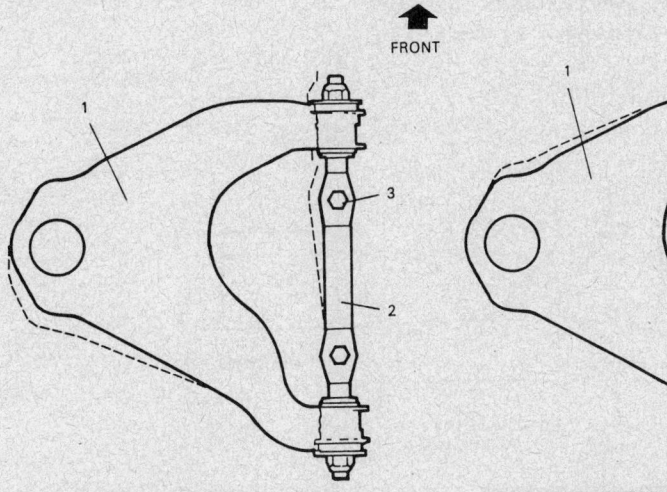
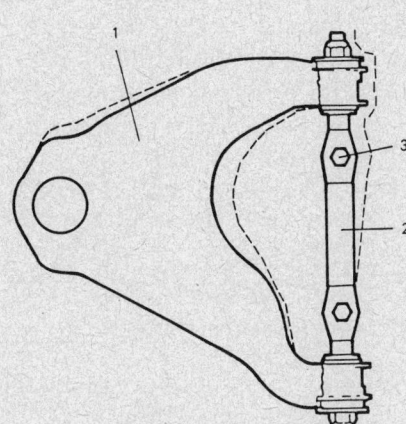
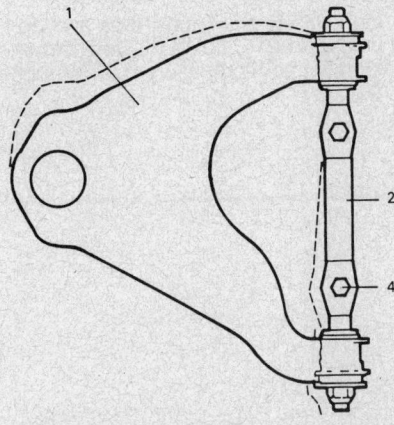
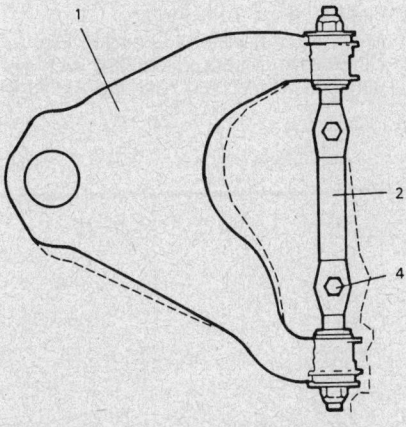

1   UPPER CONTROL ARM
2   U.C.A. SHAFT
3   FRONT BOLT
4   REAR BOLT

Fig. 1   Front camber & caster adjustment

3. **Torque** upper control arm shaft bolts to 52 ft. lbs. plus an additional 1/4 turn.

TOE-IN ADJUSTMENT

1. Loosen jam nuts on toe link rod, then rotate rods until toe-in is within specifications, **Fig. 2.**
2. **Torque** jam nuts to 47 ft. lbs. **Use care not to twist or damage rubber boots.**

REAR WHEEL ALIGNMENT

CAMBER ADJUSTMENT

1. Loosen both strut-to-knuckle attaching bolts sufficiently to allow movement between strut and knuckle.
2. Move top of tire inboard or outboard until camber is within specifications, then torque both strut-to-knuckle bolts to 140 ft. lbs. **If complete torque cannot be applied to bolts due to inaccessibility, tighten bolts just enough to hold camber position, then remove wheel and tire and apply final torque.**

TOE-IN ADJUSTMENT

1. Loosen adjuster tube clamps.
2. Rotate adjuster tube to change toe-in angle.
3. **Torque** clamps to 47 ft. lbs.

RIDE HEIGHT

Check ride height as follows:
1. Using arms, lift front of vehicle approximately two inches.
2. Gently remove hands and let vehicle settle.
3. Repeat steps 1 and 2.

FRONT WHEEL ALIGNMENT
CAMBER & CASTER ADJUSTMENT

1. Jounce front and rear bumpers three times.
2. Loosen upper control arm shaft bolts and move upper control arm as shown, **Fig. 1,** to adjust caster and camber. **If upper control arm shaft bolts are removed, paddle nut assembly must be replaced.**

Trim heights checked with correct tire pressures, fuel tank full or equivalent weight in the trunk. No passengers or added weight in car. Trunk must be empty except for spare tire and jack or simulated fuel load. Measure from known level floor to rocker panel with steering wheel in the center position.

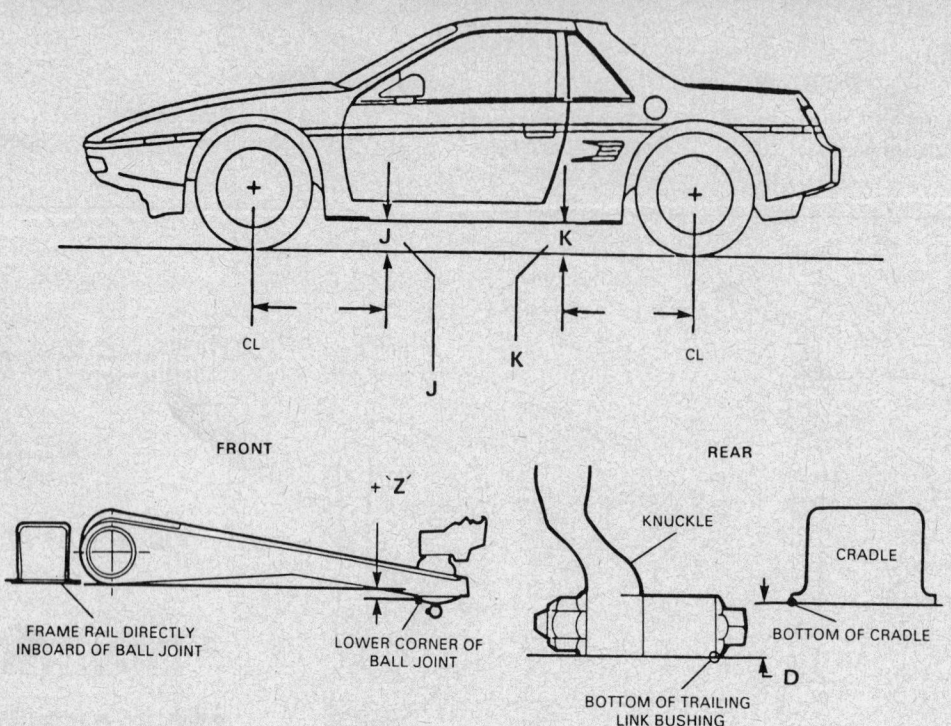

Fig. 3   Measuring ride height

4. Measure dimensions Z and J, **Fig. 3.** Dimension Z should be .2716 inch and dimension J should be 7.0-7.7 inches.

5. Repeat steps 1 through 3.
6. Measure dimensions D and K, **Fig. 3.** Dimension D should be .984 inch on vehicles with P195/70R14 tires, .866 inch with P185/75R14 tires and .511 inch with 215/60HR15 tires. Dimension K should measure 6.9-7.7 inches.

CHEVROLET LUMINA, BUICK REGAL, OLDSMOBILE CUTLASS SUPREME & PONTIAC GRAND PRIX
(W Cars)

INDEX OF SERVICE OPERATIONS

NOTE: Refer To Rear Of This Manual For Vehicle Manufacturer's Special Service Tool Suppliers.

Continued

CHEVROLET LUMINA, BUICK REGAL, OLDSMOBILE CUTLASS SUPREME & PONTIAC GRAND PRIX (W CARS)

INDEX OF SERVICE OPERATIONS—Continued

Specifications

GENERAL ENGINE SPECIFICATIONS

Year	Engine Liter/CID ①	VIN Code ②	Fuel System	Bore and Stroke	Compression Ratio	Net H.P. @ RPM ③	Maximum Torque Ft. Lbs. @ RPM	Normal Oil Pressure Pounds
1988	2.8L/V6-173	W	Fuel Injection	3.50 x 2.99	8.90	125 @ 4500	160 @ 3600	15-30
1989	2.8L/V6-173	W	Fuel Injection	3.50 x 2.99	8.90	130 @ 4500	170 @ 3600	15-30
	3.1L/V6-192	T	Fuel Injection	3.50 x 3.31	8.80	140 @ 4500	185 @ 3600	15-30
1990	2.3L/4-138	D	Fuel Injection	3.62 x 3.35	9.50	160 @ 6200	155 @ 5200	15-30
	2.3L/4-138, H.O.	A	Fuel Injection	3.62 x 3.35	10.0	180 @ 6200	160 @ 5200	15-30
	2.5L/4-151	R	Fuel Injection	4.00 x 3.00	8.30	110 @ 5200	135 @ 3200	26④
	3.1L/V6-192	T	Fuel Injection	3.50 x 3.31	8.80	135 @ 4400	180 @ 3600	15⑤
	3.1L/V6-192 ⑦	V	Fuel Injection	3.50 x 3.31	8.71	205 @ 4800	220 @ 3200	15⑤
	3.8L/V6-231	L	Fuel Injection	3.80 x 3.40	8.50	170 @ 4800	220 @ 3200	60⑥
1991	2.5L/4-151	R	Fuel Injection	4.00 x 3.00	8.30	110 @ 5200	135 @ 3200	26④
	3.1L/V6-192	T	Fuel Injection	3.50 x 3.31	8.80	135 @ 4400	180 @ 3600	15⑤
	3.4L/V6-204	X	Fuel Injection	3.62 x 3.31	9.25–9.50	⑧	215 @ 4000	15⑤

Continued

GENERAL ENGINE SPECIFICATIONS—Continued

①—CID-Cubic inch displacement.
②—The eighth digit of the VIN denotes engine code.
③—Ratings are net-as installed in vehicle.
④—At 800 RPM.
⑤—At 1100 RPM.
⑥—At 1850 RPM.
⑦—Turbocharged engine.
⑧—210 net H.P. @ 5200 RPM with manual transaxle; 200 net H.P. @ 5000 RPM with automatic transaxle.

TUNE UP SPECIFICATIONS

| Year & Engine, VIN Code ① | Spark Plug Gap | Ignition Timing BTDC | | | | Curb Idle Speed ③ | | Fast Idle Speed | | Fuel Pump Pressure |
		Firing Order Fig. ②	Man. Trans.	Auto. Trans.	Mark Fig.	Man. Trans.	Auto Trans.	Man. Trans.	Auto. Trans.	
1988										
2.8L/V6-173,W	.045	④	⑤	⑤	⑥	⑦	⑦	⑦	⑦	40–46⑧
1989										
3.1L/V6-192,T	.045	④	⑤	⑤	⑥	⑦	⑦	⑦	⑦	40–46⑧
2.8L/V6-173,W	.045	④	⑤	⑤	⑥	⑦	⑦	⑦	⑦	40–46⑧
1990										
2.3L/4-138,D	.035	B	⑤	⑤	⑥	⑦	⑦	⑦	⑦	40.5–47⑧
2.3L/4-138 H.O.,A	.035	B	⑤	—	⑥	⑦	—	⑦	—	51⑧
2.5L/4-151,R	.060	⑩	—	⑤	⑥	—	⑦	—	⑦	9–13⑪
3.1L/V6-192,T	.045	④	—	⑤	⑥	⑦	⑦	⑦	⑦	40–46⑧
3.1L/V6-192,V	.045	④	—	⑤	⑥	⑦	⑦	⑦	⑦	40–46⑧
3.8L/V6-231,L	.060	⑨	—	⑤	⑥	—	⑦	—	⑦	40–47⑧
1991										
2.5L/4-151,R	.060	⑩	—	⑤	⑥	—	⑦	—	⑦	26–32⑪
3.1L/V6-192,T	.045	④	—	⑤	⑥	—	⑦	—	⑦	40–47⑧
3.4L/V6-204,X	.045	④	⑤	⑤	⑥	⑦	⑦	⑦	⑦	40–47⑧

①—The eighth digit of Vehicle Identification Number (VIN) denotes engine code.
②—Before removing wires from distributor cap, determine location of No. 1 wire in cap, as distributor position may have been altered from that shown at the end of this chart.
③—Not adjustable.
④—Cylinder numbering as viewed from front of vehicle, front bank 2, 4, 6; rear bank 1, 3, 5. Firing order, 1-2-3-4-5-6. Refer to Fig. A for spark plug wire connections at coil unit.
⑤—Computer controlled, no adjustment.
⑥—Equipped with a crankshaft position sensor.
⑦—Idle speed is controlled by an idle air control (IAC) valve or idle speed control (ISC) motor.
⑧—With shop towel wrapped around fuel pressure valve to prevent fuel spillage, connect a suitable fuel pressure gauge to fuel pressure valve. Check fuel pressure with ignition switch On, engine not running.
⑨—Cylinder numbering as viewed from front of vehicle, front bank, 1, 3, 5; rear bank, 2, 4, 6. Firing order 1-6-5-4-3-2. Two different types of computer controlled coil ignition systems are used. Refer to Figs. C and D for spark plug wire connections at coil unit.
⑩—Cylinder numbering from front of engine, 1, 2, 3, 4. Firing order 1-3-4-2. Refer to Fig. E for spark plug wire connections at coil unit.
⑪—Wrap shop towel around fuel hose to steel line connection in engine compartment to prevent fuel spillage. Disconnect fuel hose from steel line and install a suitable fuel pressure gauge between hose and line. Ensure gauge connections are tight, then start engine and check fuel pressure readings.

Continued

TUNE UP SPECIFICATIONS—Continued

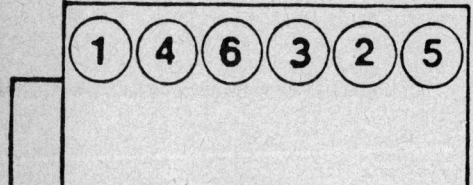

Fig. A

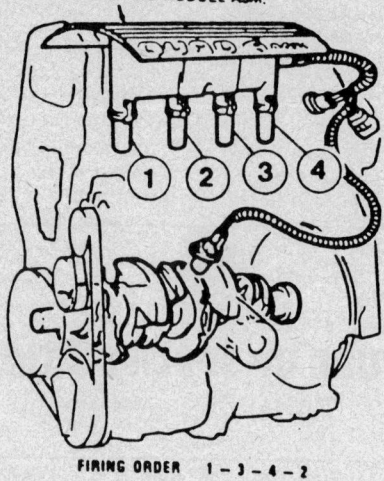

FIRING ORDER   1 - 3 - 4 - 2

Fig. B

COMPUTER CONTROLLED
COIL IGNITION

Fig. C

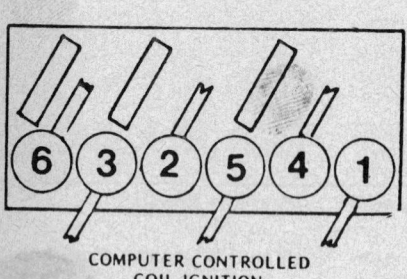

COMPUTER CONTROLLED
COIL IGNITION

Fig. D

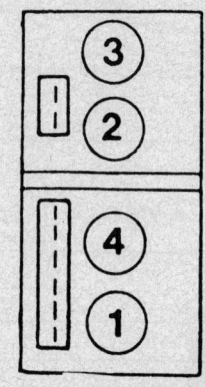

Fig. E

ALTERNATOR SPECIFICATIONS

Year	Model	Rated Hot Output Amps.
1988	1101107	100
1989	1101466	100
1990	1101143	100
	1101231	100
	1101466	100
	1101649	105
	1102604	105
1991	1101143	100
	1101466	100
	1101583	105

STARTING MOTOR APPLICATIONS

Refer to "Starter Section" for specifications.

Year	Engine/VIN	Starter Ident. No.
1988	2.8L/V6-173,W	10455019
1989	2.8L/V6-173,W	10455019
1989	3.1L/V6-192,T	10455019
1990	2.5L/4-151,R	10455019
	3.1L/V6-192,T	10455019
	3.1L/V6-192,V	10455019
	2.3L/4-138,D	10455044
	2.3L/4-138,A	10455044
	3.8L/V6-231,L	10455024
1991	2.5L/4-151,R	10455019
	3.1L/V6-192,T	10455025
	3.4L/V6-204,X	10455047

WHEEL ALIGNMENT SPECIFICATIONS

Year	Model	Caster Angle, Degrees Limits	Caster Angle, Degrees Desired	Camber Angle, Degrees Limits	Camber Angle, Degrees Desired	Toe-In Degrees
Front						
1988	Grand Prix & Regal	+1.5 to +2.5	+1.5	+.20 to +1.2	+.7	①
	Cutlass Supreme	+1.3 to +2.3	+1.8	+.20 to +1.2	+.7	①
1989	Cutlass Supreme & Grand Prix	+1.3 to +2.3	+1.8	+.20 to +1.2	+.7	①
	Regal	+1.5 to +2.5	+1.5	+.20 to +1.2	+.7	①
1990	Cutlass Supreme, Lumina & Regal	+1.5 to +2.5	+2.0	+.20 to +1.2	+.7	①
	Grand Prix	+1.3 to +2.3	+1.8	+.20 to +1.2	+.7	①
1991	Lumina	+1.3 to +2.3	+1.8	+.20 to +1.2	+.7	①
Rear						
1988	Regal	—	—	−.44 to +.56	+.06	①
	Cutlass Supreme	—	—	−.23 to +.77	+.27	①
	Grand Prix	—	—	−.11 to +.89	+.39	−.2
1989	Regal	—	—	−.11 to +.89	+.39	−.1
	Cutlass Supreme	—	—	−.23 to +.77	+.27	①
	Grand Prix	—	—	−.01 to +.99	+.49	−.1
1990	Lumina & Regal	—	—	−.11 to +.89	+.39	①
	Cutlass Supreme ②	—	—	−.40 to +.60	+.10	①
	Cutlass Supreme ③	—	—	−.65 to +.35	+.15	①
	Grand Prix	—	—	−.01 to +.99	+.49	①
1991	Lumina	—	—	−.65 to +.35	+.15	−.1

① — Toe-in 0° per wheel.
② — 14 inch tires.
③ — Except 14 inch tires.

COOLING SYSTEM & CAPACITY DATA

Year	Model or Engine/ VIN	Cooling Capacity, Qts.		Radiator Cap Relief Pressure, Lbs.	Thermo. Opening Temp.	Fuel Tank Gals.	Engine Oil Refill Qts. ①	Transaxle Oil	
		Less A/C	With A/C					Manual Transaxle Pts.	Auto. Transaxle Qts. ②
1988	2.8L/V6-173,W	12.3	12.6	15	195	16.0	4	5.0	8
1989	2.8L/V6-173,W	12.3	12.6	15	195	16.0	4	5.0	8
	3.1L/V6-192,T	12.6	12.6	15	195	16.0	4	2.5	6
1990	2.3L/4-138,A	8.9	8.9③	15	192	16.5	4	4.4	⑤
	2.3L/4-138,D	9.2	9.2④	15	192	16.5	4	4.4	⑤
	2.5L/4-151,R	9.4	9.4	15	195	17.1	4	—	6
	3.1L/V6-192,T	12.5	12.5	15	195	⑥	4	4.4	⑤
	3.1L/V6-192,V	12.5	13.2	15	195	16.5	4	4.4	⑤
	3.8L/V6-231,L	11.1	11.1	15	195	16.5	4	—	6
1991	2.5L/4-151,R	9.4	9.4	15	195	16.0	4	—	6
	3.1L/V6-192,T	12.6	12.6	15	195	16.0	4	—	6
	3.4L/V6-204,X	12.8	12.8	15	195	16.0	4	—	6

①—Additional oil may be required to bring oil level to full mark when changing oil filter.
②—Capacity approximate. Make final check with dipstick and add fluid as necessary.
③—With heavy duty radiator, 9.2 qts.
④—With heavy duty radiator, 9.4 qts.
⑤—Hydra-Matic 3T40, 7 qts.; Hydra-Matic 4T60, 6 qts.
⑥—Except Lumina, 16.5 gals.; Lumina, 16 gals.

Electrical
INDEX

FUSE PANEL & FLASHER LOCATION

On all models, the fuse panel is located behind the instrument panel, under the glove compartment. The turn signal flasher is located under the instrument panel, to the right of the steering column. The hazard warning flasher is located in the convenience center, under the glove box assembly.

IGNITION LOCK REPLACE

1. Disconnect battery ground cable.
2. Remove steering column from vehicle. On vehicles with tilt column, column should be tilted to the full up position for removal.
3. Remove and discard two lower spring retainers.
4. Remove lower bearing spring and lower bearing seat.
5. Remove nut retainer and jam nut, then the steering wheel.
6. Remove cancel cam assembly, then the hazard knob screw and hazard warning knob.
7. Position turn signal switch so that turn signal switch screws and housing screw can be removed through opening in switch.
8. Remove housing screw and column housing cover, then the turn signal

switch screws.

9. Remove wiring protector from opening in instrument panel bracket on jacket assembly and separate from wires.

10. **On 1989-91 models,** disconnect pivot/pulse switch connector then remove the pivot screw and pivot/pulse switch assembly.

11. **On all models,** disconnect turn signal switch connector from ignition and dimmer switch assembly connector.

12. Disconnect 17 way secondary lock from turn signal connector.

13. Using terminal remover tool No. J-35689-A or equivalent, disconnect wires on buzzer switch from turn signal connector and wrap wire ends with tape.

14. Remove turn signal switch assembly from column.

15. **On 1989-91 models,** proceed as follows:
    a. Remove and discard two lower spring retainers.
    b. Remove lower bearing spring and seat.
    c. Remove adapter screws then the adapter and bearing assembly.

16. **On models with tilt columns,** proceed as follows:
    a. Insert phillips head screwdriver into square opening in spring retainer, push down and turn left to release retainer and wheel tilt spring.
    b. Remove spring retainer, tilt spring and tilt spring guide.
    c. Using pivot pin remover tool No. J-21854-01 or equivalent, remove two pivot pins.

17. **On all models,** place lock cylinder in Run position.

18. **On models with tilt column,** pull tilt lever to release steering column housing. Remove the steering shaft assembly and steering column housing as a complete unit.

19. **On 1988 non-tilt models,** remove housing screws the steering shaft assembly and steering column housing as a complete unit.

20. On 1989-91 non-tilt models, proceed as follows:
    a. Place opening in retaining ring over flat on steering shaft.
    b. Remove retaining ring using a suitable screwdriver.
    c. Remove thrust washer, upper bearing spring and washer.
    d. Remove steering shaft from lower end of jacket and bowl assembly.
    e. Remove housing screws and steering column housing.
    f. Remove housing spacer the the bearing using a suitable drift. Discard bearing.

21. **On all models,** place lock cylinder in Off-Lock position and remove key.

22. Remove buzzer switch by lifting switch tab with screwdriver and pulling gently on wires.

23. Remove lock retaining screw and the lock cylinder.

24. Reverse procedure to install, noting the following:

a. **Torque** lock retaining screw to 22 inch lbs.
b. **Torque** steering column housing screws to 88 inch lbs.
c. **Torque** turn signal switch and column housing cover screws to 35 inch lbs.
d. **Torque** hazard knob screw to 7 inch lbs.
e. **Torque** jam nut to 30 ft. lbs.
f. Install new lower spring retainers, compressing spring until retainers are positioned 1.14 inch from lower end of steering shaft.

STARTER
REPLACE
2.3L/4-138 ENGINES

1. Disconnect battery ground cable.
2. Loosen air inlet hose clamp from throttle body, then remove air cleaner assembly.
3. Disconnect coolant reservoir hose from radiator filler neck and plug to prevent leakage.
4. Remove coolant reservoir attaching bolts.
5. Remove intake manifold brace bolts.
6. Raise and support vehicle.
7. Position a suitable drain pan under vehicle, then remove oil filter.
8. Remove starter motor attaching bolts, then lower starter onto frame member.
9. Disconnect starter motor wiring, then remove starter.
10. Reverse procedure to install, noting the following:
    a. **Torque** starter motor attaching bolts to 32 ft. lbs.
    b. Check engine oil level, adding oil as necessary.

2.5L/4-151 ENGINE

1. Disconnect battery ground cable.
2. Raise and support vehicle.
3. Remove flywheel cover attaching bolts, then the cover.
4. Remove stud from starter motor bracket.
5. Remove starter motor attaching bolts, lower starter and disconnect starter wiring.
6. Remove starter motor, then the bracket from starter.
7. Reverse procedure to install, noting the following:
    a. When removing starter, note if any shims are used between starter and mounting surface. If shims are found, reinstall in original location.
    b. **Torque** starter motor attaching bolts to 32 ft. lbs.
    c. **Torque** starter motor bracket stud to 18 ft. lbs.

2.8L/V6-173 ENGINE
1988

Less Heavy Duty Cooling

1. Disconnect battery ground cable.
2. Raise and support vehicle.
3. Disconnect solenoid wires and battery cables.

4. Remove starter motor cover attaching bolts and the cover.
5. Remove two starter motor to engine attaching bolts, then remove starter.
6. Reverse procedure to install. When removing starter, note if any shims are used between starter and mounting surface. If shims are found, reinstall in original location.

With Heavy Duty Cooling

1. Disconnect battery ground cable.
2. Raise and support vehicle and drain coolant.
3. Remove oil filter, then the coolant hose below oil filter closest to starter.
4. Disconnect wiring at starter motor.
5. Remove starter motor cover attaching bolts and the cover.
6. Remove two starter motor to engine attaching bolts, then remove starter.
7. Reverse procedure to install. When removing starter, note if any shims are used between starter and mounting surface. If shims are found, reinstall in original location.

1989

1. Disconnect battery ground cable.
2. Remove air cleaner assembly.
3. Raise and support vehicle.
4. **On models with engine oil cooler,** proceed as follows:
    a. Position a suitable drain pan under vehicle, then remove oil filter.
    b. Position hose next to starter motor aside.
5. **On all models,** remove nut attaching starter brace to A/C compressor.
6. Remove nut attaching starter brace to engine, then the brace.
7. Remove bolts attaching flywheel inspection cover, then the cover.
8. Remove starter motor attaching bolts, lower starter and disconnect starter wiring.
9. Remove starter motor and shims (if used).
10. Reverse procedure to install, noting the following:
    a. When removing starter, note if any shims are used between starter and mounting surface. If shims are found, reinstall in original location.
    b. **Torque** starter motor attaching bolts to 32 ft. lbs.
    c. **Torque** starter brace nuts to 23 ft. lbs.
    d. **On models with oil cooler,** check engine oil level, adding oil as necessary.

3.1L/V6-192 ENGINE

1. Disconnect battery ground cable.
2. Remove air cleaner assembly.
3. Raise and support vehicle.
4. **On models with engine oil cooler,** proceed as follows:
    a. Position a suitable drain pan under vehicle, then remove oil filter.
    b. Position hose next to starter motor aside.
5. **On all models,** remove nut attaching starter brace to A/C compressor.
6. Remove nut attaching starter brace to engine, then the brace.

7. Remove bolts attaching flywheel inspection cover, then the cover.
8. Remove starter motor attaching bolts, lower starter and disconnect starter wiring.
9. Remove starter motor and shims (if used).
10. Reverse procedure to install, noting the following:
   a. When removing starter, note if any shims are used between starter and mounting surface. If shims are found, reinstall in original location.
   b. **Torque** starter motor attaching bolts to 32 ft. lbs.
   c. **Torque** starter brace nuts to 23 ft. lbs.
   d. **On models with oil cooler,** check engine oil level, adding oil as necessary.

3.4L/V6-204 ENGINE
Manual Transaxle

1. Disconnect battery ground cable.
2. Remove air cleaner assembly.
3. Raise and support vehicle.
4. Place a suitable drain pan under vehicle and remove oil filter.
5. Disconnect electrical connections from oil pressure sensor.
6. Disconnect the crank sensor wire from ignition module.
7. Remove oil cooler adapter stud and set oil cooler aside.
8. Disconnect starter electrical connections.
9. Remove starter mounting bolts and starter.
10. Reverse procedure to install, **torquing** starter bolts to 32 ft. lbs.

Automatic Transaxle

1. Disconnect battery ground cable.
2. Remove air cleaner assembly.
3. Raise and support vehicle.
4. Place a suitable drain pan under vehicle and remove oil filter.
5. Disconnect electrical connections from oil pressure sensor.
6. Disconnect the crank sensor wire from ignition module.
7. Remove oil cooler adapter stud and set oil cooler aside.
8. Remove wiring harness from bell-housing clamp and lower radiator tie bar.
9. Disconnect power steering oil cooler lines from front crossmember.
10. Remove flywheel inspection cover.
11. Disconnect electrical connections from starter. **Disconnect and move electrical connections on cooling fan if necessary to gain access.**
12. Remove starter mounting bolts and starter assembly from vehicle.
13. Reverse procedure to install, **torquing** starter mounting bolts to 32 ft. lbs.

3.8L/V6-231 ENGINE

1. Disconnect battery ground cable.
2. Remove right side cooling fan.
3. Remove serpentine drive belt.
4. Remove A/C compressor upper support brace.
5. Lay A/C compressor in fan opening.
6. Raise and support vehicle.

7. Disconnect engine oil cooler lines at flex connection.
8. Remove bolts from flywheel inspection cover.
9. Remove bolts from starter.
10. Disconnect starter motor wiring.
11. Remove starter motor.
12. Reverse procedure to install, **torquing** starter motor attaching bolts to 32 ft. lbs.

PIVOT & PULSE SWITCH & TURN SIGNAL SWITCH ASSEMBLIES
REPLACE

1. Disconnect battery ground cable.
2. Remove nut retainer and jam nut, then the steering wheel.
3. Remove turn signal cancel cam assembly.
4. Remove hazard knob screw and the hazard warning knob.
5. Position turn signal switch so that turn signal switch screws and housing screw can be removed through openings in switch.
6. Remove housing screw and the column housing cover.
7. **On models with tilt columns,** remove shoe pin retainer cap.
8. **On all models,** remove pivot switch screw and the pivot and pulse switch assembly.
9. Remove turn signal switch screws.
10. Remove wiring protector from opening in instrument panel bracket on jacket assembly and separate from wires.
11. Disconnect turn signal switch connector from ignition and dimmer switch assembly connector.
12. Disconnect 17 way lock from turn signal connector.
13. Using terminal remover tool No. J-35689-A or equivalent, disconnect wires on buzzer switch assembly from turn signal connector.
14. Remove turn signal switch assembly from column.
15. Reverse procedure to install, noting the following:
   a. **Torque** turn signal switch and column housing cover screws to 35 inch lbs.
   b. **Torque** pivot switch screw to 20 inch lbs.
   c. **Torque** hazard knob screw to 7 inch lbs.
   d. **Torque** jam nut to 30 ft. lbs.

IGNITION & DIMMER SWITCH ASSEMBLY
REPLACE

REMOVAL

1. Place shift lever in P position and the lock cylinder in Off-Lock position.
2. Disconnect battery ground cable.
3. Remove steering column from vehicle.

4. Disconnect turn signal switch connector from ignition and dimmer switch assembly connector.
5. **On 1989-91 models,** disconnect pivot and pulse switch connector from ignition and dimmer switch connector.
6. **On all models,** remove bowl shield screw, bowl shield nut and the bowl shield.
7. Remove dimmer and ignition switch assembly as follows:
   a. Remove dimmer switch nut, then the upper mounting stud.
   b. Remove dimmer switch, then the dimmer switch actuator rod.
   c. Remove lower mounting stud, then the ignition switch from ignition switch actuator rod.

INSTALLATION

Lock cylinder set must be in the Off-Lock position when installing ignition switch to insure proper switch slider positioning.

1. Place ignition switch slider in far left position and move back one detent to right, then insert a 3/32 inch drill bit in adjustment hole on ignition switch to hold switch slider in proper position during installation.
2. Install ignition switch to switch rod.
3. Install ignition switch to steering column jacket assembly with lower mounting stud, **torquing** to 35 inch lbs.
4. Remove adjustment tool from ignition switch.
5. Install dimmer switch actuator rod through hole in instrument panel bracket and into hole in dimmer switch rod cap.
6. Install dimmer switch assembly on lower mounting stud with dimmer switch nut and upper mounting stud but do not tighten.
7. To adjust dimmer switch, insert a 3/32 inch drill bit and push switch against actuator rod to remove all lash.
8. **Torque** dimmer switch nut and upper mounting stud to 35 inch lbs., then remove adjustment tool from dimmer switch.
9. Install bowl shield to column bowl and upper mounting stud, then install shield screw, **torquing** to 35 inch lbs.
10. Install bowl shield nut, **torquing** to 35 inch lbs.
11. Connect turn signal switch connector to ignition and dimmer switch assembly connector and snap in place.
12. **On 1989-91 models,** connect pivot and pulse switch connector to ignition and dimmer switch connector.
13. **On all models,** install steering column and connect battery ground cable.

RADIO
REPLACE

CUTLASS SUPREME & REGAL

1. Remove five Phillips head screws at top of instrument cluster trim plate and pull top of trim plate out.

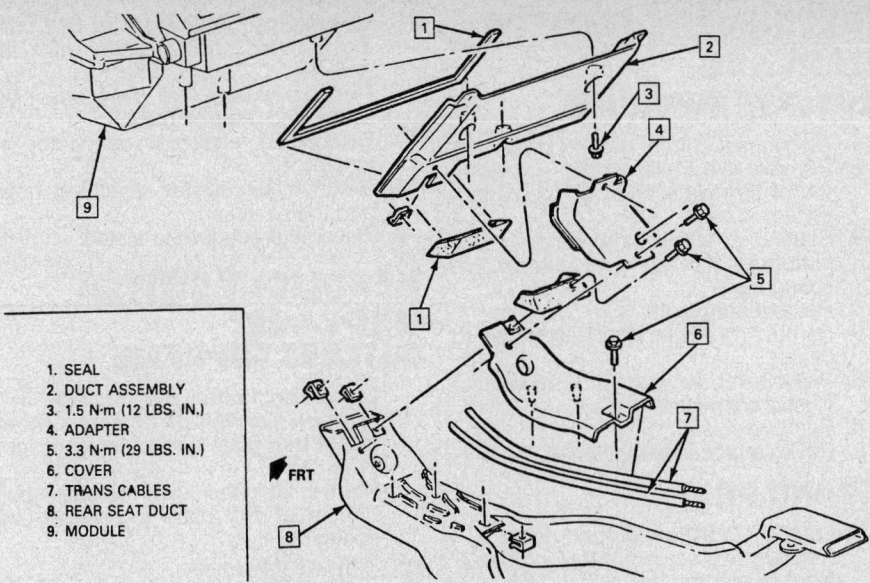

1. SEAL
2. DUCT ASSEMBLY
3. 1.5 N·m (12 LBS. IN.)
4. ADAPTER
5. 3.3 N·m (29 LBS. IN.)
6. COVER
7. TRANS CABLES
8. REAR SEAT DUCT
9. MODULE

Fig. 1   Removing heater core

2. Starting at either side, carefully pull bottom of trim plate to release five spring clips.
3. Remove trim plate.
4. Remove two screws retaining radio and pull out far enough to disconnect antenna, speaker and electrical connectors, then remove radio.
5. Reverse procedure to install.

GRAND PRIX

1. Remove steering column trim cover as follows:
   a. Disconnect ALDL connector from trim cover.
   b. Remove attaching screws from bottom of trim cover.
   c. Remove cover by carefully pulling rearward to disengage from three retaining clips on top of cover.
2. Remove bolts from left side of accessory trim plate.
3. Open glove compartment door, remove bolts from right side of accessory trim plate, then the trim plate.
4. Remove bolts attaching top of radio and nuts attaching bottom of radio.
5. Pull radio out and disconnect electrical and antenna connectors, then remove radio.
6. Reverse procedure to install.

LUMINA

1. Remove right side instrument panel trim plate by unsnapping from instrument panel carrier.
2. Remove two screws retaining radio and pull out far enough to disconnect antenna, speaker and electrical connectors, then remove radio.
3. Reverse procedure to install.

STEERING WHEEL
REPLACE

When removing a steering wheel with accessory controls in the hub, use caution to avoid damaging the electronic circuits. Steering wheel puller bolts should be turned in no more than five turns to avoid contact with the electronic circuits.

1. Disconnect battery ground cable.
2. Remove trim plate and retainer.
3. Disconnect horn wire from cam tower.
4. Turn ignition switch to On position.
5. Scribe an alignment mark on steering wheel hub in line with slash mark on steering shaft.
6. Loosen steering wheel nut, positioning it flush with end of shaft.
7. Using a suitable puller, loosen steering wheel.
8. Remove steering shaft nut and steering wheel.
9. Reverse procedure to install, aligning scribe mark and **torquing** steering shaft nut to 30 ft. lbs.

BLOWER MOTOR
REPLACE

1989–91 MODELS & 1988 MODELS WITH A/C

1. Disconnect battery ground cable.
2. Remove right sound insulator panel from under instrument panel.
3. Remove rear retaining screws from electrical convenience center, then loosen front screw and slide convenience center out.
4. Disconnect electrical connector at motor and remove harness from clip.
5. remove blower motor mounting screws and the blower motor.
6. Reverse procedure to install.

1988 MODELS LESS A/C

1. Disconnect battery ground cable.
2. Disconnect blower motor and resistor electrical connectors.
3. Remove blower motor retaining screws and the blower motor.
4. Remove fan from blower motor as necessary.
5. Reverse procedure to install.

HEATER CORE
REPLACE

1989–91 MODELS WITH A/C & ALL 1988 MODELS

1. Disconnect battery ground cable and drain cooling system.
2. Remove upper dash weatherstripping and the upper secondary cowl.
3. Disconnect heater hoses from heater core.
4. Remove sound insulator, rear seat duct adapter and the heater duct, **Fig. 1.**
5. Remove heater core cover and the heater core.
6. Reverse procedure to install.

1989–91 MODELS LESS A/C
Models With 2.5L/4-151 Engine

1. Disconnect battery ground cable and drain cooling system.
2. Rotate engine as follows:
   a. Position transaxle in N.
   b. Remove coolant reservoir and position aside. It is not necessary to disconnect coolant reservoir hoses.
   c. Remove torque strut-to-engine bracket nut and bolt.
   d. Using a prybar at engine torque strut bracket, rotate engine and transaxle assembly forward.
   e. Align slave hole in torque strut with engine bracket hole.
   f. Retain engine in this position using torque strut-to-engine bracket bolt.
3. Remove upper secondary cowl panel.
4. Remove heater hose retaining bracket nuts.
5. Remove upper nut securing lower secondary cowl panel.
6. Disconnect heater hoses from heater core.
7. Blow air through heater core nipples to remove coolant from core.
8. Remove lower right sound insulator panel.
9. Remove rear seat duct adapter, then the heater floor duct, **Fig. 1.**
10. Remove lower left sound insulator panel.
11. Remove heater core cover attaching screws, then the cover, **Fig. 1.**
12. Remove heater core retaining bolt, then the heater core.
13. Reverse procedure to install.

Models With 2.8L/V6-173 & 3.1L/V6-192 Engine

1. Disconnect battery ground cable and drain cooling system.
2. Rotate engine as follows:
   a. Position transaxle in N.
   b. Remove torque strut-to-engine bracket bolts and position strut aside.
   c. Install passenger side torque strut-to-engine bracket bolt in engine bracket.
   d. Remove coolant reservoir and position aside. It is not necessary to disconnect coolant reservoir hoses.
   e. Place a pry bar in bracket so that it contacts bracket and bolt.
   f. Rotate engine by pulling forward on pry bar.
   g. Align slave hole in driver side torque strut with engine bracket hole.
   h. Retain engine in this position using torque strut-to-engine bracket bolt.
3. Remove upper secondary cowl panel.
4. Remove heater hose retaining bracket nuts.
5. Remove upper nut securing lower secondary cowl panel.
6. Disconnect heater hoses from heater core.
7. Blow air through heater core nipples to remove coolant from core.
8. Remove lower right sound insulator panel.
9. Remove rear seat duct adapter, then the heater floor duct, **Fig. 1**.
10. Remove lower left sound insulator panel.
11. Remove heater core cover attaching screws, then the cover, **Fig. 1**.
12. Remove heater core retaining bolt, then the heater core.
13. Reverse procedure to install.

EVAPORATOR CORE
REPLACE

1. Disconnect battery ground cable and discharge A/C system.
2. Drain cooling system.
3. Remove upper weatherstrip from body and upper secondary cowl.
4. Remove lower secondary cowl upper nut.
5. Disconnect evaporator core block connections at cowl.
6. Disconnect heater hoses from heater core.
7. Remove right lower instrument panel sound insulator panel.
8. Remove rear seat duct adapter and lower heater duct.
9. Remove lower left instrument panel sound insulator panel.
10. Remove heater core cover screws and heater core.
11. Remove evaporator core cover and evaporator core.
12. Reverse procedure to install.

INSTRUMENT CLUSTER
REPLACE
CUTLASS SUPREME

1. Disconnect battery ground cable.
2. Remove five Phillips head screws at top of trim plate and pull top of trim plate out.
3. Starting at either side, carefully pull bottom of trim plate to release five spring clips.
4. Remove trim plate.
5. Remove four bolts attaching cluster to carrier.
6. Pull cluster forward and disconnect cluster connector.
7. Remove cluster.
8. Reverse procedure to install.

GRAND PRIX

1. Disconnect battery ground cable.
2. Remove two screws at top of instrument cluster trim plate.
3. Remove two Phillips head screws from under glove compartment.
4. remove two Phillips head screws connecting door hinges to instrument panel.
5. Open glove compartment door, holding at bottom, then lift door up and pull out to release door stops.
6. Remove three Phillips head screws at top of glove compartment.
7. Remove two Phillips head screws holding plastic clips under compartment.
8. Slide glove compartment out of instrument panel.
9. Disconnect electrical connectors for light and trunk release switch.
10. Remove one screw above glove compartment, then lift front of pad and pull rearward to release clips.
11. Remove four instrument cluster attaching screws.
12. Lift cluster and disconnect electrical connector, then remove cluster.
13. Reverse procedure to install.

LUMINA

1. Disconnect battery ground cable.
2. Remove instrument panel pad as follows:
   a. Remove five screws from under lower edge of instrument panel pad.
   b. Remove pad by lifting front and pulling rearward to release, then lifting up and out.
3. Disconnect electrical connectors from cluster.
4. Remove three cluster attaching screws, disconnect shift indicator cable, then remove cluster assembly.
5. Reverse procedure to install.

REGAL

1. Disconnect battery ground cable.
2. Carefully pry off speaker grilles.
3. Remove screw from under each speaker grille.
4. Remove five screws from under lower edge of instrument panel pad.
5. Remove pad by lifting front and pulling rearward to release, then lifting up and out.
6. Remove cluster trim plate attaching screw and the trim plate.
7. Disconnect electrical connector at cluster.
8. Remove six cluster attaching bolts and the cluster.
9. Reverse procedure to install.

HEADLIGHT SWITCH
REPLACE
CUTLASS SUPREME

1. Disconnect battery ground cable.
2. Remove five Phillips head screws at top of trim plate and pull top of trim plate out.
3. Starting at either side, carefully pull bottom of trim plate to release five spring clips.
4. Remove trim plate.
5. Remove two screws securing left air outlet trim plate.
6. Remove left air outlet trim plate by pulling carefully at bottom to release spring clips.
7. Disconnect electrical connector.
8. Remove headlight switch retaining screws and the switch.
9. Reverse procedure to install.

GRAND PRIX

1. Remove screw from instrument panel, under switch.
2. Remove switch assembly by carefully pulling out to release two spring clips at top.
3. Reverse procedure to install.

LUMINA

1. Disconnect battery ground cable.
2. Remove left instrument panel trim plate by pulling rearward to disengage retaining clips.
3. Remove two switch assembly attaching screws, pull switch out far enough to disconnect wiring connectors, then remove switch assembly.
4. Reverse procedure to install.

REGAL

1. Disconnect battery ground cable.
2. Carefully pry off speaker grilles.
3. Remove screw from under each speaker grille.
4. Remove five screws from under lower edge of instrument panel pad.
5. Remove pad by lifting front and pulling rearward to release, then lifting up and out.
6. Remove cluster trim plate attaching screw and the trim plate.
7. Remove four switch assembly attaching bolts and the switch assembly.
8. Reverse procedure to install.

WINDSHIELD WIPER SWITCH
REPLACE

Refer to procedure outlined under "Pivot & Pulse Switch & Turn Signal Switch Assembly, Replace."

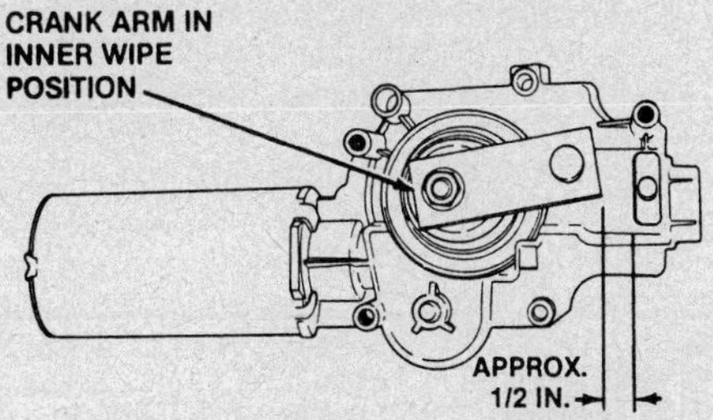

Fig. 2 Placing crank arm in inner wipe position

STOP LIGHT SWITCH
REPLACE

1. Disconnect battery ground cable.
2. Remove three fasteners from left side sound insulator panel.
3. Slide steering shaft protective sleeve toward front of dash.
4. Disconnect vacuum hose at cruise control cut-off switch.
5. Remove retainer pin which holds stop light switch to steering column bracket.
6. Disconnect electrical connectors.
7. Disconnect switch arm from pedal by pushing the arm to left and toward front of dash.
8. Release switch by pulling down and releasing top snap clip.
9. Reverse steps 3 through 8 to install, then adjust switch as follows:
   a. Depress brake pedal as far as possible and hold.
   b. Using a stiff wire with a hooked end, gently pull on the switch set lever and listen for an audible click.
10. Install left sound insulator panel.

NEUTRAL SAFETY SWITCH
REPLACE

1. Place vehicle in N.
2. Disconnect battery ground cable, then raise and support vehicle.
3. Disconnect electrical connector.
4. Remove switch harness from two retention clips, then lower vehicle.
5. Disconnect vacuum lines and electrical connector at cruise control servo, if equipped.
6. Detach servo, if equipped, and position out of way.
7. Disconnect shift lever at transaxle. Do not disconnect lever from cable.
8. Remove switch.
9. Reverse procedure to install, noting the following:
   a. Align groove on inner sleeve of switch with groove on switch body.
   b. **Torque** switch attaching bolts to 18 ft. lbs.
   c. **Torque** shift lever attaching nut to 15 ft. lbs.
   d. **Torque** cruise control servo re-

taining nut to 27 inch lbs.

WINDSHIELD WIPER MODULE
REPLACE

The windshield wiper module consists of both the wiper motor and the wiper transmission.
1. Disconnect battery ground cable.
2. Raise hood and remove washer hose, protective cap and nut from each wiper arm.
3. Lift each wiper arm and insert a suitable pin or pop rivet completely through the two holes located next to pivot of arm, then, using wiper arm removal tool No. J-8966 or equivalent, lift each arm off its transmission shaft.
4. Remove lower reveal molding attaching screws, then lower hood and remove lower reveal molding upward and rearward.
5. Raise hood, then remove air inlet panel screws, underhood lamp switch (if equipped) and the air inlet panel. **Attach holding wire or string to upper portion of switch before removing retaining nut to prevent switch from falling between panels.**
6. Disconnect wiring harness connectors at motor and the washer hose at firewall.
7. If motor is inoperative, motor crank arm must be rotated to inner wipe position, **Fig. 2.** Engage upper jaw of pliers against top edge of crank arm and lower jaw against crank arm nut, **Fig. 3.**
8. Remove three screws from bellcrank housing, then lower transmission.
9. Remove wiper module from vehicle.
10. Reverse procedure to install.

WINDSHIELD WIPER TRANSMISSION
REPLACE

EXCEPT 1991 LUMINA

1. Remove module as previously outlined.
2. Remove two transmission socket screws, then remove socket from link ball.
3. Remove righthand, lefthand, and bellcrank mounting screws and remove transmission from module.
4. Connect new transmission to module.
5. Ensure wiper motor is inner wipe position, **Fig. 2.**
6. Using suitable tool, align holes in module and bellcrank and install transmission socket screws.
7. Ensure body seal is in proper place on righthand side of module and install wiper module as previously described.
8. Install passenger side wiper arm and blade. Measure from tip of blade to bottom edge of glass, ensuring distance is approximately $9^1/8$ inches (231 mm), then tighten nut install protective cap and reconnect washer hose.

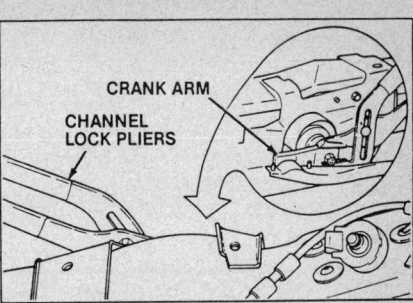

Fig. 3 Moving crank arm to inner wipe position

9. Install driver side wiper arm and blade. Measure from tip of blade to bottom edge of glass, ensuring distance is approximately 2 inches (53 mm), then tighten nut, install protective cap and reconnect washer hose.
10. Run wiper at high and low speeds with wet and tacky windshield, ensuring wiper parks properly and there is no interference between blades.

1991 LUMINA

1. With wipers in park position, disconnect washer hose from plastic connector.
2. Remove protective cap.
3. Lift wiper arm and insert a suitable pin completely through the two holes located next to pivot of arm.
4. Remove wiper arm retaining nut.
5. Lift arm off its drive shaft using an up and down rocking motion.
6. Remove top vent screen shroud.
7. Disconnect transmission drive linkage assembly in cowl area.
8. Remove transmission to body attaching screws.
9. Remove transmission and linkage from vehicle.
10. Reverse steps 6 through 9 to install transmission.
11. Install wiper arms one inch below park position.
12. Remove pin and lower wiper arm into position.
13. **Torque** a new wiper arm retaining nut to 14.7-17.7 ft. lbs.
14. Run wiper system and ensure correct operation.
15. Replace washer hose and install protective cap.

WINDSHIELD WIPER MOTOR
REPLACE

1988-90

1. Remove module as previously outlined.
2. Remove crank arm from motor. **Do not remove crank arm from transmission.**
3. Reverse procedure to install, **torquing** crank arm nut to 25-38 ft. lbs.

1991

1. With wipers in park position, disconnect washer hose from plastic con-

nector.
2. Remove protective cap.
3. Lift wiper arm and insert a suitable pin completely through the two holes located next to pivot of arm.
4. Remove wiper arm retaining nut.
5. Lift arm off its drive shaft using an up and down rocking motion.
6. Remove top vent screen shroud.

7. Disconnect wiper arm drive link from crank arm.
8. Disconnect wiper motor electrical connections.
9. Remove wiper motor attaching bolts then wiper motor guiding crank arm through hole.
10. Reverse steps 6 through 9 to install.
11. Install wiper arms one inch below park

position.
12. Remove pin and lower wiper arm into position.
13. **Torque** a new wiper arm retaining nut to 14.7-17.7 ft. lbs.
14. Run wiper system and ensure correct operation.
15. Replace washer hose and install protective cap.

2.3L/4-138 Engine

NOTE: Refer To "Buick Somerset & Skylark, Oldsmobile Cutlass Calais & Pontiac Grand Am" For Procedures Not Covered In This Section.

INDEX

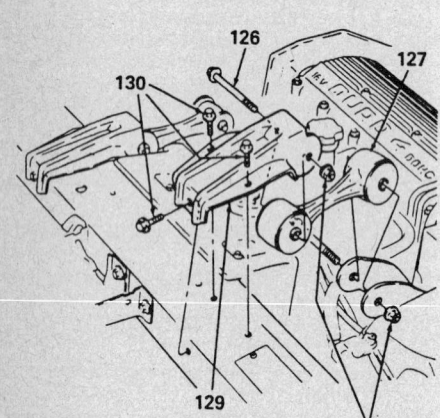

126. BOLT – 50 N·m (35 LBS. FT.)
127. TORQUE STRUT
128. NUT – 50 N·m (35 LBS. FT.)
129. BRACKET
130. BOLT – 23 N·m (17 LBS. FT.)

Fig. 1 Torque strut mount & bracket

ENGINE TORQUE STRUT & MOUNT
REPLACE

TORQUE STRUT

1. Disconnect battery ground cable.
2. Remove torque strut-to-engine bracket bolt, **Fig. 1.**
3. Remove torque strut-to-body mount bolt.
4. Remove torque strut.
5. Reverse procedure to install. Torque nuts and bolts to specifications shown in **Fig. 1.**

ENGINE MOUNT

1. Disconnect battery ground cable.
2. Remove mount retaining nuts from below frame mounting bracket, **Fig. 2.**
3. Raise engine to provide clearance using engine support tool No. J-28467 or equivalent.
4. Remove mount-to-engine bracket nuts, then the mount.
5. Reverse procedure to install. Torque nuts and bolts to specifications shown in **Fig. 2.**

ENGINE
REPLACE

1. Disconnect battery ground cable.
2. Scribe hood hinge locations, then remove hood.
3. Drain cooling system, then disconnect heater hoses from heater core and thermostat housing.
4. Disconnect upper radiator hose.
5. **On models equipped with A/C,** discharge A/C system, then disconnect A/C hoses from A/C compressor.
6. **On all models,** disconnect and mark two vacuum hoses from front of engine.
7. Disconnect electrical connectors from alternator, A/C compressor (if equipped) and fuel injector wiring harness. Position injector harness aside.
8. Disconnect electrical connections from starter motor solenoid.
9. Disconnect ground connections from front of engine, then the battery ground cable from transaxle.
10. Disconnect electrical connectors from ignition coil and module assembly, both coolant sensors, oil pressure sensor/switch, knock sensor and oxygen sensor.

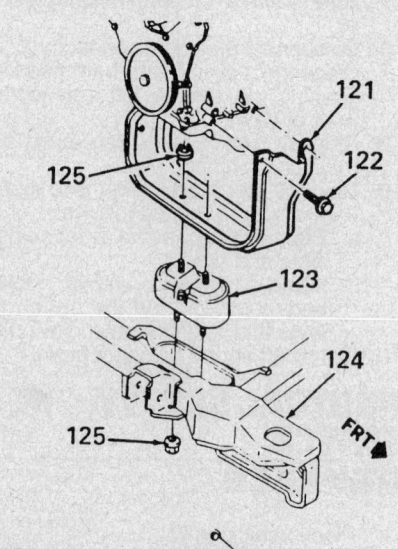

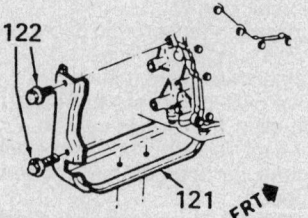

121. ENGINE MOUNT BRACKET
122. BOLT – 85 N·m (63 LBS. FT.)
123. ENGINE MOUNT
124. FRAME
125. NUT – 52 N·m (38 LBS. FT.)

Fig. 2 Lower engine mount

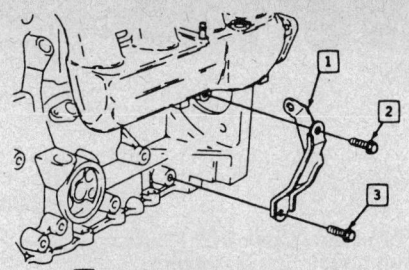

[1] BRACE, INTAKE MANIFOLD
[2] BOLT/SCREW - 25 N.m (18 LBS.FT.)
[3] BOLT/SCREW - 54 N.m (40 LBS. FT.)

Fig. 3 Intake manifold brace

11. Disconnect electrical connectors from idle air control (IAC) and throttle position sensor (TPS) on throttle body and position wiring harness aside.
12. Disconnect power brake unit vacuum hose from throttle body.
13. Disconnect throttle cable and remove throttle cable bracket.
14. Remove power steering pump pivot bolt and drive belt.
15. Disconnect power steering pump hydraulic lines, then remove power steering pump and brackets.
16. Depressurize fuel system, then disconnect fuel lines.
17. Remove torque strut mounts.
18. **On models with automatic transaxles,** remove transaxle fill tube.
19. **On all models,** remove exhaust heat shield, then remove bolts attaching exhaust pipe to exhaust manifold.
20. Remove engine-to-transaxle attaching bolts.
21. Raise and support vehicle, then remove remaining engine-to-transaxle attaching bolts.
22. Remove exhaust-to-transaxle brace.
23. Disconnect lower radiator hose.

24. Remove flywheel or torque converter cover.
25. **On models with automatic transaxle,** scribe a mark indicating relationship of torque converter to flywheel, then remove torque converter-to-flywheel attaching bolts.
26. **On all models,** remove transaxle to engine brace.
27. Remove lower engine mount.
28. Lower vehicle and support transaxle.
29. Install suitable engine lifting fixture, then remove engine from vehicle.
30. Reverse procedure to install.

INTAKE MANIFOLD REPLACE

1. Disconnect battery ground cable, then drain cooling system.
2. Disconnect vacuum hose and electrical connector from MAP sensor.
3. Disconnect electrical connectors from MAT sensor, purge solenoid and fuel injector harness. Position injector harness aside.
4. Disconnect vacuum hoses from intake manifold, hose from fuel pressure regulator and purge solenoid to canister.
5. Remove throttle body to air cleaner duct, then the vent tube to air cleaner duct.
6. Disconnect power brake unit vacuum line with retaining bracket to power steering bracket and position aside.
7. Disconnect coolant lines from throttle body.
8. Remove throttle body from intake manifold and position aside.
9. Remove oil/air separator (crankcase ventilation system) attaching bolts. Leave hoses connected to separator. Disconnect hoses from oil fill tube,

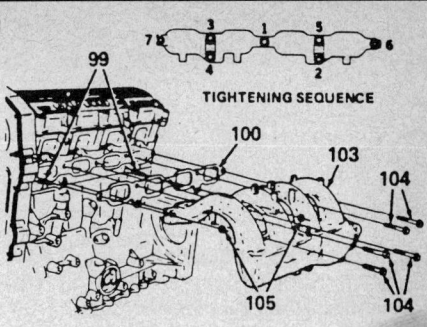

TIGHTENING SEQUENCE

99. STUD
100. INTAKE MANIFOLD GASKET
103. INTAKE MANIFOLD
104. BOLT
105. NUT

Fig. 4 Intake manifold installation & bolt tightening sequence

chain cover, intake duct and intake manifold. Remove oil/air separator and hoses as an assembly.
10. Remove oil fill cap and dipstick as an assembly.
11. Remove one oil fill tube retaining bolt, then pull fill tube upward to unseat from block.
12. Rotate oil fill tube as necessary to gain access for oil/air separator nipple, then remove oil fill tube.
13. Remove intake manifold support brace, **Fig. 3.**
14. Remove intake manifold attaching nuts and bolts, then the intake manifold and gasket.
15. Reverse procedure to install. **Torque** intake manifold attaching nuts and bolts to 18 ft. lbs. in sequence shown in **Fig. 4.**

2.5L/4-151 Engine

NOTE: Refer To "Chevrolet Celebrity, Buick Century, Oldsmobile Cutlass Ciera & Pontiac 6000" Chapter For Service Procedures.

2.8L/V6-173 & 3.1L/V6-192 Engines

INDEX

IDLE LEARN PROCEDURE

On 1990-91 models with 3.1L/V6-192 engine, any time vehicle power has been interrupted the programed position of the IAC valve pintle is lost. The following procedures must be performed to update the ECM memory with the correct IAC valve pintle position for the vehicle and provide a stable idle speed.

EXCEPT 1990 LUMINA

1. Restore vehicle power.
2. Connect TECH I scan tool to ALDL connector located under the lefthand side of the dash panel.
3. Select "IAC System."
4. Select "Idle Learn" in the "Misc. Test" mode.
5. Proceed as directed.

1990 LUMINA

1. Restore vehicle power.
2. Set parking brake and block wheels.
3. Start engine and place gear selector to drive for automatic transaxles or neutral for manual transaxles.
4. Allow the engine to run until it reaches normal operation temperatures, then an additional two minutes.

FUEL SYSTEM PRESSURE RELIEF

To reduce the risk of fire and personal injury, it is necessary to relieve the fuel system pressure before servicing fuel system components.

1988 CUTLASS SUPREME & REGAL

1. Disconnect fuel tank electrical harness connector.
2. Start engine and run until fuel supply remaining in fuel pipes is consumed.
3. Engage starter for three seconds to ensure relief of pressure.
4. Turn ignition to Off position and connect fuel tank electrical harness connections.

EXCEPT 1988 CUTLASS SUPREME & REGAL

1. Connect fuel gage tool No. J-34730, or equivalent, to the fuel pressure connection. Wrap a shop towel around fitting while connecting gage to catch any leaking fuel.
2. Install bleed hose into a suitable container and open valve to bleed system pressure.

MOUNTS
REPLACE

ENGINE MOUNT

1. Disconnect battery ground cable.
2. Remove mount retaining nuts from below cradle mounting bracket, **Fig. 1.**
3. Raise engine enough to provide clearance, then remove mount to engine bracket attaching nuts and the mount.
4. Reverse procedure to install, torquing nuts and bolts to specifications.

TRANSAXLE MOUNT

1. Disconnect battery ground cable.

2. Support transaxle with suitable jack.
3. Remove crossmember to mount attaching nuts, **Fig. 2.**
4. Remove bracket to transaxle attaching bolts.
5. Remove mount and bracket assembly.
6. Separate mount from bracket.
7. Reverse procedure to install, torquing nuts and bolts to specifications.

ENGINE
REPLACE

1. Disconnect battery ground cable, then drain coolant.
2. Scribe alignment marks, then remove hood.
3. Remove air flow tube from air cleaner and throttle valve, then the air cleaner assembly. On turbocharged models, remove turbocharger assembly.
4. Disconnect necessary electrical wiring, then the throttle and T.V. cables.
5. Relieve fuel pressure as follows:
   a. Connect fuel pressure gauge tool No. J-34730-1 or equivalent to fuel pressure connection. Wrap shop cloth around fitting while connecting gage.
   b. Insert bleed hose into suitable container and open valve to bleed system pressure.
6. Disconnect fuel lines.
7. Remove AIR pump belt, then the serpentine drive belt cover and belt.
8. Disconnect radiator hoses at engine.
9. Remove A/C compressor bolts from front bracket.
10. Remove power steering pump and position aside.
11. Disconnect heater hoses from engine.

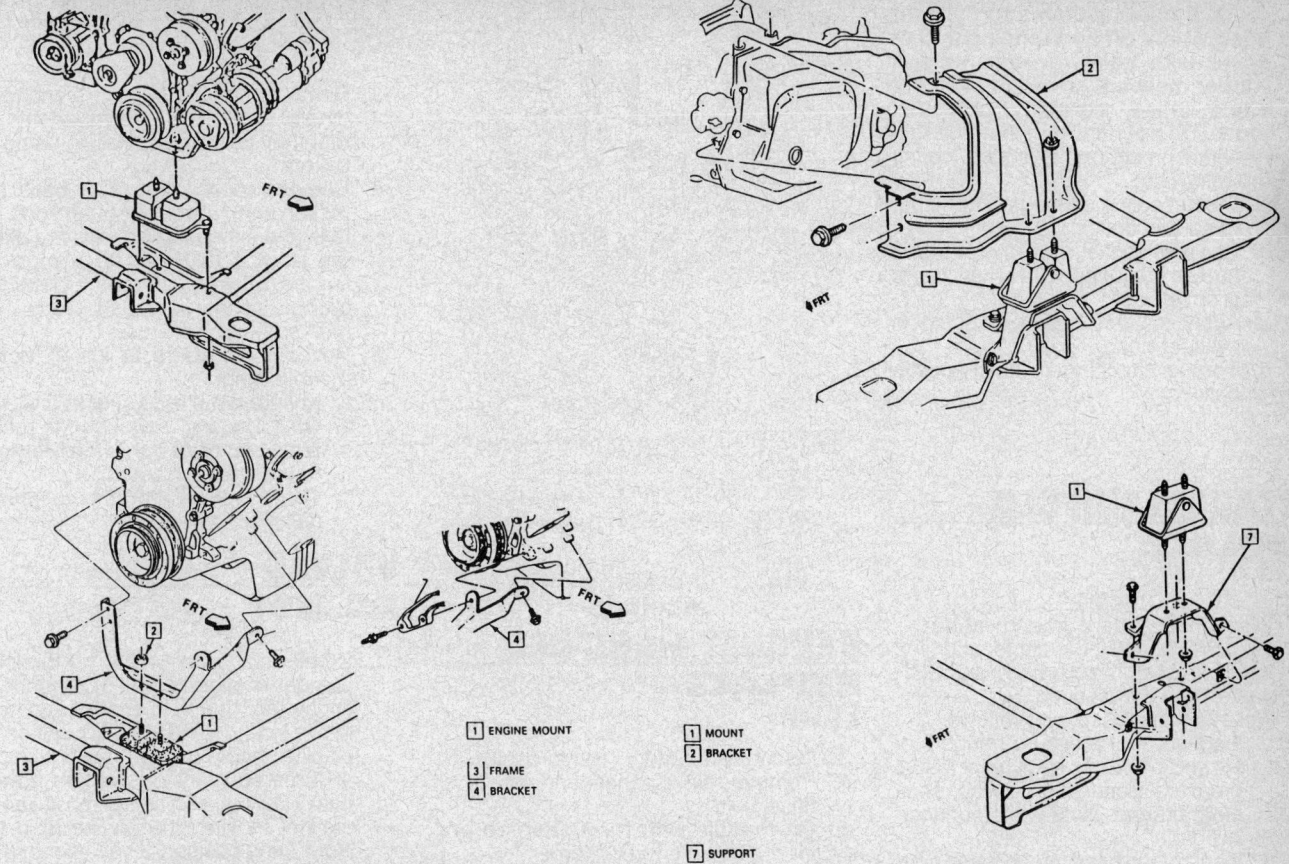

Fig. 1 Engine mount

1 ENGINE MOUNT	1 MOUNT
3 FRAME	2 BRACKET
4 BRACKET	
	7 SUPPORT

Fig. 2 Transaxle mount

12. Disconnect brake booster vacuum supply line.
13. Disconnect EGR from exhaust.
14. Raise and support vehicle.
15. Remove A/C compressor bolts at rear bracket, then position compressor aside.
16. Remove flywheel cover, then disconnect starter and position aside.
17. Remove torque converter bolts, then the transaxle bracket.
18. Remove engine front mount retaining nuts.
19. Disconnect exhaust pipe at crossover, then lower vehicle.
20. Remove engine torque struts, then the coolant recovery bottle.
21. Disconnect crossover pipe at left manifold.
22. **On except 1991 Lumina models,** pull engine assembly forward and support in this position.
22. **On all models,** disconnect crossover pipe at right manifold.
23. Disconnect bulkhead connector.
24. **On except 1991 Lumina models,** remove engine support and allow engine to roll to normal position.
25. **On all models,** remove engine to transaxle attaching bolts, attach lifting device to engine and support transaxle.
26. Remove engine assembly.
27. Reverse procedure to install.

ROCKER ARM COVER REPLACE
LEFT

1. Disconnect battery ground cable and drain coolant.
2. Disconnect ignition wire clamps from coolant tube, then loosen coolant tube below thermostat housing at engine block.
3. Disconnect coolant tube at each end.
4. Disconnect coolant tube hose at water pump.
5. Remove coolant tube.
6. Remove tube from between rocker cover and air inlet hose.
7. Remove ignition wire guide.
8. Remove cover attaching bolts and the cover. **If cover adheres to cylinder head, shear off by bumping end of cover with palm of hand or soft rubber mallet. If cover still will not come loose, carefully pry until loose. Do not distort sealing flange.**
9. Reverse procedure to install, noting the following:
   a. Clean sealing surfaces on cylinder head and cover.
   b. Use new gasket, ensuring gasket is seated properly in rocker cover groove.
   c. Apply suitable sealer in notch in cylinder head.
   d. Torque attaching bolts to specifications.

RIGHT

1. Disconnect battery ground cable and drain coolant.
2. Disconnect vacuum hoses at plenum.
3. Remove air cleaner assembly.
4. Disconnect EGR tube at crossover pipe.
5. Remove ignition wire guide, then disconnect ignition wire harness at plenum and spark plugs.
6. Disconnect two coolant hoses at throttle base.
7. Disconnect necessary electrical connectors at plenum.
8. Disconnect throttle, TV and cruise control cables.
9. Disconnect bracket at right side of plenum.
10. Disconnect brake booster vacuum supply hose from plenum.
11. Remove serpentine belt cover and the belt.
12. Detach coolant recovery bottle and position out of way.
13. Remove engine struts, then pull engine forward and secure in forward position, using slave feature on strut.
14. Remove alternator attaching bolts and position alternator out of way.
15. Remove PCV valve.

16. Remove cover attaching bolts and the cover. **If cover adheres to cylinder head, shear off by bumping end of cover with palm of hand or soft rubber mallet. If cover still will not come loose, carefully pry until loose. Do not distort sealing flange.**
17. Reverse procedure to install, noting the following:
    a. Clean sealing surfaces on cylinder head and cover.
    b. Use new gasket, ensuring gasket is seated properly in rocker cover groove.
    c. Apply suitable sealer in notch in cylinder head.
    d. Torque attaching bolts to specifications.

INTAKE MANIFOLD
REPLACE

1. Disconnect battery ground cable.
2. Remove accelerator cable and T.V. cable bracket, throttle body and EGR valve, then the plenum.
3. Relieve fuel pressure as follows:
   a. Connect fuel pressure gauge tool No. J-34730-1 or equivalent to fuel pressure connection. Wrap shop cloth around fitting while connecting gage.
   b. Insert bleed hose into suitable container and open valve to bleed system pressure.
4. Disconnect fuel inlet and return pipes from fuel rail.
5. Remove serpentine belt cover and belt.
6. Detach power steering pump and alternator and position out of way.
7. Remove alternator bracket.
8. Disconnect idle air vacuum hose at throttle body.
9. Disconnect wires at injectors and remove fuel rail.
10. Remove breather tube and runners, then the rocker arm covers.
11. Drain cooling system.
12. Disconnect radiator hose from thermostat outlet.
13. Disconnect wires at coolant sensor and oil sending switch, then remove coolant sensor.
14. Disconnect bypass hose at fill neck and head.
15. Disconnect heater inlet pipe from manifold.
16. Remove manifold attaching bolts and the manifold. **Retain Belleville washers in same positions on four center bolts.**
17. Reverse procedure to install, noting the following:
    a. Remove old gasket material and the loose sealant from front and rear ridges of cylinder block, then clean sealing surfaces.
    b. Apply bead of suitable sealant as shown, **Fig. 3.**
    c. Torque intake manifold nuts and bolts to specification, **Fig. 3.**

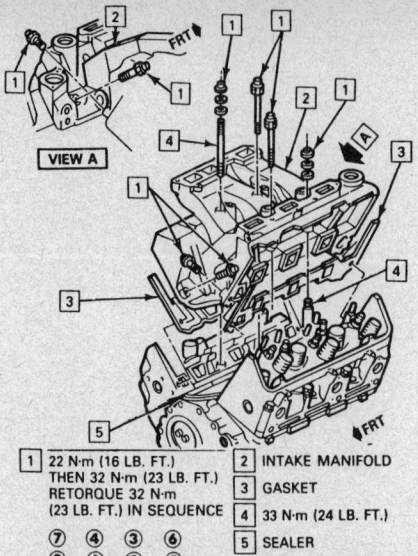

1	22 N·m (16 LB. FT.) THEN 32 N·m (23 LB. FT.) RETORQUE 32 N·m (23 LB. FT.) IN SEQUENCE	2	INTAKE MANIFOLD
		3	GASKET
	⑦ ④ ③ ⑥	4	33 N·m (24 LB. FT.)
	⑧ ① ② ⑤	5	SEALER

Fig. 3 Installing intake manifold

EXHAUST MANIFOLD
REPLACE
LEFT

1. Disconnect battery ground cable.
2. Remove air cleaner and breather hose.
3. **On models with turbocharged engines,** remove turbocharger.
4. **On all models,** disconnect torque struts from engine.
5. Remove coolant recovery bottle, then the serpentine belt cover and belt.
6. Remove A/C compressor, then the A/C strut and bracket.
7. Remove heat shield, then disconnect exhaust crossover pipe.
8. Remove manifold attaching bolts, then the manifold.
9. Reverse procedure to install, torquing manifold attaching bolts to specifications.

RIGHT

1. Disconnect battery ground cable, then raise and support vehicle.
2. Disconnect exhaust pipe from exhaust manifold, then lower vehicle.
3. **On models with turbocharged engines,** remove turbocharger.
4. **On all models,** disconnect engine torque struts, then remove coolant recovery bottle.
5. Pull engine forward and secure in forward position.
6. Remove air cleaner and breather hose, then the mass air flow sensor.
7. Remove heat shield, then disconnect crossover pipe at manifold.
8. Disconnect accelerator and T.V. cable at throttle lever, then remove accelerator and T.V. cable bracket from plenum and position out of way.
9. Remove manifold attaching bolts and the manifold.
10. Reverse procedure to install, torquing manifold attaching bolts to specifications.

VALVE MECHANISM
REPLACE

1. Remove rocker arm covers and rocker arms, identifying components so that they can be installed in same location.
2. Remove rocker arm pivot balls and rocker arms, then the push rods. Intake and exhaust push rods are different lengths (exhaust push rods are longer). Intake push rods are marked orange, exhaust push rods are marked blue.
3. Reverse procedure to install, noting the following:
   a. Ensure push rods seat in lifter.
   b. Coat bearing surfaces of rocker arms and pivot balls with Molykote or equivalent lubricant.
   c. Torque rocker arm nuts to specifications.

VALVES
ADJUST

1. Crank engine until mark on torsional damper is aligned with TDC mark on timing tab. Check to ensure engine is in the No. 1 cylinder firing position by placing fingers on No. 1 cylinder rocker arms as mark on damper comes near TDC mark on timing tab. If valves are not moving, the engine is in the No. 1 firing position. If valves move as damper mark nears TDC mark on timing tab, engine is in the No. 4 cylinder firing position and should be rotated one revolution to reach the No. 1 cylinder firing position.
2. With engine in the No. 1 cylinder firing position, adjust the following valves: Exhaust-1, 2,3; Intake-1, 5, 6. To adjust valves, back off adjusting nut until lash is felt at push rod, then tighten adjusting nut until all lash is removed. This can be determined by rotating the push rod while tightening the adjusting nut. When all lash has been eliminated, turn adjusting nut an additional 1 1/2 turns.
3. Crank engine one revolution until mark on torsional damper and TDC mark are again aligned. This is the No. 4 cylinder firing position. With engine in this position, the following valves can be adjusted: Exhaust-4, 5 & 6; Intake-2, 3 & 4.
4. Install rocker arm covers, then start engine and check timing and idle speed.

VALVE STEM OIL SEAL AND/OR VALVE SPRING
REPLACE

1. Remove rocker arm cover, then the spark plug.
2. Remove rocker arm and push rod.
3. Install air line adapter tool No. J-23590 or equivalent to spark plug port and apply compressed air to hold valves in place.

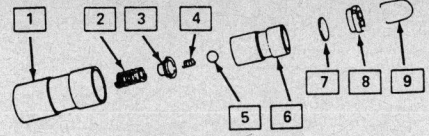

1—LIFTER BODY
2—PLUNGER SPRING
3—BALL CHECK RETAINER
4—BALL CHECK SPRING
5—BALL CHECK
6—PLUNGER
7—OIL METERING VALVE
8—PUSH ROD SEAT
9—RETAINER RING

Fig. 4   Exploded view of valve lifter

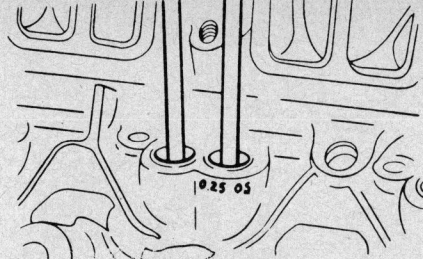

Fig. 5   Oversize lifter marking

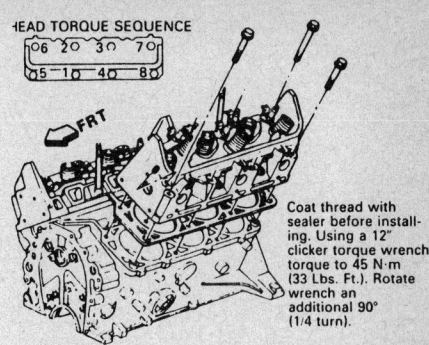

Coat thread with sealer before installing. Using a 12" clicker torque wrench torque to 45 N·m (33 Lbs. Ft.). Rotate wrench an additional 90° (1/4 turn).

Fig. 6   Installing cylinder head

4. Using valve spring compressor tool No. J-5892 or equivalent, compress valve spring and disassemble valve assembly.
5. Remove valve stem oil seal.
6. Reverse procedure to install, noting the following:
   a. When assembling valve assembly, use plastic seat provided and press over valve guide boss.
   b. If necessary, use grease to retain valve locks.

VALVE LIFTERS

Roller type valve lifters, **Fig. 4**, are used in this engine. Valve lifters must be replaced whenever camshaft is replaced.

Valve lifters should be kept in order so that they will be reinstalled in their original positions. Some engines will have both standard and .010 inch oversize valve lifters.

Where oversize lifters are used, the cylinder case will be marked "0.25 OS" with white paint on the lifter boss, **Fig. 5**.

If lifters are removed, they must be installed in their original location. If replacement is necessary, use lifters with a narrow flat ground along the lower 3/4 of the lifter. These flats provide additional oil to the cam lobe and lifter surfaces.

VALVE ARRANGEMENT
FRONT TO REAR

Cowl side . . . . E-I-E-I-I-E
Radiator side . . . . E-I-I-E-I-E

CYLINDER HEAD
REPLACE
LEFT

1. Disconnect battery ground cable, then drain coolant.
2. Remove rocker covers and intake manifold as previously outlined.
3. Remove exhaust crossover, then the oil lever indicator bracket.
4. Remove left exhaust manifold as previously outlined.
5. Disconnect plug wires at left head, then remove push rods. Intake and exhaust push rods are different lengths (exhaust push rods are lon-

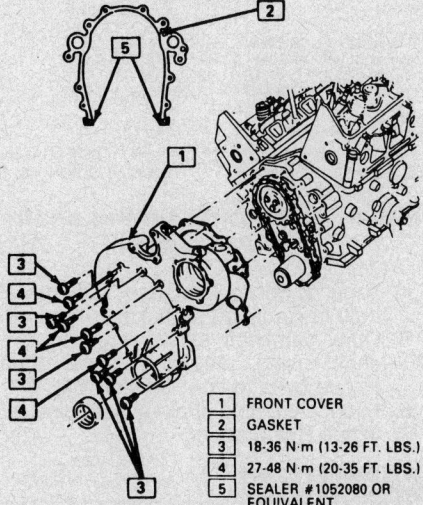

1 FRONT COVER
2 GASKET
3 18-36 N·m (13-26 FT. LBS.)
4 27-48 N·m (20-35 FT. LBS.)
5 SEALER #1052080 OR EQUIVALENT

Fig. 7   Installing timing cover

ger). Intake push rods are marked orange, exhaust push rods are marked blue.
6. Remove cylinder head attaching bolts, then the cylinder head.
7. Reverse procedure to install, noting the following:
   a. Clean gasket surfaces on head, cylinder block and intake manifold, cylinder block bolt threads and the cylinder head bolts.
   b. Place gasket in position over dowel pins with "This Side Up" marking facing upward.
   c. Coat cylinder head bolt threads with suitable sealant.
   d. Torque cylinder head bolts to specifications in proper sequence, **Fig. 6**.
   e. Torque rocker arm nuts to specifications.

RIGHT

1. Disconnect battery ground cable, then drain cooling system.
2. Raise and support vehicle and disconnect exhaust from crossover, then lower vehicle.
3. Disconnect torque struts from engine.
4. Detach coolant recovery bottle and position aside.
5. Pull engine forward and secure.
6. Remove exhaust crossover heat shield and disconnect crossover from right manifold.
7. Remove right exhaust manifold as previously outlined.

8. Disconnect spark plug wires from right cylinder head.
9. Remove rocker covers and intake manifold as previously outlined.
10. Remove push rods. Intake and exhaust push rods are different lengths (exhaust push rods are longer). Intake push rods are marked orange, exhaust push rods are marked blue.
11. Remove cylinder head attaching bolts, then the cylinder head.
12. Reverse procedure to install, noting the following:
   a. Clean gasket surfaces on head, cylinder block and intake manifold, cylinder block bolt threads and the cylinder head bolts.
   b. Place gasket in position over dowel pins with "This Side Up" marking facing upward.
   c. Coat cylinder head bolt threads with suitable sealant.
   d. Torque cylinder head bolts to specification in proper sequence, **Fig. 6**.
   e. Torque rocker arm nuts to specifications.

TIMING COVER
REPLACE

1. Disconnect battery ground cable and drain cooling system.
2. Remove serpentine drive belt tensioner, then the alternator.
3. Remove serpentine drive belt cover, then the drive belt.
4. Detach power steering pump and position aside.
5. Raise and support vehicle.
6. Remove inner splash shield, then the flywheel cover.
7. Remove starter, then, using torsional dampener remover tool No. J-24420 or equivalent, the crankshaft balancer.
8. Remove serpentine drive belt idler pulley, then the oil pan.
9. Remove lower timing cover attaching bolts, then lower cover.
10. Disconnect radiator hose at water pump and heater coolant hose from cooling system fill pipe.
11. Disconnect bypass, overflow and canister purge hoses.
12. Remove upper timing cover attaching bolts, then the cover.

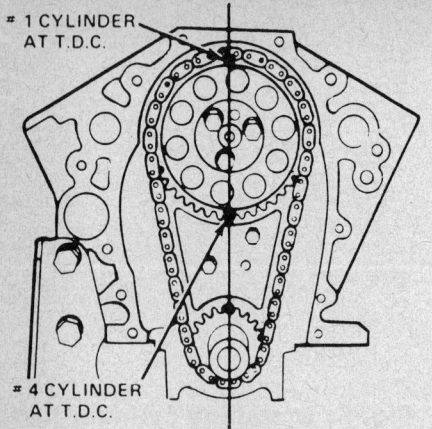

Fig. 8 Aligning timing marks

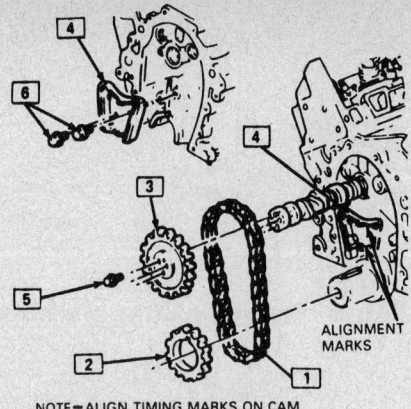

NOTE—ALIGN TIMING MARKS ON CAM
& CRANK SPROCKETS USING ALIGNMENT
MARKS ON DAMPER STAMPING OR CAST
ALIGNMENT MARKS ON CYL & CASE.

1	TIMING CHAIN	4	DAMPER
2	CRANK SPROCKET	5	20-27 N·m (15-20 FT. LBS.)
3	CAMSHAFT SPROCKET	6	18-24 N·m (13-18 FT LBS.)

Fig. 9 Replacing timing chain
& sprockets

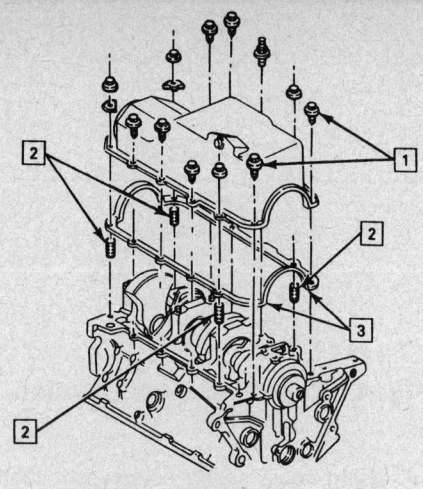

1	25 N·m (18 LB. FT.)
2	17 N·m (13 LB. FT.) ALL OTHERS 10 N·m (89 LB. IN.)
3	SEALER (1052917)

Fig. 10 Installing oil pan

13. Reverse procedure to install, noting the following:
   a. Clean sealing surfaces on front cover and cylinder block.
   b. Use new gasket and be careful not to damage sealing surfaces.
   c. Apply sealant and torque timing cover attaching bolts as shown, **Fig. 7.**

FRONT COVER OIL SEAL
REPLACE

1. Remove inner splash shield.
2. Using torsional dampener remover tool No. J-24420 or equivalent, remove crankshaft balancer.
3. Using suitable tool, pry out seal, being careful not to damage crankshaft.
4. Reverse procedure to install, noting the following:
   a. Lubricate new seal with clean engine oil and insert in front cover with lip facing engine.
   b. Use front cover alignment and oil seal installer tool No. J-35468 or equivalent to drive seal into place.

TIMING CHAIN & SPROCKETS
REPLACE
REMOVAL

1. Remove timing cover as previously outlined.
2. Position No. 1 piston at TDC with marks on camshaft and crankshaft sprockets aligned, **Fig. 8.**
3. Remove camshaft sprocket and chain. If sprocket does not come off easily, a light blow on lower edge of sprocket should dislodge it.
4. Remove crankshaft sprocket.

INSTALLATION

1. Install crankshaft sprocket.
2. Apply Molykote or equivalent to sprocket thrust surface.
3. Hold sprocket with chain hanging down and align marks on camshaft and crankshaft sprockets, **Fig. 9.**

4. Align dowel in camshaft with dowel hole in camshaft sprocket.
5. Draw camshaft sprocket onto camshaft using attaching bolts, then torque bolts to specification, **Fig. 9.**
6. Lubricate timing chain with engine oil.
7. Install timing cover.

CAMSHAFT
REPLACE

1. Remove engine as previously outlined.
2. Remove valve lifters, then the timing cover as previously outlined.
3. Remove timing chain and sprocket as previously outlined, then the camshaft.
4. Reverse procedure to install, noting the following:
   a. If installing new camshaft, coat camshaft lobes with GM E.O.S. 1052367 or equivalent.
   b. Lubricate camshaft journals with engine oil.

CAM LOBE LIFT SPECIFICATIONS

Intake............................. .2626
Exhaust............................ .2732

OIL PAN
REPLACE

1. Disconnect battery ground cable, then remove serpentine drive belt cover, drive belt and belt tensioner.
2. Using engine support fixture tool No. J-28467 or equivalent, and an extra support leg, support engine.
3. Raise and support vehicle, then drain engine oil.
4. Remove right wheel and tire assembly, then the right splash shield.
5. Remove steering gear pinch bolt, then

the transaxle mount retaining nuts. **Failure to disconnect intermediate shaft from rack and pinion stub shaft may cause damage to steering gear and/or intermediate shaft. This damage may cause loss of steering control.**
6. Remove engine to cradle mount retaining nuts.
7. Remove front engine horse collar bracket from block.
8. Remove outboard flywheel/starter plastic shield, then the inboard flywheel metal shield.
9. Detach starter and allow to hang from body.
10. Place jack under cradle front center crossmember.
11. Loosen rear cradle bolts. **Do not remove.**
12. Remove front cradle bolts and lower front of cradle.
13. **On 1991 models,** Disconnect DIS sensor wire.
14. **On all models,** remove eight oil pan retaining bolts and four oil pan retaining nuts, then the oil pan.
15. Reverse procedure to install, noting the following:
   a. Clean oil pan flanges, oil pan rail, front cover, rear main bearing cap and the threaded holes.
   b. Use new gasket.
   c. Apply suitable sealant as shown and torque nuts and bolts to specification, **Fig. 10.**

REAR MAIN SEAL
REPLACE
REMOVAL

1. Disconnect battery ground cable.
2. Using engine support fixture tool No. J-28467 or equivalent, and an extra support leg, support engine, then remove transaxle.
3. Remove flywheel.

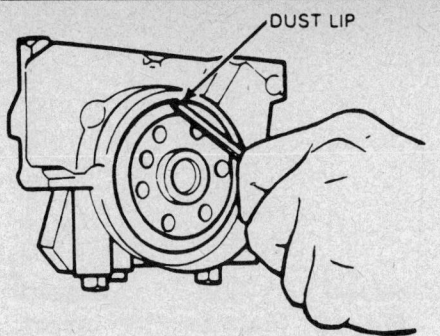

Fig. 11 Removing rear main seal

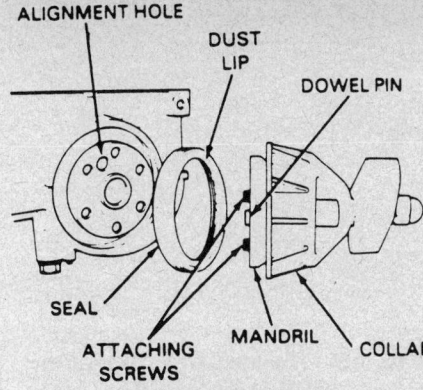

Fig. 12 Installing rear main seal

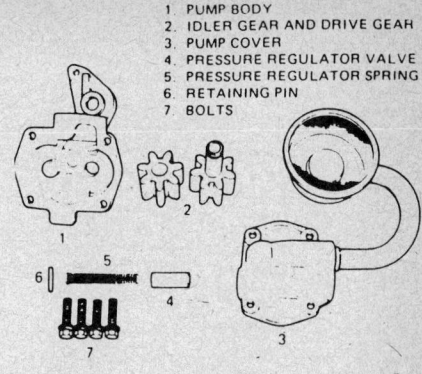

1. PUMP BODY
2. IDLER GEAR AND DRIVE GEAR
3. PUMP COVER
4. PRESSURE REGULATOR VALVE
5. PRESSURE REGULATOR SPRING
6. RETAINING PIN
7. BOLTS

Fig. 13 Exploded view of oil pump

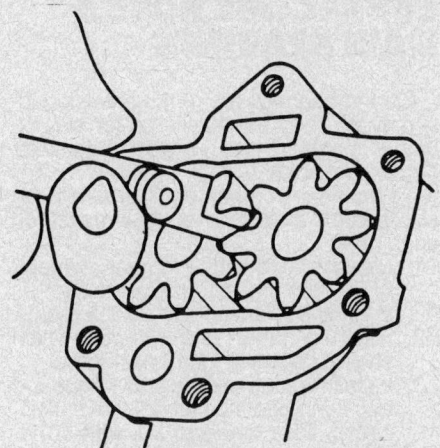

Fig. 14 Measuring oil pump gear lash

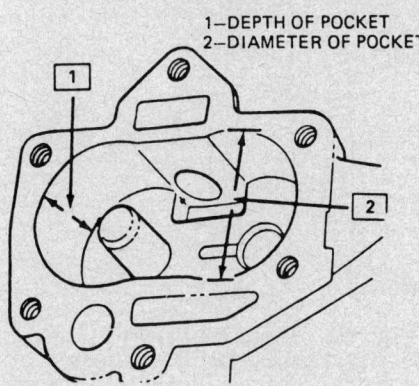

1—DEPTH OF POCKET
2—DIAMETER OF POCKET

Fig. 15 Measuring oil pump gear pocket

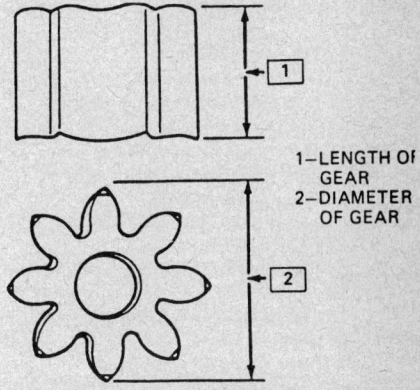

1—LENGTH OF GEAR
2—DIAMETER OF GEAR

Fig. 16 Measuring oil pump gears

4. Using suitable tool, remove seal by inserting tool in through dust lip at an angle, **Fig. 11**, and pry seal out by moving handle of tool toward end of crankshaft pilot, repeating around circumference of seal as necessary. **Be careful not to damage crankshaft O.D. surface.**

INSTALLATION

1. Check I.D. of bore for nicks or burrs and repair as required.
2. Inspect crankshaft for burrs or nicks on surface which contacts seal, repairing or replacing crankshaft as necessary.
3. Install seal as follows:
   a. Apply engine oil to I.D. and O.D. of new seal, then slide seal over mandrel until back of seal bottoms squarely against collar of rear main bearing seal installer tool No. J-34686 or equivalent, **Fig. 12**.
   b. Align dowel pin of tool with dowel pin in crankshaft by hand, or by **torquing** attaching screws to 45 inch lbs., **Fig. 12**.
   c. Turn "T" handle of tool so that collar pushes seal into bore, turning handle until collar is tight against case.
   d. Loosen "T" handle of tool until it comes to a stop, then remove attaching screws.
   e. Ensure seal is seated squarely in bore.
4. Install flywheel, then the transaxle.

OIL PUMP SERVICE
REMOVAL

1. Remove oil pan as previously described.
2. Remove pump and driveshaft extension.

DISASSEMBLY

1. Drain oil from pump.
2. Remove pump cover and pump gears, **Fig. 13**.
3. Remove pressure regulator valve. If valve is stuck, sock pump housing in carburetor cleaning solvent. **Pressure regulator valve spring may be under pressure. Remain retaining pin carefully.**
4. Clean sludge, oil and/or varnish from all parts. Varnish may be removed by soaking in carburetor or cleaning solvent.

INSPECTION

1. Inspect pump housing and cover for cracks or damaged threads, replacing as necessary. **Do not attempt to repair pump housing.** Replace spring as necessary.
2. Inspect idler gear shaft. If loose in housing, replace pump.
3. Inspect pressure regulator valve for scoring or sticking. Burrs may be removed with a fine oil stone.

4. Inspect pressure regulator valve spring for loss of tension or bending.
5. Inspect suction pipe and screen assembly for looseness if permanently pressed into pump body. If pipe is loose or has been removed, pump body cover must be replaced. Check for broken wire mesh or screen.
6. Inspect gears for chipping, galling or wear.
7. Measure gear lash in several positions, **Fig. 14**, as follows:
   a. **On 1988-89 models,** gear lash should be .009-.015 inch.
   b. **On 1990 models except 1990 Grand Prix STE and Lumina,** gear lash should be .0037-.0077 inch.
   c. **On 1990 Lumina models,** gear lash should be .009-.015 inch.
   d. **On 1990 Grand Prix STE models,** gear lash should be .004-.008 inch.
   e. **On 1991 models,** gear lash should be .0037-.0077 inch.
8. Measure pump housing gear pocket depth, **Fig. 15.** as follows:
   a. **On 1988-89 models,** pump depth should be 1.195-1.195 inches.
   b. **On 1990 models with an aluminum pump body,** pump depth should be 1.195-1.195 inches.
   c. **On 1990 models with a cast pump body except 1990 Grand Prix STE,** pump depth should be 1.202-1.205 inches.

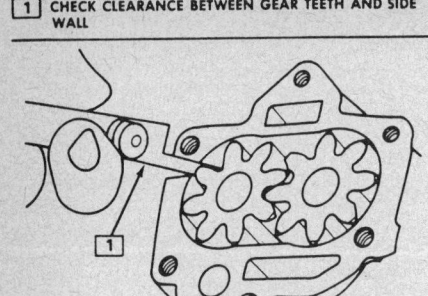

Fig. 17 Measuring gear side clearance

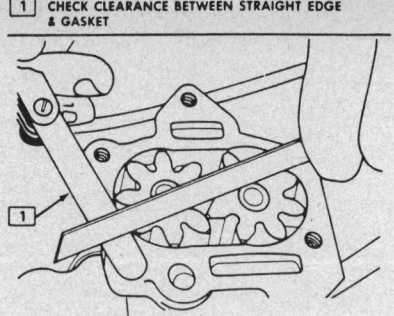

Fig. 18 Measuring oil pump end clearance

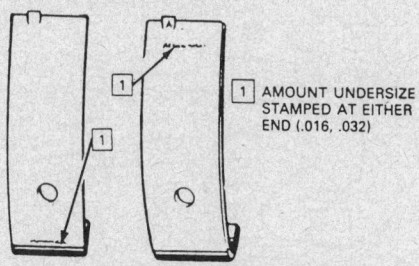

Fig. 19 Main bearing insert markings. 1988 models

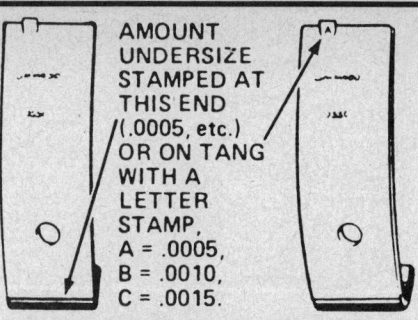

Fig. 20 Main bearing insert markings. 1989–90 models

d. **On 1990 Grand Prix STE models,** pump depth should be 1.434-1.436 inches.
e. **On 1991 models,** pump depth should be 1.202-1.205 inches.
9. Measure pump housing gear pocket diameter, **Fig. 15.** as follows:
   a. Pump housing diameter should be 1.503-1.506 inches.
10. Measure pump gear diameters, **Fig. 16,** as follows:
    a. **On 1988-89 models,** gear diameter should be 1.498-1.500 inches.
    b. **On 1990 Lumina models,** gear diameter should be 1.498-1.500 inches.
    c. **On 1990-91 models except Lumina,** gear diameter should be 1.498-1.499 inches.
11. Measure pump gear length, **Fig. 16,** as follows:
    a. **On except 1990 Grand Prix STE models,** gear length should be 1.199-1.200 inches.
    b. **On 1990 Grand Prix STE models,** gear length should be 1.438-1.439 inches.
12. Measure pump gear side clearance, **Fig. 17,** as follows:
    a. **On except 1990 Grand Prix STE models,** gear side clearance should be .003-.004 inches.
    b. **On 1990 Grand Prix STE models,** gear side clearance should be .0025-.0040 inches.
13. Measure oil pump end clearance, **Fig. 18,** as follows:
    a. **On except 1988-89 models,** end clearance should be .002-.005 inch.
    b. **On 1990 Lumina models,** end clearance should be .002-.005 inch.
    c. **On 1990 models with an aluminum pump body except 1990 Lumina,** end clearance should be .0016-.0067 inch.
    d. **On 1990 models with a cast pump body except 1990 Grand Prix STE,** end clearance should be .002-.006 inch.
    e. **On 1990 Grand Prix STE models,** end clearance should be .003-.007 inch.

ASSEMBLY

1. Lubricate all internal parts with engine oil.
2. Install pump gears.
3. Prime engine oil galleries by removing engine oil pump drive unit and rotating oil pump, using drill motor, appropriate socket and extension.
4. Install cover and gasket. **Use only original equipment gaskets as gasket thickness is critical to proper pump operation.**
5. Install pin, ensuring it is properly secured.
6. **Torque** pump cover attaching bolts to 89 inch. lbs.

INSTALLATION

1. Apply sealer No. 1050026, Fel-Pro set and seal, or equivalents to new pipe and tap into place with a plastic hammer, using oil suction pipe installer tool No. J-21182 or equivalent.
2. Install oil pump and driveshaft extension, engaging driveshaft extension into drive gear.
3. Install pump to rear bearing cap bolt, torquing to specifications.
4. Clean oil pan of oil and sludge and replace oil filter.
5. Install oil pan, then fill crankcase and check oil pressure. If pressure does not build up almost immediately, remove oil pan and check oil pump suction pipe attachment to pump. If necessary, disassemble oil pump, fill all cavities with petroleum jelly and reassemble. **Running engine without measurable oil pressure will cause extensive damage.**

CONNECTING RODS & MAIN BEARINGS

Engine bearings are of the precision insert type. They are available for service use in standard and various undersizes, **Figs. 19 and 20.**

To determine correct replacement insert size, bearing clearance must be measured as follows:

1. Measure crankshaft journal diameter in several places, approximately 90° apart and average the measurements.
2. Measure taper and run-out, which should be .0002 inch (maximum).
3. Install bearing inserts and torque rod and main bearing cap bolts to specification, then measure I.D. with an inside micrometer. Measure connecting rod I.D. in same direction as length of rod.
4. Select a suitable set of inserts to provide specified clearance limits. **Do not mix inserts of different nominal size in same bearing bore.** If clearance limits cannot be met, crankshaft journal must be reconditioned and undersized bearing inserts installed.

WATER PUMP
REPLACE

1. Disconnect battery ground cable and drain engine coolant.
2. Remove serpentine drive belt, then disconnect radiator and heater hose.
3. Remove water pump attaching bolts, then the water pump, **Fig. 21.**
4. Reverse procedure to install. noting the following:
   a. Clean water pump mating surfaces.
   b. **Torque** water pump attaching bolts to 89 inch lbs.

COOLING SYSTEM BLEED

1. **On 1988 models,** proceed as follows:
   a. Open vent valve located on thermostat housing, **Fig. 22.**
   b. Fill cooling system through radiator neck until coolant can be seen flowing from vent valve.
   c. Close vent valve and continue to fill cooling system to the base of the radiator neck.

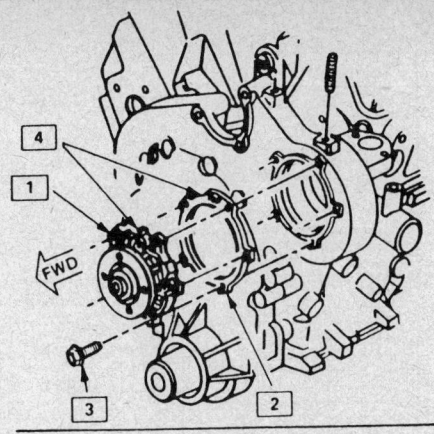

1. WATER PUMP
2. GASKET
3. 10 N·m (89 LB. IN.)
4. LOCATOR – MUST BE VERTICAL

Fig. 21   Water pump mounting

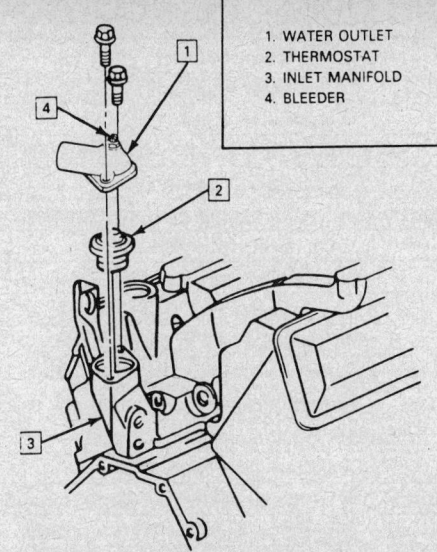

1. WATER OUTLET
2. THERMOSTAT
3. INLET MANIFOLD
4. BLEEDER

Fig. 22   Cooling system bleed vent. 1988 models.

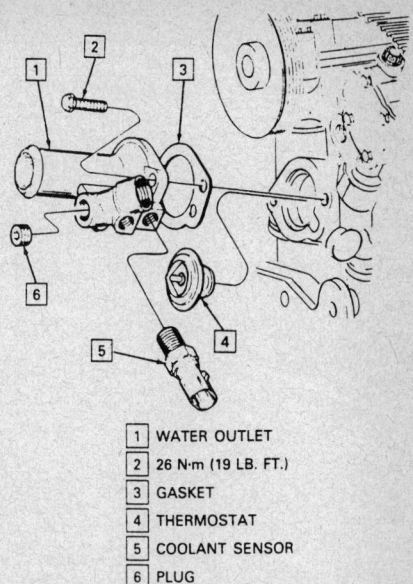

1. WATER OUTLET
2. 26 N·m (19 LB. FT.)
3. GASKET
4. THERMOSTAT
5. COOLANT SENSOR
6. PLUG

Fig. 23   Cooling system bleed vent. 1989–91 models.

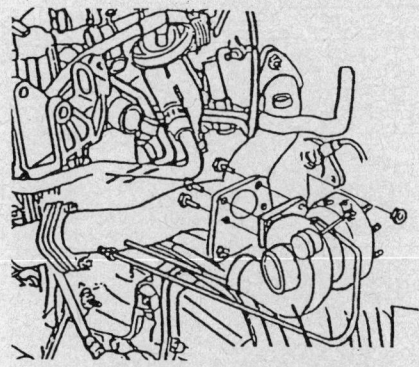

Fig. 24   Turbocharger mounting

2. **On 1989-91 models,** proceed as follows:
   a. Open vent valves located on the thermostat housing and throttle body return pipe above the water pump, **Fig. 23.** Turn both vents screws two to three turns.
   b. Fill cooling system to the base of the radiator neck.
   c. Close both vent valves. **Do not over tighten vent valves.**
3. **On all models,** install radiator cap.
4. Add sufficient coolant to the recovery tank.
5. Start engine and observe low coolant warning lamp.
6. If lamp remains On, repeat bleed procedure.

TURBOCHARGER REPLACE

1. Disconnect battery ground cable, then drain cooling system.

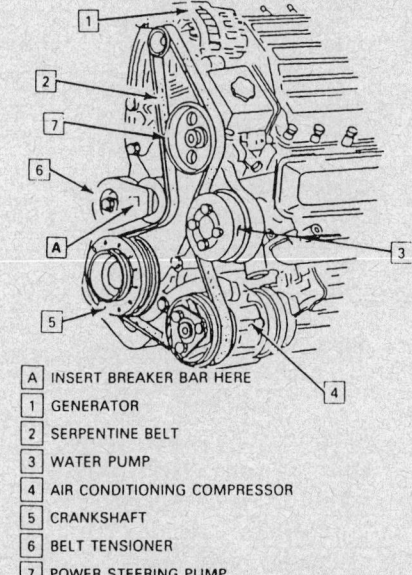

A   INSERT BREAKER BAR HERE
1   GENERATOR
2   SERPENTINE BELT
3   WATER PUMP
4   AIR CONDITIONING COMPRESSOR
5   CRANKSHAFT
6   BELT TENSIONER
7   POWER STEERING PUMP

Fig. 25   Serpentine drive belt routing

2. Remove intercooler-to-intake manifold duct attaching bolt from thermostat housing, then the duct.
3. Remove air cleaner-to-turbocharger duct from turbocharger.
4. Remove air cleaner inlet duct, then the air cleaner and duct assembly.
5. Remove turbocharger-to-intercooler duct from turbocharger.
6. Remove turbocharger heat shields.
7. Disconnect oxygen sensor electrical connector, then remove oxygen sensor.
8. Remove water return line from turbocharger.

9. Remove oil supply line from turbocharger.
10. Disconnect vacuum line from turbocharger compressor outlet, then the vacuum line from actuator assembly.
11. Remove actuator arm-to-wastegate retaining clip, then the actuator arm from wastegate.
12. Remove wastegate actuator from turbocharger.
13. **On models with cruise control,** remove cruise control servo and position aside.
14. Remove turbocharger downpipe from turbocharger.
15. Loosen turbocharger water supply hose clamp, then remove hose.
16. Remove turbocharger oil drain hose from drain pipe.
17. Remove turbocharger-to-exhaust crossover attaching bolts, then the turbocharger, **Fig. 24.**
18. Reverse procedure to install, noting the following:
    a. Transfer oil and water lines.
    b. Torque nuts and bolts to specifications.
    c. Prime turbocharger with oil before starting the engine. Crank engine with fuel pump fuse removed until normal operating oil pressure is reached.

SERPENTINE DRIVE BELT ROUTING

Refer to **Fig. 25** for serpentine drive belt routing.

TIGHTENING SPECIFICATIONS

Year	Component	Torque/ft. lbs.
1988–91	Camshaft Rear Cover	7
	Camshaft Sprocket	21
	Connecting Rod Bearing Cap Nuts	⑥
	Crankshaft Balancer	77
	Crossover/Turbocharger Support Bracket	19
	Cylinder Head Bolts	②
	Drive Belt Tensioner Bolt	⑦
	Engine Bracket To Engine Bolt	④ ⑤
	Engine Mount Bracket To Engine	63
	Engine Mount To Engine Mount Bracket	32
	Engine Mount To Frame	32
	Engine Strut Bracket To Engine	⑧
	Exhaust Crossover Nut	18
	Exhaust Downpipe Bracket To Cylinder Head	35 ⑫
	Exhaust Downpipe Bracket To Downpipe	18 ⑫
	Exhaust Downpipe To Turbocharger	17
	Exhaust Manifold Bolts	⑨
	Exhaust Manifold Heat Shield	90 ①
	Intake Manifold Bolts	24
	Intake Manifold Nuts	23
	Intake Manifold Studs	23
	Intercooler To Support	89 ① ⑫
	Main Bearing Cap Bolts	⑩
	Oil Cooler Connector	29
	Oil Filter	11
	Oil Level Indicator Retainer Nut	18
	Oil Pan	③
	Oil Pump Drive Bolt	25
	Oil Pump	25–35
	Oxygen Sensor	31
	Rocker Arm Adjusting Nuts	14–20
	Rocker Arm Covers	7
	Spark Plugs	20
	Strut Bracket To Upper Tie Bar	16
	Strut To Engine Bracket Bolt	⑪
	Strut To Tie Bar Bracket	32
	Thermostat Housing	19
	Timing Chain Cover	③
	Timing Chain Dampener	15
	Transaxle Bracket To Transaxle	60
	Transaxle Mount To Frame	38
	Transaxle Mount To Transaxle Bracket	30
	Transaxle Mount To Transaxle Mount Support	38
	Turbocharger Coolant Feed	21
	Turbocharger Coolant Return	21
	Turbocharger Oil Feed	15
	Turbocharger Oil Return	30
	Turbocharger To Exhaust Manifold Crossover	17
	Water Pump	19

① —Inch lbs.
② —Torque in sequence to 33 ft. lbs.
  then turn an additional 90°.
③ —Refer to text.
④ —1991 models.
⑤ —Bracket side bolts, 59 ft. lbs.;
  bracket front bolts, 81 ft. lbs.
⑥ —1988–89 models, 37 ft. lbs.; 1990–91

models, 39 ft. lbs.
⑦ —1988–90 models, 40 ft. lbs.; 1991
  models, 32 ft. lbs.
⑧ —Except 1990 models, 34 ft. lbs.; 1990
  models, 52 ft. lbs.
⑨ —Except 1990 Oldsmobile STE models,
  19 ft. lbs.; 1990 Grand Prix STE
  models, 19 ft. lbs.

⑩ —1988–89 models, 70 ft. lbs.; 1990–91
  models, 73 ft. lbs.
⑪ —1988–90 models except 1990 Grand
  Prix STE models, 32 ft. lbs. ; 1990
  Grand Prix STE models, 51 ft. lbs.;
  1991 models, 41 ft. lbs.
⑫ —Turbocharged engines.

3.4L/V6-204 ENGINE

INDEX

IDLE LEARN PROCEDURE

On 1991 models with 3.4L/V6-204 engine, any time vehicle power has been interrupted the programed position of the IAC valve pintle is lost. The following procedures must be performed to update the ECM memory with the correct IAC valve pintle position for the vehicle and provide a stable idle speed.
1. Restore vehicle power.
2. Connect TECH I scan tool to ALDL connector located under the lefthand side of the dash panel.
3. Select "IAC System."
4. Select "Idle Learn" in the "Misc. Test" mode.
5. Proceed as directed.

FUEL SYSTEM PRESSURE RELIEF

To reduce the risk of fire and personal injury, it is necessary to relieve the fuel system pressure before servicing fuel system components.
1. Disconnect battery ground cable.
2. Loosen fuel tank filler cap to relieve tank pressure.
3. Connect fuel pressure gage tool No. J-34730-1, or equivalent, to the fuel pressure valve. Wrap a shop towel around fitting while connection gage to avoid spillage.
4. Install bleed hose into an approved container and open valve to bleed system pressure.

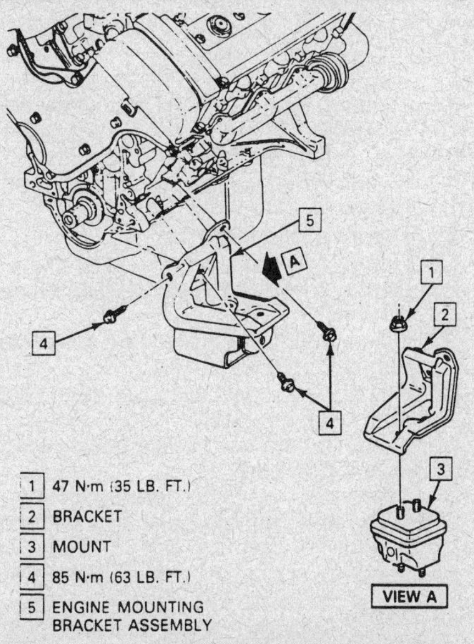

1	47 N·m (35 LB. FT.)
2	BRACKET
3	MOUNT
4	85 N·m (63 LB. FT.)
5	ENGINE MOUNTING BRACKET ASSEMBLY

Fig. 1   Front engine mounting bracket

5. Fuel system components are now safe to service.
6. Drain fuel remaining in pressure gauge in a suitable container.

MOUNTS REPLACE

FRONT

1. Remove air cleaner assembly.
2. Disconnect engine torque strut.

3. Install engine support tool Nos. J-28467, J-28467-90 and J-36462, or equivalent.
4. Raise and support vehicle.
5. Remove right front tire and wheel assembly.
6. Remove righthand engine splash shield.
7. Drain engine oil into a suitable container and remove oil filter.
8. Remove front engine mount nuts at mount bracket and frame, **Fig. 1.**
9. Install drive axle boot protector and lower vehicle.
10. Raise engine.
11. Raise and support vehicle.
12. Remove front mount.
13. Reverse procedure to install.

REAR

1. Remove air cleaner assembly and disconnect engine torque strut.
2. Install engine support tool Nos. J-28467, J-28467-90 and J-36462, or equivalent, then raise and support vehicle.
3. Remove right front tire and wheel assembly, righthand engine and drive axle splash shields.
4. Install drive axle boot protector.
5. Remove engine mount nuts at frame, **Figs. 2 and 3.**
6. Lower vehicle and raise engine.
7. Raise and support vehicle.
8. Remove power rack and pinion mounting bolts and hang rack on frame.
9. Disconnect right ball joint from lower control arm.
10. Install a suitable jack under righthand side of frame.

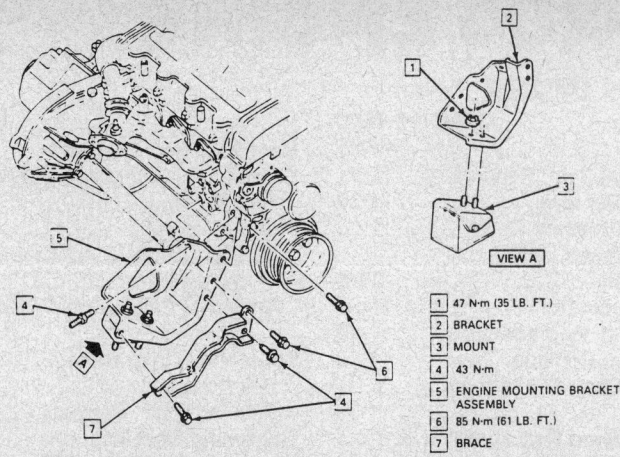

1	47 N·m (35 LB. FT.)
2	BRACKET
3	MOUNT
4	43 N·m
5	ENGINE MOUNTING BRACKET ASSEMBLY
6	85 N·m (61 LB. FT.)
7	BRACE

Fig. 2   Rear engine mounting bracket. Manual transaxles

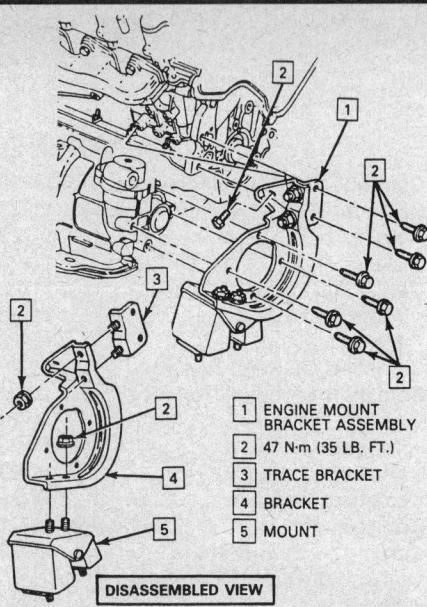

1	ENGINE MOUNT BRACKET ASSEMBLY
2	47 N·m (35 LB. FT.)
3	TRACE BRACKET
4	BRACKET
5	MOUNT

Fig. 3   Rear engine mounting bracket. Automatic transaxles

11. Remove righthand frame mounting bolts.
12. Loosen lefthand frame mounting bolts.
13. Lower righthand side of frame approximately three inches.
14. Remove upper engine mount nuts at mount.
15. Remove mount.
16. Reverse procedure to install.

ENGINE
REPLACE

MODELS w/MANUAL TRANSAXLES

1. Disconnect battery cables and remove battery jump terminal.
2. Remove air cleaner and duct assembly.
3. Drain cooling system and remove coolant recovery tank.
4. Disconnect control cables at throttle body.
5. Remove serpentine drive belt as outlined under "Serpentine Drive Belt."
6. Disconnect wiring harness cover and upper engine wire connectors at right strut tower.
7. Disconnect engine ground near air cleaner bracket.
8. Relieve fuel system pressure as outlined under "Fuel System Pressure Relief" then disconnect fuel lines at fuel rail.
9. Disconnect heater hose quick connect at intake manifold and bracket.
10. Disconnect and remove engine torque strut.
11. Remove upper and lower radiator hoses.
12. Disconnect heater hoses at water pump.
13. Remove engine torque strut bracket at frame.
14. Remove right and left engine coolant fan retaining screws.
15. Remove upper radiator support.
16. Remove both engine cooling fans.

17. Disconnect electrical bulkhead connector at right fire wall.
18. Disconnect ECM and set on engine.
19. Remove convenience center, wiring harness cover, harness clips and low coolant sensor connector and position entire harness assembly on top of engine.
20. Discharge A/C system and disconnect A/C lines near accumulator.
21. Remove shift control cable at lever bracket.
22. Mark then disconnect all necessary vacuum lines.
23. Raise and support vehicle.
24. Remove both front tire and wheel assemblies.
25. Remove both flywheel covers.
26. Drain engine oil into a suitable container.
27. Remove starter motor.
28. Remove flywheel to converter bolts.
29. Remove right and left engine splash shields.
30. Disconnect front brake ABS electrical connectors, if equipped.
31. Disconnect front exhaust pipe and converter assembly.
32. Remove both front brake calipers and support on body.
33. Disconnect steering column intermediate shaft pinch bolt and remove shaft from stub.
34. Position transaxle jack under power train.
35. Disconnect and plug transaxle cooler lines.
36. Remove frame bolts.
37. Lower powertrain from vehicle.
38. Disconnect electrical connectors and harness from left lower side of engine.
39. Remove A/C compressor with lines attached.
40. Disconnect electrical, alternator and sensor connectors and ground connections from rear of engine.
41. Remove exhaust crossover pipe.
42. Remove right axle from from transaxle as outlined under "Drive Axle, Replace" in the "Front Wheel Drive Axles" section.
43. Remove drive axle shield.

44. Remove engine mounts as outlined under "Mounts, Replace."
45. Remove power steering pump assembly.
46. Remove transaxle to engine bolts.
47. Install engine lifting device and remove engine assembly from transaxle.
48. Reverse procedure to install.

MODELS w/AUTOMATIC TRANSAXLES

1. Relieve fuel system pressure as outlined under "Fuel System Pressure Relief."
2. Remove air cleaner assembly.
3. Mark and remove hood assembly.
4. Disconnect battery ground cable and drain cooling system.
5. Discharge A/C system and remove coolant recovery tank.
6. Remove heater hoses from engine.
7. Disconnect engine torque strut mount and stud.
8. Disconnect and remove engine cooling fans.
9. Remove radiator hoses from engine.
10. Disconnect control cables from bracket and throttle body.
11. Disconnect bulkhead connections from cowl.
12. Disconnect fuel lines from engine.
13. Remove exhaust crossover pipe.
14. Remove lower transaxle to engine bolts including ground wires.
15. Remove power steering pump from engine and position aside.
16. Disconnect EGR pipe from EGR valve.
17. Raise and support vehicle.
18. Remove right tire and wheel assembly then the right splash shield.

19. Disconnect A/C manifold from A/C compressor.
20. Remove flywheel and steel torque converter inspection covers then starter.
21. Remove front exhaust pipe and converter.
22. Disconnect motor mounts as outlined under "Mounts, Replace."
23. Disconnect electrical connections at front and rear of engine then from alternator.
24. Remove torque converter bolts.
25. Remove right ball joint bolt and separate joint from control arm.
26. Remove drive axle assembly.
27. Lower vehicle.
28. Support transaxle using a suitable jack and install lifting device on engine.
29. Disconnect quick connects near ECM.
30. Remove remaining transaxle to engine bolts.
31. Disconnect necessary vacuum lines from rear of engine.
32. Remove engine assembly.
33. Reverse procedure to install.

INTAKE PLENUM
REPLACE

1. Relieve fuel system pressure as outlined under "Fuel System Pressure Relief."
2. Remove air cleaner assembly.
3. Disconnect battery ground cable and drain cooling system.
4. Remove control cables at throttle body.
5. Disconnect fuel rail cover bolts and remove fuel pipes at fuel rail.
6. Disconnect heater hose at intake manifold.
7. Disconnect vacuum lines from PVC valve and throttle body of plenum.
8. Disconnect AIR solenoid, EGR valve, canister purge solenoid, MAP sensor and throttle position sensor connectors.
9. Remove EGR bolts and EGR valve.
10. Disconnect fuel line bracket and heater hose at throttle body of plenum.
11. Disconnect all necessary vacuum lines at plenum.
12. Remove wire loom bracket for rear bank of spark plug wires.
13. Remove nuts at plenum and plenum bracket.
14. Remove plenum from vehicle.
15. Reverse procedure to install.

INTAKE MANIFOLD
REPLACE

1. Relieve fuel system pressure as outlined under "Fuel System Pressure Relief."
2. Disconnect fuel rail as follows:
   a. Remove intake manifold plenum as outlined under "Intake Plenum, Replace."
   b. Remove fuel line bracket bolts.
   c. Disconnect fuel lines at fuel rail using a suitable back-up wrench on the fuel rail fittings.

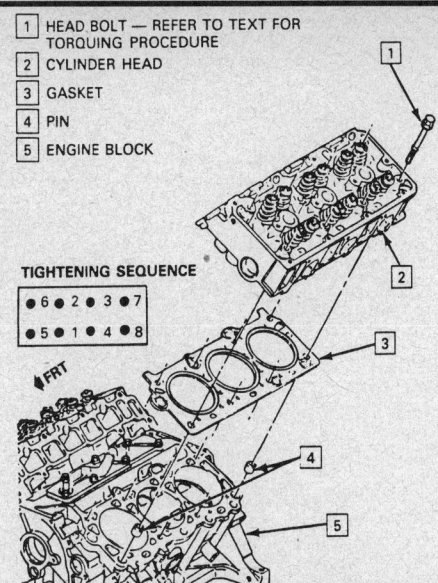

1 HEAD BOLT — REFER TO TEXT FOR TORQUING PROCEDURE
2 CYLINDER HEAD
3 GASKET
4 PIN
5 ENGINE BLOCK

TIGHTENING SEQUENCE

Fig. 4   Cylinder head bolt tightening sequence

   d. Disconnect vacuum lines at pressure regulator.
   e. Remove fuel rail bolts.
   f. Disconnect injector electrical connectors.
   g. Remove fuel rail from vehicle.
3. Disconnect heater hose pipe bracket from thermostat housing.
4. Remove temperature sensor from intake manifold.
5. Disconnect radiator hose from thermostat housing.
6. Remove intake manifold bolts and intake manifold.
7. Reverse procedure to install, inserting rubber isolators fully into manifold flange before tightening fasteners to specifications.

EXHAUST MANIFOLD
REPLACE

FRONT

1. Remove air cleaner assembly.
2. Remove exhaust crossover pipe.
3. Remove engine torque strut bracket to frame bolts and lift strut out of the way.
4. Remove upper radiator shroud, right side cooling fan heat shield and right cooling fan assembly.
5. **On models with manual transaxles,** remove front hose from air pipe.
6. **On all models,** remove exhaust manifold nuts then the manifold and heat shield.
7. Reverse procedure to install.

REAR
Automatic Transaxles

1. Remove rear cam carrier as outlined under "Camshaft Carrier, Replace."
2. Remove exhaust crossover pipe.
3. Raise and support vehicle.
4. Disconnect front exhaust pipe at manifold.

5. Lower vehicle.
6. Disconnect oxygen sensor connector.
7. Remove exhaust manifold nuts then the manifold and heat shield.
8. Reverse procedure to install.

Manual transaxles

1. Remove air cleaner assembly.
2. Disconnect battery ground cable.
3. Remove exhaust crossover pipe.
4. Raise and support vehicle.
5. Disconnect front exhaust manifold pipe.
6. Disconnect and remove oxygen sensor.
7. Remove exhaust manifold heat shield and disconnect EGR pipe at manifold.
8. Remove exhaust manifold nuts then the exhaust manifold.
9. Reverse procedure to install.

VALVE STEM OIL SEAL & VALVE SPRING
REPLACE

HEAD ON ENGINE

1. Remove camshaft carrier as outlined under "Camshaft Carrier, Replace."
2. Remove spark plugs and install spark plug port adapter tool No. J-22794, or equivalent, and apply compressed air to hold valves in place.
3. Compress valve spring using valve spring compressor tool No. J-38606, or equivalent.
4. Remove valve stem locks and release spring tension.
5. Remove valve cap, valve spring and valve stem oil seal. **Wrap tape over valve lock grooves to prevent damage to valve seals.**
6. Reverse procedure to install.

HEAD OFF ENGINE

1. Compress valve spring using valve spring compressor tool No. J-38606, or equivalent.
2. Remove valve stem locks and release spring tension.
3. Remove valve cap, valve spring and valve stem oil seal. **Wrap tape over valve lock grooves to prevent damage to valve seals.**
4. Reverse procedure to install.

VALVE LIFTERS

1. Remove camshaft carrier as outlined under "Camshaft Carrier, Replace."
2. Remove six lifter hold down hoses.
3. Remove lifters.
4. Reverse procedure to install.

CYLINDER HEAD
REPLACE

FRONT

1. Relieve fuel system pressure as outlined under "Fuel System Pressure Relief."
2. Remove intake manifold, camshaft

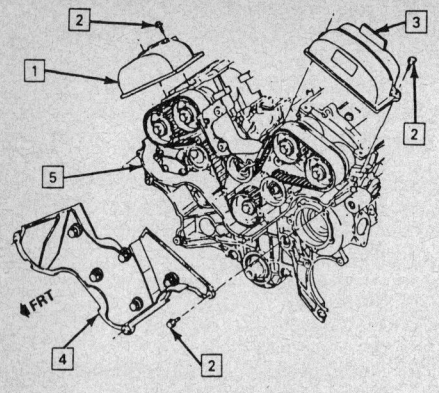

1	TIMING BELT COVER (RIGHT)
2	10 N·m (89 LB. IN.)
3	TIMING BELT COVER (LEFT)
4	TIMING BELT COVER (CENTER)
5	FRONT COVER

Fig. 5 Timing belt covers

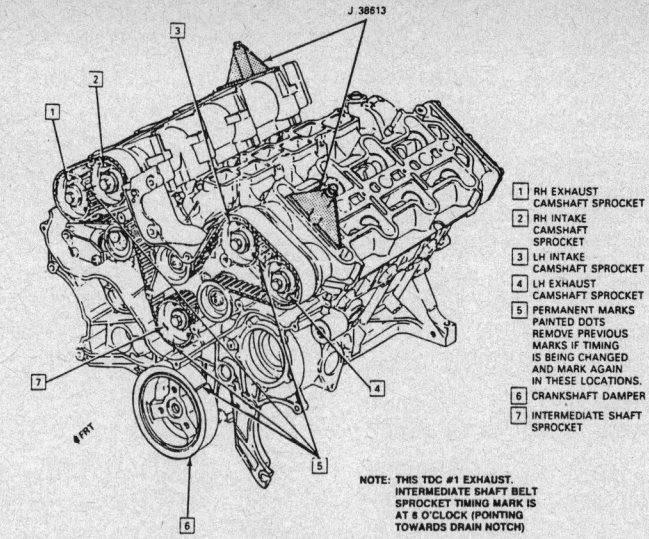

1	RH EXHAUST CAMSHAFT SPROCKET
2	RH INTAKE CAMSHAFT SPROCKET
3	LH INTAKE CAMSHAFT SPROCKET
4	LH EXHAUST CAMSHAFT SPROCKET
5	PERMANENT MARKS PAINTED DOTS REMOVE PREVIOUS MARKS IF TIMING IS BEING CHANGED AND MARK AGAIN IN THESE LOCATIONS.
6	CRANKSHAFT DAMPER
7	INTERMEDIATE SHAFT SPROCKET

NOTE: THIS TDC #1 EXHAUST. INTERMEDIATE SHAFT BELT SPROCKET TIMING MARK IS AT 6 O'CLOCK (POINTING TOWARDS DRAIN NOTCH).

Fig. 6 Engine timing marks

carrier and exhaust manifold as outlined under "Intake Manifold, Replace," " Camshaft Carrier, Replace" and "Exhaust Manifold, Replace."
3. Remove right cooling fan assembly.
4. Remove oil level indicator tube.
5. Disconnect temperature sending unit connector.
6. Remove cylinder head bolts then the cylinder head.
7. Reverse procedure to install, noting the following:
   a. Install cylinder head gasket with metal tabs between cylinders facing up.
   b. **Torque** cylinder head bolts in sequence shown in **Fig. 4** to 33 ft. lbs. plus an additional 90° turn using torque/angle meter tool No. J-36660, or equivalent.

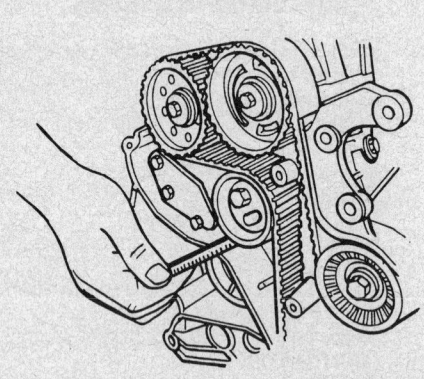

Fig. 7 Actuator measurement

REAR

1. Relieve fuel system pressure as outlined under "Fuel System Pressure Relief."
2. Remove intake manifold, camshaft carrier and exhaust manifold as outlined under "Intake Manifold, Replace," " Camshaft Carrier, Replace" and "Exhaust Manifold, Replace."
3. Disconnect oxygen sensor connector.
4. Remove rear timing belt tensioner bracket.
5. Remove cylinder head bolts then the cylinder head and gasket.
6. Reverse procedure to install, noting the following:
   a. Install cylinder head gasket with metal tabs between cylinders facing up.
   b. **Torque** cylinder head bolts in sequence shown in **Fig. 4** to 33 ft. lbs. plus an additional 90° using torque/angle meter tool No. J-36660, or equivalent.

SECONDARY TIMING BELT SERVICE
COVER, REPLACE
Right

1. Disconnect battery ground cable.
2. Remove secondary timing belt right cover bolts then the belt cover, **Fig. 5.**
3. Reverse procedure to install.

Left

1. Disconnect battery ground cable.
2. Remove spark plug cover as follows:
   a. Disconnect vacuum hose from camshaft carrier cover.
   b. Remove spark plug cover bolts then the cover.
3. Remove secondary timing belt left cover bolts then the cover, **Fig. 5.**
4. Reverse procedure to install.

Center

1. Disconnect battery ground cable.
2. Remove ECM harness cover.

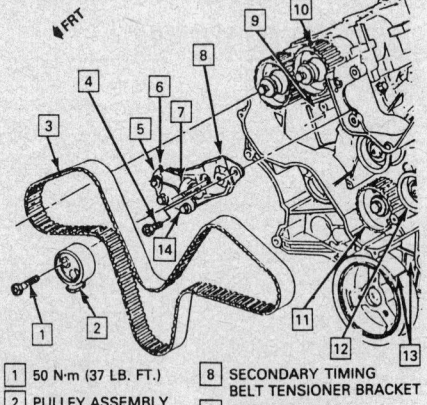

1	50 N·m (37 LB. FT.)	8	SECONDARY TIMING BELT TENSIONER BRACKET
2	PULLEY ASSEMBLY	9	CYLINDER HEAD
3	SECONDARY TIMING BELT	10	DRIVEN SPROCKET
4	50 N·m (37 LB. FT.)	11	DRIVE SPROCKET
5	ACTUATOR	12	IDLER ASSEMBLY
6	LOCK PIN (PAPER CLIP)	13	CRANKSHAFT REFERENCE MARKS
7	SIDE PLATE	14	25 N·m (18 LB. FT.)

Fig. 8 Secondary timing belt system

3. Remove serpentine belt tensioner as outlined under "Serpentine Drive Belt."
4. Remove secondary timing belt right and left covers as outlined under "Secondary Timing Belt, Service."
5. Disconnect power steering pipe retaining clip nut at alternator stud.
6. Remove secondary timing belt center cover bolts then the belt cover, **Fig. 5.**
7. Reverse procedure to install.

TENSIONER PLATE & ACTUATOR, REPLACE
Removal

1. Remove power steering pump as outlined under "Power Steering Pump, Replace" in the "Front Suspension & Steering" section.

2. Remove secondary timing belt center cover as outlined under "Secondary Timing Belt, Service."
3. Rotate engine clockwise to align timing marks on camshaft sprockets, **Fig. 6.**
4. Verify tensioner pulley position to determine if length of belt is satisfactory as follows:
   a. Insert a flat, narrow .02 inch thick, ruler along the tensioner pulley and engage the steps in the tensioner base and note the reading at the top of the tensioner pulley, **Fig. 7.**
   b. If reading is 1.56–1.68 inch, belt is in acceptable range.
   c. If reading is 1.70–1.84 inch, belt is to be replaced.
5. Loosely clamp two camshaft sprockets on each side of engine together using clamping pliers, or equivalent. **Do not mar camshaft sprockets with clamping device.**
6. Hold belt to righthand exhaust camshaft sprocket with a C-clamp and a wide pad on belt. **No deflection of camshaft sprocket should be noted, if deflection is noted, loosen clamping device.**
7. Remove tensioner side plate retaining bolts from tensioner and remove the side plate from the actuator and base, **Fig. 8.**
8. Rotate actuator assembly around the arm pivot and out of the mounting base. Removal of tensioner from base allows it to extend to its maximum travel. **Do not lose or damage tapered bushing when removing tensioner assembly.**
9. Set actuator on table in vertical position to allow oil to drain to boot end, for 5 minutes prior to refilling.
10. Form a double loop in a .032 inch diameter paper clip leaving a 1.85 inch straight length as shown in **Fig. 9.**
11. Remove rubber end plug from rear of tensioner assembly. The assembly is filled with oil and removal of plug may allow oil to escape.
12. Insert paper clip through center hole in vent plug and into pilot hole.
13. Insert a small screwdriver into screw slot inside end of plunger.
14. Retract tensioner plunger by rotating screw in a clockwise direction while pushing rod tip against the table top, until fully retracted.
15. Rotate screw slot to align with vent hole, and push the straight section of paper clip into screw slot to retain plunger in retracted position.
16. If tensioner oil has been lost, fill tensioner with SAE 5W 30 Mobil 1, or equivalent, engine oil through end hole. Fill to bottom of plug hole only when plunger is fully retracted and pin is installed.

Installation
1. Install rubber end plug to rear of actuator assembly.
2. Insert actuator bushing into side plate.

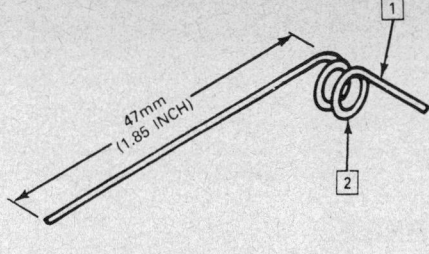

[1] PAPER CLIP
[2] DOUBLE LOOP

Fig. 9   Reworked paper clip

3. Install actuator assembly into mounting base by inserting tapered trunnion of tensioner into matching hole of bushing in bracket and installing side plate bolts. Ensure installed actuator assembly rotates freely.
4. Gently rotate tensioner pulley 11 ft. lbs. counterclockwise into belt using square lug in arm and engage actuator shaft in arm socket.
5. Pull out paper clip and allow pulley to move into belt.
6. Remove sprocket clamp and any other belt holding device.
7. Repeat step 4 and applying 12-15 ft. lbs. of torque to set initial tension on belt.
8. Rotate engine clockwise three times to seat belt. Ensure sprocket reference marks are aligned properly.
9. Verify tensioner pulley position to determine if length of belt is satisfactory as follows:
   a. Insert a flat, narrow .02 inch thick, ruler along the tensioner pulley and engage the steps in the tensioner base and note the reading at the top of the tensioner pulley, **Fig. 7.**
   b. If reading is 1.56–1.68 inch, belt is in acceptable range.
   c. If reading is 1.70–1.84 inch, belt is to be replaced.
10. Install secondary timing belt center cover as outlined under "Secondary Timing Belt, Service."
11. Install power steering pump as outlined under "Power Steering Pump, Replace" in the "Front Suspension & Steering" section.

BELT, REPLACE
Removal
1. Remove secondary timing belt actuator as outlined under "Secondary Timing Belt, Service."
2. If belt is to be reused, mark rotation direction on timing belt.
3. Remove tensioner pulley/arm assembly as outlined under "Secondary Timing Belt, Service."
4. Remove timing belt, by carefully sliding it off pulleys.

Installation
1. Install actuator and side plate. **Ensure reference marks on sprockets are properly aligned.**
2. Install timing belt by routing it around idlers and sprockets as follows, **Fig. 8.**
   a. Start at intermediate camshaft sprocket and work counterclockwise.
   b. Ensure belt is installed in direction of rotation.
   c. Engage teeth into sprockets, place rubber hose behind belt at intermediate sprocket and accumulate slack at tensioner location.
3. Install tensioner pulley to mounting base as follows:
   a. Use a flat magnet, tape or cup plug to hold pivot tube in pulley during this step.
   b. After starting pivot bolt, rotate arm counterclockwise to position square lug at 6 o'clock position.
   c. **Torque** pivot bolt to 37 ft. lbs.
4. Install actuator as outlined under "Secondary Timing Belt, Replace."

TENSIONER PULLEY, ARM & BRACKET, REPLACE
1. Remove secondary timing belt tensioner plate and actuator as outlined under "Secondary Timing Belt, Service."
2. Remove tensioner pulley bolt and pulley/arm assembly.
3. Remove mounting bracket bolts then the mounting bracket.
4. Reverse procedure to install, ensuring correct replacement color code on bracket is used.

TIMING CHAIN & SPROCKETS REPLACE
1. Raise and support vehicle.
2. Remove starter and flywheel cover.
3. Remove oil pan as outlined under "Oil Pan, Replace."
4. Remove engine as outlined under "Engine, Replace."
5. Remove front cover as outlined under "Front Cover, Replace."
6. Mark reference points on the intermediate sprocket, chain link, front face of cylinder and crankshaft sprocket, **Fig. 10.**
7. Retract timing chain tensioner as outlined under "Timing Chain Tensioner, Replace."
8. Remove timing chain and crankshaft sprocket using universal puller bridge tool No. J-8433, or equivalent, and special legs and protector tool No. J-38611, or equivalent. If intermediate gear does not slide off easily with timing chain, rotate crankshaft back and forth to help loosen gear.
9. Reverse procedure to install, noting the following:
   a. Aligning marks made during disassembly.
   b. Large chamfer and counterbore of crankshaft sprocket are installed

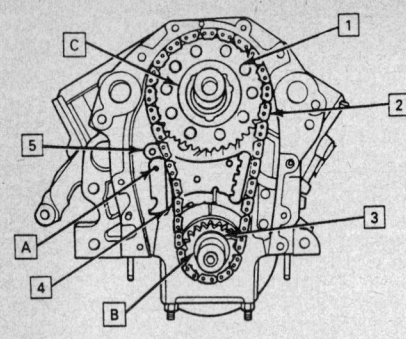

1 INTERMEDIATE SHAFT SPROCKET
2 TIMING CHAIN
3 CRANKSHAFT SPROCKET
4 TIMING CHAIN TENSIONER
5 25 N·m (18 LB. FT.)
A SPRING PIN HOLE
B CHAMFER AND COUNTER BORE INWARD
C SPROCKETS OUTWARD

Fig. 10 Timing chain assembly

toward the crankshaft.
c. Intermediate shaft sprocket spline sockets are installed away from the case.
d. Crankshaft sprocket must be pressed on for the final .31 inch to seated position using crankshaft gear installer tool No. J-38612, or equivalent.

TIMING CHAIN TENSIONER
REPLACE

1. Remove timing chain as outlined under "Timing Chain, Replace."
2. Retract tensioner shoe using tensioner retractor tool No. J-33875, or equivalent, as follows, **Fig. 11.**
   a. Insert tool on both sides of tensioner. Pull on thru pin in tensioner arm to retract spring located in tensioner arm.
   b. While compressing spring, use a suitable tool and insert in hole to retain spring.
3. Remove timing chain and sprockets as outlined under "Timing Chain & Sprockets, Replace."
4. Remove tensioner mounting bolts then the tensioner.
5. Inspect tensioner for wear, cracks or other damage.
6. With tensioner shoe retracted, install tensioner to engine block.
7. Lightly coat tensioner chain surfaces with oil.
8. Install timing chain as outlined under "Timing Chain, Replace."

CAMSHAFT CARRIER COVER
REPLACE
FRONT

1. Disconnect oil/air breather hose from cover.

---

2. Remove spark plug wires from plugs.
3. Remove rear spark plug wire cover.
4. Remove camshaft carrier cover bolts then the cover and O-ring.
5. Reverse procedure to install, ensuring bolt isolators are fully seated into cover before tightening cover bolts.

REAR

1. Remove intake plenum as outlined under "Intake Plenum, Replace."
2. Remove secondary timing belt right cover as outlined under "Secondary Timing Belt, Service."
3. Remove spark plug wires and oil/air separator hose at camshaft cover.
4. Remove camshaft cover bolts then the camshaft cover and gaskets.
5. Reverse procedure to install, ensuring bolt isolators are fully seated into cover before tightening cover bolts.

CAMSHAFT CARRIER
REPLACE
FRONT

1. Remove left camshaft carrier cover as outlined under "Camshaft Carrier Cover, Replace."
2. Remove secondary timing belt as outlined under "Secondary Timing Belt, Service."
3. Install fuel line hoses under camshaft and between lifters to hold lifters in carrier as shown in **Fig. 12.**
4. Remove exhaust crossover pipe.
5. Remove engine torque strut and strut bracket on engine.
6. Remove camshaft carrier bolts and nut then the camshaft carrier and gasket.
7. Reverse procedure to install, noting the following:
   a. Remove oil from camshaft carrier to cylinder head bolt holes, **Fig. 13.**
   b. Use petroleum jelly in lifter bores, along with hoses to keep lifters in place.

REAR

1. Remove right camshaft carrier cover as outlined under "Camshaft Carrier Cover, Replace."
2. Remove secondary timing belt as outlined under "Secondary Timing Belt, Service."
3. Install fuel line hoses under camshaft and between lifters to hold lifters in carrier as shown in **Fig. 12.**
4. Remove front engine lift hook.
5. Remove camshaft carrier bolts and nut then the camshaft carrier and gasket.
6. Reverse procedure to install, noting the following:
   a. Remove oil from camshaft carrier to cylinder head bolt holes **Fig. 13.**
   b. Use petroleum jelly in lifter bores, along with hoses to keep lifters in place.

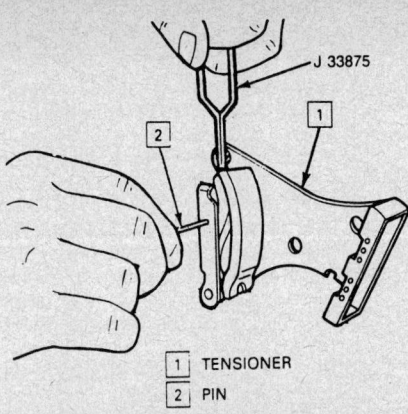

1 TENSIONER
2 PIN

Fig. 11 Retracting timing chain tensioner

CAMSHAFT SPROCKET
REPLACE
REMOVAL

1. Remove camshaft carrier covers as outlined under "Camshaft Carrier Cover, Replace."
2. Remove secondary timing belt and covers as outlined under "Secondary Timing Belt, Service."
3. Remove clamping device from sprocket.
4. Rotate camshafts so flats on camshaft to be serviced are facing up, **Fig. 13.**
5. Install camshaft hold down tool No. J-38613, or equivalent, and **torque** bolt to 22 ft. lbs., **Fig. 12.**
6. Remove camshaft sprocket bolt and washer using camshaft holding tool Nos. J38613 and J-38614, or equivalent.
7. Remove camshaft sprocket using sprocket remover tool No. J-38616, or equivalent.
8. Remove flat ring from sprocket bore.

INSTALLATION

1. Install new flat ring to large bore of sprocket.
2. Wipe camshaft noses with a light coat of oil.
3. Install camshaft sprocket on camshaft.
4. Install lock ring far enough to minimize tipping.
5. Lightly oil camshaft sprocket bolt threads and washer before using. Install bolt and washer into camshaft and seat bolt finger tight then back off 1/4-1/2 turn. **Final torque specification will be reached after performing procedure outlined under "Camshaft Timing."**
6. Repeat steps 1 through 5 for remaining camshafts.
7. Check each sprocket for binding by rotating it around the camshaft.
8. Install secondary timing belt as outlined under "Secondary Timing Belt, Service."
9. Set camshaft timing as outlined under "Camshaft Timing."

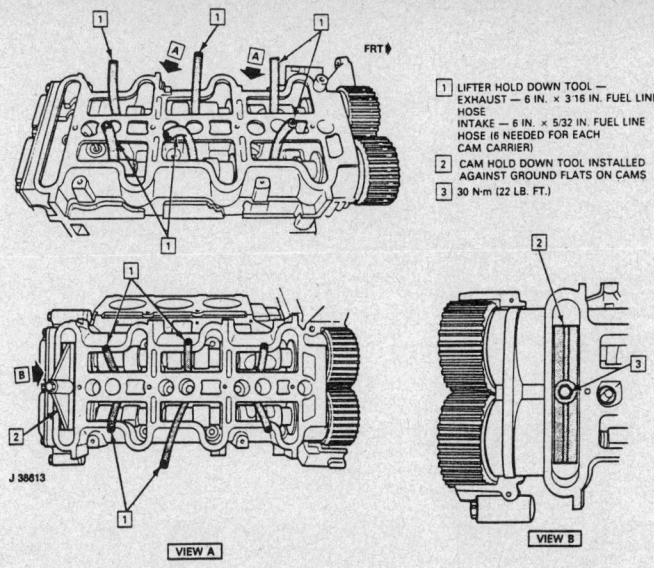

1. LIFTER HOLD DOWN TOOL — EXHAUST – 6 IN. × 3/16 IN. FUEL LINE HOSE
INTAKE – 6 IN. × 5/32 IN. FUEL LINE HOSE (6 NEEDED FOR EACH CAM CARRIER)
2. CAM HOLD DOWN TOOL INSTALLED AGAINST GROUND FLATS ON CAMS
3. 30 N·m (22 LB. FT.)

VIEW A   VIEW B

Fig. 12 Lifter and camshaft hold down tool

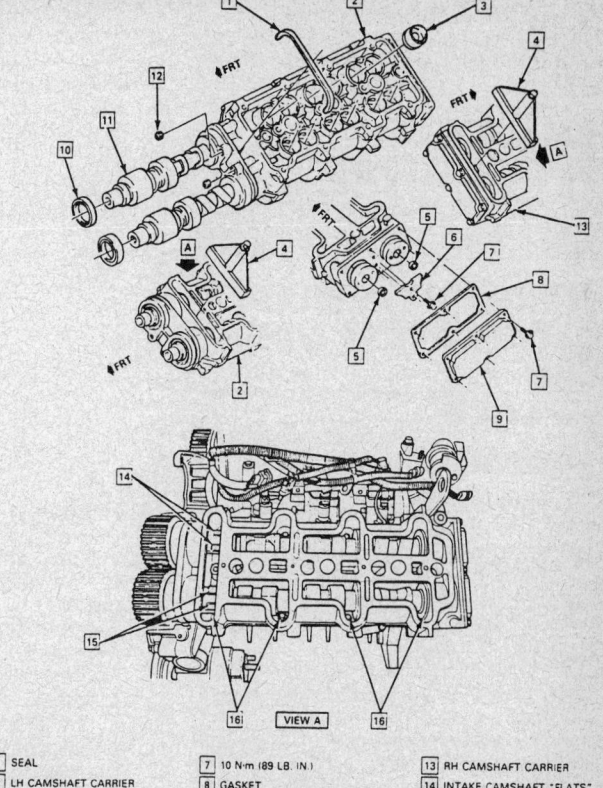

VIEW A

1	SEAL	7	10 N·m (89 LB. IN.)	13	RH CAMSHAFT CARRIER
2	LH CAMSHAFT CARRIER	8	GASKET	14	INTAKE CAMSHAFT "FLATS"
3	LIFTER	9	THRUST PLATE COVER	15	EXHAUST CAMSHAFT "FLATS"
4	CAM HOLD DOWN TOOL	10	CAMSHAFT OIL SEAL	16	BEFORE INSTALLING CAM CARRIER TO CYLINDER HEAD, REMOVE OIL FROM THESE BOLT HOLES.
5	CAMSHAFT PLUG	11	CAMSHAFT		
6	THRUST PLATE	12	OIL GALLERY PLUG		

Fig. 13 Camshaft carrier components

CAMSHAFT
REPLACE

1. Remove camshaft carrier as outlined under "Camshaft Carrier, Replace."
2. Remove lifters as outlined under "Lifter, Replace."
3. Install cam shaft hold down tool No. J-38613, or equivalent.
4. Remove camshaft sprockets as outlined under "Camshaft Sprocket, Replace."
5. Remove camshaft carrier thrust plate cover, **Fig. 13.**
6. Remove thrust plate and bolts, **Fig. 13.**
7. Remove camshaft hold down tool.
8. Remove camshaft by carefully removing it out the back of the carrier. **All camshaft journals are the same diameter and care must be taken when removing camshaft to avoid damage to bearing surfaces.**
9. Reverse procedure to install, noting the following:
   a. Coat camshaft lobes and journals with GM engine oil supplement (EOS), or equivalent.
   b. Adjust camshaft timing as outlined under "Camshaft Timing."

CAMSHAFT OIL SEAL
REPLACE

1. Remove camshaft as outlined under "Camshaft, Replace."
2. Remove camshaft seal by prying seal out with a suitable screwdriver.
3. Reverse procedure to install, using seal installation tool No. J-38619, or equivalent.

CAMSHAFT TIMING

If only one bank is to be timed, ensure bank to bank camshaft timing relationship is one revolution apart. Timing flats should be 180° opposite when finally timed.

1. Remove spark plugs.
2. Remove camshaft sprockets as outlined under "Camshaft Sprocket, Replace."
3. Rotate camshaft flats Up and install camshaft hold down tool No. J-38613, or equivalent. **torque** tool bolt to 22 ft. lbs.
4. Install secondary timing belt and tensioner pulley arm assembly as outlined under "Secondary Timing Belt, Service."
5. Ensure freeness of rotation of tensioner pulley arm assembly.
6. Rotate tensioner pulley 11 ft. lbs. counterclockwise into the belt using cast square lug on body and engage ball end of actuator into socket on pulley arm.
7. Remove tensioner lock pin, using needle nose pliers, or equivalent, allowing tensioner shaft to extend and the pulley to move into belt.
8. Remove sprocket and belt holding devices, then rotate tensioner pulley counterclockwise applying 12-15 ft. lbs. of torque.
9. Rotate engine clockwise three times to seat belt. Align crankshaft reference marks during final rotation to TDC.
10. Set lock ring on right exhaust and intake camshaft into bore by threading in attaching bolt as follows:
    a. Hold sprocket from turning using sprocket holding tool No. J-38614, or equivalent.
    b. Running **torque**, before seating, of bolt should be 44-66 ft. lbs.
    c. If less torque is required before seating, the shim and lock rings must be replaced and inspect nose of camshaft for brinelling.
    d. If more torque is required before seating, the shim and lock rings must be replaced and inspect bolt threads for burrs and/or foreign material.
    e. Seating of lock ring is accomplished when edge of ring is flush with sprocket hub.
    f. **Torque** sprocket bolt to 81 ft. lbs. to complete this step.
11. Remove camshaft holding tool.
12. Rotate engine clockwise an odd number of revolutions and realign the intermediate shaft marks at TDC. Ensure timing marks on damper lines up with front cover marks.
13. Repeat steps 2 through 9 for left intake and exhaust camshaft then repeat step 10.
14. Remove holding tools then the old timing marks.
15. Mark the position of each sprocket at TDC of number one exhaust position with permanent paint, **Fig. 6.**
16. Install secondary timing belt and cov-

ers as outlined under "Secondary Timing Belt, Service."

17. Install camshaft carrier covers as outlined under "Camshaft Carrier Cover, Replace."

CAM LOBE LIFT SPECIFICATIONS

Intake 370inch
Exhaust 370inch

INTERMEDIATE SHAFT BELT SPROCKET & OIL SEAL
REPLACE

REMOVAL

1. Verify the relationship of intermediate sprocket to front cover.
2. Raise and support vehicle.
3. Remove starter motor and install flywheel holding tool No. J-37096, or equivalent.
4. Lower vehicle.
5. Rotate engine and position to factory alignment marks. Remove sprocket bolt and washer.
6. Mark position of sprocket on nose end of intermediate shaft.
7. Remove secondary timing belt as outlined under "Secondary Timing Belt, Service."
8. Reverse center bolt and engage self-tapping screws of sprocket remover tool No. J-38616, or equivalent, into three equally spaced holes on belt sprocket and remove intermediate shaft timing belt sprocket.
9. Remove intermediate shaft belt sprocket oil seal.

INSTALLATION

1. Install oil seal using seal installer tool No. J-38619, or equivalent.
2. Lubricate seal surfaces of intermediate shaft sprocket.
3. Align timing marks and install sprocket into position engaging locating tangs of sprocket into mating sockets of chain sprocket.
4. Verify engagement by measuring from face of belt sprocket to front cover. If measurement is more than 1.65 inches, tangs are not engaged.
5. Install O-ring in position on end of intermediate shaft.
6. Lightly lubricate threads of sprocket bolt and torque bolt to specification.
7. Raise and support vehicle. Remove flywheel holding tool and install starter assembly.
8. Lower vehicle and install secondary timing belt and covers.

INTERMEDIATE SHAFT & BEARINGS
REPLACE

1. Remove engine assembly as outlined under "Engine, Replace."

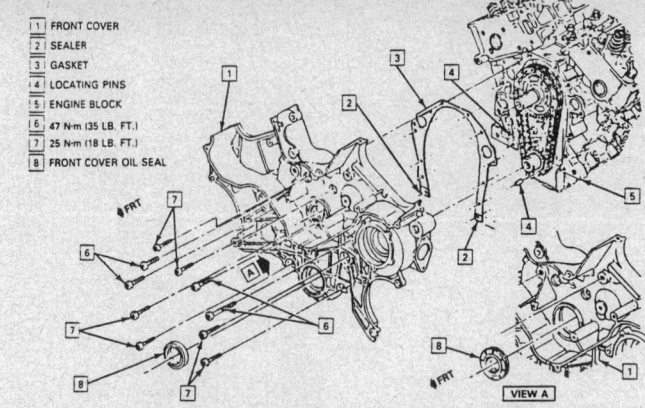

2. Remove oil pump drive assembly as outlined under "Oil Pump, Service."
3. Remove timing chain as outlined under "Timing Chain & Sprockets, Replace."
4. Remove intermediate shaft thrust plate and screws.
5. Remove intermediate shaft. **All intermediate shaft journals are the same diameter and care should be taken not to damage bearings or journals during removal.**
6. Remove intermediate shaft bearing using bearing remover/installer tool No. J-33049, or equivalent.
7. Reverse procedure to install, noting the following:
   a. Align oil holes in bearing with oil holes in cylinder block. Install oil feed holes at 4 and 7 o'clock for front bearing and 4 o'clock for bearings 2, 3 and 4.
   b. Apply oil to intermediate shaft journals prior to installation.
   c. Replace O-ring seal after sprocket installation.

INTERMEDIATE SHAFT REAR COVER
REPLACE

1. Remove transaxle assembly as outlined under "Transaxle, Replace" in the "Clutch & Manual Transaxle" or the "Automatic Transaxle" section.
2. Remove intermediate shaft rear cover bolts then the cover and gasket.
3. Reverse procedure to install.

CRANKSHAFT PULLEY & DAMPER
REPLACE

1. Remove serpentine drive belt as outlined under "Serpentine Drive Belt."
2. Raise and support vehicle.
3. Remove right tire and wheel assembly then the engine splash shield.
4. Remove starter as outlined under "Starter, Replace" in the "Electrical" section.

5. Remove crankshaft damper bolt using flywheel holding tool No. J-37096, or equivalent.
6. Remove crankshaft pulley bolt and pulley.
7. Remove crankshaft damper using crankshaft damper removal tool No. J-24430, or equivalent.
8. Reverse procedure to install, noting the following:
   a. Coat front cover oil seal with engine oil.
   b. Install suitable sealant to keyway of damper before installation.
   c. Install damper using crankshaft damper installer tool No. J-29113, or equivalent.

FRONT COVER
REPLACE

1. Remove secondary timing belt tensioner mounting bracket and idler pulleys as outlined under "Secondary Timing Belt, Service."
2. Remove engine front lift hook.
3. Remove engine torque strut bracket from frame and pull strut and bracket out of the way.
4. Remove upper radiator support.
5. Remove righthand cooling fan heat shield then the cooling fan assembly.
6. Remove lower radiator hose from coolant pump.
7. **On models with manual transaxles,** remove front air hose at air pipe.
8. **On all models,** remove heater hose at front cover and heater pipe bracket at frame.
9. Raise and support vehicle.
10. Remove right tire and wheel assembly then the engine splash shield.
11. Remove crankshaft pulley and damper as outlined under "Crankshaft Pulley & Damper, Replace."
12. Drain engine oil into a suitable container and remove oil filter.
13. Remove A/C compressor mounting bolts.
14. Remove lower front cover bolts, **Fig. 14.**
15. **On models with automatic transaxles,** remove drive axle assembly.

Fig. 14   Front cover & oil seal

(Legend in figure:)
1 FRONT COVER
2 SEALER
3 GASKET
4 LOCATING PINS
5 ENGINE BLOCK
6 47 N·m (35 LB. FT.)
7 25 N·m (18 LB. FT.)
8 FRONT COVER OIL SEAL

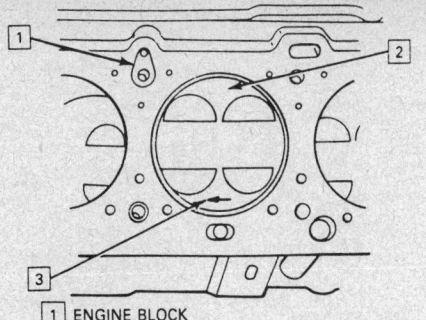

1. ENGINE BLOCK
2. PISTON
3. ARROW FACES TOWARDS FRONT OF ENGINE

Fig. 15   Piston marking

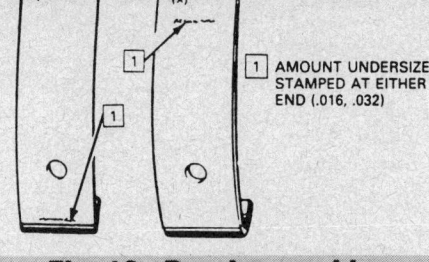

1. AMOUNT UNDERSIZE STAMPED AT EITHER END (.016, .032)

Fig. 16   Bearing marking

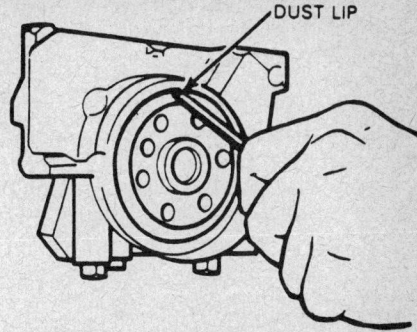

DUST LIP

Fig. 18   Removing rear main seal

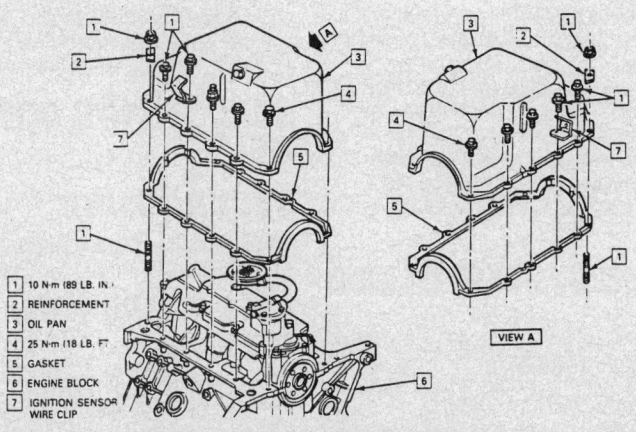

1. 10 N·m (89 LB. IN.)
2. REINFORCEMENT
3. OIL PAN
4. 25 N·m (18 LB. FT.)
5. GASKET
6. ENGINE BLOCK
7. IGNITION SENSOR WIRE CLIP

VIEW A

Fig. 17   Oil pan assembly

16. **On all models,** remove rear alternator bracket then the starter motor.
17. Lower vehicle.
18. Remove intermediate timing belt sprocket as outlined under "Intermediate Shaft Belt Sprocket & Oil Seal, Replace."
19. Remove upper alternator retaining bolts.
20. Remove forward lamp relay center screws and position relay center aside.
21. Remove oil cooler hose from front cover.
22. Remove water pump pulley.
23. Remove front cover upper bolts then the front cover and gasket.
24. Reverse procedure to install, noting the following:
    a. Apply GM sealer part No. 1052080, or equivalent, to lower edges od sealing surface of front cover.
    b. Apply suitable thread sealant to large bolts.
    c. Tighten attaching bolts to specifications.

FRONT COVER OIL SEAL
REPLACE

1. Remove crankshaft pulley and damper as outlined under "Crankshaft Pulley & Damper, Replace."

2. Pry out seal using a suitable pry tool.
3. Reverse procedure to install, lubricate seal with oil and install using seal installer tool No. J-34995, or equivalent.

PISTON & CONNECTING RODS

When installing piston and rod assemblies into cylinder block, ensure that arrow on top of piston faces toward the front of the engine, **Fig. 15.**

CONNECTING RODS & MAIN BEARINGS

Connecting rod and main bearing are of the precision insert type. They are available for service use in standard and two undersizes of .016 and .032 inch. Bearing undersize amount is stamped at either end of the bearing, **Fig. 16.**

OIL DISTRIBUTION COVER
REPLACE

1. Remove intake manifold as outlined under "Intake Manifold, Replace."
2. Remove oil distribution cover mounting bolts then the cover and gasket.
3. Reverse procedure to install.

OIL PAN & BAFFLE
REPLACE

1. Remove air cleaner assembly.
2. Install engine support fixture tool Nos. J-28467-A, J-28467-90 and J-36462, or equivalent.
3. Raise and support vehicle.
4. Remove right tire and wheel assembly and steering gear heat shield.
5. Remove steering gear bolts then hang steering gear from frame.
6. Separate ball joints from control arms.
7. Remove power steering cooler line clips from frame.
8. Disconnect engine mounts at frame as outlined under "Mounts, Replace."
9. Support frame assembly and remove frame bolts then remove frame assembly.
10. Disconnect and remove starter assembly.
11. Remove flywheel cover.
12. Remove oil pan nuts and bolts then the oil pan and gasket.
13. Remove oil baffle nuts. Rotate pick up tube and remove oil baffle.
14. Reverse procedure to install, tightening oil pan bolts to specifications shown in **Fig. 17.**

OIL PUMP
REPLACE

1. Remove oil pan and baffle as outlined under "Oil Pan & Baffle, Replace."
2. Remove oil pump bolt then the oil pump and drive shaft extension.
3. Install shaft extension on oil pump, engage shaft extension into drive gear.
4. Tighten oil pump bolt to specification.
5. Install oil pan and baffle.

OIL PUMP DRIVE
REPLACE

1. Remove rear cylinder head as outlined under "Cylinder Head, Replace."
2. Remove oil pump drive bolt and clamp.
3. Remove oil pump drive assembly and O-ring.
4. Reverse procedure to install.

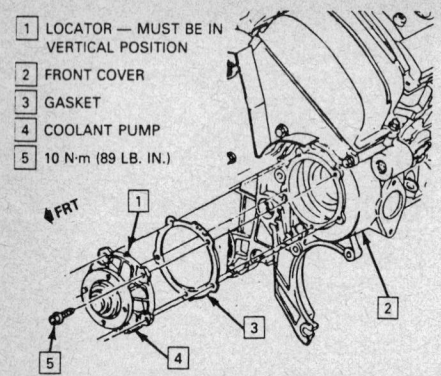

1. LOCATOR — MUST BE IN VERTICAL POSITION
2. FRONT COVER
3. GASKET
4. COOLANT PUMP
5. 10 N·m (89 LB. IN.)

Fig. 19   Water pump assembly

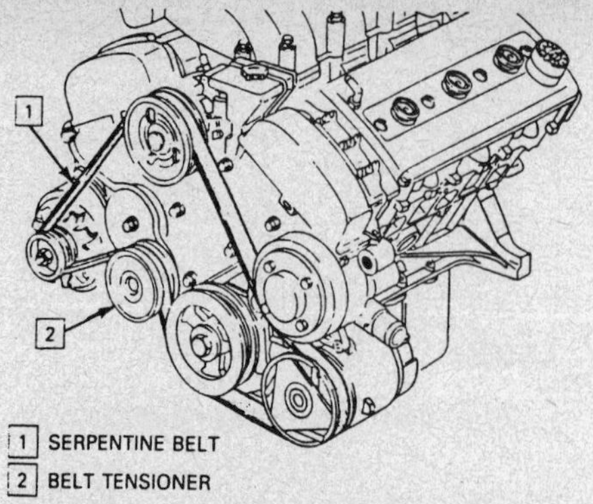

1. SERPENTINE BELT
2. BELT TENSIONER

Fig. 20   Serpentine drive belt routing

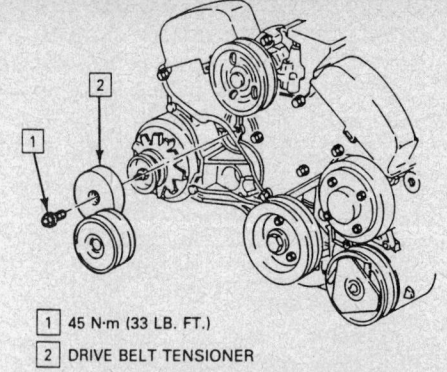

1. 45 N·m (33 LB. FT.)
2. DRIVE BELT TENSIONER

Fig. 21   Serpentine drive belt tensioner

REAR MAIN SEAL
REPLACE

1. Remove transaxle assembly as outlined under "Transaxle, Replace" in the "Clutch & Manual Transaxle" or the "Automatic Transaxle" section.
2. Remove flywheel assembly.
3. Remove oil seal using a suitable pry tool as shown in **Fig. 18.**
4. Reverse procedure to install, using seal installer tool No. J-34686, or equivalent.

WATER PUMP
REPLACE

1. Remove air cleaner assembly.

2. Disconnect battery ground cable.
3. Drain engine coolant into a suitable container.
4. Remove serpentine drive belt as outlined under "Serpentine Drive Belt."
5. Remove water pump pulley.
6. Remove water pump bolts then the water pump and gasket, **Fig. 19.**
7. Reverse procedure to install.

COOLING SYSTEM BLEED

1. Open air bleed vents on thermostat housing and heater water inlet pipe.
2. Add 3.6 quarts of engine antifreeze through the radiator neck.
3. Add clean water slowly to the system until level of coolant has reached base of radiator neck.

4. Close bleed vents and add clean water if necessary to bring coolant level to the base of radiator neck.

SERPENTINE DRIVE BELT

BELT ROUTING

Refer to **Fig. 20.** for serpentine drive belt routing.

BELT TENSIONER, REPLACE

1. Remove serpentine drive belt as outlined under "Serpentine Drive Belt."
2. Remove tensioner bolt then the tensioner, **Fig. 21.**
3. Reverse procedure to install.

TIGHTENING SPECIFICATIONS

Year	Component	Torque/ft. lbs.
1991	A/C Compressor To Front Cover Bolt	37
	AIR Pipe	15
	Camshaft Carrier Bolt	18
	Camshaft Carrier Cover Bolt	89①
	Camshaft Carrier Thrust Plate Bolt	89①
	Camshaft Sprocket Bolt	81
	Clutch Cover Bolt	18
	Upper Radiator Mounting Panel Bolt	89①
	Cooling Fan Attaching Bolt	89①
	Connecting Rod Cap Nut	39
	Crankshaft Damper Mounting Bolt	78
	Crankshaft Main Cap Bolt	②
	Crankshaft Pulley To Crankshaft Damper Bolt	37
	Crankshaft Sensor Bolt	14
	Cylinder Head Bolt	③
	EGR Tube Assembly Bolt	18
	EGR VAlve Assembly Bolt	18
	Engine Mount To Bracket Nut	35
	Engine Mounting Bracket To Engine Bolt	61④
	Exhaust Crossover Nut	18
	Exhaust Heat Shield Nut	116①

Continued

TIGHTENING SPECIFICATIONS—Continued

Year	Component	Torque/ft. lbs.
	Exhaust Mounting Nut	116 ①
	Exhaust Stud	13
	Flywheel To Engine Bolt	61
	Front Cover Bolts (Large)	35
	Front Cover Bolts (Small)	18
	Front Engine Mounting Bracket To Engine Bolt	63
	Fuel Pipe Clip Bolt	53 ①
	Fuel Pipe Retaining Screw	89 ①
	Fuel Rail Bolt	89 ①
	Idler Pulley Bolt	37
	Ignition Coil Bolt	18
	Ignition Coil Nut	125 ①
	Intake Manifold Bolt	18
	Intake Plenum Bolt	18
	Intake Plenum Nut	89 ①
	Intermediate Shaft Thrust Plate Screw	89 ①
	Intermediate Shaft Belt Sprocket Bolt	95
	Knock Sensor	71 ①
	Oil Cooler Connector	24
	Oil Cooler Fitting	13
	Oil Distribution Cover Bolt	18
	Oil Level Indicator Bolt	89 ①
	Oil Pan Baffle Nut	18
	Oil Pan Bolt	89 ① ⑤
	Oil Pan Bolt	18 ⑥
	Oil Pan Nut	89 ①
	Oil Pump Drive Bolt	35
	Oil Pump To Rear Main Bolt	40
	Power Steering Pump To Bracket Bolt	25
	Rear Camshaft Cover Bolt	89 ①
	Rear Engine Mounting Brace To Bracket Bolt	61
	Rear Engine Mounting Brace To Bracket Nut	35 ④
	Secondary Timing Belt Idler Bolt	37
	Secondary Timing Belt Tensioner Bracket Bolt	37
	Secondary Timing Belt Tensioner Pulley Bolt	37
	Secondary Timing Belt Tensioner Side Plate Bolt	18
	Serpentine Drive Belt Tensioner Bolt	33
	Spark Plug	11
	Starter Mounting Bolt	32
	Tensioner Mounting Bolt	18
	Timing Belt Cover Bolt	89 ①
	Timing Chain Tensioner Bolt	18
	Torque Strut and Engine Lift Bracket Bolt	52
	Trace Bracket To Rear Engine Mounting Bracket Bolt	35 ⑦
	Water By-Pass Nut	18
	Water Outlet Bolt	18
	Water Pump Bolt	89 ①

① —Inch lbs.
② —Torque to 37 ft. lbs plus an additional ¾ turn.
③ —Refer to text.
④ —Manual Transaxle.
⑤ —Except two rear bolts.
⑥ —Two rear bolts.
⑦ —Automatic Transaxle.

3.8L/V6-231 ENGINE

NOTE: Refer To "Chapter 5" For Service Procedures On The 3800 VIN L Engine Not Covered In This Section.

INDEX

MOUNT
REPLACE

ENGINE MOUNT

1. Disconnect battery ground cable.
2. Remove mount nuts from below frame mounting bracket.
3. Raise and support engine to gain clearance using engine support fixture tool Nos. J-28467-A, J-28467-90 and J-35953, or equivalent.
4. Remove mount to engine nuts then the mount.
5. Reverse procedure to install, **torquing** nuts to 32 ft. lbs and bolts to 70 ft. lbs.

TRANSMISSION MOUNT

1. Disconnect battery ground cable.
2. Remove engine torque strut from engine.
3. Raise and support vehicle.
4. Remove left tire and wheel assembly and lower splash shield.
5. Support transaxle using a suitable jack.
6. Remove mount nuts then the mount.
7. Reverse procedure to install, noting the following:
    a. **Torque** upper bracket to engine bolts to 61 ft. lbs.
    b. **Torque** lower bracket to engine bolts to 35 ft. lbs.
    c. **Torque** upper bracket to engine mount nuts to 22 ft. lbs.
    d. **Torque** lower bracket to frame

bolts to 38 ft. lbs.
    e. **Torque** frame bracket to mount nuts to 35 ft. lbs.

ENGINE
REPLACE

1. Mark and remove hood assembly.
2. Disconnect battery ground cable.
3. Remove air cleaner assembly.
4. Relieve fuel system pressure as follows:
    a. Disconnect battery ground cable.
    b. Loosen fuel filler cap.
    c. Connect fuel pressure gauge tool No. J-34730-1, or equivalent, to the fuel pressure valve.
    d. Place bleed hose into a suitable container.
    e. Open valve and relieve fuel system pressure.
5. Remove fuel lines from rail and mounting bracket.
6. Remove coolant bottle and inner fender electrical cover.
7. Remove fuel injector sight cover.
8. Remove throttle cables, bracket and vacuum line from throttle body.
9. Remove heat shield from exhaust crossover pipe then then crossover pipe.
10. Remove engine torque strut from engine.
11. Remove the engine cooling fan.
12. Remove vacuum line from transaxle module.
13. Remove serpentine drive belt.
14. Remove power steering pump and al-

ternator from engine.
15. Disconnect all necessary electrical connectors.
16. Remove upper and lower radiator and heater hoses from engine.
17. Remove transaxle to engine bolts and ground wire harness with bolt.
18. Raise and support vehicle.
19. Remove right tire and wheel assembly and inner splash shield.
20. Remove flywheel cover and scribe torque convertor to flywheel for installation.
21. Remove flywheel to convertor bolts.
22. Disconnect wire harness clamps from frame near radiator.
23. Remove A/C compressor and position aside.
24. Remove starter motor.
25. Remove transaxle to engine bolt through wheelwell using suitable extension.
26. Disconnect engine mount to frame nuts.
27. Remove oil filter.
28. Disconnect front exhaust pipe from manifold.
29. Disconnect oil cooler piper from hose connections.
30. Lower vehicle.
31. Install lifting device and remove engine assembly.
32. Reverse procedure to install, noting the following:
    a. Align engine with transaxle dowel pins.
    b. **Torque** torque strut bolts to 41 ft. lbs.
    c. **Torque** flywheel to convertor bolts to 46 ft. lbs.

Clutch & Manual Transaxle

INDEX

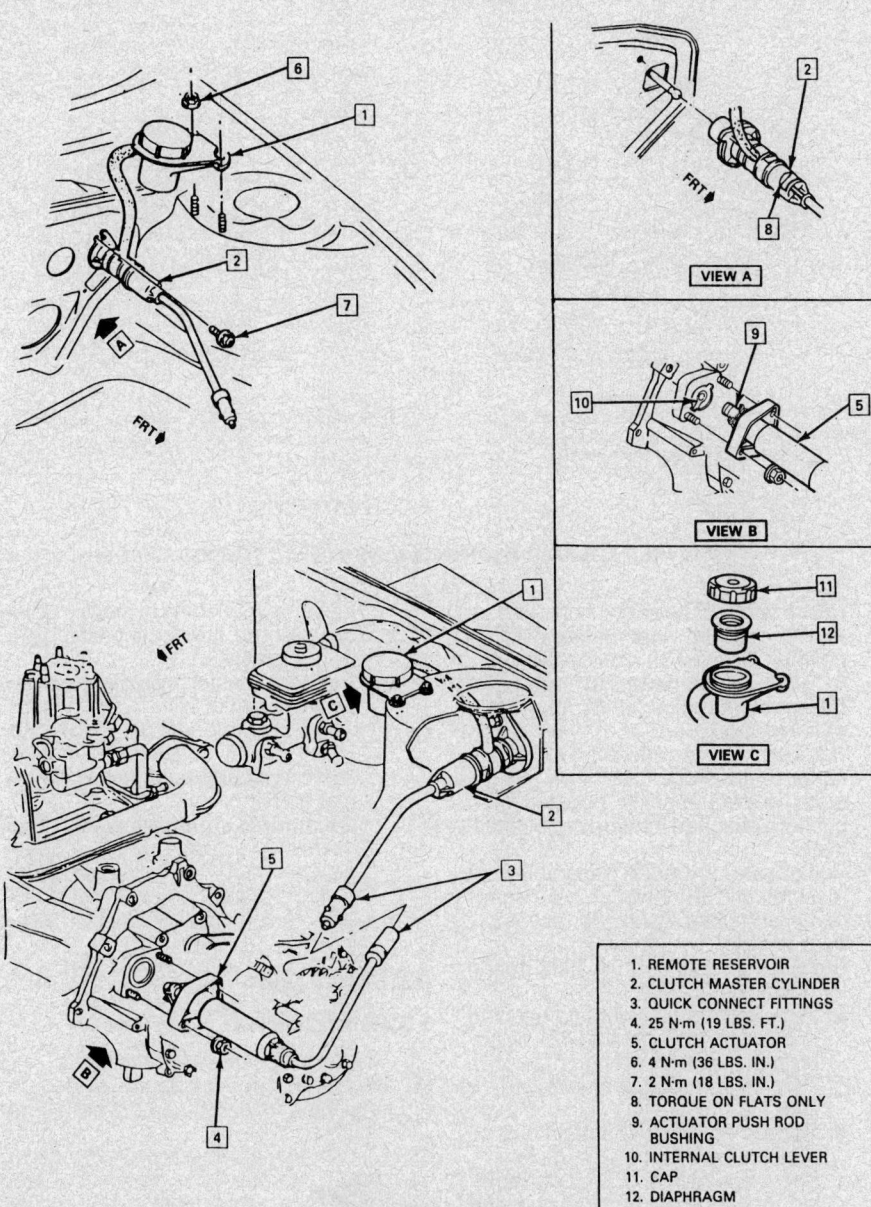

Fig. 1 Clutch hydraulic system. 1988

1. REMOTE RESERVOIR
2. CLUTCH MASTER CYLINDER
3. QUICK CONNECT FITTINGS
4. 25 N·m (19 LBS. FT.)
5. CLUTCH ACTUATOR
6. 4 N·m (36 LBS. IN.)
7. 2 N·m (18 LBS. IN.)
8. TORQUE ON FLATS ONLY
9. ACTUATOR PUSH ROD BUSHING
10. INTERNAL CLUTCH LEVER
11. CAP
12. DIAPHRAGM

DESCRIPTION

EXCEPT 1989–1990 MODELS

The hydraulic system components (master cylinder and clutch actuator) **Fig. 1 and 2** can be serviced separately. If a component fails, that component may be replaced. The clutch hydraulic system is serviced as two major assemblies, the master cylinder and actuator assemblies. Each assembly has been bled of air and filled with brake fluid. Individual components of these assemblies are not available separately.

Whenever powertrain components are lowered for any reason (removal or access to other components), the clutch actuator must be removed from the transaxle case. Refer to procedure outlined under "Clutch Actuator." **Failure to remove actuator may result in hydraulic system damage.**

Prior to any operation that requires removal of the actuator, the clutch master cylinder pushrod must be disconnected from the clutch pedal. **Failure to disconnect pushrod will result in permanent damage to the actuator if the clutch pedal is depressed without resistance from clutch loads.** Master cylinder pushrod bushing must also be replaced whenever it has been removed from the clutch pedal.

1989–90 MODELS

The hydraulic system components (master cylinder, hydraulic line and clutch actuator) **Fig. 3** are serviced as a single assembly. If a component fails, the entire system must be replaced as an assembly. The clutch hydraulic system cannot be bled. Replacement hydraulic system assemblies are pre-filled with hydraulic fluid and do not require bleeding. Individual components of the hydraulic system are not available separately.

Whenever powertrain components are lowered for any reason (removal or access to other components), the clutch actuator must be removed from the transaxle case. Refer to procedure outlined under "Clutch Actuator." **Failure to remove actuator may result in hydraulic system damage.**

Prior to any operation that requires removal of the actuator, the clutch master cylinder pushrod must be disconnected from the clutch pedal. **Failure to disconnect pushrod will result in permanent damage to the actuator if the clutch pedal is depressed without resistance from clutch loads.** Master cylinder pushrod bushing must also be replaced whenever it has been removed from the clutch pedal.

CLUTCH HYDRAULIC SYSTEM SERVICE

MASTER CYLINDER

1988 Models

1. Disconnect battery ground cable.
2. Remove sound insulator at pedals, then the master cylinder pushrod from clutch pedal.
3. Disconnect quick connect fittings in clutch hydraulic line. Insert tool No. J-36221 or equivalent and depress white plastic sleeve to separate connection.
4. Remove lefthand upper secondary cowl, then the two nuts attaching master cylinder reservoir to strut tower.
5. Remove anti-rotation screw located next to master cylinder flange at pedal support plate.
6. Using wrench flats on front end of master cylinder body, twist master cylinder counterclockwise to release twist lock attachment to plate. **Do not torque on hose connection on top of master cylinder body, or damage may occur.**
7. Pull master cylinder assembly with pushrod attached forward out of pedal plate, then lift reservoir off strut tower studs and remove complete assembly from vehicle.
8. Reverse procedure to install, noting the following:
   a. Install master cylinder into opening in pedal plate and rotate 45° by applying torque on wrench flats only.
   b. **Torque** anti-rotation screw to 18 inch lbs. and reservoir retaining nuts to 36 inch lbs.
   c. Lubricate and install "new" bushing in master cylinder pushrod.
   d. Install master cylinder pushrod to clutch pedal, with bushing tangs snapped into pedal pin groove.
   e. Re-adjust cruise control, if required, by pulling upward on clutch pedal pad. **Do not exceed 20 lbs.**

1989—91 Models

1. Disconnect battery ground cable.
2. Remove sound insulator, then disconnect master cylinder pushrod from clutch pedal.
3. Remove two nuts attaching master cylinder reservoir to strut tower.
4. Remove anti-rotational screw located next to master cylinder flange at pedal support plate.

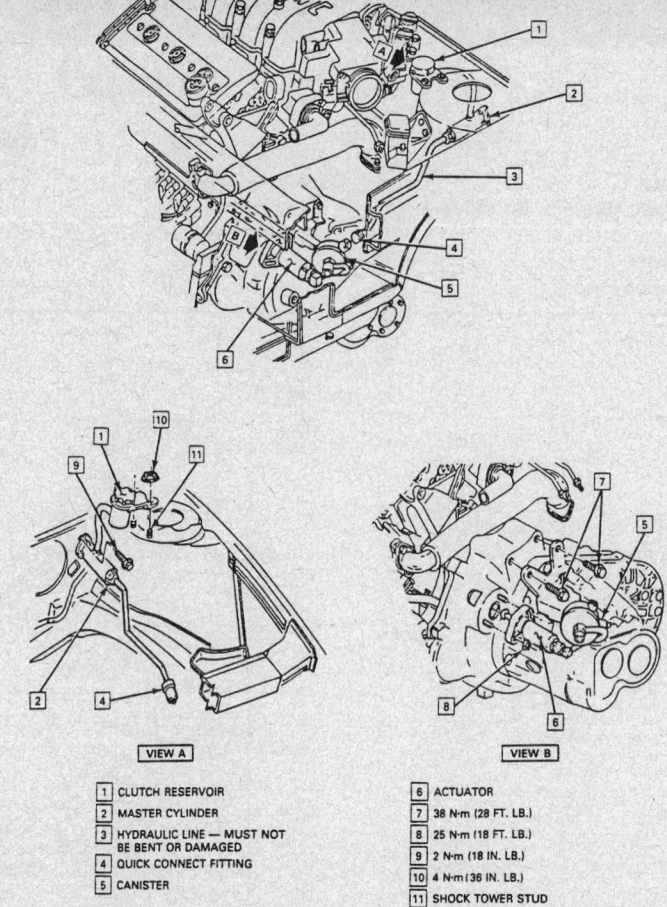

1 CLUTCH RESERVOIR
2 MASTER CYLINDER
3 HYDRAULIC LINE — MUST NOT BE BENT OR DAMAGED
4 QUICK CONNECT FITTING
5 CANISTER
6 ACTUATOR
7 38 N·m (28 FT. LB.)
8 25 N·m (18 FT. LB.)
9 2 N·m (18 IN. LB.)
10 4 N·m (36 IN. LB.)
11 SHOCK TOWER STUD

Fig. 2   Clutch hydraulic system. 1991

5. Using wrench flats on front end of master cylinder, twist master cylinder counterclockwise to release twist lock to plate attachment. **Do not twist hose connections on top of master cylinder body.**
6. Remove two nuts attaching clutch actuator to transaxle case, then the actuator from transaxle housing with pushrod attached forward out of pedal plate.
7. Pull master cylinder assembly. Lift reservoir off strut tower studs, then remove complete hydraulic assembly from vehicle.
8. Reverse procedure to install, noting the following:
   a. Install master cylinder into opening in pedal plate and rotate 45° by applying torque on wrench flats only.
   b. **Torque** anti-rotational screw to 18 inch lbs.
   c. **Torque** reservoir attaching nuts to 36 inch lbs.
   d. Install actuator on transaxle housing. Actuator pushrod busing and retaining straps should be left assembled. Actuator straps will break during normal operation. Pushrod bushing must enter pocket in internal fork housing as actuator is installed on housing studs.
   e. **Torque** actuator attaching nuts evenly to 18 ft. lbs.

   f. Install new bushing in master cylinder pushrod. Lubricate bushing prior to installation.
   g. Connect master cylinder pushrod to clutch pedal, with bushing tangs snapped into pedal pin groove.
   h. Press clutch pedal down several times, ensuring pedal effort is normal and firm.
   i. **On models equipped with cruise control,** adjust cruise control clutch switch. Refer to procedure outlined under "Cruise Control, Adjust" in the "Cruise Control" section.

ACTUATOR

1988 MODELS

1. Disconnect battery ground cable.
2. Remove sound insulator at pedals, then the master cylinder pushrod from clutch pedal.
3. Disconnect quick connect fittings in clutch hydraulic line. Insert tool No. J-36221 or equivalent and depress white plastic sleeve to separate connection.
4. Remove two nuts holding actuator assembly to transaxle housing, then the actuator from transaxle housing.
5. Reverse procedure to install noting the following:
   a. Install new , pre-filled actuator as-

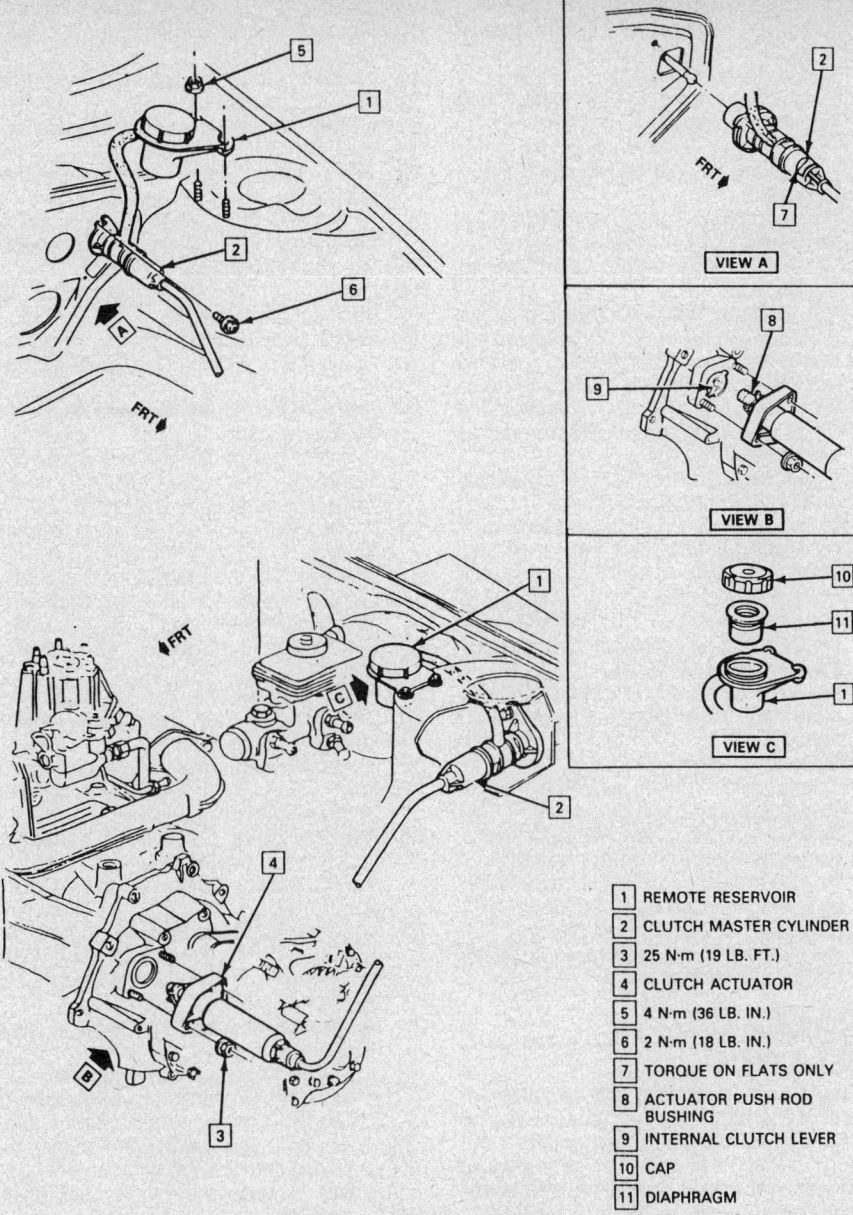

1	REMOTE RESERVOIR
2	CLUTCH MASTER CYLINDER
3	25 N·m (19 LB. FT.)
4	CLUTCH ACTUATOR
5	4 N·m (36 LB. IN.)
6	2 N·m (18 LB. IN.)
7	TORQUE ON FLATS ONLY
8	ACTUATOR PUSH ROD BUSHING
9	INTERNAL CLUTCH LEVER
10	CAP
11	DIAPHRAGM

Fig. 3 Clutch hydraulic system. 1989-90

sembly on transaxle housing. Actuator pushrod bushing and retaining straps should be left assembled. Actuator straps will break during normal operation. Pushrod bushing must enter pocket in internal fork lever as actuator is installed on housing studs.

b. **Torque** two retaining nuts evenly to 18 ft. lbs.

c. Lubricate and install "new" bushing in master cylinder pushrod.

d. Install master cylinder pushrod to clutch pedal, with bushing tangs snapped into pedal pin groove.

e. Re-adjust cruise control, if required, by pulling upward on clutch pedal pad. **Do not exceed 20 lbs.**

1989—91 Models
Removal

Whenever powertrain components are lowered for any reason (removal or access to other components), the clutch actuator must be removed from the transaxle case. **Failure to remove actuator may result in hydraulic system damage.**

1. Disconnect battery ground cable.
2. Remove sound insulator, then disconnect master cylinder pushrod from clutch pedal.
3. Remove two actuator attaching nuts, then the actuator from transaxle housing.

Installation

1. Inspect actuator pushrod for lever

bushing and replace if missing.
2. Install actuator on transaxle housing studs with pushrod centered in pocket of internal lever in housing. An axial load on pushrod may be required to compress actuator piston spring.
3. Install actuator attaching nuts, **torquing** nuts evenly to 18 ft. lbs.
4. Install new bushing in master cylinder pushrod. Lubricate bushing prior to installation.
5. Connect master cylinder pushrod to clutch pedal, with bushing tangs snapped into pedal pin groove.
6. Press clutch pedal down several times, ensuring pedal effort is normal and firm.
7. **On models equipped with cruise control**, adjust cruise control clutch switch. Refer to procedure outlined under "Cruise Control, Adjust."
8. Install sound insulator, then connect battery ground cable.

MASTER CYLINDER BLEED
EXCEPT 1989—90
Manual Method

During this procedure, fluid level in master cylinder must be maintained. Use a maximum of 50 lbs. pedal pressure to check pedal firmness.

1. Disconnect quick connect fittings in clutch hydraulic line. Insert quick disconnect tool No. J-36221 or equivalent and depress white plastic sleeve to separate connection.
2. Remove cap and diaphragm, and fill reservoir with DOT 3 brake fluid.
3. Remove lefthand upper secondary cowl, then remove air from supply hose by squeezing it until no more air bubbles are seen in reservoir.
4. Pump clutch pedal slowly by hand until slight resistance is felt.
5. Holding pedal pressure, bleed air from system by depressing internal valve at quick connect fitting. **Do not use a sharp object.**
6. Repeat steps 4 and 5 until pedal is firm and no air bubbles are seen.
7. Reconnect clutch hydraulic line, then replace reservoir cap and diaphragm.

Pressure Method

During this procedure, fluid level in master cylinder must be maintained.

1. Disconnect quick connect fittings in clutch hydraulic line. Insert quick disconnect tool No. J-36221, or equivalent, and depress white plastic sleeve to separate connection.
2. Remove cap and diaphragm, and fill reservoir with DOT 3 brake fluid.
3. Install pressure bleed adapter cap No. J-36234 or equivalent to reservoir and connect pressure bleeder.
4. Apply pressure not to exceed 30 lbs. to hydraulic system.
5. Depress internal valve at quick connect fitting. **Do not use a sharp object.**
6. Release internal valve when air is no longer visible.
7. Open internal valve and slowly depress clutch pedal. **Close internal**

valve before releasing clutch pedal.

8. Repeat this procedure until air is no longer visible.
9. Reconnect clutch hydraulic line, then replace reservoir cap and diaphragm.

CLUTCH
ADJUST

This clutch is equipped with a hydraulic slave cylinder (actuator) and there is no provision for adjustment.

CLUTCH
REPLACE

REMOVAL

Prior to any operation that requires removal of the actuator, the master cylinder pushrod must be disconnected from the clutch pedal. **Failure to disconnect pushrod will result in permanent damage to the actuator if the clutch pedal is depressed without resistance from clutch loads.** Master cylinder pushrod bushing must also be replaced whenever it has been removed from the clutch pedal.

1. Disconnect battery ground cable.
2. Remove sound insulator from inside vehicle, then disconnect clutch master cylinder push rod from clutch pedal.
3. **On except 1989-90 models,** disconnect quick connect fittings in clutch hydraulic line. Insert tool No. J-36221 or equivalent and depress white plastic sleeve to separate connection.
4. **On all models,** remove actuator to transaxle attaching nuts, then the actuator.
5. Remove transaxle assembly. Refer to procedure outlined under "Transaxle, Replace."
6. Place alignment marks on clutch cover assembly and flywheel to ensure reassembly in same position.
7. Loosen attaching bolts one turn at a time, until spring pressure is relieved.
8. Support clutch cover, then remove bolts.
9. Remove clutch cover and driven disc.

INSTALLATION

1. Position clutch disc and clutch cover, matching light side of clutch cover (marked with paint) with heavy side of flywheel (stamped with an X). Stamped letters on clutch disc identify "flywheel side." Support clutch disc and clutch cover with clutch alignment arbor tool No. J-35822 or equivalent.
2. Install clutch cover to flywheel bolts in three holes marked "L," then install remaining clutch cover to flywheel bolts, remove tool and **torque** bolts to 15 ft. lbs. on 1988-90 models and 21 ft. lbs. in two steps on 1991 models.
3. Lightly lubricate clutch fork ends which contact bearing and completely pack I.D. recess of release bearing

with suitable grease. Levers on clutch fork shaft must bear on large ears of release bearing. Levers fit between large ears and small tangs on bearing. Fork shaft must move freely with bearing in place.
4. Tie actuator lever through actuator hole to studs, holding release bearing in position.
5. Install transaxle assembly. **Clutch lever must not be moved toward flywheel until transaxle is bolted to engine.**
6. **On except 1989-90 models,** align actuator and master cylinder quick connect fittings in hydraulic line and insert master cylinder fitting into actuator fitting until it locks in place.
7. **On all models,** remove tie from actuator lever.
8. Inspect actuator rod for lever bushing and replace if missing.
9. Install actuator on housing studs with pushrod bushing centered in pocket of internal lever in housing. It may require an axial load on the push rod to compress the actuator piston spring.
10. Install actuator retaining nuts, **torquing** evenly to 18 ft. lbs.
11. Install new bushing in master cylinder push rod, lubricating before installation.
12. Connect master cylinder push rod to clutch pedal, with bushing tangs snapped into pedal pin groove.
13. Depress clutch pedal several times, ensuring effort is normal and firm.
14. Readjust cruise control, if necessary, by pulling upward on clutch pedal with a force of not more than 20 lbs.
15. Install sound insulator and connect battery ground cable.

TRANSAXLE
REPLACE

Prior to any operation that requires removal of the actuator, the master cylinder pushrod must be disconnected from the clutch pedal. **Failure to disconnect pushrod will result in permanent damage to the actuator if the clutch pedal is depressed without resistance from clutch loads.** Master cylinder pushrod bushing must also be replaced whenever it has been removed from the clutch pedal.

1. Disconnect battery ground cable.
2. Install engine support fixture tool No. J-28467-A, or equivalent, together with support leg tool No. J-36462 or equivalent.
3. Remove air cleaner housing and air intake tube.
4. Remove clutch actuator from transaxle. Refer to procedure outlined under "Clutch Hydraulic System, Service."
5. Disconnect electrical connector at speedometer driven gear sensor.
6. Remove nut and retaining clamp securing shift and select cables to transaxle.
7. Remove two nuts from cable ball studs at transaxle levers.
8. Disconnect exhaust crossover pipe at left exhaust manifold.
9. Disconnect EGR tube from crossover

pipe.
10. Remove crossover to exhaust pipe connecting bolts.
11. Loosen crossover to right exhaust manifold clamp.
12. Swing crossover upward to gain access to top transaxle bolts.
13. Remove two upper transaxle mounting bolts and two upper transaxle mounting studs, leaving one lower mounting bolt and one lower mounting stud attached.
14. Disconnect electrical connector at back-up lamp switch.
15. Raise and support vehicle, then remove drain plug to drain transaxle fluid.
16. Remove four clutch housing cover retaining screws.
17. Remove both front tire and wheel assemblies, then the left and right wheelhouse splash shields.
18. Disconnect power steering cooler lines from frame, then remove power steering rack and pinion heat shield.
19. Disconnect power steering rack and pinion at frame.
20. Disconnect ball joints at steering knuckle.
21. Remove transaxle mount upper retaining bolts, then the engine mount lower retaining nuts.
22. Remove subframe retaining bolts from body, then remove subframe from vehicle.
23. Remove drive axles from transaxle and support from body.
24. Detach starter assembly and support from body.
25. Securely attach transaxle to suitable jack, then remove remaining transaxle mounting bolt and stud and remove transaxle.
26. Reverse procedure to install, noting the following:
    a. **Torque** transaxle to engine attaching bolts and studs to 55 ft. lbs.
    b. Using frame or lower control arm for leverage, seat drive axle into transaxle, using screwdriver/pry bar at groove provided on inner joint.
    c. Verify that axle snap ring is seated by tapping on inner groove with screwdriver. Also, grasp inner housing and pull outboard. **Do not pull on axle shaft.** If snap ring is seated, axle will remain in place.
    d. After positioning frame with body mount bolts installed but not tightened, align frame to body by inserting two 19 mm (.74 inch) diameter by 203 mm (8 inch) long pins in alignment holes on right side of frame, then **torque** body mount bolts to 100 ft. lbs. **Alignment pins must not be removed until all body mount bolts are torqued to specification. Alignment pins must be kept perpendicular to frame. Right side body mounts (nearest alignment pins) should be tightened first to maintain correct front wheel alignment.**
    e. **Torque** clutch housing cover retaining screws to 115 inch lbs.

TIGHTENING SPECIFICATIONS

Year	Component	Torque/ft. lbs.
1988-91	Back-Up Lamp Switch	25
	Cable Ball Stud Nut	18
	Cable Retaining Clamp Nut	89 ①
	Clutch Actuator Nut	18
	Clutch Cover To Flywheel	②
	Clutch Fluid Reservoir Nut	36 ①
	Clutch Housing Cover Screw	116 ①
	Clutch Master Cylinder Anti-Rotation Screw	18 ①
	Clutch Pedal Pivot Nut	23
	Control Assembly Bolt	18
	Flywheel To Crankshaft Bolt	52
	Shift Lever Nut	61
	Shift Linkage Bracket Bolt	17
	Speedometer Signal Assembly Bolt	80 ①
	Transaxle Mount To Frame Nut	42
	Transaxle Mount To Transaxle Bolt	35
	Transaxle Mounting Bolt	55

① —Inch lbs.
② —1988–90 models, 15 ft. lbs: 1991 models, 21 ft. lbs.

Rear Suspension

INDEX

DESCRIPTION

These vehicles use a tri-link independent rear suspension system with a transverse leaf spring and tubular struts with large lateral links attached to the body crossmember. The three mounting points are the crossmember, strut tower and trailing arm. The crossmember is stamped steel and the composite fiberglass mono leaf spring is transversely mounted to the under side of the crossmember, with its padded ends free riding on the cast knuckle assembly.

REAR HUB & BEARING ASSEMBLY REPLACE

The rear hub and bearing assembly is not serviceable. If the hub and/or bearing is damaged, the complete assembly must be replaced.

1. Raise and support vehicle, then remove tire and wheel assembly.
2. Remove brake caliper, leaving hose attached, and suspend out of way.
3. Remove brake rotor.
4. Disconnect anti-lock brake system electrical harness connector, if equipped.
5. Remove hub and bearing assembly mounting bolts, then the assembly.
6. Reverse procedure to install, torquing hub and bearing assembly mounting bolts to specifications.

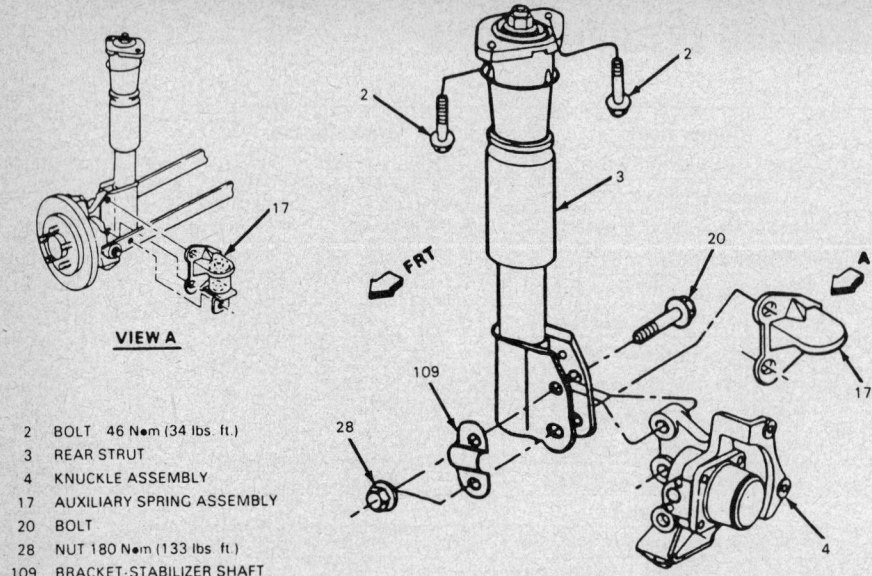

2	BOLT 46 N•m (34 lbs. ft.)
3	REAR STRUT
4	KNUCKLE ASSEMBLY
17	AUXILIARY SPRING ASSEMBLY
20	BOLT
28	NUT 180 N•m (133 lbs. ft.)
109	BRACKET-STABILIZER SHAFT

Fig. 1 Auxiliary spring replacement

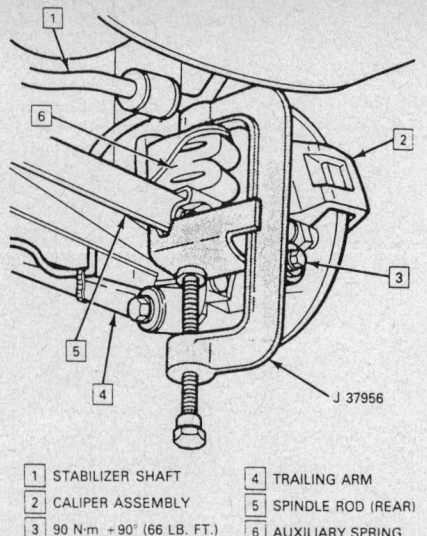

1	STABILIZER SHAFT		4	TRAILING ARM
2	CALIPER ASSEMBLY		5	SPINDLE ROD (REAR)
3	90 N•m +90° (66 LB. FT.) –90°		6	AUXILIARY SPRING

Fig. 2 Compressing auxiliary spring

AUXILIARY SPRING ASSEMBLY REPLACE

1. Raise and support vehicle, then remove wheel and tire assembly.
2. Remove leaf spring rear retention plate bolt.
3. Remove leaf spring retention bolt only enough to rotate plate clear of rod.
4. Install rear auxiliary spring compressor tool No. J-37956 or equivalent ensuring pin in stationary end of clamp is inserted in hole of upper auxiliary spring bracket, **Figs 1 and 2**.
5. Remove plug from upper bracket, then seat rod in tool channel and hand tighten.
6. Remove rod-to-knuckle bolt, then loosen tool forcing screw to allow spring to expand.
7. Remove auxiliary spring attaching bolts, then the spring and tool. **When removing auxiliary spring, ensure rod/bushing clears transverse spring and boss on knuckle.**
8. Reverse procedure to install, noting the following:
   a. Compress auxiliary spring with spring compressor tool enough to install rod-to-knuckle bolt.
   b. Install rod-to-knuckle bolt, using Loctite or equivalent. Torque to specifications.
   c. Properly position leaf spring retention plate, install bolt and torque to specifications.

TRANSVERSE SPRING ASSEMBLY REPLACE

Do not use corrosive cleaning agents, engine degreaser or solvents on or near the fiberglass leaf spring.
1. Raise and support vehicle.

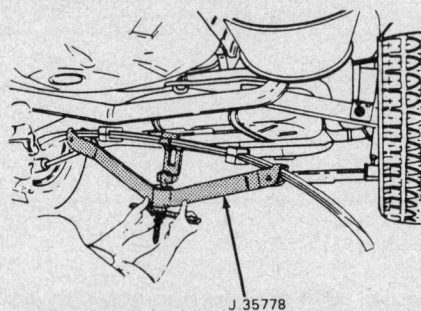

Fig. 3 Removing transverse spring assembly

2. Remove three jack pad attaching bolts and the pad.
3. Remove left and right spring retention plate attaching bolts.
4. Remove right side trailing link to knuckle attaching nut and bolt.
5. Disconnect anti-lock brake system electrical harness connector, if equipped.
6. Assemble rear spring leaf spring compressor tool No. J-35778 or equivalent to transverse spring.
7. Loosen tool handle to base of tool shank.
8. Hang center shank of tool at spring center. It is not necessary to separate tool body and shank. **Attach from front side of vehicle only.**
9. Attach tool body to spring. **Always center spring on roller of tool.**
10. Fully compress spring, then slide spring to left side. It may be necessary to pry the spring, using a screwdriver/pry bar, to the opposite side, using the wheel for leverage.
11. Relax the spring until removal clearance is achieved, then remove spring, **Fig. 3**.
12. Reverse procedure to install, noting the following:
    a. Torque trailing link to knuckle attaching bolt to specifications.
    b. Torque spring retention plate

mounting bolts to specifications. Rear spring retention plates are designed with tabs on one end. Tabs must be aligned with support assembly.
c. Torque jack pad mounting bolts to specifications.

STABILIZER SHAFT ASSEMBLY REPLACE

1. Raise and support vehicle, then remove rear wheel and tire assemblies.
2. Remove right and lefthand stabilizer shaft link bolts, then open brackets to remove insulator.
3. Remove right and lefthand strut to knuckle to stabilizer shaft nuts, **Fig. 4**. **Do not remove strut to knuckle bolts.**
4. Remove insulator brackets from bolts and from stabilizer shaft, then the stabilizer shaft.
5. Reverse procedure to install, noting the following:
   a. It may be necessary to pry stabilizer shaft to one side for installation clearance at strut. Use caution when prying.
   b. Torquing stabilizer shaft link bolts and strut to knuckle bolts to specifications.

TRI-LINK SUSPENSION ASSEMBLY REPLACE

TRAILING LINK

1. Raise and support vehicle.
2. Disconnect anti-lock brake system electrical harness connector, if equipped.
3. Remove trailing link to knuckle attaching nut and bolt, then the trailing link to

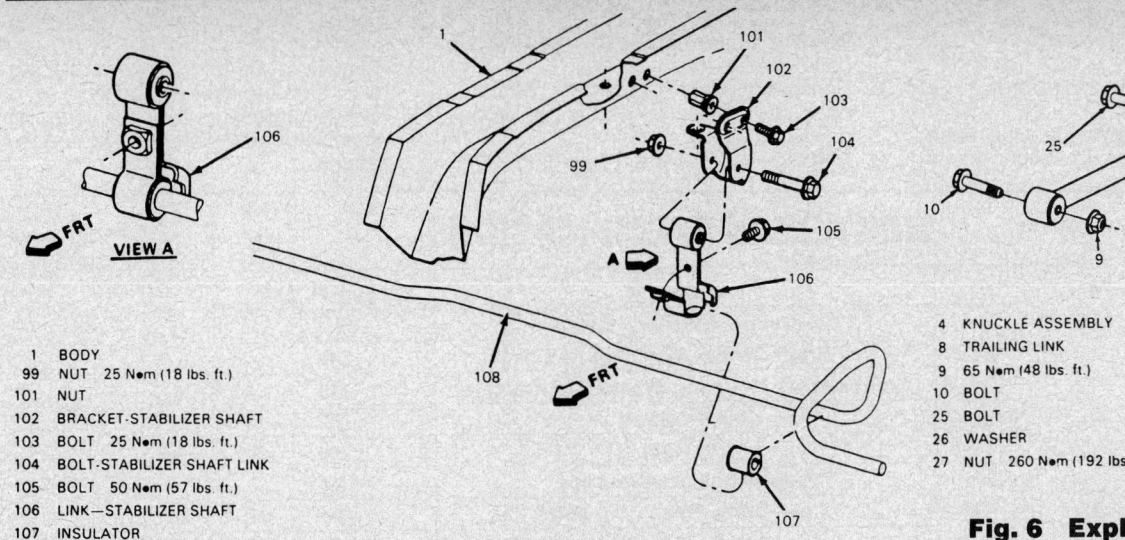

1	BODY
99	NUT 25 N·m (18 lbs. ft.)
101	NUT
102	BRACKET-STABILIZER SHAFT
103	BOLT 25 N·m (18 lbs. ft.)
104	BOLT-STABILIZER SHAFT LINK
105	BOLT 50 N·m (57 lbs. ft.)
106	LINK—STABILIZER SHAFT
107	INSULATOR
108	STABILIZER SHAFT

Fig. 4   Stabilizer shaft assembly replacement

4	KNUCKLE ASSEMBLY
8	TRAILING LINK
9	65 N·m (48 lbs. ft.)
10	BOLT
25	BOLT
26	WASHER
27	NUT 260 N·m (192 lbs. ft.)

Fig. 6   Exploded view of trailing link

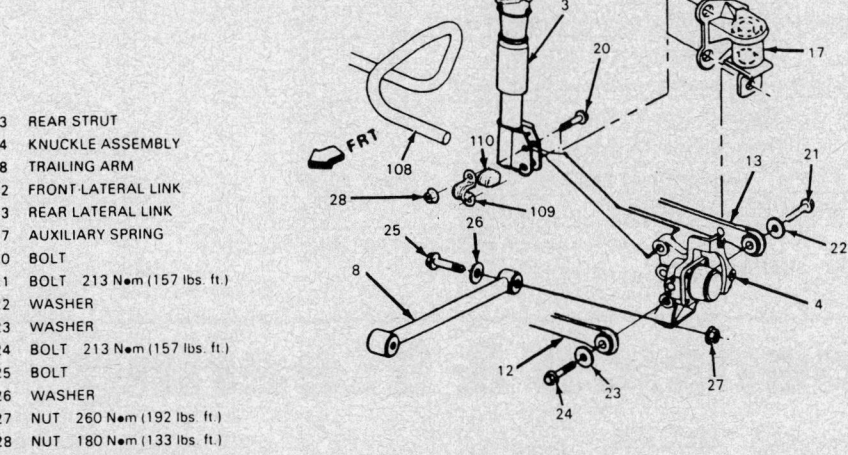

3	REAR STRUT
4	KNUCKLE ASSEMBLY
8	TRAILING ARM
12	FRONT·LATERAL LINK
13	REAR LATERAL LINK
17	AUXILIARY SPRING
20	BOLT
21	BOLT 213 N·m (157 lbs. ft.)
22	WASHER
23	WASHER
24	BOLT 213 N·m (157 lbs. ft.)
25	BOLT
26	WASHER
27	NUT 260 N·m (192 lbs. ft.)
28	NUT 180 N·m (133 lbs. ft.)
108	STABILIZER SHAFT
109	BRACKET·STABILIZER SHAFT
110	INSULATOR

Fig. 5   Exploded view of tri-link suspension assembly

body attaching nut and bolt, **Figs. 5 and 6.**
4. Remove trailing link.
5. Reverse procedure to install, torquing trailing link to body nut and trailing link to knuckle nut to specifications.

FRONT LATERAL LINK

1. Raise and support vehicle, then remove tire and wheel assembly.
2. Remove rod to knuckle bolt, then the exhaust pipe heat shield.
3. Lower to fuel tank to gain access.
4. Remove lateral link to knuckle attaching bolt.
5. Remove lateral link to suspension crossmember attaching nut and bolt, then the lateral link.
6. Reverse procedure to install, **torquing** lateral link to suspension crossmember nut to 140 ft. lbs. and the lateral link to knuckle attaching bolt to 157 ft. lbs.

REAR LATERAL LINK

1. Raise and support vehicle, then remove tire and wheel assembly.
2. Remove transverse spring as previously outlined.
3. Remove lower auxiliary spring bracket from rod.
4. Remove rear lateral link attaching nut from crossmember.
5. Push bolt forward enough to provide clearance for link removal, then remove rear lateral link.
6. Reverse procedure to install, **torquing** lateral link to crossmember attaching nut to 157 ft. lbs. and the rear lateral link to knuckle attaching bolt to 140 ft. lbs.

KNUCKLE ASSEMBLY
REPLACE

1. Raise and support vehicle, then remove tire and wheel assembly.

2. Place scribe marks on strut and knuckle to ensure installation in same position.
3. Remove jack pad.
4. Install rear leaf spring compressor tool No. J-35778 or equivalent onto transverse spring assembly and tighten to hold spring pressure. **Do not remove spring or retention plates.**
5. Remove auxiliary spring as previously outlined.
6. Disconnect front link from knuckle.
7. Remove brake caliper, leaving hose attached, and suspend caliper out of way.
8. Remove brake rotor, then the hub and bearing assembly as previously described.
9. Disconnect anti-lock brake system electrical harness connector, if equipped.
10. Disconnect trailing link from knuckle, **Fig. 5.**
11. Remove strut to knuckle attaching nuts, then the stabilizer shaft bracket.
12. Remove strut to knuckle attaching bolts, then the knuckle.
13. Reverse procedure to install, torquing strut to knuckle attaching bolts and trailing link retaining nut to specifications.

STRUT ASSEMBLY
REPLACE

1. Remove upper strut mount cover from inside rear compartment, then raise and support vehicle and remove tire and wheel assembly.
2. Install rear leaf spring compressor tool No. J-35778 or equivalent onto transverse spring assembly and tighten to hold spring pressure. **Do not remove spring or retention plates.**

3. Scribe strut and knuckle to ensure installation in same position.
4. Remove jack pad.
5. Remove auxiliary spring as previously outlined.
6. Remove brake caliper, leaving hose attached, and suspend caliper out of

way.
7. Remove brake rotor, then the brake hose bracket attaching bolt.
8. Remove upper strut attaching bolts at body and allow assembly to drop down.
9. Remove stabilizer shaft bracket by re-

moving strut to knuckle attaching nuts.
10. Remove strut to knuckle attaching bolts, then the strut assembly.
11. Reverse procedure to install, torquing upper strut attaching bolts to specifications.

TIGHTENING SPECIFICATIONS

Year	Component	Torque/Ft. Lbs.
1988-91	Caliper Bleeder Valve	62①
	Front Caliper Mounting Bolt	79
	Front Caliper Mounting Bracket To Knuckle	148
	Jack Pad Bolt	18
	Lug Nuts	100
	Proportioning Valve Caps	20
	Rear Caliper Mounting Bolt	92
	Rod To Knuckle	66②
	Rod To Support Crossmember	81③
	Spring Retention Plate Bolt	15
	Stabilizer Shaft Link Bolt	40
	Stabilizer Shaft Link To Body Bracket Nut	18
	Strut To Knuckle Nut	133
	Suspension Crossmember To Body Bolt	85
	Trailing Arm To Knuckle	192
	Trailing Link To Body Nut	48
	Upper Strut Bolt	34
	Wheel/Hub/Bearing To Knuckle Bolt	52

① —Inch lbs.
② —Turn an additional 90° after reaching specified torque.
③ —Turn an additional 60° after reaching specified torque.

Front Suspension & Steering

INDEX

DESCRIPTION

The front suspension system on these vehicles is of the MacPherson strut design. This design incorporates MacPherson struts with coil springs and a one piece configuration with lower control arms. The use of tapered top coil springs on top of the struts provides a well controlled ride and allows a lower hood profile.

STRUT CARTRIDGE REPLACE

Do not service strut unless weight of vehicle is on suspension.

REMOVAL

1. Scribe alignment marks on cover plate, remove cover plate retaining nuts, then the cover plate.
2. Using No. 50 Torx bit and strut rod remover/installer tool No. J-35669, or equivalents, remove strut shaft.
3. Remove strut mount bushing by prying with suitable tool.
4. Using strut mount plate wrench tool No. J-35670 or equivalent, remove jounce bumper retainer.
5. Attach strut extension rod tool No. J-35668 or equivalent to strut shaft and compress shaft down into cartridge, then remove tool and pull out

jounce bumper.
6. Attach strut extension rod tool No. J-35668 or equivalent to strut shaft and extend shaft, then remove tool and, using strut cap nut wrench tool No. J-35671 or equivalent, unscrew closure nut.
7. Remove strut cartridge.
8. Remove oil from strut tube using suction device.

INSTALLATION

1. Using strut cap nut wrench tool No. J-35671 or equivalent, install self contained replacement cartridge.
2. Install jounce bumper, then using strut mount plate wrench tool No. J-35670

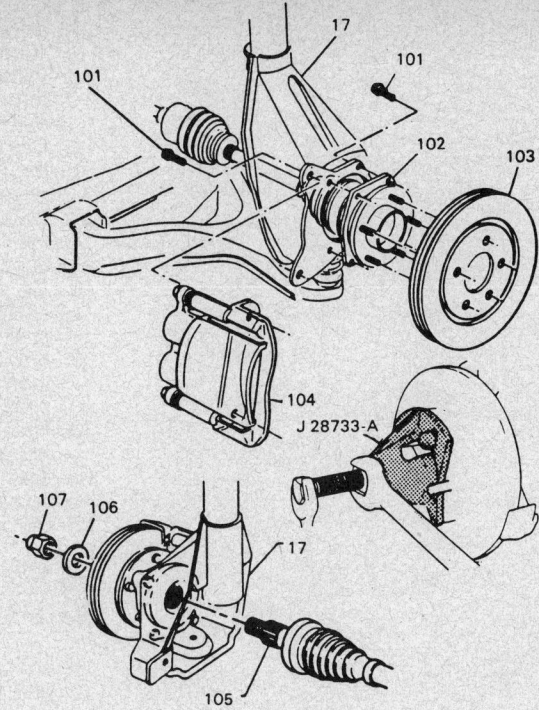

17   KNUCKLE/STRUT ASSEMBLY
101   BOLT   70 N·m (52 lbs. ft.)
102   HUB/BEARING ASSEMBLY
103   ROTOR
104   CALIPER AND BRACKET ASSEMBLY
105   DRIVE AXLE
106   WASHER
107   AXLE NUT   250 N·m (184 lbs. ft.)

Fig. 1   Removing hub & bearing assembly

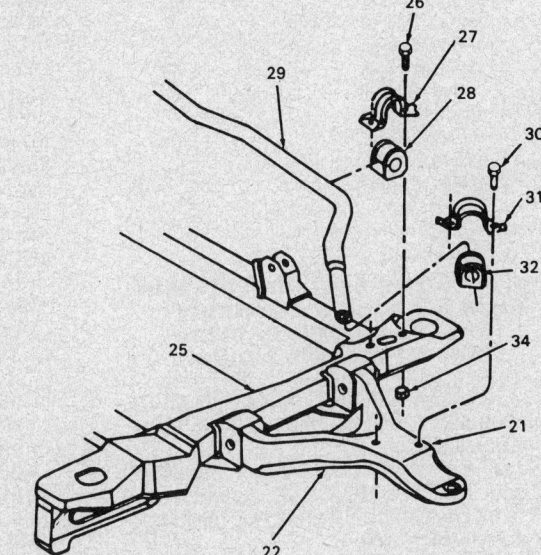

21   WELD NUTS
22   LOWER CONTROL ARM
25   FRAME
26   CLAMP BOLT
27   CLAMP
28   INSULATOR
29   STABILIZER SHAFT
30   BOLT   47 N·m (35 lbs. ft.)
31   CLAMP
32   INSULATOR
34   NUT   47 N·m (35 lbs. ft.)

Fig. 2   Replacing stabilizer shaft & insulators

or equivalent, the jounce bumper retainer.

3. **On all models**, install strut mount bushing. If necessary, use strut extension rod tool No. J-35668 or equivalent after bushing is partially installed and position strut shaft as required. Lubricate bushing with a soap solu-tion to ease installation.

4. Using No. 50 Torx bit and strut rod remover/installer tool No. J-35669, or equivalents, install strut shaft nut, tor-quing to specifications.

5. Install strut mount cover, aligning scribe marks. Torque cover plate nuts to specifications.

HUB & BEARING ASSEMBLY
REPLACE

1. Remove wheel cover, then loosen drive axle shaft nut and washer one turn. **Do not remove nut at this time. Failure to follow proper removal sequence may cause bearing damage.**

2. Loosen lug nuts, then raise and sup-port vehicle and remove wheel and tire assembly.

3. Remove brake caliper and bracket as-sembly, then the brake rotor, **Fig. 1.**

4. Remove drive axle shaft nut and washer.

5. Loosen hub and bearing assembly to knuckle attaching bolts.

6. Using front hub spindle remover tool No. J-28733-A or equivalent, push axle splines back out of hub and bear-ing assembly.

7. Remove hub and bearing assembly to knuckle attaching bolts.

8. **On models with anti-lock brakes (ABS),** remove ABS sensor mounting bolt and position sensor aside.

9. **On all models,** remove hub and bearing assembly. **Protect axle boots from damage during han-dling.**

10. Reverse procedure to install, **torqu-ing** hub and bearing assembly to knuckle attaching bolts to specifica-tions, lug nuts to 100 ft. lbs. and the drive axle nut to specifications.

STABILIZER SHAFT & INSULATORS
REPLACE

1. Loosen lug nuts, then raise and sup-port vehicle and remove wheel and tire assembly.

2. Move steering shaft dust shield to gain access to pinch bolt.

3. Remove pinch bolt from lower inter-mediate steering shaft.

4. Loosen all insulator clamp attaching nuts and bolts, **Fig. 2.**

5. Place suitable jack under center of rear frame crossmember.

6. Loosen two front frame to body bolts four turns.

7. Remove two rear frame to body bolts.

8. Lower rear of frame just enough to gain access for stabilizer shaft remov-al.

9. Remove insulators and clamps from frame and control arms.

10. Pull stabilizer shaft rearward, swing down and remove from left side of ve-hicle.

11. Reverse procedure to install, noting the following:
   a. Coat new insulators with rubber lu-bricant.
   b. Torque clamp to frame nuts and clamp to lower control arm bolts to specifications.
   c. **Torque** frame attaching bolts to 100 ft. lbs.
   d. Torque pinch bolt to specifications.
   e. **Torque** lug nuts to 100 ft. lbs.

STRUT & KNUCKLE ASSEMBLY SERVICE

REMOVAL

1. Disconnect battery ground cable.
2. Scribe alignment marks on cover plate, then loosen three cover plate retaining nuts.
3. Loosen lug nuts, then raise and support vehicle and remove wheel and tire assembly.
4. Remove brake caliper and bracket assembly, leaving hose attached, and support caliper out of way.
5. Remove brake rotor, then the hub and bearing to knuckle attaching bolts.
6. **On models with anti-lock brakes (ABS),** remove ABS sensor mounting bolt and position sensor aside.
7. **On all models,** separate axle from transaxle and carefully remove drive axle assembly.
8. Remove tie rod to knuckle attaching nut.
9. Using tie rod puller/ball joint remover tool No. J-35917 or equivalent, separate tie rod from knuckle.
10. Remove lower ball joint to knuckle attaching nut.
11. Using tool No. J-35917 or equivalent, separate ball joint from lower control arm.
12. Remove ball joint heat shield, then the cover plate retaining nuts.
13. Remove strut and knuckle assembly.

SERVICE

Springs are under high tension. Do not remove strut shaft nut without using a suitable spring compressing tool.

1. Mount strut and knuckle assembly into strut spring compressor tool No. J-34013-A and strut compressor adapter tool No. J-34013-88, or equivalents, then compress spring with compressor forcing screw just enough to release tension from upper spring insulator.
2. Using Torx bit and strut rod nut remover/installer tool No. J-35669, or equivalents, remove strut shaft nut.
3. Relieve all spring tension, then remove spring and strut components, **Fig. 3.**
4. Install spring seat and bearing.
5. Install lower spring insulator. Lower spring coil end must be visible between the step and the first retention tab of insulator.
6. Install front suspension spring.
7. Install dust shield to lower spring seat.
8. Install jounce bumper.
9. Install upper spring insulator. Upper spring coil end must be between step and location mark on insulator.
10. Using strut mount plate wrench tool No. J-35670 or equivalent, install jounce bumper retainer to strut mount.
11. Install strut mount and upper strut mount bushing.
12. Using strut spring compressor and strut compressor adapter tools Nos. J-34013-A and J-34013-88, or equivalents, compress strut assembly.

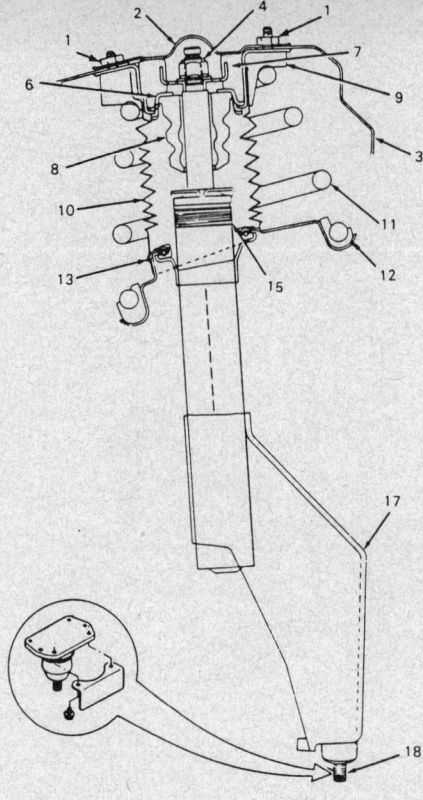

1	COVER PLATE NUT
2	COVER PLATE
3	SHOCK TOWER
4	STRUT SHAFT NUT
6	JOUNCE BUMPER RETAINER
7	STRUT MOUNT
8	JOUNCE BUMPER
9	SPRING INSULATOR
10	DUST SHIELD
11	SPRING
12	SPRING INSULATOR
13	SPRING SEAT AND BEARING
15	CLOSURE NUT
17	KNUCKLE STRUT ASSEMBLY
18	BALL JOINT

Fig. 3 Cross-sectional view of strut & knuckle assembly. 1988–89 models shown, 1990–91 models similar

13. Align strut cartridge shaft with strut extension rod tool No. J-35668 or equivalent.
14. Using strut rod nut remover/installer tool No. J-35669 or equivalent and Torx bit, install strut shaft nut, torquing to specifications.

INSTALLATION

1. Install strut mount cover plate and upper strut mount to body attaching nuts. Do not tighten nuts until vehicle is lowered to floor.
2. Install ball joint heat shield.
3. Install lower ball joint to control arm attaching nut, **torquing** to 15 ft. lbs., then tighten an addition 90°.
4. Further tighten to next slot in nut with cotter pin hole in stud and install new cotter pin. **Do not tighten more than an additional 60° to align with hole**

and do not loosen nut at any time during installation.

5. Install tie rod to knuckle attaching nut, torquing to specifications, and install cotter pin.
6. Carefully install drive axle assembly through opening in knuckle and insert drive axle into transaxle.
7. Install hub and bearing to knuckle attaching bolts, torquing to specifications.
8. **On models with anti-lock brakes (ABS),** position ABS sensor and install mounting bolt.
9. **On all models,** install brake rotor, then the brake caliper and bracket assembly.
10. Install wheel and tire assembly and lower vehicle.
11. **Torque** lug nuts to 100 ft. lbs. and the cover plate nuts to specifications.
12. Connect battery ground cable.

LOWER CONTROL ARM
REPLACE

1. Loosen lug nuts, then raise and support vehicle and remove wheel and tire assembly.
2. Remove stabilizer shaft to lower control arm insulator bracket bolts.
3. Remove lower ball joint cotter pin and nut, then, using tie rod puller/ball joint remover tool No. J-35917 or equivalent, separate ball joint from lower control arm.
4. Remove lower control arm to frame attaching nuts and bolts, then the lower control arms.
5. If bushing replacement is necessary, refer to **Fig. 4.** Coat threads of control arm bushing service tool set No. J-21474-19 or equivalent with an extreme pressure lubricant. To facilitate installation, coat outer casing of bushing with suitable lubricant.
6. Reverse procedure to install, noting the following:
   a. Lower control arm to frame bolts must be installed as shown, **Fig. 5.**
   b. Torque lower control arm to frame bolts to specifications.
   c. **Torque** lower ball joint nut 15 ft. lbs. and tighten an additional 90°, then further tighten to align next slot in nut with cotter pin hole in stud. **Do not tighten more than 60° to align with hole and do not loosen nut at any time during installation.**
   d. Torque stabilizer shaft bolts to specifications.
   e. **Torque** lug nuts to 100 ft. lbs.

STEERING GEAR
REPLACE

1. Remove air cleaner, then raise and support vehicle. **Provide additional support at rear of vehicle.**
2. Remove front wheel and tire assemblies.
3. Remove intermediate shaft lower pinch bolt at steering gear.

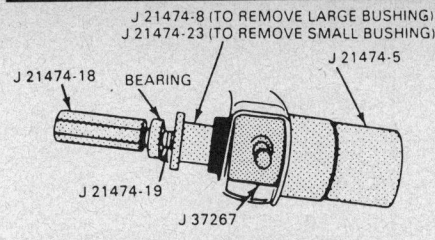

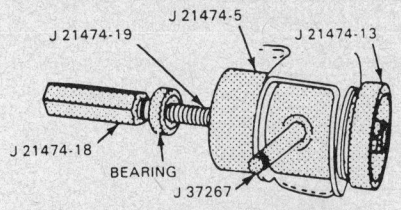

Fig. 4 Replacing lower control arm bushings

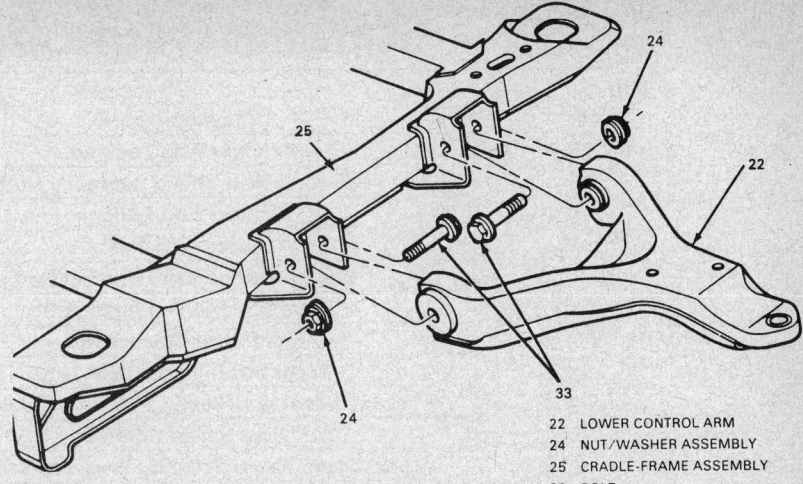

22 LOWER CONTROL ARM
24 NUT/WASHER ASSEMBLY
25 CRADLE-FRAME ASSEMBLY
33 BOLT

Fig. 5 Installing lower control arm

4. Remove intermediate shaft from stub shaft. **Failure to disconnect intermediate shaft from rack and pinion shaft stub may result in damage to steering gear and/or intermediate shaft. This damage can cause loss of steering control.**
5. Disconnect electrical connector at switch.
6. Using tie rod puller/ball joint remover tool No. J-35917 or equivalent, disconnect tie rod ends from knuckle and strut assembly.
7. Support body with suitable stands, then remove rear frame mounting bolts and lower rear frame no more than five inches. **Do not lower rear of frame too far. Damage to engine components nearest to cowl may result.**
8. Remove heat shield, then the pipe retaining clip from steering gear.
9. Disconnect inlet pipes and outlet line from power steering gear.
10. Remove remaining brackets and clips.
11. Remove rack and pinion mounting nuts and bolts, then the rack and pinion assembly through the left wheel opening.
12. Reverse procedure to install, noting the following:
    a. Torque rack and pinion mounting bolts to specifications.
    b. Replace O-rings as necessary.
    c. Torque power steering line fitting to specifications.
    d. Torque heat shield attaching screws to specifications.
    e. **Torque** rear frame attaching bolts to 100 ft. lbs.
    f. Torque tie rod end castle nuts to specifications.
    g. Torque intermediate shaft lower pinch bolt to specifications.
13. After completing installation, bleed power steering system as follows:
    a. Turn wheels all the way to left.
    b. Add power steering to Cold mark on fluid level indicator.
    c. Start engine and run at fast idle, then add fluid, if necessary, to bring level to Cold mark.

d. Bleed system by turning wheels from side to side without hitting stops. Keep fluid level at Cold mark.
e. Return wheels to center position and continue running engine for 2-3 minutes.
f. Road test vehicle to ensure steering functions normally and is free of noise.
g. Check fluid level and ensure level is at Hot mark after system has stabilized at its normal operating temperature.

POWER STEERING PUMP REPLACE

EXCEPT 2.3L/4-138 ENGINES

1. Disconnect battery ground cable.
2. Disconnect inlet and outlet hoses from pump.
3. Remove serpentine belt guard as necessary.
4. Remove belt from pulley, using 1/2 inch breaker bar.
5. Remove pump assembly.
6. Transfer pulley as necessary.
7. Reverse procedure to install, them bleed power steering system as follows:
    a. Turn wheels all the way to left.
    b. Add power steering to Cold mark on fluid level indicator.
    c. Start engine and run at fast idle, then add fluid, if necessary, to bring level to Cold mark.
    d. Bleed system by turning wheels from side to side without hitting stops. Keep fluid level at Cold mark.
    e. Return wheels to center position and continue running engine for 2-3 minutes.
    f. Road test vehicle to ensure steering functions normally and is free of noise.
    g. Check fluid level and ensure level

is at Hot mark after system has stabilized at its normal operating temperature.

2.3L/4-138 ENGINES

1. Disconnect battery ground cable.
2. Disconnect left side torque strut from engine.
3. Separate throttle cable bracket from engine torque strut bracket and position aside. Do not remove cables.
4. Remove engine torque strut bracket.
5. Disconnect inlet and outlet hoses from pump.
6. Remove serpentine belt guard as necessary.
7. Remove belt from pulley, using 1/2 inch breaker bar.
8. Remove rear bracket to pump bolts.
9. **On models except high output**, remove rear bracket to transaxle bolts.
10. **On all models**, remove rear bracket.
11. Remove front bracket to engine bolt, then the pump assembly with bracket.
12. Transfer pulley and bracket as necessary.
13. Reverse procedure to install, them bleed power steering system as follows:
    a. Turn wheels all the way to left.
    b. Add power steering to Cold mark on fluid level indicator.
    c. Start engine and run at fast idle, then add fluid, if necessary, to bring level to Cold mark.
    d. Bleed system by turning wheels from side to side without hitting stops. Keep fluid level at Cold mark.
    e. Return wheels to center position and continue running engine for 2-3 minutes.
    f. Road test vehicle to ensure steering functions normally and is free of noise.
    g. Check fluid level and ensure level is at Hot mark after system has stabilized at its normal operating temperature.

TIGHTENING SPECIFICATIONS

Year	Component	Torque/Ft. Lbs.
1988–91	Adjuster Plug Locknut	50
	Ball Joint Heat Shield Retaining Nuts	54①
	Cylinder End Fittings	20
	Drive Axle Nut	184
	Engine Torque Strut Bracket Bolt	40④
	Front Bracket To Engine Bolt	67④
	Front Strut Closure Nut	82
	Front Strut Piston Shaft Nut	72
	Front Wheel Hub/Bearing To Knuckle Bolts	52
	Heat Shield Screws	54①
	Idle Speed Power Steering Pressure Switch	116①
	Inner Tie Rod To Rack	70
	Intermediate Shaft Pinch Bolt	35
	Lower Ball Joint Nut	②
	Lower Control Arm To Frame Bolts	56
	Lug Nuts	100
	Pinion Locknut	26
	Pinion Preload	16①⑤
	Power Steering Cooler Pipe Retaining Screw	71①
	Pump Mounting Bolt	21③
	Pump To Front Or Rear Bracket Bolt	19④
	Rack And Pinion Fittings	20
	Rack And Pinion Mounting Bolts	59
	Stabilizer Bar Insulator Clamp To Frame Nuts	35
	Stabilizer Bar Insulator Clamp To Lower Control Arm Bolt	39
	Strut Mount Cover Plate Nuts	18
	Tie Rod End Jam Nut	50
	Tie Rod End Nuts	40
	Union Fitting To Hydraulic Pump Housing	55
	Valve End Fittings	12

①—Inch lbs.
②—Refer to text.
③—Except models with 2.3L/4-138 engines.
④—Models with 2.3L/4-138 engines.
⑤—Maximum.

Wheel Alignment

INDEX

Page No.

PRELIMINARY CHECK

1. Ensure tires are inflated to correct pressure, and check for uneven wear.
2. Check front wheel bearings and related suspension components for damage and replace as necessary, to eliminate improper alignment due to faulty components.
3. Check ball joints and tie rods.
4. Check vehicle trim heights.
5. Check steering gear for looseness at frame.
6. Check struts for improper operation.
7. Check for loose control arms.
8. Check for loose or missing stabilizer shaft attachments.

WHEEL ALIGNMENT
ADJUST

When adjusting wheel alignment, always adjust both front and rear alignment, proceeding in the following order.
1. Rear wheel camber
2. Rear wheel toe and tracking
3. Front wheel camber and toe.

CAMBER ADJUSTMENT

FRONT

1. Open hood and remove three strut cover plate nuts and the cover plate.
2. Lift front of vehicle just to the point that strut stud clears strut tower and cover top of strut. **Do not over extend drive axle. Do not lift by suspension.**
3. Use strut alignment templet tool No. J-36892 or equivalent to mark holes, then file three holes. File inboard or outboard of existing hole depending or camber requirement. Do not file more than .2 inch in either direction. **Paint exposed metal with red oxide primer and, after primer has dried, paint area with paint matching body color.**
4. Lower front of vehicle and guide strut studs into slotted holes.
5. Install three strut cover plate nuts.
6. Set camber to specifications by moving strut, then **torque** strut cover plate nuts to 17 ft. lbs.

REAR
1988–90

1. Loosen lug nuts, then raise and support vehicle and remove lug nuts and the wheel and tire assembly.
2. Using suitable jack, support suspension under rear knuckle and hub assembly.
3. Thread tool J-37098 or equivalent into auxiliary spring assembly and tighten to hold assembly in compressed state.
4. Remove brake caliper, leaving hose attached, and support caliper out of way.
5. Remove brake rotor and the brake hose bracket bolt.
6. Scribe strut and knuckle to ensure installation in same position.
7. Remove strut bolts at body and let assembly drop down.
8. Remove stabilizer shaft bracket, then the strut to knuckle attaching bolts.
9. Remove rear auxiliary spring to rear lateral link attaching bolt and nut, then the rear auxiliary spring assembly.
10. Remove strut assembly.
11. Place strut in vise and file lower strut attaching hole oblong.
12. Place auxiliary spring assembly in vise and file lower strut attaching hole oblong.
13. Place stabilizer bracket in vise and file lower stabilizer bracket to strut attaching hole oblong.
14. Reverse procedure to install, **torquing** upper strut bolts to 34 ft. lbs. and the lug nuts to 100 ft. lbs.
15. adjust camber by moving strut and knuckle assembly, then **torque** strut to knuckle attaching nuts to 136 ft. lbs.

1991

1. Raise and support vehicle.
2. Remove tire and wheel assembly.
3. Remove auxiliary spring as outlined under "Auxiliary Spring Assembly, Replace."
4. Remove strut/upper auxiliary spring bracket/stabilizer shaft bracket, if equipped.
5. Place strut in vise.
6. File lower strut to knuckle attaching hole oblong.

7. Place auxiliary spring assembly in vise.
8. File lower strut attaching hole oblong.
9. Place stabilizer bracket in vise.
10. File lower stabilizer bracket to strut attaching hole oblong.
11. Attach strut assembly/stabilizer shaft bracket/upper auxiliary spring bracket to knuckle.
12. Install strut to body bolts and break hose bracket.
13. Install auxiliary spring and install tire and wheel assembly.
14. Adjust camber then **torque** strut to knuckle nuts to 136 ft. lbs.
15. Check and adjust toe if necessary.

TOE ADJUSTMENT

FRONT

1. Remove small seal clamps.
2. With steering wheel in straight ahead position, loosen jam nuts on tie rods.
3. Rotate inner tie rod to obtain proper toe angle, then ensure that number of threads showing on each tie rod is approximately equal.
4. Ensure tie rod ends are square, then **torque** jam nuts to 46 ft. lbs.
5. Ensure seals are not twisted and install seal clamps.

REAR
1988–90

1. Loosen inboard cam nuts of rear support rod.
2. Rotate cam to obtain proper toe angle, **Fig. 1.**
3. **Torque** cam nuts to 140 ft. lbs.

1991

1. Install rear toe adjusting tool No. J-38118, or equivalent, after lubricating threads.
2. Hand tighten turnbuckle portion of tool in direction of adjustment. Equal amounts of threads should be showing on both sides of turnbuckle.
3. Loosen rear rod nut at crossmember a minimum of four turns.

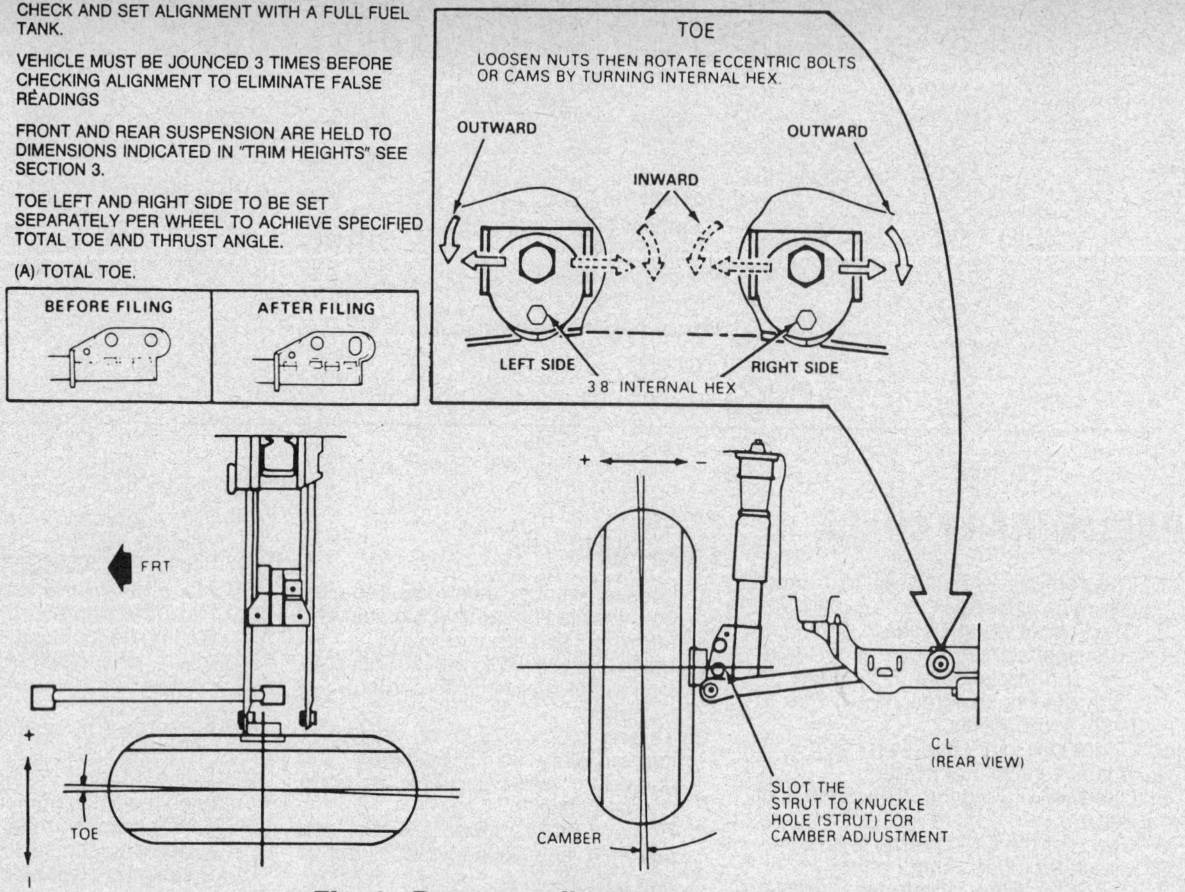

CHECK AND SET ALIGNMENT WITH A FULL FUEL TANK.

VEHICLE MUST BE JOUNCED 3 TIMES BEFORE CHECKING ALIGNMENT TO ELIMINATE FALSE READINGS

FRONT AND REAR SUSPENSION ARE HELD TO DIMENSIONS INDICATED IN "TRIM HEIGHTS" SEE SECTION 3.

TOE LEFT AND RIGHT SIDE TO BE SET SEPARATELY PER WHEEL TO ACHIEVE SPECIFIED TOTAL TOE AND THRUST ANGLE.

(A) TOTAL TOE.

Fig. 1   Rear toe adjustment

4. Rotate turnbuckle portion of tool to reach correct toe specification.
5. **Torque** rear rod to crossmember nut to 81 ft. lbs. plus an additional 60° turn.
6. Remove tool.

RIDE HEIGHT

Check ride height as follows, referring to **Figs. 2 and 3** for ride height location and **Figs. 4 through 13** for specification charts:

1. Ensure vehicle is on level ground.
2. Ensure tires are inflated to proper pressures.
3. Fuel tank should be full to obtain accurate readings.
4. Trunk should be empty except for spare tire and jack.
5. Bounce the car three times at the front and rear to normalize suspension.
6. Measure from lowest point on the ball joint housing to control arm bolt centerline, "D" and "K" positions.
7. Measure from level floor to rocker panel at "Z" and "J" positions.

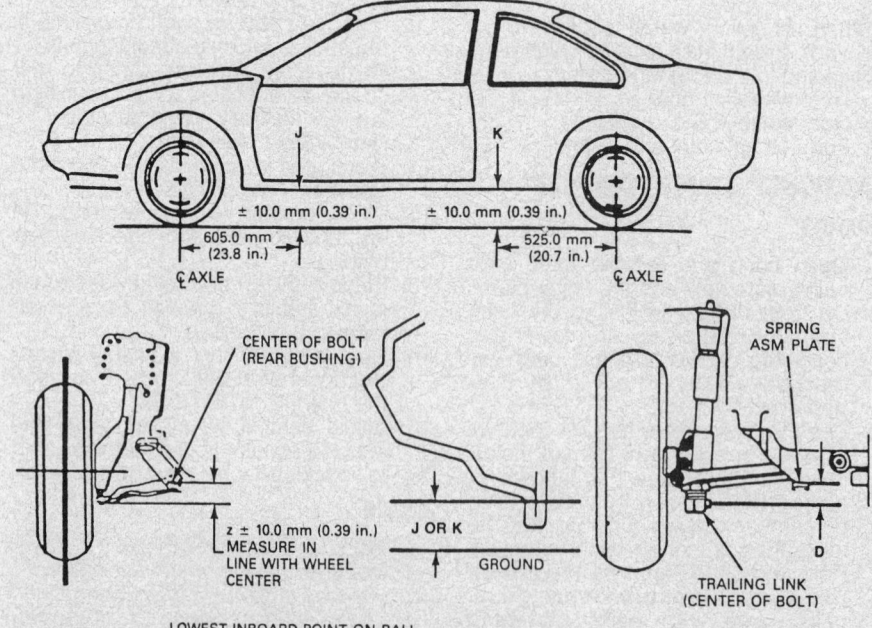

Fig. 2   Ride height measurement location. 1988 models

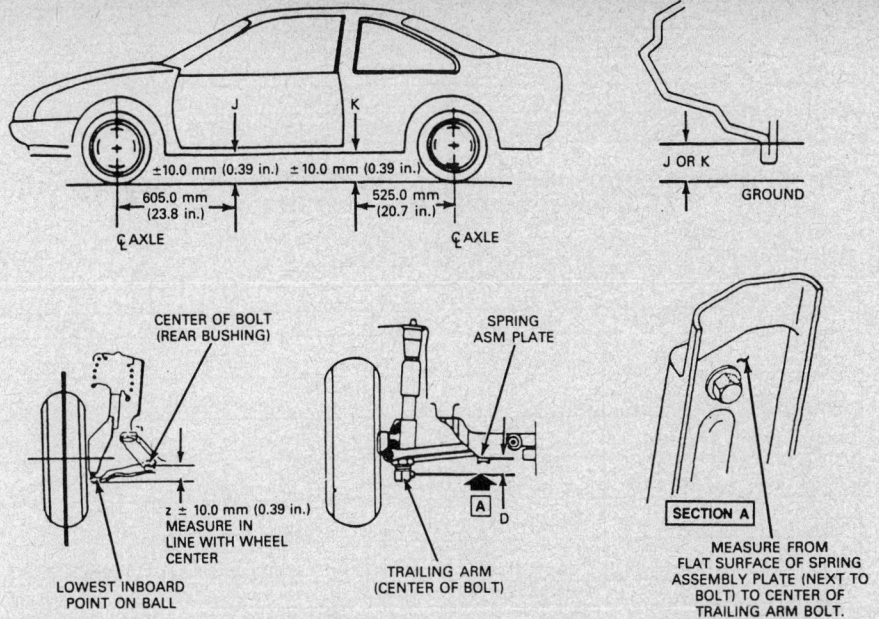

Fig. 3   Ride height measurement location. 1989–91 models

SUSP	TIRE SIZE	Z CURB	D CURB	J CURB	K CURB
STD	P195/75R14	77	97	249	249
FE3	195/70 R15	82	103	249	249
F41	205/70 R14	82	103	249	249

Fig. 4   Ride height specification chart (FE1, std. suspension; FE3, sport suspension; F41, handling package). 1988 Regal

SUSP	TIRE SIZE	Z CURB	D CURB	J CURB	K CURB
STD	P195/75R14	80	112	251	257
FE2	P205/70R14	82	114	251	257
FE3	P215/65R15	70	103	251	257

Fig. 5   Ride height specification chart (FE1, std. suspension; FE3, sport suspension; FE2, handling package). 1988 Cutlass Supreme

SUSP	TIRE SIZE	Z SHIPPED	Z CURB	D SHIPPED	D CURB	J SHIPPED	J CURB	K SHIPPED	K CURB
STD	195-751R14	81	80	124	112	254	251	267	257
STD	195-70-R15	77	75	120	109	254	251	267	257
FE3	215-65-R15	71	70	115	103	254	251	267	257

Fig. 6   Ride height specification chart (FE1, std. suspension; FE3, sport suspension). 1988–89 Grand Prix

MODEL SUSP	TIRE SIZE	Z CURB	D CURB	J CURB	K CURB
FE1	P205-70R14	83	105	249	249
FE3	P215-60R16	69	92	249	249

Fig. 7   Ride height specification chart (FE1, std. suspension; FE3, sport suspension). 1989 Regal

MODEL SUSP	TIRE SIZE	Z CURB	D CURB	J CURB	K CURB
FEI	P195-75R14	81mm (3.2 in.)	115mm (4.5 in.)	251mm (9.9 in.)	257mm (10.1 in.)
FE3	P215-65R15	71mm (2.8 in.)	106mm (4.2 in.)	251mm (9.9 in.)	257mm (10.1 in.)
FE3	P215-60R16	69mm (2.7 in.)	103mm (4.0 in.)	251mm (9.9 in.)	257mm (10.1 in.)

Fig. 8   Ride height specification chart (FE1, std. suspension; FE3, sport suspension). 1989 Cutlass Supreme

MODEL		Z	D	J	K
SUSP	TIRE SIZE	CURB	CURB	CURB	CURB
FE1	P205-70-R14	86mm (3.39 in.)	106mm (4.22 in.)	249mm (9.80 in.)	249mm (9.80 in.)
FE1	P205-70-R15	73mm (2.87 in.)	94mm (3.70 in.)	249mm (9.80 in.)	249mm (9.80 in.)
FE3	P215-60-R16	72mm (2.83 in.)	93mm (3.66 in.)	249mm (9.80 in.)	249mm (9.80 in.)

Fig. 9   Ride height specification chart (FE1, std. suspension; FE3, sport suspension). 1990 Regal

MODEL		Z	D	J	K
SUSP	TIRE SIZE	CURB	CURB	CURB	CURB
FE1 (Except Z7S)	P195-75R14	84mm (3.30 in.)	105mm (4.13 in.)	249mm (9.80 in.)	249mm (9.80 in.)
FE1 (Except Z7S)	P195-70R15	79mm (3.11 in.)	100mm (3.94 in.)	249mm (9.80 in.)	249mm (9.80 in.)
FE1 (Except Z7S)	P195-75R15	84mm (3.30 in.)	104mm (4.09 in.)	249mm (9.80 in.)	249mm (9.80 in.)
FE1 (Except Z7S)	P205-65R15	81mm (3.19 in.)	102mm (4.02 in.)	249mm (9.80 in.)	249mm (9.80 in.)
FE3 (Except Z7S)	P215-60R16	71mm (2.80 in.)	93mm (3.66 in.)	249mm (9.80 in.)	249mm (9.80 in.)
FE3 (Except Z7S)	P215-65R15	74mm (2.91 in.)	95mm (3.74 in.)	249mm (9.80 in.)	249mm (9.80 in.)
FE1 (Z7S)	P195-70R15	81mm (3.19 in.)	101mm (3.98 in.)	249mm (9.80 in.)	249mm (9.80 in.)
FE1 (Z7S)	P205-65R15	83mm (3.27 in.)	104mm (4.09 in.)	249mm (9.80 in.)	249mm (9.80 in.)
FE3 (Z7S)	P215-60R16	73mm (2.87 in.)	94mm (3.70 in.)	249mm (9.80 in.)	249mm (9.80 in.)

Fig. 10   Ride height specification chart (FE1, std. suspension; FE3, sport suspension; Z7S, convertible). 1990 Cutlass Supreme

MODEL		Z	D	J	K
SUSP	TIRE SIZE	CURB	CURB	CURB	CURB
FE1	P195-70R15	80mm (3.15 in.)	110mm (4.33 in.)	251mm (9.88 in.)	257mm (10.12 in.)
FE1	P195-75R14	84mm (3.31 in.)	114mm (4.49 in.)	251mm (9.88 in.)	257mm (10.12 in.)
FE1	P205-65R15	81mm (3.19 in.)	113mm (4.45 in.)	251mm (9.88 in.)	257mm (10.12 in.)
FE3	P215-60R16	72mm (2.83 in.)	103mm (4.06 in.)	251mm (9.88 in.)	257mm (10.12 in.)
FE3	P245-502R16	74mm (2.91 in.)	107mm (4.21 in.)	251mm (9.88 in.)	257mm (10.12 in.)

Fig. 11   Ride height specification chart (FE1, std. suspension; FE3, sport suspension). 1990 Grand Prix

MODEL		Z	D	J	K
Susp	Tire Size	Curb	Curb	Curb	Curb
FE1	P195-75R14	83	103	249	249
F41	P195-70R15	79	99	249	249
F41	P215-60R16	71	92	249	249
F41	P205-65R15	81	101	249	249

Fig. 12   Ride height specification chart (FE1, std. suspension; F41, handling package). 1990 Lumina

MODEL		Z	D	J	K
SUSP	TIRE SIZE	CURB	CURB	CURB	CURB
FE1 (Coupe)	P195-75R14	83mm (3.27 in.)	104 mm (4.09 in.)	249mm (9.80 in.)	249mm (9.80 in.)
FE1 (Sedan)	P195-75R14	84mm (3.31 in.)	105 mm (4.13 in.)	249mm (9.80 in.)	249mm (9.80 in.)
F41	P205-70R15	73mm (2.87 in.)	92 mm (3.62 in.)	249mm (9.80 in.)	249mm (9.80 in.)
F41	P225-60R16	66mm (2.60 in.)	86 mm (3.39 in.)	249mm (9.80 in.)	249mm (9.80 in.)
FE3	P225-60R16	67mm (2.64 in.)	87 mm (3.43 in.)	249mm (9.80 in.)	249mm (9.80 in.)

Fig. 13   Ride height specification chart (FE1, std. suspension; F41, handling package; FE3, sport suspension). 1991 Lumina

NOTE: Refer To Rear Of This Manual For Vehicle Manufacturer's Special Service Tool Suppliers.

Specifications

GENERAL ENGINE SPECIFICATIONS

Year	Engine CID①/Liter	Engine VIN Code②	Fuel System	Bore & Stroke	Compression Ratio	Net H.P. @ RPM③	Maximum Torque Ft. Lbs. @ RPM	Normal Oil Pressure Pounds
1988	1.6L/4-97	4	2 Bbl	3.19 x 3.08	9.0	112 @ 6600	86 @ 2800	④
1988	1.6L/4-97	5	Fuel Injection	3.19 x 3.08	9.4	108 @ 6600	97 @ 4800	④
1990	1.6L/4-97	5	Fuel Injection	3.19 x 3.08	9.4	108 @ 6600	97 @ 4800	④
1990–91	1.6L/4-97	6	Fuel Injection	3.19 x 3.08	9.5	102 @ 5800	101 @ 4800	—

①—CID-Cubic inch displacement.
②—The eighth digit of the VIN denotes engine code.

③—Ratings are net-as installed in vehicle.

④—At idle, 4.3 psi; At 3000 RPM, 36–71 psi.

TUNE UP SPECIFICATIONS

Year & Engine/VIN①	Spark Plug Gap	Firing Order Fig.②	Ignition Timing BTDC Man. Trans.	Ignition Timing BTDC Auto. Trans.	Mark Fig.	Curb Idle Speed③ Man. Trans.	Curb Idle Speed③ Auto Trans.	Fast Idle Speed Man. Trans.	Fast Idle Speed Auto. Trans.	Fuel Pump Pressure
1988										
1.6L/4-97 (4)	.043	A	—	—	B	650	750N	3000⑤	3000⑤	3.5
1.6L/4-97 (5)	.043	A	—	—	B	800	800N	—	—	38–44④
1990–91										
1.6L/4-97 (5)	.043	A	—	—	B	800	800N	—	—	38–44④
1.6L/4-97 (6)	.031	A	—	—	B	—	—	—	—	38–44④

①—The eighth digit of the Vehicle Identification Number (VIN) denotes engine code.
②—Before removing wires from distributor cap, determine location of No. 1 wire in cap, as distributor position may have been altered from that shown at the end of this chart.

③—Idle speed is adjusted in Neutral.
④—With ignition switch On and engine not running.
⑤—On high step of fast idle cam.

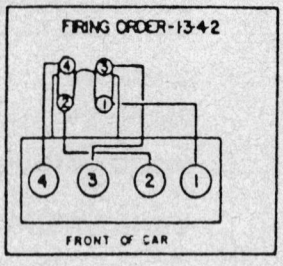

Fig. A

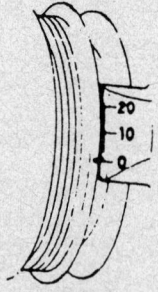

Fig. B

ALTERNATOR SPECIFICATIONS

Year	Rated Hot Output Amps.
1988	60
1990–91	60

WHEEL ALIGNMENT SPECIFICATIONS

Year	Model	Location	Caster Angle, Degrees Limits	Caster Angle, Degrees Desired	Camber Angle, Degrees Limits	Camber Angle, Degrees Desired	Toe-In Inch
1988	Nova, except 16 valve engine	Front	+.13° to +1.63°	+.88°	−1° to +.5°	−.25°	.04
1988	Nova, 16 valve engine	Front	+.2° to +1.48°	+.73°	−1° to +.5°	−.25°	.04
1988	Nova	Rear	—	—	−1.26° to +.24°	−.51°	.15
1990–91	Prizm, A/T Except GSi models	Front	+.67° to +2.17°	+1.42°	−.92° to +.55°	+.17°	.39
	Prizm, M/T Except GSi models	Front	+.57° to +2.08°	+1.33°	−1.33° to +.17°	+.58°	.39
	Prizm, A/T GSi models	Front	+.67° to +2.17°	+1.42°	−.91° to +.59°	+.16°	.04
	Prizm, M/T GSi models	Front	+.57° to +2.08°	+1.33°	−1° to +.50°	−.25°	.04
	Prizm, A/T Except GSi models	Rear	—	—	−.17° to +1.33°	+.58°	1.57
	Prizm, M/T Except GSi models	Rear	—	—	−.8° to +1.42°	+.67°	1.57
	Prizm, A/T GSi models	Rear	—	—	−1.50° to .0°	−.75°	.16
	Prizm, M/T GSi models	Rear	—	—	−1.50° to .0°	−.75°	.16

COOLING SYSTEM & CAPACITY DATA

Year	Engine (VIN)	Cooling Capacity, Qts. Manual Trans.	Cooling Capacity, Qts. Auto. Trans.	Radiator Cap Relief Pressure, Lbs.	Thermo. Opening Temp.	Fuel Tank Gals.	Engine Oil Refill Qts.	Transaxle Oil Man. Transaxle Pts.	Transaxle Oil Auto. Transaxle Qts. ①
1988	1.6L/4-97 (4)	6.3	6.3	12.8	180	13.2	3.2②	2.7	5.8
1988	1.6L/4-97 (5)	6.4	6.4	12.8	180	13.2	3.6②	2.7	8.3
1990–91	1.6L/4-97 (5)	6.0	③	14.2	180	13.2	3.6②	2.7	④
	1.6L/4-97 (6)	6.0	③	14.2	180	13.2	3.2②	2.7	④

① —Approximate make final check with dipstick.
② —With filter change add .3 qt.
③ —Except 16 valve engine, 3.17; 16 valve engine, 3.6 less filter, 3.9 with filter.
④ —A131L models, 5.8; A240E models, 8.3.

Electrical
INDEX

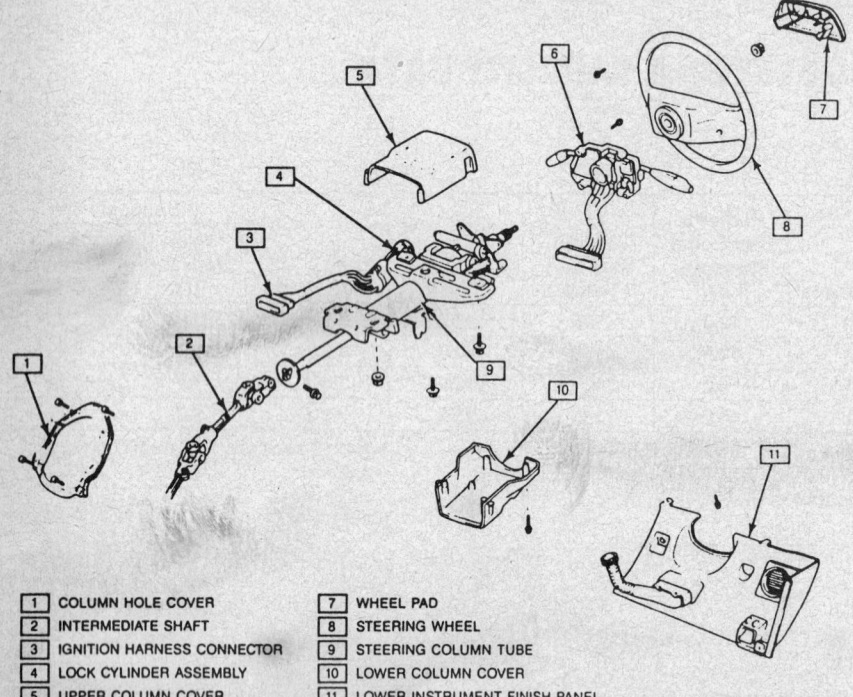

1 COLUMN HOLE COVER	7 WHEEL PAD
2 INTERMEDIATE SHAFT	8 STEERING WHEEL
3 IGNITION HARNESS CONNECTOR	9 STEERING COLUMN TUBE
4 LOCK CYLINDER ASSEMBLY	10 LOWER COLUMN COVER
5 UPPER COLUMN COVER	11 LOWER INSTRUMENT FINISH PANEL
6 MULTI-FUNCTION SWITCH	

Fig. 1   Steering column assembly. Prizm

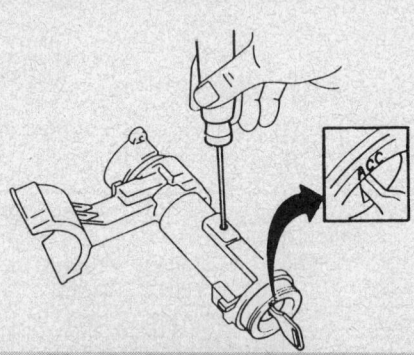

Fig. 2   Ignition cylinder removal. Prizm

FUSE PANEL & FLASHER LOCATION

There are three fuse blocks; the first is on the left front kick panel, the second is on the right front kick panel and the third is behind the battery. The flasher location is under the dash, left of the steering column.

STEERING WHEEL
REPLACE

1. Disconnect battery ground cable.
2. Remove steering column center cover and pad assembly.
3. Remove steering wheel retaining nut.
4. Using steering wheel puller tool No.

J-1859-03, or equivalent, remove steering wheel.
5. Reverse procedure to install, ensuring proper position of steering wheel.

IGNITION LOCK
REPLACE
NOVA

1. Remove steering wheel assembly.
2. Remove instrument lower finish panel, air duct and column lower cover.
3. Disconnect ignition and turn signal switch electrical connector.
4. Remove switch assembly from column upper cover.
5. Remove three screws and retainer from upper bracket.

6. Remove snap ring, insert key into ignition and release steering lock.
7. Tap out tapered head bolt.
8. Remove lock cylinder and retaining screw.
9. Reverse procedure to install.

PRIZM

1. Remove steering wheel as outlined under "Steering Wheel, Replace."
2. Remove upper and lower steering column covers, **Fig. 1**.
3. Disconnect ignition switch electrical connections.
4. Using a center punch, mark center of tapered-head bolts securing lock cylinder housing.
5. Drill into tapered-head bolts using a .12-.16 inch (3-4 mm) drill bit.
6. Remove tapered-head bolts using a bolt extractor.
7. Place ignition switch in ACC position.
8. Push down stop key and remove cylinder, **Fig. 2**.
9. Reverse procedure to install, tightening new tapered-head bolts until bolt heads break off.

IGNITION SWITCH
REPLACE

Refer to **Fig. 3** for ignition switch replacement.

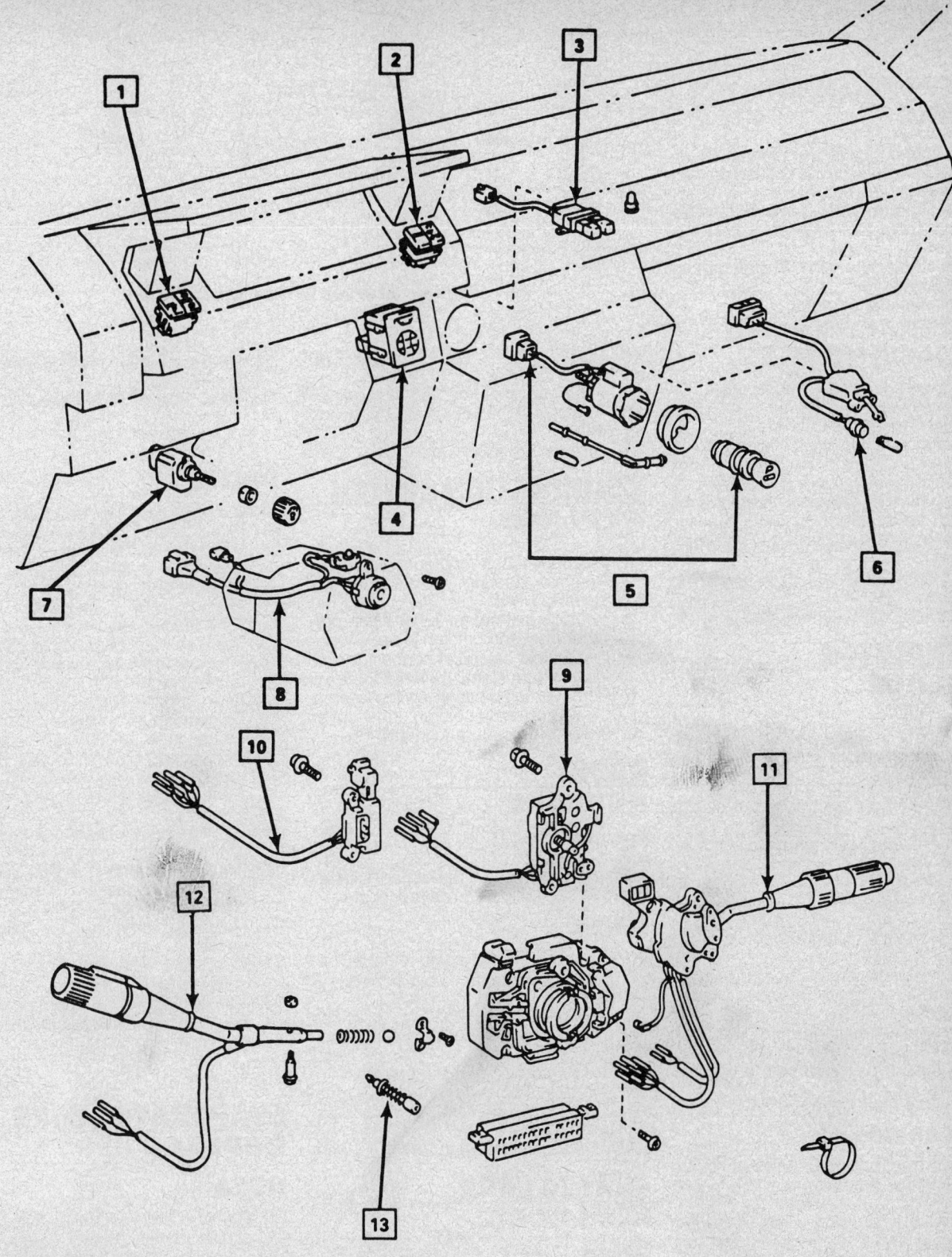

1. Defogger Switch
2. Rear Wiper Switch
3. A/C Switch
4. Mirror Switch
5. Lighter
6. Heater Blower Switch
7. Light Control Rheostat

8. Ignition/Starter Switch
9. Headlight Dimmer Switch
10. Turn Signal and Hazard Warning Switch
11. Wiper and Cruise Control Switch
12. Light Control Switch
13. Horn Contact

Fig. 3 Switches, installation

STARTER
REPLACE
EXCEPT PRIZM GSI MODELS

1. Disconnect battery ground cable.
2. Disconnect electrical connectors from starter motor, **Fig. 4.**
3. **On Nova models,** remove transmission cable and bracket at transmission.
4. **On all models,** remove starter motor attaching bolts.
5. Remove starter motor.
6. Reverse procedure to install.

PRIZM GSI MODELS

1. Disconnect battery ground cable.
2. Remove rear cooling fan.
3. Raise and support vehicle.
4. Remove right and left splash shields.
5. Disconnect oxygen sensor connector.
6. Disconnect forward exhaust pipe.
7. Disconnect electrical connections from starter assembly.
8. Remove starter assembly attaching bolts.
9. Remove starter assembly from vehicle.
10. Reverse procedure to install.

DISTRIBUTOR
REPLACE
NOVA
4A-LC Engine

1. Disconnect battery ground cable.
2. Disconnect distributor wire at electrical connector.
3. Disconnect distributor vacuum hoses, then the vacuum advance unit.
4. Disconnect distributor cap with spark plug cables connected, then position aside.
5. Disconnect distributor hold-down bolts.
6. Note position of rotor, then pull distributor outward until it stops rotating counterclockwise.
7. Reverse procedure to install. Check to ensure marks made during removal are correctly aligned during installation.
8. Adjust ignition timing.

4A-GE Engine

1. Disconnect battery ground cable.
2. Disconnect distributor wire at connector.
3. Remove spark plug wires from ignition coil and spark plugs.
4. Remove distributor hold-down bolts, then the distributor and O-ring.
5. Reverse procedure to install.

PRIZM

1. Disconnect battery ground cable.
2. Disconnect distributor electrical connectors.
3. Remove distributor cap and spark plug cables and position aside.

4. Mark distributor housing and rotor position.
5. Remove distributor mounting bolts.
6. Remove distributor and O-ring form engine.
7. Reverse procedure to install.

COMBINATION SWITCH
REPLACE

1. Disconnect battery ground cable.
2. Remove steering wheel cover and steering wheel.
3. Remove instrument lower finish panel, air duct and column lower cover.
4. Disconnect electrical connector from ignition/turn signal switch, **Fig. 3.**
5. Remove combination switch assembly with steering column upper cover.
6. Reverse procedure to install.

RADIO
REPLACE
NOVA

Refer to "Instrument Panel Pad/Cluster, Replace" for radio removal procedure.

PRIZM

1. Disconnect battery ground cable.
2. Remove steering column covers.
3. Remove console trim bezel.
4. Disconnect rear wiper/washer, cruise control and defogger electrical connections.
5. Remove radio attaching screws.
6. Remove radio from console.
7. Disconnect radio connections and antenna cable.
8. Reverse procedure to install.

HEATER CORE
REPLACE
NOVA

1. Disconnect battery ground cable, then drain cooling system.
2. Disconnect heater hose at engine compartment.
3. Remove six clips attaching lower part of case.
4. Remove lower part of case, then using suitable tool, pry open lower part of case.

5. Remove heater core assembly from heater case.
6. Reverse procedure to install.

PRIZM

1. Remove steering wheel as outlined under "Steering Wheel, Replace."
2. Remove trim bezel, instrument panel assembly, cluster assembly, center console and all console trim as outlined under "Instrument Panel Pad/Cluster, Replace."
3. Remove cup holder from console.
4. Remove radio as outlined under "Radio, Replace."
5. Drain cooling system.
6. Disconnect all cables and ducts from heater case.
7. Disconnect blower switch harness and heater control assembly.
8. Remove two center console support braces.
9. Remove heater hoses from case and grommets from cowl.
10. Remove mounting bolts, nuts and clips from heater and air distribution cases.
11. Remove heater and air distribution cases.
12. Remove screws and clips from case, separate case halves.
13. Remove heater core from case.
14. Reverse procedure to install.

EVAPORATOR CORE
REPLACE
NOVA

1. Remove A/C module as follows:
   a. Disconnect battery ground cable and discharge refrigerant.
   b. Disconnect refrigerant lines from evaporator fittings, then plug lines and open fittings.
   c. Remove evaporator inlet and outlet fitting grommets.
   d. Remove glove box and instrument panel cover.
   e. Disconnect main A/C harness connector and electrical connector from A/C switch.

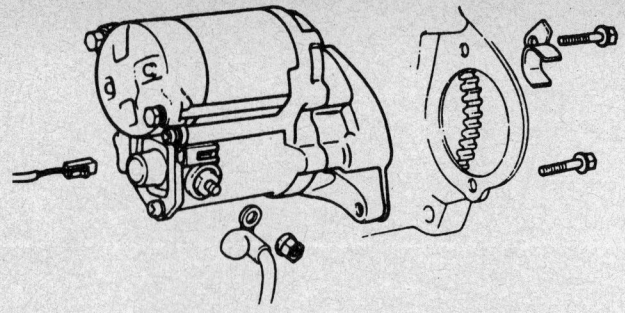

Fig. 4   Starter motor installation

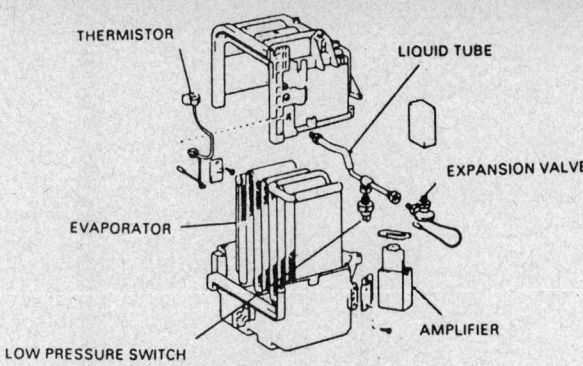

Fig. 5 Evaporator core. Nova

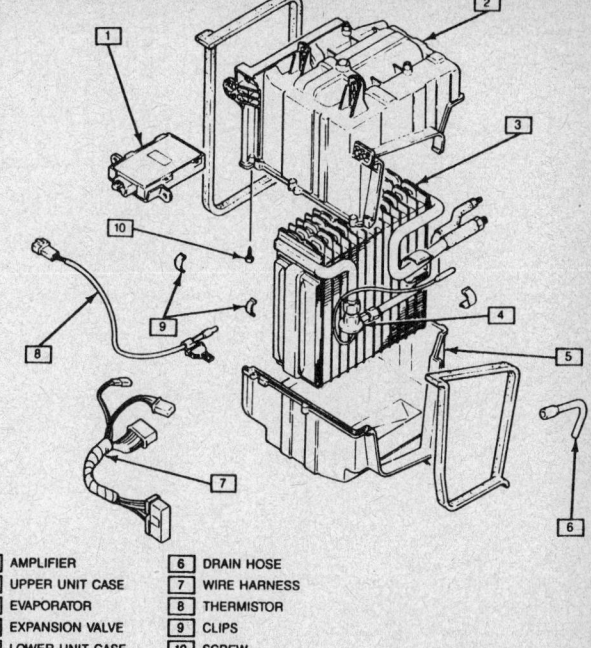

1	AMPLIFIER	6	DRAIN HOSE
2	UPPER UNIT CASE	7	WIRE HARNESS
3	EVAPORATOR	8	THERMISTOR
4	EXPANSION VALVE	9	CLIPS
5	LOWER UNIT CASE	10	SCREW

Fig. 6 Evaporator core. Prizm

f. Remove 4 nuts and 3 bolts securing A/C module, then lower module.

g. Remove A/C amplifier and harness assembly from A/C module.

2. Remove thermistor retaining screw and thermistor, **Fig. 5.**
3. Remove clamps and two screws joining evaporator case, then remove lower case.
4. Remove two screws securing upper case to evaporator.
5. Remove heat insulator and clamp from outlet tube.
6. Remove inlet tube from expansion valve and expansion valve from evaporator.
7. Remove pressure switch.
8. Reverse procedure to install.

PRIZM

1. Disconnect battery ground cable.
2. Discharge refrigeration system.
3. Remove and cap suction and liquid tube from evaporator case outlet and inlet fittings.
4. Remove grommets from inlet and outlet fittings.
5. Remove glove box compartment.
6. Disconnect wiring harness connectors.
7. Remove case attaching screws and remove evaporator case from behind instrument panel.
8. Separate upper and lower case halves, **Fig. 6.**
9. Disconnect liquid tube from inlet fitting of the expansion tube.
10. Remove packing and heat sensing tube from suction tube of evaporator.
11. Remove expansion valve.
12. Reverse procedure to install.

BLOWER MOTOR
REPLACE

NOVA

1. Disconnect battery ground cable.
2. Remove evaporator assembly, if equipped.
3. Disconnect electrical connector from blower motor.
4. Disconnect air source selector control cable from blower assembly side.

5. Loosen nuts and bolts, then remove blower assembly.
6. Reverse procedure to install.

PRIZM

1. Disconnect battery ground cable.
2. Disconnect rubber air duct running between motor and heater assembly.
3. Disconnect blower motor electrical connectors.
4. Remove blower motor attaching screws.
5. Remove blower motor from under instrument panel.
6. Reverse procedure to install.

WIPER MOTOR
REPLACE
FRONT

1. Disconnect battery ground cable.
2. Disconnect wiper motor electrical connection.
3. Remove wiper motor attaching bolts.
4. Disconnect wiper linkage from wiper motor output arm.
5. Remove wiper motor.
6. Reverse procedure to install.

REAR

1. Disconnect battery ground cable.
2. Remove wiper arm assembly.
3. Remove liftgate trim panel.
4. Disconnect wiper motor electrical connector.
5. Remove wiper motor attaching bolts.
6. Remove rear wiper motor assembly.
7. Reverse procedure to install.

INSTRUMENT PANEL PAD/CLUSTER
REPLACE
NOVA

1. Disconnect battery ground cable.
2. Remove steering wheel assembly.
3. Remove left speaker grille.
4. Remove steering column lower trim cover.
5. Remove hood release lever.
6. Remove heater duct.
7. Remove meter hood, A/C registers and hood, **Fig. 7.**
8. Remove combination meter, disconnect speedometer cable and electrical connectors. Remove meter from instrument panel.
9. Remove end finish panel.
10. Remove panel under cover.
11. Remove right side speaker grille.
12. Remove speaker bracket and speaker.
13. Remove glove compartment door and hinge.
14. Remove glove compartment door lock striker.
15. Remove center cluster finish panel.
16. Remove radio equipment assembly.
17. Remove lower center cluster finish panel.
18. Disconnect vacuum lines and electrical connectors, then remove heater control panel.
19. Remove side defroster nozzle.
20. Remove instrument panel pad assembly.
21. Reverse procedure to install.

PRIZM
Cluster, Replace

1. Disconnect battery ground cable.

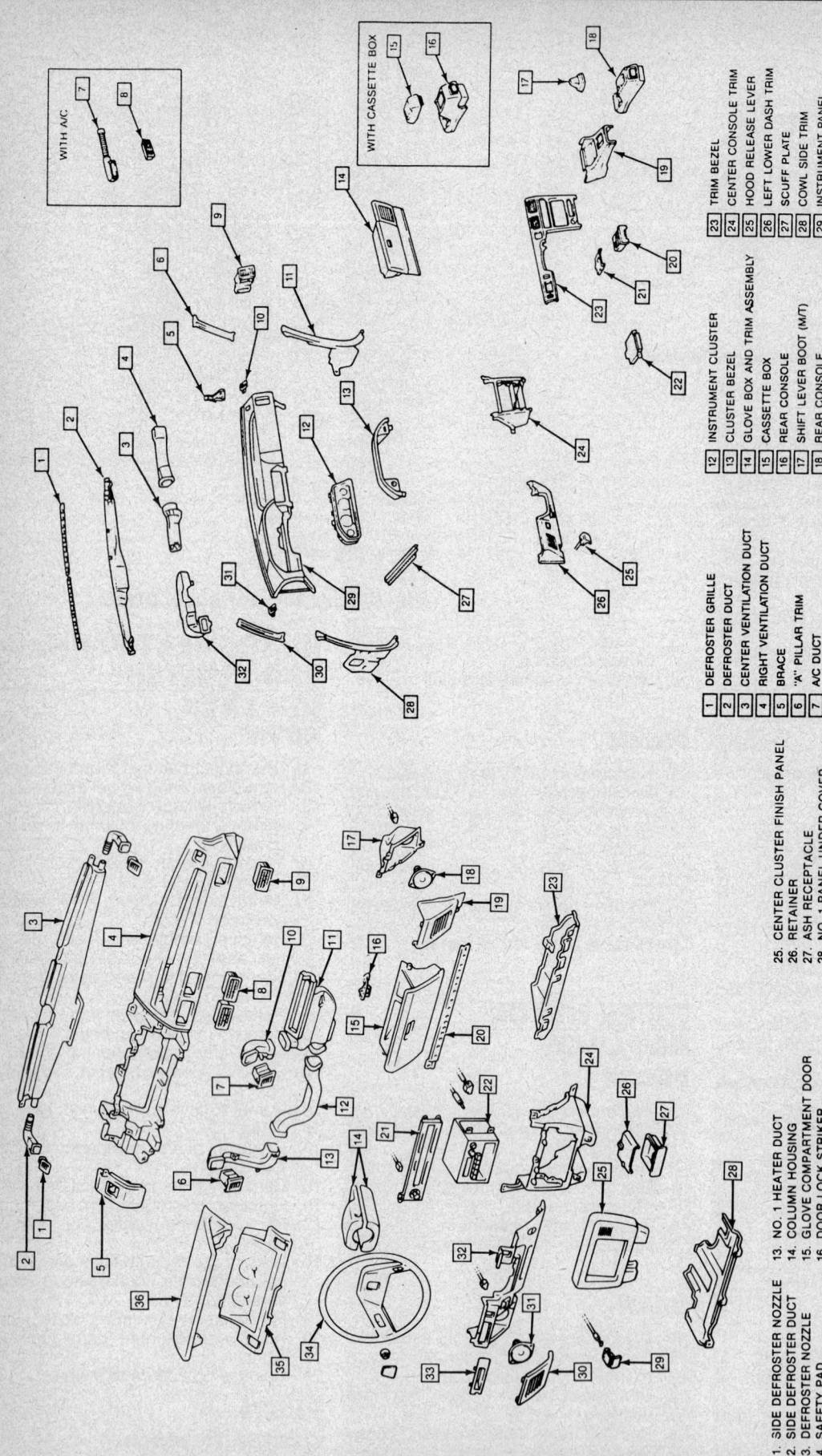

Fig. 8 Instrument panel & related components. Prizm

1	DEFROSTER GRILLE
2	DEFROSTER DUCT
3	CENTER VENTILATION DUCT
4	RIGHT VENTILATION DUCT
5	BRACE
6	"A" PILLAR TRIM
7	A/C DUCT
8	LOWER A/C DEFLECTOR
9	RIGHT VENTILATION DEFLECTOR
10	RIGHT WINDOW DEFLECTOR
11	COWL SIDE TRIM
12	INSTRUMENT CLUSTER
13	CLUSTER BEZEL
14	GLOVE BOX AND TRIM ASSEMBLY
15	CASSETTE BOX
16	REAR CONSOLE
17	SHIFT LEVER BOOT (M/T)
18	REAR CONSOLE
19	FRONT CONSOLE
20	ASHTRAY
21	RETAINER
22	CUP HOLDER
23	TRIM BEZEL
24	CENTER CONSOLE TRIM
25	HOOD RELEASE LEVER
26	LEFT LOWER DASH TRIM
27	SCUFF PLATE
28	COWL SIDE TRIM
29	INSTRUMENT PANEL
30	"A" PILLAR TRIM
31	LEFT WINDOW DEFLECTOR
32	LEFT VENTILATION DUCT

Fig. 7 Instrument panel & related components. Nova

1.	SIDE DEFROSTER NOZZLE
2.	SIDE DEFROSTER DUCT
3.	DEFROSTER NOZZLE
4.	SAFETY PAD
5.	END FINISH PANEL
6.	NO. 1 REGISTER
7.	NO. 2 REGISTER
8.	CENTER REGISTER
9.	SIDE REGISTER
10.	NO. 3 HEATER DUCT
11.	DUCT
12.	NO. 2 HEATER DUCT
13.	NO. 1 HEATER DUCT
14.	COLUMN HOUSING
15.	GLOVE COMPARTMENT DOOR
16.	DOOR LOCK STRIKER
17.	SPEAKER BRACKET
18.	SPEAKER
19.	NO. 2 SPEAKER PANEL
20.	HINGE
21.	HEATER CONTROL PANEL
22.	RADIO
23.	NO. 2 PANEL UNDER COVER
24.	LOWER CENTER CLUSTER FINISH PANEL
25.	CENTER CLUSTER FINISH PANEL
26.	RETAINER
27.	ASH RECEPTACLE
28.	NO. 1 PANEL UNDER COVER
29.	ENGINE HOOD RELEASE LEVER
30.	NO. 1 SPEAKER PANEL
31.	SPEAKER
32.	LOWER FINISH PANEL
33.	FINISH PANEL
34.	STEERING WHEEL
35.	COMBINATION METER
36.	METER HOOD

2. Disconnect hood release lever.
3. Remove lefthand lower dash trim panel screws and pull out trim, **Fig. 8.**
4. Disconnect speaker connector.
5. Remove A/C duct from lower A/C register, if equipped.
6. Remove lefthand lower trim panel.
7. Remove upper and lower steering column covers.
8. Remove center console trim panel screws and pull out trim.
9. Disconnect and remove cruise control/defogger and rear wiper/washer switches from trim panel.
10. Disconnect and remove cigar lighter lamp from trim panel.
11. Remove center trim panel.
12. Remove cluster bezel attaching screws.

13. Disconnect hazard flasher and dimmer switch electrical connections.
14. Remove cluster bezel.
15. Remove instrument cluster attaching screws.
16. Disconnect speedometer cable and electrical connectors from cluster.
17. Remove instrument cluster.
18. Reverse procedure to install.

Instrument Panel, Replace

1. Disconnect battery ground cable.
2. Remove steering wheel as outlined under "Steering Wheel, Replace."
3. Remove instrument cluster as outlined under "Cluster, Replace."

4. Remove cup holder.
5. Remove radio as outlined under "Radio, Replace."
6. Remove glove box and trim assembly.
7. Remove four attaching screws from heater and A/C control unit.
8. Remove center console trim.
9. Remove five attaching bolts from instrument panel.
10. Disconnect three electrical connectors and relay unit on the lefthand side of instrument panel.
11. Disconnect the electrical connector on the righthand side of instrument panel.
12. Detach defroster duct retainers and remove instrument panel.
13. Reverse procedure to install.

1.6L/4-97 Engine

INDEX

ENGINE MOUNT
REPLACE

EXCEPT 16 VALVE ENGINE

1. Disconnect battery ground cable.
2. Raise and support vehicle.
3. Loosen center engine mount.
4. Lower vehicle.
5. Support engine assembly.
6. Disconnect engine mount at engine assembly.
7. Raise engine assembly.
8. Remove engine mount.
9. Reverse procedure to install.

16 VALVE ENGINE
Nova

1. Disconnect battery ground cable.
2. Support engine using engine support tool No. J-28467, or equivalent.
3. Raise and support vehicle.

4. Remove hole covers from center member.
5. Remove two bolts and nuts from front, rear and righthand engine mount.
6. Lower vehicle and remove bolts from lefthand engine mount.
7. Remove engine mount through bolts.
8. Remove engine mounts.
9. Reverse procedure to install.

Prizm

1. Disconnect battery ground cable.
2. Support engine using engine support tool No. J-28467-A, or equivalent.
3. Raise and support vehicle.
4. Remove right lower stone shield.
5. Remove two lower engine mount to engine bracket nuts.
6. Lower vehicle.
7. Remove bolts and right engine mount support.
8. Remove upper bolt from engine mount to engine bracket.
9. Remove windshield washer reservoir.
10. Remove right engine mount through

bolt and engine mount.
11. Reverse procedure to install.

ENGINE
REPLACE

EXCEPT 16 VALVE ENGINE

1. Disconnect battery ground cable.
2. Drain coolant and engine oil.
3. Drain transmission fluid.
4. Mark hood hinges, then remove hood.
5. Remove air cleaner assembly.
6. Disconnect upper radiator hose at outlet and overflow hose.
7. Disconnect coolant hose at cylinder head rear coolant pipe.
8. Disconnect coolant hose at thermostat housing.
9. Disconnect fuel lines from fuel pump.
10. Mark, then disconnect all vacuum lines and electrical connectors from engine assembly.
11. Remove drive belts.

12. Disconnect speedometer cable from transaxle assembly.
13. Raise and support vehicle.
14. Disconnect exhaust pipe from exhaust manifold.
15. Disconnect air hose from converter pipe, if applicable.
16. Disconnect transaxle cooler lines from radiator.
17. Remove left and righthand under covers.
18. Remove power steering pump and A/C compressor, if equipped and position aside.
19. Disconnect cable and bracket from transaxle.
20. Disconnect steering knuckles from lower control arms.
21. Disconnect driveshafts from transaxle.
22. Remove flywheel cover.
23. Remove flex plate to torque converter attaching bolts.
24. Disconnect front and rear mounting from center crossmember.
25. Disconnect cable and remove center member.
26. Lower vehicle.
27. Remove radiator and fan assembly.
28. Install suitable engine lifting equipment on to engine lifting eyes.
29. Remove righthand motor mount through bolt.
30. Remove lefthand transaxle mount bolt and mount.
31. Remove engine and transaxle as an assembly.
32. Reverse procedure to install.

16 VALVE ENGINE

1. Disconnect battery ground and positive cables, then remove battery and engine compartment hood.
2. Remove right and left side engine under covers.
3. Drain engine oil into suitable container.
4. Drain coolant from radiator and engine block into suitable container.
5. **On models equipped with man. trans.,** drain transaxle fluid into suitable container.
6. **On all models,** remove air cleaner assembly and coolant reservoir tank.
7. Remove radiator and coolant fan as an assembly.
8. Disconnect heater hoses from coolant inlet housing.
9. Disconnect fuel pressure hose from fuel filter, then the heater and air hoses from air valve.
10. Disconnect fuel return hose from fuel pressure regulator.
11. **On models equipped with man. trans.,** remove clutch slave cylinder without disconnecting hydraulic line and position aside.
12. **On all models,** disconnect vacuum hose from charcoal canister.
13. Disconnect transaxle shift control cables from transaxle.
14. Disconnect speedometer cable, then the cruise control cable (if equipped), accelerator cable and accelerator link.
15. **On models equipped with cruise control,** remove cruise control actuator.

16. **On Nova models,** proceed as follows:
    a. Disconnect ignition coil wiring, then remove coil.
    b. Remove righthand side interior cowl panel, then disconnect No. 4 junction block connectors.
    c. Remove Electronic Control Unit (ECU) cover, then disconnect ECU connectors.
    d. Pull engine main wire harness into engine compartment, then disconnect the following:
    e. No. 2 junction block connectors (located in engine compartment).
    f. Starter cable from battery positive.
    g. Ground strap terminals.
    h. Washer change valve connector.
    i. Cruise control vacuum pump and vacuum switch connectors (if equipped).
    j. Solenoid resistor connector.
17. **On Prizm models,** Disconnect engine main electrical harness from all related sensors and switches.
18. **On all models,** disconnect brake booster hose from intake manifold.
19. Remove A/C compressor and power steering pump (if equipped) with lines attached and position aside.
20. Disconnect oxygen sensor electrical connector, then remove oxygen sensor.
21. Disconnect oil cooler hoses from oil cooler.
22. Raise and support vehicle, then disconnect catalytic converter clamp, engine pipe clamp and engine pipe from exhaust manifold.
23. Disconnect front and rear engine mounts-to-center member attaching bolts, then remove front mount through bolt and mount.
24. Remove center member-to-frame attaching bolts, then the center member.
25. Remove axle-to-side gear shaft attaching bolts, then disconnect right side lower arm from steering knuckle and separate. Remove axle shafts from side gear shafts and position aside with suitable wire.
26. Lower vehicle to ground level.
27. Attach suitable lifting equipment to engine/transaxle assembly, then remove right and left side mounts.
28. Carefully lift engine/transaxle assembly from vehicle and place on suitable stand.
29. Remove radiator fan temperature switch connector and cold start injector time switch connector.
30. Disconnect vacuum hoses from Bi-Metal Vacuum Switching Valves (BVSV), then remove coolant inlet housing attaching bolts and nut.
31. Disconnect hoses from coolant bypass tubes, then remove coolant inlet housing.
32. Disconnect back-up lamp switch connector, water temperature sensor connector and water temperature switch connector.
33. **On models equipped with auto. trans.,** neutral start switch connectors and transaxle solenoid connector.

34. **On models equipped with auto. trans.,** rotate crankshaft as necessary to gain access to and remove six torque converter attaching bolts.
35. **On all models,** remove starter assembly, then separate transaxle from engine.
36. Reverse procedure to install.

CYLINDER HEAD REPLACE

EXCEPT 16 VALVE ENGINE

1. Disconnect battery ground cable.
2. Drain cooling system.
3. Remove air cleaner assembly.
4. Raise and support vehicle.
5. Drain engine oil.
6. Disconnect exhaust pipe from exhaust manifold and exhaust bracket from engine.
7. Disconnect air hose from converter pipe.
8. Loosen power steering pivot bolt, if equipped.
9. Lower vehicle.
10. Disconnect accelerator and throttle cable from carburetor and bracket.
11. Mark, then disconnect all vacuum lines and electrical connectors from cylinder head assembly.
12. Disconnect fuel lines from fuel pump.
13. Disconnect upper radiator hose, water outlet and heater hose.
14. Remove power steering bracket, if equipped.
15. Place No. 1 cylinder at TDC of compression stroke, then disconnect spark plug wires and remove distributor assembly.
16. Remove PCV valve and wiring harness.
17. Remove No. 1 (upper) timing belt cover bolts, **Fig. 1.**
18. Remove cylinder head cover and gasket.
19. Remove alternator drive belt and water pump pulley bolts.
20. Remove No. 1 (upper) timing cover and gasket.
21. Mark camshaft timing pulley position and timing belt rotational direction.
22. Loosen idler pulley and move aside slightly to release timing belt tension, then snug down pulley bolt.
23. Pull timing belt away from camshaft timing pulley.
24. Loosen and remove cylinder head bolts gradually in three steps and in sequence shown in **Fig. 2.**
25. Remove cylinder head with intake and exhaust manifolds attached.
26. Reverse procedure to install, noting the following:
    a. Install cylinder head, then gradually tighten cylinder head bolts in three steps and in sequence shown in **Fig. 3,** to 43 ft. lbs.
    b. Install camshaft timing pulley and timing belt in original (marked) position as removed.

16 VALVE ENGINE
Nova

1. Disconnect battery ground cable.

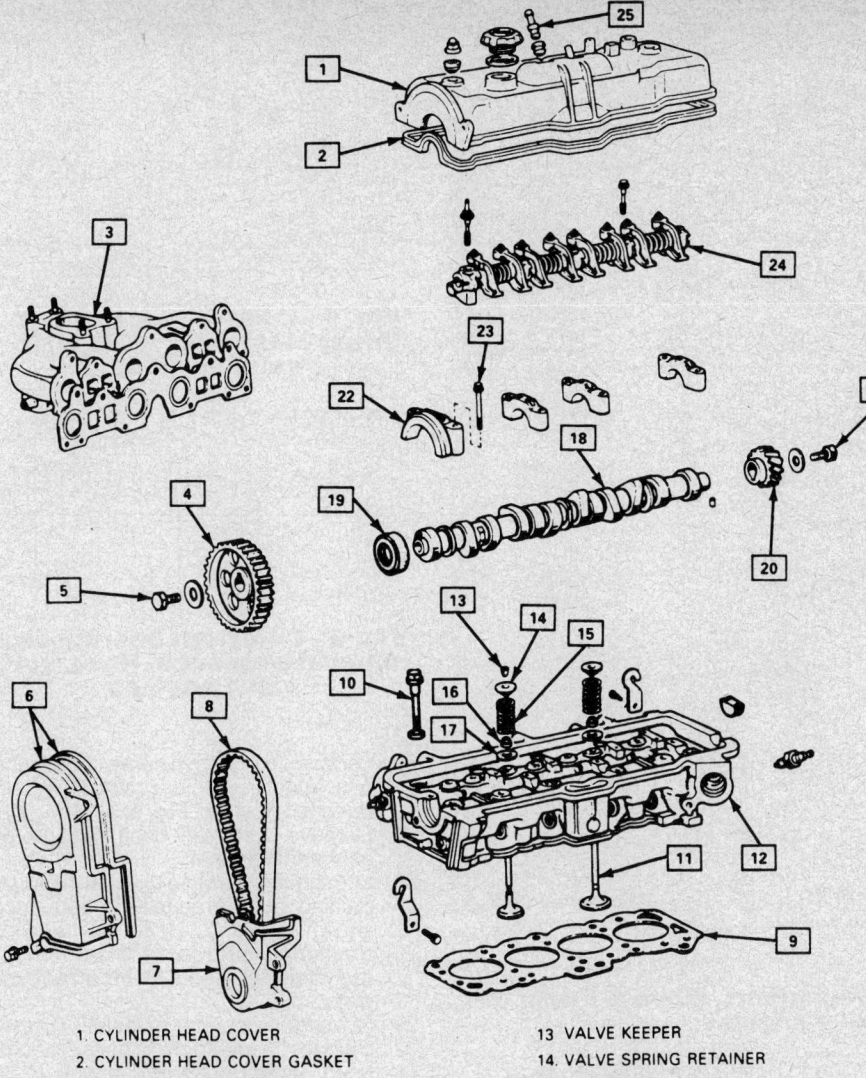

Fig. 1 **Cylinder head & related components. Except 16 valve engine**

1. CYLINDER HEAD COVER
2. CYLINDER HEAD COVER GASKET
3. EXHAUST MANIFOLD
4. CAMSHAFT TIMING PULLEY
5. 47 N·m (34 FT.LBS)
6. TIMING BELT UPPER COVER AND GASKET
7. TIMING BELT LOWER COVER
8. TIMING BELT
9. HEAD GASKET
10. 59 N·m (43 FT.LBS)
11. VALVE
12. CYLINDER HEAD

13. VALVE KEEPER
14. VALVE SPRING RETAINER
15. VALVE SPRING
16. VALVE STEM OIL SEAL
17. VALVE SPRING SEAT
18. CAMSHAFT
19. CAMSHAFT OIL SEAL
20. DRIVE GEAR
21. 29 N·m (22 FT.LBS)
22. CAMSHAFT BEARING CAP
23. 13 N·m (9 FT.LBS)
24. ROCKER ARM ASSEMBLY
25. PCV VALVE

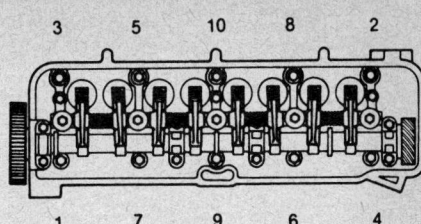

Fig. 2 **Cylinder head bolt loosening sequence. Except 16 valve engine**

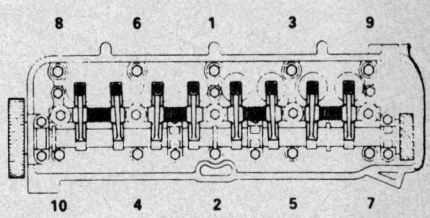

Fig. 3 **Cylinder head bolt tightening sequence. Except 16 valve engine**

2. Remove engine under cover, then drain coolant into suitable container.
3. Remove air cleaner assembly, then disconnect cruise control cable (if equipped) and accelerator cable and link.
4. Disconnect heater hose from rear cylinder head cover.
5. Identify, then disconnect vacuum hoses from throttle body.
6. Remove cruise control actuator (if equipped), ignition coil and coolant outlet hose.
7. Remove brake booster vacuum hose, then the PCV hose.
8. Remove EGR valve and tubes, then the cold start injector pressure hose.
9. Remove fuel system pulsation damper and pressure regulator.
10. Disconnect heater bypass hoses from auxiliary air valve.
11. Disconnect water temperature sensor connector and water temperature switch connector (if equipped), then identify and remove vacuum hoses from vacuum tubes. Remove vacuum tubes attaching bolts, then the vacuum tubes, cylinder head rear cover and wire clamp.
12. Disconnect all wires necessary for cylinder head removal, then lay wire harness aside.
13. Remove distributor, then the front exhaust pipe, **Fig. 4.**
14. Remove exhaust manifold insulator, oxygen sensor and the manifold support bracket.
15. Remove exhaust manifold, then the oxygen sensor gasket.
16. Remove fuel delivery pipe and fuel injectors.
17. Remove intake manifold and intake air control valve.
18. Remove power steering drive belt and alternator drive belt.
19. Remove cylinder head center cover, then the valve covers.
20. Remove coolant outlet, coolant bypass pipe and drive belt adjusting bar and gasket.
21. Remove spark plugs, then set crankshaft pulley at TDC compression stroke. **Ensure valve lifters for No. 1 cylinder are loose. If not, rotate crankshaft pulley an additional 360° to set engine at TDC compression.**
22. Position suitable jack and wooden block under engine and raise slightly, then remove right side engine mount through bolt and mount.
23. Remove water pump pulley, then on models equipped with A/C, the A/C compressor idler pulley. On all models, remove No. 2 and 3 timing belt covers.
24. If timing belt is to be replaced, refer to "Timing Belt, Replace" for procedure. If timing belt is to be reused, proceed as follows:
  a. Place alignment marks on the camshaft timing pulleys and belt.
  b. Loosen idler pulley bolt, then push idler pulley as far left as possible and temporarily tighten it.
  c. Remove timing belt from camshaft timing pulleys. **Support timing**

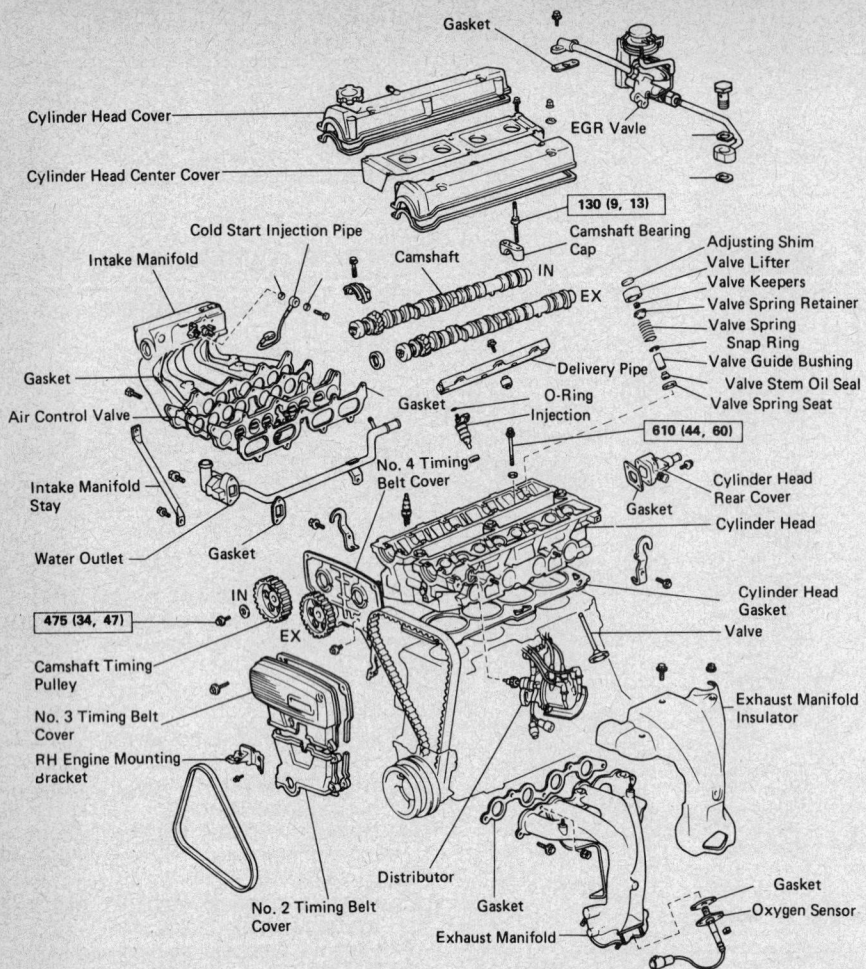

Fig. 4 Cylinder head & related components. Nova & Prizm GSi models w/16 valve engine

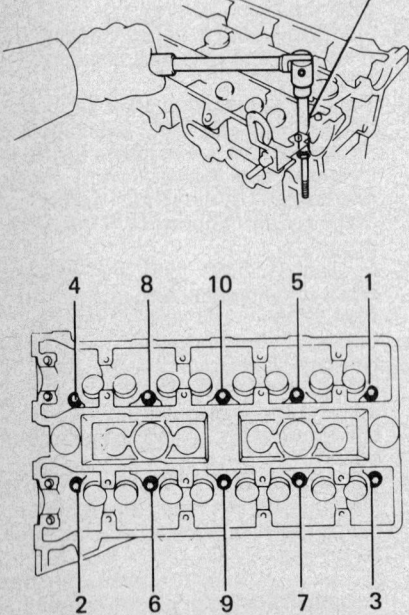

Fig. 7 Cylinder head bolt loosening sequence. Nova & Prizm GSi model w/16 valve engines

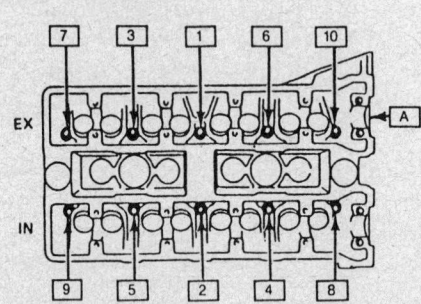

A   CYLINDER HEAD

Fig. 8 Cylinder head bolt tightening sequence. Nova & Prizm GSi models w/16 valve engines

belt so meshing of crankshaft timing pulley and timing belt does not shift.

d. Remove camshaft timing pulleys, right mounting bracket attaching bolts and mount and No. 4 timing belt cover.

25. Measure camshaft thrust clearance, **Fig. 5.** If clearance is greater than .0118 inch, replace camshaft and/or cylinder head.

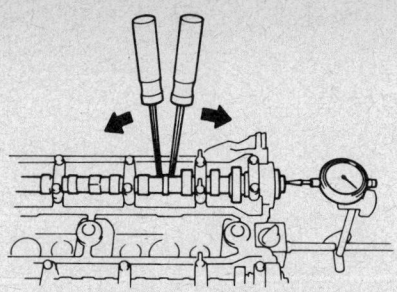

Fig. 5 Measuring camshaft thrust clearance. Nova w/16 valve engines

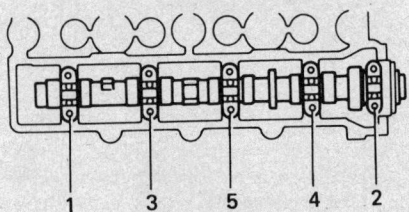

Fig. 6 Camshaft bearing cap removal sequence. Nova w/16 valve engines

26. Loosen and remove camshaft bearing cap attaching bolts gradually in sequence shown in **Fig. 6.**
27. Remove camshaft bearing caps, oil seal and camshaft.
28. Loosen and remove cylinder head attaching bolts gradually in sequence shown in **Fig. 7. Head warpage or cracking could result from removing cylinder head in incorrect order.**
29. Reverse procedure to install. **Torque** cylinder head attaching bolts gradually in three steps in sequence as shown in, **Fig. 8,** to 44 ft. lbs. Torque bearing cap attaching bolts gradually in three steps in reverse sequence as disassembly, **Fig. 6,** to specifications.

Prizm Except GSi Model

1. Disconnect battery ground cable.
2. Drain coolant into a suitable container.
3. Raise and support vehicle.
4. Remove righthand lower stone shield.
5. Disconnect two mount nut and stud protectors, then remove two rear transaxle mount to main crossmember mount nuts.
6. Remove two center mount to center crossmember nuts.
7. Lower vehicle.
8. Remove air cleaner assembly.
9. Disconnect throttle, cruise control and transaxle kick down cables.
10. Mark then disconnect all necessary electrical and vacuum connections.
11. Disconnect fuel inlet line.
12. Disconnect cold start injector pipe and the fuel rail.
13. Remove heater hoses water outlet and inlet housings, **Fig. 9.**
14. Remove spark plugs and PVC valve.
15. Remove cylinder head cover.
16. Loosen the A/C compressor, power

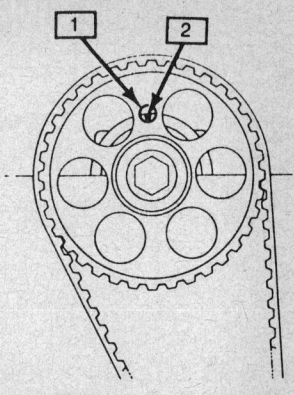

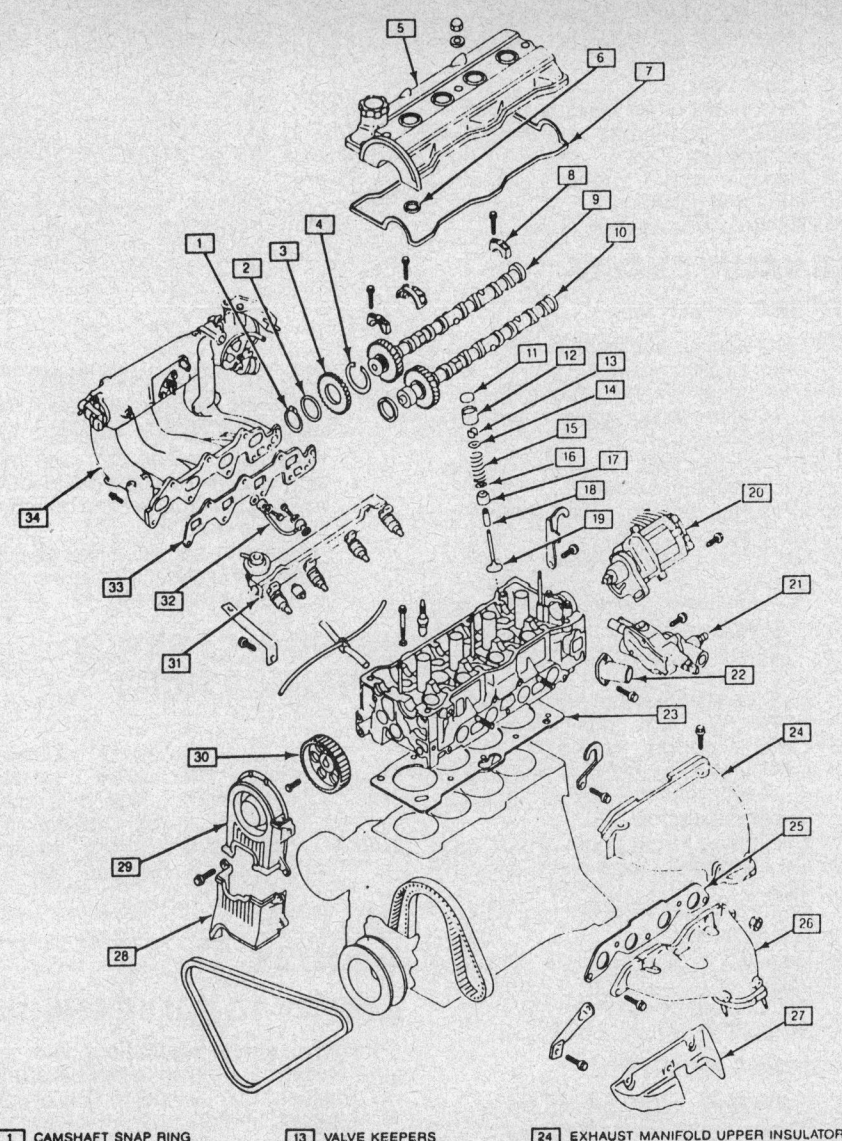

| 1 | CAMSHAFT GEAR HOLE |
| 2 | EXHAUST CAMSHAFT CAP MARK |

Fig. 10 Aligning camshaft gear hole. Prizm except GSi models

pulley and align its groove with the "0" mark of timing belt cover. **Ensure that camshaft gear hole is aligned with exhaust camshaft cap mark, Fig. 10.**

31. Remove plug from lower timing belt cover and place alignment marks on camshaft timing gear and belt.
32. Loosen idler pulley mount bolt and push idler pulley toward left then tighten temporarily.
33. Remove timing belt from camshaft timing gear. **Support timing belt so meshing of crankshaft timing gear and belt do not shift. Do not allow oil, water or dust to come in contact with timing belt.**
34. Remove cylinder head bolts in sequence shown in **Fig. 11.**
35. Remove cylinder head with intake and exhaust manifolds attached.
36. Reverse procedure to install, **torquing** cylinder head bolts in several steps in sequence shown in **Fig. 12** to 44 ft. lbs.

Prizm GSi Model

1. Disconnect battery ground cable.
2. Drain cooling system into a suitable container.
3. Remove air cleaner assembly, then disconnect cruise control cable (if equipped), accelerator cable and link.
4. Disconnect heater hose from rear cylinder head cover.
5. Identify, then disconnect vacuum hoses from throttle body.
6. Remove cruise control actuator (if equipped), ignition coil and coolant outlet hose.
7. Remove ignition coil.
8. Remove water outlet hose and outlet from cylinder head.
9. Remove brake booster vacuum hose, then the PCV hose.
10. Remove EGR valve and tubes, then the cold start injector pressure hose.
11. Disconnect water by-pass hoses from auxiliary air valve.
12. Remove vacuum pipe and cylinder rear cover.
13. Remove distributor as outlined under "Distributor, Replace" in the "Electrical" section.

1	CAMSHAFT SNAP RING	13	VALVE KEEPERS	24	EXHAUST MANIFOLD UPPER INSULATOR
2	WAVE WASHER	14	VALVE SPRING RETAINER	25	EXHAUST MANIFOLD GASKET
3	CAMSHAFT SUB-GEAR	15	VALVE SPRING	26	EXHAUST MANIFOLD
4	CAMSHAFT GEAR SPRING	16	VALVE SPRING SEAT	27	EXHAUST MANIFOLD LOWER INSULATOR
5	CYLINDER HEAD COVER	17	VALVE STEM OIL SEAL	28	CENTER TIMING BELT COVER
6	SPARK PLUG TUBE GASKET	18	VALVE GUIDE BUSHING	29	UPPER TIMING BELT COVER
7	CYLINDER HEAD COVER GASKET	19	VALVE	30	CAMSHAFT TIMING GEAR
8	CAMSHAFT BEARING CAP	20	DISTRIBUTOR	31	FUEL RAIL
9	CAMSHAFT (INTAKE)	21	WATER INLET HOUSING	32	COLD-START INJECTOR PIPE
10	CAMSHAFT (EXHAUST)	22	WATER OUTLET HOUSING	33	INTAKE MANIFOLD GASKET
11	ADJUSTING SHIM	23	HEAD GASKET	34	INTAKE MANIFOLD
12	VALVE LIFTER				

Fig. 9 Cylinder head & related components. Prizm except GSi models

steering pump and alternator brackets then remove accessary drive belts.
17. Remove A/C idler pulley.
18. Remove cruise control actuator and bracket.
19. Remove windshield washer reservoir.
20. Support engine using engine support tool No. J-28467-A, or equivalent.
21. Remove right engine mount through bolt and raise engine.
22. Remove water pump pulley and lower engine.
23. Remove engine wiring harness from upper timing belt cover.

24. Raise and support vehicle.
25. Remove cylinder head to cylinder block bracket then the exhaust manifold support bracket.
26. Disconnect exhaust pipe from exhaust manifold.
27. Remove upper and center timing belt covers.
28. Remove right engine mount bracket.
29. Remove distributor as outlined under "Distributor, Replace" in the "Electrical" section.
30. Place No. 1 cylinder at TDC on its compression stroke. Turn crankshaft

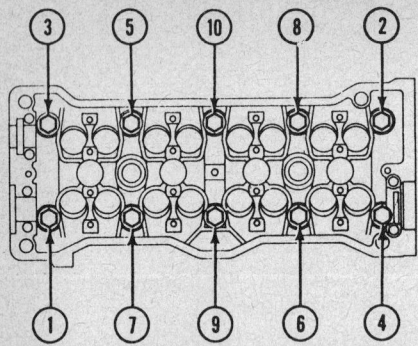

Fig. 11   Cylinder bolt removal sequence. Prizm except GSi models

14. Disconnect exhaust manifold from cylinder head as outlined under "Intake & Exhaust Manifold, Replace."
15. Remove delivery pipe with injectors.
16. Remove intake manifold as outlined under "Intake & Exhaust Manifold, Replace."
17. Remove power steering and alternator drive belts.
18. Remove cylinder head cover and spark plugs.
19. Set crankshaft pulley at TDC of compression stroke. **Ensure valve lifters for No. 1 cylinder are loose. If not, rotate crankshaft pulley an additional 360° to set engine at TDC compression.**
20. Disconnect right engine mount.
21. Remove water pump pulley then timing belt covers and timing belt as outlined under "Timing Belt Cover, Replace" and "Timing Belt & Camshaft Timing Pulley, Replace."
22. Remove camshaft as outlined under "Camshaft, Replace."
23. Remove cylinder head bolts in sequence shown in **Fig. 7.**
24. Remove cylinder head from engine block.
25. Reverse procedure to install, torquing cylinder head bolts to specification in sequence shown in **Fig. I.**

INTAKE & EXHAUST MANIFOLDS
REPLACE
EXCEPT 16 VALVE ENGINE

1. Disconnect battery ground cable.
2. Remove air cleaner assembly.
3. Disconnect vacuum lines.
4. Disconnect throttle valve cable.
5. Disconnect accelerator cable.
6. Disconnect electrical connector from carburetor.
7. Disconnect fuel line from fuel pump.
8. Disconnect all necessary vacuum lines and remove carburetor assembly.
9. Remove early fuel evaporation (EFE) gasket.
10. Disconnect vacuum line, then remove dashpot bracket.
11. Remove heat shield.
12. Raise and support vehicle.
13. Disconnect exhaust pipe from exhaust manifold.

14. Remove exhaust bracket from engine.
15. Disconnect air hose from converter pipe.
16. Lower vehicle.
17. Disconnect brake vacuum hose.
18. Remove accelerator and throttle cable bracket.
19. Remove intake and exhaust manifolds and gaskets.
20. Reverse procedure to install.

16 VALVE ENGINE
Intake Manifold

1. Disconnect battery ground cable.
2. Drain cooling system.
3. Remove air cleaner assembly.
4. **On GSi models,** remove upper radiator hose.
5. **On all models,** disconnect throttle and accelerator cables.
6. Mark then remove all necessary vacuum hoses.
7. **On except GSi models,** proceed as follows:
   a. Disconnect throttle position, cold start, air control valve and vacuum sensors and injector electrical connectors.
   b. Remove cold start injector pipe.
   c. Remove water hose from air valve.
8. **On GSi models,** proceed as follows:
   a. Remove fuel delivery pipe and injectors then the temperature sensor connector.
   b. Remove water outlet bypass pipe.
9. **On all models,** raise and support vehicle.
10. Remove intake manifold bracket.
11. Lower vehicle.
12. Remove intake manifold attaching bolts.
13. Remove intake manifold.
14. Reverse procedure to install.

Exhaust Manifold

1. Disconnect battery ground cable.
2. Remove exhaust manifold heat shield or insulator.
3. Raise and support vehicle.
4. Disconnect front exhaust pipe.
5. **On except GSi models,** remove exhaust manifold support bracket.
6. **On all models,** lower vehicle.
7. **On except GSi models,** disconnect oxygen sensor.
8. **On all models,** remove exhaust manifold attaching bolts then exhaust manifold.
9. Reverse procedure to install.

ROCKER ARM SHAFT & ROCKER ARMS
REPLACE
EXCEPT 16 VALVE ENGINE

1. Remove cylinder head cover attaching bolts, then the cylinder head cover.
2. Loosen each rocker support bolt a little at a time and in sequence shown in **Fig. 13.**
3. During installation, proceed as follows:
   a. Loosen adjusting screw locknuts.

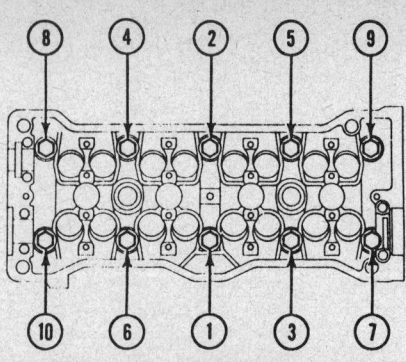

Fig. 12   Cylinder bolt tightening sequence. Prizm except GSi models

b. Assemble rocker arm assembly and face the oil holes of the rocker shaft to the right, left and bottom as shown in **Fig. 14.**
c. Install and tighten rocker support bolts gradually in three steps in sequence shown in **Fig. 15.**

VALVE CLEARANCE SPECIFICATIONS

Year	Engine/VIN	Intake Inches	Exhaust Inches
1988	1.6L/4-97, 4	.008	.012
	1.6L/4-97, 5	.008–.012	.010–.014
1990–91	1.6L/4-97, 5	.008–.012	.010–.014
	1.6L/4-97, 6	.006–.010	.008–.012

VALVES
ADJUST
EXCEPT 16 VALVE ENGINE

Perform valve adjustment with engine at normal operating temperature.
1. Position No. 1 cylinder to TDC of compression stroke.
2. Turn crankshaft in normal direction of rotation to align timing marks at TDC, then set groove on pulley to the "0" position.
3. Ensure rocker arms on No. 1 cylinder are loose and rockers on No. 4 are tight. If not, turn crankshaft one complete revolution and align marks.
4. Adjust valve clearances of the valves shown in **Fig. 16,** to specification.
5. Turn crankshaft one revolution and align the timing marks.
6. Adjust remaining valves as shown in **Fig. 17,** to specification.

16 VALVE ENGINE

Measure and adjust valve clearance while the engine is cold.
1. Disconnect battery ground cable.
2. Remove cylinder head cover.
3. Set No. 1 cylinder at TDC on the compression stroke.
4. Turn crankshaft to align groove in crankshaft pulley with "0" mark on No. 1 timing belt cover. **Ensure that valve lifters on No. 1 cylinder have free play. If not, rotate crankshaft pulley 360° and align the "0" mark on timing belt cover.**

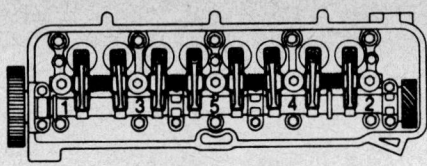

Fig. 13 Rocker arm support loosening sequence. Except 16 valve engine

VALVE CLEARNACE (HOT):
INTAKE   0.20mm (0.008 in.)
EXHAUST 0.30mm (0.012 in.)

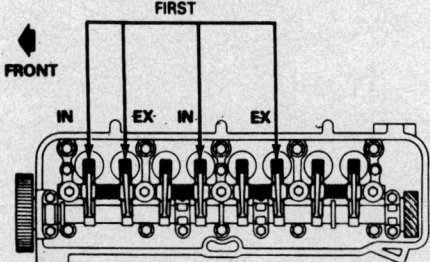

Fig. 16 First valve clearance adjustment. Except 16 valve engine

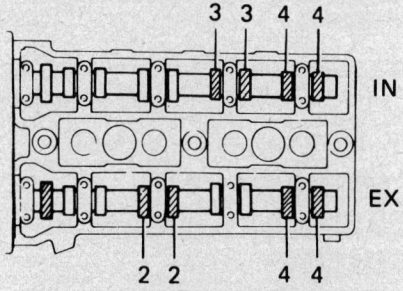

Fig. 19 Second valve clearance adjustment. 16 valve engine

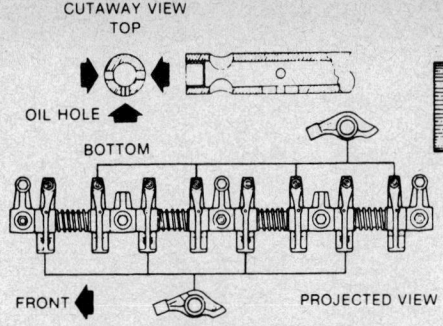

Fig. 14 Rocker shaft oil holes. Except 16 valve engine

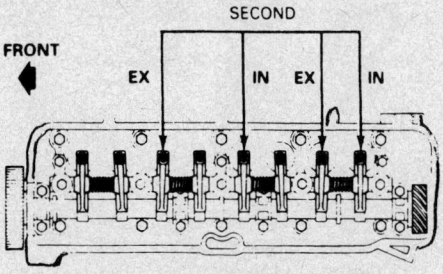

Fig. 17 Second valve clearance adjustment. Except 16 valve engine

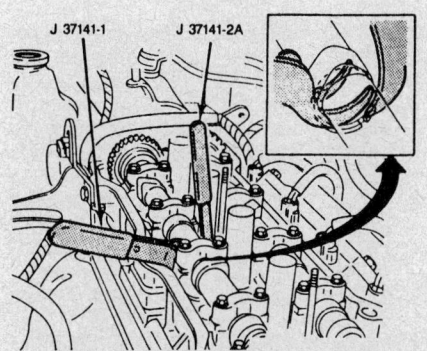

Fig. 20 Depressing valve spring. 16 valve engine

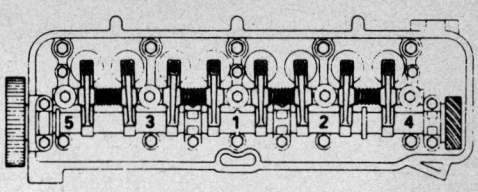

Fig. 15 Rocker arm torque sequence. Except 16 valve engine

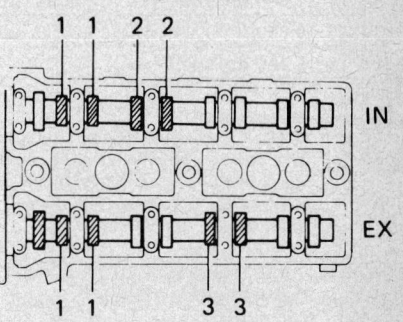

Fig. 18 First valve clearance adjustment. 16 valve engine

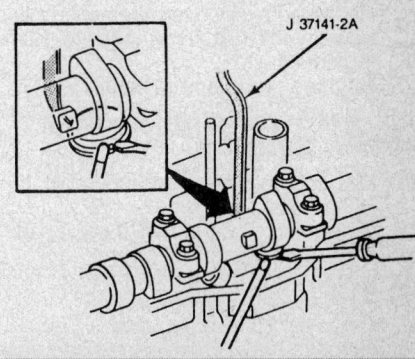

Fig. 21 Removing adjusting shim. 16 valve engine

5. Measure and record valve lash clearance between the cam lobe and the adjusting shim on cylinders shown in **Fig. 18**.
6. Rotate crankshaft 360° and align groove with "0" mark timing belt cover.
7. Measure and record valve lash clearance between the cam lobe and the adjusting shim on cylinders shown in **Fig. 19**.
8. If clearance is not within specifications, obtain the valve clearance adjustment tool set No. J-37141-A, or equivalent.
9. Insert valve spring compression tool No. J-37141-1, or equivalent, between the camshaft and lifter adjusting shim. This action will compress the valve spring and push lifter down.
10. Insert lifter holding tool No. J-37141-2A, or equivalent, between camshaft and lifter. Position bottom edge of tool on lifter and not on adjusting shim. The lifter appears to be a

sleeve around the adjusting shim. This action will hold the lifter away from camshaft, **Fig. 20**.
11. Remove spring compression tool No. J-37141-1. Lifter holding tool No. J-37141-2A should hold lifter down away from camshaft.
12. Remove adjusting shim with a small screwdriver and magnetic finger, **Fig. 21**.
13. Measure thickness of removed shim.
14. Calculate thickness of new shim required by using the following formula:
   a. T = Thickness of shim removed.
   b. A = Valve clearance measured.
   c. N = Thickness of shim required.
   d. For intake valves use formula; N = T + (A - .008 inch (.20 mm)).
   e. For exhaust valves use formula; N = T + (A - .010 inch (.25 mm)).
   f. Select a shim from **Fig. 22** with a thickness as close as possible to

the calculated valve.
15. Install new adjusting shims as required.
16. Depress valve spring using spring compression tool No. J-37141-1 and remove the lifter holding tool No. J-37141-2A.
17. Install cylinder head cover and connect battery ground cable.

TIMING BELT COVER REPLACE

EXCEPT 16 VALVE ENGINE

No. 1 (Upper) Timing Belt Cover, Replace

1. Disconnect battery ground cable.
2. Loosen water pump pulley bolts.
3. Remove alternator drive belt.
4. Remove power steering pump drive belt, if equipped.
5. Remove water pump pulley.
6. Drain cooling system.
7. Disconnect upper radiator hose at outlet.

AVAILABLE SHIMS

Shim No.	Thickness	Shim No.	Thickness
02	2.500 (0.0984)	20	2.950 (0.1161)
04	2.550 (0.1004)	22	3.000 (0.1181)
06	2.600 (0.1024)	24	3.050 (0.1201)
08	2.650 (0.1043)	26	3.100 (0.1220)
10	2.700 (0.1063)	28	3.150 (0.1240)
12	2.750 (0.1083)	30	3.200 (0.1260)
14	2.800 (0.1102)	32	3.250 (0.1280)
16	2.850 (0.1122)	34	3.300 (0.1299)
18	2.900 (0.1142)		

Intake valve clearance (cold):
   0.15 − 0.25 mm (0.006 − 0.010 in.)
Example: A 2.800 mm shim is installed and the measured clearance is 0.450 mm. Replace the 2.800 mm shim with shim No. 24 (3.050 mm).

Fig. 22 Valve shim size chart. 16 valve engine

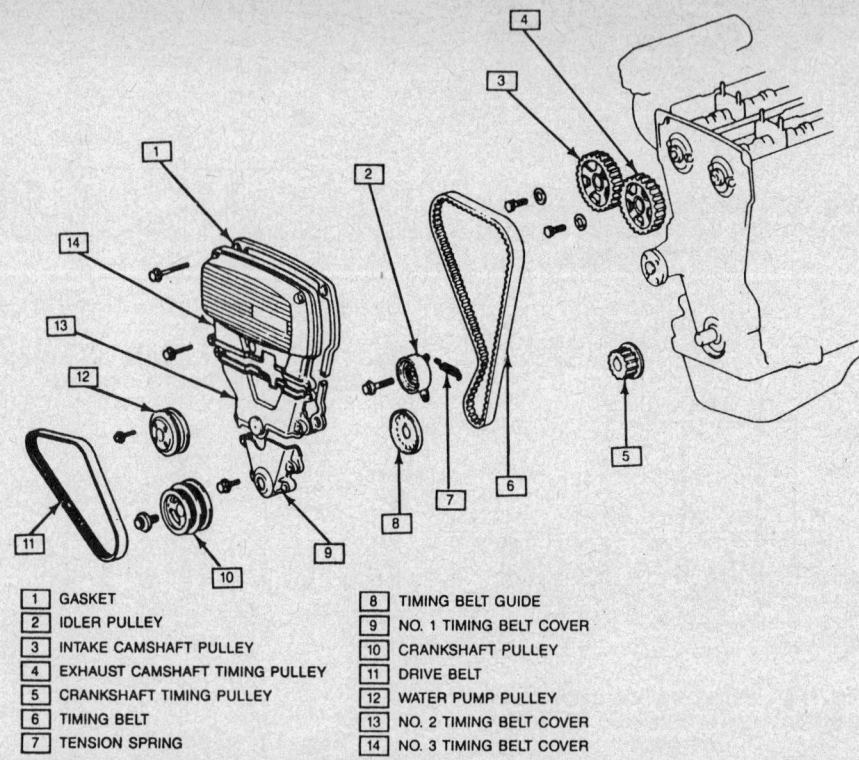

1	GASKET	8	TIMING BELT GUIDE
2	IDLER PULLEY	9	NO. 1 TIMING BELT COVER
3	INTAKE CAMSHAFT PULLEY	10	CRANKSHAFT PULLEY
4	EXHAUST CAMSHAFT TIMING PULLEY	11	DRIVE BELT
5	CRANKSHAFT TIMING PULLEY	12	WATER PUMP PULLEY
6	TIMING BELT	13	NO. 2 TIMING BELT COVER
7	TENSION SPRING	14	NO. 3 TIMING BELT COVER

Fig. 23 Timing belt components. Nova & Prizm GSi models w/16 valve engine

8. Disconnect all necessary vacuum lines.
9. Remove upper No. 1 timing cover attaching bolts.
10. Raise and support vehicle.
11. Remove lower cover attaching bolts.
12. Lower vehicle, then remove No. 1 timing cover.
13. Reverse procedure to install.

No. 2 (Lower) Timing Belt Cover, Replace

1. Disconnect battery ground cable.
2. Remove alternator belt.
3. Remove A/C drive belt, if equipped.
4. Raise and support vehicle.
5. Remove righthand under cover.
6. Remove flywheel cover.
7. Remove crankshaft pulley.
8. Remove No. 2 timing cover and gasket.
9. Reverse procedure to install.

No. 3 (Middle) Timing Belt Cover, Replace

1. Remove No. 1 timing belt cover as described previously.
2. Loosen A/C idler pulley mount nut and adjusting bolt, then remove A/C belt, if equipped.
3. Remove A/C idler pulley and adjusting bolt, if equipped.
4. Remove alternator and position aside.
5. Remove No. 3 timing belt cover and gasket.
6. Reverse procedure to install.

16 VALVE ENGINE
Nova & Prizm GSi Models

1. Disconnect battery ground cable.
2. Remove righthand wheel and lower splash shield.
3. Drain coolant.
4. Disconnect accelerator and cruise control cables.
5. Remove cruise control actuator and ignition coil.
6. Remove water outlet hose.
7. Remove accessary drive belts.
8. Remove spark plugs.

9. Set No. 1 cylinder at TDC on the compression stroke. Turn crankshaft pulley to align its groove with idler pulley bolt. Remove oil filter cap and ensure that you see hole in camshaft. If hole cannot be seen, turn crankshaft 360° and check again.
10. Disconnect righthand engine mount.
11. Remove water pump pulley.
12. Remove crankshaft pulley using holder tool No. J-8614-0, or equivalent1 and puller tool No. J-1859-03, or equivalent.
13. Remove timing belt cover attaching screws and belt covers, **Fig. 23**.
14. Reverse procedure to install.

Prizm

1. Disconnect battery ground cable.
2. Raise and support vehicle.
3. Remove right lower stone shield.
4. Lower vehicle.
5. Disconnect engine wiring harness from upper timing belt cover.
6. Remove accessory drive belts.
7. Remove crankshaft pulley using puller tool J-1859-03, or equivalent.
8. Remove cylinder head cover and windshield washer reservoir.
9. Support engine using support tool No. J-28467-A, or equivalent.
10. Remove right engine mount through bolt.
11. Raise and support vehicle.
12. Remove two rear transaxle mount to main crossmember nuts.
13. Remove two center transaxle mount to center crossmember nuts.
14. Lower vehicle.
15. Raise engine and remove water pump pulley.

16. Remove timing belt covers attaching screws and timing belt covers, **Fig. 24.**
17. Reverse procedure to install.

TIMING BELT & CAMSHAFT TIMING PULLEY
REPLACE
EXCEPT 16 VALVE ENGINE

1. Disconnect battery ground cable.
2. Drain cooling system.
3. Loosen water pump pulley bolts.
4. Remove alternator drive belt.
5. Remove power steering pump belt, if equipped.
6. Remove water pump pulley.
7. Loosen A/C idler pulley mount nut and adjusting bolt, then remove drive belt, if applicable.
8. Remove A/C idler pulley and adjusting bolt, if applicable.
9. Raise and support vehicle.
10. Remove righthand under cover.
11. Remove flywheel cover and crankshaft pulley.
12. Remove No. 2 timing belt cover with gasket.
13. Disconnect engine mounting center member.
14. Lower vehicle.
15. Disconnect upper radiator hose at outlet.
16. Disconnect all necessary vacuum hoses.
17. Remove No. 1 timing belt cover and gasket.

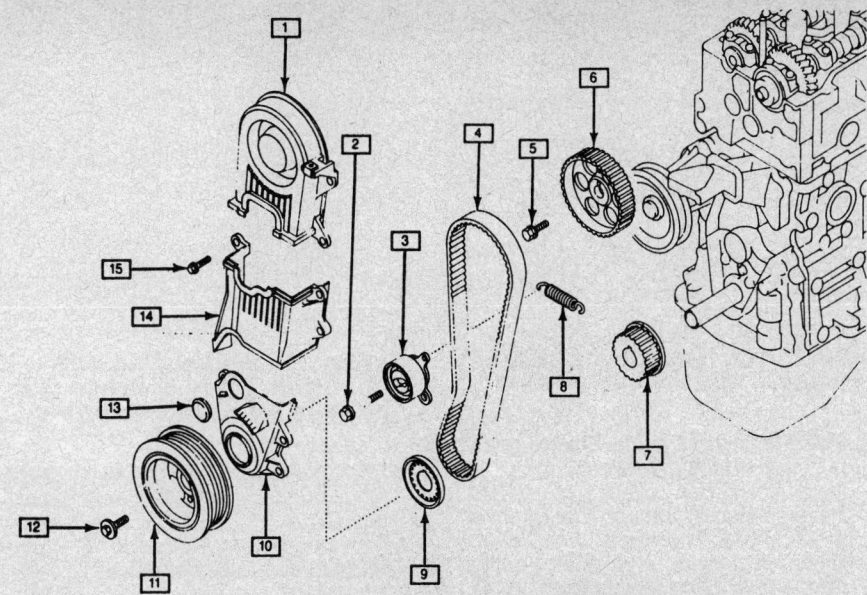

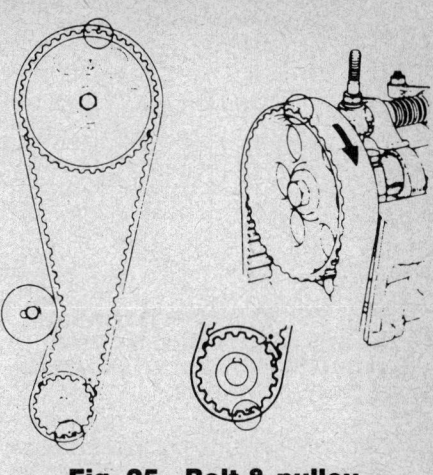

Fig. 25 Belt & pulley alignment. Except 16 valve engine

1	UPPER TIMING BELT COVER	6	CAMSHAFT TIMING PULLEY	11	CRANKSHAFT PULLEY
2	BOLT	7	CRANKSHAFT TIMING GEAR	12	BOLT
3	IDLER PULLEY	8	TENSION SPRING	13	INSPECTION PLUG
4	TIMING BELT	9	TIMING BELT GUIDE	14	CENTER TIMING BELT COVER
5	BOLT	10	LOWER TIMING BELT COVER	15	BOLT

Fig. 24 Timing belt components. Prizm except GSi models w/16 valve engine

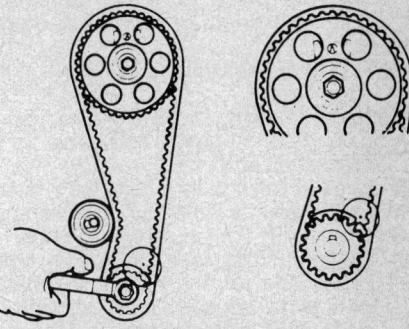

Fig. 28 Timing mark alignment. Except 16 valve engine

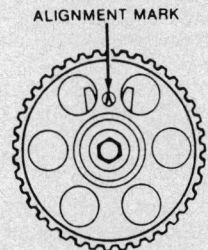

Fig. 26 Camshaft timing pulley alignment. Except 16 valve engine

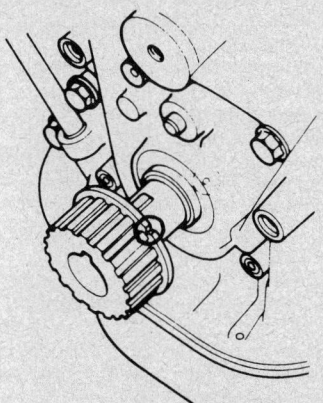

Fig. 27 Crankshaft timing pulley alignment. Except 16 valve engine

18. Remove alternator and position aside.
19. Remove No. 3 timing belt cover.
20. Support engine with a suitable jack.
21. Position No. 1 cylinder at TDC of compression stroke by turning crankshaft until the timing mark is aligned with the TDC mark. The rocker arms on the No. 1 cylinder should be loose. If not, turn crankshaft one complete turn.
22. Disconnect righthand engine mount.
23. Loosen idler pulley to relieve belt tension.
24. Lower engine and remove timing belt. **If reusing the timing belt, draw a direction arrow on the belt (in direction of engine rotation) and place alignment marks on the pulleys and belt as shown in Fig. 25.**
25. Remove idler pulley bolt, pulley and return spring.
26. Remove camshaft timing pulley.
27. During installation of belt and timing pulley, proceed as follows:
   a. Align camshaft knock pin and camshaft timing pulley. Torque bolt to specifications.
   b. Align bearing cap mark and the center of the small hole on the camshaft timing pulley as shown in **Fig. 26.**
   c. Align TDC marks on the oil pump body and crankshaft timing pulley as shown in **Fig. 27.**
   d. Remove any oil or water on the crankshaft timing pulley and keep it clean.
   e. Install timing belt idler pulley and tension spring. Pry timing belt idler pulley toward the left as far as it will go and temporarily tighten it.
   f. Install timing belt. If reusing the original timing belt, align the points marked during removal and install the belt with the arrow pointing in the direction of engine rotation.
   g. Raise engine slightly, then loosen timing belt idler pulley mounting bolt. Temporarily install the crank pulley bolt and turn the crankshaft two revolutions clockwise from TDC to TDC.
   h. Check valve timing. Ensure each pulley aligns with the marks as shown in **Fig. 28.**
   i. Reverse remaining removal procedure to complete installation procedure.

16 VALVE ENGINE
NOVA & PRIZM GSI MODELS
Removal

1. Disconnect battery ground cable, then remove right front wheel and engine under cover.
2. Drain radiator coolant, then disconnect cruise control cable (if equipped), accelerator cable and link.
3. Remove cruise control actuator (if equipped), then the ignition coil and coolant outlet hose.
4. Remove accessory drive belts, then the spark plugs.
5. Turn crankshaft pulley and align groove with "0" mark on the No. 1 timing belt cover, then remove oil filler cap and ensure cavity in camshaft is visible indicating TDC compression. If

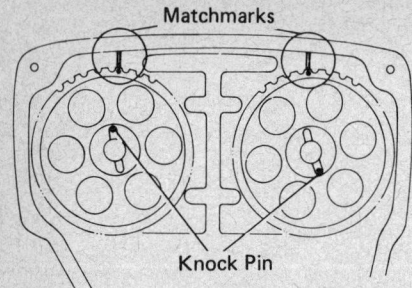

Fig. 29 Camshaft timing pulley alignment. Nova & Prizm GSi models w/16 valve engine

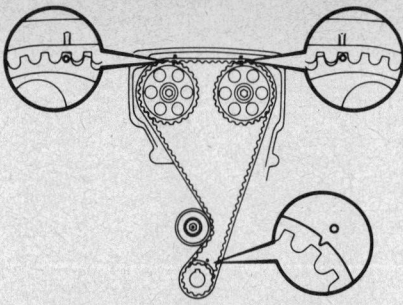

Fig. 30 Belt & pulley alignment. Nova & Prizm GSi models w/16 valve engine

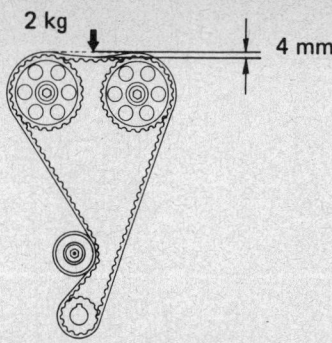

Fig. 31 Measuring belt deflection. Nova & Prizm GSi models w/16 valve engine

camshaft cavity is not visible, rotate crankshaft an additional 360° to set engine at TDC compression.
6. Raise engine with suitable jack, then remove right side engine mount through bolt and the mount. **Insert suitable piece of wood between jack and engine to prevent damage.**
7. Remove crankshaft pulley using suitable tools.
8. Remove timing belt covers and gaskets, then the timing belt guide from crankshaft sprocket.
9. Loosen idler pulley bolt, then push idler pulley as far left as possible and temporarily tighten idler pulley bolt.
10. Remove timing belt, idler pulley bolt, pulley and tension spring. **If timing belt is to be reused, mark direction and belt-to-sprocket reference marks to ensure correct position during installation.**
11. Remove cylinder head covers, then using suitable wrench positioned on camshaft flats, remove camshaft sprocket attaching bolts and sprockets.

Installation

1. Install camshaft sprockets, aligning marks as shown in **Fig. 29**. Install sprocket attaching bolts and torque to specifications.
2. Install cylinder head covers, then the crankshaft sprocket, idler pulley and tension spring. Pry idler pulley towards the left as far as possible and temporarily tighten attaching bolt.
3. Install timing belt. **If belt is being reused, ensure it is installed in the same position as removed.**
4. Slowly loosen timing belt idler bolt, then temporarily install crankshaft pulley bolt.
5. Turn crankshaft two complete revolutions clockwise from TDC of compression stroke to TDC of compression stroke.
6. Check valve timing. Ensure each sprocket is aligned as shown in **Fig. 30.**
7. Tighten timing belt idler pulley bolt to 27 ft. lbs.
8. Measure timing belt deflection as shown in **Fig. 31**. If deflection is not .16 inch with 4.4 lbs. of pressure, readjust as necessary with idler pulley.
9. Remove crankshaft pulley bolt, then

install timing belt guide. Ensure guide cup side is facing outward.
10. Install timing belt covers and gaskets.
11. Reverse steps 1 through 5 of removal procedure to complete installation. When installing crankshaft pulley torque pulley bolt to sepcification.

PRIZM EXCEPT GSI MODELS
Removal

1. Disconnect battery ground cable.
2. Remove timing belt covers as outlined under "Timing Belt Covers, Removal." **If timing belt is to be reused, mark direction and belt-to-sprocket reference marks to ensure correct position during installation.**
3. Remove timing belt guide from crankshaft sprocket.
4. Loosen idler pulley bolt, then push idler pulley as far left as possible and temporarily tighten idler pulley bolt.
5. Remove timing belt, idler pulley bolt, pulley and tension spring.
6. Remove idler pulley bolt, pulley and return spring.
7. Remove crankshaft timing pulley.
8. Remove camshaft timing gear by securing the camshaft with a wrench and removing the bolt, **Fig. 32. Ensure not to damage cylinder head or camshaft with wrench.**

Installation

1. Install camshaft timing gear.
2. Install crankshaft timing gear.
3. Position No. 1 cylinder at TDC.
4. Align camshaft timing gear hole with the exhaust camshaft cap mark, **Fig. 10.**
5. Install idler pulley, mount bolt and tensioner spring. Pry idler to left and temporarily tighten.
6. Install timing belt. If reusing original timing belt, align points made during disassembly with arrow pointing in proper direction.
7. Loosen timing belt idler pulley mount bolt.
8. Temporarily install crankshaft pulley bolt and turn crankshaft 2 revolutions from TDC to TDC. **Always turn the crankshaft clockwise.**
9. Ensure all components are properly aligned.
10. Install the timing belt idler pulley bolt.
11. Ensure timing belt deflection is

.20-.24 inch. If belt is not within specification, the idler pulley must be adjusted.
12. Reverse remaining removal procedure to complete procedure.

CAMSHAFT
REPLACE

EXCEPT 16 VALVE ENGINE

1. Disconnect battery ground cable.
2. Remove cylinder head cover.
3. Drain cooling system.
4. Loosen water pump pulley bolts and remove alternator drive belt.
5. Raise and support vehicle.
6. Remove power steering pivot bolt, if equipped.
7. Remove bolt that goes through both the No. 1 and No. 2 timing covers.
8. Lower vehicle.
9. Remove power steering drive belt, if equipped.
10. Remove water pump pulley.
11. Disconnect upper radiator hose at outlet.
12. Disconnect all necessary vacuum lines.
13. Remove No. 1 timing belt cover and gasket.
14. Disconnect spark plug wires and electrical connectors.
15. Remove distributor.
16. Disconnect fuel lines, then remove fuel pump.
17. Remove distributor gear bolt.
18. Remove rocker arm assembly.
19. Turn crankshaft clockwise and position No. 1 cylinder to TDC of compression stroke.
20. Place alignment marks on the camshaft timing pulley and belt.
21. Loosen idler pulley mount bolt and push idler pulley toward the left as far as it will go and temporarily tighten it. Remove belt.
22. Support belt so that the meshing of the crankshaft timing pulley and timing belt does not shift.
23. Do not allow belt to contact oil, water or dust.
24. Remove camshaft bearing caps and camshaft.
25. Reverse procedure to install, noting the following:
   a. Install camshaft bearing caps with

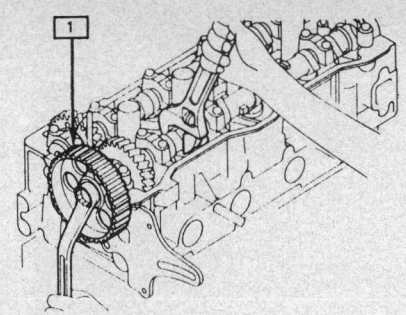

[1] CAMSHAFT TIMING GEAR

Fig. 32 Camshaft timing gear. Prizm except GSi models

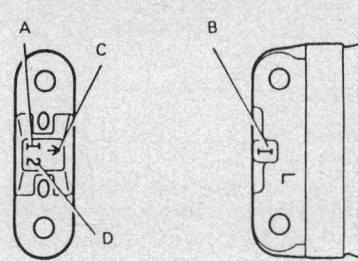

A I = INTAKE   E = EXHAUST
B I = INTAKE   E = EXHAUST
C FRONT MARK
D I.D. FOR BEARING
NO. 2 THRU NO: 5

Fig. 35 Installing camshaft bearing caps. Nova & Prizm GSi models w/16 valve engine

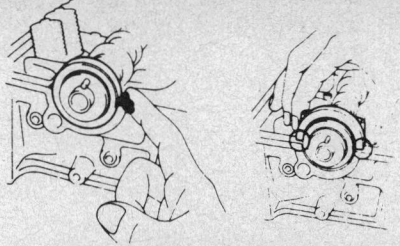

Fig. 33 Applying RTV sealant to oil seal. Except 16 valve engine

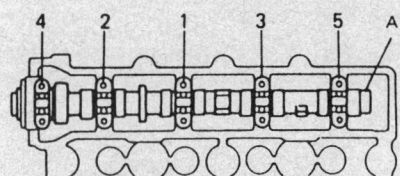

A CAMSHAFT

Fig. 36 Camshaft bearing caps tightening sequence. Nova & Prizm GSi models w/16 valve engine

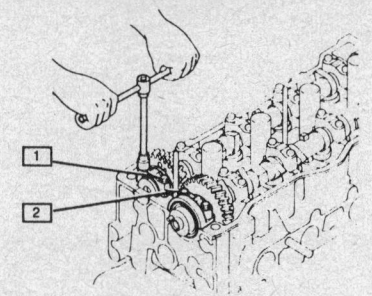

[1] INTAKE BEARING CAP BOLT
[2] EXHAUST BEARING CAP BOLT

Fig. 38 Number 1 bearing cap bolts. Prizm except GSi models

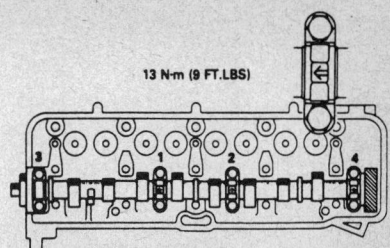

13 N·m (9 FT.LBS)

Fig. 34 Camshaft bearing cap torque specifications & sequence. Except 16 valve engine

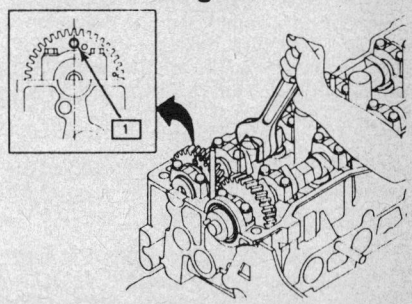

[1] SERVICE BOLT HOLE (INTAKE CAMSHAFT)

Fig. 37 Aligning service bolt hole. Prizm except GSi models

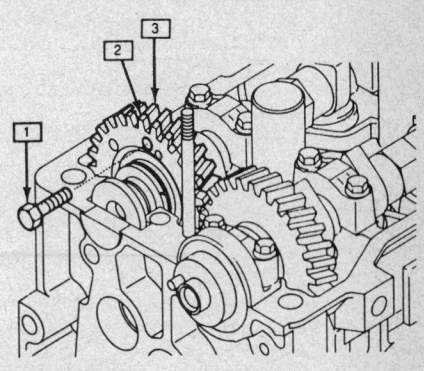

[1] SERVICE BOLT
[2] SUB-GEAR
[3] MAIN GEAR

Fig. 39 Fastening sub-gear to main gear. Prizm except GSi models

the arrows on caps facing toward the front.

b. When installing No. 1 bearing cap and oil seal, apply suitable liquid sealer to seal outer circumference, then coat mating areas shown in **Fig. 33**, with RTV sealant.

c. Ensure timing belt and timing pulley alignment marks align properly.

d. Torque bearing caps to specifications and in sequence shown in **Fig. 34**.

16 VALVE ENGINE

NOVA & PRIZM GSI MODELS
Removal

1. Disconnect battery ground cable.
2. Remove cylinder head cover.
3. Remove timing belt covers as outlined under "Timing Belt Cover, Replace."
4. Remove timing belt as outlined under "Timing Belt & Camshaft Timing Pulley, Replace."
5. Remove camshaft bearing caps.
6. Remove camshaft.

Installation

1. Install camshaft(s). Exhaust camshaft has distributor drive gear.
2. Install camshaft bearing caps on each

journal with arrows pointed toward the front, **Fig. 35**.

3. Torque cap bolts in three passes to sepcification in sequence shown in **Fig. 36**.
4. Install timing belt and covers as previously described.
5. Install cylinder head cover and connect battery ground cable.

PRIZM EXCEPT GSI MODELS
Removal

1. Disconnect battery ground cable.
2. Remove cylinder head cover.
3. Remove timing belt covers as outlined under "Timing Belt Cover, Replace."
4. Remove timing belt as outlined under "Timing Belt & Camshaft Timing Pulley, Replace."
5. Remove camshaft timing gear by holding the camshaft with a wrench and removing the camshaft bolt. Use

caution not to damage camshaft or cylinder head with wrench.

6. With the No. 1 cylinder in TDC position, the service bolt hole of the intake camshaft gear should be in position as shown in **Fig. 37**.
7. Alternately loosen the No. 1 (front) intake and exhaust camshaft bearing cap bolts in several steps, **Fig. 38**.
8. Remove No. 1 bearing caps.
9. Fasten the intake camshaft sub-gear to the main gear with a service bolt, **Fig. 39**.
10. Uniformly loosen each intake camshaft bearing cap bolt in several steps in sequence shown in **Fig. 40**.
11. Remove intake camshaft bearing caps and camshaft. **The camshaft**

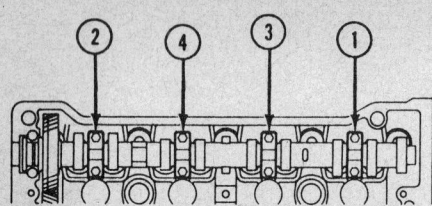

Fig. 40 Camshaft removal sequence. Prizm except GSi models

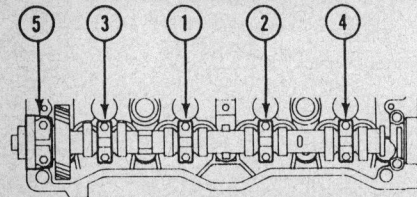

Fig. 43 Camshaft tightening sequence. Prizm except GSi models

must be held level while it is being removed. If the camshaft is not kept level, the portion of the cylinder head receiving the shaft trust may crack or be damaged. If the camshaft cannot be lifted out straight and level, retighten the No. 3 bearing cap and alternately loosen the bolts of the bearing cap in several steps while pulling up on the camshaft gear.

12. Rotate exhaust camshaft 105°, using a suitable wrench.
13. Place lockpin in position shown in **Fig. 41**.
14. Uniformly loosen each exhaust camshaft bearing cap bolt in several steps in sequence shown in **Fig. 40**.
15. Remove exhaust camshaft bearing caps and camshaft.
16. Disassemble intake camshaft by inserting pins into service holes in camshaft sub-gear, **Fig. 42**.
17. Using a screwdriver, turn sub-gear clockwise and remove pin C.
18. Remove snap ring, wave washer, camshaft sub gear, and camshaft gear spring.
19. Remove exhaust camshaft oil seal.

Installation

1. Install ring, wave washer, camshaft sub-gear and camshaft gear spring.
2. Install pins A and B, **Fig. 42**, into service holes of camshaft sub-gear.
3. Using a screwdriver, align holes of camshaft drive gear and sub-gear by turning camshaft sub-gear clockwise.
4. Install pin C.
5. Install the exhaust camshaft on cylinder head so that No. 1 and No. 3 cam lobes push their valves lifters evenly.
6. Install bearing caps on journals with arrows pointing toward the crankshaft pulley.
7. Tighten each bearing cap to specification in several steps in sequence shown in **Fig. 43**.
8. Apply mulit-purpose grease to a new exhaust camshaft oil seal and install oil seal using seal installer tool No. J-35403 or equivalent.

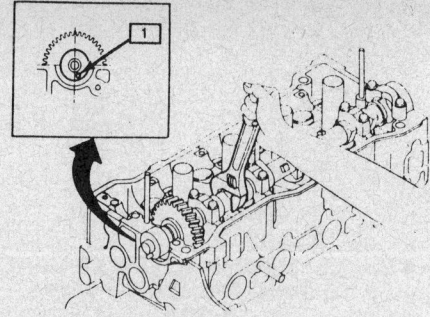

| 1 | KNOCKPIN POSITION |

Fig. 41 Knockout pin position. Prizm except GSi models

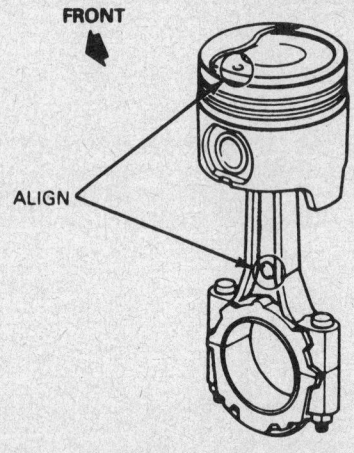

FRONT

ALIGN

Fig. 44 Piston & rod assembly

9. Position lock pin of exhaust camshaft so that No. 4 cylinder cam lobes push their lifters.
10. Engage intake camshaft gear with exhaust camshaft gear by matching alignment marks.
11. Roll camshaft into position keeping timing gears engaged.
12. Install intake camshaft bearing cap No. 2 through No. 5 with arrows pointing toward the crankshaft pulley. No. 1 bearing cap will be install later in this procedure.
13. Tighten intake camshaft bearing cap bolts to specifications in several steps in sequence shown in **Fig. 43**.
14. Remove pins from intake camshaft sub-gear.
15. Install No. 1 bearing cap. If No. 1 bearing cap does not fit properly, push the camshaft gear backward by prying apart the cylinder head and camshaft gear with a suitable pry tool.
16. Turn exhaust camshaft one revolution from TDC to TDC of No. 1 cylinder.
17. Ensure alignment marks on exhaust and intake gear align.
18. Install camshaft timing gear and secure camshaft and install timing gear bolt, **Fig. 32**.
19. Install timing belt as outlined under "Timing Belt & Camshaft Timing Pulley, Replace."

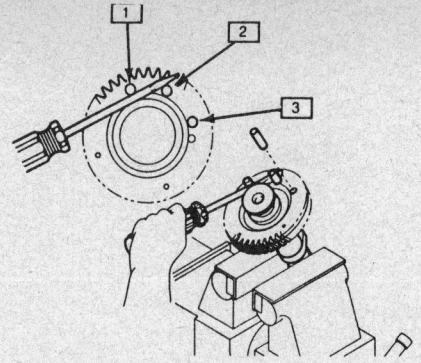

1	PIN A
2	PIN B
3	PIN C

Fig. 42 Disassembling intake camshaft. Prizm except GSi models

Cylinder Block	No.	1	2	3	1	2	3	1	2	3
Crankshaft	No.	0	0	0	1	1	1	2	2	2
Bearing	No.	1	2	3	2	3	4	3	4	5

Fig. 45 Main & Rod bearing identification. Nova & Prizm GSi models w/16 valve engine

BEARING SELECTION TABLE

Crankshaft Block Mark	1	2	3	1	2	3	1	2	3
Crankshaft Mark	0	0	0	1	1	1	2	2	2
Bearing Mark	1	2	3	3	2	4	3	4	5

Fig. 46 Main & Rod bearing identification. Prizm except GSi models

20. Install timing belt covers as outlined under "Timing Belt Cover, Replace."
21. Install cylinder head cover and connect battery ground cable.

PISTONS & RODS ASSEMBLE

Assemble pistons to connecting rods as shown in **Fig. 44**.

MAIN & ROD BEARINGS

Main and rod service bearings are available in 5 standard sizes, marked 1 through 5. If replacing a bearing, replace with one having the same number. If the number of the bearing cannot be determined, select a bearing according to the numbers imprinted on the cylinder block and crankshaft then refer to **Fig. 45 & 46** for proper bearing number.

CRANKSHAFT REAR OIL SEAL

REPLACE

NOVA

1. Remove transaxle and flywheel assembly.

MAXIMUM CLEARANCE: 0.35 mm (0.0138 in.)   MAXIMUM CLEARANCE: 0.1 mm (0.004 in.)

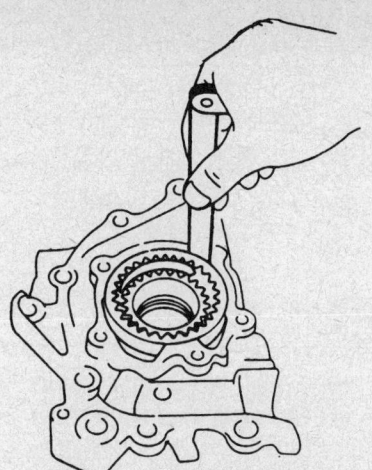

Fig. 47   Oil pump body clearance check. Except 16 valve engine

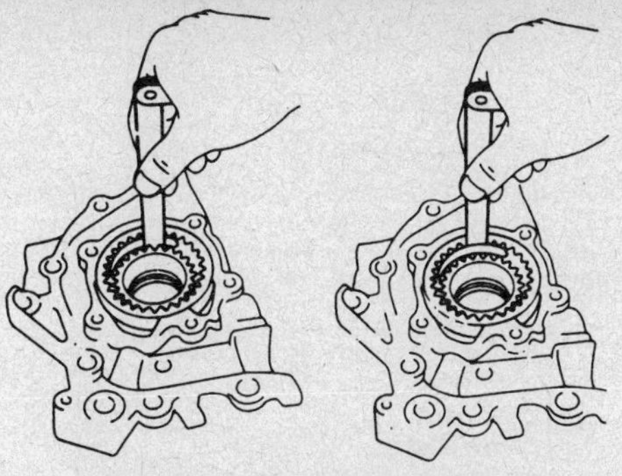

Fig. 48   Oil pump gear tip clearance check. Except 16 valve engine

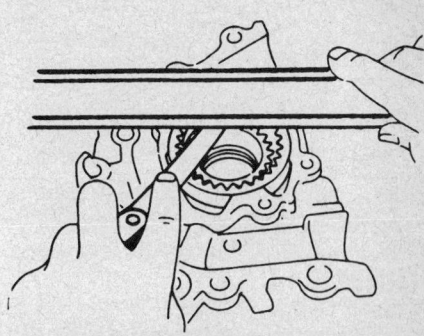

Fig. 49   Oil pump side clearance check. Except 16 valve engine

2. Remove rear end plate.
3. Carefully pry oil seal from groove.
4. Replace old oil seal with a new one, then apply a suitable lubricant.
5. Assemble rear end plate onto engine, then insert and securely tighten attaching bolts.
6. Assemble flywheel assembly to engine, then install transaxle.

PRIZM

1. Remove transaxle and flywheel assembly.
2. Remove rear end plate.
3. Remove rear main oil seal retainer.
4. Carefully knock out oil seal from retainer.
5. Replace old oil seal with a new one, then apply a suitable lubricant.
6. Assemble retainer, rear end plate onto engine, then insert and securely tighten attaching bolts.
7. Assemble flywheel assembly to engine, then install transaxle.

OIL PAN
REPLACE
EXCEPT 16 VALVE ENGINE

1. Disconnect battery ground cable.
2. Raise and support vehicle.
3. Drain engine oil.
4. Remove righthand under cover.
5. Remove oil pan bolts.
6. Remove oil pan.
7. Reverse procedure to install.

16 VALVE ENGINE
Nova & Prizm GSI Models

1. Disconnect battery ground cable.
2. Raise and support vehicle.
3. Drain engine oil.
4. Remove righthand under cover.
5. Disconnect front exhaust pipe and bracket.
6. Remove oil pan bolts.
7. Remove oil pan.
8. Reverse procedure to install.

Prizm Except GSI Models

1. Disconnect battery ground cable.
2. Raise and support vehicle.
3. Drain engine oil.

4. Remove right and left stone covers.
5. Disconnect oxygen sensor connector.
6. Disconnect exhaust pipe from catalytic converter.
7. Disconnect exhaust pipe from exhaust manifold.
8. Remove oil pan bolts and pan.
9. Reverse procedure to install.

OIL PUMP
REPLACE
EXCEPT 16 VALVE ENGINE

1. Remove Nos. 1, 2 and 3 timing belt covers as described previously.
2. Remove oil pan attaching bolts, then the oil pan.
3. Remove righthand under cover.
4. Remove flywheel cover and crankshaft pulley.
5. Mark position of camshaft and crankshaft timing pulleys and timing belt rotational direction.
6. Loosen idler pulley bolt, move pulley over to relieve belt tension and tighten bolt.
7. Pull timing belt off of crankshaft timing pulley.
8. Remove dipstick tube.
9. Remove timing belt idler pulley.
10. Remove oil pump bolts and oil pump.
11. Reverse procedure to install, noting the following:
    a. Using a feeler gauge, measure clearance between the driven gear and body, **Fig. 47**.
    b. If clearance is greater than .008 inch, replace gear and/or body.
    c. Using a feeler gauge, measure clearance between both gear tips and crescent as shown in **Fig. 48**.
    d. If clearance is greater than .0138 inch, replace gear and/or body.
    e. Using a feeler gauge and flat block, measure side clearance as shown in **Fig. 49**.
    f. If clearance is greater than .004 inch, replace gear and/or body.

16 VALVE ENGINE
Nova

1. Remove oil pan as outlined under "Oil Pan, Replace.
2. Remove oil strainer attaching bolts and nuts, then remove strainer and gasket.
3. Remove seven oil pump attaching

bolts, then the oil pump.
4. Reverse procedure to install.

PRIZM

1. Disconnect battery ground cable.
2. Remove timing belt as outlined under "Timing Belt Cover, Replace" and "Timing Belt & Camshaft Timing Pulley, Replace."
3. Raise and support vehicle.
4. Remove crankshaft timing gear pulley.
5. Remove oil pan as outlined under "Oil Pan, Replace."
6. Remove oil pump bolts and oil pump assembly.
7. Reverse procedure to install, noting the following:
    a. Using feeler gauge, measure driven gear to housing clearance, **Fig. 50**. If clearance is greater than .0078 inch, replace the oil pump.
    b. Using feeler gauge, measure drive gear to driven gear clearance, **Fig. 51**. If clearance is greater than .0012 inch, replace the gear set.
    c. Using feeler gauge, measure oil pump body to gear clearance, **Fig. 52**. If clearance is greater than .004 inch replace the oil pump.

WATER PUMP
REPLACE
NOVA

1. Drain cooling system.
2. Remove the accessory drive belts.
3. Loosen water pump pulley bolts then remove water pump pulley.
4. Disconnect water inlet and by-pass hoses from water inlet pipe.
5. Remove water inlet pipe and O-ring from water pump.
6. Remove oil dipstick and plug hole.
7. **On except 16 valve engines,** remove No. 1 timing belt cover as outlined under "Timing Belt Cover, Removal."
8. **On 16 valve engines,** remove No. 2 and 3 timing belt covers as outlined under "Timing Belt Cover, Removal."
9. **On all engines,** remove water pump bolts and water pump, **Figs. 53 and 54.**
10. Reverse procedure to install.

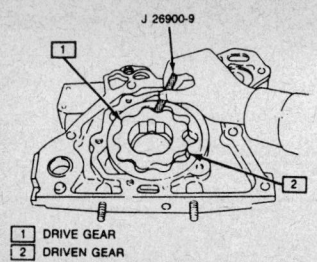

1 DRIVE GEAR
2 DRIVEN GEAR

Fig. 50 Oil pump gear to housing clearance check. Prizm

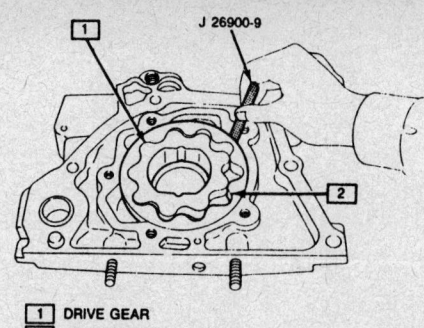

1 DRIVE GEAR
2 DRIVEN GEAR

Fig. 51 Oil pump gear to gear clearance check. Prizm

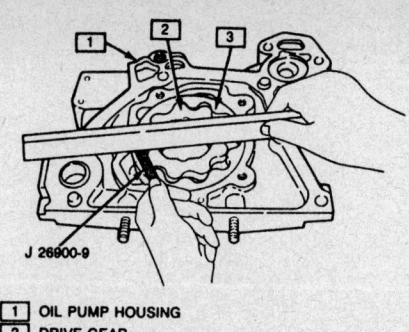

1 OIL PUMP HOUSING
2 DRIVE GEAR
3 DRIVEN GEAR

Fig. 52 Oil pump side clearance check. Prizm

PRIZM

1. Drain cooling system.
2. Raise and support engine.
3. Remove nut for rear engine mount.
4. Lower vehicle.
5. Remove windshield washer reservoir, cruise control module and bracket.
6. Remove through bolt from right engine mount.
7. With a suitable jack, raise engine.
8. Loosen water pump pulley bolts.
9. Remove accessary drive belts.
10. Remove water pump pulley.
11. Lower engine into place.
12. Disconnect water inlet and by-pass hoses from water inlet pipe.
13. Remove water inlet pipe and O-ring.
14. Remove and plug oil dipstick.
15. Remove upper timing belt cover as outlined under "Timing Belt Cover, Removal."
16. Remove water pump bolts and water pump, **Fig. 54.**
17. Reverse procedure to install.

COOLING SYSTEM BLEED

These engines do not require a specified bleed procedure. After filling cooling system, run engine to operating temperature with radiator/pressure cap off. Air will then be automatically bled through cap opening.

BELT TENSION DATA

Component	New Ft. Lbs.	Used Ft. Lbs.
Alternator	140–180	110–150
Power Steering	100–150	60–100
A/C	135–185	80–120

FUEL PUMP
REPLACE

1. Drain fuel tank.
2. Disconnect all fuel and electrical connections.
3. Raise and support vehicle.
4. Support fuel tank with a suitable jack.
5. Loosen and remove fuel tank support straps.
6. Lower fuel tank from vehicle.
7. Remove fuel tank bracket from fuel tank.
8. Remove fuel pump from fuel tank bracket.
9. Remove fuel pump filter from pump.
10. Reverse procedure to install, noting the following:
    a. **Torque** fuel tank bracket bolts to 30 inch lbs.
    b. **Torque** fuel tank flare nut to 22 ft. lbs.

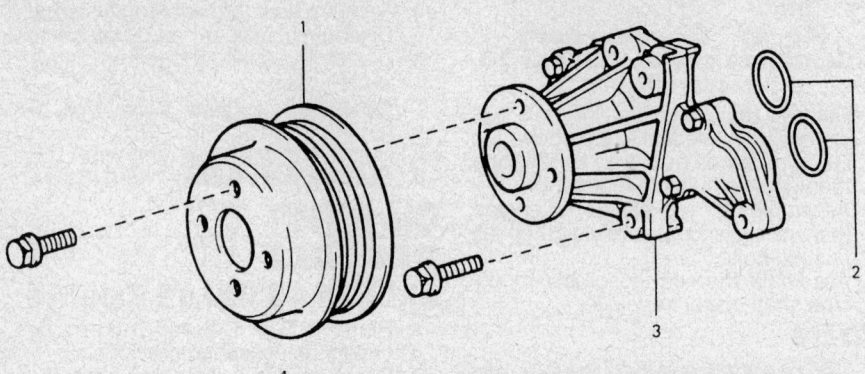

1 WATER PUMP PULLEY
2 O RING
3 WATER PUMP ASSEMBLY
4 WATER PUMP PULLEY (W PS)

Fig. 53 Water pump removal. Except 16 valve engine

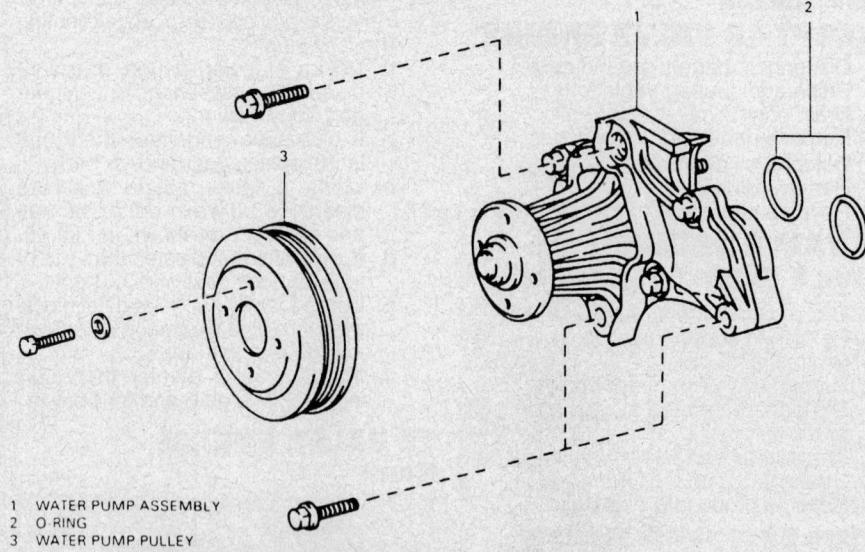

1 WATER PUMP ASSEMBLY
2 O RING
3 WATER PUMP PULLEY

Fig. 54 Water pump removal. 16 valve engine

TIGHTENING SPECIFICATIONS

Year	Component	Torque/ft. lbs.
1988–91	Camshaft Bearing Cap Bolts ②	9
	Camshaft Bearing Cap Bolts ③ ④	115 ①
	Camshaft Timing Gear Bolt ③	43
	Camshaft Timing Pulley Bolt ② ④	34
	Cold Start Injector Pipe Union Bolt ③	13
	Cold Start Injector Pipe ②	13
	Connecting Rod Bearing Cap Nuts ③ ④	36
	Crankshaft Pulley Bolt ①	105
	Crankshaft Pulley Bolt ②	101
	Crankshaft Pulley Bolt ③	87
	Cylinder Head Bolts ②	22
	Cylinder Head Bolts ③	44
	Cylinder Head Cover Cap Nuts ③	15
	Delivery Pipe Bolt ②	13
	Driveshaft To Transaxle Bolts ②	27
	Engine Mount To Center Member Bolts ②	35
	Engine Mount Support Bolts ④	35
	Engine Mount Through Bolt ②	58
	Engine Mount Through Bolt ④	64
	Engine Mount To Bracket Bolt ④	45
	Engine Mount To Engine Bracket Nuts ④	45
	Engine Mounting Center Mounting Bolts ②	29
	Exhaust Manifold Bolt ②	18
	Exhaust Manifold Nuts And Bolts ③	18
	Exhaust Manifold Nuts ④	18
	Exhaust Manifold Support Bolts ③	18
	Exhaust Manifold Insulator Bolts ③	18
	Exhaust Pipe To Exhaust Manifold Bolts ③	18
	Exhaust Pipe To Exhaust Manifold Nuts ②	46
	Flywheel Bolts ②	58
	Flywheel To Crankshaft Attaching Bolts (Automatic) ③ ④	47
	Flywheel To Crankshaft Attaching Bolts (manual) ③ ④	58
	Front Mount Through Bolt ③	58
	Idler Pulley Bolt ④	27
	Intake Manifold Bolts ③	14
	Intake Manifold Bolts ② ④	20
	Intake Manifold Bracket Bolts ④	20
	Lower Control Arm Bolt And Nuts ②	47
	Main Bearing Cap Bolts	44
	No. 1 Fuel Pipe Union Bolt ②	22
	Oil Cooler Center Bolts ④	20
	Oil Pan Bolts ④	53 ①
	Oil Pan Nuts And Bolts ③	44 ①
	Oil Pump Bolts ③	16
	Oil Pump Bolts ④	89 ①
	Oil Pump Cover Screws ③ ④	89 ①
	Oil Strainer/Pick Up Assembly Bolts And Nuts ③	89 ①
	Power Steering Drive Belt Pulley Mount Nut ②	32
	Pressure Regulator Bolts ③	65

Continued

TIGHTENING SPECIFICATIONS — Continued

Year	Component	Torque/ft. lbs.
1988-91 (Cont'd.)	Pressure Regulator Bolts ②	82
	Rear End Plate Bolts ③	89 ①
	Rear Main Oil Seal Retainer Bolts ③	84 ①
	Rear Main Seal Retainer Bolts ④	89 ①
	Rear Oil Seal Retainer Bolt ②	82
	Relief Valve Plug ④	27
	Right Engine Mount Through Bolt ③	64
	Rod Bearing Cap Nut ②	36
	Spark Plugs	13
	Starter Bolts ②	29
	Timing Belt Cover Bolt ③ ④	44 ①
	Timing Belt Idler Pulley Bolt ② ③	27
	Transaxle Mount To Center Crossmember Nuts ③ ④	45
	Transaxle Mount To Main Crossmember Nuts ③ ④	45

①—Inch lbs.
②—Nova.
③—Prizm except GSi models.
④—Prizm GSi models.

Clutch & Manual Transaxle
INDEX

CLUTCH PEDAL
ADJUST

1. Check height as shown in **Fig. 1**.
2. If it is necessary to adjust pedal height, remove instrument lower finish panel and air duct.
3. Loosen locknut and turn stopper bolt until the height is correct, then tighten locknut.
4. Push in on clutch pedal until resistance is felt, then check pushrod and pedal freeplay. Pushrod play should be .039-.197 inch, while freeplay should be .20-.59 inch.
5. To adjust, loosen locknut and turn pushrod until freeplay and pushrod play are within specification, then tighten locknut.
6. Recheck pedal height and adjust as necessary.
7. Reinstall air duct and lower finish panel.

CLUTCH
REPLACE

1. Remove transaxle assembly from vehicle.
2. Loosen each set bolt one turn at a time until spring tension is released.
3. Remove attaching bolts and pull off clutch assembly, **Fig. 2**.
4. Remove release bearing fork and boot from the transaxle.

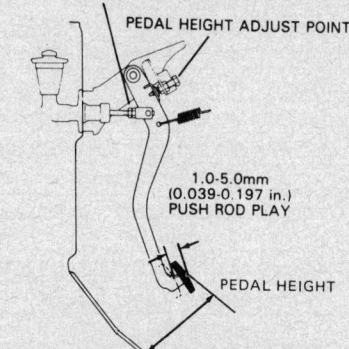

PUSH ROD PLAY AND FREEPLAY ADJUST POINT
PEDAL HEIGHT ADJUST POINT
1.0-5.0mm (0.039-0.197 in.) PUSH ROD PLAY
PEDAL HEIGHT

Fig. 1   Clutch pedal adjustment

5. Reverse procedure to install. Torque bolts to specifications.

MANUAL TRANSAXLE
REPLACE
NOVA

1. Disconnect battery ground cable.
2. Remove air inlet tube.
3. Disconnect speedometer cable.
4. Disconnect thermostat housing at transaxle.
5. Disconnect ground wire at transaxle.
6. Disconnect clutch slave cylinder and lay aside.
7. Disconnect clutch cables.
8. Disconnect back-up light switch.
9. Remove upper bellhousing bolts.
10. Remove transaxle mount upper bolt.

11. Install engine support tool No. J-28467, or equivalent.
12. Raise and support vehicle.
13. Remove lefthand wheel.
14. Remove right, left and center splash shields.
15. Remove center beam.
16. Remove transaxle inspection cover.
17. Disconnect lefthand and righthand lower control arms at knuckle.
18. Disconnect right and left axle shafts at transaxle.
19. Remove starter.
20. Support transaxle using a suitable jack.
21. Remove three backside transaxle to engine bolts.
22. Remove remaining bellhousing bolt.
23. Remove transaxle from vehicle.
24. Reverse procedure to install.

PRIZM

1. Disconnect battery ground and positive cables.
2. Support engine using support tool No. J-28467-A, or equivalent.
3. Remove battery and battery tray.
4. Remove air cleaner assembly.
5. Disconnect back-up switch.
6. Disconnect ground cable at transaxle.
7. Remove two actuator mounting bolts.
8. Remove actuator line bracket.
9. Remove shift cable retainers, end clips and cables from bracket and lay aside.
10. Remove left transaxle mount cover, brace and through bolt.
11. Remove two upper transaxle to engine bolts.

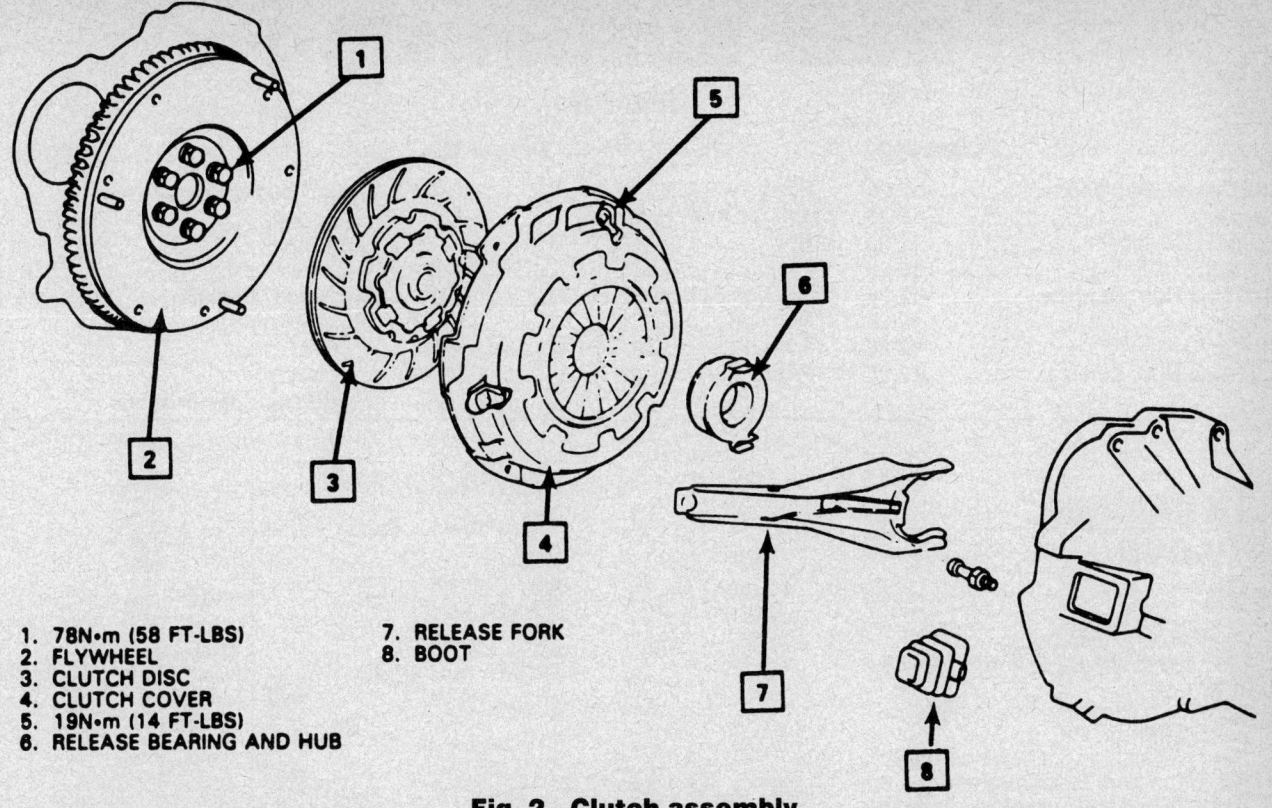

1. 78N•m (58 FT-LBS)
2. FLYWHEEL
3. CLUTCH DISC
4. CLUTCH COVER
5. 19N•m (14 FT-LBS)
6. RELEASE BEARING AND HUB
7. RELEASE FORK
8. BOOT

Fig. 2 Clutch assembly

12. Remove starter assembly.
13. Disconnect speedometer cable.
14. Raise and support vehicle.
15. Remove right and left stone shields.
16. Drain transaxle oil.
17. Remove drive axles.
18. Remove three center crossmember to radiator support bolts.
19. Remove front and center mount bolt shields.
20. Remove front, center and rear mount nuts.
21. Remove two center crossmember to main crossmember bolts.
22. Remove exhaust hangers.
23. Support main crossmember using a suitable jack.
24. Remove eight main crossmember to underbody bolts.
25. Remove two lower A-frame bracket to underbody bolts. **Lower main crossmember slowly while holding**

onto the center crossmember. **Center crossmember will be free to fall at this time and could cause serious bodily injury.**
26. Remove front through bolt and mount.
27. Remove front mount bracket from transaxle.
28. Remove center mount from transaxle.
29. Remove transaxle inspection cover.
30. Remove two lower transaxle bracket to mount bolts.
31. Lower vehicle.
32. Remove remaining transaxle mount to bracket bolts.
33. Lower transaxle using engine support tool No. J-28467, or equivalent to gain clearance to remove transaxle.
34. Remove transaxle mount.
35. Raise and support vehicle.
36. Support transaxle using a suitable jack.
37. Remove front and rear lower transax-

le to engine bolts.
38. Lower transaxle from vehicle.
39. Reverse procedure to install

SHIFT LEVER FREEPLAY ADJUST

NOVA

1. Remove shift lever cover.
2. Using a suitable spring scale attached to top of lever, select a shim that will allow a preload of .1–.2 lbs.
3. Shims are available in .031, .035, .039, .043 and .047 inch thicknesses.

PRIZM

Shift cables on these models are not adjustable. If cables are out of adjustment, replacement of the defective cable(s) will be required.

TIGHTENING SPECIFICATIONS

Year	Component	Torque/ft. lbs.
1988–91	Pedal Assembly Bracket To Instrument Panel Bolts	11
	Clutch Cover Bolts	14
	Flywheel Bolts	58
	Transaxle Case Cover Bolts	13
	Transaxle Case Bolts	22
	Back-Up Light Switch	30

Rear Suspension

INDEX

AXLE CARRIER
REPLACE
NOVA

1. Remove rear axle hub.
2. Disconnect brake line from wheel cylinder.
3. Remove bolt and nut holding axle carrier to strut rod, **Fig. 1.**
4. Remove bolt and nut holding axle carrier to the front suspension arm.
5. Remove bolt and nut holding axle carrier to the rear suspension arm.
6. Remove bolts and nuts holding axle carrier to the strut, then remove axle carrier assembly.
7. Reverse procedure to install.

KNUCKLE
REPLACE
PRIZM

1. Raise and support vehicle.
2. Support suspension using a suitable jack. Place jack under suspension supports, not the suspension arms.
3. Lower vehicle slightly so weight rests on jack.
4. Remove tire and wheel assembly.
5. **On except GSi models,** remove brake drum assembly.
6. **On GSi models,** remove rear disc brake assembly.
7. **On all models,** remove rear axle hub as outlined under "Rear Axle Hub, Replace," **Fig. 2.**
8. **On except GSi models,** disconnect brake line from brake hose and backing plate.
9. **On GSi models,** disconnect brake hose from caliper assembly.
10. **On all models,** remove strut rod from knuckle as outlined under "Strut Rod, Replace."
11. Remove front and rear suspension arms from knuckle as outlined under "Suspension Arm, Replace."
12. Disconnect strut assembly as outlined under "Strut/Coil Spring, Replace."
13. Remove knuckle.
14. Reverse procedure to install, torquing attaching bolts to specifications.

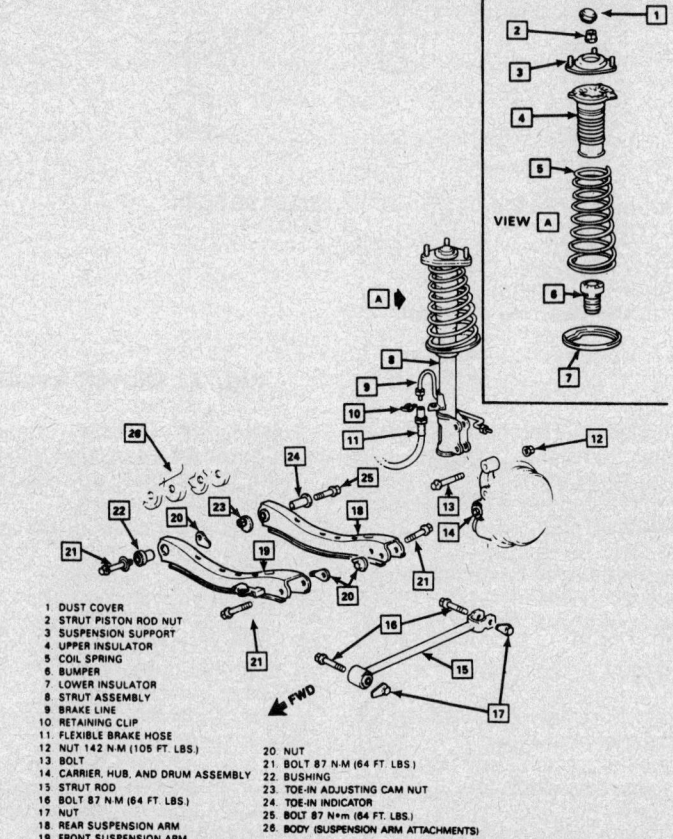

1 DUST COVER
2 STRUT PISTON ROD NUT
3 SUSPENSION SUPPORT
4 UPPER INSULATOR
5 COIL SPRING
6 BUMPER
7 LOWER INSULATOR
8 STRUT ASSEMBLY
9 BRAKE LINE
10 RETAINING CLIP
11 FLEXIBLE BRAKE HOSE
12 NUT 142 N-M (105 FT. LBS.)
13 BOLT
14 CARRIER, HUB, AND DRUM ASSEMBLY
15 STRUT ROD
16 BOLT 87 N-M (64 FT. LBS.)
17 NUT
18 REAR SUSPENSION ARM
19 FRONT SUSPENSION ARM
20 NUT
21 BOLT 87 N-M (64 FT. LBS.)
22 BUSHING
23 TOE-IN ADJUSTING CAM NUT
24 TOE-IN INDICATOR
25 BOLT 87 N•m (64 FT. LBS.)
26 BODY (SUSPENSION ARM ATTACHMENTS)

Fig. 1   Rear suspension assembly. Nova

REAR AXLE HUB
REPLACE
NOVA

1. Raise and support vehicle.
2. Remove wheel and tire assembly.
3. Remove brake drum, **Fig. 3.**
4. Remove four bolts attaching axle hub and rear brake assembly.
5. Remove hub, brake assembly and O-ring.
6. Reverse procedure to install.

PRIZM

1. Raise and support vehicle.
2. Support suspension using a suitable jack. Place jack under suspension supports, not the suspension arms.
3. Lower vehicle slightly so weight rests on jack.
4. Remove tire and wheel assembly.
5. **On except GSi models,** remove brake drum assembly.
6. **On GSi models,** remove rear disc brake assembly.
7. **On all models,** remove axle hub and rear suspension knuckle mounting bolts, **Fig. 4.**
8. Reverse procedure to install, using a new O-ring seal when installing.

REAR AXLE HUB
SERVICE
PRIZM

1. Remove rear axle hub as outlined under "Rear Axle Hub, Replace."
2. Unstake wheel bearing locknut and remove.

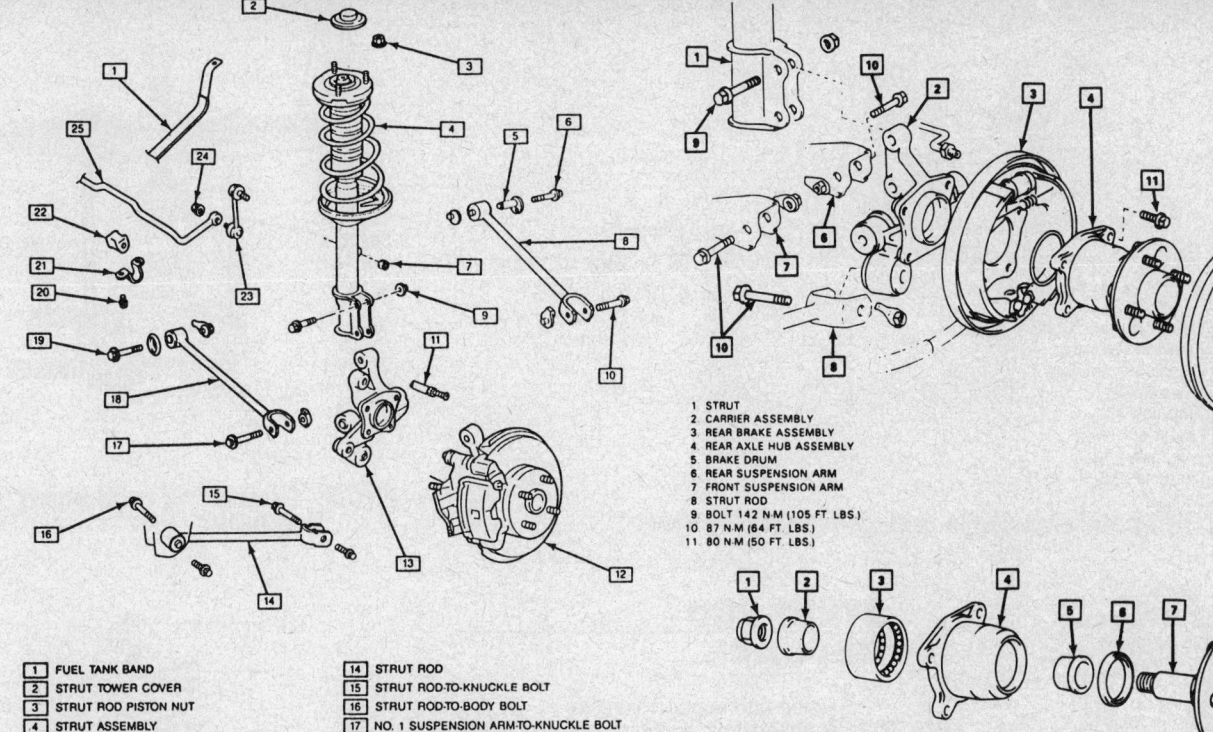

1 STRUT
2 CARRIER ASSEMBLY
3 REAR BRAKE ASSEMBLY
4 REAR AXLE HUB ASSEMBLY
5 BRAKE DRUM
6 REAR SUSPENSION ARM
7 FRONT SUSPENSION ARM
8 STRUT ROD
9 BOLT 142 N·M (105 FT. LBS.)
10 87 N·M (64 FT. LBS.)
11 80 N·M (50 FT. LBS.)

1 NUT 123 N·M (90 FT. LBS)
2 INNER BEARING INNER RACE
3 BEARING OUTER RACE WITH BEARINGS INSTALLED
4 REAR AXLE HUB (BEARING CASE)
5 OUTER BEARING INNER RACE
6 AXLE SEAL
7 AXLE

Fig. 3 Rear hub assembly. Nova

1 FUEL TANK BAND	**14** STRUT ROD
2 STRUT TOWER COVER	**15** STRUT ROD-TO-KNUCKLE BOLT
3 STRUT ROD PISTON NUT	**16** STRUT ROD-TO-BODY BOLT
4 STRUT ASSEMBLY	**17** NO. 1 SUSPENSION ARM-TO-KNUCKLE BOLT
5 REAR TCE ADJUSTMENT BOLT	**18** NO. 1 SUSPENSION ARM
6 NO. 2 SUSPENSION ARM-TO-BODY BOLT	**19** NO. 1 SUSPENSION ARM-TO-BODY BOLT
7 STABILIZER BAR LINK-TO-STRUT ASSEMBLY NUT	**20** STABILIZER BRACKET BOLT
8 NO. 2 SUSPENSION ARM	**21** STABILIZER BAR BRACKET
9 STRUT ASSEMBLY-TO-KNUCKLE NUT	**22** BUSHING
10 NO. 2 SUSPENSION ARM-TO-KNUCKLE BOLT	**23** STABILIZER BAR LINK
11 BRAKE LINE	**24** STABILIZER BAR LINK NUT
12 REAR DISC BRAKE ASSEMBLY	**25** STABILIZER BAR
13 REAR SUSPENSION KNUCKLE	

Fig. 2 Rear suspension assembly. Prizm

3. Remove axle shaft from hub assembly using a bearing removal tool Nos. J-22912, J-38278 and J-8433, or equivalent, **Figs. 4 and 5.**
4. Remove bearing inner and outer race.
5. Remove oil seal from axle shaft using seal installer/remover tool No. J-26941, or equivalent, and slide hammer.
6. Reverse procedure to install, using a new bearing locknut.

STRUT/COIL SPRING ASSEMBLY
REPLACE
NOVA

Do not attempt to disassemble strut, since cylinder is filled with high pressure gas. When discarding strut, drill a .090 inch hole in bottom of strut to relieve all gas pressure.
1. Remove quarter window garnish molding and back window panel.
2. Raise and support vehicle, then remove tire and wheel assembly.
3. Remove brake line at flex hose on strut, **Fig. 1.**
4. Disconnect flexible hose from shock absorber.

5. Remove bolts attaching strut to axle carrier.
6. Remove the strut suspension support to body bolts.
7. Reverse procedure to install.

PRIZM

1. Raise and support vehicle.
2. Support suspension using a suitable jack. Place jack under suspension supports, not the suspension arms.
3. Lower vehicle slightly so weight rests on jack.
4. Remove tire and wheel assembly.
5. Disconnect brake hose from brake hose bracket.
6. Disconnect stabilizer bar link from strut assembly as outlined under "Stabilizer Bar, Replace."
7. Disconnect strut assembly mounting bolts from knuckle.
8. Remove seat back side cushion (sedan) or rear sill side panel (hatchback).
9. Disconnect strut assembly mounting nuts holding strut support.
10. Remove strut assembly from vehicle.
11. Reverse procedure to install.

STRUT/COIL SPRING ASSEMBLY
SERVICE
DISASSEMBLY

1. Remove strut assembly as outlined under "Strut/Coil Spring Assembly, Replace."
2. Mount strut assembly in strut holding/spring compression tool No. J-34013, or equivalent.
3. Remove strut piston rod to suspension support nut.
4. Remove suspension support, coil spring, insulator and bumper.

ASSEMBLY

1. Mount strut in holding/spring compression tool No. J-34013, or equivalent.
2. Align coil spring end with lower seat hollow and install coil spring.
3. Install spring bumper and insulator.
4. Align suspension support with piston rod and install.
5. Align suspension support with strut lower bracket as shown in **Fig. 6.**
6. Compress spring slightly, install a new strut rod piston nut and torque to specification.

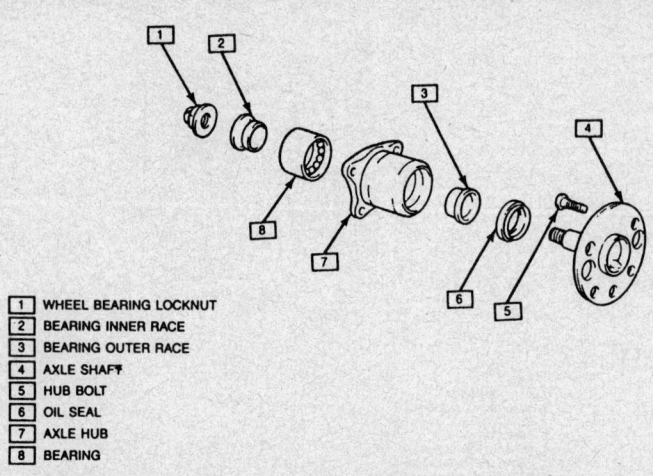

1 WHEEL BEARING LOCKNUT
2 BEARING INNER RACE
3 BEARING OUTER RACE
4 AXLE SHAFT
5 HUB BOLT
6 OIL SEAL
7 AXLE HUB
8 BEARING

Fig. 4   Rear axle hub assembly. Prizm

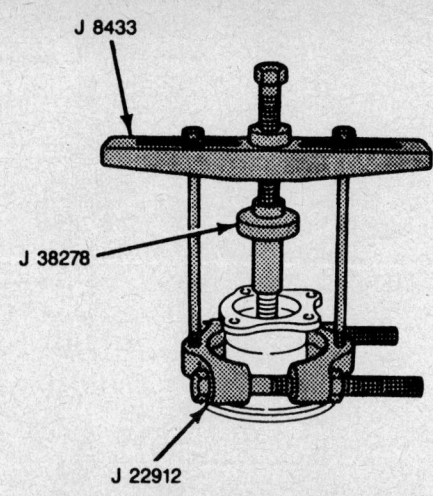

Fig. 5   Removing axle shaft from hub. Prizm

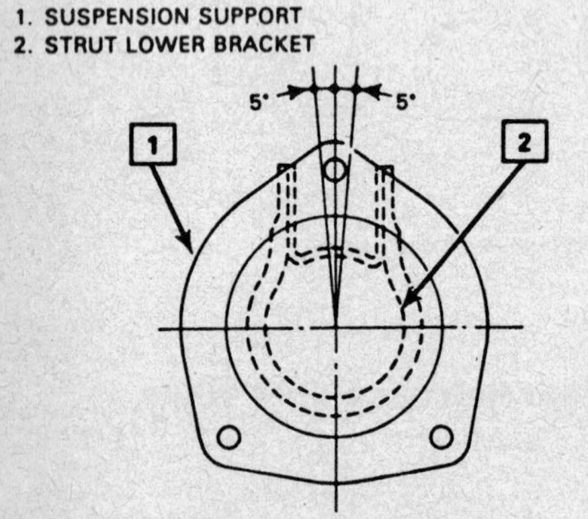

1. SUSPENSION SUPPORT
2. STRUT LOWER BRACKET

Fig. 6   Aligning suspension support plate. Prizm

SUSPENSION ARM
REPLACE
REAR

1. Raise and support vehicle.
2. Remove bolt and nut attaching rear suspension arm to axle carrier.
3. Remove cam and bolt attaching rear suspension arm to body, then the rear suspension arm.
4. Note location of cam plate mark before removing bolt and cam.
5. Reverse procedure to install.

FRONT

1. Raise and support vehicle.
2. Remove bolt and nut attaching front suspension arm to axle carrier.
3. Remove bolt and nut attaching front suspension arm to the body, then the front suspension arm.
4. Reverse procedure to install.

STRUT ROD
REPLACE

1. Raise and support vehicle.
2. Remove bolt and nut attaching strut rod to axle carrier.
3. Remove bolt and nut attaching strut rod to body, then the strut rod assembly from the vehicle.
4. Reverse procedure to install.

STABILIZER ARM
REPLACE
NOVA
Removal

1. Raise and support vehicle.
2. Remove rear tire and wheel assembly.
3. Remove attaching hardware holding stabilizer links to front suspension arm, **Fig. 7.**
4. Remove bolts holding stabilizer bar to body.
5. Remove stabilizer bar from vehicle.
6. Remove and discard bolts from stabilizer bar and links.
7. Remove collar using a sliding tee handle.
8. Remove bushing.

Installation

1. Install new bushing and collar using a sliding tee handle.
2. Install but do not tighten stabilizer links to stabilizer bar.
3. Install but do not tighten stabilizer bar to body.
4. Install stabilizer links to suspension arms and tighten to specification.
5. Torque bracket bolts holding stabilizer bar to body to specification.

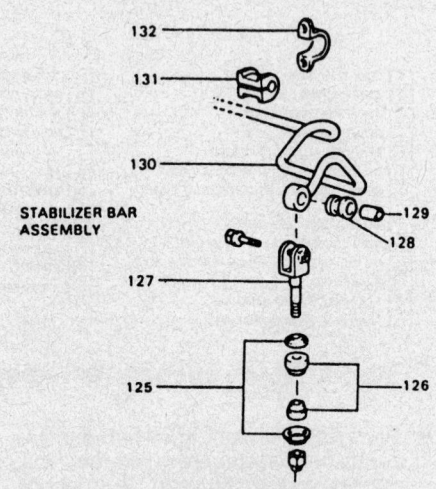

STABILIZER BAR
ASSEMBLY

125   RETAINER
126   CUSHION
127   STABILIZER LINK
128   BUSHING
129   COLLAR
130   STABILIZER BAR
131   BUSHING
132   BRACKET

Fig. 7   Stabilizer bar assembly. Prizm

6. Torque bolts holding stabilizer bar to links to specification.
7. Install tire and wheel assembly and lower vehicle.

PRIZM

1. Support fuel tank with a suitable jack.
2. Disconnect fuel tank straps.
3. Disconnect stabilizer bar links from strut assemblies, **Fig. 2.**
4. Disconnect stabilizer bar bracket mounting bolts.
5. Remove stabilizer bar from vehicle.
6. Reverse procedure to install.

TIGHTENING SPECIFICATIONS

Year	Component	Torque/Ft. lbs.
1988-91	Axle Hub Bolts ①	59
	Axle Hub Mounting Bolts ②	59
	Mounting Bracket Bolt ①	34
	Rear Axle Carrier Bolts ①	105
	Rear Suspension Arm Bolts ①	64
	Stabilizer Bar Bracket Mounting Bolts ②	14
	Stabilizer Bar Link To Strut Assembly ③	26
	Stabilizer Bar Links To Strut Assembly ②	26
	Stabilizer Bar To Stabilizer Bar Links Nuts ②	26
	Stabilizer Bar to Stabilizer Links ①	22
	Stabilizer Bracket Bolts ①	9
	Stabilizer Link to Suspension Arm ①	11
	Strut Assembly To Body Nuts ②	29
	Strut Assembly To Knuckle Nuts ②	105
	Strut Piston Rod Nut ①	36
	Strut Rod To Body Nut ②	87
	Strut Rod To Knuckle Nuts ②	87
	Strut to Axle Carrier Nut ①	105
	Suspension Arm Bolts ①	64
	Suspension Arm Bolts ②	87
	Suspension Support Nuts ①	17
	Wheel Bearing Locknut ②	90
	Wheel Nuts	76

① —Nova.
① —Prizm.

Front Suspension & Steering

INDEX

DESCRIPTION

The front suspension, **Figs. 1 through 4**, on this vehicle is a MacPherson strut design. The upper end of the strut is anchored to the body by a strut support. The strut and strut support are isolated by a rubber mount. The lower end of the strut is connected to the upper end of the steering knuckle. The lower end of the knuckle is attached to the ball joint, which is attached to the suspension control arm assembly. Movement of the steering wheel is transmitted to the tie-rod end and then to the knuckle, turning the wheel and tire assembly.

STRUT/COIL SPRING
REPLACE
NOVA

1. Open hood, then remove strut to body attaching nuts.
2. Loosen wheel lug nuts. Loosen axle shaft nut if knuckle will be removed.
3. Raise and support vehicle until wheels are clear from ground.
4. Remove tire and wheel assembly.
5. Disconnect brake flex hose clip at strut bracket.
6. Disconnect brake flex hose to brake pipe connection. Remove brake hose clip.
7. Pull brake hose back through strut bracket opening, then tape or cap brake hose and caliper.

8. Remove two brake caliper mounting bracket bolts, then the caliper.
9. Mark adjusting cam, then remove both strut to knuckle attaching nuts and bolts.
10. Remove strut assembly and camber adjusting cam from knuckle.
11. Reverse procedure to install. Torque strut to knuckle attaching nuts and bolts to specifications.

PRIZM

1. Raise and support vehicle.
2. Support suspension using a suitable jack. Place jack under suspension supports, not the control arm.
3. Lower vehicle slightly so weight rests on jack.
4. Install a drive joint seal protector tool No. J-34754, or equivalent.

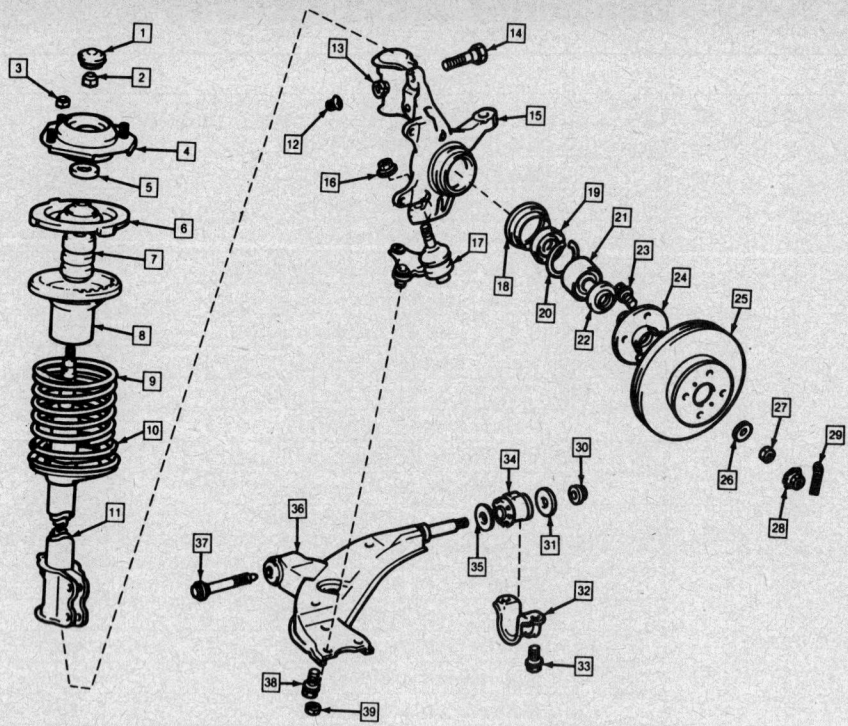

1. COVER, DUST
2. NUT, ABSORBER SHAFT
3. NUT, STRUT SUPPORT
4. SUPPORT, STRUT
5. SEAL, SUPPORT
6. SEAT, SPRING
7. BUMPER, SPRING
8. INSULATOR, UPPER
9. SPRING, COIL
10. INSULATOR, LOWER
11. ABSORBER, SHOCK/STRUT
12. NUT, STRUT TO KNUCKLE
13. CAM, CAMBER ADJUST
14. BOLT, STRUT TO KNUCKLE
15. KNUCKLE, STEERING
16. NUT, BALL JOINT TO KNUCKLE
17. JOINT, LOWER BALL
18. DEFLECTOR, DUST
19. SEAL, INNER HUB
20. RING, SNAP

21. BEARING, FRONT AXLE HUB
22. SEAL OUTER HUB
23. STUD, WHEEL
24. HUB, FRONT AXLE
25. DISC, FRONT BRAKE
26. WASHER, FRONT HUB
27. NUT, FRONT HUB
28. CAP, FRONT HUB
29. PIN, COTTER
30. NUT, CONTROL ARM
31. RETAINER, BUSHING
32. BRACKET, BUSHING
33. BOLT, BUSHING BRACKET
34. BUSHING, CONTROL ARM
35. RETAINER, BUSHING
36. ARM, LOWER CONTROL
37. BOLT, CONTROL ARM
38. BOLT, BALL JOINT
39. NUT, BALL JOINT

Fig. 1   Disassembled view of front suspension. Nova except 16 valve engine

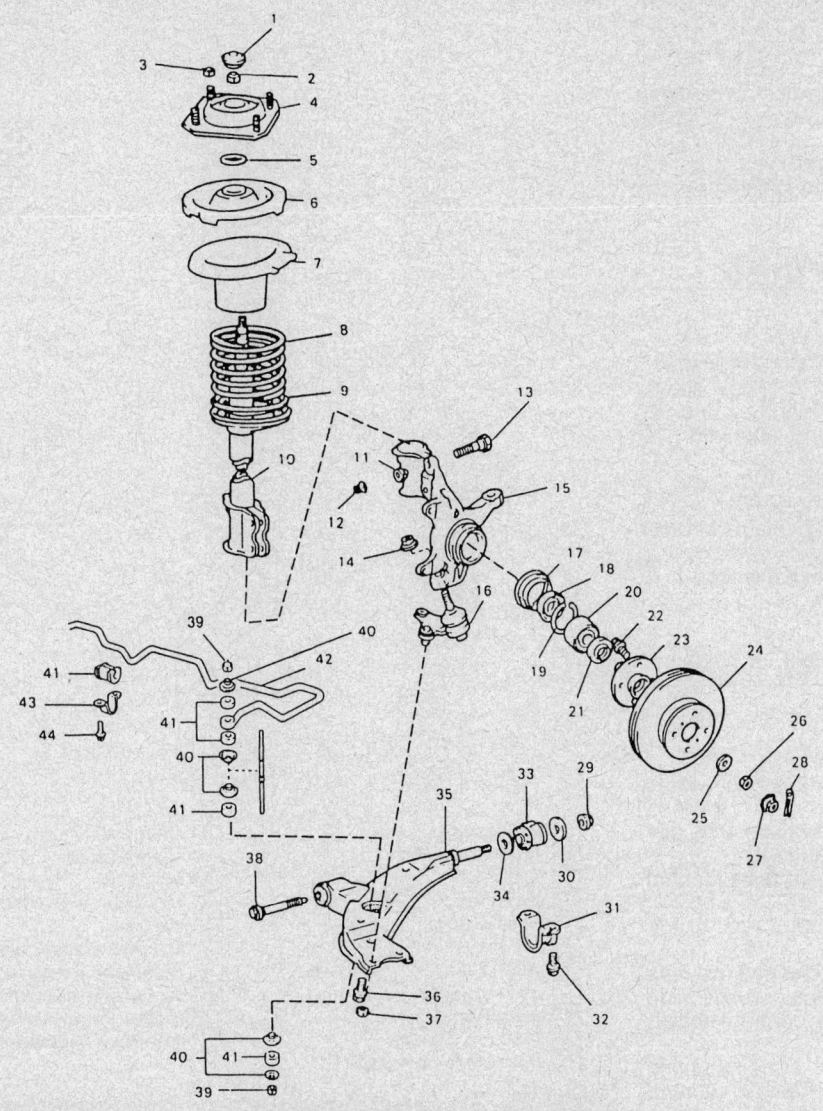

1	COVER, DUST	16	JOINT, LOWER BALL	31	BRACKET, BUSHING
2	NUT, STRUT SHAFT	17	DEFLECTOR, DUST	32	BOLT, BUSHING BRACKET
3	NUT, STRUT SUPPORT	18	SEAL, INNER GREASE	33	BUSHING, CONTROL ARM
4	SUPPORT, STRUT	19	RING, SNAP	34	RETAINER, BUSHING
5	SEAL, SUPPORT	20	BEARING, FRONT AXLE HUB	35	ARM, LOWER CONTROL
6	SEAT, SPRING	21	SEAL, OUTER HUB	36	BOLT, BALL JOINT
7	INSULATOR, UPPER	22	STUD, WHEEL	37	NUT, BALL JOINT
8	SPRING, COIL	23	HUB, FRONT AXLE	38	BOLT, CONTROL ARM
9	INSULATOR, LOWER	24	DISC, FRONT BRAKE	39	NUT, STABILIZER BAR TO CONTROL ARM
10	ABSORBER, SHOCK/STRUT	25	WASHER, FRONT HUB	40	RETAINER, STABILIZER BAR TO CONTROL ARM
11	CAM, CAMBER ADJUST	26	NUT, FRONT HUB	41	INSULATOR, STABILIZER BAR
12	NUT, STRUT TO KNUCKLE	27	CAP, FRONT HUB	42	STABILIZER BAR
13	BOLT, STRUT TO KNUCKLE	28	PIN, COTTER	43	BRACKET, STABILIZER BAR TO BODY
14	NUT, BALL JOINT TO KNUCKLE	29	NUT, CONTROL ARM	44	BOLT, STABILIZER BAR BRACKET
15	KNUCKLE, STEERING	30	RETAINER, BUSHING		

Fig. 2 Disassembled view of front suspension. Nova w/16 valve engine

5. Remove brake hose from disc brake caliper.
6. Remove clip from brake hose.
7. Remove brake hose from brake hose bracket.
8. Remove bolts and nuts attaching strut assembly to steering knuckle.
9. Remove strut assembly mounting nuts holding suspension support plate.
10. Remove strut assembly.
11. Reverse procedure to install.

STRUT/COIL SPRING
SERVICE

1. Using strut holding/spring compression tool No. J-34013-A, or equivalent, compress spring slightly. **Ensure spring seat is secure and will not turn.**
2. Remove strut rod piston nut.
3. Remove suspension support, dust seal, spring seat and insulator and bumper.
4. Reverse procedure to assemble.

LOWER CONTROL ARM
REPLACE

1. Raise and support vehicle.
2. Remove lower control arm attaching nuts and bolts.
3. **On models with stabilizer bar,** disconnect stabilizer bar links.
4. **On Nova models,** remove control arm from vehicle.
5. **On Prizm models,** proceed as follows:
   a. Remove the six bolts and two nuts and remove the suspension crossmember with control arms attached.
   b. Remove control arm mounting bolts and nuts. Remove control arm from crossmember.
6. **On all models,** reverse procedure to install. Torque control arm to body front nuts and bolts to specifications.

LOWER CONTROL ARM BUSHING
REPLACE

1. Remove control arm as outlined under "Lower Control Arm, Replace."
2. Using a suitable tool, remove lower control arm bushing from lower control arm.
3. Reverse procedure to install. Torque bushing nut to specifications.

LOWER BALL JOINT
REPLACE

1. Raise and support vehicle.
2. Support suspension using a suitable

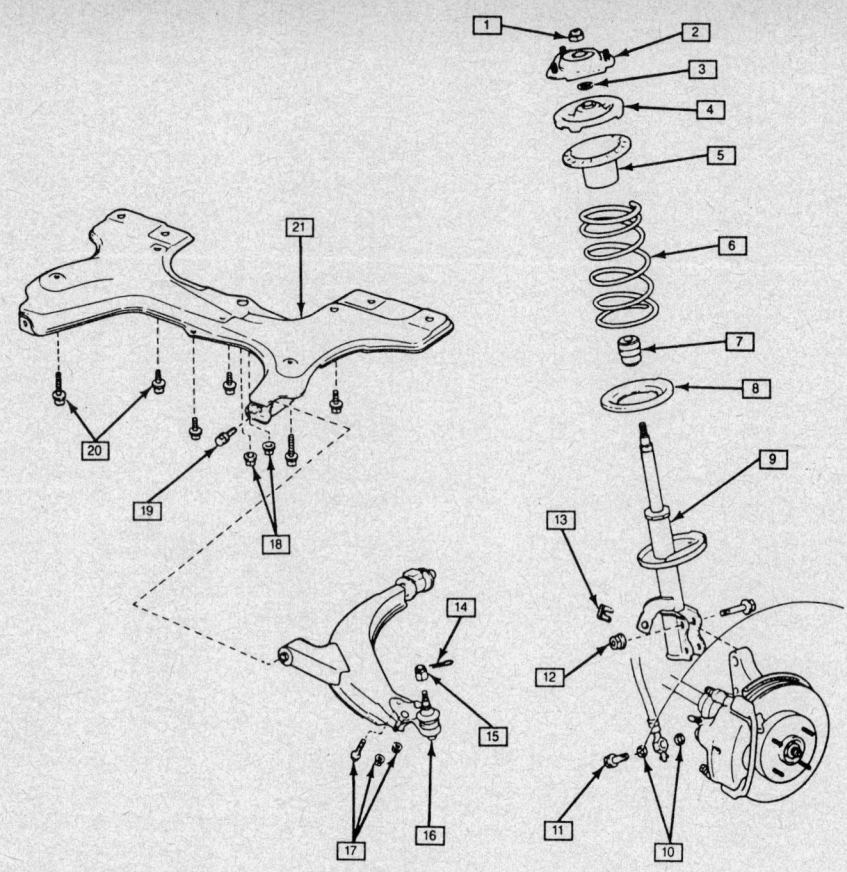

1	STRUT ROD PISTON NUT
2	SUSPENSION SUPPORT
3	DUST SEAL
4	SPRING SEAT
5	UPPER INSULATOR
6	COIL SPRING
7	SPRING BUMPER
8	LOWER INSULATOR
9	SHOCK ABSORBER
10	BRAKE LINE GASKETS
11	BRAKE LINE-TO-CALIPER BOLT
12	STRUT MOUNTING NUT AND BOLT
13	BRAKE HOSE CLIP
14	COTTER PIN
15	BALL JOINT CASTLE NUT
16	BALL JOINT
17	BALL JOINT MOUNTING NUT AND BOLT
18	CROSSMEMBER MOUNTING NUTS
19	CROSSMEMBER-TO-CONTROL-ARM BOLT
20	CROSSMEMBER MOUNTING BOLTS
21	SUSPENSION CROSSMEMBER

Fig. 3   Disassembled view of front suspension. Prizm except GSi models

jack. Place jack under suspension supports, not the control arm.
3. Lower vehicle slightly so weight rests on jack.
4. Loosen wheel lug nuts.
5. Remove tire and wheel assembly.
6. Install inner drive joint seal protector tool No. J-34754, or equivalent. **Care must be taken not to allow tri-pot joints to over extend. Over extended tri-pot joints could result in separation of internal components and possible join failure.**
7. Using ball joint removal tool No. J-35413 or equivalent, separate ball joint from knuckle assembly.
8. Remove two nuts and bolts attaching ball joint and control arm.
9. Remove ball joint.
10. Reverse procedure to install. Torque knuckle to ball joint nut to specifications. During installation, always replace a self-locking nut with a new one.

STEERING KNUCKLE
REPLACE

NOVA

1. Loosen wheel and hub nuts.
2. Raise and support vehicle.
3. Remove tire and wheel assembly.
4. Remove brake hose retaining clip at strut.
5. Disconnect flex hose from brake line.
6. Remove caliper bracket to knuckle mounting bolts, then support caliper.
7. Remove disc assembly.
8. Remove drive axle unit. Use puller J-25287 or equivalent, to push out drive axle assembly.
9. Remove cotter pin and tie rod to knuckle attaching nut. Use tie rod removal tool No. J-24319-01 or equivalent to separate the tie rod assembly.
10. Remove ball joint to control arm attaching nuts and bolt.

11. Mark camber relationship for installation, then remove two strut to knuckle attaching nuts and bolts, then the knuckle.
12. Reverse procedure to install. Torque control arm nuts and bolts, ball joint to knuckle, strut to lower bracket bolts, tie rod to knuckle and brake caliper bracket to knuckle attaching bolts sepcification.

PRIZM

1. Remove locknut cap and bearing locknut.
2. Remove brake caliper and support with wire.
3. Remove disc brake rotor.
4. Separate tie rod from steering knuckle using tie rod puller tool No. J-6627-A, or equivalent.
5. Remove lower ball joint bolt and nuts and separate it from lower control arm.
6. Remove two strut to steering knuckle nuts.
7. Install drive joint protector tool No. J-34754, or equivalent.
8. Tap driveshaft with a plastic hammer and drive out drive shaft.
9. Remove two strut to steering knuckle bolts.
10. Remove steering knuckle assembly.
11. Reverse procedure to install.

HUB
REPLACE

1. Remove knuckle from vehicle and mount into a suitable vise.
2. Using a suitable screwdriver, remove dust deflector.
3. Using seal remover tool No. J-26941 or equivalent, remove inner grease seal from knuckle, **Fig. 5.**
4. Remove inner bearing snap ring and disc brake dust shield.
5. Push out hub using hub remover tool Nos. J-25287 and J-35378 or equivalents.
6. Using tools mentioned in step 5, remove outer bearing race from hub.
7. Using seal remover tool No. J-26941 or equivalent, remove outer grease seal.
8. Using bearing remover tool Nos. J-35399 and J-35379 or equivalents, remove bearing assembly.
9. Reverse procedure to install. Use bearing installation tool Nos. J-8092 and J-35411 to install hub bearing assembly. Use seal installation tool No. J-35737 to install outer grease seal. Install hub using tool Nos. J-8092 and J-35399. Use tool No. J-35737 to install inner grease seal. Use ring installation tool No. J-35379 to install dust deflector ring. Ensure dust deflector ring faces down (open end down).

STABILIZER BAR
REPLACE

1. Raise and support vehicle.
2. Disconnect stabilizer bar links from lower control arms.

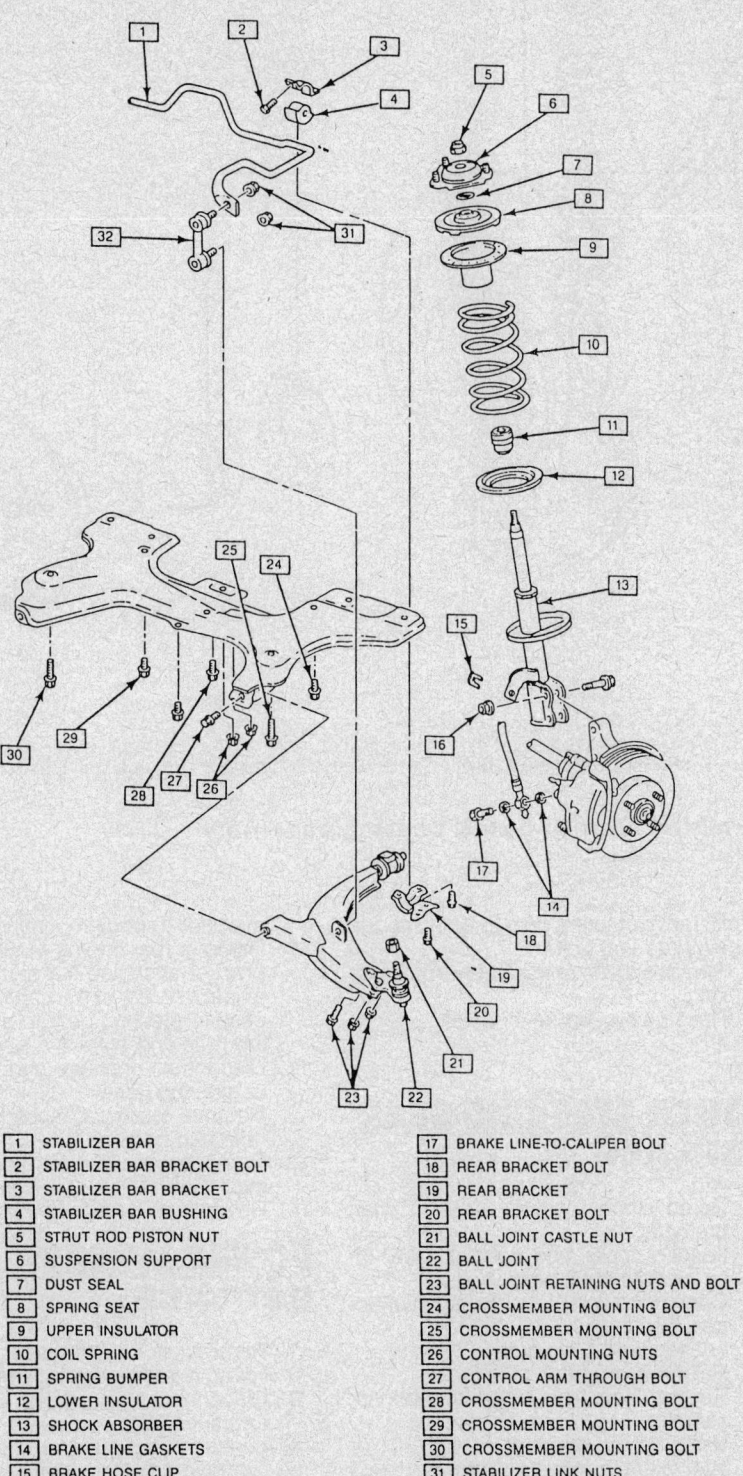

1	STABILIZER BAR
2	STABILIZER BAR BRACKET BOLT
3	STABILIZER BAR BRACKET
4	STABILIZER BAR BUSHING
5	STRUT ROD PISTON NUT
6	SUSPENSION SUPPORT
7	DUST SEAL
8	SPRING SEAT
9	UPPER INSULATOR
10	COIL SPRING
11	SPRING BUMPER
12	LOWER INSULATOR
13	SHOCK ABSORBER
14	BRAKE LINE GASKETS
15	BRAKE HOSE CLIP
16	STRUT MOUNTING NUT AND BOLT
17	BRAKE LINE-TO-CALIPER BOLT
18	REAR BRACKET BOLT
19	REAR BRACKET
20	REAR BRACKET BOLT
21	BALL JOINT CASTLE NUT
22	BALL JOINT
23	BALL JOINT RETAINING NUTS AND BOLT
24	CROSSMEMBER MOUNTING BOLT
25	CROSSMEMBER MOUNTING BOLT
26	CONTROL MOUNTING NUTS
27	CONTROL ARM THROUGH BOLT
28	CROSSMEMBER MOUNTING BOLT
29	CROSSMEMBER MOUNTING BOLT
30	CROSSMEMBER MOUNTING BOLT
31	STABILIZER LINK NUTS
32	STABILIZER LINK

Fig. 4   Disassembled view of front suspension. Prizm GSi models

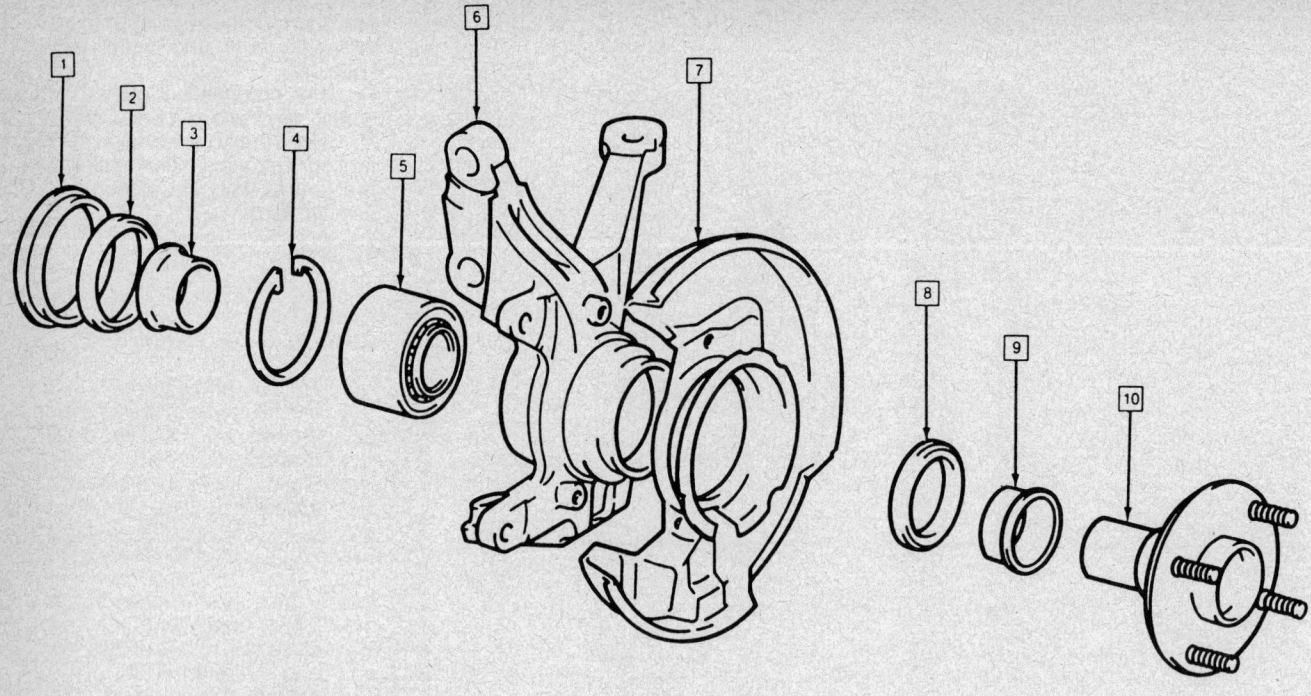

PARTS LIST

1 DEFLECTOR. DUST	3 RACE. INNER BEARING	5 BEARING. AXLE HUB
2 SEAL INNER GREASE	4 RING. SNAP	6 KNUCKLE. STEERING FRONT

7 SHIELD. DUST	9. RACE. OUTER BEARING
8 SEAL. OUTER GREASE	10. HUB. DRIVE AXLE

Fig. 5   Disassembled view of hub & bearing assembly

3. Remove stabilizer bar brackets from body.
4. Disconnect exhaust pipe from manifold and/or catalytic converter.
5. Remove stabilizer bar from vehicle.
6. Reverse procedure to install.

MANUAL STEERING GEAR
REPLACE

1. Disconnect battery ground cable.
2. Remove intermediate shaft cover.
3. Loosen upper pinch bolt. Remove lower pinch bolt from pinion shaft.
4. Loosen wheel lug nuts.
5. Raise and support vehicle.
6. Remove both front wheel and tire assemblies.
7. Remove cotter pins from tie rod ends.
8. Disconnect both tie rod ends from steering knuckles. Use tool No. J-24319-01, or equivalent only, to separate tie rod joints.

POWER STEERING GEAR
REPLACE

1. Remove intermediate steering shaft protector.
2. Loosen upper, and remove lower intermediate shaft pinch bolts.
3. Open hood and place drain pan under gear assembly.
4. Loosen wheel lug nuts.
5. Raise and support vehicle.
6. Remove both front wheel and tire assemblies.
7. Using tie rod remover J-24319-01 or equivalent, remove both tie rod ends from knuckles.
8. Support transaxle with a suitable jack.
9. Remove rear center engine mounting

9. Remove steering gear to body mounting nuts and bolts.
10. Remove steering assembly from vehicle.
11. Reverse procedure to install.

member to body mounting bolts.
10. Remove rear engine mount to mount bracket attaching nut and bolt. Raise and lower rear of transaxle to gain access to steering gear to body attaching nuts and bolts.
11. Disconnect pressure and return lines at steering gear.
12. Remove four gear to body mounting nuts and bolts.
13. Remove gear through access opening.
14. Reverse procedure to install.

POWER STEERING PUMP
REPLACE

1. Remove air cleaner assembly.
2. Remove return hose clamp.
3. Disconnect and cap pressure and return lines from pump.
4. Loosen pump pulley and remove.
5. Remove adjusting bolt, pivot bolt and drive belt.
6. Remove pump assembly.
7. Reverse procedure to install.

TIGHTENING SPECIFICATIONS

Year	Component	Torque/ft. lbs.
1988–91	Axle Shaft Nuts ①	137
	Ball Joint To Knuckle Nuts ①	82
	Ball Joint To Knuckle Nuts ②	94
	Ball Joint To Lower Control Arm Nuts ①	59
	Ball Joint To Lower Control Arm Nuts ②	105
	Brake Caliper Bolts	65
	Control Arm Rear Bracket To Crossmember Nuts ②	14
	Lower Control Arm Bushing Nuts ①	76
	Lower Control Arm Bushing Nuts ②	101
	Lower Control Arm To Body Nuts ①	⑥
	Lower Control Arm To Body Nuts ②	③
	Rear Bracket Bolts ②	94
	Rear Bracket To Crossmember Bolt ②	14
	Stabilizer Bar Link Nuts ①	13
	Stabilizer Bar Link Nuts ②	26
	Stabilizer Bar To Body Bolts ①	14
	Stabilizer Bar To Body Bolts ②	29
	Strut Piston Nut	34
	Strut To Knuckle Nuts & Bolts ①	④ 105
	Strut To Knuckle Nuts & Bolts ①	④ 166
	Strut To Knuckle Nuts & Bolts ②	194
	Suspension Support Plates ①	23 ④
	Suspension Support Plates ①	29 ⑤
	Tie Rod To Knuckle Nuts	36
	Wheel Bearing Locknuts ②	137
	Wheel Lug Nuts ①	76

①—Nova.
②—Prizm.
③—Front, 152 ft. lbs; Rear, 94 ft. lbs.
④—Except 16 valve engine.
⑤—16 valve engine.
⑥—Front, 105 ft. lbs; Rear, 72 ft. lbs.

Wheel Alignment

INDEX

FRONT WHEEL ALIGNMENT

CASTER & CAMBER

Except Prizm GSi Models

Camber is adjusted by first loosening the upper and lower strut to knuckle nuts and bolts, then rotating cam to obtain correct specification.

Caster cannot be adjusted. Should caster be found out of specification, locate cause first. If components are damaged, bent, loose, dented or worn, they should be replaced. To prevent an incorrect reading of camber or caster, jounce the bumper three times before checking, **Fig. 1.**

After adjustment, tighten nuts to specification.

Prizm GSi Models

Caster and camber cannot be adjusted. Should caster be found out of specification, locate cause first. If components are damaged, bent, loose, dented or worn, they should be replaced. To prevent an incorrect reading of camber or caster, jounce the bumper three times before checking.

TOE-IN

Toe-in is adjusted by changing tie rod length. Loosen boot clamps and slide from the boot assembly. Loosen right and left tie rod end locknuts, then turn right and left tie rods to align toe-in to specification. Right and left tie rods must be equal in length, **Fig. 2.**

After adjustment, install boot clamps, tighten nuts to specification and ensure rack boots are not twisted.

Torque strut-to-knuckle nut to specifications, and tie rod locking nut to 35 ft. lbs. for

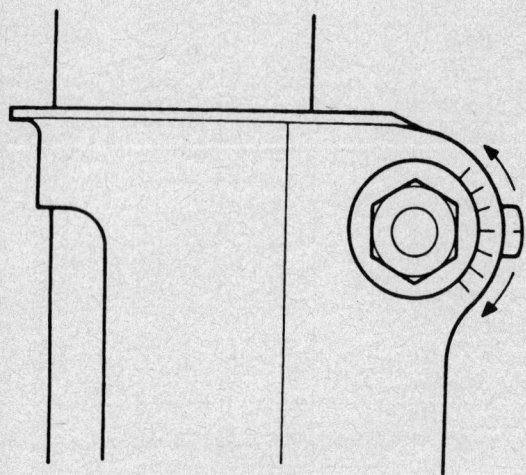

Fig. 1 Front camber

Fig. 2 Front camber adjustment

REAR TOE   ADJUSTMENT MECHANISM

Rear suspension arm No. 2 is equipped with toe   adjustment cams.

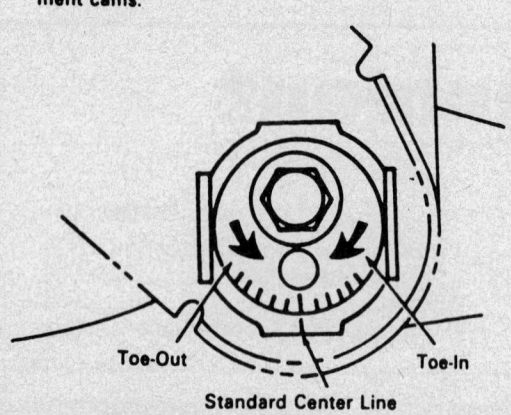

Toe-Out   Toe-In

Standard Center Line

Toe   Adjustment

(1) Measure the distance and find the difference between the left and right disc wheels and the centerline of the adjustment cam. (If the difference is not within standard specifications, check each part for deformation.)

(2) Turn each cam an equal amount in the opposite direction. (Toe   changes about 2 mm for each turn of the cam on each side.)

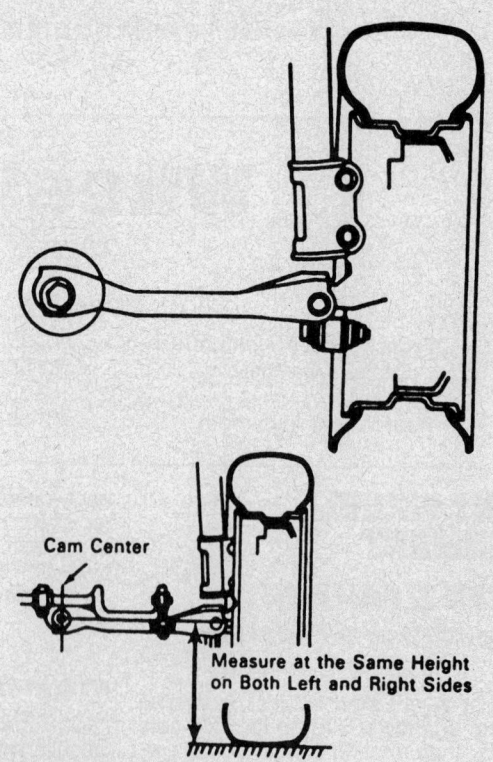

Cam Center

Measure at the Same Height on Both Left and Right Sides

Fig. 3 Rear toe adjustment

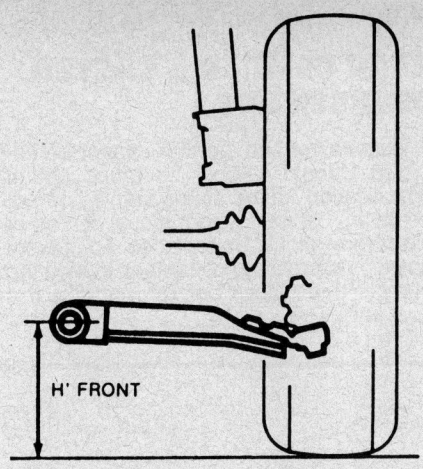

Fig. 4   Ride height. Front

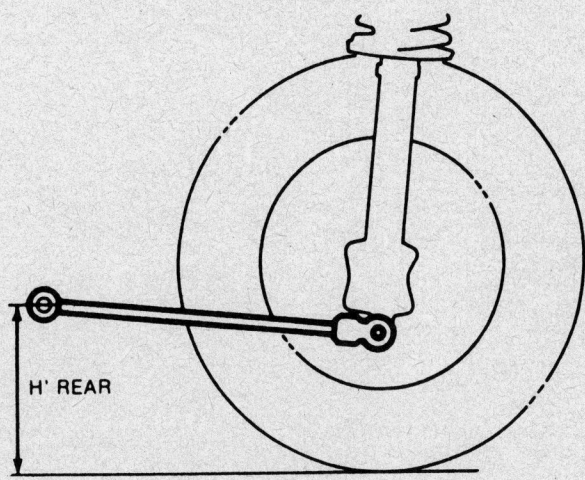

Fig. 5   Ride height. Rear

	TIRE SIZE	FRONT	REAR
4A-LC	P175/70 R 13	192 mm	258 mm
	P155/80 R 13	191 mm	257 mm
4A-GE	P175/70 HR 13	183 mm	259 mm

Fig. 6   Ride height measurement chart

Nova models or 41 ft. lbs for Prizm models.

REAR WHEEL ALIGNMENT

REAR TOE ADJUSTMENT

Toe-in can be adjusted by rotating the cam located on the rear lower control arm. Loosen bolt and rotate nut to give the correct specification. Measure distance between left and right wheel discs and cen-terline of adjustment cam, **Fig. 3.**

REAR CAMBER & CASTER ADJUSTMENT

Rear caster and camber cannot be adjusted. Should camber be found out of specification, locate cause first. If components are damaged, bent loose, dented or worn, they should be replaced. To prevent an incorrect reading of camber, jounce the bumper three times before checking. If a tie rod or tie rod end is replaced, check toe and steering angle with turning radius gages. If steering angle is not correct, check right and left tie rods for equal length. If tie rod length is change to correct steering, reinspect toe.

RIDE HEIGHT

Refer to **Figs. 4 and 5** for vehicle height and **Fig. 6,** for specification chart.

CHEVROLET SPRINT & GEO METRO (M Cars)

INDEX OF SERVICE OPERATIONS

NOTE: Refer To The Rear Of This Manual For Vehicle Manufacturer's Special Tool Suppliers.

Continued

CHEVROLET SPRINT & GEO METRO

INDEX OF SERVICE OPERATIONS—Continued

Specifications

GENERAL ENGINE SPECIFICATIONS

Year	Engine Liter /CID ①	VIN Code ②	Fuel System	Bore & Stroke Inches	Comp. Ratio	Net. H.P. @ RPM ③	Maximum Torque, Ft. Lbs. @ RPM	Normal Oil Pressure, Psi @ 3000 RPM
1988	1.0L/3-61④	5	2 Bbl. Hitachi	2.91 x 3.03	9.5	48 @ 5100	77 @ 3200	42.7–54
	1.0L/3-61⑤	5	2 Bbl. Hitachi	2.91 x 3.03	9.8	46 @ 4700	78 @ 3200	42.7–54
	1.0L/3-61 Turbo	2	EFI⑥	2.91 x 3.03	8.3	70@5500	107@3500	42.7–59.7
1989	1.0L/3-61⑦	5	EFI⑥	2.91 x 3.03	9.5	49 @ 4700	58 @ 3300	42.7–54
	1.0L/3-61⑧	5	EFI	2.91 x 3.03	9.5	55 @ 5700	58 @ 3300	42.7–54
1990	1.0L/3-61	—	EFI⑥	2.91 x 3.03	9.5	49 @ 4700	58 @ 3300	42.7–54
1991	1.0L/3-61	—	EFI⑧	2.91 x 3.03	9.5	55 @ 5700	58 @ 3300	—

① —CID= Cubic Inch Displacement.
② —The eighth digit of the VIN denotes engine code.
③ —As installed in-vehicle.
④ —Except 1988 Sprint Metro.
⑤ —1988 Sprint Metro.
⑥ —Electronic Port Fuel Injection.
⑦ —Except LSi models.
⑧ —LSi models.

TUNE UP SPECIFICATIONS

Year & Engine/VIN Code	Spark Plug Gap	Firing Order Fig.	Ignition Timing BTDC ① Man. Trans.	Ignition Timing BTDC ① Auto. Trans.	Mark Fig.	Curb Idle Speed Man. Trans.	Curb Idle Speed Auto. Trans. ⑦	Fast Idle Speed Man. Trans.	Fast Idle Speed Auto. Trans.	Fuel Pump Pressure, Psi.
1988										
1.0L/3-61/5 Except Turbo	.041	②	10	6	B	750	850N	2400	2400	3.5
1.0L/3-61/2 Turbo	.041	②	12	—	B	750	—	③	—	35–43④
1989–91										
1.0L/3-61/5	.041	②	⑤	⑤	B	750	700N	③	③	13–20⑥

① —BTDC: Before Top Dead Center.
② —Cylinder numbering front of engine to rear 1, 2, 3. Firing, 1-3-2. Refer to Fig. A for spark plug wire connections at distributor cap.
③ —Controlled by an idle speed control motor.
④ —To relieve system fuel pressure, remove fuel tank filler cap to release vapor pressure, then reinstall cap. With engine idling, disconnect fuel pump relay electrical connector. After engine has stopped operating, crank engine several times in three second intervals. After fuel pressure has been relieved, attach a suitable fuel pressure gauge to fuel feed hose, then reconnect fuel pump relay electrical connector. Start engine, then check fuel pressure with engine idling & vacuum hose disconnected from fuel pressure regulator.
⑤ —With distributor vacuum advance hose disconnected, 6° BTDC; with distributor vacuum advance hose connected, 12° BTDC.
⑥ —To relieve fuel system pressure, remove fuel pump relay from main fuse panel located in engine compartment. Operate engine until it stalls, then crank engine several times in three second intervals. Remove fuel tank filler cap to release vapor pressure, then reinstall cap. Place ignition switch in off position, then install fuel pump relay. After fuel pressure has been relieved, attach a suitable fuel pressure gauge to fuel feed hose. Start engine, then check fuel pressure with engine idling.
⑦ —N: Neutral.

Continued

TUNE UP SPECIFICATIONS — Continued

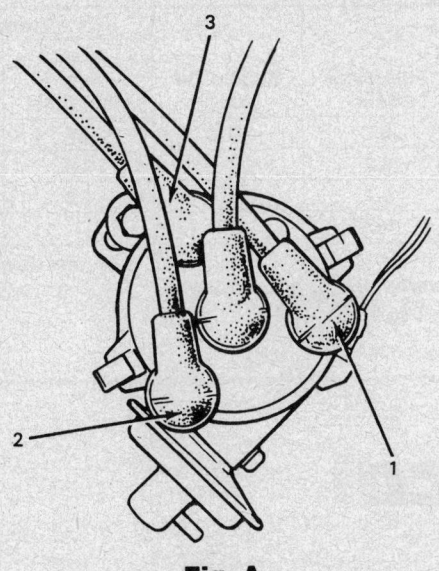

Fig. A

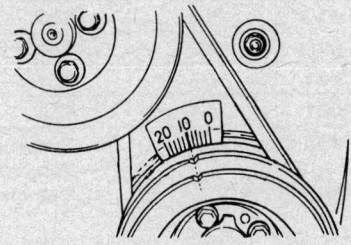

Fig. B

ALTERNATOR & REGULATOR SPECIFICATIONS

Year	Alternator			Voltage Regulator	
	Model	Current Rating Amps	RPM	Model	Voltage @ 77°F
1988	Nippondenso	45	2500	Integral	14.2-14.8
1989-91	Nippondenso	50	2500	Integral	14.2-14.8

STARTER MOTOR APPLICATIONS

Refer To "Starter Motors" For Starter Specifications.

Model	Year	Part No.
Models w/Auto. Trans.	1988	96054321
	1989-91	96060305
Models w/Man. Trans.	1988-91	96051950

FRONT WHEEL ALIGNMENT SPECIFICATIONS

Year	Models	Caster Angle, Degrees		Camber Angles, Degrees		Toe-In Inch	Turning Angle, Degrees	
		Limits	Desired	Limits	Desired		Inner Wheel	Outer Wheel
1988	All	+1⅙ to +5⅙	+3⅙	-¾ to +1¼	+¼	0	38	32
1989-91	All	+1 to +5	+3	-1 to +1	0	0	38	32

REAR WHEEL ALIGNMENT SPECIFICATIONS

Year	Model	Camber Angle, Degrees	Toe-In, Inch
1988	All	0	0
1989-91	All	0	.079

COOLING SYSTEM & CAPACITY DATA

Year	Engine	Cooling System			Fuel Tank Gals.	Engine Oil Qts. ①	Transaxle	
		Capacity, Qts.	Radiator Cap Relief Pressure, Psi	Thermostat Open Temp. °F			Man. Pints	Auto. Qts. ①
1988	1.0L/3-61 ③	4.5	12.8	190	8.7	3.7 ②	4.8	⑤
	1.0L/3-61 ④	4.8	12.8	180	8.2	3.7 ②	4.8	—
1989	1.0L/3-61	4.5	12.8	190	8.7	3.7 ②	4.8	⑤
1990–91	1.0L/3-61	4.1	12.8	190	10.6	3.3	—	—

①—Make final check with dipstick.
②—Includes filter.
③—Except turbocharger engine.
④—Turbocharged engine.
⑤—Pan only, 1.08 qts; after overhaul less torque converter, 3.7 qts.; after overhaul with new torque converter, 4.2 qts.

Electrical

INDEX

FUSE PANEL LOCATION

On **1988 models,** the fuse panel is located on the instrument panel to the left of the steering column.

On **1989-91 models,** the main fuse panel (alternator and ignition switch fuses and main fuse for junction fuse panel) is located in the engine compartment on the left hand fender apron. The junction fuse panel (fuses for other components) is located under the left hand side of the instrument panel.

FLASHER LOCATION

The turn signal and hazard flasher is located under the left hand side of the instrument panel near the fuel panel.

STARTER REPLACE

1. Disconnect battery ground cable.
2. Disconnect solenoid lead and battery cable from starter terminals.
3. Remove two starter mounting bolts, then starter.
4. Reverse procedure to install. **Torque** starter mounting bolts to 17 ft. lbs.

DISTRIBUTOR REPLACE

1. Remove negative battery cable.
2. Disconnect electrical connectors and vacuum lines.
3. Remove distributor cap, then mark rotor position on housing assembly.
4. Mark distributor housing assembly position on engine.
5. Remove distributor flange bolts, then remove distributor from engine.
6. Reverse procedure to install. Ensure alignment marks match.

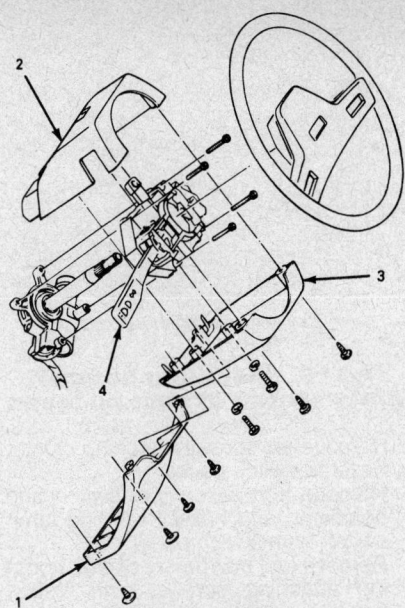

1. STEERING JOINT COVER
2. UPPER COLUMN COVER
3. LOWER COLUMN COVER
4. TURN SIG./DIMMER SWITCH

Fig. 1   Turn signal/dimmer switch removal

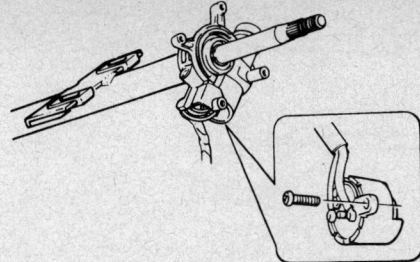

Fig. 2   Ignition switch removal

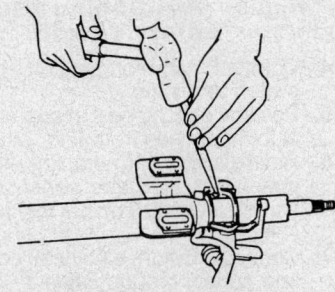

1. CENTER PUNCH (WITH SHARP POINT)
2. IGNITION SWITCH MOUNTING BOLTS

Fig. 4   Removing ignition lock retaining bolts

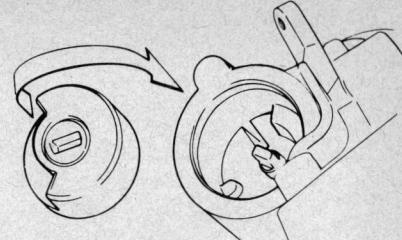

Fig. 3   Ignition switch installation

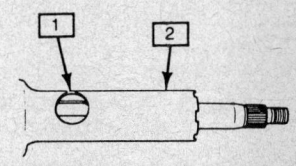

1. STEERING SHAFT
2. STEERING COLUMN

Fig. 5   Aligning steering shaft & column

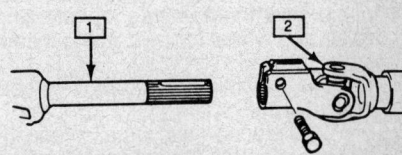

1. LOWER JOINT ASSEMBLY
2. UPPER JOINT ASSEMBLY

Fig. 7   Steering shaft to coupling alignment

TURN SIGNAL/DIMMER SWITCH
REPLACE

1. Disconnect battery ground cable.
2. Remove steering wheel, refer to "Horn Sounder and Steering Wheel, Replace."
3. Remove steering column covers, **Fig. 1.**
4. Disconnect turn signal/dimmer switch electrical connector.
5. Remove turn signal/dimmer switch attaching screws, then remove switch **Fig. 1.**
6. Reverse procedure to install.

IGNITION SWITCH
REPLACE

1988

1. Disconnect battery ground cable.
2. Remove turn signal/dimmer switch as described under "Turn Signal/Dimmer Switch, Replace."
3. Remove ignition switch to lock housing attaching screw, then remove ignition switch, **Fig. 2.**
4. Reverse procedure to install. Position ignition switch to lock housing as shown in **Fig. 3.**

1989–91

Refer to "Ignition Lock, Replace" procedure.

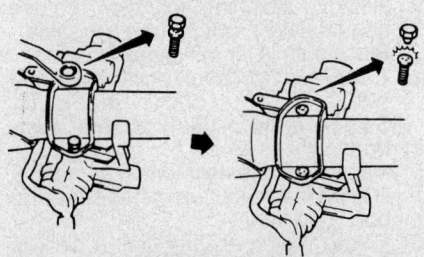

Fig. 6   Ignition lock retaining bolt installation

IGNITION LOCK
REPLACE
REMOVAL

1. Disconnect battery ground cable.
2. Remove turn signal/dimmer switch as described under "Turn Signal/Dimmer Switch, Replace."
3. Disconnect ignition switch and key warning electrical connectors.
4. Lift up floor mat at steering shaft and remove steering column coupling cover cover.
5. Remove upper steering shaft coupling bolt, then connect ignition switch and key warning electrical connectors.
6. Remove steering column attaching nuts, then remove column assembly.
7. Using a center punch, loosen and remove steering lock attaching bolts, **Fig. 4.**
8. Place ignition switch in ACC or On position and remove from steering column.

INSTALLATION

1. Position oblong hole on steering shaft

at center of hole in steering column, **Fig. 5.**
2. Place ignition switch in ACC or On position.
3. Position ignition switch to steering column, then place switch in Lock position.
4. Align ignition switch hub with oblong hole on steering shaft, then rotate steering shaft to ensure it locks.
5. Install replacement ignition switch attaching bolts. Tighten bolts until bolt head breaks off, **Fig. 6.**
6. Place ignition switch in On or ACC and check for smooth steering shaft rotation. Also check steering shaft lock for proper operation.
7. Insert steering shaft into coupling, aligning flat on end of steering shaft with bolt hole on coupling, **Fig. 7.**
8. Position steering column mounting brackets to mounting studs, then install and **torque** attaching nuts to 10 ft. lbs.
9. Install steering shaft coupling bolt and **torque** to 18 ft. lbs.
10. Install steering shaft coupling cover.
11. Install turn signal/dimmer switch as described under "Turn Signal/Dimmer Switch, Replace."

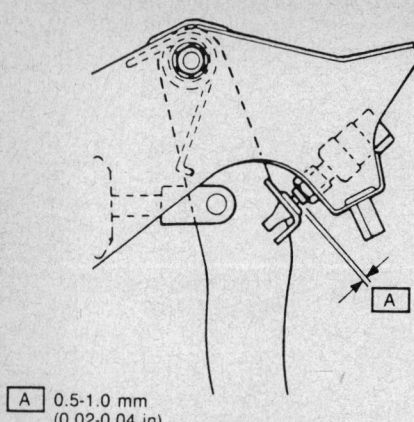

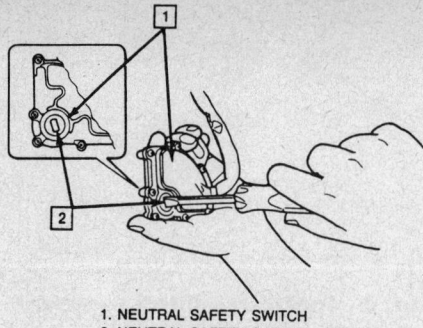

1. NEUTRAL SAFETY SWITCH
2. NEUTRAL SAFETY SWITCH JOINT

Fig. 9   Positioning neutral safety switch

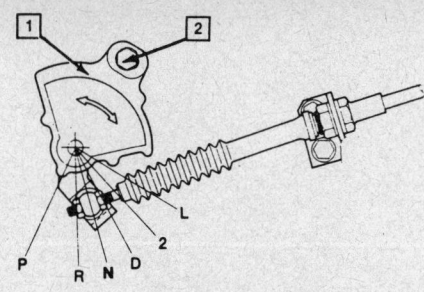

1. NEUTRAL SAFETY SWITCH
2. BOLT

Fig. 10   Installing neutral safety switch to manual lever

A 0.5-1.0 mm
(0.02-0.04 in)

Fig. 8   Stoplamp switch adjustment

HORN SOUNDER & STEERING WHEEL
REPLACE

1. Disconnect battery ground cable.
2. Pull steering wheel pad from steering wheel.
3. **On all models,** disconnect ground wire from steering wheel pad, then remove pad.
4. Remove steering wheel nut, then place alignment marks on steering shaft and wheel for use during installation.
5. Using a suitable puller, remove steering wheel.
6. Reverse procedure to install. When installing steering wheel, align marks made during removal. **Torque** steering wheel nut to 24 ft. lbs.

HEADLAMP SWITCH
REPLACE

1. Disconnect battery ground cable.
2. Remove steering column trim panel.
3. Lower steering column.
4. Remove instrument cluster bezel screws and pull bezel out.
5. Remove headlamp switch from bezel.
6. Remove cluster to instrument panel attaching screws.
7. Pull cluster rearward to reach and disconnect headlamp switch connector.
8. Remove headlamp switch.
9. Reverse procedure to install.

STOPLAMP SWITCH
ADJUST

Pull up brake pedal and adjust switch position so that clearance between end of thread and brake pedal contact plate A is .02-.04 inch, **Fig. 8.** Tighten locknut.

CLUTCH START SWITCH
ADJUST

1. Disconnect battery ground cable.
2. Disconnect electrical connector at clutch start switch.
3. Loosen switch locknut, then back-off switch adjustment.

4. Connect an ohmmeter between switch terminals.
5. Position clutch pedal at approximately .6 to 1.2 inches from floor and hold.
6. Rotate switch into bracket until ohmmeter just indicates continuity, then tighten locknut. **Torque** locknut to 10 ft. lbs.
7. Connect switch electrical connector and battery ground cable.

NEUTRAL SAFETY SWITCH
REPLACE

1. Disconnect battery ground cable.
2. Remove attaching bolt, then remove neutral safety switch from transaxle.
3. Place shift lever in Neutral position.
4. Using a screwdriver, position neutral safety switch a shown in **Fig. 9.** **Switch should click at this position.**
5. Install neutral safety switch to manual shift shaft and loosely install attaching bolt.
6. Rotate switch slightly until a click is heard, then tighten attaching bolt to 9.5 to 16.5 ft. lbs., **Fig. 10.**
7. Connect electrical connector to switch and battery ground cable to battery, then check switch for proper operation.

INSTRUMENT CLUSTER
REPLACE

1988

1. Disconnect battery ground cable.
2. Remove steering column trim panel.
3. Lower steering column.
4. Remove instrument panel cluster bezel screws and bezel, **Figs. 11 and 12.**
5. Remove two switches from bezel.
6. Remove cluster screws and cluster.
7. Remove lens.
8. Reverse procedure to install.

1989-91

1. Disconnect battery ground cable.
2. Remove four screws attaching cluster switch panel to instrument panel.
3. Disconnect electrical connectors from switches, then pull instrument cluster bezel and switch panel slightly outward as an assembly.

4. Remove six screws attaching cluster bezel to switch panel.
5. Remove front w/s wiper switch and headlamp and hazard warning lamp switch from switch panel.
6. Remove four instrument cluster housing attaching screws from switch housing.
7. Disconnect instrument cluster electrical connectors and speedometer cable.
8. Remove instrument cluster, **Fig. 13.**
9. Reverse procedure to install.

INSTRUMENT CLUSTER PRINTED CIRCUIT
REPLACE

1988

1. Disconnect battery ground cable.
2. Disconnect speedometer cable at transmission.
3. Remove steering column trim panel.
4. Lower steering column.
5. Remove steering column trim cover.
6. Remove switch from bezel, allow bezel and other switch to hang.
7. Remove cluster screws and remove cluster.
8. Disconnect electrical connector and speedometer cable.
9. Remove cluster lens.
10. Remove speedometer head assembly. Remove clock and tachometer, if necessary.
11. Remove all bulbs.
12. Remove seat belt buzzer.
13. Remove coolant temperature gauge and fuel gauge.
14. Remove seat belt buzzer timer.
15. Remove printed circuit.
16. Reverse procedure to install.

1989-91

1. Disconnect battery ground cable.
2. Remove instrument cluster as described under "Instrument Cluster, Replace."
3. Remove eight gauge and speedometer to cluster housing attaching screws.
4. Remove indicator lamps from cluster housing.
5. Remove printed circuit from cluster housing.
6. Reverse procedure to install.

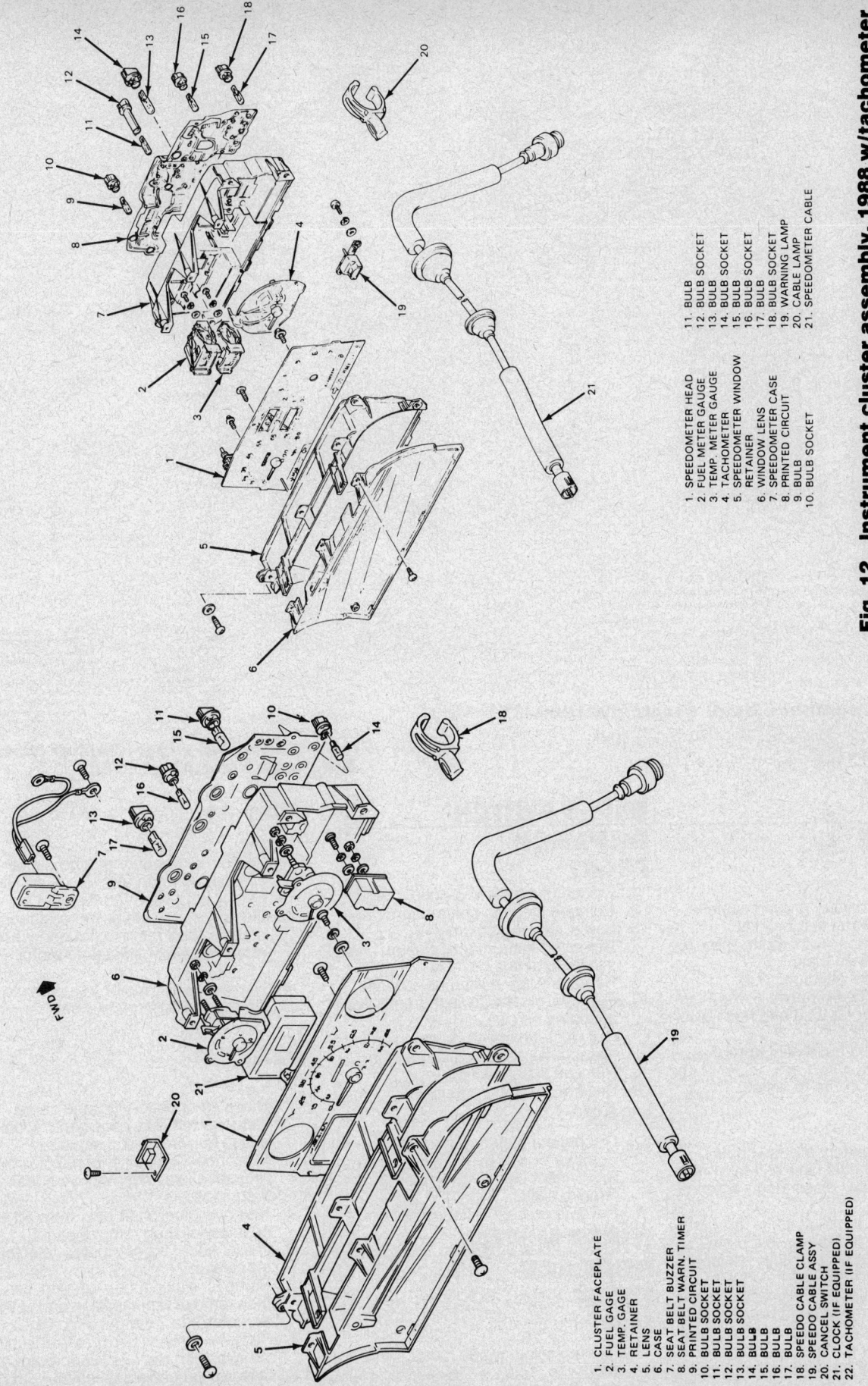

Fig. 12 Instrument cluster assembly. 1988 w/tachometer

1. SPEEDOMETER HEAD
2. FUEL METER GAUGE
3. TEMP. METER GAUGE
4. TACHOMETER
5. SPEEDOMETER WINDOW RETAINER
6. WINDOW LENS
7. SPEEDOMETER CASE
8. PRINTED CIRCUIT
9. BULB
10. BULB SOCKET
11. BULB
12. BULB SOCKET
13. BULB SOCKET
14. BULB SOCKET
15. BULB
16. BULB SOCKET
17. BULB
18. BULB SOCKET
19. WARNING LAMP
20. CABLE LAMP
21. SPEEDOMETER CABLE

Fig. 11 Instrument cluster assembly. 1988 less tachometer

1. CLUSTER FACEPLATE
2. FUEL GAGE
3. TEMP. GAGE
4. RETAINER
5. LENS
6. CASE
7. SEAT BELT BUZZER
8. SEAT BELT WARN. TIMER
9. PRINTED CIRCUIT
10. BULB SOCKET
11. BULB SOCKET
12. BULB SOCKET
13. BULB SOCKET
14. BULB
15. BULB
16. BULB
17. BULB
18. SPEEDO CABLE CLAMP
19. SPEEDO CABLE ASSY
20. CANCEL SWITCH
21. CLOCK (IF EQUIPPED)
22. TACHOMETER (IF EQUIPPED)

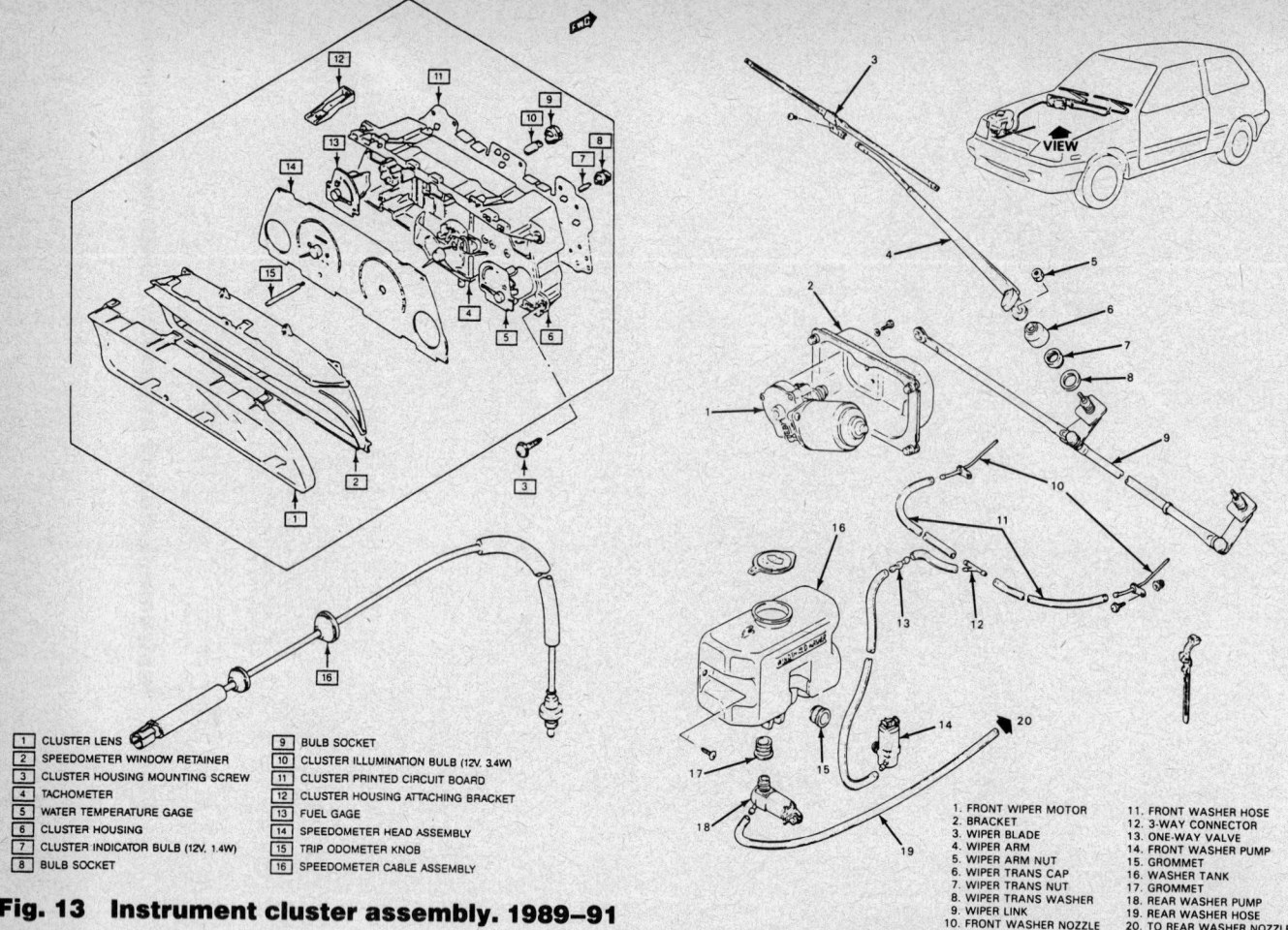

1	CLUSTER LENS
2	SPEEDOMETER WINDOW RETAINER
3	CLUSTER HOUSING MOUNTING SCREW
4	TACHOMETER
5	WATER TEMPERATURE GAGE
6	CLUSTER HOUSING
7	CLUSTER INDICATOR BULB (12V. 1.4W)
8	BULB SOCKET
9	BULB SOCKET
10	CLUSTER ILLUMINATION BULB (12V. 3.4W)
11	CLUSTER PRINTED CIRCUIT BOARD
12	CLUSTER HOUSING ATTACHING BRACKET
13	FUEL GAGE
14	SPEEDOMETER HEAD ASSEMBLY
15	TRIP ODOMETER KNOB
16	SPEEDOMETER CABLE ASSEMBLY

Fig. 13 Instrument cluster assembly. 1989–91

1. FRONT WIPER MOTOR	11. FRONT WASHER HOSE
2. BRACKET	12. 3-WAY CONNECTOR
3. WIPER BLADE	13. ONE-WAY VALVE
4. WIPER ARM	14. FRONT WASHER PUMP
5. WIPER ARM NUT	15. GROMMET
6. WIPER TRANS CAP	16. WASHER TANK
7. WIPER TRANS NUT	17. GROMMET
8. WIPER TRANS WASHER	18. REAR WASHER PUMP
9. WIPER LINK	19. REAR WASHER HOSE
10. FRONT WASHER NOZZLE	20. TO REAR WASHER NOZZLE

Fig. 14 Front windshield wiper/washer motor & linkage assembly. 1988

RADIO
REPLACE

1988

1. Disconnect battery ground cable.
2. Remove ashtray and bracket.
3. Remove knobs from radio, then remove radio face plate.
4. Remove radio attaching nuts.
5. Pull radio slightly outward, then disconnect antenna lead and radio electrical connector.
6. Remove radio assembly from instrument panel.
7. Reverse procedure to install.

1989–91

1. Disconnect battery ground cable.
2. Remove one attaching bolt from rear of radio, then disconnect antenna lead.
3. Using radio removal forks or other suitable tool at hole on each side of radio face plate, pull radio assembly outward from instrument panel.
4. Disconnect electrical connector from radio, then remove radio from vehicle.
5. Reverse procedure to install. Radio removal forks or other suitable tool is not necessary for radio installation.

WIPER SWITCH
REPLACE
FRONT

1. Disconnect battery ground cable.
2. Remove steering column trim panel.
3. Lower steering column.
4. Remove instrument cluster bezel screws and pull bezel out.
5. Remove wiper switch from bezel.
6. Remove cluster to instrument panel attaching screws.
7. Pull cluster rearward to reach and disconnect wiper switch connector.
8. Remove wiper switch.
9. Reverse procedure to install.

REAR

1. Disconnect battery ground cable.
2. Remove switch by pushing forward.
3. Disconnect electrical connector, then remove switch.
4. Reverse procedure to install.

WIPER MOTOR
REPLACE
FRONT
1988

When replacing wiper motor, refer to, **Fig. 14.**

1989–91

1. Disconnect battery ground cable.
2. Disconnect connect electrical connector from wiper motor.
3. Remove three wiper motor attaching screws, then remove nut and washer attaching wiper linkage to motor, **Fig. 15.**
4. Remove wiper motor from vehicle.
5. Reverse procedure to install.

REAR

1. Disconnect battery ground cable.
2. Remove left and right hand speaker grilles from rear lid, if equipped.
3. Disconnect electrical connector from rear speakers, then remove speakers, if equipped.
4. Remove nine push pins from lid access panel, then remove panel.
5. Disconnect wiper motor electrical connector.
6. Remove wiper motor ground screw, then remove wiper linkage arm to wiper motor attaching nut, **Fig. 16.**
7. Remove three wiper motor attaching screws, then remove wiper motor.
8. Reverse procedure to install.

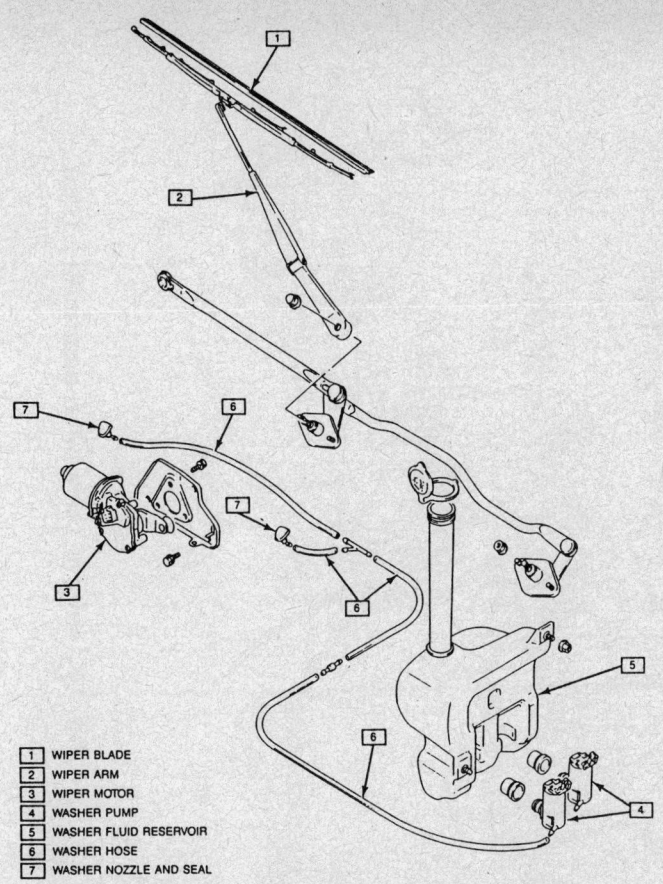

1 WIPER BLADE
2 WIPER ARM
3 WIPER MOTOR
4 WASHER PUMP
5 WASHER FLUID RESERVOIR
6 WASHER HOSE
7 WASHER NOZZLE AND SEAL

Fig. 15 Front windshield wiper/washer motor & linkage assembly. 1989–91

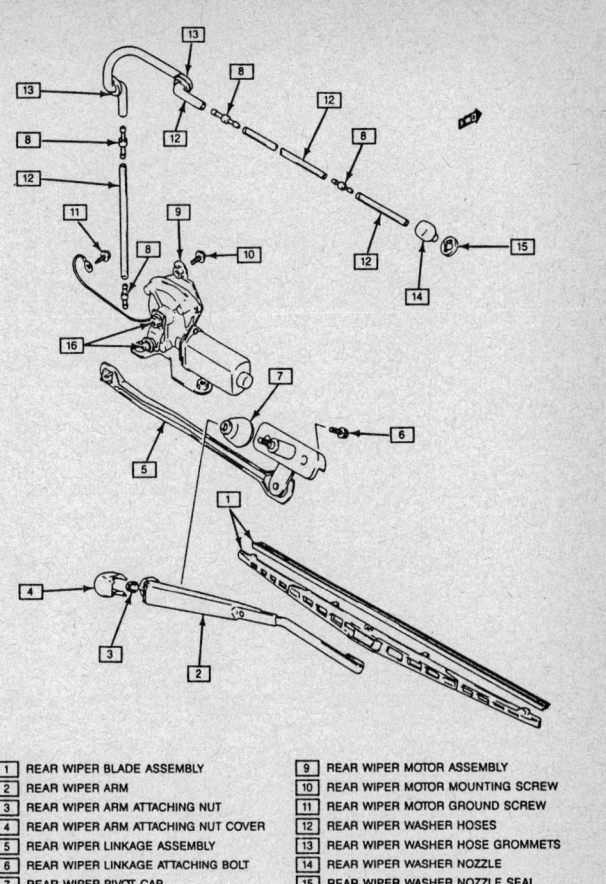

1 REAR WIPER BLADE ASSEMBLY	9 REAR WIPER MOTOR ASSEMBLY
2 REAR WIPER ARM	10 REAR WIPER MOTOR MOUNTING SCREW
3 REAR WIPER ARM ATTACHING NUT	11 REAR WIPER MOTOR GROUND SCREW
4 REAR WIPER ARM ATTACHING NUT COVER	12 REAR WIPER WASHER HOSES
5 REAR WIPER LINKAGE ASSEMBLY	13 REAR WIPER WASHER HOSE GROMMETS
6 REAR WIPER LINKAGE ATTACHING BOLT	14 REAR WIPER WASHER NOZZLE
7 REAR WIPER PIVOT CAP	15 REAR WIPER WASHER NOZZLE SEAL
8 REAR WIPER WASHER HOSE CONNECTORS	16 REAR WIPER CRANKING ARM AND ATTACHING NUT

Fig. 16 Rear windshield wiper/washer motor & linkage assembly. 1989–91

WIPER LINKAGE
REPLACE
FRONT
1988

When replacing wiper motor linkage, refer to **Fig. 14**.

1989–91

1. Disconnect battery ground cable.
2. Remove both wiper arm and blade assemblies.
3. Remove five push pins and left hand cowl panel.
4. Remove three push pins and left hand cowl panel.
5. Remove front wiper motor from vehicle as described under "Wiper Motor, Replace."
6. Remove four nuts attaching wiper motor linkage, then remove wiper motor linkage through left hand cowl cover opening, **Fig. 15**.
7. Reverse procedure to install.

REAR

1. Disconnect battery ground cable.
2. Remove wiper blade and arm assembly, **Fig. 16**.
3. Remove rear wiper motor as described under "Wiper Motor, Replace."

4. Remove two nuts attaching wiper linkage to rear lid.
5. Remove linkage trough left hand side of rear lid.
6. Reverse procedure to install.

BLOWER MOTOR
REPLACE

1988

1. Disconnect battery ground cable.
2. Disconnect defroster hose on driver's side, **Fig. 17**.
3. Disconnect blower motor lead wire.
4. Remove three blower motor mounting screws and blower motor, **Fig. 18**.
5. Reverse procedure to install.

1989–91

1. Disconnect battery ground cable.
2. Remove two screws attaching glove compartment striker to instrument panel.
3. Remove one screw attaching rear of glove compartment upper panel, then remove upper panel.
4. Disconnect blower motor and blower resistor electrical connectors.
5. Disconnect fresh air control cable from blower motor housing.
6. Remove three blower motor housing attaching bolt, then remove blower

motor housing, **Fig 19**.
7. Remove air hose, then remove three attaching screws and separate blower motor from housing, **Fig. 20**.
8. Reverse procedure to install.

HEATER CORE
REPLACE

1988

1. Disconnect battery ground cable.
2. Drain cooling system.
3. Disconnect water hoses from heater core.
4. Remove glove compartment.
5. Disconnect defroster hoses from heater housing, **Fig. 17**.
6. Disconnect connectors from blower motor and heater resistor.
7. Disconnect 3 control cables from heater case side levers.
8. Pull out center vent louvre.
9. Disconnect right and left side vent ducts from center vent duct.
10. Remove center vent duct.
11. Remove ashtray upper plate.
12. Remove instrument member stay.
13. Remove two heater assembly mounting nuts.
14. Loosen heater case top side mounting bolts from glove compartment side.

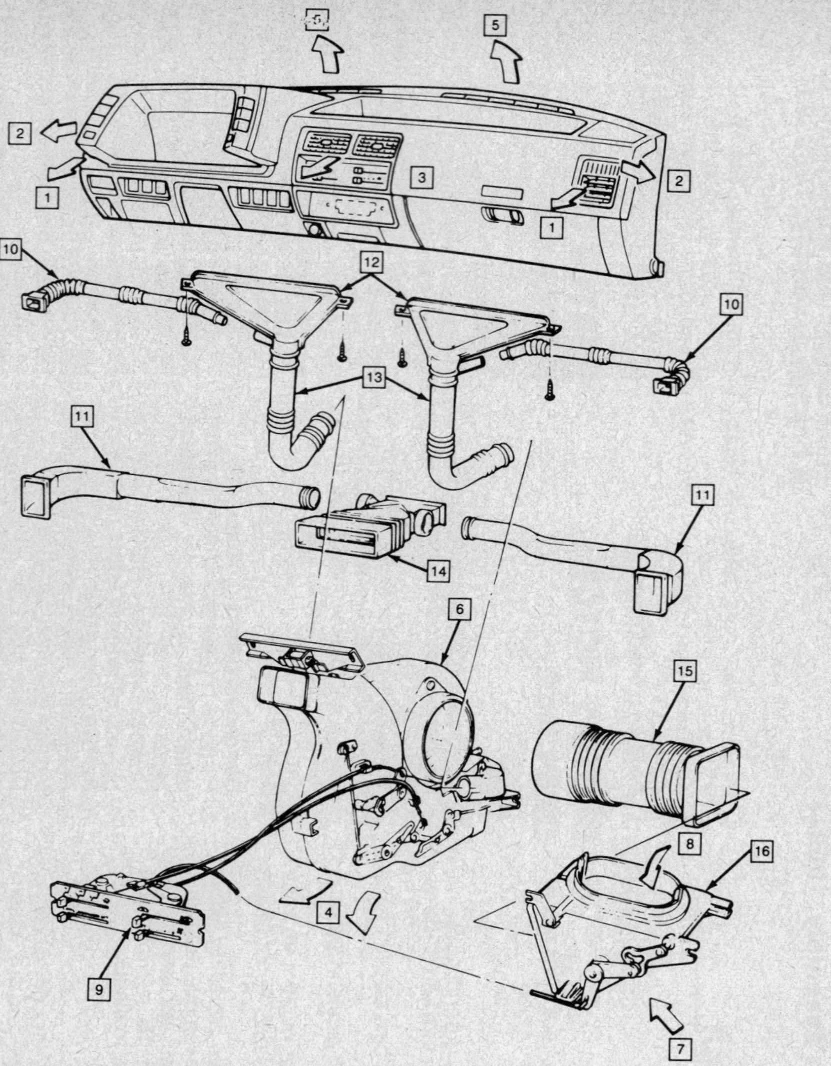

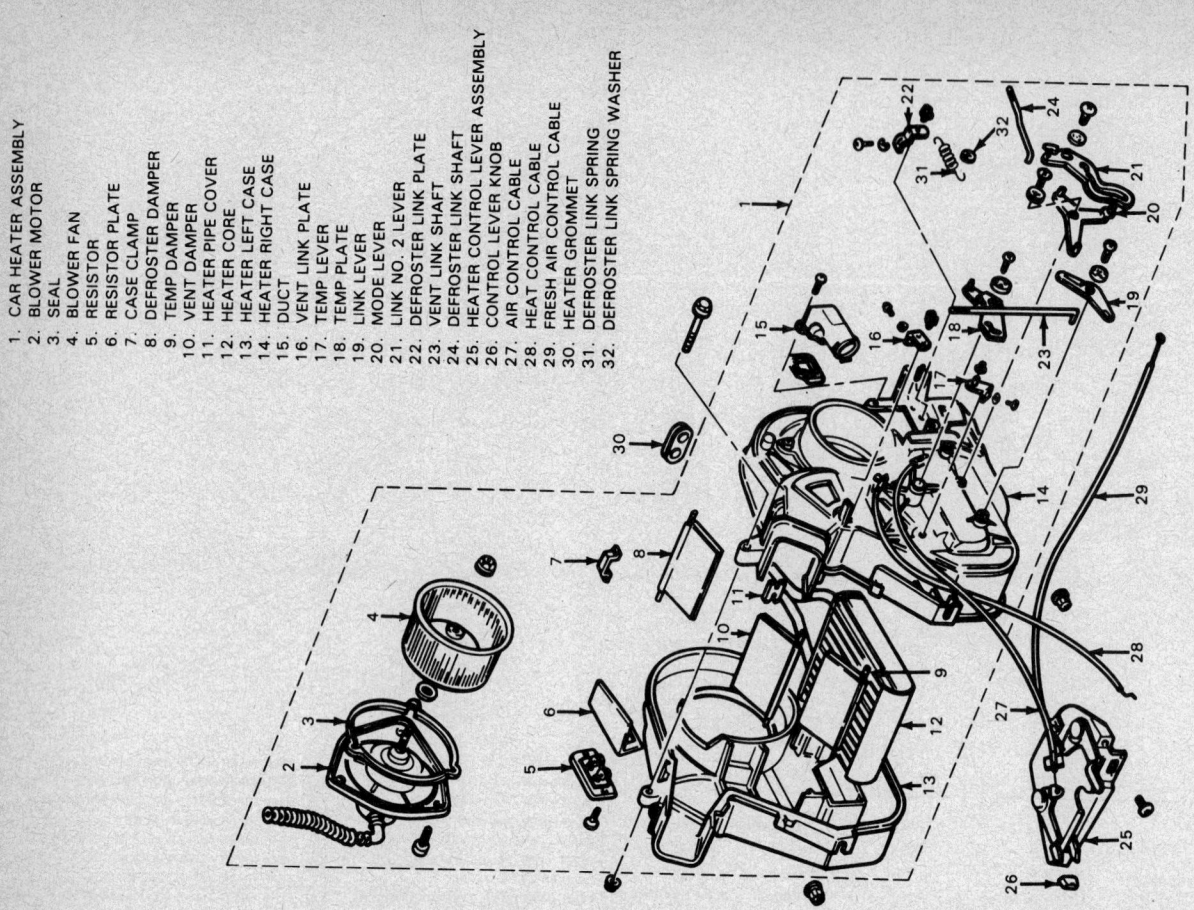

1. CAR HEATER ASSEMBLY
2. BLOWER MOTOR
3. SEAL
4. BLOWER FAN
5. RESISTOR
6. RESISTOR PLATE
7. CASE CLAMP
8. DEFROSTER DAMPER
9. TEMP DAMPER
10. VENT DAMPER
11. HEATER PIPE COVER
12. HEATER CORE
13. HEATER LEFT CASE
14. HEATER RIGHT CASE
15. DUCT
16. VENT LINK PLATE
17. TEMP LEVER
18. TEMP PLATE
19. LINK LEVER
20. MODE LEVER
21. LINK NO. 2 LEVER
22. DEFROSTER LINK PLATE
23. VENT LINK SHAFT
24. DEFROSTER LINK SHAFT
25. HEATER CONTROL LEVER ASSEMBLY
26. CONTROL LEVER KNOB
27. AIR CONTROL CABLE
28. HEAT CONTROL CABLE
29. FRESH AIR CONTROL CABLE
30. HEATER GROMMET
31. DEFROSTER LINK SPRING
32. DEFROSTER LINK SPRING WASHER

Fig. 18 Heater core case assembly. 1988

1. SIDE VENT OUTLET
2. SIDE DEFROSTER OUTLET
3. CENTER VENT OUTLET
4. FLOOR OUTLET
5. FRONT DEFROSTER OUTLET
6. BLOWER MOTOR
7. INSIDE AIR
8. OUTSIDE AIR
9. CONTROL LEVER
10. DEFROSTER HOSE
11. SIDE VENT DUCT
12. DEFROSTER NOZZLE
13. DEFROSTER HOSE
14. CENTER VENT DUCT
15. AIR DUCT
16. AIR DAMPER

Fig. 17 Heater & defroster assembly. 1988

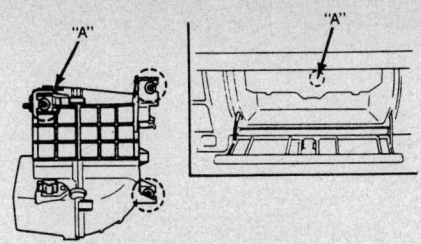

Fig. 19 Blower motor case attaching screw locations. 1989-91

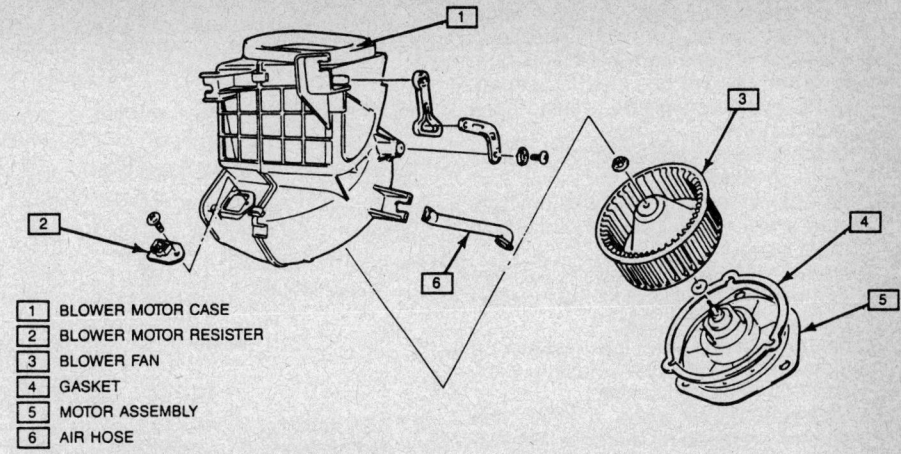

1	BLOWER MOTOR CASE
2	BLOWER MOTOR RESISTER
3	BLOWER FAN
4	GASKET
5	MOTOR ASSEMBLY
6	AIR HOSE

Fig. 20 Blower motor & case assembly. 1989-91

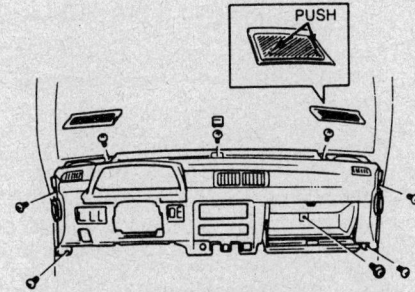

Fig. 21 Instrument panel attaching screw locations. 1989-91

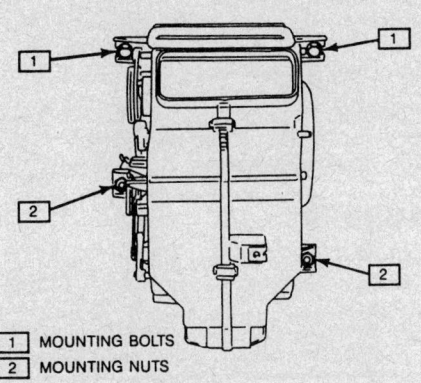

1	MOUNTING BOLTS
2	MOUNTING NUTS

Fig. 22 Heater case attaching bolt & nut locations. 1989-91

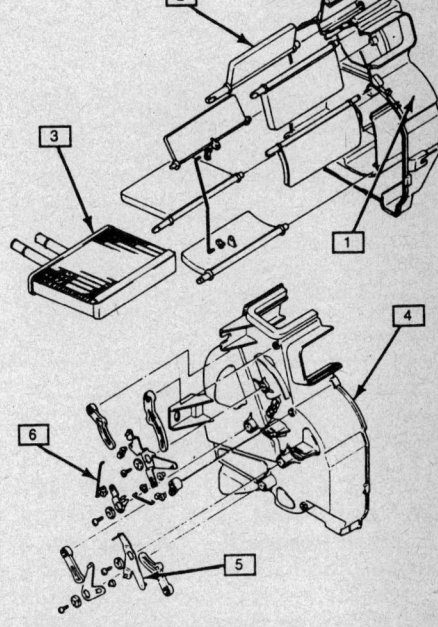

1	HEATER CASE
2	CONTROL DOOR (DAMPER)
3	HEATER CORE
4	HEATER CASE
5	CONTROL LEVEL LINKAGE
6	CONTROL SHAFT

Fig. 23 Exploded view of heater case assembly. 1989-91

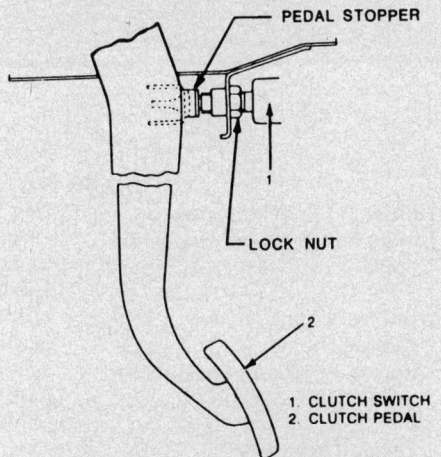

1	CLUTCH SWITCH
2	CLUTCH PEDAL

Fig. 24 Clutch switch adjustment

15. Remove heater control assembly.
16. Remove retaining clips from heater case halves, **Fig. 18.**
17. Remove heater core from housing.
18. Reverse procedure to install.

1989-91

1. Disconnect battery ground cable.
2. Drain cooling system, then disconnect heater hoses from heater core.
3. **On models equipped with automatic transaxle, remove console as follows:**
   a. Position shift control lever in Low position.
   b. Remove four console attaching screws, then carefully pull console

outward at bottom to disengage retaining pins.
   c. Move front seats fully forward, then remove two attaching screws and parking brake lever cover.
   d. Remove four screws attaching shift control lever to console.
   e. Remove Park lock out knob from shift control console, if equipped.
   f. Remove console from vehicle.
4. Remove Instrument cluster as described under "Instrument Cluster, Replace."
5. Remove turn signal/dimmer switch as described under "Turn Signal/Dimmer Switch, Replace."
6. Remove ashtray and bracket, then remove cigar lighter assembly.
7. Disconnect electrical connector, then carefully remove A/C switch through front of instrument panel bezel, if equipped.
8. Remove radio as described under "Radio, Replace."
9. Remove knobs from heater control.
10. Remove two instrument panel bezel to instrument panel attaching screws, then remove bezel.
11. Remove two screws attaching heater control panel, then pull control panel slightly outward and disconnect blower switch electrical connector.

12. Remove screw attaching hood release lever to instrument panel.
13. Remove two attaching screws from left and right hand side of instrument panel, **Fig. 21.**
14. Remove four attaching screws from instrument panel support member.
15. Remove two attaching screws from heater control assembly.
16. Remove attaching screw from rear glove of compartment upper panel.
17. Remove instrument panel access cover, then remove attaching screw at panel.
18. Remove radio speaker trim covers,

then one speaker to instrument panel attaching screw from each speaker.

19. Remove left and right hand kick panels, then remove one instrument panel attaching screw from behind each kick panel.
20. Disconnect electrical connectors from radio speakers.
21. Disconnect electrical connectors from instrument panel, then remove instrument panel.
22. Remove two mounting bolts and two mounting nuts attaching heater case to dash panel, **Fig. 22.**
23. Remove heater case from vehicle.
24. Remove heater case retaining clips and two attaching screws.
25. Separate heater case halves, then carefully remove heater core, **Fig. 23.**
26. Reverse procedure to install.

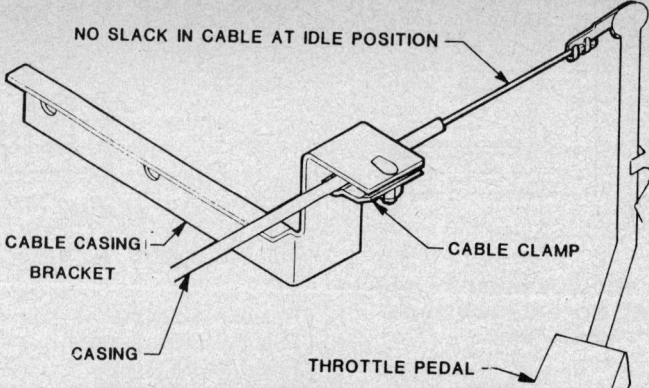

Fig. 25 Servo cable adjustment

EVAPORATOR
REPLACE
1988

1. Disconnect battery ground cable.
2. Discharge refrigerant from A/C system.
3. Remove glove compartment upper striker lid.
4. Remove ashtray and air damper.
5. Disconnect defroster hose.
6. Disconnect A/C control cable from evaporator side.
7. Disconnect heater-to-evaporator connecting band.

8. Disconnect compressor suction hose and receiver/dryer outlet hose from cooling unit. **Cap hose and fittings immediately.**
9. Remove evaporator case attaching bolts, then evaporator case assembly.
10. Detach clamps, then separate evaporator case upper and lower halves.
11. Remove case cover attaching screws, then remove evaporator.
12. Detach outlet pipe, expansion valve and thermo switch assembly.
13. Reverse procedure to install.

1989–91

1. Disconnect battery ground cable.
2. Discharge refrigerant from A/C system.
3. Remove glove compartment striker, then one attaching screw from rear of

glove compartment upper panel and remove panel.
4. Remove blower motor, then disconnect blower resistor electrical connectors.
5. Remove fresh/recirc control cable from blower case assembly.
6. Remove blower case from vehicle.
7. Disconnect air conditioner and evaporator thermistor electrical connectors.
8. Remove compressor suction line and receiver/dryer outlet line from evaporator. **Cap hose and fittings immediately.**
9. Remove evaporator case from vehicle.
10. Remove A/C amplifier from evaporator case by releasing two lower lock tabs, then slide amplifier upward to disengage from evaporator case.
11. Reverse procedure to install.

Engine
INDEX

ENGINE MOUNTS
REPLACE
FRONT

1. Disconnect battery ground cable.
2. Remove engine mount nut, then raise and support vehicle.

3. Support engine using an engine support fixture.
4. Remove engine mount and frame bracket, then remove mount from bracket.
5. Reverse procedure to install.

REAR

1. Disconnect battery ground cable.

2. Remove engine mount nut, then raise and support vehicle.
3. Remove nut retaining mount to body bracket.
4. Support engine using an engine support fixture.
5. Remove frame bracket, then remove mount.

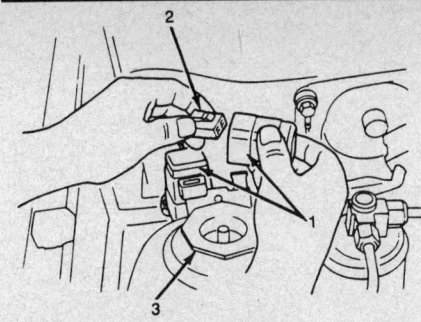

1. FUEL PUMP RELAY OR MAIN RELAY
2. FUEL PUMP RELAY LEAD WIRE
   (PINK, PINK/WHITE, WHITE/BLUE, WHITE/BLUE)
3. RIGHT FRONT SUSPENSION STRUT

Fig. 1 Fuel pump relay location. 1988 1.0L/3-61 Turbo engine

6. Reverse procedure to install.

ENGINE
REPLACE
1988

1. **On turbo engine,** relieve system fuel pressure as follows:
   a. Remove fuel tank filler cap to release vapor pressure, then reinstall cap.
   b. With engine idling, disconnect fuel pump relay electrical connector, **Fig. 1.**
   c. After engine has stopped operating, crank engine several times in three second intervals.
   d. After fuel pressure has been relieved, place ignition switch in off position and connect fuel relay electrical connector.
   e. If engine cannot be started, position shop towels around union bolt of high pressure line, then slowly loosen union bolt until fuel pressure is relieved. After fuel pressure has been relieved, tighten union bolt.
2. **On all models,** disconnect battery cables.
3. Disconnect windshield washer hose, then remove hood.
4. Remove battery and tray.
5. Remove air cleaner.
6. Drain cooling system and disconnect radiator hoses at engine.
7. Disconnect cooling fan wires.
8. Remove radiator and fan as an assembly.
9. Disconnect fuel lines at fuel pump.
10. Disconnect heater hoses at engine.
11. Disconnect vacuum hoses.
12. Disconnect brake booster vacuum hose at intake manifold.
13. Disconnect accelerator cable from carburetor.
14. Disconnect speedometer cable from transmission.
15. Disconnect outside air duct.
16. Disconnect clutch cable and bracket from transmission.
17. Disconnect wiring harnesses at engine and transmission.
18. Remove A/C compressor adjusting bolt, if equipped.
19. Remove drive belt splash shield.
20. Raise and support vehicle.

21. Disconnect exhaust pipe from manifold.
22. Loosen A/C compressor pivot bolt, if equipped.
23. Remove A/C compressor drive belt, if equipped.
24. Remove A/C compressor bracket from engine, if equipped.
25. Disconnect gearshift control shaft from transmission.
26. Disconnect gearshift extension rod from transmission.
27. Disconnect ball joints.
28. Drain transaxle.
29. Remove drive axles from transaxle.
30. Drain engine oil.
31. Disconnect engine torque rods.
32. Remove transmission mount nut.
33. Lower vehicle.
34. Remove engine side mount.
35. Remove engine mount nuts.
36. Using a hoist, remove engine and transaxle as an assembly.
37. Reverse procedure to install.

1989–91

1. Relieve fuel system pressure as follows:
   a. Remove fuel pump relay from main fuse panel located in engine compartment, **Fig. 2.**
   b. Operate engine until it stalls, then crank engine several times in three second intervals.
   c. Remove fuel tank filler cap to release vapor pressure, then reinstall cap.
   d. Place ignition switch in off position, then install fuel pump relay.
2. Disconnect battery ground cable.
3. Disconnect windshield washer hose, then remove hood.
4. Remove air cleaner assembly.
5. Drain cooling system, then remove radiator and engine cooling fan.
6. Disconnect high tension lead from ignition coil.
7. Disconnect electrical connector from distributor.
8. Disconnect electrical connectors from coolant temperature sender, engine coolant temperature sensor, engine cooling fan switch and engine oil pressure sender.
9. Disconnect electrical connector from EGR vacuum switching valve.
10. Disconnect electrical connectors from idle speed control valve, throttle position switch, fuel injector and pressure sensor.
11. Disconnect electrical connectors and wiring from alternator and starter motor.
12. Disconnect electrical connector from oxygen sensor.
13. Disconnect battery ground cable from transaxle.
14. **On models with manual transaxle,** disconnect electrical connector from back-up lamp switch.
15. **On models with automatic transaxle,** disconnect electrical connectors from neutral safety switch, speed sensor and direct clutch and second brake solenoids.
16. **On all models,** disconnect intake manifold to power brake unit vacuum hose.
17. Disconnect evaporative emission

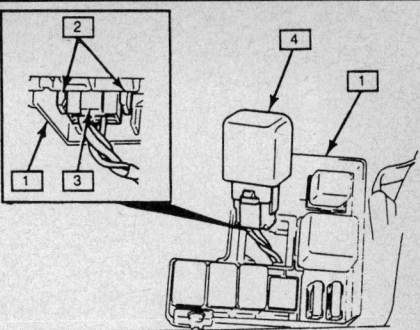

1. MAIN FUSE BOX
2. LOCK TABS
3. FUEL PUMP RELAY ELECTRICAL CONNECTOR
4. FUEL PUMP RELAY

Fig. 2 Fuel pump relay location. 1989–91 1.0L/3-61 engine

canister hoses from intake manifold and tube connections.
18. Disconnect fuel hoses from throttle body.
19. Disconnect heater hoses from engine.
20. Disconnect accelerator cable from throttle body.
21. **On models with manual transaxle,** disconnect clutch cable from from fork and housing.
22. **On models with automatic transaxle,** disconnect shift control and fluid pressure control cables from transaxle.
23. **On all models,** disconnect speedometer cable from transaxle.
24. Raise and support vehicle, then disconnect exhaust pipe from exhaust manifold.
25. Drain engine crankcase, then drain fluid from transaxle.
26. **On models with manual transaxle, disconnect control shaft and extension rod from transaxle.**
27. **On all models,** separate drive axles from transaxle. Support drive axles from chassis using wire.
28. **On models with automatic transaxle, remove engine torque rod bracket from transaxle.**
29. Lower vehicle and install an engine lifting fixture.
30. Remove engine and transaxle mounting bolts, then remove engine and transaxle assembly from vehicle.
31. Reverse procedure to install.

CYLINDER HEAD
REPLACE
1988

1. **On turbo engine, relieve system fuel pressure as follows:**
   a. Remove fuel tank filler cap to release vapor pressure, then reinstall cap.
   b. With engine idling, disconnect fuel pump relay electrical connector, **Fig. 1.**
   c. After engine has stopped operating, crank engine several times in three second intervals.
   d. After fuel pressure has been relieved, place ignition switch in off position and connect fuel relay electrical connector.

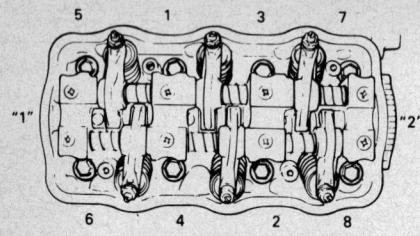

"1" CAMSHAFT PULLEY SIDE
"2" DISTRIBUTOR SIDE

Fig. 3 Cylinder head bolt tightening sequence. 1988

e. If engine cannot be started, position shop towels around union bolt of high pressure line, then slowly loosen union bolt until fuel pressure is relieved. After fuel pressure has been relieved, tighten union bolt.
2. Disconnect battery ground cable.
3. Drain cooling system.
4. Remove air cleaner, valve cover and distributor.
5. Disconnect accelerator cable from carburetor.
6. Disconnect emission control hoses from carburetor and intake manifold.
7. Disconnect cooling system hoses from intake manifold.
8. Disconnect wiring from carburetor and intake manifold.
9. Disconnect fuel lines from fuel pump.
10. Disconnect brake booster vacuum hose from intake manifold.
11. Disconnect oxygen sensor lead.
12. Disconnect exhaust pipe from manifold and second air valve.
13. Remove fuel pump.
14. Remove rocker shafts, rocker arms, springs and camshaft.
15. Disconnect engine side mounting at cylinder head.
16. Remove cylinder head bolts.
17. Remove cylinder head with carburetor, intake and exhaust manifolds.
18. Reverse procedure to install. **Torque** cylinder head bolts to specification listed at the end of this section in sequence shown in **Fig. 3.**

1989–91

1. Relieve fuel system pressure as follows:
   a. Remove fuel pump relay from main fuse panel located in engine compartment, **Fig. 2.**
   b. Operate engine until it stalls, then crank engine several times in three second intervals.
   c. Remove fuel tank filler cap to release vapor pressure, then reinstall cap.
   d. Place ignition switch in off position, then install fuel pump relay.
2. Disconnect battery ground cable.
3. Drain cooling system, then remove air cleaner assembly.
4. Disconnect coil wire from distributor cap.
5. Disconnect electrical connector from distributor.
6. Disconnect electrical connectors from coolant temperature sender, engine

coolant temperature sensor and engine cooling fan switch.
7. Disconnect electrical connector from EGR vacuum switching valve.
8. Disconnect electrical connectors from idle speed control valve, throttle position switch and fuel injector.
9. Disconnect oxygen sensor electrical connector, then detach wiring harness from clamps.
10. Disconnect ground wires from intake manifold.
11. Disconnect heater hose from intake manifold and radiator hose from thermostat housing.
12. Disconnect fuel hoses from throttle body.
13. Disconnect MAP sensor hose from intake manifold.
14. Disconnect evaporative emission hoses from intake manifold and tube.
15. Disconnect power brake unit vacuum hose from intake manifold.
16. Disconnect accelerator cable from throttle body.
17. Raise and support vehicle, then disconnect exhaust pipe from exhaust manifold.
18. Lower vehicle, then remove cylinder head cover.
19. Remove cylinder head attaching bolts, then remove cylinder head.
20. Reverse procedure to install. **Torque** cylinder head bolts to specification listed at the end of this section in sequence shown in **Fig. 4.**

INTAKE MANIFOLD
REPLACE
1988 CARBURETED ENGINES

1. Disconnect battery ground cable.
2. Drain coolant.
3. Disconnect warm air hose, cool air hose, second air hose, vacuum hose and EGR modulator from air cleaner case.
4. Remove accelerator cable from carburetor.
5. Remove electric lead wires at carburetor and intake manifold.
6. Remove all hoses from carburetor and intake manifold.
7. Remove intake manifold from cylinder head.
8. Reverse procedure to install.

TURBO ENGINES

1. Relieve system fuel pressure as follows:
   a. Remove fuel tank filler cap to release vapor pressure, then reinstall cap.
   b. With engine idling, disconnect fuel pump relay electrical connector, **Fig. 1.**
   c. After engine has stopped operating, crank engine several times in three second intervals.
   d. After fuel pressure has been relieved, place ignition switch in off position and connect fuel relay electrical connector.
   e. If engine cannot be started, position shop towels around union bolt of high pressure line, then slowly

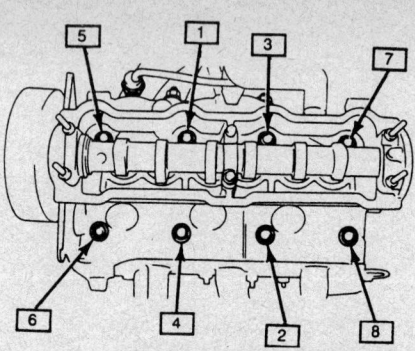

Fig. 4 Cylinder head bolt tightening sequence. 1989–91

loosen union bolt until fuel pressure is relieved. After fuel pressure has been relieved, tighten union bolt.
2. Disconnect battery ground cable.
3. Drain cooling system.
4. Remove surge tank together with throttle body.
5. Remove fuel injector couplers.
6. Remove fuel hoses from delivery pipe.
7. Remove delivery pipe together with injectors.
8. Remove water temperature gauge wire (Yellow/White).
9. Remove starter injector time switch coupler (Brown).
10. Remove water temperature sensor coupler (Green).
11. Remove radiator fan switch coupler.
12. Remove water hoses.
13. Remove EGR valve vacuum hoses.
14. Remove intake manifold.
15. Reverse procedure to install.

1989–91 EFI ENGINES

1. Relieve fuel system pressure as follows:
   a. Remove fuel pump relay from main fuse panel located in engine compartment, **Fig. 2.**
   b. Operate engine until it stalls, then crank engine several times in three second intervals.
   c. Remove fuel tank filler cap to release vapor pressure, then reinstall cap.
   d. Place ignition switch in off position, then install fuel pump relay.
2. Disconnect battery ground cable.
3. Drain cooling system, then remove air cleaner assembly.
4. Disconnect electrical connectors from coolant temperature sender, engine and coolant temperature sensor.
5. Disconnect electrical connector from EGR vacuum switching valve.
6. Disconnect electrical connectors from idle speed control valve, throttle position switch and fuel injector.
7. Disconnect ground wires from intake manifold.
8. Disconnect fuel hoses from throttle body.
9. Disconnect coolant hoses from intake manifold.
10. Disconnect MAP sensor hose from intake manifold.
11. Disconnect evaporative emission hoses from intake manifold and tube.
12. Disconnect power brake unit vacuum

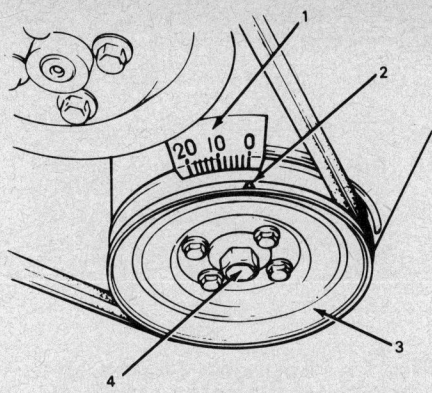

1. TIMING TAB
2. TIMING NOTCH
3. CRANKSHAFT PULLEY
4. CRANKSHAFT PULLEY BOLT

Fig. 5   Aligning crankshaft pulley

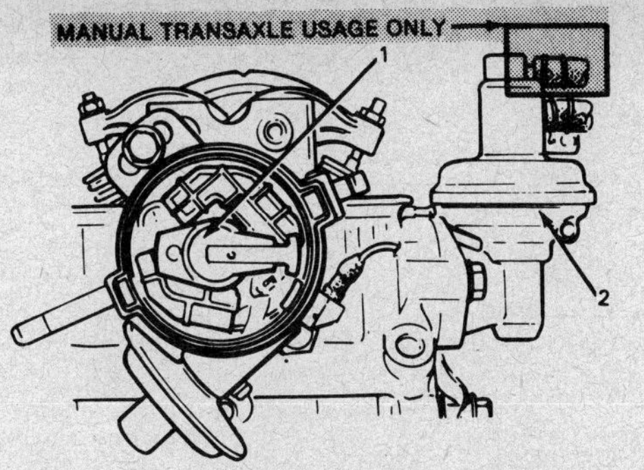

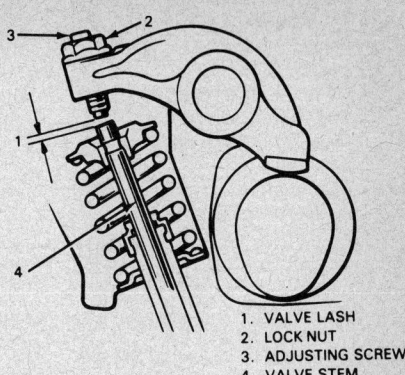

1. ROTOR
2. FUEL PUMP

Fig. 6   Distributor rotor at TDC position

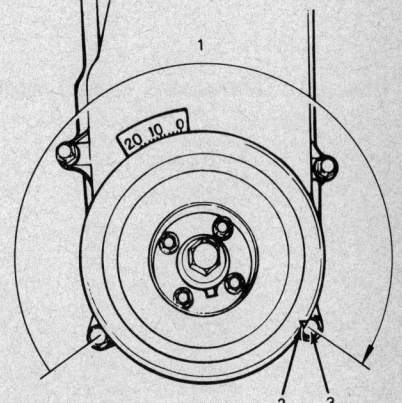

1. VALVE LASH
2. LOCK NUT
3. ADJUSTING SCREW
4. VALVE STEM

Fig. 7   Adjusting valve lash

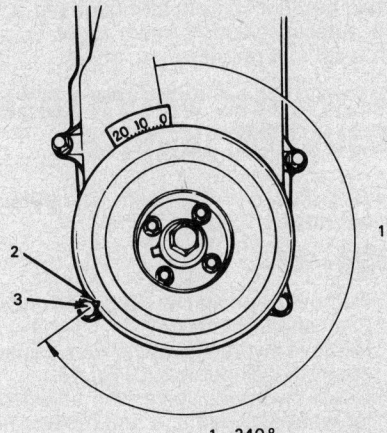

1. 240°
2. TIMING NOTCH
3. LEFT ATTACHING BOLT

Fig. 8   Crankshaft pulley alignment w/left side timing belt cover bolt

6. Remove air conditioning belt.
7. Lower vehicle and remove air compressor lower adjusting brace.
8. Remove spark plug wires.
9. Remove oxygen sensor wire from sensor and block.
10. Remove exhaust manifold hot air shroud.
11. Remove exhaust manifold.
12. Reverse procedure to install.

TURBO ENGINES

1. Remove turbocharger as outlined under "Turbocharger, Replace."
2. Remove exhaust manifold attaching bolts, then exhaust manifold.

1989–91 EFI ENGINES

1. Disconnect battery ground cable.
2. Disconnect oxygen sensor electrical connector, then release wiring harness from clamps.
3. Disconnect exhaust pipe from exhaust manifold.
4. Remove exhaust manifold attaching bolts and nuts, then remove exhaust manifold from cylinder head.
5. Reverse procedure to install.

VALVE CLEARANCE SPECIFICATIONS

1988

Valve clearance with engine cold is .006 inch for intake valves and .008 inch for exhaust valves. Valve clearance with engine hot is .010 inch for intake valve and .012 inch for exhaust valves.

1989–91

These engines are equipped with hydraulic valve lash adjusters and no adjustment is required.

VALVE ARRANGEMENT

FRONT TO REAR

1.0L/3-61 . . . . I-E-I-E-I-E

1. 240°
2. TIMING NOTCH
3. RIGHT ATTACHING BOLT

Fig. 9   Crankshaft pulley alignment w/right side timing belt cover bolt

VALVES

ADJUST

1988

1. Remove air cleaner and cylinder head cover.
2. Turn crankshaft clockwise and align timing notch on crankshaft pulley with 0 mark on timing tab. **Fig. 5.**
3. Remove distributor cap. Engine is at TDC when distributor rotor is positioned as shown in **Fig. 6.** If engine is not at TDC, turn crankshaft 360 degrees so timing notch is at 0 mark again.
4. Using feeler gauge, measure No. 1 cylinder intake and exhaust valve clearances at 1 in **Fig. 7.**
5. Adjust valve lash, if necessary, by turning adjusting screw after loosening locknut, **Fig. 7.** After adjustment, tighten locknut to specified torque.
6. After checking No. 1 cylinder, turn crankshaft 240 degrees clockwise and align timing notch on pulley with left mounting bolt of timing belt cover, **Fig. 8.** Check and, if necessary, adjust intake and exhaust valves of No. 3 cylinder.

hose from intake manifold.
13. Disconnect PCV valve hose from cylinder head cover.
14. Disconnect accelerator cable from throttle body.
15. Disconnect all other electrical connectors and hoses to permit intake manifold and throttle body removal.
16. Remove intake manifold to cylinder head attaching nuts and bolts, then remove intake manifold and throttle body as an assembly.
17. Reverse procedure to Install.

EXHAUST MANIFOLD

REPLACE

1988 CARBURETED ENGINES

1. Disconnect battery ground cable.
2. Raise and support vehicle.
3. Remove exhaust pipe at manifold.
4. Remove lower heat shield bolt.
5. Remove air pipe at manifold.

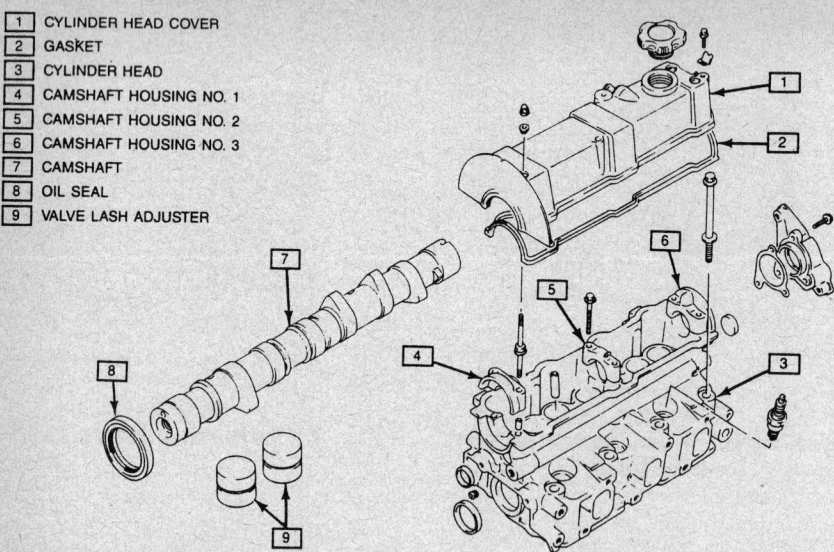

1. CYLINDER HEAD COVER
2. GASKET
3. CYLINDER HEAD
4. CAMSHAFT HOUSING NO. 1
5. CAMSHAFT HOUSING NO. 2
6. CAMSHAFT HOUSING NO. 3
7. CAMSHAFT
8. OIL SEAL
9. VALVE LASH ADJUSTER

Fig. 10 Camshaft & hydraulic valve lash adjusters. 1989–91

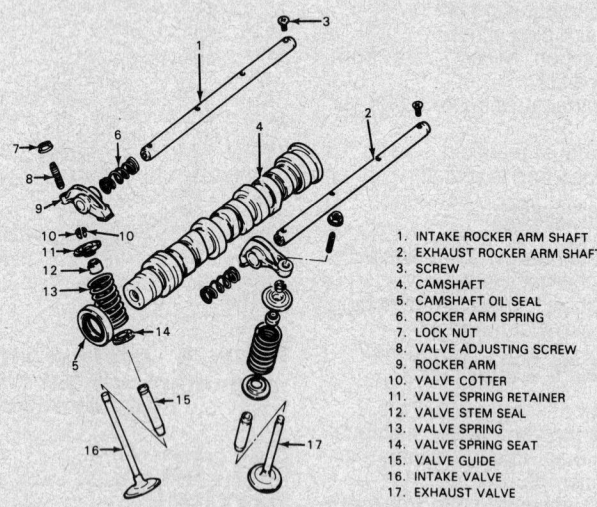

1. INTAKE ROCKER ARM SHAFT
2. EXHAUST ROCKER ARM SHAFT
3. SCREW
4. CAMSHAFT
5. CAMSHAFT OIL SEAL
6. ROCKER ARM SPRING
7. LOCK NUT
8. VALVE ADJUSTING SCREW
9. ROCKER ARM
10. VALVE COTTER
11. VALVE SPRING RETAINER
12. VALVE STEM SEAL
13. VALVE SPRING
14. VALVE SPRING SEAT
15. VALVE GUIDE
16. INTAKE VALVE
17. EXHAUST VALVE

Fig. 12 Exploded view of valve train assembly. 1988

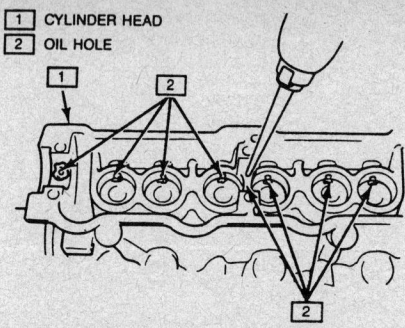

1. CYLINDER HEAD
2. OIL HOLE

Fig. 11 Applying engine oil to camshaft oil holes. 1989–91

7. Rotate crankshaft 240 degrees clockwise from left mounting bolt, and align timing notch with right mounting bolt as shown in **Fig. 9.** Check and, if necessary, adjust intake and exhaust valves of No. 2 cylinder.
8. After checking and adjusting valves, install distributor cap, cylinder head cover and air cleaner.

VALVE GUIDES

1988

Valves and valve guides are available in standard size only. The Valve guide can be driven from cylinder bore using valve guide remover tool No. J-37968-1 or equivalent. The valve guide should be driven from the combustion chamber side of the cylinder head out through the valve spring side.

The cylinder head valve guide bore should be reamed with an 11 mm reamer prior to valve guide installation. Heat cylinder head to 176 to 212°F, then drive valve guide into cylinder head bore using tool No. J-37968. Valve guide should be driven in until tool contacts cylinder head. Valve guide protrusion should be .55 inch from cylinder head surface. After installation, ream valve guide with a 7 mm reamer.

1989–91

Valves and valve guides are available in standard size only. The Valve guide can be driven from cylinder bore using valve guide remover tool No. J-37968-1 or equivalent. The valve guide should be driven from the combustion chamber side of the cylinder head out through the valve spring side.

The cylinder head valve guide bore should be reamed with an 11 mm reamer prior to valve guide installation. Heat cylinder head to 176 to 212°F, then drive valve guide into cylinder head bore using valve guide remover tool No. J-37968-1 and valve guide installer No. J-37968-2. Valve guide should be driven in until tool contacts cylinder head. Valve guide protrusion should be .45 inch from cylinder head surface. After installation, ream valve guide with a 5.5 mm reamer.

HYDRAULIC VALVE LASH ADJUSTER SERVICE

Hydraulic valve lash adjusters should not be disassembled.

1989–91

1. Remove camshaft as described under "Camshaft, Replace."
2. Remove hydraulic valve lash adjusters from cylinder head, **Fig. 10.**
3. Check hydraulic valve lash adjusters for wear and damage and replace as necessary.
4. Using a micrometer, measure outside diameter of hydraulic valve lash adjuster. Outside diameter should be 1.2188 to 1.2194 inches.
5. Measure hydraulic valve lash adjuster bore in cylinder head. Bore diameter should be 1.2205 to 1.2214 inches.
6. To determine hydraulic valve lash adjuster to cylinder head bore clearance, subtract adjuster outside diameter from cylinder head adjuster bore diameter. Adjuster to bore clearance should be .0010 to .0025 inch. If clearance is greater than .0059 inch, replace adjuster or cylinder head as necessary.
7. Place valve lash adjuster in clean engine oil prior to installation. Also pour engine oil through camshaft journal oil holes, until oil is emitted from hydraulic valve lash adjuster oil holes, **Fig. 11.**
8. Apply engine oil to valve lash adjuster, then position adjuster in cylinder head bore and install camshaft.

ROCKER ARMS & SHAFT
REPLACE

1988

1. Disconnect battery ground cable.

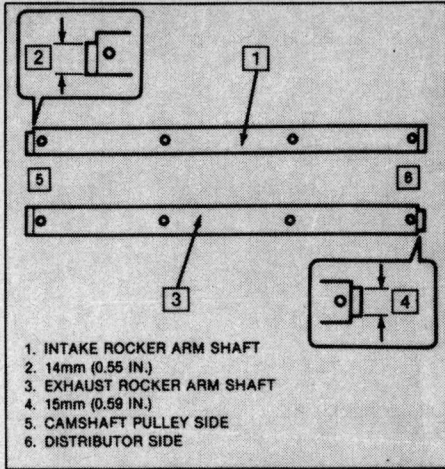

Fig. 13   Rocker arm shaft identification. 1988

1. INTAKE ROCKER ARM SHAFT
2. 14mm (0.55 IN.)
3. EXHAUST ROCKER ARM SHAFT
4. 15mm (0.59 IN.)
5. CAMSHAFT PULLEY SIDE
6. DISTRIBUTOR SIDE

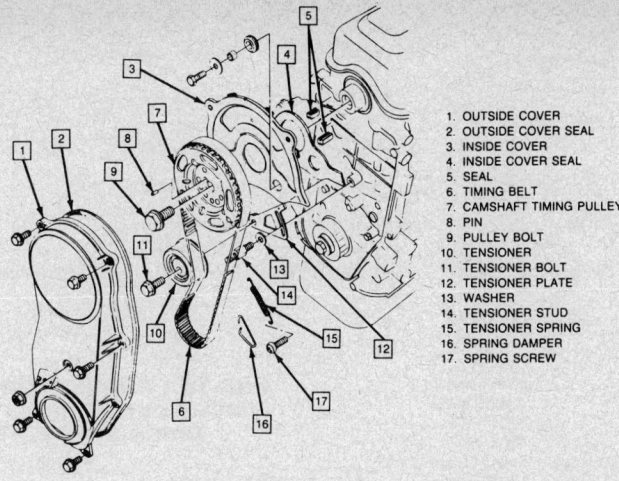

Fig. 14   Timing belt & cover assembly. 1988

1. OUTSIDE COVER
2. OUTSIDE COVER SEAL
3. INSIDE COVER
4. INSIDE COVER SEAL
5. SEAL
6. TIMING BELT
7. CAMSHAFT TIMING PULLEY
8. PIN
9. PULLEY BOLT
10. TENSIONER
11. TENSIONER BOLT
12. TENSIONER PLATE
13. WASHER
14. TENSIONER STUD
15. TENSIONER SPRING
16. SPRING DAMPER
17. SPRING SCREW

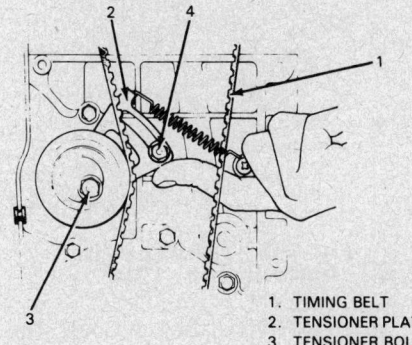

Fig. 15   Timing belt removal. 1988

1. TIMING BELT
2. TENSIONER PLATE
3. TENSIONER BOLT
4. TENSIONER STUD

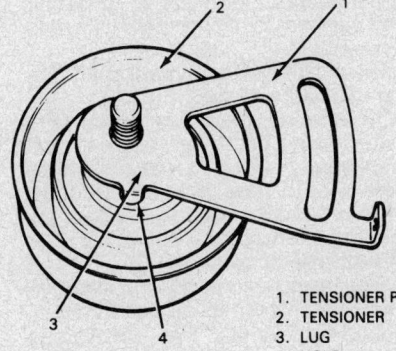

Fig. 16   Tensioner assembly

1. TENSIONER PLATE
2. TENSIONER
3. LUG
4. HOLE

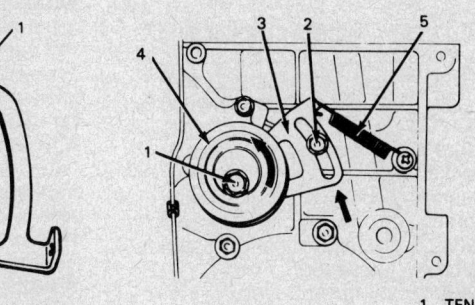

Fig. 17   Checking tensioner plate movement

1. TENSIONER BOLT
2. TENSIONER STUD
3. TENSIONER PLATE
4. TENSIONER
5. SPRING

2. Remove air cleaner assembly, then remove cylinder head cover.
3. Remove distributor from cylinder head.
4. Loosen valve adjusting screw locknuts, then back-off valve adjusting screws.
5. Remove rocker arm shaft bracket attaching screws, then remove rocker arm shaft rocker arms and springs, **Fig. 12.**
6. Check rocker arm camshaft shaft surface and adjusting screw for wear and damage.
7. Position rocker arm shaft on V-blocks and measure run-out using a dial indicator. Rocker arm shaft run-out limit is .004 inch.
8. Measure inside diameter of rocker arm bore. Inside diameter should be .629 to .630 inch, if not replace.
9. Measure Rocker arm shaft outside diameter. Outside diameter should be .628 to .629 inch, if not replace.
10. Rocker arm to rocker arm shaft clearance should be .0005 to .0017 inch. If clearance exceeds .0035 inch, replace rocker arm or shaft as necessary.
11. Reverse procedure to install. Lubricate rocker arms and shafts with engine oil, then install rocker arms,

springs and shafts. Intake and exhaust rocker arm shafts are different, refer to **Fig. 13,** for identification and proper installation.

TIMING BELT & COVER REPLACE

1988
Removal

1. Disconnect battery ground cable.
2. Loosen water pump pulley bolts.
3. Remove A/C compressor adjusting bolt, if equipped.
4. Loosen alternator adjusting bolt.
5. Raise and support vehicle.
6. Remove drive belt splash shield.
7. Remove plug in right fender well.
8. Remove A/C compressor drive belt, if equipped.
9. Remove alternator belt.
10. Remove crankshaft pulley and water pump pulley.
11. Remove bolts at bottom of timing belt cover, **Fig. 14.**
12. Lower vehicle.
13. Remove bolts at top of timing belt cover and cover.
14. Remove cylinder head cover.
15. Loosen rocker arm adjusting screws.

16. Remove distributor cap.
17. Loosen tensioner bolt and stud, and remove belt as shown in **Fig. 15.**
18. Remove tensioner, tensioner plate and tensioner spring.

Inspection

1. Check timing belt for wear or cracks. Replace as necessary.
2. Check tensioner for smooth rotation.

Installation

1. Install tensioner plate to tensioner. Insert lug of tensioner plate into hole of tensioner, **Fig. 16.**
2. Install tensioner, tensioner plate and spring. Hand tighten tensioner bolt and stud only. Check that plate movement is in direction shown in **Fig. 17.** If no movement occurs between plate and tensioner, remove tensioner and plate and reinsert plate lug into tensioner hole.
3. Turn camshaft pulley clockwise and align timing mark on camshaft pulley with V mark on inside belt cover, **Fig. 18.**
4. Using 17 mm wrench, turn crankshaft clockwise and align punch mark on timing belt pulley with arrow mark on oil pump, **Fig. 19.**

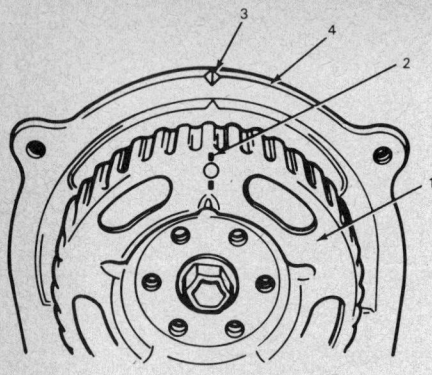

1. CAMSHAFT TIMING PULLEY
2. TIMING MARK
3. "V" MARK
4. BELT INSIDE COVER

Fig. 18 Camshaft pulley alignment. 1988

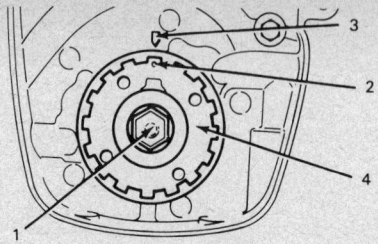

1. CRANK TIMING BELT PULLEY BOLT
2. PUNCH MARK
3. ARROW MARK
4. CRANK TIMING BELT PULLEY

Fig. 19 Aligning timing belt pulley punch mark with oil pump arrow. 1988

5. With all 4 marks aligned, install timing belt on sprockets so that drive side of belt is free of any slack and so tensioner plate is positioned as shown in **Fig. 20**.
6. To ensure timing belt is free of slack, turn crankshaft one rotation clockwise after installing belt. After removing slack, first torque tensioner stud, and then tensioner to specification listed at the end of this section.
7. Install timing belt outer cover.
8. Install crankshaft pulley and torque bolts to specification listed at the end of this section.
9. Refer to "Valves, Adjust" procedure and adjust intake and exhaust valves.
10. Install water pump pulley and drive belt.
11. Install cylinder head cover and air cleaner.
12. Connect battery ground cable.

1989–91
Removal

1. Disconnect battery ground cable, then raise and support vehicle.
2. Remove fender apron extension from right hand side of vehicle.
3. Remove water pump drive belt, then remove water pump pulley.
4. Remove four attaching bolts and crankshaft pulley.
5. Remove outer timing belt cover, **Fig. 21**.
6. Align camshaft and crankshaft timing marks, **Fig. 22**.
7. Remove timing belt tensioner, tensioner plate, spring and damper.
8. Remove timing belt.

Inspection

Check timing belt for wear and cracks and replace as necessary. Check timing belt tensioner for smoothness of rotation and replace as necessary.

Installation

1. Position lug on tensioner plate to hole in tensioner, **Fig. 16**.
2. Position tensioner and tensioner plate

to engine, then install and hand tighten attaching bolt. Ensure that tensioner and tensioner plate move in the same direction, **Fig. 17**. If movement is not as indicated, remove tensioner and reinsert tensioner plate lug into tensioner.
3. Ensure camshaft and crankshaft timing marks are aligned, **Fig. 22**.
4. With tensioner plate pushed upward, install timing belt over camshaft and crankshaft pulleys. **Arrow on timing belt should face toward direction of crankshaft rotation. When installing timing belt, keep drive side of belt free of slack.**
5. Install tensioner spring and damper, then hand tighten tensioner stud.
6. Rotate crankshaft two revolutions clockwise direction to remove slack from belt. **Ensure slack is removed from drive belt and that camshaft and crankshaft timing marks are aligned.**
7. Tighten tensioner stud, then tighten tensioner bolt to torque listed at the end of this section.
8. Install timing belt outer cover and crankshaft pulley. **Ensure seal is between oil pump housing and water pump.**
9. Install water pump pulley and drive belt.
10. Install right hand side fender apron extension, then lower vehicle and connect battery ground cable.

CAMSHAFT REPLACE

1988

1. Disconnect battery ground cable.
2. Remove air cleaner and cylinder head cover.
3. Remove distributor and case from cylinder head.
4. Loosen all valve adjusting screw locknuts and turn adjusting screws completely back to allow rocker arms to move freely.
5. Remove rocker arm shaft screws and rocker arm shafts, then, remove rocker arms and springs, **Fig. 12**.
6. Remove fuel pump and push rod from cylinder head.

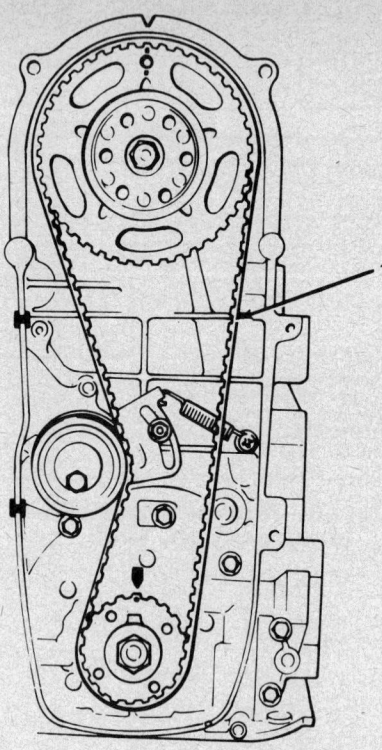

1. DRIVE SIDE OF BELT

Fig. 20 Timing belt installation. 1988

7. Refer to "Timing Belt & Cover, Replace" procedure to remove crankshaft pulley and timing belt outer cover.
8. Using tool J-34836, remove timing belt sprocket and timing belt inner cover, **Fig. 23**.
9. Remove camshaft from cylinder head.
10. Reverse procedure to install. **Torque** camshaft sprocket to specification listed at the end of this section. Refer to **Fig. 13** for rocker shaft identification.

1989–91
Removal

1. Disconnect battery ground cable.
2. Remove air cleaner assembly, then remove cylinder head cover.
3. Remove distributor from cylinder head.
4. Remove timing belt as described under "Timing Belt, Replace."
5. After timing belt has been remove, position crankshaft sprocket key as shown in, **Fig. 24**.
6. Hold camshaft in position by inserting a rod into .39 inch hole in camshaft, then remove camshaft sprocket retaining bolt, **Fig. 25**. Place shop cloth under rod to prevent damage to cylinder head surface.
7. Remove camshaft housings to cylinder head attaching bolts and studs, **Fig. 10**.
8. Remove camshaft from cylinder head. **Hydraulic valve lash adjusters should also be removed and**

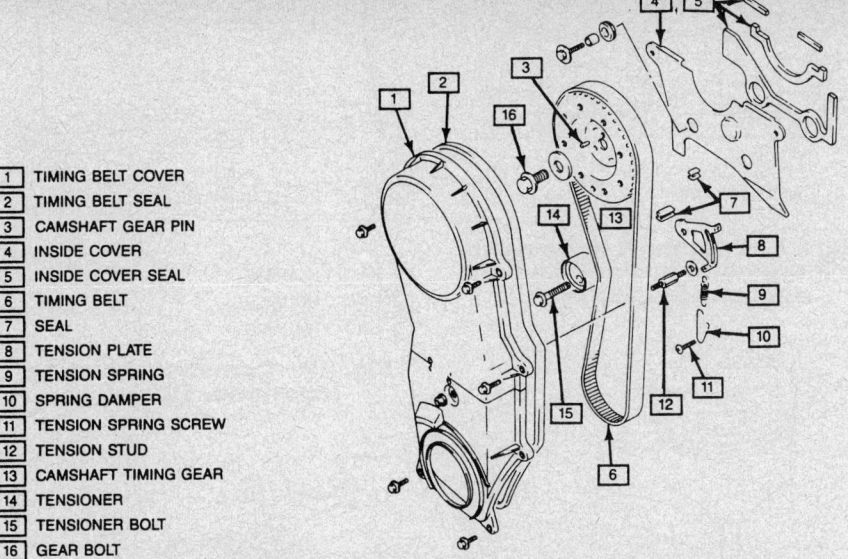

1	TIMING BELT COVER
2	TIMING BELT SEAL
3	CAMSHAFT GEAR PIN
4	INSIDE COVER
5	INSIDE COVER SEAL
6	TIMING BELT
7	SEAL
8	TENSION PLATE
9	TENSION SPRING
10	SPRING DAMPER
11	TENSION SPRING SCREW
12	TENSION STUD
13	CAMSHAFT TIMING GEAR
14	TENSIONER
15	TENSIONER BOLT
16	GEAR BOLT

Fig. 21 Timing belt & cover assembly. 1989–91

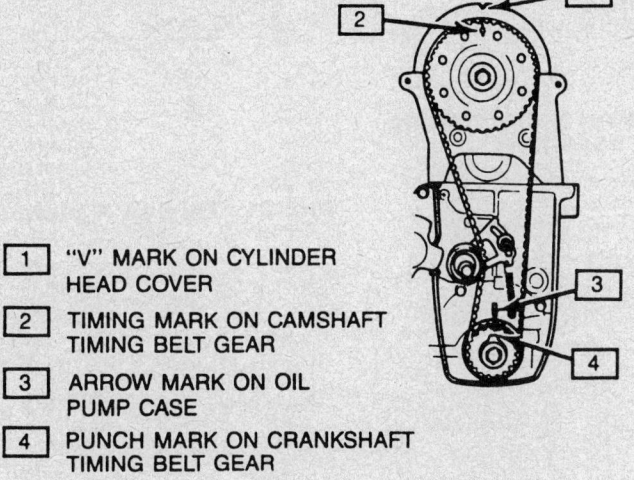

1	"V" MARK ON CYLINDER HEAD COVER
2	TIMING MARK ON CAMSHAFT TIMING BELT GEAR
3	ARROW MARK ON OIL PUMP CASE
4	PUNCH MARK ON CRANKSHAFT TIMING BELT GEAR

Fig. 22 Aligning camshaft & crankshaft sprocket timing marks. 1989–91

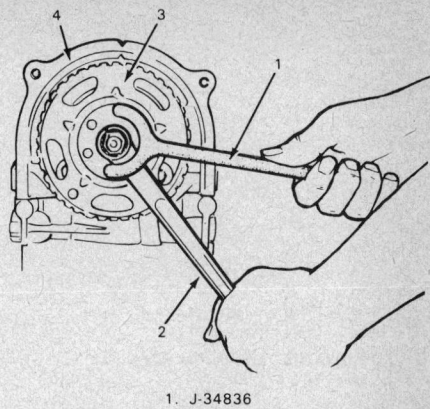

1. J-34836
2. WRENCH
3. CAMSHAFT TIMING BELT PULLEY
4. TIMING BELT INSIDE COVER

Fig. 23 Timing belt sprocket removal. 1988

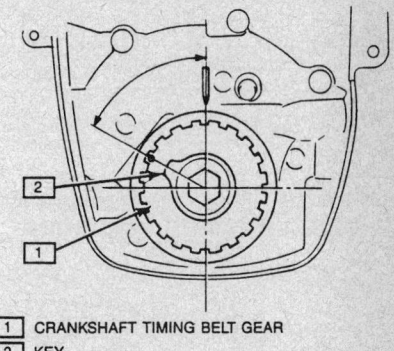

1	CRANKSHAFT TIMING BELT GEAR
2	KEY

Fig. 24 Positioning crankshaft sprocket key. 1989–91

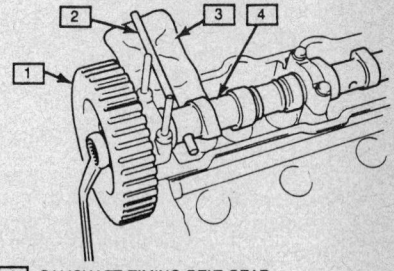

1	CAMSHAFT TIMING BELT GEAR
2	ROD
3	SHOP CLOTH
4	CAMSHAFT

Fig. 25 Camshaft sprocket bolt removal & installation. 1989–91

placed in engine oil until installation.

Installation

1. Pour engine oil into camshaft journal oil holes until oil is emitted from hydraulic valve lash adjuster holes, **Fig. 11.**
2. Lubricate valve lash adjusters with engine oil and install on cylinder head.
3. Lubricate camshaft with engine oil, then position on cylinder head with sprocket pin hole positioned as shown in **Fig. 26.**
4. Lubricate camshaft journal bores in camshaft housing with engine oil.
5. Apply sealant to cylinder head mating surface of camshaft housings No. 1 and No. 3, **Fig. 27.**
6. Position camshaft housings over camshaft and onto cylinder head mating surface. **Arrow on camshaft** housing should face camshaft sprocket side of cylinder head. Camshaft housings are numbered from 1 to 3. The housings are positioned on the cylinder head in numerical order, starting with No. 1 at camshaft sprocket side of cylinder head, **Fig. 28.**
7. Apply engine oil to camshaft housing attaching bolts and studs, then loosely install bolts and studs. Tighten bolts and studs in sequence shown in **Fig. 29.** to **torque** listed at the end of this section.
8. Apply engine oil to camshaft oil seal lip, then install seal. Seal surface should be flush with housing surface.
9. Hold camshaft in position by inserting a rod into .39 inch hole in camshaft, then install and tighten camshaft sprocket retaining bolt, **Fig. 25.** Place shop cloth under rod to prevent damage to cylinder head surface.
10. Install cylinder head cover.
11. Install timing belt as described under "Timing Belt, Replace."
12. Install ignition distributor, then install air cleaner assembly.
13. Connect battery ground cable, then adjust ignition timing.

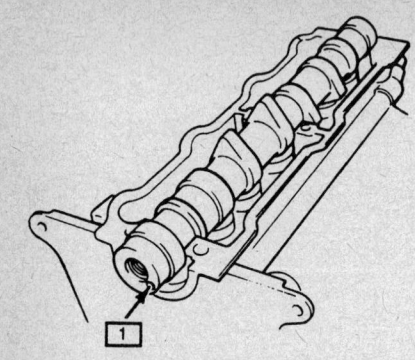

[1] TIMING BELT GEAR PIN HOLE

Fig. 26   Position camshaft sprocket pin hole. 1989-91

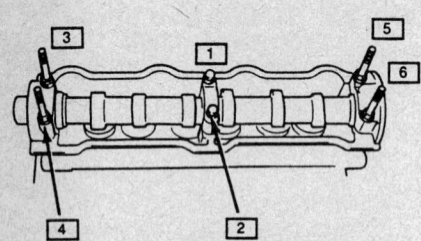

[3] [5] [1] [6] [4] [2]

Fig. 29   Camshaft housing bolt tightening sequence. 1989-91

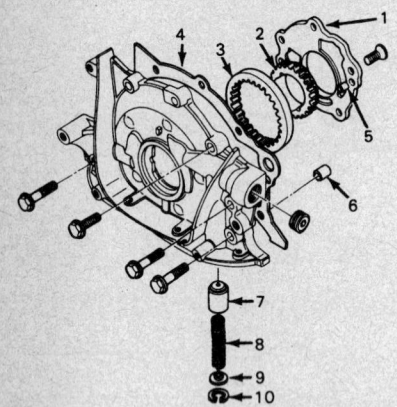

1. GEAR PLATE
2. INNER GEAR
3. OUTER GEAR
4. GASKET
5. PIN
6. PIN
7. RELIEF VALVE
8. SPRING
9. RETAINER
10. RETAINER RING

Fig. 32   Rotor type (Trochoid) oil pump. 1988-91 all

PISTON & ROD ASSEMBLY

Refer to **Fig. 30** when assembling piston and connecting rod. When installing piston and connecting rod, arrow on piston head should face front of engine and oil hole in

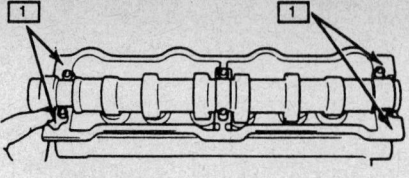

[1] APPLY SEALANT

Fig. 27   Camshaft housing to cylinder head surface sealant application. 1989-91

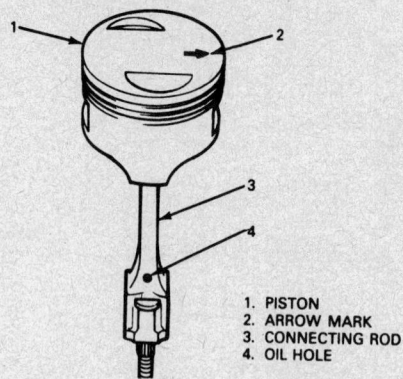

1. PISTON
2. ARROW MARK
3. CONNECTING ROD
4. OIL HOLE

Fig. 30   Piston & connecting rod assembly

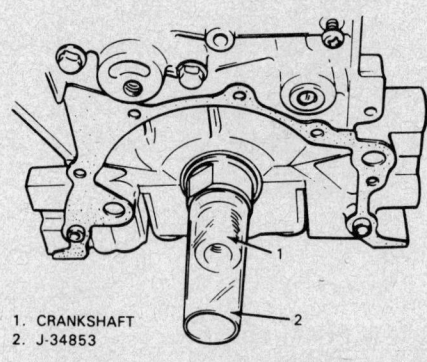

1. CRANKSHAFT
2. J-34853

Fig. 33   Crankshaft oil seal guide tool installation

connecting rod should face intake manifold. When installing connecting rod cap, arrow on cap should face front of engine.

Measure rod bearing side clearance using a feeler gauge. Connecting rod bearing side clearance should be .0039 to .0078 inch.

PISTONS, PINS & RINGS

Pistons and rings are available in standard size and oversizes of .010 and .020 inch. Piston pins are supplied with pistons in matched sets.

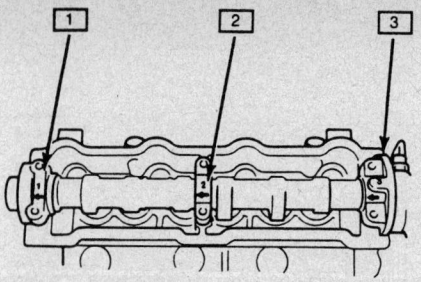

[1] NO. 1 HOUSING
[2] NO. 2 HOUSING
[3] NO. 3 HOUSING

Fig. 28   Camshaft housing locations. 1989-91

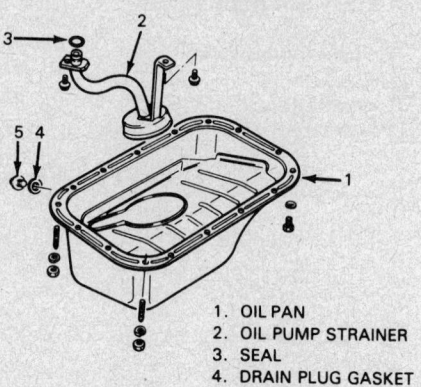

1. OIL PAN
2. OIL PUMP STRAINER
3. SEAL
4. DRAIN PLUG GASKET
5. DRAIN PLUG

Fig. 31   Oil pan & pick-up tube

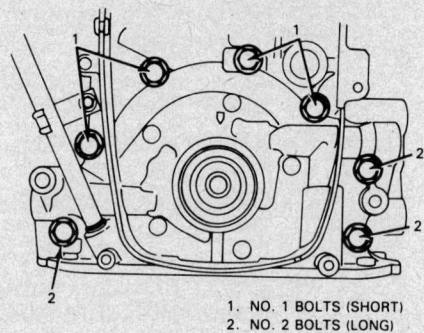

1. NO. 1 BOLTS (SHORT)
2. NO. 2 BOLTS (LONG)

Fig. 34   Oil pump bolt location

MAIN & ROD BEARINGS

Main and rod bearings are available in standard size and under size of .010 inch. Crankshaft thrust bearings are available in standard size and under size of .005 inch.

CRANKSHAFT REAR OIL SEAL
REPLACE

1. Remove transaxle as described under "Transaxle, Replace."

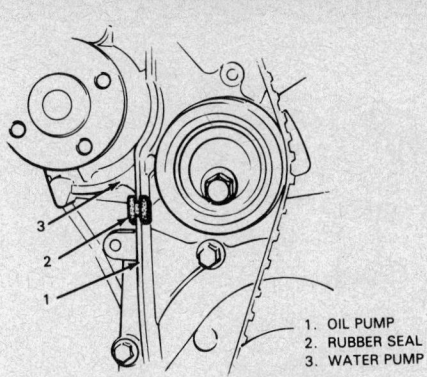
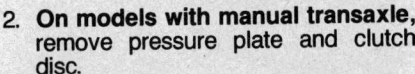

Fig. 35 Rubber seal installation

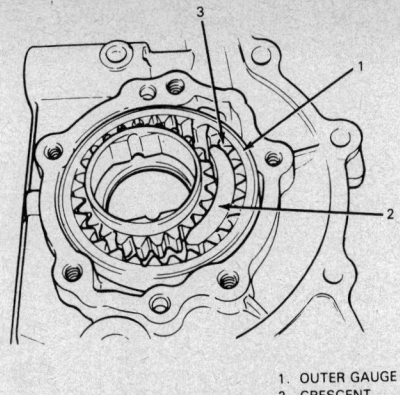
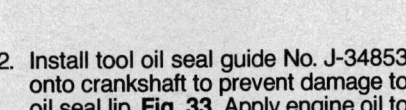

1. OIL PUMP
2. RUBBER SEAL
3. WATER PUMP

Fig. 36 Checking oil pump gear radial clearance. Rotor type similar

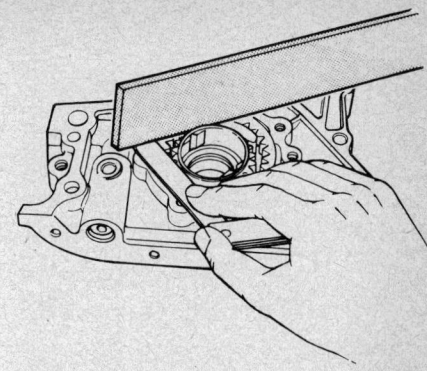

1. OUTER GAUGE
2. CRESCENT
3. CLEARANCE

Fig. 37 Checking oil pump gear side clearance. Rotor type similar

2. **On models with manual transaxle,** remove pressure plate and clutch disc.
3. **On all models,** remove flywheel.
4. Remove seal retainer, then remove seal from retainer.
5. Reverse procedure to install.

OIL PAN
REPLACE

1. Disconnect battery ground cable.
2. Raise and support vehicle.
3. Drain oil pan.
4. Remove flywheel dust cover.
5. Disconnect exhaust pipe at manifold.
6. Remove oil pan bolts and pan, **Fig. 31.**
7. Remove oil pump screen.
8. Reverse procedure to install. Apply continuous bead of silicon type sealer to oil pan flange inside bolt holes. When tightening oil pan attaching bolts, start at center and working outward. **Torque** bolts to specification listed at the end of this section.

OIL PUMP
REPLACE

REMOVAL

1. Refer to "Timing Belt, Replace" procedure to remove timing belt.
2. Refer to "Oil Pan, Replace" procedure to remove oil pan.
3. Remove crankshaft timing belt sprocket.
4. Remove alternator mounting bracket, if necessary.
5. Remove A/C compressor mounting bracket, if so equipped.
6. Remove alternator adjusting bolt and upper cover bolt, if necessary.
7. Remove oil pump bolts and pump, **Figs. 32.**

INSTALLATION

1. Install oil pump pins and gasket on engine block.

2. Install tool oil seal guide No. J-34853 onto crankshaft to prevent damage to oil seal lip, **Fig. 33.** Apply engine oil to your special tool.
3. Install oil pump onto crankshaft and engine block. Note location of mounting bolts, **Fig. 34. No. 1 bolts are shorter then No. 2 bolts in length. Install bolts as shown in Fig. 34, and tighten to torque** listed at the end of this section.
4. After installing oil pump, check that oil seal lip is not twisted, then remove tool.
5. Install rubber seal between oil pump and water pump, **Fig. 35.**
6. If necessary, trim edges of oil pump seal flush with oil pan mating surface.
7. Install timing belt guide, key and crankshaft timing sprocket. Note that timing belt guide must be installed so that curved side faces oil pump.
8. Install timing belt and tensioner components.
9. **On 1988 models, adjust intake and exhaust valves.**
10. **On all models,** adjust water pump belt tension.
11. Fill crankcase.
12. Connect battery ground cable.
13. Run engine to check that oil pressure is correct.

OIL PUMP SERVICE

1. Remove dipstick tube from oil pump.
2. Remove gear/rotor plate screws and gear plate.
3. Remove outer and inner gears/rotors.
4. Inspect oil seal lip for damage and replace as necessary.
5. Inspect outer and inner gears/rotors, gear/rotor plate, and oil pump case for excessive wear or damage.
6. Using feeler gauge, check radial clearance between outer gear/rotor and crescent, **Fig. 36.** If clearance exceeds .0122 inch, replace outer gear/rotor.
7. Using straightedge and feeler gauge, measure side clearance which should not exceed .0059 inch, **Fig. 37.**

8. Wash, clean and dry all oil pump parts.
9. Apply light coat of engine oil to inner and outer gears/rotors, oil seal lip portion, and inside surfaces of oil pump case and plate.
10. Install outer and inner gears/rotors in pump case.
11. Install gear/rotor plate and tighten screws securely. Check that gears turn smoothly by hand.
12. Install O-ring in pump case, then dipstick tube.

WATER PUMP
REPLACE

1. Disconnect battery ground cable.
2. Drain cooling system.
3. Remove drive belt, water pump pulley, crankshaft pulley, timing belt outside cover, timing belt and timing belt tensioner.
4. Remove water pump mounting bolts and nuts, and water pump.
5. Install water pump on engine block.
6. Install rubber seals between water pump and oil pump, and between water pump and cylinder head, **Fig. 38.**
7. Install timing belt tensioner, timing belt, timing belt outside cover, crankshaft pulley, water pump pulley and drive belt.
8. Tighten drive belt so it deflects .25-.35 inch on span between water pump pulley and crankshaft pulley.
9. **On 1988 models,** adjust intake and exhaust valves.
10. **On all models,** install valve cover and air cleaner.
11. Fill cooling system.
12. Connect battery ground cable.

COOLING SYSTEM BLEED

These engines do not require a specified bleed procedure. After filling cooling system, run engine to operating temperature with radiator/pressure cap off. Air will then be automatically bled through cap opening.

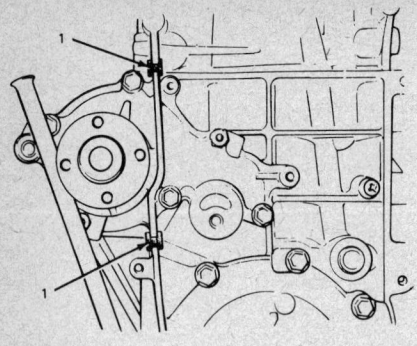

1. RUBBER SEAL

Fig. 38   Installing rubber seals

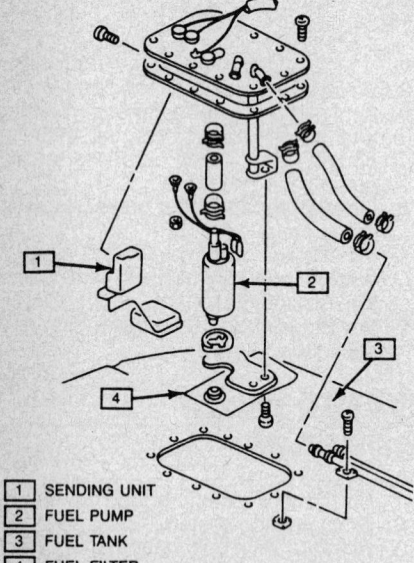

1	SENDING UNIT
2	FUEL PUMP
3	FUEL TANK
4	FUEL FILTER

Fig. 39   Electric fuel pump & sending unit removal

BELT TENSION DATA

Belt & Year	Belt Deflection Inch ①
A/C Compressor	
1988	.31–.47
1989–91	.20–.25
Alternator & Water Pump	
1988	.24–.35
1989–91 New	.20–.27
1989–91 Used	.24–.31

①—With thumb pressure applied.

FUEL PUMP
REPLACE
MECHANICAL TYPE

1. Disconnect battery ground cable.
2. Remove filler cap from fuel tank to release vapor pressure. Reinstall cap.

Engine Oiling system

3. Remove air cleaner from carburetor.
4. Disconnect fuel inlet, outlet and return hoses from fuel pump.
5. Remove fuel pump from cylinder head.
6. Remove fuel pump rod from cylinder head.
7. Reverse procedure to install.

ELECTRIC TYPE

1. **On turbo models,** relieve system fuel pressure as follows:
   a. Remove fuel tank filler cap to release vapor pressure, then reinstall cap.
   b. With engine idling, disconnect fuel pump relay electrical connector, **Fig. 1.**
   c. After engine has stopped operating, crank engine several times in three second intervals.
   d. After fuel pressure has been relieved, place ignition switch in off position and connect fuel relay electrical connector.
   e. If engine cannot be started, position shop towels around union bolt of high pressure line, then slowly loosen union bolt until fuel pressure is relieved. After fuel pressure has been relieved, tighten union bolt.
2. **On 1989-91 models,** relieve fuel system pressure as follows:
   a. Remove fuel pump relay from main fuse panel located in engine compartment, **Fig. 2.**
   b. Operate engine until it stalls, then crank engine several times in three second intervals.

   c. Remove fuel tank filler cap to release vapor pressure, then reinstall cap.
   d. Place ignition switch in off position, then install fuel pump relay.
3. **On all models,** disconnect battery ground cable.
4. Remove rear seat cushion, then disconnect fuel pump and sending unit electrical connectors, then push harness through floor pan grommet.
5. Drain fuel tank, then disconnect inlet hose from fuel filter.
6. Disconnect fuel filler hose from fuel tank.
7. Disconnect vapor hoses and fuel feed and return hoses at fuel tank and pump.
8. Remove fuel tank mounting bolts, then lower fuel tank from vehicle.
9. Remove fuel pump to fuel tank attaching bolts, then remove fuel pump, **Fig. 39.**
10. Separate fuel; pump from motor and sending unit as necessary.
11. Reverse procedure to install.

TURBOCHARGER
REPLACE

1. Disconnect battery ground cable, then drain cooling system.
2. Remove hood and front grille.
3. Remove intercooler.
4. Disconnect radiator hoses, then disconnect engine cooling fan motor electrical connector.
5. Remove front upper member.
6. Discharge A/C system, then remove A/C condenser.
7. Remove radiator.
8. Remove front bumper from damper

flange.
9. Remove exhaust pipe bolts.
10. Remove A/C compressor.
11. Remove turbocharger cover.
12. Unclamp oxygen sensor wire.
13. Remover turbocharger side cover.
14. Remove lower exhaust pipe support

bracket bolt.
15. Remove upper exhaust pipe together with lower exhaust pipe.
16. Remove air outlet pipe.
17. Remove air inlet hose clamp bolt on cylinder head, then remove air inlet pipe.

18. Remove oil pipe from cylinder block, then remove oil drain hose.
19. Remove water pipe cylinder head clamp bolt, then disconnect water hoses.
20. Remove turbocharger.
21. Reverse procedure to install.

TIGHTENING SPECIFICATIONS

Torque specifications are for clean and lightly lubricated threads only. Dry or dirty threads produce increased friction which prevents accurate measurement of tightness.

Year	Component	Torque/Ft. Lbs.
1988	Air Inlet Pipe To Turbocharger	6-8.5
	Air Outlet Pipe To Turbocharger	6-8.5
	Camshaft Sprocket Bolt	41-46
	Connecting Rod Cap Bolts	24-26
	Crankshaft Pulley Bolts	7-9
	Crankshaft Sprocket Bolt	47-54
	Cylinder Head Bolts	46-50.5
	Exhaust Manifold To Cylinder Head	14-20
	Flywheel To Crankshaft	41-47
	Intake Manifold To Cylinder Head	14-20
	Main Bearing Cap Bolts	36-41
	Oil Drain Pipe To Turbocharger	3-5
	Oil Inlet Pipe To Turbocharger	8-10.5
	Oil Inlet Stand To Turbocharger	7.5-10.5
	Oil Pan Drain Plug	22-29
	Oil Pan To Engine	7-9
	Oil Pressure Switch	9-10
	Oil Pump To Engine	7-9
	Rocker Arm Adjusting Screw Locknut	11-13
	Rocker Arm Shaft Bracket	7-9
	Spark Plug	18-21.5
	Timing Belt Tensioner Bolt	13-20
	Timing Belt Tensioner Stud	6-9
	Turbocharger To Exhaust Manifold	13.5-20
	Upper Exhaust Pipe To Turbocharger Nut	13.5-20
	Water Pump To Engine	7.5-9
1989-91	Alternator Mounting Bolts & Nuts	17
	Camshaft Housing To Cylinder Head	8
	Camshaft Sprocket Bolt	44
	Connecting Rod Cap Bolts	26
	Crankshaft Pulley Bolts	8
	Crankshaft Sprocket Bolt	81
	Cylinder Head Bolts	54
	Cylinder Head Cover	4
	Exhaust Manifold To Cylinder Head	17
	Flywheel To Crankshaft	45
	Ignition Distributor To Cylinder Head	10
	Intake Manifold To Cylinder Head	17
	Main Bearing Cap Bolts	40
	Oil Pan Drain Plug	26
	Oil Pan To Engine	8
	Oil Pressure Switch	10
	Oil Pump Pickup Tube Bolts	8

Continued

TIGHTENING SPECIFICATIONS—Continued

Year 1989-91	Component	Torque/Ft. Lbs.
	Oil Pump Rotor Plate Screws	8
	Oil Pump To Engine	8
	Spark Plug	18
	Starter Mounting Bolts	17
	Timing Belt Cover Nuts & Bolts	8
	Timing Belt Tensioner Bolt	20
	Timing Belt Tensioner Stud	8
	Water Pump To Engine	7.5-9

Clutch & Manual Transaxle
INDEX

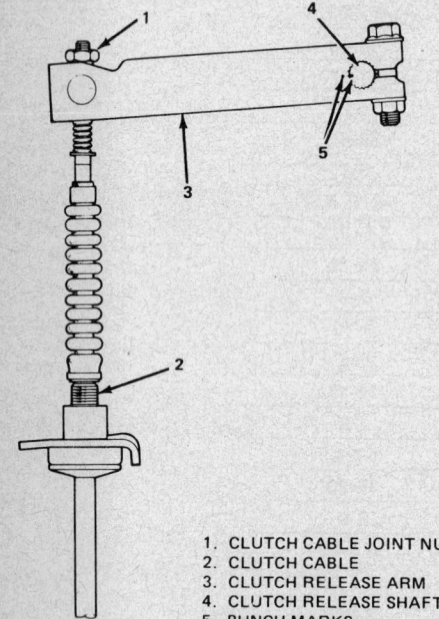

1. CLUTCH CABLE JOINT NUT
2. CLUTCH CABLE
3. CLUTCH RELEASE ARM
4. CLUTCH RELEASE SHAFT
5. PUNCH MARKS

Fig. 1 Clutch cable adjustment. 1988

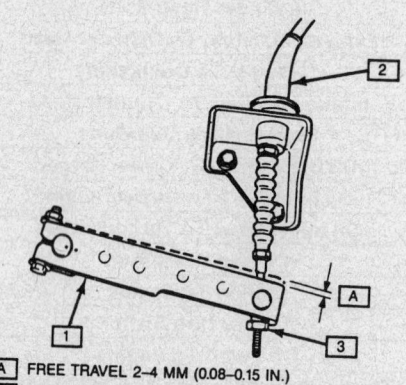

A	FREE TRAVEL 2-4 MM (0.08-0.15 IN.)
1	RELEASE LEVER
2	CLUTCH CABLE
3	JOINT NUT

Fig. 2 Clutch cable adjustment. 1989-91

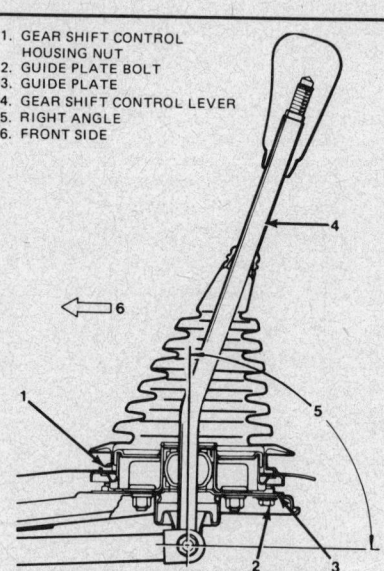

1. GEAR SHIFT CONTROL HOUSING NUT
2. GUIDE PLATE BOLT
3. GUIDE PLATE
4. GEAR SHIFT CONTROL LEVER
5. RIGHT ANGLE
6. FRONT SIDE

Fig. 3 Shift linkage adjustment. 1988

CLUTCH PEDAL HEIGHT
ADJUST

Using clutch pedal stop bolt, adjust height of clutch pedal so it is even with brake pedal.

CLUTCH RELEASE ARM PLAY
ADJUST
1988

1. Move arm by hand and check that arm play is .08 to .16 inch.

2. If play is out of specification, adjust clutch cable joint nut as necessary, **Fig. 1.**

1989-91

1. Measure clutch pedal freeplay. Clutch pedal freeplay should be .6 to .8 inch.
2. If clutch pedal freeplay is not within specifications, adjust clutch cable joint nut to provide a free travel of .08 to .15 inch at release lever, **Fig. 2.**

SHIFT LINKAGE, ADJUST
1988

1. Loosen gear shift control housing nuts and guide plate bolts.
2. Adjust guide plate by moving it forwards or backwards until shift lever is positioned in middle of guide plate and at a right angle, **Fig. 3.**
3. When guide plate is positioned properly, tighten guide plate bolts and housing nuts.

1989-91

Check gear shift control lever vertical endplay. Vertical endplay should be 0 to .007 inch. Check distance between instrument panel and gear shift control lever, with transaxle in neutral, **Fig. 4.** Distance should be approximately 10.6 inches, if not adjust.

CLUTCH CABLE
REPLACE

1. Disconnect battery ground cable at battery.
2. Remove clutch cable joint nut, then disconnect cable from release arm.
3. Remove clutch cable bracket bolts and bracket.
4. Remove cable retaining bolts at clutch pedal.
5. Remove clutch cable from vehicle.
6. Reverse procedure to install. Refer to

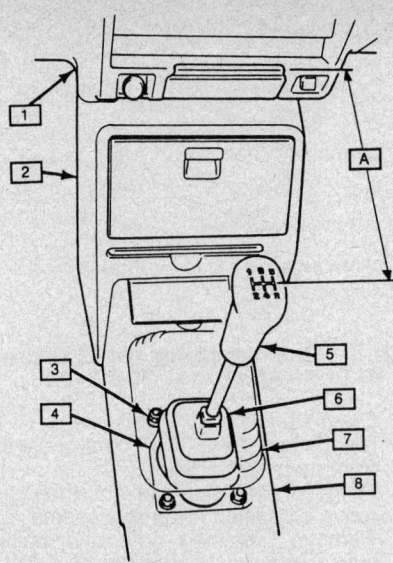

A	CONTROL LEVER POSITION DISTANCE
1	INSTRUMENT PANEL
2	CONSOLE BOX
3	CONTROL LEVER HOUSING NUT
4	BOOT COVER
5	CONTROL LEVER KNOB
6	CONTROL LEVER BOOT
7	BOOT NO. 2
8	SHIFT CONTROL LEVER COVER

Fig. 4   Positioning gearshift control lever. 1989–91

"Clutch Pedal Height, Adjust" procedure to adjust cable.

CLUTCH
REPLACE

1. Refer to "Transaxle, Replace" procedure to remove transaxle.
2. Install suitable tool into pilot bearing to support clutch assembly during removal.
3. Check for X mark or white painted letter on pressure plate and corresponding mark stamped on flywheel. If no markings are found, mark flywheel and pressure plate for assembly purposes.
4. Loosen pressure plate to flywheel mounting bolts 1 turn at a time until spring pressure is released, **Fig. 5**. It may be necessary to use flywheel holder tool No. J-35271 or equivalent to hold flywheel in position when loosening bolts.
5. Remove bolts, pressure plate and clutch disc.
6. Reverse procedure to install. Lubricate splines of transaxle input shaft and pilot bearing surface and release bearing with lithium wheel bearing grease. **Torque** pressure plate attaching bolts to 17 ft. lbs.

MANUAL TRANSAXLE
REPLACE

1988

1. Disconnect battery ground cable.

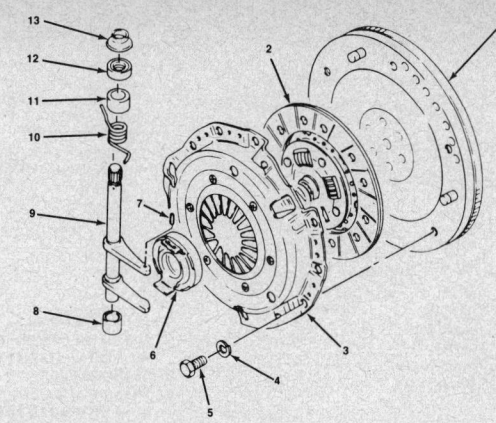

1. FLYWHEEL
2. DISC
3. CLUTCH COVER
4. LOCK WASHER
5. BOLT
6. RELEASE BEARING
7. RELEASE FORK PIN
8. NO. 2 BUSHING
9. RELEASE SHAFT
10. RETURN SPRING
11. NO. 1 BUSHING
12. SHAFT SEAL
13. SHAFT COVER

Fig. 5   Clutch assembly

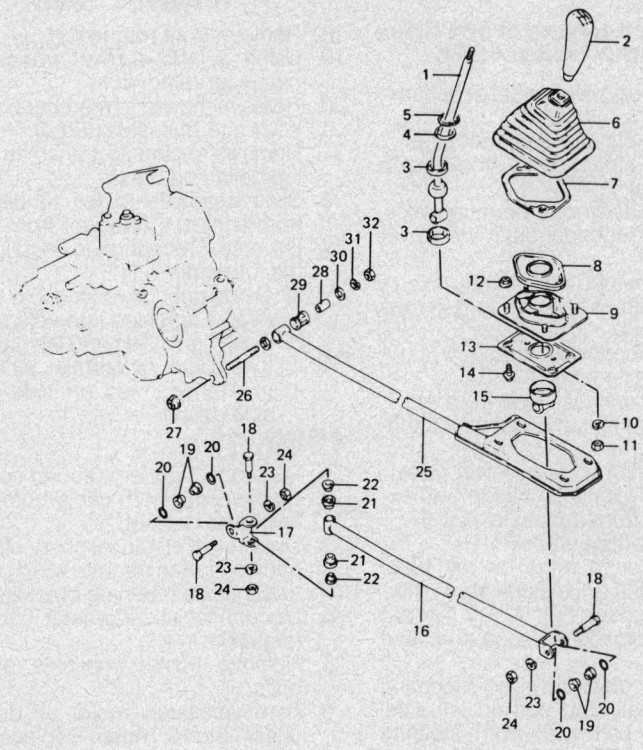

1. GEAR SHIFT CONT. LEVER	17. GEAR SHIFT CONT. JOINT
2. KNOB	18. CONT. SHAFT BOLT
3. LEVER SEAT	19. BUSHING
4. LEVER SHIM	20. BUSHING SEAL
5. LEVER RING	21. OUTER BUSHING
6. BOOT	22. INNER BUSHING
7. BOOT COVER	23. LOCK WASHER
8. HOUSING DUST COVER	24. SHAFT BOLT NUT
9. GEAR SHIFT CONT. HOUSING	25. EXTENSION ROD
10. LOCK WASHER	26. ROD STUD
11. NUT	27. STUD NUT
12. HOUSING NUT	28. SPACER
13. GUIDE PLATE	29. BUSHING
14. GUIDE PLATE BOLT	30. WASHER
15. REAR BOOT	31. LOCK WASHER
16. GEAR SHIFT CONT. SHAFT	32. ROD NUT

Fig. 6   Shift linkage components

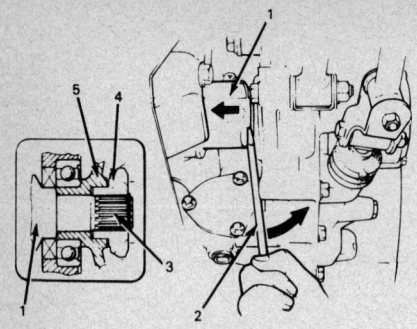

1. INBOARD JOINT OF DRIVE AXLE
2. PRY BAR
3. SNAP RING
4. DIFF. SIDE GEAR
5. DIFF. CARRIER

Fig. 7 Disengaging front drive axle snap rings. 1988

2. Disconnect negative cable at transaxle.
3. Remove air cleaner and heat pipe.
4. Disconnect clutch cable from clutch release lever.
5. Remove starter motor from transaxle.
6. Disconnect speedometer cable at transaxle.
7. Disconnect wiring from transaxle.
8. Disconnect front and rear torque rods from transaxle.
9. Raise and support vehicle.
10. Drain transaxle lubricant.
11. Disconnect exhaust pipe from manifold and from first exhaust pipe hanger.
12. Remove clutch housing lower plate.
13. Disconnect gearshift linkage and extension rod from transaxle, **Fig. 6.**
14. Remove left front wheel.
15. Disengage snap rings on left hand and right hand drive axles from differential side gears, **Fig. 7.** Pry inboard joint out to disengage snap ring fitted on spline.
16. Disconnect stabilizer bar mounting bolts and ball stud bolt on left side. Disconnect ball stud from steering knuckle by pushing down on stabilizer bar.
17. Pull inboard joint of left drive axle out of transaxle.

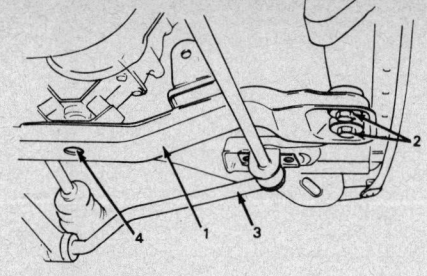

1. MOUNTING MEMBER
2. MOUNTING MEMBER BOLTS
   50 – 60 N·m (37-43 FT. LBS.)
3. STABILIZER BAR
4. TRANSAXLE MOUNT NUT
   40 – 50 N·m (29-36 FT. LBS.)

Fig. 8 Mounting member removal. 1988

18. Remove front torque rod.
19. Using a jack, support transaxle securely for removal.
20. Remove mounting member bolts from body and transaxle, **Fig. 8.**
21. Remove engine to transaxle mounting bolts and nuts.
22. Slide transaxle to left to disengage from engine, then lower from vehicle.
23. Reverse procedure to install, noting the following:
    a. Guide right drive axle into transaxle as it is raised into vehicle.
    b. Push right hand and left hand drive axles into differential side gears until snap rings on axle engage side gears.

1989–91

1. Disconnect battery ground cable.
2. Disconnect clutch cable from release lever and bracket.
3. Disconnect electrical connectors from transaxle, then remove wiring harness to transaxle retaining brackets.
4. Disconnect speedometer cable from transaxle.
5. Remove upper transaxle attaching bolts.
6. Remove starter motor as described under "Starter Motor, Replace."
7. Disconnect vacuum hose from pressure sensor.
8. Install an engine support fixture, then raise and support vehicle.

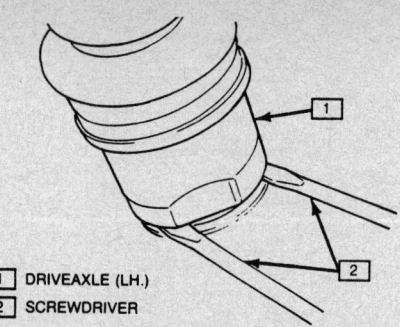

1. DRIVEAXLE (LH.)
2. SCREWDRIVER

Fig. 9 Disengaging front drive axle snap rings. 1989–91

9. Drain lubricant from transaxle.
10. Disconnect gear shift control lever from gear shift shaft.
11. Remove extension rod nut, then remove extension rod with washers.
12. Remove attaching nuts and bolts, then remove exhaust pipe.
13. Remove clutch housing lower cover.
14. Remove left front wheel and tire assembly.
15. Disconnect left tie rod end and ball joint from steering knuckle.
16. **On all models,** separate drive axles from transaxle, **Fig. 9.** Support drive axles from chassis using wire.
17. Remove lower transaxle to engine attaching bolts and nuts.
18. Support transaxle using a jack.
19. Remove two rear engine mounting nuts, then remove transaxle left hand mounting bracket attaching nuts and bolts and bracket.
20. Lower transaxle and engine assembly to disconnect assembly from stud bolts at rear engine mounting, the pull transaxle outward toward left hand side to disconnect input shaft from clutch assembly.
21. Lower transaxle, then remove from vehicle.
22. Reverse procedure to install. Lubricate splines of transaxle input shaft and pilot bearing surface and release bearing with lithium wheel bearing grease. When installing transaxle, guide right drive axle into transaxle as it is raised into vehicle. **Torque** transaxle to engine bolts to 37 ft. lbs.

TIGHTENING SPECIFICATIONS

Year	Component	Torque/Ft. Lbs.
1988–91	Cable Bracket Bolts	17
	Clutch Cable Outer Bolts	4.4
	Clutch Cover Bolts	17
	Engine Mounting Nuts	37
	Extension Rod Nut	13
	Extension Rod Stud Bolt	24
	Flywheel Bolts	45
	Gear Shift Control Shaft Bolts And Nuts	13
	Release Arm Bolt	10
	Switch Lock Nut	10
	Transmission Case Bolts	14
	Transmission To Engine Bolts	37

Rear Axle & Suspension

INDEX

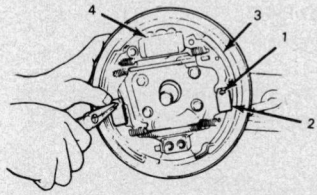

Fig. 1   Brake shoe hold down spring removal. 1988

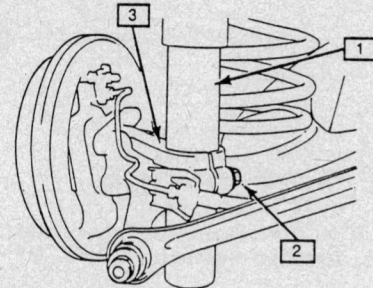

1	STRUT
2	MOUNT BOLT
3	KNUCKLE

Fig. 4   Strut lower mounting bolt. 1989-91

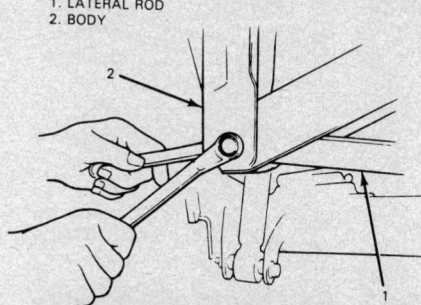

1. LATERAL ROD
2. BODY

Fig. 2   Lateral rod body side bolt location. 1988

12. Lower rear axle slowly, until tension of suspension spring is relieved. Remove spring.
13. Remove trailing arm front side bolt and lower rear axle.
14. Remove trailing arm bushing with suitable tool.
15. Reverse procedure to install. **When press fitting bushing into trailing arm, direct its slit side toward front and rear.**
16. Refer to end of this section for torque specifications.

SHOCK ABSORBER
REPLACE

1988

1. Raise and support vehicle.
2. Remove shock absorber lower mounting bolt and lock washer.
3. Remove upper mounting locknut and absorber nut.
4. Remove shock absorber.
5. Reverse procedure to install.

STRUT
REPLACE

1989-91

1. Raise and support rear of vehicle, then remove wheel and tire assembly.
2. Support suspension using a jack.
3. Remove strut upper support nuts, then push downward on strut, **Fig. 3.**
4. Remove strut lower mounting bolt, **Fig. 4.**
5. Separate strut from rear suspension knuckle, by compressing strut. If strut is difficult to remove, open slit on

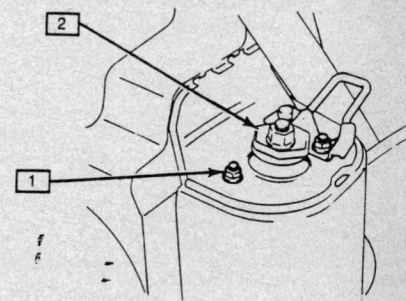

| 1 | SUPPORT NUT |
| 2 | STRUT |

Fig. 3   Strut upper attaching nuts. 1989-91

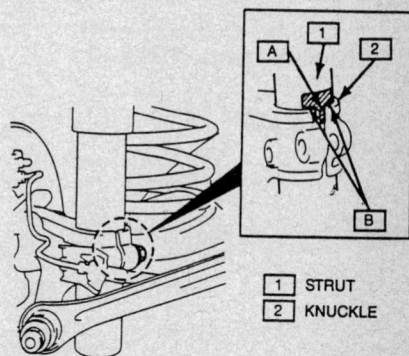

| 1 | STRUT |
| 2 | KNUCKLE |

Fig. 5   Position strut to rear suspension knuckle. 1989-91

knuckle just enough to allow strut removal.
6. Reverse procedure to install. When installing strut, align projection on strut with slit on rear suspension knuckle, **Fig. 5.**

COIL SPRING
REPLACE
1988 MODELS

Refer to "Rear Axle, Replace 1988 Models," and repeat steps 1 through 12 for coil spring removal.

COIL SPRING & SUSPENSION ARM
REPLACE
1989-91

1. Raise and support rear of vehicle,

REAR AXLE
REPLACE

1988 MODELS

1. Raise and support vehicle.
2. Remove rear brake drums.
3. Disconnect brake hoses from lines.
4. Disconnect brake hoses and retainers from trailing arm.
5. Plug brake hoses to prevent loss of brake fluid.
6. Remove brake shoe hold down spring by turning shoe hold down pin as shown in **Fig. 1.**
7. Disconnect parking brake cable from parking brake shoe lever and remove brake shoes. Remove cable from back plate.
8. Remove brake back plate from rear axle.
9. Support center of axle with a jack.
10. Remove lateral rod body side bolt, **Fig. 2.**
11. Remove shock absorber lower mounting bolt.

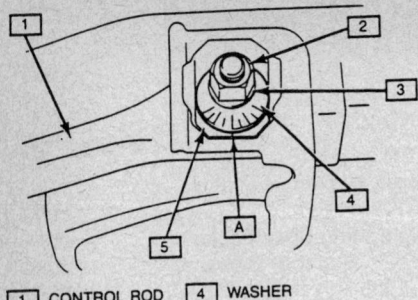

1	CONTROL ROD	4	WASHER
2	INSIDE NUT	5	CAR BODY
3	LOCK WASHER		

Fig. 6   Control rod inner bolt. 1989–91

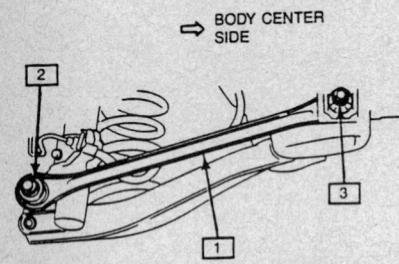

1	CONTROL ROD
2	OUTSIDE NUT
3	INSIDE NUT

Fig. 9   Control arm installation. 1989–91

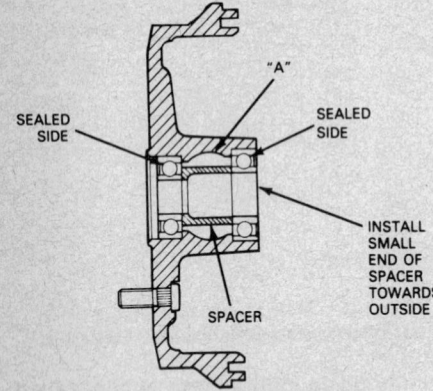

Fig. 11   Wheel bearing installation. 1988

then remove wheel and tire assembly.

2. Place alignment marks on control rod and control rod washer (A), Fig. 6, for setting toe during installation.
3. Remove control rod to body attaching bolt, then separate control rod from bracket.
4. From wheel side of control rod, remove nut from rear suspension knuckle stud, then disconnect control rod.
5. Loosen, but do not remove suspension arm rear attaching nut.
6. Loosen rear suspension knuckle lower mounting nut. Position a jack under suspension arm, then remove knuckle lower mounting nut.
7. Raise lower arm slightly to allow re-

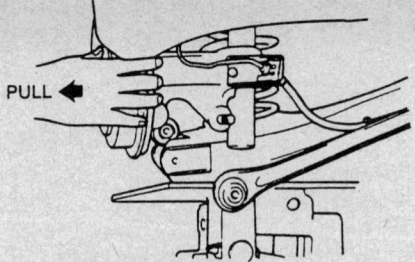

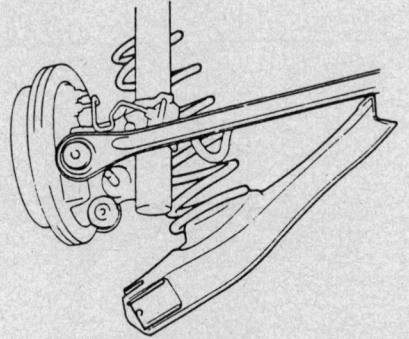

Fig. 7   Removing coil spring. 1989–91

moval of rear suspension knuckle lower mounting bolt.

8. Disengage rear suspension knuckle from suspension arm, then carefully lower suspension arm and remove coil spring, Fig. 7.
9. Remove remaining suspension arm attaching bolts and nuts and remove suspension arm, if necessary.
10. Reverse procedure to install. When installing spring, position spring end to stepped portion of suspension arm, Fig. 8. When installing control rod to body bracket, align marks made on washer and control rod during removal. **Do not torque control rod or suspension arm attaching nuts and bolts until after vehicle has been lowered.**

CONTROL ROD
REPLACE
1989–91

1. Raise and support rear of vehicle, then remove wheel and tire assembly.
2. Remove E-ring, then detach brake hose from control rod.
3. Place alignment marks on control rod and control rod washer at body bracket for setting toe during installation, Fig. 6.
4. Remove control rod to rear suspension knuckle attaching nut, Fig. 9.
5. Remove control rod to body bracket bolt, then remove control rod.
6. Reverse procedure to install. Position control rod to vehicle as shown in Fig. 10. When installing control rod to body bracket, align marks made on washer and control rod during removal. **Do not torque control rod attaching nuts and bolts until after vehicle has been lowered.**

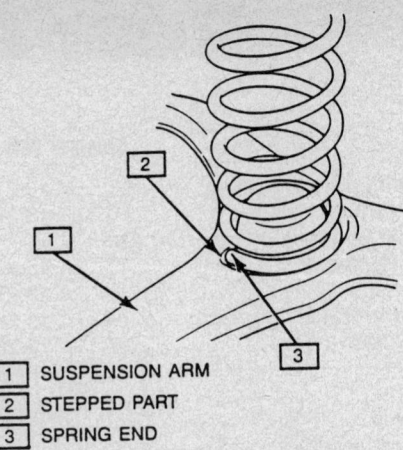

1	SUSPENSION ARM
2	STEPPED PART
3	SPRING END

Fig. 8   Positioning coil spring to suspension arm. 1989–91

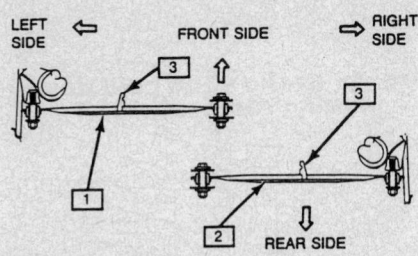

1	LEFT SIDE CONTROL ROD
2	RIGHT SIDE CONTROL ROD
3	BRAKE HOSE MOUNTING BRACKET

Fig. 10   Positioning control arm to vehicle. 1989–91

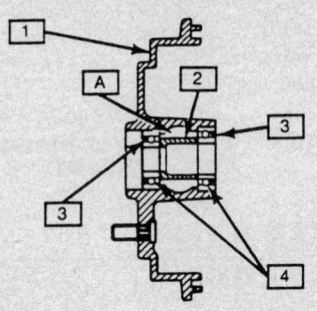

1	BRAKE DRUM	3	SEALED SIDE
2	SPACER	4	WHEEL BEARING

Fig. 12   Wheel bearing installation. 1989–91

REAR SUSPENSION KNUCKLE
REPLACE
1989–91

1. Raise and support rear of vehicle, then remove wheel and tire assembly.
2. Remove brake drum, then disconnect brake hose from rear suspension knuckle bracket.
3. Disconnect brake line from wheel cylinder. Cap brake line and wheel cylinder fitting bore.

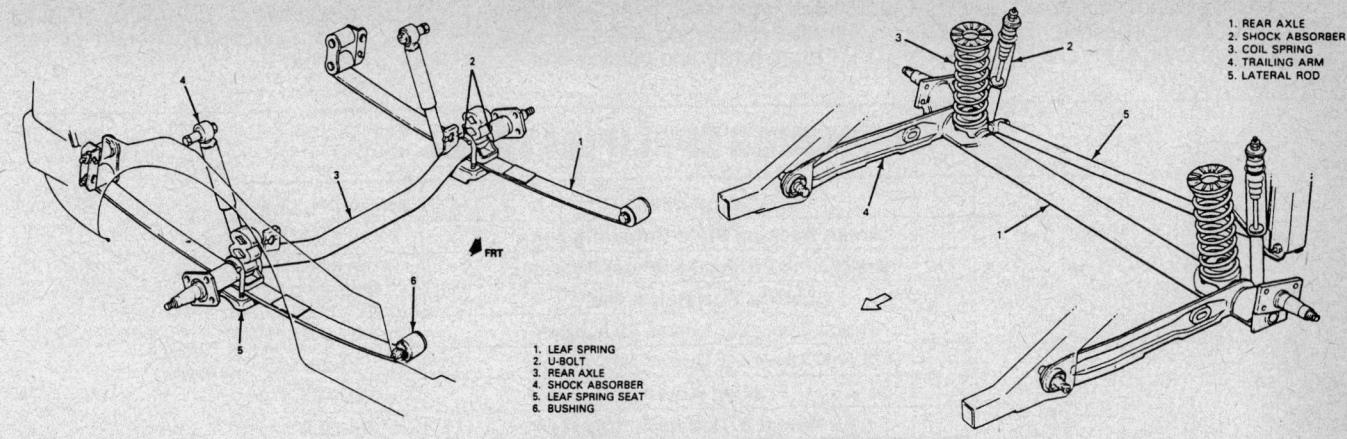

1. LEAF SPRING
2. U-BOLT
3. REAR AXLE
4. SHOCK ABSORBER
5. LEAF SPRING SEAT
6. BUSHING

1. REAR AXLE
2. SHOCK ABSORBER
3. COIL SPRING
4. TRAILING ARM
5. LATERAL ROD

Rear axle & suspension. 1988

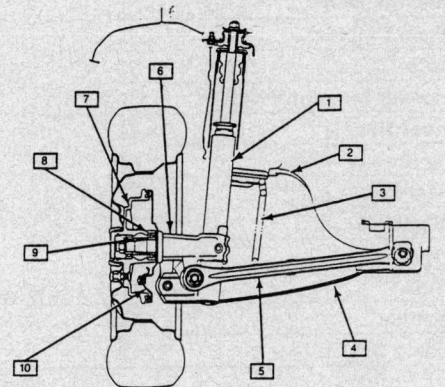

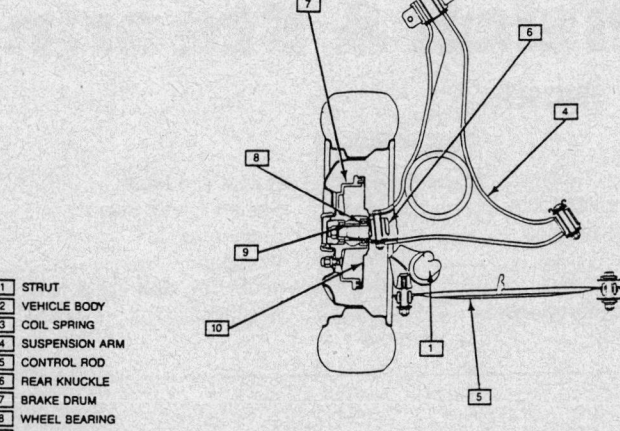

1	STRUT
2	VEHICLE BODY
3	COIL SPRING
4	SUSPENSION ARM
5	CONTROL ROD
6	REAR KNUCKLE
7	BRAKE DRUM
8	WHEEL BEARING
9	BEARING SPACER
10	BRAKE BACK PLATE

Rear suspension. 1989–91

ing surface of brake backing plate and rear suspension knuckle. When installing brake drum, **torque** wheel bearing nut to specification listed at the end of this section, then stake nut in place using a chisel. After completing installation, adjust and bleed brake system, then check for proper brake operation before moving vehicle.

WHEEL BEARING
REPLACE

1988

1. Raise and support vehicle.
2. Remove brake drum.
3. Using drift, drive bearings out of brake drum.
4. Using bearing installer J-34482 or equivalent, install bearings with stamped side outward. Refer to **Fig. 11** for spacer positioning.
5. Install brake drum.
6. Lower vehicle.

1989–91
Removal

1. Raise and support rear of vehicle, then remove wheel and tire assembly.
2. Remove wheel bearing dust cap from brake drum.
3. Using a chisel, unstake wheel bearing nut, then remove wheel bearing nut and washer.
4. Loosen parking brake cable adjusting nuts, then remove plug from backing plate and back off drum brake adjustment.
5. Using a suitable puller, remove brake. drum.
6. Using a brass drift, remove wheel bearings from brake drum.
7. Reverse procedure to install, noting the following:
   a. Fill Hub cavity (A), **Fig. 12**, with lithium wheel bearing grease.
   b. Install wheel bearings and spacer using bearing and hub installer tools Nos. J-7079-2 and J-34842 or equivalent. **Wheel bearing should be installed with sealed side facing outward, Fig. 12.**

4. Remove brake backing plate attaching bolts, then remove brake backing plate.
5. Position a jack under suspension arm.
6. Place alignment marks on control rod and control rod washer at body bracket for setting toe during installation.
7. Remove control rod to body bracket attaching nut and washer.
8. Remove control rod to rear suspension knuckle stud nut, then remove control rod.
9. Remove strut to rear suspension knuckle attaching bolt.

10. Remove strut to suspension arm attaching bolt, then separate rear suspension knuckle from suspension arm and strut. **If strut is difficult to remove, open slit on knuckle just enough to allow strut removal.**
11. Reverse procedure to install. When installing control rod to body bracket, align marks made on washer and control rod during removal. **Do not torque control rod or suspension arm attaching nuts and bolts until after vehicle has been lowered.** Prior to installation, apply sealer to mat-

c. Install brake drum on spindle. Torque wheel bearing nut to specification listed at the end of this section, then stake nut in position.
d. After completing installation, adjust drum brake and parking brake.
e. Bleed and check brake system for proper operation prior to moving vehicle.

TIGHTENING SPECIFICATIONS

Year	Component	Torque/Ft. Lbs.
1988	Brake Backing Plate Retaining Nuts	13.5-20
	Brake Line Fitting To Wheel Cylinder	10.5-13
	Lateral Rod Bolt & Nut	32.5-50.5
	Shock Absorber Lower Attachment	32.5-50.5
	Shock Absorber Upper Attachment	13-20
	Trailing Arm Nut	50.5-65
	Wheel & Tire Assembly	29-50.5
	Wheel Bearing Retaining Nut	58-86.5 ①
1989-91	Brake Backing Plate Retaining Nuts	17
	Brake Line Fitting To Wheel Cylinder	12
	Control Rod Nuts	59
	Rear Suspension Knuckle Arm Lower Mounting Nut	37
	Suspension Arm Front Nut	44
	Suspension Arm Mounting Bracket Bolt	33
	Suspension Arm Rear Nut	37
	Strut Lower Mounting Bolt	44
	Strut Support Nut	24
	Strut Upper Nut	37
	Wheel & Tire Assembly	44
	Wheel Bearing Retaining Nut	74 ①

①—After tightening nut, stake nut in position.

Front Suspension & Steering

INDEX

STRUT
REPLACE

1. Raise and support vehicle allowing front suspension to hang free.
2. Remove front wheel and tire assembly.
3. Remove E-clip from brake hose and disengage hose from strut bracket, **Figs. 1 and 2.**
4. Support lower control arm and knuckle assembly, then remove strut to knuckle bolts.
5. Remove upper strut mount nuts, then remove strut from vehicle.
6. Reverse procedure to install.

STRUT SERVICE

1. Mount strut in a spring compressor.
2. **On 1988 models,** compress spring to about ½ its height. Do not bottom spring.
3. **On 1989-91 models,** compress spring approximately ½ inch.
4. **On all models,** remove nut from strut shaft and remove components, **Figs. 3 and 4.**
5. Reverse procedure to assemble. Compress spring so strut shaft protrudes through cap by about 1 inch. Torque nut to specification listed at the end of this section.

STABILIZER BAR
REPLACE

1988

1. Raise and support vehicle.
2. Remove both front wheel and tire assemblies.
3. Remove stabilizer bar bracket bolts, **Fig. 5.**
4. Remove nuts from stabilizer bar ends and disconnect stabilizer bar ends from suspension control arms.
5. Reverse procedure to install. Refer to **Fig. 6** for proper orientation of stabilizer bar.

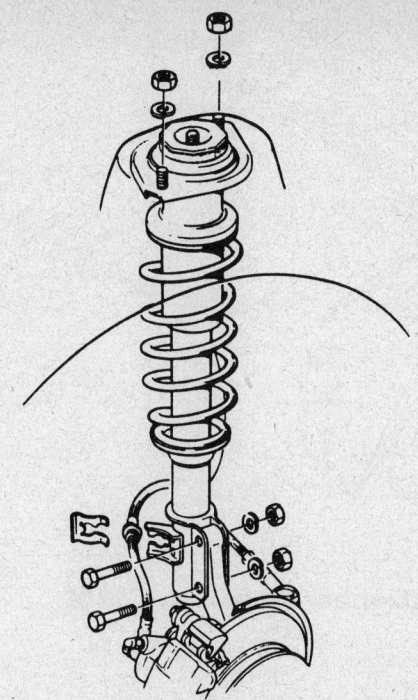

Fig. 1   Strut attaching nut bolt locations. 1988

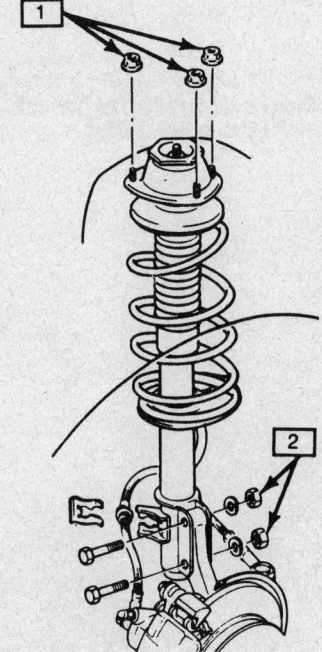

1 STRUT SUPPORT NUTS
2 STRUT BRACKET BOLTS

Fig. 2   Strut attaching nut bolt locations. 1989–91

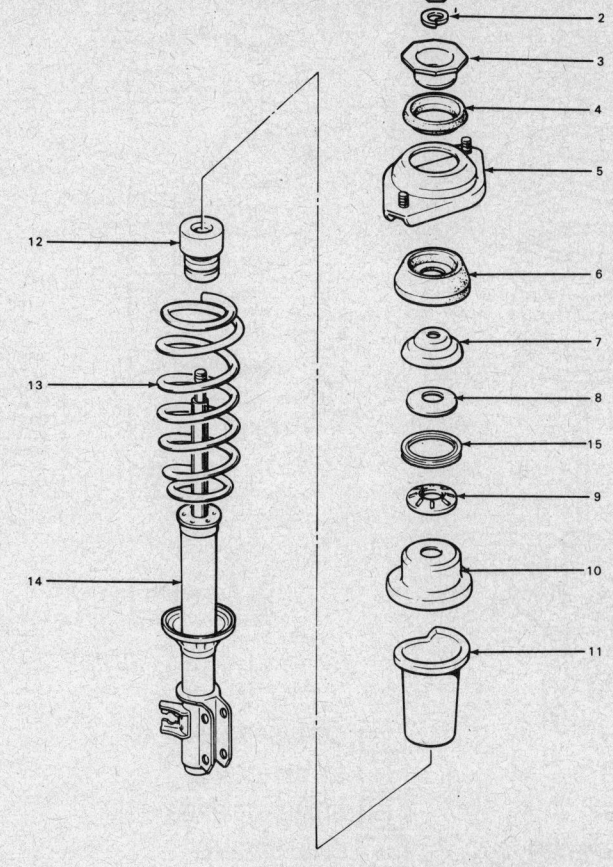

1. STRUT NUT	6. STRUT MOUNT	11. STRUT SPRING SEAT
2. STRUT LOCK WASHER	7. STRUT MOUNT SEAT	12. BUMP STOPPER
3. STRUT INNER SUPPORT	8. STRUT BEARING SEAT	13. COIL SPRING
4. STRUT REBOUND STOPPER	9. STRUT BEARING	14. STRUT ASSEMBLY
5. STRUT SUPPORT	10. SPRING UPPER SEAT	15. STRUT BEARING DUST SEAL

Fig. 3   Strut assembly exploded view. 1988

WHEEL HUB, BEARING & KNUCKLE
REPLACE

When checking wheel bearings, raise and support front of vehicle, then rotate wheel and tire assembly to check bearing for smoothness of rotation and noise. Also check wheel bearing endplay with a dial indicator. Wheel bearing endplay should not exceed .016 inch.

1. Raise and support vehicle, then remove front wheel and tire assembly.
2. **On 1988 models,** remove cotter pin and driveshaft castle nut.
3. **On 1989-91 models,** unstake, then remove hub retaining nut.
4. **On all models,** remove caliper bolts, then caliper with brake line attached. Suspend caliper from chassis with wire.
5. Refer to **Fig. 7,** and measure dimension A for assembly reference. Pull hub out of knuckle.
6. Disconnect tie rod end from knuckle with tie rod end remover tool No. J-21687-02 or equivalent.
7. Remove strut to knuckle bolts and then ball joint stud pinch bolt, **Fig. 8.**
8. Remove knuckle.
9. Using a drift, remove outer, then inner bearing from knuckle.
10. Apply suitable grease to balls and oil seal lips of wheel bearings. Fill area A, **Fig. 9,** to approximately 40 percent of capacity with suitable grease.
11. Install wheel bearings using bearing installer tool No. J-34856 or equivalent. **Install wheel bearings with sealed side facing outward. Also ensure spacer is spacer is snug and centered between inner and outer bearings.**
12. Install wheel bearing seal (5), **Fig. 9,** using seal installer tool No. J-34881 or equivalent.
13. Install spacer on hub with bevel side first, **Fig. 10.**
14. Check that wheel bearing spacer bore is aligned with bearing bores. If not, move spacer until aligned.
15. Using plastic hammer, tap hub lightly into knuckle, taking care that alignment is maintained.
16. Using wheel hub installer tool No. J-34856 and handle No. J-7079-2 or equivalent, drive hub until dimension

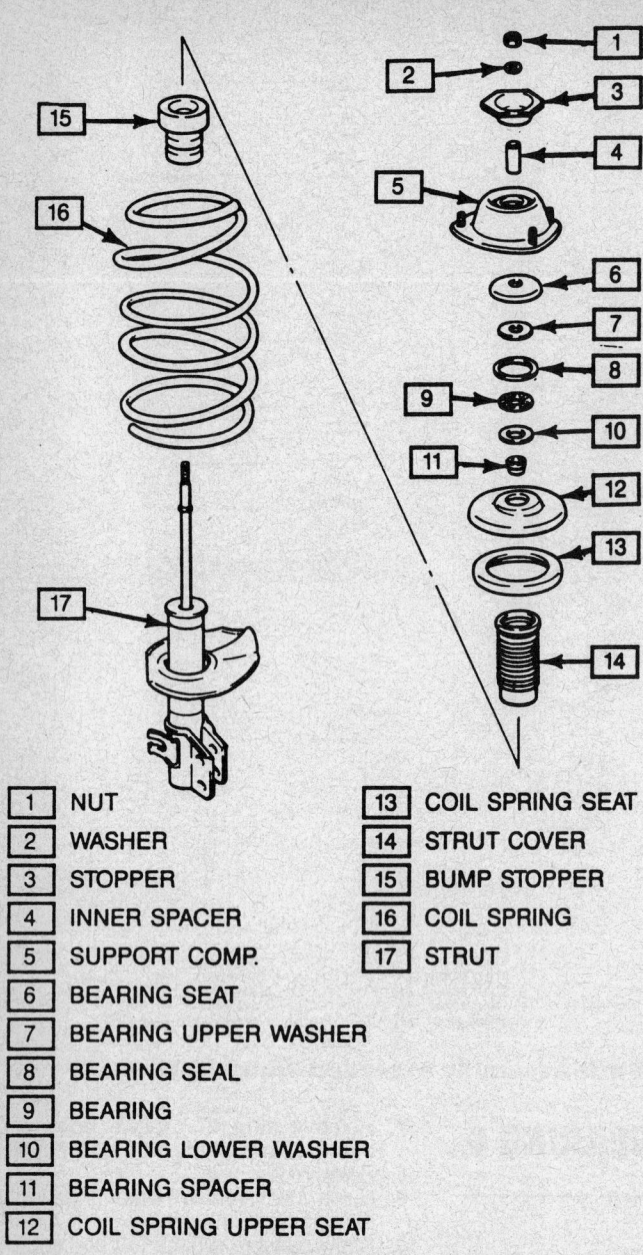

1	NUT	13	COIL SPRING SEAT
2	WASHER	14	STRUT COVER
3	STOPPER	15	BUMP STOPPER
4	INNER SPACER	16	COIL SPRING
5	SUPPORT COMP.	17	STRUT
6	BEARING SEAT		
7	BEARING UPPER WASHER		
8	BEARING SEAL		
9	BEARING		
10	BEARING LOWER WASHER		
11	BEARING SPACER		
12	COIL SPRING UPPER SEAT		

Fig. 4   Strut assembly exploded view. 1989–91

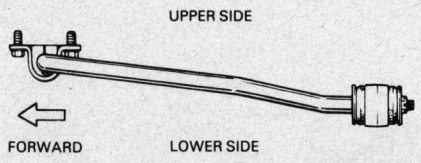

1. SPLIT PIN
2. CASTLE NUT
3. STABILIZER BAR WASHER
4. STABILIZER BAR BUSH
5. SUSPENSION CONTROL ARM
6. STABILIZER BAR
7. MOUNT BUSH
8. MOUNT BUSH BRACKET
9. MOUNT BRACKET BOLT

Fig. 5   Stabilizer bar & bushings. 1988

UPPER SIDE

FORWARD   LOWER SIDE

Fig. 6   Correct installation of stabilizer bar. 1988

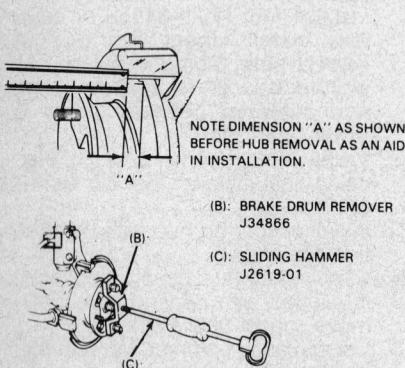

NOTE DIMENSION "A" AS SHOWN BEFORE HUB REMOVAL AS AN AID IN INSTALLATION.

"A"

(B): BRAKE DRUM REMOVER J34866

(C): SLIDING HAMMER J2619-01

Fig. 7   Checking dimension "A" to assure proper installation of hub

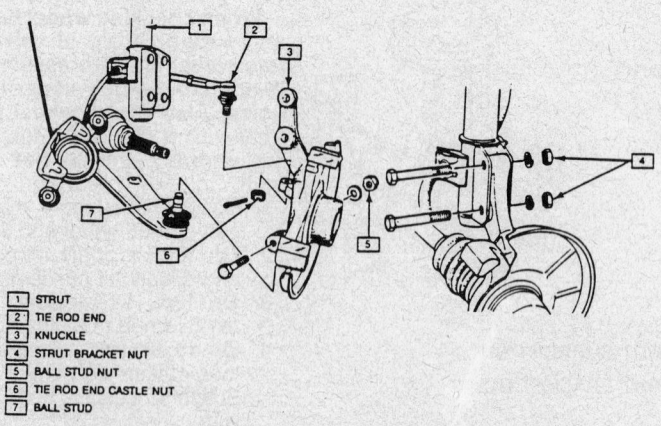

1	STRUT
2	TIE ROD END
3	KNUCKLE
4	STRUT BRACKET NUT
5	BALL STUD NUT
6	TIE ROD END CASTLE NUT
7	BALL STUD

Fig. 8   Removing steering knuckle

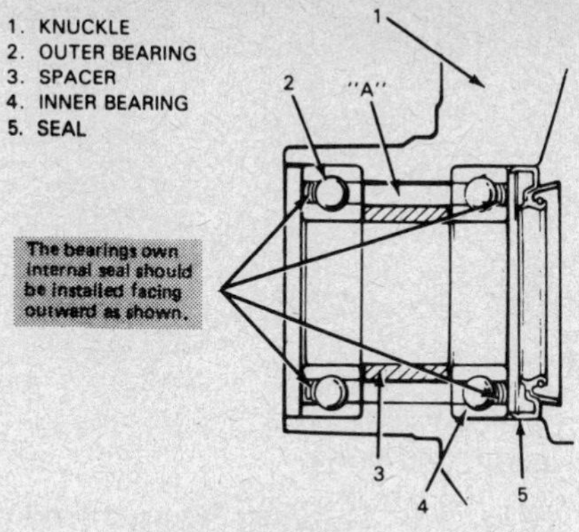

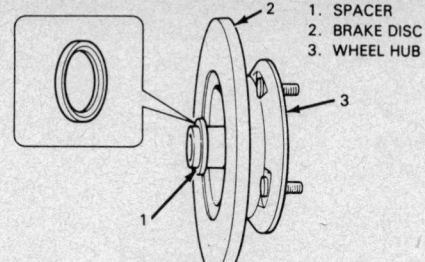

1. KNUCKLE
2. OUTER BEARING
3. SPACER
4. INNER BEARING
5. SEAL

The bearings own internal seal should be installed facing outward as shown.

1. SPACER
2. BRAKE DISC
3. WHEEL HUB

Fig. 10 Installing spacer on wheel hub

Fig. 9 Steering knuckle hub bearings & seal

A, noted in step 4, is obtained.
17. Install brake caliper.
18. Torque caliper bolts to specification listed at the end of this section.
19. Torque drive shaft castle nut to specification listed at the end of this section.
20. **On 1988 models,** install cotter pin.
21. **On 1989-91 models,** stake nut in position.
22. Install wheel and tire assembly, then lower vehicle.

LOWER CONTROL ARM & BUSHING
REPLACE

1988

1. Raise and support vehicle.
2. Remove stabilizer bar cotter pin, castle nut, washer and bushing, **Fig. 11.**
3. Remove stabilizer bar bracket bolts on same side as control arm to be removed.
4. Remove ball joint stud bolt (2), **Fig. 11.**
5. Remove control arm bolt (5), **Fig. 11,** and control arm.
6. If control arm bushing is to be replaced, proceed as follows:
   a. Remove lower control arm as described above.
   b. Position control arm and bushing over wheel hub installer tool No. J-34865 or equivalent, then press bushing from control arm, **Fig. 12.**
   c. Apply soapy water to bushing and control arm bore, then position control arm and bushing to tool.
   d. Press bushing into control arm, until an equal amount of bushing is exposed from each side of control arm, **Fig. 12.**
7. Reverse procedure to install.

1989-91

1. Raise and support vehicle, then remove wheel and tire assembly.
2. Remove ball joint stud to steering knuckle pinch bolt, **Fig. 13.**
3. Remove control arm bracket nut, then remove bracket bolts.
4. Remove control arm and bracket.
5. If control arm bushing are to be replaced, proceed as follows:
   a. Remove lower control arm as described under "Lower Control Arm, Replace."
   b. Press rear bushing from control arm, **Fig. 13.**
   c. Cut flange off front bushing, then press front bushing from control arm, **Fig. 14.**
   d. Apply soap and water to outer surface of front bushing, then press front bushing into control arm until it is centered.
   e. Position rear bushing to control arm, then drive bushing into control arm, **Figs. 15 and 16.**
6. Reverse procedure to install.

1. STABILIZER BAR
2. BALL STUD BOLT
3. KNUCKLE
4. BALL STUD
5. STABILIZER BAR MOUNT BRACKET BOLT
6. CONTROL ARM BOLT
7. SUSPENSION CONTROL ARM
8. STABILIZER BAR BUSHING
9. WASHER
10. CASTLE NUT
11. SPLIT PIN

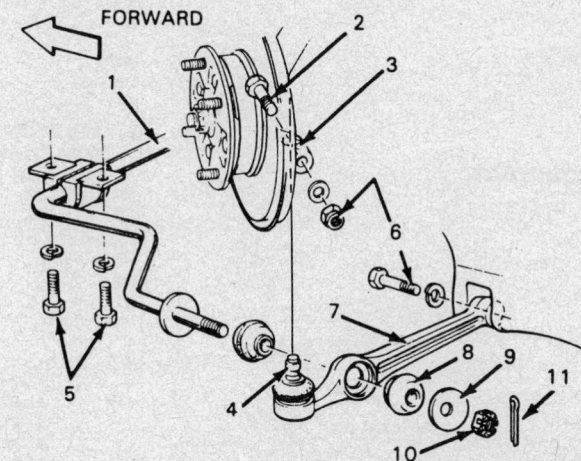

FORWARD

Fig. 11 Lower control arm replacement. 1988

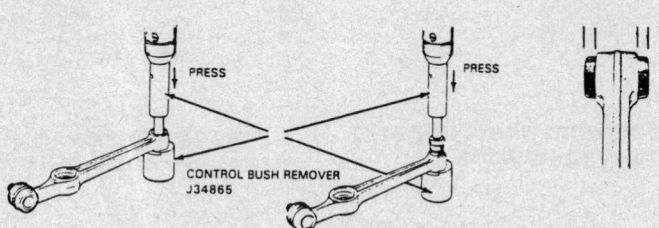

PRESS   PRESS

CONTROL BUSH REMOVER J34865

Fig. 12 Lower control arm bushing replacement. 1988

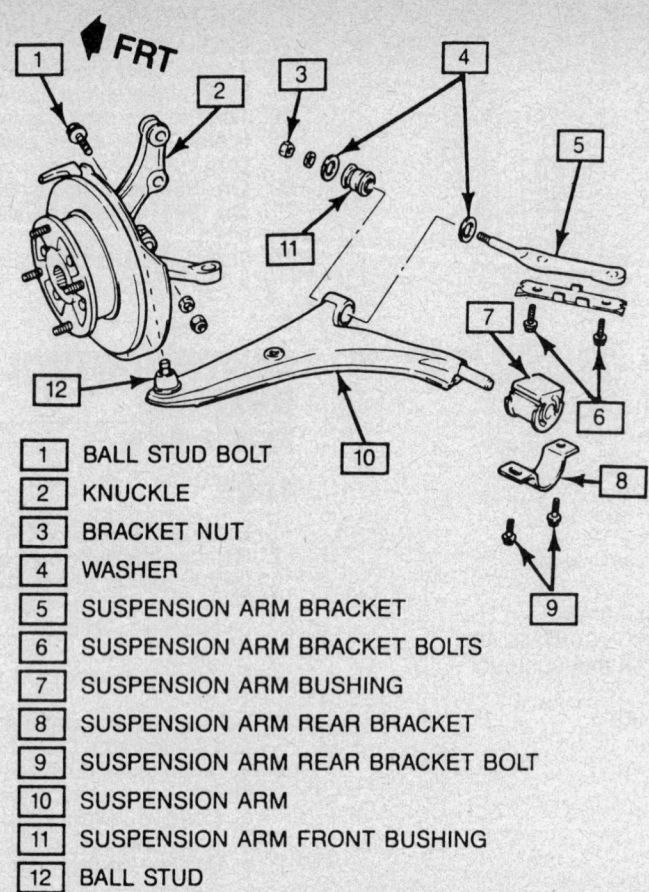

1 BALL STUD BOLT
2 KNUCKLE
3 BRACKET NUT
4 WASHER
5 SUSPENSION ARM BRACKET
6 SUSPENSION ARM BRACKET BOLTS
7 SUSPENSION ARM BUSHING
8 SUSPENSION ARM REAR BRACKET
9 SUSPENSION ARM REAR BRACKET BOLT
10 SUSPENSION ARM
11 SUSPENSION ARM FRONT BUSHING
12 BALL STUD

Fig. 13 Lower control arm replacement. 1989–91

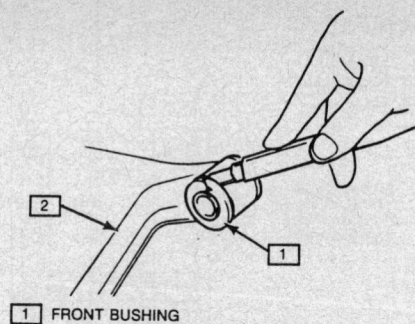

1 FRONT BUSHING
2 SUSPENSION ARM

Fig. 14 Cutting flange from control arm front bushing. 1989–91

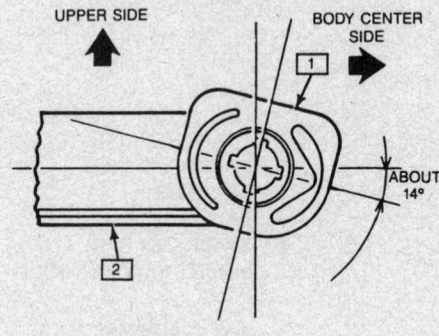

1 REAR BUSHING
2 SUSPENSION ARM

Fig. 15 Rear bushing to control arm installation. 1989–91

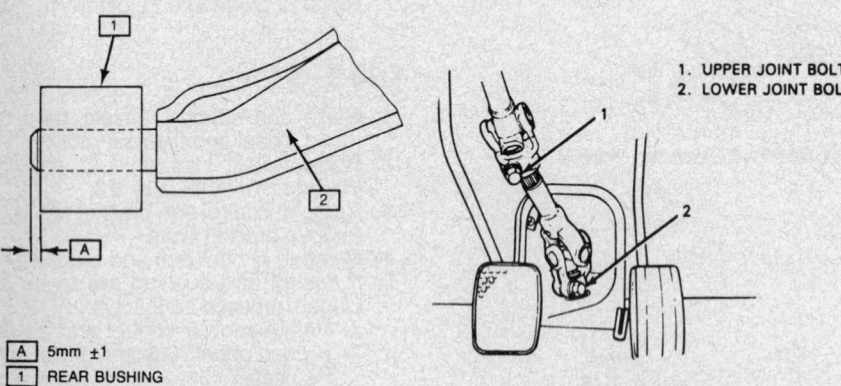

A 5mm ±1
1 REAR BUSHING
2 SUSPENSION ARM

Fig. 16 Rear bushing positioning. 1989–91

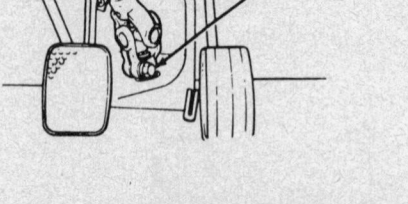

1. UPPER JOINT BOLT
2. LOWER JOINT BOLT

Fig. 17 Steering shaft upper & lower joint bolts

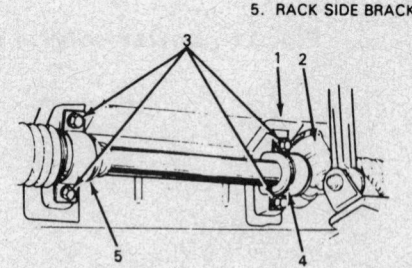

1. CAR BODY
2. STEERING GEAR CASE
3. CASE MOUNT BOLT
4. PINION SIDE BRACKET
5. RACK SIDE BRACKET

Fig. 18 Steering gear attaching bolts & brackets

MANUAL STEERING GEAR
REPLACE

1. Slide driver's seat rearward.
2. Pull off front part of floor mat on driver's side, then remove steering shaft joint cover.
3. Loosen steering shaft upper joint bolt without removing, **Fig. 17.**
4. Remove steering shaft lower joint bolt and disconnect lower joint from pinion.
5. Raise and support vehicle.
6. Remove front wheel and tire assemblies.
7. Remove cotter pins and castle nuts from tie rod ends.
8. Using tie rod end remover J-21687-02 or equivalent, disconnect tie rods from knuckles.
9. Remove steering gear housing mounting bolts, brackets and steering gear, **Fig. 18.**
10. Reverse procedure to install.

TIGHTENING SPECIFICATIONS

Year	Component	Torque/Ft. Lbs.
1988	Ball Joint Stud Nut	36.5-50.5
	Control Arm Bolt	36.5-50.5
	Disc Brake Caliper Attaching Bolts	17.5-26
	Hub Bearing Nut	108.5-195 ①
	Steering Gear Mounting Bracket Bolts	14.5-21.5
	Steering Shaft Coupling Bolts	14.5-21.5
	Strut Bracket Nut	50.5-65
	Strut Nut	29-43
	Strut Support Nut	13.5-20
	Stabilizer Bar Attaching Bolt	22-39.5
	Stabilizer Bar Castle Nut	29-65
	Tie Rod End Castle Nut	22-39.5
	Tie Rod End Locknut	25.5-39.5
	Wheel & Tire Assembly	29-50.5
1989-91	Ball Joint Stud Nut	44
	Control Arm Bracket Bolt	69
	Control Arm Bracket Nut	92
	Control Arm Rear Bracket Bolt	32
	Disc Brake Caliper Attaching Bolts	17.5-26
	Hub Bearing Nut	129 ②
	Steering Gear Mounting Bracket Bolts	18
	Steering Shaft Coupling Bolts	18
	Strut Bracket Nut	59
	Strut Nut	37
	Strut Support Nut	20
	Tie Rod End Castle Nut	32
	Tie Rod End Locknut	33
	Wheel & Tire Assembly	44

①—After tightening, install cotter pin.
②—After tightening, stake nut in position.

Wheel Alignment

INDEX

DESCRIPTION

Wheel alignment, is the angular relationship between the wheels, suspension attaching parts and ground. The angle of the knuckle away from the vertical, pointing in or out of wheels, tilt of the wheels from vertical (when viewed from front of vehicle) and tilt of suspension members from vertical (when viewed from side of vehicle), all of these are involved in proper alignment, Fig. 1.

CASTER

Caster is tilting of the front steering axis

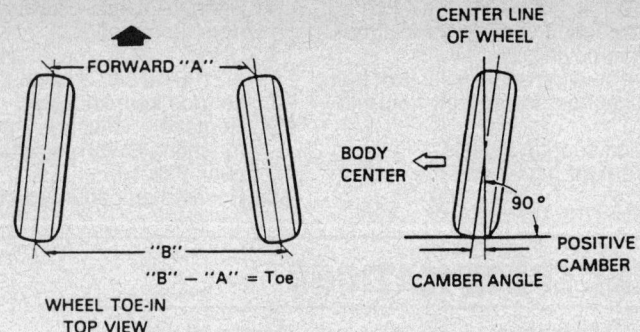

Fig. 1 Suspension geometry

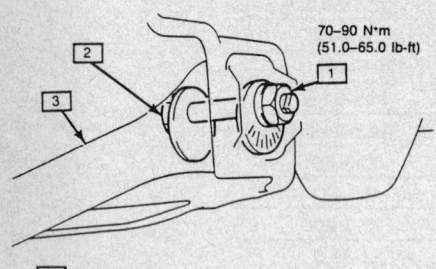

[1] INSIDE NUT
[2] INSIDE BOLT (CAM BOLT)
[3] CONTROL ROD

Fig. 3 Rear wheel toe adjustment. 1989–91

either forward or backward from the vertical (when viewed from side of vehicle). A backward tilt is positive (+) and a forward tilt is negative (−). On short and long arm type suspensions you cannot see a caster angle without using a special instrument, but if you look straight down from the top of the upper control arm to the ground you would find that ball joints do not line up (fore and aft) when a caster angle other than 0° is present.

CAMBER

Camber is the tilting of front and rear wheels from the vertical when viewed from front of vehicle. When wheels tilt outward at top, camber is positive (+). When wheels tilt inward, camber is negative (MI). Amount of tilt is measured in degrees from the vertical and this is camber angle.

TOE

Toe is the turning in or out of wheels. The purpose of toe is to ensure parallel rolling of wheels. Excessive toe-in or toe-out may increase tire wear. Toe also serves to offset small deflections of the suspension which occurs when vehicle is moving.

PRELIMINARY CHECK

Steering and vibration problems are not always the result of alignment. An additional problem to be checked is tire lead due to worn or improperly manufactured tires. "Lead" is the deviation of the vehicle from a straight path on a level road without

hand pressure on the steering wheel.

To insure correct alignment readings and alignment specifications, the following checks and inspections should be made.
1. Check tire for proper inflation and thread wear.
2. Check for loose ball joints and tie rod ends. If excessive looseness is noted, replace defective parts before adjusting toe.
3. Check for wheel and tire assembly run-out.
4. Check trim heights. If not within specifications, correct before adjusting toe.
5. Check for loose control arms.
6. Check for loose or missing stabilizer bar components.
7. Consideration must be given to excess loads, such as tool boxes, kegs, etc. If excess load is normally carried in vehicle, it should remain during alignment checks.

FRONT WHEEL ALIGNMENT
CAMBER & CASTER ADJUSTMENT

1. Position vehicle on an alignment fixture following manufacturer's instructions and check caster and camber angles. Bumper should be bounced three times before inspection, to prevent incorrect reading.
2. Camber and caster cannot be adjusted. Should either be found out of specification, locate the cause first.
3. If improper alignment is caused by damaged, worn or loose suspension parts, they should be replaced. If vehicle body or chassis is damaged, it should be repaired.

TOE ADJUSTMENT

1. Loosen right and left tie rod end locknuts, **Fig. 2**.
2. Apply grease between tie rods and rack boots.
3. Turn right and left tie rods by the same amount to align toe to specification. **Right and left tie rods should become equal in length.**
4. After adjustment, tighten locknuts and ensure rack boots are not twisted.

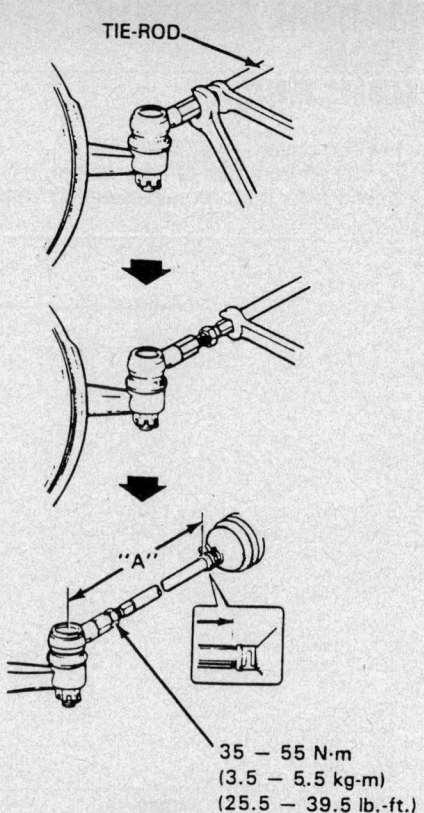

35 — 55 N·m
(3.5 — 5.5 kg-m)
(25.5 — 39.5 lb.-ft.)

Fig. 2 Front wheel toe adjustment

STEERING ANGLE

When a tie rod or tie rod end is replaced, check toe and steering angle with turning radius gages. If steering angle is not correct, check right and left tie rods for equal length.

REAR WHEEL ALIGNMENT
1989–91
Camber

Camber cannot be adjusted. Should camber be found out of specification, locate the cause. If improper alignment is caused by damaged, worn or loose suspension parts, they should be replaced. If vehicle body or chassis is damaged, it should be repaired.

Toe

The rear wheel toe is adjusted by the inner control arm cam bolt, **Fig. 3**. If toe is found to out of specification, loosen left and right inner control arm cam bolt nuts, then rotate cam bolts by equal amounts to correct toe setting. After completing adjustment, torque cam bolt nuts to 51 to 65 ft. lbs.

CHEVROLET/GEO SPECTRUM (R Car)

INDEX OF SERVICE OPERATIONS

NOTE: Refer To The Rear Of This Manual For Vehicle Manufacturer's Special Tool Suppliers.

Continued

INDEX OF SERVICE OPERATIONS—Continued

Specifications
GENERAL ENGINE SPECIFICATIONS

Year	Engine Liter/CID ①	Engine VIN Code ②	Fuel System	Bore & Stroke Inches	Comp. Ratio	Net H.P. @ RPM ③	Maximum Torque Ft. Lbs. @ RPM	Normal, Oil Psi.
1988	4-1.5L/90 Turbo	9	Fuel Inj.	3.03 x 3.11	8.1	110 @ 5400	120 @ 3400	64
1988–89	4-1.5L/90	7	2 Barrel	3.03 x 3.11	9.6	70 @ 5400	87 @ 3400	64

①—CID: Cubic inch displacement.
②—The 8th digit of the VIN denotes engine code.

③—Ratings are net as installed in vehicle.

TUNE UP SPECIFICATIONS

Year & Engine/VIN Code	Spark Plug Gap	Firing Order	Ignition Timing BTDC ① Man. Trans.	Ignition Timing BTDC ① Auto. Trans.	Mark Fig.	Curb Idle Speed Man. Trans.	Curb Idle Speed Auto. Trans. ②	Fast Idle Speed Man. Trans.	Fast Idle Speed Auto. Trans.	Fuel Pump Pressure Psi.
1988										
4-1.5L/90-9 Turbo	.043	1-3-4-2	15	—	A	950	—	—	—	35.6 ⑤
1988–89										
4-1.5L/90-K, 7 Except Turbo	.040	1-3-4-2	15③	10③	A	750	1000N	850④	980④	3.84–4.7

①—BTDC: Before Top Dead Center.
②—N: Neutral.
③—With distributor vacuum advance hose disconnected & plugged.
④—On 1st step of fast idle cam.

⑤—Place shop towels around fuel hose connection between pressure regulator & fuel distributor pipe, then carefully disconnect hose. Connect a suitable fuel pressure gauge between pressure regulator & fuel distributor pipe. Check fuel pressure with engine idling & vacuum hose at pressure regulator disconnected & plugged.

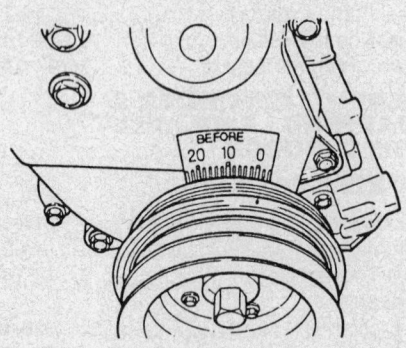

Fig. A

ALTERNATOR & REGULATOR SPECIFICATIONS

Year	Alternator				Model	Regulated Voltage At 5000 RPM②
	Model	Rated Hot Output Amps.	Cold Output At 5000 RPM ①			
1988–89	Less A/C	50	48		Integral	14.2–14.8
	With A/C	60	62		Integral	14.2–14.8

①—At 13.5 volts.
②—Cold at 10 amps.

STARTING MOTOR APPLICATIONS

Refer to "Starter Motors" for starter specifications.

Year	Engine/VIN Code	Part No.
1988–89	4-1.5L/90-K,7 ①	94449782
	4-1.5L/90-K,7 ②	94141664
	4-1.5L/90-9 Turbo	94439315

①—Man. trans.
②—Auto. trans.

FRONT WHEEL ALIGNMENT SPECIFICATIONS

Year	Model	Caster Angle Degrees		Camber Angle Degrees				Toe	Steering Angle Degrees @ Full Lock	
		Limits	Desired	Limits		Desired			Outer Wheel	Inner Wheel
				Left	Right	Left	Right			
1988–89	All	+1¾ to +2¾	+2¼	−.69 to +1.31	−.69 to +1.31	+.31	+.31	①	—	—

①—Toe, −.34 to +.34°.

REAR WHEEL ALIGNMENT SPECIFICATIONS

Year	Model	Camber, Degrees		Toe
		Limits	Desired	
1988–89	All	−¾ to +¾	0	①

①—Toe, −.43 to +.43 degrees.

COOLING SYSTEM & CAPACITY DATA

Year	Model	Cooling Capacity Qts.		Radiator Cap Relief Pressure, Lbs.	Thermo Opening Temp. °F	Fuel Tank Gals.	Engine Oil Refill, Qts.①	Transmission Oil	
		Less A/C	With A/C					5 Speed, Pints	Auto. Trans., Qts. ①
1988	All	6.7	6.7	15	180	11	3②	5.6	6.7
1989	All	6.7	6.7	15	180	11	3②	4.02	6.7

①—Approximate; make final check with dipstick.
②—Add .4 qts. with filter change.

Electrical
INDEX

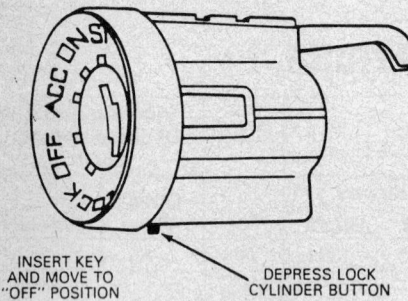

Fig. 1 Ignition lock replacement

LOCK CYLINDER REMOVAL

INSERT KEY AND MOVE TO "OFF" POSITION

DEPRESS LOCK CYLINDER BUTTON

FUSE PANEL LOCATION

The fuse panel is located on the instrument panel behind door to left of steering column.

FLASHER LOCATION

The flasher unit is located under lower left hand side of the instrument panel near the steering column.

STARTER
REPLACE

1. Disconnect battery ground cable.
2. Disconnect magnetic switch lead wire and battery cable from starter motor.
3. Remove starter motor attaching bolts and the starter.
4. Reverse procedure to install.

DISTRIBUTOR
REPLACE

1. Disconnect battery ground cable.
2. Mark and disconnect spark plug wires, electrical connectors and vacuum lines from distributor assembly.
3. Mark position of distributor assembly in block and rotor on distributor, then remove rotor.
4. Remove distributor hold-down bolt, then pull distributor assembly upward from engine.
5. Reverse procedure to install.

TURN SIGNAL/DIMMER SWITCH
REPLACE

1. Disconnect battery ground cable.
2. Remove horn shroud.
3. Remove steering wheel assembly.
4. Remove steering cowl attaching screws, then steering cowl.
5. Disconnect combination switch and ignition switch electrical connectors.
6. Remove combination switch attaching screws, then combination switch.
7. Reverse procedure to install.

IGNITION LOCK
REPLACE

1. Disconnect battery ground cable.
2. Remove steering wheel and cowl.
3. Remove combination switch.
4. Place ignition lock in Off position, then depress lock cylinder button and remove ignition lock, **Fig. 1.**
5. Reverse procedure to install.

IGNITION SWITCH
REPLACE

1. Disconnect battery ground cable.
2. Remove steering wheel and cowl.
3. Remove combination switch.
4. Disconnect electrical connector from ignition switch.
5. Remove ignition switch attaching screws and the switch.
6. Reverse procedure to install.

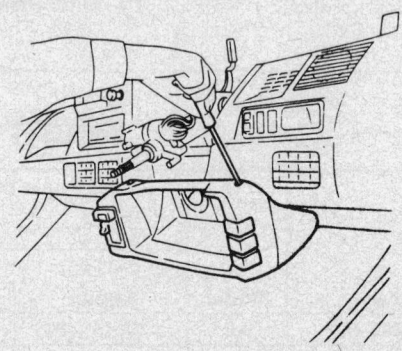

Fig. 2 Instrument cluster bezel removal

HORN SOUNDER & STEERING WHEEL
REPLACE

1. Disconnect battery ground cable.
2. Position a suitable screwdriver between steering wheel shroud and steering wheel, then pry shroud free.
3. Remove screws attaching horn shroud to steering wheel from rear side of wheel.
4. Lift horn shroud slightly and disconnect horn electrical connector, then remove shroud.
5. Remove steering wheel to steering shaft attaching nut and washer.
6. Using tool No. J-1859-03 or other suitable puller, carefully remove steering wheel from shaft.
7. Reverse procedure to install. **Torque** steering wheel to steering shaft attaching nut to 22 ft. lbs.

HEADLAMP SWITCH
REPLACE

1. Disconnect battery ground cable.

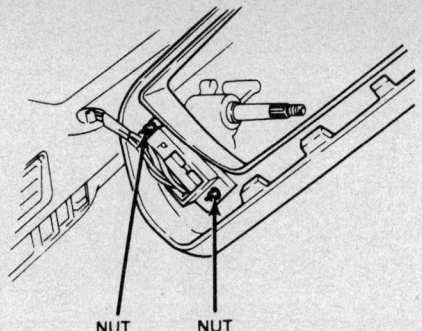

Fig. 3 Headlamp switch replacement

NUT   NUT

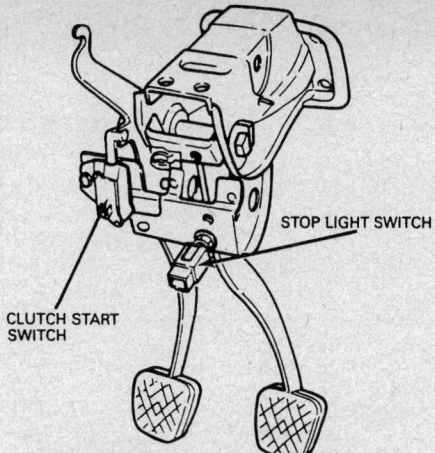

STOP LIGHT SWITCH

CLUTCH START SWITCH

Fig. 4 Stoplamp & clutch start switch locations

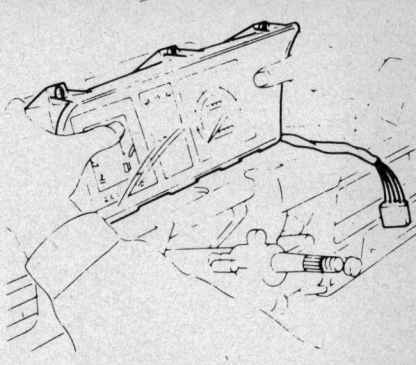

Fig. 5 Instrument cluster replacement

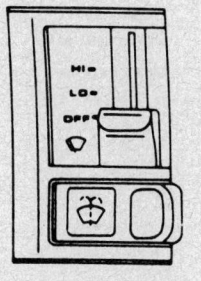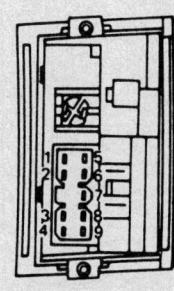

Fig. 6 Front wiper switch replacement

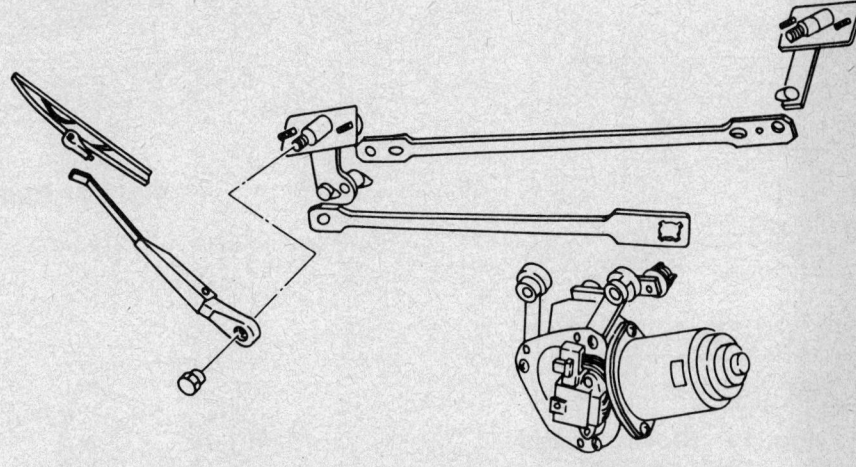

Fig. 8 Front wiper motor assembly

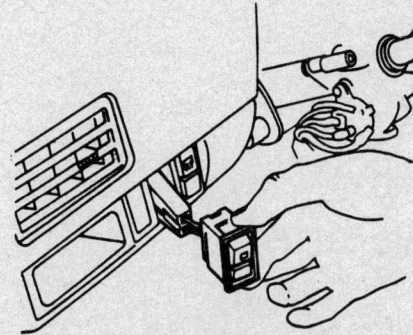

Fig. 7 Rear wiper switch replacement

2. Remove instrument cluster bezel attaching screws and the bezel, **Fig. 2.**
3. Disconnect electrical connectors from headlamp switch and windshield wiper switch.
4. Remove 2 nuts from rear of headlamp switch, then remove the switch from cluster bezel, **Fig. 3.**
5. Reverse procedure to install.

STOPLAMP SWITCH
REPLACE

1. Disconnect battery ground cable.
2. Disconnect electrical connector from stoplamp switch.

3. Loosen stoplamp switch locknut, then unthread switch from bracket, **Fig. 4.**
4. Reverse procedure to install, noting the following:
   a. Thread stoplamp switch into bracket until tip of switch is gently resting on pedal arm.
5. Carefully thread stoplamp switch in, until freeplay between brake pedal and push rod is just eliminated, then tighten locknut.

NEUTRAL SAFETY SWITCH
REPLACE

1. Disconnect battery ground cable.
2. Disconnect neutral safety switch electrical connector at left hand fender.
3. Raise and support front of vehicle.
4. Remove neutral safety switch from transaxle.
5. Reverse procedure to install. After completing installation, check and adjust transaxle fluid to proper level.

CLUTCH START SWITCH
REPLACE

1. Disconnect battery ground cable.
2. Disconnect electrical connector from clutch start switch.
3. Remove screw attaching clutch start switch to clutch pedal stop bracket, **Fig. 4.**
4. Disconnect clutch start switch from clutch pedal and remove from vehicle.
5. Reverse procedure to install.

INSTRUMENT CLUSTER
REPLACE

1. Disconnect battery ground cable.
2. Remove instrument cluster bezel attaching screws and the bezel, **Fig. 2.**
3. Disconnect electrical connectors from headlamp switch and wiper switch.
4. Remove instrument cluster attaching screws, then pull cluster outward and disconnect electrical connectors and speedometer cable, **Fig. 5.**
5. Remove instrument cluster.
6. Reverse procedure to install.

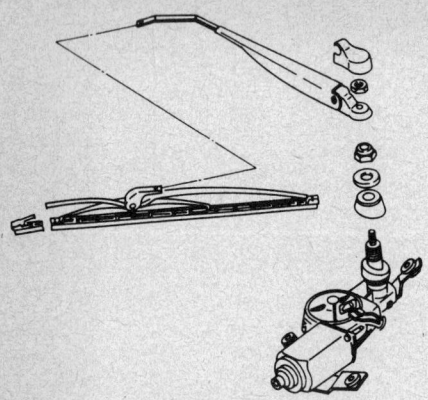

Fig. 9 Rear wiper motor assembly

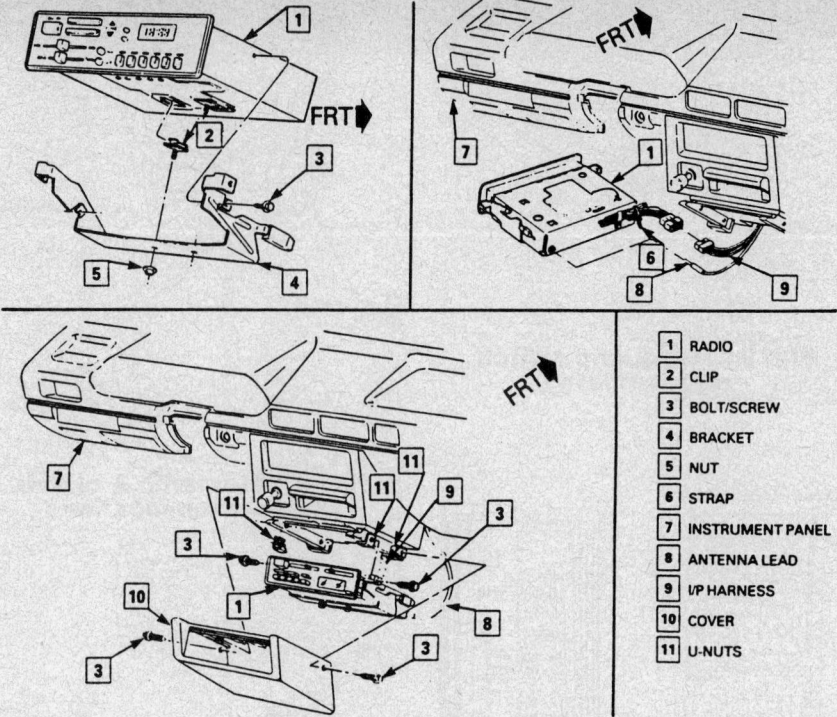

1	RADIO
2	CLIP
3	BOLT/SCREW
4	BRACKET
5	NUT
6	STRAP
7	INSTRUMENT PANEL
8	ANTENNA LEAD
9	I/P HARNESS
10	COVER
11	U-NUTS

Fig. 10 Radio replacement

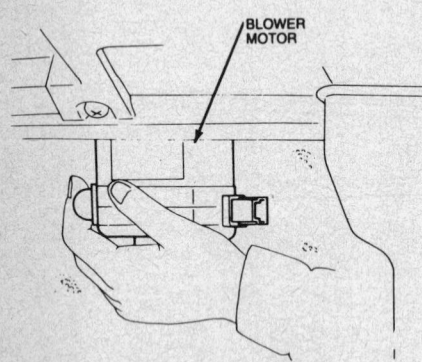

Fig. 11 Blower motor replacement

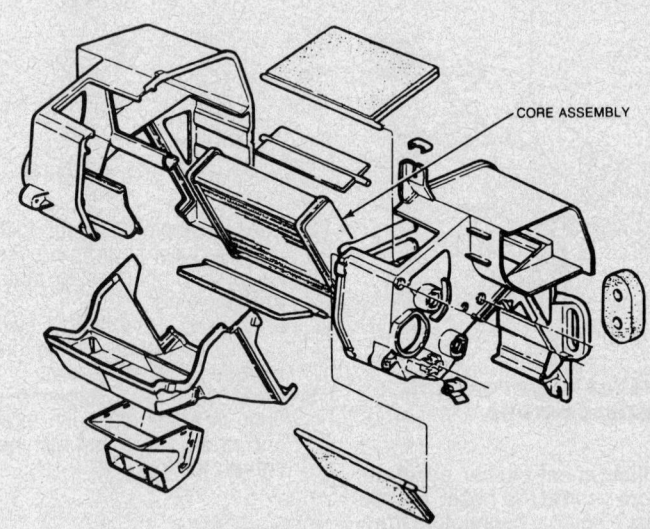

Fig. 12 Heater core assembly

WINDSHIELD WIPER SWITCH
REPLACE
FRONT

1. Disconnect battery ground cable.
2. Remove instrument cluster bezel attaching screws and pull bezel out.
3. Disconnect electrical connectors from headlamp switch and wiper switch.
4. Remove bezel inside attaching nuts and bracket, then push switch out of bezel, **Fig. 6.**
5. Reverse procedure to install.

REAR

1. Disconnect battery ground cable.
2. Pry switch panel open with a screwdriver and pull switch out.
3. Disconnect electrical connector, then remove switch, **Fig. 7.**
4. Reverse procedure to install.

WINDSHIELD WIPER MOTOR & TRANSMISSION
REPLACE
FRONT

1. Disconnect battery ground cable.
2. Remove wiper arm locknuts and the wiper arms.
3. Remove cowl cover, then the wiper motor cover.
4. Disconnect electrical connector from wiper motor.
5. Separate wiper drive arm from wiper link.
6. Disconnect wiper link from wiper motor arm.
7. Remove wiper motor attaching bolt, then the wiper and link, **Fig. 8.**
8. Reverse procedure to install.

REAR

1. Disconnect battery ground cable.
2. Remove trim pad assembly.
3. Remove wiper arm assembly.
4. Remove wiper motor fasteners, then disconnect electrical connector and remove motor, **Fig. 9.**
5. Reverse procedure to install.

RADIO
REPLACE

Refer to **Fig. 10,** when replacing radio.

BLOWER MOTOR
REPLACE

1. Disconnect battery ground cable.
2. Disconnect blower motor electrical connector from motor case.
3. **On models equipped with A/C,** disconnect rubber hose from case.
4. **On all models,** rotate blower motor counterclockwise and remove from case, **Fig. 11.**
5. Reverse procedure to install.

HEATER CORE
REPLACE

1. Disconnect battery ground cable.
2. Disconnect heater hoses from core. **When disconnecting heater hoses at core tube connection, take care not to use excessive force, or damage to core may result.**
3. Remove 6 retaining clips, then the lower part of heater case.
4. Carefully pry open lower part of heater case and remove heater core, **Fig. 12.**
5. Reverse procedure to install.

EVAPORATOR
REPLACE

1. Disconnect battery ground cable.
2. Discharge refrigerant from A/C system.
3. Remove insulator from evaporator outlet and blower joint.
4. Remove thermo switch from upper case.
5. Remove clips retaining upper and lower evaporator case halves, then the upper case half.
6. Carefully pull thermo switch capillary tube from evaporator core.
7. Remove thermo switch.
8. Remove evaporator core with expansion valve, inlet and outlet lines connected.
9. Peel off insulation tape from expansion valve and equalizer line connection.
10. Disconnect expansion valve intake pipe connection, equalizer line and evaporator outlet line.
11. Remove evaporator core. Cap all open lines and fittings.
12. Reverse procedure to install.

Engine

INDEX

ENGINE MOUNT
REPLACE
RIGHT ENGINE MOUNT

1. Disconnect battery ground cable.
2. Using a suitable jack, support engine.
3. Remove two attaching bolts, then remove plate from righthand side of engine.
4. Remove right engine mount attaching bolt and the mount, **Figs. 1. and 2**
5. Reverse procedure to install.

TORQUE ROD

1. Disconnect battery ground cable.
2. Remove bolt from engine side of rod, then remove nut and bolt from body side of rod, **Figs. 1 and 2.**
3. Remove torque rod from vehicle.
4. Reverse procedure to install.

FRONT & REAR ENGINE MOUNTS

1. Disconnect battery ground cable.
2. Raise and support vehicle, then support engine.
3. Remove through bolts and nuts from front and rear engine mounts, **Figs. 1 and 2.**
4. Remove four beam attaching bolts and the beam. **Fig. 3.**
5. Remove front and rear engine mounts.
6. Reverse procedure to install.

ENGINE
REPLACE

1. Disconnect battery ground cable.
2. Drain cooling system, then remove air cleaner.
3. Disconnect throttle cable assembly.
4. Disconnect heater hose from intake manifold, then the thermostat housing from cylinder head.
5. Disconnect coolant hose from thermostat housing, then remove distributor from cylinder head.
6. Disconnect oxygen sensor electrical connector.
7. Support engine using a suitable jack, then remove right engine mount.
8. Disconnect all vacuum hoses, lines and electrical connectors necessary for engine removal. **On models equipped with turbocharger, depressurize fuel system.**
9. **On all models,** scribe hood hinge locations and remove hood.
10. Disconnect flex hose from exhaust manifold.
11. Disconnect lower radiator hose from engine block.
12. Remove A/C compressor drive belt and power steering pump drive belt, as equipped.
13. **On model turbocharger,** disconnect fuel line at fuel pump.
14. **On all models,** remove upper starter attaching bolt.
15. Raise and support vehicle.

16. Drain crankcase and remove oil filter.
17. Disconnect oil temperature switch electrical connector.
18. Disconnect exhaust pipe bracket from cylinder block.
19. Disconnect exhaust pipe from exhaust manifold.
20. Unfasten A/C compressor, if equipped, and position aside, leaving refrigerant lines attached.
21. Remove flywheel cover and the converter attaching bolts.
22. Disconnect starter wire and remove starter motor.
23. Install flywheel holder tool No. J-35271 or equivalent.
24. Disconnect alternator electrical connectors.
25. Remove right front wheel and tire assembly.
26. Remove right front inner splash shield.
27. Support and lower engine by lowering crossmember enough to gain access to crankshaft pulley bolts.
28. Remove crankshaft pulley, then raise engine and crossmember.
29. Remove engine support, then lower vehicle.
30. Support transaxle with a suitable jack, then remove engine to transaxle bolts and the engine from vehicle.
31. Reverse procedure to install.

INTAKE MANIFOLD
REPLACE
EXCEPT TURBOCHARGED ENGINE

1. Disconnect battery ground cable, then drain cooling system.
2. Remove alternator adjusting plate bolt.
3. Disconnect all hoses and electrical connectors from air cleaner, then remove air cleaner assembly.
4. Disconnect all hoses, electrical connectors and cables from carburetor, then remove carburetor assembly.
5. Disconnect all coolant and vacuum hoses and electrical connectors from intake manifold.
6. Remove intake manifold, attaching bolts and the intake manifold.
7. Reverse procedure to install noting the following:
   a. Using a straightedge and feeler gauge, check intake manifold to cylinder head contact surface for warpage.
   b. Intake manifold must be replaced if warpage exceeds .0157 inch (0.4 mm).

TURBOCHARGED ENGINE

Refer to **Fig. 4**, for removal and installation of intake manifold.

EXHAUST MANIFOLD
REPLACE
EXCEPT TURBOCHARGED ENGINE

1. Disconnect battery ground cable.

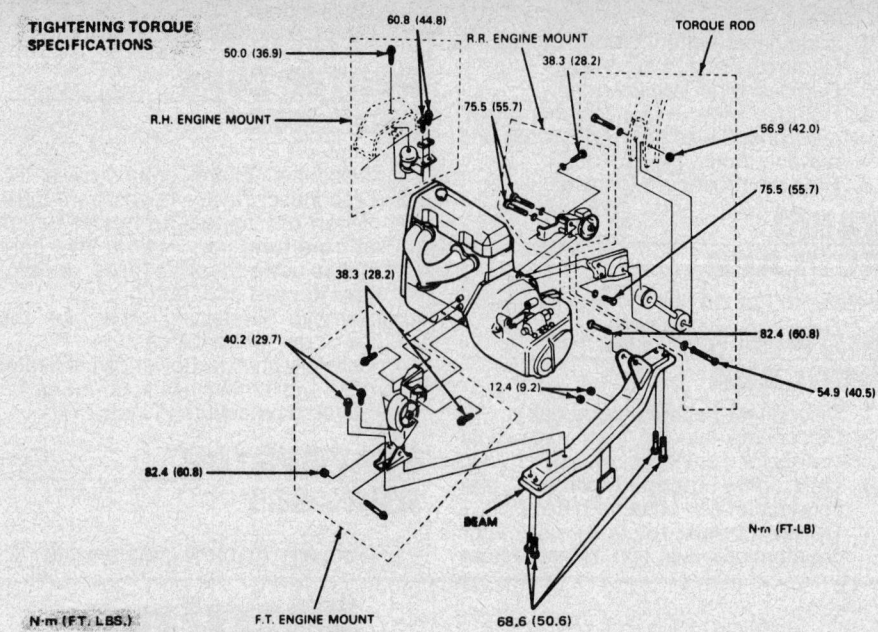

Fig. 1 Engine mount replacement. Except turbocharged engine

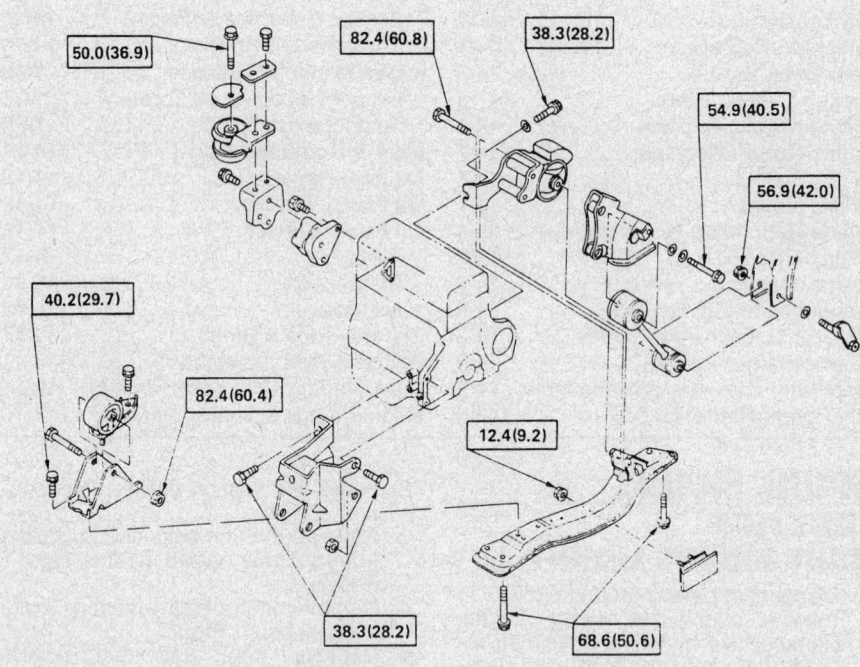

Fig. 2 Engine mount replacement. Turbocharged engine

2. Disconnect oxygen sensor electrical connector.
3. Disconnect TCA flex hose, then remove hot air cover.
4. Raise and support vehicle.
5. Disconnect exhaust pipe from exhaust manifold, then lower vehicle.
6. Remove exhaust manifold attaching nuts and bolts, then the exhaust manifold, **Fig. 5.**
7. Reverse procedure to install, noting the following:
   a. Using a straight-edge and feeler gauge, check exhaust manifold to cylinder head contact surface for warpage.
   b. Exhaust manifold must be replaced if warpage exceeds .0157 inch (0.4 mm).

TURBOCHARGED ENGINE

Refer to **Fig. 4**, for removal and installation of exhaust manifold.

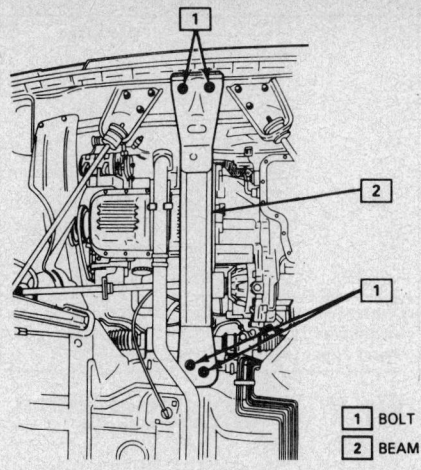

Fig. 3 Engine beam removal

| 1 | BOLT |
| 2 | BEAM |

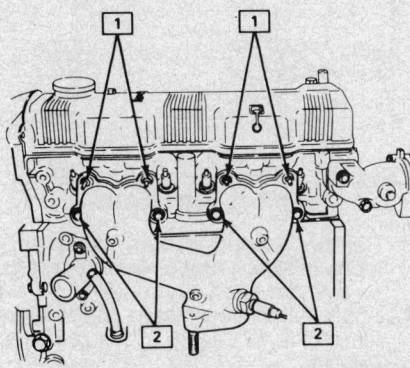

| 1 | NUT |
| 2 | BOLT |

Fig. 5 Exhaust manifold replacement. Except turbocharged models

CYLINDER HEAD REPLACE

1. Disconnect battery ground cable.
2. Remove turbocharger, if applicable.
3. Drain cooling system, then remove air cleaner assembly.
4. Disconnect flex hose from exhaust manifold.
5. Disconnect electrical connector from oxygen sensor.
6. Disconnect exhaust pipe bracket from block, then the exhaust pipe from manifold.
7. Disconnect spark plug wires from plugs.
8. Disconnect thermostat housing and distributor from cylinder head.
9. Disconnect vacuum advance hoses, then the fuel lines from fuel pump.
10. Disconnect ground cable from intake manifold.
11. Disconnect necessary hoses and the throttle valve cable.
12. Disconnect vacuum switching valve electrical connector.
13. Disconnect heater hoses from intake manifold.
14. Remove power steering pump drive belt, if equipped.
15. Support engine using a suitable jack.
16. Remove right side engine mount and bracket from front cover.
17. Remove A/C compressor drive belt, if equipped.
18. Remove alternator drive belt, then align timing marks and remove front cover.
19. Loosen tension pulley, then remove timing belt.
20. Remove alternator bracket bolt from intake manifold.

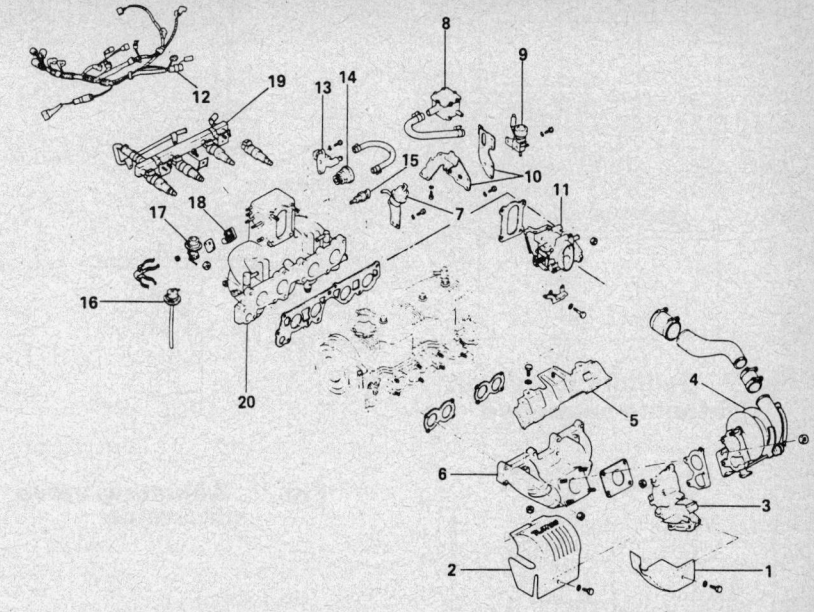

1. Heat shield (lower)
2. Heat shield (upper)
3. Wastegate manifold
4. Turbocharger assembly
5. Heat shield (manifold)
6. Exhaust manifold and hanger
7. Pressure regulator
8. Oil separator
9. VSV
10. Bracket and hanger
11. Throttle valve assembly
12. Engine harness assembly
13. IACV
14. Relief valve
15. MAT sensor
16. Back pressure transducer
17. EGR valve
18. Adaptor
19. Fuel injector with pipe
20. Intake manifold

Fig. 4 Removal & installation of intake & exhaust manifolds & turbocharger assembly

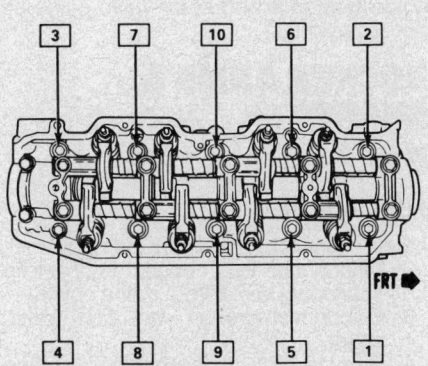

Fig. 6 Cylinder head bolt loosening sequence

21. **On models equipped with power steering,** remove power steering pump through bolt from pump bracket, then the pump mounting bracket from block.
22. **On all except turbocharged models,** disconnect fuel line from fuel pump, then remove the pump.
23. **On turbocharged models,** depressurize fuel system, then disconnect fuel lines from fuel rail.
24. **On all models,** disconnect coolant hoses from intake manifold.
25. Remove cylinder head attaching bolts in sequence, **Fig. 6.**
26. Remove cylinder head.
27. Reverse procedure to install. Torque cylinder head attaching bolts to specifications in sequence, **Fig. 7.**

VALVE ARRANGEMENT
FRONT TO REAR

All . . . . I-E-E-I-I-E-E-I

CAMSHAFT LOBE LIFT

Year	Engine	Intake & Exhaust,
1988–89	4-1.5L/90	1.426

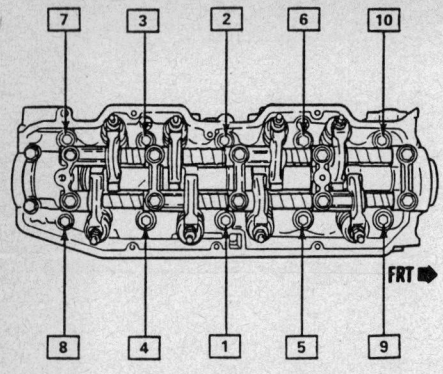

Fig. 7   Cylinder head bolt tightening sequence

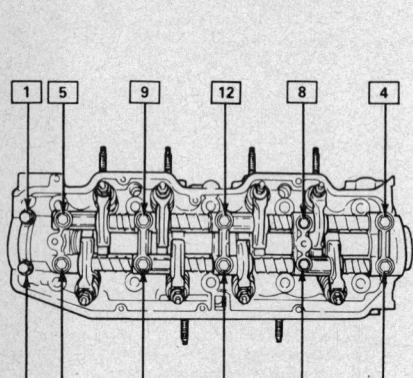

Fig. 10   Rocker arm shaft removal & installation sequence

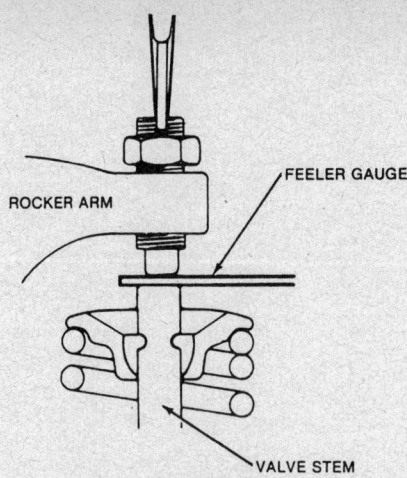

Fig. 8   Adjusting valve clearance

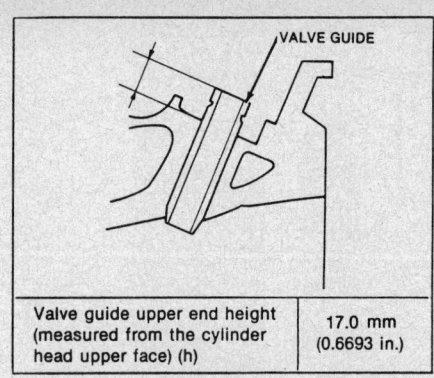

Valve guide upper end height (measured from the cylinder head upper face) (h)	17.0 mm (0.6693 in.)

Fig. 9   Valve guide installed height

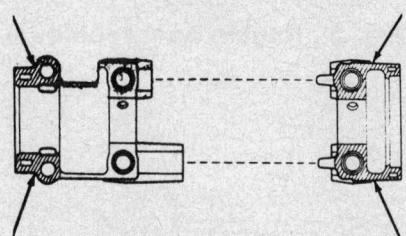

Fig. 11   Applying sealant to rocker brackets

VALVE CLEARANCE SPECIFICATIONS

Year	Engine	Intake Inch,	Exhaust Inch,
1988–89	4-1.5L/90	.006	.010

VALVES
ADJUST

1. Turn crankshaft in normal direction of rotation until No. 1 piston is at TDC of compression stroke.
2. Measure valve clearance between rocker arm and valve stem, **Fig. 8**, for No. 1 cylinder intake and exhaust valves, No. 2 cylinder intake valve and No. 3 cylinder exhaust valve. Adjust valve clearance as necessary to specification listed under "Valve Clearance Specifications."
3. Rotate crankshaft one complete turn to bring No. 4 cylinder to TDC. Measure valve clearance for No. 2 cylinder exhaust valve, No. 3 cylinder intake valve and No. 4 intake and exhaust valves. Adjust clearances as necessary.

VALVE GUIDES
REPLACE

Valves guides can be driven out through the combustion chamber side of the the cylinder head, using tool No. J-35267 or equivalent. Prior to installation, apply engine oil to outer surface of replacement valve guide. Drive valve guide into bore on cylinder head from camshaft side. Valve guide should be driven to a height of .6693 inch form upper cylinder head surface, **Fig. 9**. After installation, check valve stem to guide clearance and ream valve guide as necessary.

ROCKER ARMS & SHAFTS
REPLACE
REMOVAL

1. Disconnect battery ground cable.
2. Disconnect PCV hoses and unclip spark plug wires from valve cover.
3. Disconnect ground wire from valve cover.
4. Remove right side engine mounting rubber.
5. Support engine with a suitable jack.
6. Remove bolts and plate from side of engine.
7. Remove bracket from front cover.
8. Remove 4 front cover attaching bolts.
9. Remove valve cover attaching bolts.
10. Loosen front cover, then remove valve cover.
11. Remove rocker arm bracket bolts in sequence, **Fig. 10**.
12. Remove rocker arm shaft and rocker arms.

INSTALLATION

1. Lightly lubricate rocker arms and shafts with clean engine oil.
2. Install rocker shafts with identification marks to the front of engine.

3. Remove residual oil from contact surfaces of Nos. 1 and 5 rocker brackets on cylinder head.
4. Apply suitable sealant to contact surfaces of Nos. 1 and 5 rocker brackets, **Fig. 11**.
5. Install rocker assembly, tightening rocker arm bolts to specifications in sequence, **Fig. 10**.

TIMING BELT
REPLACE
REMOVAL

1. Remove engine as described under "Engine, Replace."
2. Remove accessory drive belts, then the engine mounting bracket from front cover.
3. Rotate crankshaft to position No. 4 piston at TDC of compression stroke.
4. Remove starter motor, then install flywheel holder tool No. J-35271 or equivalent.
5. Remove crankshaft bolt, then the boss and crank pulley.
6. Remove front cover, then loosen tension pulley fixing bolt.
7. Loosen timing belt tension using a hex wrench in the tension pulley hole.
8. Remove timing belt.

INSTALLATION

1. Install crankshaft timing pulley, ensuring Woodruff key is properly positioned, **Fig. 12**.
2. Position pulley on crankshaft, aligning pulley timing groove with mark on oil pump, **Fig. 12**.
3. Ensure camshaft pulley timing mark is aligned with upper surface of cylinder

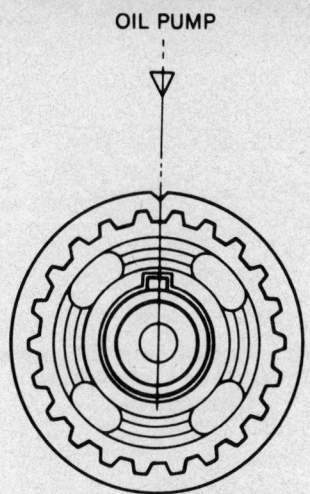

Fig. 12 Crankshaft pulley alignment

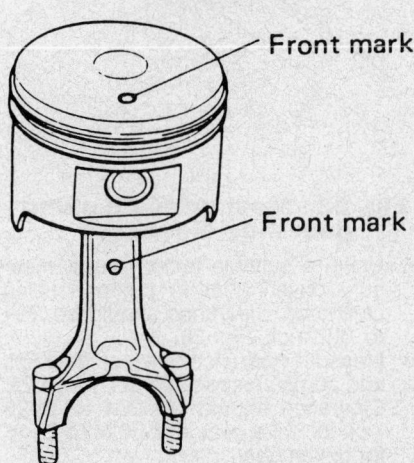

Fig. 15 Piston & rod assembly

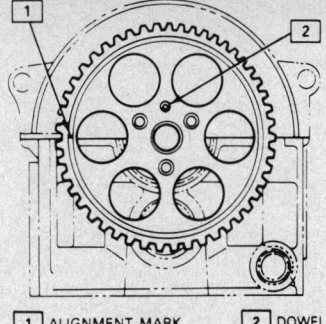

Fig. 13 Camshaft pulley alignment

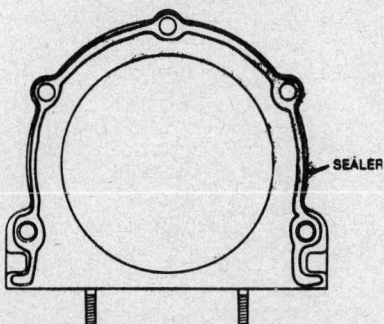

Fig. 16 Applying sealant to rear seal retainer

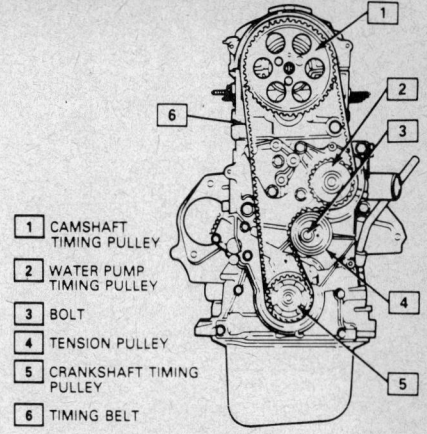

Fig. 14 Timing belt installation

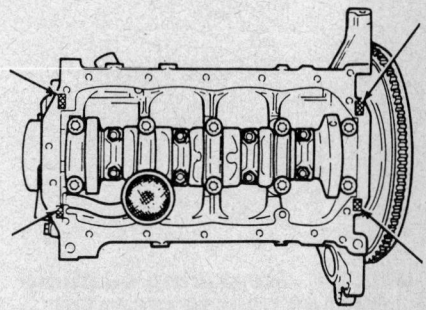

Fig. 17 Sealant application for oil pan installation

head and dowel pin is in up position, **Fig. 13.**
4. Position timing belt arrow mark in direction of engine rotation and install belt over pulleys, **Fig. 14,** in the following order: crankshaft, camshaft, water pump, tension.
5. Loosen tension pulley bolt. Insert a hex wrench into tension pulley hole, then temporarily tighten bolt while holding pulley stationary.
6. Turn crankshaft two complete revolutions and align crankshaft timing pulley groove with mark on oil pump.
7. Loosen tension pulley bolt, then apply tension to belt and torque bolt to specification listed at the end of this section, while holding pulley stationary.
8. Turn crankshaft back approximately 50° and set crankshaft at that position.
9. Check belt tension using suitable tension gauge. Tension should measure 39.6 to 48.4 lbs.
10. Check valve clearances as previously described.
11. Apply suitable sealant to cylinder head mating surface and four points

of each arched area of Nos. 1 and 5 rocker brackets.
12. Install valve cover.
13. Install timing cover and torque bolts to specification listed at the end of this section.
14. Install crankshaft pulley and torque bolt to specifications.
15. Install starter motor.
16. Install engine mount bracket.
17. Install engine.

CAMSHAFT
REPLACE

1. Disconnect battery ground cable.
2. Align mark on crankshaft pulley with "0" mark on front cover.
3. Remove valve cover, then loosen camshaft pulley bolts. Use care not to rotate engine when loosening camshaft pulley bolt.
4. Loosen timing belt tensioner, then remove timing belt.
5. Remove rocker arm shafts as previously described.
6. Remove camshaft pulley, then the distributor and camshaft.
7. Reverse procedure to install. Ensure dowel pin is in up position when installing camshaft.

PISTON & ROD ASSEMBLY

Assemble piston and rod as shown in, **Fig. 15.** Installing piston and rod assembly with front mark on piston toward front of engine. After installing piston and rod,

check connecting rod side clearance. Clearance should be .0079 to .0138 inch.

PISTONS, PINS & RINGS

Pistons and rings are available in standard size and oversizes of .020 and .040 inch. Piston pins are available in standard size only.

MAIN & ROD BEARINGS

Main and rod bearings are available in standard size and undersizes of .010 and .020 inch.

REAR BEARING MAIN SEAL
REPLACE

1. Remove transaxle as described under "Transaxle, Replace."
2. Disconnect exhaust pipe bracket.
3. Remove oil pan as described under "Oil Pan, Replace."
4. Remove rear retainer, then the rear main oil seal.
5. Clean retainer mating surface and apply suitable sealant as shown, **Fig. 16.**
6. Apply clean engine oil to seal lip, then install retainer and the seal using tool No. J-35264 or equivalent.

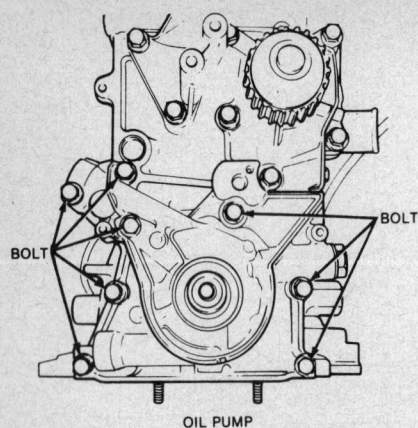

Fig. 18 Oil pump replacement

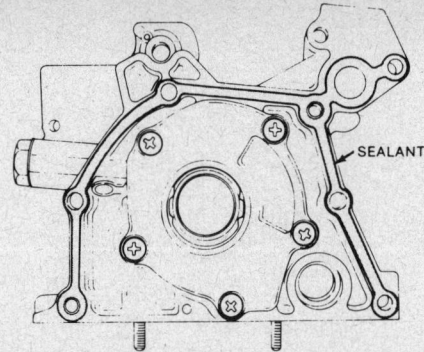

Fig. 19 Applying sealant to oil pump mating surface

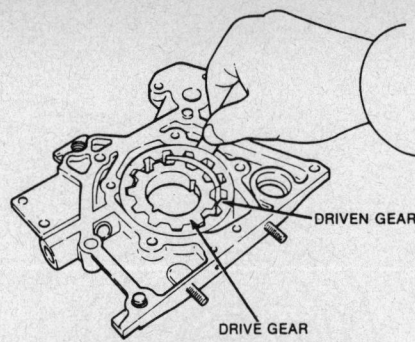

Fig. 20 Measuring oil pump driven gear to housing clearance

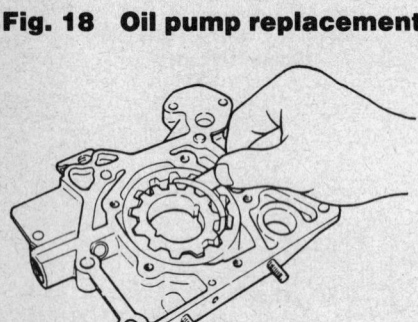

Fig. 21 Measuring oil pump driven gear to crescent clearance

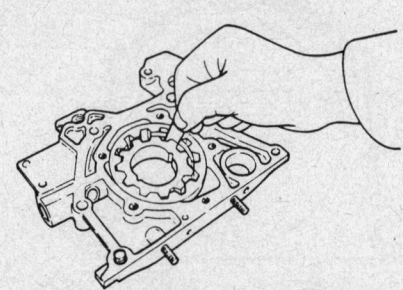

Fig. 22 Measuring oil pump drive gear to crescent clearance

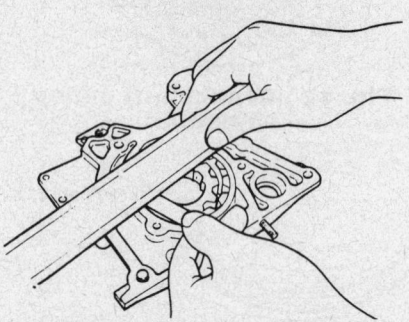

Fig. 23 Measuring oil pump gear side clearance

OIL PAN
REPLACE

1. Disconnect battery ground cable.
2. Raise and support vehicle.
3. Drain engine oil, then disconnect exhaust pipe bracket from block.
4. Disconnect exhaust pipe from exhaust manifold.
5. Disconnect righthand tension rod under bumper.
6. Remove oil pan attaching bolts and the oil pan.
7. Reverse procedure to install. Ensure pan and cylinder case mating surfaces are clean prior to mounting pan. Apply TB-1207-B or other suitable sealer to locations indicated in, **Fig. 17**, prior to oil pan installation.

OIL PUMP
REPLACE

1. Remove engine assembly as previously described.
2. Drain crankcase, then remove alternator drive belt.
3. Remove starter motor, then install flywheel holder tool No. J-35271 or equivalent.
4. Remove crankshaft pulley and boss.
5. Remove front cover, then the timing belt.
6. Remove crankshaft timing pulley and tension pulley.

7. Remove oil pan attaching bolts and the oil pan.
8. Remove oil strainer attaching bolt and the strainer.
9. Remove oil attaching bolts and the oil pump, **Fig. 18**.
10. Reverse procedure to install. Apply suitable sealant to oil pump mating surface, **Fig. 19**. When installing oil pump, lubricate front seal with engine oil prior to installation. Position seal protector No. J-35270 on crankshaft to prevent damage to seal when installing oil pump.

OIL PUMP SERVICE
DISASSEMBLY

1. Remove relief valve plug and washer, then remove valve and spring form pump housing bore.
2. Remove oil pump cover attaching bolts, then remove cover and gears.
3. If necessary, carefully remove oil seal from oil pump cover using a suitable screwdriver.

INSPECTION

1. Check to ensure relief valve slides freely in pump housing bore. If valve does not slide freely, replace oil pump.
2. Check relief valve spring for wear and damage and replace as necessary.
3. Check oil pump housing for wear and damage and replace as necessary.
4. Check oil pump strainer and pick-up tube for wear and damage and replace as necessary.

5. Using a suitable feeler gauge, measure driven gear to pump housing clearance. Clearance should be .004 to .007 inch, **Fig. 20**.
6. Measure clearance between gear tips and pump crescent, **Figs. 21 and 22**. Clearance should be .004 to .0093 inch for drive gear and .0024 to .0115 for driven gear.
7. Using a straight edge and feeler gauge, measure gear side clearance, **Fig. 23**. If clearance exceeds .0039 inch, the pump assembly should be replaced.

ASSEMBLY

1. Lubricate relief valve and spring with engine oil, then position spring and valve into pump housing bore.
2. Install relief valve plug and torque to specification listed at the end of this section.
3. Lubricate drive and driven gear with engine oil, then position in pump housing.
4. If removed, install replacement oil seal on oil pump cover using tool No. J-35269 or equivalent. After installing oil seal, apply engine oil to seal lips.
5. Install pump cover and gasket, then torque cover attaching screws to specification listed at the end of this section.

WATER PUMP
REPLACE

1. Drain cooling system.
2. Remove power steering pump drive belt.

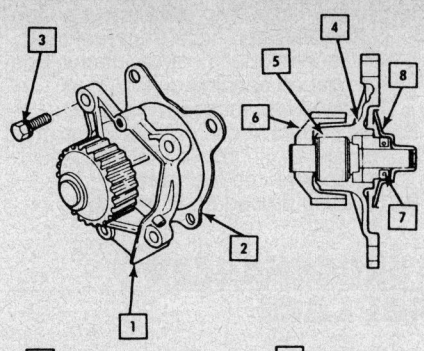

1	COOLANT PUMP ASSEMBLY	5	BEARING UNIT
2	GASKET	6	PULLEY
3	BOLT	7	SEAL UNIT
4	COOLANT PUMP BODY	8	IMPELLER

Fig. 24   Water pump replacement

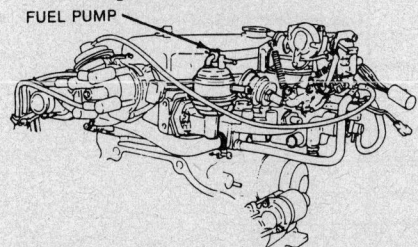

FUEL PUMP

Fig. 25   Mechanical type fuel pump location. Models less turbocharger

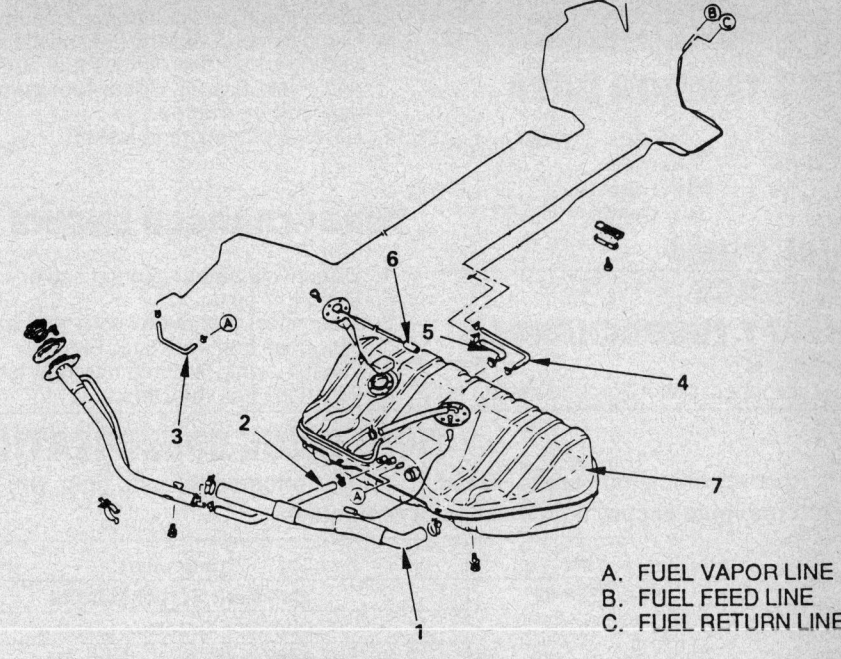

A. FUEL VAPOR LINE
B. FUEL FEED LINE
C. FUEL RETURN LINE

1. Fuel filler pipe assembly
2. Breather hose
3. Hose; fuel tank to vapor canister
4. Hose; fuel tank to return pipe
5. Hose; fuel tank to fuel feed pipe
6. Wiring connector
7. Fuel tank assembly

Fig. 26   Electric type fuel pump location. Models w/turbocharger

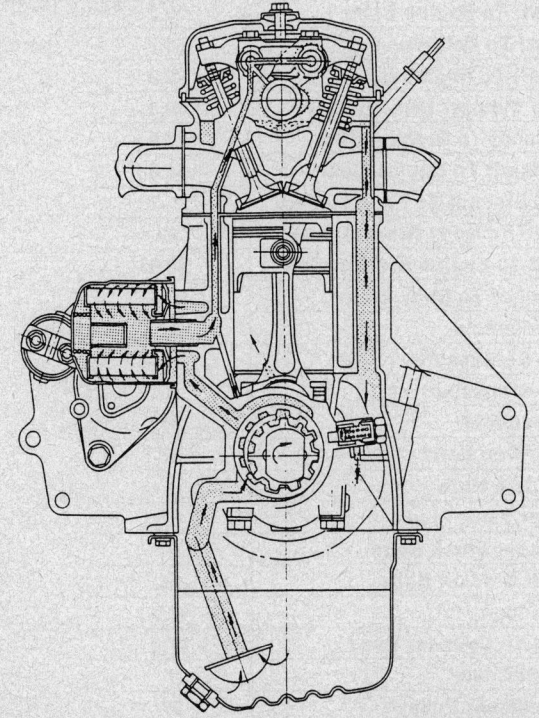

Engine oiling system. Except turbocharged engine

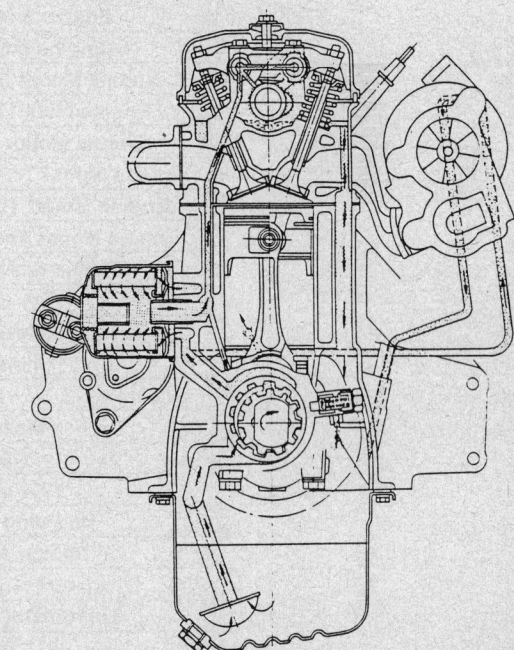

Engine oiling system. Turbocharged engine

of this section.

COOLING SYSTEM BLEED

These engines do not require a specified bleed procedure. After filling cooling system, run engine to operating with radia-

3. Remove timing belt as previously described.
4. Remove tension pulley and tension spring.

5. Remove water pump attaching bolts and the water pump, **Fig. 24.**
6. Reverse procedure to install. Torque bolts to specification listed at the end

CHEVROLET/GEO SPECTRUM

tor/pressure cap off. Air will then be automatically bled through cap opening.

BELT TENSION DATA

Engine	Belt	Tension, Lbs.
4-1.5L/90	Alternator	90
	Power Steer.	90
	A/C Comp.	90

FUEL PUMP
REPLACE
EXCEPT TURBOCHARGED ENGINE

1. Disconnect battery ground cable.

2. Disconnect fuel lines from fuel pump.
3. Remove fuel pump and heat shield attaching bolts, then remove fuel pump and shield, **Fig. 25.** Cover fuel pump opening on engine.
4. Reverse procedure to install.

TURBOCHARGED ENGINE

1. Disconnect battery ground cable.
2. Drain fuel tank.
3. Disconnect fuel return hose and fuel filter hose from fuel tank, **Fig. 26.**
4. Loosen clamp and remove fuel tank filler hose from fuel tank.

5. Remove clip, then disconnect evaporative emission hose from fuel tank.
6. Disconnect electrical connector from fuel gauge sending unit.
7. Remove fuel tank from vehicle.
8. Disconnect hose from fuel pump, then remove fuel pump to fuel tank attaching screws and fuel pump.
9. Reverse procedure to install.

TURBOCHARGER
REPLACE

Refer to **Fig. 4,** for removal and installation of turbocharger.

TIGHTENING SPECIFICATIONS

Torque specifications are for clean & lightly lubricated threads only. Dry or dirty threads produce increase friction which prevents accurate measurement of tightness.

Year	Component	Torque/Ft. Lbs.
1988-89	Camshaft Sprocket Bolts	7
	Carburetor To Intake Manifold	7.2
	Connecting Rod Cap Bolts	25
	Coolant Outlet To Thermostat Housing	17.4
	Crankshaft Pulley Bolt	108
	Cylinder Head Bolts	58 ②
	Cylinder Head Cover Bolts	7
	Engine Mount (Front) Bracket To Support Member Bolts	29.7
	Engine Mount (Front) To Bracket Bolts	60.8
	Engine Mount (Front) To Engine Bolts	28.2
	Engine Mount (Rear) To Bell Housing	55.7
	Engine Mount (Rear) To Engine Bolt	28.2
	Engine Mount (Rear) To Support Member Bolt	60.8
	Engine Mount (Right Hand) To Bracket Bolts	36.9
	Engine Mount (Right Hand) To Engine Bolts	44.8
	Engine Mount Torque Rod Bracket To Engine Bolts	55.7
	Engine Mount Torque Rod To Body Bracket Bolt	42
	Engine Mount Torque Rod To Engine Bracket Bolt	40.5
	Engine Support Member To Body Bolts	50.6
	Exhaust Manifold	17
	Flexplate To Crankshaft	①
	Flywheel To Crankshaft	①
	Intake Manifold	17
	Main Bearing Cap Bolts	65
	Oil Pan Bolts & Nuts	7
	Oil Pump Relief Valve Plug	27
	Oil Pump To Cylinder Block Bolts	7
	Rocker Arm Shaft Bracket Bolts	16
	Spark Plugs	13.7
	Thermostat Housing To Cylinder Head	17.4
	Timing Belt Cover	7
	Timing Belt Tensioner Pulley	37
	Torque Converter To Flexplate	30
	Transaxle To Engine Bolts	55
	Water Pump Bolts	17.4

① —Apply Loctite 262 or equivalent to bolt threads prior to installation. Torque bolts to 22 ft. lbs., then tighten each bolt an additional 45°.

② —Apply engine oil to bolt threads & bolt head contact surface prior to installation.

Clutch & Manual Transaxle

INDEX

Page No.

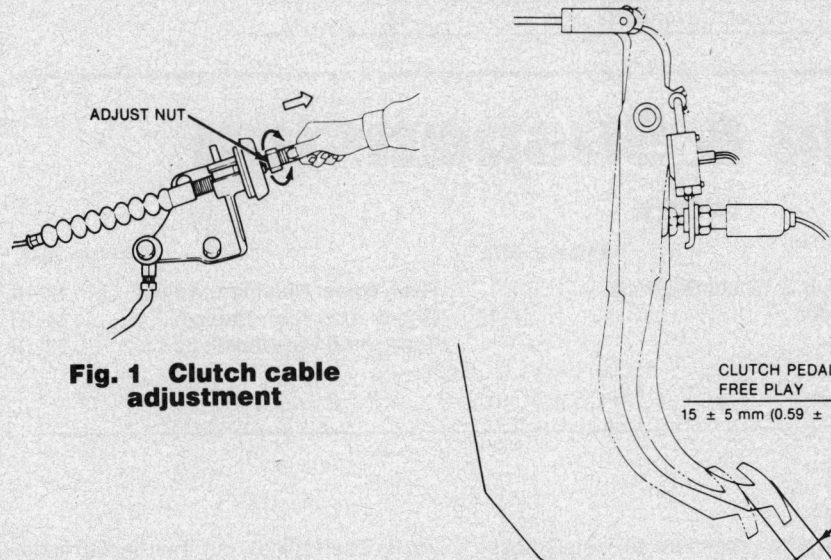

Fig. 1 Clutch cable adjustment

CLUTCH PEDAL
FREE PLAY

15 ± 5 mm (0.59 ± .20 IN.)

Fig. 2 Clutch pedal free travel measurement

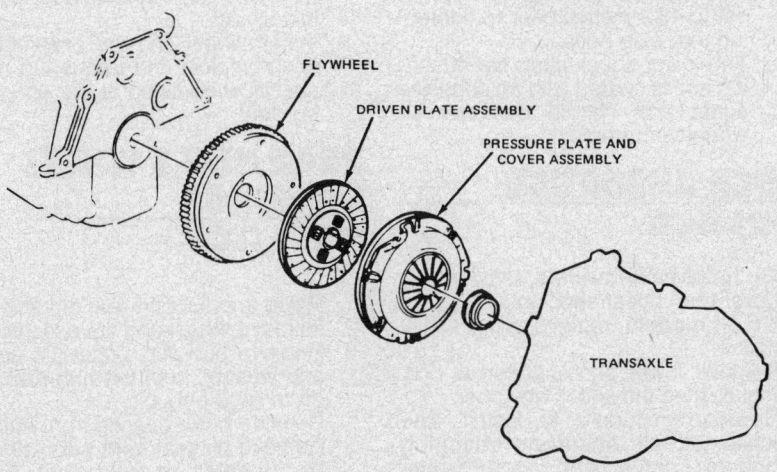

FLYWHEEL

DRIVEN PLATE ASSEMBLY

PRESSURE PLATE AND
COVER ASSEMBLY

TRANSAXLE

Fig. 3 Exploded view of clutch assembly

CLUTCH
REPLACE

1. Remove transaxle as described under "Transaxle, Replace."
2. Install alignment tool No. J-35282 or equivalent into pilot bearing to support clutch.
3. Mark clutch cover and flywheel, if not already done, for assembly reference.
4. Loosen clutch cover to flywheel attaching bolts evenly, one at a time, until spring pressure is relieved.
5. Remove bolts, clutch cover, disc and tool from flywheel, **Fig. 3**.
6. Reverse procedure to install. Lubricate input shaft splines and release bearing with grease 1051344 or equivalent during installation.

TRANSAXLE
REPLACE

1. Disconnect battery ground cable.
2. Drain transaxle oil.
3. Disconnect ground cable and electrical connectors from transaxle.
4. Disconnect speedometer cable and clutch cable from transaxle.
5. Disconnect shift and select cables from transaxle.
6. Remove air cleaner heat tube.
7. Remove upper engine to transaxle attaching bolts.
8. Raise and support vehicle.
9. Remove left front wheel and tire assembly.
10. Remove splash shield.
11. Disconnect left tie rod end from steering knuckle.
12. Remove left tension rod.
13. Disconnect drive axles from transaxle, using care to avoid damaging oil seals.
14. Remove dust cover from clutch housing.
15. Support transaxle using a suitable jack.
16. Remove remaining transaxle to engine attaching bolts.
17. Slide transaxle assembly toward driver's side, away from engine. Carefully lower jack while guiding right shaft out of transaxle and remove assembly from vehicle.
18. Reverse procedure to install, noting the following:
    a. When installing transaxle, guide right axle shaft into its bore as assembly is raised.
    b. **Torque** transaxle to engine attaching bolts to 55 ft. lbs.
    c. **Torque** left tension rod attaching bolts to 80 ft. lbs.

CLUTCH PEDAL
ADJUST

1. Disconnect battery ground cable.
2. Loosen clutch cable adjusting nut, **Fig. 1**, then pull cable rearward until it turns freely.
3. Turn adjusting nut as needed to adjust cable length. Release cable when pedal freeplay is within specifications, **Fig. 2**.
4. Tighten locknut securely.

TIGHTENING SPECIFICATIONS

Torque specifications are for clean & lightly lubricated threads only. Dry or dirty threads produce increase friction which prevents accurate measurement of tightness.

Year	Component	Torque/Ft. Lbs.
1988-89	Tension Rod Bolts	80
	Transaxle To Engine Bolts	55
	Transaxle To Clutch Bolts	22–33
	Clutch Cover Bolts	13

Rear Axle & Suspension

INDEX

DESCRIPTION

The semi-independent suspension, **Fig. 1**, consists of an axle with trailing arms and twisting cross beam, two coil springs, shock absorbers, upper spring insulators and spring compression bumpers. The axle assembly is attached to the underbody through rubber bushings located at the front end of rear axle. The rear axle brackets are integral with the underbody side rails. The two coil springs support the weight of the vehicle in the rear. Each spring is retained between a seat in the underbody and a seat welded to the top of the rear axle. A rubber cushion isolates the coil spring upper end from the underbody seat.

REAR AXLE & COIL SPRINGS
REPLACE

1. Raise and support rear of vehicle.
2. Remove both rear wheel and tire assemblies.
3. Remove brake line, retaining clip and flexible hose from center of axle.
4. Remove tension spring, then disconnect parking brake cable and cable joint.
5. Support axle with a suitable jack.
6. Remove lower shock absorber bolt and disconnect shock from axle, **Fig. 1.**
7. Lower jack supporting axle and remove coil spring, **Fig. 2.**
8. Remove axle to body attaching bolts, then lower rear axle assembly from vehicle.

9. Reverse procedure to install, noting the following:
   a. When installing coil springs, the thinner end of spring must be attached at upper end and the bottom of spring must be positioned as shown, **Fig. 3.**
   b. Rear trim height, **Fig. 4,** must be set to 15.2 inches prior to tightening rear axle bolts.
   c. The lower shock absorber attaching bolt is coated with an adhesive agent and should be replaced whenever removed.

SHOCK ABSORBER
REPLACE

1. **On hatchback models,** remove trim cover from upper shock nut.
2. **On all models,** remove upper shock nut.
3. Remove lower shock absorber bolt, **Fig. 5,** then the shock absorber.
4. Reverse procedure to install. **The lower shock absorber attaching bolt is coated with an adhesive agent and should be replaced whenever removed.**

REAR WHEEL BEARING
ADJUST

1. Raise and support rear of vehicle.
2. Remove wheel and tire assembly.
3. Remove bearing dust cap, then remove cotter pin and loosen spindle nut.
4. While rotating hub and drum assembly, **torque** spindle nut to 22 ft. lbs.

5. Loosen spindle nut, then tighten finger tight.
6. Install spindle nut retainer and cotter pin. **If cotter pin holes are not aligned, tighten nut slightly to align.**
7. Apply suitable wheel bearing grease to inner area of bearing dust cap, then install cap.
8. Install wheel and tire assembly and lower vehicle and torque lug nuts to specification listed at the end of this section.

REAR HUB & WHEEL BEARINGS
REPLACE

1. Raise and support rear of vehicle.
2. Remove wheel and tire assembly.
3. Remove hub cap, cotter pin and nut and washer, then the hub and brake drum assembly.
4. Remove outer bearing from hub.
5. Remove oil seal from hub using tool No. J-26941 or equivalent, **Fig. 6,** then remove inner bearing from hub.
6. Tap inner bearing outer race and outer bearing outer race out of hub, **Fig. 7.**
7. Install inner and outer bearing races using tool J-35307-1 and J-35307-2 respectively, **Fig. 8.**
8. Install replacement oil seal in inner side of hub using tool No. J-35305 or equivalent, **Fig. 9.**
9. Pack bearings using suitable grease.
10. Reverse procedure to install. Adjust wheel bearings as described under "Rear Wheel Bearing, Adjust."

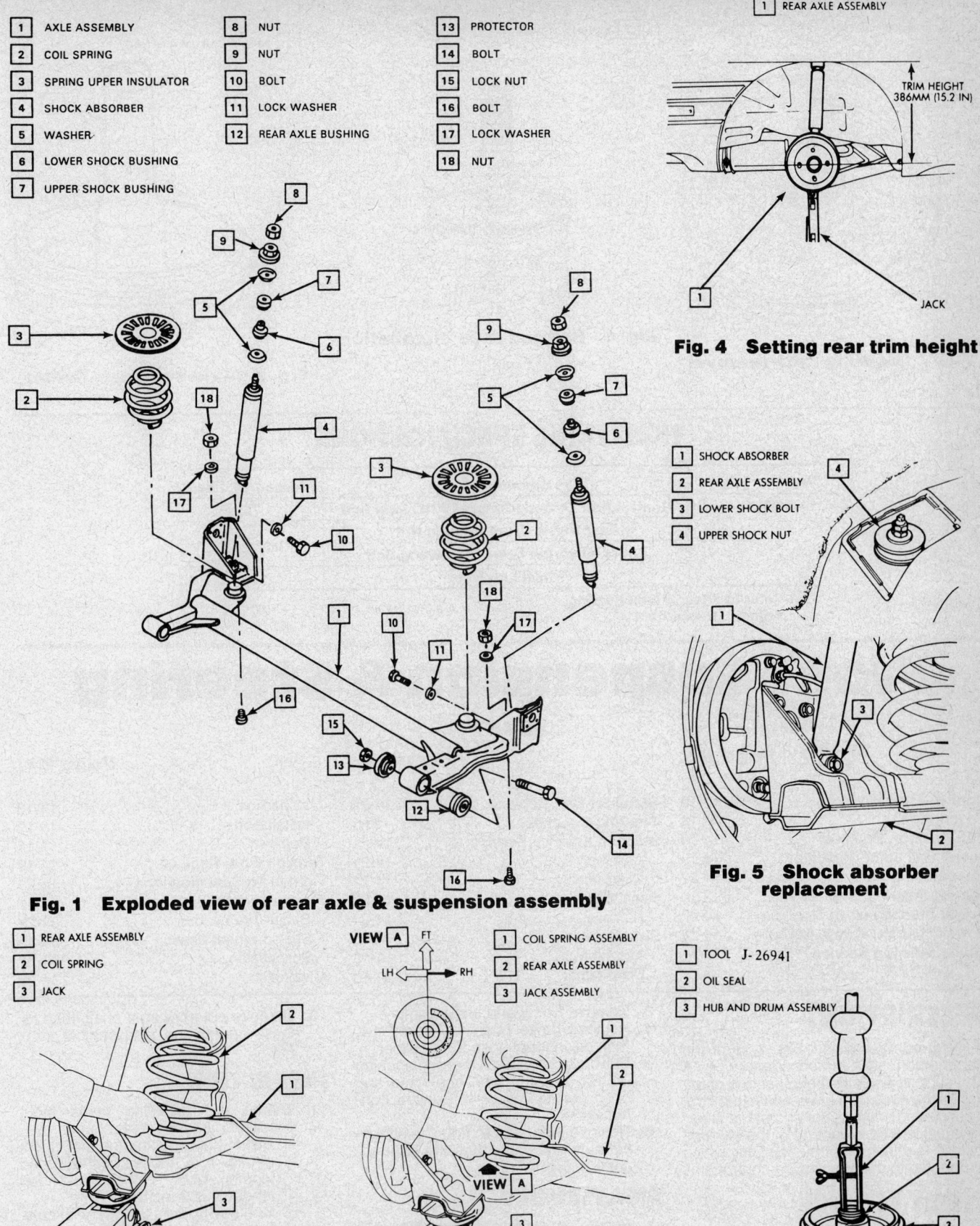

1	AXLE ASSEMBLY
2	COIL SPRING
3	SPRING UPPER INSULATOR
4	SHOCK ABSORBER
5	WASHER
6	LOWER SHOCK BUSHING
7	UPPER SHOCK BUSHING
8	NUT
9	NUT
10	BOLT
11	LOCK WASHER
12	REAR AXLE BUSHING
13	PROTECTOR
14	BOLT
15	LOCK NUT
16	BOLT
17	LOCK WASHER
18	NUT

1	REAR AXLE ASSEMBLY

TRIM HEIGHT
386MM (15.2 IN)

JACK

Fig. 4 Setting rear trim height

1	SHOCK ABSORBER
2	REAR AXLE ASSEMBLY
3	LOWER SHOCK BOLT
4	UPPER SHOCK NUT

Fig. 5 Shock absorber replacement

Fig. 1 Exploded view of rear axle & suspension assembly

1	REAR AXLE ASSEMBLY
2	COIL SPRING
3	JACK

VIEW A
FT
LH RH

1	COIL SPRING ASSEMBLY
2	REAR AXLE ASSEMBLY
3	JACK ASSEMBLY

VIEW A

1	TOOL J-26941
2	OIL SEAL
3	HUB AND DRUM ASSEMBLY

Fig. 2 Coil spring removal

Fig. 3 Coil spring installation

Fig. 6 Axle seal removal

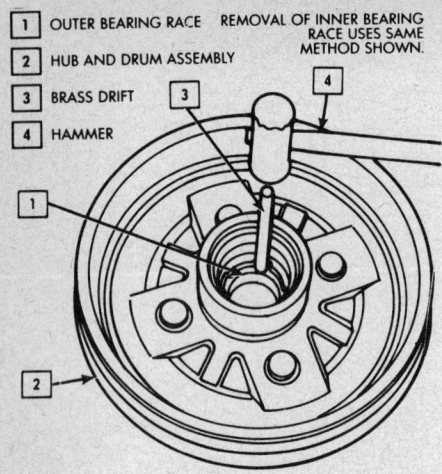

1 OUTER BEARING RACE REMOVAL OF INNER BEARING
2 HUB AND DRUM ASSEMBLY RACE USES SAME METHOD SHOWN.
3 BRASS DRIFT
4 HAMMER

Fig. 7   Bearing race removal

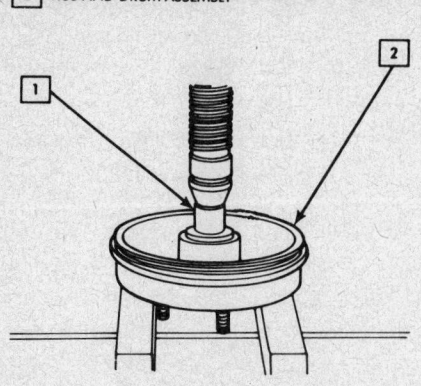

1 TOOL J-35307-1 and J-35307-2
2 HUB AND DRUM ASSEMBLY

Fig. 8   Bearing race installation

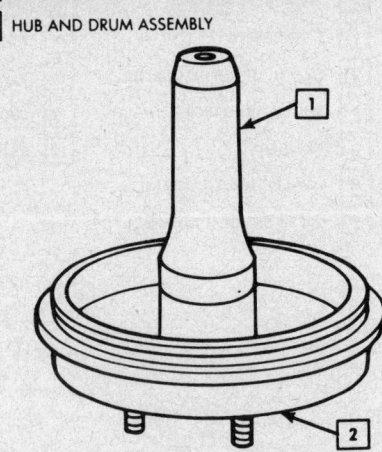

1 TOOL J-35305
2 HUB AND DRUM ASSEMBLY

Fig. 9   Axle seal installation

TIGHTENING SPECIFICATIONS

Year	Component	Torque/Ft. Lbs.
1988-89	Control Arm To Body Bracket Attaching Bolt	72
	Rear Hub & Drum Spindle Nut	①
	Shock Absorber Lower Attaching Bolt	30
	Wheel Lug Nuts	65

①—Refer to "Rear Wheel Bearing, Adjust" procedure.

Front Suspension & Steering

INDEX

DESCRIPTION

The front suspension, **Fig. 1**, is of the MacPherson strut, independent type. A strut support anchors the upper end of the strut to the body. The lower end of the strut is connected to the upper end of the steering knuckle. The lower end of the steering knuckle is attached to the ball joint, which is mounted to the suspension control arm.

STRUT SERVICE
REMOVAL

1. Remove both strut to body attaching nuts.
2. Raise and support front of vehicle.
3. Remove wheel and tire assembly.
4. Remove brake hose clip from strut, then disconnect hose from caliper.
5. Pull brake hose back through opening in strut bracket, then cap hose and open port in caliper to prevent contamination.
6. Remove both strut to knuckle attaching nuts and bolts, then the strut assembly, **Fig. 1**.

DISASSEMBLY

1. Secure strut spring compressor in a vise or suitable holding fixture.
2. Install strut into compressing tool, **Fig. 2**, and compress spring just enough to release spring tension.
3. Remove nut from strut shaft, then release spring and disassemble strut, **Fig. 3**.

INSPECTION

1. Ensure the following items meet specified measurements:
   a. **Strut:** piston diameter, 1.18 inch; stroke, 5.75 inches; compressed length, 14.65 inches; extended length, 20.39 inches.
   b. **Coil spring free length:** with auto. trans. and A/C, 13.5 inches; with auto. trans. less A/C 13.7; with manual trans. and A/C, 13.7 inches; with man. trans. less A/C, 13.9 inches.

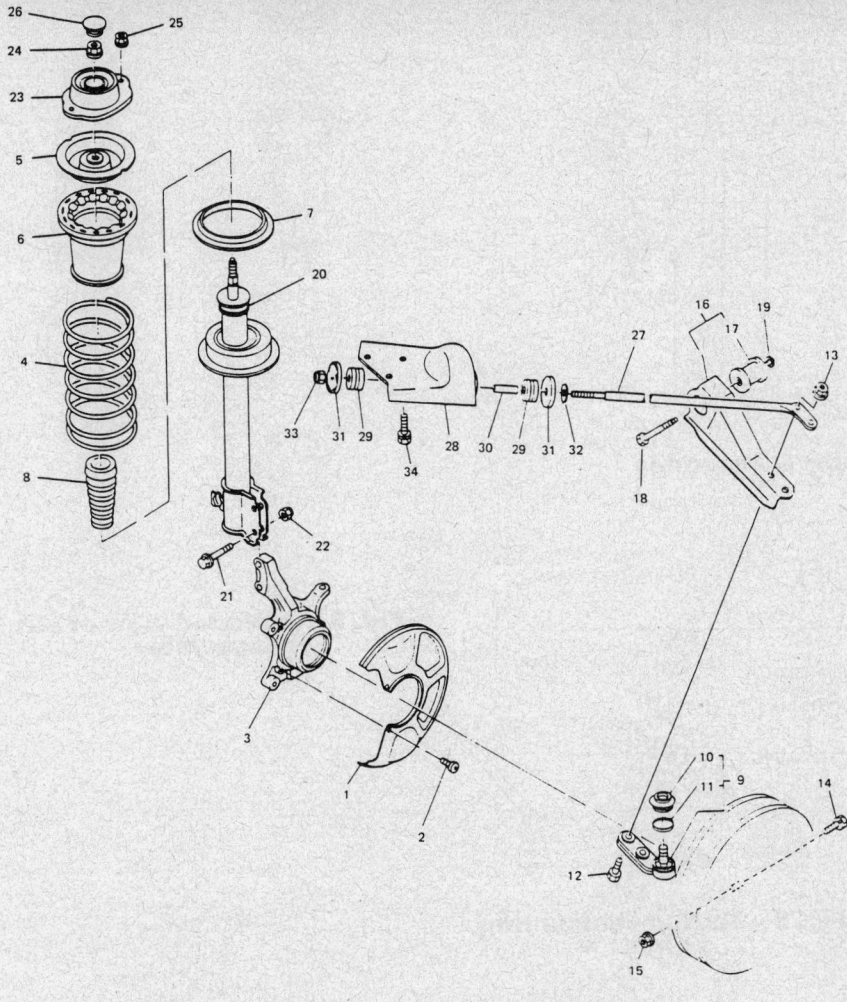

2. Check shock for oil leaks and defective operation.
3. Check coil spring for wear, cracks or distortion.
4. Check upper strut mounting for abnormal noise, binding or defective turning, or any other defects.

ASSEMBLY

1. Assemble strut in compressor tool, **Fig. 4**, ensuring "IN" marking on inside of spring upper seat faces inside of vehicle.
2. Compress spring just enough to allow installation of shaft nut.
3. Install shaft nut and tighten until shaft begins to rotate.
4. Release spring compressing tool, then torque shaft nut to specification listed at the end of this section.

INSTALLATION

1. Install strut to knuckle attaching bolts and torque to specification listed at the end of this section.
2. Route flex hose back through strut bracket opening. Connect fitting to caliper and torque to specification listed at the end of this section.
3. Install wheel and tire assembly.
4. Lower vehicle to a height where upper mount can be aligned with holes in body, then install and torque nuts to specification listed at the end of this section.
5. Lower vehicle to ground and tighten wheel nuts.

CONTROL ARM
REPLACE

1. Raise and support front of vehicle.
2. Remove lower control arm to tension rod attaching nuts and bolts.
3. Remove control arm to body attaching bolt and nut.
4. Remove control arm, **Fig. 1.**
5. Reverse procedure to install, noting the following:
   a. Replace self-locking nuts when installing arm.
   b. When attaching control arm to body, first jack up lower part of arm to 15.18 inches, **Fig. 5**, then torque attaching bolts to specifications listed at the end of this section, **Fig. 6.**

LOWER BALL JOINT
REPLACE

1. Raise and support front of vehicle.
2. Remove wheel and tire assembly.
3. Remove two nuts and bolts attaching ball joint, tension rod and control arm.
4. Remove ball joint to knuckle pinch bolt, then the ball joint, **Fig. 7.**
5. Reverse procedure to install.

TENSION ROD
REPLACE

1. Raise and support front of vehicle.
2. Remove stabilizer bar to tension rod

1. Cover, Dust	18. Bolt, Arm
2. Screw, Dust	19. Washer, Lock
3. Knuckle, Steering	20. Strut Asm., Front
4. Spring, Coil	21. Bolt, Strut
5. Seat, Upper	22. Nut, Lock
6. Seat, Rubber	23. Mount Asm., Strut Upper
7. Seat, Lower, Rubber	24. Nut, Flange (Strut Shaft)
8. Rubber, Bumper	25. Nut, Strut
9. Ball Joint, Lower Control Arm	26. Cap, Strut Upper
10. Boot, Ball Joint	27. Rod, Tension
11. Ring, Boot Clip	28. Bracket, Support
12. Bolt, Control Arm	29. Cushion, Rubber
13. Nut, Lock	30. Spacer, Tension Rod
14. Bolt, Arm End (Pinch)	31. Washer, Tension Rod
15. Nut, Lock	32. Washer, Tension Rod
16. Arm Asm., Lower	33. Nut, Lock
17. Bushing, Arm	34. Bolt, Support

Fig. 1 Exploded view of front suspension assembly

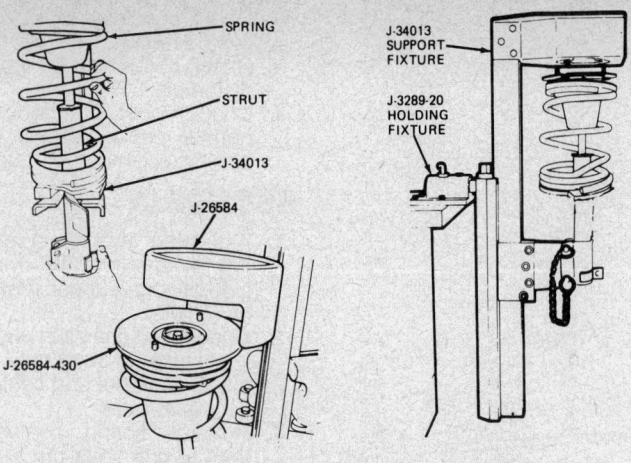

Fig. 2   Strut disassembly & assembly

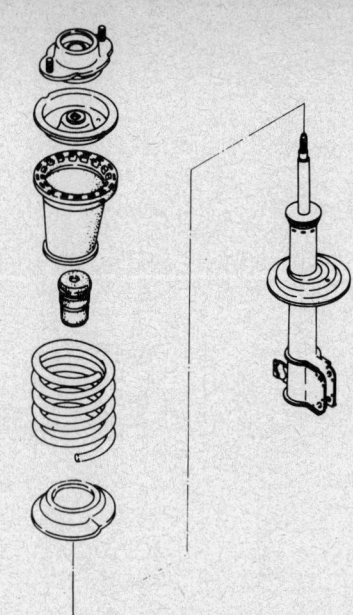

Fig. 3   Exploded view of strut assembly

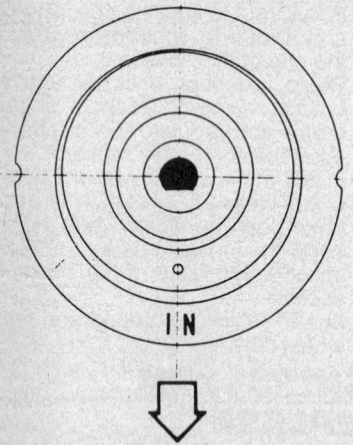

INSIDE OF VEHICLE

Fig. 4   Positioning spring upper seat

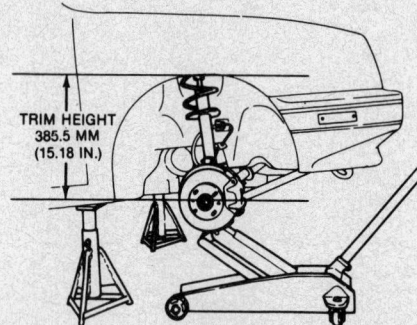

Fig. 5   Setting vehicle trim height

bracket and insulator attaching nuts and bolts, if equipped.
3. Remove tension rod to body attaching nut and washer.
4. Remove tension rod to control arm attaching nuts and bolts and the tension rod, **Fig. 8.**
5. Reverse procedure to install, using new self-locking nut.

STABILIZER BAR
REPLACE

1. Raise and support front of vehicle.
2. Remove four stabilizer bar bracket and insulator attaching nuts and bolts, then the stabilizer bar, **Fig. 8.**
3. Reverse procedure to install. Align stabilizer bar front side insulator as shown, **Fig. 9.**

HUB & ROTOR
REPLACE

1. Raise and support front of vehicle.
2. Loosen wheel lug nuts, then remove wheel and tire assembly.

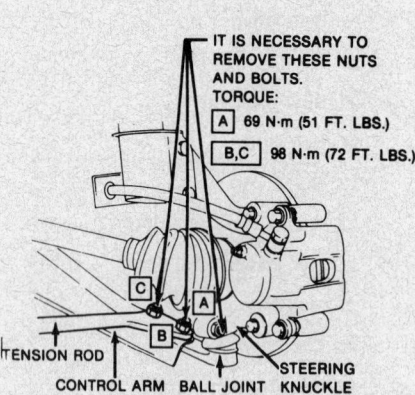

Fig. 7   Ball joint replacement

3. Remove caliper to knuckle attaching bolts, then position caliper aside.
4. Unstake nut, then remove nut and rotor, **Fig. 10.**
5. Using tool Nos. J-34866 and J-2619-01, remove hub, **Fig. 11.**
6. Reverse procedure to install. Replace all bearings, seals and self locking nuts. After tightening nut to specified torque, stake nut, **Fig. 12.**

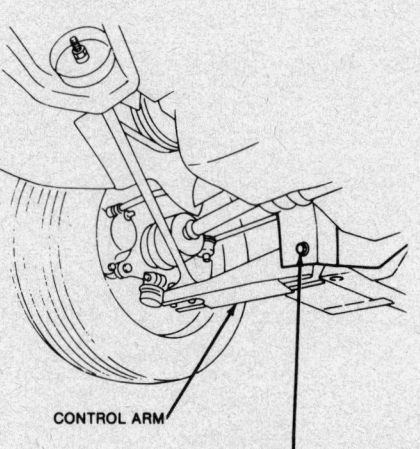

Fig. 6   Control arm installation

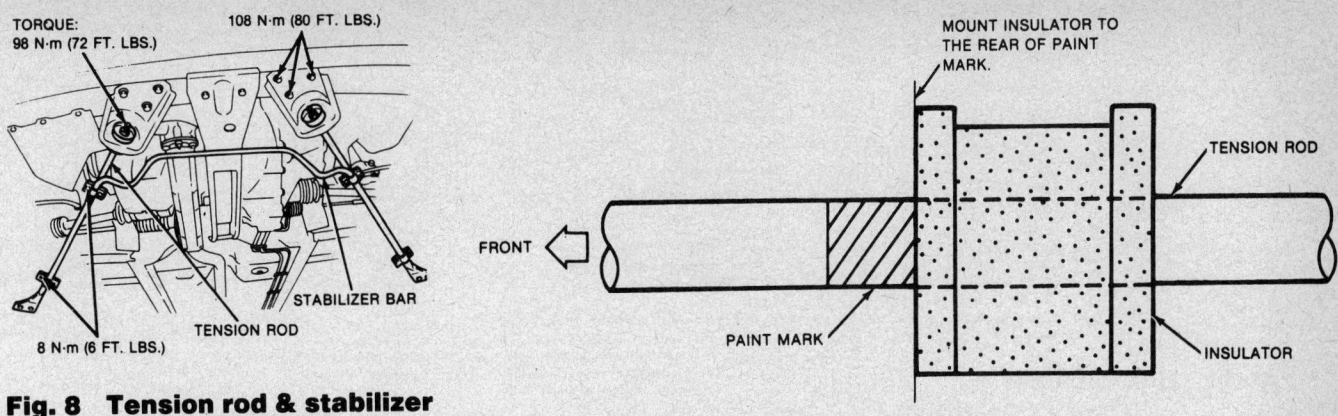

Fig. 8   Tension rod & stabilizer bar replacement

MOUNT INSULATOR TO THE REAR OF PAINT MARK.

TENSION ROD

FRONT

PAINT MARK

INSULATOR

FRONT SIDE BRACKET

PAINT MARKS:
MANUAL TRANS-BLUE (RS) RED (LS)
AUTO TRANS-WHITE (LS) BLUE (RS)

Fig. 9   Stabilizer bar insulator alignment

TORQUE:
98 N·m (72 FT. LBS.)
108 N·m (80 FT. LBS.)
8 N·m (6 FT. LBS.)
STABILIZER BAR
TENSION ROD

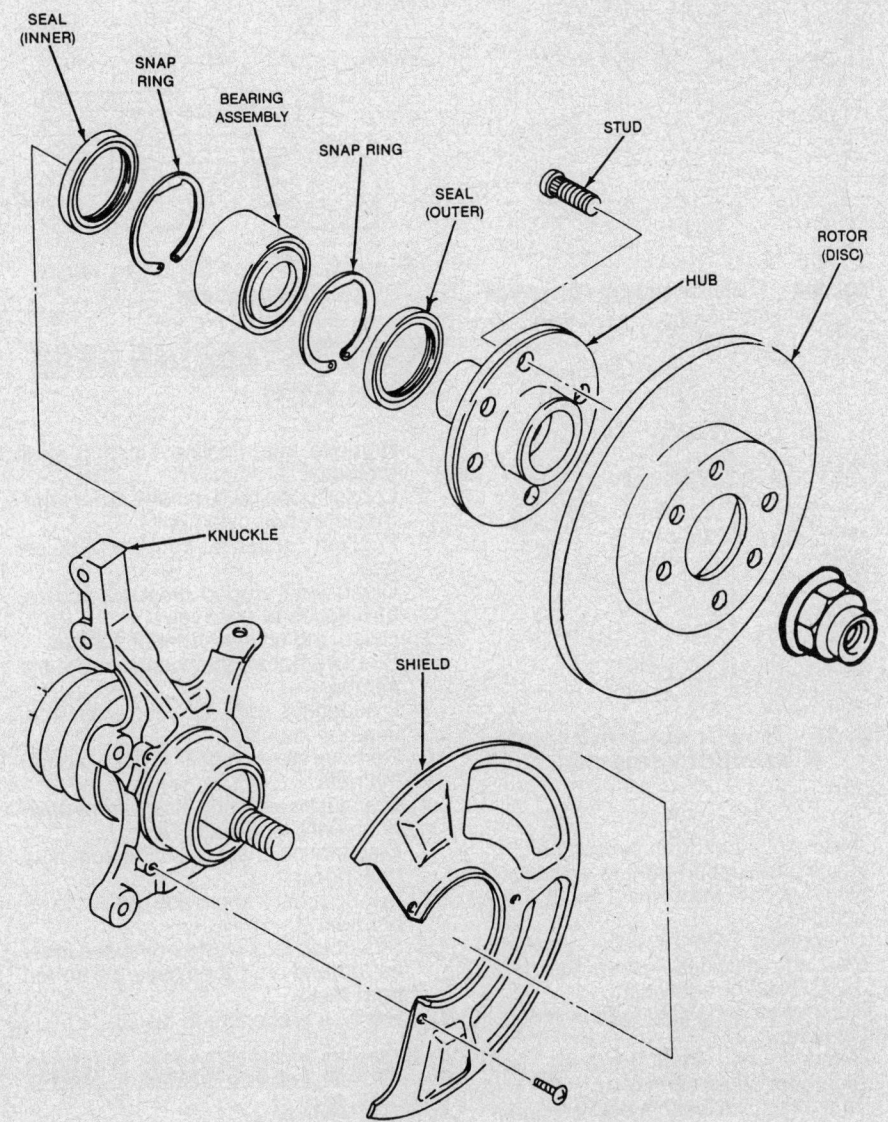

SEAL (INNER)
SNAP RING
BEARING ASSEMBLY
SNAP RING
SEAL (OUTER)
STUD
ROTOR (DISC)
HUB
KNUCKLE
SHIELD

Fig. 10   Exploded view of steering knuckle & hub assembly.

STEERING KNUCKLE SERVICE

REMOVAL

1. Raise and support front of vehicle.
2. Remove wheel and tire assembly.
3. Remove brake hose retaining clip from strut, then disconnect hose from caliper.
4. Unfasten caliper from steering knuckle and support caliper.
5. Remove rotor, then the hub as mentioned previously.
6. Remove splash shield.
7. Remove tie rod using tool No. J-21687-02 or equivalent.
8. Remove two ball joint to control arm and tension rod attaching nuts and bolts.
9. Remove steering knuckle to strut attaching nuts and bolts and the steering knuckle, **Fig. 13.**

DISASSEMBLY

1. Remove inner seal, snap rings and inner bearing race from steering knuckle.
2. Press hub bearing from knuckle, **Fig. 14.**
3. Press outer bearing race from hub, **Fig. 15. The hub bearing, both inner and outer seals and races must not be reused.**

ASSEMBLY

1. Install outer snap ring to knuckle.
2. Install hub bearing assembly using a suitable press.
3. Install inner snap ring, then the inner and outer seals using tool J-35303 or equivalent.
4. Install outer race using tool No. J-3502 or equivalent.

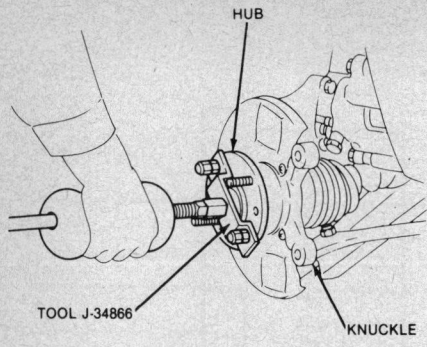

Fig. 11 Hub removal

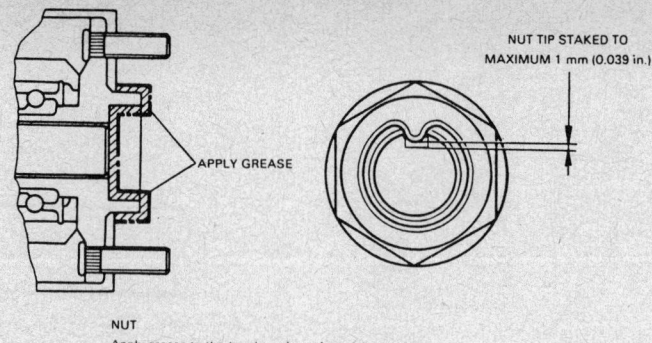

NUT
Apply grease to the head inside surfaces, the nut fitting surfaces, and the nut threads. Tighten the nut to 186 N•m (137 lbs. ft.) torque. Stake the nut tip after tightening it to the specified torque.

NOTE: Always replace the used nut with a new nut. Never attempt to reuse the old nut.

Fig. 12 Hub spindle nut installation.

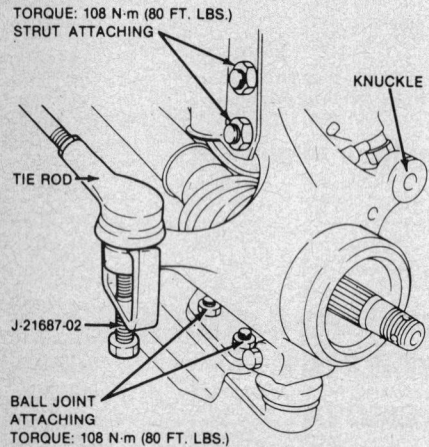

Fig. 13 Steering knuckle removal

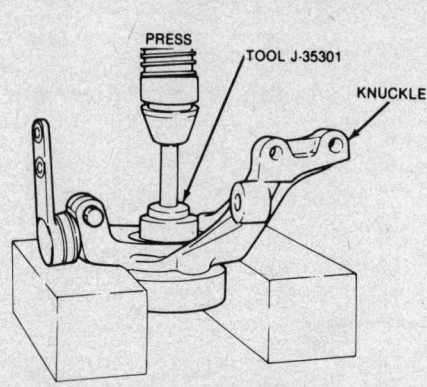

Fig. 14 Hub bearing removal

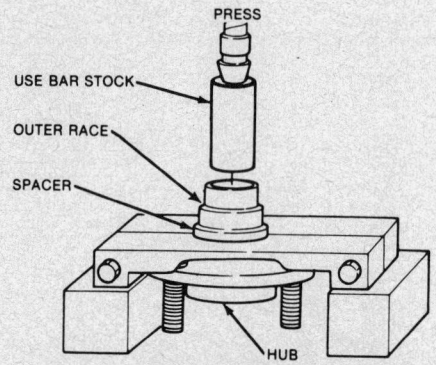

Fig. 15 Outer bearing race removal

INSTALLATION

1. Install ball joint to control arm attaching nuts and bolts and torque to specification listed at the end of this section.
2. Install strut to knuckle attaching nuts and bolts and torque to specification listed at the end of this section.
3. Install tie rod to knuckle attaching nut and torque to specification listed at the end of this section.
4. Install brake rotor.
5. Install brake caliper to knuckle attaching bolts and torque to specification listed at the end of this section.
6. Install brake hose to caliper and torque fitting to specification listed at the end of this section.
7. Install wheel and tire assembly, then lower vehicle.
8. Apply suitable grease to axle shaft threads and nut. After tightening nut to specified torque, stake nut, **Fig. 12.**
9. Tighten wheel nuts, then bleed brake system.

MANUAL STEERING GEAR
REPLACE

1. Remove intermediate shaft cover.
2. Loosen upper pinch bolt, then remove

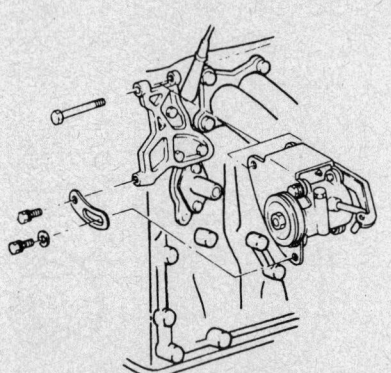

Fig. 16 Power steering pump & bracket removal

lower pinch bolt from pinion shaft.
3. Raise and support front of vehicle.
4. Remove both front wheel and tire assemblies.
5. Disconnect both tie rod ends from steering knuckles using tool No. J-21687-02 or equivalent.
6. Remove steering gear to body mounting nuts.
7. Remove band from left boot, then slide boot off steering gear.
8. Straighten lock washer between inner tie rod and rack, then separate tie rod from rack.
9. Reverse procedure to install.

POWER STEERING GEAR
REPLACE

1. Remove intermediate steering shaft protector.
2. Loosen upper and remove lower intermediate shaft pinch bolts.
3. Position suitable container below gear.
4. Clean area around pressure and return hoses at gear valve.
5. Raise and support front of vehicle.
6. Remove both front wheel and tire assemblies.
7. Disconnect both tie rod ends from steering knuckles.
8. Remove steering gear to dash mounting nuts.
9. Cut plastic retaining straps from power steering pipes and hose.
10. Disconnect inner boot band from right rack boot.
11. Pull boot back to provide access to inner tie rod.
12. Straighten lock washer between inner tie rod and rack, then separate tie rod from rack.
13. Reverse procedure to install.

POWER STEERING PUMP
REPLACE

1. Position suitable container below pump.

2. Remove pressure hose clamp.
3. Disconnect pressure and return hoses from pump.

4. Remove adjusting bolt, pivot bolt and drive belt.
5. Remove pump and pump bracket,

Fig. 16.
6. Remove pulley from pump.
7. Reverse procedure to install.

TIGHTENING SPECIFICATIONS

Year	Component	Torque/Ft. Lbs.
1988-89	Brake Hose To Disc Brake Caliper	13
	Control Arm To Crossmember Bolt	41
	Disc Brake Caliper To Steering Knuckle Bolts	41
	Front Hub Spindle Nut	137①
	Inner Tie Rod To Rack Nut	65
	Lower Ball Joint To Control Arm Nuts	80
	Lower Ball Joint To Steering Knuckle Pinch Bolt	51
	Power Steering Pump Mounting Bolts	15
	Steering Gear Mounting Bolts	30
	Strut Shaft Nut	43
	Strut To Steering Knuckle Attaching Bolts	87
	Strut Upper Attaching Nuts	41
	Tension Rod Clamp Bolts	6
	Tension Rod Support Bracket Attaching Bolts	40
	Tension Rod To Control Arm Nuts	80
	Tension Rod To Support Bracket Nut	72
	Tie Rod End To Steering Knuckle	29
	Wheel & Tire Assembly	65

①—Nut must be staked after tightening.

Wheel Alignment

INDEX

DESCRIPTION

Wheel alignment, is the angular relationship between the wheels, suspension attaching parts and ground. The angle of the knuckle away from the vertical, pointing in or out of wheels, tilt of the wheels from vertical (when viewed from front of vehicle) and tilt of suspension members from vertical (when viewed from side of vehicle), all of these are involved in proper alignment, **Fig. 1.**

CASTER

Caster is tilting of the front steering axis either forward or backward from the vertical (when viewed from side of vehicle). A backward tilt is positive (+) and a forward tilt is negative (−). On short and long arm type suspensions you cannot see a caster angle without using a special instrument, but if you look straight down from the top

of the upper control arm to the ground you would find that ball joints do not line up (fore and aft) when a caster angle other than 0° is present.

CAMBER

Camber is the tilting of front and rear wheels from the vertical when viewed from front of vehicle. When wheels tilt outward at top, camber is positive (+). When wheels tilt inward, camber is negative (MI). Amount of tilt is measured in degrees from the vertical and this is camber angle.

TOE

Toe is the turning in or out of wheels. The actual amount of toe is normally .078 inch (2 mm). The purpose of toe is to ensure parallel rolling of wheels. Excessive toe-in or toe-out may increase tire wear. Toe also serves to offset small deflections of the suspension which occurs when vehicle is moving.

PRELIMINARY CHECK

Steering and vibration problems are not always the result of alignment. An additional problem to be checked is tire lead due to worn or improperly manufactured tires. "Lead" is the deviation of the vehicle from a straight path on a level road without hand pressure on the steering wheel.

To insure correct alignment readings and alignment specifications, the following checks and inspections should be made.
1. Check tire for proper inflation and thread wear.
2. Check for loose ball joints and tie rod ends. If excessive looseness is noted, replace defective parts before adjusting toe.
3. Check for wheel and tire assembly run-out.
4. Check trim heights. If not within specifications, correct before adjusting toe.
5. Check for loose control arms.

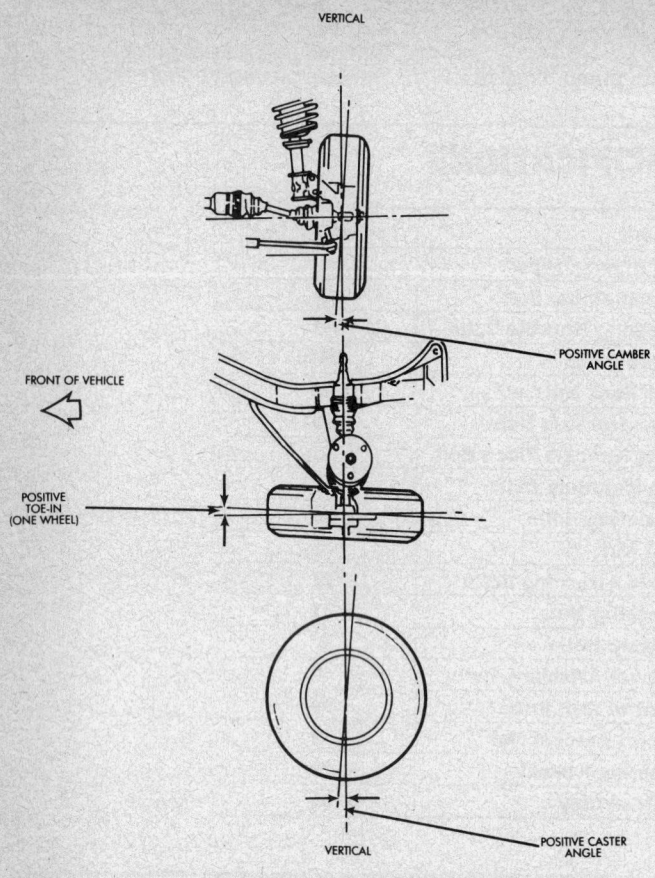

Fig. 1 Suspension geometry

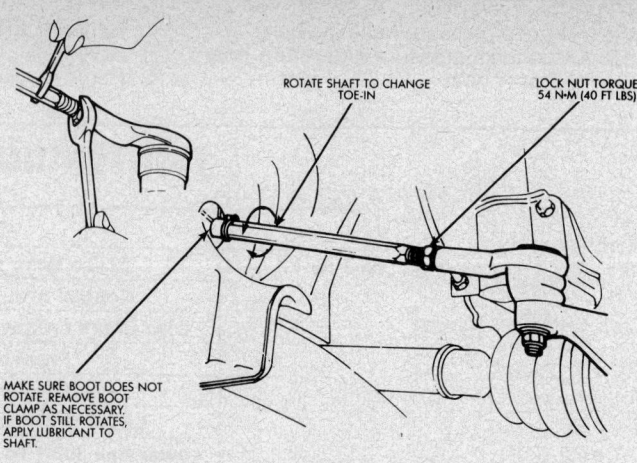

Fig. 2 Adjusting toe-in

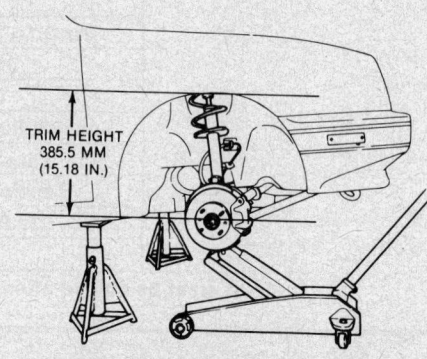

Fig. 3 Adjusting front trim height

6. Check for loose or missing stabilizer bar components.
7. Consideration must be given to excess loads, such as tool boxes, etc. If excess load is normally carried in vehicle, it should remain during alignment checks.

ADJUSTMENTS

CASTER & CAMBER

Caster and camber angles are pre-set and cannot be adjusted. If caster and/or camber are out of specifications, the cause must be found. If worn or damaged suspension components are the cause, they should be replaced. If problem is body related, the body should be repaired as needed.

TOE-IN

Toe-in is adjusted by altering tie rod length. To perform adjustment, loosen small end boot clamps and slide from the boot. Loosen right and left tie rod end locknuts, then turn both tie rods, **Fig. 2**, the same amount to bring toe-in within specifications. Ensure right and left tie rods are equal in length, then tighten locknuts. When adjustment is complete, ensure boots are not twisted.

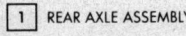

1 REAR AXLE ASSEMBLY

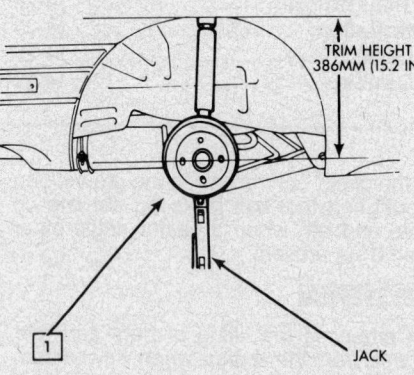

Fig. 4 Adjusting rear trim height

STEERING ANGLE

When a tie rod or tie rod end is replaced, check toe and steering angle using suitable turning radius gauges. If steering angle is not $37\frac{2}{3}°$ inside and $32\frac{1}{2}°$ outside, check right and left tie rods for equal length. If tie rod length is changed to correct steering angle, reinspect toe in.

TRIM HEIGHT
Front

1. Loosen wheel lug nuts.
2. Raise and support vehicle using suitable jack stands.
3. Remove wheel and tire assemblies.
4. Loosen control arm to body, then tension rod attaching bolts.
5. Using a suitable jack, jack up the lower part of control arm to 15.18 inches, **Fig. 3**, **torque** control arm to body attaching bolts to 41 ft. lbs. and tension rod bolts to 80 ft. lbs.

Rear

1. Loosen wheel lug nuts.
2. Raise and support vehicle using suitable jack stands.
3. Remove wheel and tire assemblies.
4. Loosen rear axle attaching bolts.
5. Using a suitable jack, jack up lower part of rear axle and set rear trim height to 15.2 inches, **Fig. 4.**, then **torque** rear axle bolts to 72 ft. lbs.

GEO STORM
(R Car)
INDEX OF SERVICE OPERATIONS

NOTE: Refer To The Rear Of This Manual For Vehicle Manufacturer's Special Tool Suppliers.

Continued

GEO STORM

INDEX OF SERVICE OPERATIONS—Continued

Specifications
GENERAL ENGINE SPECIFICATIONS

Year	Engine Liter/CID①	VIN Code②	Fuel System	Bore & Stroke	Comp. Ratio	Net HP @ RPM③	Maximum Torque Ft. Lbs. @ RPM	Normal Oil Pressure Psi
1990–91	1.6L/4-97④	6	MFI	3.15 x 3.11	9.1	95 @ 5800	97 @ 4800	—
1990–91	1.6L/4-97⑤	5	MFI	3.15 x 3.11	9.8	130 @ 7000	102 @ 5800	—

①—CID: Cubic Inch Displacement.
②—The eighth digit of the VIN denotes engine code.
③—Ratings are net, as installed in vehicle.
④—3 valves each cylinder.
⑤—4 valves each cylinder.

TUNE UP SPECIFICATIONS

Year & Engine/VIN Code	Spark Plug Gap	Ignition Timing BTDC① Firing Order Fig.	Man. Trans.	Auto. Trans.	Mark Fig.	Curb Idle Speed Man. Trans.	Auto. Trans.	Fast Idle Speed Man. Trans.	Auto. Trans.	Fuel Pump Pressure Psi
1988										
1.6L/4-97(6)	.041	②	①	①	A	③	③	③	③	35–42
1.6L/4-97(5)	.043	②	①	①	B	③	③	③	①	35–42

①—TDC: Top Dead Center.
②—1-3-4-2.
③—Idle speeds are ECM controlled.

Continued

TUNE UP SPECIFICATIONS—Continued

Fig. A   12 valve, Crankshaft pulley timing alignment

1 TIMING MARK

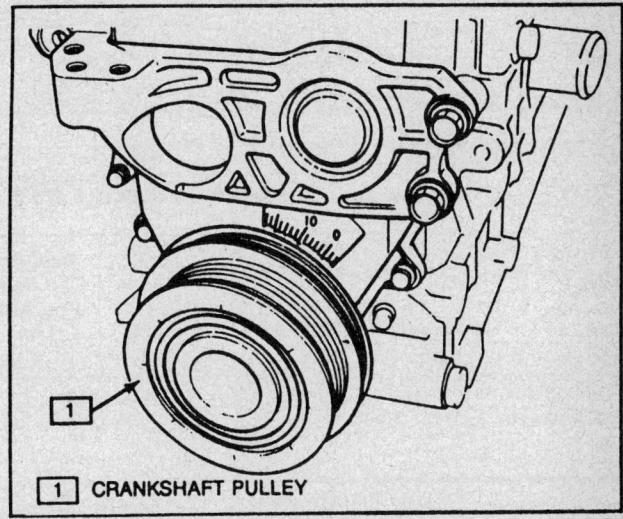

1 CRANKSHAFT PULLEY

Fig. B   16 valve, Crankshaft pulley timing alignment

ALTERNATOR & REGULATOR SPECIFICATIONS

Year	Model	Alternator Rated Output Amps.	Regulated Voltage
1990–91	3 & 4 A/T ①	85	13.8–14.2
1990–91	M/T ②	61	13.8–14.2

①—Delco Remy DRX 06950.
①—Delco Remy DRX 06841.

STARTER MOTOR APPLICATIONS

Refer to "Starter Motor & Switches", section for specifications.

Year	Engine	Model	Make	Ident. No.
1990–91	1.6L/4-97	3 A/T	Denso	128000-7120
	1.6L/4-97	4 A/T	Denso	128000-7000
	1.6L/4-97	Manual Transaxle	Denso	128000-7400

FRONT WHEEL ALIGNMENT SPECIFICATIONS

Year	Model	Caster Angle, Degrees ①		Camber Angle, Degrees		Toe In Inch	
		Limits	Desired	Limits	Desired	Limits	Desired
1990–91	All	2–4	3.0	−1.25– +.25	−0.5	−0.039– +0.039	0

①—Not adjustable

REAR WHEEL ALIGNMENT SPECIFICATIONS

Year	Model	Toe In Inch		Camber	
		Limits	Desired	Limits	Desired
1990–91	All	0.118–0.246	0.157	—	—

COOLING SYSTEM & CAPACITY DATA

Year	Model	Cooling Capacity Qts.		Radiator Cap Relief Pressure, Lbs.	Thermo. Opening Temp. °F.	Fuel Tank Gals.	Engine Oil w/Filter Qts. ①	Transmission Oil	
		Vin 6	Vin 5					Manual Transaxle, Qts.	Auto Transaxle, Qts.
1990–91	All	②	③	14.2	180°F	12.4	④	4.2	⑤

①—Approximate, make final check with dipstick.
②—With M/T, 7.1 qts.; With A/T, 7.6 qts.
③—With M/T, 7.3 qts.; With A/T, 7.8 qts.
④—Vin 6, 3.5 qts.; Vin 5, 4.2 qts.
⑤—With 3 speed, 6.9 qts., With 4 speed, 6.8 qts.

Electrical

INDEX

FUSE PANEL & FLASHER LOCATION

The fuse panel is located below lefthand side of instrument panel, **Fig. 1.**

Turn signal and hazard flasher is located above fuse panel, under lefthand side of instrument panel.

STARTER MOTOR
REPLACE

1. Disconnect battery ground cable, then battery positive cable from starter.
2. On models with manual transaxle, disconnect ignition switch lead from starter solenoid.
3. On models with automatic transaxle, disconnect ignition switch lead from starter solenoid pigtail.
4. On all models, remove two starter motor mounting bolts, then the motor.
5. Reverse procedure to install, **torque** starter attaching bolts to 29 ft. lbs. and battery positive cable nut to 26 ft. lbs.

Fig. 1   Fuse panel location

DISTRIBUTOR
REPLACE

1. Disconnect battery ground cable.
2. Remove all distributor electrical connections, then distributor cap.
3. Mark distributor housing position on engine, and the rotor position on distributor housing assembly.
4. Remove distributor mounting bolt, **Fig. 2,** then distributor from engine.
5. Remove O ring from distributor shaft.
6. Reverse procedures to install, using new O-ring gaskets.

TURN SIGNAL/DIMMER SWITCH
REPLACE

On all models equipped with the SIR or inflatable restraint systems, disable system as described in "Passive Restraint Systems" before performing any repair procedures on or near steering column.

1. Disconnect battery ground cable.
2. Remove steering wheel as described in "Steering Wheel, Replace."
3. Remove lower switch panel, dash lighter panel and hood release cable.
4. Remove lap air deflector attaching screws, then the lap air reflector.

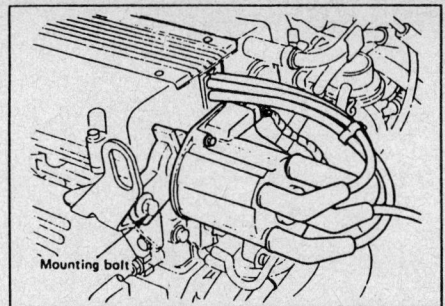

Fig. 2 Distributor assembly

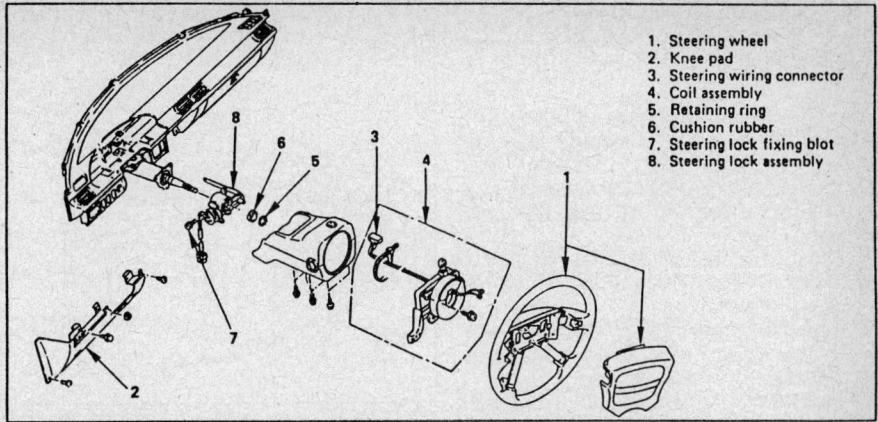

1. Steering wheel
2. Knee pad
3. Steering wiring connector
4. Coil assembly
5. Retaining ring
6. Cushion rubber
7. Steering lock fixing blot
8. Steering lock assembly

Fig. 3 Steering column assembly

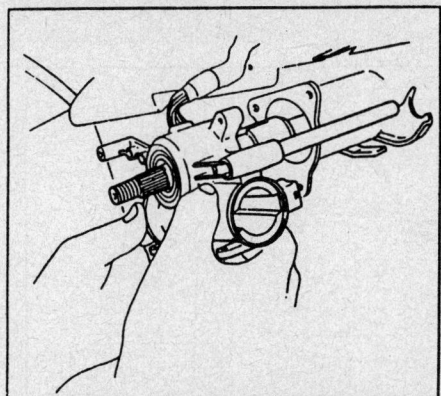

Fig. 4 Ignition switch assembly

Fig. 5 SIR module removal

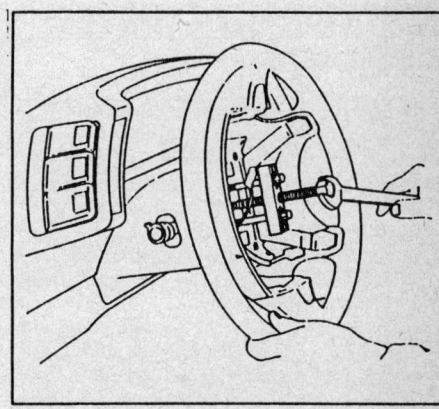

Fig. 6 Steering wheel removal

5. Remove left lower dash trim panel attaching screws, then lower dash trim panel.
6. Remove upper steering column mounting bolts and lower column.
7. Remove two piece steering column cover attaching screws and cover.
8. Disconnect coil assembly wiring harness from turn signal switch, then remove four retaining screws and coil assembly, **Fig. 3**.
9. Remove turn signal switch retaining screws, then turn signal switch.
10. Reverse procedure to install.

IGNITION LOCK
REPLACE

On all models equipped with the SIR or inflatable restraint systems, disable system as described in "Passive Restraint Systems" before performing any repair procedures on or near steering column.

1. Disconnect battery ground cable.
2. Remove steering wheel as described in "Steering Wheel, Replace."
3. Remove turn signal assembly as described in "Turn Signal/Dimmer Switch, Replace."
4. Turn key to Off position, depress retaining pin, then remove ignition lock cylinder from switch.
5. Reverse procedure to install.

IGNITION SWITCH
REPLACE

On all models equipped with the SIR or inflatable restraint systems, disable system as described in "Passive Restraint Systems" before performing any repair procedures on or near steering column.

1. Disconnect battery ground cable.
2. Remove steering wheel as described in "Steering Wheel, Replace."
3. Remove turn signal assembly as described in "Turn Signal/Dimmer Switch, Replace."
4. Remove ignition lock as described in "Ignition Lock, Replace."
5. Disconnect electrical connector from ignition switch, then remove snap ring and spacer collar from steering shaft, **Fig. 4**.
6. Disconnect back drive cable from ignition switch, then remove ignition switch retaining bolts and ignition switch from steering column.
7. Reverse procedure to install.

HORN SOUNDER & STEERING WHEEL
REPLACE

On all models equipped with the SIR or inflatable restraint systems, disable system as described in "Passive Restraint Systems" before performing any repair procedures on or near steering column.

1. Disconnect battery ground cable.
2. Remove SIR module mounting screws and SIR module, **Fig. 5**.
3. Remove steering wheel retaining nut.
4. Using puller tool NO. J 1859-03 or equivalent, remove steering wheel from column, **Fig. 6**.
5. Remove horn switch retaining screws and horn switch from steering wheel, **Fig. 7**.
6. Remove rear steering wheel cover attaching screws, then the cover.
7. Reverse procedure to install, **torque** steering wheel nut to 25 ft. lbs.

HEADLAMP SWITCH
REPLACE

On all models equipped with the SIR or inflatable restraint systems, disable system as described in "Passive Restraint Systems" before performing any repair procedures on or near steering column.

1. Disconnect battery ground cable.
2. Refer to "Dash Panel Service" to remove meter hood.
3. Remove meter cluster from meter hood, then two clips attaching headlamp control harness.
4. Remove four headlamp control switch retaining screws, then the headlamp control switch with illumination box, Fig. 8.
5. Disconnect electrical connector, then two illumination box retaining screws and illumination box.
6. Reverse procedure to install.

INSTRUMENT CLUSTER
REPLACE

On all models equipped with the SIR or inflatable restraint systems, disable system as described in "Passive Restraint Systems" before performing any repair procedures on or near steering column.

1. Disconnect battery ground cable.
2. Refer to "Dash Panel Service", then remove meter hood.
3. Remove four dash gauge retaining screws, then disconnect electrical connectors and speedometer cable, Fig. 9.
4. Remove dash gauge assembly.
5. Reverse procedure to install, ensuring that all electrical connectors are securely connected.

WINDSHIELD WIPER SWITCH
REPLACE

FRONT

On all models equipped with the SIR or inflatable restraint systems, disable system as described in "Passive Restraint Systems" before performing any repair procedures on or near steering column.

1. Disconnect battery ground cable.
2. Remove meter hood as described in "Dash Panel Service."
3. Remove meter cluster, then the two attaching clips from wiper/washer switch harness.
4. Remove four switch attaching screws, then the switch with illumination bulb.
5. Reverse procedure to install.

REAR

1. Disconnect battery ground cable.
2. Remove trim bezel.
3. Remove rear wiper switch, then disconnect electrical connector.
4. Reverse procedure to install.

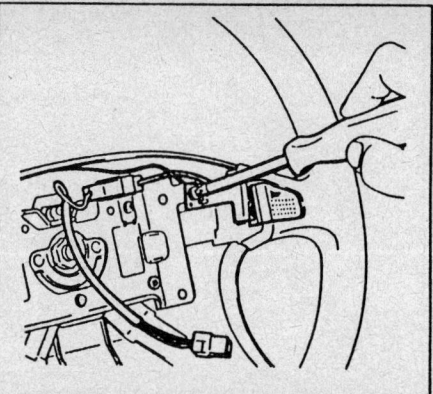

Fig. 7   Horn harness connector

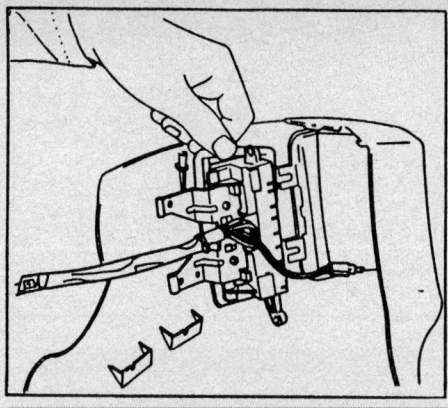

Fig. 8   Headlamp control switch

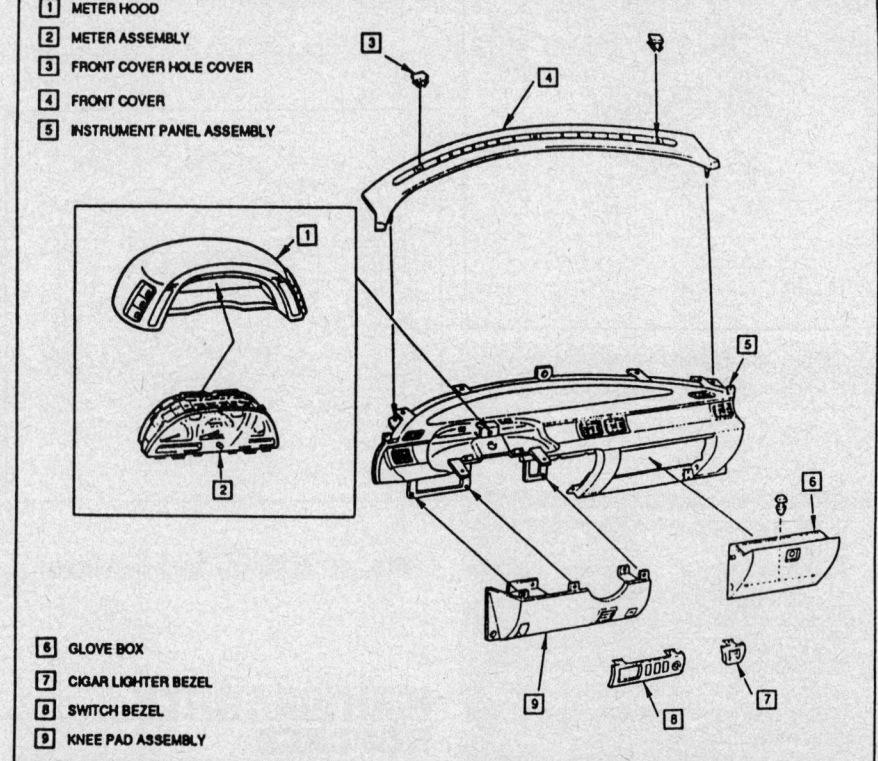

1. METER HOOD
2. METER ASSEMBLY
3. FRONT COVER HOLE COVER
4. FRONT COVER
5. INSTRUMENT PANEL ASSEMBLY
6. GLOVE BOX
7. CIGAR LIGHTER BEZEL
8. SWITCH BEZEL
9. KNEE PAD ASSEMBLY

Fig. 9   Instrument panel

CLUTCH START SWITCH
REPLACE

1. Disconnect battery ground cable.
2. Disconnect electrical connector from clutch switch that is mounted above clutch pedal.
3. Remove front locknut, then the switch.
4. Remove rear locknut.
5. Reverse the procedure to install.

CLUTCH START SWITCH
ADJUST

Loosen clutch switch locknut, then rotate clutch switch until threaded portion bottoms on switch bracket, then tighten locknut.

STOP LAMP SWITCH
REPLACE

1. Remove stop lamp switch lock nut, then the stop lamp switch.
2. Reverse procedure to install.

STOP LAMP SWITCH
ADJUST

Loosen stop lamp switch locknut. Thread stop lamp switch into bracket until tip of switch is gently resting on pedal arm. Carefully thread stop lamp switch inward until freeplay between brake pedal and push rod is eliminated, then tighten locknut.

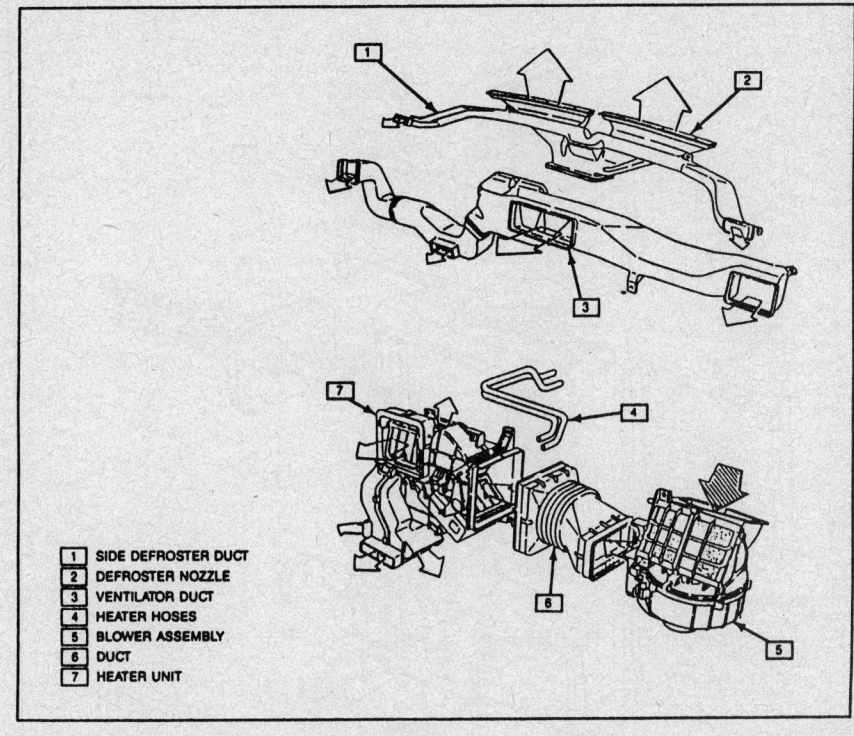

Fig. 10 Heater assembly

1 SIDE DEFROSTER DUCT
2 DEFROSTER NOZZLE
3 VENTILATOR DUCT
4 HEATER HOSES
5 BLOWER ASSEMBLY
6 DUCT
7 HEATER UNIT

RADIO
REPLACE

1. Remove four heater control knobs, then four radio bezel screws from radio bezel, **Fig. 9.**
2. Disconnect illumination lamp and harness from radio bezel.
3. Remove three righthand side panel retaining screws, then four radio bracket retaining screws.
4. Remove radio from I/P, then disconnect electrical and antenna connectors.
5. Reverse procedure to install.

HEATER CORE
REPLACE

1. Disconnect battery ground cable.
2. Drain cooling system, then disconnect heater hoses at engine compartment.
3. Remove instrument panel assembly, referring to "Dash Panel Service" for procedure.
4. Remove evaporator assembly as described in "Evaporator Core, Replace."

5. Remove duct between blower assembly and heater unit, **Fig. 10,** then the center ventilation duct.
6. Remove four heater unit retaining nuts, then the heater unit.
7. Remove three duct mounting screws, then the five mode control to heater core case retaining screws.
8. Remove mode control case, but do not remove the link assembly at this time.
9. Remove five screws so that two halves of the heater core case may be separated, **Fig. 10.**
10. Remove heater core.
11. Reverse procedure to install.

BLOWER MOTOR
REPLACE

1. Disconnect battery ground cable.
2. Disconnect blower motor electrical connector.
3. Remove four blower motor attaching screws, then the blower motor, **Fig. 10.**
4. Reverse procedure to install.

EVAPORATOR CORE
REPLACE

1. Disconnect battery ground cable.
2. Discharge A/C system as described in "Air Conditioning."
3. Remove A/C lines from expansion valve, capping all fittings immediately to keep moisture out of system.
4. Remove retaining clip and expansion valve from the evaporator.
5. Remove glove box assembly from I/P, then the lower dash reinforcement bracket.
6. Disconnect electrical connector from thermostat switch and blower motor resistor.
7. Remove air inlet cable from blend door, then retaining nuts from evaporator case.
8. Remove evaporator assembly from dash, then retaining clip from evaporator case.
9. Remove four case retaining screws, then separate case, **Fig. 11.**
10. Remove evaporator core and evaporator grommet from case.
11. Reverse procedure to install.

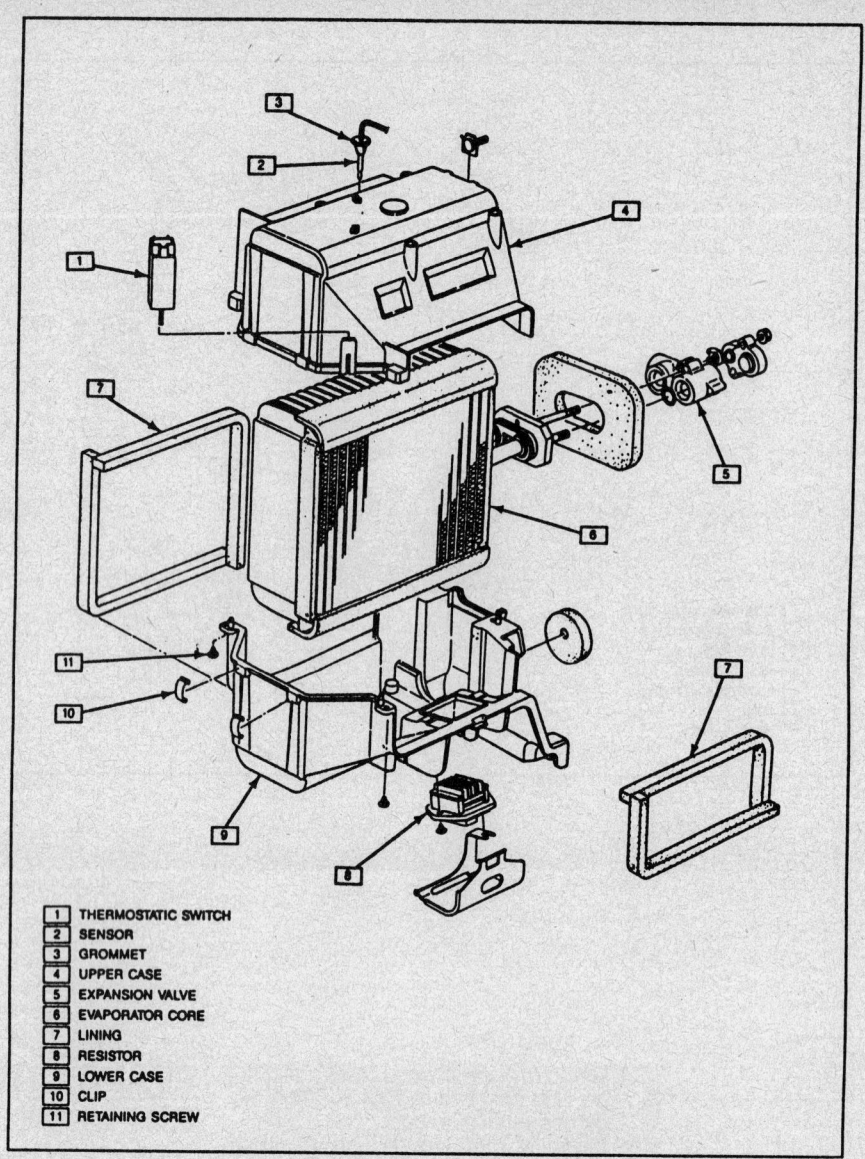

1. THERMOSTATIC SWITCH
2. SENSOR
3. GROMMET
4. UPPER CASE
5. EXPANSION VALVE
6. EVAPORATOR CORE
7. LINING
8. RESISTOR
9. LOWER CASE
10. CLIP
11. RETAINING SCREW

Fig. 11 Evaporator assembly

1.6L/4-97 Engine

INDEX

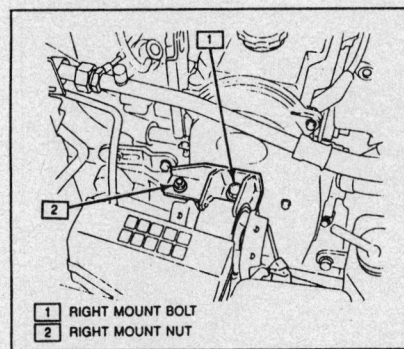

| 1 | RIGHT MOUNT BOLT |
| 2 | RIGHT MOUNT NUT |

Fig. 1   Right engine mount

ENGINE MOUNTS
REPLACE
RIGHT MOUNT

1. Disconnect battery ground cable.
2. Using engine support tool No. J28467-A or equivalent, support engine.
3. Raise and support vehicle.
4. Remove bolt and nut from mounting bridge bracket, **Fig. 1.**
5. Remove engine mount through bolt, then the engine mount.
6. Reverse procedure to install.

TORQUE ROD

1. Disconnect battery ground cable, then raise and support vehicle.
2. Remove torque rod bracket attaching nut and bolts, **Fig. 2.**
3. Remove torque rod center bolt and nut, then remove torque rod and bracket assembly.
4. Reverse procedure to install.

REAR MOUNT

1. Disconnect battery ground cable.
2. Support engine using engine support tool, No. J28467-A or equivalent.
3. Raise and support vehicle.
4. Remove dampener weight from the engine mounting, then the bolt from transaxle case.
5. Remove center bolts from the center beam, then the rear engine mount.
6. Reverse procedure to install.

LEFT MOUNT

1. Disconnect battery cables, then remove battery.
2. Remove cover plate, then the left engine mount bolts from transaxle case.
3. Remove left engine mount center bolt, then left engine mount.
4. Reverse procedure to install.

ENGINE
REPLACE

1. Disconnect battery cables.
2. Remove battery, battery tray and hood.
3. Drain engine coolant, then remove accelerator cable from throttle valve.
4. Remove breather hose from intake air duct, then intake air duct from throttle valve.
5. Remove air cleaner assembly.
6. Disconnect MAP sensor hose from MAP sensor, then the brake booster vacuum hose and two canister hoses from pipes of the common chamber.
7. Remove two cable harness connectors near LH shock tower.
8. Disconnect ignition coil electrical connectors, then the ignition coil and bracket as an assembly.
9. Disconnect engine harness ground cable from LH inner fender, then the chassis harness terminal from relay and fuse box.

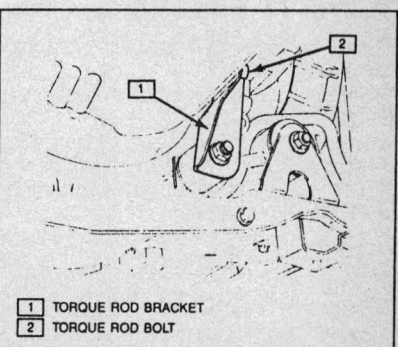

| 1 | TORQUE ROD BRACKET |
| 2 | TORQUE ROD BOLT |

Fig. 2   Torque rod engine mount

10. Disconnect cooling fan and oxygen sensor harness connectors.
11. Disconnect ground cable terminal at rear of cylinder head cover and four connectors from automatic transaxle control system harness.
12. **On models with manual transaxle,** disconnect clutch cable by loosening two adjusting nuts.
13. Remove two transaxle shift cables by disconnecting cotter pin and removing clip from shift cable bracket.
14. **On models with automatic transaxle,** disconnect transaxle shift cable by removing cotter pin, then the joint from shift cable lever.
15. **On all models,** remove two heater hoses from engine, speedometer cable from transaxle and upper radiator hose from radiator.
16. Remove fuel feed pipe and fuel return hose near the filter, then the coolant coolant recovery tank with bracket as an assembly.
17. Remove power steering belt, power steering pump and bracket.
18. Remove cooling fan and shroud, then raise and support vehicle.

19. Remove righthand and lefthand under covers, then the lower radiator hose.
20. Remove two transaxle oil cooler lines from transaxle.
21. Remove two air conditioning compressor bracket bolts from engine and set aside.
22. Remove front tire and wheel assemblies, then the drive axles.
23. Remove front exhaust pipe from exhaust manifold, then lower vehicle.
24. Lower vehicle and attach a suitable engine hoist to the lifting bracket, applying slight pressure.
25. Remove engine and transaxle mounts.
26. Remove engine and transaxle as an assembly.
27. Remove transaxle from engine.
28. Reverse procedure to install.

COMMON CHAMBER/INTAKE MANIFOLD REPLACE

12 VALVE ENGINE

Refer to **Figs. 3, 4 and 5** for 12 valve engine breakdown.
1. Remove battery ground cable, then ignition coil wires.
2. Remove accelerator cable from throttle valve and common chamber, then two cable harness connectors at lefthand shock tower.
3. Disconnect cable harness from intake air control valve, MAT and TPS sensors.
4. Remove breather hose from intake air duct, then intake air duct from throttle valve and PCV hose from the cylinder head cover.
5. Remove EGR valve and canister vacuum hoses from throttle valve, then the EGR pipe from EGR valve and exhaust manifold.
6. Remove common chamber bracket and throttle valve assembly attaching bolts, then the throttle valve.
7. Remove coolant bypass pipe clip bolt and MAP sensor from common chamber.
8. Remove brake booster and canister vacuum hoses from common chamber and throttle valve.
9. Remove pressure regulator and EGR vacuum hoses from common chamber.
10. Remove engine hanger bolt, then the common chamber retaining nuts and bolts.
11. Remove common chamber from engine assembly.
12. Reverse procedure to install.

16 VALVE ENGINE

Refer to **Figs. 6 through 9**, when working on 16 valve engines.
1. Disconnect battery ground cable.
2. Remove accelerator cable clip and PCV hose from intake air duct, then the intake air duct from vehicle.

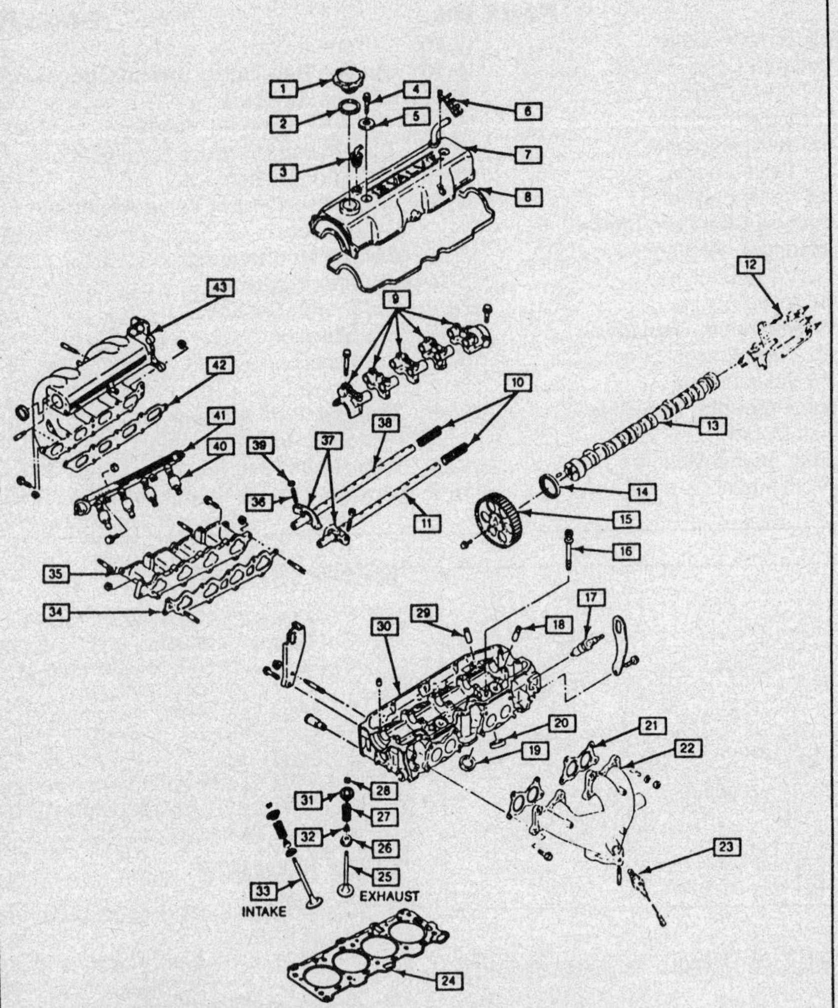

1	OIL FILLER CAP
2	GASKET
3	PCV VALVE
4	CYLINDER HEAD COVER BOLT
5	GASKET
6	CABLE CLIP
7	CYLINDER HEAD COVER
8	GASKET
9	ROCKER BRACKET
10	ROCKER SPRING
11	ROCKER SHAFT (EXHAUST)
12	DISTRIBUTOR
13	CAMSHAFT
14	CAMSHAFT OIL SEAL
15	TIMING PULLEY
16	CYLINDER HEAD BOLT
17	SPARK PLUG
18	VALVE GUIDE (EXHAUST)
19	SEAT INSERT (EXHAUST VALVE)
20	SEAT INSERT (INTAKE VALVE)
21	EXHAUST MANIFOLD GASKET
22	EXHAUST MANIFOLD
23	OXYGEN SENSOR
24	CYLINDER HEAD GASKET
25	EXHAUST VALVE
26	LOWER SPRING SEAT
27	VALVE SPRING
28	SPLIT COLLAR
29	VALVE GUIDE (INTAKE)
30	CYLINDER HEAD
31	UPPER SPRING SEAT
32	VALVE STEM SEAL
33	INTAKE VALVE
34	INDUCTION PORT GASKET
35	INDUCTION PORT
36	ADJUSTING SCREW
37	ROCKER ARM
38	ROCKER SHAFT (INTAKE)
39	NUT
40	COMMON RAIL
41	FUEL RAIL
42	COMMON CHAMBER GASKET
43	COMMON CHAMBER

Fig. 3   12 valve single overhead camshaft engine

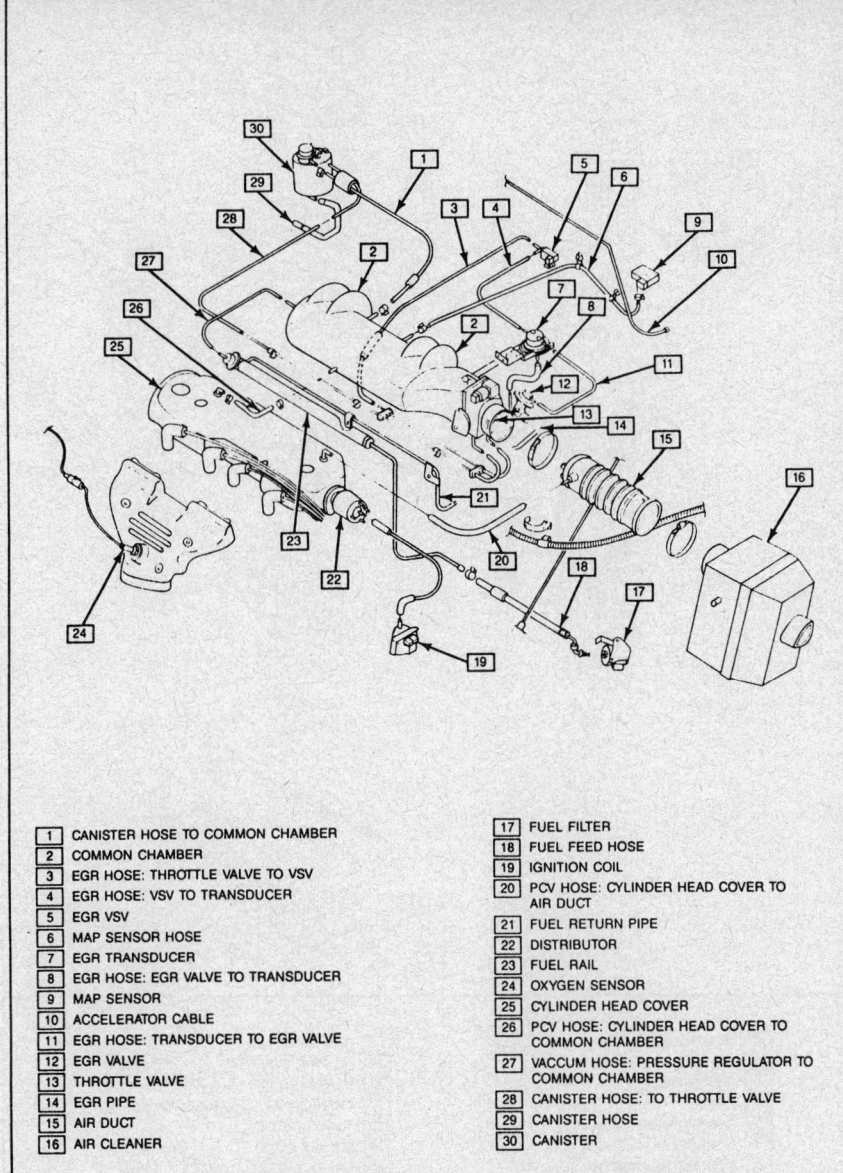

Fig. 4 12 valve single overhead camshaft engine

1	CANISTER HOSE TO COMMON CHAMBER
2	COMMON CHAMBER
3	EGR HOSE: THROTTLE VALVE TO VSV
4	EGR HOSE: VSV TO TRANSDUCER
5	EGR VSV
6	MAP SENSOR HOSE
7	EGR TRANSDUCER
8	EGR HOSE: EGR VALVE TO TRANSDUCER
9	MAP SENSOR
10	ACCELERATOR CABLE
11	EGR HOSE: TRANSDUCER TO EGR VALVE
12	EGR VALVE
13	THROTTLE VALVE
14	EGR PIPE
15	AIR DUCT
16	AIR CLEANER

17	FUEL FILTER
18	FUEL FEED HOSE
19	IGNITION COIL
20	PCV HOSE: CYLINDER HEAD COVER TO AIR DUCT
21	FUEL RETURN PIPE
22	DISTRIBUTOR
23	FUEL RAIL
24	OXYGEN SENSOR
25	CYLINDER HEAD COVER
26	PCV HOSE: CYLINDER HEAD COVER TO COMMON CHAMBER
27	VACCUM HOSE: PRESSURE REGULATOR TO COMMON CHAMBER
28	CANISTER HOSE: TO THROTTLE VALVE
29	CANISTER HOSE
30	CANISTER

3. Remove accelerator cable from throttle valve, then MAP sensor hose from MAP sensor.
4. Remove vacuum hose from brake booster and two canister hoses from pipes on common chamber, then remove canister pipe bracket.
5. Remove fuel pressure regulator vacuum hose, then remove induction control valve vacuum hose.
6. Remove throttle valve from common chamber, then disconnect alternator harness clip and three fuel injector harness cable clips.
7. Loosen EGR pipe bracket at exhaust manifold and loosen EGR clip at thermostat housing.
8. Remove two common chamber bracket bolts on lefthand side of engine and engine hanger bolt on righthand side of common chamber.
9. Remove ten bolts and two nuts from common chamber induction control valve assembly, then the common chamber.
10. Reverse procedure to install.

INDUCTION CONTROL VALVE ASSEMBLY REPLACE

1. Disconnect battery ground cable, then ignition coil wires.
2. Remove common chamber as described in ""Common Chamber/Intake Manifold, Replace."
3. Remove two oil cooler pipe clip nuts from studs located under induction control valve.
4. Remove fuel feed pipe and return fuel hose, then two fuel rail retaining bolts.
5. Remove two fuel injector harness bracket retaining bolts, then the fuel injector harness and fuel rail with fuel injectors attached from injection control valve assembly.
6. Disconnect VSV harness connector from induction control valve.
7. Remove seven bolts and two nuts from induction control valve assembly, then the induction control assembly.
8. Reverse procedures to install, **torquing** induction control valve retaining bolts to 17 ft. lbs.

EXHAUST MANIFOLD REPLACE

1. Disconnect battery ground cable
2. Remove heat protector, then disconnect oxygen sensor electrical connector.
3. Remove the EGR pipe from exhaust manifold and EGR valve, then the front exhaust pipe from exhaust manifold.
4. Remove exhaust manifold retaining nuts and bolts, then the exhaust manifold.
5. Reverse procedure to install.

CYLINDER HEAD REPLACE

12 VALVE ENGINE

1. Disconnect battery ground cable, then drain coolant.
2. Disconnect accelerator cable from throttle valve.
3. Remove breather hose from intake air duct, then the intake air duct from the throttle valve.
4. Remove MAP sensor hose from MAP sensor, then the brake booster vacuum hose.
5. Remove two canister hoses and EGR vacuum hoses from common chamber.
6. Disconnect oxygen sensor harness from oxygen sensor, ignition coil ground from thermostat housing flange and coolant temperature sensor from thermo unit harness.
7. Remove cable harness clip from bracket at coolant outlet pipe, then two cable harness connectors near lefthand strut tower.
8. Remove two heater hoses from engine and upper radiator hose from radiator.
9. Remove fuel feed hose and return hose, then raise and support vehicle.
10. Remove righthand under cover and exhaust pipe from exhaust manifold, then lower vehicle.

11. Remove right side engine mount, then the alternator and power steering belts.
12. Remove engine mounting bracket from timing cover, timing cover and timing belt.
13. Remove cylinder head center cover, cylinder head bolts, then the cylinder head.
14. Reverse procedure to install, noting the following:
    a. Using tightening sequence shown in **Fig. 10**, torque cylinder head bolts in two steps. First to 29 ft. lbs, then to 58 ft. lbs.
    b. Install timing belt as described in "Timing Belt Replace."

16 VALVE ENGINE

1. Disconnect battery ground cable, then drain coolant.
2. Disconnect accelerator cable from intake air duct, then accelerator cable clips from cylinder head cover and common chamber.
3. Disconnect accelerator cable from throttle valve and remove PCV hose from intake duct side.
4. Remove intake air duct from throttle valve, then MAP sensor hose from MAP sensor.
5. Remove brake booster vacuum hose from brake booster, then two canister hoses from pipes on common chamber.
6. Remove two canister pipes and MAP sensor pipe from common chamber, then canister pipe support bracket.
7. Disconnect oxygen sensor harness connector, ignition coil ground cable from thermostat housing flange, coolant temperature sensor and thermo unit harness connector at thermostat housing.
8. Disconnect two ground cable terminals from right side of common chamber, then ground cable from rear RH side of common chamber.
9. Disconnect starter and alternator cable clip.
10. Remove two heater hoses from engine, then upper radiator hose.
11. Remove throttle valve heating hose from coolant bypass pipe, then coolant bypass pipe bracket from cylinder head and fuel feed pipe and return fuel hose.
12. Raise and support vehicle, then remove righthand side under cover.
13. Remove front exhaust pipe from exhaust manifold, then lower vehicle.
14. Remove right side engine mount, then cylinder head center cover.
15. Remove spark plug wires from spark plugs and clips, then PCV hose from cylinder head cover.
16. Remove upper timing cover and cylinder head cover.
17. Remove timing belt, then cylinder head bolts as shown in **Fig. 11**.
18. Raise cylinder head and remove oil cooler pipe from oil cooler.

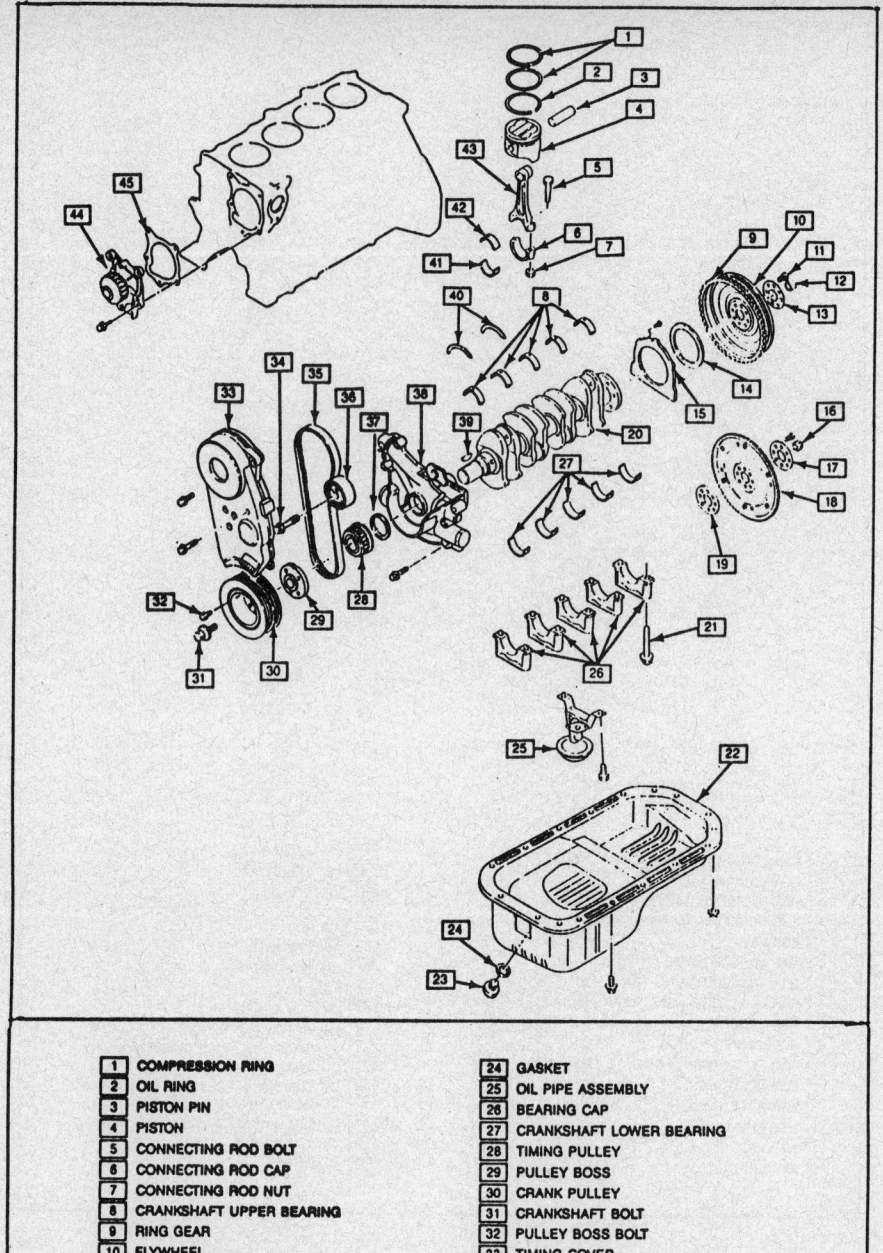

1	COMPRESSION RING	24	GASKET
2	OIL RING	25	OIL PIPE ASSEMBLY
3	PISTON PIN	26	BEARING CAP
4	PISTON	27	CRANKSHAFT LOWER BEARING
5	CONNECTING ROD BOLT	28	TIMING PULLEY
6	CONNECTING ROD CAP	29	PULLEY BOSS
7	CONNECTING ROD NUT	30	CRANK PULLEY
8	CRANKSHAFT UPPER BEARING	31	CRANKSHAFT BOLT
9	RING GEAR	32	PULLEY BOSS BOLT
10	FLYWHEEL	33	TIMING COVER
11	FLYWHEEL BOLT	34	TENSION PULLEY BOLT
12	SLEEVE (M/T)	35	TIMING BELT
13	WASHER (M/T)	36	TENSION PULLEY
14	OIL SEAL	37	OIL SEAL
15	REAR RETAINER	38	OIL PUMP ASSEMBLY
16	SLEEVE (A/T)	39	KEY
17	WASHER (A/T)	40	THRUST WASHER
18	RING GEAR ASSEMBLY	41	CONNECTING ROD LOWER BEARING
19	SPACER (A/T)	42	CONNECTING ROD UPPER BEARING
20	CRANKSHAFT	43	CONNECTING ROD
21	BEARING CAP BOLT	44	WATER PUMP ASSEMBLY
22	OIL PAN	45	GASKET
23	PLUG		

Fig. 5   12 valve cylinder block components

19. Remove cylinder head.
20. Reverse procedure to install, using tightening sequence shown in **Fig. 12**, torque cylinder head bolts in two steps. First to 29 ft. lbs., then to 58 ft. lbs.

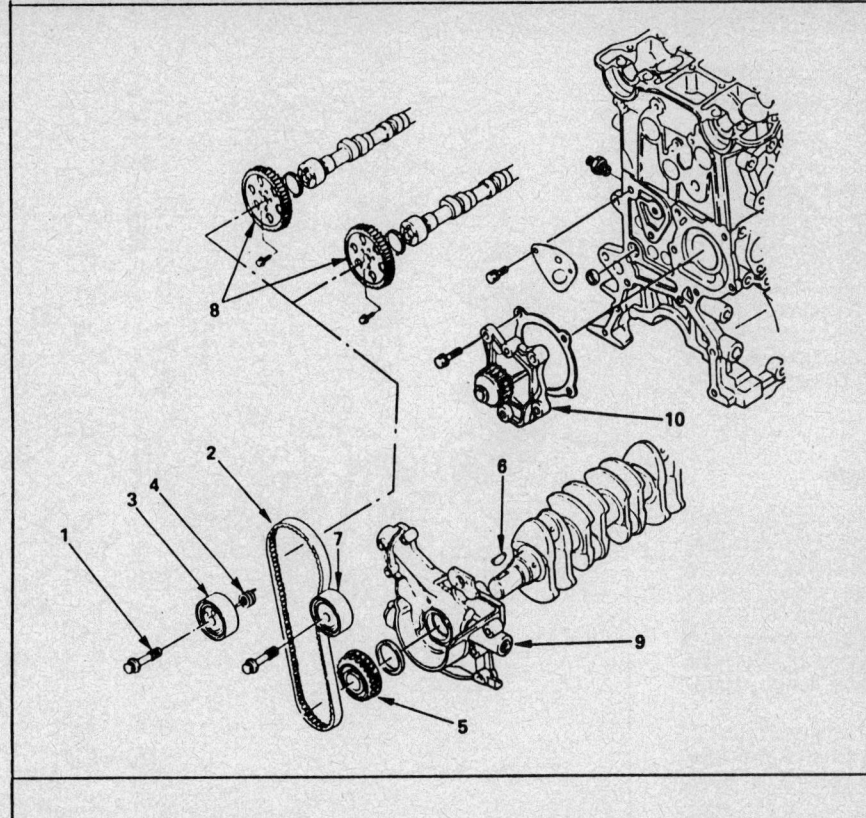

1. Tension pulley lock bolt
2. Timing belt
3. Tension pulley
4. Tension spring
5. Crankshaft timing pulley
6. Key
7. Idle pulley
8. Camshaft timing pulley
9. Oil pump assembly
10. Water pump assembly

Fig. 6 16 valve dual overhead camshaft engine

CAMSHAFT LOBE HEIGHT

12 VALVE ENGINE

Year	Liter/CID	Intake & Exhaust
1990–91	1.6L/4-97	1.426 ①

① —Minimum height.

16 VALVE ENGINE

Year	Liter/CID	Intake & Exhaust
1990–91	1.6L/4-97	1.503 ①

① —Minimum height.

VALVE CLEARANCE SPECIFICATIONS

12 VALVE ENGINE

Year	Engine	Intake Inch	Exhaust Inch
1990–91	1.6L/4-97	.006	.010

16 VALVE ENGINE

Year	Engine	Intake Inch	Exhaust Inch
1990–91	1.6L/4-97	.004–.008	.008–.012

VALVES
ADJUST

12 VALVE ENGINE

1. Set number one cylinder at TDC on the compression stroke, then turn crankshaft pulley to align its notched line with the 0 mark on timing cover.
2. Ensure that valves on No. 1 cylinder have play and valves No. 4 cylinder do not. If not as specified, turn crankshaft pulley 360° and align the 0 mark on lower timing cover, **Fig. 13.**
3. Measure valve lash between rocker arm and valve stem as follows:
   a. Intake and exhaust valves on No. 1 cylinder.
   b. Intake valve on No. 2 cylinder.
   c. Exhaust valves on No. 3 cylinder.
4. Valve lash should be 0.006 inch on intake and 0.010 on exhaust valves.
5. If lash is not as specified, adjust valve

lash by loosening adjustment screw locknut and turn adjustment screw until lash is within specifications, **Fig. 14.**

6. Tighten adjustment lock nut, then rotate crankshaft 360° and measure lash as follows:
   a. Intake and exhaust on No. 4 cylinder.
   b. Intake valves on No. 3 cylinder.
   c. Exhaust valves on No. 2 cylinder.
7. Valve lash should be 0.006 inch on intake and 0.010 on exhaust valves.
8. If lash is not as specified, adjust valve lash by loosening adjustment screw locknut and turn adjustment screw until lash is within specifications.
9. Install cylinder head cover.

16 VALVE ENGINE

The 16 valve engine is not equipped with rocker arms. Valve adjustment is performed by using selective shims. Measure valve lash when engine is cold.

1. Disconnect battery ground cable.
2. Remove cylinder head cover and camshafts as described in "Cylinder Head Cover, Replace" and "Camshafts, Replace."
3. Remove selective shims and tappets. **Be sure to arrange shims and tappets in order of removal to ensure proper installation.**
4. Valve lash adjustment must be done while engine is cold. Use Valve Lash Spring Spacer tool Nos. J 38413-2 (left) and J 38413-3 (right) or equivalent to make adjustments.
5. Set No. 1 cylinder to TDC, then align crankshaft pulley to 0 mark on the timing cover.
6. Ensure valves on No. 1 cylinder have play and valves on No. 4 cylinder do not have play. If valves are not set as above, rotate crankshaft pulley 360° and align with 0 mark on timing cover, then recheck valves.
7. Measure and record valve lash between cam lobe and selective shim as follows:
   a. On No. 1 cylinder, intake and exhaust valves.
   b. On No. 2 cylinder, intake valves.
   c. On No. 3 cylinder, exhaust valves.
8. Rotate crankshaft pulley 360° and ensure that rear camshaft bearing caps are removed so that selective shims may be removed.
9. Measure and record valve lash between cam lobe and selective shim as follows:
   a. On No. 4 cylinder, intake and exhaust valves.
   b. On No. 3 cylinder, intake valves.
   c. On No. 2 cylinder, exhaust valves.
10. Valve clearance on the exhaust valve must be between 0.008-0.012 inch. If clearance is not as specified, replace shim by turning the camshaft lobe downward and inserting tool, J 38413-2 (Left) or J 38413-3 (Right) between camshaft journal and the cam lobe next to selective shim. Turn cam lobe upward and remove selec-

tive shim, **Fig. 15 and 16.**
11. Refer to **Fig. 17,** for available exhaust shims.
12. Valve clearance on the intake valve must be between 0.004-0.008 inch. If clearance is not as specified, replace

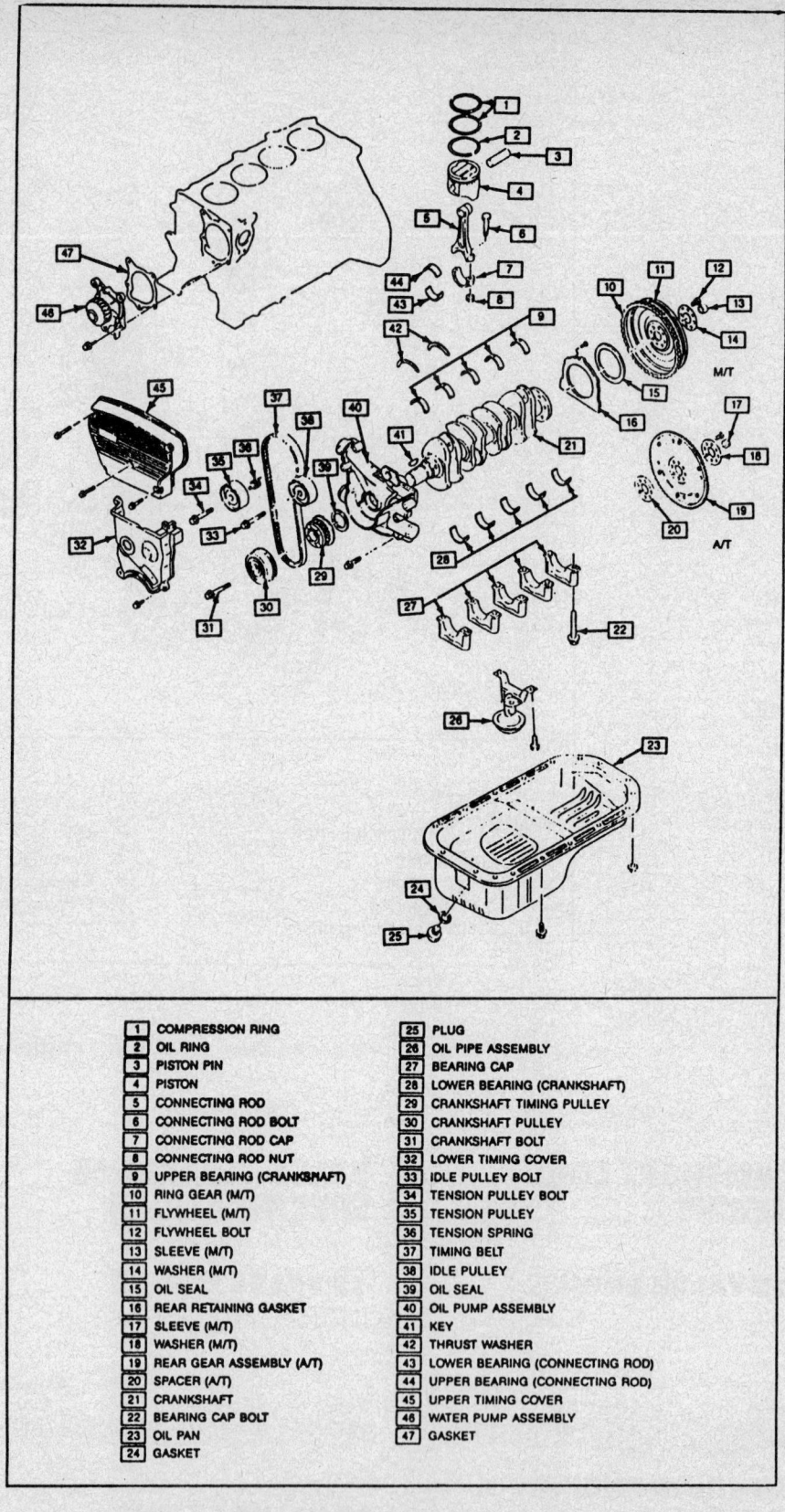

1	COMPRESSION RING	25	PLUG
2	OIL RING	26	OIL PIPE ASSEMBLY
3	PISTON PIN	27	BEARING CAP
4	PISTON	28	LOWER BEARING (CRANKSHAFT)
5	CONNECTING ROD	29	CRANKSHAFT TIMING PULLEY
6	CONNECTING ROD BOLT	30	CRANKSHAFT PULLEY
7	CONNECTING ROD CAP	31	CRANKSHAFT BOLT
8	CONNECTING ROD NUT	32	LOWER TIMING COVER
9	UPPER BEARING (CRANKSHAFT)	33	IDLE PULLEY BOLT
10	RING GEAR (M/T)	34	TENSION PULLEY BOLT
11	FLYWHEEL (M/T)	35	TENSION PULLEY
12	FLYWHEEL BOLT	36	TENSION SPRING
13	SLEEVE (M/T)	37	TIMING BELT
14	WASHER (M/T)	38	IDLE PULLEY
15	OIL SEAL	39	OIL SEAL
16	REAR RETAINING GASKET	40	OIL PUMP ASSEMBLY
17	SLEEVE (M/T)	41	KEY
18	WASHER (M/T)	42	THRUST WASHER
19	REAR GEAR ASSEMBLY (A/T)	43	LOWER BEARING (CONNECTING ROD)
20	SPACER (A/T)	44	UPPER BEARING (CONNECTING ROD)
21	CRANKSHAFT	45	UPPER TIMING COVER
22	BEARING CAP BOLT	46	WATER PUMP ASSEMBLY
23	OIL PAN	47	GASKET
24	GASKET		

Fig. 7   16 valve cylinder block components

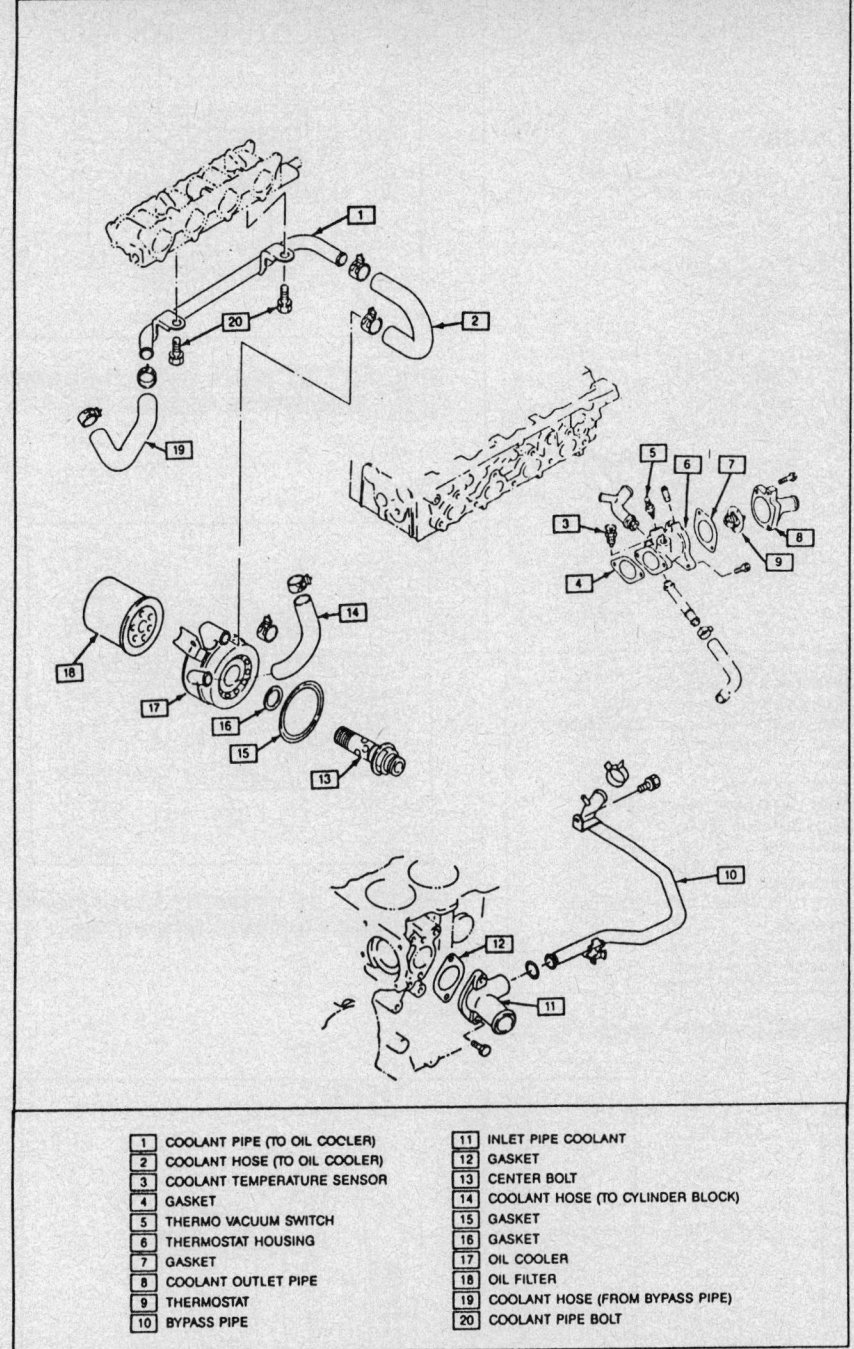

1	COOLANT PIPE (TO OIL COOLER)	**11**	INLET PIPE COOLANT
2	COOLANT HOSE (TO OIL COOLER)	**12**	GASKET
3	COOLANT TEMPERATURE SENSOR	**13**	CENTER BOLT
4	GASKET	**14**	COOLANT HOSE (TO CYLINDER BLOCK)
5	THERMO VACUUM SWITCH	**15**	GASKET
6	THERMOSTAT HOUSING	**16**	GASKET
7	GASKET	**17**	OIL COOLER
8	COOLANT OUTLET PIPE	**18**	OIL FILTER
9	THERMOSTAT	**19**	COOLANT HOSE (FROM BYPASS PIPE)
10	BYPASS PIPE	**20**	COOLANT PIPE BOLT

Fig. 8   16 valve cylinder head attaching components

shim by turning the camshaft lobe downward and inserting tool, J 38413-2 (Left) or J 38413-3 (Right) between camshaft journal and the cam lobe next to selective shim. Turn cam lobe upward and remove selective shim.

13. Refer to **Fig. 17,** for available intake shims.
14. Install cylinder head cover.

VALVE GUIDES
REPLACE

Using valve guide remover, J 37985 or suitable tool, drive valve guides from cylinder head with a hammer. Install valve guides using a J 38462 installer with the J 37985 valve guide remover.

ROCKER ARMS & SHAFT
REPLACE

1. Disconnect battery ground cable.
2. Remove PCV hoses and spark plug wires from the clip.
3. Remove two bolts from timing belt cover, then loosen lower timing belt cover bolts.
4. Remove cylinder head cover bolts, then cylinder head cover.
5. Remove rocker arm bracket bolts in order shown in **Fig. 18.**
6. Remove rocker arm shaft and rocker arm assembly, then remove rocker arms from shafts.
7. Reverse procedure to install, noting the following:
   a. Apply GM 1052942 sealant or equivalent to No. 1 and No. 5 rocker brackets.
   b. Using tightening sequence shown in **Fig. 19, torque** bolts to 22 ft. lbs.
   c. Make necessary valve lash adjustments.

TIMING BELT
REPLACE

12 VALVE ENGINE
Removal

1. Disconnect battery ground cable.
2. Remove alternator and power steering belts, then support engine using a J 28467-A engine support fixture or equivalent.
3. Remove right side engine mount, then the timing belt cover.
4. Rotate crankshaft so that No. 1 cylinder is at TDC, aligning the camshaft pulley timing mark, **Fig. 20.**
5. Remove crankshaft pulley bolt, then raise and support vehicle.
6. Remove crankshaft pulley, then lower vehicle.
7. Loosen tension pulley retaining bolt ½ turn and remove timing belt.

Installation

1. Align camshaft pulley timing marks, **Fig. 20,** then raise and support vehicle.
2. Align crankshaft pulley to TDC, then place timing belt over crankshaft pulley and install crankshaft pulley.
3. Lower vehicle, then install timing belt over, camshaft pulley, water pump pulley and tensioner pulley in order as shown in **Fig. 21.**
4. **Torque** timing belt tensioner to 31 ft. lbs., then rotate crankshaft two turns to ensure that crankshaft timing mark and camshaft pulley marks are correct.
5. Install timing belt cover, then raise and support vehicle.
6. **Torque** crankshaft pulley center bolt to 87 ft. lbs. and pulley side bolts to 89 inch lbs.
7. Lower vehicle, then install belts, right side engine mount and remove engine support fixture.
8. Connect battery ground cable.

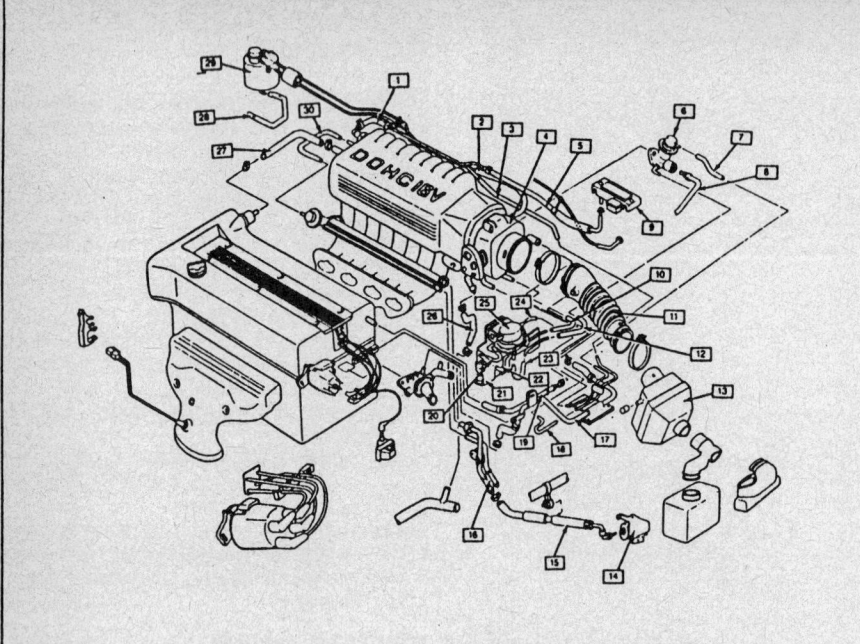

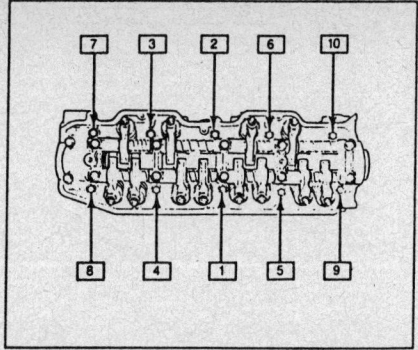

Fig. 10   12 valve cylinder head tightening sequence

#	COMPONENT	#	COMPONENT
1	MAP SENSOR HOSE: CYLINDER HEAD COVER TO PIPE	17	THROTTLE VALVE HEATING HOSE: THERMOSTAT HSG TO T-VALVE
2	CANISTER HOSE: TO THROTTLE VALVE	18	CANISTER HOSE: PIPE TO THROTTLE VALVE
3	CANISTER HOSE: TO PIPE	19	PCV HOSE: CYLINDER HEAD COVER TO AIR DUCT
4	THROTTLE VALVE	20	EGR HOSE: VSV TO TRANSDUCER
5	MAP SENSOR HOSE: PIPE TO MAP SENSOR	21	VSV: EGR
6	EGR VALVE	22	EGR HOSE: PIPE TO VSV
7	EGR HOSE: PIPE TO EGR VALVE	23	EGR HOSE: EGR VALVE TO TRANSDUCER
8	EGR PIPE	24	EGR HOSE: TRANSDUCER TO PIPE
9	MAP SENSOR	25	EGR TRANSDUCER
10	EGR HOSE: THROTTLE VALVE TO PIPE	26	THROTTLE VALVE HEATING HOSE: T-VALVE TO BYPASS PIPE
11	AIR DUCT	27	PCV HOSE: CYLINDER HEAD COVER TO AIR DUCT
12	EGR HOSE: TRANSDUCER TO EGR VALVE	28	CANISTER HOSE
13	AIR CLEANER	29	CANISTER
14	FUEL FILTER	30	VACUUM HOSE: FUEL PRESSURE REGULATOR TO COMMON CHAMBER
15	FUEL FEED PIPE		
16	FUEL RETURN PIPE		

Fig. 9   16 valve intake and exhaust components

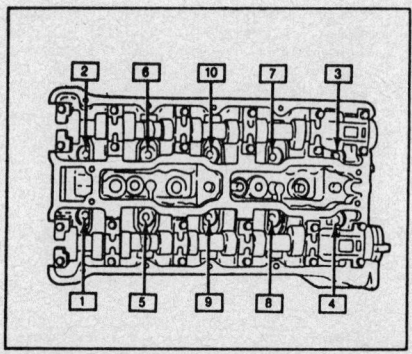

Fig. 11   16 valve cylinder head bolt removal sequence

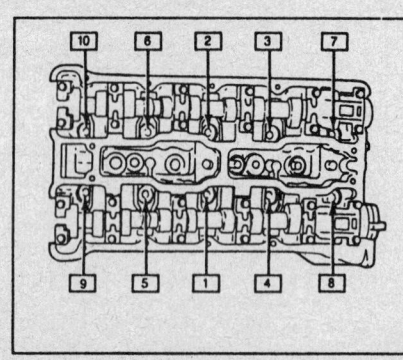

Fig. 12   16 valve cylinder head tightening sequence

1 TIMING MARK

Fig. 13   12 valve Crankshaft pulley timing mark

16 VALVE ENGINE

Removal

1. Disconnect battery ground cable.
2. Support engine using support fixture J 28467-A or equivalent, then remove right side engine mount.
3. Remove power steering and alternator drive belts, then upper timing belt cover.
4. Raise and support vehicle, then re-move crankshaft pulley bolt and crankshaft pulley.
5. Lower vehicle and remove lower timing cover.
6. Align crankshaft pulley to TDC, then loosen tension pulley retaining bolt ½ turn and remove timing belt.

Installation

1. Align camshaft pulleys timing marks, **Fig. 22.**
2. Raise and support vehicle, then align crankshaft pulley to TDC.
3. Install timing belt over crankshaft pulley, then install crankshaft pulley, but do not tighten.
4. Lower vehicle, then install timing belt over crankshaft pulley, water pump pulley, idler pulley, exhaust camshaft pulley, intake camshaft pulley and then tensioner pulley as shown in **Fig. 23.**

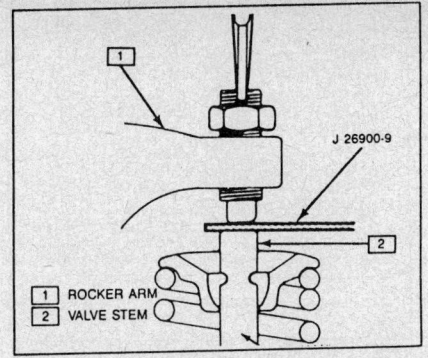

Fig. 14   12 valve clearance adjustment

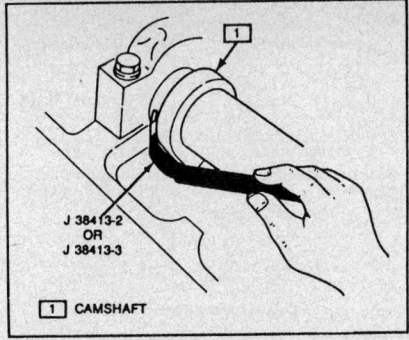

Fig. 15   16 valve lash service

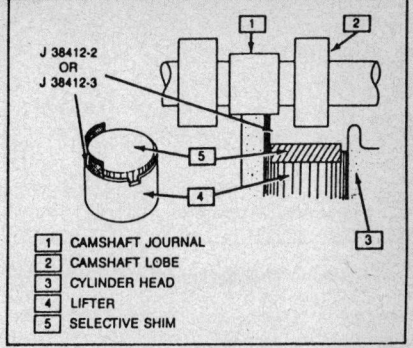

1	CAMSHAFT JOURNAL
2	CAMSHAFT LOBE
3	CYLINDER HEAD
4	LIFTER
5	SELECTIVE SHIM

Fig. 16   16 valve clearance adjustment

Thickness of available adjuster (Shim)

NO in Chart	Thickness (mm)	NO in Chart	Thickness (mm)
1	2.55	11	3.05
2	2.60	12	3.10
3	2.65	13	3.15
4	2.70	14	3.20
5	2.75	15	3.25
6	2.80	16	3.30
7	2.85	17	3.35
8	2.90	18	3.40
9	2.95	19	3.45
10	3.00		

Note; Thickness mark is printed on the surface to be contacted with tappet.

Fig. 17   Valve shim chart

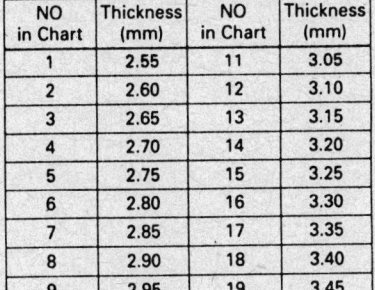

| 1 | ALIGNMENT MARK |
| 2 | DOWEL |

Fig. 20   12 valve cam pulley timing mark

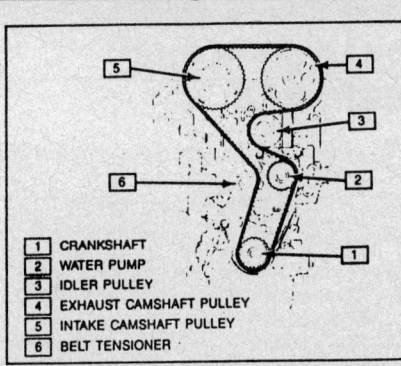

1	CRANKSHAFT
2	WATER PUMP
3	IDLER PULLEY
4	EXHAUST CAMSHAFT PULLEY
5	INTAKE CAMSHAFT PULLEY
6	BELT TENSIONER

Fig. 23   16 valve timing belt

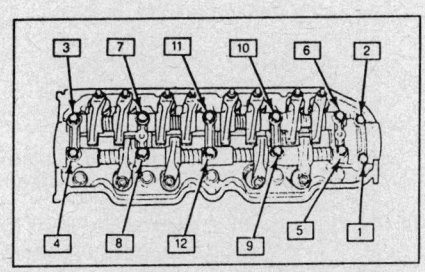

Fig. 18   Rocker arm shaft removal

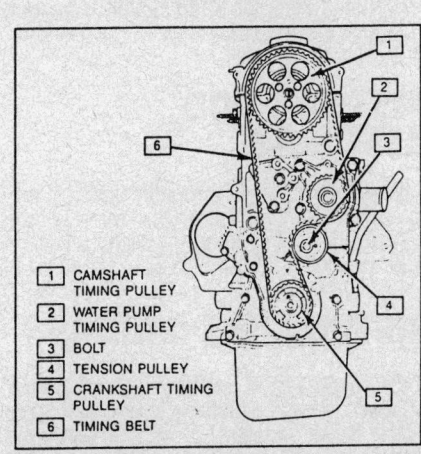

1	CAMSHAFT TIMING PULLEY
2	WATER PUMP TIMING PULLEY
3	BOLT
4	TENSION PULLEY
5	CRANKSHAFT TIMING PULLEY
6	TIMING BELT

Fig. 21   12 valve timing belt

5. **Torque** timing belt tensioner to 31 ft. lbs., then rotate crankshaft two turns to ensure that crankshaft timing pulley mark and camshaft pulley marks are correctly aligned.
6. Install lower timing cover
7. Raise and support vehicle, then **torque** crankshaft pulley bolt to 87 ft. lbs.
8. Lower vehicle and install upper timing cover.
9. Install alternator and power steering belts, then right side engine mount.
10. Remove engine support and install battery ground cable.

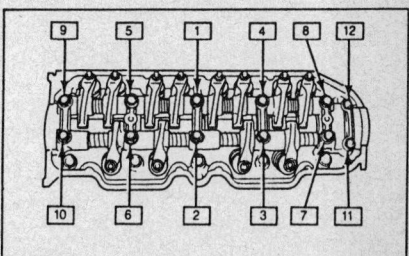

Fig. 19   Rocker arm shaft tightening sequence

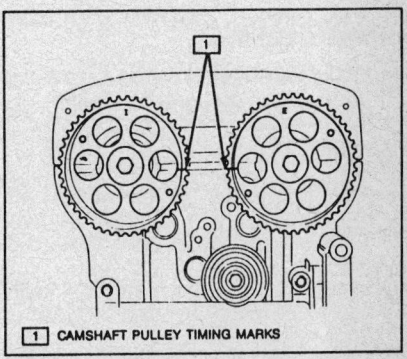

| 1 | CAMSHAFT PULLEY TIMING MARKS |

Fig. 22   16 valve cam pulley timing mark

CAMSHAFT REPLACE

12 VALVE ENGINE
Removal

1. Disconnect battery ground cable.
2. Remove PCV hoses and spark plug wires from the clip.
3. Remove two bolts from the timing belt cover, then loosen lower timing belt cover bolts.
4. Remove cylinder head cover bolts, then cylinder head cover.
5. Rotate crankshaft to TDC on compression stroke by aligning the camshaft pulley timing marks, **Fig. 20.**
6. Loosen timing belt tensioner, then remove timing belt.
7. Remove distributor, camshaft bearing cap retaining bolts and covers.
8. Remove camshaft and camshaft seal.

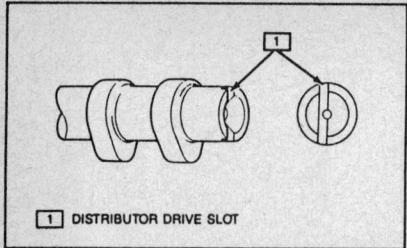

Fig. 24   Distributor drive slot

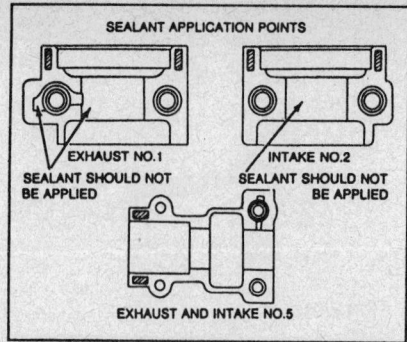

Fig. 25   Camshaft bearing cap sealant

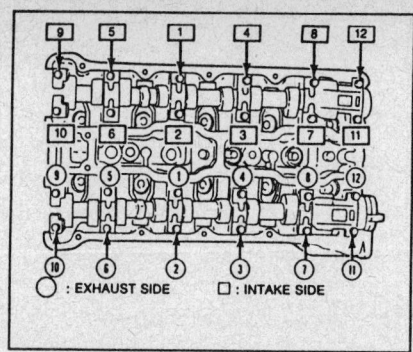

Fig. 26   Camshaft bearing cap tightening sequence

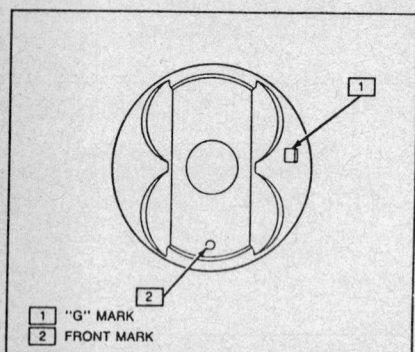

Fig. 27   Piston mark location

Installation

1. Install camshaft in cylinder head with dowel pin in the upright position.
2. Install camshaft bearing caps, but do not tighten.
3. Apply GM 1052942 sealant or equivalent to No. 1 and No. 5 camshaft bearing caps.
4. **Torque** camshaft bearing caps to 89 inch lbs.
5. Install new camshaft oil seal using seal installation tool No. J 35268 or equivalent.
6. Install distributor, camshaft timing pulley and timing belt, referring to "Timing Belt Replace" for procedure.
7. Install cylinder head cover, then battery ground cable.

16 VALVE ENGINE
Removal

1. Disconnect battery ground cable.
2. Remove cylinder head cover, then rotate crankshaft to TDC by aligning camshaft pulley timing marks.
3. Loosen timing belt tensioner, then remove camshaft pulleys from camshaft.
4. Remove distributor, then camshaft bearing caps bolts. **Bolts must be kept in the order they were taken out. To ensure that they will be installed into the same threaded hole.**
5. Remove the camshaft, then the camshaft seals.

Installation

1. Install camshaft into cylinder head, ensuring that dowel pin is in the up position and distributor drive slot is at end of exhaust camshaft, **Fig. 24.**
2. Install bearing caps and bolts in order that they were removed, but do not tighten at this time.
3. Apply GM 1052942 sealant or equivalent to No. 1 and No. 5 camshaft bearing caps, **Fig. 25.**
4. **Torque** camshaft bearing cap bolts to 89 inch lbs. using sequence shown in **Fig. 26.**
5. Install new camshaft oil seal using tool J 35268 oil sealer installer or equivalent.
6. Install distributor, camshaft timing pulleys, then the timing belt.
7. Install cylinder head cover, then battery ground cable.

PISTON & ROD ASSEMBLE

Align front marks on piston and rod assemblies, **Fig. 27.**. Ensure that mark is facing front of engine when installing into cylinder block.

PISTON, PINS & RINGS

There are three standard size pistons and two oversized pistons. When installing piston rings, ensure that code marks are facing upwards. Install pin into piston and rod as shown in **Fig. 28.**

MAIN & ROD BEARINGS

Rod bearings come in three standard sizes and two oversize, 0.0098 inch and 0.0196 inch. If after replacing rod bearing, thrust clearance is still excessive, replace crankshaft. Connecting rod bearing cap nuts should be **torqued** in three steps to 36 ft. lbs.

When replacing a main bearing, always replace it with one that has the same number. If you can not read number, refer to **Fig. 29,** for sizes of main bearings. When servicing the crankshaft, inspect all journals for wear or damage. Install upper half

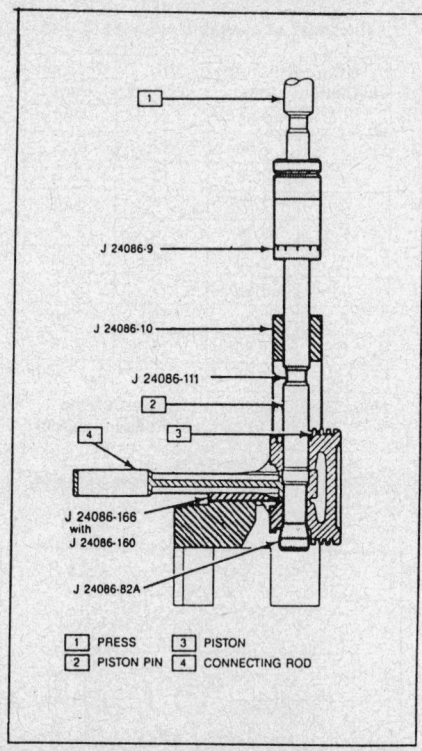

Fig. 28   Piston pin remover and installer

of bearings into cylinder block, and the lower half into main bearing caps. If oil clearance can not be brought within specifications using a standard bearing, regrind crankshaft for next oversize bearing.

REAR MAIN SEAL REPLACE

1. Disconnect battery ground cable, then raise and support vehicle.
2. Remove right and left under covers, then the oil pan as described in "Oil Pan, Replace."
3. Remove transaxle as described in "Transaxle, Replace" in "Clutch & Manual Transaxle" section.
4. Mark flywheel and engine position for installation reference, then remove flywheel.

① Size mark	Main Bearing Bore Diameter (mm)	Crank Shaft Main Journal Diameter (mm)	② Size Mark	Crank Shaft Bearing Size Mark (Upper Side)	Crank Shaft Bearing Size Mark (Lower Side)	Oil Clearance (mm) (Reference)
1	55.992-56.000	51.918-51.928	— —	Blue	Blue	0.022-0.048
		51.929-51.938	—	Black	Black	0.020-0.046
2	55.984-55.991	51.918-51.928	— —			0.022-0.048
		51.929-51.938	—	Brown	Brown	0.020-0.046
3	55.976-55.983	51.918-51.928	— —			0.022-0.048
		51.929-51.938	—	Green	Green	0.020-0.046
Under Size 0.25	55.976-56.000	51.668-51.688		Stamp of Size	Stamp of Size	0.020-0.088
Under Size 0.50		51.418-51.438				

Fig. 29 Main bearing selection table

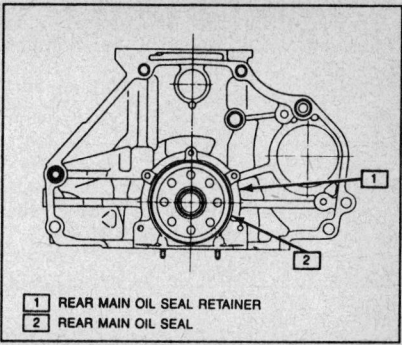

1 REAR MAIN OIL SEAL RETAINER
2 REAR MAIN OIL SEAL

Fig. 30 Rear main oil seal retainer

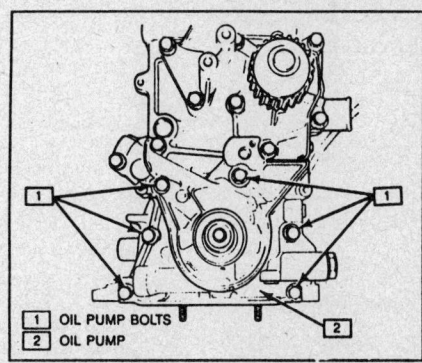

1 OIL PUMP BOLTS
2 OIL PUMP

Fig. 31 Oil pump removal

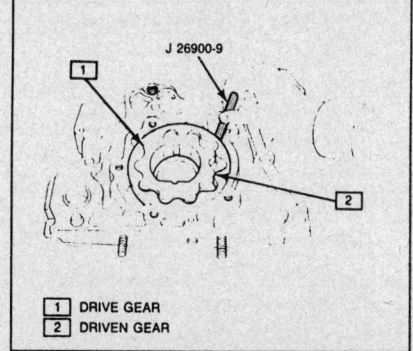

1 DRIVE GEAR
2 DRIVEN GEAR

Fig. 32 Measuring oil pump drive to driven gear

6. Reverse procedure to install. Use new oil pan gasket, applying Gm 1052942 sealant or equivalent to gasket surface. **Torque** stiffener bolts to 50 ft. lbs.

OIL PUMP SERVICE
REMOVAL
1. Disconnect battery ground cable.
2. Remove timing belt cover, alternator and power steering belts, then raise and support vehicle.
3. Remove crankshaft pulley, then oil pump attaching bolts and oil pump, **Fig. 31.**

INSPECTION
1. Measure oil pump driven gear to housing clearance, **Fig. 32,** using suitable feeler gauge. If clearance is more than 0.078 inch, replace oil pump.
2. Measure oil pump drive gear to driven gear clearance, **Fig. 33.** If the clearance is more than 0.012 inch, replace the gear set.
3. Measure oil pump body to gear clearance, **Fig. 34,** using a feeler gauge and precision straightedge. If the clearance is more than 0.004 inch, replace oil pump.

INSTALLATION
1. Apply GM 1052942 sealant or equivalent to oil pump gasket surface.

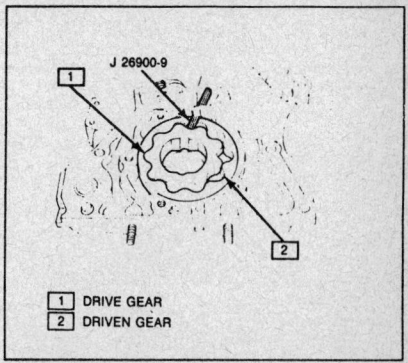

1 DRIVE GEAR
2 DRIVEN GEAR

Fig. 33 Measuring oil pump driven gear to housing

2. Install oil pump, **torque** oil pump to block bolts to 89 inch lbs.
3. Install crankshaft pulley, then lower vehicle.
4. Install timing belt cover, then the power steering and alternator belts.
5. Connect battery ground cable.

WATER PUMP
REPLACE
12 VALVE ENGINE
1. Disconnect battery ground cable, then drain coolant system.
2. Remove power steering belt, then timing belt cover and timing belt. See "Timing Belt Replace".
3. Remove water pump to block retaining bolts, then water pump.
4. Reverse procedure to install.

16 VALVE ENGINE
1. Disconnect battery ground cable, then drain cooling system.
2. Remove right front engine mount as outlined under "Engine Mount, Replace."
3. Remove engine mount bridge.
4. Remove upper timing belt cover assembly.
5. Remove power steering belt.
6. Remove lower timing belt cover assembly.
7. Loosen timing belt tensioner, then remove timing belt at water pump pulley.
8. Remove water pump attaching bolts, then remove water pump.
9. Reverse procedure to install.

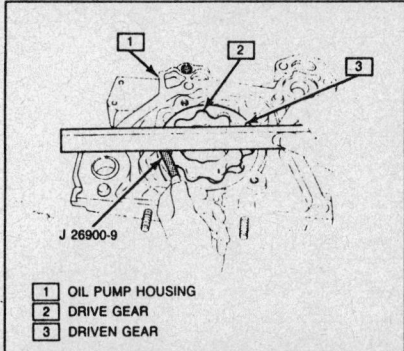

J 26900-9

1 OIL PUMP HOUSING
2 DRIVE GEAR
3 DRIVEN GEAR

Fig. 34 Measuring oil pump body to gear clearance

5. Remove flywheel spacer and rear main seal retainer.
6. Remove rear main seal from retainer, **Fig. 30.**
7. Reverse procedure to install.

OIL PAN
REPLACE
1. Disconnect battery ground cable.
2. Raise and support vehicle, then drain crankcase oil.
3. Remove righthand under cover, then exhaust pipe from exhaust manifold.
4. Remove torque rod and flywheel dust cover.
5. Remove stiffener from cylinder block, then oil pan.

BELT TENSION DATA

Engine	Belt	Tension Lbs.
1.6L/4-97	Alternator	①
	Power Steering	②

① —New belt - adjust to 140 to 180 lbs; used belt - adjust to 110 to 150 lbs.

② —On models with A/C, tension gauge should read 145 lbs; on models less A/C - gauge should read 90 lbs.

FUEL PUMP
REPLACE

1. Disconnect battery ground cable, then loosen fuel filler cap to relieve tank vapor pressure.
2. Disconnect fuel fitting, wrapping a shop towel around fitting to prevent spraying.
3. Siphon or pump fuel into approved container.
4. Raise and support vehicle with suitable floor jacks.
5. Remove exhaust pipe from catalytic converter, then fuel filler neck hose from fuel tank.
6. Remove fuel overflow pipe hose from fuel tank.
7. Disconnect fuel gauge sending unit and fuel pump electrical connectors.
8. Remove fuel vapor, fuel supply and fuel return hose from the fuel tank.
9. Support fuel tank using a suitable transaxle jack or equivalent, then remove six tank retaining bolts and tank.
10. Remove eight fuel pump mounting screws, then fuel pump/bracket from fuel tank.
11. Remove fuel pump supply hose extension from bracket, gasket from pump bracket or tank and filter from pump pick-up tube.
12. Disconnect electrical connector wires from pump.
13. Remove pump from bracket, then outlet hose from pump.
14. Reverse procedure to install.

TIGHTENING SPECIFICATIONS

Year	Component	Torque/Ft. Lbs.
1990-91	Camshaft Bearing Caps	89①
	Camshaft Pulley Retaining Bolts	43
	Common Chamber Bolts & Nuts	17
	Connecting Rod Bearing Cap Nuts	36
	Crankshaft Pulley Center Bolt	87
	Cylinder Head Bolts	②
	Cylinder Head Cover Bolts	③
	EGR Pipe Bracket Bolts	32
	Exhaust Manifold Bolts & Nuts	30
	Flexplate Retaining Bolts	47
	Flywheel Retaining Bolts	58
	Fuel Pump Screws	30①
	Fuel Pump Supply Hose Fitting	25
	Fuel Tank Bolts	25
	Induction Port Retaining Bolts	17
	Left Engine Mount Center Bolt	50
	Left Engine Mount To Transaxle Case Bolts	35
	Main Bearing Cap Bolts	44
	Mounting Bridge Bracket Bolt	29
	Oil Pan Bolts & Nuts	89①
	Oil Pump Bolts	89①
	Oil Pump Cover Screws	89①
	Rear Main Seal Retainer Bolts	89①
	Rear Mount Center Bolt	76
	Rear Mount Transaxle Case Bolt	37
	Relief Valve Plug	27
	Right Mount Through Bolt	50
	Rocker Arm Bracket Bolts	16
	Stiffener Bolts	50
	Throttle Valve Bolts	17
	Timing Belt Tensioner	31
	Torque Rod Center Bolt	50
	Torque Rod Bracket Bolts & Nut	28
	Water Pump Bolts (DOHC)	17
	Water Pump Bolts (SOHC)	17.4

① —Inch lbs.
② —Refer to text.
③ —On vehicles with VIN Code 5 tighten to 26 inch lbs., on vehicles with VIN Code 6 tighten to 89 inch lbs.

Clutch & Manual Transaxle

INDEX

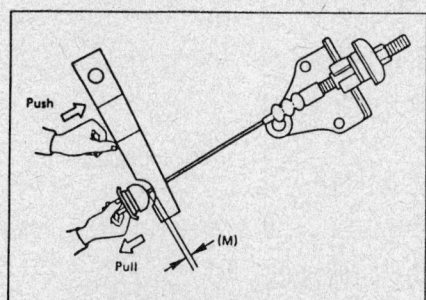

Clutch lever free play (M)	2±1 (0.08±0.04)
Clutch pedal free play (L)	10±5 (0.39±0.20)

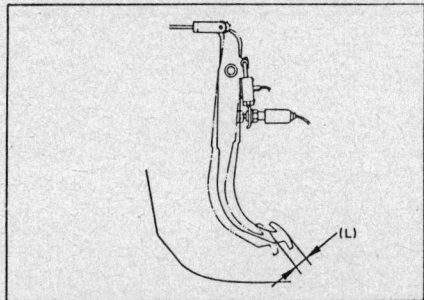

Fig. 1   Clutch cable adjustment

CLUTCH CABLE
REPLACE

1. Disconnect battery ground cable.
2. **On models equipped with turbocharger,** remove inter cooler.
3. **On all models,** loosen clutch cable adjusting nuts, then disconnect cable from release arm and cable bracket.
4. Disconnect cable from clutch pedal and front of dash, then remove cable from vehicle.
5. Reverse procedure to install, applying grease to pin of clutch cable.

CLUTCH CABLE
ADJUST

1. Measure clutch pedal free play, **Fig. 1,** to confirm adjustments are within specifications.
2. If freeplay is not within specifications, turn adjustment nut clockwise or counterclockwise to adjust cable.
3. Repeat step 2 so that play between clutch release arm and clutch cable is within specifications shown in **Fig. 1.**

CLUTCH
REPLACE

1. Remove transaxle assembly as outlined under "Transaxle, Replace."
2. Mark clutch cover assembly position to flywheel for installation alignment.
3. Remove clutch cover bolts evenly, releasing spring tension.
4. Remove clutch cover and disc.
5. Reverse procedure to install. Torque clutch cover bolts to specifications.

MANUAL TRANSAXLE
REPLACE
REMOVAL

1. Disconnect battery cables, then remove battery and battery tray.
2. Drain transaxle fluid, then remove air cleaner assembly.
3. Disconnect wire connectors and ground cable.
4. Disconnect engine wiring harness clip, then remove ignition coil ground cable.
5. Remove battery bracket and ignition coil assembly.
6. Remove speedometer cable, clutch cable and shifter cable, then using tool No. J 28467-A or equivalent, support engine assembly.
7. Raise and support vehicle, then remove wheel and tire assembly.
8. Remove front under covers, then remove ball joints at steering knuckles.
9. Remove front drive axles, then remove front exhaust pipe.
10. Remove torque rod and bracket, then left transaxle mount.
11. Remove front transaxle through bolt, then center beam with rear transaxle mount.
12. Remove engine stiffener and flywheel dust cover.
13. Using suitable jacks, support transaxle, then remove transaxle attaching bolts.
14. Remove transaxle assembly.

INSTALLATION

1. Install transaxle assembly, then torque attaching bolts to specifications.
2. Remove transaxle support, then install flywheel dust cover.

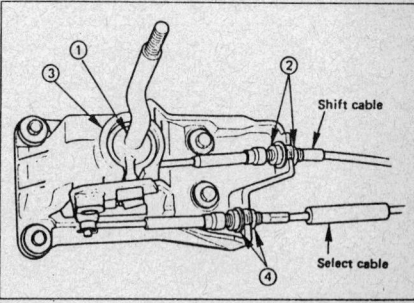

Fig. 2   Shift cable adjustment

3. Install engine stiffener, then install center beam with rear transaxle mount, then install front and left transaxle mount through bolts.
4. Torque bolts to specifications.
5. Install torque rod, bracket and front exhaust pipe.
6. Install right drive axle assemblies, then install ball joints.
7. Install front under covers, then wheel and tire assembly, then lower vehicle.
8. Remove engine support fixture.
9. Install shift cable, clutch cable and speedometer cable.
10. Install battery bracket, ignition coil assembly and ignition coil ground cable.
11. Install engine electrical harness clamp, then connect ground cable.
12. Connect electrical connectors, battery, battery tray and battery cables.

SHIFT CABLE
ADJUST

1. Place transaxle in "Neutral" position.
2. Turn adjusting nuts (2) until change lever (1) is at right angle to pivot case, as viewed from side of gear control, **Fig. 2.**
3. Turn adjusting nuts (4) until change lever (1) is at a right angle to pivot case as viewed from rear of gear control, **Fig. 3.**
4. After making adjustments, tighten adjusting nuts (2) and (4).

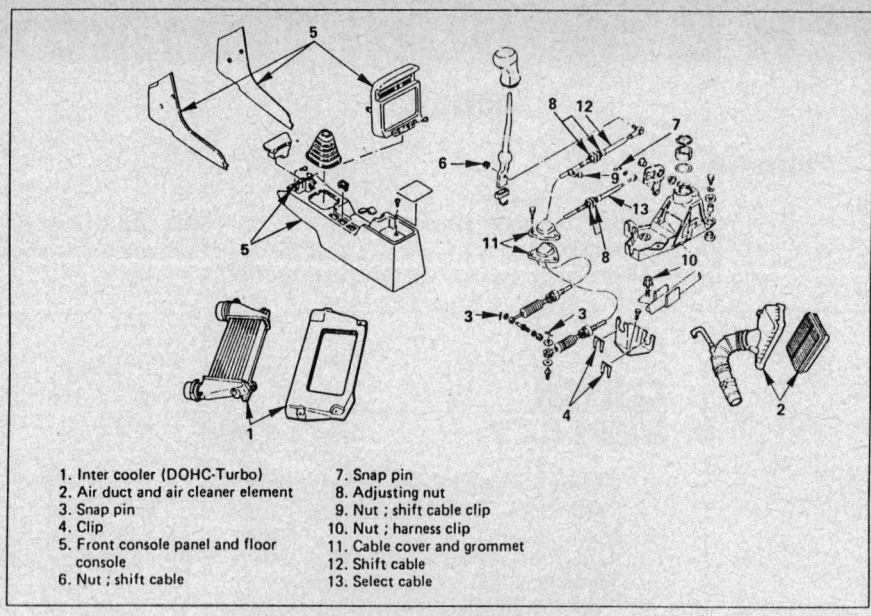

1. Inter cooler (DOHC-Turbo)
2. Air duct and air cleaner element
3. Snap pin
4. Clip
5. Front console panel and floor console
6. Nut ; shift cable
7. Snap pin
8. Adjusting nut
9. Nut ; shift cable clip
10. Nut ; harness clip
11. Cable cover and grommet
12. Shift cable
13. Select cable

Fig. 3   Shift cable assembly

TIGHTENING SPECIFICATIONS

Year	Component	Torque/ft. lbs.
1990–91	Clutch Cover Bolts	13
	Clutch Flywheel Bolts	58
	Transaxle Filler Plug	20
	Transaxle Front Mount Bracket	45
	Transaxle Front Retaining Nut	45
	Transaxle Rear Mount Bolt	29
	Transaxle Left Axle Mount Bolts	29
	Transaxle Left Through Bolt	64
	Transaxle To Engine Bolts	55
	Transaxle Center Crossmember Bolts	45

Rear Axle & Suspension

INDEX

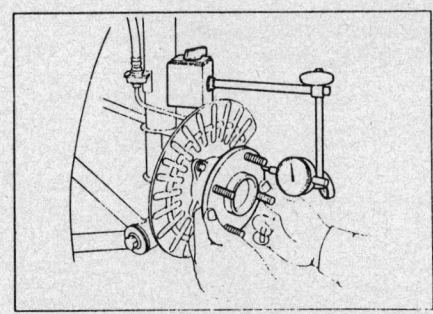

Fig. 1   Measuring hub axial play

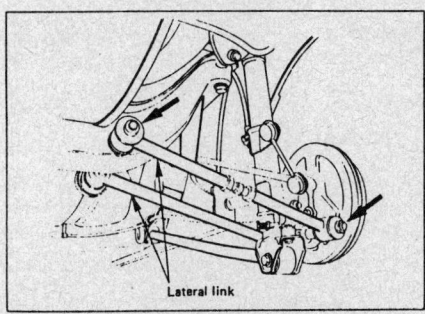

Fig. 2   Lateral link adjustment

Fig. 3   Lateral link replacement

HUB ASSEMBLY REPLACE

1. Disconnect battery ground cable.
2. Raise and support vehicle, then remove wheel and tire assembly.
3. Using suitable jack stands, support rear suspension, then remove rear brake drum assembly.
4. Check hub axial play at hub flange, **Fig. 1**, using suitable dial indicator. If axial play is greater then 0.020 inch, replace hub assembly.
5. Remove four hub to knuckle bolts, then the hub assembly.
6. Reverse procedures to install.

LATERAL LINK REPLACE

1. Place vehicle on level surface, then disconnect battery ground cable.
2. Raise and support vehicle, then remove tire and wheel assemblies. Refer to **Figs. 2 and 3** when servicing lateral links.
3. Remove lateral link bolt on lefthand side and push crossmember down to prevent interference with fuel tank.
4. Remove righthand side lateral link mounting bolts from rear crossmember and rear suspension knuckle.
5. Remove lateral links.
6. Reverse procedures to install.

STRUT ASSEMBLY REPLACE

1. Place vehicle on level surface, then disconnect battery ground cable.
2. Raise and support vehicle, then remove tire and wheel assemblies.
3. Support suspension with jackstands, then lower vehicle slightly so weight rest on jackstands and not suspension arms.
4. Remove flexible brake hose and clip at strut.
5. Remove stabilizer bar link from strut, then strut to knuckle bolts.
6. Open rear hatch and remove strut tower cover, then loosen nuts for strut mount and remove strut assemblies, **Figs. 4 and 5,**.
7. Reverse procedure to install.

STABILIZER BAR REPLACE

Refer to Figs. 7 and 8 when replacing stabilizer bar.
1. Disconnect battery ground cable, then raise and support vehicle.
2. Place jack stands under suspension support, then lower vehicle slightly so that vehicle weight rests on support not on suspension arms.
3. Remove bracket with rubber bushing from body, then the stabilizer bar.
4. Reverse procedure to install.

TRAILING LINK REPLACE

1. Place vehicle on level surface, then disconnect battery ground cable.
2. Raise and support vehicle, then remove tire and wheel assemblies.
3. Remove trailing link bolts, then trailing link, **Fig. 6**.
4. Reverse procedure to install, noting the following:
   a. It will be necessary to reset trim height before you torque trailing link bolts. Refer to "Trim Height, Adjust" in "Wheel Alignment" section.
   b. **Torque** trailing link bolts to 94 ft. lbs.

REAR SUSPENSION KNUCKLE REPLACE

1. Raise and support vehicle, then remove tire and wheel assemblies.
2. Place jack stands under suspension support, then lower vehicle slightly so that vehicle weight rests on support not on suspension arms.
3. Remove rear brake drum, then hub unit assembly as described in "Hub Assembly, Replace."
4. Remove backing plate with brake assembly and set aside.
5. Remove through bolt from lateral link at axial side.
6. Remove suspension knuckle from strut.
7. Reverse procedure to install.

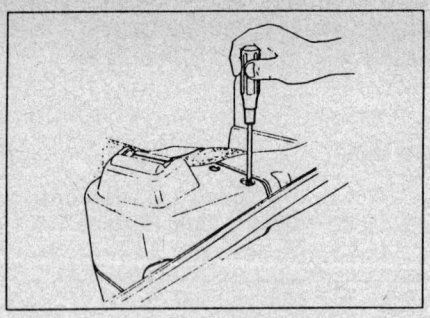

Fig. 4 Removing strut tower cover

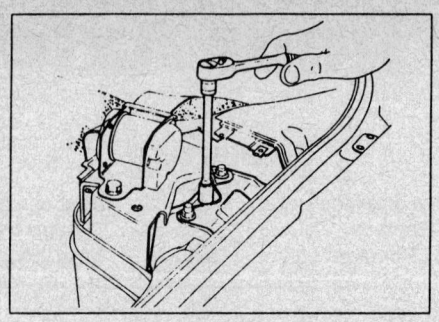

Fig. 5 Removing upper strut mounting nuts

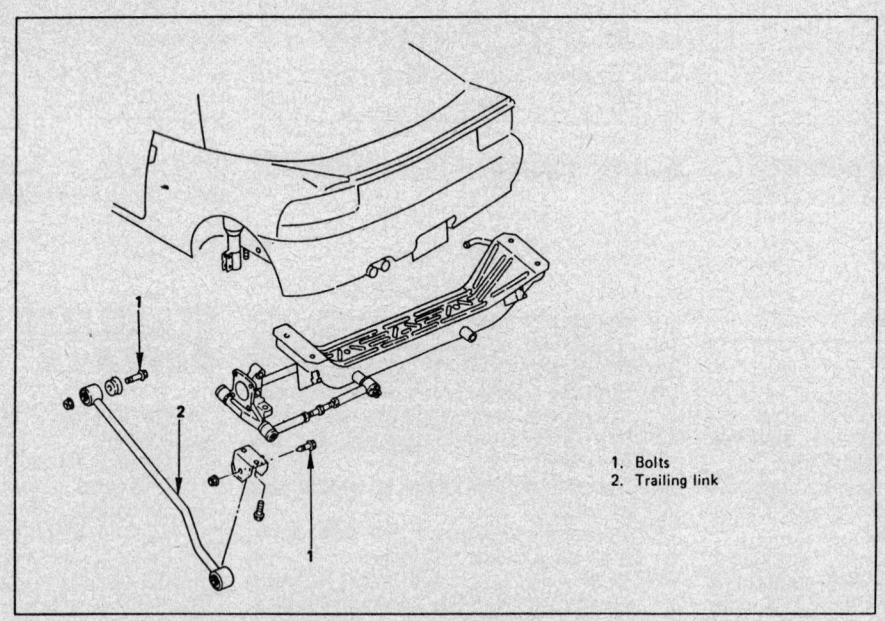

1. Bolts
2. Trailing link

Fig. 6 Trailing link removal

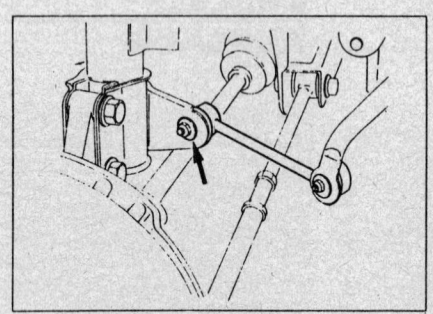

Fig. 7 Stabilizer bar connection

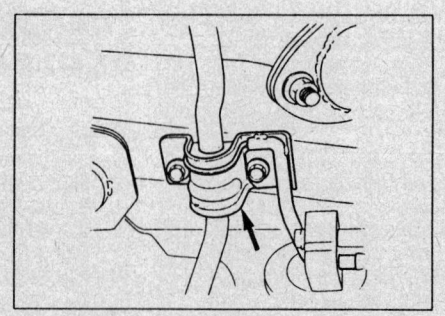

Fig. 8 Stabilizer brackets

TIGHTENING SPECIFICATIONS

Year	Component	Torque/ft. lbs.
1990–91	Crossmember Bolts	94
	Hub Assembly	49
	Lateral Link Bolts	94
	Link Bolts	19
	Stabilizer Bar Brackets	71
	Stabilizer Bar Link	19
	Strut Rod Piston Nut	36
	Strut To Knuckle Bolts	116
	Strut Tower Nuts	50
	Trailing Link Bolts	94
	Wheel & Tire	87

①—Inch lbs.

Front Suspension & Steering

INDEX

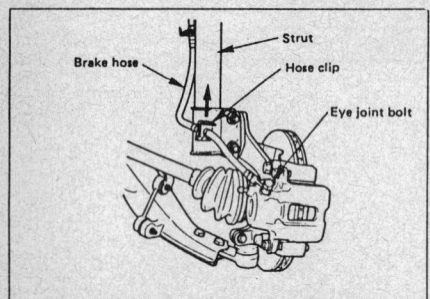

Fig. 1   Front brake hose removal

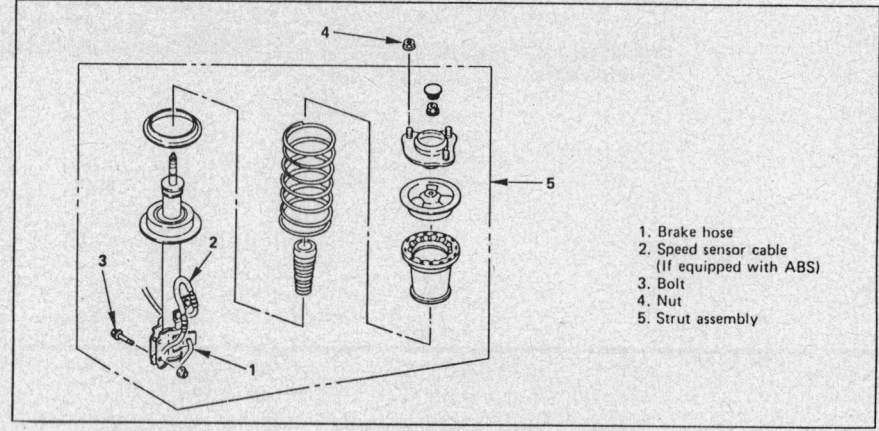

1. Brake hose
2. Speed sensor cable (If equipped with ABS)
3. Bolt
4. Nut
5. Strut assembly

Fig. 2   Front strut assembly

STRUT ASSEMBLY
REPLACE

1. Disconnect battery ground cable.
2. Raise and support vehicle, then remove wheel and tire assembly.
3. Using suitable jack stands, support front suspension.
4. Disconnect front caliper brake hose, clip and bracket, then drain brake fluid, **Fig. 1.**
5. Cap brake hose to prevent fluid leakage and dirt from entering system.
6. Remove strut assembly lower attaching bolts and nuts, **Fig. 2.**
7. Remove upper strut mount attaching nuts, **Fig. 3,** then remove strut assembly.
8. Reverse procedure to install. Torque attaching nuts and bolt to specifications.

LOWER CONTROL ARM
ASSEMBLY
REPLACE

1. Disconnect battery ground cable.

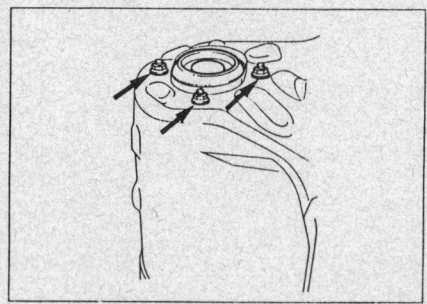

Fig. 3   Upper strut mount

2. Raise and support vehicle, then remove wheel and tire assembly.
3. Remove stabilizer bar link to control arm assembly.
4. Remove lower ball joint attaching nuts, **Fig. 4.**
5. Remove control arm front bushing attaching bolt.
6. Remove control arm rear bushing at-

taching bolts, then remove control arm assembly.
7. Reverse procedure to install. Torque attaching nuts and bolt to specifications.

STABILIZER BAR
REPLACE

1. Disconnect battery ground cable.
2. Using tool No. J28467-A or equivalent, remove engine assembly.
3. Raise and support vehicle, then using suitable jack stands, support front suspension.
4. Remove wheel and tire assembly, then remove front exhaust pipe.
5. Disconnect power steering gear lines, **Fig. 5.**
6. Remove steering shaft and boot inside vehicle, **Fig. 6.**
7. Remove lower ball joint assemblies.
8. Using tool No. J 21687-02 or equivalent, remove tie rod at steering knuckle, **Fig. 7.**

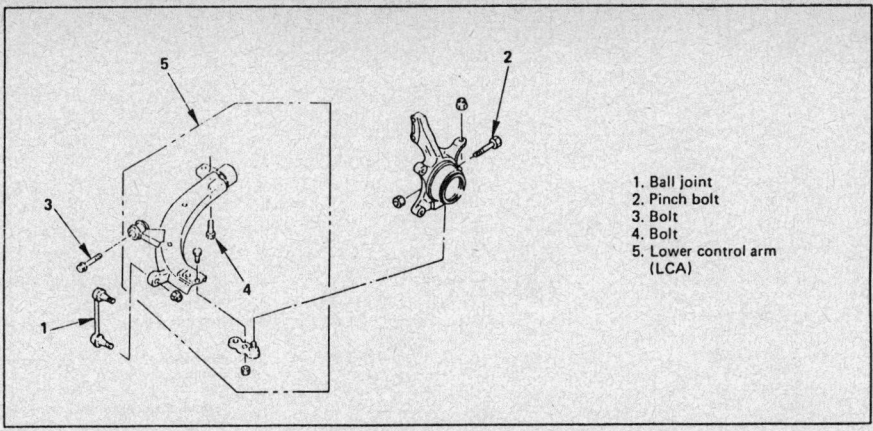

1. Ball joint
2. Pinch bolt
3. Bolt
4. Bolt
5. Lower control arm (LCA)

Fig. 4   Lower control arm assembly

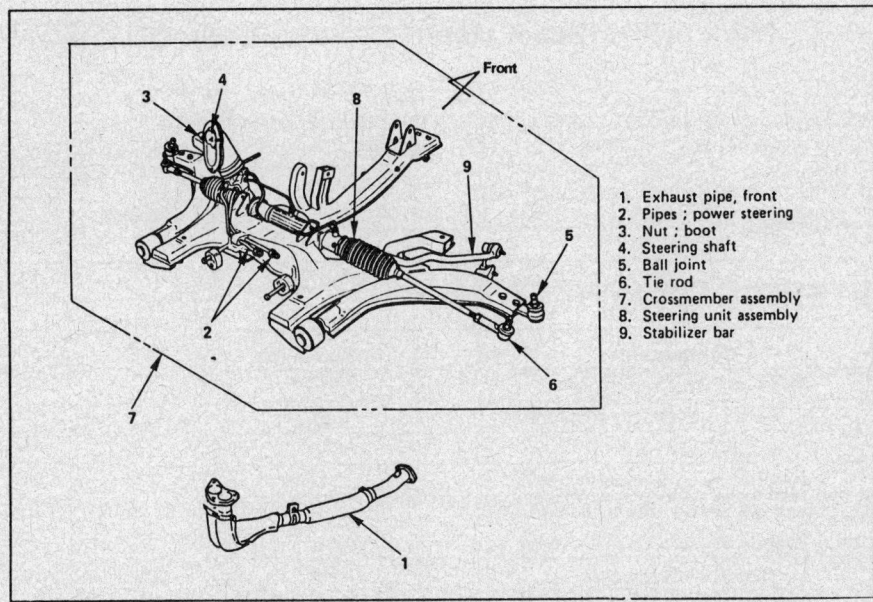

Front

1. Exhaust pipe, front
2. Pipes ; power steering
3. Nut ; boot
4. Steering shaft
5. Ball joint
6. Tie rod
7. Crossmember assembly
8. Steering unit assembly
9. Stabilizer bar

Fig. 5   Front crossmember assembly

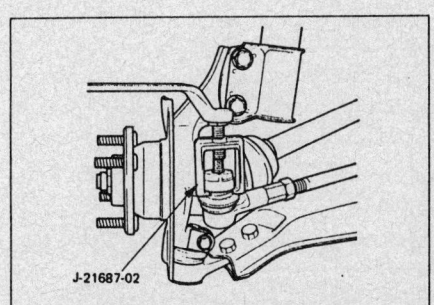

J-21687-02

Fig. 6   Steering shaft

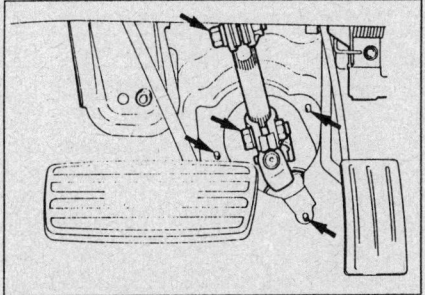

Fig. 7   Tie rod removal

9. Remove engine torque rod center beam attaching nut and bolt.
10. Remove rear engine mount.
11. Remove center beam attaching bolts, then remove crossmember attaching bolts.
12. Remove center beam, crossmember, steering gear and stabilizer bar assembly.
13. Remove steering gear assembly, then remove stabilizer bar.
14. Reverswe procedure to install. Torque attaching nuts and bolts to specifications.

WHEEL HUB, BEARING & KNUCKLE
REPLACE
REMOVAL

1. Disconnect battery ground cable.
2. Raise and support vehicle, then remove wheel and tire assembly.
3. Remove brake caliper attaching bolts, support caliper and position aside, **Fig. 8.**
4. Remove brake rotor assembly.
5. Using suitable gauge measure hub bearing endplay. If endplay exceeds .0002 inch, replace hub bearing.
6. Stake hub axle attaching nut, then remove hub axle attaching nut.
7. Using tool Nos. J 34866 and J 2619-01 or equivalents, remove hub assembly.
8. Using toll No. J 21687-02 or equivalent, remove tie rod, **Fig. 7.**
9. Remove lower ball joint assembly.
10. Remove lower strut to steering knuckle attaching nuts and bolts, then remove steering knuckle.

INSTALLATION

1. Install knuckle assembly into drive shaft and snug hub nuts. **Ensure that seals are not damaged when installing the shaft into the knuckle. If hub and knuckle assemblies are disassembled, seals, inter and outer must be replaced with new seals.**
2. Install ball joint of lower control arm to knuckle. Do not loosen boot on ball joint.
3. Install lower ball joint. Torque to specifications
4. Install tie rod. Torque to specifications.
5. Install hub nut and torque to specifications, then stake hub nut.
6. Install rotor, then brake caliper, torque caliper bolts to specifications.

RACK & PINION STEERING GEAR
REPLACE

1. Remove intermediate steering shaft

cover, then remove dust boot ring attaching nuts.
2. Raise and support vehicle, then remove wheel and tire assembly.
3. Remove dust boot from bulkhead, then position drain pan under vehicle.
4. Remove intermediate steering shaft pinch bolt.
5. Using Tie Rod End Remover tool No. J 21687-02 or equivalent, disconnect tie rod ends at steering knuckles.
6. Remove power steering fluid line hold down bracket.
7. Disconnect power steering high pressure line, drain power steering fluid, then remove rack to crossmember attaching bolts.
8. Remove steering gear bracket attaching nut and bolt, then position steering gear from mounts.
9. Disconnect power steering return line, then disconnect intermediate shaft knuckle.
10. Remove steering gear through right side of vehicle.
11. Reverse procedure to install.

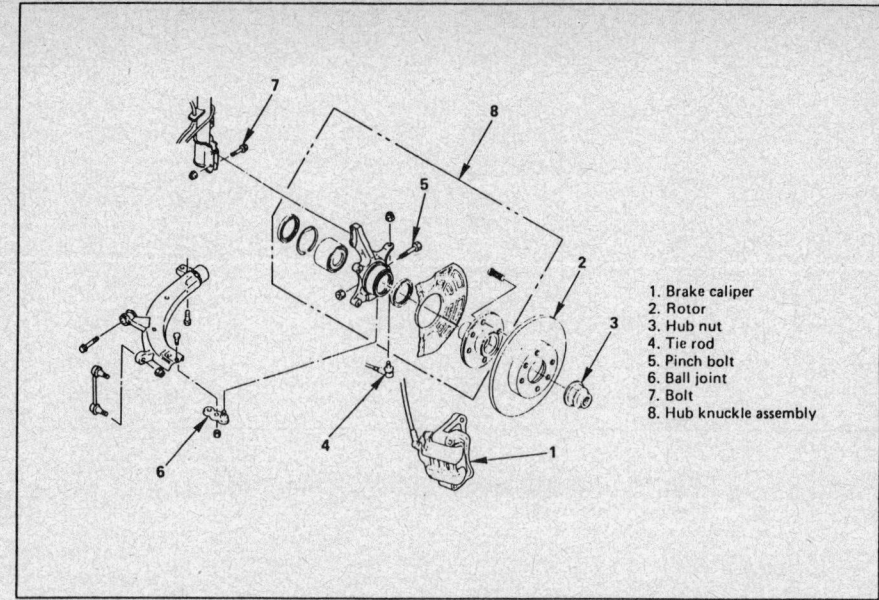

1. Brake caliper
2. Rotor
3. Hub nut
4. Tie rod
5. Pinch bolt
6. Ball joint
7. Bolt
8. Hub knuckle assembly

Fig. 8   Wheel hub & steering knuckle assembly

POWER STEERING PUMP REPLACE

1. Raise and support vehicle, then place drain pan underneath vehicle.

2. Loosen power steering pump adjusting and pivot bolts, then remove drive belt.
3. Disconnect power steering pump high pressure and return lines, cap lines to prevent contamination.
4. Remove adjusting and pivot bolts, then remove power steering pump and bracket assembly.
5. Reverse procedure to install.

TIGHTENING SPECIFICATIONS

Year	Component	Torque/ft. lbs.
1990–91	Ball Joint To Control Arm	115
	Ball Joint To Steering Knuckle	49
	Brake Caliper Bolt	72
	Control Arm To Crossmember	117
	Crossmember Assembly to Frame Bolt	137
	Engine Torque Rod To Center Beam Bolt	37
	Hub Assembly Nut	137
	Inner Tire Rod	65
	Knuckle To Strut Bolts	116
	Lower Control Arm Front Bushing	95
	Lower Control Arm Rear Bushing	51
	Lower Strut To Knuckle Bolt	115
	Outer Tie Rod Nut To Steering Knuckle	40
	Pinch Bolt To Ball Joint Of Lower Control Arm	48
	Power Steering Pump Adjusting Bolt	15
	Power Steering Pump Pivot Bolt	15
	Stabilizer Bar To Control Arm	19
	Stabilizer Bar To Crossmember	12
	Stabilizer Link Bolt	19
	Steering Gear To Crossmember	41
	Strut Rod Piston Nut	34
	Tie Rod Nut To Lower Control Arm	19
	Upper Strut Mounting Nuts	50
	Wheel & Tire Assembly	87

Wheel Alignment

INDEX

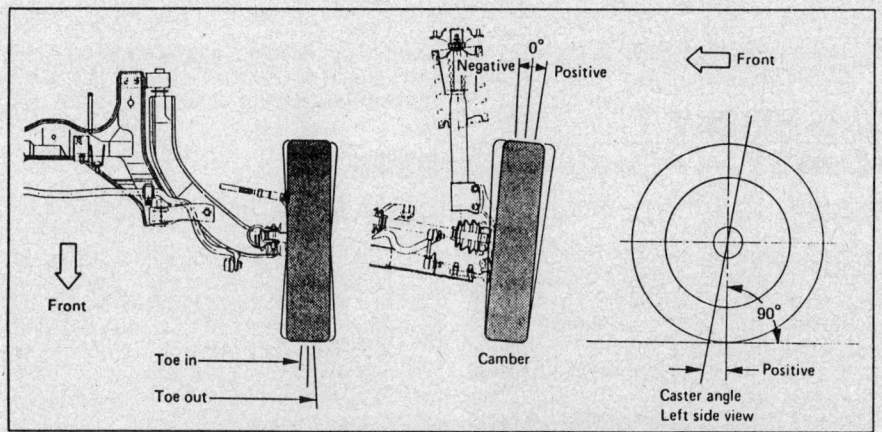

Fig. 1   Front alignment angles

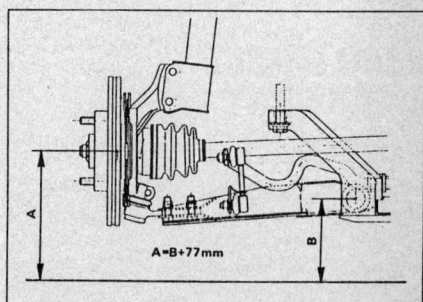

Fig. 2   Trim height

DESCRIPTION

Wheel alignment is the angular relationship between the wheels, suspension attaching parts and ground, **Fig. 1**. The angle of the knuckle away from the vertical, pointing in or out of wheels, tilt of the wheels from vertical (when viewed from front of vehicle) and tilt of suspension members from vertical (when viewed from side of vehicle), all of these are involved in proper alignment.

CASTER

Caster is tilting of the steering axis either forward or backward from the vertical (when viewed from side of vehicle). A backward tilt is positive (+) and a forward tilt is negative (-). On short and long arm type suspension you cannot see a caster angle without using a special instrument, but if you look straight down from the top of the upper control arm to the ground, you would find that ball joints do not line up what a caster angle other than 0° is present.

CAMBER

Camber is the tilting of front and rear wheels from the vertical when viewed from front of vehicle. When wheels tilt outward at top, camber is positive(+). When wheels tilt inward, camber is negative (-). Amount of tilt is measured in degrees from the vertical and this is camber angle.

TOE

Toe is the turning in or out of wheels. The purpose of toe is to ensure parallel rolling of wheels. Excessive toe-in or toe-out may increase tire wear. Toe also serves to offset small deflections of the suspension which occurs when vehicle is moving.

PRELIMINARY CHECK

Steering and vibration problems are not always the results of poor alignment. An additional problem to be checked is tire lead due to worn or improperly manufactured tires. ""Lead" is the deviation of the vehicle from a straight path on a level road without hand pressure on the steering wheel.

Refer to "Front Wheel Alignment Specifications" and "Rear Wheel Alignment Specifications" located in the front of this chapter, to insure correct specifications, if vehicle is within specification the following checks and inspections should be preformed.

1. Check tires for proper inflation and tread wear.
2. Check for loose ball joints and tie rod ends. If excessive looseness is noted, replace defective parts before adjusting toe.
3. Check for wheel and tire assembly run-out.
4. Check trim heights. If not within specifications, correct before adjusting toe.
5. Check for loose control arms.
6. Check for loose or missing stabilizer bar components.
7. Consideration must be given to excess loads. If excess load is normally carried in vehicle, it should remain during alignment checks.

FRONT WHEEL ALIGNMENT

CAMBER & CASTER ADJUSTMENT

Camber and caster are not be adjustable. If during inspection, either is found to be out of specifications, locate the cause. Check for damaged, loose, bent or worn front suspension parts. Replace worn or damaged parts as needed. To prevent any incorrect reading during inspection, bounce front bumper three or more times.

TOE ADJUSTMENT

1. Loosen right and left tie rod end lock nuts.
2. Apply grease between tie rods and rack boots.
3. Turn right and left tie rods by the same amount to align toe to specification. **Right and left tie rods should become equal in length.**
4. After adjustment, tighten locknuts and ensure rack boots are not twisted.

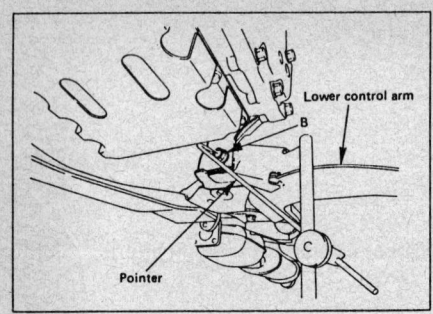

Fig. 3 Trim height, bushing center

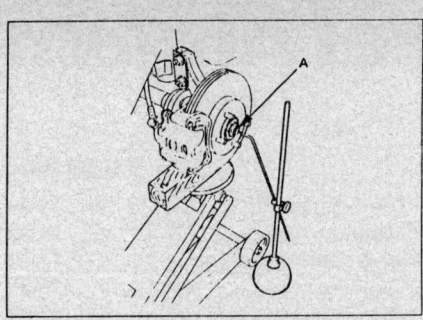

Fig. 4 Trim height, wheel level

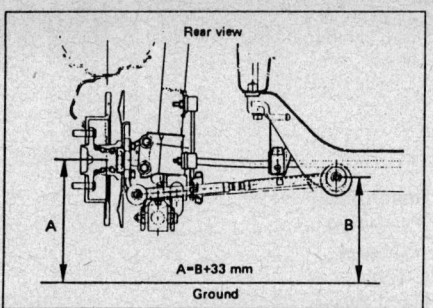

Fig. 5 Trim height center

REAR WHEEL ALIGNMENT

CAMBER

Camber cannot be adjusted. Should camber be found out of specification, locate the cause and replace vehicle parts to correct the damage. If the body or chassis is found to be damaged, the damaged area must be corrected to provide proper alignment.

TOE

1. Loosen jam nuts on rear support rod.
2. Turn hex screw in center to obtain proper toe angle.

3. Tighten jam nuts. **Torque** jam nuts to 65 ft. lbs.

TRIM HEIGHT
ADJUST
FRONT

When reattaching the control arm, hold the position of wheel center to keep distance of 3 inches at bushing center (B) height, **Fig. 2.** Bushing will twist if the wheel center height is too high or low. If bushing does twist, bushing will suffer premature damage.

Measure height (B) at front bushing center and set point at height of (B) plus 3 inches, **Figs. 3 and 4.** Move front rotor assembly by using a suitable floor jack until reaching specification height (A), then tighten the bushing bolts at this time.

REAR

Refer to **Fig. 5** when adjusting trim height.
1. Hold the position of wheel center to keep distance of 1.3 inch height from rear bushing center of lateral link.
2. Measure height of bushing center at rear side of crossmember. Set point at height of B + 1.299 inch.
3. Raise up rear wheel using a jack until it reaches specified height.
4. **Torque** lateral or trailing links bolts to specifications.

PONTIAC LEMANS
(T Car)
INDEX OF SERVICE OPERATIONS

NOTE: Refer To The Rear Of This Manual For Vehicle Manufacturer's Special Tool Suppliers.

INDEX OF SERVICE OPERATIONS—Continued

Specifications

GENERAL ENGINE SPECIFICATIONS

Year	Engine Liter/CID①	Engine VIN Code②	Fuel System	Bore x Stroke Inches	Compression Ratio	Net HP @ RPM ③	Maximum Torque Ft. Lbs. @ RPM
1988-91	1.6L/4-98	6	TBI④	3.11 x 3.21	8.6	74 @ 5600	90 @ 2800
1989-91	2.0L/4-121	K	TBI④	3.39 x 3.39	8.8	96 @ 4800	118 @ 3600

①—CID: Cubic Inch Displacement.
②—The eighth digit of the VIN denotes engine code.
③—Ratings are net as installed in vehicle.
④—Throttle body fuel injection.

TUNE UP SPECIFICATIONS

Year & Engine/ VIN Code①	Spark Plug Gap	Ignition Timing BTDC② Firing Order ④	Ignition Timing BTDC② Man. Trans.	Ignition Timing BTDC② Auto. Trans.	Ignition Timing BTDC② Mark Fig.	Curb Idle Speed③ Man. Trans.	Curb Idle Speed③ Auto. Trans.	Fast Idle Speed Man. Trans.	Fast Idle Speed Auto. Trans.	Fuel Pump Pressure Psi.
1988-91										
1.6L/4-98/6	.060	1—3—4—2	⑦	⑦	A	600⑥⑧	500⑥⑧	⑧	⑧	9-13⑤
2.0L/4-121/K	.060	B	—	—	C	600⑥⑧	500⑥⑧	⑧	⑧	9-13⑤

①—The eighth digit of the Vehicle Identification Number (VIN) denotes engine code.
②—BTDC: Before Top Dead Center.
③—N: Neutral.
④—Before disconnecting wires from distributor cap, determine location of No. 1 wire in cap, as distributor position may have been altered from that shown at the end of this chart.

⑤—Remove fuel pump fuse from fuse panel, then start engine & operate until engine stops. Crank engine for approximately 3 seconds to relieve fuel pressure from lines. Disconnect fuel supply hose, then connect a suitable fuel pressure gauge between hose & tube. Operate engine at idle & note gauge reading.
⑥—Minimum.

⑦—Align notch on crankshaft pulley with pointer. Prior to checking ignition timing, connect a jumper wire between terminals A & B of ALDL diagnostic connector. The ALDL diagnostic connector is located under the righthand side of the instrument panel.
⑧—Idle speed is controlled by the IAC (Idle Air Control) assembly.

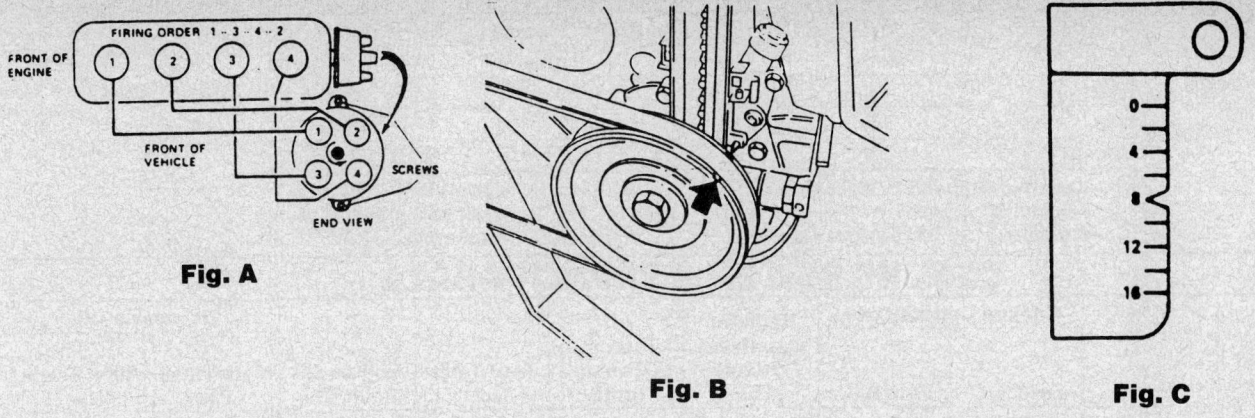

Fig. A

Fig. B

Fig. C

ALTERNATOR SPECIFICATIONS

Year	Model Number	Series	Alternator Rated Output Amps.
1988–89	1100234	10SI	38
	1100253	12SI	70
	1100261	12SI	81
	1101144	CS130	85
	1101145	CS130	100
1990–91	1101531	CS121	72
	1101563	CS121	72
	1101564	CS121	60
	1101565	CS121	72
	90244847	Bosch	55
	90244848	Bosch	65

STARTING MOTOR APPLICATIONS

Year	Engine	Starter Series	Model No.
1988–91	1.6L/4-98	5MT	1998525

FRONT WHEEL ALIGNMENT SPECIFICATIONS

Year	Model	Caster Angle, Degrees		Camber Angle, Degrees				Toe-In, Degrees
		Limits	Desired	Limits		Desired		
				Left	Right	Left	Right	
1988–91	All	+.75 to +2.75	+1.75①	+.45 to −1.05	+.45 to −1.05	−.3	−.3	0

①—Deviation from left to right side of vehicle: 1° maximum.

REAR WHEEL ALIGNMENT

| Year | Model | Camber Angle Degrees | | Toe In Degrees |
		Limits	Desired	
1988	All	0 to −1	−.5①	.33②
1989	All	—	−1③	.33②
1990-91	All	—	−1③	−.42②

①—Variation from left to right side of vehicle: .5° maximum.
②—Variation from left to right side of vehicle: .24° maximum.
③—Variation from left to right side of vehicle: .25° maximum.

COOLING SYSTEM & CAPACITY DATA

| Year | Engine | Cooling Capacity Qts. | | Radiator Cap Relief Pressure, Lbs. | Thermo. Opening Temp. | Fuel Tank Gals. | Engine Oil Refill Qts. | Transaxle Oil | |
		Less A/C	With A/C					Man. Trans. Pts.	Auto. Trans. Qts. ①
1988	All	8.1	8.1	15	195	13.2	4②	3.5	③
1989-91	All	8.1	8.1	15	195	13	4②	4.5	③

①—Approximate, make final check with dipstick.
②—Additional oil maybe required with filter change.
③—Oil pan only, 4 qts.; total capacity, 6 qts.

Electrical
INDEX

FUSE PANEL LOCATION

The fuse panel is located under the left-hand side of the instrument panel.

FLASHER LOCATION

The flasher is located on the fuse panel under the lefthand side of the instrument panel.

STARTER REPLACE

1988

1. Remove fuel pump fuse from fuse panel, then start and operate engine until it stalls. After stalling, crank engine for approximately 3 seconds to deplete fuel pressure in lines.
2. Disconnect battery ground cable.
3. Disconnect fuel lines from throttle body unit and position aside. **Place shop towel over fuel line and fitting when disconnecting.**

4. Disconnect vacuum lines from throttle body. **Tag vacuum lines so they can be installed in the same positions.**
5. Remove splash shield from distributor coil and position aside.
6. Remove upper starter motor attaching bolt using 6 and 12 inch extensions with a universal socket.
7. **On models less power brakes,** proceed as follows:
   a. Remove lower starter motor attaching bolt.
   b. Position starter motor to gain access to wiring, then disconnect wiring.
   c. Remove brake master cylinder to dash panel attaching nuts, then position master cylinder to provide clearance for starter motor removal.
8. **On models equipped with power brakes,** proceed as follows:
   a. Remove steering column cover attaching screws, then remove steering column cover.
   b. Remove steering column upper attaching nuts, then remove attaching screws at toe pan.
   c. Raise and support front of vehicle,

then disconnect steering shaft from coupling.
   d. Lower vehicle, then from inside vehicle, position steering column to provide clearance for starter motor removal.
   e. Disconnect wiring from starter motor, then remove lower starter motor attaching bolt.
9. **On all models,** remove starter motor from vehicle.
10. Reverse procedure to install.

1989-91

1. Disconnect battery ground cable.
2. Disconnect wiring at starter motor, then remove upper and lower starter attaching bolts.
3. Remove starter motor from vehicle.
4. Reverse procedure to install. **Torque** starter bolts to 33 ft. lbs.

DISTRIBUTOR REPLACE

1. Disconnect battery ground cable.
2. Remove ignition coil and spark plug wires at distributor cap.

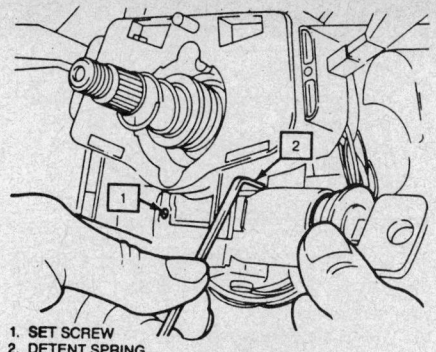

1. SET SCREW
2. DETENT SPRING

Fig. 1   Ignition lock replacement

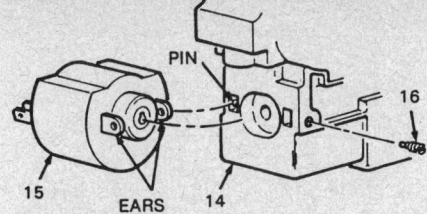

14- HOUSING ASM, IGN SWITCH
15- SWITCH ASM, IGNITION
16- SCREW, IGN SWITCH RETAINING

Fig. 2   Ignition switch replacement

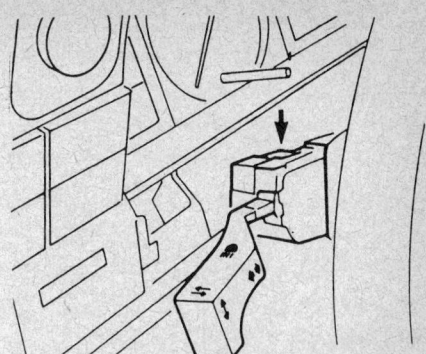

Fig. 3   Turn signal & wiper switch replacement

3. Disconnect coil and EST electrical connectors.
4. **On 1.6L/4-98 models,** remove distributor clamp attaching bolt.
5. **On 1989-91 2.0L/1-121 models,** remove distributor cam carrier attaching nuts.
6. **On all models,** mark distributor tang drive and camshaft for correct assembly, then remove distributor.
7. Reverse procedure to install.

IGNITION LOCK
REPLACE

1. Disconnect battery ground cable.
2. Remove lower instrument cluster trim.
3. Remove turn signal and wiper switch cover attaching screws and the cover.
4. Turn ignition key to position "II."
5. Depress detent spring, **Fig. 1,** then slide lock cylinder out of steering column.
6. Reverse procedure to install.

IGNITION SWITCH
REPLACE

1. Disconnect battery ground cable.
2. Remove lower instrument cluster trim.
3. Remove turn signal and wiper switch cover attaching screws and the cover.
4. Disconnect electrical connector from ignition switch.
5. Remove ignition switch setscrew, then remove ignition switch, **Fig. 2.**
6. Reverse procedure to install.

TURN SIGNAL & WIPER SWITCH
REPLACE

1. Disconnect battery ground cable.
2. Remove lower instrument cluster trim.
3. Remove screws from both sides of upper cover panel. Rotate steering wheel as necessary to gain access to all screws.
4. Remove three lower panel attaching screws, then pull handle from lock release lever and remove tilt lever, if equipped.
5. Depress switch release tabs, **Fig. 3,** then disconnect electrical connector and remove switch.
6. Reverse procedure to install.

STEERING WHEEL
REPLACE

1. Disconnect battery ground cable.
2. Remove steering wheel horn cap, then disconnect horn electrical leads.
3. Remove steering wheel retaining nut and retainer, then place alignment marks on steering wheel and steering shaft.
4. Remove steering wheel using tool No. J-36541 or equivalent.
5. Unclip steering wheel contact ring, if required.
6. Reverse procedure to install. When installing steering wheel, align marks placed on steering wheel and steering shaft. Also the turn signal cancelling cam on the steering wheel should be to the left. **Torque** steering wheel attaching nut to 13 ft. lbs.

BACK-UP LIGHT/NEUTRAL START SWITCH
REPLACE

1. Disconnect battery ground cable.
2. Disconnect shift linkage and electrical connector from switch, **Fig. 4.**
3. Remove switch attaching bolts and the switch.
4. Reverse procedure to install. Adjust switch prior to tightening attaching bolts, refer to "Back-up Light/Neutral Start Switch, Adjust."

BACK-UP LIGHT/NEUTRAL START SWITCH
ADJUST

1. Shift transaxle into Neutral.
2. Loosen switch attaching bolts, then rotate switch on shift assembly to align adjustment hole with carrier tang hole. Insert a $3/32$ drill bit into adjustment hole on switch to a depth of $3/8$ inch.
3. **Torque** attaching bolts to 22 ft. lbs., then remove drill bit.

HEADLAMP SWITCH
REPLACE

1. Disconnect battery ground cable.
2. Depress switch retaining clips using a suitable screwdriver, **Fig. 5.**
3. Disconnect electrical connector and remove switch.
4. Reverse procedure to install.

INSTRUMENT CLUSTER
REPLACE

1. Disconnect battery ground cable.
2. Remove turn signal switch housing attaching screws and the housing. Rotate steering wheel as necessary to gain access to all screws.
3. Remove two instrument panel trim plate attaching screws and the trim plate, **Fig. 6.**
4. Depress speedometer cable retainer spring and disconnect cable from cluster.
5. Remove instrument cluster attaching screws.
6. Disconnect electrical connectors from cluster, then remove cluster from vehicle, **Fig. 7.**
7. Reverse procedure to install.

RADIO
REPLACE

1. Disconnect battery ground cable.
2. Place ignition switch in On position, then set transaxle selector lever in the 1 position.
3. Using a suitable pointed plastic tool, remove package panel, **Fig. 8.**
4. Remove front center console attaching screws from under ashtray and plastic cap, **Fig. 9.**
5. **On models with automatic transaxle,** remove selector lever, then pull indicator strap from cover. Remove retaining clips and trim cover.
6. **On models with manual transaxle,** remove shift knob, trim plate and boot.
7. **On all models,** remove front console.
8. Remove four console upper attaching screws, then slide console toward rear of vehicle.
9. Remove radio from instrument panel, **Fig. 10.**

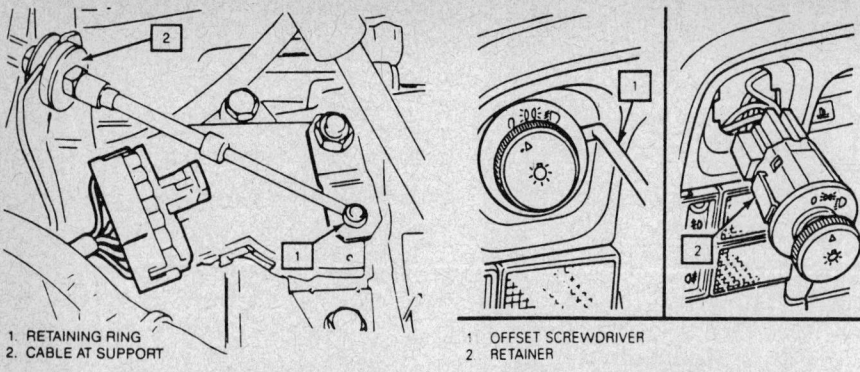

1. RETAINING RING
2. CABLE AT SUPPORT

Fig. 4   Back-up light/neutral start switch replacement

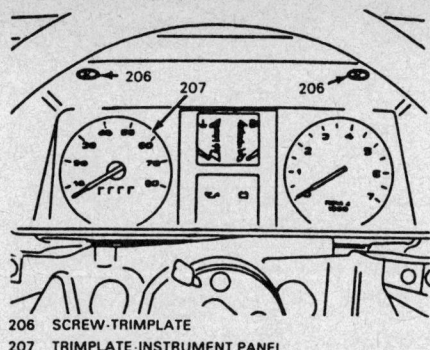

1. OFFSET SCREWDRIVER
2. RETAINER

Fig. 5   Headlamp switch replacement

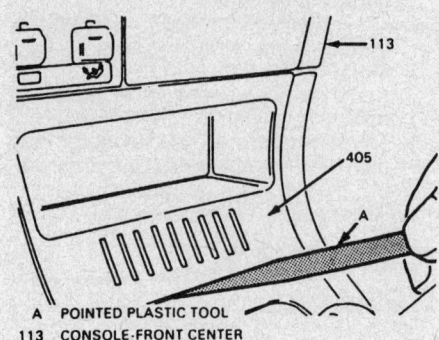

206   SCREW-TRIMPLATE
207   TRIMPLATE-INSTRUMENT PANEL

Fig. 6   Instrument cluster trim plate attaching screw locations

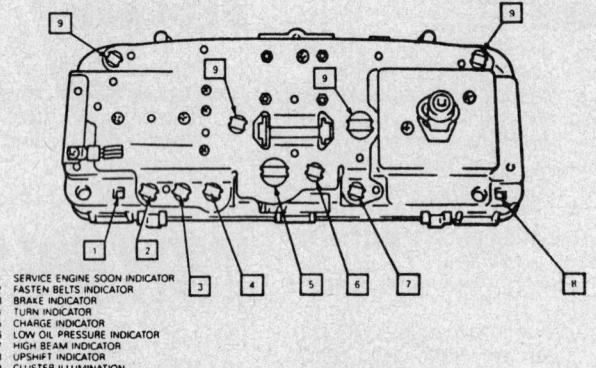

1 SERVICE ENGINE SOON INDICATOR
2 FASTEN BELTS INDICATOR
3 BRAKE INDICATOR
4 TURN INDICATOR
5 CHARGE INDICATOR
6 LOW OIL PRESSURE INDICATOR
7 HIGH BEAM INDICATOR
8 UPSHIFT INDICATOR
9 CLUSTER ILLUMINATION

Fig. 7   Instrument cluster

A   POINTED PLASTIC TOOL
113   CONSOLE-FRONT CENTER
405   PACKAGE PANEL

Fig. 8   Package panel removal

WINDSHIELD WIPER MOTOR
REPLACE

1. Disconnect battery ground cable.
2. **On 1988 models,** remove wiper arm attaching nuts, then slide arms off splined shafts.
3. **On all models,** remove cowl vent grille attaching screws and the grille.
4. Disconnect wiper motor electrical connectors.
5. Remove crank arm to wiper motor attaching nut.
6. Remove wiper motor attaching bolts and the wiper motor.
7. Reverse procedure to install.

BLOWER MOTOR
REPLACE
LESS A/C

1. Disconnect battery ground cable.
2. Remove wiper arm attaching nuts, then slide arms off splined shafts.
3. Remove four wind deflector attaching screws and the deflector halves.
4. Remove washer nozzle hoses from washer nozzles.
5. Remove seal from dash panel and clip, then the right side wiper bearing attaching nut.
6. Remove water deflector, then disconnect electrical connector from blower motor housing.
7. Remove blower motor housing attaching screws and the housing.
8. Remove housing cover attaching cover screws and the cover.
9. Remove blower motor from housing.
10. Reverse procedure to install.

WITH A/C

1. Disconnect battery ground cable.
2. Disconnect blower motor electrical connectors.
3. Disconnect air hose from lower housing.
4. Remove blower motor to case attaching screws.
5. Remove blower motor and fan assembly from housing.
6. Remove blower fan retaining nut and the fan from motor.
7. Reverse procedure to install.

HEATER CORE
REPLACE
LESS A/C

1. Disconnect battery ground cable, then drain cooling system.
2. Block off heater hoses with spring clips, then mark hoses for installation reference.
3. Disconnect heater hoses from heater core.
4. Remove package panel, then move heater control levers to lowest position.
5. Disconnect temperature control cable from actuating lever and air distributor.
6. Remove kick panel from under glove box.
7. Disconnect temperature valve linkage from righthand air distributor.
8. Lift carpeting, then remove air distributor cover attaching screws and the cover.
9. Remove heater core attaching screws, then the heater core and bracket assembly. Move temperature valve as necessary to gain access to all screws.
10. Reverse procedure to install.

WITH A/C

1. Disconnect battery ground cable.
2. Block off heater hoses with spring clips, then disconnect the hoses from heater core.
3. Disconnect evaporator drain hose from heater case.
4. **On models equipped with manual transaxle,** remove gear shift boot.
5. **On all models,** remove package shelf, then the front floor console shift plate and front center console.
6. Remove glove box attaching screws and straps, then the glove box.
7. Remove hush panel retainers and the hush panel.
8. Remove outer heater case cover retainers, then bend back tab and remove the cover.
9. Remove heater case cover retaining clips and the cover.
10. Remove heater core cover attaching screws and the cover.

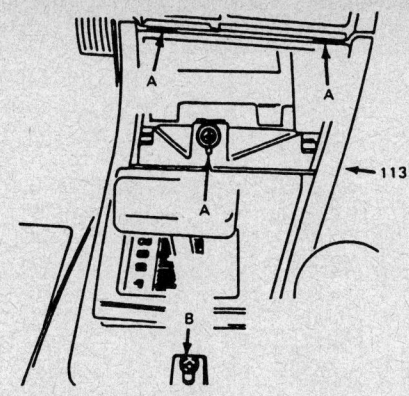

A REMOVE SCREWS
B REMOVE SCREW (UNDER CAP)
113 CONSOLE-FRONT CENTER

Fig. 9 Front console attaching screw location

11. Remove heater core clamps and the heater core.
12. Reverse procedure to install.

EVAPORATOR CORE
REPLACE

1. Disconnect battery ground cable.
2. Discharge air conditioning system.

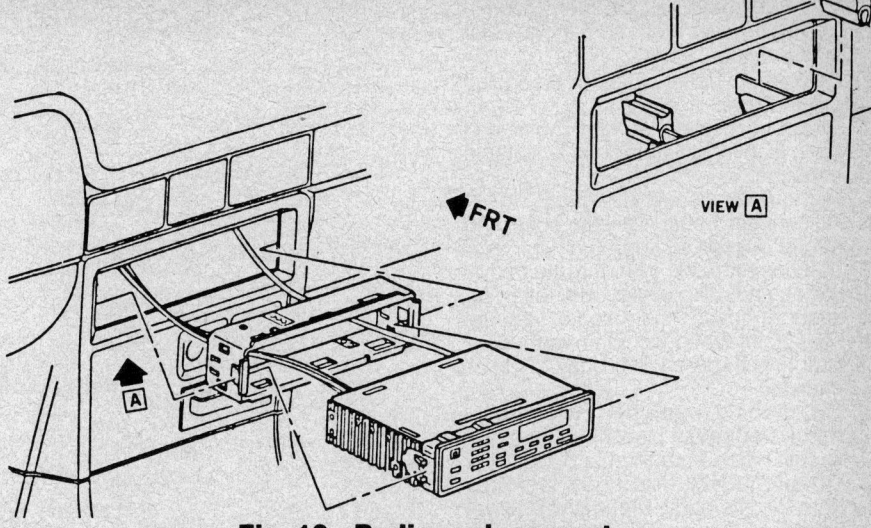

Fig. 10 Radio replacement

3. Remove heater core as previously outlined.
4. Disconnect accumulator to evaporator pipe and orifice tube to evaporator at dash panel.
5. Remove evaporator cover attaching screws, then remove evaporator cover.
6. Remove evaporator bracket attaching screws, then remove pipe clamps.
7. Remove evaporator core.
8. Reverse procedure to install.

1.6L/4-98 Engine

INDEX

ENGINE MOUNT
REPLACE

1. Disconnect battery ground cable.
2. Install engine support fixture No. J28467-A with fixture adapters J28467-70 or equivalents. **Support** tool must be positioned in center of cowl and properly tightened prior to supporting engine and transaxle assembly.
3. Remove engine mount attaching bolts and the mount, **Fig. 1.**
4. Reverse procedure to install. Tighten mount attaching bolts to torque listed at the end of this section.

ENGINE
REPLACE

1. Relieve fuel system pressure as follows:
   a. Remove fuel pump fuse from fuse panel.
   b. Start engine. After engine stalls,

crank for ten seconds to relieve residual pressure from fuel system.

   c. Turn ignition off and install fuel pump fuse.

2. Disconnect battery cables and engine ground wire.
3. Disconnect lower radiator hose and drain cooling system into a suitable container.
4. Remove air cleaner assembly.
5. Disconnect upper radiator hose and heater hose from engine.
6. Disconnect cable from throttle body.
7. Label and disconnect the following vacuum hoses; brake servo, vacuum sensor, intake manifold to vapor canister and throttle valve body to vapor canister.
8. **On models equipped with automatic transaxle,** disconnect transaxle shift cable from throttle body.
9. **On all models,** disconnect fuel lines from throttle body. **Place shop towel over fuel line and fitting when disconnecting.**
10. Disconnect electrical connectors from the following components: oxygen sensor, oil pressure switch, intake manifold temperature sensor, speed sensor, injector nozzle, back-up lamp switch, neutral start switch, throttle valve, idle air control motor and distributor.
11. Disconnect instrument panel harness connector, ground wires from camshaft housing and intake manifold and wiring harness retaining strap.
12. Remove ignition coil plugs and cable.
13. Disconnect bulkhead wiring harness connector.
14. **On models equipped with automatic transaxle,** disconnect torque converter clutch electrical connector.
15. **On all models,** raise and support vehicle.
16. **On 1990-91 models,** remove splash shield.
17. **On all models,** remove exhaust pipe and catalytic converter.
18. Pull driveshaft out of transaxle, then remove closure plug from transaxle case.
19. Disconnect interference suppression cable from transaxle.
20. Remove clutch cover plate, then remove clutch housing to engine block lower attaching bolts.
21. Lower vehicle, then attach suitable lifting equipment to engine lift hooks.
22. Support transaxle with a suitable jack, then remove right front and left front engine mount attaching bolts and the mount, then remove rear engine mount attaching bolts..
23. Remove clutch housing to engine block upper attaching bolts.
24. Separate engine from clutch housing, then carefully lift engine from vehicle.
25. Reverse procedure to install.

INTAKE MANIFOLD
REPLACE

1. Relieve fuel system pressure as follows:
   a. Remove fuel pump fuse from fuse panel.

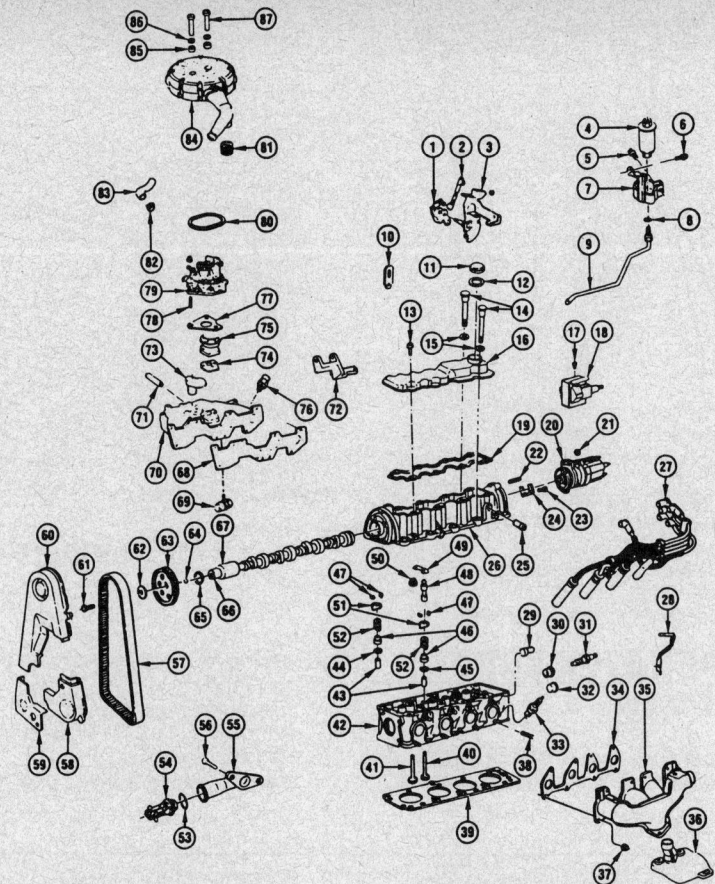

1	LEVER-ACCELERATOR CONTROL
2	ROD-THROTTLE CONTROL
3	BRACKET-ACCELERATOR CONTROL
4	FILTER-FUEL
5	BOLT
6	BOLT
7	BRACKET-FUEL FILTER
8	SEAL-FUEL FEED LINE O-RING
9	PIPE-FUEL TANK TO FILTER
10	BRACKET-ENGINE LIFT
11	CAP-OIL
12	SEAL-OIL CAP
13	BOLT
14	BOLT-CAMSHAFT CARRIER HOUSING
15	WASHER
16	COVER-CAMSHAFT HOUSING
17	BOLT
18	COIL
19	GASKET-CAMSHAFT CARRIER COVER
20	DISTRIBUTOR
21	NUT
22	BOLT
23	BOLT
24	PLATE-CAMSHAFT PRESS
25	TUBE-PCV
26	HOUSING-CAMSHAFT CARRIER
27	WIRE-SPARK PLUG
28	SUPPORT-SPARK PLUG WIRE
29	VALVE-CYLINDER HEAD BYPASS
30	ADAPTER
31	SENSOR-COOLANT TEMPERATURE
32	CAP
33	PLUG-SPARK
34	GASKET-EXHAUST MANIFOLD
35	MANIFOLD-EXHAUST
36	STOVE-EXHAUST MANIFOLD HEAT
37	NUT
38	STUD
39	GASKET-CYLINDER HEAD
40	VALVE-EXHAUST
41	VALVE-INTAKE
42	HEAD-CYLINDER
43	GUIDE
44	WASHER-INTAKE VALVE SPRING SEAT

45	ROTO CAP-EXHAUST VALVE
46	SEAL-VALVE
47	LOCK (COLLAR)-VALVE STEM
48	ADJUSTER-HYDRAULIC VALVE LASH
49	ARM-VALVE ROCKER
50	VALVE-THRUST PIECE
51	CAP-VALVE SPRING
52	SPRING-INTAKE AND EXHAUST VALVE
53	RING-SEAL
54	THERMOSTAT (92 DEGREE)
55	HOUSING-COOLING THERMOSTAT
56	BOLT-SPROCKET
57	BELT-TIMING
58	COVER-TIMING BELT LOWER REAR
59	COVER-TIMING BELT LOWER FRONT
60	COVER-TIMING BELT UPPER FRONT
61	BOLT
62	WASHER-TIMING GEAR
63	SPROCKET-CAMSHAFT TIMING
64	BALL
65	SEAL-CAMSHAFT OIL
66	PIN
67	CAMSHAFT
68	GASKET-INTAKE MANIFOLD
69	CONNECTOR-FUEL GAGE
70	MANIFOLD-INTAKE
71	CONNECTOR-INTAKE MANIFOLD
72	BRACKET-GENERAL MOUNTING
73	INSERT-INTAKE MANIFOLD TBI
74	GASKET-E.G.R.
75	VALVE-E.G.R.
76	SENSOR-INTAKE MANIFOLD COOLANT TEMPERATURE
77	GASKET-TBI
78	STUD
79	THROTTLE BODY INJECTOR (TBI)
80	GASKET-AIR CLEANER
81	HOSE-HEAT STOVE
82	CLAMP
83	HOSE-CYLINDER BLOCK VENT
84	AIR CLEANER
85	SEAL-AIR CLEANER CAP NUT
86	WASHER-AIR CLEANER CAP NUT
87	NUT-AIR CLEANER

Cylinder head & components

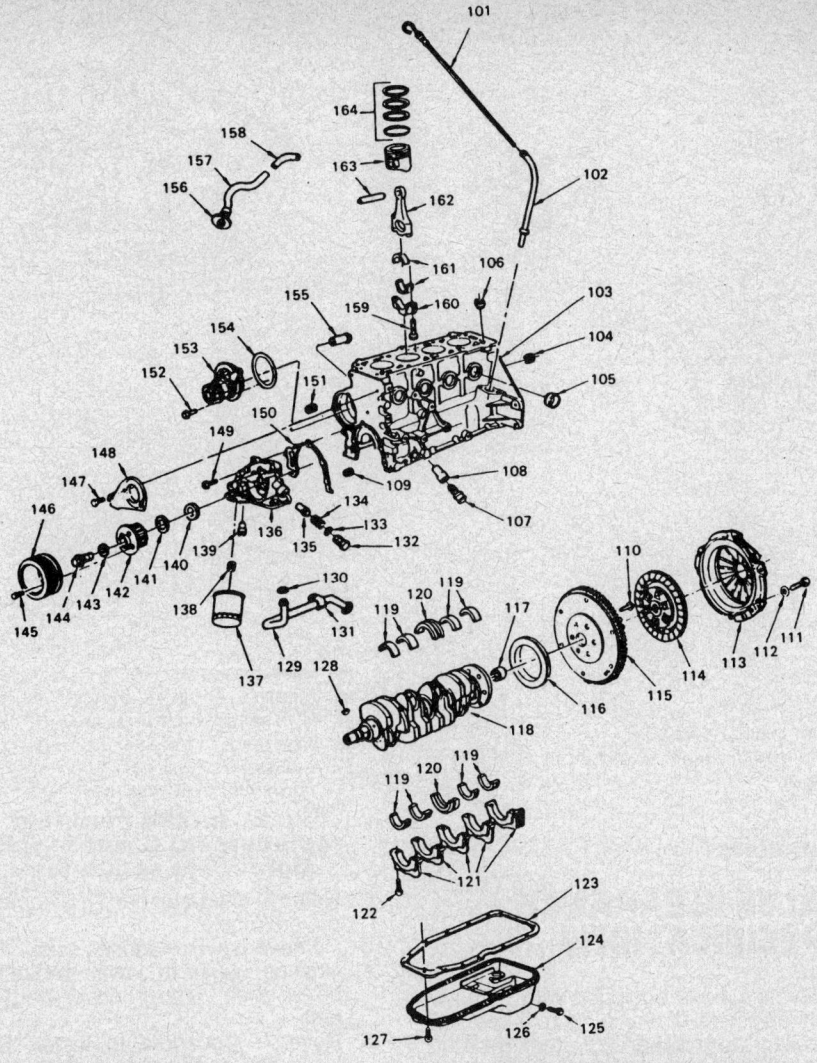

Cylinder block & components

101	INDICATOR (ROD)-OIL LEVEL
102	TUBE-OIL
103	BLOCK-ENGINE CYLINDER
104	SLEEVE-TRANSMISSION
105	PLUG-CLIP TYPE
106	SLEEVE-CYLINDER TO CYLINDER BLOCK
107	PLUG-IGNITION TIMING BUSHING
108	BUSHING-IGNITION TIMING
109	SLEEVE-OIL PLUG
110	BOLT
111	BOLT
112	WASHER
113	COVER-CLUTCH PRESSURE WITH PLATE
114	PLATE (DISC)-CLUTCH DRIVEN (M/T)
115	FLYWHEEL
116	RING-REAR CRANKSHAFT OIL SEAL
117	BEARING
118	CRANKSHAFT
119	BEARING SET-CRANKSHAFT
120	BEARING-CRANKSHAFT MAIN
121	CAP-CRANKSHAFT MAIN BEARING
122	BOLT
123	GASKET-OIL PAN
124	PAN-OIL
125	BOLT-OIL PAN DRAIN
126	GASKET (RING)-OIL PAN DRAIN BOLT
127	BOLT
128	KEY-CRANKSHAFT
129	PIPE-OIL PUMP SUCTION
130	RING-OIL PUMP SUCTION PIPE
131	BRACKET
132	BOLT-OIL PUMP PRESSURE RELIEF VALVE

133	RING-OIL PUMP PRESSURE RELIEF VALVE
134	SPRING-OIL PUMP PRESSURE RELIEF VALVE
135	PLUNGER-OIL PUMP PRESSURE RELIEF VALVE
136	PUMP-OIL
137	FILTER-OIL
138	CONNECTOR-OIL FILTER
139	VALVE-OIL PUMP BYPASS
140	RING-OIL PUMP SEAL
141	WASHER
142	GEAR-CRANKSHAFT TIMING
143	WASHER-CRANKSHAFT PULLEY
144	BOLT-CRANKSHAFT TIMING GEAR
145	BOLT-CRANKSHAFT PULLEY
146	PULLEY-CRANKSHAFT
147	SCREW-REAR TIMING BELT COVER
148	COVER-TIMING BELT UPPER REAR
149	BOLT
150	GASKET-OIL PUMP
151	PLUG
152	BOLT-COOLANT PUMP
153	PUMP-COOLANT
154	RING-COOLANT PUMP SEAL
155	NECK-CYLINDER BLOCK COOLANT INLET
156	GASKET-CYLINDER BLOCK VENT PIPE
157	PIPE-CYLINDER BLOCK VENT
158	HOSE-CYLINDER BLOCK VENT
159	BOLT-CONNECTING ROD
160	CAP-CONNECTING ROD BEARING
161	BEARING SET-CONNECTING ROD
162	ROD-CONNECTING
163	PISTON WITH PIN
164	PISTON RINGS

b. Start engine. After engine stalls, crank for ten seconds to relieve residual pressure from fuel system.
   c. Turn ignition off and install fuel pump fuse.
2. Disconnect battery ground cable.
3. Remove air cleaner assembly, then drain cooling system.
4. Unfasten alternator and position aside.
5. Disconnect throttle cable from intake manifold bracket.
6. Disconnect throttle and throttle valve cables from throttle body.
7. Disconnect electrical connectors from throttle body.
8. Disconnect fuel inlet and return lines, then the coolant hoses from intake manifold. **Place shop towel over fuel line and fitting when disconnecting.**
9. Remove manifold attaching bolts and the manifold, **Fig. 2.**
10. Reverse procedure to install. Clean manifold and cylinder head mating surfaces and install a new gasket prior to installation. Tighten intake manifold attaching nuts and bolts in sequence shown in **Fig. 2.**

EXHAUST MANIFOLD
REPLACE

1. Remove air cleaner assembly.
2. Disconnect spark plug wires and the oxygen sensor electrical connector.
3. Remove pre-heater from exhaust manifold.
4. Disconnect exhaust pipe from manifold, then remove manifold attaching nuts and the manifold, **Fig. 3.**
5. Reverse procedure to install. Clean manifold and cylinder head mating surfaces and install a new gasket prior to installation. Tighten exhaust manifold attaching nuts to specifications and in sequence shown in **Fig. 3.**

CYLINDER HEAD/CAMSHAFT CARRIER
REPLACE

1. Relieve fuel system pressure as follows:
   a. Remove fuel pump fuse from fuse panel.
   b. Start engine. After engine stalls, crank for ten seconds to relieve residual pressure from fuel system.
   c. Turn ignition off and install fuel pump fuse.
2. Disconnect battery ground cable.
3. Remove air cleaner assembly, then drain cooling system.
4. Unfasten alternator and position aside.
5. Remove distributor and ignition wires.
6. Disconnect cables from intake manifold bracket, throttle body and downshift cable.
7. Disconnect ECM electrical connectors at the throttle body and intake manifold.

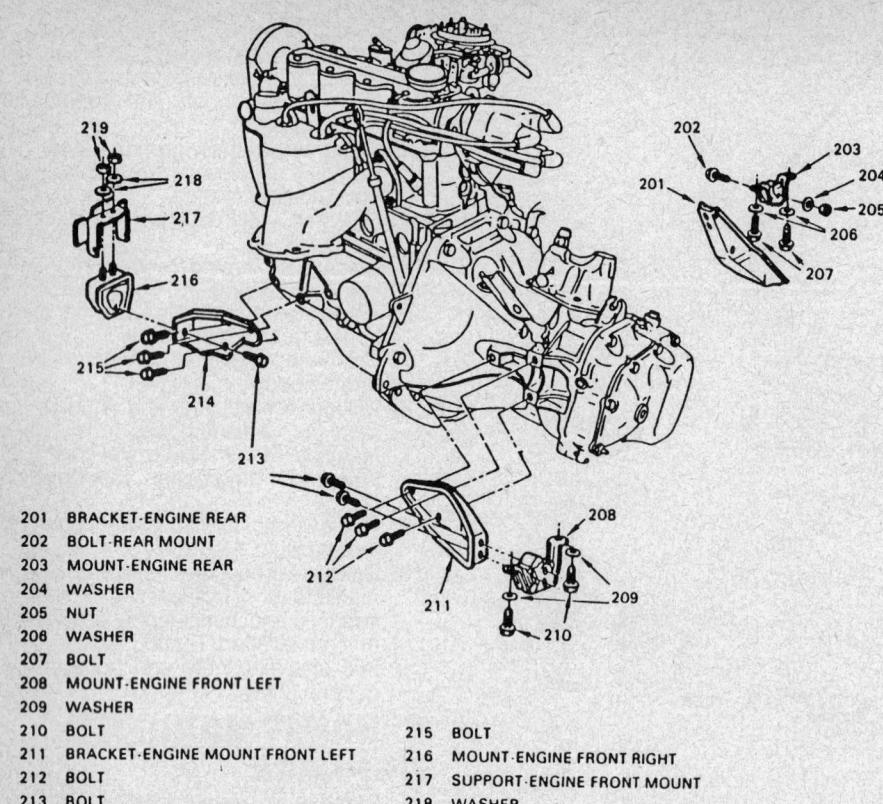

201 BRACKET-ENGINE REAR
202 BOLT-REAR MOUNT
203 MOUNT-ENGINE REAR
204 WASHER
205 NUT
206 WASHER
207 BOLT
208 MOUNT-ENGINE FRONT LEFT
209 WASHER
210 BOLT
211 BRACKET-ENGINE MOUNT FRONT LEFT
212 BOLT
213 BOLT
214 BRACKET-ENGINE MOUNT-FRONT RIGHT
215 BOLT
216 MOUNT-ENGINE FRONT RIGHT
217 SUPPORT-ENGINE FRONT MOUNT
218 WASHER
219 NUT

Fig. 1 Engine mounts

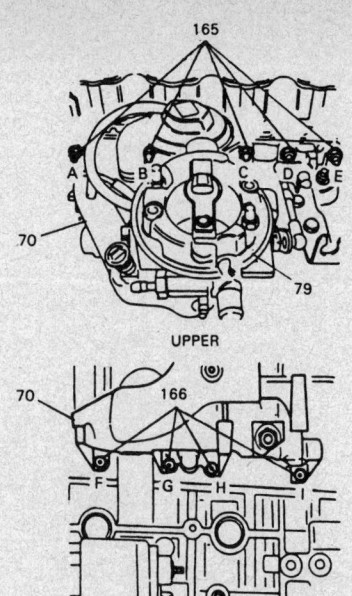

70 MANIFOLD-INTAKE
79 THROTTLE BODY INJECTION (TBI)
165 NUT-TORQUE TO 22 N•m (16 Lbs. Ft.)
166 BOLT-TORQUE TO 22 N•m (16 Lbs. Ft.)
LOOSENING SEQUENCE: C-G-B-H-D-F-E-I-A
TIGHTENING SEQUENCE: A-I-E-F-D-H-B-G-C

Fig. 2 Intake manifold replacement & nut & bolt tightening sequence

8. Disconnect fuel inlet and return lines, then the coolant and heater hoses from intake manifold and water outlet. **Place shop towel over fuel line and fitting when disconnecting.**
9. Disconnect breather and PCV hoses at camshaft carrier.
10. Remove upper radiator hose.
11. Disconnect exhaust pipe from manifold, then disconnect oxygen sensor electrical connector.
12. Disconnect engine wiring harness and the thermostat housing electrical connector.
13. Remove timing belt as described under "Timing Belt, Replace."
14. Loosen cylinder head attaching bolts gradually in sequence, **Fig. 4,** until all bolts are removed.
15. Remove valve cover, then compress valve springs using a suitable tool, **Fig. 5,** and remove rocker arms and valve lash compensators. **Identify components for installation reference.**
16. Remove cylinder head as an assembly with intake and exhaust manifolds.
17. Reverse procedure to install, noting the following:
    a. Clean all cylinder head, valve cover and block mating surfaces.
    b. Apply a continuous bead (3 mm) of anerobic sealant to cam carrier sealing surface.
    c. Install new cylinder head gasket.
    d. Tighten cylinder head attaching bolts to torque listed at the end of this section in sequence shown in **Fig. 6.**

VALVE CLEARANCE SPECIFICATIONS

This engine is equipped with hydraulic lash adjusters. If valve lash is present, check for worn rocker arm, stuck hydraulic valve lash adjuster plunger or defective valve lash adjuster.

VALVE GUIDES

Valve guides are an integral part of the cylinder head. If stem to guide clearance becomes excessive, the valve guide should be reamed to the next oversize and the appropriate oversize valve should be installed. Valve are available in oversizes of .003, .006 and .010 inch.

CAMSHAFT LIFT SPECIFICATIONS

Engine 1.6L/4-98	Year	Int. Inch	Exh. Inch
	1988–89	.221	.241
	1990–91	.220	.241

TIMING BELT FRONT COVER
REPLACE

1. Disconnect battery ground cable.

2. Remove alternator and A/C compressor drive belts.
3. Remove power steering pump.
4. Unsnap upper to lower portions of cover, then remove cover from engine.
5. Reverse procedure to install. Snap lower portion of cover in first.

TIMING BELT
REPLACE

1. Remove timing belt cover as previously described.
2. Remove air cleaner assembly, then disconnect breather hoses from valve cover.
3. Remove valve cover attaching bolts and the cover.
4. Remove timing belt.
5. Reverse procedure to install.

CAMSHAFT & CRANKSHAFT SPROCKETS
REPLACE

1. Remove timing belt cover as previously described.
2. Remove air cleaner assembly, then disconnect breather hoses from valve cover.
3. Remove valve cover attaching bolts and the cover.
4. Remove timing belt.

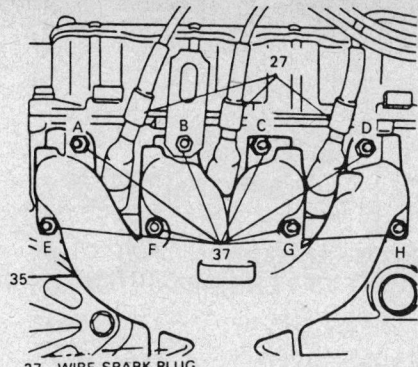

27 WIRE-SPARK PLUG
35 MANIFOLD-EXHAUST
37 NUTS-TORQUE TO 22 N·m (16 LBS. FT)
   LOOSENING SEQUENCE: H-A-E-D-F-C-G-B
   TIGHTENING SEQUENCE: B-G-C-F-D-E-A-H

Fig. 3 Exhaust manifold replacement & nut tightening sequence

5. Hold camshaft with a suitable wrench, then remove bolt, washer and camshaft sprocket, **Fig. 7.**
6. Remove retaining bolt and washer, then the crankshaft pulley and sprocket.
7. Reverse procedure to install, noting the following:
   a. Align mark on camshaft sprocket with mark on rear timing belt cover.
   b. Tighten camshaft gear attaching bolt and crankshaft sprocket retaining bolt to torque listed at the end of this section.

TIMING BELT REAR COVER
REPLACE

1. Remove camshaft sprocket as previously described.
2. Remove rear cover attaching bolts and the cover. Guide cover over water pump rear cover.
3. Reverse procedure to install.

CRANKSHAFT PULLEY
REPLACE

1. Disconnect battery ground cable.
2. Loosen and remove alternator and A/C compressor drive belts.
3. Remove crankshaft pulley attaching bolt and the pulley.
4. Reverse procedure to install. Torque attaching bolt to specification listed at the end of this section.

CAMSHAFT
REPLACE

1. Remove air cleaner assembly, then disconnect breather hoses from valve cover.
2. Remove valve cover attaching bolts and the cover.
3. Apply compressed air to spark plug hole using a suitable adapter to hole valves in place.
4. Compress valve springs using a suitable tool, **Fig. 5,** then remove rocker

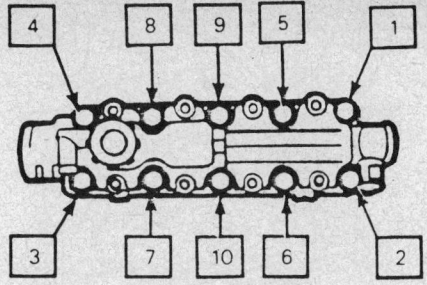

Fig. 4 Cylinder head bolt loosening sequence

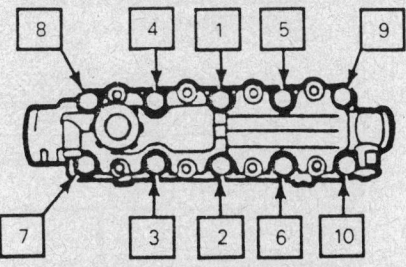

Fig. 6 Cylinder head bolt tightening sequence

arms and valve lash compensators. **Identify components for installation reference.**
5. Remove camshaft gear attaching bolt and the gear.
6. Remove distributor, then the camshaft thrust plate and camshaft.
7. Reverse procedure to install, noting following:
   a. Tighten camshaft thrust plate attaching bolts to torque listed at the end of this section.
   b. **On 1988-89 models,** ensure camshaft endplay measures .016-.064 inch.
   c. **On 1990-91 models,** ensure camshaft endplay measures .0035-.0083 inch.

CRANKSHAFT FRONT OIL SEAL
REPLACE

1. Remove crankshaft gear as previously described.
2. Remove crankshaft key and rear thrust washer.
3. Remove timing belt rear cover, then pry front seal out of groove.
4. Lubricate, then install new seal using tool No. J36534 or equivalent, **Fig. 8.**

CRANKSHAFT REAR OIL SEAL
REPLACE

1. Remove transaxle assembly.
2. Remove flywheel attaching bolts and the flywheel.
3. **On models equipped with manual**

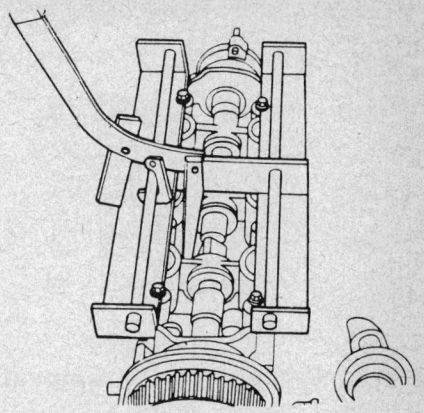

Fig. 5 Compressing valve springs

transaxle, remove clutch pressure plate and disc.
4. **On all models,** pry rear seal out of groove.
5. Lubricate outer surface of new seal, then install the seal using tool No. J36792 or equivalent.

PISTON & ROD ASSEMBLY

Assemble piston to rod, with notch on piston head toward front of engine, **Fig. 9.** Upon installation, measure rod bearing side clearance using a suitable feeler gauge. On 1988-89 models, rod bearing side clearance should be .0027-.0095 inch. On 1990-91 models, rod bearing side clearance should be .0028-.0095 inch.

PISTONS, PINS & RINGS

Pistons and rings are available in standard size and oversize of .020 inch. Pistons and pins are supplied in matched sets.

MAIN & ROD BEARINGS

Main and rod bearings are available in standard sizes and undersizes of .010 and .020 inch.

OIL PAN
REPLACE

1. Disconnect battery ground cable.
2. Raise and support vehicle.
3. **On 1990-91 models,** remove right splash shield.
4. **On all models,** drain engine oil, then disconnect exhaust pipe from exhaust manifold.
5. **On 1990-91 models equipped with manual transaxle,** remove clutch cover plate attaching bolts, then remove clutch cover plate.
6. **On all models,** remove oil pan attaching bolts and the oil pan.
7. Reverse procedure to install. Apply

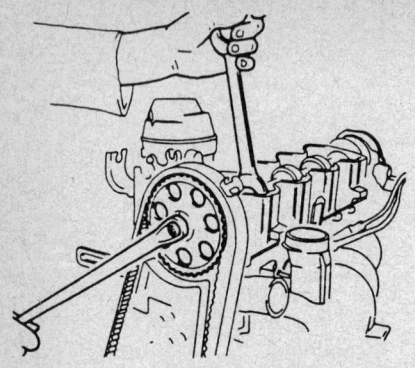

Fig. 7   Camshaft gear removal

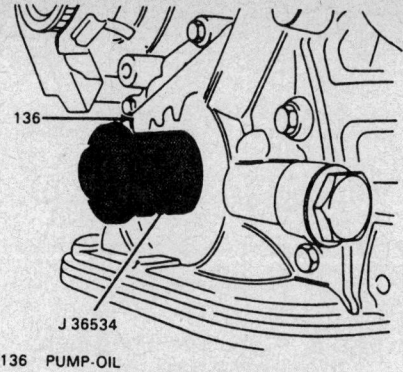

136   PUMP-OIL

Fig. 8   Crankshaft front seal installation

NOTCH TOWARD FRONT OF ENGINE

Fig. 9   Piston & rod assembly

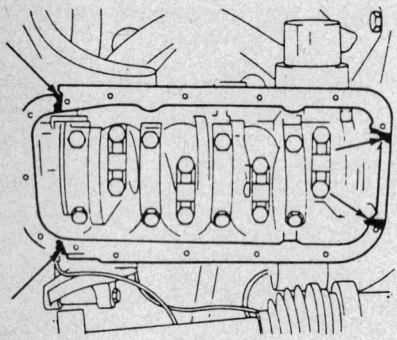

Fig. 10   Oil pan sealant application

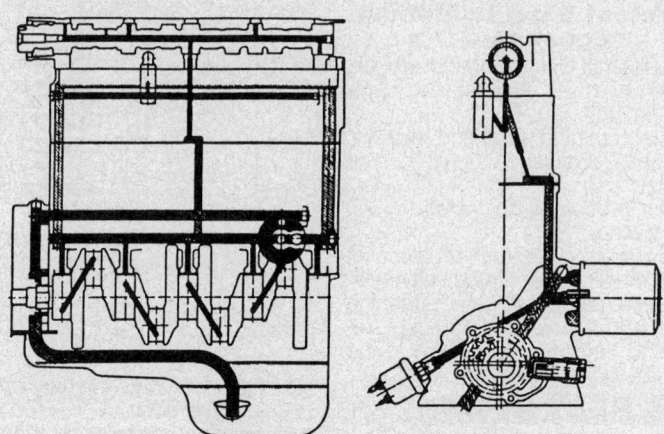

Engine oiling system

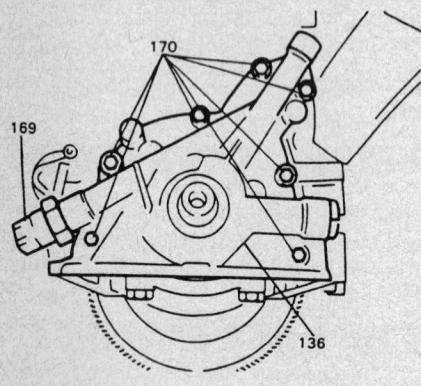

136   PUMP-OIL
169   SWITCH-OIL PRESSURE
170   BOLTS-OIL PUMP

Fig. 11   Oil pump attaching bolt locations

suitable sealant to bolt threads and oil pan seams, **Fig. 10.**

OIL PUMP
REPLACE
REMOVAL
1. Remove crankshaft gear and timing belt rear cover as previously described.
2. Disconnect electrical connector from oil pressure switch.
3. Remove oil pan as previously described.

4. Remove oil filter, then the pickup tube and oil pump, **Fig. 11.**
5. Remove crankshaft front oil seal.

INSTALLATION
1. Install oil pump using a new gasket.
2. Install pickup tube and support using a new O-ring.
3. Install oil pan, then a new front seal using tool No. J36534 or equivalent.
4. Install new oil filter, then reconnect oil pressure switch electrical connector.
5. Install rear timing belt cover and crankshaft gear.

OIL PUMP SERVICE
DISASSEMBLY
1. Drain oil from pump, then remove suction pipe and screen assembly.
2. Remove oil pump cover and gears, **Fig. 12.**
3. Carefully remove pressure regulator valve plug or cotter pin, then the valve spring and valve.

INSPECTION
1. Clean all pump components in suitable solvent.
2. Inspect pump housing and cover for

damage or casting imperfections. Replace housing if necessary.
3. Inspect idler gear shaft fit in housing. If shaft fits loosely, replace pump or timing chain cover as needed.
4. Inspect pressure regulator valve for damaging or sticking. Small burrs may be removed with an oil stone.
5. Install pressure regulator valve spring for loss of tension or damage and replace as necessary.
6. Inspect suction pipe and screen for looseness or damage and replace as necessary.
7. Inspect gears for damage and replace as necessary.
8. Inspect driveshaft for looseness or excessive wear and replace as necessary.

ASSEMBLY
1. Lubricate all internal components with clean engine oil.
2. Pack all pump cavities with petroleum jelly, then install the gears. **Ensure mark on gears faces timing cover.**
3. Install cover and gasket, then the pressure regulator valve and spring.
4. Apply Loctite sealant to pressure regulator valve plug threads, then install the plug and torque to specifications listed at the end of this section.

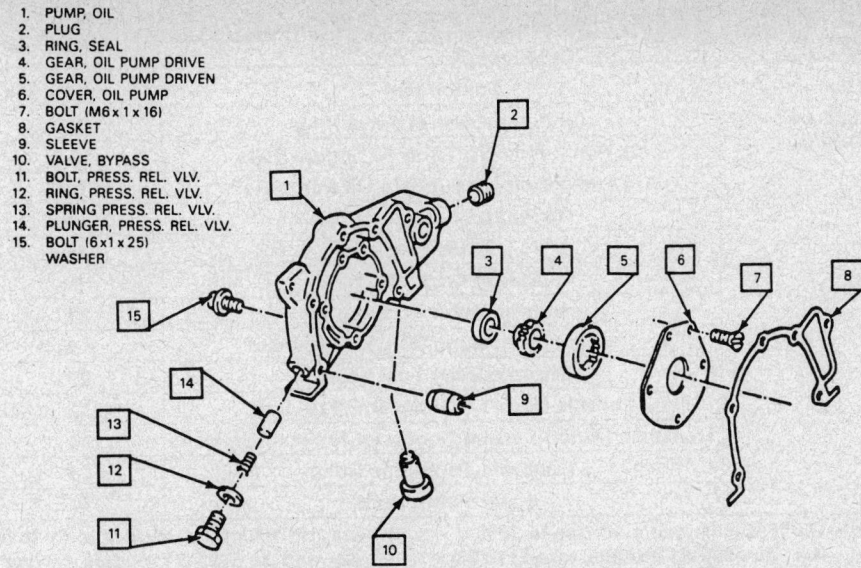

1. PUMP, OIL
2. PLUG
3. RING, SEAL
4. GEAR, OIL PUMP DRIVE
5. GEAR, OIL PUMP DRIVEN
6. COVER, OIL PUMP
7. BOLT (M6 x 1 x 16)
8. GASKET
9. SLEEVE
10. VALVE, BYPASS
11. BOLT, PRESS. REL. VLV.
12. RING, PRESS. REL. VLV.
13. SPRING PRESS. REL. VLV.
14. PLUNGER, PRESS. REL. VLV.
15. BOLT (6 x 1 x 25)
    WASHER

Fig. 12   Exploded view of oil pump assembly

WATER PUMP
REPLACE

1. Disconnect lower radiator hose and drain coolant into a suitable container.
2. Remove front cover, timing belt and rear cover as previously described.
3. Remove water pump attaching bolts and the water pump.
4. Reverse procedure to install. Apply silicone grease to pump sealing surface and new seal ring prior to installation.

BELT TENSION DATA

Year	Belt	Lbs. New	Lbs. Used
1988	All	90	79
1989–91	A/C Comp.	155	80
	Alternator, Power Steer.	90	77

FUEL PUMP
REPLACE

1. Relieve fuel system pressure as follows:
   a. Remove fuel pump fuse from fuse panel.
   b. Start engine. After engine stalls, crank for ten seconds to relieve residual pressure from fuel system.
   c. Turn ignition off and install fuel pump fuse.
2. Disconnect battery ground cable.
3. Raise rear seat, then remove cover from floor pan.
4. Disconnect electrical fuel pump connector and fuel line from fuel pump.
5. Remove fuel pump attaching bolts and the fuel pump.
6. Reverse procedure to install.

TIGHTENING SPECIFICATIONS

Torque specifications are for clean & lightly lubricated threads only. Dry or dirty threads produce increase friction which prevents accurate measurement of tightness.

Year	Component	Torque/Ft. Lbs.
1988-91	Alternator Lower Bolt	24
	Alternator Upper Bolt	20
	Camshaft Carrier Cover Bolts	6
	Camshaft Sprocket Bolt	①
	Camshaft Thrust Plate Bolts	71②
	Connecting Rod Cap Bolts	③
	Crankshaft Pulley Bolts	40④
	Cylinder Head/Camshaft Carrier Bolts	⑤
	Engine Mount Bracket (Front) Bolts	29
	Exhaust Manifold Bolts	16
	Exhaust Pipe To Manifold Nuts	⑥
	Flexplate To Crankshaft Bolts	25
	Flywheel To Crankshaft Bolts	⑦
	Intake Manifold Bolts	16
	Main Bearing Cap Bolts	⑧
	Oil Pan Bolts	71②
	Oil Pan Drain Plug	34

Continued

TIGHTENING SPECIFICATIONS—Continued

Year	Component	Torque/Ft. Lbs.
1988–91 Cont'd	Oil Pump Control Valve Plug	22
	Oil Pump Pick-Up Tube To Engine Bolts	5
	Oil Pump Pick-Up Tube To Oil Pump Bolt	5
	Oil Pump To Engine Bolts	⑨
	Spark Plug	18
	Splash Guard Bolts	9
	Starter Motor To Engine	33
	Thermostat Housing To Cylinder Head	7.5
	Throttle Body Fuel Lines	20
	Throttle Body To Intake Manifold Bolt	12
	Transaxle (Auto.) Torque Converter to Flexplate Bolts	44
	Transaxle To Engine Bolts	55
	Water Pump Bolts	⑩

①—On 1988–89 models, torque to 34 ft. lbs., on 1990–91 models, torque to 33 ft. lbs.

②—Inch lbs.

③—Torque bolts to 18 ft. lbs., then tighten an additional 30 °.

④—On 1990–91 models, torque to 40 ft. lbs. ±26 inch lbs.

⑤—Torque bolts to 18 ft. lbs. Tighten each bolt an additional 120 ° in 60 ° increments. Advance each bolt an additional 30 ° to obtain final torque. Start engine & allow to reach operating temperature, then tighten bolts an additional 30 to 50 °.

⑥—On 1988 models, torque nuts to 19 ft. lbs., on 1989 models, torque to 18 ft. lbs. and on 1990–91 models, torque nuts to 115 inch lbs.

⑦—Torque flywheel bolts to 25 ft. lbs., then advance each bolt an additional 30–45 °.

⑧—Torque bolts to 36 ft. lbs., then tighten an additional 45–60 °.

⑨—On 1988–89 models, torque bolts to 5 ft. lbs, on 1990–91 models, torque bolts to 53 inch lbs.

⑩—On 1988 models, torque bolts to 5.8 ft. lbs., on 1989 models, torque bolts to 5.9 ft. lbs. and on 1990–91 models, torque bolts to 71 inch lbs.

2.0L/4-121 Engine
INDEX

ENGINE MOUNT
REPLACE

1. Disconnect battery ground cable.
2. Support engine using tool No. J-28467-A or equivalent.
3. Remove mount to bracket attaching bolts, then remove mount to engine upper attaching bolts, Figs. 1 and 2.
4. Raise and support vehicle, then remove mount to engine lower attaching bolts and engine mount.
5. Reverse procedure to install. Apply Loctite in kit No. 1052624 or other suitable thread locking compound to bolt threads prior to installation.

ENGINE
REPLACE

1. **On all models, remove fuel pump fuse from fuse panel, then start and operate engine until it stalls. After stalling, crank engine for approximately 3 seconds to deplete fuel pressure in lines.**
2. Disconnect battery ground cable and engine ground strap.
3. Drain cooling system, then disconnect radiator and heater hoses.
4. Remove air cleaner assembly.
5. Disconnect engine wiring harness at bulkhead connector.
6. Disconnect electrical connectors at brake cylinder, cooling fan relay, cooling fan motor, windshield wiper motor and coolant temperature switch. Also disconnect electrical connectors at A/C compressor clutch and A/C relay, if equipped.

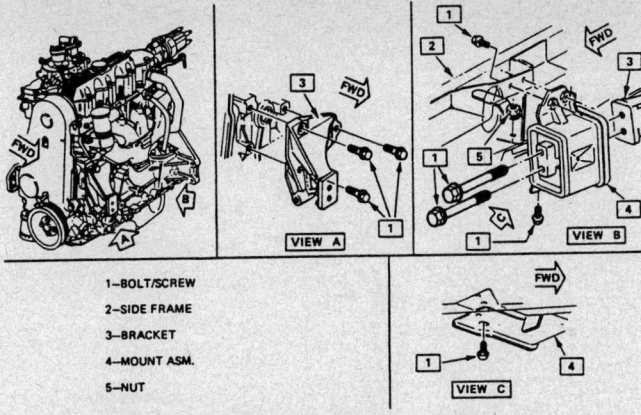

Fig. 1 Front engine mounting

1—BOLT/SCREW
2—SIDE FRAME
3—BRACKET
4—MOUNT ASM.
5—NUT

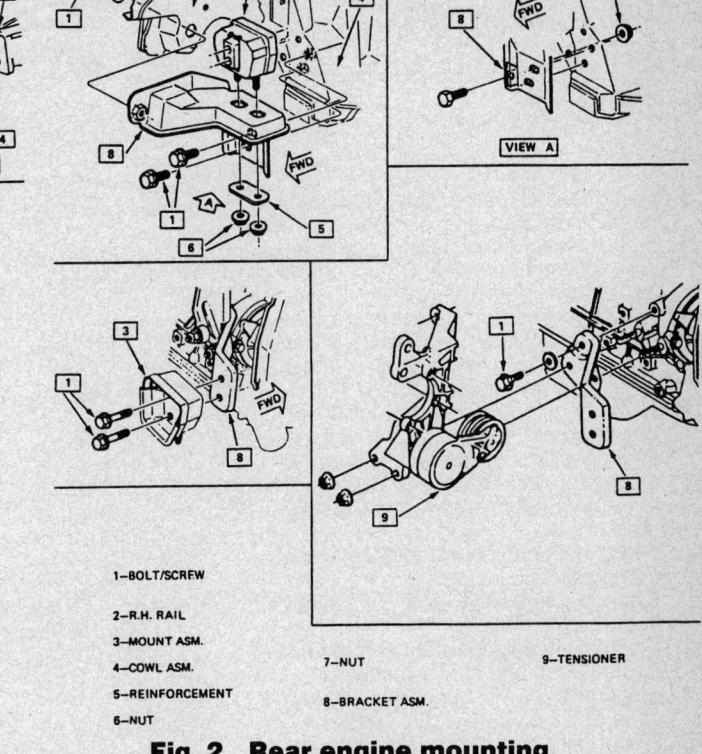

1—BOLT/SCREW
2—R.H. RAIL
3—MOUNT ASM.
4—COWL ASM.
5—REINFORCEMENT
6—NUT
7—NUT
8—BRACKET ASM.
9—TENSIONER

Fig. 2 Rear engine mounting

7. Disconnect electrical connector from ECM (Electronic Control Module) and pull harness through bulkhead connector.
8. **On 1990-91 models,** remove vacuum hoses at fuel injection, MAP sensor and canister.
9. **On all models,** disconnect throttle cable at bracket and throttle body.
10. Disconnect shift control cable at transaxle.
11. Disconnect power steering hoses at pump.
12. Raise and support front of vehicle, then disconnect exhaust pipe from exhaust manifold and position aside.
13. **On models equipped with automatic transaxle,** disconnect transmission fluid cooler lines.
14. **On all models,** disconnect fuel lines. **Place shop towel over fuel line and fitting when disconnecting.**
15. Remove heater hoses at heater core.
16. Remove front wheel and tire assemblies.
17. Remove front brake calipers with brake hoses attached and suspend from wheel opening with suitable wire.
18. Discharge A/C system, then disconnect refrigerant lines from A/C compressor, then disconnect A/C compressor electrical connectors.
19. Ensure vehicle is properly supported, then remove two center bolts from suspension support. Remove one bolt from each end of suspension support, then loosen the remaining bolts.
20. **On models with automatic transaxle,** remove transaxle rear strut.
21. **On all models,** remove transaxle front strut.
22. Support front vehicle by positioning jack stands under radiator support.
23. Position suitable jack and a wooden board (4 x 4 inches x 6 foot) across width of vehicle at rear of cowl.
24. Raise vehicle slightly and remove jack stands positioned under radiator support.
25. Position a suitable dolly with 3 wooden blocks (4 x 4 x 12 inches) as supports, under engine and transaxle assembly.
26. Carefully lower vehicle to position engine and transaxle assembly on dolly.
27. Remove remaining bolt at left and righthand sides of the front suspension supports.
28. Scribe line indicating position of strut to steering knuckle. This scribe line is used during installation to reset camber adjustment.
29. Remove engine and transaxle mount to bracket attaching bolts, then steering knuckle to strut bolts.
30. Raise vehicle, allowing engine, transaxle and suspension to remain on dolly. Prior to raising vehicle, ensure all necessary electrical wiring, cables, linkages and hoses are disconnected to permit engine and transaxle removal.
31. Separate engine from transaxle.
32. Reverse procedure to install. When installing strut to steering knuckle, align scribe lines made during removal.

INTAKE MANIFOLD REPLACE

1. Remove fuel pump fuse from fuse panel, then start and operate engine until it stalls. After stalling, crank engine for approximately 3 seconds to deplete fuel pressure in lines.
2. Disconnect battery ground cable, then drain cooling system.
3. **On 1990-91 models,** remove air cleaner and serpentine belt.
4. **On all models,** remove alternator and bracket from camshaft carrier.
5. Remove power steering pump bracket to intake manifold attaching bolts, then position pump and bracket aside with hoses attached.
6. Remove ignition coil and bracket assembly.
7. Disconnect throttle cable from intake manifold bracket and throttle body.
8. Disconnect TV cable and electrical connectors from throttle body.
9. Disconnect power brake unit vacuum hose at filter.
10. Disconnect fuel lines at throttle body. **Place shop towel over fuel line and fitting when disconnecting.**
11. Disconnect water pump to intake manifold coolant bypass hose and inlet tube.
12. Disconnect ECM electrical connector to provide access to intake manifold lower attaching nuts.
13. Remove intake manifold attaching nuts and intake manifold.
14. Reverse procedure to install. Tighten intake manifold attaching nuts in sequence shown in **Fig. 3.**

EXHAUST MANIFOLD REPLACE

1. Disconnect battery ground cable, then remove air cleaner assembly.
2. Tag, then remove spark plug wires and retainers.
3. **On 1990-91 models,** remove oil dipstick tube and breather.
4. **On all models,** disconnect electrical connector from oxygen sensor.
5. Disconnect exhaust pipe from exhaust manifold.
6. Remove exhaust manifold attaching nuts, then remove exhaust manifold.
7. Reverse procedure to install. Tighten exhaust manifold attaching nuts in sequence shown in **Fig. 4.**

CYLINDER HEAD/CAMSHAFT CARRIER
REPLACE

1. Remove fuel pump fuse from fuse panel, then start and operate engine until it stalls. After stalling, crank engine for approximately 3 seconds to deplete fuel pressure in lines.
2. Disconnect battery ground cable, then remove air cleaner assembly.
3. Drain cooling system, then remove serpentine drive belt.
4. Remove alternator and bracket assembly, then remove ignition coil.
5. Mark position of distributor rotor to distributor body and distributor body to cylinder head, then remove distributor.
6. Disconnect cables from intake manifold brackets.
7. Disconnect throttle and TV cables from throttle body.
8. Disconnect electrical connectors from throttle body and intake manifold.
9. Disconnect power brake unit vacuum hose at filter.
10. Disconnect fuel lines from throttle body unit. **Place shop towel over fuel line and fitting when disconnecting.**
11. Disconnect radiator, heater and bypass hoses from cylinder head and intake manifold.
12. Disconnect breather hose from camshaft carrier cover.
13. Disconnect exhaust pipe from exhaust manifold.
14. Disconnect electrical connectors from oxygen sensor, wiring harness, thermostat housing, coolant temperature switch and other components to permit cylinder head, intake manifold and exhaust manifold to be removed as an assembly.
15. Remove timing belt, as described under "Timing Belt, Replace," then remove timing belt rear cover.
16. With engine cold, loosen cylinder head/camshaft carrier attaching bolts in sequence shown in **Fig. 5.**
17. Remove camshaft carrier, rocker arms and hydraulic valve lash adjusters.
18. Remove cylinder head, intake manifold and exhaust manifold as an assembly. If necessary, separate intake and exhaust manifolds from cylinder head after removal from engine.
19. Reverse procedure to install. Prior to installation, the intake and exhaust manifolds must be assembled to cylinder head, if removed. Apply a continuous bead (3 mm) of anerobic sealant 1052942 or equivalent to cam carrier sealing surface prior to installation. Tighten cylinder head bolts to torque listed at the end of this section in sequence shown in **Fig. 6.**

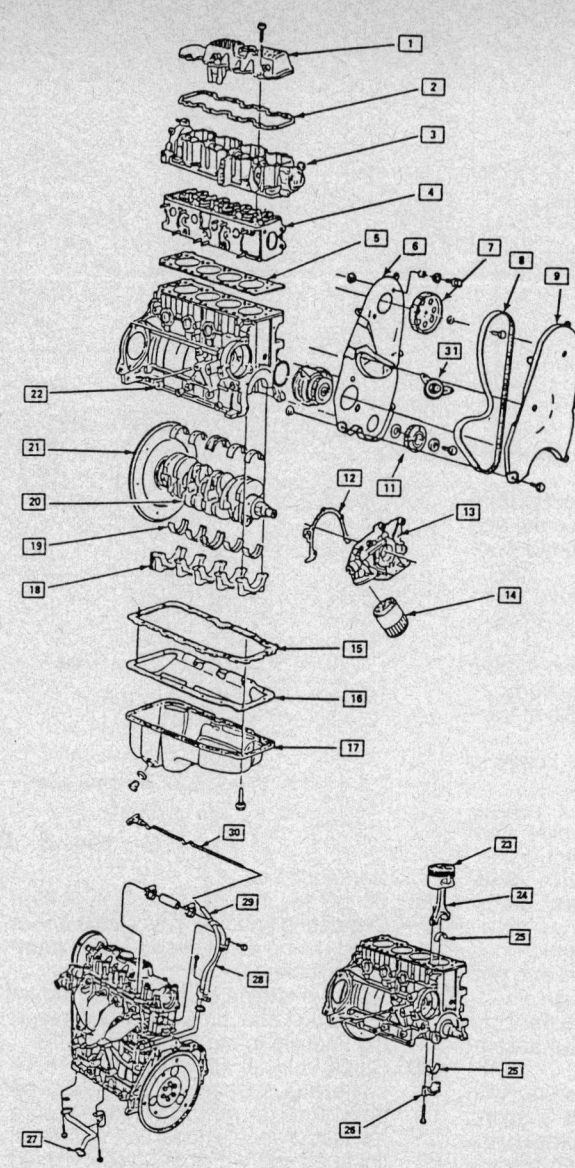

1—CAMSHAFT COVER
2—CAMSHAFT COVER GASKET
3—CAMSHAFT CARRIER
4—CYLINDER HEAD
5—CYLINDER HEAD GASKET
6—FRONT COVER BACKING
7—CAMSHAFT SPROCKET
8—TIMING BELT
9—FRONT COVER
10—WATER PUMP
11—CRANKSHAFT GEAR
12—OIL PUMP GASKET
13—OIL PUMP
14—OIL FILTER
15—OIL PAN GASKET
16—OIL SCRAPER
17—OIL PAN
18—CRANKSHAFT BEARING CAPS
19—CRANKSHAFT BEARING
20—CRANKSHAFT
21—FLYWHEEL
22—CYLINDER BLOCK
23—PISTON
24—CONNECTING ROD
25—CONNECTING ROD BEARINGS
26—CONNECTING ROD CAP
27—OIL PUMP PICKUP TUBE
28—VENT TUBE
29—TUBE
30—OIL DIPSTICK
31—TIMING BELT TENSIONER

Exploded view of engine assembly

VALVE CLEARANCE SPECIFICATIONS

This engine is equipped with hydraulic lash adjusters. If valve lash is present, check for worn rocker arm, stuck hydraulic valve lash adjuster plunger or defective valve lash adjuster.

VALVE GUIDES

Valve guides are an integral part of the cylinder head. If stem to guide clearance becomes excessive, the valve guide should be reamed to the next oversize and the appropriate oversize valve should be installed. Valves are available in oversizes of .003, .006 and .010 inch.

CAMSHAFT LIFT SPECIFICATIONS

Engine	Year	Int, Inch	Exh, Inch
2.0L/4-121	1989	.259	.259
	1990-91	.2366	.2515

ROCKER ARMS & HYDRAULIC VALVE LASH ADJUSTERS
REPLACE

1. Disconnect battery ground cable, then remove air cleaner assembly.
2. Disconnect breather hoses from camshaft carrier cover.

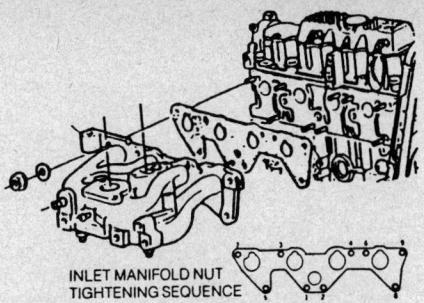

Fig. 3 Intake manifold replacement & bolt tightening sequence

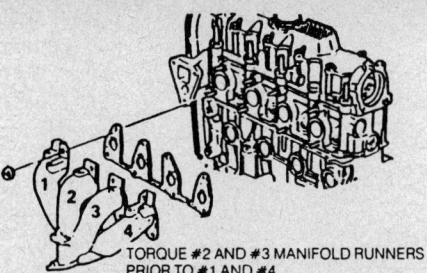

TORQUE #2 AND #3 MANIFOLD RUNNERS PRIOR TO #1 AND #4.

Fig. 4 Exhaust manifold replacement & bolt tightening sequence

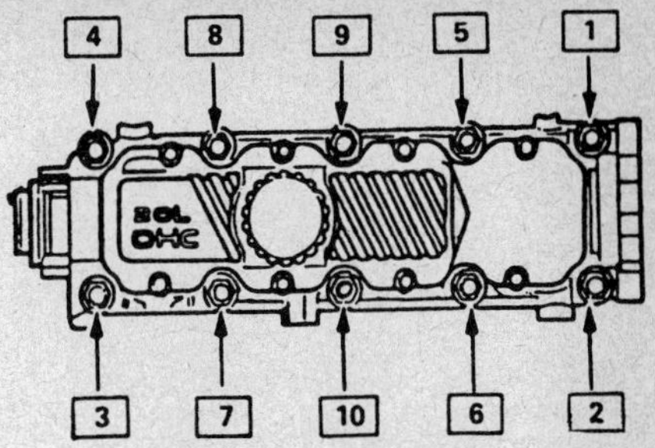

Fig. 5 Cylinder head/camshaft carrier bolt loosening sequence

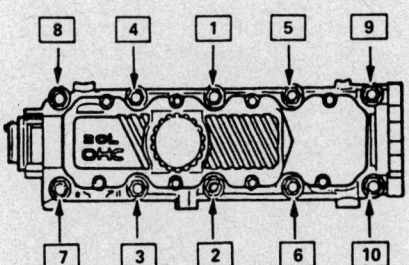

Fig. 6 Cylinder head/camshaft carrier bolt tightening sequence

3. Remove camshaft carrier cover attaching bolt, then remove cover.
4. Using tool No. J-33302-B or equivalent, compress valve and springs, **Fig. 7**, then remove remove rocker arms, thrust pieces and hydraulic valve lash adjusters, **Fig. 8**. Tag components so they can be installed in the same position.
5. Reverse procedure to install.

VALVE SPRING & VALVE STEM OIL SEAL
REPLACE

1. Remove camshaft carrier cover attaching bolts, then remove carrier cover.
2. Remove rocker arm and hydraulic valve lash adjuster for cylinder being serviced as described under "Rocker Arms and Hydraulic Valve Lash Adjusters, Replace."
3. Remove spark plug, then position adapter J-22794 or equivalent into spark plug hole. Connect a suitable compressed air source to adapter to hold valve in position.
4. Using tool No. J-33302-25 or equivalent, **Fig. 7**, compress valve springs and remove valve locks, caps, springs, spring washers, exhaust valve rotators and valve stem oil seals, **Fig. 8**.
5. Reverse procedure to install. Lubricate valve stem oil seal with engine oil prior to installation. When installing valve stem oil seal, use a suitable plastic sleeve to position seal over valve stem.

CRANKSHAFT PULLEY
REPLACE

1. Disconnect battery ground cable, then remove serpentine drive belt.
2. Remove inner fender shield.
3. Remove A/C compressor drive belt, if equipped.
4. Remove crankshaft pulley attaching bolt and remove pulley.
5. Reverse procedure to install. Prior to installation of crankshaft pulley attaching bolt, apply Loctite 242 or equivalent to bolt threads, then torque bolt to specification listed at the end of this section.

TIMING BELT FRONT COVER
REPLACE

1. Disconnect battery ground cable, then remove serpentine drive belt.
2. Loosen serpentine drive belt tensioner bolt and allow tensioner arm to swing downward.
3. Remove timing belt cover attaching bolts and nuts, then remove timing belt cover, **Fig. 9**.
4. Reverse procedure to install.

TIMING BELT
REPLACE

REMOVAL

1. Disconnect battery ground cable, then remove A/C belt, if equipped, then remove serpentine drive belt.
2. Remove power steering pump, bracket and serpentine drive belt tensioner as an assembly.
3. Remove timing timing belt cover attaching bolts, then remove timing belt cover, **Fig. 9**.
4. Loosen water pump attaching bolts, then using tool No. J-33039-A or equivalent, **Fig. 10**, on water pump eccentric, release tension.
5. Remove crankshaft pulley as described under "Crankshaft Pulley, Replace."
6. Remove timing belt from camshaft and crankshaft sprockets, **Fig. 9**.

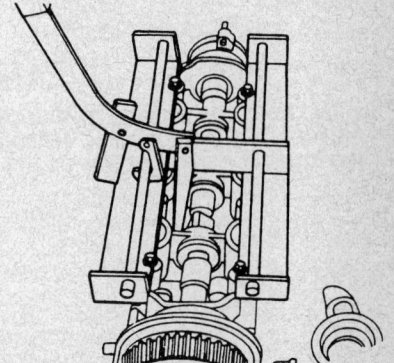

Fig. 7 Compressing valve springs

INSTALLATION

1. Align timing marks on camshaft and crankshaft sprockets with timing marks on timing belt rear cover.
2. Position timing belt to camshaft and crankshaft sprockets and tensioner, **Fig. 9**.
3. Using tool No. 33039-A or equivalent, **Fig. 10**, rotate water pump eccentric clockwise until tensioner contacts high torque stop, then tighten water pump attaching bolts slightly.
4. Rotate crankshaft pulley 2 revolutions in clockwise direction to seat timing belt on sprockets.
5. With engine at room temperature, rotate water pump eccentric counterclockwise until hole in tensioner arm is in line with hole in base. Use tool No. 33039-A or equivalent to rotate water pump eccentric.
6. Tighten water pump attaching bolts to torque listed at the end of this section. Ensure tensioner holes remain aligned.
7. Install crankshaft pulley, then install timing belt cover.
8. Install power steering pump, bracket and serpentine drive belt tensioner.
9. Install and tension A/C belt, if equipped, and serpentine drive belt, then connect battery ground cable.

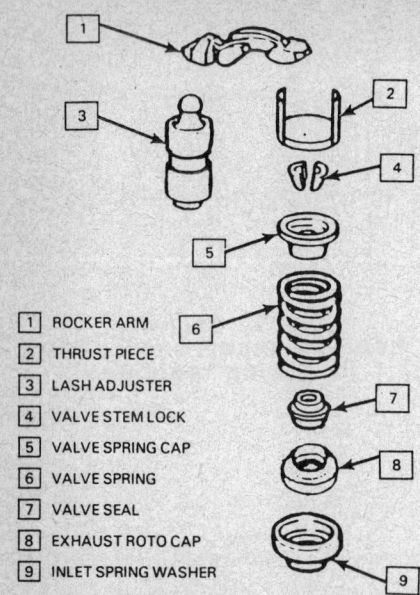

1 ROCKER ARM
2 THRUST PIECE
3 LASH ADJUSTER
4 VALVE STEM LOCK
5 VALVE SPRING CAP
6 VALVE SPRING
7 VALVE SEAL
8 EXHAUST ROTO CAP
9 INLET SPRING WASHER

Fig. 8 Rocker arms, hydraulic valve lash adjusters, valve springs & valve stem seals

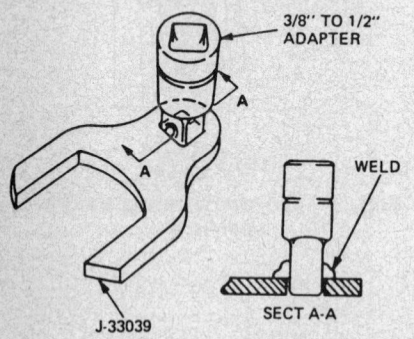

Fig. 10 Water pump eccentric adjusting tool modification

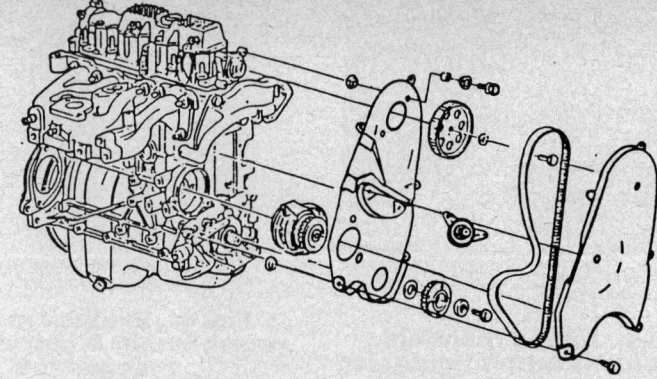

Fig. 9 Timing belt & components

Fig. 11 Camshaft sprocket replacement

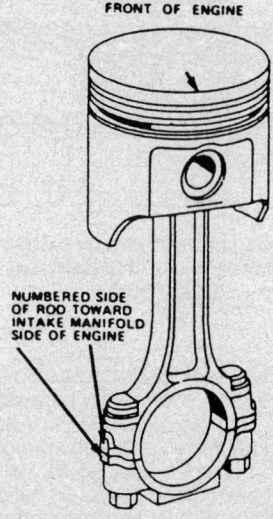

Fig. 12 Piston & rod assembly

CAMSHAFT SPROCKET REPLACE

1. Disconnect battery ground cable.
2. Remove camshaft cover carrier attaching bolts, then remove camshaft cover carrier.
3. Remove timing belt as described under "Timing Belt, Replace."
4. While holding camshaft in position with a suitable open end wrench, remove camshaft sprocket attaching bolts, then remove washer and sprocket, **Fig. 11.**
5. Reverse procedure to install. While holding camshaft in position with an open end wrench, tighten camshaft sprocket attaching bolt to torque listed at the end of this section.

CRANKSHAFT SPROCKET REPLACE

1. Disconnect battery ground cable.

2. Remove timing belt as described under "Timing Belt, Replace."
3. Remove crankshaft sprocket attaching bolt and washer, then remove crankshaft sprocket.
4. Reverse procedure to install. When installing crankshaft sprocket, ensure it is proper positioned on crankshaft key. Tighten crankshaft sprocket attaching bolt to torque listed at the end of this section.

TIMING BELT REAR COVER REPLACE

1. Disconnect battery ground cable.
2. Remove timing belt as described under "Timing Belt, Replace."
3. Remove camshaft and crankshaft sprockets as described previously.
4. Remove timing belt tensioner assembly.
5. Remove timing belt rear cover attaching bolts, then remove cover, **Fig. 9.**
6. Reverse procedure to install. Tighten timing belt rear cover attaching bolts to torque listed at the end of this section.

CAMSHAFT REPLACE

1. Disconnect battery ground cable.
2. Remove rocker arms and hydraulic valve lash adjusters as described under, "Rocker Arms and Hydraulic Valve Lash Adjusters, Replace."
3. Remove camshaft sprocket as described under "Camshaft Sprocket, Replace."
4. Remove distributor from engine.
5. Remove rear thrust plate, then slide camshaft from rear of engine.
6. Reverse procedure to install. Lubricate camshaft front carrier oil seal with engine oil prior to camshaft installation. Tighten camshaft rear thrust plate attaching bolts to torque listed at the end of this section. Camshaft endplay should be .0016-.0064 inch.

PISTON & ROD ASSEMBLY

Assemble piston to rod, with notch on piston head toward front of engine and numbered side of rod toward intake manifold side of engine, **Fig. 12.** Upon installation, measure rod bearing side clearance using a feeler gauge. Rod bearing side clearance should be .0039-.0149 inch.

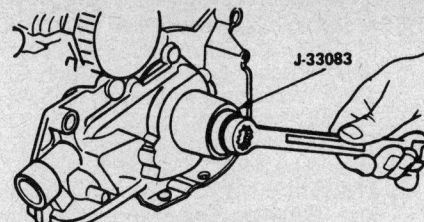

Fig. 13 Crankshaft front seal installation

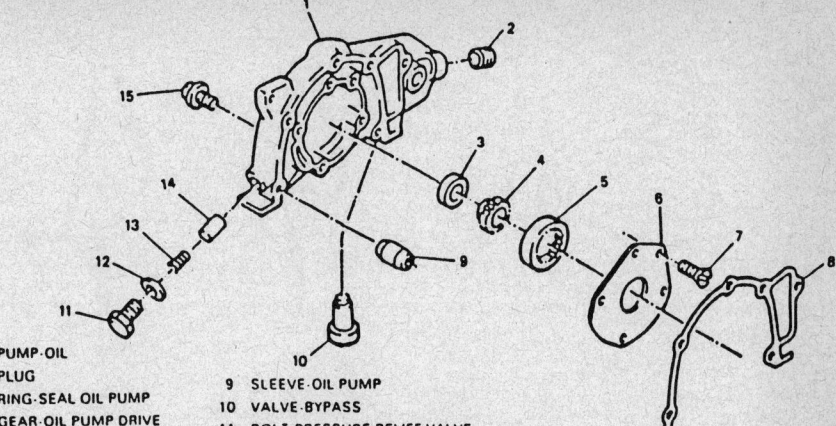

1 PUMP-OIL
2 PLUG
3 RING-SEAL OIL PUMP
4 GEAR-OIL PUMP DRIVE
5 GEAR-OIL PUMP DRIVEN
6 COVER-OIL PUMP
7 BOLT (M6 x 1 x 16)
8 GASKET-OIL PUMP
9 SLEEVE-OIL PUMP
10 VALVE-BYPASS
11 BOLT-PRESSURE RELIEF VALVE
12 RING-PRESSURE RELIEF VALVE
13 SPRING-PRESSURE RELIEF VALVE
14 PLUNGER-PRESSURE RELIEF VALVE
15 BOLT (6 x 1 x 25)

Fig. 15 Exploded view of oil pump assembly

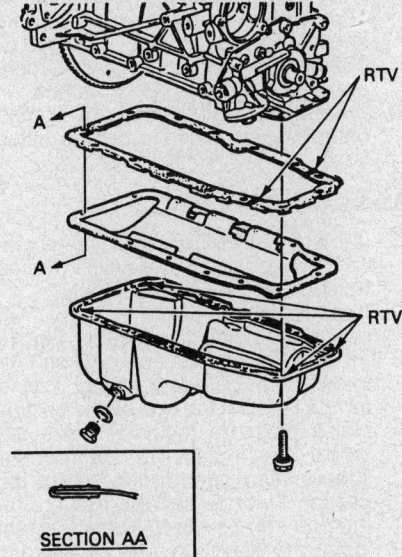

Fig. 14 Oil pan & gasket

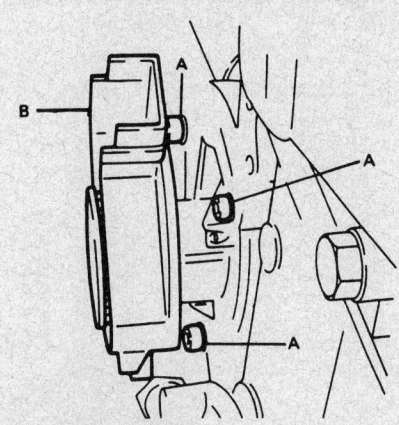

A WATER PUMP BOLTS
B LOWER REAR TIMING BELT COVER

Fig. 16 Water pump attaching bolt locations

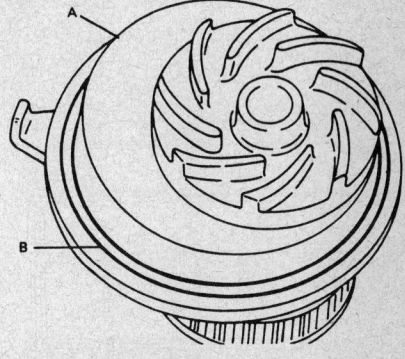

A WATER PUMP REMOVED FROM ENGINE BLOCK SHOWING IMPELLER
B SEAL-WATER PUMP

Fig. 17 Water pump seal installation

PISTONS, PINS & RINGS

Pistons and rings are available in standard size only.

MAIN & ROD BEARINGS

Main and rod bearings are available in standard sizes and undersizes of .005 and .010 inch.

CRANKSHAFT FRONT OIL SEAL
REPLACE

1. Disconnect battery ground cable.
2. Remove crankshaft pulley as described under "Crankshaft Pulley, Replace."
3. Remove key and thrust washer from crankshaft.
4. Remove timing belt rear cover as described under "Timing Belt Rear Cover, Replace."
5. Pry crankshaft front seal from oil pump.
6. Reverse procedure to install. Prior to installation, lubricate seal lip with engine oil. Use tool No. J-33083 or equivalent to install seal, **Fig. 13.**

CRANKSHAFT REAR OIL SEAL
REPLACE

1. Remove transaxle assembly as described under "Transaxle, Replace."
2. Remove flywheel attaching bolts and flywheel.
3. **On models with manual transaxle,** remove pressure plate and clutch disc.
4. **On all models,** pry crankshaft rear oil seal from engine.
5. Reverse procedure to install. Prior to installation, lubricate seal lip with engine oil. Use tool No. J-36227 or equivalent, to install seal.

OIL PAN
REPLACE

1. Disconnect battery ground cable.
2. Raise and support front of vehicle, then drain crankcase.
3. Disconnect exhaust pipe from ex-

haust manifold.
4. Remove flywheel cover attaching bolts and flywheel cover.
5. Remove oil pan attaching bolts, then remove oil pan, **Fig. 14.**
6. Reverse procedure to install. Apply sealant to oil pan gasket as shown in **Fig. 14.** Prior to installation, apply Loctite to oil pan attaching bolts. Tighten oil pan attaching bolts to torque listed at the end of this section.

OIL PUMP
REPLACE

1. Disconnect battery ground cable.
2. Remove crankshaft sprocket as described under "Crankshaft Sprocket, Replace."
3. Remove timing belt rear cover as described under "Timing Belt Rear Cover, Replace."
4. Disconnect oil pressure sender electrical connector.
5. Remove oil pan as described under "Oil Pan, Replace."
6. Remove oil filter.
7. Remove oil pump attaching bolts, then oil filter and pickup tube assembly.
8. Pry crankshaft front oil seal from oil pump.
9. Reverse procedure to install. Tighten

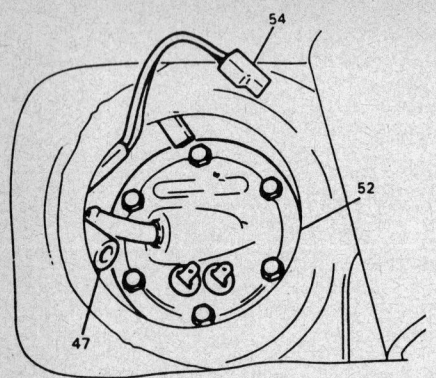

47 HOSE-FUEL PUMP
52 PUMP-FUEL
54 ELECTRICAL CONNECTOR-
   FUEL PUMP

Fig. 18 Electric fuel pump replacement

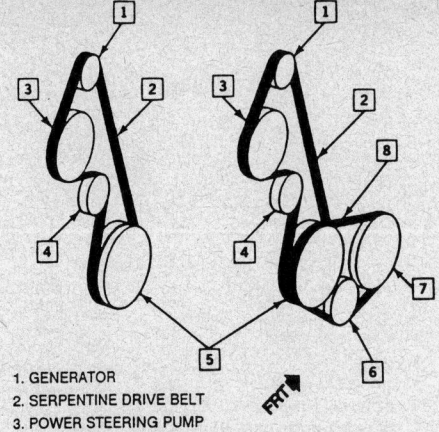

1. GENERATOR
2. SERPENTINE DRIVE BELT
3. POWER STEERING PUMP
4. SERPENTINE TENSIONER
5. CRANKSHAFT PULLEY
6. A/C TENSIONER
7. A/C COMPRESSOR
8. A/C "V" BELT

Fig. 19 Serpentine drive belt routing

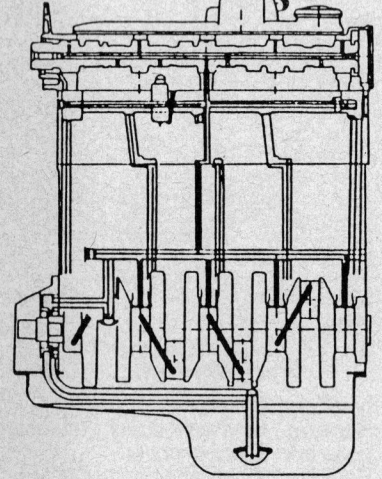

Engine oiling system

oil pump attaching bolts to torque listed at the end of this section. After installing oil pump and oil pan, lubricate crankshaft front oil seal lip with engine oil, then install seal using tool No. J-33083 or equivalent, **Fig. 13.**

OIL PUMP SERVICE

DISASSEMBLY

1. Drain oil from pump into a suitable container.
2. Remove pump driveshaft, then remove pickup tube and screen assembly.
3. Remove pump cover attaching screws, then remove pump cover and gears, **Fig. 15.**
4. Carefully remove regulator valve plug, spring and valve from pump housing. If valve is difficult to remove, soak pump housing in a suitable carburetor cleaning solvent.

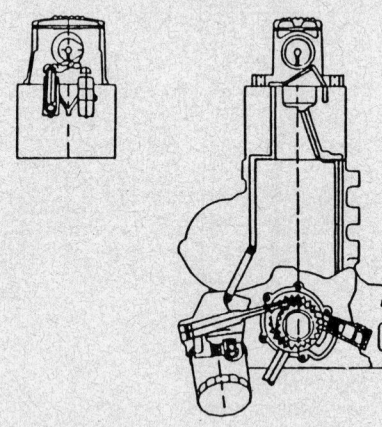

CLEANING & INSPECTION

1. Clean components in a suitable carburetor cleaning solvent.
2. Check all component wear and damage.
3. Check regulator valve spring for loss of tension and distortion.
4. Using a feeler gauge measure oil pump gear lash. Gear lash should be .004-.008 inch.
5. Check clearance between idler gear and oil pump body. On 1989 models, clearance should be .004-.007 inch. On 1990-91 models, clearance should be .0043-.0074 inch.
6. **On all models,** check clearance between drive gear and oil pump housing. Clearance should be .014-.018 inch.
7. Using a straight edge and feeler gauge, check clearance between gears and pump cover. Clearance should be .001 to .004 inch.

8. Measure oil pump housing gear pocket depth and diameter. Gear pocket depth should be .395-.397 inch. On 1989 models, gear pocket diameter should be 3.230-3.235 inch. On 1990-91 models, gear depth pocket should be 3.231-3.234 inch.
9. Measure drive and idler gear length and diameter. Drive and idler gear length should be .393-.394 inch. On 1989 models, drive gear diameter should be 2.317-2.319 inches. On 1990-91 models, drive gear diameter should be 1.612-1.613 inches. On 1989 models, idler gear diameter should be 3.225-3.227 inches. On 1990-91 models, idler gear diameter should be 3.2248-3.2269 inches.
10. **On all models,** replace any components that are found to be unsatisfactory.

ASSEMBLY

1. Lubricate all components with engine oil and pack pump all cavities with petroleum jelly prior to assembly.
2. Position gears in pump body, with gear mark facing timing cover, **Fig. 15.**
3. Install pump cover and gasket, then install and tighten attaching bolts to torque listed at the end of this section.
4. Install pressure regulator valve and spring, then install plug and torque to specification listed at the end of this section. Prior to installing plug, coat threads with Loctite 573 or equivalent.
5. Install pump pickup tube and screen.

WATER PUMP
REPLACE

1. Disconnect battery ground cable.
2. Disconnect lower radiator hose and allow cooling system to drain.
3. Remove timing belt as described under "Timing Belt, Replace."
4. Remove timing belt lower rear cover.
5. Remove water pump attaching bolts and water pump, **Fig. 16.**
6. Reverse procedure to install. Prior to installation, coat water pump seal and sealing surface with suitable silicone grease, **Fig. 17.**

BELT TENSION DATA

Year	Belt	Lbs. New	Lbs. Used
1989–91	A/C Comp.	155	80
	Serpentine Drive Belt	①	①

①—**Controlled by belt tensioner.**

FUEL PUMP
REPLACE

1. Remove fuel pump fuse from fuse panel, then start and operate engine until it stalls. After stalling, crank en-

gine for approximately 3 seconds to deplete fuel pressure in lines.
2. Disconnect battery ground cable.
3. Raise rear seat, then lift cover from vehicle floor pan.

4. Disconnect electrical connector and fuel line from fuel pump, **Fig. 18.**
5. Remove fuel pump to fuel tank attaching bolts, then remove fuel pump.
6. Reverse procedure to install.

SERPENTINE DRIVE BELT ROUTING

Refer to **Fig. 19,** for serpentine drive belt routing.

TIGHTENING SPECIFICATIONS

Torque specifications are for clean & lightly lubricated threads only. Dry or dirty threads produce increase friction which prevents accurate measurement of tightness.

Year	Component	Torque/Ft. Lbs.
1989-91	A/C Compressor Mounting Bracket To Engine	69
	A/C Compressor To Engine Mounting Bracket (Front)	69
	A/C Compressor To Engine Mounting Bracket (Rear)	50
	A/C Compressor To Rear Bracket	23
	Alternator Brace To Manifold	23
	Alternator To Bracket (Long Bolts)	32
	Alternator To Bracket (Short Bolts)	23
	Camshaft Carrier Cover Bolts	6
	Camshaft Rear Cover	7.5
	Camshaft Sprocket Bolt	33
	Camshaft Thrust Plate Bolts	6
	Connecting Rod Cap Bolts	38
	Coolant Inlet	18
	Crankshaft Pulley Bolts	20
	Crankshaft Sprocket	114
	Cylinder Head/Camshaft Carrier Bolts	①
	EGR Valve	15
	Engine Mount Bolts & Nuts	40
	Exhaust Manifold Bolts	16
	Exhaust Pipe To Exhaust Manifold	②
	Flexplate To Crankshaft Bolts	52
	Flywheel To Crankshaft Bolts	55
	Front Cover	8
	Fuel Pump Screw Fittings	15
	Idler Pulley Bolts	23
	Intake Manifold Bolts	16
	Main Bearing Cap Bolts	70
	Oil Filter Adapter, Auto. Trans.	13
	Oil Filter Adapter, Man. Trans.	26
	Oil Pan Bolts	3.7
	Oil Pan Drain Plug	33
	Oil Pump Cover	7
	Oil Pump Pressure Regulating Valve Plug	22
	Oil Pump Pick-Up Tube To Engine Bolt	4.4
	Oil Pump Pick-Up Tube To Oil Pump Bolts	6
	Oil Pump To Engine Bolts	32
	Oxygen Sensor	31
	Serpentine Drive Belt Tensioner	18
	Spark Plug	18
	Starter Motor To Engine	32
	Starter Motor To Front Bracket	9
	Thermostat Adapter	8

Continued

TIGHTENING SPECIFICATIONS—Continued

Year	Component	Torque/Ft. Lbs.
1989-91 Cont'd	Thermostat Housing	7.5
	Thermostat Outlet	9
	Throttle Body Fuel Lines	20
	Throttle Body To Intake Manifold Bolt	12
	Timing Belt Front Cover	7.5
	Timing Belt Rear Cover	7.3
	Timing Belt Tensioner	18
	Transaxle (Auto.) Torque Converter to Flexplate Bolts	44
	Transaxle To Engine Bolts	55
	Water Pump Bolts	18
	Water Pump Pulley	23

① —Torque bolts to 18 ft. lbs., then advance each bolt an additional 180° in 60° increments. Start engine & allow to reach operating temperature, then tighten bolts an additional 30 to 50°.

② —On 1989 models, torque to 15 ft. lbs. and on 1990–91 models, torque to 19 ft. lbs.

Clutch & Manual Transaxles

INDEX

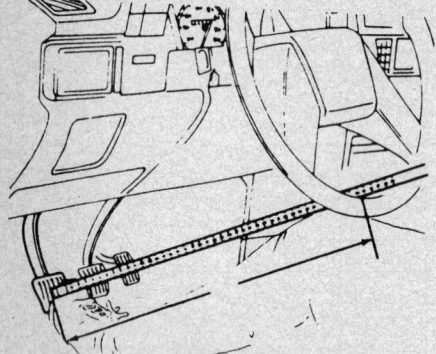

Fig. 1   Clutch pedal travel measurement

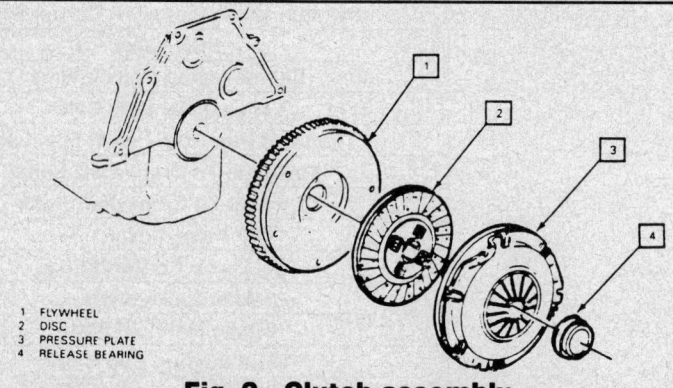

1 FLYWHEEL
2 DISC
3 PRESSURE PLATE
4 RELEASE BEARING

Fig. 2   Clutch assembly

CLUTCH PEDAL
ADJUST

1. Measure and record distance between outer edge of steering wheel and center of clutch pedal, **Fig. 1**.
2. Fully depress clutch pedal and repeat measurement made in step 1.
3. Determine clutch pedal travel by subtracting first measurement from second measurement.
4. If clutch pedal travel is not 5.43-5.71 inches, remove clip and adjust cable nut as necessary, then install clip.

CLUTCH
REPLACE
REMOVAL

1. Disconnect battery ground cable.

2. Remove clip and nut, then disconnect clutch cable from release lever. **Prior to disconnecting, measure threaded end of clutch cable at clutch release lever, so that cable may be set in the same position during installation.**
3. Raise and support vehicle.
4. Remove left front wheel and tire assembly.
5. Remove 17 mm plug from transaxle cover.
6. Mark relationship between input shaft and cluster gear, then remove snap ring from end of input shaft.
7. Remove screw at end of input shaft using tool No. J-36668 or equivalent.
8. Screw tools J-36644 and J-6125-B or equivalents into end of input shaft, then pull input shaft out of cluster gear.

9. Remove clutch cover attaching bolts and the cover.
10. Push back clutch release lever and install pressure spring clamp (tool No. J-36554 or equivalent) into pressure plate.
11. Rotate flywheel 120° and install a second clamp, then rotate an additional 120° and install a third clamp. **Pressure plate and clutch disc cannot be removed without the three spring clamps properly installed.**
12. Support pressure plate and remove attaching bolts, pressure plate and clutch disc, **Fig 2**.

INSTALLATION

1. Position new pressure in a suitable press and apply enough pressure to install three spring clamps.
2. Install pressure plate and clutch disc,

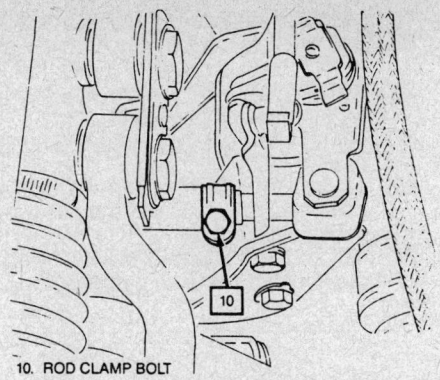

10. ROD CLAMP BOLT

Fig. 3 Shift rod clamp bolt

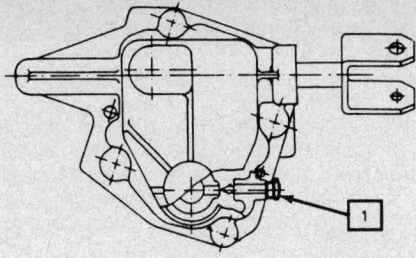

1. ADJUSTMENT HOLE PLUG

Fig. 4 Shift linkage adjustment hole plug

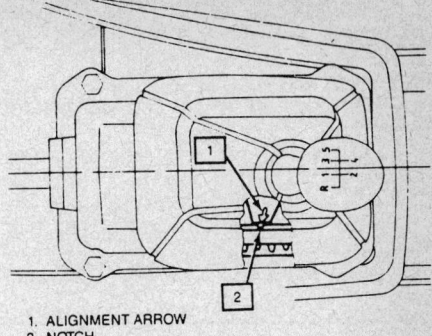

1. ALIGNMENT ARROW
2. NOTCH

Fig. 5 Shift lever alignment

noting the following:

a. Ensure long portion of clutch disc hub faces transaxle.

b. Apply suitable grease to clutch disc spline and release bearing.

c. Ensure reference marks on flywheel and pressure plate are properly aligned.

d. Install two pressure plate bolts. Align clutch disc splines with input shaft splines and marks on input shaft with marks on cluster gear, then install remaining bolts and torque all to specifications.

3. Seat input shaft in cluster gear using tool J-36644 and J-6125-B or equivalents.

4. Install screw at end of input shaft using tool No. J-36668 or equivalent, then torque to specifications.

5. Install snap ring onto input shaft. **Ensure sharp end of snap ring faces cover.**

6. Apply suitable Teflon pipe thread sealant to transaxle cover plug threads, then install the plug and torque to specifications.

7. Remove spring clamps, then install clutch cover and torque attaching bolts to specifications.

8. Lower vehicle, then connect clutch cable to release lever. Set threaded portion of clutch to measurement noted during removal and adjust as necessary.

MANUAL TRANSAXLE SHIFT LINKAGE
ADJUST

1. Disconnect battery ground cable.
2. Place gearshift lever in Neutral position, then loosen rod clamp bolt, **Fig. 3.**
3. Remove adjustment hole plug from shift lever cover, **Fig. 4,** then turn shift rod to the left until a 3/16 inch gauge pin can be inserted into adjustment hole in intermediate shift lever.
4. Remove shift boot from console, then unfasten console and lift upward to gain access to shift control lever mechanism.
5. Move gearshift lever to 1st/2nd gear position while still in Neutral.
6. Ensure lever is against stop and arrow

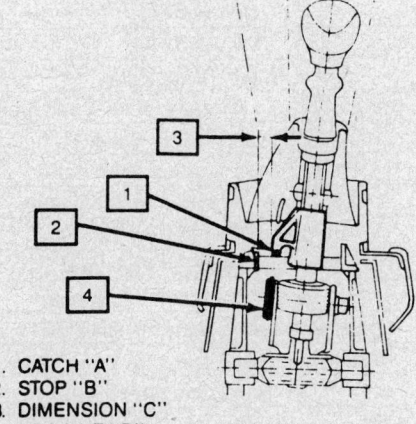

1. CATCH "A"
2. STOP "B"
3. DIMENSION "C"
4. ADJ. NUT "D"

Fig. 6 Shift lever measurements

is aligned with notch, **Fig. 5,** then **torque** rod clamp bolt to 10 ft. lbs. plus an additional 90-180°.

7. Measure clearance between catch "A," **Fig. 6,** and stop "B" with lever in neutral position. Clearance should measure .12 inch.

8. Remove gauge pin and install plug.

9. Adjust dimension "C," **Fig. 6,** to .449-.465 inch by turning adjusting nut "D" as necessary. **Bend back two locking tabs at nut prior to adjustment.**

10. Install boot then the console assembly.

11. Reconnect battery ground cable.

MANUAL TRANSAXLE REPLACE
1988

1. Disconnect battery ground cable.
2. Remove clip, then disconnect clutch cable from release lever.
3. Remove clip and bolt from universal joint.
4. Disconnect speedometer cable, speed sensor and back-up lamp switch electrical connectors.
5. Remove three upper transaxle to engine attaching bolts.
6. Install engine support fixture J28467-A or equivalent.

7. Raise and support vehicle.
8. Remove left front wheel and tire assembly.
9. Remove plug and disconnect ground wire from transaxle cover.
10. Mark relationship between input shaft and cluster gear, then remove snap ring from end of input shaft.
11. Remove screw at end of input shaft using tool No. J26668 or equivalent.
12. Screw tools J36644 and J6125-B or equivalents into end of input shaft, then pull input shaft out of cluster gear.
13. Remove flywheel cover attaching bolts and the cover.
14. Remove left lower ball joint and tie rod end.
15. Remove both drive axles from transaxle.
16. Support transaxle using a suitable jack.
17. Remove left front mount bracket attaching bolts and the bracket.
18. Remove left rear mount bracket to transaxle attaching bolts.
19. Remove lower transaxle to engine attaching bolts.
20. Lower jack while sliding right drive axle out of transaxle and remove transaxle from vehicle.
21. Reverse procedure to install, noting the following **torques:** lower transaxle to engine bolts, 55 ft. lbs.; left rear mount bracket bolts, 56 ft. lbs.; left front mount bracket to transaxle bolts, 47 ft. lbs.; left front mount bracket to mount bolts, 55 ft. lbs.; flywheel cover bolts, 62 inch lbs.; upper transaxle to engine bolt, 55 ft. lbs.; input shaft screw, 133 inch lbs.

1989–91

If only the transaxle is to be removed, the transaxle end shield along with the main shaft and driveshaft should be removed from the transaxle casing.

1. Disconnect battery ground cable.
2. Remove air cleaner.
3. Remove clutch cable at release lever attaching clip and nut.
4. Remove universal joint attaching clip and bolt.
5. Disconnect speedometer cable, speed sensor and back-up lamp electrical connectors.
6. Loosen shift rod clamp attaching bolt.
7. Remove upper transaxle to engine at-

taching bolts.

8. Install engine support fixture tool J28467-A or equivalent.
9. Raise and support vehicle.
10. Remove front wheel and tire assemblies.
11. **On 1990-91 models,** remove splash shield.
12. **On all models,** disconnect interference suppression capacitor cable at transaxle.
13. Press both ball joints from steering

knuckle.

14. Disengage axle shafts from transaxle casing.
15. Remove transaxle cover at end shield.
16. Disengage both drive axles at transaxle using tool J36639 or equivalent.
17. Mark relationship between transaxle driveshaft and cluster gear, then remove snap ring from end of input shaft.
18. Pull out left drive axle and support.

19. Support transaxle using suitable jack.
20. Remove left front mount bracket attaching bolts, then remove bracket.
21. Remove left rear mount bracket to transaxle attaching bolts.
22. Remove lower transaxle to engine attaching bolts.
23. Lower jack while guiding right drive axle out of transaxle and remove transaxle from vehicle.
24. Reverse procedure to install. Torque all attaching points to specifications.

TIGHTENING SPECIFICATIONS

Year	Component	Torque/Ft. Lbs.
1988	Ball Joint Nut	50
	Clutch Cover Plug	36
	Clutch Fork To Release Lever Shaft Bolt	26
	Flywheel Cover Bolts	62①
	Front Mount Bracket To Mount	55
	Front Mount Bracket To Transaxle	47
	Input Shaft Attaching Screw	133①
	Pressure Plate To Flywheel	11
	Rear Mount Bracket To Transaxle	56
	Release Bearing Guide Sleeve Bolts	45①
	Upper & Lower Transaxle To Engine	55
1989-91	Ball Joint Nut	50
	Clutch Cover Plug	36
	Clutch Fork To Release Lever Shaft Bolt	26
	Flywheel Cover Bolts	62①
	Front Mount Bracket To Mount	55
	Front Mount Bracket To Transaxle	48
	Input Shaft Attaching Screw	11
	Pressure Plate To Flywheel	11
	Rear Mount Bracket To Transaxle	55
	Release Bearing Guide Sleeve Bolts	45①
	Upper & Lower Transaxle To Engine	55

①—Inch lbs.

Rear Axle & Suspension
INDEX

REAR AXLE
REPLACE

REMOVAL

1. Raise and support vehicle.
2. Remove rear wheel and tire assemblies.
3. Remove exhaust heat shield from vehicle underbody.
4. Measure and record length of thread on parking brake lever pushrod.

5. Remove self-locking nut from parking brake lever pushrod and the lock plate from brake cable compensation yoke.
6. Disconnect parking brake cable from brake cable compensation yoke.
7. Disconnect parking brake cable from guides on transaxle tunnel and plastic sleeves on fuel tank and position toward muffler.
8. Raise one rear axle arm using a suitable jack.
9. Disconnect brake lines from brake pressure hoses on rear axle bracket and remove lock clips. **Cap brake line fittings.**

10. Disconnect brake pressure hoses from bracket.
11. Remove shock absorbers as described under "Shock Absorber, Replace."
12. Remove rear axle arm attaching bolt, then lower the arm and remove coil spring. If necessary, depress rear axle arm using a pry bar positioned in shock absorber bracket.
13. Repeat step 12 on opposite side.
14. Support center of rear axle assembly using a suitable jack.
15. Remove rear axle attaching bolts and carefully lower axle assembly from

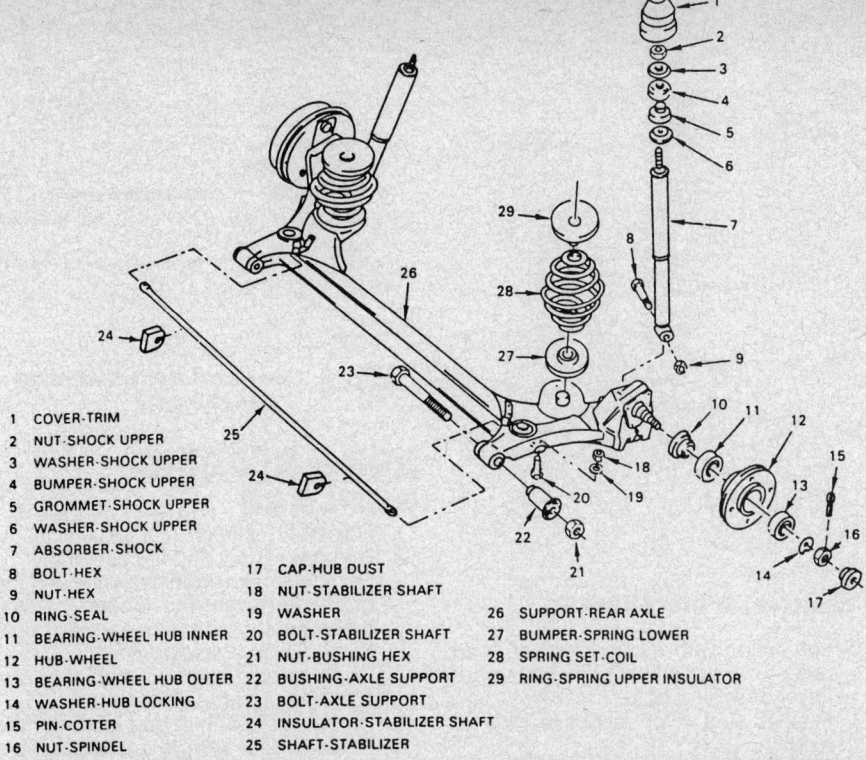

1 COVER-TRIM
2 NUT-SHOCK UPPER
3 WASHER-SHOCK UPPER
4 BUMPER-SHOCK UPPER
5 GROMMET-SHOCK UPPER
6 WASHER-SHOCK UPPER
7 ABSORBER-SHOCK
8 BOLT-HEX
9 NUT-HEX
10 RING-SEAL
11 BEARING-WHEEL HUB INNER
12 HUB-WHEEL
13 BEARING-WHEEL HUB OUTER
14 WASHER-HUB LOCKING
15 PIN-COTTER
16 NUT-SPINDEL

17 CAP-HUB DUST
18 NUT-STABILIZER SHAFT
19 WASHER
20 BOLT-STABILIZER SHAFT
21 NUT-BUSHING HEX
22 BUSHING-AXLE SUPPORT
23 BOLT-AXLE SUPPORT
24 INSULATOR-STABILIZER SHAFT
25 SHAFT-STABILIZER

26 SUPPORT-REAR AXLE
27 BUMPER-SPRING LOWER
28 SPRING SET-COIL
29 RING-SPRING UPPER INSULATOR

Fig. 1 Exploded view of rear axle & suspension assembly

vehicle, **Fig. 1.**

16. If rear axle assembly is to be replaced, proceed as follows:
   a. Remove brake drum setscrew and the drum.
   b. Remove dust cap from wheel hub.
   c. Remove wheel hub retaining nut and the wheel hub.
   d. Bend open brake line retaining clamps.
   e. Remove brake anchor plates and paper seal from rear axle arm.
   f. Remove stabilizer bar attaching bolts and the stabilizer bar.
   g. Disconnect parking brake cable from mounting.

INSTALLATION

1. If rear axle assembly is being replaced, proceed as follows:
   a. Attach stabilizer bar to rear axle and tighten attaching bolts to torque listed at the end of this section.
   b. Apply suitable sealant to brake anchor plate, then position new paper seals on plate.
   c. Apply suitable locking compound to anchor plate attaching bolts, then install the bolts and tighten to torque listed at the end of this section.
   d. Position brake lines in rear axle clamps and bend clamps closed.
   e. Apply suitable grease to wheel spindle, then install wheel hub and **torque** attaching nut to 12 ft. lbs.
   f. Adjust wheel bearings as described under "Wheel Bearings, Adjust."
   g. Install brake drums and setscrew.
   h. Position parking brake cable over exhaust muffler.

2. Raise rear axle assembly and secure to vehicle underbody. Raise one rear axle arm slightly using a suitable jack.
3. Install coil spring, ensuring lower rubber damper is properly positioned in spring seat.
4. Raise axle arm and install shock absorber. Tighten attaching bolts to torque listed at the end of this section.
5. Repeat steps 3 and 4 on opposite side.
6. Fasten brake pressure hoses to rear axle bracket and retaining clips.
7. Attach brake pressure lines to pressure hoses.
8. Install parking brake cable and adjust to dimension recorded at removal.
9. Install rear wheel and tire assemblies, then adjust wheel bearings as described under "Wheel Bearings, Adjust."
10. Tighten rear axle attaching bolts to torque listed at the end of this section, with weight of vehicle on wheels.
11. Bleed brake system, then adjust parking brake as necessary.

WHEEL BEARINGS
ADJUST

1. Raise and support rear of vehicle.
2. Remove hub dust cap, then the spindle nut cotter pin and nut.
3. **Torque** spindle nut to 18 ft. lbs. while turning wheel assembly forward by hand.
4. Back off spindle nut until just loose, then hand-tighten the nut.
5. Loosen spindle nut until either hole in spindle aligns with slot in nut, then install new cotter pin. **Do not loosen nut more than** 1/2 **turn.**

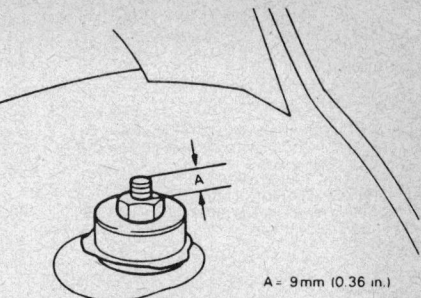

A = 9mm (0.36 in.)

Fig. 2 Shock absorber upper nut installation

6. Ensure bearing endplay measures .001 to .005 inch, then install dust cap on hub.

SHOCK ABSORBER
REPLACE

1. Open deck lid and remove trim cover, if equipped.
2. Remove upper shock absorber attaching nut.
3. Raise rear of vehicle and support rear axle using a suitable jack.
4. Remove lower attaching bolt and nut and the shock absorber. **Do not remove both shock absorbers at the same time.**
5. Reverse procedure to install, noting the following:
   a. Tighten lower attaching bolt to torque listed at the end of this section.
   b. Tighten upper attaching nut until thread extends .36 inch above the nut, **Fig. 2.**

STABILIZER BAR
REPLACE

1. Raise and support rear of vehicle.
2. Remove one rear wheel and tire assembly.
3. Remove stabilizer bar attaching bolts and nuts from both sides of axle, then remove stabilizer bar toward side of vehicle less wheel.
4. Reverse procedure to install. Tighten stabilizer bar attaching bolts to torque listed at the end of this section.

COIL SPRING
REPLACE

1. Raise and support rear of vehicle. Support control arms with suitable jackstands.
2. Remove brake line clips from body bracket and allow brake line to hang free.
3. Disconnect parking brake cable at equalizer.
4. Disconnect brake hoses and cap fittings.
5. Remove right and left shock absorber lower attaching bolts.
6. Carefully lower rear axle and remove springs and insulators.

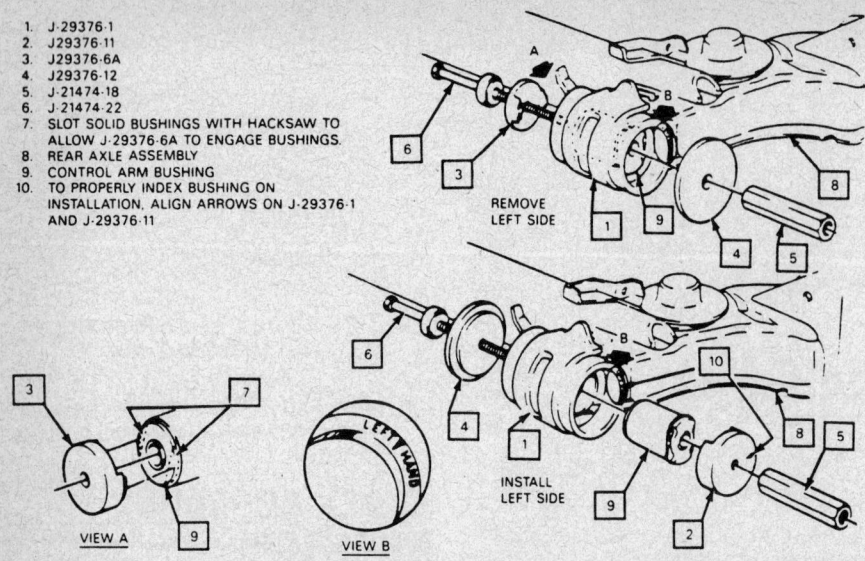

1. J-29376-1
2. J29376-11
3. J29376-6A
4. J29376-12
5. J-21474-18
6. J-21474-22
7. SLOT SOLID BUSHINGS WITH HACKSAW TO ALLOW J-29376-6A TO ENGAGE BUSHINGS.
8. REAR AXLE ASSEMBLY
9. CONTROL ARM BUSHING
10. TO PROPERLY INDEX BUSHING ON INSTALLATION, ALIGN ARROWS ON J-29376-1 AND J-29376-11

Fig. 3 Control arm bushing removal & installation

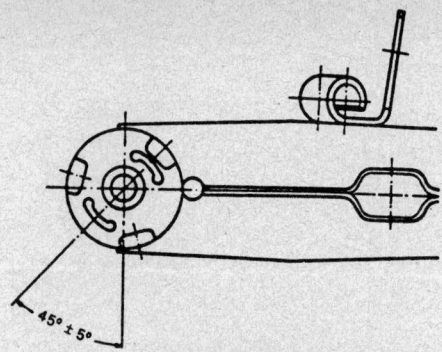

Fig. 4 Control arm bushing alignment

7. Reverse procedure to install, noting the following:
   a. Prior to installing springs, secure upper insulators to body with suitable adhesive.
   b. Tighten shock absorber lower attaching bolts to torque listed at the end of this section.

CONTROL ARM BUSHINGS
REPLACE

1. Raise and support rear of vehicle.
2. Raise one rear axle arm using a suitable jack and remove shock absorber lower attaching bolt.
3. Raise opposite rear axle arm and remove shock absorber lower attaching bolt.
4. Lower axle arm slightly and remove coil spring with rubber damper, then raise axle and install shock absorber lower attaching bolt.
5. Repeat step 4 on opposite side of axle.
6. Support center of rear axle assembly using a suitable jack.
7. Remove brake line retaining clips from vehicle underbody and position brake lines in underbody recess.
8. Remove rear axle attaching bolts, then lower axle slightly and support with tool hangar No. J-29376-13 or equivalent.
9. Heat control arm bushings to 122-158°F, then remove the bushings using tools shown in **Fig. 3.**
10. Install new bushings as shown in **Fig. 3.**
11. Reverse remainder of removal procedure to complete installation. Ensure bushings are properly aligned, **Fig. 4.**

HUB & BEARING
REPLACE

1. Raise and support rear of vehicle.
2. Remove wheel and tire assembly.
3. Remove brake drum setscrew and the drum. If necessary, loosen parking brake cable and press parking brake lever in with a screwdriver.
4. Remove dust cap from hub, then the spindle nut cotter pin and nut.
5. Remove wheel hub and lockwasher.
6. Remove seal from wheel hub using a suitable screwdriver.
7. Remove inner tapered roller bearing from hub.
8. Drive inner and outer bearing outer races out of wheel hub using a suitable drift.
9. Reverse procedure to install, noting the following:
   a. Press bearing outer races into hub using tools J-6791 and J-8092 or equivalents.
   b. Pack wheel bearings, seal lip and wheel hub with suitable wheel bearing grease.
   c. Following completion of installation, adjust wheel bearings and parking brake as needed.

TIGHTENING SPECIFICATIONS

Year	Component	Torque/Ft. Lbs.
1988	Brake Anchor Plate Bolt To Rear Axle Arm	21
	Control Arm To Body Bracket Nut	70
	Shock Absorber To Body Mount	①
	Shock Absorber To Axle Bolt	51
	Stabilizer Shaft To Axle Nuts	59
	Wheel & Tire Assembly	65
1989-91	Brake Anchor Plate Bolt To Rear Axle Arm	21
	Control Arm To Body Bracket Nut	70
	Shock Absorber To Body Mount	①
	Shock Absorber To Axle Bolt	51
	Stabilizer Shaft To Axle Nuts	59
	Wheel & Tire Assembly	66

①—Tighten until .36 inch of thread is exposed above top of nut.

Front Suspension & Steering

INDEX

STEERING KNUCKLE & STRUT ASSEMBLY
REPLACE

1. Loosen two upper strut to body attaching nuts, **Fig. 1.**
2. Loosen wheel lug nuts, then remove drive axle shaft retaining pin, nut and washer.
3. Raise and support front of vehicle. Support vehicle on suitable jackstands. Remove wheel and tire assembly.
4. Remove wheel and tire assembly.
5. Install modified outer seal protector J-28712 or equivalent.
6. Remove brake caliper and position aside, leaving brake line attached.
7. Remove brake disc attaching screws and the disc.
8. Remove outer tie rod to steering arm attaching nuts, then separate tie rod from arm using tool No. J-24319-01 or other suitable puller.
9. Remove lower ball joint retaining clip and stud nut, then separate ball joint from steering knuckle using tool J-36226 or equivalent. **Disregard "This Side Towards Wheel" marking on tool. Tool must be turned to opposite position when used on these vehicles.**
10. Support drive axle, then separate the axle from front wheel hub using tool No. J-37105 or equivalent and remove two strut to body attaching nuts and steering knuckle and strut assembly from vehicle.
11. Reverse procedure to install, noting the following:
    a. Torque strut to body attaching nuts to specification listed at the end of this section.
    b. Torque lower ball joint nut to specification listed at the end of this section.
    c. Torque tie rod attaching nut to specification listed at the end of this section.
    d. Torque disc to wheel hub bolt to specification listed at the end of this section.
    e. With weight of vehicle on wheels, **torque** new drive axle to hub nut to 74 ft. lbs., then back off nut and retorque to 15 ft. lbs. Tighten nut an additional ¼ turn, then install cotter pin. If necessary, loosen nut slightly to align cotter pin holes.

STRUT ASSEMBLY SERVICE

1. Secure strut assembly in compressor tool No. J-34013 with adapter J-34013-87 or equivalents, **Fig. 2.**
2. Turn compressor forcing screw to compress spring slightly, then remove upper bearing dust cover.
3. Remove dampener shaft nut while using a suitable socket to prevent shaft from turning.
4. Guide dampener shaft out of strut assembly while loosening compressor screw.
5. Continue to loosen compressor screw, then remove strut dampener and spring.
6. Remove thrust washer, upper strut mount, raised edge washer and plastic mount from top of strut, **Fig. 1.**
7. Remove strut shield, upper spring insulator, spring, strut bumper and on 1990-91 models, remove front brake shield.
8. **On all models,** remove strut cartridge nut and the cartridge using tool No. J-36804 or equivalent. **Exercise extreme caution as strut cartridge nut is under high torque pressure.**
9. Reverse procedure to assemble, noting the following:
    a. Install new strut cartridge nut and tighten to torque listed at the end of this section. Do not remove wax lubricant from nut.
    b. Apply suitable lubricant to upper strut bearings prior to assembly.
    c. Position spring as shown, **Fig. 3,** and move assembly upright in strut compressor before installing upper locking pin.
    d. Tighten dampener shaft nut to torque listed at the end of this section, while preventing nut from turning.

CONTROL ARM
REPLACE

1. Raise and support front of vehicle. Support vehicle on suitable jackstands placed under frame.
2. Remove wheel and tire assembly.
3. Disconnect stabilizer bar from control arm.
4. Install modified outer seal protector J-28712 or equivalent.
5. Remove ball joint retaining clip and stud nut, then separate ball joint from steering knuckle using tool No. J-36226 or equivalent. **Disregard**

"This Side Towards Wheel" marking on tool. Tool must be turned to opposite position when used on these vehicles.
6. Remove control arm attaching bolts and the control arm.
7. If necessary, replace control arm bushings as shown in **Figs. 4 through 7.**
8. Reverse procedure to install. Tighten attachments to torque listed at the end of this section.

BALL JOINT INSPECTION

1. Raise and support front of vehicle so that suspension is allowed to hang free.
2. Grasp wheel and tire assembly at 6 and 12 o'clock positions, then rock top of wheel and tire assembly inward and outward.
3. While rocking wheel and tire assembly, observe movement between steering knuckle and control arm. If any horizontal movement is present, replace ball joint.
4. If ball joint is disconnected from steering knuckle, use finger pressure to try to twist ball joint in its socket. If ball joint can be twisted in its socket, replace ball joint.

BALL JOINT
REPLACE

1. Remove control arm as previously described.
2. Drill heads off ball joint rivets, then punch out rivets using a suitable drift and remove ball joint.
3. Reverse procedure to install. Tighten ball joint retaining nuts from below the control arm to torque listed at the end of this section.

STABILIZER BAR
REPLACE

1. Raise vehicle and support so that front suspension hangs free.
2. Remove front wheel and tire assemblies.
3. Disconnect stabilizer bar link assemblies from control arms, **Fig. 1.**
4. Remove stabilizer bar bracket attaching bolts, then the bushings, brackets and stabilizer bar.
5. Reverse procedure to install. Tighten stabilizer bar to body bolts to torque listed at the end of this section and the stabilizer bar to control arm nuts to a length of 1¹⁵⁄₃₂ inch, **Fig. 8.**

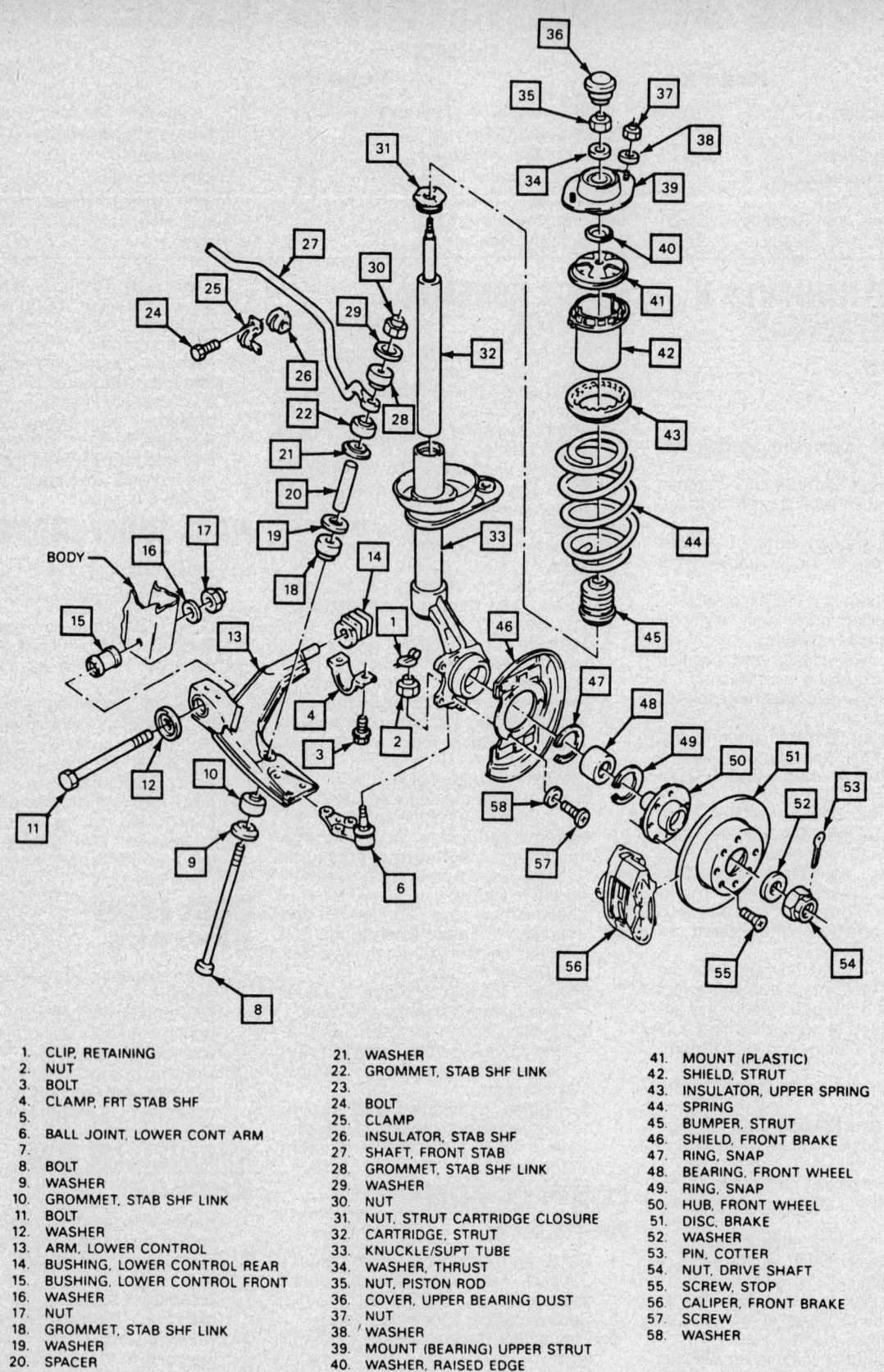

Fig. 1 Exploded view of front suspension

1. CLIP, RETAINING
2. NUT
3. BOLT
4. CLAMP, FRT STAB SHF
5.
6. BALL JOINT, LOWER CONT ARM
7.
8. BOLT
9. WASHER
10. GROMMET, STAB SHF LINK
11. BOLT
12. WASHER
13. ARM, LOWER CONTROL
14. BUSHING, LOWER CONTROL REAR
15. BUSHING, LOWER CONTROL FRONT
16. WASHER
17. NUT
18. GROMMET, STAB SHF LINK
19. WASHER
20. SPACER

21. WASHER
22. GROMMET, STAB SHF LINK
23.
24. BOLT
25. CLAMP
26. INSULATOR, STAB SHF
27. SHAFT, FRONT STAB
28. GROMMET, STAB SHF LINK
29. WASHER
30. NUT
31. NUT, STRUT CARTRIDGE CLOSURE
32. CARTRIDGE, STRUT
33. KNUCKLE/SUPT TUBE
34. WASHER, THRUST
35. NUT, PISTON ROD
36. COVER, UPPER BEARING DUST
37. NUT
38. WASHER
39. MOUNT (BEARING) UPPER STRUT
40. WASHER, RAISED EDGE

41. MOUNT (PLASTIC)
42. SHIELD, STRUT
43. INSULATOR, UPPER SPRING
44. SPRING
45. BUMPER, STRUT
46. SHIELD, FRONT BRAKE
47. RING, SNAP
48. BEARING, FRONT WHEEL
49. RING, SNAP
50. HUB, FRONT WHEEL
51. DISC, BRAKE
52. WASHER
53. PIN, COTTER
54. NUT, DRIVE SHAFT
55. SCREW, STOP
56. CALIPER, FRONT BRAKE
57. SCREW
58. WASHER

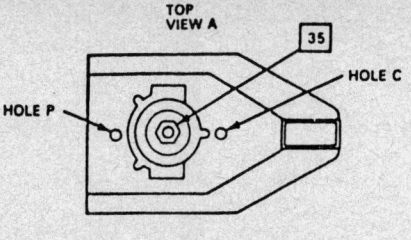

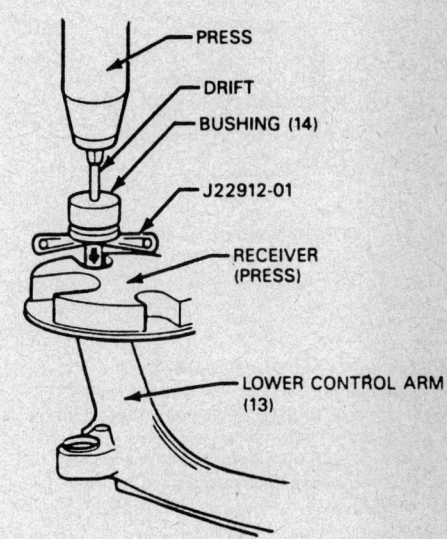

Lug on plastic front spring mount serves as installation guide: looking in direction of travel, lug points forwards on spring strut for left side of vehicle; on spring strut for right side of vehicle, lug points backwards.

33

41

Fig. 3 Spring mount alignment

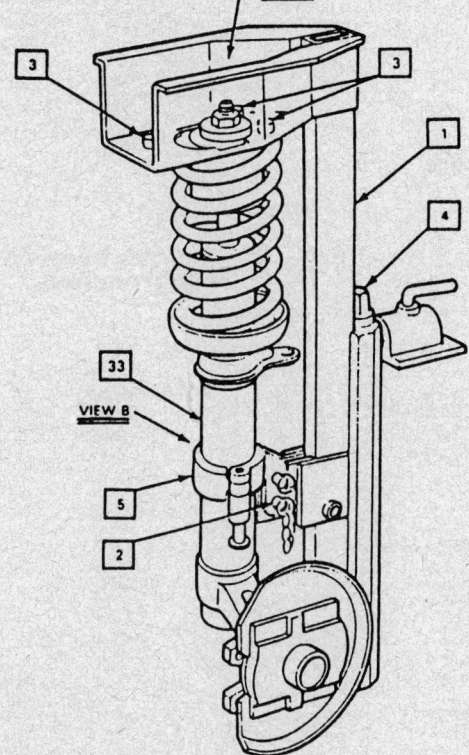

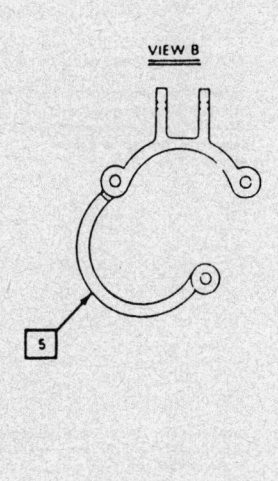

VIEW B

5

1. STRUT COMPRESSOR J 34013
2. INSTALL LOCKING PINS THROUGH STRUT ASSEMBLY
3. TIGHTEN NUTS TILL FLUSH WITH STRUT COMPRESSOR (SEE VIEW A)
4. COMPRESSOR FORCING SCREW
5. CLAMPING TOOL J 34013-87 (SEE VIEW B)
33. STRUT ASSEMBLY
35. NUT, PISTON ROD

Fig. 2 Strut disassembly

PRESS
DRIFT
BUSHING (14)
J22912-01
RECEIVER (PRESS)
LOWER CONTROL ARM (13)

Fig. 4 Control arm rear bushing removal

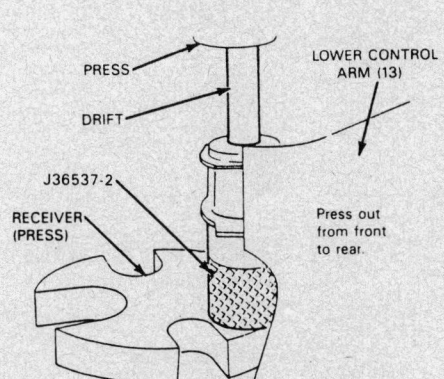

Fig. 5 Control arm front bushing removal

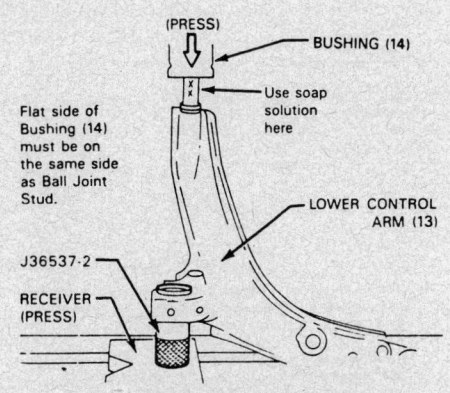

Fig. 6 Control arm rear bushing installation

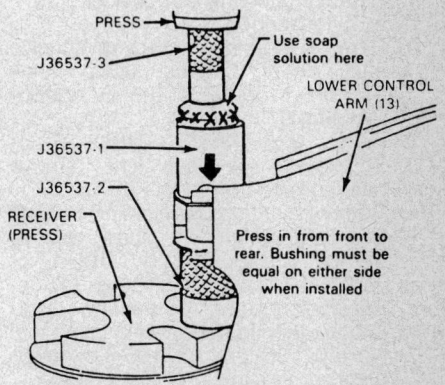

Fig. 7 Control arm front bushing installation

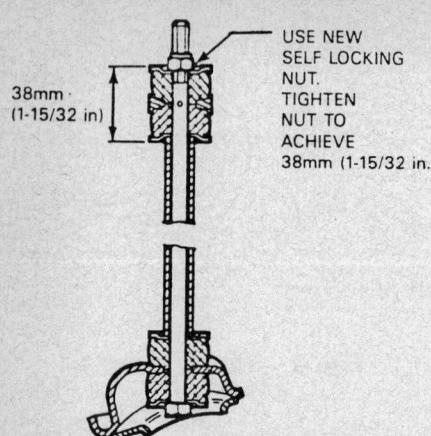

Fig. 8   Stabilizer bar attaching nut installation

38mm (1-15/32 in)

USE NEW SELF LOCKING NUT. TIGHTEN NUT TO ACHIEVE 38mm (1-15/32 in.)

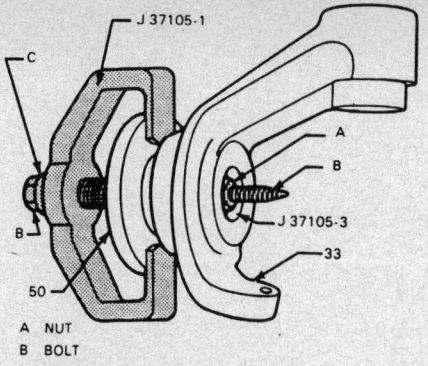

A   NUT
B   BOLT
C   BEARING
33   KNUCKLE AND SUPPORT TUBE
50   HUB

Fig. 9   Removing hub from steering knuckle

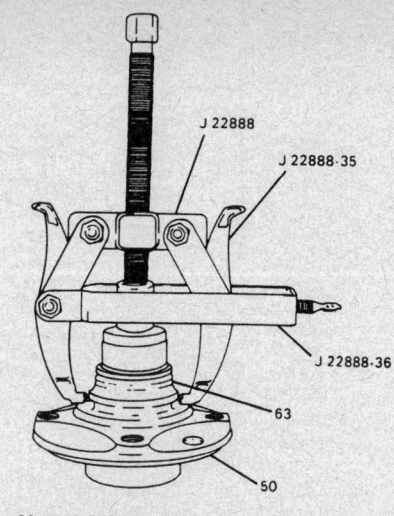

50   HUB-FRONT WHEEL
63   INNER RACE

Fig. 10   Remove bearing inner race from hub

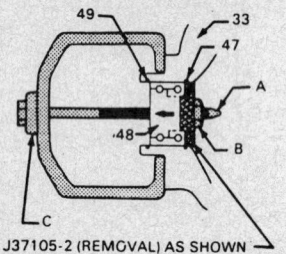

J37105-2 (REMOVAL) AS SHOWN
J37105-2 (INSTALLATION) REVERSE TOOL

A   BOLT
B   NUT
C   BEARING
33   KNUCKLE AND SUPPORT TUBE
47   RING-SNAP-MUST BE REMOVED FOR BEARING REMOVAL. INSTALL AFTER HUB (50) INSTALLATION
48   BEARING-FRONT WHEEL
49   RING-SNAP-MUST BE INSTALLED FOR BEARING INSTALLATION AND REMOVED FOR BEARING REMOVAL.

Fig. 11   Removing bearing from steering knuckle bore

HUB & BEARING
REPLACE

1. Remove steering knuckle as previously described.
2. Remove hub from steering knuckle and wheel bearing using tools J-37105-1 or J-37105-3 or equivalent, **Fig. 9**.
3. Using tool Nos. J-22888-35 or J-22888-36 or equivalent, remove bearing race from hub, **Fig. 10**.
4. Remove snap rings retaining bearing to steering knuckle, then remove bearing using tool J-37105-1 or J-37105-3 or equivalent, **Fig. 11**.
5. Position snap ring into steering knuckle bore, then install bearing using tool No. J-37105-1 or J-37105-3 or equivalent.
6. Using tool No. J-37105-1 or J-37105-3 or equivalent, pull hub onto bearing assembly and steering knuckle, then install snap ring.

After all necessary operations on the steering gear or the steering column assembly are completed (removing and reinstalling, disassembling and reassembling), the exact straight ahead position of the steering is to be checked in each case.

STEERING, POSITION STRAIGHT AHEAD

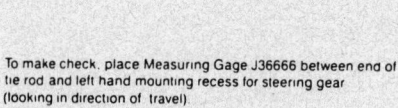

* The straight ahead position is achieved when reference dimension A = 325 mm/12.8 in

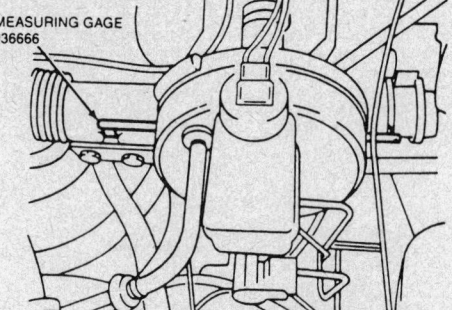

MEASURING GAGE J36666

To make check, place Measuring Gage J36666 between end of tie rod and left hand mounting recess for steering gear (looking in direction of travel).

Hold steering wheel in this exact straight ahead position.

The following conditions must be fulfilled:

1. The steering spindle clamp flange bolt must be lying horizontally on top.

2. The steering wheel must be centered on the steering spindle.

(Steering wheel spokes centered diagonally and pointing downwards)

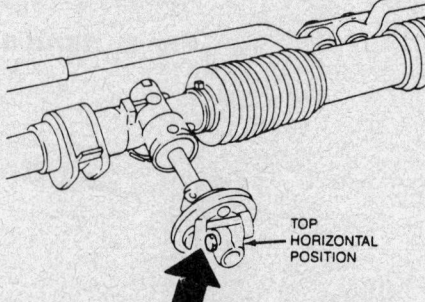

TOP HORIZONTAL POSITION

MEASURING GAGE J36666

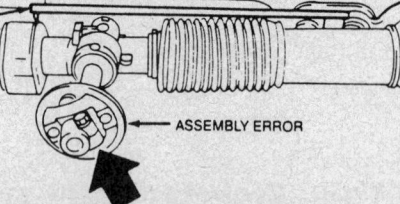

1a. If clamp flange bolt is slanted pinion is displaced one tooth on rack (assembly error) — steering pinion position must be corrected.

2a. If steering wheel is off center by more than ± 5° (clamp flange bolt must lie horizontally on top), pull steering wheel off of steering spindle using J36541 and center on spindle splines.

ASSEMBLY ERROR

Fig. 12   Adjusting steering wheel position

STEERING GEAR REPLACE

1. Disconnect battery ground cable.
2. **On 1988 models equipped with power steering and all models equipped with manual steering,** remove both pinch bolts from coupling assembly, then slide coupling up on steering spindle. Position steering wheel straight ahead as shown in **Fig. 12.**
3. **On all models,** remove air cleaner assembly.
4. Loosen both tie rods from center of steering gear housing, then pry lock plate in half, then remove both tie rod bolts from center of steering gear housing.
5. Remove steering damper brackets and mounting clamps, then remove steering damper, then push flex coupling upward on steering spindle, as equipped.
6. **On models equipped with power steering gear,** disconnect fluid lines from gear.
7. **On 1989-91 models equipped with power steering,** remove steering gear and pinion flexible coupling clamp attaching bolts.

8. **On 1988 models equipped with power steering and all models equipped with manual steering,** remove left and right mounting clamp bolt and nut, then remove clamp.
9. **On all models,** Remove instrument panel seal from gear, then remove steering gear through righthand wheel opening.
10. Reverse procedure to install, noting the following:
    a. After second reuse of mounting clamp studs, thread locking kit No. 1052624 or equivalent must be used.
    b. Tighten mounting clamp attaching nuts to torque listed at the end of this section.
    c. Tighten coupling to steering column attaching bolts to torque listed at the end of this section.

POWER STEERING PUMP REPLACE

MODELS w/1.6L/4-98 ENGINE

1. Disconnect battery ground cable.
2. Remove power steering pump drive belt, then three attaching bolts and power steering pulley.
3. Disconnect fluid lines from pump.
4. Remove pump to upper timing belt cover attaching clips, then remove clips.
5. Remove power steering pump mounting bolts, then remove pump from vehicle.
6. Reverse procedure to install. After completing installation, bleed system by cycling steering wheel from side to side without contacting stops. Keep fluid at proper level during bleeding procedure.

MODELS w/2.0L/4-121 ENGINE

1. Disconnect battery ground cable.
2. Remove power steering pump drive belt, then disconnect fluid lines from pump.
3. Remove power steering pump to bracket attaching bolts through holes in pulley.
4. Remove power steering pump from vehicle.
5. Reverse procedure to install. After completing installation, bleed system by cycling steering wheel from side to side without contacting stops. Keep fluid at proper level during bleeding procedure.

TIGHTENING SPECIFICATIONS

Year	Component	Torque/Ft. Lbs.
1988	Ball Joint To Strut/Knuckle Assembly Nut	50
	Control Arm Front Mounting Bolts	100
	Control Arm Rear Mounting Bolts	50
	Disc Brake Rotor To Hub Screw	3
	Flex Coupling To Steering Shaft Clamp Bolt	16
	Flex Coupling To Stub Shaft Clamp Bolt	16
	Hub & Bearing Nut	①
	Inner Tie Rod To Steering Gear	65
	Power Steering Fluid Line Fittings	20
	Power Steering Pump Attaching Bolts	18
	Power Steering Pump Pulley Attaching Bolts	20
	Stabilizer Bar To Body Clamp Bolts	29
	Steering Damper Bracket To Steering Gear Bolts	16
	Steering Gear Mounting Clamp Bolts & Nuts	28
	Steering Gear Retaining Bracket Nuts	16
	Strut To Body Nuts	18
	Strut Cartridge Retaining Nut	145
	Strut PushRod Nut	40
	Tie Rod End To Steering Knuckle Assembly Nut	45
	Tie Rod Pinch Bolts	16
	Wheel & Tire Assembly	65
1989–91	Ball Joint To Strut/Knuckle Assembly Nut	50
	Control Arm Front Mounting Bolts	100
	Control Arm Rear Mounting Bolts	50
	Disc Brake Rotor To Hub Screw	3

Continued

TIGHTENING SPECIFICATIONS—Continued

Year	Component	Torque/Ft. Lbs.
1988-91 Cont'd	Flex Coupling To Steering Shaft Clamp Bolt	16
	Flex Coupling To Stub Shaft Clamp Bolt	16
	Hub & Bearing Nut	①
	Inner Tie Rod To Steering Gear	66
	Power Steering Fluid Line Fittings	20
	Power Steering Pump Attaching Bolts	18
	Power Steering Pump Pulley Attaching Bolts	20
	Stabilizer Bar To Body Clamp Bolts	29
	Steering Damper Bracket To Steering Gear Bolts	16
	Steering Gear Mounting Clamp Bolts & Nuts	28
	Steering Gear Retaining Bracket Nuts	16
	Strut To Body Nuts	18
	Strut Cartridge Retaining Nut	145
	Strut PushRod Nut	40
	Tie Rod End To Steering Knuckle Assembly Nut	45
	Tie Rod Pinch Bolts	16
	Wheel & Tire Assembly	66

①—With weight of vehicle on wheels, torque new drive axle to hub nut to 74 ft. lbs., then back off nut and retorque to 15 ft. lbs. Tighten nut an additional ¼ turn, then install cotter pin. If required, loosen nut slightly to align cotter pin holes.

Wheel Alignment

INDEX

VEHICLE TRIM HEIGHT

Vehicle trim height is measured from the rocker panel to ground. From rocker panel front to ground should be 7.7 inches. From rocker panel rear to ground, trim height should be 7.5 inches. If trim height is not within limits, check control arms, struts and ball joints for wear and damage.

FRONT WHEEL ALIGNMENT

CASTER & CAMBER

Front caster and camber angles are not adjustable. If caster or camber is found to be out of specifications, inspect suspension and related body components for damage and repair or replace as necessary.

TOE

1. Loosen right and left tie rod end clamps, **Fig. 1.**
2. Turn right and left tie rod adjusters as

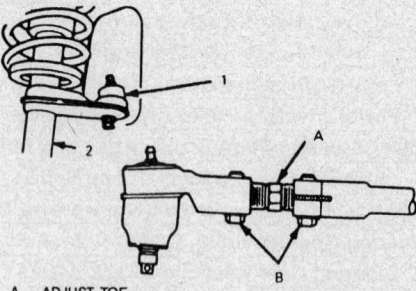

A ADJUST TOE SETTING HERE
B LOOSEN CLAMP BOLTS ADJUST TOE.
1 TIE ROD-OUTER
2 DAMPER-STRUT

Fig. 1 Front toe adjustment

necessary to bring toe within specifications.
3. **On 1988-89 models,** ensure right and left tie rods are equal in length, then **torque** clamp bolts to 41 ft. lbs.
4. **On 1990-91 models,** ensure right and left tie rods are equal in length, then **torque** clamp bolts to 15 ft. lbs.

REAR WHEEL ALIGNMENT

CASTER & CAMBER

Rear caster and camber angles are not adjustable. If caster or camber is found to be out of specifications, inspect suspension and related body components for damage and repair or replace as necessary.

TOE

Rear toe is not adjustable. If toe is found to be out of specifications, inspect rear axle assembly and wheel spindle for damage and correct as necessary.

TABLE OF CONTENTS

Troubleshooting

INDEX

Condition	Probable cause	Corrective action
INSUFFICIENT REFRIGERANT CHARGE Insufficient cooling. Bubbles appear in sight glass.	Refrigerant is low, or leaking slightly.	1. Leak test. 2. Repair leak. 3. Charge system. Evacuate, as necessary, and recharge system.
ALMOST NO REFRIGERANT No cooling action. A lot of bubbles or something like mist appears in sight glass.	Serious refrigerant leak.	Stop compressor immediately. 1. Leak test. 2. Discharge system. 3. Repair leak(s). 4. Replace receiver drier if necessary. 5. Check oil level. 6. Evacuate and recharge system.
FAULTY EXPANSION VALVE Slight cooling. Sweat or frosting on expansion valve inlet.	Expansion valve restricts refrigerant flow. • Expansion valve is clogged. • Expansion valve is in-operative. Valve stuck closed. Thermal bulb has lost charge.	If valve inlet reveals sweat or frost: 1. Discharge system. 2. Remove valve and clean it. Replace it if necessary. 3. Evacuate system. 4. Charge system. If valve does not operate: 1. Discharge system. 2. Replace valve. 3. Evacuate and charge system.

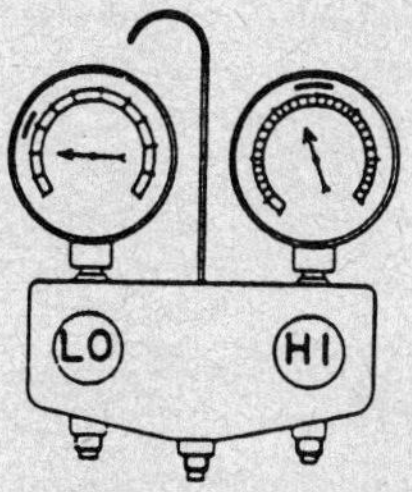

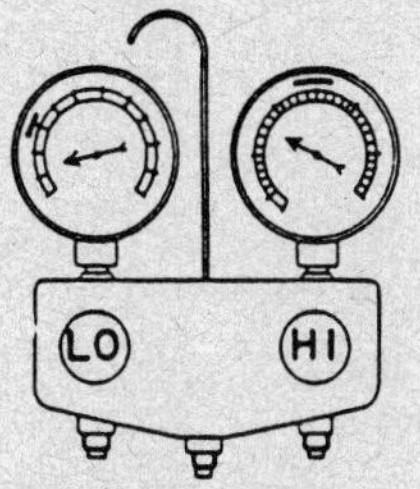

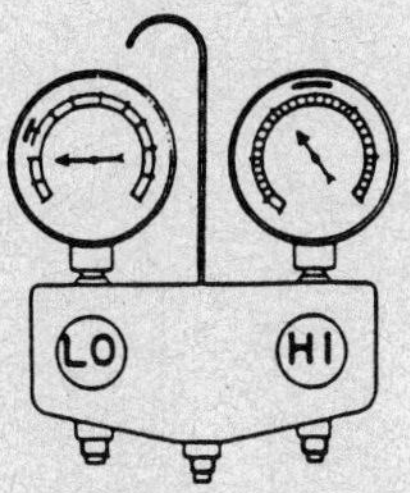

Fig. 1   Symptom diagnosis chart (part 1 of 3)

SYMPTOM DIAGNOSIS CHARTS

When diagnosing specific air conditioning system symptoms, refer to **Fig. 1.**

LEAK TESTS

Testing the refrigerant system for leaks is one of the most important phases of troubleshooting. One or more of the methods outlined will prove useful in detecting leaks or checking connections if service work is performed. Before beginning any leak test, attach a manifold gauge set and note pressure. If little or no pressure is indicated, a partial charge must be installed. Check all connections, compressor head gasket, oil filler plug and compressor shaft seal for leaks.

ELECTRONIC LEAK DETECTORS

There are a number of electronic leak detectors available to perform leak tests. Refer to operating instructions for the unit being used and observe these general procedures.
1. Move detector probe one inch per second in areas of suspected leaks.
2. Position probe below test point, as refrigerant gas is heavier than air.
3. Be sure to check service access gauge port valve fittings, particularly when valve caps are missing, as dirt accumulations can destroy the sealing area of valve core when manifold gauge set is attached. Replace missing valve caps after cleaning valve core area. **Valve caps should only be finger tightened. Using pliers to tighten valve caps may distort sealing surface of valve.**
4. Check for leaks in manifold gauge set and hoses, as well as the rest of the system.

Condition	Probable cause	Corrective action
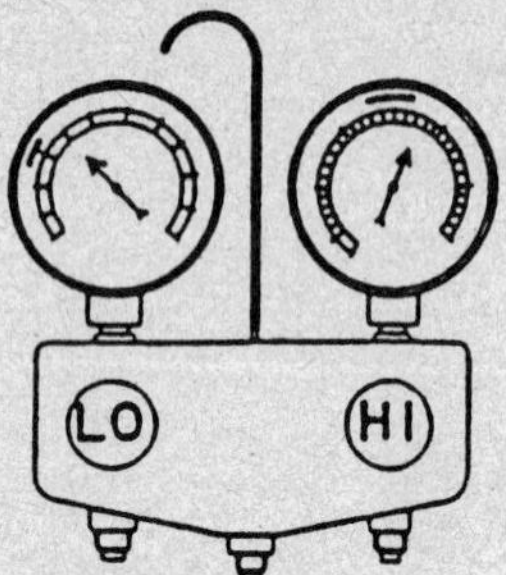 Insufficient cooling. Sweat on suction line.	Expansion valve allows too much refrigerant through evaporator.	Check valve for operation. If suction side does not show a pressure decrease, replace valve.
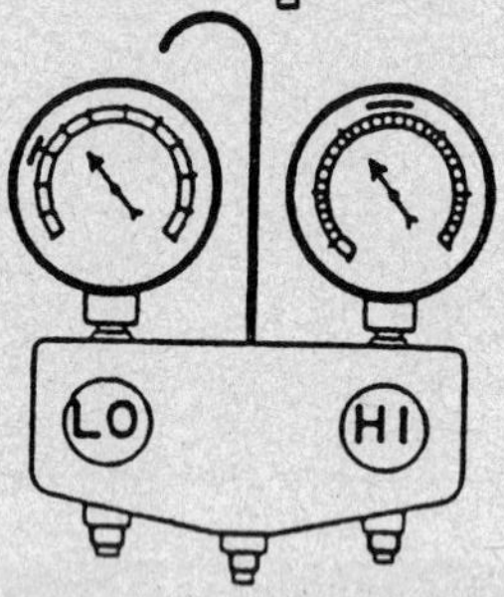 No cooling. Sweat or frosting on suction line.	Faulty expansion valve.	1. Discharge system. 2. Replace valve. 3. Evacuate and replace system.
AIR IN SYSTEM		
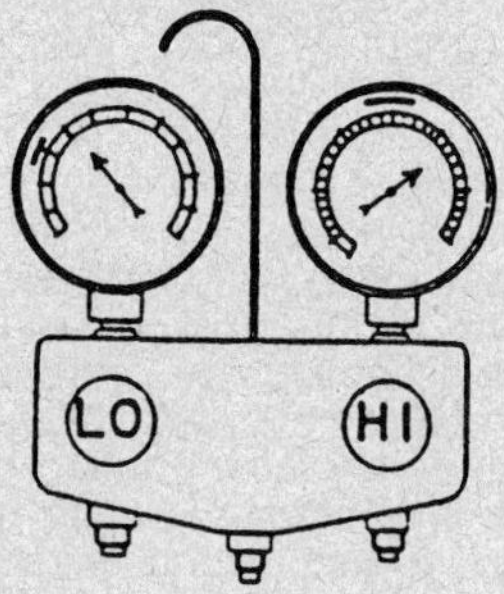 Insufficient cooling. Sight glass shows occasional bubbles.	Air mixed with refrigerant in system.	1. Discharge system. 2. Replace receiver drier. 3. Evacuate and charge system.
MOISTURE IN SYSTEM		
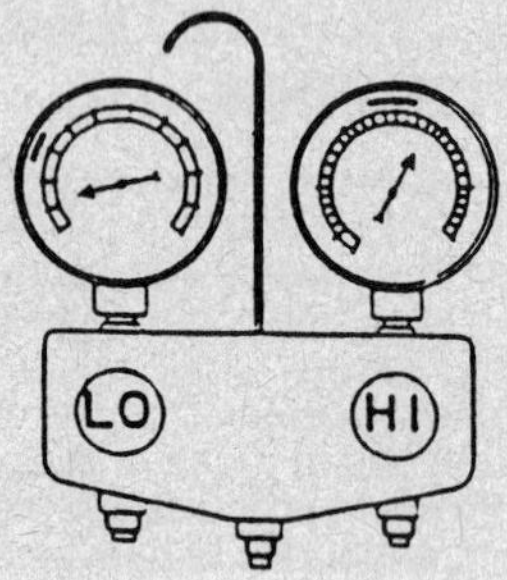 After short operation, suction side may show vacuum pressure reading. During this condition, discharge air will be warm. As a warning of this, reading vibrates around 39 kPa (0.4 kg/cm², 6 psi).	Drier is saturated with moisture. Moisture has frozen in expansion valve. Refrigerant flow is restricted.	1. Discharge system. 2. Replace receiver drier (twice if necessary). 3. Evacuate system completely. (Repeat 30-minutes evacuating three times.) 4. Recharge system.

Fig. 1 Symptom diagnosis chart (part 2 of 3)

FLAME-TYPE (HALIDE) LEAK DETECTORS

1. Adjust detector flame as low as possible to obtain maximum sensitivity. Be sure copper element is cherry red and not burned away. The flame will be almost colorless.
2. Slowly move detector along areas of suspected leaks. A slight leak will cause the flame to change to a bright yellow-green color. A significant leak will be indicated by a brilliant blue flame. Position flame under areas being tested as refrigerant gas is heavier than air. **The presence of dust in the pickup hose may cause a change in the color of the flame. If not rec-**

Condition	Probable cause	Corrective action
FAULTY CONDENSER 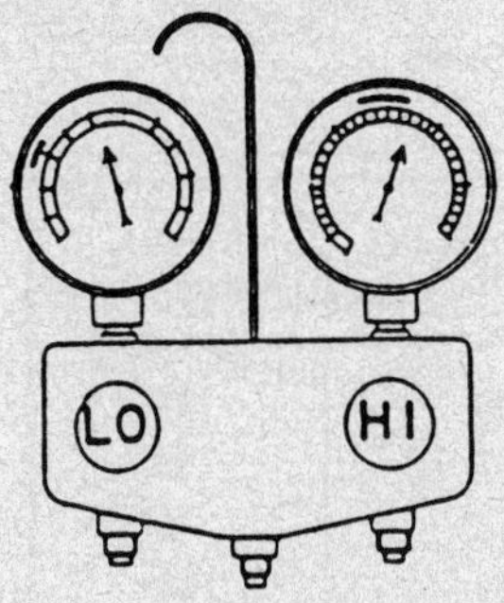 No cooling action: engine may overheat. Bubbles appear in sight glass of drier. Suction line is very hot.	Usually a malfunctioning condenser.	• Check condenser fan motor. • Check condenser for dirt accumulation. • Check engine cooling system for overheating. • Check for refrigerant overcharging. If pressure remains high in spite of all above actions taken, remove and inspect the condenser for possible oil clogging.
HIGH PRESSURE LINE BLOCKED 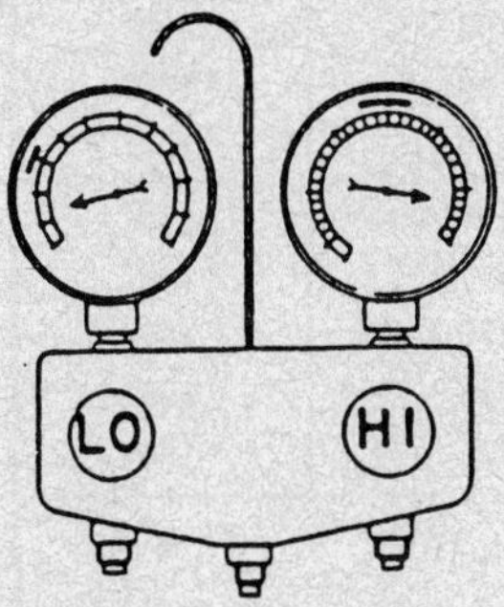 Insufficient cooling. Frosted high pressure liquid line.	Drier clogged, or restriction in high pressure line.	1. Discharge system. 2. Remove receiver drier or strainer and replace it. 3. Evacuate and charge system.
FAULTY COMPRESSOR 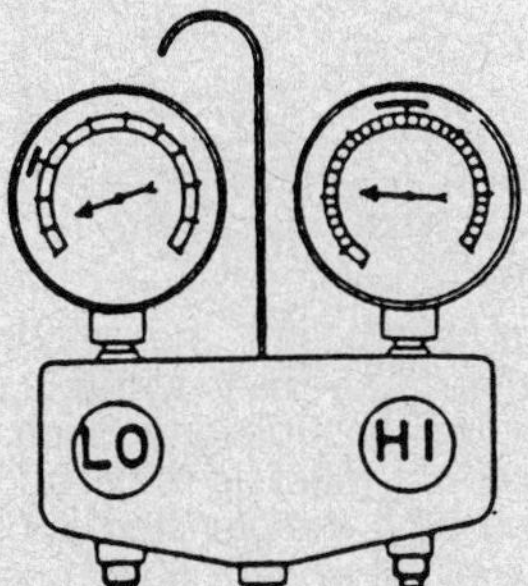 Insufficient cooling.	Internal problem in compressor, or damaged gasket and valve.	1. Discharge system. 2. Remove and check compressor. 3. Repair or replace compressor. 4. Check oil level. 5. Replace receiver drier. 6. Evacuate and charge system.

Fig. 1   Symptom diagnosis chart (part 3 of 3)

ognized, a false diagnosis could be made. **Store leak detector in a clean place and ensure hose is free of dust before leak testing.**

3. Check for leaks in the manifold gauge set and hoses, as well as the rest of the system.
4. Use a small fan to ventilate areas where the leak detector indicates refrigerant constantly. These areas are contaminated with refrigerant and must be ventilated before leak can be pinpointed.

FLUID LEAK DETECTORS

Apply leak detector solution around joints to be tested. A cluster of bubbles will form immediately if there is a leak. A white foam that forms after a short while will indicate an extremely small leak. In some confined areas such as sections of the evaporator and condenser, electronic leak detectors will be more useful.

System Testing

INDEX

GENERAL PRECAUTIONS

The Freon refrigerant used is also known as R-12. It is colorless and odorless both as a gas and a liquid. Since it boils (vaporizes) at $-21.7°F$, it will usually be in a vapor state when being handled in a repair shop. But if a portion of the liquid coolant should come in contact with the hands or face, note that its temperature momentarily will be at least $-22°F$.

Protective goggles should be worn when opening any refrigerant lines. If liquid coolant does touch the eyes, bathe the eyes quickly in cold water, then apply a bland disinfectant oil to the eyes. See an eye doctor.

When checking a system for leaks with a torch type leak detector, do not breathe the vapors coming from the flame. Do not discharge refrigerant in the area of a live flame. A poisonous phosgene gas is produced when R-12 is burned. While the small amount of gas produced by a leak detector is not harmful unless inhaled directly at the flame, the quantity of refrigerant released into the air when a system is purged can be extremely dangerous if allowed to come into contact with an open flame. Thus, when purging a system, be sure that the discharge hose is routed to a well ventilated area where no flame is present. Under these conditions the refrigerant will be quickly dissipated into the surrounding air.

Never allow the temperature of refrigerant drums to exceed $125°F$. The excessive increase in temperature will cause a corresponding increase in pressure which may cause the safety plug to release or the drum to burst.

If it is necessary to heat a drum of refrigerant when charging a system, the drum should be placed in water no hotter than $125°F$. Never use a blow torch or other open flame. If possible, a pressure release mechanism should be attached before the drum is heated.

When connecting and disconnecting service gauges on an A/C system, ensure that gauge hand valves are fully closed and that compressor service valves, if equipped, are in the back-seated (fully counterclockwise) position. Do not disconnect gauge hoses from service port adapters, if used, while gauges are connected to A/C system. To disconnect hoses, always remove adapter from service port. Do not disconnect hoses from gauge manifold while connected to A/C system, as refrigerant will be rapidly discharged.

Evaporator Pressure Gauge Reading	Evaporator Temperature F°	High Pressure Gauge Reading	Ambient Temperature
0	-21°	45	20°
0.6	-20°	55	30°
2.4	-15°	72	40°
4.5	-10°	86	50°
6.8	-5°	105	60°
9.2	0°	126	70°
11.8	5°	140	75°
14.7	10°	160	80°
17.1	15°	185	90°
21.1	20°	195	95°
22.5	22°	220	100°
23.9	24°	240	105°
25.4	26°	260	110°
26.9	28°	275	115°
28.5	30°	290	120°
37.0	40°	305	125°
46.7	50°	325	130°
57.7	60°		
70.1	70°		
84.1	80°		
99.6	90°		
116.9	100°		
136.0	110°		
157.1	120°		
179.0	130°		

Fig. 1 Pressure-temperature relationship. Conditions equivalent to 30 mph or 1750 engine RPM

After disconnecting gauge lines, check the valve areas to be sure service valves are correctly seated and Schraeder valves, if used, are not leaking.

EXERCISE SYSTEM

An important fact most owners ignore is that A/C units must be used periodically. Manufacturers caution that when the air conditioner is not used regularly, particularly during the cold months, it should be turned on for a few minutes once every two or three weeks while the engine is running. This keeps the system in good operating condition.

Checking out the system for the effects of disuse before the onset of summer is one of the most important aspects of A/C servicing.

First clean out the condenser core, mounted in all cases at the front of the radiator. All obstructions, such as leaves, bugs or dirt, must be removed, as they will reduce heat transfer and impair the efficiency of the system. Make sure the space between the condenser and the radiator also is free of foreign matter.

Make certain the evaporator water drain is open. The evaporator cools and dehumidifies the air before it enters the passenger compartment; there, the refrigerant is changed from a liquid to a vapor. As the core cools the air, moisture condenses on it but is prevented from collecting in the evaporator by the water drain.

PERFORMANCE TEST

The system should be operated for at least 15 minutes to allow sufficient time for

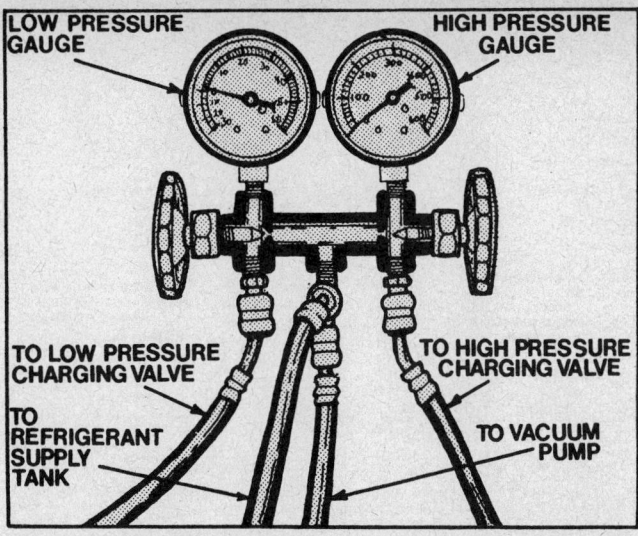

Fig. 2 Manifold gauge set hose connections

all parts to become completely stabilized. Determine if the system is fully charged by the use of test gauges and sight glass if one is installed on system. Head pressure will read from 180 psi to 220 psi or higher, depending upon ambient temperature and the type unit being tested. The sight glass should be free of bubbles if a glass is used in the system. Low side pressures should read approximately 15 psi to 30 psi, again depending on the ambient temperature and the unit being tested. It is not feasible to give a definite reading for all types of systems used, as the type control and component installation used on a particular system will directly influence the pressure readings on the high and low sides, **Fig. 1.**

The high side pressure will definitely be affected by the ambient or outside air temperature. A system that is operating normally will indicate a high side gauge reading between 150-170 psi with an 80°F ambient temperature. The same system will register 210-230 psi with an ambient temperature of 100°. No two systems will register exactly the same, therefore, allowance for variations in head pressures must be considered. Following are the most important normal readings likely to be encountered during the season.

Ambient Temp.	High Side Pressure
80	150-170
90	175-195
95	185-205
100	210-230
105	230-250
110	250-270

RELATIVE TEMPERATURE OF HIGH AND LOW SIDES

The high side of the system should be uniformly hot to the touch throughout. A difference in temperature will indicate a partial blockage of liquid or gas at this point.

The low side of the system should be uniformly cool to the touch with no excessive sweating of the suction line or low side service valve. Excessive sweating or frosting of the low side service valve usually indicates an expansion valve is allowing an excessive amount of refrigerant into the evaporator.

EVAPORATOR OUTPUT

At this point, provided all other inspection tests have been performed, and components have been found to operate as they should, a rapid cooling down of the interior of the vehicle should result. The use of a thermometer is not necessary to determine evaporator output. Bringing all units to the correct operating specifications will insure that the evaporator performs as intended.

DISCHARGING & EVACUATING SYSTEM

REFRIGERANT RECOVERY

The use of refrigerant recovery and recycling stations allows the recovery and reuse of refrigerant after contaminants and moisture have been removed.

When using a recovery or recycling station, follow the manufacturer's operating instructions, noting the following:

1. **Use extreme caution and observe all safety and service precautions related to use of refrigerants.**
2. Connect refrigerant recycling station hose(s) to vehicle A/C service port(s) and recovery station inlet fitting. Hoses used should have shut off devices or check valve within 12 inches of hose ends to minimize introduction of air into recycling station and to minimize amount of refrigerant release when hose(s) is disconnected.
3. Turn recycling station On to start recovery process. Allow recycling station to pump refrigerant from A/C system until station pressure gauge indicates vacuum.

4. After vehicle A/C system has been evacuated, close station inlet valve, if equipped.
5. Turn station Off. On some stations the pump will automatically be turned Off by a low pressure switch.
6. Allow vehicle A/C system to remain closed for approximately two minutes. Observe vacuum level indicated on gauge. If pressure does not rise, disconnect recycling station hose(s).
7. If system pressure rises, repeat steps 3 through 6 until vacuum level remains stable for two minutes.
8. Service A/C system as necessary, then evacuate and recharge A/C system.

DISCHARGING SYSTEM

1. Connect gauges into system, **Fig. 2**, and adjust controls for maximum cooling. This is necessary when the system has not been operating to return excess oil to the compressor.
2. Operate engine for 10 to 15 minutes to stabilize the system at 1500-1750 RPM.
3. Adjust engine speed to slow idle, then shut off engine and controls.
4. Open low side hand manifold valve slightly, using a container to catch oil and refrigerant. Do not discharge the refrigerant near an open flame as a toxic gas (phosgene) can result.
5. Allow all refrigerant to discharge through the low side fitting only. **Open hand valve(s) only enough to bleed refrigerant from system. Too rapid purging will draw excessive oil from compressor and system.**
6. When refrigerant ceases to bleed from the discharge hose on the low side, crack open the high side hand valve to check for any remaining pressure. If pressure does exist, allow high side to discharge slowly. This condition indicates a high side restriction, and it must be diagnosed and corrected before evacuating and charging the system.

EVACUATE SYSTEM WITH VACUUM PUMP

Vacuum pumps suitable for removing air and moisture from A/C systems are commercially available. A specification for system pump-down used here is 28 to 29 1/2 inches vacuum. This reading can be attained at or near sea level only. For each 1000 feet of altitude this operation is being performed, the reading will be 1 inch vacuum lower. As an example, at 5000 feet elevation, only 23-24 1/2 inch of vacuum can be obtained. **The system must be completely discharged before it can be evacuated. Damage to vacuum pump may result if pressurized refrigerant is allowed to enter.**

1. With hand gauges connected into system, remove cap from vacuum hose connector. Install hand gauge manifold center hose to vacuum pump connector. Open low side gauge manifold hand valve only.
2. Ensure low side gauge is calibrated correctly. It should be reading zero. If

not, adjust calibration.

3. Evacuate system with the vacuum pump until the low pressure gauge reads at least 28 inches of vacuum. Continue evacuating system for an additional 15 minutes for routine system servicing or 20 to 30 minutes, if any parts have been replaced.

4. When system evacuation is complete, close low side gauge manifold hand valve, then turn vacuum pump off.

5. Check ability of system to hold vacuum. Watch low side gauge to see that gauge does not rise at a faster rate than 1 inch vacuum every 4 to 5 minutes. If low side gauge rises at too rapid a rate, install partial charge and leak test. Evacuate system again.

6. If system holds vacuum, charge system with refrigerant.

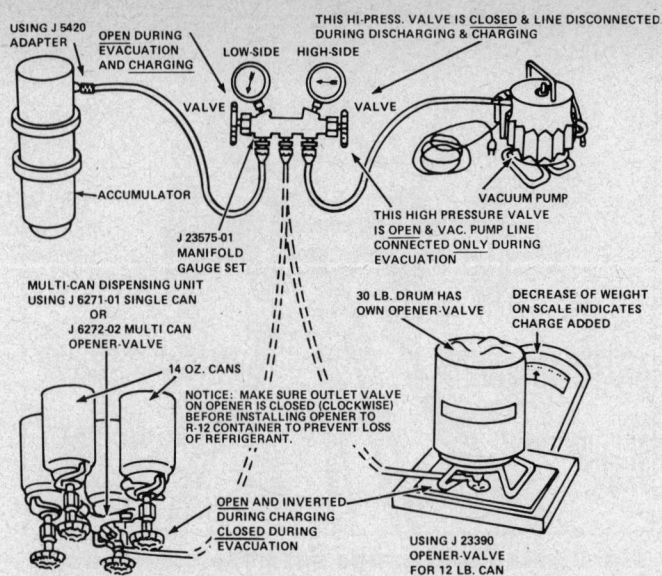

Fig. 3 Charging C.C.O.T. A/C system

EVACUATE SYSTEM USING CHARGING STATION

A vacuum pump is built into the charging station and is constructed to withstand repeated and prolonged use without damage. Complete moisture removal from the system is possible only with a vacuum pump constructed for the purpose.

The system must be completely discharged before it can be evacuated. Damage to the vacuum pump may result if pressurized refrigerant is allowed to enter.

1. Connect hose to vacuum pump, if system was discharged through charging station.

2. Open low side gauge hand valve of charging station.

3. Connect station into 110 volt current.

4. Turn vacuum pump on according to instructions for specific station being used.

5. Evacuate system with the vacuum pump until the low pressure gauge reads at least 28 inches of vacuum. Continue evacuating system for an additional 15 minutes for routine system servicing or 20 to 30 minutes, if any parts have been replaced.

6. Close low side gauge hand valve, then turn vacuum pump off.

7. Check ability of system to hold vacuum. Watch low side gauge to see that gauge does not rise at a faster rate than 1 inch vacuum every 4 to 5 minutes. If low side gauge rises at too rapid a rate, install partial charge and leak test. Then evacuate system again.

8. If system holds vacuum, charge system with refrigerant.

CHARGING THE SYSTEM

USING CHARGING STATION J-23500-01

Use instructions provided with charging station with the following exceptions:

1. Do not connect high pressure line to A/C system.

2. Always keep high pressure valve closed on charging station.

3. Perform all evacuation and charging through accumulator low-side pressure service fitting.

Use of these procedures will prevent charging station from being accidentally exposed to high-side vehicle system pressure.

USING DISPOSABLE CANS OR REFRIGERANT DRUM

Never use these cans to charge into the high pressure side of the system (compressor discharge port) or into a system that is at high temperature, because the high system pressures could be transferred into the charging can causing it to explode.

If R-12 drum is used, place on scale and note total weight before charging. During charging, watch scale to determine amount of R-12 used.

If 14 ounce R-12 cans are used, close tapping valve, then attach cans following instructions included with manifold adaptor.

Charging Of System

1. Start engine and allow to warm up (choke off, normal idle). Set A/C control lever to OFF.

2. With R-12 drum or cans inverted, open R-12 supply valve and allow 1 lb. of liquid R-12 to flow into system through low-side service fitting on accumulator, **Fig. 3.**

3. When 1 lb. of refrigerant has entered system, engage compressor by setting A/C lever to NORM and blower switch to HI to draw in remainder of charge. Cooling condenser with a large fan will speed up charging procedure by maintaining condenser temperature below charging cylinder temperature.

4. Close refrigerant supply valve and run engine for 30 seconds to clear lines and gauges.

5. With engine running, remove charging low side hose adapter from accumulator service fitting. Unscrew rapidly to avoid excessive refrigerant loss. **Do not remove a gauge line from its adapter when line is connected to A/C system. To disconnect line, always remove line adapter from service fitting. Do not remove charging hose at gauge set while attached to accumulator, as system will be discharged due to depressed Schraeder valve.**

6. Replace protective cap on accumulator fitting and turn engine off.

7. Check system for leaks.

8. Start engine and check for proper system pressures.

System Service

INDEX

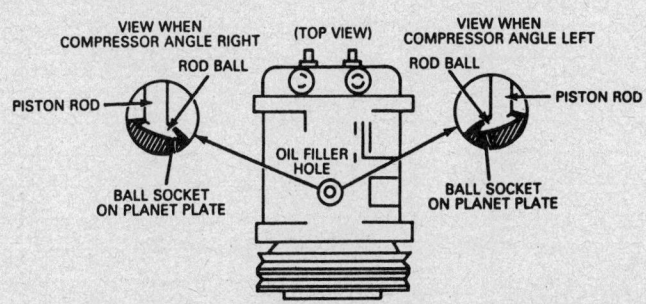

Fig. 1   Positioning internal components of compressor

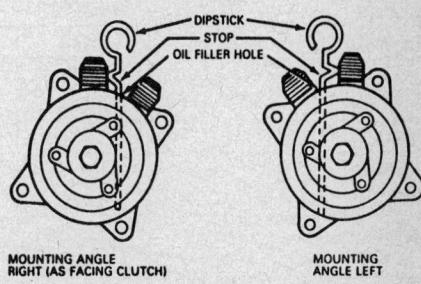

Fig. 2   Checking compressor oil level

MOUNTING ANGLE DEGREE	ACCEPTABLE OIL LEVEL IN INCREMENTS
	505
0	4-6
10	6-8
20	8-10
30	10-11
40	11-12
50	12-13
60	12-13
90	15-16

Fig. 3   Compressor oil level specifications

OIL CHARGE

When replacing certain components of an air conditioning system a oil charge must be added to the system to keep the proper level of refrigerant oil in the system. Refer to "Oil Charge Data Table" for oil charge specifications.

If the refrigerant charge is abruptly lost due to a large refrigerant leak, approximately three ounces of refrigerant oil will be carried out of the system with the refrigerant. Upon replacement of a component which caused a large refrigerant leak, add three ounces of oil to the system plus the amount required for any component replaced as outlined under "Oil Charge Data Table." If possible, add oil directly to the replacement component.

CHARGING VALVE LOCATION

On all models except Chevrolet Nova, the high pressure charging valve is located either on the high pressure line or the muffler, and the low pressure charging valve is located either on the accumulator or low pressure line. On Chevrolet Nova the high pressure charging valve is on the liquid line ahead of the strut tower, and the low pressure charging valve is on the suction line ahead of the strut tower.

CHECKING COMPRESSOR OIL LEVEL

SPRINT

Whenever a system component has been replaced or there is an obvious oil leak, follow the procedure below after repairs have been made.
1. Determine mounting angle as follows:
   a. Position angle gauge across flat surfaces of two front mounting ears, then center bubble.
   b. Read mounting angle to closest degree.
2. Remove oil filler plug. Look through oil filler plug hole and rotate clutch front plate to position internal parts as shown in **Fig. 1**.
3. Insert dipstick to its stop position, **Fig. 2**.
4. Remove dipstick, then count increments of oil. Use table in **Fig. 3**, to determine correct oil level for mounting angle of compressor.
5. Adjust oil level as necessary. then install oil filler plug.

OIL CHARGE DATA TABLE

Application			Oil Charge (Fl. Oz.) When replacing component				
Model	Year	Compressor Model	Compressor	Evaporator	Condenser	Accumulator	Receiver
BUICK							
Century	1988	[10]	[6]	2	1	[5]	—
	1989	[10]	[6]	2	1	[14]	—
	1990	[10]	[3]	3	1	[14]	—
Electra	1988–90	HR-6[2]	[3]	3	1	3.5	—
Estate Wagon	1988	R-4[2]	[3]	3	1	3.5	—
	1989	R-4[2]	[6]	3	1	2	—
	1990	R-4[2]	[3]	3	1	3.5	—
LeSabre	1988–90	HR-6[2]	[3]	3	1	3.5	—
Reatta	1988–89	HR-6[2]	[3]	3	1	3.5	—
	1990	HR-6[2]	[19]	3	1	3.5	—
Regal	1988–89	V-5[1]	[3]	3	1	3.5	—
	1990	[20]	[3]	3	1	3.5	—
Riviera	1988–89	HR-6[2]	[3]	3	1	3.5	—
	1990	HR-6[2]	[19]	3	1	3.5	—
Skyhawk	1988	V-5[1]	[3]	1	1	3.5	—
	1989	V-5[1]	[3]	3	1	3.5	—
Skylark	1988	V-5[1]	[3]	1	1	3.5	—
	1989–90	V-5[1]	[3]	3	1	3.5	—
CADILLAC							
Brougham	1988–89	R-4[2]	[6]	3	1	[5]	—
	1990	R-4[2]	[19]	3	1	[5]	—
Cimarron	1988	V-5[1]	[3]	1	1	3.5	—
DeVille	1988–90	HR-6[2]	[3]	3	1	3.5	—
Eldorado	1988–90	HR-6[2]	[6]	3	1	3.5	—
Fleetwood	1988–90	HR-6[2]	[3]	3	1	3.5	—
Seville	1988–90	HR-6[2]	[6]	3	1	3.5	—
CHEVROLET							
Beretta	1988–90	V-5[1]	[4]	2	1	[5]	—
Camaro	1988	R-4[2]	[3]	3	1	3.5	—
	1989	R-4[2]	[6]	3	1	2	—
	1990	R-4[2]	[3]	3	1	3.5	—
Caprice	1988	R-4[2]	[3]	3	1	3.5	—
	1989	R-4[2]	[6]	3	1	2	—
	1990	R-4[2]	[3]	3	1	3.5	—
Cavalier	1988	V-5[1]	[3]	1	1	3.5	—
	1989–90	V-5[1]	[3]	3	1	3.5	—
Celebrity	1988–90	V-5[1]	[3]	3	1	3.5	—
Corsica	1988–90	V-5[1]	[4]	2	1	[5]	—
Corvette	1988	10PA20[2]	[3]	3	1	3.5	—
	1989	10PA20[2]	[6]	2	1	[15]	—
	1990	10PA20[2]	[6]	3	1	3.5	—
Lumina	1990	V-5[1]	[3]	3	1	3.5	—
Monte Carlo	1988	R-4[2]	[3]	3	1	3.5	—
Nova	1988	—	[4]	—	1.4–1.7	—	.7
Spectrum	1988	DKS-13G[2]	[7]	1	.67	.67	—
Sprint	1988	—	[8]	—	.7–1.0	—	.4

Continued

OIL CHARGE DATA TABLE —Continued

Application			Oil Charge (Fl. Oz.) When replacing component				
Model	Year	Compressor Model	Compressor	Evaporator	Condenser	Accumulator	Receiver
GEO							
Metro	1989–90	—	⑧	—	.7–1.0	—	.4
Prizm	1990	—	⑯	1.4–1.7	1.4–1.7	—	.7
Spectrum	1989	DKS-13G②	⑦	1	.67	.67	—
Storm	1990	—	—	1.7	1	—	1
OLDSMOBILE							
Custom Cruiser	1988	R-4②	⑨	3	1	⑤	—
	1989	R-4②	⑥	3	1	2	—
	1990	R-4②	③	3	1	3.5	—
Cutlass Calais	1988	V-5①	③	1	1	3.5	—
	1989–90	V-5①	③	3	1	3.5	—
Cutlass Ciera	1988	⑩	⑥	2	1	⑤	—
	1989–90	⑩	⑰	⑱	1	⑭	—
Cutlass Cruiser	1988	⑩	⑥	2	1	⑤	—
	1989–90	⑩	⑰	⑱	1	⑭	—
Cutlass Supreme	1988–90	V-5①	③	3	1	3.5	—
Cutlass Supreme Classic	1988	R-4②	⑨	3	1	⑤	—
Firenza	1988	V-5①	③	1	1	3.5	—
Toronado	1988–89	HR-6②	③	3	1	3.5	—
	1990	HR-6②	⑲	3	1	3.5	—
Trofeo	1990	HR-6②	⑲	3	1	3.5	—
88	1988–90	HR-6②	③	3	1	3.5	—
98	1988–90	HR-6②	③	3	1	3.5	—
PONTIAC							
Bonneville	1988–90	HR-6②	③	3	1	3.5	—
Fiero	1988	⑫	③	3	1	3.5	—
Firebird	1988	R-4②	③	3	1	3.5	—
	1989	R-4②	⑥	3	1	2	—
	1990	R-4②	③	3	1	3.5	—
Grand Am	1988	⑬	③	1	1	3.5	—
	1989	⑬	③	3	1	3.5	—
	1990	V-5①	③	3	1	3.5	—
Grand Prix	1988–90	V-5①	③	3	1	3.5	—
LeMans	1988–90	V-5①	③	3	1	3.5	—
Safari	1988	R-4②	③	3	1	3.5	—
	1989	R-4②	⑥	3	1	2	—
Sunbird	1988	⑪	③	1	1	3.5	—
	1989–90	⑪	③	3	1	3.5	—
6000	1988–90	V-5①	③	3	1	3.5	—

①—Variable displacement compressor.
②—Fixed displacement compressor.
③—Drain oil from old compressor and measure, then drain new compressor. If more than one ounce is drained from old compressor, add same amount to new compressor. If less than one ounce is drained from compressor, add two ounces.

④—Drain oil from old compressor and measure, then drain new compressor. Add same amount of oil to new compressor as drained from old compressor.

OIL CHARGE DATA TABLE—Continued

⑤—Drain oil from accumulator and measure. Add same amount of oil to new accumulator, plus two ounces. If no oil is drained, add two ounces to new accumulator.

⑥—Drain oil from old compressor and measure, then drain new compressor. Add same amount to new compressor as drained from old compressor, plus one ounce.

⑦—Drain oil from old compressor and measure, then drain new compressor. If more than two ounces are drained from old compressor, add same amount to new compressor. If less than two ounces are drained from compressor, add two ounces.

⑧—Replacement compressors contain 2.7 ounces. Drain 1.4 ounces from new compressor before installing.

⑨—Drain oil from old compressor and measure, then drain new compressor. If more than three ounces are drained from old compressor, add same amount to new compressor. If less than three ounces are drained from compressor, add three ounces.

⑩—2.5L and 2.8L engines are equipped with V-5 compressors. 3.3L and 3.8L engines are equipped with HR-6 compressor.

⑪—2.0L less turbocharged engine is equipped with V-5 compressor. 2.0L turbocharged engine is equipped with HR-6 compressor.

⑫—2.5L engine is equipped with V-5 compressor. 2.8L engine is equipped with HR-6 compressor.

⑬—2.0L engine is equipped with HR-6 compressor. 2.3L and 2.5L engines are equipped with V-5 compressors.

⑭—On HR-6 equipped models, drain oil from accumulator and measure. Add same amount of oil to new accumulator, plus two ounces. If no oil is drained, add two ounces to new accumulator. On V-5 models add 3.5 ounces to new accumulator.

⑮—Drain oil from accumulator and measure. Add same amount of oil to new accumulator, plus three ounces. If no oil is drained, add two ounces to new accumulator.

⑯—Drain oil from old compressor and measure, then drain new compressor. Add same amount of oil to new compressor as drained from old compressor, plus .7 ounce.

⑰—On HR-6 equipped models, drain oil from old compressor and measure, then drain new compressor. Add same amount to new compressor as drained from old compressor, plus one ounce. On V-5 equipped models, drain oil from old compressor and measure, then drain new compressor. If more than one ounce is drained from old compressor, add same amount to new compressor. If less than one ounce is drained from compressor, add two ounces.

⑱—On HR-6 equipped models, add two ounces. On V-5 equipped models, add three ounces.

⑲—Drain oil from old compressor and measure, then drain new compressor. Amount drained from old compressor should not be more than five ounces. Add same amount of oil to new compressor as drained from old compressor, plus enough extra oil to equal a total of six ounces.

⑳—3.1L engine is equipped with V-5 compressor. 3.8L engine is equipped with HR-6 compressor.

A/C Data Table

| Model | Year | Refrigerant Capacity, Lbs. | Refrigeration Oil | | | Compressor Clutch Air Gap Inch |
			Viscosity	Total System Capacity, Ounces	Compressor Oil Level	
BUICK						
Century	1988–90	2.75	525	8	①	.015–.025
Electra	1988–90	2.40	525	8	①	.015–.025
Estate Wagon	1988–90	3.50	525	6	①	.020–.040
LeSabre	1988	2.40	525	8	①	.015–.025
	1989–90	2.87	525	8	①	.015–.025
Reatta	1988–90	2.40	525	8	①	.015–.025
Regal	1988–89	2.25	525	8	①	.015–.025
	1990	④	525	8	①	.015–.025
Riviera	1988–90	2.40	525	8	①	.015–.025
Skyhawk	1988–89	2.25	525	8	①	.015–.025
Skylark	1988–90	2.25	525	8	①	.015–.025
CADILLAC						
Brougham	1988	3.50	525	6	①	.020–.040
	1989–90	3.30	525	6	①	.020–.040
Cimarron	1988	2.25	525	8	①	.015–.025
DeVille	1988–89	2.40	525	8	①	.015–.025
	1990	2.87	525	8	①	.015–.025
Eldorado	1988–90	2.40	525	8	①	.015–.025
Fleetwood	1988–89	2.40	525	8	①	.015–.025
	1990	2.87	525	8	①	.015–.025
Seville	1988–90	2.40	525	8	①	.015–.025
CHEVROLET						
Beretta	1988–90	2.75	525	8	①	.015–.025
Camaro	1988	2.25	525	6	①	.020–.040
	1989–90	3.50	525	6	①	.020–.040
Caprice	1988–90	3.50	525	6	①	.020–.040
Cavalier	1988–90	2.25	525	8	①	.015–.025
Celebrity	1988–90	2.75	525	8	①	.015–.025
Corsica	1988–90	2.75	525	8	①	.015–.025
Corvette	1988–89	2.75	500	8	①	.014–.026
	1990	2.25	500	8	①	.014–.026
Lumina	1990	2.25	525	8	①	.015–.025
Monte Carlo	1988	3.25	525	6	①	.020–.040
Nova	1988	—	500	—	—	.016–.028
Spectrum	1988	1.80	500	3.35	①	.010–.020
Sprint	1988	1.50	—	—	②	.016–.031
GEO						
Metro	1989–90	1.10	—	2.7	①	.016–.028
Prizm	1990	1.10	—	—	①	.014–.026
Spectrum	1989	1.80	500	3.35	①	.010–.020
Storm	1990	1.10	—	—	—	—

Continued

A/C DATA TABLE—Continued

Model	Year	Refrigerant Capacity, Lbs.	Refrigeration Oil			Compressor Clutch Air Gap Inch
			Viscosity	Total System Capacity, Ounces	Compressor Oil Level	
OLDSMOBILE						
Custom Cruiser	1988–90	3.50	525	6	①	.020–.040
Cutlass Calais	1988–90	2.25	525	8	①	.015–.025
Cutlass Ciera	1988–90	2.75	525	8	①	.015–.025
Cutlass Cruiser	1988–90	2.75	525	8	①	.015–.025
Cutlass Supreme	1988–90	2.25	525	8	①	.015–.025
Cutlass Supreme Classic	1988	3.25	525	6	①	.020–.040
Firenza	1988	2.25	525	8	①	.015–.025
Toronado	1988–90	2.40	525	8	①	.015–.025
Trofeo	1990	2.40	525	8	①	.015–.025
88	1988	2.40	525	8	①	.015–.025
	1989–90	2.87	525	8	①	.015–.025
98	1988–90	2.40	525	8	①	.015–.025
PONTIAC						
Bonneville	1988	2.40	525	8	①	.015–.025
	1989–90	2.87	525	8	①	.015–.025
Fiero	1988	2.50	525	8	①	.015–.025
Firebird	1988	2.25	525	6	①	.020–.040
	1989–90	3.50	525	6	①	.020–.040
Grand Am	1988–90	2.25	525	8	①	.015–.025
Grand Prix	1988–90	2.25	525	8	①	.015–.025
LeMans	1988–90	2.20	525	8	①	.015–.025
Safari	1988–89	3.50	525	6	①	.020–.040
Sunbird	1988–90	2.25	525	8	①	.015–.025
6000	1988–90	③	525	8	①	.015–.025

①—Note that "Oil Level" cannot be checked. Refer to total capacity in ounces.

②—Refer to text.

③—Except STE models, 2.75 lbs.; STE models, 2.25 lbs.

④—Models less 3800 engine, 2.25 lbs.; models w/3800 engine, 2.75 lbs.

ENGINE COOLING FANS

TABLE OF CONTENTS

Variable Speed Fans

INDEX

Fig. 1   Typical variable-speed fan installed

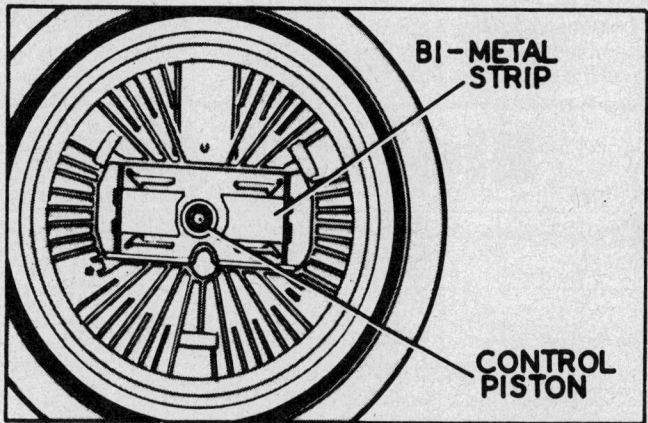

Fig. 2   Variable-speed fan with flat bi-metal thermostatic spring

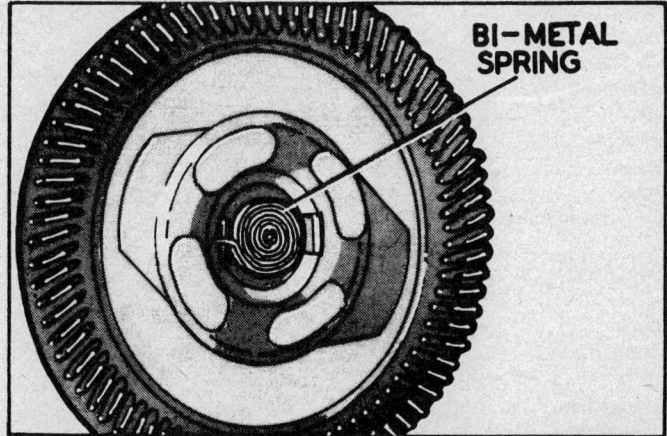

Fig. 3   Variable-speed fan with coiled bi-metal thermostatic spring

DESCRIPTION

The fan drive clutch, **Fig. 1,** is a fluid coupling containing silicone oil. Fan speed is regulated by the torque-carrying capacity of the silicone oil. The more silicone oil in the coupling the greater the fan speed, and the less silicone oil the slower the fan speed.

Two types of fan drive clutches are in use. On one, **Fig. 2,** a bi-metallic strip and control piston on the front of the fluid cou-pling regulates the amount of silicone oil entering the coupling. The bi-metallic strip bows outward with an increase in sur-rounding temperature and allows a piston to move outward. The piston opens a valve regulating the flow of silicone oil into the coupling from a reserve chamber. The silicone oil is returned to the reserve chamber through a bleed hole when the valve is closed.

On the other type of fan drive clutch, **Fig. 3,** a heat-sensitive, bi-metal spring con-nected to an opening plate brings about a similar result. Both units cause the fan speed to increase with a rise in tempera-ture and to decrease as the temperature goes down.

In some cases a Flex-Fan is used in-stead of a Fan Drive Clutch. Flexible blades vary the volume of air being drawn through the radiator, automatically in-creasing the pitch at low engine speeds.

FAN DRIVE CLUTCH TEST

Do not operate the engine until the fan has been first checked for possible cracks and separations.

Run the engine at a fast idle speed (1000 RPM) until normal operating tem-perature is reached. This process can be speeded up by blocking off the front of the radiator with cardboard. Regardless of temperatures, the unit must be operated for at least five minutes immediately be-fore being tested.

Stop the engine and, using a glove or a cloth to protect the hand, immediately check the effort required to turn the fan. If considerable effort is required, it can be assumed that the coupling is operating satisfactorily. If very little effort is required to turn the fan, it is an indication that the coupling is not operating properly and should be replaced.

If the clutch fan is the coiled bi-metal spring type, it may be tested while the vehicle is being driven. To check, disconnect the bi-metal spring, **Fig. 4**, and rotate 90° counterclockwise. This disables the temperature-controlled free-wheeling feature and the clutch performs like a conventional fan. If this cures the overheating condition, replace the clutch fan.

SERVICE PROCEDURE

To prevent silicone fluid from draining into fan drive bearing, do not store or place drive unit on bench with rear of shaft pointing downward.

The removal procedure for either type of fan clutch assembly is generally the same for all cars. Merely unfasten the unit from the water pump and remove the assembly from the car.

The type of unit shown in **Fig. 2** may be partially disassembled for inspection and cleaning. Take off the capscrews that hold

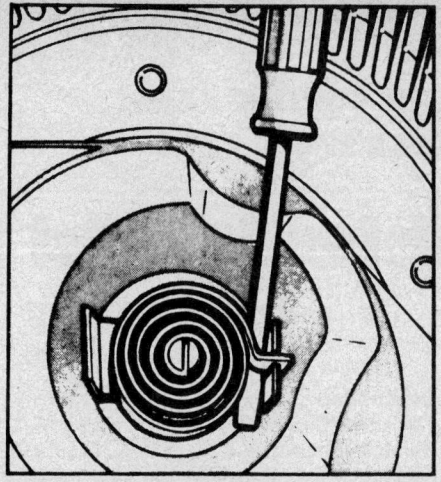

Fig. 4   Disconnecting bi-metal spring

the assembly together and separate the fan from the drive clutch. Next remove the metal strip on the front by pushing one end of it toward the fan clutch body so it clears the retaining bracket. Then push the strip to the side so that its opposite end will spring out of place. Now remove the small control piston underneath it.

Check the piston for free movement of the coupling device. If the piston sticks, clean it with emery cloth. If the bi-metal strip is damaged, replace the entire unit. These strips are not interchangeable.

When reassembling, install the control piston so that the projection on the end of it will contact the metal strip. Then install the metal strip. After reassembly, clean the clutch drive with a cloth soaked in solvent. Avoid dipping the clutch assembly in any type of liquid. Install the assembly in the reverse order of removal.

The coil spring type of fan clutch cannot be disassembled, serviced or repaired. If it does not function properly it must be replaced with a new unit.

Electric Cooling Fans

NOTE: Wire Code Identification and Symbol Identification located in the front of this manual can be used as an aid when using wiring circuits found in this section.

INDEX

Continued

INDEX—Continued

Continued

INDEX—Continued

On models equipped with electric engine cooling fans, the battery ground cable should be disconnected whenever underhood service is performed.

NOVA

DIAGNOSIS

Refer to **Fig. 1** when testing this system.

ON-VEHICLE

Temperature Below 181°F

1. Turn ignition switch onto confirm that fan stops. If fan does not stop, check fan relay and temperature switch, then check for separated connector or severed wire between relay and temperature switch.
2. Disconnect temperature switch wire and confirm that fan rotates. If fan does not rotate, check fan relay, fan motor, ignition relay and fuse and check for short circuit between fan relay and temperature switch.

Temperature Above 194°F

Start engine and raise engine temperature to above 194°F. Confirm that fan rotates. If not, replace temperature switch.

OFF-VEHICLE

1. Inspect temperature switch as follows:
   a. Using ohmmeter, ensure there is no continuity when coolant temperature is above 194°F.
   b. Ensure there is continuity when coolant temperature is below 181°F.
2. Inspect ignition relay. located in en-

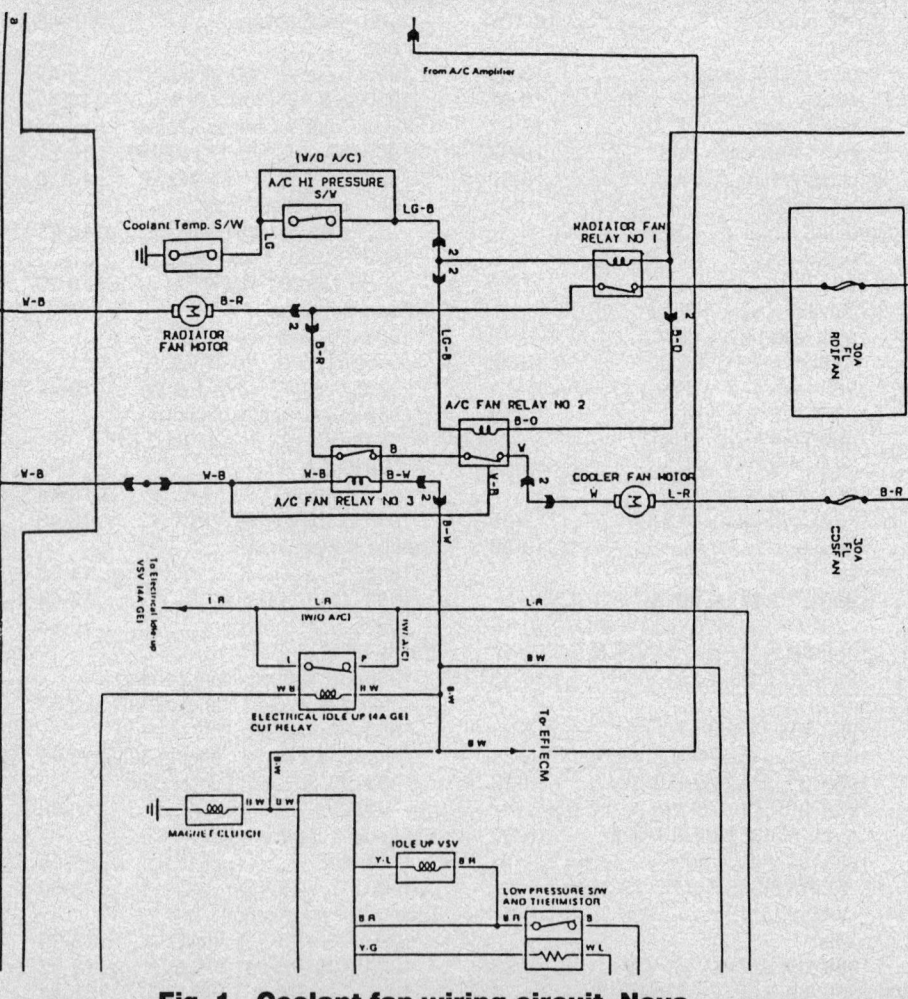

Fig. 1   Coolant fan wiring circuit. Nova

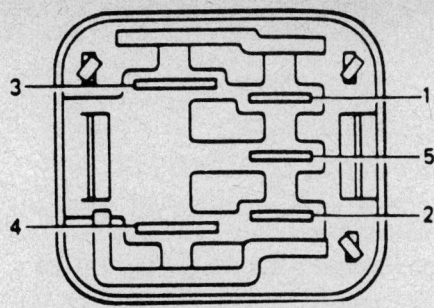

Fig. 2 Ignition relay terminal identification. Nova

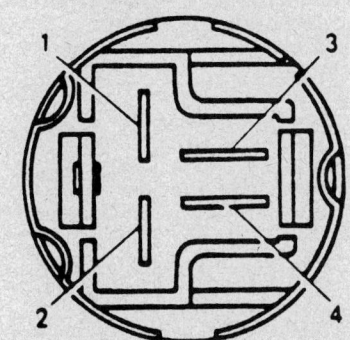

Fig. 3 Fan motor relay terminal identification. Nova

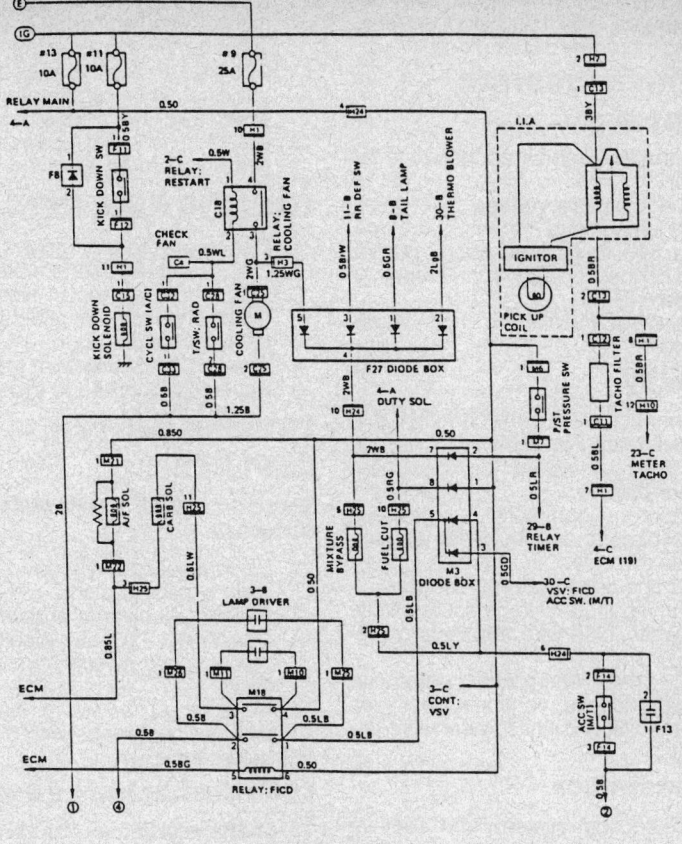

Fig. 4 Coolant fan wiring circuit. Spectrum

gine compartment relay box, as follows:

  a. Using ohmmeter, measure resistance between terminals 1 and 2, **Fig. 2**. Resistance should be 50-80 ohms.

  b. Connect 12 volt battery across terminals 1 and 2 and, using ohmmeter, ensure there is continuity between terminals 3 and 4 and no continuity between terminals 4 and 5.

  c. If results in steps a and b are not as specified, replace ignition relay.

3. Inspect fan motor relay, located in engine compartment relay box, as follows:

  a. Using ohmmeter, measure resistance between terminals 1 and 2, **Fig. 3**. Resistance should be 50-80 ohms.

  b. Connect 12 volt battery across terminals 1 and 2 and, using ohmmeter, check for continuity between terminals 3 and 4.

  c. If results are not as specified in steps a and b, replace fan motor relay.

4. To inspect fan motor, connect battery and ammeter to fan motor connector and check that motor rotates smoothly and current is 3.4-5 amps.

FAN, REPLACE

1. Disconnect battery ground cable.
2. Disconnect connector at fan motor.
3. Remove fan, then the fan shroud.
4. Separate fan blade from motor.
5. Reverse procedure to install.

SPECTRUM

SYSTEM DESCRIPTION

Radiator cooling fan operation is controlled by a cooling fan relay, radiator mounted thermosensor and the A/C compressor cycling switch. Battery voltage is applied to the fan relay control coil through the restart relay and voltage is applied to the relay switch circuit through a non-switched fuse in the fuse panel. The relay control coil circuit is completed to ground either through the thermosensor or through the A/C compressor clutch cycling switch.

During normal operation the thermosensor contacts close when coolant temperature is above 185°F and voltage is applied to the cooling fan motor through the relay switching circuit. When coolant thermosensor contacts are open and the temperature is below 185°F, the thermosensor cooling fan does not operate. However, when the A/C clutch is energized the fan relay coil circuit is completed to ground through the A/C switch and the cooling fan operates regardless of coolant temperature.

DIAGNOSIS & TESTING

Refer to **Fig. 4** when testing this system.

SYSTEM TEST

1. Start engine and run until it reaches normal operating temperature.
2. Monitor coolant temperature using suitable thermometer and observe cooling fan operation.
3. Cooling fan should begin to operate when coolant temperature reaches 186-192°F., and fan should stop running when coolant temperature drops to 178-183°F.
4. If fan fails to operate, proceed as follows:

  a. Ground white/blue fan test lead located in harness at left rear of engine compartment.

  b. If fan operates, replace thermosensor and recheck system operation.

  c. If fan fails to operate, check for blown fuse, defective relay, damaged or disconnected wiring, disconnected fan ground lead or defective fan motor.

5. **On models with A/C**, place control in maximum cooling position.
6. If cooling fan does not operate when compressor clutch is engaged, check

for open circuit between fan relay and A/C switch, defective switch or defective compressor clutch diode.

COMPONENT TESTING

Fan Motor

1. Disconnect electrical connector to fan motor.
2. Connect battery voltage to terminal using jumper wire.
3. If fan fails to operate, check ground strap connection, **Fig. 4,** and repair as needed.
4. If ground is satisfactory, motor is defective.

Fan Relay

1. Disconnect electrical connector and remove relay. **Fan relay is located in left front of engine compartment above battery.**
2. Connect ohmmeter between white/black and white/green wire terminals on relay.
3. Meter should indicate no continuity.
4. Connect battery voltage across white and white/blue wire terminals on relay.
5. With relay energized, ohmmeter should indicate continuity between white/black and white/green wire terminals.

Thermosensor

1. Drain cooling system and remove thermosensor from radiator, **Fig. 4.**
2. Connect an ohmmeter between sensor terminals.
3. Heat thermosensor in suitable solution while observing ohmmeter.
4. Meter should indicate continuity when temperature reaches 186-192°F.
5. Allow sensor to cool while observing meter. Meter should indicate no continuity as temperature drops below 178-183°F.
6. If sensor fails to operate as outlined, sensor is defective.

SPRINT & METRO

TROUBLESHOOTING

Fan Motor Does Not Operate

1. Blown fuse.
2. Defective fan motor.
3. Defective thermo switch.

Fan Motor Operates Continuously

1. Defective thermo switch.

SYSTEM DIAGNOSIS

Fan Motor

1. Apply battery voltage to fan motor electrical connector.
2. If motor fails to operate, it should be replaced.

Thermo Switch

1. Connect an ohmmeter to thermo switch.
2. Immerse switch in water, then heat

water gradually and check for continuity. Continuity should exist when water temperature reaches a range of 201-208°F and above, and should not exist when temperatures are between 192-199°F and below.
3. If switch does not operate as specified, it should be replaced.

COOLING FAN, REPLACE

1. Disconnect battery ground cable.
2. Disconnect air cleaner inlet tube.
3. Disconnect fan motor electrical connector, then remove attaching screws, fan motor and shroud.
4. Remove fan blade from motor.
5. Reverse procedure to install.

THERMO SWITCH, REPLACE

Except 1988 Turbocharged Models

1. Disconnect battery ground cable, then drain cooling system.
2. Remove air cleaner and air inlet tube.
3. Disconnect switch electrical lead, then remove switch from thermostat cap.
4. Reverse procedure to install, wrapping switch threads with sealing tape before installation.

1988 Turbocharged Models

1. Disconnect battery ground cable, then drain cooling system.
2. Remove throttle body intake air hose.
3. Remove fan thermo switch coupler and thermo switch.

CIMARRON

SYSTEM DESCRIPTION

The coolant fan is controlled by the coolant fan relay. The coolant fan relay is electrically operated by the ECM which receives input signals from the coolant temperature sensor and A/C system.

The ECM activates the coolant fan relay when, the engine coolant is above 223°F, the A/C is turned On, coolant temperature sensor fails, A/C pressure exceeds 200 psi or the vehicle speed is less than 74 mph. Any of these input signals causes the ECM to ground circuit 335, energizing the coolant fan relay. The coolant fan runs with battery voltage across its terminals.

TROUBLESHOOTING

1. If coolant fan does not operate, check ALT/FAN fuse.
2. If coolant fan runs with ignition switch Off, replace coolant fan relay.
3. If coolant fan runs with ignition switch in RUN position, check that ECM connector C1 pin D12 is grounded through the coolant fan A/C pressure switch.

SYSTEM CHECK

1. With engine cool and idling and mode selector in NORM position, coolant fan should turn On.

2. With engine cool, move mode selector to Off, coolant fan should turn Off after 30 seconds.
3. With engine warm, run engine at a fast idle for several minutes. Coolant fan should turn On.

SYSTEM DIAGNOSIS

Refer to **Fig. 5** when performing diagnostic procedures on this systems.

Coolant Fan Does Not Run

1. With the ignition switch in RUM position, connect a fused jumper between terminal B and ground at the ALDL connector. If coolant fan turns On, problem is ECM related.
2. If coolant fan does not operate, disconnect C3 connector from the ECM and connect a fused jumper between terminal E8 and ground then turn ignition switch to RUN position. If coolant fan runs, problem is ECM related.
3. If coolant fan does not operate, leave jumper from step 2 in place and turn ignition switch to RUN position then disconnect coolant fan relay and connect a test lamp between the following terminals:
   a. Terminal 5 and ground. If lamp does not light, check ALT/FAN fuse and brown/white wire for an open.
   b. Terminals 5 and 2. If lamp does not light, check dark green/white wire for an open.
   c. Terminal 1 and ground. If lamp does not light, check red wire and fusible link D for an open.
4. If test lamp lights in steps 3a through 3c, connect a fused jumper between terminals 1 and 4 on the disconnected fan relay connector. If coolant fan runs, replace coolant fan relay.
5. If coolant fan does not run, leave jumper in place from step 4 and connect a test lamp between the following terminals:
   a. Terminal B and ground. If lamp does not light, check black/red wire for an open.
   b. Terminals B and A. If lamp does not light, check black wire for an open.
   c. If test lamp lights in step a and b, replace coolant fan.

Coolant Fan Runs Continuously

1. Place ignition switch in RUN position and connect a test lamp between terminals 5 and 2 of the disconnected coolant fan relay connector. If test lamp does not light, replace coolant fan relay.
2. If test lamp lights, check dark green/white wire for a short to ground. If wire is satisfactory, problem is ECM related.

COOLANT FAN, REPLACE

1. Disconnect battery ground cable.
2. Remove air cleaner and duct assembly.
3. Scribe alignment mark on primary hood latch and remove.

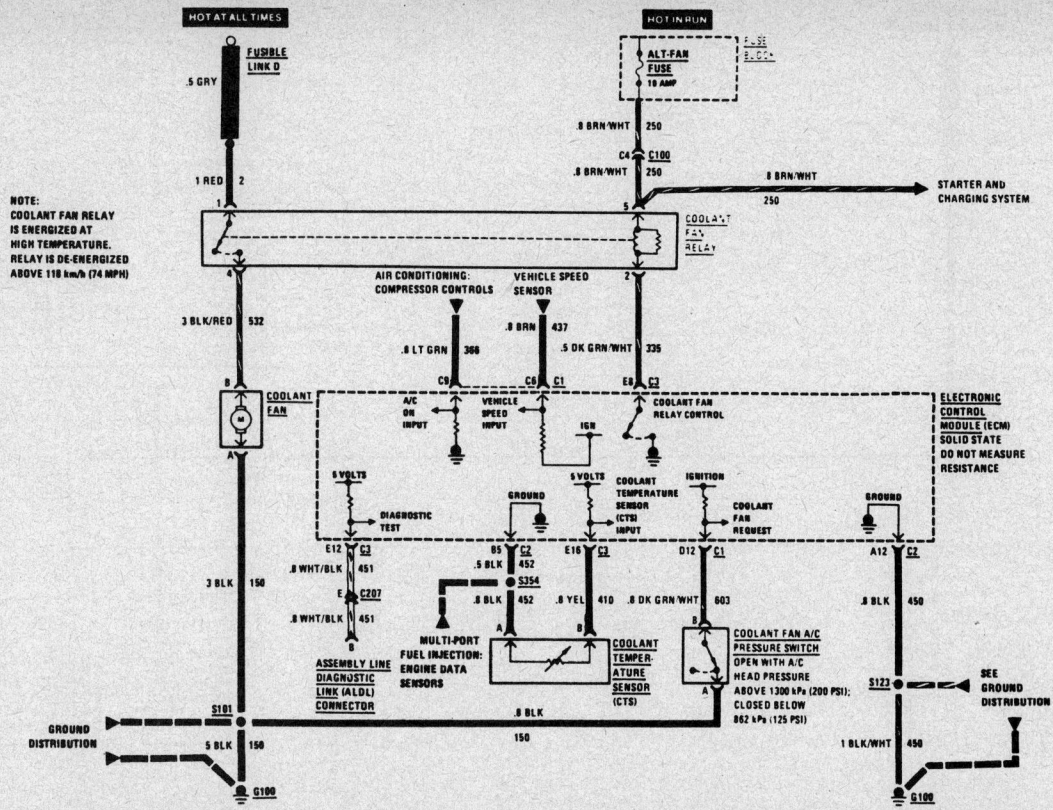

Fig. 5   Coolant fan wiring circuit. 1988 Cimarron, 2.8L/V6-173 VIN W

4. Drain engine coolant to a level below upper radiator hose.
5. Remove radiator upper hose and position out of the way.
6. Remove transaxle cooling lines from radiator.
7. Disconnect coolant fan electrical connector.
8. Remove fan assembly from radiator support.
9. Reverse procedure to install.

BERETTA & CORSICA

SYSTEM DIAGNOSIS

Refer to **Figs. 6 and 7** when performing diagnostic procedures on these systems.

1988 MODELS WITH 2.0L/4-121 ENGINE

1. Turn ignition switch to ON position, engine not operating.
2. Ensure coolant temperature is less than approximately 230°F.
3. Ensure A/C, if equipped, is OFF.
4. Check fan operation. If fan operates, proceed as follows:
   a. Check dark green/white wire (circuit) 335 for short to ground.
   b. Check for faulty relay.
5. If fan does not operate, proceed as follows:
   a. Ground diagnostic terminal and note fan operation.
   b. If fan does not operate, check fuse.
   c. If fuse is blown, check for short to ground in pink/black wire (circuit) 39. If wire is satisfactory, check for

a faulty relay.
   d. If fuse is satisfactory, disconnect relay electrical connector. Connect a suitable test lamp between harness connector terminals 39 pink/black wire and 335 dark green/white wire. If test lamp lights, connect test lamp between harness connector terminal wires (circuits) 2 and ground. If test lamp lights, jump harness connector terminals 2 red wire and 702 black/red wire. Check fan operation. If fan operates, replace relay. If fan does not operate check for an open circuit 702 black/red wire, open ground circuit 150 black wire or a defective fan motor.
   e. If test lamp does not light, connect a test lamp between harness connector terminal 39 pink/black wire and chassis ground.
   f. If test lamp lights, check for an open in dark green/white wire (circuit) 335. If circuit is satisfactory, check ECM terminal E8 or ECM. If test lamp does not light, repair open circuit 39 pink/black wire.

1988 MODELS WITH 2.8L/V6-173 ENGINES

1. Turn ignition switch to ON (engine not operating) and A/C, if equipped, OFF.
2. Ensure coolant temperature is below 212°F.
3. Coolant fan should not be operating. If coolant fan is operating, disconnect fan relay. Fan should stop. If fan stops, connect a suitable test lamp to dark

green/white wire (circuit) 335 and to battery (12 volts). If test lamp lights, circuit 335 is shorted to ground or the ECM is defective. If test lamp does not light, replace relay assembly.
4. If coolant fan does not operate, ground diagnostic terminal. Fan should operate. If coolant fan does not operate, proceed to step 5. If coolant fan operates, re move ground from diagnostic terminal. Start and operate engine at idle. Ensure A/C, if equipped is off. Fan should be OFF (while coolant temperature is below 212°F). If coolant fan operates, replace ECM. If coolant fan does not operate, check A/C system, fan control switch, circuits 935 (for short) and A/C pressure fan control switch.
5. If fan is not operating, disconnect fan control relay. Turn ignition switch to ON (engine not operating). Probe harness terminals A and D with a suitable test lamp connected to ground. If no light ON (one or both), repair open of shot to ground in wire (circuit) that did not light (test lamp light). If test lamp lights for both, ground diagnostic terminal and probe dark green/white wire (circuit) 335 with a test lamp connected to battery (12 volts). If test lamp is OFF, repair open or short in wire (circuit) 335 or faulty connection at ECM or defective ECM. If test lamp lights, jump harness terminals A and E together using a fused jumper wire. Fan should operate. If fan operates, replace relay. If does not operate, connect a test lamp across cooling fan

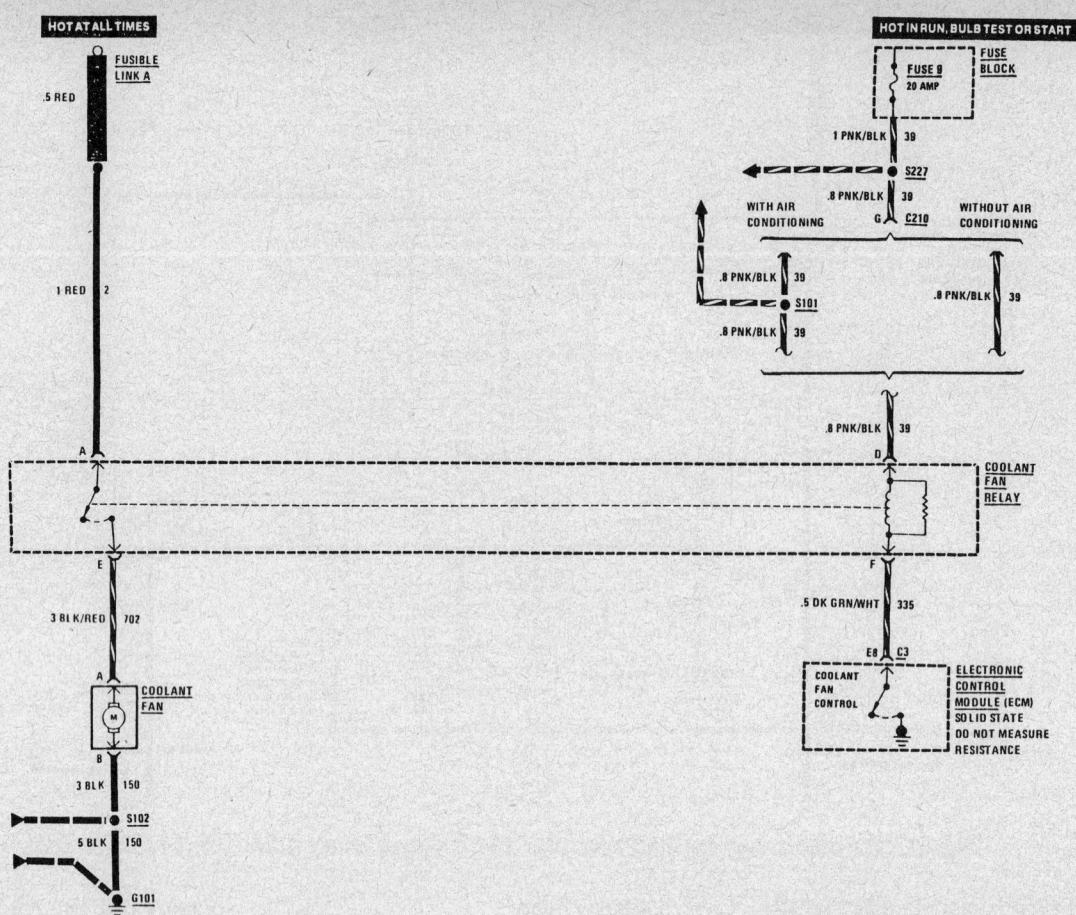

Fig. 6 Coolant fan wiring circuit. 1988 Beretta & Corsica

motor harness connector terminals (with A and E terminals still jumped). If test lamp lights, replace motor. If test lamp is OFF, probe each terminal with a test lamp connected to ground. If light comes on (one), repair open in ground black wire (circuit 150). If test lamp is OFF, repair open in circuit between relay and cooling fan motor.

1989–90 MODELS

1. If coolant fan does not operate, check fuse No. 9 and Fuse Link A.
2. If coolant fan runs with ignition switch in the OFF position, replace the coolant fan relay.

SYSTEM CHECK

1. With engine cold and at idle speed, move A/C selector switch to the NORM position, coolant fan should come on. Move the A/C selector to the OFF position, coolant fan should turn off.
2. Run engine at fast idle for several minutes, coolant fan should come on before coolant temperature indicator comes on or if equipped with temperature gauge before gauge reads H.
3. If coolant fan does not operate as described above refer to "Coolant Fan Does Not Run At All" or "Coolant Fan Does Not Turn Off With Ignition Switch In Run."

Coolant Fan Does Not Run At All

1. With ignition off, connect a fused jumper wire between the Assembly Line Diagnostic Link (ALDL) connector terminal B and ground.
2. Turn ignition switch to the RUN position. If coolant fan does not run, proceed to step 3. If coolant fan runs, problem is ECM related.
3. Turn ignition switch off, then disconnect jumper wire from the ALDL connector.
4. Connect fused jumper wire between coolant fan relay terminal F and ground, turn ignition switch to the RUN position. If coolant fan does not run, proceed to step 5. If coolant fan runs, locate and repair open circuit in dark green/white wire No. 335.
5. Turn ignition switch off, then disconnect jumper wire from coolant fan relay terminal F.
6. Disconnect coolant fan relay connector, connect a test lamp between terminal D pink/black wire and ground. Turn ignition switch to RUN. If test lamp lights, proceed to step 7. If test lamp does not light, check fuse 9, if fuse is satisfactory, locate and repair open circuit in pink/black wire.
7. Connect test lamp between terminals D pink/black wire and F dark green/white wire. If test lamp lights, proceed to step 8. If test lamp does not light, check dark green/white wire for an open circuit, repair if necessary. If circuit is satisfactory, problem is ECM related.
8. Connect test lamp to terminal A red wire and ground. If test lamp lights, proceed to step 9. If test lamp does not light, locate and repair open circuit in red wire.
9. With ignition switch off and coolant fan relay connector disconnected, connect a fused jumper wire between terminal A red wire and terminal E black/red wire. Turn ignition switch to RUN. If coolant fan does not run, proceed to step 10. If coolant fan runs, replace coolant fan relay.
10. With ignition switch in RUN and jumper wire connected as in step 9, connect a test lamp between terminal B black/red wire and ground. If test lamp lights, proceed to step 11. If test lamp does not light, locate and repair open circuit in black/red wire.
11. Connect test lamp between terminal B

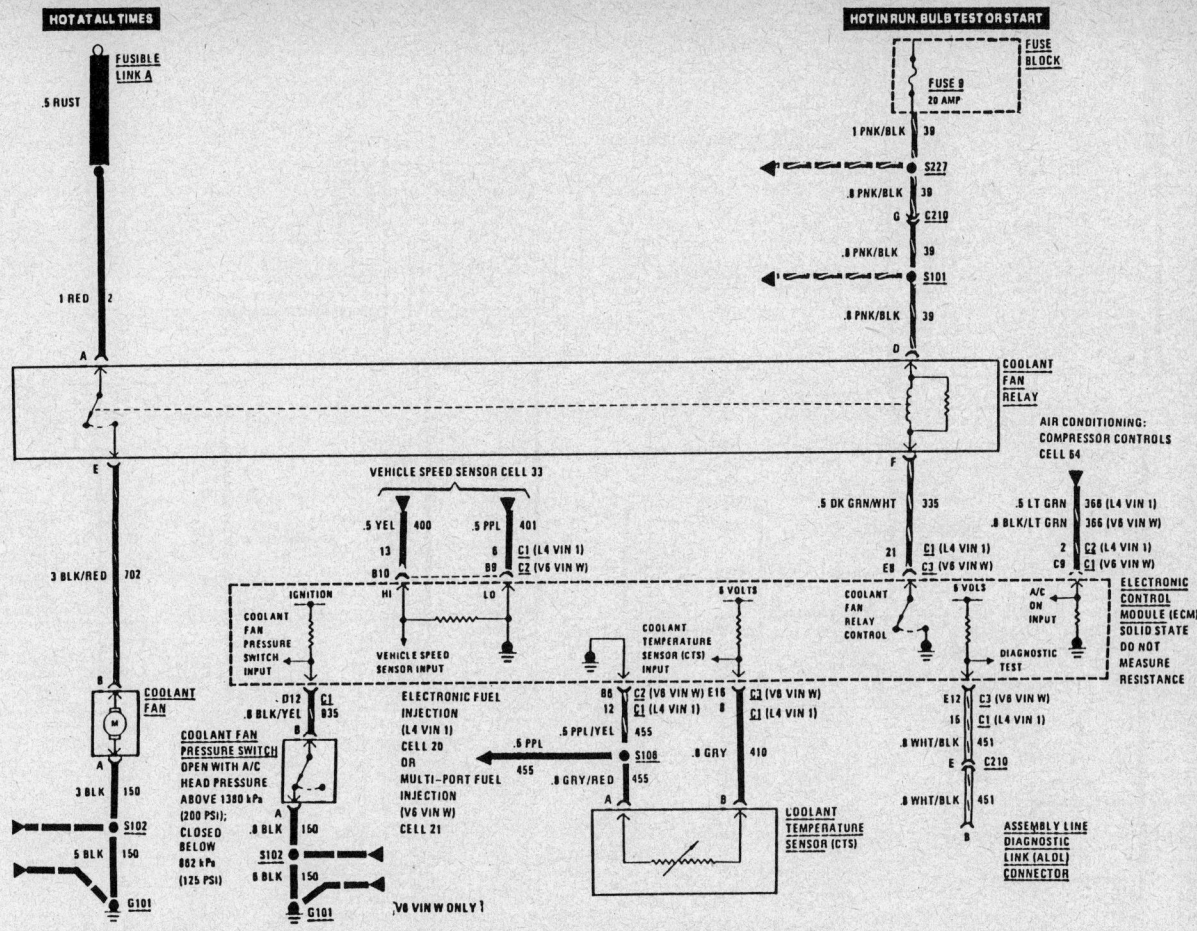

Fig. 7   Coolant fan wiring circuit. 1989–90 Beretta & Corsica

black/red wire and terminal A black wire. If test lamp lights, replace coolant fan. If test lamp does not light, locate and repair open circuit in black wire.

Coolant Fan Does Not Turn Off With Ignition Switch In Run

1. Disconnect coolant fan relay connector, then turn ignition switch to the RUN position.
2. Connect a test lamp between terminal D pink/black wire and terminal F dark green/white wire. If test lamp does not light, replace the coolant fan relay. If test lamp lights, check dark green/white wire for an open circuit. If dark green/white wire is satisfactory, problem is ECM related.

COOLING FAN, REPLACE

1. Disconnect battery ground cable.
2. Disconnect electrical connectors from motor and fan frame.
3. Remove fan assembly from radiator.
4. Reverse procedure to install. **Torque** attaching bolts to 7 ft. lbs.

CELEBRITY & 6000

SYSTEM DESCRIPTION

2.5L/4-151 VIN R

Voltage is available at all times through fusible link A to the coolant fan relay contacts. With ignition switch in RUN position, voltage is available through the C/H fuse to the coolant fan relay coil.

Depending on coolant temperature, the coolant switch fan contact will be open or closed.

With the coolant fan switch contact closed, voltage is applied through the C/H fuse to the coolant fan relay coil, and the coolant fan relay contacts close. Voltage is applied through fusible link A to the coolant fan relay contacts and the coolant fan to ground. The coolant fan operates.

The coolant fan is energized when the A/C compressor operates. This ensures adequate air flow over the A/C condenser.

The coolant fan runs when the function selector is in MAX, NORM or BI-LEVEL position, the A/C low pressure cut-out switch is closed, and the ECM completes a voltage path to ground.

2.8L/V6-173 VIN W & T

Voltage is available at all times through the battery junction block and fusible link F

to the coolant fan relay contacts. With ignition switch in RUN position, voltage is available through C/H fuse to the coolant fan relay coil.

When the ECM receives a signal from the coolant temperature sensor, ground is provided for the coolant fan relay between the module's coolant fan control terminal and ground terminal. Voltage is applied through the C/H fuse to the coolant fan relay coil, and the ECM to ground. The coolant fan relay contacts close. Voltage is applied through the battery junction block to the coolant fan relay contacts, and the coolant fan to ground. The coolant fan operates.

The coolant fan is energized when the A/C compressor operates. This ensures adequate air flow over the A/C condenser.

The coolant fan runs when the A/C high pressure switch closes and the ECM provides ground between the module's coolant fan control terminal and ground terminal.

TROUBLESHOOTING

1. Check C/H fuse.
2. Replace coolant fan relay if coolant fan runs with ignition switch off.

SYSTEM CHECK

1. With engine cold and idling, move

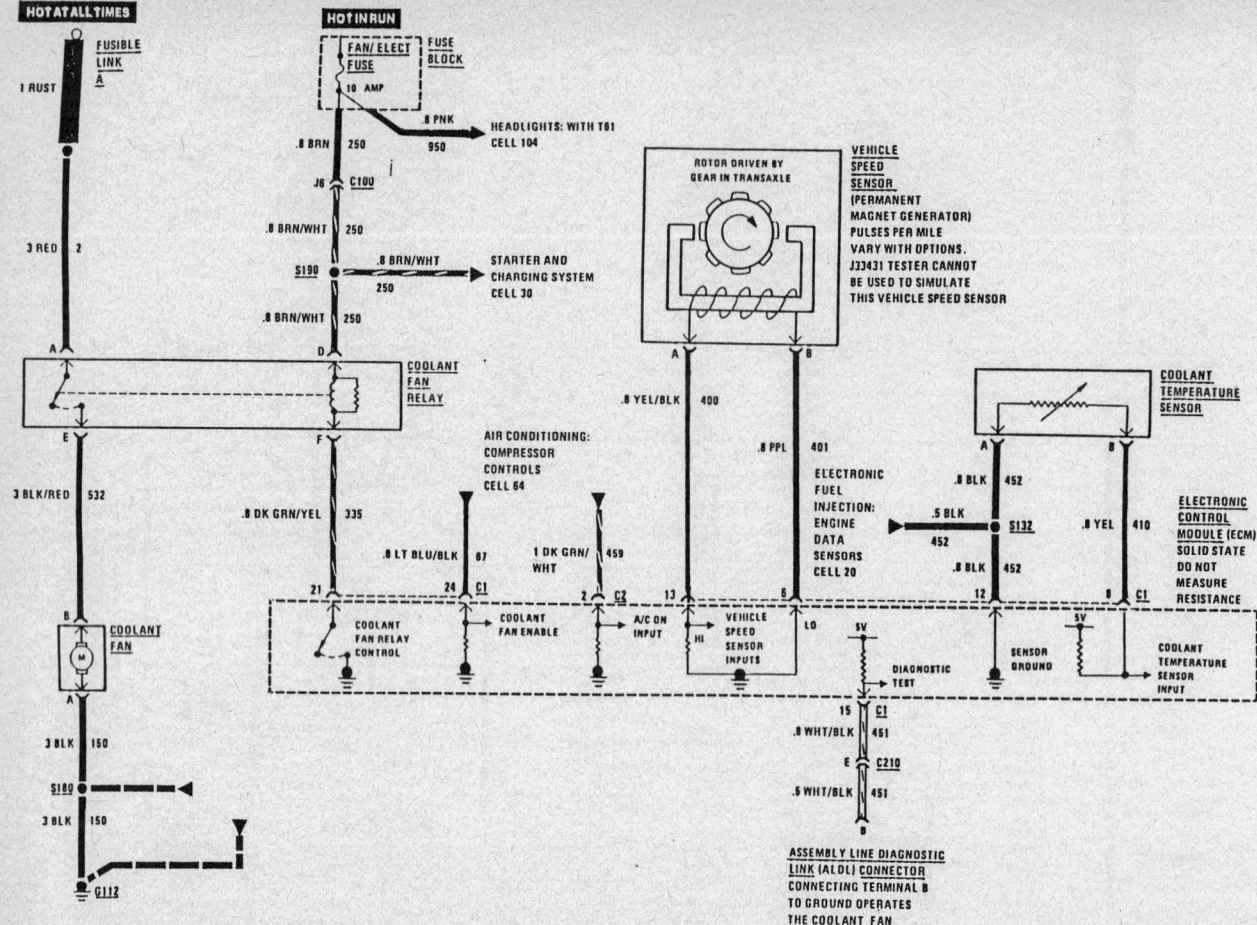

Fig. 8   Coolant fan wiring circuit. 1988–90 Celebrity & 1990 6000 w/2.5L/4-151 engine, VIN R

A/C selector, if equipped, to NORM. Coolant fan should run.

2. With engine coolant below operating temperature, move A/C selector to OFF. Coolant fan should turn off.

3. With engine warm, run engine at fast idle for several minutes. Coolant fan should turn on before coolant temperature indicator comes on or coolant temperature gauge needle reaches H.

DIAGNOSIS

Refer to **Figs. 8 through 15** when performing diagnostic procedures on this system.

Coolant Fan Does Not Run

1. Connect fused jumper between ALDL connector terminal B and ground and turn ignition switch to RUN position. If coolant fan runs, problem is ECM related.

2. If coolant fan does not run, connect fused jumper between dark green/white wire of ECM connector C1 (VIN R) or C3 (VIN W) and ground and turn ignition switch to RUN position. If coolant fan runs, problem is ECM related.

3. If coolant fan does not run, leave

fused jumper connected as in step 2, disconnect coolant fan relay connector, turn ignition switch to RUN position and connect test lamp between terminals as follows:

a. Between D wire terminal and ground. If lamp does not illuminate, check C/H fuse and brown/white wire for open.

b. Between D and F wire terminals. If lamp does not illuminate, check dark green/white wire for open.

c. Between red wire terminal and ground. If lamp does not illuminate, check red wire and fusible link A for open.

4. If lamp illuminates in steps a, b and c, disconnect coolant fan relay connector and connect fused jumper between A and E wire terminals. If coolant fan runs, replace coolant fan.

5. If coolant fan does not run, leave fused jumper connected as in step 4, disconnect coolant fan connector and connect test lamp between terminals as follows:

a. Between B wire terminal and ground. If lamp does not illuminate, check black/red wire (VIN R and T) or yellow wire (VIN W and T) for open.

b. Between B and black wire terminals. If lamp does not illuminate, check black wire for open.

c. If lamp illuminates in steps a and b, replace coolant fan.

Coolant Fan Runs Continuously, 1988 Models

1. Place ignition switch in RUN position, connect a test lamp between brown/white and dark green/white wire terminals of coolant fan relay connector.

2. If lamp does not illuminate, replace coolant fan relay.

3. If lamp illuminates, check dark green/white wire for short to ground. If wire is satisfactory, problem is ECM related.

Coolant Fan Runs Continuously, 1989–90 Models

1. Place ignition switch in RUN position, disconnect ECM connector C1 on VIN R or C3 on VIN W and T. If coolant fan does not turn off, proceed to step 2. If coolant fan turns off, problem is ECM related.

2. Remove FAN/ELEC fuse. If fan turns

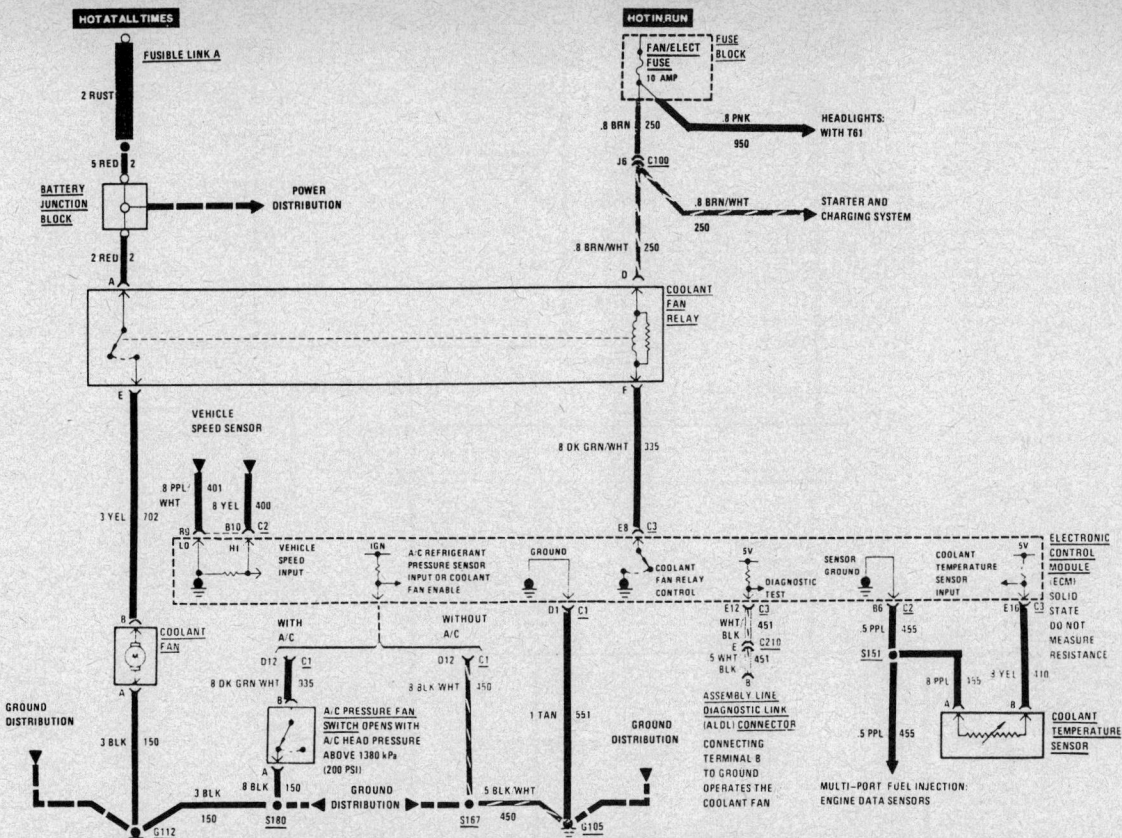

Fig. 9   Coolant fan wiring circuit. 1988–89 Celebrity w/2.8L/V6-173 engine, VIN W

off, locate and repair short to ground in dark green/yellow or dark green/white wires. If fan stays on, replace coolant fan relay.

COOLANT FAN, REPLACE

1. Disconnect battery ground cable.
2. Disconnect wiring harness from fan motor and fan frame.
3. Remove fan assembly from radiator support.
4. Reverse procedure to install.

CALAIS

SYSTEM DESCRIPTION

2.3L/4-138 VINS A & D

A two speed coolant fan is used with the VIN D engine. The coolant fan is turned on and off by the coolant fan relays.

For low speed operation, the low speed relay coil is grounded through the ECM when vehicle speed is less than 45 mph and the engine coolant reaches 208°F, or when the A/C is turned on. The contacts close and voltage is applied through the coolant fan resistor to the coolant fan. The fan runs at low speed.

For high speed operation, the high speed relay coil is grounded through the ECM when the coolant temperature reaches 228°F. The contacts close and voltage is applied to the coolant fan. The fan runs at high speed. The coolant fan will contin-

ue to run at high speed after the ignition switch is turned off until the coolant temperature lowers.

2.5L/4-151 VIN U & 3.3L/V6-204 VIN N

The coolant fan is controlled by the coolant fan relay. The coolant fan relay is electrically operated by the ECM. The ECM receives input signals from the coolant temperature sensor, the vehicle speed sensor and the A/C mode selector. The ECM activates the coolant fan relay when the engine coolant, which is sensed by the coolant temperature sensor, is above 227°F, when the A/C is turned on or when the coolant temperature sensor fails. Any of these input signals causes the ECM to ground circuit 335 when vehicle speed is less than 35 mph. With circuit 335 grounded, the coolant fan relay is energized and its contacts close, turning the coolant fan on.

3.0L/V6-181 VIN L

A two speed coolant fan is used with the VIN L engine. The coolant fan is turned on and off by the coolant fan relays.

For low speed operation, the low speed relay coil is grounded through the ECM or low speed contacts of the coolant fan A/C dual pressure switch. The ECM grounds the coil when vehicle speed is less than 45 mph and engine coolant temperature reaches 208°F. The low speed contacts of the coolant fan A/C dual pressure switch ground the coil of the coolant fan relay when head pressure is above 150 psi.

With the low speed relay coil grounded, the associated contacts close. Voltage is applied through the coolant fan resistor to the coolant fan. The resistor drops part of the battery voltage and the coolant fan runs at low speed.

For high speed operation, the high speed relay coil is grounded through the high speed contacts of the coolant fan A/C pressure switch or the coolant fan temperature switch. The coolant fan A/C dual pressure switch high speed contacts close at a refrigerant pressure higher than the pressure that closed the low speed contacts (300 psi). The coolant fan temperature switch closes when coolant temperature reaches 228°F.

With the high speed relay coil grounded, the associated contacts close. Battery voltage is applied to the coolant fan. The fan runs at high speed.

TROUBLESHOOTING

1. If coolant fan does not operate, check fuse 21.
2. **On VIN U,** if coolant fan runs with ignition switch in OFF position, replace coolant fan relay.
3. **On VIN L,** if coolant fan runs in high speed with ignition switch in OFF position, replace high speed coolant fan relay.
4. **On VIN L,** if coolant fan runs in low speed with ignition switch in OFF position, replace high speed coolant fan relay.

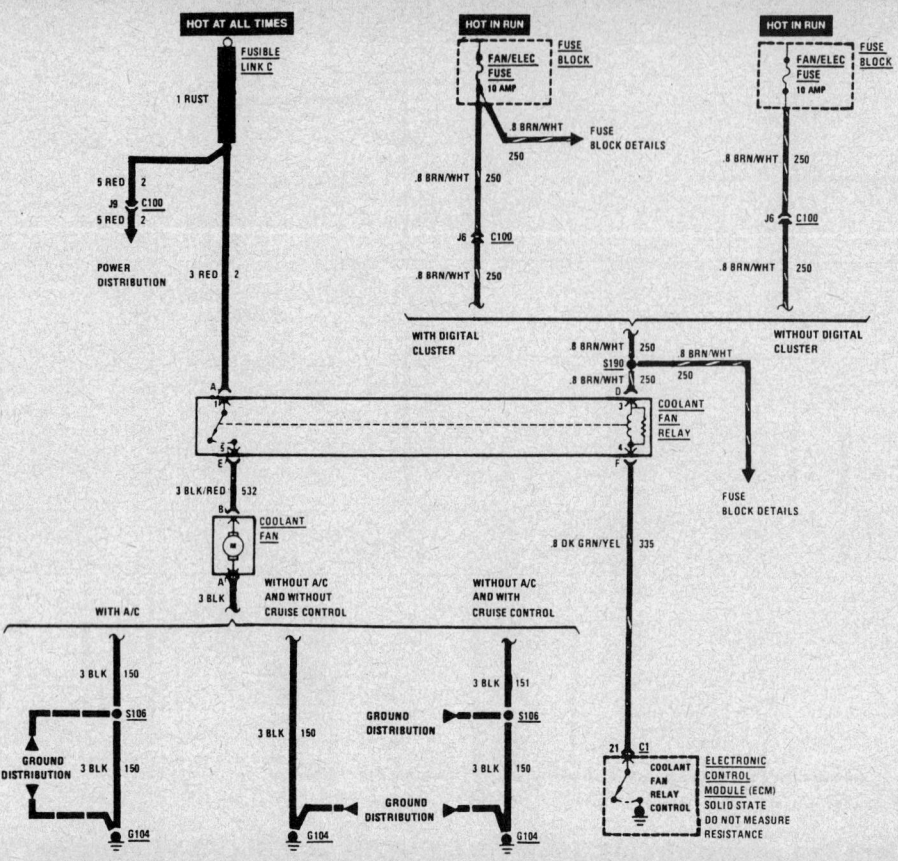

Fig. 10   Coolant fan wiring circuit. 1988 6000, 2.5L/4-151 VIN R

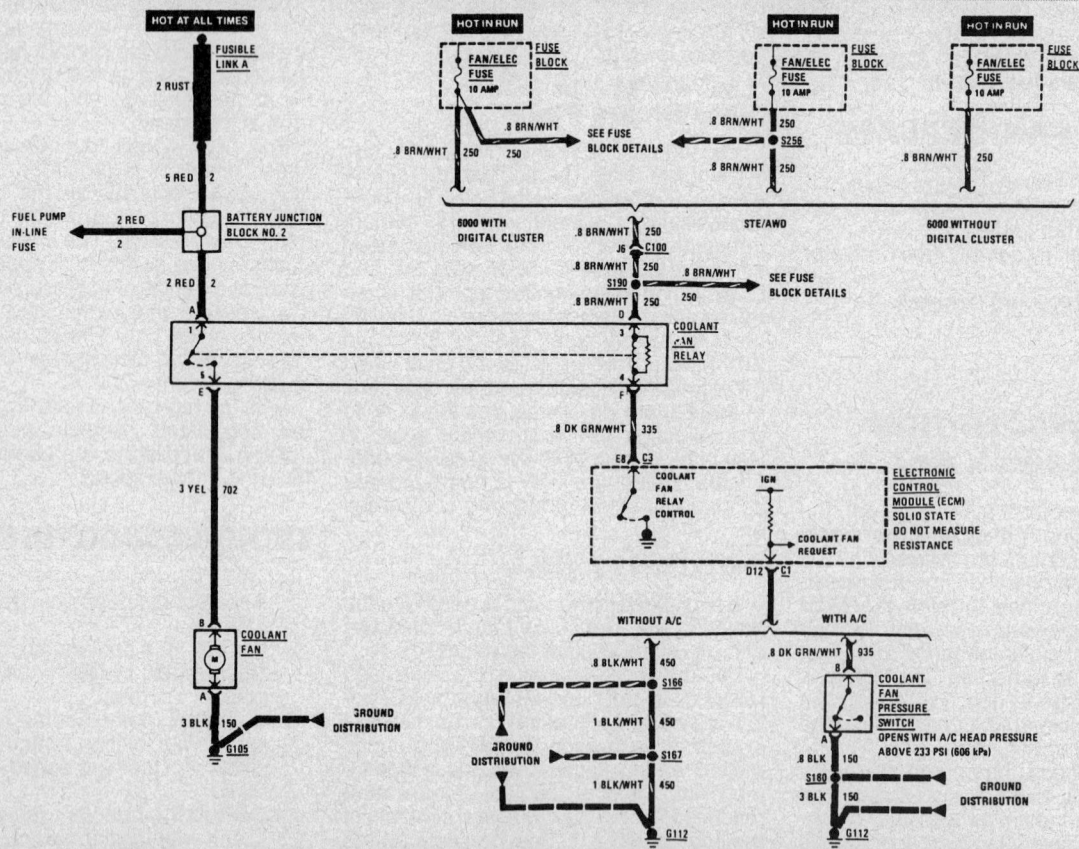

Fig. 11   Coolant fan wiring circuit. 1988 6000, 2.8L/V6-173 VIN W

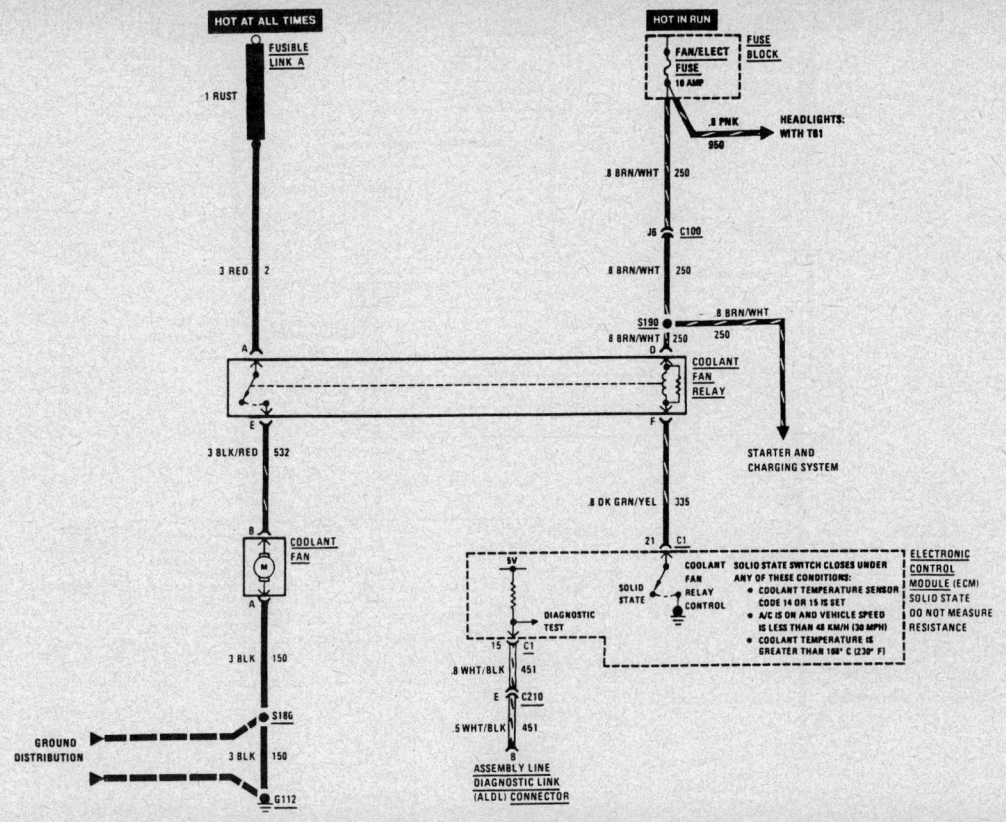

Fig. 12   Coolant fan wiring circuit. 1989 6000, 2.5L/4-151 VIN R

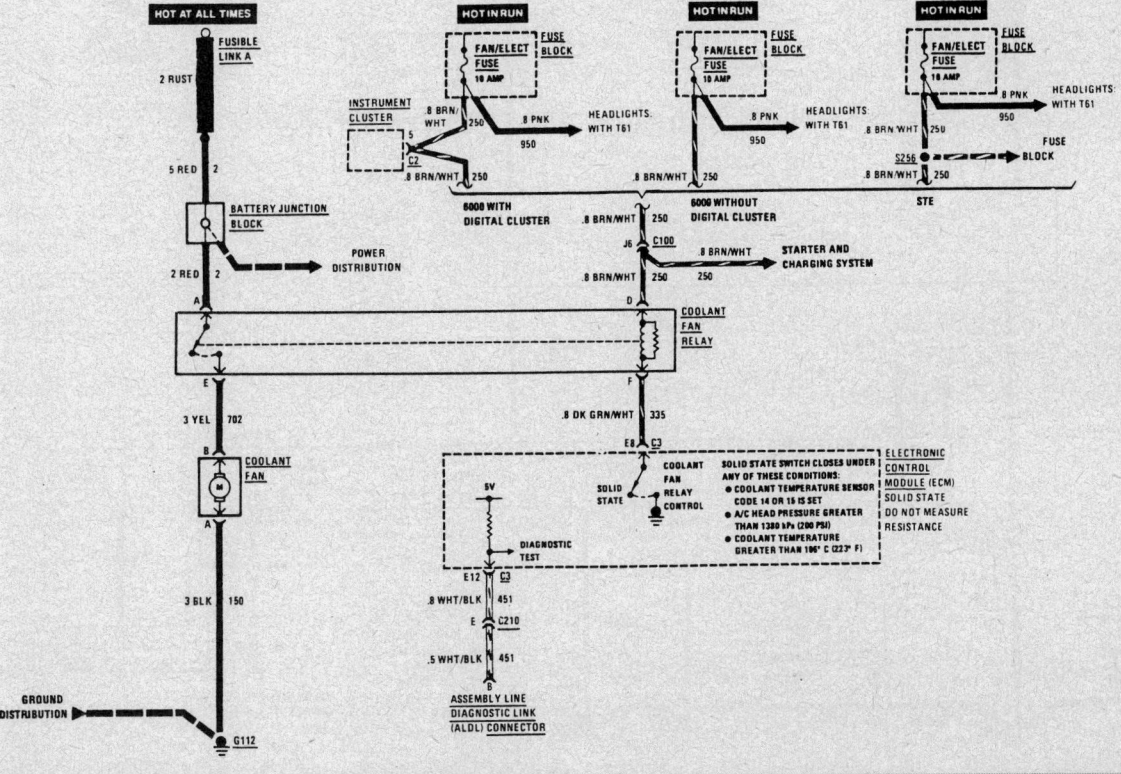

Fig. 13   Coolant fan wiring circuit, with daytime running lights. 1989 6000, 3.1L/V6-191 VIN T

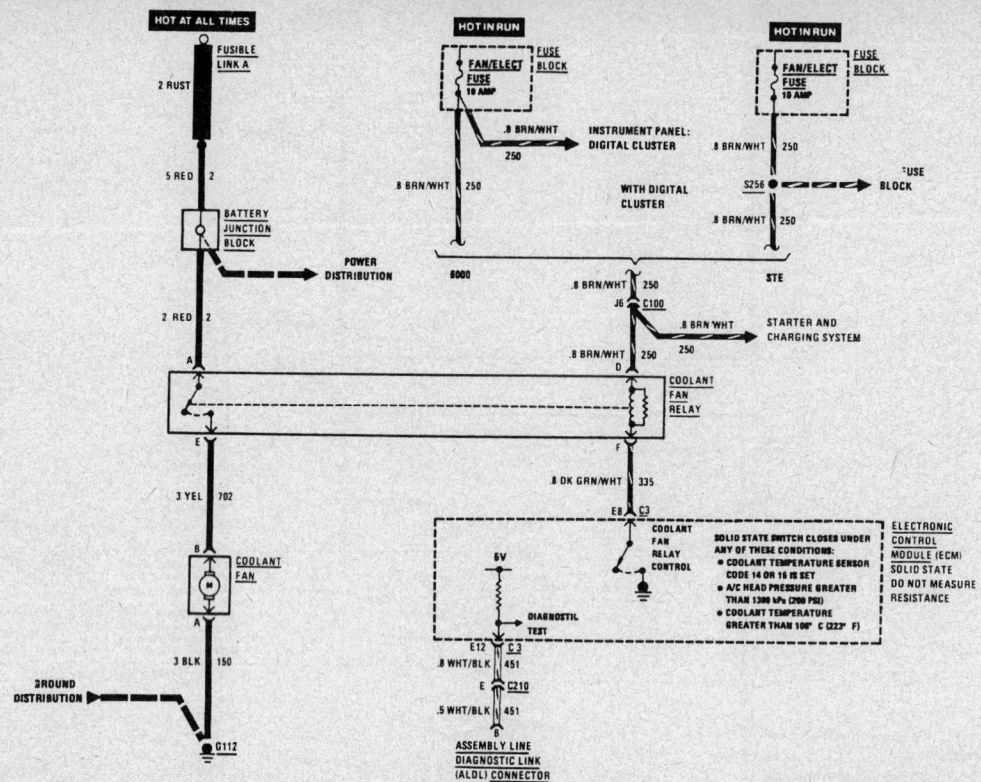

Fig. 14 Coolant fan wiring circuit, less daytime running lights. 1989 6000, 3.3L/V6-204 VIN T

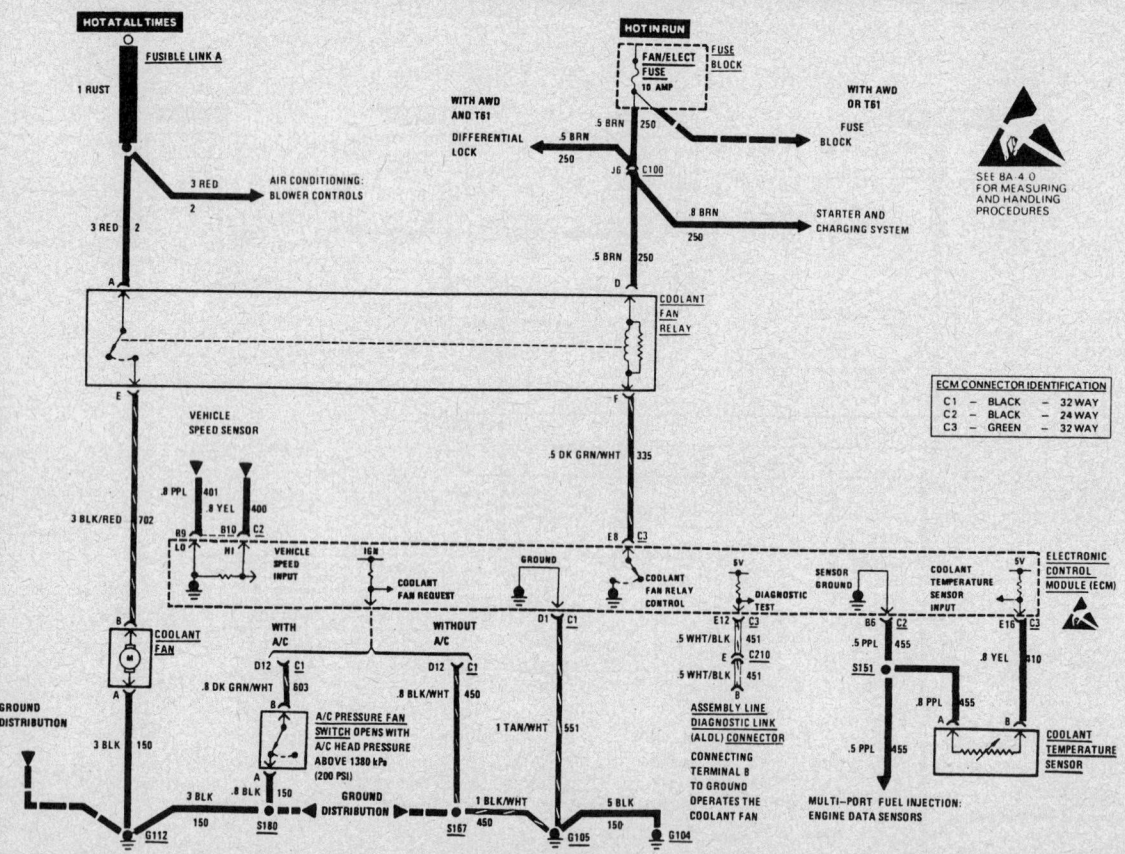

Fig. 15 Coolant fan wiring circuit. 1990 Celebrity & 6000, 3.1L/V6-191 VIN T

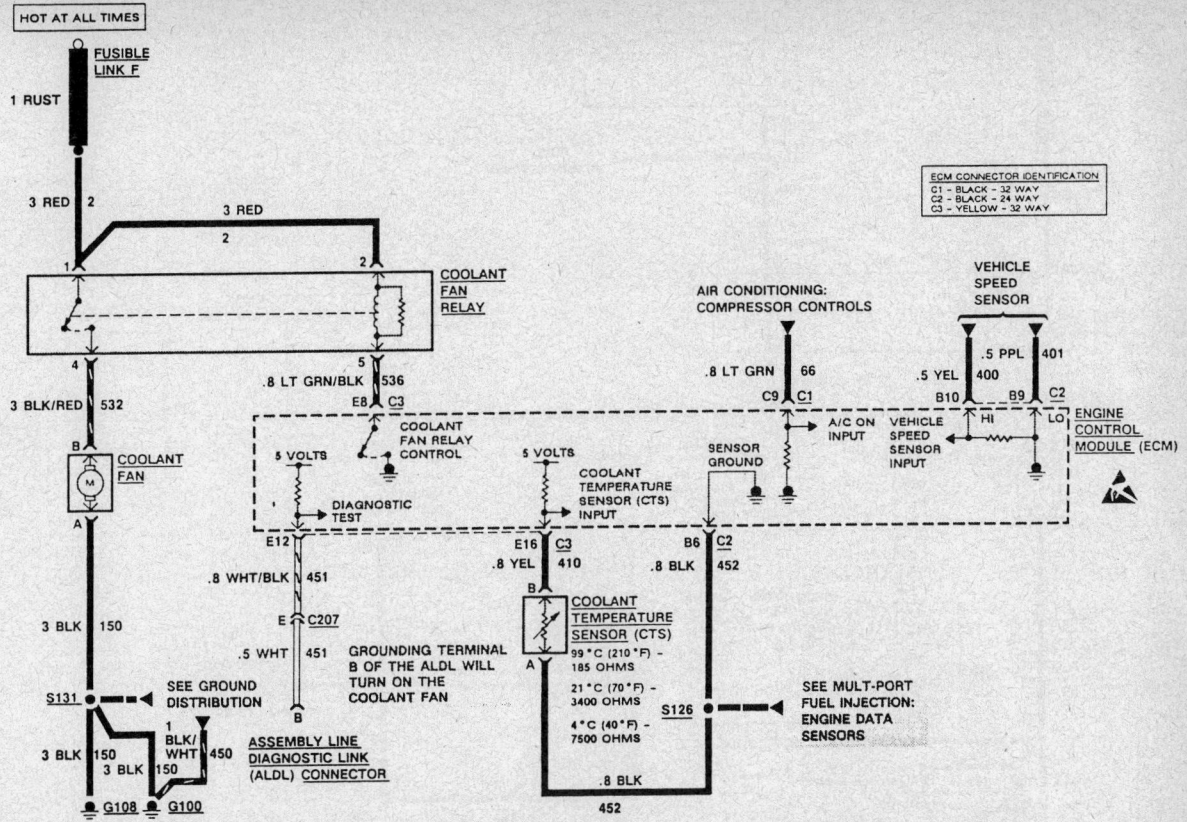

Fig. 16   Coolant fan wiring circuit. 1988-90 Calais w/2.3L/4-138 & 2.3L/4-138 HO engines, VINS A & D

SYSTEM CHECK

1. With ambient air temperature above 70°F, open all doors, start vehicle and set A/C mode selector, if equipped, to MAX. Coolant fan should turn on in a short period of time.
2. With engine coolant below operating temperature, move A/C mode selector to OFF position. Coolant fan should turn off in a short period of time.
3. Run engine at fast idle for several minutes. The coolant fan should turn on before coolant temperature indicator comes on or coolant temperature gage needle reaches HOT.

DIAGNOSIS

Refer to **Figs. 16 through 18** when performing the following diagnostic procedures.

VIN U

Coolant Fan Does Not Turn On

1. With ignition switch in RUN position, ground white wire terminal of ALDL connector. If coolant fan runs, problem is ECM related.
2. If coolant fan does not run, turn ignition switch to RUN position and ground dark green/white wire at ECM black/red connector with fused jumper. If coolant fan runs, problem is ECM related.

3. If coolant fan does not run, leave fused jumper connected as in step 2, turn ignition switch to RUN position, disconnect coolant fan relay connector and measure voltage from brown wire terminal to ground. If battery voltage is not present, check fuse 21, brown wire and dark green/white wire for open.
4. If battery voltage is present, leave fused jumper connected as in step 2, turn ignition switch to RUN position and measure voltage between brown and dark green/white wire terminals. If battery voltage is not present, check dark green/white wire for open.
5. If battery voltage is present, disconnect coolant fan relay connector and measure voltage from red wire (1) terminal to ground. If battery voltage is not present, check red wire (2) and fusible link for open.
6. If battery voltage is present, disconnect coolant fan relay connector and connect a 20 amp fused jumper between red (1) and black/red wire terminals. If coolant fan runs, replace coolant fan relay.
7. If coolant fan does not run, leave fused jumper connected as in step 6, disconnect coolant fan connector and measure voltage between black/red wire terminal and ground. If battery voltage is not present, check black red wire for open.
8. If battery voltage is present, leave fused jumper connected as in step 6

and measure voltage between black/red and black wire terminals.
9. If battery voltage is not present, check black wire for open.
10. If battery voltage is present, replace coolant fan motor.

Coolant Fan Does Not Turn Off With Engine Coolant Cool, A/C Mode Selector Off & Ignition Switch In RUN Position

1. Turn ignition switch to RUN position, disconnect coolant fan relay connector and connect test lamp between brown/white and dark green/white wire terminals. If lamp does not illuminate, replace coolant fan relay.
2. If lamp illuminates, check dark green/white wire for short to ground. If wire is satisfactory, problem is ECM related.

Coolant Fan Does Not Turn On With A/C Mode Selector On, And Head Pressure Above 150 psi, But Does Turn On With Engine Hot

1. Turn ignition switch to RUN position and place A/C mode selector in MAX position. Measure voltage between terminal C1/24 dark green/white of the ECM and ground.
2. If battery voltage is present, problem is ECM related.
3. If no battery voltage is present, check dark green/white wire for an open.

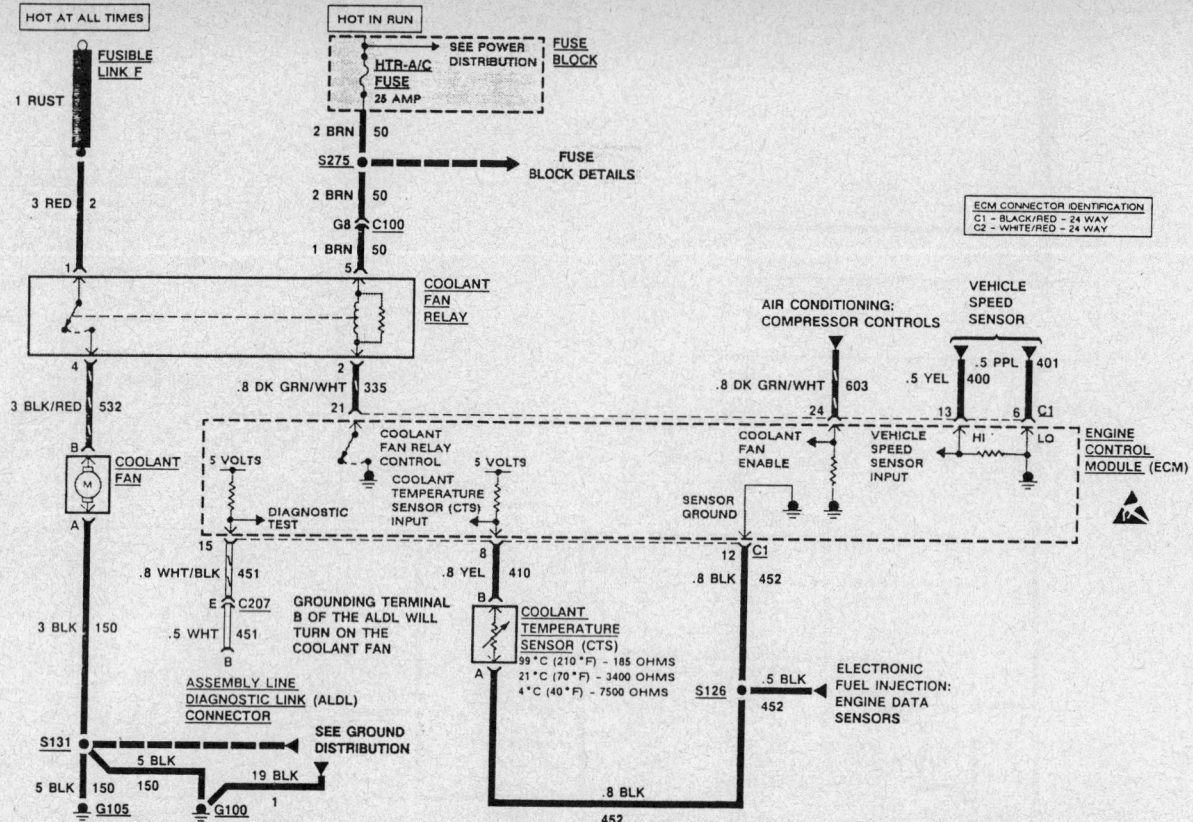

Fig. 17 Coolant fan wiring circuit. 1988–90 Calais w/2.5L/4-151 engine, VIN U

VINS A, D & L

Coolant Fan Does Not Run In Low Or High Speed

1. Disconnect high speed coolant fan relay connector and connect a 20 amp fused jumper between red (1) (VINS A & D) or red/white (1) (VIN L) and black/pink wire terminals. If coolant fan runs, proceed to "Coolant Fan Does Not Run In Low Speed" and "Coolant Fan Does Not Run In High Speed."
2. If coolant fan does not run, leave fused jumper connected as in step 1, disconnect coolant fan connector and measure voltage from black/pink wire terminal to ground. If battery voltage is not present, check fusible link F, red (2) wire or red/white (2) wire and black/pink wire for open.
3. If battery voltage is present, leave jumper connected as in step 1 and measure voltage from black/pink to black wire terminal at coolant fan connector.
4. If battery voltage is not present, check black wire for open.
5. If battery voltage is present, check coolant fan connector terminal contact and, if satisfactory, replace coolant fan.

Coolant Fan Does Not Run In Low Speed

1. With ignition switch in RUN position, ground white wire terminal of ALDL connector. If coolant fan runs, problem is ECM related.
2. If coolant fan does not run, turn ignition switch to run position and ground dark green wire terminal of ECM black, 32 pin connector (VIN L) or ECM yellow connector (VINS A & D) with fused jumper. If coolant fan runs, problem is ECM related.
3. If coolant fan does not run, leave fused jumper connected as in step 2, turn ignition switch to RUN position, disconnect low speed coolant fan relay and measure voltage from brown/white (VIN L) or brown (VINS A & D) wire terminal to ground. If battery voltage is not present, check fuse 21, brown wire and brown/white wire for open.
4. If battery voltage is present, leave fused jumper connected as in step 2, turn ignition switch to RUN position and measure voltage from brown/white (VIN L) or brown (VINS A & D) and dark green wire terminals. If battery voltage is not present, check dark green wire for open.
5. If battery voltage is present, disconnect low speed coolant fan relay connector and measure voltage from red or red/white wire terminal (1) to ground. If battery voltage is not present, check red or red/white wire (2) for open.
6. If battery voltage is present, disconnect low speed coolant fan relay connector and connect a 20 amp fused jumper between red or red/white (1) and black/red wire terminals.
7. If coolant fan does not run, check black/red wire and coolant fan resistor for open.
8. If coolant fan runs, check low speed coolant fan relay connector terminal contact and, if satisfactory, replace low speed coolant fan relay.

Coolant Fan Does Not Run In High Speed (VIN L)

1. Disconnect connector from coolant fan temperature switch and ground connector terminal with a fused jumper. If coolant fan runs, check coolant fan temperature switch terminal contact and, if satisfactory, replace coolant fan temperature switch.
2. If coolant fan does not run, leave fused jumper connected as in step 1, disconnect high speed coolant fan relay connector, turn ignition switch to RUN position and measure voltage from brown wire terminal to ground. If battery voltage is not present, check brown wire and fuse 21 for open.
3. If battery voltage is present, leave fused jumper connected as in step 1, turn ignition switch to RUN position and measure voltage between brown and light green/black wire terminals. If battery voltage is not present, check light/green black wire for open.
4. If battery voltage is present, measure voltage between red/white (1) (1988) wire terminal and ground. If battery voltage is not present, check red/white (2) (1988) wire and fusible link F for open.
5. If battery voltage is present, disconnect high speed coolant fan relay con-

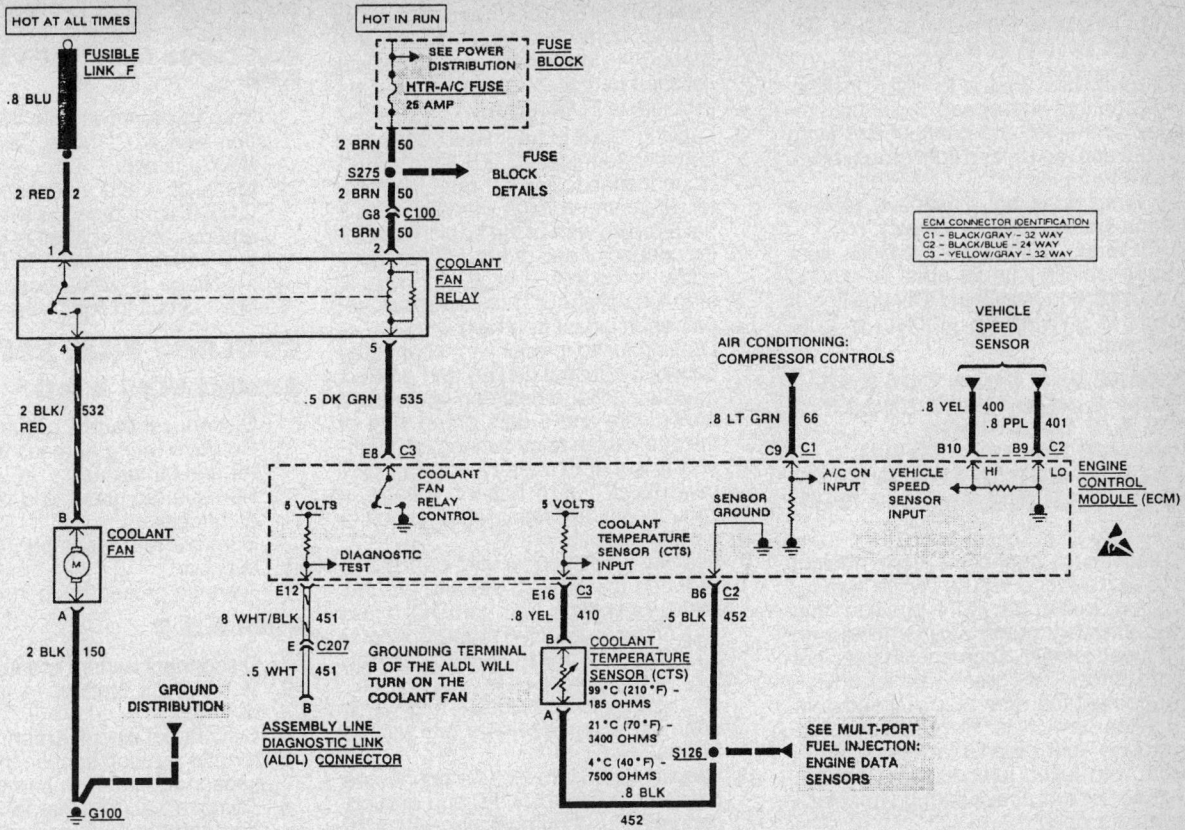

Fig. 18   Coolant fan wiring circuit. 1989-90 Calais w/3.3L/V6-204 engine, VIN N

nector and connect a 20 amp fused jumper between red/white (1) (1988) and black/pink wire terminals.

6. If coolant fan runs, check black pink wire for open.
7. If coolant fan does not run, check high speed coolant fan relay connector terminal contact and, if satisfactory, replace high speed coolant fan relay.

Coolant Fan Does Not Run In High Speed

1. With ignition switch in RUN position, ground light green/black wire terminal of ECM yellow connector with a fused jumper. If coolant fan runs, problem is ECM related.
2. If coolant fan does not run, leave fused jumper connected as in step 1, disconnect high speed coolant fan relay connector, turn ignition switch to RUN position and measure voltage from red wire terminal (2) to ground. If battery voltage is not present, check red wire (2) for open.
3. If battery voltage is present, leave fused jumper connected as in step 1, turn ignition switch to RUN position and measure voltage between red (2) and light green/black wire terminals. If battery voltage is not present, check light green black wire for open.
4. If battery voltage is present, measure voltage between red wire terminal (1) and ground. If battery voltage is not present, check red wire (2) for open.
5. If battery voltage is present, discon-

nect high speed coolant fan relay connector and connect a 20 amp fused jumper between red (1) and black/pink wire terminals.

6. If coolant fan does not run, check black/pink wire for open.
7. If coolant fan runs, check high speed coolant fan relay connector terminal contact and, if satisfactory, replace high speed coolant fan relay.

Coolant Fan Runs Continuously In Low Speed With Engine Coolant Cool & A/C Off (VIN L)

1. Turn ignition switch to RUN position and disconnect coolant fan A/C dual pressure switch connector. If coolant fan does not run, replace A/C coolant fan dual pressure switch.
2. If coolant fan runs, disconnect low speed coolant fan relay connector, turn ignition switch to RUN position and connect test lamp between brown/white and dark green wire terminals.
3. If lamp does not illuminate, replace low speed coolant fan relay.
4. If lamp illuminates, check dark green wires for short to ground. If wires are satisfactory, problem is ECM related.

Coolant Fan Runs Continuously In Low Speed With Engine Coolant Cool & A/C Off (VINS A & D)

1. Disconnect low speed coolant fan re-

lay connector, turn ignition switch to RUN position and connect test lamp between brown and dark green wire terminals.

2. If lamp does not illuminate, replace low speed coolant fan relay.
3. If lamp illuminates, check dark green wire for short to ground. If wire is satisfactory, problem is ECM related.

Coolant Fan Runs Continuously In High Speed With Engine Coolant Cool & A/C Off (VIN L)

1. Turn ignition switch to RUN position and disconnect coolant fan temperature switch. If coolant fan does not run, replace coolant fan temperature switch.
2. If coolant fan runs, turn ignition switch to RUN position and disconnect coolant fan A/C dual pressure switch. If coolant fan does not run, replace coolant fan A/C dual pressure switch.
3. If coolant fan runs, turn ignition switch to RUN position, disconnect high speed coolant fan relay connector and connect test lamp between brown and light green/black wire terminals.
4. If lamp does not illuminate, replace high speed coolant fan relay.
5. If lamp illuminates, check light green/black wires for short to ground.

Coolant Fan Runs Continuously In High Speed With Engine Coolant Cool & A/C Off (VINS A & D)

1. Turn ignition switch to RUN position, disconnect high speed coolant fan relay connector and connect test lamp between red (2) and light green/black wire terminals.
2. If lamp does not illuminate, replace high speed coolant fan relay.
3. If lamp illuminates, check light green/black wire for short to ground with ignition switch in RUN position. If wire is satisfactory, problem is ECM related.

Coolant Fan Does Not Run In Low And/Or High Speed With A/C On & Head Pressure Above 150 psi, But Does Run In Low & High Speed With Engine Hot (VIN L)

1. Disconnect connector from coolant fan A/C dual pressure switch, turn ignition switch to RUN position and ground dark green wire terminal with a fused jumper. If coolant fan does not run, check dark green wire for open.
2. If coolant fan runs at low speed, turn ignition switch to RUN position and ground light green/black wire terminal with fused jumper. If coolant fan does not run, check light green/black wire for open.
3. If coolant fan runs at high speed, turn ignition switch to RUN position and connect fused jumper between light green/black and black/white wire terminals.
4. If coolant fan does not run, check black/white wire for open.
5. If coolant fan runs at high speed, check coolant fan A/C dual pressure switch connector terminal contact and, if satisfactory, replace coolant fan A/C dual pressure switch.

Coolant Fan Does Not Run In Low And/Or High Speed With A/C On & Head Pressure Above 150 psi, But Does Run In Low & High Speed With Engine Hot (VINS A & D)

1. With engine idling, turn on A/C and observe engine operation.
2. If engine slows down when compressor clutch engages, check light green/black wire for open. If wire is satisfactory, problem is ECM related.
3. If engine does not slow down when compressor clutch engages, problem is ECM related.

VIN N

Coolant Fan Does Not Turn On

1. Ground terminal B white wire of the Assembly Line Diagnostic Link (ALDL) connector, then turn ignition switch to the RUN position. If coolant fan does not run, proceed to step 2. If coolant fan runs, problem is ECM related.

2. Connect a fused jumper wire between terminal C3/E8 dark green wire of the Engine Control Module (ECM) and ground. If coolant fan does not run, proceed to step 3. If coolant fan runs, problem is ECM related.
3. Leaving fused jumper wire connected between terminal C3/E8 and ground, disconnect coolant fan relay connector. Measure voltage between terminal 2 brown wire of the coolant fan relay connector and ground. If voltage is equal to battery voltage, proceed to step 4. If voltage is zero, locate and repair open circuit in brown wire.
4. Leaving fused jumper wire connected between terminal C3/E8 and ground, measure voltage between terminals 2 brown wire and 5 dark green wire of the coolant fan relay connector. If voltage is equal to battery voltage, proceed to step 5. If battery voltage is zero, locate and repair open circuit in dark green wire.
5. Leaving fused jumper wire connected between terminal C3/E8 and ground, measure voltage from terminal 1 red wire of the coolant fan relay connector and ground. If voltage is equal to battery voltage, proceed to step 6. If battery voltage is zero, locate and repair open circuit in either the red wire or fusible link F.
6. Leaving fused jumper wire connected between terminal C3/E8 and ground, connect a fused jumper wire with a 20 amp fuse between terminals 1 red wire and terminal 4 black/red wire of the coolant fan relay connector. If coolant fan does not run, proceed to step 7. If coolant fan runs, replace coolant fan relay.
7. With fused jumper wires still connected at the ECM and coolant fan relay connector, measure voltage between terminals B black/red wire and ground. If voltage is equal to battery voltage, proceed to step 8. If battery voltage is zero, locate and repair open circuit in black/read wire.
8. With fused jumper wires still connected at the ECM and coolant fan relay connector, measure voltage between terminals B black/red wire and A black wire of the coolant fan connector. If voltage is equal to battery voltage, replace coolant fan motor. If voltage is zero, locate and repair open circuit in black wire.

Coolant Fan Does Not Turn Off With Engine Coolant Cool, A/C Mode Selector Off & Ignition Switch In RUN Position

1. Disconnect coolant fan relay connector, then connect a test lamp between terminals 2 brown wire and 5 dark green wire and turn ignition to the RUN position. If test lamp lights, proceed to step 2. If test lamp does not light, replace coolant fan relay.
2. Inspect dark green wire for a possible short to ground, repair as necessary. If dark green wire is satisfactory, problem is ECM related.

Coolant Fan Does Not Run With A/C On & Head Pressure Above 150 psi, But Does Run With Engine Hot

1. Turn ignition switch to the RUN position and A/C mode selector to the MAX position.
2. Measure voltage between terminal C1/C9 light green wire of the ECM and ground. If voltage is equal to battery voltage, problem is ECM related. If voltage is zero, locate and repair open circuit in light green wire.

COOLANT FAN, REPLACE
Except VINS A & D

1. Disconnect battery ground cable.
2. Remove wiring harness from fan motor and fan frame.
3. Remove fan guard and hose support as necessary.
4. Remove fan assembly from radiator support.
5. Reverse procedure to install.

VINS A & D

1. Disconnect battery ground cable.
2. Remove air cleaner to throttle body duct.
3. Disconnect electrical connectors from throttle position sensor, IAC and MAP sensor and position harness aside.
4. Remove vacuum harness assembly from throttle body and position aside.
5. Disconnect MAP sensor vacuum hose at intake manifold.
6. Remove coolant fan shroud attaching bolts and the shroud together with MAP sensor.
7. Remove coolant fan to upper radiator support attaching bolt, remaining upper radiator support bolt and the upper radiator support.
8. Remove electrical connector from coolant fan.
9. Lift fan assembly out of two lower insulators, rotate bracket so two lower bracket legs point upward, move fan assembly toward driver's side until fan blade overlaps radiator tank to core seam by approximately one inch and remove fan assembly upward. **Because of minimum clearance, care must be taken not to damage lock tang on throttle position sensor with fan bracket.**
10. Reverse procedure to install.

CUTLASS CIERA & CUTLASS CRUISER

SYSTEM DESCRIPTION
2.5L/4-151 VIN R

The coolant fan is turned on and off by the ECM based on inputs from the coolant temperature sensor, vehicle speed sensor and the A/C system. Battery voltage is applied at all times to terminal E of the coolant fan relay and when the ignition switch is in RUN position, battery voltage is applied to terminal C of the relay. The ECM energizes the coolant fan relay by grounding the dark green/white wire. The relay

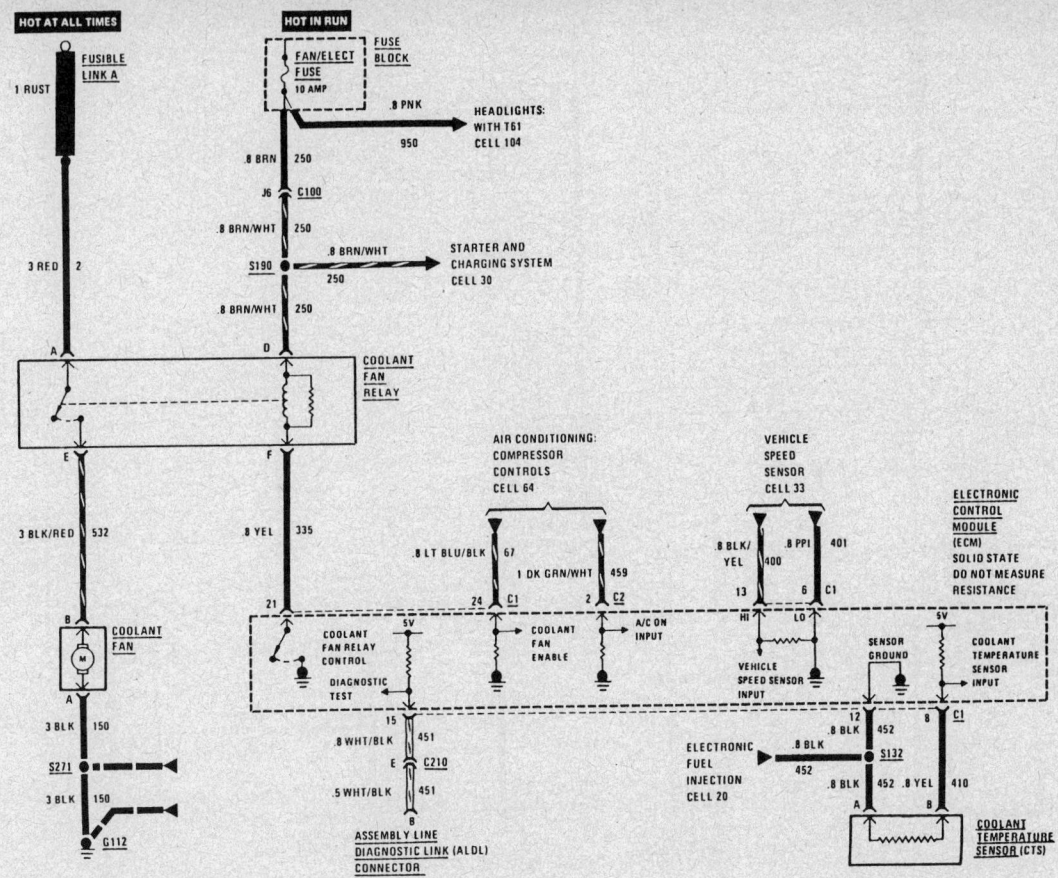

Fig. 19   Coolant fan wiring circuit. 1988–90 Cutlass Ciera & Cutlass Cruiser w/2.5L/4-151 engine, VIN R

energizes and battery voltage is applied to the cooling fan. THe ECM opens circuit 335 to de-energize the relay and turn off the coolant fan. The ECM will turn on the coolant fan when A/C is on and vehicle speed is less than 35 mph or when coolant temperature is above approximately 225°F and vehicle speed is less than 35 mph.

2.8L/V6-173 VIN W

The coolant fan is turned on and off by the ECM based on inputs from the coolant temperature sensor, vehicle speed sensor and the fan pressure switch. Battery voltage is applied at all times to terminal E of the coolant fan relay and when the ignition switch is in RUN position, battery voltage is applied to terminal C of the relay. The ECM energizes the coolant fan relay by grounding the dark green/white wire. The relay energizes and battery voltage is applied to the coolant fan. The ECM opens circuit 335 to de-energize the relay and turn off the coolant fan. The ECM will turn on the coolant fan when vehicle speed is less than 40 mph and coolant temperature exceeds 234°F or when vehicle speed is less than 40 mph and A/C head pressure exceeds 233 psi.

3.8L/V6-231 VINS N & 3

Two types of coolant fans are used with this engine. The coolant fans are turned on

and off either by the coolant fan relay, the coolant fan delay relay, the pusher coolant fan relay or the puller coolant fan relay depending on the specific application or engine requirement.

For operation without A/C, the coolant fan relay is controlled by the coolant fan switch or the ECM. For operation with A/C, the coolant fan relay is controlled by the coolant fan switch, the A/C high pressure switch and the ECM.

When one of these components grounds the coil of the coolant fan relay, the contacts close and the fan comes on.

THe heavy duty coolant system, used on some models, consists of two coolant fans. The puller coolant fan is controlled by the puller coolant fan relay. This relay is controlled by the ECM, the puller contacts of the A/C dual pressure switch and the coolant fan switch. The pusher coolant fan is controlled by the pusher coolant fan relay. This relay is controlled by the coolant fan switch and the pusher contacts of the A/C high pressure switch. When any one of these components grounds the coil of one of the relays, that particular fan runs.

When a ground path is provided for the pusher coolant fan relay, the puller coolant fan relay also receives the ground path. When the pusher coolant fan runs, so does the puller coolant fan.

On all vehicles, the coolant fan delay relay operates the coolant fan(s) for a short

period of time after the engine is turned off. A solid state timer relay removes the path to ground for the coolant fan delay relay coil to turn off the fan.

TROUBLESHOOTING

1. **On VINs R and W,** check C/H-FAN fuse.
2. **On VIN 3,** check FAN-C/H fuse.
3. **On VINs R and W,** if coolant fan runs with ignition switch off, replace coolant fan relay.

SYSTEM CHECK
Less Heavy Duty Cooling

1. With ambient air temperature above 60°F, start vehicle and set A/C selector, if equipped, to MAX. Coolant fan should turn on in a short period of time.
2. With engine coolant below operating temperature, move A/C selector to OFF. Coolant fan should turn off in a short period of time.
3. Run engine at fast idle until engine coolant becomes hot. The coolant fan should turn on and run before coolant temperature indicator comes on or the coolant temperature gage needle reaches HOT.
4. **On VIN 3,** with engine coolant above 226°F, turn engine off. Coolant fan

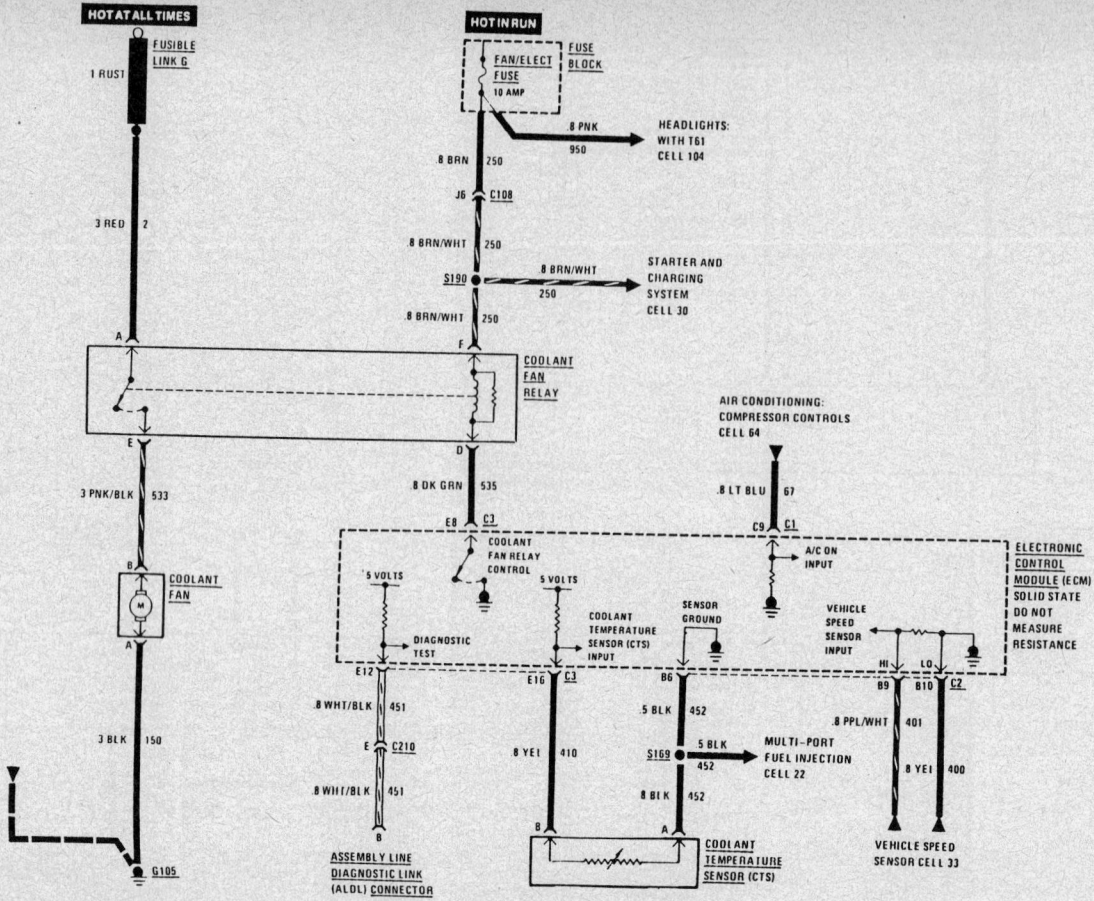

Fig. 20   Coolant fan wiring circuit (less heavy duty). 1989–90 Cutlass Ciera & Cutlass Cruiser w/3.3L/V6-204 engine, VIN N

should run for approximately 10 minutes or until coolant temperature falls below 226°F.

With Heavy Duty Cooling

1. With ambient air temperature above 60°F, start vehicle and set A/C selector, if equipped, to MAX. Puller coolant fan should be turned on in a short period of time by the A/C dual pressure switch and pusher coolant fan should be turned on a short time later by the A/C dual pressure switch.
2. With engine coolant below operating temperature, move A/C selector to OFF. Both fans should turn off in a short period of time.
3. Run engine at fast idle until engine coolant becomes hot. The puller coolant fan should be turned on by the ECM when coolant temperature exceeds 208°F and the pusher coolant fan should be turned on by the coolant fan switch when coolant temperature exceeds 226°F.
4. With engine coolant above 226°F, turn engine off. Puller coolant fan should run for approximately 10 minutes or until coolant temperature falls below 226°F.

SYSTEM DIAGNOSIS

Refer to **Figs. 19** through **22** when performing the following diagnostic procedures.

1988–89 VINS R & W
Coolant Fan Does Not Turn On

1. With ignition switch in RUN position ground white/black wire terminal of ALDL connector. If coolant fan runs, problem is ECM related.
2. If coolant fan does not run, turn ignition switch to RUN position and ground dark green/white wire terminal of ECM connector C1 (VIN R) or ECM yellow connector (VIN W) with a fused jumper. If coolant fan runs, problem is ECM related.
3. If coolant fan does not run, leave fused jumper connected as in step 2, turn ignition switch to RUN position, disconnect coolant fan relay connector and measure voltage from brown/white wire terminal to ground. If battery voltage is not present, check C/H-FAN fuse, brown wire and brown/white wire for open.
4. If battery voltage is present, leave fused jumper connected as in step 2, turn ignition switch to RUN position and measure voltage between

brown/white and dark green/white wire terminals. If battery voltage is not present, check dark green/white wire for open.
5. If battery voltage is present, disconnect coolant fan relay connector and measure voltage from red wire terminal to ground. If battery voltage is not present, check red wire and fusible link A (VIN R) or fusible link F (VIN W) for open.
6. If battery voltage is present, disconnect coolant fan relay connector and connect a 20 amp fused jumper between red and black/red wire terminals. If coolant fan runs, replace coolant fan relay.
7. If coolant fan does not run, leave fused jumper connected as in step 6, disconnect connector from coolant fan and measure voltage between black/red wire terminal and ground. If battery voltage is not present, check black/red wire for open.
8. If battery voltage is present, leave fused jumper connected as in step 6 and measure voltage between black/red and black wire terminals.
9. If battery voltage is not present, check black wire for open.
10. If battery voltage is present, replace coolant fan motor.

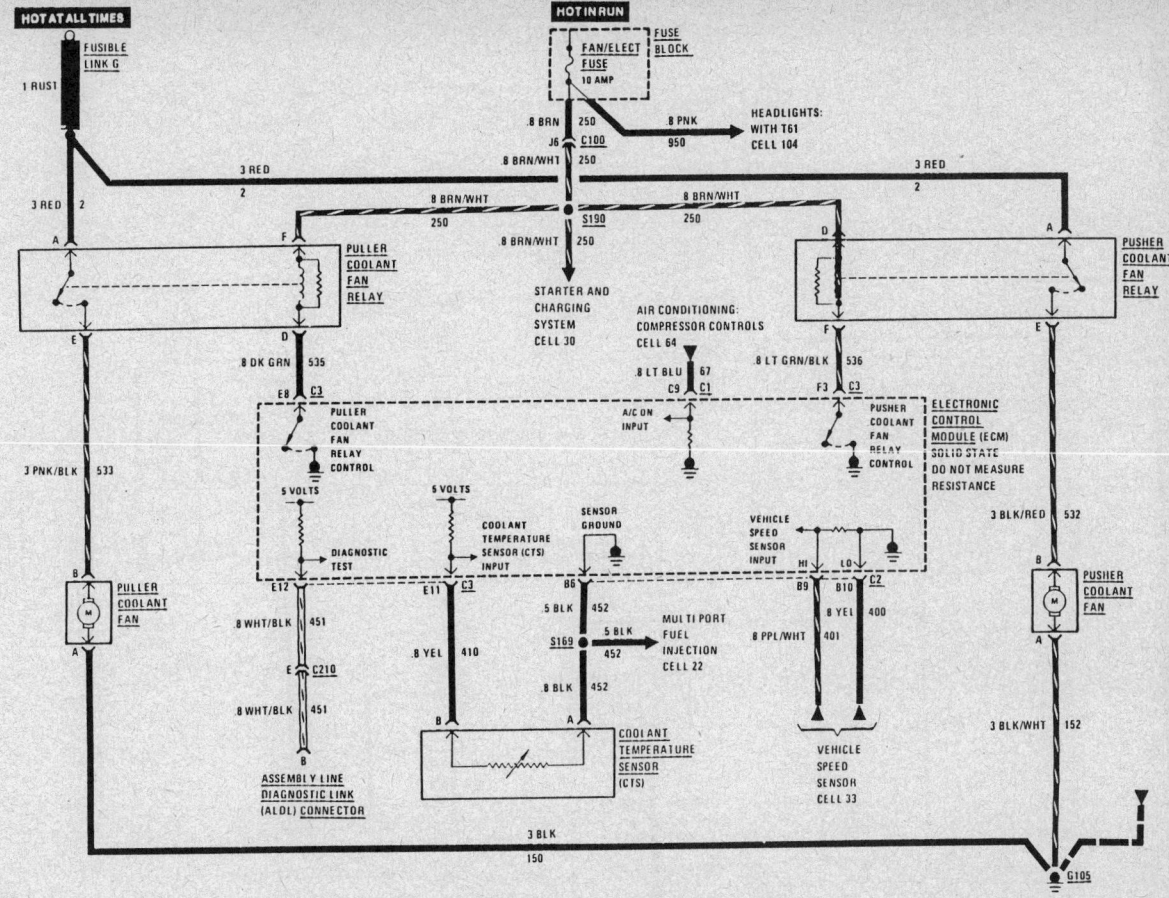

Fig. 21   Coolant fan wiring circuit (with heavy duty). 1989 Cutlass Ciera & Cutlass Cruiser w/3.3L/V6-204 engine, VIN N

Coolant Fan Does Not Turn Off With Engine Coolant Cool, A/C Off & Ignition Switch In RUN Position

1. Turn ignition switch to RUN position, disconnect coolant fan relay connector and connect test lamp between brown/white and dark green/white wire terminals.
2. If lamp does not illuminate, replace coolant fan relay.
3. If lamp illuminates, check dark green/white wire for short to ground. If wire is satisfactory, problem is ECM related.

1988–89 V6-VINS N & 3

1. On models less heavy duty cooling, proceed as follows:
   a. If coolant fan does not turn on, perform test A.
   b. If coolant fan does not run for delay period after engine is turned off with coolant temperature above 226°F, perform test B.
   c. If coolant fan runs continuously with A/C, if equipped, off, coolant temperature cool and engine running, perform test G.
   d. If coolant fan does not run with A/C on and A/C system is operating normally, turn ignition switch to RUN position, disconnect A/C high

pressure switch connector and connect a fused jumper between dark green and black/white wires. If fan runs, replace A/C high pressure switch. If fan does not run, check dark green and black/white wires for open.
   e. If coolant fan does not turn off after 10 minutes when ignition switch is off, disconnect coolant fan relay connector. If coolant fan turns off, replace coolant fan relay. If fan does not turn off, replace coolant fan delay relay.
2. On models with heavy duty cooling, proceed as follows:
   a. If puller coolant fan does not come on, perform test A.
   b. If puller coolant fan does not run for delay period after engine is turned off with coolant temperature above 226°F, perform test B.
   c. If pusher coolant fan does not turn on with coolant temperature above 226°F or with A/C on and A/C head pressure above 300 psi, perform test C.
   d. If puller and pusher coolant fans run with A/C on but not with A/C off and coolant temperature is above 226°F, check dark green/white wire between splice S155 and coolant fan switch for open and, if wire is satisfactory, re-

place coolant fan switch.
   e. If pusher and/or puller coolant fans do not run with A/C on and A/C system is operating normally, perform test D.
   f. If pusher coolant fan runs with ignition switch in OFF position, replace pusher coolant fan relay.
   g. If puller coolant fan does not turn off after 10 minutes when ignition switch is off, disconnect puller coolant fan relay connector. If fan turns off, replace puller coolant fan relay. If fan does not turn off, replace coolant fan delay relay.
   h. If puller and pusher coolant fans run continuously with A/C off, coolant temperature cool and engine running, perform test E.
   i. If puller fan runs continuously with A/C off, coolant temperature cool and engine running, perform test F.
   j. If pusher fan runs with ALDL connector white/black wire terminal grounded, replace coolant fan relay diode.

Test A: Fan Open Test

1. Disconnect connector from coolant fan switch, ground connector terminal with a fused jumper and turn ignition switch to RUN position. If fan runs, replace coolant fan switch and proceed to step 3.

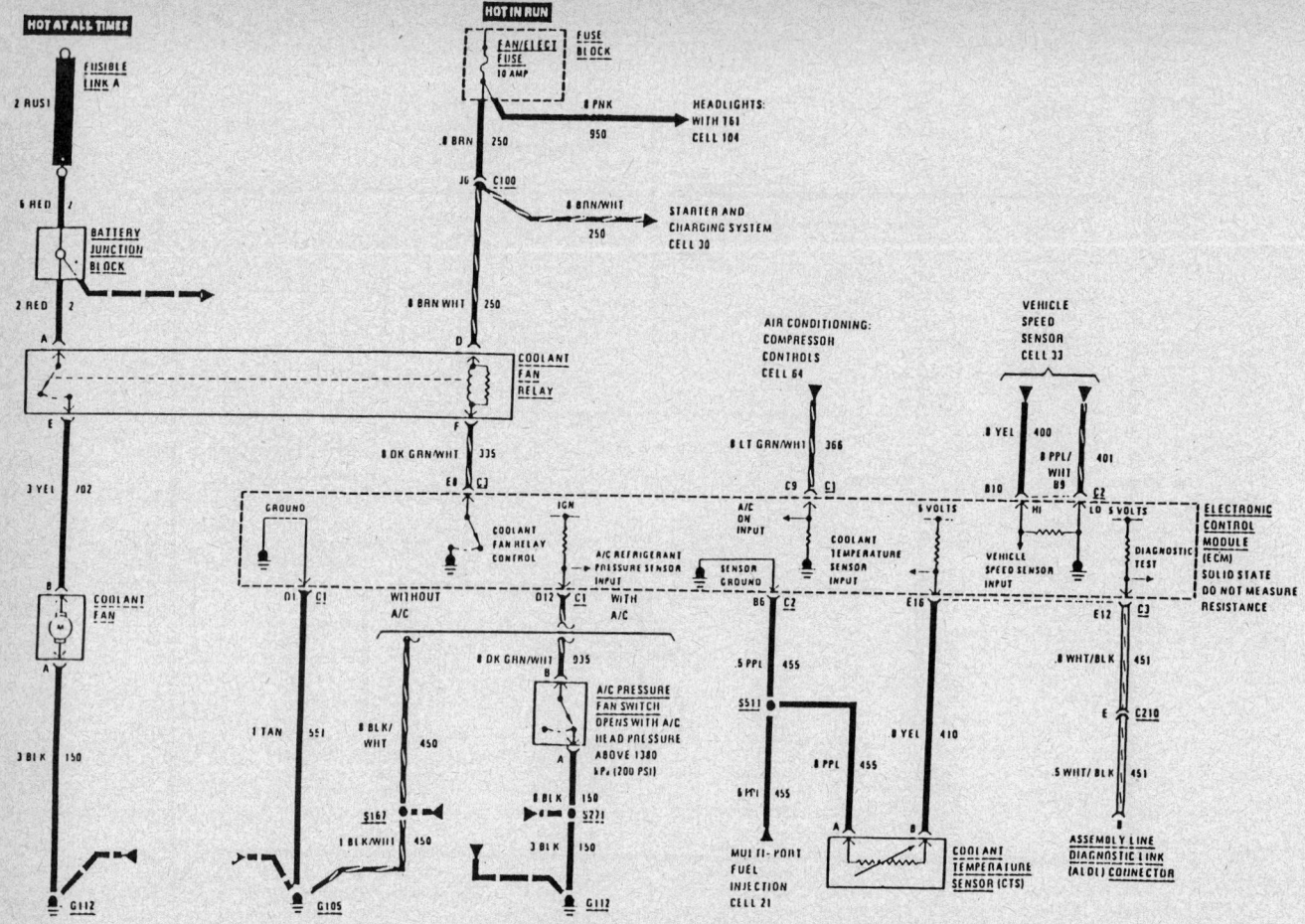

Fig. 22 Coolant fan wiring circuit. 1988–89 Cutlass Ciera & Cutlass Cruiser w/2.8L/V6-173 engine, VIN W

2. If fan does not run, check and repair dark green wire, dark green/white wire and coolant fan relay diode, then proceed to step 3.
3. Turn ignition switch to RUN position and ground white/black wire terminal of ALDL connector with a fused jumper. If fan runs, problem is ECM related.
4. If fan does not run, turn ignition switch to RUN position and ground dark green wire terminal of ECM 32 pin connector with a fused jumper. If fan runs, problem is ECM related.
5. If fan does not run, leave fused jumper connected as in step 4, turn ignition switch to RUN position, disconnect coolant fan relay connector (less heavy duty cooling) or puller coolant fan relay connector (with heavy duty cooling) and measure voltage from brown and red wire terminals to ground. If battery voltage is not present at one or both terminals, check attached circuit for open.
6. If battery voltage is present at both terminals, leave fused jumper connected as in step 4 and measure voltage between brown and dark green wire terminals. If battery voltage is not present, check dark green wire circuit for open.
7. If battery voltage is present, connect

20 amp fused jumper between red and black/red wire terminals at the relay connector. If fan runs, replace relay.
8. If fan does not run, leave fused jumper connected as in step 7, disconnect coolant fan connector (less heavy duty cooling) or puller coolant fan connector (with heavy duty cooling) and measure voltage from black/red wire terminal to ground. If battery voltage is not present, check black/red wire for open.
9. If battery voltage is present, move ground lead of voltmeter to black wire terminal of fan connector.
10. If battery voltage is not present, check black wire for open.
11. If battery voltage is present, replace coolant fan motor.

Test B: Fan delay Test

1. Cycle ignition switch, then turn to OFF position, disconnect connector from coolant fan switch and ground connector terminal with a fused jumper. If fan runs, replace coolant fan switch.
2. If fan does not run, disconnect connector from coolant fan delay relay and measure voltage from orange wire terminal of ECM 24 pin connector and from red wire terminal of ECM 32

pin connector to ground. If battery voltage is not present at one or both terminals, check attached circuit for open.
3. If battery voltage is present at both terminals, turn ignition switch to RUN position and measure voltage from pink/black wire terminal of ECM 24 pin connector to ground. If battery voltage is not present, check pink/black wire for open.
4. If battery voltage is present, turn ignition switch to OFF position and measure voltage from pink/black wire terminal of ECM 24 pin connector and ground. If there is more than 2 volts, check pink/black wire for short to battery.
5. If battery voltage is not present, measure voltage between orange and black/white wire terminals of ECM 24 pin connector. If battery voltage is not present, check black/white wire for open.
6. If battery voltage is present, ground coolant fan switch connector terminal with a fused jumper and measure voltage between red and dark green/white wire terminals at relay connector.
7. If battery voltage is not present, check dark green/white wire for open.

8. If battery voltage is present, replace coolant fan delay relay.

Test C: Pusher Fan Test

1. Disconnect connector from coolant fan switch, ground connector terminal with a fused jumper and turn ignition switch to RUN position. If fan runs, replace coolant fan switch.
2. If fan does not run, leave fused jumper connected as in step 1, disconnect connector from pusher coolant fan relay, turn ignition switch to run position and measure voltage from brown and red wire terminals to ground. If battery voltage is not present at one or both terminals, check attached circuit for open.
3. If battery voltage is present at both terminals leave fused jumper connected as in step 1, turn ignition switch to RUN position and measure voltage between brown and dark green/white wire terminals. If battery voltage is not present, check dark green/white wire for open.
4. If battery voltage is present, connect 20 amp fused jumper between red and black/pink wire terminals at relay connector. If fan runs, replace pusher coolant fan relay.
5. If fan does not run, leave fused jumper connected as in step 4, disconnect connector from pusher coolant fan and measure voltage from red wire terminal to ground. If battery voltage is not present, check black/red wire for open.
6. If battery voltage is present, move ground lead of voltmeter to black/white wire terminal of fan connector.
7. If battery voltage is not present, check black/white wire for open.
8. If battery voltage is present, replace coolant fan motor.

Test D: A/C Dual Pressure Switch Test

1. Disconnect connector from A/C dual pressure switch, turn ignition switch to RUN position and measure voltage from dark green and green/white wire terminals. If battery voltage is not present at one or both terminals, check attached circuit for open.
2. If battery voltage is present at both terminals, measure voltage between dark green and black/white wire terminals.
3. If battery voltage is present, check black/white wire for open.
4. If battery voltage is present, replace A/C dual pressure switch.

Test E: Puller, Pusher Fan Short Test

1. Turn ignition switch to RUN position and disconnect coolant fan switch connector. If fans turn off, replace coolant fan switch.
2. If fans run, disconnect A/C dual pressure switch connector. If fans turn off, replace A/C dual pressure switch.
3. If fans run, check dark green/white wires for short to ground.
4. If wires are satisfactory, replace pusher coolant fan relay and, if puller cool-

ant fan still runs continuously, proceed to test F.

Test F: Puller Fan Short Test

1. Turn ignition switch to RUN position and disconnect A/C dual pressure switch. If fan turns off, replace A/C dual pressure switch.
2. If fan runs, disconnect puller fan relay connector and connect test lamp between brown and dark green wire terminals.
3. If lamp does not illuminate, replace puller coolant fan relay.
4. If lamp illuminates, check dark green wires for short to ground. If wires are satisfactory, problem is ECM related.

Test G: Coolant Fan Short Test

1. Turn ignition switch to RUN position and disconnect coolant fan switch connector. If fan turn off, replace coolant fan switch.
2. If fan runs on vehicles with A/C, proceed as follows:
   a. Disconnect connector from A/C high pressure switch.
   b. If fan turns off, replace A/C high pressure switch.
3. If fan runs in step 1 on vehicles less A/C or in step 2a on vehicles with A/C, disconnect connector from coolant fan relay and connect test lamp between brown and dark green wire terminals. If lamp does not illuminate, replace coolant fan relay.
4. If lamp illuminates, check dark green and dark green/white wires for short to ground. If wires are satisfactory, problem is ECM related.

1990 VINS R & N
Coolant Fan Does Not Turn On

1. With ignition switch in RUN position ground white/black wire terminal of ALDL connector. If coolant fan runs, problem is ECM related.
2. If coolant fan does not run, turn ignition switch to RUN position and ground terminal C1/24 (VIN R) or C3/E8 (VIN N) wire terminal of ECM connector a fused jumper. If coolant fan runs, problem is ECM related.
3. If coolant fan does not run, leave fused jumper connected as in step 2, turn ignition switch to RUN position, disconnect coolant fan relay connector and measure voltage from brown/white wire terminal to ground. If battery voltage is not present, check C/H-FAN fuse, brown wire for open.
4. If battery voltage is present, leave fused jumper connected as in step 2, turn ignition switch to RUN position and measure voltage between brown/white and dark green/white (VIN R) or dark green/yellow (VIN N) wire terminals. If battery voltage is not present, check dark green/white or dark green/yellow wire for open.
5. If battery voltage is present, disconnect coolant fan relay connector and measure voltage from red wire terminal to ground. If battery voltage is not present, check red wire and fusible link for open.

6. If battery voltage is present, disconnect coolant fan relay connector and connect a 20 amp fused jumper between terminals A and E. If coolant fan runs, replace coolant fan relay.
7. If coolant fan does not run, leave fused jumper connected as in step 6, disconnect connector from coolant fan and measure voltage between B wire terminal and ground. If battery voltage is not present, check black/red or black/pink wire for open.
8. If battery voltage is present, leave fused jumper connected as in step 6 and measure voltage between B and A wire terminals.
9. If battery voltage is not present, check black wire for open.
10. If battery voltage is present, replace coolant fan motor.

Coolant Fan Does Not Turn Off With Engine Coolant Cool, A/C Off & Ignition Switch In RUN Position

1. Turn ignition switch to RUN position, disconnect coolant fan relay connector and connect test lamp between F and D wire terminals.
2. If lamp does not illuminate, replace coolant fan relay.
3. If lamp illuminates, check dark green/yellow or dark green wire for short to ground. If wire is satisfactory, problem is ECM related.

Coolant fan does not turn on with A/C ON

1. Turn ignition switch to RUN position, place A/C mode selector in MAX position. Measure voltage between terminal C1/24 (VIN R) or C1/C9 (VIN N) of the ECM and ground.
2. If battery voltage is present, problem is ECM related.
3. If zero voltage is present, check light blue/black (VIN R) or light blue (VIN N) wire for open, repair as necessary.
4. If wire is satisfactory, problem is ECM related.

COOLANT FAN, REPLACE

1. Disconnect battery ground cable.
2. Disconnect wiring harness from motor and the fan frame.
3. Remove fan guard and hose support as necessary.
4. Remove fan assembly from radiator support.
5. reverse procedure to install.

CAMARO & FIREBIRD

SYSTEM DESCRIPTION

**2.8L/V6-173 VIN S,
3.1L/V6-192 VIN T,
5.0L/V8-305 VIN F &
5.7L/V8-350 VIN 8**

The coolant fan is controlled by the ECM. In the 6 cylinder, the coolant fan is also controlled by the redundant cooling fan switch. When the ECM grounds circuit 335, the coolant fan relay is energized and battery voltage is applied to the coolant fan. If the ECM fails on the 6 cylinder en-

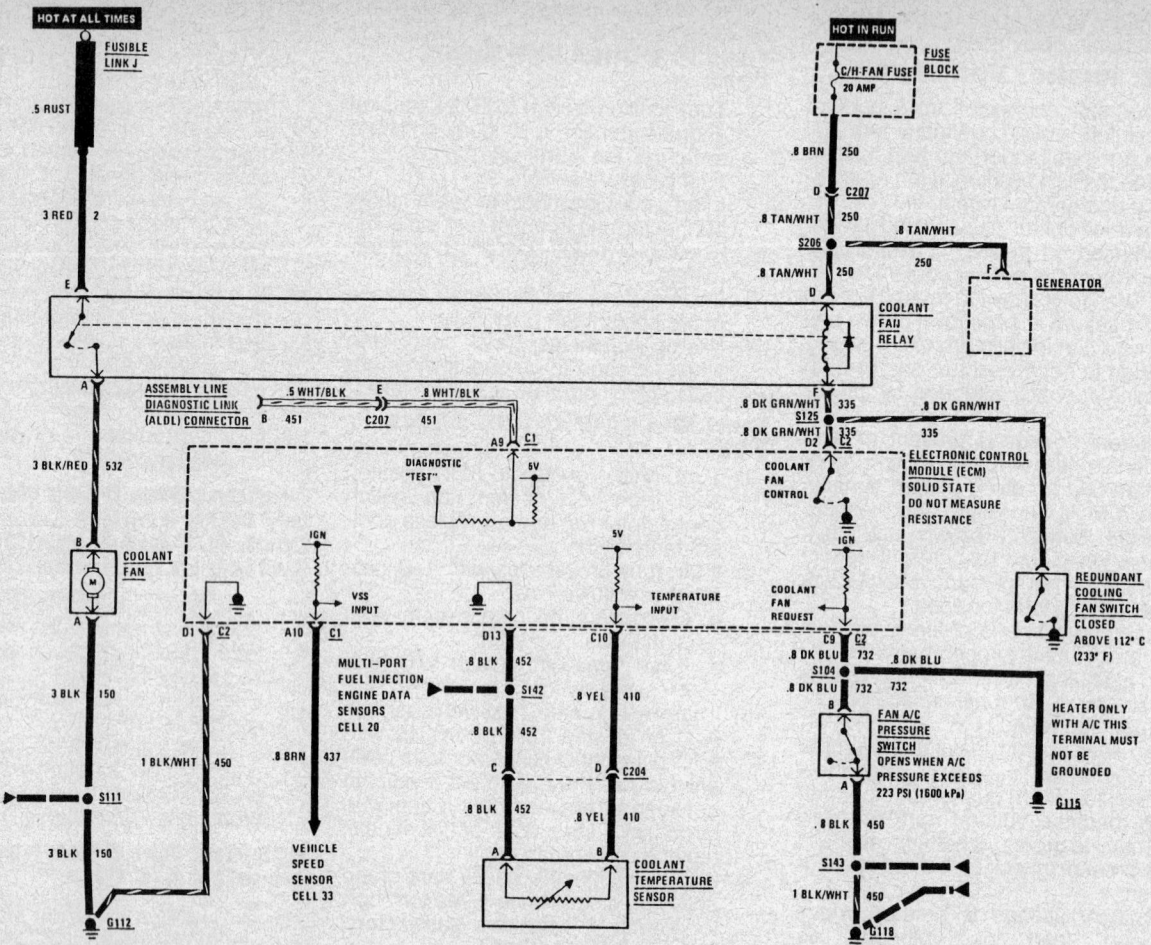

Fig. 23   Coolant fan wiring circuit. 1988–89 Firebird w/2.8L/V6-173 engine, VIN S

gine, the redundant coolant fan switch will ground the 335 circuit and energize the coolant fan relay. The ECM will ground the coolant fan relay when the coolant temperature sensor indicates the coolant temperature is greater than 222°F or when A/C control head pressure is greater than 233 psi and vehicle speed is less than 40 mph.

The auxiliary coolant fan, used on the 8 cylinder engines, is controlled by the fan pressure switch and the auxiliary coolant fan switch. If one of these switches closes, the auxiliary coolant fan relay is turned on. When a switch is closed, terminal D11 of ECM connector C2 is grounded. This tells the ECM that the auxiliary coolant fan should be on.

5.0L/V8-305 VIN H & 5.7L/V8-305 VIN E

The coolant fan is activated by the coolant fan switch. The switch closes when coolant temperature is over 238°F completing a path to ground through the coolant fan relay windings. The relay contacts then close and voltage is applied to the coolant fan. When the coolant temperature drops to 214°F, the switch opens and the coolant fan stops.

In A/C equipped vehicles, the A/C control head completes a path to ground for the coolant fan relay. Voltage is then applied to the coolant fan.

TROUBLESHOOTING

1. Check C/H-FAN fuse if coolant fan does not run.
2. Check that ground G112 (6 cylinder), G117 (V8 VINs E and H) or G104 (V8 VINs F and 8) is clean and tight.
3. Check fusible link J (6 cylinder) or H (8 cylinder).
4. If coolant fan runs with ignition switch off, replace coolant fan relay.

SYSTEM CHECK

1. With engine cold and idling, turn A/C selector, if equipped, to NORM. On VINs E and H, coolant fan should turn on. On VINs S, F and 8, coolant fan, and auxiliary coolant fan if equipped, should turn on when A/C control head pressure exceeds 233 psi.
2. With engine coolant below operating temperature, move A/C selector to off. On VINs E and H, coolant fan should turn off. On VINs S, F and 8, coolant fan, and auxiliary coolant fan if equipped, should turn off when A/C control head pressure falls below 233 psi.
3. With engine warm, run engine at fast idle foe several minutes. Coolant fan and, on 1988 models, the auxiliary

coolant fan if equipped, turns on before coolant temperature indicator lights or before coolant temperature gage needle indicates hot.
4. **On 1988 models,** turn ignition switch to OFF position. Coolant fan, and auxiliary coolant fan if equipped, should turn off.

DIAGNOSIS

Refer to **Figs. 23 through 31** when performing the following diagnostic procedures.

2.8L/V6-173 VIN S

If coolant fan does not run at all, perform test A. If coolant fan does not run with engine hot but does run with A/C on, perform test B. If coolant fan runs at all times with engine cool and A/C off, perform test C.

Test A: Coolant Fan Open Test

1. Connect fused jumper between ALDL connector terminal B and ground and turn ignition switch to RUN position. If coolant fan runs, problem is ECM related.
2. If coolant fan does not run, Connect fused jumper to coolant fan relay connector between dark green/white wire and ground and turn ignition

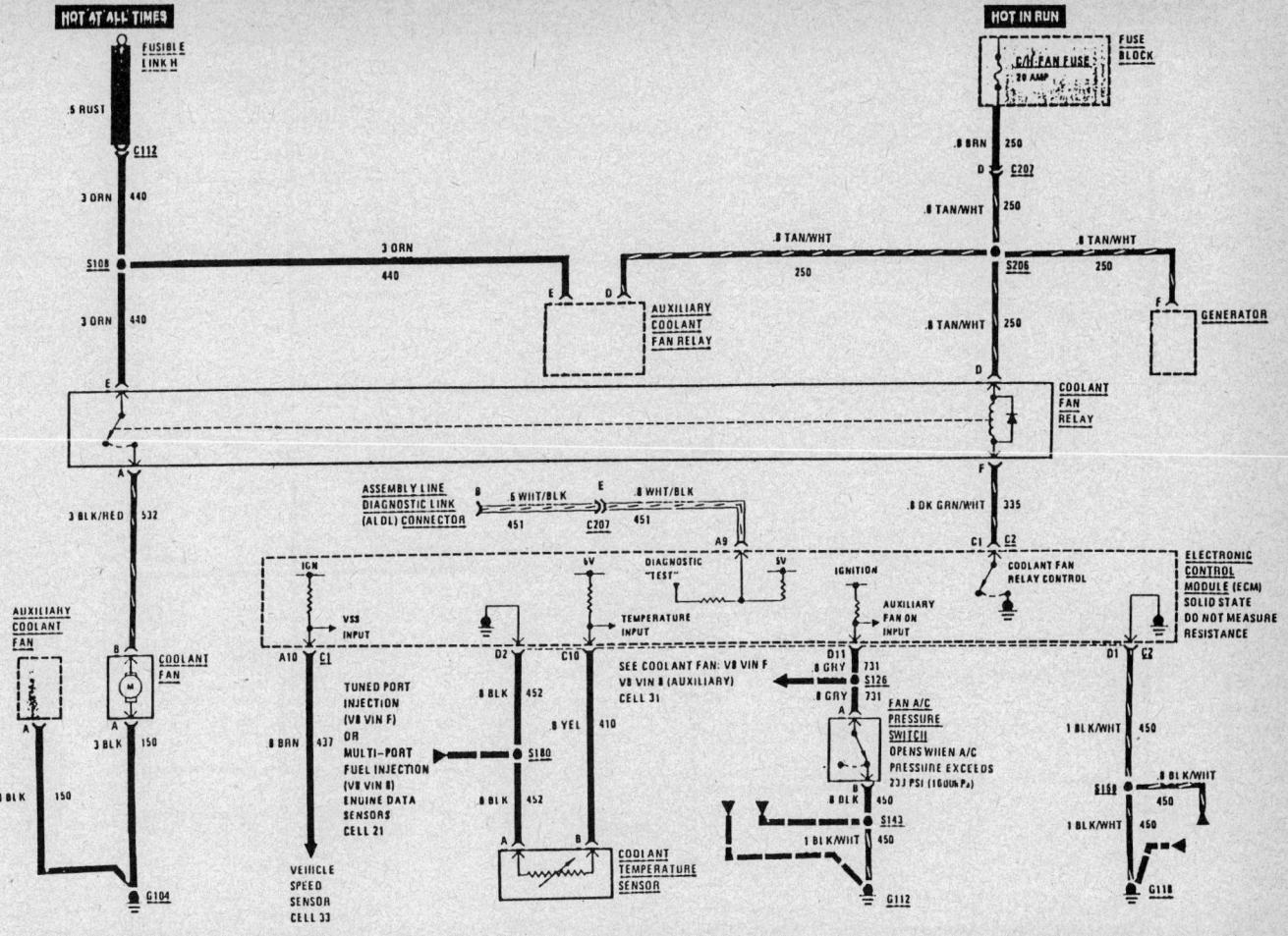

Fig. 24 Coolant fan wiring circuit. 1988–90 Firebird w/5.0L/V8-305 & 5.7L/V8-350 engines, VINS F & 8

switch to RUN position. If coolant fan runs, check dark green/white wire for open. If wire is satisfactory, problem is ECM related.

3. If coolant fan does not run, disconnect coolant fan relay connector, turn ignition switch to run position and connect test lamp between terminals as follows:
   a. Connect between brown (1988) wire terminal and ground. If lamp does not illuminate, check C/H-FAN fuse, brown wire for open.
   b. Connect between red wire terminal and ground. If lamp does not illuminate, check fusible link J and red wire for open.
4. If lamp illuminates in steps a and b, disconnect coolant fan relay connector and connect fused jumper between red and black/red wire terminals. If coolant fan runs, replace coolant fan relay.
5. If coolant fan does not run, leave fused jumper connected as in step 4, disconnect coolant fan connector and connect test lamp between terminals as follows:

a. Connect between black/red wire terminal and ground. If lamp does not illuminate, check black/red wire for open.
b. Connect between black/red and black wire terminals. If lamp does not illuminate, check black wire for open.
c. If lamp illuminates in steps a and b, replace coolant fan.

Test B: Coolant Fan Switch Test

1. Disconnect redundant coolant fan switch connector, connect fused jumper between dark green/white wire terminal and ground and turn ignition switch to RUN position.
2. If coolant fan runs, replace redundant cooling fan switch. If coolant fan still runs, problem is ECM related.
3. If coolant fan does not run, check dark green/white wire for open.

TEST C: Coolant Fan Short Test

1. With ignition switch in RUN position, remove redundant coolant fan switch connector. If coolant fan turns off, re-

place redundant coolant fan switch.
2. If coolant fan does not turn off, remove C/H-FAN fuse.
3. If coolant fan turns off, check dark green/white wires for short to ground. If wires are satisfactory, problem is ECM related.
4. If coolant fan does not turn off, replace coolant fan relay.

3.1L/V6-192 VIN T

If coolant fan does not run at all, perform test A. If coolant fan does not turn off with engine coolant cool, A/C Off and ignition switch in RUN position, perform test B. If coolant fan does not turn On with A/C On and head pressure above 223 psi, but does turn On with engine hot, perform test C.

Test A: Coolant Fan Open Test

1. Connect fused jumper between ALDL connector terminal B and ground and turn ignition switch to RUN position. If coolant fan runs, problem is ECM related.
2. If coolant fan does not run, connect fused jumper to coolant fan relay con-

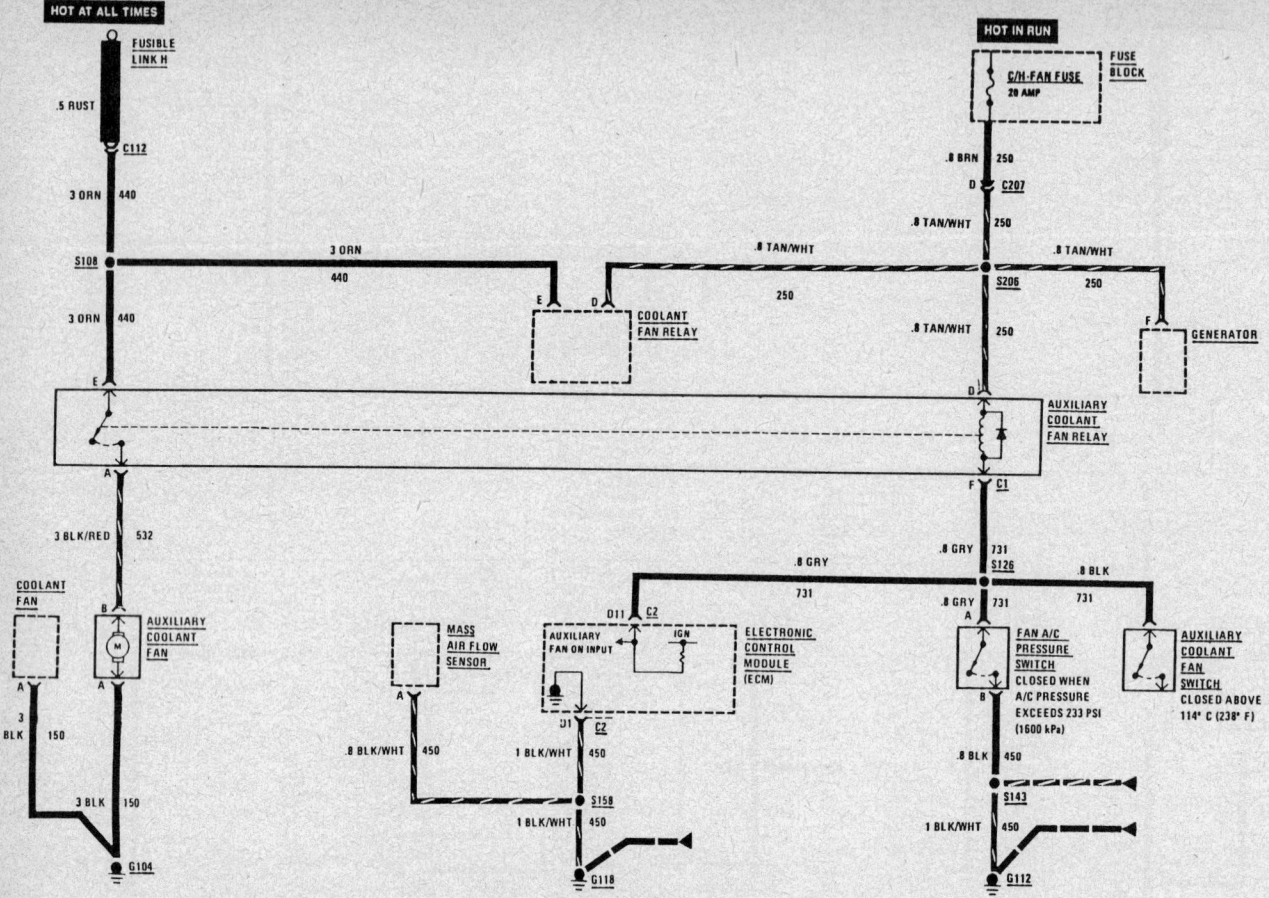

Fig. 25 Coolant fan wiring circuit (auxiliary cooling fan). 1988–90 Firebird w/5.0L/V8-305 & 5.7L/V8-350 engines, VINS F & 8

nector between dark green/white wire and ground and turn ignition switch to RUN position. If coolant fan runs, check dark green/white wire for open. If wire is satisfactory, problem is ECM related.

3. If coolant fan does not run, disconnect coolant fan relay connector, turn ignition switch to run position and connect test lamp between terminals as follows:
   a. Connect between terminal D and ground. If lamp does not illuminate, check C/H-FAN fuse, tan/white wire for open.
   b. Connect between red wire terminal and ground. If lamp does not illuminate, check fusible link J and red wire for open.

4. If lamp illuminates in steps a and b, disconnect coolant fan relay connector and connect fused jumper between red and black/red wire terminals. If coolant fan runs, replace coolant fan relay.

5. If coolant fan does not run, leave fused jumper connected as in step 4, disconnect coolant fan connector and connect test lamp between terminals as follows:
   a. Connect between black/red wire terminal and ground. If lamp does

not illuminate, check black/red wire for open.
   b. Connect between black/red and black wire terminals. If lamp does not illuminate, check black wire for open.
   c. If lamp illuminates in steps a and b, replace coolant fan.

Test B: Coolant Fan Does Not Turn Off With Engine Coolant Cool, A/C Off And Ignition Switch In RUN Position

1. Disconnect coolant fan relay, connect a test lamp between terminals D and F of the fan relay connector. If lamp does not light, replace coolant fan relay.

2. If test lamp lights, check and repair dark green/white wire for a short to ground. If wire is satisfactory, connect a fused jumper between terminal C2/D12 of the ECM and ground.

3. After waiting two minutes if fan continues to run, problem is ECM related.

4. If fan stops, disconnect fan A/C pressure switch connector and connect a fused jumper between terminal B and ground.

5. After two minutes if fan continues to run, check dark blue wire for an open.

6. If fan stops, connect a fused jumper between terminals B and A of the fan A/C pressure switch connector. If fan continues to run, Repair open in black/white wire.

7. If fan stops, replace fan A/C pressure switch.

Test C: Coolant Fan Does Not Turn On With A/C On And Head Pressure Above 223 psi, But Does Turn On With Engine Hot

1. With ignition switch in RUN position and A/C mode selector in MAX position, disconnect fan A/C pressure switch connector. Measure voltage between terminal B and ground. If zero volts is present, repair short to ground in dark green/white wire.

2. If battery voltage is present, problem is ECM related.

5.0L/V8-305 VIN F & 5.7L/V8-350 VIN 8

If coolant fan does not run at all, perform test A. If coolant fan runs at all times with A/C off and engine cools, perform test B. On 1988 models, if auxiliary coolant fan does not run at all, perform test C and, if auxiliary fan runs at all times with A/C off and engine cool, perform test D.

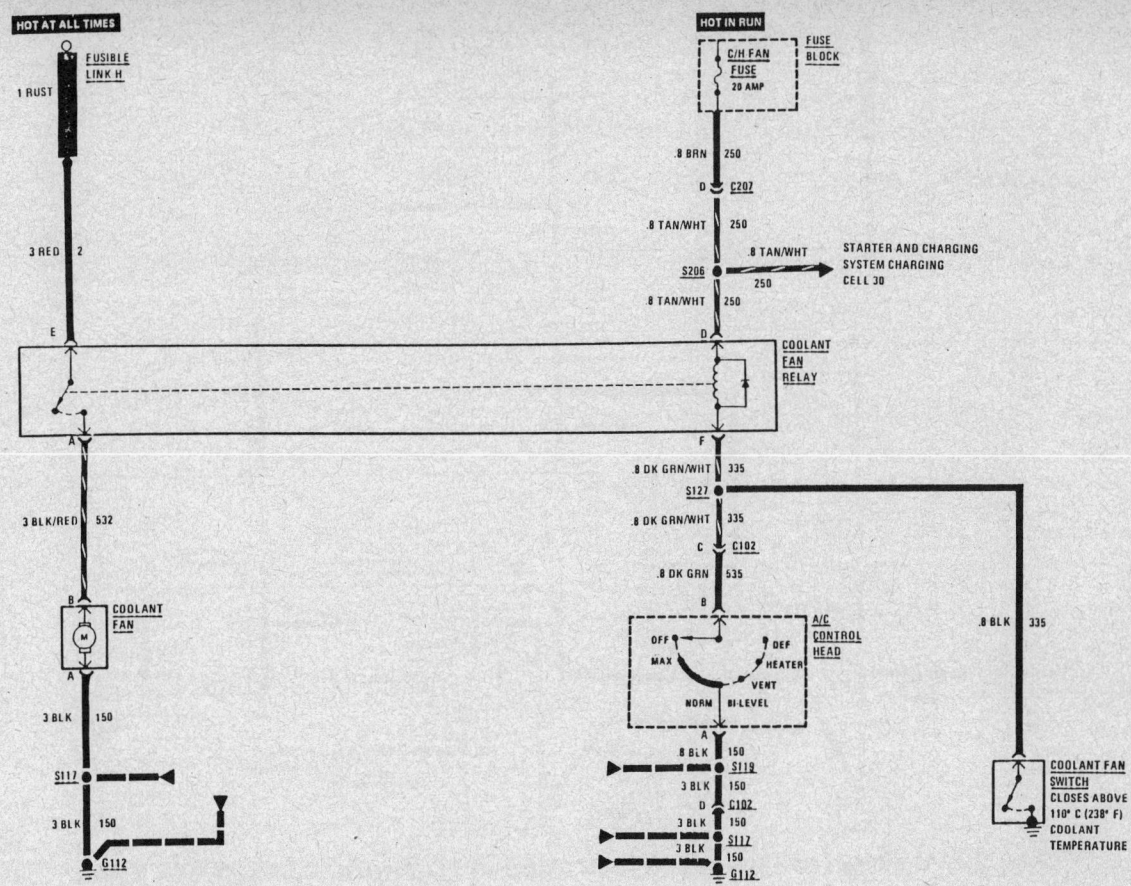

Fig. 26   Coolant fan wiring circuit. 1988 Camaro & Firebird w/5.0L/V8-305 VIN E

Test A: Coolant Fan Open Test

1. Connect fused jumper between ALDL connector b terminal and ground and turn ignition switch to RUN position. If coolant fan runs, problem is ECM related.
2. If coolant fan does not run, connect fused jumper between coolant fan relay connector dark green/white wire terminal and ground and turn ignition switch to RUN position. If coolant fan runs, check dark green/white wire for open. If wire is satisfactory, problem is ECM related.
3. If coolant fan does not run, disconnect coolant fan relay connector, turn ignition switch to RUN position and connect test lamp between terminals as follows:
   a. Connect between brown (1988) wire terminal and ground. If lamp does not illuminate, check C/H-FAN fuse, brown wire and, on 1988 models, tan/white wire for open.
   b. Connect between orange wire terminal and ground. If lamp does not illuminate, check fusible link H and orange wire for open.
4. If lamp illuminates in steps a and b, disconnect coolant fan relay connector and connect fused jumper be-

tween orange and black/red wire terminals. If coolant fan runs, replace coolant fan relay.
5. If coolant fan does not run, leave fused jumper connected as in step 4, disconnect coolant fan connector and connect test lamp between terminals as follows:
   a. Connect between black/red wire terminal and ground. If lamp does not illuminate, check black/red wire for open.
   b. Connect between black/red and black wire terminals. If lamp does not illuminate, check black wire for open.
   c. If lamp illuminates in steps a and b, replace coolant fan.

Test B: Coolant Fan Short Test

1. With ignition switch in RUN position, remove C/H-FAN fuse.
2. If coolant fan turns off, check dark green/white wire for short to ground. If wire is satisfactory, problem is ECM related.
3. If coolant fan does not turn off, replace coolant fan relay.

Test C: Auxiliary Coolant Fan Open Test

1. Connect fused jumper between auxiliary coolant fan relay connector dark

green/white wire and ground and turn ignition switch to RUN position. If auxiliary coolant fan runs, check dark green/white and gray wires for open and, if wires are satisfactory, check switches.
2. If auxiliary coolant fan does not run, disconnect auxiliary coolant fan relay connector, turn ignition switch to RUN position and connect test lamp between terminals as follows:
   a. Connect between orange wire (D) terminal and ground. If lamp does not illuminate, check orange and brown wires for open.
   b. Connect between orange wire wire (E) terminal and ground. If lamp does not illuminate, check orange wire for open.
3. If lamp illuminates in steps a and b, disconnect auxiliary coolant fan relay connector and connect fused jumper between orange (E) and black/red wire terminals. If auxiliary coolant fan runs, replace auxiliary coolant fan relay.
4. If auxiliary coolant fan does not run, leave fused jumper connected as in step 3, disconnect auxiliary coolant fan connector and connect test lamp between terminals as follows:
   a. Connect between black/red wire terminal and ground. If test lamp does not illuminate, check

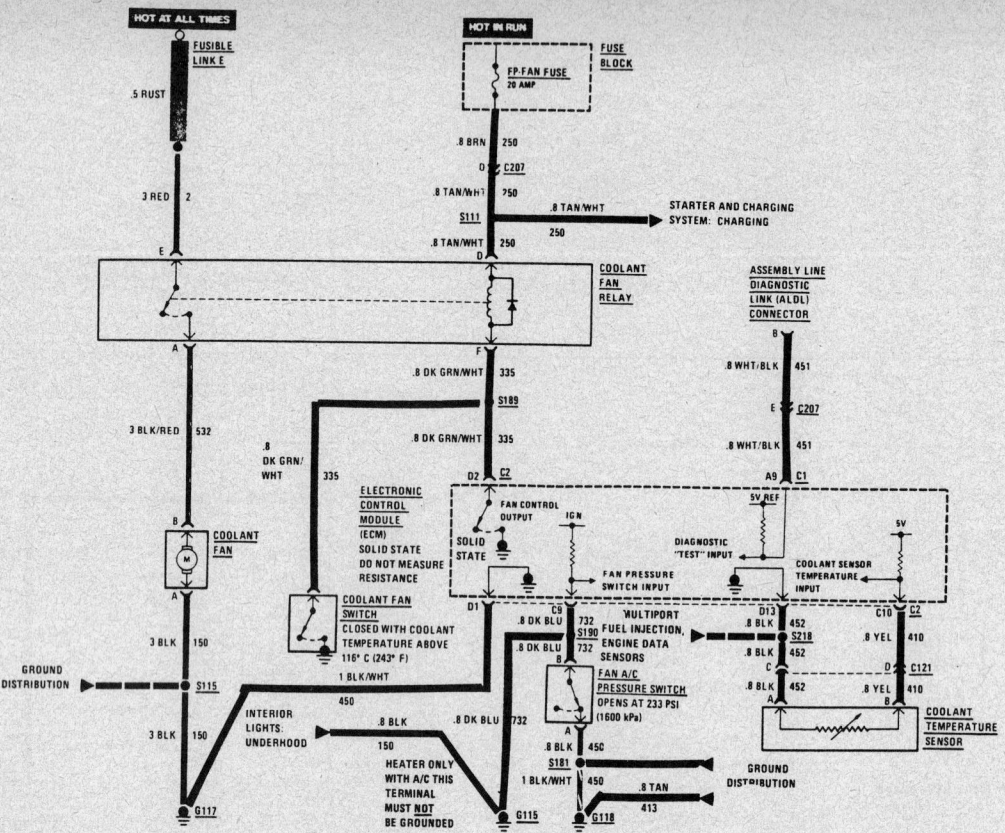

Fig. 27 Coolant fan wiring circuit. 1988–89 Camaro, 2.8L/V6-173 VIN S

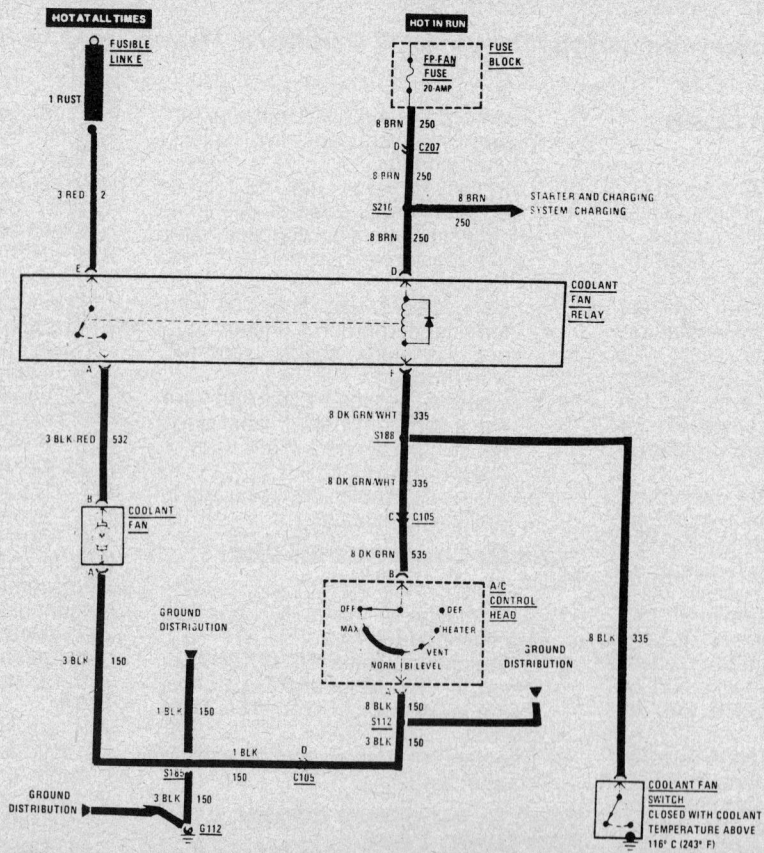

Fig. 28 Coolant fan wiring circuit. 1989–90 Camaro, 5.0L/V8-305 VIN E

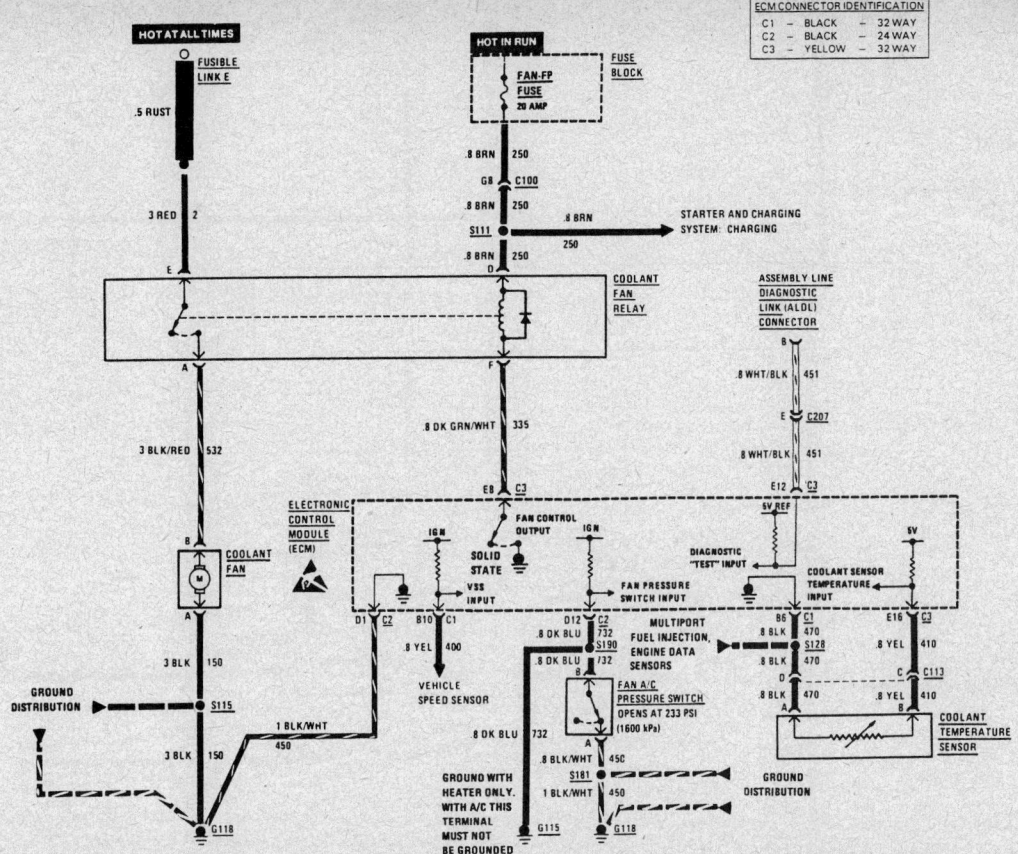

Fig. 29   Coolant fan wiring circuit. 1990 Firebird, 3.1L/V6-191 VIN T

black/red wire for open.
b. Connect between black/red and black wire terminals. If lamp does not illuminate, check black wire for open.
c. If lamp illuminates in steps a and b, replace auxiliary coolant fan.

Test D: Auxiliary Coolant Fan Short Test

1. With ignition switch in RUN position, disconnect auxiliary coolant fan switch. If auxiliary coolant fan turns off, replace auxiliary coolant fan switch.
2. If auxiliary coolant fan does not turn off, disconnect fan pressure switch. If auxiliary coolant fan turns off, replace fan pressure switch.
3. If auxiliary coolant fan does not turn off, remove C/H-FAN fuse.
4. If auxiliary coolant fan does not turn off, replace auxiliary coolant fan relay.
5. If auxiliary coolant fan turns off, check dark green/white and gray wires for open.

5.0L/V8-305 VIN H

If coolant fan does not run with engine hot and A/C on, perform test A. If coolant fan does not run with engine hot but does run with A/C on, perform test B. If coolant fan does not run with A/C on but does run with engine hot, perform test C. If coolant fan runs at all times with A/C off and engine cool, perform test D. If auxiliary coolant fan does not run with ignition switch off

and engine coolant hot, perform test E. If auxiliary coolant fan runs with ignition switch in RUN position, replace auxiliary coolant fan relay.

Test A: Coolant Fan Open Test

1. Connect fused jumper between between coolant fan relay connector dark green wire and ground and turn ignition switch to RUN position. If coolant fan runs, check dark green wire for open.
2. If coolant fan does not run, disconnect coolant fan relay connector, turn ignition switch to run position and connect test lamp between terminals as follows:
   a. Connect between brown/white wire terminal and ground. If lamp does not illuminate, check C/H-FAN fuse brown and brown/white wires for open.
   b. Connect between rust wire terminal and ground. If lamp does not illuminate, check fusible link F, fusible link B and red wire for open.
3. If lamp illuminates in steps a and b, disconnect coolant fan relay connector and connect fused jumper between between rust and black/red wire terminals. If coolant fan runs, replace coolant fan relay.
4. If coolant fan does not run, leave fused jumper connected as in step 3, disconnect coolant fan connector and connect test lamp between terminals

as follows:
a. Connect between black/red wire terminal and ground. If lamp does not illuminate, check black red wire for open.
b. Connect between black/red and black wire terminals. If lamp does not illuminate, check black wire for open.
c. If lamp illuminates in steps a and b, replace coolant fan.

Test B: Coolant Fan Switch Test

1. Disconnect coolant fan switch connector, turn ignition switch to RUN position and connect fused jumper between black wire terminal and ground.
2. If coolant fan runs, replace coolant fan switch.
3. If coolant fan does not run, check black wire for open.

Test C: A/C Control Head Test

1. Disconnect A/C control head connector, turn ignition switch to RUN position and connect fused jumper between terminals as follows:
   a. Connect between dark green wire connector and ground. If coolant fan does not run, check dark green wire for open.
   b. Connect between dark green and black wire terminals. If coolant fan does not run, check black wire for open.

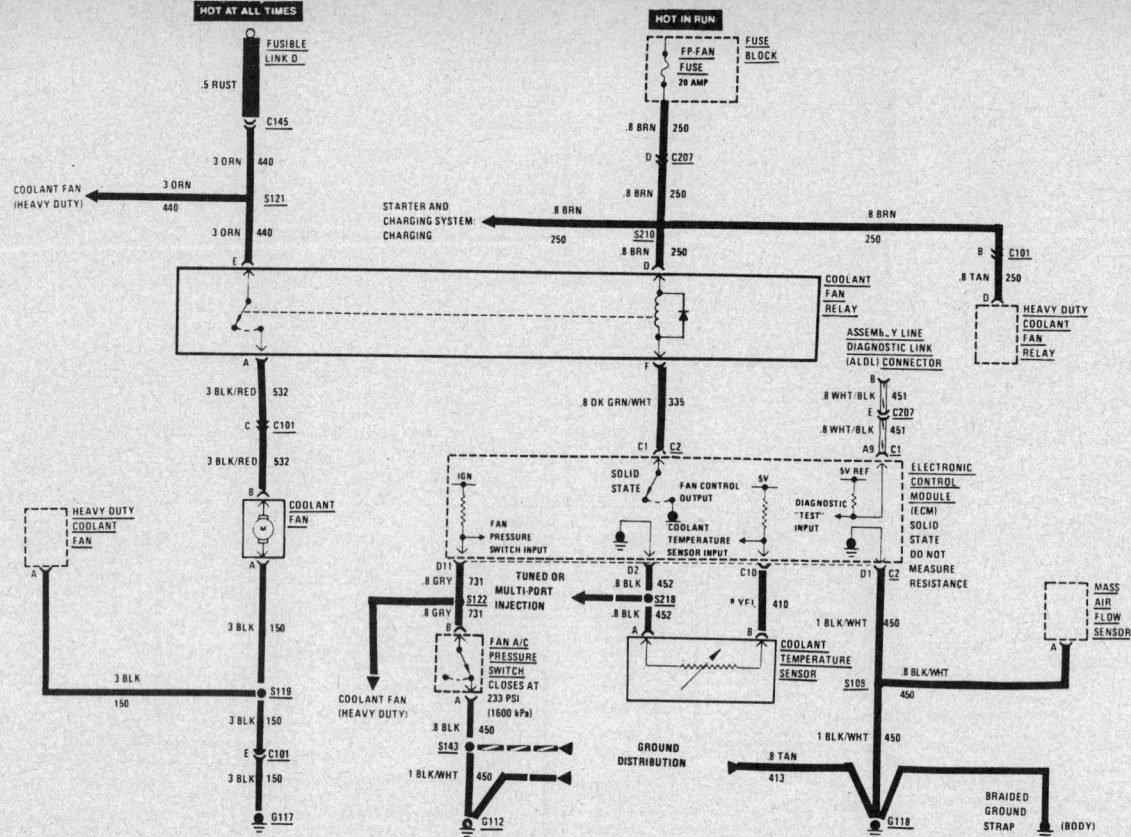

Fig. 30   Coolant fan wiring circuit. 1988–90 Camaro, 5.0L/V8-305 & 5.7L/V8-350 VINS F & 8

2. If lamp illuminates in steps a and b, replace A/C control head.

Test D: Coolant Fan Short Test

1. With ignition switch in RUN position, remove coolant fan switch. If fan turns off, replace coolant fan switch.
2. If fan does not turn off, remove C/H-FAN fuse. If fan does not turn off, replace coolant fan relay.
3. If fan turns off, disconnect A/C control head and reconnect C/H-FAN fuse.
4. If fan continues to run, check dark green and black wires for short to ground.
5. If fan turns off, replace A/C control head.

5.0L/V8-305 VIN E

If coolant fan does not run with engine hot and A/C on, perform test A. If coolant fan does not run with engine hot but does run with A/C on, perform test B. If coolant fan does not run with A/C on but does run with engine hot, perform test C. If coolant fan runs at all times with A/C off and engine cool, perform test D.

Test A: Coolant Fan Open Test

1. Connect fused jumper between dark

green wire of coolant fan relay connector and ground and turn ignition switch to RUN position. If coolant fan runs, check dark green wire for open.
2. If coolant fan does not run, disconnect coolant fan relay connector, turn ignition switch to RUN position and connect test lamp between terminals as follows:
   a. Connect between brown wire terminal and ground. If lamp does not illuminate, check C/H-FAN fuse and brown wire for open.
   b. Connect between red wire terminal and ground. If lamp does not illuminate, check fusible link H and red wire for open.
3. If lamp illuminates in steps a and b, disconnect coolant fan relay connector and connect fused jumper between red and black/red wire terminals. If coolant fan runs, replace coolant fan relay.
4. If coolant fan does not run, leave fused jumper connected as in step 3, disconnect coolant fan connector and connect test lamp between terminals as follows:
   a. Connect between black/red wire terminal and ground. If lamp does not illuminate, check black/red wire for open.
   b. Connect between black/red and black wire terminals. If lamp does not illuminate, check black wire for open.

c. If lamp illuminates in steps a and b, replace coolant fan.

Test B: Coolant Fan Switch Test

1. Disconnect coolant fan switch connector, turn ignition switch to RUN position and connect fused jumper between black wire terminal and ground.
2. If coolant fan runs, replace coolant fan switch.
3. If coolant fan does not run, check black wire for open.

Test C: A/C Control Head Test

1. Disconnect A/C control head 5 pin connector, turn ignition switch to RUN position and connect fused jumper between terminals as follows:
   a. Connect between dark green wire terminal and ground. If coolant fan does not run, check dark green/white and dark green wires for open.
   b. Connect between dark green and black wire terminals. If coolant fan does not run, check black wire for open.
2. If coolant fan runs in steps a and b, replace A/C control head.

Test D: Coolant Fan Short Test

1. With ignition switch in RUN position, remove coolant fan switch. If fan turns

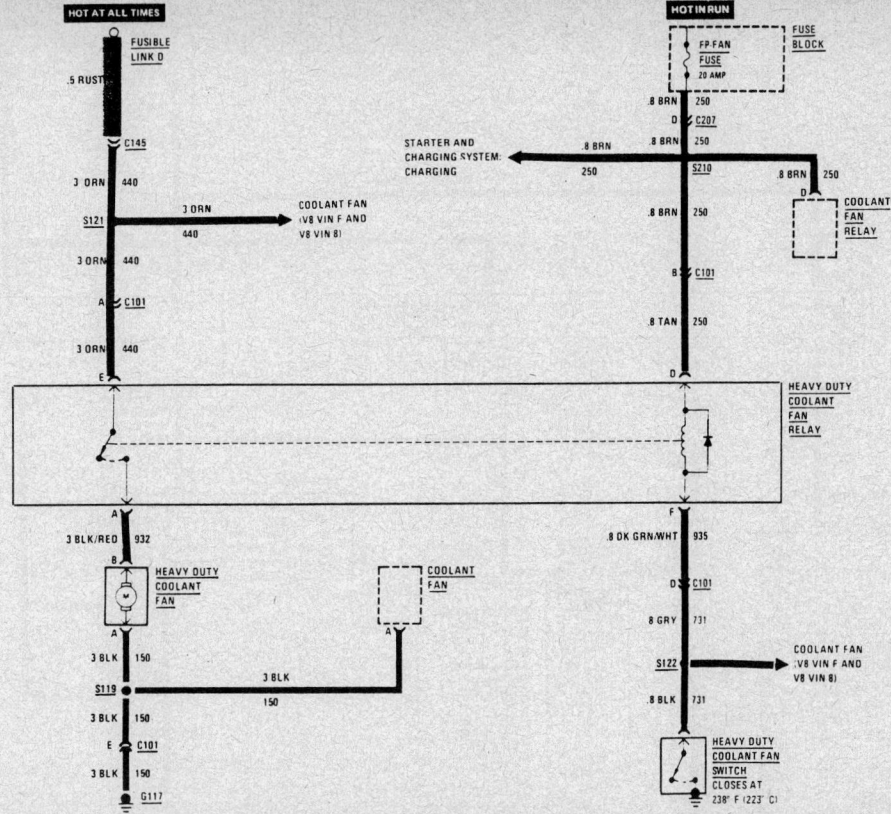

Fig. 31 Coolant fan wiring circuit (heavy duty). 1988–90 Camaro 5.0L/V8-305 & 5.7L/V8-350 VINS F & 8

off, replace coolant fan switch.
2. If fan does not turn off, remove C/H-FAN fuse. If fan does not turn off, replace coolant fan relay.
3. If fan turns off, disconnect A/C control head and reconnect C/H-FAN fuse.
4. If fan does not turn off, check dark green/white and black wires for short to ground.
5. If fan turns off, replace A/C control head.

COOLANT FAN, REPLACE

1. Disconnect battery ground cable.
2. Remove harness from fan motor and fan frame.
3. Remove fan frame to radiator support attaching bolts.
4. Remove fan and frame assembly.
5. Reverse procedure to install.

1988 BONNEVILLE

SYSTEM DESCRIPTION

3.8L/V6-231 VIN C

A two speed coolant fan is turned on and off by the low and high speed coolant fan relays.

For low speed operation, the low speed relay coil is grounded through the ECM. The ECM grounds the coil when vehicle speed is less than 35 mph and engine coolant is above 208°F, or when the ECM receives an A/C input.

With the low speed relay coil grounded, its contacts close. Voltage is applied

through the coolant fan resistor to the coolant fan. The resistor reduces voltage supplied to the fan so the fan runs at low speed.

For high speed operation, the high speed relay coil is grounded through the high speed contacts in the A/C dual pressure switch or by the ECM. The A/C dual pressure switch high speed contacts close at a refrigerant pressure above 300 psi. The ECM switch closes when coolant temperature rises above 226°F.

With high speed coil grounded, its contacts close. Battery voltage is applied to the coolant fan. The fan runs at high speed.

The coolant fan with heavy duty, if equipped, whenever coolant fan runs at high speed. The A/C dual pressure switch and ECM also control the auxiliary coolant fan relay which supplies battery voltage to the auxiliary coolant fan when energized.

3.8L/V6-231 VIN 3

The coolant fan is turned on when the contacts of the coolant fan relay close and supply voltage to the fan from fusible link C. Terminal 2 of the relay coil is supplied with battery voltage from fuse 6 whenever ignition switch is in RUN position. When a ground is furnished to terminal 5 of the relay coil, the relay contacts close, starting the fan. Terminal 5 may be grounded either by the ECM, when engine coolant temperature is above 208°F, by the A/C pressure switch, when refrigerant pressure exceeds 260 psi or by the temperature switch when engine coolant temperature

is above 226°F (without heavy duty coolant fan).

The heavy duty coolant fan operate in a manner similar to the coolant fan. Its relay is energized when engine coolant temperature is above 226°F by the temperature switch or when refrigerant pressure is above 300 psi by the A/C dual pressure switch. When the heavy duty coolant fan relay is energized, battery voltage is applied to the heavy duty coolant fan and it runs.

TROUBLESHOOTING

1. Visually inspect fuse 6.
2. Check fusible link C.
3. If either fan runs with ignition switch off, replace associated coolant fan relay.

SYSTEM CHECK

1. With engine cold and idling, move A/C selector switch, if equipped, to NORM. The coolant fan should turn on.
2. With engine coolant below operating temperature, move A/C selector switch to OFF. Coolant fan should turn off.
3. Run engine at fast idle for several minutes. The coolant fan should turn on before the coolant temperature indicator comes on.

SYSTEM DIAGNOSIS

Refer to **Figs. 32 through 35** when performing diagnostic procedures on these systems.

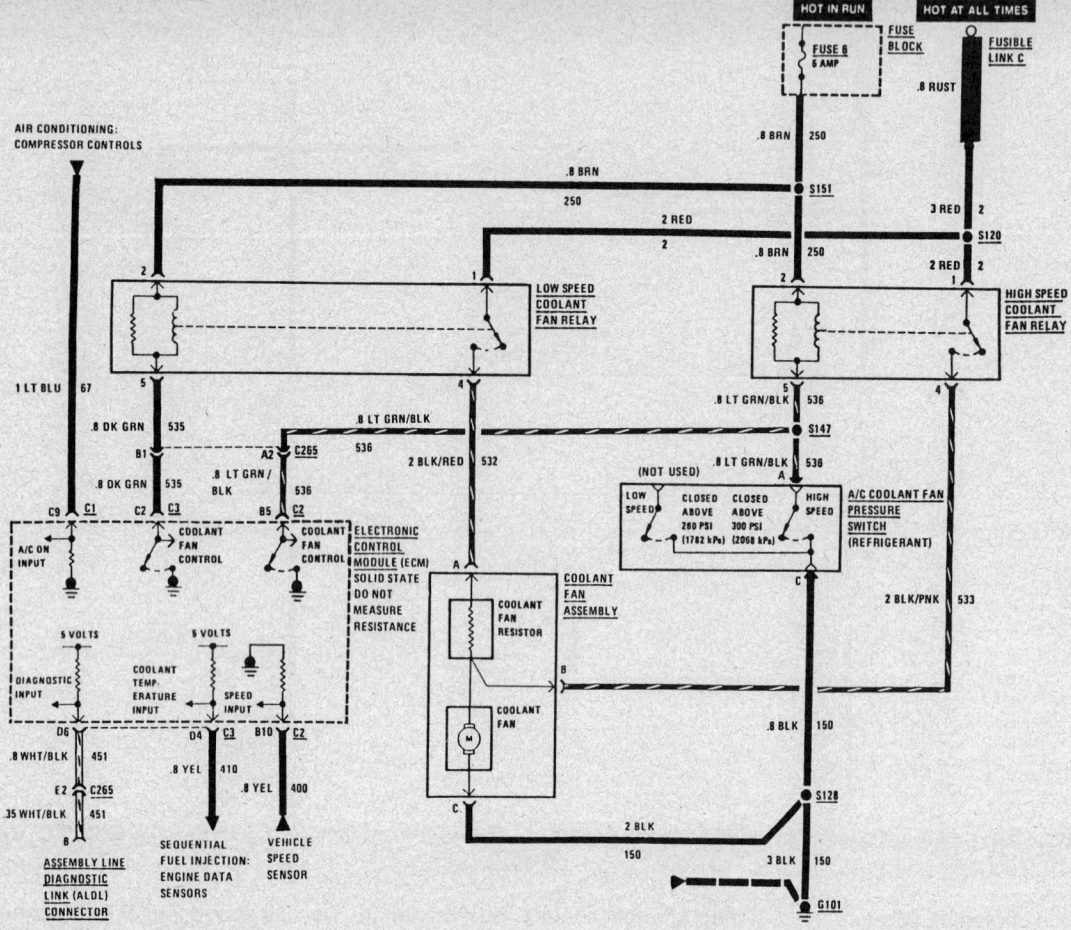

Fig. 32 Coolant fan wiring circuit (less heavy duty). 1988 Bonneville w/3.8L/V6-231 VIN C

VIN 3

Coolant Fan Does Not Run

1. Connect fused jumper at ALDL connector between white/black wire terminal and ground and turn ignition switch to RUN position. If coolant fan runs, problem is ECM related.
2. If coolant fan runs, turn ignition switch to RUN position and connect fused jumper between ECM connector C1 dark green wire terminal and ground. If coolant fan runs, problem is ECM related.
3. If coolant fan does not run, leave fused jumper connected as in step 2, disconnect coolant fan relay connector, turn ignition switch to RUN position and connect test lamp between terminals as follows:
   a. Connect between brown wire terminal and ground. If lamp does not illuminate, check fuse 6 and brown wire for open.
   b. Connect between brown and dark green wire terminals. If lamp does not illuminate, check dark green wire and coolant fan diode.
   c. Connect between red wire terminal and ground. If lamp does not illuminate, check fusible link C and red wire for open.

4. If lamp illuminates in steps a, b and c, disconnect coolant fan relay connector and connect fused jumper between red and black/red wire terminals. If coolant fan runs, replace coolant fan relay.
5. If coolant fan does not run, leave fused jumper connected as in step 4, disconnect coolant fan connector, turn ignition switch to RUN position and connect test lamp between terminals as follows:
   a. Connect between red/black wire terminal and ground. If lamp does not illuminate, check red/black wire for open.
   b. Connect between red/black and black wire terminals. If lamp does not illuminate, check black wire for open.
   c. If lamp illuminates in steps a and b, replace coolant fan.

Auxiliary Coolant Fan Does Not Run

1. Turn ignition switch to RUN position and connect a fused jumper between light green/black wire and ground at temperature switch. If auxiliary coolant fan runs, replace temperature switch.
2. If auxiliary coolant fan does not run,

leave fused jumper connected as in step 1, disconnect auxiliary coolant fan relay connector, turn ignition switch to RUN position and connect test lamp between terminals as follows:
   a. Connect between brown wire terminal and ground. If lamp does not illuminate, check fuse 6 and brown wire for open.
   b. Connect between brown and light green/black wire terminals. If lamp does not illuminate, check light green/black wire for open.
   c. Connect between red wire terminal and ground. If lamp does not illuminate, check fusible link C and red wire for open.
3. If lamp illuminates in steps a, b and c, disconnect auxiliary coolant fan relay connector and connect fused jumper between red and white wire terminals. If auxiliary coolant fan runs, replace auxiliary coolant fan relay.
4. If auxiliary coolant fan does not run, leave fused jumper connected as in step 3, disconnect auxiliary coolant fan connector, turn ignition switch to RUN position and connect test lamp between terminals as follows:
   a. Connect between white wire terminal and ground. If lamp does not il-

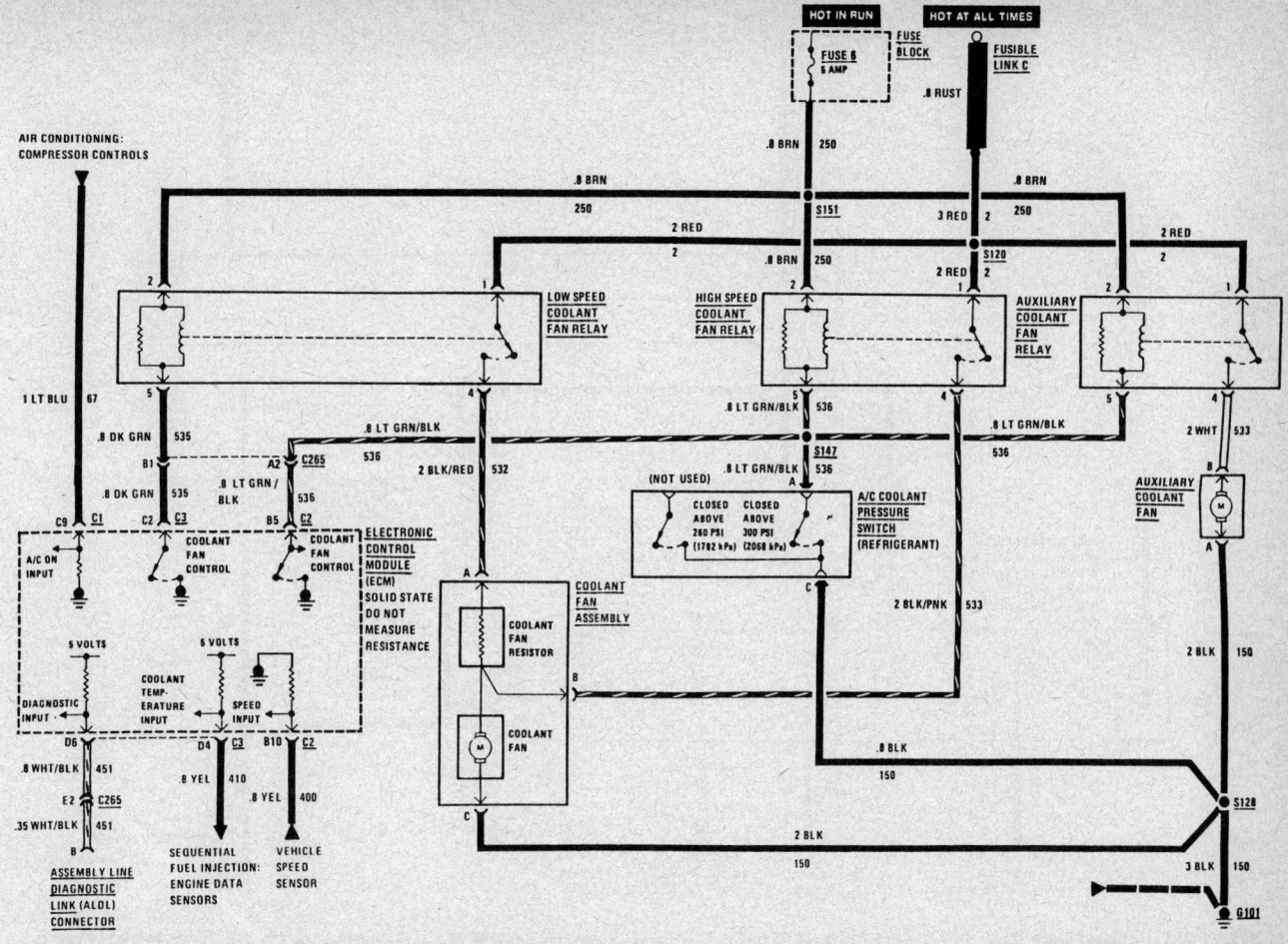

Fig. 33 Coolant fan wiring circuit (with heavy duty). 1988 Bonneville w/3.8L/V6-231 VIN C

luminate, check white wire for open.

b. Connect between white and black wire terminals. If lamp does not illuminate, check black wire for open.

c. If lamp illuminates in steps a and b, replace auxiliary coolant fan.

Coolant Fan Does Not Turn Off

1. Remove temperature switch connector, if equipped, while engine is cool. If coolant fan stops, replace temperature switch.
2. If coolant fan does not stop, remove A/C pressure switch connector. If coolant fan stops, replace A/C pressure switch.
3. If coolant fan does not stop, remove ECM connector C1 with ignition switch in RUN position and engine not running. If coolant fan stops, problem is ECM related.
4. If coolant fan does not stop, remove fuse 6.
5. If coolant fan stops, check dark green/white wire for short to ground.
6. If coolant fan does not stop, replace coolant fan relay.

Auxiliary Coolant Fan Does Not Turn Off

1. Remove A/C pressure switch connector.

2. If auxiliary coolant fan stops, replace A/C pressure switch.
3. If auxiliary coolant fan does not stop, remove fuse 6.
4. If auxiliary coolant fan stops, check light green/black wire for short to ground.
5. If auxiliary coolant fan does not stop, replace auxiliary coolant fan relay.

Coolant Fan Or Auxiliary Coolant Fan Does Not Run With A/C On & Functioning Properly But Does Run With Engine Hot

1. Disconnect A/C pressure switch connector, turn ignition switch to RUN position and connect fused jumper between terminals as follows:
   a. Connect between dark green wire terminal and ground. If coolant fan does not run, check dark green wire for open.
   b. Connect between dark green and black wire terminals. If coolant fan does not run, check black wire for open.
2. If coolant fan runs in steps a and b, replace A/C pressure switch.

VIN C

Coolant Fan Does Not Run

1. Disconnect high speed coolant fan re-

lay connector and connect a 20 amp fused jumper between red and white wire terminals. If coolant fan runs, proceed to "Coolant Fan Does Not Run In Low Speed" and "Coolant Fan Does Not Run In High Speed."

2. If coolant fan runs, leave fused jumper connected as in step 1, disconnect coolant fan assembly connector and measure voltage from white wire terminal to ground. If battery voltage is not present, check fusible link C, red wire and white wire for open.
3. If battery voltage is present, leave fused jumper connected as in step 1 and measure voltage between white and black wire terminals at coolant fan assembly connector. If battery voltage is not present, check black wire for open.
4. If battery voltage is present, check coolant fan assembly connector terminals and, if satisfactory, replace coolant fan assembly.

Coolant Fan Does Not Run In Low Speed

1. Turn ignition switch to RUN position and ground black terminal of ALDL connector with fused jumper. If coolant fan runs, problem is ECM related.
2. If coolant fan does not run, turn ignition switch to RUN position and ground dark green wire terminal at

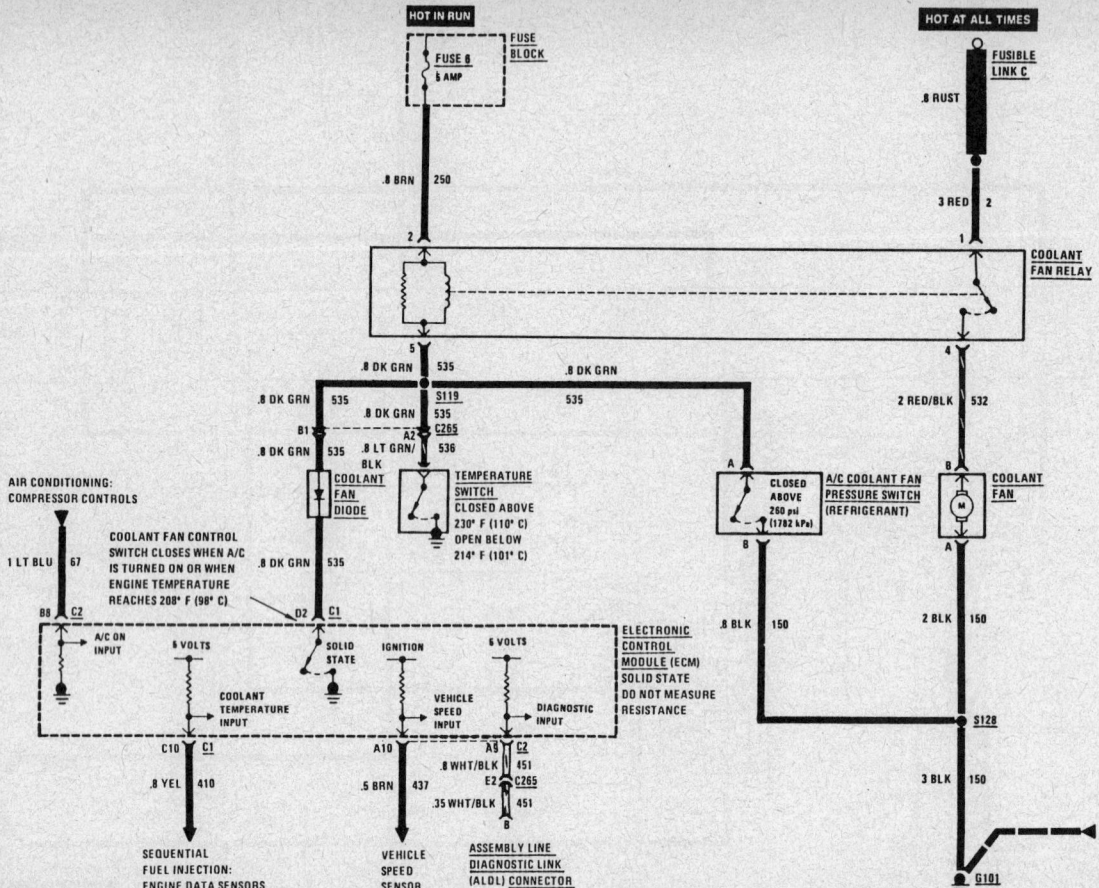

Fig. 34 Coolant fan wiring circuit (less heavy duty). 1989 Bonneville w/3.8L/V6-231 VIN 3

ECM connector C3 with fused jumper. If coolant fan runs, problem is ECM related.

3. If coolant fan does not run, leave fused jumper connected as in step 2, place ignition switch in RUN position, disconnect low speed coolant fan relay connector and measure voltage from brown wire terminal to ground. If battery voltage is not present, check fuse 6 and brown wire for open.

3. If battery voltage is present, leave fused jumper connected as in step 2, turn ignition switch to RUN position and measure voltage between brown and dark green wire terminals at low speed coolant fan relay connector. If battery voltage is not present, check dark green wire for open.

4. If battery voltage is present, measure voltage from red wire terminal to ground at low speed coolant fan relay connector. If battery voltage is not present, check red wire for open.

5. If battery voltage is present, disconnect low speed coolant fan relay connector and connect fused jumper with 20 amp fuse between red and black/red wire terminals. If coolant fan runs, check low speed coolant fan relay connector terminals and, if satisfactory, replace low speed coolant fan relay.

6. If coolant fan does not run, check black/red wire for open. If wire is satisfactory, check black/red wire termi-

nal contact at coolant fan assembly and, if satisfactory, replace coolant fan assembly.

Coolant Fan Does Not Run In High Speed

1. Disconnect connector C2 from ECM and ground terminal B5 with a fused jumper. If coolant fan runs, problem is ECM related.

2. If coolant fan does not run, leave fused jumper connected as in step 1, disconnect high speed coolant fan relay, turn ignition switch to RUN position and measure voltage from brown wire terminal to ground. If battery voltage is not present, check brown wire and fuse 6 for open.

3. If battery voltage is present, leave fused jumper connected as in step 1, turn ignition switch to RUN position and measure voltage between brown and light green/black wire terminals at high speed coolant fan relay. If battery voltage is not present, check light green/black wire for open.

4. If battery voltage is present, measure voltage between red wire terminal and ground. If battery voltage is not present, check red wire for open.

5. If battery voltage is present disconnect high speed coolant fan relay connector and connect fused jumper with 20 amp fuse between red and white wire terminals. If coolant fan runs, check auxiliary coolant fan connector

terminals and, if satisfactory, replace auxiliary coolant fan motor.

6. If coolant fan does not run, check white wire for open. If wire is satisfactory, check auxiliary coolant fan relay connector terminal contact and, if satisfactory, replace auxiliary coolant fan relay.

Auxiliary Coolant Fan Does Not Run

1. Disconnect connector from A/C dual pressure switch and ground light green/black wire terminal with fused jumper. If auxiliary coolant fan runs, check A/C system and, if satisfactory, replace A/C dual pressure switch.

2. If auxiliary coolant fan does not run, leave fused jumper connected as in step 1, disconnect auxiliary coolant fan relay connector, turn ignition switch to RUN position and measure voltage from brown wire terminal to ground. If battery voltage is not present, check brown wire and fuse 6 for open.

3. If battery voltage is present, leave fused jumper connected as in step 1, turn ignition switch to RUN position and measure voltage between brown and light green/black wire terminals. If battery voltage is not present, check light green/black wire for open.

4. If battery voltage is present, measure voltage between red wire terminal and ground. If battery voltage is not pres-

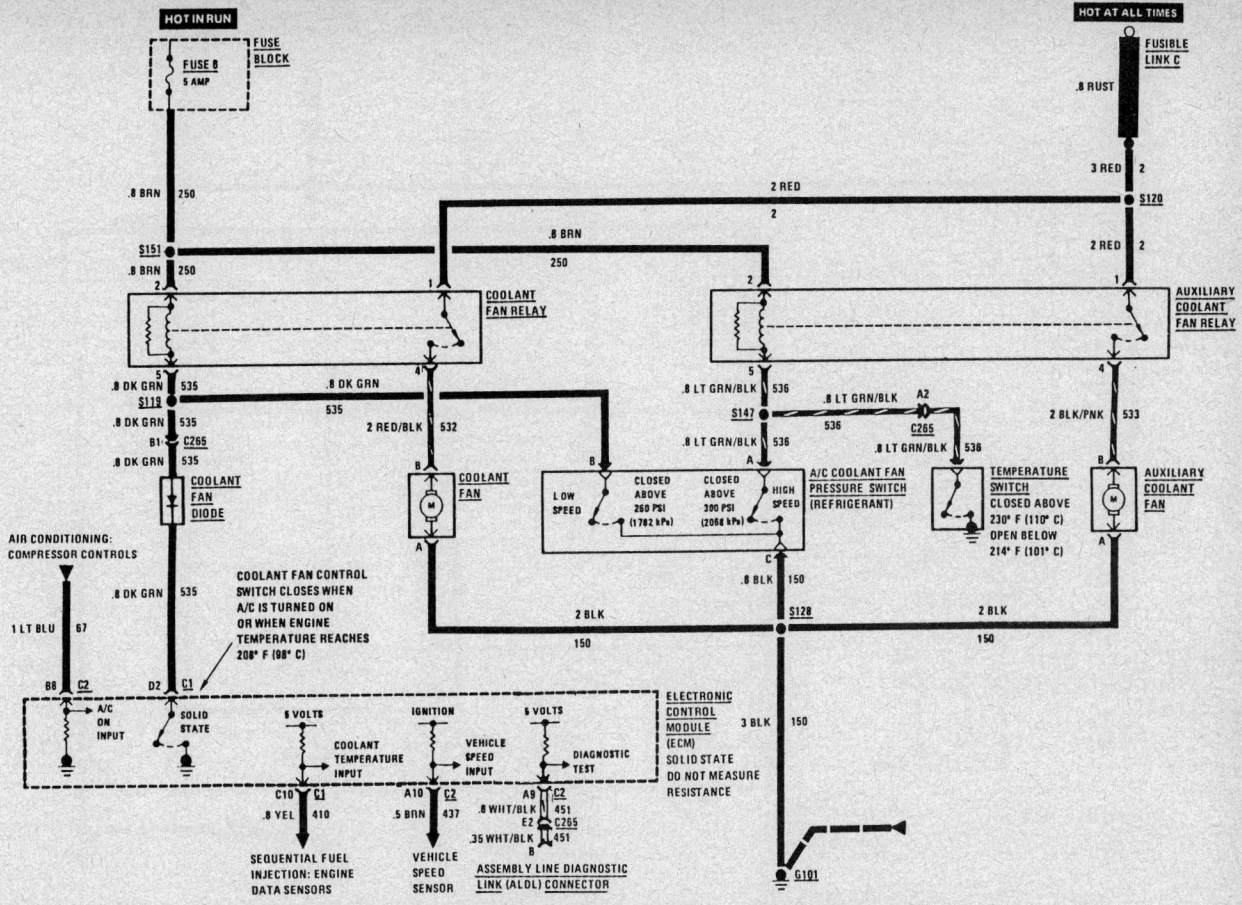

Fig. 35 Coolant fan wiring circuit (with heavy duty). 1989 Bonneville w/3.8L/V6-231 VIN 3

ent, check red wire for open.

5. If battery voltage is present, disconnect auxiliary coolant fan relay connector and connect fused jumper with 20 amp fuse between red and white wire terminals. If auxiliary coolant fan runs, check auxiliary coolant fan relay connector terminal contact and, if satisfactory, replace auxiliary coolant fan relay.

6. If auxiliary coolant fan does not run, leave fused jumper connected as in step 5, disconnect auxiliary coolant fan connector and measure voltage between white wire terminal and ground. If battery voltage is not present, check white wire for open.

7. If battery voltage is present, leave fused jumper connected as in step 5, and measure voltage between white and black wire terminals.

8. If battery voltage is not present, check black wire for open.

9. If battery voltage is present, check auxiliary coolant fan connector terminals and, if satisfactory, replace auxiliary coolant fan motor.

Coolant Fan Runs Continuously In Low Speed With Ignition Switch In RUN Position, Engine Coolant Cool & A/C Off

1. Place ignition switch in RUN position

and disconnect ECM connector C3. If coolant fan stops, problem is ECM related.

2. If coolant fan runs, disconnect low speed coolant fan relay connector, turn ignition switch to RUN position and connect test lamp between brown and dark green wire terminals.

3. If lamp does not illuminate, replace low speed coolant fan relay.

4. If light illuminates, check dark green wire for short to ground.

Coolant Fan Runs Continuously In High Speed And/Or Auxiliary Coolant Fan Runs Continuously With Ignition Switch IN RUN Position, Engine Coolant Cool & A/C Off

1. Turn ignition switch to RUN position and disconnect ECM connector C2. If coolant fan(s) stop(s), problem is ECM related.

2. If coolant fan(s) run(s), place ignition switch in RUN position and disconnect A/C dual pressure switch. If coolant fan(s) do(es) not run, check A/C system and, if satisfactory, replace A/C dual pressure switch.

3. If coolant fan(s) run(s), place ignition switch in RUN position, disconnect high speed coolant fan relay connec-

tor and/or auxiliary coolant fan relay connector and connect test lamp between brown and light green/black wire terminals.

4. If lamp does not illuminate, replace suspect relay.

5. If lamp illuminates, check light green/black wires for short to ground.

Low Speed Coolant Fan Does Not Operate Immediately After Selecting A/C

1. Disconnect ECM connector C1, turn ignition switch to RUN position, place A/C selector at NORM position and measure voltage at terminal C9.

2. If battery voltage is not present, problem is in A/C compressor controls.

3. If battery voltage is present, problem is ECM related.

High Speed Coolant Fan And/Or Auxiliary Coolant Fan Do Not Operate With A/C Pressure Above 300 psi

1. Disconnect connector from A/C dual pressure switch, turn ignition switch to RUN position and ground light green/black wire terminal with fused jumper. If coolant fan and/or auxiliary coolant fan does not run, check light green/black wire for open.

2. If coolant fan runs at high speed and

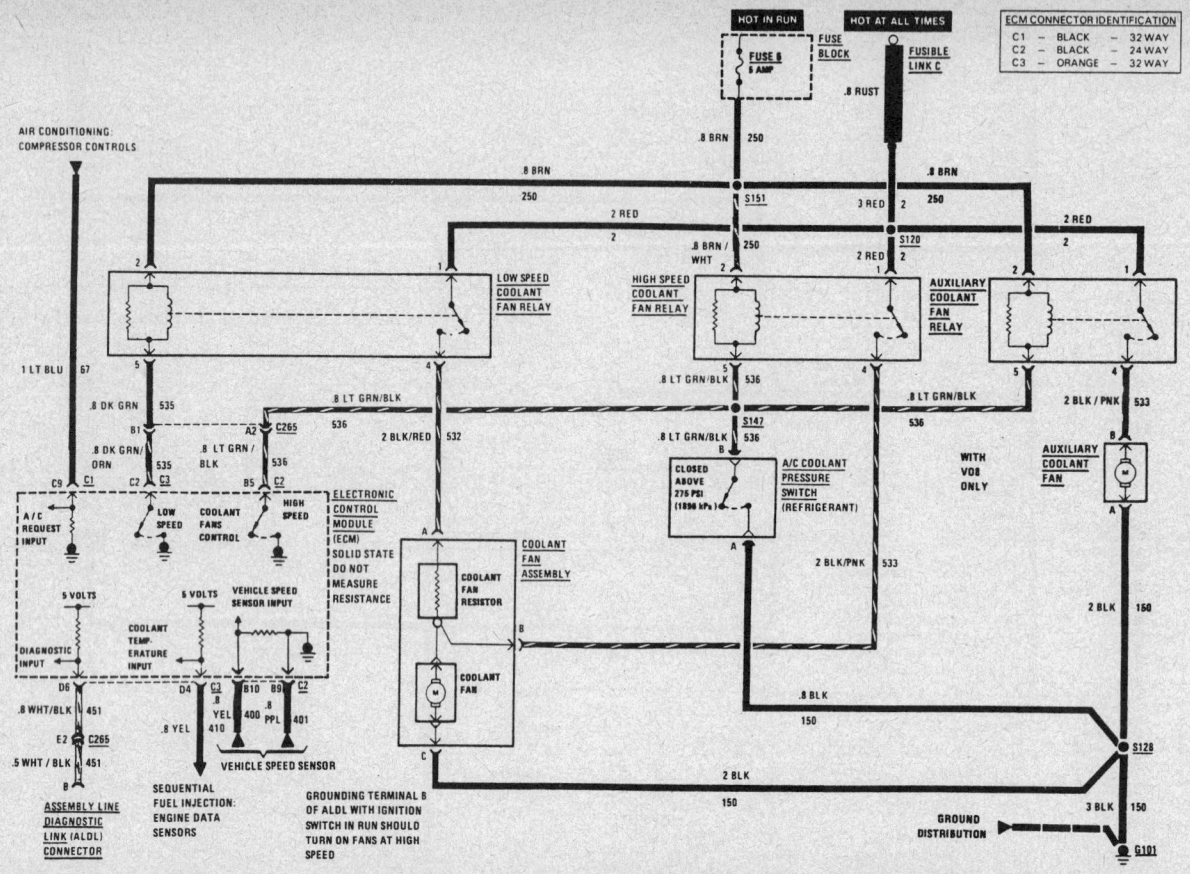

Fig. 36   Coolant fan wiring circuit. 1989–90 Bonneville

auxiliary coolant fan runs, turn ignition switch to RUN position and connect fused jumper between light green/black and black wire terminals.
3. If coolant fan(s) do not run, check black wire for open.
4. If coolant fan(s) continue to run, check A/C dual pressure switch connector terminal contact and A/C system and, if satisfactory, replace A/C dual pressure switch.

COOLANT FAN, REPLACE

1. Disconnect battery ground cable.
2. Remove harness from fan motor and fan frame.
3. Remove fan frame to radiator support attaching bolts.
4. Remove fan and frame assembly.
5. Reverse procedure to install.

1989–90 BONNEVILLE

SYSTEM DESCRIPTION

3.8L/V6-231 VIN C

A two speed coolant fan is turned on and off by the low and high speed coolant fan relays.

For low speed operation, the low speed relay coil is grounded through the ECM. The ECM grounds the coil when engine coolant is above 213°F. When the vehicle speed is greater than 47 mph, the ECM will turn off the low speed coolant fan if it is op-

erating.

With the low speed relay coil grounded, its contacts close. Voltage is applied through the coolant fan resistor to the coolant fan. The resistor reduces voltage supplied to the fan so the fan runs at low speed.

For high speed operation, the high speed relay coil is grounded through the high speed contacts in the A/C dual pressure switch or by the ECM. The A/C dual pressure switch high speed contacts close at a refrigerant pressure above 275 psi. The ECM switch closes when coolant temperature rises above 226°F.

With high speed coil grounded, its contacts close. Battery voltage is applied to the coolant fan. The fan runs at high speed.

The coolant fan with heavy duty, if equipped, operates whenever coolant fan runs at high speed. The A/C dual pressure switch and ECM also control the auxiliary coolant fan relay which supplies battery voltage to the auxiliary coolant fan when energized.

TROUBLESHOOTING

1. Visually inspect fuse 6.
2. Check fusible link C.
3. If either fan runs with ignition switch off, replace associated coolant fan relay.

SYSTEM CHECK

1. With engine cold and idling, move A/C selector switch, if equipped, to NORM. The coolant fan should run for 60 seconds at low speed. When A/C head pressure exceeds 275 psi, coolant fan runs at high speed and auxiliary coolant fan runs.
2. With engine coolant below operating temperature, move A/C selector switch to OFF. Coolant fan should turn off.
3. Run engine at fast idle for several minutes. The coolant fan should turn on before the coolant temperature indicator comes on.

SYSTEM DIAGNOSIS

Refer to **Fig. 36** when performing diagnostic procedures on these systems.

Coolant Fan Does Not Run

1. Disconnect high speed coolant fan relay connector and connect a 20 amp fused jumper between terminals 1 and 4. If coolant fan runs, proceed to "Coolant Fan Does Not Run In Low Speed" and "Coolant Fan Does Not Run In High Speed."
2. If coolant fan does not run, leave fused jumper connected as in step 1, disconnect coolant fan assembly connector and measure voltage from terminal B and ground. If battery voltage

is not present, check fusible link C, red wire and black/pink wire for open.

3. If battery voltage is present, leave fused jumper connected as in step 1 and measure voltage between terminals B and C at coolant fan assembly connector. If battery voltage is not present, check black wire for open.

4. If battery voltage is present, check coolant fan assembly connector terminals and, if satisfactory, replace coolant fan assembly.

Coolant Fan Does Not Run In Low Speed

1. Disconnect low speed coolant fan relay connector and connect a fused jumper between terminals 1 and 4. If coolant fan does not run, check red, black wire and coolant fan resistor and wiring.

2. If coolant fan runs at low speed, remove fused jumper and turn ignition switch to RUN position. Measure voltage between terminal 2 and ground at low speed coolant relay connector. If zero volts is present, check fuse 6 and brown wire for open.

3. If battery voltage is present, reconnect low speed coolant fan relay and place ignition switch in RUN position. Ground terminal C2 of ECM connector C3 with a fused jumper. If coolant fan runs at low speed, problem is ECM related.

4. If coolant fan does not run on low speed, check dark green/orange and dark green wires for open. Ensure condition of low speed coolant fan relay terminals.

5. If wires and relay are satisfactory, replace low speed coolant fan relay.

Coolant Fan Does Not Run In High Speed

1. Place ignition switch in RUN position and ground terminal B of the ALDL connector with a fused jumper.

2. If coolant fan runs, problem is ECM related.

3. If coolant fan does not run on high speed, remove fused jumper from ALDL connector and connect a 20 amp fused jumper between terminals 1 and 4 of the high speed coolant fan relay connector. If coolant fan does not run, check red, black/pink wires and coolant fan assembly wiring for an open.

4. If coolant fan runs on high speed, remove fused jumper and place ignition switch in RUN position. Measure voltage between terminal 2 and ground at the high speed coolant fan relay connector. If zero volts is present, check brown/white wire for an open.

5. If battery voltage is present, reconnect high speed coolant fan relay and place ignition switch in RUN position. Ground terminal B5 of ECM connector C2 with a fused jumper. If coolant fan does not operate, check light green/black wire for an open. Ensure condition of the high speed coolant fan relay. If satisfactory replace high speed coolant fan relay.

6. If coolant fan run, problem is ECM related.

Auxiliary Coolant Fan Does Not Run

1. If coolant fan does not operate in high speed, problem is ECM related.

2. If coolant fan runs in high speed, disconnect auxiliary cooling fan relay connector and place ignition switch in RUN position. Measure voltage between terminal 2 and ground. If zero volts is present, check brown wire for an open.

3. If battery voltage is present, measure voltage between terminal 1 and ground. If zero volts is present, check red wire for an open.

4. If battery voltage is present, connect a fused jumper between terminals 1 and 4 at the auxiliary fan relay connector. If auxiliary coolant fan runs, check condition of auxiliary coolant fan relay and light green/black wire. If satisfactory, replace auxiliary cooling fan relay.

5. If auxiliary cooling fan does not run, leave jumper connected to terminals 1 and 4 and disconnect the connector from the auxiliary cooling fan. Measure voltage between terminal B and ground. If zero volts is present, check for an open in the black/pink wire.

6. If Battery voltage is present, measure voltage between terminals B and A. If zero volts are present, check for an open in the black wire.

7. If battery voltage is present, check auxiliary cooling fan connector terminals. if satisfactory, replace the auxiliary cooling fan motor.

Coolant Fan Runs Continuously In Low Speed With Ignition Switch in RUN Position, Engine Coolant Cool & A/C Off

1. Place ignition switch in RUN position and disconnect low speed coolant fan relay. Connect test lamp between terminals 2 and 5 at low speed fan relay.

2. If test lamp does not light, replace low speed coolant fan relay.

3. If test lamp lights, check dark green wire for short to ground. if wires are satisfactory, problem is ECM related.

Coolant Fan Runs Continuously In High Speed And/Or Auxiliary Coolant Fan Runs Continuously With Ignition Switch IN RUN Position, Engine Coolant Cool & A/C Off

1. Turn ignition switch to RUN position and disconnect A/C coolant fan pressure switch connector. If coolant fan(s) stops, replace A/C coolant fan pressure switch.

2. If coolant fan(s) runs, place ignition switch in RUN position and disconnect high speed coolant relay connector and/or auxiliary coolant fan relay connector.

3. Connect a test lamp between terminals 2 and 5. If test lamp does not light, replace suspected relay.

4. If test lamp lights, check light green/black wires for a short to ground. If wires are satisfactory, problem is ECM related.

Low Speed Coolant Fan Does Not Operate Immediately After Selecting A/C

1. Disconnect ECM connector C1, turn ignition switch to RUN position, place A/C selector at NORM position and measure voltage at terminal C9.

2. If battery voltage is not present, problem is in A/C compressor controls.

3. If battery voltage is present, problem is ECM related.

High Speed Coolant Fan And/Or Auxiliary Coolant Fan Do Not Operate With A/C Pressure Above 275 psi.

1. Disconnect connector from A/C dual pressure switch, turn ignition switch to RUN position and connect light green/black and black wire terminal with fused jumper. If coolant fan and/or auxiliary coolant fan does not run, check light green/black and black wire for open.

2. If coolant fan runs, ensure condition of switch terminal contacts. If satisfactory, replace A/C coolant pressure switch.

COOLANT FAN, REPLACE

1. Disconnect battery ground cable.
2. Remove harness from fan motor and fan frame.
3. Remove fan frame to radiator support attaching bolts.
4. Remove fan and frame assembly.
5. Reverse procedure to install.

CAVALIER
SYSTEM DESCRIPTION

The coolant fan is turned on and off by the ECM based on inputs from the coolant temperature sensor, vehicle speed sensor and the A/C system, if equipped. Battery voltage is applied at all times to terminal 1 of the coolant fan relay and, when the ignition switch is in RUN position, battery voltage ia applied to terminal 5 of the relay. The ECM energizes the coolant fan relay by grounding circuit 335. The relay energizes and battery voltage is applied to the coolant fan.

TROUBLESHOOTING

1. **On 4 cylinder models,** check GAGES fuse or fuse 1.
2. **On 6 cylinder models,** check C-H fuse or fuse 17.
3. If coolant fan runs with ignition switch off, replace coolant fan relay.

SYSTEM CHECK

1. With ambient temperature above 60°F and engine cold and idling, move A/C selector, if equipped to NORM position. Coolant fan should turn on in a short period of time.
2. With engine coolant below operating temperature, move A/C selector switch to OFF position. Coolant fan should turn off.
3. With engine warm, run engine at fast idle for several minutes. Coolant fan should turn on.

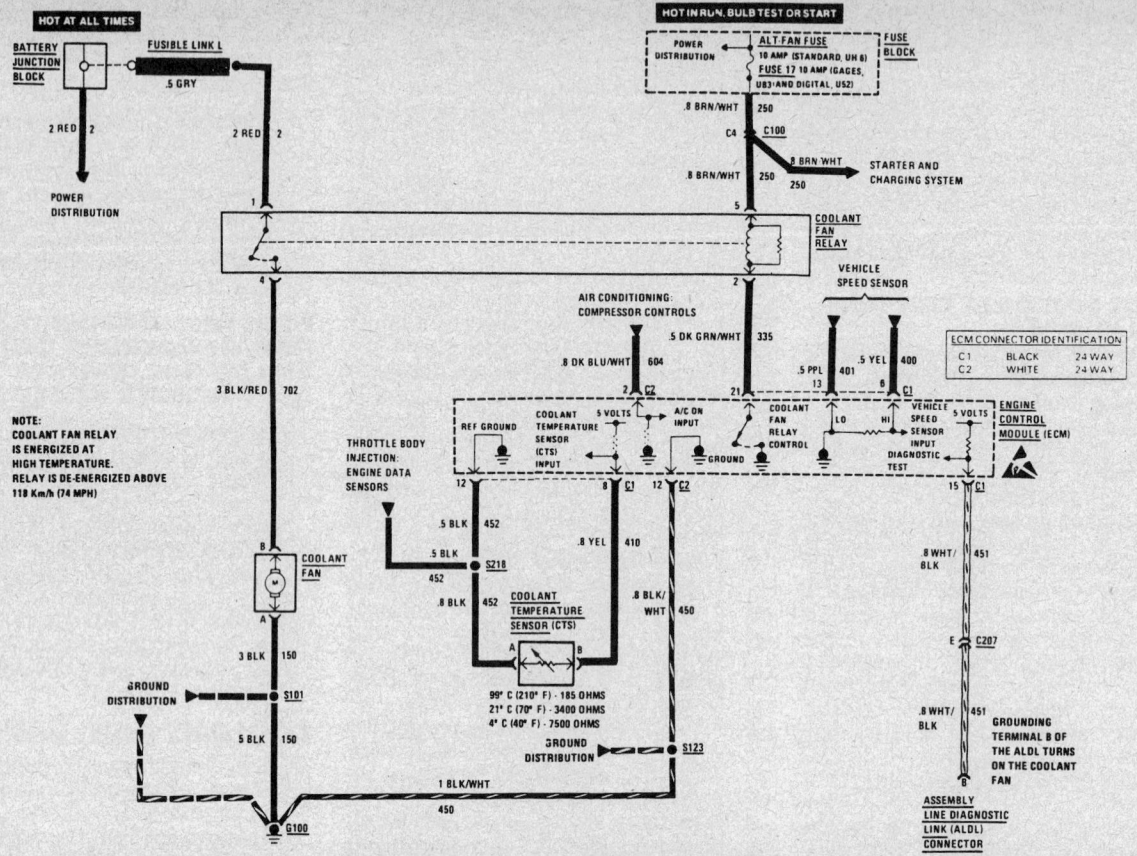

Fig. 37   Coolant fan wiring circuit. 1988–89 Cavalier, 2.0L/4-122 VIN 1

DIAGNOSIS

Refer To **Figs. 37 through 40** when performing diagnostic procedures on these systems.

Coolant Fan Does Not Run

1. Turn ignition switch to RUN position and connect fused jumper between ALDL connector white/black wire terminal and ground. If coolant fan runs, problem is ECM related.
2. If coolant fan does not run, turn ignition switch to RUN position and connect fused jumper between ECM connector C1 (4 cylinder) or C3 (6 cylinder) and ground. If coolant fan runs, problem is ECM related.
3. If coolant fan does not run, leave fused jumper connected as in step 2, disconnect coolant fan relay connector, turn ignition switch to RUN position and connect test lamp between terminals as follows:
   a. Connect between terminal 5 and ground. If lamp does not illuminate, check fuse and pink/black or brown/white wire for open.
   b. Connect between terminals 5 and 2. If lamp does not illuminate, check dark green/yellow or dark green/white wire for open.
   c. Connect between red wire terminal and ground. If lamp does not illuminate, check red wire and fusible link L for open.

4. If lamp illuminates in steps a, b and c, disconnect coolant fan relay connector and connect fused jumper between red and black/pink (4 cylinder) or black/red (6 cylinder) wire terminals. If coolant fan runs, replace coolant fan relay.
5. If coolant fan does not run, leave fused jumper connected as in step 4, disconnect coolant fan connector and connect test lamp between terminals as follows:
   a. Connect between black/pink (4 cylinder) or black/red (6 cylinder) wire terminal and ground. If lamp does not illuminate, check black/pink or black/red wire for open.
   b. Connect between black/pink or black/red and black wire terminals. If lamp does not illuminate, check black wire for open.
   c. If lamp illuminates in steps a and b, replace coolant fan.

Coolant Fan Runs Continuously

1. With ignition switch in RUN position, disconnect coolant fan relay connector and connect test lamp between pink/black (4 cylinder) or brown/white (6 cylinder) and dark green/yellow wire terminals.
2. If lamp does not illuminate, replace coolant fan relay.
3. If lamp illuminates, check dark green/yellow wire for short to ground.

If wire is satisfactory, problem is ECM related.

COOLANT FAN, REPLACE

1. Disconnect battery ground cable.
2. Disconnect wiring harness from motor and fan frame.
3. Remove fan assembly from radiator support.
4. Reverse procedure to install.

CUTLASS SUPREME, GRAND PRIX & REGAL

SYSTEM DESCRIPTION
Less Heavy Duty Cooling

The coolant fan is controlled by the coolant fan relay. The coolant fan relay is electrically operated by the ECM. The ECM receives input signals from the coolant temperature sensor, the vehicle speed sensor and the A/C mode selector. The ECM activates the coolant fan relay when the engine coolant, which is sensed by the coolant temperature sensor, is above 227°F with A/C off and 223°F with A/C on. The ECM grounds circuit 335 when vehicle speed is less than 70 mph. With circuit 335 grounded, the coolant fan relay is energized and its contacts close, turning the coolant fan on. The coolant fan runs until the ignition switch is turned off or coolant temperature decreases to 220°F with A/C off or 216°F with A/C on.

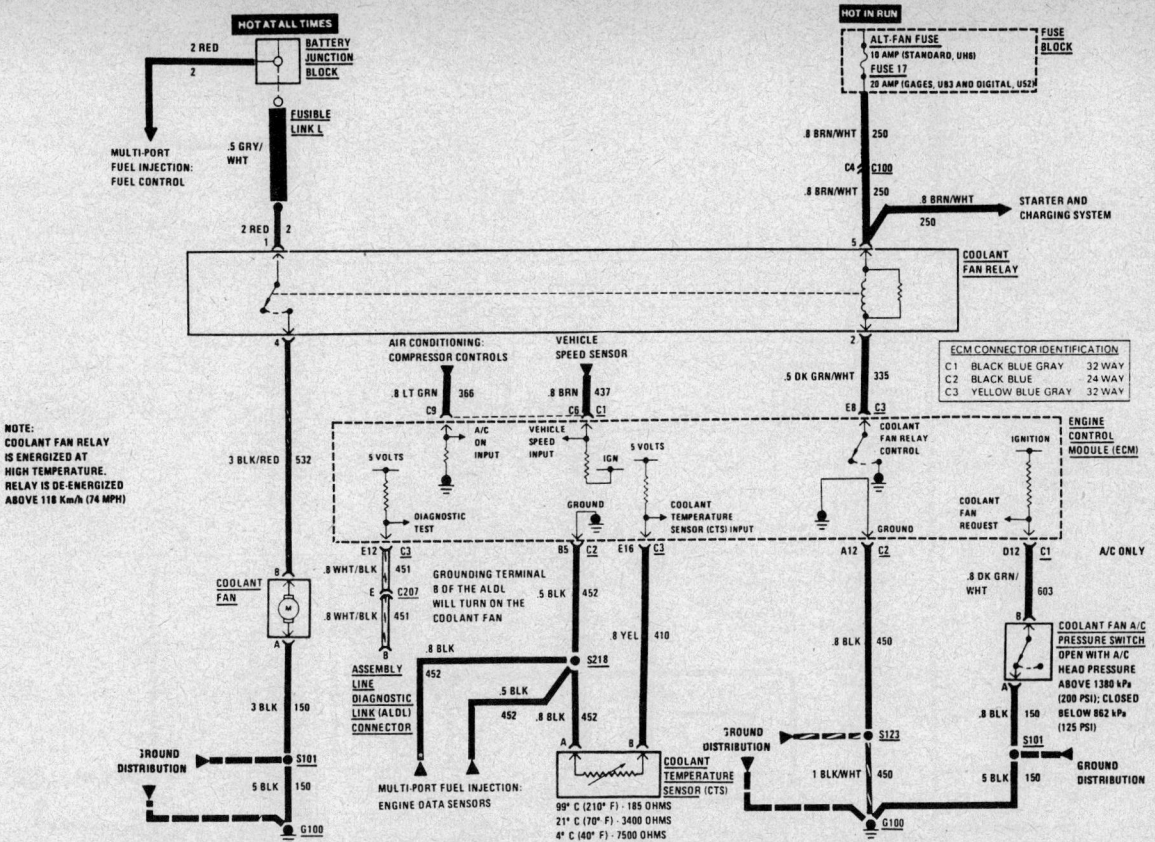

Fig. 38   Coolant fan wiring circuit. 1988–89 Cavalier, 2.8L/V6-173 VIN W

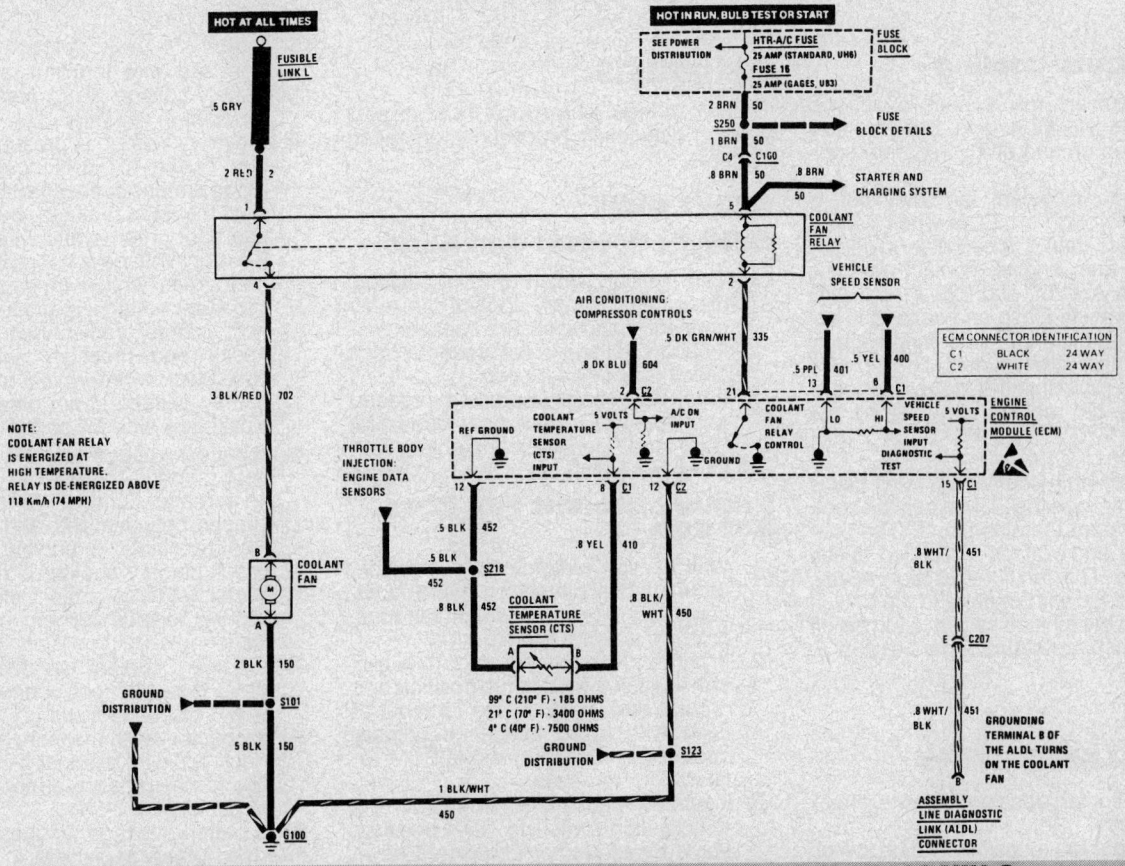

Fig. 39   Coolant fan wiring circuit. 1990 Cavalier, 2.2L/4-133 VIN G

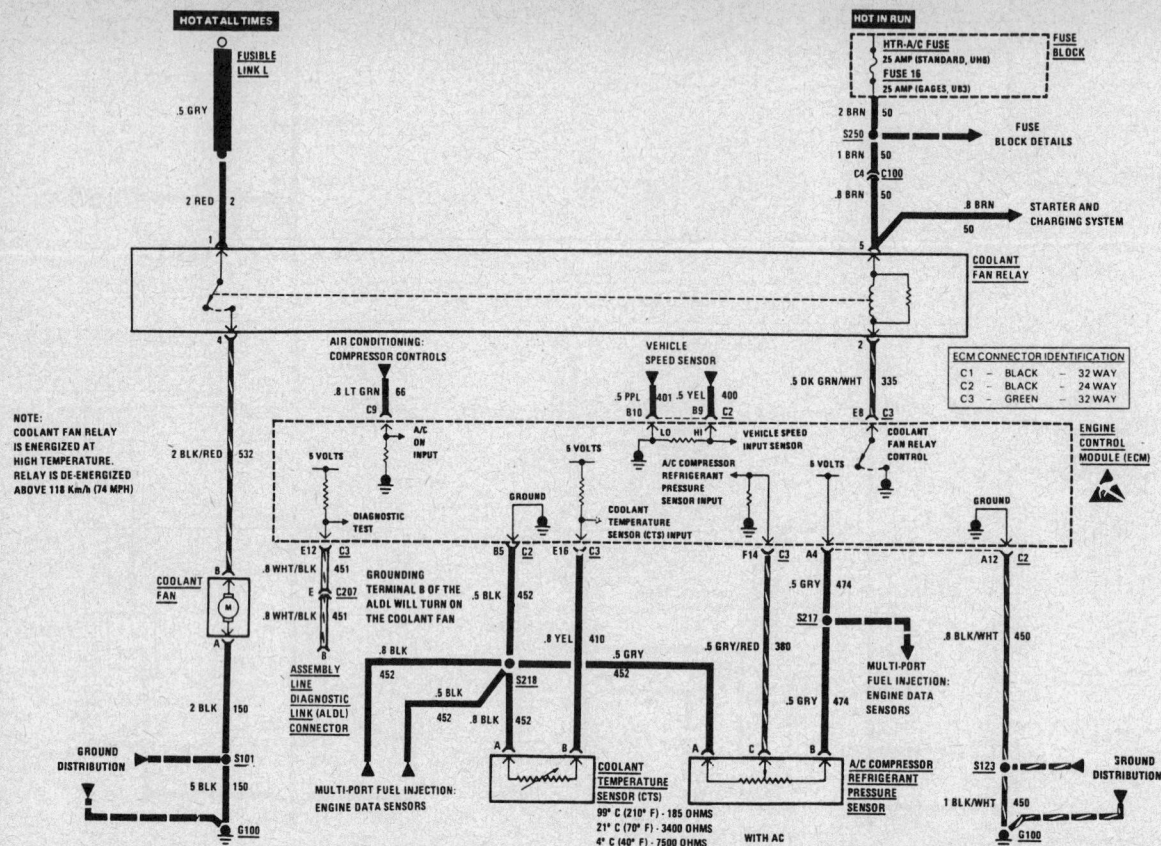

Fig. 40   Coolant fan wiring circuit. 1990 Cavalier, 3.1L/V6-191 VIN T

Heavy Duty Cooling

A two coolant fan system is optional with the V6 VIN W engine. Each coolant fan is turned on and off by separate coolant fan relays.

The primary coolant fan relay coil is grounded through the ECM when vehicle speed is less than a speed determined by the ECM and engine coolant reaches 227°F with A/C off and 223°F with A/C on. The contacts close and voltage is applied through the primary coolant fan relay to the primary coolant fan. The primary coolant fan runs until the ignition switch is turned off, or coolant temperature decreases to 220°F with A/C off or 216°F with A/C on.

The heavy duty coolant fan relay coil is grounded through the ECM when the coolant temperature reaches 245°F. The contacts close and voltage is applied to the coolant fan. The fan runs at high speed. The coolant fan will continue to run at high speed after the ignition switch is turned off until coolant temperature lowers to 238°F.

TROUBLESHOOTING

1. If coolant fan does not operate, check IGN fuse.
2. If coolant fan runs with ignition switch in OFF position, replace coolant fan relay.

DIAGNOSIS

Refer To **Figs. 41 through 46** when performing diagnostic procedures on these systems.

HEAVY DUTY

Neither Coolant Fan Runs

1. Turn ignition switch to RUN position, disconnect primary coolant fan relay connector and measure voltage.
2. If battery voltage is not present, check pink/black wire for open.
3. If battery voltage is present, proceed to "Primary Coolant Fan Does Not Run" and "Heavy Duty Coolant Fan Does Not Run."

Primary Coolant Fan Does Not Run

1. With ignition switch in RUN position, ground white/black terminal of ALDL connector. If primary coolant fan runs, problem is ECM related.
2. If primary coolant fan does not run, turn ignition switch to run position and ground dark green/white terminal at ECM with fused jumper. If primary coolant fan runs, problem is ECM related.
3. if primary coolant fan does not run, turn ignition switch to RUN position, leave fused jumper connected as in step 2, disconnect primary coolant fan relay connector and measure voltage

from red wire terminal to ground. If battery voltage is not present, check for open in red wire.

4. If battery voltage is present, turn ignition switch to RUN position, leave fused jumper connected as in step 2 and measure voltage between red and dark green/white wire terminals. If battery voltage is not present, check dark green/white wire for open.
5. If battery voltage is present, disconnect primary coolant fan relay connector and measure voltage from pink/black wire terminal to ground. If battery voltage is not present, check pink/black wire for open.
6. If battery voltage is present, disconnect primary coolant fan relay connector and connect 20 amp fused jumper between red and black/red wire terminals. If coolant fan runs, check primary coolant fan relay connector terminal contact and, if satisfactory, replace primary coolant fan relay.
7. If primary coolant fan does not run, leave fused jumper connected as in step 6, disconnect primary coolant fan connector and measure voltage at black/red wire terminal. If battery voltage is not present, check black/red wire for open.
8. If battery voltage is present, leave fused jumper in place as in step 6 and measure voltage between black/red and black wire terminals.

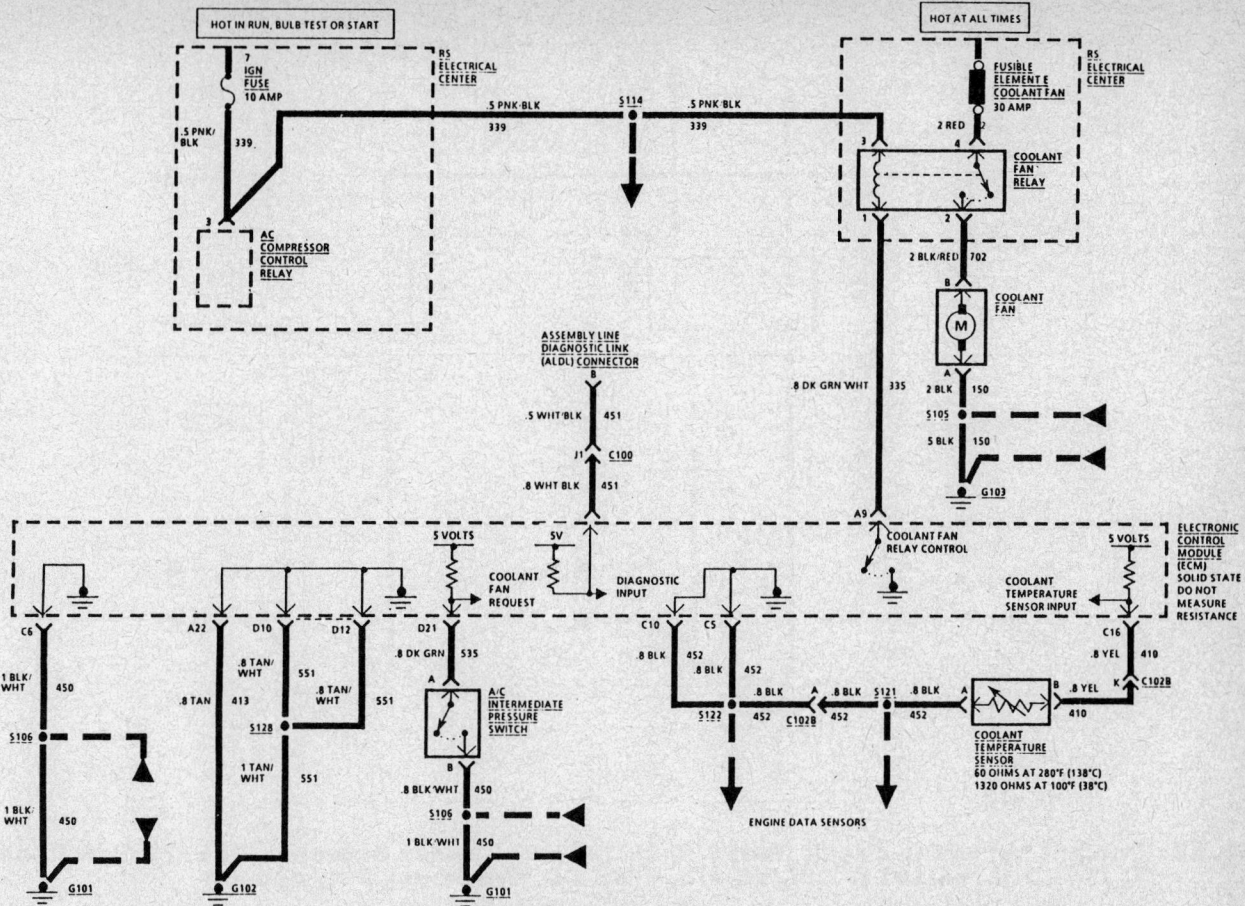

Fig. 41   Coolant fan wiring circuit. 1988–89 Cutlass Supreme, Grand Prix and Regal (less heavy duty cooling), 3.1L/V6-191 & 2.8L/V6-173 VINS T & W

9. If battery voltage is not present, check black wire for open.
10. If battery voltage is present, check primary coolant fan connector terminals for cleanness and tightness and, if satisfactory, replace primary coolant fan.

Heavy Duty Coolant Fan Does Not Run

1. With ignition switch in RUN position, ground dark blue/white wire terminal at ECM with fused jumper. If coolant fan runs, problem is ECM related.
2. If coolant fan does not run, leave fused jumper connected as in step 1, disconnect heavy duty coolant fan relay connector, turn ignition switch to RUN position and measure voltage from pink/black wire terminal to ground. If battery voltage is not present, check pink/black wire for open.
3. If battery voltage is present, leave fused jumper connected as in step 1, turn ignition switch to RUN position and measure voltage between pink/black and dark blue/white wire terminals. If battery voltage is not present, check dark blue/white wire for open.
4. If battery voltage is present, measure voltage between red wire terminal and ground. If battery voltage is not pres-

ent, check red wire for open.
5. If battery voltage is present, disconnect heavy duty coolant fan relay connector and connect 20 amp fused jumper between red and black/red wire terminals.
6. If coolant fan does not run, check black/red wire for open.
7. If coolant fan runs, check high speed coolant fan relay connector terminal contact and, if satisfactory, replace high speed coolant fan relay.

Primary Coolant Fan Runs Continuously With Engine Coolant Cool & A/C Mode Selector Off

1. Disconnect primary coolant fan relay connector, turn ignition switch to RUN position and connect test lamp between pink/black and dark green/white wire terminals.
2. If lamp does not illuminate, replace primary coolant fan relay.
3. If lamp illuminates, check dark green/white wire for short to ground. If wire is satisfactory, problem is ECM related.

Heavy Duty Coolant Fan Runs Continuously With Engine Coolant Cool & A/C Mode Selector Off

1. Disconnect heavy duty coolant fan re-

lay connector, turn ignition switch to RUN position and connect test lamp between pink/black and dark blue/white terminals.
2. If lamp does not illuminate, replace heavy duty coolant fan relay.
3. If lamp illuminates, check dark green/white wire for short to ground. If wire is satisfactory, problem is ECM related.

EXCEPT HEAVY DUTY
Coolant Fan Does Not Run

1. With ignition switch in RUN position, ground white/black wire terminal of ALDL connector. If coolant fan runs, problem is ECM related.
2. If coolant fan does not run, ground dark green/white wire terminal at ECM with a fused jumper. If coolant fan runs, problem is ECM related.
3. If coolant fan does not run, leave fused jumper connected as in step 2, disconnect coolant fan relay connector and measure voltage from red wire terminal to ground. If battery voltage is not present, check fusible link E and red wire for open.
4. If battery voltage is present, leave fused jumper connected as in step 2 and measure voltage from pink/black wire terminal to ground. If battery voltage is not present, check pink/black

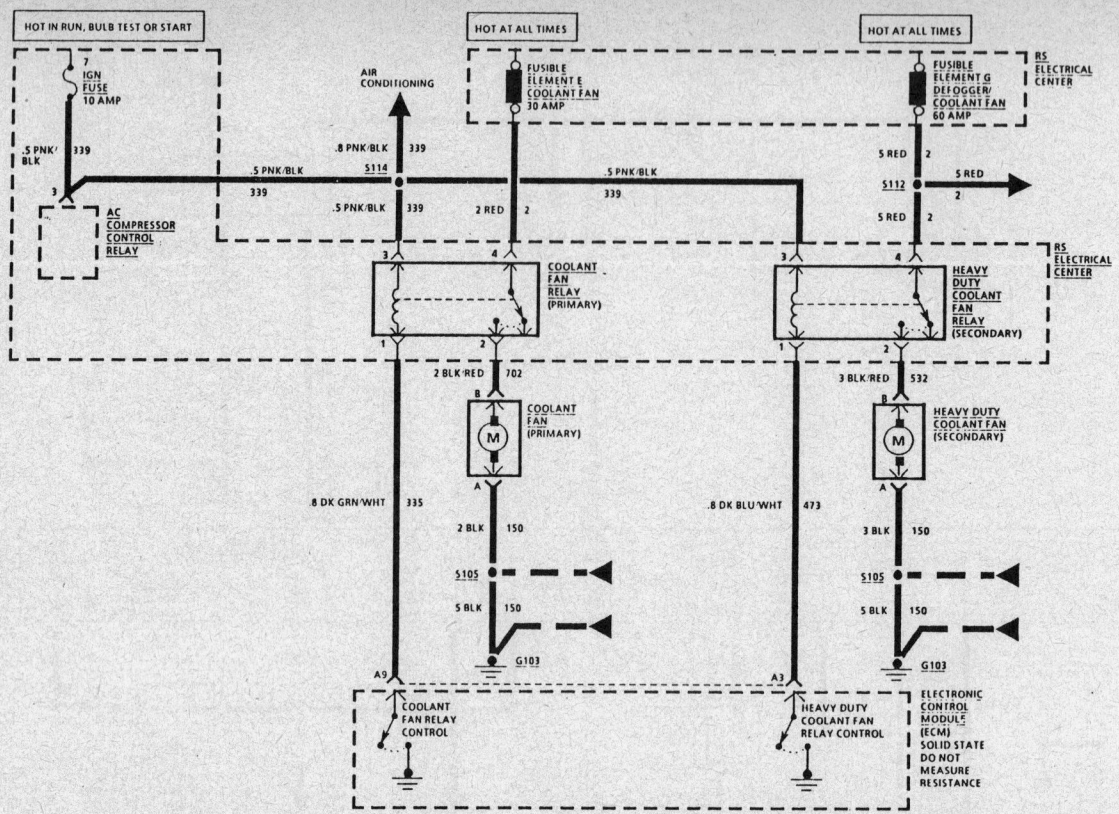

Fig. 42 Coolant fan wiring circuit (Part 1 of 2). 1988-89 Cutlass Supreme, Grand Prix & Regal, 3.1L/V6-191 & 2.8L/V6-173, VINS T & W w/heavy duty cooling

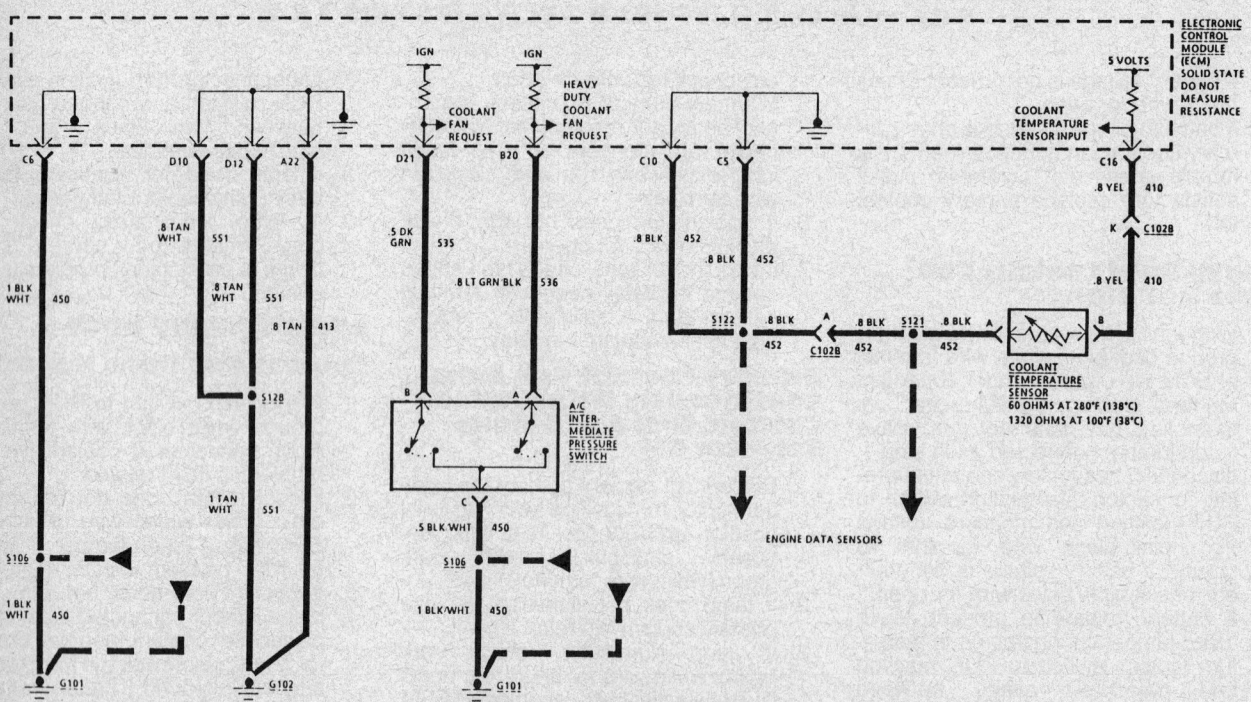

Fig. 42 Coolant fan wiring circuit (Part 2 of 2). 1988-89 Cutlass Supreme, Grand Prix & Regal, 3.1L/V6-191 & 2.8L/V6-173, VINS T & W w/heavy duty cooling

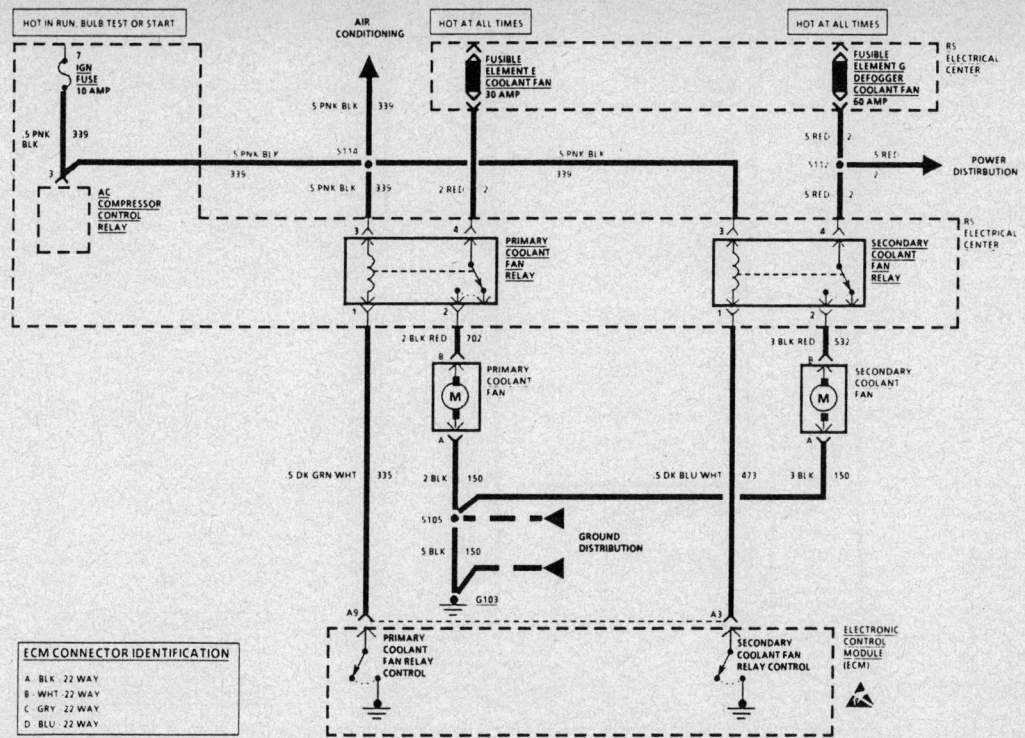

Fig. 43   Coolant fan wiring circuit (Part 1 of 2). 1990 Cutlass Supreme & Grand Prix, 3.1L/V6-191 VIN T

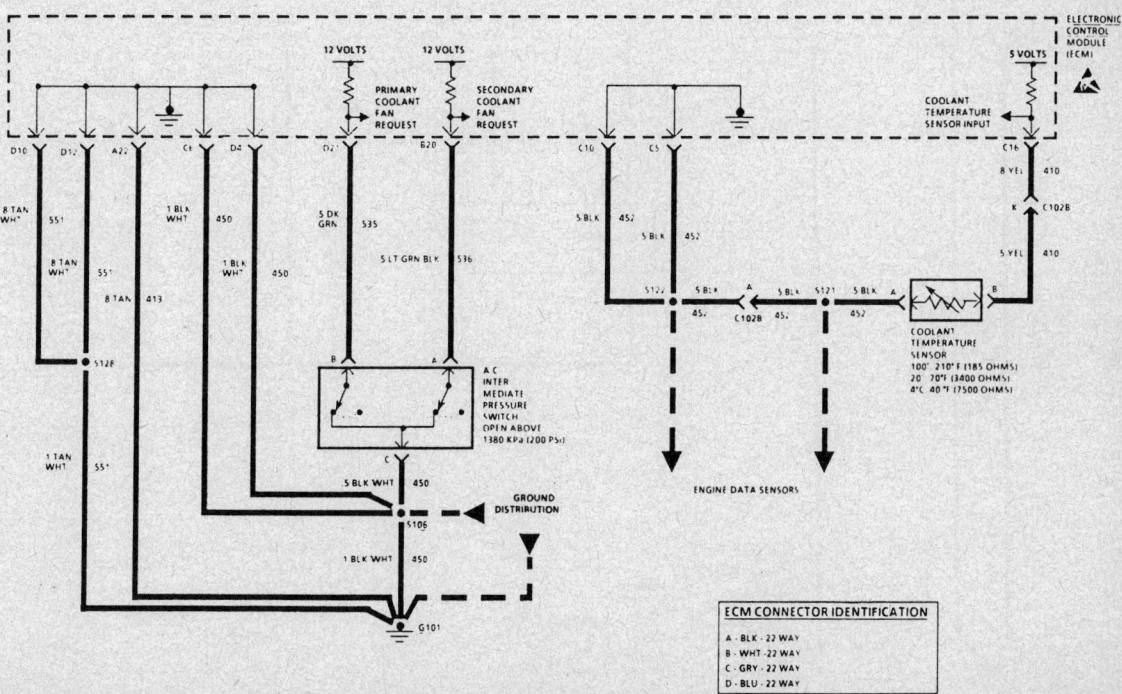

Fig. 43   Coolant fan wiring circuit (Part 2 of 2). 1990 Cutlass Supreme & Grand Prix, 3.1L/V6-191 VIN T

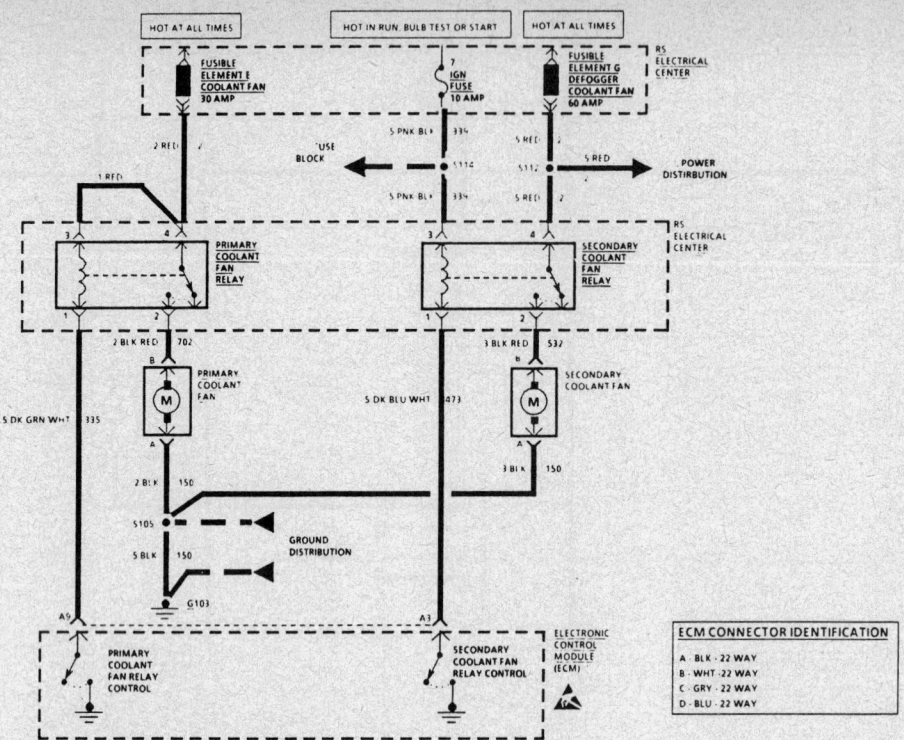

Fig. 44   Coolant fan wiring circuit (Part 1 of 2). 1990 Cutlass Supreme, 2.3L/4-138 VIN A & 1990 Grand Prix, 2.3L/4-138 VIN D

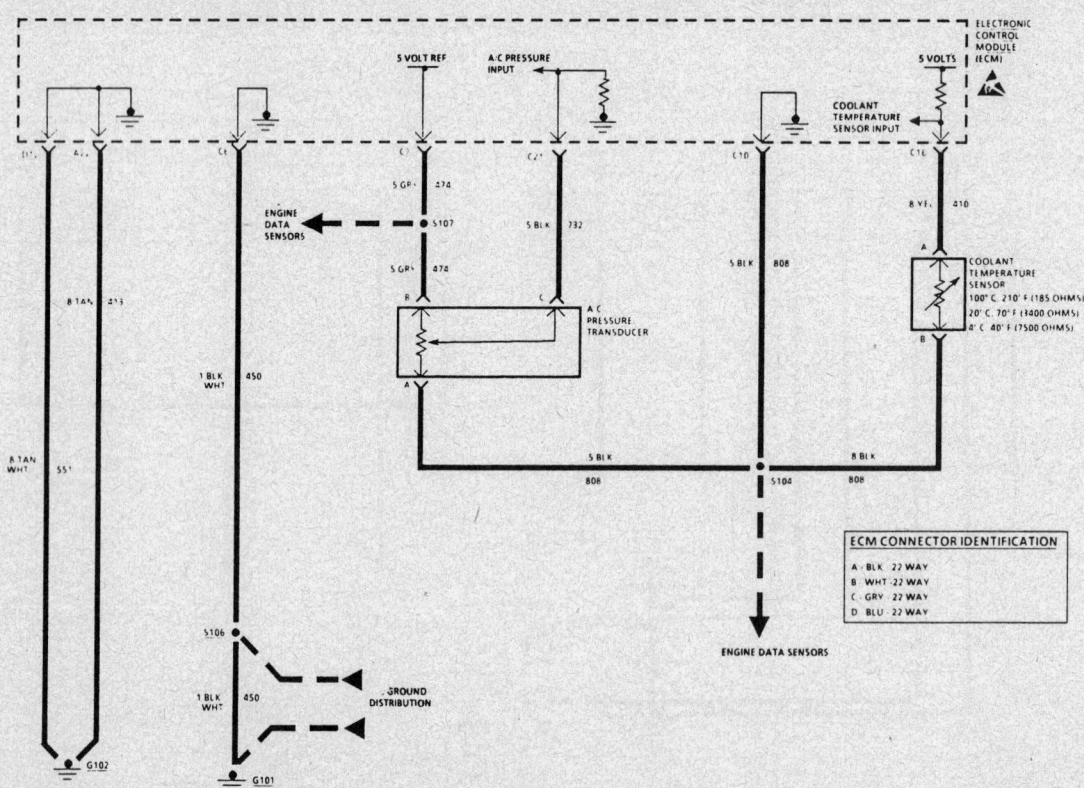

Fig. 44   Coolant fan wiring circuit (Part 2 of 2). 1990 Cutlass Supreme, 2.3L/4-138 VIN A & 1990 Grand Prix, 2.3L/4-138 VIN D

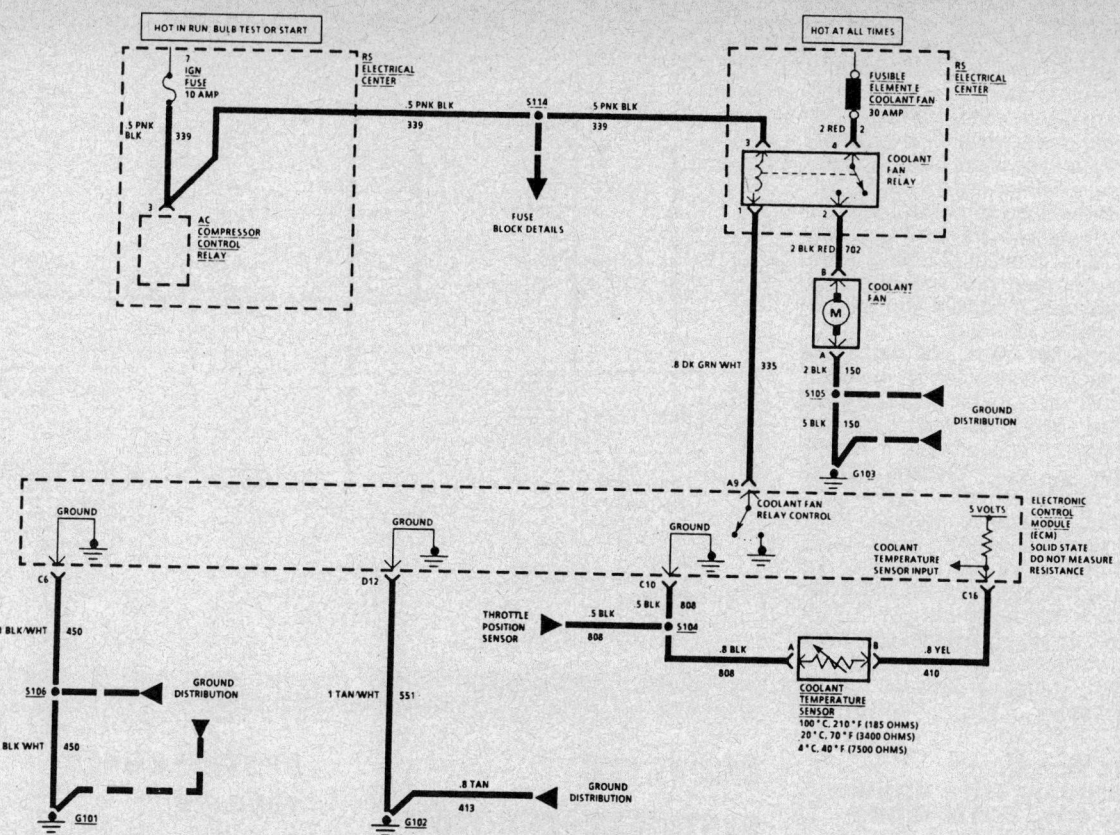

Fig. 45   Coolant fan wiring circuit. 1990 Grand Prix, 2.5L/4-151 VIN R

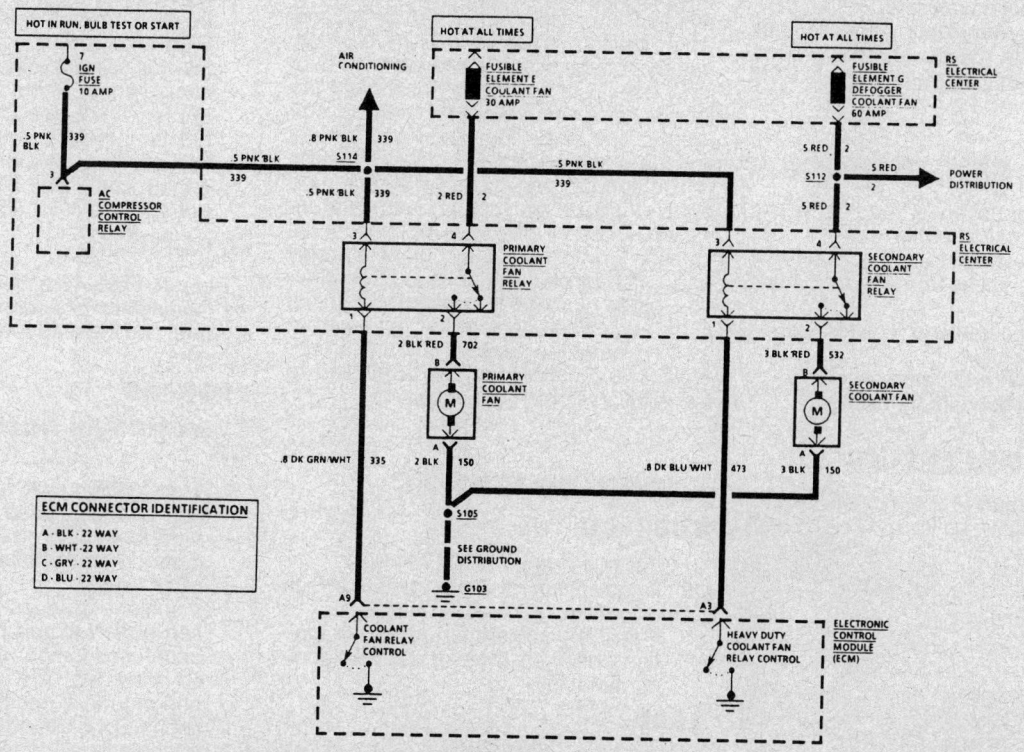

Fig. 46   Coolant fan wiring circuit (Part 1 of 2). 1990 Regal, 3.1L/V6-191 VIN T

wire for open.

5. If battery voltage is present, leave fused jumper connected as in step 2, disconnect coolant fan relay connector and measure voltage between red and dark green/white wire terminals. If battery voltage is not present, check dark green/white wire for open.

6. If battery voltage is present, disconnect primary coolant fan relay connector and connect 20 amp fused jumper between red and black/red wire terminals. If coolant fan runs, replace coolant fan relay.

7. If coolant fan does not run, leave fused jumper connected as in step 6, disconnect coolant fan connector and measure voltage between black/red wire terminal and ground. If battery voltage is not present, check black/red wire for open.

8. If battery voltage is present, leave fused jumper connected as in step 6, disconnect coolant fan connector and measure voltage between black/red and black wire terminals.

9. If battery voltage is not present, check black wire for open.

10. If battery voltage is present, replace coolant fan.

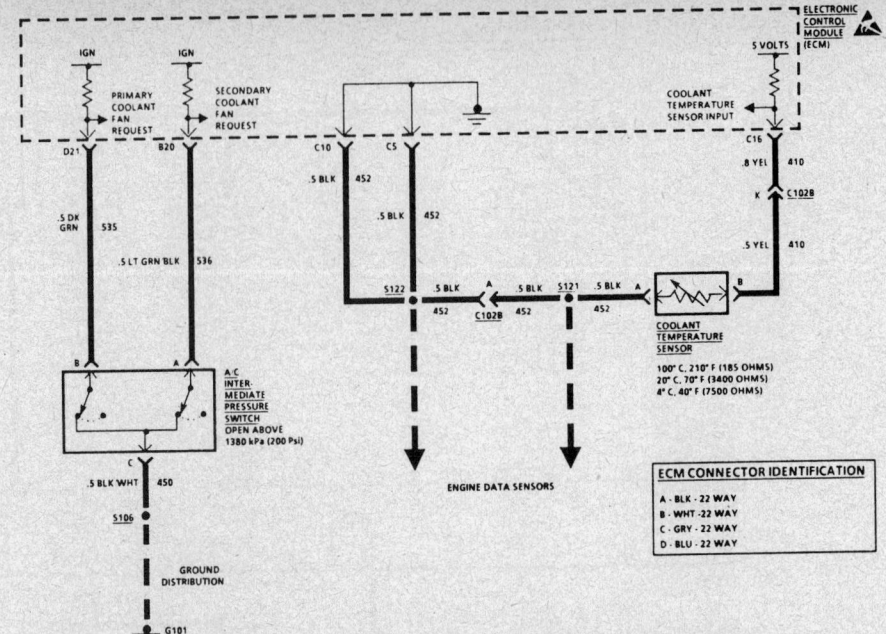

Fig. 46 Coolant fan wiring circuit. (Part 2 of 2). 1990 Regal, 3.1L/V6-191 VIN T

Coolant Fan Runs Continuously With Engine Coolant Cool & A/C Mode Selector Off

1. Disconnect coolant fan relay connector and connect test lamp between pink/black and dark green/white wire terminals. If lamp does not illuminate, replace coolant fan relay.

2. If lamp illuminates, check dark green/white wire for short to ground. If wire is satisfactory, problem is ECM related.

COOLANT FAN, REPLACE

1. Disconnect battery ground cable.
2. Remove coolant bottle.
3. Remove engine strut(s).
4. Remove harness from fan motor and fan frame.
5. Remove fan frame to radiator support attaching bolts.
6. Remove fan and frame assembly.
7. Reverse procedure to install.

SERVICE BULLETINS

On 1988 Grand Prix, a condition of reduced A/C cooling at idle may be present. This can be caused by an A/C intermediate pressure switch (internal corrosion) which will not allow the engine coolant fan to engage with A/C ON.

To correct this condition, disconnect switch harness connector, cover the connector end with tape to prevent water entry and tape back to wiring harness. This will allow the coolant fan to run whenever A/C is ON. The switch is located on the high pressure (liquid line) clamped to the left-hand side of the engine compartment rail, near the condenser and directly below the suction line.

CORVETTE
SYSTEM DESCRIPTION

The coolant fan is turned on and off by the ECM based on inputs from the coolant temperature sensor, the vehicle speed sensor and the A/C coolant fan switch, if equipped. Battery is applied at all times to terminal E of the coolant fan relay and, when ignition switch is in RUN position, battery voltage is applied to terminal D of relay. The ECM energizes the coolant fan by grounding circuit 935 (1988–89) or 409 (1990). The relay energizes, and battery voltage is applied to the coolant fan motor.

The auxiliary coolant fan relay is turned on and off by the coolant temperature switch. Battery voltage is applied at all times to terminal E of the coolant fan relay and, when ignition switch is in RUN position, battery voltage is applied to terminal D of relay. When coolant fan temperature switch closes, the auxiliary coolant fan energizes and battery voltage is applied to the auxiliary coolant fan motor.

TROUBLESHOOTING
1988–89

1. Visually check the C. FAN fuse.
2. If coolant fan runs with ignition switch off, replace coolant fan relay.
3. If auxiliary coolant fan runs with ignition switch off, replace auxiliary coolant fan relay.

1990

1. Check for an open Gauges fuse.
2. Check for an open fusible link D or E.
3. Check for corrosion on coolant fan and coolant fan relay terminals.
4. Ensure grounds are clean and tight.

SYSTEM CHECK
1988–89

1. With ambient temperature above 60°F and the engine cold and idling, move A/C function selector, if equipped, to NORM. Coolant fan should turn on after a short period.
2. Move A/C function selector to OFF position. Coolant fan should turn off.
3. With engine warmed up, run it at fast idle for several minutes. Coolant fan should come on before auxiliary coolant fan, if equipped, and before coolant temperature indicator comes on and auxiliary coolant fan, if equipped, should come on before coolant temperature indicator comes on.

DIAGNOSIS

Refer to **Figs. 47 and 48** when performing diagnostic procedures on 1988-89 systems and **Figs. 49 through 51** for 1990 systems.

1988–89
Coolant Fan Does Not Turn On

1. Turn ignition switch to RUN position and connect fused jumper between ALDL connector white/black wire and ground. If coolant fan runs, problem is ECM related.
2. If coolant fan does not run, turn ignition switch to run position and connect fused jumper at ECM connector C1 between dark green/white wire and ground. If coolant fan runs, problem is ECM related.
3. If coolant fan does not run, leave fused jumper connected as in step 2, disconnect coolant fan relay connector, turn ignition switch to RUN position and connect test lamp between

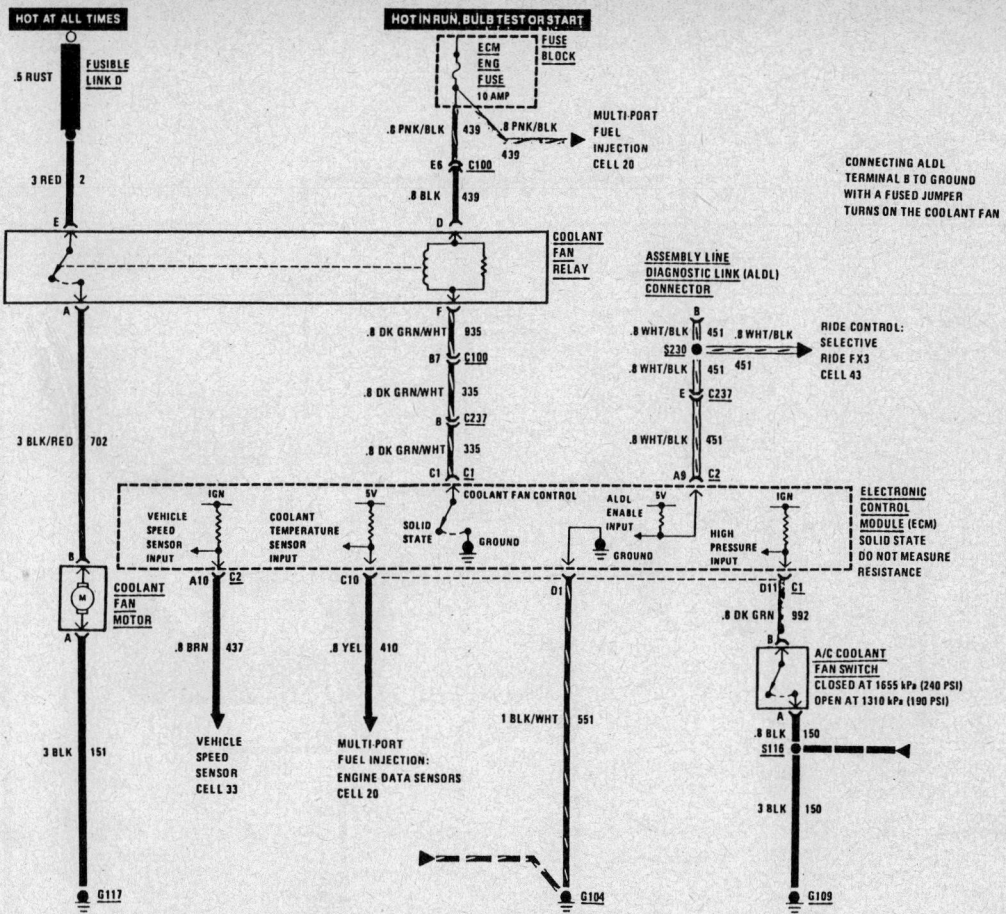

Fig. 47 Coolant fan wiring circuit. 1988–89 Corvette

terminals as follows:
a. Connect between dark blue wire terminal and ground. If lamp does not illuminate, check C. FAN fuse and dark blue wire for open.
b. Connect between dark blue and dark green/white wire terminals. If lamp does not illuminate, check dark green/white wire for ground.
c. Connect between red wire terminal and ground. If lamp does not illuminate, check fusible link D and red wire for open.
4. If lamp illuminates in steps a, b and c, disconnect coolant fan relay connector and connect 20 amp fused jumper between red and black/red wire terminals. If coolant fan runs, replace coolant fan relay.
5. If coolant fan does not run, leave fused jumper connected as in step 4, disconnect coolant fan motor connector and connect test lamp between terminals as follows:
a. Connect between black/red wire terminal and ground. If lamp does not illuminate, check black/red wire for open.
b. Connect between black/red and black wire terminals. If lamp does not illuminate, check black wire for open.
c. If lamp illuminates in steps a and b,

replace coolant fan motor.

Auxiliary Coolant Fan Does Not Turn On

1. Disconnect coolant fan temperature switch connector, turn ignition switch to RUN position and connect fused jumper between dark green/white wire terminal and ground. If auxiliary coolant fan runs, replace coolant fan temperature switch.
2. If auxiliary coolant fan does not run, leave fused jumper connected as in step 1, disconnect auxiliary coolant fan relay connector, turn ignition switch to RUN position and connect test lamp between terminals as follows:
a. Connect between dark blue wire terminal and ground. If lamp does not illuminate, check C. FAN fuse and dark blue wire for ground.
b. Connect between dark blue and dark green/white wire terminals. If lamp does not illuminate, check dark green/white wire for open.
c. Connect between red wire terminal and ground. If lamp does not illuminate, check fusible link E and red wire for open.
3. If lamp illuminates in steps a, b and c,

disconnect auxiliary coolant fan relay connector and connect 20 amp fused jumper between red and red/black wire terminals. If auxiliary coolant fan runs, replace auxiliary coolant fan relay.
4. If auxiliary coolant fan does not run, leave fused jumper connected as in step 3, disconnect auxiliary coolant fan motor connector and connect test lamp between terminals as follows:
a. Connect between black/red wire terminal and ground. If lamp does not illuminate, check black/red wire for open.
b. Connect between black/red and black wire terminals. If lamp does not illuminate, check black wire for open.
c. If lamp illuminates in steps a and b, replace auxiliary coolant fan motor.

Coolant Fan Does Not Turn Off

1. With ignition switch in RUN position, disconnect ECM connector C1. If fan turns off, problem is ECM related.
2. If fan does not turn off, disconnect coolant fan relay connector, connect test lamp between dark blue and dark green/white wire terminals and turn ignition switch to RUN position.

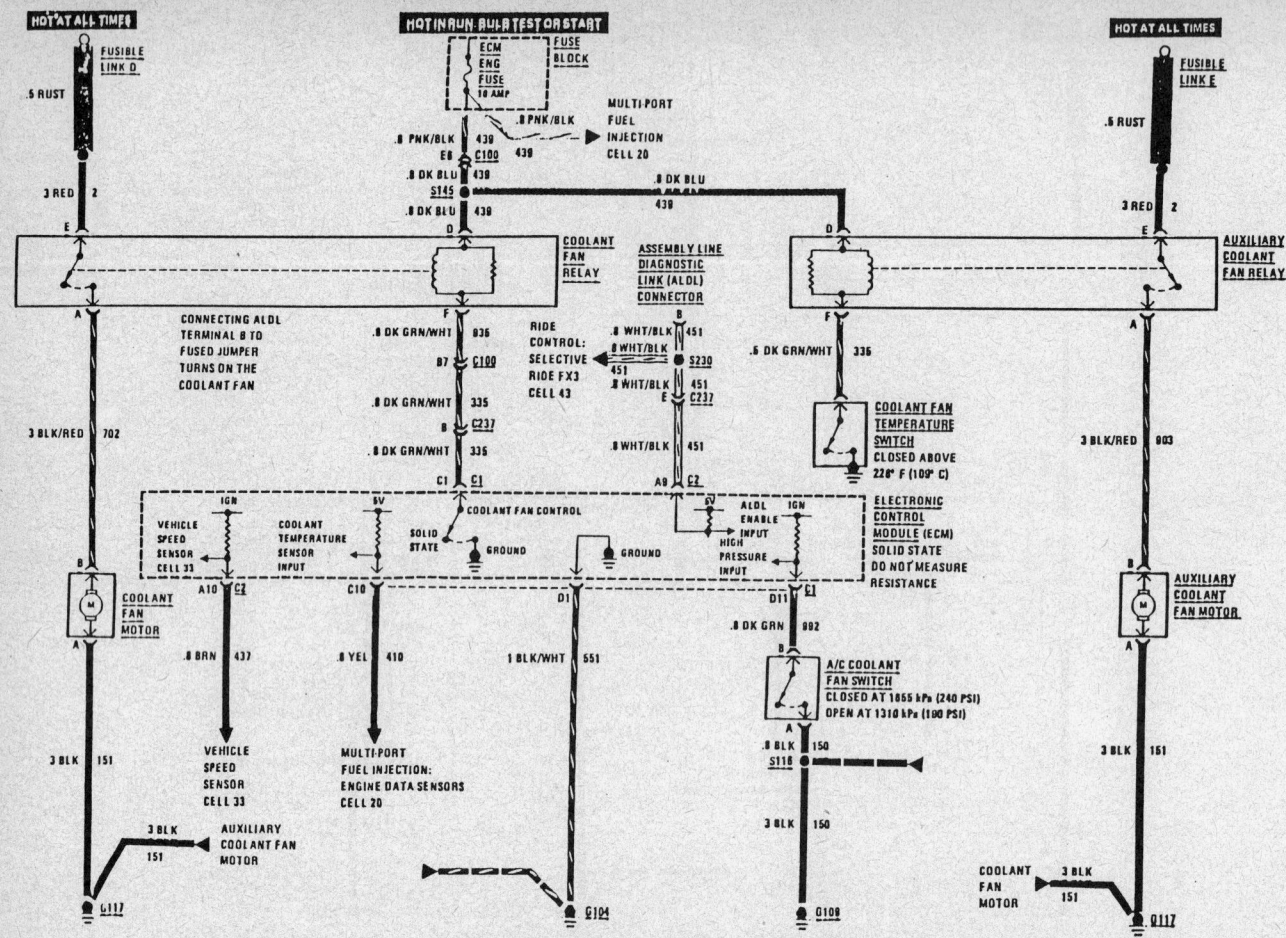

Fig. 48 Auxiliary coolant fan wiring circuit. 1988–89 Corvette

3. If lamp illuminates, check dark green/white wire for short to ground.
4. If lamp does not illuminate, replace coolant fan relay.

Auxiliary Coolant Fan Does Not Turn Off

1. With ignition switch in RUN position, disconnect coolant fan temperature switch. If fan turns off, replace coolant fan temperature switch.
2. If fan does not turn off, disconnect auxiliary coolant fan relay, connect test lamp between dark blue and dark green/white wire terminals and turn ignition switch to RUN position.
3. If lamp illuminates, check dark green/white wire for short to ground.
4. If lamp does not illuminate, replace auxiliary coolant fan relay.

COOLANT FAN, REPLACE

1. Disconnect battery ground cable.
2. Disconnect fan wires and fan at shroud.
3. Remove fan assembly.
4. Reverse procedure to install.

DEVILLE & FLEETWOOD
SYSTEM DESCRIPTION
4.5L/V8-273 VIN 5

The body computer module (BCM) controls both coolant fans according to inputs received from the ECM. The BCM receives signals telling it what the coolant and refrigerant temperatures are. The refrigerant high side temperature sensor, located between the condenser and the orifice tube, transmits the refrigerant temperature to the ECM. The ECM sends the coolant temperature through the data link to the BCM.

The speed of the coolant fans is controlled by the BCM. If the BCM determines that the fans should be at low or medium speed, it grounds the corresponding relay. The coolant fan resistor reduces the amount of voltage applied to the coolant fans.

When the ignition switch is first turned to RUN, the BCM grounds the coolant fan relay. This prevents the high speed coolant fan relay from being energized. If the BCM determines that the coolant fan should be at high speed, it de-energizes the coolant fan relay then grounds the high speed coolant fan relay. The fans run at high speed, since voltage is applied directly from the fusible link to the coolant fans.

If the BCM fails, it does not energize the coolant fan relay. This allows the high speed coolant fan relay to be energized when the ignition switch is in RUN position.

4.5L/V8-273 VIN 3

This system uses two coolant fans. These fans are wired in parallel so both fans run at the same time.

The ECM has two coolant fan control outputs, one for high speed and one for low speed. When the ECM low speed output is turned on at C2 terminal A11, it grounds the coil of the low speed coolant fan relay. The relay closes completing a circuit to the coolant fans. The coolant fan resistor drops the voltage to both fans. High speed operation is similar and involves grounding C2 terminal B8, the ECM high speed output, and the high speed coolant fan relay coil. The coolant fan resistor is not used for high speed operation.

The ECM controls its coolant fan outputs based on signals received from the coolant temperature and refrigerant high side temperature sensors. The coolant temperature sensor is wired directly to the ECM. The refrigerant temperature sensor is wired to the BCM. Its temperature signal is processed by the BCM and sent over a serial data line to the ECM in digital form.

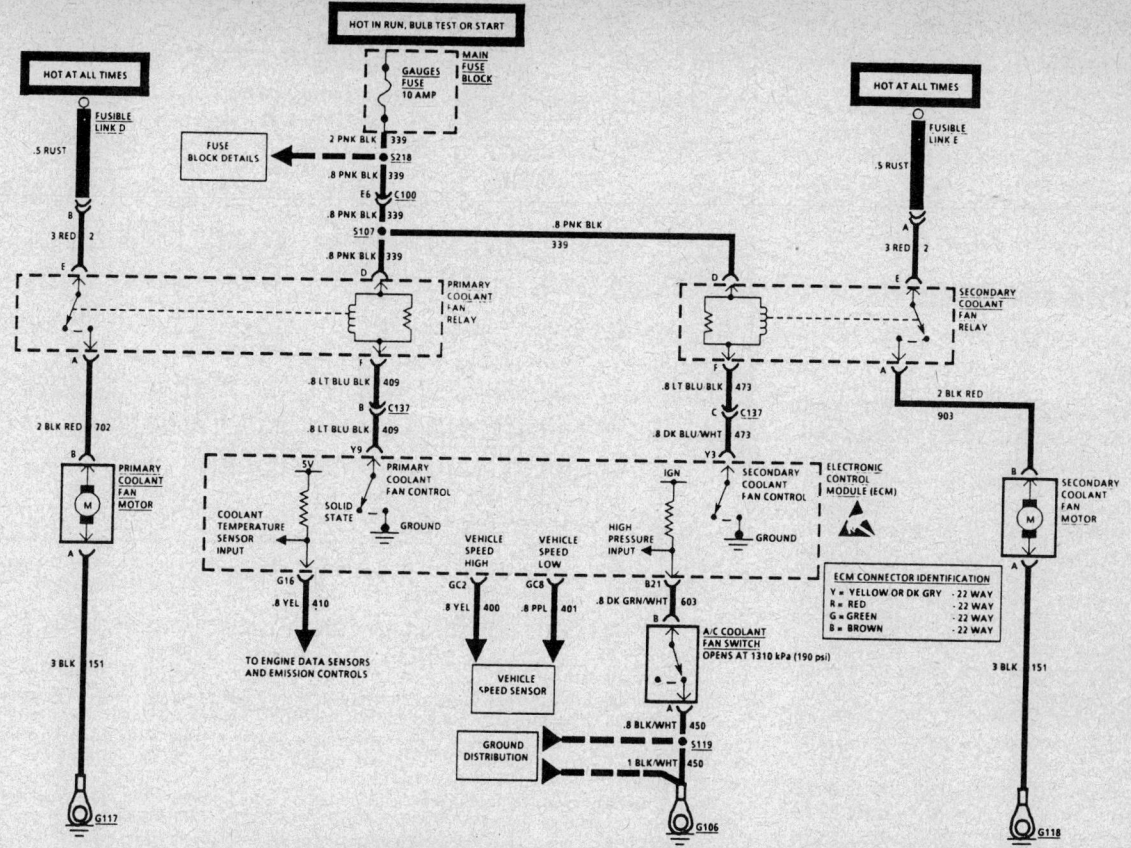

Fig. 49   Coolant fan wiring circuit. 1990 Corvette, 5.7L/V8-350 VIN 8

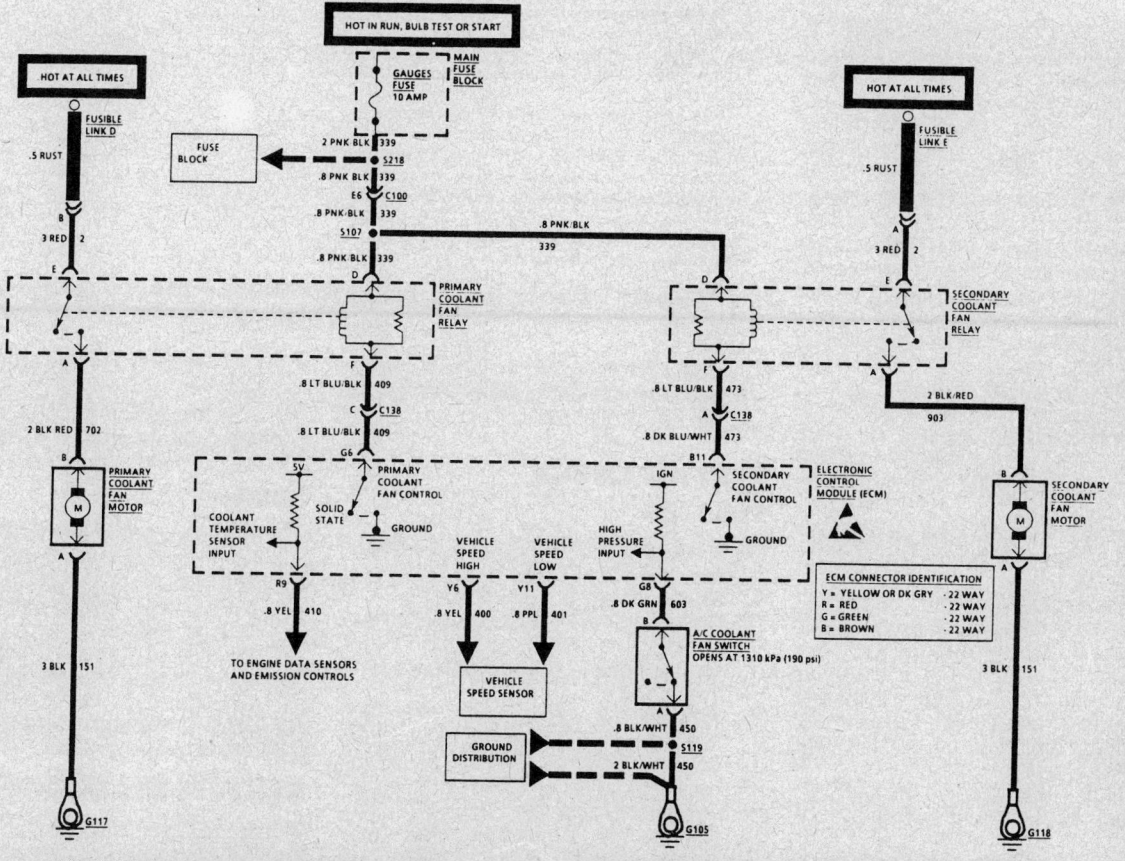

Fig. 50   Coolant fan wiring circuit. 1990 Corvette, 5.7L/V8-350 VIN J

TROUBLESHOOTING

1. If coolant fans do not operate, check fuse 6 and fusible link D.
2. If only one fan fails to operates, check wires to that fan. If wires are satisfactory, replace coolant fan motor.
3. If the coolant fans operate on high speed only, check resistor wiring and resister.

ENTERING DIAGNOSTIC MODE

1988–89

1. Turn ignition On, then depress Off and Warmer buttons on the Climate Control Panel (CCP), **Fig. 52**. Hold buttons until all display panel segments illuminate, indicating beginning of diagnostic readout. **The two display panels must be illuminated to ensure all segments are operating. Do not attempt diagnosis unless all segments appear, as a misdiagnosis could result. If any segments are inoperative, the display panel must be replaced.**
2. Depress and release ECON button on CCP. Display will switch from Code .7.0 to Code F.8.5.
3. Exit diagnostic mode by depressing AUTO button on CCP or turn ignition Off for ten seconds until the temperature setting is displayed.

1990

1. Turn ignition On, then depress OFF and WARMER buttons on the Climate Control Panel (CCP), **Fig. 52**. Hold buttons until all display panel segments illuminate, indicating beginning of diagnostic readout. **The two display panels must be illuminated to ensure all segments are operating. Do not attempt diagnosis unless all segments appear, as a misdiagnosis could result. If any segments are inoperative, the display panel must be replaced.**
2. After all ECM and BCM codes have been displayed or if no codes are present, .7.0 will be displayed. At this point press the HI button, fuel data center should display E.9.5.
3. Press ECON and WARMER to enter ECM output override and to receive E.0.0 display.
4. Advance the display by depressing the HI button on the ECC until E.5.8 is displayed.
5. Depressing the WARMER button will run coolant fans at low speed and a 10 will be displayed on the fuel data center.
6. Depressing the COOLER button will run coolant fans at high speed and a 11 will be displayed on the fuel data center.
7. When 00 is displayed on the fuel data center the coolant fans will not be running.
8. To exit diagnostic mode, depress AUTO button on CCP or turn ignition

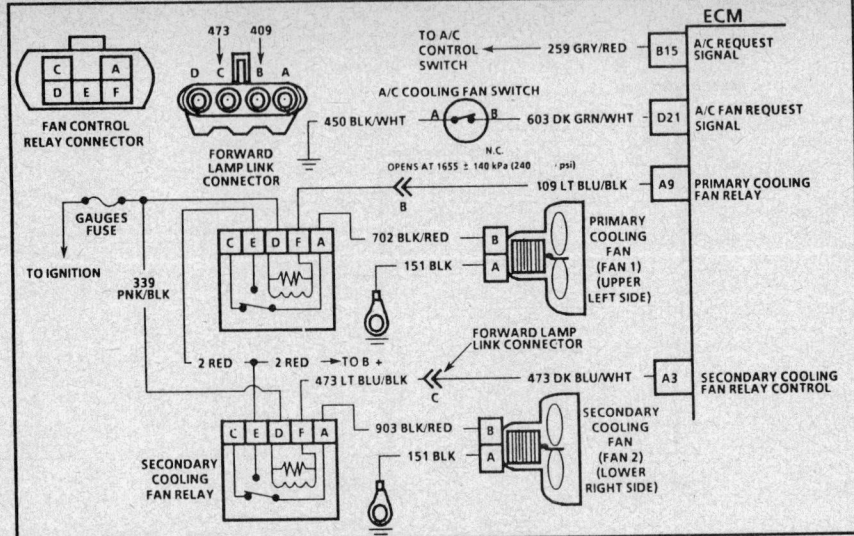

CHART C-12

ELECTRIC COOLING FAN CONTROL CIRCUIT DIAGNOSIS
5.7L (VIN 8) "Y" CARLINE (PORT)

Circuit Description:

The cooling fans are controlled by the ECM based on various inputs. Battery voltage is supplied to the fan relays on terminal "E" and ignition voltage to terminal "D". Grounding CKT 409 (relay terminal "F") will energize the primary cooling fan relay (Fan 1) and supply battery voltage to the primary cooling fan motor. Grounding CKT 473 (relay terminal "F") will energize the secondary cooling fan relay (Fan 2) and supply battery voltage to the secondary fan motor.

The A/C cooling fan switch, mounted in the A/C high pressure line, will close when head pressure exceeds 1655 kPa (240 psi) and this input causes the ECM to ground CKT 473 or CKT 409 if other criteria are met.

If a Code 14, 15, 52 or 62 sets or the ECM is operating in the fuel back-up mode, the ECM will turn "ON" the cooling fans.

Diagnostic Aids:

If the owner complained of an overheating problem it must be determined if the complaint was due to an actual boil over, or the warning indicator light, or engine coolant temperature gage indicated overheating.

The gage accuracy can also be checked by comparing the Coolant Temperature Sensor (CTS) reading using a "Scan" tool and comparing its reading with the gage reading. If the engine is actually overheating and the gage indicates overheating, but the cooling fan is not coming "ON," the Coolant Temperature Sensor (CTS) has probably shifted out of calibration and should be replaced.

If the engine is overheating and the cooling fans are "ON," the cooling system should be checked,

Fig. 51   Coolant fan diagnostic chart (Part 1 of 4). 1990 Corvette

Off for ten seconds until the temperature setting is displayed. Stored codes will not be cleared.

SYSTEM CHECK

1988–89

1. Enter diagnostic mode as outlined under "Entering Diagnostic Mode" and select cooling fan override.
2. Press and hold the LO button on the CCP. Coolant fans should be OFF. If On, their speed should decrease until they turn OFF.
3. Release the LO button. Press and hold the HI button on the CCP. Coolant fans should begin at low speed, increase to medium speed and then increase to high speed.
4. Release the HI button. Coolant fans should remain ON for 4½ minutes on 1988 models and 90 seconds on 1989 models then return to BCM control.
5. Releasing HI or LO button will return fan speed to automatic BCM control.
6. Exit diagnostic mode.

1990

1. Start engine and let idle. Coolant fans should run at low speed after a few minutes.
2. With engine idling, restrict air flow through radiator by covering half of grill side of the radiator. Coolant fans should run at high speed after a few minutes.
3. Uncover radiator. Coolant fans should return to low speed.

SYSTEM DIAGNOSIS

Refer to **Figs. 53 through 55** when performing diagnostic procedures on these systems.

CHART C-12

ELECTRIC COOLING FAN CONTROL CIRCUIT DIAGNOSIS
5.7L (VIN 8) "Y" CARLINE (PORT)

- INSTALL "SCAN" TOOL.
- IGNITION "ON," ENGINE "OFF," A/C "OFF."
- ENGINE COOLANT AND ENGINE OIL TEMPERATURE BELOW 100°C (212°F). ARE BOTH COOLING FANS "OFF?"

YES

- SELECT A/C MODE WITH THE A/C CONTROL SWITCH. DOES "SCAN" TOOL INDICATE A/C REQUEST DISPLAY AS "YES?"

YES

- IGNITION "ON," ENGINE RUNNING.
- USING "SCAN" TOOL SELECT:
  - MISCELLANEOUS TEST
  - OUTPUT TESTS
  - FAN RELAYS
  - FAN RELAY #1
- ENABLE "OUTPUT TEST."
  DOES PRIMARY COOLING FAN (FAN#1) OPERATE?

YES

- USING "SCAN" TOOL SELECT FAN RELAY #2.
- ENABLE "OUTPUT TEST."
  DOES SECONDARY COOLING FAN (FAN#2) OPERATE?

YES

- DOES "SCAN" TOOL INDICATE A/C FAN REQUEST DISPLAY AS "NO?"

YES

- IGNITION "OFF."
- DISCONNECT A/C COOLING FAN SWITCH.
- IGNITON "ON."
- DOES "SCAN" TOOL INDICATE A/C FAN REQUEST DISPLAY AS "YES?"

YES — NO TROUBLE FOUND.

NO — SHORT TO GROUND ON CKT 603 OR FAULTY ECM.

NO — DIAGNOSIS OF A/C CLUTCH CIRCUIT

NO — REFER TO 2 OF 2

NO — REFER TO 2 OF 2

NO

- IGNITION "OFF."
- DISCONNECT A/C COOLING FAN SWITCH.
- CONNECT A JUMPER WIRE FROM THE A/C COOLING FAN HARNESS TERMINAL "B" TO GROUND.
- IGNITION "ON."
  DOES SCAN TOOL INDICATE A/C FAN REQUEST DISPLSAY AS "YES?"

NO

- CONNECT JUMPER WIRE ACROSS A/C COOLING FAN SWITCH.
  DOES "SCAN" TOOL INDICATE A/C FAN REQUEST DISPLAY AS "YES?"

YES — FAULTY CONNECTION OR OPEN CKT 603 OR FAULTY ECM.

NO — HIGH A/C PRESSURE OR FAULTY CONNECTION OR FAULTY A/C COOLING FAN SWITCH.

YES — FAULTY CONNECTION OR OPEN CKT 450.

NO

- DISCONNECT FAN RELAY FOR FAN THAT IS OPERATING DID THE FAN STOP?

YES

- IGNITION "OFF."
- PROBE FAN RELAY HARNESS CONNECTOR TERMINAL "F" WITH TEST LIGHT TO 12V. IS TEST LIGHT "ON"?

YES

PRIMARY FAN (FAN#1)

CKT 409 SHORTED TO GROUND OR FAULTY ECM.

SECONDARY FAN (FAN#2)

CKT 473 SHORTED TO GROUND OR FAULTY ECM.

NO — FAULTY RELAY.

NO — CKT FROM RELAY TO FAN IS SHORTED TO VOLTAGE. (CKT 702 OR CKT 903)

Fig. 51 Coolant fan diagnostic chart (Part 2 of 4). 1990 Corvette

1988–89

Coolant Fans Do Not Operate In Low Speed

1. Disconnect BCM connector C1 and turn ignition switch to RUN position. Connect a fused jumper between gray/black wire terminal and ground. If coolant fans run at low speed, replace BCM module.
2. If coolant fans do not operate, leave jumper installed in step 1 and disconnect coolant fan relay connector. Measure voltage between coolant fan relay connector terminals as follows:
   a. Between terminal 2 and ground. If zero volts is present, check brown wire for an open.
   b. Between terminals 2 and 5. If zero volts is present, check gray/black wire for an open.
   c. Between terminal 1 and ground. If zero volts is present, check red wire for an open.

3. If battery voltage is present in steps a through c, connect a fused jumper to terminals 1 and 4 on the disconnected low speed coolant fan relay connector. If fans run at low speeds, replace low speed coolant fan relay.
4. If fans do not operate, check red (1988) or black/red (1989) wire for an open. If wire is satisfactory, replace coolant fan resistors.

Coolant Fans Do Not Operate In Medium Speed

1. Disconnect BCM connector C1, turn ignition switch to RUN position and connect a fused jumper between terminal 17 (1988) or A7 (1989) and ground. If coolant fans run, replace BCM module.
2. If coolant fans do not run, leave jumper in place from step 1 and disconnect medium speed coolant fan relay. Measure voltage on the relay connector between the following terminals:
   a. Between terminal 2 and ground. If

zero volts is present, check brown wire for an open.
   b. Between terminals 2 and 5. If zero volts is present, check dark green/white (1988) or black/yellow (1989) wire for an open.
   c. Between terminal 1 and ground. If zero volts is present, check red wire for an open.
3. If battery voltage is present in steps a through c, connect a fused jumper between terminals 1 and 4 at the medium speed relay. If coolant fans rum at medium speed, replace medium speed coolant fan relay.
4. If fans do not run, check red/black (1988) or black/pink (1989) wires for an open. If wires are satisfactory, replace coolant fan resistors.

Coolant Fans Do Not Operate On High Speed

1. Remove coolant fan relay, turn ignition switch to RUN position. Connect a fused jumper at relay center, position D between terminal 1 and ground. If coolant fans run on high speed, proceed to step 5.
2. If coolant fans do not operate on high speed, disconnect high speed coolant fan relay, turn ignition switch to RUN position. Connect a fused jumper between the following terminals on the relay connector:
   a. Between terminal 2 and ground. If zero volts is present, check brown wire for an open.
   b. Between terminals 2 and 5. If zero volts is present, check orange/black wire for an open.
   c. Between terminal 1 and ground. If zero volts is present, check red wire for an open.
3. If battery voltage is present in steps a through c, connect a fused jumper between terminals 1 and 4 on the high speed coolant fan relay. If fans run on high speed, replace high speed coolant fan relay.
4. If fans do not operate at high speed, check white (1988) or red/black (1989) wire for an open.
5. Separate connector C1 from BCM, turn ignition switch to RUN position and reconnect the coolant fan relay. If coolant fan runs on high speed, replace BCM module.
6. If fans do not operate on high speed, leave ignition switch in RUN position and BCM connector C1 disconnected then remove coolant fan relay. Measure voltage between the following terminals at the relay center position D:
   a. Between terminals 2 and 5. If battery voltage is present, check black/yellow wire for a short to ground.
   b. Between terminals 2 and 3. If voltage is less than battery voltage, check black wire for an open.
   c. If voltage is correct for steps a and b, replace coolant fan relay.

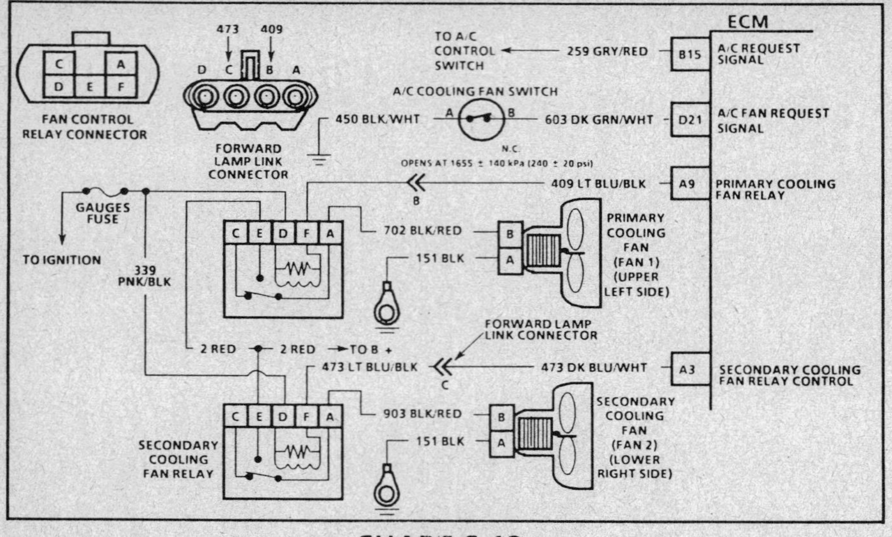

CHART C-12
(Page 2 of 2)

ELECTRIC COOLING FAN CONTROL CIRCUIT DIAGNOSIS
5.7L (VIN 8) "Y" CARLINE (PORT)

FROM CHART C-12

- IGNITION "OFF."
- DISCONNECT FAN CONTROL RELAY FOR COOLING FAN THAT DID NOT OPERATE.
- IGNITION "ON."
- PROBE HARNESS TERMINALS "D" AND "E" OF FAN RELAY WITH A TEST LIGHT CONNECTED TO GROUND.

LIGHT "ON" BOTH

LIGHT "OFF" ONE OR BOTH.

REPAIR OPEN OR SHORT TO GROUND IN CIRCUIT THAT DID NOT LIGHT.

- USING "SCAN" TOOL SELECT "FIELD SERVICE MODE."
- PROBE CONNECTOR HARNESS TERMINAL "F" WITH A TEST LIGHT CONNECTED TO 12 VOLTS.
- IS TEST LIGHT "ON"?

YES

NO

REPAIR OPEN OR SHORT TO VOLTAGE IN CIRCUIT FROM RELAY TO ECM. (CKT 409 OR CKT 473)
OR
FAULTY CONNECTION AT ECM
OR
FAULTY ECM.

- USING A JUMPER WIRE, JUMPER HARNESS TERMINALS "A" AND "D" TOGETHER. DOES FAN OPERATE?

YES

FAULTY CONNECTION
OR
FAULTY RELAY.

NO

- WITH JUMPER WIRE STILL INSTALLED
- DISCONNECT INOPERATIVE COOLING FAN MOTOR ELECTRICAL CONNECTOR
- PROBE A TEST LIGHT ACROSS THE INOPERATIVE COOLING FAN MOTOR HARNESS CONNECTOR TERMINALS
- IS TEST LIGHT "ON"?

YES

FAULTY COOLING FAN MOTOR

NO

- PROBE COOLING FAN MOTOR HARNESS CONNECTOR TERMINAL "B" WITH A TEST LIGHT CONNECTED TO GROUND.

YES

FAULTY CONNECTION
OR
OPEN CKT 151.

NO

FAULTY CONNECTION
OR
OPEN IN CIRCUIT BETWEEN RELAY AND COOLING FAN MOTOR. (CKT 702 OR CKT 903)

Fig. 51 Coolant fan diagnostic chart (Part 4 of 4). 1990 Corvette

---

ECM

B15	A/C REQUEST SIGNAL
D21	A/C FAN REQUEST SIGNAL
A9	PRIMARY COOLING FAN RELAY
A3	SECONDARY COOLING FAN RELAY CONTROL

TO A/C CONTROL SWITCH

259 GRY/RED

A/C COOLING FAN SWITCH

450 BLK/WHT

603 DK GRN/WHT

N.C.

OPEN AT 1655 ± 160 kPa (240 ± 20 psi)

409 LT BLU/BLK

PRIMARY COOLING FAN (FAN 1) (UPPER LEFT SIDE)

FORWARD LAMP LINK CONNECTOR

473 DK BLU/WHT

SECONDARY COOLING FAN (FAN 2) (LOWER RIGHT SIDE)

473   409

FORWARD LAMP LINK CONNECTOR

702 BLK/RED

151 BLK

473 LT BLU/BLK

2 RED — TO B+

2 RED

903 BLK/RED

151 BLK

PRIMARY COOLING FAN RELAY

SECONDARY COOLING FAN RELAY

339 PNK/BLK

GAUGES FUSE

TO IGNITION

FAN CONTROL RELAY CONNECTOR

CHART C-12

ELECTRIC COOLING FAN CONTROL CIRCUIT DIAGNOSIS
5.7L (VIN 8) "Y" CARLINE (PORT)

Circuit Description:

The cooling fans are controlled by the ECM based on various inputs. Battery voltage is supplied to the fan relays on terminal "E" and ignition voltage to terminal "D." Grounding CKT 409 (relay terminal "F") will energize the primary cooling fan relay (Fan 1) and supply battery voltage to the primary cooling fan motor. Grounding CKT 473 (relay terminal "F") will energize the secondary cooling fan relay (Fan 2) and supply battery voltage to the secondary fan motor.

The A/C cooling fan switch, mounted in the A/C high pressure line, will close when head pressure exceeds 1655 kPa (240 psi) and this input causes the ECM to ground CKT 473 or CKT 409 if other criteria are met.

If a Code 14, 15, 52 or 62 sets or the ECM is operating in the fuel back up mode, the ECM will turn "ON" the cooling fans.

Diagnostic Aids:

If the owner complained of an overheating problem, it must be determined if the complaint was due to an actual boil over or the warning indicator light or engine coolant temperature gage indicated overheating.

The gage accuracy can also be checked by comparing the Coolant Temperature Sensor (CTS) reading using a "Scan" tool and comparing its reading with the gage reading.

If the engine is actually overheating and the gage indicates overheating, but the cooling fan is not coming "ON," the Coolant Temperature Sensor (CTS) has probably shifted out of calibration and should be replaced.

If the engine is overheating and the cooling fans are "ON," the cooling system should be checked, refer to ENGINE COOLING.

Fig. 51 Coolant fan diagnostic chart (Part 3 of 4). 1990 Corvette

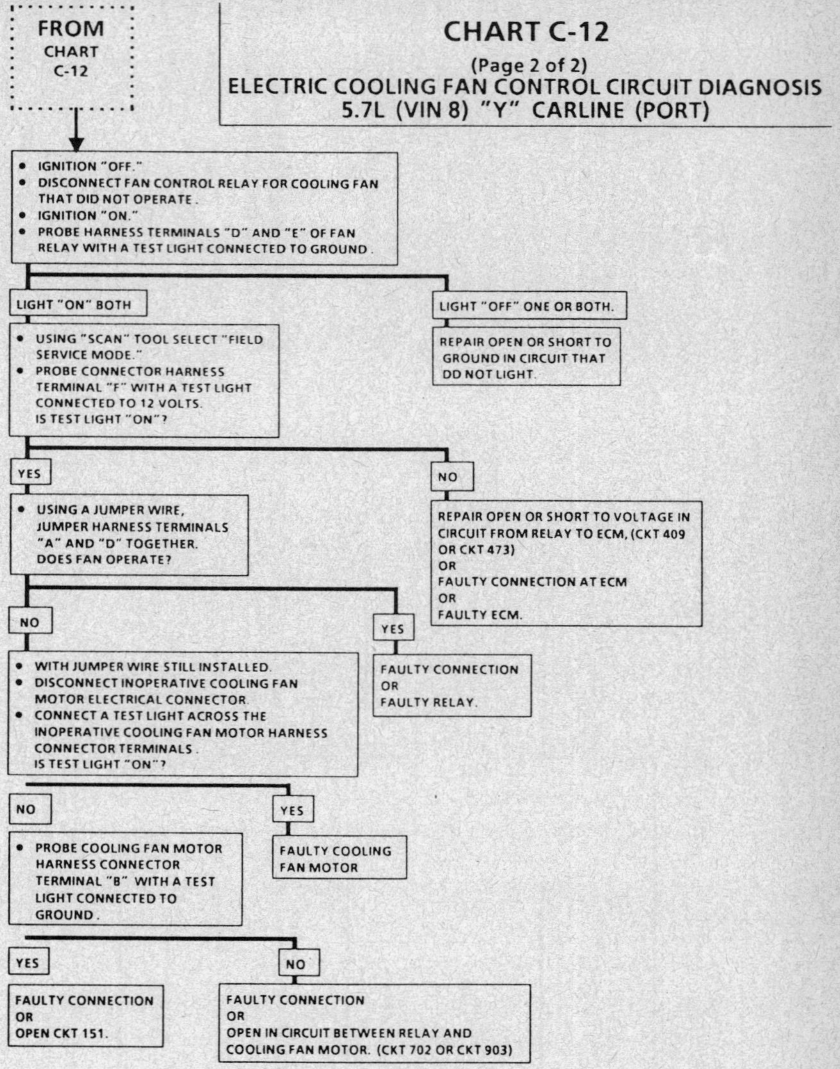

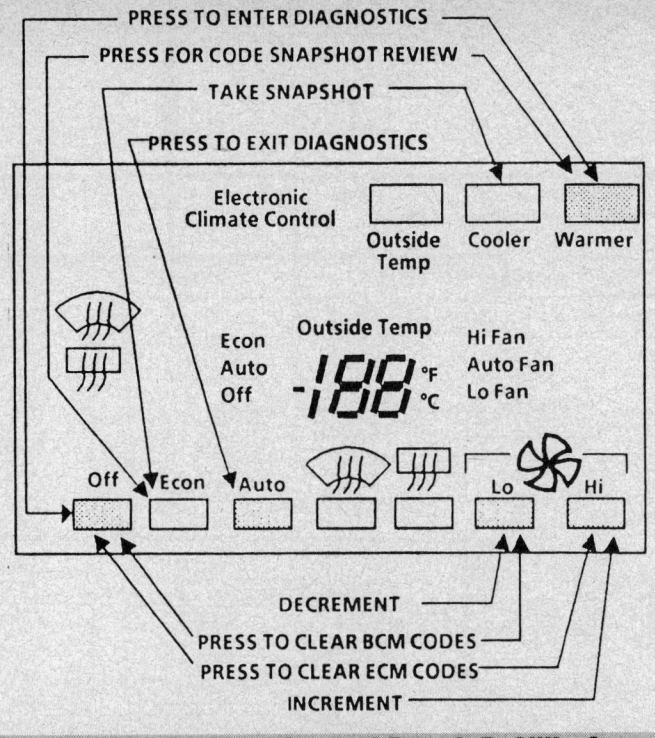

Fig. 52   Climate Control Panel. DeVille & Fleetwood

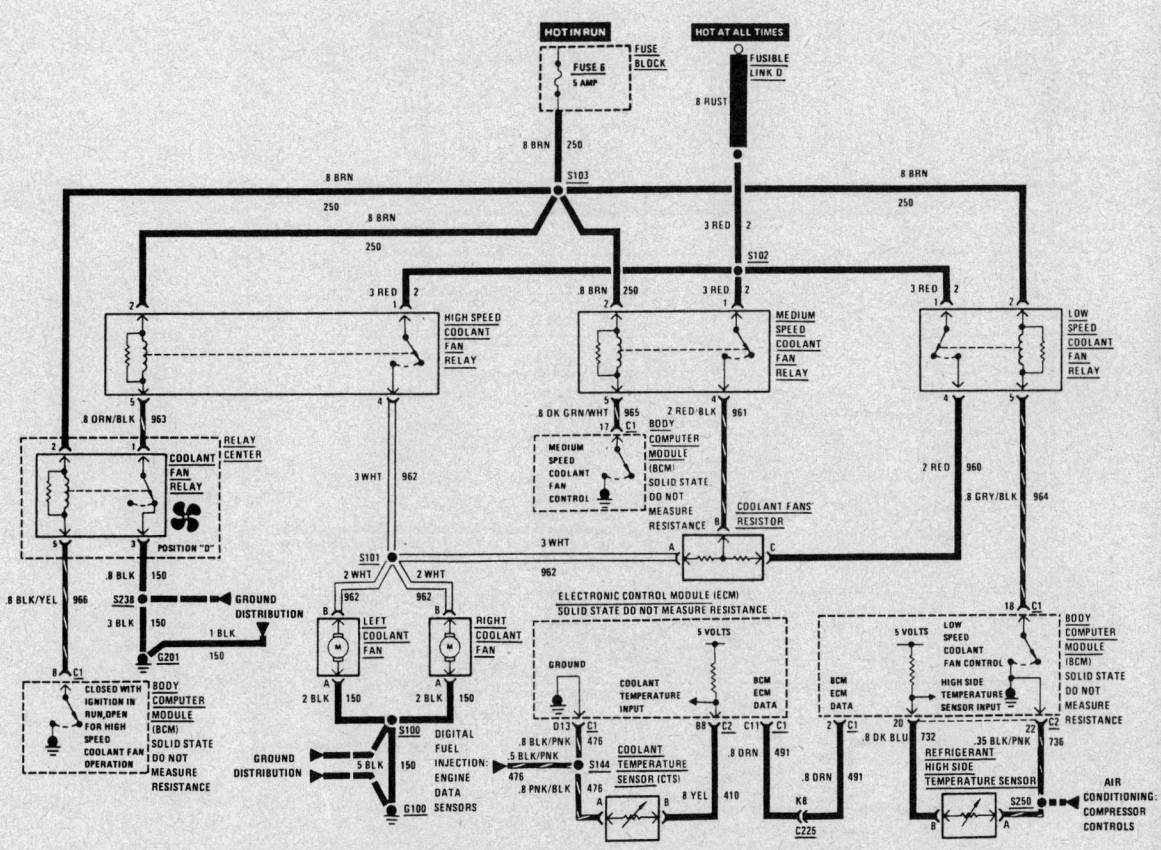

Fig. 53   Coolant fan wiring circuit. 1988 DeVille & Fleetwood

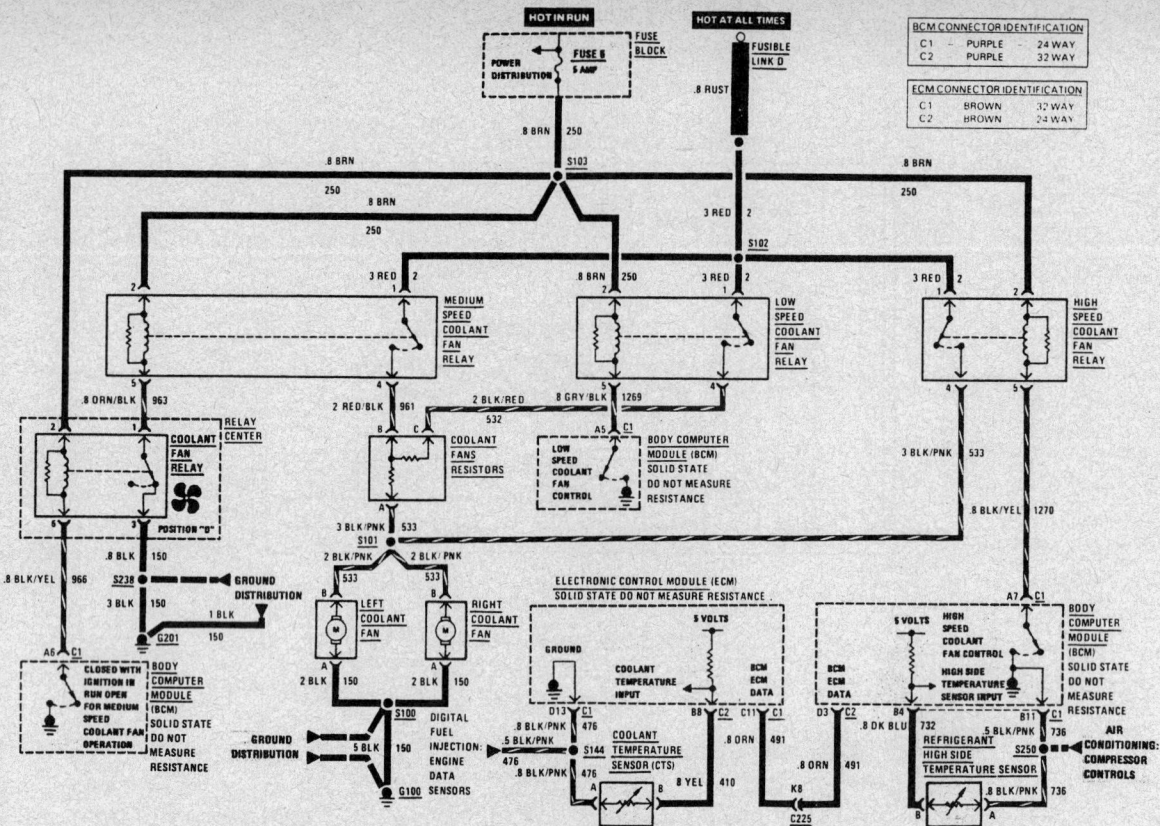

Fig. 54   Coolant fan wiring circuit. 1989 DeVille & Fleetwood

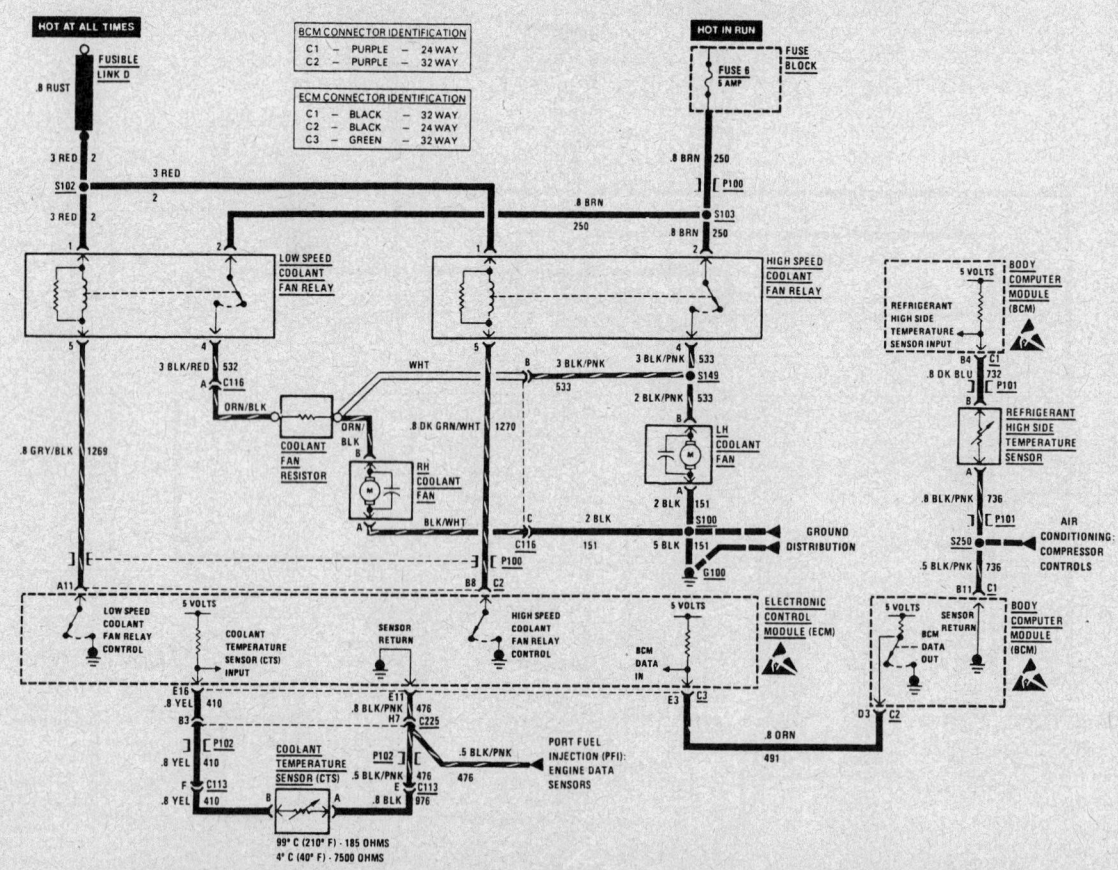

Fig. 55   Coolant fan wiring circuit. 1990 DeVille & Fleetwood

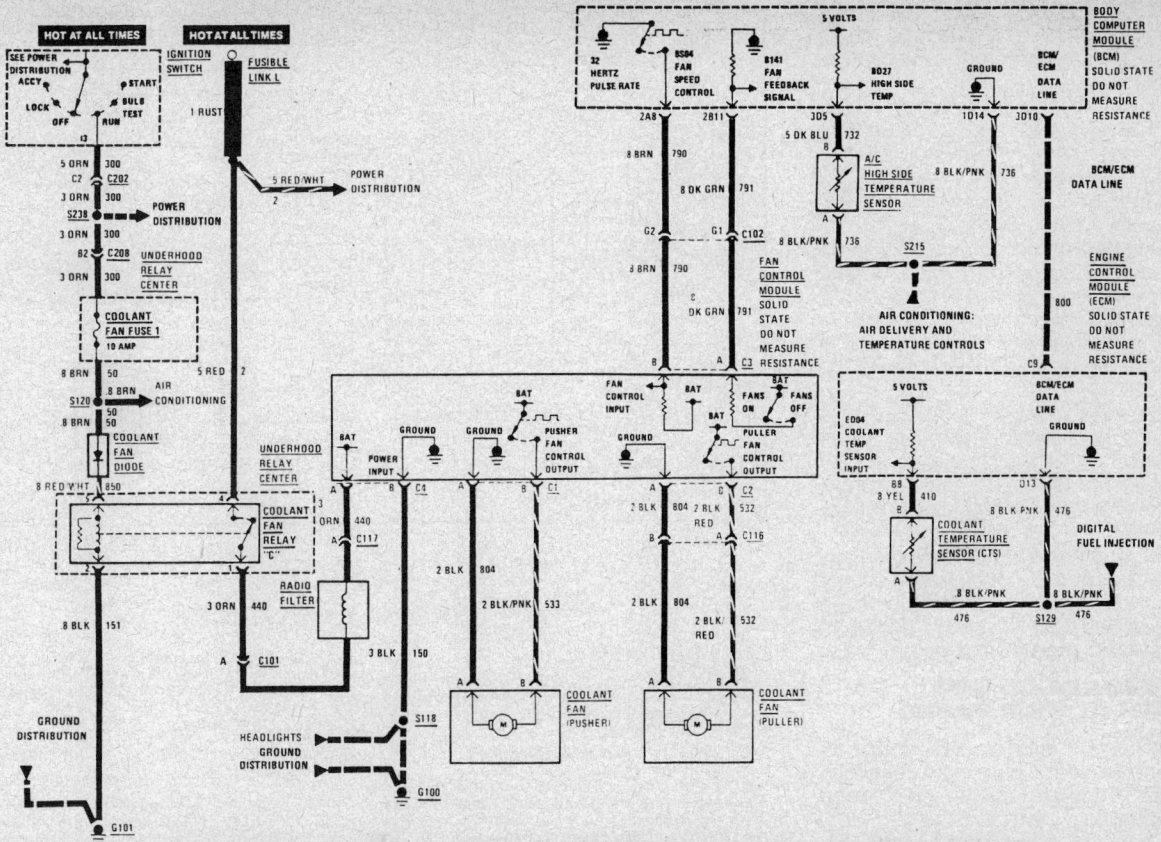

Fig. 56 Coolant fan wiring circuit. 1988–89 Eldorado & Seville

Coolant Fans Operates At All Times, With Ignition Switch In Run Position

1. Turn ignition switch to RUN position and connect a fused jumper between black/yellow wire terminal and ground at the BCM connector C1. If fans turn Off, replace BCM module.
2. **On 1988 models**, if coolant fans continue to run, leave jumper in place from step 1 and remove coolant fan relay. Measure voltage between the following terminals at the relay center position D:
   a. Between terminal 2 and ground. If zero volts is present, check brown wire for an open.
   b. Between terminals 2 and 5. If zero volts is present, check black/yellow wire for an open.
   c. If battery voltage is present in steps a and b, check orange/black wire for a short to ground. If wire is satisfactory, replace coolant fan relay.
3. **On 1989 models**, if coolant fans continue to run, leave jumper in place from step 1 and remove coolant fan relay. Measure voltage between the following terminals at the relay center position D:
   a. Between terminals 2 and 5. If voltage is more than zero, check black/yellow wire for a short to ground.
   b. Between terminals 2 and 5. If voltage is less than battery voltage, check black/yellow wire for an

open.
   c. If voltage is correct in steps a and b, check orange/black wire for a short to ground. If wire is satisfactory, replace coolant fan relay.

Coolant Fan Runs At All Times, With Ignition Switch In Any Position

Disconnect each coolant fan relay, one at a time, until coolant fans stops. When coolant fans stop, replace the relay that was just disconnected.

1990

Coolant Fans Do Not Operate At All

1. Disconnect high speed coolant fan relay, measure voltage between relay terminal 1 and ground. If zero volts is present, check red wire and fusible link D.
2. If battery voltage is present, turn ignition switch to RUN position then measure voltage between relay terminal 2 and ground. If zero volts is present, check brown wire and fuse number 6.
3. If battery voltage is present, reconnect high speed coolant fan relay then enter diagnostic mode as outlined under "Entering Diagnostic Mode." Turn coolant fans to high speed with ECM override.
4. Disconnect lefthand coolant fan connector. Measure voltage between connector terminal B and ground. If zero volts is present, check black/pink wire.

5. If battery voltage is present, check black wire between coolant fan motor and ground.

Coolant Fans Do Not Operate At Low Speed

1. Turn coolant fans on low speed as outlined under "Entering Diagnostic Mode." If coolant fans turn on proceed as follows:
   a. Start engine and turn On A/C.
   b. Enter diagnostic as outlined under "Entering Diagnostic Mode" when the fuel data center displays .7.0, depress and release the LO button on the ECC to enter ECM data display mode E.9.0.
   c. Advance the display by depressing the HI button until P.0.4 parameter is displayed. Compare parameter reading with known properly functioning vehicle. Exit diagnostic mode
   d. Enter diagnostic as outlined under "Entering Diagnostic Mode" when the fuel data center displays .7.0, depress and release the OUTSIDE TEMP button on the ECC to enter BCM data display mode F.8.0.
   e. Advance the display by depressing the HI button until P.2.7 parameter is displayed. Compare parameter reading with a known properly functioning vehicle. Exit diagnostic mode.
   f. If readings are satisfactory, replace ECM.

g. If reading are not satisfactory, check wiring to suspect sensor. If wiring is satisfactory, replace sensor.
2. If coolant fans do not operate, ensure ECM is connected and ignition switch is in RUN position connect a fused jumper between ECM connector C2 terminal A11 and ground. If coolant fans run, replace ECM.
3. If coolant fans do not operate, leave jumper installed from step 2 and check voltage at the following low speed coolant fan relay terminals:
   a. Between terminal 1 and ground. If zero volts is present check red wire.
   b. Between terminals 1 and 5. If zero volts is present, check gray/black wire.
   c. Between terminal 2 and ground. If zero volts is present, check brown wire.
4. Connect a fused jumper between terminal 2 and 4. If coolant fans do not run, check black/red wire. If black/red wire is satisfactory, check righthand coolant fan resistor and wiring.

Coolant Fans Do Not Operate At High Speed

1. Turn coolant fans on high speed as outlined under "Entering Diagnostic Mode." If coolant fans turn on proceed as follows:
   a. Start engine and turn On A/C.
   b. Enter diagnostic as outlined under "Entering Diagnostic Mode" when the fuel data center displays .7.0, depress and release the LO button on the ECC to enter ECM data display mode E.9.0.
   c. Advance the display by depressing the HI button until P.0.4 parameter is displayed. Compare parameter reading with known properly functioning vehicle. Exit diagnostic mode
   d. Enter diagnostic as outlined under "Entering Diagnostic Mode" when the fuel data center displays .7.0, depress and release the OUTSIDE TEMP button on the ECC to enter BCM data display mode F.8.0.
   e. Advance the display by depressing the HI button until P.2.7 parameter is displayed. Compare parameter reading with a known properly functioning vehicle. Exit diagnostic mode.
   f. If reading are satisfactory, replace ECM.
   g. If reading are not satisfactory, check wiring to suspect sensor. If wiring is satisfactory, replace sensor.
2. If coolant fans do not operate, ensure ECM is connected and ignition switch is in RUN position connect a fused jumper between ECM connector C2 terminal B8 and ground. If coolant fans run, replace ECM.
3. If coolant fans do not operate, leave jumper installed from step 2 and check voltage at the following high speed coolant fan relay terminals:
   a. Between terminal 1 and ground. If

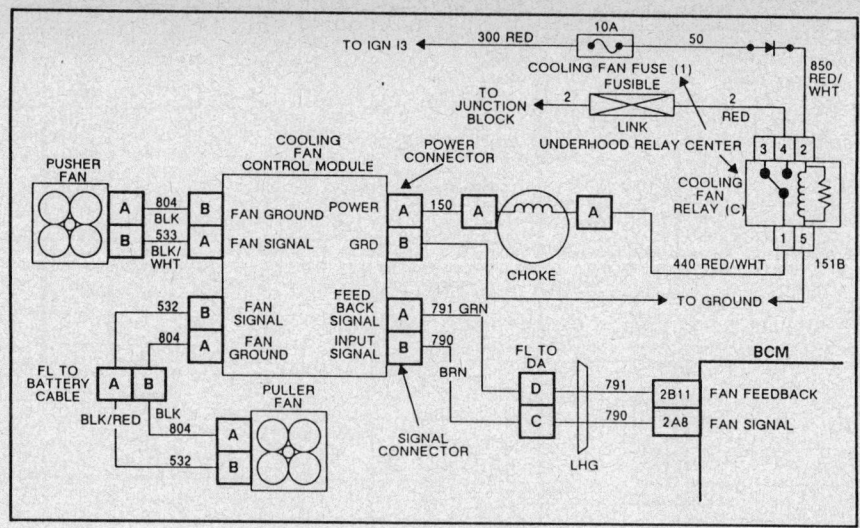

zero volts is present check red wire.
   b. Between terminals 1 and 5. If zero volts is present, check dark green/white wire.
   c. Between terminal 2 and ground. If zero volts is present, check brown wire.
4. Connect a fused jumper between terminal 2 and 4. If coolant fans do not run, check black/pink wire.

COOLANT FAN, REPLACE

1. Disconnect battery ground cable.
2. Raise and support vehicle.
3. Disconnect fan electrical connectors.
4. Remove fan to lower cradle attaching screws.
5. Lower vehicle.
6. For right fan, remove A/C accumulator from bracket and position out of the way.
7. Remove air cleaner intake duct.
8. Remove fan to upper radiator mounting panel attaching screws.
9. Remove upper radiator mounting panel.
10. Remove cooling fan(s).
11. Reverse procedure to install.

ELDORADO & SEVILLE

For system description, testing and diagnosis on 1988-89 models, refer to **Figs. 56** and **57** for procedures.

SYSTEM DESCRIPTION
1990
Circuit Operation

The ECM controls both coolant fans by controlling three relays through two outputs. There are two modes of coolant fan operation. One mode is the series mode

CODE B441
COOLING FANS PROBLEM

Circuit Description:
Code B441 is set by the BCM if it receives the improper cooling fans feedback voltage. The cooling fans control module is designed to change the feedback voltage on circuit 791 as follows:

- 7V if the fans have been turned off
- 0V if the fans have been turned on
- 7V if the fans have been turned on and an excessive current draw exists (stalled or shorted fan motors)
- 0V if both fan connectors are open.

The BCM will set Code B441 if either of the following conditions exist:

A. The BCM has commanded the fans off but the feedback voltage remains low. The BCM will keep Code B441 current for the rest of the ignition cycle and continue providing a normal control signal to the cooling fans control module. The BCM will again test this condition during the next ignition cycle to determine if the malfunction has become intermittent.

B. The BCM has commanded the fans on but the feedback voltage remains high. The BCM will command the fans off to protect the system from a possible stalled or shorted motor condition. If the control temperatures (coolant and A/C high side) should drop below the turn off points and later require the fans on, the BCM will repeat the test to determine if the malfunction has become intermittent.

Both of the above conditions will result in the "Coolant Temp/Fan" display on the CCDIC being illuminated whenever the control temperatures require cooling fans operation.

Test Description:
Numbers below refer to circled numbers on the diagnostic chart.

1. The cooling fans override feature (BS04) can be used to evaluate the system operation. If higher fan is off when "high fans" are commanded or if either fan is on when "fans off" is commanded, the appropriate diagnostic path can be followed to isolate the malfunction.

2. The cooling fans feedback input BI41 can be used to evaluate the feedback signal being received by the BCM. If the input does not agree with the actual fans operation, circuit 791 must be investigated for a possible malfunction. If the input does agree with the commanded fans operation within the appropriate time period, then the cause of Code B441 is not currently present.

Note on Intermittents

If an intermittent Code B441 is being set, manipulate the related wiring while observing the cooling fans feedback BI41 and commanding "High Fans" or "Fans Off" in the override diagnostic mode. If the failure is induced, the fans status will not agree with the commanded operation. This will help in isolating the location of the malfunction.

Fig. 57   Coolant fan diagnosis chart (Part 1 of 4). 1988–89 Eldorado & Seville

CODE B441
COOLING FANS CIRCUIT

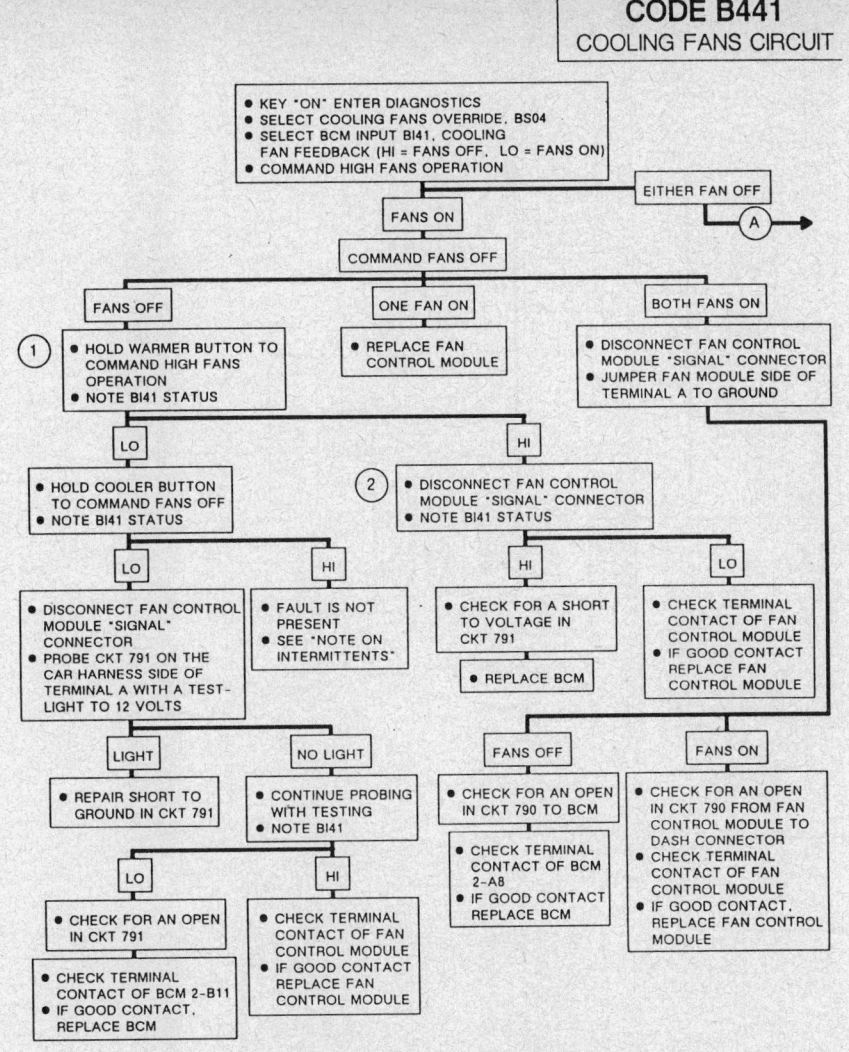

Fig. 57 Coolant fan diagnosis chart (Part 2 of 4). 1988–89 Eldorado & Seville

where only coolant fan relay B is energized by the ECM and both coolant fans run at low speed. The second mode is parallel mode where all three of the coolant fan relays are energized by the ECM and both coolant fans run at high speed. Coolant fan operation is only possible when the ignition switch is in the RUN position.

The coolant fans will run at slow speed when circuit 535 is grounded by the ECM at terminal 2A11. Coolant fan relay B is energized and voltage is applied to both coolant fans.

The coolant fans run at high speed when circuits 535 and 536 are grounded by the ECM. Grounding circuit 535 energizes coolant fan relay B and battery voltage is applied to the pusher fan. When circuit 536 is grounded coolant fan relays C and D are energized. Coolant fan relay C provides a ground for the pusher fan through circuit 804. Battery voltage is applied through coolant fan relay D to the puller fan.

Series Mode

The BCM will request the ECM to turn

On the coolant fans at low speed when A/C high side temperature is greater than 140°F and will request the ECM to turn the coolant fans Off when A/C high side temperature drops below 122°F.

The BCM will also request the ECM to turn the coolant fans On at lo speed when vehicle speed is less than 20 mph, A/C compressor clutch engagement is possible or the outside air temperature is greater than 113°F.

The ECM will turn On the coolant fans at low speed when coolant temperature is greater than 212°F and turn the coolant fans Off when coolant temperature falls below 208°F.

Parallel Mode

The BCM will request the ECM to turn the coolant fans On at high speed when A/C high side temperature is above 158°F or an A/C high side temperature sensor failure is current and A/C clutch engagement is possible. The BCM will request the ECM to turn the coolant fans Off when

A/C high side temperature drops below 138°F.

The ECM will turn the coolant fans On at high speed if coolant temperature is above 226°F or a coolant temperature sensor failure is current. The ECM will switch the coolant fans Off when coolant temperature drops below 222°F.

TROUBLESHOOTING
1990

1. If both coolant fans do not operate, check fusible link L by operating the horn.
2. If there is also a problem with A/C compressor clutch engagement, check coolant fan fuse 1 in the underhood relay center.
3. If both coolant fans operate in low speed with ignition switch OFF, check for a short to battery voltage on circuit 532. If circuit is satisfactory, replace coolant fan relay B.
4. If both coolant fans operate in high speed but not in low speed, check the 533 circuit between coolant fan relay C and S161 for an open. Also check continuity of coolant fan relay C between terminals 1 and 3.
5. For a continuous low speed operation with ignition switch in RUN only, check circuit 535 for a short to ground. If circuit is satisfactory, problem is ECM related.
6. If puller fan runs continuously with ignition switch in ON or OFF position, check circuit 533 for a short to battery voltage If circuit is satisfactory, replace coolant fan relay D.
7. If puller fan run continuously with ignition switch in RUN position only, check circuit 536 for a short to ground. If circuit is satisfactory, problem is ECM related.
8. If a no low speed,no high speed puller fan condition exists, check circuit 533 between S161 and puller fan for an open. Check circuit 804 between puller fan and S112 for and open. Check puller fan and terminal contacts.
9. If a no low speed or pusher fan runs in high speed when in system test ES08, check circuit 533 for a short to ground between pusher fan and coolant fan relay C. If circuit is satisfactory, replace coolant fan relay C.

ENTERING DIAGNOSTIC MODE
1990

Refer to **Fig. 58** when entering diagnostic mode.

Turn ignition On, then depress OFF and WARMER buttons on the Climate Control Panel (CCP), **Fig. 59.** Hold buttons until all display panel segments illuminate, indicating beginning of diagnostic readout. **The two display panels must be illuminated to ensure all segments are operating. Do not attempt diagnosis unless all segments appear, as a misdiagnosis could result. If any segments are inoperative, the display panel must be replaced.**

CODE B441 (CONT'D) COOLING FANS CIRCUIT

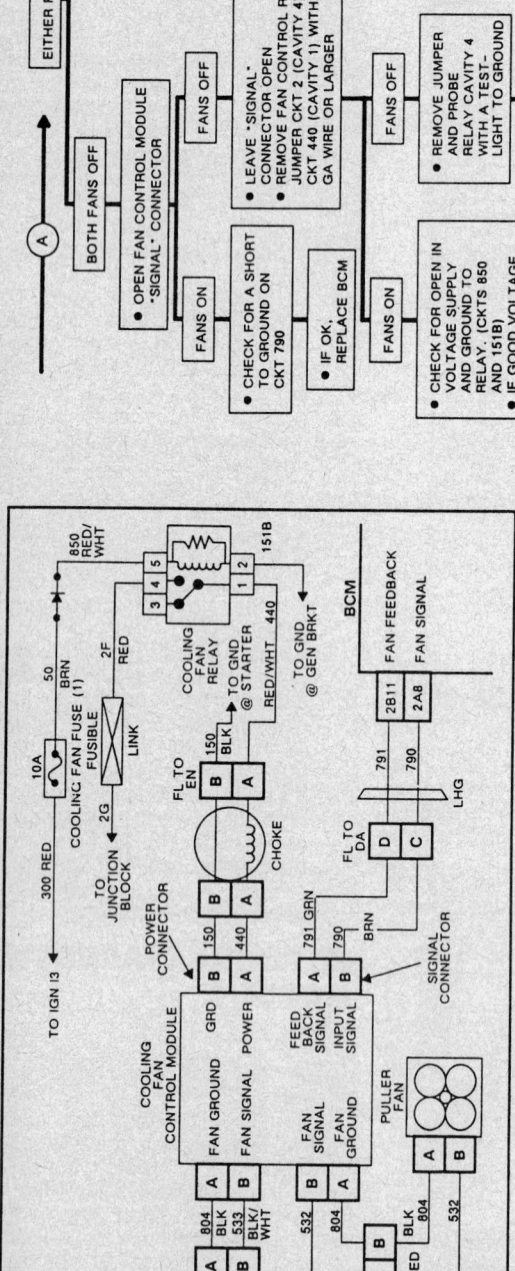

EITHER FAN OFF

ONE FAN ON
- CHECK FOR A BINDING FAN MOTOR

FAN ON
- TURN IGNITION OFF AND REMOVE FAN MOTOR CONNECTORS
- JUMPER INOPERATIVE FAN HARNESS TO OPERATIVE FAN MOTOR WITH 12 GA WIRE OR LARGER IGNITION ON
- COMMAND HIGH FANS

FAN ON
- REPLACE INOPERATIVE FAN MOTOR

FAN OFF
- CHECK FOR A SHORT TO GROUND OR OPEN IN INOPERATIVE FAN HARNESS

LIGHT
- REINSTALL RELAY
- DISCONNECT FAN CONTROL MODULE "POWER" CONNECTOR
- CONNECT TESTLIGHT BETWEEN TERMINALS ON THE RELAY SIDE OF THE HARNESS

FAN OFF
- IF OK, REPLACE FAN CONTROL MODULE

LIGHT
- CHECK FOR SHORTED FAN MOTORS
- REPLACE FAN CONTROL MODULE

BOTH FANS OFF
- OPEN FAN CONTROL MODULE "SIGNAL" CONNECTOR

FANS OFF
- LEAVE "SIGNAL" CONNECTOR OPEN REMOVE FAN CONTROL RELAY JUMPER CKT 2 (CAVITY 4) TO CKT 440 (CAVITY 1) WITH 12 GA WIRE OR LARGER

FANS OFF
- REMOVE JUMPER AND PROBE RELAY CAVITY 4 WITH A TEST-LIGHT TO GROUND

NO LIGHT
- REPAIR OPEN IN CKT 2F

NO LIGHT
- CONNECT TESTLIGHT BETWEEN CKT 440 IN CAR HARNESS AND GROUND

LIGHT
- REPAIR OPEN IN CKT 150

NO LIGHT
- REPAIR OPEN IN CKT 440

FANS ON
- CHECK FOR A SHORT TO GROUND ON CKT 790

FANS ON
- IF OK, REPLACE BCM

FANS ON
- CHECK FOR OPEN IN VOLTAGE SUPPLY AND GROUND TO RELAY. (CKTS 850 AND 151B)
- IF GOOD VOLTAGE SUPPLY AND GROUND, REPLACE RELAY

WHEN ALL DIAGNOSIS AND REPAIRS ARE COMPLETED, CLEAR CODES AND VERIFY PROPER OPERATION

Fig. 57 Coolant fan diagnosis chart (Part 4 of 4). 1988–89 Eldorado & Seville

---

CODE B441 (CONT'D) COOLING FANS PROBLEM

Circuit Description:

Code B441 is set by the BCM if it receives the improper cooling fans feedback voltage. The cooling fans control module is designed to change the feedback voltage on circuit 791 as follows:

- 7V if the fans have been turned off
- 0V if the fans have been turned on
- 7V if the fans have been turned on and an excessive current draw exists (stalled or shorted fan motors)
- 0V if both fan connectors are open.

The BCM will set Code B441 if either of the following conditions exist:

A. The BCM has commanded the fans off but the feedback voltage remains low. The BCM will keep Code B441 current for the rest of the ignition cycle and continue providing a normal control signal to the cooling fans control module. The BCM will again test this condition during the next ignition cycle to determine if the malfunction has become intermittent.

B. The BCM has commanded the fans on but the feedback voltage remains high. The BCM will command the fans off to protect the system from a possible stalled or shorted motor condition. If the control temperatures (coolant and A/C high side) should drop below the turn off points and later require the fans on, the BCM will repeat the test to determine if the malfunction has become intermittent.

Both of the above conditions will result in the "Coolant Temp/Fan" message on the CCDIC being illuminated whenever the control temperatures require cooling fans operation.

Note on Intermittents

If an intermittent Code B441 is being set, manipulate the related wiring while observing the cooling fans feedback B141 and commanding "High Fans" or "Fans Off" in the override diagnostic mode. If the failure is induced, the fans status will not agree with the commanded operation. This will help in isolating the location of the malfunction.

Fig. 57 Coolant fan diagnosis chart (Part 3 of 4). 1988–89 Eldorado & Seville

START
ENTER DIAGNOSTICS BY SIMULTANEOUSLY PRESSING THE CCP'S "OFF" AND "WARM" BUTTONS UNTIL ALL DISPLAYS ARE LIT.
SEGMENT CHECK LEVEL
PRESS "OFF" = RETURN TO NORMAL OPERATION
DIAGNOSTIC CODE LEVEL
PRESS "OFF" = RETURN TO SEGMENT CHECK
SYSTEM LEVEL
ECM?
BCM?
IPC?
SIR?
PRESS "OFF" = RETURN TO DIAGNOSTIC CODES
PRESS "LO" = DISPLAY NEXT SYSTEM
PRESS "HI" = PROCEED TO FIRST TEST TYPE FOR SELECTED SYSTEM.
TEST TYPE LEVEL
DATA?
INPUTS?
OUTPUTS?
OVERRIDE?
CLEAR CODES?
SNAPSHOT?
DISPLAY VIN?
PRESS "OFF" = RETURN TO NEXT SYSTEM
PRESS "LO" = DISPLAY NEXT AVAILABLE TEST TYPE
PRESS "HI" = PROCEED TO FIRST TEST CHOICE FOR SELECTED TEST TYPE
TEST CHOICE LEVEL
"X X X X"
TEST NUMBER
TEST TYPE
D = DATA
I = INPUT
O = OUTPUT
S = OVERRIDE
SYSTEM
E = ECM
B = BCM
I = IPC
S = SIR
PRESS "OFF" = RETURN TO NEXT TEST TYPE FOR SELECTED SYSTEM.
PRESS "LO" = DISPLAY PREVIOUS TEST NUMBER.
PRESS "HI" = DISPLAY NEXT HIGHER TEST NUMBER
NOTE: "CLEAR CODES?" SELECTION DISPLAYS "CODES CLEAR" AND AUTOMATICALLY RETURNS TO NEXT TEST TYPE FOR SELECTED SYSTEM.

Fig. 58 How to operate Service Mode. 1990 Eldorado & Seville

Cooler
Warmer
Off AutoEcon
LoNormHi
Off
AUTO
Econ
Lo
NORM
HI
Electronic Climate Control
Outside Temp
Date
Time
Temp Time
Range
Inst Econ
Avg Econ
Eng Data
Fuel Used
Reset Recall
Engl Metric
Driver Information Center
date/time set

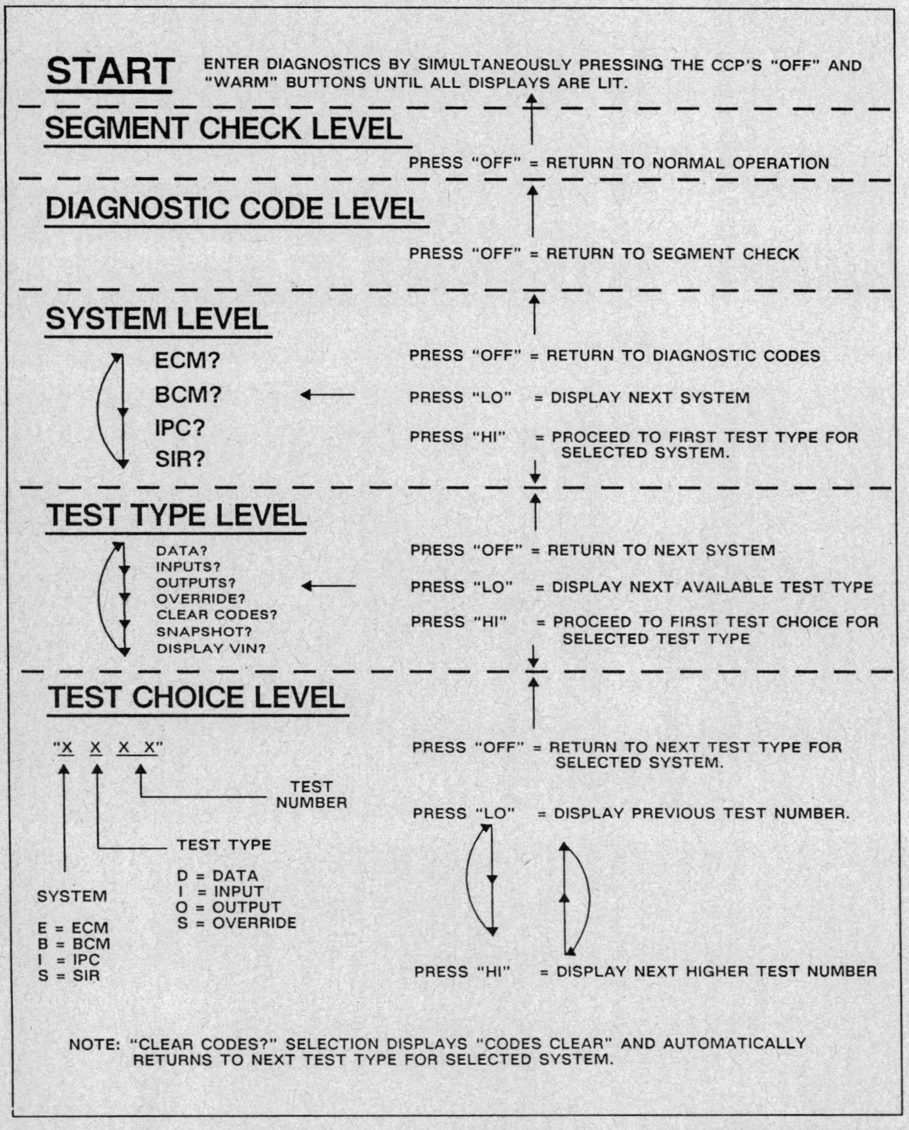

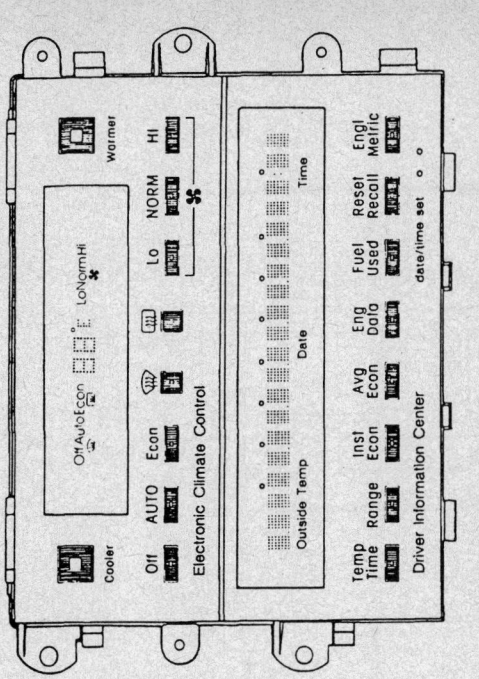

Fig. 59 Climate Control/Driver Information Center (CCDIC) Display. 1990 Eldorado & Seville

Cooler (output #1, ECM terminal 2A11)	warmer (output #2, ECM terminal 2B8)	
Diagnostic Display	Diagnostic Display	Correct Result
0	0	Both Fans off
0	1	Puller Fan high speed Pusher Fan off
1	0	Both Fans low speed
1	1	Both Fans high speed

Fig. 60 System check table. 1990 Eldorado & Seville

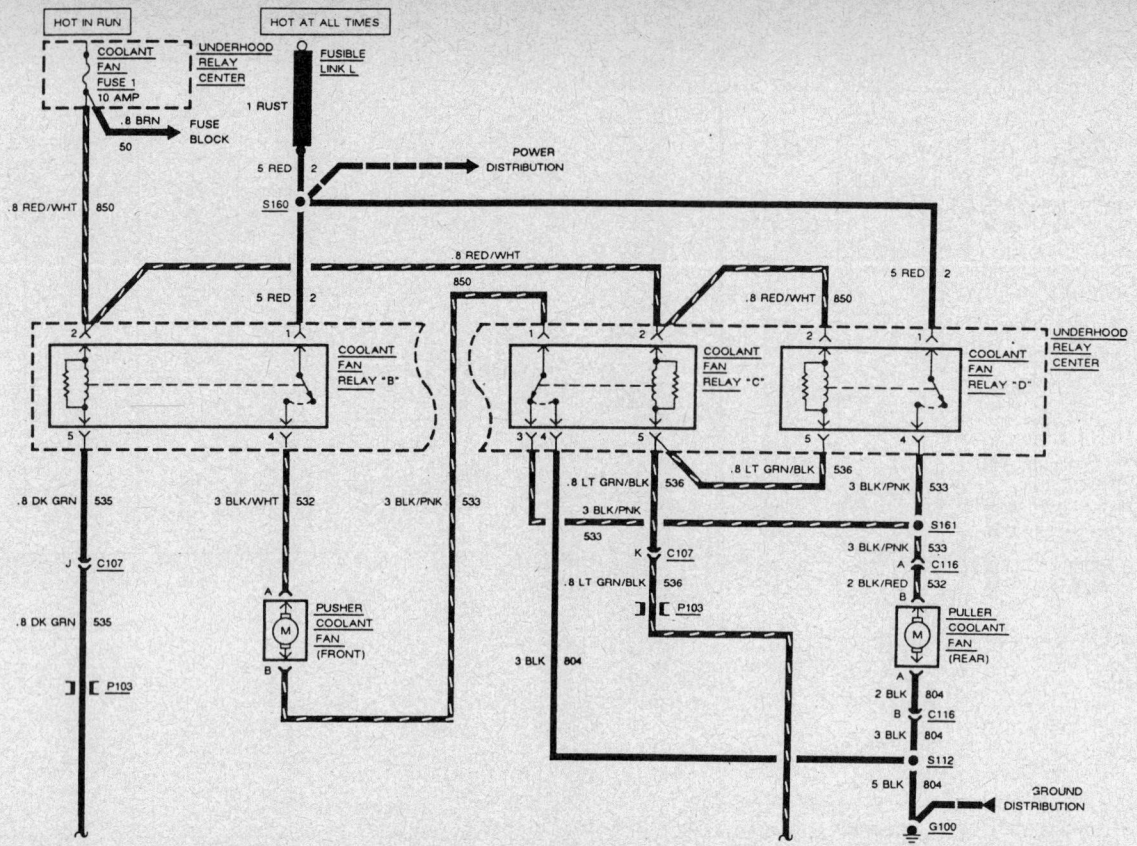

Fig. 61   Coolant fan wiring circuit (Part 1 of 2). 1990 Eldorado & Seville

After all ECM and BCM codes have been displayed, "ECM" will be displayed. At this point pressing the OFF button will return to diagnostic codes. Pressing the LO button will display the next system and pressing the HI button will proceed to the first test type for the system selected.

Having selected a system, the first available test type will be displayed. While selecting a specific test type, the OFF button will stop the test type and return the display to the next available system. Pressing the LO button will display the next available test type and pressing the HI button will select the displayed test type.

After selecting the test type, the first available test will be displayed. If dashes ever appear, this test is not allowed while vehicle is running. While selecting a specific test, pressing the OFF button will stop the test selection process and return the display to the next available test type. Pressing the LO button will display the next smaller test number for the selected test type. Pressing the HI button will display the next larger test number for the selected test type.

Pressing the RESET/RECALL button will halt diagnostics and return to normal display and operation.

SYSTEM CHECK

1990

1. Enter diagnostics as outlined under "Entering Diagnostic Mode."
2. Enter ECM override and select ES08,

coolant fan output override mode.
3. Operate the COOLER and WARMER buttons as indicated in **Fig. 60** to check the operation of the coolant fan system.
4. If all the results in **Fig. 60** are correct the coolant fans, relays and wiring are satisfactory. If a system still exists proceed to "Diagnosis."

DIAGNOSIS

1990

Refer To **Fig. 61** when performing diagnostic procedures on these systems.

Both Coolant Fans Do Not Operate At All

1. If horn operate, proceed to step 2. If horns do not operate, check the following:
   a. Check fusible link L for an open.
   b. Check circuits 2, 532 and 533 for a short to ground before replacing fusible link.
   c. Check circuit 2 to S160 and circuit 804 between S112 and G100 for an open.
2. Measure voltage between underhood relay center position B terminal 2 to ground with the relay removed and ignition switch in RUN position. If battery voltage is not present, check circuit 850 and coolant fan fuse 1 for an open.
3. If battery voltage is present, check wiring to both coolant fans and the fan terminal contacts. If wiring or terminal

contact is unsatisfactory, repair/replace as necessary.
4. If wiring and terminal contacts are satisfactory, check circuits 535 and 536 for an open. If both circuits are satisfactory, problem is ECM related.
5. If one or both circuits are unsatisfactory, repair/replace as necessary.

No Low Speed, No High Speed Pusher Fan

1. Disconnect coolant fan relay B from the underhood relay center. Turn ignition switch in RUN position and measure voltage between terminal 1 and ground then terminal 2 and ground of the relay center position B. If zero volts is present at one or both terminals, check circuits 2 and/or 850 for an open.
2. If battery voltage is present, enter diagnostics and select ECM override ES08 as outlined under "Diagnosis," set the display to 10. Connect a test lamp between terminals 2 and 5 at position B of the relay center. If test lamps does not light, check circuit 535 for an open or short to battery voltage. If wiring is satisfactory, problem is ECM related.
3. If test lamps lights, connect a fused jumper between terminals 1 and 4 at position B of relay center. If coolant fan runs at low speed, check or replace coolant fan relay B.
4. If the coolant fan does not run at high

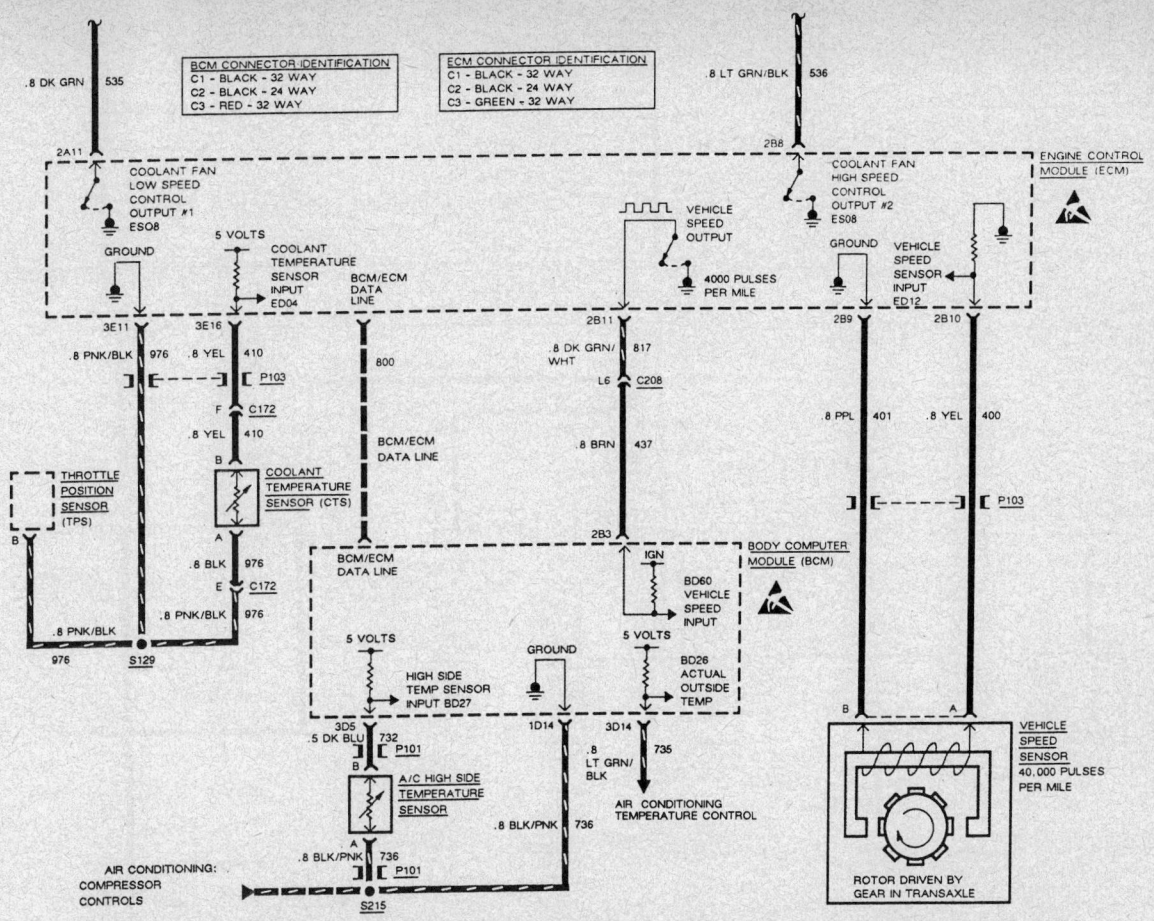

Fig. 61 Coolant fan wiring circuit (Part 2 of 2). 1990 Eldorado & Seville

speed, leave jumper in place and disconnect coolant fan relay C. If coolant fan runs at high speed, check/replace relay C.

5. If pusher fan does not run at high speed, check circuits 532 and 533 for an open to pusher fan. Also check pusher fan terminal contact. If satisfactory, replace pusher fan.

No High Speed Pusher Fan

1. Disconnect coolant relay C from the underhood relay center and with the ignition switch in RUN position, measure voltage between terminals 2 and 4.
2. If battery voltage is present, check terminal contact at relay C. If satisfactory, replace coolant fan relay C.
3. If zero volts is present, check circuit 804 for an open.

No High Speed Puller Fan

1. Disconnect coolant fan relay D from the underhood relay center. With the ignition switch in RUN position, measure voltage between terminal 1 and ground then between terminal 2 and ground of the relay center position D. If battery voltage is not present at one or both terminals, check circuits 2 and 850 for an open.
2. If battery voltage is present at both terminals, enter diagnostics and select ECM override ES08 and set dis-

play to 01. Connect a test lamp between terminals 2 and 5 of the relay center position D. If lamp does not light, check circuit 536 for an open.
3. If test lamp lights, connect a fused jumper between terminals 1 and 4 of the relay center position D. If puller fan does not run, check circuit 533 for an open.
4. If the puller fan runs at high speed, check terminal contact at relay D. If satisfactory, replace coolant fan relay D.

No High Speed Both Fans

1. Disconnect coolant fan relays C and D. Turn ignition switch to RUN position, measure voltage between terminal 2 and ground at position C then between terminals 2 and 1 at position D. If battery voltage is not present at one or both terminals, check associated circuit for an open.
2. If battery voltage is present at both terminals, check circuit 536 for an open or short to battery voltage. If circuit 536 is satisfactory, problem is ECM related.
3. If circuit 635 is not satisfactory, repair/replace as necessary.

COOLANT FAN, REPLACE

1. Disconnect battery ground cable.
2. **On front cooling fan,** proceed as follows:

   a. Remove radiator cover panel.
   b. Disconnect and remove fan control module and bracket.
   c. Remove front grill.
3. **On rear coolant fan,** proceed as follows:
   a. Remove air cleaner duct.
   b. Remove A/C hose bracket.
4. **On both fans,** disconnect electrical connections.
5. Remove cooling fan(s).
6. Reverse procedure to install.

EIGHTY-EIGHT & NINETY-EIGHT

SYSTEM DESCRIPTION

3.8L/V6-231 VIN C

A two speed coolant fan is turned on and off by the low and high speed coolant fan relays.

For low speed operation, the low speed relay coil is grounded through the ECM. The ECM grounds the coil when engine coolant is above 208°F.

With low speed relay coil grounded, its contacts close. Voltage is applied through the coolant fan resistor to the coolant fan. The resistor reduces voltage supplied to the fan so the fan runs at low speed.

For high speed operation, the high speed relay coil is grounded through the

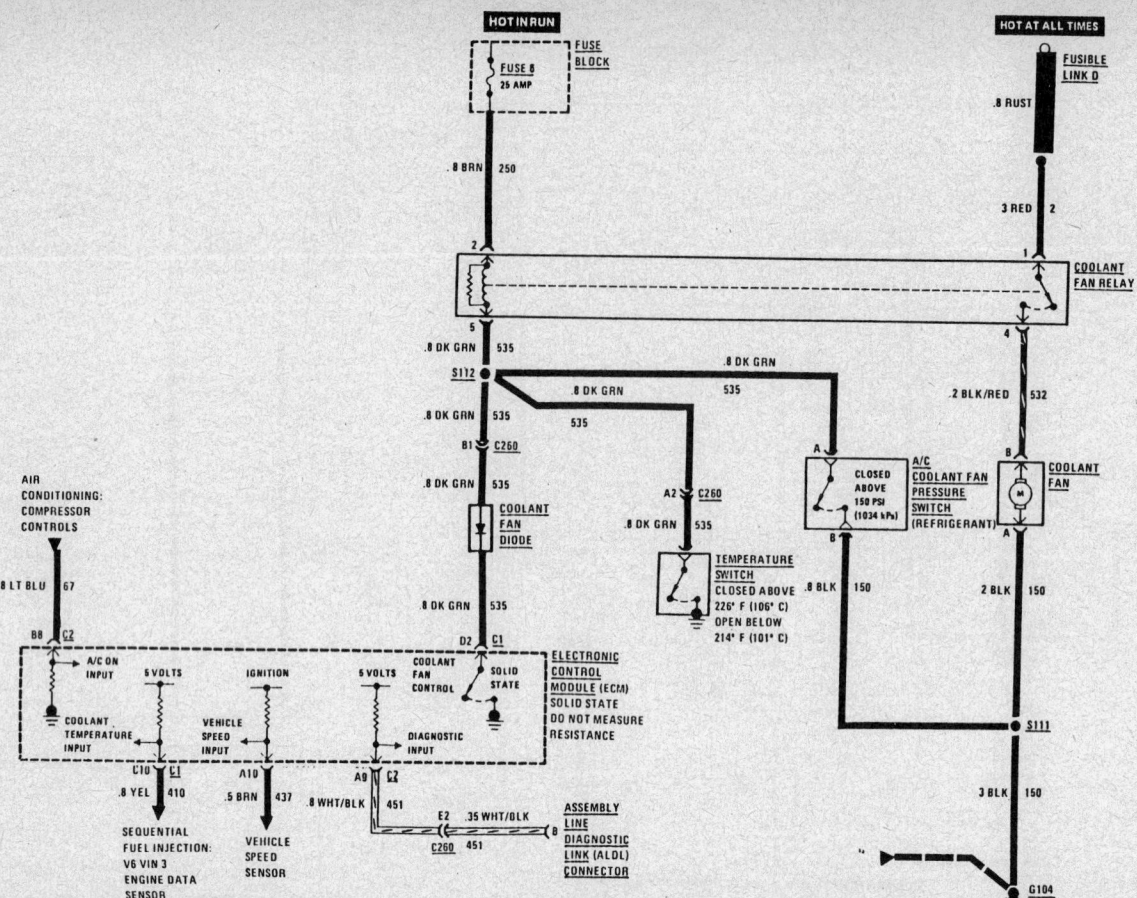

Fig. 62 Coolant fan wiring circuit (less auxiliary cooling fan). 1988–89 88 3.8L/w/V6-231 engine, VIN 3

high speed contacts in the A/C coolant fan pressure switch or by the ECM. The A/C coolant fan pressure switch high speed contacts close at a refrigerant pressure above 275 psi.

With the high speed coil grounded, its contacts close. Battery voltage is applied to the coolant fan. The fan runs at high speed.

The auxiliary coolant fan, if equipped, operates whenever the coolant fan runs at high speed. The A/C coolant fan pressure switch and ECM also control the auxiliary coolant fan relay, if equipped, which supplies battery voltage to the auxiliary coolant fan when energized.

88 w/3.8L/V6-231 VIN 3

The coolant fan is turned on when the contacts of the coolant fan relay close and supply voltage to the fan from fusible link D. Terminal 2 of the relay coil is supplied with battery voltage from fuse 6 whenever the ignition switch is in RUN position. The relay contacts will close, starting the fan, when a ground is furnished to terminals 5 of the relay coil. Terminal 5 may be grounded either by the ECM when engine coolant temperature is above 208°F, by the A/C coolant fan pressure switch when refrigerant pressure exceeds 150 psi or by the temperature switch when engine coolant temperature is above 226°F (less auxiliary coolant fan).

The auxiliary coolant fan operates in a manner similar to the coolant fan. Its relay is energized when engine coolant temperature is above 226°F by the temperature switch or when refrigerant pressure is above 275 psi by the A/C coolant fan pressure switch. When the auxiliary coolant fan relay is energized, battery voltage is applied to the auxiliary coolant fan. The auxiliary coolant fan runs.

98 w/3.8L/V6-231 VIN 3

A two speed coolant fan is turned on and off by the low and high speed coolant fan relays.

For low speed operation, the low speed relay coil is grounded through the ECM or the low speed contacts of the A/C coolant fan pressure switch. The ECM grounds the coil when engine coolant temperature is above 208°F. The A/C coolant fan pressure switch low speed contacts close with refrigerant pressure above 150 psi.

With the low speed relay coil grounded, its contacts close. Voltage is applied through the coolant fan resistor to the coolant fan. The resistor reduces voltage supplied to the fan so the fan runs at low speed.

For high speed operation, the high speed relay coil is grounded through the high speed contacts in the A/C coolant fan pressure switch or by the temperature switch. The A/C dual pressure switch high speed contacts close a refrigerant pres-

sure above 275 psi. The temperature switch closes when coolant temperature rises above 226°F.

With the high speed coil grounded, its contacts close. Battery voltage is applied to the coolant fan. The fan runs at high speed.

The auxiliary coolant fan, if equipped, operates whenever the coolant fan runs at high speed. The A/C coolant fan pressure switch and temperature switch also control the auxiliary coolant fan relay, which supplies battery voltage to the auxiliary coolant fan when energized.

TROUBLESHOOTING

1. Visually inspect fuse 6.
2. Check fusible link D.
3. If either fan runs with ignition switch in OFF position, replace associated coolant fan relay.

SYSTEM CHECK
3.8L/V6-231 VIN C & 98 w/3.8L/V6-231 VIN 3

1. With ambient temperature above 60°F and engine cold and idling, move A/C selector switch, if equipped, to NORM. Coolant fan should run at low speed. When A/C head pressure exceeds 275 psi, coolant fan should run at high speed and auxiliary coolant fan should run.

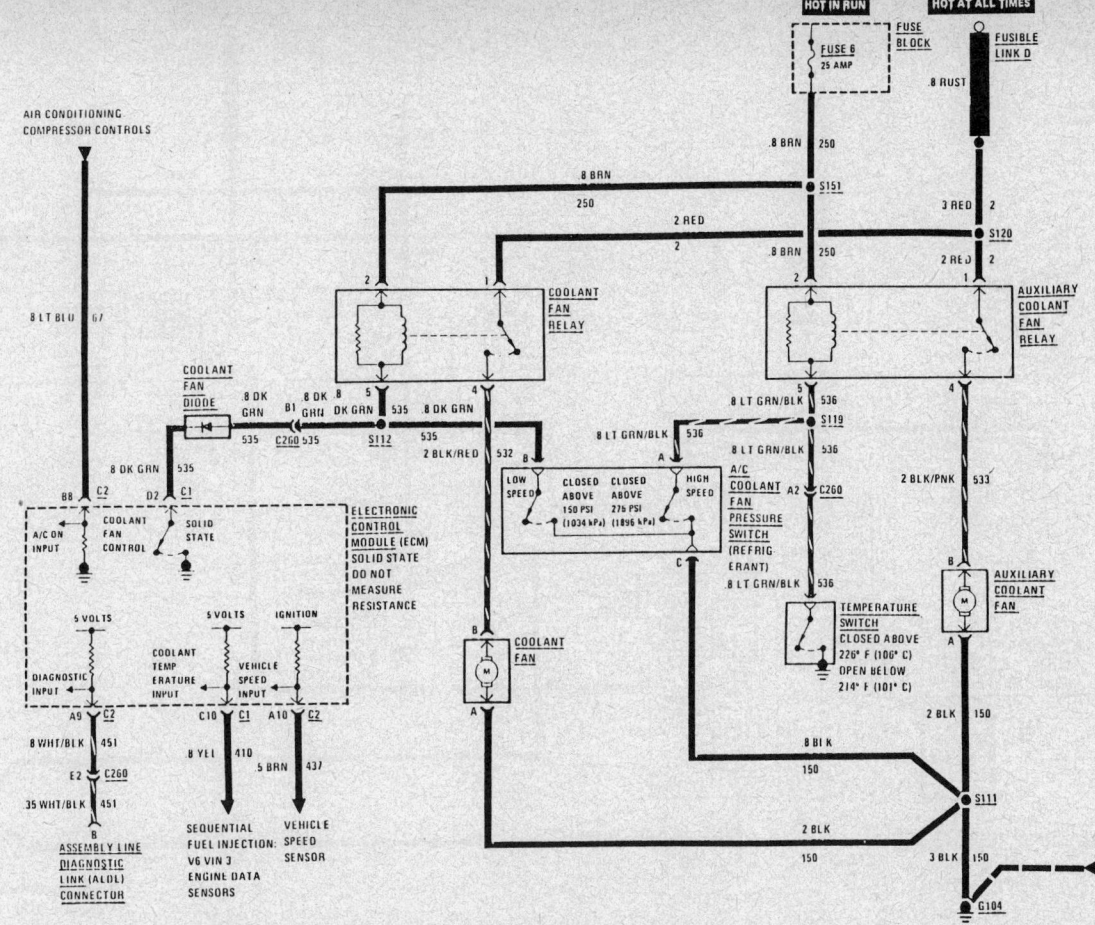

Fig. 63 Coolant fan wiring circuit (with auxiliary cooling fan). 1988–89 88 w/3.8L/V6-231 engine, VIN 3

2. With engine coolant below 208°F, move A/C selector switch to OFF position. Coolant fan(s) should turn off.
3. Run engine at fast idle for several minutes. When engine temperature exceeds 208°F, ECM should turn coolant fan on and coolant fan should run at low speed. When engine temperature exceeds 226°F, coolant fan should run at high speed and auxiliary coolant fan should run.

88 w/3.8L/V6-231 VIN 3

1. With ambient temperature above 60°F and engine cold and idling, move A/C selector switch, if equipped, to NORM. When A/C head pressure exceeds 150 psi, coolant fan should run. When A/C head pressure exceeds 275 psi, auxiliary coolant fan, if equipped, should run.
2. With engine coolant below 208°F, move A/C selector switch to OFF position. When A/C coolant fan pressure switch contacts open, coolant fan(s) should turn off.
3. Run engine at fast idle for several minutes. When engine coolant temperature exceeds 208°F, ECM should turn coolant fan on. When engine coolant temperature exceeds 226°F, the auxiliary coolant fan should run.

DIAGNOSIS

Refer To **Figs. 62 through 65** when performing diagnostic procedures on these systems.

3.8L/V6-231 VIN C & 98 w/3.8L/V6-231 VIN 3
Coolant Fan Does Not Run In Low Or High Speed

1. Disconnect high speed coolant relay connector and connect a 20 amp fused jumper between red and black/pink wire terminals. If coolant fan runs, proceed to "Coolant Fan Does Not Run In Low Speed" and "Coolant Fan Does Not Run In High Speed."
2. If coolant fan does not run, leave fused jumper connected as in step 1, disconnect coolant fan assembly connector and measure voltage from black/pink wire terminal to ground. If battery voltage is not present, check fusible link D, red wire and black/pink wire for open.
3. If battery voltage is present, leave fused jumper connected as in step 1, and measure voltage between black/pink and black wire terminals. If battery voltage is not present, check black wire for open.
4. If battery voltage is present, check

coolant fan assembly connector terminals and, if satisfactory, replace coolant fan assembly.

Coolant Fan Does Not Run In High Speed

1. Turn ignition switch to RUN position and ground white/black wire terminal of ALDL connector with a fused jumper. If coolant fan runs, problem is ECM related.
2. If coolant fan does not run, place ignition switch in RUN position dark green wire terminal of ECM connector C3 (VIN C) or C1 (VIN3) with a fused jumper. If coolant fan runs, problem is ECM related.
3. If coolant fan does not run, leave fused jumper connected as in step 2, turn ignition switch to RUN position, disconnect low speed coolant fan relay connector and measure voltage from brown wire terminal to ground. If battery voltage is not present, check fuse 6 and brown wire for open.
4. If battery voltage is present, leave fused jumper connected as in step 2, turn ignition switch to RUN position and measure voltage between brown and dark green wire terminals. If battery voltage is not present, check dark green wire for open.
5. If battery voltage is present, discon-

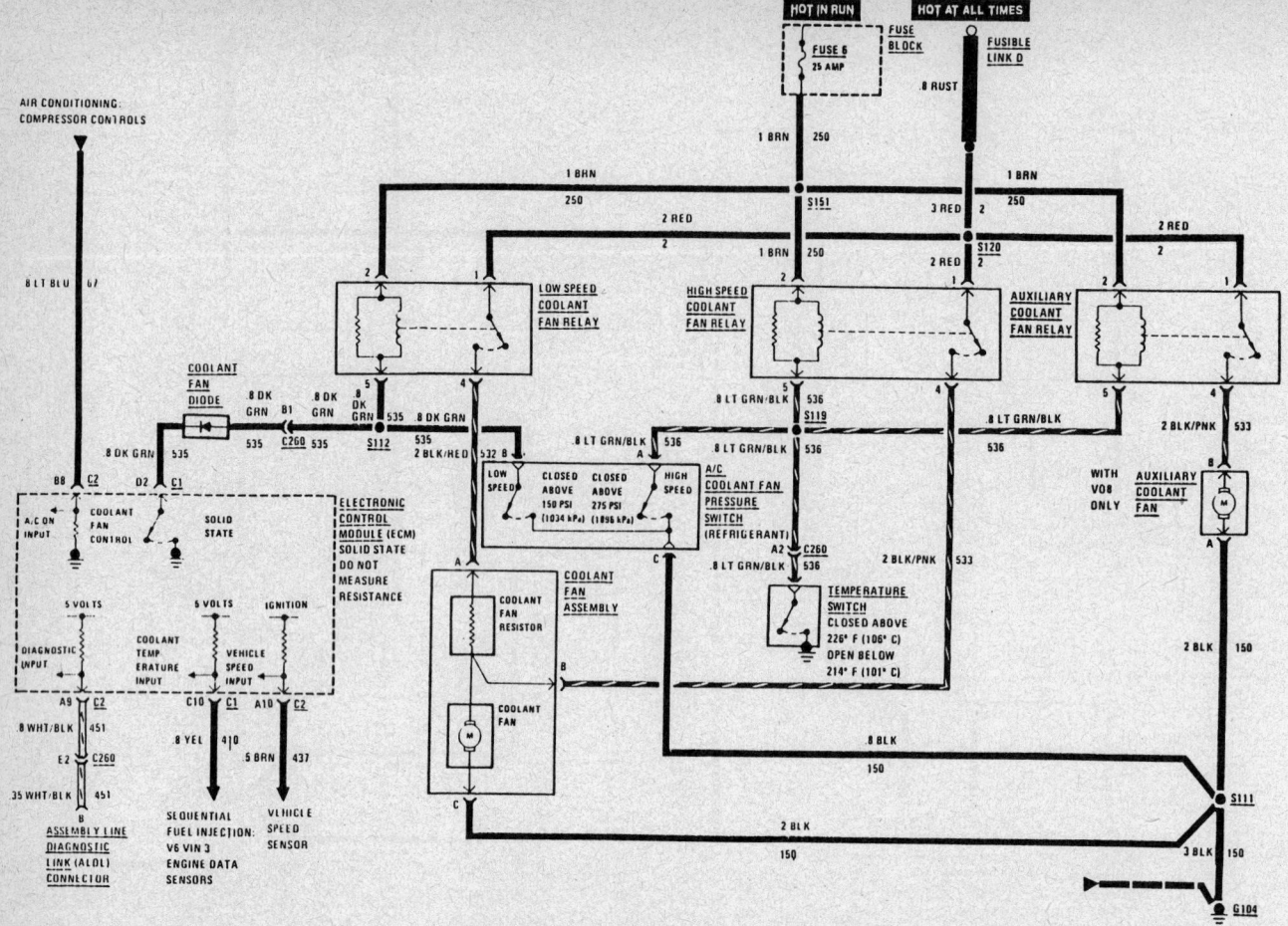

Fig. 64   Coolant fan wiring circuit. 1988–89 98 w/3.8L/V6-231 engine, VIN 3

nect low speed coolant fan connector and connect a 20 amp fused jumper between red and black/red wire terminals. If coolant fan runs, check low speed coolant fan relay connector terminals and, if satisfactory, replace low speed coolant fan relay.

6. If coolant fan does not run, check black/red wire for open. If wire is satisfactory, check black/red wire terminal contact at coolant fan assembly and, if satisfactory, replace coolant fan assembly.

Coolant Fan Does Not Run In High Speed

1. Turn ignition switch to RUN position and ground light green/black wire terminal of A/C coolant fan with a fused jumper. If coolant fan runs on VIN C, check light green/black wire to ECM for open. If coolant fan runs on VIN 3, check light green/black wire to temperature switch for open. If wire is satisfactory, problem is ECM related.

2. If coolant fan does not run, leave fused jumper connected as in step 1, disconnect high speed coolant fan relay connector, turn ignition switch to RUN position and measure voltage from brown wire terminal to ground. If battery voltage is not present, check brown wire and fuse 6 for open.

3. If battery voltage is present, leave fused jumper connected as in step 1, turn ignition switch to RUN position and measure voltage between brown and light green/black wire terminals. If battery voltage is not present, check light green/black wire for open.

4. If battery voltage is present, measure voltage between red wire terminal and ground. If battery voltage is not present, check red wire for open.

5. If battery voltage is present, disconnect high speed coolant fan relay connector and connect a 20 amp fused jumper between red and black/pink wire terminals. If coolant fan runs, check high speed coolant fan relay connector terminal contact and, if satisfactory, replace high speed coolant fan relay.

6. If coolant fan does not run, check black pink wire for open. If wire is satisfactory, check wire terminal contact at coolant fan assembly and, if satisfactory, replace coolant fan assembly.

Auxiliary Coolant Fan Does Not Run

1. If coolant fan does not run in high speed, proceed to "Coolant Fan Does Not Run In High Speed."

2. If coolant fan runs in high speed, disconnect auxiliary coolant fan relay

connector, turn ignition switch to RUN position and measure voltage from brown wire terminal to ground. If battery voltage is not present, check brown wire for open.

3. If battery voltage is present, measure voltage between red wire terminal and ground. If battery voltage is not present, check red wire for open.

4. If battery voltage is present, disconnect auxiliary coolant fan connector and connect a 20 amp fused jumper between red and black/pink wire terminals. If auxiliary coolant fan runs, check auxiliary coolant fan relay connector terminal contact and the light green/black wire to splice S119 and, if satisfactory, replace auxiliary coolant fan relay.

5. If auxiliary coolant fan does not run, leave fused jumper connected as in step 4, disconnect connector from auxiliary coolant fan relay and measure voltage between black/pink wire terminal and ground. If battery voltage is not present, check black/pink wire for open.

6. If battery voltage is present, leave fused jumper connected as in step 4, and measure voltage between black/pink and black wire terminals.

7. If battery voltage is not present, check black wire for open.

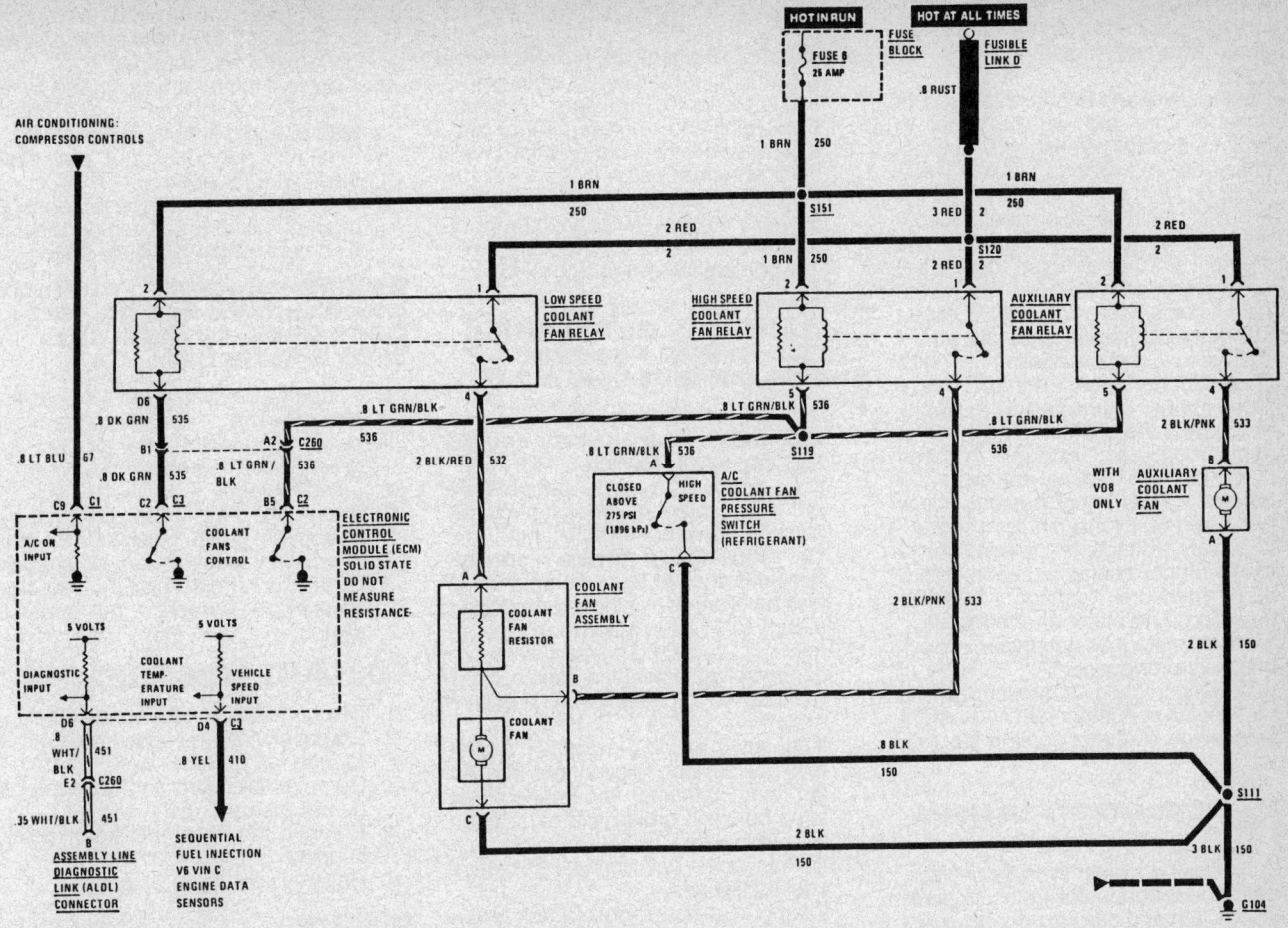

Fig. 65   Coolant fan wiring circuit. 1988–90 88 & 98 w/3.8L/V6-231 engine, VIN C

8. If battery voltage is present, check auxiliary coolant fan connector terminals and, if satisfactory, replace auxiliary coolant fan motor.

Coolant Fan Runs Continuously In Low Speed With Ignition Switch In Run Position, Engine Coolant Cool & A/C Off

1. Disconnect low speed coolant fan relay connector, turn ignition switch to RUN position and connect test lamp between brown and dark green wire terminals.
2. If lamp does not illuminate, replace low speed coolant fan relay.
3. If lamp illuminates, check dark green wire for short to ground and, on VIN 3, the A/C coolant fan pressure switch. If wire and switch are satisfactory, problem is ECM related.

Coolant Fan Runs Continuously In High Speed And/Or Auxiliary Coolant Fan Runs Continuously With Ignition Switch In RUN Position, Engine Coolant Cool & A/C Off

1. Turn ignition switch to RUN position and disconnect A/C coolant fan pressure switch connector. If coolant fan(s) stop(s), replace A/C coolant

fan pressure switch.
2. If coolant fan(s) run(s), turn ignition switch to RUN position, disconnect high speed coolant fan relay connector and/or auxiliary coolant fan relay connector and connect test lamp between brown and light green/black wire terminals.
3. If lamp does not illuminate, replace suspect relay.
4. If lamp illuminates, check light green/black wires for short to ground and, if wires are satisfactory on VIN 3, check temperature switch. If wires are satisfactory on VIN C, problem is ECM related.

Coolant Fan And/Or Auxiliary Coolant Fan Does Not Run With A/C On, But Does Operate Normally With Engine Hot

1. If coolant fan does not operate in low speed with A/C on:
   a. On VIN C, problem is ECM related.
   b. On VIN 3, check A/C coolant fan pressure switch and dark green and black wires to A/C coolant fan pressure switch.
2. If coolant fan operates in low speed with A/C on, check whether coolant fan operates at high speed and auxiliary coolant fan runs when A/C pressure is above 275 psi.

3. If not, check A/C coolant fan pressure switch and light green black wire and black wire to A/C coolant fan pressure switch.

88 w/VIN 3
Coolant Fan Does Not Run

1. Turn ignition switch to run position and ground white/black wire terminal of ALDL connector with a fused jumper. If coolant fan runs, check temperature switch operation, if equipped. If not equipped with temperature switch or temperature switch is satisfactory, problem is ECM related.
2. If coolant fan does not run, turn ignition switch to run position and ground dark green wire terminal of ECM connector C1 with a fused jumper. If coolant fan runs, problem is ECM related.
3. If coolant fan does not run, leave fused jumper connected as in step 2, turn ignition switch to RUN position, disconnect coolant fan relay connector and measure voltage from brown wire terminal to ground. If battery voltage is not present, check fuse 6 and brown wire for open.
4. If battery voltage is present, leave fused jumper connected as in step 2, turn ignition switch to RUN position and measure voltage between brown

and dark green wire terminals. If battery voltage is not present, check dark green wire and coolant fan diode for open.

5. If battery voltage is present, measure voltage from red wire terminal to ground. If battery voltage is not present, check red wire and fusible link D for open.

6. If battery voltage is present, disconnect coolant fan relay connector and connect a 20 amp fused jumper between red and black/red wire terminals. If coolant fan runs, check coolant fan relay connector terminals and, if satisfactory, replace coolant fan relay.

7. If coolant fan does not run, leave fused jumper connected as in step 6, disconnect the coolant fan connector and measure voltage between black/red wire terminal and ground. If battery voltage is not present, check black/red wire for open.

8. If battery voltage is present, leave fused jumper connected as in step 6 and measure voltage between black/red and black wire terminals.

9. If battery voltage is not present, check black wire for open.

10. If battery voltage is present, check coolant fan connector terminals and, if satisfactory, replace coolant fan motor.

Auxiliary Coolant Fan Does Not Run

1. Turn ignition switch to RUN position, disconnect connector from temperature switch and ground connector terminal with a fused jumper. If auxiliary coolant fan runs, check temperature switch terminal contact and, if satisfactory, replace temperature switch.

2. If auxiliary coolant fan does not run, leave fused jumper connected as in step 1, disconnect auxiliary coolant fan relay connector, turn ignition switch to RUN position and measure voltage from brown wire terminal to ground. If battery voltage is not present, check brown wire for open.

3. If battery voltage is present, leave fused jumper connected as in step 1, turn ignition switch to RUN position and measure voltage between brown and light green/black wire terminals. If battery voltage is not present, check light green/black wire for open.

4. If battery voltage is present, measure voltage between red wire terminal and ground. If battery voltage is not present, check red wire for open.

5. If battery voltage is present, disconnect auxiliary coolant fan relay connector and connect a 20 amp fused jumper between red and black/pink wire terminals. If auxiliary coolant fan runs, check auxiliary coolant fan relay connector terminal contact and, if satisfactory, replace auxiliary coolant fan relay.

6. If auxiliary coolant fan does not run, leave fused jumper connected as in step 5, disconnect connector from auxiliary coolant fan and measure voltage between black/pink wire terminal and ground. If battery voltage is

not present, check black/pink wire for open.

7. If battery voltage is present, leave fused jumper connected as in step 5 and measure voltage between black/pink and black wire terminals.

8. If battery voltage is not present, check black wire for open.

9. If battery voltage is present, check auxiliary coolant fan connector terminals and, if satisfactory, replace auxiliary coolant fan motor.

Coolant Fan Runs Continuously With Ignition Switch In RUN Position, Engine Coolant Cool & A/C Off

1. **On models less auxiliary coolant fan,** turn ignition switch to RUN position and disconnect temperature switch. If coolant fan does not run, replace temperature switch.

2. **On models with auxiliary coolant fan,** or if coolant fan runs on models less auxiliary coolant fan, turn ignition switch to RUN position and disconnect A/C coolant fan pressure switch connector. If coolant fan does not run, replace A/C coolant fan pressure switch.

3. If coolant fan runs, turn ignition switch to RUN position, disconnect coolant fan relay connector and connect test lamp between brown and dark green wire terminals.

4. If lamp does not illuminate, replace coolant fan relay.

5. If lamp illuminates, check dark green wires and coolant fan diode for short to ground. If wires and diode are satisfactory, problem is ECM related.

Auxiliary Coolant Fan Runs Continuously With Ignition Switch In RUN Position, Engine Coolant Cool & A/C Off

1. Turn ignition switch to RUN position and disconnect temperature switch connector. If auxiliary coolant fan does not run, replace coolant fan temperature switch.

2. If auxiliary coolant fan runs, turn ignition switch to RUN position and disconnect A/C coolant fan pressure switch. If auxiliary coolant fan does not run, replace A/C coolant fan pressure switch.

3. If auxiliary coolant fan runs, turn ignition switch to RUN position, disconnect auxiliary coolant fan relay connector and connect test lamp between brown and light green/black wire terminals.

4. If lamp does not illuminate, replace auxiliary coolant fan relay.

5. If lamp illuminates, check light green/black wires for short to ground.

Coolant Fan Does Not Run With A/C On, But Does Operate Normally With Engine Hot

1. Turn ignition switch to RUN position, disconnect A/C coolant fan pressure switch connector and ground dark

green wire terminal with a fused jumper. If coolant fan does not run, check dark green wire for open.

2. If coolant fan runs, turn ignition switch to RUN position and move ground lead of fused jumper to black wire.

3. If coolant fan does not run, check black wire for open.

4. If coolant fan runs, check connector terminals and, if satisfactory, replace A/C coolant fan pressure switch.

Auxiliary Coolant Fan Does Not Run With A/C On, But Does Operate Normally With Engine Hot

1. Turn ignition switch to RUN position, disconnect A/C coolant fan pressure switch connector and ground light green/black wire terminal with a fused jumper.

2. If auxiliary coolant fan does not run, check light green/black wire for open.

3. If auxiliary coolant fan runs, check connector terminal and, if satisfactory, replace A/C coolant fan pressure switch.

COOLANT FAN, REPLACE

1. Disconnect battery ground cable.
2. Remove wiring harness from fan motor and fan frame.
3. Remove fan guard and hose support as necessary.
4. Remove fan assembly from radiator support.
5. Reverse procedure to install.

FIERO
SYSTEM DESCRIPTION
2.5L/4-151 VIN R

The coolant fan is turned on and off by the ECM based on inputs from the coolant temperature sensor, vehicle speed sensor and the A/C system. Battery voltage is applied at all times to terminal A of the coolant fan relay. The ECM energizes the coolant fan relay by grounding circuit 335. The relay energizes and battery voltage is applied to the coolant fan.

The A/C control head also energizes the coolant fan relay by grounding circuit 335 whenever the A/C function selector is in MAX, NORM or B/L.

2.8L/V6-173 VIN 9

The coolant fan is operated by the coolant fan relay. Battery voltage is applied at all times through fusible link A to terminal A of the coolant fan relay. With ignition switch in RUN position, voltage is applied through the FAN E fuse to terminal D of the relay coil.

When coolant temperature exceeds 235°F, the coolant temperature switch closes. By grounding circuit 335, the relay coil is energized and battery voltage is applied to the coolant fan.

If equipped with A/C, the A/C high pressure cut-out switch and A/C control head also energize the coolant fan relay by grounding circuit 335 whenever the A/C high pressure cut-out switch closes above 280 psi and the A/C function selector is in MAX, NORM or B/L.

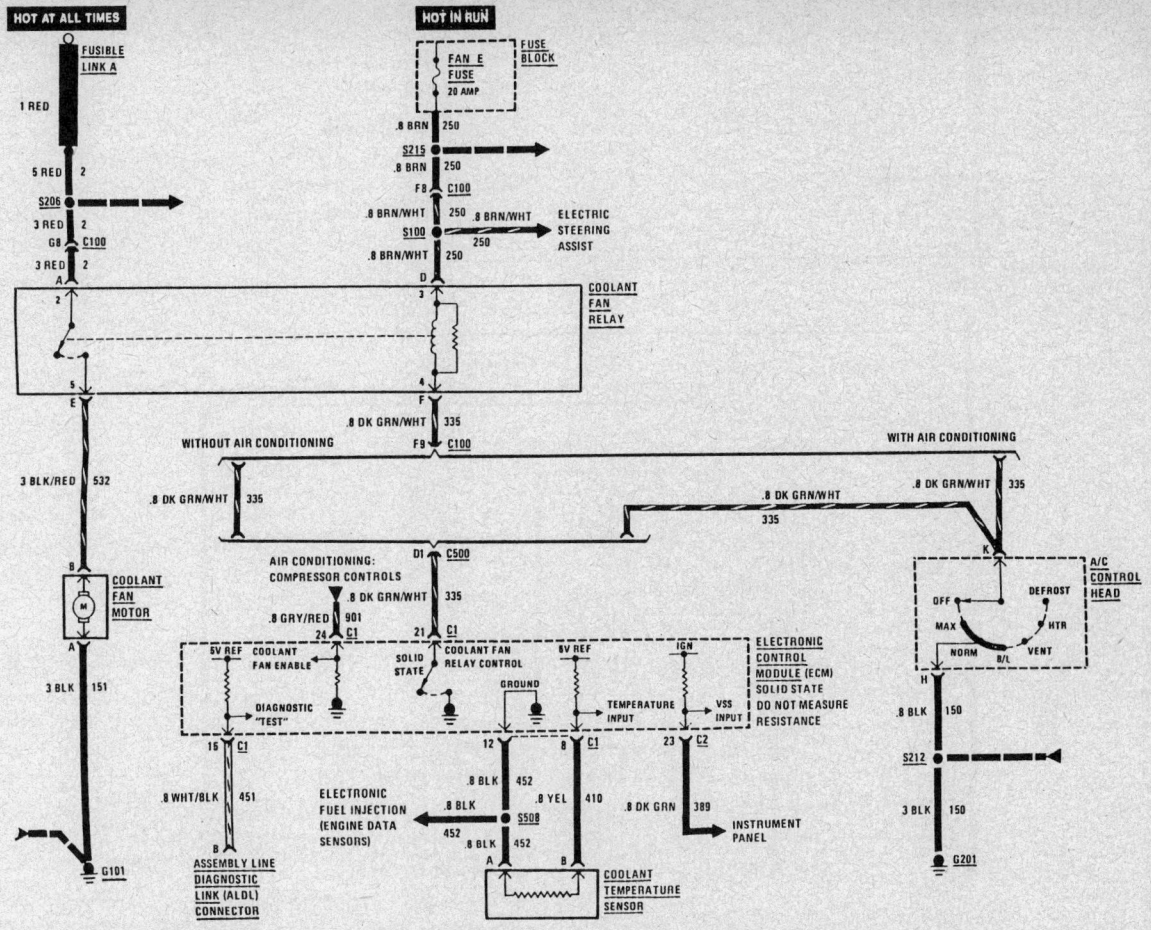

Fig. 66   Coolant fan wiring circuit. 1988 Fiero w/2.5L/4-151 engine

TROUBLESHOOTING

4 CYLINDER

1. Check FAN E fuse and fusible link A if coolant fan does not run.
2. If coolant fan operates with ignition switch in OFF position, replace coolant fan relay.
3. Check ground G201 by operating radio.
4. Check ground G101 by operating the front park/turn lights.

6 CYLINDER

1. Check FAN E fuse and fusible link A if coolant fan does not run.
2. Check ground G101 by operating the front park/turn lights.
3. If coolant fan runs with ignition switch in OFF position, replace coolant fan relay.

SYSTEM CHECK

1. With engine cold and idling, move A/C function selector, if equipped, to NORM position. Coolant fan and engine blower should turn on.
2. With engine coolant below operating temperature, move A/C function selector to OFF position. Coolant fan and engine blower should turn off.

3. With engine warm, run engine at fast idle for several minutes. Coolant fan and engine blower should turn on before temperature indicator comes on.

DIAGNOSIS

Refer to **Figs. 66 and 67** when performing diagnostic procedures on these systems.

4 CYLINDER

Coolant Fan Does Not Run

1. Turn ignition switch to RUN position and connect fused jumper between ALDL connector white/black wire terminal and ground. If coolant fan runs, problem is ECM related.
2. If coolant fan does not run, turn ignition switch to RUN position, turn A/C function selector to OFF position and connect fused jumper between ECM connector dark green/white wire and ground. If coolant fan runs, problem is ECM related.
3. If coolant fan does not run, leave fused jumper connected as in step 2, disconnect coolant fan relay connector, turn ignition switch to RUN position and connect test lamp between terminals as follows:
   a. Connect between brown/white

wire and ground. If lamp does not illuminate, check FAN E fuse and brown/white wire for open.
   b. Connect between brown/white and dark green/white wire terminals. If lamp does not illuminate, check dark green/white wire for open.
   c. Connect between red wire terminal and ground. If lamp does not illuminate, check fusible link A and red wire for open.
4. If lamp illuminates in steps a, b and c, disconnect coolant fan relay connector and connect 20 A fused jumper between red and black/red wire terminals. If coolant fan runs, replace coolant fan relay.
5. If coolant fan does not run, leave fused jumper connected as in step 4, disconnect coolant fan motor connector and connect test lamp between terminals as follows:
   a. Connect between black/red wire terminal and ground. If lamp does not illuminate, check black/red wire for open.
   b. Connect between black/red and black wire terminals. If lamp does not illuminate, check black wire for open.
   c. If lamp illuminates in steps a and b, replace coolant fan motor.

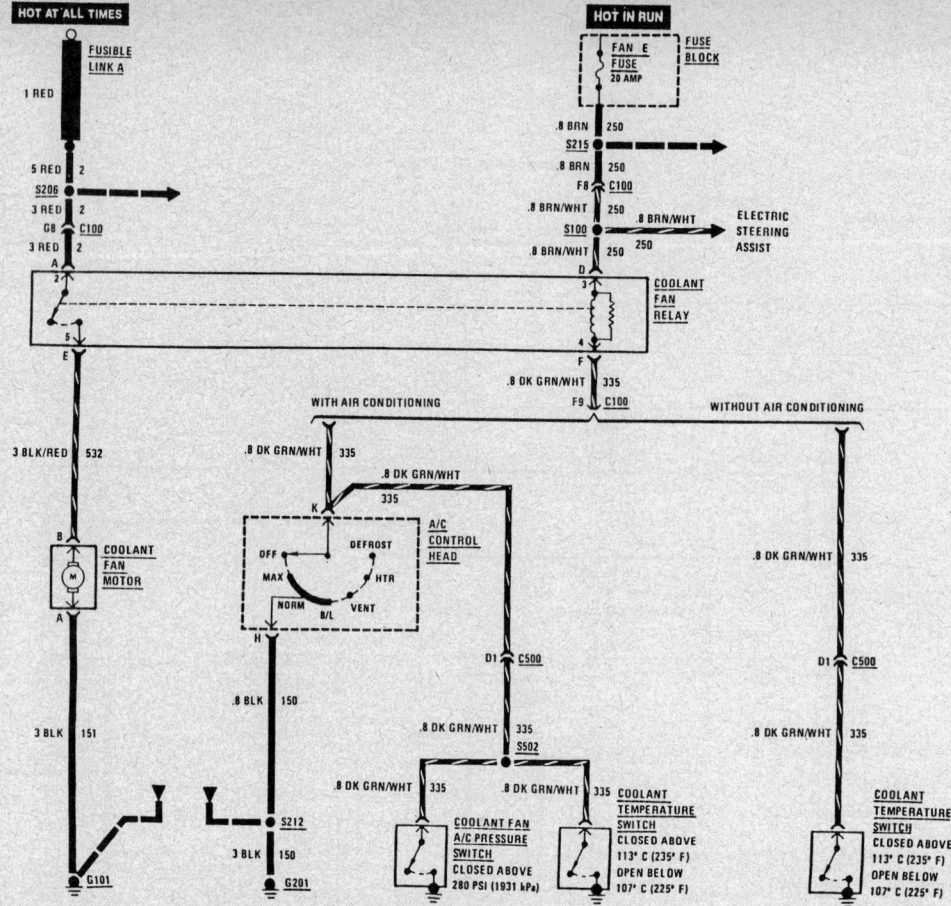

Fig. 67   Coolant fan wiring circuit. 1988 Fiero w/2.8L/V6-173 engine

Coolant Fan Does Not Run With A/C On

1. Disconnect A/C control head connector, turn ignition switch to RUN position and connect fused jumper between terminals as follows:
   a. Connect between dark green/white wire terminal and ground. If coolant fan does not run, check dark green/white wire for open.
   b. Connect between dark green/white and black wire terminals. If coolant fan does not run, check black wire for open.
2. If coolant fan runs in steps a and b, replace A/C control head.

Coolant Fan Runs Continuously

1. With ignition switch in RUN position, disconnect coolant fan relay connector and connect test lamp between brown/white and dark green/white wire terminals. If lamp does not illuminate, replace coolant fan relay.
2. If lamp illuminates, disconnect A/C control head connector. If coolant fan does not run, replace A/C control head.

3. If coolant fan runs, disconnect ECM connector C2.
4. If coolant fan runs, check dark green/white wire for short to ground.
5. If coolant fan does not run, problem is ECM related.

6 CYLINDER

Coolant Fan Does Not Run With Engine Hot

1. Disconnect coolant temperature switch connector, turn ignition switch to RUN position, turn A/C function selector to OFF position and connect fused jumper between dark green/white wire terminal and ground. If coolant fan and engine blower run, replace coolant temperature switch.
2. If coolant fan and engine blower do not run, proceed to "Coolant Fan Does Not Run At All."

Coolant Fan & Engine Blower Do Not Run With A/C On

1. Disconnect A/C control head connector, turn ignition switch to RUN position and connect fused jumper between terminals as follows:
   a. Connect between dark

green/white wire and ground. If coolant fan and engine blower do not run, proceed to "Coolant Fan Does Not Run At All."
   b. Connect between dark green/white and black wire terminals. If coolant fan and engine blower do not run, check black wire for open.
2. If coolant fan and engine blower run in steps a and b, replace A/C control head.

Coolant Fan Does Not Run At All

1. Turn ignition switch to RUN position and connect fused jumper between coolant fan relay connector dark green/white wire and ground. If coolant fan runs, check dark green/white wire for open.
2. If coolant fan does not run, disconnect coolant fan relay connector, turn ignition switch to RUN position and connect test lamp between terminals as follows:
   a. Connect between brown/white wire terminal and ground. If test lamp does not illuminate, check FAN E fuse and brown/white wire for open.

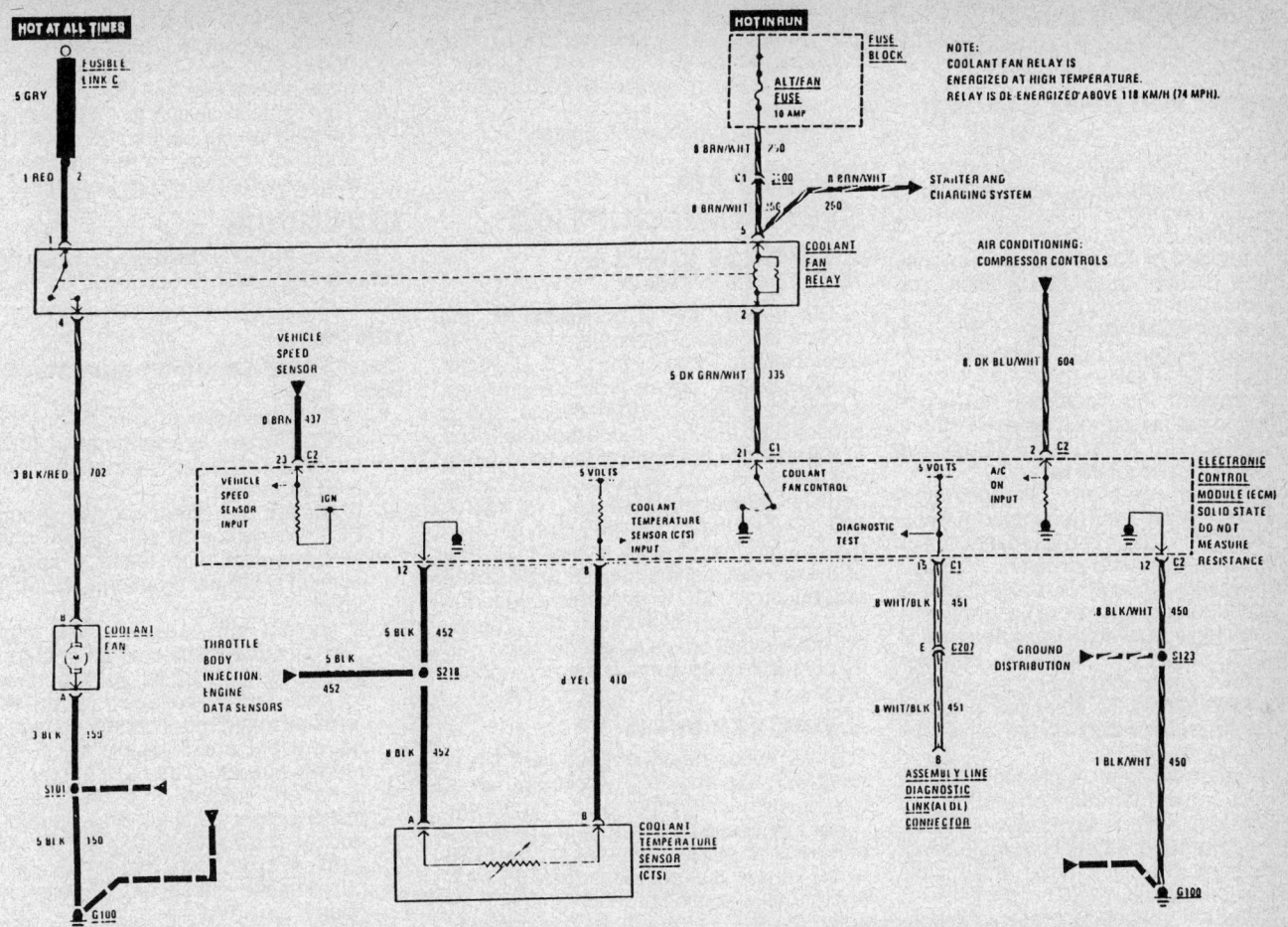

Fig. 68   Coolant fan wiring circuit. 1988 Firenza w/2.0L/4-121 engine

b. Connect between red wire terminal and ground. If lamp does not illuminate, check fusible link A and red wire for open.

3. If lamp illuminates in steps a and b, disconnect coolant fan relay connector and connect 20 amp fused jumper between red and red/black wire terminals. If coolant fan runs, replace coolant fan relay.

4. If coolant fan does not run, leave fused jumper connected as in step 3, disconnect coolant fan motor connector and connect test lamp between terminals as follows:
   a. Connect between black/red wire terminal and ground. If lamp does not illuminate, check black/red wire for open.
   b. Connect between black/red and black wire terminals. If lamp does not illuminate, check black wire for open.
   c. If lamp illuminates in steps a and b, replace coolant fan motor.

Coolant Fan & Engine Blower Run Continuously

1. With ignition switch in RUN position, disconnect coolant temperature switch connector. If coolant fan does not run, replace coolant temperature switch.

2. If coolant fan runs, disconnect A/C high pressure cut-out switch connector. If coolant fan does not run, replace A/C high pressure cut-out switch.

3. If coolant fan runs, disconnect A/C control head connector.

4. If coolant fan runs, check dark green/white wire for short to ground.

5. If coolant fan does not run, replace A/C control head.

COOLANT FAN, REPLACE

1. Disconnect battery ground cable.
2. Remove harness from fan motor and fan frame.
3. Remove fan frame to radiator support attaching bolts.
4. Remove fan and frame assembly.
5. Reverse procedure to install.

FIRENZA

SYSTEM DESCRIPTION

The coolant fan is supplied voltage by the coolant fan relay. The relay is energized when the ECM grounds circuit 335. The ECM receives input signals from the coolant temperature sensor, the vehicle speed sensor and the mode selector. The ECM activates the coolant fan relay when engine coolant is above 223°F, the A/C is turned on or the coolant temperature sensor fails. The coolant fan will not operate when the vehicle's speed is above 74 mph. With circuit 335 grounded, the coolant fan relay is energized and its contacts close. The coolant fan runs with battery voltage across its terminals. The coolant fan will run for a minimum of 30 seconds.

TROUBLESHOOTING

1. Visually inspect ALT/FAN fuse.
2. If coolant fan runs with ignition switch in OFF position, replace coolant fan relay.

SYSTEM CHECK

1. With ambient air temperature above 60°F, start vehicle and set mode selector, if equipped, to MAX. Coolant fan should turn on.
2. With engine coolant below operating temperature, move mode selector to OFF position. Coolant fan should turn off in a short time.
3. Run engine at fast idle for several minutes. Coolant fan should turn on and run before coolant temperature indicator comes on or coolant temperature gage needle reaches HOT.

DIAGNOSIS

Refer to **Fig. 68** when performing diagnostic procedures on this system.

Coolant Fan Does Not Turn On

1. With ignition switch in RUN position, ground white/black wire terminal of ALDL connector. If coolant fan runs, problem is ECM related.
2. If coolant fan does not run, turn ignition switch to RUN position and ground dark green/white wire terminal of ECM black connector with fused jumper. If coolant fan runs, problem is ECM related.
3. If coolant fan does not run, leave fused jumper connected as in step 2, turn ignition switch to RUN position, disconnect coolant fan relay connector and measure voltage from brown/white wire terminal to ground. If battery voltage is not present, check brown/white wire for open.
4. If battery voltage is present, leave fused jumper connected as in step 2, turn ignition switch to RUN position and measure voltage between brown/white and dark green/white wire terminals. If battery voltage is not present, check dark green/white wire for open.
5. If battery voltage is present, disconnect coolant fan relay connector and measure voltage from red wire terminal to ground. If battery voltage is not present, check red wire and fusible link C for open.
6. If battery voltage is present, disconnect coolant fan relay connector and connect 20 amp fused jumper between red and black/red wire terminals. If coolant fan runs, replace coolant fan relay.
7. If coolant fan does not run, leave fused jumper connected as in step 6, disconnect coolant fan connector and measure voltage between black/red wire terminal and ground. If battery voltage is not present, check black/red wire for open.
8. If battery voltage is present, leave fused jumper connected as in step 6 and measure voltage between black/red and black wire terminals.
9. If battery voltage is not present, check black wire for open.
10. If battery voltage is present, replace coolant fan.

Coolant Fan Does Not Turn Off With Engine Coolant Cool, A/C Off & Ignition Switch in RUN Position

1. Turn ignition switch to RUN position, disconnect coolant fan relay connector and connect test lamp between brown/white and dark green/white wire terminals. If lamp does not illuminate, replace coolant fan relay.
2. If lamp illuminates, check dark green/white wire for short to ground. If wire is satisfactory, problem is ECM related.

COOLANT FAN, REPLACE

1. Disconnect battery ground cable.

2. Remove air cleaner duct.
3. Remove wiring harness from motor and fan frame.
4. Remove fan assembly from radiator support.
5. Reverse procedure to install.

GRAND AM
SYSTEM DESCRIPTION
2.0L/4-121 VIN M & 2.5L/4-151 VIN U

The coolant fan is controlled by the coolant fan relay. The coolant fan relay is electrically operated by the ECM. The ECM receives input signals from the coolant temperature sensor, the vehicle speed sensor and the A/C mode selector. The ECM activates the coolant fan relay when the engine coolant, which is sensed by the coolant temperature sensor, is above 227°F, when the A/C is turned on or when the coolant temperature sensor fails. Any of these input signals causes the ECM to ground circuit 335 when vehicle speed is less than 35 mph. With circuit 335 grounded, the coolant fan relay is energized and its contacts close, turning the coolant fan on.

2.3L/4-138 VIN D

A two speed heavy duty coolant fan is used with this engine. The coolant fan is turned on and off by the coolant fan relays.

For low speed operation, the low speed relay coil is grounded through the ECM when vehicle speed is less than 45 mph and the engine coolant reaches 208°F, or when the A/C is turned on. The contacts close and voltage is applied through the coolant fan resistor to the coolant fan. The fan runs at low speed.

For high speed operation, the high speed relay coil is grounded through the ECM when the coolant temperature reaches 228°F. The contacts close and voltage is applied to the coolant fan. The fan runs at high speed.

TROUBLESHOOTING

1. If coolant fan does not operate on VINs U and D, check fusible link F and H-AC fuse.
2. If coolant fan runs with ignition switch in OFF position on VIN U, replace coolant fan relay.
3. If coolant fan runs in high speed with ignition switch in OFF position on VIN D, replace high speed coolant fan relay.
4. If coolant fan runs in low speed with ignition switch in OFF position on VIN D, replace low speed coolant fan relay.

SYSTEM CHECK

1. With ambient air temperature above 70°F, open all doors, start vehicle and set A/C mode selector, if equipped, to MAX position. Coolant fan should turn on in a short period of time.
2. With engine coolant below operating temperature, move A/C selector to OFF position. Coolant fan should turn off in a short period of time.
3. Run engine at fast idle for several

minutes. Coolant fan should turn on before coolant temperature indicator comes on or coolant temperature gage needle reaches HOT.
4. Turn ignition switch to OFF position. Coolant fan should turn off on VINs U and D or continue to run until engine coolant temperature lowers on VIN M.

DIAGNOSIS

Refer to **Figs. 69 through 71** when performing diagnostic procedures on these systems.

VIN M
Coolant Fan Does Not Turn On

1. With ignition switch in RUN position, ground white wire terminal of ALDL connector. If coolant fan runs, problem is ECM related.
2. If coolant fan does not run, ground ECM connector C3 dark green/white wire terminal with fused jumper. If coolant fan runs, problem is ECM related.
3. If coolant fan does not run, leave fused jumper connected as in step 2, disconnect coolant fan relay connector and measure voltage from red wire terminal to ground. If battery voltage is not present, check fusible link F and red (2) wire for open.
4. If battery voltage is present, leave fused jumper connected as in step 2 and measure voltage from red (2) wire terminal to ground. If battery voltage is not present, check red (2) wire for open.
5. If battery voltage is present, leave fused jumper connected as in step 2, disconnect coolant fan relay connector and measure voltage between red (2) and dark green/white wire terminals. If battery voltage is not present, check dark green/white wire for open.
6. If battery voltage is present, disconnect coolant fan relay connector and connect fused jumper with 20 amp fuse between red and black/red wire terminals. If coolant fan runs, replace coolant fan relay.
7. If coolant fan does not run, leave fused jumper connected as in step 6, disconnect coolant fan connector and measure voltage between black/red wire terminal and ground. If battery voltage is not present, check black/red wire for open.
8. If battery voltage is present, leave fused jumper connected as in step 6 and measure voltage between black/red and black wires of coolant fan connector.
9. If battery voltage is not present, check black wire for open.
10. If battery voltage is present, replace coolant fan.

Coolant Fan Does Not Turn Off With Engine Coolant Cool & A/C Mode Selector Off

1. Disconnect coolant fan relay connector and connect test lamp between red and dark green/white wire terminals. If lamp does not illuminate, replace coolant fan relay.

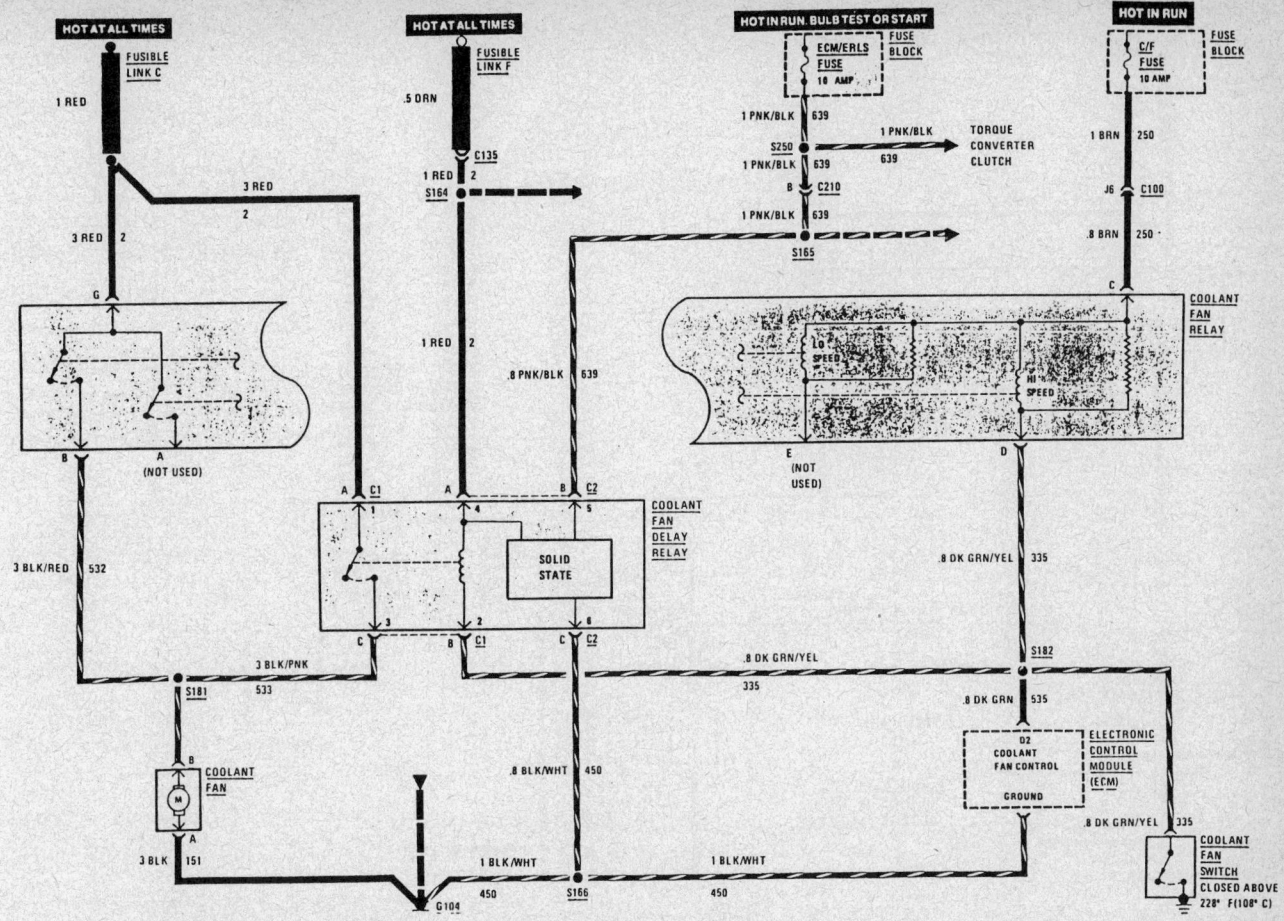

Fig. 69   Coolant fan wiring circuit. 1988–89 Grand Am w/2.0L/4-121 engine, VIN M

2. If lamp illuminates, check dark green/white wire for short to ground. If wire is satisfactory, problem is ECM related.

Coolant Fan Does Not Turn On With A/C Mode Selector On And Head Pressure Above 150 psi, But Does Run With Engine Hot

1. Place ignition in RUN position and A/C mode selector in MAX position. Measure voltage between terminal C1/C9 of the ECM and ground.
2. If zero volts is present, check blue/white wire for an open.
3. If battery voltage is present, problem is ECM related

VIN U
Coolant Fan Does Not Turn On

1. With ignition switch in RUN position, ground terminal B of ALDL connector. If coolant fan runs, problem is ECM related.
2. If coolant fan does not run, turn ignition switch to RUN position and ground ECM C1 connector dark green/white wire terminal with fused jumper. If coolant fan runs, problem is ECM related.

3. If coolant fan does not run, leave fused jumper connected as in step 2, turn ignition switch to RUN position, disconnect coolant fan relay connector and measure voltage from brown wire terminal to ground. If battery voltage is not present, check brown and brown/white wires for open.
4. If battery voltage is present, leave fused jumper connected as in step 2, turn ignition switch to RUN position and measure voltage between brown and dark green/white wire terminals. If battery voltage is not present, check dark green/white wire for open.
5. If battery voltage is present, disconnect coolant fan relay connector and measure voltage from red (1) wire terminal to ground. If battery voltage is not present, check red (2) wire and fusible link F for open.
6. If battery voltage is present, disconnect coolant fan relay connector and connect fused jumper with 20 amp fuse between red (1) and black/red wire terminals. If coolant fan runs, replace coolant fan relay.
7. If coolant fan does not run, leave fused jumper connected as in step 6, disconnect coolant fan connector and measure voltage between black/red wire terminal and ground. If battery voltage is not present, check black/red wire for open.

8. If battery voltage is present, leave fused jumper connected as in step 6, and measure voltage between black/red and black wire terminals of coolant fan connector.
9. If battery voltage is not present, check black wire for open.
10. If battery voltage is present, replace coolant fan.

Coolant Fan Does Not Turn Off With Engine Cool, A/C Mode Selector Off & Ignition Switch In RUN Position

1. Turn ignition switch to RUN position, disconnect coolant fan relay connector and connect test lamp between brown and dark green/white wire terminals. If lamp does not illuminate, replace coolant fan relay.
2. If lamp illuminates, check dark green/white wire for short to ground. If wire is satisfactory, problem is ECM related.

Coolant Fan Does Not Turn On With A/C Mode Selector On And Head Pressure Above 150 psi, But Does Run With Engine Hot

1. Place ignition in RUN position and

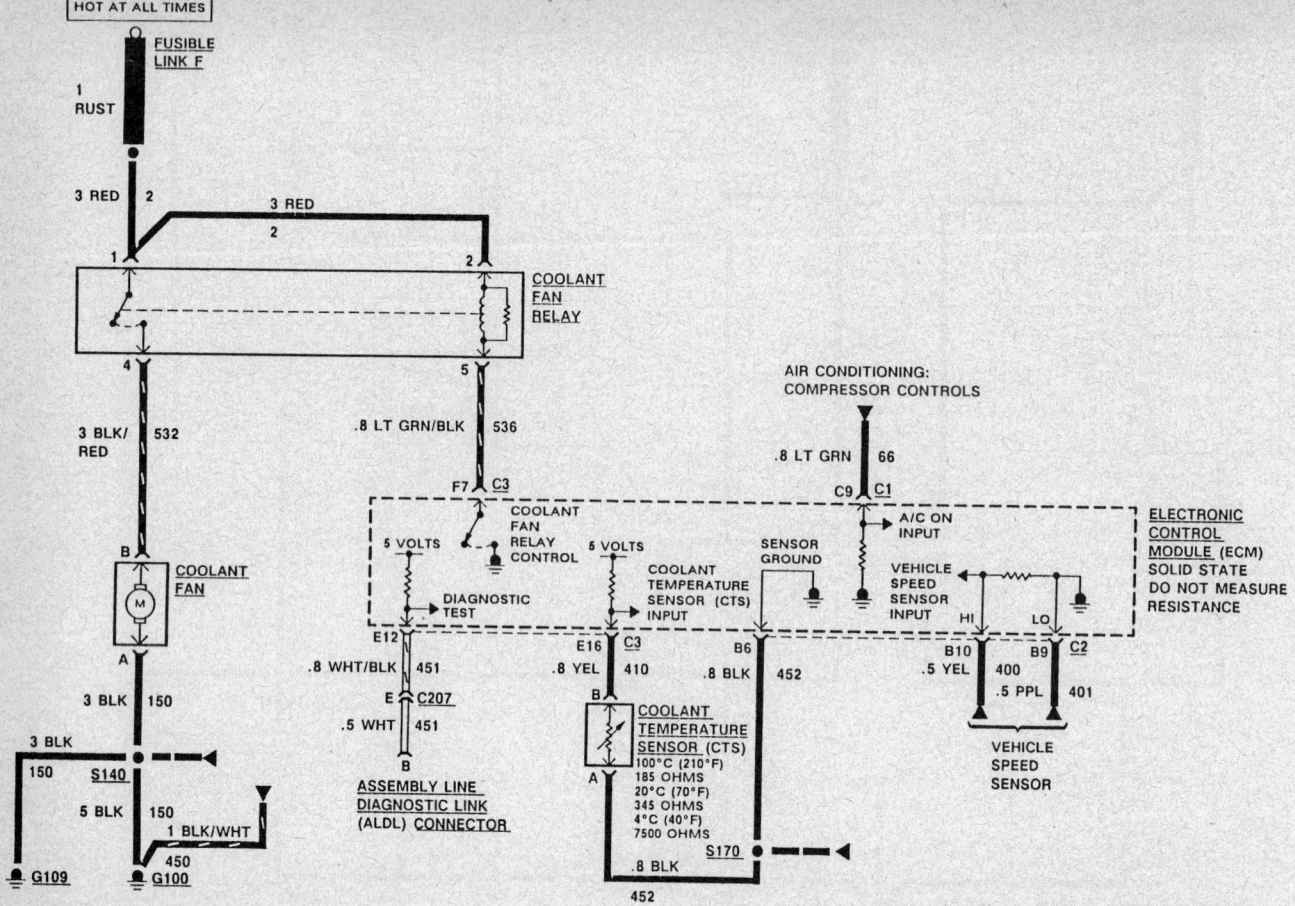

Fig. 70   Coolant fan wiring circuit. 1988–90 Grand Am w/2.3L/4-143 engine, VIN D & A

A/C mode selector in MAX position. Measure voltage between terminal C1/24 of the ECM and ground.
2. If zero volts is present, check dark green/white wire for an open.
3. If battery voltage is present, problem is ECM related

1988 VIN D

Coolant Fan Does Not Run In Low Or High Speed

1. Disconnect high speed coolant fan relay connector and connect a 20 amp fused jumper between red (1) and black/pink wire terminals. If coolant fan runs proceed to "Coolant Fan Does Not Run In Low Speed" and "Coolant Fan Does Not Run In High Speed."
2. If coolant fan does not run, leave fused jumper connected as in step 1, disconnect coolant fan connector and measure voltage from black/pink wire terminal to ground. If battery voltage is not present, check fusible link F, red (2) wire and black/pink wire for open.
3. If battery voltage is present, leave fused jumper connected as in step 1 and measure voltage from black/pink to black wire terminal of coolant fan connector. If battery voltage is not present, check black wire for open.

4. If battery voltage is present, check coolant fan connector terminal contact and, if satisfactory, replace coolant fan.

Coolant Fan Does Not Run In Low Speed

1. With ignition switch in RUN position, ground white terminal of ALDL connector. If coolant fan runs, problem is ECM related.
2. If coolant fan does not run, turn ignition switch to RUN position and ground ECM connector C3 dark green wire terminal with fused jumper. If coolant fan runs, problem is ECM related.
3. If coolant fan does not run, leave fused jumper connected as in step 2, turn ignition switch to RUN position, disconnect low speed coolant fan relay connector and measure voltage from brown wire terminal to ground. If battery voltage is not present, check H-AC fuse and brown wire for open.
4. If battery voltage is present, leave fused jumper connected as in step 2, turn ignition switch to RUN position and measure voltage between brown and dark green wire terminals. If battery voltage is not present, check dark green wire for open.
5. If battery voltage is present, discon-

nect low speed coolant fan relay connector and measure voltage from red (1) wire terminal to ground. If battery voltage is not present, check red (2) wire for open.
6. If battery voltage is present, disconnect low speed coolant fan relay connector and connect fused jumper with 20 amp fuse between red (1) and black/red wire terminals.
7. If coolant fan does not run, check black/red wire for open.
8. If coolant fan runs, check low speed coolant fan relay terminal contact and, if satisfactory, replace low speed coolant fan relay.

Coolant Fan Does Not Run In High Speed

1. With ignition switch in RUN position, ground ECM connector C3 light green/black wire terminal with fused jumper. If coolant fan runs, problem is ECM related.
2. If coolant fan does not run, leave fused jumper connected as in step 1, disconnect high speed coolant fan relay connector, turn ignition switch to RUN position and measure voltage from red (2) wire terminal to ground. If battery voltage is not present, check red wire for open.
3. If battery voltage is present, leave

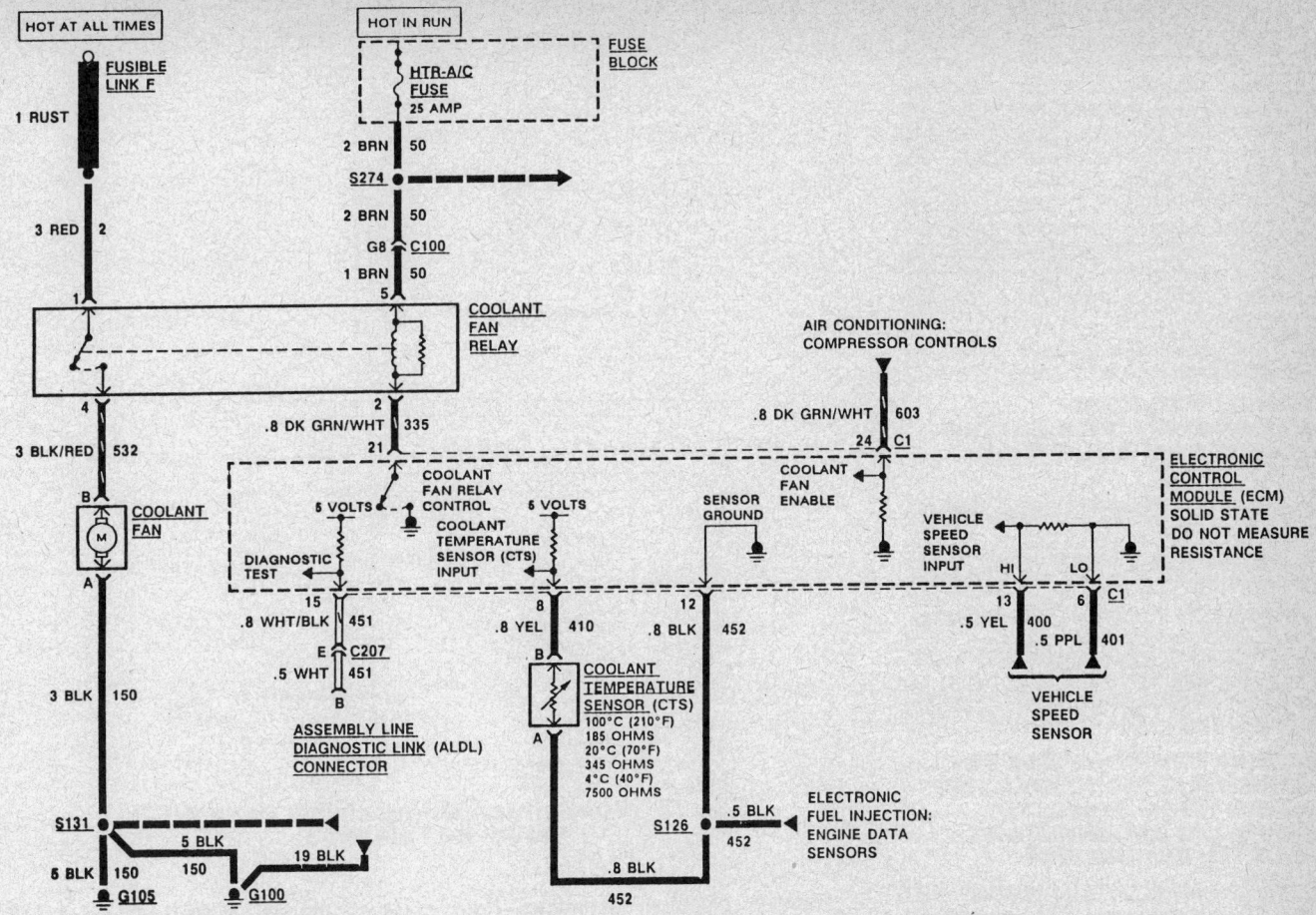

Fig. 71 Coolant fan wiring circuit. 1988–90 Grand Am w/2.5L/4-151 engine, VIN U

fused jumper connected as in step 1, turn ignition switch to RUN position and measure voltage between red (2) and light green/black wire terminals. If battery voltage is not present, check light green/black wire for open.

4. If battery voltage is present, measure voltage between red (1) wire terminal and ground. If battery voltage is not present, check red (2) wire for open.

5. If battery voltage is present, disconnect high speed coolant fan relay connector and connect a fused jumper with 20 amp fuse between red (1) and black/pink wire terminals.

6. If coolant fan does not run, check black/pink wire for open.

7. If coolant fan runs, check high speed coolant fan relay connector terminal contact and, if satisfactory, replace coolant fan.

Coolant Fan Runs Continuously In Low Speed With Engine Coolant Cool & A/C Mode Selector Off

1. Disconnect low speed coolant relay connector, turn ignition switch to RUN position and connect test lamp between brown and dark green wire terminals.

2. If lamp does not illuminate, replace low speed coolant fan relay.

3. If lamp illuminates, check dark green wire for short to ground. If wire is satisfactory, problem is ECM related.

Coolant Fan Runs Continuously In High Speed With Engine Coolant Cool & A/C Mode Selector Off

1. Disconnect high speed coolant fan relay connector, turn ignition switch to RUN position and connect test lamp between red and light green/black wire terminals

2. If lamp does not illuminate, replace high speed coolant fan relay.

3. If lamp illuminates, check light green/black wire for short to ground. If wire is satisfactory, problem is ECM related.

Coolant Fan Does Not Run In Low And/Or High Speed With A/C Mode Selector On & Head Pressure Above 150 psi, But Does Run In Low & High Speed With Engine Hot

1. With engine idling, turn on A/C and observe engine operation.

2. If engine slows when compressor clutch engages, check dark green/white wire for open. If wire is

satisfactory, problem is ECM related.

3. If engine does not slow down when compressor clutch engages, problem is ECM related.

1989–90 VIN A & D

Coolant Fan Does Not Turn On

1. Place ignition switch in RUN position. Ground terminal B of the ALDL connector. If coolant fan runs, problem is ECM related.

2. If coolant fan does not run, ground terminal C3/E8 of the ECM connector with a fused jumper. If coolant fan runs, problem is ECM related.

3. If coolant fan does not run and terminal C3/E8 is still grounded, disconnect coolant fan relay connector. Measure voltage between terminal 2 of the coolant fan relay connector to ground. If zero volts is present, check red wire and fusible link F for and open.

4. If battery voltage is present and terminal C3/E8 is still grounded, measure voltage between red wire terminal and ground of the relay connector. If zero volts is present, check red wire and fusible link F for an open.

5. If battery voltage is present, connect a fused jumper between terminals 1

and 4 of the coolant fan relay. If coolant fan runs, replace coolant fan relay.

6. If coolant fan does not run, leave jumper on relay connector and measure voltage between terminal B of the coolant fan connector to ground. If zero volts is present, check black/red wire for an open.
7. If battery voltage is present, leave jumper on relay connector and measure voltage between terminals B and A on coolant fan connector. If zero volts is present, check black wire for an open.
8. If battery voltage is present, replace coolant fan motor.

Coolant Fan Runs Continuously With Engine Coolant Cool & A/C Mode Selector Off

1. Disconnect coolant fan relay connector.
2. Connect a test lamp between terminals 2 and 5 of the relay connector. If lamp does not light, replace coolant fan relay.
3. If test lamp lights, check and repair green/ black wire for a short to ground. If wire is satisfactory, problem is ECM related.

Coolant Fan Does Not Turn On With A/C Mode Selector On And Head Pressure Above 150 psi, But Does Run With Engine Hot

1. Place ignition in RUN position and A/C mode selector in MAX position. Measure voltage between terminal C1/C9 of the ECM and ground.
2. If zero volts is present, check light green wire for an open.
3. If battery voltage is present, problem is ECM related

COOLANT FAN, REPLACE

VIN M & VIN U

1. Disconnect battery ground cable.
2. Remove wiring harness from fan motor and fan frame.
3. Remove fan guard and hose support as necessary.
4. Remove fan assembly from radiator support.
5. Reverse procedure to install.

VIN D & A

1. Disconnect battery ground cable.
2. Remove air cleaner to throttle body duct.
3. Disconnect electrical connectors from throttle position sensor, IAC and MAP sensor and position harness aside.
4. Remove vacuum harness assembly from throttle body and position aside.
5. Disconnect MAP sensor vacuum hose at intake manifold.
6. Remove coolant fan shroud attaching bolts and the shroud together with MAP sensor.
7. Remove coolant fan to upper radiator support attaching bolt, remaining upper radiator support bolt and the upper radiator support.

8. Remove electrical connector from coolant fan.
9. Lift fan assembly out of two lower insulators, rotate bracket so two lower bracket legs point upward, move fan assembly toward driver's side until fan blade overlaps radiator tank to core seam by approximately one inch and remove fan assembly upward. Because of minimum clearance, care must be taken not to damage lock tang on throttle position sensor with fan bracket.
10. Reverse procedure to install.

LEMANS

SYSTEM DESCRIPTION

Models Less A/C

Cooling fan operation is controlled by an engine temperature switch. When engine temperature reaches 221°F, the switch closes and the fan is energized. As the engine cools, the engine temperature switch opens and the cooling fan stops.

Models With A/C

Operation of the two-speed cooling fan is controlled by high and low speed cooling fan relays. When the A/C system is turned on, voltage is supplied to the A/C compressor relay, the ECM grounds the compressor relay coil and the low speed fan relay is energized. Voltage is then transferred from fuse No. 14, through the cooling fan resistor and to the fan. When the ECM determines that the en-

gine should be cooled, it will ground the high speed fan relay to apply voltage directly from the fuse to the fan motor.

DIAGNOSIS

Refer to **Figs. 72 through 75** when performing diagnostic procedures on this system.

1988 MODELS LESS A/C

Cooling Fan Does Not Run

1. Check fuse No. 11 and replace as necessary.
2. Disconnect engine temperature switch electrical connector and connect a fused jumper wire between switch terminals Z (green/white wire) and and Y (black wire). If fan runs, replace engine temperature switch. If fan does not run, proceed to step 3.
3. With ignition switch in Run position and fused jumper cable still installed, connect a suitable test lamp alternately between cooling fan connector terminal Y (brown wire) and ground and terminals Y (brown wire) and Z (green/white wire).
4. If test lamp lights at both connections, replace fan motor. If test lamp does not light when connected between terminal Y and ground, check brown wire (circuit 250) for an open and repair as necessary. If test lamp does not light at when connected between terminals Y and Z, check green/white wire (circuit 935) and black wire (circuit 150) for an open and repair as necessary.

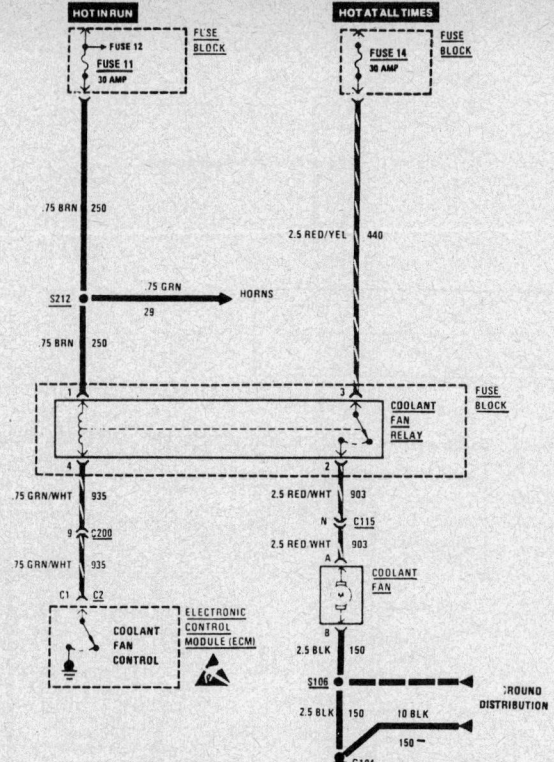

Fig. 72   Coolant fan wiring circuit (less A/C). 1988–89 LeMans

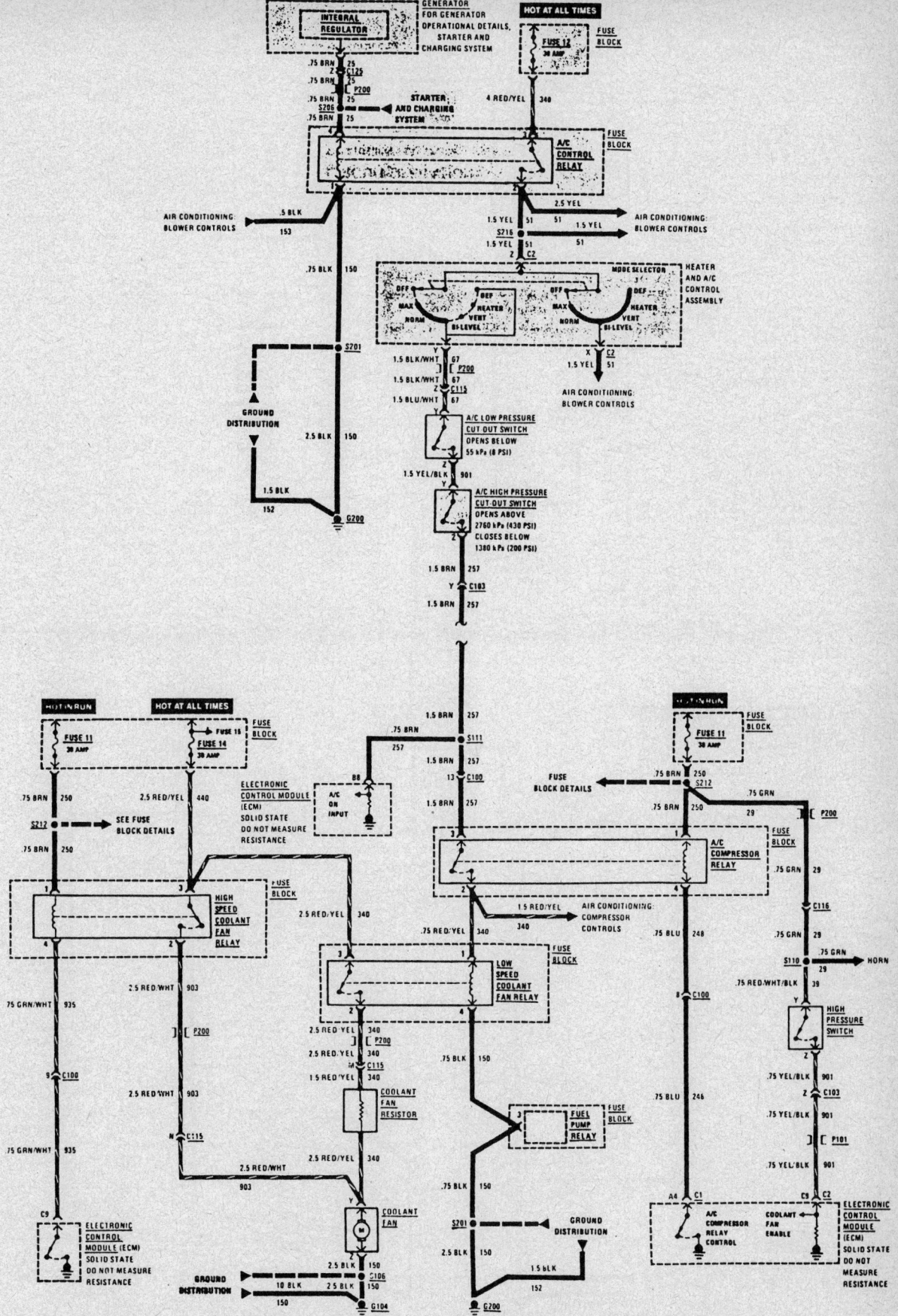

Fig. 73 Coolant fan wiring circuit (with A/C). 1988–89 LeMans

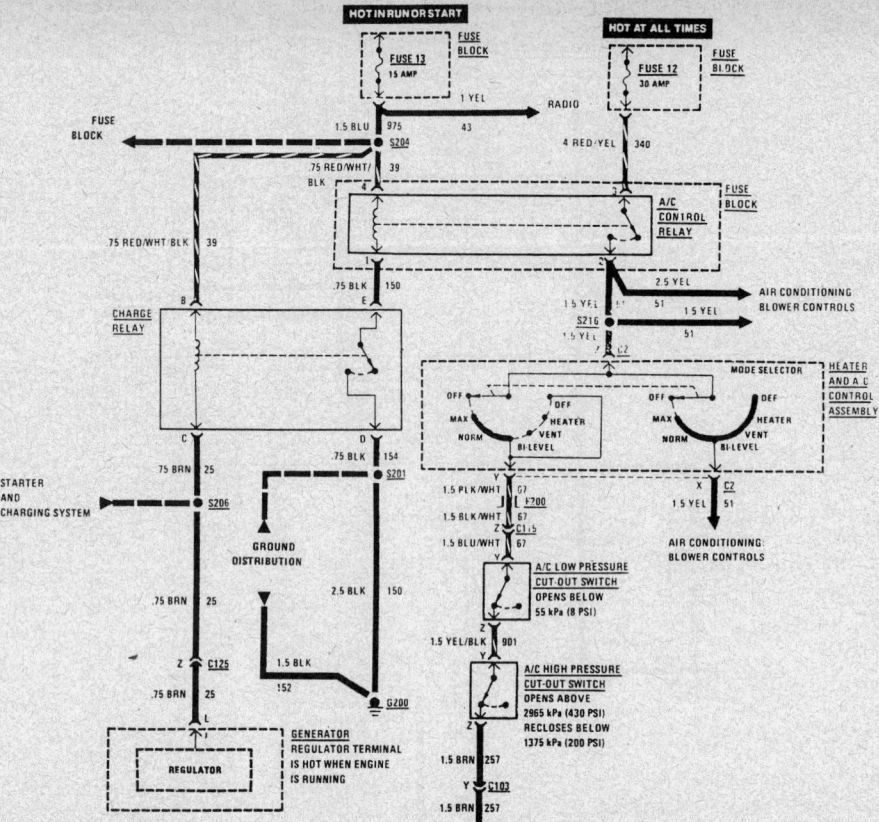

Fig. 74   Coolant fan wiring circuit (Part 1 of 2). 1990 LeMans, with A/C

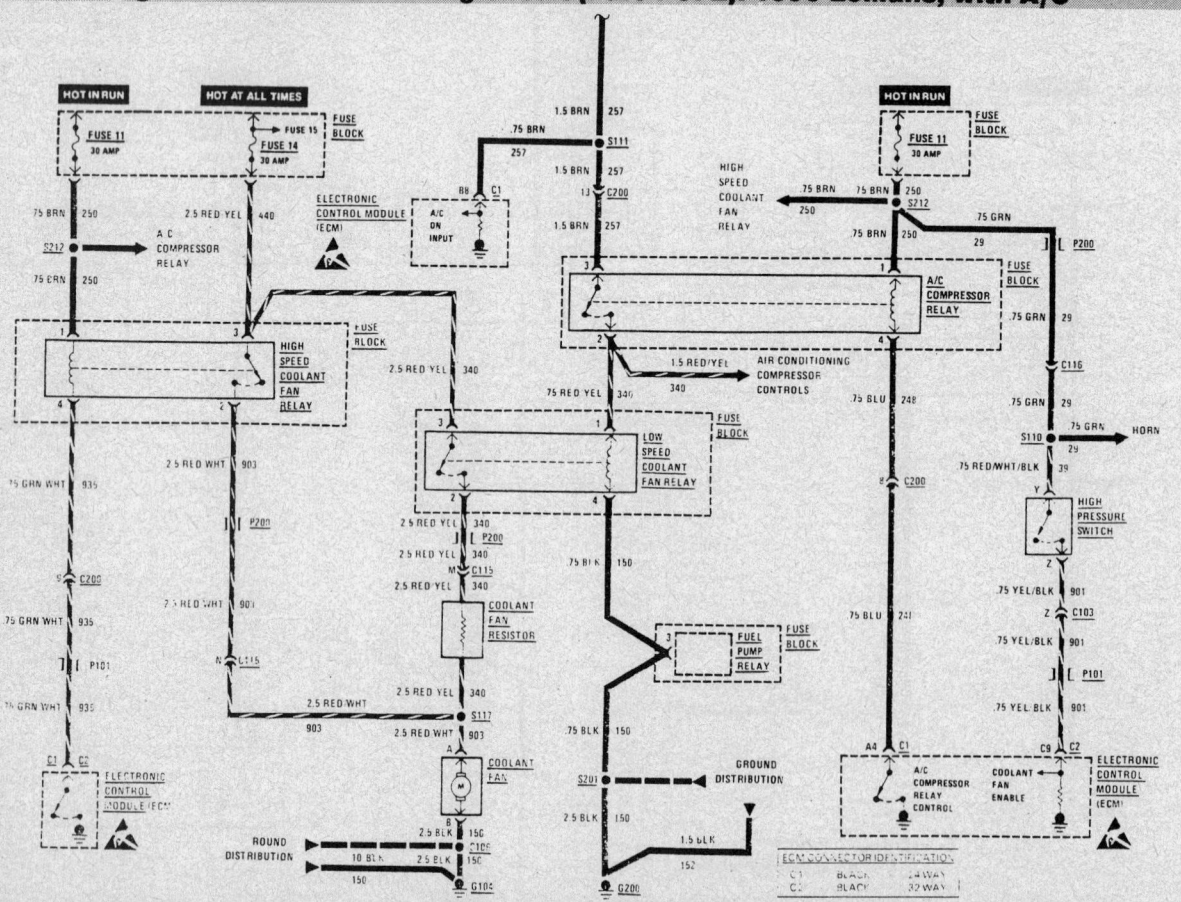

Fig. 74   Coolant fan wiring circuit (Part 2 of 2). 1990 LeMans, with A/C

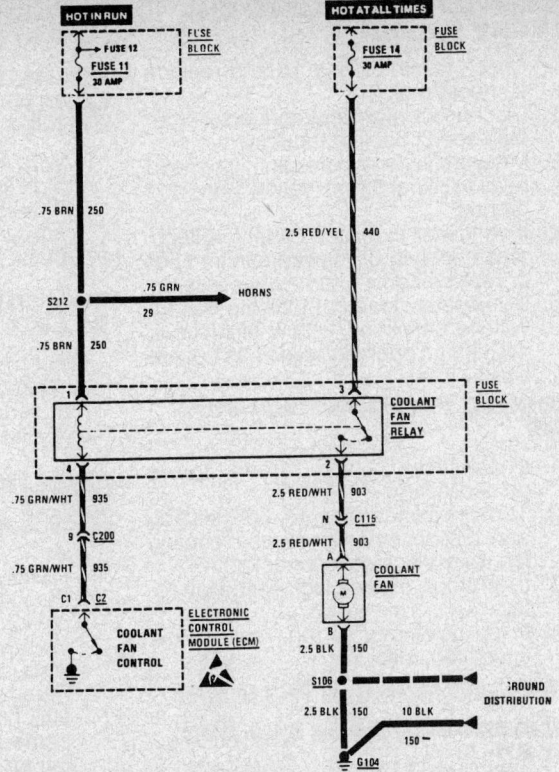

Fig. 75 Coolant fan wiring circuit. 1990 LeMans, less A/C

Cooling Fan Runs Continuously With Ignition Switch In Run

1. Check fuse No. 11 and replace as necessary.
2. Disconnect engine temperature switch electrical connector with ignition switch in Run position.
3. If fan stops, replace engine temperature switch. If fan continues to run, check green/white wire (circuit 935) for a short to ground and repair as necessary.

1989–90 MODELS LESS A/C
Coolant Fan Does Not Run

1. Check fuses 11 and 12, replace as necessary.
2. Connect a fused jumper wire between terminal B of the Assembly Line Diagnostic Link Connector (ALDL) and ground, then turn the ignition switch to the RUN position. If coolant fan does not run, proceed to step 3. If coolant fan runs, problem is ECM related.
3. Disconnect ECM C2 connector, then connect a fused jumper wire between C1 green/white connector and ground. Turn ignition switch to RUN, If coolant fan does not run, proceed to step 4. If coolant fan runs, problem is ECM related.
4. Leaving jumper wire connected from the previous step, disconnect coolant fan relay connector. Turn ignition

switch to RUN, then using a Test lamp proceed as follows:
a. Connect test lamp between terminal 1 (brown) wire and ground. If test lamp lights, proceed to step b. If test lamp does not light, locate and repair open in brown wire.
b. Connect test lamp between terminal 3 (red/yellow) wire and ground. If test lamp lights, proceed to step c. If test lamp does not light, locate and repair open in red/yellow wire.
c. Connect test lamp between terminal 1 (brown) and terminal 4 (green/white) wires. If test lamp lights, proceed to step d. If test lamp does not light, locate and repair open in green/white wire.
d. Connect test lamp between terminal 1 (brown) and terminal 2 (red/white) wires. If test lamp lights, replace high speed coolant fan relay. If test lamp does not light, proceed to step 5.
5. With coolant fan relay connector disconnected, connect fused jumper wire between terminal 2 (red/white) and terminal 3 (red/yellow).
6. Check voltage between red/white terminal and ground. If battery voltage is indicated, proceed to step 7. If battery voltage is not indicated, locate and repair open circuit in red/white wire.
7. Check voltage between red/white and black wires. If battery voltage is indicated, replace coolant fan. If battery voltage is not indicated, locate and repair open circuit in black wire.

Coolant Fan Runs Constantly When Ignition Switch Is In Run

1. Disconnect ECM connector C2, then turn ignition switch to the RUN position.
2. If coolant fan is off, problem is ECM related.
3. If coolant fan is on, locate and repair short to ground in green/white wire.

Coolant Fan Does Not Run At Low Speed

1. Disconnect Connector C1 from ECM, then turn ignition switch to the RUN position.
2. Connect a fused jumper wire between terminal A4 (blue) wire and ground. If coolant fan does not run, proceed to step 3. If coolant fan runs, problem is ECM related.
3. With ignition switch in RUN and jumper wire connected as in step 2. Disconnect low speed coolant fan relay connector and proceed as follows:
   a. Connect a test lamp between connector terminal 1 (red/yellow) and ground. If test lamp lights, proceed to step b. If test lamp does not light, locate and repair open in red/yellow wire.
   b. Connect a test lamp between connector terminals 1 (red/yellow) and 4 (black). If test lamp lights, replace low coolant fan relay. If test lamp does not light, locate and repair open in black wire.

1988 MODELS WITH A/C
Cooling Fan Does Not Run At Low Speed

1. Check fuses 11 and 14 and replace as necessary.
2. Connect a suitable fused jumper wire between ECM connector terminal A4 (blue wire) and ground. If fan runs, the electronic engine control system is at fault. If fan runs at low speed, proceed to step 3.
3. Disconnect low speed cooling fan relay electrical connector.
4. Move A/C mode selector to Norm and ignition switch to Run position, leaving fused jumper cable installed at ECM connector.
5. Connect a suitable test lamp between low speed cooling fan relay electrical connector terminal 1 (red/yellow wire) and ground. If test lamp lights, proceed to step 8. If test lamp does not light, inspect red/yellow wire (circuit 340) and repair as necessary.
6. Connect a suitable test lamp between low speed cooling fan relay electrical connector terminals 1 (red/yellow wire) and 4 (black wire). If test lamp lights, proceed to step 8. If test lamp does not light, check black wire (circuit 150) for an open and repair as necessary.
7. Connect a suitable test lamp between low speed cooling fan relay electrical connector terminal 3 (red/yellow wire) and ground. If test lamp lights, proceed to step 8. If test lamp does not light, check red/yellow wire

(circuit 340) for an open and repair as necessary.

8. Connect a suitable fused jumper wire between low speed cooling fan relay electrical connector terminals 2 (red/yellow wire) and 3 (red/yellow wire). If fan runs at low speed, replace low speed cooling fan relay. If fan does not run at low speed, proceed to step 9.

9. Disconnect cooling fan resistor electrical connector, leaving fuse jumper wire connected between low speed relay terminals 2 and 3.

10. Connect a suitable test lamp between cooling fan resistor connector terminal A (red/yellow wire) and ground. If test lamp lights, replace resistor. If test lamp does not light, check red/yellow wire (circuit 340) for an open to resistor and repair as necessary.

11. Connect a suitable test lamp between cooling fan resistor connector terminals A (red/yellow wire) and b (red/yellow wire). If test lamp lights, replace resistor. If test lamp does not light, check red/yellow wire (circuit 340) for an open to cooling fan and repair as necessary.

Cooling Fan Does Not Run At High Speed

1. Check fuses 11 and 14 and replace as necessary.

2. Turn ignition switch to Run position and connect a suitable fused jumper wire between ALDL connector terminal B and ground. If cooling fan runs at high speed, proceed to step 3. If fan does not run, the electronic engine control system is at fault.

3. With ignition in Run position, disconnect ECM electrical connector and connect a suitable fused jumper wire between connector terminal C9 (green/white wire) and ground. If cooling fan does not run at high speed, proceed to step 4. If cooling fan runs at high speed, the electronic engine control system is at fault.

4. Disconnect high speed cooling fan relay electrical connector.

5. Turn ignition switch to Run position, leaving fused jumper cable installed at ECM connector.

6. Connect a suitable test lamp between high speed cooling fan relay electrical connector terminal 1 (brown wire) and ground. If test lamp lights, replace high speed relay. If test lamp does not light, check brown wire (circuit 250) for an open and repair as necessary.

7. Connect a suitable test lamp between high speed cooling fan relay electrical connector terminals 1 (brown wire) and 4 (green/white wire). If test lamp lights, replace high speed relay. If test lamp does not light, check green/white wire (circuit 935) for an open and repair as necessary.

8. Connect a suitable test lamp between high speed cooling fan relay electrical connector terminals 1 (brown wire) and 2 (red/white wire). If test lamp lights, replace high speed relay. If test lamp does not light, check red/white wire (circuit 903) for an open and repair as necessary.

Cooling Fan Does Not Run At Any Speed

1. Check fuses 11 and 14 and replace as necessary.

2. Disconnect electrical connector from high speed cooling fan relay.

3. Measure voltage between high speed relay terminal 3 (red/yellow wire) and ground.

4. If voltmeter indicates battery voltage, repair open in black wire (circuit 150) or replace cooling fan as necessary.

5. If voltmeter does not indicate battery voltage, check red/yellow wire (circuit 440) for an open and repair as necessary.

Cooling Fan Does Not Turn Off

1. Check fuses 11 and 14 and replace as necessary.

2. Turn ignition switch to Off position and disconnect high speed cooling fan relay electrical connector.

3. If fan stops, replace high speed fan relay.

4. If fan continues to run, replace low speed fan relay.

1989–90 MODELS WITH A/C

Coolant Fan Does Not Run At All

1. Disconnect low speed coolant fan relay connector, turn ignition switch to the RUN position and the A/C to the NORM mode.

2. Using a test light, proceed as follows:
   a. Connect test lamp between terminal 1 (red/yellow) wire and ground. If test lamp lights, proceed to step b. If test lamp does not light, locate and repair open circuit in red/yellow wire.
   b. Connect test lamp between terminal 1 (red/yellow) wire and black wire. If test lamp lights, proceed to step c. If test lamp does not light, locate and repair open circuit in black wire.
   c. Connect test lamp between terminal 3 (red/yellow) wire and ground. If test lamp lights, proceed to step 3. If test lamp does not light, locate and repair open circuit in either one of the red/yellow wires.

3. Connect a fused jumper wire between terminal 3 (red/yellow) and terminal 2 (red/yellow) wires. If coolant fan does not run at low speed, proceed to step 4. If coolant fan runs at low speed, replace low speed coolant fan relay.

4. Leaving fused jumper connected from step 3, disconnect coolant fan connector.

5. Connect a test lamp between terminal A (red/yellow) wire of the coolant fan connector and ground. If test lamp lights, proceed to step 6. If test lamp does not light, locate and repair open circuit in either the red/yellow or the red/white wires in the coolant fan resistor.

6. Connect a test lamp between terminal A (red/yellow) and terminal B (Black) wires of the coolant fan connector. If test lamp lights, replace coolant fan. If

test lamp does not light, locate and repair open circuit in the black wire.

Coolant Fan Runs Constantly With Ignition Switch Off

1. With ignition switch off, disconnect high speed coolant fan relay.

2. If fan stops replace high speed coolant fan relay. If fan does not stop replace low speed coolant fan relay.

Coolant Fan Does Not Run At Low Speed

Refer to "Coolant Fan Does Not Run At Low Speed" in "1989 Models Less A/C." When performing tests A/C should be in the NORM mode.

COOLING FAN REPLACE

1. Disconnect battery ground cable.

2. Disconnect fan motor electrical connectors.

3. Remove oxygen sensor plug from air shroud.

4. Remove fan frame-to-radiator support attaching bolts, then then fan and frame assembly. A bent or damaged fan assembly must be replaced.

5. Reverse procedure to install.

SKYHAWK

SYSTEM DESCRIPTION

The coolant fan is supplied voltage by the coolant fan relay. The coolant fan relay is energized when the ECM grounds circuit 335. The ECM receives input signals from the coolant temperature sensor, vehicle speed sensor and mode selector. The ECM activates the coolant fan relay when engine coolant is above 223°F, when A/C is turned on or when coolant temperature sensor fails. The coolant fan will not operate when vehicle's speed is greater than 74 mph. The coolant fan will run for a minimum of 30 seconds.

TROUBLESHOOTING

1. If coolant fan does not operate, visually check ALT/FAN fuse and check fusible link C on 1988 models, or fusible link L on 1989 models.

2. If coolant fan runs with ignition switch off, replace coolant fan relay.

SYSTEM CHECK

1. With engine cold and idling, move mode selector to NORM, if equipped. Coolant fan should run.

2. With engine coolant below operating temperature, move mode selector to OFF. Coolant fan should turn off after approximately 30 seconds.

3. With engine warm, run engine at fast idle for several minutes. Coolant fan should turn on.

SYSTEM DIAGNOSIS

Refer to Fig. 76 when performing diagnostic procedures on this system.

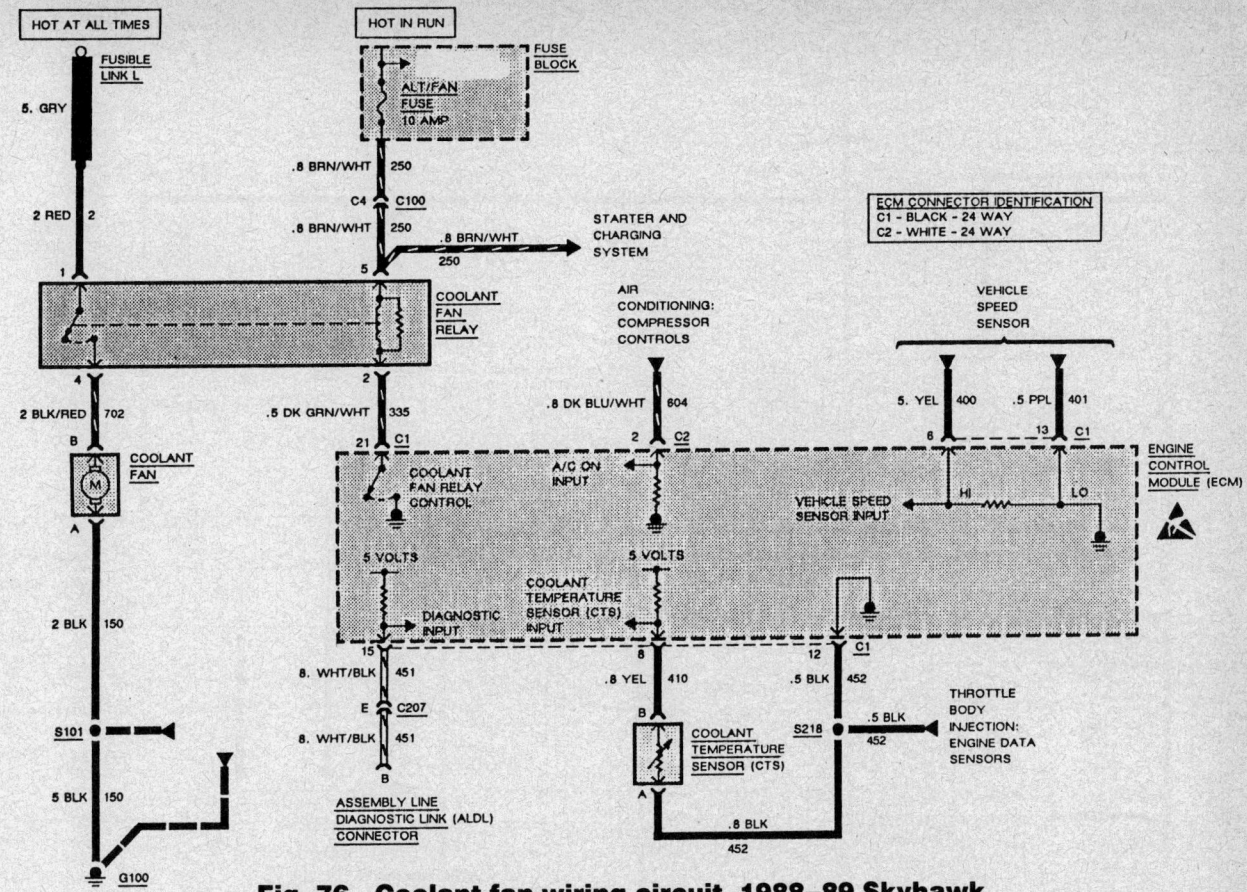

Fig. 76 Coolant fan wiring circuit. 1988–89 Skyhawk

Coolant Fan Does Not Run

1. Connect fused jumper between ALDL connector white/black wire and ground and turn ignition switch to RUN. If coolant fan runs, problem is ECM related.
2. If coolant fan does not run, connect fused jumper between ECM white connector dark green/white wire and ground and turn ignition switch to RUN. If coolant fan runs, problem is ECM related.
3. If coolant fan does not run, leave fused jumper in place from step 2, disconnect coolant fan relay connector, turn ignition switch to RUN and connect test lamp between coolant fan relay connector terminals as follows:
   a. Connect between brown/white wire terminal and ground. If test lamp does not illuminate, check brown/white wire for an open.
   b. Connect between brown/white and dark green/white wire terminals. If test lamp does not illuminate, check dark green/white wire for open.
   c. Connect between red wire terminal and ground. If test light does not illuminate, check fusible link C and red wire for open.
4. If test lamp illuminated in steps a, b and c, connect fused jumper between

coolant fan relay connector red and black/red wire terminals. If coolant fan runs, replace coolant fan relay.
5. If coolant fan does not run, leave fused jumper connected as in step 4, disconnect coolant fan connector and connect test lamp between coolant fan connector terminals as follows:
   a. Connect between black/red wire terminal and ground. If test lamp does not illuminate, check black/red wire for open.
   b. Connect between black/red and black wire terminals. If test lamp does not illuminate, check black wire for open.
6. If test lamp illuminated in steps a and b, replace coolant fan.

Coolant Fan Runs Continuously

1. Disconnect coolant fan relay, turn ignition switch to RUN and connect test lamp between brown/white and dark green/white wire terminals of coolant fan relay connector.
2. If test lamp does not illuminate, replace coolant fan relay.
3. If test lamp illuminates, check wiring between ECM and coolant fan relay for short to ground. If wire is satisfactory, problem is ECM related.

COOLANT FAN, REPLACE

1. Disconnect battery ground cable.
2. Remove air cleaner duct.
3. Disconnect wiring harness from motor and fan frame.
4. Remove coolant fan from radiator support.
5. Reverse procedure to install.

1988 SKYLARK

SYSTEM DESCRIPTION
4-138 VIN D

A two speed coolant fan is used with this engine. The coolant fan is turned on and off by the coolant fan relays.

For low speed operation, the low speed relay coil is grounded through the ECM when vehicle speed is less than 45 mph and the engine coolant temperature reaches 208°F, or when the A/C is turned on. The contacts close and voltage is applied through a resistor to the coolant fan. The fan runs at low speed.

For high speed operation, the high speed relay coil is grounded through the ECM when the engine coolant temperature reaches 228°F. The contacts close and voltage is applied directly to the coolant fan. The fan runs at high speed. The coolant fan will continue to run at high

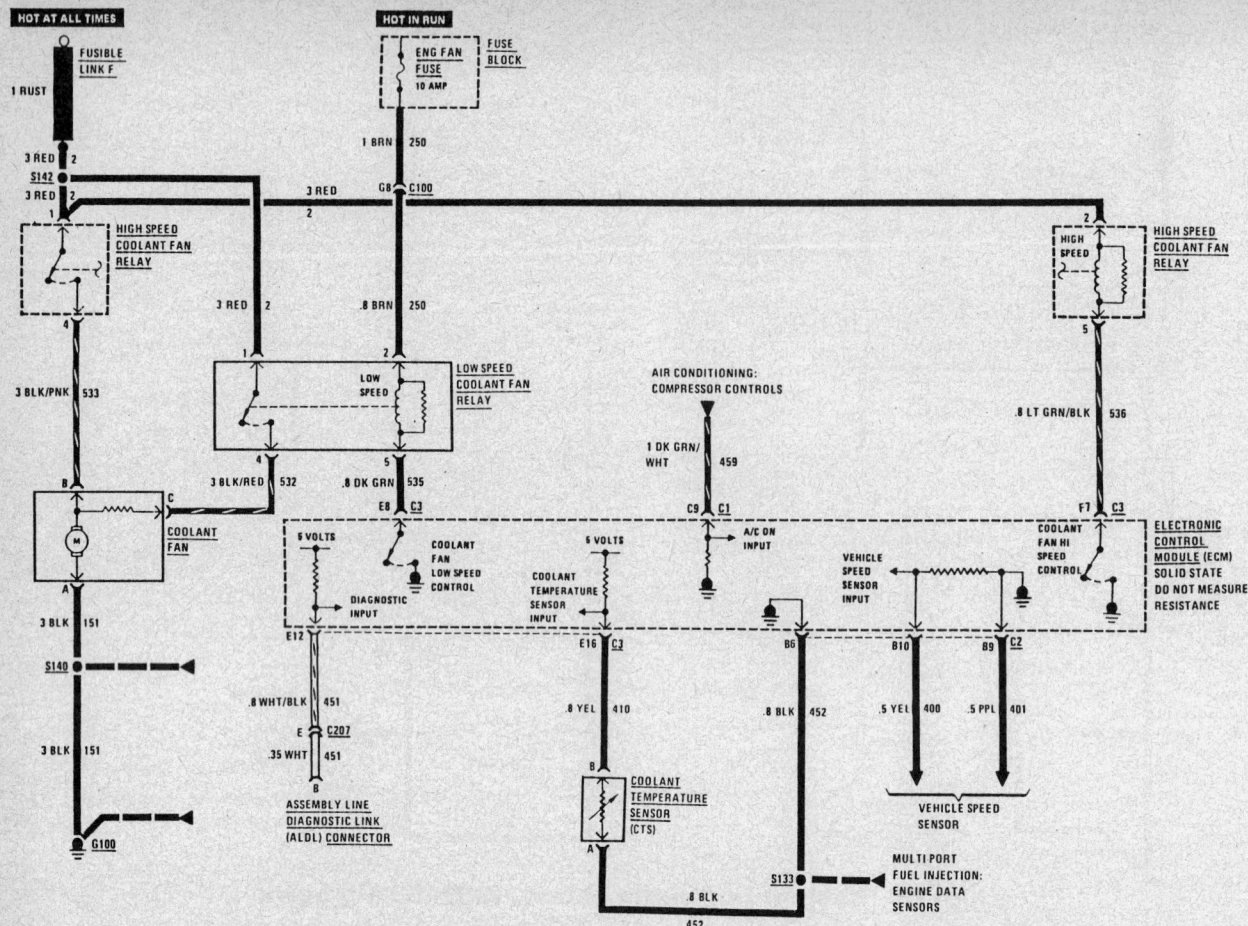

Fig. 77 Coolant fan wiring circuit. 1988 Skylark w/2.3L/4-143 engine

speed after the ignition switch is turned off, until engine coolant temperature lowers.

4-151 VIN U

The coolant fan is controlled by the coolant fan relay. The coolant fan relay is electrically operated by the ECM. THe ECM receives input signals from the coolant temperature sensor, the vehicle speed sensor and the A/C mode selector. The ECM activates the coolant fan relay when either the engine coolant temperature, which is sensed by the coolant temperature sensor, is above 227°F when the A/C is turned on, or when the coolant temperature sensor fails. Any of these input signals causes the ECM to ground circuit 335 when vehicle speed is less than 35 mph. With circuit 335 grounded, the coolant fan relay is energized and its contacts close, turning the coolant fan on.

V6-181 VIN L

A two speed coolant fan is used with this engine. The coolant fan is turned on and off by the coolant fan relays.

For low speed operation, the low speed relay coil is grounded through the ECM or the low speed contacts of the coolant fan A/C dual pressure switch. The ECM grounds the coil when vehicle speed is

less than 45 mph and the engine coolant temperature reaches 208°F. The low speed contacts of the coolant fan A/C dual pressure switch ground the coil of the coolant fan relay when head pressure is above 150 psi.

With low speed relay coil grounded, the associated contacts close. Voltage is applied through the coolant fan resistor to the coolant fan. The resistor drops part of the battery voltage and the coolant fan runs at low speed.

For high speed operation, the high speed relay coil is grounded through the high speed contacts of the coolant fan A/C dual pressure switch or the coolant fan temperature switch. The coolant fan A/C dual pressure switch high speed contacts close when head pressure is higher than the pressure that closed the low speed contacts (300 psi). The coolant fan temperature switch closes when coolant temperature reaches 228°F.

With the high speed relay coil grounded, the associated contacts close. Battery voltage is applied to the coolant fan. The fan runs at high speed.

TROUBLESHOOTING

Visually inspect the ENG FAN fuse.

SYSTEM CHECK

1. **On vehicles equipped with A/C,** with engine cold and idling, push mode selector to NORM. Coolant fan should turn on.
2. **On vehicles equipped with A/C,** push mode selector to off. Coolant fan should turn off.
3. **On all vehicles,** with engine warmed up, run it at fast idle for several minutes. Coolant temperature should turn on before coolant temperature indicator comes on.

SYSTEM DIAGNOSIS

Refer to **Figs. 77 through 79** when performing diagnostic procedures on these systems.

4-138 VIN D

Coolant Fan Does Not Run in Low Speed

1. Disconnect ECM yellow connector, turn ignition switch to RUN position and connect fused jumper between dark green wire terminal and ground. If coolant fan runs in low speed, problem is ECM related.

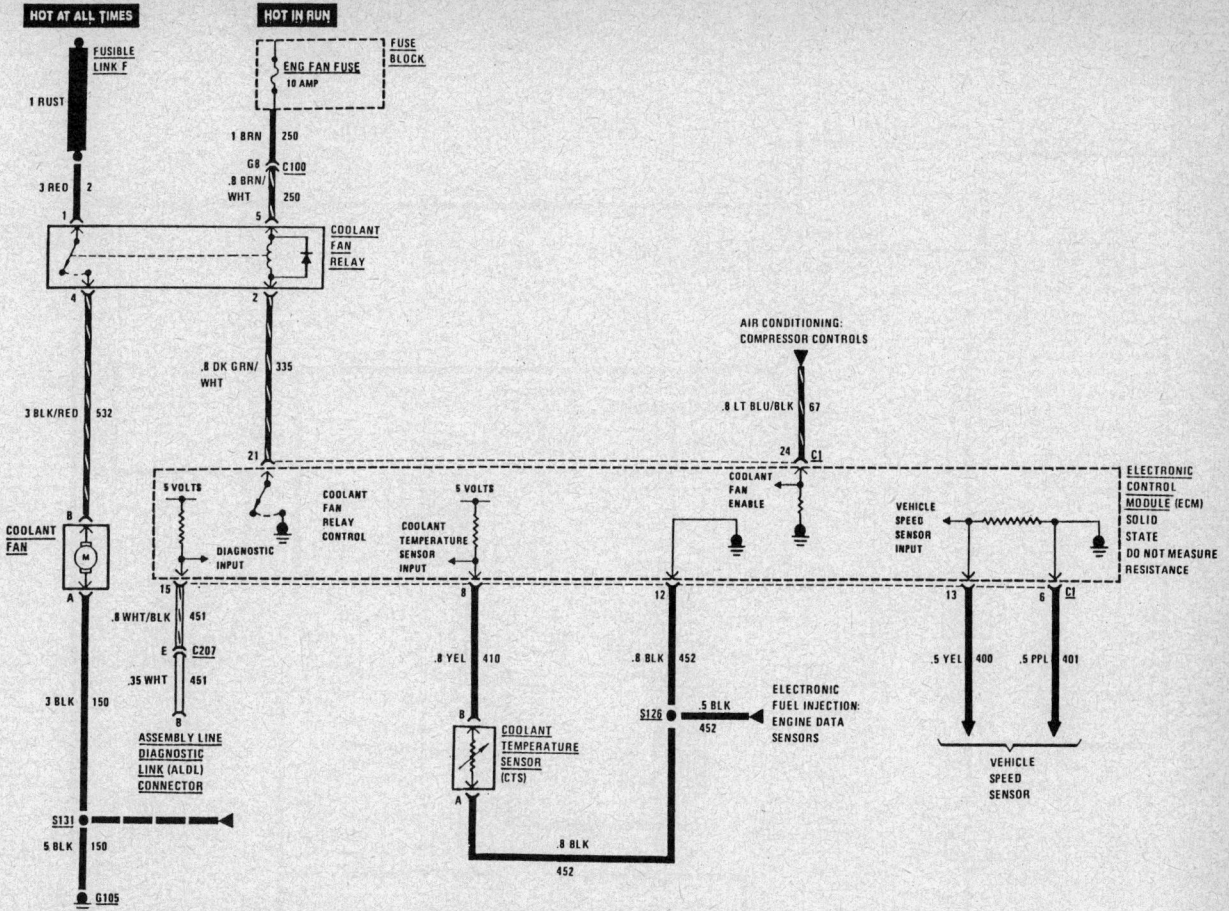

Fig. 78 Coolant fan wiring circuit. 1988 Skylark w/2.5L/4-151 engine

2. If coolant fan does not run in low speed, connect fused jumper between ALDL connector white wire terminal and ground, disconnect low speed coolant fan relay connector, turn ignition switch to RUN position and connect test lamp between terminals as follows:
   a. Connect between brown wire terminal and ground. If test lamp does not illuminate, check ENG FAN fuse and brown wire for open.
   b. Connect between brown and dark green wire terminals. If lamp does not illuminate, check dark green wire for open.
   c. Connect between red/white wire terminal and ground. If lamp does not illuminate, check fusible link F, red/white wire and red wire for opens.
3. If lamp illuminated in steps a, b and c, disconnect low speed coolant relay connector, turn ignition switch to RUN position and connect fused jumper between red/white and black/red wire terminals. If coolant fan runs at low speed, replace low speed coolant fan relay.
4. If coolant fan does not run at low speed, leave fused jumper connected as in step 2, disconnect coolant fan connector, turn ignition switch to RUN position and connect test lamp between terminals as follows:

a. Connect between black/red wire terminal and ground. If test lamp does not illuminate, check black/red wire for open.
b. Connect between black/red and black wire terminals. If lamp does not illuminate, check black wire for open.
c. If lamp illuminated in steps a and b, replace coolant fan.

Coolant Fan Does Not Run In High Speed

1. Connect fused jumper between ALDL connector white wire terminal and ground. If coolant fan runs in high speed, problem is ECM related.
2. If coolant fan does not run in high speed, disconnect ECM yellow connector and connect fused jumper between light green/black wire terminal and ground. If coolant fan runs in high speed, problem is ECM related.
3. If coolant fan does not run in high speed, connect fused jumper between ALDL connector white wire terminal and ground, reconnect ECM connector, disconnect high speed coolant fan relay connector and connect test lamp as follows:
   a. Connect between red wire terminal (2) and ground. If lamp does not illuminate, check fusible link F and red wire (2) for open.

b. Connect between red (2) and light green/black wire terminals. If lamp does not illuminate, check light green/black wire for open.
c. Connect between red wire terminal (1) and ground. If lamp does not illuminate, check fusible link F and red wire (2) for open.
4. If lamp illuminated in steps a, b and c, disconnect high speed coolant fan relay connector and connect fused jumper between red and black/pink wire terminals. If coolant fan runs at high speed, replace high speed coolant fan relay.
5. If coolant fan does not run at high speed, leave fused jumper connected as in step 2, disconnect coolant fan connector and connect test lamp between terminals as follows:
   a. Connect between black/pink wire terminal and ground. If lamp does not illuminate, check black/pink wire for open.
   b. Connect between black/pink and black wire terminals. If lamp does not illuminate, check black wire for open.
   c. If lamp illuminated in steps a and b, replace coolant fan.

Coolant Fan Does Not Turn Off

1. With ignition switch in RUN position,

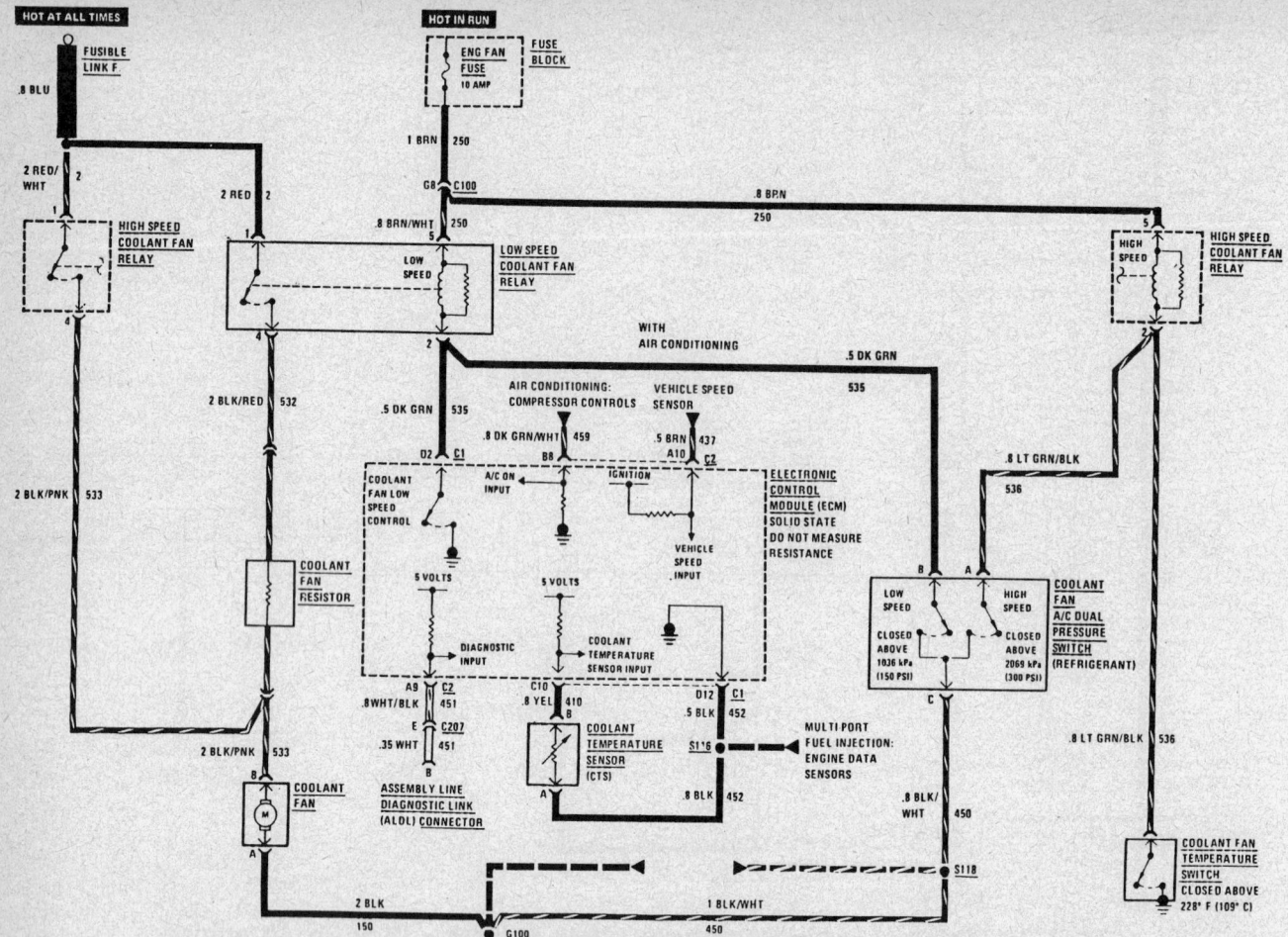

Fig. 79 Coolant fan wiring circuit. 1988 Skylark w/3.0L/V6-181 engine

disconnect yellow ECM connector. If coolant fan turns off, problem is ECM related.

2. If coolant fan does not turn off, disconnect high speed coolant fan relay. If coolant fan turns off, check light green/black wire for short to ground and, if wire is satisfactory, replace high speed coolant fan relay.

3. If coolant fan does not turn off, disconnect low speed coolant fan relay. If coolant fan turns off, check dark green wire for a short to ground and, if wire is satisfactory, replace low speed coolant fan relay.

4-151 VIN U

Coolant Fan Does Not Turn On

1. Connect a fused jumper between ALDL connector white wire terminal and ground and turn ignition switch to RUN position. If coolant fan runs, problem is ECM related.

2. If coolant fan does not run, disconnect back/red ECM connector, connect fused jumper between dark green/white wire terminal and ground and turn ignition switch to RUN position. If coolant fan runs, problem is ECM related.

3. If coolant fan does not run, leave fused jumper in place as in step 2, dis-

connect coolant fan relay connector, turn ignition switch to RUN position and connect test lamp between terminals as follows:

a. Connect between brown/white wire terminal and ground. If lamp does not illuminate, check ENG FUSE fuse, brown wire and brown/white wire for open.

b. Connect between brown/white and dark green/white wire terminals. If test lamp does not illuminate, check dark green/white wire for open.

c. Connect between red wire terminal and ground. If test lamp does not illuminate, check fusible link F and red wire for open.

d. Connect between red and black/red wire terminals. If lamp does not illuminate, proceed to step 4.

e. If lamp illuminated in steps a through d, replace coolant fan relay.

4. Leave fused jumper connected as in step 3, disconnect coolant fan connector, turn ignition switch to RUN position and connect test lamp between terminals as follows:

a. Connect between black/red wire terminal and ground. If lamp does not illuminate, check black/red wire for open.

b. Connect between black/red and black wire terminals. If lamp does not illuminate, check black wire for open.

c. If lamp illuminates in steps a and b, replace coolant fan.

Coolant Fan Does Not Turn Off

1. With ignition switch in RUN position, disconnect ECM connector. If coolant fan turns off, problem is ECM related.

2. If coolant fan does not turn off, remove ENG FAN fuse.

3. If coolant fan turns off, check dark green/white wire for short to ground.

4. If coolant fan does not turn off, replace coolant fan relay.

V6-181 VIN L

Coolant Fan Does Not Run In Low Speed

1. Connect fused jumper between ALDL connector white wire terminal and ground and turn ignition switch to RUN position. If coolant fan runs in low speed, problem is ECM related.

2. If coolant fan does not run in low speed, Disconnect ECM 32 pin connector, connect fused jumper be-

tween dark green wire terminal and ground and turn ignition switch to RUN position. If coolant fan runs in low speed, problem is ECM related.

3. If coolant fan does not run in low speed, leave fused jumper in place as in step 2, disconnect low speed coolant fan relay connector, turn ignition switch to RUN position and connect test lamp between terminals as follows:
   a. Connect between brown/white wire terminal and ground. If test lamp does not illuminate, check ENG FAN fuse, brown wire and brown/white wire for open.
   b. Connect between brown/white and dark green wire terminals. If test lamp does not illuminate, check dark green wire for open.
   c. Connect between red wire terminal and ground. If test lamp does not illuminate, check fusible link F and red wire for open.
4. If lamp illuminated in steps a, b and c, disconnect low speed coolant fan relay, connect fused jumper between red and black/red wire terminals and turn ignition switch to RUN position.
5. If coolant fan runs at low speed, replace low speed coolant fan relay.
6. If coolant fan does not run at low speed, leave fused jumper connected as in step 2, disconnect coolant fan connector, turn ignition switch to RUN position and connect test lamp between terminals as follows:
   a. Connect between black/pink wire terminal and ground. If lamp does not illuminate, check black/pink wire, coolant fan resistor and black/red wire for open.
   b. Connect between black/pink and black wire terminals. If lamp does not illuminate, check black wire for open.

Coolant Fan Does Not Work In High Speed

1. Disconnect coolant fan temperature switch connector or coolant fan A/C dual pressure switch connector, turn ignition switch to RUN position and connect fused jumper as follows:
   a. Connect between coolant fan temperature switch connector light green/black wire terminal and ground. If coolant fan does not run at high speed, proceed to step 2.
   b. **On vehicles with A/C,** connect between coolant fan A/C dual pressure switch connector light green/black wire terminal and ground. If coolant fan does not run at high speed, proceed to step 2.
   c. If coolant fan runs at high speed in steps a and b, replace suspect switch.
2. Connect fused jumper between light green/black wire at coolant fan temperature switch and ground, disconnect high speed coolant fan relay connector, turn ignition switch to RUN position and connect test lamp between terminals as follows:
   a. Connect between brown wire terminal and ground. If lamp does not

illuminate, check ENG FAN fuse and brown wire for open.
   b. Connect between brown and light green/black wire terminals. If lamp does not illuminate, check light green/black wire for an open to coolant fan temperature switch.
   c. Connect between red/white wire and ground. If lamp does not illuminate, check fusible link F and red/white wire for open.
   d. If lamp illuminated in steps a, b and c, check light green/black wire to coolant fan A/C dual pressure switch for open.
3. If wire is satisfactory, disconnect high speed coolant fan relay connector, connect fused jumper between red/white and black/pink wire terminals and turn ignition switch to RUN position. If coolant fan runs at high speed, replace high speed coolant fan relay.
4. If coolant fan does not run at high speed, leave fused jumper connected as in step 2, disconnect coolant fan connector, turn ignition switch to RUN position and connect test lamp between terminals as follows:
   a. Connect between black/pink wire terminal and ground. If test lamp does not illuminate, check black/pink wire for open.
   b. Connect between black/pink and black wire terminals. If lamp does not illuminate, check black wire for open.
   c. If test lamp illuminates in steps a and b, replace coolant fan.

Coolant Fan Does Not Turn Off

1. With ignition switch in RUN position, disconnect 32 pin ECM connector. If coolant fan turns off, problem is ECM related.
2. If coolant fan does not turn off, disconnect coolant fan temperature switch. If coolant fan stops, replace coolant fan temperature switch.
3. If coolant fan does not stop, proceed to step 4 for vehicles with A/C, or to step 5 for vehicles less A/C.
4. Disconnect coolant fan A/C dual pressure switch. If coolant fan stops, replace coolant fan A/C dual pressure switch. If not, proceed to step 6.
5. With ignition switch off, disconnect high speed coolant fan relay. If coolant fan stops, check light green/black wire for a short to ground and, if wire is satisfactory, replace high speed coolant fan relay. If not, proceed to step 6.
6. Disconnect low speed coolant fan relay. If coolant fan stops, check dark green wire for short and, if wire is satisfactory, replace low speed coolant fan relay.

Coolant Fan Does Not Run In Low/Or High Speed With Mode Selector On & Head Pressure Above 150 psi, But Does Run In Low & High Speed With Engine Hot

1. With ignition switch in RUN position,

disconnect coolant fan A/C dual pressure switch connector and connect fused jumper between dark green wire terminal and ground. If coolant fan does not run in low speed, check dark green wire for open.
2. If coolant fan runs in low speed, connect fused jumper from light green/black wire terminal to ground. If coolant fan does not run at high speed, check light green/black wire for open.
3. If coolant fan runs at high speed, connect fused jumper between light green/black and black/white wire terminals.
4. If coolant fan runs at high speed, replace coolant fan A/C dual pressure switch.
5. If coolant fan does not run at high speed, check black/white wire for an open to ground.

COOLANT FAN, REPLACE
EXCEPT 4-138 VIN D

1. Disconnect battery ground cable.
2. Disconnect wiring harness from motor and fan frame.
3. Remove fan guard and hose support as necessary.
4. Remove fan assembly from radiator support.
5. Reverse procedure to install.

4-138 VIN D

1. Disconnect battery ground cable.
2. Remove air cleaner to throttle body duct.
3. Disconnect electrical connectors from throttle position sensor, IAC and manifold absolute pressure (MAP) sensor and position harness out of way.
4. Disconnect vacuum harness assembly from throttle body and position out of way.
5. Disconnect MAP sensor vacuum hose from intake manifold.
6. Remove coolant fan shroud attaching bolts and remove shroud together with MAP sensor.
7. Remove coolant fan to upper radiator support bolt, remaining upper radiator support bolt and the upper radiator support.
8. Disconnect electrical connector from coolant fan.
9. Lift fan assembly out of two lower insulators and rotate bracket so two lower bracket legs point upward, then move fan assembly toward driver side until fan blade overlaps radiator tank to core seam by approximately one inch and remove fan assembly upward, out the top. **Due to limited access, care must be taken not to damage lock tang on throttle position sensor with fan bracket.**
10. Reverse procedure to install.

1989–90 SKYLARK
SYSTEM DESCRIPTION

The coolant fan is controlled by the coolant fan relay. The coolant fan relay is electrically operated by the ECM. The ECM receives input signals from the coolant temperature sensor, vehicle speed sensor

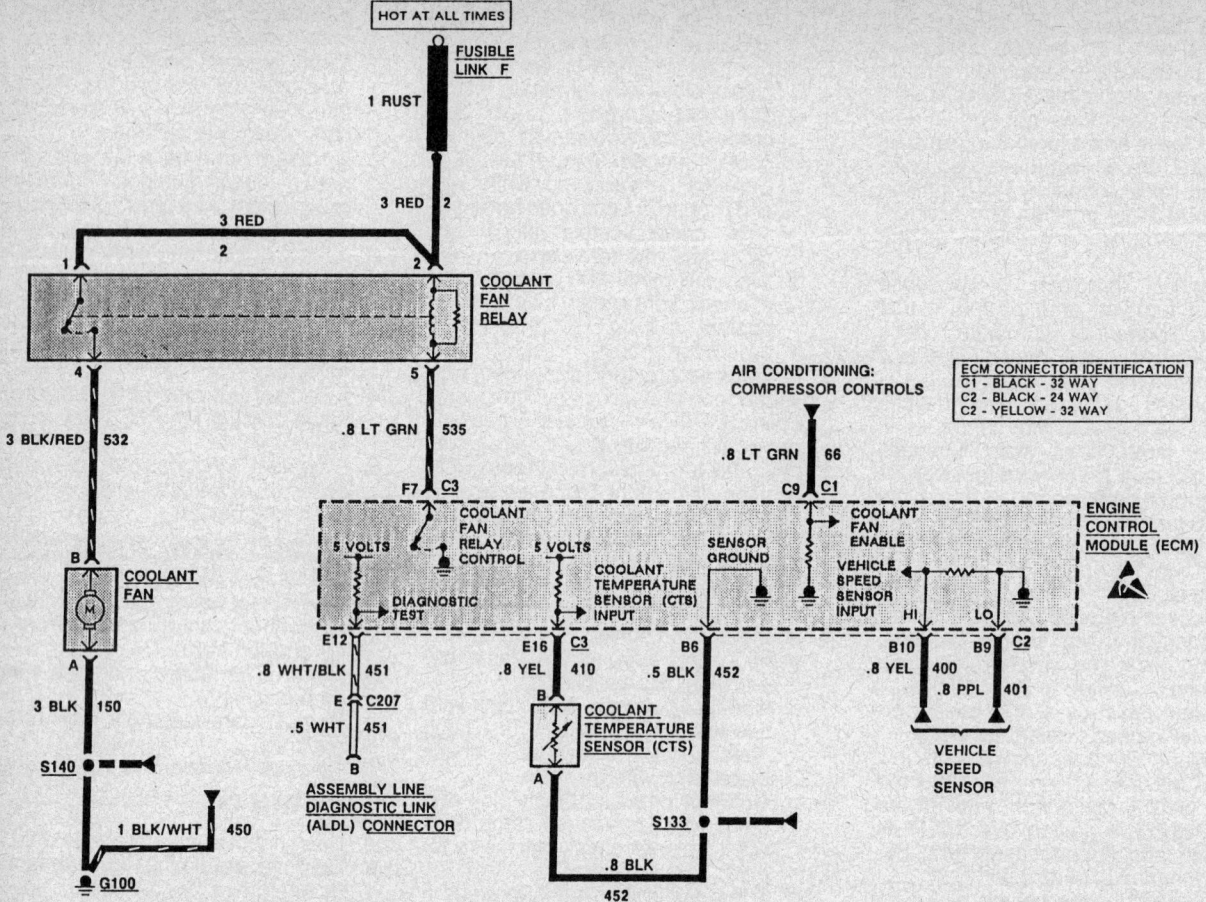

Fig. 80 Coolant fan wiring circuit. 1989–90 Skylark w/2.3L/4-138 engine

and A/C mode selector. The ECM will activate the coolant fan relay when engine temperature is above 227°F, air conditioning is turned on, or the coolant temperature sensor fails. Any of these input signals causes the ECM to ground circuit 335 on 4-151 VIN U engines, circuit 536 on 4-138 VIN D engines and circuit 535 on V6-204 VIN N engines, when vehicle speed is less than 35 mph. When circuits are grounded, the coolant fan relay is energized and its contacts close, turning the coolant fan on.

TROUBLESHOOTING

1. If the coolant fan does not run, check fusible link F.
2. **On 4-151 VIN U and V6-204 VIN N engines,** if coolant fan does not operate, check HTR-A/C fuse.
3. **On 4-151 VIN U and V6-204 VIN N engines,** if coolant fan runs with ignition switch off, replace coolant fan relay.

SYSTEM CHECK

1. With ambient air temperature above 70°F, open all doors, start car and set A/C mode selector on MAX. Coolant fan should turn on.
2. With engine coolant below operating temperature, move A/C mode selector to OFF. Coolant fan should turn off

in a short period of time.
3. Run engine at fast idle for several minutes. Coolant fan should come on before the coolant temperature indicator comes on or the coolant temperature display shows H.

SYSTEM DIAGNOSIS

Refer to **Figs. 80 through 82** when performing diagnostic procedures on these systems.

4-151 VIN U

Coolant Fan Does Not Turn On

1. Turn ignition switch to the RUN position, ground terminal B white wire of the ALDL connector.
2. If coolant fan runs, problem is ECM related.
3. If coolant fan does not run, ground terminal C1/21 dark green/white of the ECM with a fused jumper.
4. If coolant fan runs, problem is ECM related.
5. If coolant fan does not run, leaving terminal C1/21 of the ECM grounded, disconnect coolant fan relay connector. Measure voltage from terminal 5 brown wire of the coolant fan relay connector to ground.
6. If zero voltage is indicated, check brown wire and HTR-A/C fuse for an

open circuit.
7. If battery voltage is indicated, measure voltage between terminals 5 brown wire and 2 dark green/white of the coolant fan relay connector.
8. If zero voltage is indicated, check dark green/white wire for an open circuit.
9. If battery voltage is indicated, measure voltage from terminal 1 red of the coolant fan relay connector to ground.
10. If zero voltage is indicated, check red wire and fusible link F for an open circuit.
11. If battery voltage is indicated, connect a fused jumper with a 20 amp fuse between terminals 1 red wire and 4 black/red wire of the disconnected coolant fan relay connector.
12. If coolant fan runs, replace coolant fan relay.
13. If coolant fan does not run, disconnect connector from coolant fan and measure voltage from terminal B black/red of the coolant fan connector to ground.
14. If zero voltage is indicated, check black/red wire for an open circuit.
15. If battery voltage is indicated, measure voltage between terminals B black/red wire and A black wire of the coolant fan connector.
16. If zero voltage is indicated, check black wire for an open circuit.
17. If battery voltage is indicated, replace coolant fan motor.

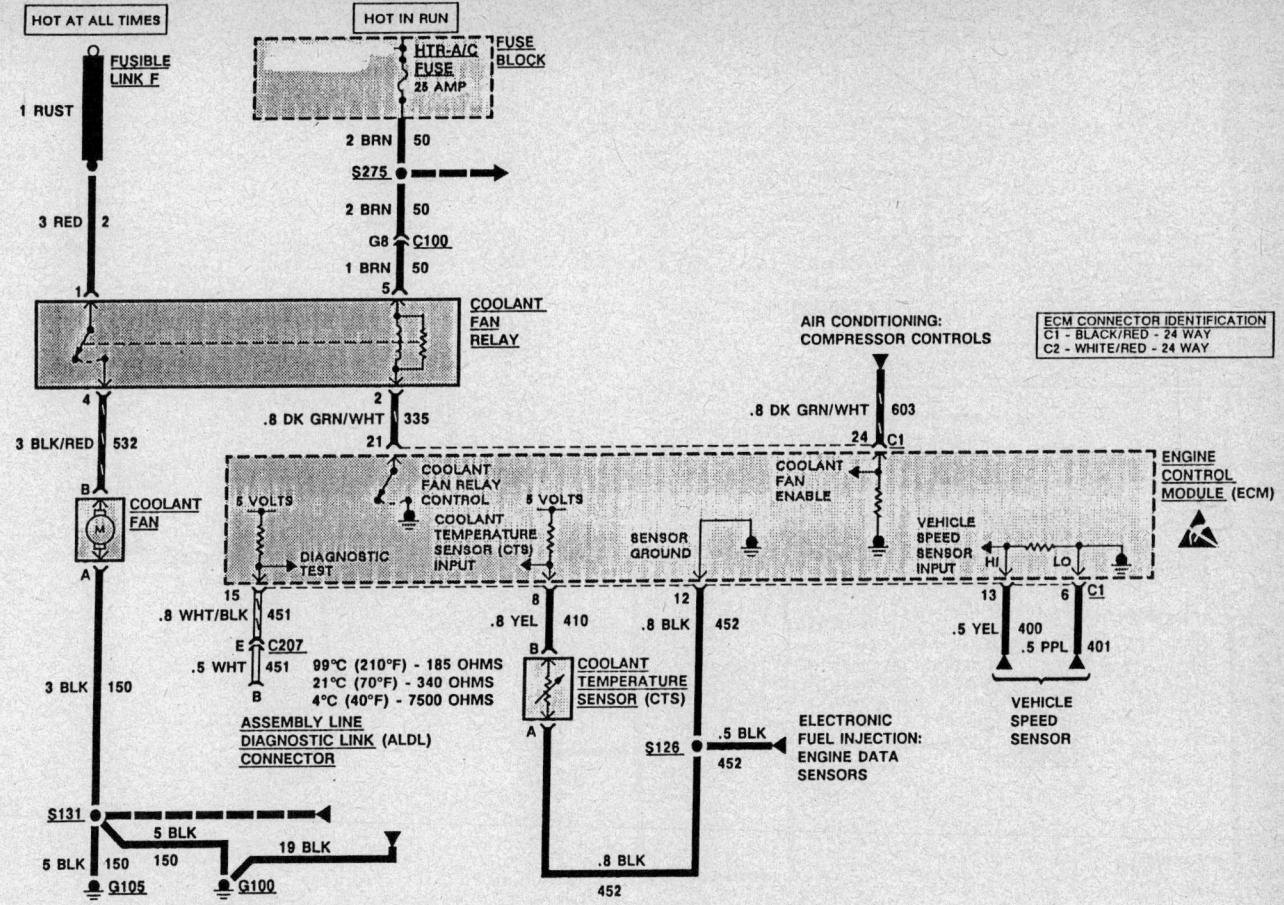

Fig. 81   Coolant fan wiring circuit. 1989–90 Skylark w/2.5L/4-151 engine

Coolant Fan Does Not Turn Off With Engine Coolant Cool, A/C Mode Selector Off & Ignition Switch In Run

1. Turn ignition switch to the RUN position, then disconnect the coolant fan relay connector.
2. Connect a test lamp between terminals 5 brown wire and 2 dark green/white wire of the coolant fan relay connector.
3. If test lamp does not light, replace coolant fan relay.
4. If test lamp lights, check dark green/white wire for an open circuit.
5. If wire is satisfactory, problem is ECM related.

Coolant Fan Does Not Turn On With A/C Mode Selector On & Head pressure Above 150 psi, But Does Run With Engine Hot

1. Turn ignition switch to run, and switch A/C mode selector to MAX position.
2. Measure voltage between terminal C1/24 dark green/white wire of the ECM and ground.
3. If zero voltage is indicated, check dark green/white wire for an open circuit.

4. If battery voltage is indicated, problem is ECM related.

4-138 VIN D
Coolant Fan Does Not Turn On

1. Turn ignition switch to RUN position, ground terminal B white wire of the ALDL connector.
2. If coolant fan runs, problem is ECM related.
3. If coolant fan does not run, ground terminal C3/F7 light green/black wire of the ECM with a fused jumper.
4. If coolant fan runs, problem is ECM related.
5. If coolant fan does not run, leaving terminal C3/F7 grounded, disconnect coolant fan relay connector.
6. Measure voltage from terminal 2 red wire of the coolant fan relay connector and ground.
7. If zero voltage is indicated, check red wire and fusible link F for an open circuit.
8. If battery voltage is indicated, measure voltage between terminals 2 red wire and 5 light green/black wire of the coolant fan relay connector.
9. If zero voltage is indicated, check light green/black wire for an open circuit.
10. If battery voltage is indicated, mea-

sure voltage from terminal 1 red wire of the coolant fan relay connector to ground.
11. If zero voltage is indicated, check red wire and fusible link F for an open circuit.
12. If battery voltage is indicated, connect a fused jumper with a 20 amp fuse between terminals 1 red wire and 4 black/red wire of the coolant fan relay connector.
13. If coolant fan runs, replace coolant fan relay.
14. If coolant fan does not run, leave fused jumper connected at coolant fan relay connector.
15. Disconnect connector from the coolant fan, measure voltage from terminal B black/red wire of the coolant fan connector and ground.
16. If zero voltage is indicated, check black/red wire for an open circuit.
17. If battery voltage is indicated, leave fused jumper connected at the coolant fan relay connector.
18. Measure voltage between terminals B black/red wire and A black wire of the coolant fan connector.
19. If zero voltage is indicated, check black wire for an open circuit.
20. If battery voltage is indicated, replace coolant fan motor.

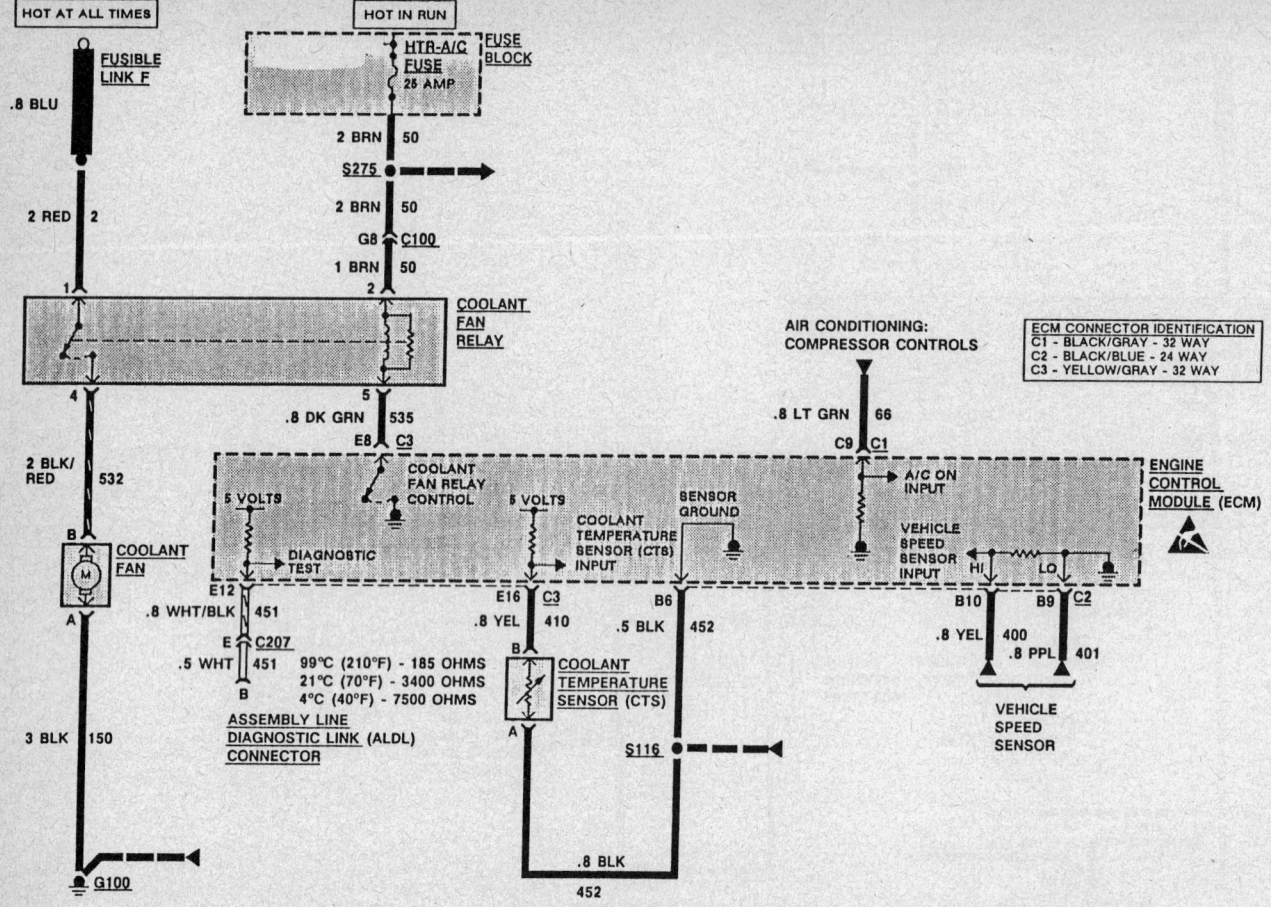

Fig. 82 Coolant fan wiring circuit. 1989–90 Skylark w/3.3L/V6-204 engine

Coolant Fan Does Not Turn Off With Engine Coolant Cool & A/C Mode Selector Off

1. Disconnect coolant relay connector, then connect a test lamp between terminals 2 red wire and 5 light green/black wire of the coolant fan relay connector.
2. If test lamp does not light, replace coolant fan relay.
3. If test lamp lights, check light green/black wire for a short to ground.
4. If wire is satisfactory, problem is ECM related.

Coolant Fan Does Not Turn On With A/C Mode Selector On & Head pressure Above 150 psi, But Does Run With Engine Hot

1. Turn ignition switch to the RUN position, switch A/C mode selector to MAX.
2. Measure voltage between terminal C1/C9 light green wire of the ECM and ground.
3. If zero voltage is indicated, check light green wire for an open circuit.
4. If battery voltage is indicated, problem is ECM related.

V6-204 VIN N

A/C Coolant Fan Does Not Turn

1. Turn ignition switch to the RUN position, then ground terminal B white wire of the ALDL connector.
2. If coolant fan runs, problem is ECM related.
3. If coolant fan does not run, ground terminal C3/E8 dark green wire of the ECM with a fused jumper.
4. If coolant fan runs, problem is ECM related.
5. If coolant fan does not run, with terminal C3/E8 dark green wire of the ECM grounded disconnect coolant fan relay connector.
6. Measure voltage from terminal 2 brown wire of the coolant fan relay to ground.
7. If zero voltage is indicated, check brown wire and HTR-A/C fuse for an open circuit.
8. If battery voltage is indicated, with ECM still grounded, measure voltage between terminals 2 brown wire and 5 dark green wire of the coolant fan relay connector.
9. If zero voltage is indicated, check dark green wire for an open circuit.

10. If battery voltage is indicated, measure voltage from terminal 1 red wire of the coolant fan relay connector to ground.
11. If zero voltage is indicated, check red wire for an open circuit.
12. If battery voltage is indicated, connect a fused jumper with a 20 amp fuse between terminals 1 red wire and 4 black/red wire of the coolant fan relay connector.
13. If coolant fan runs, replace coolant fan relay.
14. If coolant fan does not run, with fused jumper still connected at coolant fan relay connector, measure voltage between terminals B black/red wire and A black wire of the coolant fan connector.
15. If zero voltage is indicated, check black wire for an open circuit.
16. If battery voltage is indicated, replace coolant fan motor.

Coolant Fan Does Not Turn Off With Engine Coolant Cool, A/C Mode Selector Off & Ignition Switch In Run

1. Turn ignition switch to the RUN position, then disconnect coolant fan relay connector.
2. Connect a test lamp between terminals 2 brown wire and 5 dark green wire of the coolant fan relay connector.

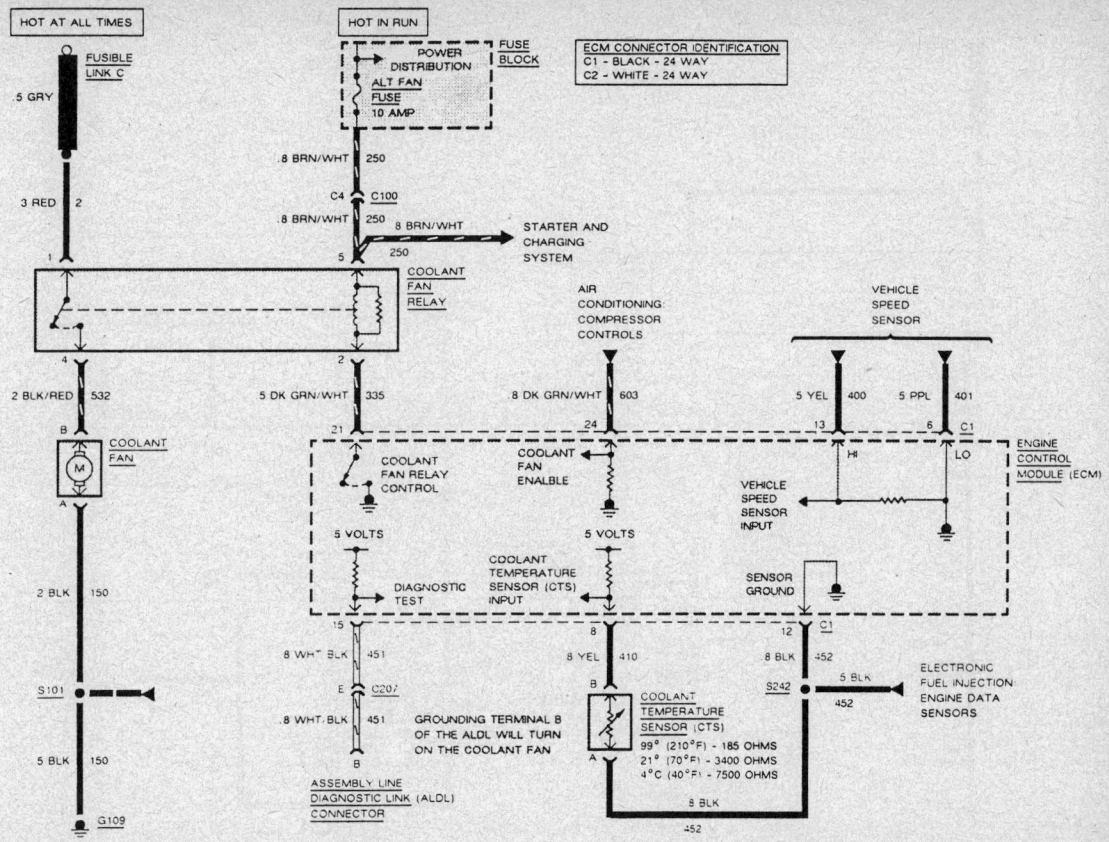

Fig. 83 Coolant fan wiring circuit. Sunbird, 2.0L/4-122 engine, VIN K

3. If test lamp does not light, replace coolant fan relay.
4. If test lamp lights, check dark green wire for a short to ground.
5. If wire is satisfactory, problem is ECM related.

Coolant Fan Does Not Turn On With A/C Mode Selector On & Head pressure Above 150 psi, But Does Run With Engine Hot

1. Turn ignition switch to the RUN position and switch A/C mode selector to the MAX position.
2. Measure voltage between terminal C1/C9 light green of the ECM and ground.
3. If zero battery voltage is indicated, check light green wire for an open circuit.
4. If battery voltage is indicated, problem is ECM related.

SUNBIRD
SYSTEM DESCRIPTION

The coolant fan is controlled by the coolant fan relay. The coolant fan relay is electrically operated by the ECM. The ECM receives input signal from the coolant temperature sensor and the A/C mode selector. The ECM activates the coolant fan relay when engine coolant, which is sensed by the coolant temperature sensor, is above 227°F, when A/C is turned on and

when coolant temperature sensor fails. Any of these input signals causes the ECM to ground circuit 335. With circuit 335 grounded, the coolant fan relay is energized and its contacts close. The battery runs with battery voltage across its terminals.

TROUBLESHOOTING
4-121 VIN K

1. If coolant fan does not operate, check C-H fuse.
2. If coolant fan runs with ignition switch off, replace coolant fan relay.

4-121 VIN M

1. If coolant fan does not operate, check fusible link C.
2. If coolant fan runs with engine on but does not run with ignition switch off and engine coolant hot, problem is ECM related.

SYSTEM CHECK

1. With engine cold and idling, move A/C mode selector, if equipped, to NORM. Coolant fan should turn on.
2. With engine coolant below operating temperature, move A/C mode selector to OFF. Coolant fan should turn off.
3. With engine warm, run engine at a fast idle for several minutes. Coolant fan should turn on.
4. Turn ignition switch off. On VIN K, coolant fan should turn off. On VIN M, coolant fan should run until engine coolant temperature lowers.

DIAGNOSIS

Refer to **Figs. 83 and 84** when performing diagnostic procedures on these systems.

Coolant Fan Does Not Run

1. Connect fused jumper between ALDL connector B and ground and turn ignition switch to RUN position. If coolant fan runs, problem is ECM related.
2. If coolant fan does not run, connect fused jumper between ECM connector C1 (VIN K) or C3 (VIN M) dark green/white wire and ground and turn ignition switch to RUN position. If coolant fan runs, problem is ECM related.
3. If coolant fan does not run, leave fused jumper connected as in step 2, disconnect coolant fan relay connector, turn ignition switch to RUN position and connect test lamp between terminals as follows:
   a. Connect between terminal 1 and ground. If lamp does not illuminate, check red wire and fusible link C for open.
   b. Connect between terminal 5 and ground. If lamp does not illuminate, check brown wire (VIN K) or red (2) wire (VIN M) for open.
   c. Connect between terminals 5 and 2. If lamp does not illuminate, check dark green/white wire for open.

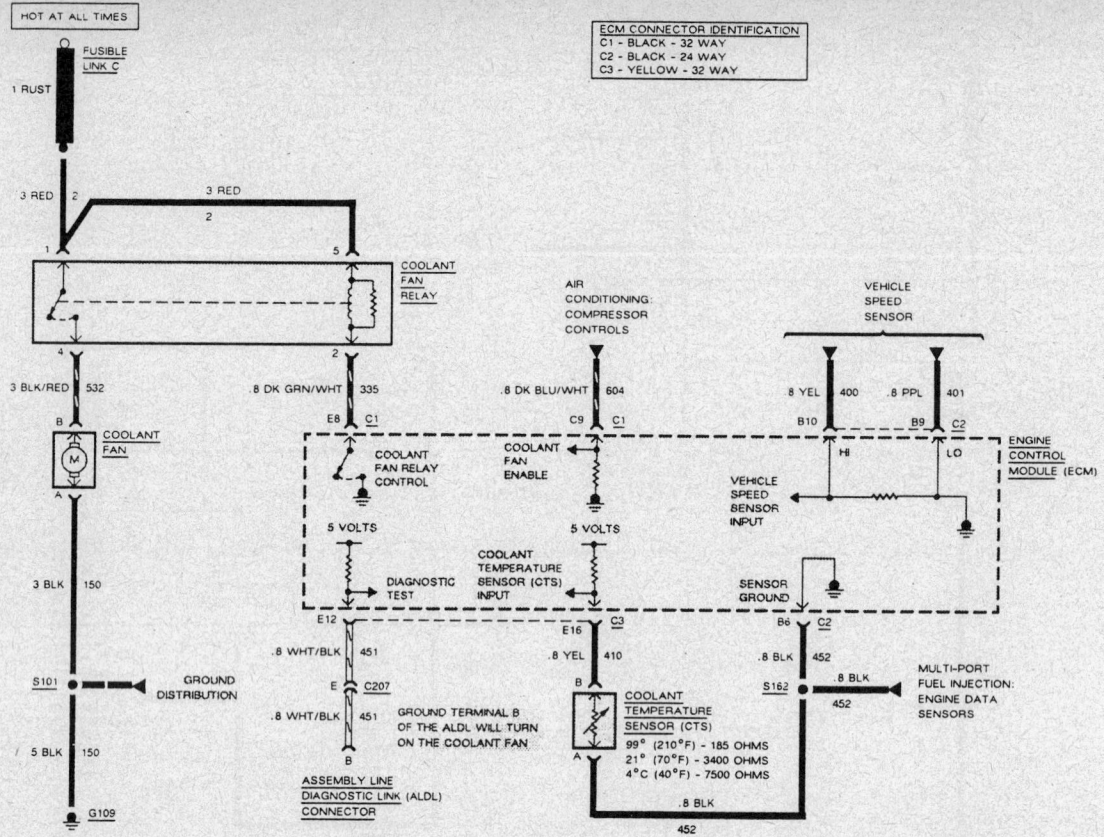

Fig. 84   Coolant fan wiring circuit. Sunbird, 2.0L/4-122 engine, VIN M

4. If lamp illuminates in steps a, b and c, disconnect coolant fan relay connector and connect fused jumper between terminals 1 and 4. If coolant fan runs, replace coolant fan relay.

5. If coolant fan does not run, connect fused jumper between terminals 1 and 4 of coolant fan relay, disconnect coolant fan connector and connect test lamp between terminals as follows:
   a. Connect between terminal B and ground. If lamp does not illuminate, check black/red wire for open.
   b. Connect between terminals B and A. If lamp does not illuminate, check black wire for open.
   c. If test lamp illuminates in steps a and b, replace coolant fan.

Coolant Fan Runs Continuously

1. Place ignition switch in RUN position, disconnect coolant fan relay connector and connect test lamp between terminals 5 and 2.

2. If test lamp does not illuminate, replace coolant fan relay.

3. If lamp illuminates, check dark green/white wire for short to ground. If wire is satisfactory, problem is ECM related.

COOLANT FAN, REPLACE

1. Disconnect battery ground cable.
2. Remove air cleaner to throttle body duct.

3. Remove electrical connector from coolant fan.

4. Lift fan assembly out of two lower insulators, rotate bracket so two lower bracket legs point upward, move fan assembly toward driver's side until fan blade overlaps radiator tank to core seam by approximately one inch and remove fan assembly upward. **Because of minimum clearance, care must be taken not to damage lock tang on throttle position sensor with the fan bracket.**

5. Reverse procedure to install.

1988 ELECTRA, PARK AVENUE & LESABRE

SYSTEM DESCRIPTION

A two speed coolant fan is turned on and off by the low and high speed coolant fan relays.

For low speed operation, the low speed coolant fan relay coil is grounded through the ECM or the low speed contacts of the A/C dual pressure switch. The ECM grounds the coil when vehicle speed is less than 35 mph and the engine coolant is warmed up. The A/C dual pressure switch low speed contacts close with high refrigerant pressure above 260 psi.

With the low speed relay coil grounded, its contacts close. Voltage is applied through the coolant fan resistor to the coolant fan. The resistor reduces battery voltage supplied to the fan so that the fan

runs at a low speed.

For high speed operation, the high speed coolant fan relay coil is grounded through the high speed contacts in the A/C dual pressure switch or by the temperature switch. The pressure switch high speed contacts close at a refrigerant pressure above 300 psi. The temperature switch closes when coolant temperature rises above 230°F.

With the high speed relay coil grounded, its contacts close. Battery voltage is applied to the coolant fan. The fan runs at high speed.

The heavy duty coolant fan is turned on and off by the heavy duty coolant fan relay. The heavy duty coolant fan relay is grounded through the high speed contacts in the A/C dual pressure switch or by the temperature switch. With the heavy duty relay coil grounded, its contacts close. Battery voltage is applied to the heavy duty coolant fan. The fan runs at high speed.

TROUBLESHOOTING

1. Check fuse 6.
2. Check that the terminals on the negative junction block are clean and tight.

SYSTEM CHECK

1. With engine cold and idling, move A/C function selector to NORM. Coolant fan should turn on.
2. Move A/C function selector to off. Coolant fan should turn off.
3. With engine warmed up, run it at fast

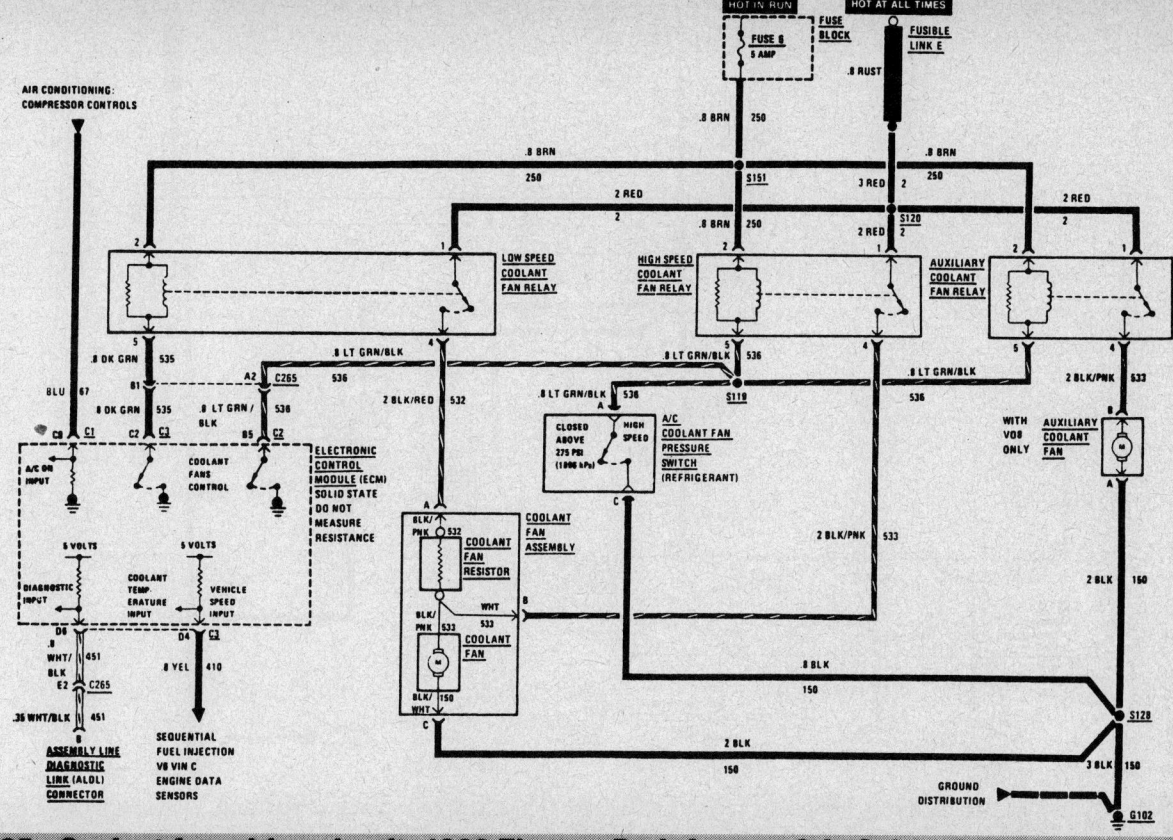

Fig. 85 Coolant fan wiring circuit. 1988 Electra, Park Avenue & LeSabre, 3.8L/V6-231 engine, VIN C

idle for several minutes. Coolant fan should turn on before coolant temperature indicator comes on, or before coolant temperature gage needle reaches H.

DIAGNOSIS

Refer to Fig. 85 through 87 when performing diagnostic procedures on this system.

Coolant Fan Does Not Run At Low Speed

1. Connect fused jumper between ALDL connector black wire terminal and ground and turn ignition switch to RUN position. If coolant fan runs, problem is ECM related.
2. If coolant fan does not run, turn ignition switch to RUN position and connect a fused jumper between dark green wire on 32 pin ECM connector and ground, or between dark green wire of A/C dual pressure switch and ground. If coolant fan runs, replace suspect switch.
3. If coolant fan does not run, leave fused jumper connected as in step 2, disconnect low speed coolant fan relay connector, turn ignition switch to RUN position and connect test lamp between terminals as follows:
   a. Connect between brown wire terminal and ground. If lamp does not illuminate, check brown wire for open.
   b. Connect between brown and dark green wire terminals. If lamp does not illuminate, check dark green

wire and diode for an open.
   c. Connect between red wire terminal and ground. If lamp does not illuminate, check fusible link D and red wire for open.
4. If lamp illuminates in steps a, b and c, disconnect low speed coolant fan relay connector and connect fused jumper between red and black/red wire terminals. If coolant fan runs, replace coolant fan relay.
5. If coolant fan does not run, leave fused jumper connected as in step 2, connect coolant fan relay connector, disconnect coolant fan assembly connector, turn ignition switch to RUN position and connect test lamp between terminals as follows:
   a. Connect between black/red wire terminal and ground. If lamp does not illuminate, check black/red wire and coolant fan resistor for open.
   b. Connect between black/red and black wire terminals. If lamp does not illuminate, check black wire for open.
   c. If lamp illuminates in steps a and b, replace coolant fan.

Coolant Fan Does Not Run At High Speed

1. Connect a fused jumper between light green/black wire of A/C switch and ground, or between light green/black wire of temperature switch and ground, and turn ignition switch to RUN position. If coolant fan runs at

high speed and heavy duty fan runs, replace suspect switch.
2. If coolant fan does not run at high speed and/or heavy duty fan does not run, connect fused jumper between light green/black wire of coolant fan temperature switch and ground, disconnect high speed coolant fan relay connector, turn ignition switch to RUN position and connect test lamp between terminals as follows:
   a. Connect between brown wire terminal and ground. If lamp does not illuminate, check fuse 6 and brown wire for open.
   b. Connect between brown and light green/black wire terminals. If lamp does not illuminate, check light green/black wire for open.
   c. Connect between red wire terminal and ground. If lamp does not illuminate, check fusible link D and red wire for open.
3. If lamp illuminates in steps a, b and c, disconnect high speed coolant fan relay connector, turn ignition switch to RUN position and connect fused jumper between red and white wire terminals. If coolant fan runs at high speed, replace fan relay.
4. If coolant fan does not run at high speed, leave fused jumper connected as in step 3, connect high speed coolant fan relay connector, disconnect coolant fan connector, turn ignition switch to RUN position and connect test lamp between terminals as follows:

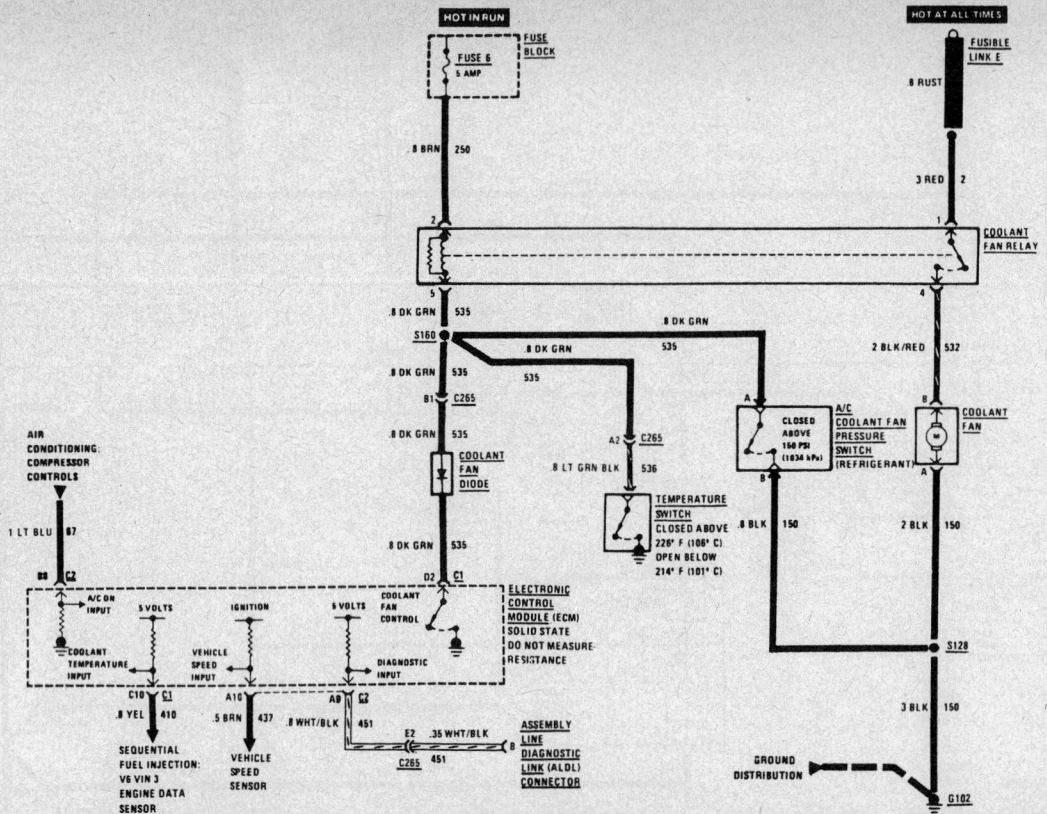

Fig. 86 Coolant fan wiring circuit. 1989 LeSabre (less heavy duty cooling), 3.8L/V6-231 engine, VIN 3

a. Connect between white wire terminal and ground. If lamp does not illuminate, check white wire and coolant fan resistor for open.
b. Connect between white and black wire terminals. If lamp does not illuminate, check black wire for open.
c. If lamp illuminates in steps a and b, replace high speed coolant fan.

Coolant Fan Does Not Turn Off

1. With ignition switch in RUN position, disconnect ECM 32 pin connector. If fan turns off, problem is ECM related.
2. If fan does not turn off, disconnect temperature switch. If fan stops, replace coolant fan temperature switch.
3. If fan does not stop, disconnect A/C dual pressure switch, if equipped. If fan stops, replace A/C dual pressure switch.
4. If fan does not stop, turn ignition switch off and disconnect high speed coolant fan relay, if equipped. If fan stops, replace high speed coolant fan relay.
5. If fan does not stop, replace low speed coolant fan relay.

Heavy Duty Coolant Fan Does Not Operate

1. Connect fused jumper between light green/black wire at coolant fan temperature switch and ground, disconnect heavy duty coolant fan relay connector, turn ignition switch to RUN position and connect test lamp between terminals as follows:

a. Connect between brown wire terminal and ground. If lamp does not illuminate, check fuse 6 and brown wire for open.
b. Connect between brown and light green/black wire terminals. If lamp does not illuminate, check light green/black wire for open.
c. Connect between red wire terminal and ground. If lamp does not illuminate, check fusible link D and red wire for open.

2. If lamp illuminates in steps a, b and c, disconnect heavy duty coolant fan relay connector, turn ignition switch to RUN position and connect a fused jumper between red and white wire terminals. If heavy duty coolant fan runs, replace heavy duty fan relay.

3. If heavy duty coolant fan does not run, leave fused jumper connected as in step 2, disconnect heavy duty coolant fan connector, turn ignition switch to RUN position and connect test lamp between terminals as follows:

a. Connect between white wire terminal and ground. If lamp does not illuminate, check white wire for open.
b. Connect between white and black wire terminals. If lamp does not illuminate, check black wire for open.
c. If lamp illuminates in steps a and b, replace heavy duty coolant fan.

Heavy Duty Coolant Fan Does Not Turn Off

1. Turn ignition switch to OFF position.

2. If fan does not stop, replace heavy duty coolant fan relay.

COOLANT FAN REPLACE

1. Disconnect battery ground cable.
2. Disconnect electrical connector from fan motor and frame.
3. Remove frame to radiator support attaching bolts.
4. Remove fan assembly.
5. Reverse procedure to install.

1989–90 ELECTRA, PARK AVENUE & LESABRE

SYSTEM DESCRIPTION

A two speed coolant fan is turned on and off by the low and high speed coolant fan relays.

For low speed operation, the low speed coolant fan relay coil is grounded through the ECM or the low speed contacts of the A/C dual pressure switch. The ECM grounds the coil when vehicle speed is less than 35 mph and the engine coolant is warmed up. The A/C dual pressure switch low speed contacts close with high refrigerant pressure above 260 psi.

With the low speed relay coil grounded, its contacts close. Voltage is applied through the coolant fan resistor to the coolant fan. The resistor reduces battery voltage supplied to the fan so that the fan runs at a low speed.

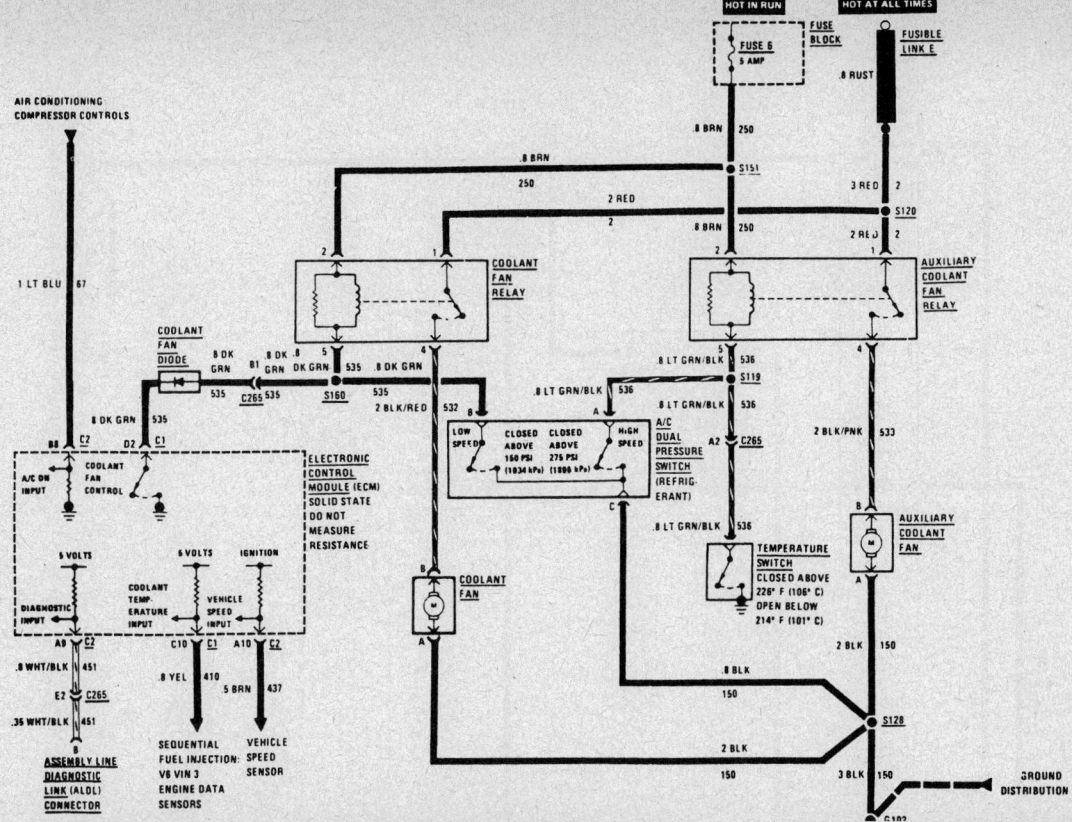

Fig. 87 Coolant fan wiring circuit. 1989 LeSabre (with heavy duty cooling), 3.8L/V6-231 engine, VIN 3

For high speed operation, the high speed coolant fan relay coil is grounded through the high speed contacts in the A/C dual pressure switch or by the temperature switch. The pressure switch high speed contacts close at a refrigerant pressure above 300 psi. The temperature switch closes when coolant temperature rises above 230°F.

With the high speed relay coil grounded, its contacts close. Battery voltage is applied to the coolant fan. The fan runs at high speed.

The heavy duty coolant fan is turned on and off by the heavy duty coolant fan relay. The heavy duty coolant fan relay is grounded through the high speed contacts in the A/C dual pressure switch or by the temperature switch. With the heavy duty relay coil grounded, its contacts close. Battery voltage is applied to the heavy duty coolant fan. The fan runs at high speed.

TROUBLESHOOTING

1. Check fuse 6.
2. Check fusible link D 3.

SYSTEM CHECK

1. With engine cold and idling, move A/C function selector to NORM. Coolant fan should turn on.
2. Move A/C function selector to off. Coolant fan should turn off.
3. With engine warmed up, run it at fast idle for several minutes. Coolant fan should turn on before coolant temperature indicator comes on, or before coolant temperature gage needle reaches H.

DIAGNOSIS

Refer to **Figs. 88 through 97** when performing diagnostic procedures on this system.

COOLANT FAN REPLACE

1. Disconnect battery ground cable.
2. Disconnect electrical connector from fan motor and frame.
3. Remove frame to radiator support attaching bolts.
4. Remove fan assembly.
5. Reverse procedure to install.

1988 CENTURY

DESCRIPTION

The coolant fan is electrically operated. It is turned on when engine coolant becomes hot enough to require cooling.

In the 4-151 VIN R and the V6-173 VIN W, the coolant fan is turned on or off by the ECM and the A/C selector switch, or the ECM and the A/C low pressure cut-off switch. Either of these switch combinations will complete the circuit and ground the coil of the coolant fan relay. It is energized, its contacts close and battery voltage is applied to the coolant fan.

In the V6-231 VIN 3, two types of coolant fans are used. The fans are turned on and off by either the coolant fan relay, the coolant fan delay relay, or the pusher fan relay.

For single speed operation without A/C, the coolant fan relay is controlled by the coolant fan switch or the ECM. For single speed operation with A/C, the coolant fan relay is controlled by the coolant fan switch, the A/C pressure switch and the ECM. When one of these components grounds the coil of the coolant fan relay, the contacts close and battery voltage is applied to the coolant fan.

The heavy duty cooling system for the V6-231 VIN 3 consists of two coolant fans. The coolant fan is controlled by the coolant fan relay. This relay is controlled by the ECM, the Lo speed contact of the A/C pressure switch and the coolant fan switch. The high speed coolant fan is controlled by the pusher fan relay. This relay is controlled by the coolant fan switch and the Hi speed contact of the A/C pressure switch. When any one of these components grounds the coil of one of the relays, the particular fan runs.

The coolant fan delay relay operates the coolant fan for a short period of time after the engine is turned off. A solid state timer relay removes the path to ground for the coolant fan delay relay coil to turn off the coolant fan.

TROUBLESHOOTING
4-151 VIN R

1. If coolant fan does not operate, check C-H fuse.
2. If coolant fan runs with ignition switch off, replace coolant fan relay.

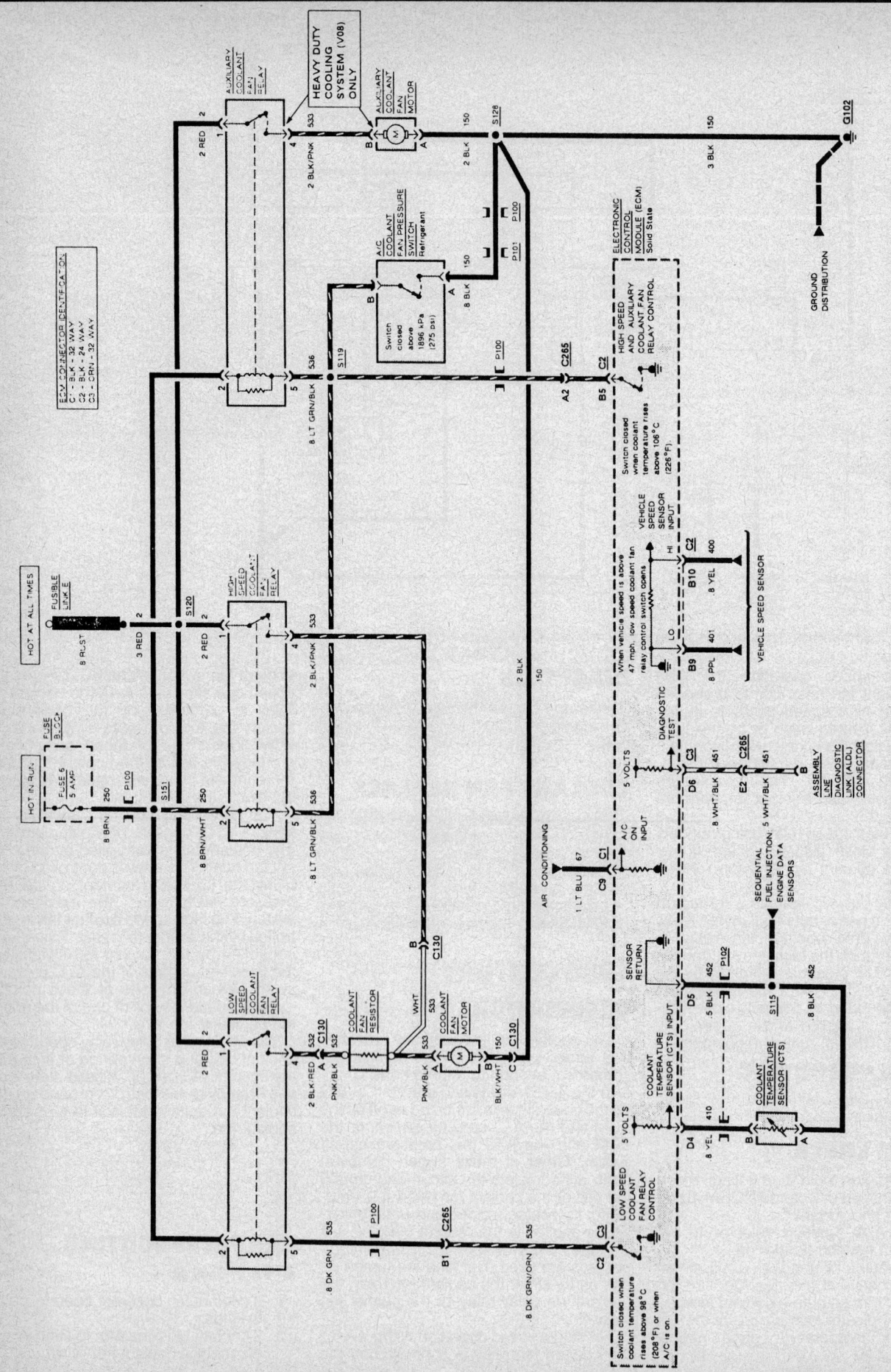

Fig. 88 Coolant fan wiring circuit. 1989 Electra & Park Avenue, 3.8L/V6-231 engine, VIN C

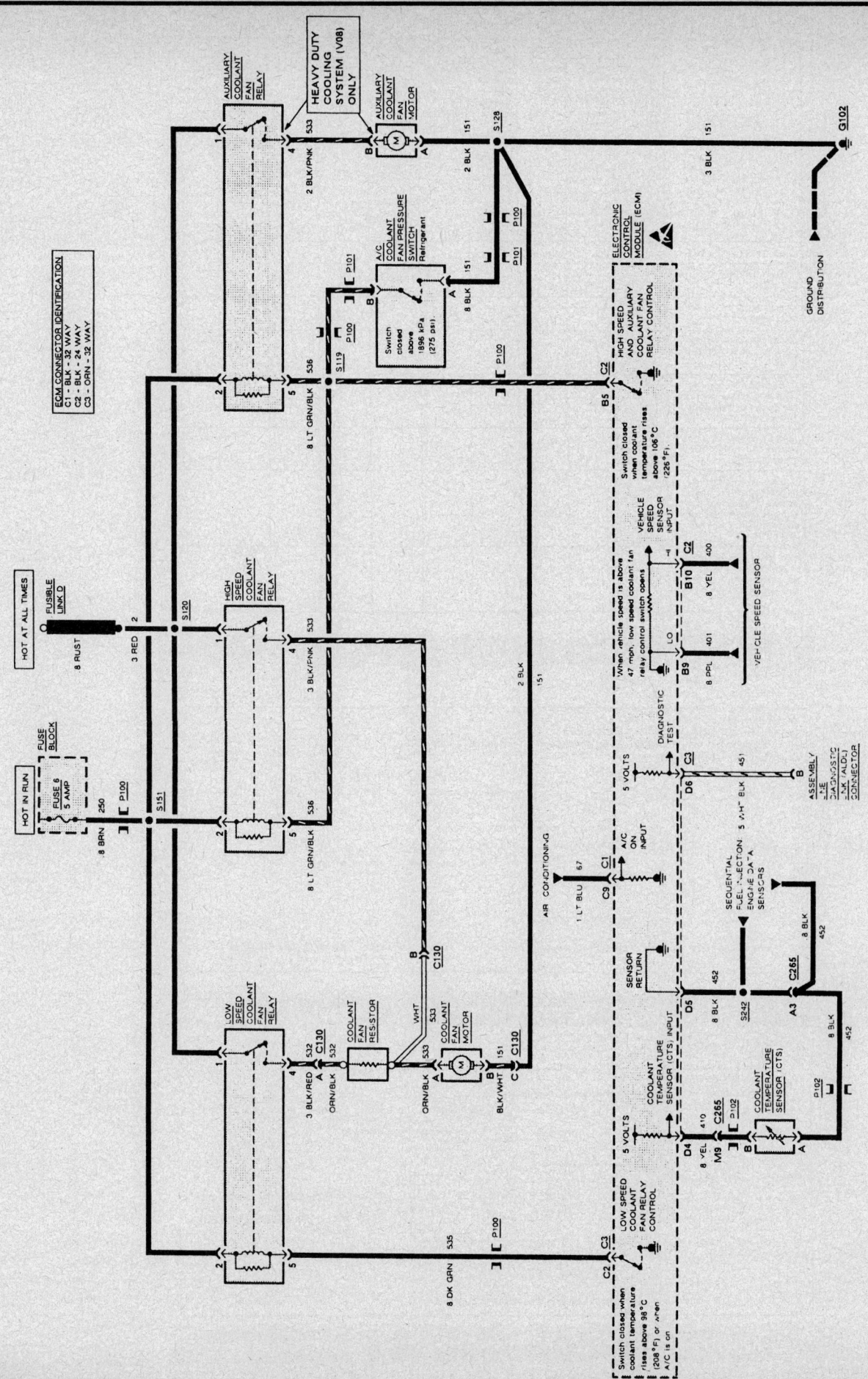

Fig. 89 Coolant fan wiring circuit. 1990 Electra, Park Avenue & LeSabre, 3.8L/V6-231 engine, VIN C

SYMPTOM	Check 67 wire for an open, see Air Conditioning. If OK, ECM diagnosis.	Check Fuse 6 by visual inspection.	Check Fusible Link D.	Do Coolant Fan Input Test A.	Do High Speed Coolant Fan Input Test B.	Do Low Speed Coolant Fan Input Test C.	Do Auxiliary Coolant Fan Input Test D.	Do Test E.	Do A/C Pressure Signal Test F.	Do Relay Ground Short Test G.
Coolant fan does not run.		• Do 1st	• Do 2nd	• Do 3rd						
Coolant fan does not run at low speed.						•				
Coolant fan does not run at high speed.					•					
Coolant fan does not run at low speed after selecting A/C.	•									
Coolant fan runs continuously in low speed with ignition switch at RUN, engine coolant cool, and A/C off.								•		
Auxiliary coolant fan does not run, but coolant fan operates normally.							•			
Coolant fan runs continuously in high speed and/or auxiliary coolant fan runs with ignition switch at RUN, engine coolant cool, and A/C off.										•
High speed coolant fan and/or auxiliary coolant fan do not operate with A/C pressure above 1896 kPa (275 psi).									•	

Fig. 90   System diagnosis guide. 1989–90 Electra & Park Avenue, 3.8L/V6-231 engine, VIN C

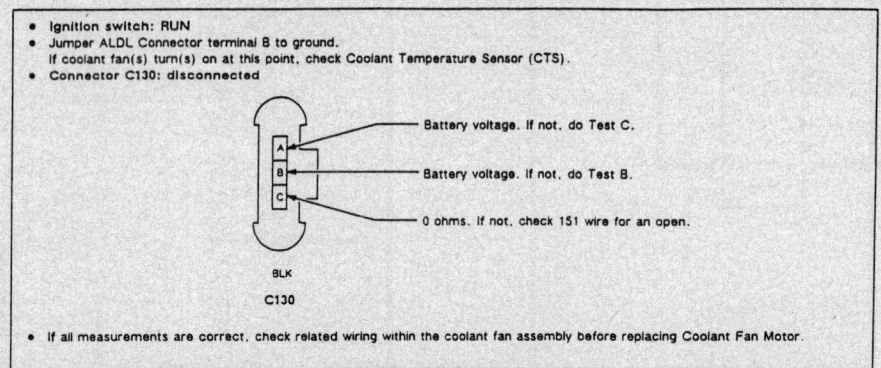

Fig. 91   Coolant fan test A. 1989–90 Electra & Park Avenue, 3.8L/V6-231 engine, VIN C

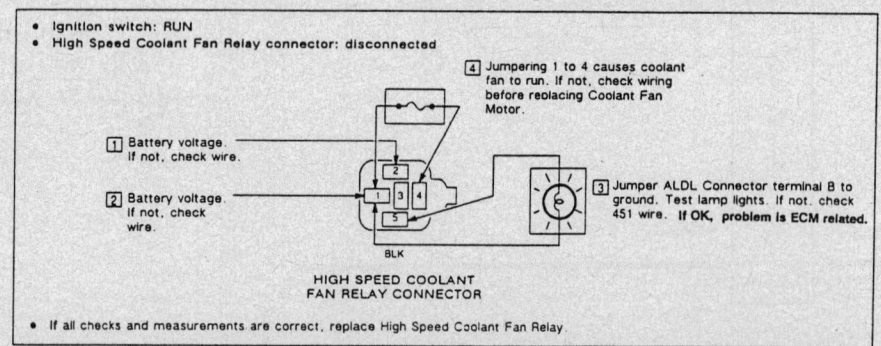

Fig. 92   Coolant fan test B. 1989–90 Electra & Park Avenue, 3.8L/V6-231 engine, VIN C

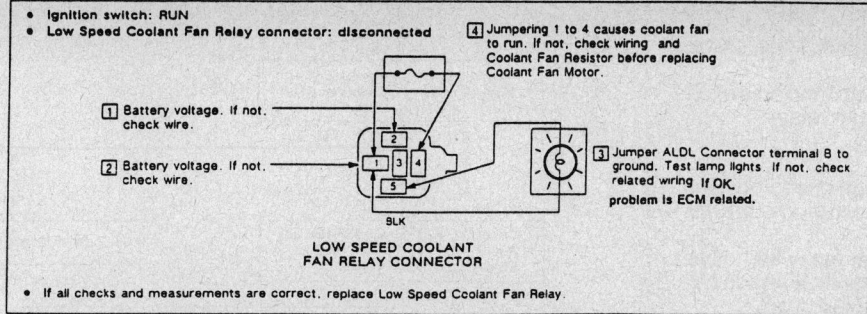

- Ignition switch: RUN
- Low Speed Coolant Fan Relay connector: disconnected

[4] Jumpering 1 to 4 causes coolant fan to run. If not, check wiring and Coolant Fan Resistor before replacing Coolant Fan Motor.

[1] Battery voltage. If not, check wire.

[2] Battery voltage. If not, check wire.

[3] Jumper ALDL Connector terminal B to ground. Test lamp lights. If not, check related wiring. If OK, problem is ECM related.

BLK

LOW SPEED COOLANT
FAN RELAY CONNECTOR

- If all checks and measurements are correct, replace Low Speed Coolant Fan Relay.

Fig. 93   Coolant fan test C. 1989–90 Electra & Park Avenue, 3.8L/V6-231 engine, VIN C

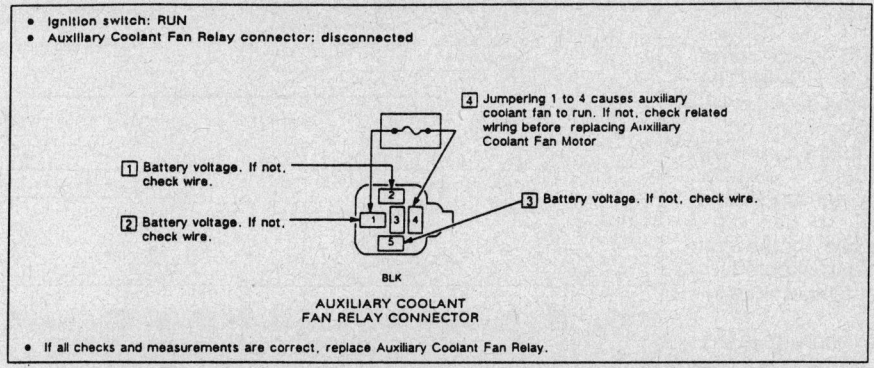

- Ignition switch: RUN
- Auxiliary Coolant Fan Relay connector: disconnected

[4] Jumpering 1 to 4 causes auxiliary coolant fan to run. If not, check related wiring before replacing Auxiliary Coolant Fan Motor

[1] Battery voltage. If not, check wire.

[2] Battery voltage. If not, check wire.

[3] Battery voltage. If not, check wire.

BLK

AUXILIARY COOLANT
FAN RELAY CONNECTOR

- If all checks and measurements are correct, replace Auxiliary Coolant Fan Relay.

Fig. 94   Coolant fan test D. 1989–90 Electra & Park Avenue, 3.8L/V6-231 engine, VIN C

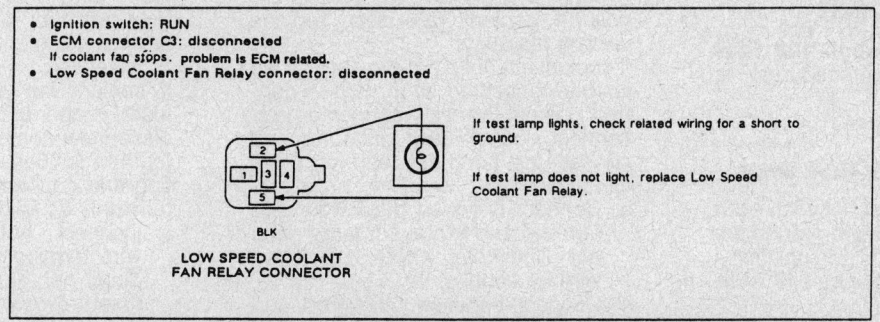

- Ignition switch: RUN
- ECM connector C3: disconnected
  If coolant fan stops, problem is ECM related.
- Low Speed Coolant Fan Relay connector: disconnected

If test lamp lights, check related wiring for a short to ground.

If test lamp does not light, replace Low Speed Coolant Fan Relay.

BLK

LOW SPEED COOLANT
FAN RELAY CONNECTOR

Fig. 95   Coolant fan test E. 1989–90 Electra & Park Avenue, 3.8L/V6-231 engine, VIN C

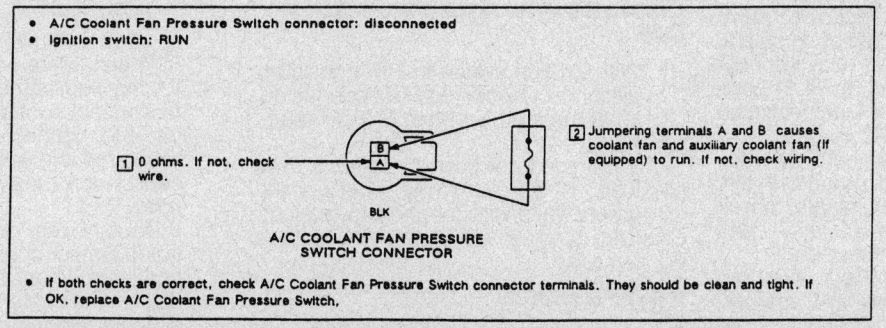

- A/C Coolant Fan Pressure Switch connector: disconnected
- Ignition switch: RUN

[1] 0 ohms. If not, check wire.

[2] Jumpering terminals A and B causes coolant fan and auxiliary coolant fan (if equipped) to run. If not, check wiring.

BLK

A/C COOLANT FAN PRESSURE
SWITCH CONNECTOR

- If both checks are correct, check A/C Coolant Fan Pressure Switch connector terminals. They should be clean and tight. If OK, replace A/C Coolant Fan Pressure Switch.

Fig. 96   Coolant fan test F. 1989–90 Electra & Park Avenue, 3.8L/V6-231 engine, VIN C

V6-173 VIN W

1. If coolant fan does not operate, check F/P fuse.
2. If coolant fan runs with ignition switch off, replace coolant fan relay.

V6-231 VIN 3

1. If coolant fan and high speed coolant fan, if equipped, do not run, check FAN fuse.
2. If high speed coolant fan, with heavy duty only, runs with ignition switch off, replace pusher fan relay.
3. If coolant fan does not run for a short period after engine is off and the engine coolant is hot, check the ECM/ERLS fuse.

SYSTEM CHECK

1. With engine cold and idling, move A/C selector switch to NORM. The coolant fan, and the high speed coolant fan if equipped, should turn on.
2. With engine coolant below operating temperature, move the A/C selector switch to off. The coolant fan should turn off.
3. Run engine at fast idle for several minutes. The coolant fan should turn on before the coolant temperature indicator comes on.
4. Run engine for a few more minutes, then turn engine off. Except on V6-231 VIN 3, the coolant fan should turn off. On V6-231 VIN 3, the coolant fan, and high speed coolant fan if equipped, should continue to run until coolant temperature lowers.

SYSTEM DIAGNOSIS

Refer to **Figs. 98 through 102** when performing diagnostic procedures on these systems.

4-151 VIN R

Coolant Fan Does Not Run

1. Connect fused jumper between ALDL connector terminal B and ground and turn ignition switch to RUN position. If coolant fan runs, problem is ECM related.
2. If coolant fan does not run, turn ignition switch to RUN position and connect a fused jumper between dark green/white wire of ECM black/red connector and ground. If coolant fan runs, problem is ECM related.
3. If coolant fan does not run, leave fused jumper connected as in step 2, disconnect coolant fan relay connector, turn ignition switch to RUN position and connect test lamp between terminals as follows:
   a. Connect between brown/white wire terminal and ground. If test lamp does not illuminate, check C-H fuse, brown wire and brown/white wire for open.
   b. Connect between red wire and ground. If lamp does not illuminate, check fusible link D and and red wire for open.
   c. Connect between red and dark green/white wire terminals. If lamp does not illuminate, check dark

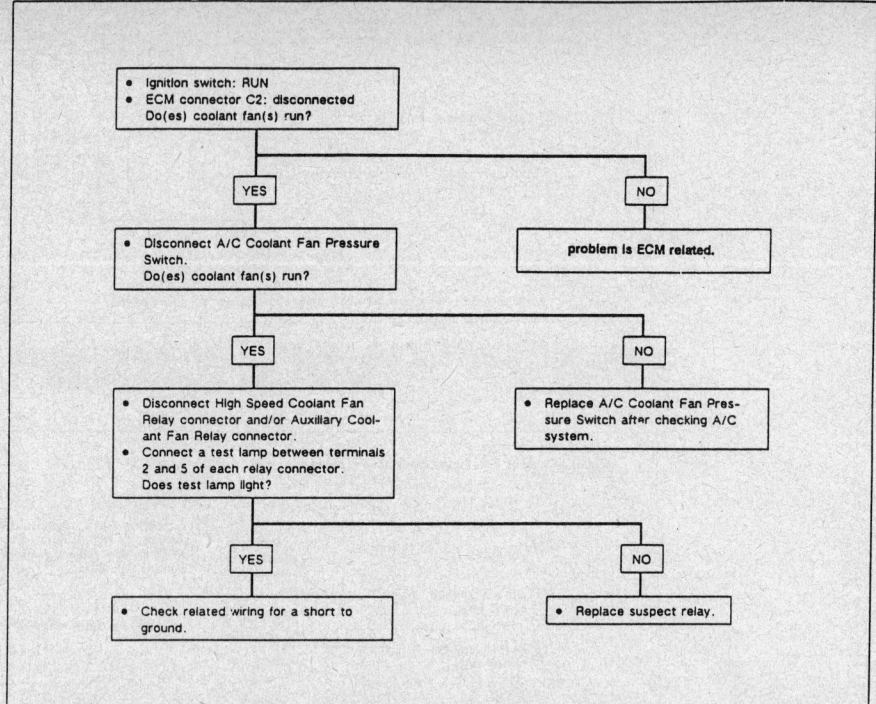

Fig. 97   Coolant fan test G. 1989–90 Electra & Park Avenue, 3.8L/V6-231 engine, VIN C

green/white wire for open.
4. If lamp illuminated in steps a, b and c, disconnect coolant fan relay connector and connect fused jumper between red and black/red wire terminals. If coolant fan runs, replace coolant fan relay.
5. If coolant fan does not run, leave fuse jumper connected as in step 2, connect coolant fan relay connector, disconnect coolant fan connector and connect test lamp between terminals as follows:
   a. Connect between black/red wire terminal and ground. If lamp does not illuminate, check black/red wire for open.
   b. Connect between black/red and black wire terminals. If lamp does not illuminate, check black wire for open.
   c. If lamp illuminates in steps a and b, replace coolant fan.

Coolant Fan Does Not Turn Off

1. With ignition switch in RUN position, disconnect black/red ECM connector. If fan turns off, problem is ECM related.
2. If fan does not turn off, remove C-H fuse. If fan turns off, check dark green/white wire for short to ground.
3. If fan does not turn off, replace coolant fan relay.

V6-173 VIN W

Coolant Fan Does Not Run

1. Turn ignition switch to RUN position and connect fused jumper between ALDL connector terminal B and

ground. If coolant fan runs, problem is ECM related.
2. If coolant fan does not run, turn ignition switch to RUN position connect fused jumper at ECM C3 connector between dark green/white wire and ground. If coolant fan runs, problem is ECM related.
3. If coolant fan does not run, leave fused jumper connected as in step 2, disconnect coolant fan relay connector, turn ignition switch to RUN position and connect test lamp between terminals as follows:
   a. Connect between brown/white wire terminal and ground. If lamp does not illuminate, check F/P fuse brown wire and brown/white wire for open.
   b. Connect between red wire terminal and ground. If lamp does not illuminate, check fusible link D and red wire for open.
   c. Connect between red and dark green/white wire terminals. If lamp does not illuminate, check dark green/white wire for open.
4. If lamp illuminated in steps a, b and c, disconnect coolant fan relay connector and connect fused jumper between red and yellow wire terminals. If coolant fan runs, replace coolant fan relay.
5. If coolant fan does not run, leave fused jumper connected as in step 2, connect coolant fan relay connector, disconnect coolant fan connector and connect test lamp between terminals as follows:
   a. Connect between yellow terminal and ground. If lamp does not illuminate, check yellow wire for open.

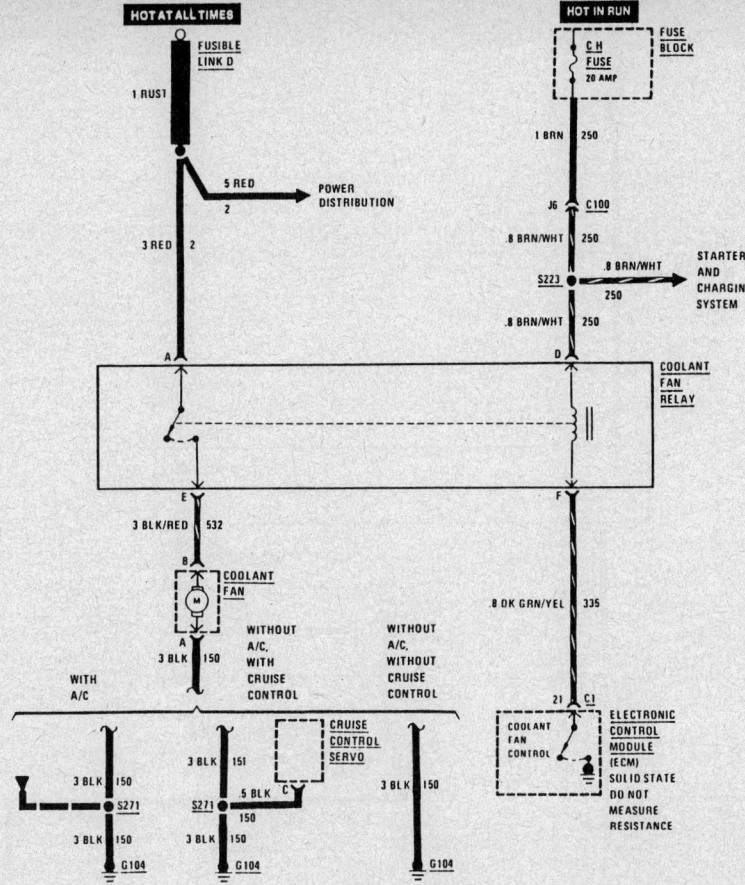

Fig. 98 Coolant fan wiring circuit. 1988 Century w/2.5L/4-151 engine, VIN R

b. Connect between yellow and black wire terminals. If lamp does not illuminate, check black wire for open.

c. If lamp illuminates in steps a and b, replace coolant fan.

Coolant Fan Does Not Turn Off

1. Disconnect ECM connector C3. If fan turns off, problem is ECM related.
2. If fan does not turn off, remove F/P fuse.
3. If fan turns off, check dark green/white wire for short to ground.
4. If fan does not turn off, replace coolant fan relay.

V6-231 VIN 3
Coolant Fan Does Not Run

1. Turn ignition switch to RUN position and connect fused jumper at ALDL connector between terminal B and ground. If coolant fan runs, problem is ECM related.
2. If coolant fan does not run, turn ignition switch to run position and connect fused jumper between dark green wire and ground at either ECM 32 pin connector pin C15 or the A/C pressure switch dark green wire, or the coolant fan switch. If fan runs, re-place suspect switch.

3. If fan does not run, leave fused jumper connected as in step 2, disconnect coolant fan relay connector, turn ignition switch to RUN position and connect test lamp between terminals as follows:
   a. Connect between brown wire terminal and ground. If lamp does not illuminate, check FAN fuse and brown wire for open.
   b. Connect between brown and dark green wire terminals. If lamp does not illuminate, check coolant fan relay diode, dark green wire and dark green/white wire for open.
   c. Connect between red wire terminal and ground. If lamp does not illuminate, check fusible link A and red wire for open.
4. If lamp illuminated in steps a, b and c, disconnect coolant fan relay connector and connect fused jumper between red and black/red wire terminals. If coolant fan runs, replace coolant fan relay.
5. If coolant fan does not run, leave fused jumper connected as in step 2, connect coolant fan relay connector, disconnect coolant fan connector, turn ignition switch to RUN position

and connect test lamp between terminals as follows:
   a. Connect between black/red wire terminal and ground. If lamp does not illuminate, check black/red wire for open.
   b. Connect between black/red and black wire terminals. If lamp does not illuminate, check black wire for open.
   c. If lamp illuminates in steps a and b, replace coolant fan.

High Speed Coolant Fan Does Not Run

1. Turn ignition switch to RUN position and connect fused jumper between dark green/white wire and ground at either the coolant fan switch or the A/C high pressure switch. If high speed coolant fan runs, replace suspect switch.
2. If high speed coolant fan does not run, connect fused jumper between coolant fan switch dark green/white wire and ground, disconnect pusher fan relay connector, turn ignition switch to RUN position and connect test lamp between terminals as follows:
   a. Connect between brown wire ter-

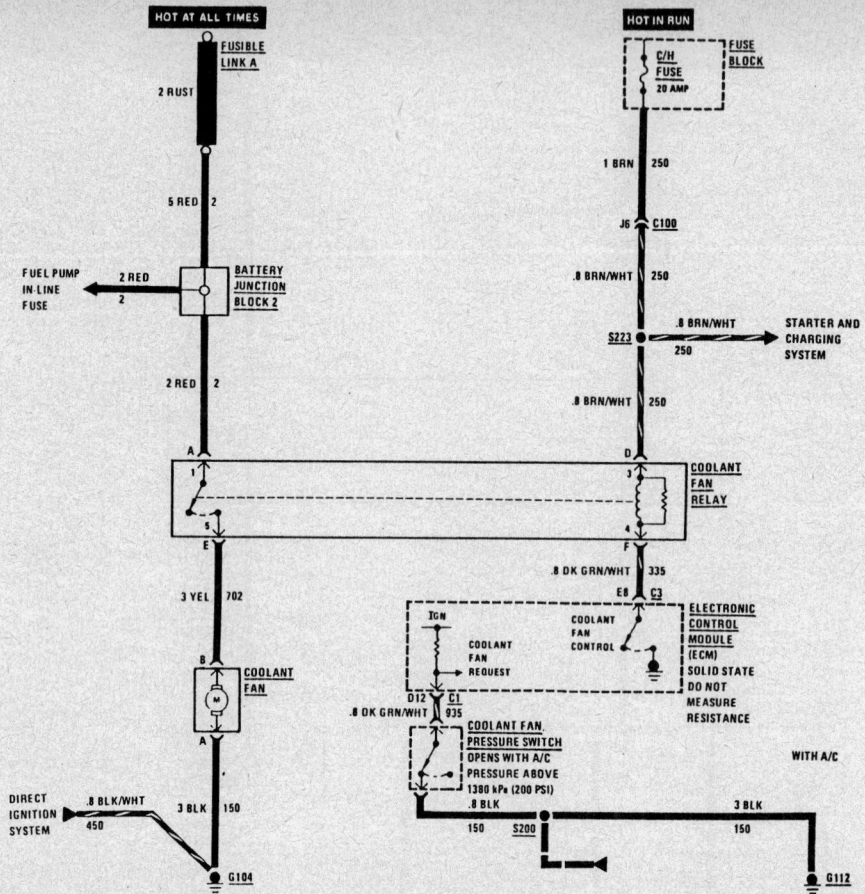

Fig. 99   Coolant fan wiring circuit. 1988 Century w/2.8L/V6-173 engine, VIN W

minal and ground. If lamp does not illuminate, check FAN fuse and brown wire for open.

b. Connect between brown and dark green/white wire terminals. If lamp does not illuminate, check dark green/white wire for open.

c. Connect between red wire terminal and ground. If lamp does not illuminate, check fusible link A and red wire for open.

3. If lamp illuminates in steps a, b and c, disconnect pusher fan relay connector and connect fused jumper between red and black/pink wire terminals. If high speed coolant fan runs, replace pusher fan relay.

4. If high speed fan does not run, connect fused jumper between coolant fan switch dark green/white wire terminal and ground, connect pusher fan relay connector, disconnect high speed coolant fan connector, turn ignition switch to RUN position and connect test lamp between terminals as follows:

a. Connect between black/red wire terminal and ground. If lamp does not illuminate, check black/red and black/pink wires for open.

b. Connect between black/red and black/white wire terminals. If lamp does not illuminate, check black/white wire for open.

c. If lamp illuminates in steps a and b, replace high speed coolant fan.

Coolant Fan And/Or High Speed Coolant Fan Does Not Turn Off

1. With ignition switch in RUN position, disconnect ECM 32 pin connector. If coolant fan turns off, problem is ECM related.

2. If coolant fan does not turn off, disconnect coolant fan switch. If coolant fan stops, replace coolant fan switch.

3. If coolant fan does not stop, disconnect A/C pressure switch, if equipped. If coolant fan stops, replace A/C pressure switch.

4. If coolant fan does not stop, turn ignition switch off and disconnect pusher fan relay, if equipped. If high speed coolant fan stops, replace pusher fan relay.

5. If high speed coolant fan does not stop, disconnect coolant fan relay.

6. If coolant fan stops, replace coolant fan relay.

7. If coolant fan does not stop, replace coolant fan delay relay.

Coolant Fan Does Not Run For a Delay Period After The Ignition Switch Is Turned To Off (Engine Coolant Hot), But Fan Does Run When Ignition Switch Is In RUN

1. With engine coolant hot, disconnect coolant fan relay and turn ignition switch to RUN position, then disconnect coolant fan delay relay connector and connect test lamp between terminals as follows:

a. Connect between connector C2 orange wire terminal and ground. If lamp does not illuminate, check fusible link G and orange wire for open.

b. Connect between connector C2 orange and black/white wire terminals. If lamp does not illuminate, check black/white wire for open.

c. Connect between connector C1 red wire terminal and ground. If lamp does not illuminate, check fusible link A and red wire for open.

d. Connect between C1 connector red and dark green/white wire terminals. If lamp does not illuminate, check dark green/white wire for

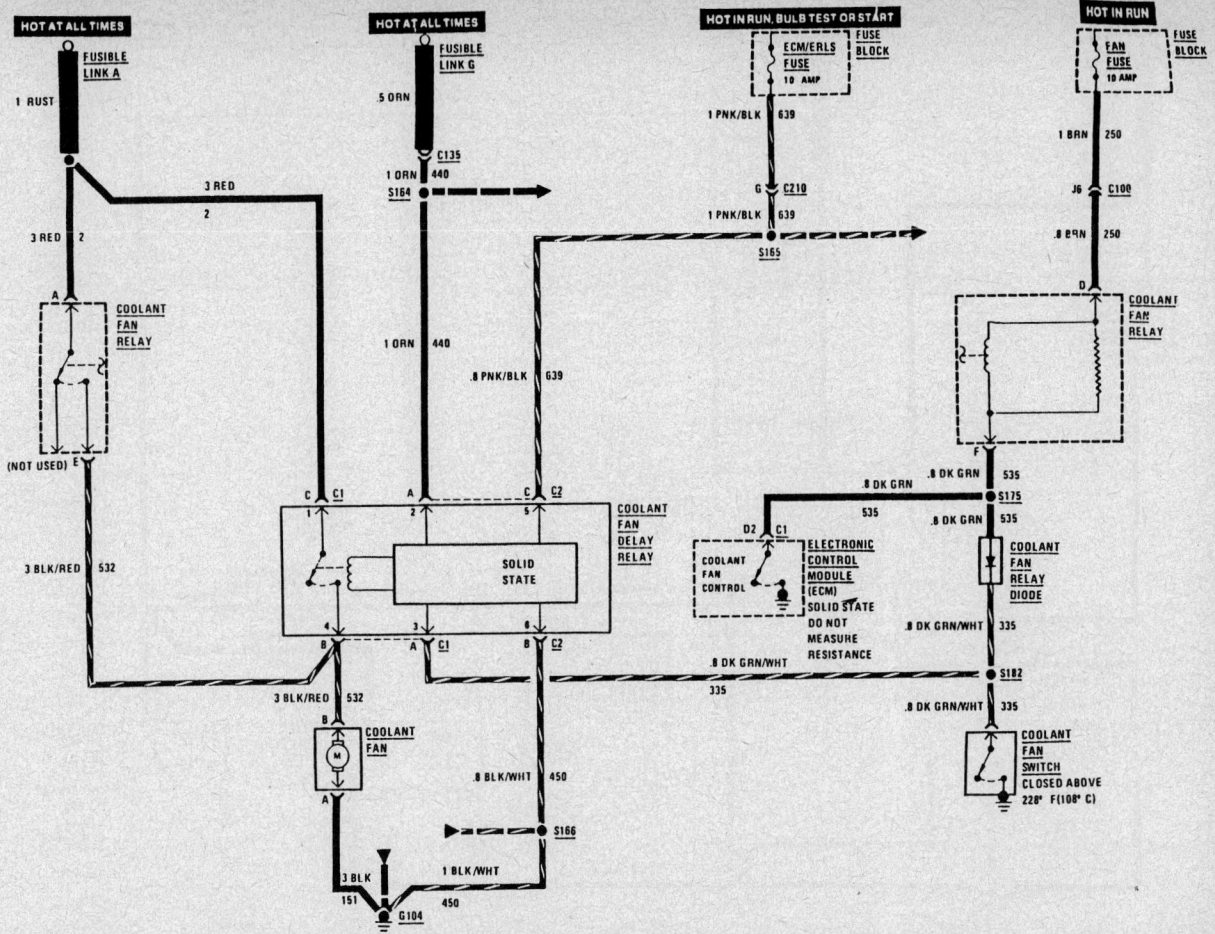

Fig. 100   Coolant fan wiring circuit (less A/C). 1988 Century w/3.8L/V6-231 engine, VIN 3

open and, if wire is satisfactory, replace coolant fan switch.
  e. Connect between connector C1 red and black/red wire terminals. If lamp does not illuminate, check black/red wire for open.
  f. Connect between Connector C2 pink/black wire terminal and ground. If lamp does not illuminate, check ECM/ERLS fuse and pink/black wire for open.
2. If lamp illuminates in steps a through f, replace coolant fan delay relay.

1989–90 CENTURY

SYSTEM DESCRIPTION

4-151 VIN R & V6-173 VIN W

The coolant fan is turned on and off by the ECM, based on inputs from the coolant temperature sensor, vehicle speed sensor and the A/C system. Battery voltage is applied at all times to terminal A of the coolant fan relay and when the ignition switch is turned to the RUN position, voltage is applied to terminal D of the relay. The ECM energizes the coolant fan relay by grounding the dark green/yellow wire circuit (335). The relay energizes and battery voltage is applied to the coolant fan. The ECM opens circuit 335 to de-energize the relay and turn off the coolant fan.

V6-204 VIN N Less Heavy Duty Cooling

The coolant fan is controlled by the coolant fan relay. The coolant fan relay is electrically operated by the ECM. The ECM receives input signals from the coolant temperature sensor, vehicle speed sensor and A/C mode selector. The ECM activates the coolant fan relay when either the engine coolant temperature is above 202°F, when A/C is turned on, or when coolant temperature sensor fails. Any of these signals will cause the ECM to ground circuit 535, turning the coolant fan on.

V6-204 VIN N w/Heavy Duty Cooling

A Pusher and a Puller coolant fan are used with a heavy duty cooling system. These fans are turned on and off by coolant fan relays which are controlled by the ECM.

The puller coolant fan relay is energized when the ECM grounds the dark green wire, circuit 535. The relay contacts close, providing battery voltage to the puller coolant fan. The ECM opens circuit 535 to de-energize the relay and turn off the puller coolant fan.

The ECM receives input signals from the coolant temperature sensor, vehicle speed sensor and A/C mode selector. The ECM

activates the puller coolant fan relay when coolant temperature exceeds 202°F, when A/C is turned on, or when coolant temperature sensor fails. Any of these input signals will cause the ECM to ground circuit 535 when vehicle speed is less than 40 mph.

The pusher fan relay is energized when the ECM grounds light green/black wire, circuit 536. This will cause relay contacts to close, providing battery voltage to the pusher coolant fan. The ECM activates the pusher coolant fan when engine coolant temperature reaches 226°F or when A/C head pressure exceeds 245 psi.

TROUBLESHOOTING

1. Check FAN/ELECT fuse.
2. **On V6-173 VIN W models less A/C,** if coolant fan does not run, check that terminal C1/D12 of the ECM is grounded.
3. **On all models,** if coolant fan runs with ignition off, replace the coolant fan relay.

SYSTEM CHECK

Models Less Heavy Duty Cooling

1. With ambient temperature above 60°F, start car and set A/C mode selector to the MAX position. Coolant fan should turn on.

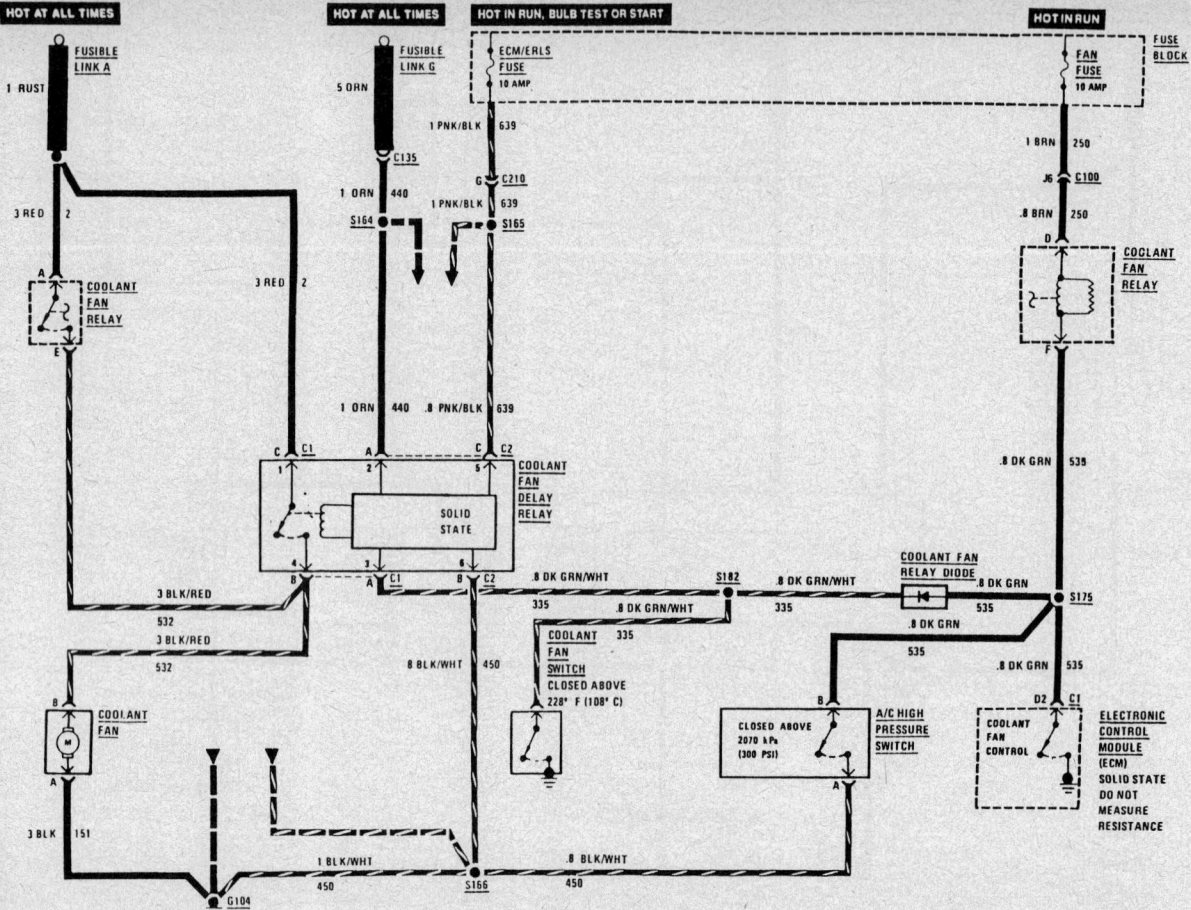

Fig. 101 Coolant fan wiring circuit (with A/C & less heavy duty). 1988 Century w/3.8L/V6-231 engine, VIN 3

2. With engine coolant below operating temperature, move A/C mode selector to OFF. Coolant fan should turn off in a short time period.
3. Run engine at fast idle until engine coolant becomes hot. Coolant fan should come on and run before coolant temperature indicator comes on or the coolant temperature gage reads hot.

Models w/Heavy Duty Cooling

1. With ambient temperature above 60°F, start car and set A/C mode selector to the MAX position. Puller coolant fan should turn on.
2. With engine coolant below operating temperature, move A/C mode selector to OFF. Puller coolant fan should turn off in a short time period.
3. Run engine at fast idle until engine coolant becomes hot. Puller coolant fan should come on when coolant temperature reaches 202°F and the pusher coolant fan should come on when coolant temperature reaches 226°F.

SYSTEM DIAGNOSIS

Refer to **Figs. 103 through 106** when performing diagnostic procedures on these systems.

MODELS LESS HEAVY DUTY COOLING

Coolant Fan Does Not Turn On

1. With ignition switch turned off, ground terminal B white/black wire of the ALDL connector.
2. Turn ignition switch to the RUN position. If coolant fan does not run, proceed to step 3. If coolant fan does not run, problem is ECM related.
3. With ignition switch in the RUN position, use a fused jumper wire and ground ECM terminal C1/21 (VIN R), or terminal C3/E38 (VIN N & W). If coolant fan does not run, proceed to step 4. If coolant fan runs, problem is ECM related.
4. Leaving fused jumper connected as in step 3 and ignition in the RUN position, disconnect coolant fan relay connector.
5. Measure voltage from the brown/white wire of the coolant fan relay connector to ground. If voltage is equal to battery voltage, proceed to step 6. If there is no voltage indicated, check FAN/ELECT fuse, and brown and brown/white wires for an open circuit.
6. Fused jumper still connected and igni-

tion switch still in RUN position, measure voltage as follows:
a. On 2.5L/4-151 VIN R engines, measure between brown/white and dark green/yellow (1989) or dark green/white (1990) wires.
b. On 2.8L/V6-173 VIN W engines, measure between brown/white and dark green/white wires.
c. On 3/3L/V6-204 VIN N engines, measure between brown/white and dark green wires.
7. If battery voltage is indicated, proceed to step 8. If zero volts are indicated, check dark green/yellow (1989 VIN R), dark green/white (1990 VIN R), dark green/white (VIN W), or dark green (VIN N) wire, for an open circuit.
8. With coolant fan relay disconnected, measure voltage between terminal A (red wire) of the connector and ground. If battery voltage is indicated, proceed to step 9. If zero volts are indicated, check red wire or fusible link for an open.
9. Connect a fused jumper with a 20 amp fuse between terminals A and E at the coolant fan relay connector. If coolant fan does not run, proceed to step 10. If coolant fan runs, replace coolant fan relay.
10. Leaving fused jumper wire connected from step 9, disconnect connector from the coolant fan.

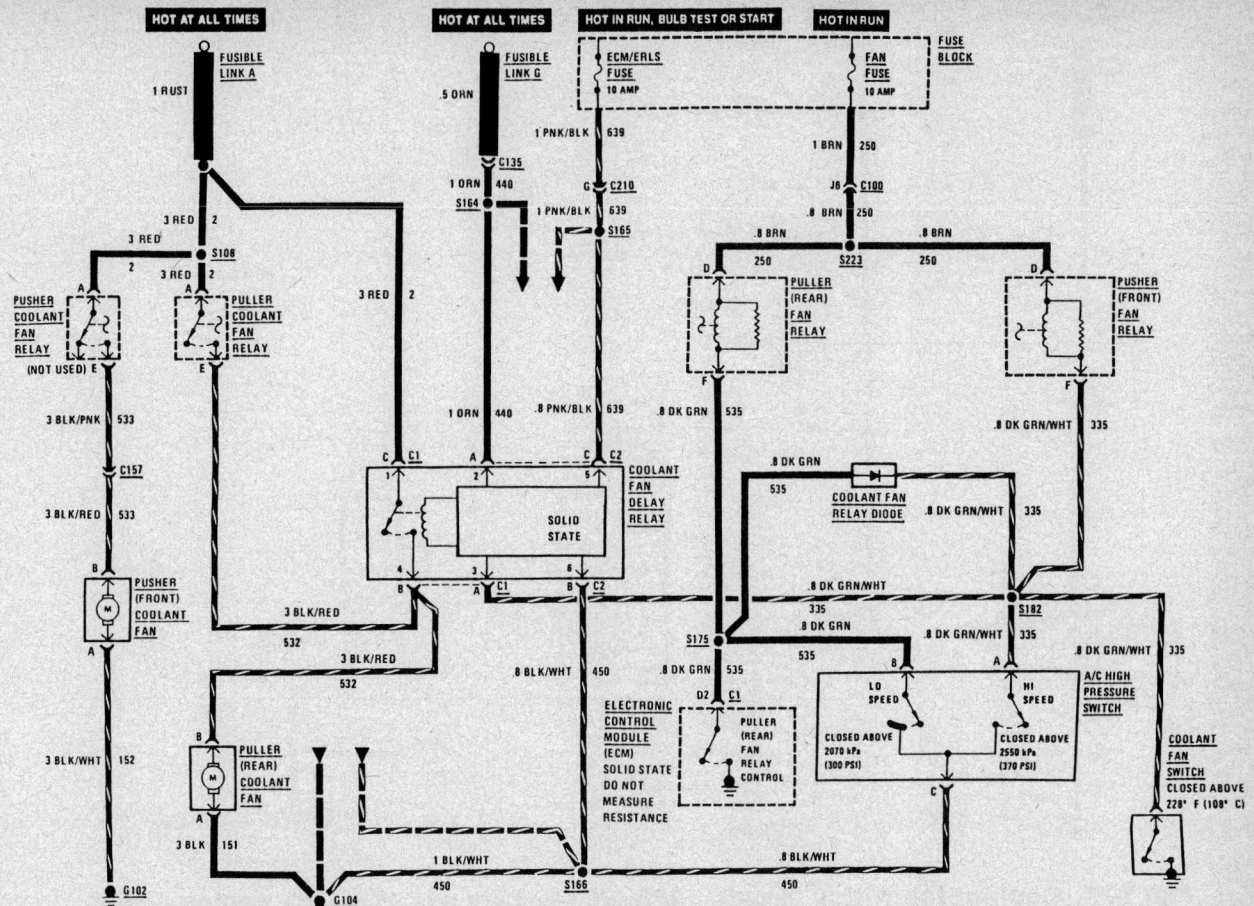

Fig. 102   Coolant fan wiring circuit (with A/C & heavy duty). 1989 Century w/3.8L/V6-231 engine, VIN 3

11. Measure voltage between terminal B of the connector and ground. If battery voltage is indicated, proceed to step 12. If zero volts are indicated, check for an open circuit in black/red (VIN R), yellow (VIN W) or pink/black (VIN N) wire.

12. Leaving fused jumper connected at the coolant fan relay connector, measure voltage between terminals A and B of the coolant fan connector. If battery voltage is indicated, replace coolant fan motor. If zero volts are indicated, check black wire for an open circuit.

Coolant Fan Does Not Turn Off With Engine Coolant Cool, A/C Off & Ignition Switch In Run

1. Turn ignition switch off, then disconnect coolant fan relay connector.

2. Connect a test lamp between terminals F and D of the coolant fan relay connector. If test lamp lights, proceed to step 3. If test lamp does not light, replace coolant fan relay.

3. Check wires for a short to ground as follows:
   a. On 2.5L/4-151 engines, check dark green/yellow (1989) or dark green/white (1990) wire.
   b. On 2.8L/V6-173 engines, check

dark green/white wire.
   c. On 3.3L/V6-204 engines, check dark green wire.

4. If all wires are satisfactory, problem is ECM related.

Coolant Fan Does Not Turn On With A/C On

1. Turn ignition switch to run, put A/C mode selector in the MAX position.

2. Measure voltage between terminal C1/24 (VIN R) or C1/C9 (VIN N) and ground.

3. If battery voltage is indicated, problem si ECM related.

4. If zero voltage is indicated, check light blue/black wire or light blue wire for an open circuit.

Coolant Fan Does Not Turn On With A/C On & A/C Head Pressure Above 200 psi

1. Disconnect ECM connector C1, measure resistance from C1/D12 dark green/white wire to ground.

2. If resistance is zero, proceed to step 3. If resistance is infinite, proceed as follows:
   a. Check dark green/white wire for an open circuit, repair if necessary.
   b. If wire is satisfactory, check that coolant fan A/C pressure switch is closed.

   c. If switch is closed, problem is ECM related.
   d. If switch is open, replace switch.

3. Leaving ECM C1 connector disconnected, turn ignition switch to RUN position.

4. Switch A/C mode selector to the MAX position, measure voltage between terminal C1/C9 light green/white wire of the ECM to ground.

5. If battery voltage is indicated, problem is ECM related.

6. If zero voltage is indicated, check light green/white wire for an open circuit.

7. If wire is satisfactory, problem is in A/C system.

MODELS WITH HEAVY DUTY COOLING

Puller Coolant Fan Does Not Turn On

1. Turn ignition switch to the RUN position, ground terminal B white/black wire of the ALDL connector.

2. If puller coolant fan runs, problem is ECM related.

3. If puller coolant fan does not run, ground terminal C3/E8 dark green wire of the ECM with a fused jumper.

4. If puller coolant fan runs, problem is ECM related.

5. If puller coolant fan does not run,

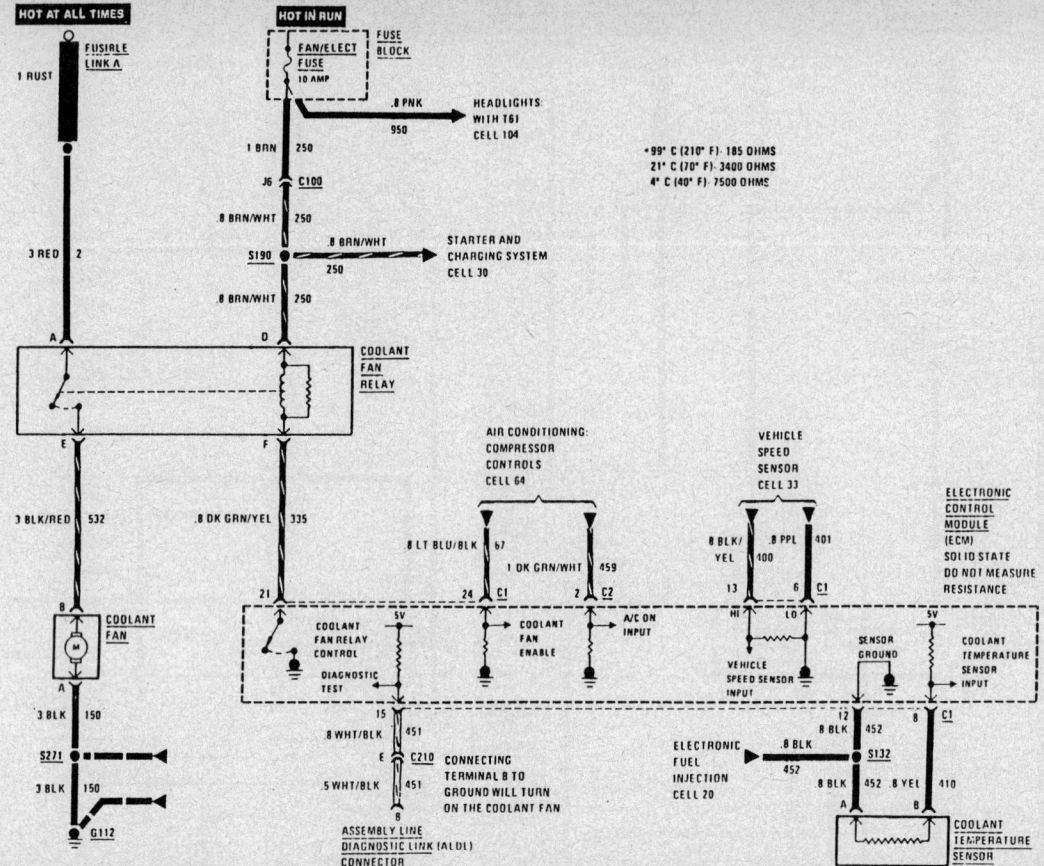

Fig. 103 Coolant fan wiring circuit. 1989–90 Century w/2.5L/4-151 engine, VIN R

leave fused jumper connected as in step 3.

6. Disconnect puller coolant fan relay connector, then measure voltage from terminal F brown/white wire to ground.
7. If zero voltage is indicated, check FAN/ELECT fuse and brown/white wire for an open circuit, repair or replace as necessary.
8. If battery voltage is indicated, measure voltage between terminals F brown/white wire and D dark green wire of the puller fan relay connector.
9. If zero voltage is indicated, check dark green 535 wire for an open circuit.
10. If battery voltage is indicated, measure voltage from terminal A red wire of the puller coolant fan relay connector to ground.
11. If zero voltage is indicated, check red wire or fusible link G for an open circuit.
12. If battery voltage is indicated, connect a fused jumper with a 20 amp fuse between terminals A red wire and E pink/black wire at puller fan relay connector.
13. If puller coolant fan runs, replace puller coolant fan relay.
14. If puller coolant fan does not run, leave fused jumper connected at the puller fan relay connector.
15. Measure voltage between terminal B pink/black and ground.
16. If zero voltage is indicated, check

pink/black wire for an open circuit.
17. If battery voltage is indicated, measure voltage between terminals B pink/black wire and A black wire of the puller coolant fan connector.
18. If zero voltage is indicated, check black wire for an open circuit.
19. If battery voltage is indicated, replace puller coolant fan motor.

Pusher Coolant Fan Does Not Turn On

1. Turn ignition switch to the RUN position, Ground terminal C3/F3 light green/black wire at the ECM terminal with a fused jumper.
2. If pusher coolant fan runs, problem is ECM related.
3. If pusher coolant fan does not run, disconnect coolant fan relay connector, then measure voltage from terminal D brown/white wire to ground.
4. If zero voltage is indicated, check FAN/ELEC fuse and brown and brown/white wires for an open circuit.
5. If battery voltage is indicated, measure voltage between terminals D brown/white and F light green/black wire of the pusher fan relay.
6. If zero voltage is indicated, check FAN/ELEC fuse, brown and brown/white wires for an open circuit.
7. If battery voltage is indicated, measure voltage between terminals D brown/white and F light green/black of the pusher coolant fan relay.

8. If zero voltage is indicated, check light green/black wire for an open circuit.
9. If battery voltage is indicated, measure voltage between terminal A red wire of the pusher coolant fan relay to ground.
10. If zero voltage is indicated, check red wire and fusible link G for an open circuit.
11. If battery voltage is indicated, connect a fused jumper with a 20 amp fuse between terminals A red wire and E black/red wire at the pusher fan relay connector.
12. If pusher coolant fan runs, replace pusher coolant fan relay.
13. If pusher coolant fan does not run, disconnect connector from the pusher coolant fan and measure voltage between terminal B black/red wire and ground.
14. If zero voltage is indicated, check black/red wire for an open circuit.
15. Measure voltage between terminals B black/red wire and A black/white of the pusher fan connector.
16. If zero voltage is indicated, check black/white wire for an open circuit.
17. If battery voltage is indicated, replace pusher coolant fan motor.

Pusher & Or Puller Coolant Fans Do Not Run With A/C On

1. Turn ignition switch to the RUN posi-

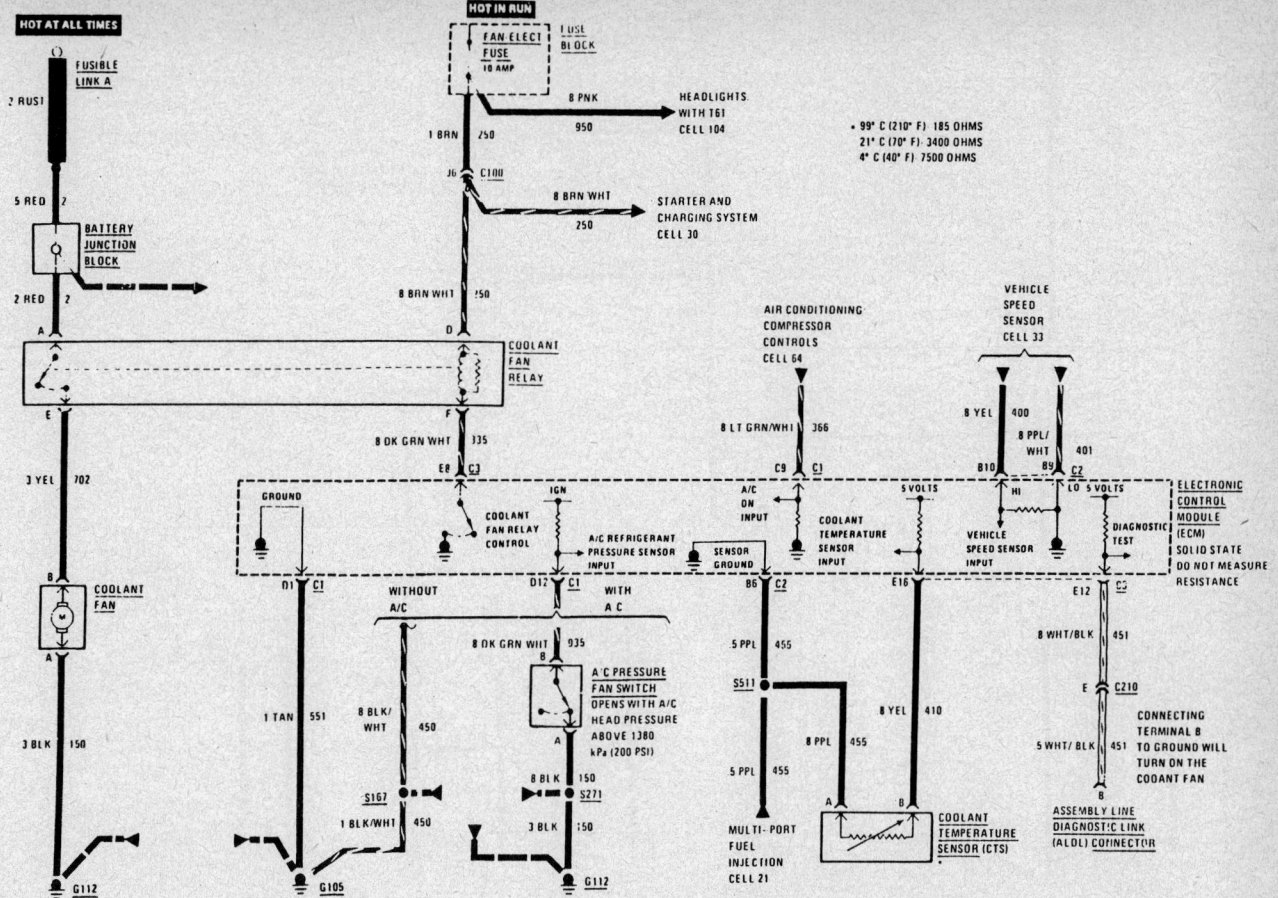

Fig. 104   Coolant fan wiring circuit. 1989 Century w/2.8L/V6-173 engine, VIN W

tion, put A/C mode selector in MAX.
2. Measure voltage at terminal C1/C9 light blue of the ECM to ground.
3. If battery voltage is indicated, problem is ECM related.
4. If zero voltage is indicated, check light blue wire for an open circuit.
5. If wire is satisfactory, problem is in the A/C system.

Pusher Coolant Fan Runs Continuously With A/C Off, Coolant Temperature Cool & Ignition In RUN Position

1. Turn ignition switch to RUN position, disconnect pusher coolant fan relay connector.
2. Connect a test lamp between terminals D brown/white wire and F light green/black wire.
3. If test lamp fails to light, replace pusher coolant fan relay.
4. If test lamp lights, check light green/black wire for a short to ground.
5. If wire is satisfactory, problem is ECM related.

Puller Coolant Fan Runs Continuously With A/C Off, Coolant Temperature Cool & Ignition In RUN Position

1. Turn ignition switch to RUN position,

disconnect puller coolant fan relay connector.
2. Connect a test lamp between terminals F brown/white wire and D dark green wire.
3. If test lamp fails to light, replace puller coolant fan relay.
4. If test lamp lights, check dark green wire for a short to ground.
5. If wire is satisfactory, problem is ECM related.

RIVERA, REATTA, TORONADO & TROFEO
SYSTEM DESCRIPTION

The coolant fans on these models consist of a fan located behind the radiator, and a fan mounted in front of the radiator.

The rear fan operates on two speeds, while the front fan operates only on high speed. Both fans are activated any time the coolant fans are in the high speed mode.

The fans will be activated by the ECM, when the engine coolant temperature sensor or the A/C high pressure sensor reach calibration points.

DIAGNOSIS

Fan system diagnosis begins with chart C-12A **Figs. 107 through 110.** Fans consist of a two speed fan and a single speed fan. When diagnosing a fan system malfunction, remember that fans are ECM controlled only.

COOLANT FAN REPLACE

1. Disconnect battery ground cable.
2. Remove wiring harness from fan motor and fan frame.
3. Remove fan assembly.
4. Reverse procedure to install.

LUMINA
SYSTEM DESCRIPTION

The coolant fan is controlled by the coolant fan relay. The coolant fan relay is electrically operated by the ECM. The ECM receives input signals from the coolant temperature sensor, A/C mode selector and on the V6 VIN T engine, the A/C intermediate pressure switch. When circuit 335 is grounded, the coolant fan relay is energized and its contacts are close, turning on the coolant fan.

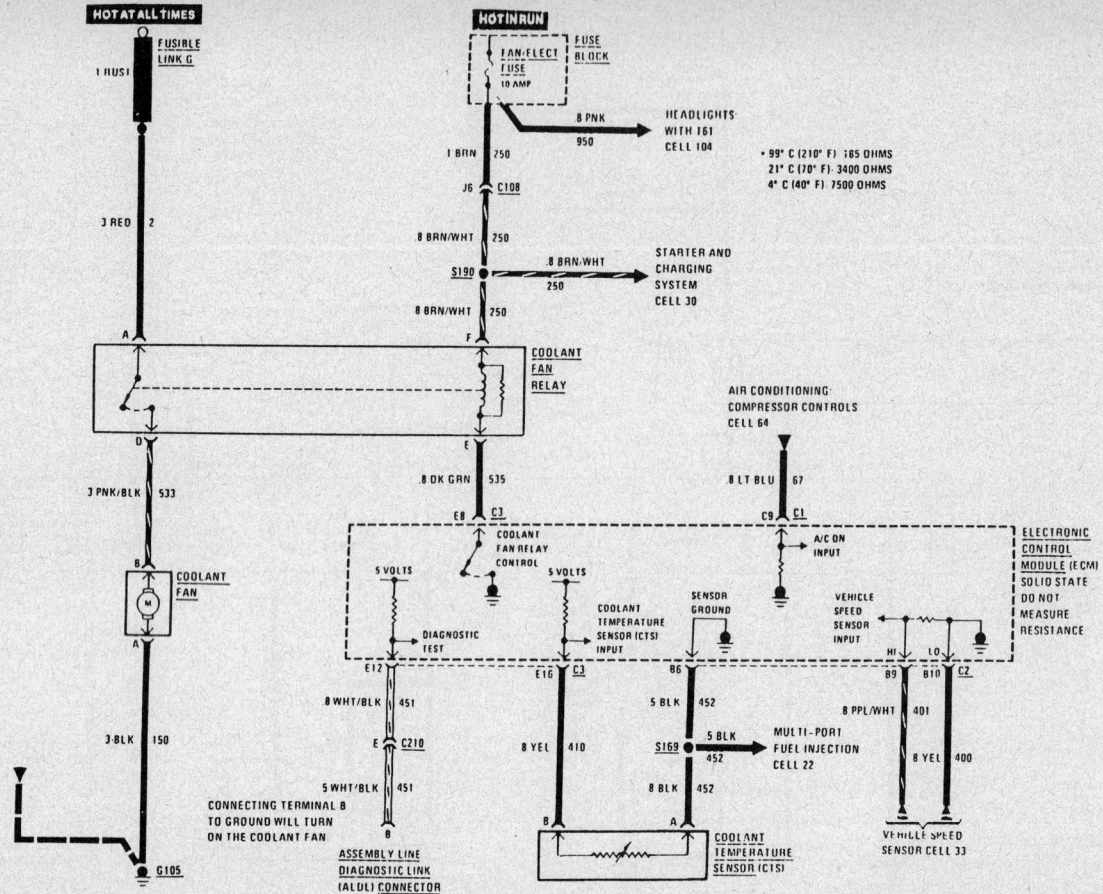

Fig. 105   Coolant fan wiring circuit (less heavy duty cooling). 1989–90 Century w/3.3L/V6-204 engine, VIN N

TROUBLESHOOTING

1. If coolant fan does not operate, check IGN fuse.
2. If coolant fan runs with ignition switch in the OFF position, replace the coolant fan relay.

DIAGNOSIS

Refer to **Fig. 111** when performing diagnostic procedures on this system.

Coolant Fan Does Not Turn On

1. With ignition switch in OFF position, ground terminal B of the ALDL connector. If coolant fan runs, problem is ECM related.
2. If coolant fan does not run, ground terminal A9 at the ECM with a fused jumper. If coolant fan runs, problem is ECM related.
3. If coolant fan does not run, leave jumper from step 2 installed and disconnect coolant fan relay connector. Measure voltage between terminal 4 and ground. If zero volts is present, check red wire for an open.
4. If battery voltage is present, measure voltage between terminal 3 and ground. If zero volts is present, check

pink/black wire for an open.
5. If battery voltage is present, disconnect coolant fan relay then measure voltage between terminals 4 and 1 on the relay connector. If zero volts is present, check dark green/white wire for an open.
6. If battery voltage is present, with coolant fan relay disconnected connect a fused jumper between terminals 4 and 2 at the connector. If coolant fan runs, replace coolant fan relay.
7. If coolant fan does not run, leave jumper installed from step 6 then disconnect the coolant fan connector and measure voltage between terminal B and ground. If zero volts is present, check black/red wire for an open.
8. If battery voltage is present, measure voltage between terminals B and A. If zero volts is present, check black wire for an open.
9. If battery voltage is present, replace coolant fan.

Coolant Fan Does Not Turn Off With Engine Coolant Cool And A/C Mode Selector Off

1. Disconnect coolant fan relay and connect a test lamp between terminals 3 and 1 on the relay connector. If test

lamp does not light, replace coolant relay.
2. If test lamp lights, check dark green/white wire for a short to ground. If wire is satisfactory, problem is ECM related.
3. If wire is not satisfactory, repair/replace as necessary.

COOLANT FAN REPLACE

1. Disconnect battery ground cable.
2. Remove air cleaner assembly.
3. Remove coolant reservoir.
4. Remove engine strut brace bolts from upper tie bar and rotate strut(s) and brace(s) rearward. **Loosen strut retaining bolts on both ends to prevent damage to strut(s).**
5. Disconnect wiring harness from fan motor(s) and fan frame(s).
6. Remove fan frame attaching bolts.
7. Remove fan assembly.
8. Reverse procedure to install.

PRIZM

SYSTEM DESCRIPTION

When the ignition switch is in either the RUN or START positions, system voltage is applied to the coils of the main engine relay and to fan relay 1. Because the main

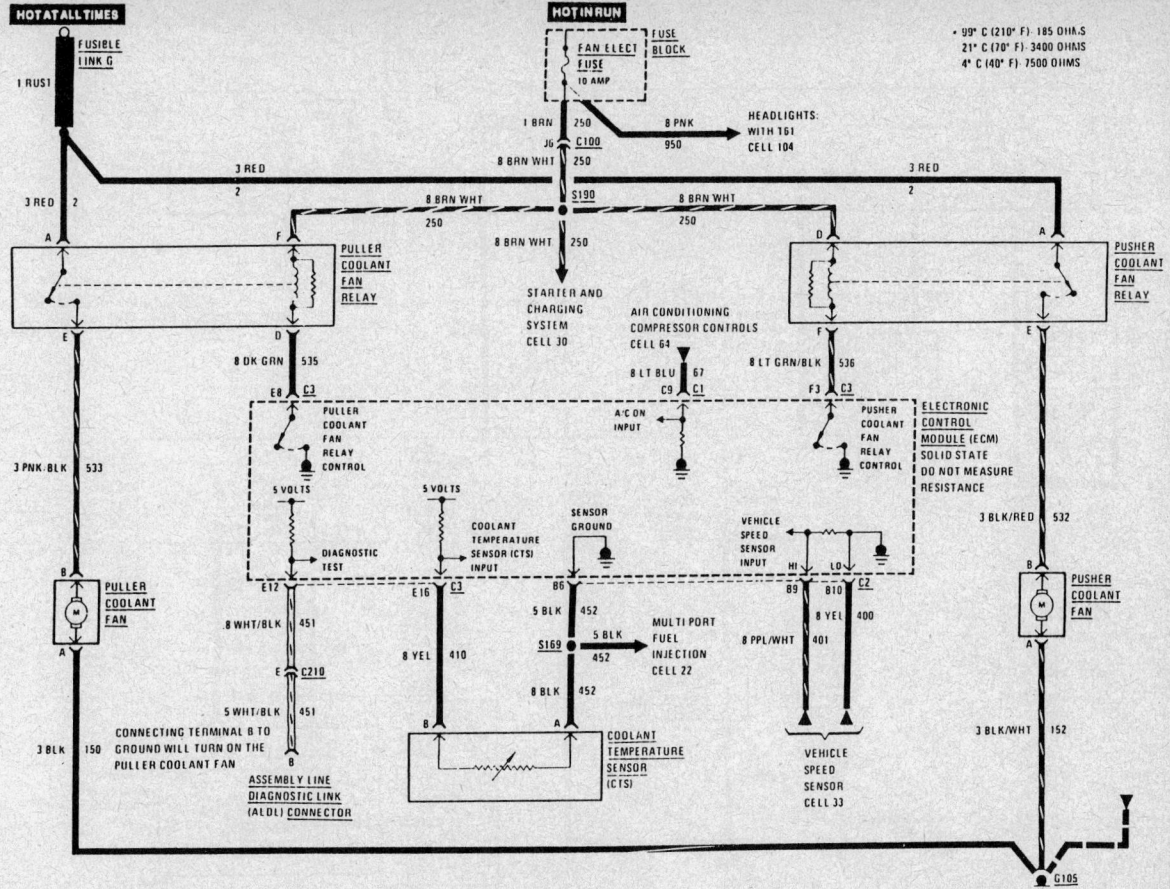

Fig. 106   Coolant fan wiring circuit (with heavy duty cooling). 1989 Century w/3.3L/V6-204 engine, VIN N

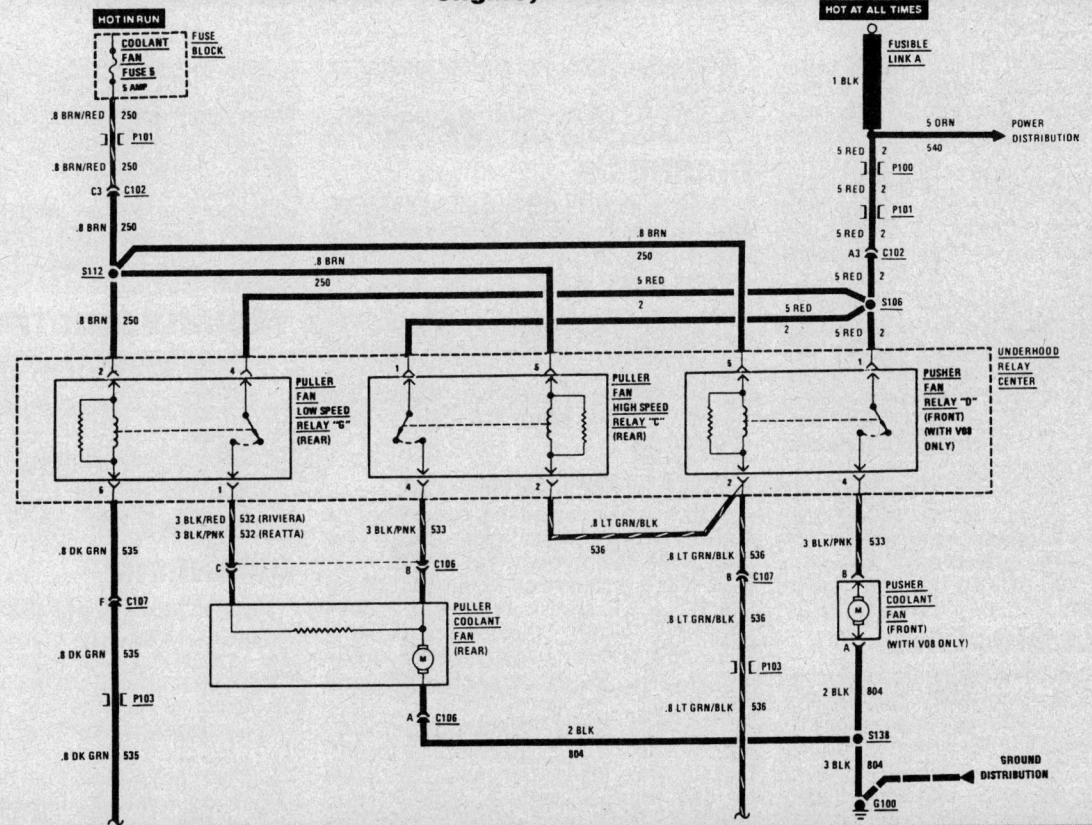

Fig. 107   Coolant fan wiring circuit (Part 1 of 2). 1988 Reatta, Riviera, Toronado & Trofeo

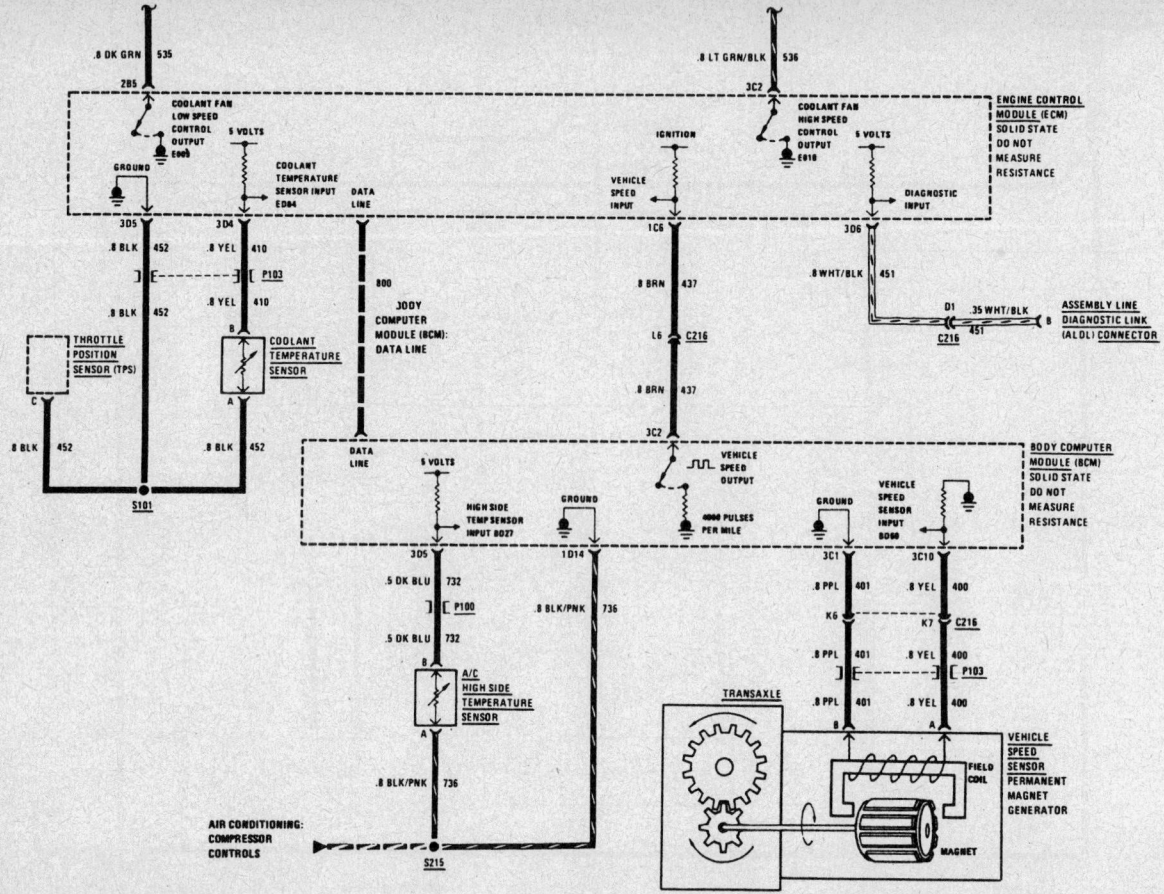

Fig. 107 Coolant fan wiring circuit (Part 2 of 2). 1988 Reatta, Riviera, Toronado & Trofeo

relay is grounded at G108, the relay is energized, its contacts close, and battery voltage is applied through the relay and the radiator fan fusible link to the contacts of fan relay 1.

When engine coolant temperature is below 194°F, the coolant fan temperature switch provides a ground for relay 1, the relay energizes and its contacts are pulled open.

Whenever engine coolant temperature reaches or exceeds 194°F, the coolant fan temperature switch opens, fan relay 1 is de-energized, its contacts close, and system voltage is applied through the relay to the coolant fan motor. Since the fan motor is grounded at G108, it start to operate as soon as voltage is applied.

When engine coolant temperature drops below 194°F, the coolant fan temperature switch closes to ground, fan relay 1 is energized the relay contacts are pulled open and system voltage is no longer applied to the fan motor.

TROUBLESHOOTING

1. Check the IGN fuse by turning the ignition switch to RUN and noting CHARGE WARNING lamp operation.
2. Check the ECM/IG fuse with a fuse tester.
3. Check the A/C fuse with a fuse tester.
4. Check all relays in junction blocks 2 and 5 are mounted securely.

5. Check radiator fan fusible link for an open.
6. Check, clean and tighten body grounds G108 and G201.

DIAGNOSIS

Refer to **Fig. 112 through 114** to perform diagnostic procedures on this system.

COOLANT FAN REPLACE

1. Disconnect battery ground cable.
2. Disconnect coolant fan electrical harness.
3. Remove coolant fan from vehicle.
4. Reverse procedure to install.

STORM
SYSTEM DESCRIPTION

With the engine running, the generator applies voltage to the restart relay. The voltage passes through the closed contacts of the restart relay to the condenser fan relay and the radiator fan relay. The triple switch closes when the refrigerant pressure is above 214 psi. When the triple switch closes, the condenser fan and radiator fan relays energize.

The condenser fan receives battery voltage from fuse E-4 through the closed contacts of the condenser fan relay. The radiator fan receives battery voltage from fusible link FL-4 through the radiator fan relay.

The thermo switch closes when the coolant temperature is above 179°F. When the thermo switch closes, the radiator fan and condenser fan operate in the same manner as when the triple switch closes.

When the ignition switch is turned to START, the restart relay is energized, the contacts are opened and the fans will not operate.

TROUBLESHOOTING

1. Check fuse C-21 and E-4 using a fuse tester.
2. Check fusible link FL-4 using a fuse tester.
3. Be sure that grounds G102 and G103 are clean and tight.
4. Check that A/C system is properly charged.

DIAGNOSIS

Refer to **Fig. 115 and 116** to perform diagnostic procedures on this system.
1. Disconnect battery ground cable.
2. Drain coolant from radiator.
3. Remove upper radiator hose.
4. Disconnect electrical connections from coolant fan motor.
5. Disconnect cable form thermo switch.
6. Remove coolant fan assembly from vehicle.
7. Reverse procedure to install.

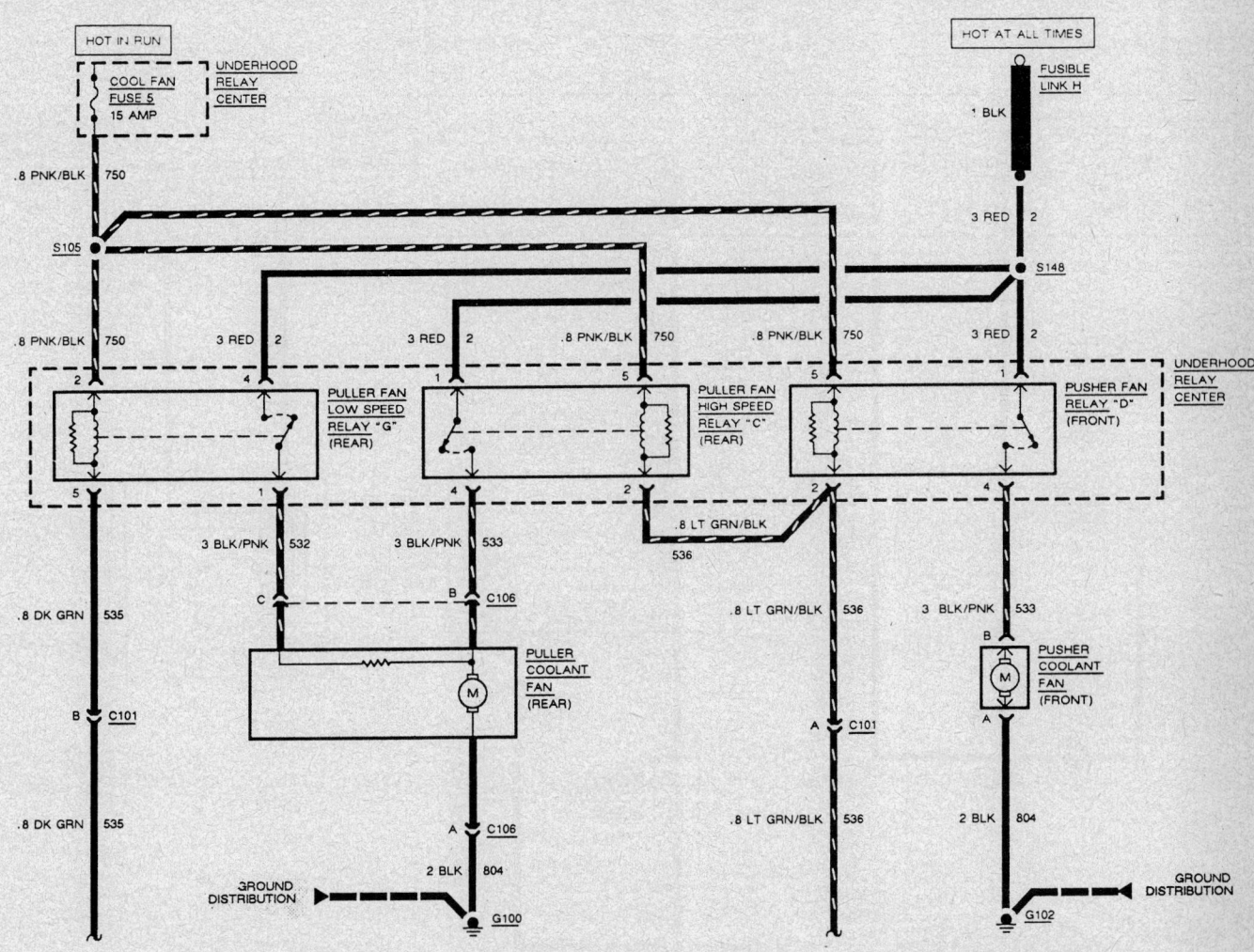

Fig. 108   Coolant fan wiring circuit (Part 1 of 2). 1989–90 Toronado & Trofeo

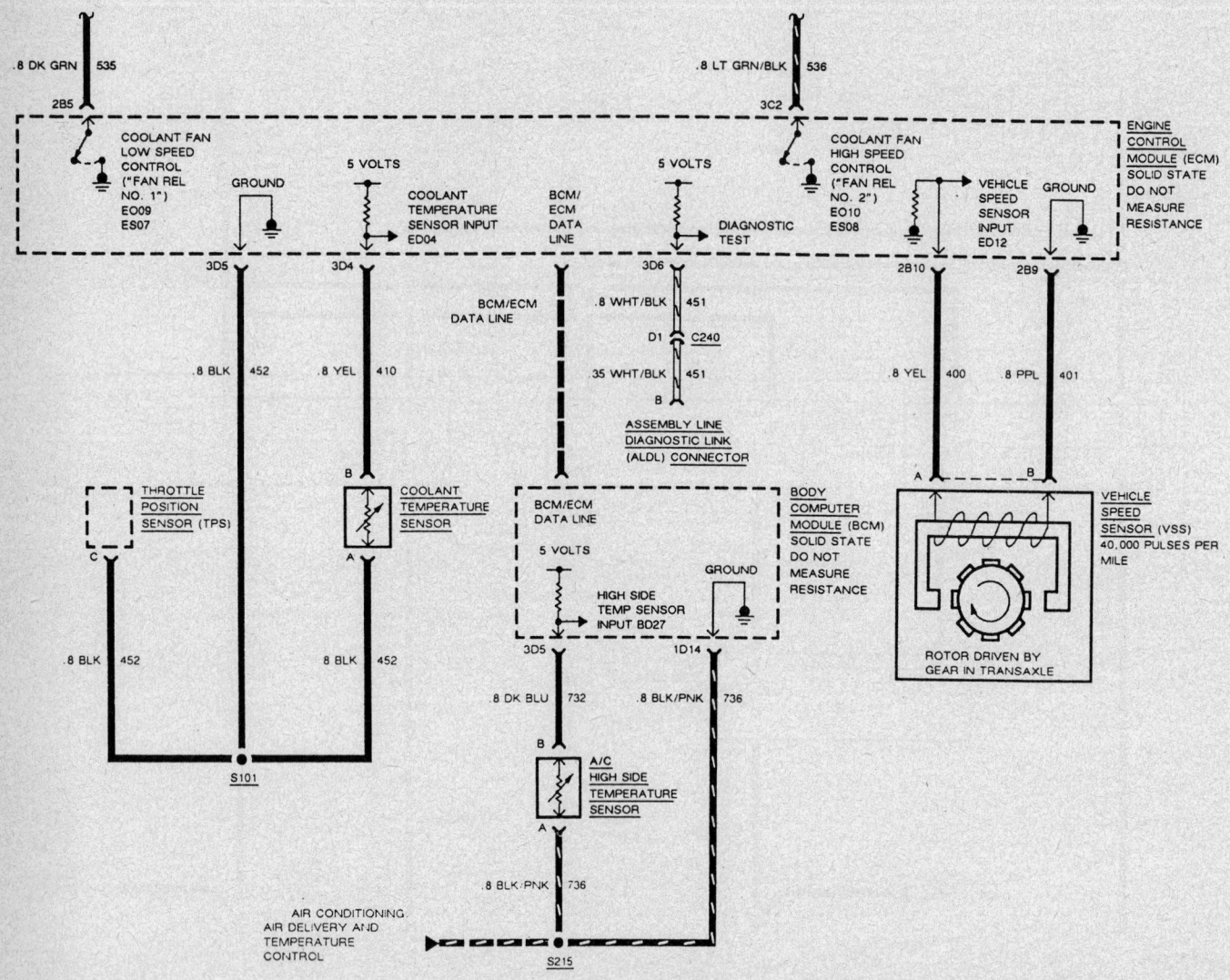

Fig. 108 Coolant fan wiring circuit (Part 2 of 2). 1989–90 Toronado & Trofeo

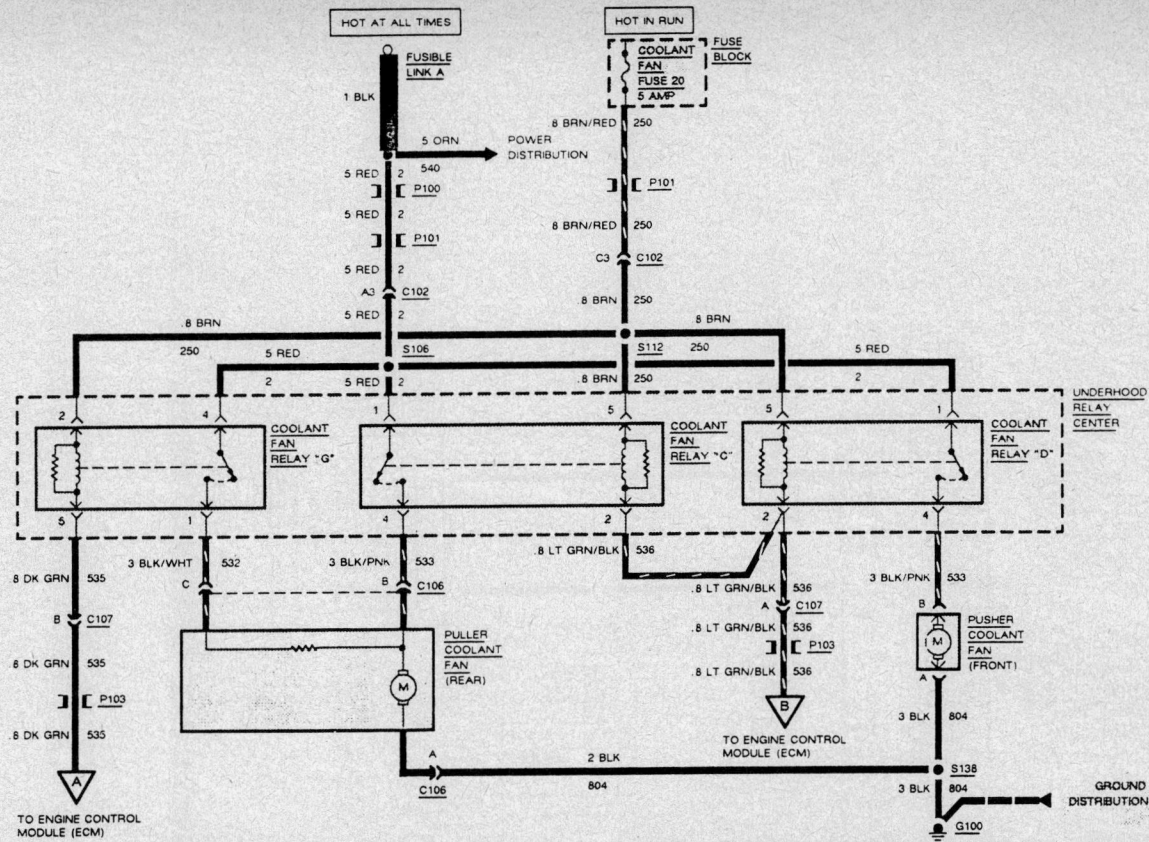

Fig. 109 Coolant fan wiring circuit (Part 1 of 2). 1989–90 Riviera

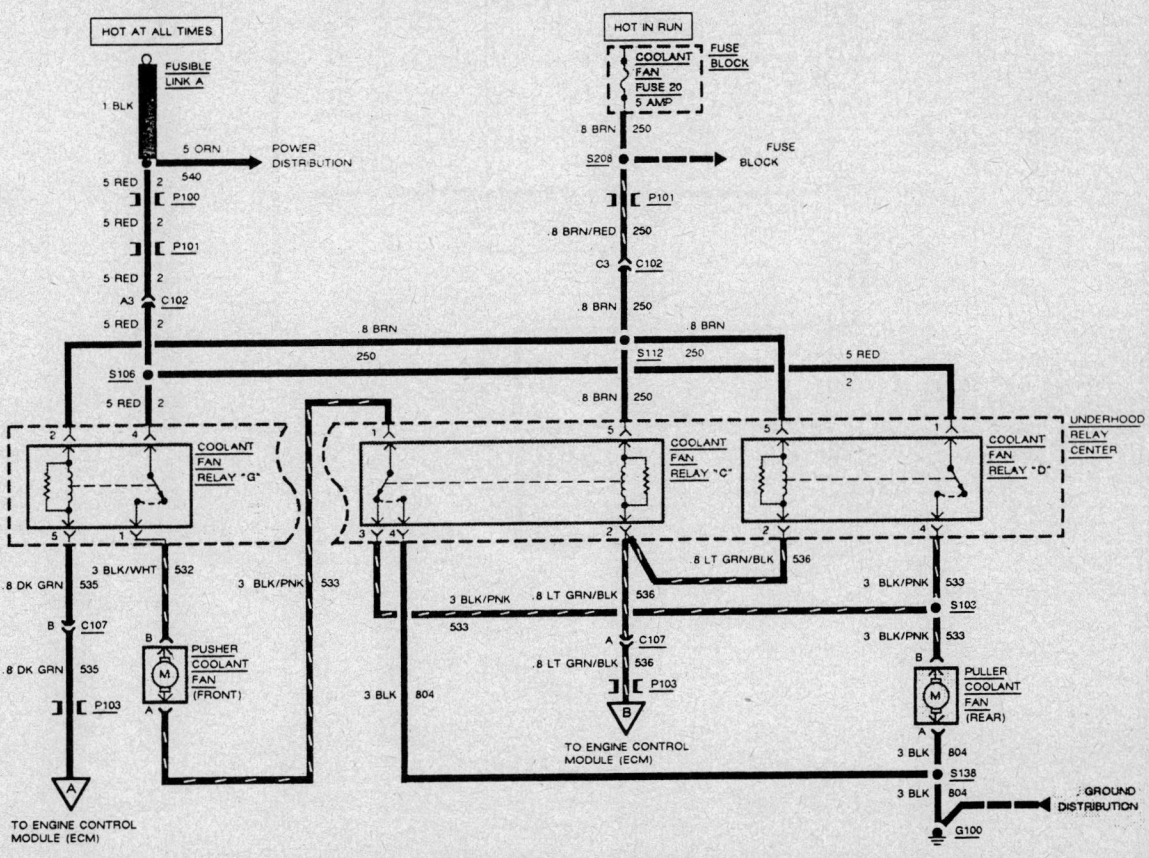

Fig. 109 Coolant fan wiring circuit (Part 1 of 2). 1989–90 Reatta

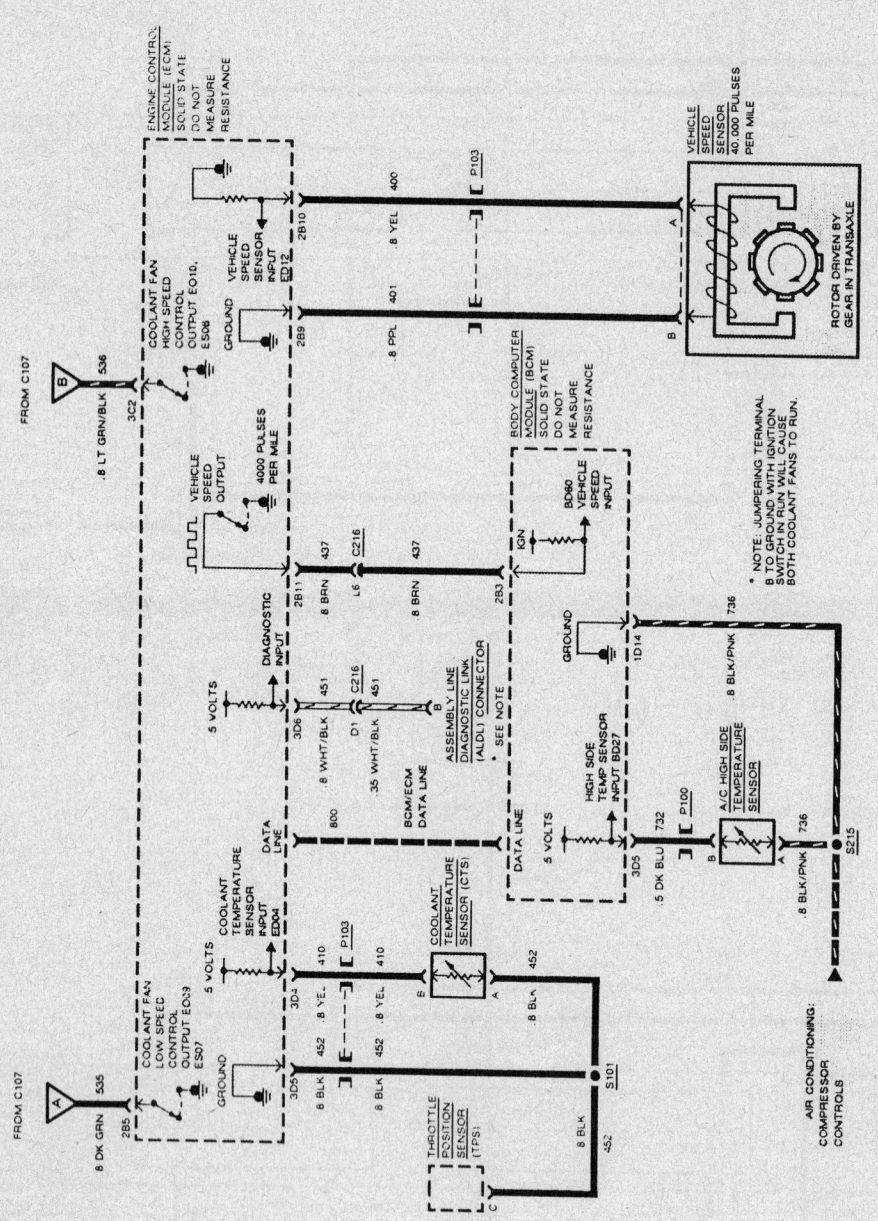

Fig. 109 Coolant fan wiring circuit (Part 2 of 2). 1989–90 Riviera & Reatta

CHART C-12A
COOLANT FANS FUNCTIONAL CHECK
3800 (VIN C) "E" CARLINE (PORT)

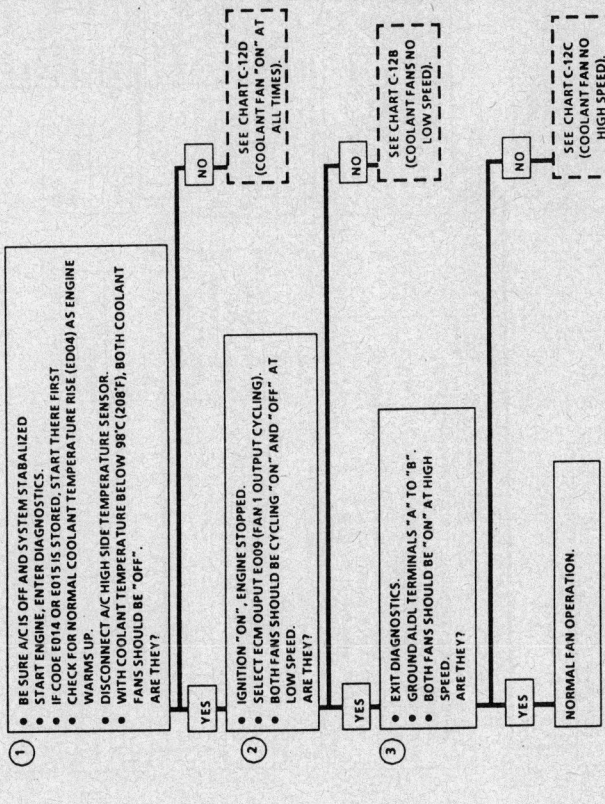

①
- BE SURE A/C IS OFF AND SYSTEM STABALIZED
- START ENGINE, ENTER DIAGNOSTICS.
- IF CODE E014 OR E015 IS STORED, START THERE FIRST
- CHECK FOR NORMAL COOLANT TEMPERATURE RISE (ED04) AS ENGINE WARMS UP.
- DISCONNECT A/C HIGH SIDE TEMPERATURE SENSOR.
- WITH COOLANT TEMPERATURE BELOW 98°C (208°F), BOTH COOLANT FANS SHOULD BE "OFF".

ARE THEY?

NO → SEE CHART C-12D (COOLANT FAN "ON" AT ALL TIMES).

YES ↓

②
- IGNITION "ON", ENGINE STOPPED.
- SELECT ECM OUPUT E009 (FAN 1 OUTPUT CYCLING).
- BOTH FANS SHOULD BE CYCLING "ON" AND "OFF" AT LOW SPEED.

ARE THEY?

NO → SEE CHART C-12B (COOLANT FANS NO LOW SPEED).

YES ↓

③
- EXIT DIAGNOSTICS.
- GROUND ALDL TERMINALS "A" TO "B".
- BOTH FANS SHOULD BE "ON" AT HIGH SPEED.

ARE THEY?

NO → SEE CHART C-12C (COOLANT FANS NO HIGH SPEED).

YES ↓

NORMAL FAN OPERATION.

WHEN ALL DIAGNOSIS AND REPAIRS ARE COMPLETED, CLEAR CODES AND VERIFY PROPER OPERATION

Fig. 110 Coolant fan diagnostic chart (Part 2 of 10). Riviera & Reatta

CHART C-12A
COOLANT FANS FUNCTIONAL CHECK
3800 (VIN C) "E" CARLINE (PORT)

ECM
- YD4 COOLANT SIGNAL
- YD5 SENSOR GRND
- BB5 FAN 1 QDR DRIVER
- YC2 FAN 2 QDR DRIVER

YEL 410 — BLK 452 — DK GRN 535 — LT GRN/BLK 536

5 AMP COOLANT FAN FUSE — 533 BLK/PNK — IGN

LOW SPEED = RELAY "G" ENERGIZED
HIGH SPEED = ALL RELAYS ENERGIZED

FAN RELAY "D" — FAN RELAY "C" — FAN RELAY "G"

533 PNK/BLK — 250 BRN — 804 BLK — 533 BLK/PNK — 532 BLK/WHT

COOLANT TEMPERATURE SENSOR

TO BATTERY JUNCTION BLOCK — 2 RED — FUSIBLE LINK

FRONT FAN — REAR FAN — 804 BLK

Circuit Description:

The ECM and three relays are used to control the two coolant fans.

LO Speed Fans Operation - Low speed of both fans are controlled by the ECM. The ECM energizes coolant fan relay "G" through terminal "BB5" when either the coolant temperature (ED04) exceeds 101°C (214°F) or A/C high side refrigerant temperature (BD27) exceeds 50°C (122°F).

High Speed Fans Operation - High speed of both fans are controlled by the ECM. The ECM energizes all three relays, when either coolant temperature (ED04) exceeds 108°C (226F°) or A/C high side refrigerant temperature (BD27) exceeds 65°C (149°F).

Test Description: Numbers below refer to circled numbers on the diagnostic chart.

1. Codes E014 or E015 could mean coolant system or sensor operation is not normal so fans operation can't be checked correctly.
2. ECM output E009 grounds fan relay "G" through the ECM for 3 seconds "ON" and 3 seconds "OFF." Fans should cycle "ON" for 3 seconds "OFF" for 3 seconds at low speed.
3. Grounding ALDL terminal "A" to "B" will cause the ECM to ground fan relays "G", "C" and "D" through the ECM. Fans should run at high speed.

Fig. 110 Coolant fan diagnostic chart (Part 1 of 10). Riviera & Reatta

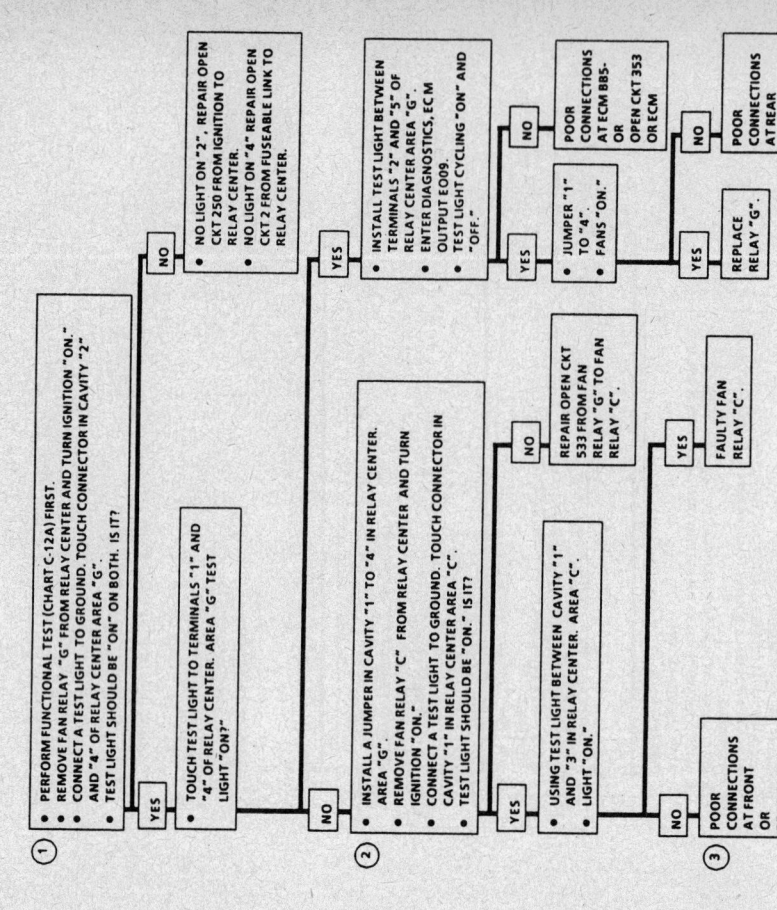

CHART C-12B
COOLANT FANS NO LOW SPEED
3800 (VIN C) "E" CARLINE (PORT)

1
- PERFORM FUNCTIONAL TEST (CHART C-12A) FIRST.
- REMOVE FAN RELAY "G" FROM RELAY CENTER AND TURN IGNITION "ON."
- CONNECT A TEST LIGHT TO GROUND. TOUCH CONNECTOR IN CAVITY "2" AND "4" OF RELAY CENTER AREA "G".
- TEST LIGHT SHOULD BE "ON" ON BOTH. IS IT?

- TOUCH TEST LIGHT TO TERMINALS "1" AND "4" OF RELAY CENTER. AREA "G" TEST LIGHT "ON"?

- NO LIGHT ON "2". REPAIR OPEN CKT 250 FROM IGNITION TO RELAY CENTER.
- NO LIGHT ON "4". REPAIR OPEN CKT 2 FROM FUSEABLE LINK TO RELAY CENTER.

- INSTALL TEST LIGHT BETWEEN TERMINALS "2" AND "5" OF RELAY CENTER AREA "G".
- ENTER DIAGNOSTICS, ECM OUTPUT E009.
- TEST LIGHT CYCLING "ON" AND "OFF."

- POOR CONNECTIONS AT ECM BB5 OR OPEN CKT 353 OR ECM

- JUMPER "1" TO "4".
- FANS "ON."

- POOR CONNECTIONS AT REAR OR FRONT FAN

- REPLACE RELAY "G".

2
- INSTALL A JUMPER IN CAVITY "1" TO "4" IN RELAY CENTER. AREA "G".
- REMOVE FAN RELAY "C" FROM RELAY CENTER AND TURN IGNITION "ON."
- CONNECT A TEST LIGHT TO GROUND. TOUCH CONNECTOR IN CAVITY "1" IN RELAY CENTER AREA "C".
- TEST LIGHT SHOULD BE "ON." IS IT?

- USING TEST LIGHT BETWEEN CAVITY "1" AND "3" IN RELAY CENTER, AREA "C". LIGHT "ON."

- REPAIR OPEN CKT 533 FROM FAN RELAY "G" TO FAN RELAY "C".

- FAULTY FAN RELAY "C".

3
- POOR CONNECTIONS AT FRONT OR REAR FAN.

Fig. 110 Coolant fan diagnostic chart (Part 4 of 10). Riviera & Reatta

---

ECM

COOLANT SIGNAL	YD4
SENSOR GRND	YD5
FAN 1 QDR DRIVER	BB5
FAN 2 QDR DRIVER	YC2

410 YEL
452 BLK
535 DK GRN
536 LT GRN/BLK

COOLANT TEMPERATURE SENSOR

TO BATTERY JUNCTION BLOCK

2 RED — FUSIBLE LINK

FAN RELAY "G"

FAN RELAY "C"

FAN RELAY "D"

533 PNK/BLK

250 BRN

533 BLK/PNK

532 BLK/WHT

533 BLK/PNK

804 BLK

533 BLK/PNK

FRONT FAN

REAR FAN

5 AMP COOLANT FAN FUSE

IGN

LOW SPEED = RELAY "G" ENERGIZED

CHART C-12B
COOLANT FANS NO LOW SPEED
3800 (VIN C) "E" CARLINE (PORT)

Circuit Description:

The ECM and three relays are used to control the two coolant fans.

LO Speed Fans Operation - Low speed of both fans are controlled by the ECM. The ECM energizes coolant fan relay "G" through terminal "BB5" when either the coolant temperature (ED04) exceeds 101°C (214°F) or A/C high side refrigerant temperature (BD27) exceeds 50°C (122°F).

High Speed Fans Operation - High speed of both fans are controlled by the ECM. The ECM energizes all three relays, when either coolant temperature (ED04) exceeds 108°C (226°F) or A/C high side refrigerant temperature (BD27) exceeds 65°C (149°F).

NOTICE: Mechanization drawing above reflects only those circuits and components used for low speed fans.

Test Description: Numbers below refer to circled numbers on the diagnostic chart.

1. Test light should be "ON" because harness terminal "2" has B+ with ignition switch turned "ON." Terminal "4" has B + all the time.

2. By jumpering "1" to "4" of relay "G" and removing relay "C" and touching a test light to terminal "1", validates the circuit up to relay "C". If light is "OFF," it is CKT 532, CKT 533 or the front fan.

3. Test light "ON" validates all circuits. If light is "ON," relay "C" is bad. If light is "OFF," it is connections at rear fan or fan motor.

Fig. 110 Coolant fan diagnostic chart (Part 3 of 10). Riviera & Reatta

CHART C-12C-A

COOLANT FAN NO HIGH SPEED REAR FAN
3800 (VIN C) "E" CARLINE (PORT)

① • PERFORM FUNCTIONAL TEST (CHART C-12A) FIRST.
• REMOVE FAN RELAY "D" FROM RELAY CENTER, AND TURN IGNITION "ON."
• CONNECT A TEST LIGHT TO GROUND, AND TOUCH TERMINAL "1" AND "5".
• TEST LIGHT SHOULD BE "ON" AT BOTH. IS IT?

YES → ② • CONNECT TEST LIGHT BETWEEN CAVITY "2" AND "5" IN RELAY CENTER. AREA "D".
• ENTER DIAGNOSTICS.
• SELECT EO10 (FAN OUTPUT CYCLING).
• TEST LIGHT SHOULD BE CYCLING "ON" AND "OFF." IS IT?

NO →
• NO LIGHT ON "5" OPEN CKT 250 FROM COOLANT FANS FUSE TO RELAY CENTER.
• NO LIGHT ON "1" OPEN CKT 2 FROM FUSEABLE LINK TO RELAY CENTER.

YES → ③ • INSTALL A JUMPER BETWEEN CAVITY "1" AND "4" OF RELAY CENTER. AREA "D".
• FAN SHOULD BE "ON." IS IT?

NO → CHECK FOR OPEN CKT 536. IF CIRCUIT IS OK, IT'S POOR CONNECTION AT ECM TERMINAL "YC2" OR FAULTY ECM.

YES → FAULTY FAN RELAY "D".

NO → ④ • REINSTALL FAN RELAY "D".
• WITH EO10 STILL SELECTED, DISCONNECT REAR FAN HARNESS CONNECTOR FROM FAN MOTOR.
• CONNECT A TEST LIGHT FROM HARNESS TERMINAL "A" TO "B".
• DOES TEST LIGHT CYCLE "OFF" AND "ON"?

YES → FAULTY REAR FAN ASSEMBLY.

NO → OPEN CKT 533 OR 804.

WHEN ALL DIAGNOSIS AND REPAIRS ARE COMPLETED, CLEAR CODES AND VERIFY PROPER OPERATION.

Fig. 110 Coolant fan diagnostic chart (Part 6 of 10). Riviera & Reatta

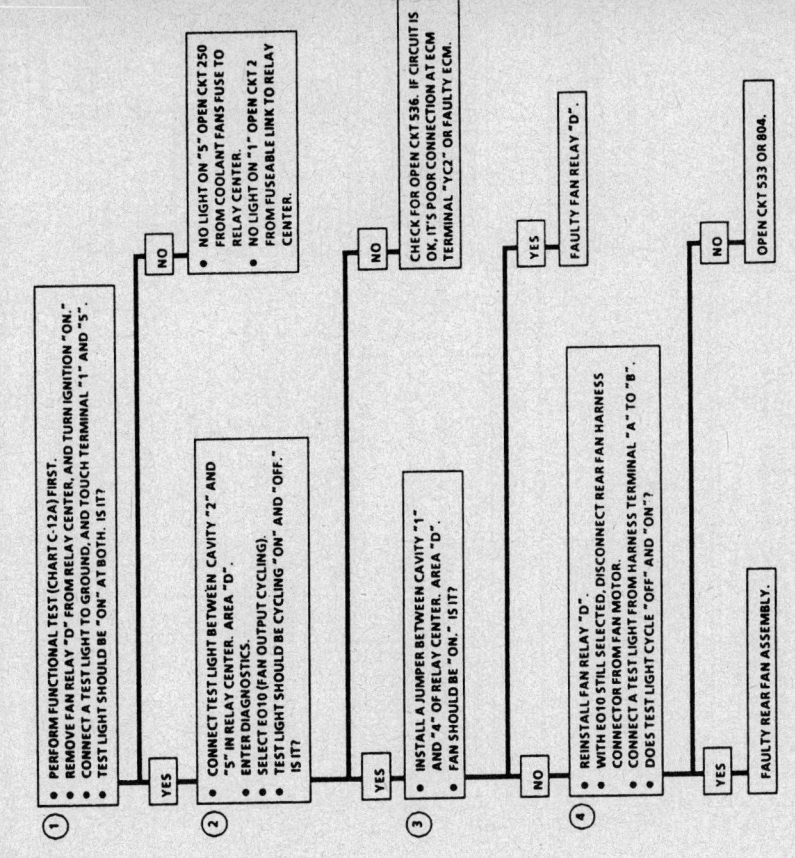

CHART C-12C-A

COOLANT FAN NO HIGH SPEED REAR FAN
3800 (VIN C) "E" CARLINE (PORT)

Fig. 110 Coolant fan diagnostic chart (Part 5 of 10). Riviera & Reatta

Circuit Description:

The ECM and three relays are used to control the two coolant fans.

LO Speed Fans Operation - Low speed of both fans are controlled by the ECM. The ECM energizes coolant fan relay "G" through terminal "BB5" when either the coolant temperature (BD27) exceeds 50°C (122°F) or A/C high side refrigerant temperature (ED04) exceeds 101°C (214°F) or A/C high side refrigerant temperature (BD27) exceeds 50°C (122°F).

High Speed Fans Operation - High speed of both fans are controlled by the ECM. The ECM energizes all three relays, when either coolant temperature (ED04) exceeds 108°C (226°F) or A/C high side refrigerant temperature (BD27) exceeds 65°C (149°F).

NOTICE: Mechanization drawing above reflects only those circuits and components used for high speed rear fan operation.

Test Description: Numbers below refer to circled numbers on the diagnostic chart.

1. Test light should be "ON" because harness terminal "5" has B+ with ignition switch turned "ON," Terminal "1" has B+ all the time.

2. Test light should be "ON" for 3 seconds and "OFF" for 3 seconds as EO10 cycles fan "ON/OFF" at 3 second intervals.

3. Jumpering harness terminals "1" and "4" bypasses the relay. If fan runs, the relay is faulty.

4. Cycling of the test light proves CKT 533 and 804 are OK, so fan motor is faulty.

CHART C-12C-B
COOLANT FAN NO HIGH SPEED FRONT FAN 3800 (VIN C) "E" CARLINE (PORT)

① (Box 1)
- PERFORM FUNCTIONAL TEST (CHART C-12A) FIRST.
- REMOVE FAN RELAY "G" FROM RELAY CENTER AND TURN IGNITION "ON."
- CONNECT A TEST LIGHT TO GROUND. TOUCH CONNECTOR IN CAVITY "2" AND "4" OF RELAY CENTER AREA "G".
- TEST LIGHT SHOULD BE "ON" ON BOTH. IS IT?

NO →
- NO LIGHT ON "2", REPAIR OPEN CKT 250 FROM IGNITION TO RELAY CENTER.
- NO LIGHT ON "4" REPAIR OPEN CKT 2 FROM FUSEABLE LINK TO RELAY CENTER.

YES →
- TOUCH TEST LIGHT TO TERMINALS "1" AND "4" OF RELAY CENTER. AREA "G" TEST LIGHT "ON"?

② (Box 2)
- INSTALL A JUMPER IN CAVITY "1" TO "4" IN RELAY CENTER. AREA "G".
- REMOVE FAN RELAY "C" FROM RELAY CENTER AND TURN IGNITION "ON."
- CONNECT A TEST LIGHT TO GROUND. TOUCH CONNECTOR IN CAVITY "1" IN RELAY CENTER. AREA "C". IS IT?
- TEST LIGHT SHOULD BE "ON."

YES →
- INSTALL TEST LIGHT BETWEEN TERMINALS "2" AND "5" OF RELAY CENTER AREA "G".
- ENTER DIAGNOSTICS, ECM OUTPUT EO09.
- TEST LIGHT CYCLING "ON" AND "OFF."

- NO → POOR CONNECTIONS AT ECM BB5- OR OPEN CKT 353 OR ECM
- YES → JUMPER "1" TO "4". FANS "ON."?
  - YES → REPLACE RELAY "G".
  - NO → POOR CONNECTIONS AT FRONT OR REAR FANS.

③ (Box 3)
- USING TEST LIGHT BETWEEN CAVITY "1" AND "4" IN RELAY CENTER. AREA "C". LIGHT "ON."

- NO → REPAIR OPEN CKT 533 FROM FAN RELAY "G" TO FAN RELAY "C".
- YES → FAULTY FAN RELAY "C".

OPEN CKT 804

Fig. 110 Coolant fan diagnostic chart (Part 8 of 10). Riviera & Reatta

---

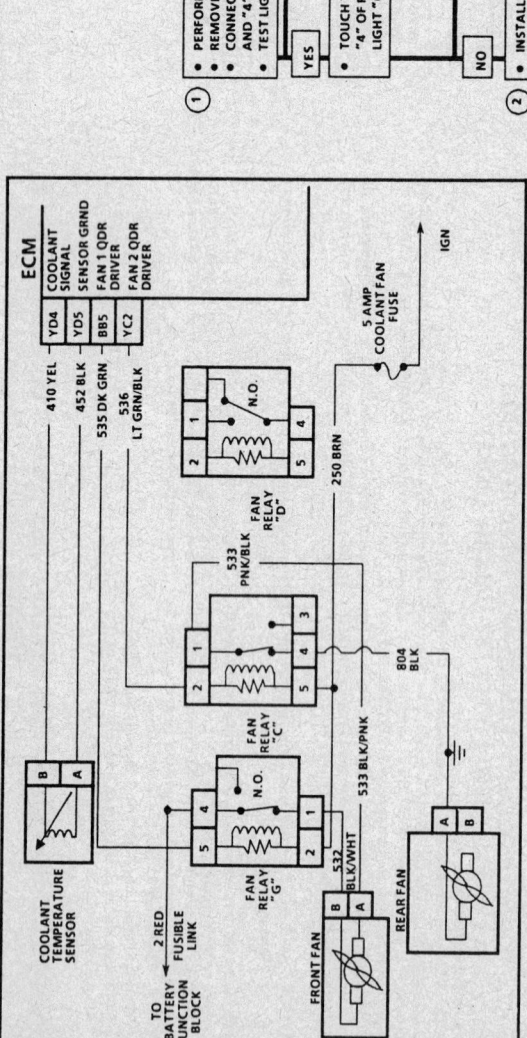

CHART C-12C-B
COOLANT FAN NO HIGH SPEED FRONT FAN 3800 (VIN C) "E" CARLINE (PORT)

ECM

410 YEL	YD4	COOLANT SIGNAL
452 BLK	YD5	SENSOR GRND
535 DK GRN	BB5	FAN 1 QDR DRIVER
536 LT GRN/BLK	YC2	FAN 2 QDR DRIVER

Circuit Description:

The ECM and three relays are used to control the two coolant fans.

LO Speed Fans Operation - Low speed of both fans are controlled by the ECM. The ECM energizes coolant fan relay "G" through terminal "BB5" when either the coolant temperature (BD27) exceeds 50°C (122°F) or A/C high side refrigerant temperature (ED04) exceeds 101°C (214°F) or

High Speed Fans Operation - High speed of both fans are controlled by the ECM. The ECM energizes all three relays, when either coolant temperature (ED04) exceeds 108°C (226°F) or A/C high side refrigerant temperature (BD27) exceeds 65°C (149°F).

NOTICE: Mechanization drawing above reflects only those circuits and components used for high speed front fan operation.

Test Description: Numbers below refer to circled numbers on the diagnostic chart.

1. Test light should be "ON" because harness terminal "2" has B+ with ignition switch turned "ON." Terminal "4" has B+ all the time. Test light "ON" validates circuit through both fan motors, relay "C" and ground connections.

2. By jumpering "1" to "4" of relay "G" and removing a test light to terminal "1", validates the circuit up to relay "C". If light is "OFF," it is CKT 532, CKT 533 or the front fan.

3. Test light "ON" validates all circuits. If light is "ON," relay "C" is bad. If light is "OFF," it is a problem with the ground CKT 804.

Fig. 110 Coolant fan diagnostic chart (Part 7 of 10). Riviera & Reatta

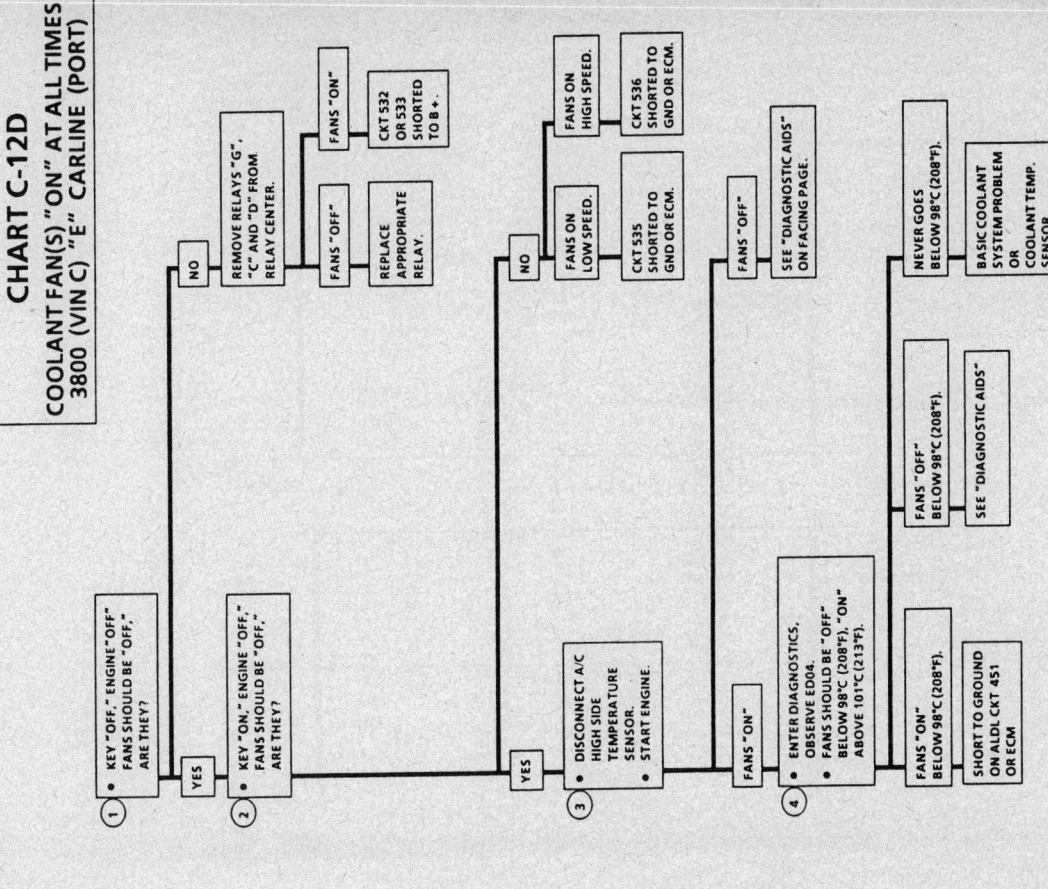

CHART C-12D

COOLANT FAN(S) "ON" AT ALL TIMES 3800 (VIN C) "E" CARLINE (PORT)

Fig. 110 Coolant fan diagnostic chart (Part 10 of 10). Riviera & Reatta

CHART C-12D

COOLANT FAN(S) "ON" AT ALL TIMES 3800 (VIN C) "E" CARLINE (PORT)

LOW SPEED = RELAY "G" ENERGIZED
HIGH SPEED = ALL RELAYS ENERGIZED

ECM

YD4	COOLANT SIGNAL
YD5	SENSOR GRND
BB5	FAN 1 QDR DRIVER
YC2	FAN 2 QDR DRIVER

Circuit Description:
The ECM and three relays are used to control the two coolant fans.
Lo Speed Fans Operation - Low speed of both fans are controlled by the ECM. The ECM energizes coolant fan relay "G" through terminal "BB5" when either the coolant temperature (BD27) exceeds 50°C (122°F) or A/C high side refrigerant temperature exceeds 101°C (214°F) or A/C high side refrigerant temperature exceeds 50°C (122°F).
High Speed Fans Operation - High speed of both fans are controlled by the ECM. The ECM energizes all three relays, when either coolant temperature (ED04) exceeds 108°C (226°F) or A/C high side refrigerant temperature (BD27) exceeds 65°C (149°F).

Test Description: Numbers below refer to circled numbers on the diagnostic chart.
1. Fans should not run when key is "OFF."
2. Fans should not run when engine is "OFF."
3. Disconnecting the A/C high side temperature sensor will remove the BCM ECM request due to the A/C high side temperature.
4. Defines fan operation based on coolant temperature only.

Diagnostic Aids:
Coolant fans should be "OFF" if:
1. Coolant temperature is less than 98°C (208°F).
2. A/C high side temperature is less than 50°C (122°F).

NOTE: On-board diagnostics may assist in diagnosing:
BD21 is coolant temperature.
BD27 is A/C high side temperature sensor.

The ECM energizes coolant fan relay "G" through terminal "BB5" when either the coolant temperature (BD27) exceeds 50°C (122°F) or A/C high side refrigerant temperature (ED04) exceeds 101°C (214°F) or A/C high side refrigerant temperature exceeds 50°C (122°F).

Disconnecting the A/C high side temperature sensor should result in BD27 reading less than –30°C. If not, problem is ECM related.

Disconnecting the coolant temperature sensor should cause BD21 to read less than –30°C (–30°F) also. If not, problem is ECM related.

BD27 should read about 50°C (122°F) when A/C system high side pressure is approximately 160 psi. Comparing these might point out a bad sensor.

NOTE: Normal coolant fan operation requires low speed if:
Engine is running, vehicle speed is less than 45 mph and coolant temperature (ED04, BD21) exceeds 101°C (214°F) or A/C high side temperature is greater than 50°C (122°F).

Fig. 110 Coolant fan diagnostic chart (Part 9 of 10). Riviera & Reatta

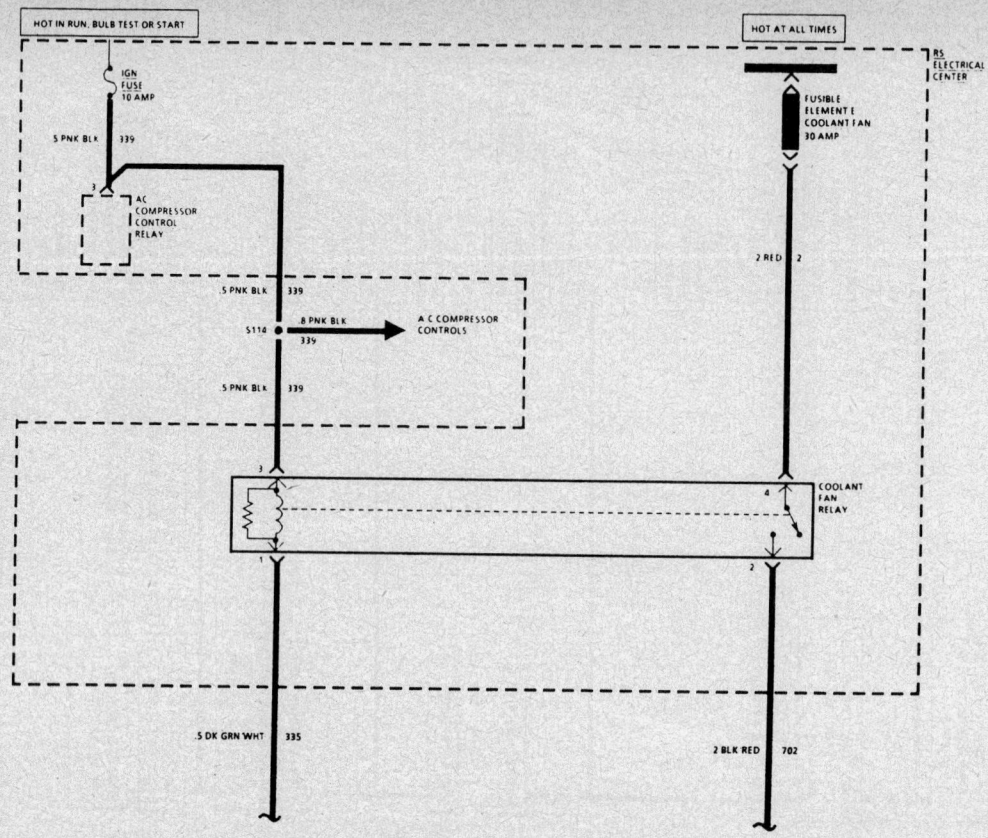

Fig. 111   Coolant fan wiring circuit (Part 1 of 2). 1990 Lumina

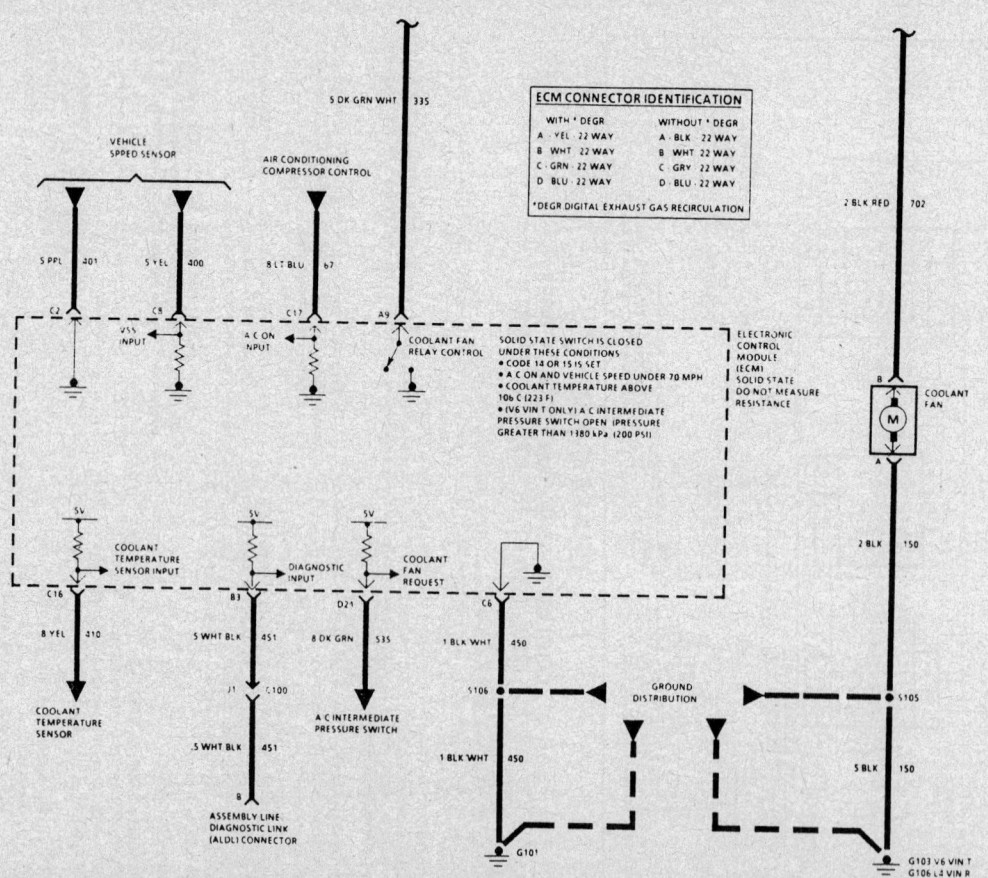

Fig. 111   Coolant fan wiring circuit (Part 2 of 2). 1990 Lumina

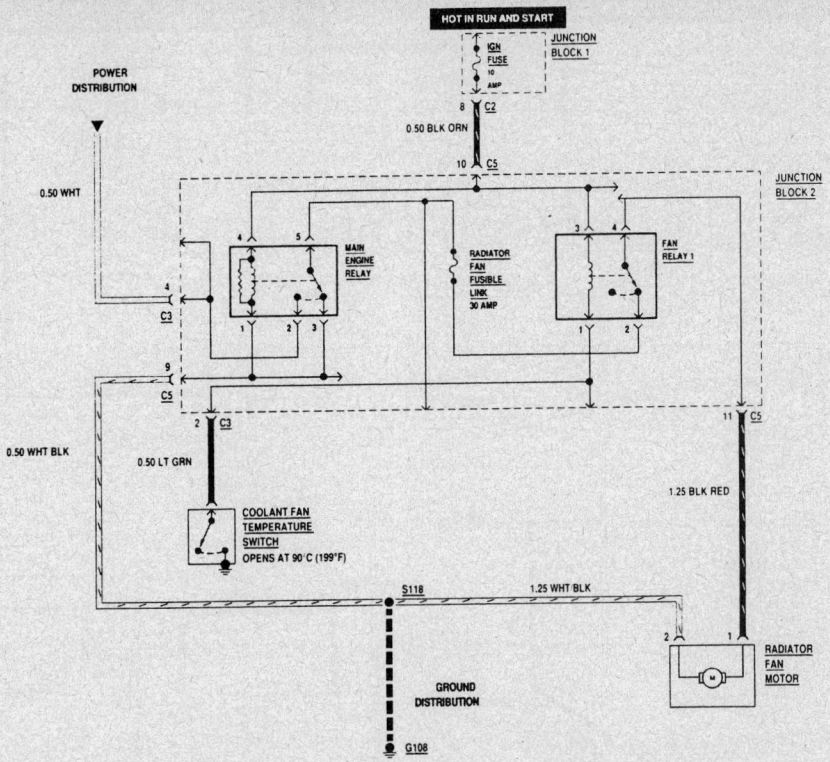

Fig. 112   Coolant fan wiring circuit. 1990 Prizm less A/C

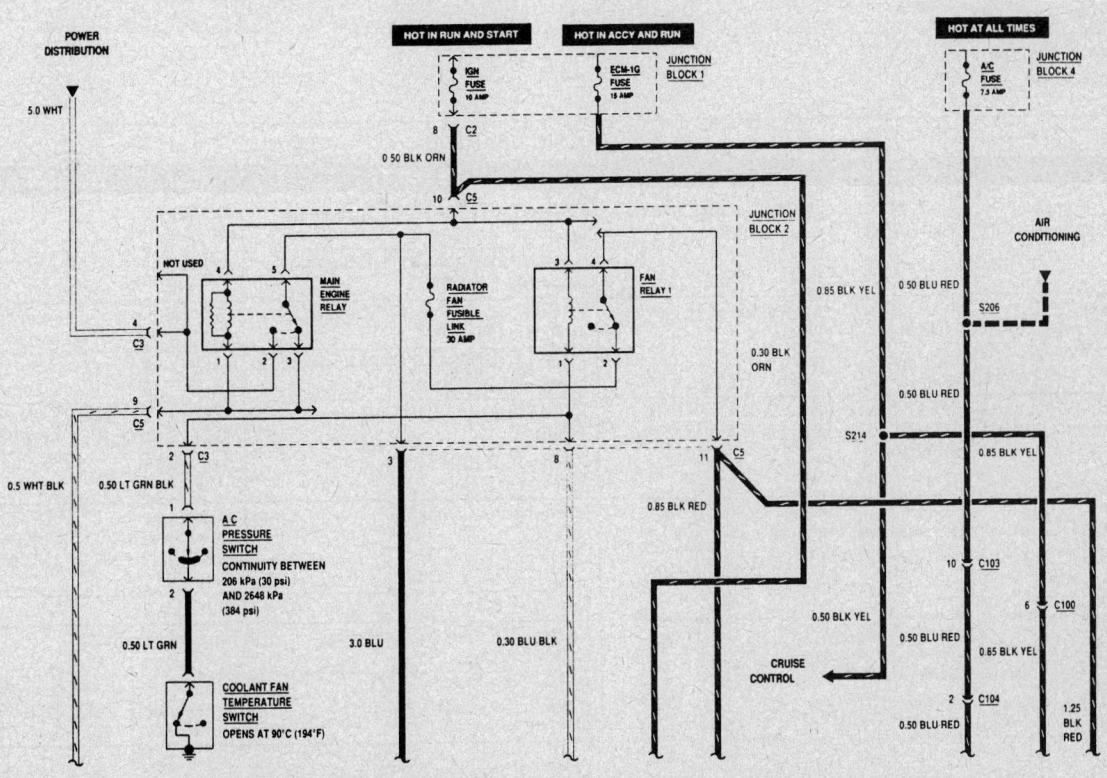

Fig. 113   Coolant fan wiring circuit (Part 1 of 2). 1990 Prizm with A/C

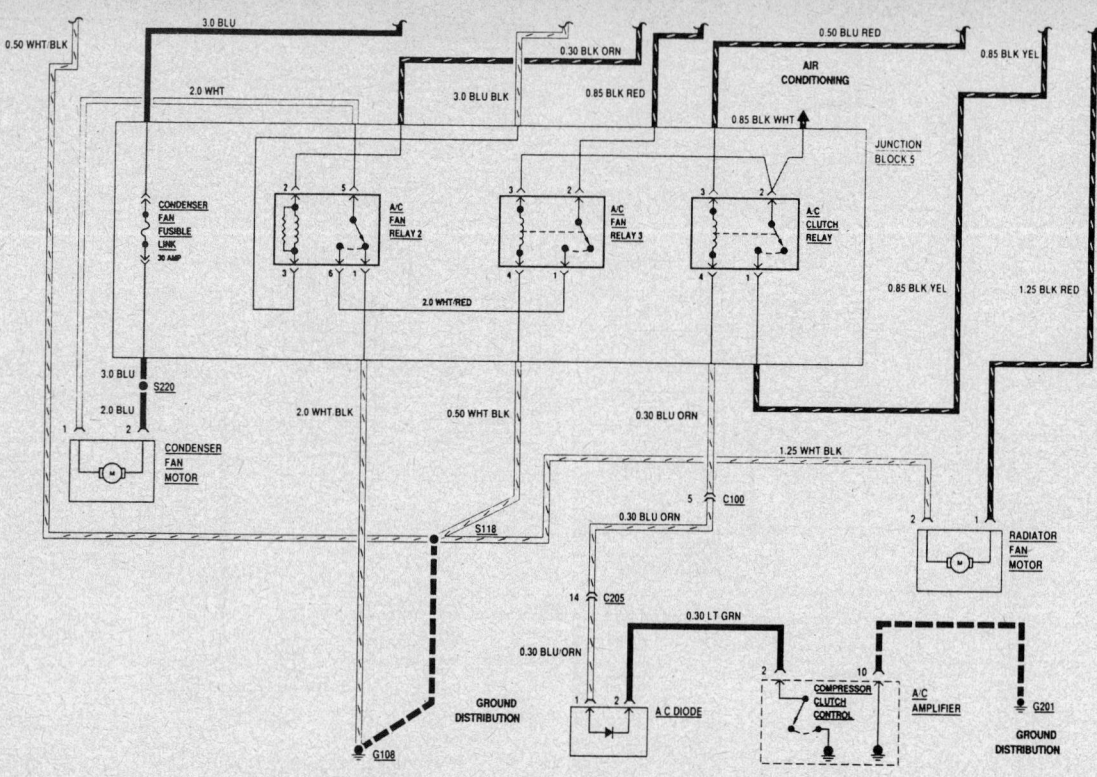

Fig. 113   Coolant fan wiring circuit (Part 2 of 2). 1990 Prizm with A/C

COOLANT FANS		DIAGNOSTIC CHART A		
	TEST	**RESULT**		**ACTION**
A1.	Start and run the engine. Make certain that engine coolant temperature is below 90°C (194°F).	RADIATOR FAN MOTOR does not operate.		GO TO **A2**.
		RADIATOR FAN MOTOR operates below 90°C (194°F).		GO TO **A3**.
A2.	Cover the front of the radiator. Run the engine until operating temperature reaches 90°C (194°F).	RADIATOR FAN MOTOR operates at 90°C (194°F).		All systems diagnosed in this cell are functioning normally.
		RADIATOR FAN MOTOR does not operate at 90°C (194°F).		GO TO **A6**.
A3.	Remove the COOLANT FAN TEMPERATURE SWITCH connector. Connect a fused jumper between the connector cavity and chassis ground.	RADIATOR FAN MOTOR stops running.		Replace COOLANT FAN TEMPERATURE SWITCH.
		RADIATOR FAN MOTOR continues to run.		GO TO **A4**.
A4.	Turn ignition switch to "OFF." Backprobe JUNCTION BLOCK 2 connector C3 with a digital multimeter from cavity 2 to chassis ground. Measure resistance.	More than 0.3 ohms.		Repair open in LT GRN wire between JUNCTION BLOCK 2 and COOLANT FAN TEMPERATURE SWITCH.
		Less than 0.3 ohms.		GO TO **A5**.
A5.	Remove jumper. Reconnect COOLANT FAN TEMPERATURE SWITCH connector. Turn ignition switch to "RUN." Remove Fan Relay 1 from JUNCTION BLOCK 2.	RADIATOR FAN MOTOR stops running.		Replace Fan Relay 1.
		RADIATOR FAN MOTOR continues to run.		Repair short to voltage in BLK/RED wire between JUNCTION BLOCK 2 and RADIATOR FAN MOTOR.

Fig. 114   System diagnosis chart (Part 1 of 2). 1990 Prizm

COOLANT FANS	DIAGNOSTIC CHART A (CONT'D)		
	TEST	RESULT	ACTION
A6.	Disconnect COOLANT FAN TEMPERATURE SWITCH connector.	RADIATOR FAN MOTOR starts running.	Replace COOLANT FAN TEMPERATURE SWITCH.
		RADIATOR FAN MOTOR does not operate.	GO TO A7.
A7.	Connect a digital multimeter from COOLANT FAN TEMPERATURE SWITCH connector to chassis ground. Measure resistance.	Less than 0.3 ohms.	Repair short to ground in LT GRN wire between JUNCTION BLOCK 2 and COOLANT FAN TEMPERATURE SWITCH.
		More than 0.3 ohms.	GO TO A8.
A8.	Leave COOLANT FAN TEMPERATURE SWITCH disconnected. Backprobe RADIATOR FAN MOTOR connector with a test lamp from cavity 1 to chassis ground. Turn ignition switch to "RUN."	Test lamp lights.	GO TO A9.
		Test lamp does not light.	GO TO A10.
A9.	Turn ignition switch to "OFF." Backprobe RADIATOR FAN MOTOR connector with a digital multimeter from cavity 2 to chassis ground. Measure resistance.	More than 0.3 ohms.	Repair WHT BLK ground wire.
		Less than 0.3 ohms.	Replace RADIATOR FAN MOTOR.
A10.	Backprobe JUNCTION BLOCK 2 connector C5 with a test lamp from cavity 11 to chassis ground.	Test lamp lights.	Repair open in BLK/RED wire between JUNCTION BLOCK 2 and RADIATOR FAN MOTOR.
		Test lamp does not light.	Replace Fan Relay 1.

Fig. 114 System diagnosis chart (Part 2 of 2). 1990 Prizm

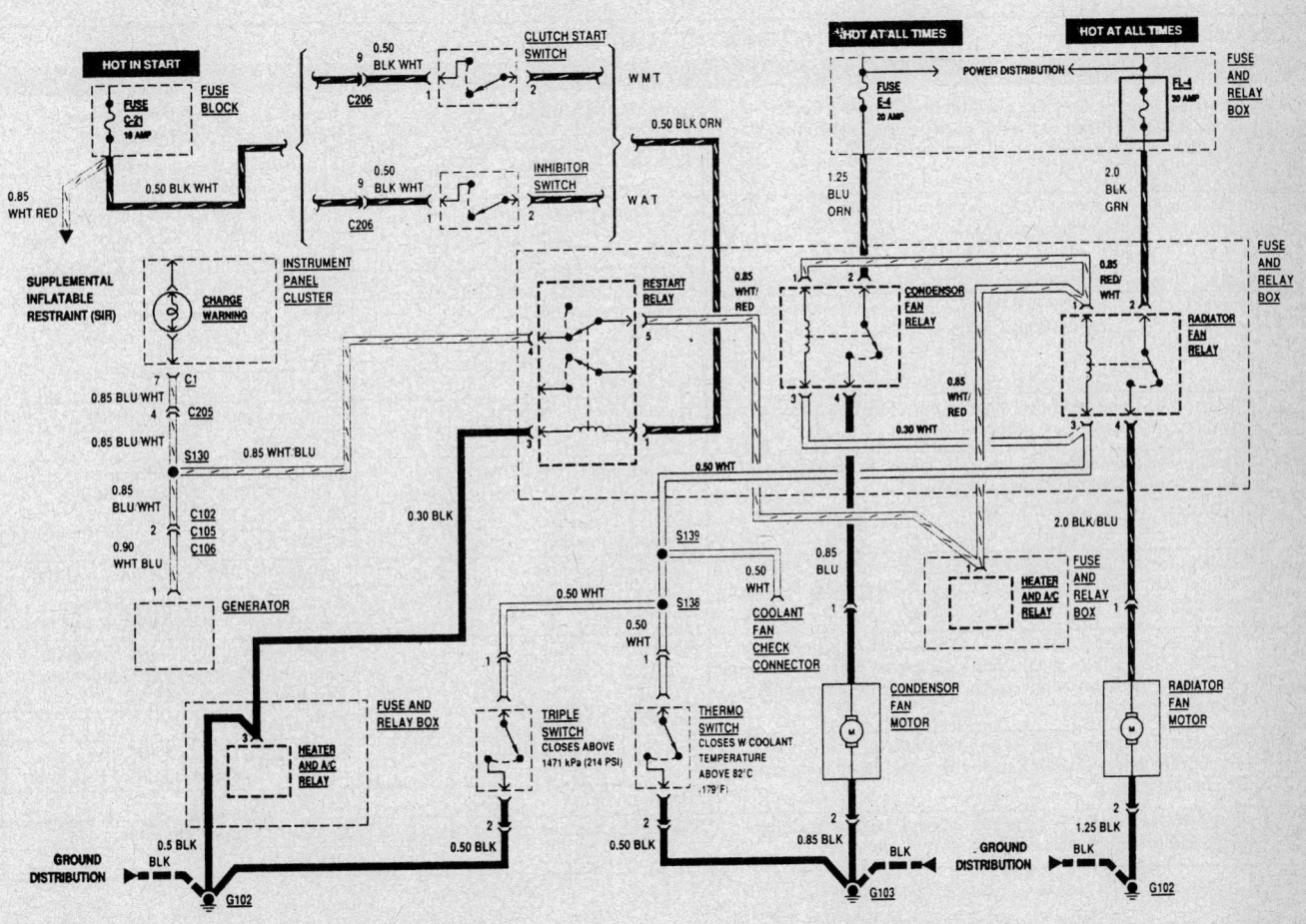

Fig. 115 Coolant fan wiring circuit. 1990 Storm

COOLANT FANS		DIAGNOSTIC CHART A	
	TEST	**RESULT**	**ACTION**
A1.	Start and run the engine until coolant temperature reaches 85°C (185°F).	RADIATOR FAN and CONDENSER FAN operate.	GO TO **A2**.
		RADIATOR FAN operates only.	GO TO **A6**.
		CONDENSER FAN operates only.	GO TO **A11**.
		Neither fan operates.	GO TO **A3**.
A2.	Disconnect THERMO SWITCH connector. Run engine with air conditioning operating for a 5 minute period.	RADIATOR FAN and CONDENSER FAN both operate at least once during the 5 minute test.	All systems diagnosed in this cell are functioning normally.
		Neither fan operates at all during the 5 minute test.	GO TO **A16**.
A3.	Connect a fused jumper from COOLING FAN CHECK CONNECTOR to chassis ground with engine still running.	RADIATOR FAN and CONDENSER FAN operate.	GO TO **A4**.
		Neither fan operates.	GO TO **A18**.
		RADIATOR FAN operates only.	GO TO **A6**.
		CONDENSER FAN operates only.	GO TO **A11**.
A4.	Disconnect THERMO SWITCH connector. Connect a jumper between cavities 1 and 2 with engine running.	Fans operate.	Replace THERMO SWITCH.
		Fans do not operate.	GO TO **A5**.

Fig. 116   System diagnosis chart (Part 1 of 4). 1990 Storm

COOLANT FANS		DIAGNOSTIC CHART A (CONT'D)	
	TEST	**RESULT**	**ACTION**
A5.	Remove jumper. Connect a digital multimeter from THERMO SWITCH connector cavity 2 to chassis ground. Measure resistance.	More than 0.3 ohms.	Repair BLK ground wire between THERMO SWITCH and G103.
		Less than 0.3 ohms.	Repair WHT wire between THERMO SWITCH and S139.
A6.	Backprobe Condenser Fan Relay connector with a test lamp from cavity 1 to chassis ground.	Test lamp does not light.	Repair open in RED/WHT wire between Radiator Fan Relay and Condenser Fan Relay.
		Test lamp lights.	GO TO **A7**.
A7.	Backprobe Condenser Fan Relay connector with a test lamp from cavity 2 to chassis ground.	Test lamp does not light.	Repair open in BLU/ORN wire between Fuse E-4 and Condenser Fan Relay.
		Test lamp lights.	GO TO **A8**.
A8.	Backprobe Condenser Fan Relay connector with a test lamp from cavity 4 to chassis ground.	Test lamp does not light.	Replace Condenser Fan Relay.
		Test lamp lights.	GO TO **A9**.
A9.	Backprobe CONDENSER FAN MOTOR connector with a test lamp from cavity 1 to chassis ground.	Test lamp does not light.	Repair open in BLU wire between CONDENSER FAN MOTOR and FUSE AND RELAY BOX.
		Test lamp lights.	GO TO **A10**.
A10.	Disconnect CONDENSER FAN MOTOR connector. Connect a digital multimeter from cavity 2 to chassis ground. Measure resistance.	Less than 0.3 ohms.	Replace CONDENSER FAN MOTOR.
		More than 0.3 ohms.	Repair BLK ground wire between CONDENSER FAN MOTOR and G103.
A11.	Remove Condenser Fan Relay and Radiator Fan Relay from FUSE AND RELAY BOX. Connect a digital multimeter from Radiator Fan Relay connector cavity 3 to chassis ground. Measure resistance.	More than 0.3 ohms.	Repair open in WHT wire between Radiator Fan Relay and Condenser Fan Relay.
		Less than 0.3 ohms.	GO TO **A12**.
A12.	Reinstall Condenser Fan Relay and Radiator Fan Relay. Backprobe Radiator Fan Relay with a test lamp from cavity 2 to chassis ground.	Test lamp does not light.	Repair open in BLK/GRN wire between FL-4 and Radiator Fan Relay.
		Test lamp lights.	GO TO **A13**.
A13.	Backprobe Radiator Fan Relay connector with a test lamp from cavity 4 to chassis ground.	Test lamp does not light.	Replace Radiator Fan Relay.
		Test lamp lights.	GO TO **A14**.

Fig. 116   System diagnosis chart (Part 2 of 4). 1990 Storm

COOLANT FANS	DIAGNOSTIC CHART A (CONT'D)	
TEST	**RESULT**	**ACTION**
A14. Backprobe RADIATOR FAN MOTOR connector with a test lamp from cavity 1 to chassis ground.	Test lamp does not light.	Repair open in BLK/BLU wire between FUSE AND RELAY BOX and RADIATOR FAN MOTOR.
	Test lamp lights.	GO TO **A15**.
A15. Disconnect RADIATOR FAN MOTOR connector. Connect a digital multimeter from cavity 2 to chassis ground. Measure resistance.	More than 0.3 ohms.	Repair BLK ground wire between RADIATOR FAN MOTOR and G102.
	Less than 0.3 ohms.	Replace RADIATOR FAN MOTOR.
A16. Disconnect TRIPLE SWITCH connector and remove Condenser Fan Relay from FUSE AND RELAY BOX. Connect a digital multimeter from TRIPLE SWITCH connector cavity 1 to Condenser Fan Relay connector cavity 3. Measure resistance.	More than 0.3 ohms.	Repair open in WHT wire between S138 and TRIPLE SWITCH.
	Less than 0.3 ohms.	GO TO **A17**.
A17. Connect a digital multimeter from TRIPLE SWITCH connector cavity 2 to chassis ground. Measure resistance.	More than 0.3 ohms.	Repair BLK ground wire between TRIPLE SWITCH and G102.
	Less than 0.3 ohms.	Replace TRIPLE SWITCH. IMPORTANT: Receiver/Dryer must be replaced as a unit in order replace TRIPLE SWITCH.
A18. Disconnect THERMO SWITCH connector. Connect a digital multimeter from cavity 2 to chassis ground. Measure resistance.	More than 0.3 ohms.	Repair BLK ground wire between THERMO SWITCH and G103.
	Less than 0.3 ohms.	GO TO **A19**.
A19. Connect a jumper across THERMO SWITCH connector cavities. Remove Condenser Fan Relay and Radiator Fan Relay from FUSE AND RELAY BOX. Connect a digital multimeter from Condenser Fan Relay connector cavity 3 to chassis ground. Measure resistance.	More than 0.3 ohms.	Repair open in WHT wire between FUSE AND RELAY BOX and THERMO SWITCH.
	Less than 0.3 ohms.	GO TO **A20**.
A20. Connect a digital multimeter from Radiator Fan Relay connector cavity 3 to chassis ground. Measure resistance.	More than 0.3 ohms.	Repair open in WHT wire between Radiator Fan Relay and Condenser Fan Relay.
	Less than 0.3 ohms.	GO TO **A21**.
A21. Backprobe GENERATOR connector with a test lamp from cavity 1 to chassis ground.	Test lamp does not light.	Replace GENERATOR.
	Test lamp lights.	GO TO **A22**.

Fig. 116   System diagnosis chart (Part 3 of 4). 1990 Storm

COOLANT FANS	DIAGNOSTIC CHART A (CONT'D)		
TEST		**RESULT**	**ACTION**
A22. Backprobe Restart Relay connector with a test lamp from cavity 5 to chassis ground.		Test lamp does not light.	Repair open in WHT/BLU wire between GENERATOR and FUSE AND RELAY BOX.
		Test lamp lights.	GO TO **A23**.
A23. Backprobe Restart Relay connector with a test lamp from cavity 5 to chassis ground.		Test lamp does not light.	Replace Restart Relay.
		Test lamp lights.	GO TO **A24**.
A24. Backprobe Heater and A/C Relay connector with a test lamp from cavity 1 to chassis ground.		Test lamp does not light.	Repair open in WHT/RED wire between Restart Relay and Heater and A/C Relay.
		Test lamp lights.	Repair open in WHT/RED wire between Heater and A/C Relay and Radiator Fan Relay.

Fig. 116   System diagnosis chart (Part 4 of 4). 1990 Storm

DASH GAUGES

INDEX

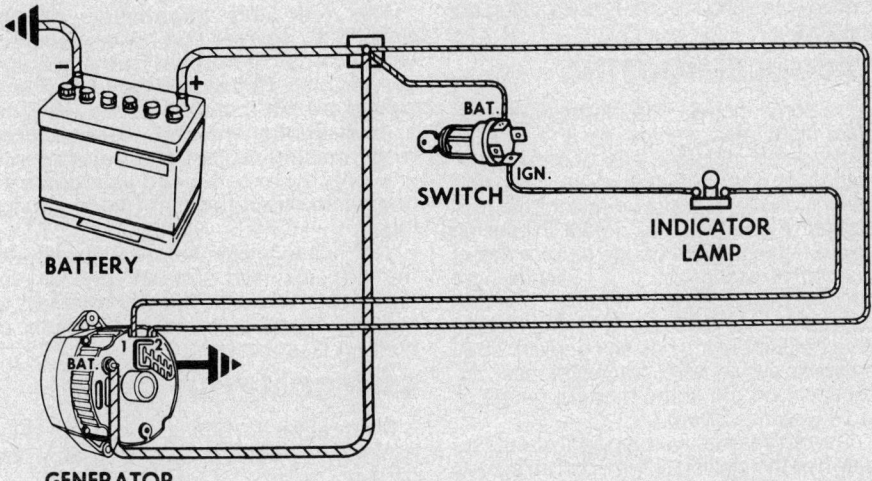

Fig. 1 Charge indicator lamp wiring. Delco SI type charging system

GENERAL TESTING

Gauge failures are often caused by defective wiring or grounds. The first step in locating a trouble should be a thorough inspection of all wiring, terminals and printed circuits. If wiring is secured by clamps, check to see whether the insulation has been severed thereby grounding the wire. In the case of a fuel gauge installation, rust may cause failure by corrosion at the ground connection of the tank unit.

VARIABLE VOLTAGE GAUGES

The variable voltage type dash gauge consists of two magnetic coils to which battery voltage is applied. The coils act on the gauge pointer and pull in opposite directions. One coil is grounded directly to the chassis, while the other coil is grounded through a variable resistor within the sending unit. Resistance through the sending unit determines current flow through its coil, and therefore pointer position.

When resistance is high in the sending unit, less current is allowed to flow through its coil, causing the gauge pointer to move toward the directly grounded coil. When resistance in the sending unit decreases, more current is allowed to pass through its coil, increasing the magnetic field. The gauge pointer is then attracted toward the coil which is grounded through the sending unit.

A special tester is required to diagnose this type gauge. Follow instructions included with the tester.

ALTERNATOR INDICATOR LAMP

DELCOTRON CHARGING SYSTEM

This system features an integral solid state regulator mounted inside the alternator slip ring end frame. The alternator indicator lamp is installed in the field wire circuit connected between the ignition Ign. terminal and alternator No. 1 terminal, **Fig. 1.** The resistance provided by the alternator warning light circuit is needed to protect the diode trio. The alternator indicator lamp should light when the ignition switch is turned on before engine is started. If lamp does not light, either lamp is burned out or indicator lamp wiring has an open circuit. After engine is started, the indicator lamp should be out at all times. If indicator lamp comes on, alternator belt may be loose, alternator or regulator may be defective, charging circuit may be defective or fuse may be blown.

Troubleshooting

1. Switch off, Lamp on:
   a. Disconnect electrical connector from alternator terminals Nos. 1 and 2.
   b. If indicator light remains lit, repair short circuit between leads.
   c. If indicator light goes out, replace alternator rectifier bridge.
2. Switch on, lamp off, engine not running:
   a. Perform tests described in step 1.
   b. If problem still exists, there may be an open circuit.
   c. To locate open circuit, check for blown fuse or fusible link, burned out bulb, defective bulb socket or an open in No. 1 lead circuit between alternator and ignition switch.
   d. If no faults are found, check charging system for proper operation.
3. Switch on, lamp on, engine running:
   a. **On models** so equipped, check condition of fuse between indicator light and ignition switch and fuse in A/C circuit.
   b. Check charging system for proper operation.

VOLTMETER

The voltmeter is a gauge which measures the electrical flow from the battery to indicate whether the battery output is within tolerances. The voltmeter reading can range from 13.5–14.0 volts under normal operating conditions. If an undercharge or overcharge condition is indicated for an extended period, the battery and charging system should be checked.

TROUBLESHOOTING

To check voltmeter, turn key and headlights on with engine off. Pointer should move to 12.5 volts. If no needle movement is observed, check connections from battery to circuit breaker. If connections are tight and meter shows no movement, check wire continuity. If wire continuity is satisfactory, the meter is inoperative and must be replaced.

ELECTRICAL TEMPERATURE GAUGES

This temperature indicating system consists of a sending unit, located on the cylinder head, electrical temperature gauge and an instrument voltage regulator. As engine temperature increases or decreases, the resistance of the sending unit changes, in turn controlling current flow through the gauge. When engine temperature is low sending unit resistance is high, current flow through the gauge is restricted, and the gauge pointer remains against the stop or moves very little. As engine temperature increases sending unit resistance decreases and current flow through the gauge increases, resulting in increased pointer movement.

TROUBLESHOOTING

Troubleshooting for the electrical temperature indicating system is the same as for the electrical oil pressure indicating system.

ELECTRICAL OIL PRESSURE GAUGES

This oil pressure indicating system incorporates an instrument voltage regulator, electrical oil pressure gauge and a sending unit which are connected in series. The sending unit consists of a diaphragm, contact and a variable resistor. As oil pressure increases or decreases, the diaphragm actuated the contact on the variable resistor, in turn controlling current flow through the gauge. When oil pressure is low, the resistance of the variable resistor is high, restricting current flow to the gauge, in turn indicating low oil pressure. As oil pressure increases, the resistance of the variable resistor is lowered, permitting an increased current flow to the gauge, resulting in an increased gauge reading.

TROUBLESHOOTING

Disconnect the oil pressure gauge lead from the sending unit, connect a 12 volt test lamp between the gauge lead and the ground and turn ignition on. If test lamp flashes, the instrument voltage regulator is functioning properly and the gauge circuit is not broken. If the test lamp remains lit, the instrument voltage regulator is defective and must be replaced. If the test lamp does not light, check the instrument voltage regulator for proper ground or an open circuit. Also, check for an open in the instrument voltage regulator to oil pressure gauge wire or in the gauge itself. **If test lamp flashes and gauge is not accurate, the gauge may be out of calibration, requiring replacement.**

OIL PRESSURE INDICATOR LAMP

Many cars utilize a warning light on the instrument panel in place of the conventional dash indicating gauge to warn the driver when the oil pressure is dangerously low. The warning light is wired in series with the ignition switch and the engine unit, which is an oil pressure switch.

The oil pressure switch contains a diaphragm and a set of contacts. When the ignition switch is turned on, the warning light circuit is energized and the circuit is completed through the closed contacts in the pressure switch. When the engine is started, build-up of oil pressure compresses the diaphragm, opening the contacts, thereby breaking the circuit and putting out the light.

TROUBLESHOOTING

On some models, the oil pressure indicator light also serves as the electric choke defect indicator. If Oil or engine indicator light does not light, check to ensure electric choke is not disconnected at carburetor. Also check for defect in electric choke heater, blown gauge fuse or defect in lamp or wiring circuit. If indicator light stays on with engine running possible causes are: oil pressure is low, switch to indicator light wiring has an open circuit, oil pressure switch wire connector has disconnected or on some models, gauge or radio fuse has blown.

The oil pressure warning light should go on when the ignition is turned on. If it does not light, disconnect the wire from the engine unit and ground the wire to the frame or cylinder block. Then if the warning light still does not go on with the ignition switch on, replace the bulb.

If the warning light goes on when the wire is grounded to the frame or cylinder block, the engine unit should be checked for being loose or poorly grounded. If the unit is found to be tight and properly grounded, it should be removed and a new one installed. The presence of sealing compound on the threads of the engine unit will cause a poor ground.

If the warning light remains lit when it normally should be out, replace the engine unit before proceeding to determine the cause for a low pressure indication.

The warning light sometimes will light up or will flicker when the engine is idling, even though the oil pressure is adequate. However, the light should go out when the engine is speeded up. There is no cause for alarm in such cases; it simply means that the pressure switch is not calibrated precisely correct.

TEMPERATURE INDICATOR LAMP

TROUBLESHOOTING

If the red light is not lit when the engine is being cranked, check for a burned out bulb, an open in the light circuit, or a defective ignition switch.

If the red light is lit when the engine is

running, check the wiring between light and switch for a ground, temperature switch defective, or overheated cooling system. **As a test circuit to check whether the red bulb is functioning properly, a wire which is connected to the ground terminal of the ignition switch is tapped into its circuit. When the ignition is in the start engine cranking position, the ground terminal is grounded inside the switch and the red bulb will be lit. When the engine is started and the ignition switch is in the on position, the test circuit is opened and the bulb is then controlled by the temperature switch.**

SPEEDOMETERS

The following information covers only that service on speedometers which can be performed by the average service man. Repairs on the units themselves are not included as they require special equipment and extreme care when making repairs and adjustments and only an experienced speedometer mechanic should attempt such servicing.

The speedometer has two main parts: the indicator head and the speedometer drive cable. When the speedometer fails to indicate speed or mileage, the cable or housing is probably broken.

SPEEDOMETER CABLE

Most cables are broken due to lack of lubrication or a sharp bend or kink in the housing.

Cable can break because the speedometer head mechanism binds. If such is the case, the speedometer head should be repaired or replaced before a new cable or housing is installed.

A jumpy pointer condition, together with a sort of scraping noise, is due, in most instances, to a dry or kinked speedometer cable. The kinked cable rubs on the housing and winds up, slowing down the pointer. The cable then unwinds and the pointer jumps.

To check for kinks, remove the cable, lay it on a flat surface and twist one end with the fingers. If it turns over smoothly the cable is not kinked. But if part of the cable flops over as it is twisted, the cable is kinked and should be replaced.

Lubrication

The speedometer cable should be lubricated with special cable lubricant every 10,000 miles.

Fill the ferrule on the upper end of the housing with the cable lubricant. Insert the cable in the housing, starting at the upper end. Turn the cable around carefully while feeding it into the housing. Repeat filling the ferrule except for the last six inches of cable. Too much lubricant at this point may cause the lubricant to work into the indicating hand.

Installation

During installation, if the cable sticks when inserted in the housing and will not go through, the housing is damaged inside or kinked. Be sure to check the housing from one end to the other. Straighten any sharp bends by relocating clamps or elbows. Replace housing if it is badly kinked or broken. Position the cable and housing so that they lead into the head as straight as possible.

Check the new cable for kinks before installing it. Use wide, sweeping, gradual curves when the cable comes out of the transmission and connects to the head so the cable will not be damaged during its installation.

If inspection indicates that the cable and housing are in good condition, yet pointer action is erratic, check the speedometer head for possible binding.

The speedometer drive pinion should also be checked. If the pinion is dry or its teeth are stripped, the speedometer may not register properly.

The transmission mainshaft nut must be tight or the speedometer drive gear may slip on the mainshaft and cause slow speed readings.

FIBER OPTIC MONITORING SYSTEM

Fiber optics are non-electric light conductors made up of coated strands which, when exposed to a light source at one end, will reflect the light through their entire length, thereby illuminating a monitoring lens on the instrument panel or fender without the use of a bulb when the exterior lights are turned on.

FUEL GAUGES

The fuel gauge system consists of a sending unit, instrument voltage regulator and an electric fuel gauge. The sending unit is a variable resistor that is controlled by a float. Corresponding to actual fuel level, the float will rise or fall. When the ignition is turned to the On position, voltage is applied to the gauge through the voltage regulator, completing the gauge ground circuit through the sending unit.

When the tank is full and the float is raised, maximum resistance (approximately 90 ohms) is produced by the sending unit, current flow through the gauge is decreased, and the gauge pointer moves slightly. As the tank empties and the float drops resistance in the sending unit decreases, current flow through the gauge increases and the gauge pointer moves toward empty.

Most analog fuel gauges are of the free floating type, which means that the gauge pointer does not remain against the full stop when the ignition is off. Rather, the pointer floats to a mid-position when no voltage is applied to the gauge.

TROUBLESHOOTING
Gauge Reads Empty When Tank Is Full

This condition is generally caused by a short in the fuel tank unit circuit.
1. Disconnect electrical connector to sending unit, then turn ignition switch to ON position.

2. If gauge reads past full, test gauge with tester BT-6508 or equivalent. If gauge reads empty, disconnect main body harness connector, near the fuse block.
3. If gauge still shows empty, check for short in printed circuit or defective gauge. If gauge reads beyond full, reconnect front body harness connector and disconnect rear body harness connector (in left wheel house).
4. If gauge shows empty, locate and repair grounded wire in harness between front and rear body harness connectors. If gauge reads beyond full, check for short between rear body harness connector, damaged float or defective sending unit.

Gauge Reads Full Or Beyond At All Times

This condition is generally caused by an open in the tank unit circuit.
1. Check tank unit ground for proper contact with body or chassis and repair as needed.
2. If tank unit ground is satisfactory, disconnect electrical connector to tank unit and connect harness side of connector to suitable ground with jumper wire, then turn on ignition.
3. If gauge reads empty, remove fuel tank and inspect wiring to sending unit. If wiring and connections are satisfactory, replace tank unit.
4. If gauge still shows full, disconnect front body harness connector and ground fuel gauge wire terminal in instrument panel side of connector.
5. If gauge still reads full, check for loose connection in cluster, open (crack) in printed circuit or defective gauge. If gauge reads empty, locate and repair open or poor connection between front body connector and tank unit connector.

Fuel Gauge Inaccurate

Tester BT-6508 or equivalent must be used to diagnose dash gauge malfunction.
1. Ensure battery is fully charged, disconnect electrical connector to tank unit and connect tester to between harness connector and suitable ground following manufacturer's instructions.
2. Set tester on empty then turn on ignition. Gauge should read empty or below.
3. Set tester on full. Gauge should read full or above.
4. If gauge does not respond to tester input, replace dash gauge. If gauge responds correctly, check for poor connections at tank unit, poor tank unit ground or defective tank unit.

LOW FUEL WARNING SYSTEM

The switch type consists of an indicator light and a low fuel warning switch located on the instrument panel.

The warning switch contacts are closed by the difference in voltage potential between the fuel gauge terminals. This voltage differential will activate the warning switch when the fuel tank is less than 1/4 full and, in turn, cause the indicator to light.

TROUBLESHOOTING

This system incorporates an indicator light. With ignition switch turned to on, the indicator should light. If not, check bulb and all electrical connections. Replace warning switch if bulb and connections prove satisfactory.

LOW WASHER FLUID INDICATOR

There are two types of low washer fluid indicating systems. They are the mechanical type and electrically controlled type. The mechanical type consists of a float and rod assembly, sending unit and a fiber optic. The electrically controlled type consists of a float, magnet, contact points and a resistor.

On the mechanical type, the upper end of the rod extends into the sending unit and has colored red and green portions. When the windshield wipers are activated, a lamp bulb in the sending unit lights either the red or green sections of the rod. The colored light is then picked up by the fiber optic and is transmitted through it to the telltale lens. The lens will show red or green depending upon washer fluid level.

The electrically controlled indicator is activated when the windshield wipers are engaged. A slight amount of current flows from the wiper motor to the washer bottle float unit. This current will either pass through the contact points or the resistor which is in parallel with the points. When the washer fluid level is high, the magnet holds the contact points open. The current will now flow through the resistor where it is reduced so the indicator will not light. When the washer fluid level is low, the float drops and the magnet will separate from the cap assembly allowing the current to pass through the contact points and activate the indicator light.

TROUBLESHOOTING

On the mechanical indicating system, if the telltale lens fails to glow when the windshield wipers are activated, check lamp bulb in sending unit and see that fiber optic is not broken.

On the electrically controlled system, the first item to check is the indicator bulb. With the windshield wipers On, connect a jumper wire between the two terminals on the washer bottle cap. The indicator should then light. If not, replace bulb. If the bulb is found to be satisfactory, remove cap and float assembly from washer bottle. Float should be able to move to the bottom of the stem and the magnet should separate from the cap. If not, replace float and cap assembly.

LOW COOLANT LEVEL INDICATOR

Some vehicles use a buzzer or indicator lamp to indicate a low coolant level condition. The buzzer or lamp is activated by a sensor, located in the radiator, when the coolant level becomes one quart or more low.

FUEL USAGE GAUGE
BUICK & CADILLAC

Operation

This system consists of green and amber indicator lights located on the fuel gauge or telltale lamp cluster, a switch mounted on the instrument panel behind the gauges and an interconnecting vacuum hose and tee. The system operates on engine vacuum through a dual contact vacuum sensing switch. When the accelerator is operated slowly and smoothly, engine vacuum remains high and the switch passes current to the green indicator light which indicates economical fuel consumption. When the accelerator pedal is depressed rapidly, vacuum decreases and the switch passes current to the amber indicator light, which indicates high fuel consumption. The amber indicator light will glow when the ignition switch is in the On position with the engine stopped.

Functional Test

1. With ignition switch in the on position, ground each terminal at the economy switch. Both green and amber indicator lights should glow. If not check for burned out bulbs.
2. With ignition switch in On position, amber indicator light should glow. If not, check for loose or disconnected wires at fuel economy switch or for poor ground. If amber indicator light still does not glow replace switch.
3. Start engine and allow to idle, the green indicator light should glow. If not, check for leaking, plugged or kinked vacuum hose between vacuum source and fuel economy switch. Check for loose or disconnected wires at economy switch or poor ground. If green indicator lamp still does not glow, replace switch.

UPSHIFT INDICATOR
DESCRIPTION

This lamp is used on most models equipped with manual transmission. The Upshift lamp is illuminated to inform the driver of ideal shift points, with improved fuel economy as the specific objective. When the light is illuminated, the transmission should be shifted to the next highest gear, if driving conditions permit such an action.

TROUBLESHOOTING

If Upshift indicator is not working properly, perform the following test. It is necessary to refer to wiring diagrams located in MOTOR's "Vacuum & Wiring Diagram Manual" for the specific year and model being serviced.

1. Disconnect ECM connector C1.
2. Place ignition switch in run.
3. Measure voltage at terminal A2 of ECM connector.
4. If battery voltage is present, further ECM diagnosis is necessary.
5. If battery voltage is not present, repair open circuit in brown/black wire, circuit 456.

DRIVER REMINDER PACKAGE
CUTLASS, TORONADO, 88 & 98

The driver reminder package incorporates several warning and reminder features into one system. The system uses three distinct sounds, and warning and reminder lights on the center instrument cluster.

If engine coolant level is three quarts or more low, a red LOW COOLANT warning light will illuminate and a fast pulsed tone will be heard. The light will remain lit and the tone will be heard until coolant is added to the cooling system. The light will also illuminate during engine starting as a bulb check.

When the headlight switch is in the On position and the ignition is off, a red LIGHTS ON warning light will illuminate and a fast-pulsed tone will be heard. Turning the headlight switch to the right will dim the instrument panel lights and shut off the tone.

When there is less than approximately three gallons of fuel in the tank, an amber LOW FUEL warning light will illuminate and a steady five second tone will be heard, however the lamp may not light until fuel level is diminished to as low as a 1/2 gallon. The light will remain lit until fuel is added to the tank. This warning light will also illuminate during engine starting as a bulb check.

The amber LOW WASH FLUID reminder light will illuminate while the windshield wipers are operated if the washer fluid reservoir is less than approximately 1/3 full. This light will remain lit during wiper operation until fluid is added.

Additional tones used to warn operator of potential problems are: engine overheating, fast pulsed tone; malfunction in the charging system, fast-pulsed tone; seat belt reminder, slow pulsed tone; key reminder, steady tone.

TABLE OF CONTENTS

General Information

INDEX

STARTER TROUBLESHOOTING

SLOW OR NOT CRANKING

When trouble develops in the starter motor circuit, and the starter cranks the engine slowly or not at all, several preliminary checks can be made to determine whether the trouble lies in the battery, in the starter, in the wiring between them, or elsewhere. Many conditions besides defects in the starter itself can result in poor cranking performance.

To make a quick check of the starter system, turn on the headlights. They should burn with normal brilliance. If they do not, the battery may be run down.

If the battery is in a charged condition so that lights burn brightly, operate the starter motor. Any one of three things will happen to the lights: (1) They will go out, (2) dim considerably or (3) stay bright without any cranking action taking place.

If Lights Go Out

If the lights go out as the starter switch is closed, it indicates that there is a poor connection between the battery and starter motor. This poor connection will most often be found at the battery terminals. Correction is made by removing the cable clamps from the terminals, cleaning the terminals and clamps, replacing the clamps and tightening them securely. A coating of corrosion inhibitor (petroleum jelly will do) may be applied to the clamps and terminals to retard the formation of corrosion.

If Lights Dim

If the lights dim considerably as the starter switch is closed and the starter operates slowly or not at all, the battery may be run down, or there may be some mechanical condition in the engine or starter motor that is throwing a heavy burden on the starter motor. This imposes a high discharge rate on the battery which causes noticeable dimming of the lights.

Check the battery state of charge. If it is charged, the trouble probably lies in either the engine or starter motor itself. In the engine, tight bearings or pistons or heavy oil place an added burden on the starter motor. Low temperatures also hamper starter motor performance since it thickens engine oil and makes the engine considerably harder to crank and start. Also, a battery is less efficient at low temperatures.

In the starter motor, a bent armature, loose pole shoe screws or worn bearings, any of which may allow the armature to drag, will reduce cranking performance and increase current draw.

In addition, more serious internal damage is sometimes found. Thrown armature windings or commutator bars, which sometimes occur on over-running clutch drive starter motors, are usually caused by excessive overrunning after starter. This is the result of such conditions as the driver keeping the starter switch closed too long after the engine has started, the driver opening the throttle too wide in starting, or improper carburetor fast idle adjustment. Any of these subject the over-running clutch to extra strain so it tends to seize, spinning the armature at high speed with resulting armature damage.

Another cause may be engine backfire during cranking which may result, among other things, from ignition timing being too far advanced.

To avoid such failures, the driver should pause a few seconds after a false start to make sure the engine has come completely to rest before another start is attempted. In addition, the ignition timing should be checked if engine backfiring has caused the trouble.

Lights Stay Bright; No Cranking Action

This condition indicates an open circuit at some point, either in the starter itself, the starter switch or control circuit. The solenoid control circuit can be eliminated momentarily by placing a heavy jumper lead across the solenoid main terminals to see if the starter will operate. This connects the starter directly to the battery and, if it operates, it indicates that the control circuit is not functioning normally. The wiring and control units must be checked to locate the trouble.

If the starter does not operate with the jumper attached, it will probably have to be removed from the engine so it can be examined in detail.

STARTER DRIVE TROUBLES

Starter drive troubles are easy to diagnose and they usually cannot be confused with ordinary starter difficulties. If the starter does not turn over at all or if it drags, look for trouble in the starter or electrical supply system. Concentrate on the starter drive or ring gear if the starter is noisy, if it turns but does not engage the engine, or if the starter won't disengage after the engine is started. After the starter is removed, the trouble can usually be located quickly.

Worn or chipped ring gear or starter pinion are the usual causes of noisy operation. Before replacing either or both of these parts try to find out what caused the damage. With the Bendix type drive, incomplete engagement of the pinion with the ring gear is a common cause of tooth damage. The wrong pinion clearance on starter drives of the over-running clutch type leads to poor meshing of the pinion and ring gear and too rapid tooth wear.

A less common cause of noise with either type of drive is a bent starter armature shaft. When this shaft is bent, the pinion gear alternately binds and then only partly meshes with the ring gear. Most manufacturers specify a maximum of .003 inch radial runout on the armature shaft.

Drive Clutch Failure

The over-running clutch type drive seldom becomes so worn that it fails to engage since it is directly activated by a fork and lever. The only thing that is likely to happen is that, once engaged, it will not turn the engine because the clutch itself is worn out. A much more frequent difficulty and one that rapidly wears ring gear and teeth is partial engagement. Proper meshing of the pinion is controlled by the end clearance between the pinion gear and the starter housing or pinion stop, if used.

On some starters, the solenoids are completely enclosed in the starter housing and the pinion clearance is not adjustable. If the clearance is not correct, the starter must be disassembled and checked for excessive wear of solenoid linkage, shift lever mechanism, or improper assembly of parts.

Failure of the over-running clutch drive to disengage is usually caused by binding between the armature shaft and the drive. If the drive, particularly the clutch, shows signs of overheating it indicates that it is not disengaging immediately after the engine starts. If the clutch is forced to over-run too long, it overheats and turns a bluish color. For the cause of the binding, look for rust or gum between the armature shaft and the drive, or for burred splines. Excess oil on the drive will lead to gumming, and inadequate air circulation in the flywheel housing will cause rust.

Over-running clutch drives cannot be overhauled in the field so they must be replaced. In cleaning, never soak them in a solvent because the solvent may enter the clutch and dissolve the sealed-in lubricant. Wipe them off lightly with kerosene and lubricate them sparingly with SAE 10 or 10W oil.

Bendix Drive Failure

When a Bendix type drive doesn't engage the cause usually is one of three things: either the drive spring is broken, one of the drive spring bolts has sheared off, or the screw shaft threads won't allow the pinion to travel toward the flywheel. In the first two cases, remove the drive by unscrewing the set screw under the last coil of the drive spring and replace the broken parts. Gummed or rusty screw shaft threads are fairly common causes of Bendix drive failure and are easily cleaned with a little kerosene or steel wool, depending on the trouble. Here again, as in the case of over-running clutch drives, use light oil sparingly, and be sure the flywheel housing has adequate ventilation. There is usually a breather hole in the bottom of the

flywheel housing which should be open.

The failure of a Bendix drive to disengage or to mesh properly is most often caused by gummed or rusty screw shaft threads. When this is not true, look for mechanical failure within the drive itself.

CHECKING CIRCUIT WITH VOLTMETER

Excessive resistance in the circuit between the battery and starter will reduce cranking performance. The resistance can be checked by using a voltmeter to measure voltage drop in the circuits while the starter is operated. There are three checks to be made:

1. Voltage drop between car frame and grounded battery terminal post.
2. Voltage drop between car frame and starter motor field frame.
3. Voltage drop between insulated battery terminal post and starter motor terminal stud, or the battery terminal stud of the solenoid.

Each of these should show no more than one-tenth (0.1) volt drop when the starter motor is cranking the engine. Do not use the starter for more than 30 seconds at a time to avoid overheating it.

If excessive voltage drop is found in any of these circuits, make correction by disconnecting the cables, cleaning the connections carefully, and then reconnecting the cables firmly in place. A coating of petroleum jelly on the battery cables and terminal clamps will retard corrosion.

On some cars, extra long battery cables may be required due to the location of the battery and starter. This may result in somewhat higher voltage drop than the above recommended 0.1 volt. The only means of determining the normal voltage drop in such cases is to check several of these vehicles. Then when the voltage drop is well above the normal figure for all cars checked, abnormal resistance will be indicated and correction can be made as already explained.

SOLENOID SWITCHES

The solenoid switch on a cranking motor not only closes the circuit between the battery and the cranking motor but also shifts the drive pinion into mesh with the engine flywheel ring gear. This is done by means of a linkage between the solenoid

switch plunger and the shift lever on the cranking motor.

There are two windings in the solenoid; a pull-in winding and a hold-in winding. Both windings are energized when the external control switch is closed. They produce a magnetic field which pulls the plunger in so that the drive pinion is shifted into mesh, and the main contacts in the solenoid switch are closed to connect the battery directly to the cranking motor. Closing the main switch contacts shorts out the pull-in winding since this winding is connected across the main contacts. The magnetism produced by the hold-in winding is sufficient to hold the plunger in, and shorting out the pull-in winding reduces drain on the battery. When the control switch is opened, it disconnects the hold-in winding from the battery. When the hold-in winding is disconnected from the battery, the shift lever spring withdraws the plunger from the solenoid, opening the solenoid switch contacts and at the same time withdrawing the drive pinion from mesh. Proper operation of the switch depends on maintaining a definite balance between the magnetic strength of the pull-in and hold-in windings.

This balance is established in the design by the size of the wire and the number of turns specified. An open circuit in the hold-in winding or attempts to crank with a discharged battery will cause the switch to chatter.

STARTER MOTOR SERVICE

To obtain full performance data on a starter motor.or to determine the cause of abnormal operation, the starter motor should be submitted to a no-load and torque test. These tests are best performed on a starter bench tester with the starter mounted on it.

From a practical standpoint, however, a simple torque test may be made quickly with the starter in the car. Make sure the battery is fully charged and that the starter circuit wires and terminals are in good condition. Then operate the starter to see if the engine turns over normally. If it does not, the torque developed is below standard and the starter should be removed for further checking.

Starter Motor Specifications

Starter Make	Starter Ident. No	Free Speed Test			Solenoid	
		Amps	Volts	RPM	Hold-In Windings	Pull-In Windings
Delco-Remy	10455001	52-76	10	6000-12000	—	—
	10455004	50-75	10	6000-11900	—	—
	10455006	45-74	10	6000-11900	13-19	23-30
	10455007	50-75	10	6000-11900	—	—
	10455010	50-75	10	6000-11900	12-15	30-36
	10455015	52-76	10	6000-12000	—	—
	10455016	50-75	10	6000-11900	—	—
	10455017	50-75	10	6000-11900	—	—
	10455019	50-75	10	6000-11900	—	—
	10455020	52-76	10	6000-12000	—	—
	10455021	55-85	10	6000-12000	—	—
	10455022	55-85	10	6000-12000	—	—
	10455024	45-74	10	6000-11900	13-19	23-30
	10455044	52-76	10	6000-12000	—	—
	1998511	50-75	10	6000-11900	—	—
	1998524	50-75	10	6000-11900	13-19	23-30
	1998525	55-85	10	6000-12000	13-19	23-30
	1998527	52-76	10	6000-12000	13-19	23-30
	1998544	48-75	10	9000-13000	—	—
	1998545	65-90	10	3500-5500	—	—
	1998548	50-75	10	6000-11900	—	—
	1998578	45-85	10	3300-5000	—	—
	1998579	70-110	10	6500-10700	—	—
	1998580	70-110	10	6500-10700	13-19	23-30
	1998591	70-110	10	6500-10700	13-19	23-30
Nippondenso	①②	35-50	11	1200-2380	—	—
	①③	60-90	11.5	3000-5950	—	—
	④②	35-90	11.5	1200-3000	—	—
	④③	60-90	11.5	3000-5950	—	—
	⑤	45-90	10	3500-5000	—	—

①—Geo models except Storm. ③—Automatic transmission. ⑤—1990 Corvette.
②—Manual transmission. ④—Geo Storm.

Delco-Remy Starters

INDEX

DESCRIPTION

The Delco-Remy starter, **Fig. 1,** has the solenoid shift lever mechanism and the solenoid plunger enclosed in the drive housing to protect them from exposure to road dirt, icing conditions and splash. They have an extruded field frame and an overrunning clutch type drive. The overrunning clutch is operated by a solenoid switch mounted to a flange on the drive housing. The diesel engine starters have a center bearing.

The solenoid is attached to the drive end housing by two screws. The cover can be removed to inspect the contacts and contact disc, but the switch is serviced as assembly only.

Most motors of this type have graphite and oil impregnated bronze bearings which ordinarily require no added lubrication except at time of overhaul when a few drops of light engine oil should be placed on each bearing before reassembly.

DIAGNOSIS

When diagnosing Delco-Remy starters, refer to **Fig. 2.**

IN-VEHICLE TESTING

FREE SPEED TEST

With the circuit connected as shown in **Fig. 3,** use a tachometer to measure armature revolutions per minute. Failure of the motor to perform to specifications may be due to tight or dry bearings, or high resistance connections.

PINION CLEARANCE

There is no provision for adjusting pinion clearance on this type motor. When the

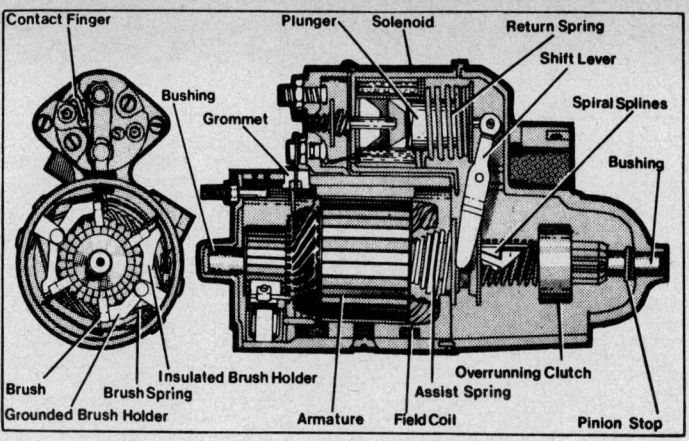

Fig. 1   Delco-Remy starter motor

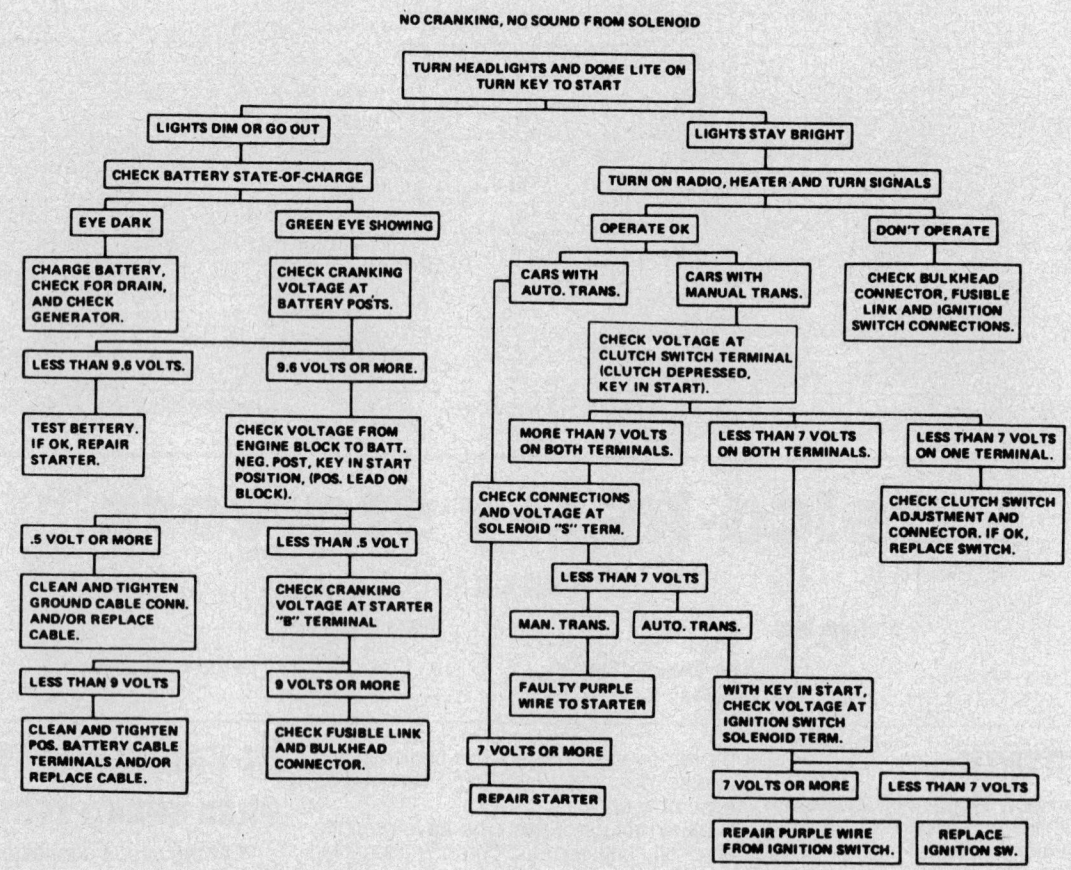

Fig. 2   Delco-Remy starter motor diagnosis (Part 1 of 2)

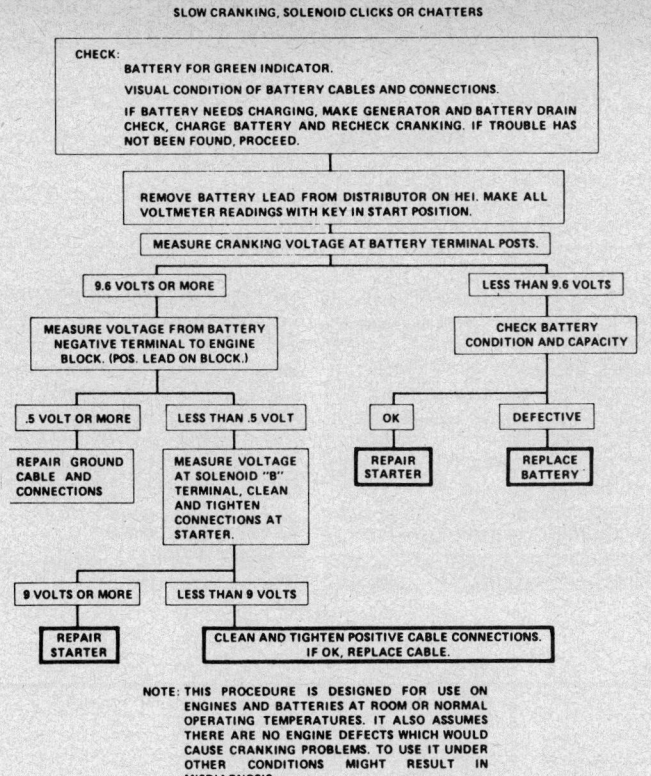

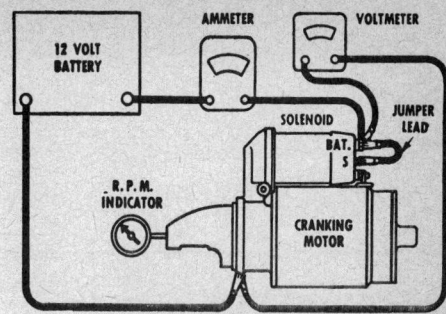

Fig. 3 Starter free speed test connections

Fig. 2 Delco-Remy starter motor diagnosis (Part 2 of 2)

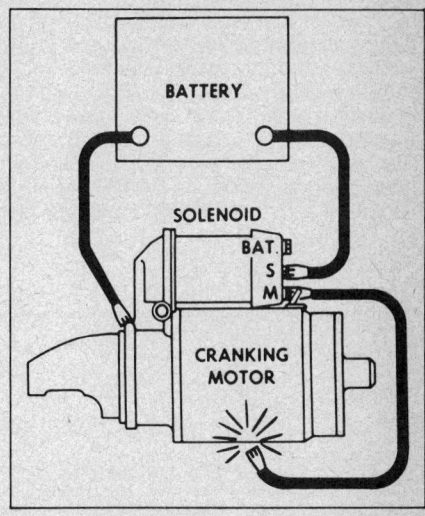

Fig. 4 Starter pinion clearance test connections

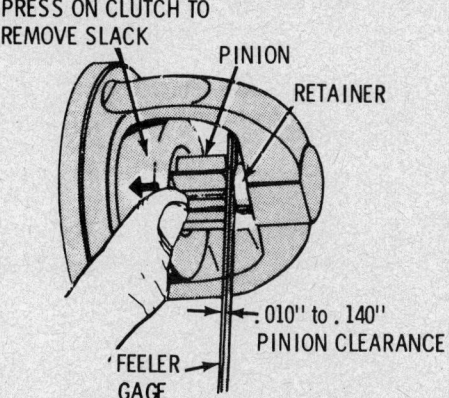

Fig. 5 Checking pinion clearance

shift lever mechanism is correctly assembled, the pinion clearance should fall within the limits of .010 to .140 inch. When the clearance is not within these limits, it may indicate excessive wear of the solenoid linkage or shift lever yoke buttons.

Pinion clearance should be checked after the motor has been disassembled and reassembled. To check, disconnect motor field coil connector from solenoid terminal and insulate end. Connect one battery lead to solenoid switch terminal and the other

lead to the solenoid frame, **Fig. 4.** Using a jumper lead connected to the solenoid motor terminal, momentarily flash the lead to the solenoid frame. This will shift the pinion into the cranking position until the battery is disconnected.

After energizing the solenoid with the clutch shifted toward the pinion stop retainer, push the pinion back toward the commutator end as far as possible to take up any slack movement; then check the clearance with feeler gauge, **Fig. 5.**

Nippondenso Starter

INDEX

DESCRIPTION

Nippondenso starters, **Figs. 1 and 2,** are either a conventional type or reduction gear types. The conventional type used on manual transmissions consists of a frame and field assembly, an armature assembly, an overruning clutch assembly, a starter solenoid assembly, a commutator end housing, a brush holder and a shift lever. The reduction gear type starters used on automatic transmissions which use all of the above components along with a reduction gear and shock absorber assembly.

When the ignition switch is turned to start and the clutch start/neutral safety switch is closed, the solenoid windings are energized, resulting in plunger and shift lever movement. This causes the pinion to engage the engine flywheel ring gear and the starter solenoid contacts to close. With the contacts closed, the starter solenoid provides a closed circuit between the battery positive terminal and the starter motor. The starter motor is grounded to the engine block, therefore the circuit is complete and engine cranking may occur.

Once the engine starts, the pinion is designed to overrun and protect the armature from excessive speeds until the ignition switch is released from the start position. When the ignition switch is released, a return spring in the solenoid assembly opens the starter solenoid contacts, breaking the circuit and disengaging the pinion.

DIAGNOSIS

Refer to **Fig. 3** when troubleshooting these starter motors.

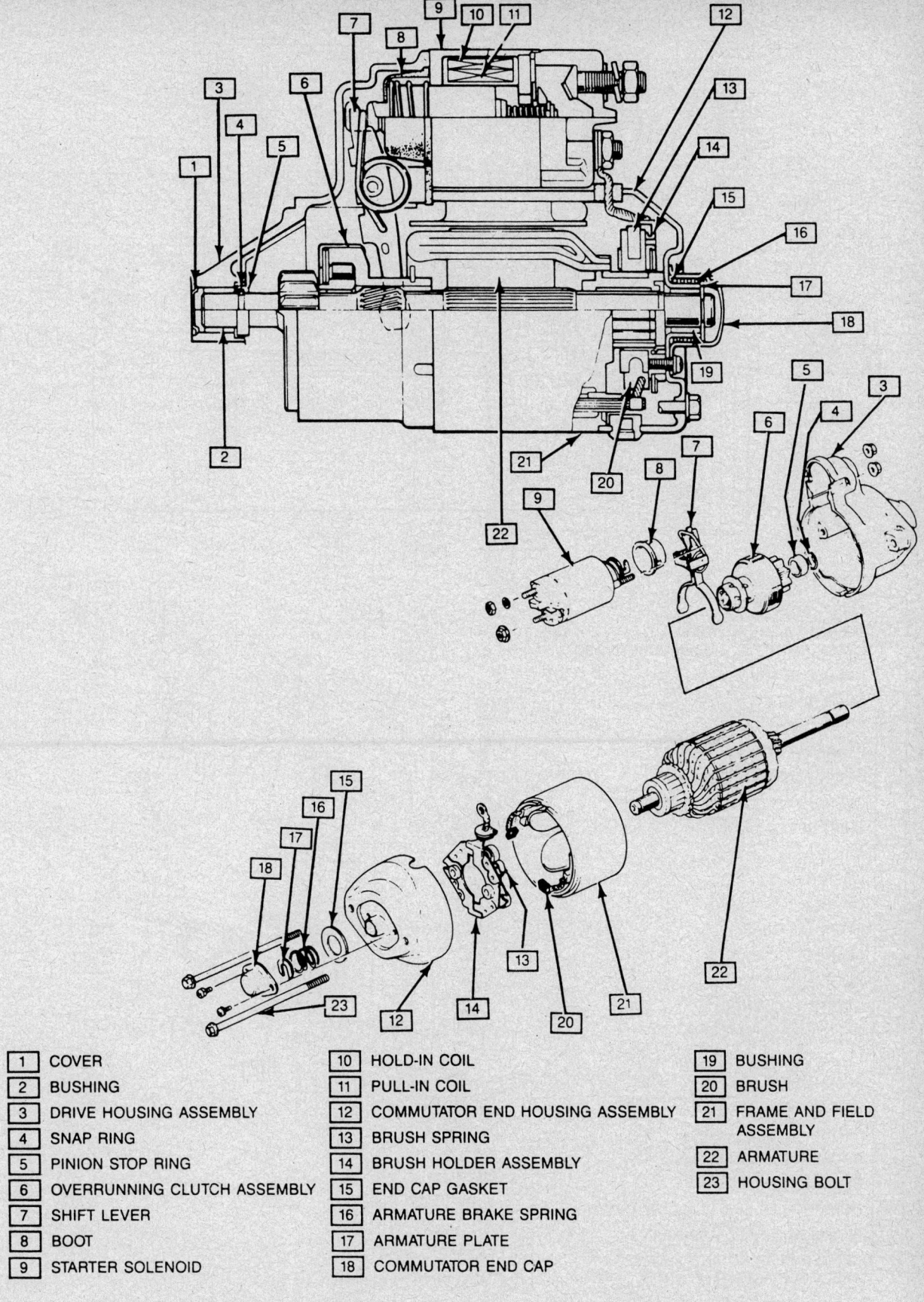

1	COVER	10	HOLD-IN COIL	19	BUSHING
2	BUSHING	11	PULL-IN COIL	20	BRUSH
3	DRIVE HOUSING ASSEMBLY	12	COMMUTATOR END HOUSING ASSEMBLY	21	FRAME AND FIELD ASSEMBLY
4	SNAP RING	13	BRUSH SPRING	22	ARMATURE
5	PINION STOP RING	14	BRUSH HOLDER ASSEMBLY	23	HOUSING BOLT
6	OVERRUNNING CLUTCH ASSEMBLY	15	END CAP GASKET		
7	SHIFT LEVER	16	ARMATURE BRAKE SPRING		
8	BOOT	17	ARMATURE PLATE		
9	STARTER SOLENOID	18	COMMUTATOR END CAP		

Fig. 1   Exploded view of starter smotor. Conventional w/manual trans

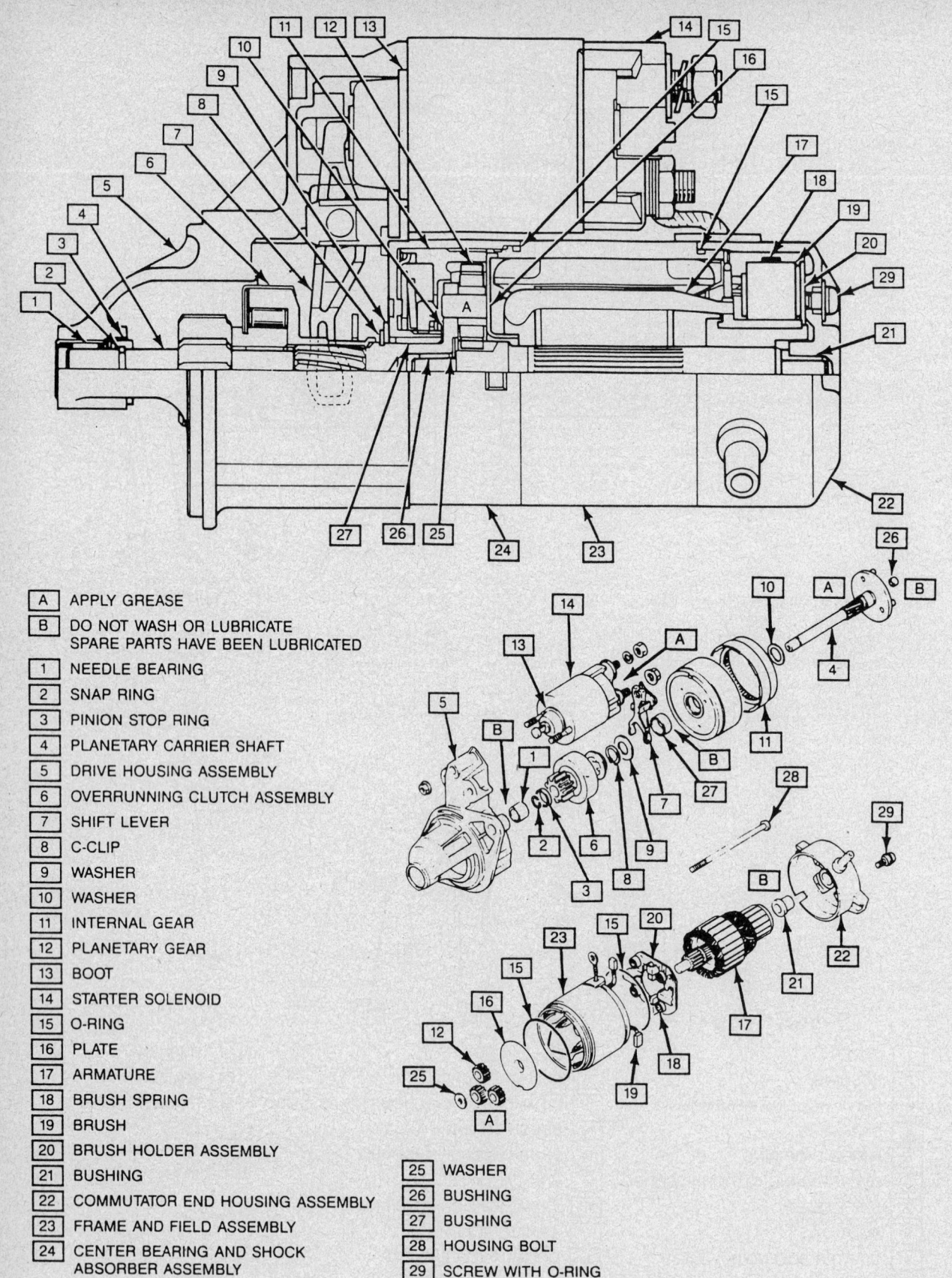

A	APPLY GREASE
B	DO NOT WASH OR LUBRICATE SPARE PARTS HAVE BEEN LUBRICATED
1	NEEDLE BEARING
2	SNAP RING
3	PINION STOP RING
4	PLANETARY CARRIER SHAFT
5	DRIVE HOUSING ASSEMBLY
6	OVERRUNNING CLUTCH ASSEMBLY
7	SHIFT LEVER
8	C-CLIP
9	WASHER
10	WASHER
11	INTERNAL GEAR
12	PLANETARY GEAR
13	BOOT
14	STARTER SOLENOID
15	O-RING
16	PLATE
17	ARMATURE
18	BRUSH SPRING
19	BRUSH
20	BRUSH HOLDER ASSEMBLY
21	BUSHING
22	COMMUTATOR END HOUSING ASSEMBLY
23	FRAME AND FIELD ASSEMBLY
24	CENTER BEARING AND SHOCK ABSORBER ASSEMBLY
25	WASHER
26	BUSHING
27	BUSHING
28	HOUSING BOLT
29	SCREW WITH O-RING

Fig. 2 Exploded view of starter motor. Reduction w/automatic trans

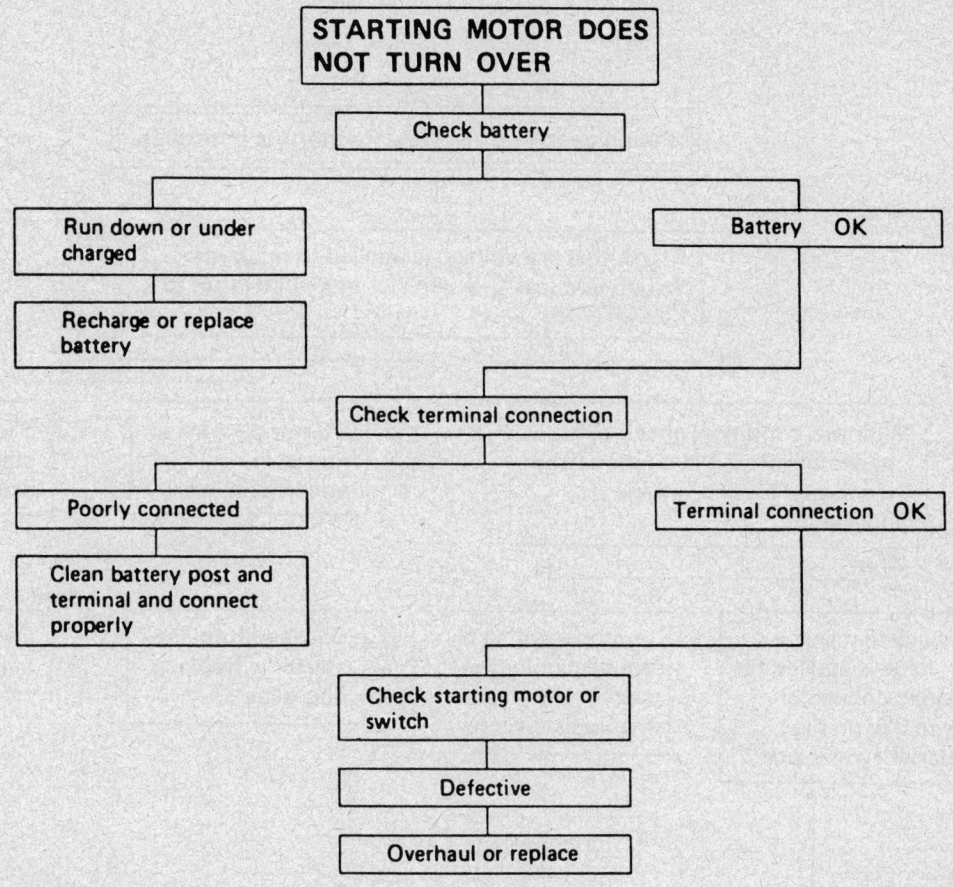

Troubleshooting Procedure

Turn on headlights and starter switch.

Headlights go out or dim considerably.	a) Battery undercharged. b) Starting motor coil circuit shorted. c) Starting motor parts defective.
Headlights stay bright	a) Starting motor circuit open. b) Starting motor coil open. c) Starting switch defective.

Fig. 3   Diagnosis chart (Part 1 of 6)

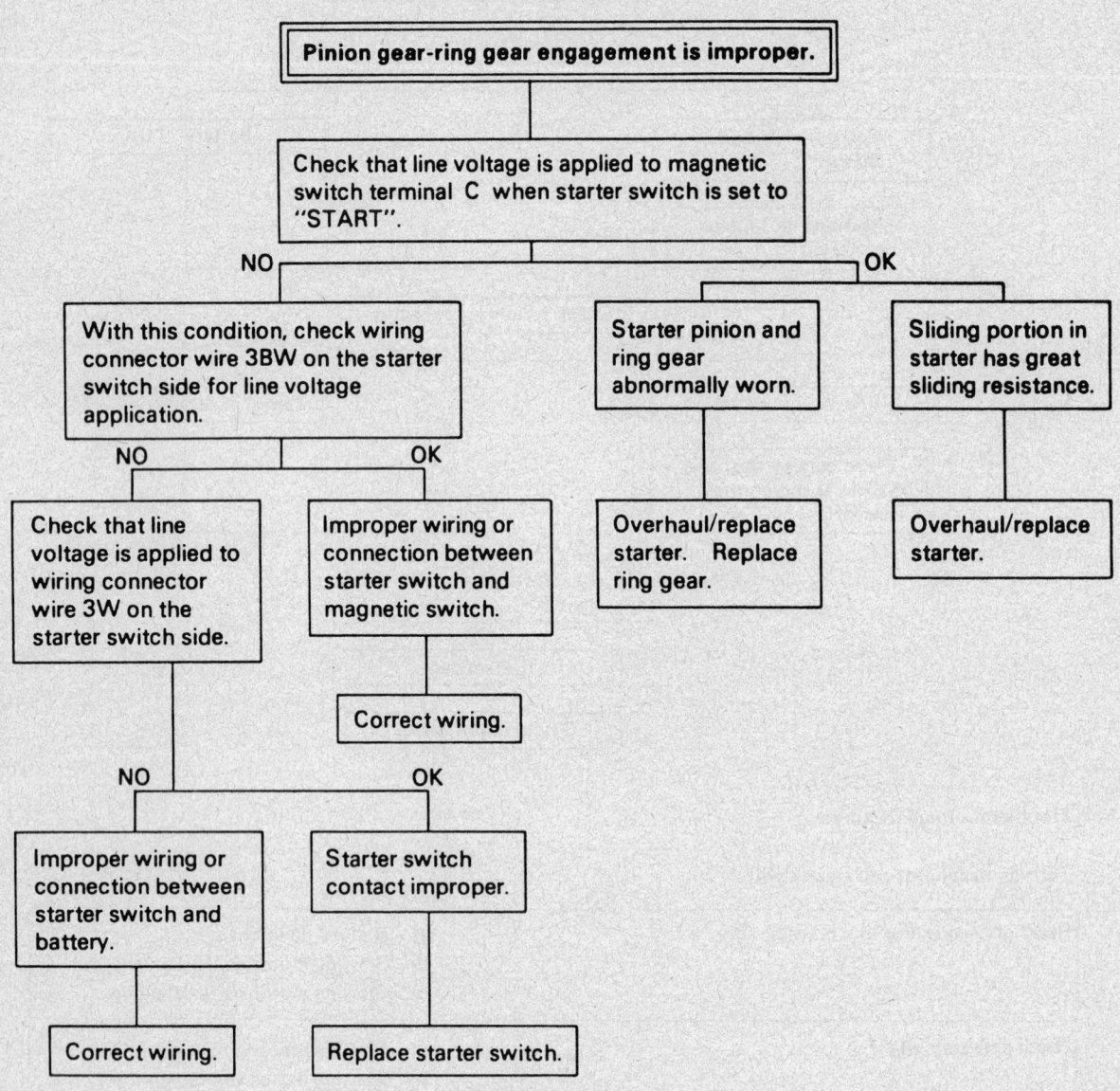

Fig. 3   Diagnosis chart (Part 2 of 6)

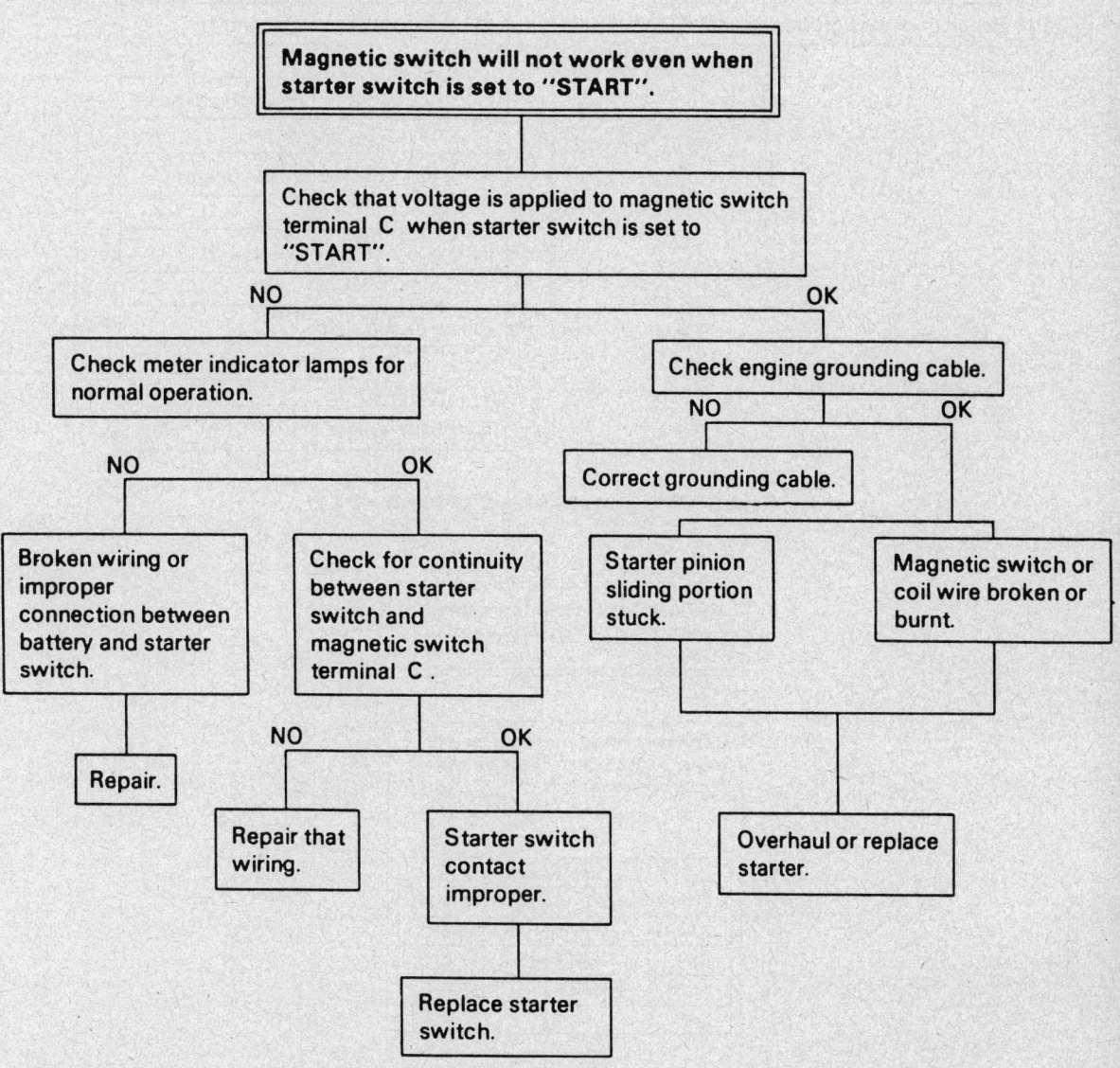

Fig. 3   Diagnosis chart (Part 3 of 6)

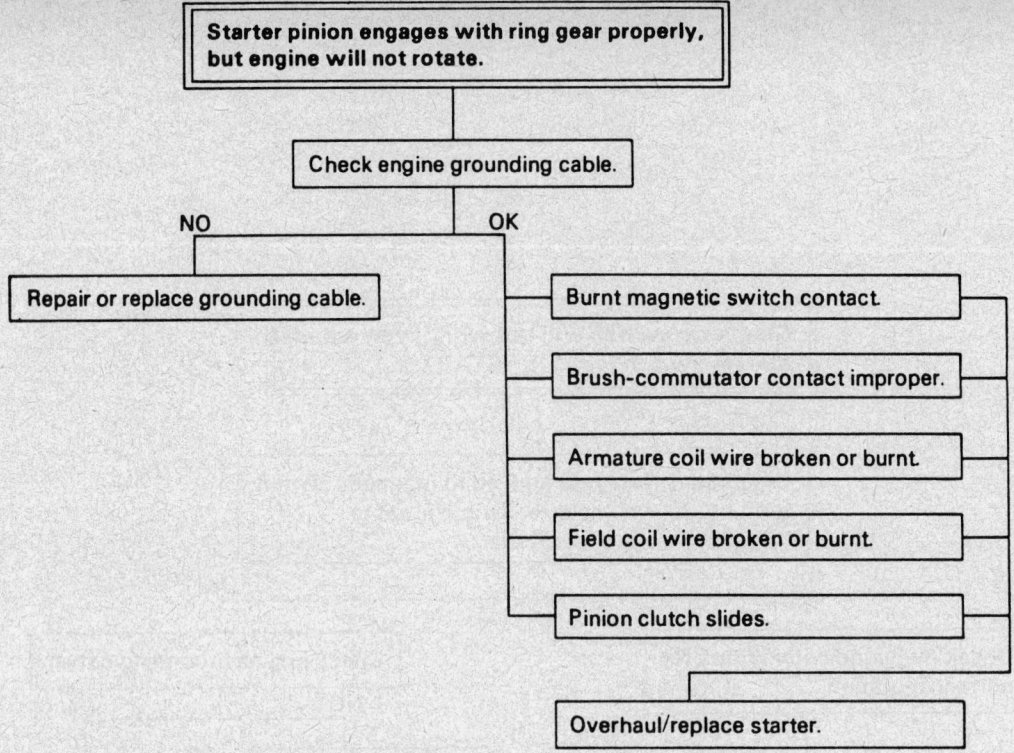

Fig. 3   Diagnosis chart (Part 4 of 6)

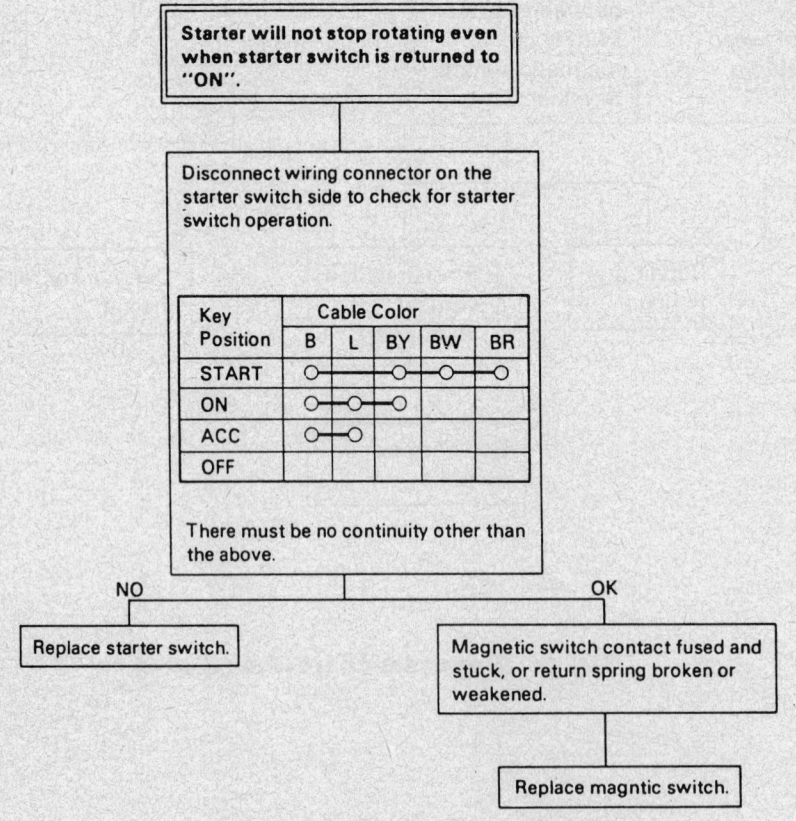

Fig. 3   Diagnosis chart (Part 5 of 6)

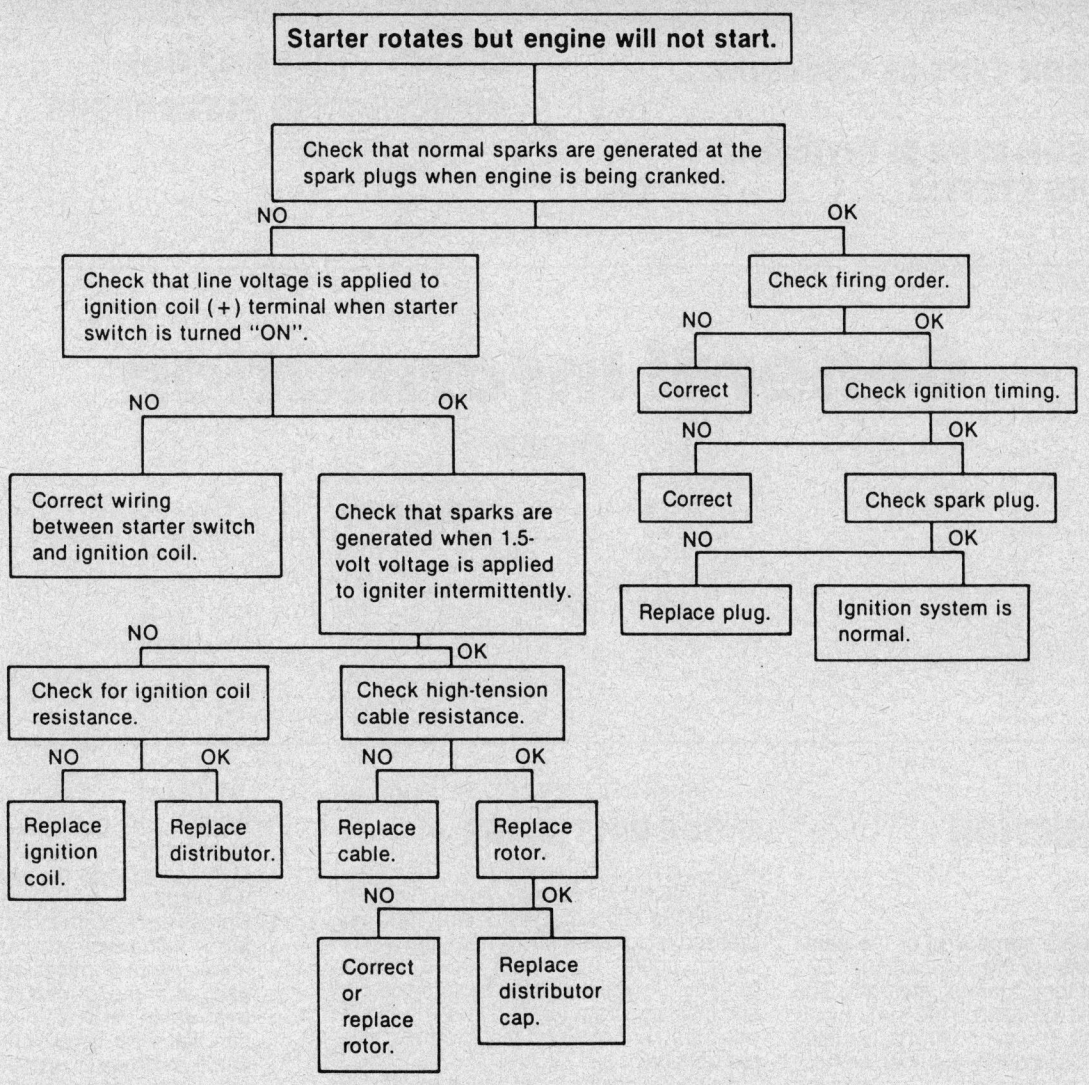

Fig. 3 Diagnosis chart (Part 6 of 6)

ALTERNATOR SYSTEMS

TABLE OF CONTENTS

General Information

INDEX

INTRODUCTION

Alternators are composed of the same functional parts as the conventional D.C. generator but they operate differently. The field is called a rotor and is the turning portion of the unit. The generating part, called a stator, is the stationary member, comparable to the armature in a D.C. generator. The regulator, similar to those used in a D.C. system, regulates the output of the alternator-rectifier system.

The power source of the system is the alternator. Current is transmitted from the field terminal of the regulator through a slip ring to the field coil and back to ground through another slip ring. The strength of the field regulates the output of the alternating current. This alternating current is then transmitted from the alternator to the rectifier where it is converted to direct current.

These alternators employ a three-phase stator winding in which the phase windings are electrically 120 degrees apart. The rotor consists of a field coil encased between interleaved sections producing. When the rotor is energized, a magnetic field with alternate north and south poles is created. By rotating the rotor inside the stator the alternating current is induced in the stator windings. This alternating current is rectified (changed to D.C.) by silicon diodes and brought out to the output terminal of the alternator.

DIODE RECTIFIERS

Six silicon diode rectifiers are used and act as electrical one-way valves. Three of the diodes have ground polarity and are pressed or screwed into a heat sink which is grounded. The other three diodes (ungrounded) are pressed or screwed into and insulated from the end head; these diodes are connected to the alternator output terminal.

Since the diodes have a high resistance to the flow of current in one direction and a low resistance in the opposite direction, they may be connected in a manner which allows current to flow from the alternator to the battery in the low resistance direction. The high resistance in the opposite direction prevents the flow of current from the battery to the alternator. Because of this feature no circuit breaker is required between the alternator and battery.

SERVICE PRECAUTIONS

1. Be certain that battery polarity is correct when servicing units. Reversed battery polarity will damage rectifiers and regulators.
2. If booster battery is used for starting, be sure to use correct polarity in hook up.
3. When a fast charger is used to charge a vehicle battery, the vehicle battery cables should be disconnected unless the fast charger is equipped with a special Alternator Protector, in which case the vehicle battery cables need not be disconnected. Also the fast charger should never be used to start a vehicle as damage to rectifiers will result.
4. Unless the system includes a load relay or field relay, grounding the alternator output terminal will damage the alternator and/or circuits. This is true even when the system is not in operation since no circuit breaker is used and the battery is applied to the alternator output terminal at all times. The field or load relay acts as a circuit breaker in that it is controlled by the ignition switch.
5. When adjusting the voltage regulator, do not short the adjusting tool to the regulator base as the regulator may be damaged. The tool should be insulated by taping or by installing a plastic sleeve.
6. Before making any on vehicle tests of the alternator or regulator, the battery should be checked and the circuit inspected for faulty wiring or insulation, loose or corroded connections and poor ground circuits.
7. Check alternator belt tension to be sure the belt is tight enough to prevent slipping under load.
8. The ignition switch should be off and the battery ground cable disconnected before making any test connections to prevent damage to the system.
9. The vehicle battery must be fully charged or a fully charged battery may be installed for test purposes.

Delcotron Type SI Integral Charging System

INDEX

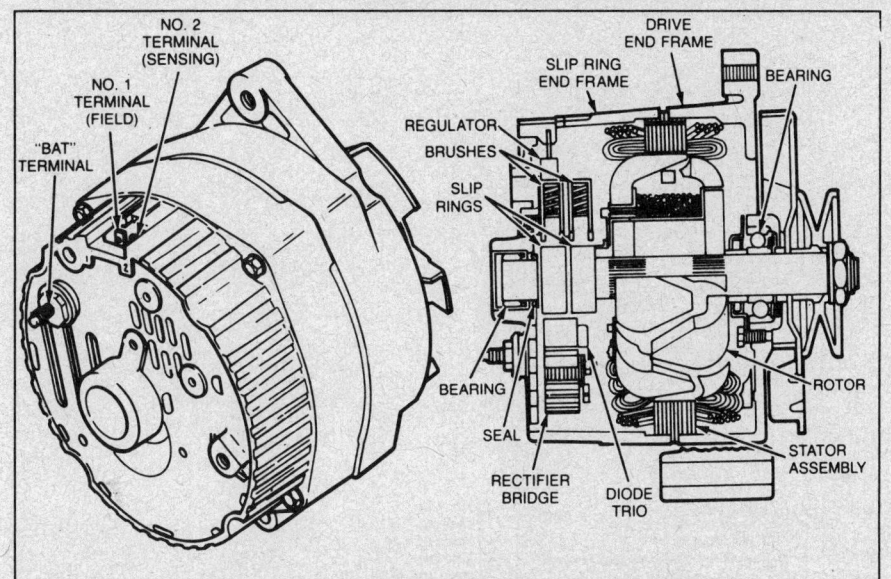

Fig. 1 Delcotron type SI alternator

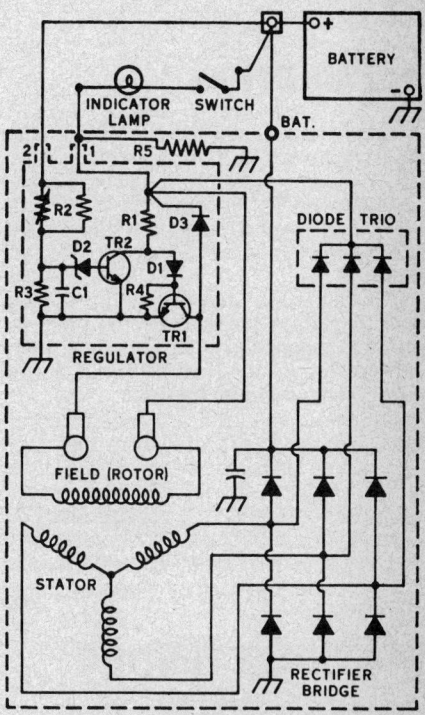

Fig. 2 Wiring diagram of charging circuit

DESCRIPTION

This unit, **Fig. 1,** feature a solid state regulator mounted inside the alternator slip ring end frame, along with the brush holder assembly. All regulator components are enclosed in a solid mold with no need or provision for adjustment of the regulator. A rectifier bridge, containing six diodes and connected to the stator windings, changes A.C. voltage to D.C. voltage which is available at the output terminal. Generator field current is supplied through a diode trio which is also connected to the stator windings. The diodes and rectifiers are protected by a capacitor which is also mounted in the end frame.

Delco Remy units incorporate a resistor in the warning indicator circuit. **Fig. 2.**

TROUBLESHOOTING

UNDERCHARGED BATTERY

1. Disconnect battery ground cable.
2. Disconnect wire at BAT terminal of alternator, connect ammeter, positive lead to BAT terminal and negative lead to wire.
3. Connect battery ground cable.
4. Turn on all accessories, then connect a carbon pile regulator across battery.
5. Operate engine at moderate speed, adjust carbon pile regulator to obtain maximum current output.

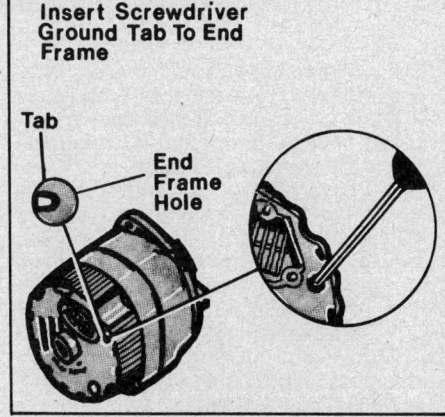

Insert Screwdriver Ground Tab To End Frame

Fig. 3 Grounding field windings

6. If ammeter reading is within 10 amps of rated output, alternator is not at fault. **Alternator rated output is stamped on alternator frame.**
7. If ammeter reading is not within 10 amps of rated output, ground field winding by inserting screwdriver in end frame hole, contacting tab, **Fig. 3. Do not insert screwdriver deeper than one inch since tab is usually located within 3/4 inch of casing surface.**
8. If reading is within 10 amps of rated

output, regulator must be replaced. If reading is not within limits, check field winding, diode trio, rectifier bridge and stator.
9. Turn off all accessories and disconnect ammeter and carbon pile regulator.

TESTING

IN-VEHICLE VOLTAGE REGULATOR TEST

1. Connect voltmeter and fast charger to 12 volt battery.
2. Connect regulator and test light as shown, observing battery polarity.
3. Test light should be on.
4. Turn on fast charger and slowly increase charge rate. Observe voltmeter, light should go out at a voltage regulator setting of 13.5-16.0 volts.

The test light is connected into the circuit, exactly as the rotor is when the regulator is inside the generator. The regulator shuts off the current to the test light when the regulator setting is reached. This voltage will vary with changes in temperature.

Nippondenso Alternator

INDEX

DESCRIPTION

This alternator has an IC integral solid state regulator. **Fig. 1.** All regulator components are enclosed into a solid mold and are attached to the slip ring end frame along with the brush holder assembly. The alternator voltage setting cannot be adjusted.

The alternator rotor bearing contain enough grease to eliminate the need for periodic lubrication. Two brushes carry current through the two slip rings to the field coil mounted on the rotor.

The stator windings are assembled on the inside of a laminated core that form part of the alternator frame. The rectifier bridge contains six diodes which electrically change stator A.C. voltage into D.C. voltage. The neutral diodes serve to convert the voltage fluctuation at the neutral point to direct current for increasing generator output.

IN-VEHICLE TESTING

SYSTEM TEST

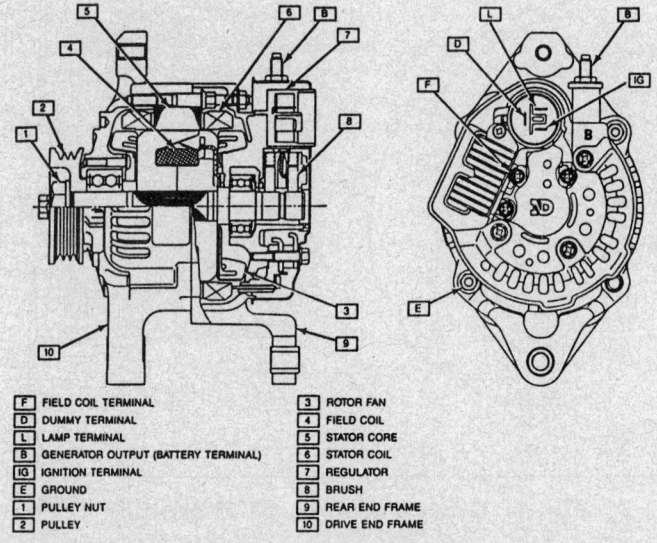

F FIELD COIL TERMINAL	**3** ROTOR FAN
D DUMMY TERMINAL	**4** FIELD COIL
L LAMP TERMINAL	**5** STATOR CORE
B GENERATOR OUTPUT (BATTERY TERMINAL)	**6** STATOR COIL
IG IGNITION TERMINAL	**7** REGULATOR
E GROUND	**8** BRUSH
1 PULLEY NUT	**9** REAR END FRAME
2 PULLEY	**10** DRIVE END FRAME

Fig. 1 Nippondenso alternator

1. Connect an ammeter and voltmeter as follows:
   a. Disconnect wire from B terminal of alternator, then connect ammeter negative probe to the wire.
   b. Connect ammeter positive probe to B terminal of alternator.
   c. Connect voltmeter positive probe to B terminal of alternator and the negative probe to ground.
2. Start engine and allow to run at 2,000 RPM, then check reading of ammeter and voltmeter. Ammeter should read less than 10 amps. Voltmeter should read 13.9-15.1 volts at 77°F.

3. If voltage reading is greater than specified voltage, replace IC regulator. If voltage reading is less than specified voltage, check the IC regulator and alternator as follows:
   a. With engine running and F terminal grounded, check voltage reading at B terminal.
   b. If voltage reading is greater than specified voltage, replace IC regulator. If voltage reading is less than specified voltage, check alternator.
4. With engine running at 2,000 RPM, turn on high beam headlights and place heater fan control switch in the HI position.
5. Check ammeter reading. If reading is less than 30 amps, repair alternator.

REGULATOR TEST

1. Connect a voltmeter and fast charger to battery.
2. Turn ignition switch On and slowly increase charge rate. Indicator lamp in vehicle will begin to dim when voltage setting is reached.
3. Observe voltmeter, light should dim at 13.5 -16.0 volts.
4. If no voltage is present, replace voltage regulator.

Delcotron Type CS Charging System

INDEX

DESCRIPTION

The CS alternator is available in three sizes: CS121, CS130 and CS144. The numerals denote the outer diameter of the stator laminations and the letters CS stand for charging system. The CS144 can be serviced. The CS121 and CS130 are serviced as an assembly only.

The CS alternators uses a new type regulator and a diode trio is not used. A delta stator, rectifier bridge, and rotor with slip rings and brushes are electrically similar to earlier alternators. A conventional fan mounted next to the pulley pulls air through the assembly for cooling. An internal fan mounted on the rotor pulls air through the slip ring end frame to cool rectifier, bridge and regulator. Air is expelled through openings in the end frame. No periodic maintenance is required.

SYSTEM OPERATION

CS130 and CS144 alternators may be used with only two connections. The battery positive BAT terminal must be connected to a battery during operation. The second required connection is through the indicator light, or a suitable external resistor to L terminal of the regulator which serves to turn unit On at start up. Three other regulator terminals are available for optional use in vehicle systems. The P terminal is connected to the stator, and may be connected to a tachometer or other device. The F terminal is connected internally to field positive, and may be used as a fault indicator. The S terminal may be connected externally to a voltage, such as battery voltage, to sense voltage to be controlled.

The regulator voltage setting varies with temperature, and limits system voltage by controlling rotor field current. Unlike others regulators, this regulator switches field current On and Off at a fixed frequency about 400 cycles per second. By varying On-Off time, correct average field current is obtained to provide proper system voltage. At high speeds, the On time may be 10% and Off time 90%. At low speeds with high electrical loads, On-Off time may be 90% and 10% respectively.

Alternator systems on· some applications are controlled by a Body Control Module (BCM). If cause of a system malfunction cannot be determined using the following test procedure, a problem in the electronic control system is indicated. For complete system diagnosis, refer to MO-

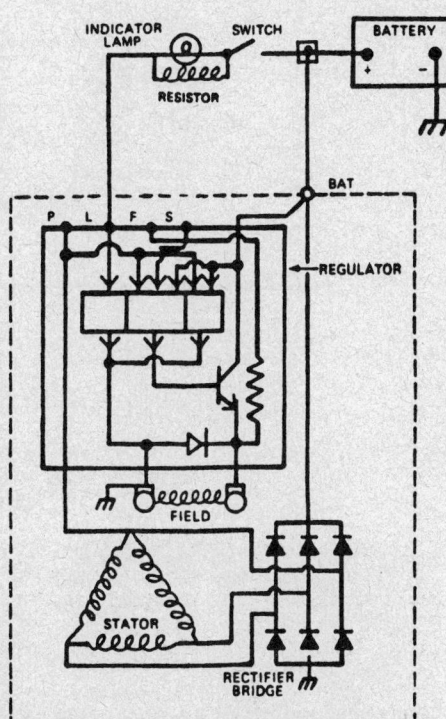

Fig. 1   CS charging system wiring diagram

TOR's Auto Engine Tune Up and Electronics Manual.

DIAGNOSIS & TESTING

CHARGING SYSTEM

When the charging system is operating normally, the indicator lamp will come On when ignition switch is turned On and will go out when the engine starts. If the lamp operates abnormally, or if an undercharge or overcharge battery condition occurs, the following may be used to diagnose the charging system.

1. An undercharged battery if often caused by accessories being left On extented periods of time, or if an accessory lamp stays On.
2. Noise from an alternator may be caused by a loose drive pulley, loose mounting bolts, worn or dirty bearings,

defective diodes or a defective stator.
3. To avoid damage to electrical equipment, refer to charging circuit wiring diagram, **Fig. 1** and proceed as follows:
   a. Do not reverse connections to the alternator.
   b. Do not short across or ground any of the terminals in charging system.
   c. Never disconnect output terminal while alternator is running.
4. Trouble in the charging system will appear as follows:
   a. Faulty indicator lamp operation.
   b. Undercharge battery, as evidenced by slow cranking or dark hydrometer.
   c. Overcharge battery, as evidenced by spewing of electrolyte from the vents.

IN-VEHICLE TESTING

EXCEPT CS144

1. Visually check belt and wiring and make any necessary repairs.
2. **On models** without charge indicator light, proceed to step 5.
3. **On all models,** with ignition switch on and engine stopped, lamp should be on. If not, disconnect harness from alternator, and ground L terminal.
   a. If lamp lights, replace alternator.
   b. If lamp does not light, locate open circuit between grounding lead and ignition switch.
4. With ignition switch on and engine stopped, lamp should be off. If not, disconnect wiring harness from alternator.
   a. If lamp goes off, replace alternator.
   b. If lamp stays on, check for grounded L terminal in wiring harness.
5. Battery undercharged or overcharged.
   a. Disconnect wiring harness connector from alternator.
   b. With ignition switch on and engine not running, connect voltmeter from ground to L terminal.
   c. Zero reading indicates open circuit between terminal and battery. Correct as required.
   d. Reconnect harness connector to alternator.
   e. Measure voltage across battery terminals with engine running at approximately 2000 RPM. If voltage is above 16 volts, replace alternator.

f. Turn on accessories and load battery with carbon pile to obtain maximum amperage. Maintain voltage at 13 volts or less. If alternator is within 15 amps of rated output, it is acceptable.

CS144

1. Visually check belt and wiring and make necessary repairs.
2. Ensure battery is fully charged.
3. Run engine at 1000-1500 RPM for 30 seconds, then measure alternator output voltage.
4. If voltage is less than 16 volts, proceed to step 5. If voltage is 16 volts or more, proceed as follows:
   a. Disassemble and inspect individual components. If rotor does not pass ohmmeter inspection, replace drive end frame and regulator. If rotor does pass ohmmeter inspection, replace regulator.
5. With ignition off and battery ground cable disconnected, connect an ammeter in the circuit at the battery terminal of alternator.
6. Reconnect battery ground cable, connect a carbon pile across the battery.
7. Run engine at 1500 RPM, then adjust carbon pile to obtain maximum current output from alternator.
8. If alternator output is less than 90 amps, proceed as follows:
   a. Disassemble and test, then reassemble.
9. If alternator output is greater than 90 amps, proceed as follows:
   a. Run engine and measure the voltage drop between the alternator housing and the battery ground terminal.
   b. If less than .2 volts, alternator is satisfactory.
   c. If more then .2 volts, check for poor ground or high resistance in ground circuit.

ON-VEHICLE OUTPUT TEST

1. Connect ammeter in series at alternator output BAT terminal, then connect voltmeter and carbon pile across battery terminal. Ensure battery is fully charged.
2. Operate engine at moderate speed. With carbon pile turned Off, check voltage across battery terminals.
3. If voltmeter reads above 16 volts, repair (CS-144) only or replace alternator.
4. If voltmeter reads below 16 volts, proceed as follows:
   a. With engine still running at moderate speed turn accessories On and load battery with carbon pile to obtain maximum amperage output. Maintain voltage above 13 volts.
   b. If output is within 15 amps of rated output, alternator is satisfactory.
   c. If output is not within 15 amps of rated output, alternator is defective and requires repair (CS-144 only) or replace alternator.

BENCH TESTING

1. Make connections as shown in **Fig. 2**, however leave the carbon pile disconnected. The ground polarity of the alternator and battery must be the same. The battery must be fully charged. Use a 30-500 ohm resistor between battery and L terminal.
2. Slowly increase alternator speed and observe voltage.
3. If voltage is uncontrolled and increases above 16 volts, the rotor field is shorted, the regulator is defective or both. A shorted rotor field can cause the regulator to become defective. **Battery must be fully charged when making this test.**
4. If voltage is below 16 volts, increase speed and adjust carbon pile obtain maximum amperage output. Maintain voltage above 13 volts.
5. If output is within 15 amps of rated output, alternator is satisfactory.
6. If output is not within 15 amps of rated output, alternator is defective and requires repair.

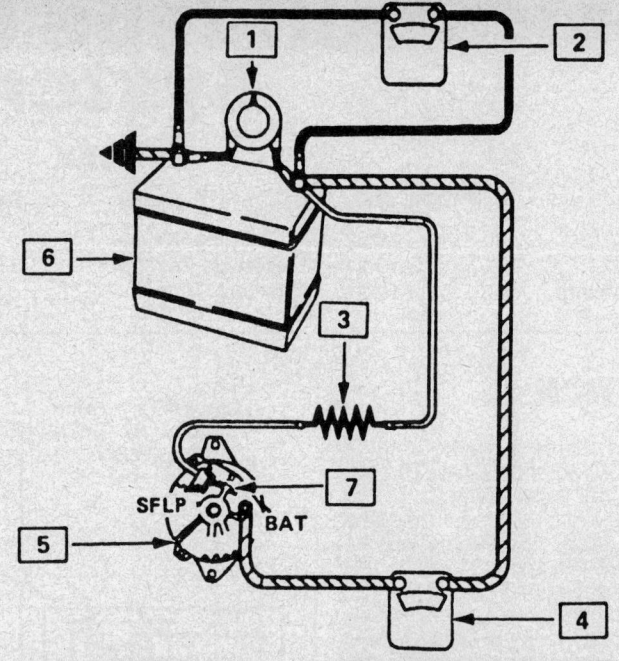

1—CARBON PILE
2—VOLTMETER
3—RESISTOR
4—TESTAMMETER
5—GENERATOR
6—BATTERY
7—CONNECT RESISTOR TO "L" TERMINAL

SFLP   BAT

Fig. 2   CS alternator bench check

DISC BRAKES

NOTE: Refer to "Applications" to determine which type brakes are used on vehicle being serviced.

TABLE OF CONTENTS

Applications

Model	Year	Application
BUICK		
Century	1988–90	Delco-Moraine Single Piston Type 2
Electra	1988–90	Delco-Moraine Single Piston Type 2
Estate Wagon	1988–90	Delco-Moraine Single Piston Type 1
LeSabre	1988–90	Delco-Moraine Single Piston Type 2
Park Avenue	1988–90	Delco-Moraine Single Piston Type 2
Reatta	1988–90	Delco-Moraine Single Piston Type 4
Regal	1988–90 (Front)	Delco-Moraine Dual Piston
	1988–90 (Rear)	Delco-Moraine Single Piston
Riviera	1988–90	Delco-Moraine Single Piston Type 4
Skyhawk	1988–89	Delco-Moraine Single Piston Type 2
Skylark	1988–90	Delco-Moraine Single Piston Type 2
CADILLAC		
Brougham	1988–90	Delco-Moraine Single Piston Type 1
Cimarron	1988	Delco-Moraine Single Piston Type 2
DeVille	1988–90	Delco-Moraine Single Piston Type 2
Eldorado	1988–90	Delco-Moraine Single Piston Type 4

Continued

APPLICATION CHARTS—Continued

Model	Year	Application
Fleetwood	1988–90	Delco-Moraine Single Piston Type 2
Seville	1988–90	Delco-Moraine Single Piston Type 4
CHEVROLET		
Beretta	1988–90	Delco-Moraine Single Piston Type 2
Camaro	1988 (Rear)	Delco-Moraine Single Piston
	1988–90 (Front Standard)	Delco-Moraine Single Piston Type 1
	1989–90 (Front Optional)	PBR Dual Piston
	1989–90 (Rear)	PBR Single Piston
Caprice	1988–90	Delco-Moraine Single Piston Type 1
Cavalier	1988–90	Delco-Moraine Single Piston Type 2
Celebrity	1988–90	Delco-Moraine Single Piston Type 2
Corsica	1988–90	Delco-Moraine Single Piston Type 2
Corvette	1988–90 (Front)	PBR Dual Piston
	1988–90 (Rear)	PBR Single Piston
Lumina	1990 (Front)	Delco-Moraine Dual Piston Type 5
	1990 (Rear)	Delco-Moraine Single Piston Type 5
Monte Carlo	1988	Delco-Moraine Single Piston Type 1
Nova	1988	Toyota/GM
Spectrum	1988	Aisin Seiki Type 1
Sprint	1988	Aisin Seiki Type 2
GEO		
Metro	1989–90	Aisin Seiki Type 1
Prizm	1990	Toyota/GM
Spectrum	1989	Aisin Seiki Type 1
Storm	1990	Aisin Seiki Type 1
OLDSMOBILE		
Custom Cruiser	1988–90	Delco-Moraine Single Piston Type 1
Cutlass Calais	1988–90	Delco-Moraine Single Piston Type 2
Cutlass Ciera	1988–90	Delco-Moraine Single Piston Type 2
Cutlass Cruiser	1988–90	Delco-Moraine Single Piston Type 2
Cutlass Supreme	1988–90 (Front)	Delco-Moraine Dual Piston
	1988–90 (Rear)	Delco-Moraine Single Piston Type 5
Cutlass Supreme Classic	1988	Delco-Moraine Single Piston Type 1
Firenza	1988	Delco-Moraine Single Piston Type 2
Toronado	1988–90	Delco Moraine Single Piston Type 4
Trofeo	1990	Delco-Moraine Single Piston Type 4
88	1988–90	Delco-Moraine Single Piston Type 2
98	1988–90	Delco-Moraine Single Piston Type 2
PONTIAC		
Bonneville	1988–90	Delco-Moraine Single Piston Type 2
Fiero	1988	Delco-Moraine Single Piston Type 6
Firebird	1988 (Rear)	Delco-Moraine Single Piston
	1988–90 (Front Standard)	Delco-Moraine Single Piston Type 1
	1989–90 (Front Optional)	PBR Dual Piston
	1989–90 (Rear)	PBR Single Piston
Grand Am	1988–90	Delco-Moraine Single Piston Type 2
Grand Prix	1988–90 (Front)	Delco-Moraine Dual Piston
	1988–90 (Rear)	Delco-Moraine Single Piston Type 5
LeMans	1988–90	DAEWOO Single Piston
Safari	1988–89	Delco-Moraine Single Piston Type 1
Sunbird	1988–90	Delco-Moraine Single Piston Type 2
6000	1988–90 (Front)	Delco-Moraine Single Piston Type 2
	1989–90 (Rear)	Delco-Moraine Single Piston Type 6

Continued

APPLICATION CHARTS—Continued

Model	Year	Application
6000STE	1988–89 (Front)	Delco-Moraine Single Piston Type 2
	1988–89 (Rear)	Delco-Moraine Single Piston Type 3

①—Single piston with dual mounting bolts.	④—Front.	⑧—Optional front.
②—4 wheel disc brakes.	⑤—Rear.	⑨—Single piston caliper.
③—Dual piston with dual mounting bolts.	⑥—Single piston rear disc brakes.	⑩—optional rear.
	⑦—Dual piston caliper.	⑪—Front and rear.

General Information

INDEX

TROUBLESHOOTING

When troubleshooting brake system, refer to **Fig. 1**.

BRAKE SHOES, LININGS & CALIPERS

Remove wheels and inspect brake disc, caliper and linings. The wheel bearings should be inspected at this time and repacked if necessary. Do not get any grease on the linings.

Do not replace individual pads or replace pads on one wheel of an axle set alone, as braking performance will be adversely affected.

If a visual inspection does not adequately determine the condition of the linings, the brake shoe and lining assemblies should be removed and inspected. If shoes do not require replacement, reinstall them in their original positions. Brake shoes and linings should also be replaced if cracked or damaged.

If the caliper is cracked or fluid leakage through the casting is evident, it must be replaced as a unit.

BRAKE ROUGHNESS

The most common cause of brake chatter on disc brakes is a variation in thickness of the disc. If roughness or vibration is encountered during highway operation or if pedal pulsation is experienced at low speeds, the disc may have excessive thickness variation. To check for this condition, measure the disc at 12 points with a micrometer at a radius approximately one inch from edge of disc. If thickness measurements vary by more than .0005 inch, the disc should be replaced with a new one.

Excessive lateral runout of braking disc may cause a "knocking back" of the pistons, possibly creating increased pedal travel and vibration when brakes are applied.

Before checking the runout, wheel bearings should be adjusted. The readjustment is very important and will be required at the completion of the test to prevent bearing failure. Be sure to make the adjustment according to the recommendations given under "Front Wheel Bearings, Adjust" in the car chapters.

BRAKE DISC SERVICE

Servicing of disc brakes is extremely critical due to the close tolerances required in machining the brake disc to insure proper brake operation.

The maintenance of these close controls of the shape of the rubbing surfaces is necessary to prevent brake roughness. In addition, the surface finish must be non-directional and maintained at a micro inch finish. This close control of the rubbing surface finish is necessary to avoid pulls and erratic performance, and to promote long lining life and equal lining wear of both left and right brakes.

In light of the foregoing remarks, refinishing of the rubbing surfaces should not be attempted unless precision equipment, capable of measuring in micro inches (millionths of an inch) is available.

To check lateral runout of a disc, mount a dial indicator on a convenient part (steering knuckle, tie rod, disc brake caliper housing) so that the plunger of the dial indicator contacts the disc at a point one inch from the outer edge, **Fig. 2**. If the total indicated runout exceeds specifications, install a new disc.

To check parallelism (thickness variation), mount dial indicators, **Fig. 3**, so the plunger contacts rotor approximately 1 inch from outer edge. If parallelism exceeds specifications, replace rotor.

GENERAL PRECAUTIONS

1. Grease or any other foreign material must be kept off the brake linings, caliper, surfaces of the disc and external surfaces of the hub, during service procedures. Handling the brake disc and caliper should be done in a way to avoid deformation of the disc and nicking or scratching brake linings.
2. If inspection reveals rubber piston seals are worn or damaged, they should be replaced immediately.
3. During removal and installation of a wheel assembly, exercise care so as not to interfere with or damage the caliper splash shield, or bleeder screw.
4. Front wheel bearings preload should be adjusted to specifications .
5. Be sure vehicle is centered on hoist before servicing any of the front end components to avoid bending or damaging the disc splash shield on full right or left wheel turns.
6. Before the vehicle is moved after any brake service work, be sure to obtain a firm brake pedal.
7. The assembly bolts of two piece caliper housings should not be disturbed unless the caliper requires service.

INSPECTION OF CALIPER

Should it become necessary to remove the caliper for installation of new parts, clean all parts in alcohol, wipe dry using lint free cloths, using an air hose to blow out drilled passages and bores. Check dust boots for punctures or tears. If punctures or tears are evident, new boots should be installed upon reassembly.

Inspect piston bores for scoring or pitting. Bores that show light scratches or corrosion can usually be cleaned with crocus cloth. However, bores that have deep scratches or scoring may be honed, provided the diameter of the bore is not increased more than .002 inches. If the bore does not clean up within this specification, a new caliper housing should be installed (black stains on the bore walls are caused by piston seals and will do no harm).

When using a hone, **Fig. 4**, be sure to in-

CAUSE	Excessive Brake Pedal Travel	Brake Pedal Travel Gradually Increases	Excessive Brake Pedal Effort	Excessive Braking Action	Brakes Slow To Respond	Brakes Slow To Release	Brakes Drag	Uneven Braking Action (Side To Side)	Uneven Braking Action (Front To Rear)	Scraping Noise From Brakes	*Brakes Squeak During Application	*Brakes Squeak During Stop	**Brakes Pulsate (Roughness)	*Brakes Groan At End of Stop	*"BRAKE" Warning Lamp Glows
Leaking Brake Line or Connection	X	XX						X							XX
Leaking Wheel Cylinder or Piston Seal	X	XX		X				X							XX
Leaking Master Cylinder	X	XX													XX
Air in Brake System	XX							X							X
Contaminated or Improper Brake Fluid					X	X	X								X
Leaking Vacuum System			XX		X										
Restricted Air Passage in Power Head			X		XX	X									
Damaged Power Head			X	X	X	X	X								
Improperly Assembled Power Head Valving			X	X	X	X	XX								
Worn Out Brake Lining - Replace			X	X				X	X	X	X	X		X	
Uneven Brake Lining Wear - Replace and Correct	X			X				X	X	X	X	X		X	X
Incorrect Lining Material-Replace			X	X				X	X			X		X	
Contaminated Brake Lining - Replace				XX				XX	X	X	X	X		X	
Linings Damaged by Abusive Use-Replace			X	XX				X	X	X	X	X		X	
Heat Spotted or Scored Brake Drums or Rotors				X				X	X		X	X	X	X	
Out-of-Round Brake Drums													X		
Improper Rotor Thickness Variation													XX		
Excessive Lateral Runout	X											X		X	
Faulty Automatic Adjusters	X						X	X	X						X
Incorrect Wheel Cylinder Sizes	X		X	X				X	X						
Weak or Incorrect Brake Shoe Retention Springs				X		X	XX	X	X	XX	X	XX			
Brake Assembly Attachments - Missing or Loose	X						X	X	X		X	X	X		
Insufficient Brake Shoe Guide Lubricant						X	X	X	X	XX	XX				
Restricted Brake Fluid Passage or Sticking Wheel Cylinder Piston		X	X		X	X	X	X	X						
Incorrect Stoplamp Switch Adjustment		X		X			X								
Brake Pedal Linkage Interference or Binding			X		X	XX	XX								X
Improperly Adjusted Parking Brake							X								X
Parking Brake Cable Siezed						X	X		X						X
Drums Tapered or Threaded										XX					
Incorrect Front End Alignment									XX						
Incorrect Wheel Bearing Runout	X									X					
Loose Front Suspension Attachments								X		XX				X	
Operator Riding Brake Pedal	X	X	X				X		X			X		X	
Improper Booster Pushrod Length	X					X	XX								
Sticking Wheel Cylinder or Caliper Pistons			X			X	X	X							
Caliper Not Sliding Freely	X						X			X			XX		
Faulty Proportioning Valve			X	X	X	X	X								

XX — Indicates more probable cause(s)
X — Indicates other causes
*May be a normal condition.
**Can usually be corrected by servicing front brakes.

Fig. 1 Troubleshooting brake system chart

stall the hone baffle before honing bore. The baffle is used to protect the hone stones from damage. Use extreme care in cleaning the caliper after honing. Remove all dust and grit by flushing the caliper with alcohol. Wipe dry with clean lint free cloth and then clean a second time in the same manner.

BLEEDING DISC BRAKES

Pressure bleeding is recommended for all hydraulic disc brake systems.

The disc brake hydraulic system can be bled manually or with pressure bleeding equipment. **On vehicles with disc brakes** the brake pedal will require more pumping and frequent checking of fluid level in master cylinder during bleeding operation.

Never use brake fluid that has been drained from hydraulic system when bleeding the brakes. Be sure the disc

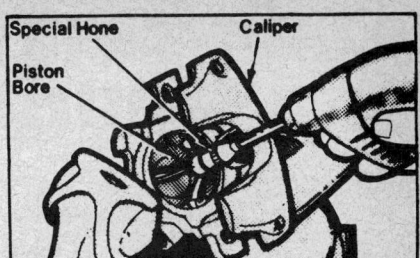

Fig. 4   Honing caliper piston bore

Fig. 2   Checking rotor for lateral runout

Fig. 3   Checking rotor parallelism (thickness variation)

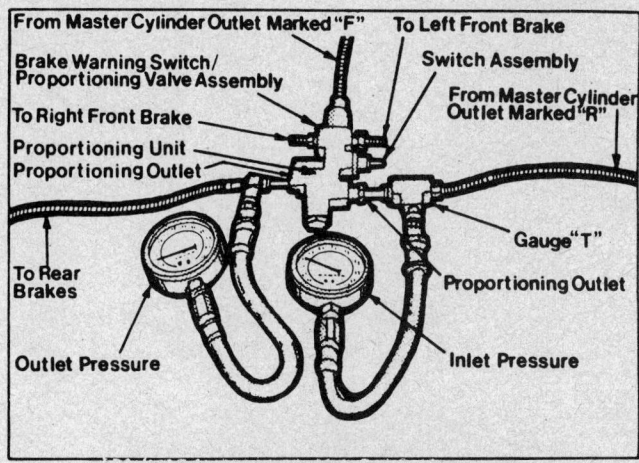

Fig. 5   Gauge hook-up for testing proportioning valve (typical)

brake pistons are returned to their normal positions and that the shoe and lining assemblies are properly seated. Before driving the vehicle, check brake operation to be sure that a firm pedal has been obtained.

PROPORTIONING VALVE

The proportioning valve (when used), **Fig. 5,** provides balanced braking action between front and rear brakes under a wide range of braking conditions. The valve regulates the hydraulic pressure applied to the rear wheel cylinders, thus limiting rear braking action when high pressures are required at the front brakes. In this manner, premature rear wheel skid is prevented.

TESTING PROPORTIONING VALVE

When a premature rear wheel slide is obtained on a brake application, it usually is an indication that the fluid pressure to the rear wheels is above the 50% reduction ratio for the rear line pressure and that malfunction has occurred within the proportioning valve.

To test the valve, install gauge set shown in **Fig. 5** in brake line between master cylinder and proportioning valve, and at output end of proportioning valve and brake line as shown. Be sure all joints are fluid tight.

Have a helper exert pressure on brake pedal (holding pressure). Obtain a reading on master cylinder output of approximately 700 psi. While pressure is being held as above, reading on valve outlet should be 550–610 psi. If the pressure readings do not meet these specifications, the valve should be removed and a new valve installed.

Aisin-Seiki Single Piston w/Dual Mounting Bolts (Type 1)

INDEX

Description

This single piston sliding caliper assembly, **Figs. 1 and 2,** is mounted to a support bracket by two slide pins. The caliper assembly slides on the two mounting pins. Upon brake application, fluid pressure against the piston forces the inboard shoe and lining assembly against the inboard side of the disc. This action causes the caliper assembly to slide until the outboard lining comes into contact with the disc.

SERVICE

CALIPER REMOVAL

1. Disconnect negative battery cable.
2. Remove approximately ²/₃ of brake fluid from master cylinder.
3. Raise and support vehicle.
4. Mark relationship between front wheel and axle, then remove wheel and tire assembly.
5. If caliper assembly is to be serviced, remove inlet fitting attaching bolt, copper washer, and inlet fitting from caliper housing. Plug opening in inlet fitting to prevent fluid loss and contamination. **Do not crimp brake hose, as this may damage internal structure of hose. If only shoe and lining assemblies are to be replaced, do not disconnect brake line fitting from caliper.**
6. Remove caliper slide pins and the caliper. If only shoe and lining assemblies are to be replaced, suspend caliper from chassis using suitable hanger. **Do not allow caliper to hang by brake hose.**
7. Remove shoe and lining assembly.
8. Remove bracket attaching bolts and the bracket.
9. Remove slide pin boot from bracket.

BRAKE SHOE & LINING, REPLACE

1. Remove approximately ²/₃ of brake fluid from master cylinder.
2. Raise and support vehicle.
3. Mark relationship between front wheel and axle, then remove wheel and tire assembly.
4. Remove 2 caliper slide pins from bracket.
5. Unfasten caliper, and support with a length of wire, leaving hydraulic lines connected.

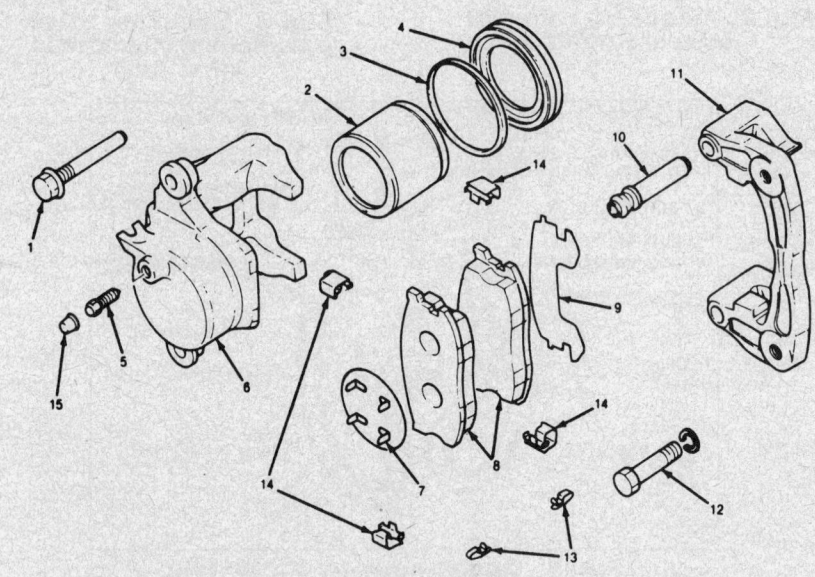

1. SLIDE PIN BOLT
2. PISTON
3. PISTON SEAL
4. PISTON BOOT
5. BLEEDER SCREW
6. CALIPER BODY
7. INNER SHIM
8. PADS
9. OUTER SHIM
10. SLIDE PIN BOOT
11. BRACKET
12. BOLT
13. WEAR INDICATOR
14. RETAINER
15. CAP

Fig. 1   Exploded view of disc brake caliper assembly. 1988 models

6. Remove brake pads, shims, wear indicators and retainers, **Fig. 1 and 2.**
7. Reverse procedure to install.

CALIPER DISASSEMBLY

1. Remove caliper assembly as outlined previously, then drain brake fluid from caliper.
2. Use clean shop towels to pad interior of caliper assembly, then remove piston by directing compressed air into caliper brake hose inlet hole, **Fig. 3. Use just enough air pressure to ease piston out of bore. Do not place fingers in front of piston for any reason when applying compressed air. This could result in serious personal injury.**
3. Remove dust boot from piston.
4. Using a small piece of wood or plastic, remove piston seal from bore. **Do not use a metal tool of any kind to remove seal as it may damage bore.**
5. Remove bleeder valve.

6. Inspect piston for scoring, nicks, corrosion, and wear and replace as needed.
7. Inspect caliper housing and seal groove for corrosion, nicks, scoring and excessive wear, and use crocus cloth to polish away corrosion from housing bore. Replace caliper housing if corrosion in and around seal groove will not clean up with crocus cloth.
8. Clean all parts with denatured alcohol. Dry with unlubricated compressed air. Blow out all passages in housing and bleeder valve.

CALIPER ASSEMBLY

1. Apply suitable grease to piston seal and cylinder wall, then install the seal. Check to ensure piston seal is not twisted.
2. Apply suitable grease to sliding portion of piston and install dust boot.
3. Insert edge of dust boot into boot

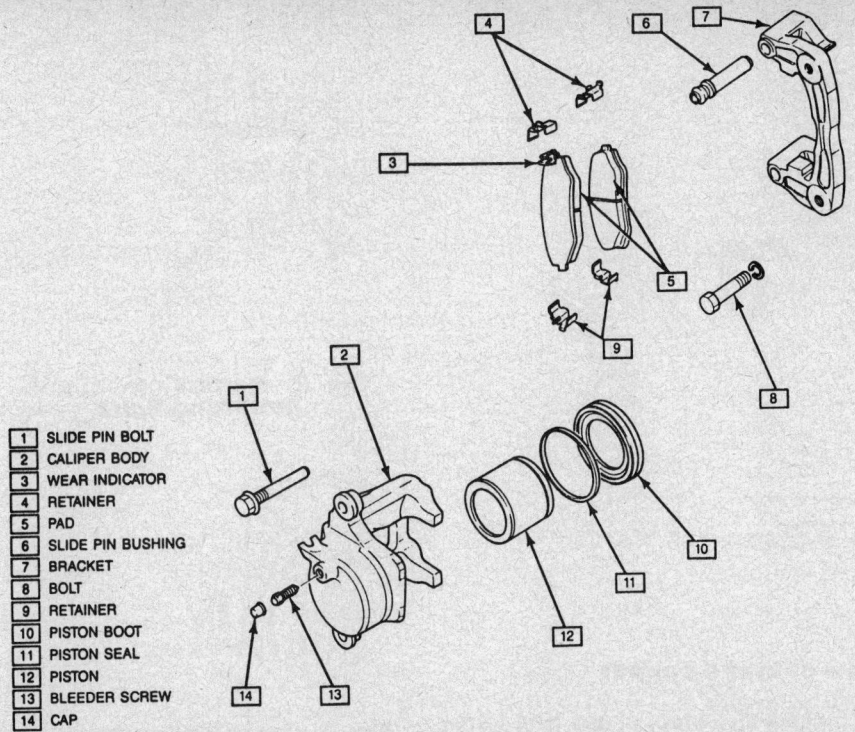

1	SLIDE PIN BOLT
2	CALIPER BODY
3	WEAR INDICATOR
4	RETAINER
5	PAD
6	SLIDE PIN BUSHING
7	BRACKET
8	BOLT
9	RETAINER
10	PISTON BOOT
11	PISTON SEAL
12	PISTON
13	BLEEDER SCREW
14	CAP

Fig. 2   Exploded view of disc brake caliper assembly. 1989–90 models

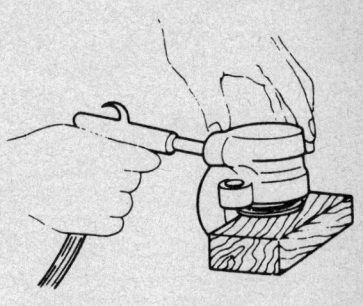

CAUTION: Do not place fingers in front of the piston in an attempt to catch or protect it when applying compressed air. This could result in serious injury.

NOTICE: Use just enough air to ease the piston out of the bore. If the piston is blown out, even with padding provided, it may be damaged.

Fig. 3   Removing caliper piston

groove, then slowly force piston fully into cylinder.
4. Install bleeder valve.

CALIPER INSTALLATION

1. Apply suitable grease to inner face of slide pin boot.

2. Install slide pin boot to bracket.
3. Install bracket and **torque** attaching bolts to 40.5 ft. lbs.
4. Install shoe and lining assembly, ensure wear indicators are located on trailing edge of shoe assemblies during forward wheel rotation.
5. Install caliper assembly to bracket.

Torque attaching bolts to 36 ft. lbs.
6. Attach flexible hose to caliper and **torque** fitting to 13.4 ft. lbs.
7. Install wheel and tire assembly, then lower vehicle.
8. Fill master cylinder to proper level and bleed brakes. **Before moving vehicle, pump brake pedal several times to be sure it is firm. Do not move vehicle until a firm pedal is obtained.**

Aisin-Seiki Single Piston w/Dual Mounting Bolts (Type 2)

INDEX

DESCRIPTION

This single piston sliding caliper assembly, **Fig. 1**, is mounted to a support bracket by two slide pins. The caliper assembly slides on the two mounting pins. Upon brake application, fluid pressure against the piston forces the inboard shoe and lining assembly against the inboard side of the disc. This action causes the caliper assembly to slide until the outboard lining comes into contact with the disc.

SERVICE

CALIPER REMOVAL

1. Remove approximately ⅔ of brake fluid from master cylinder.
2. Raise and support vehicle.

3. Mark relationship between front wheel and axle, then remove wheel and tire assembly.
4. If caliper assembly is to be serviced, remove inlet fitting attaching bolt, copper washer, and inlet fitting from caliper housing. Plug opening in inlet fitting to prevent fluid loss and contamination. **Do not crimp brake hose, as this may damage internal structure of hose. If only shoe and lining assemblies are to be replaced, do not disconnect brake line fitting from caliper.**
5. Remove caliper mounting bolts.
6. Remove caliper from knuckle. **Be careful not to drop inside pad which will come off with caliper.**

BRAKE SHOE & LINING, REPLACE

1. Raise and support vehicle and remove wheel.
2. Remove caliper mounting bolts, **Fig. 2.**
3. Remove caliper from knuckle, taking care not to drop inside pad. If only shoe and lining assemblies are to be replaced, suspend caliper from chassis using suitable hanger. **Do not allow caliper to hang by brake hose.**
4. Remove outside pad.
5. Install pad clips, No. 1 & 2, then outside pad to knuckle, **Fig. 3.**
6. Install caliper and inside pad to knuckle, **Fig. 4.** Position outer springs over

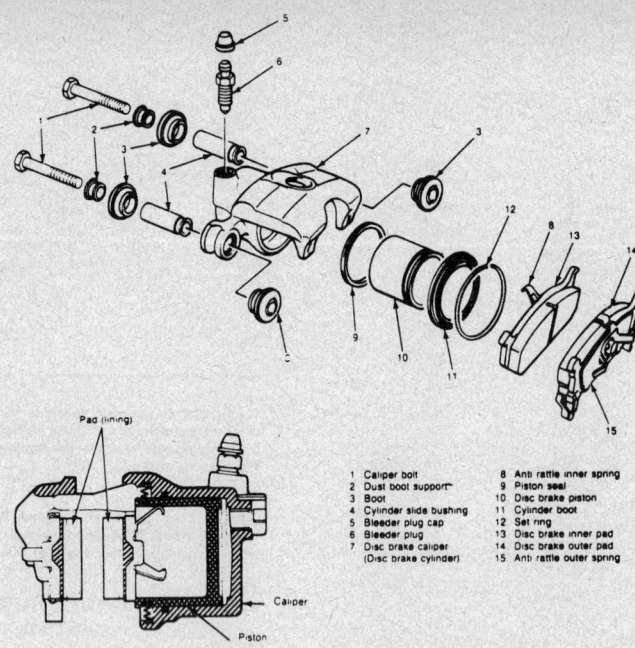

Fig. 1   Exploded view of brake caliper

1. Caliper bolt	8. Anti rattle inner spring
2. Dust boot support	9. Piston seal
3. Boot	10. Disc brake piston
4. Cylinder slide bushing	11. Cylinder boot
5. Bleeder plug cap	12. Set ring
6. Bleeder plug	13. Disc brake inner pad
7. Disc brake caliper	14. Disc brake outer pad
(Disc brake cylinder)	15. Anti rattle outer spring

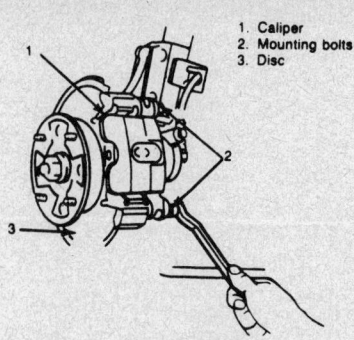

Fig. 2   Removing caliper mounting bolts

1. Caliper
2. Mounting bolts
3. Disc

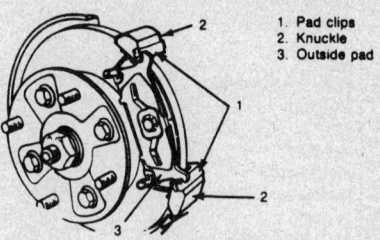

Fig. 3   Installing outside pad

1. Pad clips
2. Knuckle
3. Outside pad

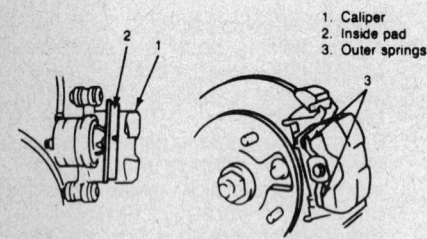

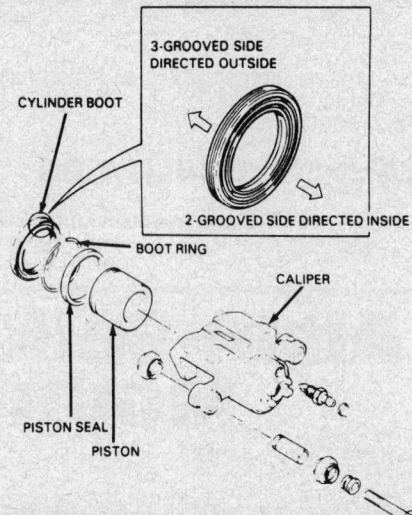

Fig. 5   Installing caliper boot

1. Caliper
2. Inside pad
3. Outer springs

Fig. 4   Installing inside pad & caliper

caliper as shown.
7. **Torque** caliper bolts to 17.5-26 ft. lbs.
8. Install front wheel.
9. Lower vehicle and perform brake test.

CALIPER DISASSEMBLY

1. Remove caliper assembly as outlined previously, then drain brake fluid from caliper.
2. Remove cylinder boot set ring and boot from cylinder groove, **Fig. 1.**
3. Use clean shop towels to pad interior of caliper assembly, then remove piston by directing compressed air into caliper brake hose inlet hole. **Use just enough air pressure to ease piston out of bore. Do not place fingers in front of piston for any reason when applying compressed air. This could result in serious personal injury.**
4. Using a small piece of wood or plastic, remove piston seal from bore. **Do not** use a metal tool of any kind to remove seal as it may damage bore.
5. Remove bleeder valve.
6. Inspect piston for scoring, nicks, corrosion, and wear and replace as needed.
7. Inspect caliper housing and seal groove for corrosion, nicks, scoring and excessive wear, and use crocus cloth to polish away corrosion from housing bore. Replace caliper housing if corrosion in and around seal groove will not clean up with crocus cloth.
8. Clean all parts with denatured alcohol. Dry with unlubricated compressed air. Blow out all passages in housing and bleeder valve.

CALIPER ASSEMBLY & INSTALLATION

1. Apply suitable grease to piston seal and cylinder wall, then install the seal. Check to ensure piston seal is not twisted.
2. Install new boot on piston so side with 2 grooves faces in toward cylinder and side with 3 grooves faces out, **Fig. 5.**
3. Install piston in caliper so it projects about .4 inch to ease installation of boot on caliper housing. Install boot on caliper housing, then install set ring.
4. Install bleeder valve.
5. Check that caliper slide bushings are lubricated with rubber grease. Check that slide bushing in each carrier hole can be moved smoothly in each direction.
6. Install caliper and inside pad on knuckle.
7. Tighten caliper bolts.
8. Connect brake hose, then bleed hydraulic system.
9. Install wheel.
10. Lower vehicle and test brakes. **Before moving vehicle, pump brake pedal several times to be sure it is firm. Do not move vehicle until a firm pedal is obtained.**

Daewoo Single Piston w/Dual Mounting Bolts

INDEX

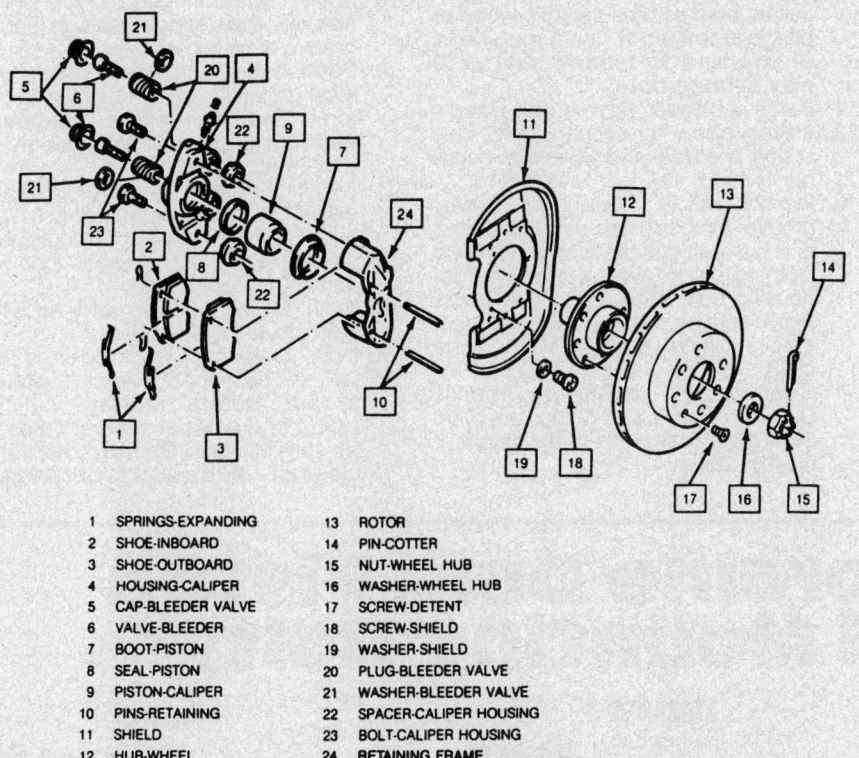

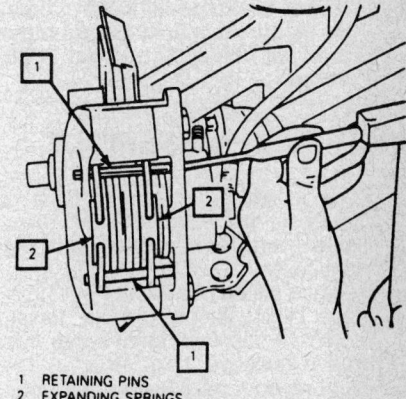

Fig. 2 Brake pad retaining pin removal

1	SPRINGS-EXPANDING	13	ROTOR
2	SHOE-INBOARD	14	PIN-COTTER
3	SHOE-OUTBOARD	15	NUT-WHEEL HUB
4	HOUSING-CALIPER	16	WASHER-WHEEL HUB
5	CAP-BLEEDER VALVE	17	SCREW-DETENT
6	VALVE-BLEEDER	18	SCREW-SHIELD
7	BOOT-PISTON	19	WASHER-SHIELD
8	SEAL-PISTON	20	PLUG-BLEEDER VALVE
9	PISTON-CALIPER	21	WASHER-BLEEDER VALVE
10	PINS-RETAINING	22	SPACER-CALIPER HOUSING
11	SHIELD	23	BOLT-CALIPER HOUSING
12	HUB-WHEEL	24	RETAINING FRAME

Fig. 1 Exploded view of brake caliper assembly

DESCRIPTION

This caliper has a single bore, **Fig. 1**, and is mounted to the steering knuckle with two mounting bolts. Upon brake application, hydraulic pressure is converted by the caliper to stopping force. This force acts equally against the piston and the bottom of the caliper bore to move the piston outward and to slide the caliper inward resulting in a clamping action on the rotor. This clamping action forces the lining against the rotor, creating friction to stop the vehicle.

SERVICE

BRAKE SHOE & LINING, REPLACE

Caliper removal is not required to replace shoe and linings.
1. Remove approximately ⅔ of brake fluid from master cylinder.

2. Raise and support vehicle.
3. Mark relationship between front wheel and hub, then remove wheel and tire assembly.
4. Carefully drive pad retaining pins from inside out, **Fig. 2**.
5. Bottom piston into caliper bore using suitable pliers, then remove brake pads.
6. Reverse procedure to install, noting the following:
   a. Install brake pads with wear sensor to the piston side.
   b. Ensure pads can be moved back and forth slightly when installed.
   c. Install retaining pins from outside in, ensuring openings align.
   d. Upon completion of installation, lower vehicle and pump brake pedal several times to properly position brake pads.

CALIPER, REPLACE

1. Remove approximately ⅔ of brake

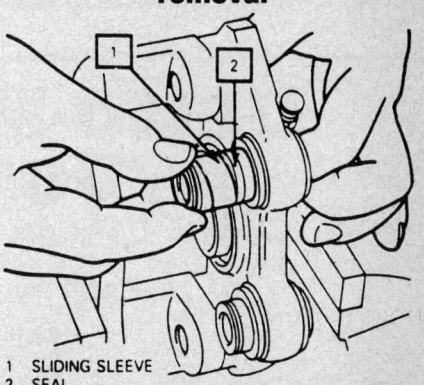

Fig. 3 Caliper sliding sleeve removal

fluid from master cylinder.
2. Raise and support vehicle.
3. Mark relationship between front wheel and hub, then remove wheel and hub assembly.
4. Bottom piston into caliper bore using suitable pliers to provide clearance between brake pads and rotor.
5. Disconnect brake hose from caliper. Plug openings in brake hose and caliper to prevent leakage and contamination. **Do not crimp brake hose, as this may damage internal structure of hose.**
6. Remove outer protective caps from caliper housing seats.
7. Remove caliper attaching bolts, and the caliper.
8. Reverse procedure to install, noting the following:

a. Original equipment caliper attaching bolts are micro-encapsulated. After removal of these bolts, threads in steering knuckle must be re-cut using a M12 X 1.5 thread tap.

b. Install new caliper attaching bolts not micro-encapsulated and **torque to 70 ft. lbs.**

c. **Torque** brake hose inlet fitting attaching bolt to 18 ft. lbs.

d. Install new outer protective caps. Ensure caps seat evenly on caliper.

e. Upon completion of installation, bleed hydraulic system, then lower vehicle. **Before moving vehicle, pump brake pedal several times to be sure it is firm. Do not move vehicle until a firm pedal is obtained.**

CALIPER DISASSEMBLY

1. Remove caliper and brake pads as previously described.
2. Remove inner protective caps for sliding sleeves.
3. Remove piston boot from housing.
4. Move sliding sleeve slightly toward protective cap and remove cap from groove in sleeve.
5. Remove boot from piston and housing.
6. Press sliding sleeves out of housing, **Fig. 3,** then remove seals using a suitable wood or plastic tool.
7. Clean outside of caliper, then drain brake fluid from caliper.
8. Use clean shop towels to pad interior of caliper assembly, then remove piston by directing compressed air into caliper brake hose inlet hole, **Use just enough air pressure to ease piston out of bore. Do not place fingers in front of piston for any reason when applying compressed air. This could result in serious personal injury.**
9. Secure caliper assembly in a suitable vise, then remove caliper retaining frame attaching bolts and the frame.
10. Remove piston seal from groove in caliper bore using a suitable wood or plastic tool. **Do not use a metal tool of any kind to remove seal as it may damage bore.**
11. Remove bleeder valve from caliper.
12. Inspect piston for scoring, nicks, corrosion, and wear and replace as needed.
13. Inspect caliper housing and seal groove for corrosion, nicks, scoring and excessive wear, and use crocus cloth to polish away corrosion from housing bore. Replace caliper housing if corrosion in and around seal groove will not clean up with crocus cloth.
14. Clean all parts with denatured alcohol. Dry with unlubricated compressed air. Blow out all passages in housing and bleeder valve.

CALIPER ASSEMBLY

1. Lubricate, then install new piston seal into caliper bore. Ensure seal is not twisted.
2. Install lubricated piston into caliper bore, ensuring piston does not jam and piston seal is properly seated. **Leave piston exposed enough to permit installation of boot in groove.**
3. Position boot in piston groove and press onto caliper housing. Seat boot using dust boot seal installer tool No. J36538 or equivalent.
4. Install caliper retaining frame, **torquing** attaching bolts to 70 ft. lbs.
5. Apply suitable grease to sliding sleeves, then install seals in center groove of sliding sleeves.
6. Position sliding sleeves in caliper with inner protective cap groove facing piston. **Leave sleeves exposed enough to permit installation of protective caps.**
7. Install new protective caps into sliding sleeve grooves and press onto caliper housing collar. Seat caps using sliding sleeve dust boot installer tool No. J36647 or equivalent.
8. Push sliding sleeves into housing, then install bleeder valve.
9. Install brake pads and caliper as previously described. Bleed hydraulic system, **Before moving vehicle, pump brake pedal several times to be sure it is firm. Do not move vehicle until a firm pedal is obtained.**

Delco-Moraine Dual Piston w/Dual Mounting Bolts

INDEX

DESCRIPTION

This dual piston sliding caliper, **Fig. 1,** is comprised of two interconnected bores and is attached to a mounting bracket with two mounting bolts. Hydraulic pressure acting on the bottom of the caliper bores forces the pistons outward, enabling the caliper to slide inward, thereby clamping the brake shoes against the rotor.

SERVICE

CALIPER REMOVAL

1. Siphon enough brake fluid out of the master cylinder to bring fluid level to ⅓ full to avoid fluid overflow when the caliper pistons are pushed back into bores.
2. Raise vehicle and remove front wheels.
3. Mark relationship between wheel to hub and bearing assembly. Remove tire and wheel assembly.
4. Using a suitable C-clamp and block of wood, push pistons back together into caliper bores.
5. If caliper assembly is to be serviced, remove inlet fitting attaching bolt, copper washer, and inlet fitting from caliper housing. Plug opening in inlet fitting to prevent fluid loss and contamination. **Do not crimp brake hose, as this may damage internal structure of hose. If only shoe and lining assemblies are to be replaced, do not disconnect brake line fitting from caliper.**
6. Remove two mounting bolts, then remove caliper. If only shoe and lining assemblies are to be replaced, suspend caliper from chassis using suitable hanger. **Do not allow caliper to hang by brake hose.**

BRAKE SHOE & LINING REMOVAL

1. Remove caliper as outlined previously.
2. Lift upward on outward shoe retaining spring of outboard shoe until it clears center lug, then remove shoe from caliper.
3. Pull inboard shoe outward to disengage retainer springs from pistons, then remove inboard shoe from caliper.

CALIPER DISASSEMBLY

1. Remove caliper assembly as outlined previously, then drain brake fluid from caliper.

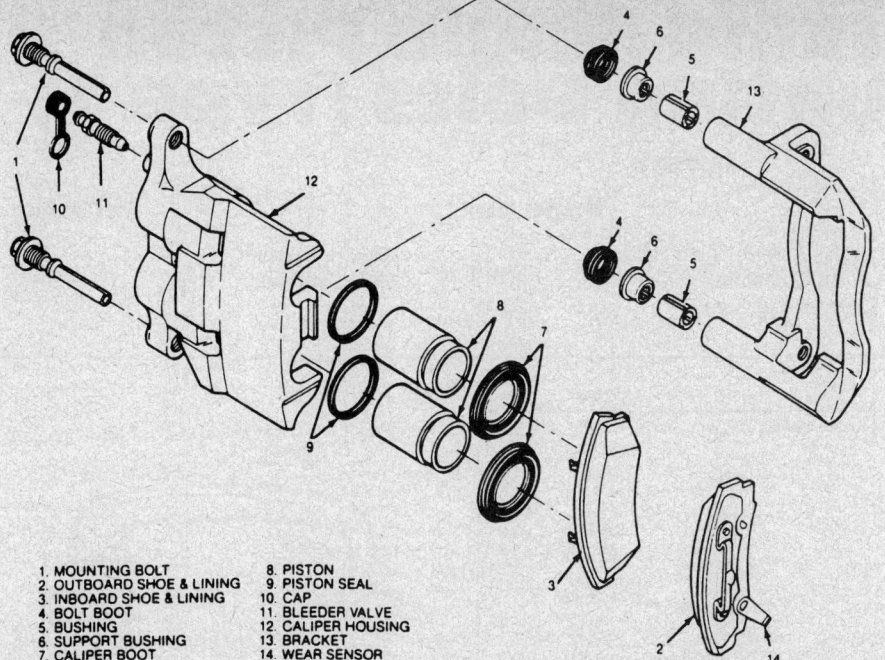

1. MOUNTING BOLT
2. OUTBOARD SHOE & LINING
3. INBOARD SHOE & LINING
4. BOLT BOOT
5. BUSHING
6. SUPPORT BUSHING
7. CALIPER BOOT
8. PISTON
9. PISTON SEAL
10. CAP
11. BLEEDER VALVE
12. CALIPER HOUSING
13. BRACKET
14. WEAR SENSOR

Fig. 1   Exploded view of Delco-Moraine 3242 series dual piston caliper

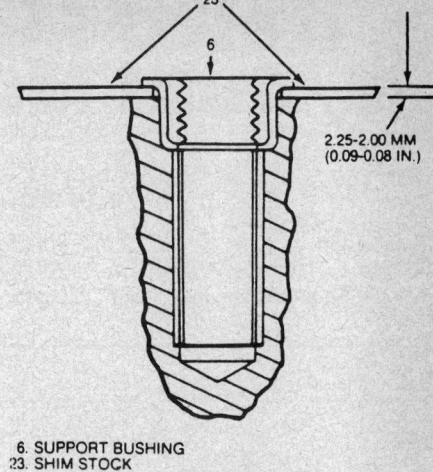

6. SUPPORT BUSHING
23. SHIM STOCK

Fig. 2   Installing support bushing

2. Position shop towel in interior part of caliper, then slowly apply compressed air to inlet port and remove pistons. **It is imperative that one piston be partially installed to facilitate removal of second piston from bore. A pad or wooden spacer may be used to prevent complete removal of first piston.**
3. Remove piston boots from caliper bores, then using suitable wooden or plastic tool, pry piston seals from caliper bore grooves. **Do not use a metal tool of any kind to remove seal as it may damage bore.**
4. Remove bleeder valve from caliper.
5. Inspect piston for scoring, nicks, corrosion, and wear and replace as needed.
6. Inspect caliper housing and seal grooves for corrosion, nicks, scoring and excessive wear, and use crocus cloth to polish away corrosion from housing bore. Replace caliper housing if corrosion in and around seal grooves will not clean up with crocus cloth.
7. Clean all parts with denatured alcohol. Dry with unlubricated compressed air. Blow out all passages in housing and bleeder valve.

MOUNTING BRACKET SERVICE
Removal

1. Remove caliper as outlined previously.

2. Using suitable torx bit, remove mounting bracket attaching bolts and the mounting bracket.

Bushing & Boot Replacement

1. Remove mounting bracket from vehicle.
2. Remove bolt boots from support bushings, **Fig. 1.**
3. Clamp bracket in a suitable vise, then pry support bushings from inner bushings in bracket ears with small screwdriver.
4. Using a paper clip, pull inner bushings from mounting bracket ears.
5. Lubricate inner bushings with silicone based grease, then install bushings flush with bracket ears.
6. Position .080–.090 inch thick shim stock on bracket ear face, then drive support bushings into inner bushings, **Fig. 2.** When properly installed, bushing should protrude .080–.090 inch above bracket ear face.
7. Snap new bolt boots over support bushing lip.

Installation

1. Coat mounting bracket attaching bolt threads with Loctite sealant or equivalent.
2. Align mounting bracket holes, then install mounting bracket and **torque** attaching bolts to 148 ft. lbs.

CALIPER ASSEMBLY

1. Install bleeder valve and **torque** to 116 inch lbs.
2. Lubricate piston seals with clean brake fluid, then carefully install seals into caliper bore grooves. **Ensure seals are not twisted.**
3. Lubricate boots and install onto pistons, then push pistons fully into caliper bores.
4. Seat boots into caliper bores using boot seal installer tool No. J-36349 or equivalent.

BRAKE SHOE & LINING INSTALLATION

1. Install inboard shoe into caliper, ensuring retainer spring tangs are fully positioned into pistons.
2. Snap outboard shoe retaining spring over housing center lug, then install outboard shoe into caliper.
3. Install brake caliper as outlined further on.

CALIPER INSTALLATION

1. Position caliper over rotor and onto mounting bracket.
2. Lubricate entire length of mounting bolts with silicone based grease, then install bolts and **torque** to 79 ft. lbs.
3. If inlet fitting was removed, install fitting using new copper washer and **torque** bolt to 32 ft. lbs.
4. Install front wheels, fill master cylinder to proper level, then bleed brake system as required. **Before moving vehicle, pump brake pedal several times to be sure it is firm. Do not move vehicle until a firm pedal is obtained.**

Delco-Moraine Single Piston w/Dual Mounting Bolts (Type 1)

INDEX

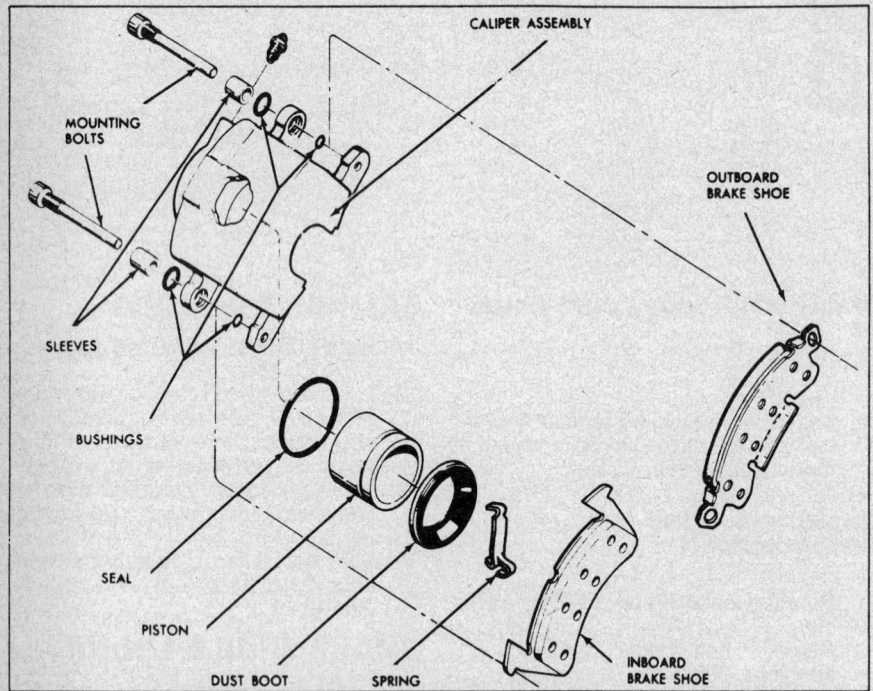

Fig. 1 Typical Delco-Moraine 3000/3075/3100 series caliper exploded view

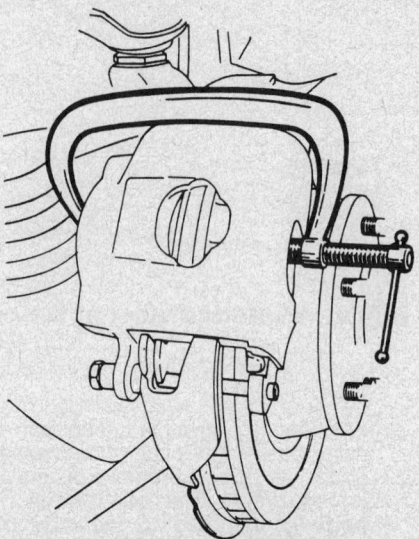

Fig. 2 Compressing piston and shoes with C-clamp

DESCRIPTION

This single piston sliding caliper assembly, **Fig. 1**, incorporates a one piece housing with the inboard side of the housing bored for the piston. A seal within the housing bore provides a hydraulic seal between the piston and housing wall.

A spring steel scraper (wear sensor) is incorporated on each inboard shoe. When the shoe lining has worn to within .030 inch of the shoe, the sensor scrapes the rotor and emits an audible high frequency sound indicating that the linings should be replaced.

The caliper assembly slides on the mounting bolts. Upon brake application, fluid pressure against the piston forces the inboard shoe and lining assembly against the inboard side of the disc. This action causes the caliper assembly to slide until the outboard lining comes into contact with the disc. As pressure builds up, the linings are pressed against the disc with increased force.

SERVICE

CALIPER REMOVAL

1. Siphon enough brake fluid out of the master cylinder to bring fluid level to 1/3 full to avoid fluid overflow when the caliper piston is pushed back into its bore.
2. Raise vehicle and remove front wheels.
3. Using a C-clamp, as illustrated in **Fig. 2**, push piston back into its bore.
4. If caliper assembly is to be serviced, remove inlet fitting attaching bolt, copper washer, and inlet fitting from caliper housing. Plug opening in inlet fitting to prevent fluid loss and contamination. **Do not crimp brake hose, as this may damage internal structure of hose. If only shoe and lining assemblies are to be replaced, do not disconnect brake line fitting from caliper.**
5. Remove two mounting bolts, **Fig. 3**, and lift caliper away from disc. If only

shoe and lining assemblies are to be replaced, suspend caliper from chassis using suitable hanger. **Do not allow caliper to hang by brake hose.**

BRAKE SHOE & LINING REMOVAL

1. Remove caliper assembly as outlined above.
2. Remove inboard shoe. Dislodge outboard shoe and position caliper on the front suspension so the brake hose will not support the weight of the caliper.
3. Remove shoe support spring from piston.
4. Remove two sleeves from inboard ears of the caliper.
5. Remove four rubber bushings from the grooves in each of the caliper ears.

CALIPER DISASSEMBLY

1. Remove caliper as outlined above.
2. Clean outside of caliper, then drain brake fluid from caliper.
3. Use clean shop towels to pad interior of caliper assembly, then remove piston by directing compressed air into caliper brake hose inlet hole, **Fig. 4.**

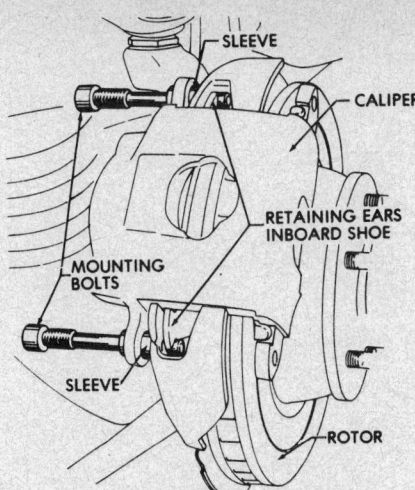

Fig. 3 Caliper & mounting bolts

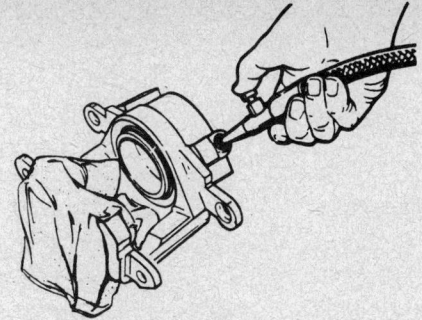

Fig. 4 Removing piston from caliper

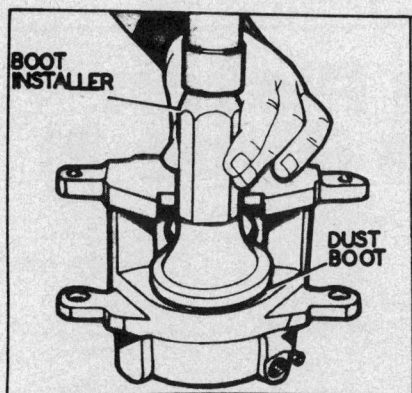

Fig. 6 Installing boot to caliper

Use just enough air pressure to ease piston out of bore. Do not place fingers in front of piston for any reason when applying compressed air. This could result in serious personal injury.

4. Carefully pry dust boot out of bore.
5. Using a small piece of wood or plastic, remove piston seal from bore. **Do not use a metal tool of any kind to remove seal as it may damage bore.**
6. Remove bleeder valve.
7. Inspect piston for scoring, nicks, corrosion, and wear and replace as needed.
8. Inspect caliper housing and seal groove for corrosion, nicks, scoring and excessive wear, and use crocus cloth to polish away corrosion from housing bore. Replace caliper housing if corrosion in and around seal groove will not clean up with crocus cloth.
9. Clean all parts with denatured alcohol. Dry with unlubricated compressed air. Blow out all passages in housing and bleeder valve.

CALIPER ASSEMBLY

1. Lubricate caliper piston bore and new piston seal with clean brake fluid. Position seal in bore groove. **Ensure seal is not twisted.**
2. Lubricate piston with clean brake fluid and assemble a new boot into the groove in the piston so the fold faces the open end of the piston, **Fig. 5.**
3. Using care not to unseat the seal, insert piston into bore and force the piston to the bottom of the bore.
4. Position dust boot in caliper counterbore and install, using suitable seal installer, **Fig. 6.** Check the boot installation to be sure the retaining ring molded into the boot is not bent and that the boot is installed below the caliper face and evenly all around. If the boot is not fully installed, dirt and moisture may enter the bore and cause corrosion.
5. Install the brake hose in the caliper using a new copper gasket.
6. Install shoes and reinstall caliper assembly.

BRAKE SHOE & LINING INSTALLATION

1. Lubricate new sleeves, rubber bushings, bushing grooves and mounting bolt ends with Delco Silicone Lube or its equivalent.
2. Install new bushings and sleeves in caliper ears. **Position the sleeve so that the end toward the shoe is flush with the machined surface of the ear.**
3. Install shoe support spring by positioning single tang end of spring into notch cut at top of inboard shoe. Press remaining end of spring over bottom edge of shoe until shoe is engaged securely.
4. Position inboard shoe with spring attached into caliper with ear end facing downward and bottom end facing upward with spring resting on inside diameter of piston. Press downward on both ends of shoe until shoe contacts piston and support spring contacts piston inside diameter. **Some inboard replacement brake pads incorporate wear sensors and have a specific left and righthand assem-**

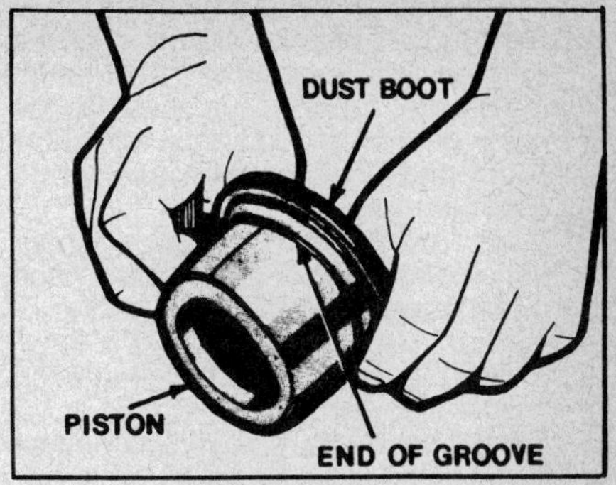

Fig. 5 Installing boot to piston

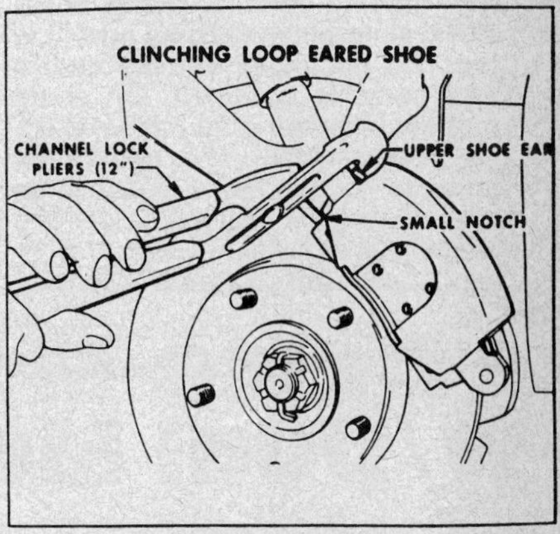

Fig. 7 Clinching loop eared brake shoe

bly. Properly installed, the wear sensor will face toward the rear of caliper.
5. Position outboard shoe in caliper with shoe ears over caliper ears and tab at bottom of shoe engaged in caliper cutout.
6. With shoes installed, lift caliper and rest bottom edge of outboard lining on outer edge of brake disc to be sure there is no clearance between outboard shoe tab and caliper abutment.
7. Install caliper and **torque** mounting bolts to 38 ft. lbs.
8. Clinch upper ears of outboard shoe by positioning pliers with one jaw on top of upper ear and one jaw in notch on bottom shoe opposite ear, **Fig. 7.** Ears are to be flat against caliper housing with no radial clearance. If clearance exists, repeat clinching procedure. **Before moving vehicle, pump brake pedal several times to be sure it is firm. Do not move vehicle until a firm pedal is obtained. On some models with low drag calipers, apply approximately 175 pounds of pressure to the brake pedal three times to properly seat the caliper and related components.**

CALIPER INSTALLATION

1. Position caliper over disc, lining up holes in caliper with holes in mounting bracket. If brake hose was not disconnected during removal, be sure not to

kink it during installation.

2. Start mounting bolts through sleeves in inboard caliper ears and the mounting bracket, making sure ends of bolts pass under ears on inboard shoe. **Right and left calipers must not be interchanged.**
3. Push mounting bolts through to engage holes in the outboard ears. Then thread mounting bolts into bracket.
4. **Torque** mounting bolts to 38 ft. lbs.
5. Check the dimensions between each caliper stop and caliper, **Fig. 8.**
6. If brake hose was removed, reconnect it and bleed the calipers.
7. Replace front wheels, lower vehicle and add brake fluid to master cylinder to bring level to ¼ inch from top. **Before moving vehicle, pump brake pedal several times to be sure it is firm. Do not move vehicle until a firm pedal is obtained. On some models with low drag calipers,** apply approximately 175 pounds of pressure to the brake pedal three times to properly seat the caliper and related components.

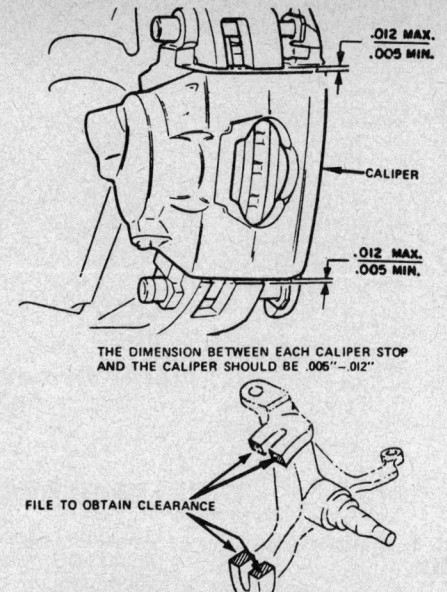

THE DIMENSION BETWEEN EACH CALIPER STOP AND THE CALIPER SHOULD BE .005"–.012"

FILE TO OBTAIN CLEARANCE

Fig. 8 Checking clearance between caliper & stops

Delco-Moraine Single Piston w/Dual Mounting Bolts (Type 2)

INDEX

DESCRIPTION

The caliper has a single piston and is mounted to the support bracket by two mounting bolts, **Figs. 1 through 3.** The caliper assembly slides on the two mounting bolts. Upon brake application, fluid pressure against the piston forces the inboard shoe and lining assembly against the inboard side of the disc. This action causes the caliper assembly to slide until the outboard lining comes into contact with the disc. As pressure builds up the linings are pressed against the disc with increased force.

SERVICE

CALIPER REMOVAL

1. Remove approximately ⅔ of brake fluid from master cylinder.
2. Raise and support front of vehicle, then remove wheel and tire assembly.
3. Position suitable pliers over inboard pad and housing as shown in **Fig. 4,** and squeeze pliers to compress caliper piston.
4. If caliper assembly is being removed

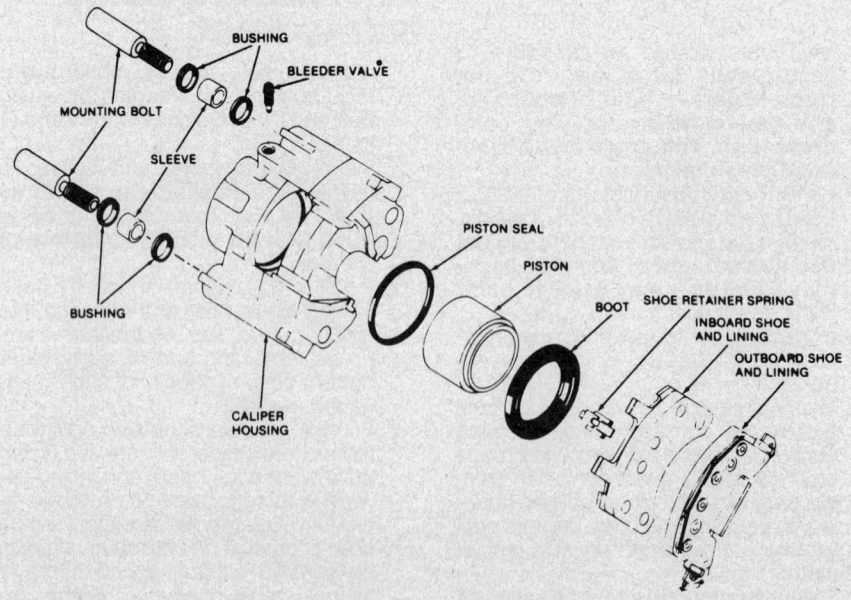

Fig. 1 Delco-Moraine 3200 series caliper exploded view

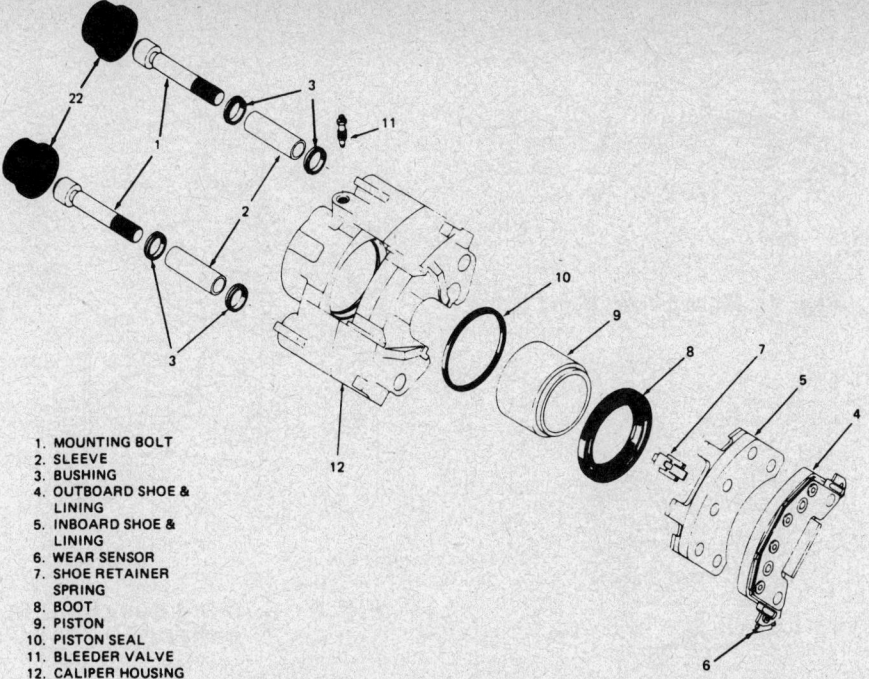

1. MOUNTING BOLT
2. SLEEVE
3. BUSHING
4. OUTBOARD SHOE & LINING
5. INBOARD SHOE & LINING
6. WEAR SENSOR
7. SHOE RETAINER SPRING
8. BOOT
9. PISTON
10. PISTON SEAL
11. BLEEDER VALVE
12. CALIPER HOUSING
22. BOOT

Fig. 2   Delco-Moraine 3257 series caliper exploded view

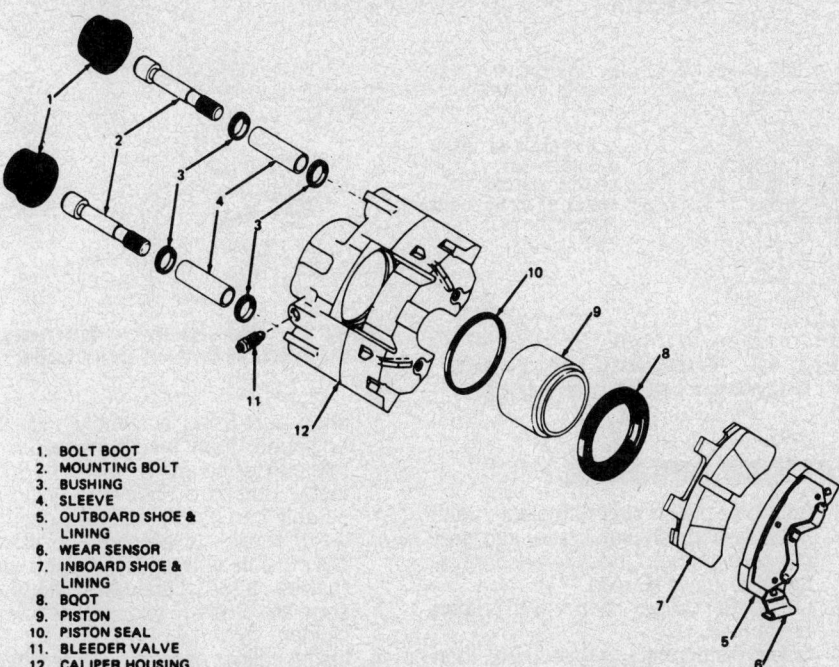

1. BOLT BOOT
2. MOUNTING BOLT
3. BUSHING
4. SLEEVE
5. OUTBOARD SHOE & LINING
6. WEAR SENSOR
7. INBOARD SHOE & LINING
8. BOOT
9. PISTON
10. PISTON SEAL
11. BLEEDER VALVE
12. CALIPER HOUSING

Fig. 3   Delco-Moraine 3264 series caliper exploded view

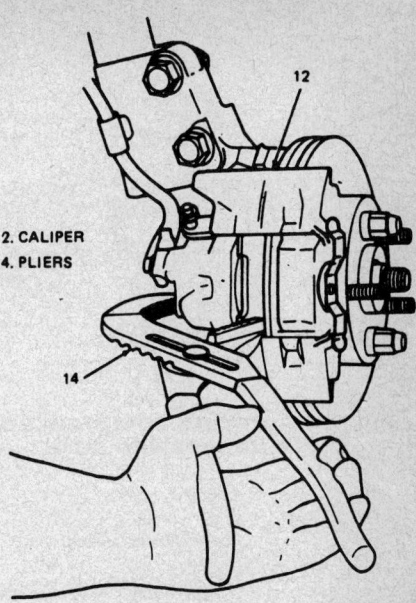

12. CALIPER
14. PLIERS

Fig. 4   Compressing caliper piston with pliers

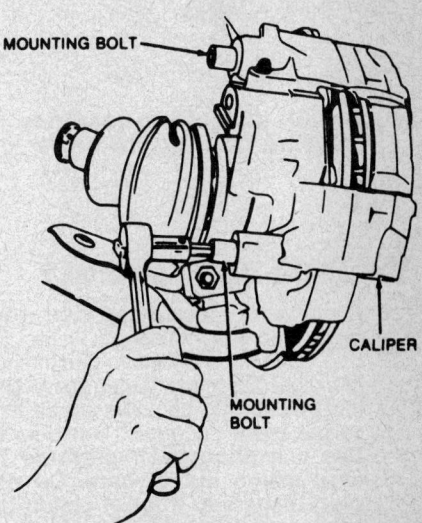

MOUNTING BOLT

CALIPER

MOUNTING BOLT

Fig. 5   Removing caliper mounting bolts

BRAKE SHOE & LINING REMOVAL

1. Remove caliper assembly as outline above.
2. Remove shoe and lining assemblies from caliper, **Figs. 1 through 3**, noting the following:
   a. **On models with tab mount outer shoe (all except series 3264),** straighten bent over shoe tabs with suitable pliers.
   b. **On models with spring mount outer shoe (series 3264),** insert screwdriver between shoe and caliper and disengage buttons on shoe from holes in caliper.
3. Remove sleeves and bushings from grooves in caliper mounting bolt holes, **Figs. 1 through 3**.

for service, remove inlet fitting attaching bolt, copper washer, and inlet fitting from caliper housing. Plug opening in inlet fitting to prevent fluid loss and contamination. **Do not crimp brake hose, as this may damage internal structure of hose. If only shoe and lining assemblies are to be replaced, do not disconnect brake line fitting from caliper.**

5. Remove Allen head caliper mounting bolts, **Fig. 5**. If bolts show signs of corrosion, use new bolts when installing caliper assembly.
6. Remove caliper assembly from disc. If only shoe and lining assemblies are to be replaced, using a length of wire suspend caliper from spring coil. Never allow caliper to hang from brake hose.

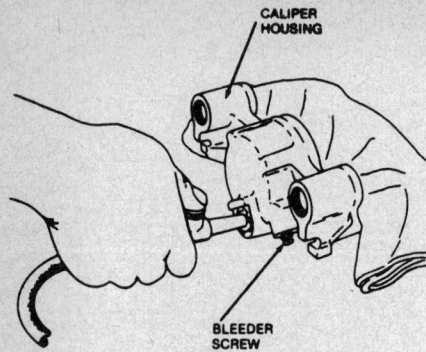

Fig. 6 Applying compressed air to caliper line port

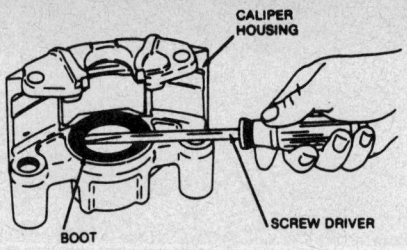

Fig. 7 Removing dust boot

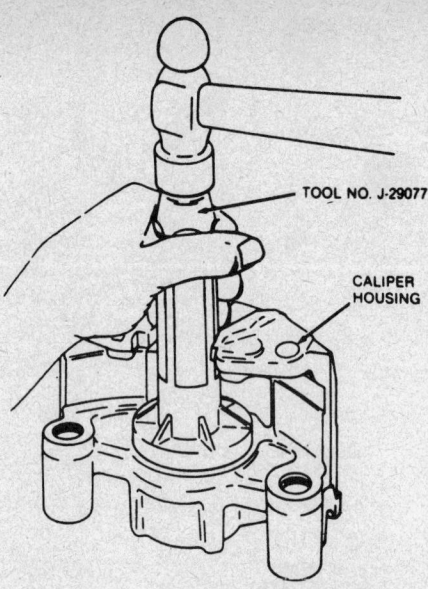

Fig. 8 Seating dust boot in caliper

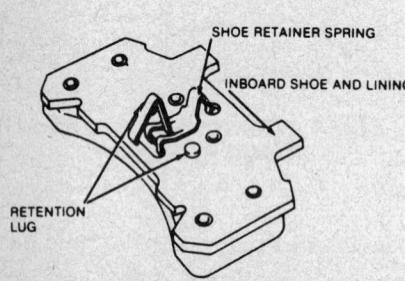

Fig. 9 Installing retainer spring on inboard shoe

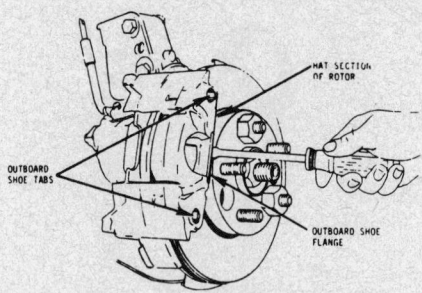

Fig. 10 Positioning screwdriver between outboard shoe flange & hat section of rotor

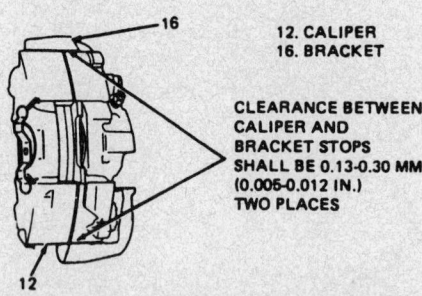

12. CALIPER
16. BRACKET

CLEARANCE BETWEEN CALIPER AND BRACKET STOPS SHALL BE 0.13-0.30 MM (0.005-0.012 IN.) TWO PLACES

Fig. 12 Checking clearance between caliper & stops

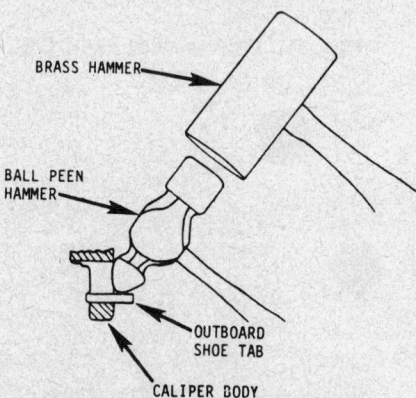

Fig. 11 Positioning hammer to clinch brake pad tabs

CALIPER DISASSEMBLY

1. Clean outside of caliper, then drain brake fluid from caliper.
2. Use clean shop towels to pad interior of caliper assembly, then remove piston by directing compressed air into caliper brake hose inlet hole, **Fig. 6.** **Use just enough air pressure to ease piston out of bore. Do not place fingers in front of piston for any reason when applying compressed air. This could result in serious personal injury.**
3. Using a screwdriver, remove dust boot from caliper bore, **Fig. 7.**
4. Using a small piece of wood or plastic, remove piston seal from bore. **Do not use a metal tool of any kind to remove seal as it may damage bore.**
5. Remove bleeder valve.
6. Inspect piston for scoring, nicks, corrosion, and wear and replace as needed.
7. Inspect caliper housing and seal groove for corrosion, nicks, scoring and excessive wear, and use crocus cloth to polish away corrosion from housing bore. Replace caliper housing if corrosion in and around seal groove will not clean up with crocus cloth.
8. Clean all parts with denatured alcohol. Dry with unlubricated compressed air. Blow out all passages in housing and bleeder valve.

CALIPER ASSEMBLY

1. Lubricate piston seal with clean brake fluid, then install piston seal into caliper bore groove. Check to ensure piston seal is not twisted.
2. Lubricate caliper bore with clean brake fluid.
3. Insert piston into caliper bore, then force piston down until piston bottoms in bore.
4. Position outer diameter of dust boot in caliper housing counterbore, then seat boot as shown in **Fig. 8.**
5. Install bleeder screw on caliper housing.

BRAKE SHOE & LINING INSTALLATION

1. Lubricate new bushings with suitable grease, install bushings in caliper grooves, then insert sleeves through bushings.
2. Install retaining spring onto inboard shoe and lining assembly, **Fig. 9,** if equipped, then install inboard shoe into caliper housing.
3. Install outboard shoe and lining assembly into caliper housing ensuring wear sensor is properly positioned. **On models with spring mount shoe (series 3264),** ensure buttons on shoe are properly engaged in holes in caliper.
4. Install caliper assembly as outlined.
5. **On models with tab mount outer shoe (except series 3264),** clinch outboard shoe to brake caliper as follows:
   a. Apply brakes several times to ensure caliper piston is extended and shoes are fully seated.
   b. Wedge a large flat blade screwdriver between outboard shoe flange and hat section of rotor, **Fig. 10.**
   c. Hold outer pad against caliper with suitable clamp or by applying moderate pressure on brake pedal.
   d. Position a ball peen hammer on outboard shoe tab, **Fig. 11,** then

using a larger brass hammer, lightly tap the ball peen hammer to bend the outboard shoe tab. Tabs must be bent around casting to approximately 45°.

e. After both tabs have been bent pressure should be released and outboard shoe should be locked into position. If shoe is loose, repeat steps a. through d. **If an outboard shoe is removed from the caliper, or the tabs unclinched for any reason, then it will be necessary to replace the shoe and lining assemblies. Do not re-clinch outboard shoe locking** tabs after having removed shoe from caliper.

CALIPER, INSTALLATION

1. Position caliper assembly over disc and align mounting bolt holes. If brake hoses were not disconnected during removal, use care not to kink hoses during installation.
2. Install mounting bolts and **torque** to 38 ft. lbs., **Fig. 5.**
3. Check the dimensions between each caliper stop and caliper, **Fig. 12.** If necessary remove caliper and file ends of bracket to provide proper clearance.
4. If brake hose fitting was disconnected during removal, install brake hose fitting and **torque** retaining bolt to 18 to 33 ft. lbs.
5. Fill master cylinder. Bleed brake system if brake line was disconnected and recheck master cylinder fluid level.
6. Install wheel and tire assembly on vehicle, then lower vehicle and check brake system operation. **Before moving vehicle, pump brake pedal several times to be sure it is firm. Do not move vehicle until a firm pedal is obtained.**

Delco-Moraine Single Piston w/Dual Mounting Bolts (Type 3)

INDEX

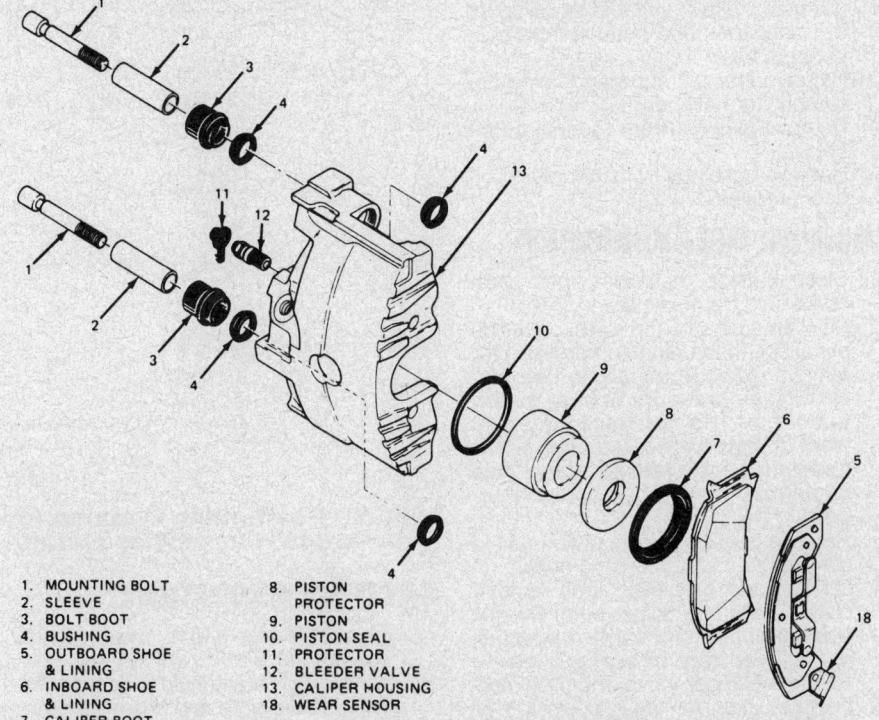

1. MOUNTING BOLT
2. SLEEVE
3. BOLT BOOT
4. BUSHING
5. OUTBOARD SHOE & LINING
6. INBOARD SHOE & LINING
7. CALIPER BOOT
8. PISTON PROTECTOR
9. PISTON
10. PISTON SEAL
11. PROTECTOR
12. BLEEDER VALVE
13. CALIPER HOUSING
18. WEAR SENSOR

Fig. 1 Delco-Moraine series 5349 front disc brake caliper exploded view

DESCRIPTION

This caliper, **Figs. 1 and 2,** has a single bore and is mounted to the support bracket with two mounting bolts. Hydraulic pressure, created by applying force to the brake pedal, is converted by the caliper into friction. The hydraulic pressure is applied equally against the piston and the bottom of the caliper bore moving the piston outward, resulting in a clamping action on the brake rotor.

Rear disc brake calipers include an integral parking brake mechanism. When the parking brake is applied, the lever turns an actuator screw which is threaded into a nut in the caliper piston. As the actuator screw turns, the piston is forced out, applying force on the rotor. The piston contains a self adjusting mechanism to keep the parking brake in proper adjustment and to ensure proper clearance when the parking brake is released.

FRONT BRAKE ASSEMBLY

CALIPER REMOVAL

1. Drain approximately ⅔ of brake fluid from master cylinder assembly.
2. Raise and support vehicle, then remove tire and wheel assembly.
3. If caliper is to be serviced or replaced, remove bolt securing inlet fitting, then disconnect brake hose, and plug end to prevent loss of fluid and contamination. **Do not crimp brake hose, as this may damage internal structure of hose. If only shoe and lining assemblies are being replaced, do not disconnect brake hose from caliper.**
4. Remove caliper retaining bolts and boots, **Fig. 1.**
5. Compress piston, placing suitable adjustable pliers over inboard surface of caliper housing and support bracket as shown in **Fig. 3.**
6. Remove caliper from disc. If shoe and lining assemblies are to be replaced, use a length of wire to suspend caliper. Do not allow caliper to hang from brake line.

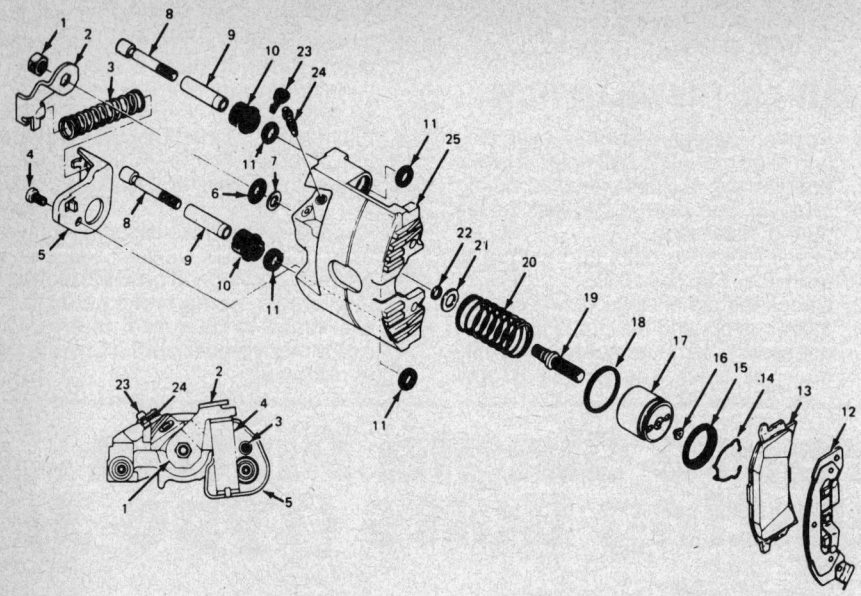

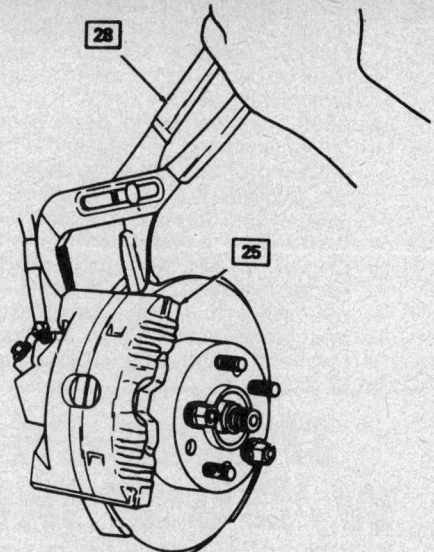

1. NUT
2. LEVER
3. RETURN SPRING
4. BOLT
5. BRACKET
6. LEVER SEAL
7. ANTI-FRICTION WASHER
8. MOUNTING BOLT
9. SLEEVE
10. BOLT BOOT
11. BUSHING
12. OUTBOARD SHOE & LINING
13. INBOARD SHOE & LINING
14. SHOE DAMPENING SPRING
15. CALIPER BOOT
16. TWO WAY CHECK VALVE
17. PISTON ASSEMBLY
18. PISTON SEAL
19. ACTUATOR SCREW
20. BALANCE SPRING
21. THRUST WASHER
22. SHAFT SEAL
23. PROTECTOR
24. BLEEDER VALVE
25. CALIPER HOUSING
26. WEAR SENSOR

25. CALIPER HOUSING
28. PLIERS

Fig. 3 Compressing front caliper piston for caliper removal

Fig. 2 Delco-Moraine series 5748 rear disc brake caliper exploded view

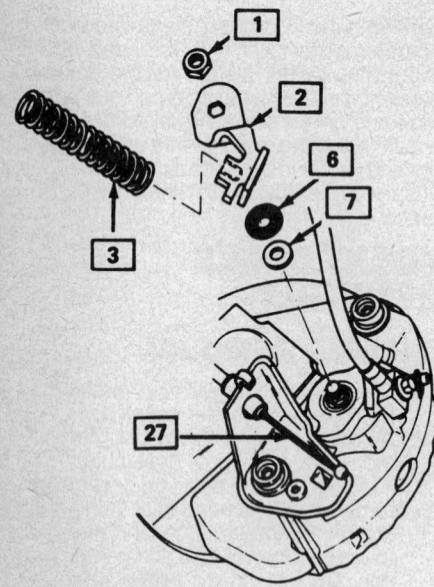

1. NUT
2. LEVER
3. RETURN SPRING
6. LEVER SEAL
7. ANTI-FRICTION WASHER
27. CABLE

Fig. 4 Parking brake lever assembly

BRAKE SHOE & LINING REMOVAL

1. Remove caliper as described under "Caliper Removal."
2. To remove outboard shoe and lining assembly, use a suitable screwdriver to disengage shoe buttons from caliper holes.
3. Remove inboard shoe and lining assembly from caliper.
4. Remove sleeves from mounting bolt holes.
5. Remove bushings from mounting bolt hole grooves.

CALIPER DISASSEMBLY

1. Clean outside of caliper, then drain brake fluid from caliper.
2. Position a clean shop towel on inside of caliper, then using compressed air, remove piston from caliper. **Use just enough air pressure to ease piston out of bore. Do not place fingers in front of piston for any reason when applying compressed air. This could result in serious personal injury.**
3. Remove dust boot from piston taking care not to scratch housing bore.
4. Using wood or plastic tool, remove piston seal from caliper bore. **Do not use metal tool since this may damage caliper bore or seal groove.**
5. Remove bleeder valve and protector.
6. Inspect piston for wear, corrosion or damage. Replace piston, if necessary.
7. Inspect caliper housing for corrosion. If corrosion exists, use a crocus cloth to remove light surface corrosion. If corrosion cannot be removed with crocus cloth, replace caliper housing.
8. Clean all parts with denatured alcohol. Dry with unlubricated compressed air. Blow out all passages in housing and bleeder valve.

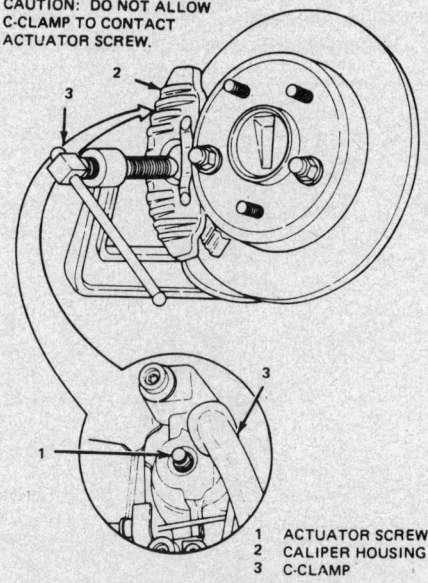

CAUTION: DO NOT ALLOW C-CLAMP TO CONTACT ACTUATOR SCREW.

1 ACTUATOR SCREW
2 CALIPER HOUSING
3 C-CLAMP

Fig. 5 Positioning C-clamp to compress rear caliper piston

CALIPER ASSEMBLY

1. Install bleeder valve onto caliper. **Torque** valve to 80-140 inch lbs.
2. Using clean brake fluid, lubricate caliper housing bore and bore seals.
3. Install piston seal into caliper bore groove. Ensure seal is not twisted in groove.
4. Install boot and piston protector onto piston.
5. Install piston into caliper bore and push piston completely to the bottom.
6. Using dust boot installer tool No. J-29381 or equivalent, install boot into caliper housing counterbore.

BRAKE SHOE & LINING INSTALLATION

1. Lubricate, then install bushings into mounting bolt hole grooves.
2. Lubricate, then install sleeves into mounting bolt holes.
3. Install inboard shoe and lining onto caliper. **Ensure tabs on inboard shoe are positioned so that they fit into corresponding holes in face of piston.**
4. Install outboard shoe and lining onto caliper. Ensure wear sensor is positioned at leading edge of brake shoe.

CALIPER INSTALLATION

1. Install caliper onto brake rotor mounting bracket.
2. Using silicone grease or equivalent, liberally coat shoulder and mounting bolt threads so caliper cavity will be filled.
3. Install caliper mounting bolts. **Torque** bolts to 21-35 ft. lbs.

REAR BRAKE ASSEMBLY
CALIPER REMOVAL

1. Drain approximately 2/3 of brake fluid from master cylinder assembly.
2. Raise and support vehicle, then remove tire and wheel assembly.
3. Loosen tension on parking brake cable at equalizer, remove cable and spring from parking brake lever, **Fig. 4**
4. While holding parking brake lever, remove locknut, parking brake lever, lever seal and anti-friction washer, **Fig. 4. Parking brake lever assembly must be removed to provide clearance for compressing caliper piston. Failure to remove lever will cause piston to be damaged when it is bottomed in bore.**
5. Remove brake line fittings from caliper if caliper is to be removed for service or replacement. **If only the shoes and linings are to be replaced, do not disconnect brake hose from caliper.**
6. Remove caliper mounting bolts, then position C-clamp onto caliper as shown in **Fig. 5**, and tighten clamp until piston bottoms in piston bore. **Do not come in contact with actuator screw.**
7. Lift caliper off rotor and mounting bracket and support caliper, as needed, to prevent stretching brake hose.

BRAKE SHOE & LINING REMOVAL

1. Remove caliper as described under "Caliper Removal."
2. Remove inboard shoe and lining assembly from caliper.
3. To remove outboard shoe and lining assembly, use a suitable screwdriver to disengage shoe buttons from caliper holes.
4. Remove sleeves from mounting bolt holes.
5. Remove bolt boots and bushings from caliper.

6. Using a suitable screwdriver, remove two-way check valve from piston end.

CALIPER DISASSEMBLY

1. Remove dampening spring from piston end by turning retainer until inside tabs line up with notches in piston, **Fig. 2**.
2. Remove nut and lever assembly.
3. Remove lever seal and anti-friction washer.
4. Place caliper into a soft jaw vise. Place a clean shop towel on inside of caliper. Remove piston using suitable wrench to rotate actuator screw to work piston out of caliper. **Rotate in parking brake apply direction**
5. Press on threaded end of actuator screw, then remove screw.
6. Remove shaft seal and thrust washer from actuator screw.
7. Remove boot from caliper housing bore. Do not use a sharp tool to remove boot from caliper.
8. Using a piece of wool or plastic, remove piston seal from groove in caliper bore. **Do not use any type of metal tool to remove piston seal, since damage to caliper bore may result.**
9. Inspect piston for wear and damage. Replace piston, if necessary.
10. Inspect piston bore for scoring, nicks, corrosion, or wear. Use a crocus cloth to polish out light corrosion. Replace caliper housing if corrosion will not clean up with crocus cloth.
11. Remove bleeder valve and protector.
12. Inspect caliper mounting bracket. If mounting bracket is damaged, replace as required.
13. Clean all parts with denatured alcohol. Dry with unlubricated compressed air. Blow out all passages in housing and bleeder valve.

CALIPER ASSEMBLY

1. Install bleeder valve. **Torque** valve to 80-140 inch lbs.
2. Install protector onto bleeder valve.
3. Install mounting bracket, if removed. **Torque** bracket bolt to 24-38 ft. lbs.
4. Lubricate new piston seal with clean brake fluid and install is caliper bore groove. **Make sure seal is not twisted.**
5. Lubricate and install boot onto piston with inside lip of boot in piston groove and boot fold toward end of piston that contacts inboard brake shoe.
6. Install thrust washer onto actuator screw with bearing, grayish, surface toward caliper housing.
7. Lubricate shaft seal with clean brake fluid, then install seal onto actuator screw.
8. Lubricate actuator screw, then install screw into piston.
9. Install balance spring into piston recess.
10. Lubricate piston assembly with clean brake fluid, then install assembly into caliper bore. Use piston installer tool No. J-23072 or equivalent to push piston completely down into bore.
11. Lubricate and install anti-friction

washer and lever seal onto actuator screw. **Ensure sealing bead on lever is against housing.** Install lever onto actuator screw. Rotate lever away from stop slightly and hold while install nut. **Torque** nut to 30-40 ft. lbs. After nut is torqued, rotate lever back to contact stop.
12. Seat boot into caliper housing counterbore. Using dust boot installer tool No. J-28678 or equivalent.
13. Install dampening spring into groove end of piston. It may be necessary to move parking brake lever off the stop to extend piston and make spring groove accessible.

BRAKE SHOE & LINING INSTALLATION

1. Lubricate, then install bushings into mounting bolt hole grooves.
2. Lubricate, then install bolt boots into mounting bolt holes.
3. Lubricate, then install sleeves into mounting bolt holes.
4. Install two-way check valve into piston end.
5. Install inboard shoe and lining into caliper. Noting the following:
   a. Ensure D-shaped tab on shoe engages D shaped notch in piston.
   b. If tab and notch do not align, use spanner wrench or equivalent to turn piston.
   c. Slide edge of metal shoe under ends of dampening spring and snap shoe into position, flat against the piston.
6. Install outboard shoe and lining assembly into piston. Ensure spring ends on outboard shoe snap into piston recess. **Brake wear sensor must be at leading edge of shoe during forward wheel rotation.**
7. After installation of caliper assembly, apply brakes slowly and firmly three times to seat linings.

CALIPER INSTALLATION

1. Liberally fill cavities in housing between bushings with silicone grease.
2. Install sleeves in caliper, then caliper over brake rotor into mounting bracket.
3. **Torque** caliper mounting bolts to 30-45 ft. lbs.
4. Install brake line fitting onto caliper, if removed. **Torque** fitting to 30 ft. lbs.
5. Install anti-friction washer.
6. Lubricate seal, then install into caliper housing. Ensure sealing bead on seal contacts housing.
7. Install lever onto actuator screw. **Lever must be pointing down.**
8. While holding lever, install nut. **Torque** nut to 30-40 ft. lbs.
9. Rotate lever back against caliper stop, then install spring.
10. Install parking brake cable. Tighten cable at equalizer until lever starts to move off caliper stop. Loosen adjustment until lever moves back against caliper stop.
11. Adjust parking brake, then install tire and wheel assembly, then lower vehicle.

DELCO-MORAINE SINGLE PISTON W/ DUAL MOUNTING BOLTS (TYPE 3)

12. Fill master cylinder with brake fluid.
13. Bleed brake system, if necessary. **Before moving vehicle, pump brake pedal several times to be sure it is firm. Do not move vehicle until a firm pedal is obtained.**

PARKING BRAKE
ADJUST

1. Apply service brake pedal three times, then apply and release parking brake lever three times.
2. Raise and support vehicle, then place alignment mark on wheel and axle flange.
3. Check parking brake hand lever for full release as follows:
   a. Turn ignition switch to "On" position and ensure "Brake" warning lamp is off.
   b. If "Brake" warning lamp is still on, with hand lever fully released, pull front parking brake cable downward to remove slack from pedal assembly.
4. Remove rear wheels, then install two lug nuts to secure rotor.
5. Ensure parking brake levers on both calipers are against lever stops on caliper housings. If levers are not against stops, check for binding in rear cables, then loosen cable adjuster until levers are properly positioned.
6. Tighten parking brake cable at adjuster until either left or right lever begins to move off stop, then loosen adjuster until lever moves back barely touching stop.
7. Operate parking brake lever several times to ensure proper adjustment. Hand lever should not travel more than 8 ratchet clicks and rear wheels should not rotate forward when hand lever is applied 5 to 8 ratchet clicks.
8. Install rear wheels aligning marks on wheel and axle flange.

Delco-Moraine Single Piston w/Dual Mounting Bolts (Type 4)

INDEX

DESCRIPTION

This caliper, **Figs. 1 and 2,** has a single bore and is mounted to the support bracket with two mounting bolts. Hydraulic pressure, created by applying force to the brake pedal, is converted by the caliper into friction. The hydraulic pressure is applied equally against the piston and the bottom of the caliper bore moving the piston outward and the housing inward, resulting in a clamping action on the brake rotor.

Rear disc brake calipers include an integral parking brake mechanism. When the parking brake is applied, the lever turns an actuator screw which is threaded into a nut in the caliper piston. As the actuator screw turns, the piston is forced out, applying force on the rotor. The piston contains a self adjusting mechanism to keep the parking brake in proper adjustment and to ensure proper clearance when the parking brake is released.

FRONT BRAKE ASSEMBLY

CALIPER REMOVAL

1. Drain approximately ⅔ of brake fluid from master cylinder assembly.
2. Raise and support vehicle, then mark position of wheel and remove tire and wheel assembly.
3. If caliper is to be serviced or replaced, remove bolt securing inlet fitting, then disconnect brake hose, and plug end

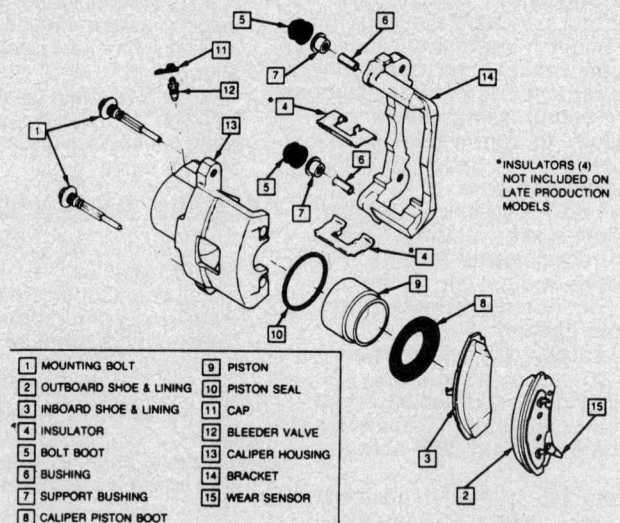

1 MOUNTING BOLT	9 PISTON
2 OUTBOARD SHOE & LINING	10 PISTON SEAL
3 INBOARD SHOE & LINING	11 CAP
4 INSULATOR	12 BLEEDER VALVE
5 BOLT BOOT	13 CALIPER HOUSING
6 BUSHING	14 BRACKET
7 SUPPORT BUSHING	15 WEAR SENSOR
8 CALIPER PISTON BOOT	

*INSULATORS (4) NOT INCLUDED ON LATE PRODUCTION MODELS.

Fig. 1   Delco-Moraine series 3264M front disc brake caliper exploded view

to prevent loss of fluid and contamination. **Do not crimp brake hose, as this may damage internal structure of hose. If only shoe and lining assemblies are being replaced, do not disconnect brake hose from caliper.**
4. Remove caliper to support mounting bolts, then lift caliper off support. If only shoe and lining assemblies are to be replaced, suspend caliper from chassis using suitable hanger. **Do not allow caliper to hang by brake hose.**
5. Remove insulators (4) from caliper support if equipped, **Fig. 1.**

BRAKE SHOE & LINING REMOVAL

1. Remove caliper assembly as outlined.
2. Remove outboard shoe and lining as-

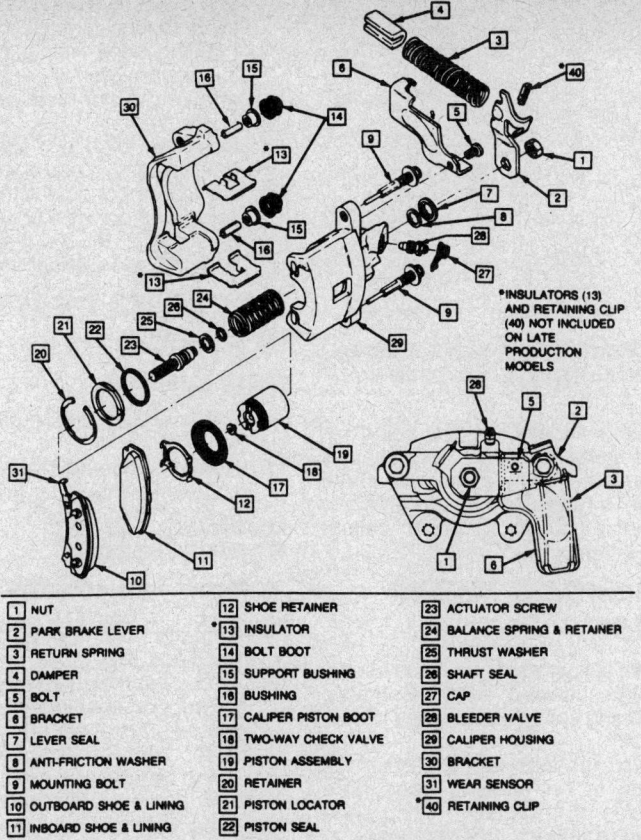

Fig. 2 Delco-Moraine series 3738M rear disc brake caliper exploded view

1	NUT	12	SHOE RETAINER	23	ACTUATOR SCREW
2	PARK BRAKE LEVER	*13	INSULATOR	24	BALANCE SPRING & RETAINER
3	RETURN SPRING	14	BOLT BOOT	25	THRUST WASHER
4	DAMPER	15	SUPPORT BUSHING	26	SHAFT SEAL
5	BOLT	16	BUSHING	27	CAP
6	BRACKET	17	CALIPER PISTON BOOT	28	BLEEDER VALVE
7	LEVER SEAL	18	TWO-WAY CHECK VALVE	29	CALIPER HOUSING
8	ANTI-FRICTION WASHER	19	PISTON ASSEMBLY	30	BRACKET
9	MOUNTING BOLT	20	RETAINER	31	WEAR SENSOR
10	OUTBOARD SHOE & LINING	21	PISTON LOCATOR	*40	RETAINING CLIP
11	INBOARD SHOE & LINING	22	PISTON SEAL		

*INSULATORS (13) AND RETAINING CLIP (40) NOT INCLUDED ON LATE PRODUCTION MODELS

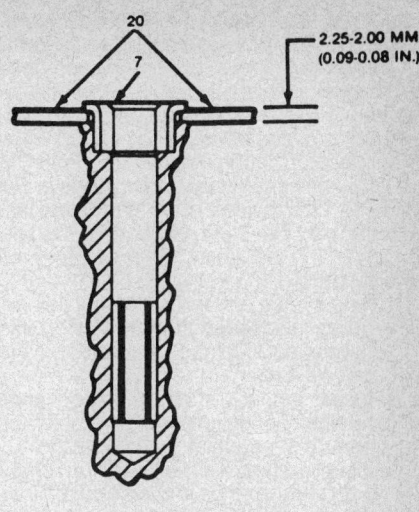

7. SUPPORT BUSHING
20. SHIM STOCK

Fig. 3 Installing support bushing

sembly, using screwdriver to disengage shoe springs from holes in caliper housing.

3. Remove inboard shoe and lining assembly, unsnapping shoe retainer spring from caliper piston bore.

4. If new shoe and lining assemblies are to be installed, compress piston into housing with suitable clamp or pliers, taking care not to damage piston.

CALIPER DISASSEMBLY

1. Drain brake fluid from caliper and clean thoroughly.

2. Use clean shop towels to pad inside of caliper, then remove piston by applying compressed air to fluid inlet port. Use only enough air pressure to ease piston from bore. **Keep fingers away from piston to avoid injury as piston is forced out.**

3. Pry dust boot from caliper, taking care not to damage housing bore.

4. With a small wood or plastic tool remove piston seal from caliper bore. **Do not use metal tool since this may damage caliper bore or seal groove.**

5. Inspect piston for scoring nicks, corrosion, wear and damage and replace as needed.

6. Inspect caliper housing and seal groove for corrosion, nicks, scoring

and excessive wear. Use crocus cloth to polish away corrosion from housing bore. Replace caliper housing if corrosion in and around seal groove will not clean up with crocus cloth.

7. Remove bleeder screw from caliper housing, **Fig. 1.**

8. Clean components with denatured alcohol and dry with unlubricated compressed air. Blow out all passages in housing and bleeder valve.

MOUNTING BRACKET SERVICE

Removal

1. Remove caliper as outlined previously.

2. Remove mounting bracket attaching bolts, then mounting bracket.

Bushing & Boot Replacement

1. Remove mounting bracket from vehicle.

2. Remove bolt boots from support bushings, **Fig. 1.**

3. Clamp bracket in a suitable vise, then pry support bushings from inner bushings in bracket ears with small screwdriver.

4. Using a paper clip, pull inner bushings from mounting bracket ears.

5. Lubricate inner bushings with silicone based grease, then install bushings flush with bracket ears.

6. Position .080–.090 inch thick shim stock on bracket ear face, then tap support bushings, with plastic mallet, into inner bushings, **Fig. 3.** When properly installed, bushing should protrude .080–.090 inch above bracket ear face.

7. Snap new bolt boots over support bushing lip.

Installation

1. Coat mounting bracket attaching bolt threads with Loctite sealant or equivalent. **Failure to use sealant on mounting bolts may result in loosening of caliper to knuckle attachment.**

2. Align mounting bracket holes, then install mounting bracket and **torque** attaching bolts to 83 ft. lbs.

CALIPER ASSEMBLY

1. Install bleeder screw and **torque** to 110 inch lbs.

2. Lubricate piston seal, piston, caliper bore and dust boot with new brake fluid.

3. Roll piston seal into seal groove in caliper bore, ensuring seal is fully seated and not twisted.

4. Install dust boot over piston, ensuring lip of boot engages piston groove.

5. Install piston in caliper bore, press piston to bottom of bore, then seat boot in caliper counterbore with suitable installer.

BRAKE SHOE & LINING INSTALLATION

A revised shoe and lining assembly is

used on 1988-89 models. The revised assembly includes a new lining material and extended shoes, eliminating the need for the stainless steel shoe abutment insulators (4), **Fig. 1.** This shoe and lining assembly can also be identified by the lining edge code: The original lining code is DM 121 FE, while the revised lining code is DM 128 FE. The revised shoe and lining assembly can be used on earlier models, however, the insulators must be removed and discarded.

1. If new shoe and lining assemblies are being installed, compress piston into caliper bore, taking care not to damage piston.
2. Install inboard shoe, snapping shoe retainer spring into piston bore, and ensure shoe is flat against piston.
3. Install outboard shoe assembly, snapping shoe springs into holes in caliper, and ensure shoe is flat against caliper housing.

CALIPER INSTALLATION

1. If first design shoe and lining assemblies are being installed, mount insulators (4), **Fig. 1,** on caliper bracket.
2. Position caliper on mounting bracket, ensuring insulators, first design, and mounting bolt boots remain in place.
3. Apply thin coating of silicone grease to caliper mounting bolts, install bolts and **torque** to 63 ft. lbs.
4. Install brake hose, if removed, and **torque** fitting bolt to 24 ft. lbs.
5. Install wheels and lower vehicle.
6. Fill master cylinder and bleed brakes as needed. **Do not attempt to move vehicle until brake pedal has been pumped several times and a firm brake pedal has been obtained.**

REAR BRAKE ASSEMBLY
CALIPER REMOVAL

1. Drain approximately ²/₃ of brake fluid from master cylinder assembly.
2. Raise and support vehicle, then remove tire and wheel assembly.
3. Loosen tension on parking brake cable at equalizer.
4. Remove retaining clip from parking brake lever, if equipped, disconnect cable, then remove spring and damper, **Fig. 2.**
5. Hold parking brake lever, remove locknut.
6. Remove lever, lever seal, and anti-friction washer.
7. Bottom piston into caliper bore to provide clearance between linings and rotor.
8. Reinstall anti-friction washer, lever seal (sealing bead against housing), lever, and locknut.
9. If caliper is to be serviced, remove inlet fitting attaching bolt, then disconnect and plug inlet fitting. **Do not crimp brake hose, as this may damage internal structure of hose. If only shoe and lining assemblies are to be replaced, do not disconnect brake line.**
10. Remove caliper mounting bolts, then lift caliper from bracket. If only shoe

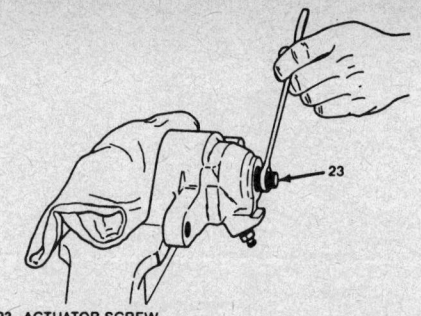

23. ACTUATOR SCREW

Fig. 4   Removing piston from caliper. Rear disc brake

and lining assemblies are being replaced, suspend caliper from chassis with suitable hanger. **Do not allow caliper to hang from brake hose.**

11. Remove insulators from caliper bracket, if equipped.

BRAKE SHOE & LINING REMOVAL

1. Remove caliper assembly as outlined.
2. Remove outboard shoe assembly, unsnapping springs from holes in caliper.
3. Remove inboard shoe assembly, pressing in on edge of shoe from open side of caliper and tilting shoe outward to release it from retainer.
4. Remove bushings from caliper mounting bracket holes, **Fig. 2,** and remove two-way check valve from end of piston with screwdriver. **If leakage is noted from piston hole after removing check valve, replace actuator and overhaul caliper.**

CALIPER DISASSEMBLY

1. Remove caliper assembly as outlined.
2. Rotate shoe retainer until tabs are aligned with recesses in piston, then remove shoe retainer, **Fig. 2.**
3. If installed remove locknut, lever, lever seal, and anti-friction washer.
4. Secure caliper assembly in vise and insulate interior of caliper with shop towels.
5. Remove piston by rotating actuator screw in parking brake apply direction to work piston from caliper bore **Fig. 4.**
6. Remove balance spring (24), then remove actuator screw by pressing on threaded end, **Fig. 2.**
7. Remove shaft seal and thrust washer from actuator screw.
8. Pry dust boot from caliper taking care not to damage caliper.
9. Remove retainer snap ring, then the locator.
10. Using wooden or plastic tool remove piston seal from caliper bore. **Do not use metal tool since this may damage caliper bore or seal groove.**
11. Inspect piston for scoring, nicks, corrosion, and wear and replace as needed.
12. Inspect caliper housing and seal groove for corrosion, nicks, scoring

and excessive wear, and use crocus cloth to polish away corrosion from housing bore. Replace caliper housing if corrosion in and around seal groove will not clean up with crocus cloth.

13. Remove bleeder screw. Remove bracket only is damaged.
14. Clean components with denatured alcohol and dry with unlubricated compressed air. Blow out all passages in housing and bleeder valve.

MOUNTING BRACKET SERVICE
Removal

1. Remove caliper as outlined previously.
2. Remove mounting bracket attaching bolts, then mounting bracket.

Bushing & Boot Replacement

1. Remove mounting bracket from vehicle.
2. Remove bolt boots from support bushings, **Fig. 2.**
3. Clamp bracket in a suitable vise, then pry support bushings from inner bushings in bracket ears with small screwdriver.
4. Using a paper clip, pull inner bushings from mounting bracket ears.
5. Lubricate inner bushings with silicone based grease, then install bushings flush with bracket ears.
6. Position .080-.090 inch thick shim stock on bracket ear face, then tap support bushings, with plastic mallet, into inner bushings, **Fig. 3.** When properly installed, bushing should protrude .080-.090 inch above bracket ear face.
7. Snap new bolt boots over support bushing lip.

Installation

1. Coat mounting bracket attaching bolt threads with Loctite sealant or equivalent. **Failure to use sealant on mounting bolts may result in loosening of caliper to knuckle attachment.**
2. Align mounting bracket holes, then install mounting bracket and **torque** attaching bolts to 83 ft. lbs.

CALIPER ASSEMBLY

1. Install bleeder valve, and **torque** to 110 inch lbs.
2. Install bracket, if removed, and **torque** to 31 ft. lbs.
3. Lubricate piston seal, piston, caliper bore and dust boot with new brake fluid.
4. Roll piston seal into seal groove in caliper bore, ensuring seal is fully seated and not twisted.
5. Lubricate piston locator with new brake fluid, then position locator on piston using piston locating tools No. J135588-1 and No. J135588-2 or equivalents.
6. Install thrust washer, grayish side towards caliper housing, on actuator

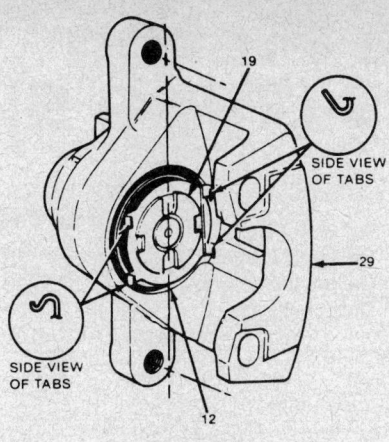

12 SHOE RETAINER
19 PISTON ASSEMBLY
29 CALIPER HOUSING

Fig. 5 Positioning caliper piston and pad retainer. Rear disc brake

and discarded.

1. Install lubricated bushings into bolt holes in caliper bracket.
2. Bottom piston in caliper bore using suitable pliers, protecting piston to prevent damage. **Do not allow pliers to contact actuator screw.**
3. Lubricate new two-way check valve, then insert valve into piston.
4. Install inboard shoe assembly as follows:
   a. Engage inboard shoe edge in straight tabs of retainer, then press down and snap shoe under S-shaped tabs, **Fig. 6.**
   b. Ensure shoe lays flat against piston and that retainer and piston are properly aligned. Note that tab on retainer are different, **Fig. 5,** and rotate retainer as needed.
   c. Ensure buttons on back of shoe engage D-shaped notches in piston. Rotate piston as needed with spanner wrench tool No. J-7624 or equivalent. Piston is properly aligned when D-shaped notches are aligned with caliper mounting bolt holes, **Fig. 5.**
5. Install outboard shoe assembly, snap shoe springs into holes in caliper and ensure pad lays flat against caliper. **Wear sensor should be at trailing edge of shoe during forward wheel rotation.**

CALIPER INSTALLATION

1. Lubricate sliding surfaces and mount insulators, if equipped, on caliper bracket.
2. Position caliper on mounting bracket ensuring insulators and retaining bolt boots remain in position.
3. Coat mounting bolts with thin film of silicone grease, install bolts and **torque** bolts to 63 ft. lbs.
4. Install brake hose using new sealing washers and **torque** fitting bolt to 15 ft. lbs.
5. Install parking brake lever as follows:
   a. Lubricate lever seal and anti-friction washer.
   b. Install washer, seal and parking brake lever. **Seal should be against caliper housing. Parking brake lever should be pointing downward.**
   c. Move lever off stop, hold lever and **torque** retaining nut to 35 ft. lbs., then rotate lever against stop.
6. Install spring and damper, connect parking brake cable, then secure assembly with retaining clip, if used.
7. Tighten brake cable at equalizer until parking brake lever moves off stop, then loosen cable until lever just contacts stop.
8. Install wheels and lower vehicle, fill master cylinder, and bleed brakes as needed. **Do not attempt to move vehicle until brake pedal has been moved several times a firm brake pedal is obtained.**

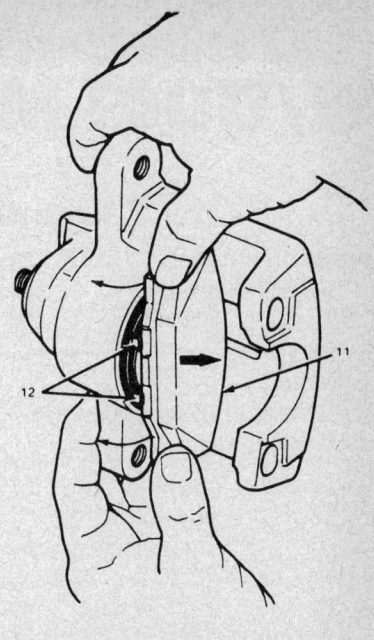

11 INBOARD SHOE & LINING
12 SHOE RETAINER

Fig. 6 Inboard shoe installation. Rear disc brake

PARKING BRAKE
ADJUST

1. Apply and release service brakes three times with a force of approximately 175 lbs.
2. Fully apply parking brake (may require up to 4 pedal strokes) using approximately 125 lbs. force on last stroke, then release. Repeat procedure two more times.
3. Inspect parking brake pedal assembly for full release by observing brake warning lamp.
4. If lamp is on and parking brake appears to be fully released, operate manual pedal release lever and pull down on front cable to remove slack from pedal assembly.
5. Raise and support vehicle and inspect parking brake levers on rear calipers.
6. If levers are not against stops, inspect rear cables for binding and position levers against stops.
7. Tighten brake cable at equalizer until either lever begins to move off stop.
8. Loosen cable until lever returns to stop. Both levers must be resting on stops after adjustment.
9. Operate parking brake several times, ensuring firm pedal can be obtained by pumping pedal less than 3 1/2 strokes.
10. Release parking brake and ensure both caliper levers are against stops.

screw.

7. Install lubricated shaft seal on actuator screw, then install actuator screw assembly into caliper housing.
8. Install balance spring in piston recess.
9. Install piston assembly, pressing piston in until locator is past snap ring groove, turn actuator screw as necessary to allow piston assembly to move toward bottom of caliper bore, then install snap ring.
10. Install lubricated dust boot over piston with inside lip in groove in piston and boot fold toward end of piston that contacts brake shoe, then bottom piston in caliper bore.
11. Install anti-friction washer and seal over end of actuator screw, ensuring seal bead is against caliper housing.
12. Install parking brake lever over actuator screw, rotate lever away from stop, hold lever and **torque** retaining nut to 35 ft. lbs., then rotate lever back to stop.
13. Seat dust boot in caliper counterbore using suitable driver.
14. Install shoe retainer on end of piston, ensuring piston and retainer are positioned as shown in **Fig. 5.**

BRAKE SHOE & LINING INSTALLATION

A revised shoe and lining assembly is used **on all 1988-89 models.** The revised assembly includes a new lining material and extended shoes, eliminating the need for the stainless steel shoe abutment insulators (13), **Fig. 2.** This shoe and lining assembly can also be identified by the lining edge code: The original lining code is DM 121 FE, while the revised lining code is DM 128 FE. The revised shoe and lining assembly can be used on earlier models, however, the insulators must be removed

Delco-Moraine Single Piston w/Dual Mounting Bolts (Type 5)

INDEX

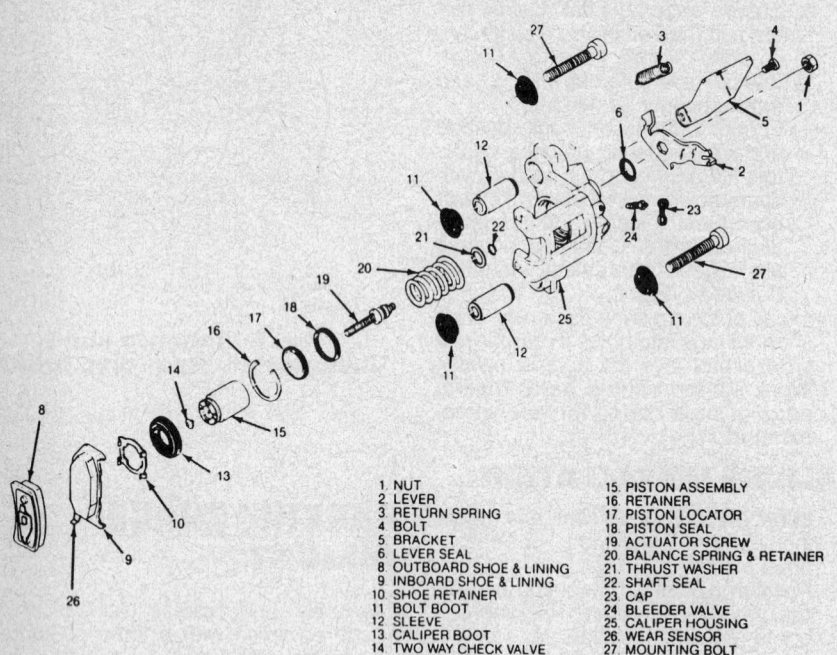

1. NUT
2. LEVER
3. RETURN SPRING
4. BOLT
5. BRACKET
6. LEVER SEAL
8. OUTBOARD SHOE & LINING
9. INBOARD SHOE & LINING
10. SHOE RETAINER
11. BOLT BOOT
12. SLEEVE
13. CALIPER BOOT
14. TWO WAY CHECK VALVE
15. PISTON ASSEMBLY
16. RETAINER
17. PISTON LOCATOR
18. PISTON SEAL
19. ACTUATOR SCREW
20. BALANCE SPRING & RETAINER
21. THRUST WASHER
22. SHAFT SEAL
23. CAP
24. BLEEDER VALVE
25. CALIPER HOUSING
26. WEAR SENSOR
27. MOUNTING BOLT

Fig. 1   Exploded view of Delco-Moraine 7735 series rear caliper

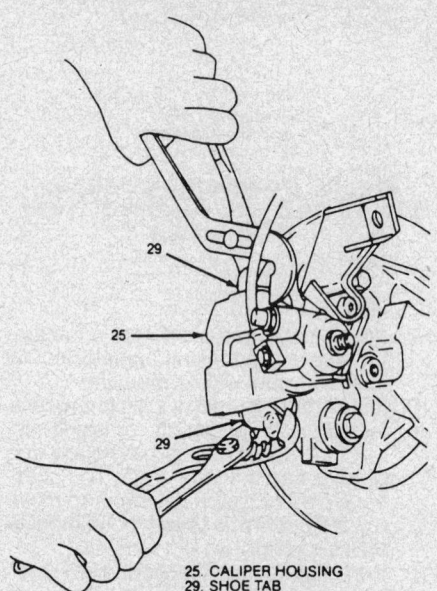

25. CALIPER HOUSING
29. SHOE TAB

Fig. 2   Bottoming piston in caliper bore

DESCRIPTION

This rear caliper, **Fig. 1,** has a single bore and is mounted to the support bracket with two mounting bolts. Hydraulic pressure, created by applying force to the brake pedal, is converted by the caliper into friction. The hydraulic pressure is applied equally against the piston and the bottom of the caliper bore moving the piston outward and the caliper housing inward, resulting in a clamping action on the brake rotor.

The caliper includes an integral parking brake mechanism. When the parking brake is applied, the lever turns an actuator screw which is threaded into a nut in the caliper piston. As the actuator screw turns, the piston is forced out, applying force on the rotor. The piston contains a self-adjusting mechanism to keep the parking brake in proper adjustment and to ensure proper clearance when the parking brake is released.

SERVICE
CALIPER REMOVAL

1. Drain approximately ⅔ of brake fluid from master cylinder assembly.
2. Raise and support vehicle, then remove tire and wheel assembly.
3. Loosen tension on parking brake cable at equalizer, then disconnect cable and remove return spring from parking brake lever, **Fig. 1.**
4. Hold parking brake lever in position, loosen retaining nut, then remove nut, lever and seal.
5. Position two adjustable pliers over inboard shoe tabs and flanges on caliper housing as shown, **Fig. 2,** then bottom piston in caliper bore.
6. Reinstall lever seal, lever and retaining nut.
7. If caliper assembly is to be serviced, remove inlet fitting attaching bolt, copper washer, and inlet fitting from caliper housing. Plug opening in inlet fitting to prevent fluid loss and contamination. **Do not crimp brake hose, as this may damage internal**

structure of hose. If only shoe and lining assemblies are to be replaced, do not disconnect brake line fitting from caliper.

8. Remove caliper mounting bolts, then lift caliper from mounting bracket. If only shoe and lining assemblies are being replaced, suspend caliper from chassis with suitable hanger. **Do not allow caliper to hang from brake hose.**

BRAKE SHOE & LINING REMOVAL

1. Remove caliper as outlined previously.
2. Remove outboard shoe assembly, disengaging buttons on shoe from holes in caliper.
3. Remove inboard shoe assembly, pressing in on edge of shoe from open side of caliper and tilting shoe outward to release it from retainer.
4. Remove two-way check valve from end of piston with screwdriver. **If leakage is noted from piston hole after removing check valve, caliper must be overhauled.**

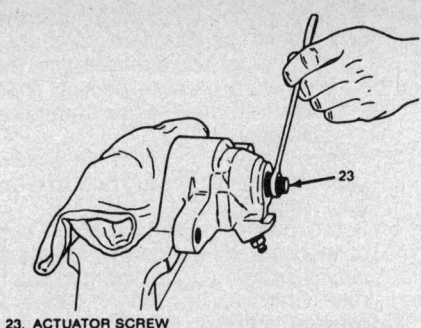

23. ACTUATOR SCREW

Fig. 3 Removing piston from caliper

CALIPER DISASSEMBLY

1. Remove caliper assembly as outlined previously.
2. Secure caliper assembly in vise and drive out sleeves and bolt boots. Insulate interior of caliper with shop towels.
3. Rotate shoe retainer until tabs are aligned with notches in piston, then remove shoe retainer, **Fig. 1.**
4. Remove locknut, lever, and lever seal, if installed.
5. Remove piston by rotating actuator screw in parking brake apply direction to work piston from caliper bore **Fig. 3.**
6. Remove balance spring (20), then remove actuator screw by pressing on threaded end, **Fig. 1.**
7. Remove seal and thrust washer from actuator screw.
8. Pry dust boot from caliper taking care not to damage caliper bore.
9. Remove piston locator retainer, then the locator.
10. Using a small piece of wood or plastic, remove piston seal from bore. **Do not use a metal tool of any kind to remove seal as it may damage bore.**
11. Remove bleeder screw. Remove bracket (5) and bolt (4), **Fig. 1**, if damaged.
12. Inspect piston for scoring, nicks, corrosion, and wear and replace as needed.
13. Inspect caliper housing and seal groove for corrosion, nicks, scoring and excessive wear, and use crocus cloth to polish away corrosion from housing bore. Replace caliper housing if corrosion in and around seal groove will not clean up with crocus cloth.
14. Clean all parts with denatured alcohol. Dry with unlubricated compressed air. Blow out all passages in housing and bleeder valve.

CALIPER ASSEMBLY

1. Install bleeder screw and **torque** to 116 inch lbs.
2. If removed, install bracket (5) and bolt (4), **Fig. 1**, then **torque** bolt to 32 ft. lbs.
3. Lubricate piston seals and bore grooves with new brake fluid, then roll piston seal into seal groove in bore,

ensuring seal is fully seated and not twisted.
4. Lubricate piston locator with new brake fluid, then position locator on piston using piston locator installer tool No. J-36627 or equivalent.
5. Install thrust washer on actuator screw, with grayish side towards caliper housing, then install lubricated shaft seal onto actuator screw.
6. Install actuator screw into piston assembly.
7. Install balance spring in piston recess in housing.
8. Install piston assembly, pressing piston in until locator is past retainer groove, turn actuator screw as necessary to allow piston assembly to move toward bottom of caliper bore, then install retainer ring.
9. Install lubricated dust boot over piston with inside lip in groove in piston and boot fold toward end of piston that contacts brake shoe, then bottom piston in caliper bore.
10. Install lubricated lever seal over end of actuator screw, ensuring seal bead is against caliper housing.
11. Install parking brake lever over actuator screw, rotate lever away from stop, then hold lever and **torque** retaining nut to 32 ft. lbs. After tightening retaining nut, rotate lever back to stop.
12. Seat dust boot in caliper counterbore using suitable driver.
13. Install shoe retainer in groove on end of piston, ensuring retainer tabs are properly aligned with piston notches.
14. Install sleeves and bolt boots into caliper housing as follows:
    a. Lubricate sleeves, bolt boots and caliper mounting bolt holes with silicone based grease.
    b. Install one bolt boot into groove in mounting bolt hole of caliper housing.
    c. Push sleeve into mounting bolt hole, past inner diameter of bolt boot, and position as shown in view A of **Fig. 4.**
    d. Install second bolt boot in groove at other end of mounting bolt hole as shown in view B of **Fig. 4.**
    e. Push sleeve in opposite direction until grooves of sleeve seat in inner diameter of both bolt boots as shown in view C of **Fig. 4.**
    f. Repeat steps b through e to install remaining bolt boots and sleeve.
15. Install caliper as outlined further on.

BRAKE SHOE & LINING INSTALLATION

1. Lubricate, then install two-way check valve into piston.
2. Install inboard shoe assembly as follows:
    a. Engage inboard shoe edge in retainer tabs closest to caliper bridge, then press down and snap shoe tabs at open side of caliper. Ensure shoe lays flat against piston.
    b. Ensure buttons on back of shoe engage D-shaped notches in piston. Rotate piston as needed with

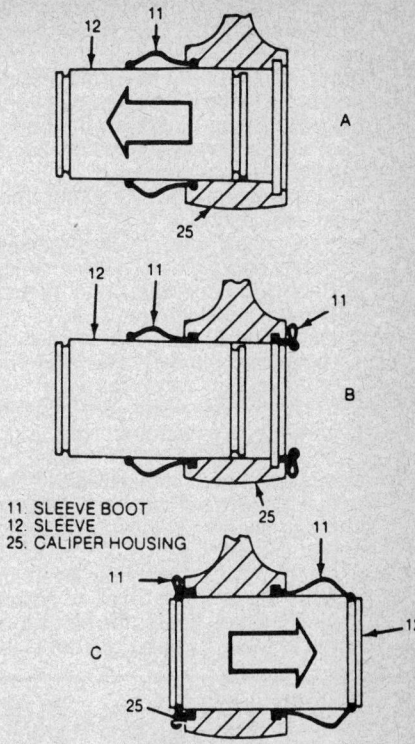

11. SLEEVE BOOT
12. SLEEVE
25. CALIPER HOUSING

Fig. 4 Bolt boot & sleeve installation

spanner wrench tool No. J-7624 or equivalent. Piston is properly aligned when one of the D-shaped notches is nearest caliper bridge.
    c. Wear sensor should be at the leading edge of shoe during forward wheel rotation.
3. Install outboard shoe assembly, snapping shoe springs into holes in caliper. Ensure pad lays flat against caliper.

CALIPER INSTALLATION

1. Push sleeves inward, away from inboard brake shoe.
2. Reconnect brake hose bracket to suspension, then position caliper over rotor and onto mounting bracket.
3. Install mounting bolts and **torque** to 79 ft. lbs. (92 ft. lbs. on 1989-90 models).
4. Reinstall bracket (5) and bolt (4), **Fig. 1**, **torque** bolt to 32 ft. lbs., then reconnect brake line to caliper using new copper washers.
5. Remove retaining nut, parking brake lever and lever seal, then clean area around seal and actuator screw.
6. Lubricate, then install lever seal. Ensure seal is fully seated against caliper.
7. Install parking brake lever onto actuator screw hex, ensuring lever faces downward, then install retaining nut.
8. While holding lever against stop on caliper, **torque** retaining nut to 35 ft. lbs.
9. Install lever return spring, then reconnect parking brake cable.

10. Install wheels and lower vehicle, then fill master cylinder and bleed brakes as needed. **Before moving vehicle, pump brake pedal several times to be sure it is firm. Do not move vehicle until a firm pedal is obtained.**

11. After installation is completed, adjust parking brake as follows:
    a. Depress brake pedal several times to seat linings.
    b. Fully apply and release parking brake approximately three times. Each full application may require two full pedal strokes.
    c. Raise and support vehicle, then remove rear wheels. Reinstall two wheel nuts to retain rotor.
    d. Turn ignition switch on, and observe brake warning light. Light should be Off. If light remains on, operate manual brake release and pull downward on front parking brake cable to remove slack from pedal assembly.
    e. Check that parking brake levers on both calipers are against caliper stops. If not, check for binding at rear cables. If cables are not bind-

ing proceed to next step.
    f. Loosen adjustment at equalizer until both parking brake levers are against caliper stops.
    g. Tighten cable at equalizer until either parking brake lever moves off caliper stop, then loosen cable until lever just contacts stop. With cable properly adjusted, a firm pedal should be obtained by pumping parking brake two full strokes. Rear wheels should be fully locked.
    h. After adjustment is completed, install wheels and lower vehicle.

PARKING BRAKE
ADJUST

1. Apply service brake pedal three times with a force of approximately 175 lbs.
2. Fully apply and release parking brake three times. Full application may require two pedal strokes.
3. Raise and support vehicle, then mark relationship between wheel and axle flange.
4. Check parking brake pedal assembly for full release as follows:

    a. Turn ignition switch to On position.
    b. If "Brake" lamp is illuminated, operate manual brake release and pull downward on front parking brake cable to remove slack from pedal assembly.
5. Remove rear wheel and tire assemblies, then install two lug nuts to retain each rotor assembly.
6. If two parking brake levers on both calipers are not against lever stops on caliper housings, check for binding in rear cables and/or loosen cables at adjuster until both left and right levers are against their stops.
7. Tighten parking brake cable at adjuster until either the left or right lever begins to move off the stop, then loosen adjustment until lever moves back barely touching stop.
8. Operate parking brake several times to check adjustments. A firm pedal feel should be obtained by pumping pedal two full strokes and rear wheels should not rotate forward when parking brake is fully applied.
9. Install wheel and tire assemblies, aligning marks made in step 3.

Delco-Moraine Single Piston w/Dual Mounting Bolts (Type 6)

INDEX

DESCRIPTION

These calipers, **Figs. 1 and 2**, have a single bore and are mounted to a support bracket with two mounting bolts. Hydraulic force, created by applying force to the brake pedal, is converted by the caliper into friction. The hydraulic force is applied equally against the piston and the bottom of the caliper bore moving the piston outward, resulting in a clamping action on the brake rotor.

The rear caliper includes an integral parking brake mechanism. When the parking brake is applied, the lever turns an actuator screw which is threaded into a nut in the caliper piston. As the actuator screw turns, the piston is forced out, applying force on the rotor. The piston contains a self-adjusting mechanism to keep the parking brake in proper adjustment and to ensure proper clearance when the parking brake is released.

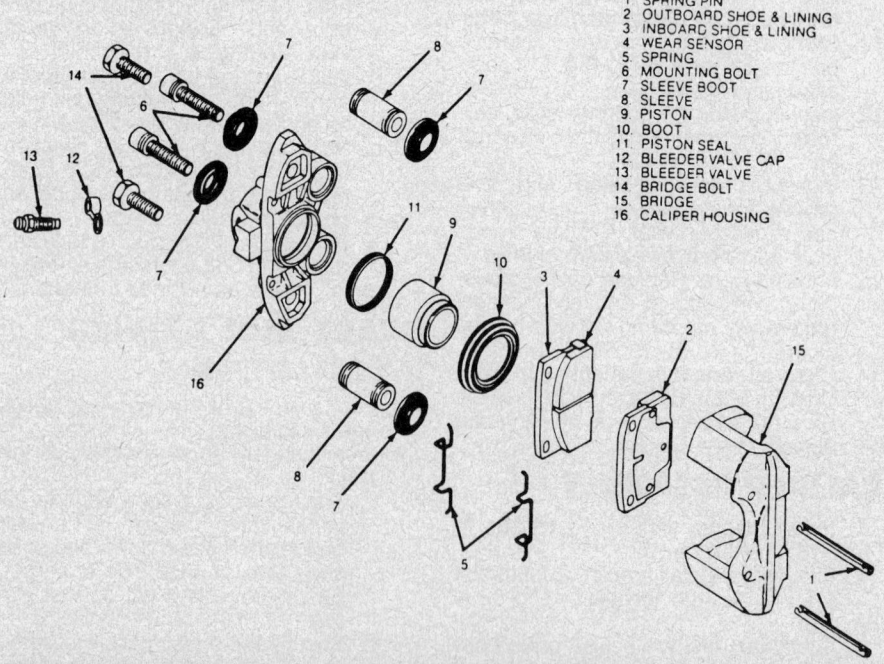

```
 1  SPRING PIN
 2  OUTBOARD SHOE & LINING
 3  INBOARD SHOE & LINING
 4  WEAR SENSOR
 5  SPRING
 6  MOUNTING BOLT
 7  SLEEVE BOOT
 8  SLEEVE
 9  PISTON
10  BOOT
11  PISTON SEAL
12  BLEEDER VALVE CAP
13  BLEEDER VALVE
14  BRIDGE BOLT
15  BRIDGE
16  CALIPER HOUSING
```

Fig. 1 Exploded view of Delco-Moraine 48H series front caliper

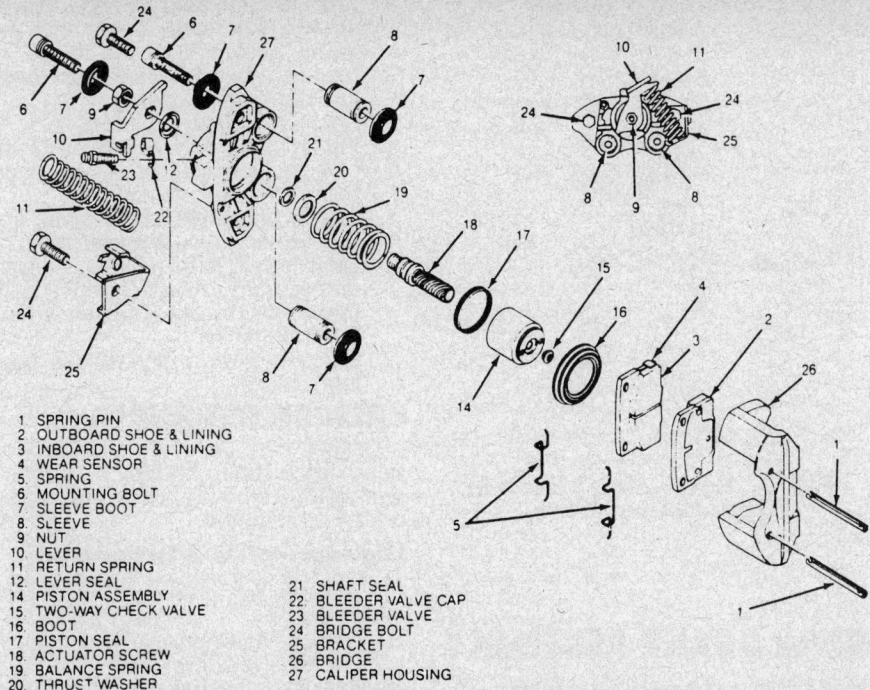

1. SPRING PIN
2. OUTBOARD SHOE & LINING
3. INBOARD SHOE & LINING
4. WEAR SENSOR
5. SPRING
6. MOUNTING BOLT
7. SLEEVE BOOT
8. SLEEVE
9. NUT
10. LEVER
11. RETURN SPRING
12. LEVER SEAL
14. PISTON ASSEMBLY
15. TWO-WAY CHECK VALVE
16. BOOT
17. PISTON SEAL
18. ACTUATOR SCREW
19. BALANCE SPRING
20. THRUST WASHER

21. SHAFT SEAL
22. BLEEDER VALVE CAP
23. BLEEDER VALVE
24. BRIDGE BOLT
25. BRACKET
26. BRIDGE
27. CALIPER HOUSING

Fig. 2 Exploded view of Delco-Moraine 48H series rear caliper

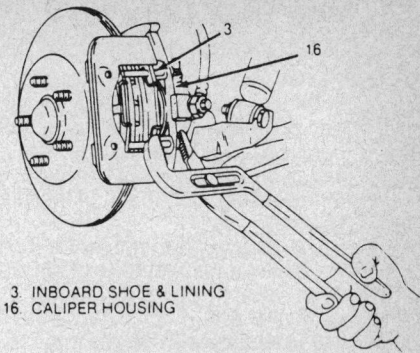

3. INBOARD SHOE & LINING
16. CALIPER HOUSING

Fig. 3 Bottoming piston in front caliper bore

FRONT BRAKE ASSEMBLY

BRAKE SHOE & LINING REMOVAL

1. Drain approximately 2/3 of brake fluid from master cylinder assembly.
2. Raise and support vehicle, then mark position of wheel and remove tire and wheel assembly. Reinstall two wheel nuts to hold rotor in position.
3. Position adjustable pliers over caliper housing and flange of inboard brake shoe, **Fig. 3**, then squeeze pliers and bottom piston in caliper bore.
4. Using suitable tools, drive spring pins (1) from caliper housing, **Fig. 1**. Use caution when performing this procedure, as retainer springs (5) may fly out and cause personal injury.
5. Remove retainer springs from inboard and outboard shoe flanges.
6. Remove outboard, then the inboard brake shoe and lining through opening in caliper. If inboard brake shoe is difficult to remove, move caliper housing inboard to provide additional clearance for removal.

CALIPER REMOVAL

1. Remove brake shoes and linings as outlined previously.
2. If caliper requires overhaul, disconnect brake line from caliper and plug openings to prevent fluid loss or contamination.
3. Remove caliper mounting bolts (6), **Fig. 1**, using suitable torx bit. Do not confuse mounting bolts with bridge bolts (14) during removal.
4. Lift up on caliper and remove from

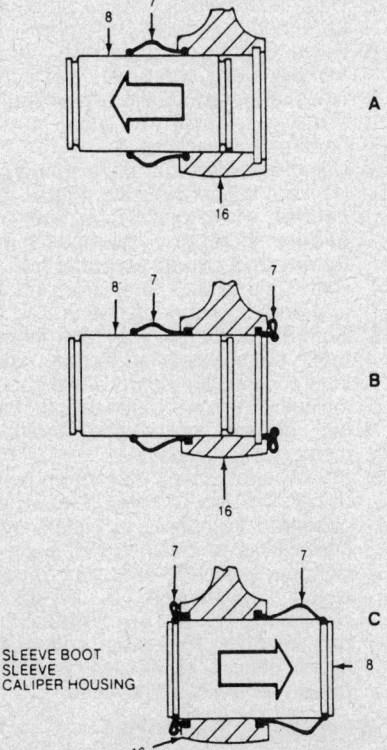

7. SLEEVE BOOT
8. SLEEVE
16. CALIPER HOUSING

Fig. 4 Sleeve boot & sleeve installation. Front caliper (rear caliper similar)

brake rotor. If overhaul is not required, suspend caliper from suspension to avoid damaging brake hose.
5. Remove sleeves and sleeve boots from caliper.

CALIPER OVERHAUL

Caliper can be overhauled without removing caliper bridge. If bridge is damaged, remove bridge bolts and bridge as required.

Disassembly & Inspection

1. Remove caliper as outlined previously.
2. Use clean shop towels to pad inside of caliper, then remove piston by applying compressed air to fluid inlet port. Use only enough air pressure to ease piston from bore. **Keep fingers away from piston to avoid injury as piston is forced out.**
3. Pry dust boot from caliper, then remove piston seal, taking care not to damage housing.
4. Clean metal components with suitable solvent and blow dry with compressed air.
5. Inspect piston for scoring nicks, corrosion, wear and damage, and replace as needed.
6. Inspect caliper housing and seal groove for damage, corrosion, nicks, scoring and excessive wear, and use crocus cloth to polish away corrosion from housing bore. Replace caliper housing if damaged, or if corrosion is excessive.
7. Remove bleeder screw from caliper housing, **Fig. 1**.

Assembly

1. Reinstall caliper bridge, if removed during disassembly. **Torque** bridge bolts to 74 ft. lbs.
2. Lubricate piston seal, piston, caliper bore and dust boot with new brake fluid.
3. Roll piston seal into seal groove in caliper bore, ensuring seal is fully seated and not twisted.
4. Install dust boot over piston, ensuring lip of boot engages piston groove.
5. Install piston in caliper bore, press piston to bottom of bore, then seat boot in caliper counterbore with suitable driver.
6. Install bleeder screw and **torque** to 116 inch lbs.

CALIPER INSTALLATION

1. Install sleeves and sleeve boots into caliper as follows:
   a. Lubricate sleeves, boots and caliper mounting bolt holes with silicone based grease.
   b. Install one sleeve boot into groove in mounting bolt hole of caliper housing.
   c. Push sleeve into mounting bolt hole, past inner diameter of sleeve boot, and position as shown in view A of **Fig. 4. Ensure sleeves are installed with large hole facing inboard, or damage to mounting bracket threads may result.**
   d. Install second sleeve boot in groove at other end of mounting bolt hole as shown in view B of **Fig. 4.**
   e. Push sleeve in opposite direction until grooves of sleeve seat in inner diameter of both sleeve boots as shown in view C of **Fig. 4.**
   f. Repeat steps b through e to install remaining boots and sleeve.
2. Position caliper over rotor and onto mounting bracket, then install mounting bolts and **torque** to 74 ft.lbs.
3. If caliper was overhauled, reconnect brake line using new copper washers.
4. Install brake shoes and linings as outlined further on.
5. If caliper was overhauled, fill master cylinder to proper level, then bleed brake system.

BRAKE SHOE & LINING INSTALLATION

1. Install inboard shoe and lining, ensuring wear sensor is positioned at leading edge of shoe during forward rotation of wheel.
2. Install outboard shoe and lining.
3. Using a brass drift and hammer, drive in one spring pin until pin just begins to emerge from inboard face of caliper.
4. Tap in other spring pin as noted above, but stop when pin is just through outboard section of caliper housing.
5. Position pins so slots face each other, then install retainer springs as follows:
   a. Hook one end of spring under pin installed in step 3, ensuring mid-section of spring is positioned over shoe flange. Repeat procedure for remaining spring.
   b. Using a screwdriver, press down on other end of springs while sliding remaining spring pin inboard as outlined in step 3.
   c. After installation, ensure retainer springs are equally centered on shoe flanges, and that spring ends project under pins an equal amount.
6. Install wheels, lower vehicle, then fill master cylinder to proper level.
7. Apply brake pedal several times to correctly seat linings.

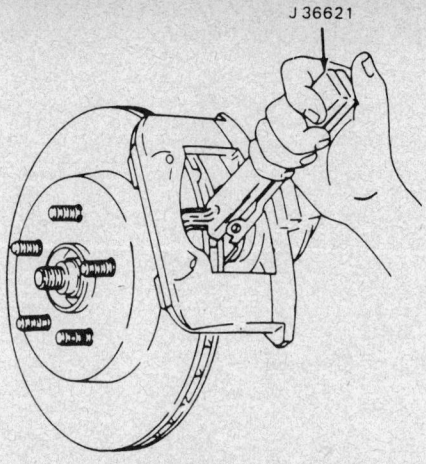

J36621

Fig. 5 Bottoming piston in rear caliper bore

REAR BRAKE ASSEMBLY

BRAKE SHOE & LINING REMOVAL

1. Drain approximately 2/3 of brake fluid from master cylinder assembly.
2. Raise and support vehicle, release parking brake, then mark position of wheel and remove tire and wheel assembly. Reinstall two wheel nuts to hold rotor in position.
3. Using suitable tools, drive spring pins (1) from caliper housing, **Fig. 2. Use caution when performing this procedure, as retainer springs (5) may fly out and cause personal injury.**
4. Remove retainer springs from inboard and outboard shoe flanges.
5. Remove outboard, then the inboard brake shoe and lining through opening in caliper. If inboard brake shoe is difficult to remove, move caliper housing inboard to provide additional clearance for removal.
6. Pry two-way check valve from piston using small screwdriver. If leakage is observed from hole in piston, overhaul caliper as outlined further on.
7. Bottom piston into caliper bore using piston adjusting tool No. J-36621 or equivalent, **Fig. 5. Turn lefthand piston counterclockwise and righthand piston clockwise to move piston assembly into bore.**

CALIPER REMOVAL

1. Remove brake shoes and linings as outlined previously.
2. Loosen parking brake cable adjustment, then disconnect parking brake cable and remove return spring from parking brake lever.
3. If caliper assembly is to be serviced, remove inlet fitting attaching bolt, copper washer, and inlet fitting from caliper housing.Plug opening in inlet fitting to prevent fluid loss and contamination. **Do not crimp brake**

hose, as this may damage internal structure of hose. If only shoe and lining assemblies are to be replaced, do not disconnect brake line fitting from caliper.
4. Remove caliper mounting bolts (6), **Fig. 2,** using suitable torx bit. Do not confuse mounting bolts with bridge bolts (24) during removal.
5. Lift up on caliper and remove from brake rotor. If only shoe and lining assemblies are to be replaced, suspend caliper from chassis using suitable hanger. **Do not allow caliper to hang by brake hose.**
6. Remove sleeves and sleeve boots from caliper.

CALIPER OVERHAUL

Caliper can be overhauled without removing caliper bridge. If bridge is damaged, remove bridge bolts and bridge as required.

Disassembly & Inspection

1. Remove caliper as outlined previously.
2. Remove parking brake lever retaining nut, lever and lever seal.
3. Insulate interior of caliper with shop towels, then remove piston by rotating actuator screw in parking brake apply direction to work piston from caliper bore.
4. Remove actuator screw (18) by pressing on threaded end, then the balance spring (19), **Fig. 2.**
5. Remove seal and thrust washer from actuator screw.
6. Pry dust boot from caliper taking care not to damage caliper bore.
7. Using a small piece of wood or plastic, remove piston seal from bore. **Do not use a metal tool of any kind to remove seal as it may damage bore.**
8. Remove bleeder valve.
9. Inspect piston for scoring, nicks, corrosion, and wear and replace as needed.
10. Inspect caliper housing and seal groove for corrosion, nicks, scoring and excessive wear, and use crocus cloth to polish away corrosion from housing bore. Replace caliper housing if corrosion in and around seal groove will not clean up with crocus cloth.
11. Clean all parts with denatured alcohol. Dry with unlubricated compressed air. Blow out all passages in housing and bleeder valve.

Assembly

1. Reinstall caliper bridge, if removed during disassembly. **Torque** bridge bolts to 74 ft. lbs., then install bleeder valve.
2. Lubricate piston seal, piston, caliper bore and dust boot with new brake fluid.
3. Roll piston seal into seal groove in caliper bore, ensuring seal is fully seated and not twisted.
4. Install thrust washer on actuator screw, with copper side of washer facing toward piston assembly, then install shaft seal onto actuator screw.

5. Install lubricated shaft seal on actuator screw.
6. Install boot onto piston assembly.
7. Install actuator screw and balance spring into caliper bore. Ensure end of spring fully bottoms in recess at bottom of bore.
8. Install piston and boot assembly, push piston into bore, then turn actuator screw as necessary until piston fully bottoms in caliper.
9. Install lever seal over end of actuator screw, ensuring rubber sealing bead is against lever and copper colored side is against caliper housing.
10. Install parking brake lever over actuator screw, rotate lever away from stop, then hold lever and **torque** retaining nut to 35 ft. lbs. After tightening retaining nut, rotate lever back to stop.
11. Seat dust boot in caliper counterbore using suitable driver.

CALIPER INSTALLATION

1. Install sleeves and sleeve boots into caliper as follows:
   a. Lubricate sleeves, boots and caliper mounting bolt holes with silicone based grease.
   b. Install one sleeve boot into groove in mounting bolt hole of caliper housing.
   c. Push sleeve into mounting bolt hole, passed inner diameter of sleeve boot, and position as shown in view A of **Fig. 4**. **Ensure sleeves are installed with large hole facing inboard, or damage to mounting bracket threads may result.**
   d. Install second sleeve boot in groove at other end of mounting bolt hole as shown in view B of **Fig. 4.**
   e. Push sleeve in opposite direction until grooves of sleeve seat in inner diameter of both sleeve boots as shown in view C of **Fig. 4.**
   f. Repeat steps b through e to install remaining boots and sleeve.
2. Position caliper over rotor and onto mounting bracket, then install mounting bolts and **torque** to 74 ft.lbs.
3. If caliper was overhauled, reconnect brake line using new copper washers.
4. Install brake shoes and linings as outlined further on.
5. If caliper was overhauled, fill master cylinder to proper level, then bleed brake system.
6. Install lever return spring, then reconnect parking brake cable.
7. Install wheels and lower vehicle. **Do not attempt to move vehicle until brake pedal has been moved several times and full braking action is restored.**
8. After installation is completed, adjust parking brake as follows:
   a. Depress brake pedal several times to seat linings.
   b. Fully apply and release parking brake approximately three times.
   c. Turn ignition switch on, and observe brake warning light. Light should be Off. If light remains on, operate manual brake release and pull downward on front parking brake cable to remove slack from pedal assembly.
   d. Raise and support vehicle.
   e. Check that parking brake levers on both calipers are against caliper stops. If not, check for binding at rear cables. If cables are not binding proceed to next step.
   f. Tighten cable at equalizer until either parking brake lever moves off caliper stop, then loosen cable until lever just contacts stop. With cable properly adjusted, parking brake lever should not travel more than six ratchet clicks and rear wheels should be fully locked at three to six ratchet clicks.
   g. After adjustment is completed, install wheels and lower vehicle.

BRAKE SHOE & LINING INSTALLATION

1. Lubricate, then install new two-way check valve into piston assembly.
2. Install inboard shoe and lining, ensuring wear sensor is positioned at leading edge of shoe during forward rotation of wheel.
3. Install outboard shoe and lining.
4. Using a brass drift and hammer, drive in one spring pin until pin just begins to emerge from inboard face of caliper.
5. Tap in other spring pin as noted above, but stop when pin is just through outboard section of caliper housing.
6. Position pins so slots face each other, then install retainer springs as follows:
   a. Hook one end of spring under pin installed in step 3, ensuring mid-section of spring is positioned over shoe flange. Repeat procedure for remaining spring.
   b. Using a screwdriver, press down on other end of springs while sliding remaining spring pin inboard as outlined in step 3.
   c. After installation, ensure retainer springs are equally centered on shoe flanges, and that spring ends project under pins an equal amount.
7. Install wheels, lower vehicle, then fill master cylinder to proper level.
8. Apply brake pedal several times to correctly seat linings.

PARKING BRAKE ADJUST

1. Apply service brake pedal three times with a force of approximately 175 lbs.
2. Apply and release parking brake three times.
3. Raise and support vehicle.
4. Mark relationship between wheel and axle flange.
5. Ensure parking brake lever is fully released, then turn ignition switch on and note brake warning lamp. If warning lamp is lit, pull down on front parking brake cable to remove slack from pedal.
6. Remove rear wheel and tire assemblies. Retain rotors with two lug nuts.
7. Ensure parking brake levers on both calipers are in contact with lever stops on caliper housings. If not, check for binding in rear cables and/or loosen cables as necessary.
8. Tighten parking brake cable at adjuster until either lever begins to move off stop, then loosen until lever moves back and contacts stop.
9. Operate parking brake lever several times and ensure proper operation. When properly adjusted, the lever should not travel more than six clicks and the rear wheels should not rotate forward when lever is applied three to six clicks.

Delco-Moraine Single Piston Rear Disc Brake

INDEX

DESCRIPTION

Upon application of the brakes, **Figs. 1 & 2,** the cone and piston move out as one part. The nut remains stationary on the high lead screw and a gap develops between the cone and nut. When lining wear occurs, the cone and piston do not return to their original position, thereby leaving a small gap equal to the lining wear between the nut and cone. The adjusting spring causes the nut to rotate on the high lead screw to close the gap and adjust the caliper.

Upon application of parking brake, the lever rotation causes the high lead screw to turn and the nut to move down the screw, thereby loading through the cone and the cone-clutch interface of the piston, resulting in a clamp load on the linings. When the parking brake is released, the cone rotates on the clutch interface to adjust the caliper. The clutch interface prevents the cone from turning when the parking brake is applied.

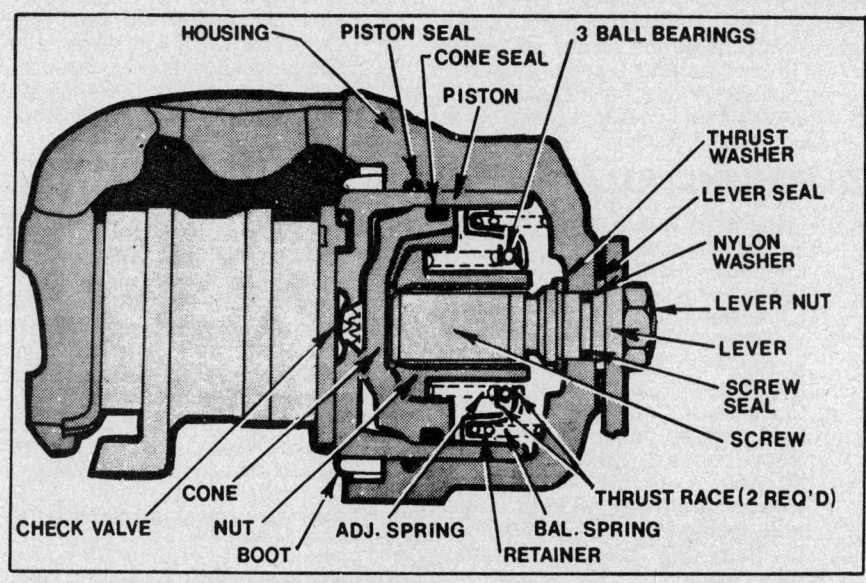

Fig. 1   Typical Delco-Moraine rear disc brake cross-sectional view

SERVICE

CALIPER REMOVAL

Do not mix power steering fluid with brake fluid. If brake seals contact steering fluid or steering seals contact brake fluid, damage will result.
1. Remove two thirds of the total brake fluid capacity from the master cylinder front reservoir, to prevent overflow of brake fluid.
2. Support vehicle on a hoist and remove tire and wheel assembly.
3. Install one nut with flat side facing rotor to prevent rotor from falling out when caliper is removed.
4. Loosen parking brake cable tension at equalizer, then remove cable from parking brake lever and remove return spring, locknut, lever, lever seal and anti-friction washer. **Lever must be held in place while removing nut.**
5. Clean surface in area of lever seal, then using a 7 inch (or larger) C-clamp, with the solid end on lever stop and screw end on back of outboard lining, turn clamp until piston is bottomed in caliper. **Do not position C-clamp on actuator screw.**
6. Before removing clamp, lubricate housing surface under lever seal with silicone lubricant.
7. Install anti-friction washer, a new lever seal and lever. **Install lever on hex**

with arm pointing downward.
8. Rotate lever toward front of vehicle and while holding in this position, install nut and **torque** to 25 ft. lbs. and rotate lever back to stop.
9. Disconnect brake line from caliper and plug openings to prevent loss of fluid and contamination. **Do not crimp brake hose, as this may damage internal structure of hose.**
10. Remove the brass bolt from block, if applicable. **If brake line nut is seized, brass bolt and block can be removed with brake line attached by removing bolt. Plug openings to prevent loss of fluid and entry of dirt.**
11. Remove caliper mounting bolts and remove caliper.
12. Reverse procedure to install and **torque** caliper mounting bolts to 30 ft. lbs. **When installing brass bolt and block, use two new copper gaskets. Torque bolt or connector to 30 ft. lbs.**

CALIPER DISASSEMBLY

1. Clamp caliper in a vise and remove the two mounting sleeves and four

bushings, **Fig. 2.**
2. Remove shoe dampening spring from end of piston.
3. If installed, remove locknut, lever, lever seal, and anti-friction washer.
4. Rotate parking brake lever in parking brake apply direction to remove piston from housing, **Fig. 3.** If piston will not move, Use a ⁹⁄₁₆ inch wrench, rotate actuator screw clockwise on right-hand caliper or counterclockwise on lefthand caliper until the piston moves from housing. **Pad caliper with shop cloths when removing piston.**
5. Remove balance spring, then remove actuator screw by pressing on thread end.
6. Remove shaft seal, and thrust washer from actuator screw.
7. Remove dust boot. **Take care not to scratch caliper housing or bore.**
8. Using a small piece of wood or plastic, remove piston seal from bore. **Do not use a metal tool of any kind to remove seal as it may damage bore.**
9. Remove bleeder screw, fitting, copper washers, and bolt. Remove bracket only if damaged.
10. Inspect piston for scoring, nicks, corrosion, and wear and replace as need-

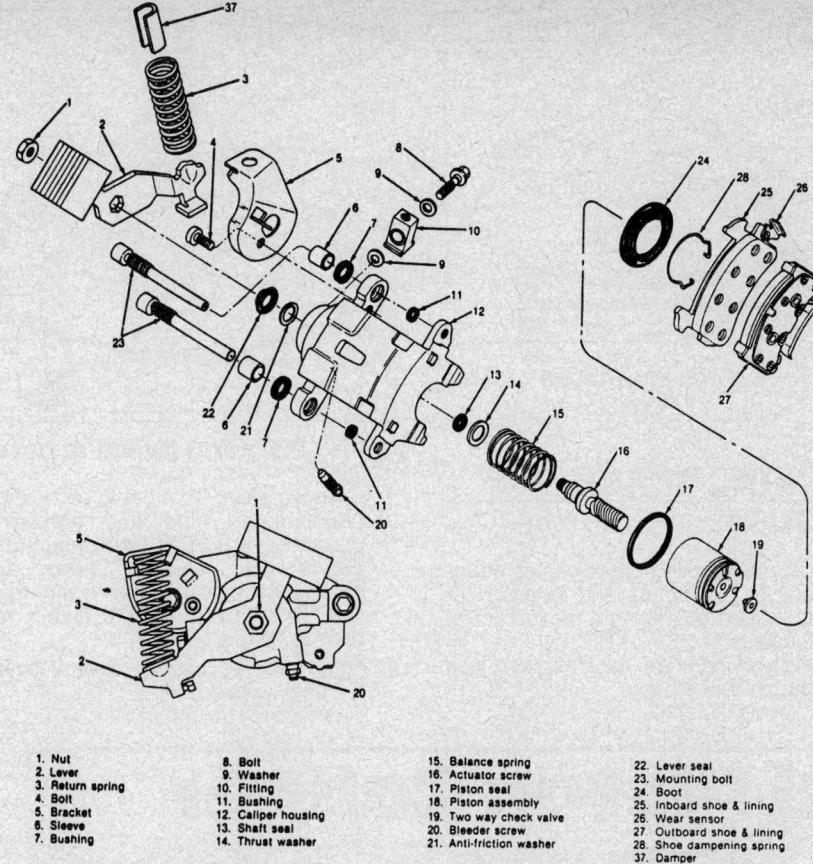

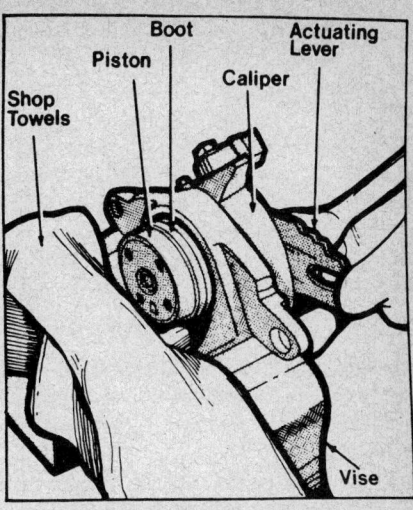

Fig. 3 Removing piston from bore

1. Nut	8. Bolt	15. Balance spring	22. Lever seal
2. Lever	9. Washer	16. Actuator screw	23. Mounting bolt
3. Return spring	10. Fitting	17. Piston seal	24. Boot
4. Bolt	11. Bushing	18. Piston assembly	25. Inboard shoe & lining
5. Bracket	12. Caliper housing	19. Two way check valve	26. Wear sensor
6. Sleeve	13. Shaft seal	20. Bleeder screw	27. Outboard shoe & lining
7. Bushing	14. Thrust washer	21. Anti-friction washer	28. Shoe dampening spring
			37. Damper

Fig. 2 Rear disc brake caliper exploded view (Typical)

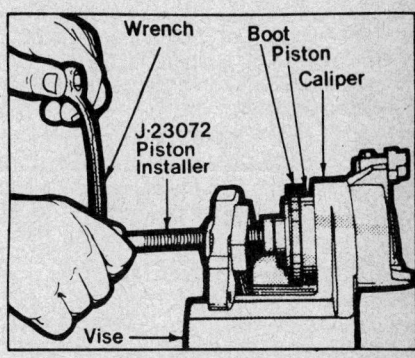

Fig. 5 Installing piston into caliper

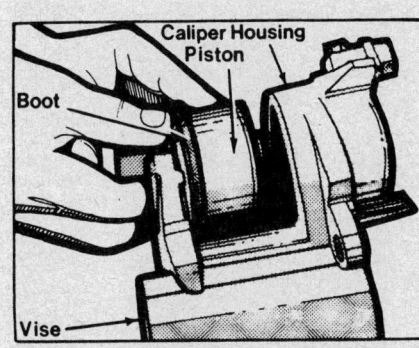

Fig. 4 Positioning piston in caliper

ed.

11. Inspect caliper housing and seal groove for corrosion, nicks, scoring and excessive wear, and use crocus cloth to polish away corrosion from housing bore. Replace caliper housing if corrosion in and around seal groove will not clean up with crocus cloth.

12. Clean all parts with denatured alcohol. Dry with unlubricated compressed air. Blow out all passages in housing and bleeder valve.

CALIPER ASSEMBLY

1. Install bleeder screw and **torque** to 116 inch lbs., then install bracket, if removed, and **torque** to 31 ft. lbs.

2. Install fitting and bolt, if equipped, using new copper washer and **torque** to 24 ft. lbs.

3. Lubricate and install new piston seal. **Make sure is not twisted.**

4. Install new boot onto piston assembly with lip of boot located in piston groove and boot fold toward end of piston that contact inboard brake shoe.

5. Install new thrust washer on actuator screw, with copper side of washer towards the piston assembly.

6. Install lubricated shaft seal on actuator screw, then install actuator screw in piston.

7. Coat piston seal with clean brake fluid. Install balance spring into piston and install assembly into caliper housing, **Fig. 4.**

8. With piston installer tool No. J-23072 or equivalent push piston fully into caliper housing, **Fig. 5. The piston must be pushed straight into caliper to prevent damage to the actuator screw seal as it passes through hole in rear of piston bore.**

9. Before removing piston installer tool No. J-23072, install lubricated anti-friction washer, new lever seal, lever and locknut. Position lever away from stop, rotate forward and hold lever in position, then **torque** nut to 35 ft. lbs.

10. Remove piston installer tool No. J-23072, rotate lever back to stop and install return spring.

11. With dust boot installer tool No. J-26296 or equivalent, drive boot until seal bottoms in caliper housing, **Fig. 6.**

12. Install dampening spring in groove in end of piston.

BRAKE SHOE & LINING REPLACEMENT

1. Remove caliper as described previously and remove shoe and lining.

2. Remove and discard the two caliper mounting sleeves and the four bushings. Using silicone lubricant, install new bushings and seals. **Sleeves are installed in inner bushings.**

3. Remove and discard piston two-way check valve and install a new one, **Fig. 7. If leakage is noted from end of piston after check valve is removed caliper must be overhauled.**

4. Position new inboard shoe assembly on piston. The D-shaped tab must fit into indentation in piston. If piston requires rotation, use spanner wrench

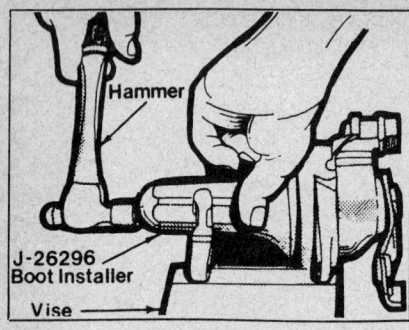

Fig. 6 Driving boot into caliper

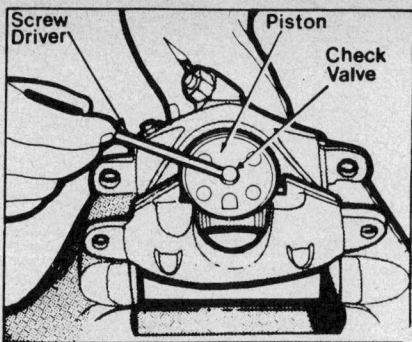

Fig. 7 Removing piston check valve

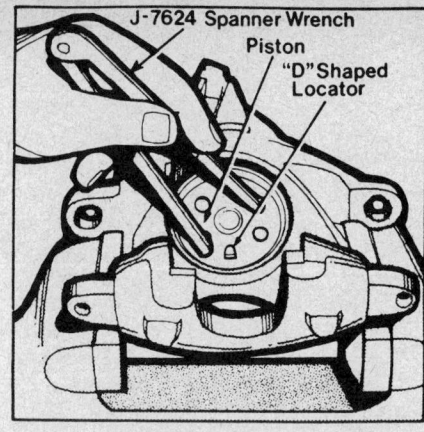

Fig. 8 Rotating piston in bore

to rotate piston, **Fig. 8. Install new spring retainers** as applicable.

5. Install new outboard shoe assembly onto caliper. Install caliper and **torque** mounting bolts to 30 ft. lbs.
6. Position channel lock pliers over brake shoe ears, if equipped, and bottom edge of caliper. While holding moderate force on brake pedal, clinch outboard shoe.

PARKING BRAKE ADJUST

1. Lubricate parking brake cables at underbody rub points and at equalizer hooks and ensure free movement of all cables.
2. With parking brake fully released, jack up both rear wheels.

3. Remove slack from cable by holding brake cable stud and tightening equalizer nut. **After tightening nut, check that caliper levers are against stops on caliper housing. If not, loosen cable until levers return to stops.**
4. Actuate parking brake several times to check adjustment.

PBR Dual Piston Caliper

INDEX

DESCRIPTION

This front caliper, **Fig. 1,** consists of dual pistons and an aluminum housing which is suspended on the shoe and lining assemblies. Hydraulic pressure, created by applying force to the brake pedal, acts equally against the pistons and the bottom of the caliper bores to move the pistons outward. This action slides the caliper inward, resulting in a clamping action on the brake rotor. This clamping action forces the linings against the rotor, creating the friction necessary to stop the vehicle.

SERVICE

CALIPER REMOVAL

1. Remove 2/3 of the total brake fluid capacity from master cylinder reservoir.
2. Raise and support vehicle, then remove tire and wheel assembly.
3. Install two wheel retaining nuts to retain rotor in position.
4. If caliper requires overhaul, remove inlet fitting attaching bolt, then disconnect inlet fitting from caliper housing. Discard the two gaskets, then plug openings in inlet fitting and caliper to prevent loss or contamination of fluid.

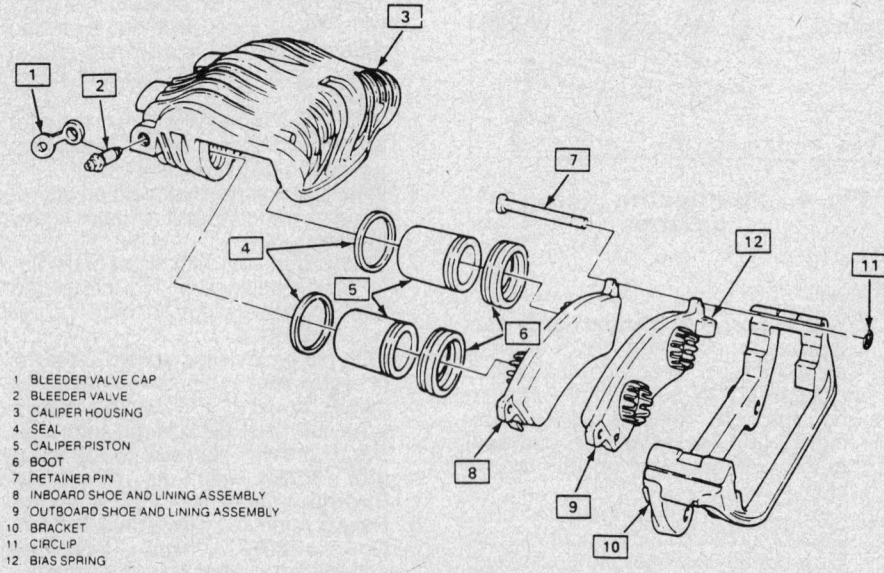

1 BLEEDER VALVE CAP
2 BLEEDER VALVE
3 CALIPER HOUSING
4 SEAL
5 CALIPER PISTON
6 BOOT
7 RETAINER PIN
8 INBOARD SHOE AND LINING ASSEMBLY
9 OUTBOARD SHOE AND LINING ASSEMBLY
10 BRACKET
11 CIRCLIP
12 BIAS SPRING

Fig. 1 Exploded view of PBR dual piston front caliper

Do not crimp brake hose, as this may damage internal structure of hose.

5. Remove circlip (11) and retaining pin (7), **Fig. 1**, then pull caliper off rotor and mounting bracket. If only shoe and linings require replacement, suspend caliper from upper control arm to prevent damage to brake hose.

BRAKE SHOE & LINING REMOVAL

1. Remove brake caliper as outlined previously.
2. Position suitable pliers over caliper and center of inboard shoe and lining as shown, **Fig. 2**, then squeeze pliers to bottom pistons in caliper bores.
3. Remove shoe and lining assemblies.

CALIPER DISASSEMBLY

1. Remove shoe and lining assemblies as previously described.
2. Pad interior of caliper housing with shop towels to prevent damage to pistons during removal.
3. Position shop towel in interior part of caliper, then slowly apply compressed air to inlet port and remove pistons. **It is imperative that one piston be partially installed to facilitate removal of second piston from bore. A pad or wooden spacer may be used to prevent complete removal of first piston.**
4. Remove dust boots from pistons.
5. Using a small piece of wood or plastic, remove piston seal from bore. **Do not use a metal tool of any kind to remove seal as it may damage bore.**
6. Remove bleeder valve cap and bleeder valve.
7. Inspect piston for scoring, nicks, corrosion, and wear and replace as needed.
8. Inspect caliper housing and seal groove for corrosion, nicks, scoring

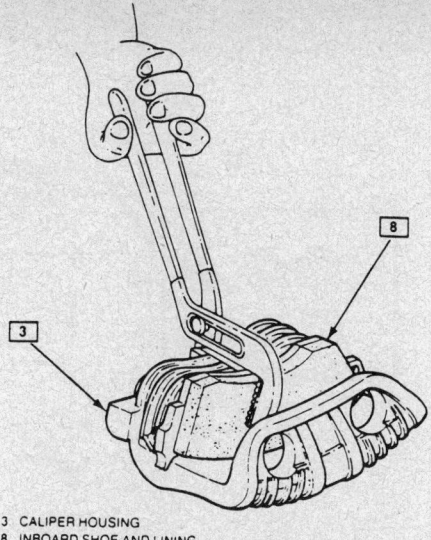

3 CALIPER HOUSING
8 INBOARD SHOE AND LINING

Fig. 2   Bottoming pistons in caliper bore

and excessive wear, and use crocus cloth to polish away corrosion from housing bore. Replace caliper housing if corrosion in and around seal groove will not clean up with crocus cloth.
9. Clean all parts with denatured alcohol. Dry with unlubricated compressed air. Blow out all passages in housing and bleeder valve.

CALIPER ASSEMBLY

1. Install cap onto bleeder valve, then install bleeder valve into caliper.
2. Using clean brake fluid, lubricate piston seals, then install seals into caliper bore grooves. Ensure seals are not twisted during installation.

3. Using clean brake fluid, lubricate caliper bores and piston assemblies.
4. Install boot over end of piston. Place piston into caliper bore, then push downward until fully bottomed in bore. Ensure boot is properly seated into groove around piston and into groove in caliper bore.
5. Repeat step 4 for remaining piston.
6. Install shoes and linings as outlined further on, then bleed brake system.

BRAKE SHOE & LINING INSTALLATION

1. Install inboard shoe and lining, ensuring tangs on shoe fully engage pistons. When properly installed, shoe should be flush with piston.
2. Install outboard shoe and lining into caliper housing, ensuring insulators are fully seated into holes in outboard side of housing.
3. Install caliper as outlined further on.

CALIPER INSTALLATION

1. Ensure guiding surfaces on shoe and lining assemblies and mounting bracket are seated correctly, then position caliper over rotor and onto mounting bracket.
2. Press caliper housing downward to compress bias springs (12), **Fig. 1**, then install new retainer pin and circlip. **Two sets of retainer pins are available for service, one for base calipers and one for heavy duty. Since the circlip grooves are cut in different positions, ensure the correct retainer pin is used.**
3. If caliper was overhauled, reconnect inlet fitting using new gaskets, then bleed brake system as required.
4. Reinstall wheel and tire assembly, then lower vehicle.
5. Fill master cylinder to proper level, then pump brake pedal firmly and slowly three times to bring pads into contact with brake rotor.

PBR Single Piston Caliper

INDEX

DESCRIPTION

This rear caliper, **Fig. 1**, consists of a single piston and an aluminum housing which is suspended in a mounting bracket through two slide pins. Hydraulic pressure, created by applying force to the brake pedal, acts equally against the piston and the bottom of the caliper bore to move the piston outward. This action slides the caliper inward, resulting in a clamping action on the brake rotor. This clamping action

forces the linings against the rotor, creating the friction necessary to stop the vehicle.

The parking brake mechanism on this caliper is completely independent of the hydraulic brake system. When the parking brake is applied, the lever on the caliper causes the pushrod, actuating collar and clamp rod assembly to move outward. This causes the caliper to move inward, mechanically forcing the linings against the rotor.

SERVICE
BRAKE SHOE & LINING REMOVAL

1. Remove ²/₃ of the total brake fluid capacity from master cylinder reservoir.
2. Raise and support vehicle, then remove tire and wheel assembly.
3. Install two wheel retaining nuts to retain rotor in position.
4. Position one end of a suitable

C-clamp against inlet fitting bolt, and the other end against outboard shoe and lining, then tighten clamp as shown, **Fig. 2**, until piston fully bottoms in caliper bore.

5. Remove upper guide pin bolt and discard.
6. Loosen lower guide pin bolt, then pivot caliper downward on the lower guide pin bolt to expose the shoe & lining assemblies. Use care to avoid damaging brake hose.
7. Remove shoes and linings from mounting bracket.

BRAKE SHOE & LINING INSTALLATION

1. Install outboard shoe and lining onto mounting bracket, ensuring insulator on shoe is positioned toward caliper housing.
2. Install inboard shoe and lining. Ensure wear sensor is positioned nearest caliper piston. When properly installed, sensor should be in trailing position when wheel is rotated in forward direction.
3. Pivot caliper into position over shoes and linings. Ensure springs on outboard shoe do not protrude through inspection hole in housing. If protrusion is evident, lift caliper housing and readjust position of outboard shoe and lining.
4. Install new upper guide pin bolt and **torque** to 26 ft. lbs., then **torque** lower bolt to 16 ft. lbs.
5. Fill master cylinder to proper level, then pump brake pedal firmly and slowly three times to bring pads into contact with brake rotor.

CALIPER REMOVAL

1. Disable parking brake automatic adjuster as follows:
   a. Working from inside vehicle, remove driver seat cushion, then the parking brake lever cover screws and cover.
   b. Using .080 inch gauge wire, fabricate a tool to disengage drive pawl from sector, **Fig. 3**.
   c. Using tool mentioned above, disengage drive pawl from sector, then insert a nail through anchor

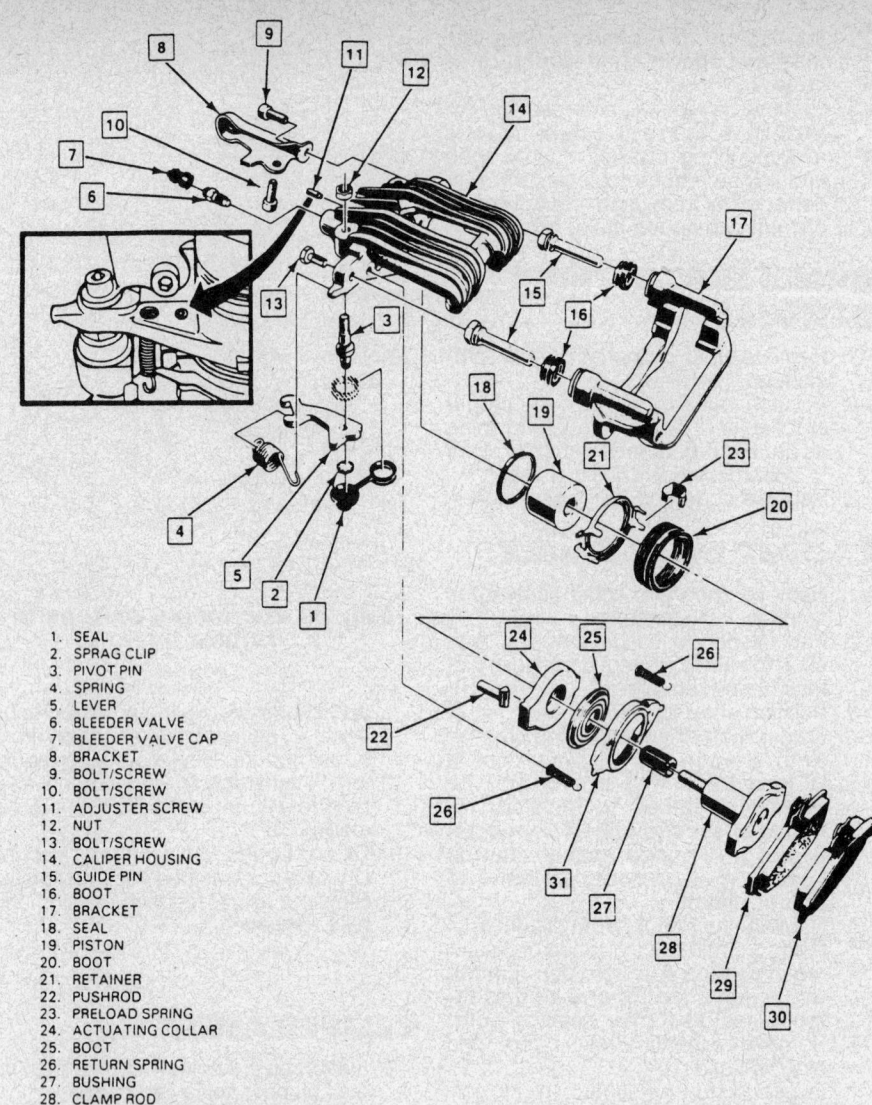

1. SEAL
2. SPRAG CLIP
3. PIVOT PIN
4. SPRING
5. LEVER
6. BLEEDER VALVE
7. BLEEDER VALVE CAP
8. BRACKET
9. BOLT/SCREW
10. BOLT/SCREW
11. ADJUSTER SCREW
12. NUT
13. BOLT/SCREW
14. CALIPER HOUSING
15. GUIDE PIN
16. BOOT
17. BRACKET
18. SEAL
19. PISTON
20. BOOT
21. RETAINER
22. PUSHROD
23. PRELOAD SPRING
24. ACTUATING COLLAR
25. BOOT
26. RETURN SPRING
27. BUSHING
28. CLAMP ROD
29. INBOARD SHOE AND LINING ASSEMBLY
30. OUTBOARD SHOE AND LINING ASSEMBLY
31. RETAINER

Fig. 1   Exploded view of PBR single piston rear caliper

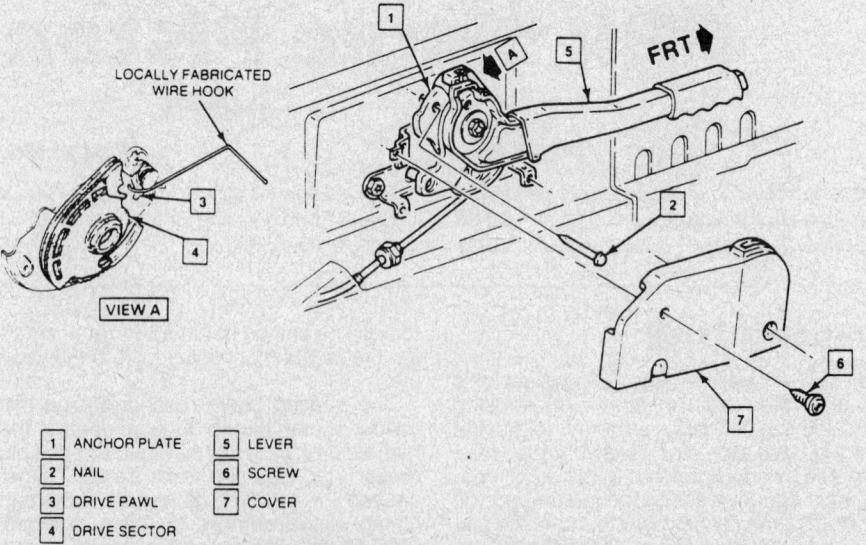

LOCALLY FABRICATED WIRE HOOK

VIEW A

FRT

1	ANCHOR PLATE	5	LEVER
2	NAIL	6	SCREW
3	DRIVE PAWL	7	COVER
4	DRIVE SECTOR		

Fig. 3   Disabling parking brake automatic adjuster mechanism

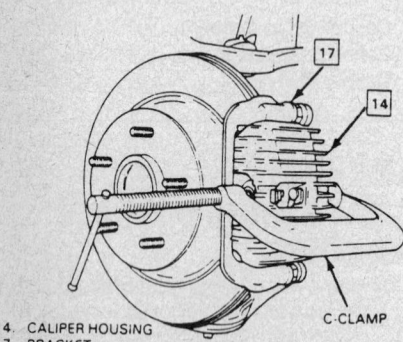

14. CALIPER HOUSING
17. BRACKET

Fig. 2   Bottoming piston in caliper bore

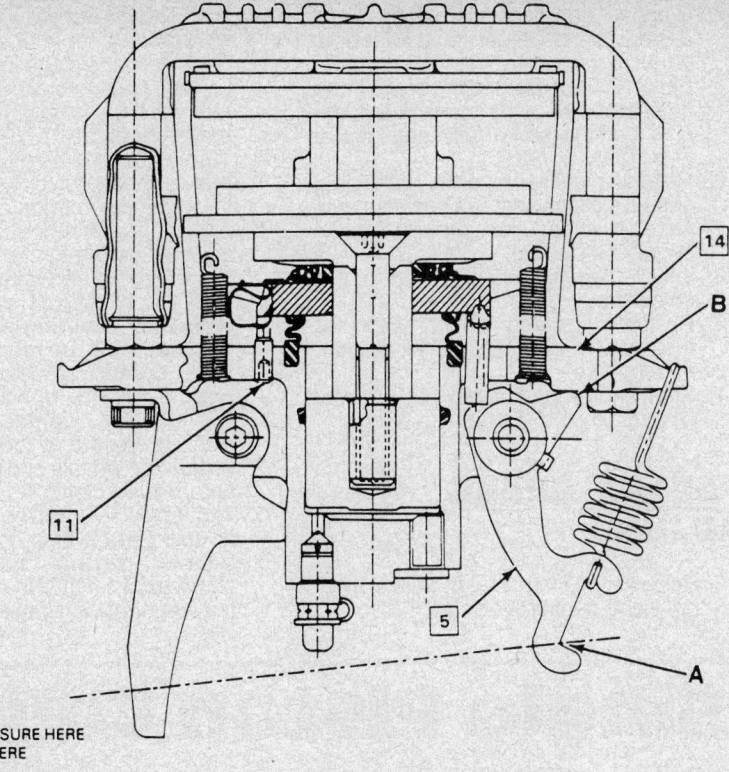

A. APPLY PRESSURE HERE
B. MEASURE HERE
5. LEVER
11. ADJUSTER SCREW
14. CALIPER HOUSING

Fig. 4 Parking brake free travel adjustment

plate to keep drive pawl in disengaged position.

d. Pull up on lever until it aligns with pawl, then depress button until lever is fully downward.

e. Visually inspect that anchor plate is fully against stud. If not, repeat procedure as needed.

f. Pull front parking brake cable rearward to slacken cable at caliper assembly.

2. Raise and support vehicle, then remove tire and wheel assembly.

3. Install two wheel retaining nuts to retain rotor in position.

4. If caliper requires overhaul, remove inlet fitting attaching bolt, then disconnect inlet fitting from caliper housing. Discard the two gaskets, then plug openings in inlet fitting and caliper to prevent loss or contamination of fluid.

5. Remove caliper lever return spring. Discard spring if coils are open.

6. Disconnect parking brake cable from lever (5) and caliper bracket (8), **Fig. 1.**

7. Remove upper and lower guide pin bolts, then remove caliper from rotor and mounting bracket. If caliper does not require overhaul, suspend it from suspension to prevent damage to brake line.

CALIPER DISASSEMBLY

1. Remove caliper as previously outlined.

2. Remove the two return springs from actuating collar, then pull collar out of caliper housing and remove clamp rod (28) and bushing (27), **Fig. 1.** Discard bushing.

3. Bend back boot retainer tabs, then remove retainers (21, 31), boots (20, 25) and pushrod (22) from actuating collar. Remove preload spring (23) from retainer (31), then discard retainers and boots.

4. Use clean shop towels to pad interior of caliper assembly, then remove piston by directing compressed air into caliper brake hose inlet hole, **Use just enough air pressure to ease piston out of bore. Do not place fingers in front of piston for any reason when applying compressed air. This could result in serious personal injury.**

5. Using a small piece of wood or plastic, remove piston seal from bore. **Do not use a metal tool of any kind to remove seal as it may damage bore.**

6. Remove bleeder valve cap and bleeder valve.

7. Remove seal (1), sprag clip (2) and lever (5) from pivot pin (3). Discard sprag clip.

8. Clean all metal components with suitable solvent, then dry with compressed air.

9. Inspect parking brake lever components, piston, caliper bore and mounting bracket for scoring, excessive wear or corrosion. Replace parts as necessary.

CALIPER ASSEMBLY

1. Using clean brake fluid, lubricate piston seal, then install seal into caliper bore groove. Ensure seal is not twisted during installation.

2. Using clean brake fluid, lubricate caliper bore and piston.

3. Place piston into caliper bore, then push downward until fully bottomed in bore.

4. Apply lubricant provided in repair kit to actuating collar (24), then install pushrod (22), new boots (20, 25) and new retainers (21, 31) onto collar, **Fig. 1.** Clamp retainers firmly against collar, then bend tabs on retainer (21) to hold assembly together.

5. Reconnect preload spring (23) onto retainer (31).

6. Apply lubricant provided in repair kit to clamp rod (28), then slide rod through holes in boot (25) and actuating collar (24). Ensure boot is firmly positioned against reaction plate on clamp rod.

7. Lubricate new compliance bushing (27), then install bushing onto clamp rod (28).

8. Lubricate grooved bead of inner boot (20), boot groove in caliper housing and actuating collar with lubricant provided in repair kit.

9. Push clamp rod to bottom of piston mating hole, then pull actuating collar (24) and seat inner boot (20) into boot groove in caliper housing.

10. Ensure pushrod (22) is positioned in hole in caliper housing, then install bleeder cap and valve.

11. If removed, install pivot pin (3) and new nut (12) onto caliper, **torque** nut to 16 ft. lbs., then lubricate parking brake lever (5) and pivot pin.

12. Install pivot pin seal (1), parking brake lever and new sprag clip (2), ensuring teeth of sprag clip face away from lever, then snap seal cap over pivot pin.

13. Install the two collar return springs (26) onto retainer (31). Ensure retainer enters springs at end of second coil.

14. Install adjustment screw (11) into caliper housing until actuating collar is parallel to piston bore face of housing.

15. Lubricate guide pins with suitable grease, then slide boots onto pins.

16. Fill boots with grease, then install into mounting bracket. Ensure boots are properly positioned in grooves in pins and mounting bracket.

17. Install caliper and bleed brake system, then adjust parking brake free travel as outlined under "Caliper Installation."

CALIPER INSTALLATION

1. Install shoe and lining assemblies, if removed, as outlined previously.

2. Position caliper over rotor and onto mounting bracket, then install upper and lower guide pin bolts. **Torque** upper bolt to 26 ft. lbs. and lower bolt to 16 ft. lbs.

3. Attach parking brake cable to caliper bracket and lever, then install lever return spring.

4. If removed, install inlet fitting using

new gaskets, then bleed brake system.

5. If caliper was overhauled, adjust parking brake free travel as follows:
   a. Have an assistant apply a light load to brake pedal until rotor can no longer be turned by hand.
   b. Apply pressure to caliper lever in direction shown in **Fig. 4.**
   c. Measure free travel between caliper lever and housing. Free travel should be .024-.028 inch. If free travel is not as specified, proceed to next step.
   d. Remove adjustment screw, then clean thread adhesive from threads.
   e. Coat threads with new adhesive, reinstall adjustment screw, then turn as required until specified free travel is obtained. **Turning screw clockwise increases free travel, while counterclockwise rotation decreases travel.**
   f. Release brake pedal, then firmly apply brake pedal three times and recheck free travel. Repeat adjustment procedure as necessary.

6. Remove nail from anchor plate installed during caliper removal procedure.
7. Apply and release parking brake three times, then lift lever upward and ensure parking brake fully engages at 7-9 clicks.
8. Release parking brake. No brake drag should exist and no gap between caliper housings and parking levers should be evident.
9. Install parking brake lever cover, screws and driver's cushion.
10. Reinstall tire and wheel assembly, then check and refill master cylinder as required.
11. Start engine and pump brake pedal several times to seat brake linings.

PARKING BRAKE
ADJUST

1. Release parking brake lever, then raise and support vehicle.

2. Remove rear wheels then install lug nuts on two opposite wheel studs to hold brake rotor in position.
3. Back caliper pistons into bores.
4. Loosen parking brake cable adjusting nut until there is no tension on parking brake shoes.
5. Turn each brake rotor until parking brake shoe star adjuster is visible through hole in rotor.
6. Adjusting one side at a time, tighten adjuster until rotor cannot be turned by hand, then back star wheel off 5 to 7 notches. **Adjust parking brake shoes by inserting a suitable tool through hole in rotor. On drivers side, tighten adjuster by moving handle of tool upwards. On passenger side, tighten adjuster by moving handle of tool downward.**
7. Install rear wheels and pull parking lever up two notches.
8. Tighten cable adjusting nut at equalizer until there is drag on wheels.
9. Release parking brake lever and check adjustment. No drag should be felt when rotating wheels.

Toyota/GM Single Piston Caliper

INDEX

DESCRIPTION

The caliper is a single bore design and is mounted to a carrier assembly. Hydraulic pressure, created by applying brake pedal, is converted by the caliper to a stopping force. This force acts equally against the piston and bottom of caliper bore to move the piston outward and to slide caliper inward resulting in a clamping action on the rotor. The clamping action forces linings against the rotor, creating friction necessary to stop the vehicle.

FRONT CALIPER
REPLACE
REMOVAL

1. Siphon 2/3 of the brake fluid from master cylinder, raise and support vehicle, and remove wheels.
2. Reinstall 2 wheel nuts to retain rotor, then remove caliper mounting bolts, **Fig. 1.**
3. Remove union nut securing brake hose to caliper and drain fluid into suitable container. **If caliper is only being removed for brake pad replacement, do not disconnect brake hose.**
4. Compress piston as needed, then re-

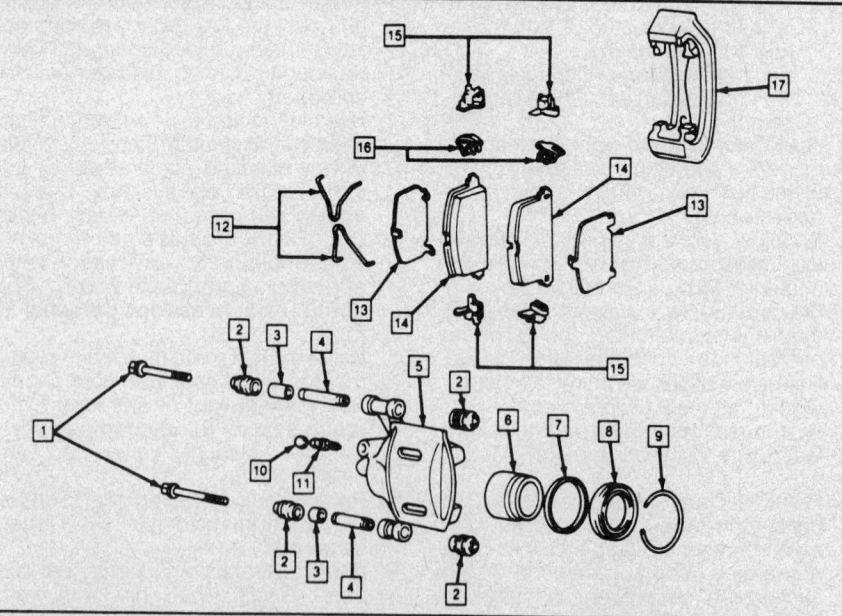

1. MOUNTING BOLT	6. PISTON	10. CAP	14. PAD
2. DUST BOOT	7. PISTON SEAL	11. BLEEDER SCREW	15. PAD SUPPORT PLATE
3. COLLAR	8. BOOT	12. ANTI-RATTLE SPRING	16. PAD WEAR INDICATOR PLATE
4. SLIDE BUSHING	9. SET RING	13. ANTI-SQUEAL SHIM	17. MOUNTING BRACKET
5. CALIPER HOUSING			

Fig. 1 Toyota/GM front brake caliper exploded view

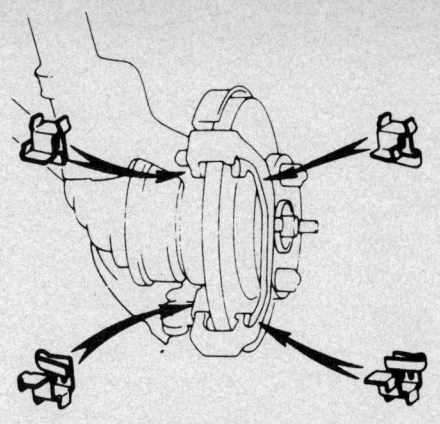

Fig. 2   Front caliper support installation

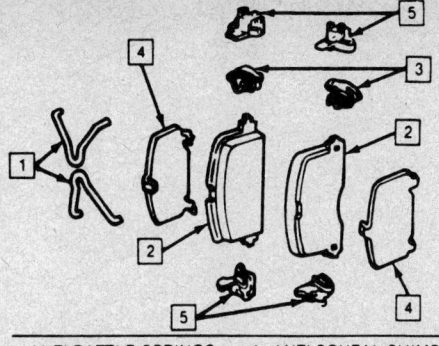

1. ANTI-RATTLE SPRINGS
2. BRAKE PADS
3. WEAR INDICATOR
4. ANTI-SQUEAL SHIMS
5. SUPPORT PLATES

Fig. 3   Front brake pad assembly

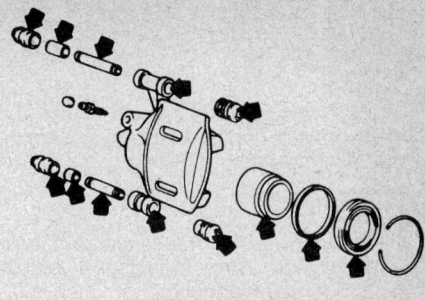

Fig. 4   Lubrication points for front caliper assembly

move caliper. If brake hose remains connected, secure caliper aside to prevent hose from being stretched.

INSTALLATION

1. Seat piston in caliper bore, taking care not to damage piston.
2. Ensure support plates, **Fig. 2,** and anti-rattle springs are properly positioned, then mount caliper over rotor onto mounting bracket.
3. Install caliper mounting bolts and **torque** bolts to 18 ft. lbs.
4. Install brake hose and mounting bolts, using new copper gaskets, then **torque** bolt to 17 ft. lbs.
5. Refill master cylinder and bleed brake system.

FRONT BRAKE PADS
REPLACE

Replace brake pads on one wheel at a time to prevent opposite side caliper piston from being forced out of bore.

REMOVAL

1. Remove caliper as outlined, leaving brake hose connected, and secure caliper aside.
2. Remove 2 anti-rattle clips, then the brake brake pads, **Fig. 3.**
3. Remove pad wear indicator plates and anti-squeal shims.
4. Remove support plates.

INSTALLATION

1. Install new support plates on caliper mounting bracket, **Fig. 2.**
2. Install new wear indicators and anti-squeal shims on each pad, **Fig. 3,** then position pads in caliper mounting bracket. **Ensure arrow on wear indicator is pointing in rotating direction of rotor.**
3. Install anti-rattle springs.
4. Seat piston in caliper bore, then install caliper and mounting bolts, and

torque bolts to 18. ft lbs.
5. Refill master cylinder and bleed brakes as needed.

FRONT CALIPER OVERHAUL
DISASSEMBLY

1. Remove 2 caliper slide bushings, 4 dust boots and spacer collars, **Fig. 1.**
2. Pry out caliper dust boot retaining ring and remove dust boot.
3. Place clean shop towels in caliper web to protect piston, then apply compressed air to caliper fluid inlet to force piston from bore. **Keep fingers clear of caliper web when removing piston. Use only enough air pressure to ease piston out of bore, or piston may be damaged.**
4. Remove piston seal from caliper bore, taking care not to mar machined surface of caliper.
5. Remove bleeder valve.
6. Clean components with alcohol and wipe dry with clean, lint free shop towels. Blow out caliper body and fluid passages with clean, filtered compressed air.
7. Inspect caliper and piston for damage, distortion, excessive wear and pitting, and replace as needed.
8. Replace mounting bolts, collars and caliper slides if they are damaged or worn.

ASSEMBLY

1. Apply lithium soap base glycol grease to components shown in **Fig. 4.**
2. Install piston seal in caliper, ensuring seal is squarely seated in groove.
3. Press piston into bore, ensuring piston enters bore straight.
4. Seat piston dust boot in caliper groove, then install retaining ring.
5. Install 2 collars and 4 slide bushing dust boots, **Fig. 1,** rotating boots as they are pressed in to ensure they are

fully seated.
6. Install slide bushings through dust boots, ensuring boots remain seated in caliper grooves.

REAR CALIPER
REPLACE
REMOVAL

1. Siphon 2/3 of the brake fluid from master cylinder, raise and support vehicle, and remove wheels.
2. Reinstall 2 wheel nuts to retain rotor.
3. Remove union nut securing brake hose to caliper and drain fluid into suitable container.
4. Remove clip from parking brake and disconnect parking brake cable.
5. Remove caliper mounting bolt, lift caliper, then remove parking brake pin clip.
6. While pushing parking brake crank, **Fig. 5,** remove pin.
7. Lift caliper and remove from vehicle.

INSTALLATION

1. Position caliper over mounting bracket, then install mounting bolt and **torque** to 14 ft. lbs.
2. Install parking brake clip.
3. Install brake hose and union bolt, using new copper gaskets, then **torque** bolt to 22 ft. lbs.
4. Refill master cylinder and bleed brake system.
5. Adjust parking brake as follows:
   a. Pull upward on parking brake lever several times, then fully release lever.
   b. Depress brake pedal several times to automatically adjust brake.
   c. When properly adjusted, parking brake crank should just contact stopper pin.

REAR BRAKE PADS
REPLACE

Replace brake pads on one wheel at a time to prevent opposite side caliper piston from being forced out of bore.

REMOVAL

1. Siphon ²/₃ of the brake fluid from master cylinder, raise and support vehicle, and remove wheels.
2. Reinstall 2 wheel nuts to retain rotor.
3. Remove caliper mounting bolt, then swing caliper upward to expose brake compone nts. **Do not remove main pin from caliper.**
4. Remove brake pads, anti-squeal shims, anti-rattle springs and the two support plates, **Fig. 5.**

INSTALLATION

1. Install new pad support plates to lower part of mounting bracket.
2. Install new anti-rattle springs to upper side of mounting bracket.
3. Position new anti-squeal shims to backside of each brake pad, then install pads onto mounting bracket. Ensure pads are positioned so wear indicators are on top side.
4. Using brake piston driver tool No. J-37149 or equivalent, **Fig. 6,** slowly turn piston clockwise and press into caliper bore until it locks in position at bottom of bore.
5. With pad protrusion fitted into piston stopper groove, swing caliper downward and install mounting bolt. **Torque** bolt to 14 ft. lbs.
6. Fill master cylinder to proper level, then depress brake pedal several times to seat linings and to actuate parking brake automatic adjuster.

REAR CALIPER OVERHAUL

DISASSEMBLY

1. Remove sliding bushing and the four dust boots, **Fig. 5.**
2. Using a suitable screwdriver, remove caliper set ring and boot.
3. Using brake piston driver tool No. J-37149 or equivalent, rotate piston out of caliper bore.

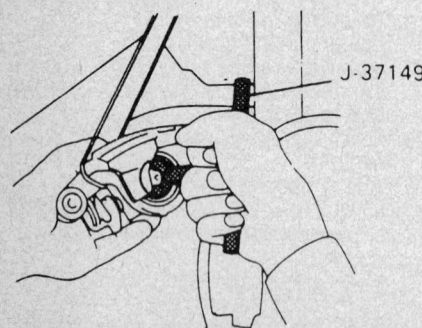

Fig. 6   Pressing piston into caliper bore

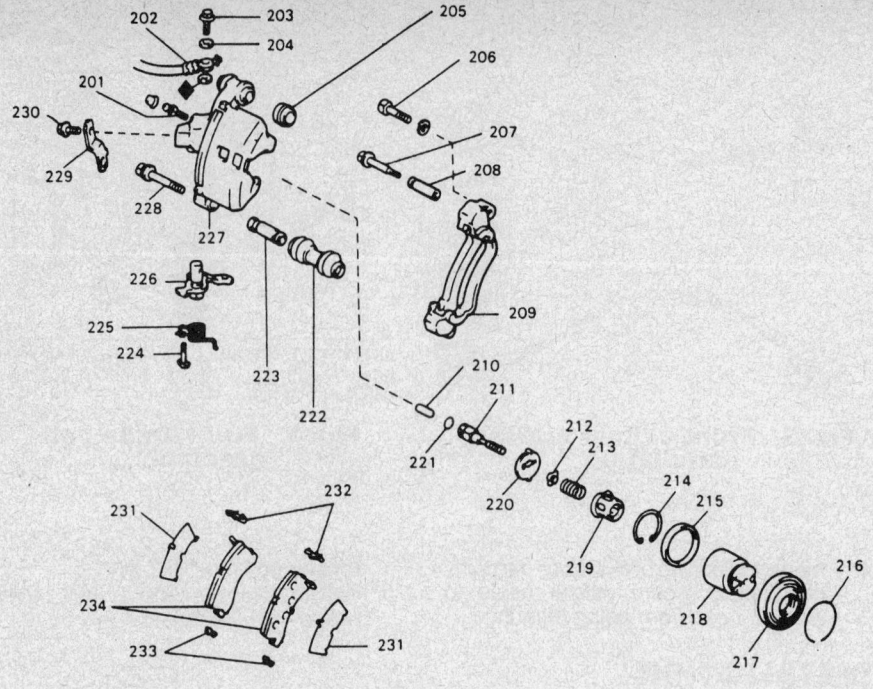

kg•cm (FT LB N•m)

ILL NO.	DESCRIPTION	ILL NO.	DESCRIPTION
201	BLEEDER SCREW	218	PISTON
202	BRAKE HOSE	219	ADJUSTING BOLT SPRING RETAINER
203	UNION BOLT	220	ADJUSTING BOLT STOPPER
204	GASKET	221	O-RING
205	MAIN PIN BOOT	222	DUST BOOT
206	MOUNTING BRACKET BOLT	223	SLIDE BUSHING
207	MAIN PIN	224	STOPPER PIN
208	SLIDING BUSHING	225	SPRING
209	MOUNTING BRACKET	226	PARKING BRAKE CRANK
210	PARKING BRAKE STRUT	227	CALIPER HOUSING
211	ADJUSTING BOLT	228	MOUNTING BOLT
212	ADJUSTING BOLT SPRING PLATE	229	CABLE SUPPORT BRACKET
213	SPRING	230	CABLE SUPPORT BRACKET BOLT
214	SNAP RING	231	ANTI-SQUEAL SHIM
215	PISTON SEAL	232	ANTI-RATTLE SPRING
216	SET RING	233	PAD SUPPORT PLATE
217	BOOT	234	PAD

Fig. 5   Toyota/GM rear brake caliper exploded view

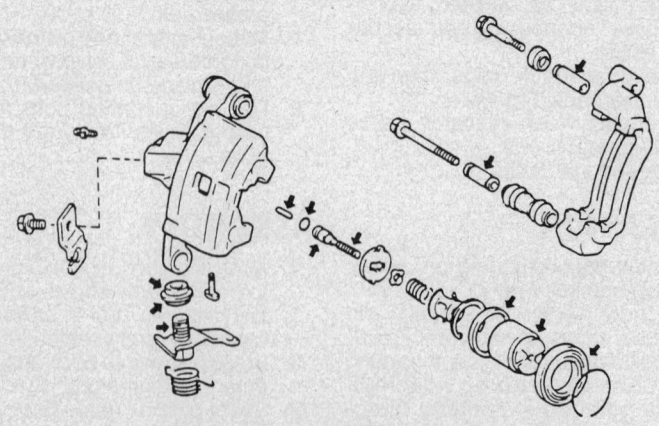

Fig. 7   Lubrication points for rear caliper assembly

4. Pry piston seal from caliper bore.
5. Position adjusting bolt guide nut tool No. J-37150 or equivalent over adjusting bolt, tighten tool, then remove snap ring from caliper bore and pull out adjusting bolt and components.
6. Remove parking brake strut and cable support bracket, then the parking brake crank torsion spring.
7. Remove parking brake crank, then the crank boot by tapping on metal portion of boot with screwdriver or similar tool. **Do not remove crank boot unless boot is damaged or excessively worn.**
8. Using a suitable punch, drive stopper pin from caliper.
9. Inspect all components for damage, wear or corrosion, and replace as necessary.

ASSEMBLY

1. Clean all parts not included in repair kit and dry with compressed air.
2. Lubricate all components indicated in **Fig. 7** with lithium based grease.
3. Install stopper pin into caliper until pin protrudes .98 inch outward as shown in **Fig. 8**.
4. If removed during disassembly, tap parking brake crank boot into position in caliper using a 24mm socket.
5. Install parking brake crank. Ensure crank boot aligns with groove of crank seal.
6. Install cable support bracket, then press surface of bracket flush against

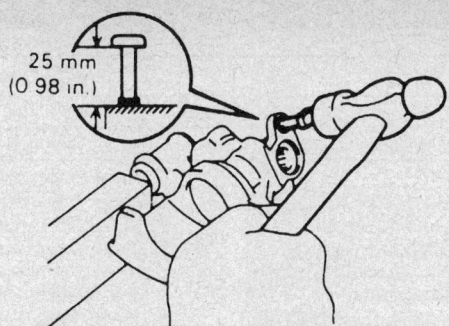

Fig. 8 Installing stopper pin

caliper and **torque** bolt to 34 ft. lbs. When properly installed, clearance between parking brake crank and support bracket should be .236 inch.
7. Install torsion spring, then check that parking brake crank subassembly touches stopper pin.
8. Install parking brake strut. **Before adjusting strut, ensure needle bearing rollers do not catch on caliper bore.**
9. Position new O-ring onto adjusting bolt, then assemble stopper, plate, spring and spring retainer onto bolt. Hand tighten assembly using adjusting bolt guide nut tool No. J-37150 or equivalent. When properly assembled, inscribed surface of stopper should face upward and notches of spring retainer should align with notches of stopper.

10. Position adjusting bolt subassembly into caliper, then install snap ring, ensuring opening faces toward bleeder side of caliper. Pull upward on adjusting bolt and ensure bolt does not move.
11. Check operation of parking brake by moving crank by hand. Adjusting bolt should move smoothly, with no evidence of binding.
12. Install piston seal into caliper bore, then using brake piston driver tool No. J-37149 or equivalent, install piston and bottom in bore by turning tool clockwise.
13. Align center of piston stopper groove with protrusion of caliper bore.
14. Install boot and set ring into caliper.
15. Using a 21mm socket and suitable vise, press new main pin boot into caliper housing.
16. Install sliding bushing and bolt, then install caliper as outlined previously.

PARKING BRAKE
ADJUST

1. Check that parking brake lever travel is correct by pulling parking brake lever all the way up and counting the number of clicks.
2. Parking brake lever travel should be 4 to 7 clicks. If not, remove console, loosen locknut and turn adjusting nut until travel is correct.

Tightening Specifications

Component	Torque/Ft. Lbs.
Brake Hose To Caliper Fitting Inlet Bolt	29
Brake Hose To Strut	20
Brake Pedal To Bracket Nut	29
Brake Pipes Connection	13
Brake Shield Bolts	89①
Booster To Pedal Bracket	15
Caliper Bleeder Valve	116①
Combination Valve Mounting	14
Front Brake Pipe To Engine Outer Side Rail	20
Front Caliper Mounting Bolts	38②③
Front Caliper Mounting Bracket To Knuckle	148
Hydraulic Unit To Pushrod Bracket	37
Master Cylinder To Booster Nut	20④⑤
Parking Brake Lever Assembly Bolts	18
Parking Brake Release Handle Screw	27①
Proportioning Valve Caps	20
Proportioning Valves	29⑥
Rear Caliper Mounting Bolt	92
Reservoir Screw	1.1⑥
Stopper Bolt	6⑥
Union Nut To Vacuum Hose On Intake Manifold	11⑦
Wheel Cylinder Bleeder Screw	48①
Wheel Cylinder To Backing Plate	12
Junction Block To Axle Housing	20

Continued

TIGHTENING SPECIFICATIONS—Continued

Component	Torque/Ft. Lbs.
Wheel Hub Bolt	⑥
Wheel Speed Sensor Mounting Bolts	9

①—Inch lbs.
②—Except 1988–89 Spectrum; 1988–90 Cutlass Supreme, Grand Prix, LeMans, Regal & 1990 Lumina; 1989–90 Metro & Prizm; 1990 Storm & Toranado/Trofeo models.
③—1988–89 Spectrum 36 ft. lbs.; 1988–90 Cutlass Supreme, Grand Prix, Regal & 1990 Lumina, 79 ft. lbs.; 1988–90 LeMans, 70 ft. lbs.; 1989–90 Metro & Prizm, 18 ft. lbs.; 1990 Storm, 76 ft. lbs.; 1990 Toronado/Trofeo, 63 ft. lbs.
④—Except 1988–89 Spectrum; 1988–90

Cutlass Supreme, Grand Prix, LeMans & Regal; 1989–90 Metro & Prizm; 1990 Lumina & Storm models.
⑤—1988–89 Spectrum, 9 ft. lbs.; 1988–90 Cutlass Supreme, Grand Prix, Regal & 1990 Lumina, 28 ft. lbs.; 1989–90 Metro & 1990 Storm, 115 inch lbs.; 1988–90 LeMans & 1989–90 Prizm, 13 ft. lbs.
⑥—Spectrum.
⑦—LeMans.
⑧—1989–90 Prizm, 59 ft. lbs.; 1990 Storm, 49 ft. lbs.

Disc Brake Caliper Specifications

Year	Model	Caliper Bore Dia. Inch
BUICK: REAR WHEEL DRIVE		
1988–90	All	2.94
BUICK SOMERSET REGAL & SKYLARK, OLDS. CALAIS, PONT. GRAND AM		
1988–90	All	2.24
CADILLAC: REAR WHEEL DRIVE		
1988–90	Brougham	2.94
BUICK REATTA & RIVIERA, CAD. ELDORADO & SEVILLE, OLDS. TORONADO/TROFEO		
1988–90	All	⑤
BUICK ELECTRA & LESABRE, CAD. DEVILLE, FLEETWOOD, OLDS. 88 & 98; PONT. BONNEVILLE		
1988–90	All	2.50
CHEVROLET (CAMARO, CAPRICE, CORVETTE & MONTE CARLO)		
1988	Camaro	①
1989–90	Camaro	④
1988–90	Caprice	2.94
1988	Monte Carlo	2.50
1988–90	Corvette	②
CAD. CIMARRON & OLDS. FIRENZA, CHEV. BERETTA, CAVALIER, CORSICA, PONTIAC SUNBIRD & BUICK SKYHAWK		
1988–90	Except Beretta & Corsica	2.24
1988–90	Beretta & Corsica	2.25

①—Front, 2.50 inches; rear, 1.89 inches.
②—Front, 1.50 inches; rear, 1.60 inches.
③—Except heavy duty, 2.24 inches; heavy duty, 2.50 inches.

Year	Model	Caliper Bore Dia. Inch
CHEV. CELEBRITY, BUICK CENTURY, OLDS. CUTLASS CIERA, PONT. 6000 & CUTLASS CRUISER		
1988–90	All	③
OLDSMOBILE: REAR WHEEL DRIVE		
1988–90	Cutlass RWD	2.50
	Custom Cruiser	2.94
PONTIAC: REAR WHEEL DRIVE		
1988	Fiero	—
1988	Firebird	①
1989–90	Firebird	④
1988–89	Safari	2.94
BUICK REGAL, OLDS. CUTLASS SUPREME, PONT. GRAND PRIX & CHEVROLET LUMINA		
1988–90	All	—
CHEVROLET NOVA, SPECTRUM & SPRINT; GEO METRO, PRIZM, SPECTRUM & STORM		
1988	Nova	—
1988–89	Spectrum	—
1988–90	Metro & Sprint	1.89
1990	Prizm	—
1990	Storm	—
PONTIAC LEMANS		
1988–90	All	—

④—Front standard, 2.50 inches; front heavy duty, 1.50 inches; rear, 1.60 inches.
⑤—Front, 2.50 inches; rear, 1.50 inches.

Disc Brake Rotor Specifications

Car	Year	Nominal Thickness	Minimum Refinish Thickness ①	Thickness Variation (Parallelism)	Lateral Runout (T.I.R.)	Finish (Micro-inch)
BUICK: REAR WHEEL DRIVE						
All	1988–90	1.043	.980	.0005	.005	—
BUICK RIVIERA, CAD. ELDORADO & SEVILLE, OLDS. TORONADO & BUICK REATTA						
All ②	1988–90	1.035	.971	.0005	.004	10-50
All ③	1988–90	.494	.444	.0005	.003	10-50
BUICK SOMERSET, OLDS. CALAIS, PONT. GRAND AM & 1988–90 BUICK SKYLARK						
All	1988–90	.885	.830	.0005	.004	—
BUICK ELECTRA, LESABRE & PARK AVE., CAD. DEVILLE, FLEETWOOD, OLDS. 88 & 89, PONT. BONNEVILLE						
All	1988	1.043	.980	.0005	.004	10-50
	1989–90	1.043	.972	.0005	.004	—
BUICK REGAL, OLDS CUTLASS SUPREME & PONT. GRAND PRIX; CHEVROLET LUMINA						
All ②	1988	1.040	1.019	.0005	.003	—
	1989–90	1.040	.984	.0005	.004	—
All ③	1988	.492	.426	.0005	.003	—
	1989–90	.492	.441	.0005	.004	—
CADILLAC: REAR WHEEL DRIVE						
Brougham	1988–90	1.031	.972	.0005	.004	—
CHEVROLET (CAMARO, CAPRICE, CORVETTE & MONTE CARLO)						
Camaro ②	1988–90	1.043	.980	.0005	.004	30-80
Camaro ③	1988	1.042	.986	.0005	.005	40-80
	1989–90	.795	.744	—	.005	—
Corvette	1988–90 ④	.795	.744	.0005	.006	—
	1988–90 ⑤	1.110	1.059	.0005	.006	—
Caprice & Monte Carlo	1988–90	1.043	.980	.0005	.004	30-80
CHEV. BERETTA, CAVALIER & CORSICA. BUICK SKYHAWK, CAD. CIMARRON, OLDS. FIRENZA, PONT. SUNBIRD						
All	1988–90	.885	.830	.0005	.004	—
CHEV. CELEBRITY; BUICK CENTURY; OLDS. CUTLASS CRUISER, CUTLASS CIERA; PONT. 6000						
All	1988	.885	.830	.0005	.004	12-50
Except 6000 STE & 6000 (AWD)	1989–90 ⑥	.885	.830	.0005	.004	—
	1989–90 ⑦	1.043	.972	.0005	.004	—
6000 (AWD)	1990 ③	.756	.702	.0005	.003	—
6000STE	1989 ③	.756	.744	.0005	.005	—
CHEVROLET SPECTRUM & SPRINT; GEO METRO, SPECTRUM & STORM						
Spectrum	1988–89	.433	.378	—	.006	—
Sprint & Metro	1988–90	.394	.315	—	.003	—
Storm	1990	.866	.811	—	.005	—
CHEVROLET NOVA & GEO PRIZM						
Nova ②	1988	.531	.492	—	.006	—
Nova ③	1988	.354	.315	—	.006	—
Prizm	1990	.709	.669	.0005	.0035	—
PONTIAC LEMANS						
All	1988–90	.500	.420	.0004	.004	—
OLDSMOBILE: REAR WHEEL DRIVE						
Except Cutlass & Toronado	1988	1.035	1.020	.0005	.004	—
	1989–90	1.043	.980	.0005	.004	—
Cutlass	1988	1.020	.984	.0005	.004	—

Continued

DISC BRAKE ROTOR SPECIFICATIONS—Continued

Car	Year	Nominal Thickness	Minimum Refinish Thickness ①	Thickness Variation (Parallelism)	Lateral Runout (T.I.R.)	Finish (Micro-inch)
PONTIAC: REAR WHEEL DRIVE						
Fiero ② ③	1988	.756	.702	.0005	.003	—
Firebird ②	1988-90	1.043	.980	.0005	.004	30-80
Firebird ③	1988	1.042	.986	.0005	.005	40-80
	1989–90	.795	.744	.0005	.005	—
Safari	1988–89	1.043	.980	.0005	.004	40-80

①—All brake rotors have a discard dimension cast into them. This is a wear dimension, not a refinish dimension. Any rotor that does not meet specifications should be discarded.
②—Front.
③—Rear.
④—Except heavy duty front rotors.
⑤—Heavy duty front rotors.
⑥—Light duty.
⑦—Medium and heavy duty.

DRUM BRAKES

NOTE: Refer to "Applications" to determine which type brakes are used on vehicle being serviced.

Applications

	Type No.		Type No.		Type No.
BUICK		Camaro	2	Custom Cruiser	1
		Caprice	1	Cutlass Except Ciera (RWD)	2
Century	4	Cavalier	4	Cutlass Ciera	4
Electra:		Celebrity	4	Cutlass Cruiser	4
1988-90 Estate Wagon	1	Corsica	5	Firenza	4
1988-90 Except Estate Wagon	5	Monte Carlo	2	88	5
LeSabre	5	Nova	6	98	5
Skyhawk	4	Spectrum	7	**PONTIAC**	
Skylark	4	Sprint	8		
Somerset	4	**GEO**		Bonneville	4
CADILLAC				Firebird	2
		Metro	8	Grand Am	4
Cimarron	4	Prizm	6	LeMans	3
DeVille (FWD)	5	Spectrum	7	Safari	1
Fleetwood (FWD):		Storm	7	Sunbird	4
1988	4	**OLDSMOBILE**		6000	4
1989-90	5				
CHEVROLET		Calais	4		
Beretta	4				

General Information

INDEX

SERVICE PRECAUTIONS

When working on or around brake assemblies, care must be taken to prevent breathing asbestos dust, as many manufacturers incorporate asbestos fibers in the production of brake linings. During routine service operations the amount of asbestos dust from brake lining wear is at a low level due to a chemical breakdown during use, and a few precautions will minimize exposure.

1. Do not sand or grind brake linings unless suitable local exhaust ventilation equipment is used to prevent excessive asbestos exposure.
2. Wear a suitable respirator approved for asbestos dust use during all repair procedures.
3. When cleaning brake dust from brake parts, use a vacuum cleaner with a highly efficient filter system. If a suitable vacuum cleaner is not available, use a water soaked rag. **Do not use compressed air or dry brush to clean brake parts.**
4. Keep work area clean using same equipment as for cleaning brake parts.
5. Properly dispose of rags and vacuum cleaner bags by placing them in plastic bags.
6. Do not smoke or eat while working on

brake systems. **Never use gasoline, kerosene, alcohol, motor oil, transmission fluid, or any fluid containing mineral oil to clean brake system components. These fluids will damage the rubber caps and seals. If system contamination is suspected, check brake fluid in the reservoir for dirt, discoloration, or separation (breakdown) of the brake fluid into distinct layers. Drain and flush the hydraulic system with clean brake fluid if contamination is suspected.**

GENERAL INSPECTION

BRAKE DRUMS

Any time the brake drums are removed for brake service, the braking surface diameter should be checked with a suitable brake drum micrometer at several points to determine if they are within the safe oversize limit stamped on the brake drum outer surface. If the braking surface diameter exceeds specifications, the drum must be replaced. If the braking surface diameter is within specifications, drums should be cleaned and inspected for cracks, scores, deep grooves, taper, out of round and heat spotting. If drums are cracked or heat spotted, they must be replaced. Minor scores should be removed with sandpaper. Grooves and large scores can only be removed by machining with special equipment, as long as the braking surface is within specifications stamped on brake drum outer surface. Any brake drum sufficiently out of round to cause vehicle vibration or noise while braking or showing taper should also be machined, removing only enough stock to true up the brake drum.

After a brake drum is machined, wipe the braking surface diameter with a denatured alcohol soaked cloth. If one brake drum is machined, the other should also be machined to the same diameter to maintain equal braking forces.

BRAKE LININGS & SPRINGS

Inspect brake linings for excessive wear, damage, oil, grease or brake fluid contamination. If any of the above conditions exists, brake linings should be replaced. Do not attempt to replace only one set of brake shoes; they should be replaced as an axle set only to maintain equal braking forces. Examine brake shoe webbing, hold-down and return springs for signs of overheating indicated by a slight blue color. If any component exhibits overheating signs, replace hold-down and return springs with new ones. Overheated springs lose their pull and could cause brake linings to wear out prematurely. Inspect all springs for sags, bends and external damage and replace as necessary.

Inspect hold-down retainers and pins for bends, rust and corrosion. If any of the above is found, replace as required.

BACKING PLATE

Inspect backing plate shoe contact surface for grooves that may restrict shoe movement and cannot be removed by lightly sanding with emery cloth or other suitable abrasive. If backing plate exhibits above condition, it should be replaced. Also inspect for signs of cracks, warpage and excessive rust, indicating need for replacement.

ADJUSTER MECHANISM

Inspect all components for rust, corrosion, bends and fatigue. Replace as necessary. On adjuster mechanism equipped with adjuster cable, inspect cable for kinks, fraying or elongation of eyelet and replace as necessary.

PARKING BRAKE CABLE

Inspect parking brake cable end for kinks, fraying and elongation and replace as necessary. Use a small hose clamp to compress clamp where it enters backing plate to remove.

Types 1 & 2

INDEX

REMOVAL

1. Raise and support rear of vehicle, then remove tire and wheel assembly.
2. Remove brake drum. If brake lining is dragging on brake drum, back off brake adjustment by rotating adjustment screw. Refer to individual car chapter for procedure. **If brake drum is rusted or corroded to axle flange and cannot be removed, lightly tap axle flange to drum mounting surface with a suitable hammer.**
3. Using brake spring pliers or equivalent, unhook primary and secondary return springs, **Figs. 1 and 2. Observe location of brake parts being removed to aid during installation.**
4. Remove brake hold-down springs with suitable tool.
5. Lift actuating lever, then unhook actuating link from anchor pin and remove.
6. Remove actuating lever(s) and return spring.
7. Spread shoes apart and remove parking brake strut and spring.
8. Disconnect parking brake cable from lever, then remove brake shoes from backing plate.

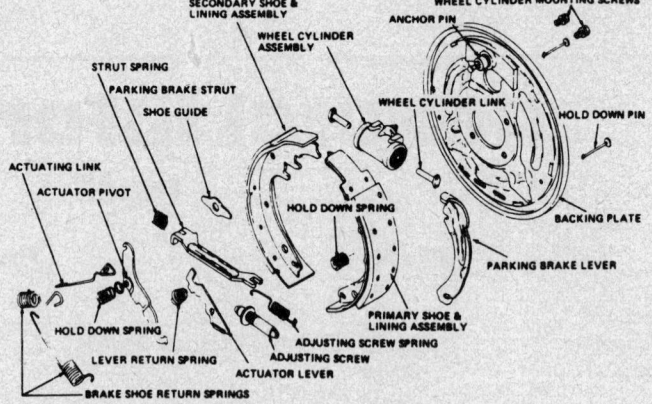

Fig. 1 Drum brake assembly. Type 1 typical

9. Separate brake shoes by removing adjusting screw and spring, then unhook parking brake lever from shoe assembly.
10. Clean dirt from brake drum, backing plate and all other components. **Do not use compressed air or dry brush to clean brake parts. Many brake parts contain asbestos fibers which, if inhaled, can cause serious injury. Clean brake parts with a water soaked rag or a suitable vacuum cleaner to minimize airborne dust.**

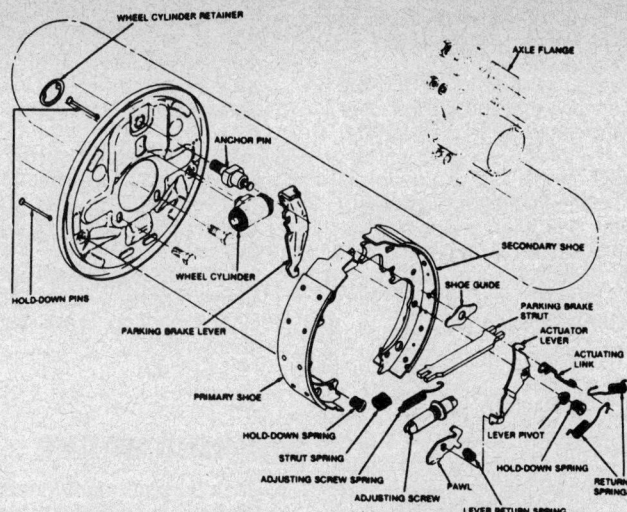

Fig. 2 Drum brake assembly. Type 2

Fig. 3 Brake shoe gauge measuring inside diameter of brake drum

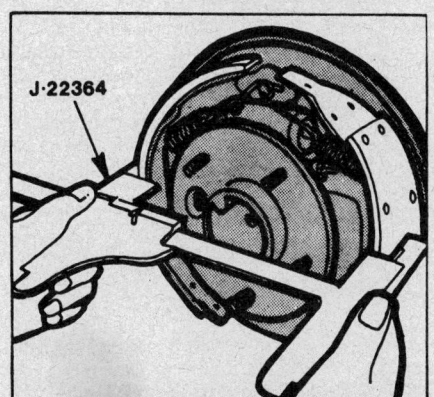

Fig. 4 Brake shoe gauge measuring outside diameter of brake shoes

INSPECTION

1. Inspect components for damage and unusual wear. Replace as necessary.
2. Inspect wheel cylinders. Boots which are torn, cut or heat damaged indicate need for wheel cylinder replacement. **On type 1 brakes,** remove wheel cylinder links. Fluid spill from boot center hole indicates cup leakage and need for wheel cylinder replacement. **On type 2 brakes,** use a small screwdriver to pry center hole of boot away from piston. If fluid spills from center hole, cup leakage is indicated and wheel cylinder should be replaced. **On all types,** light fluid coatings on piston within cylinder is considered normal.
3. Inspect backing plate for evidence of axle seal leakage. If leakage exists, refer to individual car chapters for axle seal replacement procedures.
4. Inspect backing plate attaching bolts, and ensure they are tight.
5. Using fine emery cloth or other suitable abrasive, clean rust and dirt from shoe contact surface on backing plate.

INSTALLATION

1. Lubricate parking brake lever fulcrum with suitable brake lube, then attach lever to brake shoe. Ensure lever operates smoothly.
2. Connect brake shoes with adjusting screw spring, then position adjusting screw. **Ensure adjusting screw star wheel does not contact adjusting screw spring after installation and also ensure righthand thread adjusting screw is installed on left side of vehicle and lefthand thread adjusting screw is installed on right side of vehicle. When brake shoe installation is completed, ensure starwheel lines up with adjusting hole in backing plate.**
3. Lightly lubricate backing plate shoe contact surfaces with suitable brake lube, then the area where parking brake cable contacts backing plate.
4. Install brake shoes on backing plate while engaging wheel cylinder links (if equipped) with shoe webbing. Connect parking brake cable to parking brake lever. **The primary shoe (short lining) faces towards front of vehicle.**
5. Install actuating levers, actuating link and return spring, **Figs. 1 and 2.**
6. Install hold-down springs with suitable tool.
7. Install primary and secondary shoe return springs using brake spring pliers or equivalent.
8. Using suitable brake drum to shoe gauge, measure brake drum inside diameter. Adjust brake shoes to dimension obtained on outside portion of gauge.
9. Install brake drum, wheel and tire assembly.
10. If any hydraulic connections have been opened, bleed brake system.
11. Adjust parking brake. Refer to individual car chapters for procedures.
12. Inspect all hydraulic lines and con-

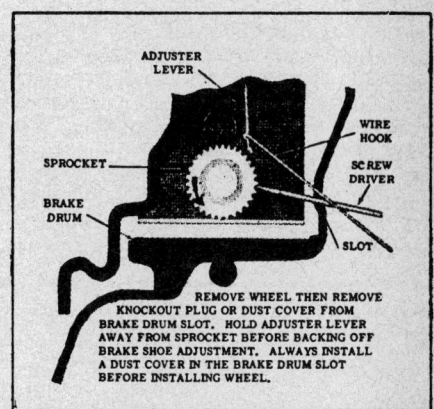

Fig. 5 Backing off brake shoe adjustment

nections for leakage and repair as necessary.
13. Check master cylinder fluid level and replenish as necessary.
14. Check brake pedal for proper feel and return.
15. Lower vehicle and road test. **Do not severely apply brakes immediately after installation of new brake linings or permanent damage may occur to linings, and/or brake drums may become scored. Brakes must be used moderately during first several hundred miles of operation to ensure proper burnishing of linings.**

BRAKE ADJUSTMENTS

These brakes have self-adjusting shoe mechanisms that assure correct lining-to-drum clearances at all times. The automatic adjusters operate only when the brakes are applied as the car is moving rearward.

Although the brakes are self-adjusting, an initial adjustment is necessary after the brake shoes have been relined or replaced, or when the length of the adjusting screw has been changed during some other service operation.

Frequent usage of an automatic transmission forward range to halt reverse vehicle motion may prevent the automatic adjusters from functioning, thereby inducing low pedal heights. Should low pedal heights be encountered, it is recommended that numerous forward and reverse stops be made until satisfactory pedal height is obtained. **If a low pedal condition cannot be corrected by making numerous reverse stops (provided the hydraulic system is free of air)it indicates that the self-adjusting mechanism is not functioning. Therefore, it will be necessary to remove the brake drum, clean, free up and lubricate the adjusting mechanism. Then adjust the brakes as follows, being sure the parking brake is fully released.**

SERVICE BRAKE

Type 1

In as much as there is no way to adjust these brakes with the drums installed, the following procedure is mandatory after new linings are installed, or it becomes necessary to change the length of the brake shoe adjusting screw.

1. With brake drums removed, position the caliper shown in **Fig. 3**, to the inside diameter of the drum, then tighten the clamp screw.

2. Next position brake shoe end of the caliper tool over the brake shoes as shown in **Fig. 4**.
3. Rotate the gauge slightly around the shoes to ensure that the gauge contacts the linings at the largest diameter.
4. Adjust brake shoes until the gauge is a snug fit on the linings at the point of largest lining diameter. **If it is necessary to back off the brake shoe adjustment, it will be necessary to hold the adjuster lever away from the adjuster screw, Fig. 5.**

Type 2

1. Using a suitable punch, knock out lanced area in backing plate or drum. If drum is installed on vehicle when this is done, remove drum and clean brake compartment of all metal. **When adjustment is completed, a new hole cover must be installed in the backing plate.**
2. Using brake adjusting tool No. J-6166 or equivalent, turn brake adjusting screw to expand brake shoes at each wheel until wheel can just be turned by hand. Drag should be equal on all wheels.
3. **On all except Camaro,** back off adjusting screw at each wheel 30 notches.

4. **On Camaro,** back off screw 12 notches.
5. **On all models,** if shoe still drags slightly on drum, back off adjusting screw an additional one or two notches.
6. When adjusting screw has been backed off approximately 12 notches, brakes should be free of drag. Heavy drag at this point indicates tight parking brake cables.
7. Install adjusting hole cover in brake backing plate.
8. Check parking brake for proper adjustment.

PARKING BRAKE

1. Jack up both rear wheels.
2. Apply parking brake three notches.
3. **Type 1,** tighten adjusting nut until right rear wheel can just be rotated rearward but is locked when forward rotation is attempted.
4. **Type 2,** tighten adjusting nut until left rear wheel can just be rotated rearward but is locked when forward rotation is attempted.
5. Release parking brake and check to ensure rear wheels rotate freely in either direction with no brake drag.

Type 3

INDEX

REMOVAL

1. Raise and support vehicle.
2. Mark relationship between rear wheel and hub, then remove wheel and tire assembly.
3. Remove brake drum detent screw, then the brake drum. If drum is difficult to remove, proceed as follows:
   a. Ensure parking brake cable is released.
   b. Loosen parking brake cable.
   c. Remove access hole plug from backing plate, then move parking brake lever until lever stop rests on brake shoe.
4. Remove upper and lower return springs, then the adjuster actuator and actuator spring, **Fig. 1**.
5. Press brake shoes outward slightly and remove adjuster assembly.
6. Remove hold-down springs, washers and pins using a suitable tool.
7. Remove brake shoes from backing plate and parking brake cable.

INSPECTION

1. If any parts are of doubtful strength or quality due to heat discoloration, or are worn, replace them.

2. Inspect wheel cylinder dust boots for signs of excessive wear or damage.
3. Inspect adjusting screw for smooth operation over full length.
4. Clean adjusting screw components in denatured alcohol.
5. Apply suitable lubricant to adjuster screw threads, inside diameter of socket and socket face. Adequate lubrication is achieved when a continuous bead of lubricant is at open end of adjuster nut and socket when threads are fully engaged.
6. Clean dirt and/or rust from brake drum, backing plate and all other components. **Do not use compressed air or dry brush to clean brake parts. Many brake parts contain asbestos fibers which, if inhaled, can cause serious injury. Clean brake parts with a water soaked rag or a suitable vacuum cleaner to minimize airborne dust.**
7. Ensure adjuster nut turns freely on adjuster screw.

INSTALLATION

1. Lubricate backing plate at points shown, **Fig. 2**.

2. Connect parking brake lever to parking brake cable.
3. Ensure parking brake cable is properly routed, then install shoes and lining to backing plate with hold-down spring, washer and pin.
4. Position adjuster shoe and lining and lower return spring against backing plate. Ensure spring is properly positioned under anchor plate.
5. Install hold-down spring, washer and pin.
6. Turn adjuster in to stop, then install adjuster assembly, **Fig. 3**. Ensure spring clip is positioned toward backing plate.
7. Install adjuster actuator onto pin and actuator spring.
8. Install spring connecting link to pin and press into brake hole.
9. Connect upper spring from connecting link to brake shoe.
10. Install brake drum and detent screw, then the wheel and tire assembly.
11. Adjust service and parking brakes as necessary.

SERVICE BRAKE
ADJUST

1. Raise and support vehicle.

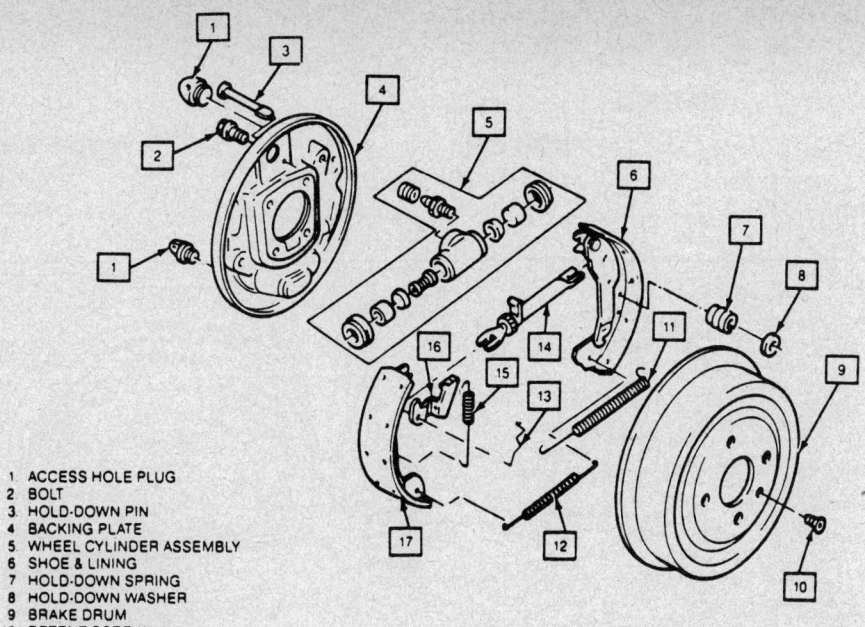

1. ACCESS HOLE PLUG
2. BOLT
3. HOLD-DOWN PIN
4. BACKING PLATE
5. WHEEL CYLINDER ASSEMBLY
6. SHOE & LINING
7. HOLD-DOWN SPRING
8. HOLD-DOWN WASHER
9. BRAKE DRUM
10. DETENT SCREW
11. UPPER RETURN SPRING
12. LOWER RETURN SPRING
13. SPRING CONNECTING LINK
14. ADJUSTER ASSEMBLY
15. ACTUATOR SPRING
16. ADJUSTER ACTUATOR
17. ADJUSTER SHOE & LINING

Fig. 1   Drum brake assembly. Type 3

Fig. 2   Backing plate lubrication points

2. Mark relationship between rear wheels and hubs, then remove wheel and tire assemblies.
3. Remove brake drum set screw, then the brake drum. If drum is difficult to remove, proceed as follows:
   a. Ensure parking brake cable releases.
   b. Loosen parking brake cable.
   c. Remove access hole plug from backing plate, then move parking brake lever until lever stop rests on brake shoe.
4. Turn adjuster assembly in as far as possible, **Fig. 3**.
5. Ensure parking brake lever stops make contact with edge of shoe web. If contact is not evident, loosen parking brake cable at equalizer as necessary.
6. Install brake drums and wheels. then lower vehicle.
7. Depress brake pedal at least ten times until clicking of adjustment actuator is no longer heard.
8. Adjust parking brake as necessary.

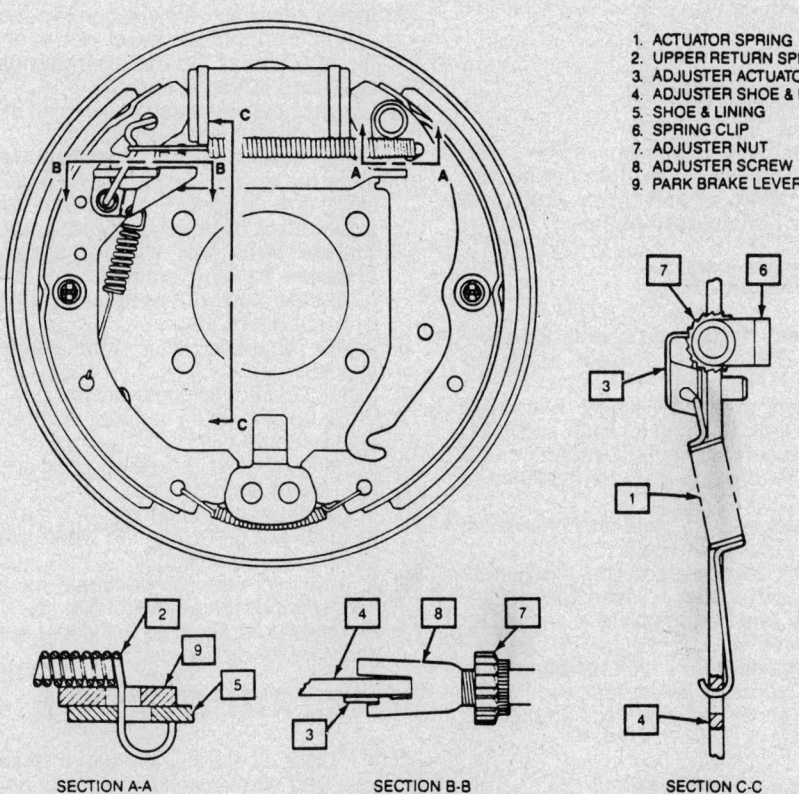

1. ACTUATOR SPRING
2. UPPER RETURN SPRING
3. ADJUSTER ACTUATOR
4. ADJUSTER SHOE & LINING
5. SHOE & LINING
6. SPRING CLIP
7. ADJUSTER NUT
8. ADJUSTER SCREW
9. PARK BRAKE LEVER

SECTION A-A

SECTION B-B

SECTION C-C

Fig. 3   Cross-sectional view of drum brake assembly

PARKING BRAKE
ADJUST

1. Adjust service brakes as previously described.
2. Ensure parking brakes are fully released.
3. Raise and support vehicle.
4. Ensure parking brake cable moves freely, then turn self-locking nut until rear wheels are difficult to turn.
5. Back off self-locking nut until rear wheels are just free to turn.

Type 4

INDEX

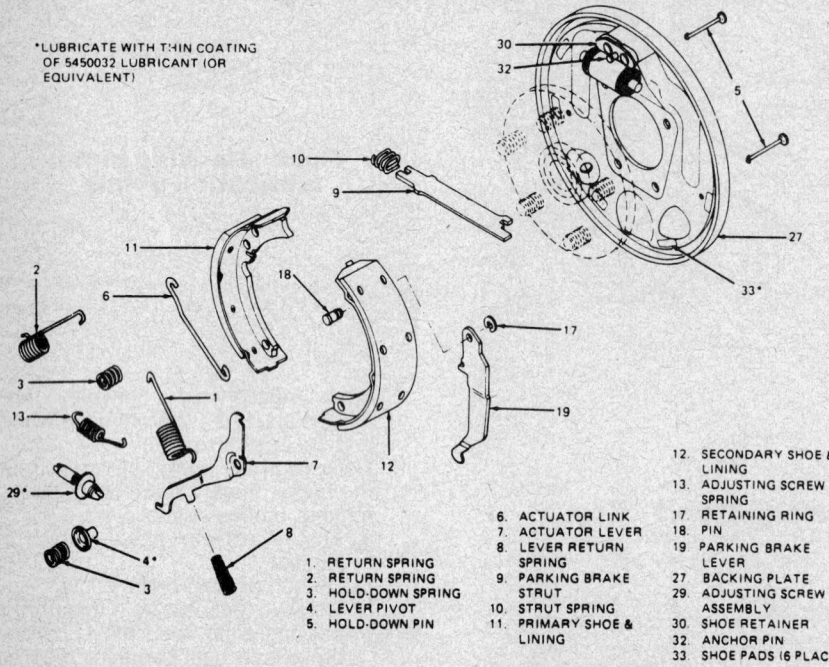

*LUBRICATE WITH THIN COATING OF 5450032 LUBRICANT (OR EQUIVALENT)

1. RETURN SPRING
2. RETURN SPRING
3. HOLD-DOWN SPRING
4. LEVER PIVOT
5. HOLD-DOWN PIN
6. ACTUATOR LINK
7. ACTUATOR LEVER
8. LEVER RETURN SPRING
9. PARKING BRAKE STRUT
10. STRUT SPRING
11. PRIMARY SHOE & LINING
12. SECONDARY SHOE & LINING
13. ADJUSTING SCREW SPRING
17. RETAINING RING
18. PIN
19. PARKING BRAKE LEVER
27. BACKING PLATE
29. ADJUSTING SCREW ASSEMBLY
30. SHOE RETAINER
32. ANCHOR PIN
33. SHOE PADS (6 PLACES)

Fig. 1 Drum brake assembly. Type 4

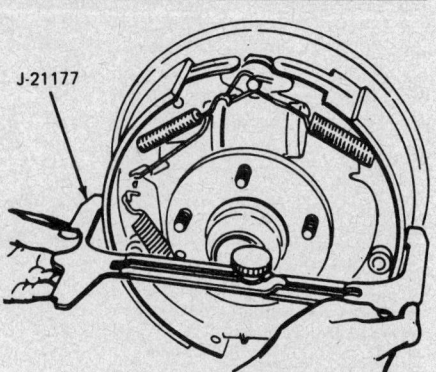

Fig. 2 Measuring brake drum inside diameter

REMOVAL

1. Raise and support rear of vehicle, then remove tire and wheel assembly.
2. Remove brake drum. If brake lining is dragging on brake drum, back off brake adjustment by rotating adjusting screw. Refer to individual car chapter for procedure. **If brake drum is rusted or corroded to axle flange and cannot be removed, lightly tap axle flange to drum mounting surface with a suitable hammer.**
3. Using brake spring pliers or equivalent, remove brake return springs, **Fig. 1.**
4. Using suitable pliers, remove hold-down springs and lever pivot.
5. While lifting up on actuator lever, disconnect actuating link.
6. Remove actuator lever and return spring.
7. Remove parking brake strut and spring.
8. Disconnect parking brake cable, then remove brake shoe and lining assembly.
9. Remove adjusting screw assembly and spring as follows:
   a. Note position of adjusting spring.
   b. Remove retaining ring, pin, and parking brake lever from secondary shoe.
   c. Remove adjusting screw and spring. **Do not interchange adjusting screws from right and left brake assemblies.**

INSPECTION

1. Inspect brake components for damage and/or wear. Replace as necessary.
2. Inspect wheel cylinders. Excessive fluid indicates cup leakage and need for wheel cylinder replacement.
3. Inspect backing plate for evidence of axle seal leakage.
4. Inspect backing plate attaching bolts. Ensure bolts are tight.
5. Check adjuster operation. If adjusters are worn, frozen or loose, replace adjuster and backing plate assembly as required.
6. Using fine emery cloth or other suitable abrasive, clean rust and/or dirt from shoe contact surface on backing plate.

INSTALLATION

1. Install parking brake lever, pin and retaining ring onto secondary shoe.
2. Apply silicone brake lubricant onto adjuster screw threads, inside diame-

ter of socket and socket face. Adequate lubrication is achieved when a continuous bead of lubricant is at open end of pivot nut and socket when adjuster threads are completely engaged.

3. Install adjusting screw assembly and spring. **Spring coils must not overlap star wheel. Do not interchange right and lefthand springs.**
4. Connect parking brake cable, then install shoe and lining assembly.
5. Using a suitable tool, spread brake shoes apart, then install parking brake strut and spring. **Ensure parking brake strut is properly positioned. Ensure strut end without spring engages parking brake lever. Ensure strut end with spring engages primary brake shoe.**
6. Install actuator lever and return spring.
7. Install actuator link onto anchor pin.
8. While holding up on actuator lever, install link onto lever.
9. Install hold-down pins, lever pivot and hold-down springs.
10. Install shoe return springs.
11. Install brake drum, tire and wheel assembly.
12. If any hydraulic connections have been opened, bleed brake system.
13. Adjust brakes. Refer to individual car chapters for procedure.

BRAKE ADJUSTMENTS

The rear drum brakes have self-adjusting shoe mechanisms that assure correct lining-to-drum clearances at all times. The automatic adjusters operate only when the service brakes are applied.

Although the brakes are self-adjusting, an initial adjustment is necessary after the brake shoes have been replaced, or when the length of the star wheel adjuster has been changed during some other service operation.

SERVICE BRAKE

1. Raise and support vehicle, then remove rear wheels and brake drums.
2. Check to make sure parking brake cable linkage and levers on secondary brake shoe are in "free" position.
3. Using brake shoe measuring tool No. J-21177 or equivalent, measure drum inside diameter, **Fig. 2.**
4. Turn brake adjusting screw to expand shoes to .050 inch less than diameter obtained on outside caliper portion of brake shoe measuring tool No. J-21177, **Fig. 3.**
5. Adjust parking brake. **Whenever rear drum brakes are serviced, the parking brake linkage cable at the equalizer must always be readjusted to prevent possible damage to brake shoes.**
6. Install brake drums, wheels and tires and lower vehicle to ground.
7. Drive vehicle and apply and release

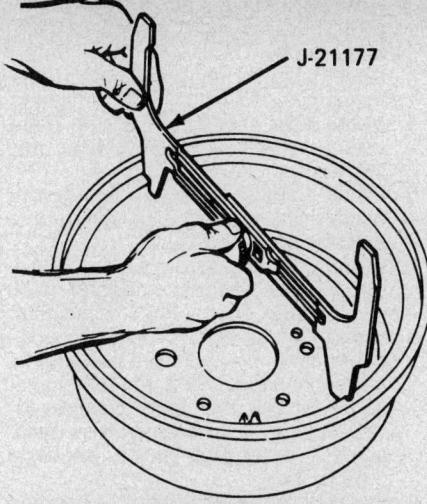

Fig. 3   Adjusting brake shoe clearance

service brake 30-35 times with normal pedal force. Allow about one second between brake applications until

satisfactory pedal height is obtained.

PARKING BRAKE

1. Adjust service brakes.
2. apply and release parking brake approximately 8 times, then release.
3. Ensure parking brake is fully released by turning ignition on. Brake warning lamp should be off. If brake warning lamp is lit, determine reason and repair as necessary.
4. Apply parking brake four clicks.
5. Raise and support vehicle.
6. Remove access hole cover from backing plate.
7. Adjust parking brake cable until a 1/8 inch drill bit can be inserted perpendicularly through access hole into space between shoe web and parking brake lever. Adjustment is correct when the 1/8 inch drill can be inserted, but a 1/4 inch drill cannot.
8. Release parking brake, then ensure rear wheels rotate freely. Repeat adjustment if necessary.
9. Install access hole cover, then lower vehicle.

Type 5

INDEX

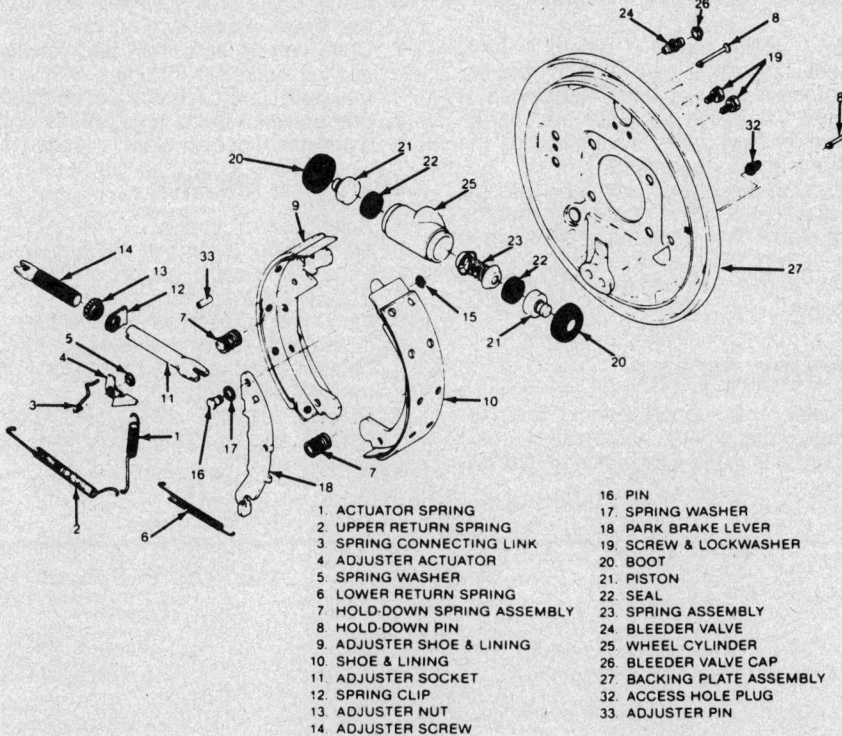

1. ACTUATOR SPRING
2. UPPER RETURN SPRING
3. SPRING CONNECTING LINK
4. ADJUSTER ACTUATOR
5. SPRING WASHER
6. LOWER RETURN SPRING
7. HOLD-DOWN SPRING ASSEMBLY
8. HOLD-DOWN PIN
9. ADJUSTER SHOE & LINING
10. SHOE & LINING
11. ADJUSTER SOCKET
12. SPRING CLIP
13. ADJUSTER NUT
14. ADJUSTER SCREW
15. RETAINING RING
16. PIN
17. SPRING WASHER
18. PARK BRAKE LEVER
19. SCREW & LOCKWASHER
20. BOOT
21. PISTON
22. SEAL
23. SPRING ASSEMBLY
24. BLEEDER VALVE
25. WHEEL CYLINDER
26. BLEEDER VALVE CAP
27. BACKING PLATE ASSEMBLY
32. ACCESS HOLE PLUG
33. ADJUSTER PIN

Fig. 1   Drum brake assembly. Type 5

REMOVAL

1. Raise and support vehicle.
2. Mark relationship of wheel to axle flange, then remove wheel and tire assembly.
3. Mark relationship of brake drum to axle flange, then remove drum. **If brake drum is difficult to remove, back off parking brake cable adjustment, remove inspection hole plug from backing plate, insert screwdriver through hole and press in to push parking brake lever off stop.**
4. Using suitable tool, remove actuator spring, then upper return spring, **Fig. 1.**
5. Remove spring connecting link, adjuster actuator, and spring washer.
6. Remove hold-down springs and pins.
7. Disconnect parking brake cable, then remove shoe and lining assembly together with lower return spring.
8. Remove adjusting screw assembly, and lower return spring.
9. Remove retaining ring, pin, spring washer and parking brake lever from shoe and lining assembly.

INSPECTION

1. If any parts are of doubtful strength or

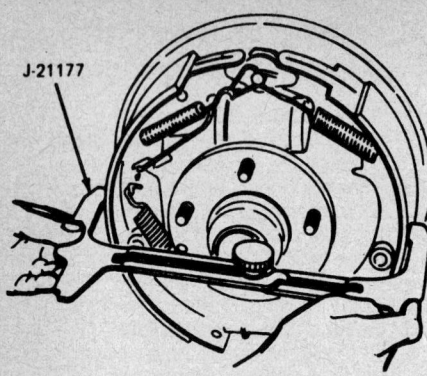

Fig. 2   Measuring brake drum inside diameter

quality due to heat discoloration, or are worn, replace them.
2. Inspect wheel cylinder dust boots for signs of excessive wear or damage.
3. Inspect adjusting screw for smooth operation over full length.
4. Clean adjusting screw components in denatured alcohol. **Ensure spring clip is installed in correct position, Fig. 1.**
5. Apply suitable lubricant to adjuster screw threads, inside diameter of socket and socket face. Adequate lubrication is achieved when a continuous bead of lubricant is at open end of adjuster nut and socket when threads are fully engaged.
6. Clean dirt and/or rust from brake drum, backing plate and all other components. **Do not use compressed air or dry brush to clean brake parts. Many brake parts contain asbestos fibers which, if inhaled, can cause serious injury. Clean brake parts with a water soaked rag or a suitable vacuum cleaner to minimize airborne dust.**
7. Ensure adjuster nut turns freely on adjuster screw.

INSTALLATION

1. Press adjuster pin and spring washer into shoe and lining so that pin projects .275-.283 inch from the side on which the adjuster actuator is installed.
2. Install adjuster shoe and lining, to front of vehicle on left side or to rear of vehicle on right side.
3. Install parking brake lever on shoe and lining with spring washer, pin and

retaining ring. Install spring washer with concave side against parking brake lever.
4. Attach adjuster shoe and lining to remaining shoe with lower return spring.
5. Install both shoes on backing plate, securing with hold-down pins and springs.
6. Install adjuster actuator, spring connecting link and actuator spring onto adjuster shoe and lining.
7. Install adjusting screw assembly, ensuring adjuster screw engages notch in adjuster shoe. Ensure adjuster screw spring clip is properly positioned and the adjuster actuator is properly engaged in notch in adjuster screw. **Do not over extend upper return spring. The spring will be damaged if extended length exceeds 5.49 inches.**
8. Install upper return spring by inserting angled hook end of spring through parking brake lever and shoe lining, using suitable tool to pull spring straight across and then down to hook into crook in spring connecting link.
9. Back off parking brake adjustment until parking brake lever rests on brake shoe.
10. Install brake drum and tire and wheel assembly, then lower vehicle.
11. Apply and release service brake at least 25 times, then continue to pump brake pedal until clicking noise at drum brake self adjusters stops on both sides.
12. Adjust parking brake. Refer to individual car chapters for procedure.

BRAKE ADJUSTMENTS

The rear drum brakes have self-adjusting shoe mechanisms that assure correct lining-to-drum clearances at all times. The automatic adjusters operate only when the brakes are applied as the vehicle is moving rearward.
Although the brakes are self-adjusting, an initial adjustment is necessary after the brake shoes have been replaced, or when the length of the star wheel adjuster has been changed during some other service operation.

SERVICE BRAKE

1. Raise and support vehicle, then remove rear wheels and brake drums.
2. Check to make sure parking brake ca-

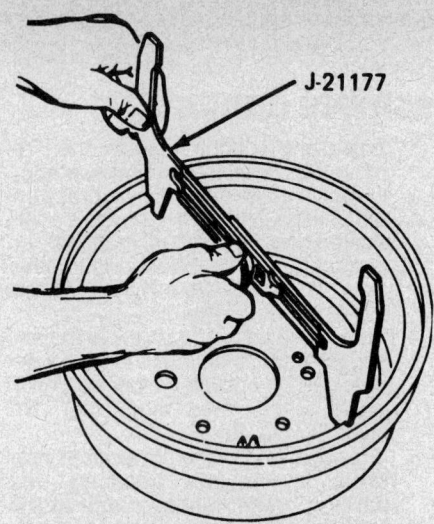

Fig. 3   Adjusting brake shoe clearance

ble linkage and levers on secondary brake shoe are in "free" position.
3. Using brake shoe measuring tool No. J-21177 or equivalent, measure drum inside diameter, **Fig. 2.**
4. Turn brake adjusting screw to expand shoes to .050 inch less than diameter obtained on outside caliper portion of brake shoe measuring tool No. J-21177, **Fig. 3.**
5. Adjust parking brake. **Whenever rear drum brakes are serviced, the parking brake linkage cable at the equalizer must always be readjusted to prevent possible damage to brake shoes.**
6. Install brake drums, wheels and tires and lower vehicle to ground.
7. Drive vehicle and apply and release service brake 30-35 times with normal pedal force. Allow about one second between brake applications until satisfactory pedal height is obtained.

PARKING BRAKE

1. Adjust service brakes.
2. Lift parking lever five ratchet, then raise and support rear of vehicle.
3. Ensure equalizer nut groove is lubricated with grease, then tighten adjusting nut until rear wheel can be rotated backward, but is locked when forward rotation is attempted.
4. Release parking brake lever. Both wheels should rotate freely with no brake drag.

Type 6

INDEX

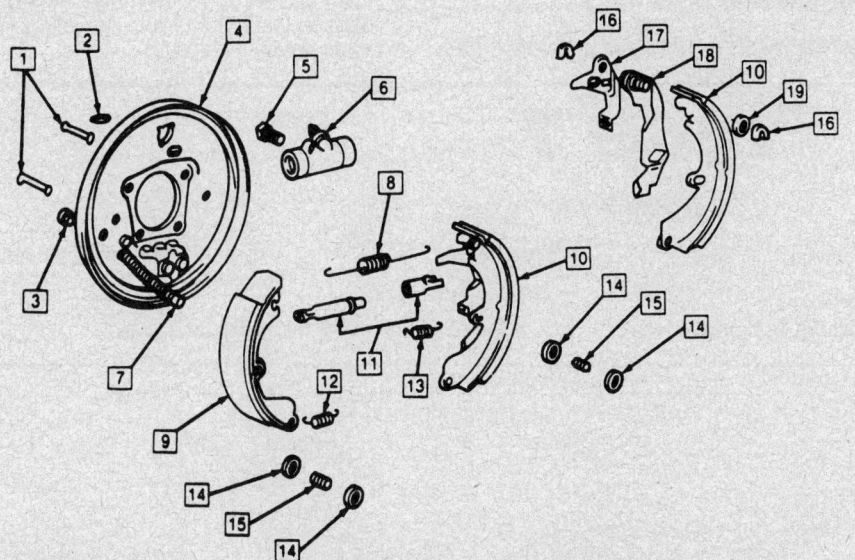

1. HOLD-DOWN PIN
2. PLUG
3. INSPECTION HOLE PLUG
4. BACKING PLATE
5. BOLT
6. WHEEL CYLINDER
7. PARKING BRAKE CABLE
8. RETURN SPRING
9. FRONT SHOE
10. REAR SHOE
11. STRUT
12. ANCHOR SPRING
13. ADJUSTING LEVER SPRING
14. RETAINER
15. HOLD-DOWN SPRING
16. C-WASHER
17. AUTOMATIC ADJUSTING LEVER
18. PARKING BRAKE LEVER
19. SHIM

Fig. 1   Drum brake assembly. Type 6

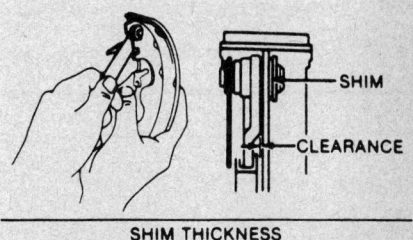

SHIM THICKNESS	
THICKNESS	THICKNESS
0.2 MM (0.008 IN.)	0.5 MM (0.020 IN.)
0.3 MM (0.012 IN.)	0.6 MM (0.024 IN.)
0.4 MM (0.016 IN.)	0.9 MM (0.035 IN.)

Fig. 2   Checking lever to shoe clearance

REMOVAL

1. Raise and support vehicle.
2. Mark relationship of wheel to axle, then remove wheel and tire assembly.
3. Remove brake drum. If drum is difficult to remove, insert screwdriver through hole in backing plate and hold automatic adjusting lever away from adjusting bolt, then, using a second screwdriver, reduce brake shoe adjustment.
4. Remove return spring, **Fig.1**
5. Remove hold-down spring, retainers and pin retaining front shoe.
6. Disconnect anchor spring from front shoe, then remove front shoe.
7. Remove anchor spring.
8. Remove hold-down spring, retainers and pin retaining rear shoe.
9. Using screwdriver, disconnect parking brake cable from anchor plate.
10. Using pliers, disconnect parking brake cable from lever and remove rear shoe together with strut.
11. Remove adjusting lever spring, then the strut together with return spring.

12. Remove parking brake lever and automatic adjusting lever from rear shoe by prying out "C" washer and removing shims and levers.
13. Clean dirt from brake drum, backing plate and all other components. **Do not use compressed air or dry brush to clean brake parts. Many brake parts contain asbestos fibers which, if inhaled, can cause serious injury. Clean brake parts with a water soaked rag or a suitable vacuum cleaner to minimize airborne dust.**

INSPECTION

1. Check brake drum, shoes, strut, auto adjuster lever, springs and backing plate for wear, distortion, cracks or other abnormal conditions.
2. If any parts are of doubtful strength or quality due to damage, heat discoloration, stress or wear, replace them.
3. Measure brake drum inside diameter and the brake shoe lining thickness.
4. Inspect lining and drum for proper contact.

INSTALLATION

1. Apply suitable lubricant to backing plate brake shoe contact points, anchor plate brake shoe contact points, strut and adjusting bolt contact points and the strut and brake shoe contact points.
2. Install parking brake lever and automatic adjusting lever to rear shoe as follows:
   a. Temporarily install levers and shim with a new "C" washer.
   b. Using feeler gauge, measure clearance between shoe and lever, **Fig. 2.**
   c. If clearance is not 0-.0138 inch, adjust by installing replacement shim.
   d. Using pliers, stake "C" washer.
3. Set strut and return spring in place on rear shoe and install adjusting lever spring.
4. Install rear shoe as follows:
   a. Using pliers, connect parking brake cable to lever.
   b. Pass parking brake cable through notch in anchor plate.
   c. Set rear shoe in place with end of shoe inserted in wheel cylinder and other end in anchor plate.
   d. Install hold-down spring, retainers and pin.
5. Install front shoe as follows:
   a. Install anchor spring between front and rear shoes.
   b. Set front shoe in place with end of shoe inserted in wheel cylinder and the strut in place.
   c. Install hold-down spring, retainers and pin.

GENERAL MOTORS—Drum Brakes

d. Connect return spring.
6. Check operation of automatic adjuster mechanism as follows:
   a. Move parking brake lever of rear shoe back and forth and check whether adjusting bolt turns. If bolt does not turn, check brakes for incorrect installation.
   b. Adjust strut length to shortest possible distance.
   c. Install brake drum.
   d. Pull parking brake lever all the way up until a clicking sound can no longer be heard.
7. Check clearance between brake shoes and drum. Remove drum and

measure brake drum inside diameter and diameter of brake shoes.
8. If clearance is not .024 inch, check parking brake system.
9. Install brake drum and the wheel and tire assembly.
10. Fill master cylinder as necessary and bleed brake system.
11. Check for fluid leakage.

SERVICE BRAKE ADJUST

Adjustment is accomplished automati-

cally by pulling the parking brake lever all the way up until a clicking sound can no longer be heard.

PARKING BRAKE ADJUST

1. Check that parking brake lever travel is correct by pulling parking brake lever all the way up and counting the number of clicks.
2. Parking brake lever travel should be 4-7 clicks. If not, remove console, loosen locknut and turn adjusting nut until travel is correct.

Type 7

INDEX

REMOVAL

1. Raise and support rear of vehicle.
2. Remove wheels, then brake hubs and drums.
3. Remove return spring and auto adjuster spring.
4. Remove leading shoe hold-down spring and pin, **Fig. 1.**
5. Remove leading shoe and auto adjuster.
6. Remove trailing shoe hold-down spring and pin, then shoe.
7. Disconnect parking brake cable from lever, then remove trailing shoe.
8. Remove parking brake lever from trailing shoe.

INSPECTION

1. If any parts are of doubtful strength or quality due to heat discoloration, or are worn, replace them.
2. Inspect wheel cylinder dust boots for signs of excessive wear or damage.
3. Inspect auto adjuster gear for smooth operation over full length.
4. Clean adjusting gear components in denatured alcohol.
5. Apply suitable lubricant to adjuster screw threads, inside diameter of socket and socket face. Adequate lubrication is achieved when a continuous bead of lubricant is at open end of adjuster nut and socket when threads are fully engaged.
6. Clean dirt and/or rust from brake drum, backing plate and all other components. **Do not use compressed air or dry brush to clean brake parts. Many brake parts contain asbestos fibers which, if inhaled, can cause serious injury. Clean brake parts with a water soaked rag or a suitable vacuum cleaner to minimize airborne dust.**

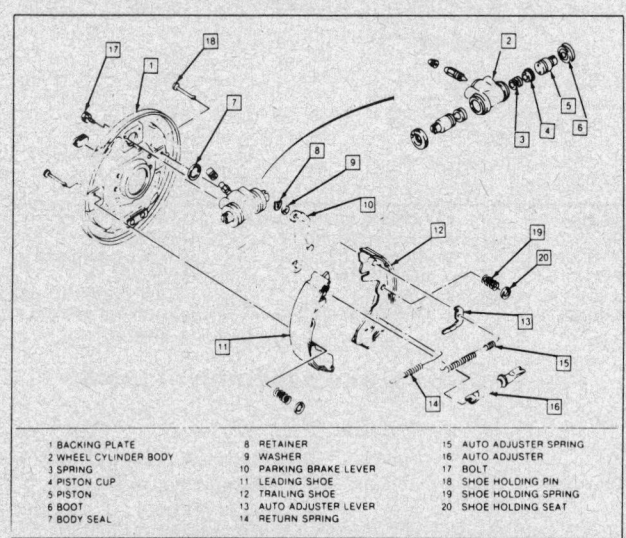

Fig. 1   Rear drum brake assembly. Type 7

1 BACKING PLATE
2 WHEEL CYLINDER BODY
3 SPRING
4 PISTON CUP
5 PISTON
6 BOOT
7 BODY SEAL
8 RETAINER
9 WASHER
10 PARKING BRAKE LEVER
11 LEADING SHOE
12 TRAILING SHOE
13 AUTO ADJUSTER LEVER
14 RETURN SPRING
15 AUTO ADJUSTER SPRING
16 AUTO ADJUSTER
17 BOLT
18 SHOE HOLDING PIN
19 SHOE HOLDING SPRING
20 SHOE HOLDING SEAT

7. Ensure adjuster gear turns freely on adjuster screw.

INSTALLATION

1. Apply suitable lubricant to backing plate and cylinder piston brake shoe contact points, adjuster and parking lever pin contact points.
2. Install parking brake lever to trailing shoe, then connect parking brake cable to lever.
3. Install trailing shoe to backing plate with hold-down pin and spring, then install brake adjuster.
4. Install leading shoe to backing plate with hold-down pin and spring.

5. Install auto adjuster lever and auto adjuster spring, then install return spring.
6. Install brake drum, then adjust brakes. Refer to individual car chapters for procedure.
7. Adjust bearing preload. Refer to individual car chapters for procedure.
8. If hydraulic connections have been opened, bleed system

SERVICE BRAKE ADJUST

1. Measure brake drum inside diameter and brake shoe diameter, **Fig. 2.**

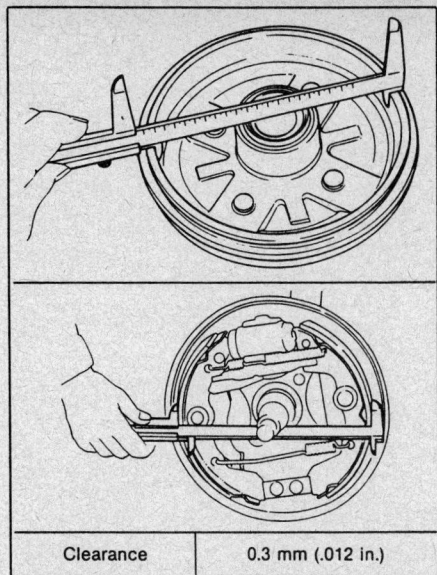

| Clearance | 0.3 mm (.012 in.) |

Fig. 2   Drum brake adjustment

2. Ensure clearance between diameters is as specified, **Fig. 2**.

PARKING BRAKE
ADJUST

Parking brake stroke should measure 7 to 9 notches with approximately 14 lbs. pressure applied. Lever stroke is automatically adjusted when rear brakes are adjusted. If stroke is not within specifications after adjusting rear brakes, it may be adjusted by rotating the cable turnbuckle.

BRAKE PEDAL HEIGHT
ADJUST

1. Ensure pedal is fully returned by pedal return spring, then measure brake pedal height, Fig. 3.
2. If measurement does not meet specifications, preform adjustment as follows:
   a. Loosen stop light switch and the locknut on pushrod.
   b. Adjust pushrod until brake pedal extends approximately 6.07 inches from floorboard.
   c. Position tip of stoplamp switch to rest lightly on pedal arm rubber stop.

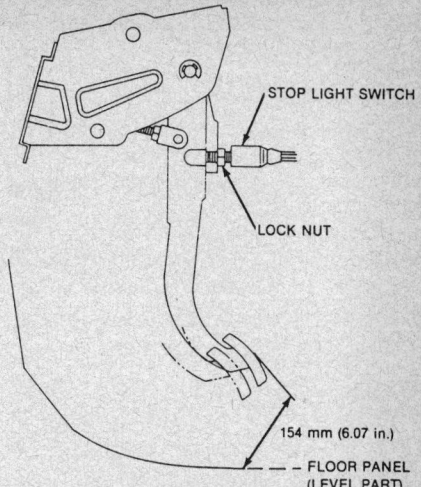

Fig. 3   Brake pedal height adjustment

d. Carefully rotate stoplamp switch until freeplay between pedal arm and pushrod is eliminated from brake pedal.
e. Tighten locknut.

Type 8
INDEX

REMOVAL

1. Raise and support vehicle.
2. Remove spindle cap by hammering lightly at 3 points around cap.
3. Remove cotter pin or unfasten staked portion of nut, then remove castle nut and washer.
4. Loosen parking brake cable adjusting nuts.
5. Remove backing plate plug, **Fig. 1**.
6. Insert screwdriver into plug hole until it contacts shoe hold down spring and push in direction shown.**Fig. 1**. This pushes hold down spring up and releases parking brake shoe lever from hold down spring, resulting in added clearance between shoe and drum.
7. Using slide hammer tool No. J-2619-01 and brake drum remover tool No. J-34866 or equivalents, pull off brake drum.
8. Remove brake shoe hold down springs by turning hold down pins.
9. Disconnect parking brake cable from parking brake shoe lever and remove brake shoes.
10. Remove spring 1 in **Fig. 2**, pull primary shoe in direction of arrow and disengage strut 4 and return spring 2.
11. Disconnect return spring 3 from shoe.
12. Disconnect parking brake shoe lever from shoe.

INSPECTION

1. If any parts are of doubtful strength or quality due to heat discoloration, or are worn, replace them.
2. Inspect wheel cylinder dust boots for signs of excessive wear or damage. If any leakage is apparent replace or rebuild wheel cylinder.
3. Clean dirt and/or rust from brake drum, backing plate and all other components. **Do not use compressed air or dry brush to clean brake parts. Many brake parts contain asbestos fibers which, if inhaled, can cause serious injury. Clean brake parts with a water soaked rag or a suitable vacuum cleaner to minimize airborne dust.**

INSTALLATION

1. Assemble brake shoes, levers and springs as shown in **Fig. 3**.
2. Push shoe hold down springs down into place. Turn hold down pins to engage springs.
3. To minimize dimension 'A-A,' **Fig. 4**, push strut towards backplate while pushing out on shoe as shown.
4. Position tab of spring clip behind parking lever.
5. Install brake drum and **torque** castle nut to 58–86.5 ft. lbs. Install cotter pin.
6. Install spindle cap.
7. Install wheel.
8. Depress brake pedal several times to obtain proper drum to shoe clearance and adjust parking brake.
9. Check that brake drum does not drag.
10. Lower vehicle and test brake operation.

SERVICE BRAKE
ADJUST

Adjustment is accomplished automati-

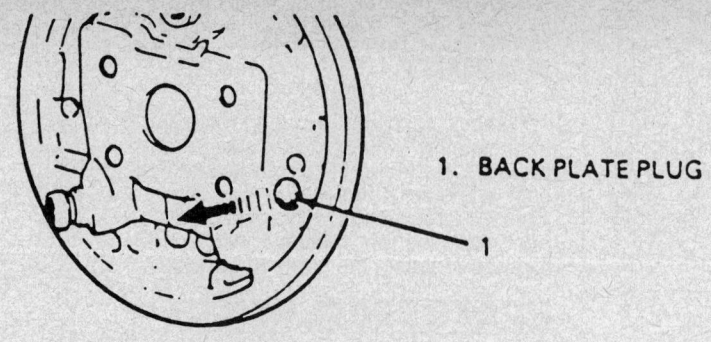

1. BACK PLATE PLUG

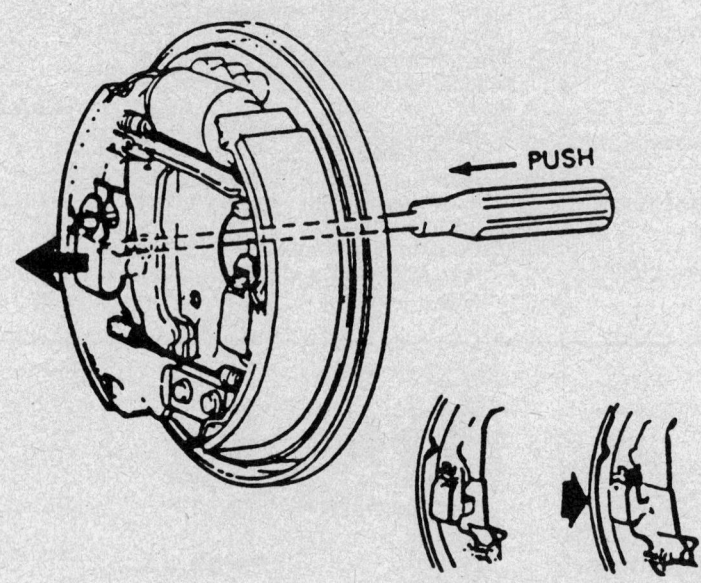

PUSH

Fig. 1   Removing backing plate plug

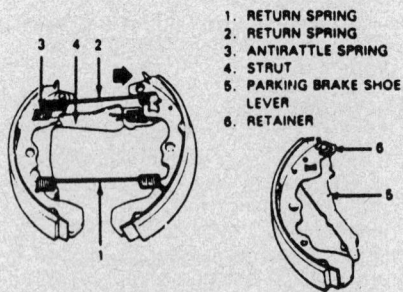

1. RETURN SPRING
2. RETURN SPRING
3. ANTIRATTLE SPRING
4. STRUT
5. PARKING BRAKE SHOE LEVER
6. RETAINER

Fig. 2   Brake shoe return spring identification

cally by applying brake pedal 3 to 5 times with 66 lbs. of pressure. Brake pedal should be cycled 3 to 5 times when replacement components are installed to assure proper adjustment.

PARKING BRAKE
ADJUST

On 1988 models, parking brake lever should be adjusted so lever comes up 3 to 8 notches with 44 lbs. of pull applied. On 1989-90 models, parking brake lever should be adjusted so lever comes up 4 to 9 notches with 44 to 55 lbs. of pull applied.

Adjust travel by loosening adjustment nuts, **Fig. 5.**

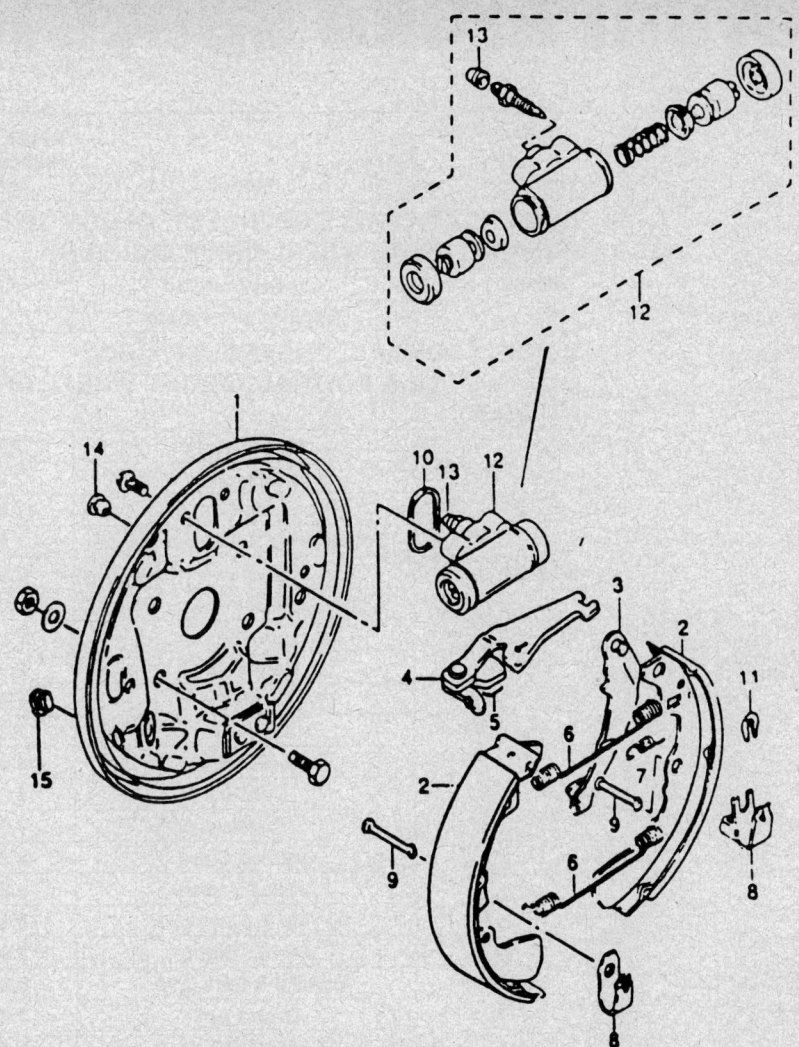

1. Brake back plate
2. Brake shoe
3. Parking brake shoe lever
4. Brake strut
5. Quadrant spring
6. Shoe return spring
7. Antirattle spring
8. Shoe hold down spring
9. Shoe hold down pin
10. Packing
11. Parking level retainer
12. Wheel cylinder
13. Bleeder plug cap
14. Rubber plug
15. Rubber plug

Fig. 3   Assembling rear brake unit. Type 8

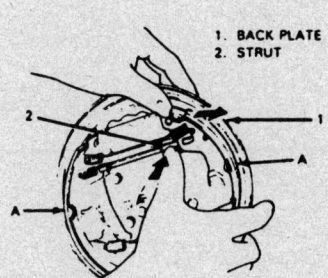

1. BACK PLATE
2. STRUT

Fig. 4   Brake lining installation

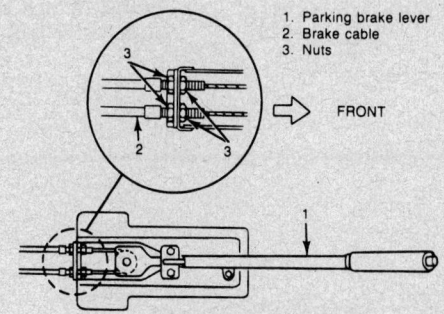

1. Parking brake lever
2. Brake cable
3. Nuts

FRONT

Fig. 5   Parking brake adjustment

Drum Brake Specifications

Year	Model	Brake Drum Inside Dia. Inch
BUICK, CADILLAC, CHEVROLET, OLDSMOBILE & PONTIAC (REAR WHEEL DRIVE MODELS)		
1988–90	Except Cadillac	①
	Cadillac Brougham	11
BUICK, CADILLAC, CHEVROLET, GEO, OLDSMOBILE & PONTIAC (FRONT WHEEL DRIVE MODELS)		
1988	Cimarron	7.87
	Firenza	7.87
	Nova	7.87
	Somerset & Somerset Regal	7.87
1988–89	Skyhawk	7.87
	Spectrum	7.09
1988–90	Beretta	8.87
	Bonneville	8.86
	Calais	7.87
	Cavalier	7.87
	Celebrity	8.86
	Century	8.86
	Corsica	7.87
	Cutlass Ciera	8.86
	Cutlass Cruiser	8.86
	DeVille & Fleetwood	8.86
	Eighty-Eight	8.86
	Electra & Park Ave.	8.86
	Grand Am	7.87
	LeMans	8.87
	LeSabre	8.86
	Ninety-Eight	8.86
	Skylark	7.87
	Sunbird	7.87
	6000	8.86
1989—90	Metro	7.09
1990	Prizm	7.87
	Storm	7.87

① —With 4.75 inch bolt circle, 9.5 inches;
   with 5 inch bolt circle, 11 inches.

AUTOMATIC TRANSMISSIONS/TRANSAXLES

TABLE OF CONTENTS

Aisin Warner A131L Automatic Transaxle

INDEX

IDENTIFICATION

The transaxle identification number is stamped at top of transaxle rear cover at rear of transaxle.

DESCRIPTION

The A131L 3 speed automatic transaxle is used on Chevrolet Nova vehicles & 1989—90 Geo prizm. The torque converter is equipped with an integral lock-up clutch. For higher performance, greater fuel economy and quietness, a high efficiency torque converter, wider gear ratio, compact high-precision valve body, high efficiency oil pump and a light weight durable integral transaxle case are used.

TROUBLESHOOTING

FLUID DISCOLORED OR SMELLS BURNED

1. Contaminated fluid.
2. Faulty torque converter.
3. Faulty transaxle.

VEHICLE DOES NOT MOVE IN ANY DRIVE GEAR

1. Improperly adjusted transaxle control cable.
2. Faulty valve body or primary regulator.
3. Faulty transaxle.

VEHICLE DOES NOT MOVE IN ANY RANGE

1. Faulty park lock pawl.
2. Faulty valve body or primary regulator.
3. Faulty torque converter.
4. Broken converter drive plate.
5. Blocked oil pump intake strainer.
6. Faulty transmission.

INCORRECT SHIFT LEVER POSITION

1. Improperly adjusted transaxle control cable.
2. Faulty manual valve and lever.
3. Faulty transaxle.

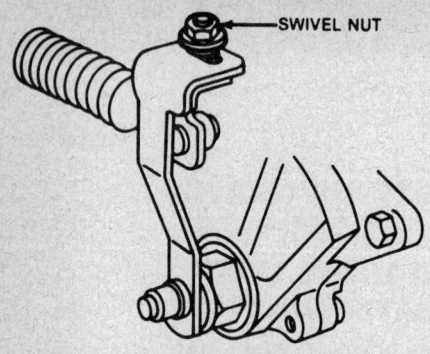

Copyrighted Material Reprinted with Permission from Hydra-Matic Div., GM Corp.

Fig. 1   Manual shift linkage adjustment

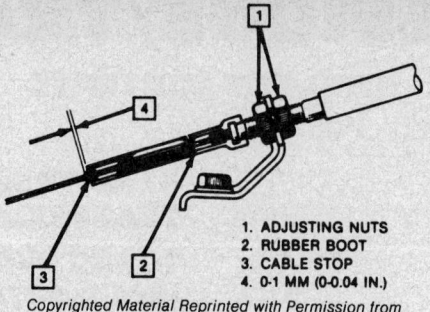

1. ADJUSTING NUTS
2. RUBBER BOOT
3. CABLE STOP
4. 0-1 MM (0-0.04 IN.)

Copyrighted Material Reprinted with Permission from Hydra-Matic Div., GM Corp.

Fig. 2   Throttle cable adjustment

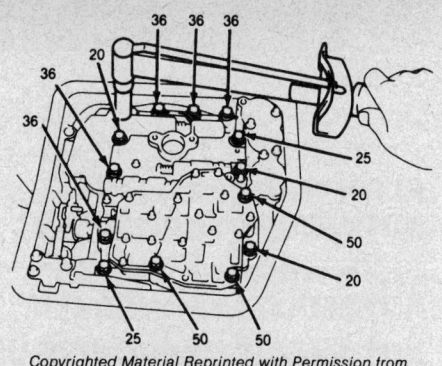

Copyrighted Material Reprinted with Permission from Hydra-Matic Div., GM Corp.

Fig. 3   Valve body bolt identification

HARSH ENGAGEMENT INTO ANY DRIVE RANGE

1. Improperly adjusted transaxle control cable.
2. Faulty valve body or primary regulator.
3. Faulty accumulator pistons.
4. Faulty transaxle.

DELAYED UPSHIFTS & DOWNSHIFTS

1. Improperly adjusted throttle cable.
2. Faulty governors.
3. Faulty valve body.

SLIPS ON UPSHIFTS OR SHUDDERS ON TAKE-OFF

1. Improperly adjusted transaxle control cable.
2. Improperly adjusted throttle cable.
3. Faulty valve body.
4. Faulty transaxle.

DRAG OR BINDING ON UPSHIFT

1. Improperly adjusted transmission control cable.
2. Faulty valve body.
3. Faulty transaxle.

HARSH DOWNSHIFT

1. Improperly adjusted throttle cable.
2. Faulty accumulator pistons.
3. Faulty valve body.
4. Faulty transaxle.

NO DOWNSHIFT WHEN COASTING

1. Faulty governor.
2. Faulty valve body.

INCORRECT DOWNSHIFT

1. Improperly adjusted throttle cable.
2. Faulty governor.
3. Faulty valve body.
4. Faulty transaxle.

NO KICKDOWN

1. Improperly adjusted throttle cable.

2. Faulty governor.
3. Faulty valve body.

NO ENGINE BRAKING

1. Faulty valve body.
2. Faulty transaxle.

NO HOLD IN PARK

1. Improperly adjusted transaxle control cable.
2. Faulty parking lock pawl and rod.

MAINTENANCE

CHANGING FLUID

1. Raise and support vehicle, then place a suitable container under transaxle drain plug.
2. Remove drain plug and drain fluid, then reinstall and tighten drain plug.
3. With engine off, add 2.4 quarts of Dexron II type transmission fluid.
4. Start engine, then move selector lever through all ranges and end in "Park."
5. With engine idling, check fluid level, then if necessary, add fluid as necessary to bring fluid to "Cool" level on dipstick.

IN-VEHICLE ADJUSTMENTS

MANUAL SHIFT LINKAGE, ADJUST

1. Loosen swivel nut on lever, then push manual lever fully toward right side of vehicle, **Fig. 1.**
2. Return lever two notches to Neutral position, then place selector lever in Neutral position.
3. Manually hold lever lightly toward R range, then tighten swivel nut.

THROTTLE CABLE, ADJUST

1. Hold accelerator pedal in fully depressed position, then loosen cable adjusting nuts. **Fig. 2.**
2. Adjust cable to obtain .04 inch between end of boot and stopper on cable, then tighten adjusting nut.
3. Fully depress accelerator pedal and recheck adjustment, then road test vehicle.

NEUTRAL SAFETY SWITCH, ADJUST

1. Loosen neutral start switch attaching bolts, then place selector lever in Neutral position.
2. Disconnect electrical connector, then connect a suitable ohmmeter between terminals.
3. Rotate switch until meter indicates continuity, then **torque** switch retaining bolts to 48 inch lbs. to secure adjustment.
4. Reconnect electrical connector to switch then ensure engine starts with selector lever in Neutral and Park only.

IN-VEHICLE REPAIRS

VALVE BODY, REPLACE
Removal

1. Clean area around pan, then drain transmission fluid.
2. Remove oil pan and gasket, then the oil strainer.
3. Remove oil apply tube bracket attaching bolts, then the apply tube.
4. Remove oil tubes using a suitable screwdriver, then the manual detent spring.
5. Remove manual valve attaching bolts, then the manual valve assembly.
6. Remove valve body to cable bracket attaching bolt, then disconnect throttle cable.
7. Remove valve body attaching bolts, then valve body, governor, apply gasket and governor oil gasket.

Installation

1. Install governor oil gasket, then the governor and governor apply gasket.
2. Hold valve body in place, then manually retain cam in downward position and slip cable end into slot.
3. Position valve body into place, then insert and finger tighten 14 attaching bolts. **Torque** bolts to 7 ft. lbs. **Attaching bolt lengths (mm) are indicated in Fig. 3.**
4. Align manual valve with pin on manu-

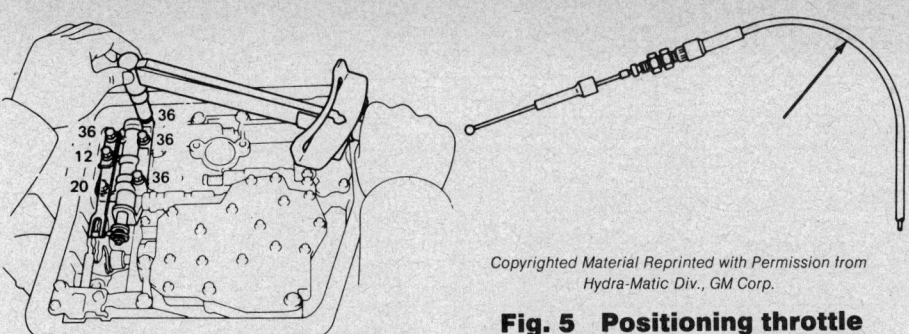

Fig. 4   Manual valve body bolt identification

al valve lever, then install manual valve body.

5. Insert and finger tighten attaching bolts, then **torque** to 7 ft. lbs. **Attaching bolt lengths (mm) are indicated in Fig. 4.**
6. Install detent spring, then insert and finger tighten attaching bolts. **Torque** attaching bolts to 7 ft. lbs.
7. Ensure manual lever is in contact with center of roller at tip of detent spring, then install oil tubes.
8. Install apply tube bracket, then the oil strainer.
9. Insert magnet into pan, then install oil pan with new gasket.
10. Insert oil pan attaching bolts, then **torque** to 43 inch lbs.
11. Install drain plug with new gasket, then **torque** to 36 ft. lbs.
12. Fill transaxle to specifications, then ensure proper fluid level.

THROTTLE CABLE, REPLACE

Removal
1. Disconnect throttle cable from engine, then the transaxle control cable from manual shift lever.
2. Remove manual shift lever, then the neutral start switch.
3. Remove valve body as previously described, then the retaining plate bolt and retaining plate.
4. Pull cable from transaxle case.

Installation
1. Insert cable into transaxle case, then install retaining plate and bolt.
2. Install valve body as previously described, then position cable stop for adjustment reference as follows. **Cable stop is not staked in place on replacement cable.**
   a. Bend cable to a radius of approximately 7.87 inches as shown, **Fig. 5.**
   b. Lightly pull inner cable from housing until a slight resistance is felt, then hold in position.
   c. Stake stopper onto inner cable so that .031–.059 inch clearance exists between stop and cable housing.
3. Connect throttle cable to throttle linkage, then adjust cable as previously described.

Fig. 5   Positioning throttle cable for stopper installation

4. Install neutral safety switch, then the manual shift lever. Adjust switch as previously described.
5. Ensure transaxle fluid level is to specifications, then road test vehicle.

GOVERNOR VALVE, REPLACE

Removal
1. Remove transaxle cover, then the left-hand driveshaft.
2. Remove governor cover, then the O-ring.
3. Remove governor body with thrust washer.
4. Remove washer, then the governor body adapter.

Installation
1. Install governor body adapter, then the governor body with thrust washer.
2. Install governor cover with O-ring, then the lefthand driveshaft.
3. Install transaxle dust cover, then ensure transaxle fluid level is to specifications.
4. Road test vehicle.

SECOND BRAKE SERVO ASSEMBLY, REPLACE

Removal
1. Raise and support vehicle, then remove shift cable bracket at transaxle.
2. Remove snap ring.
3. Remove cover.
4. Remove piston, then the outer spring.

Installation
1. Insert piston, less outer spring, then install snap ring.
2. Install brake apply rod tool No. J-35679, then observe groove on plunger of tool.
3. Push button on tool, **Fig. 6.** This allows tool to push brake apply rod into case. If groove is visible, piston stroke is correct (.059–.118 inch). If stroke is greater than specified, replace piston rod with 2.870 inch or 2.811 inch rod as needed.
4. Remove snap ring, then install piston and outer spring.
5. Install spring compressor tool No. J-35549 to compress spring, then insert snap ring.
6. Install cover, then the shift cable bracket.
7. Lower vehicle.

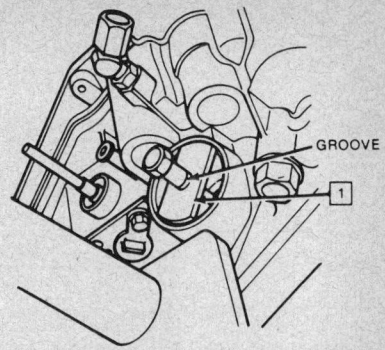

Fig. 6   Second brake servo plunger installation

TRANSAXLE REPLACE

1. Disconnect battery ground cable.
2. Remove air intake tube, then disconnect speedometer cable at transaxle.
3. Disconnect thermostat housing and ground cable at transaxle, then remove upper mount to bracket attaching bolt.
4. Disconnect transaxle electrical connectors, then the T.V. cable at carburetor.
5. Remove 2 upper bellhousing attaching bolts, then support engine using a suitable support tool.
6. Raise and support vehicle, then remove left wheel assembly.
7. Remove left and right splash shields, then the center splash shield.
8. Remove center beam, then disconnect shift cable at transaxle.
9. Remove shift cable bracket, then the cooler bracket.
10. Disconnect cooler lines at outlets, then remove inspection cover.
11. Remove torque converter attaching bolts, then the left control arm at ball joint.
12. Remove right and left axle shafts at transaxle, then the starter attaching bolts.
13. Remove 3 rear transaxle attaching bolts, then support transaxle, using a suitable jack.
14. Remove remaining transaxle attaching bolts, then the remaining bellhousing attaching bolts.
15. Remove transaxle from vehicle.
16. Reverse procedure to install, noting the following:
    a. **Torque** transaxle housing attaching bolts to 47 ft. lbs. for 12 mm bolts or 34 ft. lbs. for 10 mm bolts.
    b. **Torque** lefthand engine mount bolts to 38 ft. lbs.
    c. Install white torque converter bolt first, then the five yellow bolts. **Torque** bolts evenly to 13 ft. lbs.
    d. **Torque** engine mount center support bolts to 29 ft. lbs.
    e. **Torque** front and rear mount bolts to 29 ft. lbs.

TIGHTENING SPECIFICATIONS

Component	Torque/Ft. Lbs.
Counter Driven Gear To Shaft	127
Drain Plug To Oil Pan	36
Lefthand Bearing Retainer To Case	14
Manual Valve To Case	7
Neutral Start Switch To Case	4
Oil Filter To Valve Body	7
Oil Pan To Case	3
Oil Pump To Case	16
Parking Paw Bracket To Case	5
Ring Gear To Differential Case	71
Stator Shaft To Pump	7
Transaxle Rear Cover To Case	18
Upper Valve Body To Lower Valve Body	4
Valve Body To Case	7

Aisin Warner A240E Automatic Transaxle

INDEX

TRANSAXLE IDENTIFICATION

The transaxle identification number is stamped on top of the transaxle rear cover at the rear of the transaxle.

DESCRIPTION

The A240E 4 speed automatic transaxle is used on the 1988 Chevrolet Nova. The torque converter is equipped with an Electronic lock-up clutch and is computer controlled.

TROUBLESHOOTING

FLUID DISCOLORED OR SMELLS BURNED

1. Contaminated fluid.
2. Faulty torque converter.
3. Faulty transaxle.

VEHICLE DOES NOT MOVE IN ANY DRIVE GEAR

1. Improperly adjusted transaxle control cable.
2. Faulty valve body or primary regulator.
3. Faulty transaxle.

VEHICLE DOES NOT MOVE IN ANY RANGE

1. Faulty parking pawl.
2. Incorrect shift lever position.
3. Faulty torque converter.
4. Damaged converter drive plate.
5. Blocked oil pump strainer.
6. Faulty transaxle.

INCORRECT SHIFT LEVER POSITION

1. Improperly adjusted transaxle linkage.
2. Faulty manual valve or lever.
3. Faulty transaxle.

HARSH ENGAGEMENT INTO ANY DRIVE RANGE

1. Improperly adjusted transaxle control cable.
2. Faulty valve body or primary regulator.
3. Faulty accumulator pistons.
4. Faulty transaxle.

DELAYED UPSHIFTS & DOWNSHIFTS

1. Improperly adjusted throttle cable.
2. Faulty governor.
3. Faulty valve body.

SLIPS ON UPSHIFTS OR SHUDDERS ON TAKE-OFF

1. Improperly adjusted transaxle control cable.
2. Improperly adjusted throttle cable.
3. Faulty valve body.
4. Faulty transaxle.

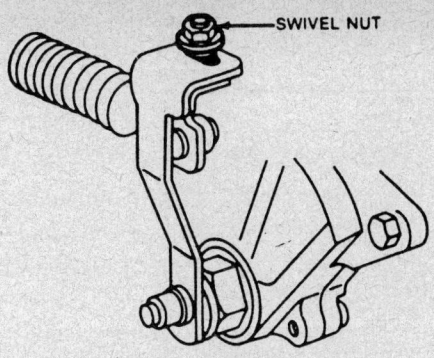

Copyrighted Material Reprinted with Permission from Hydra-Matic Div., GM Corp.

Fig. 1   Manual shift linkage adjustment

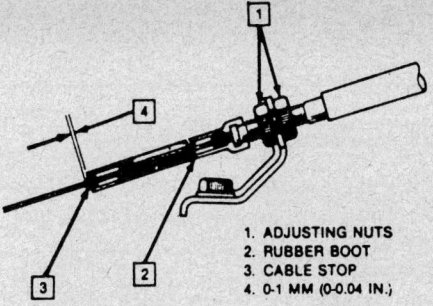

1. ADJUSTING NUTS
2. RUBBER BOOT
3. CABLE STOP
4. 0-1 MM (0-0.04 IN.)

Copyrighted Material Reprinted with Permission from Hydra-Matic Div., GM Corp.

Fig. 2   Throttle cable adjustment

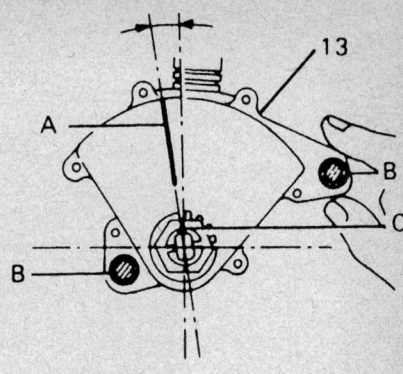

A   NEUTRAL BASIC LINE
B   BOLT
C   GROOVE
13   NEUTRAL START SWITCH

Copyrighted Material Reprinted with Permission from Hydra-Matic Div., GM Corp.

Fig. 3   Neutral safety switch adjustment

DRAG OR BINDING ON UPSHIFTS

1. Improperly adjusted transaxle control cable.
2. Faulty valve body.
3. Faulty transaxle.

HARSH DOWNSHIFT

1. Improperly adjusted throttle cable.
2. Faulty accumulator piston.
3. Faulty valve body.
4. Faulty transaxle.

NO DOWNSHIFT WHEN COASTING

1. Faulty governor.
2. Faulty valve body.

INCORRECT DOWNSHIFT

1. Improperly adjusted throttle cable.
2. Faulty governor.
3. Faulty valve body.
4. Faulty transaxle.

NO KICKDOWN

1. Improperly adjusted throttle cable.
2. Faulty governor.
3. Faulty valve body.

NO ENGINE BREAKING IN 2

1. Faulty valve body.
2. Faulty transaxle.

NO HOLD IN PARK

1. Improperly adjusted transaxle control linkage.
2. Faulty parking pawl.

MAINTENANCE

CHANGING FLUID

1. Raise and support vehicle, then position suitable drain pan under transaxle oil pan.
2. Remove transaxle drain plug and allow fluid to drain, then re-install drain plug.

3. Add 2.4 qts. of Dexron Type II transmission fluid to transaxle.
4. Start engine and move selector lever through all selector lever positions, then return to Park.
5. With engine idling, check fluid level and add fluid as necessary.

IN-VEHICLE ADJUSTMENTS

MANUAL LINKAGE, ADJUST

1. Loosen swivel nut on lever, then push manual lever fully forward toward the right side of the vehicle, **Fig. 1.**
2. Return lever two notches to the Neutral position, then place selector lever in Neutral position.
3. Manual hold lever tightly toward R range, then tighten swivel nut.

THROTTLE CABLE, ADJUST

1. Hold accelerator pedal in the fully depressed position, the loosen cable adjusting nuts, **Fig. 2.**
2. Adjust cable to obtain .04 inch clearance between end of boot and stopper on cable, then tighten adjusting nut.
3. Fully depress accelerator pedal and recheck adjustment, then road test vehicle.

NEUTRAL SAFETY SWITCH, ADJUST

1. Loosen neutral safety switch attaching bolts.
2. Place selector lever in the Neutral position.
3. Disconnect electrical connector.
4. Align groove with neutral basic line, **Fig. 3.**
5. **Torque** switch attaching bolts to 48 inch lbs.
6. Connect electrical connector and check to ensure engine starts on when selector lever is Neutral or Park.

TRANSAXLE

REPLACE

1. Disconnect battery ground cable.
2. Remove air cleaner assembly.
3. Disconnect neutral safety switch electrical connector.
4. Disconnect speed sensor electrical connector, if equipped.
5. Disconnect solenoid valve electrical connector.
6. Disconnect speedometer cable.
7. Disconnect throttle cable.
8. Disconnect shift control cable.
9. Disconnect and cap oil cooler lines.
10. Disconnect coolant inlet hose.
11. Raise and support vehicle, then drain fluid from transaxle.
12. Remove engine undercover.
13. Remove dust covers from crossmember, then remove front and rear mount bolts.
14. Support transaxle assembly using a suitable transmission jack, then remove engine center crossmember attaching bolts and crossmember.
15. Disconnect exhaust pipe from exhaust manifold.
16. Carefully disconnect left driveshaft.
17. Remove starter motor.
18. Remove stiffener plate and engine rear plate.
19. Using a suitable wrench, hold crankshaft pulley in position, then remove torque converter to flywheel attaching bolts.
20. With transaxle properly supported, remove engine rear attaching bolts.
21. Remove transaxle from vehicle.
22. Reverse procedure to install. Using suitable calipers and a straightedge, measure installed surface to transaxle housing surface. This distance should be .079 inch or more. **Torque** 12 mm transaxle top engine attaching bolts to 47 ft. lbs. and 10 mm attaching bolts to 34 ft. lbs. **Torque** engine rear mount attaching bolts to 38 ft. lbs. **Torque** torque converter attaching bolts to 20 ft. lbs. **Torque** engine center crossmember attaching bolts to 29 ft. lbs. **Torque** front and rear mount attaching bolts to 29 ft. lbs.

TIGHTENING SPECIFICATIONS

Component	Torque/Ft. Lbs.
Accumulator Piston To Valve Body	7
Drain Plug To Oil Pan	13
Neutral Safety Switch To Case	4
Oil Cooler Lines To Case	25
Oil Pan To Transaxle Case	3
Oil Pump To Transaxle Housing	18
Ring Gear To Differential Case	71
Stator Shaft To Pump Body	7
Torque Convertor To Flexplate	20
Transaxle Case To Front/Rear Mounts	29
Transaxle Housing To Transaxle Case	22
Transaxle Rear Cover To Case	22
Transaxle To Engine Mounting Bolts	47①
Transaxle To Engine Mounting Bolts	34②
Valve Body Cover To Valve Body	7
Valve Body To Case	7

①—10 mm bolts.
②—12 mm bolts.

KF 100 Automatic Transaxle (Spectrum)

INDEX

DESCRIPTION

The KF 100 automatic transaxle is a compact type unit where the transmission and differential are integral and use the same type lubricant (Dexron II). Power is transferred from the output gear through the ring gear to the idler gear.

The output gear, idler gear and differential gear case are supported by tapered roller bearings. The preload on the roller bearings can be adjusted by using shims.

The final gear is a helical type design requiring no tooth contact adjustment.

TROUBLESHOOTING

NO 1-2 SHIFT

1. Incorrectly adjusted shift linkage.
2. Damaged or disconnected vacuum lines.
3. Damaged or disconnected vacuum diaphragm or rod.
4. Faulty control valve or governor valve.
5. Faulty band servo or brake band.

NO 2-3 SHIFT

1. Incorrectly adjusted shift linkage.
2. Damaged or disconnected vacuum lines.
3. Damaged or disconnected vacuum diaphragm or rod.
4. Faulty control valve or governor valve.
5. Faulty band servo or brake band.
6. Damaged front clutch.

1-2 SHIFT POINTS TOO HIGH OR LOW

1. Damaged or disconnected solenoid wiring.
2. Damaged or disconnected vacuum lines.
3. Incorrectly adjusted kickdown switch or damaged and/or disconnected wiring.
4. Abnormal hydraulic pressures.
5. Faulty down shift solenoid.
6. Damaged or disconnected vacuum diaphragm or rod.
7. Faulty control valve or governor valve.

2-3 SHIFT POINTS TOO HIGH OR LOW

1. Faulty solenoid wiring.
2. Damaged or disconnected vacuum

lines.
3. Incorrectly adjusted kickdown switch or damaged and/or disconnected wiring.
4. Abnormal hydraulic pressures.
5. Faulty downshift solenoid.
6. Faulty vacuum diaphragm or control rod.
7. Faulty control valve or governor valve.

SLIPS OUT OF 2ND GEAR

1. Faulty or incorrectly adjusted linkage.
2. Abnormal hydraulic pressures.
3. Faulty control valve.
4. Faulty band servo and brake band.

NO KICKDOWN

1. Faulty solenoid wiring.
2. Incorrectly adjusted linkage.
3. Damaged or disconnected vacuum lines.
4. Faulty kickdown switch and/or wiring.
5. Faulty downshift solenoid.
6. Faulty control valve.

VEHICLE DOES NOT MOVE IN ANY GEAR POSITION

1. Incorrect transaxle fluid level.
2. Incorrectly adjusted linkage.
3. Loose or missing torque converter mounting bolts.
4. Damaged ring gear.
5. Abnormal hydraulic pressures.
6. Damaged torque converter.
7. Faulty oil pump and/or control valve.
8. Damaged transaxle shafts.

VEHICLE DOES NOT MOVE IN D

1. Incorrectly adjusted linkage.
2. Abnormal hydraulic pressures.
3. Faulty oil pump.
4. Faulty control valve.
5. Faulty one-way clutch.
6. Faulty rear clutch.

VEHICLE DOES NOT MOVE IN D2

1. Incorrectly adjusted linkage.
2. Abnormal hydraulic pressures.
3. Faulty control valve.
4. Faulty band servo or brake band.

VEHICLE DOES NOT MOVE IN REVERSE

1. Incorrectly adjusted linkage.
2. Abnormal hydraulic pressures.
3. Defective oil pump.
4. Faulty control valve.
5. Faulty low-reverse brake.
6. Faulty front clutch.
7. Faulty rear clutch.

VEHICLE MOVES IN NEUTRAL

1. Incorrect transaxle fluid level.
2. Incorrectly adjusted linkage.
3. Faulty rear clutch.

VEHICLE DOES NOT MOVE IN ANY FORWARD GEAR

1. Incorrectly adjusted linkage.
2. Abnormal hydraulic pressures.
3. Defective oil pump.
4. Faulty control valve.
5. Defective front clutch.

SLIPS WHEN SHIFTING FROM N TO D

1. Incorrect transaxle fluid level.
2. Incorrectly adjusted linkage.
3. Damaged or disconnected vacuum lines.
4. Abnormal hydraulic pressures.
5. Faulty vacuum diaphragm or rod.
6. Faulty control valve.
7. Defective rear clutch.

SLIPS WHEN SHIFTING FROM P-R OR N-R

1. Incorrect transaxle fluid level.
2. Incorrectly adjusted linkage.
3. Damaged or disconnected vacuum lines.
4. Abnormal hydraulic pressures.
5. Faulty vacuum diaphragm or rod.
6. Defective oil pump.
7. Faulty control valve.
8. Faulty low-reverse brake.
9. Faulty front clutch.

SLIPS IN DRIVE

1. Incorrect transaxle fluid level.
2. Incorrectly adjusted linkage.
3. Damaged or disconnected vacuum lines.
4. Abnormal hydraulic pressures.
5. Faulty vacuum diaphragm or rod.
6. Defective torque converter.
7. Defective oil pump.
8. Faulty control valve.
9. Defective one-way clutch.
10. Defective rear clutch.

SLIPS IN 1 OR 2

1. Faulty band servo or brake band.
2. Faulty low-reverse brake.
3. Faulty rear clutch.

SLIPS IN REVERSE

1. Incorrect transaxle fluid level.
2. Incorrectly adjusted linkage.
3. Damaged or disconnected vacuum lines.
4. Abnormal hydraulic pressures.
5. Faulty vacuum diaphragm or rod.
6. Faulty torque converter.
7. Defective oil pump.
8. Defective control valve.
9. Defective low-reverse brake.
10. Defective front clutch.

VIBRATION IN DRIVE

1. Loose or broken torque converter mounting bolts.
2. Damaged ring gear.
3. Damaged torque converter.

NOISE IN NEUTRAL & PARK

1. Loose or broken torque converter mounting bolts.
2. Damaged torque converter.
3. Defective oil pump.

MAINTENANCE

MAINTENANCE INTERVALS

Check transaxle fluid level every 7,500 miles, adding Dexron II automatic transmission fluid as necessary.

Change transaxle fluid and service sump filter every 30,000 miles under normal driving conditions, or every 15,000 miles if vehicle is operated under severe conditions such as city driving during hot weather or driving over hilly or mountainous terrain.

CHECKING FLUID LEVEL

To ensure accuracy of transaxle fluid level reading, wait 30 minutes before checking vehicle which has just been driven for a long period of time at highway speeds or in city traffic during hot weather.
1. Park vehicle on a level surface and apply parking brake.
2. Place transaxle in Park position and idle engine for two minutes.
3. With the brake applied, move shift lever through all gear ranges, then return to Park position.
4. Remove and touch dipstick to determine fluid temperature. If fluid is cool or warm, level should be between cold notch (marked "C") and center notch; If fluid is hot, level should be between center notch and hot notch (marked "H"). Add Dexron II fluid as necessary. **Do not overfill.**

CHANGING FLUID

1. Remove drain plug at bottom of differential and drain fluid.
2. Remove oil pan and discard pan gasket.
3. Clean drain pan, then using a new gasket, install gasket and pan to transaxle. **Torque** pan bolts to 5 ft. lbs.
4. Install drain plug and fill transaxle through oil filler tube with Dexron II automatic transmission fluid.

IN-VEHICLE ADJUSTMENTS
MANUAL LINKAGE, ADJUST
Park Lock Cable

1. Ensure shift control cable is properly adjusted.
2. Remove 4 screws securing console assembly.
3. Place shift control lever in Park, then turn ignition switch to Lock position.
4. Loosen upper and lower nuts securing cable to floor bracket.
5. Rotate lower nut clockwise until con-

trol lever cannot be moved out of Park.

6. Securely tighten upper adjusting nut.
7. Rotate key to Off position and ensure shift control lever can be moved out of Park position.
8. Install console assembly.

Shift Control Cable

1. Loosen nuts on control link, then place transaxle manual lever into Neutral detent.
2. Place shift control lever in Neutral position.
3. Rotate link assembly clockwise to remove slack in shift cable.
4. While holding link, tighten rear adjusting nut **Fig. 1**, until it just contacts link.
5. Tighten front adjusting nut until it just contacts link, then tighten both adjusting nuts.
6. Ensure when selector lever is shifted from Park through D1, a clicking can be felt at each shift position. Ensure the gear selected corresponds to that indicated by the gear selection plate.
7. Ensure lever can be shifted between Drive and Neutral without depressing the shifter button.
8. If the shift lever can be shifted from Drive to Reverse without depressing the shifter button or if the button is loose, adjust by loosening the locknut and twisting the selector lever knob.

IN-VEHICLE REPAIRS

SHIFTER CONTROL, REPLACE

1. Disconnect battery ground cable.
2. Remove floor console.
3. Disconnect shift cable from control.
4. Disconnect park lock cable from shifter.
5. Remove bolts attaching control assembly to floor. Remove control assembly.
6. Reverse procedure to install.

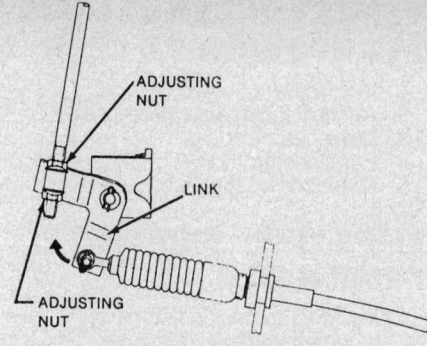

Copyrighted Material Reprinted with Permission from Hydra-Matic Div., GM Corp.

Fig. 1   Shift cable adjustment

SPEEDOMETER DRIVEN GEAR, REPLACE

1. Disconnect battery ground cable.
2. Disconnect speedometer cable from transaxle assembly.
3. Remove retainer bolt, retainer, speedometer driven gear and O-ring seal.
4. Reverse procedure to install.

SERVO ASSEMBLY, REPLACE

1. Disconnect battery ground cable.
2. Raise and support vehicle.
3. Remove left front wheel and tire assembly.
4. Remove left lower control tension rod assembly.
5. Disconnect tie rod from left steering arm.
6. Remove one oil pan attaching bolt nearest servo cover.
7. Install servo piston compressor J-35278 or equivalent, and compress the servo cover. Remove cover and retaining ring, then the cover.
8. Remove tool and servo assembly from transaxle assembly.
9. Reverse procedure to install.

TRANSAXLE REPLACE

1. Disconnect battery ground cable.
2. Disconnect air intake hose from air cleaner assembly.
3. Disconnect shift cable from transaxle.
4. Disconnect speedometer cable from transaxle.
5. Disconnect vacuum hose from vacuum diaphragm.
6. Disconnect engine harness clamp from transaxle.
7. Disconnect ground cable from transaxle.
8. Mark, then disconnect all electrical connectors from transaxle assembly.
9. Disconnect, then cap transaxle fluid lines.
10. Remove three upper transaxle to engine attaching bolts.
11. Raise and support vehicle.
12. Remove both front wheel and tire assemblies.
13. Remove splash shield.
14. Disconnect both tie rod ends at steering knuckle.
15. Remove both tension rod brackets, then disconnect tension rods from controls arms.
16. Disconnect both driveshaft assemblies from transaxle.
17. Remove flywheel dust cover.
18. Remove converter to flywheel attaching bolts.
19. Remove rear mount through bolts from transaxle assembly.
20. Remove starter motor attaching bolts, then the starter motor.
21. Position a suitable jack under transaxle assembly.
22. Remove lower transaxle to engine attaching bolts.
23. Carefully remove transaxle from vehicle.
24. Reverse procedure to install. **Torque** transaxle to engine attaching bolts to 56 ft. lbs. Torque converter to flywheel attaching bolts to 30 ft. lbs.

TIGHTENING SPECIFICATIONS

Component	Torque/Ft. Lbs.
Center And Rear Mount, Mounting Nuts	45
Center Crossmember To Main Crossmember	45
Center Crossmember To Radiator Support	45
Center Mount To Transaxle Bolts	45
Control Assembly Bolts	15
Cooling Line	20
Cooling Line Fittings	15
Differential Drain And Fill Plug	29
Fill Tube To Case Bolt	97 ①
Flywheel To Torque Converter Bolts	31
Front Mount Bracket To Transaxle Bolts	13
Front Mount, Mounting Bolts	45
Front Mount Through Bolt	64
Governor Cover Retainer Bolts	97 ①
Left Mount Brace Bolts	13
Left Mount Bracket Bolts	45
Left Mount Through Bolt	64
Lower A-Frame To Underbody Bolts	94
Main Crossmember To Underbody Bolts	152
Manual Valve And Manual Detent Bolts	89 ①
Neutral Start Switch Bolts	69 ①
Oil Apply Tube Retainer Bolts	44 ①
Oil Filter Mounting Bolts	89 ①
Pan Bolts	44 ①
Rear Mount Through Bolt	64
Side Case Cover Bolts	44 ①
Starter Bolts	29
Transaxle Drain Plug	29
Transaxle To Engine Bolts	34
Valve Body Bolts	89 ①
Exhaust Hanger Bracket Nuts	115 ①

①—Inch lbs.

Turbo Hydra-Matic 125C (3T40) Automatic Transaxle

INDEX

IDENTIFICATION

This transaxle may be identified by a model tag attached to the oil pan flange pad to the right of the oil dipstick at the rear of the transaxle.

DESCRIPTION

This automatic transaxle is designed for use with FWD and mid-engine RWD vehicles. The unit consists primarily of a 3 element torque converter, Fig. 1, compound planetary gear set and dual sprockets, drive link assembly and a pressure plate and damper assembly. A differential and final drive gear set is also incorporated in the transaxle case. Three multiple disc clutches, a roller clutch and a band provide the friction elements required to obtain the desired functions of the planetary gear set. Hydraulic pressure required to operate the friction elements and automatic control is provided by a vane type pump.

TROUBLESHOOTING

NO DRIVE IN DRIVE RANGE; INTERMEDIATE, LOW & REVERSE OK

1. Low fluid level.
2. Forward clutch feed in input shaft restricted.
3. Leak between case cover and driven sprocket passages. Check gaskets.

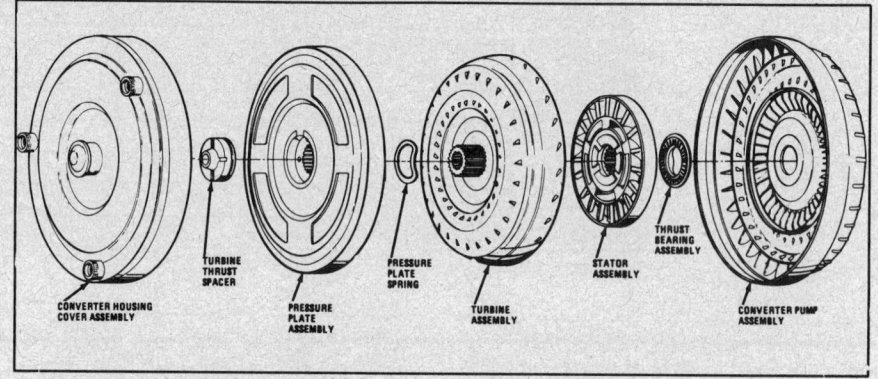

Copyrighted Material Reprinted with Permission from Hydra-Matic Div., GM Corp.

Fig. 1   Exploded view of torque converter clutch

1-2 SHIFT COMPLAINTS

Before diagnosing 1-2 shift problems, check and correct transmission fluid and set T.V. cable to specifications.

Slow, Early Or Drawn Out Shifts With End Bump

1. Disconnected or binding T.V. cable.
2. Low oil pressure. Check oil pressure in neutral at full T.V.
3. Intermediate servo piston oil seal missing or damaged.
4. Servo piston damaged.
5. Leak between servo apply pin and case.
6. Intermediate servo band apply pin binding in case.
7. T.V. plunger, T.V. shift valve or 1-2 accumulator valve binding.
8. 1-2 accumulator piston, seal, spring or bore damaged.
9. Incorrect or leaking spacer plate and/or gaskets.
10. Case porous in 2nd, servo apply and/or 1-2 accumulator passages.
11. Burned intermediate band.
12. Case cover improperly torqued.

Hunts 1-2-1 At Low Speed

1. Governor springs distorted and/or weights binding.

Firm, Harsh Or Delayed Shifts

1. Disconnected or binding T.V. cable.
2. High oil pressure. Check oil pressure in neutral at minimum T.V.
3. Compare 1-2 shift feel at part throttle in Drive range to 1-2 shift feel at part throttle in intermediate range. If inter-

mediate range is firmer, follow steps 2 through 12 under "Slow, Early or Drawn Out Shifts With End Bump." If shift feels the same for both ranges, proceed to next step.

4. Intermediate servo piston, piston seal or piston bore damaged.
5. Missing servo orifice bleed cup plug.
6. Leak between servo apply pin and and case or wrong apply pin.
7. Incorrect T.V. link.
8. T.V. plunger, T.V. shift valve or 1-2 accumulator valve binding.
9. 1-2 accumulator piston piston, seal spring or bore damaged.
10. Incorrect or leaking spacer plate and/or gaskets.
11. Leaking 2nd oil passage in case or case cover.

2-3 SHIFT COMPLAINTS

Before diagnosing 2-3 shift problems, check transmission fluid level and adjust T.V. cable and manual linkage as required.

Delayed Harsh Upshift

1. High oil pressure.
2. Direct clutch accumulator exhaust hole plugged or not drilled.
3. Direct clutch exhaust valve check ball No. 1 missing, improperly located or leaking.
4. Valve body throttle valve and plunger binding.
5. T.V. shift valve binding.

Slow, Early Or Drawn Out Shifts With End Bump

1. Low oil pressure.
2. Intermediate servo piston to case seal ring missing or damaged.
3. Servo piston or bore (case) damaged.
4. Orifice plug missing from case servo bore area.
5. Accumulator exhaust check valve not seated.
6. Direct clutch feed orifice in spacer plate restricted.
7. Spacer plate or gaskets leaking or incorrectly installed.
8. Check ball No. 5 not seated.
9. Direct clutch case cover passages porous or incorrect cover gasket.
10. Driven sprocket support passages interconnected, leaking or restricted.
11. Driven sprocket support oil seal rings damaged or missing. Support inner sleeve loose or out of position.
12. Direct clutch check ball, check ball capsule or seals damaged or leaking.
13. Direct clutch piston or housing cracked, apply ring missing or incorrect number of clutch plates.

FAILS TO SHIFT 2-3 OR DELAYED 2-3 SHIFT

Check transmission fluid level, set T.V. cable to specifications and check manual linkage before diagnosing shift problems.

1. Incorrect, broken, disconnected or binding T.V. cable.
2. Worn governor cover.
3. Governor thrust washer and seal worn or missing.
4. Governor spring unseated, weights

binding or exhaust check balls missing.
5. Governor driven gear stripped or missing.
6. Intermediate servo piston, bore or seal ring damaged.
7. Intermediate servo orifice bleed cup in case missing or case porous in servo bore area.
8. Direct clutch accumulator cup plug or accumulator exhaust check valve leaking or missing.
9. Binding throttle lever and bracket assembly or wrong or disconnected T.V. link.
10. 2-3 shift valve, 2-3 T.V. valve or shift T.V. valve sticking or binding.
11. Governor feed to 2-3 T.V. valve or direct clutch feed orifice restricted.
12. Valve body spacer plate or gaskets leaking, damaged or incorrectly installed.
13. Missing or improperly located No. 5 check ball.
14. Governor shaft case sleeve or driven sprocket support oil seal damaged or missing.
15. Direct clutch piston, piston housing or seals damaged.
16. Direct clutch plates or check ball capsule damaged. Backing plate snap ring out of groove.
17. Leaking case center gasket or loose case cover bolts.
18. Leaking, interconnected or restricted driven sprocket support passages.
19. Driven sprocket support oil seal rings missing or damaged.
20. Driven sprocket support sleeve loose or out of position.

DELAY IN DRIVE & REVERSE

1. Low fluid level.
2. Low line pressures. A 3 to 5 second delay in Drive or reverse with engine off for 60 minutes or longer indicates converter drain back.
3. Damaged turbine shaft Teflon seals. Replace with solid seals.

NO UPSHIFTS, DELAYED UPSHIFTS OR FULL THROTTLE UPSHIFTS

1. Improperly adjusted linkage
2. T.V. cable improperly adjusted, disconnected or broken.
3. Oil level low.
4. Governor cover worn or thrust washer missing.
5. Governor seal worn or cut.
6. Governor spring not seated or weights binding on pin.
7. Governor ball missing or driven gear stripped.
8. Intermediate servo apply pin sticking.
9. Intermediate servo seals cut or damaged, piston sticking or porosity in servo case bore.
10. Valves sticking in control valve assembly or spacer plate gaskets leaking.
11. Governor feed orifice to 1-2 and 2-3 shift valve clogged.

12. Valve body spacer drive to governor orifice clogged.
13. Intermediate band worn or burned.
14. Porosity in case cover, missing cup plugs or 2nd oil passage leaking.

2ND SPEED START, MISSES 1ST

1. Governor springs distorted or out of place. Governor weights binding.
2. 1-2 Shift or throttle valves stuck in upshift position.

SHIFTS 2-1 AT HIGH SPEEDS, PASSING GEAR

1. Damaged governor assembly.
2. Sticking intermediate servo.
3. Direct clutch orifice controlled by No. 2 check ball restricted.
4. 1-2 accumulator piston or seal missing or leaking.

SLIPS OR CHATTERS IN 1ST

1. Low fluid level.
2. Wrong or incorrectly adjusted T.V. cable.
3. Low oil pressure.
4. Restricted feed to forward clutch.
5. Burned forward clutch.
6. Rough machined surface on driven sprocket support.
7. Incorrect case cover gaskets.

SHIFTS 1-3 (MISSES 2ND)

1. Intermediate servo sticking, leaking or damaged.
2. Stuck or unseated accumulator exhaust check valve.
3. 1-2 valve sticking in control valve pump assembly.
4. Wrong or incorrectly installed spacer plate or gasket.
5. Governor feed passage to 1-2 valve blocked.
6. Intermediate band apply feed orifice blocked.
7. Case or case cover intermediate servo apply passage blocked.
8. Burned, improperly installed or broken intermediate band.

NO FULL THROTTLE 3-2 DOWNSHIFT

1. Wrong, improperly adjusted or binding T.V. cable or link.
2. Accelerator pedal and/or linkage will not open carburetor to wide open position.
3. Binding shift T.V. or throttle valve.
4. Spacer plate holes plugged and/or gaskets damaged or improperly positioned.

NO INTERMEDIATE RANGE (2ND GEAR)

1. Intermediate servo oil seal ring missing or damaged.
2. Intermediate band broken, burned or improperly positioned.
3. 1-2 accumulator piston or pin damaged or missing.

NO OVERRUN BRAKING IN LOW, REVERSE OK

1. Manual linkage improperly adjusted.
2. Lo-reverse pipe or piston seals leaking.
3. Damaged low blow off valve assembly.

TRANSAXLE NOISY

1. Low fluid level.
2. Screen plugged or screen O-ring damaged.
3. Coolant in fluid.
4. Transaxle grounded to body.
5. Roller bearing damaged or worn.
6. If noisy in 3rd gear or on turns only, check differential and final drive unit.

HIGH OR LOW FLUID PRESSURE

1. Throttle valve cable improperly adjusted or binding.
2. Throttle lever and bracket assembly binding or damaged.
3. Throttle valve or plunger binding.
4. Shift throttle valve binding.
5. Line boost valve binding.
6. Throttle valve boost valve or reverse boost valve binding.
7. Pressure regulator valve and spring binding.
8. Pressure relief valve damaged.
9. Manual valve disconnected.
10. Pump damaged.

NO DRIVE IN FORWARD RANGE, REVERSE TIES UP

1. Driven sprocket support sleeve turned.

NO FORWARD OR REVERSE IN ANY RANGE

Ties Up

1. Internal mechanical damage.
2. Broken differential.
3. Object between link and sprocket locking link assembly.

Slippage

1. Low fluid level.
2. Converter to flex plate bolts missing.
3. Low line pressure in drive.
4. Manual linkage binding.
5. Input shaft to forward clutch drum broken loose.
6. Reaction carrier broken at low roller clutch cam.
7. Broken chain assembly.

NO DRIVE IN FORWARD RANGES, REVERSE OK

1. Low line pressure in Drive.
2. Binding manual linkage.
3. Driven sprocket support drive oil passage or case cover gasket restricted.
4. Drive oil passage leak in case cover.
5. Driven sprocket support sleeve loose or improperly located.
6. Burned forward clutch.
7. Leaking valve body pipe in control valve assembly.

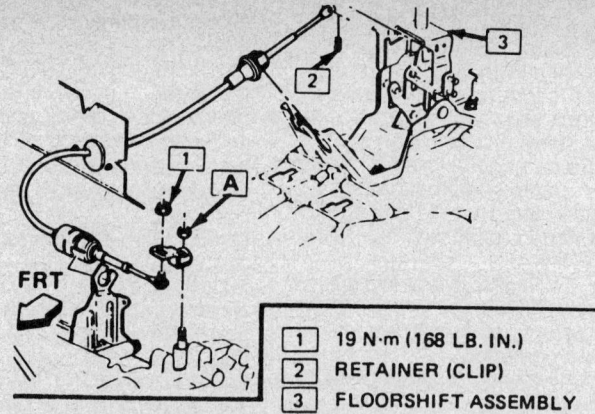

1	19 N·m (168 LB. IN.)
2	RETAINER (CLIP)
3	FLOORSHIFT ASSEMBLY

A LEVER MUST BE HELD OUT OF PARK WHEN TORQUING NUT. IMPACT TYPE TOOLS MUST NOT BE USED.

Copyrighted Material Reprinted with Permission from Hydra-Matic Div., GM Corp.

Fig. 2 Typical manual cable mounting. Cavalier, Cimarron, Firenza, Skyhawk, Sunbird & 2000; 1988 Calais, Grand Am & Somerset Regal; 1988 Skylark

NO REVERSE, ALL FORWARD RANGES OK

Ties Up

1. Forward clutch not releasing due to burned clutch plates, piston seal ring missing or sticking exhaust check ball.

Slippage

1. Low Line Pressure in reverse.
2. Restricted case to low and reverse clutch housing cup plug assembly.
3. Low and reverse clutch piston or seal leakage.
4. Low and reverse pipe O-ring or washer damaged or missing.
5. Incorrect gasket for driven sprocket support height.
6. Low 1st orifice in spacer plate plugged or missing.
7. Burned direct clutch.
8. Burned low and reverse clutch.

MAINTENANCE

To check fluid, drive vehicle for at least 15 minutes to bring fluid to operating temperature (200°F). With vehicle on a level surface and engine idling in Park and parking brake applied, the level on the dipstick should be at the "Full" mark. To bring the fluid level from the ADD mark to the FULL mark requires one pint of fluid. If vehicle cannot be driven sufficiently to bring fluid to operating temperature, the level on the dipstick should be between the two dimples on the dipstick with fluid temperature at 70°F. Note that the two dimples are located above the FULL mark.

If additional fluid is required, use only Dexron II automatic transmission fluid.

An early change to a darker color from the usual red color and or a strong odor that is usually associated with overheated fluid is normal and should not be considered as a positive sign of required maintenance or unit failure.

When adding fluid, do not overfill, as foaming and loss of fluid through the vent may occur as the fluid heats up. Also, if fluid level is too low, complete loss of drive may occur especially when cold, which can cause transmission failure.

Every 100,000 miles, the oil should be drained, the oil pan removed, the screen cleaned and fresh fluid added. For vehicles subjected to more severe use such as heavy city traffic especially in hot weather, prolonged periods of idling or towing, this maintenance should be performed every 15,000 miles.

CHANGING FLUID

1. Raise and support vehicle, then position drain pan under oil pan.
2. Remove front and side oil pan attaching bolts, then loosen rear pan attaching bolts.
3. Carefully pry oil pan loose from transaxle case and allow fluid to drain.
4. Remove remaining attaching bolt, oil pan and gasket. Thoroughly clean pan before reinstalling.
5. Remove and discard screen and O-ring seal.
6. Install replacement screen and O-ring seal, locating screen against dipstick stop.
7. Install gasket on oil pan, then install pan and **torque** attaching bolts to 8 ft. lbs.
8. Lower vehicle and add approximately 4 qts. of fluid.
9. With selector in park, parking brake applied and engine at idle speed and operating temperature, check fluid level and add fluid as necessary. **Do not race engine. Move shift lever through ranges, then back to "Park" position.**

IN-VEHICLE ADJUSTMENTS
MANUAL LINKAGE, ADJUST

Except Fiero

1. Place transaxle shift lever in "Neutral"

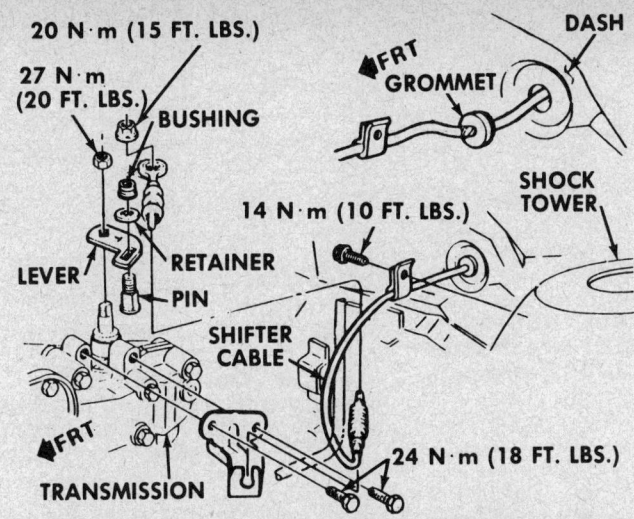

Copyrighted Material Reprinted with Permission from Hydra-Matic Div., GM Corp.

Fig. 3   Typical manual cable mounting. Celebrity, Century, Cutlass Ciera & 6000

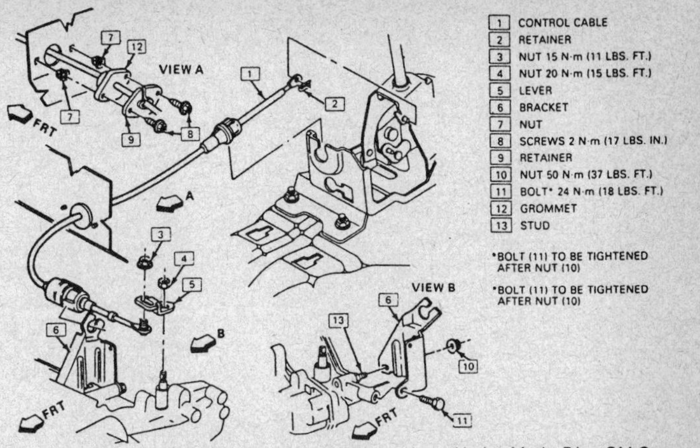

1	CONTROL CABLE
2	RETAINER
3	NUT 15 N·m (11 LBS. FT.)
4	NUT 20 N·m (15 LBS. FT.)
5	LEVER
6	BRACKET
7	NUT
8	SCREWS 2 N·m (17 LBS. IN.)
9	RETAINER
10	NUT 50 N·m (37 LBS. FT.)
11	BOLT* 24 N·m (18 LBS. FT.)
12	GROMMET
13	STUD

*BOLT (11) TO BE TIGHTENED AFTER NUT (10)
*BOLT (11) TO BE TIGHTENED AFTER NUT (10)

Copyrighted Material Reprinted with Permission from Hydra-Matic Div., GM Corp.

Fig. 4   Manual cable mounting (Floor shift). 1988–90 Corsica & Beretta

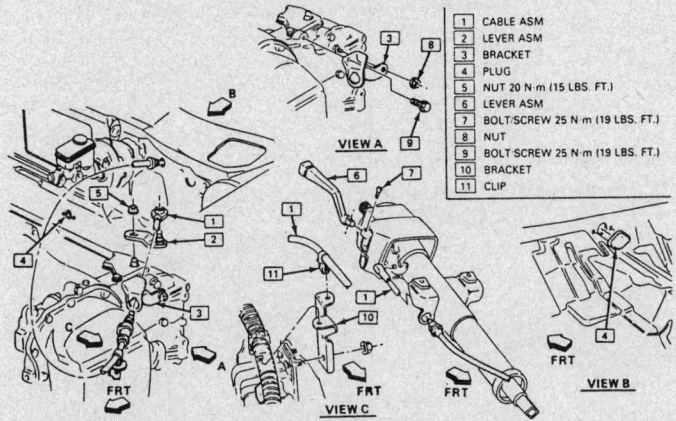

1	CABLE ASM
2	LEVER ASM
3	BRACKET
4	PLUG
5	NUT 20 N·m (15 LBS. FT.)
6	LEVER ASM
7	BOLT·SCREW 25 N·m (19 LBS. FT.)
8	NUT
9	BOLT·SCREW 25 N·m (19 LBS. FT.)
10	BRACKET
11	CLIP

Copyrighted Material Reprinted with Permission from Hydra-Matic Div., GM Corp.

Fig. 5   Manual cable mounting (Column shift). 1988–90 Corsica & Beretta

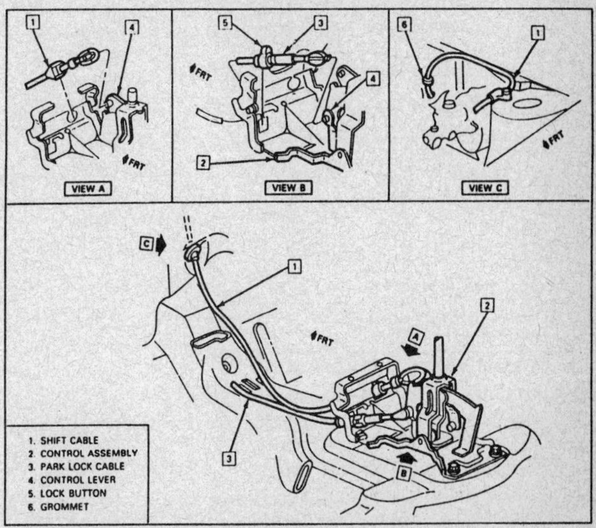

1. SHIFT CABLE
2. CONTROL ASSEMBLY
3. PARK LOCK CABLE
4. CONTROL LEVER
5. LOCK BUTTON
6. GROMMET

Copyrighted Material Reprinted with Permission from Hydra-Matic Div., GM Corp.

Fig. 6   Manual cable mounting. Cutlass Supreme, Grand Prix & Lumina

---

position.
2. Place transaxle lever in "Neutral" position by moving transaxle lever clockwise to the "L" detent, then move lever counterclockwise through three detent positions to "Neutral."
3. Loosely assemble retainer, bushing and shift cable to pin, **Figs. 2 through 6**, then **torque** attaching nut to specifications.

Fiero

1. Place transaxle shift lever in "Neutral" position.
2. Place transaxle lever in "Neutral" position by rotating transaxle lever clockwise from "Park," through "Reverse" and into "Neutral."
3. Insert shift cable threaded pin through slotted hole in lever and hand start nut, **Fig. 7**.
4. **Torque** nut to 15-25 ft. lbs. while holding lever out of "Park" position.

DETENT/T.V. CABLE, ADJUST
Except LeMans & 1988 Fiero

1. Depress and hold metal lock tab, **Figs. 8 and 9**.
2. Move slider back through fitting in direction away from throttle idler lever until slider stops against fitting, then release lock tab.
3. Rotate throttle idler lever to full travel stop position to set automatic cable adjuster on cable to correct setting, then release throttle idler lever.

1988 Fiero

1. Ensure cable is in the full non-adjusted position, **Fig. 10**.
2. Ensure cable is connected at transaxle and is working freely.
3. Check cable for kinks and twisting.
4. Ensure accelerator cable is properly installed.
5. Adjust cable by rotating idler pulley counterclockwise to 65 inch lbs.

LeMans

1. Remove air cleaner assembly.
2. Remove spring clip to release cable tension, **Fig. 11**.
3. Depress accelerator cable until it contacts kickdown switch, then install cable spring clip. **With accelerator depressed, ensure throttle valve is fully open.**

IN-VEHICLE, REPAIRS
VALVE BODY, REPLACE
Except LeMans

1. Remove valve body cover and gasket.
2. Remove solenoid retaining bolt and the solenoid, then disconnect converter clutch wires from 3rd gear pressure switch.
3. Remove screws attaching throttle lever and bracket assembly, then remove throttle lever and bracket assembly with T.V. cable link.
4. Remove the auxiliary valve body screws except for the one screw shown in **Fig. 12**. Loosen, but do not remove, this screw.

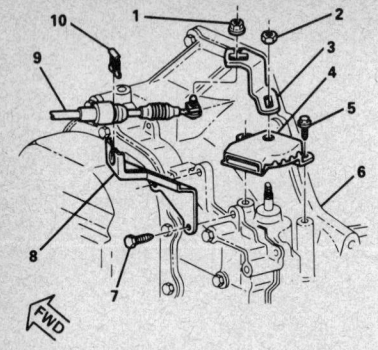

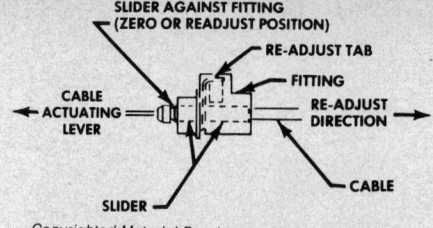

Fig. 8 Downshift cable adjustment. Except 1988–90 models w/2.0L/4-121 overhead cam engine & 1988 Fiero

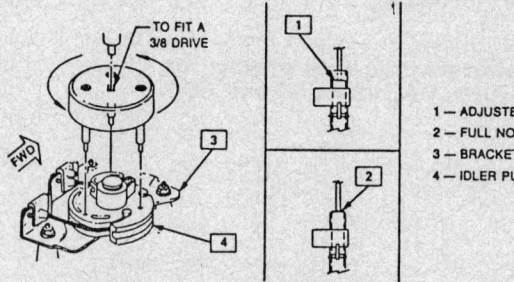

1	BOLT	4	CABLE
2	READJUST BUTTON	5	CABLE END (TO TRANSAXLE)
3	CABLE CASING		

Fig. 9 Downshift cable adjustment. 1988–90 models w/2.0L/4-121 overhead cam engine

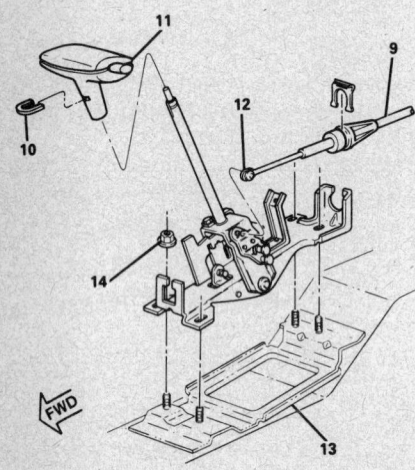

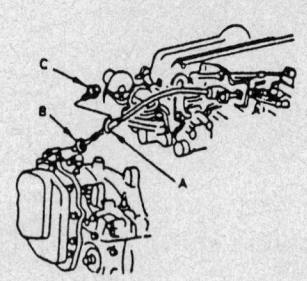

1 — ADJUSTED POSITION
2 — FULL NON-ADJUSTED POSITION
3 — BRACKET ASSEMBLY (ENGINE)
4 — IDLER PULLEY

Fig. 10 Downshift cable adjustment. 1988 Fiero

1 — NUT/CABLE ASSY.	8 — BRACKET
2 — NUT/SHIFTING LEVER	9 — CABLE ASSY.
3 — LEVER/SHIFTING	10 — RETAINER ASSY.
4 — SWITCH/NEUTRAL START AND BACK-UP	11 — T HANDLE
5 — BOLT/NEUTRAL START SWITCH (2)	12 — SNAP SECURELY ONTO PIN
6 — TRANSAXLE	13 — GEAR SHIFT SUPPORT
7 — BOLT/BRACKET	14 — NUT 23 N·M (17 FT. LB.)

Fig. 7 Manual cable mounting. 1988 Fiero

5. Remove remaining valve body retaining screws, then the valve body and pump assembly.
6. Separate valve body from auxiliary valve body.
7. Reverse procedure to install. **Torque** all 6 mm bolts to 8 ft. lbs. and all 8 mm bolts to 18 ft. lbs.
8. Using new gasket, install valve body cover to transaxle and **torque** bolts to 12 ft. lbs. Transaxle valve body covers and oil pans can have a raised rib, depressed rib or flat sealing flange. RTV sealant should be used on all oil pans and valve body covers that have a flat sealing flange. Gaskets should be used on all oil pans and valve body covers that have either depressed or raised rib sealing flanges.

LeMans

1. Disconnect battery ground cable, then disconnect T.V. cable.

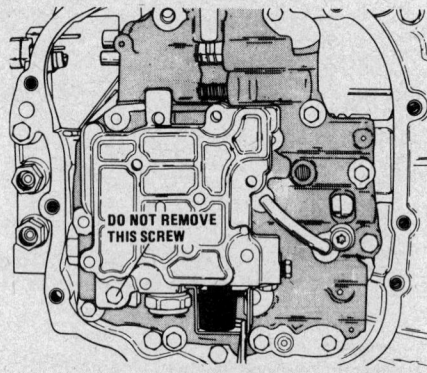

A CABLE-THROTTLE VALVE
B RING-SEAL
C BOLT

Fig. 11 T.V. cable at transaxle. LeMans

2. Raise and support vehicle.
3. Remove left front wheel and tire assembly.
4. Remove valve body cover attaching bolts and the cover.
5. Remove bolt securing TCC solenoid-to-auxiliary valve body and solenoid.
6. Disconnect TCC solenoid electrical connector from transaxle case.
7. Remove T.V. linkage bracket-to-valve body attaching bolt.
8. Remove remaining valve body attaching bolts and the valve body. Do not remove bolt "A."
9. Reverse procedure to install.

INTERMEDIATE SERVO, REPLACE

1. Remove oil pan and gasket, then remove screen and O-ring.

Fig. 12 Valve body & auxiliary valve body retaining screws

2. Remove reverse oil pipe retaining brackets, intermediate servo cover and gasket.
3. Remove intermediate servo assembly.
4. Reverse procedure to install. **Torque** intermediate servo cover screws to 8 ft. lbs.

GOVERNOR, REPLACE

1. Raise and support vehicle.
2. Remove engine to transaxle brace attaching bolts, then the heat shield, if equipped.
3. Remove speedometer cable or wire connector from transaxle.
4. Remove speedometer driven gear and sleeve assembly or speed sensor, as equipped.
5. Remove governor cover and O-ring.

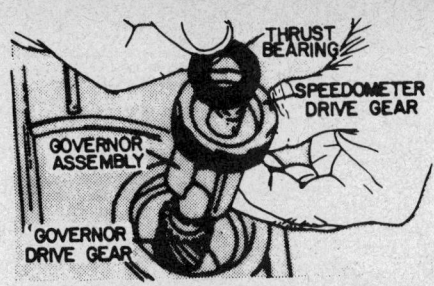

Copyrighted Material Reprinted with Permission from Hydra-Matic Div., GM Corp.

Fig. 13 Removing & installing governor assembly

6. Remove speedometer drive gear thrust washer and gear, then the governor assembly, **Fig. 13**.

TRANSAXLE REPLACE

LEMANS

1. Disconnect battery ground cable, then remove air cleaner assembly.
2. Disconnect capacitor cable from transaxle.
3. Disconnect throttle valve cable from throttle and transaxle.
4. Disconnect selector cable from transaxle lever.
5. Remove selector cable bracket, leaving cable attached to bracket.
6. Disconnect electrical connectors from speed sensor, torque converter clutch and neutral safety switch.
7. Disconnect speedometer drive cable from transaxle.
8. Remove top three engine to transaxle attaching bolts.
9. Install engine support fixture No. J28467-A with adapter No. J228467-70 or equivalent.
10. Raise and support vehicle.
11. Remove both front wheel and tire assemblies.
12. Remove lower ball joint retaining clips and stud nuts, then separate ball joints from steering knuckles using ball joint tool No. J36226 or equivalent. **Disregard "This Side Towards Wheel" marking on tool. Tool must be turned to opposite position when used on these vehicles.**
13. Remove both axle shafts from transaxle.
14. Disconnect oil cooler lines from transaxle.
15. Remove converter cover attaching bolts and the cover.
16. Mark relationship between flywheel and torque converter for installation reference, then remove torque converter-to-flywheel attaching bolts.
17. Remove left transaxle mount attaching bolts and the mount.
18. Support transaxle with a suitable jack, then remove rear transaxle mount attaching bolts and the mount.
19. Remove right transaxle mount attaching bolts and the mount.
20. Remove remaining transaxle-to-engine attaching bolts,

then carefully lower transaxle from vehicle.
21. Reverse procedure to install, noting the following **torques:** transaxle retaining bolts, 54 ft. lbs.; right transaxle mount bolts, 30 ft. lbs.; left and rear transaxle mount bolts, 16 ft. lbs.; torque converter to flywheel bolts, 44 ft. lbs.

CELEBRITY, CENTURY, CUTLASS CIERA & 6000

1. Disconnect battery ground cable, then remove air cleaner.
2. Disconnect T.V. cable from transaxle and carburetor, then remove strut shock bracket bolts from transaxle.
3. Remove oil cooler lines from strut bracket.
4. Remove all transaxle to engine attaching bolts except the one nearest the starter. Loosen, but do not remove this bolt.
5. Disconnect speedometer cable at upper and lower couplings, then remove shift linkage retaining clip, washer and bracket bolts.
6. Disconnect oil cooler lines at transaxle.
7. Remove front and left sections of cradle as follows:
   a. Install engine support fixture No. J-22825-1 and adapter No. J-22825-45 or equivalents, then **torque** fasteners to 30 ft. lbs.
   b. Position support hook into lifting bracket and tighten coupling nut only enough to remove slack from hook. **Engine support fixture must be located in center of cowl for 4 cylinder engines and on strut towers for 6 cylinder engines. Support fixture is not designed to support entire weight of engine and transaxle. Improper use may result in vehicle damage and/or personal injury.**
   c. Remove intermediate shaft to steering gear stub shaft attaching bolt, then raise and support vehicle.
   d. Support engine with suitable jack, then remove left front wheel/tire assembly.
   e. Remove power steering line brackets and steering gear mounting bolts.
   f. Disconnect drive line vibration absorber, if equipped.
   g. Disconnect left lower ball joint at steering knuckle, then remove both front stabilizer bar reinforcements and bushings.
   h. Using a 1/2 inch drill bit, drill through spot weld located between rear holes of left stabilizer bar mounting, **Fig. 14**.
   i. Disconnect engine and transaxle mounts from cradle, then remove side crossmember bolts.
   j. Remove left side body mount bolts, then the left and front cradle assembly.
8. Install axle shaft boot protectors, then position axle shaft puller behind axle

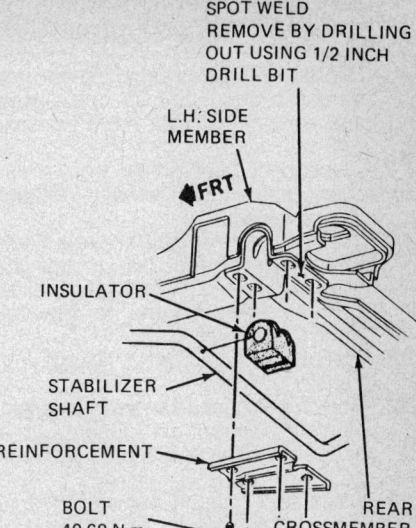

Copyrighted Material Reprinted with Permission from Hydra-Matic Div., GM Corp.

Fig. 14 Drilling cradle spot weld

shaft cones and pull cones away from transaxle.
9. Remove left axle shaft and plug bore in transaxle to avoid fluid leakage.
10. Remove starter, then the converter shield.
11. Remove the three flywheel to converter attaching bolts.
12. Remove engine to transaxle bracket extension bolts, then the rear transaxle mount bracket assembly. Raise transaxle if necessary.
13. Support transaxle with a jack, then remove the one remaining engine to transaxle bolt located near the starter.
14. Slide transaxle towards drivers side and remove from vehicle.
15. Reverse procedure to install. Note the following when installing transaxle:
   a. Position a 1/2 inch drill bit into drilled hole, **Fig. 14**, before tightening cradle bolts.
   b. Slide right axle shaft into case as transaxle is being installed.
   c. Check front suspension alignment after transaxle installation.
   d. Check and adjust T.V. cable if necessary.
   e. **Torque** transaxle mount bolts to 22 ft. lbs.
   f. **Torque** transaxle-to-engine mount bolts to 55 ft. lbs.

CIMARRON

1. Disconnect battery ground cable.
2. Remove air intake duct from air cleaner, then the left fender brace.
3. Disconnect M.A.T. sensor electrical connector from air cleaner.
4. Disconnect mass air flow sensor electrical connector, then the PCV pipe clamp from air intake duct.
5. Remove air intake duct from throttle body, then the mass air flow sensor attaching bolt.
6. Remove air cleaner bracket attaching bolts from battery tray, then the air cleaner mass air flow sensor and air intake duct as an assembly.

7. Disconnect T.V. cable from throttle body.
8. Remove T.V. cable attaching bolt from transaxle, then pull up cable cover and disconnect cable from transaxle rod.
9. Disconnect heat shield from crossover pipe, then remove exhaust crossover pipe.
10. Install suitable engine support fixture, then remove transaxle mount and bracket assembly. **It may be necessary to raise engine to facilitate mount removal.**
11. Disconnect shift control linkage from transaxle.
12. Remove upper transaxle-to-engine attaching bolts, then loosen, but do not remove, the bolt nearest the starter.
13. Raise and support vehicle, then remove front wheels.
14. Remove ball joint cotter pin, then loosen castle nut until ball joint separates from control arm.
15. Remove stabilizer bar to LEFTHAND lower control arm attaching bolt.
16. Remove six LEFTHAND front suspension support assembly attaching bolts, then position axle shaft removing tools J-28468 and J-23907 behind axle shaft cones and pull cones away from transaxle.
17. Remove axle shafts and plug transaxle bore to prevent fluid leakage.
18. Remove transaxle control cable brackets-to-transaxle attaching nut, then the engine-to-transaxle stud.
19. Remove speedometer cable from transaxle, then the transaxle stabilizer from transaxle.
20. Remove torque converter shield, then the torque converter-to-flex plate attaching bolts.
21. Remove and plug transaxle cooler lines.
22. Remove starter, then loosen brake and fuel line brackets at lefthand side of underbody.
23. Remove remaining transaxle-to-engine attaching bolts, then lower transaxle from vehicle.
24. Reverse procedure to install, noting the following:
    a. Follow the tightening sequence shown in **Fig. 15** when installing the front suspension support assembly.
    b. Readjust T.V. cable.
    c. Check front suspension alignment.

CALAIS, FIRENZA, GRAND AM, SKYHAWK, SOMERSET REGAL, SUNBIRD & SKYLARK

1. Disconnect battery ground cable.
2. On models except 3.0L/V6-181 engine, remove air cleaner assembly.
3. On models with 3.0L/V6-181 engine, remove mass air flow sensor and air intake duct.
4. On all models, disconnect T.V. cable from throttle lever and transaxle.
5. Remove fluid level indicator and fill tube.

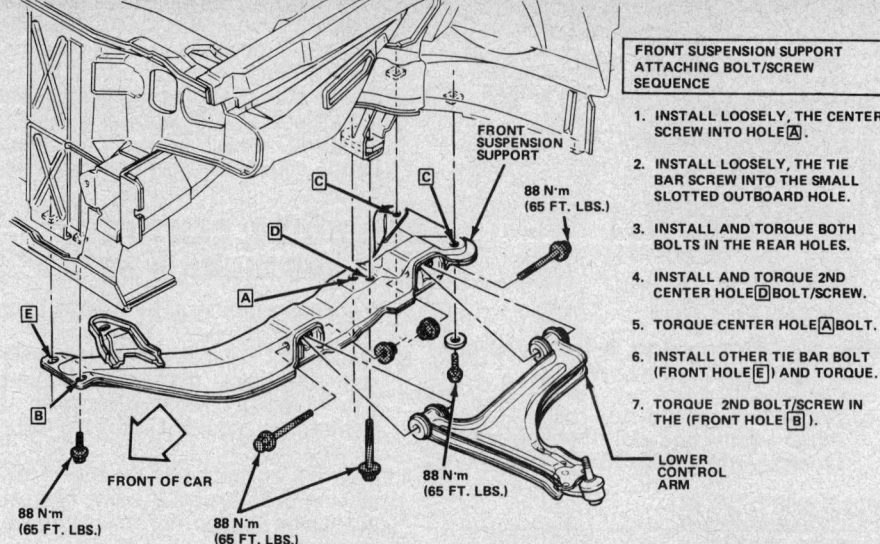

Copyrighted Material Reprinted with Permission from Hydra-Matic Div., GM Corp.

Fig. 15   Front suspension support attaching bolt sequence

6. Install suitable engine support fixture, then insert a 1/4 x 2 inch bolt in hole at right front motor mount to ensure proper driveline alignment.
7. Remove wiring harness-to-transaxle attaching nut, then disconnect the following electrical connectors:
    a. Speed sensor.
    b. TCC connector.
    c. Park/neutral and back-up lamp switch. **On Calais, Grand Am, Somerset Regal and Skylark, it may be easier to reach the park/neutral and back-up lamp switch when vehicle is raised.**
8. Remove shift linkage from transaxle, then the top two transaxle-to-engine attaching bolts and left upper transaxle mount and bracket assembly.
9. Remove transaxle-to-vent pipe rubber hose.
10. Remove remaining upper engine-to-transaxle attaching bolts, then raise and support vehicle.
11. Remove front wheels, then drain transaxle fluid.
12. Remove shift linkage and bracket from transaxle.
13. Install drive axle boot seal protector J-33162 or equivalent on inner seals. **Some vehicles may use a silicone (gray) boot on the inboard axle joint. Use protector J-33162 on these boots. All other boots are made from a thermo-plastic material (black) and do not require use of a boot seal protector.**
14. Separate ball joints from control arms, then remove both drive axles.
15. Remove transaxle mounting strut, then the left stabilizer bar link pin bolt.
16. Remove left stabilizer bar frame bushing clamp attaching nuts, then the left frame support assembly.
17. On Firenza, Skyhawk and Sunbird, remove starter and speedometer cable.
18. On all models, remove transaxle converter cover.
19. Scribe alignment mark on flexplate and torque converter, then remove torque converter-to-flexplate attaching bolts.
20. Remove and plug transaxle cooler lines.
21. Remove transaxle-to-engine support bracket.
22. Position suitable jack under transaxle, then remove remaining engine-to-transaxle attaching bolts.
23. Lower transaxle from vehicle.
24. Reverse procedure to install, noting the following:
    a. Torque converter-to-flexplate attaching bolts to 46 ft. lbs.
    b. Readjust T.V. cable.
    c. Check front suspension alignment.

FIERO

1. Disconnect battery ground cable, then remove air cleaner together with right and left engine vent covers.
2. Disconnect throttle valve cable at transaxle and throttle body, then disconnect shift cable at transaxle.
3. Disconnect electrical connectors at neutral safety switch, transaxle converter clutch and speedometer pick-up.
4. Disconnect transaxle wiring harness at transaxle to engine retaining bolts.
5. Remove transaxle oil cooler line support bracket, then remove five transaxle to engine retaining bolts.
6. Remove shift cable bracket and neutral safety switch harness.
7. Install a suitable engine support fixture, then raise vehicle and support.
8. Remove rear wheel and tire assemblies.
9. If drive axle is equipped with gray boots, install boot protectors J-33162 or equivalent.
10. Remove fixed adjusting link/lateral control arm through bolts.
11. Disconnect trailing arms at knuckles. On vehicle equipped with Tri-Pot joints, care must be taken not to allow

Tri-Pot joints to become overextended. When driveshafts are disconnected, overextending may result in separation of internal components, which may result in joint failure.

12. Remove rear axle shafts from transaxle. Support shafts from chassis using wire.
13. Remove splash shields, then disconnect brake cables at calipers and brake control cable at frame.
14. Disconnect exhaust pipe at exhaust manifold.
15. Remove two engine mount to cradle attaching nuts and two transaxle mount to cradle attaching nuts.
16. Remove two front and two rear cradle retaining bolts, then remove cradle.
17. Remove starter motor, then remove flexplate shield and flexplate attaching bolts.
18. Disconnect and plug oil cooler lines.
19. Support transaxle with a suitable transmission jack, then remove right rear support bracket.
20. Remove remaining transaxle to engine attaching bolts and disconnect ground cable.
21. Remove transaxle from vehicle.
22. Reverse procedure to install noting the following:
    a. **Torque** trailing arm at knuckle to 44 ft. lbs., then tighten an additional 90°.
    b. **Torque** fixed adjusting link/lateral control arm through bolts to 37 ft. lbs., then tighten an additional 90°.

CORSICA & BERETTA

4 Cylinder Engines

1. Disconnect battery ground cable, then remove air cleaner assembly and air intake duct.
2. Disconnect T.V. cable from throttle lever and transaxle.
3. Remove fluid lever indicator and fill tube.
4. Install engine support fixture J-28467 and adapter J-35953, or equivalent.
5. Remove wire harness-to-transaxle attaching nut, then disconnect electrical connectors from speed sensor, TCC connector, park/neutral and back-up lamp switch.
6. Disconnect shift linkage from transaxle, then remove the two top transaxle-to-engine attaching bolts, transaxle mount and bracket assembly.
7. Remove transaxle-to-vent pipe rubber hose, then the remaining upper engine-to-transaxle attaching bolts.
8. Raise and support vehicle, then remove both front wheels.
9. Remove shift linkage and bracket assembly from transaxle.
10. Install drive axle boot seal protectors J-34754 or equivalent on inner seals. **Failure to install seal protectors can result in seal damage and possible joint failure.**
11. Remove lefthand splash shield, then both drive axles.
12. Remove transaxle mounting strut, then left stabilizer bar link pin bolt.
13. Remove left stabilizer bar frame bush-

ing clamp attaching nuts, then the left frame support assembly.
14. Disconnect speedometer connector from transaxle.
15. Remove transaxle converter cover.
16. Scribe alignment marks on flexplate and torque converter, then remove torque converter-to-flexplate attaching bolts.
17. Remove transaxle cooler lines. **Plug lines to prevent leakage or dirt from entering the system.**
18. Remove transaxle-to-engine support bracket, then position a suitable jack under transaxle.
19. Remove remaining engine-to-transaxle attaching bolts, then lower transaxle from vehicle.
20. Reverse procedure to install noting then following:
    a. Torque converter-to-flexplate attaching bolts to 46 ft. lbs.
    b. **Torque** transaxle-to-engine mounting bolts to 55 ft. lbs.
    c. **Torque** transaxle mount bolts to 40 ft. lbs., transaxle mount nuts to 23 ft. lbs. and transaxle mount through bolts to 82 ft. lbs.
    d. Readjust T.V. cable and shift linkage.
    e. Check for proper oil level and leaks.
    f. Check front suspension alignment.

V6 Engines

1. Disconnect battery ground cable.
2. Remove air cleaner, mounting bracket, MAF sensor and air tube as an assembly.
3. Remove exhaust crossover bolts at RH manifold, then lefthand manifold bolts at cylinder head. **If necessary, raise and support manifold/crossover assembly.**
4. Disconnect T.V. cable from throttle lever and transaxle, then transaxle-to-vent pipe rubber hose.
5. Disconnect shift cable from transaxle.
6. Disconnect neutral start switch and T.C.C. electrical connectors.
7. Remove fluid level indicator and fill tube.
8. Install engine support fixture J-28467 and adapter J-35953 or equivalent.
9. Remove nut attaching wiring harness from transaxle.
10. Remove transaxle mount through bolt, then mount bracket and mount from transaxle.
11. Remove upper transaxle-to-engine attaching bolts, then raise and support vehicle.
12. Remove both front wheels, then lefthand splash shield.
13. Remove transaxle converter cover, then scribe alignment marks on flex plate and torque converter for reassembly.
14. Remove torque converter-to-flex plate attaching bolts.
15. Remove torsional strut and lateral strut from transaxle, then transaxle bracket bolts.
16. Disconnect speedometer connector from transaxle, then shift cable bracket.

17. Install drive axle boot seal protectors J-34754 or equivalent on inner seals. **Failure to install seal protectors can result in seal damage and possible joint failure.**
18. Remove both drive axles.
19. Remove left stabilizer bar link pin bolt, left stabilizer bar frame bushing attaching nuts, then the left frame support assembly.
20. Remove transaxle cooler lines. **Plug lines to prevent leakage or dirt from entering the system.**
21. Position a suitable jack under transaxle, then remove remaining transaxle-to-engine attaching bolts.
22. Remove transaxle assembly from vehicle.
23. Reverse procedure to install noting the following:
    a. Torque converter-to-flexplate attaching bolts to 46 ft. lbs.
    b. **Torque** transaxle-to-engine mounting bolts to 55 ft. lbs.
    c. **Torque** transaxle mount bolts to 40 ft. lbs., transaxle mount nuts to 23 ft. lbs. and transaxle mount through bolts to 82 ft. lbs.
    d. Readjust T.V. cable and shift linkage.
    e. Check for proper oil level and leaks.
    f. Check front suspension alignment.

CAVALIER

1. Disconnect battery ground cable, then remove air cleaner assembly.
2. **On 1989—90 models**, drain cooling system, then disconnect heater core hoses using clamp tool No. J-37097 or equivalent.
3. **On all models**, disconnect T.V. cable from throttle lever and transaxle.
4. Remove fluid level indicator and fill tube.
5. Install engine support fixture tool No. J-28467 or equivalent.
6. **On 1988 models**, insert a 1/4 X 2 inch bolt into hole at right front motor mount to maintain driveline alignment.
7. **On all models**, remove wire harness to transaxle attaching nut, then disconnect electrical connectors from speed sensor, TCC connector, park/neutral and back-up lamp switch.
8. Disconnect shift linkage from transaxle, then remove two top transaxle to engine attaching bolts, transaxle mount and bracket assembly.
9. Remove transaxle to vent pipe rubber hose, then the remaining upper engine to transaxle attaching bolts.
10. Raise and support vehicle, then remove both front wheels.
11. Drain transaxle fluid.
12. Remove shift linkage and bracket assembly from transaxle.
13. Install drive axle boot seal protectors No. J-34754 oe equivalent on inner seals, then disconnect both ball joints from control arms. Failure to install seal protectors can result in seal damage and possible joint failure.
14. Remove both drive axles.
15. Remove transaxle mounting strut, then left stabilizer bar link pin bolt.

16. Remove left stabilizer bar frame bushing clamp attaching nuts, then the left frame support assembly.
17. **On models equipped with 2.0L/4-121 engine,** disconnect exhaust pipe from manifold.
18. **On models equipped with 2.8L/V6-173 engine,** remove front exhaust manifold and pipe.
19. **On all models,** disconnect speedometer connector from transaxle, then remove starter motor.
20. Remove transaxle convertor cover.
21. Scribe alignment marks on flexplate and torque convertor, then remove torque convertor to flexplate attaching bolts.
22. Remove transaxle cooler lines. **Plug lines to prevent leakage or dirt from entering system.**
23. Remove transaxle to engine support bracket, then position a suitable jack under transaxle.
24. Remove remaining transaxle to engine attaching bolts, then lower transaxle from vehicle.
25. Reverse procedure to install, noting the following:
    a. **Torque** ball joint-to-knuckle to 55 ft. lbs.; flywheel-to-torque convertor to 35 ft.lbs.; stabilizer links to 13 ft. lbs.; starter to 32 ft.lbs.; starter bracket to 24 ft. lbs.; torque convertor cover 115 inch lbs.; transaxle mount strut to 31 ft.lbs.; transaxle-to-engine to 55 ft. lbs.; upper transaxle mount bracket to 38 ft. lbs.; upper transaxle mount-to-transaxle to 31 ft.lbs.
    b. Add necessary transaxle fluid.
    c. Adjust shift linkage as outlined under "Manual Linkage, Adjust."
    d. Adjust T.V. cable as outlined under "Detent/T.V. Cable, Adjust."
    e. Check front suspension alignment after transaxle installation.

CUTLASS SUPREME, GRAND PRIX & LUMINA

1. Disconnect battery ground cable.
2. **On Cutlass Supreme and Grand Prix models,** remove coolant recovery reservoir.
3. **On all models,** disconnect shift control and T.V. cable from transaxle.
4. Remove throttle cable bracket. Remove brake booster hose if equipped.
5. Remove both torque struts from engine.
6. Remove left torque strut from bracket.
7. Disconnect oil cooler lines from transaxle.
8. Install engine support fixture No. J28467-A with adapter No. J28467-90 or equivalents.
9. Raise and support vehicle.
10. Remove front wheels.
11. Remove caliper bracket assemblies and rotors.
12. Remove lower engine splash shields.
13. Remove nuts and washers from driveshafts.
14. Using front hub spindle remover tool No. J28733 or equivalent, separate axle splines from hub/bearing assemblies.
15. Remove hub/bearing assembly to knuckle attaching bolts. If equipped remove ABS sensor attaching bolts and position sensor aside.
16 Remove hub/bearing assemblies.
17. Using axle shaft remover tool No. J33008, extension tool No. J29794 and slide hammer tool No. J2619-01 or equivalents, separate right and left side axles from transaxle.
18. Remove axle assemblies from knuckles.
19. Disconnect tie rod ends and ball joints from steering knuckle.
20. **On Lumina models,** remove oil filter.
21. Remove and support A/C compressor. **Do not disconnect refrigerant lines.**
22. **On all models,** remove heat shield from rack and pinion, then disconnect electrical connector.
23. Remove main engine wiring harness to transaxle case retaining bolts.
24. Secure rack and pinion unit to exhaust system, then remove rack and pinion to frame attaching bolts.
25. Remove power steering line to frame retaining bolts.
26. Remove engine and transaxle to frame mounts.
27. Support frame with jackstands, then remove frame bolts. Remove frame and jackstands from vehicle.
28. Remove flywheel access cover, then the torque convertor bolts.
29. Remove starter retaining bolts, then support starter.
30. Disconnect battery ground cable from transaxle.
31. Remove transaxle fill tube bolt.
32. Remove transaxle mount bracket.
33. Lower vehicle.
34. Disconnect transaxle electrical connector.
35. Remove transaxle fill tube.
36. Using engine support, lower left side of engine approximately four inches.
37. Raise and support vehicle.
38. **On Cutlass Supreme and Grand Prix models,** remove fuel line bracket from transaxle.
39. **On all models,** position a suitable jack under transaxle, remove transaxle retaining bolts and lower transaxle from vehicle.
40. Reverse procedure to install noting the following:
    a. **Torque** auxiliary oil cooler bolt to 18 ft lbs, and nut to 89 inch lbs.; bracket to transaxle front stud to 35 ft. lbs.; bracket to transaxle rear bolt to 61 ft.lbs.; bracket to transaxle top stud 40 ft.lbs.; console shift control assembly nut to 18 ft.lbs.; convertor cover to 89 inch lbs.; engine to transaxle brace bolt to 35 ft. lbs.; fill tube to 18 ft. lbs.; flywheel to torque convertor to 44 ft.lbs.; mount to bracket to 22 ft.lbs.; neutral switch to 18 ft.lbs.; shift control bracket to transaxle to 18 ft. lbs.; shift control lever to transaxle nut to 15 ft. lbs.; TCC solenoid to 125 inch lbs.; transaxle cooler pipe clip bolt to 35 ft.lbs. transaxle to engine bolt to 55 ft. lbs.
    b. Add necessary transaxle fluid.
    c. Check engine oil level.
    d. Adjust shift linkage as outlined under "Manual Linkage, Adjust."
    e. Adjust T.V. cable as outlined under "Detent/T.V. Cable, Adjust."
    f. Check front suspension alignment.

TIGHTENING SPECIFICATIONS

Component	Torque/Ft. Lbs.
Case Cover To Case	18
Case To Drive Sprocket Support	18
Cooler Connector	23
Governor Cover To Case	8
Intermediate Servo Cover	8
Line Pressure Take-Off	8
Manual Detent Spring Assembly To Case	8
Oil Pan And Valve Body Cover	8
Parking Lock Bracket To Case	18
Pressure Switch	8
Pump Cover To Case Cover	8 ①
Pump Cover To Case Cover	18 ②
Pump Cover To Valve Body	8
Reverse Pipe Retainer To Case	18
Solenoid To Valve Body	8
Speedometer Driven Gear To Governor Cover	75 ③
T.V. Cable To Case	75 ③
Valve Body To Case	18
Valve Body To Case Cover	8
Valve Body To Driven Sprocket Support	18

① —6 mm bolts.
② —8 mm bolts.
③ —Inch lbs.

Turbo Hydra-Matic 440-T4 (4T60) Automatic Transaxle
INDEX

IDENTIFICATION

This transaxle may be identified by the following codes stamped into the horizontal cast rib on the right rear side of the transaxle housing.

DESCRIPTION

The 440-T4 transaxle is a fully automatic unit which provides four forward speeds including an overdrive top gear. The transmission unit includes a three element hydraulic torque converter and lock-up clutching element, four multiple disc clutch, two bands and a compound reaction planetary gear set, **Fig. 1.** Power transmitted to the drive wheels from the planetary gear through a final drive gear set and differential assembly.

The converter is designed to provide **torque** multiplication during acceleration and at slow vehicle speed, and lock-up during normal operation for increase operating economy. Operation of the converter lock-up is controlled automatically by the engine fuel system electronic control module. In addition, the converter drives the vane type oil pump by means of a shaft splined to the converter cover.

The torque converter hydraulically couples the engine to the planetary gears through a turbine and shaft assembly which drives the transmission output shaft by means of a drive link chain and sprock-

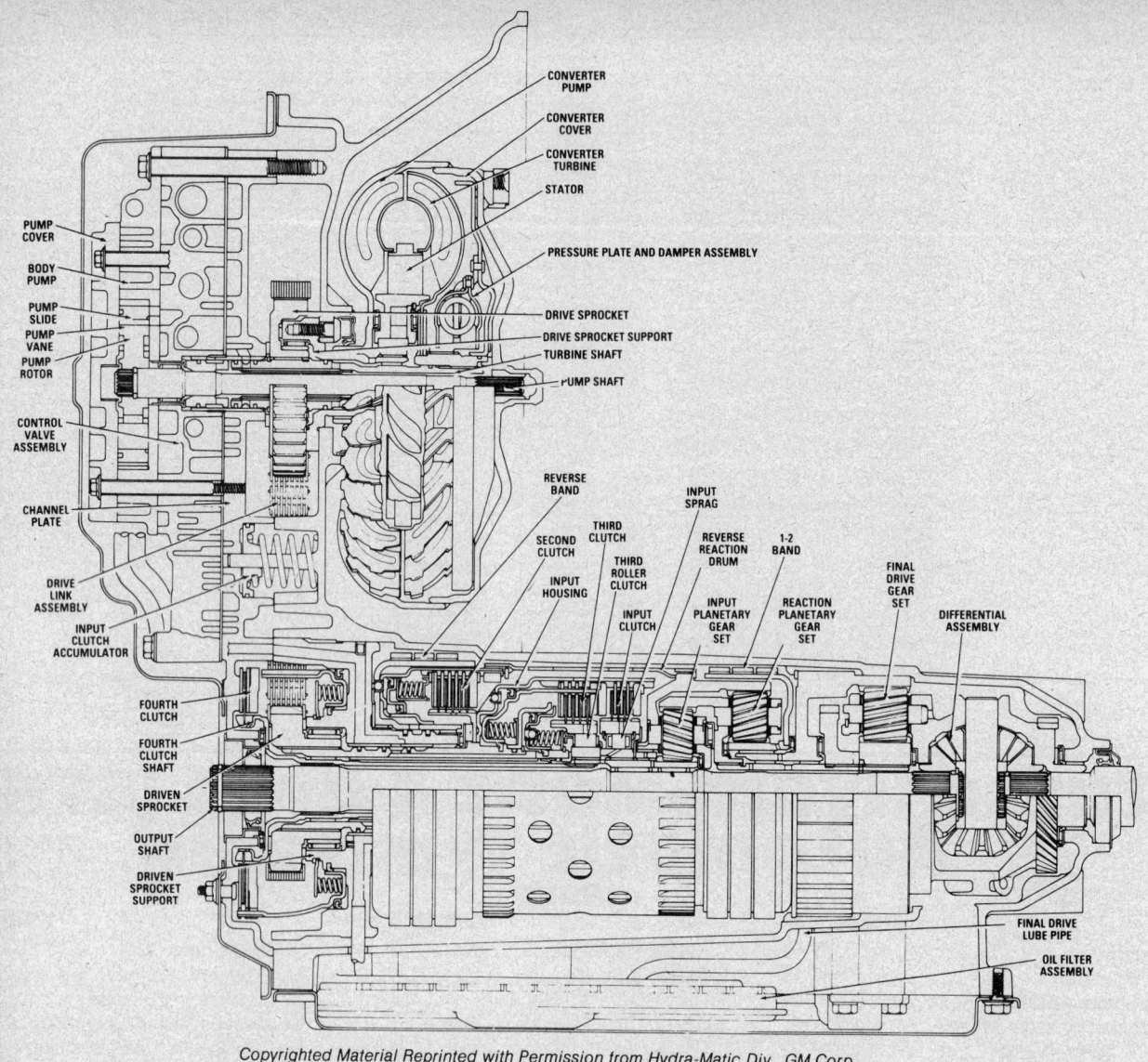

Copyrighted Material Reprinted with Permission from Hydra-Matic Div., GM Corp.

Fig. 1 Turbo Hydra-Matic 440-T4 automatic transaxle

ets.

TROUBLESHOOTING

OIL LEAK

1. Side cover distorted.
2. Oil pan attaching bolts loose.
3. Oil pan gaskets damaged.
4. T.V. cable, fill tube and/or electrical connector seal damaged.
5. Manual shaft seal assembly damaged.
6. Governor cover and/or servo covers O-rings damaged.
7. Cooler fittings and/or pressure taps insufficiently tightened, or threads stripped.
8. Converter seal damaged, or garter spring missing.
9. Axle seals damaged, or garter spring missing.
10. Modulator O-ring damaged.
11. Parking plunger guide O-ring damaged.
12. Speedometer O-ring damaged.

OIL FORCED OUT VENT OR FOAMING OIL

1. High fluid level.
2. Overheated or contaminated oil.
3. Damaged filter or filter seal.
4. Leaking accumulator cover pipe or drive socket support lubrication pipes.
5. Thermo element not closing properly.
6. Thermo element improperly installed or incorrect pin height.
7. Defective or improperly installed modulator port gasket.
8. Plugged drive sprocket support drain back holes.

OIL PRESSURE HIGH OR LOW

1. Incorrect fluid level.
2. Contaminated fluid or engine overheating.
3. Vacuum line leaking.
4. Modulator leaking or modulator diaphragm damaged.
5. Nicked, scored or stuck modulator valve.
6. Pressure regulator valve or spring damaged.
7. Pressure relief valve spring damaged or ball missing.
8. Oil pump damaged or restricted.
9. Aspirator "T" blocked or incorrectly installed.

DELAYED ENGAGEMENT

1. Low oil level.
2. Cooler check ball not seating.
3. Damaged or defective reverse servo seal.
4. Damaged or defective 1-2 servo seal.
5. Leaking 1-2 servo oil pipes.

NO DRIVE IN D RANGE

1. Low fluid level.
2. Low oil pressure.
3. Manual linkage improperly adjusted or disconnected.
4. Torque converter stator roller clutch sluggish or converter not properly at-

tached to flex plate.
5. Drive axles disengaged.
6. Damaged or broken drive link chain, sprockets or bearings.
7. Damaged 1-2 servo or incorrect apply pin.
8. 1-2 servo oil pipes or pipe seals leaking.
9. Damaged oil pump or pump driveshaft.
10. Input clutch reverse check ball out of position.
11. Burned input clutch plates, damaged clutch seals or damaged piston.
12. Leaking input housing check ball.
13. Damaged input shaft seals or blocked input shaft passages.
14. Defective input sprag or improper sprag and input sun gear assembly. **When servicing transaxle for intermittent or complete loss of drive, the input sprag assembly should always be replaced. A sprag causing intermittent loss of drive may appear in satisfactory condition while still being susceptible to "pop-out" during operation.**
15. Third roller clutch burned due to lack of lubrication.
16. Damaged input carrier and/or reaction carrier.
17. Damaged or improperly installed output shaft.
18. Burned or improperly installed 1-2 band.
19. Damaged final drive assembly and/or final drive sun gear shaft.
20. Broken parking pawl spring.

SLIPS IN DRIVE
1. Incorrect oil level.
2. Cut or damaged vacuum line to modulator or defective modulator.
3. Low oil pressure.
4. Damaged 1-2 servo or servo piston seal.
5. Plugged filter screen.
6. Leaking servo oil pipes or pipe seals.
7. Defective converter stator clutch.
8. Defective input clutch accumulator or damaged input shaft seals.
9. Damaged or defective input clutch or leaks at ball capsule.

NO 1-2 UPSHIFT, 1ST SPEED ONLY
1. Governor weights binding.
2. Governor springs or gear damaged.
3. Leaking governor oil pipes.
4. Leaking governor retainer or blocked governor screen.
5. Leaking accumulator cover, retainer or oil pipes.
6. 1-2 shift valve sticking or binding.
7. Valve body spacer plate or gaskets damaged or improperly positioned.
8. Damaged driven sprocket support oil rings.
9. Damaged or improperly assembled second clutch.
10. Clutch housing check ball damaged.
11. Damaged reverse reaction drum splines or missing drum plate.

HARSH OR SOFT 1-2 SHIFT
1. Incorrect oil pressure.

2. Accumulator cover bolts improperly tightened.
3. Accumulator pistons, seals or springs damaged.
4. Control valve assembly accumulator valve binding.
5. Check ball No. 8 missing or improperly installed.

INCORRECT SHIFT SPEED
1. T.V. cable disconnected or improperly adjusted.
2. T.V. link, lever or bracket damaged.
3. T.V. valve and plunger binding.
4. Governor pressure incorrect.

NO 2-3 UPSHIFT, 1ST & 2ND SPEEDS ONLY
1. Governor damaged.
2. Accumulator cover oil hole blocked.
3. Leaking drive sprocket support oil pipe.
4. 2-3 shift valve binding or sticking.
5. Control valve assembly bolts improperly torqued.
6. Leaking or improperly positioned check balls.
7. Sticking 2-3 accumulator valve.
8. Leaking 1-2 servo release oil pipe.
9. Improperly installed channel plate gasket.
10. Blocked oil passage to driven sprocket support.
11. Damaged input housing and shaft seals or blocked oil passages.
12. Damaged third clutch assembly.
13. Damaged third clutch piston check ball.
14. Damaged third roller clutch assembly.
15. Third roller clutch improperly assembled on input sun gear shaft.

HARSH OR SOFT 2-3 SHIFT
1. Incorrect oil pressure.
2. Leaking 1-2 servo check ball and capsule assembly.
3. Leaking 1-2 servo release oil pipe or pipe seals.
4. Improperly located 1-2 servo feed passage check ball.

NO 3-4 UPSHIFT
1. Incorrect throttle valve adjustment.
2. Defective governor.
3. Leaking governor feed or return oil pipes.
4. 3-4 shift valve binding or stuck.
5. Damaged fourth clutch shift spline.
6. Damaged or improperly assembled fourth clutch.

HARSH OR SOFT 3-4 SHIFT
1. Incorrect oil pressure.
2. Accumulator cover and pistons seal damaged or cover bolts improperly tightened.
3. Check ball No. 1 improperly located.

NO CONVERTER CLUTCH OPERATION
Models w/ECM
1. ECM malfunction.
2. Damaged, loose or corroded connectors.

3. Pinched wires.
4. Third clutch switch inoperative.
5. Inoperative solenoid.
6. Solenoid screen blocked.
7. Solenoid seal leaking.
8. Converter clutch shift valve and/or apply valve sticking.
9. Damaged or defective torque converter.
10. Damaged turbine shaft seals.
11. Damaged pump shaft seals.
12. Converter clutch blow-off check ball not properly seated in channel plate.

Models Less ECM
1. Damaged electrical connectors.
2. Pinched wires.
3. Inoperative governor pressure switch.
4. Inoperative third clutch switch.
5. Inoperative fourth clutch switch.
6. Inoperative solenoid valve.
7. Stuck converter clutch shift valve.
8. Stuck converter clutch apply valve.
9. Missing No. 10 check ball.
10. Improperly seated or damaged converter clutch blow-off check ball.
11. Damaged turbine shaft seals.
12. Damaged oil pump driveshaft seal.
13. Damaged TCC accumulator piston or seal.

CONVERTER CLUTCH DOES NOT RELEASE
1. No ECM signal to solenoid or defective solenoid, if equipped.
2. Sticking converter clutch apply piston.

ROUGH CONVERTER CLUTCH OPERATION
1. Sticking converter clutch regulator valve.
2. Turbine shaft seals damaged or missing.
3. Converter clutch blow-off valve check ball damaged.
4. Damaged converter clutch accumulator piston or seal.
5. Damaged or incorrect TCC blow-off spring.

HARSH 4-3 DOWNSHIFT
1. Control valve assembly check ball No. 1 missing.

HARSH 3-2 DOWNSHIFT
1. Improper vacuum signal or defective modulator.
2. Sticking 1-2 servo control valve.
3. No. 12 check ball missing.
4. Sticking 3-2 control valve.
5. No. 4 check ball missing.
6. Sticking 3-2 coast valve.
7. No. 2 check ball missing or improperly positioned.

HARSH 2-1 DOWNSHIFT
1. Control valve assembly check ball No. 8 missing.
2. No. 2 check ball missing or improperly positioned.

NO REVERSE IN R RANGE
1. Incorrect oil pressure.
2. Damaged reverse servo piston or seal.

TURBO HYDRA-MATIC 440-T4 (4T60) AUTOMATIC TRANSAXLE

3. Reverse servo improperly assembled or improper apply pin installed.
4. Damaged or defective oil pump.
5. Damaged input clutch accumulator piston seal.
6. Damaged drive link assembly.
7. Burned, damaged or improperly installed reverse band.
8. Damaged or defective input clutch.
9. Defective input sprag.
10. Reverse reaction drum splines, input carrier and/or reaction carrier damaged.

SLIPS IN REVERSE

1. Incorrect oil pressure.
2. Damaged reverse servo seal.
3. Damaged reverse reaction carrier splines.
4. Refer to "Slips In Drive" comments.

WILL NOT HOLD IN PARK

1. Damaged or disconnect manual linkage.
2. Damaged parking pawl spring, pawl and/or parking gear.
3. Damaged actuator assembly or actuator spring.

HARSH N-D OR D-N SHIFT

1. Improper vacuum signal to modulator or defective modulator.
2. Aspirator T-fitting improperly installed or plugged.
3. No. 9 check ball missing from control valve (harsh into reverse).
4. No. 12 check ball missing from control valve (harsh into drive).
5. Thermal element does not close when hot.

TAKES OFF WHEN HOT

1. Excessive oil pressure.
2. Sticking 1-2 shift valve.

NO VISCOUS CLUTCH OPERATION

1. Improper operation of ECM.
2. Damaged ECM thermistor.
3. Damaged ECM temperature switch.

MAINTENANCE

To check fluid, drive vehicle for at least 15 minutes to bring fluid to operating temperature (200°F). With vehicle on a level surface and engine idling in Park and parking brake applied, the level on the dipstick should be at the FULL mark. To bring the fluid level from the ADD mark to the FULL mark requires one pint of fluid. If vehicle cannot be driven sufficiently to bring fluid to operating temperature, the level on the dipstick should be between the two dimples on the dipstick with fluid temperature at 70°F. Note that the two dimples are located above the FULL mark.

If additional fluid is required, use only Dexron II automatic transmission fluid.

An early change to a darker color from the usual red color and/or a strong odor that is usually associated with overheated fluid is normal and should not be considered as a positive sign of required maintenance or unit failure.

When adding fluid, do not overfill, as foaming and loss of fluid through the vent may occur as the fluid heats up. Also, if fluid level is too low, complete loss of drive may occur especially when cold, which can cause transmission failure.

Every 100,000 miles, the oil should be drained, the oil pan removed, the screen cleaned and fresh fluid added. For vehicles subjected to more severe use such as heavy city traffic especially in hot weather, prolonged periods of idling or towing, this maintenance should be performed every 15,000 miles.

CHANGING FLUID

1. Raise and support vehicle, then position drain pan under oil pan.
2. Remove front and side oil pan attaching bolts, then loosen rear pan attaching bolts.
3. Carefully pry oil pan loose from transaxle case and allow fluid to drain.
4. Remove remaining attaching bolt, oil pan and gasket. Thoroughly clean pan before reinstalling.
5. Remove and discard screen and O-ring seal.
6. Install replacement screen and O-ring seal, locating screen against dipstick stop.
7. Install gasket on oil pan, then install pan and **torque** attaching bolts to 10 ft. lbs.
8. Lower vehicle and add approximately 6 qts. of fluid.
9. With selector in park, parking brake applied and engine at idle speed and operating temperature, check fluid level and add fluid as necessary. **Do not race engine or move shift lever through ranges.**

IN-VEHICLE ADJUSTMENTS
MANUAL LINKAGE, ADJUST

1. Lift up on cable lock button, located

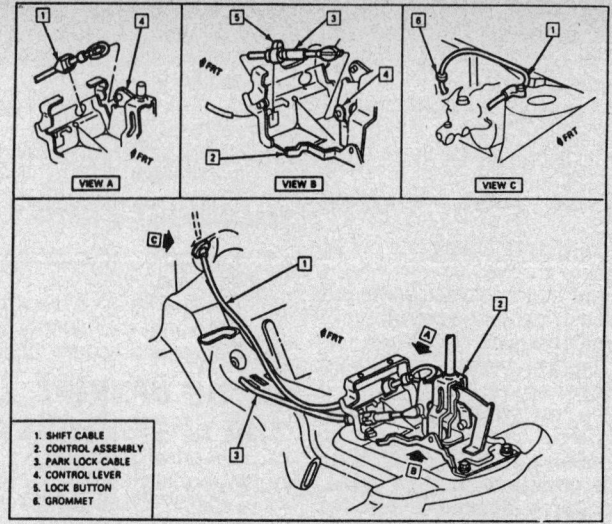

1. SHIFT CABLE
2. CONTROL ASSEMBLY
3. PARK LOCK CABLE
4. CONTROL LEVER
5. LOCK BUTTON
6. GROMMET

Fig. 2   Manual linkage adjustment

near transaxle cable bracket.
2. Place transaxle manual control lever in Neutral position. Neutral position can be obtained by rotating the manual lever counterclockwise to Park position, then rotate lever clockwise from Park, through Reverse to Neutral.
3. Place transaxle selector lever in the Neutral position.
4. Push down on cable lock button **Fig. 2.**

T.V. CABLE, ADJUST
Except 1988–90 Cutlass Supreme, Gran Prix & Regal

1. Ensure ignition is in the Off position.
2. Depress and hold metal adjustment tab at engine end of T.V. cable, **Fig. 3.**
3. Move slider until it contacts fitting, then release tab.
4. Check cable for sticking or binding and road test vehicle. **Recheck cable after engine has reached normal operating temperature, as cable may appear to operate properly with engine cold.**

1988–90 Cutlass Supreme, Grand Prix & Regal

1. With engine not operating, ensure T.V. and accelerator cables are properly installed into idle pulley.
2. Position adjustment tool into idler and rotate in a counterclockwise direction to 65 inch lbs.
3. It should be noted that during adjustment, several clicks will be heard.
4. If readjustment is necessary, depress and hold readjustment button.
5. Pull cable housing outward until slider contacts adjustment, then release button.
6. Position adjustment tool on idler and rotate in a counterclockwise direction to 65 inch lbs.
7. Measure slider position. Slider should be within 2mm of its original position.
8. After completing adjustment, road test the vehicle.

TURBO HYDRA-MATIC 440-T4 (4T60) AUTOMATIC TRANSAXLE

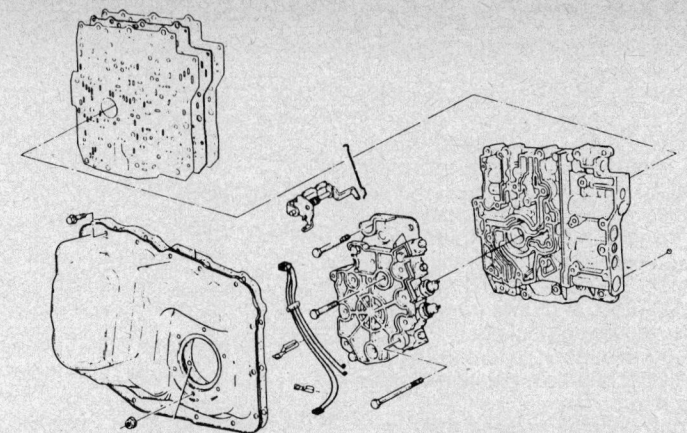

Copyrighted Material Reprinted with Permission from Hydra-Matic Div., GM Corp.

Fig. 3   T.V. cable adjustment

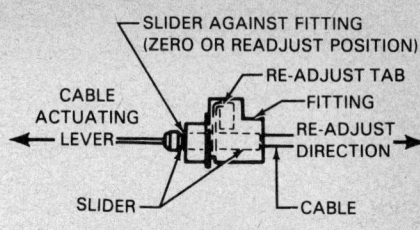

Copyrighted Material Reprinted with Permission from Hydra-Matic Div., GM Corp.

Fig. 4   Valve body replacement

IN-VEHICLE REPAIRS

VALVE BODY, REPLACE

1988–90 CUTLASS SUPREME, GRAND PRIX & REGAL

On these models, the transaxle must be removed from the vehicle to replace the valve body.

Celebrity, Century, Cutlass Ciera & 6000

1. Disconnect battery ground cleaner and remove air cleaner assembly.
2. Install engine support assembly J-28467 or equivalent.
3. Rotate steering wheel until bolt securing intermediate shaft to steering gear is facing up. Remove bolt, then disconnect intermediate shaft from steering gear stub shaft.
4. Remove upper case side cover retaining bolts.
5. Raise and support vehicle. Position jack and block of wood under engine to act as support during cradle removal, then remove left front wheel.
6. Disconnect brake line support clip from underbody.
7. Remove power steering line brackets, steering gear brackets and driveline vibration damper as needed.
8. Remove pinch bolt from left steering knuckle and disconnect lower ball joint.
9. Disconnect stabilizer bar from left control arm, then remove both front stabilizer bar reinforcements and bushings from left and right side members.
10. Drill through spot weld located between rear holes of left front stabilizer bar mounting using a 1/2 inch bit.
11. Disconnect engine and transaxle mounts from cradle.
12. Remove side member-to-crossmember attaching bolts.
13. Remove bolts securing left side body mount.
14. Remove left side member and front crossmember assembly. **It may be necessary to pull or gently pry crossmember loose.**
15. Disconnect and remove AIR pipe.
16. Remove jack and lower vehicle, then lower transaxle by adjusting engine support fixture.
17. Remove remaining bolts securing transaxle side cover pan.
18. Disconnect drive axle and remove nuts surrounding flange at channel plate. **Do not pry against case side cover to remove axle. Insert pry bar behind axle and use suitable block of wood as fulcrum when removing axle.**
19. Remove case side cover pan and gaskets.
20. Remove valve body retaining bolts, valve body and oil pump as an assembly, **Fig. 4. Do not remove 3 pump cover-to-valve body attaching bolts.**
21. Reverse procedure to install.

Electra, LeSabre, Reatta, Riviera, Toronado, 88 & 98

1. Disconnect battery ground cable.
2. Disconnect vacuum hoses from cruise control servo unit, if equipped.
3. Disconnect electrical connector from neutral/back-up lamp switch.
4. Raise and support vehicle, then remove left front wheel.
5. Remove inner splash shield.
6. Disconnect left tie rod from steering knuckle using suitable puller.
7. Disconnect stabilizer link from left control arm.
8. Install drive axle boot protectors, as needed. **Models using silicone (gray) boots on drive axle joints require the use of seal protectors J-33162 or equivalent. Models using thermoplastic boots (black) do not require the use of seal protectors.**
9. Disconnect ball joint from left steering knuckle.
10. Disconnect left drive axle from transaxle, using suitable puller, and secure drive axle aside, taking care not to extend drive axle joints.

11. Remove pinch bolt securing intermediate shaft to steering gear and disconnect intermediate shaft from gear.
12. Position suitable jack under transaxle oil pan and raise jack until weight of transaxle is supported.
13. Remove 3 bolts securing frame to body on left side.
14. Lower transaxle just enough to gain access to side cover pan bolts.
15. Disconnect cooler lines from transaxle and plug lines and open fittings.
16. Remove side cover bolts, side cover and gaskets.
17. Remove valve body retaining bolts, valve body, oil pump and gaskets as an assembly, **Fig. 4. Do not remove 3 pump cover-to-valve body attaching bolts.**
18. Reverse procedure to install.

DeVille & Fleetwood

1. Disconnect battery ground cable and remove air cleaner.
2. Install engine support fixture J-28467 or equivalent.
3. Remove upper side cover retaining bolts and the fuel pipe bracket.
4. Raise and support vehicle, then remove left front wheel.
5. Disconnect stabilizer shaft from left control arm, noting position of bushings and spacers.
6. Support control arm using suitable jack, then disconnect ball joint from left steering knuckle using suitable puller.
7. Remove left engine splash shield.
8. Remove vacuum pump mounting bolts and secure pump aside, leaving hoses connected.
9. Install drive boot seal protectors J-34754 or equivalent.
10. Disconnect left drive axle from transaxle and secure aside, using care to avoid extending drive axle joints.
11. Support transaxle using suitable jack and remove left front transaxle mount.
12. Remove right front engine mount as follows. **Vehicle should be supported at each front frame horn to prevent vehicle from tipping on hoist.**
   a. Disconnect brace between engine bracket and engine.
   b. Remove 2 nuts securing mount to frame.
   c. Remove 2 nuts securing transaxle bracket to mount.
   d. Remove 2 nuts securing transaxle mount to frame bracket.
   e. Raise engine using support fixture, then remove stud and 2 bolts se-

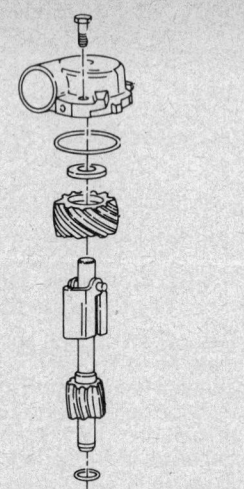

Fig. 5 Governor replacement

curing mount bracket to block.
   f. Remove mount and bracket by pulling forward.
13. Loosen left and right rear transaxle mounts.
14. Remove left cradle mounts, then separate left cradle and remove from vehicle.
15. Loosen, but do not remove, right cradle mounts.
16. Remove jacks, ensuring vehicle remains stable, then lower vehicle.
17. Note position of engine support fixture support rods and lower engine/transaxle assembly as follows. **In order to obtain maximum clearance for side cover removal it is necessary to tilt front of engine downward.**
   a. Move left rear support rod until it extends approximately 6 inches above "T" nut.
   b. Lower left front support rod until top is flush with top of "T" nut.
18. Raise and support vehicle.
19. Disconnect transaxle cooler lines from bracket and secure aside.
20. Remove remaining side cover retaining bolts and nuts securing axle opening cover.
21. Remove side cover pan and gaskets.
22. Remove wiring harness and VCC solenoid, disconnecting harness from pressure switches and case connector.
23. Remove T.V. lever, bracket and link assembly.
24. Remove oil pump retaining bolts and the pump assembly. **Do not remove 3 pump cover-to-valve body attaching bolts.**
25. Remove valve body retaining bolts and the valve body, noting position of 4 control valve-to-spacer plate check balls.
26. Remove oil pump driveshaft.
27. Remove spacer plate and gaskets, noting position of 8 spacer-to-channel plate check balls.
28. Reverse procedure to install.

Eldorado & Seville

1. Disconnect battery ground cable and remove air cleaner assembly.
2. Remove inner engine cooling fan assembly.
3. Disconnect vacuum hoses from cruise control servo and vacuum modulator.
4. Disconnect electrical connectors from cruise control servo, distributor, oil pressure sending unit and transaxle.
5. Disconnect T.V. cable from throttle lever and bracket, and from transaxle.
6. Remove vacuum modulator.
7. Install engine support fixture J-28467 or equivalent and note position of left side support hooks.
8. Raise and support vehicle, then remove left front wheel.
9. Remove right and left wheel housing lower splash shields.
10. Remove left stabilizer bar link and support left control arm with suitable jack.
11. Remove left ball joint cotter pin and nut, then disconnect ball joint using suitable puller.
12. Remove 4 nuts securing transaxle to cradle and bracket.
13. Remove A/C compressor splash shield, No. 1 cradle mount insulator cover and the left side engine mount and damper fasteners.
14. Remove 6 right front cradle joining bolts.
15. Remove left stabilizer mount retaining bolts.
16. Remove 2 left rear cradle joining bolts.
17. Disconnect wire loom and vacuum hoses from retainers on cradle and transaxle.
18. Disconnect hoses from AIR pump and disconnect pipe retainer from rear of cradle.
19. Lower vehicle.
20. Raise engine/transaxle assembly 2 inches using support fixture hooks at flywheel end of engine.
21. Raise and support vehicle.
22. Remove No. 1 insulator bolt and separate right front corner of cradle assembly, then remove left cradle section.
23. Disconnect AIR valve from transaxle and position aside.
24. Remove stud bolts securing transaxle bracket to bellhousing, noting position of bolts for installation reference.
25. Lower vehicle, then lower engine/transaxle assembly to position noted in step 7.
26. Remove transaxle mount bracket upper stud bolts and the bracket, rotating bracket clockwise to aid removal.
27. Lower left side of transaxle to limit allowed by support hooks.
28. Raise vehicle and install suitable drive axle boot seal protectors.
29. Disconnect drive axle and secure toward rear of vehicle, using care to avoid overextending drive axle joints.
30. Remove case side cover pan bolt, pan and gaskets.
31. Remove wiring harness and VCC solenoid from pressure Twitches and case connector.

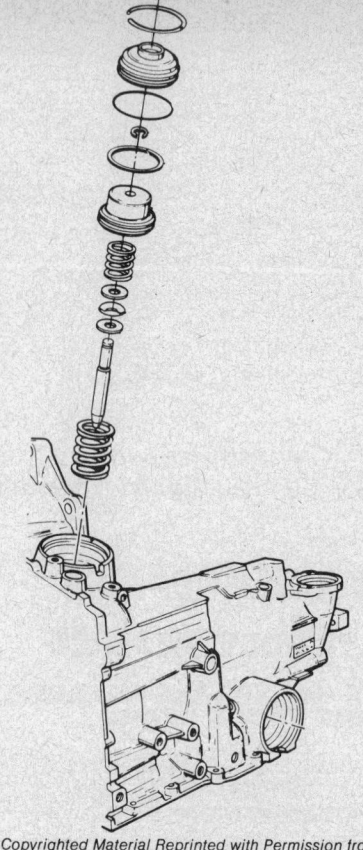

Fig. 6 Reverse servo replacement

32. Remove T.V. lever, bracket and link assembly.
33. Remove oil pump retaining bolts and the pump assembly. **Do not remove 3 pump cover-to-valve body attaching bolts.**
34. Remove valve body retaining bolts and the valve body, noting position of 4 control valve-to-spacer plate check balls.
35. Remove oil pump driveshaft.
36. Remove spacer plate and gaskets, noting position of 8 spacer-to-channel plate check balls.
37. Reverse procedure to install.

GOVERNOR, REPLACE

1. Raise and support vehicle.
2. Remove speed sensor assembly.
3. Remove governor cover attaching bolts, then the cover and seal.
4. Remove governor complete with sleeve and speedometer drive gear, **Fig. 5.**
5. Reverse procedure to install.

ACCUMULATOR, REPLACE

1. Raise and support vehicle.
2. Drain transaxle fluid and remove oil pan.
3. Remove oil filter and seal, then the accumulator cover attaching bolts and cover.
4. Remove accumulator piston, oil seal and spring.
5. Reverse procedure to install.

REVERSE SERVO, REPLACE

1. Disconnect exhaust crossover pipe.
2. Depress servo cover, then remove snap ring and servo cover.
3. Remove servo piston, sealing ring, apply pin and servo spring, **Fig. 6.**
4. Reverse procedure to install.

1-2 SERVO, REPLACE

1. Depress servo cover, then remove snap ring and servo cover.
2. Remove servo piston, sealing ring, apply pin and servo spring, **Fig. 7.**
3. Reverse procedure to install.

TRANSAXLE REPLACE

CELEBRITY, CENTURY, CUTLASS CIERA & 6000

1. Disconnect battery ground cable.
2. Remove air cleaner assembly, then disconnect T.V. cable at both ends.
3. Disconnect shift linkage from transaxle.
4. Install engine support fixture, then disconnect converter clutch electrical connector.
5. Remove 3 transaxle-to-engine attaching bolts.
6. Disconnect vacuum line from modulator.
7. Raise and support vehicle.
8. Remove left front wheel, then the lower ball joint pinch nut.
9. Remove brake line bracket from strut, then disconnect drive axles from transaxle.
10. Remove cradle-to-stabilizer attaching bolts.
11. Remove stabilizer-to-control arm attaching bolts, then the left front cradle assembly.
12. Disconnect speedometer cable from transaxle, then remove extension housing-to-engine block support bracket.
13. Disconnect cooler lines from transaxle, then remove right and left insulator attaching bolts.
14. Remove flywheel splash shield.
15. Mark relationship of flywheel to converter, then remove flywheel attaching bolts.
16. Remove all remaining transaxle-to-engine attaching bolts except one.
17. Support transaxle with a suitable jack, then remove remaining bolt and carefully lower transaxle from vehicle.
18. Reverse procedure to install.

BONNEVILLE, ELECTRA, LESABRE, 88 & 98

1. Disconnect battery ground cable.
2. Disconnect electrical connector from mass air flow sensor.
3. Loosen two hose clamps at air intake duct, then remove intake duct and mass air flow sensor as an assembly.

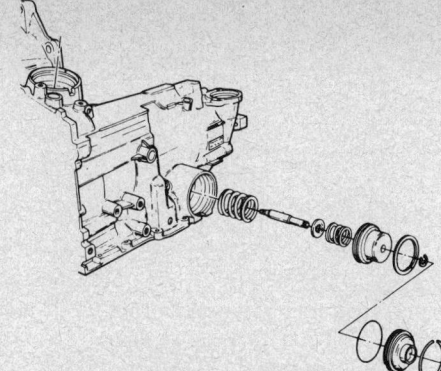

Copyrighted Material Reprinted with Permission from Hydra-Matic Div., GM Corp.

Fig. 7   1-2 servo replacement

4. Disconnect T.V. cable at both ends.
5. On models equipped with cruise control, disconnect cable from throttle body and the vacuum hoses from servo, then remove servo assembly.
6. On all models, disconnect shift control linkage from transaxle.
7. Disconnect electrical connectors from park/neutral switch, torque converter clutch and vehicle speed sensor.
8. Disconnect vacuum modulator hose from modulator.
9. Remove 3 upper transaxle-to-engine attaching bolts, then install suitable engine support fixture.
10. Turn steering wheel to the full left position, then remove both front wheels.
11. Remove right front ball joint nut and separate control arm from steering knuckle.
12. Remove right drive axle from case, using care to avoid damaging the seal.
13. Remove left drive axle, using a suitable pry bar with axle boot seal protectors installed.
14. Disconnect electrical connector from aspirator, then remove left front transaxle mount.
15. Remove right front transaxle mount attaching nuts.
16. Remove left rear transaxle mount-to-transaxle attaching bolts, then the right rear transaxle mount.
17. Remove engine support bracket-to-transaxle case attaching bolts.
18. Remove stabilizer link-to-control arm bolt.
19. Remove flywheel cover attaching bolts and the cover.
20. Mark relationship of flywheel to converter, then remove flywheel attaching bolts.
21. Remove rear cradle-to-front cradle attaching bolts.
22. Install suitable transaxle support fixture, then cradle assembly by swinging to one side and supporting with a suitable stand.
23. Disconnect cooler lines from transaxle, then remove remaining lower transaxle-to-engine attaching bolts.
24. Carefully lower transaxle from vehicle.
25. Reverse procedure to install.

DEVILLE & FLEETWOOD

1. Disconnect battery ground cable and

remove air cleaner assembly.
2. Remove T.V. cable and cable-to-cooler line bracket.
3. Remove exhaust crossover pipe.
4. Disconnect shift cable bracket and manual lever from transaxle, then secure cable, bracket and lever aside.
5. Disconnect electrical connectors from transaxle, cruise control servo and neutral/back-up lamp switch.
6. Remove upper bolts and studs securing bellhousing to engine block (positions 2, 3, 4 and 5), **Fig. 8.**
7. Disconnect vacuum line from modulator.
8. Install engine support fixture J-28467 or equivalent, noting the following:
   a. Ensure fixture is installed in extreme forward position across both strut towers.
   b. The two-piece, link-type hook should be used at passenger side rear engine hook, and both drivers side hooks should be positioned vertically.
   c. Hooks should be tightened to remove all looseness and slack, but it is not necessary to actually raise engine.
9. Raise and support vehicle, then remove front wheels.
10. Support lower control arms using suitable jacks, then disconnect both ball joints from steering knuckles using suitable puller.
11. Install suitable drive axle boot seal protectors, separate drive axles from transaxle, then secure drive axles aside. **Care must be taken not to overextend driveshaft pot joints, as joint will be damaged.**
12. Remove left stabilizer link and mounting clamp bolts, then clamp, bushings and spacers, noting position for installation.
13. Remove A/C compressor and left engine splash shields, left No. 1 mount cover and wiring harness cover.
14. Remove vacuum pump from left cradle and secure aside, then disconnect electrical connector from vehicle speed sensor.
15. Remove fasteners securing right and left front engine/transaxle mounts to cradle.
16. Remove left No. 1 mount bolts, then separate and remove left cradle assembly.
17. Disconnect and plug cooler lines, then unfasten cooler line bracket.
18. Remove transaxle-to-engine support bracket.
19. Remove right rear mount-to-transaxle bracket and fasteners securing left rear mount to transaxle.
20. Remove flexplate dust cover and colts securing flexplate to torque converter.
21. Support transaxle with suitable jack, then remove bellhousing-to-engine bolts at positions No. 1 and 6, **Fig. 8. To remove bolt No. 6, it is necessary to use a suitable extension and access bolt through right wheel house opening.**
22. Separate and remove transaxle as-

sembly.

23. Reverse procedure to install.

ELDORADO & SEVILLE

1. Disconnect battery ground cable and remove air cleaner assembly.
2. Disconnect and remove T.V. cable.
3. Remove cruise control servo.
4. Disconnect electrical connectors from distributor, oil pressure sending unit and transaxle.
5. Remove engine oil cooler line bracket.
6. Disconnect shift cable bracket and manual lever from transaxle, then secure cable, bracket and lever aside.
7. Remove fuel line bracket and disconnect neutral safety switch electrical connector.
8. Remove vacuum modulator.
9. Remove T.V. cable support bracket and remaining engine oil cooler line bracket.
10. Remove bellhousing bolts No. 2, 3, 4 and 6, **Fig. 8.**
11. Disconnect AIR crossover pipe fitting and reposition pipe.
12. Remove radiator hose bracket and fasteners securing transaxle mount to bracket.
13. Install engine support bracket J-28467 or equivalent, and note position of support hooks.
14. Raise and support vehicle and remove front wheels.
15. Remove left and right stabilizer link bolts, ball joint cotter pins and ball joint retaining nuts.
16. Support control arms using suitable jacks, then disconnect left and right ball joints using suitable puller.
17. Remove A/C compressor splash shield and No. 1 cradle mount cover.
18. Disconnect AIR pipe end hose connections and rear mounting clip.
19. Disconnect vacuum hoses and wire loom from front of cradle.
20. Remove fasteners securing engine mount, damper and transaxle mount to cradle and wire loom to transaxle bracket.
21. Lower vehicle, then raise transaxle 2 inches from position noted in step 13 using left support hooks of engine support fixture.
22. Raise and support vehicle.
23. Remove left side stabilizer mounting bolts and bolts joining cradle at right front and left rear corners.
24. Remove No. 1 cradle mount bolts. Separate cradle at right front corner, then remove left cradle section.
25. Disconnect AIR management valve bracket from transaxle mounting bracket and secure valve and bracket assembly to transaxle stud bolt.
26. Lower vehicle, then lower engine/transaxle assembly to position noted in step 13.
27. Remove transaxle mounting bracket.
28. Raise and support vehicle.
29. Remove bracket from right transaxle mount to transaxle and bolts securing engine/transaxle brace to transaxle.
30. Disconnect electrical connector from vehicle speed sensor.

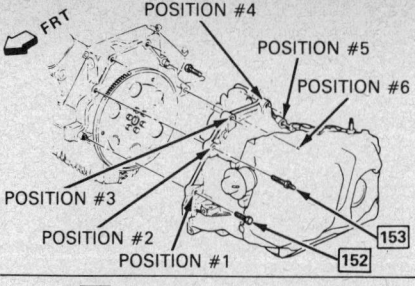

152 BOLT (75 N·m/55 FT. LBS.)
153 STUD (75 N·m/55 FT. LBS.)

Copyrighted Material Reprinted with Permission from Hydra-Matic Div., GM Corp.

Fig. 8 Transaxle bolt identification. DeVille, Eldorado, Fleetwood & Seville

31. Remove flexplate dust covers and bolts securing flexplate to torque converter.
32. Support transaxle with suitable jack, then remove bellhousing bolts No. 1 and 6, **Fig. 8.** To remove bolt No. 6, use suitable extension to gain access through right front wheel house opening.
33. Disconnect cooler lines from transaxle, then plug lines and open fittings.
34. Install suitable drive axle boot seal protectors, separate drive axles from transaxle and secure axles aside. **Care must be taken not to overextend drive axle pot joints, as joint will be damaged.**
35. Separate and remove transaxle assembly.
36. Reverse procedure to install.

REATTA, RIVIERA & TORONADO

1. Disconnect battery ground cable and install engine support fixture J-28467 or equivalent.
2. Disconnect vacuum hose from modulator and electrical connectors from transaxle.
3. Disconnect T.V. cable from throttle body and transaxle.
4. Remove cruise control servo, if equipped.
5. Disconnect selector cable bracket and manual selector lever from transaxle, then secure cable, bracket and lever assembly aside.
6. Remove neutral start/back-up lamp switch assembly.
7. Remove top 3 bellhousing bolts, bolts securing wiring harness and the driveline damper bracket.
8. Raise and support vehicle.
9. Disconnect cooler lines from transaxle, then plug lines and open fittings.
10. Remove flexplate dust cover and bolts securing flexplate to torque converter.
11. Remove engine mount nuts and left transaxle mounting bolts.
12. Remove sway bar links from lower control arms.
13. Ensure control arm is properly supported, then remove cotter pin and nut and disconnect left ball joint.
14. Disconnect left drive axle from tran-

saxle, taking care not to overextend drive axle pot joints. **Use drive axle boot seal protector J-33162 or equivalent on models with silicone (gray) drive axle boots. Models with thermoplastic (black) boots do not require the use of protectors.**
15. Remove left side frame (cradle) as follows:
   a. Remove bolt securing lower control arm assembly to frame and the strut rod nut, then rotate control arm aside.
   b. Remove engine splash shield.
   c. Disconnect wiring harness from front crossmember.
   d. Remove lower nut securing driveline vibration damper and 2 nuts securing front engine mount to frame.
   e. Disconnect left transaxle mount from frame.
   f. Remove 3 bolts from rear left side of rail and 4 bolts from right end of front crossmember.
   g. Remove left front frame mount cover and mounting bolt.
   h. Separate and remove left frame section.
16. Support transaxle with suitable jack, then remove 2 remaining bellhousing bolts.
17. Remove engine-to-transaxle brace.
18. Disconnect right drive axle and secure aside, taking care not to overextend drive axle pot joints.
19. Separate and remove transaxle.
20. Reverse procedure to install.

1988–90 CUTLASS SUPREME, GRAND PRIX & REGAL

1. Disconnect battery ground cable, then install a suitable engine support fixture.
2. Remove air cleaner assembly and intake air tube.
3. Install engine support fixture tool Nos. J28467 and J36462 or equivalents.
4. Disconnect shift control cable at transaxle, then remove cable from mounting bracket.
5. Disconnect T.V. cable at throttle linkage.
6. Remove exhaust crossover pipe to lefthand exhaust manifold attaching bolts.
7. Disconnect EGR tube from crossover pipe, then disconnect crossover pipe from exhaust pipe.
8. Loosen crossover pipe to righthand exhaust manifold attaching bolts, then swing crossover pipe upward to gain access to the two top bellhousing bolts.
9. Remove the four upper bellhousing attaching bolts. Do not remove the two lower bellhousing attaching bolts at this time.
10. Disconnect torque converter clutch electrical connector at transaxle.
11. Disconnect vacuum line from vacuum modulator and park/neutral switch

electrical connector.
12. Disconnect electrical connector or speedometer cable from transaxle.
13. Raise and support vehicle, then remove both wheel and tire assemblies.
14. Remove right and left wheel housing splash shields.
15. Detach power steering cooler lines from cradle.
16. Remove heat shield, then detach steering gear from cradle.
17. Disconnect right and left ball joints at steering knuckle. Use ball joint remover tool No. J35917 or equivalent to separate ball joints at steering knuck-le.
18. Remove transaxle mount upper attaching nuts, then remove engine mount lower attaching nuts.
19. Remove bolts attaching cradle to body, then remove cradle.
20. Disconnect transaxle oil cooler lines, then detach lines at bracket.
21. Remove torque converter cover.
22. Remove drive axles from transaxle and support from body using suitable wire. When separating right drive axle from transaxle, use drive axle boot seal protector tool No. J33162 or equivalent. The left drive axle can be removed from the transaxle by inserting a suitable pry bar into groove located on inner joint. Use care not to damage drive axle boots.
23. Remove starter motor.
24. Remove converter to flywheel attaching bolts, then remove righthand engine to transaxle support bracket at transaxle.
25. Support transaxle with a suitable transmission jack, then remove remaining transaxle retaining bolts.
26. Carefully lower transaxle assembly from vehicle.
27. Reverse procedure to install.

TIGHTENING SPECIFICATIONS

Component	Torque/Ft. Lbs.
Accumulator Cover To Case	20
Case To Drive Sprocket Support	20
Case Side Cover To Channel Plate Nut	10
Channel Plate To Case	20
Channel Plate To Driven Sprocket Support	20
Governor To Case	20
Manual Detent Spring To Channel Plate	10
Manual Shaft Inside Detent Lever Nut	25
Modulator To Case	20
Oil Scoop To Case	10
Pipe Plug	10
Pressure Switch	10
Pump Body To Case	20
Pump Body To Valve Body	10
Pump Cover To Channel Plate	10
Pump Cover To Pump Body	20
Pump Cover To Valve Body	10
Pump Plug (Orifice)	7
Retainer, Governor Oil Pipe	20
Servo Pipe Bracket To Valve Body	10
Side Cover To Case	10
Solenoid To Valve Body	10
Transaxle Oil Pan To Case	10
Valve Body To Case	20
Valve Body To Channel Plate	10

Turbo Hydra-Matic 200-4R Automatic Transmission

INDEX

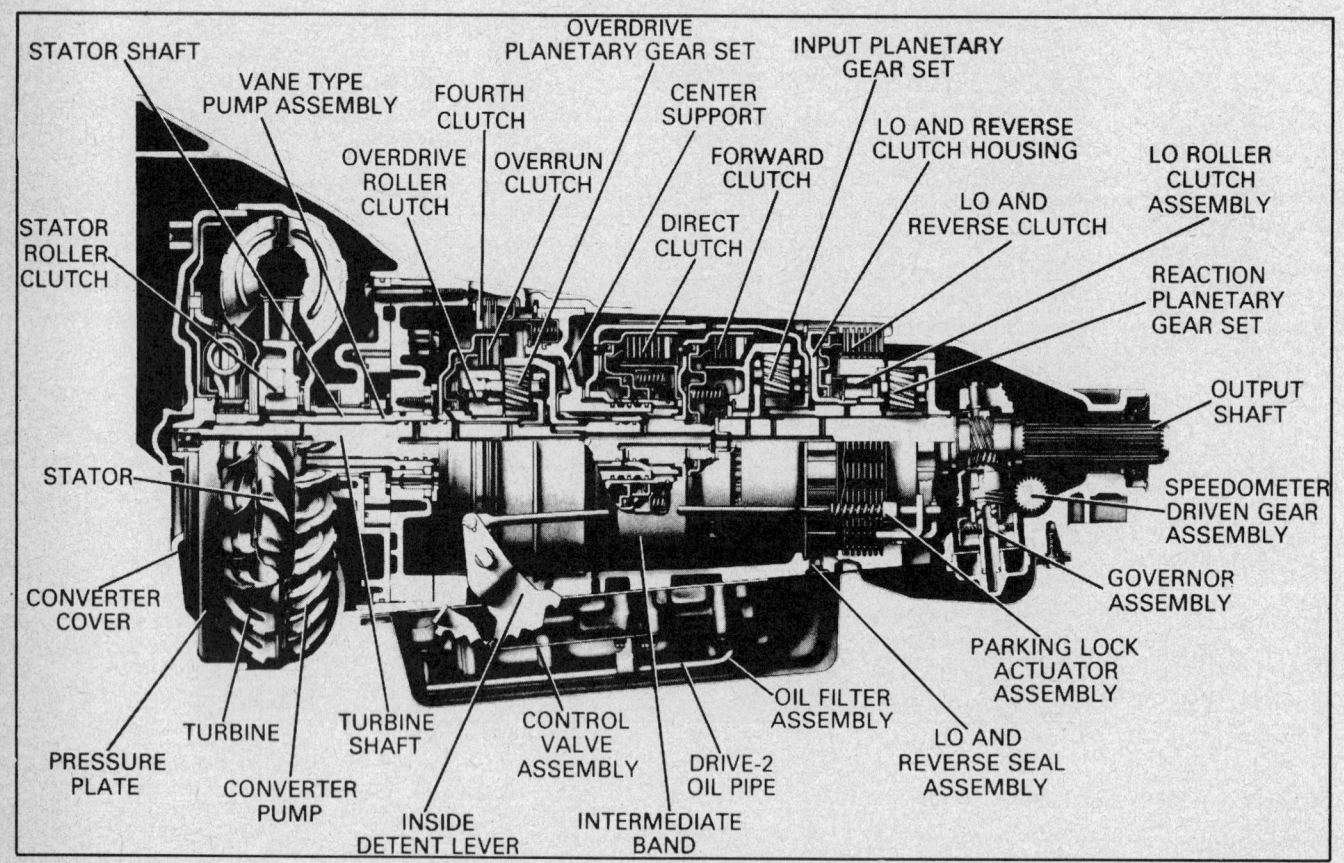

Fig. 1 THM 200-4R cross-sectional view

IDENTIFICATION

The transmission identification number is stamped on the lefthand side of the transmission.

DESCRIPTION

This transmission is a fully automatic unit consisting primarily of a three-element hydraulic torque converter with a converter clutch, a compound planetary gear set and an overdrive unit, **Fig. 1.** Five multiple-disc clutches and a band provide the friction elements required to obtain the desired function of the compound planetary gear set and the overdrive unit.

The torque converter couples the engine to the overdrive unit and planetary gears through oil and provides torque multiplication. The combination of the compound planetary gear set and the overdrive unit provides four forward ratios and one reverse. Fully automatic changing of the gear ratios is determined by vehicle speed and engine torque.

The hydraulic system in this transmission is pressurized by a variable capacity vane type pump to provide the working pressure required to operate the friction elements and automatic controls.

TROUBLESHOOTING

NO DRIVE

1. Low fluid level.
2. Manual linkage improperly adjusted.
3. Low fluid pressure.
   a. Plugged or restricted oil filter.
   b. Cut or missing oil filter O-ring seals.
   c. Faulty pressure regulator valve.
   d. Damaged pump rotor tangs.
   e. Porosity in oil filter to pump intake bore.
4. Springs missing in overdrive unit roller clutch.
5. Overdrive unit rollers galled or missing.
6. Forward Clutch.
   a. Forward clutch does not apply—piston cracked, seals missing, damaged; clutch plates burned; snap ring out of groove.
   b. Missing or damaged forward clutch oil seal rings; leak in feed circuits; pump to case gasket improperly positioned or damaged.
   c. Stuck or missing clutch housing ball check.
   d. Cup plug leaking or missing in the rear of the forward clutch shaft in the clutch apply passage.
7. Low and reverse roller clutch springs missing.
8. Low and reverse roller clutch rollers galled or missing.

HIGH OR LOW OIL PRESSURE

1. Throttle valve cable improperly adjusted, binding, unhooked, broken, or wrong link.
2. Damaged or leaking throttle valve assembly.
   a. Throttle lever and bracket assembly binding, unhooked or improperly positioned.
   b. Binding throttle valve or plunger valve.
3. Pressure regulator valve binding.
4. Throttle valve boost valve.
   a. Valve binding.
   b. Wrong valve (causing low oil pressure only).
5. Reverse boost valve binding.
6. Manual valve unhooked or improperly positioned.
7. Pressure relief valve ball missing or spring damaged.
8. Pump.
   a. Slide stuck.
   b. Slide seal damaged or missing.
   c. Decrease air bleed orifice missing or damaged causing high oil pressure.
   d. Decrease air bleed orifice plugged causing low oil pressure.
9. Throttle valve limit valve binding.
10. Line bias valve binding in open position causing high oil pressure.
11. Line bias valve binding in closed position causing low oil pressure.
12. Incorrect orifices or passages in control valve assembly spacer plate or case.

1-2 SHIFT ONLY AT FULL THROTTLE

1. Throttle valve cable binding, unhooked, broken, or improperly adjusted.
2. Throttle lever and bracket assembly binding or unhooked.
3. Throttle valve exhaust ball lifter or No. 5 ball binding, improperly positioned, or unhooked.
4. No. 5 ball sealed causing full throttle valve pressure regardless of throttle valve position.
5. Throttle valve and plunger binding.
6. Control valve body gaskets leaking, damaged, or incorrectly installed.
7. Porous case assembly.

NO 1-2 SHIFT

1. Governor and governor feed passages.
   a. Plugged governor oil feed orifice in spacer plate.
   b. Check balls missing in governor assembly.
   c. Missing or leaking inner governor cover rubber O-ring seal.
   d. Governor shaft seal missing or damaged.
   e. Stripped governor driven gear.
   f. Governor weights binding on pin.
   g. Governor driven gear not engaged with governor shaft.
2. Control valve assembly.
   a. 1-2 shift, low 1st/Detent, or 1-2 throttle valve stuck in downshift position.
   b. Spacer plate gaskets improperly positioned.
3. Case.
   a. Case channels porous or 2nd oil feed hole undrilled.
   b. Excessive leakage between case bore and intermediate band apply rings.
   c. Intermediate band anchor pin missing or unhooked from band.
   d. Broken or missing band.
4. Intermediate servo assembly.
   a. Missing servo cover oil seal.
   b. Porosity in serve; cover, inner piston, or outer piston.
   c. Incorrect intermediate band apply pin.
   d. Incorrect usage of cover and piston.
5. 1-2 accumulator.
   a. Loose 1-2 accumulator housing bolts.
   b. Damaged 1-2 accumulator housing face.
   c. Missing or damaged accumulator plate.

NO 2-3 SHIFT

1. Control valve assembly and spacer plate.
   a. 2-3 shift valve or 2-3 throttle valve stuck in the downshift position.

b. Leaking, damaged or incorrectly installed valve body gaskets.
   c. Reverse/3rd check ball not seating, damaged or missing.
2. Case channels porous.
3. Center support.
   a. Plugged or undrilled center support direct clutch feed passage.
   b. Damaged steel oil seal rings on center support.
4. Direct clutch.
   a. Inner oil seal ring on piston damaged or missing.
   b. Center oil seal ring on direct clutch hub damaged or missing.
   c. Check ball and/or retainer damaged or missing from direct clutch piston.
   d. Damaged or missing direct clutch piston or housing.
   e. Damaged or missing direct clutch plates.
   f. Direct clutch backing plate snap ring not in groove.
   g. Release spring guide improperly located, preventing piston check ball from seating in retainer.
5. Intermediate servo assembly (third clutch accumulator oil passages).
   a. Broken or missing servo to case oil seal ring on intermediate servo piston.
   b. Intermediate servo and/or capsule missing or damaged.
   c. Plugged or undrilled exhaust hole in case between servo piston seal rings.
   d. Bleed orifice cup plug missing from intermediate servo pocket in case.

NO DRIVE IN R OR SLIPS IN R

1. Binding or improperly adjusted throttle valve cable.
2. Improperly adjusted manual linkage.
3. Binding throttle valve.
4. Throttle valve limit valve binding.
5. Binding line bias valve.
6. Reverse boost valve binding in pressure regulator bore.
7. Reverse/3rd or Low/Reverse check ball missing or seat in spacer plate damaged.
8. Reverse clutch.
   a. Cracked piston, or missing inner or outer seals.
   b. Clutch plates burned.
   c. Missing or damaged reverse oil seal in case.
   d. Missing clutch plate or wave plate.
9. Center support.
   a. Loose or missing center support attaching bolts.
   b. Blocked or undrilled passages.
   c. Porosity.
10. Direct clutch housing.
    a. Cracked housing or piston.
    b. Missing or damaged inner or outer piston seal.
    c. Missing or damaged check ball in either the direct clutch housing or the piston.
    d. Plates burned.
11. Plugged Low/Reverse overrun clutch orifice in spacer plate.

DRIVE IN NEUTRAL

1. Manual linkage improperly adjusted or disconnected.
2. Forward clutch.
   a. Clutch does not release.
   b. Sticking exhaust check ball.
   c. Plates burned together.
3. Case cross leaking to forward clutch passage (D4).

SLIPPING 1-2 SHIFT

1. Low fluid level.
2. Spacer plate gaskets damaged or incorrectly installed.
3. Accumulator valve.
   a. Valve sticking in valve body causing low 1-2 accumulator pressure.
   b. Weak or missing spring.
4. 1-2 accumulator piston.
   a. Leaking seal, broken or missing spring.
   b. Leak between piston and pin.
   c. Binding 1-2 accumulator piston.
   d. Damaged 1-2 accumulator piston bore.
5. Intermediate band apply pin.
   a. Incorrect selection of apply pin.
   b. Excessive leakage between apply pin and case.
   c. Apply pin feed hole not completely drilled.
6. Intermediate servo assembly.
   a. Porosity in piston.
   b. Damaged or missing cover to servo oil seal ring.
   c. Leak between servo apply pin and case.
7. Improperly adjusted throttle valve cable.
8. Throttle valve binding, causing low throttle valve pressure.
9. Binding throttle valve limit valve.
10. Line bias valve sticking, causing low line pressure.
11. Worn or burned intermediate band.
12. Case porosity in 2nd clutch passage.

ROUGH 1-2 SHIFT

1. Throttle valve cable binding or improperly adjusted.
2. Binding throttle valve to throttle valve plunger.
3. Binding throttle valve limit valve.
4. Binding accumulator valve.
5. Binding line bias valve.
6. Intermediate servo assembly.
   a. Incorrect selection apply pin.
   b. Damaged or missing servo piston to case oil seal ring.
   c. Bleed cup plug missing in case.
7. 1-2 accumulator.
   a. Oil ring damaged.
   b. Piston stuck.
   c. Broken or missing spring.
   d. Damaged bore.
8. 1-2 shift check ball No. 8 missing or sticking.

SLIPPING 2-3 SHIFT

1. Low fluid level.
2. Improperly adjusted throttle valve cable.
3. Binding throttle valve.
4. Spacer plate and gaskets.

---

a. Direct clutch orifice partially blocked in spacer plate.
   b. Gaskets out of position or damaged.
5. Intermediate servo assembly.
   a. Damaged or missing servo to case oil seal ring.
   b. Damaged piston or servo bore.
   c. Intermediate servo orifice bleed cup plug in case missing.
   d. Case porous in the servo bore area.
6. Direct clutch feed.
   a. Direct clutch feed channels porous.
   b. Loose case to support bolts causing leakage.
   c. Cracked direct clutch piston or housing.
   d. Cut or missing piston seals.
   e. Burned direct clutch plates.
   f. Check ball in piston and/or housing missing, damaged, or leaking.
   g. Check ball capsule damaged.
   h. Release spring guide improperly located preventing check ball from seating in piston.
7. Center support.
   a. Channels cross feeding, leaking, or restricted.
   b. Damaged or missing oil seal rings.

ROUGH 2-3 SHIFT

1. Missing or improperly positioned throttle valve cable.
2. Throttle valve and plunger.
   a. Throttle valve plunger binding.
   b. Throttle valve binding.
3. Throttle valve limit valve binding.
4. Intermediate servo assembly exhaust hole undrilled or plugged between intermediate servo piston seals, preventing intermediate servo piston from completing its stroke.
5. 3-2 exhaust check ball No. 4 missing or improperly positioned.
6. 3rd accumulator check ball No. 2 missing or improperly positioned.

SLIPPING 3-4 SHIFT

1. Low fluid level.
2. Control valve assembly and spacer plate.
   a. Gaskets of space plate damaged or incorrectly installed.
   b. Accumulator valve sticking causing low 3-4 accumulator pressure.
   c. Weak or missing accumulator valve spring.
3. 3-4 accumulator.
   a. Piston stuck.
   b. Damaged bore or oil ring.
4. Center support porosity.
5. Loose center support attaching bolts.
6. Fourth clutch piston surface or seals damaged.
7. Improper clutch plate usage.
8. Burned fourth clutch plates.
9. Case.
   a. Porosity.
   b. 1-2 accumulator housing bolts loose.
   c. 3-4 accumulator piston seal damaged.
   d. 3-4 accumulator leaking between the piston and pin.

---

e. 3-4 accumulator bore damaged.

ROUGH 3-4 SHIFT

1. Throttle valve cable improperly positioned or missing.
2. Throttle valve and plunger.
   a. Throttle valve plunger binding.
   b. Throttle valve binding.
3. Throttle valve limit valve binding.
4. 3-4 accumulator.
   a. Piston stuck.
   b. Bore damaged.
5. Fourth clutch piston binding.

NO CONVERTER CLUTCH APPLICATION

1. Electrical problem.
   a. 12 volts not being supplied to clutch solenoid.
   b. Defective solenoid.
   c. Damaged electrical connector.
   d. Defective pressure switch.
   e. Wire grounded.
2. Converter clutch shift valve or throttle valve stuck.
3. Pump Assembly.
   a. Plugged converter signal oil orifice in pump.
   b. Damaged or missing solenoid O-ring.
   c. Orifice cup plug missing in oil cooler passage in pump.
   d. Damaged or improperly positioned pump to case gasket.
   e. Converter clutch application valve stuck.
   f. Cup plug missing from application passage.

ROUGH CONVERTER CLUTCH APPLICATION

1. Damaged converter clutch pressure plate.
2. Damaged or missing check ball in end of turbine shaft.

CONVERTER CLUTCH DOES NOT RELEASE

1. Converter clutch apply valve stuck.
2. Damaged converter.
3. Missing cup plug in pump release passage.
4. Missing or damaged turbine shaft end seal.
5. Hole not drilled through turbine shaft.

FIRST SPEED ONLY, NO 1-2 SHIFT

1. Governor and governor feed passages:
   a. Governor oil feed orifice in spacer plate clogged.
   b. Governor ball, or balls missing in governor assembly.
   c. Inner governor cover O-ring leaking, or missing.
   d. Governor shaft seal damaged, or missing.
   e. Governor driven gear not engaged with governor shaft.
   f. Governor driven gear stripped.
   g. Governor weights binding.
2. Control valve assembly.
   a. Spacer plate gaskets improperly installed.

b. 1-2 shift, Lo 1st/Detent, or 1-2 throttle valve stuck in downshift position.
3. Case:
   a. Porosity.
   b. 2nd oil feed hole not drilled out.
   c. Leakage between case bore and intermediate band apply rings.
   d. Intermediate band anchor pin missing, or disconnected from band.
   e. Broken, or missing band.
4. 1-2 Accumulator:
   a. Missing or damaged accumulator plate.
   b. 1-2 accumulator housing bolts loose, or face damage.

FIRST & SECOND SPEEDS ONLY

1. Control valve assembly and spacer plate:
   a. 2-3 throttle valve, or shift valve stuck in downshift position.
   b. Valve body gaskets damaged, leaking, or improperly installed.
   c. Reverse/3rd check ball not seating, damaged, or missing.
2. Porosity in case channels.
3. Center support:
   a. clutch feed passages clogged, or not drilled through.
   b. oil seal rings damaged.
4. Direct clutch:
   a. Inner oil seal ring damaged, or missing on piston.
   b. center oil seal ring damaged, or missing on clutch hub.
   c. Backing plate snap ring out of groove.
   d. Direct clutch plates damaged, or missing
   e. Clutch piston and/or housing damaged, or missing.
   f. Release spring guide improperly located, preventing piston check ball from seating.
   g. Check ball and/or retainer damaged, or missing.
5. Intermediate servo assembly (third clutch accumulator oil passages):
   a. Servo to case oil seal ring damaged, or missing.
   b. Bleed orifice cup missing from intermediate servo pocket in case.
   c. Exhaust hole in case between servo piston seal rings clogged, or not drilled out.
   d. Intermediate servo and/or capsule damaged or missing.

FIRST, SECOND & THIRD SPEED ONLY, NO 3-4 SHIFT

1. Control valve assembly and spacer plate.
   a. 3-4 shift valve or 3-4 throttle valve stuck.
   b. Plugged spacer plate orifice.
2. Center support.
   a. Plugged or undrilled oil passages.
   b. Loose or missing center support attaching bolts.
   c. Cracked or damaged fourth clutch piston.

d. Damaged, missing or improperly assembled fourth clutch piston seals.
   e. Improper plate usage.
   f. Burned fourth clutch plates.
   g. Binding overrun clutch plates.
3. Case porosity.
4. Orifice cup plug missing in 3-4 accumulator passage in case.
5. Leakage between accumulator piston and pin.
6. 3-4 accumulator bore damaged.

NO MANUAL 2ND OR 3RD

1. Turbine shaft and overrun clutch:
   a. D-3 oil passage not drilled or plugged turbine shaft.
   b. D-3 oil passage not drilled through to overrun clutch hub.
   c. Oil seals missing or damaged in overrun clutch piston.
   d. Overrun clutches burned.
   e. Overrun clutch backing plate snap ring out of groove.

NO ENGINE BRAKING IN L1

1. Improperly adjusted manual linkage.
2. D-3 orifice in spacer plate plugged.
3. Control valve body gaskets leaking, damaged, or incorrectly installed.
4. D-2 oil pipe leaking or out of position.
5. L1 overrun clutch valve binding in valve body.
6. L1/Reverse check ball No. 10 improperly positioned or missing.
7. L1/Detent check ball No. 9 improperly positioned or missing.
8. PT/D-3 check ball No. 3 improperly positioned or missing.
9. Turbine shaft and overrun clutch. No manual 3rd or 2nd should also be a complaint with the following:
   a. Plugged or undrilled D-3 oil passage in turbine shaft.
   b. D-3 oil passage not drilled through in overrun clutch hub.
   c. Missing or damaged oil seals in the overrun clutch piston.
   d. Burned overrun clutches.
   e. Overrun clutch backing plate snap ring out of groove.
10. Case porosity.
11. L1/Reverse clutch assembly. No reverse should also be a complaint with any of the following conditions:
    a. Broken or missing piston seals.
    b. Clutch housing snap ring out of case.
    c. Cracked/porous piston or housing.
    d. Missing or damaged cup plug or rubber seal between case and L1/Reverse clutch housing.

NO ENGINE BRAKING IN L2

1. Manual linkage improperly adjusted.
2. Valve body gaskets leaking, damaged, or improperly installed.
3. Leaking or out of position D-2 oil pipe.
4. Plugged D-3 orifice in spacer plate.
5. PT/D-3 check ball No. 3 improperly positioned or missing.
6. Porous case.

7. Missing or damaged intermediate servo cover to case oil seal ring.
8. Intermediate band off anchor pin.
9. Broken or burned intermediate band.
10. D-3 oil passage not drilled through in overrun clutch hub.
11. Missing or damaged oil seals in the overrun clutch piston.
12. Undrilled or plugged D-3 oil hole in turbine shaft.
13. Burned overrun clutches.
14. Overrun clutch backing plate snap ring out of groove.

NO ENGINE BRAKING IN 3RD GEAR

1. Control valve assembly and spacer plate.
   a. Manual linkage improperly adjusted.
   b. D-3 orifice in spacer plate clogged.
   c. Valve body gaskets damaged, leaking or improperly installed.
   d. PT/D-3 check ball No. 3 improperly positioned or missing.
2. Turbine shaft and overrun clutch.
   a. D-3 oil passage clogged or undrilled in turbine shaft.
   b. D-3 oil hole not drilled through in overrun clutch hub.
   c. Overrun clutches burned.
   d. Overrun clutch backing plate snap ring out of groove.
   e. Oil seals damaged or missing in clutch piston.
3. Overrun clutch backing plate snap ring out of groove.

NO ENGINE BRAKING IN D

1. Manual linkage improperly adjusted.
2. Plugged D-3 orifice in spacer plate.
3. Leaking, damaged, or incorrectly installed valve body gaskets.
4. PT/D-3 check ball No. 3 improperly positioned or missing.
5. Undrilled or plugged D-3 oil passage in turbine shaft.
6. D-3 oil hole not drilled through in overrun clutch hub.
7. Missing or damaged oil seals in the overrun clutch piston.
8. Burned overrun clutches.
9. Overrun clutch backing plate snap ring out of groove.

WILL NOT HOLD IN PARK

1. Manual linkage improperly adjusted.
2. Internal linkage.
   a. Parking pawl binding in case.
   b. Damaged actuator rod, spring, or plunger.
   c. Broken parking pawl.
   d. Loose or damaged parking bracket.
   e. Missing or improperly positioned manual shaft to case pin.
3. Inside detent lever and pin assembly.
   a. Loose nut.
   b. Worn or damaged hole in lever.
4. Manual detent roller and spring assembly.
   a. Roller assembly to valve body bolt loose.
   b. Pin or roller damaged, improperly positioned, or missing.

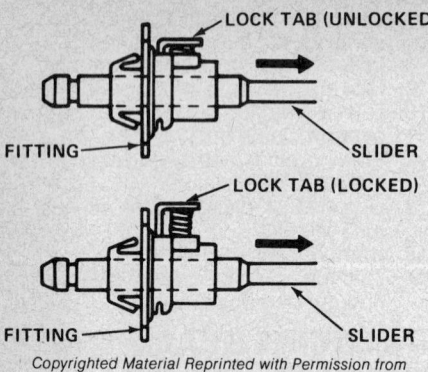

Fig. 2 Self adjusting throttle valve linkage

NO PART THROTTLE DOWNSHIFTS

1. Binding throttle valve.
2. Throttle valve limit valve binding.
3. Plugged or undrilled spacer plate hole.
4. Improperly positioned or damaged valve body gaskets.
5. Throttle valve modulator downshift valve stuck.
6. Improperly set throttle valve cable.

NO PART THROTTLE 4-3 DOWNSHIFT

On selected models with a part throttle passage in the throttle plunger bushing.

1. Throttle plunger bushing passages not open.
2. 3-4 throttle valve bushing passages not open.
3. PT/D-3 check ball No. 3 incorrectly positioned or missing.
4. Improperly positioned or damaged valve body gaskets.
5. Improperly set throttle valve cable.
6. Throttle valve limit valve binding.

LOW OR HIGH SHIFT POINT

1. Binding or improperly adjusted throttle valve cable.
2. Throttle valve limit valve binding.
3. Throttle valve binding.
4. Throttle valve modulator upshift valve binding.
5. Throttle valve modulator downshift valve binding.
6. Improperly positioned, leaking, or damaged valve body gaskets.
7. Throttle valve plunger binding.
8. 1-2, 2-3, or 3-4 throttle valves binding in bushings.
9. Pressure regulator valve binding.
10. Throttle valve exhaust ball No. 5 and lifter improperly positioned, unhooked, or missing.
11. Throttle lever and bracket assembly.
    a. Binding, unhooked, or loose at mounting valve body bolt.
    b. Not positioned at the throttle valve plunger bushing pin locator.
12. Broken or missing governor shaft to cover seal ring.

13. Broken or missing governor cover gasket.
14. Porous case.

MAINTENANCE

To check fluid, drive vehicle for at least 15 minutes to bring fluid to operating temperature (200°F). With vehicle on a level surface and engine idling in Park and parking brake applied, the level on the dipstick should be at the "F" mark. To bring the fluid level from the ADD mark to the FULL mark requires 1 pint of fluid. If vehicle cannot be driven sufficiently to bring fluid to operating temperature, the level on the dipstick should be between the two dimples on the dipstick with fluid temperature at 70°F.

If additional fluid is required, use only Dexron II automatic transmission fluid.

An early change to a darker color from the usual red color and or a strong odor that is usually associated with overheated fluid is normal and should not be considered as a positive sign of required maintenance of unit failure.

When adding fluid, do not overfill, as foaming and loss of fluid through the vent may occur as the fluid heats up. Also, if fluid level is too low, complete loss of drive may occur especially when cold, which can cause transmission failure.

Every 100,000 miles, the oil should be drained, the oil pan removed, the screen cleaned and fresh fluid added. For vehicles subjected to more severe use such as heavy city traffic especially in hot weather, prolonged periods of idling or towing, this maintenance should be performed every 15,000 miles.

DRAINING BOTTOM PAN

1. Remove front and side oil pan attaching bolts, then loosen the rear oil pan attaching bolts.
2. Carefully pry oil pan loose and allow fluid to drain into a suitable container.
3. Remove the oil pan and gasket, then remove the screen attaching bolts and remove screen.
4. Thoroughly clean oil screen and oil pan with solvent.
5. Install oil screen using a new gasket, then install oil pan using a new gasket and **torque** attaching bolts to 10-13 ft. lbs.
6. Add approximately 3 quarts of fluid, then with engine idling and parking brake applied, move selector lever through each range and return selector lever to PARK.
7. Check fluid level and add fluid as required to bring level between the two dimples on the dipstick.

IN-VEHICLE ADJUSTMENTS
THROTTLE VALVE LINKAGE, ADJUST

1. With engine off, disconnect throttle valve linkage retaining lock.
2. Rotate throttle lever to wide open position and hold in this position.

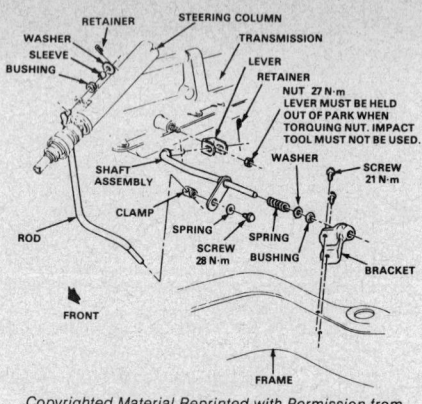

Fig. 3 Column mounted shift linkage adjustment

3. Connect throttle valve linkage retaining lock.

Self Adjusting Linkage

1. With engine off, depress locking tab and move slider rearward through fitting until slider contacts fitting, **Fig. 2.**
2. Release locking tab, then move carburetor throttle lever to wide open position and release.
3. Check cable for sticking or binding, then test vehicle for proper operation.
4. If transmission does not shift properly, raise and support vehicle and remove transmission oil pan. Inspect throttle lever and bracket assembly on valve body for damage. Check to ensure throttle valve exhaust rod is not worn or damaged. Check to ensure lifter spring holds lifter rod against bottom of valve body and that throttle valve plunger is not sticking.

MANUAL LINKAGE, ADJUST
Column Mounted

1. Position transmission shift lever in Neutral.
2. Position transmission manual valve lever in Neutral detent.
3. With clamp spring washer and screw assembled onto equalizer lever and control rod, hold clamp against equalizer lever, then snug tighten clamp screw against control rod, **Fig. 3.**

Console Mounted

1. Position console shift lever in Park position.
2. Position transmission manual valve lever in Park detent.
3. Position pin, **Fig. 4,** until pin fits loosely in transmission lever, then tighten attaching nut.

IN-VEHICLE REPAIRS
INTERMEDIATE SERVO, REPLACE

1. Raise and support vehicle.
2. Remove four catalytic converter heat shield screws, then position heat

3. Install servo cover depressor tool No. J-29714 or equivalent, using two oil pan screws.
4. Depress servo cover, then remove retaining ring.
5. Remove servo cover, then the O-ring. O-ring may be located in the case.
6. Remove the servo assembly.
7. Reverse procedure to install.

SPEEDOMETER DRIVEN GEAR, REPLACE

1. Disconnect speedometer cable.
2. Remove bolt, retainer, speedometer driven gear and the O-ring seal.
3. Reverse procedure to install.

REAR OIL SEAL, REPLACE

1. Remove propeller shaft.
2. Pry seal from extension housing with a suitable tool.
3. Drive new oil seal into extension housing, using a suitable tool.
4. Install propeller shaft.

VALVE BODY, REPLACE

1988

1. Drain transmission oil pan.
2. Remove oil pan and filter.
3. Remove screw and washer securing T.V. cable to transmission and disconnect the cable.
4. Remove throttle lever and bracket assembly. Use caution not to bend throttle lever link.
5. Disconnect electrical connectors at the 4-3 pressure switch and the 4th clutch pressure switch.
6. Remove solenoid attaching bolts, clips and solenoid assembly.
7. Remove manual detent roller and spring assembly.
8. Remove valve body retaining bolts while supporting valve body. Secure manual valve and remove valve body. Use caution not to lose the three check balls.
9. Reverse procedure to install. **Torque** valve body bolts to 12 ft. lbs.

1989—90

1. Remove transmission oil pan and filter.
2. Remove screw and washer securing T.V. cable to the transmission.
3. Disconnect electrical connectors.
4. Remove bolts securing the electrical connector clips.
5. Remove bolts securing the solenoid assembly, then solenoid with O-ring.
6. Disconnect case electrical connector, then remove O-ring seal.
7. If equipped, remove temperature switch and attaching bolt.
8. Remove pressure switch, then the T.V. lever and bracket assembly, from cable link.
9. Remove T.V. lever bracket assembly,

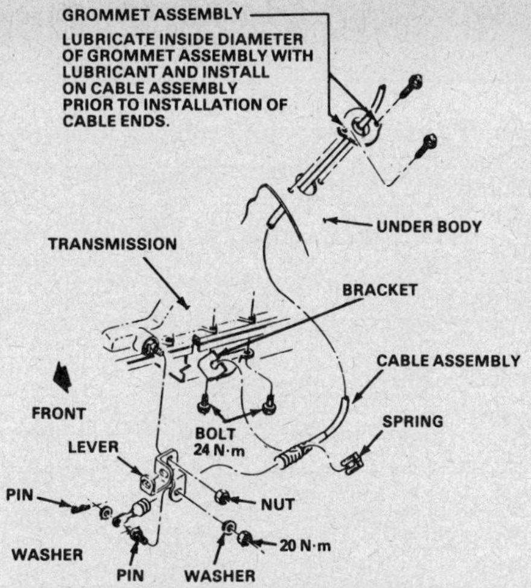

GROMMET ASSEMBLY

LUBRICATE INSIDE DIAMETER OF GROMMET ASSEMBLY WITH LUBRICANT AND INSTALL ON CABLE ASSEMBLY PRIOR TO INSTALLATION OF CABLE ENDS.

UNDER BODY

TRANSMISSION

BRACKET

CABLE ASSEMBLY

FRONT

SPRING

LEVER

BOLT 24 N·m

PIN

NUT

WASHER

PIN   WASHER

20 N·m

Fig. 4   Console mounted shift linkage adjustment

then manual detent roller and spring assembly.
10. Remove the signal oil pipe retainer and signal pipe.
11. Support the control valve assembly, then remove the remaining valve body bolts and control valve assembly. **Care must be taken when removing the control valve assembly to prevent loss of three check balls located in the assembly. Do Not carry assembly by attached pipe.**
12. Remove the check balls.
13. Lay control valve assembly down with the sensor plate side up. Do not damage the switches.
14. Reverse procedure to install. **Torque** valve body bolts to 11 ft. lbs.

1-2 & 3-4 ACCUMULATOR, REPLACE

1988

1. Remove valve body.
2. While supporting 1-2 accumulator housing, remove housing retaining bolts. Then, remove housing and gasket.
3. Support valve body spacer plate, gaskets and accumulator plate to prevent loss of the eight check balls and the 3-4 accumulator spring piston and pin located in the case. Remove remaining retaining bolt on accumulator plate. **The intermediate band anchor pin may become dislodged after removing spacer plate and gaskets.**
4. Reverse procedure to install.

1989—90

1. Remove transmission pan attaching bolts, then the pan.
2. Remove housing to valve body bolts.

3. Remove housing and pin assembly.
4. Remove 1-2 accumulator piston from housing pin and assembly. Apply low air pressure, 3 psi, to orifice housing.
5. Remove the accumulator piston seal ring from the 1-2 accumulator piston.
6. Remove the spacer plate and gaskets.
7. Remove the 3-4 accumulator piston, spring and pin.
8. Remove piston seal ring from piston.
9. Reverse procedure to install.

GOVERNOR, REPLACE

1. Drain transmission oil pan.
2. Remove oil pan and filter.
3. Remove governor attaching bolts, cover and gasket. The governor may come out with the cover. Also, it may be necessary to rotate output shaft counterclockwise while removing governor.
4. Reverse procedure to install.

TRANSMISSION
REPLACE

1. Disconnect battery ground cable and remove air cleaner.
2. Disconnect throttle valve cable from carburetor.
3. Remove transmission oil level dipstick. Remove upper bolt on dipstick tube.
4. Raise and support vehicle.
5. Mark driveshaft and companion flange for reference during installation, then remove driveshaft.
6. Disconnect speedometer cable and manual shift linkage from transmission.
7. Disconnect torque converter clutch solenoid electrical connector.
8. Remove flywheel undercover. Mark flywheel and converter for reference during installation. Remove three flywheel to converter attaching bolts.
9. Remove catalytic converter support bracket bolts and the tunnel strap.
10. Remove transmission crossmember to transmission mount bolts. Remove transmission crossmember to frame bolts.
11. Support transmission with a jack, then move crossmember rearward.
12. Lower transmission slightly and disconnect throttle valve cable and oil cooler lines.
13. Support engine with a jack, then remove engine to transmission mounting bolts.
14. Lower jack and remove transmission from vehicle. Use caution not to drop torque converter as transmission is removed. Install a converter holding tool to secure converter.
15. Reverse procedure to install noting the following:
   a. **Torque** converter-to-flexplate bolts to 46 ft. lbs.
   b. Adjust T.V. cable and linkage.

TIGHTENING SPECIFICATIONS

Component	Torque/Ft. Lbs.
Accumulator 1-2 Housing Bolts	8
Catalytic Converter Bracket	15
Center Support Bolts	18
Converter Cover Housing Bolts	7
Converter To Flex Plate Bolts	45
Cooler Connector	28
Direct Clutch Pressure Take-Off	7
Equalizer Lever To Control Rod	21
Filler Tube To transmission Bolt	35
Floor Pan Reinforcement	20
Fluid Level indicator Tube Brace To Transmission	7
Governor Cover To Case	18
Line Pressure Take-Off	7
Low Gear Block Out To Transmission Oil Pan Screw	13
Manual Shaft Hex Nut	23
Mount To Transmission Support Nut	25①
Mount To Transmission Support Nut	35②
Oil Cooler Lines To Transmission	16①
Oil Cooler Lines To Transmission	28②
Oil Cooler Pipes To Radiator Connector	28
Oil Pan Bolts	10③
Oil Pan Bolts	8④
Oil Pump Cover To Pump Body	18
Oil Pump To Case	18
Parking Paw Lock Bracket Bolt	18
Pressure Switch	10
Propeller Shaft Strap Bolts	16
Solenoid To Case	10
Speedometer Retainer To Case	10
Stator Shaft To Pump Cover	10
Starter Bolts	30
Transmission Support To Frame	40①
Transmission Support To Frame	25②
Transmission To Engine Bolts	35
T.V. Cable To Case	7
Valve Body Bolts	10③
Valve Body Bolts	11④

① —1988–89 models.   ③ —1988 models.
② —1990 models.   ④ —1989–90 models.

Turbo Hydra-Matic 700-R4 (4L60) Automatic Transmission

INDEX

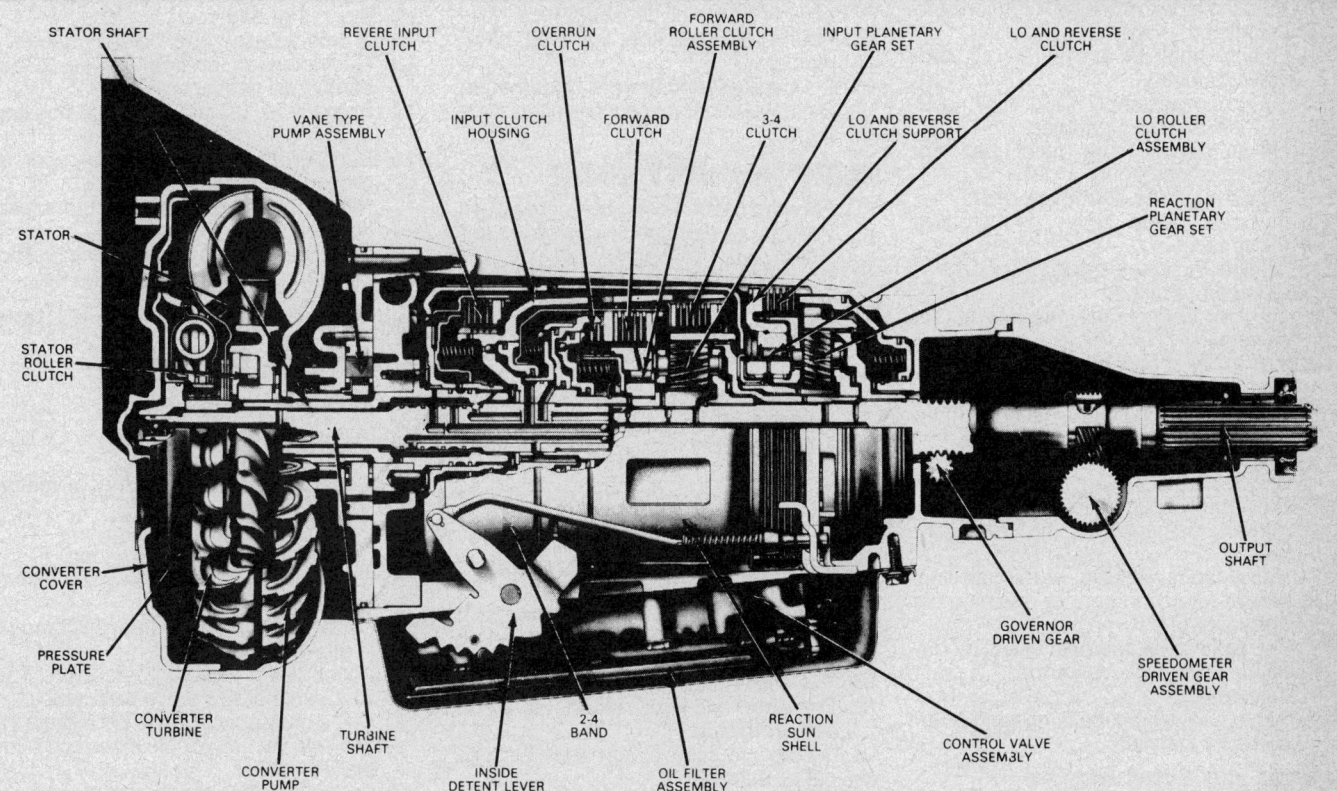

Fig. 1   700-R4 automatic transmission

IDENTIFICATION

Transmission identification code can be located in one of two positions: right rear pan to case mounting flange or right side transmission to engine mounting flange. The second and third digits of the transmission identification code denotes transmission model.

DESCRIPTION

The model 700-R4, **Fig. 1,** is a fully automatic transmission consisting of a 3-element hydraulic torque converter with the addition of a converter clutch.

Also two planetary gear sets, five multiple-disc type clutches, two roller or one-way clutches and a band are used which provide the friction elements to produce four forward speeds, the last of which is overdrive.

The torque converter, through oil, couples the engine power to the gear sets and hydraulically provides additional torque multiplication when required. Also, through the converter clutch, the converter drive and driven members operate as one unit when applied, providing mechanical drive from the engine through the transmission.

The gear ratio changes are fully automatic in relation to the vehicle speed and engine torque. Vehicle speed and engine torque are directed to the transmission providing the proper gear ratio for maximum efficiency and performance at all throttle openings.

A hydraulic system pressurized by a variable capacity vane-type pump, provides the operating pressure required for the operation of the friction elements and automatic controls.

TROUBLESHOOTING

OIL PRESSURE HIGH OR LOW

1. Oil pump assembly pressure regulator valve stuck.
2. Oil pump assembly pressure regulator valve spring damaged.
3. Oil pump rotor guide missing or incorrectly installed.
4. Oil pump rotor cracked or damaged.
5. T.V. valve and reverse boost valve or bushing stuck, damaged or incorrectly installed.
6. Orifice hole in pressure regulator valve plugged.
7. Oil pump assembly slide sticking or excessive rotor clearance.
8. Oil pump pressure relief ball not sealed or damaged.
9. Oil pump cover or body porous.
10. Incorrect pump cover or defective pump faces.
11. Oil filter intake pipe and filter body restricted or cracked.
12. Oil filter O-ring seal missing, cut or damaged.
13. T.V. exhaust ball stuck or damaged.
14. Throttle lever and bracket assembly or throttle link binding, damaged or incorrectly installed.
15. Valve body manual valve scored or damaged.
16. Valve body spacer plate or gaskets incorrect, damaged or incorrectly installed.
17. Valve body throttle valve sticking, sleeve rotated in bore or retaining pin not seated.
18. T.V. limit valve, line bias valve, modulated downshift valve or 2-3 shift valve stuck.
19. Valve body check balls missing or incorrectly installed.

HIGH OR LOW SHIFT POINTS

1. T.V. cable binding or incorrectly adjusted.
2. T.V. exhaust ball stuck or damaged.
3. Throttle lever and bracket assembly binding, damaged or incorrectly installed.
4. Sticking oil pump slide, pressure regulator valve or T.V. boost valve.
5. Valve body modulated T.V. up or down valves sticking.
6. T.V. limit valve, throttle valve or plunger sticking.

7. Valve body spacer plate or gaskets damaged or incorrect.

FIRST SPEED ONLY—NO UPSHIFT

1. Governor valve sticking.
2. Governor driven gear loose or damaged.
3. Governor driven gear retaining pin missing.
4. Nicks or burrs on output shaft, governor sleeve or case bore.
5. Governor support pin in case too long or short.
6. Governor weights or springs missing, binding or damaged.
7. 1-2 shift valve sticking.
8. Valve body spacer plate or gaskets damaged or incorrectly installed.
9. Case to valve body face not flat or damaged.
10. Governor screen restricted or damaged.
11. Restricted or blocked 2-4 servo assembly apply passages.
12. Nicks or burrs on 2-4 servo assembly pin or pin bore in case.
13. Missing or damaged 2-4 servo assembly piston or pin seals.
14. Fourth servo piston installed backwards.
15. 2-4 band assembly worn or damaged.
16. 2-4 band assembly anchor pin not engaged.

SLIPS IN FIRST GEAR

1. Forward clutch assembly plates worn.
2. Porosity or damage in forward clutch piston.
3. Forward clutch piston inner and outer seals missing, cut or damaged.
4. Input housing to forward clutch housing O-ring seal missing, cut or damaged.
5. Forward clutch housing damaged.
6. Forward clutch housing retainer and ball assembly not sealing or damaged.
7. Turbine shaft seals missing, cut or damaged.
8. Valve body accumulator valve stuck.
9. Valve body face not flat, damaged lands or interconnected passages.
10. Valve body spacer plate or gaskets incorrect, damaged or incorrectly installed.
11. T.V. cable binding or broken.
12. Damaged ring grooves on 1-2 accumulator piston.
13. 1-2 accumulator piston seal missing, cut or damaged.
14. 1-2 accumulator cover gasket missing or damaged.
15. Leak between 1-2 accumulator piston and pin.
16. Broken 1-2 accumulator spring.
17. Fourth servo piston installed backwards.
18. Incorrect oil pressure. Refer to "High Or Low Oil Pressure."

1-2 SHIFT SPEED HIGH OR LOW

1. T.V. cable binding, broken or incorrectly adjusted.

2. Faulty governor assembly. Refer to "First Speed Only — No Upshift."
3. Throttle lever and bracket assembly damaged, binding or incorrectly installed.
4. T.V. link missing, binding or damaged.
5. T.V. exhaust check ball and T.V. plunger sticking.
6. Valve body or oil pump assembly face not flat.

1-2 SHIFT SLIPPING OR ROUGH

1. Throttle lever and bracket assembly incorrectly installed or damaged.
2. T.V. cable damaged.
3. Throttle valve sticking.
4. T.V. bushing turned in its bore.
5. 1-2 shift valve train stuck.
6. Valve body assembly gaskets or spacer plate incorrect, damaged or incorrectly installed.
7. T.V. limit valve, line bias valve or accumulator valve stuck.
8. Valve body face not flat.
9. 2-4 servo assembly apply pin too long or short.
10. 2-4 servo seals or O-ring seals missing, cut or damaged.
11. 2-4 servo assembly bore damaged.
12. Restricted or missing 2-4 servo assembly oil passages.
13. Porosity in 1-2 accumulator housing or piston.
14. Second accumulator piston seal or groove damaged.
15. Nicks or burrs in 1-2 accumulator housing.
16. 2-4 band worn or incorrectly installed.
17. Oil pump assembly faces not flat.

NO 2-3 SHIFT OR 2-3 SHIFT SLIPPING, ROUGH OR HUNTING

1. Internal converter damage.
2. Governor valve stuck.
3. Governor assembly drive gear retaining pin missing or loose.
4. Governor weights binding.
5. Governor drive gear damaged.
6. Governor support pin in case too long or short.
7. Oil pump stator shaft sleeve scored or improperly installed.
8. Accumulator valve, throttle valve, T.V. limit valve or 2-3 valve train stuck.
9. Valve body spacer plate or gaskets incorrect, damaged or incorrectly installed.
10. Forward or 3-4 clutch plates worn.
11. Excessive clutch plate travel.
12. Cut or damaged piston seals in input housing assembly.
13. Porosity in 3-4 clutch housing or piston.
14. 3-4 piston check ball stuck, damaged or incorrectly sealing.
15. Restricted input housing assembly apply passages.
16. Forward clutch piston retainer and ball assembly not seating.
17. Input housing assembly sealing balls loose or missing.
18. Third accumulator retainer and ball

19. Second apply piston seals missing, cut or damaged.
20. 2-4 servo pin seals missing, cut or damaged.

NO 3-4 SHIFT OR ROUGH 3-4 SHIFT

1. Governor weights bonding.
2. Governor valve stuck.
3. Governor drive gear retaining pin missing or loose.
4. Governor drive gear damaged.
5. Governor support pin in case too long or short.
6. Oil pump assembly faces not flat.
7. Pump cover retainer and ball assembly missing or damaged.
8. Accumulator valve, throttle valve, T.V. limit valve, 3-2 control valve, 1-2 shift valve train or 2-3 shift valve train stuck.
9. Manual valve link bent or damaged.
10. Valve body assembly spacer plates or gaskets incorrect, damaged or incorrectly installed.
11. Incorrect 2-4 servo assembly band apply pin.
12. Missing or damaged 2-4 servo seals.
13. Porosity in 2-4 servo pistons, cover and case.
14. Damaged 2-4 servo piston seal grooves.
15. Plugged or missing orifice cup plug in 2-4 servo assembly.
16. Third accumulator retainer and ball assembly leaking.
17. Porosity in 3-4 accumulator piston or bore.
18. 3-4 accumulator piston seal or seal grooves damaged.
19. Plugged or missing orifice cup plug.
20. Restricted case oil passage.
21. Faulty input housing assembly. Refer to" No 2-3 Shift Or 2-3 Shift Slipping, Rough Or Hunting."
22. 2-4 band assembly worn or incorrectly installed.

NO REVERSE OR SLIPS IN REVERSE

1. 3-4 apply ring stuck in applied position.
2. Forward clutch not releasing.
3. Turbine shaft seals missing, cut or damaged.
4. Manual linkage incorrectly adjusted.
5. Oil pump retainer and ball assembly missing or damaged.
6. Oil pump stator shaft sleeve scored or damaged.
7. Reverse boost valve stuck, damaged or incorrectly installed.
8. Oil pump cup plug missing.
9. Oil pump converter clutch apply valve stuck.
10. Oil pump face not flat or restricted oil passage.
11. 2-3 shift valve stuck.
12. Valve body spacer plate and gaskets incorrect, damaged or incorrectly installed.
13. Reverse input clutch plate worn.
14. Reverse input housing and drum assembly cracked at weld.
15. Reverse input clutch plate retaining ring out of groove.

16. Reverse input clutch return spring assembly retaining ring out of groove.
17. Reverse input clutch seals cut or damaged.
18. Reverse input clutch retainer and ball assembly not sealing.
19. Restricted oil apply passage in reverse input clutch.
20. Lo and reverse clutch plates worn.
21. Lo and reverse clutch plate retaining ring incorrectly installed.
22. Porosity in low and reverse clutch piston.
23. Low and reverse clutch seals damaged or oil apply passage restricted.
24. Case cover plate gasket missing, damaged or incorrectly torqued.

NO PART THROTTLE OR DELAYED DOWNSHIFTS

1. Throttle linkage incorrectly adjusted.
2. 2-4 servo assembly apply pin cut or damaged.
3. 2-4 servo cover retaining ring missing or incorrectly installed.
4. Fourth apply piston damaged or incorrectly installed.
5. 2-4 servo inner housing damaged or incorrectly installed.
6. Governor weights binding.
7. Governor valve stuck.
8. Throttle valve, 3-2 control valve or T.V. modulated downshift valve stuck.
9. T.V. sleeve turned in bore.
10. 4-3 sequence valve body channel blocked.
11. Number 5 check ball missing from valve body.

NO OVERRUN BRAKING — MANUAL 3-2-1

1. Throttle linkage incorrectly adjusted.
2. Throttle valve or 4-3 sequence valve stuck.
3. Number 3 check ball incorrectly installed.
4. Valve body spacer plate and gaskets incorrect, damaged or incorrectly installed.
5. Turbine shaft oil passages plugged or not drilled.
6. Turbine shaft seal rings damaged.
7. Turbine shaft sealing balls loose or missing.
8. Porosity in forward or overrun clutch piston.
9. Overrun piston seals cut or damaged.
10. Overrun piston check ball not seating.

NO CONVERTER CLUTCH APPLY

1. 12 volts not being applied to the transmission.
2. Defective outside electrical connector.
3. Defective inside electrical connector, wiring harness or solenoid.
4. Solenoid shorted or incorrectly grounded.
5. Incorrect or damaged pressure switches.
6. Internal converter damage.
7. Oil pump converter clutch apply valve stuck or incorrectly installed.
8. Oil pump converter clutch apply valve

retaining ring incorrectly installed.
9. Oil pump to case gasket incorrectly installed.
10. Oil pump orifice cup plug clogged.
11. Oil pump solenoid O-ring seal cut or damaged.
12. Oil pump orifice cup plug missing from cooler in passage.
13. High or uneven oil pump body to cover bolt torque.
14. Converter clutch shift valve or throttle valve stuck.
15. Turbine shaft O-ring seal cut or damaged.
16. Turbine shaft retainer and ball assembly plugged.

CONVERTER SHUDDER

1. Internal torque converter damage.
2. Converter clutch shift valve stuck.
3. Oil pump converter clutch apply valve stuck.
4. Restricted oil pump oil passage.
5. Crack in oil filter body or restriction in filter neck.
6. Oil filter O-ring seal cut or damaged.
7. Low oil pressure or engine not properly tuned.
8. Turbine shaft O-ring cut or damaged.
9. Turbine shaft retainer and ball assembly damaged.

NO CONVERTER CLUTCH RELEASE

1. Oil pump converter clutch apply valve stuck.
2. Internal torque converter damage.
3. Solenoid grounded.

DRIVES IN NEUTRAL

1. Forward clutch burned or not releasing.
2. Manual linkage disconnected or incorrectly adjusted.
3. Internal leakage in case or case face not flat.

SECOND GEAR START IN DRIVE RANGE

1. Governor valve stuck.
2. Governor support pin too long or missing.
3. Forward sprag clutch assembly installed backwards.

NO PARK

1. Parking linkage actuator rod assembly bent or damaged.
2. Parking linkage actuator rod spring binding or improperly crimped.
3. Parking linkage actuator rod not attached to inside detent lever.
4. Parking linkage bracket damaged or not torqued properly.
5. Inside detent lever not torqued properly.
6. Detent roller improperly installed.
7. Parking pawl binding or damaged.

RATCHETING NOISE

1. Parking pawl return spring weak, damaged or incorrectly installed.

OIL OUT OF THE VENT

1. Chamfer in oil pump body rotor pocket too large.
2. T.V. limit valve stuck.

VIBRATION IN REVERSE & WHINING NOISE IN PARK

1. Broken vane rings in oil pump.

MAINTENANCE

Fluid level should be checked at every engine oil change. Frequency of change for transmission fluid is dependent on the type of driving conditions in which the vehicle is used. If the transmission is subjected to severe service such as: use in heavy city traffic when the outside temperature regularly reaches 90°F, use in very hilly or mountainous areas, commercial use such as taxi or delivery service, the fluid should be changed every 15,000 miles. Otherwise, change the fluid every 100,000 miles, using Dexron II or equivalent automatic transmission fluid. To check fluid at operating temperature (190°-200°F), which is obtained only after 15 miles of highway-type driving:

1. Apply parking brake and block wheels.
2. Place selector lever in park and start, but do not race, engine. Move selector lever through each range.
3. Check fluid immediately with selector lever in park, engine running at slow idle, and vehicle on level surface. Fluid level should be at full hot mark.

CHANGING FLUID

1. Raise and support vehicle.
2. Place drain pan under transmission oil pan, loosen pan bolts on front of pan, pry carefully with screwdriver to loosen oil pan, and allow fluid to drain.
3. Remove remaining oil pan bolts, oil pan, and gasket.
4. Drain fluid from pan, then clean pan and dry thoroughly with compressed air.
5. Remove oil filter to valve body bolt, then remove filter and gasket, replace with new filter and gasket and install filter attaching bolt. **Torque** to specification.
6. Install new gasket on oil pan, then install oil pan and **torque** bolts to 8 ft. lbs.
7. Lower vehicle and add five quarts of automatic transmission fluid through filler tube.
8. With selector lever in park and parking brake applied, start engine and let idle. Do not race engine.
9. Move selector lever through each range, return to park position, check fluid, and add additional fluid to bring level between dimples on dipstick.

ADDING FLUID TO FILL DRY TRANSMISSION & CONVERTER

1. Add fluid through filler tube until oil level is between add and hot marks on dipstick.

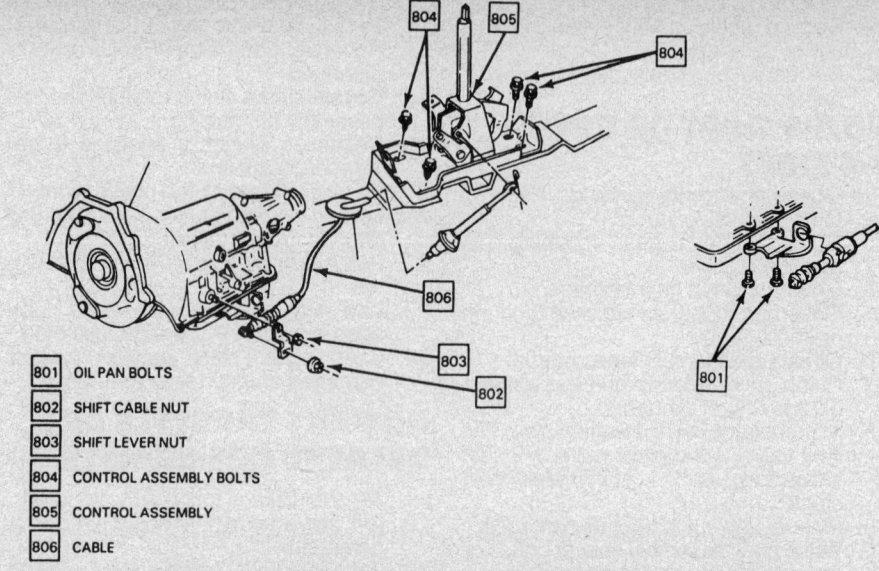

801	OIL PAN BOLTS
802	SHIFT CABLE NUT
803	SHIFT LEVER NUT
804	CONTROL ASSEMBLY BOLTS
805	CONTROL ASSEMBLY
806	CABLE

Copyrighted Material Reprinted with Permission from Hydra-Matic Div., GM Corp.

Fig. 2   Shift linkage adjustment. Camaro & Firebird

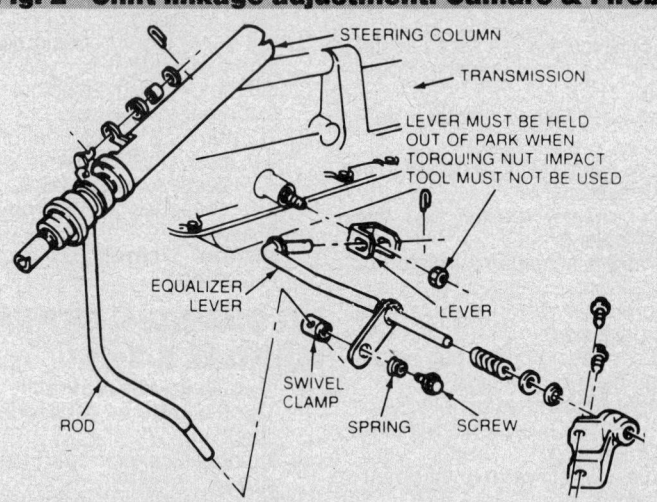

Copyrighted Material Reprinted with Permission from Hydra-Matic Div., GM Corp.

Fig. 3   Column shift manual linkage. Caprice & Monte Carlo

2. Place selector lever in park, depress accelerator to place carburetor on fast idle cam, and move selector lever through each range. Do not race engine.
3. With selector lever in park, engine running at idle (1-3 minutes), and vehicle on level surface, check fluid level and add additional fluid to bring level between dimples on dipstick.

IN-VEHICLE ADJUSTMENTS

MANUAL LINKAGE, ADJUST

CAMARO & FIREBIRD

1. Place transmission control lever in Neutral position.
2. Loosen cable attaching nut(s) or bolt(s) at shift lever **Fig. 2.**
3. Rotate shift lever clockwise to the Park detent, then back to the Neutral detent.
4. **Torque** cable attaching nuts or bolts to 11 ft. lbs. Control lever must be held in position when tightening nut.
5. Check cable adjustment by rotating transmission control lever through each detent position.

CAPRICE & MONTE CARLO

1. Loosen swivel clamp screw.
2. Position shift lever in neutral gate.
3. Position transmission lever in neutral detent.
4. While holding swivel clamp flush against equalizer lever, tighten swivel clamp screw, **Fig. 3. Do not exert force in either direction on rod or equalizer lever while tightening swivel clamp screw.**

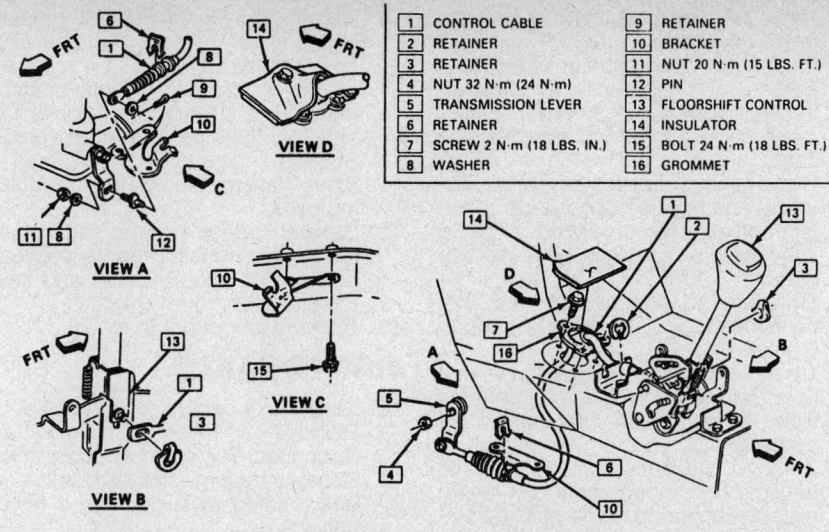

1	CONTROL CABLE	9	RETAINER
2	RETAINER	10	BRACKET
3	RETAINER	11	NUT 20 N·m (15 LBS. FT.)
4	NUT 32 N·m (24 N·m)	12	PIN
5	TRANSMISSION LEVER	13	FLOORSHIFT CONTROL
6	RETAINER	14	INSULATOR
7	SCREW 2 N·m (18 LBS. IN.)	15	BOLT 24 N·m (18 LBS. FT.)
8	WASHER	16	GROMMET

Copyrighted Material Reprinted with Permission from Hydra-Matic Div., GM Corp.

Fig. 4   Manual Linkage. Corvette

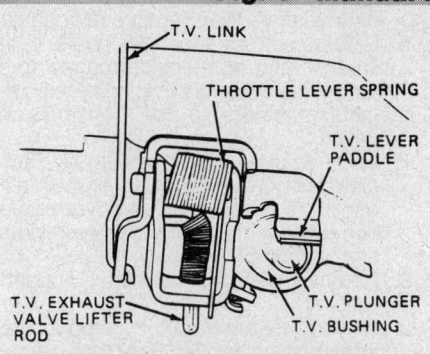

Copyrighted Material Reprinted with Permission from Hydra-Matic Div., GM Corp.

Fig. 6   Throttle lever & bracket assembly

CORVETTE

1. Place transmission control lever in Neutral position **Fig. 4**.
2. Loosen cable attachment at shift lever.
3. Rotate shift lever clockwise to Park position and then back to Neutral position.
4. **Torque** cable attachment to 15 ft. lbs. Lever must be held in position when tightening attachment.
5. Check control cable by rotating control lever through each detent.

T.V. CABLE, ADJUST

The T.V. cable should not be thought of as an automatic downshift cable. It controls line pressures, shift points, shift feel, part throttle downshifts, and detent downshifts. The function of the cable is similar to the combined functions of a vacuum modulator and detent downshift cable. The T.V. cable operates the throttle lever and bracket assembly, **Figs. 5 and 6**.

1. Stop engine.
2. Depress readjust tab and move slider through fitting, away from lever assembly, until slider stops against fitting. Release readjust tab.

3. Open carburetor lever to full throttle stop position to automatically adjust cable, then release carburetor lever and check cable for sticking or binding.
4. Road test vehicle. If delayed or only full throttle shifts still occur, proceed as follows:
   a. Remove oil pan and inspect throttle lever and bracket assembly, **Fig. 7**.
   b. Check T.V. exhaust valve lifter rod for distortion, or binding in control valve assembly or spacer plate.
   c. Make sure T.V. exhaust check ball moves up and down in conjunction with lifter.
   d. Make sure lifter spring holds lifter rod up against control valve assembly.
   e. Make sure T.V. plunger is not stuck.
   f. Inspect transmission for correct throttle lever to cable link.

IN-VEHICLE REPAIRS

SERVO ASSEMBLY, REPLACE

1. **On Corvette models**, raise and support vehicle, then disconnect exhaust system and remove propeller shaft and torque arm. **On all 1988-90 Corvette models, the driveline support beam must be removed before disconnecting propeller shaft.**
2. **On all models**, remove two oil pan bolts and install servo cover depressor tool No. J-29714 or equivalent on oil pan flange to depress servo cover.
3. Remove servo cover retaining ring, then remove tool.
4. Remove cover and seal ring which may be in case.
5. Remove servo piston and bore-apply pin assembly.
6. Reverse procedure to install.

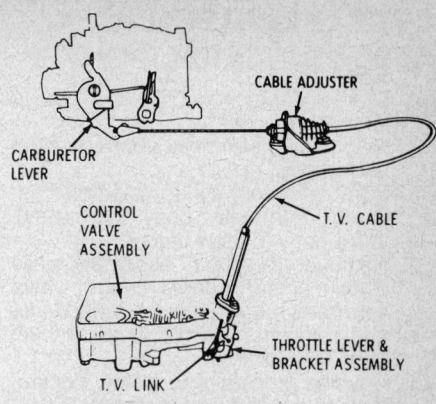

Copyrighted Material Reprinted with Permission from Hydra-Matic Div., GM Corp.

Fig. 5   T.V. cable & linkage

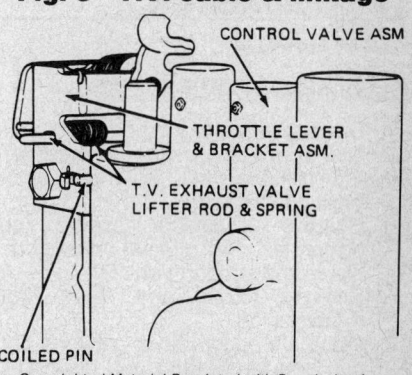

Copyrighted Material Reprinted with Permission from Hydra-Matic Div., GM Corp.

Fig. 7   Throttle lever & bracket assembly alignment

SPEEDOMETER DRIVEN GEAR, REPLACE

1. Disconnect speedometer cable or P.M. generator electrical connector from transmission.
2. Remove retainer bolt, retainer, P.M. generator (if equipped), speedometer driven gear and O-ring seal.
3. Reverse procedure to install, using new O-ring and adjusting fluid level.

REAR OIL SEAL, REPLACE

1. Remove driveshaft, and tunnel strap, if equipped.
2. Using suitable tool, pry out lip oil seal.
3. Coat outer casting of new oil seal with suitable sealer and drive into place with seal installer tool No. J-21426.
4. Install tunnel strap if used, then install driveshaft.

GOVERNOR, REPLACE

1. Raise and support vehicle, then if necessary, remove exhaust system.
2. Remove governor cover from case using extreme care not to damage cover. If cover is damaged, it must be replaced.
3. Remove governor.
4. Reverse procedure to install and check fluid level.

CONTROL VALVE ASSEMBLY, REPLACE

1. Drain and remove oil pan and remove filter and gasket.
2. Disconnect electrical connectors at valve body.
3. Remove detent spring and roller assembly from valve body and remove valve body to case bolts.
4. Remove valve body assembly while disconnecting manual control valve link from range selector inner lever and removing throttle lever bracket from T.V. link.
5. Reverse procedure to install. **Torque** bolts to 8 ft. lbs. and replenish fluid.

TRANSMISSION REPLACE

CAMARO & FIREBIRD

1. Disconnect battery ground cable.
2. Remove oil dipstick tube, if necessary, then disconnect all transmission electrical connectors.
3. Remove air cleaner assembly and disconnect T.V. cable at upper end.
4. Raise and support vehicle.
5. Remove torque arm clamp from transmission.
6. Place a wooden block between floor pan and torque arm and disconnect torque arm from rear axle.
7. Remove propeller shaft, then disconnect speedometer cable, or P.M. generator, and T.V. cable from transmission.
8. Disconnect transmission cooler lines and shift linkage.
9. Remove exhaust bracket, then the upper-to-lower support bolts.
10. Support transmission with a jack and remove transmission rear lower support.
11. Remove flywheel cover, then mark relationship between flywheel and converter and remove torque converter attaching bolts.
12. Remove transmission-to-engine attaching bolts and carefully lower transmission from vehicle.
13. Reverse procedure to install.

CAPRICE

1. Remove air cleaner assembly, then, disconnect T.V. cable at its upper end. Remove transmission oil dipstick and bolt holding dipstick tube, if accessible.
2. Raise and support vehicle and remove driveshaft.
3. Disconnect speedometer cable, shift linkage, and all electrical leads at transmission as well as any clips that retain the leads to the transmission case.
4. Remove flywheel cover, mark flywheel and torque converter to maintain original balance. Remove torque converter to flywheel bolts and/or nuts.
5. **On gasoline engine vehicles,** disconnect catalytic converter support bracket.
6. **On all models equipped,** remove floor pan reinforcement if it interferes with removal or installation of driveshaft.
7. Remove transmission support to transmission mount bolt and transmission support to frame bolts and insulators, if used.
8. Position a jack under transmission, raise transmission slightly, and slide transmission support rearward.
9. Lower transmission to gain access to oil cooler lines and T.V. cable attachments, disconnect oil cooler lines and T.V. cable, and cap all openings.
10. Support engine with suitable tool, remove transmission to engine bolts, and disconnect transmission assembly.
11. Install torque converter holding fixture tool J-21366 or equivalent, and remove transmission assembly from vehicle.
12. Reverse procedure to install.

CORVETTE

1. Disconnect battery ground cable.
2. Disconnect T.V. cable at upper end, then remove transmission oil dipstick.
3. Raise and support vehicle.
4. **On 1988-90 convertible models,** remove upper and lower underbody braces.
5. **On all models,** disconnect speedometer cable or P.M. generator electrical connector, shift linkage and all electrical leads from transmission as well as any clips that retain the leads to transmission case.
6. Remove flywheel cover, then mark flywheel and torque converter to maintain original balance. Remove torque converter to flywheel bolts and/or nuts.
7. Remove exhaust system components as necessary.
8. Install a jack under transmission, then raise transmission slightly.

9. Remove driveline beam and propeller shaft.
10. Lower transmission to gain access to oil cooler lines and T.V. cable attachments, then disconnect oil cooler lines and T.V. cable and cap all openings.
11. Support engine using a jack, then remove transmission-to-engine attaching bolts.
12. Separate transmission assembly from engine, then install torque converter holding tool No. J-21366 and lower transmission from vehicle.
13. Reverse procedure to install.

MONTE CARLO

1. Disconnect battery ground cable.
2. Remove air cleaner assembly and disconnect T.V. cable at upper end.
3. Remove transmission oil dipstick and bolt holding dipstick tube, if necessary.
4. Raise and support vehicle.
5. Remove floor pan reinforcement, if necessary for removal or installation of driveshaft, then remove driveshaft.
6. Disconnect speedometer cable, shift linkage, and all electrical connectors as well as any clips that retain electrical connectors to the transmission case.
7. Remove flexplate cover, mark flexplate and torque converter to maintain original balance, then remove torque converter to flexplate attaching nuts and/or bolts.
8. Remove catalytic converter support bracket.
9. Remove transmission support to transmission mount bolt, then transmission support to frame bolts and insulator, if used.
10. Position a jack under transmission, raise transmission slightly and slide transmission support rearward.
11. Lower transmission slightly to gain access to oil cooler lines and T.V. cable attachments, then disconnect oil cooler lines and T.V. cable, and cap all openings.
12. Support engine with suitable tool, then remove transmission to engine bolts and disconnect transmission assembly. **Take care not to damage any cables, lines or linkage.**
13. Using torque converter holding fixture tool No. J-21366 or equivalent, remove transmission assembly from vehicle.
14. Reverse procedure to install noting the following:
    a. **Torque** converter to flexplate attaching bolts to 46 ft. lbs.
    b. Adjust T.V. cable and linkage.

TIGHTENING SPECIFICATIONS

Component	Torque/Ft. Lbs.
Accumulator Cover To Case	8
Auxiliary Valve Body To Case	8
Case Extension To Case	26
Connector Cooler Pipe	28
Detent Spring To Valve Body	18
Manual Shaft To Inside Detent Lever	23
Oil Pan To Case	8
Oil Passage Cover To Case	8
Park Brake Bracket To Brace	18
Pressure Switches	8
Pump Assembly To Case	18
Pump Cover To Body	18
Solenoid Assembly To Pump	8
Torque Convertor To Flywheel Bolt	46
Transmission To Engine Bolts	35
Underbody Brace Stud Nut	20
Underbody Brace To Frame Bolt	47
Valve Body To Case	8
Torque Converter Cover Bolt	89 ①

① —Inch lbs.

Automatic Overdrive Unit (Doug Nash), Corvette

INDEX

DESCRIPTION

The automatic overdrive unit used on the 1988 Corvette, **Fig. 1,** and the 4 speed manual transmission is essentially a combination of two separate transmission units. The first unit is a conventional 4 speed (83 mm) manual system with a 1.1 ratio in 4th gear. The second unit is a two speed overdrive system electronically controlled by the ECM which operates with a 1.1 and a .68 to 1 ratio or 1.1 and a .59 to 1 ratio. The two speed or overdrive unit performs its functions using a planetary gear set in combination with two sets of clutch components.

The ECM is programmed to control the shift solenoid and the overdrive unit. The overdrive mode cannot occur when the transmission is in first gear. It can occur when the transmission is in the remaining three gears.

The hydraulic circuit, **Fig. 2** consists of a rotor type pump on the overdrive unit output shaft, a shift valve, solenoid, accumulator valve and a pressure relief valve locat- ed in the valve body assembly. In the normal (direct drive) mode, fluid circulates from the pump through a 115-125 psi pressure relief, and through the cooler lines then back to the pan or sump. When the overdrive switch is closed by the ECM, the solenoid plunger is activated, opening the shift valve passage for fluid flow into the piston. When the solenoid de-energizes, the shift valve returns to its original position.

TROUBLESHOOTING

Refer to **Fig. 3** for automatic overdrive unit troubleshooting procedure.

IN-VEHICLE ADJUSTMENTS

PARK LOCK CABLE, ADJUST

1. Lift adjusting key upward and release cable, **Fig. 4.**
2. Place steering column lock lever into lock park position.
3. Place transmission shift lever into Reverse.
4. Insert a .060 inch feeler gauge against reverse stop, then pull reverse lever until reverse pawl contacts feeler gauge.
5. Push adjusting key downward to set cable.
6. Remove feeler gauge and pull back on shift lever.
7. Ensure reverse pawl hits reverse stop and locks shifter lever in Reverse.

T.V. CABLE, ADJUST

1. Depress and hold metal lock tab, **Fig. 5.**
2. Move slider back, away from throttle body lever until slider contacts fitting.
3. Release metal lock tab.
4. Rotate throttle lever to the Full throttle stop position to obtain a minimum of one click adjustment.

IN-VEHICLE REPAIRS

SIDE COVER, REPLACE

1. Place transmission shift lever into 2nd gear.
2. Raise and support vehicle.
3. Disconnect electrical connector(s) from side cover switch(s), then remove switch(s) from side cover, if applicable.
4. Remove shift levers from shifter shafts.
5. Remove side cover attaching bolts, then the side cover.
6. Reverse procedure to install.

SHIFTER ASSEMBLY, REPLACE

Removal

1. Disconnect battery ground cable.
2. Disconnect electrical connector from power seat switch(s).
3. Remove left seat from vehicle.
4. Remove knob from shift lever.
5. Remove console cover attaching screws, then the console cover.
6. Remove glove compartment lock and left side panel from console.
7. Remove shifter cover.
8. Disconnect three rods from shifter.
9. Disconnect park lock cable from shifter, then disconnect overdrive switch electrical connector, if applicable.
10. Remove shifter cross bolt and shifter mounting bracket.
11. Remove shifter mounting bolt from body panel, then the shifter assembly from vehicle.

Installation

1. Position shifter into underbody and install mounting bolt. **Torque** bolt to 40-51 ft. lbs.
2. Position mounting bracket onto shifter and install bracket bolts. **Torque** cross bolt to 15-22 ft. lbs. **Torque** mounting bracket to underbody mount bolt to 10-15 ft. lbs.
3. Install three shifter rods onto shifter assembly.
4. Install park lock cable onto shifter. Adjust cable as outlined previously, then reconnect overdrive switch electrical connector, if applicable.
5. Reverse removal steps 1 through 7 for remaining installation procedure.

T.V. CABLE, REPLACE

Refer to **Fig. 6** for T.V. cable routing and attachments. Refer to "T.V. Cable, Adjust" for adjustment procedure.

OVERDRIVE SWITCH, REPLACE

1. Disconnect battery ground cable.
2. Remove instrument cluster trim plate adjusting screws, then the headlight switch knob, tilt column lever and trim plate.
3. Remove instrument panel accessory trim plate attaching screws, then the plate.
4. Remove console trim plate attaching screws, pull trim plate rearward, then disconnect cigar lighter electrical connector.
5. Remove shift boot-to-trim plate attaching screws, then the trim plate.
6. Carefully pry overdrive switch button from shifter knob.
7. Disconnect overdrive switch rod from shifter. Count the number of turns required to disconnect rod for installation reference.
8. Loosen overdrive switch-to-shifter retaining nut, then remove switch and slide block. **Use care to prevent losing slide block return spring.**
9. Disconnect switch electrical connector, then remove switch-to-slide block retaining pin.
10. Reverse procedure to install, noting the following:
    a. When installing switch rod, screw rod into switch block the same number of turns noted during removal.
    b. After installing switch button, ensure button is flush with top of shift knob. If not, remove button and turn rod in or out as required.

OIL FILTER, REPLACE

1. Disconnect battery ground cable.
2. Raise and support vehicle.
3. Position a drain pan under overdrive unit oil pan. Remove oil pan attaching bolts from front and side of pan.
4. Loosen rear pan attaching bolts approximately 4 turns.
5. Carefully pry oil pan loose, allowing fluid to drain.
6. Remove remaining pan attaching bolts.
7. Clean oil pan with solvent and dry

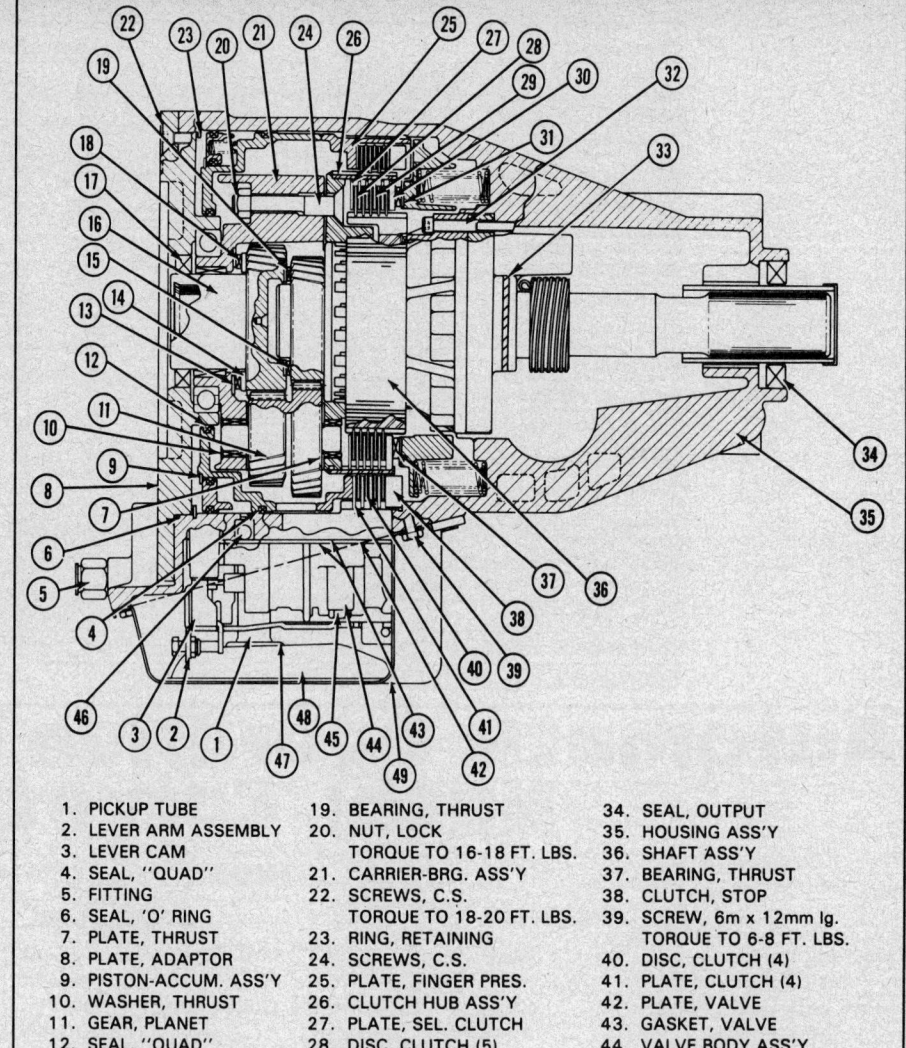

1. PICKUP TUBE	19. BEARING, THRUST	34. SEAL, OUTPUT
2. LEVER ARM ASSEMBLY	20. NUT, LOCK	35. HOUSING ASS'Y
3. LEVER CAM	TORQUE TO 16-18 FT. LBS.	36. SHAFT ASS'Y
4. SEAL, "QUAD"	21. CARRIER-BRG. ASS'Y	37. BEARING, THRUST
5. FITTING	22. SCREWS, C.S.	38. CLUTCH, STOP
6. SEAL, 'O' RING	TORQUE TO 18-20 FT. LBS.	39. SCREW, 6m x 12mm lg.
7. PLATE, THRUST	23. RING, RETAINING	TORQUE TO 6-8 FT. LBS.
8. PLATE, ADAPTOR	24. SCREWS, C.S.	40. DISC, CLUTCH (4)
9. PISTON-ACCUM. ASS'Y	25. PLATE, FINGER PRES.	41. PLATE, CLUTCH (4)
10. WASHER, THRUST	26. CLUTCH HUB ASS'Y	42. PLATE, VALVE
11. GEAR, PLANET	27. PLATE, SEL. CLUTCH	43. GASKET, VALVE
12. SEAL, "QUAD"	28. DISC, CLUTCH (5)	44. VALVE BODY ASS'Y
13. WASHER, THRUST	29. PLATE, CLUTCH (4)	45. SCREW, HEX. 6m x 45mm
14. WASHER, THRUST	30. PLATE, BEARING	TORQUE TO 6-8 FT. LBS.
15. WASHER, THRUST	31. WASHER, THRUST	46. BALL, 5/16" STEEL
16. GEAR, SUN	32. SCREW, ALLEN 6m x 40mm	47. GROMMET
17. SEAL, INPUT	TORQUE TO 6-8 FT. LBS.	48. OIL FILTER
18. BEARING, THRUST	33. SEAL, PUMP	49. OIL PAN

Fig. 1   Cross-sectional view of overdrive unit

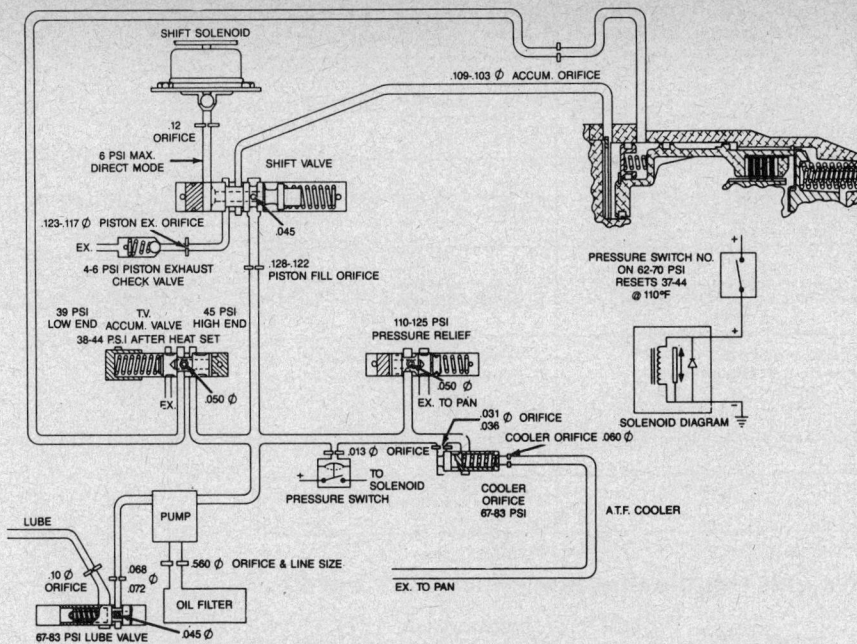

Fig. 2 Overdrive unit hydraulic circuit. 1988

CONDITION	PROBABLE CAUSE	CORRECTION
Overdrive Inop	a. Insufficient Lubricant b. Speedometer Inop c. Blown Fuse d. Temperature Gage Inop e. O/D Switch at Shifter Knob f. Solenoid Inop · Check for (12 volts at O/D Connector—Engine at operating temp.—wheels off the ground shift trans from 1st into 2nd gear at 12-15 MPH—solenoid should energize at this point) g. Solenoid Check Ball Missing h. Low Pressure Switch i. Shift Valve Inop j. Pressure Regulator Valve Inop k. Drive Pin Broken or Missing in Pump	a. Fill to correct level b. Replace speedometer sensors. Replace speedometer drive or driven gears. c. Replace fuse d. Replace gage or sending unit e. Replace switch or repair wires f. Replace solenoid or repair wires. g. Install check ball h. Replace switch i. Free up valve or replace valve body j. Free up valve or replace valve body k. Replace pin or pump gears
Overdrive in All Gears	a. Solenoid Plunger Stuck b. Solenoid Exhaust Hole Plugged c. Shift Valve Stuck	a. Replace Solenoid b. Clear exhaust passage c. Free up shift valve or replace valve body
Harsh Up Shifts	a. Stuck T.V. Valve b. Stuck Accumulator Piston c. Accumulator Seal Damaged	a. Free up valve or replace valve body b. Free up or replace c. Replace seal
Harsh Down Shifts	a. Stuck T.V. Valve	a. Free up valve or replace valve body
Soft Up Shift	a. Stuck T.V. Valve b. O/D Clutch Plates Burn't	a. Free up valve or replace valve body b. Replace clutch plates and disc's
Soft Downshift	a. Stuck T.V. Valve	a. Free up valve or replace valve body
No Downshift	a. E.C.M., throttle position switch	a. Repair or replace E.C.M. or throttle position switch
Slips on Upshift	a. Direct Clutch Plates Burn't b. Excessive Clutch Pack Clearance	a. Replace direct clutch plates and disc's b. Adjust clutch pack clearance
Chatters on Upshifts	a. Piston Seals Damaged b. Direct Clutch Plates Burn't c. Low mainline pressure	a. Replace seals b. Replace direct clutch plates and disc's c. Check lines for restrictions. Check pump.

Fig. 3 Overdrive unit troubleshooting chart (Part 1 of 2)

thoroughly with compressed air.
8. Remove filter from overdrive unit.
9. Install a new filter.
10. During oil pan installation, note the following:
   a. Apply a bead of RTV sealant number 1052366 or equivalent, onto oil pan flange and install oil pan onto overdrive housing. **The RTV sealant must be wet when installing oil pan onto overdrive housing. RTV sealant should be applied around inside of bolt holes, Fig. 7.**
   b. Install magnet onto oil pan as shown in **Fig. 8.**
   c. Install oil pan attaching bolts. **Torque** bolts to 6-8 ft. lbs.
11. Fill overdrive unit with Dexron II automatic transmission fluid.

VALVE BODY, REPLACE

1. Disconnect battery ground cable.
2. Disconnect T.V. cable from throttle body lever, if applicable.
3. Remove transmission oil pan and filter assembly as described previously.
4. Disconnect tan colored electrical connector from low pressure cut-off switch.
5. Disconnect T.V. cable from throttle body lever, if applicable, then remove bolt retaining T.V. cable to valve body.
6. Remove remaining valve body to transmission case attaching bolts.
7. Remove valve body and spacer plate assembly from overdrive unit. **Care must be taken when removing valve body to prevent loss of the check ball, Fig. 8. Check ball is spring loaded under the valve body.**
8. To install valve body, reverse removal procedure and note the following, if applicable:
   a. Remove T.V. cable attaching bolt from overdrive case. Install throttle setting gauge tool No. J-34671-1 or equivalent into T.V. cable bore, then hook T.V. cable onto top step, **Fig. 9.**
   b. Unhook T.V. cable from top step, then connect T.V. cable onto lower step.
   c. Position throttle setting gauge tool No. J-34671-2 or equivalent, between piston and solenoid bracket, **Fig. 10.** Adjust screw/bolt on T.V. lever until bolt contacts cam stop.

OVERDRIVE SOLENOID, REPLACE

1. Disconnect battery ground cable.
2. Remove transmission oil pan and filter assembly as described previously.
3. Disconnect T.V. cable from throttle body lever, if applicable.
4. Remove valve body as described previously.
5. Using valve body spring compressor tool No. J-34529 or equivalent, compress shift valve spring, then remove retaining pin.
6. Using valve body spring compressor tool No. J-34529 or equivalent, compress relief valve springs, then re-

CONDITION	PROBABLE CAUSE	CORRECTION
O/D Overheats	a. Insufficient Lubricant b. Stuck Cooler Valve c. Cooler Line Restriction d. Restriction in Radiator	a. Fill to correct level b. Free up cooler valve or replace valve c. Flush lines or replace d. Flush radiator or replace
No Reverse	a. Direct Clutch Plates Burn't	a. Replace direct clutch plates and disc's
Noisy in Direct Drive	a. Front Carrier Bearing b. Thrust Bearing in Direct Clutch	a. Replace carrier cover b. Replace thrust bearing
Noisy in Overdrive	a. Pinion Roller Bearings b. Pinion Gears (scored, chipped or burn't) c. Input Sun Gear (scored, chipped or burn't) d. Output Sun Gear (scored, chipped or burn't)	a. Replace carrier cover or housing b. Replace pinion gears c. Replace input sun gear d. Replace output sun gear
No Direct Drive	a. Sprag Clutch Damaged	a. Replace Sprag Clutch

Copyrighted Material Reprinted with Permission from Hydra-Matic Div., GM Corp.

Fig. 3   Overdrive unit troubleshooting chart (Part 2 of 2)

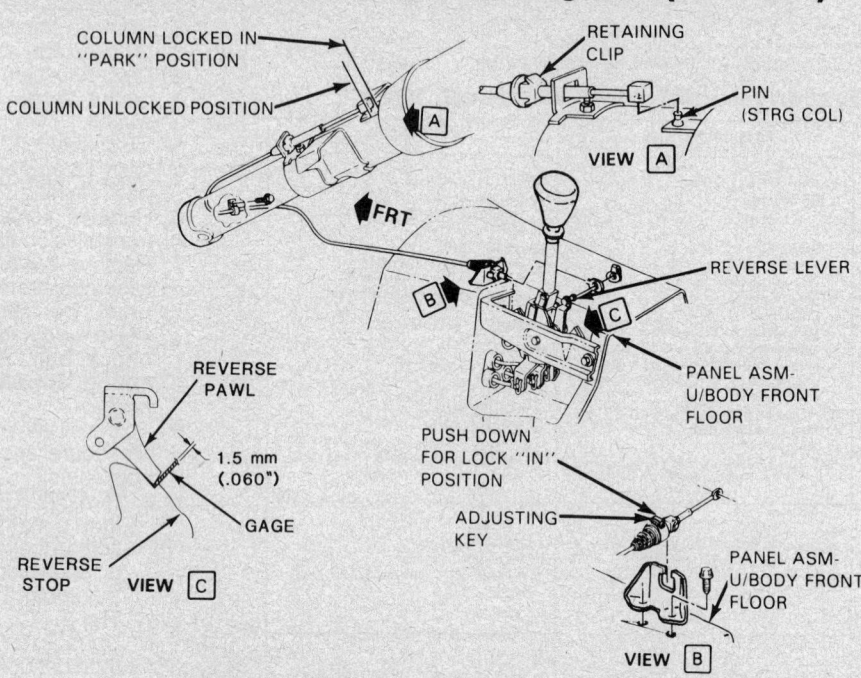

Copyrighted Material Reprinted with Permission from Hydra-Matic Div., GM Corp.

Fig. 4   Park lock cable adjustment

move retaining pin.
7. Remove solenoid valve body attaching bolts.
8. Remove solenoid valve and check ball assembly from valve body.
9. Reverse procedure to install.

PRESSURE SWITCH, REPLACE

1. Disconnect battery ground cable.
2. Remove transmission oil pan and filter assembly as described previously.
3. Disconnect electrical connectors from pressure switch.
4. Remove switch from valve body.
5. Reverse procedure to install.

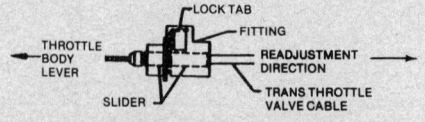

Copyrighted Material Reprinted with Permission from Hydra-Matic Div., GM Corp.

Fig. 5   T.V. cable adjustment

OVERDRIVE UNIT OUTPUT SEAL, REPLACE

1. Disconnect battery ground cable.
2. Raise and support vehicle. On models equipped with convertible top, remove upper and lower underbody braces.
3. Remove exhaust system as follows:
   a. Disconnect AIR pipe from catalytic converter.
   b. Disconnect AIR pipe clamps from exhaust pipe.
   c. Disconnect oxygen sensor lead.
   d. Remove muffler to support hanger attaching bolts.
   e. Disconnect exhaust pipes from exhaust manifolds.
4. Support transmission, then remove bolts attaching support beam at the axle and transmission.
5. Mark relationship of propeller shaft to companion flange. Remove trunnion bearing straps, then the rear universal joint. Tape bearings caps to trunnion to prevent bearing loss.
6. Slide slip yoke from transmission and remove propeller shaft.
7. Using a suitable tool, remove seal

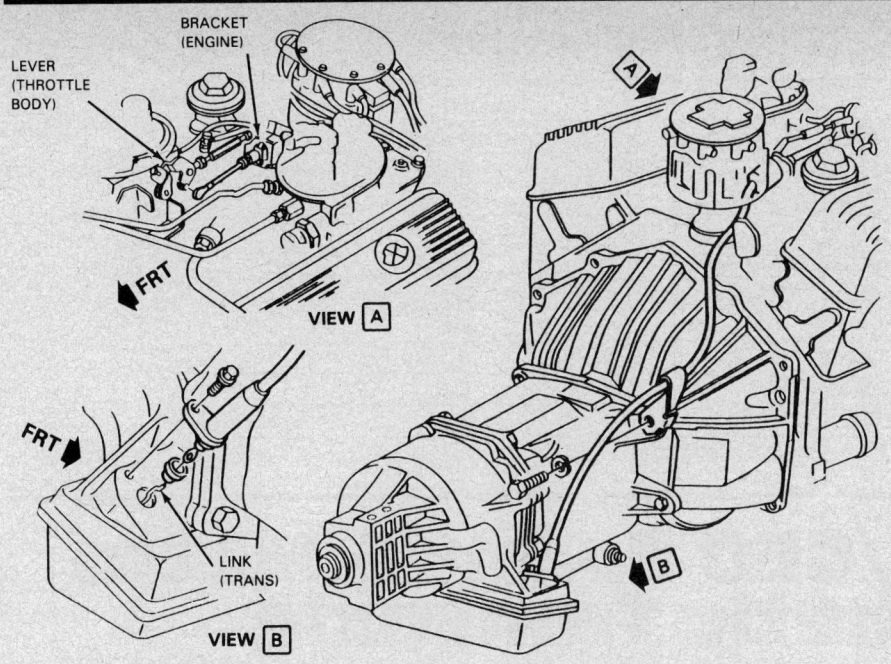

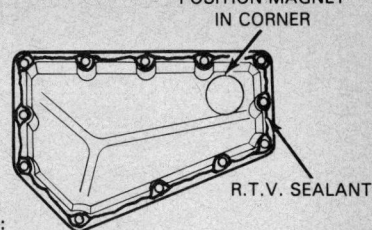

NOTE:

1. INSTALL THE OIL PAN ON HOUSING WHILE R.T.V. SEALANT IS WET.
   PAN AND HOUSING FLANGE SURFACE MUST BE DRY AND FREE OF OIL FILM.

Copyrighted Material Reprinted with Permission from Hydra-Matic Div., GM Corp.

Fig. 7   Magnet & RTV sealant location

Copyrighted Material Reprinted with Permission from Hydra-Matic Div., GM Corp.

Fig. 6   T.V. cable routing & attachments

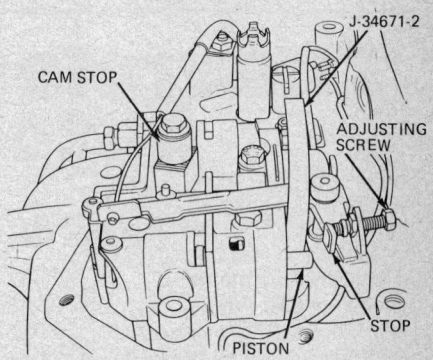

Copyrighted Material Reprinted with Permission from Hydra-Matic Div., GM Corp.

Fig. 10   Positioning throttle setting gauge tool No. J-34671-2 between piston & solenoid bracket

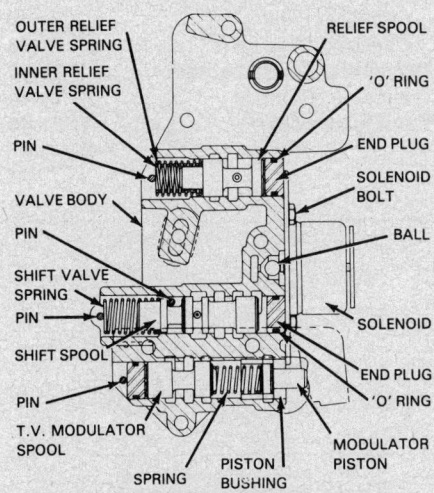

Copyrighted Material Reprinted with Permission from Hydra-Matic Div., GM Corp.

Fig. 8   Valve body components

from overdrive output shaft.
8. Coat new seal lip with automatic transmission fluid.
9. Using output seal installer tool No. J-21426 or equivalent, install new seal onto overdrive output shaft seal groove.
10. Reverse removal steps to complete installation.

OVERDRIVE UNIT
REPLACE

Transmission and overdrive unit are removed as an assembly.
1. Disconnect battery ground cable.
2. Remove air cleaner assembly from engine.

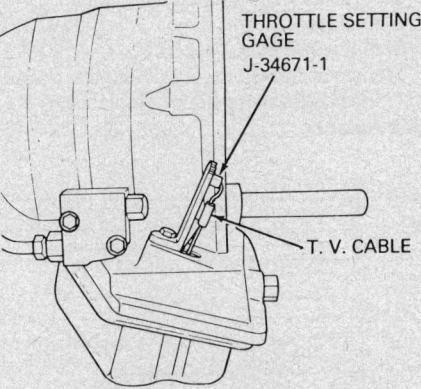

Copyrighted Material Reprinted with Permission from Hydra-Matic Div., GM Corp.

Fig. 9   Hooking T.V. cable onto throttle setting gauge

3. Disconnect T.V. cable from left TBI unit, if applicable.
4. Remove distributor cap and position aside.
5. Raise and support vehicle. On models with convertible top, remove upper and lower underbody braces.
6. Remove exhaust system as follows:
   a. Disconnect AIR pipe from catalytic converter.
   b. Disconnect AIR pipe clamps from exhaust pipe.
   c. Disconnect oxygen sensor lead.
   d. Remove muffler to support hanger attaching bolts.
   e. Disconnect exhaust pipes from exhaust manifolds.
   f. Remove exhaust hanger at transmission.
7. Position a jack under transmission.
8. Remove bolts attaching driveline beam at axle and transmission.

9. Remove driveline beam from vehicle.
10. Mark relationship of the propeller shaft to the axle companion flange. Remove trunnion bearing straps, then disconnect rear universal joint from axle. Slide propeller shaft slip yoke out from the overdrive unit and remove shaft from the vehicle.
11. Disconnect fluid cooler lines from overdrive unit.
12. Disconnect T.V. cable from overdrive unit, if applicable.
13. Disconnect shift linkage from shift cover.
14. Disconnect electrical connector from side cover switches, back-up light switch and overdrive unit. Disconnect speedometer cable.
15. Place a jack under engine oil pan with a block of wood placed between jack and pan.
16. Lower transmission slightly.
17. Remove transmission to bellhousing attaching bolts.
18. Slide transmission and overdrive unit rearward to disengage input shaft from clutch.
19. Lower transmission and overdrive unit from vehicle.
20. Remove seven transmission to overdrive unit attaching bolts and separate overdrive unit from transmission.
21. Reverse procedure to install.

TIGHTENING SPECIFICATIONS

Component	Torque/Ft. Lbs.
Adapter Plate To Case Bolts	18–20
Carrier Cover Retaining Nuts	16–18
Cooler Block To Case Bolts	6–8
Oil Pan To Case Bolts	6–8
Overdrive Case To Reverse Housing Bolts	34–36
Pressure Plate Access Plugs	55①
Pressure Tap Plugs	55①
Pump Cover To Pump Cavity	10–12
Pump Housing To Case Bolts	6–8
Valve Body To Case Bolts	6–8

①—Inch lbs.

Chevrolet/GEO Sprint & Metro Automatic Transaxle

INDEX

TROUBLESHOOTING

In conjunction with the prerequisites noted below, refer to charts, **Figs. 1 through 3,** when troubleshooting the transaxle:

1. Engine coolant is at normal operating temperature.
2. Engine idle speed is 800-900 RPM.
3. Transaxle fluid level is correct and at normal operating temperature.
4. Accelerator cable, oil pressure control cable and selector cable are properly adjusted.
5. Gear shift control system wiring is in good condition.
6. Vacuum switch hose is properly connected.

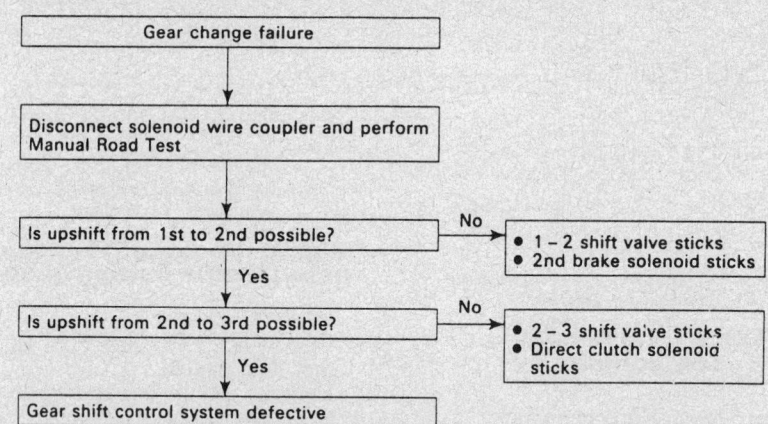

Copyrighted Material Reprinted with Permission from Hydra-Matic Div., GM Corp.

Fig. 1   Transaxle troubleshooting chart. Gear change failure

MAINTENANCE

CHECKING FLUID LEVEL

1. Drive vehicle for approximately 15 minutes to bring fluid up to normal operating temperature.
2. With vehicle on level surface, apply parking brake and block drive wheels.
3. With selector lever in Park, start engine, then move selector lever through each range and return to Park.
4. Remove dipstick and check fluid level.
5. Fluid level should be between the two "HOT" marks on dipstick.

6. Add fluid as required to bring fluid to specified level. When adding fluid use only Dexron II type transaxle fluid or equivalent.

CHANGING FLUID

Under normal driving conditions, fluid should be changed and oil strainer cleaned every 100,000 miles. Under harsh driving conditions fluid should be changed every 15,000 miles. To service, proceed as follows:

1. Raise and support front of vehicle.
2. Remove drain plug and drain fluid from oil pan.
3. Remove stabilizer shaft mount bolts, then the transaxle mounting member.
4. Remove oil pan attaching bolts and the oil pan.
5. Remove oil strainer-to-valve body attaching bolts, then the oil strainer.
6. Clean strainer and oil pan in solvent. Engine magnet in oil pan is positioned directly below oil strainer.

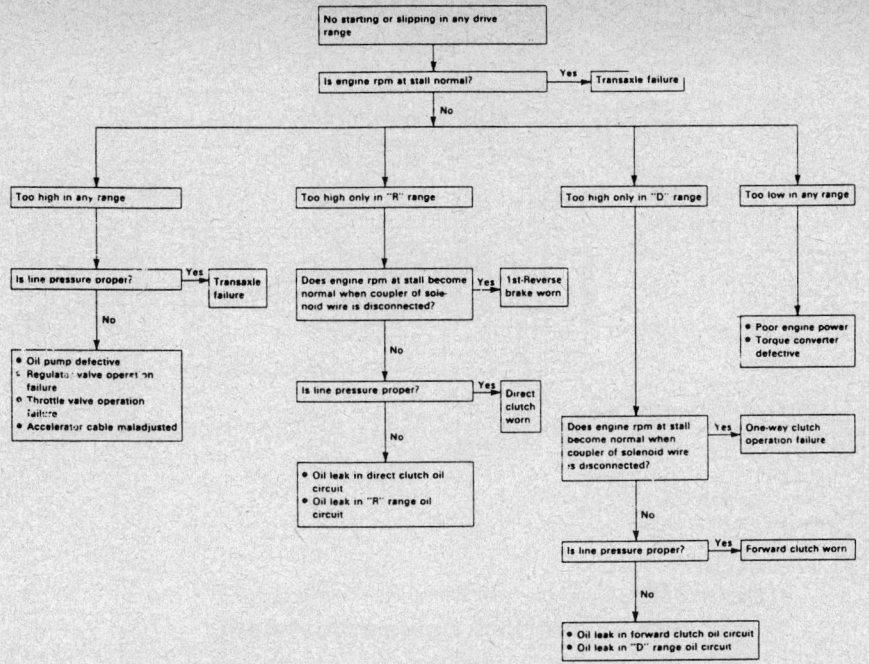

Copyrighted Material Reprinted with Permission from Hydra-Matic Div., GM Corp.

Fig. 2   Transaxle troubleshooting chart. No starting or slipping in any drive range

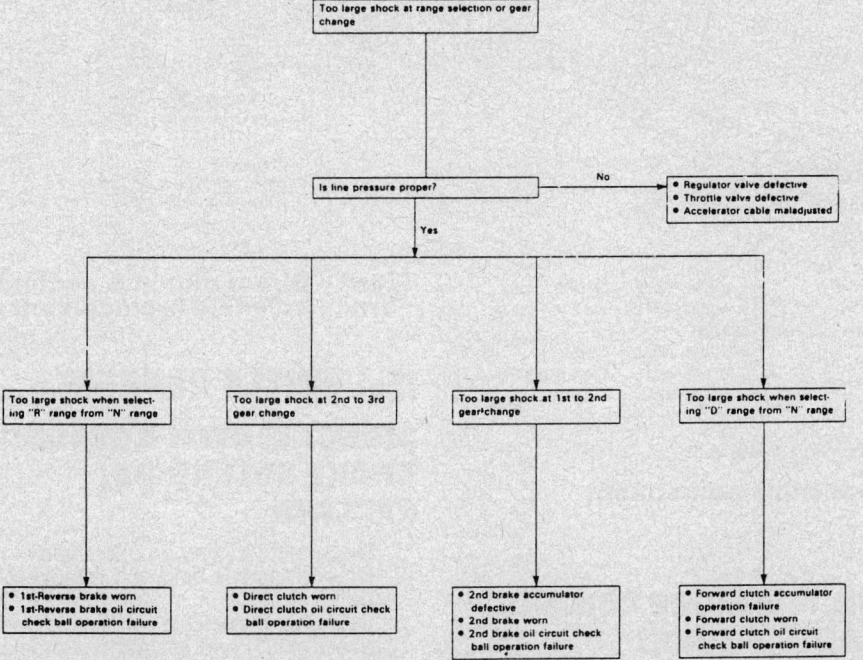

Copyrighted Material Reprinted with Permission from Hydra-Matic Div., GM Corp.

Fig. 3   Transaxle troubleshooting chart. Too large shock at range selection of gear change

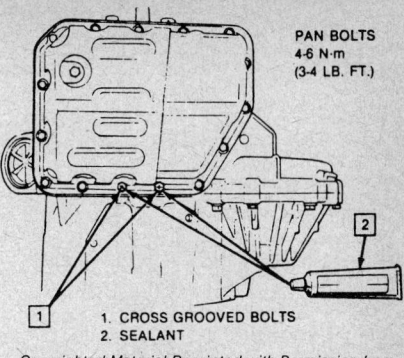

PAN BOLTS
4-6 N·m
(3-4 LB. FT.)

1. CROSS GROOVED BOLTS
2. SEALANT

Copyrighted Material Reprinted with Permission from Hydra-Matic Div., GM Corp.

Fig. 4   Oil pan installation

WHEN SHIFT LOCK SOLENOID IS NOT OPERATED:

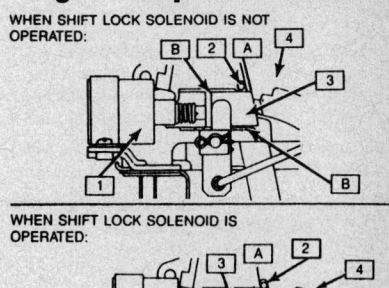

WHEN SHIFT LOCK SOLENOID IS OPERATED:

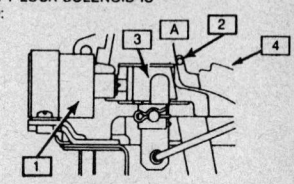

1	SHIFT LOCK SOLENOID
2	DETENT PIN
3	LOCK PLATE
4	DETENT PLATE
A	MORE THAN 1.0 MM (0.040 IN)
B	APPLY GREASE HERE

Copyrighted Material Reprinted with Permission from Hydra-Matic Div., GM Corp.

Fig. 5   Interlock solenoid adjustment

IN-VEHICLE ADJUSTMENTS
INTERLOCK DRIVE SOLENOID, ADJUST

1. Shift selector lever to Park.
2. Adjust solenoid position so that solenoid operates as follows:
   a. When ignition switch is turned Off (solenoid is not operated) and On (solenoid is operated), lock plate should be positioned as shown in **Fig. 5.**
   b. There should be no clearance between lock plate and guide plate as shown in **Fig. 6.**
3. After adjusting solenoid position, tighten solenoid screws.
4. After tightening solenoid screws, check the following:
   a. When ignition switch is turned Off, selector lever is locked in Park range and cannot be shifted into any other range.
   b. When ignition switch is turned On, selector lever can be shifted into any other range.
   c. If manual release knob is pulled with ignition switch Off, selector lever can be shifted into any other range.

7. Install oil strainer and attaching bolts. **Torque** bolts to 4-5 ft. lbs.
8. Install oil pan using new gasket. **Torque** attaching bolts to 3-4 ft. lbs. Two of the oil pan attaching bolts have crossed grooves on the bolt head. When installing these two bolts, coat threads with sealant and install in positions shown in **Fig. 4.**

9. Reinstall stabilizer shaft and transaxle mounting member. **Torque** stabilizer shaft mount bolts to 22-40 ft. lbs. and transaxle member attaching bolts to 37-43 ft. lbs.
10. Lower vehicle and refill oil pan with approximately 1.5 quarts of Dexron II type transaxle fluid or equivalent.
11. Check fluid level as previously described and adjust as necessary.

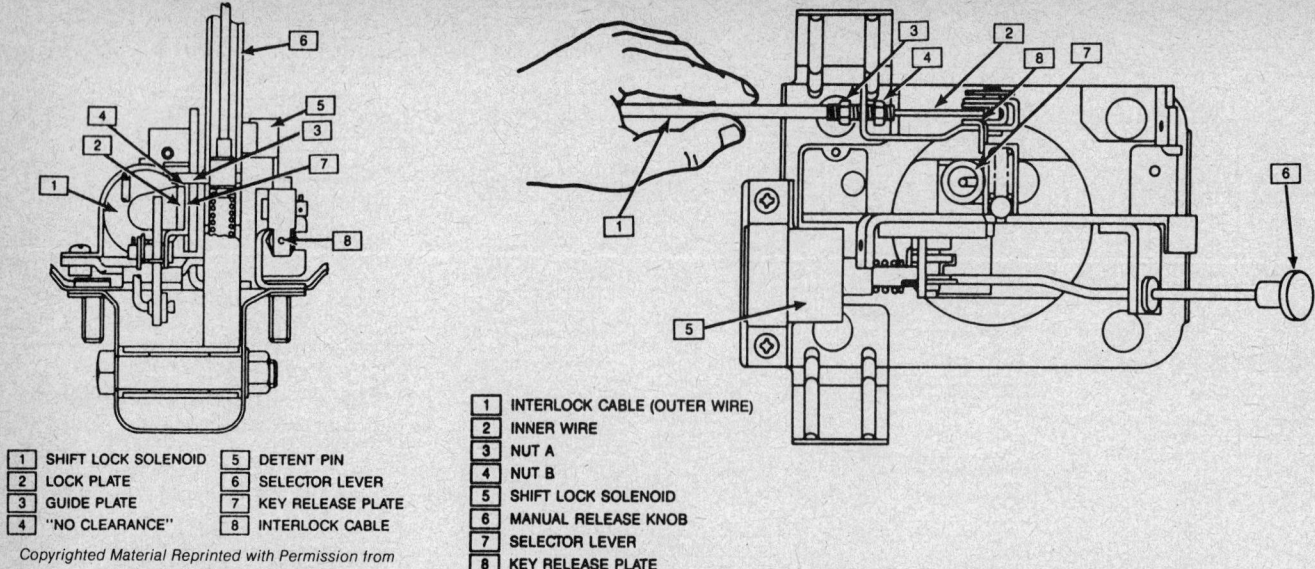

1	SHIFT LOCK SOLENOID	5	DETENT PIN
2	LOCK PLATE	6	SELECTOR LEVER
3	GUIDE PLATE	7	KEY RELEASE PLATE
4	"NO CLEARANCE"	8	INTERLOCK CABLE

Copyrighted Material Reprinted with Permission from Hydra-Matic Div., GM Corp.

Fig. 6   Interlock solenoid lock plate clearance

1	INTERLOCK CABLE (OUTER WIRE)
2	INNER WIRE
3	NUT A
4	NUT B
5	SHIFT LOCK SOLENOID
6	MANUAL RELEASE KNOB
7	SELECTOR LEVER
8	KEY RELEASE PLATE

Copyrighted Material Reprinted with Permission from Hydra-Matic Div., GM Corp.

Fig. 7   Interlock cable adjustment

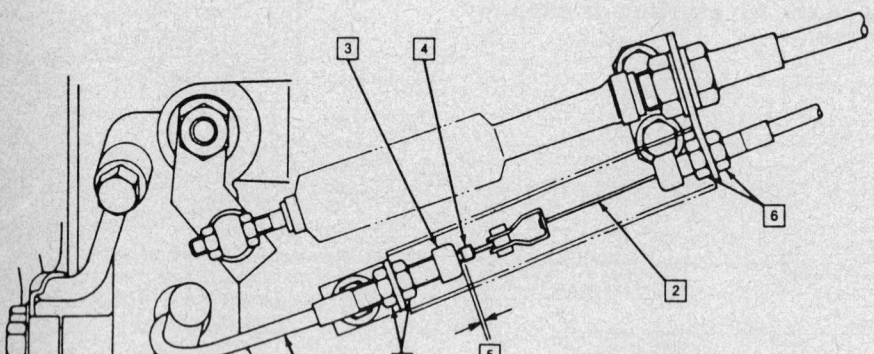

1. OIL PRESSURE CONTROL CABLE
2. ACCELERATOR CABLE
3. BOOT
4. INNER CABLE STOPPER
5. CLEARANCE (0-0.5 MM. 0-0.02 IN.)
6. ADJUSTING NUTS Ⓐ
7. ADJUSTING NUTS Ⓑ

Copyrighted Material Reprinted with Permission from Hydra-Matic Div., GM Corp.

Fig. 8   Oil pressure control cable adjustment

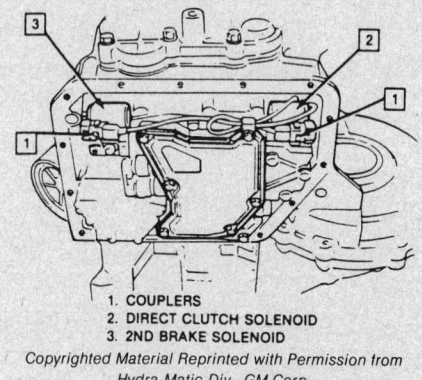

1. COUPLERS
2. DIRECT CLUTCH SOLENOID
3. 2ND BRAKE SOLENOID

Copyrighted Material Reprinted with Permission from Hydra-Matic Div., GM Corp.

Fig. 9   Direct clutch & second brake solenoid replacement

IN-VEHICLE REPAIRS

DIRECT CLUTCH & SECOND BRAKE SOLENOIDS, REPLACE

1. Disconnect battery ground cable.
2. Drain transaxle fluid and remove oil pan.
3. Disconnect electrical connectors from direct clutch and second brake solenoids, then remove the solenoids, **Fig. 9.**
4. Remove solenoid wire harness with grommet from upper side.
5. Reverse procedure to install.

OIL PRESSURE CONTROL CABLE, REPLACE

1. Remove cable cover, then disconnect oil pressure control cable from accelerator cable, **Fig. 10.**
2. Drain transaxle fluid and remove oil pan.
3. Disconnect oil pressure control cable from throttle valve cam, then remove

INTERLOCK CABLE, ADJUST

1. Shift selector lever to Park.
2. Loosen nuts (A) and (B) as shown in **Fig. 7.**
3. With outer wire pulled forward so that there is no deflection on inner wire, tighten nut (A), then nut (B) hand-tight.
4. Tighten nuts (A) and (B) again, then check the following:
   a. With selector lever in Park, ensure ignition key can be turned from "ACC" to "LOCK" position and removed from ignition switch.
   b. With selector lever shifted in any drive range other than Park, ignition key cannot be turned from Acc to Lock position.

OIL PRESSURE CONTROL CABLE, ADJUST

1. Check and, if necessary, adjust accelerator cable.
2. Start engine and allow to reach normal operating temperature.
3. Remove control cable cover and check that boot to inner cable stopper clearance is 0-.020 inch as shown, **Fig. 8.**
4. If clearance is not as specified, loosen, then tighten adjusting nuts (A) until specified clearance is obtained. If clearance is still not within specifications, turn adjusting nuts (B) and repeat procedure outlined above.

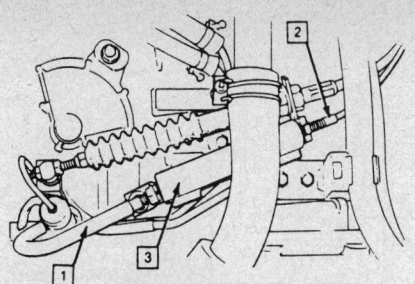

1. OIL PRESSURE CONTROL CABLE
2. ACCELERATOR CABLE
3. CABLE COVER

Copyrighted Material Reprinted with Permission from Hydra-Matic Div., GM Corp.

Fig. 10   Oil pressure control cable replacement

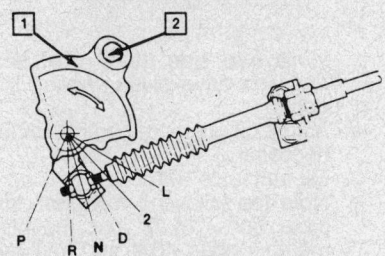

1. SHIFT LEVER SWITCH
2. BOLT

Copyrighted Material Reprinted with Permission from Hydra-Matic Div., GM Corp.

Fig. 13   Shift lever switch adjustment

the cable from transaxle case.
4. Reverse procedure to install, then adjust cable as previously described.

TRANSAXLE SELECTOR LEVER, REPLACE

1. Disconnect battery ground cable.
2. Remove selector lever knob, then the console assembly.
3. Remove selector indicator assembly, then disconnect cable from selector lever.
4. Disconnect back drive cable and the back drive solenoid electrical connector.
5. Raise and support vehicle.
6. Remove four housing attaching nuts, then the housing seat and housing with selector lever.
7. Reverse procedure to install.

TRANSAXLE SELECTOR CABLE, REPLACE

Removal

1. Remove console assembly, then the selector indicator assembly.
2. Disconnect selector cable from selector lever, floor and transaxle.
3. Raise and support vehicle.
4. Remove selector cable from front panel.

Installation

1. Raise and support vehicle.
2. Position selector cable in front panel, then lower vehicle.

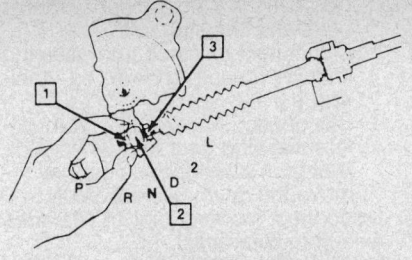

1. NUT Ⓐ
2. MANUAL SELECT CABLE JOINT
3. NUT Ⓑ

Copyrighted Material Reprinted with Permission from Hydra-Matic Div., GM Corp.

Fig. 11   Transaxle selector cable installation

3. Apply grease to selector cable pin, then connect cable to lever.
4. Install selector indicator, then the console assembly.
5. Connect cable to bracket on transaxle, then slide cable into manual select joint hole and position manual shift lever in Neutral range.
6. Turn nut (A), **Fig. 11**, by hand until it contacts manual select cable joint, then tighten nut (B) with wrench.
7. After tightening cable nuts, check the following:
   a. With selector lever in Park, vehicle can not move when pushed.
   b. With selector lever in Neutral, vehicle cannot be driven.
   c. With selector in Drive, Second or Low ranges, vehicle can be driven.
   d. With selector lever in Reverse, vehicle can be backed up.

SHIFT LEVER SWITCH, REPLACE

Removal

1. Disconnect battery ground cable.
2. Disconnect electrical connectors from shift lever switch.
3. Remove shift lever switch from manual shift shaft.

Installation

1. Shift manual shift lever to Manual range.
2. Using a screwdriver, turn shift lever switch to the position shown in **Fig. 12** and ensure a click is heard from joint at this position.
3. Install switch to manual shift shaft, then move the shaft in direction of arrow, **Fig. 13**, until a click is heard. Stop at this position and torque attaching bolts to 9.5-16.5 ft. lbs.
4. Connect electrical connectors to switch, then install clamp.
5. Apply parking brake and block wheels, then check the following:
   a. With selector lever in Park and ignition switch On, starter motor operates.
   b. With selector lever in Neutral and ignition switch On, starter motor operates.
   c. After moving selector lever from Neutral to Low, then back to Neu-

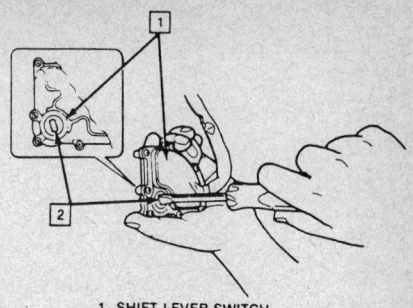

1. SHIFT LEVER SWITCH
2. SHIFT LEVER SWITCH JOINT

Copyrighted Material Reprinted with Permission from Hydra-Matic Div., GM Corp.

Fig. 12   Shift lever switch installation

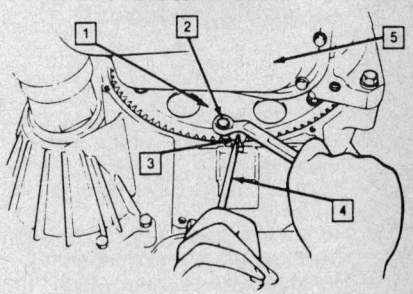

1. DRIVE PLATE
2. DRIVE PLATE BOLT
3. NOTCH
4. STANDARD SCREWDRIVER
5. ENGINE OIL PAN

Copyrighted Material Reprinted with Permission from Hydra-Matic Div., GM Corp.

Fig. 14   Drive plate bolt removal

tral, starter motor operates with ignition switch On.
   d. With selector lever in Park and ignition switch On, starter motor operates.
   e. In any range other than Park or Neutral, starter motor cannot be operated.
   f. With selector lever in Reverse and ignition switch On (engine not running), back-up lamps light.

TRANSAXLE REPLACE

1. Disconnect battery ground cable.
2. Remove air suction guide from air cleaner.
3. Disconnect battery cables and remove battery and tray.
4. Remove ground cable from transaxle.
5. Disconnect solenoid and shift lever connectors.
6. Remove wire harness and speedometer cable from transaxle.
7. Remove oil pressure control cable from accelerator cable, then the accelerator cable from transaxle.
8. Disconnect select cable from transaxle, then remove starter.
9. Drain transaxle fluid.
10. Disconnect oil outlet and inlet hoses from oil pipes. Plug all openings.
11. Raise and support vehicle.
12. Remove exhaust system components as necessary, then the clutch housing lower plate.

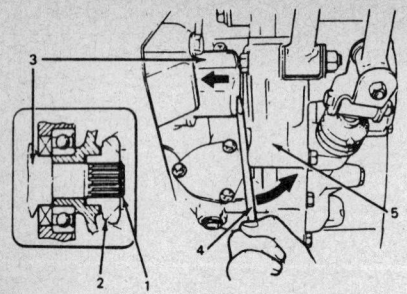

1. SNAP RING
2. DIFFERENTIAL SIDE GEAR
3. DIFFERENTIAL SIDE JOINT
4. TIRE LEVER
5. TRANSAXLE

Copyrighted Material Reprinted with Permission from Hydra-Matic Div., GM Corp.

Fig. 15 Differential side gear snap ring removal

13. Remove drive plate attaching bolts using a screwdriver in notch provided to hold drive plate, **Fig. 14.**
14. Remove LH front drive axle as follows:
    a. Remove wheel center cap, then the cotter pin and driveshaft nut.
    b. Remove wheel nuts, then the wheel and tire assembly.
    c. Remove snap ring from spline of differential side joint using a screwdriver, **Fig. 15.**

d. Remove stabilizer bar bracket bolts and ball stud bolt.
e. Disconnect ball stud from steering knuckle by pulling down on stabilizer bar.
f. Disconnect inboard joint from differential side gear and wheel side joint from steering knuckle, then remove the drive axle assembly.
15. Disconnect inboard joint of RH drive axle from differential.
16. Remove RH side transaxle mounting member bolts, then secure transaxle using a jack.
17. Remove LH side transaxle mounting bolts.
18. Remove engine-to-transaxle attaching bolts.
19. Remove transaxle from engine by sliding toward left side and carefully lowering jack.
20. Reverse procedure to install, noting the following:
    a. Apply suitable grease around the cup at center of torque converter.
    b. Measure distance A, **Fig. 16.** Distance should measure more than .85 inch. If distance is less than specified, converter installation is improper and must be corrected.
    c. Guide right drive axle into differential side gear as transaxle is being raised.
    d. After installing inboard joints into differential side gear, push inboard

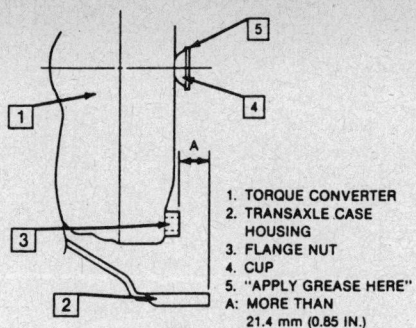

1. TORQUE CONVERTER
2. TRANSAXLE CASE HOUSING
3. FLANGE NUT
4. CUP
5. "APPLY GREASE HERE"
A: MORE THAN 21.4 mm (0.85 IN.)

Copyrighted Material Reprinted with Permission from Hydra-Matic Div., GM Corp.

Fig. 16 Torque converter installation

joints into side gears until snap rings on drive axles engage side gears.
e. Adjust oil pressure control cable if necessary.
f. Fill transaxle with fluid.
g. Note the following **torques**: drive plate bolts, 14 ft. lbs.; mounting member bolts, 40 ft. lbs.; transaxle mounting nuts, 33–40 ft. lbs.; transaxle mounting bolts, 40 ft. lbs.; stabilizer shaft mounting bolts, 31 ft. lbs.; ball stud bolt, 44 ft. lbs.; wheel nuts, 40 ft. lbs.

TIGHTENING SPECIFICATIONS

Component	Torque/Ft. Lbs.
Drive Plate Bolts To Torque Converter	13–14
Lower Valve Body Bolts	6–8
Manual Shift Lever Nuts	20–23
Oil Drain Plug	13–16
Oil Pan Bolts	3–4
Oil Pump Case Bolts	13–19
Oil Pump Cover Bolts	6–8
Oil Strainer Bolts	4
Rear Cover Case Bolts	12–16
Rear Cover Case Nuts	8–10
Reduction Driven Gear Nut	80–108
Solenoid Bolt	5–6
Throttle Valve Cam Bolt	4–6
Transaxle Case Housing Bolts	12–16
Upper Valve Body Bolts	4
2nd Brake Band Cover Bolts	5–6

KF 400 & JF403E Automatic Transaxles (Storm)

INDEX

DESCRIPTION

KF 400

The KF 400 is a 3-speed automatic transaxle. Power is transferred from the output gear through the ring gear to the idler gear.

The output gear, idler gear and differential gear case are supported by tapered roller bearings. The preload on the roller bearings can be adjusted by using shims.

The final drive gear is a helical type design.

JF403E

The JF430E is a 4-speed automatic transaxle. This transaxle utilizes a microcomputer as a control unit to evaluate driving conditions including throttle opening and vehicle speed.

This transaxle also incorporates a shift mode change control. The economy mode (ECON switch ON) is suitable for economical driving. The normal mode (ECON switch OFF) is suitable for hill climbing and/or acceleration.

MAINTENANCE

Check transaxle fluid level every 7,500 miles, adding Dexron II automatic transmission fluid as necessary.

Change transaxle fluid and filter every 30,000 miles under normal driving conditions, or every 15,000 miles if vehicle is operated under severe conditions such as city driving during hot weather or driving over hilly or mountainous terrain.

CHECKING FLUID LEVEL

1. Park vehicle on level ground.
2. Start engine and operate for 15 minutes to allow fluid to reach operating temperature.
3. Move gear selector through all gear positions, then to park.
4. Remove and check fluid level on dipstick, add Dexron II as necessary. **Do not overfill.**
5. Remove speedometer gear at the transaxle and check differential fluid level on speedometer gear housing, add Dexron II as necessary.

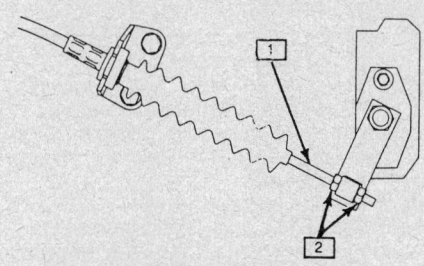

Copyrighted Material Reprinted with Permission from Hydra-Matic Div., GM Corp.

Fig. 1   Shift cable adjustment

CHANGING FLUID

1. Raise and support vehicle.
2. Remove drain plug at bottom of differential and drain fluid.
3. Remove oil pan and discard pan gasket.
4. Clean drain pan, then using a new gasket, install gasket and pan to transaxle. **Torque** pan bolts to 71 inch lbs.
5. Install drain plug and fill transaxle through oil filler tube and speedometer gear housing with Dexron II automatic transmission fluid.

IN-VEHICLE ADJUSTMENTS

MANUAL LINKAGE, ADJUST

Shift Control Cable, Adjust

1. Place the ignition key in the LOCK position.
2. Set the gear selector lever in the Park position.
3. Loosen the adjuster nuts at the transaxle **Fig. 1.**
4. Ensure shift lever at the transaxle is in the "PARK" position.
5. Pull the cable forward and tighten forward adjuster nut until it contacts shift lever.
6. Tighten rear adjuster nut until it contacts shift lever, then tighten both adjuster nuts.

Back Drive Cable, Adjust

1. Place shift lever in Park position.
2. Place ignition switch to the LOCK position.
3. Pull cable forward at shift lever bracket, then tighten forward adjuster nut until contact is made against the bracket.
4. Tighten rear nut until it makes contact with shift lever bracket, then tighten both adjuster nuts.

IN-VEHICLE REPAIRS

SHIFTER CONTROL, REPLACE

1. Disconnect battery ground cable.
2. Remove ashtray, shift trim bezel, heater control knobs, then radio bezel.
3. Remove lower console, then shift knob from lever.
4. Disconnect back drive cable for shift control.
5. Disconnect shift lock out module from shift control, then electrical connections.
6. Disconnect shift control cable from shift control.
7. Remove shift control retaining bolts, then shift control.
8. Remove solenoid and switch assembly from shift control.
9. Reverse procedure to install.

SPEEDOMETER DRIVEN GEAR, REPLACE

1. Disconnect battery ground cable.
2. Remove air breather tube, then air intake duct from air cleaner assembly.
3. Disconnect speedometer cable at transaxle.
4. Remove speedometer driven gear retaining bolt, then gear and O-ring seal.
5. Reverse procedure to install, noting the following:
   a. Replace speedometer O-ring seal.
   b. **Torque** speedometer driven gear retaining bolt to 71 inch lbs.

CONTROL VALVE ASSEMBLY, REPLACE

KM 400

1. Disconnect negative battery cable.

2. Raise and support vehicle.
3. Remove left and right undercovers.
4. Drain transaxle fluid.
5. Remove oil pan attaching bolts, then oil pan.
6. Remove control valve assembly bolts, then control valve assembly.
7. Reverse procedure to install, noting the following:
   a. **Torque** control valve assembly bolts to 71 inch lbs.
   b. **Torque** oil pan bolts to 71 inch lbs.
   c. Refill transaxle fluid as described under "Changing Fluid."

JF403E

1. Disconnect negative battery cable, then the terminal assembly connector.
2. Remove the terminal assembly clip.
3. Raise and support vehicle.
4. Remove left and right undercovers, then drain the transaxle.
5. Remove oil pan protector and oil pan.
6. Remove the fifteen control valve assembly bolts.
7. Remove control valve and terminal assemblies from transaxle.
8. Remove terminal valve assembly from control valve assembly.
9. Reverse procedure to install. **Torque**

control valve assembly bolts and oil pan bolts to 71 inch lbs.

TRANSAXLE
REPLACE

1. Disconnect negative battery cable.
2. Remove battery and battery tray.
3. Remove air duct, then air breather tube from air cleaner assembly.
4. **On KF 400 models,** disconnect vacuum diaphragm at vacuum hose.
5. **On all models,** disconnect electrical connectors from transaxle, then shift cable from lever.
6. Disconnect shift cable bracket from transaxle case.
7. remove breather hose from transaxle, then the speedometer cable.
8. Install engine support fixture tool No. J 28467-A or equivalent to engine.
9. Remove left transaxle mount through bolt, then four transaxle to engine mounting bolts.
10. Raise and support vehicle.
11. Remove left and right undercovers, then front wheel and tire assemblies.
12. Disconnect left control arm from steering knuckle.

13. Drain transaxle fluid.
14. Disconnect drive axles from transaxle.
15. Remove front transaxle mount through bolt, then dampener from rear mount through bolt.
16. Remove rear transaxle mount through bolt, then two front center crossmember mounting bolts.
17. Disconnect front pipe to exhaust manifold.
18. Remove two rear crossmember mounting bolts.
19. Remove center crossmember bolts from vehicle, place suitable transaxle jack under transaxle.
20. Remove rear mount to transaxle case bolt, then front mount retaining bolt.
21. Remove front mount bracket from the engine, then the flywheel cover.
22. Remove flywheel to torque converter bolts.
23. Disconnect oil cooler lines from transaxle.
24. Remove two rear mount transaxle bolts, then carefully lower transaxle from vehicle.
25. Reverse procedure to install. **Torque** transaxle mount through bolt to 64 ft. lbs. and flywheel to torque converter bolts to 31 ft. lbs.

TIGHTENING SPECIFICATIONS

Component	Torque/Ft. Lbs.
Center Crossmember Bolts	45
Control Valve Assembly Bolts	71①
Drain Plug	20
Flywheel To Torque Converter Bolts	31
Front Transaxle Mount Bracket Bolts	45
Front Transaxle Mount Retaining Nut	45
Front Transaxle Mount Through Bolt	64
Governor Cover Retaining Bolts	71①
Left Transaxle Mount Bolts	29
Left Transaxle Mount Through Bolt	64
Lower Filler Tube To Case Bolt	97①
Neutral Safety Switch Retaining Screws	26①
Oil Cooler Lines Union Bolts	10
Oil Filter Bolts	71①
Oil Pan Bolts	71①
Oil Pressure Tap Plug	80①
Rear Transaxle Mount Bolts	29
Shift Cable Grommet Bolts	89①
Shift Cable Locknut	20
Shift control retaining bolts	20
Shifter control Bolts	20
Speedometer Driven Gear Retaining Bolt	71①
Transaxle To Engine Mounting Bolts	31
Upper Filler Tube To Case Bolt	97①

①—Inch lbs.

FRONT WHEEL DRIVE AXLES

INDEX

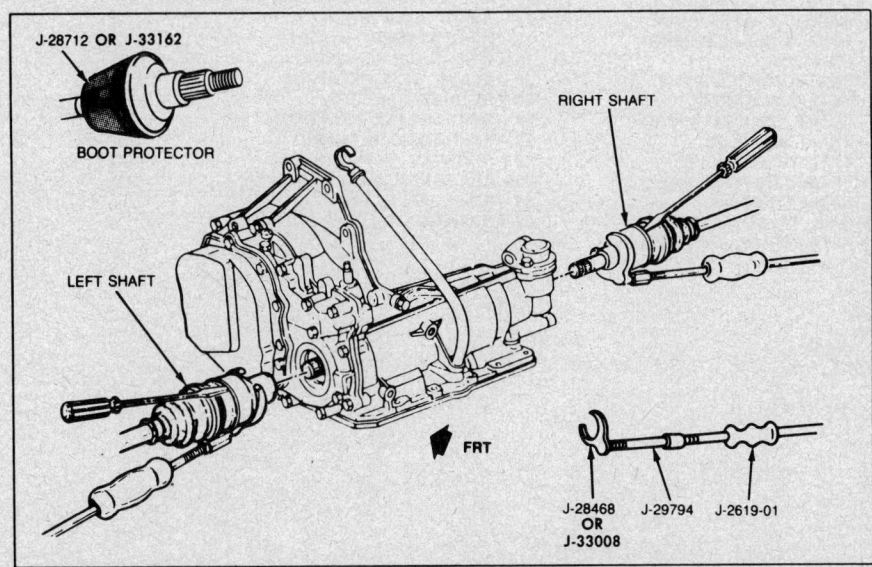

Fig. 1 Front wheel drive components & axle shaft removal. Except Metro, Spectrum, Sprint & Storm (Typical)

3. Worn C.V. joint.
4. Binding or tight C.V. joint.

DESCRIPTION

The front wheel drive system, **Figs. 1, and 2**, consists of left and righthand output shafts and drive axles. Each drive axle consists of an axle shaft, with a ball type constant velocity joint at the outboard end and a tri-pot joint at the inboard end.

On all models except Metro, Spectrum, Sprint and Storm, a ball type constant velocity joint is used at the outboard end, while a tri-pot type joint is used at the inboard end, **Fig. 3**. Snap rings are used to lock the male splines of the axle shafts into the transaxle gears, except for the left side inboard joint used with the automatic transaxles. The left side inboard joint used on automatic transaxle models utilizes a female spline which installs over a transaxle stub shaft.

On some manual transmissions, a constant velocity joint is used on the inboard end of the drive axle, **Fig. 4**.

On Storm models, a ball type constant velocity joint is used at the outboard end, while a tri-pot type joint is used at the inboard end.

On Spectrum models, the drive axles are completely flexible assemblies containing an inner and outer constant velocity joint joined by an axle shaft, **Fig. 5**. Three types of constant velocity joints are used: the manual transaxle utilizes a Birfield outer and double offset inner, and the automatic uses a tripod inner and a Birfield outer.

On Metro and Sprint models, a constant velocity ball joint is used on the outboard side of the drive axle and a constant velocity tripod joint on the inboard side, **Fig. 6**.

TROUBLESHOOTING

CLICKING NOISE IN TURNS

Worn or damaged outboard joint.

CLUNK WHEN ACCELERATING FROM COAST TO DRIVE

Worn or damaged constant velocity joint.

SHUDDER OR VIBRATION DURING ACCELERATION

1. Excessive C.V. joint angle.
2. Incorrect toe in or out.
3. Incorrect trim height.
4. Worn or damaged inboard or outboard C.V. joints.
5. Sticking tri-pot joint spider assembly.

VIBRATION AT HIGHWAY SPEEDS

1. Out-of-balance front tires or wheels.
2. Out-of-round front tires.

DRIVE AXLE
REPLACE

On models equipped with tri-pot joints on inboard axles, care must be taken not to overextend joints. When either or both ends are disconnected, overextending the tri-pot joint could result in internal joint separation.

On vehicles equipped with ball type constant velocity inboard joints, install inner drive joint seal protector J-34754, on inboard seal and install axle boot protector J-28712 on outboard seal if necessary. On vehicles equipped with tri-pot inboard joints, install axle boot seal protector J-28712 on outboard seal and J-33162 on inboard seal, if necessary.

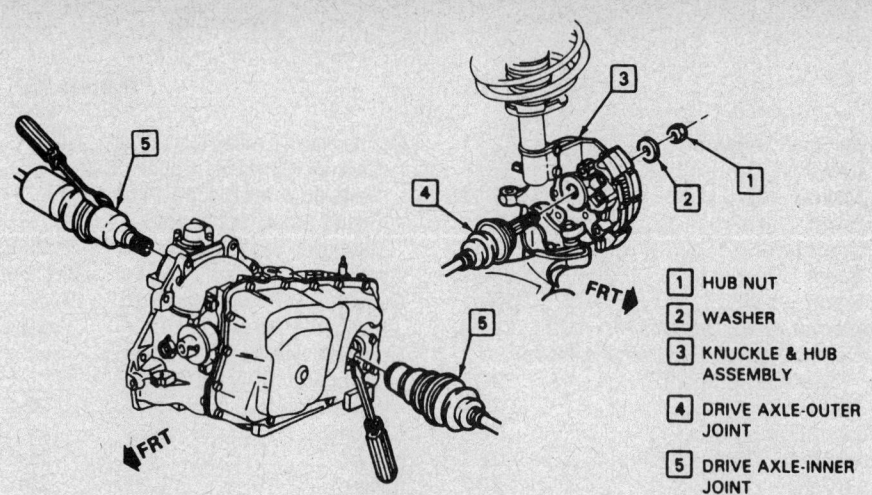

1	HUB NUT
2	WASHER
3	KNUCKLE & HUB ASSEMBLY
4	DRIVE AXLE-OUTER JOINT
5	DRIVE AXLE-INNER JOINT

Fig. 2   Front wheel drive components & axle shaft installation. Except Metro, Spectrum, Sprint & Storm (Typical)

Key No.	Part Name
1 – RACE, C.V. JOINT OUTER	15 – HOUSING ASM, TRI-POT
2 – CAGE, C.V. JOINT	16 – HOUSING ASM, DAMPER & TRI-POT (RH)
3 – RACE, C.V. JOINT INNER	17 – SHAFT, AXLE (RH)
4 – RING, SHAFT RETAINING	18 – RING, SPACER
5 – BALL (6)	19 – RING, RACE RETAINING
6 – PROTECTOR, CLAMP (2)	20 – CLAMP, SEAL RETAINING
7 – SEAL, C.V. JOINT	21 – RETAINER, NEEDLE
8 – CLAMP, SEAL RETAINING	22 – RING, NEEDLE RETAINER
9 – SHAFT, AXLE (LH)	23 – RING, JOINT RETAINING
10 – SEAL, TRI-POT JOINT	24 – HOUSING, TRI-POT (RH)
11 – SPIDER, TRI-POT JOINT	25 – SHAFT ASM, DAMPER &
12 – ROLLER, NEEDLE	26 – RING, DEFLECTOR
13 – BALL, TRI-POT JOINT (3)	27 – BUSHING, TRILOBAL TRI-POT
14 – RETAINER, BALL & NEEDLE (3)	

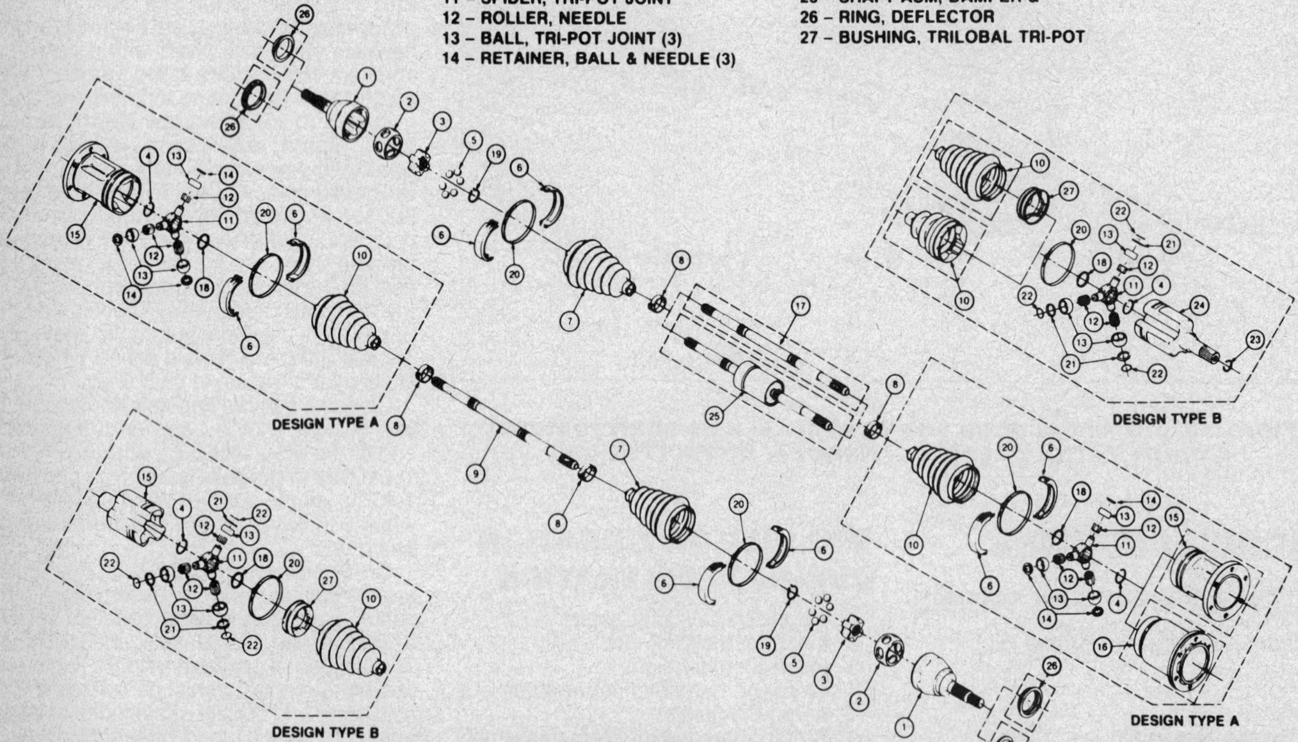

DESIGN TYPE A

DESIGN TYPE B

DESIGN TYPE B

DESIGN TYPE A

Fig. 3   Exploded view of drive axle with tri-pot inboard joint. Except Metro, Spectrum, Sprint & Storm.

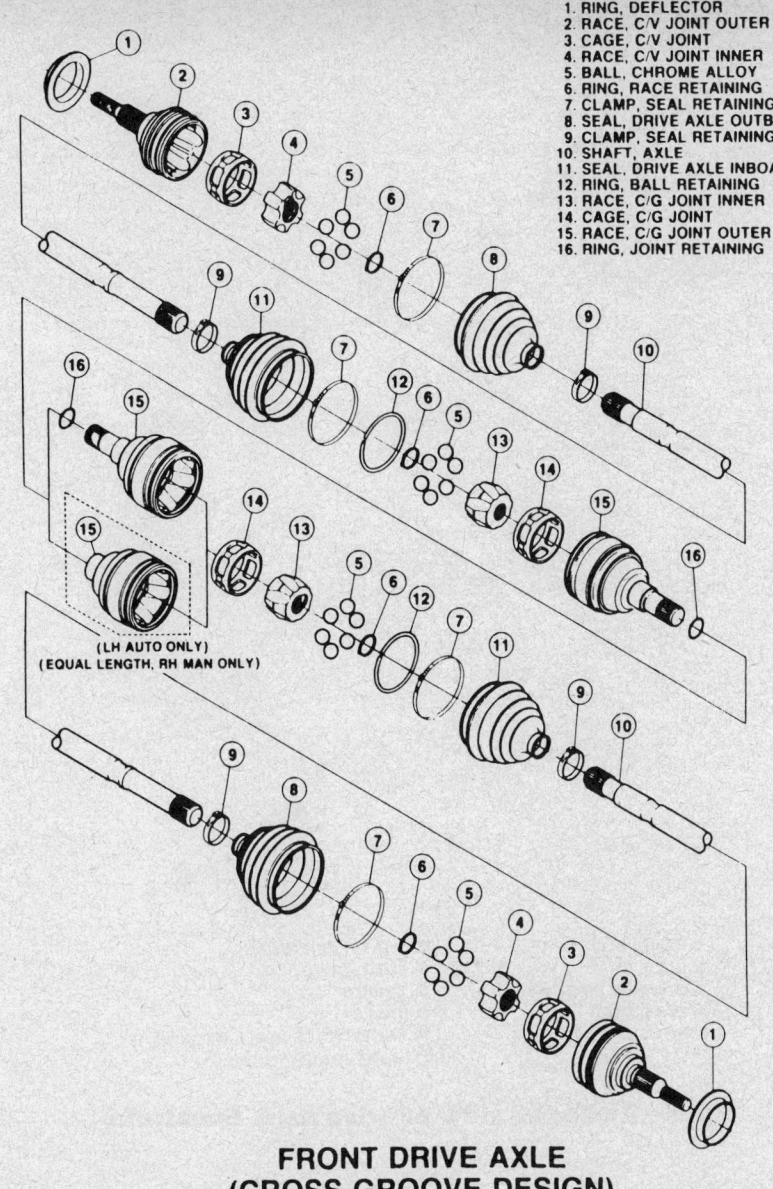

1. RING, DEFLECTOR
2. RACE, C/V JOINT OUTER
3. CAGE, C/V JOINT
4. RACE, C/V JOINT INNER
5. BALL, CHROME ALLOY
6. RING, RACE RETAINING
7. CLAMP, SEAL RETAINING
8. SEAL, DRIVE AXLE OUTBOARD
9. CLAMP, SEAL RETAINING
10. SHAFT, AXLE
11. SEAL, DRIVE AXLE INBOARD
12. RING, BALL RETAINING
13. RACE, C/G JOINT INNER
14. CAGE, C/G JOINT
15. RACE, C/G JOINT OUTER
16. RING, JOINT RETAINING

(LH AUTO ONLY)
(EQUAL LENGTH, RH MAN ONLY)

**FRONT DRIVE AXLE
(CROSS-GROOVE DESIGN)**

Fig. 4   Exploded view of cross-groove design drive axle. Models w/manual transmission except Metro, Spectrum, Sprint & Storm

ELDORADO, REATTA, RIVIERA, SEVILLE, TORONADO, 1988 DEVILLE & FLEETWOOD

Removal

1. Remove hub nut, then raise and support vehicle and remove wheel and tire assembly.
2. Remove brake caliper and rotor assembly.
3. Remove stabilizer link or stabilizer bar from control arm.
4. Remove tie rod end at steering knuckle, then remove lower ball joint stud at steering knuckle.
5. Remove axle from transaxle using a prybar or screwdriver and a wood block as a fulcrum to protect case cover.
6. Drive axle from hub and bearing assembly using drive axle spindle remover tool No. J-28733.
7. Remove axle from vehicle.

Installation

1. Install drive axle at steering knuckle.
2. Install lower ball joint stud at steering knuckle.
3. Install stabilizer link or stabilizer bar to lower control arm.
4. Install tie rod end at steering knuckle.
5. Install brake caliper, rotor and new caliper mounting bolts.
6. Install new torque prevailing nut and washer.
7. Insert a screwdriver or drift into caliper and rotor to prevent rotor from turning, **Fig. 7.**

then install hub nut and **torque** to 74 ft lbs., **Fig. 7.**
8. Seat the drive axle into the transaxle by placing a screwdriver into the groove on the joint housing and tapping until seated, then grasp the inner housing and pull outward. If the snap ring is properly seated, the axle will remain in place, **Fig. 2.**
9. Install the front wheel and tire assembly and lower vehicle.

BONNEVILLE, CAVALIER, CELEBRITY, CENTURY, CIMARRON, CUTLASS CALAIS, DELTA 88 & 98, ELECTRA, FIRENZA, GRAND AM, LESABRE, PARK AVENUE, SKYHAWK, SKYLARK & SUNBIRD

Removal

1. Raise and support vehicle, then remove tire and wheel assembly.
2. Install a brass drift or a screwdriver to prevent the rotor from turning, **Fig. 7.**
3. Remove shaft nut and washer using shaft nut socket tool No. J-34826.
4. Remove brake caliper from steering knuckle and suspend caliper assembly.
5. Remove rotor from hub and bearing assembly, then stabilizer shaft or link from control arm.
6. Remove ball joint from steering knuckle.
7. Remove drive axle from transaxle using axle shaft remover tool No. J-33008, axle shaft remover tool No. J-29794 and slide hammer tool No. J-2619-01 if necessary, **Fig. 1.**
8. Remove drive axle from hub and bearing assembly using front hub spindle remover tool No. J-28733-A, **Fig. 8.**

Installation

1. Install drive axle into hub and bearing assembly and transaxle.
2. Install lower ball joint to steering knuckle.
3. Install stabilizer shaft or link to control arm.
4. Install rotor to hub and bearing assembly.
5. Insert a screwdriver or drift into caliper and rotor to prevent rotor from turning, **Fig. 7.**
6. Install a new hub nut and washer, **torque** to 185 ft. lbs. **On Bonneville, Electra, LeSabre, Park Avenue and Sunbird models, torque** to 191 ft. lbs.
7. Seat the drive axle into the transaxle by placing a screwdriver into the groove on the joint housing and tapping until seated.
8. Ensure drive axle is seated by pulling outward on the housing. Do not pull on the drive axle.
9. Install tire and wheel assembly and lower vehicle.

CUTLASS SUPREME, GRAND PRIX, LUMINA & REGAL

Removal

1. Raise and support vehicle, then remove tire and wheel assembly.
2. Remove brake caliper and bracket assembly, then the rotor.
3. Remove the four bolts holding the hub/bearing assembly to the knuckle.
4. **On vehicles equipped with The Anti-Lock Brake System (ABS)**, remove the ABS sensor mounting bolt, then position the sensor aside to avoid damage.
5. **On vehicles equipped with 125C and HM-282 transaxles and right shaft of vehicles with 440-T4 transaxles**, separate the drive axle from the transaxle using axle shaft remover tool No. J-3308, extension tool No. J-29794 and puller tool No. J-2619-01. **Fig. 1. On the left shaft of vehicles equipped with 440-T4 transmissions**, using the frame for leverage, separate the drive axle from the transaxle with a screwdriver or prybar in the groove provided on the inner joint, **Fig. 2**.
6. **On all transmissions**, remove the axle/bearing assembly through the knuckle.

Installation

1. **On all transmissions**, Install the axle/bearing assembly through the knuckle and into the transaxle. **If equipped with ABS**, install the ABS assembly.
2. Loosely secure the bearing to knuckle bolts.
3. Seat the drive axle into the transaxle by placing a screwdriver into the groove on the joint housing and tapping until seated, then grasp the inner housing and pull outward. If the snap ring is properly seated, the axle will remain in place, **Fig. 2**.

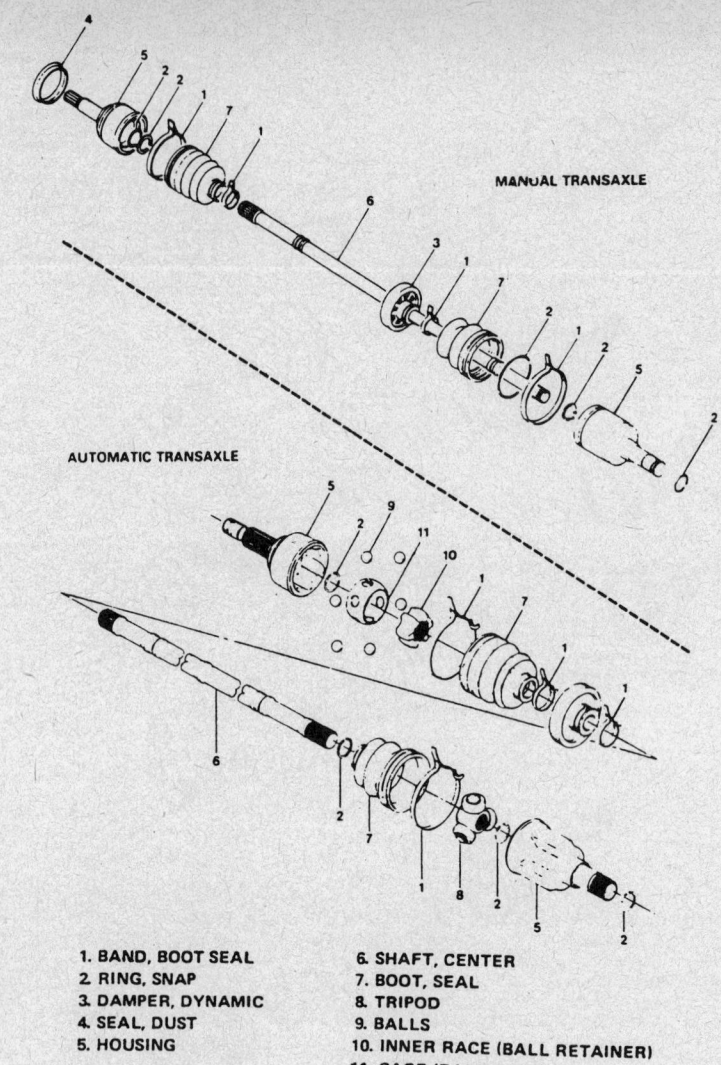

MANUAL TRANSAXLE

AUTOMATIC TRANSAXLE

1. BAND, BOOT SEAL
2. RING, SNAP
3. DAMPER, DYNAMIC
4. SEAL, DUST
5. HOUSING
6. SHAFT, CENTER
7. BOOT, SEAL
8. TRIPOD
9. BALLS
10. INNER RACE (BALL RETAINER)
11. CAGE (BALL GUIDE)

Fig. 5   Exploded view of drive axle. Spectrum

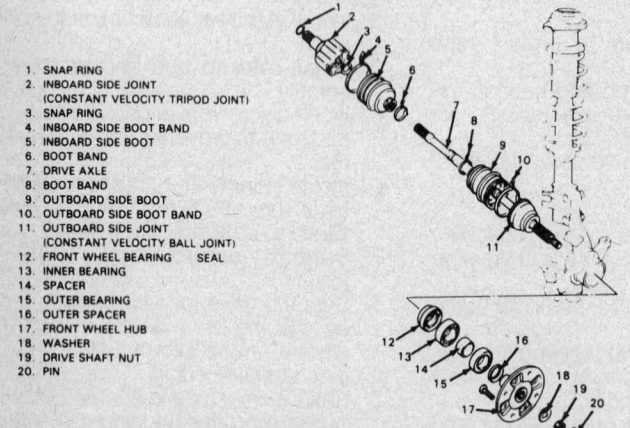

1. SNAP RING
2. INBOARD SIDE JOINT (CONSTANT VELOCITY TRIPOD JOINT)
3. SNAP RING
4. INBOARD SIDE BOOT BAND
5. INBOARD SIDE BOOT
6. BOOT BAND
7. DRIVE AXLE
8. BOOT BAND
9. OUTBOARD SIDE BOOT
10. OUTBOARD SIDE BOOT BAND
11. OUTBOARD SIDE JOINT (CONSTANT VELOCITY BALL JOINT)
12. FRONT WHEEL BEARING   SEAL
13. INNER BEARING
14. SPACER
15. OUTER BEARING
16. OUTER SPACER
17. FRONT WHEEL HUB
18. WASHER
19. DRIVE SHAFT NUT
20. PIN

Fig. 6   Exploded view of drive axle. Sprint

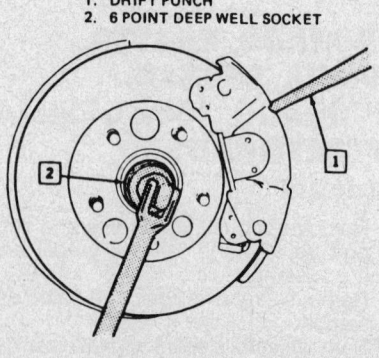

1. DRIFT PUNCH
2. 6 POINT DEEP WELL SOCKET

Fig. 7   Removing & installing axle shaft nut

4. Using a new nut and washer, install the hub and bearing assembly to axle, **torque** hub and bearing assembly to knuckle attaching bolts to 52 ft. lbs.
5. Install rotor and brake assembly.
6. Install tire and wheel assembly.
7. **Torque** drive axle nut to 184 ft. lbs, then lower vehicle.

1989–90 DEVILLE & FLEETWOOD
Removal

1. Raise and support vehicle, then remove tire and wheel assembly.
2. Install a brass drift or a screwdriver to prevent the rotor from turning, **Fig. 7**.
3. Remove shaft nut and washer.
4. Remove lower ball joint cotter and nut, then loosen ball joint using ball joint separator tool No. J-29330. **If removing right axle,** turn wheel to left, **if removing left axle,** turn wheel to the right.
5. Separate the joint by using a pry bar between the suspension support and lower control arm.
6. Pull out on lower knuckle area and with a plastic or rubber mallet strike the end of the axle shaft to disengage axle from hub and bearing.
7. Separate hub and bearing assembly from drive axle and move strut and knuckle assembly rearward.
8. Remove inner joint from transaxle using axle shaft remover tool No. J-28468 or J-33008 if equipped with intermediate shaft, **Fig. 1**.

Installation

1. Seat the drive axle into the transaxle by placing a screwdriver into the groove on the joint housing and tapping until seated, then grasp the inner housing and pull outward. If the snap ring is properly seated, the axle will remain in place, **Fig. 2**.
2. Drive axle into hub and bearing assembly.
3. Install lower ball joint to knuckle, **torque** to 45 ft. lbs., then install cotter pin.
4. Install washer and new shaft nut.
5. Insert a screwdriver or drift into caliper and rotor to prevent rotor from turning. **Fig. 7**.
6. Install hub nut, **torque** to 185 ft. lbs.
7. Install tire and wheel assembly and lower vehicle.

METRO

1. Remove wheel center cap.
2. Remove claulking, driveshaft nut and washer.
3. Raise and support vehicle.
4. Remove wheel and tire assembly.
5. Drain transaxle fluid.
6. Pry inboard driveshaft from transaxle using a large screwdriver or equivalent.
7. Remove lower ball joint retaining nut, then separate suspension arm from steering knuckle.
8. Remove drive axle assembly from transaxle, then from steering knuckle.

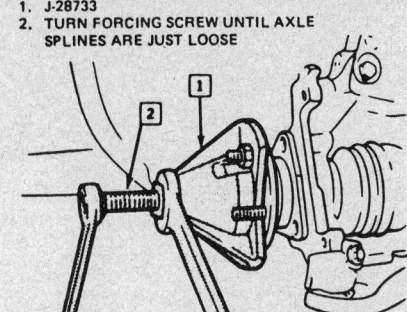

1. J-28733
2. TURN FORCING SCREW UNTIL AXLE SPLINES ARE JUST LOOSE

Fig. 8 Removing drive axle from hub & bearing assembly

9. Reverse procedure to install, noting the following:
   a. Clean front wheel bearing seal, then apply grease to seal.
   b. Check seal for breakage or deterioration, replace if necessary.
   c. Apply sealant to drain plug for manual transaxle.
   d. Install the wheel side joint to the steering knuckle, then the differential-side joint to the transaxle. Push drive axle into transaxle by hand until snap ring is seated in spline. **Torque** hub nut to 129 ft. lbs. and ball joint stud bolt to 44 ft. lbs.

PRIZM

1. Disconnect battery ground cable.
2. Raise and support vehicle.
3. Drain transaxle fluid.
4. Remove hub nut cap, then cotter pin, hub nut and washer.
5. Remove tie rod end from steering knuckle.
6. Remove brake caliper from steering knuckle.
7. Disconnect control arm from steering knuckle.
8. Remove brake rotor.
9. Remove drive axle from hub assembly using a plastic hammer. **If shaft is difficult to remove, use crankshaft gear puller (Tool No. J 25287) or equivalent.**
10. Remove drive axle assembly from transaxle using slide hammer (Tool No. J 2619-01) and axle shaft puller (Tool No. J 35762).
11. Reverse procedure to install, noting the following:
    a. Install drive axle in transaxle first, then hub assembly.
    b. **Torque** lower control arm bolts to 105 ft. lbs.
    c. **Torque** tie rod end nut to 36 ft. lbs.
    d. **Torque** brake caliper mounting bolts to 65 ft. lbs.
    e. **Torque** drive axle hub nut to 137 ft.lbs.

STORM

1. Disconnect battery ground cable.
2. Raise and support vehicle.
3. Drain transaxle fluid.

4. Remove wheel assembly.
5. Unstake hub nut, then remove nut.
6. Remove tie rod end from steering knuckle.
7. Disconnect lower control arm from steering knuckle.
8. Remove drive axle from hub assembly, using a plastic hammer.
9. Remove drive axle assembly from transaxle, using slide hammer (Tool No. J 2619-01) and axle shaft puller (Tool No. J 35762).
10. Remove drive axle from vehicle.
11. Reverse procedure to install, noting the following:
    a. **Torque** lower control arm bolts to 105 ft. lbs.
    b. **Torque** tie rod end to 36 ft. lbs.
    c. **Torque** hub nut to 137 ft. lbs., then stake nut.

LEMANS
Removal

1. Loosen both upper strut mount attaching bolts.
2. Remove wheel cover, then loosen wheel lug nuts and remove cotter pin and drive axle shaft-to-hub nut and washer.
3. Raise and support vehicle.
4. Remove wheel and tire assembly.
5. Remove ball joint retaining clip and stud nut, then separate ball joint from steering knuckle using ball joint separator tool No. J-36226 or equivalent. **Disregard "This Side Towards Wheel" marking on tool. Tool must be turned to opposite position when used on these vehicles.**
6. Remove tie rod nut, then separate tie rod from steering knuckle using tie rod separator tool No. J-24319-01 or equivalent.
7. Separate drive axle shaft from wheel hub using axle shaft to hub separator tool No. J-3666-1 or equivalent.
8. Position a drain pan under transaxle, then remove drive axle from transaxle using axle shaft to transaxle separator tool No. J-36639 and slide hammer tool No. J-23907 or equivalents.

Installation

1. Install drive axle into transaxle, using care to avoid damaging seal. Pull on outer joint race to ensure it will not come out of transaxle.
2. Install drive axle into knuckle hub bearing.
3. Install steering knuckle onto lower ball joint, then connect tie rod to the knuckle. **Torque** tie rod nut to 45 ft. lbs. and ball joint stud nut to 50 ft. lbs., then tie rod nut cotter pin and stud nut retaining clip.
4. Install drive axle shaft-to-wheel hub washer and nut.
5. Install wheel and tire assembly, then lower vehicle.
6. With weight of vehicle on wheels, **torque** new drive axle-to-hub nut to 74 ft. lbs., then back off nut and **retorque** to 15 ft. lbs. Tighten nut an additional ¼ turn, then install cotter pin. If necessary, loosen nut slightly to align cotter pin holes.

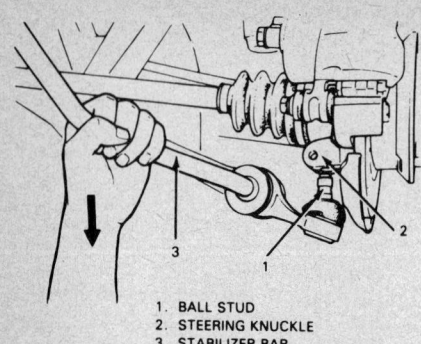

1. BALL STUD
2. STEERING KNUCKLE
3. STABILIZER BAR

Fig. 9 Removing ball joint stud from steering knuckle. Sprint

7. **Torque** upper strut mount attaching nuts to 22 ft. lbs.
8. Check transaxle fluid and replenish as needed.

6000
Removal

1. Raise and support vehicle, then remove tire and wheel assembly.
2. Insert drift or screwdriver into caliper to prevent rotor from turning, **Fig. 7**.
3. Remove hub nut and washer using hub nut socket tool No. J-34826 and discard the shaft nut, **Fig. 7**.
4. Remove brake caliper from steering knuckle and suspend caliper assembly.
5. Remove rotor from hub and bearing assembly.
6. Remove stabilizer shaft from control arm.
7. Remove ball joint from steering knuckle.
8. Using axle shaft remover tool No. J-33008 with extension J-29794 on slide hammer, remove drive axle from transaxle, then vehicle, **Fig. 1**.
9. Remove drive axle from hub and bearing assembly using puller No. J-28733, **Fig. 8**.

Installation

1. Install drive axle into hub and bearing assembly, then the transmission.
2. Install the lower ball joint to the steering knuckle.
3. Install the stabilizer shaft to the control arm.
4. Install caliper to steering knuckle, then install washer and a new torque prevailing shaft nut.
5. Insert a screwdriver or drift into caliper and rotor to prevent rotor from turning, **Fig. 7**.
6. Install hub nut, **torque** to 185 ft. lbs. **Fig. 7**.
7. Seat the drive axle into the transaxle by placing a screwdriver into the groove on the joint housing and tapping until seated, then grasp the inner housing and pull outward. If the snap ring is properly seated, the axle will remain in place, **Fig. 2**.
8. Install tire and wheel assembly and lower vehicle.

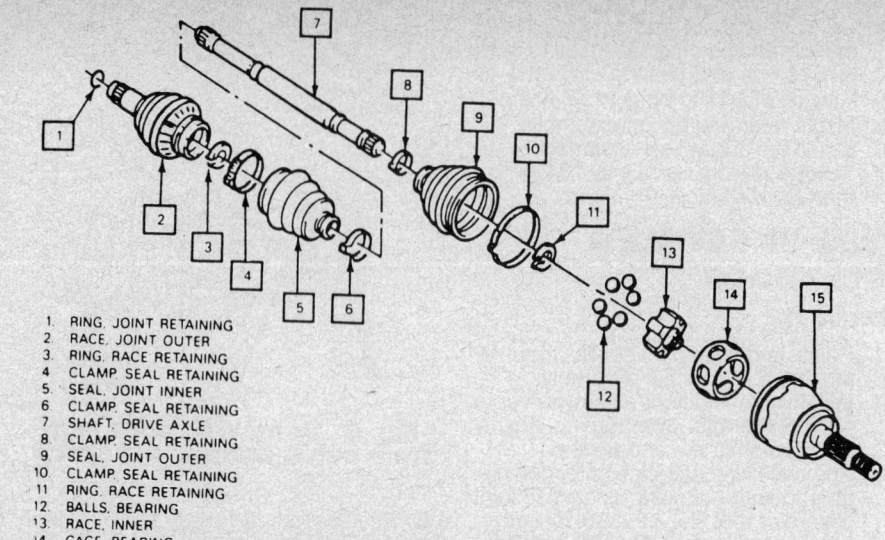

1. RING, JOINT RETAINING
2. RACE, JOINT OUTER
3. RING, RACE RETAINING
4. CLAMP, SEAL RETAINING
5. SEAL, JOINT INNER
6. CLAMP, SEAL RETAINING
7. SHAFT, DRIVE AXLE
8. CLAMP, SEAL RETAINING
9. SEAL, JOINT OUTER
10. CLAMP, SEAL RETAINING
11. RING, RACE RETAINING
12. BALLS, BEARING
13. RACE, INNER
14. CAGE, BEARING
15. RACE, JOINT OUTER

Fig. 10 Exploded view of front drive axle assembly. LeMans

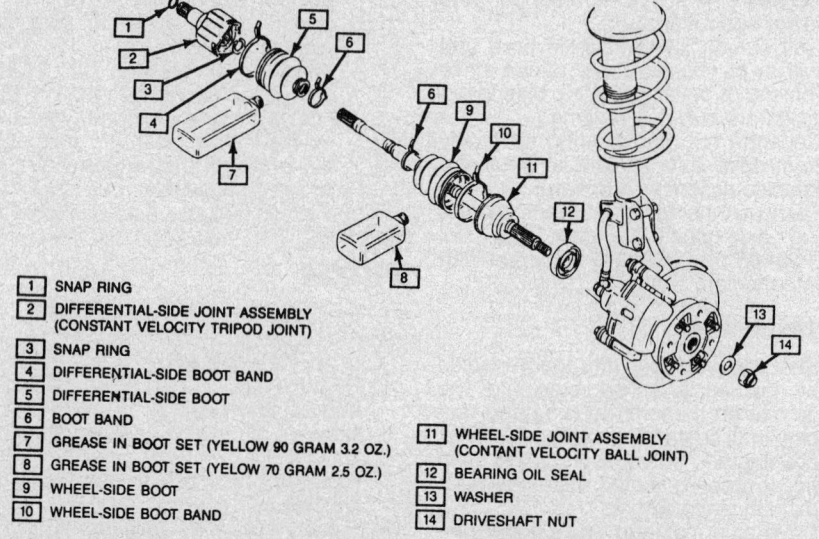

1	SNAP RING
2	DIFFERENTIAL-SIDE JOINT ASSEMBLY (CONSTANT VELOCITY TRIPOD JOINT)
3	SNAP RING
4	DIFFERENTIAL-SIDE BOOT BAND
5	DIFFERENTIAL-SIDE BOOT
6	BOOT BAND
7	GREASE IN BOOT SET (YELLOW 90 GRAM 3.2 OZ.)
8	GREASE IN BOOT SET (YELOW 70 GRAM 2.5 OZ.)
9	WHEEL-SIDE BOOT
10	WHEEL-SIDE BOOT BAND
11	WHEEL-SIDE JOINT ASSEMBLY (CONTANT VELOCITY BALL JOINT)
12	BEARING OIL SEAL
13	WASHER
14	DRIVESHAFT NUT

Fig. 11 Exploded view of drive axle. Metro

SPECTRUM

1. Remove wheel cover, cotter pin and driveshaft nut, then loosen wheel nuts.
2. Raise and support vehicle.
3. Remove front wheel and tire assembly.
4. Drain transaxle oil.
5. Detach snap ring installed on spline of inboard joint using a large screwdriver.
6. Remove knuckle and hub assembly.
7. Unfasten inboard joint from differential side gear and outboard joint from steering knuckle, then remove drive axle assembly.
8. Reverse procedure to install.

SPRINT

1. Remove wheel center cap.
2. Remove cotter pin, then drive shaft nut.
3. Loosen wheel lug nuts.
4. Raise and support vehicle.

5. Remove front wheel.
6. Drain transaxle fluid.
7. Using a suitable lever, pry inboard drive shaft joint from differential side gear to disengage snap ring on shaft spline.
8. Remove 2 stabilizer bar mount bracket bolts and ball joint stud bolt. Pull down on stabilizer bar to disconnect ball joint stud from steering knuckle, **Fig. 9**.
9. Disconnect inboard joint from differential side gear, then outboard joint from steering knuckle. Remove drive shaft.
10. Reverse procedure to install. **Torque** drive shaft nut to 108.5-195 ft. lbs.

CORSICA & BERETTA
Removal

1. Remove hub nut, then raise and support vehicle and remove wheel and tire assembly.
2. Remove disc brake caliper and caliper support.

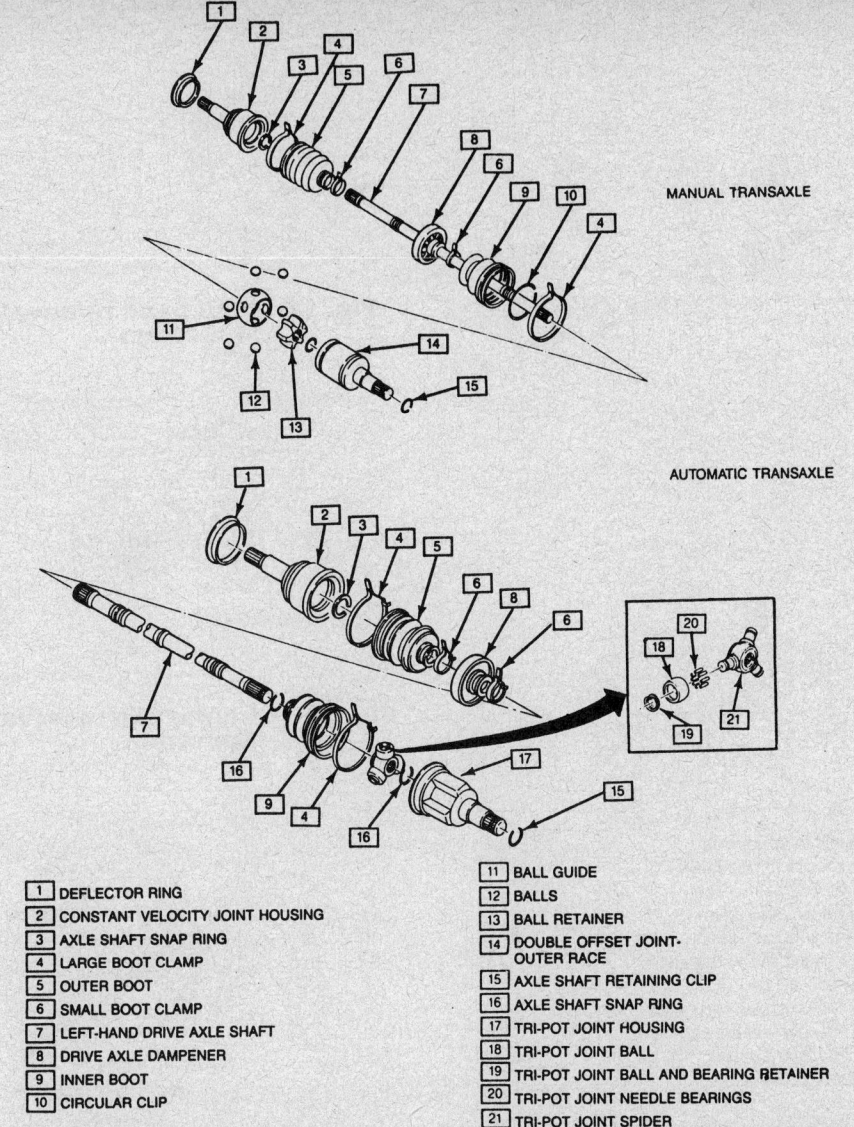

MANUAL TRANSAXLE

AUTOMATIC TRANSAXLE

1	DEFLECTOR RING
2	CONSTANT VELOCITY JOINT HOUSING
3	AXLE SHAFT SNAP RING
4	LARGE BOOT CLAMP
5	OUTER BOOT
6	SMALL BOOT CLAMP
7	LEFT-HAND DRIVE AXLE SHAFT
8	DRIVE AXLE DAMPENER
9	INNER BOOT
10	CIRCULAR CLIP

11	BALL GUIDE
12	BALLS
13	BALL RETAINER
14	DOUBLE OFFSET JOINT-OUTER RACE
15	AXLE SHAFT RETAINING CLIP
16	AXLE SHAFT SNAP RING
17	TRI-POT JOINT HOUSING
18	TRI-POT JOINT BALL
19	TRI-POT JOINT BALL AND BEARING RETAINER
20	TRI-POT JOINT NEEDLE BEARINGS
21	TRI-POT JOINT SPIDER

Fig. 12 Exploded view of front drive axle assembly. Storm

3. **On 1989-90 Corsica models,** remove lower control arm ball joint nut and cotter pin.
4. **On 1988 Corsica models,** remove strut to steering knuckle attaching bolts then pull steering knuckle assembly out of strut bracket.
5. **On 1989-90 models,** use front hub spindle remover tool No. J-28733 and remove drive axle from hub and bearing assembly, **Fig. 8.**
6. Drain transaxle.
7. **On 1988 Corsica models,** using axle shaft remover tool No. J-33008 with extension No. J-29794 remove drive axle from transaxle, then temporarily support with a wire or rope, **Fig. 1.**
8. **On 1989-90 models,** using axle shaft remover No. J-33008 with extension No. J-29794 on slide hammer, remove drive axle from transaxle, then vehicle **Fig. 1.**
7. **On 1988 Corsica models,** use front hub spindle remover tool No. J-28733

and remove drive axle from hub and bearing assembly, **Fig. 8.**

Installation
1. Loosely install drive axle to strut and transaxle.
2. **On 1988 Corsica models,** position steering knuckle to strut bracket and install bolts.
3. **On all models,** install rotor and brake caliper.
4. Install a brass drift or a screwdriver to prevent the rotor from turning, **Fig. 7,** then install hub nut and washer and **torque** to 71 ft. lbs. Remove drift or screwdriver.
5. Using screwdriver in groove provided on inner retainer, install axle shaft on transaxle, **Fig. 2.** Tap on screwdriver until axle shaft is seated in transaxle.
6. Remove boot seal protector, then install wheel and tire.
7. Lower vehicle, then **torque** hub nut to 191 ft. lbs. and fill axle with proper fluid.

NOVA
Removal

1. Remove hub nut cotter pin, the the hub nut and washer.
2. Loosen wheel lug nuts, then raise and support vehicle.
3. Remove wheel and tire assembly, then lower control arm to ball joint attaching nuts and bolts.
4. Using ball remover tool No. J-24319-01, remove tie rod end from steering knuckle.
5. Remove brake caliper support-to-steering knuckle attaching bolts, then the caliper. Support caliper to prevent brake hose damage.
6. Remove rotor, then using puller tool No. J-25287, push axle assembly from hub.
7. Using tool Nos. J-2619-01 and J-35762, pull axle assembly from transaxle. **When removing axle assembly, do not pull on axle shaft. To prevent axle boot damage, do not allow them to contact any parts during removal.**

Installation

Prior to installing axle assembly, inspect knuckle inner grease seal. Replace if distorted or worn. Also check for foreign material at hub bearing area.
1. Install axle assembly into transaxle. Use a long brass drift and hammer positioned on the tri-pot housing ribs to drive in.
2. Install axle into wheel hub, then lower control arm to ball joint. **Torque** ball joint nuts and bolts to 47 ft. lbs.
3. Install tie rod end. **Torque** nut to 38 ft. lbs.
4. Install rotor, then the brake caliper. **Torque** attaching bolts to 65 ft. lbs.
5. Install tire and wheel assembly, then drive axle nut and washer.
6. Lower vehicle to floor, then **torque** lug nuts to 76 ft. lbs. and drive axle nut to 137 ft. lbs.
7. Install nut cap and cotter pin.

DRIVE AXLE, DISASSEMBLY
LEMANS

1. Secure axle shaft in a soft-jawed vise.
2. Cut off seal clamps and remove seals, then spread bearing retaining rings, **Fig. 10.**
3. Mark relationship between shaft and joints for assembly reference, then tap joints off shaft using a plastic mallet.
4. Inspect all components for excessive wear or damage and replace as necessary.

SPRINT

1. Remove boot band from inboard joint, **Fig. 6.**
2. Remove housing from inboard joint.
3. Remove snap ring, then spider from shaft.

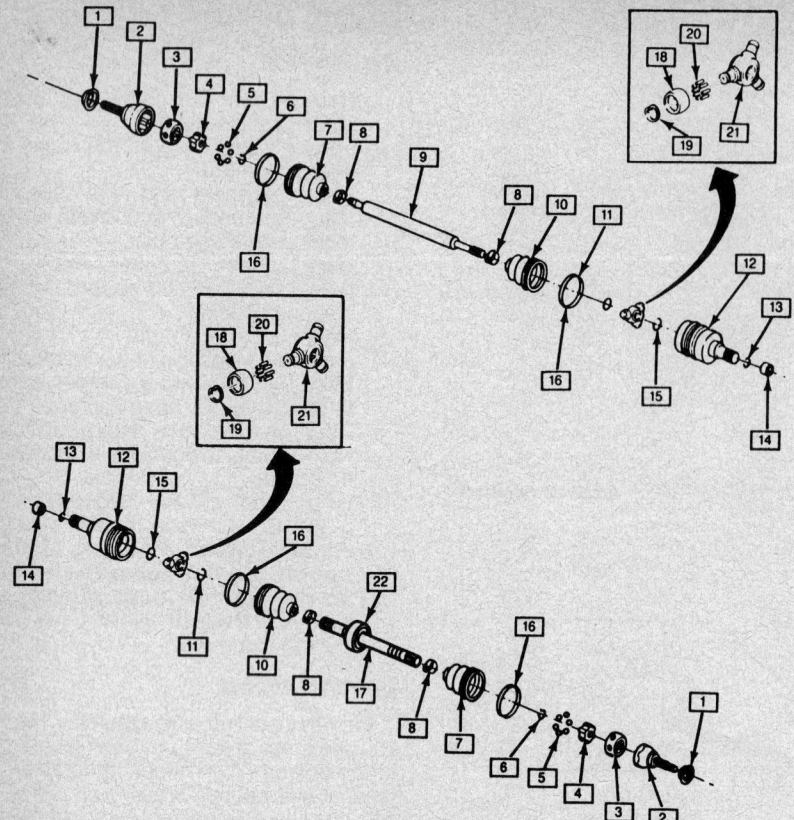

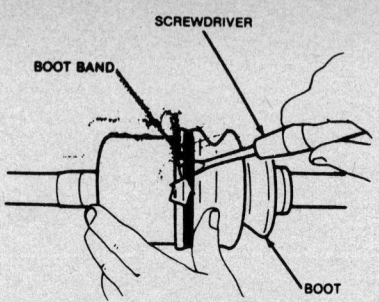

Fig. 14   Boot band removal. Spectrum

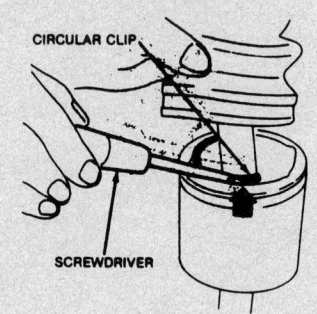

Fig. 15   Circular clip removal. Spectrum

1 DEFLECTOR RING	12 TRI-POT JOINT HOUSING
2 CONSTANT VELOCITY JOINT OUTER RACE	13 AXLE SHAFT RETAINING PINS
3 CASE	14 DRIVE AXLE DUST COVER
4 CONSTANT VELOCITY JOINT INNER RACE	15 AXLE SHAFT SNAP RING
5 BALLS	16 LARGE BOOT CLAMPS
6 AXLE SNAFT SHAP RING	17 LEFT HAND DRIVE AXLE SHAFT
7 OUTBOARD BOOT	18 TRI-POT JOINT BALL
8 SMALL BOOT CLAMP	19 TRI-POT JOINT BALL AND BEARING RETAINER
9 RIGHT HAND DRIVE AXLE SHAFT	20 TRI-POT JOINT NEEDLE BEARINGS
10 TRI-POT BOOT	21 TRI-POT JOINT SPIDER
11 AXLE SHAFT RETAINING RING	22 DRIVE AXLE DAMPENER

Fig. 13   Exploded view of front drive axle assembly. Prizm

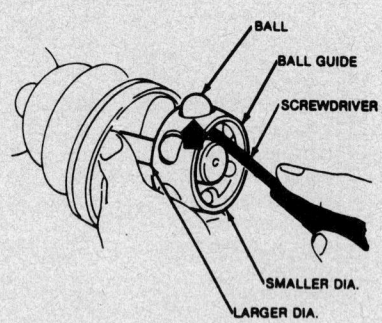

Fig. 16   Bearing removal. Spectrum

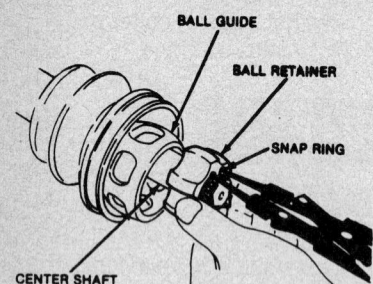

Fig. 17   Snap ring removal. Spectrum

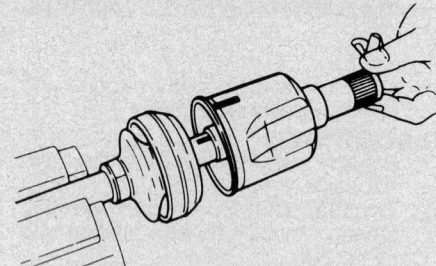

Fig. 18   Removing housing from shaft. Spectrum

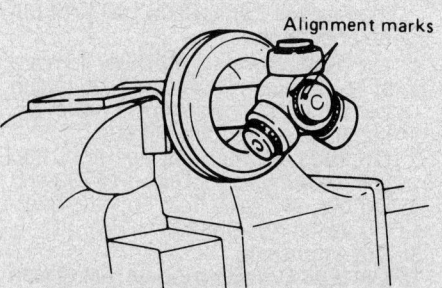

Fig. 19   Tripod removal. Spectrum

4. Remove inside and outside boots from shaft. **Do not disassemble outboard joint. If joint is defective, it must be replaced as an assembly. Do not disassemble inboard joint spider as it is serviced as an assembly.**

METRO

Do not disassemble outboard joint or

differential side ball joint. If any malfunction is detected in these components, replace as an assembly.
1. Remove tripod joint boot band, **Fig. 11**
2. Remove tripod joint housing.
3. Using snap ring pliers, remove snap ring from shaft.
4. Remove tripod joint spider from shaft.
5. Remove boot band from inner drive shaft joint, then boot.
6. Release boot bands from outer boot,

then remove boot.

STORM
Double Offset Joint

1. Secure axle assembly in a soft-jawed

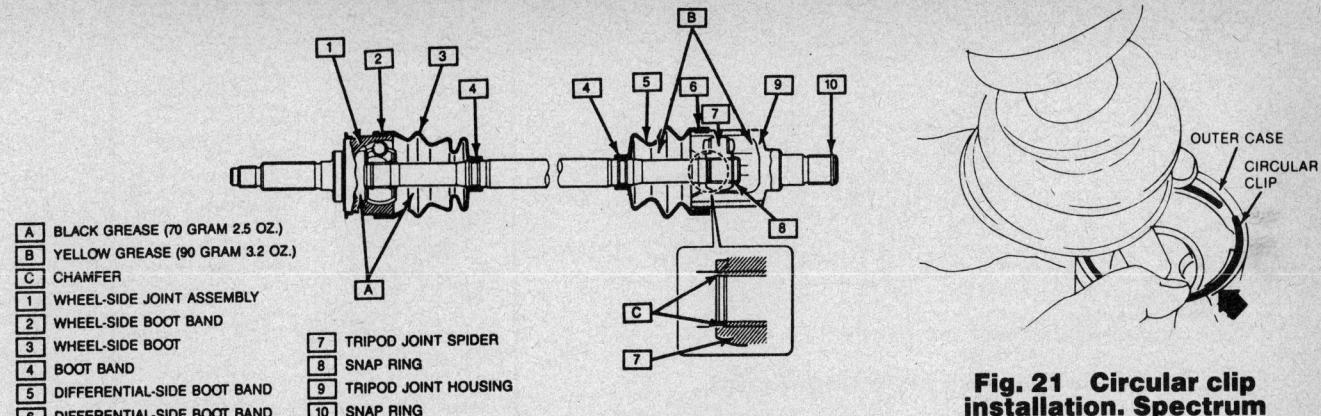

A BLACK GREASE (70 GRAM 2.5 OZ.)
B YELLOW GREASE (90 GRAM 3.2 OZ.)
C CHAMFER
1 WHEEL-SIDE JOINT ASSEMBLY
2 WHEEL-SIDE BOOT BAND
3 WHEEL-SIDE BOOT
4 BOOT BAND
5 DIFFERENTIAL-SIDE BOOT BAND
6 DIFFERENTIAL-SIDE BOOT BAND

7 TRIPOD JOINT SPIDER
8 SNAP RING
9 TRIPOD JOINT HOUSING
10 SNAP RING

Fig. 20 Assembling drive axle assembly. Metro

Fig. 21 Circular clip installation. Spectrum

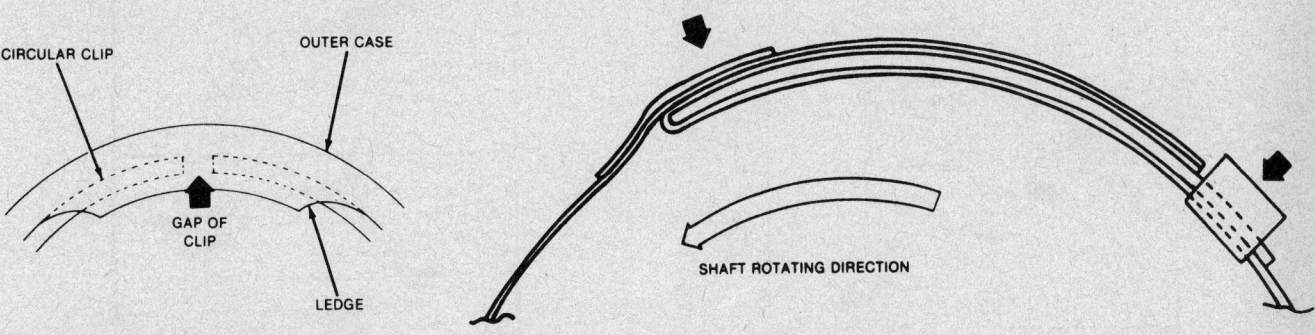

Fig. 22 Circular clip alignment. Spectrum

Fig. 23 Boot band installation (double offset joint). Spectrum

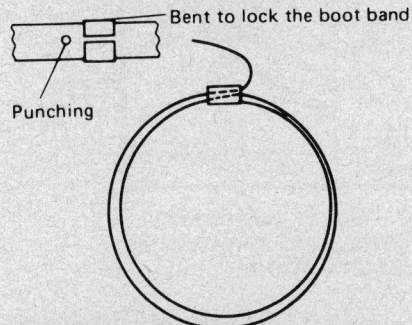

Bent to lock the boot band

Punching

Fig. 24 Boot band installation (tripod joint). Spectrum

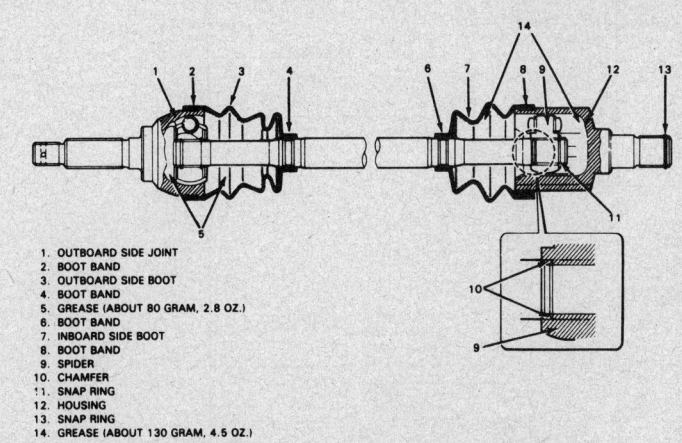

1. OUTBOARD SIDE JOINT
2. BOOT BAND
3. OUTBOARD SIDE BOOT
4. BOOT BAND
5. GREASE (ABOUT 80 GRAM, 2.8 OZ.)
6. BOOT BAND
7. INBOARD SIDE BOOT
8. BOOT BAND
9. SPIDER
10. CHAMFER
11. SNAP RING
12. HOUSING
13. SNAP RING
14. GREASE (ABOUT 130 GRAM, 4.5 OZ.)

Fig. 25 Drive axle assembly. Sprint

vise.
2. Remove boot band from differential side joint.
3. Move boot slightly and remove circular clip.
4. Separate case from shaft and remove 6 balls using a suitable screwdriver.
5. Turn ball guide on an angle and move it to center shaft side.
6. Remove snap ring from shaft **Fig. 12**, then slide out ball guide and retainer.
7. Remove boot from shaft, and if necessary, tap damper off shaft with brass hammer.

Tripod Joint

1. Secure axle assembly in a soft-jawed vise.
2. Using a screwdriver, remove boot

band from differential side joint.
3. Place alignment marks on both housing and shaft, then remove housing from shaft.
4. Remove snap ring from shaft, then make alignment marks on both shaft and tripod.
5. Using a hammer and brass drift, remove tripod from shaft. **Ensure care is taken not to hit roller.**
6. Remove boot from shaft, and if neces-

sary, tap damper off shaft with brass hammer.

PRIZM

1. Secure axle assembly in a soft-jawed vise.
2. Remove boot retaining clamps, **Fig. 13.**
3. Remove race retaining ring using snap ring pliers.
4. Disconnect inner race from drive axle

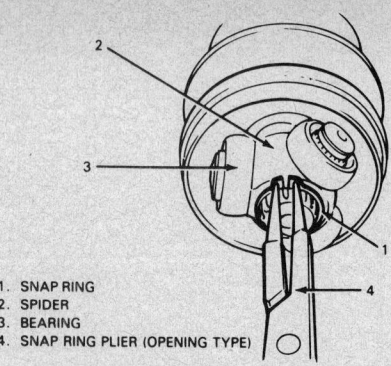

1. SNAP RING
2. SPIDER
3. BEARING
4. SNAP RING PLIER (OPENING TYPE)

Fig. 26 Installing axle snap ring. Sprint

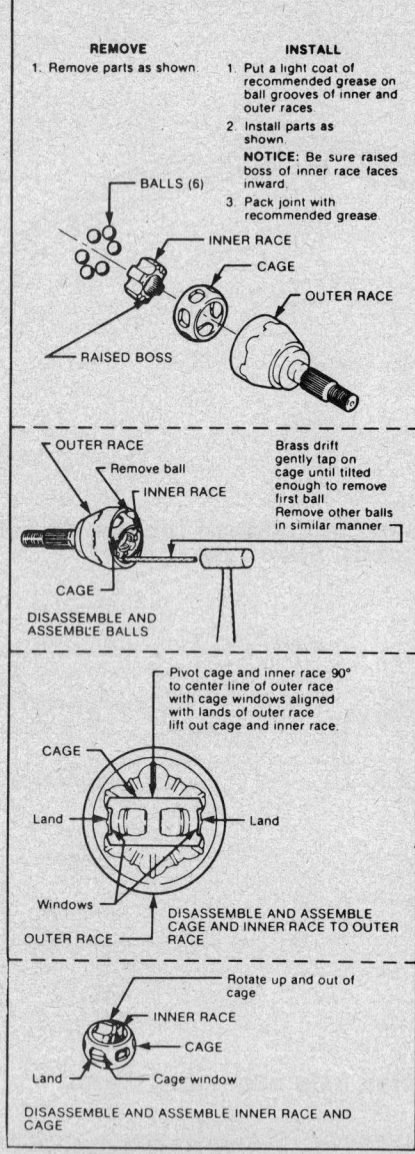

Fig. 28 Outer constant velocity joint disassembly & assembly

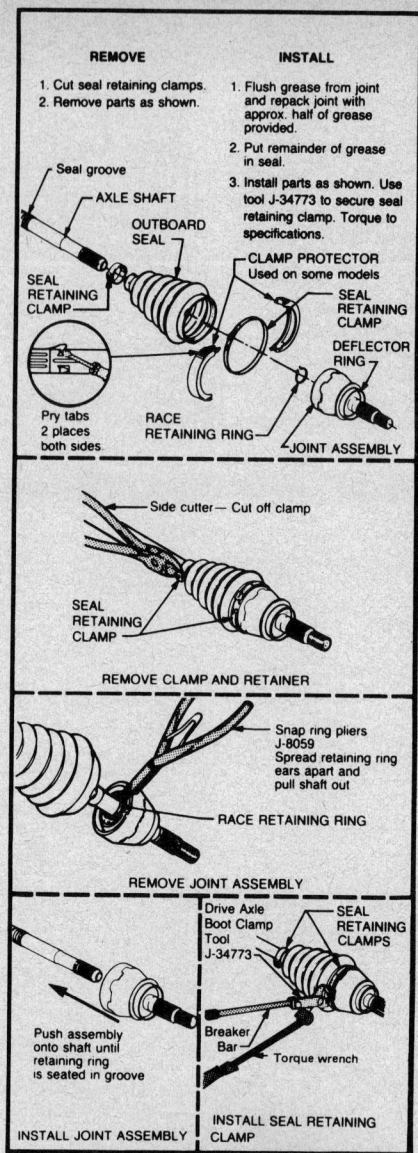

Fig. 27 Outer constant velocity joint seal removal & installation

2. Remove boot band from differential side joint, **Fig. 14.**
3. Move boot slightly and remove circular clip, **Fig. 15.**
4. Separate case from shaft and remove 6 balls with a screwdriver, **Fig. 16.**
5. Turn ball guide on an angle and move it to center shaft side.
6. Remove snap ring from shaft, **Fig. 17**, then slide out ball guide and retainer.
7. Remove boot from shaft.

Birfield Joint

The Birfield joint must be serviced as an assembly only, however, then boot may be removed in the same manner as described for the Double Offset type joint.

Tripod Joint

1. Secure axle assembly, **Fig. 5**, in a soft-jawed vise.
2. Using a screwdriver, remove boot band from differential side joint.

shaft.
5. Remove boot from axle shaft.
6. Tilt cage, then remove ball bearings.
7. Tilt cage and inner race 90°, then pull from outer race.

SPECTRUM
Double Offset Joint

1. Secure axle assembly, **Fig. 5**, in a soft-jawed vise.

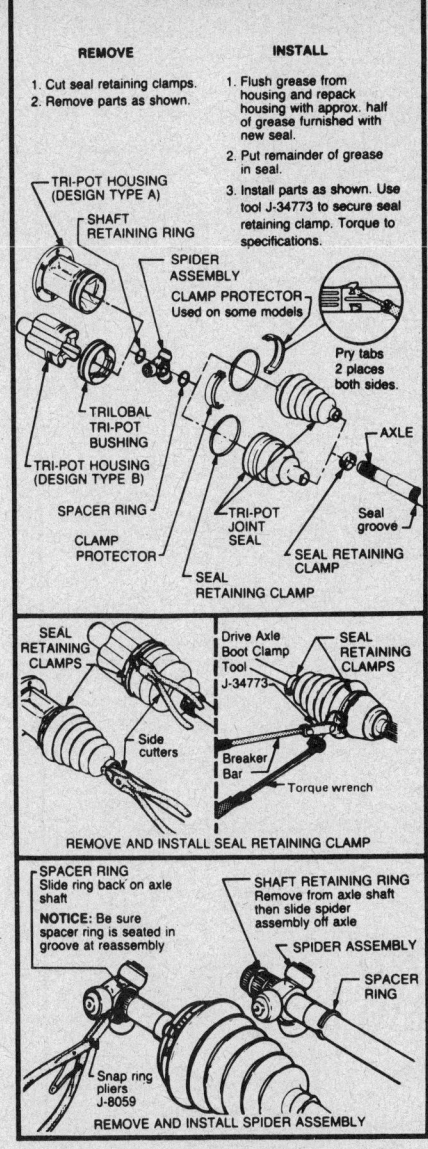

Fig. 29   Inner tri-pot seal removal & installation. Models less bearing blocks

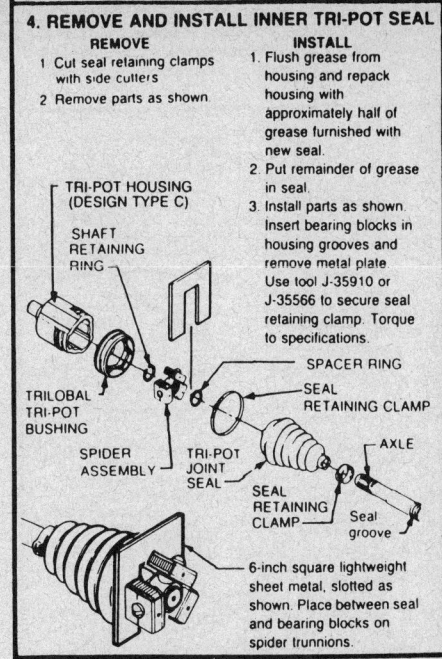

Fig. 30   Inner tri-pot seal removal & installation (Part 1 Of 2). Models w/bearing blocks

3. Make alignment marks on both housing and shaft, then remove housing from shaft, **Fig. 18.**
4. Remove snap ring from shaft, then make alignment marks on both shaft and tripod, **Fig. 19.**
5. Using a hammer and brass drift, remove tripod from shaft. **Take care not to hit roller.**
6. Remove boot from shaft, and if necessary, dynamic damper.

AXLE SHAFT, ASSEMBLY
METRO

Throughly inspect parts for wear prior to assembly. Replace any excessively worn parts. Ensure wheel-side joint assembly and tripod joint housing are washed and air dried, and that the boots are cleaned with a cloth.

1. Apply joint grease liberally to wheel-side joint, **Fig. 20.**
2. Install wheel-side boot on shaft, then fill inside of boot with joint grease, approximately 80 grams.
3. Install boot bands.
4. Install transaxle-side boot clamp, then boot onto shaft.
5. Apply yellow grease liberally to transaxle-side joint.
6. Install spider joint on shaft with beveled side facing wheel-side joint.
7. Install spider joint snap ring.
8. Fill inside of transaxle-side boot with joint grease, approximately 130 grams.
9. Install spider joint housing, then boot band.
10. Check boots for distortion or dents, correct as necessary.

STORM

1. Install boot clamp on shaft, then boot.

2. Install ball guide and ball retainer on shaft, then snap ring.
3. Move ball guide into place, then install six balls into ball guide.
4. Install circular clip in outer race.
5. Pack one half of joint with General Motors grease (Part No.7845393).
6. Remove drive axle from vise.

PRIZM

1. Apply General Motors grease (Part No. 7845393) to tripot housing and spider joint.
2. Install boot clamp on drive axle shaft, then boot.
3. Install spider joint assembly on drive axle using a brass drift and hammer.
4. Install outboard snap ring.
5. Install spider assembly in tripot housing.
6. Connect boot and boot clamp to tripot housing.
7. Remove drive shaft assembly from vise.

LEMANS

1. Pack joints with suitable grease, then tap joint assemblies into shaft splines until retaining rings are properly seated.
2. Install inner joint on long side of shaft and outer joint on short side of shaft.
3. Install joint seals and with new clamps. Secure clamps using seal clamp installer tool No. J-22610 or equivalent.

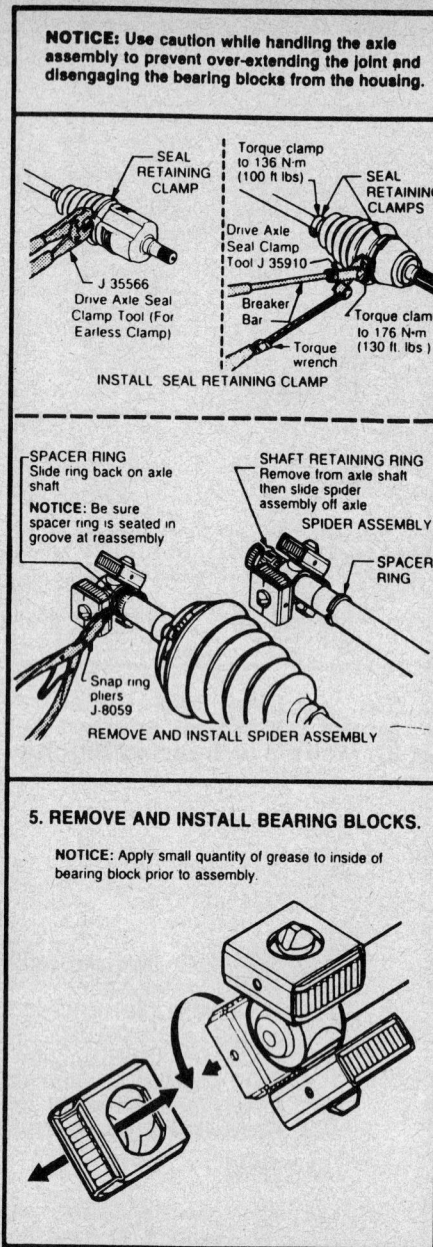

Fig. 30 Inner tri-pot seal removal & installation (Part 2 Of 2). Models w/bearing blocks

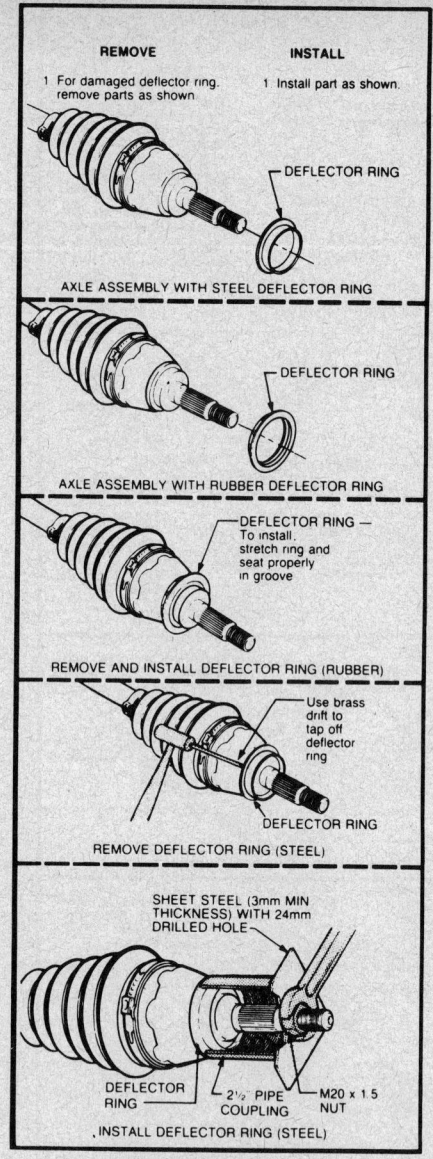

Fig. 31 Inboard thermo-plastic seal installation

SPECTRUM
Double Offset Joint

1. Assemble in the reverse order of disassembly, noting the following:
   a. Use care to avoid damaging boot when installing boot on shaft.
   b. Install and align circular clip as shown, **Figs. 21 and 22.**
   c. To install boot band, first insert a screwdriver into end of boot, then install band as shown, **Fig. 23.** Ensure band end clip is securely tightened around the band and boot is not twisted.

Tripod Joint

Assemble in the reverse order of disassembly, noting the following:
1. Tape spline section of shaft with tape to prevent damage to boot when installing.
2. Install tripod onto shaft with shorter spline positioned on the outer side.
3. Ensure all alignment marks align before assembling.
4. Wind boot band twice, **Fig. 24,** then tighten band using pliers. Finally, lock band using a punch.

SPRINT

1. Liberally apply black grease included in outboard boot kit to outboard joint.
2. Install outboard boot on shaft. Fill inside of boot with about 2.8 oz. of joint grease, **Fig. 25.**
3. Install inboard boot on shaft.
4. Liberally apply yellow joint grease included in inboard boot kit to inboard joint.
5. Install inboard spider on drive shaft with chamfered side toward outboard joint as shown in **Fig. 25.**
6. Install snap ring in shaft groove, **Fig. 26.**
7. Fill inside of inboard boot with about 4.5 oz. of joint grease and install housing, **Fig. 25.** Attach boot to housing with boot band.
8. Check boots for distortion and correct as necessary.

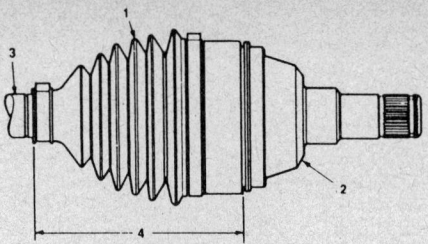

1. INBOARD THERMOPLASTIC SEAL
2. CROSS-GROOVE JOINT
3. AXLE SHAFT
4. 133 mm (5¼") – JOINT AND SEAL ARE TO BE COMPRESSED TO THIS DIMENSION BEFORE CRIMPING CLAMPS.

Fig. 32   Inboard thermo-plastic seal collapsed dimension. Models w/cross-groove joint

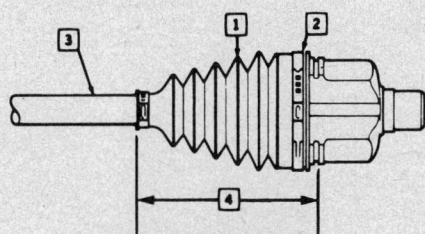

1. INBOARD THERMOPLASTIC SEAL
2. TRILOBAL TRIPOT JOINT
3. AXLE SHAFT
4. 130 MM (5 1/16") – JOINT AND SEAL ARE TO BE COMPRESSED TO THIS DIMENSION BEFORE CRIMPING CLAMPS.

Fig. 33   Inboard thermo-plastic seal collapsed dimension. Models w/trilobal trishaft joint

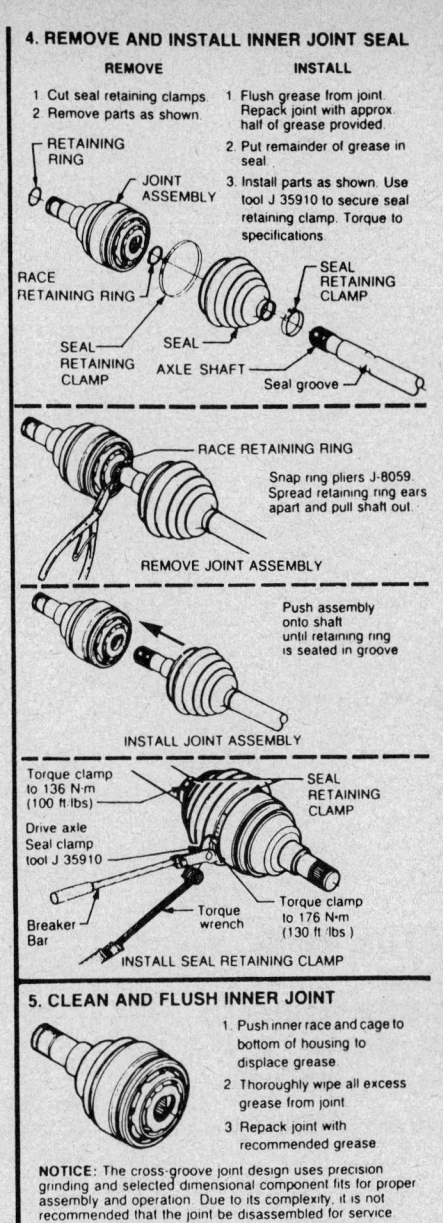

4. REMOVE AND INSTALL INNER JOINT SEAL

REMOVE	INSTALL
1. Cut seal retaining clamps.	1. Flush grease from joint. Repack joint with approx. half of grease provided.
2. Remove parts as shown.	2. Put remainder of grease in seal.
	3. Install parts as shown. Use tool J 35910 to secure seal retaining clamp. Torque to specifications.

RETAINING RING
JOINT ASSEMBLY
RACE RETAINING RING
SEAL RETAINING CLAMP
SEAL RETAINING CLAMP
SEAL
AXLE SHAFT
Seal groove

RACE RETAINING RING

Snap ring pliers J-8059. Spread retaining ring ears apart and pull shaft out.

REMOVE JOINT ASSEMBLY

Push assembly onto shaft until retaining ring is seated in groove.

INSTALL JOINT ASSEMBLY

Torque clamp to 136 N·m (100 ft.lbs)
Drive axle Seal clamp tool J 35910
SEAL RETAINING CLAMP
Breaker Bar
Torque wrench
Torque clamp to 176 N·m (130 ft.lbs.)

INSTALL SEAL RETAINING CLAMP

5. CLEAN AND FLUSH INNER JOINT

1. Push inner race and cage to bottom of housing to displace grease.
2. Thoroughly wipe all excess grease from joint.
3. Repack joint with recommended grease.

NOTICE: The cross-groove joint design uses precision grinding and selected dimensional component fits for proper assembly and operation. Due to its complexity, it is not recommended that the joint be disassembled for service.

Fig. 34   Cross groove inner joint seal removal & installation. Models w/cross groove inner joint

OUTER CONSTANT VELOCITY JOINT & SEAL REPLACE

EXCEPT GEO MODELS, LEMANS, SPECTRUM & SPRINT

For removal and installation procedures refer to **Figs. 27, and 28.**

GEO MODELS, LEMANS, SPECTRUM & SPRINT

For replacement procedure, refer to "Drive Axle Disassembly."

INNER TRI-POT SEAL REPLACE

EXCEPT GEO MODELS, LEMANS, SPECTRUM & SPRINT

For removal and installation procedures, refer to **Figs. 29 and 30.** On 1988 models, when installing the thermo-plastic seal, the drive axle must be collapsed as shown in **Figs. 31, 32, and 33** to prevent distortion of the seal.

GEO MODELS, LEMANS, SPECTRUM & SPRINT

For replacement procedure, refer to "Drive Axle Disassembly."

INNER CONSTANT VELOCITY JOINT & SEAL REPLACE

CROSS GROOVE DESIGN FRONT AXLE

For removal and installation procedures refer to **Fig. 34.**

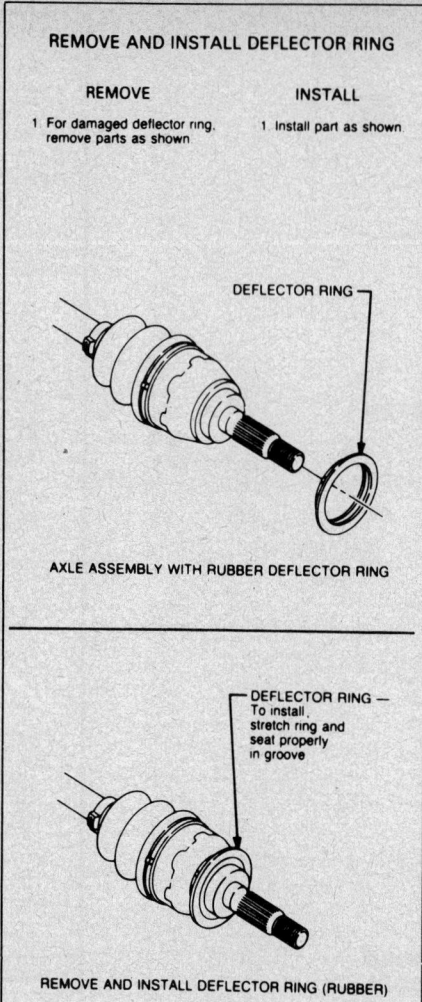

REMOVE AND INSTALL DEFLECTOR RING

REMOVE	INSTALL
1. For damaged deflector ring, remove parts as shown.	1. Install part as shown.

DEFLECTOR RING

AXLE ASSEMBLY WITH RUBBER DEFLECTOR RING

DEFLECTOR RING —
To install stretch ring and seat properly in groove

REMOVE AND INSTALL DEFLECTOR RING (RUBBER)

G60050-4D-C

Fig. 35   Deflector ring removal & installation. Models except Geo, LeMans, Nova, Spectrum & Sprint

DEFLECTOR RING
REPLACE
EXCEPT GEO MODELS, LEMANS, NOVA, SPECTRUM & SPRINT

For removal and installation procedures, refer to **Fig. 35.**

GEO MODELS

1. Disconnect battery ground cable.
2. Raise and support vehicle.
3. Remove drive axle assembly.
4. Remove deflector ring using shaft removal fork (Part No. J-37780).
5. Reverse procedure to install.

ALL WHEEL DRIVE

INDEX

DESCRIPTION

PROPELLER SHAFT

Torque is transmitted from the transaxle to the rear axle differential carrier through the propeller shafts and universal joint/C.V. (Constant Velocity) joint assemblies.

These propeller shafts are the balanced tubular type. A pinion flange is used at the transaxle to connect the C.V. joint on the forward end of the front propeller shaft. The rear end of the front propeller shaft has a double cardan universal joint that is bolted to a center bearing. A spline at the front end of the rear shaft slips through the center bearing and into the double cardan joint at the rear of the front shaft. A ball-type center bearing mounted in a rubber cushion provides support for both propeller shafts. A universal joint is used to connect the rear propeller shaft to the rear axle differential carrier.

REAR AXLE

All parts necessary to transmit power from the propeller shaft to the rear axle shafts are enclosed in a differential carrier assembly. The rear axle has a hypoid type ring gear and pinion with the centerline of the pinion gear below the centerline of the ring gear. Two preloaded tapered roller bearings support the hypoid pinion gear in the carrier. The inner race of the rear pinion bearing is a tight press fit on the pinion stem. The inner race of the front bearing combines a light press fit to a close sliding fit on the pinion flange end of the pinion stem. The outer race of each bearing is pressed against a shoulder recessed in the carrier. Tightening the pinion nut compresses a collapsible spacer which bears against the inner race of the front bearing and a shoulder on the pinion stem. This spacer is used to enable automatic bearing preload adjustment and maintain a preload on both front and rear pinion bearings. Adjustment of the pinion is obtained by placing shims between the head of the drive pinion and the rear pinion bearing. The rear axle differential case is of a one-piece construction and is supported in the carrier by two tapered roller bearings. These bearings are preloaded.

AXLE SHAFT ASSEMBLIES

The axle shafts transmit the rotating force from the rear axle to the hub/bearing assemblies. These shafts include: a solid axle shaft, an inner tripod joint designed to stroke axially that has a triobular housing with a bushing and a thermoplastic boot clamped on the axle, an outer fixed center joint which also uses a thermoplastic boot. The axle joint assemblies have been lubricated and sealed at the factory and do not require periodic lubrication.

DIAGNOSIS & TESTING

REAR AXLE

Many noises suspected as coming from the rear axle actually originate from other places such as tires, road surfaces, wheel bearings, engine, transaxle, exhaust system or body drumming. Before disassembling the rear axle, a careful and thorough check is necessary. Also it should be noted that the rear axle gears are not absolutely quiet and that some noise from the rear axle should be accepted as normal. Use the following procedure, to check for axle noise under normal operating conditions.

1. Ensure rear axle lubricant is at proper level.
2. Drive vehicle down a level asphalt road to reduce tire noise and body drumming until rear axle lubricant is thoroughly warm.
3. Note speed that noise is occurring. Stop vehicle and shift transaxle to neutral, run engine slowly up and down through engine speeds, corresponding to vehicle speed where noise was most pronounced, to determine if noise is caused by Exhaust, muffler roar or another engine condition.
4. Separate tire noise from rear axle noise as follows:
   a. Tire noise changes with different road surfaces but axle noise does not.
   b. Temporarily inflate all tires to 50 psi. If noise is different from before, noise is tire related. If noise is the same as before, noise is probably coming from the rear axle.
   c. Rear axle noise usually stops when coasting at speeds under 30 mph. Tire noise will continue, with a lower tone as speed is reduced.
   d. Compare noise when pulling to noise when coasting, rear axle noise will usually change, tire noise will remain the same.
   e. Check if noise changes with various speeds or sudden acceleration and deceleration. Exhaust and axle noise will usually vary with these conditions, while tire noise will remain the same and is more noticeable at speeds of 20-30 mph.
   f. Drive vehicle over smooth pavements or dirt roads (not gravel) with tires at normal pressure. If noise is caused by tires, it will change or disappear and appear again with changes in road surface.
5. Front wheel bearing noise will sometimes be confused with rear axle noise, to check for front wheel bearing noise, proceed as follows:
   a. Front wheel bearing noise will remain the same when vehicle is in drive or coasting.
   b. Lightly applying the brake pedal while holding vehicle speed constant will often cause front bearing noise to diminish.
   c. Raise and support vehicle, then check for front wheel bearing noise by spinning and shaking the front tires.
6. Rear suspension bushings, frame insulators and spring insulators dampen rear axle noise when installed correctly. Ensure that no metal contact exists between spring and spring opening in frame or between upper and lower control arm bushings and rear module. Any metal-to-metal contact may result in telegraphing road noise and normal axle noise.

AXLE NOISES

Gear Noise

Gear noise (whine) is audible from speeds 35-50 mph under the following driving conditions; drive — acceleration or heavy pull, road load — vehicle driving load or constant speed, float — vehicle slows down gradually but engine still pulls slightly, coast — throttle closed and vehicle in gear.

Bearing Noise

When bearings are worn or damaged they usually produce a rough growl or grating noise, rather than the whining noise produced by a bad gear. Bearings frequently produce a "wow-wow" noise at bearing RPM, this sound would indicate a worn or damaged pinion or rear axle side bearing. This noise could easily be confused with a rear wheel bearing noise. Inspect and replace as required.

Rear Wheel Bearing Noise

A defective rear wheel bearing will produce a noise which continues when vehicle is coasting at a low speed and transaxle in neutral. Noise may diminish when braking lightly. To check bearings, raise rear wheels, then spin wheels by hand and listen at hubs for bearing noise.

Knock At Low Speeds

Low speed knock could be the result of a worn universal joint or a side gear hub counterbore in differential case worn oversize. Inspect and replace propeller shaft or differential case and side gear as required.

Backlash Clunk

An excessive clunk when accelerating or decelerating can be caused by a worn rear axle pinion shaft, worn case, excessive clearance between axle shaft and side gear splines, excessive clearance between side gear hub and counterbore in case, worn pinion and side gear teeth, worn thrust washers and excessive drive pinion and ring gear backlash. Replace worn parts as needed and adjust pinion and ring gear backlash.

PROPELLER SHAFT

Refer to **Fig. 1** for propeller shaft diagnosis.

Propeller Shaft Runout Measurement

1. Raise and support vehicle so that wheels can rotate.
2. Attach a dial indicator using a magnetic base to a smooth place on vehicle underbody. **Do not attach dial indicator base at a weld.**
3. Take dial indicator readings at propeller shaft check points, **Figs. 2 and 3**, and compare readings with **Fig. 4. The splined end of the rear propeller shaft is needed for smooth operation of a two piece driveline. Ensure dial indicator readings are accurate.**
4. With transaxle in neutral, hand rotate axle pinion flange or transaxle output shaft and measure rear propeller shaft runout. Then measure front propeller shaft runout on transaxle output shaft end. If runout exceeds specification, rotate propeller shaft 180° at companion flange and install and check runout.
5. If runout is still over specification at one or more check points, replace propeller shaft after checking for vibration or noise. Check runout on propeller shaft replacement.
6. If new propeller shaft runout is over specification, check for a bent companion flange.

ON-VEHICLE SERVICE

DIFFERENTIAL FLUID CHECK

1. Raise and support vehicle, then remove rear axle drain plug.

PROBLEM	PROBABLE CAUSE	CORRECTION
C.V./Universal Joint Noise	• Worn C.V. joint • Worn center bearing • Worn universal joint bearings • Improper lubrication • Loose flange bolts	• Replace propeller shaft • Replace propeller shaft • Replace propeller shaft • Lubricate as directed • Tighten bolts to "Specifications"
Ping, Snap, or Click in Driveline (Usually Heard on Initial Load after the Transmission is in Gear; Forward or Reverse)	• Loose rear module brace bolts or rear axle module hold down bolts • Worn rear module brace bushings or rear axle module hold down bushings	• Tighten bolts to specifications • Replace worn or damaged bushings
Knocking or Clunking in the Driveline when Operating the Vehicle in a Floating Condition in High or Neutral Gear at 16 km/h (10 mph)	• Worn or damaged universal joint. • Side gear hub counterbore in the differential is worn oversize • Worn center bearing	• Replace propeller shaft • Replace differential case and/or the side gears • Replace propeller shaft
Roughness or Vibration	• Propeller shaft not properly indexed to transmission or rear axle flange • Bent or dented propeller shafts • Undercoating on propeller shafts • Tire unbalance, 40-89 km/h (30-55 mph) Not throttle conscious • Tight universal joint • Worn universal joint • Burrs or gouges on pinion flange. Check snap ring locating surfaces of pinion yoke • Propeller shaft or pinion flange is unbalanced	• Reindex propeller shaft • Replace propeller shafts • Clean propeller shafts • Balance or replace as required • Impact yokes with a shaft hammer to free up. If unable to free up or if joint feels rough when rotated, replace propeller shafts • Replace propeller shafts • Rework or replace the pinion flange • Check for a missing balance weight on the propeller shaft. Rotate the pinion flange 180°

Fig. 1   Propeller shaft diagnosis (Part 1 of 2)

2. Fill fluid until it reaches bottom of drain hole with S.A.E. 80-90 weight GL-5 gear lubricant or equivalent.
3. **Torque** drain plug to 24 ft. lbs.

PROPELLER SHAFT, REPLACE

ORIGINAL SHAFT

Removal

1. Raise and support vehicle so that wheels can spin.
2. Scribe transmission output shaft flange opposite "painted" marking on front propeller shaft.
3. Scribe rear axle pinion flange opposite "painted" marking on rear propeller shaft.
4. Scribe center support mounting plate to floor pan of vehicle. **Do not loosen, remove or disconnect four bolts adjacent to center double cardan joint. Disturbing these fasteners may result in a driveline vibration.**

5. Remove four rear propeller shaft to rear axle pinion flange attaching bolts, **Fig. 5.**
6. With the aid of an assistant to support propeller shaft, proceed as follows:
   a. Remove three center bearing support to underbody retaining bolts.
   b. Remove four front propeller shaft to transaxle output shaft flange connecting bolts.
   c. Remove propeller shaft from vehicle.

Installation

1. With the aid of an assistant to support propeller shaft, proceed as follows:
   a. Align rear propeller shaft flange to rear axle pinion flange, using reference marks.
   b. Loosely install nuts to center bearing support and bolts to rear axle flange. **The center mount plate must be installed at the scribed position so that front C.V. joint is**

PROBLEM	PROBABLE CAUSE	CORRECTION
	• Excessive looseness at the slip spline	• Replace necessary parts
	• Distorted or damaged yokes or flanges	• Install new yokes or flanges
	• Yokes out of phase	• Remove pinion flange, turn 180° from the original position and install. Tighten bolts to specification.
	• Propeller shaft runout at 80 km/h (50 mph). Throttle conscious	• Check propeller shaft runout at a front and rear. Should be less than specified. If above, rotate propeller shaft 80° and recheck. Replace the propeller shaft if runout is still over specification.
Scraping Noise	• Slinger, pinion flange, or end yoke rubbing on rear axle or center bearing.	• Correct the interference
Roughness Above 56 km/h (35 mph) Felt and/or Heard Squeak	• Tires unbalanced or worn.	• Balance or replace as required
	• Lack of lubricant	• Lubricate joint and splines. Also check for worn or brinelled parts.
	• Center bearing worn	• Replace propeller shafts.
	• Worn universal joint	• Replace propeller shafts
Whine or whistle	• Center bearing, worn	Place the vehicle on a hoist with rear wheels free to rotate and diagnose for source of noise, replace propeller shaft, if required.
Shudder on Acceleration (Low Speed)	• Loose or missing bolts at the center bearing or flanges	• Replace or tighten bolts to specifications
	• Incorrectly set driveline angle	• Shim under the transmission support mount to change the driveline angle
	• Worn universal joint/C.V. joint	• Replace propeller shafts

Fig. 1   Propeller shaft diagnosis (Part 2 of 2)

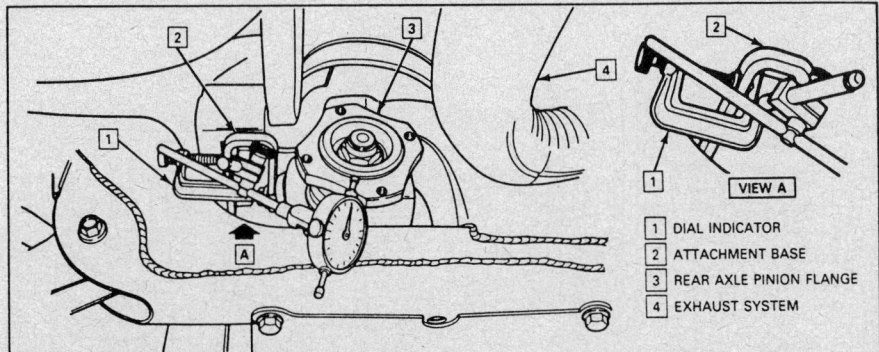

1	DIAL INDICATOR
2	ATTACHMENT BASE
3	REAR AXLE PINION FLANGE
4	EXHAUST SYSTEM

Fig. 2   Measuring rear propeller shaft runout

correctly located within its travel limits.
  c. **Torque** rear propeller shaft flange to rear axle pinion flange bolts to 40 ft. lbs.
2. Align front propeller shaft to transaxle output flange, using reference marks.
3. **Torque** center support bearing nuts to 25 ft. lbs and front propeller shaft flange bolts to 40 ft. lbs.

NEW SHAFT

Removal

1. Raise and support vehicle so that wheels can rotate.
2. Remove four rear propeller shaft to rear axle pinion flange attaching bolts, **Fig. 5.**
3. With the aid of an assistant to support

propeller shaft, proceed as follows:
  a. Remove three center bearing support to underbody retaining bolts.
  b. Remove four front propeller shaft to transaxle output shaft flange connecting bolts.
  c. Remove propeller shaft from vehicle.

Installation

1. Using a dial indicator, measure and mark bolt hole corresponding to high point of radial runout on both transaxle output flange and rear axle pinion flange, **Figs. 2 and 3.**
2. Attach center bearing bracket from old propeller shaft to new propeller shaft assembly.
3. With the aid of an assistant to support propeller shaft, proceed as follows:
  a. Align point marks supplied on flanges of propeller shaft to marks applied in step 1.
  b. Loosely install nuts to center bearing support and bolts to rear axle pinion flange.
  c. **Torque** rear propeller shaft to rear axle pinion flange bolts to 40 ft. lbs.
  d. Push propeller shaft forward until a click is heard, temporarily install a 15/16 inch thick spacer between output flange and front propeller shaft flange as shown in **Fig. 6.** Clamp in this position.
4. Install center bracket retaining nuts and **torque** to 20 ft. lbs.
5. Remove spacer and extend front C.V. joint to meet output flange and **torque** to 40 ft. lbs.
6. Refer to **Fig. 7** for proper C.V. joint plunge location.

DIFFERENTIAL CARRIER ASSEMBLY, REPLACE

1. Disconnect battery ground cable.
2. Release air pressure from Electronic Level Control (ELC).
3. Raise and support vehicle, then drain lubricant from differential carrier housing.
4. Remove rear tire and wheel assemblies.
5. Remove propeller shaft as described in "Propeller Shaft, Replace."
6. Remove rear module assembly as follows:
  a. Open rear compartment lid.
  b. Loosen parking brake cable at tensioner, and disconnect parking brake cable ends at spindle brackets, **Fig. 8.**
  c. Remove parking brake springs, bracket bolts and brackets.
  d. Separate parking brake cable at tensioner.
  e. Remove calipers and suspend with wire.
  f. Remove anti-lock sensor retaining bolts and position sensors out of the way.
  g. Disconnect ELC electrical connections, air lines and height sensor arm from bracket stud.
  h. Remove bolt securing brake line/ELC sensor bracket to left-hand control arm.

i. Remove exhaust system support bolt located above the frame.
j. Remove eight frame brace to underbody bracket bolts.
k. Install rear Mono-Leaf Spring Compressor tool No. J 33432 or equivalent, onto leaf spring.
l. Place a transmission jack under rear module and install bolts into existing jacking plate bores.
m. Remove strut upper attaching bolts and nuts, gaining access through the rear luggage compartment.
n. Release spring tension and remove spring compressor tool.
o. Remove four frame mounting bolts and lower module assembly enough to disconnect differential vent tube.
p. Lower module assembly completely.

7. Remove drive axle as described under "Drive Axle, Replace."
8. Remove three differential carrier to rear module retaining bolts, then the differential from module.
9. Reverse procedure to install, noting the following:
   a. **Torque** differential carrier to rear module bolts to 60 ft. lbs.
   b. Align scribe marks and **torque** lower strut mount to knuckle attaching bolts to 148 ft. lbs.
   c. **Torque** hub and bearing assembly attaching bolts to 61 ft. lbs.
   d. **Torque** caliper attaching bolts to 38 ft. lbs.
   e. **Torque** axle shaft nut to 185 ft. lbs.
   f. **Torque** four rear module frame mount bolts to 103 ft. lbs.
   g. **Torque** upper strut mount retaining bolts to 40 ft. lbs.
   h. **Torque** underbody bracket to frame brace bolts to 28 ft. lbs.
   i. **Torque** exhaust support bolt to 11 ft. lbs.
   j. **Torque** brake line/ELC sensor bracket to lefthand control arm attaching bolt to 18 ft. lbs.

DRIVE AXLE, REPLACE
Removal

1. Raise and support vehicle, then remove tire and wheel assemblies.
2. Disconnect parking brake cable end from bracket.
3. Insert a drift punch or screwdriver through caliper into rotor to prevent rotor from turning.
4. Remove axle shaft nut and washer, **Fig. 9.**
5. Remove brake rotor.
6. Install spring compressor tool J 33432 or equivalent onto spring, then remove three bolts attaching hub and bearing assembly to knuckle.
7. Using hub spindle remover tool No. J 28733-A or equivalent, remove hub and bearing assembly from knuckle.
8. Scribe position of upper bolt that attaches the lower strut mount to the knuckle, then remove bolts and nut attaching strut mount to knuckle.
9. Swing knuckle downward and away from drive axle shaft. **Drive axle seal protector J 34754 Fig. 10 should be**

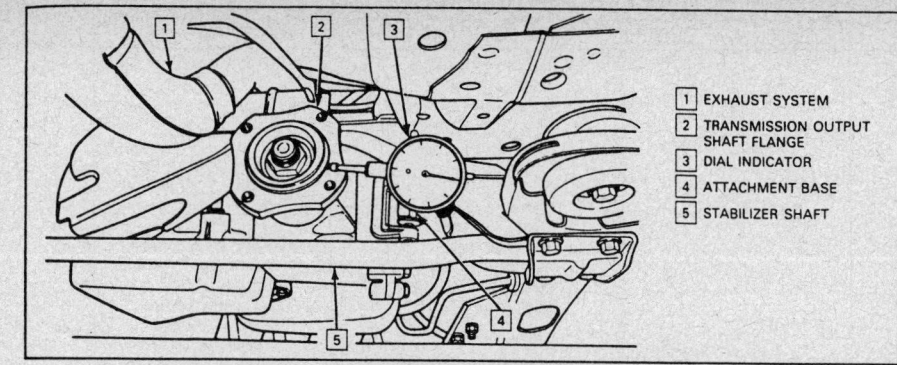

Fig. 3   Measuring front propeller shaft runout

1	EXHAUST SYSTEM
2	TRANSMISSION OUTPUT SHAFT FLANGE
3	DIAL INDICATOR
4	ATTACHMENT BASE
5	STABILIZER SHAFT

Propeller Shaft	Front Check	Center Check	Rear Check
Two-Piece Front	–	1.5 mm (0.06 in.)	–
Two-Piece Rear	0.8 mm (0.03 in.)	0.6 mm (0.02 in.)	0.6 mm (0.02 in.)

Fig. 4   Propeller shaft runout specifications

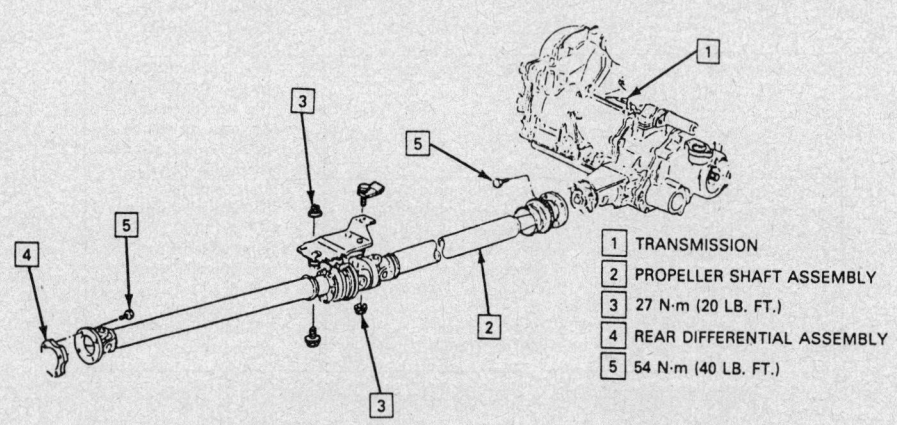

1	TRANSMISSION
2	PROPELLER SHAFT ASSEMBLY
3	27 N·m (20 LB. FT.)
4	REAR DIFFERENTIAL ASSEMBLY
5	54 N·m (40 LB. FT.)

Fig. 5   Propeller shaft assembly

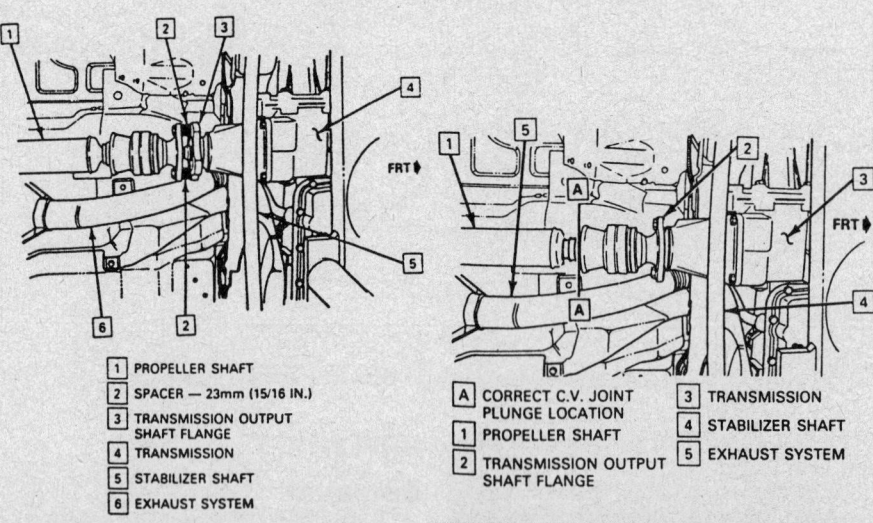

1	PROPELLER SHAFT
2	SPACER — 23mm (15/16 IN.)
3	TRANSMISSION OUTPUT SHAFT FLANGE
4	TRANSMISSION
5	STABILIZER SHAFT
6	EXHAUST SYSTEM

Fig. 6   Installing spacer between output flange & propeller shaft flange

A	CORRECT C.V. JOINT PLUNGE LOCATION	3	TRANSMISSION
1	PROPELLER SHAFT	4	STABILIZER SHAFT
2	TRANSMISSION OUTPUT SHAFT FLANGE	5	EXHAUST SYSTEM

Fig. 7   Checking C.V. joint plunge location

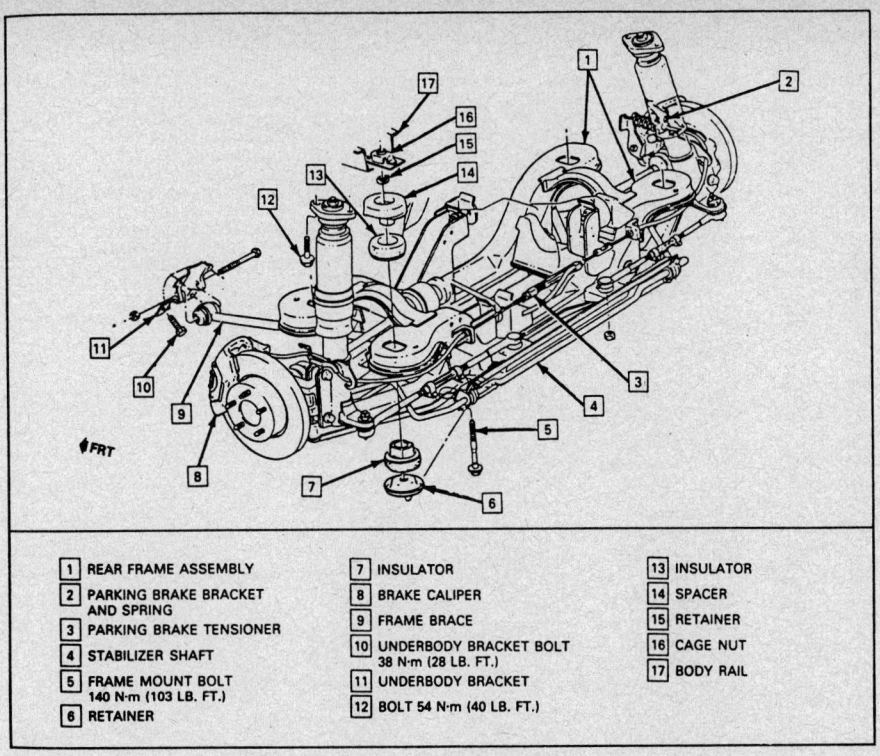

Fig. 8 Rear module assembly

1	REAR FRAME ASSEMBLY	**7**	INSULATOR	**13**	INSULATOR	
2	PARKING BRAKE BRACKET AND SPRING	**8**	BRAKE CALIPER	**14**	SPACER	
3	PARKING BRAKE TENSIONER	**9**	FRAME BRACE	**15**	RETAINER	
4	STABILIZER SHAFT	**10**	UNDERBODY BRACKET BOLT 38 N·m (28 LB. FT.)	**16**	CAGE NUT	
5	FRAME MOUNT BOLT 140 N·m (103 LB. FT.)	**11**	UNDERBODY BRACKET	**17**	BODY RAIL	
6	RETAINER	**12**	BOLT 54 N·m (40 LB. FT.)			

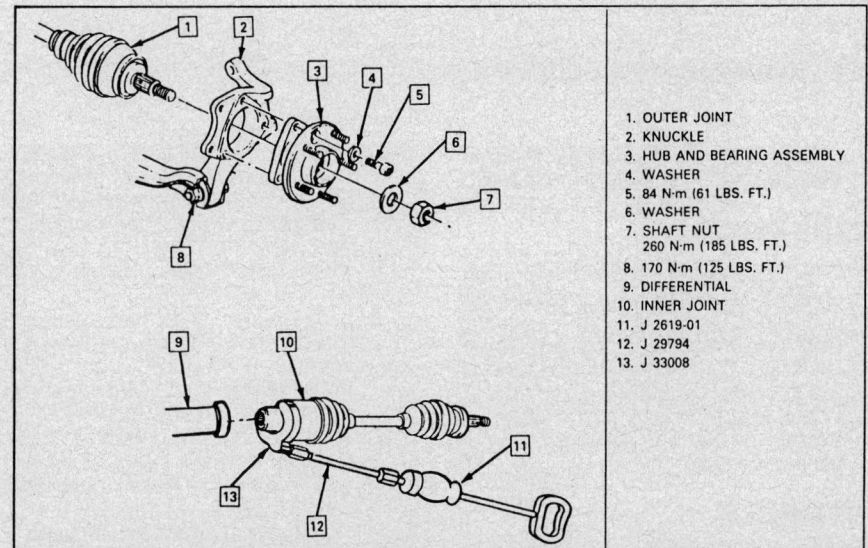

Fig. 9 Drive axle assembly

1. OUTER JOINT
2. KNUCKLE
3. HUB AND BEARING ASSEMBLY
4. WASHER
5. 84 N·m (61 LBS. FT.)
6. WASHER
7. SHAFT NUT 260 N·m (185 LBS. FT.)
8. 170 N·m (125 LBS. FT.)
9. DIFFERENTIAL
10. INNER JOINT
11. J 2619-01
12. J 29794
13. J 33008

modified and installed on drive axle prior to performing service procedures. Failure to observe this could result in seal damage and possible joint failure.

10. Using drive axle removal tool No. J 33008, slide hammer tool J 2619-01 and axle shaft remover extension tool No. J 29794 or equivalents, remove axle shaft from differential.

Installation

1. Insert drive axle into differential. Ensure positive engagement by pulling outward on inner axle end. Grasp housing only. Do not grasp and pull on axle shaft.
2. Swing knuckle up to lower strut mount.
3. Position nut plate and install lower strut mount bolts to knuckle. Prior to

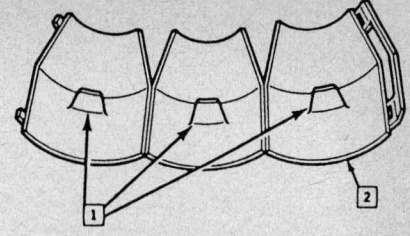

1	REMOVE TABS
2	J 34754 DRIVE AXLE SEAL PROTECTOR

Fig. 10 Modifying seal protector tool

tightening bolts, align scribe marks top with top bolt. **Torque** bolts to 148 ft. lbs.

4. Remove seal protector J 34754 from drive axle boot.
5. Install hub and bearing assembly to knuckle and axle spline.
6. **Torque** hub and bearing attaching bolts to 61 ft. lbs.
7. Remove spring compressor tool No. J 33432 or equivalent.
8. Install rotor, then brake caliper to rotor. **Torque** caliper attaching bolts to 38 ft. lbs.
9. Connect anti-lock brake sensor to knuckle, then adjust sensor gap as follows:
   a. Loosen sensor adjustment screw.
   b. Using a feeler gauge, set gap at .028 inch.
   c. **Torque** adjustment screw to 18 inch lbs.
10. Connect parking brake cable end to bracket.
11. Using drift punch or screwdriver to prevent rotor from turning, install new shaft nut and washer, then **torque** to 185 ft. lbs.
12. Install tire and wheel assemblies, then check camber adjustment. **Camber adjustment should not be necessary if lower strut mount-to-knuckle bolts were properly aligned with scribe marks.**

DRIVE AXLE, SERVICE

Refer to **Figs. 11** and **12** for drive axle service.

REAR DIFFERENTIAL, SERVICE

DISASSEMBLE

1. Mount differential in suitable holding device.
2. Remove righthand differential mounting bracket attaching bolts, **Fig. 13**.
3. Remove righthand output shaft, then seal and seal retainer.
4. Remove lefthand output shaft, then left side axle tube extension.
5. Remove differential carrier assembly retaining bolts, then insert a screwdriver into slots provided **Fig. 14** and pry to separate case.
6. Remove bolt and lock tab from side bearing adjuster sleeve as shown in **Fig. 15**.
7. Using side bearing adjuster wrench

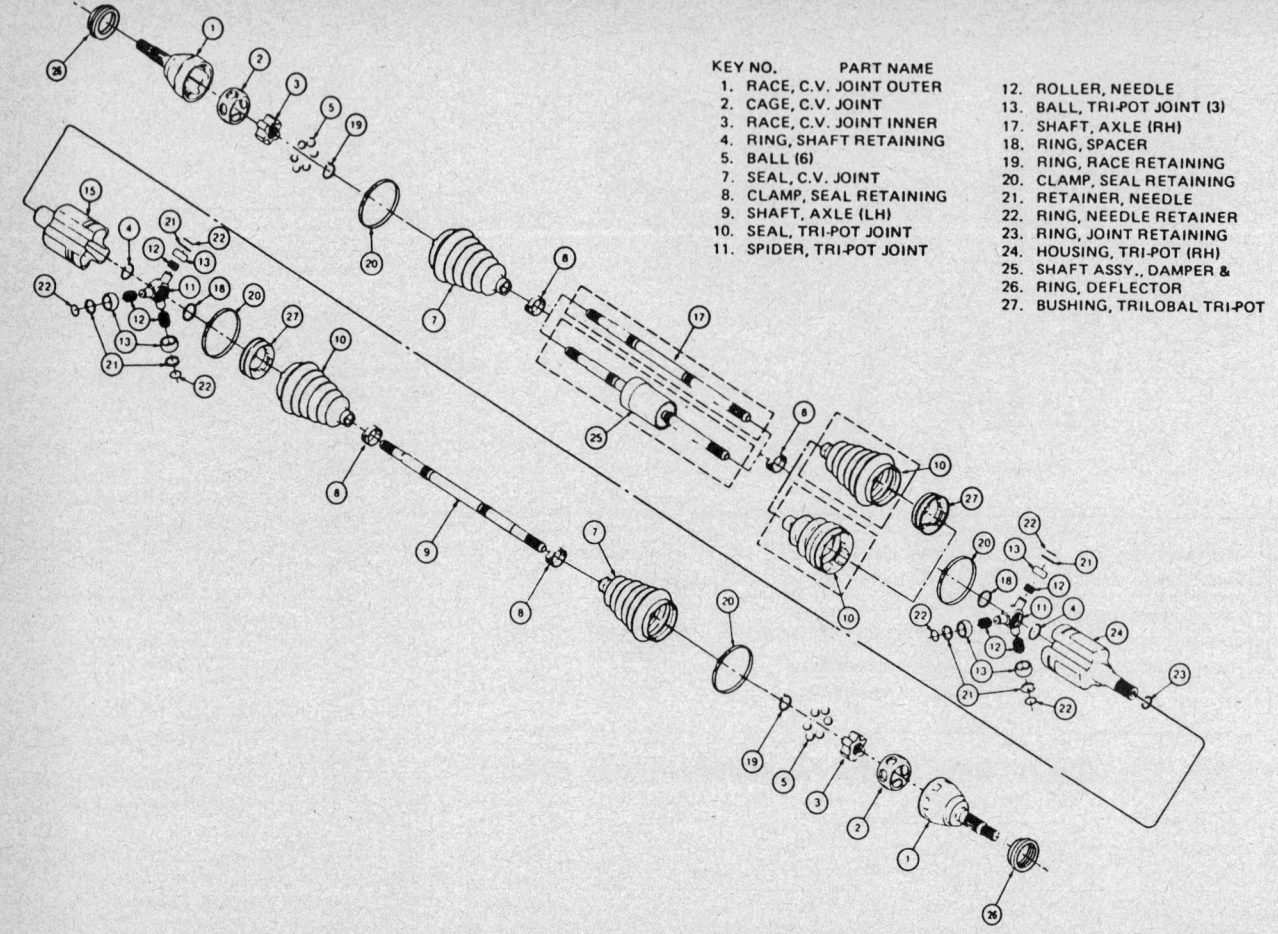

KEY NO.   PART NAME

1. RACE, C.V. JOINT OUTER
2. CAGE, C.V. JOINT
3. RACE, C.V. JOINT INNER
4. RING, SHAFT RETAINING
5. BALL (6)
7. SEAL, C.V. JOINT
8. CLAMP, SEAL RETAINING
9. SHAFT, AXLE (LH)
10. SEAL, TRI-POT JOINT
11. SPIDER, TRI-POT JOINT

12. ROLLER, NEEDLE
13. BALL, TRI-POT JOINT (3)
17. SHAFT, AXLE (RH)
18. RING, SPACER
19. RING, RACE RETAINING
20. CLAMP, SEAL RETAINING
21. RETAINER, NEEDLE
22. RING, NEEDLE RETAINER
23. RING, JOINT RETAINING
24. HOUSING, TRI-POT (RH)
25. SHAFT ASSY., DAMPER &
26. RING, DEFLECTOR
27. BUSHING, TRILOBAL TRI-POT

Fig. 11   Exploded view of drive axle

tool No. J 33792 or equivalent, turn adjusting sleeve until bearing cup is pushed out of the case.
8. Using bearing removal tool No. J 21551 or equivalent, remove side bearing from sleeve.
9. Using pinion flange removal tool No. J 8614-01 or equivalent, remove pinion flange nut and washer.
10. Using pinion bearing remover kit J 33837-1 or equivalent, remove pinion flange and deflector, **Fig. 16.**
11. Remove pinion, spacer and shims.
12. Using pinion bearing removal kit tool No. J 33837-1 or equivalent, remove outer bearing, bearing cup and seal from carrier case.
13. Using pinion bearing removal kit tool No. J 33837-1 or equivalent, push out inner bearing cup as shown in **Fig. 17.**
14. Remove differential pinion shaft retaining screw, then the pinion shaft from differential case.
15. Remove differential pinion gears and washers.
16. Scribe marks on side gears and case for assembly reference, then remove side gears and side thrust washers.
17. Remove drive gear and ring gear from differential case. **Do not pry between ring gear and case. Drive gear off with a brass drift and hammer.**
18. Using bearing cone remover tool No.

J 22912-01 or equivalent, remove side bearings from differential case.

INSPECTION

1. Check bearing for a smooth feel when applying as much hand pressure as possible.
2. Check sealing surface of pinion flange for nicks, burrs or a rough surface which could result in seal damage.
3. Check ring gear and pinion gear for excessive wear and scoring. Replace set if necessary.

ASSEMBLE

Prior to assembly, lubricate all seal lips, bearings, gears and bearing surfaces with axle lubricant.
1. Install thrust washers and side gears into differential case. If original gears and washers are used, align marks scribed during disassembly and install them in their original positions.
2. Refer to **Fig. 13**, then install pinion gears and thrust washers as follows:
   a. Position one pinion gear (13) between side gears (11) and rotate gears until pinion gear is directly opposite large opening in case.
   b. Place other pinion gear (13) between side gears and ensure holes

in both pinion gears are aligned.
   c. Rotate pinion gears towards opening in case just enough to insert thrust washers (12) between gears and case.
   d. Align holes in gears, thrust washers and case.
   e. Install pinion shaft into case and through holes in gears and washers.
   f. Install pinion shaft retaining screw and **torque** to 26 ft. lbs.
3. Attach ring gear onto differential case, then install new drive gear bolts and **torque** to 63 ft. lbs. **Always use new drive gear bolts.**
4. Using bearing installation tool No. J 33790 or equivalent, install side bearing into differential case.
5. Using bearing cup installation tool No. J 33837-1, J 33837-3 and J 33837-4 or equivalents, install outer bearing cup, **Fig. 18.**
6. Using bearing cup installation tool No. J 33837-1, J 33837-3 and J 33837-4 or equivalents, install inner bearing cup, **Fig. 19.**
7. To select the proper shim thickness it will be necessary to measure pinion depth. To measure pinion depth, obtain pinion shim setting gauge tool No. J 33838 or equivalent and a dial indicator, then proceed as follows:

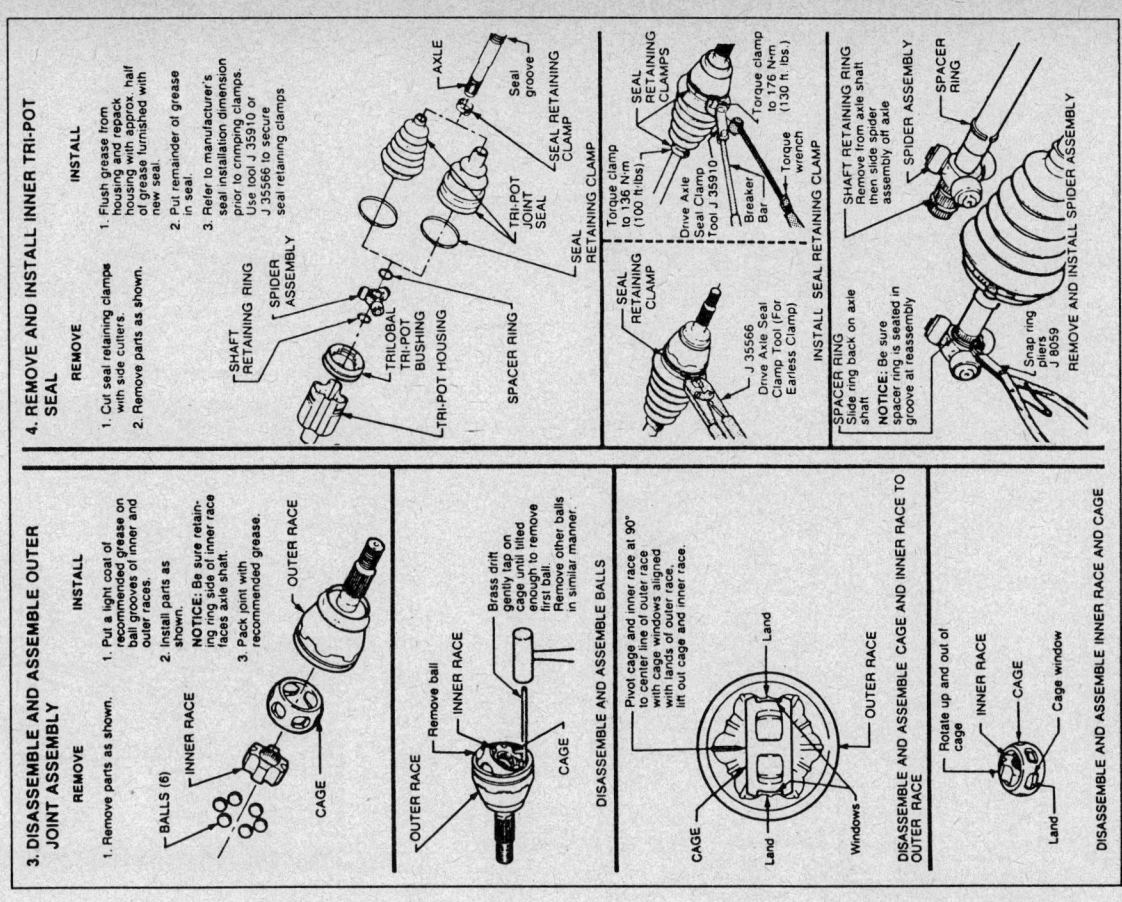

Fig. 12 Drive axle service (Part 2 of 2)

Fig. 12 Drive axle service (Part 1 of 2)

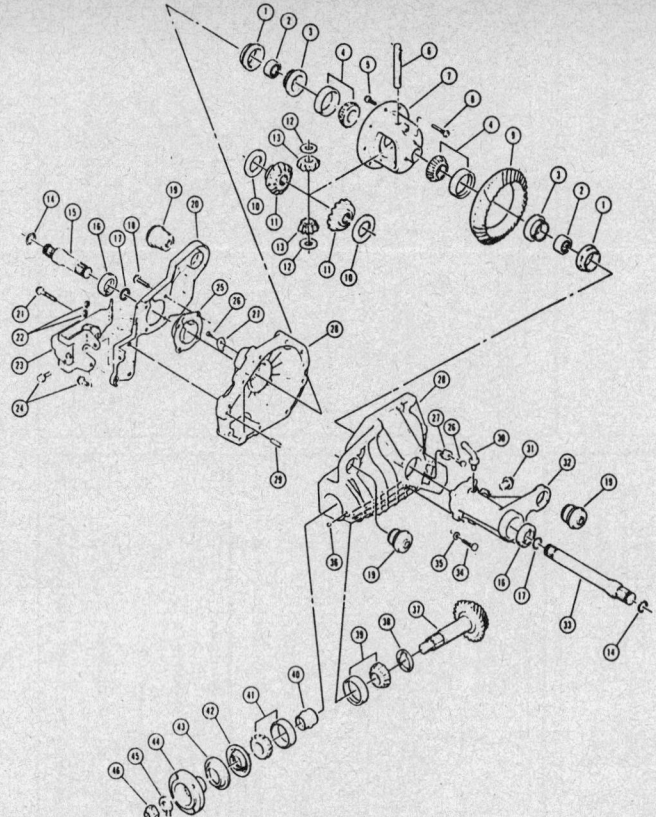

Key No. Part Name

1 - INSERT, DIFF CARRIER BRG ADJ
2 - BEARING ASM, DIFF OUTPUT SHAFT
3 - SLEEVE, DIFF CARRIER BRG ADJ
4 - BEARING ASM, DIFF SIDE
5 - BOLT, DRIVE GEAR
6 - SHAFT, DIFF PINION GEAR
7 - CASE, DIFFERENTIAL
8 - SCREW, DIFF PINION SHAFT
9 - GEAR, RING
10 - WASHER, DIFF SIDE GEAR THRUST
11 - GEAR, DIFFERENTIAL SIDE
12 - WASHER, DIFF PINION GEAR
13 - GEAR, DIFF PINION
14 - RING, DIFF SHAFT OUTER
15 - SHAFT, RH DIFF OUTPUT
16 - SEAL, SHAFT
17 - RING, DIFF SHAFT INNER
18 - BOLT
19 - BUSHING ASM, DIFF CARRIER
20 - BRACKET, RH DIFF MOUNTING
21 - BOLT, DIFF CARRIER ASM
22 - NUT, HEXAGON

23 - DAMPENER ASM
24 - BOLT, HEX HD
25 - RETAINER ASM, SHAFT SEAL
26 - BOLT, DIFF ADJ LOCK
27 - LOCK, DIFF ADJUSTER
28 - CARRIER ASM, DIFF
29 - PIN, DIFF CARRIER
30 - CONNECTOR, REAR AXLE VENT HOSE
31 - PLUG, DIFF FILLER
32 - EXTENSION, AXLE TUBE
33 - SHAFT, LH DIFF OUTPUT
34 - BOLT
35 - WASHER
36 - PLUG, DIFF COVER
37 - PINION, DRIVE
38 - SHIM, PINION BEARING
39 - BEARING ASM, INNER PINION
40 - SPACER, PINION BEARING
41 - BEARING ASM, OUTER PINION
42 - SEAL ASM, PINION FLANGE
43 - DEFLECTOR, PINION FLANGE
44 - FLANGE, PINION
45 - WASHER, PINION FLANGE
46 - NUT, PINION FLANGE

Fig. 13   Exploded view of rear differential

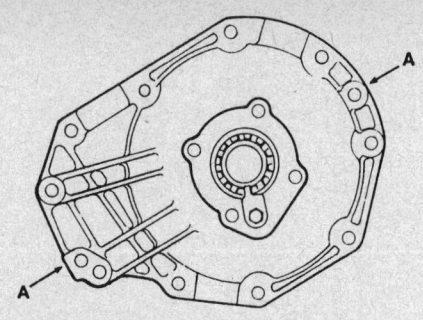

A - CARRIER PRY POINTS

Fig. 14   Separating carrier case

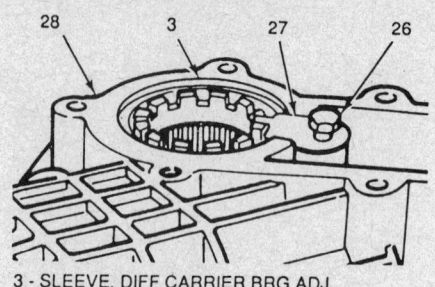

3 - SLEEVE, DIFF CARRIER BRG ADJ
26 - BOLT, DIFF ADJ LOCK
27 - LOCK, DIFF ADJUSTER
28 - CARRIER ASM, DIFF

Fig. 15   Removing lock tab

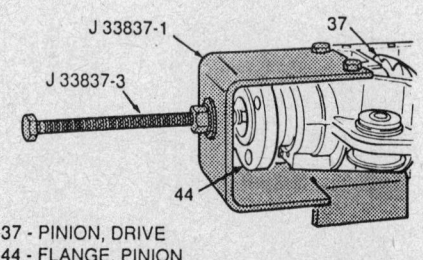

37 - PINION, DRIVE
44 - FLANGE, PINION

Fig. 16   Pinion flange removal

a. Lubricate inner and outer pinion bearings with axle lubricant.
b. Holding pinion bearings in position, install pinion shim setting gauge tool No. J 33838 or equivalent as shown in **Fig. 20.**
c. Preload inner and outer pinion bearings to 20 inch lbs. by tightening mounting bolt on tool and holding end of tool shaft with a wrench.
d. Set dial indicator at zero, then position it in pinion shim setting gauge tool, **Fig. 20.**
e. Push dial indicator down until needle rotates approximately three turns clockwise. Tighten dial indicator in this position.
f. Set button of pinion shim setting gauge tool on differential bearing bore.
g. Rotate tool slowly back and forth

until dial indicator reads lowest point of bore. Set dial indicator to zero. Repeat rocking action of tool to verify zero setting.
h. After zero setting is obtained and verified, move tool button out of side bearing bore.
i. Record dial indicator reading, then choose a shim that corresponds with dial indicator reading. For example; if reading is .033 inch install a .033 inch thick shim.
8. Using pinion bearing installer tool No. J 33785 or equivalent, install inner pinion bearing onto pinion gear.
9. Install new pinion bearing spacer onto pinion gear, then outer pinion bearing into case.
10. Using pinion oil seal installer tool No. J 33782 or equivalent, install pinion flange seal into case.

11. Install pinion gear into carrier case.
12. Install pinion flange deflector, pinion flange, pinion flange washer and nut.
13. Tighten nut until no end play is detectable while holding flange with pinion flange remover tool No. J 8614-01 or equivalent. **Bearing preload is determined by tightening this pinion nut. Tightening the nut can add many additional inch lbs. of torque. The pinion nut must be tightened carefully and in small increments, checking preload after each slight amount of tightening. Check bearing preload using an inch lb. wrench. Maximum preload is 20 inch lbs.**
14. Rotate pinion several times to ensure that bearing are seated. Check preload again. If preload has been changed by rotating pinion, reset pre-

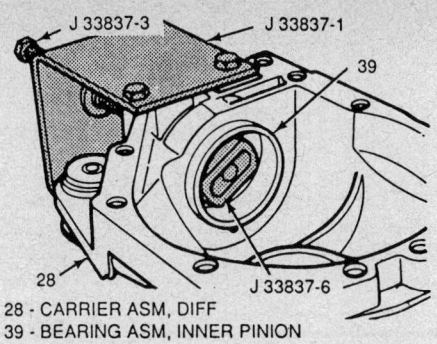

28 - CARRIER ASM, DIFF
39 - BEARING ASM, INNER PINION

Fig. 17 Bearing cup removal

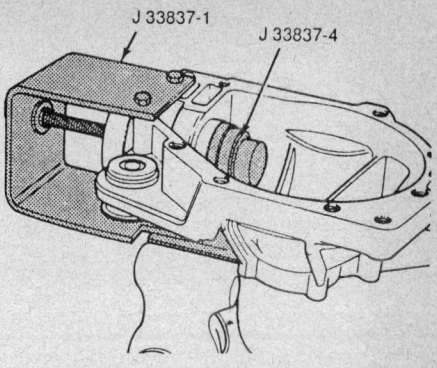

Fig. 18 Outer bearing cup installation

Fig. 19 Inner bearing cup installation

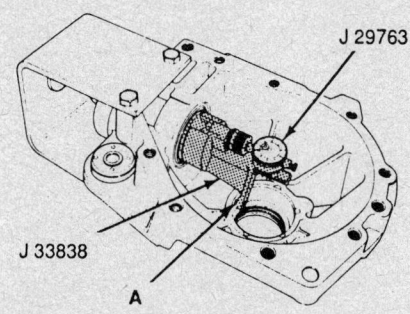

A - LOCATE BUTTON IN THE BORE

Fig. 20 Pinion shim measurement

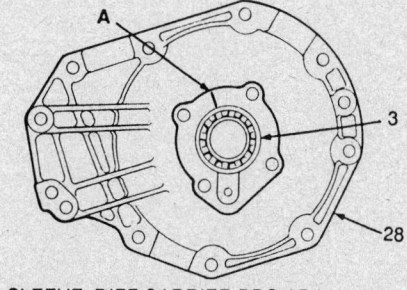

3 - SLEEVE, DIFF CARRIER BRG ADJ
28 - CARRIER ASM, DIFF
A - MARK LOCATION ON THE CASE

Fig. 21 Marking location of adjusting sleeves

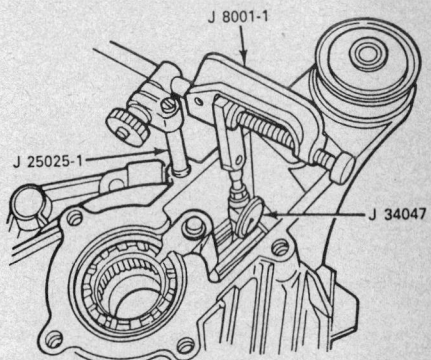

Fig. 22 Measuring backlash at ring gear

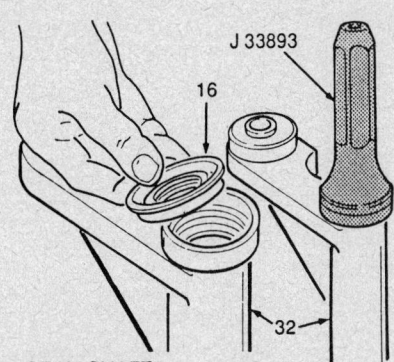

16 - SEAL, SHAFT
32 - EXTENSION, AXLE TUBE

Fig. 23 Installing shaft seal

load to specification.
15. Using output shaft bearing installer or equivalent, install differential output bearings into differential carrier adjusting sleeves.
16. Thread both sleeves into carrier case, then using bearing cup installer tool No. J 23423-A install bearing cups into carrier case.
17. Install differential case assembly into carrier case half that contains the pinion gear.
18. Using side bearing adjuster wrench tool No. J 33792 or equivalent, turn left hand adjusting sleeve inward toward differential case until backlash is felt between ring and pinion gear.
19. Assemble carrier case halves. **Do not use sealer at this time.**
20. If carrier halves do not make complete contact, back out righthand adjusting sleeve.
21. Install case attaching bolts and **torque** to 37 ft. lbs.
22. Measure ring and pinion gear backlash as follows:
   a. Using side bearing adjuster wrench tool No. J 33792 or equivalent, tighten righthand adjusting sleeve until no backlash is present, approximately 100 ft. lbs.
   b. Tighten lefthand adjusting sleeve to approximately 100 ft. lbs.
   c. Scribe location of adjusting

sleeves in relation to carrier case halves so that notches in adjusting sleeves can be counted when turned, **Fig. 21.**
   d. Using side bearing adjuster wrench tool No. J 33792 or equivalent, turn righthand adjusting sleeve out two notches.
   e. Turn lefthand adjusting sleeve inward one notch, then rotate pinion several times to seat bearings.
   f. Using dial indicator clamp tool No. J 8001-1, dial indicator mount J 25025-1 and gear lash gauge J 34047 or equivalents, and mount indicator as shown in **Fig. 22.**

   g. Use small button on indicator stem so that contact can be made near heel end of ring gear tooth to obtain an accurate backlash reading.
   h. Record backlash readings at three or four points around the ring gear. **Pinion must be held stationary when recording backlash.**
   i. Backlash should measure between .003-.010 inch with no more than .002 inch variation between the different measurement points. If backlash differs more than .002 inch between measuring points, check for burrs, distorted case flange, uneven bolting condition, or foreign matter between case and ring gear.
   j. If backlash is not within specification, adjust sleeves as necessary. To increase backlash, turn left sleeve inward and right sleeve outward. To decrease backlash, turn left sleeve outward and right sleeve inward. **When adjusting backlash, always maintain "one notch" preload at side bearings. For example; if it is necessary to turn right sleeve one notch inward, then left sleeve must be turned one notch outward.**
   k. When backlash is correct, mark position of sleeves so they can be kept in the same location.

23. Loosen righthand adjustment sleeve, then remove four carrier case attaching bolts.
24. Apply sealer No. 1052357, Loctite 514 or equivalent, on one carrier case surface.
25. Install four carrier case attaching bolts and **torque** to 35 ft. lbs.
26. Reposition righthand sleeve to previously marked position, then install both differential adjuster lock tabs with lock bolts and **torque** to 71 inch lbs.
27. Attach dampner assembly to differential mounting bracket, **torque** bolts and nuts to 35 ft. lbs.
28. Install shaft seal into shaft seal retainer assembly.
29. Install shaft seal retainer assembly.
30. Install differential mounting bracket, **torque** mounting bracket attaching bolts to 25 ft. lbs.
31. Install righthand differential output shaft and snap into position.
32. Using output shaft seal installer tool No. J 33893 or equivalent, install seal into tube extension, **Fig. 23.**
33. Apply sealer No. 1052357, Loctite 514 or equivalent to carrier surface, then install lefthand differential output shaft into tube extension.
34. Install tube extension with washers and bolts, **torque** bolts to 18 ft. lbs.
35. Press vent hose connector into position, then install filler plug and **torque** to 26 ft. lbs.

HYDRAULIC BRAKE SYSTEM

INDEX

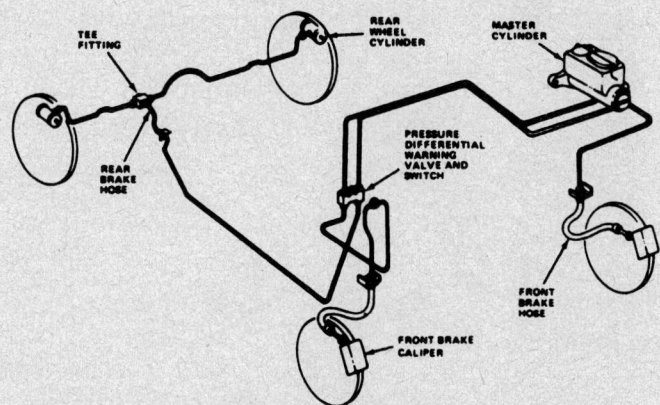

**Fig. 1   Front & rear split brake system
(typical)**

SYSTEM OPERATION

DUAL MASTER CYLINDER

Front & Rear Split System

When the brake pedal is depressed, both the primary (front brake) and the secondary (rear brake) master cylinder pistons are moved simultaneously to exert hydraulic fluid pressure on their respective systems, **Figs. 1 and 2.**

If the rear (secondary) brake system fails, initial brake pedal movement will cause the unrestricted secondary piston to bottom in the master cylinder bore. Primary piston movement will displace hydraulic fluid in the primary section of the master cylinder to actuate the front brake system.

If the front (primary) brake system fails, initial brake pedal movement will cause the unrestricted primary piston to bottom out against the secondary piston. Continued downward movement of the brake pedal moves the secondary piston to displace hydraulic fluid in the rear brake system to actuate the rear brakes.

Diagonally Split System

This system operates on the same principle as conventional front and rear split systems, using primary and secondary master cylinders which move simultaneously to exert hydraulic pressure on their respective systems. The hydraulic brake lines on this system, however, have been diagonally split front to rear (left front to right rear and right front to left rear) in place of separate lines to the front and rear wheels, **Fig. 3.**

In the event of a system failure, the remaining non-failed system will do all the braking on one front wheel and one rear wheel, thus maintaining 50% of the total braking force.

COMPONENT DESCRIPTION

BRAKE WARNING LAMP SWITCHES

There are four basic types of brake warning lamp switches as shown, **Figs. 4 through 7.** When a pressure differential occurs between the front and rear brake systems, the valves will shuttle toward the side with the low pressure.

In the switch shown in **Fig. 4,** movement of the differential valve forces the switch plunger upward over the tapered shoulder of the valve to close the switch contacts and light the dual brake warning lamp, signaling a brake system failure.

In **Fig. 5,** the valve assembly consists of two valves in a common bore that are spring loaded toward the centered position. The spring-loaded switch contact

plunger rests on top of the valves in the centered position (right view). When a pressure differential occurs between the front and rear brake systems, the valves will shuttle toward the side with the low pressure. The spring-loaded switch plunger is "triggered" and the ground circuit for the warning lamp is completed, lighting the lamp (left view).

In **Fig. 6,** as pressure falls in one system, the other system's normal pressure forces the piston to the inoperative side, contacting the switch terminal, causing the warning lamp on the instrument panel to glow.

Fig. 7 shows the switch mounted directly in the master cylinder assembly. Whenever there is a specified differential pressure, the switch piston will activate the brake failure warning switch and cause the brake warning lamp to glow.

Testing Warning Lamp Operation

The warning lamp should illuminate when the ignition switch is in the start position, and turn off when the switch returns to run. If the brake lamp remains on after the ignition returns to run, check fluid level in master cylinder reservoir and inspect parking brake. If the warning lamp does not turn on during cranking, check for defective bulb or blown fuse.

COMBINATION VALVE

The combination valve, **Fig. 8** is a metering valve, failure warning switch, and a proportioner in one assembly and is used on disc brake applications. The metering valve delays front disc braking until the rear drum brake shoes contact the drum. The failure warning switch is actuated in event of front or rear brake system failure, in turn activating a dash warning lamp. The proportioner balances front to rear braking action during rapid deceleration.

Metering Valve

When the brakes are not applied, the metering valve permits the brake fluid to flow through the valve, thus allowing the fluid to expand and contract with temperature changes.

When the brakes are initially applied, the metering valve stem moves to the left, preventing fluid to flow through the valve to the front disc brakes. This is accomplished by the smooth end of the metering valve stem contacting the metering valve seal lip at 4 to 30 psi, **Fig. 9**. The metering valve spring holds the retainer against the seal until a predetermined pressure is produced at the valve inlet port which overcomes the spring pressure and permits hydraulic pressure to actuate the front disc brakes, **Fig. 10**. The increased pressure into the valve is metered through the valve seal, to the front disc brakes, producing an increased force on the diaphragm. The diaphragm then pulls the pin, in turn pulling the retainer and reduces the spring pressure on the metering valve seal. Eventually, the pressure reaches a point at which the spring is pulled away by the diaphragm pin and retainer, leaving the metering valve unrestricted, permitting full pressure to pass through the metering valve.

Failure Warning Switch

If the rear brake system fails, the front system pressure forces the switch piston to the right, **Fig. 11**. The switch pin is then forced up into the switch, completing the electrical circuit and activates the dash warning lamp.

When repairs are made and pressure returns to the system, the piston moves to the left, resetting the switch. The detent on the piston requires approximately 100 to 450 psi to permit full reset of the piston. In event of front brake system failure, the piston moves to the left and the same sequence of events is followed as for rear system failure except the piston resets to the right.

Proportioning or Pressure Control Valve

During rapid deceleration, a portion of vehicle weight is transferred to the front wheels. This resultant loss of weight at rear wheels must be compensated for to avoid early rear wheel skid. The proportioner or pressure control valve reduces rear brake system pressure, delaying rear wheel skid. When the proportioner or pressure control valve is incorporated in the combination valve assembly, pressure developed within the valve acts against the large end of the piston, overcoming the spring pressure, moving the piston left, **Fig. 12**. The piston then contacts the stem seat and restricts line pressure through the valve.

During normal braking operation, the proportioner or pressure control valve is not functional. Brake fluid flows into the proportioner or pressure control valve between the piston center hole and the valve stem, through the stop plate and to the rear brakes. Spring pressure loads the piston during normal braking, causing it to rest against the stop plate, **Fig. 13**.

On diagonally split brake systems, two proportioners or pressure control valves are used. One controls the left rear brake, the other the right rear brake. The proportioners or pressure control valves are installed in the master cylinder rear brake outlet ports, **Fig. 14**.

BRAKE DISTRIBUTION VALVE & SWITCH

This switch assembly, **Fig. 15**, is used on some diagonally split brake systems and Corvette four wheel disc brake systems. It is connected to the outlet ports of the master cylinder and to the brake warning lamp and warns the driver if either the primary or secondary brake system has failed.

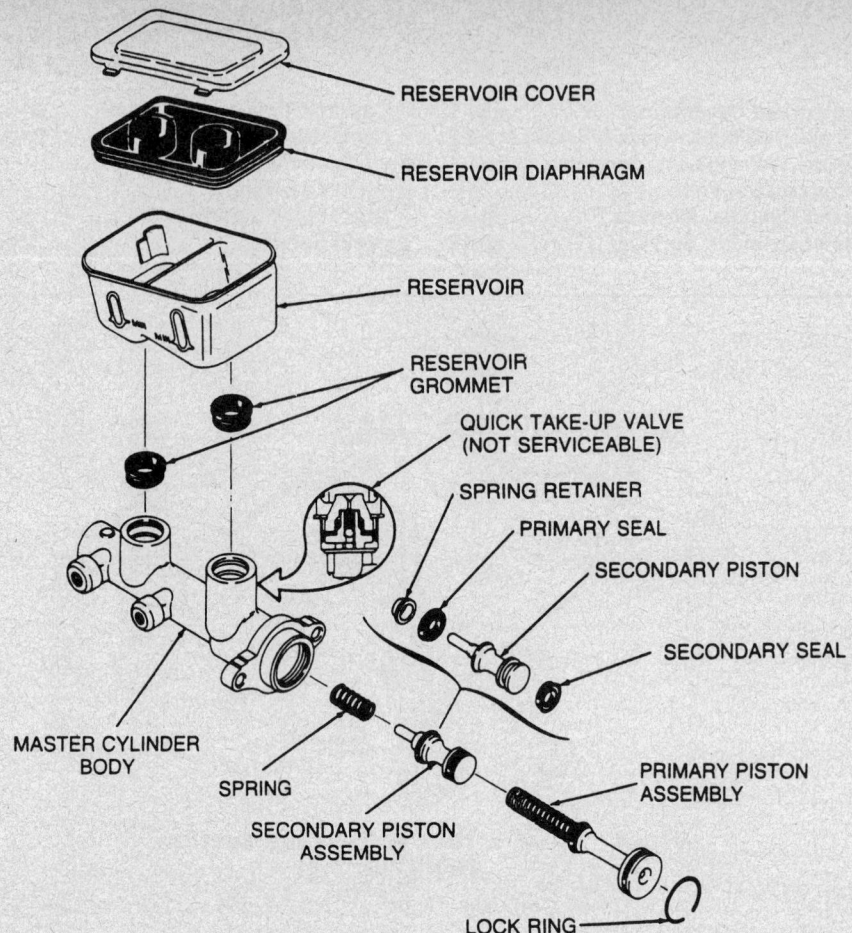

Fig. 2   Dual master cylinder assembly. Composite type

- RESERVOIR COVER
- RESERVOIR DIAPHRAGM
- RESERVOIR
- RESERVOIR GROMMET
- QUICK TAKE-UP VALVE (NOT SERVICEABLE)
- SPRING RETAINER
- PRIMARY SEAL
- SECONDARY PISTON
- SECONDARY SEAL
- PRIMARY PISTON ASSEMBLY
- LOCK RING
- MASTER CYLINDER BODY
- SPRING
- SECONDARY PISTON ASSEMBLY

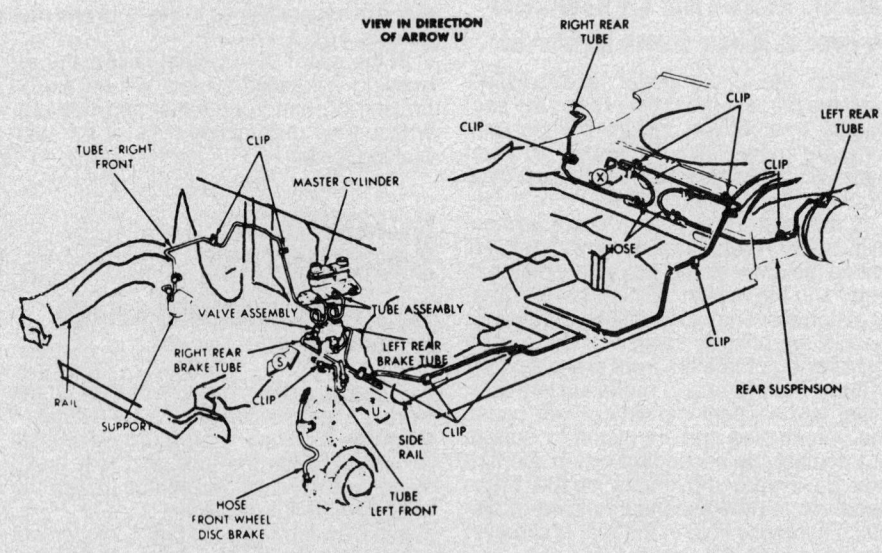

Fig. 3   Diagonally split brake system (typical)

VIEW IN DIRECTION OF ARROW U — RIGHT REAR TUBE — CLIP — LEFT REAR TUBE — TUBE - RIGHT FRONT — CLIP — MASTER CYLINDER — CLIP — HOSE — VALVE ASSEMBLY — TUBE ASSEMBLY — RIGHT REAR BRAKE TUBE — LEFT REAR BRAKE TUBE — CLIP — REAR SUSPENSION — RAIL — SUPPORT — CLIP — SIDE RAIL — HOSE FRONT WHEEL DISC BRAKE — TUBE LEFT FRONT

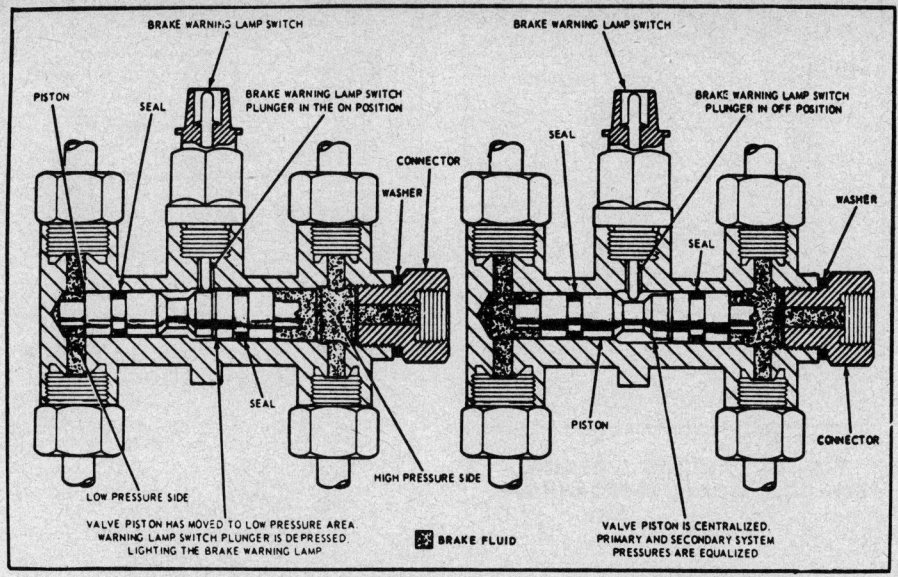

Fig. 4 Pressure differential valve & brake warning lamp switch

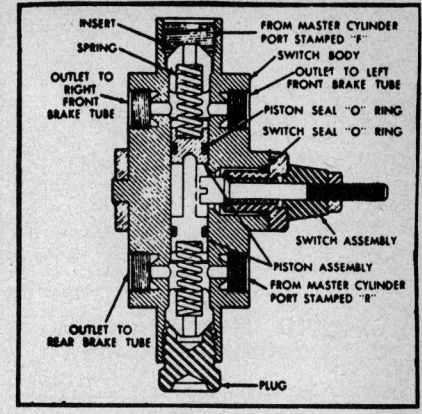

Fig. 6 Pressure differential valve & brake warning lamp switch

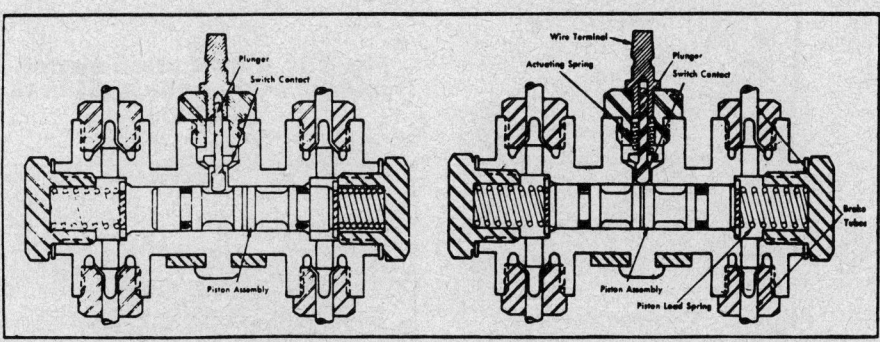

Fig. 5 Pressure differential valve & brake warning lamp switch

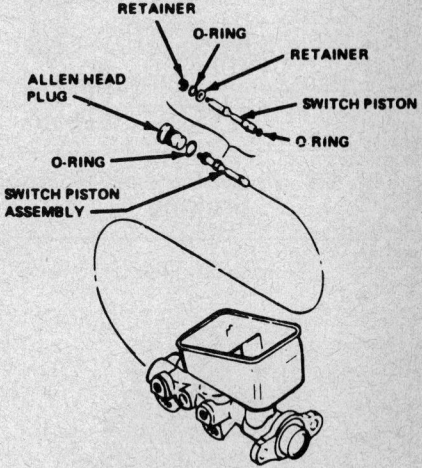

Fig. 7 Dual master cylinder with built in warning lamp switch

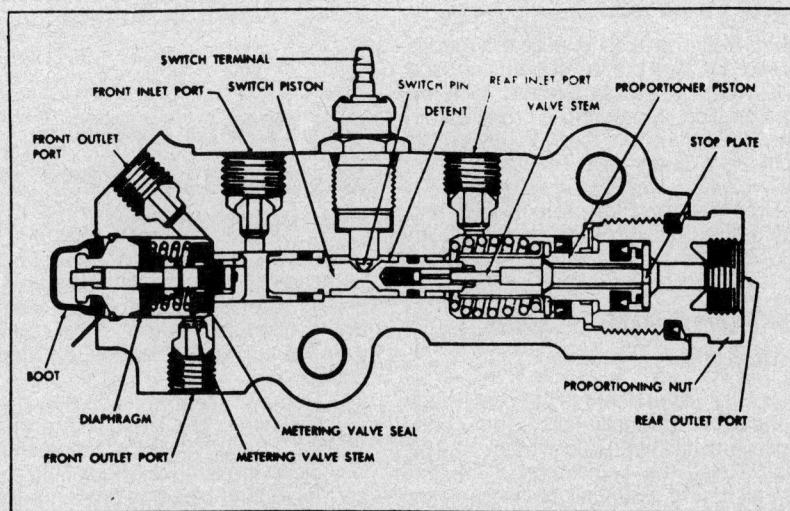

Fig. 8 Combination valve

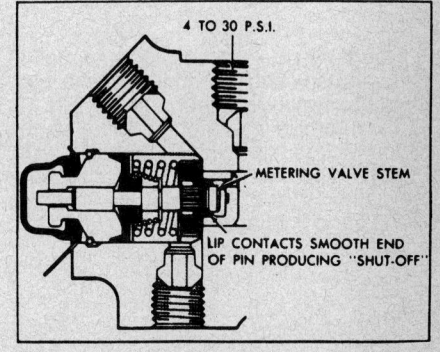

Fig. 9 Metering valve. Initial braking

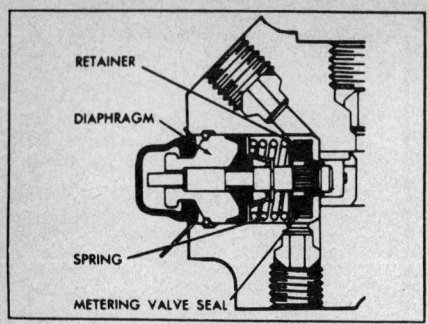

Fig. 10   Metering valve. Continued braking

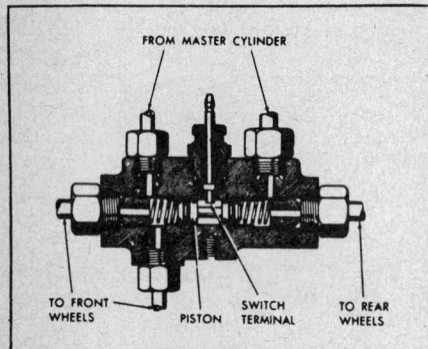

Fig. 13   Proportioner. Normal braking

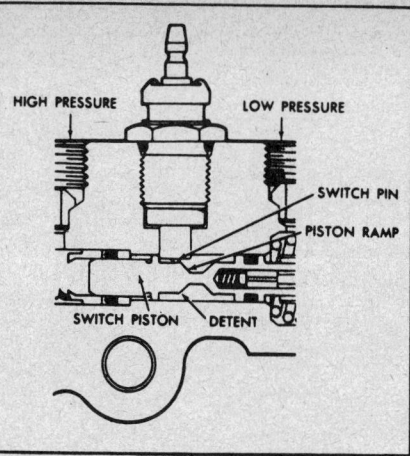

Fig. 11   Failure warning switch. Rear system failure

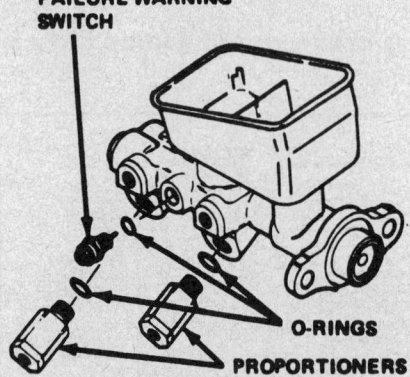

Fig. 14   Proportioners installed in master cylinder

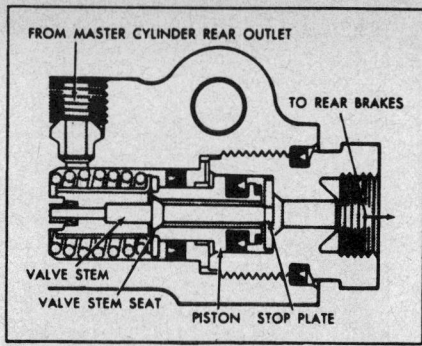

Fig. 12   Proportioner. Rapid deceleration

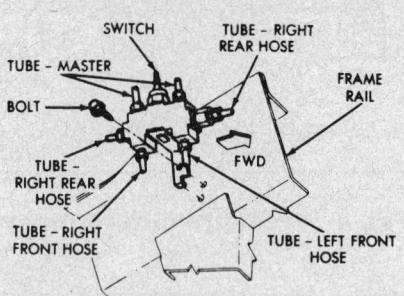

Fig. 15   Distribution switch (typical). Diagonally split brake systems

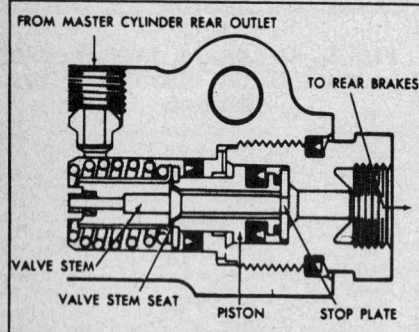

Fig. 16   Brake distribution switch. Normal

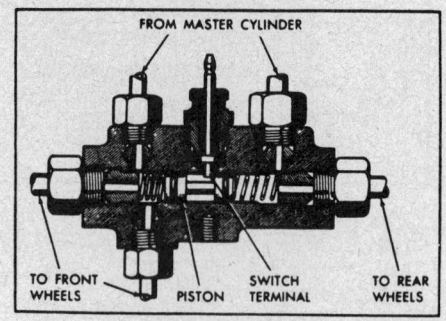

Fig. 17   Brake distribution switch. Failed

When hydraulic pressure is equal in both primary and secondary brake systems, the switch remains centered, **Fig. 16.** If pressure fails in one of the systems, the piston moves toward the inoperative side, **Fig. 17.** The shoulder of the piston contacts the switch terminal, providing a ground and lighting the warning lamp.

TROUBLESHOOTING

When troubleshooting the hydraulic brake system, perform the following checks and inspections as outlined below. If problem still exists within system, refer to **Fig. 18** first, then to **Fig. 19** as necessary.

ROAD TESTING

When testing brakes, ensure the road is level and dry. Test brakes at both light and heavy pedal pressure. Do not lock up brakes or slide tires during a brake test.

Check the tires on the vehicle before performing a brake test. Tires should be equally inflated, identical in size and with equal tread pattern. Excessive camber and caster will cause the brakes to pull. An overloaded vehicle will also brake erratically.

CHECKING FOR FLUID LEAKAGE

Start engine and depress the brake pedal. If the pedal gradually falls under constant pressure, the hydraulic system may be leaking. Raise the vehicle on a lift and check all tubing lines and backing plates for signs of leakage. It may be necessary to lift or remove the carpeting or floor mats to check for booster or master cylinder leakage.

SYSTEM SERVICE

BLEEDING BRAKES
Manual Bleeding

Pressure bleeding is recommended for all hydraulic systems. However, if a pressure bleeder is unavailable, use the following procedure. **Brake fluid damages painted surfaces.** Immediately clean any spilled fluid.

1. Remove vacuum reserve by pumping brakes several times with engine off.
2. Fill master cylinder reservoir with clean brake fluid. Check fluid level often during bleeding procedure; do not let reservoir fall below half full.
3. If necessary, bleed master cylinder as follows:
   a. Disconnect master cylinder for-

BRAKE DIAGNOSIS CHART — DISC, DRUM SYSTEMS

CAUSE \ SYMPTOM	Excessive Brake Pedal Travel	Brake Pedal Travel Gradually Increases	Excessive Brake Pedal Effort	Excessive Brake Action	Brakes Respond Slow to Braking	Brakes Slow to Release	Brakes Slow to Respond	Brakes Drag Action	Uneven Braking Action (Side to Side)	Uneven Braking Action (Front to Rear)	Scraping Noise from Brakes	Brakes Squeak During Application	Brakes Squeak During Stop	Brakes Chatter (Roughness)	Brakes Groan at End of Stop	Brakes Tell-Tale Glows
Leaking Brake Line or Connection	X	XX	X								X					XX
Leaking Wheel Cylinder or Piston Seal	X	XX	X	X						X	X					X
Leaking Master Cylinder	X	XX	X								X					X
Air in Brake System	XX		X								X					XX
Contaminated or Improper Brake Fluid	X					X	X	X	X							X
Leaking Vacuum System				XX		X										
Restricted Air Passage in Power Booster			X	X		XX	X	X								
Damaged Power Booster			X	X	X	X	XX	X								
Worn Out Brake Lining				X		X					X	X	X	XX	X	
Uneven Brake Lining Wear-Replace	X					X					X	X	X	XX	X	
Glazed Brake Lining-Sand				XX		X					X			X		X
Incorrect Lining Material-Replace				X		X					X	X	X	X	X	X
Contaminated Brake Lining-Replace				X	XX	X				XX	XX	X		X	X	X
Lining Damaged by Abusive Use-Replace				X	XX					X	X	X		X	X	X
Excessive Brake Lining Dust-Remove				X	XX					XX	XX	X		X		X
Heat Spotted or Scored Drums or Rotors						X					X	X		X	XX	X
Out-of-Round or Vibrating Brake Drums														XX		
Backing Plate Interference on the Drum											X					
Out-of-Parallel Brake Rotors	X													XX		
Excessive Rotor Run-out	X													X		
Faulty Automatic Adjusters	X					X				X	X	X				X
Incorrect Wheel Cylinder Sizes				X	X					X	X					
Weak or Incorrect Brake Shoe Retention Springs						X	X	X	X	X	X		X	XX		
Brake Assembly Attachments-Missing or Loose	X									X	X	X		X	X	
Insufficient Brake Shoe Guide Lubricant										X	X	X	XX	XX		
Restricted Brake Fluid Passage or Sticking Wheel Cylinder Piston			X	X		X	X	X	X	X						X
Improperly Adjusted Stoplight Switch or Cruise Control Vacuum Dump								X								
Faulty Metering Valve	X			X	X	X	X	X			X					X
Faulty Porportioning Valve				X	X	X	X				X					X
Brake Pedal Linkage Interference or Binding				X		X	XX	XX								
Improperly Adjusted Parking Brake								X			X					XX
Incorrect Front End Alignment									XX							
Incorrect Tire Pressure									X	X						
Incorrect Wheel Bearing Adjustment	X								X	X		X		X		
Loose Front Suspension Attachments									X	X		XX		X	X	
Out-of-Balance Wheel Assemblies														XX		
Operator Riding Brake Pedal				X					X		X				X	X
Sticking Caliper or Wheel Cylinder Pistons				X					XX	X	X					

XX — Indicates more probable cause(s)   X — Indicates other causes

Fig. 18   Brake diagnosis chart (part 1 of 6). Front disc/rear drum system

ward brake line connection until fluid flows from reservoir. Reconnect and tighten brake line.

b. Instruct an assistant to slowly de-press brake pedal one time and hold.

c. Crack open front brake line connection again, purging air from cylinder.

d. Retighten connection and slowly release brake pedal.

e. Wait 15 seconds, then repeat until

BRAKE DIAGNOSIS CHART — 4 WHEEL DISC SYSTEMS

SYMPTOM

CAUSE	Excessive Brake Pedal Travel	Gradually Increases Brake Pedal Travel	Excessive Effort	Excessive Brake Action	Brakes Slow to Respond	Brakes Slow to Release	Brakes Drag	Uneven Action (Side to Side)	Uneven Braking Action (Front to Rear)	Scraping Noise from Brakes	Brakes Squeak During Application	Brakes Squeak During Stop	Brakes Squeak (Roughness)	Brakes Chatter End of Stop	Brakes Groan at End of Stop	Brakes Tell-Tale Glows / Excessive Parking Brake Pedal Travel	No Reserve Stopping
Leaking Brake Line or Connection	X	XX	X						X							XX	
Leaking Piston Seal	X	XX	X	X				X	X							X	
Leaking Master Cylinder	X	XX	X						X							X	
Air in Brake System	XX		X						X							XX	
Contaminated or Substandard Brake Fluid	X					X	X	X	X							X	
Leaking Vacuum System					XX		X									XX	
Restricted Air Passage in Power Booster				X	X		XX	X									
Damaged Power Booster				X	X	X		X	XX								XX
Worn Out Brake Lining					X	X			X	X	X	X			X		
Uneven Brake Lining Wear-Replace	X					X			X	X	X	X	XX		X	X	
Glazed Brake Lining-Sand				XX		X			X	X		X	X				
Incorrect Lining Material-Replace				X	X		X		X	X			X		X		
Contaminated Brake Lining-Replace					XX		X		XX	XX	X	X	X		X		
Lining Damaged by Abusive Use-Replace				X	XX				X	X	X	X	X		X		
Heat Spotted or Scored Rotors					X				X	X		X	X	XX	X		
Out-of-Parallel Brake Rotors	X													XX			
Excessive Run-Out Rotor	X													X			
Faulty Automatic Adjusters	X				X			X	X	X					X	X	
Brake Assembly Attachments-Missing or Loose	X							X	X	X	X		X	X	X		
Restricted Brake Fluid Passage				X	X		X	X	X							X	
Improperly adjusted Stoplight Switch or Cruise Control Vacuum Dump									X								
Faulty Proportioning Valve				X	X	X	X	X	X							X	
Brake Pedal Linkage Interference or Binding				X		X	XX	XX									
Improperly Adjusted Parking Brake Cables								X		X						X	
Improper Length Master Cylinder Push Rod	X				X		X	XX	X								
Incorrect Front End Alignment								XX									
Incorrect Tire Pressure								X	X								
Faulty Wheel Bearing - Replace	X										X			X			
Loose Front Suspension Attachments								X	X		XX			X	X		
Out-of-Balance Wheel Assemblies														XX			
Operator Riding Brake Pedal				X				X	X						X		
Sticking Caliper Piston						X	X	XX	X	X							
Park Brake Switch Circuit Grounded																XX	
Park Brake Not Releasing								X		X						XX	

XX - Indicates more probable cause(s)

X - Indicates other causes

Fig. 18   Brake diagnosis chart (part 2 of 6). Four wheel disc system

all air is purged.

f. Bleed the rearward (nearest the cowl) brake line connection by repeating steps a through e.

4. Loosen, then slightly retighten bleeder valves at all four wheels. Repair any broken, stripped or frozen valves at this time.

5. Proceed to appropriate wheel first and follow set sequence according to "Wheel Bleeding Sequence."

6. Place transparent tube over bleeder valve, then allow tube to hang down into transparent container, **Fig. 20.** Ensure end of tube is submerged in

BRAKE DIAGNOSIS — GASOLINE

CONDITION	POSSIBLE CAUSE	CORRECTION
EXCESSIVE PEDAL EFFORT.	1. MALFUNCTIONING POWER BOOSTER.	1. CHECK POWER BOOSTER AND REPAIR IF NECESSARY.
	2. PARTIAL BRAKE SYSTEM FAILURE.	2. CHECK FRONT AND REAR BRAKE SYSTEM AND REPAIR AS NECESSARY. ALSO CHECK BRAKE WARNING LIGHT. IF A FAILED SYSTEM IS FOUND, THE LIGHT SHOULD HAVE INDICATED A FAILURE.
	3. EXCESSIVELY WORN LININGS.	3. CHECK AND REPLACE IN AXLE SETS.
	4. FADING BRAKES DUE TO INCORRECT LINING OR EXCESSIVE BRAKING.	4. REPLACE WITH ORIGINAL EQUIPMENT LINING.
	5. LINING GLAZED.	5. SAND LINING AND ROTORS OR DRUMS.
	6. WORN DRUMS.	6. REPLACE.
EXCESSIVE PEDAL TRAVEL.	1. PARTIAL BRAKE SYSTEM FAILURE.	1. CHECK BOTH FRONT AND REAR BRAKE SYSTEMS FOR A FAILURE AND REPAIR. ALSO CHECK WARNING LIGHT. IT SHOULD HAVE INDICATED A FAILURE.
	2. INSUFFICIENT FLUID IN MASTER CYLINDER.	2. FILL RESERVOIRS WITH APPROVED BRAKE FLUID. CHECK FOR LEAKS. CHECK WARNING LIGHT.
	3. AIR TRAPPED IN SYSTEM. (PEDAL SPONGY).	3. BLEED SYSTEM.
	4. REAR BRAKE SYSTEM NOT ADJUSTING.	4. REPAIR AUTO ADJUSTERS AND ADJUST REAR BRAKES.
	5. BENT SHOE AND LINING.	5. REPLACE SHOES AND LININGS IN AXLE SETS.
NOISE (HIGH PITCHED SQUEAK WITHOUT BRAKE APPLIED).	1. FRONT LININGS WORN OUT (WEAR OUT SENSOR MAKING NOISE).	1. REPLACE LININGS.
NOISE (METALLIC SCRAPING NOISE FROM REAR).	1. BRAKE DRUM CONTACTING STATIONARY BACKING PLATE.	1. SEE TURNING BRAKE DRUM.
BRAKE SQUEAK WITH BRAKES APPLIED.	1. INSULATOR ON OUTBOARD SHOE DAMAGED.	1. REPLACE INSULATOR.
	2. INCORRECT LININGS.	2. REPLACE WITH ORIGINAL EQUIPMENT LININGS.
BRAKE ROUGHNESS OR CHATTER (PEDAL PULSATES).	1. EXCESSIVE ROTOR LATERAL RUNOUT.	1. CHECK PER INSTRUCTIONS. IF NOT WITHIN SPECIFICATIONS, REPLACE OR MACHINE THE ROTOR.
	2. ROTOR THICKNESS VARIATION NOT WITHIN SPECIFICATIONS.	2. CHECK PER INSTRUCTIONS. IF NOT WITHIN SPECIFICATIONS, REPLACE OR MACHINE THE ROTOR.
	3. WHEEL BEARINGS NOT ADJUSTED (EXCEPT ELDORADO AND SEVILLE).	3. ADJUST WHEEL BEARINGS TO CORRECT SPECIFICATIONS.
	4. REAR DRUMS OUT OF ROUND.	4. CHECK RUNOUT AND IF NOT WITHIN SPECIFICATIONS, TURN THE DRUMS (NOT OVER THE MAXIMUM).

Fig. 18   Brake diagnosis chart (part 3 of 6). Models w/gasoline engine

clean brake fluid.
7. Instruct an assistant to slowly depress brake pedal one time and hold.

8. Crack open bleeder valve, purging air from cylinder. Retighten bleeder screw and slowly release pedal.

9. Wait 15 seconds, then repeat steps 7 and 8. Repeat these steps until all air is bled from system.

BRAKE DIAGNOSIS — GASOLINE

CONDITION	POSSIBLE CAUSE	CORRECTION
BRAKE ROUGHNESS OR CHATTER (PEDAL PULSATES). (CONT'D.)	5. DISC BRAKE SHOE REVERSED (STEEL AGAINST IRON).	5. REPLACE SHOE AND LINING AND MACHINE ROTOR WITHIN SPECIFICATIONS.
	6. SEVILLE OR ELDORADO; FRONT TIRES FLAT SPOTTED OR HAVE HIGH RADIAL FORCE VARIATION.	6. SUBSTITUTE KNOWN GOOD TIRES
	7. UNEVEN PAD WEAR CAUSED BY CALIPER NOT SLIDING DUE TO IMPROPER CLEARANCE OR DIRT.	7. REMOVE CALIPER AND CORRECT AS NECESSARY.
	8. UNEVEN ROTOR WEAR CAUSING A THICKNESS VARIATION BETWEEN THE TWO BRAKING SURFACES.	8. MACHINE ROTOR AS FOLLOWS: a. MACHINE ROTORS TO OBTAIN A THICKNESS VARIATION NO GREATER THAN .0005" AND A LATERAL RUNOUT NO GREATER THAN .004". b. CHECK CALIPER FREENESS. WITH ROTOR REMOVED, INSTALL CALIPER AND MOUNTING BOLTS (PINS). CHECK FOR .005" - .012" CLEARANCE AT BOTH TOP AND BOTTOM OF CALIPER. IF LESS THAN .005" IS FOUND, FILE WITH A FLAT FILE UNTIL AT LEAST .005" IS OBTAINED. **DO NOT EXCEED A MAXIMUM** OF .012" PER END OF .024" TOTAL CLEARANCE. CALIPER CLEARANCE TO INBOARD AND OUTBOARD REACTION PADS MUST BE EQUAL WITHIN .004" BOTH AT THE TOP AND BOTTOM OF THE CALIPER. THIS IS TO ENSURE CORRECT ALIGNMENT OF CALIPER TO KNUCKLE DURING A BRAKE APPLICATION. c. REMOVE CALIPER AFTER FREENESS CHECK. CLEAN PINS (DO NOT USE ABRASIVES) AND REPLACE SLEEVES AND "O" RINGS. APPLY A LIGHT COATING OF SILICONE GREASE OR EQUIVALENT TO ALL CONTACT POINTS AND "O" RINGS. d. INSTALL RECONDITIONED ROTORS. AND, EXCEPT ELDORADO AND SEVILLE, SET BEARING ADJUSTMENT END PLAY. e. INSPECT LININGS. CLEAN FOREIGN MATERIAL FROM RIVET HOLES. f. REINSTALL CALIPERS. g. PUMP BRAKE PEDAL TO SEAT SHOES BEFORE ATTEMPTING TO MOVE CAR.
PULLS.	1. INCORRECT TIRE PRESSURES.	1. INFLATE EVENLY ON BOTH SIDES TO THE RECOMMENDED PRESSURES.
	2. FRONT END OUT OF ALIGNMENT.	2. CHECK AND ALIGN TO SPECIFICATIONS.
	3. UNMATCHED TIRES ON SAME AXLE.	3. TIRES WITH APPROXIMATELY THE SAME AMOUNT OF TREAD SHOULD BE USED ON THE SAME AXLE.

Fig. 18   Brake diagnosis chart (part 4 of 6). Models w/gasoline engine

BRAKE DIAGNOSIS — GASOLINE

CONDITION	POSSIBLE CAUSE	CORRECTION
PULLS. (CONT'D.)	4. RESTRICTED BRAKE LINES OR HOSES.	4. CHECK FOR SOFT HOSES AND DAMAGED LINES. REPLACE WITH NEW HOSES AND NEW DOUBLE-WALLED STEEL BRAKE TUBING.
	5. MALFUNCTIONING CALIPER ASSEMBLY.	5. CHECK FOR STUCK OR SLUGGISH PISTONS, PROPER LUBRICATION OF CALIPER BUSHINGS.
	6. DEFECTIVE OR DAMAGED SHOE AND LINING (GREASE OR BRAKE FLUID ON LINING OR BENT SHOE).	6. INSTALL NEW SHOE AND LINING IN COMPLETE AXLE SETS.
	7. MALFUNCTIONING REAR BRAKES.	7. CHECK FOR INOPERATIVE AUTO ADJUSTING MECHANISM, DEFECTIVE LINING (GREASE OR BRAKE FLUID ON LINING) OR DEFECTIVE WHEEL CYLINDERS. REPAIR AS NECESSARY.
	8. LOOSE SUSPENSION PARTS.	8. CHECK ALL SUSPENSION MOUNTINGS.
	9. LOOSE CALIPERS.	9. CHECK AND TORQUE BOLTS TO SPECIFICATIONS.
GRABBING OR UNEVEN BRAKING.	1. ALL CONDITIONS LISTED UNDER "PULLS."	1. ALL CONDITIONS LISTED UNDER "PULL."
	2. MALFUNCTION OF COMBINATION VALVE. PROPORTIONER SECTION CAUSING EARLY REAR WHEEL SLIDE.	2. REPLACE COMBINATION VALVE.
	3. MALFUNCTION OF POWER BRAKE UNIT.	3. CHECK OPERATION AND REPAIR, IF NECESSARY.
	4. BINDING BRAKE PEDAL MECHANISM.	4. CHECK AND LUBRICATE, IF NECESSARY. POSSIBLY REPLACE PEDAL BUSHING AND/OR SPACER.
DRAGGING BRAKES (A VERY LIGHT DRAG IS PRESENT IN ALL DISC BRAKES IMMEDIATELY AFTER PEDAL IS RELEASED).	1. MASTER CYLINDER PISTONS NOT RETURNING CORRECTLY.	1. WITH RESERVOIR COVER OFF, CHECK FOR FLUID SPURT AT BYPASS HOLES AS PEDAL IS DEPRESSED. REBUILD MASTER CYLINDER.
	2. RESTRICTED BRAKE LINES OR HOSES.	2. CHECK FOR SOFT HOSES OR DAMAGED LINES AND REPLACE WITH NEW HOSES AND NEW DOUBLE-WALLED STEEL BRAKE TUBING.
	3. INCORRECT PARKING BRAKE ADJUSTMENT ON REAR BRAKES.	3. CHECK AND READJUST TO CORRECT SPECIFICATIONS.
	4. POWER BOOSTER OUTPUT ROD TOO LONG.	4. REPLACE WITH CORRECT LENGTH.
	5. BRAKE PEDAL NOT RETURNING FREELY.	5. STOP LIGHT SWITCH OR CRUISE CONTROL NOT ADJUSTED PROPERLY. a. PEDAL PIVOT NOT LUBRICATED. b. INTERFERENCE WITH WIRING.
	6. PARKING BRAKE CABLE BINDING.	6. REPLACE.

Fig. 18   Brake diagnosis chart (part 5 of 6). Models w/gasoline engine

BRAKE DIAGNOSIS — DIESEL

CONDITION	POSSIBLE CAUSE	CORRECTION
EXCESSIVE BRAKE PEDAL EFFORT.	1. LOOSE OR BROKEN POWER STEERING PUMP BELT. 2. NO FLUID IN POWER STEERING RESERVOIR. 3. LEAKS IN POWER STEERING, BOOSTER OR ACCUMULATOR HOSES. 4. LEAKS AT TUBE FITTINGS, POWER STEERING, BOOSTER OR ACCUMULATOR CONNECTIONS. 5. EXTERNAL LEAKAGE AT ACCUMULATOR. 6. FAULTY BOOSTER PISTON SEAL CAUSING LEAKAGE AT BOOSTER FLANGE VENT. 7. FAULTY BOOSTER INPUT ROD SEAL WITH LEAKAGE AT INPUT ROD END. 8. FAULTY BOOSTER COVER SEAL WITH LEAKAGE BETWEEN HOUSING AND COVER. 9. FAULTY BOOSTER SPOOL PLUG SEAL.	1. TIGHTEN OR REPLACE THE BELT. 2. FILL RESERVOIR AND CHECK FOR EXTERNAL LEAKS. 3. REPLACE FAULTY PARTS. 4. TIGHTEN FITTINGS OR REPLACE TUBE SEATS, IF FAULTY. 5. REPLACE "O" RING AND RETAINER. 6. REPAIR WITH NEW SEAL KIT. 7. REPLACE BOOSTER. 8. REPAIR WITH NEW SEAL KIT. 9. REPAIR WITH SPOOL PLUG SEAL KIT.
SLOW BRAKE PEDAL RETURN.	1. EXCESSIVE SEAL FRICTION IN HYDRAULIC BOOSTER. 2. FAULTY SPOOL ACTION. 3. BROKEN PISTON RETURN SPRING. 4. RESTRICTION IN RETURN LINE FROM HYDRAULIC BOOSTER TO PUMP RESERVOIR. 5. BROKEN SPOOL RETURN SPRING.	1. REPAIR WITH NEW SEAL KIT. 2. FLUSH STEERING SYSTEM WHILE PUMPING BRAKE PEDAL. 3. REPLACE SPRING. 4. REPLACE LINE. 5. REPLACE SPRING.
GRABBY BRAKES.	1. BROKEN SPOOL RETURN SPRING. 2. FAULTY SPOOL ACTION CAUSED BY CONTAMINATION IN SYSTEM.	1. REPLACE SPRING. 2. FLUSH STEERING SYSTEM WHILE PUMPING BRAKE PEDAL.
BOOSTER CHATTERS — PEDAL VIBRATES	1. POWER STEERING PUMP SLIPS. 2. LOW FLUID LEVEL IN POWER STEERING PUMP RESERVOIR. 3. FAULTY SPOOL OPERATION CAUSED BY CONTAMINATION IN SYSTEM.	1. TIGHTEN BELT. 2. FILL RESERVOIR AND CHECK FOR EXTERNAL LEAKS. 3. FLUSH STEERING SYSTEM WHILE PUMPING BRAKE PEDAL.
ACCUMULATOR LEAK DOWN — SYSTEM DOES NOT HOLD CHARGE	1. CONTAMINATION IN STEERING HYDRO-BOOST SYSTEM. 2. INTERNAL LEAKAGE IN ACCUMULATOR SYSTEM.	1. FLUSH STEERING SYSTEM WHILE PUMPING BRAKE PEDAL. 2. REPAIR UNIT USING ACCUMULATOR REBUILD KIT AND SEAL KIT.

Fig. 18 Brake diagnosis chart (part 6 of 6). Models w/diesel engine

---

HARD PEDAL

CAUSE	CORRECTION
Broken or damaged hydraulic brake lines.	Inspect and replace as necessary.
Vacuum failure.	Check for: Faulty vacuum check valve or grommet-replace. Collapsed or damaged vacuum hose-replace. Plugged or loose vacuum fitting-repair. Faulty air valve seal or support plate seal-replace. Damaged floating control valve-replace. Bad stud welds on front or rear housing of power head-replace unless easily repaired.
Defective diaphragm.	Replace
Restricted air filter element.	Replace
Worn or distorted reaction plate or levers.	Replace plate or levers.
Cracked or broken power piston or retainer.	Replace power piston and piston rod retainer.

GRABBY BRAKES
(Apparent Off-On Condition)

CAUSE	CORRECTION
Broken or damaged hydraulic brake lines.	Inspect and replace as necessary.
Insufficient fluid in master cylinder.	Fill reservoirs with approved brake fluid-check for leaks.
Defective master cylinder seals.	Repair or replace as necessary.
Cracked master cylinder casting.	Replace
Leaks at front disc brake calipers or rear wheel cylinders in pipes or connections.	Inspect and repair as necessary.
Air in hydraulic system.	Bleed system.

BRAKES FAIL TO RELEASE

CAUSE	CORRECTION
Blocked passage in power piston.	Inspect and repair or replace as necessary.
Air valve sticking shut.	Check for proper lubrication of air valve "O" ring.
Broken piston return spring.	Replace
Broken air valve spring.	Replace
Tight pedal linkage.	Repair or replace as necessary.

Fig. 19   Power brake diagnosis chart

Pressure Bleeding

1. Loosen, then slightly retighten bleeder valves at all four wheels. Repair any broken, stripped or frozen valves at this time.
2. Using a diaphragm type pressure bleeder, install suitable bleeder adapter to master cylinder, **Fig. 21.**
3. Charge bleeder ball to 20-25 psi.
4. Connect pressure bleeder line to adapter.
5. Open line valve on pressure bleeder, then depress bleed-off valve on adapter until a small amount of brake fluid is released.
6. Raise and support vehicle.
7. Proceed to appropriate wheel first and follow set sequence according to "Wheel Bleeding Sequence."
8. Place transparent tube over bleeder valve, then allow tube to hang down into transparent container, **Fig. 20.** Ensure end of tube is submerged in clean brake fluid.
9. Open bleeder valve 1/2 to 3/4 turn and allow fluid to flow into container until all air is purged from line.

Wheel Bleeding Sequence

Rear wheel drive models except Corvette: if manual bleeding, RR-LR-RF-LF; if pressure bleeding, bleed front brakes together and rear brakes together.

Front wheel drive models except Spectrum: RR-LF-LR-RF.

1988–89 Corvette: RF-RR-LR-LF.

Spectrum: LF-RR-RF-LR.

Flushing Hydraulic System

If brake fluid is old, rusty or contaminated, or whenever new parts are installed in

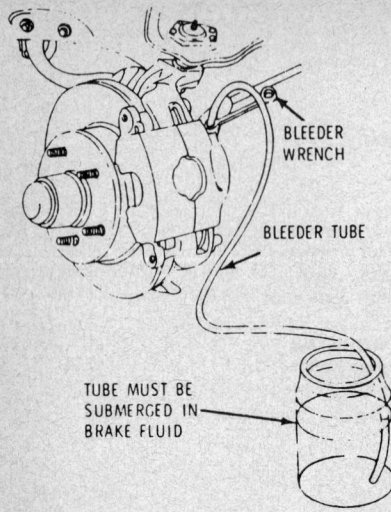

Fig. 20 Bleeding brakes

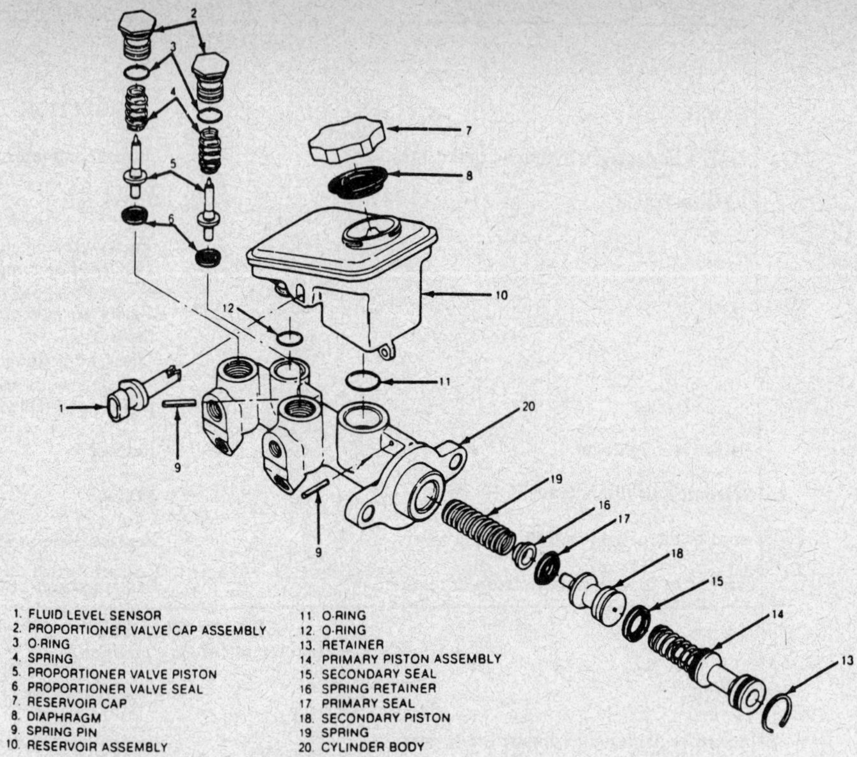

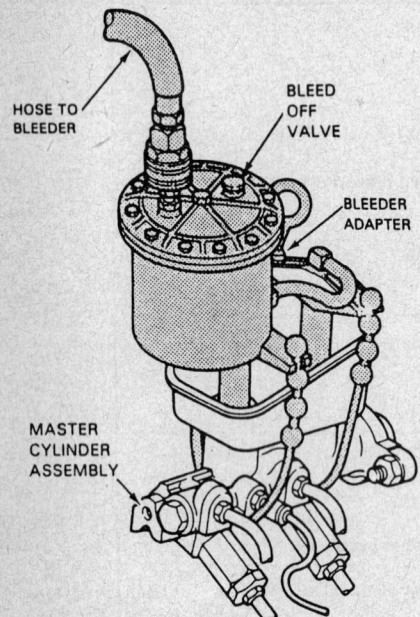

Fig. 21 Installing pressure bleeder adapter

hydraulic system, the system must be flushed. Bleed brakes, allowing at least one quart of clean brake fluid to pass through system. Any rubber parts in hydraulic system which were exposed to contaminated fluid must be replaced.

MASTER CYLINDER
REPLACE

1. Disconnect master cylinder push rod from brake pedal.
2. Disconnect wire connector from brake warning pressure switch.
3. Disconnect brake lines from master cylinder.
4. Remove two master cylinder mounting nuts, then the master cylinder.
5. Reverse procedure to install.

1. FLUID LEVEL SENSOR
2. PROPORTIONER VALVE CAP ASSEMBLY
3. O-RING
4. SPRING
5. PROPORTIONER VALVE PISTON
6. PROPORTIONER VALVE SEAL
7. RESERVOIR CAP
8. DIAPHRAGM
9. SPRING PIN
10. RESERVOIR ASSEMBLY
11. O-RING
12. O-RING
13. RETAINER
14. PRIMARY PISTON ASSEMBLY
15. SECONDARY SEAL
16. SPRING RETAINER
17. PRIMARY SEAL
18. SECONDARY PISTON
19. SPRING
20. CYLINDER BODY

Fig. 22 Compact master cylinder assembly

MASTER CYLINDER SERVICE
COMPOSITE TYPE

Refer to **Figs. 2** and **22** when performing the following procedures.

Disassembly

1. Remove master cylinder from vehicle as follows:
   a. Disconnect and plug hydraulic lines.
   b. Remove two master cylinder attaching nuts, then the master cylinder.
2. Remove reservoir cover and diaphragm. Discard old brake fluid in reservoir.
3. Inspect cover and diaphragm. Replace if cut, cracked or deformed.
4. Remove fluid level switch, if equipped.
5. **On models with compact master cylinder,** remove proportioner valve assembly, **Fig. 22.**
6. Depress primary piston and remove lock ring.
7. Plug primary fluid outlet (outlet nearest to cowl when master cylinder is installed), then apply compressed air into secondary fluid outlet to remove primary and secondary pistons.
8. Remove spring retainer and seals from secondary piston.
9. Clamp master cylinder in a vise as shown in **Fig. 23**, then remove reservoir using a pry bar. Remove reservoir grommets.
10. Inspect master cylinder bore for corrosion. **Do not use abrasive material on master cylinder bore.** Replace if bore is corroded.

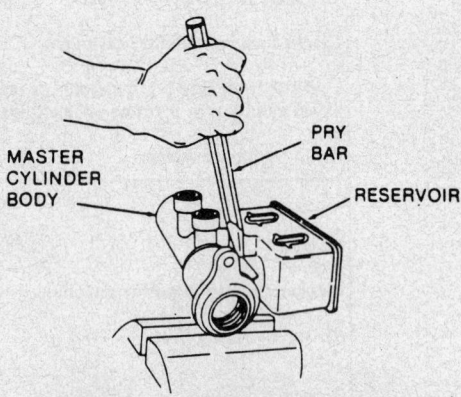

Fig. 23 Removing master cylinder reservoir. Composite type

Assembly

Clean all parts not included in repair kit with brake fluid. **Do not dry with compressed air.** Lubricate all rubber parts with clean brake fluid prior to installation.

1. Lubricate new reservoir grommets with silicone brake lube, then press grommets into master cylinder body. Ensure grommets are properly seated.
2. Lay reservoir upside down on flat, hard surface. Press master cylinder body onto reservoir using rocking motion.
3. Install new seals on secondary piston, then the spring retainer.
4. Install spring and secondary piston assembly into cylinder.

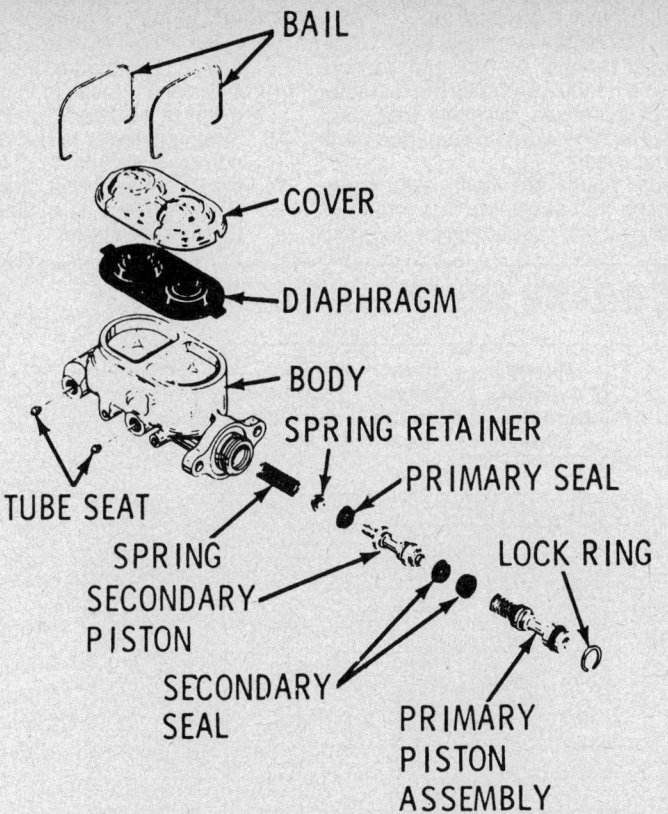

Fig. 24   Cast iron type master cylinder

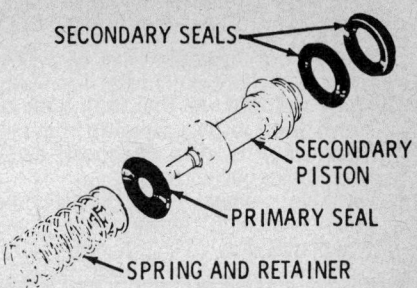

Fig. 25   Secondary piston and seals. Cast iron type master cylinder

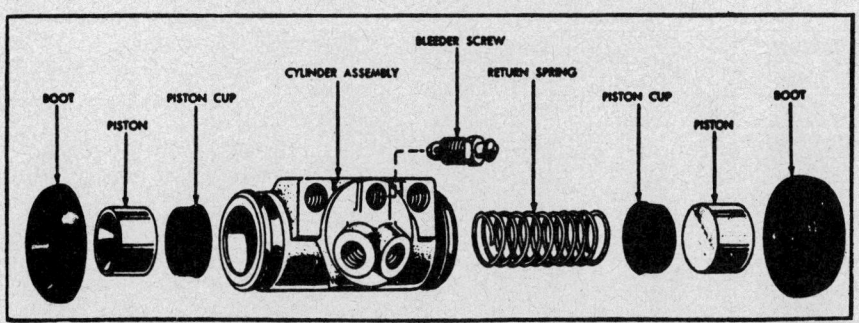

Fig. 26   Disassembled view of wheel cylinder (typical)

5. Install primary piston. Depress primary piston into cylinder, then install lock ring.
6. Install fluid level switch, if equipped.
7. **On models with compact master cylinder,** install proportioner valve assembly, **Fig. 22.**
8. Fit diaphragm into reservoir cover, then install cover onto reservoir.
9. Install master cylinder in vehicle by reversing steps 2a and 2b on "Disassembly" procedure. Bleed brakes.

CAST IRON TYPE

Refer to **Figs. 24 and 25** while performing the following procedures.

Disassembly

1. Remove master cylinder from vehicle.
2. Clean outside of master cylinder, then remove reservoir cover and diaphragm.

3. Turn master cylinder over, then pump pushrod by hand to remove any remaining brake fluid.
4. Clamp master cylinder in a vise, with vise jaws gripping mounting flange and fluid ports pointing up. **Do not clamp master cylinder body in vise.**
5. Remove lock ring and primary piston assembly from cylinder bore.
6. Apply compressed air to secondary outlet port to remove secondary piston spring and retainer.
7. Using a $^{13}/_{64}$ inch drill, enlarge hole in tube fitting insert of fluid outlet holes. Place a heavy washer over outlet hole, then thread a $^{1}/_{4}$ X 20 X $^{3}/_{4}$ screw into insert. Tighten screw until insert is unseated, then remove insert, screw and washer.
8. Remove primary and secondary seal from secondary piston.

Inspection

Clean all parts not included in repair kit with brake fluid. **Do not dry with compressed air.**
1. Inspect cylinder bore for scoring and corrosion. Replace master cylinder if necessary.
2. Polish discolored or stained cylinder with crocus cloth, then rinse in clean brake fluid. Ensure compensating port is clean.

Assembly

Lubricate all rubber parts with clean brake fluid prior to installation.
1. With master cylinder in a vise, insert brass tube fitting inserts from overhaul kit into outlet holes.
2. Using spare brake line tube, thread tube nut into outlet hole and turn down until tube fitting insert bottoms into outlet hole. Remove tube nut and inspect outlet hole for burrs.
3. Install inner secondary seal into groove in secondary piston.
4. Install primary seal over end of secondary piston, with flat side of seal against flange of piston.
5. Install outer secondary seal into groove in end of secondary piston.
6. Install secondary piston spring retainer into secondary piston spring, then place the retainer and spring over end of secondary piston, with retainer seated inside lip of primary cup.
7. Hold master cylinder with open end down, then place secondary piston assembly into bore, with spring seated against end of bore.
8. Clamp master cylinder in a vise with open end of bore facing up.
9. Insert new primary piston assembly, spring end first, into bore.
10. Hold primary piston down, then install lock ring in groove on inside of bore.
11. Install new reservoir diaphragm into reservoir cover with beaded side out, then secure cover onto cylinder.
12. Install master cylinder in vehicle. Bleed brakes.

WHEEL CYLINDER OVERHAUL

1. Raise and support vehicle.

2. Remove wheel, drum and brake shoes.
3. Disconnect hydraulic line at wheel cylinder. **Do not pull metal line away from cylinder, as this may kink or bend line.** Line will separate from cylinder when cylinder is moved away from brake backing plate.
4. Remove wheel cylinder-to-brake plate attaching screws, then the wheel cylinder.
5. Remove boots, pistons, springs and cups from cylinder, **Fig. 26.**
6. Clean all parts with brake fluid.
7. Inspect cylinder bore. A scored bore may be honed as long as the diameter is not increased by more than .005 inch. Replace worn or damaged parts as necessary.
8. Ensure hands are clean before proceeding with assembly. Lubricate cylinder wall and rubber cups with brake fluid, then install springs, cups, pistons and boots in housing.
9. Wipe end of hydraulic line to remove any foreign matter, then place wheel cylinder in position. Enter tubing into cylinder and start threads on fitting.
10. Secure cylinder to backing plate, then complete tightening of tubing fitting.
11. Install brake shoes, drum and wheel.
12. Bleed system as outlined previously, then adjust brakes.

HYDRAULIC BRAKE SPECIFICATIONS

Model	Year	Master Cylinder Bore Dia., Inch	Front Caliper Bore Dia., Inch	Rear Caliper Bore Dia., Inch	Wheel Cylinder Bore Dia., Inch
BUICK					
Century	1988–90	①	—	—	②
Electra	1988–89	③	2.52	—	.874
Estate Wagon	1988—90	1.125	2.952	—	1.00
LeSabre	1988–89	③	2.52	—	.874
Park Avenue	1988–89	③	2.52	—	.874
Reatta	1988–90	④	2.52	1.50	—
Regal	1988—90	.945	1.65	1.378	—
Riviera	1988–90	④	2.52	1.50	—
Skyhawk	1988	⑤	2.244	—	.625
	1989	.874	2.244	—	.625
Skylark	1988	⑥	2.244	—	.625
	1989–90	.874	2.244	—	.625
CADILLAC					
Brougham	1988–90	⑦	.930	—	1.00
Cimarron	1988	⑧	—	—	.625
DeVille	1990	③	2.52	—	.874
Eldorado	1988–90	⑦	2.52	1.50	—
Fleetwood (FWD)	1990	③	2.52	—	.874
Seville	1988–90	⑦	2.52	1.50	—
CHEVROLET					
Beretta	1988	.945	2.24	—	.748
	1989–90	.875	2.25	—	.748
Camaro	1988–90	⑨	⑩	1.60	.748
Caprice	1988–90	1.125	2.952	—	.748 ⑬
Cavalier	1988	.937	2.24	—	.625
	1989–90	.874	2.244	—	.625
Celebrity	1988	.875 ⑪	2.24	—	.687 ⑫
	1989–90	.874 ⑬	2.24	—	⑭
Corsica	1988	.945	2.24	—	.748
	1989–90	.875	2.25	—	.748
Corvette	1988–90	.862	1.50	1.60	—
Lumina	1990	.945	1.65	1.378	—
Monte Carlo	1988	.937	2.50	—	.750
Nova	1988	.889	2.04	1.27	.698
Sprint	1988	.750	2.01	—	.690
GEO					
Metro	1989–90	.810	1.889	—	.620
Prizm Except GSI	1990	.812	2.01	—	.690
Prizm GSI	1990	.874	2.13	1.19	—
Spectrum	1989	.810	2.13	—	.690
Storm	1990	⑮	2.00	—	.600

Continued

HYDRAULIC BRAKE SPECIFICATIONS—Continued

Model	Year	Master Cylinder Bore Dia., Inch	Front Caliper Bore Dia., Inch	Rear Caliper Bore Dia., Inch	Wheel Cylinder Bore Dia., Inch
OLDSMOBILE					
Calais	1988	⑯	—	—	.625
	1989–90	.874	2.244	—	.625
Custom Cruiser	1988–90	1.125	2.952	—	1.00
Cutlass Ciera	1988	.875 ⑪	2.24	—	.687
	1989–90	.874	2.244	—	⑭
Cutlass Ciera Wagon	1988–90	.875 ⑪	2.24	—	.812
Cutlass Supreme	1988–90	.945	1.65	1.378	—
Cutlass Supreme Classic (RWD)	1988	.9375	2.50	—	.750
	1989–90	.874 ⑬	2.24	—	⑭
Cutlass Supreme Cruiser (FWD)	1988	.875 ⑪	2.24	—	.687 ⑫
Firenza	1988	⑰	—	—	.625
Toronado	1988–90	⑱	2.52	1.50	—
Trofeo	1988–90	⑱	2.52	1.50	—
88	1988	③	2.52	—	.937
	1989–90	.937	2.52	—	.937
98	1988	③	2.52	—	.937
	1989–90	.937	2.52	—	.937
PONTIAC					
Bonneville	1988	③	2.52	—	.937
	1989–90	.937	2.52	—	.937
Fiero	1988	1.00	1.929	1.889	—
Firebird	1988	⑨	2.50	1.875	.748
	1989–90	⑨	2.5 ⑲	1.60	.748
Grand Am	1988	⑳	2.244	—	.625
Grand Am	1989–90	.874	2.244	—	.625
Grand Prix	1988–90	.945	1.65	1.378	—
LeMans	1988	.815	.685	—	.690
Sunbird	1988	.937	2.24	—	.625
	1989–90	.874	2.244	—	.625
Trans Am	1988	⑨	2.50	1.875	.748
	1989–90	⑨	2.5 ⑲	1.60	.748
6000	1988	.875 ⑪	2.244	1.92	.687 ⑫
	1989–90	.874 ⑬	2.244	1.92	⑭

①—Light duty, .874. Medium & heavy duty, .944.
②—Sedan/coupe, .689. Wagon: medium duty, .811, heavy duty, .748.
③—Less anti-lock brakes main bore, .945, Quick Take Up bore, 1.252. w/anti-lock brakes, .937.
④—Main bore, 1.126, Quick Take Up bore, 1.574. w/anti-lock brakes, 1.00.
⑤—VIN code prior to 409093, .937. After 409094, .874.
⑥—VIN code prior to 011292, .937. After 011292, .874.
⑦—Main bore, 1.126. Quick Take Up bore, 1.574.
⑧—VIN code prior to 502420, .937. After 502419, .874.
⑨—Disc & drum system, .945. Four wheel disc system, 1.00.

⑩—Standard, 2.52. Heavy duty, 1.50.
⑪—Heavy duty, .937.
⑫—Heavy duty wagon, .812.
⑬—Heavy duty, .944.
⑭—Coupe/sedan standard, .689. Coupe/sedan medium duty & wagon standard, .811. All heavy duty, .748.
⑮—Single overhead cam, .810. Dual overhead cam, .875.
⑯—VIN code prior to 216877, .937. After 216876, .874.
⑰—VIN code prior to 304666, .937. After 304666, .874.
⑱—Less anti-lock brakes main bore, 1.126, Quick Take Up bore, 1.574. Anti-lock brake system. 1.00.
⑲—Heavy duty, 1.50.
⑳—VIN code prior to 637905, .937. After 637904, .874.

POWER BRAKE UNITS

INDEX

APPLICATIONS

BUICK

Century	Tandem diaphragm
Electra	Tandem diaphragm
Estate Wagon	Tandem diaphragm
LeSabre	Tandem diaphragm
Park Avenue	Tandem diaphragm
Reatta	Tandem diaphragm
Regal	Tandem diaphragm
Riviera	Tandem diaphragm
Skyhawk	Tandem diaphragm
Skylark	Tandem diaphragm

CADILLAC

Brougham	Tandem diaphragm
Cimarron	Tandem diaphragm
DeVille	Tandem diaphragm
Eldorado	Tandem diaphragm
Fleetwood (FWD)	Tandem diaphragm
Seville	Tandem diaphragm

CHEVROLET

Beretta	Tandem diaphragm
Camaro	Tandem diaphragm
Caprice	Tandem diaphragm
Cavalier	Tandem diaphragm
Celebrity	Tandem diaphragm
Corsica	Tandem diaphragm
Corvette	Single diaphragm
Lumina	Tandem diaphragm
Monte Carlo	Tandem diaphragm
Nova	Single diaphragm
Sprint	Single diaphragm

GEO

Metro	Single diaphragm
Prizm	Single diaphragm
Spectrum	Single diaphragm
Storm	Single diaphragm

OLDSMOBILE

Calais	Tandem diaphragm
Custom Cruiser	Tandem diaphragm
Cutlass Ciera	Tandem diaphragm
Cutlass Ciera Wagon	Tandem diaphragm
Cutlass Supreme	Tandem diaphragm
Cutlass Supreme Classic (RWD)	Tandem diaphragm
Cutlass Supreme Cruiser (FWD)	Tandem diaphragm
Firenza	Tandem diaphragm
Toronado	Tandem diaphragm
Trofeo	Tandem diaphragm
88	Tandem diaphragm
98	Tandem diaphragm

PONTIAC

Bonneville	Tandem diaphragm
Fiero	Tandem diaphragm
Firebird	Tandem diaphragm
Grand Am	Tandem diaphragm
Grand Prix	Tandem diaphragm
LeMans	Single diaphragm
Sunbird	Tandem diaphragm
Trans Am	Tandem diaphragm
6000	Tandem diaphragm

GENERAL SERVICE

Two basic types of power assist mechanisms are used: vacuum assist diaphragm assemblies, which use engine vacuum or, in some cases vacuum pressure developed by an external vacuum pump. The second type is a hydraulic pressure assist mechanism, which use pressure developed by an external pump (usually the power steering pump). Both systems act to increase the force exerted on the master cylinder piston by the operator. This in turn increases the hydraulic pressure delivered to the wheel cylinders, while decreasing driver effort necessary to obtain acceptable stopping performance.

Vacuum assist units are similar in operation and get their energy by opposing engine vacuum to atmospheric pressure. A piston and cylinder, flexible diaphragm (bellows) utilize this energy to provide brake assistance. The fundamental difference between these types of vacuum assist systems lies simply in how the diaphragm within the power unit is suspended when the brakes are not applied.

In order to properly diagnose vacuum assist system malfunctions it is important to know whether the diaphragm within a power unit is air suspended or vacuum suspended. Air-suspended units are under atmospheric pressure until the brakes are applied. Engine vacuum is then admitted, causing the piston or diaphragm to move (or the bellows to collapse). Vacuum-suspended types are balanced with engine vacuum until the brake pedal is depressed, allowing atmospheric pressure to unbalance the unit and apply force to the brake system.

Regardless of whether the brakes are vacuum or hydraulically assisted, certain general service procedures apply. Only specified, clean brake fluid should be used in brake system. On hydro boost systems, use of the specified hydraulic fluid in the boost circuit is essential to proper system operation. Care must be taken not to mix the fluids of the two separate operating circuits. Use of improper fluids, or contaminated fluid will cause damage to the seals and valves.

PRECAUTIONS

1. After disassembling a power brake unit, soak all metal parts in solvent.
2. Use only alcohol on parts containing rubber. After the parts have been thoroughly cleaned and rinsed in solvent, they should be rewashed in clean alcohol before assembly.
3. Use an compressed air to blow dirt and cleaning fluid from the recesses and internal passages.
4. Always use all the parts furnished in the repair kit.
5. **Use extreme caution when disassembling power assist mechanisms, as suddenly releasing internal spring tension could cause damage or personal injury.**
6. **On models with hydro-boost assist systems,** do not disassemble the accumulator. If the accumulator is damaged or diagnosed as defective, it must be replaced as an assembly.

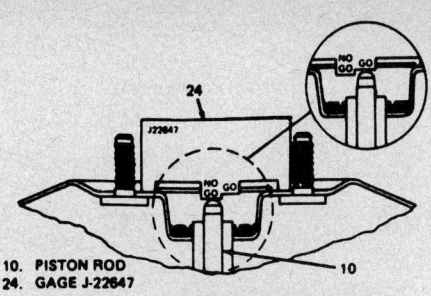

10. PISTON ROD
24. GAGE J-22647

Fig. 1 Master cylinder pushrod adjustment. Delco-Moraine type vacuum booster

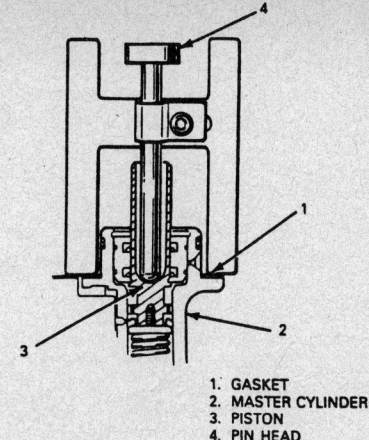

1. GASKET
2. MASTER CYLINDER
3. PISTON
4. PIN HEAD

Fig. 2 Master cylinder adjustment tool

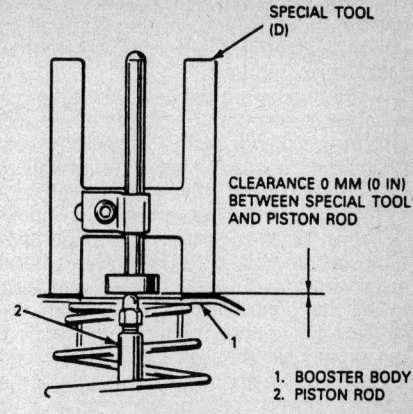

1. BOOSTER BODY
2. PISTON ROD

Fig. 3 Booster piston rod adjustment

PUSHROD ADJUSTMENT

Proper adjustment of the master cylinder pushrod is necessary to ensure proper operation of the power brake system. A pushrod that is too long will cause the master cylinder piston to close off the compensating port, preventing hydraulic pressure from being released and resulting in brake drag. A pushrod that is too short will cause excessive brake pedal travel and cause groaning noises to come from the booster when the brakes are applied. A properly adjusted pushrod that remains assembled to the booster with which it was matched during production should not require service adjustment. However, if the booster, master cylinder or pushrod are serviced, the pushrod may require adjustment.

There are two methods that can be used to check for proper pushrod length and installation: the gauge method and air method. Usually, if the power unit pushrod requires adjustment, use the power unit repair kit gauge. The gauge measures from the end of the pushrod to the power unit shell.

GAUGE METHOD
Delco-Moraine Type

On these models, the master cylinder pushrod length is fixed and is usually only checked after the unit has been overhauled.

1. Assemble booster unit and install pushrod, ensuring pushrod is fully seated.
2. Position go/no go gauge furnished in repair kit over pushrod as shown in **Fig. 1**
3. If pushrod height is not within limits of gauge, install service adjustable pushrod and adjust rod to obtain correct height.
4. Install power unit and check adjustment, ensuring master cylinder compensating port is open with engine running and brake pedal released.

Single Diaphragm Type

This unit is used on late model Chevrolet Sprint, GEO Metro & Spectrum. The length of the booster piston rod is adjusted to provide specified clearance between the piston rod end and master cylinder piston. Before making an adjustment, push

piston rod several times to ensure reaction disc is in place. Ensure gasket is installed to master cylinder and keep inside of booster at atmospheric pressure.

1. Place booster pin rod gauge No. J-34873 or equivalent on master cylinder and push pin until it contacts piston, **Fig. 2**.
2. Turn tool upside down and place it on booster. Adjust booster piston rod length until rod end contacts pin head.
3. Adjust clearance by turning adjusting bolt of piston rod, **Fig. 3**. If negative pressure is applied to booster with engine at idle, piston to piston rod clearance should measure 0.004–0.020 inch.

AIR METHOD

1. Be sure master cylinder attaching nuts are tight.
2. Remove master cylinder filler cap.
3. With brake released, force compressed air into the hydraulic outlet of the master cylinder. **Regulate air pressure to a value of approximately 5 psi, to prevent spraying brake fluid from master cylinder. Care must be taken not to allow brake fluid to contact painted surfaces of vehicle, skin or eyes, as damage or personal injury will result.**
4. If air passes through the compensating port, which is the smaller of the two holes in the bottom of the master cylinder reservoir, the adjustment is satisfactory.
5. If air does not flow through the compensating port, adjust the pushrod as required, either by means of the adjustment screw (if provided) or by adding shims between the master cylinder and power unit shell until the air flows freely.
6. Reconnect brake lines and bleed system.

POWER BOOSTER
REPLACE

1. Disconnect brake unit push rod from brake pedal.
2. Remove two master cylinder to power brake unit mounting nuts.
3. Position master cylinder away from brake unit, leaving brake lines attached. **Do not bend or kink brake lines.**
4. Disconnect vacuum hose from vacuum check valve. Cap all open hose ends and fittings to prevent contamination.
5. Remove power brake unit to dash panel attaching nuts, then the brake unit.
6. Reverse procedure to install.

DELCO-MORAINE SINGLE DIAPHRAGM TYPE
DESCRIPTION

This power brake unit is a suspended type vacuum brake booster which utilizes engine intake manifold vacuum and atmospheric pressure to assist in braking, **Fig. 4.**

The unit consists of a vacuum power section and a hydraulic master cylinder section. The vacuum power section contains a power piston with rolling diaphragm mechanism and power piston return spring.

The control valve consists of an air valve and floating vacuum control valve assembly. The reaction mechanism consists of a hydraulic piston, reaction plate and a series of levers. The valve operating rod, (which operates the air valve), projects from the power section and is connected to the brake pedal linkage.

A vacuum check valve, attached to the front vacuum chamber and connected to the intake manifold, traps vacuum in the power unit at the highest level of vacuum. In addition, some models are equipped with a vacuum switch mounted on the front housing. The switch serves to illuminate the brake failure warning lamp when vacuum applied to the booster falls below a predetermined level.

As the brakes are applied, the valve operating rod and control piston move forward in the power piston assembly. This action compresses the valve return spring, bringing the poppet valve into contact with the vacuum valve seat in the valve housing. When this is done the vacuum port will be closed. Any additional movement of the valve operating rod in the applied direction, moves the control valve away from the poppet valve to open the atmospheric port. This admits air through the air filter and passages to the chamber at the right of the vacuum power piston assembly. This creates vacuum on the left side of the diaphragm and atmospheric pressure on the right side. Because of this a force is developed, moving the vacuum power piston assembly, master cylinder pushrod, and hydraulic piston to the left. The compensating port closes and hydraulic fluid is forced through the residual check valve and brake tubes into the brake wheel cylinders.

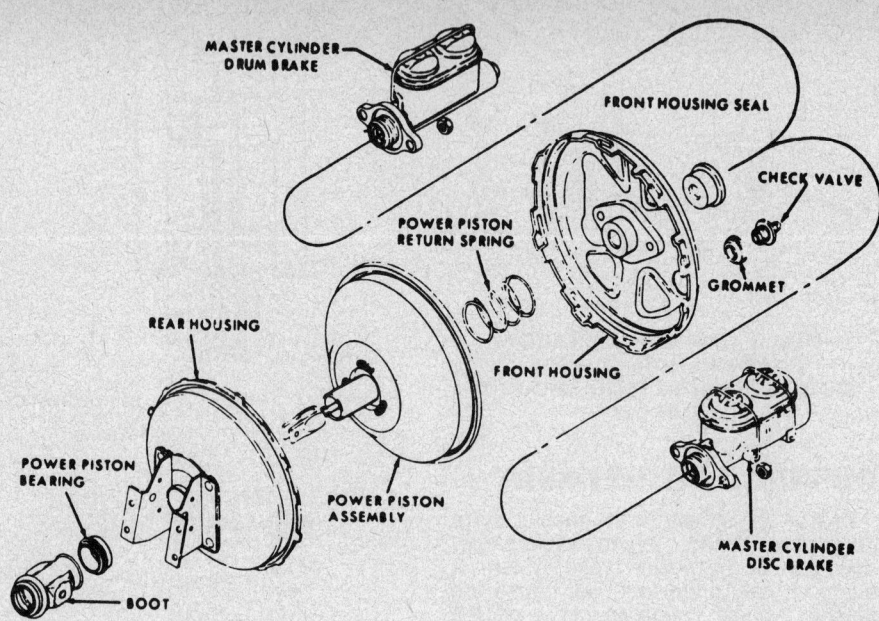

TROUBLESHOOTING
Hard Pedal

1. Internal vacuum leak.
2. Faulty control valve.

Brakes Grab

1. Faulty control valve.

Slow Or No Release

1. Faulty pushrod adjustment.
2. Bind in linkage.

OVERHAUL

1. Remove piston rod from booster, **Fig. 5**, then push rod clevis and nut.
2. Attach booster to special tool, **Fig. 6**, and scribe a mark on booster No. 1 and No. 2 body halves for assemble reference. Turn thumbscrew enough to rotate body halves.
3. Turn thumbscrew out enough to allow body halves to separate, then remove piston return spring. **Hold both bodies to prevent either body from jumping off by spring force.**
4. Remove boot, air cleaner elements, air cleaner separator and booster piston from body No. 2, then remove diaphragm from booster piston by hand. **Do not use a screwdriver or other sharp tool.**
5. Compress air valve spring, by moving rod up or down, **Fig. 7**, then remove valve stopper key.
6. Remove booster air valve assembly from booster piston, then reaction disc.
7. Remove oil seal from booster No. 2 body, **Fig. 8**, and discard.
8. Refer to **Fig. 9**, before assembling booster, and follow recommended inspection and replacement of parts.

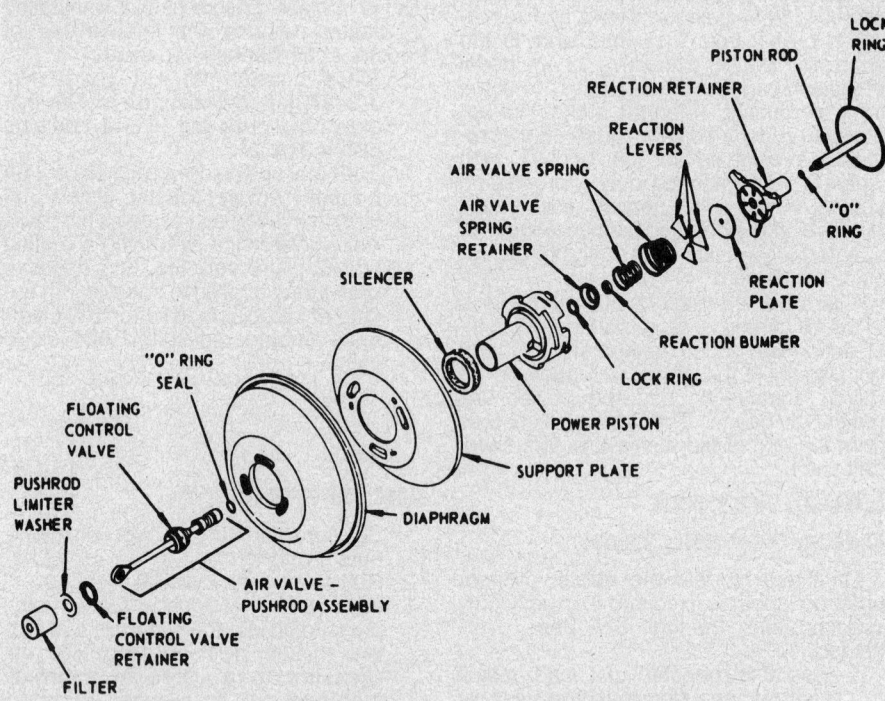

Fig. 4   Delco-Moraine single diaphragm booster

9. Reverse procedure to assemble, noting the following:
   a. Apply silicone grease on oil seal before assembling.
   b. Apply silicone grease to entire mating surface of piston and diaphragm.
   c. Ensure diaphragm is seated securely in its outer groove of body No. 2. Use care when assembling body halves.
   d. Ensure diaphragm is not caught by projections around body No. 1, and that halves mate correctly before rotating tool.

DELCO-MORAINE TANDEM DIAPHRAGM TYPE
DESCRIPTION

This unit utilizes a vacuum power chamber, consisting of a front and rear shell, housing divider, front and rear diaphragm, plate assemblies, hydraulic pushrod and a diaphragm return spring, **Figs. 10 and 11.**

The unit operates in much the same manner as the single diaphragm unit described previously. The diaphragm and

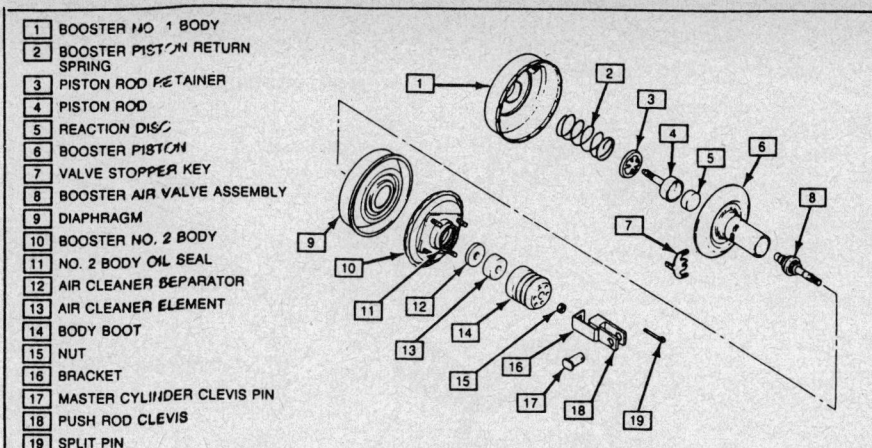

1. BOOSTER NO. 1 BODY
2. BOOSTER PISTON RETURN SPRING
3. PISTON ROD RETAINER
4. PISTON ROD
5. REACTION DISC
6. BOOSTER PISTON
7. VALVE STOPPER KEY
8. BOOSTER AIR VALVE ASSEMBLY
9. DIAPHRAGM
10. BOOSTER NO. 2 BODY
11. NO. 2 BODY OIL SEAL
12. AIR CLEANER SEPARATOR
13. AIR CLEANER ELEMENT
14. BODY BOOT
15. NUT
16. BRACKET
17. MASTER CYLINDER CLEVIS PIN
18. PUSH ROD CLEVIS
19. SPLIT PIN

Fig. 5   Single diaphragm booster

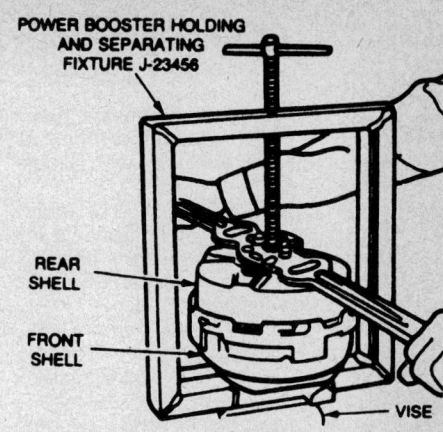

Fig. 6   Typical brake booster holding & support fixture installation. Delco-Moraine units

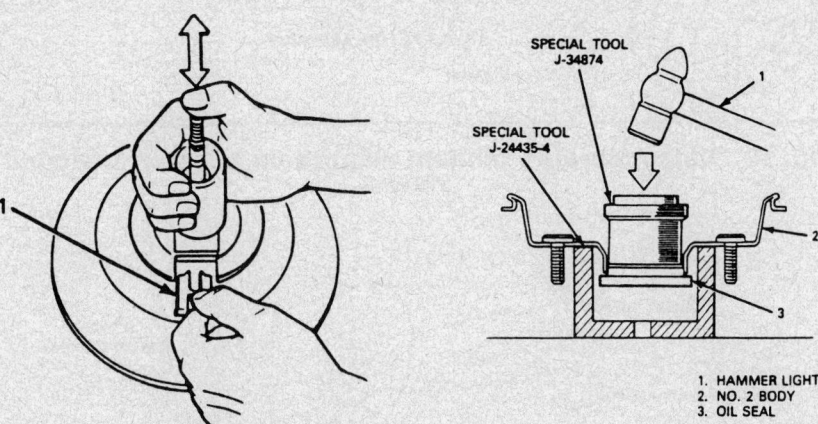

Fig. 7   Removal of valve stopper key

Fig. 8   Oil seal removal tool

1. HAMMER LIGHTLY
2. NO. 2 BODY
3. OIL SEAL

Part	Inspect For	Corrective Action
1. Booster piston	Cracks, distortion or damage.	Replace.
2. Air valve assembly (Control valve and spring)	Damaged or worn seal surfaces.	Replace.
3. Reaction disc	Damage or wear.	Replace.
4. Diaphragm, boot, and rubber	Damage.	Replace.
5. Piston rod and retainer	Damage or bend.	Replace.
6. Booster No. 1 & No. 2 body	1. Scratches, scores, pits, dents, or other damage affecting rolling or sealing of diaphragm or other seals.	Replace, unless easily repaired.
	2. Cracks, damage at ears, damaged threads on studs.	Replace, unless easily repaired.
	3. Bent or nicked locking lugs.	Replace, unless easily repaired.
	4. Loose studs.	Replace.
7. Air filters and separator	Dirt.	Replace.

Fig. 9   Booster inspection chart

plate assemblies utilize the pressure differential between the engine intake manifold vacuum and atmospheric pressure to assist in braking.

TROUBLESHOOTING
Hard Pedal
1. Internal vacuum leak.

2. Faulty control valve.

Brakes Grab
1. Faulty control valve.

Slow Or No Release
1. Faulty pushrod adjustment.
2. Bind in linkage.

OVERHAUL
Disassembly
1. Remove pedal pushrod boot, silencer, check valve, vacuum switch and grommets, as equipped, then the front housing seal.
2. Scribe matching marks between front and rear housing sections, then mount booster assembly in suitable holding fixture with rear housing facing up.
3. Apply pressure to housing with holding fixture forcing screw and rotate rear housing counterclockwise to unlock housing halves.
4. Slowly release spring tension, then remove booster assembly from holding fixture. **Do not allow spring tension to release suddenly, as damage or personal injury may result.**
5. Lift off rear housing, then remove primary power piston bearing from housing.
6. Remove power piston group and return spring from front housing, **Fig. 10.**
7. Remove master cylinder piston rod and reaction retainer from front of piston, then the silencer from the rear of the assembly, **Fig. 11.**
8. Hold piston assembly at edges of divider and strike pedal pushrod against work surface to dislodge diaphragm retainer.
9. Remove primary diaphragm and support plate, secondary power piston bearing and housing divider, then the secondary diaphragm and support plate from piston, noting installation position of components, **Fig. 12.**
10. Clean and inspect components as outlined in "General Service," then replace as needed. **Do not disassemble power piston. If service is required, power piston must be replaced as an assembly.**

Assembly
1. Position power piston assembly on work surface with pedal pushrod facing up.

2. Lubricate inner lip of secondary diaphragm, fit diaphragm over support plate, then install assembly onto power piston.

3. Install secondary power piston bearing into divider with flat surface of bearing on side of divider with 6 lugs, **Fig. 11.**

4. Install guide sleeve J-28458 or equivalent over power piston, lubricate inner diameter of secondary bearing, then install divider assembly with lugged side facing up.

5. Lubricate inner lip of primary diaphragm. Fit diaphragm over support plate, then install diaphragm assembly on power piston.

6. Ensure diaphragms and support plates are properly positioned, install new diaphragm retainer, then seat retainer on power piston using guide sleeve J-28458 or equivalent and hammer.

7. Install primary power piston bearing in rear housing, then lubricate inner diameter of bearing.

8. Mount front housing in holding fixture J-23456 or equivalent, then install diaphragm return spring, power piston group and the rear housing assembly, **Fig. 10.**

9. Ensure housing scribe marks are properly aligned, then press housing sections together with holding fixture forcing screw. **Assembly of housing can be facilitated by applying vacuum to front housing port. Block opening for vacuum switch, if equipped.**

10. Rotate rear housing clockwise to lock housing, then stake two tabs 180° apart to secure assembly. Do not stake tabs which have previously been used.

11. Lubricate grommets and front seal, install grommets, check valve and vacuum switch, as equipped, then the front housing seal.

12. Install silencer and pedal pushrod boot.

GIRLOCK SINGLE DIAPHRAGM TYPE
DESCRIPTION

This booster is a single diaphragm, vacuum suspended un it with a lightweight cast alloy housing, **Fig. 12.** Vacuum is applied to the front and rear housings. When the brake pedal is released, negative pressure is equalized on both sides of the diaphragm and power piston assembly. Spring tension holds the piston at the rest position. When the brakes are applied, the atmospheric port in the power piston is opened. Negative pressure in the front chamber pulls the diaphragm and vacuum piston assembly, reaction disc and output rod forward. Pressure on the master cylinder piston is increased. When the brakes are released, the atmospheric port in the valve assembly is closed. Negative pressure is equalized on both sides of the diaphragm and piston assembly. Spring tension forces the piston back to the rest position. When the atmospheric port is

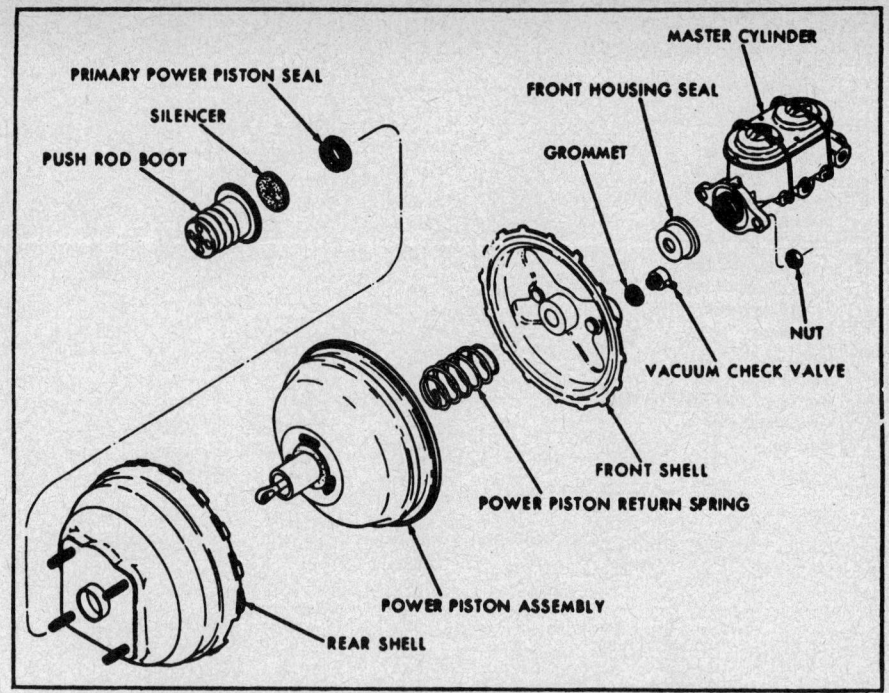

Fig. 10 Delco-Moraine tandem diaphragm booster exploded view

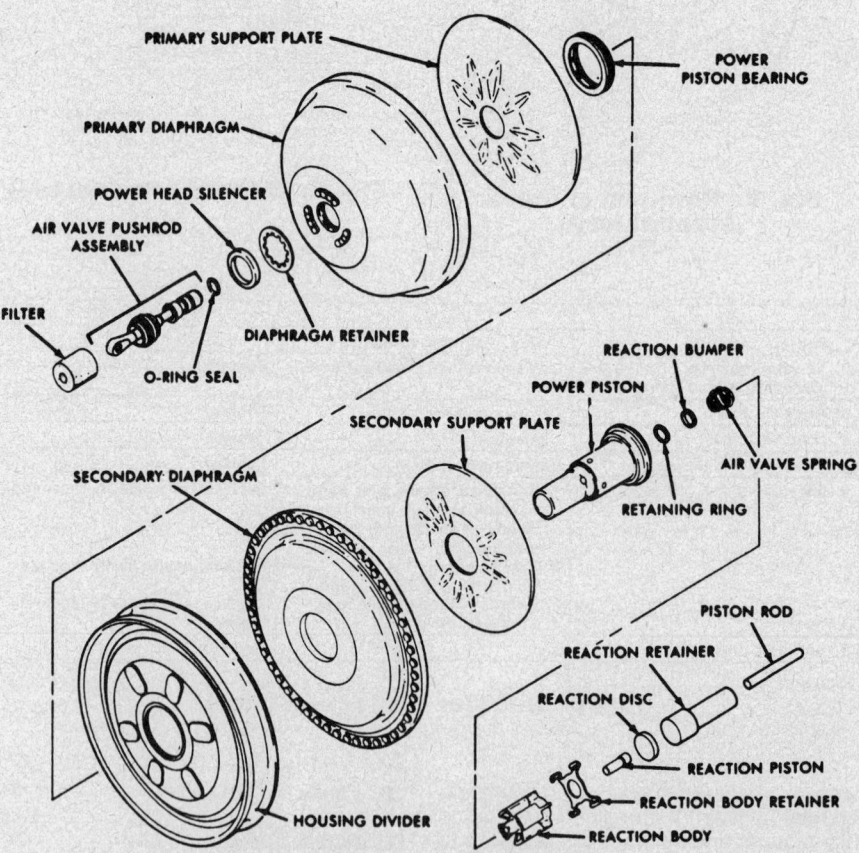

Fig. 11 Power head assembly exploded view. Delco-Moraine tandem diaphragm booster

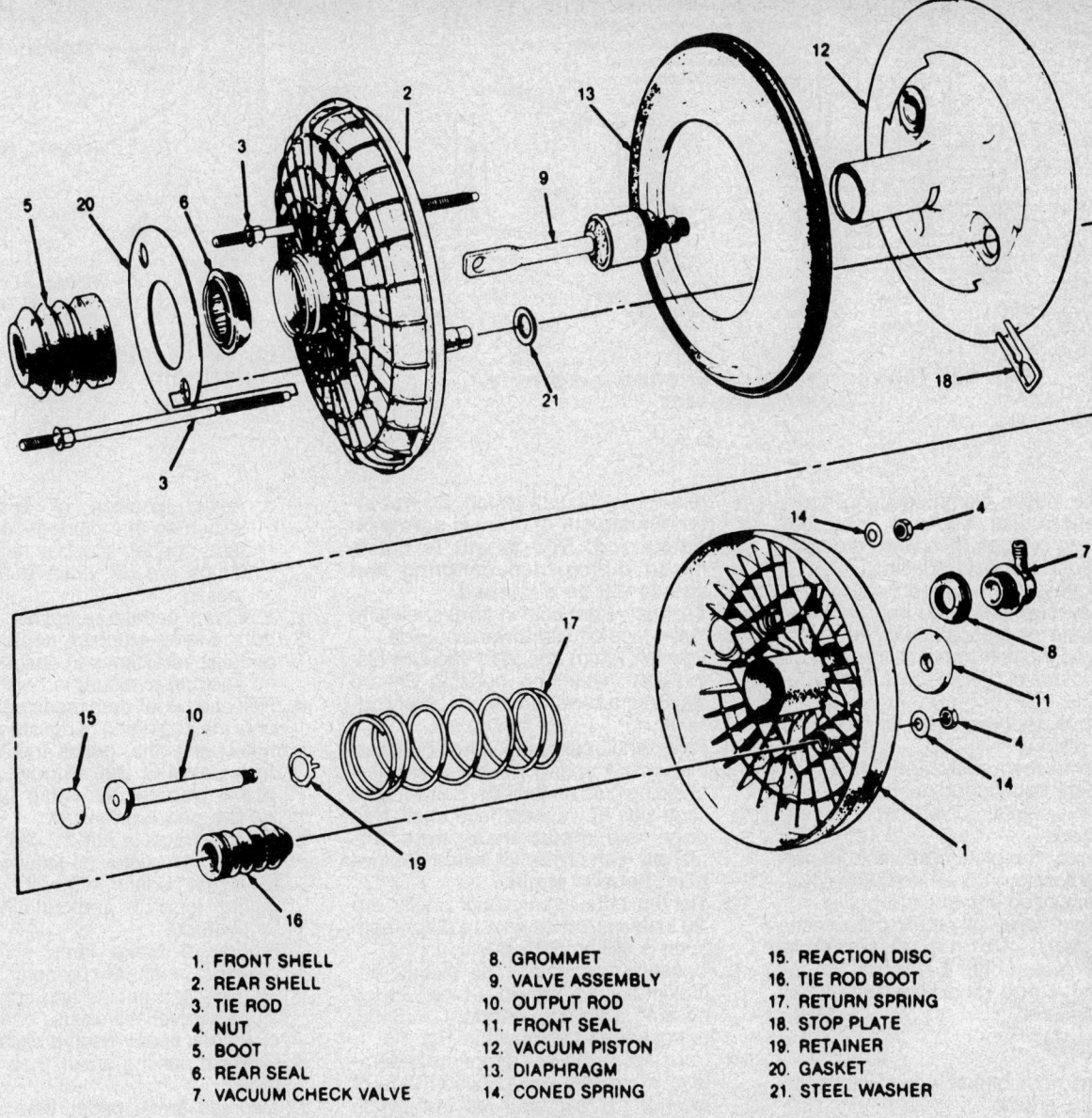

1. FRONT SHELL
2. REAR SHELL
3. TIE ROD
4. NUT
5. BOOT
6. REAR SEAL
7. VACUUM CHECK VALVE

8. GROMMET
9. VALVE ASSEMBLY
10. OUTPUT ROD
11. FRONT SEAL
12. VACUUM PISTON
13. DIAPHRAGM
14. CONED SPRING

15. REACTION DISC
16. TIE ROD BOOT
17. RETURN SPRING
18. STOP PLATE
19. RETAINER
20. GASKET
21. STEEL WASHER

Fig. 12 Girlock brake booster exploded view

opened, air is drawn into the rear chamber through a filter in the valve assembly.

TROUBLESHOOTING
Brakes Grab

1. Contaminated, damaged or dirty linings.
2. Damaged booster.
3. Improperly assembled booster valve.

Excessive Pedal Effort

1. Leak in booster vacuum supply system.
2. Glazed linings.
3. Restricted filter or booster valve air passage.
4. Damaged booster or improperly assembled booster valve.

Brakes Slow To Respond

1. Restricted filter or booster valve air passage.
2. Contaminated brake fluid.
3. Leak in booster vacuum supply system.
4. Damaged booster or improperly assembled booster valve.

Brakes Slow To Release Or Drag

1. Damaged booster assembly.
2. Improperly assembled booster valve.
3. Pedal linkage damaged or improperly adjusted.
4. Restricted booster air passage.
5. Insufficient caliper guide lubrication; damaged or defective calipers.
6. Contaminated brake fluid.

OVERHAUL
Disassembly

1. Remove vacuum check valve from front housing.
2. Loosen tie rod nuts several turns (approximately 1/2 inch), but do not remove nuts.
3. Pry housing shells apart using a thin blade screw driver, taking care not to chip or mar housing shells, or cut diaphragm.
4. Clamp housing shells together with suitable holding fixtures, then remove tie rod nuts and spring washers. **Failure to secure housing shells prior to removing tie rod nuts may allow housing shells to separate due to spring tension, causing damage and/or personal injury.**

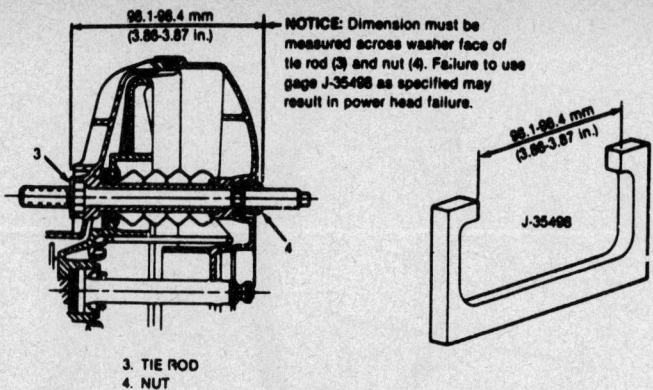

Fig. 13   Measuring booster shell assembly. Girlock booster

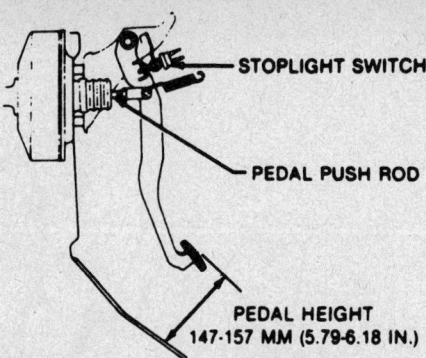

Fig. 14   Typical brake pedal adjustment. Chevrolet Nova

5. Slowly loosen clamp securing housing shells, then separate front shell and remove return spring, grommet and front seal from housing.
6. Remove pedal pushrod boot, gasket and tie rods from rear shell, **Fig. 12.**
7. Separate diaphragm bead from rear shell, tie rod boots from posts on shell, then remove vacuum piston assembly.
8. Remove diaphragm and tie rod boots from piston.
9. Remove rear seal from shell and washers from tie rod posts.
10. Remove output rod, retainer and reaction disc.
11. Remove stop plate from vacuum piston, pressing on open end while pulling on closed end of plate.
12. Remove valve assembly from vacuum piston. **Do not disassemble valve assembly. If service is required, entire valve assembly must be replaced.**

Assembly

Lubricate components where indicated with silicone grease.
1. Lubricate outer surface of valve assembly, then insert valve into vacuum piston and secure valve with stop plate, **Fig. 12.** Ensure plate is in fully locked position.
2. Lubricate reaction disc, then install disc in vacuum piston.
3. Install new tie rod boots in openings in vacuum piston, then liberally coat insides of boots with silicone grease.
4. Lubricate outer lip of diaphragm, then fit diaphragm into vacuum piston.
5. Press rear seal into shell, lubricate inner diameter of seal, then install washers over tie rod posts on rear shell.
6. Mount vacuum piston assembly in rear shell, pushing tie rod boots over posts. Ensure diaphragm bead is properly located around perimeter of shell.
7. Install tie rods through bores in rear shell.
8. Mount rear shell assembly in fixture J-23456-51A or equivalent, lubricate output rod, then install rod and new

retainer in vacuum piston. **Do not alter adjustment of convex screw on output rod. Rod length is determined during manufacturing and should not be disturbed.**
9. Seat new front seal in front shell with metal face of seal toward outside.
10. Position return spring in vacuum piston, then install front housing. Ensure diaphragm bead remains properly positioned.
11. Press shell halves together by hand, then install spring washers and new retaining nuts on tie rods. Ensure concave side of washers face shell. **Use only new replacement nuts furnished with repair kit when assembling booster shells.**
12. Tighten nuts evenly until shells are .20 inch apart, then ensure diaphragm bead is still properly positioned.
13. Continue tightening nuts evenly, approximately 1/2 turn at a time. Gauge housing assembly with tool J-35498, or equivalent as shown in **Fig. 13.**
14. Housing shells are properly assembled when distance between face of washer (3) and face of nut (4) is 3.87-4.86 inches, **Fig. 13.**
15. Reverse steps 1 and 2 of disassembly procedure to complete assembly.

TOYOTA/GM SINGLE DIAPHRAGM TYPE

ADJUSTMENTS
Brake Pedal

1. With engine running and brake pedal in rest position, measure distance between face of pedal and floor mat, **Fig. 14.**
2. If distance is not 5.79-6.18 inches, adjust pedal height as follows:
   a. Remove left lower instrument panel trim section and air duct.
   b. Loosen stop lamp switch sufficiently to gain clearance for pedal adjustment.
   c. Loosen locknut and rotate pedal pushrod as needed to obtain specified pedal height, then tighten locknut.

   d. Adjust position of brake light switch so that plunger lightly contacts pedal stopper and brake lamps are off when pedal is released.
   e. Check pedal free travel.
3. With engine stopped, depress brake pedal several times to ensure there is no vacuum pressure in booster.
4. Release pedal, then press pedal down until the beginning of resistance is felt, measuring the pedal travel. **Pedal free travel is the amount that the brake booster air valve is moved by the pedal pushrod.**
5. If pedal travel is not .12-.24 inch, adjust pedal freeplay as follows:
   a. Adjust pedal free travel by loosening locknut and rotating pedal pushrod.
   b. Ensure brake lamp switch and pedal height are properly adjusted, then start engine and confirm that free travel still exists.
   c. Check pedal reserve distance.
6. Release parking brake, then start engine.
7. Depress brake pedal, then measure distance from face of pedal to floor mat. If pedal reserve distance is not more than 2.56 inch with an applied force of 110.2 lbs., check and repair brake system as needed.

Booster Pushrod

The following adjustment procedure is performed with the brake booster removed, using gauge J-34873-A or equivalent. This procedure should produce a clearance of .004-.020 inch between booster pushrod and master cylinder piston, with idling vacuum applied to booster.
1. Position gauge on rear of master cylinder, with gasket in place, **Fig. 15.**
2. Lower gauge pin until lightly contacting master cylinder piston, then secure position of gauge pin.
3. Invert gauge and position gauge over pushrod on booster, **Fig. 16.**
4. Adjust length of pushrod so that tip of pushrod lightly contacts head of gauge pin with gauge resting on booster shell.

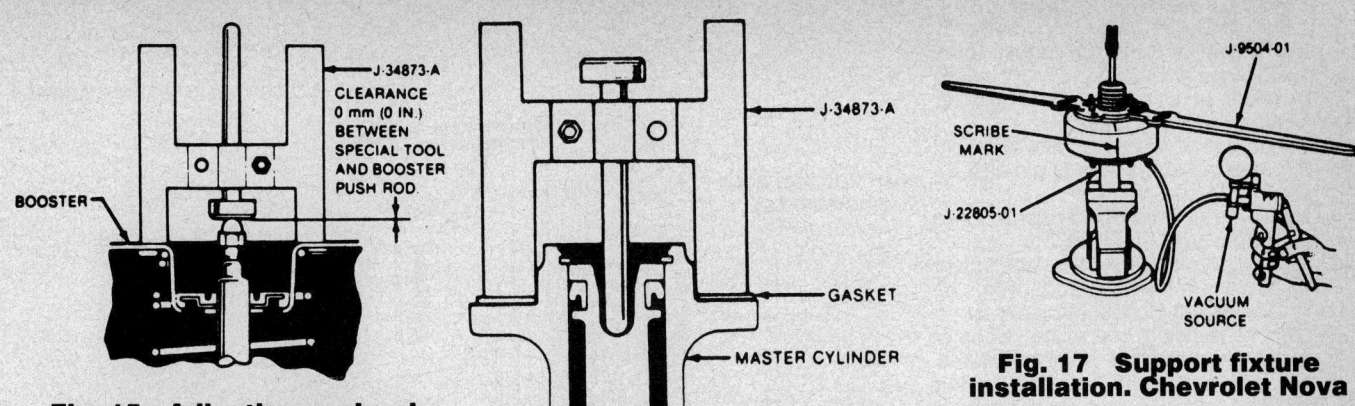

Fig. 15   Adjusting pushrod gauge on master cylinder. Chevrolet Nova

Fig. 16   Checking pushrod height. Chevrolet Nova

Fig. 17   Support fixture installation. Chevrolet Nova

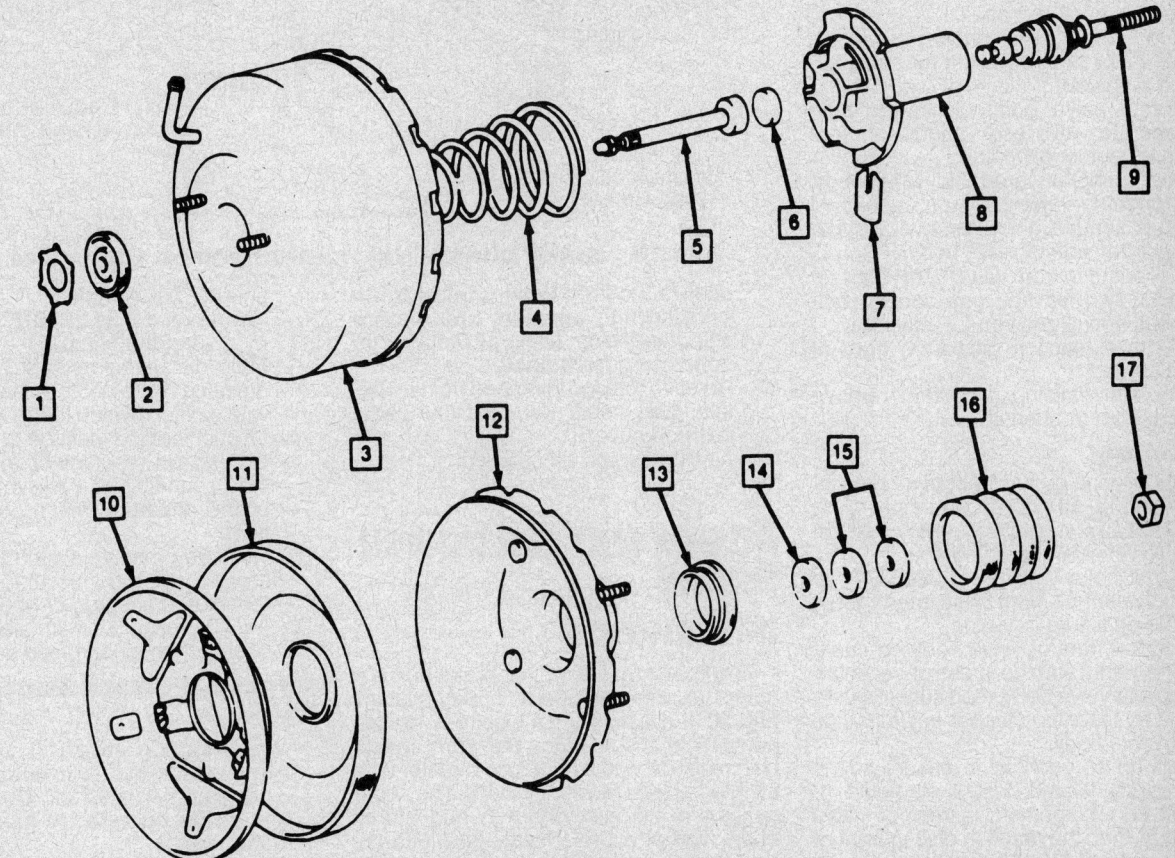

Fig. 18   Toyota/GM brake booster exploded view

TROUBLESHOOTING

Low Or Spongy Brake Pedal

1. Worn linings.
2. Air, or leaks in hydraulic system.
3. Defective master cylinder.
4. Defective wheel cylinder or calipers.
5. Improperly adjusted pedal linkage or booster pushrod.
6. Defective rear brake adjuster.

Brakes Drag

1. Improperly adjusted parking brake, or binding cables.

2. Improperly adjusted, or binding pedal linkage.
3. Improperly adjusted booster pushrod.
4. Defective booster return spring.
5. Sticking caliper or wheel cylinder piston.
6. Defective master cylinder.

Brakes Grab

1. Contaminated, worn, or defective brake linings.
2. Drum or brake rotor out of round.
3. Defective brake booster.

Hard Pedal/Brakes Inefficient

1. Contaminated, glazed, or defective brake linings.
2. Frozen caliper piston.
3. Defective vacuum pump, or leak in booster vacuum supply system.
4. Defective brake booster.

OVERHAUL

Disassembly

1. Attach holding fixture J-22805-01 or equivalent to front of booster, then

mount fixture in vise, **Fig. 17.** Mounting holes of holding fixture may have to be elongated toward inside in order to accommodate booster master cylinder studs.

2. Scribe matching marks between front and rear booster shells to aid assembly.
3. Remove nut from pedal pushrod and boot from rear shell, **Fig. 18.**
4. Attach lever J-9504-01 or equivalent to booster mounting studs, **Fig. 17.** Rotate rear shell counterclockwise to unlock housing, separate booster shells, then remove holding fixtures. **Do not suddenly release spring tension when separating booster shells.**
5. Remove diaphragm spring and pushrod from front shell.
6. Remove diaphragm and piston assembly from rear shell.
7. Support rear shell inboard of mounting studs, then drive out rear seal using a spacer.
8. Rotate valve body clockwise, then separate valve body and diaphragm from booster piston.
9. Push pedal pushrod into valve body, supporting valve body on cushioned work surface, then remove stopper key from side of valve body.
10. Pull pushrod from valve body, then remove two felt and one sponge element, noting position for assembly.
11. Remove reaction disc from front of valve body.
12. Pry out retaining ring, then remove seal from front shell.

Assembly

Apply silicone grease to components indicated in **Fig. 19** prior to assembly.

1. Install new seal in front shell, then secure with new retaining ring.
2. Install holding fixture J-22805-01 or equivalent on front shell, then mount holding fixture in vise.
3. Support front of valve body on cushioned work surface, press pedal pushrod into valve body, then secure pushrod by inserting stopper key into side of valve body.
4. Pull up on pushrod to ensure key is properly seated. Install elements (2 felt and 1 sponge) in rear of valve body, then the reaction disc in front of valve body, **Fig. 18.**
5. Mount diaphragm on booster piston.
6. Insert valve body assembly into booster piston, then rotate valve body counterclockwise to lock in position.
7. Support rear shell from inside, inboard of mounting studs, and drive new rear seal into place using a spacer.
8. Install diaphragm assembly into rear shell, then the pushrod and return spring into front shell.
9. Position rear shell and diaphragm assembly over front shell, then re-install rotating lever J-9504-01 or equivalent, ensuring matching marks will be aligned when assembly is rotated to locked position.
10. Apply vacuum to inlet port in front shell, then rotate rear housing clockwise to the locked position. **If rear**

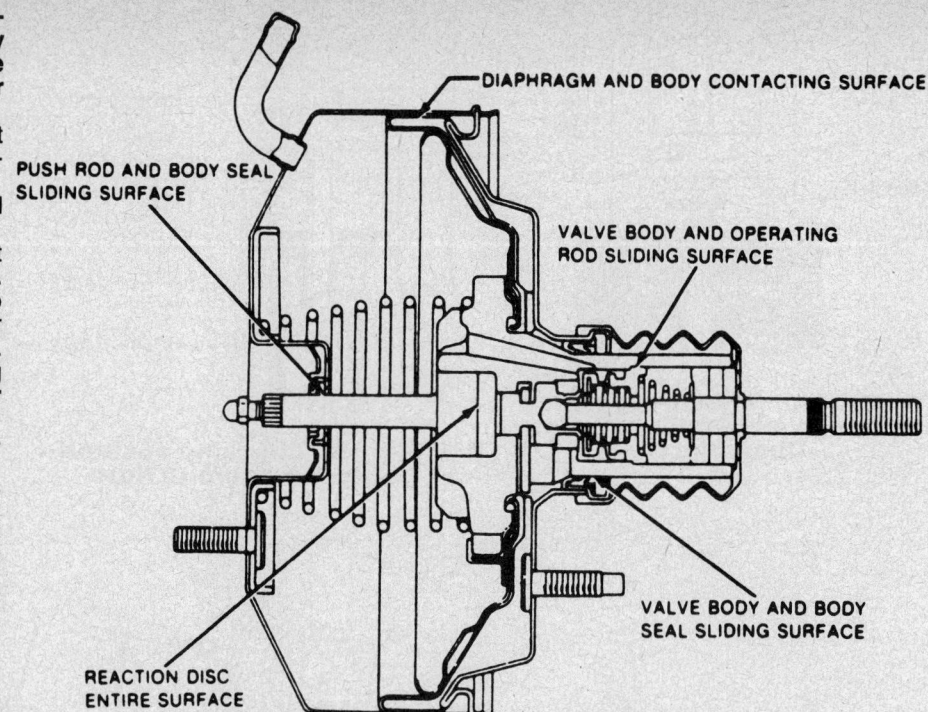

Fig. 19   Brake booster lubrication points. Chevrolet Nova

shell is too tight to be rotated when pressed into position, apply more silicone grease to lip of diaphragm contacting front shell.

11. Remove rotating lever and holding fixture, then install rear boot and pedal pushrod nut.
12. Adjust pushrod as outlined.

POWER MASTER POWER BRAKE

DESCRIPTION

The Power Master power brake unit is a complete, integral power brake system, **Fig. 20.** It consists of an electro-hydraulic pump, fluid accumulator, pressure switch, fluid reservoir and a hydraulic booster with an integral dual master cylinder. The accumulator is nitrogen charged and stores brake fluid at approximately 510-675 psi for hydraulic booster operation. The electro-hydraulic pump operates between pressure switch limits with the ignition switch in the On position.

When the pressure switch senses accumulator pressure below 510 psi, the 12 volt electro-hydraulic operates to increase accumulator fluid pressure to 675 psi.

When the brake pedal is depressed, fluid from the accumulator acts on the booster power piston, which in turn operates the master cylinder.

DIAGNOSIS & TESTING
Preliminary Procedure

1. Bleed, then refill brakes as necessary.
2. Ensure pump cycle time and reservoir fluid levels are maintained within prescribed limits. Brake fluid temperature

should be 60-80°F. If necessary, warm brake fluid to 60°F (minimum), by cycling the pump.

3. Fully discharge accumulator by depressing brake pedal at least 10 times, with ignition switch in the Off position.
4. Inspect for fluid leakage at brake pedal push rod, reservoir cover, hose and pipe connections, reservoir attaching points, pressure switch and accumulator.
5. Remove pressure switch from Power Master unit, then install tool J-35126 test gauge adapter, or equivalent.
6. Attach pressure switch electrical connector, then close bleed valve.

Function Check Sequence Test

1. Turn ignition switch to On position. The electro-hydraulic pump will operate and then shut off. **Do not allow pump to operate for more than 20 seconds.**
2. Ensure pump stops at 635-735 psi (as observed on test gauge). The pressure will settle to a slightly lower value after shut off, then remain steady.
3. Slowly bleed off accumulator pressure with bleed valve, returning brake fluid to the pump reservoir. Ensure pump operates again at a pressure of 490-530 psi.
4. Slowly apply brake pedal (reservoir cover off) and hold at a steady medium force. Observe pressure gauge for indication of continuous pressure drop. Pressure drop should not cause pump to recycle within 30 seconds of first apply.
5. Turn ignition switch to Off position, then remove pressure switch electrical connector.

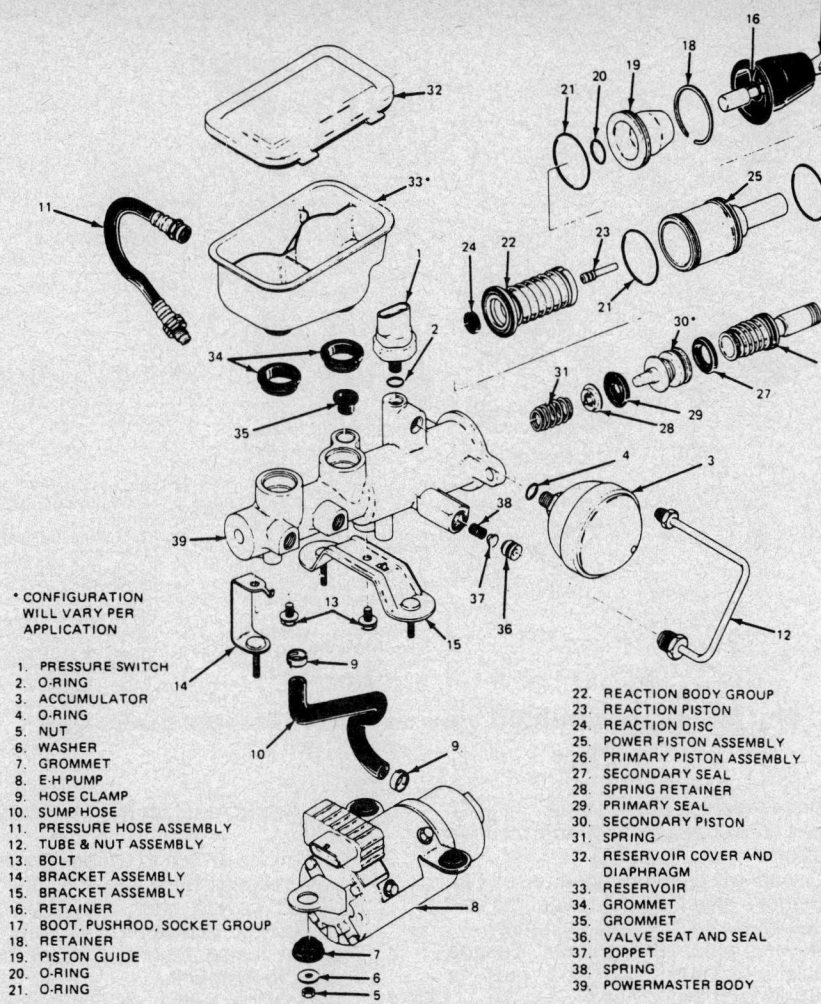

* CONFIGURATION
WILL VARY PER
APPLICATION

1. PRESSURE SWITCH
2. O-RING
3. ACCUMULATOR
4. O-RING
5. NUT
6. WASHER
7. GROMMET
8. E-H PUMP
9. HOSE CLAMP
10. SUMP HOSE
11. PRESSURE HOSE ASSEMBLY
12. TUBE & NUT ASSEMBLY
13. BOLT
14. BRACKET ASSEMBLY
15. BRACKET ASSEMBLY
16. RETAINER
17. BOOT, PUSHROD, SOCKET GROUP
18. RETAINER
19. PISTON GUIDE
20. O-RING
21. O-RING

22. REACTION BODY GROUP
23. REACTION PISTON
24. REACTION DISC
25. POWER PISTON ASSEMBLY
26. PRIMARY PISTON ASSEMBLY
27. SECONDARY SEAL
28. SPRING RETAINER
29. PRIMARY SEAL
30. SECONDARY PISTON
31. SPRING
32. RESERVOIR COVER AND
   DIAPHRAGM
33. RESERVOIR
34. GROMMET
35. GROMMET
36. VALVE SEAT AND SEAL
37. POPPET
38. SPRING
39. POWERMASTER BODY

Fig. 20 Power Master power brake unit

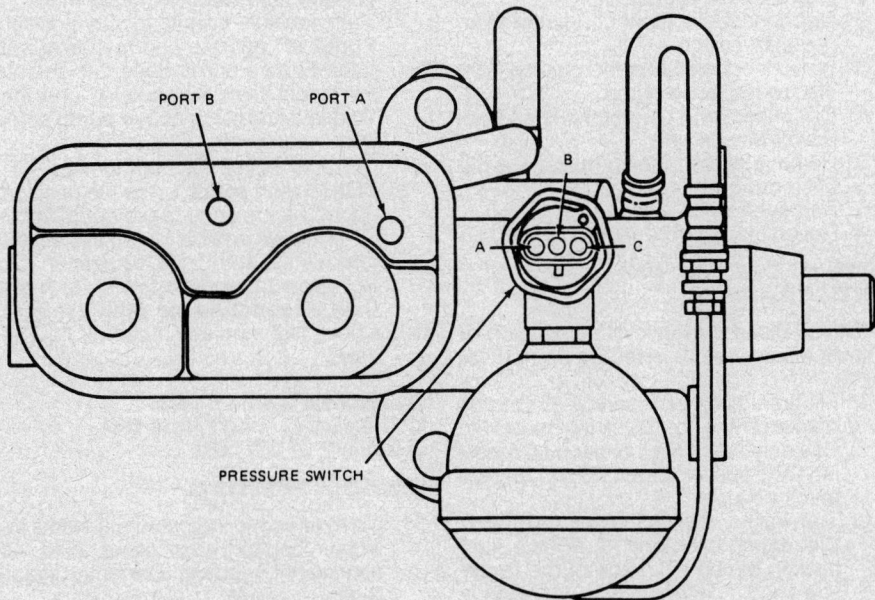

Fig. 21 Ports & terminals. Power Master brake unit

6. Attach an ohmmeter to switch terminals B and C, **Fig. 21.**
7. With ignition switch in the Off position, slowly bleed off accumulator pressure. Pressure switch terminals B and C should close off at approximately 355-435 psi. This is a low pressure warning signal.
8. Continue to bleed off accumulator pressure and note sudden drop off in gauge pressure reading at approximately 200-330 psi. This sudden drop is the accumulator pre-charge pressure.
9. Ensure the pump sump fluid level is at the full mark on the inside of the reservoir when accumulator is completely depressurized.
10. Turn ignition switch to the On position, then cycle pump several times to remove air by opening and closing bleeder valve.
11. Pump on time should be less than 10 seconds each cycle. During pump on/off cycles, note sump reservoir fluid level. Fluid will normally just cover the sump hose port when the pump is off and half full when pump comes on.

TROUBLESHOOTING

Test gauge adapter tool J-35126, a volt/ohmmeter and 6 inches of plastic tubing (1/4 inch diameter) are required for the following procedure.

Brake Warning Light On After Engine Start

1. Begin with parking brake applied. Temporarily release parking brake and observe light. Re-apply, if light remains on.
2. Check for excessive brake pedal travel.
3. Check for hard brake pedal force to stop.

Pump Motor Will Not Operate

1. Check ignition, 30 amp fuse and pressure switch terminals A and C.
2. Check motor and/or motor relay and wiring.

Pump Motor Operates, But Does Not Shut Off After 20 Seconds

1. Check reservoir fluid level.
2. Check reservoir port A for back flow.
3. Check pump pressure.

Pump Self Cycles Without Brake Applied

1. Check for accumulator precharge pressure.

Pump Self Cycles While Holding Brake Apply Force

1. Check accumulator precharge pressure.
2. Check for fluid back flow at reservoir port A.

Fluid Level In Pump Reservoir Does Not Cycle Between Full And Nearly Empty When Accumulator Is Fully Charged and Fully Depressurized

1. Check for air in fluid.
2. Check accumulator precharge pressure.

Fluid Level In Pump Reservoir Does Not Cycle Between Half Full And Nearly Empty At Pressure Switch Limits

1. Check for a full reservoir with a fully depressurized accumulator.
2. Check for accumulator precharge pressure if reservoir level after pump cycle is not nearly empty.

Pump And Motor Noisy

1. Check for grounded tube and hose.
2. Check reservoir fluid level.
3. Check motor mount grommets.

Fluid Leakage

1. Check pump reservoir for excess fluid fill with accumulator fully depressurized.
2. Check for tight reservoir cover and diaphragm.
3. Wipe dry, then identify source of leakage.

Pump Cycle Time At Pressure Switch Limits Exceeds 10 Seconds

1. Check for air in system.
2. Check for normal pressure switch points.
3. Check for obstructed pump inlet and outlet fluid circuits.
4. Check for a defective pump.

SYSTEM SERVICE

Depressurizing Power Master Unit

With ignition switch in the Off position, apply and release brake pedal a minimum of 10 times, using approximately 50 lbs of force on the pedal.

Pressure Switch, Replace

1. Depressurize system, then disconnect electrical connector from pressure switch.
2. Remove pressure switch and O-ring.
3. Reverse procedure to install. **Torque** pressure switch to 15-20 ft. lbs.

Accumulator, Replace

1. Depressurize system.
2. Remove accumulator and O-ring.
3. Reverse procedure to install. Install a new O-ring, then **torque** accumulator to 15-20 ft. lbs.

Electro-Hydraulic Pump & Pressure Hose, Replace

1. Depressurize system.
2. Remove reservoir cover and diaphragm.
3. Remove hose clamp, then disconnect electro-hydraulic pump to sump hose.

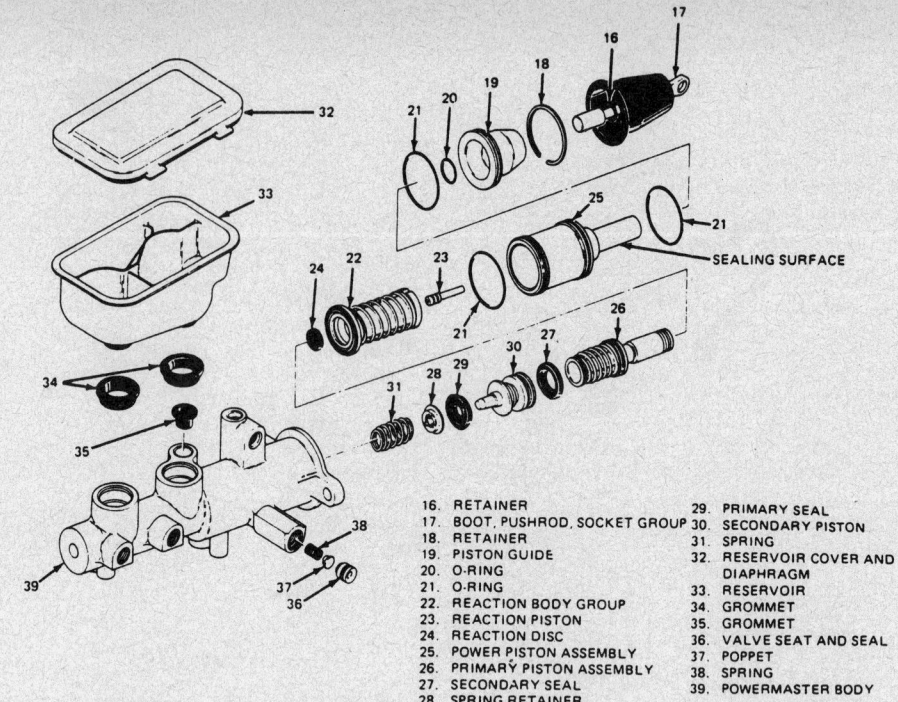

16. RETAINER
17. BOOT, PUSHROD, SOCKET GROUP
18. RETAINER
19. PISTON GUIDE
20. O-RING
21. O-RING
22. REACTION BODY GROUP
23. REACTION PISTON
24. REACTION DISC
25. POWER PISTON ASSEMBLY
26. PRIMARY PISTON ASSEMBLY
27. SECONDARY SEAL
28. SPRING RETAINER
29. PRIMARY SEAL
30. SECONDARY PISTON
31. SPRING
32. RESERVOIR COVER AND DIAPHRAGM
33. RESERVOIR
34. GROMMET
35. GROMMET
36. VALVE SEAT AND SEAL
37. POPPET
38. SPRING
39. POWERMASTER BODY

SEALING SURFACE

Fig. 22   Disassembled view of Power Master brake unit

4. Drain reservoir pump sump.
5. Disconnect electrical connector from electro-hydraulic pump.
6. Disconnect pressure hose assembly.
7. Remove attaching nuts, washers and electro-hydraulic pump assembly.
8. Reverse procedure to install. **Torque** electro-hydraulic attaching nuts to 23-35 inch lbs.

Power Master Unit, Replace

1. Depressurize system.
2. Disconnect electrical connector from pressure switch.
3. Disconnect electrical connector from electro-hydraulic pump.
4. Disconnect and plug brake lines from Power Master unit.
5. Remove two attaching nuts, then the push rod from brake pedal.
6. Remove Power Master unit.
7. Reverse procedure to install.

Power Master Fill Procedure

Bench bleed master cylinder portion of Power Master before installing unit on vehicle.

1. Fill both sides of reservoir to the full marks on the inside of the reservoir. Use only new, clean brake fluid meeting DOT specifications shown on reservoir cover.
2. Turn ignition switch to the On position. With pump operating, the brake fluid level in the booster side of the reservoir should decrease as brake fluid is moved to the accumulator. If the booster side of the reservoir begins to run dry, add brake fluid to just cover the reservoir pump port until the pump

stops. **Pump must shut off within 20 seconds.**
3. Turn ignition switch to Off position after 20 seconds have elapsed. Check for leaks or flow back into reservoir from booster return port.
4. Properly install reservoir cover assembly to reservoir.
5. Turn ignition switch to Off position and apply, then release brake pedal approximately 10 times.
6. Remove reservoir cover and adjust booster fluid level to the full mark.
7. Turn ignition switch to On position. Pump will operate and refill accumulator. Ensure pump does not operate for longer than 20 seconds and that fluid level remains above pump sump port in reservoir.
8. Correctly install reservoir cover.
9. With ignition switch in the On position, apply, then release brake pedal to cycle pump on and off 10-15 cycles and remove air from booster section. **Do not allow pump to operate for more than 20 seconds for each cycle.**
10. Check high and low reservoir fluid levels.

BLEEDING MASTER CYLINDER SECTION OF POWER MASTER

Manual Method

1. Fill reservoir to indicated full marks inside reservoir with brake fluid as specified on cover. Correctly install reservoir cover.
2. Remove brake line connectors from master cylinder outlet ports and allow cylinder to gravity bleed until fluid runs out of the brake line ports. Con-

nect brake lines to master cylinder ports. Tighten connector closest to cowl area.

3. Slowly apply brake pedal to full travel at approximately 50 lbs force. Tighten forward brake line connector, then release pedal completely. Wait 5 seconds. Apply brake pedal and hold. Open forward connector 1/2 turn to purge air from connector. Tighten connector, then release brake pedal again.

4. Repeat step 3 until all air is purged from forward connector port. Tighten connector. Maintain reservoir brake fluid levels.

5. Repeat steps 3 and 4 except at the rear brake line connector.

6. With brake lines, cylinders and master cylinder completely bled, check pedal travel and observe that brake warning indicator does not light during hard apply.

Pressure Method

Pressure bleeding equipment must be of the diaphragm type. It must have a rubber diaphragm between the air supply and the brake fluid to prevent air, moisture and other contaminants from entering the hydraulic system.

1. Fill master cylinder section of reservoir approximately half full with new brake fluid.

2. Install the special bleeder adapter J-35360 or equivalent onto Power Master.

3. Charge bleeder ball to 20-25 psi.

4. Connect line to adapter. Open line valve and depress bleed off valve on top of adapter until a few drops of fluid appear.

5. Raise and support vehicle.

6. Attach bleeder hose to bleeder valve and submerge opposite end into a clean container partially filled with brake fluid.

7. Open bleeder valve 1/2 to 3/4 turn and allow fluid to flow until no air is seen in fluid.

8. **The bleeding sequence is as follows:**
   a. Right rear.
   b. Left rear.
   c. Right front.
   d. Left front.

9. After the bleeding procedure is completed, **toque** brake line connector to 10-15 ft. lbs.

OVERHAUL
Disassembly

1. Remove reservoir cover and diaphragm, **Fig. 22.** Drain fluid from reservoir.

2. Remove pressure switch and O-ring.

3. Remove accumulator and O-ring.

4. Remove electro-hydraulic pump and pressure hose assembly.

5. Remove sump hose, clamps, tube, nut assembly and brackets. **Do not scratch or damage outside diameter seal surface at push rod end of power master assembly and bores in Power Master body.**

6. Remove retainer from Power Master body groove.

7. Remove boot, retainer, pushrod and power piston group.

8. Remove retainer, boot, push rod, socket group and piston guide from power piston assembly.

9. Remove O-ring from piston guide and O-rings from power piston assembly and piston guide.

10. Remove reaction body group from power piston assembly.

11. Remove reaction piston and reaction disc from reaction body group. **Do not attempt further disassembly of reaction body group or power piston assembly. If damage is found or isolated to the reaction body group or power piston assembly, replace complete reaction body group or power piston assembly.**

12. Remove primary piston assembly and secondary piston assembly.

13. Remove secondary seal, spring retainer and primary seal from secondary piston.

14. Remove spring from body bore.

15. Position Power Master body into a vise. **Do not clamp vise jaws across Power Master body.**

16. Remove reservoir.

17. Remove reservoir grommets.

18. Remove valve seat and seal. Discard seal.

19. Remove poppet and springs. Discard poppet and springs.

20. Clean all components except the pressure switch and electro-hydraulic pump in denatured alcohol.

21. Blow dry using low pressure compressed air. Use clean brake fluid to lubricate components, O-rings and body bores prior to assembly.

Assembly

1. Position Power Master body into a vise.

2. Install new spring and poppet into Power Master body.

3. Install a new valve seat and seal into Power Master body.

4. Bottom out valve seat and seal by threading nut of tube and nut assembly into Power Master body port.

5. Remove Power Master body from vise.

6. Install grommets into Power Master body. **Ensure grommets are correctly seated.**

7. Install reservoir onto Power Master body.

8. Install spring into Power Master body.

9. Install secondary seal, primary seal and spring retainer onto secondary piston.

10. Install secondary piston assembly into Power Master body.

11. Install primary piston assembly into Power Master body.

12. Install reaction piston and a new reaction disc into reaction body group.

13. Install two O-rings onto power piston assembly.

14. Install reaction body group into power piston assembly.

15. Install power piston assembly into Power Master body. Install O-rings onto piston guide.

16. Install piston guide into Power Master body over power piston.

17. Install retainer, while depressing piston guide and power piston.

18. Install boot, push rod, socket group and socket into end portion of power piston assembly. Install retainer.

19. Install brackets, sump hose, clamps, tube and nut assembly.

20. Install electro-hydraulic pump and pressure hose assembly.

21. Install accumulator and O-ring.

22. Install pressure switch and O-ring.

23. Install reservoir cover and diaphragm onto reservoir.

VACUUM PUMPS

INDEX

ELECTRICAL VACUUM PUMP

DESCRIPTION

Some GM transverse mounted gasoline engine models are equipped with an external electrical vacuum pump which aids the power brake system at times of low engine vacuum. The system is comprised of an electric motor, hoses, a controller containing an internal on-off switch and a timer/relay. The pump is located under the battery in a plastic and metal casing, **Fig. 1.** Under normal conditions, the system works identically to conventional brake systems.

The vacuum pump outlet hose is connected to the intake manifold and the inlet hose is connected to the brake booster check valve, **Fig. 2.** A charcoal filter is installed in the outlet hose to prevent harmful vapors from damaging the internal pump components.

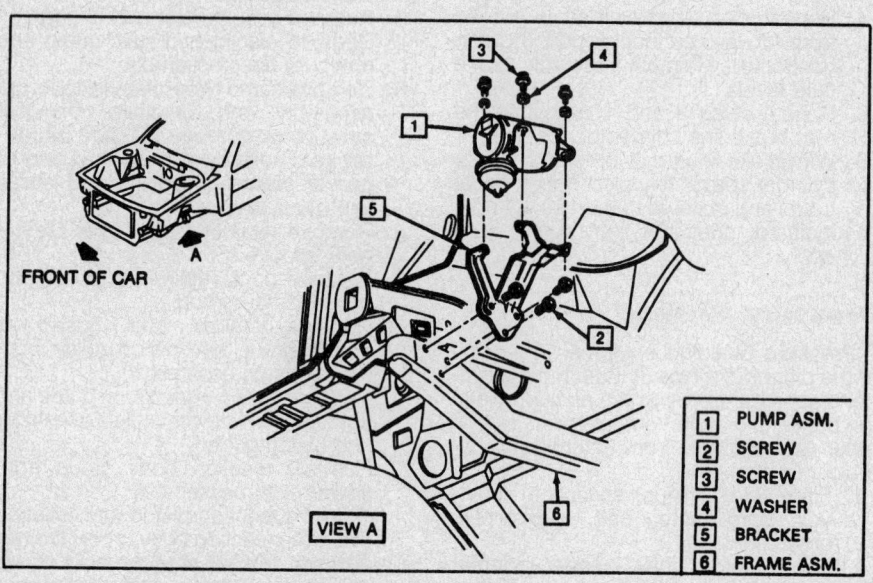

1	PUMP ASM.
2	SCREW
3	SCREW
4	WASHER
5	BRACKET
6	FRAME ASM.

Fig. 1   Electrical vacuum pump

PERFORMANCE CHECK

1. Attach a suitable vacuum gauge to the intake side of the vacuum pump, gauge should read approximately 21 inches of vacuum after 10 seconds of pump operation with outlet side vented to atmosphere.
2. With pump operating and intake port blocked off, pump current draw should not exceed 8 amps at 13.5 volts.
3. Replace pump as necessary.

SYSTEM SERVICE

Vacuum Pump, Replace

1. Raise and support front of vehicle.
2. Remove lefthand side splash shield.
3. Carefully remove locking type electrical connectors and vacuum hoses from pump.
4. Remove three vacuum pump retaining nuts, then the pump.
5. Reverse procedure to install.

1	HOSE ASM - VACUUM PUMP
2	BOLT/SCREW
3	VACUUM PUMP ASSEMBLY
4	CRUISE CONTROL SERVO
5	CLIP

Fig. 2   Vacuum hose routing

ANTI-LOCK BRAKES

TABLE OF CONTENTS

1989–90 Cutlass Supreme, Grand Prix & Regal (Delco-Moraine III Type)

NOTE: Wire Code Identification and Symbol Identification located in the front of this manual can be used as an aid when using wiring circuits found in this section.

INDEX

Continued

INDEX —Continued

OPERATING PRECAUTIONS

Some of the following procedures require that hydraulic lines, hoses and fittings be disconnected for inspection of testing. This Delco-Moraine brake system uses a hydraulic booster/modulator called a Powermaster III, which, when completely charged, contains brake fluid under high pressure. Before disconnecting any hydraulic lines, hoses or fittings, ensure the Powermaster III is completely depressurized as described further on. Failure to depressurize the Powermaster III may result in personal injury and/or damage to painted surfaces and/or the vehicle.

COMPUTER SYSTEM SERVICE PRECAUTIONS

The Delco-Moraine system is designed to withstand normal current draws associated with vehicle operation. During testing of opens or shorts, do not ground or apply voltage to any of the circuits unless instructed to do so by the appropriate diagnostic procedure.

DESCRIPTION

The Delco-Moraine anti-lock brake system (DM ABS-III), operates on all four wheels. It is designed to reduce the tendency of a wheel to lose traction (lock), while braking. In most instances, the base power brake system operates. Anti-lock braking occurs only when a combination of wheel speed sensors and a microprocessor determine a wheel is about to loose traction during braking. The DM ABS-III then adjusts brake pressure to both front wheels and/or both rear wheels to reduce the tendency of the wheels to lock-up. This system helps the driver maintain steering during braking, over a variety of road surfaces.

SYSTEM COMPONENTS

The main components of the Delco-Moraine ABS-III, are the Powermaster III hydraulic booster/master cylinder, four wheel speed sensors, speed sensor rings, remote proportioner valve assembly and an anti-lock brake controller.

ANTI-LOCK BRAKE CONTROLLER

The anti-lock brake controller monitors the speed of each wheel to determine if a wheel is approaching lock-up. If this condition is detected, the controller pulses the appropriate solenoids in the Powermaster III, to adjust brake pressures. The controller also monitors the system for malfunctions, provides diagnostic information and shuts system down in case of a serious malfunction. The controller is located beneath the front passenger seat, in a protective plastic case. The controller is non-serviceable.

POWERMASTER III

The Powermaster III is a booster/modulator designed to provide base (normal) and anti-lock braking power. Fluid pressure is created and maintained by a combination of an electric motor/pump and accumulator. The accumulator is pre-charged to 1200 psi and the electric pump maintains system pressure at 2700 psi. During anti-lock braking, the fluid pressure is modulated by three solenoid assemblies. One assembly for each front wheel and one assembly for the rear brakes. Each solenoid assembly can apply, hold, or release pressure in the line it controls. Each front wheel can be modulated separately (first one, then the other), but the rear brakes have to be modulated together. This system is commonly called a Select-Low 3-Channel System. The Powermaster III is located in the left rear corner of engine compartment.

FRONT WHEEL SPEED SENSORS & RINGS

Front speed sensors are bolted to the strut assemblies above the axle shafts. The speed sensor rings are located on the outer the constant velocity joints, directly beneath the wheel speed sensors. As a ring moves past a speed sensor, an oscillating voltage is sent to the controller. The frequency of this signal increases and decreases with wheel speed. No repair or gap adjustment to the wheel speed sensor is permitted.

PRE-DIAGNOSIS INSPECTION

ITEM	INSPECT FOR:	CORRECTIVE ACTION
BRAKE FLUID RESERVOIR, MASTER CYLINDER UNIT, BRAKE CALIPERS AND BRAKE HOSES AND LINES	– LOW FLUID LEVEL – EXTERNAL LEAKS – BLINDING OR STICKING CALIPERS	– FILL RESERVOIR – REPAIR LEAKS AS REQUIRED – REPAIR AS NEEDED
PARKING BRAKE	– FULL RELEASE	– RELEASE PARKING BRAKE – ADJUST CABLE IF REQUIRED
BATTERY	– ADEQUATE CHARGE ("GREEN EYE")	– CHARGE OR REPLACE BATTERY AS REQUIRED – SERVICE CHARGING SYSTEM AS REQUIRED (SEE SECTION 6D)

FUSES AND FUSIBLE ELEMENTS
FUSE BLOCK
 • ABS 2 FUSE 12   10 AMP
 • STOP FUSE 10   20 AMP
 • INDIC FUSE 11   10 AMP
ANTILOCK BRAKE POWER CENTER
 • CONTROLLER FUSE   10 AMP
 • ELECT BRAKE VALVE FUSE 15 AMP
 • FUSIBLE ELEMENT K
   PUMP MOTOR   30 AMP
 • FUSIBLE ELEMENT L
   ELECT BRAKE VALVE   30 AMP
	– BLOWN FUSE OR FUSIBLE ELEMENT	– REPLACE FUSE OR FUSIBLE ELEMENT AND VERIFY OPERATION

CONNECTORS • ANTILOCK BRAKE CONTROLLER • PUMP MOTOR RELAY • PUMP MOTOR • ACCUMULATOR SWITCH • REAR ENABLE RELAY • FRONT ENABLE RELAY • RIGHT FRONT SOLENOID • LEFT FRONT SOLENOID • REAR SOLENOID • WHEEL SPEED SENSORS • LAMP DRIVER MODULE • ANTILOCK BRAKE DIODE	– PROPER ENGAGEMENT OF CONNECTOR – LOOSE WIRES IN CONNECTOR	– PROPERLY ENGAGE CONNECTORS – REPAIR LOOSE WIRES
GROUND G106	– CLEAN AND TIGHT CONNECTION	– TIGHTEN – REPAIR LOOSE WIRES
INDICATORS OPERATION DURING BULB TEST • ANTILOCK WARNING INDICATOR • BRAKE WARNING INDICATOR	– LIGHTS	– CHECK CONNECTIONS – REPLACE BULB AND VERIFY OPERATION

Fig. 1   Pre-diagnosis inspection procedure and corrective actions

REAR WHEEL SPEED SENSORS & RINGS

Rear wheel speed sensors and speed sensor rings are integral parts of the rear wheel hub and bearing assemblies. Each sensor and ring is self-contained sealed from the environment. If a sensor or ring is malfunctioning or damaged, the entire rear hub and bearing assembly must be replaced. No repair or gap adjustment to the wheel speed sensor is permitted.

REMOTE PROPORTIONER VALVE

The proportioner valve proportions brake pressure to the rear brakes. Proportioning occurs only after a preset input pressure has been reached. Beyond this preset pressure, the valve limits output pressure to the rear brakes at a set percentage of the total system output. The separate parts of the remote proportioner valve cannot be serviced. The valve must be replaced if it is malfunctioning.

BRAKE WARNING INDICATOR

The red brake warning lamp illuminates after engine is started to indicate one or all of the following; parking brake is applied, fluid level is low, or accumulator pressure is below 1800 psi. Any of these three conditions can damage brake system or greatly reduce braking action. If the red brake warning lamp is on, check above possible causes. The brake warning lamp can be tested for proper operation by when ignition switch is in the Start position. The indicator should be on in this position.

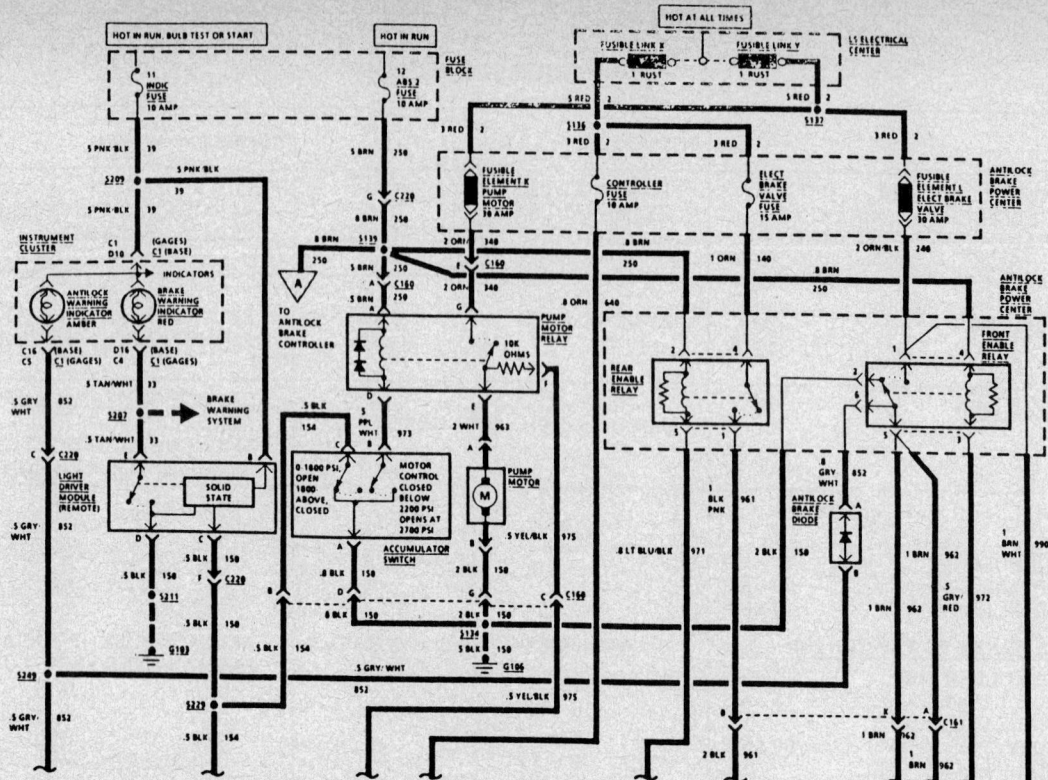

**Fig. 2   Anti-Lock brake system wiring diagram (Part 1 of 2).
1989 models**

ANTI-LOCK WARNING INDICATOR

The anti-lock warning indicator illuminates after the engine is running to indicate the following conditions. Constant illumination indicates the anti-lock brake controller has detected a fault and disabled part or all of the anti-lock brake system. The base power brake system will not be disabled. A flashing light indicates the anti-lock brake controller has detected a fault, but still retaining ABS operation. Prolonged operation with a flashing indicator may further damage the ABS system. The anti-lock warning indicator can be tested for proper operation with ignition switch in the Start position. The indicator should illuminate in this position. The indicator should also illuminate for approximately three seconds after engine is started.

OPERATION

During ABS operation, the Delco-Moraine ABS-III system cycles (pulses), the brakes, adjusting line pressures, to obtain optimum stopping distance and vehicle control. During this cycling, the brake pedal will pulsate and clicking noises will be heard from the solenoids as they control the cycling. Clicking of the solenoids and pulsating of the brake pedal at this time and during a short period after vehicle starting is normal.

During ABS braking, to optimize stopping distance, the ABS will pump the brake pedal. The driver should press steadily and firmly on the brake pedal. **The driver should never pump the brake pedal when ABS is activated.**

During ABS operation, some tire noise may be heard. This noise is normal and results from slippage of the tire on the road surface. The amount of tire slippage will depend upon road and tire conditions. A tire will also seem to lock momentarily. This is a result of rapid changes in wheel speed and is also normal. A wheel that locks and stays locked for more than one second is not normal and should be serviced immediately.

PRE-DIAGNOSIS INSPECTION

Refer to **Fig. 1**, for pre-diagnosis procedure and corrective actions.

DIAGNOSIS

A bi-directional scan tool connected to the assembly line diagnostic link (ALDL), is needed to access fault codes in the Delco-Moraine anti-lock braking system. Follow manufacturers directions for accessing fault codes. Refer to **Figs. 2 through 71**, for diagnosing trouble codes.

The ABS controller, when accessed with a bi-directional scan tool, identifies faults as specifically as possible. This diagnosis will also determine whether or not the fault is intermittent. There are 58 diagnostic fault codes. The first five codes stored, are stored in order of occurrence, from least recent to most recent. Fault codes will not disappear when ignition is turned Off, or when the battery is disconnected. Fault codes can only be read and erased with a bi-directional scan tool. If no faults occur within 50 drive cycles, all fault codes will be cleared. A drive cycle is defined as turning the ignition switch to the On position and vehicle is driven at speeds over 10 mph.

If a fault is detected, which disables the front ABS, the rear anti-lock brakes will continue to operate. The front brakes will have use of the normal power brake system only. If a fault is detected, which disables the rear ABS, the entire ABS will shut down, leaving normal power brake capability only.

Always turn ignition switch to the Off position prior to troubleshooting. This will ensure all diagnostic data is preserved. If ignition switch is not turned to the Off position, any information stored for a fault, in the last drive cycle, will be lost.

On 1988 models, if ignition switch is not turned Off prior to reading fault codes, and no other fault codes have occurred within the last 50 drive cycles, code 255 will set. If other fault codes did occur during the last 50 drive cycles, only information for the last drive cycle will be lost.

NOTE ON INTERMITTENTS

If an intermittent fault cannot be diagnosed using Indicator Lamp Sequence chart, the problem will most probably be caused by a defective electrical connection or wiring. When an intermittent problem is encountered, check questionable

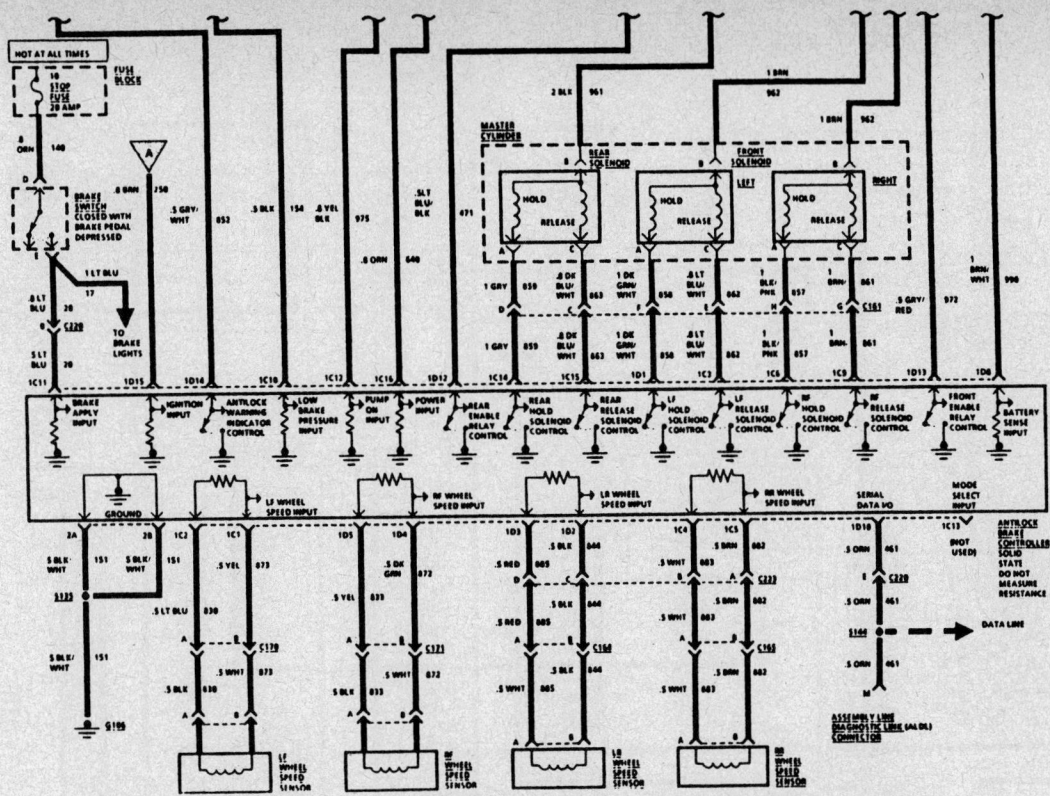

Fig. 2 Anti-Lock brake system wiring diagram (Part 2 of 2).
1989 models

circuits and electrical connectors for the following:

1. Poor mating of connector halves or terminals not fully seated in connector body.
2. Improperly formed or damaged terminals. All connector terminals in the problem circuit should be carefully removed to increase contact tension.
3. Poor terminal wire connection.

If a visual check does not locate cause of problem, operate vehicle with EBCM connected and attempt to duplicate condition and use Indicator Lamp Sequence chart to isolate potential cause.

SYSTEM SERVICE

BRAKE PEDAL TRAVEL

When the vehicle is stopped and the ABS is pressurized, it is possible to push the pedal, until it bottoms near the floor. This travel is normal while system is pressurized. Excessive travel occurs when braking action does not begin within the first 1.25 inches of pedal travel, while system is pressurized. Excessive pedal travel also exists when pedal travel exceeds 3 inches, when applying light pressure, while Powermaster III unit is depressurized.

DEPRESSURIZING POWERMASTER III

The Powermaster III must be depressurized prior to performing any service operations.

1. Turn ignition switch to the Off position, or disconnect negative battery cable.
2. Firmly apply, then release the brake pedal a minimum of 40 times. A noticeable change in pedal feel (from soft to hard), will occur when accumulator is completely discharged.
3. Do not turn ignition switch to the On or Start position after depressurizing Powermaster III, unless instructed by service procedure, or until service operations have been completed.

CHECKING FLUID LEVEL

1. Park vehicle on a level surface, then depressurize Powermaster III, see "Depressurizing Powermaster III."
2. Clean reservoir cover, then remove cover and diaphragm assembly from the Powermaster III. Note fluid level in reservoir chambers.
3. If any chamber is underfilled, **Fig. 72**, check for signs of leakage. Make repairs as necessary. **Fill chambers with clean DOT 3 fluid only.**
4. If chamber is overfilled, adjust fluid level. **Do not contaminate fluid in brake system with dirt, dust, lubricants, oils, or other substance.**
5. Replace diaphragm assembly and cover.
6. Turn ignition switch to the On position. Allow system to pressurize.
7. Depressurize Powermaster III, then check fluid level.
8. If reservoir chamber is again overfilled, repair or replace components as necessary.

POWERMASTER III BLEEDING

Pressure Bleeding

If a Powermaster III unit has been replaced, or air is suspected in the brake lines, the entire braking system must be bled.

If only a hydraulic portion of the Powermaster III unit has been replaced, without allowing air into the brake lines, it may only be necessary to manually bleed the Powermaster III unit.

Pressure bleeding must be done with diaphragm type bleeding equipment. Use only DOT 3 type brake fluid from a sealed container.

1. Turn ignition switch to the Off position, then depressurize the Powermaster III unit, see "Depressurizing Powermaster III."
2. Clean reservoir cover and diaphragm assembly, then remove assembly.
3. Check fluid in both reservoir sections, then fill to proper level, using clean DOT 3 brake fluid, if necessary.
4. Install bleeder adapter tool No. J-37115 or equivalent and secure with attachment cable. Ensure cable does not interfere with bleeder valve access.
5. Attach bleeder adapter to pressure bleed equipment, charge to 5-10 psi. for approximately 30 seconds, then slowly increase pressure to 30-35 psi.

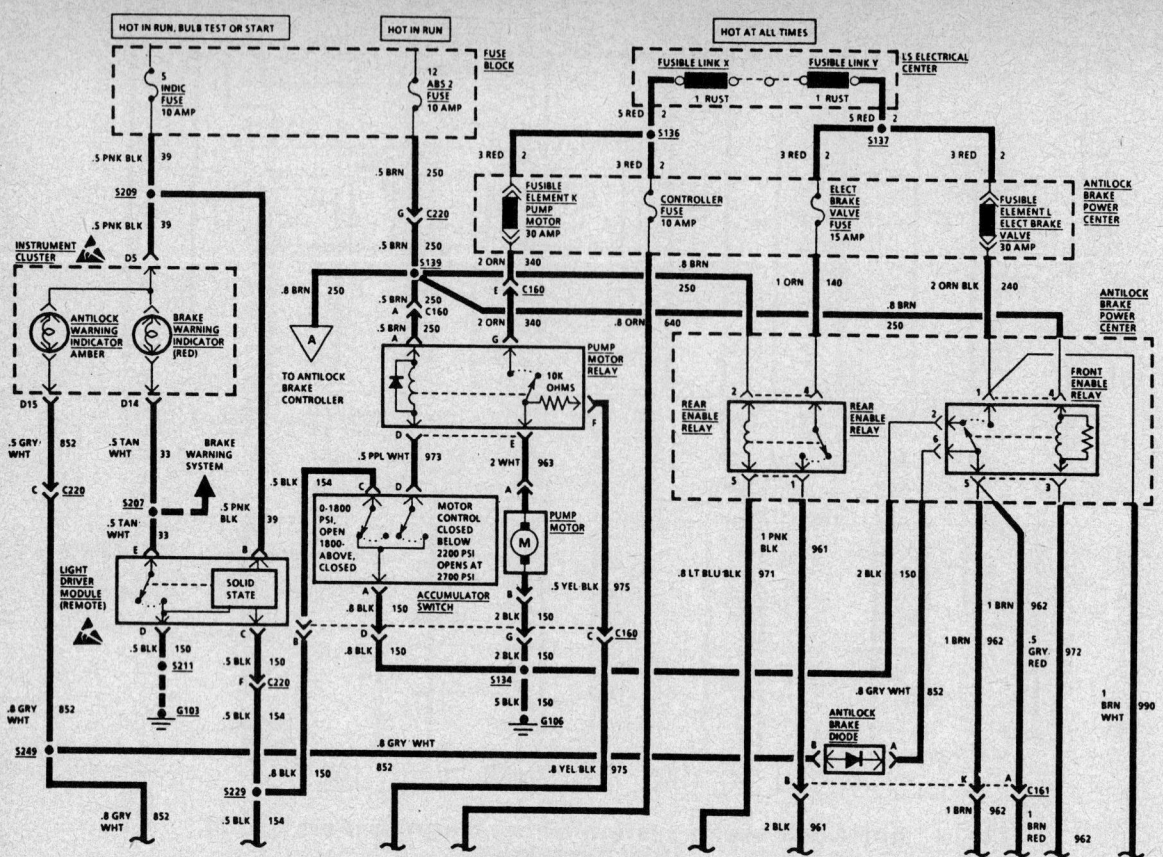

Fig. 3   Anti-Lock brake system wiring diagram (Part 1 of 2). 1990 models except Grand Prix STE

6. Bleed adapter tool No. J-37115 or equivalent by connecting a clear plastic hose to adapter bleeder screw and submerging opposite end in a clean container partially filled with brake fluid.

7. Slowly open bleeder valve, allowing fluid to flow until no more air is seen in fluid, then close valve.

8. Raise and support vehicle, then bleed brakes in sequence: right rear, left rear, right front, then left front, as described below.

9. Attach bleeder hose to bleeder valve, then submerge opposite end in a clean container partially filled with brake fluid.

10. Slowly open bleeder valve and allow fluid to flow for 20-30 seconds. To aid in releasing entrapped air, lightly tap on caliper castings with a rubber mallet.

11. Close valve when fluid begins to run with no bubbles. **Repeat steps 9-11 for each wheel, following wheel sequence in step 8.**

12. Lower vehicle, then attach bleeder hose to bleeder valve on inboard side of Powermaster III unit and submerge opposite end of hose in a clean container partially filled with brake fluid.

13. Slowly open bleeder valve and allow fluid to flow for 20-30 seconds.

14. Close valve when fluid begins to run with no bubbles.

15. Repeat steps 13-15 for outboard side bleeder valve.

16. Remove bleeder adapter tool No. J-37115 or equivalent from Powermaster III unit, then check fluid level in both reservoirs. Fill if necessary.

17. Snap reservoir cover into place, then apply moderate to heavy force to the brake pedal.

18. With the pedal applied, turn ignition switch to the On position for 5 seconds, then turn ignition switch to the Off position. Do this 10 times in succession to cycle solenoids. **Do not start engine, or place ignition switch in the Start position.**

19. Depressurize Powermaster III unit, then wait two minutes for air to clear from reservoir.

20. Attach bleeder hose to bleeder valve on inboard side of Powermaster III unit and submerge opposite end in a clean container partially filled with brake fluid.

21. With the ignition switch in the On position, apply light force to the brake pedal, then slowly open bleeder valve and allow fluid to flow until no air is seen.

22. Close valve when no air is seen in fluid.

23. Repeat steps 21-23, on outboard side bleeder valve.

24. Turn ignition switch to the Off position, then depressurize Powermaster III unit.

25. Remove reservoir cover and diaphragm assembly, then check fluid level in reservoirs. Use clean DOT 3 fluid to fill if necessary.

26. Snap reservoir cover onto reservoir, then turn ignition switch to the On position. Allow pump to run.

27. Turn ignition switch to the Off position if pump runs longer than 60 seconds, inspect pump for malfunction.

28. Apply brake pedal and note travel and feel. If pedal feels firm and smooth, without excessive travel, system is properly bled.

29. If pedal feels soft, spongy, or has excessive travel, see "Excessive Pedal Travel."

30. If a bump is noted upon initial pedal apply, or pedal apply does not feel smooth and uniform, see "Non-Uniform Pedal Apply."

32. Road test vehicle. If any of the above symptoms appear, refer to appropriate procedure.

Manual Bleeding

1. Turn ignition switch to the Off position, then depressurize Powermaster III unit.

2. Clean reservoir and diaphragm assembly, then remove reservoir cover assembly.

3. Fill reservoir to proper level wit DOT 3 brake fluid, then reinstall cover assembly.

4. Raise and support vehicle, then attach a clear bleeder hose to right front bleeder valve and submerge opposite end in clean container partially filled with brake fluid.

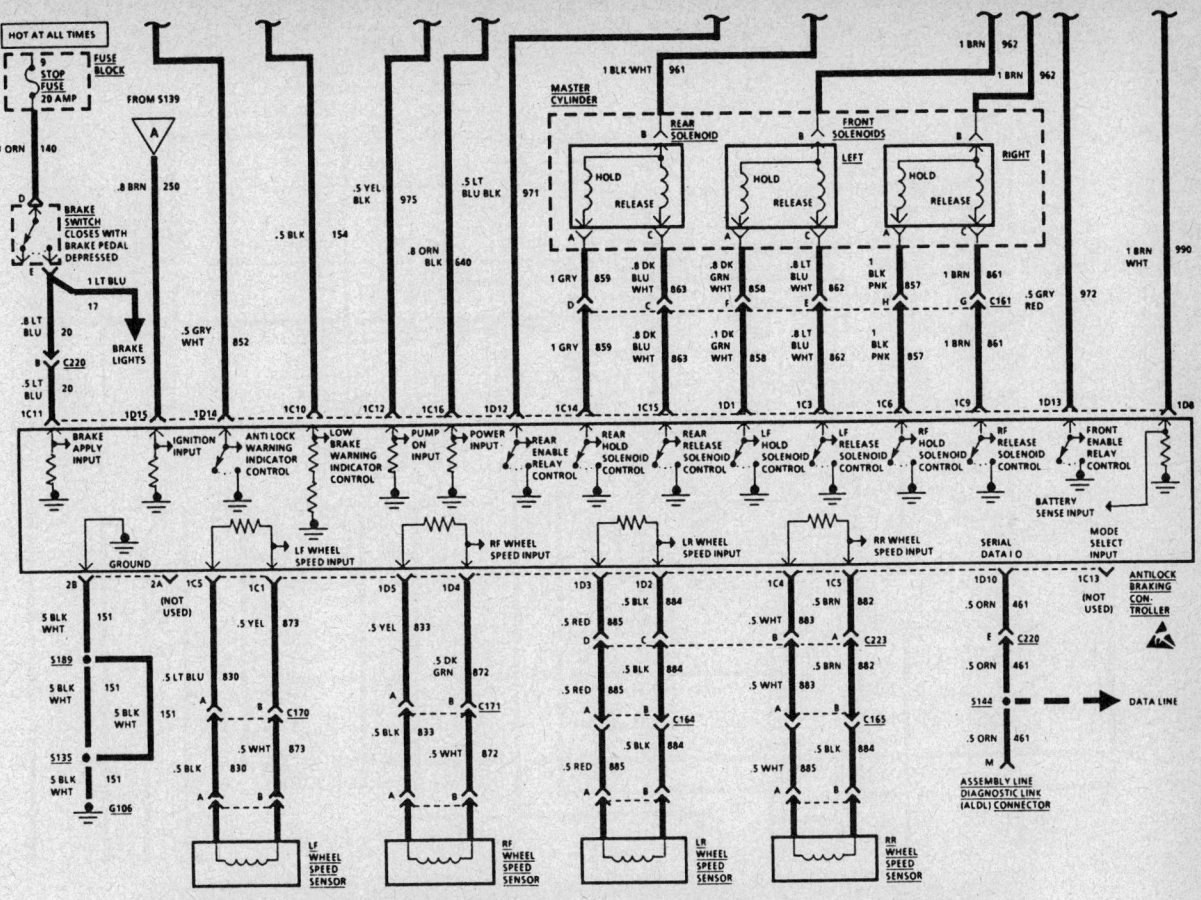

Fig. 3   Anti-Lock brake system wiring diagram (Part 2 of 2). 1990 models except Grand Prix STE

5. Open bleeder valve, then slowly depress bleeder valve. To aid in releasing trapped air, lightly tap on caliper castings with a rubber mallet.
6. Close bleeder valve, then release brake valve.
7. Check, then add brake fluid if necessary.
8. Repeat steps 4-7 until pedal feels firm and no air is observed bleeder hose.
9. Repeat steps 4-8 for left front brake.
10. Turn ignition switch to the On position, allowing pump to run. If pump runs longer than 60 seconds, inspect pump for malfunctions.
11. Attach clear bleeder hose to right rear bleeder valve and submerge opposite end in a clean container partially filled with brake fluid.
12. Turn ignition switch to the On position, open bleeder valve, then slowly depress brake pedal part-way, until fluid begins to flow from hose. **Do not depress brake pedal fully.**
13. Hold pedal for 15 seconds. To aid in freeing entrapped air, tap lightly on caliper casting with a rubber mallet.
14. Close bleeder valve, then release brake pedal.
15. Repeat steps 12-14, until no air is observed in the fluid.
16. Turn ignition switch to the Off position, depressurize Powermaster III unit, then check brake fluid. Add fluid as needed.
17. Repeat steps 10-16 for left rear

wheel.
18. Repeat steps 10-16 for inboard bleeder valve of Powermaster III unit.
19. Repeat steps 10-16 for outboard bleeder valve of Powermaster III unit.
20. Turn ignition switch to the Off position, then depressurize Powermaster III unit. Check brake fluid level and fill as needed.
21. Apply moderate to heavy force on brake pedal.
22. With pedal applied, turn ignition switch to the On position for 5 seconds, then turn ignition switch to the Off position. Repeat this step 10 times. **Do not turn ignition switch to the Start position, or start motor.**
23. Depressurize Powermaster III unit, then wait two minutes for air to clear from within reservoir.
24. Attach bleeder hose to bleeder valve on inboard side of Powermaster III unit and submerge opposite end in clean container partially filled with brake fluid.
25. Turn ignition switch to the On position, then apply light force to brake pedal.
26. With pedal applied, slowly open bleeder valve and allow fluid to flow until no air is seen in fluid.
27. Close valve when no air is seen in fluid.
28. Repeat steps 24-27, for outboard bleeder valve.
29. Turn ignition switch to the Off position, then depressurize Powermaster III

unit.
30. Remove reservoir cover and diaphragm assembly, check and fill reservoirs with DOT 3 brake fluid as needed.
31. Install reservoir cover, then turn ignition switch to the On position. Allow pump to run. If pump runs for longer than 60 seconds, inspect pump for malfunctions.
32. Apply brake pedal, noting feel and travel.
33. If pedal feels firm and smooth, without excessive travel, system is properly bled.
34. If pedal feels soft, spongy, or has excessive travel, see "Excessive Pedal Travel."
35. If a bump is noted upon initial pedal apply, or pedal apply does not feel smooth and uniform, see "Non-Uniform Pedal Apply."
36. Road test vehicle. If any of the above symptoms appear, refer to appropriate procedure.

EXCESSIVE PEDAL TRAVEL

Excessive pedal travel exists when braking action does not start within the first 1.25 inches of pedal travel, while the Powermaster III unit is pressurized. When the Powermaster III unit is not pressurized, excessive pedal travel exists when brake pedal moves more than 3 inches while applying light pedal pressure.

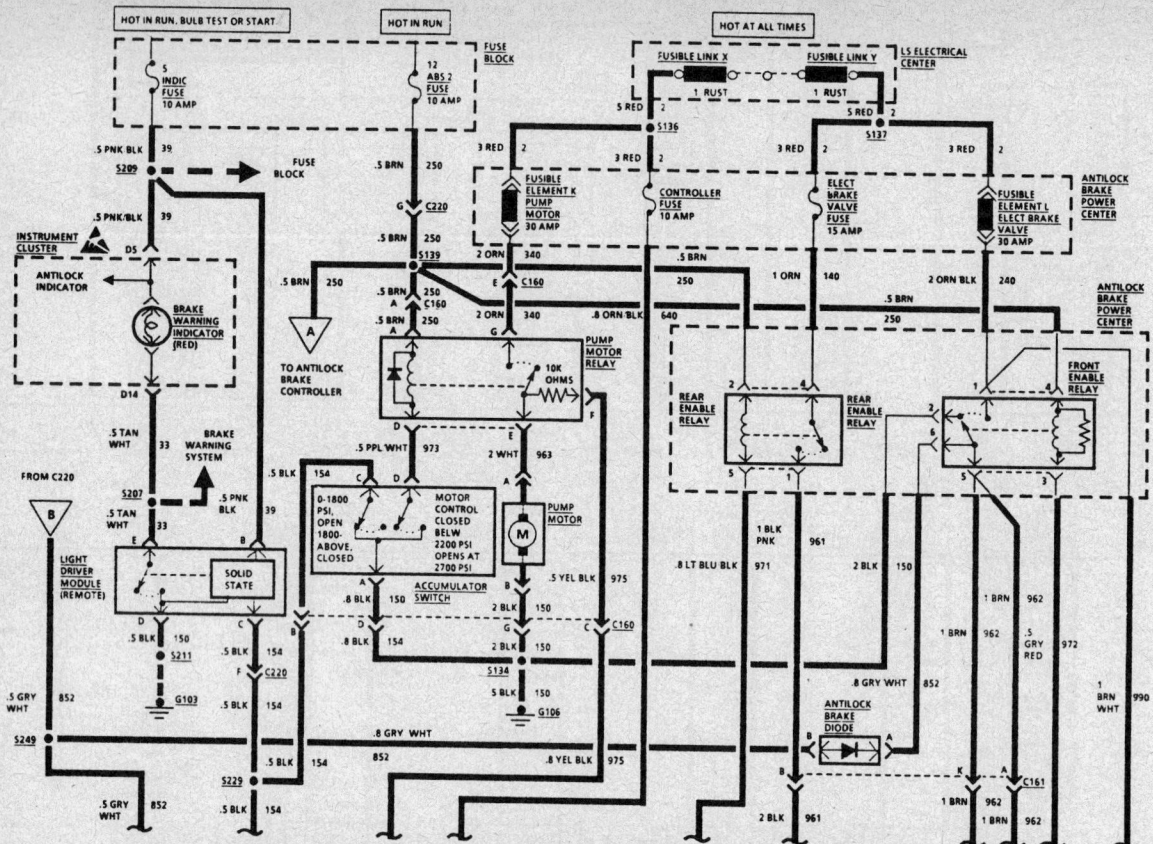

**Fig. 4   Anti-Lock brake system wiring diagram (Part 1 of 3).
1990 Grand Prix STE**

1. Apply moderate to heavy force on brake pedal, turn ignition switch to the On position for 5 seconds, then turn ignition switch to the Off position. **Do not turn ignition switch to the Start position, or start motor.**
2. Release brake pedal, then repeat step 1, twice.
3. Bleed front brakes, as described in "Pressure Bleeding."
4. If excessive pedal travel exists, check brake fluid level, then for leaks in braking system.

NON-UNIFORM PEDAL APPLY

1. Raise rear of vehicle until Powermaster III unit is level with ground, or sloping downward slightly.
2. Depressurize Powermaster III unit.
3. Wait two minutes, then turn ignition switch to the On position. Allow pump to pressurize unit. **Do not turn ignition switch to the Start position or start engine.**
4. If condition still exists, raise rear of vehicle, as described in step 1, then bleed rear brakes. See "Pressure Bleeding," or "Manual Bleeding."

PUMP RUNS CONTINUOUSLY

Only perform this procedure if pump runs for more than 60 seconds. **Do not allow brake fluid to come into contact with painted surfaces.**

1. Turn ignition switch to the Off position, then depressurize Powermaster III unit.
2. Loosen, but do not remove tube nuts from both front master cylinder chambers.
3. Apply brake pedal as far as possible. Check that brake fluid runs from around tube nuts.
4. With pedal still applied, tighten tube nuts.
5. Quickly release brake pedal, then reapply with a sharp, rapid motion with full force.
6. Continue from step 25, of "Pressure Bleeding."

DELCO-MORAINE POWERMASTER III ELECTRICAL CONNECTORS

The Powermaster III unit is equipped with electrical connectors which utilize a connector position assurance locking pin. This locking pin assures proper alignment and engagement of the connector, **Fig. 73.**
Always remove the locking pin prior to disconnecting electrical connector. Use extreme caution as to not damage locking pin during removal or installation. Note position of rubber seals when disconnecting connectors for installation purposes. Always reinstall locking pins after reconnecting connector.

COMPONENT REPLACEMENT

FLUID LEVEL SENSOR SWITCH, REPLACE

1. Disconnect 2-pin connector (1), from fluid level sensor switch (2), **Fig. 74.**
2. Remove fluid level sensor switch from reservoir.
3. Depress locking tabs at inboard end of switch, under reservoir on opposite end of 2-pin connector.
4. Reverse procedure to install. Ensure sensor switch locking tabs snap into place.

BLEEDER VALVES, REPLACE

1. Depressurize Powermaster III, see "Depressurizing Powermaster III."
2. Remove bleeder valves (4), **Fig. 74.** Clean valves in denatured alcohol, then dry with compressed air. **Do not use lubricated compressed air.**
3. Reverse procedure to install, noting the following:
   a. **Torque** bleeder valve to 40-90 inch lbs.
   b. Bleed Powermaster III as described in "Powermaster III Bleeding."

Continued on page 25-49

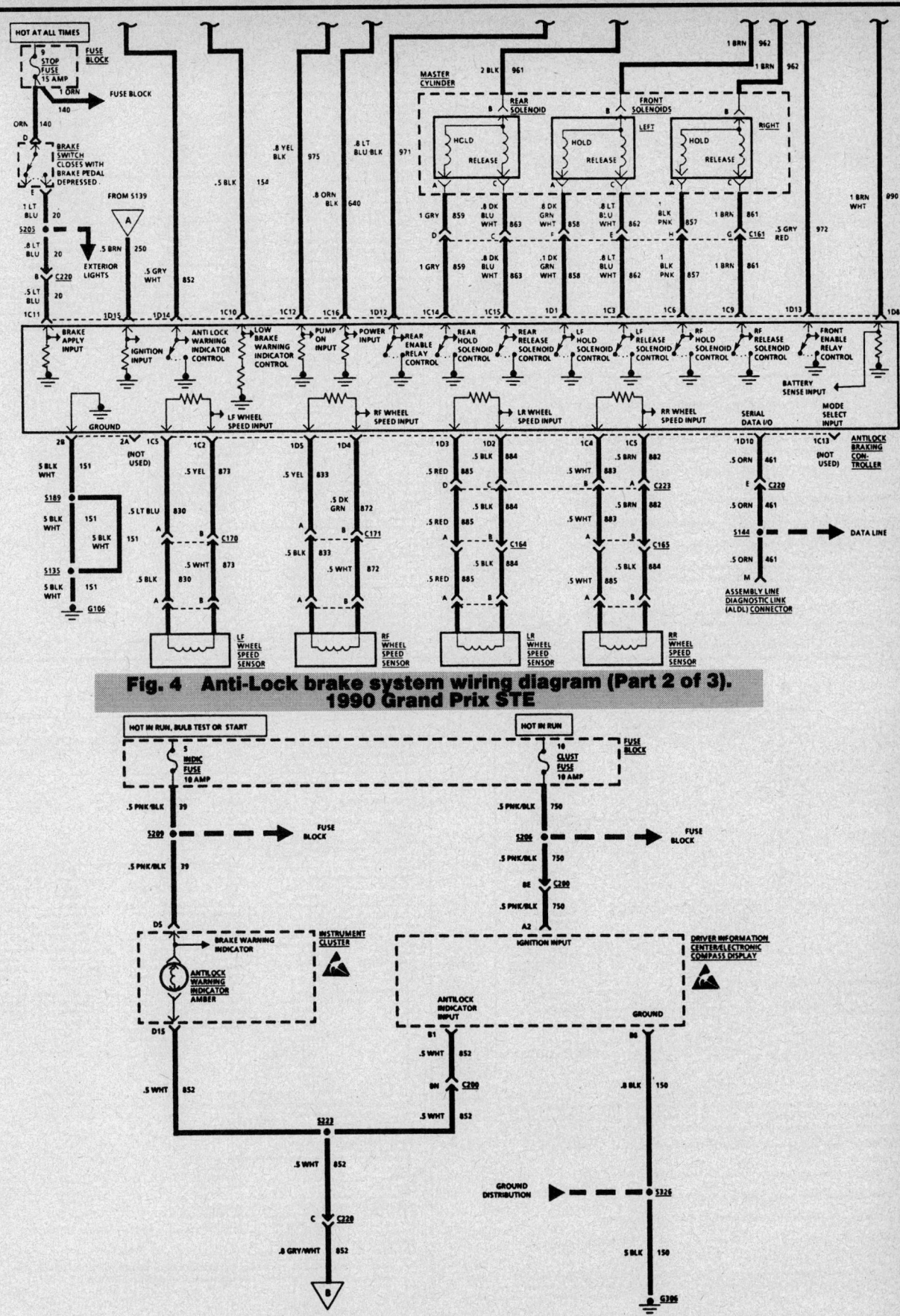

**Fig. 4 Anti-Lock brake system wiring diagram (Part 2 of 3).
1990 Grand Prix STE**

**Fig. 4 Anti-Lock brake system wiring diagram (Part 3 of 3).
1990 Grand Prix STE**

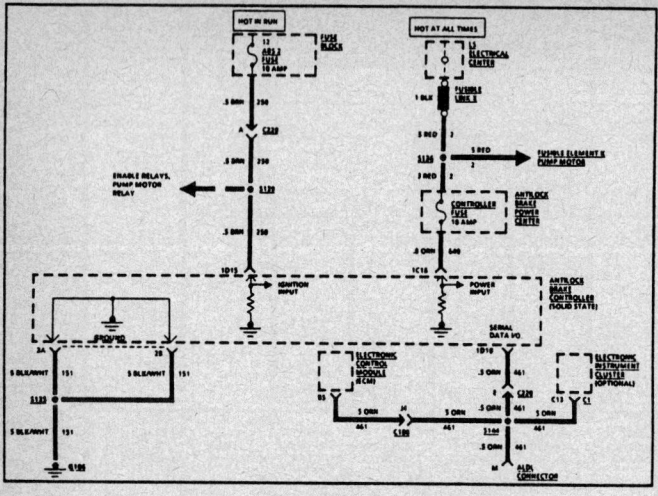

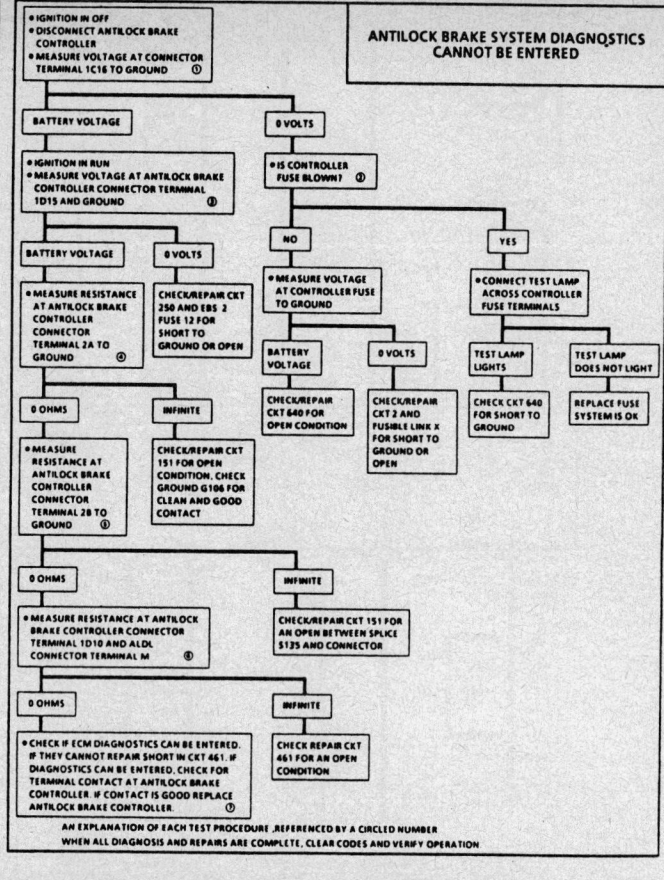

ANTILOCK BRAKE SYSTEM DIAGNOSTICS CANNOT BE ENTERED

The Antilock Brake System will be disabled and the Antilock Warning Indicator will be on if a loss of power or ground occurs at the Antilock Brake Controller. A loss of power or ground at the controller or a open or shorted serial data line will also prevent access to the Antilock Brake System's diagnostics.

TEST DESCRIPTION: The following provides an explanation of the procedures being followed in the facing trouble tree.

① Determines if voltage is being applied to the Antilock Brake Controller at Terminal 1C16.

② Indicates whether the fault is due to open condition or a possible short to ground in CKT 640.

③ Determines if voltage is being applied to Antilock Brake Controller at Terminal 1D15.

④ & ⑤ A measurement of infinite resistance indicates an open condition in the Antilock Brake Controller's ground circuits, although only one complete ground path is required for proper operation. Both ground paths should be checked to assure redundancy.

⑥ A measurement of infinite resistance indicates an open condition exists in the data line CKT 461. If an open condition exists in the data line the controller would be unable to communicate with a bi-directional scan tool.

⑦ If a short to ground existed in CKT 461, communication with the ECM would not be possible. If communication with the ECM is possible a poor terminal connection at the Antilock Brake Controller is indicated or the controller is defective.

Fig. 5   Anti-lock brake system diagnostics cannot be entered. 1989 models

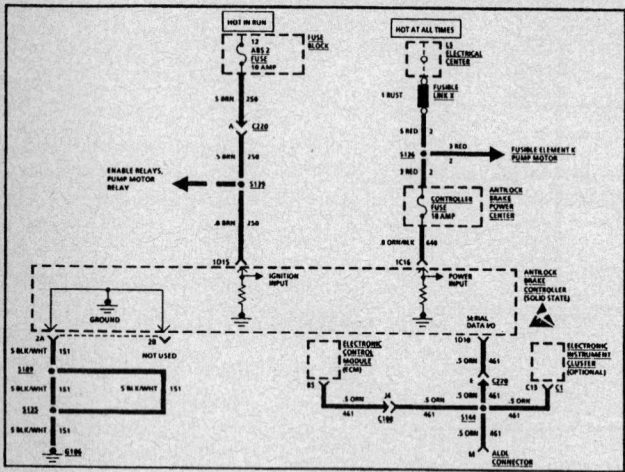

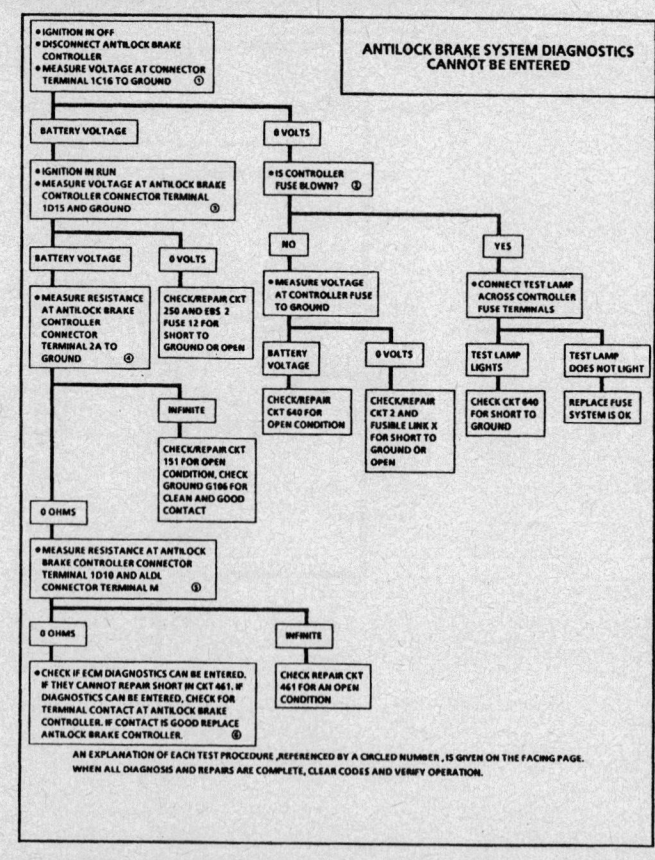

ANTILOCK BRAKE SYSTEM DIAGNOSTICS CANNOT BE ENTERED

The Antilock Brake System will be disabled and the Antilock Warning Indicator will be on if a loss of power or ground occurs at the Antilock Brake Controller. A loss of power or ground at the controller or a open or shorted serial data line will also prevent access to the Antilock Brake System's diagnostics.

TEST DESCRIPTION: The following provides an explanation of the procedures being followed in the facing trouble tree.

① Determines if voltage is being applied to the Antilock Brake Controller at Terminal 1C16.

② Indicates whether the fault is due to open condition or a possible short to ground in CKT 640.

③ Determines if voltage is being applied to Antilock Brake Controller at Terminal 1D15.

④ A measurement of infinite resistance indicates an open condition in the Antilock Brake Controller's ground circuit.

⑤ A measurement of infinite resistance indicates an open condition exists in the data line CKT 461. If an open condition exists in the data line the controller would be unable to communicate with a bi-directional scan tool.

⑥ If a short to ground existed in CKT 461, communication with the ECM would not be possible. If communication with the ECM is possible a poor terminal connection at the Antilock Brake Controller is indicated or the controller is defective.

Fig. 6   Anti-lock brake system diagnostics cannot be entered. 1990 models

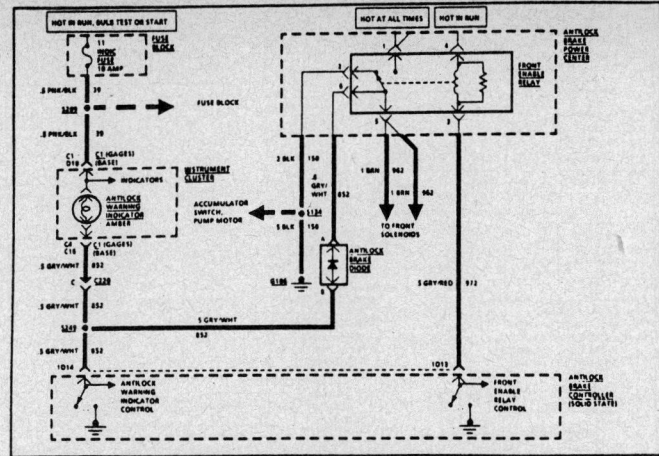

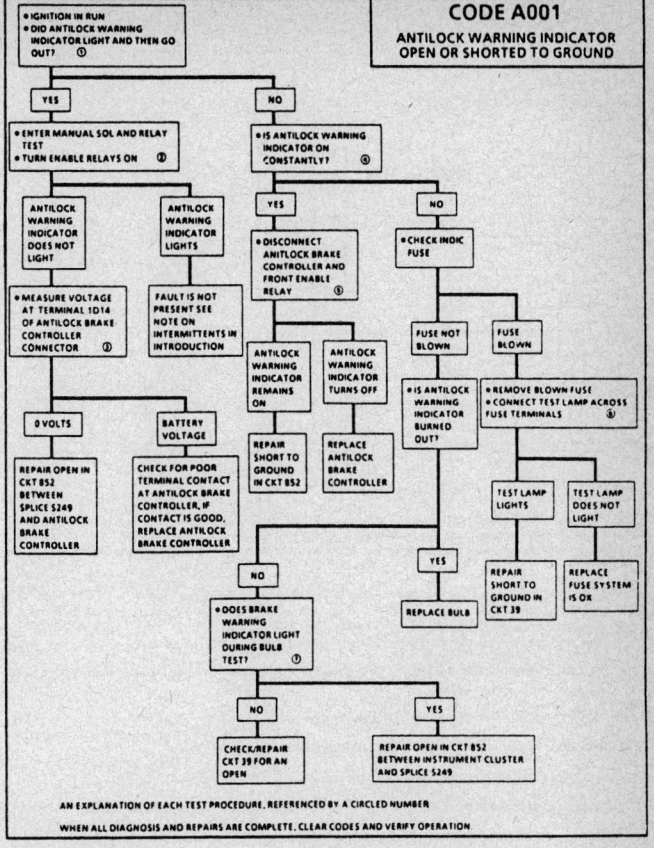

CODE A001

Antilock Warning Indicator open or shorted to ground.

When the Front Enable Relay is energized, its contacts close. This opens the ground path from the Antilock Warning Indicator. Voltage from the INDIC Fuse should now be present at terminal 1D14.

CODE A001 will set when all of the following conditions exist:
- The Front Enable Relay is energized.
- The Antilock Warning Indicator Control is open.
- The Antilock Brake Controller senses no voltage at terminal 1D14.

TEST DESCRIPTION: The following provides an explanation of the procedures being followed in the facing trouble tree.

① If the Antilock Warning Indicator lights, the circuit from the Indicator to ground G106 must be good.

② By energizing the Front Enable Relay, one can determine if CKT 852 to Antilock Brake Controller is defective. In this mode, the Controller should ground the Indicator causing it to light.

③ Voltage at terminal 1D14 indicates that CKT 852 is OK. The fault must then be internal to the Controller.

④ This determines if the problem is an open or short to ground.

⑤ Isolates the Antilock Warning Indicator from its possible grounds and therefore determines whether a short to ground is present in CKT 852 or whether the Antilock Brake Controller is defective.

⑥ Checks for a short to ground in CKT 39.

⑦ Determines whether open is in CKT 852 or CKT 39.

Fig. 7   Code A001, anti-lock warning indicator open or shorted to ground

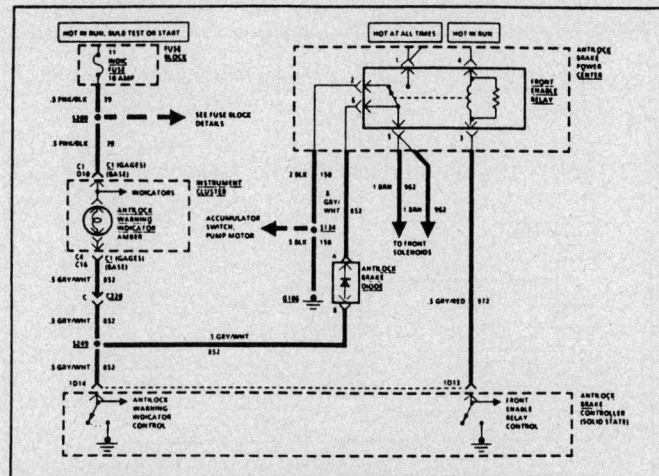

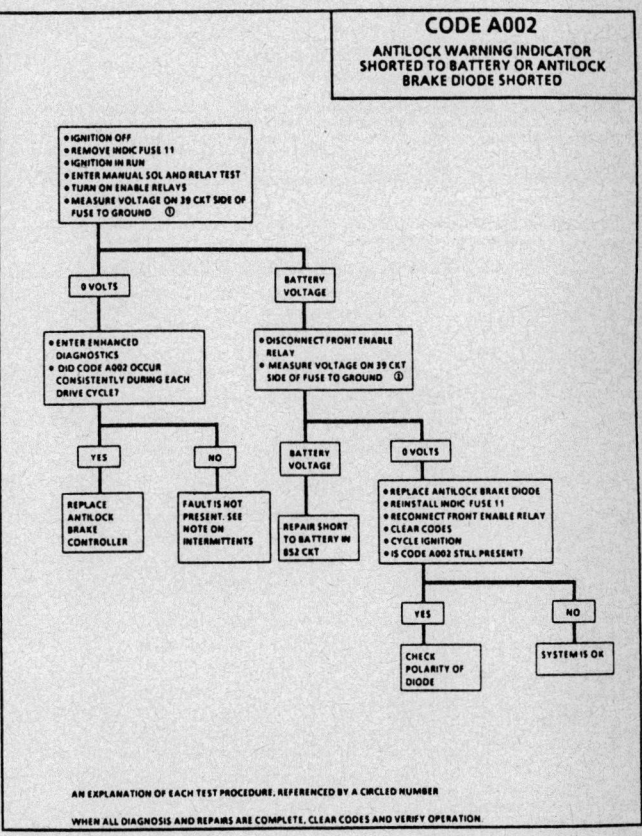

CODE A002

Antilock Warning Indicator shorted to Battery or Antilock Brake Diode shorted.

The Antilock Brake Diode prevents battery voltage from being applied to the Antilock Warning Indicator when the Front Enable Relay is energized. If the Antilock Brake Controller is inoperative, the Antilock Brake Diode allows the Antilock Warning Indicator to be grounded through the deenergized Front Enable Relay.

CODE A002 will set during system initialization when all of the following conditions exist:
- The Front Enable Relay is energized.
- The Antilock Warning Indicator Control is closed.
- The Antilock Brake Controller senses battery voltage at terminal 1D14.

TEST DESCRIPTION: The following provides an explanation of the procedures being followed in the facing trouble tree.

① Isolates the Antilock Warning Indicator circuit from it's power source and therefore determines whether another voltage source is shorted into the circuit or whether the Antilock Brake Controller is defective.

② Determines whether the Antilock Brake Diode is shorted or whether a short to battery exists in CKT 852.

Fig. 8   Code A002, anti-lock warning indicator shorted to battery, or anti-lock brake diode shorted

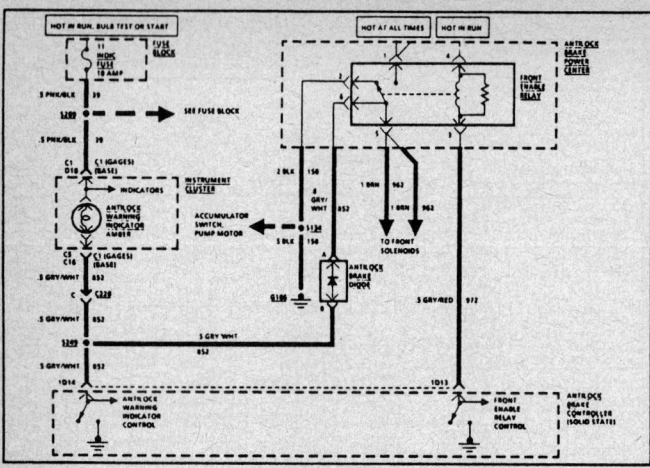

CODE A003

Antilock Brake Diode open or ground open

If the Antilock Brake Controller loses power or ground, the Antilock Warning Indicator is grounded through the 852 CKT, the Antilock Brake Diode, the open contacts of the Front Enable Relay, and CKT 150. The Antilock Brake Diode prevents Battery Voltage from being applied to the Antilock Warning Indicator when the Front Enable Relay is energized.

CODE A003 will set during system initialization when all of the following conditions exist:
- The Front Enable Relay is deenergized.
- The Antilock Warning Indicator Control is open.
- The Antilock Brake Controller senses battery voltage at terminal 1D14.

TEST DESCRIPTION: The following provides an explanation of the procedures being followed in the facing trouble tree.

① If code A039 is also set, the ground CKT 150 must be open.

② Determines if an open condition exists or if a possible intermittent condition exists.

③ Checks if the condition exists between splice S249 and the Front Enable Relay.

④ Indicates if an open condition exists in CKT 852 between splice S249 and the Antilock Brake Diode.

⑤ Determines if an open condition exists in CKT 852 to Front Enable Relay, or in Antilock Brake Diode.

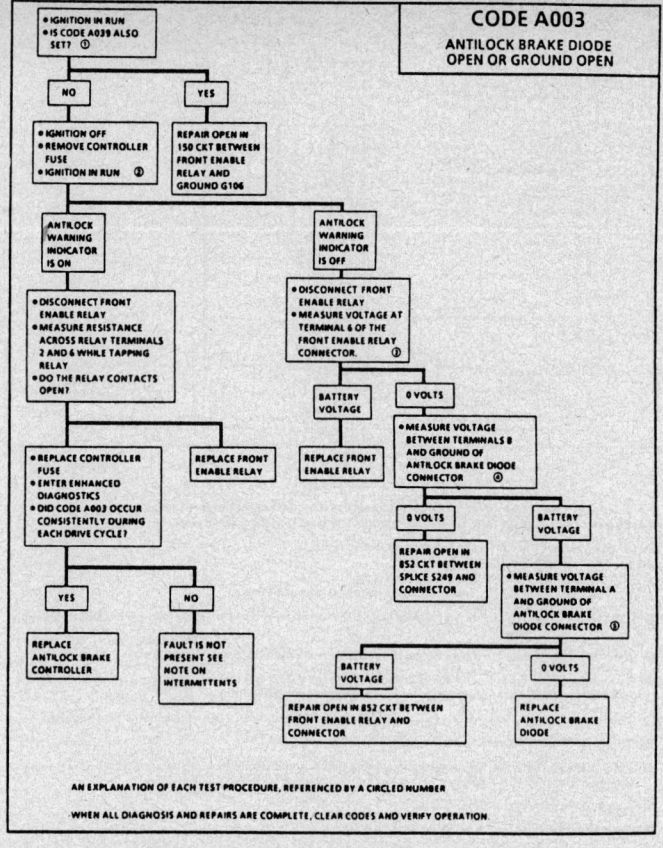

Fig. 9   Code A003, anti-lock brake diode open or ground open

CODE A004

Enable Relay or Solenoid fault detected (FR FAULT)

CODE A004   is a pretest which the Antilock Brake Controller uses in order to detect that a malfunction has occurred in the solenoid or enable relay circuits. Once the Controller has set Code 4 it will initiate a series of tests in order to pinpoint the malfunction. Code A004 will always set along with another Code. The other code which is set will indicate the nature of the malfunction and where it occurred.

TEST DESCRIPTION: The following provides an explanation of the procedures being followed in the facing trouble tree.

① If another code is set a fault exists in the solenoid or enable relay circuits. The other code will indicate the nature of the malfunction and where it occurred.

② If Code A004 sets and no other codes have been set, an internal malfunction in the Antilock Brake Controller is indicated.

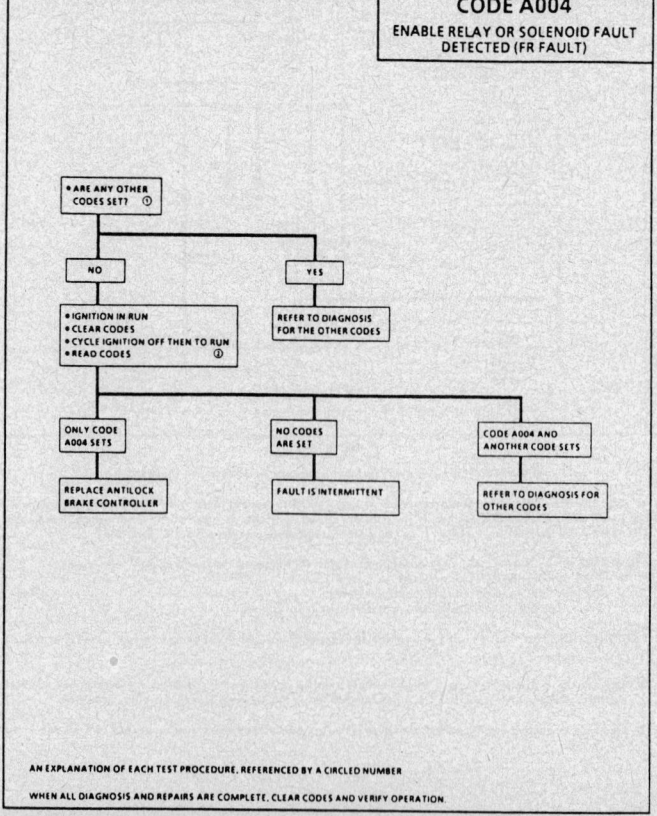

Fig. 10   Code A004, enable relay or solenoid fault detected (FR fault)

1989-90 CUTLASS SUPREME, GRAND PRIX & REGAL (DELCO-MORAINE III TYPE)

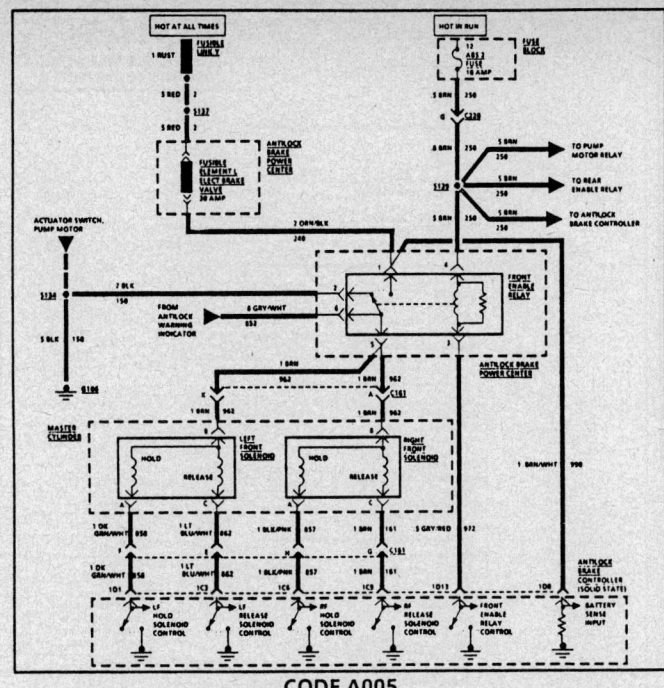

CODE A005

FRONT ENABLE RELAY COIL OPEN, CONTACTS OPEN, FUSE OPEN

CODE A005

Front Enable Relay Coil open, contacts open, fuse open

If the Ignition is in RUN and the Antilock Brake Controller does not detect any faults, the Controller will close the Front Enable Relay Control. This grounds the Front Enable Relay Coil and the Relay becomes energized. The contacts close, and voltage is applied from Fusible Element L to the Left Front Solenoid and the Right Front Solenoid. If the Controller is not closing any of the Solenoid Controls, the Controller will sense battery voltage at terminals 1D1, 1C3, 1C6, and 1C9.

CODE A005 will set when all of the following conditions exist:
- The Front Enable Relay Control is closed (Front Enable Relay energized).
- The Antilock Brake Controller senses no voltage at terminals 1D1, 1C3, 1C6 and 1C9.

AN EXPLANATION OF EACH TEST PROCEDURE, REFERENCED BY A CIRCLED NUMBER, IS GIVEN BELOW

WHEN ALL DIAGNOSIS AND REPAIRS ARE COMPLETE, CLEAR CODES AND VERIFY OPERATION.

TEST DESCRIPTION: The following provides an explanation of the procedures being followed in the above trouble tree.

① If voltage is present at Front Enable Relay, but not at terminal 1D13, and open in CKT 972 is indicated.

② If Code A007 is also set, none of the solenoids are receiving voltage. This indicates a problem with connector C161.

③ If the test lamp lights, it shows that CKT 250, CKT 972, and the Antilock Brake Controller are good. This indicates that the fault is in the Front Enable Relay or connector, or the fault is intermittent.

Fig. 11   Code A005, front enable relay coil open, contacts open, fuse open. (1 of 2)

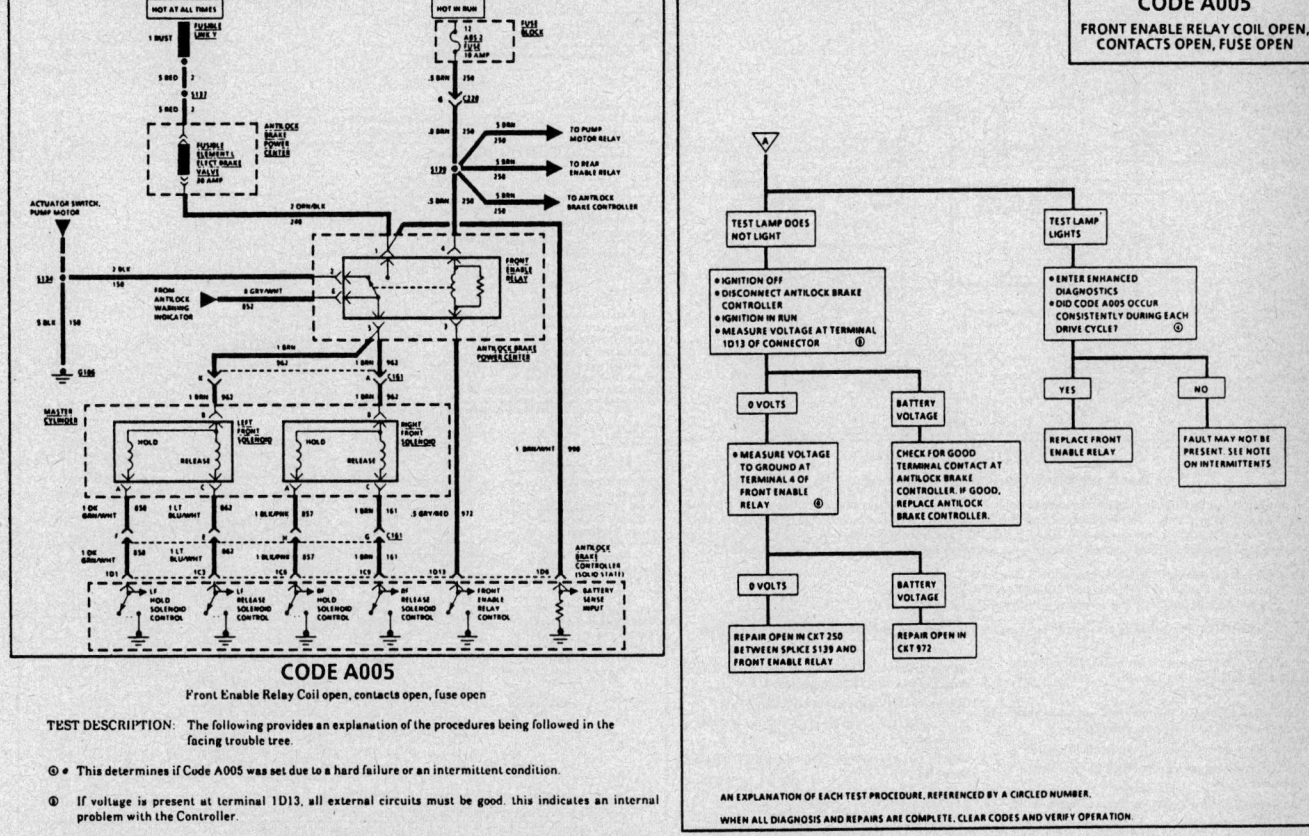

CODE A005

Front Enable Relay Coil open, contacts open, fuse open

TEST DESCRIPTION: The following provides an explanation of the procedures being followed in the facing trouble tree.

② • This determines if Code A005 was set due to a hard failure or an intermittent condition.

① If voltage is present at terminal 1D13, all external circuits must be good. this indicates an internal problem with the Controller.

③ If voltage is present at Front Enable Relay, but not at terminal 1D13, an open in CKT 972 is indicated.

CODE A005

FRONT ENABLE RELAY COIL OPEN, CONTACTS OPEN, FUSE OPEN

AN EXPLANATION OF EACH TEST PROCEDURE, REFERENCED BY A CIRCLED NUMBER, IS

WHEN ALL DIAGNOSIS AND REPAIRS ARE COMPLETE, CLEAR CODES AND VERIFY OPERATION.

Fig. 11   Code A005, front enable relay coil open, contacts open, fuse open. (2 of 2)

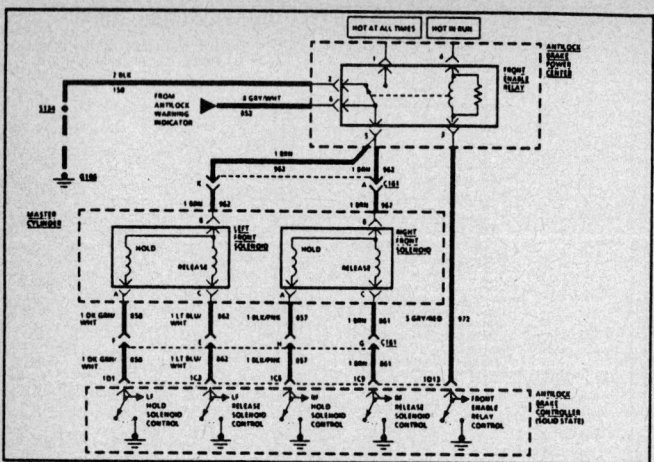

CODE A006

Front Enable Relay Coil shorted to Battery.

Battery Voltage is applied to the Front Enable Relay and CKT 972 whenever the Ignition is in RUN and the Front Enable Relay Control is open.

When the Front Enable Relay Control is closed, ground is applied to terminal 3 of the Front Enable Relay. CKT 972 is now grounded, so voltage is no longer present at terminal 1D13 of the Antilock Brake Controller.

CODE A006 will set when all of the following conditions exist:
- The Front Enable Relay control is closed (Front Enable Relay energized).
- The Antilock Brake Controller senses Battery voltage at Terminal 1D13.
- The Antilock Brake Controller senses no voltage at Terminals 1D1, 1C3, 1C6 and 1C9.

TEST DESCRIPTION: The following provides an explanation of the procedures being followed in the facing trouble tree.

① Code A008 will also be set if both Enable Relay Connectors are disconnected simultaneously.

② With the Front Enable Relay disconnected it can be determined whether a short to Battery exists in CKT 972 (Battery voltage present at Terminal 3 of Front Enable Relay connector).

③ Determines if a short exists internally in the Front Enable Relay.

④ It is possible for an open Relay Coil to set this Code. Code A005 will now set if this fault is present.

⑤ If Code A006 is a consistent failure, the Controller is faulty.

CODE A006 — FRONT ENABLE RELAY COIL SHORTED TO BATTERY

- IGNITION IN RUN
- IS CODE A008 ALSO SET? ①

NO →
- DISCONNECT FRONT ENABLE RELAY
- MEASURE VOLTAGE AT TERMINAL 3 OF FRONT ENABLE RELAY CONNECTOR ②

  - **0 VOLTS**
    - MEASURE RESISTANCE ACROSS TERMINALS 4 AND 3 OF THE FRONT ENABLE RELAY ③
      - **APPROX 60-80 OHMS**
        - IGNITION OFF
        - RECONNECT FRONT ENABLE RELAY
        - IGNITION IN RUN
        - IS CODE A005 NOW SET? ④
          - **NO**
            - ENTER ENHANCED DIAGNOSTICS
            - DID CODE A006 OCCUR CONSISTENTLY DURING EACH DRIVE CYCLE? ⑤
              - **NO** → FAULT MAY NOT BE PRESENT. SEE NOTE ON INTERMITTENTS
              - **YES** → REPLACE ANTILOCK BRAKE CONTROLLER
          - **YES** → REFER TO CODE A005
      - **APPROX 0 OHMS** → REPLACE FRONT ENABLE RELAY
  - **BATTERY VOLTAGE** → REPAIR SHORT TO BATTERY IN 972 CKT

YES → CHECK BOTH ENABLE RELAY CONNECTIONS

AN EXPLANATION OF EACH TEST PROCEDURE, REFERENCED BY A CIRCLED NUMBER

WHEN ALL DIAGNOSIS AND REPAIRS ARE COMPLETE, CLEAR CODES AND VERIFY OPERATION.

Fig. 12   Code A006, front enable relay coil shorted to battery

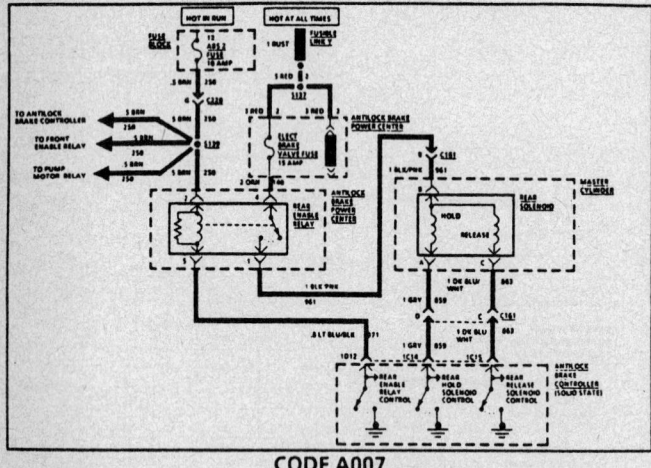

CODE A007

Rear Enable Relay Coil open, contacts open, fuse open

If the Ignition is in RUN and the Antilock Brake Controller does not detect any faults, the Controller will close the Rear Enable Relay Control. This grounds the Rear Enable Relay and the Relay becomes energized. The contacts close, and voltage is applied from the ELECT BRAKE VALVE Fuse to the Rear Solenoid. If the Controller is not closing either of the Rear Solenoid Controls, the Controller will sense Battery voltage at terminals 1C14 and 1C15.

CODE A007 will set when all the following conditions exist:
- The Rear Enable Relay Control is closed (Rear Enable Relay energized).:
- The Antilock Brake Controller senses no voltage at Terminals 1C14 and 1C15.

TEST DESCRIPTION: The following provides an explanation of the procedures being followed in the trouble tree.

① If Code A005 is also set, none of the Solenoids are receiving voltage. This indicates a problem with connector C161.

② Code A054 will set if the relay coil circuit is open. Diagnostics are covered under code A054.

③ Determines if power feed to Relay contacts is good.

④ If Battery voltage is measured CKT 961 and Rear Solenoid are good.

⑤ Determines if open exists in Rear Solenoid or in CKT 961.

⑥ This determines if Code A007 was set due to a hard failure or an intermittent condition.

⑦ Checks for short to ground in CKT 140.

⑧ If test lamp lights, a short to ground in CKT 961 is indicated.

⑨ Checks for good power feed to ELECT BRAKE VALVE Fuse.

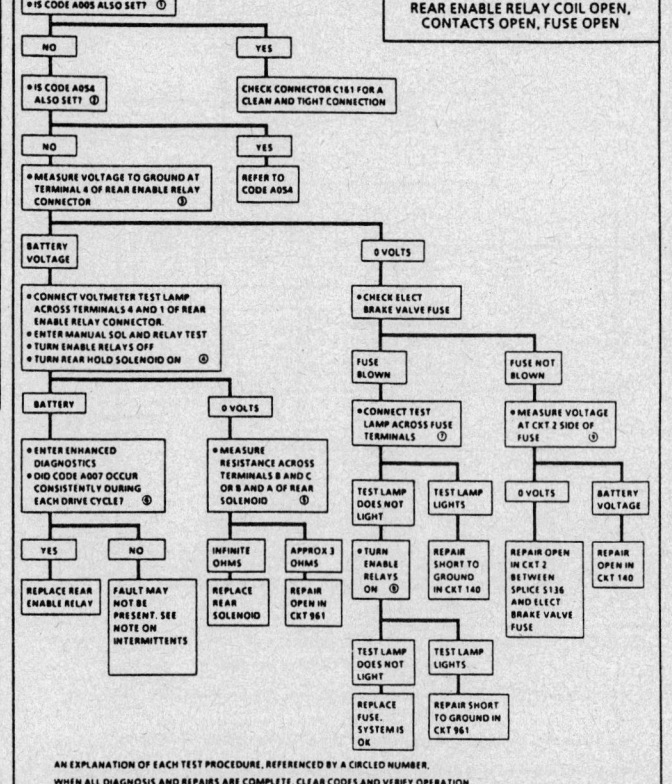

CODE A007 — REAR ENABLE RELAY COIL OPEN, CONTACTS OPEN, FUSE OPEN

- IGNITION IN RUN
- IS CODE A005 ALSO SET? ①

NO →
- IS CODE A054 ALSO SET? ②
  - **NO →**
    - MEASURE VOLTAGE TO GROUND AT TERMINAL 4 OF REAR ENABLE RELAY CONNECTOR ③
      - **BATTERY VOLTAGE**
        - CONNECT VOLTMETER TEST LAMP ACROSS TERMINALS 4 AND 1 OF REAR ENABLE RELAY CONNECTOR.
        - ENTER MANUAL SOL AND RELAY TEST
        - TURN ENABLE RELAYS OFF
        - TURN REAR HOLD SOLENOID ON ④
          - **BATTERY**
            - ENTER ENHANCED DIAGNOSTICS
            - DID CODE A007 OCCUR CONSISTENTLY DURING EACH DRIVE CYCLE? ⑥
              - **YES** → REPLACE REAR ENABLE RELAY
              - **NO** → FAULT MAY NOT BE PRESENT. SEE NOTE ON INTERMITTENTS
          - **0 VOLTS**
            - MEASURE RESISTANCE ACROSS TERMINALS B AND C OR B AND A OF REAR SOLENOID ⑤
              - **INFINITE OHMS** → REPLACE REAR SOLENOID
              - **APPROX 3 OHMS** → REPAIR OPEN IN CKT 961
      - **0 VOLTS**
        - CHECK ELECT BRAKE VALVE FUSE
          - **FUSE BLOWN**
            - CONNECT TEST LAMP ACROSS FUSE TERMINALS ⑦
              - **TEST LAMP DOES NOT LIGHT**
                - TURN ENABLE RELAYS ON ⑧
                  - **TEST LAMP DOES NOT LIGHT** → REPLACE FUSE. SYSTEM IS OK
                  - **TEST LAMP LIGHTS** → REPAIR SHORT TO GROUND IN CKT 961
              - **TEST LAMP LIGHTS** → REPAIR SHORT TO GROUND IN CKT 140
          - **FUSE NOT BLOWN**
            - MEASURE VOLTAGE AT CKT 2 SIDE OF FUSE ⑨
              - **0 VOLTS** → REPAIR OPEN IN CKT 2 BETWEEN SPLICE S136 AND ELECT BRAKE VALVE FUSE
              - **BATTERY VOLTAGE** → REPAIR OPEN IN CKT 140
  - **YES →** REFER TO CODE A054
- **YES →** CHECK CONNECTOR C161 FOR A CLEAN AND TIGHT CONNECTION

AN EXPLANATION OF EACH TEST PROCEDURE, REFERENCED BY A CIRCLED NUMBER

WHEN ALL DIAGNOSIS AND REPAIRS ARE COMPLETE, CLEAR CODES AND VERIFY OPERATION.

Fig. 13   Code A007, rear enable relay coil open, contacts open, fuse open. 1989 models

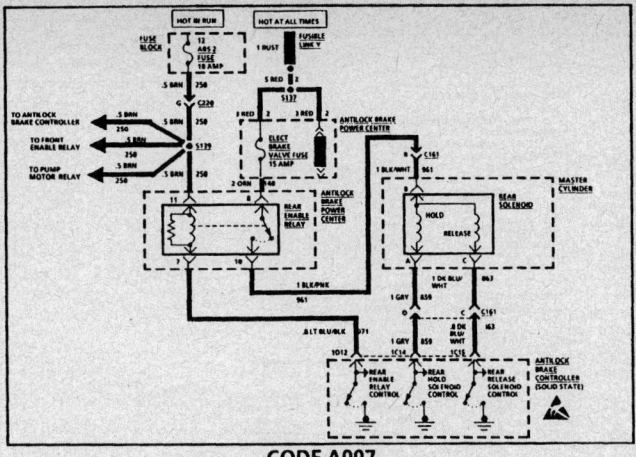

CODE A007

Rear Enable Relay Coil open, contacts open, fuse open

If the Ignition is in RUN and the Antilock Brake Controller does not detect any faults, the Controller will close the Rear Enable Relay Control. This grounds the Rear Enable Relay and the Relay becomes energized. The contacts close, and voltage is applied from the ELECT BRAKE VALVE Fuse to the Rear Solenoid. If the Controller is not closing either of the Rear Solenoid Controls, the Controller will sense Battery voltage at terminals 1C14 and 1C15.

CODE A007 will set when all the following conditions exist:
- The Rear Enable Relay Control is closed (Rear Enable Relay energized).
- The Antilock Brake Controller senses no voltage at Terminals 1C14 and 1C15.

TEST DESCRIPTION: The following provides an explanation of the procedures being followed in the trouble tree.

① If Code A005 is also set, none of the Solenoids are receiving voltage. This indicates a problem with connector C161.

② Code A054 will set if the relay coil circuit is open. Diagnostics are covered under code A054.

③ Determines if power feed to Relay contacts is good.

④ If Battery voltage is measured CKT 961 and Rear Solenoid are good.

⑤ Determines if open exists in Rear Solenoid or in CKT 961.

⑥ This determines if Code A007 was set due to a hard failure or an intermittent condition.

⑦ Checks for short to ground in CKT 140.

⑧ If test lamp lights, a short to ground in CKT 961 is indicated.

⑨ Checks for good power feed to ELECT BRAKE VALVE Fuse.

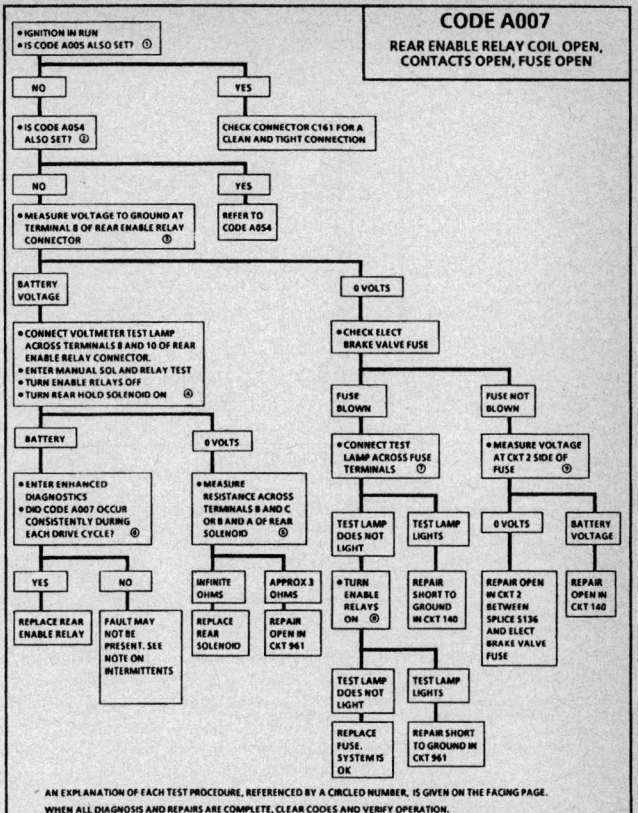

Fig. 14   Code A007, rear enable relay coil open, contacts open, fuse open. 1990 models

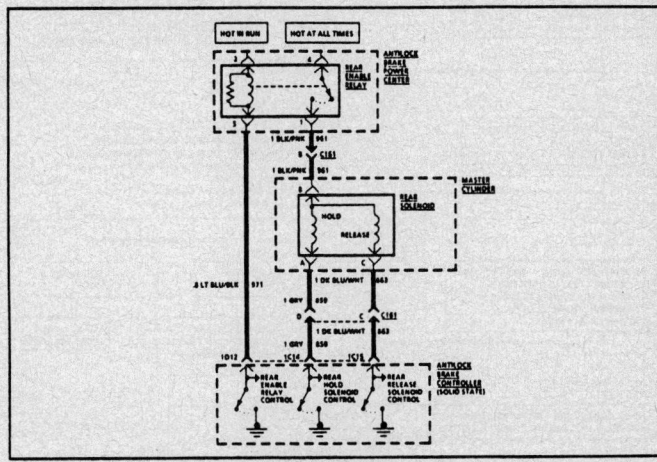

CODE A008

Rear Enable Relay Coil shorted to Battery

Battery voltage is applied to the Rear Enable Relay and CKT 971 whenever the Ignition is in RUN and the Rear Enable Relay Control is open. When the Rear Enable Relay Control is closed, ground is applied to terminal 7 of the Rear Enable Relay. CKT 971 is now grounded, so voltage is no longer present at terminal 1D12 of the Antilock Brake Controller.

CODE A008 will set when all the following conditions exist:
- The Rear Enable Relay Control is closed (Rear Enable Relay energized).
- The Antilock Brake Controller senses Battery voltage at Terminal 1D12.
- The Antilock Brake Controller senses no voltage at Terminals 1C14 and 1C15.

TEST DESCRIPTION: The following provides an explanation of the procedures being followed in the facing trouble tree.

① With the Rear Enable Relay disconnected it can be determined whether a short to Battery exists in the 971 CKT (Battery voltage present at Terminal 7 of Rear Enable Relay connector).

② Determines if a short exists internally in the Rear Enable Relay or whether the Antilock Brake Controller is defective.

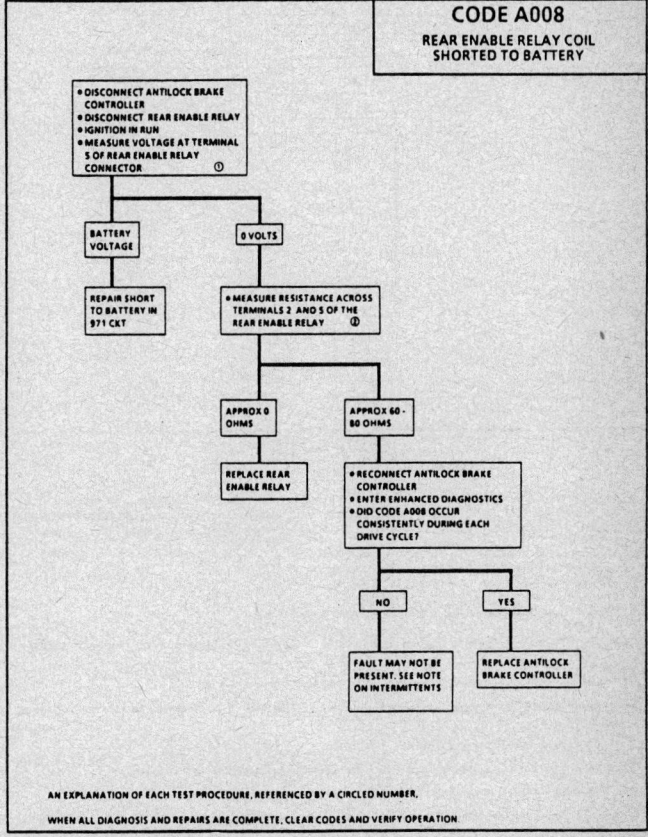

Fig. 15   Code A008, rear enable relay coil shorted to battery. 1989 models

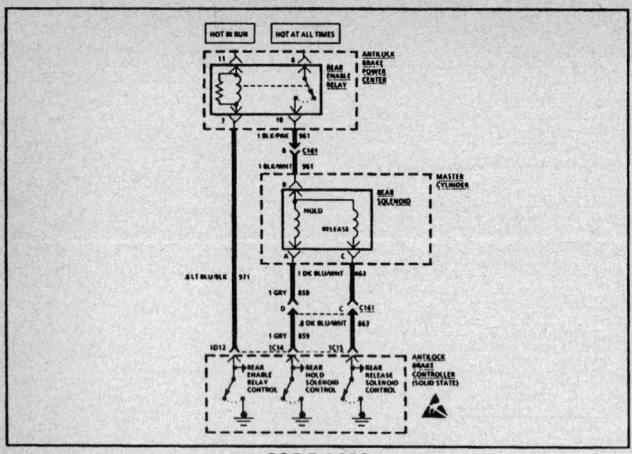

CODE A008

Rear Enable Relay Coil shorted to Battery

Battery voltage is applied to the Rear Enable Relay and CKT 971 whenever the Ignition is in RUN and the Rear Enable Relay Control is open. When the Rear Enable Relay Control is closed, ground is applied to terminal 7 of the Rear Enable Relay. CKT 971 is now grounded, so voltage is no longer present at terminal 1D12 of the Antilock Brake Controller.

CODE A008 will set when all the following conditions exist:
- The Rear Enable Relay Control is closed (Rear Enable Relay energized).
- The Antilock Brake Controller senses Battery voltage at Terminal 1D12.
- The Antilock Brake Controller senses no voltage at Terminals 1C14 and 1C15.

TEST DESCRIPTION: The following provides an explanation of the procedures being followed in the facing trouble tree.

① With the Rear Enable Relay disconnected it can be determined whether a short to Battery exists in the 971 CKT (Battery voltage present at Terminal 7 of Rear Enable Relay connector).

② Determines if a short exists internally in the Rear Enable Relay or whether the Antilock Brake Controller is defective.

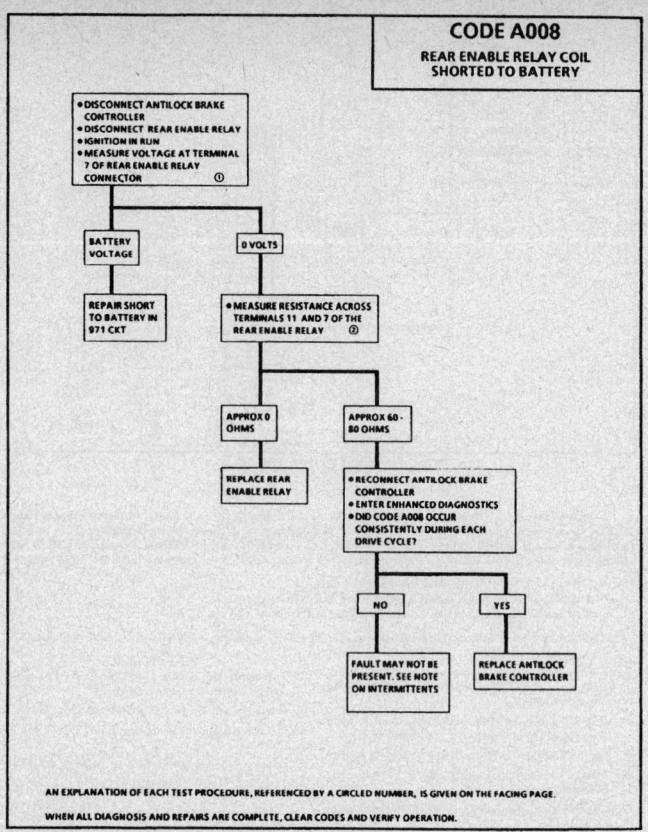

CODE A008
REAR ENABLE RELAY COIL SHORTED TO BATTERY

AN EXPLANATION OF EACH TEST PROCEDURE, REFERENCED BY A CIRCLED NUMBER, IS GIVEN ON THE FACING PAGE.

WHEN ALL DIAGNOSIS AND REPAIRS ARE COMPLETE, CLEAR CODES AND VERIFY OPERATION.

Fig. 16   Code A008, rear enable relay coil shorted to battery. 1990 models

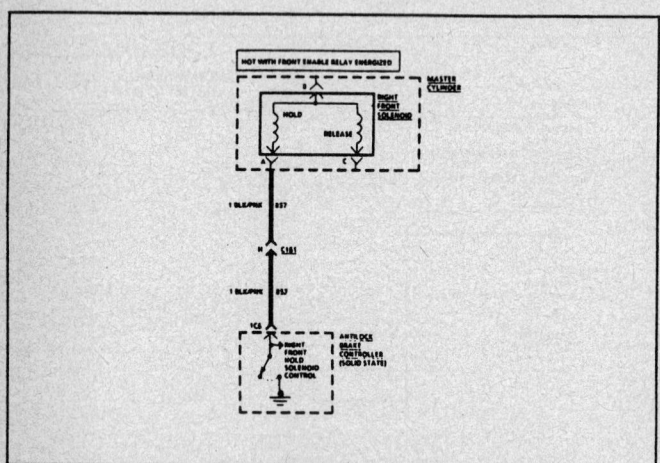

CODE A009

Right Front Hold Solenoid open or shorted to ground

When the Front Enable Relay is energized, voltage is applied to the Right Front Solenoid. If the Antilock Brake Controller determines that the Right Front Hold Solenoid should be activated, it will close the Right Front Hold Solenoid Control. Ground is now applied at terminal A of the Right Front Solenoid, so the Right Front Hold Solenoid is on.

CODE A009 will set when all the following conditions exist:
- The Front Enable Relay is energized.
- The Right Front Hold Solenoid control is open.
- The Antilock Brake Controller senses no voltage at terminal 1C6.

TEST DESCRIPTION: The following provides an explanation of the procedures being followed in the facing trouble tree.

① If Code A012 is also set, the power feed to the Right Front Solenoid is open.

② Voltage at terminal 1C6 will cause the scan tool to display a HI feedback. A LO feedback indicates that voltage is not present.

③ A short to ground must be present if the test lamp lights.

④ If short to ground does not exist with Controller disconnected, short is internal to Controller.

⑤ CKT 962 is OK if the test lamp lights. Open must be internal to solenoid.

⑥ If continuity to ground through the Front Enable Relay contacts is present, open must be internal to Controller.

⑦ Determines if open is in Solenoid or 857 CKT.

CODE A009
RIGHT FRONT HOLD SOLENOID OPEN OR SHORTED TO GROUND

AN EXPLANATION OF EACH TEST PROCEDURE, REFERENCED BY A CIRCLED NUMBER.

WHEN ALL DIAGNOSIS AND REPAIRS ARE COMPLETE, CLEAR CODES AND VERIFY OPERATION.

Fig. 17   Code A009, right front hold solenoid open or shorted to ground

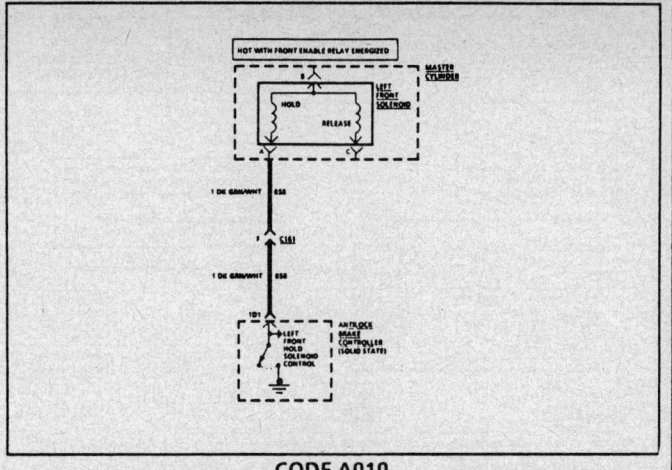

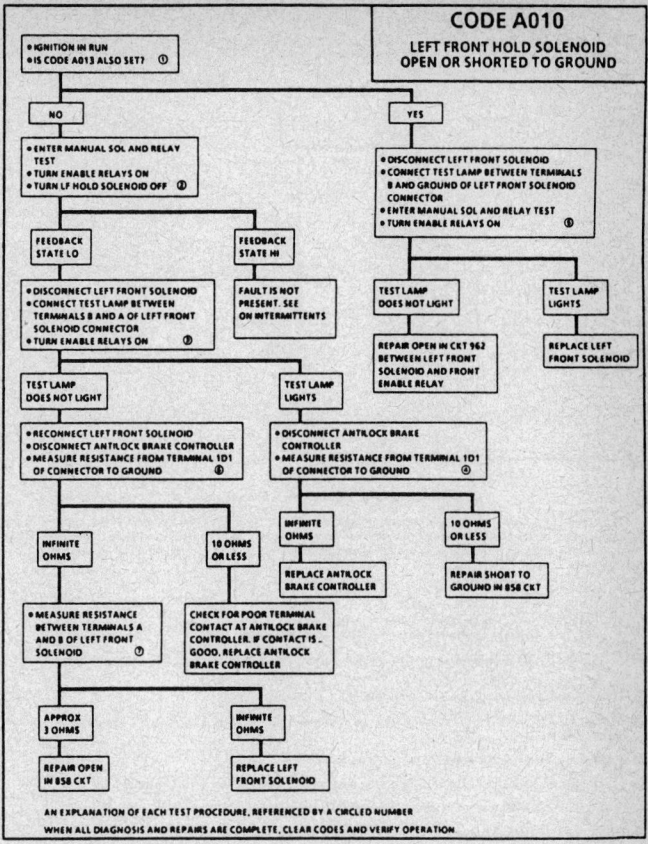

CODE A010
Left Front Hold Solenoid open or shorted to ground

When the Front Enable Relay is energized, voltage is applied to the Left Front Solenoid. If the Antilock Brake Controller determines that the Left Front Hold Solenoid should be activated, it will close the Left Front Hold Solenoid Control. Ground is now applied at terminal A of the Left Front Solenoid, so the Left Front Hold Solenoid is on.

CODE A010 will set when all the following conditions exist:
- The Front Enable Relay is energized.
- The Left Front Hold Solenoid Control is open.
- The Antilock Brake Controller senses no voltage at Terminal 1D1.

TEST DESCRIPTION: The following provides an explanation of the procedures being followed in the facing trouble tree.

① If Code A013 is also set, the power feed to the Left Front Solenoid is open.

② Voltage at terminal 1D1 will cause the scan tool to display HI feedback. A LO feedback indicates that voltage is not present.

③ A short to ground must be present if the test lamp lights.

④ If short to ground does not exist with controller disconnected, short is internal to Controller.

⑤ CKT 962 is OK if the test lamp lights. Open must be internal to solenoid.

⑥ If continuity to ground through the Front Enable Relay Contacts is present, open must be internal to Controller.

⑦ Determines if open is in solenoid or 858 CKT.

Fig. 18 Code A010, left front hold solenoid open or shorted to ground

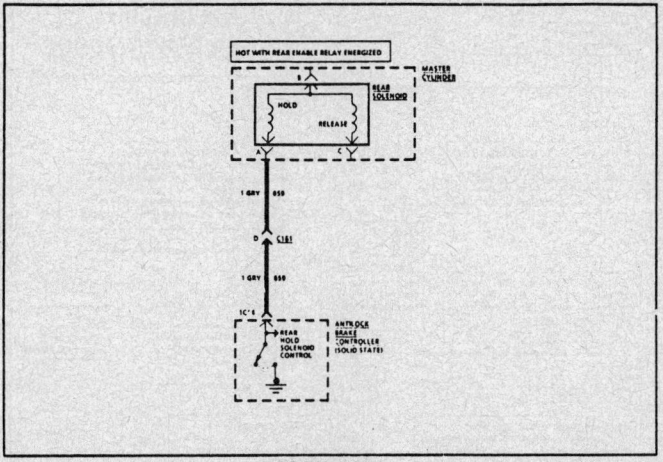

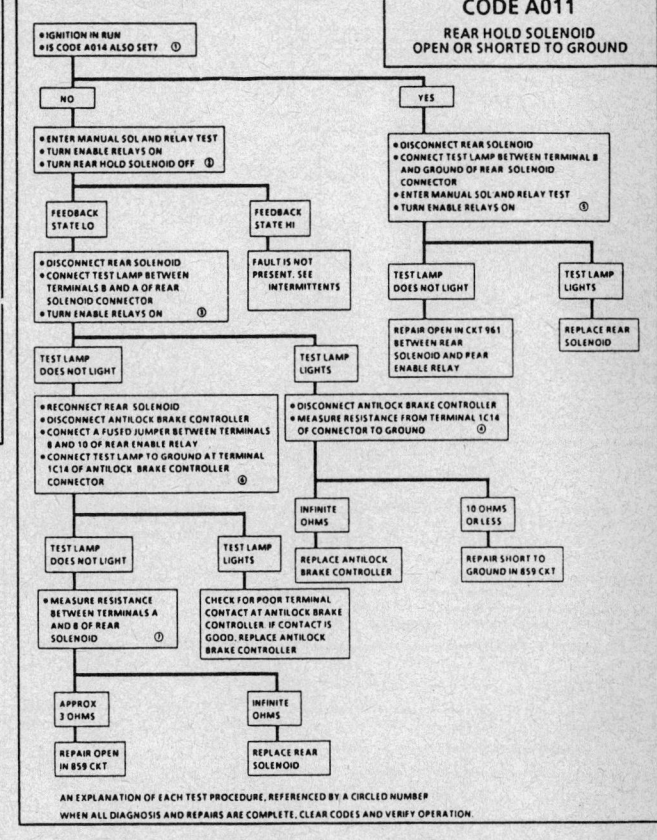

CODE A011
Rear Hold Solenoid open or shorted to ground

When the Rear Enable Relay is energized, voltage is applied to the Rear Solenoid. If the Antilock Brake Controller determines that the Rear Hold Solenoid should be activated, it will close the Rear Hold Solenoid Control. Ground is now applied at terminal A of the Rear Solenoid, so the Rear Hold Solenoid is on.

CODE A011 will set when all the following conditions exist:
- The Rear Enable Relay is energized.
- The Rear Hold Solenoid Control is open.
- The Antilock Brake Controller senses no voltage at Terminal 1C14.

TEST DESCRIPTION: The following provides an explanation of the procedures being followed in the facing trouble tree.

① If Code A014 is also set, the power feed to the Rear Solenoid is open.

② Voltage at terminal 1C14 will cause the scan tool to display a HI feedback. A LO feedback indicates that voltage is not present.

③ A short to ground must be present if the test lamp lights.

④ If short to ground does not exist with Controller disconnected, short is internal to Controller.

⑤ CKT 961 is OK if the test lamp lights. Open must be internal to solenoid.

⑥ If test lamp lights, Rear Hold Solenoid and CKT 859 are good. Open must be internal to Controller.

⑦ Determines if open is in Solenoid or 859 CKT.

Fig. 19 Code A011, rear hold solenoid open or shorted to ground

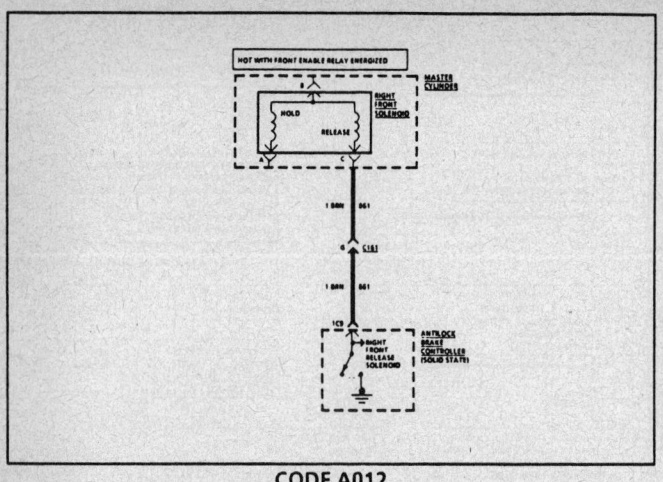

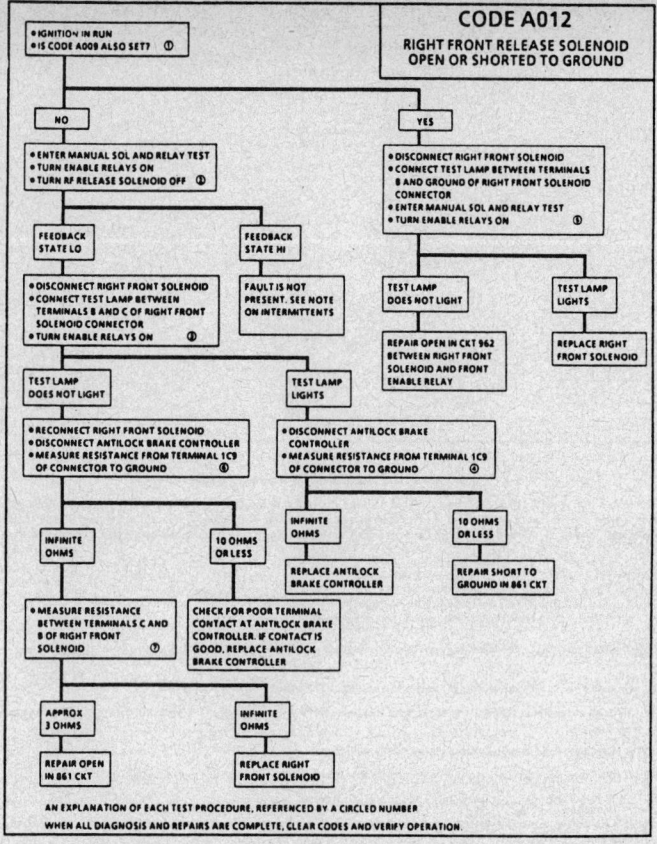

CODE A012
Right Front Release Solenoid open or shorted to ground

When the Front Enable Relay is energized, voltage is applied to the Right Front Solenoid. If the Antilock Brake Controller determines that the Right Front Release Solenoid should be activated, it will close the Right Front Release Solenoid Control. Ground is now applied at terminal C of the Right Front Solenoid, so the Right Front Release Solenoid is on.

CODE A012 will set when all the following conditions exist:
- The Front Enable Relay is energized.
- The Right Front Release Solenoid Control is open.
- The Antilock Brake Controller senses no voltage at Terminal 1C9.

TEST DESCRIPTION: The following provides an explanation of the procedures being followed in the facing trouble tree.

① If Code A009 is also set, the power feed to the Right Front Solenoid is open.

② Voltage at terminal 1C9 will cause the scan tool to display a HI feedback. A LO feedback indicates that voltage is not present.

③ A short to ground must be present if the test lamp lights.

④ If short to ground does not exist with Controller disconnected, short is internal to Controller.

⑤ CKT 962 is OK, if the test lamp lights. Open must be internal to solenoid.

⑥ If continuity to ground through the Front Enable Relay is present, open must be internal to Controller.

⑦ Determines if open is in Solenoid or 861 CKT.

Fig. 20   Code A012, right front release solenoid open or shorted to ground

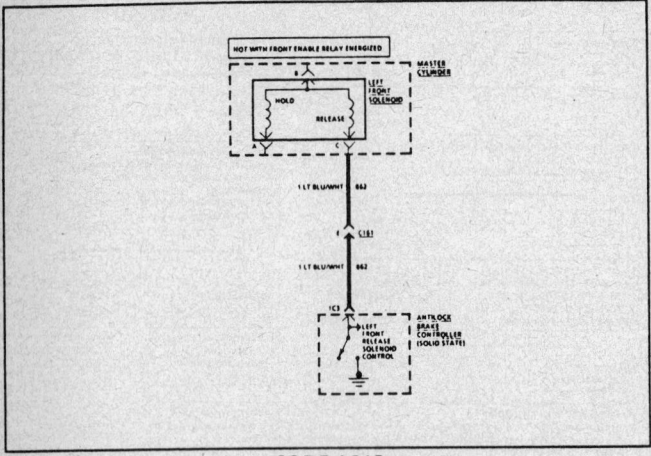

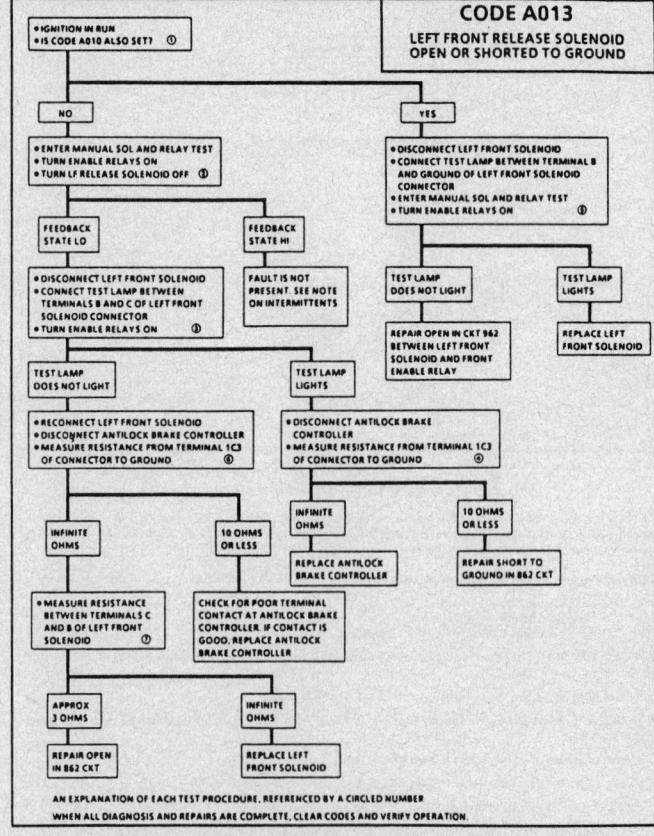

CODE A013
Left Front Release Solenoid open or shorted to ground

When the Front Enable Relay is energized, voltage is applied to the Left Front Solenoid. If the Antilock Brake Controller determines that the Left Front Release Solenoid should be activated, it will close the Left Front Release Solenoid Control. Ground is now applied at terminal C of the Left Front Solenoid, so the Left Front Release Solenoid is on.

CODE A013 will set when all the following conditions exist:
- The Front Enable Relay is energized.
- The Left Front Release Solenoid Control is open.
- The Antilock Brake Controller senses no voltage at Terminal 1C3.

TEST DESCRIPTION: The following provides an explanation of the procedures being followed in the facing trouble tree.

① If Code A010 is also set, the power feed to the Left Front Solenoid is open.

② Voltage at terminal 1C3 will cause the scan tool to display a HI feedback. A LO feedback indicates that voltage is not present.

③ A short to ground must be present if the test lamp lights.

④ If short to ground does not exist with controller disconnected, short is internal to controller.

⑤ CKT 962 is OK if the test lamp lights. Open must be internal to solenoid.

⑥ If continuity to ground through the Front Enable Relay is present, open must be internal to Controller.

⑦ Determines if open is in solenoid or 862 CKT.

Fig. 21   Code A013, left front release solenoid open or shorted to ground

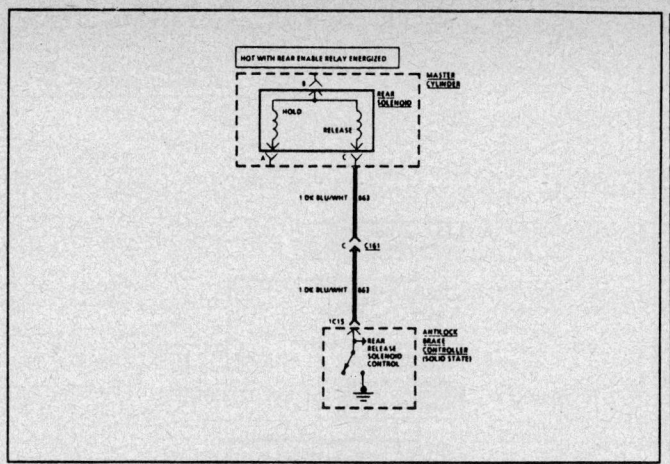

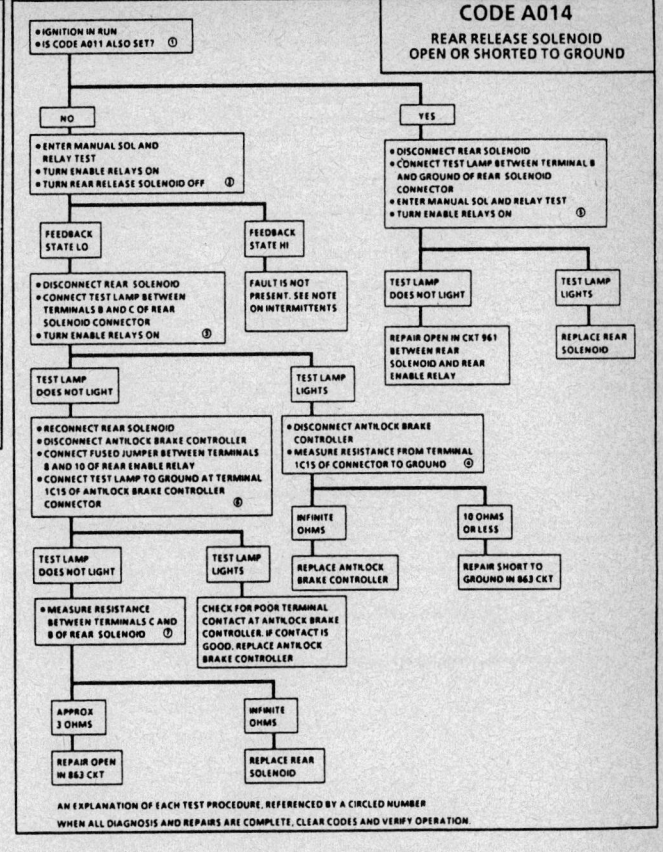

CODE A014

Rear Release Solenoid open or shorted to ground

When the Rear Enable Relay is energized, voltage is applied to the Rear Solenoid. If the Antilock Brake Controller determines that the Rear Release Solenoid should be activated, it will close the Rear Release Solenoid Control. Ground is now applied at terminal C of the Rear Solenoid, so the Rear Release Solenoid is on.

CODE A014 will set when all the following conditions exist:
* The Rear Enable Relay is energized.
* The Rear Release Solenoid Control is open.
* The Antilock Brake Controller senses no voltage at terminal 1C15.

TEST DESCRIPTION: The following provides an explanation of the procedures being followed in the facing trouble tree.

① If Code A011 is also set, the power feed to the Rear Solenoid is open.

② Voltage at terminal 1C15 will cause the scan tool to display a HI feedback. A LO feedback indicates that voltage is not present.

③ A short to ground must be present if the test lamp lights.

④ If short to ground does not exist with controller disconnected, short is internal to controller.

⑤ CKT 962 is OK if test lamp lights. Open must be internal to solenoid.

⑥ If test lamp lights, Rear Release Solenoid and CKT 863 are good. Open must be internal to controller.

⑦ Determines if open is in Solenoid or 863 CKT

Fig. 22 Code A014, rear release solenoid open or shorted to ground

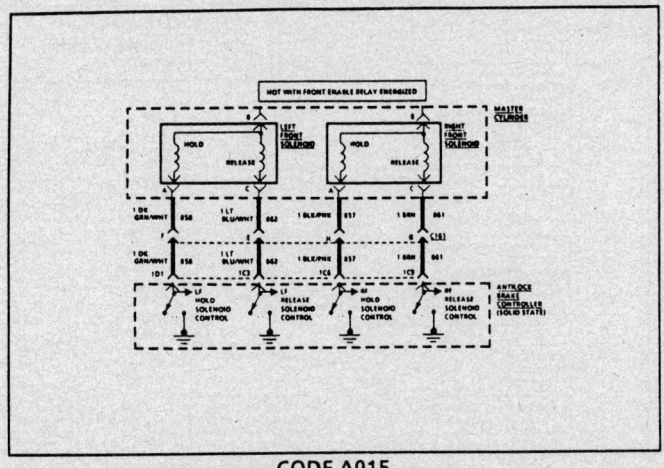

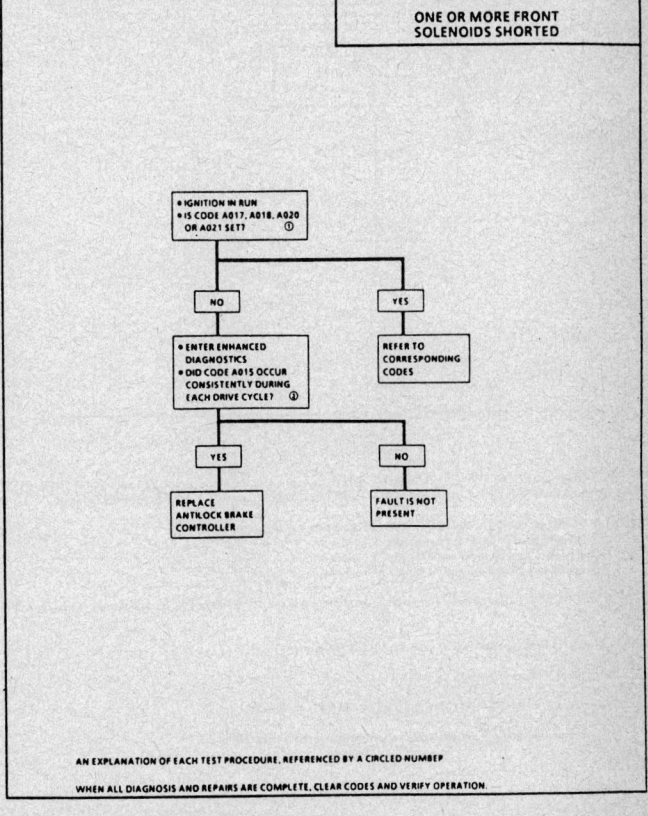

CODE A015

One or more Front Solenoids shorted

CODE A015 will set when the Antilock Brake Controller senses Battery voltage at Terminal 1D1, 1C3, 1C6 or 1C9 when the corresponding Solenoid Control is closed.

TEST DESCRIPTION: The following provides an explanation of the procedures being followed in the facing trouble tree.

① The reason for referring to these codes is that the fault that caused Code A015 to set will be linked to a specific circuit.

② If the failure is consistent, Antilock Brake Controller has an internal fault.

Fig. 23 Code A015, one or more front solenoids shorted

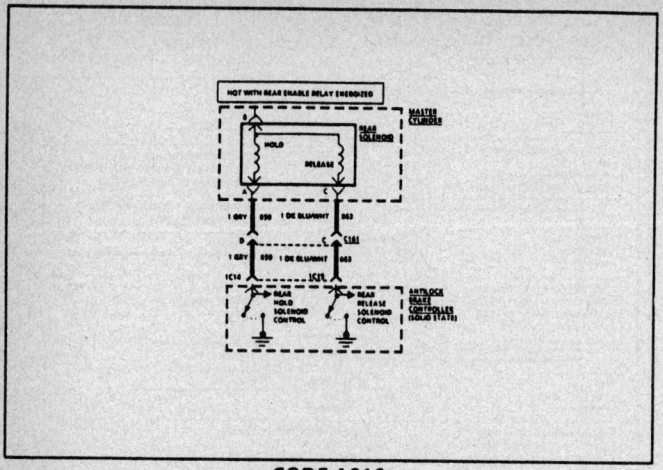

CODE A016
One or both Rear Solenoids shorted

CODE A016 will set when the Antilock Brake Controller senses Battery voltage at Terminal 1C14 or 1C15 when the corresponding Solenoid Control is closed.

TEST DESCRIPTION: The following provides an explanation of the procedures being followed in the facing trouble tree.

① The reason for refering to these codes is that the fault that caused Code A016 to set will be linked to a specific circuit.

② If the failure is consistent, Antilock Brake Controller has an internal fault.

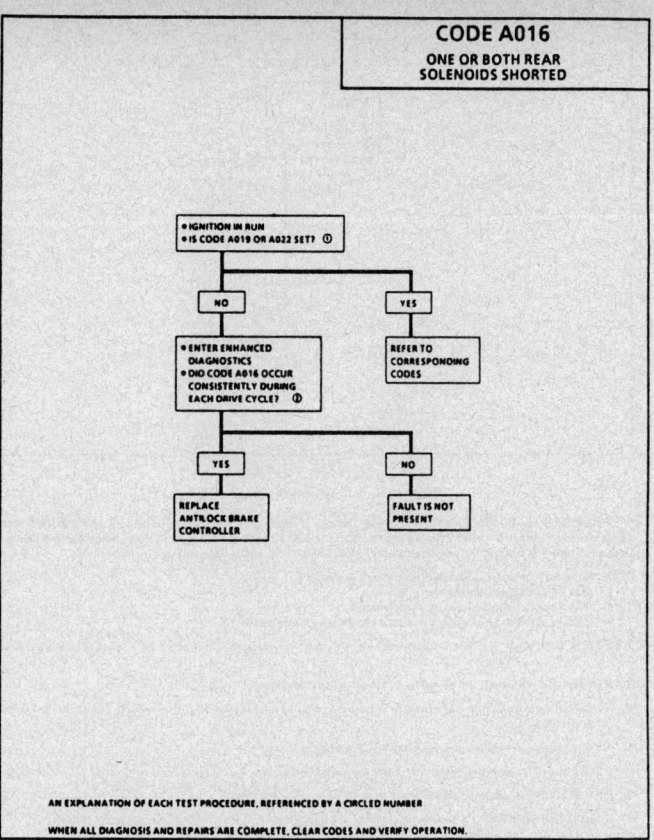

CODE A016
ONE OR BOTH REAR SOLENOIDS SHORTED

AN EXPLANATION OF EACH TEST PROCEDURE, REFERENCED BY A CIRCLED NUMBER

WHEN ALL DIAGNOSIS AND REPAIRS ARE COMPLETE, CLEAR CODES AND VERIFY OPERATION.

Fig. 24   Code A016, one or both rear solenoids shorted

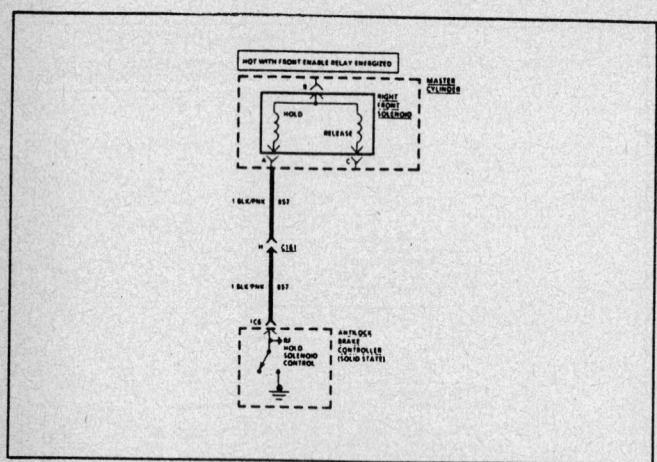

CODE A017
Right Front Hold Solenoid shorted

When the Front Enable Relay is energized, voltage is applied to the Right Front Solenoid. If the Right Front Hold Solenoid Control is closed, ground is applied to CKT 857. This activates the Right Front Hold Solenoid.

CODE A017 will set during initialization when all the following conditions exist:
• The Front Enable Relay is energized.
• The Right Front Hold Solenoid Control is closed.
• The Antilock Brake Controller senses Battery voltage at Terminal 1C6.

TEST DESCRIPTION: The following provides an explanation of the procedures being followed in the facing trouble tree.

① This determines if condition that set code A017 is still present.

③ Determines if short to Battery exists.

② Determines if short to Battery is in 857 CKT or internal to controller.

④ If Right Front Solenoid is not shorted, fault must be internal to controller.

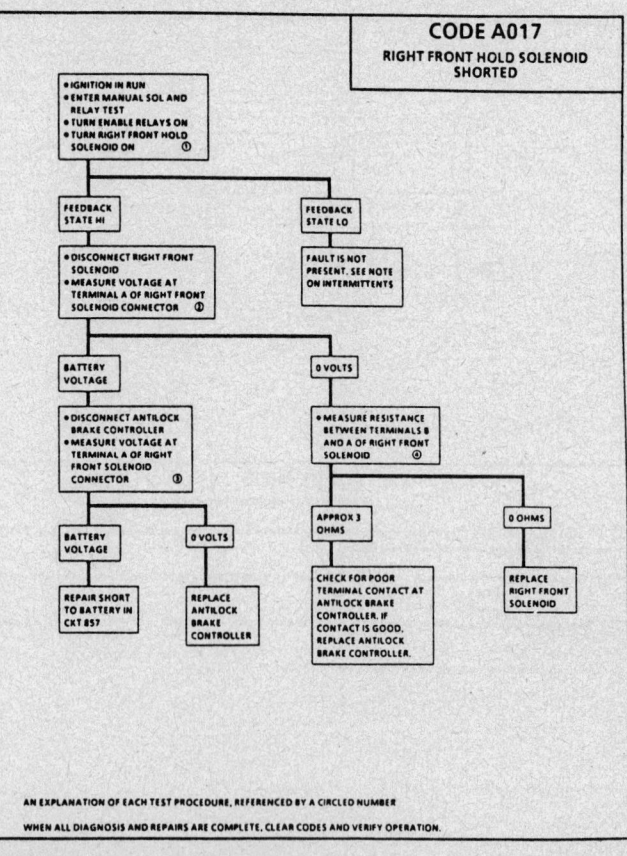

CODE A017
RIGHT FRONT HOLD SOLENOID SHORTED

AN EXPLANATION OF EACH TEST PROCEDURE, REFERENCED BY A CIRCLED NUMBER

WHEN ALL DIAGNOSIS AND REPAIRS ARE COMPLETE, CLEAR CODES AND VERIFY OPERATION.

Fig. 25   Code A017, right front hold solenoid shorted

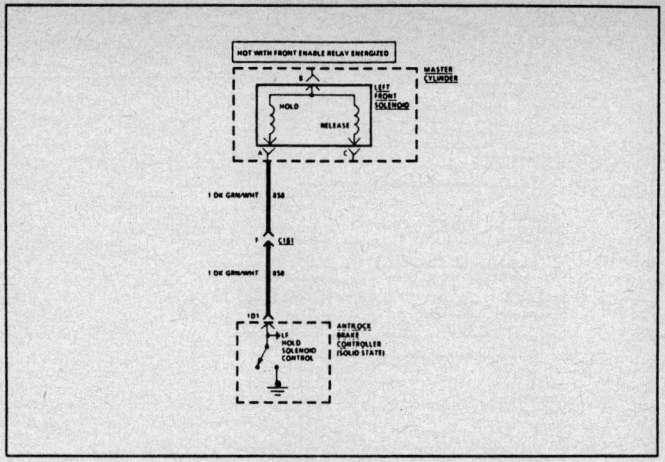

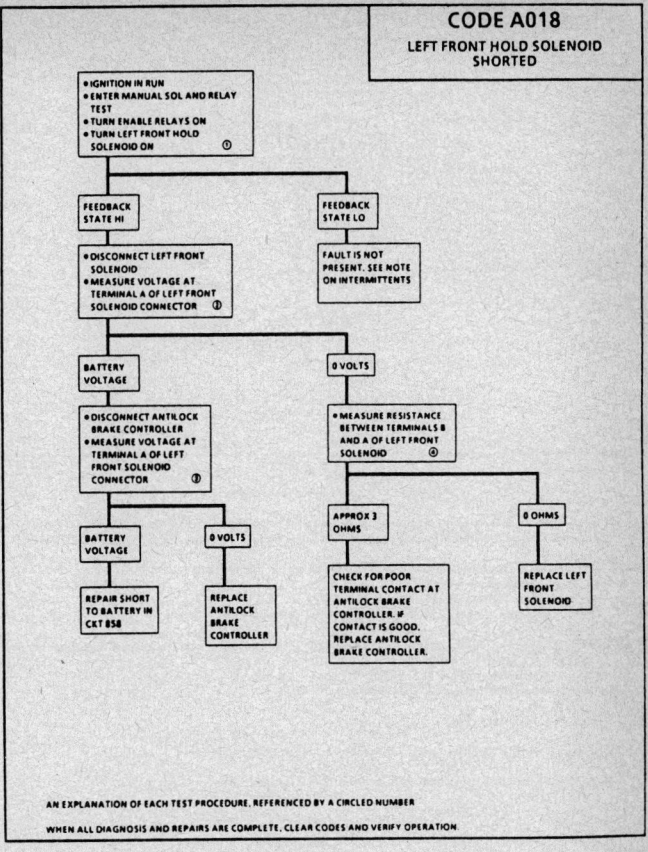

CODE A018

Left Front Hold Solenoid shorted

When the Front Enable Relay is energized, voltage is applied to the Left Front Solenoid. If the Left Front Hold Solenoid Control is closed, ground is applied to CKT 858. This activates the Left Front Hold Solenoid.

CODE A018 will set during initialization when all the following conditions exist:
- The Front Enable Relay is energized.
- The Left Front Hold Solenoid Control is closed.
- The Antilock Brake Controller senses Battery voltage at Terminal 1D1.

TEST DESCRIPTION: The following provides an explanation of the procedures being followed in the facing trouble tree.

① This determines if condition that set code A018 is still present.

② Checks if short to Battery exists.

③ Determines if short to Battery is in 858 CKT or internal to controller

④ If Left Front Solenoid is not shorted, fault must be internal to controller.

Fig. 26   Code A018, left front hold solenoid shorted

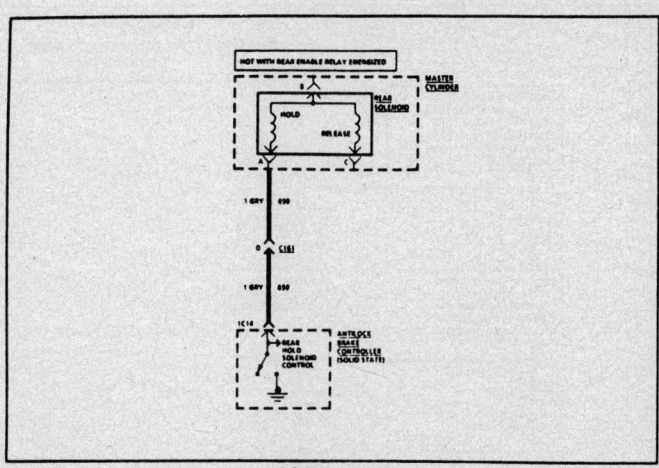

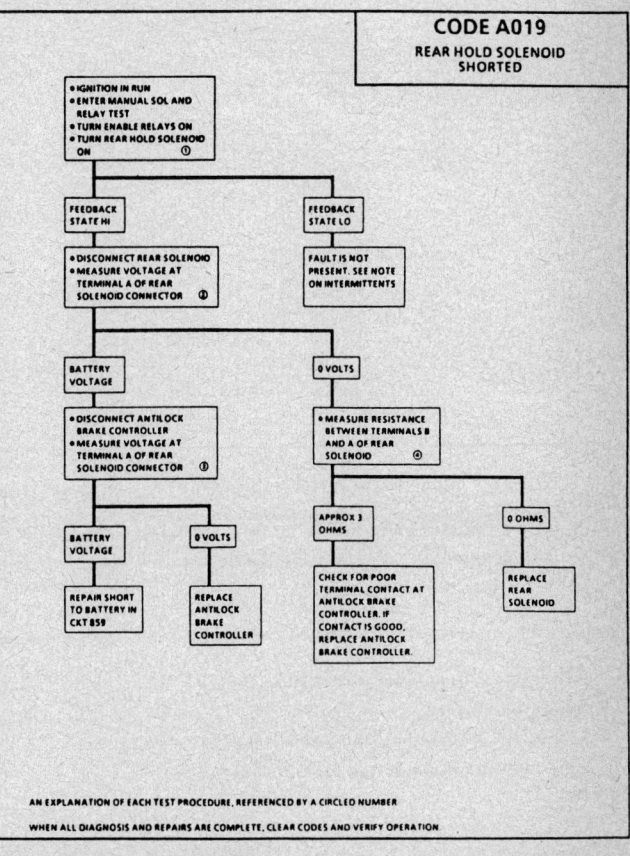

CODE A019

Rear Hold Solenoid shorted

When the Rear Enable Relay is energized, voltage is applied to the Rear Solenoid. If the Rear Hold Solenoid Control is closed, ground is applied to CKT 859. This activates the Rear Hold Solenoid.

CODE A019 will set during initialization when all the following conditions exist:
- The Rear Enable Relay is energized.
- The Rear Hold Solenoid Control is closed.
- The Antilock Brake Controller senses Battery voltage at Terminal 1C14.

TEST DESCRIPTION: The following provides an explanation of the procedures being followed in the facing trouble tree.

① This determines if condition that set code A019 is still present.

② Checks if short to Battery exists.

③ Determines if short to Battery is in 859 CKT or internal to controller.

④ If Rear Solenoid is not shorted, fault must be internal to controller.

Fig. 27   Code A019, rear hold solenoid shorted

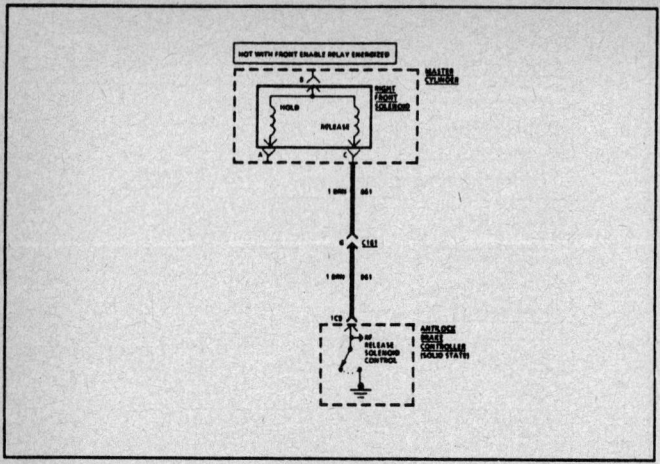

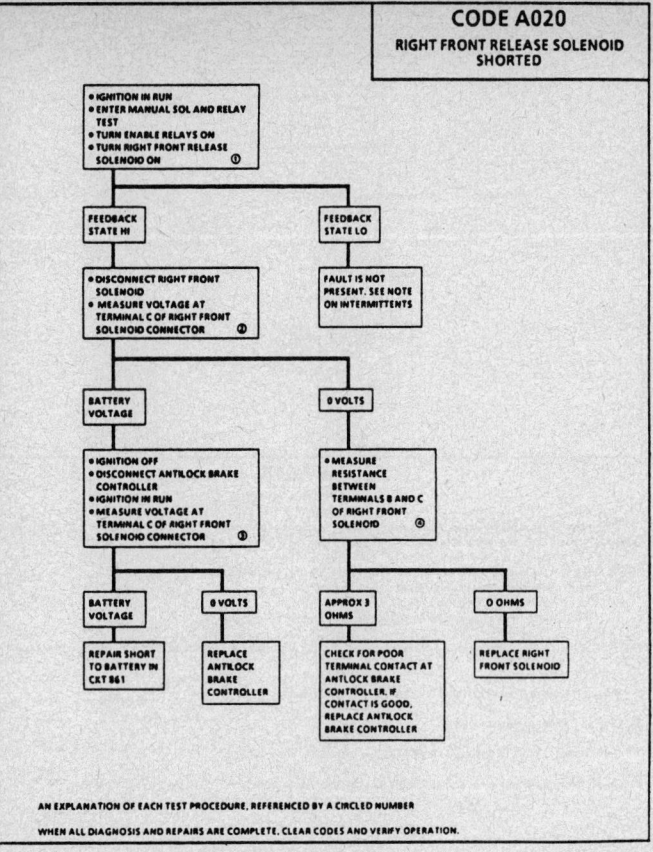

CODE A020
Right Front Release Solenoid shorted

When the Front Enable Relay is energized, voltage is applied to the Right Front Solenoid. If the Right Front Release Solenoid Control is closed, ground is applied to CKT 861. This activates the Right Front Release Solenoid.

CODE A020 will set during initialization when all the following conditions exist:
- The Front Enable Relay is energized.
- The Right Front Release Solenoid Control is closed.
- The Antilock Brake Controller senses Battery voltage at Terminal 1C9.

TEST DESCRIPTION: The following provides an explanation of the procedures being followed in the facing trouble tree.

① This determines if condition that set Code A020 is still present.

② Checks if short to Battery exists.

③ Determines if short to Battery is in 861 CKT or internal to Controller.

④ If Right Front Solenoid is not shorted, fault must be internal to Controller.

Fig. 28   Code A020, right front release solenoid shorted

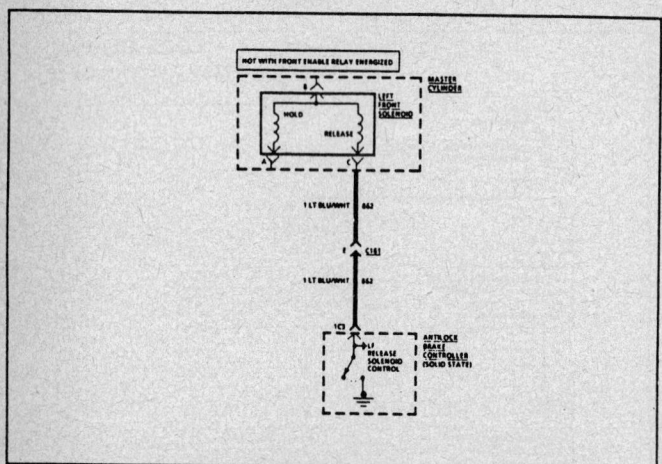

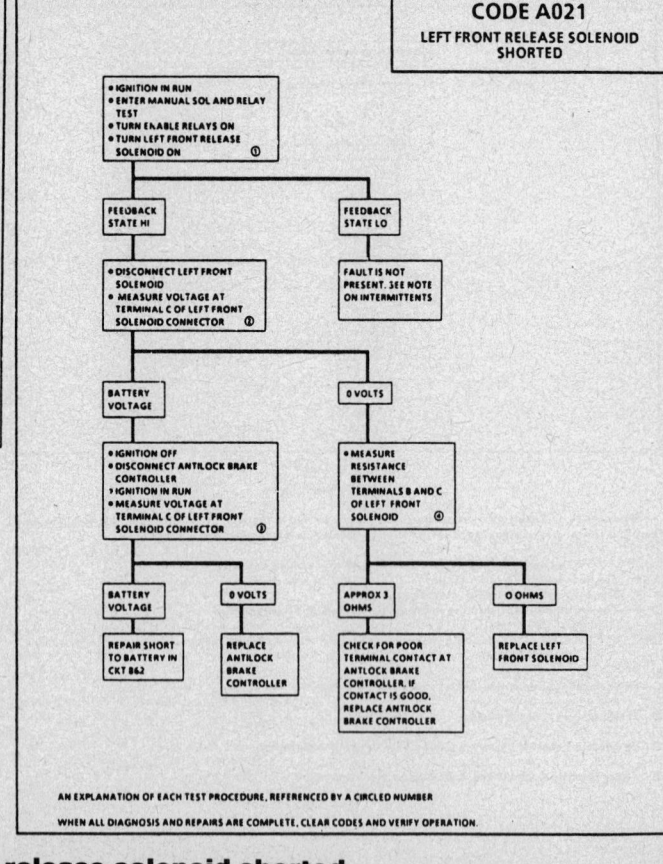

CODE A021
Left Front Release Solenoid shorted

When the Front Enable Relay is energized, voltage is applied to the Left Front Solenoid. If the Left Front Release Solenoid Control is closed, ground is applied to CKT 862. This activates the Left Front Release Solenoid.

CODE A021 will set during initialization when all the following conditions exist:
- The Front Enable Relay is energized.
- The Left Front Release Solenoid Control is closed.
- The Antilock Brake Controller senses Battery voltage at Terminal 1C3.

TEST DESCRIPTION: The following provides an explanation of the procedures being followed in the facing trouble tree.

① This determines if condition that set Code A021 is still present.

② Checks if short to Battery exists.

③ Determines if short to Battery is in 862 CKT or internal to Controller.

④ If Left Front Solenoid is not shorted, fault must be internal to Controller.

Fig. 29   Code A021, left front release solenoid shorted

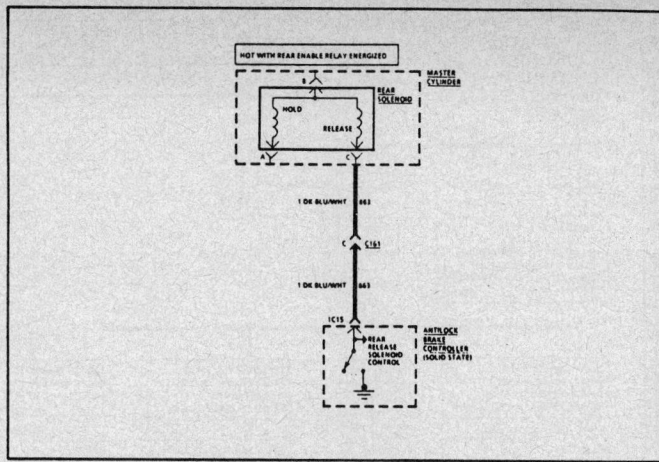

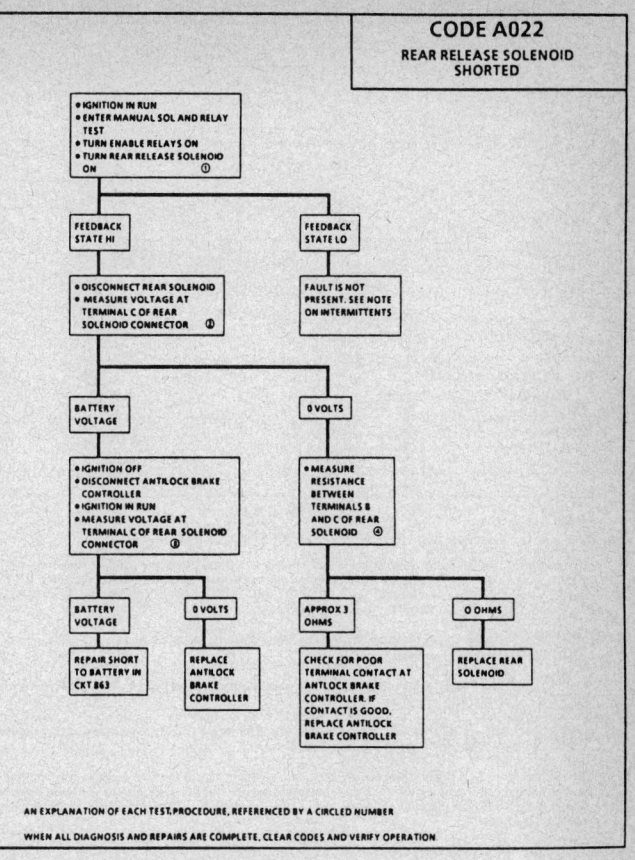

CODE A022
Rear Release Solenoid shorted

When the Rear Enable Relay is energized, voltage is applied to the Rear Solenoid. If the Rear Release Solenoid Control is closed, ground is applied to CKT 863. This activates the Rear Release Solenoid.

CODE A022 will set during initialization when all the following conditions exist:
- The Rear Enable Relay is energized.
- The Rear Release Solenoid Control is closed.
- The Antilock Brake Controller senses Battery voltage at Terminal 1C15.

TEST DESCRIPTION: The following provides an explanation of the procedures being followed in the facing trouble tree.

① This determines if condition that set Code A022 is still present.

② Checks if short to Battery exists.

③ Determines if short to Battery is in 863 CKT or internal to Controller.

④ If Rear Solenoid is not shorted, fault must be internal to Controller.

Fig. 30   Code A022, rear release solenoid shorted

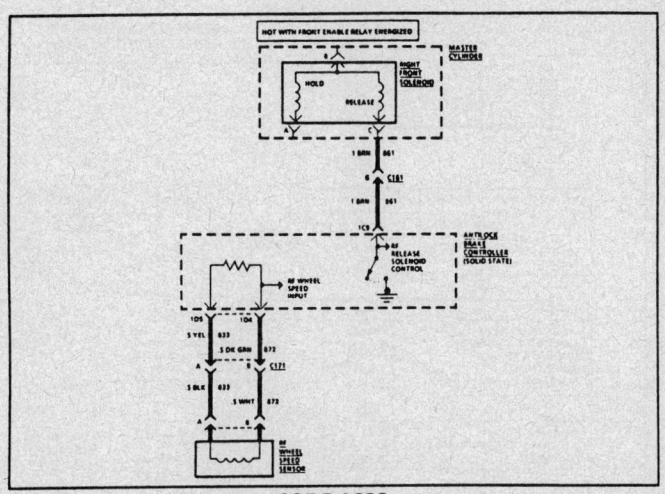

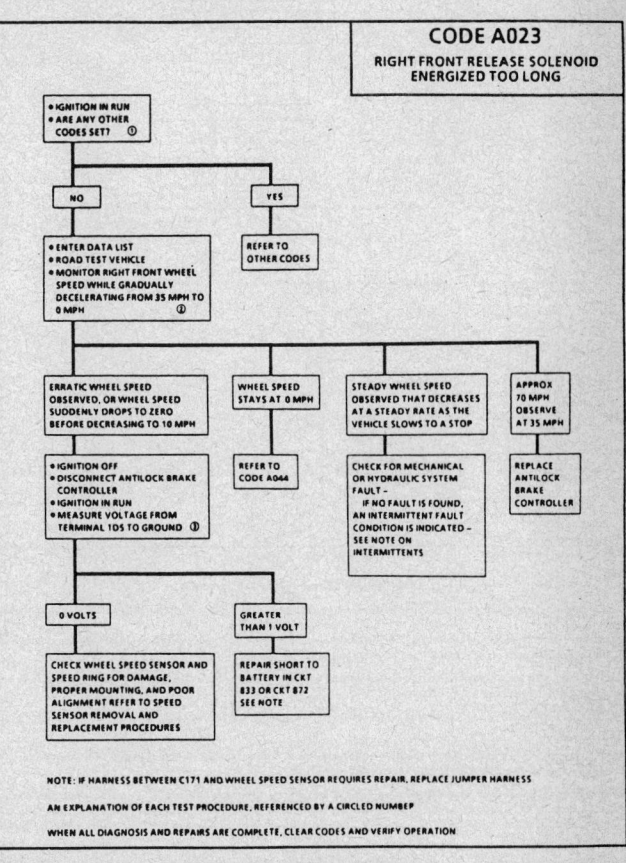

CODE A023
Right Front Release Solenoid energized too long

By monitoring the Right Front Wheel Speed Sensor, the Antilock Brake Controller can determine if the Right Front Wheel is locking up. If this condition occurs, the controller will activate the Right Front Release Solenoid by closing the Right Front Release Solenoid Control. The Solenoid Control will be closed until the Controller determines that the Right Front Wheel has increased to an acceptable speed.

CODE A023 will set when the Antilock Brake Controller senses that the Right Front Release Solenoid has been energized longer than proper operation requires.

TEST DESCRIPTION: The following provides an explanation of the procedures being followed in the facing trouble tree.

① If any other codes are set they should be addressed first. The reason for this is that the fault that caused the solenoid to be energized too long will be better identified.

② By examining the Right Front Wheel Speed input, it can be determined if the fault is due to erratic wheel speed inputs which occur only at low speeds. If the wheel speed input is found to be steady at a low speed a mechanical or hydraulic problem is indicated –   A wheel speed that stays at 0 MPH indicates an open – refer to Code A044.

③ This checks for a possible short to voltage on CKT 833 and CKT 872.

Fig. 31   Code A023, right front release solenoid energized too long

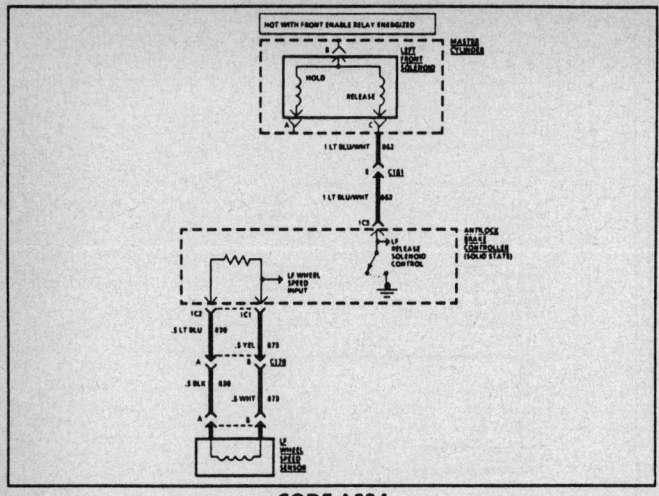

CODE A024
Left Front Release Solenoid energized too long

By monitoring the Left Front Wheel Speed Sensor, the Antilock Brake Controller can determine if the Left Front Wheel is locking up during an ABS stop. If this condition occurs, the Controller will activate the Left Front Release Solenoid by closing the Left Front Release Solenoid Control. The Solenoid Control will be closed until the Controller determines that the Left Front Wheel has increased to an acceptable speed.

CODE A024 will set when the Antilock Brake Controller senses that the Left Front Release Solenoid has been energized longer than proper operation requires.

TEST DESCRIPTION: The following provides an explanation of the procedures being followed in the facing trouble tree.

① If any other codes are set they should be addressed first. The reason for this is that the fault that caused the solenoid to be energized too long will be better identified.

② By examining the Left Front Wheel Speed input, it can be determined if the fault is due to erratic wheel speed inputs which occur only at low speeds. If the wheel speed input is found to be steady at a low speed a mechanical or hydraulic problem is indicated   A wheel speed that stays at 0 MPH indicates an open – refer to Code A045.

③ This checks for a possible short to voltage on CKT 830 and CKT 873.

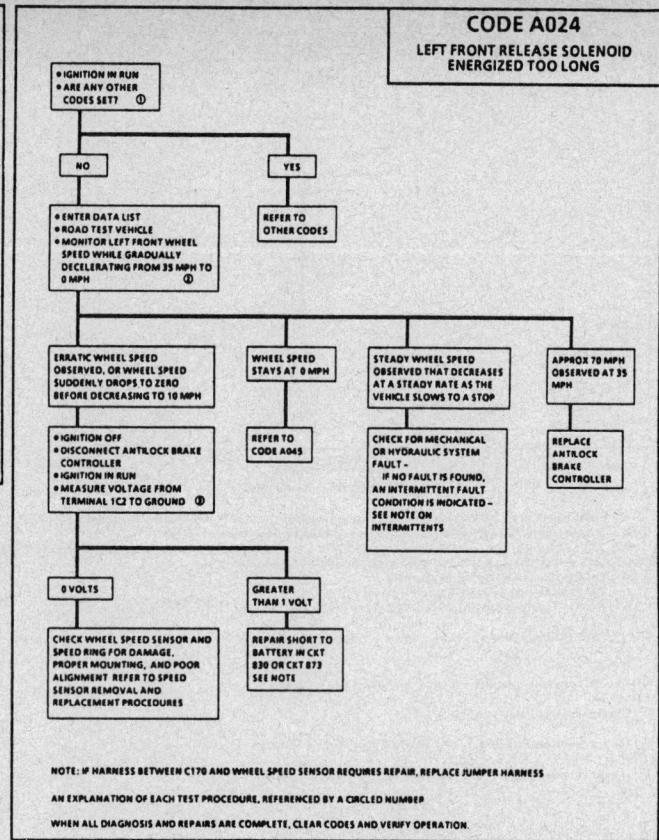

Fig. 32   Code A024, left front release solenoid energized too long

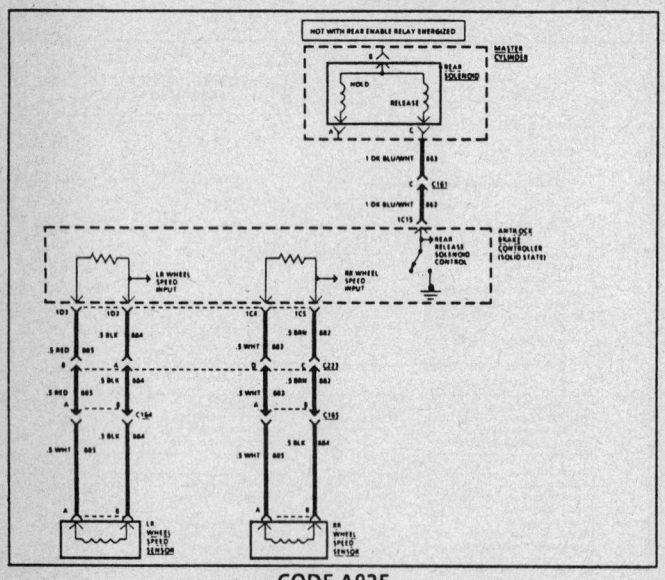

CODE A025
Rear Release Solenoid energized too long

By monitoring the Rear Wheel Speed Sensors, the Antilock Brake Controller can determine if a rear wheel is locking up during an ABS stop. If the condition occurs, the Controller will activate the Rear Release Solenoid by closing the Rear Release Solenoid Control. The Solenoid Control will be closed until the Controller determines that both rear wheels have increased to acceptable speeds.

CODE A025 will set when the Antilock Brake Controller senses that the Rear Release Solenoid has been energized longer than proper operation requires.

TEST DESCRIPTION: The following provides an explanation of the procedures being followed in the facing trouble tree.

① If any other codes are set they should be addressed first. The reason for this is that the fault that caused the solenoid to be energized too long will be better identified.

② By examining the rear wheel speed inputs, it can be determined if the fault is due to erratic wheel speed inputs which occur only at low speeds. If the wheel speed input is found to be steady at low speed, a mechanical or hydraulic problem is indicated-   A wheel speed that stays at 0 MPH indicates an open – refer to Code A046 or A047.

③ This checks for a possible short to ground on the suspect Wheel Speed Sensor Circuit.

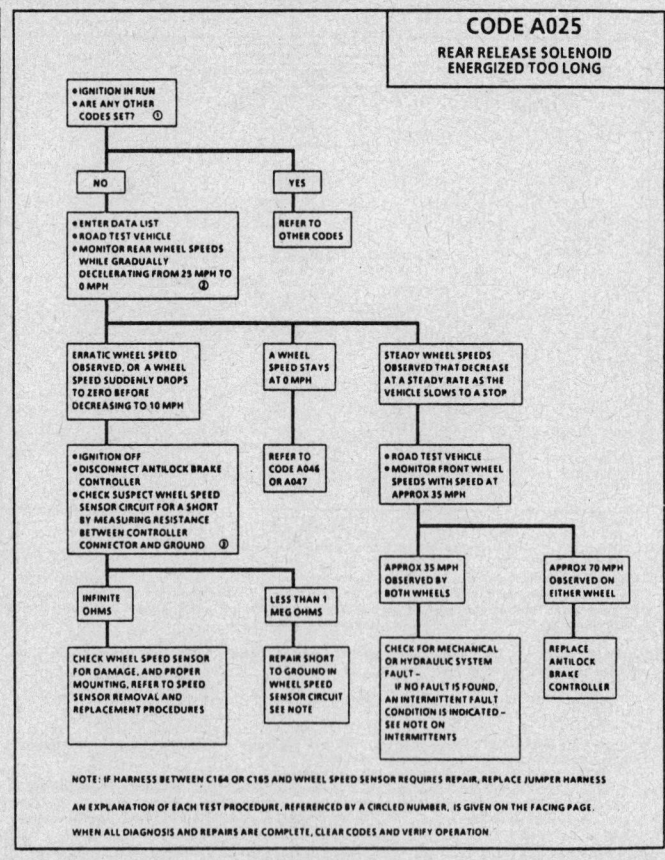

Fig. 33   Code A025, rear release solenoid energized too long

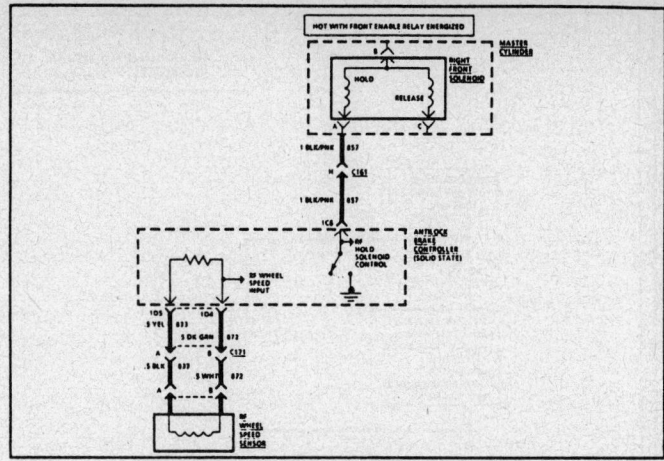

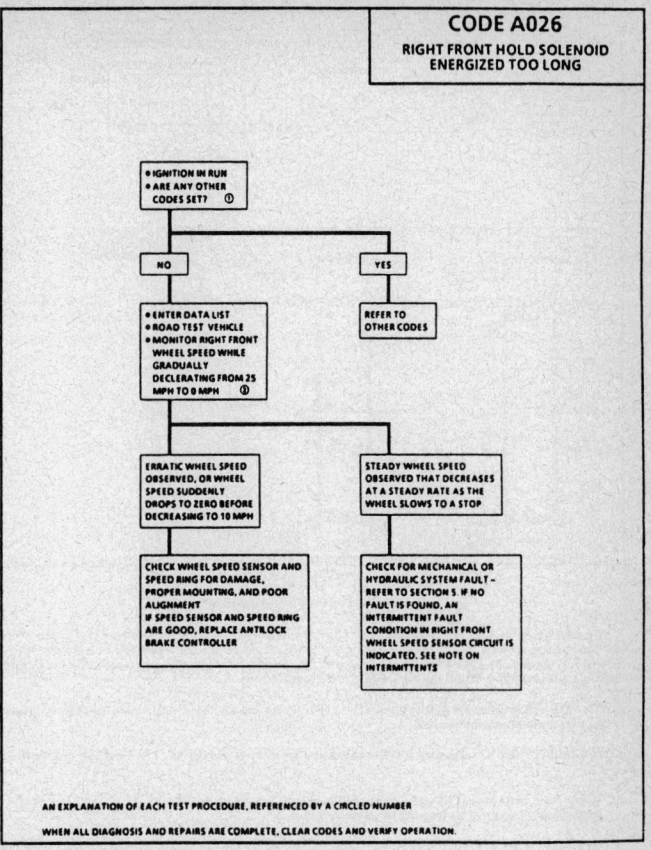

CODE A026
Right Front Hold Solenoid energized too long

By monitoring the Right Front Wheel Speed Sensor, the Antilock Brake Controller can determine if the Right Front Wheel is not decelerating properly during an ABS stop. If this condition occurs, the Controller will activate the Right Front Hold Solenoid by closing the Right Front Hold Solenoid Control. The Solenoid Control will be closed until the Controller determines that the Right Front Wheel has decreased to an acceptable speed.

CODE A026 will set when the Antilock Brake Controller senses that the Right Front Hold Solenoid has been energized longer than proper operation requires.

TEST DESCRIPTION: The following provides an explanation of the procedures being followed in the facing trouble tree.

① If any other codes are set they should be addressed first. The reason for this is that the fault that caused the solenoid to be energized too long will be better identified.

② By examining the Right Front Wheel Speed input, it can be determined if the fault is due to erratic wheel speed inputs which occur only at low speeds. If the wheel speed input is found to be steady at a low speed a mechanical or hydraulic problem is indicated

Fig. 34   Code A026, right front hold solenoid energized too long

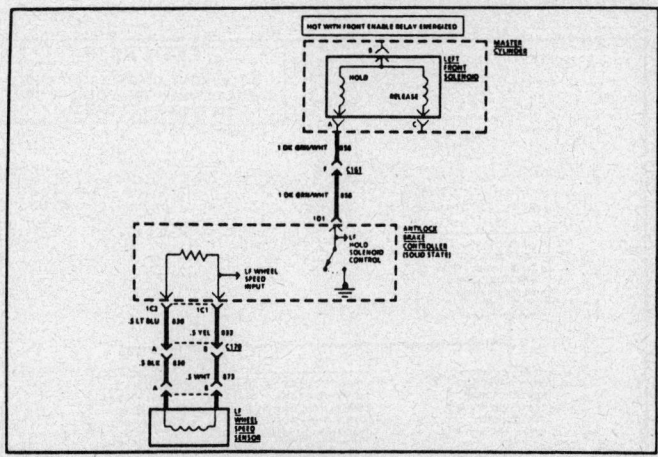

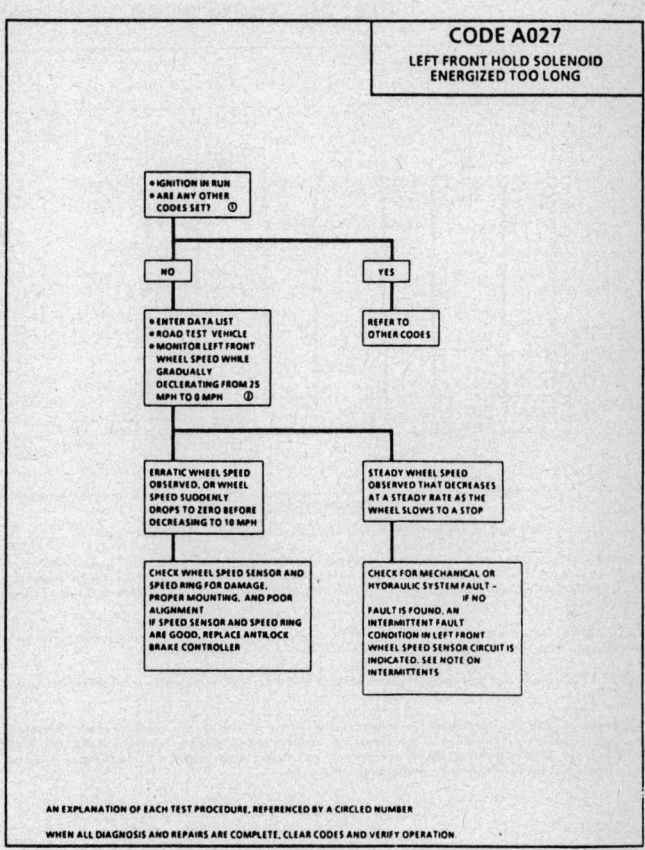

CODE A027
Left Front Hold Solenoid energized too long

By monitoring the Left Front Wheel Speed Sensor, the Antilock Brake Controller can determine if the Left Front Wheel is not decelerating properly during an ABS stop. If this condition occurs, the Controller will activate the Left Front Hold Solenoid by closing the Left Front Hold Solenoid Control. The Solenoid Control will be closed until the Controller determines that the Left Front Wheel has decreased to an acceptable speed.

CODE A027 will set when the Antilock Brake Controller senses that the Left Front Hold Solenoid has been energized longer than proper operation requires.

TEST DESCRIPTION: The following provides an explanation of the procedures being followed in the facing trouble tree.

① If any other codes are set they should be addressed first. The reason for this is that the fault that caused the solenoid to be energized too long will be better identified.

② By examining the Left Front Wheel Speed input, it can be determined if the fault is due to erratic wheel speed inputs which occur only at low speeds. If the wheel speed input is found to be steady at a low speed a mechanical or hydraulic problem is indicated

Fig. 35   Code A027, left front hold solenoid energized too long

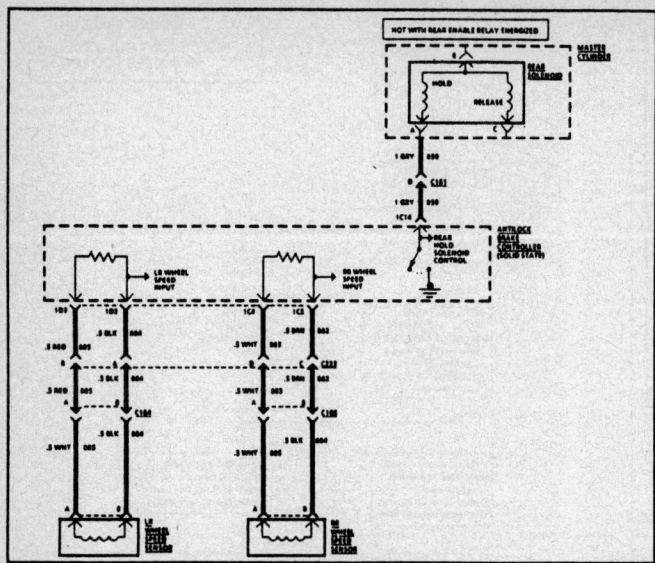

CODE A028
Rear Hold Solenoid energized too long

By monitoring the Rear Wheel Speed Sensors, the Antilock Brake Controller can determine if a Rear Wheel is not decelerating properly during an ABS stop. If this condition occurs, the Controller will activate the Rear Hold Solenoid by closing the Rear Hold Solenoid Control. The Solenoid Control will be closed until the Controller determines that the Rear Wheel has decreased to an acceptable speed.

CODE A028 will set when the Antilock Brake Controller senses that the Rear Hold Solenoid has been energized longer than proper operation requires.

TEST DESCRIPTION: The following provides an explanation of the procedures being followed in the facing trouble tree.

① If any other codes are set they should be addressed first. The reason for this is that the fault that caused the solenoid to be energized too long will be better identified.

② By examining the rear wheel speed inputs, it can be determined if the fault is due to erratic wheel speed inputs which occur only at low speeds. If the wheel speed input is found to be steady at low speed a mechanical or hydraulic problem is indicated

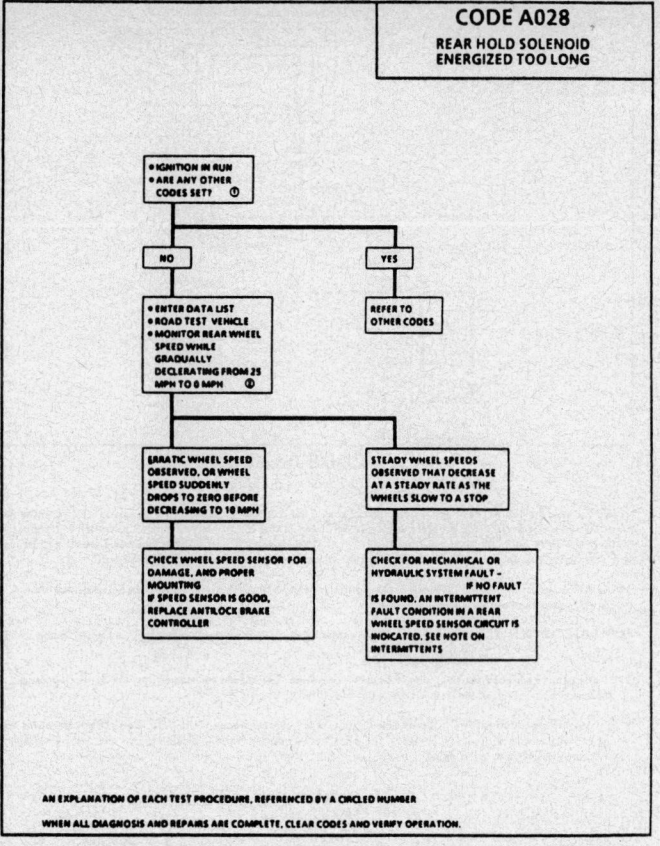

CODE A028
REAR HOLD SOLENOID
ENERGIZED TOO LONG

AN EXPLANATION OF EACH TEST PROCEDURE, REFERENCED BY A CIRCLED NUMBER

WHEN ALL DIAGNOSIS AND REPAIRS ARE COMPLETE, CLEAR CODES AND VERIFY OPERATION.

Fig. 36   Code A028, rear hold solenoid energized too long

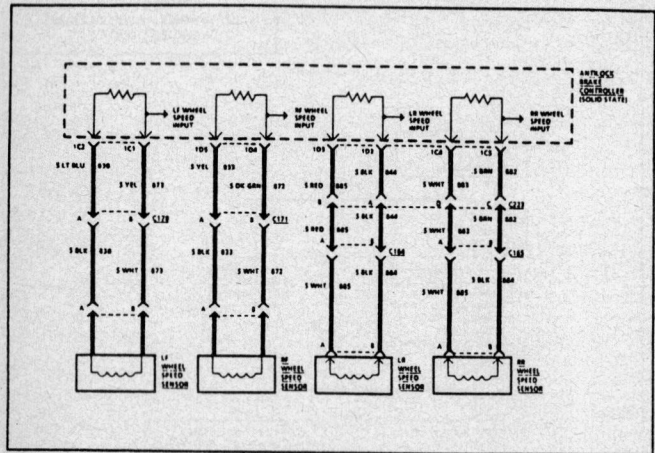

CODE A030
Both front, or one front and one rear wheel Speed Sensor open or shorted to ground

The Antilock Brake Controller monitors the Wheel Speed Sensors. If one or more wheel speed inputs are not receiving data from the Wheel Speed Sensor, the Controller can not detect wheel lockup. When only one speed input is not receiving data, Code A044, A045, A046 or A047 will be set. This Code (A030) is set when more than one speed input is faulty.

CODE A030 will set when the Antilock Brake Controller senses that either both Front Wheel Speed Sensors or a Front and a Rear Wheel Speed Sensor input are 0 mph for greater than 20 seconds.

TEST DESCRIPTION: The following provides an explanation of the procedures being followed in the facing trouble tree.

① By observing all four Wheel Speed Sensor inputs (while driving vehicle), you can determine which Wheel Speed Sensor circuits are faulty (no wheel speed observed). Faults can be diagnosed by refering to Codes A044, A045, A046, and A047 (right front, left front, right rear or left rear wheel speed = 0). In the case where an intermittent fault condition is indicated refer to introduction.

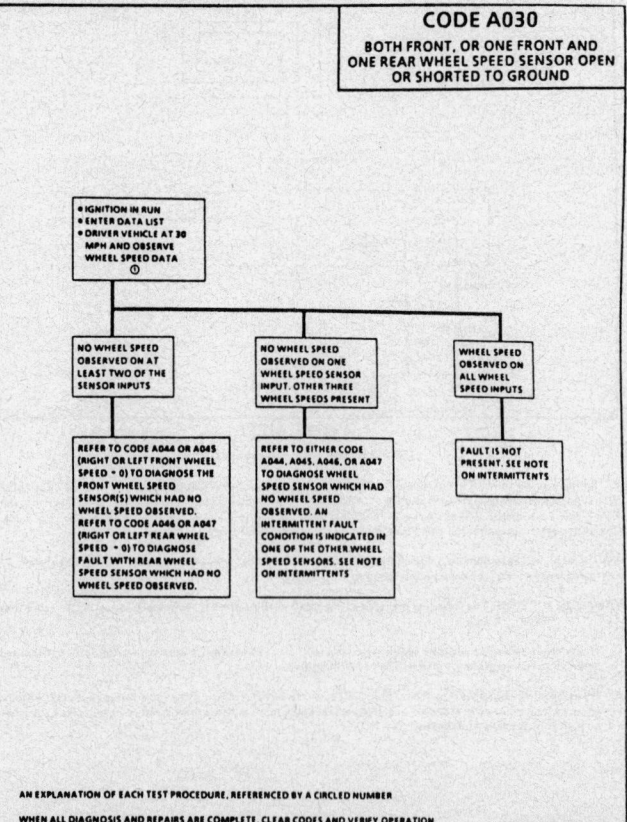

CODE A030
BOTH FRONT, OR ONE FRONT AND
ONE REAR WHEEL SPEED SENSOR OPEN
OR SHORTED TO GROUND

AN EXPLANATION OF EACH TEST PROCEDURE, REFERENCED BY A CIRCLED NUMBER

WHEN ALL DIAGNOSIS AND REPAIRS ARE COMPLETE, CLEAR CODES AND VERIFY OPERATION.

Fig. 37   Code A030, both front, or one front and one rear wheel speed sensor open or shorted to ground

1989-90 CUTLASS SUPREME, GRAND PRIX & REGAL (DELCO-MORAINE III TYPE)

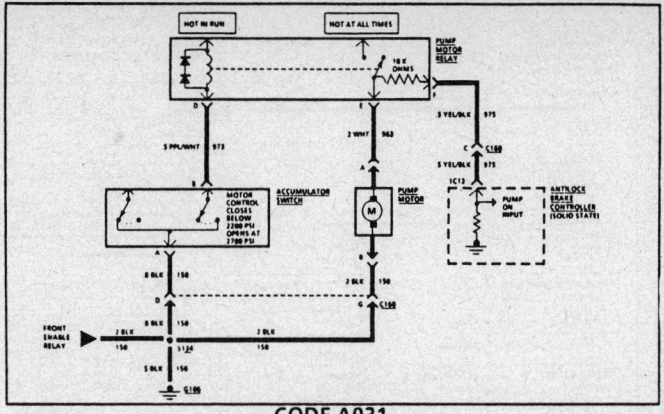

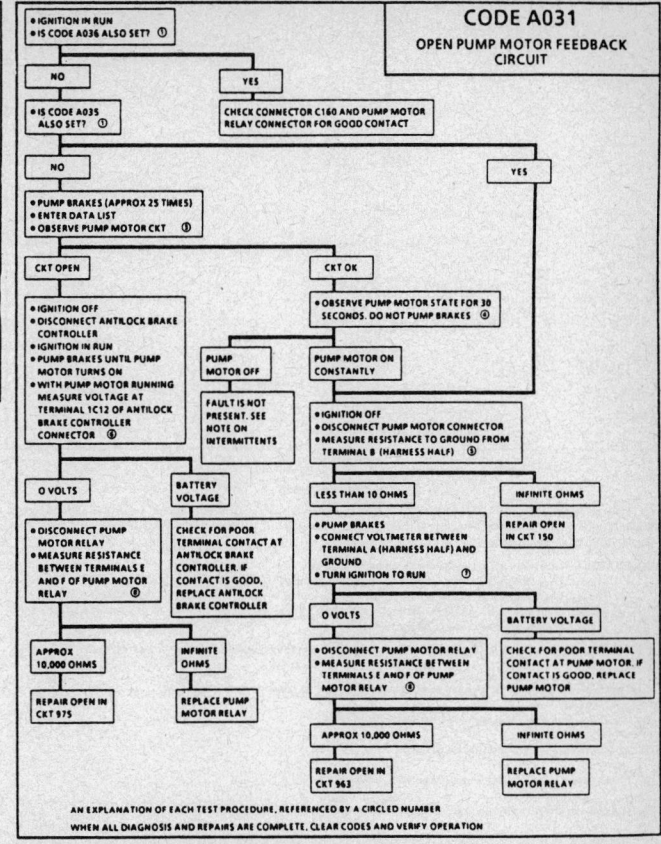

CODE A031
Open Pump Motor feedback circuit

Whenever the Pump Motor Relay contacts are open, the Pump On Input is grounded through the Pump Motor Relay and the Pump Motor. The Pump On Input will have voltage applied to it when the Pump Motor Relay Contacts are closed (the Pump Motor also has voltage applied to it). If the Pump On Input does not sense ground or the proper voltage, the Controller will set Code A031.

CODE A031 will set when the Antilock Brake Controller detects an open condition in the Pump Motor circuit between the Pump Motor Relay and ground or detects an open condition in the Pump On Input circuit between the Pump Motor Relay and the Antilock Brake Controller.

TEST DESCRIPTION: The following provides an explanation of the procedures being followed in the facing trouble tree.

① If Code A036 is also set, the problem is isolated to poor connections at either the Pump Motor Relay or Connector C160.

② Code A035, when set with Code A031, indicates that the Pump Motor circuit is open.

③ This step determines if the Pump Motor Feedback circuit is open.

④ If the Pump Motor is always on, there must be an open in the Pump Motor circuit which is preventing the Pump Motor from operating.

⑤ Determines if the open condition exists in CKT 150 between the Pump Motor and ground G106.

⑥ Battery voltage at terminal 1C12 indicates a problem with the connection at the Controller or the Controller itself.

⑦ Detects if circuit to Pump Motor is good. This would indicate a faulty Pump Motor.

⑧ Determines that the open condition is internal to the Pump Motor Relay if the resistance across terminals E and F of the Pump Motor Relay is infinite.

Fig. 38   Code A031, open pump motor feedback circuit

CODE A032
Open Brake Switch or hydraulic leak

CODE A032 will set when the Antilock Brake Controller receives three pump on inputs without receiving a brake switch on input. This allows a brake switch fault to be detected without an Antilock Braking condition present. Refer to Code A056 for diagnosis.

Fig. 39   Code A032, Open brake switch or hydraulic leak. 1989 models

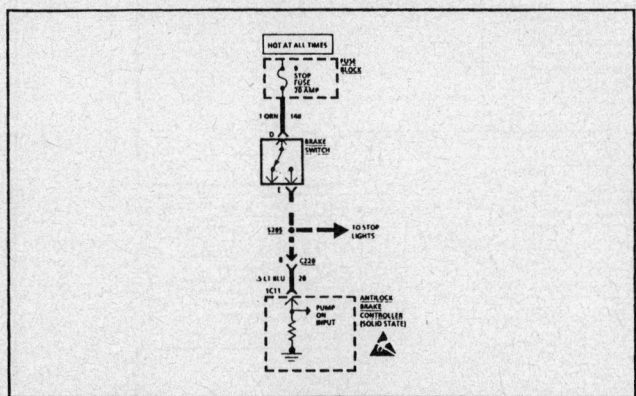

CODE A032
Open Brake Switch or Hydraulic Leak

Voltage is applied at all times to the Brake Switch. When the Brake Switch is closed, voltage is applied to the Brake Lights and terminal 1C11 of the Antilock Brake Controller. If the Brake Apply Input receives voltage, the Controller determines that the brakes are being applied.

CODE A032 will set when all the following conditions exsist:
- The Antilock Brake Controller receives three pump on inputs without receiving a brake switch on input. This allows a brake switch fault to be detected without an Antilock Braking condition present.

TEST DESCRIPTION: The following provides an explanation of the procedures being following in the facing trouble tree.

① & ③ Checks for a improperly adjusted or intermittent Brake Switch.

② If Code A062 is also set, the pump motor was cycling too fast. See Code A062.

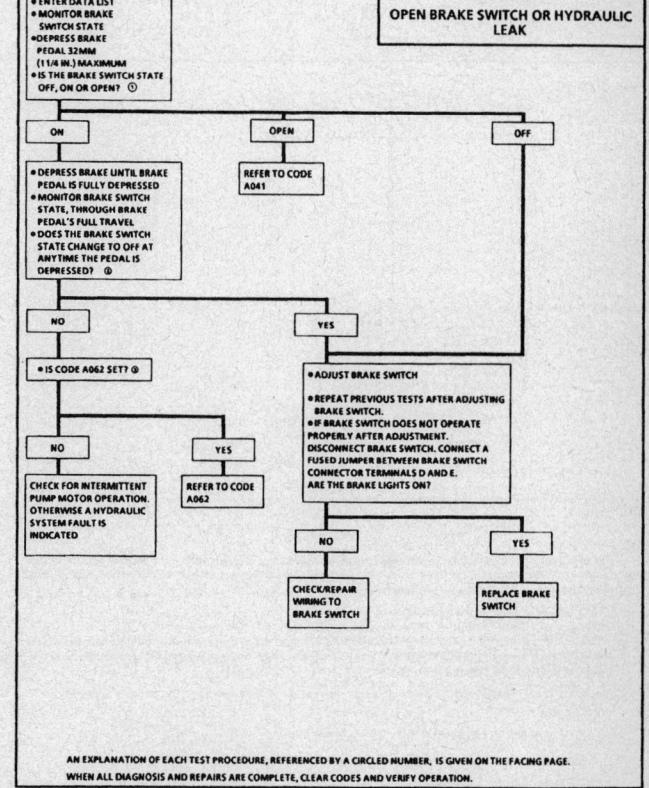

Fig. 40   Code A032, Open brake switch or hydraulic leak. 1990 models

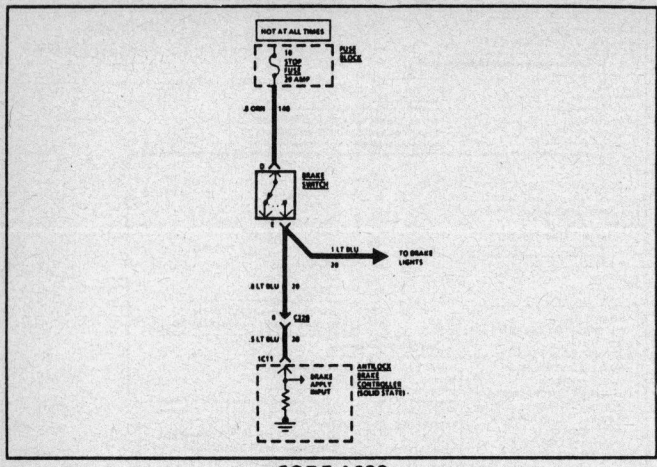

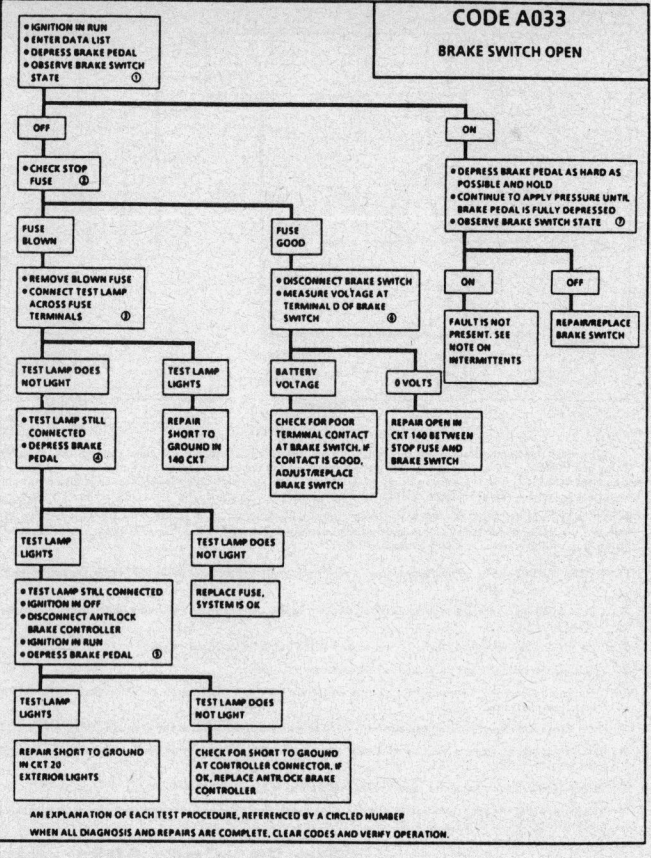

CODE A033

Brake Switch open

Voltage is applied at all times to the Brake Switch. When the Brake Switch is closed, voltage is applied to the Brake Lights and terminal 1C11 of the Antilock Brake Controller. If the Brake Apply Input receives voltage, the Controller determines that the brakes are being applied.

CODE A033 will set when all of the following conditions exist:
- The Antilock Brake Controller senses no voltage at terminal 1C11 (brake apply input is lo).
- The Antilock Brake Controller senses that two wheels (one of which is in the front) are decelerating at a rate greater than normally possible without using the brakes (vehicle is slowing down fast enough that the controller knows the brakes are being applied).

TEST DESCRIPTION: The following provides an explanation of the procedures being followed in the facing trouble tree.

① This determines whether an open condition currently exists under normal conditions.

② Checks if open condition is caused by an open Stop Fuse.

③ Isolates a short to ground in the 140 CKT.

④ If test lamp lights, a short to ground exists.

⑤ Isolates the short to ground to external circuits or to the Antilock Brake Controller.

⑥ Determines if an open condition exists in the CKT 140 or if the Brake Switch is defective.

⑦ An intermittent open Brake Switch may be possible. This step checks for this condition.

Fig. 41   Code A033, brake switch is open. 1989 models

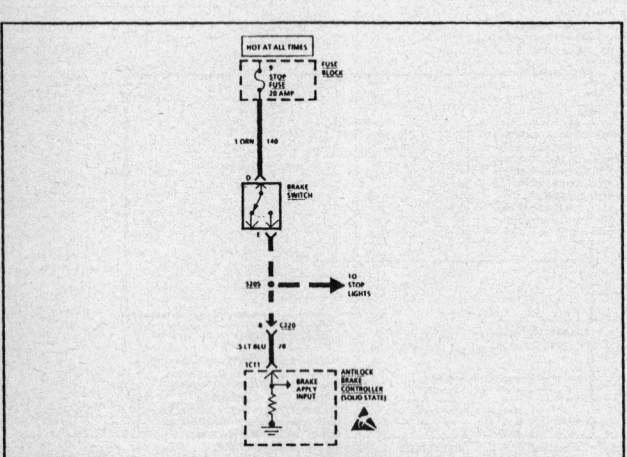

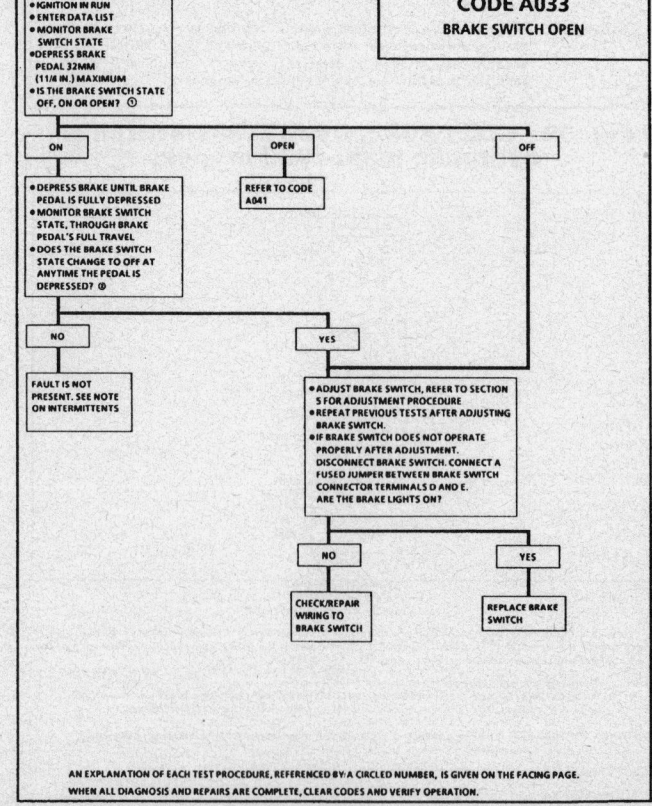

CODE A033

Brake Switch open

Voltage is applied at all times to the Brake Switch. When the Brake Switch is closed, voltage is applied to the Brake Lights and terminal 1C11 of the Antilock Brake Controller. If the Brake Apply Input receives voltage, the Controller determines that the brakes are being applied.

CODE A033 will set when all of the following conditions exist:
- The Antilock Brake Controller senses no voltage at terminal 1C11 (brake apply input is lo).
- The Antilock Brake Controller senses that two wheels (one of which is in the front) are decelerating at a rate greater than normally possible without using the brakes (vehicle is slowing down fast enough that the controller knows the brakes are being applied).

TEST DESCRIPTION: The following provides an explanation of the procedures being followed in the facing trouble tree.

① & ② Checks for improperly adjusted or intermittent Brake Switch.

Fig. 42   Code A033, brake switch is open. 1990 models

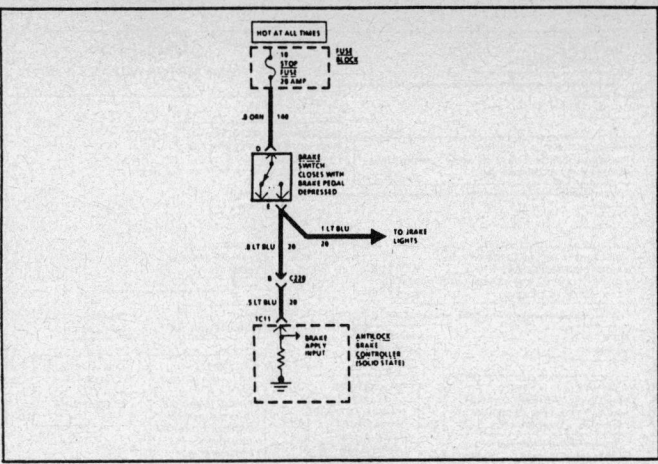

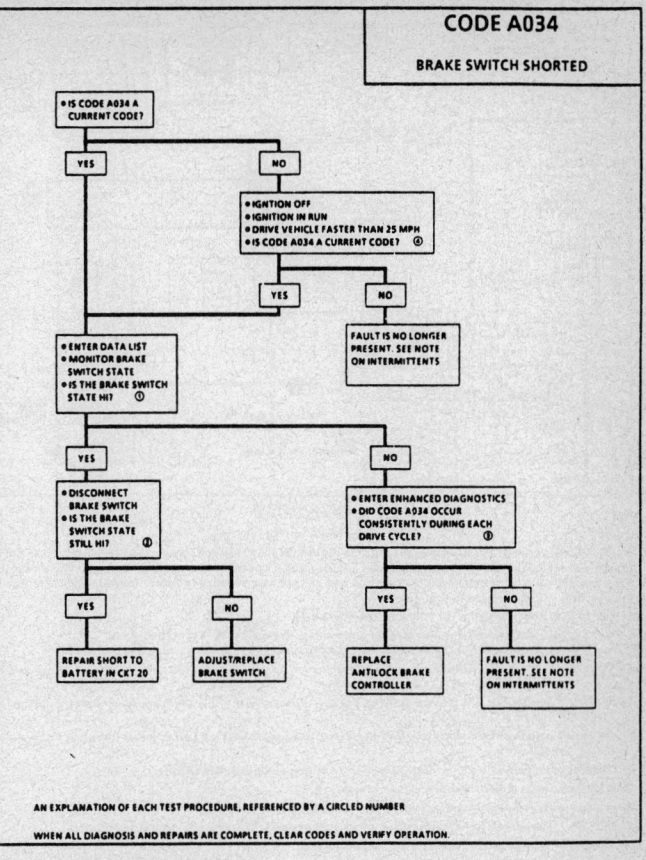

CODE A034

Brake Switch shorted

When the Brake Pedal is depressed, the Brake Switch closes. This applies voltage from the Stop Fuse to the Antilock Brake Controller and the brake lights. Before the Controller will initiate an Antilock Brake Stop, it must first sense voltage at the Brake Apply Input.

CODE A034 will set when all of the following conditions exist:
- The Antilock Brake Controller senses battery voltage at terminal 1C11 for a complete ignition cycle in which the vehicle speed surpasses 25 mph.
- The Antilock Brake Controller senses Battery voltage at terminal 1C11 during any following ignition cycle in which the vehicle speed surpasses 25 mph.

TEST DESCRIPTION: The following provides an explanation of the procedures being followed in the facing trouble tree.

① Confirms that a short exists in the circuit (brake lights on).

② Determines whether a short to Battery exists in the CKT 20; or whether the Brake Switch is shorted or maladjusted.

③ If Code A034 is a consistent failure, but CKTS and Brake Switch are good, the Antilock Brake Controller must have an internal fault.

④ This step verifies that the code is not about to become a current code by passing the second condition (see above).

Fig. 43   Code A034, brake switch shorted

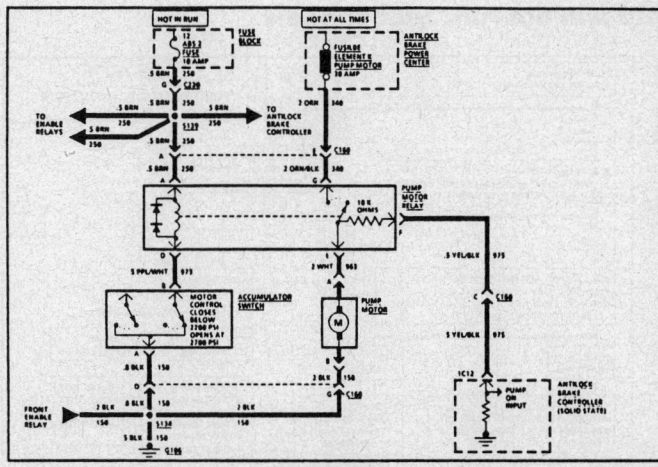

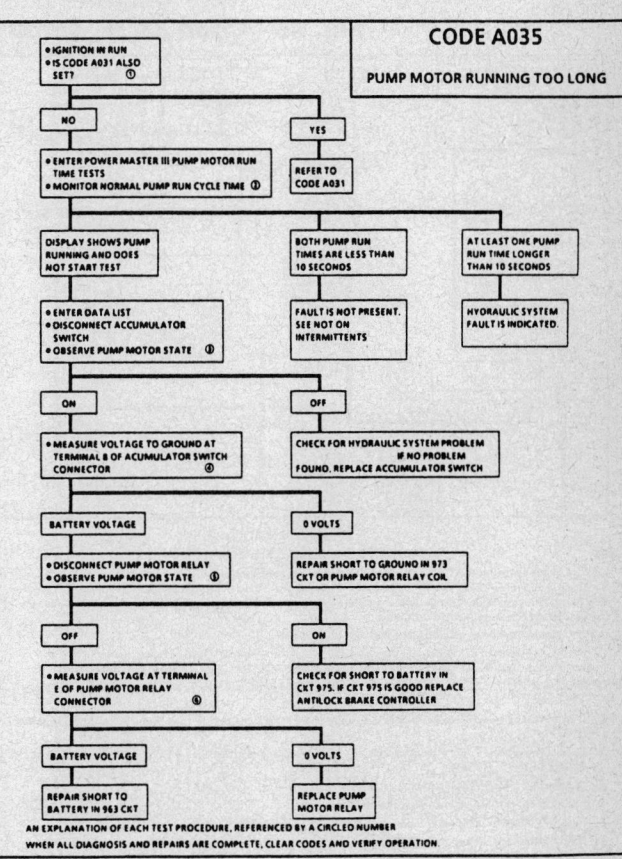

CODE A035

Pump Motor running too long

The Accumulator Switch Motor Control closes when the pressure drops below 2200 PSI. This grounds the Pump Motor Relay Coil causing voltage to be applied to the Pump Motor and Pump On Input. Whenever the Pump Motor is on, the Pump On Input will have voltage applied to it.

CODE A035 will set when the Antilock Brake Controller senses voltage at Terminal 1C12 "Pump on input" for more than 3 minutes.

TEST DESCRIPTION: The following provides an explanation of the procedures being followed in the facing trouble tree.

① When Code A035 and A031 are both set, the problem is isolated to the Pump Motor Circuit.

② This step determines if the Pump Motor is running constantly (electrical fault), running longer than normal (hydraulic fault), or running too long intermittently.

③ It can be determined if the accumulator switch is causing the fault by disconnecting the accumulator switch and observing the Pump Motor State. OFF indicates a defective accumulator switch or hydraulic failure.

④ Determines if a short to ground exists in 973 wire.

⑤ This step detects if a short to Battery exists by isolating the 975 wire and Antilock Brake Controller from the Pump Motor Circuit.

⑥ Determines if a short to ground exists in the 963 wire, or whether the Pump Motor Relay is defective.

Fig. 44   Code A035, pump motor running too long

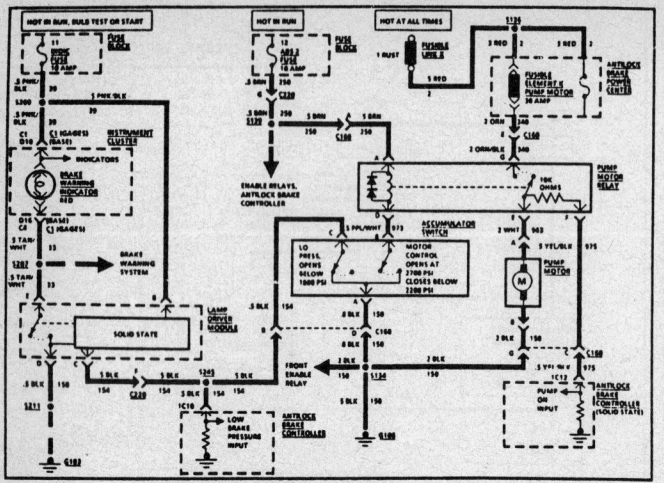

CODE A036

Pump Motor will not run

The Pump On Input will have voltage applied to it when the Pump Motor Relay contacts are closed. If the Brake Pressure drops below 1800 PSI, the Accumulator Switch opens. This removes ground from the Lamp Driver Module. The Lamp Driver Module then closes the switch to turn on the Brake Warning Indicator, and also applies voltage to the Low Brake Pressure Input of the Controller.

CODE A036 will set when all of the following conditions exist:
- The Antilock Brake Controller does not sense voltage at terminal 1C12 (Pump on input).
- The Antilock Brake Controller senses voltage at terminal 1C10 (Brake Warning Indicator is on).

TEST DESCRIPTION: The following provides an explanation of the procedures being followed in the facing trouble tree.

① If code A031 is also set, the problem is isolated to poor connections at either the Pump Motor Relay or Connector C160.
② By observing if the Pump Motor operates, the fault is isolated to either the Low Pressure Circuit or Pump Motor Relay Circuit.
③ Determines if fault is in Pump Motor Relay Circuit or Accumulator Switch Circuit.
④ This step checks if there is an actual fault present.
⑤ Battery voltage at terminal A indicates a good Relay Coil power feed.
⑥ If Pump Motor operates, the fault is either a hydraulic system failure or faulty Accumulator Switch.
⑦ Checks for an open ground circuit to Accumulator Switch.
⑧ Determines if 973 CKT is open.
⑨ At this point, a good Relay Contact power feed indicates a faulty Pump Motor Relay.

Fig. 45   Code A036, pump motor will not run. 1989 models

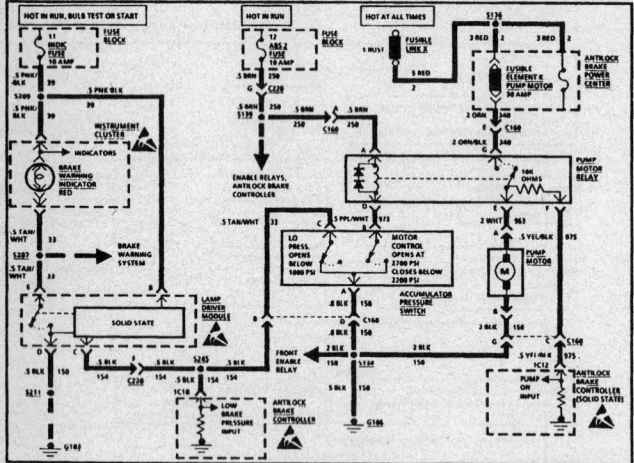

CODE A036

Pump Motor will not run

The Pump On Input will have voltage applied to it when the Pump Motor Relay contacts are closed. If the Brake Pressure drops below 1800 PSI, the Accumulator Switch opens. This removes ground from the Lamp Driver Module. The Lamp Driver Module then closes the switch to turn on the Brake Warning Indicator, and also applies voltage to the Low Brake Pressure Input of the Controller.

CODE A036 will set when all of the following conditions exist:
- The Antilock Brake Controller does not sense voltage at terminal 1C12 (Pump on input).
- The Antilock Brake Controller senses voltage at terminal 1C10 (Brake Warning Indicator is on).

TEST DESCRIPTION: The following provides an explanation of the procedures being followed in the facing trouble tree.

① If code A031 is also set, the problem is isolated to poor connections at either the Pump Motor Relay or Connector C160.
② By observing if the Pump Motor operates, the fault is isolated to either the Low Pressure Circuit or Pump Motor Relay Circuit.
③ Determines if fault is in Pump Motor Relay Circuit or Accumulator Switch Circuit.
④ This step checks if there is an actual fault present.
⑤ Battery voltage at terminal A indicates a good Relay Coil power feed.
⑥ If Pump Motor operates, the fault is either a hydraulic system failure or faulty Accumulator Switch.
⑦ Checks for an open ground circuit to Accumulator Switch.
⑧ Determines if 973 CKT is open.
⑨ At this point, a good Relay Contact power feed indicates a faulty Pump Motor Relay.

Fig. 46   Code A036, pump motor will not run. 1990 models

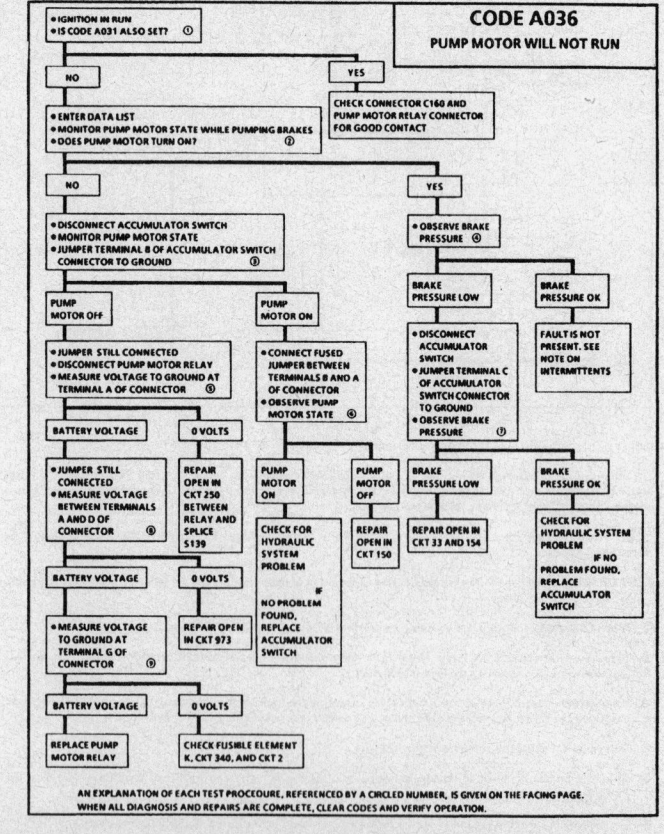

CODE A036

PUMP MOTOR WILL NOT RUN

AN EXPLANATION OF EACH TEST PROCEDURE, REFERENCED BY A CIRCLED NUMBER, IS GIVEN ON THE FACING PAGE. WHEN ALL DIAGNOSIS AND REPAIRS ARE COMPLETE, CLEAR CODES AND VERIFY OPERATION.

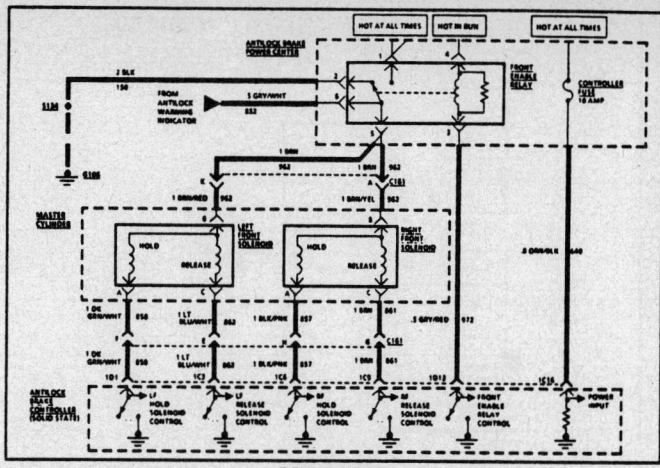

CODE A037
Front Enable Relay Coil shorted to ground

When the Front Enable Relay Control is open, the Front Enable Relay is deenergized. This prevents voltage from being applied to the Front Solenoids and Solenoid Controls. If the Front Enable Relay is deenergized and the Ignition is in RUN, voltage should be present at terminal 1D13.

CODE A037 will set during system initialization when all of the following conditions exist:
- The Front Enable Relay Control is open (Front Enable Relay deenergized).
- The Antilock Brake Controller senses no voltage at Terminal 1D13.
- The Antilock Brake Controller senses Battery voltage at Terminals 1D1, 1C3, 1C6 and 1C9.

TEST DESCRIPTION: The following provides an explanation of the procedures being followed in the facing trouble tree.

① By isolating the Front Enable Relay Coil from its ground and observing the Antilock Warning Indicator, it can be determined whether the Front Enable Relay has deenergized (Antilock Warning Indicator lights) which indicates a possible defective Antilock Brake Controller or whether the Front Enable Relay has remained energized (Antilock Warning Indicator does not light) which indicates a short to ground in the 972 wire.

② If Code A037 is a consistent failure, the Antilock Brake Controller has an internal fault.

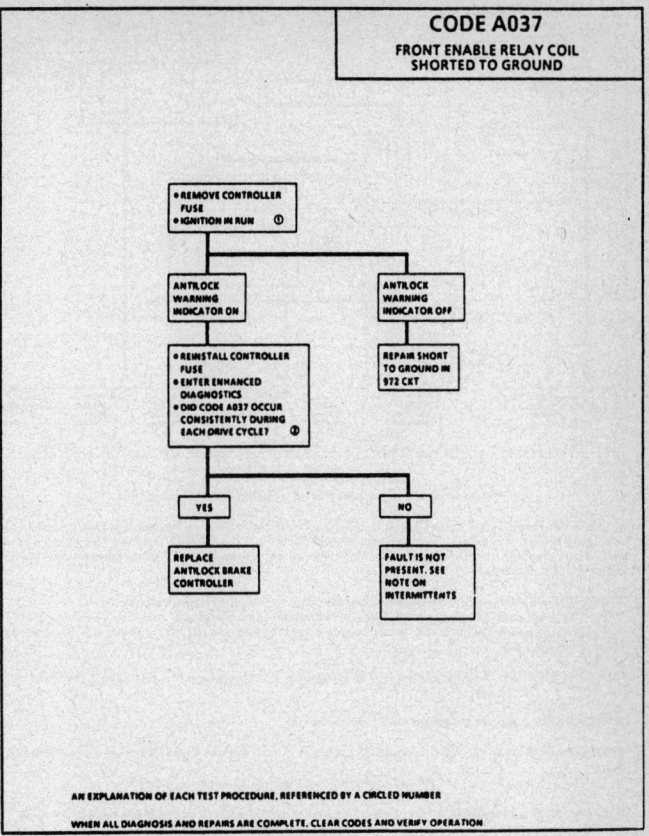

CODE A037
FRONT ENABLE RELAY COIL SHORTED TO GROUND

AN EXPLANATION OF EACH TEST PROCEDURE, REFERENCED BY A CIRCLED NUMBER

WHEN ALL DIAGNOSIS AND REPAIRS ARE COMPLETE, CLEAR CODES AND VERIFY OPERATION

Fig. 47 Code A037, front enable relay coil shorted to ground

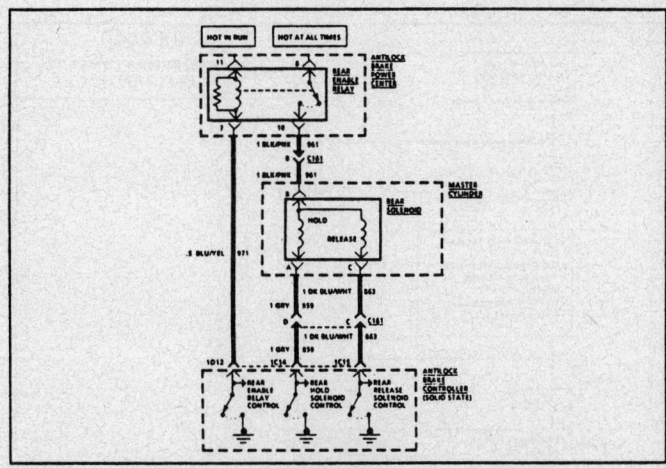

CODE A038
Rear Enable Relay Coil shorted to Ground

When the Rear Enable Relay Control is open, the Rear Enable Relay is deenergized. This prevents voltage from being applied to the Rear Solenoid and Solenoid controls. If the Rear Enable Relay is deenergized and the Ignition is in RUN, voltage should be present at terminal 1D12.

CODE A038 will set during system initialization when all the following conditions exist:
- The Rear Enable Relay control is open (Rear Enable Relay deenergized).
- The Antilock Brake Controller senses no voltage at Terminal 1D12.
- Antilock Brake Controller senses Battery voltage at Terminal 1C14 and 1C15.

TEST DESCRIPTION: The following provides an explanation of the procedures being followed in the facing trouble tree.

① By isolating the Rear Enable Relay Control from its ground and measuring the voltage at Terminal 1D12 of the Antilock Brake Controller connector it can be determined whether the Rear Enable Relay has deenergized (Battery voltage at Terminal 1D12) which indicates a possible defective Antilock Brake Controller or whether the Rear Enable Relay has remained energized (0 volts at Terminal 1D12) which indicates a short to ground in the 971 circuit.

② If Code A038 is a consistent failure, the Antilock Brake Controller has an internal fault.

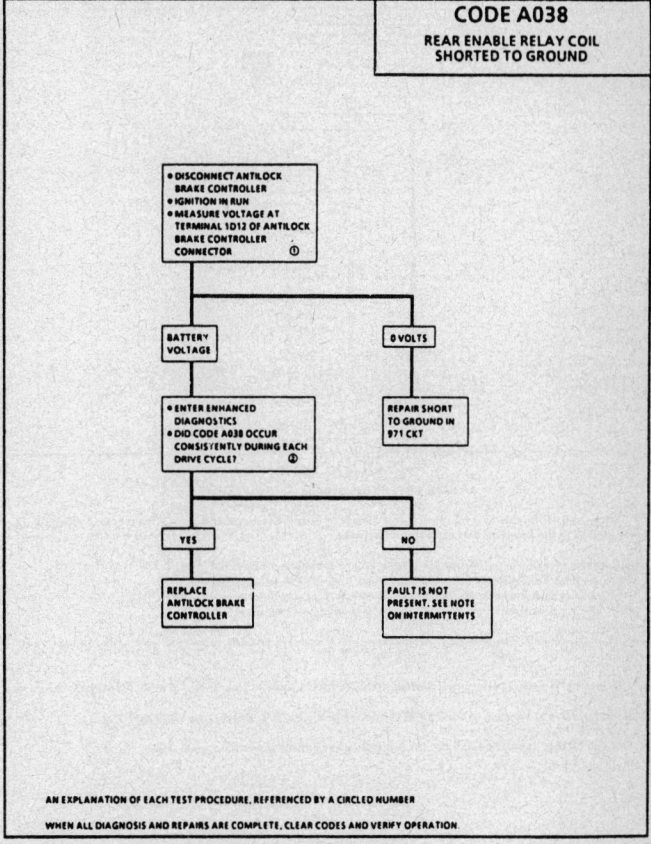

CODE A038
REAR ENABLE RELAY COIL SHORTED TO GROUND

AN EXPLANATION OF EACH TEST PROCEDURE, REFERENCED BY A CIRCLED NUMBER

WHEN ALL DIAGNOSIS AND REPAIRS ARE COMPLETE, CLEAR CODES AND VERIFY OPERATION.

Fig. 48 Code A038, rear enable relay coil shorted to ground

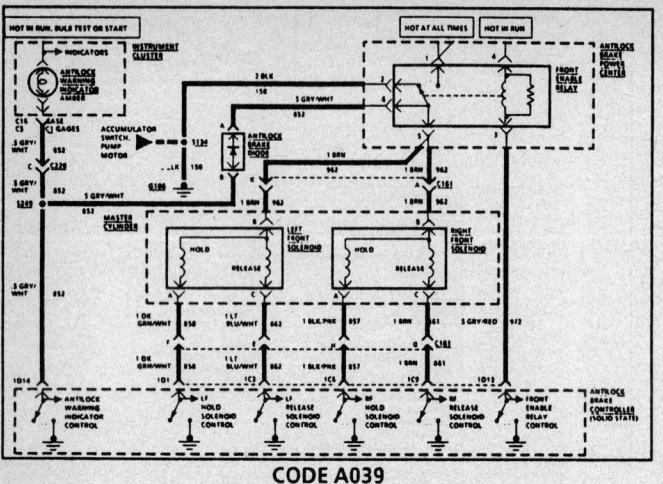

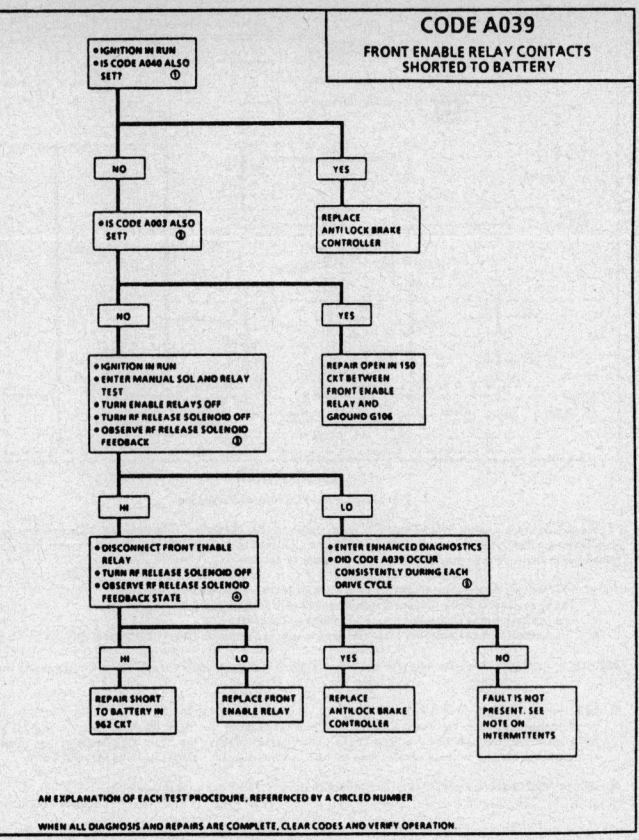

CODE A039

Front Enable Relay contacts shorted to Battery or relay ground open.

When the Front Enable Relay Control is open, the Front Enable Relay is deenergized. This prevents voltage from being applied to the Front Solenoids and Solenoid Controls. If the 150 CKT from the Front Enable Relay is open, Battery voltage from the Antilock Warning Indicator will be applied to the solenoids even when the Front Enable Relay is deenergized.

CODE A039 will set during system initialization when all of the following conditions exist:
- The Front Enable Relay Control is open (Front Enable Relay deenergized).
- The Antilock Brake Controller senses Battery voltage at Terminals 1D1, 1C3, 1C6 and 1C9 (Front Solenoid controls).

TEST DESCRIPTION: The following provides an explanation of the procedures being followed in the facing trouble tree.

① If Code A003 is also set, the ground CKT 150 must be open.

② Determines if a short to Battery is present in the circuit or if the Antilock Brake Controller is possibly defective.

③ Isolates a short to Battery in CKT 962 or determines if the Front Enable relay is defective.

④ If Code A039 is a consistent failure, the Antilock Brake Controller has an internal fault.

Fig. 49 Code A039, front enable relay contacts shorted to battery

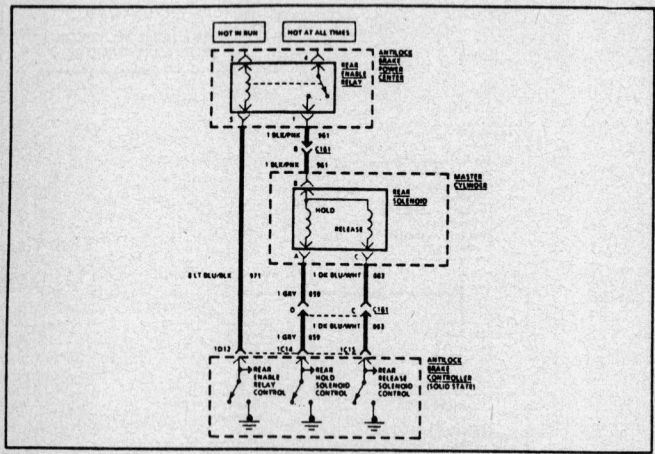

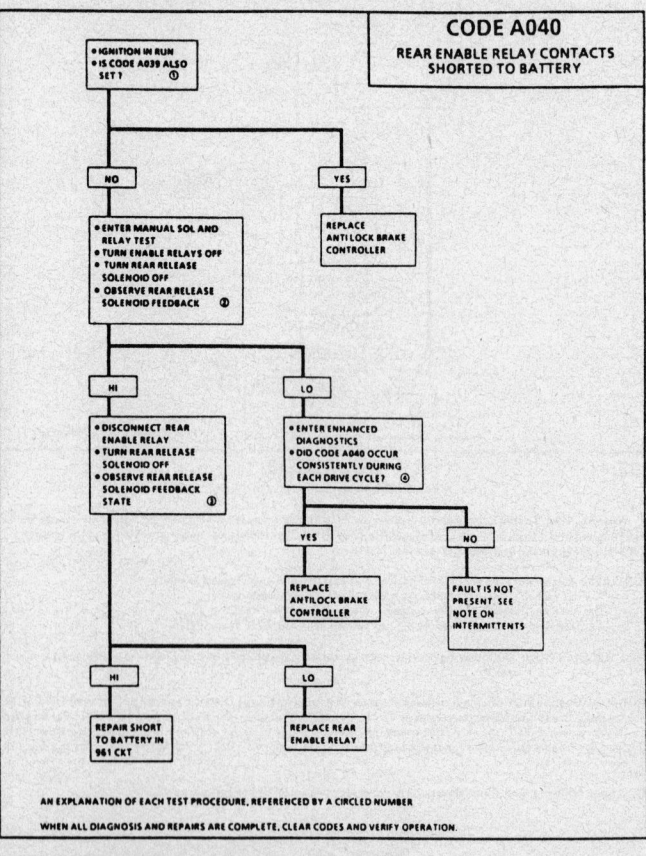

CODE A040

Rear Enable Relay contacts shorted to Battery.

When the Rear Enable Relay Control is open, the Rear Enable Relay is deenergized. This prevents voltage from being applied to the Rear Solenoid and Solenoid Controls.

CODE A040 will set during initialization when all of the following conditions exist:
- The Rear Enable Relay Control is open (Rear Enable Relay deenergized).
- The Antilock Brake Controller senses Battery voltage at both terminals 1C14 and 1C15.
- The Antilock Brake Controller senses Battery voltage at terminal 1D12.

TEST DESCRIPTION: The following provides an explanation of the procedures being followed in the facing trouble tree.

② Determines if a short to Battery is present in the circuit or if the Antilock Brake Controller is possibly defective.

③ Isolates a short to Battery in the CKT 961 or determines if the Rear Enable Relay is defective.

④ If Code A040 is a consistent failure, the Antilock Brake controller has an internal fault.

Fig. 50 Code A040, rear enable relay contacts shorted to battery

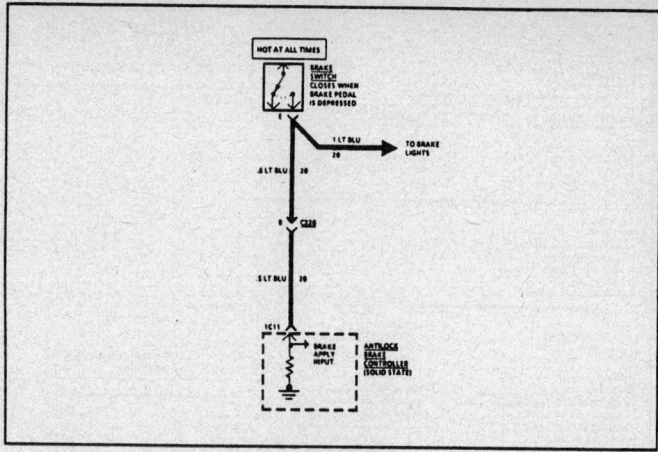

CODE A041
Brake Switch circuit open

The Antilock Brake Controller determines that the Brake Pedal is pressed when battery voltage is sensed at the Brake Apply Input. If battery voltage is not present, the Controller should sense ground through CKT 20, CKT 17, and the Brake Lights. It should be noted that this code will set if the Hazard Lights are turned on and the High Level Stop Light is open or burned out.

CODE A041 will set when all the following conditions exist:
* Brake Switch is open (Battery voltage not sensed at Brake Apply Input)
* Antilock Brake Controller does not sense ground at Brake Apply Input (through CKT 20 and CKT 17)

TEST DESCRIPTION: The following provides an explanation of the procedures being followed in the facing trouble tree.

① Determines if the open condition exists in CKT 20 between the Brake Switch and the brake lights (High Level Stop Light did not light with brake pedal depressed) or if the open condition exists in CKT 20 between the Brake Switch and the Antilock Brake Controller (High Level Stop Light did light with Brake Pedal depressed).

② By observing the Brake Switch State when it is known that the Brake Switch is closed it can be determined if the Antilock Brake Controller is sensing the proper input (a proper input at this point would indicate an intermittent fault condition).

③ Isolates the open condition to CKT 20 between the Brake Switch and the Antilock Brake Controller if 0 volts was measured at Terminal 1C11 of Antilock Brake Controller. If Battery voltage was measured at Terminal 1C11 it indicates that the Antilock Brake Controller is defective.

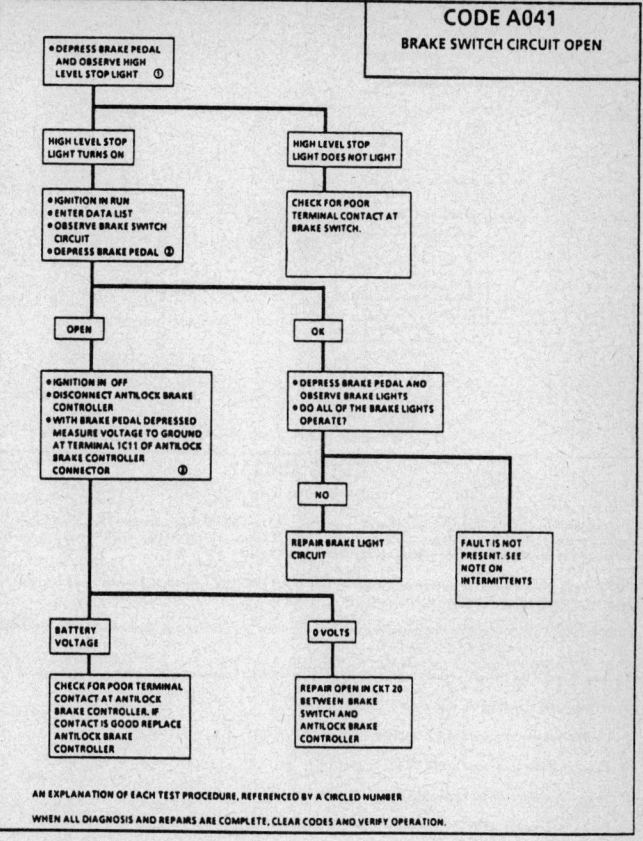

Fig. 51   Code A041, brake switch circuit open

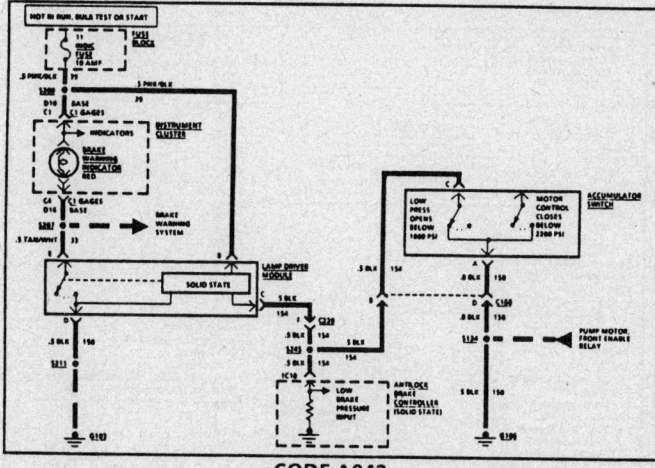

CODE A042
Low Brake Pressure Circuit open

When the Low Pressure Switch in the Accumulator Switch is closed (pressure greater than approximately 1800 PSI), the Antilock Brake Controller senses ground at the Low Brake Pressure Input. If the Low Pressure Switch is open (pressure less than 1800 PSI) the Lamp Driver Module loses ground at terminal C. The Lamp Driver Module turns on the Brake Warning Indicator and applies voltage to the Low Brake Pressure Input. If the Controller does not sense ground or battery voltage at the Low Brake Pressure Input, it will set Code A042.

CODE A042 will set when the Antilock Brake Controller senses that an open condition exists in the 154 CKT between the Controller and the Lamp Driver Module.

TEST DESCRIPTION: The following provides an explanation of the procedures being followed in the facing trouble tree.

① If the Brake Warning Indicator lights constantly, there must be an open in the 154 CKT between the Lamp Driver Module and Splice S245.

② Determines if open condition is currently present.

③ Isolates the open condition to CKT 154 between splice S245 and the Antilock Brake Controller or determines a defective Antilock Brake Controller.

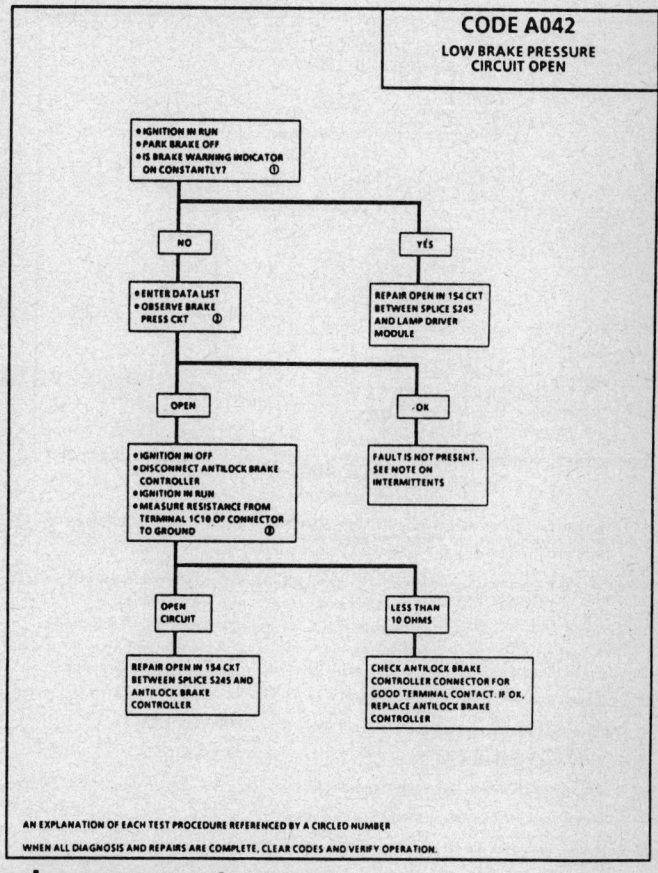

Fig. 52   Code A042, low brake pressure circuit open

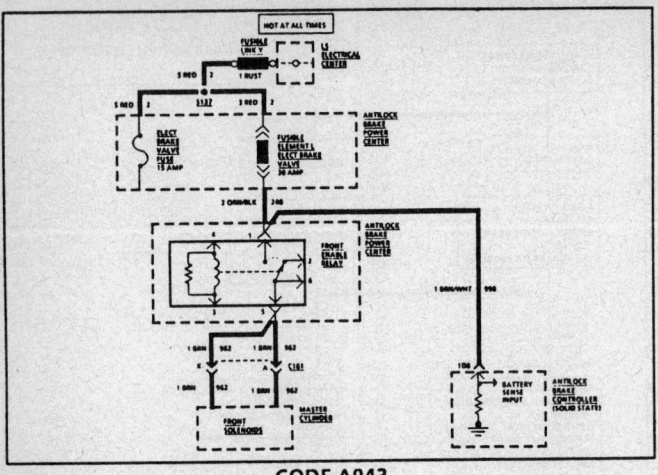

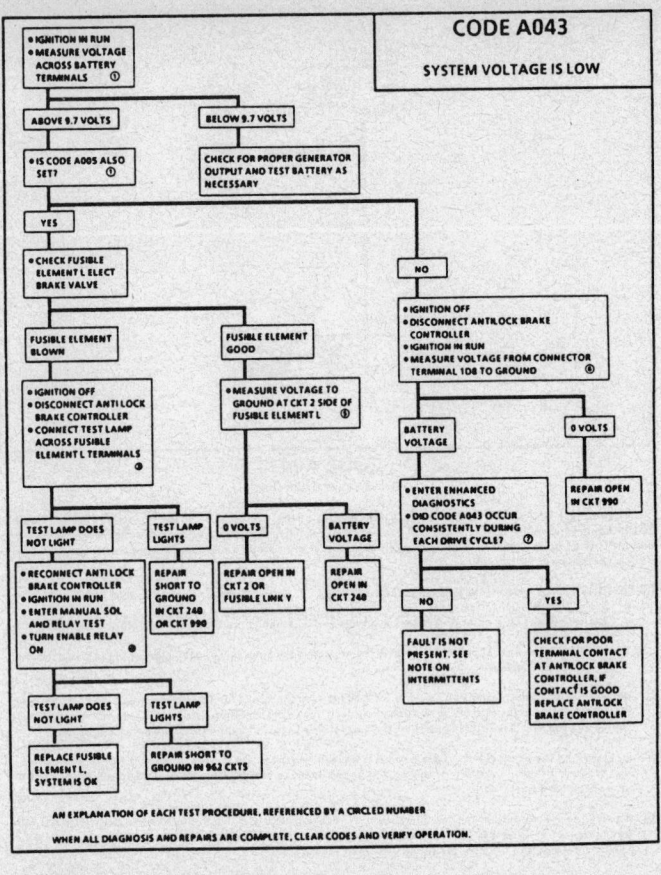

CODE A043
System voltage is low

Voltage from Fusible Element L is applied at all times to the Front Enable Relay terminal 1 and the Antilock Brake Controller Battery Sense Input. Since the Antilock Brake Controller needs greater than 9.7 volts to properly operate, Code A043 is set when the applied voltage is less than 9.7 volts.

CODE A043 will set when the voltage being supplied to terminal 1D8 of the Antilock Brake Controller is below 9.7 volts and vehicle speed has exceeded 10 mph.

TEST DESCRIPTION: The following provides an explanation of the procedures being followed in the facing trouble tree.

① Determines if the Battery or charging system is faulty, or isolates the problem to the Antilock Brake system.

② If Code A005 is not set, the problem is in the 990 CKT.

③ Checks for short to ground in 240 CKT and 990 CKT.

④ Checks for short to ground in 962 CKTS.

⑤ Determines if open is present before or after Fusible Element L.

⑥ Indicates if open is in 990 CKT or possibly internal to Controller.

⑦ Determines if fault is a constant failure internal to Controller or an intermittent.

Fig. 53   Code A043, system voltage is low. 1989 models

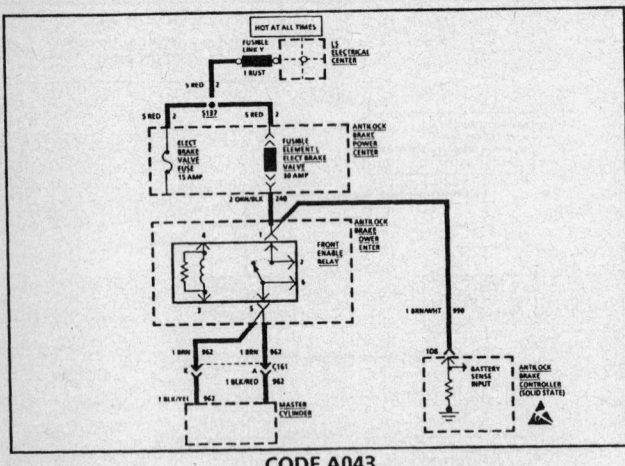

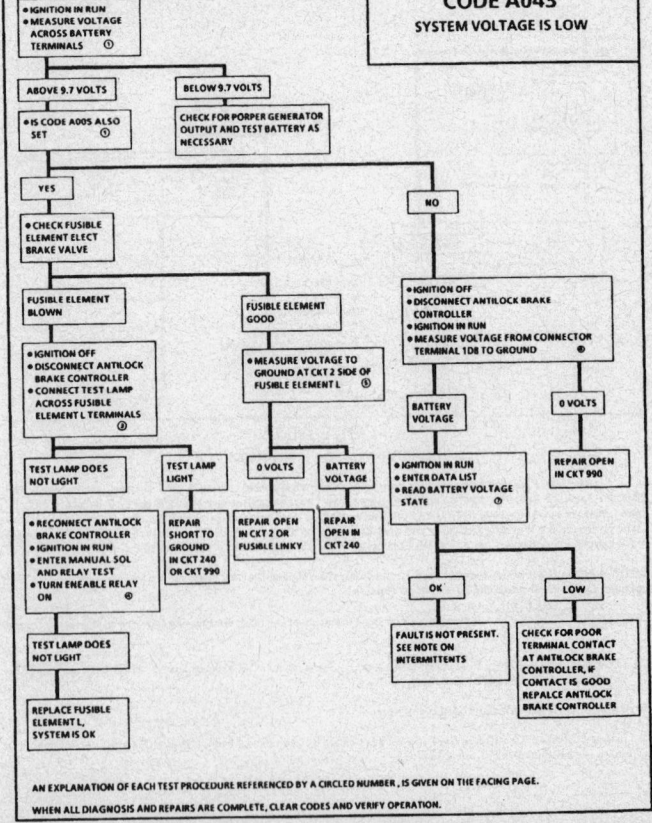

CODE A043
System voltage is low

Voltage from Fusible Element L is applied at all times to the Front Enable Relay terminal 1 and the Antilock Brake Controller Battery Sense Input. Since the Antilock Brake Controller needs greater than 9.7 volts to properly operate, Code A043 is set when the applied voltage is less than is less than 9.7 volts.

CODE A034 will set when the voltage being supplied to terminal 1D8 of the Antilock Brake Controller is below 9.7 volts and vehicle speed has exceeded 10 mph.

TEST DESCRIPTION: The following provides an explanation of the procedures being followed in the facing trouble tree.

① Determines if the Battery or charging system is faulty, or isolates the problem to the Antilock Brake system.

② If Code A005 is not set, the problem is in the 990 CKT.

③ Checks for short to ground in 962 CKTS.

④ Checks for short to ground in 962 CKTS.

⑤ Determines if open is present before or after Fusible Element L.

⑥ Indicates if open is in 990 CKT or possibly internal to Controller.

⑦ Determines if fault is a constant failure internal to Controller or an intermittent.

Fig. 54   Code A043, system voltage is low. 1990 models

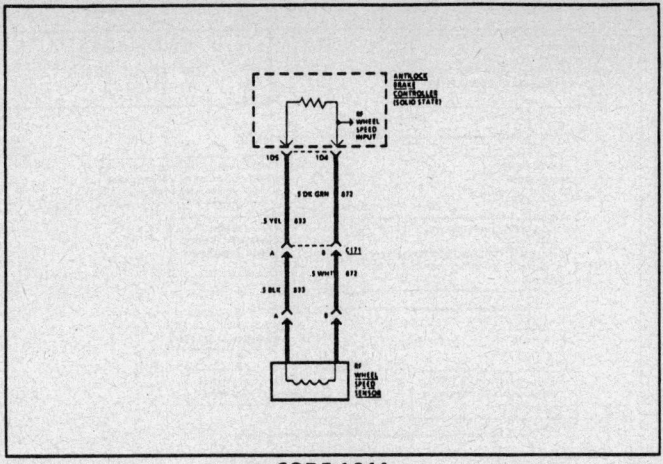

CODE A044

Right Front Wheel Speed = 0

The Wheel Speed Sensor generates a signal that indicates the speed of the wheel. Voltage pulses are produced as the magnetic teeth pass a coil. The frequency of this AC voltage is used by the Controller to determine how fast the wheel is turning. By comparing this wheel speed to the other wheel speeds, the Controller can detect if wheel lock-up is about to occur.

CODE A044 will set when all of the following conditions exist:
- The Antilock Brake Controller senses the right front wheel speed to be 0 mph.
- The Antilock Brake Controller senses that the other three wheel speeds are greater than 5 mph and are operating correctly.

TEST DESCRIPTION: The following provides an explanation of the procedures being followed in the following trouble tree.

① By observing the Right Front Wheel speed input, you can verify what type of input the controller is sensing. An unsteady or erratic wheel speed input indicates that a fault is present in the Wheel Speed Sensor or its related circuitry. If a steady wheel speed is observed, an intermittent fault condition is indicated.

② Indicates a defective Wheel Speed Sensor by isolating a short to ground internal to the sensor.

③ If resistance measured across the Wheel Speed Sensor is infinite, the fault is due to an open condition internal to the Speed Sensor.

④ Determines a short to Battery is present in CKT 833 if Battery voltage is measured at Terminal A of the harness side of the Wheel Speed Sensor Connector

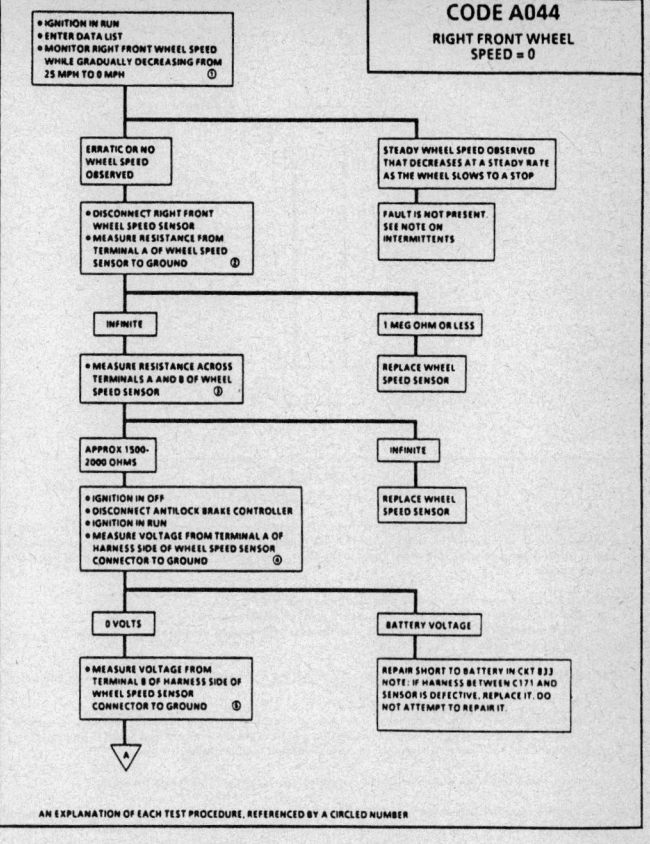

Fig. 55 Code A044, right front wheel speed at 0 mph (Part 1 of 2)

⑤ Determines a short to Battery is present in CKT 872 if Battery voltage is measured at Terminal B of the harness side of the Wheel Speed Sensor Connector.

⑥ With Terminal A of CKT 833 connected to ground, the resistance from Terminal 1D5 to ground should be zero. If infinite resistance is measured, an open condition is indicated in CKT 833.

⑦ With Terminal B of CKT 872 connected to ground, the resistance from Terminal 1D4 to ground should be zero. If infinite resistance is measured, an open condition is indicated in CKT 872.

⑧ At this point, all the connecting circuitry has tested good. The fault may be due to a poorly mated connector at the Wheel Speed Sensor or the Antilock Brake Controller. Other possible causes could be due to damage to the Speed Sensor or Speed Ring. Check for proper mounting, or poor alignment. If everything above tests good, replace the Antilock Brake Controller.

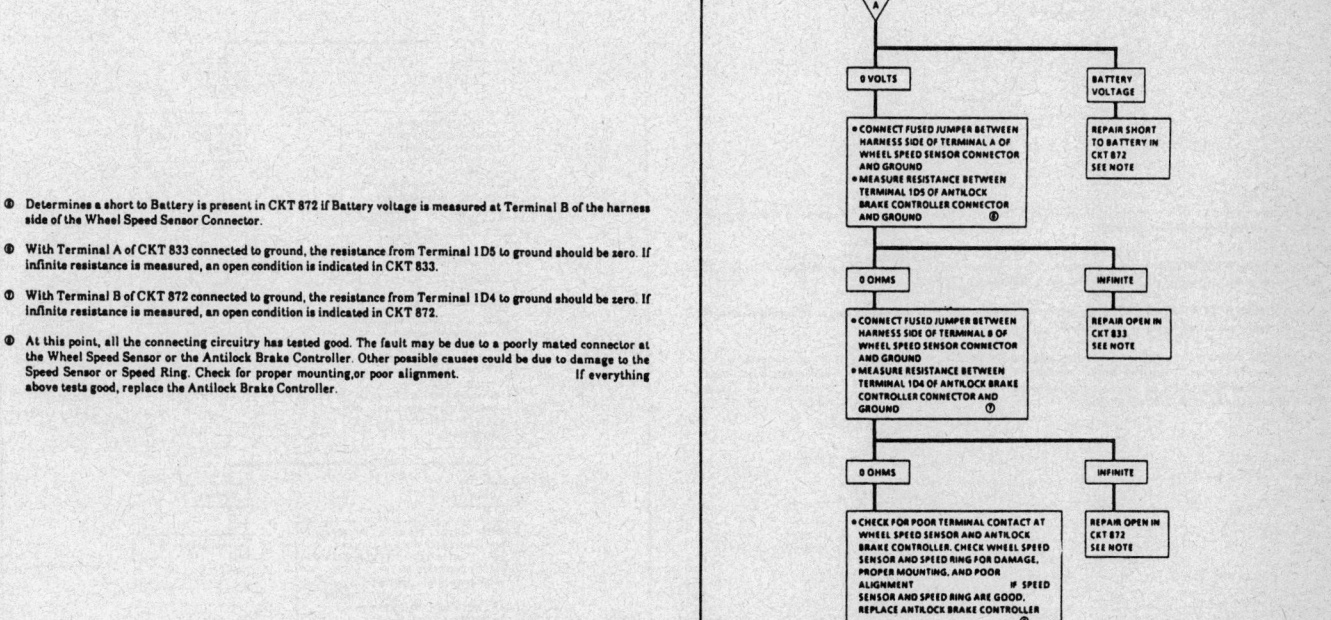

Fig. 55 Code A044, right front wheel speed at 0 mph (Part 2 of 2)

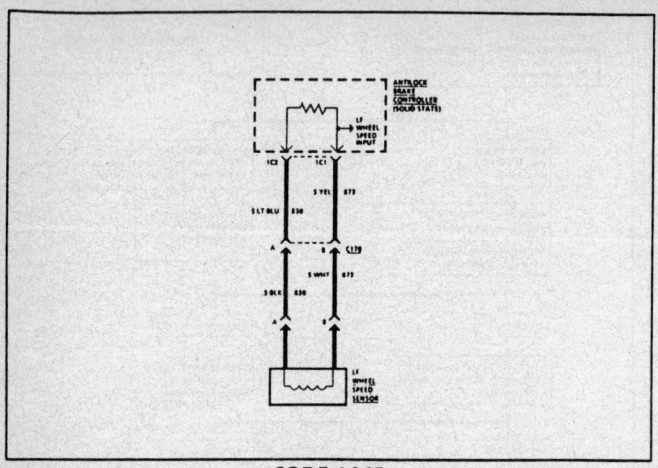

CODE A045
Left Front Wheel Speed = 0

The Wheel Speed Sensor generates a signal that indicates the speed of the wheel. Voltage pulses are produced as the magnetic teeth pass a coil. The frequency of this AC voltage is used by the Controller to determine how fast the wheel is turning. By comparing this wheel speed to the other wheel speeds, the Controller can detect if wheel lock-up is about to occur.

CODE A045 will set when all of the following conditions exist:
- The Antilock Brake Controller Senses the left front wheel speed to be 0 mph.
- The Antilock Brake Controller senses that the other three wheel speeds are greater than 5 mph and are operating correctly.

TEST DESCRIPTION: The following provides an explanation of the procedures being followed in the following trouble tree.

① By observing the Left Front Wheel speed input, you can verify what type of input the controller is sensing. An unsteady or erratic wheel speed input indicates that a fault is present in the Wheel Speed Sensor or its related circuitry. If a steady wheel speed is observed, an intermittent fault condition is indicated.

② Indicates a defective Wheel Speed Sensor by isolating a short to ground internal to the sensor.

③ If resistance measured across the Wheel Speed Sensor is infinite, the fault is due to an open condition internal to the Speed Sensor.

④ Determines a short to Battery is present in CKT 830 if Battery voltage is measured at Terminal A of the harness side of the Wheel Speed Sensor Connector.

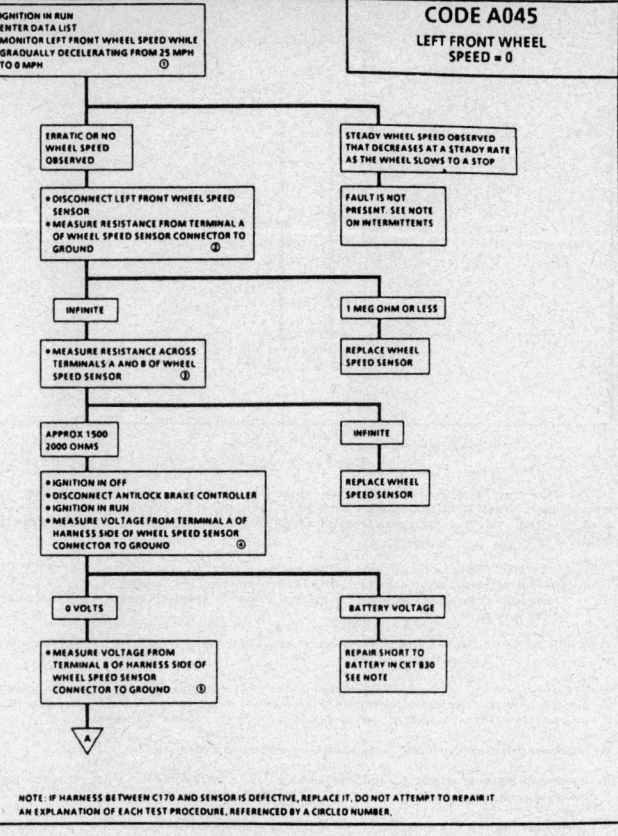

Fig. 56 Code A045, left front wheel speed at 0 mph (Part 1 of 2)

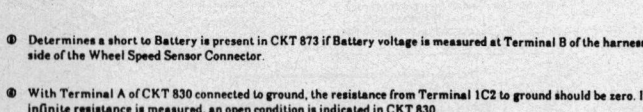

⑤ Determines a short to Battery is present in CKT 873 if Battery voltage is measured at Terminal B of the harness side of the Wheel Speed Sensor Connector.

⑥ With Terminal A of CKT 830 connected to ground, the resistance from Terminal 1C2 to ground should be zero. If infinite resistance is measured, an open condition is indicated in CKT 830.

⑦ With Terminal B of CKT 873 connected to ground, the resistance from Terminal 1C1 to ground should be zero. If infinite resistance is measured, an open condition is indicated in CKT 873.

⑧ At this point, all the connecting circuitry has tested good. The fault may be due to a poorly mated connector at the Wheel Speed Sensor or the Antilock Brake Controller. Other possible cause could be due to damage to the Speed Sensor or Speed Ring. Check for proper mounting or poor alignment. If everthing above tests good, replace the Antilock Brake Contoller.

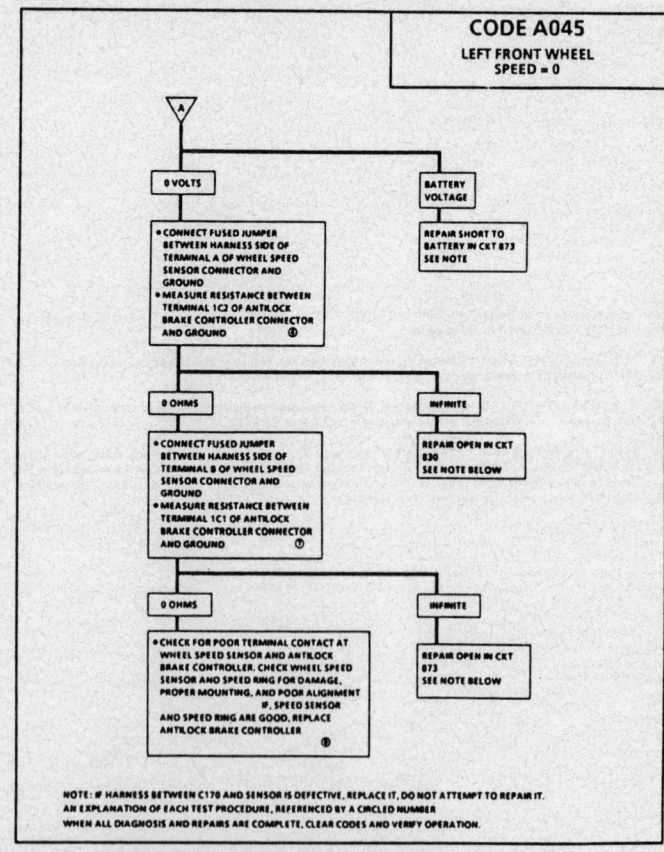

Fig. 56 Code A045, left front wheel speed at 0 mph (Part 2 of 2)

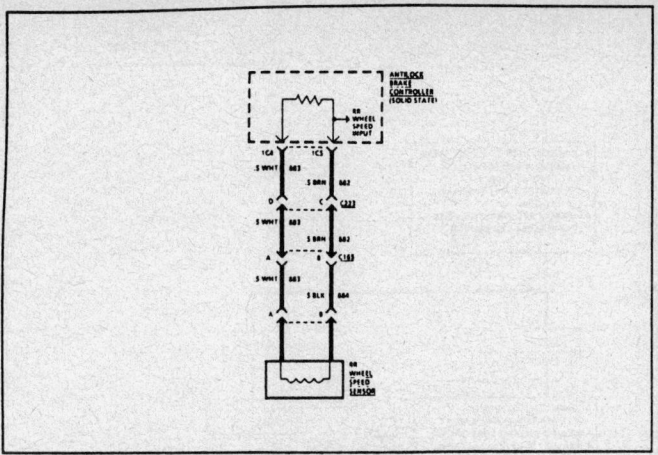

CODE A046

Right Rear Wheel Speed = 0

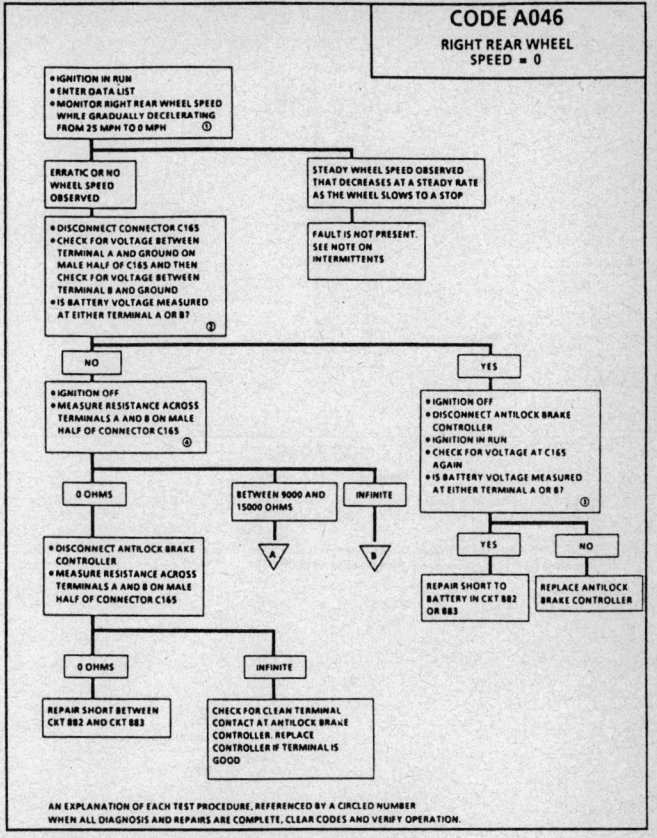

The Wheel Speed Sensor generates a signal that indicates the speed of the wheel. Voltage pulses are produced as the magnetic teeth pass the coil. The frequency of this AC voltage is used by the Controller to determine how fast the wheel is turning. By comparing this wheel speed to the other wheel speeds, the Controller can detect if wheel lock-up is about to occur.

CODE A046 will set when all of the following conditions exist:
- The Antilock Brake Controller Senses the right rear wheel speed to be 0 mph.
- The Antilock Brake Controller senses that the other three wheel speeds are greater than 5 mph and are operating correctly.

TEST DESCRIPTION: The following provides an explanation of the procedures being followed in the following trouble tree.

① Observation of erratic or no wheel speed input indicates the fault is present and is not intermittent.

②&③ Step 2 determines if a short to battery is the fault. If battery voltage is measured step 3 isolates the short to the harness or controller

④ If 9000 to 15000 ohms was measured, the possibility of an open or short in the circuit between the Antilock Brake Controller and Connector C165 has been eliminated.

Fig. 57 Code A046, right rear wheel speed at 0 mph (Part 1 of 3)

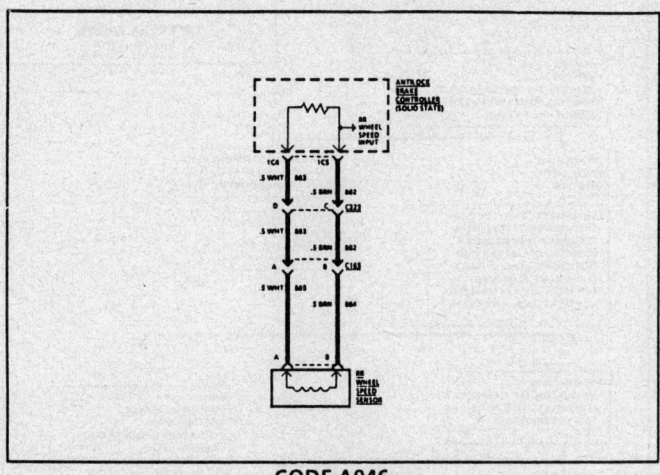

CODE A046

Right Rear Wheel Speed = 0

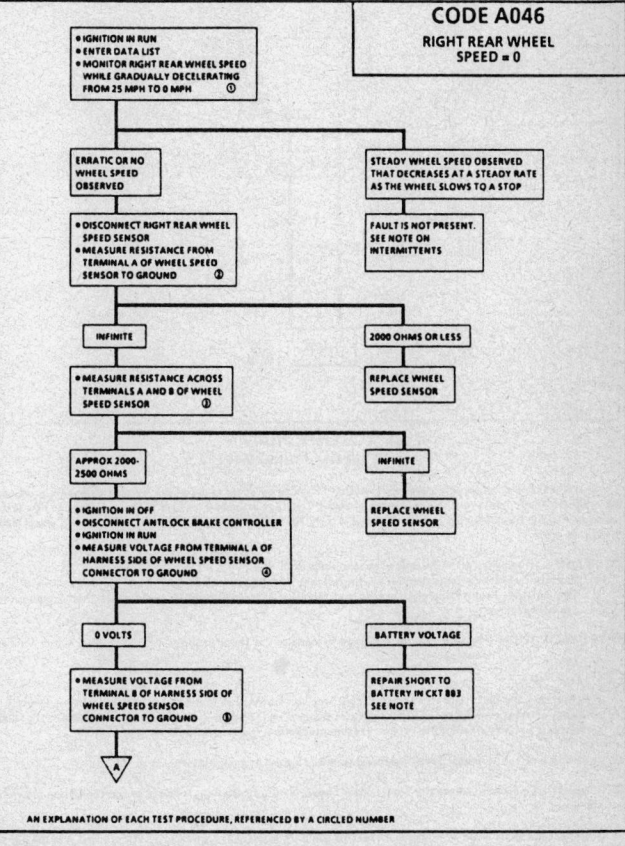

TEST DESCRIPTION: The following provides an explanation of the procedures being followed in the following trouble tree.

⑤ If more than 10 ohms is measured the circuits between the controller and C165 are ok. This isolates the fault to be between the Wheel Speed Sensor and C165. Since this area of circuit is exposed to the elements and road debris, it should be carefully inspected for damage.

⑥ This procedure isolates the fault to a short to ground (1500 to 2500 ohms) or open (above 2500 ohms) or a shorted sensor circuit (below 1500 ohms)

⑦ & ⑧ Determines if the fault is in the harness or the Wheel Speed Sensor. If the harness between C165 and the sensor is defective, replace it. Do not attempt to repair the harness.

Fig. 57 Code A046, right rear wheel speed at 0 mph (Part 2 of 3)

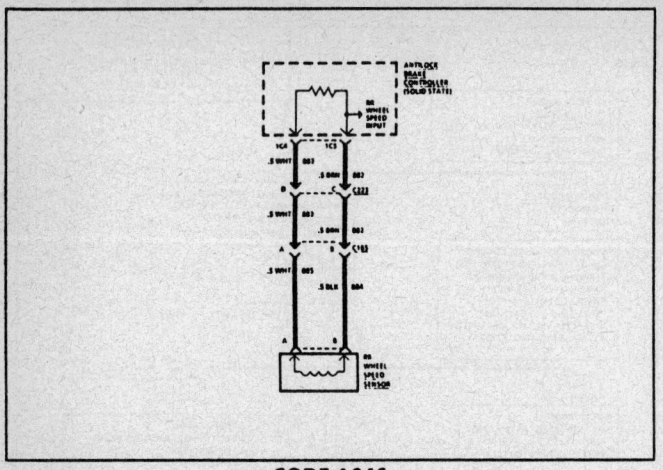

CODE A046

Right Rear Wheel Speed = 0

ⓦ With CKT 883 connected to ground, the resistance from Terminal 1C4 to ground should be zero. If infinite resistance is measured, an open condition is indicated in CKT 883.

ⓘ With CKT 882 connected to ground, the resistance from Terminal 1C5 to ground should be zero. If infinite resistance is measured, an open condition is indicated in CKT 882.

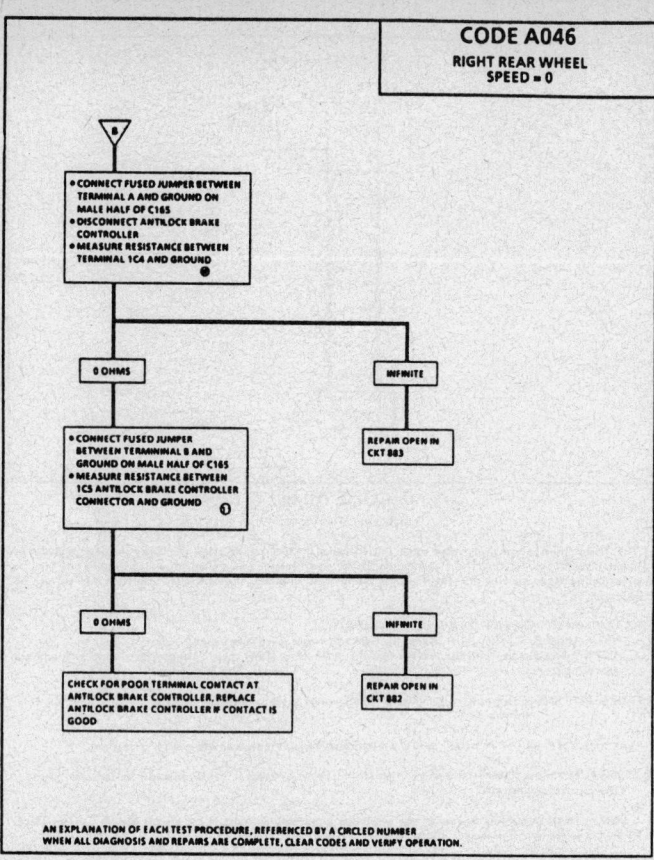

CODE A046

RIGHT REAR WHEEL SPEED = 0

AN EXPLANATION OF EACH TEST PROCEDURE, REFERENCED BY A CIRCLED NUMBER WHEN ALL DIAGNOSIS AND REPAIRS ARE COMPLETE, CLEAR CODES AND VERIFY OPERATION.

Fig. 57   Code A046, right rear wheel speed at 0 mph (Part 3 of 3)

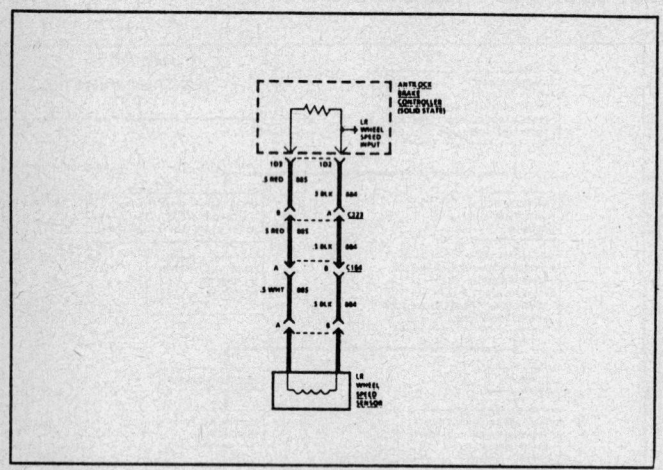

CODE A047

Left Rear Wheel Speed = 0

The Wheel Speed Sensor generates a signal that indicates the speed of the wheel. Voltage pulses are produced as the magnetic teeth pass a coil. The frequency of this A/C voltage is used by the Controller to determine how fast the wheel is turning. By comparing this wheel speed to the other wheel speeds, the Controller can detect if wheel lock-up is about to occur.

CODE A047 will set when all of the following conditions exist:
- The Antilock Brake Controller senses the left rear wheel speed to be 0 mph.
- The Antilock Brake Controller senses that the other three wheel speeds are greater than 5 mph and are operating correctly.

TEST DESCRIPTION: The following provides an explanation of the procedures being followed in the following trouble tree.

ⓘ By observing the Left Rear Wheel speed input, you can verify what type of input the controller is sensing. An unsteady or erratic wheel speed input indicates that a fault is present in the Wheel Speed Sensor or it's related circuitry. If a steady wheel speed is observed, an intermittent fault condition is indicated.

ⓘ Indicates a defective Wheel Speed Sensor by isolating a short to ground internal to the sensor.

ⓘ If resistance measured across the Wheel Speed Sensor is infinite, the fault is due to an open condition internal to the Speed Sensor.

ⓘ Determines a short to Battery is present in CKT 885 if Battery voltage is measured at Terminal A of the harness side of the Wheel Speed Sensor Connector.

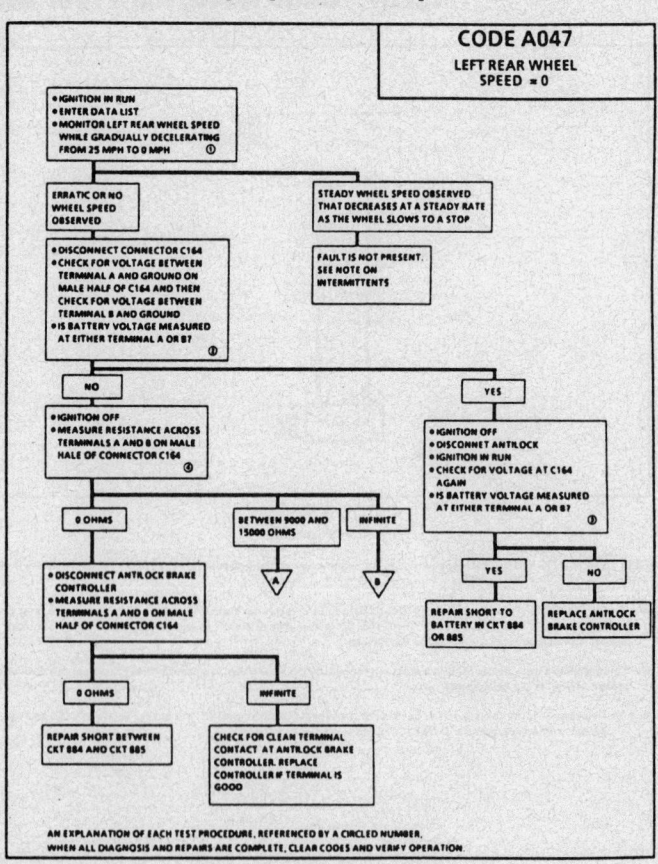

CODE A047

LEFT REAR WHEEL SPEED = 0

AN EXPLANATION OF EACH TEST PROCEDURE, REFERENCED BY A CIRCLED NUMBER, WHEN ALL DIAGNOSIS AND REPAIRS ARE COMPLETE, CLEAR CODES AND VERIFY OPERATION.

Fig. 58   Code A047, left rear wheel speed at 0 mph (Part 1 of 3)

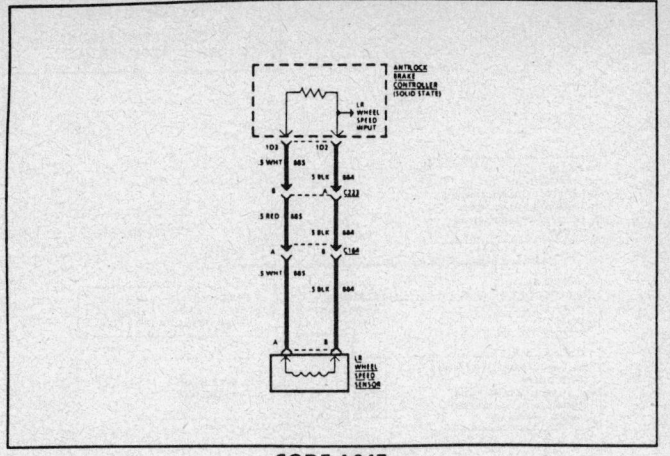

CODE A047

Left Rear Wheel Speed = 0

TEST DESCRIPTION: The following provides an explanation of the procedures being followed in the following trouble tree.

④ If more than 10 ohms is measured the circuit between the controller and C164 are ok. This isolates the fault to be between the Wheel Speed Sensor and C164. Since this area of circuit is exposed to the elements and road debris, it should be carefully inspected for damage.

⑤ This procedure isolates the fault to a short to ground (1500 to 2500 ohms) or open (above 2500 ohms) or a shorted sensor circuit (below 1500 ohms).

⑦ & ⑧ Determines if the fault is in the harness or the Wheel Speed Sensor. If the harness between C164 and the sensor is defective, replace it, do not attempt to repair the harness.

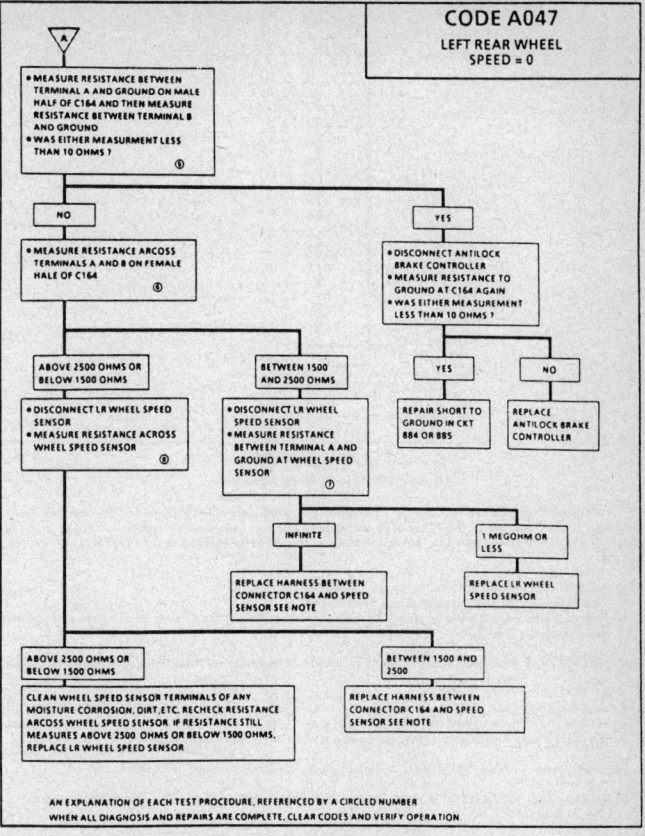

Fig. 58 Code A047, left rear wheel speed at 0 mph (Part 2 of 3)

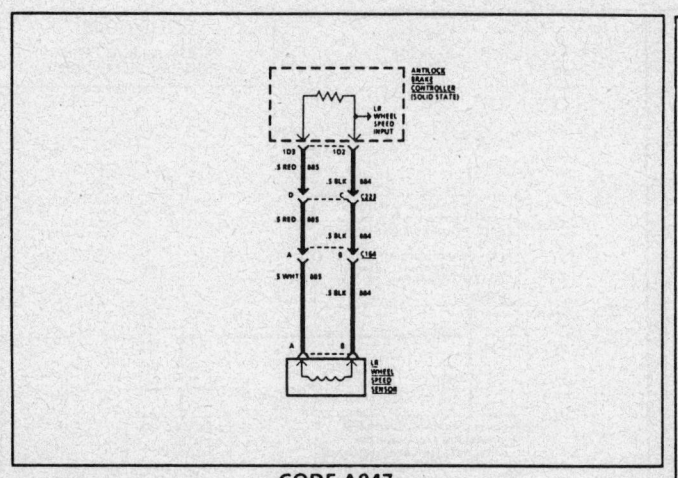

CODE A047

Left Rear Wheel Speed = 0

⑩ With CKT 884 connected to ground, the resistance from Terminal 1D2 to ground should be zero. If infinite resistance is measured, an open condition is indicated in CKT 884.

⑪ With CKT 885 connected to ground, the resistance from Terminal 1D3 to ground should be zero. If infinite resistance is measured, an open condition is indicated in CKT 885.

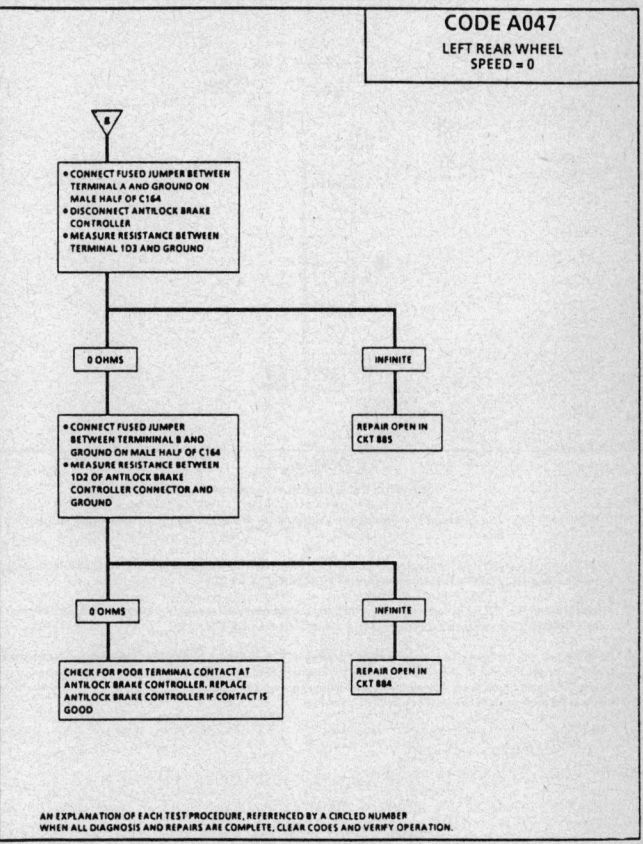

Fig. 58 Code A047, left rear wheel speed at 0 mph (Part 3 of 3)

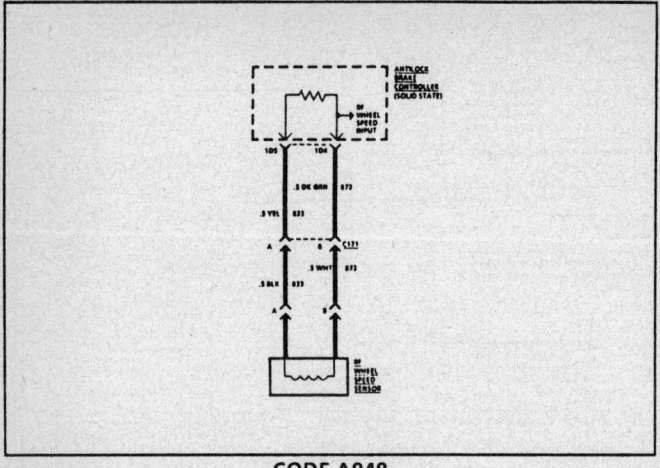

CODE A048
Excessive Right Front Wheel Acceleration

The Antilock Brake Controller uses the signal from the Wheel Speed Sensor to detect if wheel lock-up is impending. If the frequency of the AC voltage produced by the wheel speed sensor indicates that the wheel is accelerating or decelerating faster than physically possible, the Controller determines the signal is faulty and sets the code.

CODE A048 will set when all of the following conditions exist:
- The Brakes are not being applied (Brake Switch is off).
- The Antilock Brake Controller senses that the Right Front Wheel has accelerated or decelerated greater than physically possible.

TEST DESCRIPTION: The following provides an explanation of the procedures being followed in the facing trouble tree.

① By observing the Right Front Wheel speed input, you can verify what type of input the controller is sensing. An unsteady or erratic wheel speed input indicates that a fault is present in the Wheel Speed Sensor or its related circuitry. If a steady wheel speed is observed, an intermittent fault condition is indicated.

② Indicates a defective Wheel Speed Sensor by isolating a short to ground internal to the sensor.

③ If resistance measured across the Wheel Speed Sensor is infinite, the fault is due to an open condition internal to the Speed Sensor.

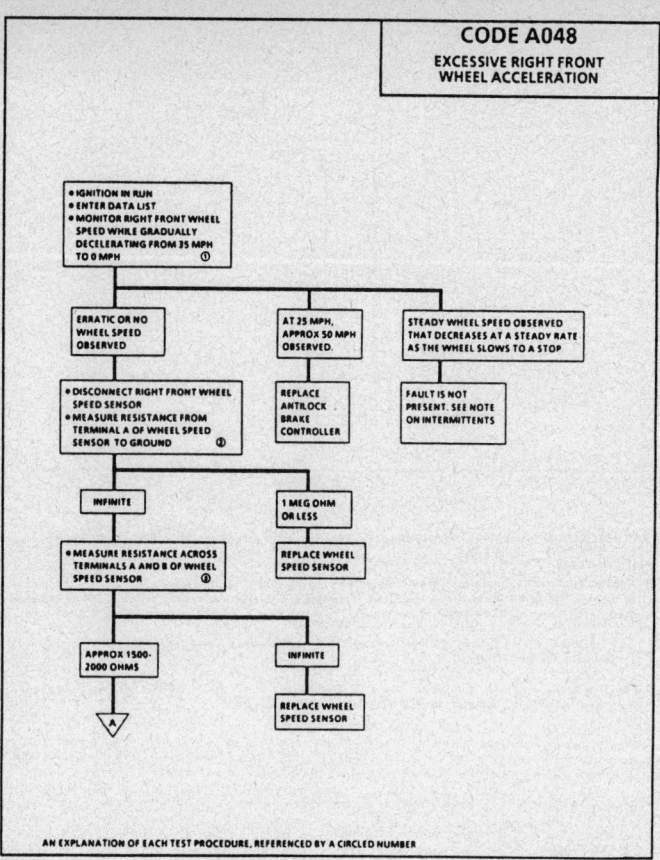

Fig. 59 Code A048, excessive right front wheel acceleration. (Part 1 of 2)

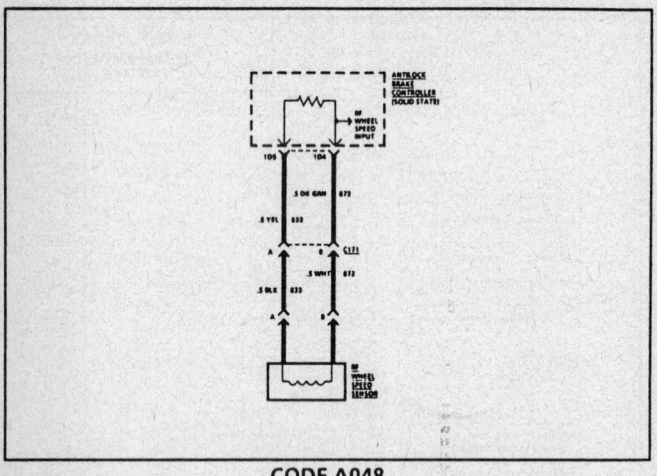

CODE A048
Excessive Right Front Wheel Acceleration

TEST DESCRIPTION: The following provides an explanation of the procedures being followed in the facing trouble tree.

④ With Terminal A of CKT 833 connected to ground, the resistance from Terminal 1D5 to ground should be zero. If infinite resistance is measured, an open condition is indicated in CKT 833.

⑤ With Terminal B of CKT 872 connected to ground, the resistance from Terminal 1D4 to ground should be zero. If infinite resistance is measured, an open condition is indicated in CKT 872.

⑥ At this point, all the connecting circuitry has tested good. The fault may be due to a poorly mated connector at the Wheel Speed Sensor or the Antilock Brake Controller. Other possible causes could be due to damage to the Speed Sensor or Speed Ring. Check for proper mounting or poor alignment.   If everything above tests good, replace the Antilock Brake Controller.

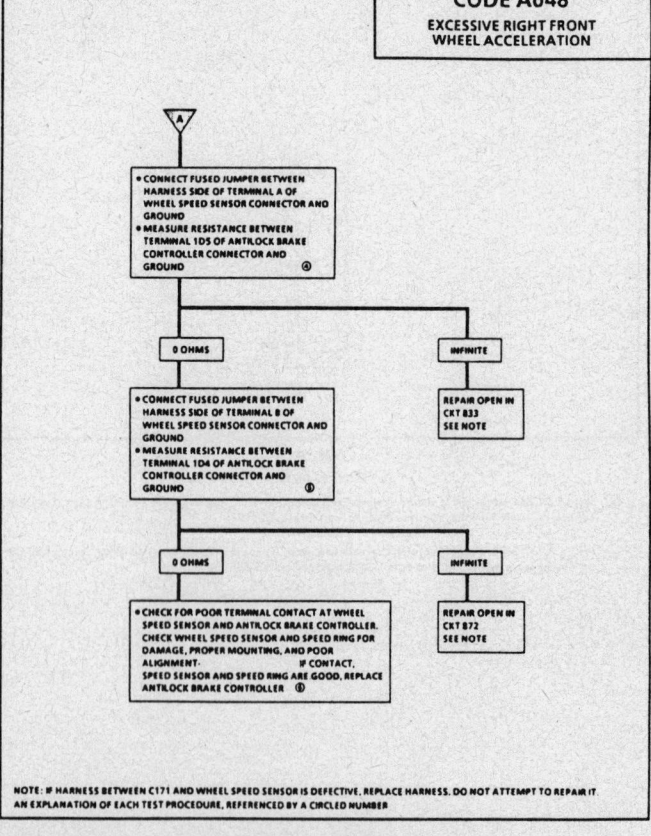

Fig. 59 Code A048, excessive right front wheel acceleration. (Part 2 of 2)

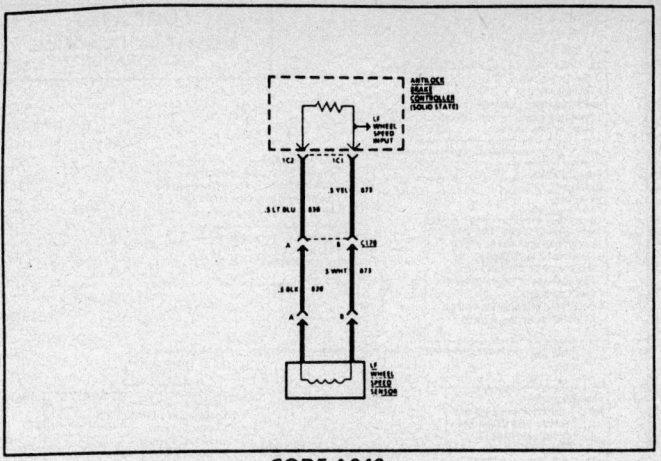

CODE A049
Excessive Left Front Wheel Acceleration

The Antilock Brake Controller uses the signal from the Wheel Speed Sensor to detect if wheel lock-up is impending. If the frequency of the AC voltage produced by the Wheel Speed Sensor indicates that the wheel is accelerating or decelerating faster than physically possible, the Controller determines the signal is faulty and sets the code.

CODE A049 will set when all of the following conditions exist:
- The Brakes are not being applied (Brake Switch is off).
- The Antilock Brake Controller senses that the Left Front Wheel has accelerated or decelerated greater than physically possible.

TEST DESCRIPTION: The following provides an explanation of the procedures being followed in the facing trouble tree.

① By observing the Left Front Wheel speed input, you can verify what type of input the controller is sensing. An unsteady or erratic wheel speed input indicates that a fault is present in the Wheel Speed Sensor or its related circuitry. If a steady wheel speed is observed, an intermittent fault condition is indicated.

② Indicates a defective Wheel Speed Sensor by isolating a short to ground internal to the sensor.

③ If resistance measured across the Wheel Speed Sensor is infinite, the fault is due to an open condition internal to the Speed Sensor.

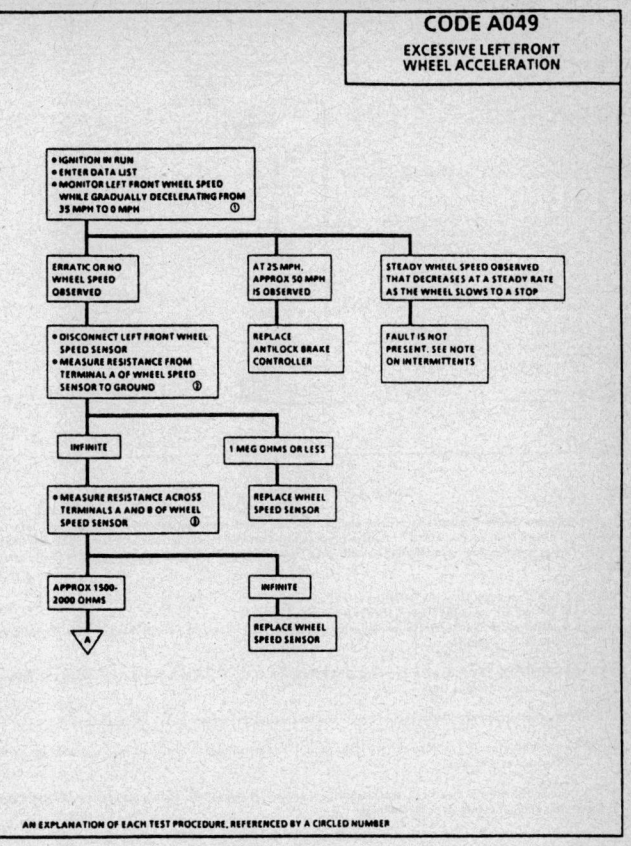

CODE A049
EXCESSIVE LEFT FRONT WHEEL ACCELERATION

AN EXPLANATION OF EACH TEST PROCEDURE, REFERENCED BY A CIRCLED NUMBER

Fig. 60   Code A049, excessive left front wheel acceleration. (Part 1 of 2)

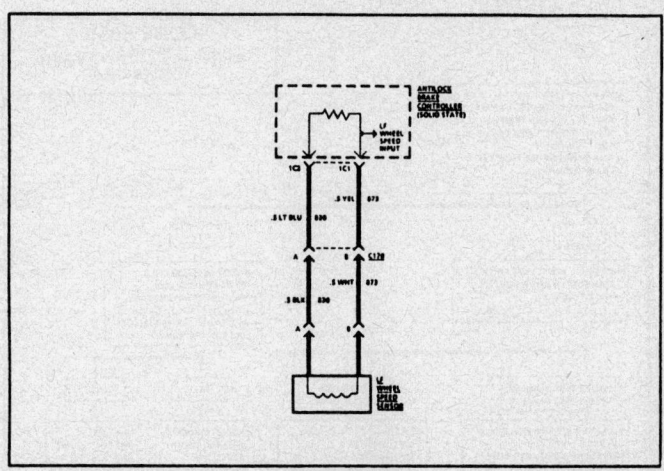

CODE A049
Excessive Left Front Wheel Acceleration

TEST DESCRIPTION: The following provides an explanation of the procedures being followed in the facing trouble tree.

④ With Terminal A of CKT 830 connected to ground, the resistance from Terminal 1C2 to ground should be zero. If infinite resistance is measured, an open condition is indicated in CKT 830.

⑤ With Terminal B of CKT 873 connected to ground, the resistance from Terminal 1C1 to ground should be zero. If infinite resistance is measured, an open condition is indicated in CKT 873.

⑥ At this point, all the connecting circuitry has tested good. The fault may be due to a poorly mated connector at the Wheel Speed Sensor or the Antilock Brake Controller. Other possible causes could be due to damage to the Speed Sensor or Speed Ring. Check for proper mounting, or poor alignment.   If everything above tests good, replace the Antilock Brake Controller.

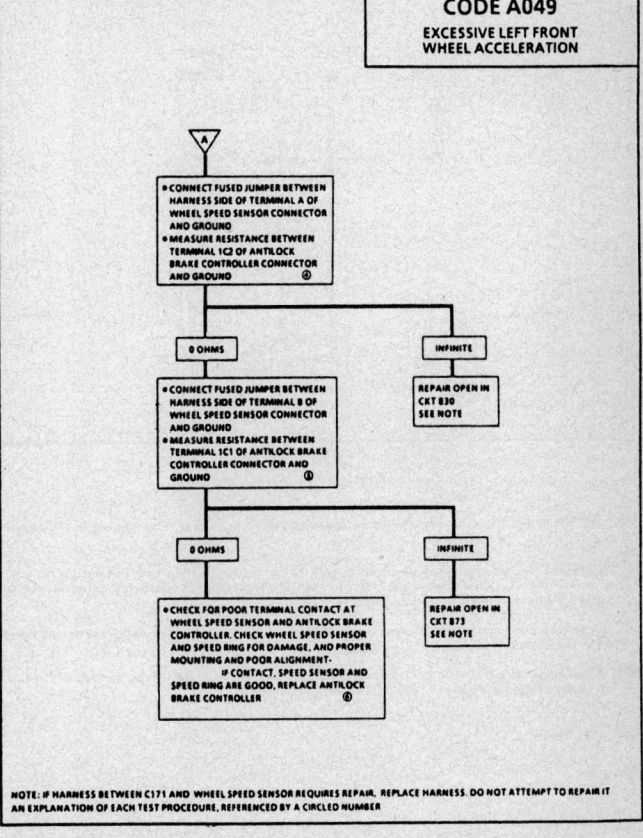

CODE A049
EXCESSIVE LEFT FRONT WHEEL ACCELERATION

NOTE: IF HARNESS BETWEEN C171 AND WHEEL SPEED SENSOR REQUIRES REPAIR, REPLACE HARNESS. DO NOT ATTEMPT TO REPAIR IT
AN EXPLANATION OF EACH TEST PROCEDURE, REFERENCED BY A CIRCLED NUMBER

Fig. 60   Code A049, excessive left front wheel acceleration. (Part 2 of 2)

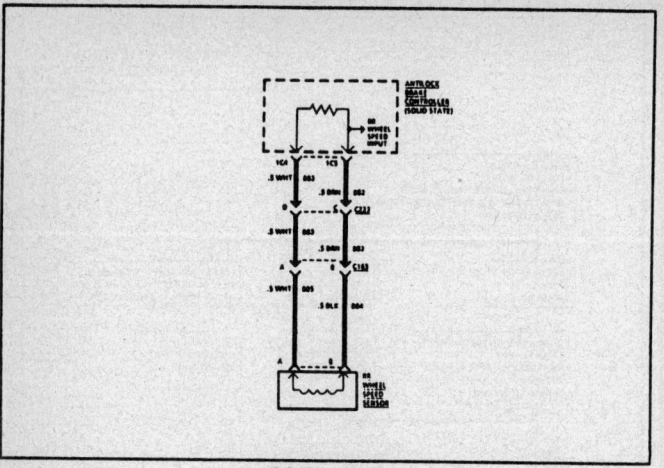

CODE A050
Excessive Right Rear Wheel Acceleration

The Antilock Brake Controller uses the signal from the wheel speed sensor to detect if wheel lock-up is impending. If the frequency of the AC voltage produced by the wheel speed sensor indicates that the wheel is accelerating or decelerating faster than physically possible, the Controller determines the signal is faulty and sets the code.

CODE A050 will set when all of the following conditions exist:
- The Brakes are not being applied (Brake Switch is off).
- The Antilock Brake Controller senses that the Right Rear Wheel has accelerated or decelerated greater than physically possible.

TEST DESCRIPTION: The following provides an explanation of the procedures being followed in the following trouble tree.

① Observation of erratic or no wheel speed input indicates the fault is present and is not intermittent.

②& ③ Step 2 determines if a short to battery is the fault. If battery voltage is measured, step 3 isolates the short to the harness or controller.

④ If 9000 to 15000 ohms is measured, the possibility of an open or short in the circuit between the Antilock Brake Controller and Connector C165 is eliminated.

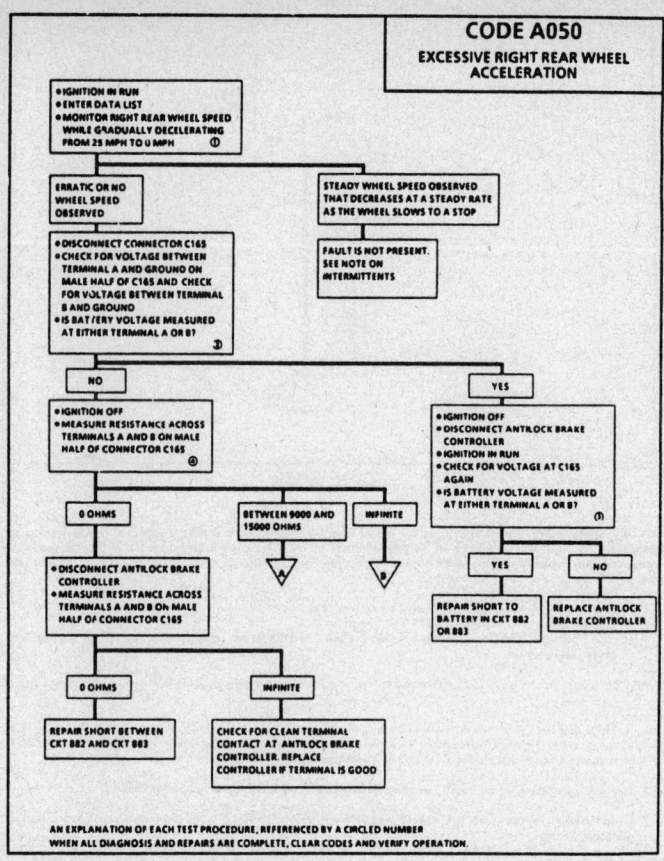

Fig. 61   Code A050, excessive right rear wheel acceleration. (Part 1 of 3)

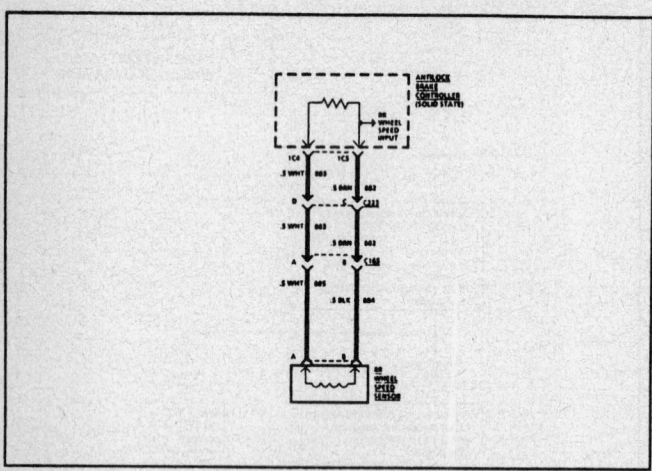

CODE A050
Excessive Rear Rear Wheel Speed Acceleration

TEST DESCRIPTION: The following provides an explanation of the procedures being followed in the following trouble tree.

⑤ If more than 10 ohms is measured, the circuit between the Controller and C165 are ok. This isolates the fault to be between the Wheel Speed Sensor and C165. Since this area of the circuit is exposed to the elements and road debris it should be carefully inspected for damage.

⑥ This procedure isolates the fault to a short to ground (1500 to 2500 ohms) or open (above 2500 ohms) or a shorted sensor circuit (below 1500 ohms)

⑦ & ⑧ Determine if the fault is in the harness or the Wheel Speed Sensor. If the harness between C165 and the sensor is defective, replace it. Do not attempt to repair the harness.

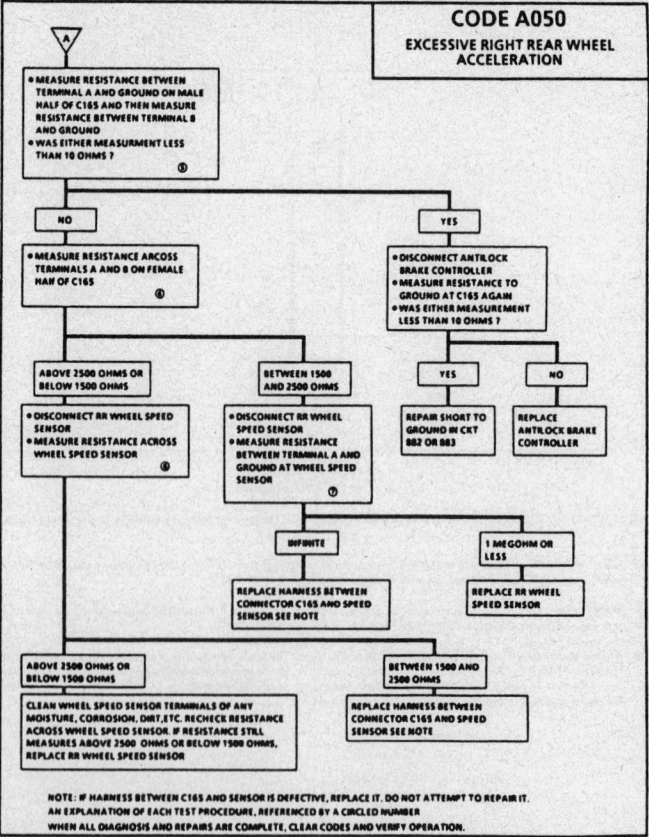

Fig. 61   Code A050, excessive right rear wheel acceleration. (Part 2 of 3)

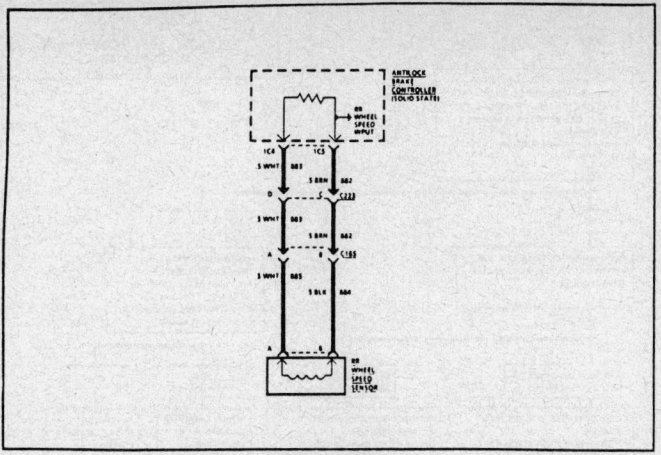

CODE A050

Excessive Right Rear Wheel Speed Acceleration

ⓐ With CKT 883 connector to ground, the resistance from Terminal 1C4 to ground should be zero. If infinite resistance is measured, an open condition is indicated in CKT 883.

ⓑ With CKT 882 connector to ground, the resistance from Terminal 1C5 to ground should be zero. If infinite resistance is measured, an open condition is indicated in CKT 882.

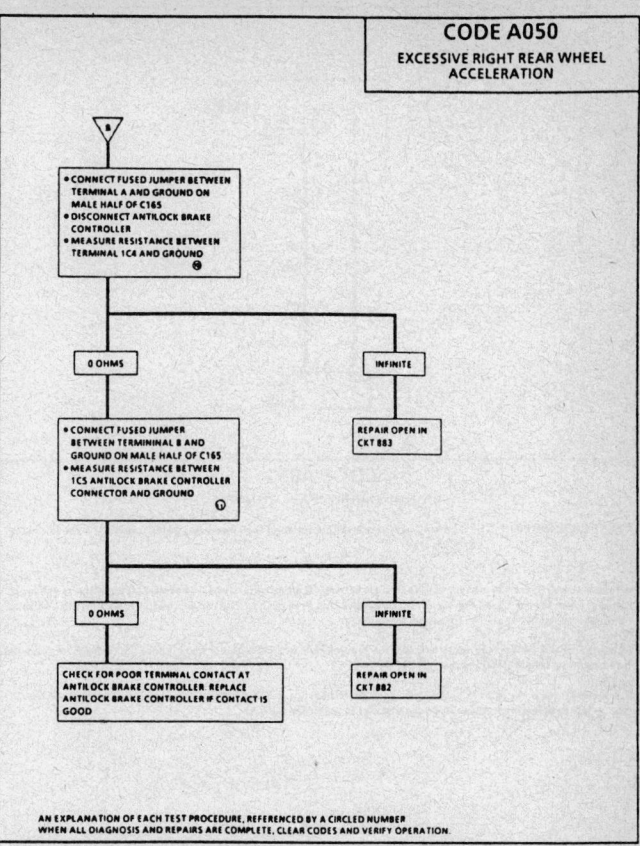

CODE A050
EXCESSIVE RIGHT REAR WHEEL ACCELERATION

AN EXPLANATION OF EACH TEST PROCEDURE, REFERENCED BY A CIRCLED NUMBER WHEN ALL DIAGNOSIS AND REPAIRS ARE COMPLETE, CLEAR CODES AND VERIFY OPERATION.

Fig. 61   Code A050, excessive right rear wheel acceleration. (Part 3 of 3)

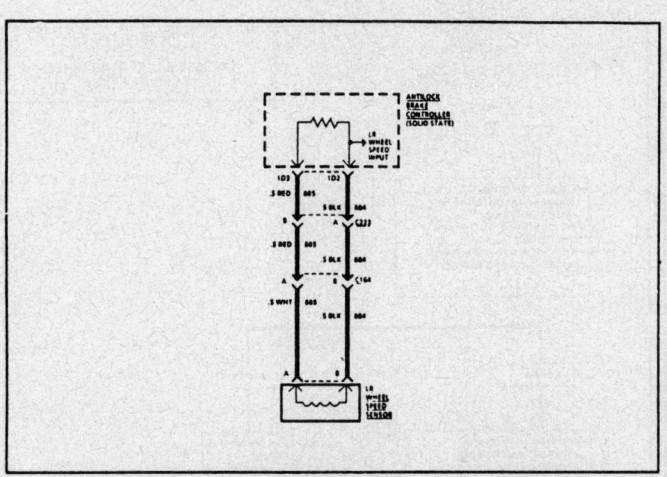

CODE A051

Excessive Left Rear Wheel Acceleration

The Antilock Brake Controller uses the signal from the wheel speed sensor to detect if wheel speed lock-up is impending. If the frequency of the AC voltage produced by the wheel speed sensor indicates that the wheel is accelerating or decelerating faster than physically possible, the Controller determines the signal is faulty and sets the code.

CODE A051 will set when all of the following conditions exist:
- The Brakes are not being applied (Brake Switch is off).
- The Antilock Brake Controller senses that the Left Rear Wheel has accelerated or decelerated greater than physically possible.

TEST DESCRIPTION: The following provides an explanation of the procedures being followed in the following trouble tree.

① Observation of erratic or no wheel speed input indicates the fault is present and is not intermittent.

②&③ Step 2 determines is if a short to Battery is the fault. If Battery voltage is measured, step 3 isolates the short to the harness or controller.

④ If 9000 to 15000 ohms were measured, the possibility of an open or short in the circuit between the Antilock Brakes Controller and Connector 164 has been eliminated.

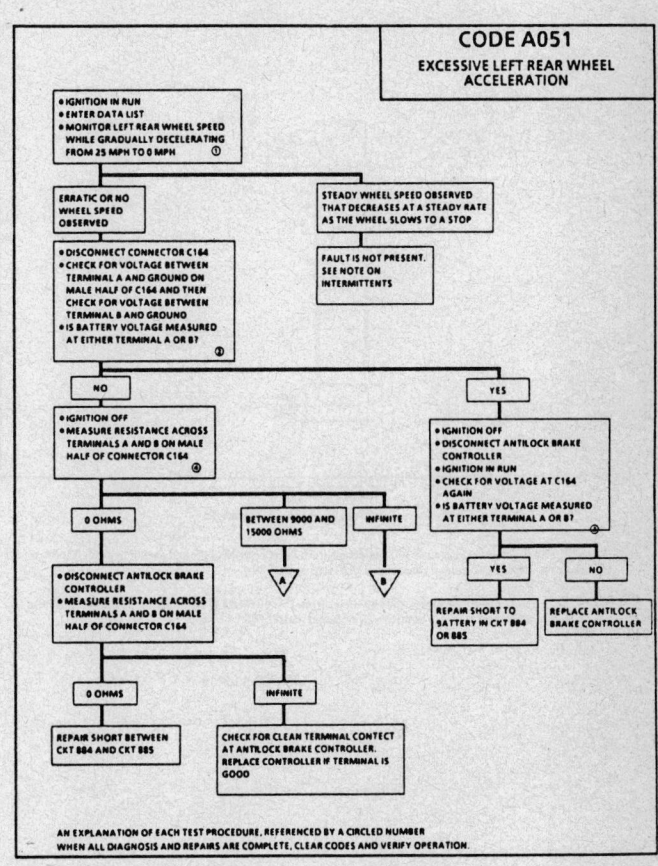

CODE A051
EXCESSIVE LEFT REAR WHEEL ACCELERATION

AN EXPLANATION OF EACH TEST PROCEDURE, REFERENCED BY A CIRCLED NUMBER WHEN ALL DIAGNOSIS AND REPAIRS ARE COMPLETE, CLEAR CODES AND VERIFY OPERATION.

Fig. 62   Code A051, excessive left rear wheel acceleration. (Part 1 of 3)

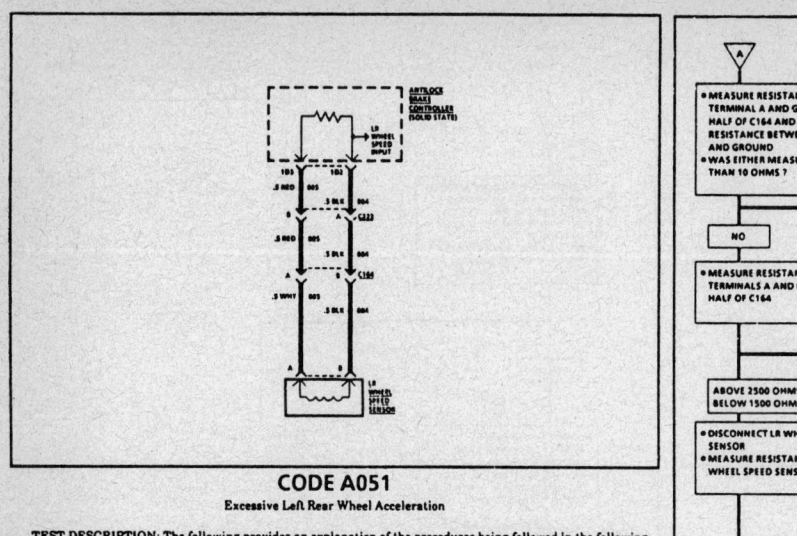

CODE A051
Excessive Left Rear Wheel Acceleration

TEST DESCRIPTION: The following provides an explanation of the procedures being followed in the following trouble tree

① If more than 10 ohms is measured, the circuits between the controller and C164 are OK. This isolates the fault between the Wheel Speed Sensor and C164. Since this area of the circuit is exposed to the elements and road debris, it should be carefully inspected for damage.

④ This procedure isolates the fault to a short to ground(1500 to 2500 ohms) or open (above 2500 ohms) or a shorted sensor circuit (below 1500 ohms).

⑦&⑧ Determines if the fault is in the harness or the Wheel Speed Sensor. If the harness between C164 and the sensor is defective, replace it, do not attempt to repair the harness.

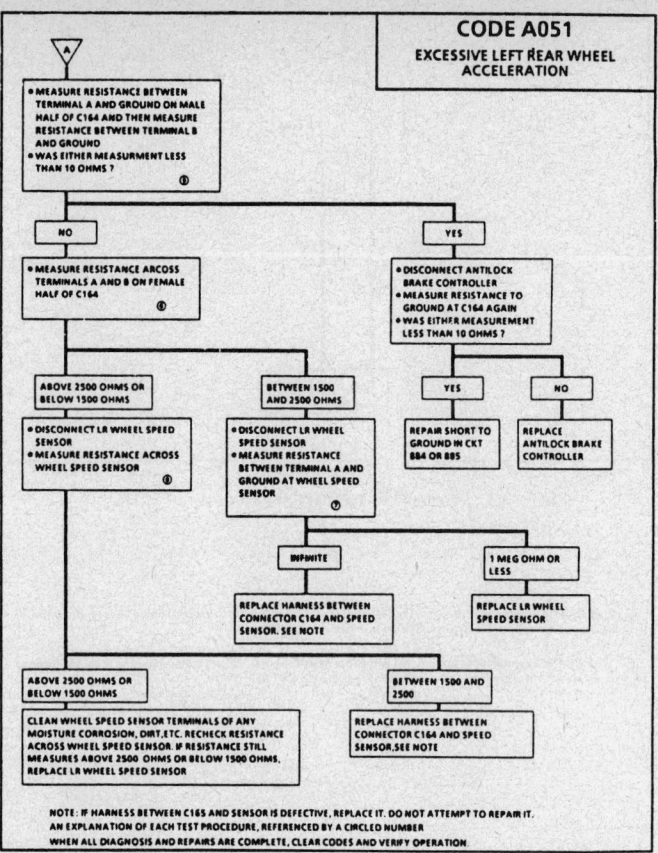

Fig. 62 Code A051, excessive left rear wheel acceleration. (Part 2 of 3)

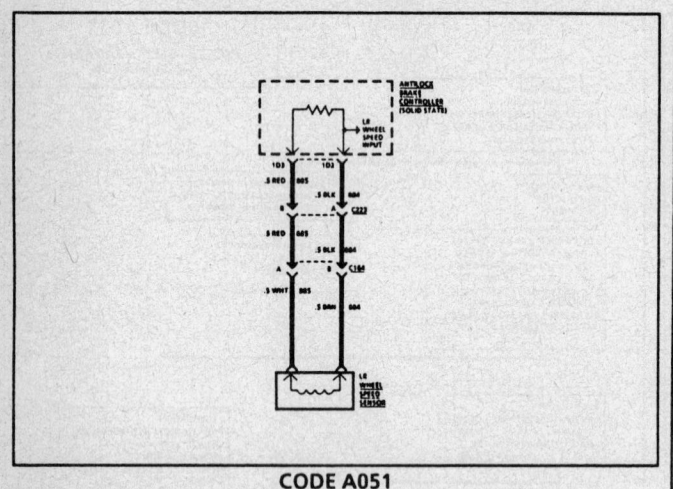

CODE A051
Excessive Left Rear Wheel Speed Acceleration

⑩ With CKT 884 connector to ground, the resistance from Terminal 1D2 to ground should be zero. If infinite resistance is measured, an open condition is indicated in CKT 884.

⑪ With CKT 885 connector to ground, the resistance from Terminal 1D3 to ground should be zero. If infinite resistance is measured, an open condition is indicated in CKT 885.

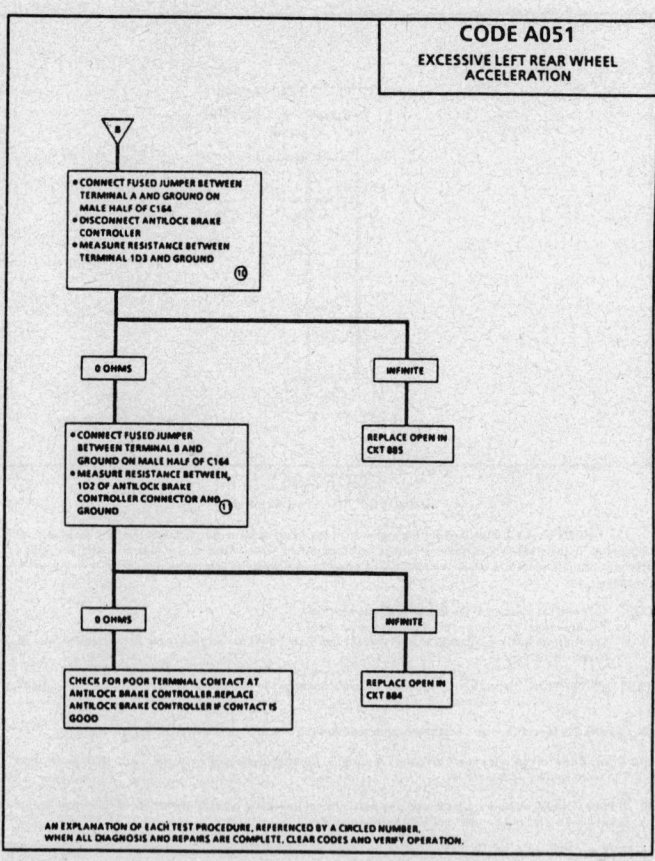

Fig. 62 Code A051, excessive left rear wheel acceleration. (Part 3 of 3)

Anti-Lock Brakes—GENERAL MOTORS

CODE A052

Antilock Brake Controller Calibration Error

CODE A052 will set when the Antilock Brake Controller detects a malfunction internal to itself. If this code is set, replace the Antilock Brake Controller.

Fig. 63   Code A052, anti-lock brake control calibration error

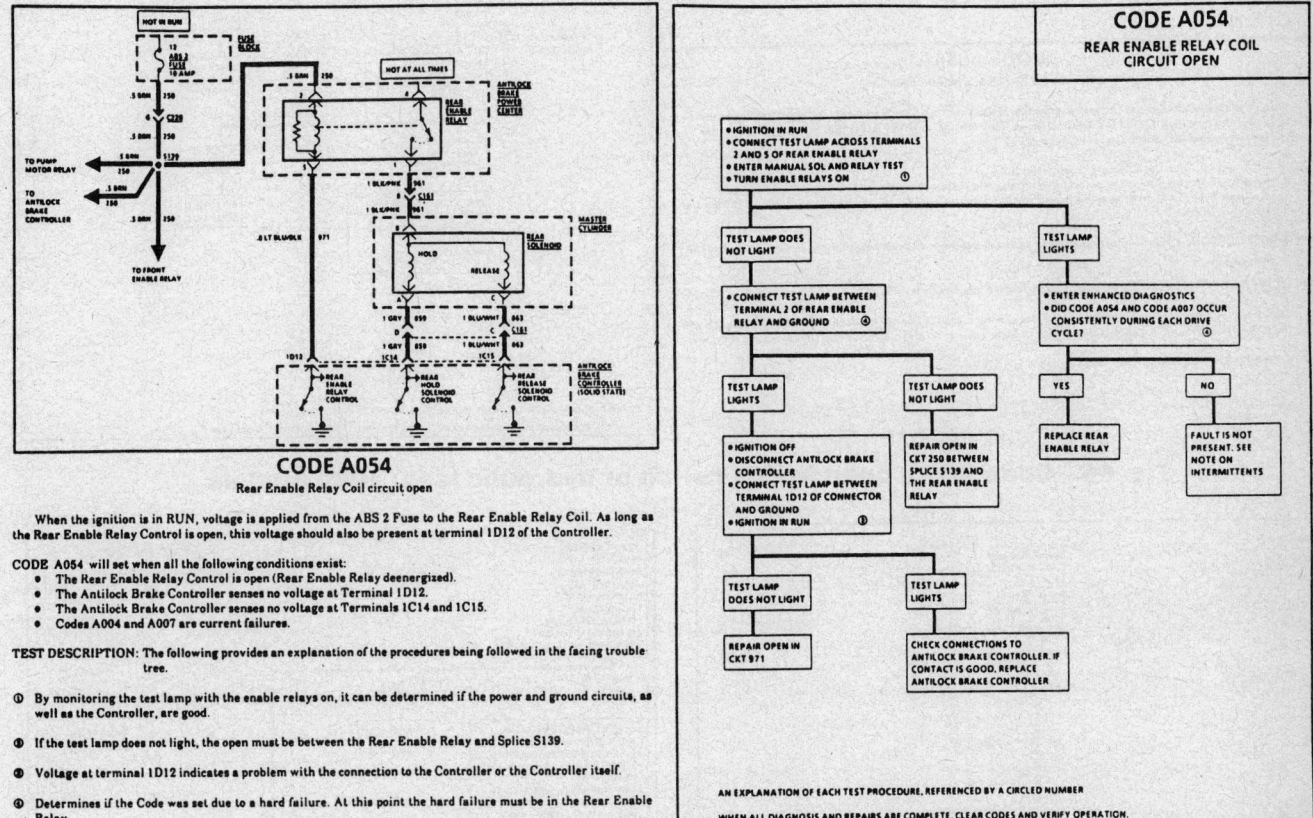

CODE A054

Rear Enable Relay Coil circuit open

When the ignition is in RUN, voltage is applied from the ABS 2 Fuse to the Rear Enable Relay Coil. As long as the Rear Enable Relay Control is open, this voltage should also be present at terminal 1D12 of the Controller.

CODE A054 will set when all the following conditions exist:
- The Rear Enable Relay Control is open (Rear Enable Relay deenergized).
- The Antilock Brake Controller senses no voltage at Terminal 1D12.
- The Antilock Brake Controller senses no voltage at Terminals 1C14 and 1C15.
- Codes A004 and A007 are current failures.

TEST DESCRIPTION: The following provides an explanation of the procedures being followed in the facing trouble tree.

① By monitoring the test lamp with the enable relays on, it can be determined if the power and ground circuits, as well as the Controller, are good.

② If the test lamp does not light, the open must be between the Rear Enable Relay and Splice S139.

③ Voltage at terminal 1D12 indicates a problem with the connection to the Controller or the Controller itself.

④ Determines if the Code was set due to a hard failure. At this point the hard failure must be in the Rear Enable Relay.

Fig. 64   Code A054, rear enable relay coil circuit open

CODE A055

Antilock Brake Controller internal voltage fault

CODE A055 will set when the Antilock Brake Controller detects a malfunction internal to itself. If this code is set, replace the Antilock Brake Controller.

Fig. 65   Code A055, anti-lock brake controller internal voltage fault

1989-90 CUTLASS SUPREME, GRAND PRIX & REGAL (DELCO-MORAINE III TYPE)

25-45

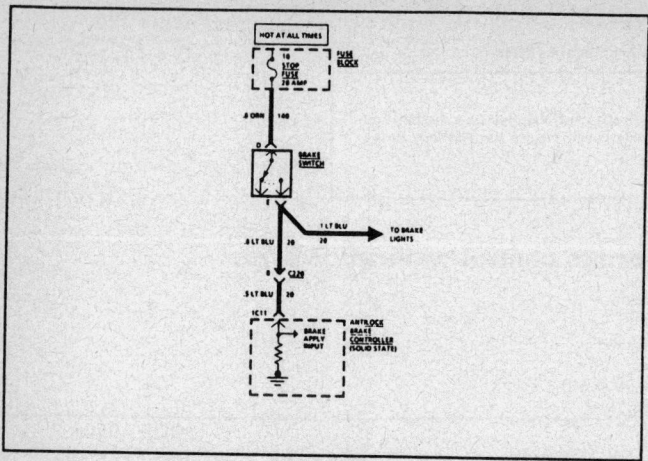

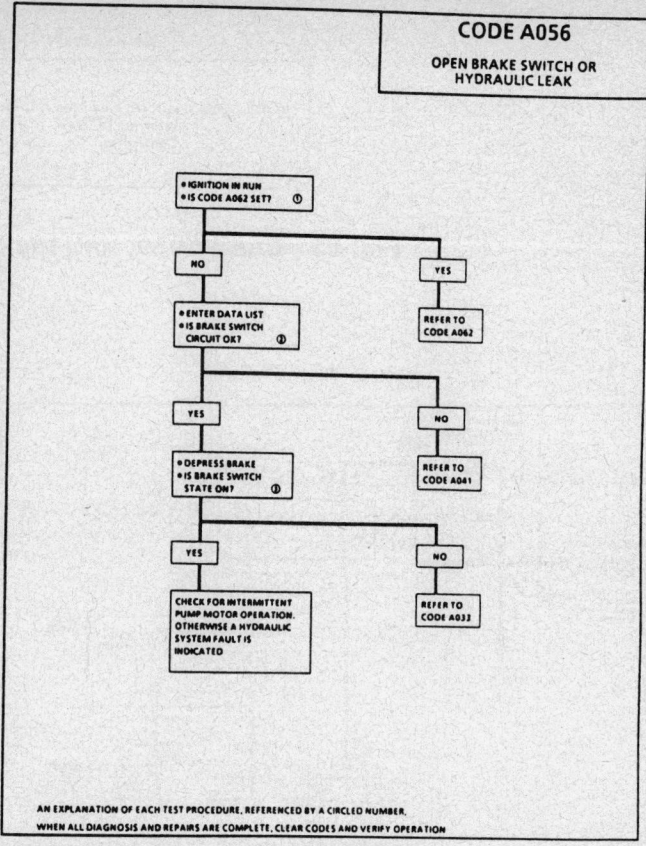

CODE A056
Open Brake Switch or Hydraulic Leak

Voltage is applied at all times to the Brake Switch. When the Brake Switch is closed, voltage is applied to the Brake Lights and terminal 1C11 of the Antilock Brake Controller. If the Brake Apply Input receives voltage, the Controller determines that the brakes are being applied.

CODE A056 will set when the following condition exists:
- Code A032 was set during the preceding ignition cycle. Code A056 will remain a current code until the Antilock Brake Controller senses a Brake Switch transition and the ignition cycle is completed (Ignition turned to OFF).

TEST DESCRIPTION: The following provides an explanation of the procedures being followed in the facing trouble tree.

① If Code A062 is also set, the pump motor was cycling too fast. See Code A062.

② Code A041 will diagnose an open between the Brake Switch and the Controller, or between the brake switch and the stop light to ground. An open High Level Stop Light can also set this code if the Hazard Lights are operated.

③ Code A033 will diagnose an open brake switch or CKT 140.

Fig. 66   Code A056, open brake switch or hydraulic leak. 1989 models

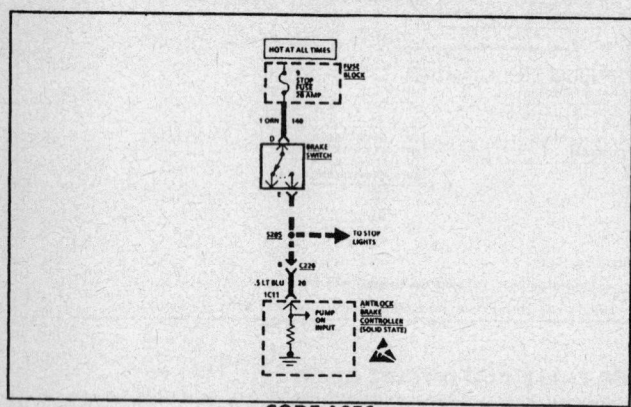

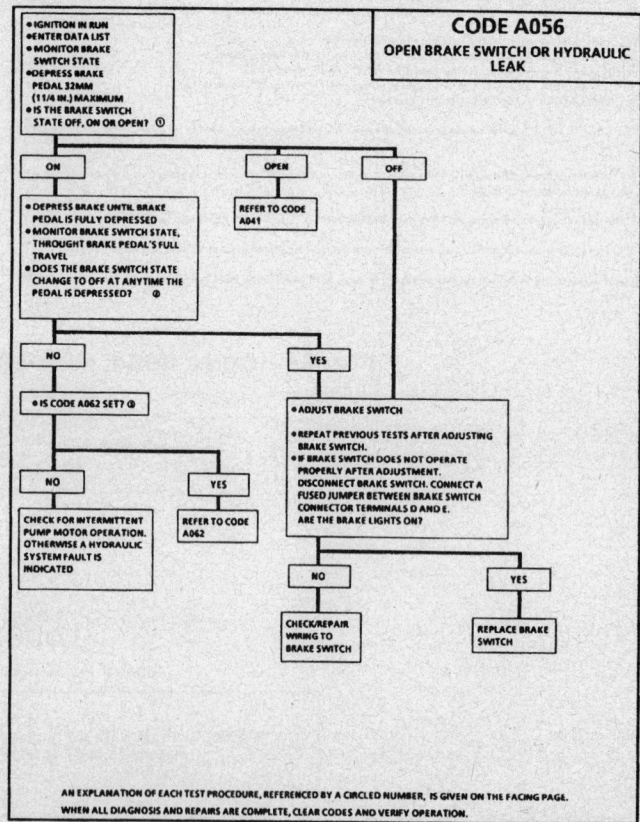

CODE A056
Open Brake Switch or Hydraulic Leak

Voltage is applied at all times to the Brake Switch. When the Brake Switch is closed, voltage is applied to the Brake Lights and terminal 1C11 of the Antilock Brake Controller. If the Brake Apply Input receives voltage, the Controller determines that the brakes are being applied.

CODE A056 will set when all the following conditions exsist:
- The Antilock Brake Controller receives three jump on inputs without receiving a brake switch on input. This allows a brake switch fault to be detected without an Antilock Braking condition present.

TEST DESCRIPTION: The following provides an explanation of the procedures being following in the facing trouble tree.

① & ② Checks for an improperly adjusted Brake Switch.

③ If Code A062 is also set, the pump motor was cycling too fast. See Code A062.

Fig. 67   Code A056, open brake switch or hydraulic leak. 1990 models

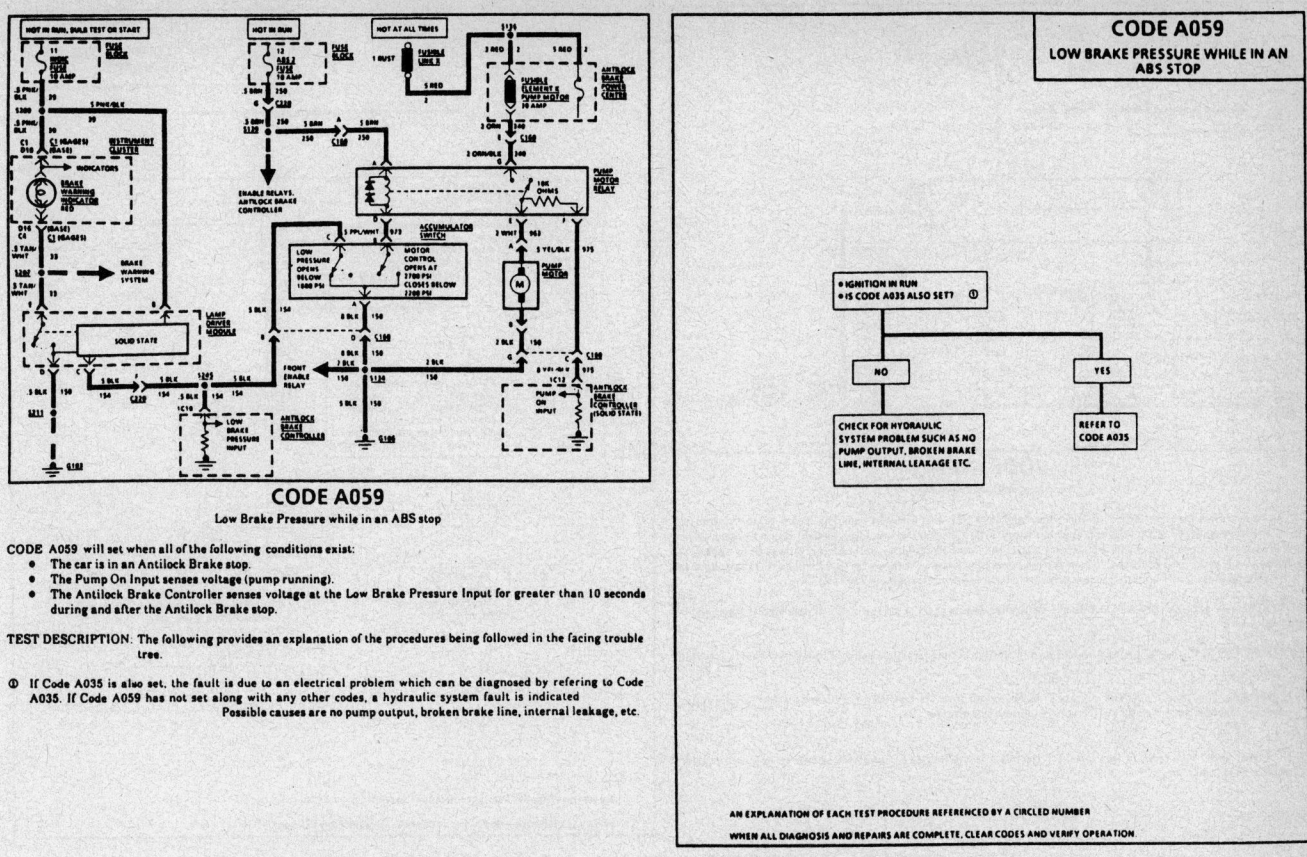

CODE A059

Low Brake Pressure while in an ABS stop

CODE A059 will set when all of the following conditions exist:
- The car is in an Antilock Brake stop.
- The Pump On Input senses voltage (pump running).
- The Antilock Brake Controller senses voltage at the Low Brake Pressure Input for greater than 10 seconds during and after the Antilock Brake stop.

TEST DESCRIPTION: The following provides an explanation of the procedures being followed in the facing trouble tree.

① If Code A035 is also set, the fault is due to an electrical problem which can be diagnosed by referring to Code A035. If Code A059 has not set along with any other codes, a hydraulic system fault is indicated. Possible causes are no pump output, broken brake line, internal leakage, etc.

Fig. 68   Code A059, low brake pressure while in an ABS stop

CODE A060

Antilock Brake Controller Internal fault

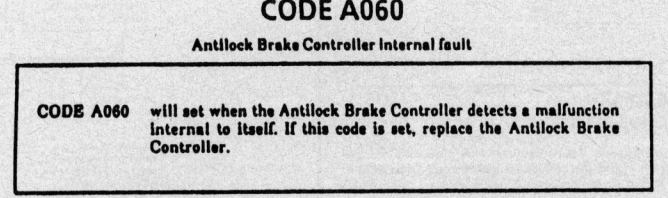

CODE A060 will set when the Antilock Brake Controller detects a malfunction internal to itself. If this code is set, replace the Antilock Brake Controller.

Fig. 69   Code A060, anti-lock brake controller internal fault

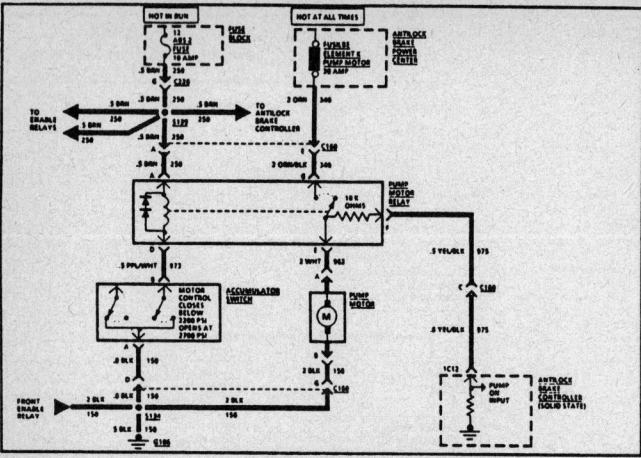

CODE A062
Low Accumulator Pre-charge

The Accumulator is precharged to approximately 1200 PSI with nitrogen gas. The Pump Motor maintains system pressure between 2200 PSI and approximately 2700 PSI. The Accumulator Switch Motor Control closes when the pressure drops below 2200 PSI. This grounds the Pump Motor Relay Coil causing voltage to be applied to the Pump Motor and Pump On Input. Whenever the Pump Motor is on, the Pump On Input will have voltage applied to it. The Pump Motor will run until system pressure is restored to approximately 2700 PSI.

CODE A062 will set when the Antilock Brake Controller detects short pump run times of less than 1.4 seconds in duration.

TEST DESCRIPTION: The following provides an explanation of the procedures being followed in the facing trouble tree.

① If the pump run time from "OK pressure" to "pump off time" is less than six seconds a low accumulator precharge or poor accumulator switch point condition is indicated.

② If normal pump run cycle is less than 1.7 seconds a miscalibrated accumulator switch or low accumulator precharge is indicated.

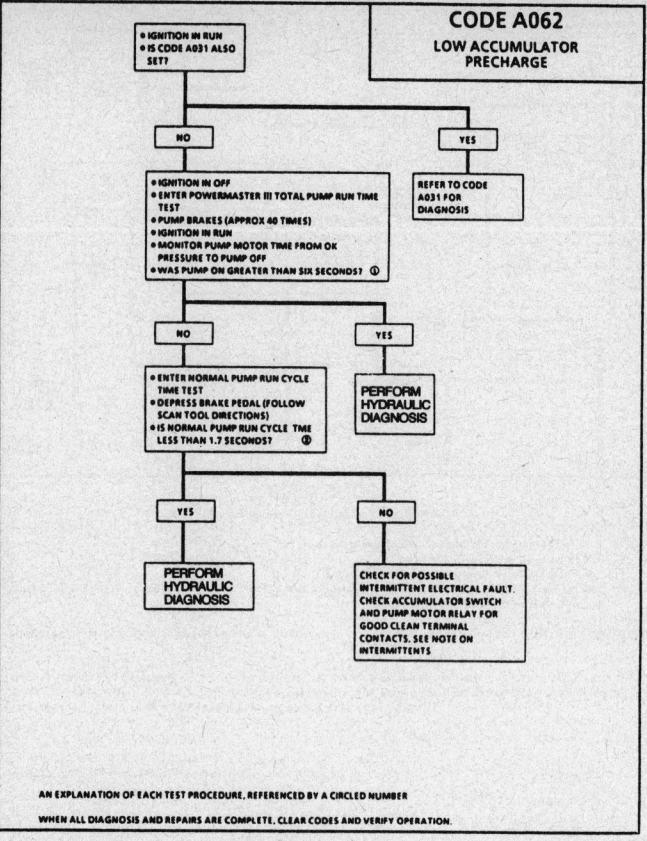

Fig. 70   Code A062, low accumulator precharge

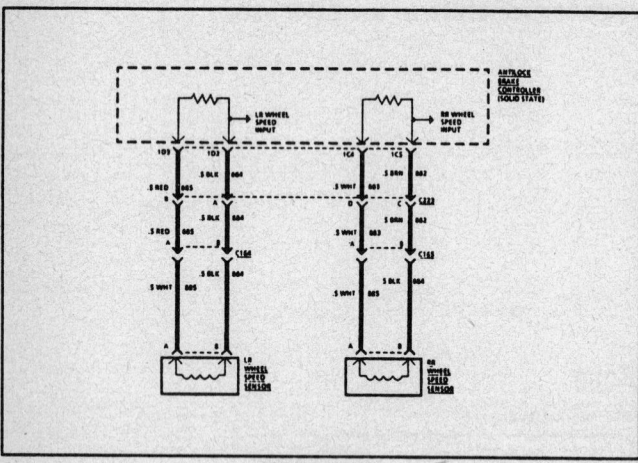

CODE A063
Both Rear Wheel Speed Sensors open

The Antilock Brake Controller monitors the Wheel Speed Sensors. If one or both rear wheel speeds are zero, the Controller cannot accurately detect wheel lock-up. Since three good wheel speeds are needed to set Codes A046 or A047, these Codes cannot determine if both wheel speed sensors are faulty. Code A063 can detect if both Rear Wheel Speed Sensors are malfunctioning.

CODE A063 will set when all of the following conditions exist:
• The Antilock Brake Controller senses both front wheel speeds are greater than 10 mph and are operating correctly.
• The Antilock Brake Controller senses both rear wheel speeds are 0 mph for more than 20 seconds.

TEST DESCRIPTION: The following provides an explanation of the procedures being followed in the facing trouble tree.

① If the front wheel were spinning while the vehicle was being serviced on a lift code, A063 would set. The code should be cleared and the vehicle road tested to insure this was the reason code A063 set.

② Determines whether the fault is due to a hard failure or a possible intermittent failure.

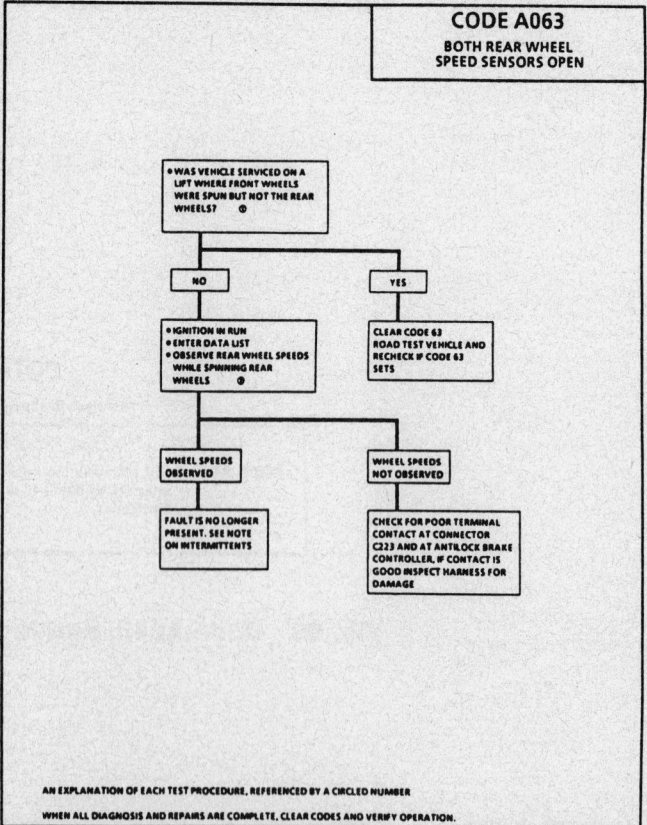

Fig. 71   Code A063, both rear wheel speed sensors open

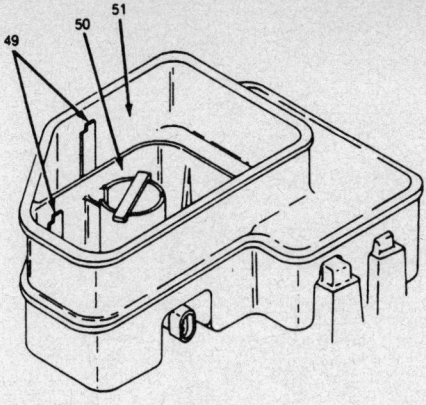

49. FLUID LEVEL MARKS
50. FRONT CHAMBER
51. REAR CHAMBER

Fig. 72   Fluid level fill marks

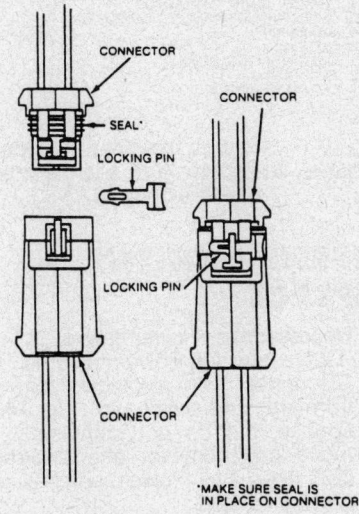

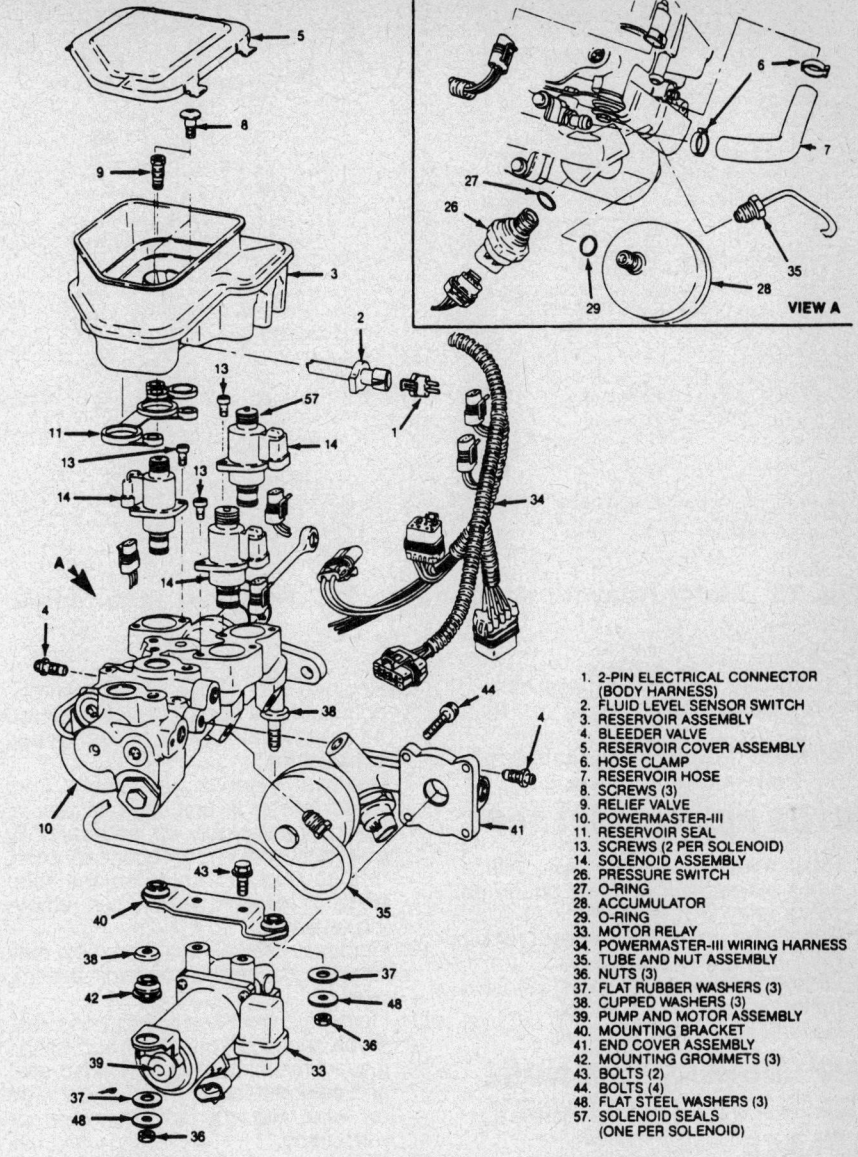

1. 2-PIN ELECTRICAL CONNECTOR (BODY HARNESS)
2. FLUID LEVEL SENSOR SWITCH
3. RESERVOIR ASSEMBLY
4. BLEEDER VALVE
5. RESERVOIR COVER ASSEMBLY
6. HOSE CLAMP
7. RESERVOIR HOSE
8. SCREWS (3)
9. RELIEF VALVE
10. POWERMASTER-III
11. RESERVOIR SEAL
13. SCREWS (2 PER SOLENOID)
14. SOLENOID ASSEMBLY
26. PRESSURE SWITCH
27. O-RING
28. ACCUMULATOR
29. O-RING
33. MOTOR RELAY
34. POWERMASTER-III WIRING HARNESS
35. TUBE AND NUT ASSEMBLY
36. NUTS (3)
37. FLAT RUBBER WASHERS (3)
38. CUPPED WASHERS (3)
39. PUMP AND MOTOR ASSEMBLY
40. MOUNTING BRACKET
41. END COVER ASSEMBLY
42. MOUNTING GROMMETS (3)
43. BOLTS (2)
44. BOLTS (4)
48. FLAT STEEL WASHERS (3)
57. SOLENOID SEALS (ONE PER SOLENOID)

Fig. 74   Powermaster III, exploded view

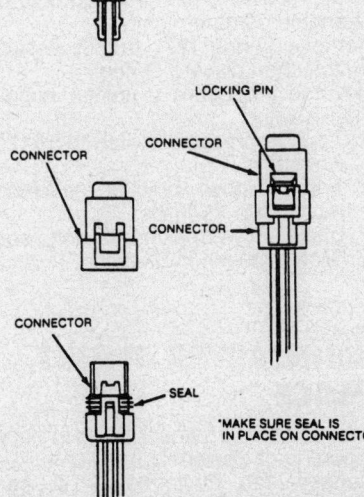

Fig. 73   Connector position assurance locking pins

ACCUMULATOR, REPLACE

The accumulator is nitrogen-charged and holds brake fluid under high pressure. It cannot be serviced and must be replaced as an assembly.

1. Depressurize the Powermaster III, see "Depressurizing Powermaster III."
2. Remove the accumulator (28), by turning hex nut on the end of accumulator with a 17 mm socket, **Fig. 74.**
3. Remove from vehicle by sliding out from underneath Powermaster III, toward left front wheelwell.
4. Remove O-ring (29), from accumulator.
5. Reverse procedure to install, noting the following:
   a. Lightly lubricate, then install a new O-ring on accumulator.
   b. **Torque** accumulator to 23-36 ft. lbs.

c. Bleed Powermaster III as described in "Powermaster III Bleeding."

TUBE & NUT ASSEMBLY (HIGH PRESSURE SIDE), REPLACE

1. Depressurize the Powermaster III, see "Depressurizing Powermaster III."
2. Remove air cleaner, duct and stud.
3. Remove tube and nut assembly (35), from Powermaster III unit (10). Plug all openings to prevent fluid loss and contamination, **Fig. 74.**
4. Inspect tube and nut assembly for crack, deformation and scratches or nicks on sealing surfaces. Replace tube and nut assembly if any of the above conditions are found.
5. Reverse procedure to install, noting the following:

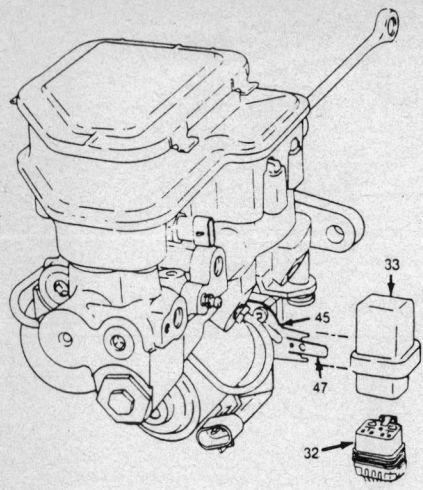

32. 5-PIN CONNECTOR
33. MOTOR RELAY
45. RELAY BRACKET
47. RELAY BRACKET RELEASE TAB

Fig. 75 Motor relay location

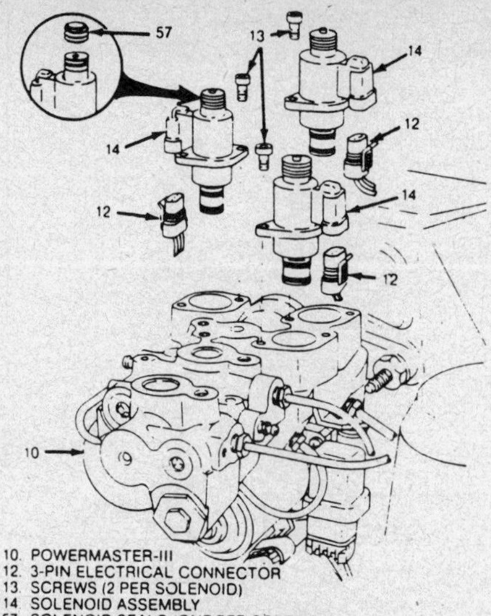

a. **Torque** tube and nut assembly to Powermaster III unit to 10-15 ft. lbs.
b. Bleed Powermaster III unit, see "Powermaster III Bleeding."

MOTOR RELAY, REPLACE

1. Push relay bracket tab (47), with a small screwdriver, to clear button on motor relay (33), **Fig. 75.**
2. Pull motor relay from relay bracket (45).
3. Disconnect 5-pin connector (32), from motor relay.
4. Reverse procedure to install.

RESERVOIR COVER, HOSE & RESERVOIR ASSEMBLY, REPLACE

Clean reservoir cover assembly (5) and surrounding area before removing, **Fig. 74.**
1. Depressurize Powermaster III, see "Depressurizing Powermaster III."
2. Unsnap reservoir cover assembly, then remove from reservoir (3).
3. Inspect reservoir cover assembly for cuts, cracks, nicks and deformation. Replace any damaged parts.
4. Remove fluid level sensor switch, as described in "Fluid Level Sensor Switch, Replace."
5. To gain access, loosen but do not remove cowl bracket attaching nuts, then pull Powermaster III forward slightly.
6. Use a clean syringe to remove as much brake fluid from reservoir as possible. **Brake fluid will cause damage to all painted surfaces.**
7. Cover electrical connectors and engine/body parts with clean shop towels to catch any brake fluid dripped from reservoir. Use a suitable container to catch brake fluid when upper end reservoir hose is disconnected from reservoir.

8. Remove upper hose clamp, then disconnect hose from reservoir. **Discard all used brake fluid. Never reuse brake fluid.**
9. Remove reservoir assembly from Powermaster III unit, then lift rear of reservoir assembly up and carefully pull away from under secondary dash. Use caution as to not damage solenoids or solenoid seals when removing reservoir.
10. Remove reservoir seal. This seal may remain attached to reservoir assembly.
11. Remove lower hose clamp, hose, reservoir seal and solenoid if necessary.
12. Inspect reservoir assembly, hose, seal and solenoid for any type of damage or wear. Replace any damaged or worn parts.
13. Reverse procedure to install, noting the following:
    a. **Torque** cowl bracket attaching nuts to 15-25 ft. lbs.
    b. Bleed Powermaster III, see "Powermaster III Bleeding."

SOLENOID ASSEMBLIES, REPLACE

Clean reservoir cover assembly (5) and surrounding area before removing, **Fig. 74.**
1. Depressurize Powermaster III, see "Depressurizing Powermaster III."
2. Clean surrounding area, then remove reservoir cover and assembly.
3. Disconnect 3-pin connector (12), from solenoid assembly (14), **Fig. 76.**
4. Remove solenoid attaching screws (13), then the solenoid assembly. Ensure lower solenoid O-rings are in place and in good condition.
5. Reverse procedure to install, noting the following:
    a. **Torque** solenoid assembly attaching screws to 33-45 ft. lbs.
    b. Bleed Powermaster III, see "Powermaster III Bleeding."

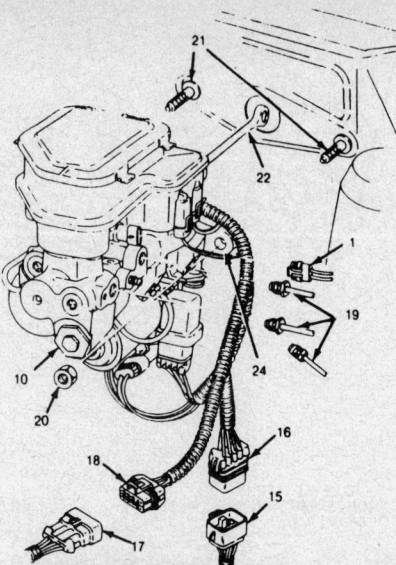

10. POWERMASTER-III
12. 3-PIN ELECTRICAL CONNECTOR
13. SCREWS (2 PER SOLENOID)
14. SOLENOID ASSEMBLY
57. SOLENOID SEALS (ONE PER SOLENOID)

Fig. 76 Solenoid assemblies

1. 2-PIN ELECTRICAL CONNECTOR (BODY HARNESS)
10. POWERMASTER-III
15. VEHICLE 7-PIN CONNECTOR
16. 7-PIN WIRING HARNESS CONNECTOR
17. VEHICLE 10-PIN CONNECTOR
18. 10-PIN WIRING HARNESS CONNECTOR
19. BRAKE PIPE
20. NUTS (2)
21. COWL BRACKET STUD
22. PUSHROD
24. MOUNTING BRACKET

Fig. 77 Powermaster III brake tube, mounting & electrical connections

PRESSURE SWITCH, REPLACE

1. Depressurize Powermaster III, see "Depressurizing Powermaster III."
2. Disconnect 3-pin electrical connector from pressure switch (26), **Fig. 74.**
3. Loosen, but do not completely remove cowl bracket attaching nuts (20), then pull Powermaster III unit slightly forward.
4. Raise and support vehicle. Using switch socket tool No. J-37117 or equivalent, swivel joint and extensions, remove switch through bottom of engine compartment.
5. Remove O-ring (27), from pressure switch, then discard O-ring.
6. Reverse procedure to install, noting the following:
    a. **Torque** pressure switch to 15-20 ft. lbs.
    b. **Torque** cowl bracket attaching nuts to 15-25 ft. lbs.
    c. Bleed Powermaster III unit, see "Powermaster III Bleeding."

POWERMASTER III UNIT, REPLACE

Do not use wiring harness to aid in lifting or supporting of Powermaster III unit.
1. Depressurize Powermaster III, see "Depressurizing Powermaster III."
2. Disconnect 7-pin connector (15), from Powermaster III harness connector (16), **Fig. 77.**

3. Disconnect 10-pin connector (17), from Powermaster III wiring harness connector (18).
4. Disconnect 2-pin connector (1), from fluid level sensor switch (2).
5. Remove three brake pipes (19), from Powermaster III unit. Plug open lines and fittings to prevent fluid loss and contamination.
6. Remove hair pin clip (located inside vehicle), and pushrod (22), from brake pedal.
7. Remove two attaching nuts (20), from cowl bracket studs, then remove Powermaster III unit.
8. Reverse procedure to install, noting the following:
   a. **Torque** two cowl bracket attaching nuts to 15-25 ft. lbs.
   b. **Torque** tube-to-Powermaster III unit nuts to 10-15 ft. lbs.
   c. Bleed Powermaster III unit, see "Powermaster III Bleeding."

ANTI-LOCK BRAKE CONTROLLER, REPLACE

The anti-lock brake controller can be removed from vehicle without removing front seat.

1. Turn ignition switch to the Off position, slide passenger seat forward, then tip seat forward.
2. Remove bolts securing case cover, then remove anti-lock controller. It is not necessary to remove the harness connectors to slide controller out of the case.
3. Remove connectors from controller.
4. Reverse procedure to install, tightening case cover bolts hand tight.

PROPORTIONER VALVE ASSEMBLY, REPLACE

The proportioner valve is not repairable and must be serviced as a complete assembly. The use of rubber hoses or hydraulic lines other than those specified may lead to functional problems and major repairs.

1. Depressurize Powermaster III, see "Depressurizing Powermaster III."
2. Remove input brake line, then two output brake lines, from proportioner valve assembly. Input brake line has a 12 mm threaded nut and output brake lines have 10 mm threaded nuts. Plug open lines and fittings to prevent fluid loss and contamination.
3. Remove proportioner valve assembly.
4. Reverse procedure to install, noting the following:
   a. **Torque** tube nuts to 10-15 ft. lbs.
   b. Bleed system, see "Manual Bleeding," or "Pressure Bleeding."

FRONT WHEEL SPEED SENSORS, REPLACE

1. Raise and support vehicle, then remove sensor connector from wiring harness.
2. Remove two front wheel speed sensor bolts, then one bracket connector bolt.
3. Remove front speed sensor.
4. Reverse procedure to install, noting the following:
   a. **Torque** 15 mm bolts to 52-65 ft. lbs.
   b. **Torque** 10 mm bolts to 6-9 ft. lbs.

Bonneville, DeVille, Electra, Fleetwood, Park Avenue, 88, 98 & 6000 (Teves Type)

NOTE: Wire Code Identification and Symbol Identification located in the front of this manual can be used as an aid when using wiring circuits found in this section.

INDEX

Continued

OPERATING PRECAUTIONS

Some of the following procedures require that hydraulic lines, hoses and fittings be disconnected for inspection of testing. This Teves brake system uses a hydraulic accumulator which, when completely charged, contains brake fluid under high pressure. Before disconnecting any hydraulic lines, hoses or fittings, ensure the accumulator is completely depressurized as described further on. Failure to depressurize the hydraulic accumulator may result in personal injury and/or damage to painted surfaces and/or the vehicle.

Certain components in the system are not intended to be serviced individually. Do not attempt to remove or disconnect certain system components, such as the hydraulic accumulator or valve block. Only those components with removal procedures should be serviced.

Torque bolts attaching the brake caliper mounting bracket to the front and rear knuckles must be replaced any time they are removed or become loose. Tightening or loosening the torque bolts, which use encapsulated thread locking compound, is not recommended. Failure to replace the brake caliper mounting bracket torque bolts, after they have been loosened or removed, may result in loosening of the caliper to knuckle assembly, causing reduced vehicle braking ability.

COMPUTER SYSTEM SERVICE PRECAUTIONS

This Teves anti-lock brake system interfaces directly with the Electronic Brake Control Module (EBCM) and on some models, the Body Computer Module (BCM). These modules are designed to withstand normal current draws associated with vehicle operation. However, care must be taken to avoid overloading any of the EBCM or BCM circuits. During testing of opens or shorts, do not ground or apply voltage to any of the circuits unless instructed to do so by the appropriate diagnostic procedure. These circuits should only be tested with a high impedance multimeter (J-35029-A or equivalent), or special tools described further on. Power should never be removed or applied to any control module with the ignition switch in the On position. Before removing or connecting battery cables, fuses, or connectors, always turn the ignition switch to the Off position.

GENERAL SERVICE PRECAUTIONS

On models equipped with Supplemental Inflatable Restraint (SIR) system, serious injury can result from unintended airbag deployment.

The SIR system is designed to retain sufficient voltage to deploy the airbag for a short time after power has been disconnected. To avoid serious injury, disarm the SIR as follows:

1. Turn ignition switch to Off position.
2. Remove SIR fuse from fuse panel.
3. Disconnect yellow two-way connector at base of steering column, if equipped, as follows:
   a. Remove lefthand sound insulator retaining screws and nuts.
   b. Remove courtesy lamp from sound insulator, then the sound insulator from vehicle.
   c. Remove Connector Position Assurance (CPA) pin, then disconnect yellow two-way connector at base of steering column.
4. Wait at least 10 minutes before any further work is attempted. Serious injury may result from unintended airbag deployment if service is attempted immediately after SIR fuse is removed.
5. Reverse procedure to arm SIR system, noting the following:
   a. Turn ignition switch to On position.
   b. Observe INFALATABLE RESTRAINT indicator lamp.
   c. If lamp does not flash 7-9 times then remain Off, refer to "Passive Restraint Systems" for diagnosis.

If welding work is to be performed on the vehicle using an electric arc welder, the EBCM and valve block connectors should be disconnected before the welding operation begins. The EBCM and valve block connectors should never be connected or disconnected with the ignition switch in the On position. Some components of the anti-lock brake system are not serviceable separately and must be replaced as assemblies.

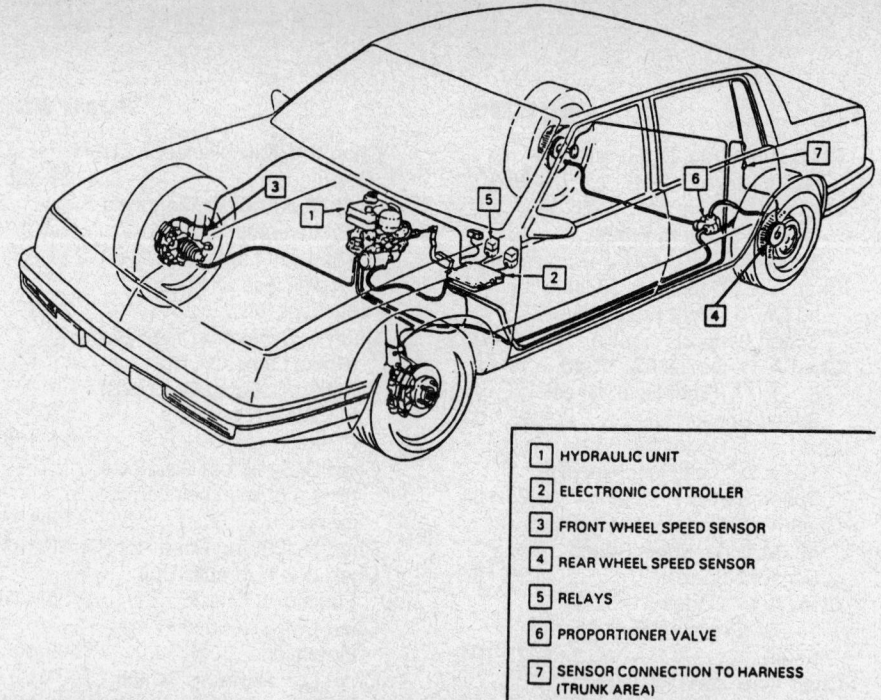

1	HYDRAULIC UNIT
2	ELECTRONIC CONTROLLER
3	FRONT WHEEL SPEED SENSOR
4	REAR WHEEL SPEED SENSOR
5	RELAYS
6	PROPORTIONER VALVE
7	SENSOR CONNECTION TO HARNESS (TRUNK AREA)

Fig. 1 Anti-Lock Brake System (ABS)

DESCRIPTION

The purpose of this Teves anti-lock brake system, is to prevent wheel lockup under heavy brake application.

The anti-lock function is desirable because a vehicle which is stopped without locking the wheels will normally stop in a shorter distance than a vehicle with locked wheels, while retaining directional stability and some steering capability. This allows the vehicle's operator to retain greater control of the vehicle during heavy brake application.

SYSTEM COMPONENTS

The anti-lock brake system, **Fig. 1**, consists of a pump motor assembly, fluid accumulator, pressure switch, fluid reservoir with integral filter, hydraulic booster/master cylinder, wheel speed sensors, Electronic Brake Control Module (EBCM) and a valve block assembly.

ELECTRONIC BRAKE CONTROL MODULE (EBCM)

The EBCM monitors speed of each wheel to determine if any wheel is beginning to lock. If a locking condition is sensed, brake pressures are automatically adjusted to provide for maximum stopping without wheel lock.

TIMER FLASHER MODULE

On some models, the pump circuit includes a timer flasher module, located in the instrument panel behind driver side close out panel, which monitors pump running time. If pump runs for more than three minutes, the timer flasher module will cause BRAKE warning lamp to flash.

HYDRAULIC UNIT

Main components of hydraulic unit are hydraulic booster master cylinder, valve

block assembly, pump motor assembly, pressure switch, accumulator and fluid level sensor, **Fig. 2**.

When brake pedal is depressed, hydraulic booster/master cylinder operates front brakes in normal manner and also provides modulated accumulator pressure to rear brakes.

The valve block assembly is a series of solenoid controlled valves which cycle very quickly to apply and release hydraulic pressure to each wheel.

The pump and motor assembly supplies high pressure brake fluid to accumulator. This high pressure fluid is used for power assist and also to apply rear brakes.

The pressure switch monitors accumulator pressure. When pressure drops below the lower limit, pressure switch activates pump motor relay which turns on pump. Once pressure reaches upper limit, pressure switch deactivates the relay and shuts off pump. If pressure leak or pump failure occur, pressure switch will signal EBCM to disable anti-lock function. The pressure switch will also light BRAKE lamp located in instrument panel.

The accumulator is pressure storage device which can hold brake fluid under very high pressures. The accumulator has an internal diaphragm with nitrogen trapped on one side. As pump fills accumulator, diaphragm moves and compresses trapped nitrogen.

The fluid level sensor is located in fluid reservoir. This sensor has two functions. It can signal the EBCM that there is a low fluid condition. The EBCM will then disable the Anti-Lock function. The sensor will also light the BRAKE lamp located in instrument panel.

ANTI-LOCK WARNING LAMP

Vehicles equipped with the Anti-Lock system have an amber ANTI-LOCK warn-

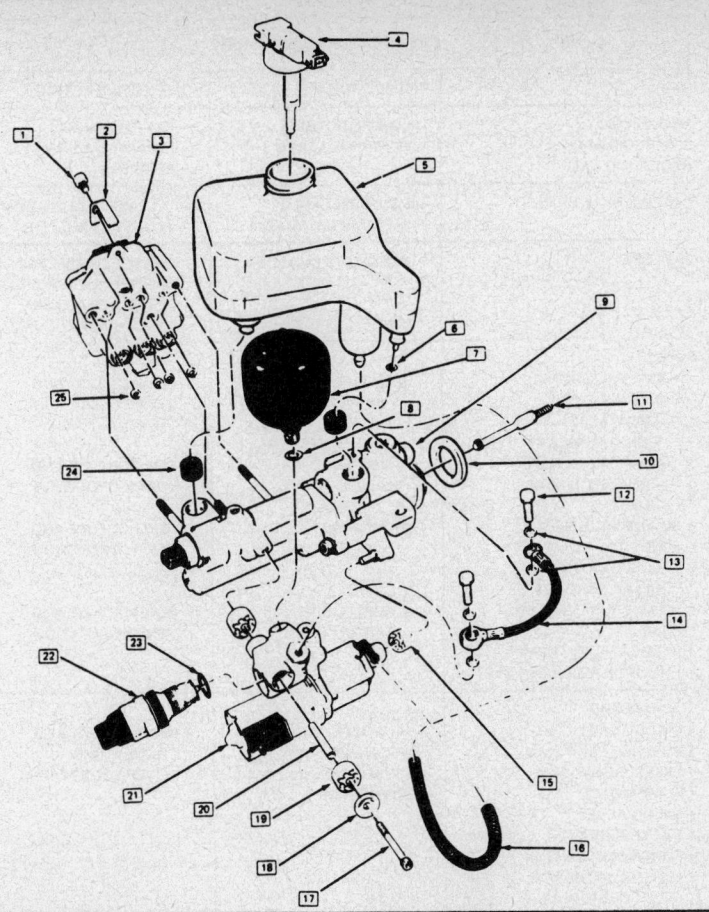

Fig. 2 Anti-lock brake hydraulic unit

1	RESERVOIR RETAINER SCREW
2	RESERVOIR RETAINER
3	VALVE BLOCK ASSEMBLY
4	FLUID LEVEL SENSOR
5	BRAKE FLUID RESERVOIR
6	RESERVOIR O-RING SEAL
7	ACCUMULATOR
8	ACCUMULATOR O-RING SEAL
9	MASTER CYLINDER AND BOOSTER ASSEMBLY
10	HYDRAULIC UNIT TO PUSHROD ASSEMBLY SEAL
11	PUSHROD
12	HIGH PRESSURE HOSE FITTING
13	HIGH PRESSURE HOSE O-RING SEAL
14	HIGH PRESSURE HOSE
15	PUMP INSULATOR
16	RETURN HOSE
17	PUMP MOUNTING BOLT
18	PUMP WASHER
19	PUMP INSULATOR
20	PUMP MOUNTING BOLT SLEEVE
21	PUMP AND MOTOR ASSEMBLY
22	PRESSURE SWITCH
23	PRESSURE SWITCH O-RING SEAL
24	RESERVOIR GROMMET
25	VALVE BLOCK TO MASTER CYLINDER O-RING SEAL

ing lamp in the instrument panel. The ANTI-LOCK warning lamp will illuminate if a malfunction in the system is detected by the electronic controller. In case of an electronic malfunction, the controller will turn the ANTI-LOCK warning lamp on, then disable the anti-lock braking function. If ANTI-LOCK and BRAKE warning lamp come on at the same time, there may be something wrong with hydraulic brake system.

The ANTI-LOCK lamp will illuminate during engine starting and will usually stay on approximately three seconds after ignition switch is returned to the Run position. If the car has not been started in several hours, the ANTI-LOCK lamp may stay on for as long as thirty seconds. The ABS pump is recharging the hydraulic accumulator to normal operating pressures. The lamp will stay on until charging is complete. If lamp stays on longer than thirty seconds after engine is started or comes on while driving, the brake system should be inspected for a malfunction.

BRAKE WARNING LAMP

The Anti-Lock brake system uses a three circuit design so that some braking capacity is still available if hydraulic pressure is lost in one circuit. The BRAKE warning lamp is located at the lefthand side of instrument cluster and is designed to alert driver of conditions that would result in reduced braking ability.

The BRAKE warning lamp should turn on under several conditions. The BRAKE lamp will illuminate during engine cranking, when parking brake is not fully released, low brake fluid level, or low accumulator pressure. If BRAKE warning lamp stays on any longer than thirty seconds after starting engine or comes on during driving, there may be a malfunction in brake hydraulic system.

OPERATION

Under normal driving conditions the Anti-Lock brake system functions the same as standard brake system. However, with the detection of wheel lock-up, a

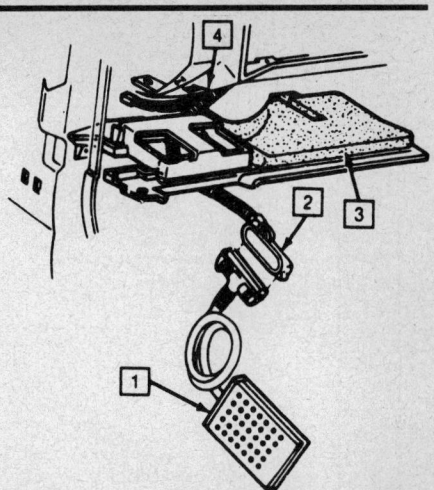

Fig. 3 Installing break-out box

slight bump or kick-back will be felt in brake pedal. This pedal "bump" will be followed by a series of short pedal pulsations which occur in rapid succession. Brake pedal pulsation will continue until there is no longer a need for the anti-lock function or until vehicle is stopped. A slight ticking or popping noise may be heard during brake application. This noise is normal and indicates that the anti-lock function is being used.

When anti-lock system is in use, brake pedal may rise even as brakes are being applied. Maintaining a constant force on the pedal will provide shortest stopping distance.

REQUIRED TEST EQUIPMENT

Some diagnostic procedures require use of a pressure gauge and Pin-Out Box tool No. J-35592 or equivalent.

1. Install Pin-Out Box tool No. J-35592 or equivalent as follows:
   a. Turn ignition switch to the Off position.
   b. Depending on model, different procedures are required for EBCM removal. EBCM is either held in with two retainers, three screws, or a twist-type mount. EBCM is located on left side dash close out panel, **Fig. 3.**
   c. Remove 35 pin harness connector from EBCM, depress locking plate, then turn toward front of car.
   d. Inspect 35 pin harness connector for damage, then connect pin-out box connector to harness connector.
2. **On 1988 models,** install pressure gauge tool No. J-35604 or equivalent as follows:
   a. Depressurize accumulator, refer to ""Depressurizing Hydraulic Accumulator," procedure.
   b. Remove pressure hose fitting from pump body, **Fig. 4,**. Use caution not to drop two O-ring seals when removing fitting.
   c. Install one O-ring seal on pressure gauge fitting, then insert gauge fitting into pressure hose coupling.
   d. Install remaining O-ring seal on gauge fitting on underside of pressure hose coupling, then thread

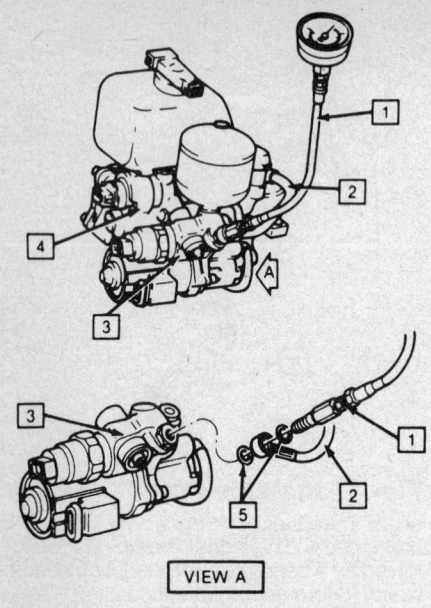

1 J-35604 PRESSURE GAGE ASSEMBLY
2 HIGH PRESSURE HOSE
3 PUMP AND MOTOR ASSEMBLY
4 HYDRAULIC UNIT
5 SEALS (O-RINGS)

Fig. 4 Installing pressure gauge

gauge fitting into pump body. **Torque** fitting to 15 ft. lbs.
3. **On 1989-90 models,** install pressure gauge as follows:
   a. Depressurize accumulator, refer to ""Depressurizing Hydraulic Accumulator," procedure.
   b. Remove accumulator, then install pressure gauge tool No. J-35604-88 or equivalent. **Torque** pressure gauge to 32 ft. lbs.
   c. Install, then tighten accumulator to pressure gauge. When removing the gauge, inspect O-ring for damage. Replace as necessary.

Diagnosis

On models equipped with Supplemental Inflatable Restraint (SIR) system, serious injury can result from unintended airbag deployment.

The SIR system is designed to retain sufficient voltage to deploy the airbag for a short time after power has been disconnected. To avoid serious injury, disarm the SIR as follows:
1. Turn ignition switch to Off position.
2. Remove SIR fuse from fuse panel.
3. Disconnect yellow two-way connector at base of steering column, if equipped, as follows:
   a. Remove lefthand sound insulator retaining screws and nuts.
   b. Remove courtesy lamp from sound insulator, then the sound insulator from vehicle.
   c. Remove Connector Position Assurance (CPA) pin, then disconnect yellow two-way connector at

base of steering column.
4. Wait at least 10 minutes before any further work is attempted. Serious injury may result from unintended airbag deployment if service is attempted immediately after SIR fuse is removed.
5. Reverse procedure to arm SIR system, noting the following:
   a. Turn ignition switch to On position.
   b. Observe INFALATABLE RESTRAINT indicator lamp.
   c. If lamp does not flash 7-9 times then remain Off, refer to "Passive Restraint Systems" for diagnosis.

1988 MODELS & 1989-90 6000

Diagnosis of system malfunctions requires three basic steps which must be followed in order to isolate the fault accurately and quickly. The proper diagnostic procedure consists of the following steps: Pre-Diagnosis Inspection, Lamp Sequence Determination and Component Test Charts.

PRE-DIAGNOSIS INSPECTION

The pre-diagnosis inspection consists of a quick visual check of specific system components which could create an apparent Anti-Lock system malfunction. Performing this inspection prior to diagnosing specific symptoms, may result in diagnosis of a simple defect which may be the cause of an inoperative system. This inspection should be the first step in diagnosing a complaint. For visual inspection procedure, refer to **Figs. 5 and 6**.

LAMP SEQUENCE DETERMINATION

The second step in diagnosing this system is determination of warning lamp behavior. This system uses two warning lamps, a red BRAKE warning lamp and an

PRE-DIAGNOSIS INSPECTION		
ITEM	INSPECT FOR:	CORRECTIVE ACTION
BRAKE FLUID RESERVOIR AND HYDRAULIC UNIT	– LOW FLUID LEVEL – EXTERNAL LEAKS	– FILL RESERVOIR – REPAIR LEAKS AS REQUIRED
PARKING BRAKE	– FULLY RELEASED – IMPROPERLY ADJUSTED	– RELEASE PARKING BRAKE – ADJUST CABLE
BATTERY	ADEQUATE CHARGE	– CHARGE OR REPLACE BATTERY AS REQUIRED – SERVICE CHARGING SYSTEM AS REQUIRED
FUSES • 5 AMP ELECTRONIC BRAKE FUSE – LOCATED IN CONVENIENCE CENTER	– BLOWN FUSE	– REPLACE FUSE AND VERIFY OPERATION
• 10 AMP GAGES FUSE – LOCATED IN FUSE BLOCK	– BLOWN FUSE	– REPLACE FUSE AND VERIFY OPERATION
• 30 AMP MAIN RELAY FUSE – LOCATED ON MAIN RELAY BRACKET	– BLOWN FUSE	– REPLACE FUSE AND VERIFY OPERATION
• 30 AMP PUMP MOTOR FUSE – LOCATED ON PUMP MOTOR RELAY BRACKET	– BLOWN FUSE	– REPLACE FUSE AND VERIFY OPERATION
CONNECTORS • MAIN RELAY • PUMP MOTOR RELAY • PRESSURE SWITCH • PUMP MOTOR • MAIN VALVE • VALVE BLOCK • FLUID LEVEL SENSOR • ELECTRONIC BRAKE CONTROL MODULE (EBCM) • 4 SENSOR CONNECTORS	– PROPER ENGAGEMENT OF CONNECTOR – LOOSE WIRES IN CONNECTOR	– PROPERLY ENGAGE CONNECTORS – REPAIR LOOSE WIRES
CONNECTORS (WITH ALL WHEEL DRIVE) • DIFFERENTIAL LOCK ENGAGED SWITCH CONNECTOR AT TRANSAXLE TRANSFER CASE • DIFFERENTIAL LOCK ENGAGED SWITCH JUMPER CONNECTOR TO EBCM WIRING HARNESS AT LEFT SIDE OF DASH PANEL	-- PROPER ENGAGEMENT OF CONNECTOR -- LOOSE WIRES IN CONNECTOR	-- PROPERLY ENGAGE CONNECTORS -- REPAIR LOOSE WIRES

Fig. 5 Pre-diagnosis inspection chart (Part 1 of 2). 1988-90 6000

PRE-DIAGNOSIS INSPECTION (CONT.)

ITEM	INSPECT FOR:	CORRECTIVE ACTION
GROUNDS		
• BODY GROUNDS	-- LOOSE CONNECTIONS	-- TIGHTEN CONNECTIONS
-- LOCATED ON MAIN RELAY BRACKET	-- BROKEN EYELETS	-- REPAIR WIRE OR EYELET
• HYDRAULIC UNIT GROUND	-- CORROSION	-- CLEAN CONTACT SURFACES
-- ON HYDRAULIC UNIT		
JUNCTION BLOCK	-- CORROSION	-- CLEAN CONTACT SURFACES
	-- LOOSE JUNCTION BLOCK OR CONNECTIONS	-- TIGHTEN CONNECTIONS
	-- BROKEN WIRES	-- REPAIR OR REPLACE WIRES AS NECESSARY

Fig. 5   Pre-diagnosis inspection chart (Part 2 of 2). 1988–90 6000

PRE-DIAGNOSIS INSPECTION

ITEM	INSPECTION FOR:	INSPECTION FOR:
BRAKE FLUID RESERVOIR, HYDRAULIC UNIT	– LOW FLUID LEVEL – EXTERNAL LEAKS	– FILL RESERVOIR – REPAIR LEAKS AS REQUIRED
PARKING BRAKE	FULL RELEASE	– RELEASE PARKING BRAKE – ADJUST CABLE OR VACUUM RELEASE VALVE IF REQUIRED
BATTERY	ADEQUATE CHARGE ("GREEN EYE")	– CHARGE OR REPLACE BATTERY AS REQUIRED – SERVICE CHARGING SYSTEM AS REQUIRED
FUSES FUSES • ELECTRONIC BRAKE FUSE – 5 AMP – LOCATED IN FUSE PANEL	BLOWN FUSE	– REPLACE FUSE AND VERIFY OPERATION
• MAIN RELAY FUSE – 30 AMP WITH RED WIRE – LOCATED IN FUSE HOLDER ON RELAY BRACKET	BLOWN FUSE	– REPLACE FUSE AND VERIFY OPERATION
• – PUMP MOTOR FUSE – 30 AMP WITH YELLOW WIRE – LOCATED IN FUSE HOLDER ON RELAY BRACKET	BLOWN FUSE	– REPLACE FUSE AND VERIFY OPERATION
CONNECTORS • MAIN RELAY – CONNECTOR WITH 5 WIRES ATTACHED • PUMP MOTOR RELAY – CONNECTOR WITH 4 WIRES ATTACHED • PRESSURE SWITCH • PUMP MOTOR • MAIN VALVE • VALVE BLOCK • FLUID LEVEL SENSOR • ELECTRONIC BRAKE CONTROL MODULE (EBCM)	– IMPROPER ENGAGEMENT OF CONNECTOR – LOOSE WIRES IN CONNECTOR	– PROPERLY ENGAGE CONNECTORS – REPAIR LOOSE WIRES
GROUNDS • BODY GROUNDS – LOCATED ON STUD AT LEFT FENDER RAIL • HYDRAULIC UNIT GROUND – ON HYDRAULIC UNIT	– LOOSE CONNECTIONS – BROKEN EYELETS – CORROSION	– TIGHTEN – REPAIR WIRE OR EYELETS – CLEAN CONTACT SURFACES

Fig. 6   Pre-diagnosis inspection chart. Except 1988–90 6000

amber ANTI-LOCK lamp. By observing when these lamps illuminate, individual components and sub-systems may be isolated.

Normal indicator lamp sequence is shown in **Figs. 7 and 8.** Indicator lamp sequences are shown graphically in **Fig. 9 and 10,** and described below.

Vehicle Status

Each lamp sequence graphs, **Figs. 9 and 10,** are divided into seven areas which represent vehicle status. Behavior of BRAKE and ANTI-LOCK lamps are represented in horizontal rows below vehicle status headers.

Lamp Status

BRAKE and ANTI-LOCK lamp status is indicated by shaded areas in horizontal rows below each vehicle status header, **Figs. 9 and 10.** Righthand diagonal shading indicates illumination of ANTI-LOCK lamp. Lefthand diagonal shading indicates illumination of BRAKE lamp. A vehicle status block which is not entirely shaded means that the lamp is only on for a portion of the test period.

LAMP SEQUENCE TEST PROCEDURE

The following procedure should be used to determine proper light sequence used for further diagnosis. When evaluating vehicle condition, use caution if reduced braking ability is evident.

1. Turn ignition switch to Off position for a minimum of 15 seconds.
2. Turn ignition switch to On position, then observe BRAKE and ANTI-LOCK lamps, noting the following:
   a. If accumulator has been discharged, both indicator lamps may remain on for approximately 30 seconds. If this occurs, allow lamps to turn off and turn ignition switch to Off position for another 15 second period, then proceed to step 3.
   b. If lamps do not go out within 30 seconds, proceed to step 4.
3. Turn ignition switch to On position and observe warning lamps. At this point, BRAKE lamp should remain off. ANTI-LOCK lamp should come on for 3-6 seconds, then go out.
4. Turn ignition switch to "Start" position and observe warning lamps. Both warning lamps should light.
5. Start engine and release key to Run position and observe warning lamps. BRAKE lamp should turn off immediately. ANTI-LOCK lamp should remain on for 3-6 seconds, then go out.
6. Drive vehicle at a minimum speed of 20 mph for a short period of time and observe warning lamps. Both lamps should remain off for this step and remainder of test. Note as accurately as possible conditions under which either lamp comes on.

INDICATOR LAMP SEQUENCE

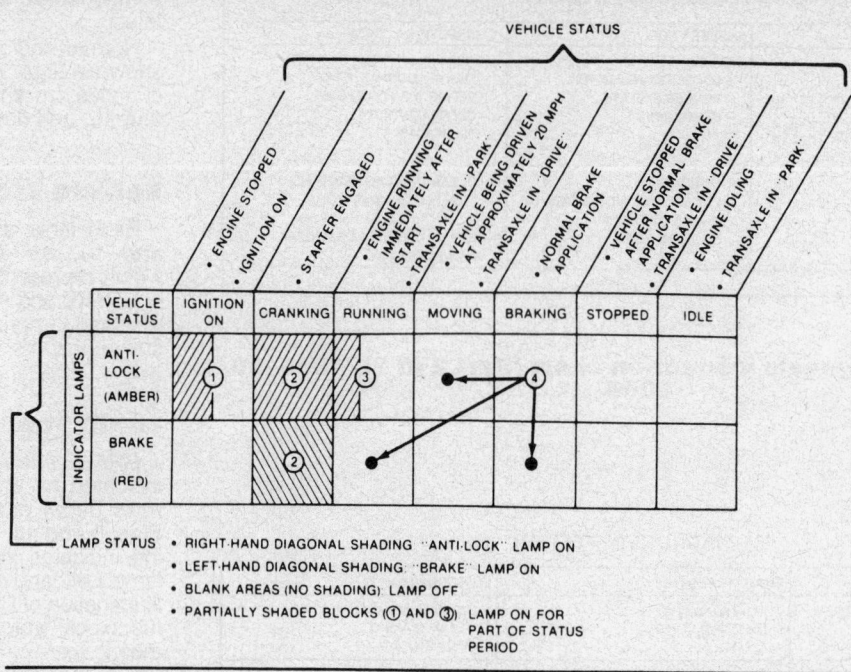

NORMAL LAMP SEQUENCE

① WITH CHARGED ACCUMULATOR, "ANTI-LOCK" LIGHT WILL COME ON FOR 3-5 SECONDS WITH "IGNITION ON". IF ACCUMULATOR IS DISCHARGED, LAMP MAY STAY ON FOR UP TO 30 SECONDS.

② "BRAKE" AND "ANTI-LOCK" LAMPS WILL BOTH TURN ON DURING CRANKING

③ IMMEDIATELY AFTER ENGINE STARTING, "ANTI-LOCK" LAMP WILL TURN ON FOR 3-5 SECONDS

④ BOTH LAMPS SHOULD REMAIN OFF AT ALL OTHER TIMES

Fig. 7   Normal indicator lamp sequence. Except 1989–90 6000

7. Stop vehicle using normal brake application. Both lights should remain off.
8. Place transaxle in PARK, then allow vehicle to idle for several seconds and observe warning lamps. Both should remain off.
9. From information obtained in above test, determine lamp sequence and/or symptom which most closely matches vehicle condition, then perform indicated tests, **Figs. 9 and 10.**

DIAGNOSTIC PROCEDURE

Diagnostic procedures in this section may be helpful in determining the cause of intermittent problems in Anti-Lock brake system electrical components. In most cases, a specific fault must be present to locate a problem effectively using Indicator Lamp Sequence chart, **Figs 9 and 10,** along with Pin-Out Checks and trouble trees, **Figs. 11 through 47,** for all 1988 models except 1988 6000 and **Figs. 48-90,** for 1988-90 6000.

NOTE ON INTERMITTENTS

If an intermittent fault cannot be diagnosed using Indicator Lamp Sequence chart, the problem will most probably be caused by a defective electrical connection or wiring. When an intermittent problem is encountered, check questionable circuits, **Figs. 91 and 92,** and electrical connectors, **Figs. 93 and 94,** for the following:

1. Poor mating of connector halves or terminals not fully seated in connector body.
2. Improperly formed or damaged terminals. All connector terminals in the problem circuit should be carefully removed to increase contact tension.
3. Poor terminal wire connection.

If a visual check does not locate cause of problem, operate vehicle with EBCM connected and attempt to duplicate condition and use Indicator Lamp Sequence chart to isolate potential cause.

Circuits which could possibly cause intermittent operation of ANTI-LOCK lamp are as follows:

1. Wheel speed sensor circuits — low or intermittent output.
2. Ignition enable circuit — interruption of 12 volt input.
3. EBCM switch loop circuit (low fluid/low pressure sensors — intermittent open.
4. Main relay circuit — open in coil or switched battery power.

1989–90 MODELS EXCEPT 6000

SELF-DIAGNOSIS

This anti-lock brake system is equipped with a self-diagnostic capability which may be used to assist in isolation of ABS faults. This feature includes 42 trouble codes which can be displayed by the EBCM through the flashing of the amber "ANTI-LOCK" lamp in the instrument panel cluster. In order to access and understand any ABS trouble code which may be present, it is necessary to enter the ABS diagnostic mode and read the trouble codes using the following procedures.

DISPLAYING ABS TROUBLE CODES

The following information is to be used for reference when directed by the appropriate diagnostic procedure. Do not attempt to diagnose an ABS condition at this time. Refer to "Basic Diagnostic Procedure" before attempting diagnosis.

The EBCM will store any failure code into memory. These codes will remain stored in the EBCM until they are erased. To clear codes proceed to "Clearing ABS Codes." Disconnecting the EBCM, battery cables, or turning the ignition switch to the Off position, will not clear the trouble codes from memory.

WARNING/INDICATOR LAMP SEQUENCE

WARNING/INDICATOR LAMP SEQUENCE

WARNING/INDICATOR LAMP	COLOR	IGNITION ON*	CRANKING*	RUNNING*	MOVING*	BRAKING*	STOPPED*	IDLE*	"LOCK-NORMAL" SWITCH MOVED TO "LOCK"	MOVED TO "NORMAL"
"BRAKE"	RED	OFF	ON	OFF	OFF	OFF	OFF	OFF	OFF	OFF
"ANTI-LOCK"	AMBER	ON, THEN OFF	ON	ON, THEN OFF	OFF	OFF	OFF	OFF	ON	ON, THEN OFF
"LOCK-NORMAL" SWITCH	AMBER	OFF	OFF	OFF	OFF	OFF	OFF	OFF	FLASH	OFF
"LOCK"	AMBER	OFF	OFF	OFF	OFF	OFF	OFF	OFF	OFF, THEN ON	ON, THEN OFF

* "LOCK-NORMAL" SWITCH SET TO "NORMAL"

NORMAL SEQUENCE

1 — WITH IGNITION "ON," "ANTILOCK" WARNING LAMP WILL COME ON FOR 3-5 SECONDS IF ACCUMULATOR IS CHARGED. "ANTILOCK" WARNING LAMP MAY STAY ON FOR UP TO 30 SECONDS IF ACCUMULATOR IS DISCHARGED.

2 — "BRAKE" AND "ANTILOCK" WARNING LAMPS WILL TURN ON DURING CRANKING.

3 — IMMEDIATELY AFTER THE ENGINE STARTS, "ANTILOCK" WARNING LAMP WILL BE ON FOR 3-5 SECONDS.

4 — WHEN "LOCK-NORMAL" SWITCH IS MOVED TO "LOCK," AMBER SWITCH INDICATOR LAMP WILL FLASH.

5 — THE "LOCK" AND "ANTILOCK" LAMPS WILL TURN ON WHEN THE TRANSFER CASE DIFFERENTIAL VACUUM-ACTUATED LOCK LOCKS THE DIFFERENTIAL.

6 — WHEN "LOCK-NORMAL" SWITCH IS MOVED BACK TO "NORMAL," "ANTILOCK" WARNING LAMP WILL REMAIN ON FOR 3-5 SECONDS AND THEN GO OFF. SWITCH INDICATOR LAMP WILL IMMEDIATELY STOP FLASHING AND REMAIN OFF.

7 — THE "LOCK" INDICATOR LAMP WILL GO OFF WHEN THE TRANSFER CASE DIFFERENTIAL SPRING MECHANISM UNLOCKS THE DIFFERENTIAL.

8 — ALL FOUR LAMPS WILL REMAIN OFF AT ALL OTHER TIMES.

Fig. 8   Warning/Indicator lamp sequence chart. 1989–90 6000

READING ABS TROUBLE CODES

1. With ignition switch turned to the On position, allow pump/motor to charge the accumulator. If accumulator is discharged, the "BRAKE" and ""ANTI-LOCK" lamps will remain on for up to 30 seconds.
2. If the "ANTI-LOCK" lamp does not go off within 30 seconds, note that lamp did not go off, then proceed to step 3.
3. With ignition switch turned to the Off position, place a jumper wire between Assembly Line Diagnostic Link (ALDL), pin H and A or between ALDL pin H and body ground. The ALDL is located on the driver's side of the vehicle near the parking brake pedal assembly.
4. Turn ignition switch to the RUN position, then count the lamp flashes to identify the first digit. If the lamp turns on for four seconds, then turns off (and remains off), no trouble codes are present. Proceed to "ABS Functional Check," then proceed with diagnosis as directed. If the EBCM has stored any trouble codes, the "ANTI-LOCK" lamp will turn on for approximately four seconds and will then start flashing. These flashes represent the first digit of the trouble code.
5. Count lamp flashes for the second digit. The lamp will pause (remain off), for approximately three seconds after flashing the first digit. It will then flash the second digit of the trouble code. When the ""ANTI-LOCK" lamp flashes the second digit of the trouble code, be careful to count only the number of times the lamp turns on and goes out. When the EBCM is done flashing the second digit, the "ANTI-LOCK" lamp will remain on. The last pulse, when the lamp remains on, should not be counted as a flash, Fig. 95.
6. Record trouble codes obtained.
7. Check for additional trouble codes. Without turning the ignition switch to the Off position, disconnect the jumper wire from ALDL pin H. Connect the jumper again to ALDL pin. If an additional code is present, the "ANTI-LOCK" lamp will begin flashing the first digit as described previously. Count lamp flashes for the first and second digits as was done for the first code. Record the additional trouble code if present.
8. Repeat steps 6 and 7, until no additional trouble codes are displayed. Up to seven trouble codes can be displayed. The "ANTI-LOCK" lamp will remain on continuously when all trouble codes have been displayed. ABS trouble codes cannot be cleared unless all codes have been displayed.
9. After recording all ABS codes, remove jumper from the ALDL, install ALDL cover, then proceed with the "ABS Functional Check."

HISTORY & CURRENT ABS CODES

The ABS trouble codes which may be stored by the EBCM are not specifically designated as current or history codes, as are BCM and ECM codes. The anti-lock lamp, may be used to assist in differentiating between current and history codes as follows:

1. If the anti-lock lamp is on before entering the ABS diagnostic mode, at least one of the stored codes is current.
2. If the anti-lock lamp is off before entering the ABS diagnostic mode, none of the stored codes are current.
3. If more than one ABS code is stored and the anti-lock lamp is on before diagnostic mode was entered, it is impossible to determine which is a current code and which is a history code.
4. If the Anti-Lock lamp remains on continuously throughout the diagnostic procedure, see symptom diagnosis information as directed by the "ABS Functional Check." If the anti-lock lamp does not come on at all, see symptom diagnosis information as directed by the "ABS Functional Check" as well.

Continued on page 25-100

LAMP SEQUENCE CHART

SEQ. NO.	LAMP SEQUENCE	SYMPTOM DESCRIPTION	PERF. TEST
	SEE LAMP SEQUENCE DETERMINATION PROCEDURE IN THIS SECTION BEFORE USING THIS CHART		
1	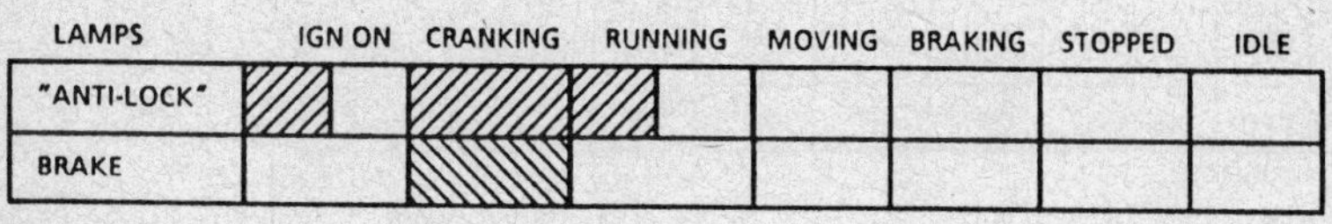 LAMPS — IGN ON, CRANKING, RUNNING, MOVING, BRAKING, STOPPED, IDLE — "ANTI-LOCK" / BRAKE	NORMAL LAMP SEQUENCE WITH — EXCESSIVE PEDAL TRAVEL OR SPONGY PEDAL — ANTI-LOCK BRAKING OPERATION OR VALVE CYCLING DURING NORMAL STOP ON DRY PAVEMENT — POOR VEHICLE TRACKING DURING ANTI-LOCK BRAKING	G C D
2	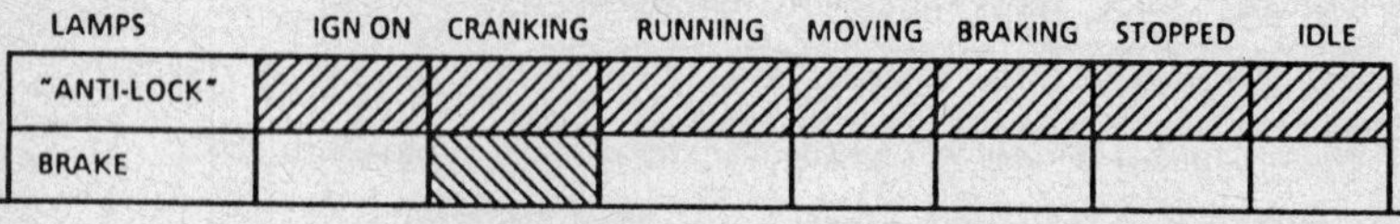 LAMPS — "ANTI-LOCK" / BRAKE	CONTINUOUS "ANTI-LOCK" LAMP NORMAL "BRAKE" LAMP	A
3	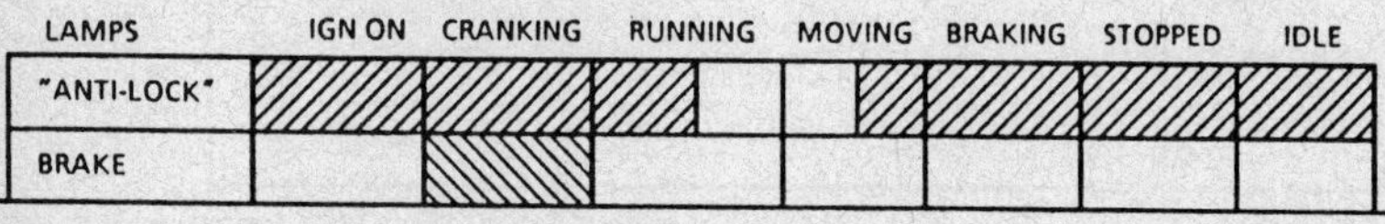 LAMPS — "ANTI-LOCK" / BRAKE	"ANTI-LOCK" LAMP COMES ON AFTER VEHICLE STARTS MOVING NORMAL BRAKE LIGHT	C
4	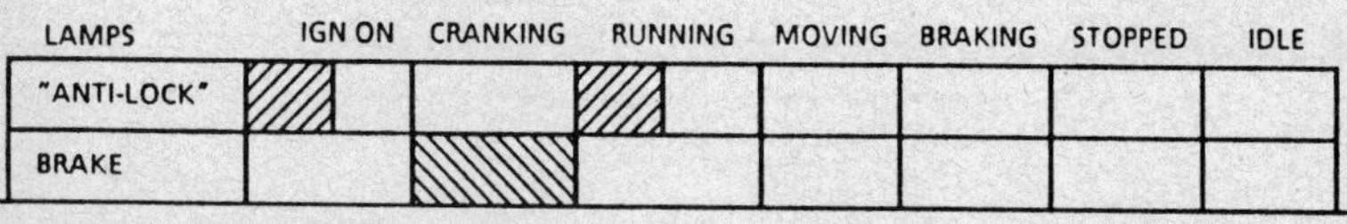 LAMPS — "ANTI-LOCK" / BRAKE	NO "ANTI-LOCK" LAMP WHILE CRANKING NORMAL "BRAKE" LAMP	A-19
5	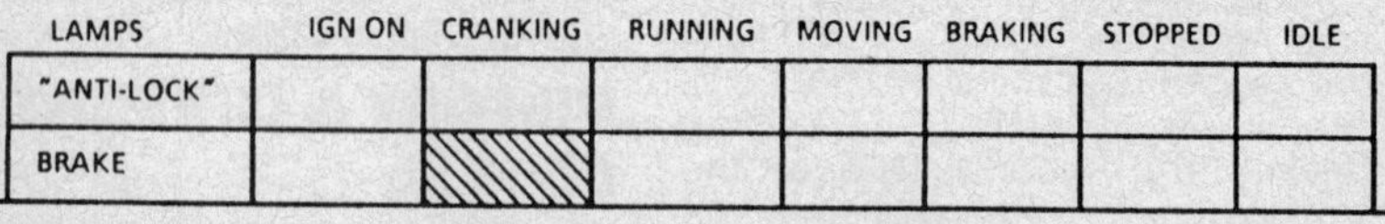 LAMPS — "ANTI-LOCK" / BRAKE	NO "ANTI-LOCK" LAMP NORMAL "BRAKE" LAMP	E
6	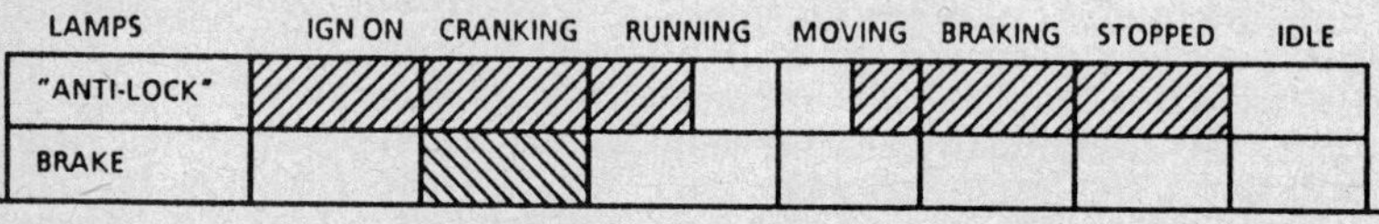 LAMPS — "ANTI-LOCK" / BRAKE	INTERMITTANT "ANTI-LOCK" WHILE DRIVING NORMAL "BRAKE" LAMP	F
7	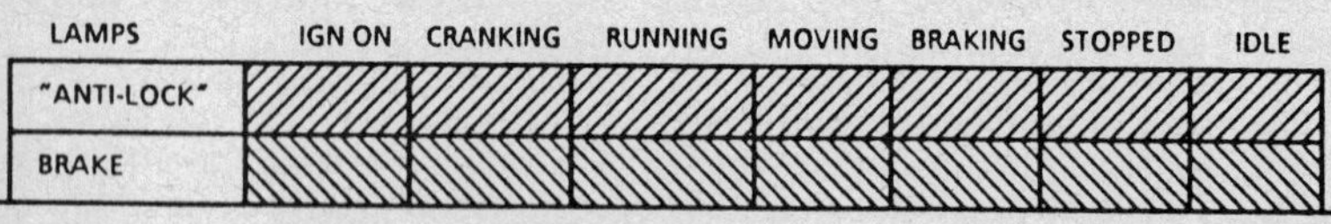 LAMPS — "ANTI-LOCK" / BRAKE	CONTINUOUS "ANTI-LOCK" LAMP CONTINUOUS "BRAKE" LAMP	B
8	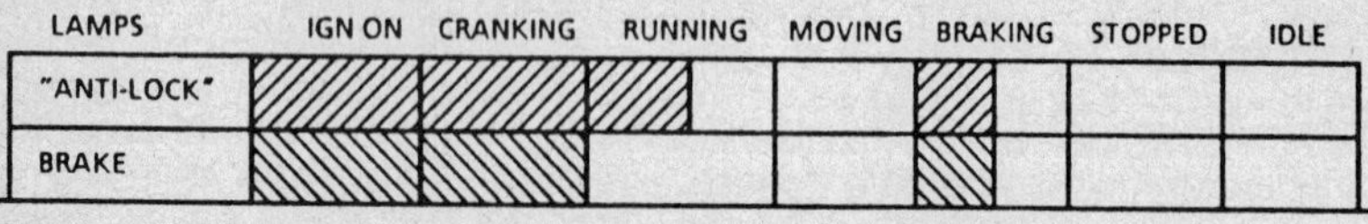 LAMPS — "ANTI-LOCK" / BRAKE	"ANTI-LOCK" AND "BRAKE" LAMPS COME ON WHILE BRAKING	B
9	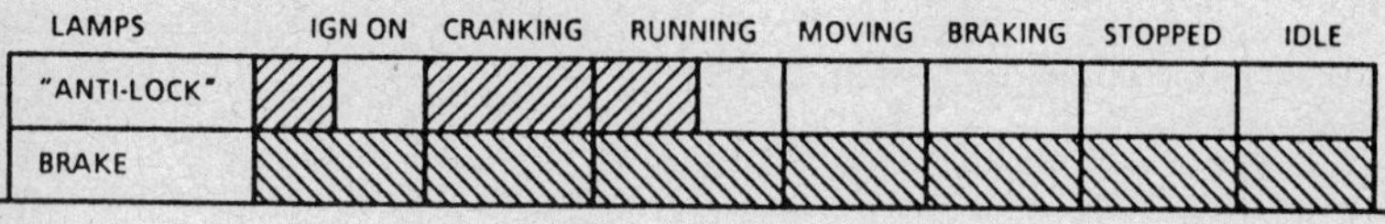 LAMPS — "ANTI-LOCK" / BRAKE	NORMAL "ANTI-LOCK" LAMP CONTINUOUS "BRAKE" LAMP	B

Fig. 9 Indicator lamp sequence chart. 1988 models, except 6000

SEE LAMP SEQUENCE DETERMINATION PROCEDURE
IN THIS SECTION BEFORE USING THIS CHART

SEQUENCE NUMBER	LAMP SEQUENCE	SYMPTOM DESCRIPTION	SEE FIGURE
1	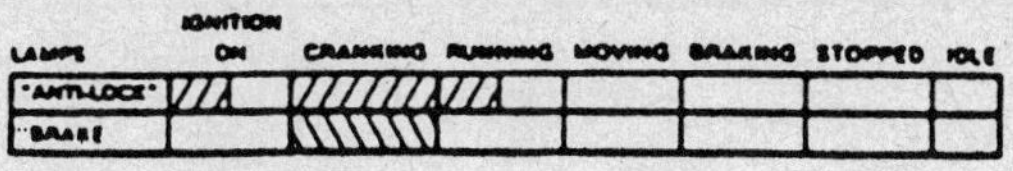	NORMAL LAMP SEQUENCE WITH — EXCESSIVE PEDAL TRAVEL OR SPONGY PEDAL — ANTI-LOCK BRAKING OPERATION OR VALVE CYCLING DURING NORMAL STOPS ON DRY PAVEMENT — POOR VEHICLE TRACKING DURING ANTI-LOCK BRAKING	89 62 78
2	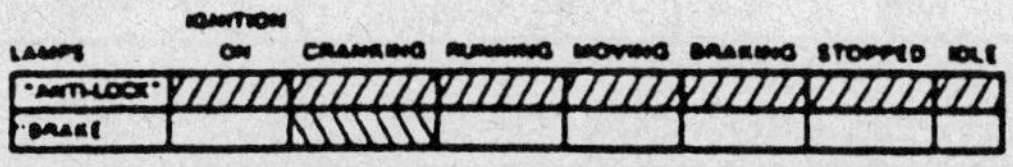	CONTINUOUS "ANTI-LOCK" LAMP NORMAL "BRAKE" LAMP	
3	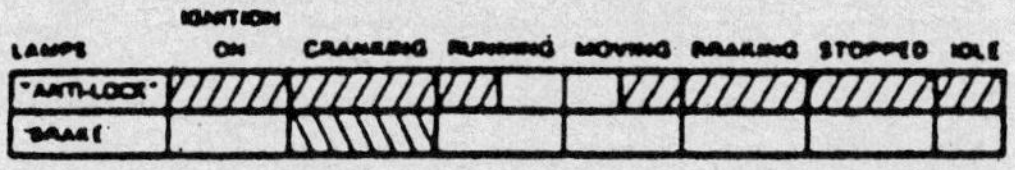	"ANTI-LOCK" LAMP COMES ON AFTER VEHICLE STARTS MOVING NORMAL BRAKE LAMP	60
4	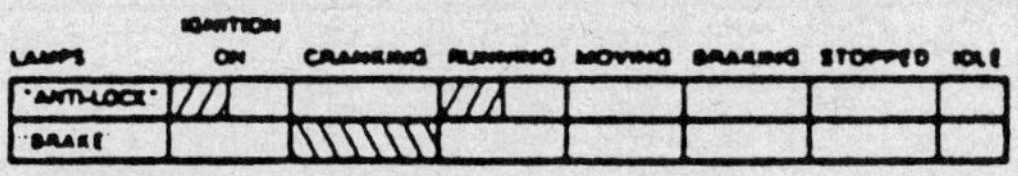	NO "ANTI-LOCK" LAMP WHILE CRANKING NORMAL "BRAKE" LAMP	87
5	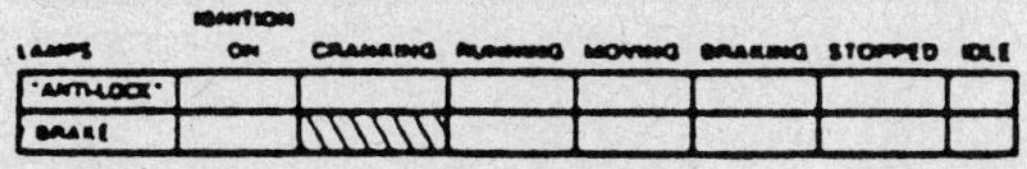	NO "ANTI-LOCK" LAMP NORMAL "BRAKE" LAMP	86
6	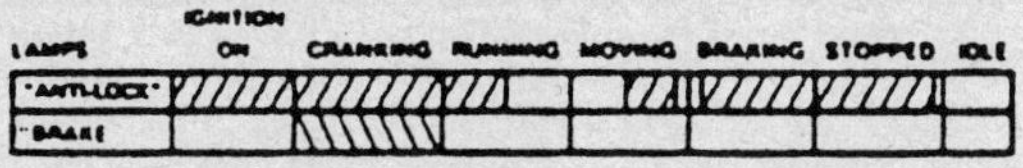	INTERMITTANT "ANTI-LOCK" LAMP WHILE DRIVING NORMAL "BRAKE" LAMP	82
7	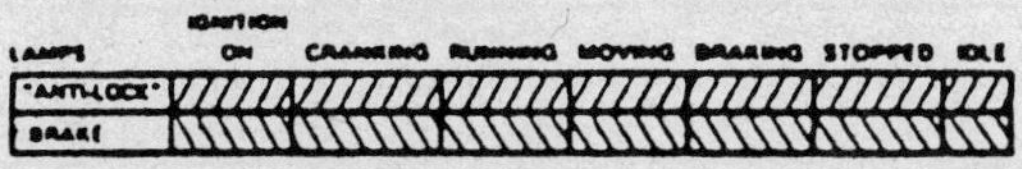	CONTINUOUS "ANTI-LOCK" LAMP CONTINUOUS "BRAKE" LAMP	88
8	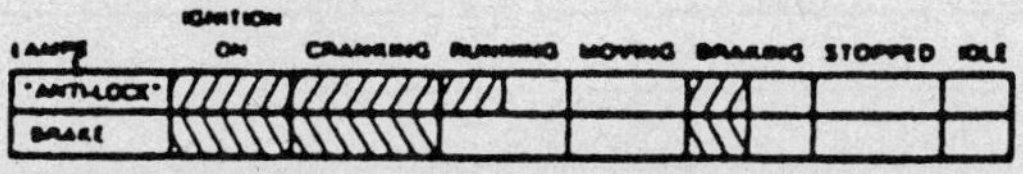	"ANTI-LOCK" AND "BRAKE" LAMPS COME ON WHILE BRAKING	88
9	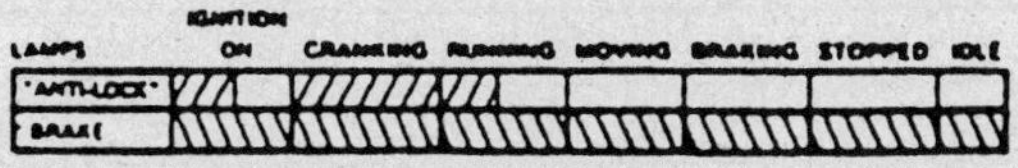	NORMAL "ANTI-LOCK" LAMP CONTINUOUS "BRAKE" LAMP	88
10	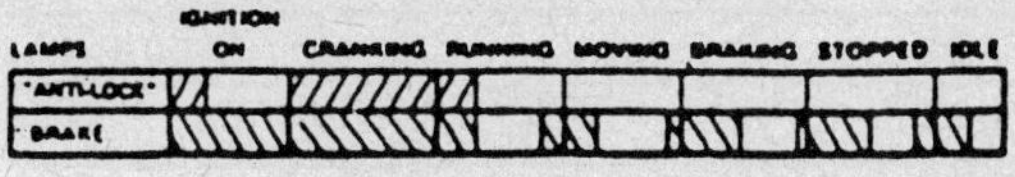	NORMAL OR CONTINUOUS "ANTI-LOCK" LAMP FLASHING "BRAKE" LAMP	88

LAMP STATUS • SHADED AREAS: LAMP ON

• BLANK AREAS (NO SHADING): LAMP OFF

• PARTIALLY SHADED AREAS: LAMP ON FOR PART OF TEST PERIOD

Fig. 10 Indicator lamp sequence chart. 1988–90 6000

TEST A
PIN-OUT CHECKS

- CONNECT BREAK-OUT BOX J-35592 TO 35-PIN EBCM HARNESS CONNECTOR AS DESCRIBED IN THIS SECTION
- PERFORM CHECKS WITH HIGH IMPEDANCE DIGITAL MULTIMETER J-34029-A OR EQUIVALENT
- ALL CHECKS ARE MADE WITH ENGINE STOPPED

CIRCUIT TO BE TESTED	IGNITION SWITCH POSITION	MULTIMETER SCALE/RANGE	MEASURE BETWEEN PIN NUMBERS	SPECIFICATION	IF RESULT NOT WITHIN SPECIFICATION, SEE CHART
IGNITION ENABLE	RUN	20 DCV	2(+)*.1(−)*	10 V MINIMUM	A-1
MAIN RELAY GROUND	OFF	200Ω	1,3	CONTINUITY	A-2
	OFF	200Ω	1,20	CONTINUITY	
MAIN RELAY COIL	OFF	200Ω	1,8	45-105 Ω	A-3

BEFORE PERFORMING THIS TEST: • REMOVE GAGE (FUSE #3) FROM FUSE PANEL
• PLACE FUSED JUMPER BETWEEN BREAK-OUT BOX PINS 2 & 8

MAIN RELAY POWER	ON	20 DCV	3(+),1(−)	10 V MINIMUM	A-4
	ON	20 DCV	20(+),1(−)	10 V MINIMUM	

BEFORE PROCEEDING: • REMOVE JUMPER FROM PINS 2 &8
• INSTALL GAGE FUSE

EBCM SWITCH LOOP	OFF	200Ω	9,10	LESS THAN 5Ω	A-5
	OFF	200Ω	1,9	NO CONTINUITY	A-6
RR SENSOR RESISTANCE	OFF	2kΩ	4,22	800-1400Ω	A-7
LF SENSOR RESISTANCE	OFF	2kΩ	5,23	800-1400Ω	A-8
LR SENSOR RESISTANCE	OFF	2kΩ	6,24	800-1400Ω	A-9
RF SENSOR RESISTANCE	OFF	2kΩ	7,25	800-1400Ω	A-10
MAIN VALVE SOLENOID	OFF	200Ω	11,18	2-5Ω	A-11
VALVE BLOCK GROUND	OFF	200Ω	1,11	LESS THAN 2Ω	A-12
RF INLET VALVE	OFF	200Ω	11,15	5-7Ω	A-13
LF INLET VALVE	OFF	200Ω	11,35	5-7Ω	A-14
REAR INLET VALVE	OFF	200Ω	11,17	5-7Ω	A-15
RF OUTLET VALVE	OFF	200Ω	11,34	3-5Ω	A-16
LF OUTLET VALVE	OFF	200Ω	11,16	3-5Ω	A-17
REAR OUTLET VALVE	OFF	200Ω	11,33	3-5Ω	A-18

BEFORE PERFORMING THIS TEST: • REMOVE MAIN RELAY FROM CONNECTOR ON RELAY BRACKET (5 WIRES ATTACHED)

DIODE	OFF	DIODE ▆◀—	27(+), 3(−)	CONTINUITY	A-19
	OFF	DIODE ▆◀—	3(+), 27(−)	NO CONTINUITY	

BEFORE PROCEEDING: • INSTALL MAIN RELAY

• WITH BRAKE PEDAL RELEASED

	ON	20 DCV	12(+), 1(−)	O V	A-20
BRAKE LIGHT SWITCH					

• WITH BRAKE PEDAL APPLIED

	ON	20 DCV	12(+), 1(−)	10 V MINIMUM	A-20

*(+) OR (−) INDICATES MULTIMETER POLARITY
IF ALL TEST RESULTS ARE WITHIN SPECIFICATION, RECONNECT EBCM AND VERIFY CONTINUOUS "ANTI-LOCK" LAMP OPERATION

- IF NORMAL OPERATION RESUMES, SEE NOTE ON INTERMITTANTS
- IF LAMP REMAINS ON, SEE CHART A-21

Fig. 11   Test A, pin-out checks. 1988 models except 6000

CHART A-1
IGNITION ENABLE CIRCUIT

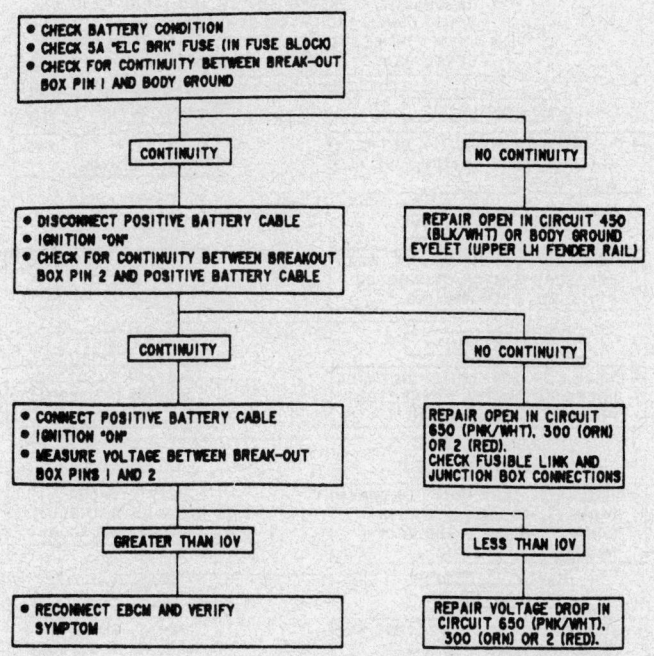

Fig. 12   Chart A-1, ignition enable circuit. 1988 models except 6000

CHART A-2
MAIN RELAY GROUND CIRCUIT

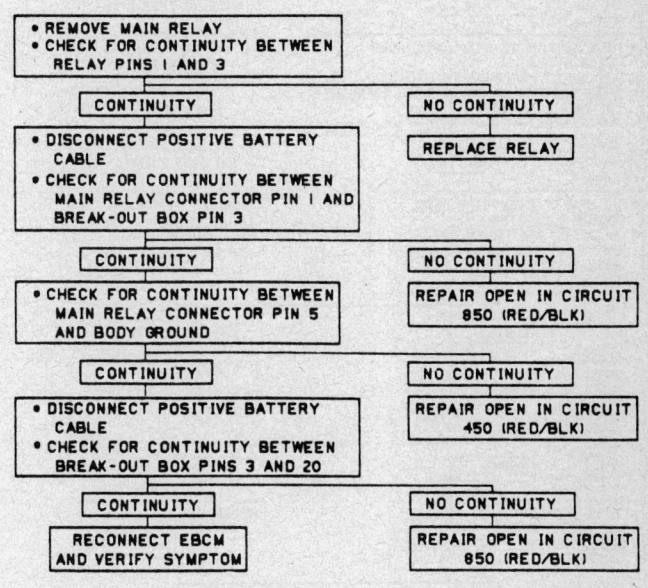

Fig. 13   Chart A-2, main relay ground circuit. 1988 models except 6000

CHART A-3
MAIN RELAY COIL CIRCUIT

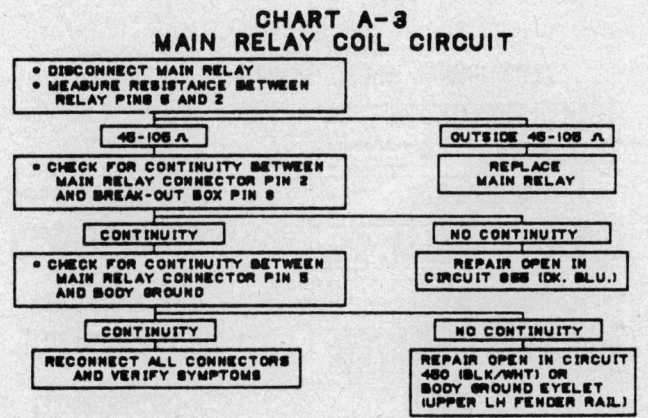

Fig. 14   Chart A-3, main relay coil circuit. 1988 models except 6000

CHART A-4
MAIN RELAY POWER CIRCUIT

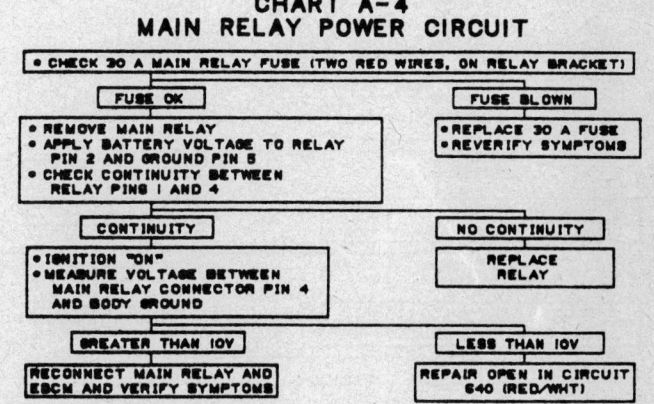

Fig. 15   Chart A-4, main relay power circuit. 1988 models except 6000

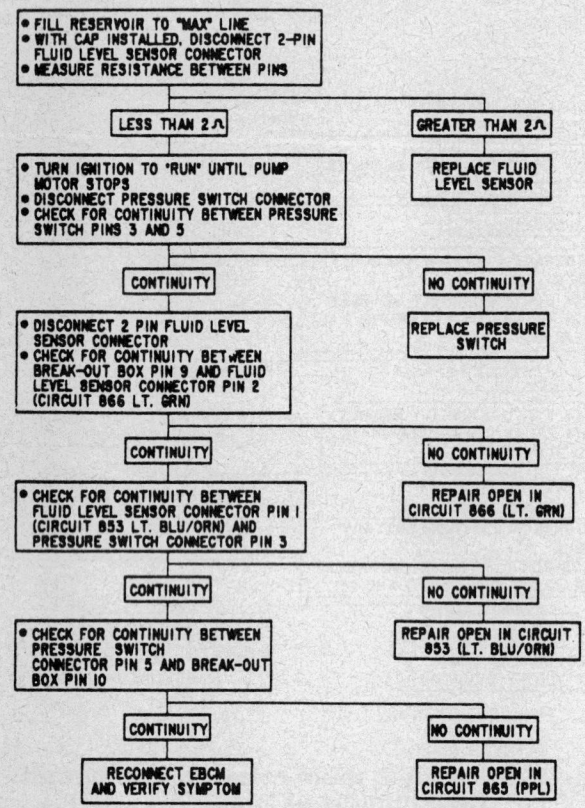

Fig. 16   Chart A-5, EBCM loop open. 1988 models except 6000

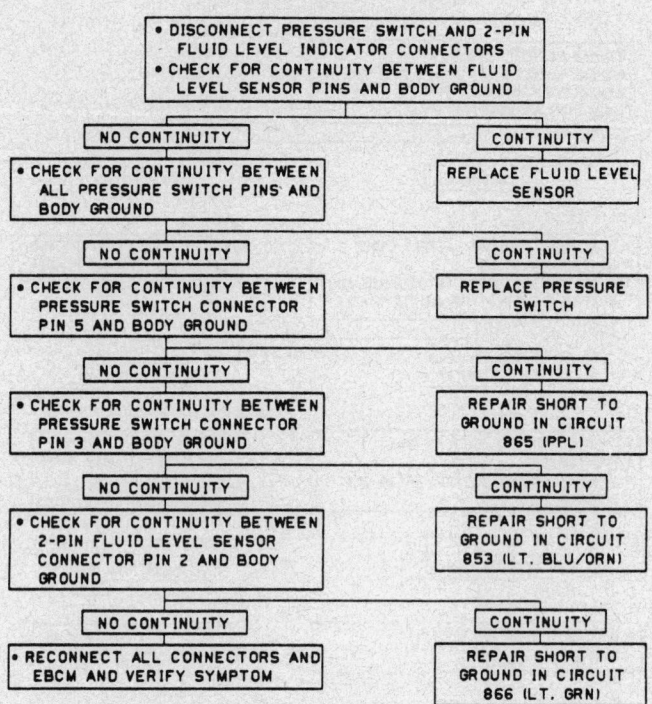

Fig. 17   Chart A-6, EBCM loop short. 1988 models except 6000

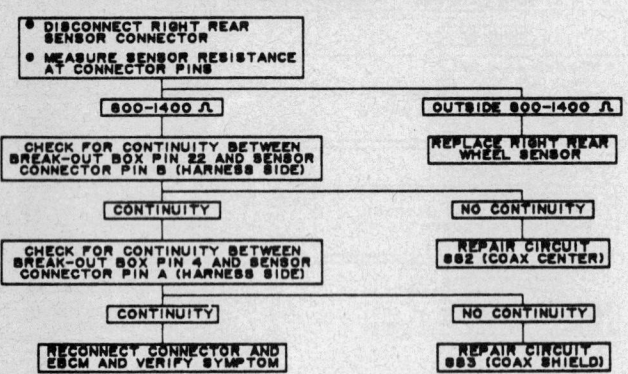

Fig. 18   Chart A-7, right rear wheel sensor. 1988 models except 6000

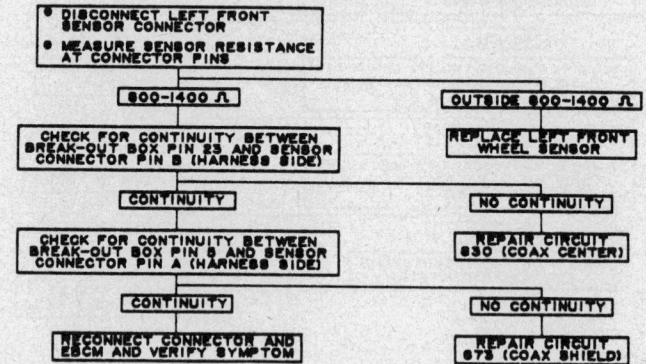

Fig. 19   Chart A-8, left front wheel sensor. 1988 models except 6000

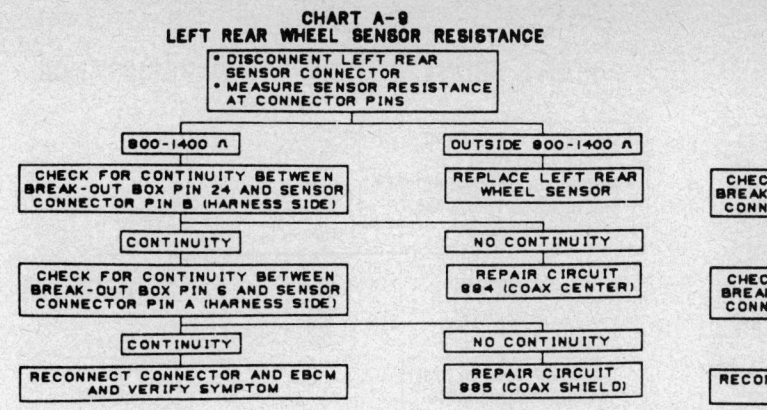

Fig. 20   Chart A-9, left rear wheel sensor. 1988 models except 6000

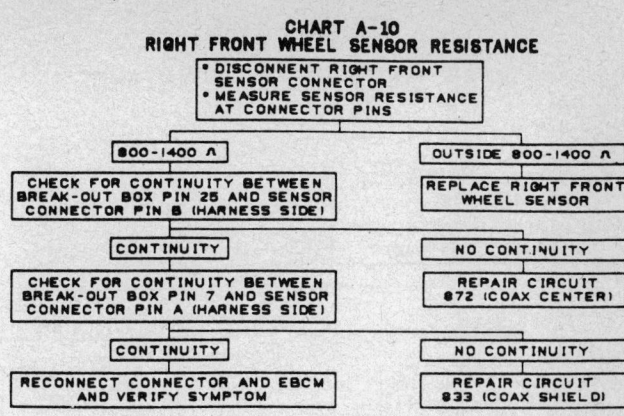

Fig. 21   Chart A-10, right front wheel sensor. 1988 models except 6000

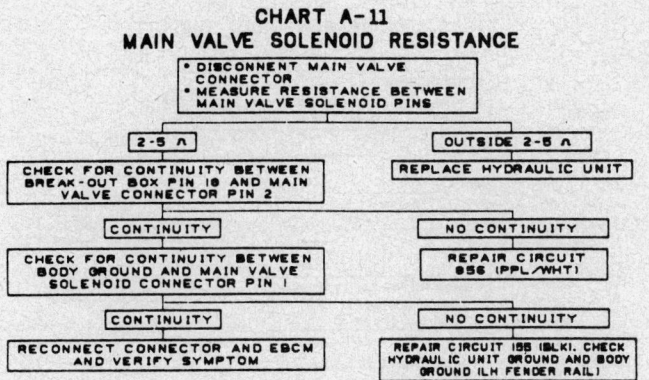

Fig. 22   Chart A-11, main valve solenoid resistance. 1988 models except 6000

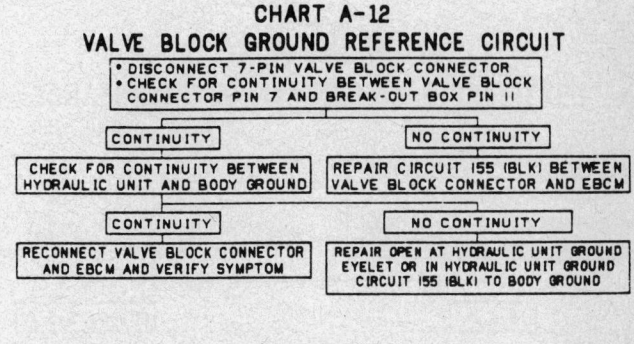

Fig. 23   Chart A-12, valve block ground reference. 1988 models except 6000

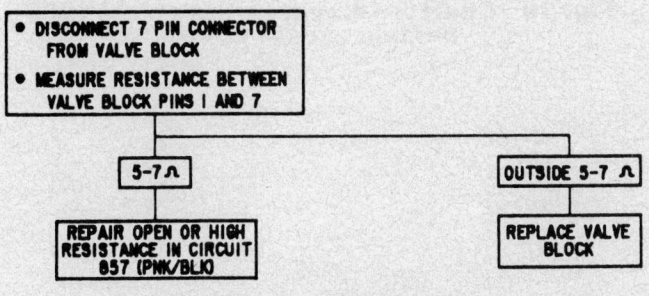

Fig. 24   Chart A-13, right front inlet valve. 1988 models except 6000

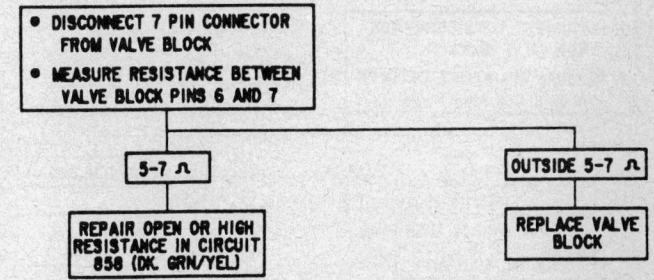

Fig. 25   Chart A-14, left front inlet valve. 1988 models except 6000

CHART A-15

REAR INLET VALVE RESISTANCE

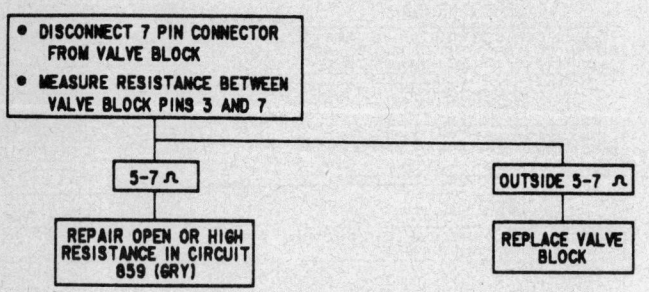

Fig. 26   Chart A-15, rear inlet valve. 1988 models except 6000

CHART A-16

RIGHT FRONT OUTLET VALVE RESISTANCE

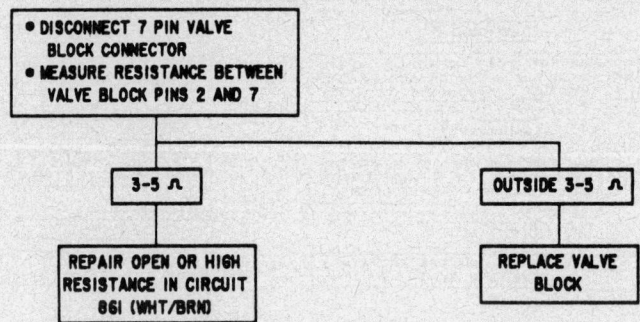

Fig. 27   Chart A-16, right front outlet valve. 1988 models except 6000

CHART A-17

LEFT FRONT OUTLET VALVE RESISTANCE

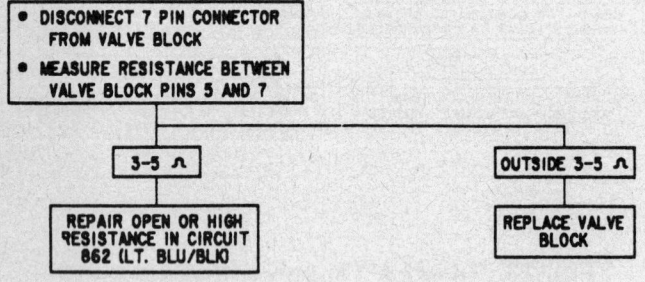

Fig. 28   Chart A-17, left front outlet valve. 1988 models except 6000

CHART A-19

DIODE AND DIODE CIRCUIT

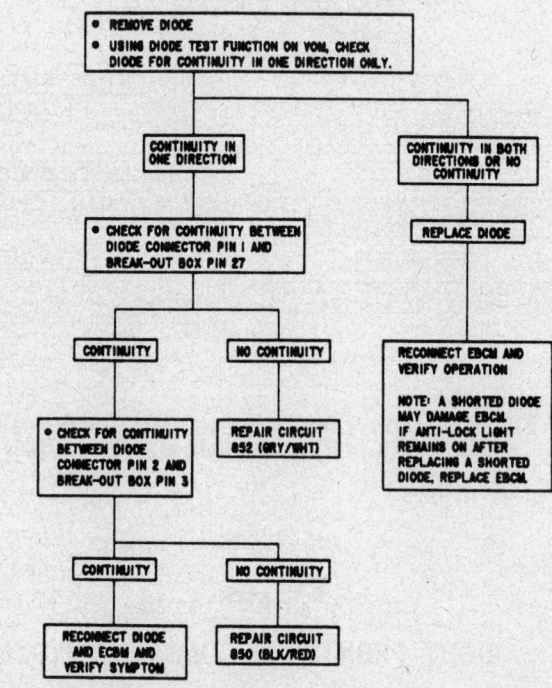

CHART A-18

REAR OUTLET VALVE RESISTANCE

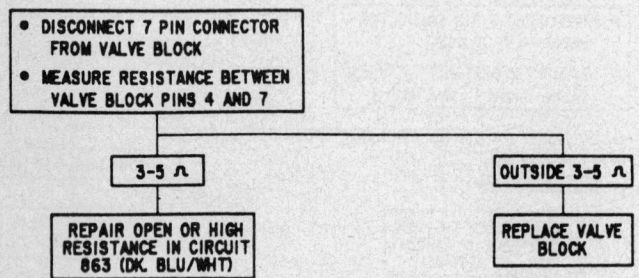

Fig. 29   Chart A-18, rear outlet valve. 1988 models except 6000

Fig. 30   Chart A-19, diode & diode circuit. 1988 models except 6000

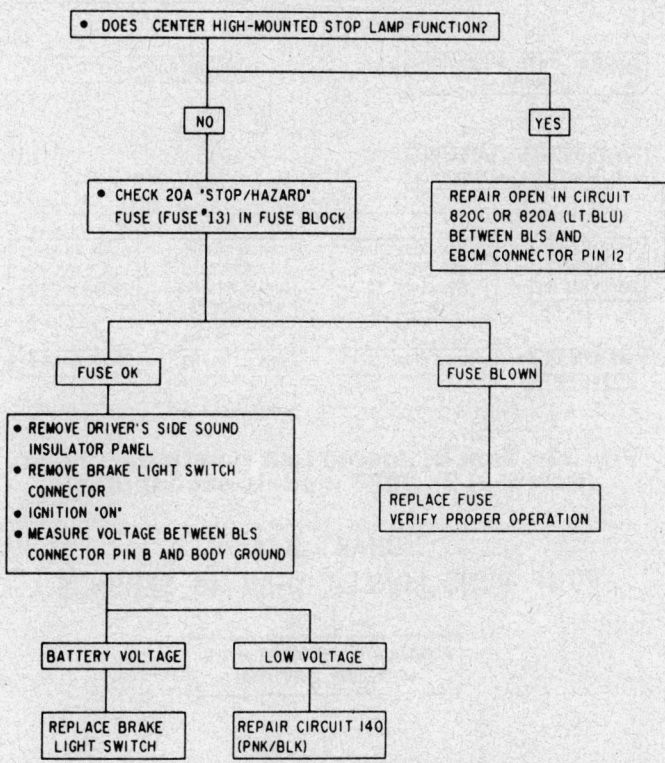

Fig. 31 Chart A-20, brake light switch input. 1988 models except 6000

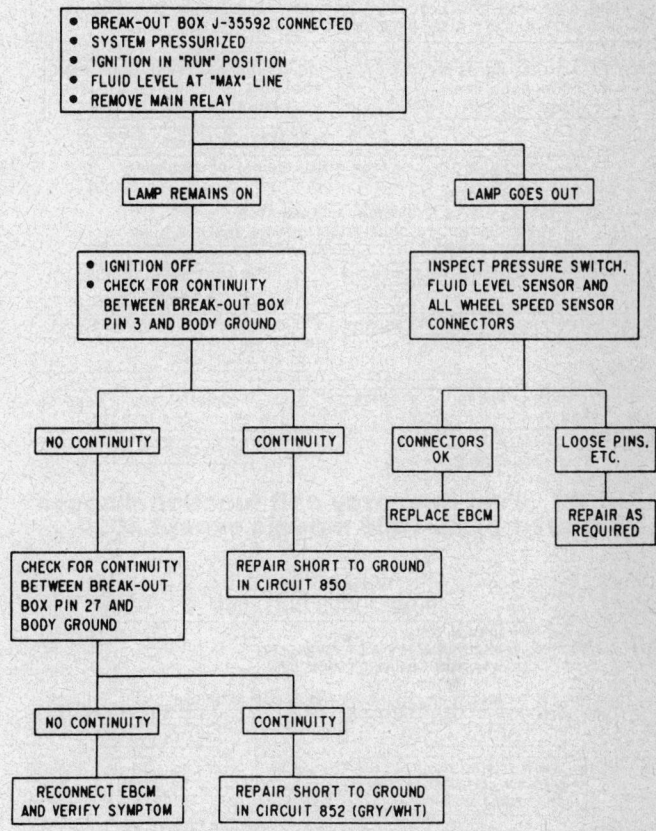

Fig. 32 Chart A-21, ANTI-LOCK lamp circuit. 1988 models except 6000

TEST B
ENERGY UNIT
FUNCTIONAL CHECK

- DEPRESSURIZE HYDRAULIC ACCUMULATOR
- TURN IGNITION TO "RUN" POSITION

PUMP RUNS → IF COMPLAINT IS CONTINUOUS "BRAKE" LAMP OPERATION, CHECK FOR INOPERATIVE OR GROUNDED PARKING BRAKE SWITCH AND REPAIR AS REQUIRED

PUMP DOES NOT RUN → GO TO CHART B-1

DETERMINE ACCUMULATOR PRE-CHARGE PRESSURE
- IGNITION "OFF"
- DEPRESSURIZE HYDRAULIC ACCUMULATOR
- INSTALL PRESSURE GAGE J-35604 AS DESCRIBED IN THIS SECTION
- TURN IGNITION TO "RUN" AND OBSERVE GAGE. PUMP MOTOR WILL START AND GAGE NEEDLE WILL QUICKLY JUMP TO THE PRE-CHARGE PRESSURE AND THEN SLOWLY RISE. RECORD PRE-CHARGE PRESSURE

PRE-CHARGE PRESSURE 4000-8000 KPA (580-1160 PSI)

PRE-CHARGE PRESSURE LESS THAN 4000 KPA (580 PSI) OR GREATER THAN 8000 KPA (1160 PSI) → REPLACE ACCUMULATOR

DETERMINE ACCUMULATOR FINAL CHARGE PRESSURE
- IGNITION "OFF"
- DEPRESSURIZE HYDRAULIC ACCUMULATOR
- TURN IGNITION TO "RUN" POSITION AND OBSERVE PUMP

PUMP STOPS WITHIN 45 SECONDS → RECORD FINAL CHARGE PRESSURE

PUMP CONTINUES TO RUN AFTER 45 SECONDS
- RECORD ACCUMULATOR PRESSURE
- IGNITION "OFF"
- GO TO CHART B-2

FINAL CHARGE PRESSURE GREATER THAN 25,800 KPA (2500 PSI)

FINAL CHARGE PRESSURE LESS THAN 25,800 KPA (2500 PSI) → GO TO CHART B-3

CONTINUED

Fig. 33   Test B, energy unit functional check (Part 1 of 2). 1988 models except 6000

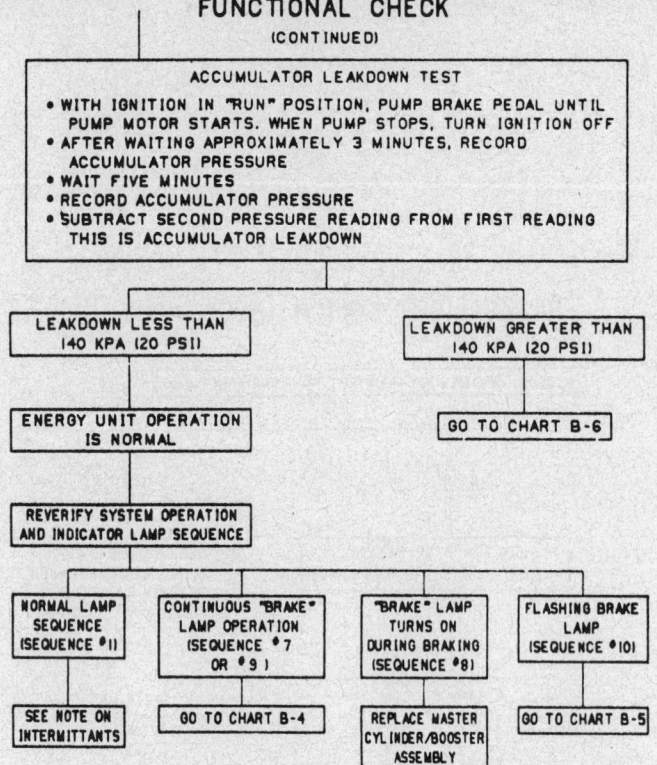

TEST B
ENERGY UNIT
FUNCTIONAL CHECK
(CONTINUED)

ACCUMULATOR LEAKDOWN TEST
- WITH IGNITION IN "RUN" POSITION, PUMP BRAKE PEDAL UNTIL PUMP MOTOR STARTS. WHEN PUMP STOPS, TURN IGNITION OFF
- AFTER WAITING APPROXIMATELY 3 MINUTES, RECORD ACCUMULATOR PRESSURE
- WAIT FIVE MINUTES
- RECORD ACCUMULATOR PRESSURE
- SUBTRACT SECOND PRESSURE READING FROM FIRST READING THIS IS ACCUMULATOR LEAKDOWN

LEAKDOWN LESS THAN 140 KPA (20 PSI) → ENERGY UNIT OPERATION IS NORMAL → REVERIFY SYSTEM OPERATION AND INDICATOR LAMP SEQUENCE

LEAKDOWN GREATER THAN 140 KPA (20 PSI) → GO TO CHART B-6

NORMAL LAMP SEQUENCE (SEQUENCE #1) → SEE NOTE ON INTERMITTANTS

CONTINUOUS "BRAKE" LAMP OPERATION (SEQUENCE #7 OR #9) → GO TO CHART B-4

"BRAKE" LAMP TURNS ON DURING BRAKING (SEQUENCE #8) → REPLACE MASTER CYLINDER/BOOSTER ASSEMBLY

FLASHING BRAKE LAMP (SEQUENCE #10) → GO TO CHART B-5

Fig. 33   Test B, energy unit functional check (Part 2 of 2). 1988 models except 6000

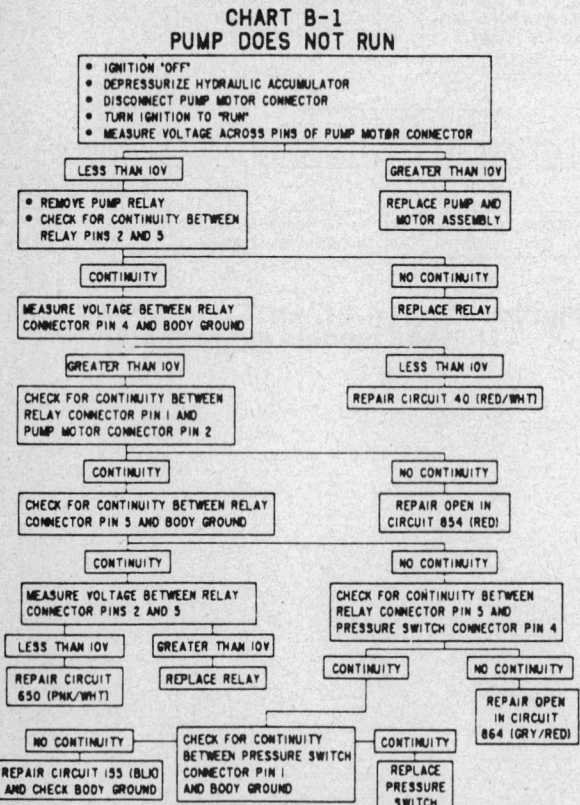

CHART B-1
PUMP DOES NOT RUN

- IGNITION "OFF"
- DEPRESSURIZE HYDRAULIC ACCUMULATOR
- DISCONNECT PUMP MOTOR CONNECTOR
- TURN IGNITION TO "RUN"
- MEASURE VOLTAGE ACROSS PINS OF PUMP MOTOR CONNECTOR

LESS THAN 10V
- REMOVE PUMP RELAY
- CHECK FOR CONTINUITY BETWEEN RELAY PINS 2 AND 5

GREATER THAN 10V → REPLACE PUMP AND MOTOR ASSEMBLY

CONTINUITY → MEASURE VOLTAGE BETWEEN RELAY CONNECTOR PIN 4 AND BODY GROUND

NO CONTINUITY → REPLACE RELAY

GREATER THAN 10V → CHECK FOR CONTINUITY BETWEEN RELAY CONNECTOR PIN 1 AND PUMP MOTOR CONNECTOR PIN 2

LESS THAN 10V → REPAIR CIRCUIT 40 (RED/WHT)

CONTINUITY → CHECK FOR CONTINUITY BETWEEN RELAY CONNECTOR PIN 5 AND BODY GROUND

NO CONTINUITY → REPAIR OPEN IN CIRCUIT 854 (RED)

CONTINUITY → MEASURE VOLTAGE BETWEEN RELAY CONNECTOR PINS 2 AND 5

NO CONTINUITY → CHECK FOR CONTINUITY BETWEEN RELAY CONNECTOR PIN 5 AND PRESSURE SWITCH CONNECTOR PIN 4

LESS THAN 10V → REPAIR CIRCUIT 650 (PNK/WHT)

GREATER THAN 10V → REPLACE RELAY

CONTINUITY

NO CONTINUITY → REPAIR OPEN IN CIRCUIT 864 (GRY/RED)

NO CONTINUITY → REPAIR CIRCUIT 155 (BLK) AND CHECK BODY GROUND

CHECK FOR CONTINUITY BETWEEN PRESSURE SWITCH CONNECTOR PIN 1 AND BODY GROUND

CONTINUITY → REPLACE PRESSURE SWITCH

Fig. 34   Chart B-1, pump does not run. 1988 models except 6000

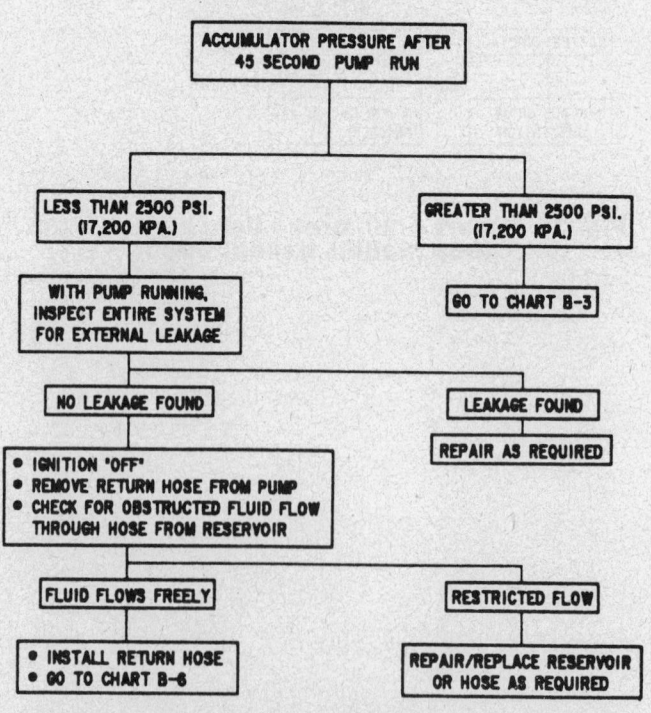

CHART B-2
PUMP RUNS LONGER THAN 45 SECONDS

ACCUMULATOR PRESSURE AFTER 45 SECOND PUMP RUN

LESS THAN 2500 PSI. (17,200 KPA.) → WITH PUMP RUNNING, INSPECT ENTIRE SYSTEM FOR EXTERNAL LEAKAGE

GREATER THAN 2500 PSI. (17,200 KPA.) → GO TO CHART B-3

NO LEAKAGE FOUND
- IGNITION "OFF"
- REMOVE RETURN HOSE FROM PUMP
- CHECK FOR OBSTRUCTED FLUID FLOW THROUGH HOSE FROM RESERVOIR

LEAKAGE FOUND → REPAIR AS REQUIRED

FLUID FLOWS FREELY
- INSTALL RETURN HOSE
- GO TO CHART B-6

RESTRICTED FLOW → REPAIR/REPLACE RESERVOIR OR HOSE AS REQUIRED

Fig. 35   Chart B-2, pump runs longer than 45 seconds. 1988 models except 6000

BONNEVILLE, DEVILLE, ELECTRA, FLEETWOOD, PARK AVENUE, 88, 98 & 6000 (TEVES TYPE)

CHART B-3
PRESSURE SWITCH PERFORMANCE

I. SWITCH STATUS - PRESSURIZED
- TURN IGNITION TO "RUN" UNTIL PUMP STOPS
- IGNITION "OFF"
    - NOTE: IF PUMP CONTINUES TO RUN AFTER 45 SECONDS, TURN IGNITION OFF AND PROCEDE
- CHECK PRESSURE SWITCH PINS FOR THE FOLLOWING CONDITIONS USING VOM

MEASURE BETWEEN PINS	SCALE	SPECIFICATION
B,D	200 Ω	NO CONTINUITY
C,D	200 Ω	NO CONTINUITY
A,E	200 Ω	CONTINUITY
ALL PINS,BODY GROUND	200 Ω	NO CONTINUITY

IF ANY CONDITION IS NOT MET, REPLACE PRESSURE SWITCH AND VERIFY SYSTEM OPERATION

II. SWITCH STATUS - DEPRESSURIZED
- DEPRESSURIZE HYDRAULIC ACCUMULATOR
- CHECK PRESSURE SWITCH PINS FOR THE FOLLOWING CONDITIONS USING VOM

MEASURE BETWEEN PINS	SCALE	SPECIFICATION
B,D	200 Ω	CONTINUITY
C,D	200 Ω	CONTINUITY
A,E	200 Ω	NO CONTINUITY
ALL PINS,BODY GROUND	200 Ω	NO CONTINUITY

IF ANY CONDITION IS NOT MET, REPLACE PRESSURE SWITCH AND VERIFY SYSTEM OPERATION

PRESSURE SWITCH

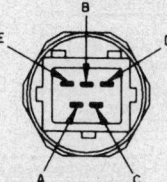

CONTINUED
↓

CHART B-3
(CONTINUED)

III. SWITCH THRESHOLDS
- DEPRESSURIZE HYDRAULIC ACCUMULATOR
- INSTALL PRESSURE GAGE J-35604 AS DESCRIBED IN THIS SECTION
- CONNECT PRESSURE SWITCH CONNECTOR AND TURN IGNITION TO "RUN" UNTIL PUMP STOPS
- USING VOM, MONITOR FOR CONTINUITY BETWEEN PRESSURE SWITCH PINS AS SHOWN BELOW WHILE SLOWLY BLEEDING OFF ACCUMULATOR PRESSURE BY PUMPING THE BRAKE PEDAL. CONTINUITY SHOULD BE GAINED OR LOST AS INDICATED.
- PRESSURIZE SYSTEM BETWEEN EACH TEST BY RECONNECTING PRESSURE SWITCH AND TURNING IGNITION TO "RUN" UNTIL PUMP STOPS

MEASURE BETWEEN PINS	SWITCH STATUS	PRESSURE RANGE
C,D	CONTINUITY SHOULD BE GAINED AT:	1980-2080 PSI (13,650-14,350 KPA)
B,D	CONTINUITY SHOULD BE GAINED AT:	1500-1550 PSI (10,350-10,700 KPA)
A,E	CONTINUITY SHOULD BE LOST AT:	1500-1550 PSI (10,350-10,700 KPA)

IF ANY CONDITION IS NOT MET, REPLACE PRESSURE SWITCH AND VERIFY PROPER OPERATION

- DEPRESSURIZE HYDRAULIC ACCUMULATOR
- WITH IGNITION OFF, CONNECT PRESSURE SWITCH CONNECTOR
- TURN IGNITION TO "RUN" AND OBSERVE GAGE, "ANTI-LOCK" LAMP, "BRAKE" LAMP AND PUMP MOTOR. EVENTS SHOULD OCCUR AT PRESSURES INDICATED IN CHART BELOW

EVENT	PRESSURE
"ANTI-LOCK" LAMP TURNS OFF	1900-1975 PSI (13,100-13,600 KPA)
"BRAKE" LAMP TURNS OFF	1900-1975 PSI (13,100-13,600 KPA)
PUMP MOTOR STOPS	2550-2670 PSI (17,580-18,400 KPA)

IF ANY CONDITION IS NOT MET, REPLACE PRESSURE SWITCH AND VERIFY PROPER OPERATION

PRESSURE SWITCH

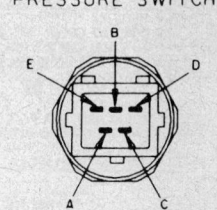

Fig. 36   Chart B-3, pressure switch performance (Part 1 of 2). 1988 models except 6000

Fig. 36   Chart B-3, pressure switch performance (Part 2 of 2). 1988 models except 6000

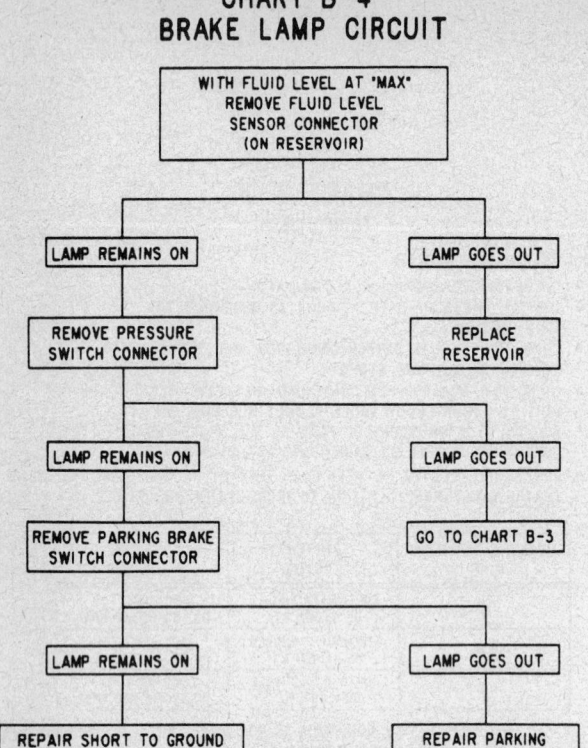

CHART B-4
BRAKE LAMP CIRCUIT

Fig. 37   Chart B-4, brake lamp circuit. 1988 models except 6000

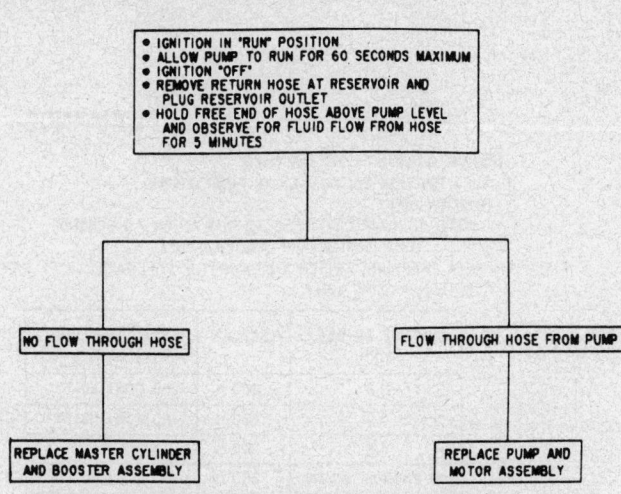

CHART B-5
HYDRAULIC UNIT LEAKDOWN

Fig. 38   Chart B-5, hydraulic unit leakdown. 1988 models except 6000

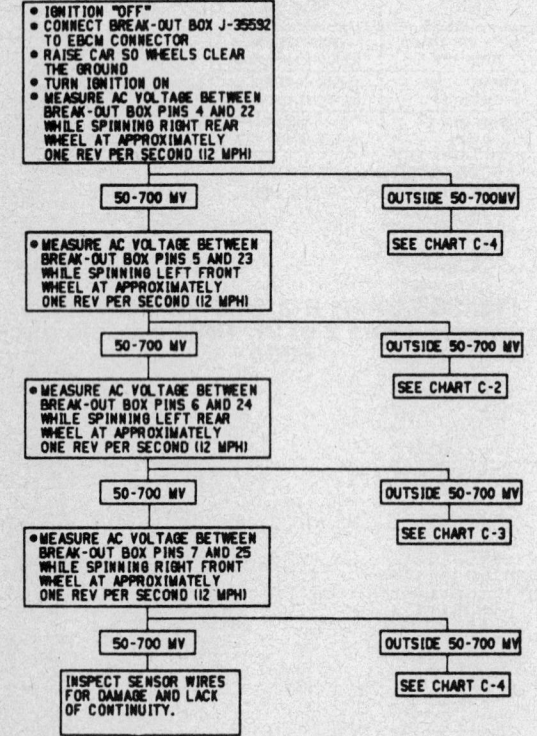

TEST C
WHEEL SPEED SENSOR OUTPUT

Fig. 39   Test C, wheel speed sensor output. 1988 models except 6000

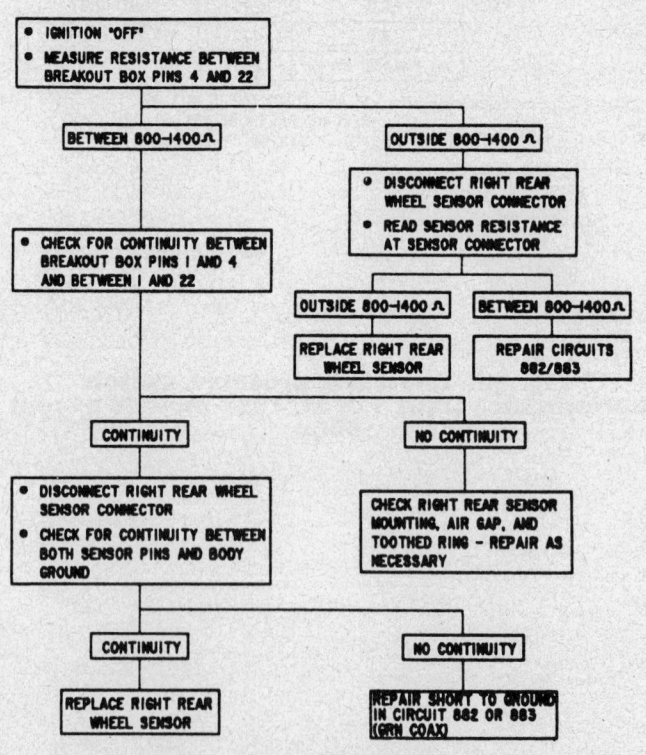

CHART C-1
RIGHT REAR WHEEL SENSOR OUTPUT

Fig. 40   Chart C-1, right rear sensor output. 1988 models except 6000

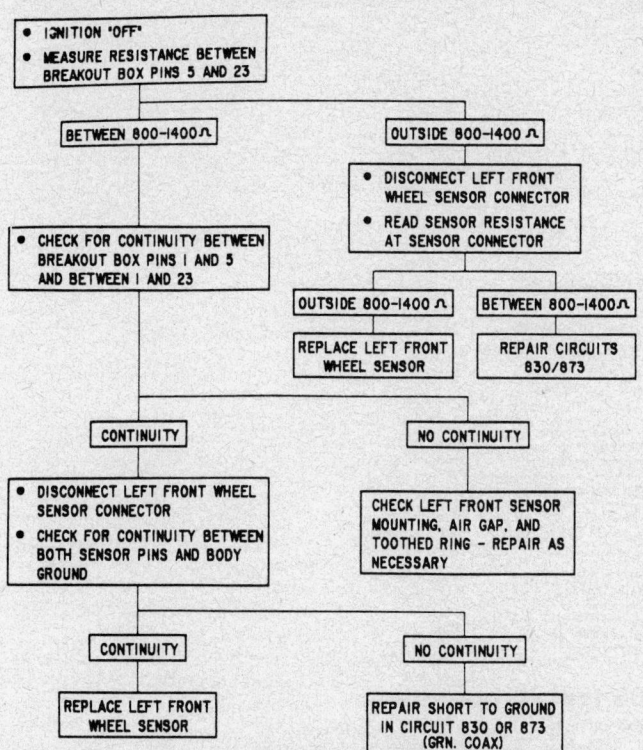

Fig. 41   Chart C-2, left front sensor output. 1988 models except 6000

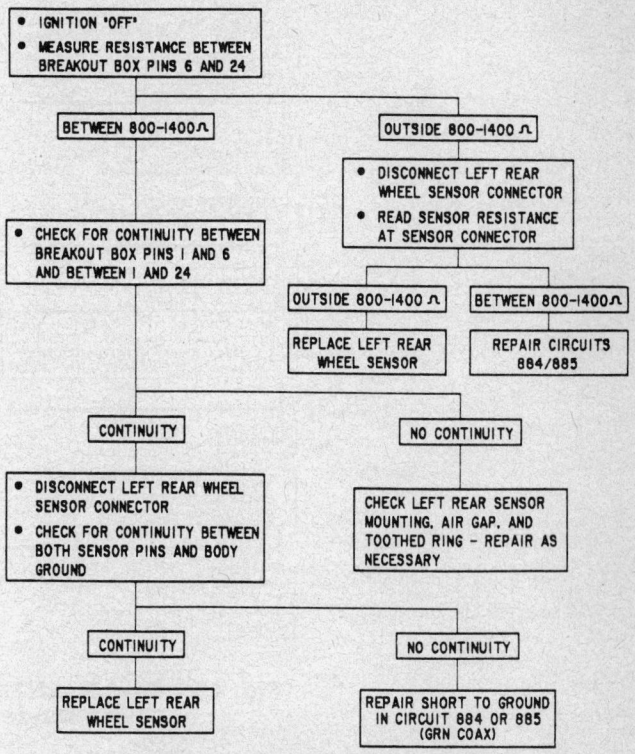

Fig. 42   Chart C-3, left rear sensor output. 1988 models except 6000

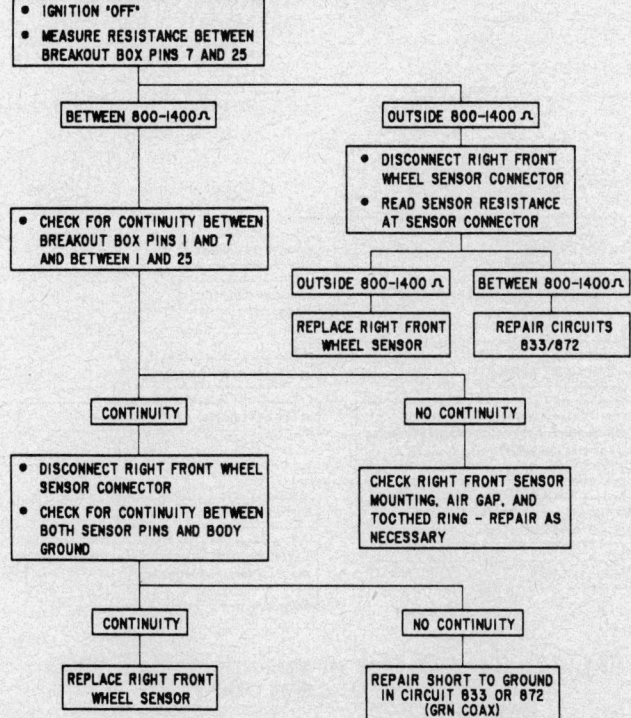

Fig. 43   Chart C-4, right front sensor output. 1988 models except 6000

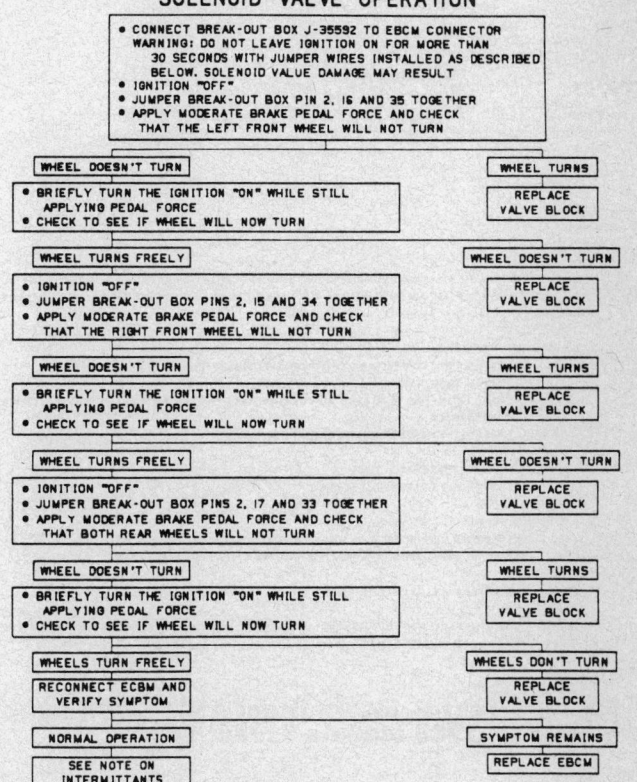

Fig. 44   Test D, solenoid valve operation. 1988 models except 6000

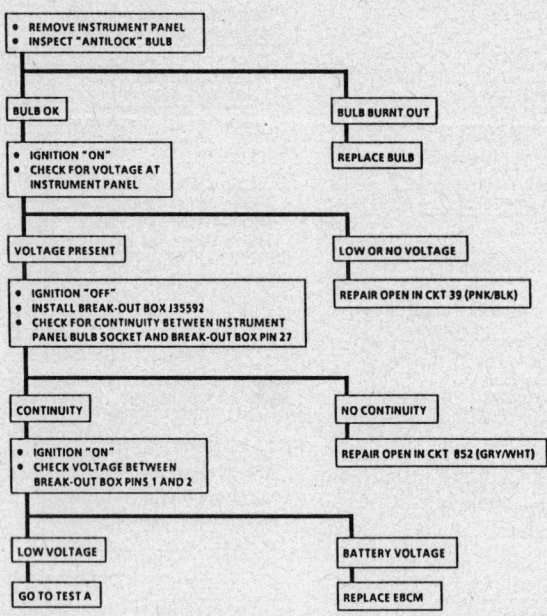

TEST E
"ANTILOCK" LAMP INOPERATIVE

- REMOVE INSTRUMENT PANEL
- INSPECT "ANTILOCK" BULB

BULB OK

- IGNITION "ON"
- CHECK FOR VOLTAGE AT INSTRUMENT PANEL

BULB BURNT OUT

REPLACE BULB

VOLTAGE PRESENT

- IGNITION "OFF"
- INSTALL BREAK-OUT BOX J35592
- CHECK FOR CONTINUITY BETWEEN INSTRUMENT PANEL BULB SOCKET AND BREAK-OUT BOX PIN 27

LOW OR NO VOLTAGE

REPAIR OPEN IN CKT 39 (PNK/BLK)

CONTINUITY

- IGNITION "ON"
- CHECK VOLTAGE BETWEEN BREAK-OUT BOX PINS 1 AND 2

NO CONTINUITY

REPAIR OPEN IN CKT 852 (GRY/WHT)

LOW VOLTAGE

GO TO TEST A

BATTERY VOLTAGE

REPLACE EBCM

Fig. 45   Test F, ANTI-LOCK lamp inoperative. 1988 models except 6000

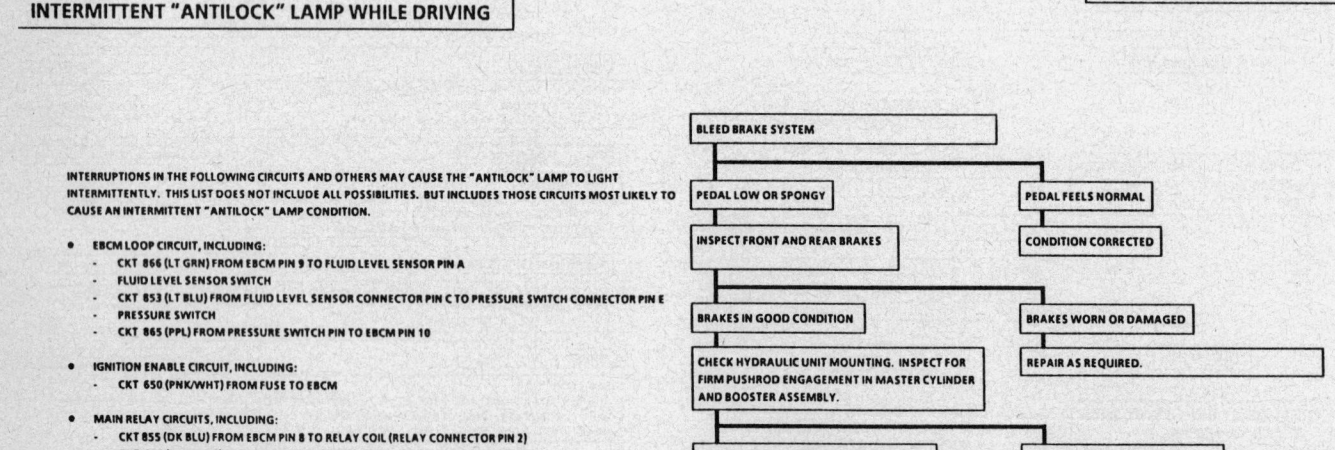

TEST F
INTERMITTENT "ANTILOCK" LAMP WHILE DRIVING

TEST G
LOW OR SPONGY PEDAL

INTERRUPTIONS IN THE FOLLOWING CIRCUITS AND OTHERS MAY CAUSE THE "ANTILOCK" LAMP TO LIGHT INTERMITTENTLY. THIS LIST DOES NOT INCLUDE ALL POSSIBILITIES. BUT INCLUDES THOSE CIRCUITS MOST LIKELY TO CAUSE AN INTERMITTENT "ANTILOCK" LAMP CONDITION.

- EBCM LOOP CIRCUIT, INCLUDING:
  - CKT 866 (LT GRN) FROM EBCM PIN 9 TO FLUID LEVEL SENSOR PIN A
  - FLUID LEVEL SENSOR SWITCH
  - CKT 853 (LT BLU) FROM FLUID LEVEL SENSOR CONNECTOR PIN C TO PRESSURE SWITCH CONNECTOR PIN E
  - PRESSURE SWITCH
  - CKT 865 (PPL) FROM PRESSURE SWITCH PIN TO EBCM PIN 10

- IGNITION ENABLE CIRCUIT, INCLUDING:
  - CKT 650 (PNK/WHT) FROM FUSE TO EBCM

- MAIN RELAY CIRCUITS, INCLUDING:
  - CKT 855 (DK BLU) FROM EBCM PIN 8 TO RELAY COIL (RELAY CONNECTOR PIN 2)
  - CKT 803 (BLK/WHT) FROM RELAY COIL TO EBCM PIN 1 (RELAY CONNECTOR PIN T)

- ALL WHEEL SPEED SENSOR CIRCUITS

INSPECT CONNECTORS AND WIRES IN THESE CIRCUITS. IF NO TROUBLE IS FOUND, SEE NOTE ON INTERMITTENTS IN THIS SECTION AND PERFORM TEST A.

BLEED BRAKE SYSTEM

PEDAL LOW OR SPONGY

INSPECT FRONT AND REAR BRAKES

PEDAL FEELS NORMAL

CONDITION CORRECTED

BRAKES IN GOOD CONDITION

CHECK HYDRAULIC UNIT MOUNTING. INSPECT FOR FIRM PUSHROD ENGAGEMENT IN MASTER CYLINDER AND BOOSTER ASSEMBLY.

BRAKES WORN OR DAMAGED

REPAIR AS REQUIRED.

COMPONENTS IMPROPERLY INSTALLED. DAMAGED OR MISADJUSTED.

REPAIR AS REQUIRED.

PUSHROD IMPROPERLY ENGAGED

INSPECT PUSHROD GROMMET AND MOUNTING BRACKET. REPAIR AS REQUIRED.

Fig. 46   Test G, intermittent ANTI-LOCK lamp. 1988 models except 6000

Fig. 47   Test H, low or spongy pedal. 1988 models except 6000

PIN-OUT CHECKS

- CONNECT J 35592 TO 35-PIN EBCM HARNESS CONNECTOR AS DESCRIBED IN THIS SECTION
- PERFORM CHECKS WITH HIGH IMPEDANCE DIGITAL MULTIMETER J 34029-A OR EQUIVALENT
- ALL CHECKS ARE MADE WITH ENGINE OFF

CIRCUIT TO BE TESTED	IGNITION SWITCH POSITION	MULTIMETER SCALE/RANGE	MEASURE BETWEEN PIN NUMBERS	SPECIFICATION	IF RESULT NOT WITHIN SPECIFICATION, SEE FIGURE		
IGNITION ENABLE	RUN	20 DCV	2(+)*,1(-)*	10 V MINIMUM	49	50	51
MAIN RELAY GROUND	OFF	200 ∧	1,3	CONTINUITY	53		
	OFF	200 ∧	1,20	CONTINUITY			
MAIN RELAY COIL	OFF	200 ∧	1,8	45-105 ∧	54		

BEFORE PERFORMING THIS TEST: • REMOVE GAGE FUSE FROM FUSE BOX
• PLACE FUSED JUMPER BETWEEN J 35592 PINS 2 & 8

MAIN RELAY POWER	ON	20 DCV	3(+),1(-)	10 V MINIMUM	55
	ON	20 DCV	20(+),1(-)	10 V MINIMUM	

BEFORE PROCEEDING: • REMOVE JUMPER FROM PINS 2 & 8
• INSTALL GAGE FUSE

EBCM SWITCH LOOP	OFF	200 ∧	9,10	LESS THAN 5 ∧	56	57
	OFF	200 ∧	1,9	NO CONTINUITY		58
RR SENSOR RESISTANCE	OFF	2k ∧	4,22	800-1400 ∧	62	59
LF SENSOR RESISTANCE	OFF	2k ∧	5,23	800-1400 ∧	64	59
LR SENSOR RESISTANCE	OFF	2k ∧	6,24	800-1400 ∧	66	59
RF SENSOR RESISTANCE	OFF	2k ∧	7,25	800-1400 ∧	68	59
MAIN VALVE SOLENOID	OFF	200 ∧	11,18	2-5 ∧	69	70
VALVE BLOCK GROUND	OFF	200 ∧	1,11	LESS THAN 2 ∧	71	
RF INLET VALVE	OFF	200 ∧	11,15	5-7 ∧	72	
LF INLET VALVE	OFF	200 ∧	11,35	5-7 ∧	73	
REAR INLET VALVE	OFF	200 ∧	11,17	5-7 ∧	74	
RF OUTLET VALVE	OFF	200 ∧	11,34	3-5 ∧	75	
LF OUTLET VALVE	OFF	200 ∧	11,16	3-5 ∧	76	
REAR OUTLET VALVE	OFF	200 ∧	11,33	3-5 ∧	77	

*(+) OR (-) INDICATES MULTI-METER POLARITY
IF ALL TEST RESULTS ARE WITHIN SPECIFICATION, RECONNECT EBCM AND VERIFY CONTINUOUS "ANTILOCK" WARNING LAMP OPERATION
- IF NORMAL OPERATION RESUMES, SEE NOTE ON INTERMITTENTS
- IF LAMP REMAINS ON, SEE FIGURE 82

Fig. 48   Pin-Out checks. 1988–90 6000

IGNITION ENABLE CIRCUIT

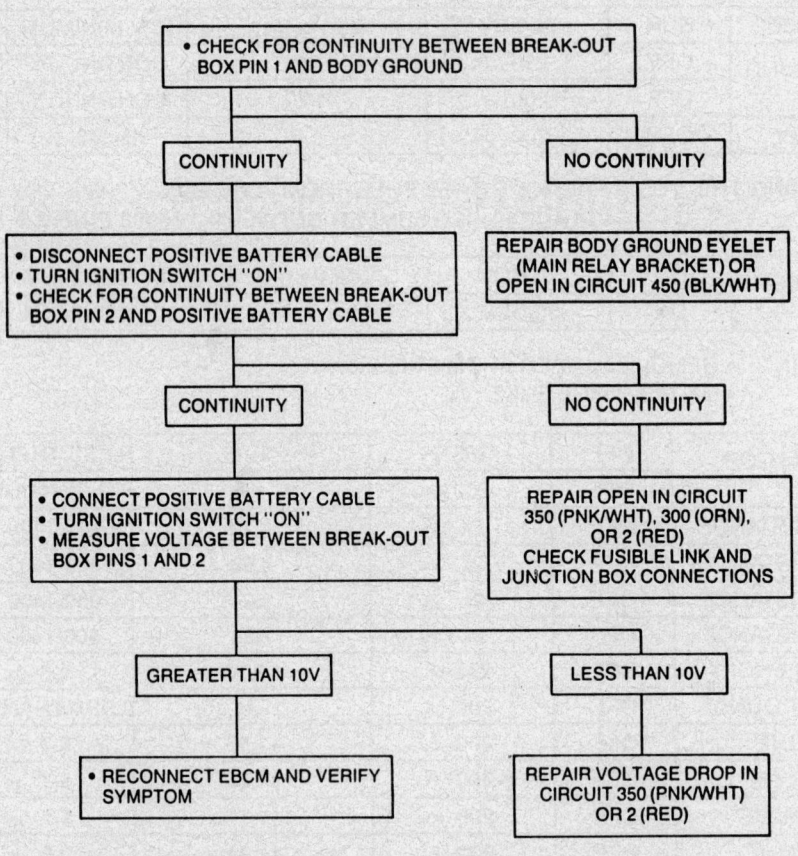

Fig. 49   Ignition enable circuit. 1988 6000

IGNITION ENABLE CIRCUIT

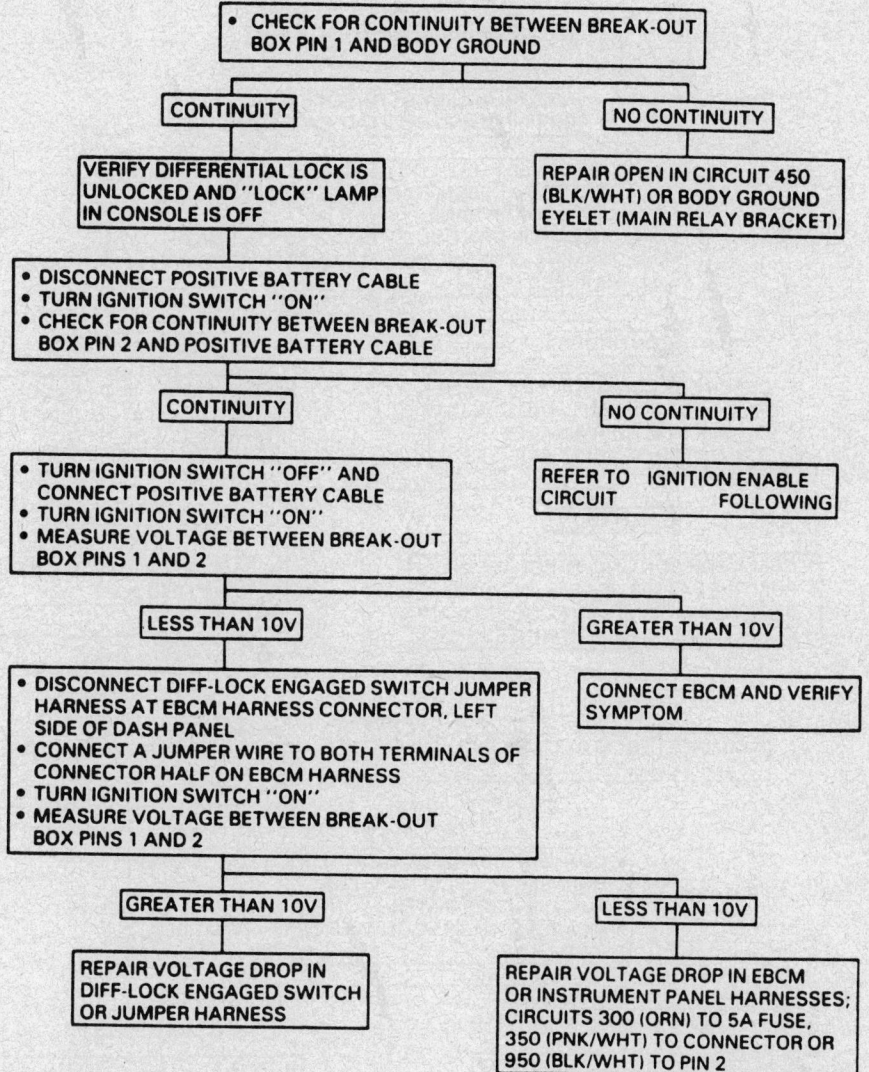

Fig. 50   Test-A, ignition enable circuit. 1989–90 6000

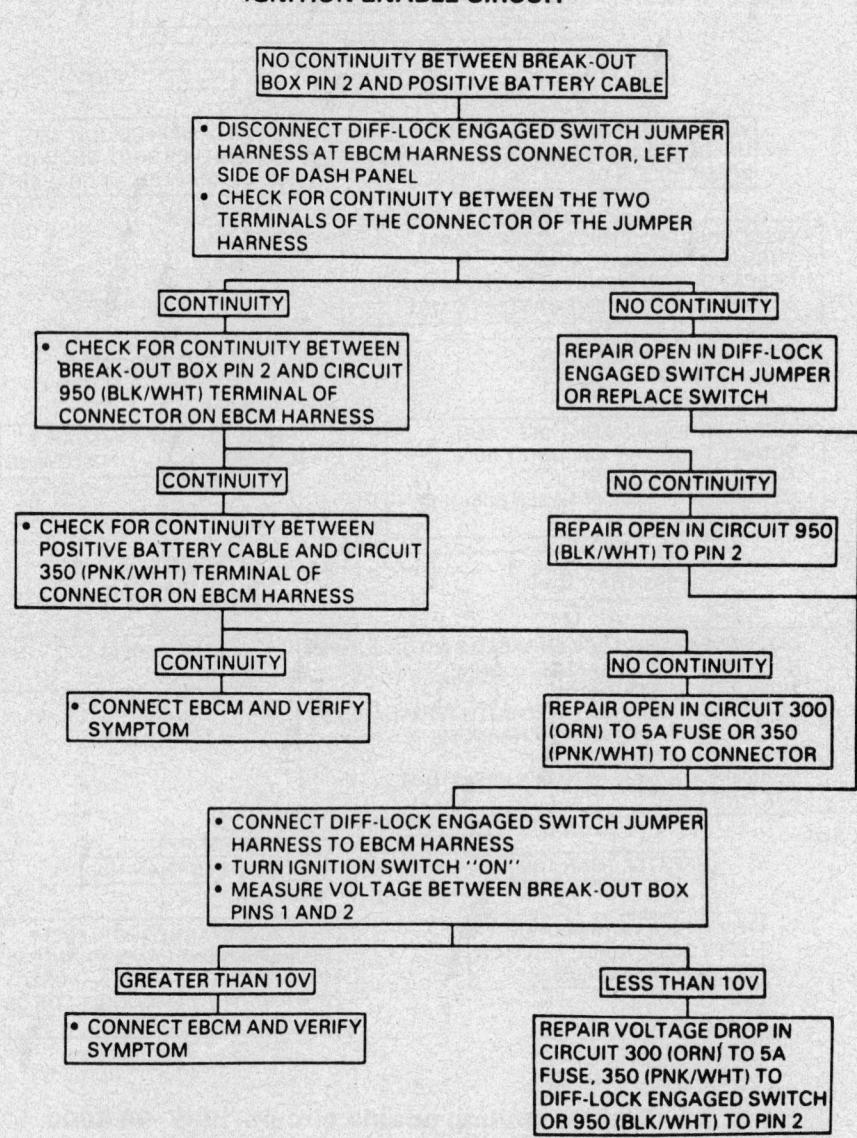

IGNITION ENABLE CIRCUIT

NO CONTINUITY BETWEEN BREAK-OUT BOX PIN 2 AND POSITIVE BATTERY CABLE

- DISCONNECT DIFF-LOCK ENGAGED SWITCH JUMPER HARNESS AT EBCM HARNESS CONNECTOR, LEFT SIDE OF DASH PANEL
- CHECK FOR CONTINUITY BETWEEN THE TWO TERMINALS OF THE CONNECTOR OF THE JUMPER HARNESS

CONTINUITY
- CHECK FOR CONTINUITY BETWEEN BREAK-OUT BOX PIN 2 AND CIRCUIT 950 (BLK/WHT) TERMINAL OF CONNECTOR ON EBCM HARNESS

NO CONTINUITY
REPAIR OPEN IN DIFF-LOCK ENGAGED SWITCH JUMPER OR REPLACE SWITCH

CONTINUITY
- CHECK FOR CONTINUITY BETWEEN POSITIVE BATTERY CABLE AND CIRCUIT 350 (PNK/WHT) TERMINAL OF CONNECTOR ON EBCM HARNESS

NO CONTINUITY
REPAIR OPEN IN CIRCUIT 950 (BLK/WHT) TO PIN 2

CONTINUITY
- CONNECT EBCM AND VERIFY SYMPTOM

NO CONTINUITY
REPAIR OPEN IN CIRCUIT 300 (ORN) TO 5A FUSE OR 350 (PNK/WHT) TO CONNECTOR

- CONNECT DIFF-LOCK ENGAGED SWITCH JUMPER HARNESS TO EBCM HARNESS
- TURN IGNITION SWITCH "ON"
- MEASURE VOLTAGE BETWEEN BREAK-OUT BOX PINS 1 AND 2

GREATER THAN 10V
- CONNECT EBCM AND VERIFY SYMPTOM

LESS THAN 10V
REPAIR VOLTAGE DROP IN CIRCUIT 300 (ORN) TO 5A FUSE, 350 (PNK/WHT) TO DIFF-LOCK ENGAGED SWITCH OR 950 (BLK/WHT) TO PIN 2

Fig. 51   Test-B, ignition enable circuit. 1989–90 6000

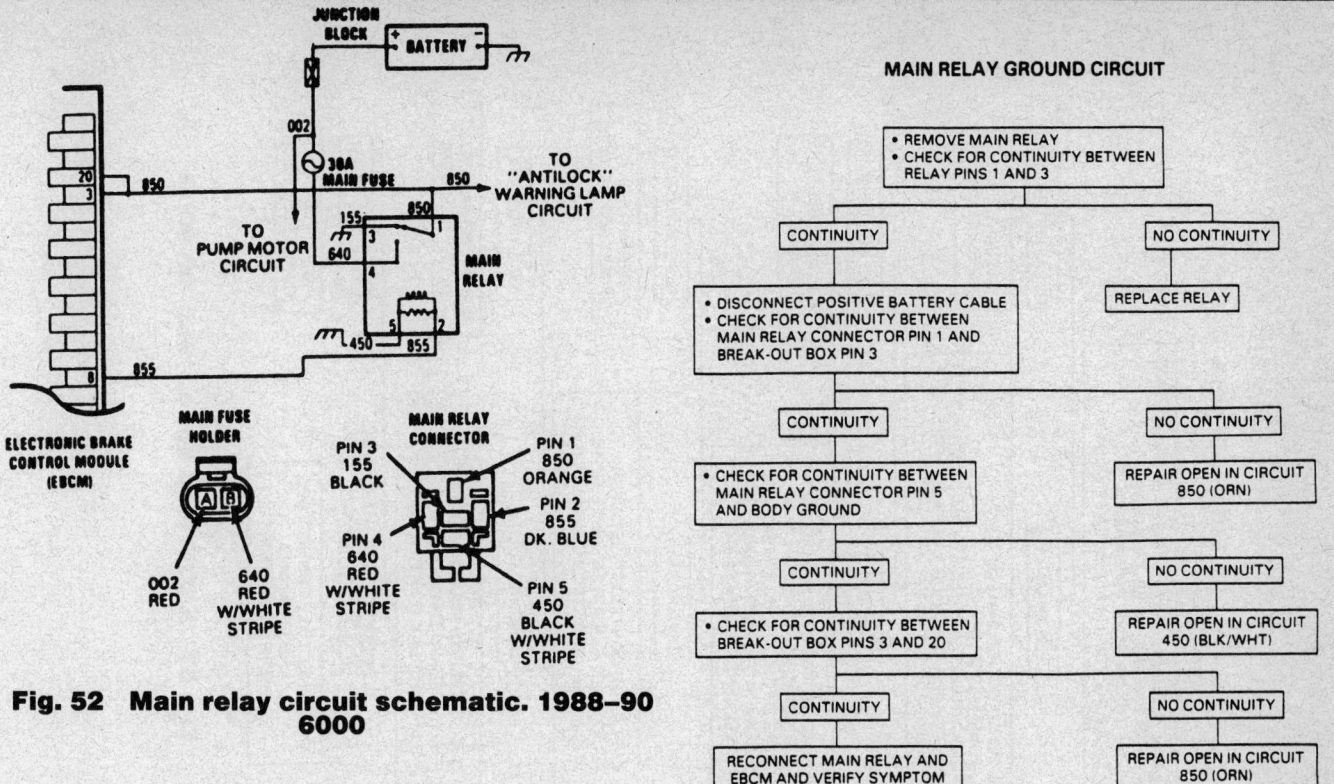

Fig. 52   Main relay circuit schematic. 1988–90 6000

MAIN RELAY GROUND CIRCUIT

- REMOVE MAIN RELAY
- CHECK FOR CONTINUITY BETWEEN RELAY PINS 1 AND 3

CONTINUITY →
- DISCONNECT POSITIVE BATTERY CABLE
- CHECK FOR CONTINUITY BETWEEN MAIN RELAY CONNECTOR PIN 1 AND BREAK-OUT BOX PIN 3

NO CONTINUITY → REPLACE RELAY

CONTINUITY →
- CHECK FOR CONTINUITY BETWEEN MAIN RELAY CONNECTOR PIN 5 AND BODY GROUND

NO CONTINUITY → REPAIR OPEN IN CIRCUIT 850 (ORN)

CONTINUITY →
- CHECK FOR CONTINUITY BETWEEN BREAK-OUT BOX PINS 3 AND 20

NO CONTINUITY → REPAIR OPEN IN CIRCUIT 450 (BLK/WHT)

CONTINUITY →
RECONNECT MAIN RELAY AND EBCM AND VERIFY SYMPTOM

NO CONTINUITY → REPAIR OPEN IN CIRCUIT 850 (ORN)

Fig. 53   Main relay ground circuit. 1988–90 6000

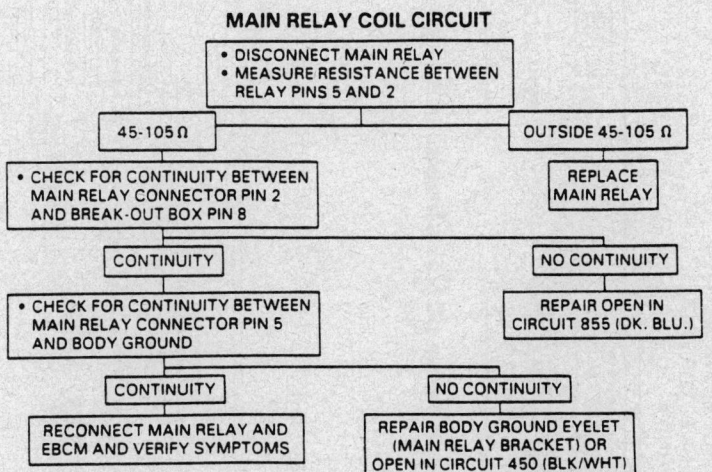

MAIN RELAY COIL CIRCUIT

- DISCONNECT MAIN RELAY
- MEASURE RESISTANCE BETWEEN RELAY PINS 5 AND 2

45-105 Ω →
- CHECK FOR CONTINUITY BETWEEN MAIN RELAY CONNECTOR PIN 2 AND BREAK-OUT BOX PIN 8

OUTSIDE 45-105 Ω → REPLACE MAIN RELAY

CONTINUITY →
- CHECK FOR CONTINUITY BETWEEN MAIN RELAY CONNECTOR PIN 5 AND BODY GROUND

NO CONTINUITY → REPAIR OPEN IN CIRCUIT 855 (DK. BLU.)

CONTINUITY →
RECONNECT MAIN RELAY AND EBCM AND VERIFY SYMPTOMS

NO CONTINUITY → REPAIR BODY GROUND EYELET (MAIN RELAY BRACKET) OR OPEN IN CIRCUIT 450 (BLK/WHT)

Fig. 54   Main relay coil circuit. 1988–90 6000

EBCM LOOP OPEN

- FILL RESERVOIR AS DESCRIBED IN THIS SECTION WITH CAP INSTALLED, DISCONNECT 2-PIN FLUID LEVEL SENSOR CONNECTOR, MEASURE RESISTANCE BETWEEN PINS
  - GREATER THAN 2 Ω → REPLACE FLUID LEVEL SENSOR
  - LESS THAN 2 Ω → TURN IGNITION SWITCH TO "RUN" UNTIL PUMP MOTOR STOPS, DISCONNECT PRESSURE SWITCH CONNECTOR, CHECK FOR CONTINUITY BETWEEN PRESSURE SWITCH PINS 3 AND 5
    - NO CONTINUITY → REPLACE PRESSURE SWITCH
    - CONTINUITY → DISCONNECT 2 PIN FLUID LEVEL SENSOR CONNECTOR, CHECK FOR CONTINUITY BETWEEN BREAK-OUT BOX PIN 9 AND FLUID LEVEL SENSOR CONNECTOR PIN 2
      - NO CONTINUITY → REPAIR OPEN IN CIRCUIT 866 (LT. GRN)
      - CONTINUITY → CHECK FOR CONTINUITY BETWEEN FLUID LEVEL SENSOR CONNECTOR PIN 1 AND PRESSURE SWITCH CONNECTOR PIN 3
        - NO CONTINUITY → REPAIR OPEN IN CIRCUIT 853 (LT. BLU/ORN)
        - CONTINUITY → CHECK FOR CONTINUITY BETWEEN PRESSURE SWITCH CONNECTOR PIN 5 AND BREAK-OUT BOX PIN 10
          - NO CONTINUITY → REPAIR OPEN IN CIRCUIT 865 (PPL)
          - CONTINUITY → RECONNECT ALL CONNECTORS AND EBCM AND VERIFY SYMPTOM

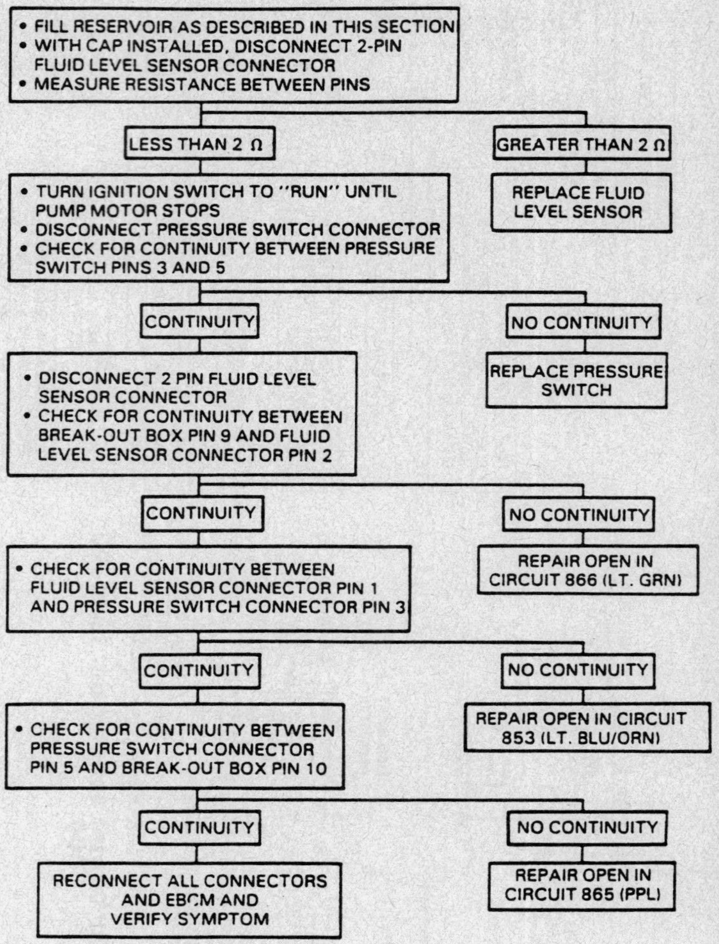

Fig. 57   EBCM loop open. 1988-90 6000

MAIN RELAY POWER CIRCUIT

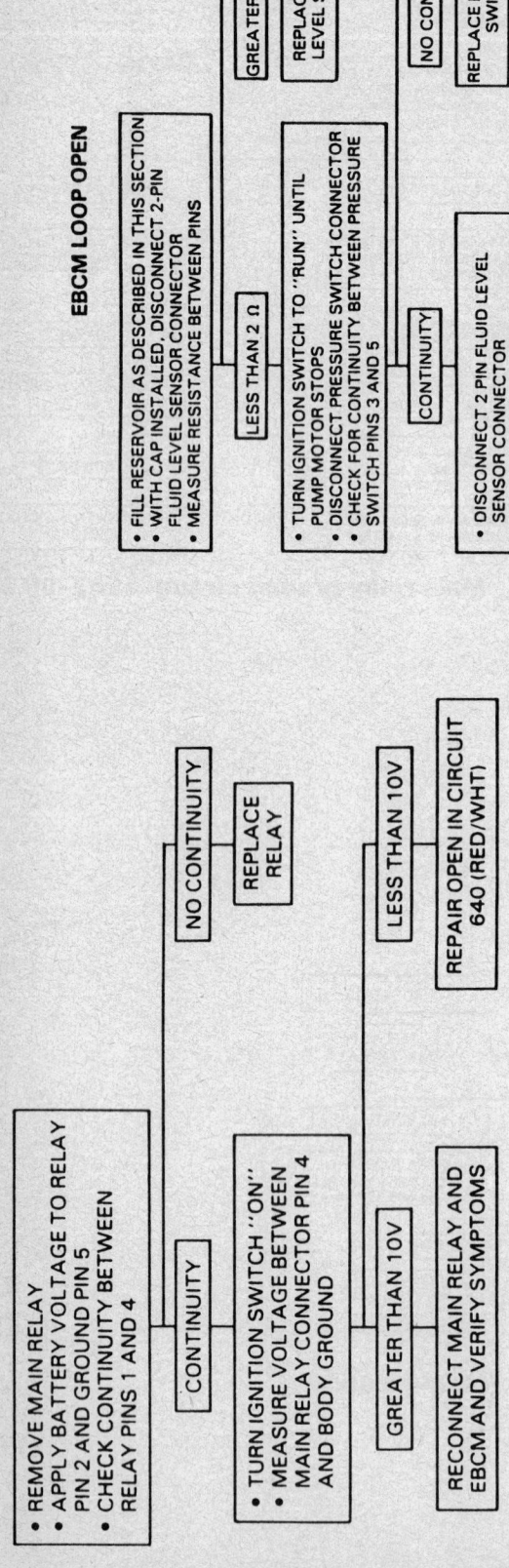

- REMOVE MAIN RELAY, APPLY BATTERY VOLTAGE TO RELAY PIN 2 AND GROUND PIN 5, CHECK CONTINUITY BETWEEN RELAY PINS 1 AND 4
  - NO CONTINUITY → REPLACE RELAY
  - CONTINUITY → TURN IGNITION SWITCH "ON", MEASURE VOLTAGE BETWEEN MAIN RELAY CONNECTOR PIN 4 AND BODY GROUND
    - GREATER THAN 10V → RECONNECT MAIN RELAY AND EBCM AND VERIFY SYMPTOMS
    - LESS THAN 10V → REPAIR OPEN IN CIRCUIT 640 (RED/WHT)

Fig. 55   Main relay power circuit. 1988-90 6000

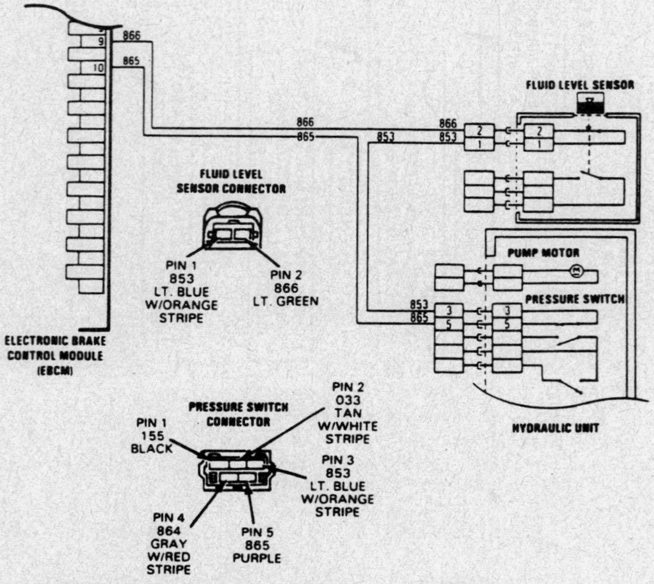

FLUID LEVEL SENSOR
PRESSURE SWITCH
PUMP MOTOR
HYDRAULIC UNIT

866
853
853
866
865
853
865

FLUID LEVEL SENSOR CONNECTOR
PIN 2 866 LT. GREEN
PIN 1 853 LT. BLUE W/ORANGE STRIPE

PRESSURE SWITCH CONNECTOR
PIN 2 033 TAN W/WHITE STRIPE
PIN 3 853 LT. BLUE W/ORANGE STRIPE
PIN 5 865 PURPLE
PIN 4 864 GRAY W/RED STRIPE
PIN 1 155 BLACK

ELECTRONIC BRAKE CONTROL MODULE (EBCM)

Fig. 56   EBCM loop circuit schematic. 1988-90 6000

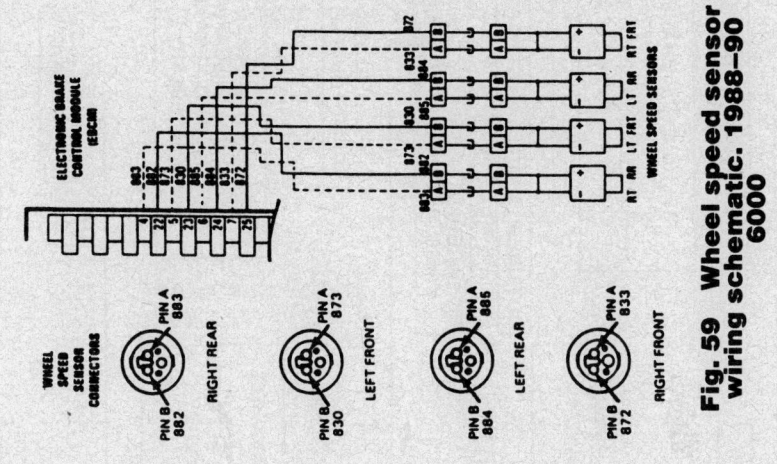

Fig. 59 Wheel speed sensor wiring schematic. 1988-90 6000

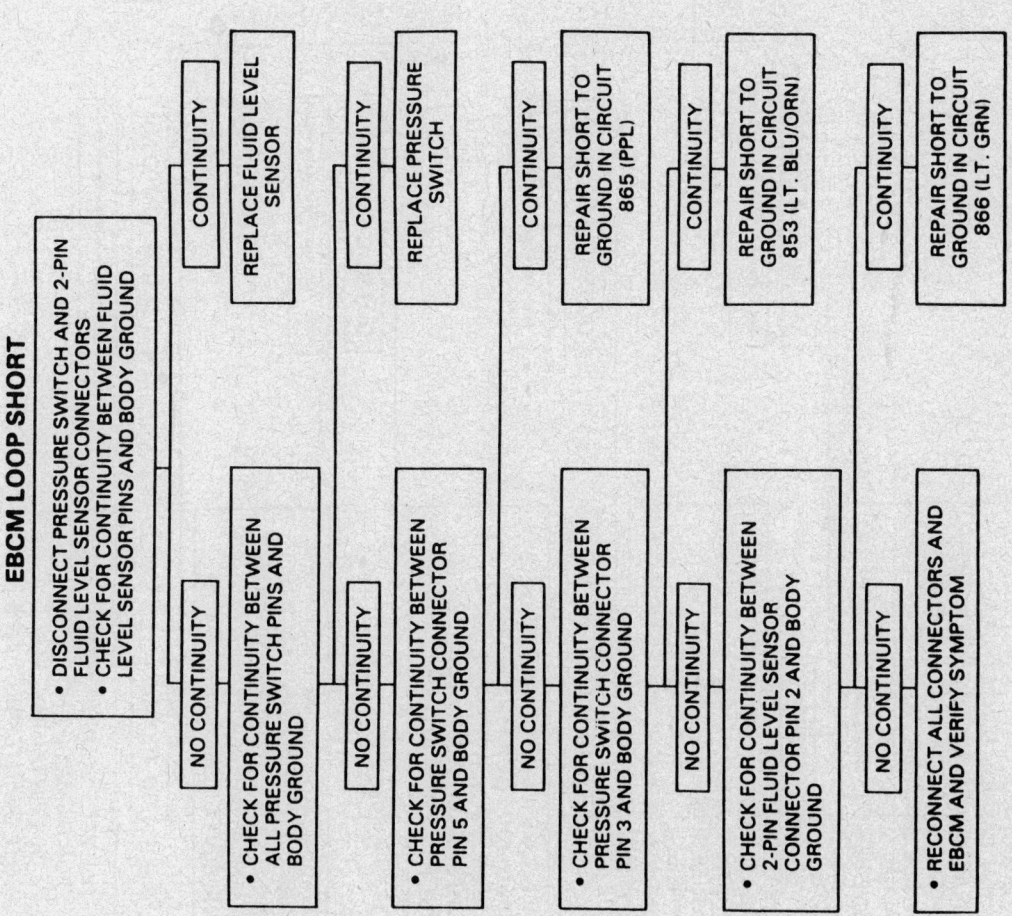

Fig. 58 EBCM loop short. 1988-90 6000

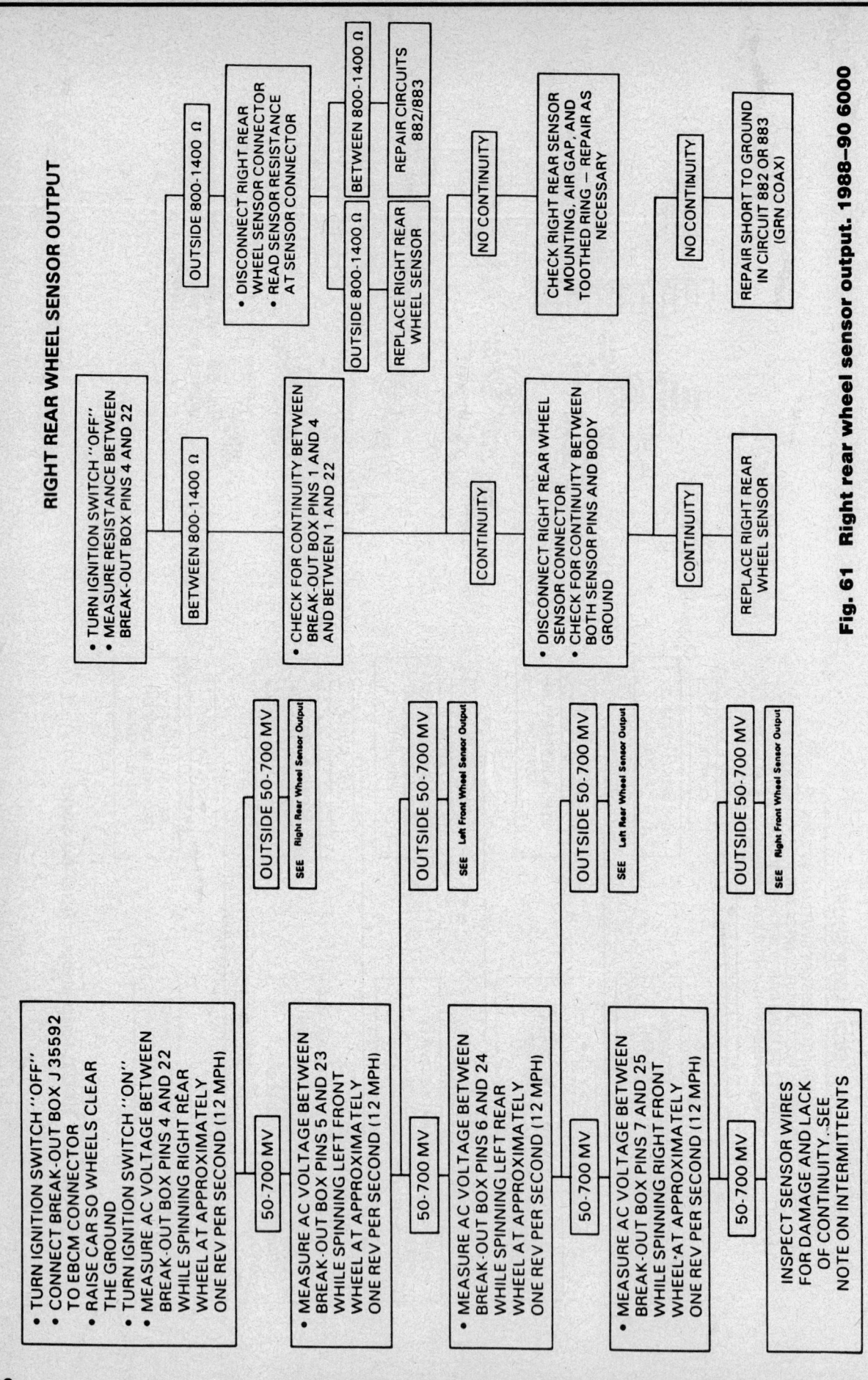

RIGHT REAR WHEEL SENSOR OUTPUT

Fig. 61 Right rear wheel sensor output. 1988–90 6000

WHEEL SPEED SENSOR OUTPUT

Fig. 60 Wheel speed sensor output. 1988–90 6000

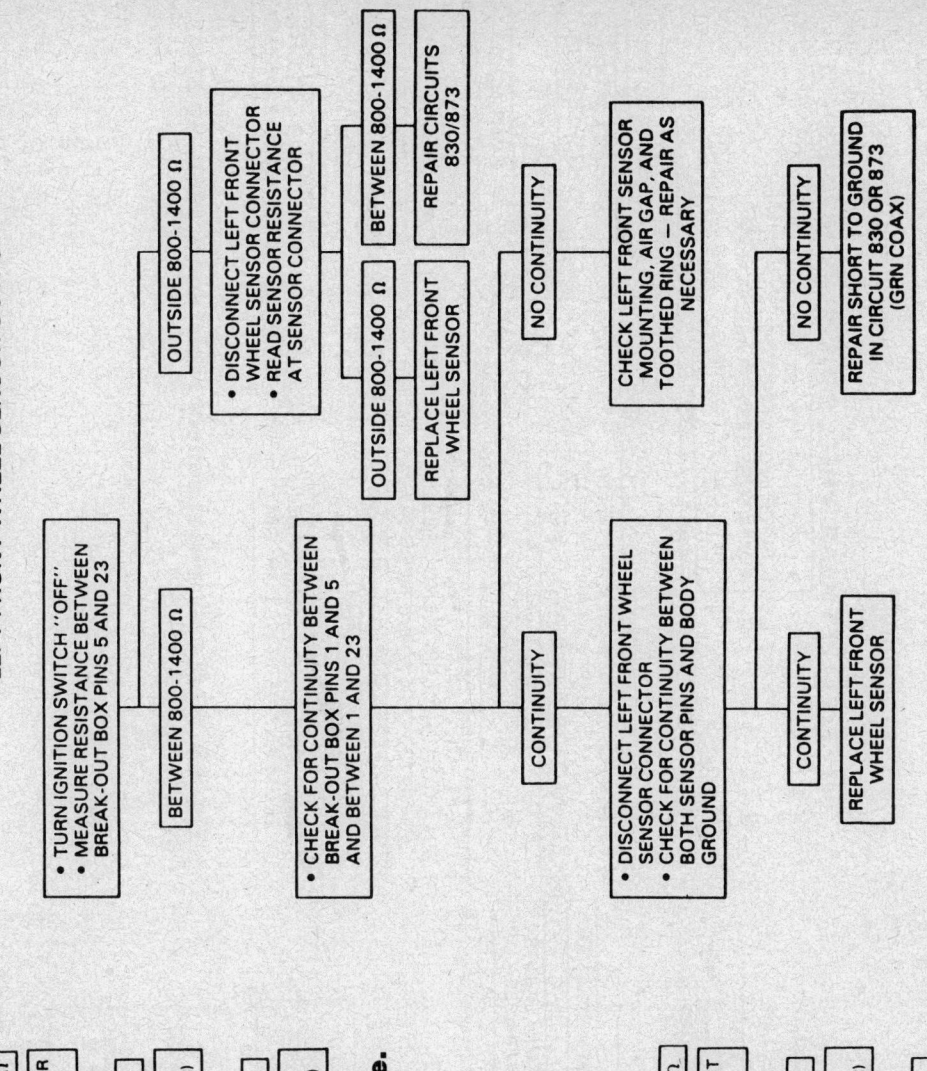

LEFT FRONT WHEEL SENSOR OUTPUT

- TURN IGNITION SWITCH "OFF"
- MEASURE RESISTANCE BETWEEN BREAK-OUT BOX PINS 5 AND 23

OUTSIDE 800-1400 Ω
- DISCONNECT LEFT FRONT WHEEL SENSOR CONNECTOR
- READ SENSOR RESISTANCE AT SENSOR CONNECTOR
  - BETWEEN 800-1400 Ω → REPAIR CIRCUITS 830/873
  - OUTSIDE 800-1400 Ω → REPLACE LEFT FRONT WHEEL SENSOR

BETWEEN 800-1400 Ω
- CHECK FOR CONTINUITY BETWEEN BREAK-OUT BOX PINS 1 AND 5 AND BETWEEN 1 AND 23
  - NO CONTINUITY → CHECK LEFT FRONT SENSOR MOUNTING, AIR GAP, AND TOOTHED RING – REPAIR AS NECESSARY
    - NO CONTINUITY → REPAIR SHORT TO GROUND IN CIRCUIT 830 OR 873 (GRN COAX)
    - CONTINUITY → REPLACE LEFT FRONT WHEEL SENSOR
  - CONTINUITY → DISCONNECT LEFT FRONT WHEEL SENSOR CONNECTOR / CHECK FOR CONTINUITY BETWEEN BOTH SENSOR PINS AND BODY GROUND

Fig. 63 Left front wheel sensor output. 1988–90 6000

RIGHT REAR WHEEL SENSOR RESISTANCE

- DISCONNECT RIGHT REAR SENSOR CONNECTOR
- MEASURE SENSOR RESISTANCE AT CONNECTOR PINS
  - OUTSIDE 800-1400 Ω → REPLACE RIGHT REAR WHEEL SENSOR
  - 800-1400 Ω → CHECK FOR CONTINUITY BETWEEN BREAK-OUT BOX PIN 22 AND SENSOR CONNECTOR PIN B (HARNESS SIDE)
    - NO CONTINUITY → REPAIR CIRCUIT 882 (COAX CENTER)
    - CONTINUITY → CHECK FOR CONTINUITY BETWEEN BREAK-OUT BOX PIN 4 AND SENSOR CONNECTOR PIN A (HARNESS SIDE)
      - NO CONTINUITY → REPAIR CIRCUIT 883 (COAX SHIELD)
      - CONTINUITY → RECONNECT CONNECTOR AND EBCM AND VERIFY SYMPTOM

Fig. 62 Right rear wheel sensor resistance. 1988–90 6000

LEFT FRONT WHEEL SENSOR RESISTANCE

- DISCONNECT LEFT FRONT SENSOR CONNECTOR
- MEASURE SENSOR RESISTANCE AT CONNECTOR PINS
  - OUTSIDE 800-1400 Ω → REPLACE LEFT FRONT WHEEL SENSOR
  - 800-1400 Ω → CHECK FOR CONTINUITY BETWEEN BREAK-OUT BOX PIN 23 AND SENSOR CONNECTOR PIN B (HARNESS SIDE)
    - NO CONTINUITY → REPAIR CIRCUIT 830 (COAX CENTER)
    - CONTINUITY → CHECK FOR CONTINUITY BETWEEN BREAK-OUT BOX PIN 5 AND SENSOR CONNECTOR PIN A (HARNESS SIDE)
      - NO CONTINUITY → REPAIR CIRCUIT 873 (COAX SHIELD)
      - CONTINUITY → RECONNECT CONNECTOR AND EBCM AND VERIFY SYMPTOM

Fig. 64 Left front wheel sensor resistance. 1988–90 6000

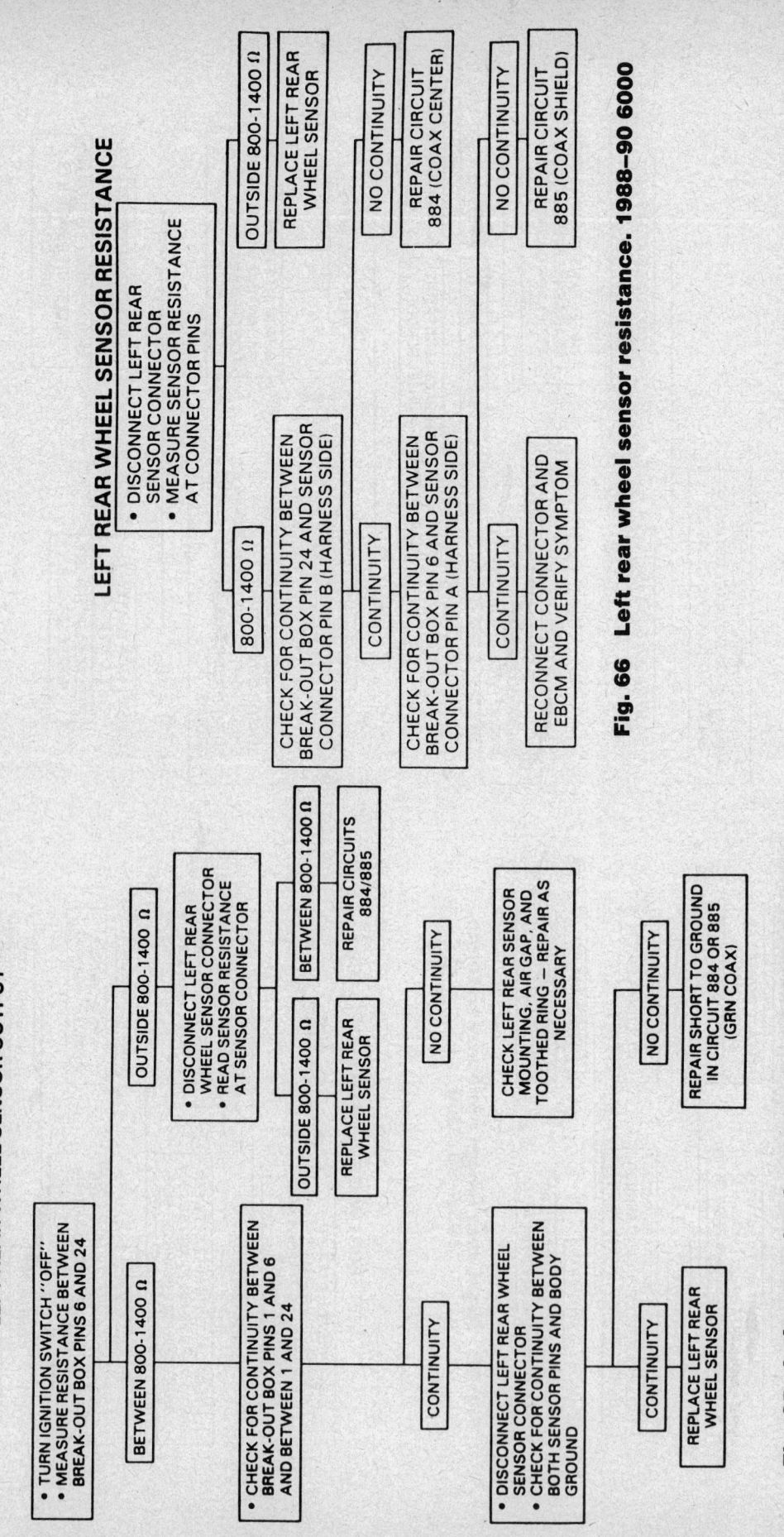

LEFT REAR WHEEL SENSOR RESISTANCE

- DISCONNECT LEFT REAR SENSOR CONNECTOR
- MEASURE SENSOR RESISTANCE AT CONNECTOR PINS

OUTSIDE 800-1400 Ω → REPLACE LEFT REAR WHEEL SENSOR

800-1400 Ω

CHECK FOR CONTINUITY BETWEEN BREAK-OUT BOX PIN 24 AND SENSOR CONNECTOR PIN B (HARNESS SIDE)

NO CONTINUITY → REPAIR CIRCUIT 884 (COAX CENTER)

CONTINUITY

CHECK FOR CONTINUITY BETWEEN BREAK-OUT BOX PIN 6 AND SENSOR CONNECTOR PIN A (HARNESS SIDE)

NO CONTINUITY → REPAIR CIRCUIT 885 (COAX SHIELD)

CONTINUITY

RECONNECT CONNECTOR AND EBCM AND VERIFY SYMPTOM

Fig. 66   Left rear wheel sensor resistance. 1988–90 6000

LEFT REAR WHEEL SENSOR OUTPUT

- TURN IGNITION SWITCH "OFF"
- MEASURE RESISTANCE BETWEEN BREAK-OUT BOX PINS 6 AND 24

BETWEEN 800-1400 Ω

OUTSIDE 800-1400 Ω

- DISCONNECT LEFT REAR WHEEL SENSOR CONNECTOR
- READ SENSOR RESISTANCE AT SENSOR CONNECTOR

BETWEEN 800-1400 Ω → REPAIR CIRCUITS 884/885

OUTSIDE 800-1400 Ω → REPLACE LEFT REAR WHEEL SENSOR

CHECK FOR CONTINUITY BETWEEN BREAK-OUT BOX PINS 1 AND 6 AND BETWEEN 1 AND 24

NO CONTINUITY

CHECK LEFT REAR SENSOR MOUNTING, AIR GAP, AND TOOTHED RING – REPAIR AS NECESSARY

CONTINUITY

DISCONNECT LEFT REAR WHEEL SENSOR CONNECTOR
CHECK FOR CONTINUITY BETWEEN BOTH SENSOR PINS AND BODY GROUND

NO CONTINUITY → REPAIR SHORT TO GROUND IN CIRCUIT 884 OR 885 (GRN COAX)

CONTINUITY → REPLACE LEFT REAR WHEEL SENSOR

Fig. 65   Left rear wheel sensor output. 1988–90 6000

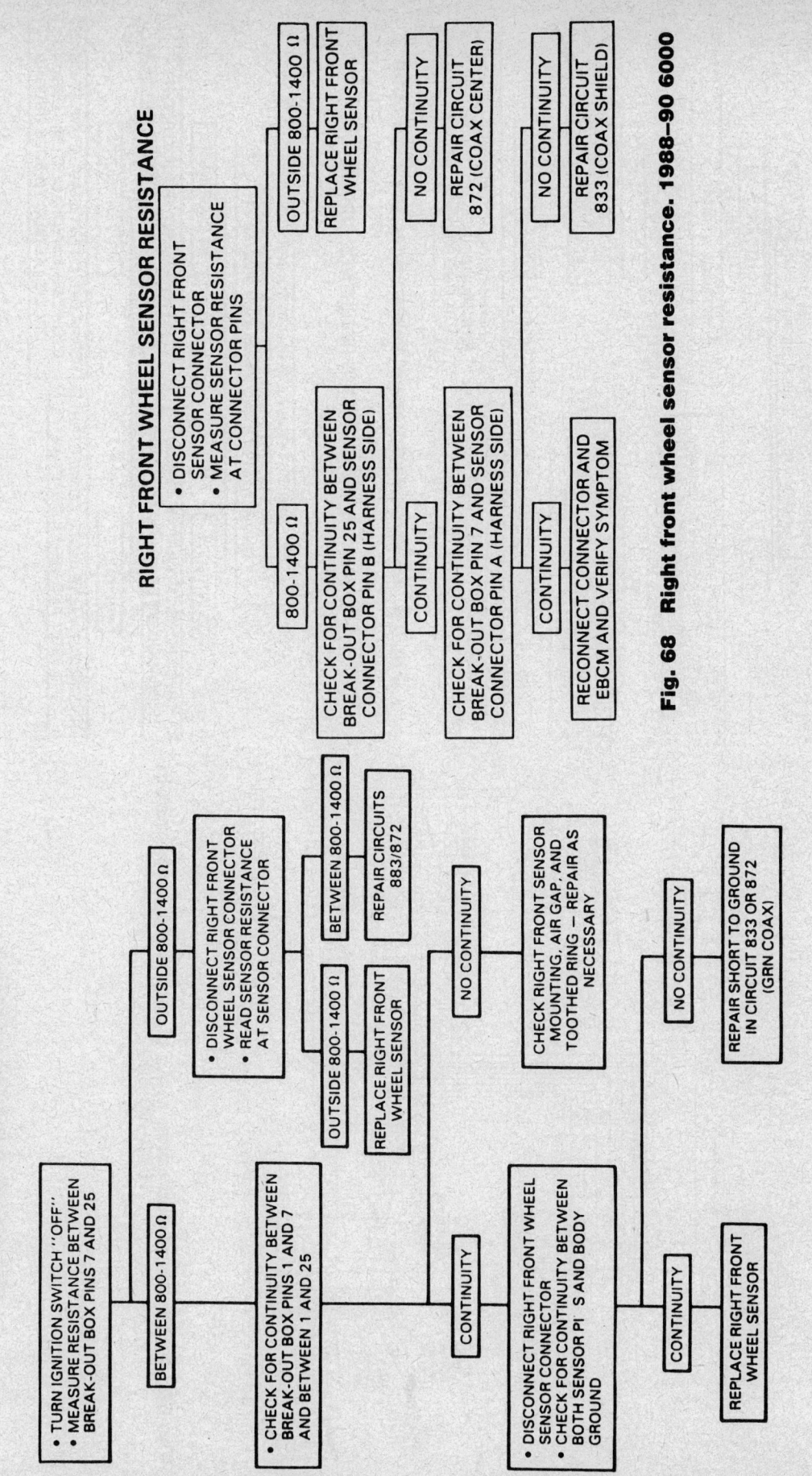

RIGHT FRONT WHEEL SENSOR RESISTANCE

- DISCONNECT RIGHT FRONT SENSOR CONNECTOR
- MEASURE SENSOR RESISTANCE AT CONNECTOR PINS

OUTSIDE 800-1400 Ω → REPLACE RIGHT FRONT WHEEL SENSOR

800-1400 Ω → CHECK FOR CONTINUITY BETWEEN BREAK-OUT BOX PIN 25 AND SENSOR CONNECTOR PIN B (HARNESS SIDE)

NO CONTINUITY → REPAIR CIRCUIT 872 (COAX CENTER)

CONTINUITY → CHECK FOR CONTINUITY BETWEEN BREAK-OUT BOX PIN 7 AND SENSOR CONNECTOR PIN A (HARNESS SIDE)

NO CONTINUITY → REPAIR CIRCUIT 833 (COAX SHIELD)

CONTINUITY → RECONNECT CONNECTOR AND EBCM AND VERIFY SYMPTOM

Fig. 68   Right front wheel sensor resistance. 1988–90 6000

RIGHT FRONT WHEEL SENSOR OUTPUT

- TURN IGNITION SWITCH "OFF"
- MEASURE RESISTANCE BETWEEN BREAK-OUT BOX PINS 7 AND 25

OUTSIDE 800-1400 Ω → DISCONNECT RIGHT FRONT WHEEL SENSOR CONNECTOR; READ SENSOR RESISTANCE AT SENSOR CONNECTOR

BETWEEN 800-1400 Ω → REPAIR CIRCUITS 883/872

OUTSIDE 800-1400 Ω → REPLACE RIGHT FRONT WHEEL SENSOR

BETWEEN 800-1400 Ω → CHECK FOR CONTINUITY BETWEEN BREAK-OUT BOX PINS 1 AND 7 AND BETWEEN 1 AND 25

NO CONTINUITY → CHECK RIGHT FRONT SENSOR MOUNTING, AIR GAP, AND TOOTHED RING — REPAIR AS NECESSARY

CONTINUITY → DISCONNECT RIGHT FRONT WHEEL SENSOR CONNECTOR; CHECK FOR CONTINUITY BETWEEN BOTH SENSOR PI'S AND BODY GROUND

NO CONTINUITY → REPAIR SHORT TO GROUND IN CIRCUIT 833 OR 872 (GRN COAX)

CONTINUITY → REPLACE RIGHT FRONT WHEEL SENSOR

Fig. 67   Right front wheel sensor output. 1988–90 6000

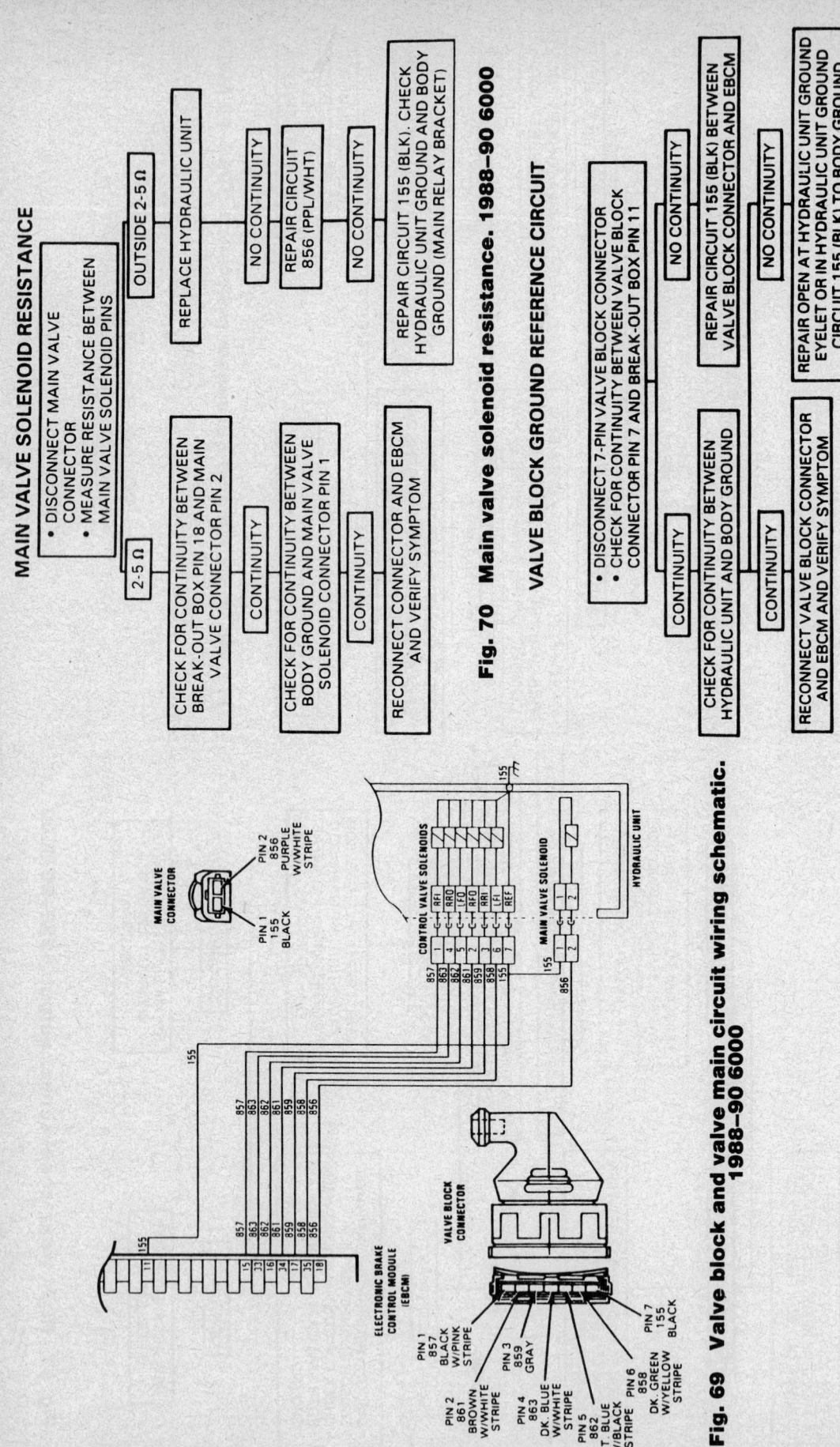

MAIN VALVE SOLENOID RESISTANCE

- DISCONNECT MAIN VALVE CONNECTOR
- MEASURE RESISTANCE BETWEEN MAIN VALVE SOLENOID PINS

OUTSIDE 2-5 Ω → REPLACE HYDRAULIC UNIT

NO CONTINUITY → REPAIR CIRCUIT 856 (PPL/WHT)

NO CONTINUITY → REPAIR CIRCUIT 155 (BLK). CHECK HYDRAULIC UNIT GROUND AND BODY GROUND (MAIN RELAY BRACKET)

2-5 Ω → CHECK FOR CONTINUITY BETWEEN BREAK-OUT BOX PIN 18 AND MAIN VALVE CONNECTOR PIN 2

CONTINUITY → CHECK FOR CONTINUITY BETWEEN BODY GROUND AND MAIN VALVE SOLENOID CONNECTOR PIN 1

CONTINUITY → RECONNECT CONNECTOR AND EBCM AND VERIFY SYMPTOM

Fig. 70 Main valve solenoid resistance. 1988–90 6000

VALVE BLOCK GROUND REFERENCE CIRCUIT

- DISCONNECT 7-PIN VALVE BLOCK CONNECTOR
- CHECK FOR CONTINUITY BETWEEN VALVE BLOCK CONNECTOR PIN 7 AND BREAK-OUT BOX PIN 11

NO CONTINUITY → REPAIR CIRCUIT 155 (BLK) BETWEEN VALVE BLOCK CONNECTOR AND EBCM

NO CONTINUITY → REPAIR OPEN AT HYDRAULIC UNIT GROUND EYELET OR IN HYDRAULIC UNIT GROUND CIRCUIT 155 (BLK) TO BODY GROUND

CONTINUITY → CHECK FOR CONTINUITY BETWEEN HYDRAULIC UNIT AND BODY GROUND

CONTINUITY → RECONNECT VALVE BLOCK CONNECTOR AND EBCM AND VERIFY SYMPTOM

Fig. 71 Valve block ground reference circuit. 1988–90 6000

Fig. 69 Valve block and valve main circuit wiring schematic. 1988–90 6000

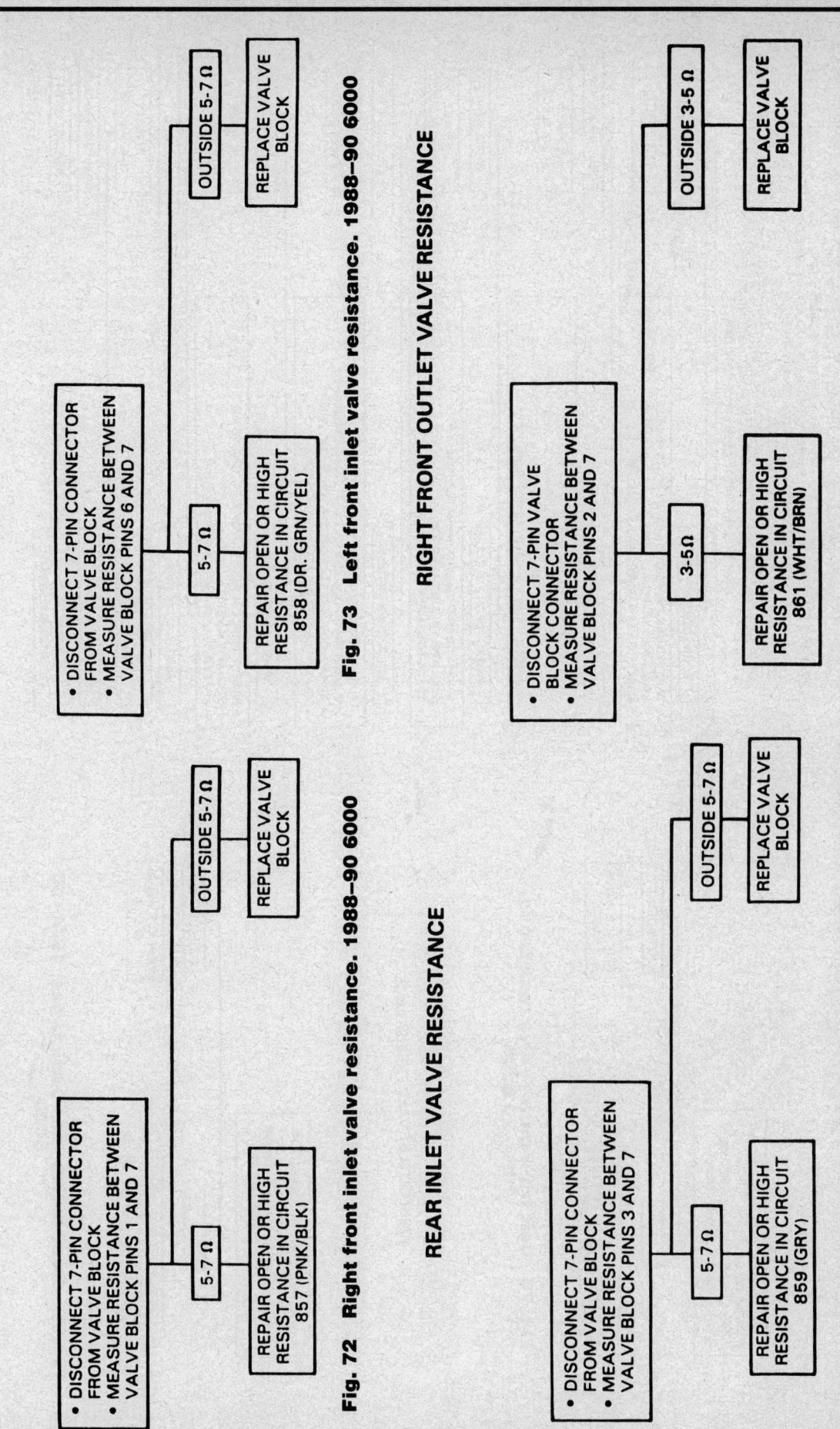

RIGHT FRONT INLET VALVE RESISTANCE

- DISCONNECT 7-PIN CONNECTOR FROM VALVE BLOCK
- MEASURE RESISTANCE BETWEEN VALVE BLOCK PINS 1 AND 7

5-7 Ω → REPAIR OPEN OR HIGH RESISTANCE IN CIRCUIT 857 (PNK/BLK)

OUTSIDE 5-7 Ω → REPLACE VALVE BLOCK

Fig. 72   Right front inlet valve resistance. 1988–90 6000

LEFT FRONT INLET VALVE RESISTANCE

- DISCONNECT 7-PIN CONNECTOR FROM VALVE BLOCK
- MEASURE RESISTANCE BETWEEN VALVE BLOCK PINS 6 AND 7

5-7 Ω → REPAIR OPEN OR HIGH RESISTANCE IN CIRCUIT 858 (DR. GRN/YEL)

OUTSIDE 5-7 Ω → REPLACE VALVE BLOCK

Fig. 73   Left front inlet valve resistance. 1988–90 6000

REAR INLET VALVE RESISTANCE

- DISCONNECT 7-PIN CONNECTOR FROM VALVE BLOCK
- MEASURE RESISTANCE BETWEEN VALVE BLOCK PINS 3 AND 7

5-7 Ω → REPAIR OPEN OR HIGH RESISTANCE IN CIRCUIT 859 (GRY)

OUTSIDE 5-7 Ω → REPLACE VALVE BLOCK

Fig. 74   Rear inlet valve resistance. 1988–90 6000

RIGHT FRONT OUTLET VALVE RESISTANCE

- DISCONNECT 7-PIN VALVE BLOCK CONNECTOR
- MEASURE RESISTANCE BETWEEN VALVE BLOCK PINS 2 AND 7

3-5 Ω → REPAIR OPEN OR HIGH RESISTANCE IN CIRCUIT 861 (WHT/BRN)

OUTSIDE 3-5 Ω → REPLACE VALVE BLOCK

Fig. 75   Right front outlet valve resistance. 1988–90 6000

SOLENOID VALVE OPERATION

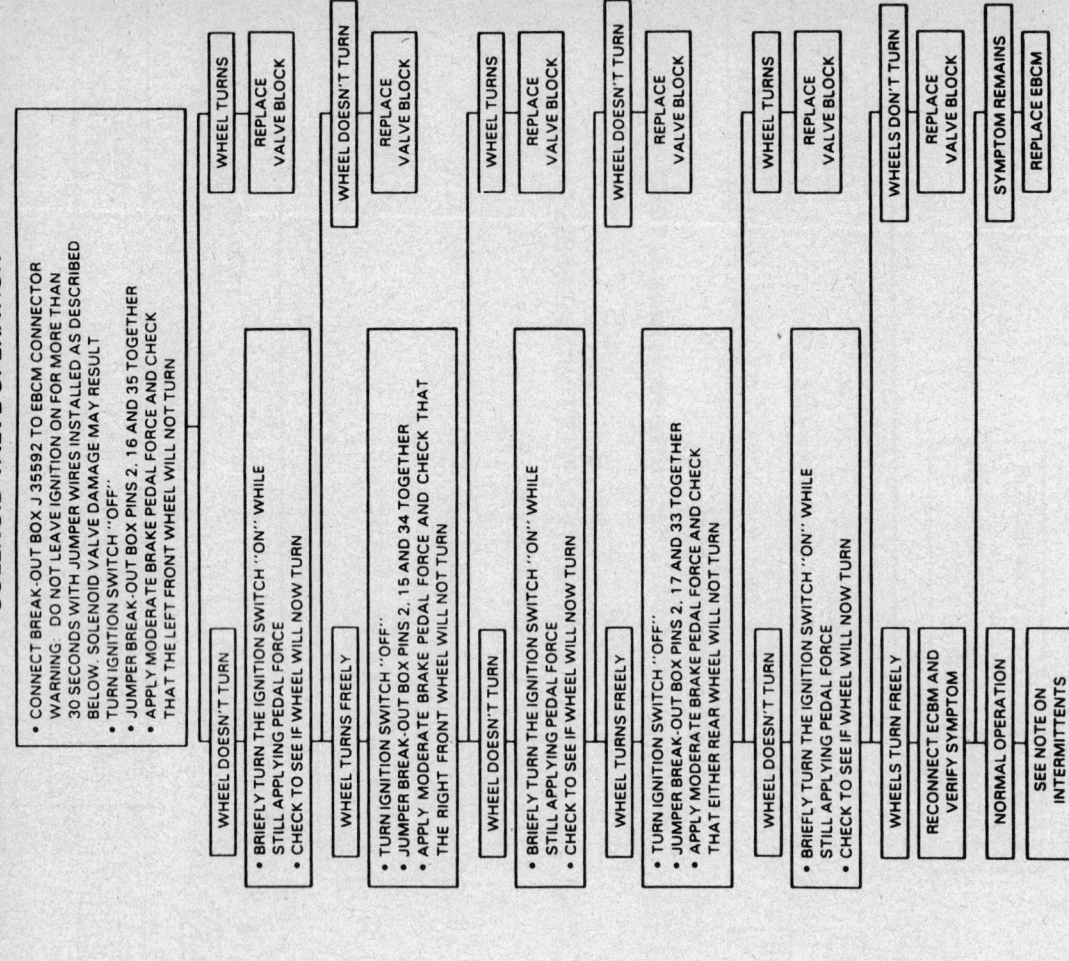

- CONNECT BREAK-OUT BOX J 35592 TO EBCM CONNECTOR
  WARNING: DO NOT LEAVE IGNITION ON FOR MORE THAN
  30 SECONDS WITH JUMPER WIRES INSTALLED AS DESCRIBED
  BELOW. SOLENOID VALVE DAMAGE MAY RESULT
- TURN IGNITION SWITCH "OFF"
- JUMPER BREAK-OUT BOX PINS 2, 16 AND 35 TOGETHER
- APPLY MODERATE BRAKE PEDAL FORCE AND CHECK
  THAT THE LEFT FRONT WHEEL WILL NOT TURN

WHEEL DOESN'T TURN
- BRIEFLY TURN THE IGNITION SWITCH "ON" WHILE
  STILL APPLYING PEDAL FORCE
- CHECK TO SEE IF WHEEL WILL NOW TURN

WHEEL TURNS → REPLACE VALVE BLOCK

WHEEL TURNS FREELY
- TURN IGNITION SWITCH "OFF"
- JUMPER BREAK-OUT BOX PINS 2, 15 AND 34 TOGETHER
- APPLY MODERATE BRAKE PEDAL FORCE AND CHECK THAT
  THE RIGHT FRONT WHEEL WILL NOT TURN

WHEEL DOESN'T TURN → REPLACE VALVE BLOCK

WHEEL DOESN'T TURN
- BRIEFLY TURN THE IGNITION SWITCH "ON" WHILE
  STILL APPLYING PEDAL FORCE
- CHECK TO SEE IF WHEEL WILL NOW TURN

WHEEL TURNS → REPLACE VALVE BLOCK

WHEEL TURNS FREELY
- TURN IGNITION SWITCH "OFF"
- JUMPER BREAK-OUT BOX PINS 2, 17 AND 33 TOGETHER
- APPLY MODERATE BRAKE PEDAL FORCE AND CHECK
  THAT EITHER REAR WHEEL WILL NOT TURN

WHEEL DOESN'T TURN → REPLACE VALVE BLOCK

WHEEL DOESN'T TURN
- BRIEFLY TURN THE IGNITION SWITCH "ON" WHILE
  STILL APPLYING PEDAL FORCE
- CHECK TO SEE IF WHEEL WILL NOW TURN

WHEEL TURNS → REPLACE VALVE BLOCK

WHEELS TURN FREELY
- RECONNECT ECBM AND VERIFY SYMPTOM

WHEELS DON'T TURN → REPLACE VALVE BLOCK

NORMAL OPERATION

SYMPTOM REMAINS → REPLACE EBCM

SEE NOTE ON INTERMITTENTS

Fig. 78 Solenoid valve operation. 1988-90 6000

LEFT FRONT OUTLET VALVE RESISTANCE

- DISCONNECT 7-PIN CONNECTOR
  FROM VALVE BLOCK
- MEASURE RESISTANCE BETWEEN
  VALVE BLOCK PINS 5 AND 7

OUTSIDE 3-5 Ω → REPLACE VALVE BLOCK

3-5 Ω → REPAIR OPEN OR HIGH RESISTANCE IN CIRCUIT 862 (LT. BLU/BLK)

Fig. 76 Left front outlet valve resistance. 1988-90 6000

REAR OUTLET VALVE RESISTANCE

- DISCONNECT 7-PIN CONNECTOR
  FROM VALVE BLOCK
- MEASURE RESISTANCE BETWEEN
  VALVE BLOCK PINS 4 AND 7

OUTSIDE 3-5 Ω → REPLACE VALVE BLOCK

3-5 Ω → REPAIR OPEN OR HIGH RESISTANCE IN CIRCUIT 863 (DK. BLU/WHT)

Fig. 77 Rear outlet valve resistance. 1988-90 6000

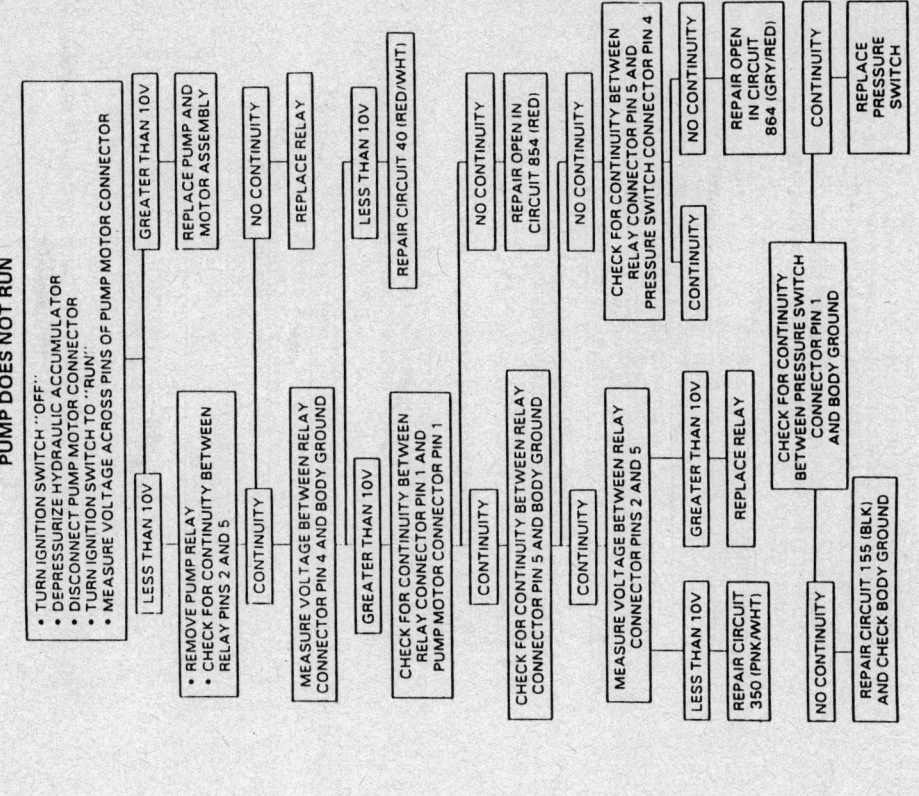

PUMP DOES NOT RUN

- TURN IGNITION SWITCH "OFF"
- DEPRESSURIZE HYDRAULIC ACCUMULATOR
- DISCONNECT PUMP MOTOR CONNECTOR
- TURN IGNITION SWITCH TO "RUN"
- MEASURE VOLTAGE ACROSS PINS OF PUMP MOTOR CONNECTOR

Fig. 80 Pump inoperative. 1988–90 6000

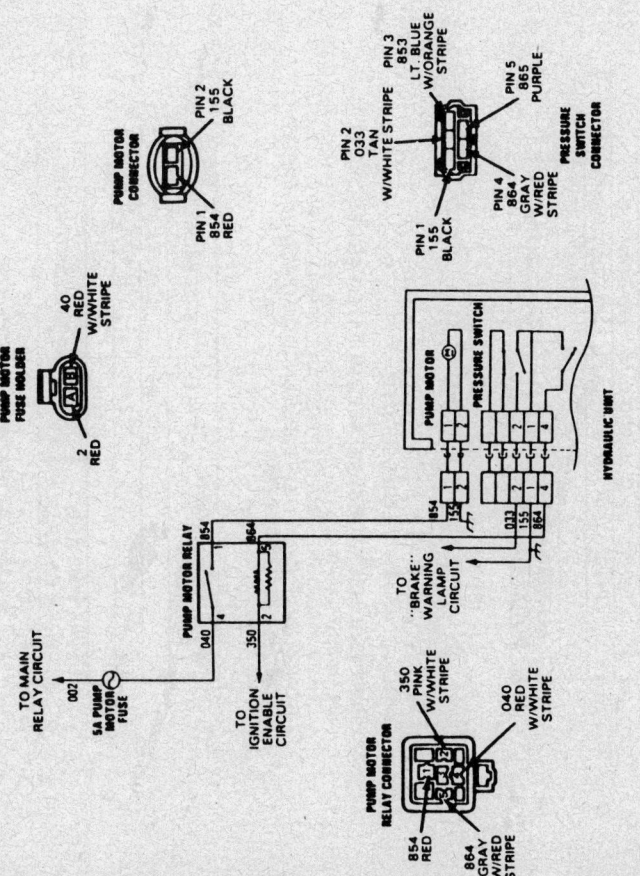

Fig. 79 Pump motor circuit schematic. 1988–90 6000

PRESSURE SWITCH PERFORMANCE

I. SWITCH STATUS — PRESSURIZED

• TURN IGNITION SWITCH TO "RUN" UNTIL PUMP STOPS
• TURN IGNITION SWITCH "OFF"
  NOTE: IF PUMP CONTINUES TO RUN AFTER 45 SECONDS, TURN IGNITION SWITCH OFF AND PROCEED
• CHECK PRESSURE SWITCH PINS FOR THE FOLLOWING CONDITIONS USING HIGH IMPEDANCE DIGITAL MULTIMETER J34029-A OR EQUIVALENT

MEASURE BETWEEN PINS	SCALE	SPECIFICATION
1, 2	200 Ω	NO CONTINUITY
1, 4	200 Ω	NO CONTINUITY
3, 5	200 Ω	CONTINUITY
ALL PINS AND BODY GROUND	200 Ω	NO CONTINUITY

IF ANY CONDITION IS NOT MET, REPLACE PRESSURE SWITCH

II. SWITCH STATUS — DEPRESSURIZED

• DEPRESSURIZE HYDRAULIC ACCUMULATOR AS DESCRIBED IN THIS SECTION
• CHECK PRESSURE SWITCH PINS FOR THE FOLLOWING CONDITIONS USING HIGH IMPEDANCE DIGITAL MULTIMETER J34029-A OR EQUIVALENT

MEASURE BETWEEN PINS	SCALE	SPECIFICATION
1, 2	200 Ω	CONTINUITY
1, 4	200 Ω	CONTINUITY
3, 5	200 Ω	NO CONTINUITY
ALL PINS AND BODY GROUND	200 Ω	NO CONTINUITY

IF ANY CONDITION IS NOT MET, REPLACE PRESSURE SWITCH

CONTINUED →

Fig. 81 Pressure switch performance, (Part 1 of 2). 1988–90 6000

PRESSURE SWITCH PERFORMANCE (CONT.)

III. SWITCH THRESHOLDS

• DEPRESSURIZE HYDRAULIC ACCUMULATOR AS DESCRIBED IN THIS SECTION
• INSTALL PRESSURE GAGE J 35604 AS DESCRIBED IN THIS SECTION
• CONNECT PRESSURE SWITCH CONNECTOR AND TURN IGNITION SWITCH TO "RUN" UNTIL PUMP STOPS
• USING HIGH IMPEDANCE DIGITAL MULTIMETER J34029-A OR EQUIVALENT, MONITOR FOR CONTINUITY BETWEEN PRESSURE SWITCH PINS AS SHOWN BELOW WHILE SLOWLY BLEEDING OFF ACCUMULATOR PRESSURE BY PUMPING THE BRAKE PEDAL. CONTINUITY SHOULD BE GAINED OR LOST AS INDICATED.
• PRESSURIZE SYSTEM BETWEEN EACH TEST BY RECONNECTING PRESSURE SWITCH AND TURNING IGNITION SWITCH TO "RUN" UNTIL PUMP STOPS

MEASURE BETWEEN PINS	SWITCH STATUS	PRESSURE RANGE
1, 4	CONTINUITY SHOULD BE GAINED AT:	1980-2080 PSI (13,650-14,350 KPA)
1, 2	CONTINUITY SHOULD BE GAINED AT:	1500-1550 PSI (10,350-10,700 KPA)
3, 5	CONTINUITY SHOULD BE LOST AT:	1500-1550 PSI (10,350-10,700 KPA)

IF ANY CONDITION IS NOT MET, REPLACE PRESSURE SWITCH

• DEPRESSURIZE HYDRAULIC ACCUMULATOR AS DESCRIBED IN THIS SECTION
• WITH IGNITION "OFF," CONNECT PRESSURE SWITCH CONNECTOR
• TURN IGNITION TO "RUN" AND OBSERVE GAGE, "ANTILOCK" LAMP, "BRAKE" LAMP AND PUMP MOTOR. EVENTS SHOULD OCCUR AT PRESSURES INDICATED IN CHART BELOW

EVENT	PRESSURE
"ANTILOCK" LAMP TURNS OFF	1900-1975 PSI (13,100-13,600 KPA)
"BRAKE" LAMP TURNS OFF	1900-1975 PSI (13,100-13,600 KPA)
PUMP MOTOR STOPS	2550-2670 PSI (17,580-18,400 KPA)

IF ANY CONDITION IS NOT MET, REPLACE PRESSURE SWITCH

Fig. 81 Pressure switch performance, (Part 2 of 2). 1988–90 6000

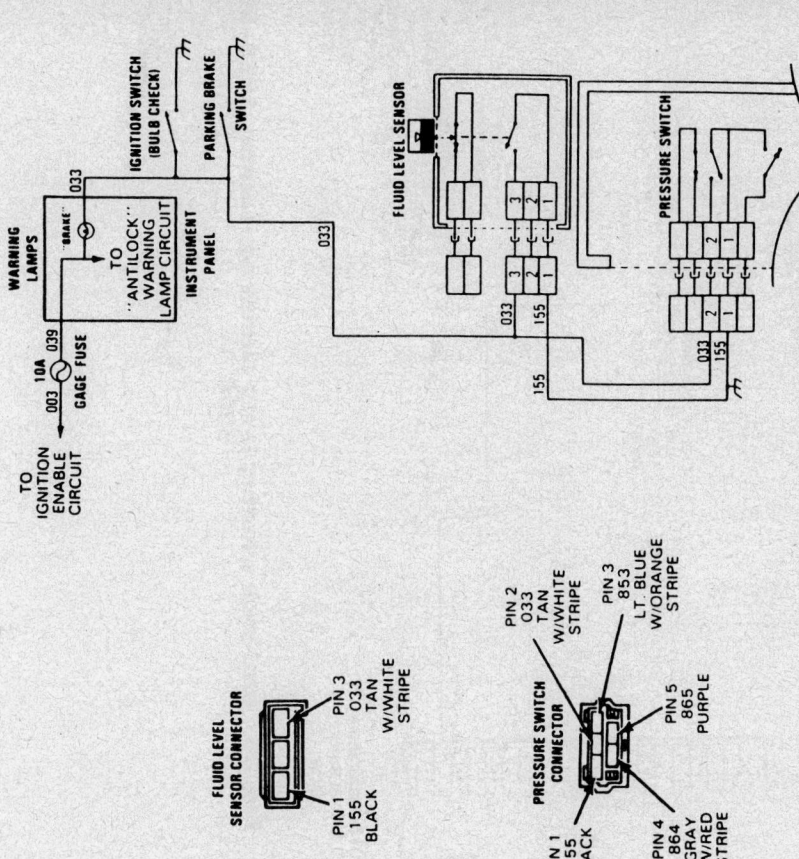

Fig. 83 Brake warning lamp circuit schematic. 1988–90 6000

FLUID LEVEL
SENSOR CONNECTOR

PIN 3
033
TAN
W/WHITE
STRIPE

PIN 1
155
BLACK

PRESSURE SWITCH
CONNECTOR

PIN 2
033
TAN
W/WHITE
STRIPE

PIN 3
853
LT. BLUE
W/ORANGE
STRIPE

PIN 5
865
PURPLE

PIN 1
155
BLACK

PIN 4
864
GRAY
W/RED
STRIPE

INTERMITTENT "ANTILOCK" WARNING LAMP WHILE DRIVING

INTERRUPTIONS IN THE FOLLOWING CIRCUITS MAY CAUSE THE "ANTILOCK" LAMP TO LIGHT INTERMITTENTLY. THIS LIST DOES NOT INCLUDE ALL POSSIBILITIES, BUT INCLUDES THOSE CIRCUITS MOST LIKELY TO CAUSE THE "ANTILOCK" WARNING LAMP TO LIGHT INTERMITTENTLY.

• EBCM SWITCH LOOP, INCLUDING
 – CIRCUIT 866 (LT. GRN) FROM EBCM TO FLUID LEVEL SENSOR
 – 2-PIN FLUID LEVEL SENSOR SWITCH
 – CIRCUIT 853 (LT. BLU/ORN) FROM FLUID LEVEL SENSOR TO PRESSURE SWITCH
 – CIRCUIT 865 (PPL) FROM PRESSURE SWITCH TO EBCM

• IGNITION ENABLE CIRCUIT, INCLUDING
 – BRAKE FUSE (#5 IN CONVENIENCE CENTER 5A)
 – CIRCUIT 350 (PNK/WHT) FROM RELAY COIL TO GROUND
 – DIFFERENTIAL LOCK ENGAGED SWITCH AND JUMPER (ALL WHEEL DRIVE)
 – 951 CIRCUIT TO DIFFERENTIAL LOCK CONTROL RELAY IN THE CONSOLE (ALL WHEEL DRIVE)

• MAIN RELAY CIRCUITS, INCLUDING
 – CIRCUIT 855 (DK. BLU) FROM EBCM TO RELAY COIL
 – CIRCUIT 450 (BLK/WHT) FROM RELAY COIL TO GROUND

• ALL WHEEL SPEED SENSOR CIRCUITS

INSPECT CONNECTORS AND WIRES IN THESE CIRCUITS. IF NO TROUBLE IS FOUND, SEE NOTE ON INTERMITTENTS IN THIS SECTION AND PERFORM.

Fig. 82 Intermittent anti-lock warning lamp. 1988–90 6000

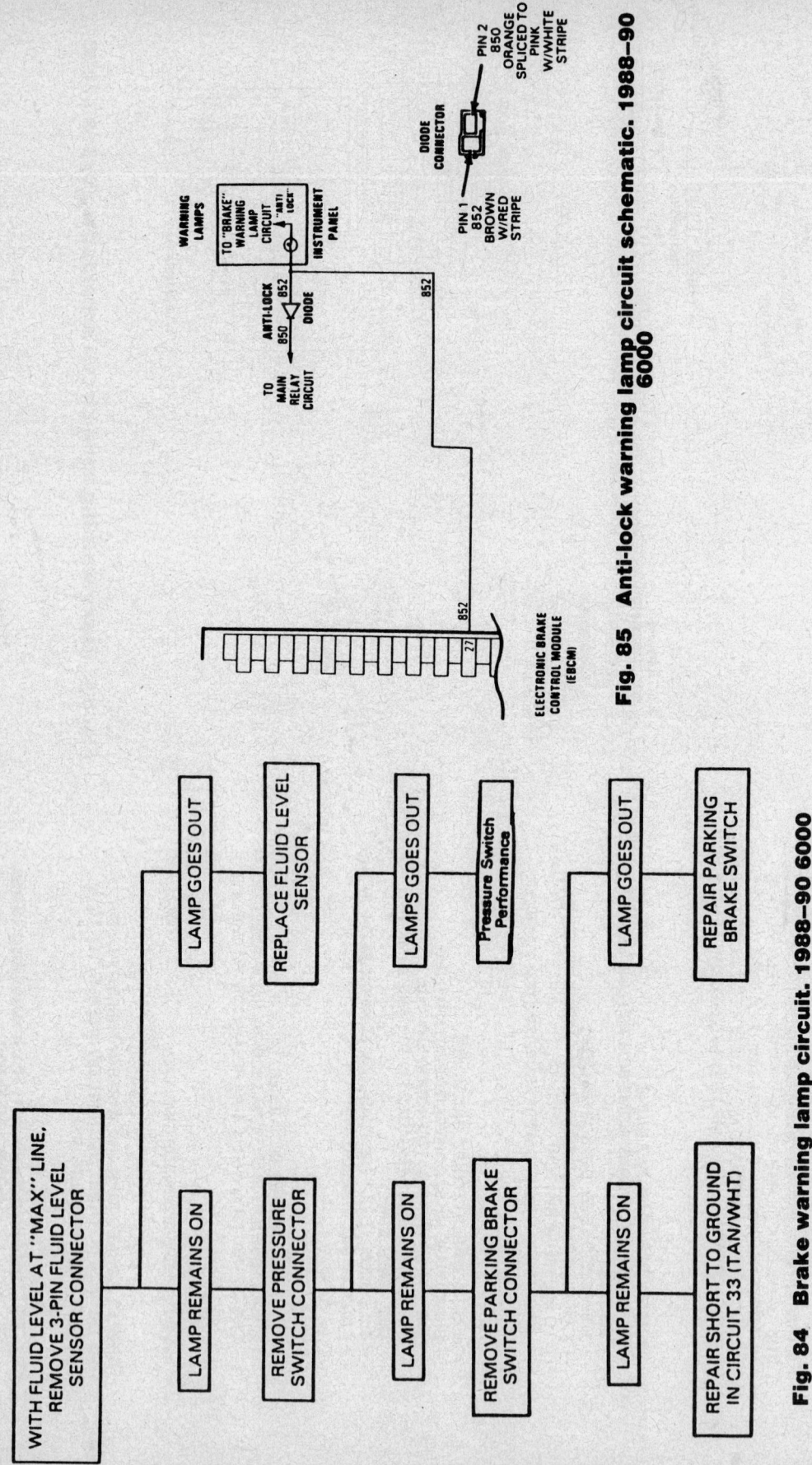

Fig. 85 Anti-lock warning lamp circuit schematic. 1988-90 6000

Fig. 84 Brake warning lamp circuit. 1988-90 6000

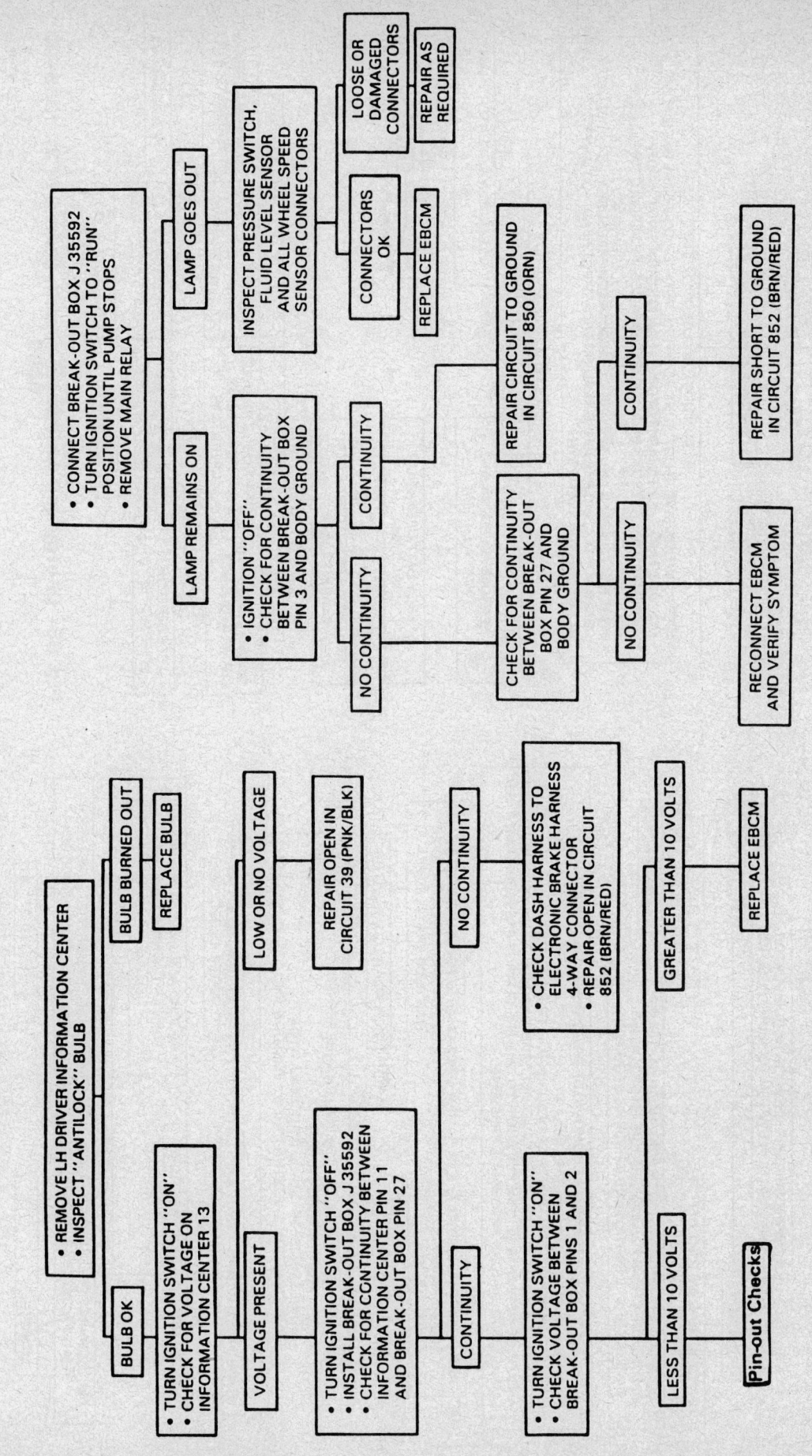

"ANTILOCK" WARNING LAMP CIRCUIT

- CONNECT BREAK-OUT BOX J 35592
- TURN IGNITION SWITCH TO "RUN" POSITION UNTIL PUMP STOPS
- REMOVE MAIN RELAY

LAMP GOES OUT → INSPECT PRESSURE SWITCH, FLUID LEVEL SENSOR AND ALL WHEEL SPEED SENSOR CONNECTORS

- LOOSE OR DAMAGED CONNECTORS → REPAIR AS REQUIRED
- CONNECTORS OK → REPLACE EBCM

LAMP REMAINS ON →
- IGNITION "OFF"
- CHECK FOR CONTINUITY BETWEEN BREAK-OUT BOX PIN 3 AND BODY GROUND

- NO CONTINUITY → CHECK FOR CONTINUITY BETWEEN BREAK-OUT BOX PIN 27 AND BODY GROUND
  - CONTINUITY → RECONNECT EBCM AND VERIFY SYMPTOM
  - NO CONTINUITY → RECONNECT EBCM AND VERIFY SYMPTOM
- CONTINUITY → REPAIR CIRCUIT TO GROUND IN CIRCUIT 850 (ORN)
  - CONTINUITY → REPAIR SHORT TO GROUND IN CIRCUIT 852 (BRN/RED)

Fig. 87 Anti-lock warning lamp circuit. 1988–90 6000

"ANTILOCK" WARNING LAMP INOPERATIVE

- REMOVE LH DRIVER INFORMATION CENTER
- INSPECT "ANTILOCK" BULB

- **BULB BURNED OUT** → REPLACE BULB
- **BULB OK** →
  - TURN IGNITION SWITCH "ON"
  - CHECK FOR VOLTAGE ON INFORMATION CENTER 13

  - **LOW OR NO VOLTAGE** → REPAIR OPEN IN CIRCUIT 39 (PNK/BLK)
  - **VOLTAGE PRESENT** →
    - TURN IGNITION SWITCH "OFF"
    - INSTALL BREAK-OUT BOX J 35592
    - CHECK FOR CONTINUITY BETWEEN INFORMATION CENTER PIN 11 AND BREAK-OUT BOX PIN 27

    - **NO CONTINUITY** →
      - CHECK DASH HARNESS TO ELECTRONIC BRAKE HARNESS 4-WAY CONNECTOR
      - REPAIR OPEN IN CIRCUIT 852 (BRN/RED)
    - **CONTINUITY** →
      - TURN IGNITION SWITCH "ON"
      - CHECK VOLTAGE BETWEEN BREAK-OUT BOX PINS 1 AND 2

      - **GREATER THAN 10 VOLTS** → REPLACE EBCM
      - **LESS THAN 10 VOLTS** → **Pin-out Checks**

Fig. 86 Anti-lock warning lamp inoperative. 1988–90 6000

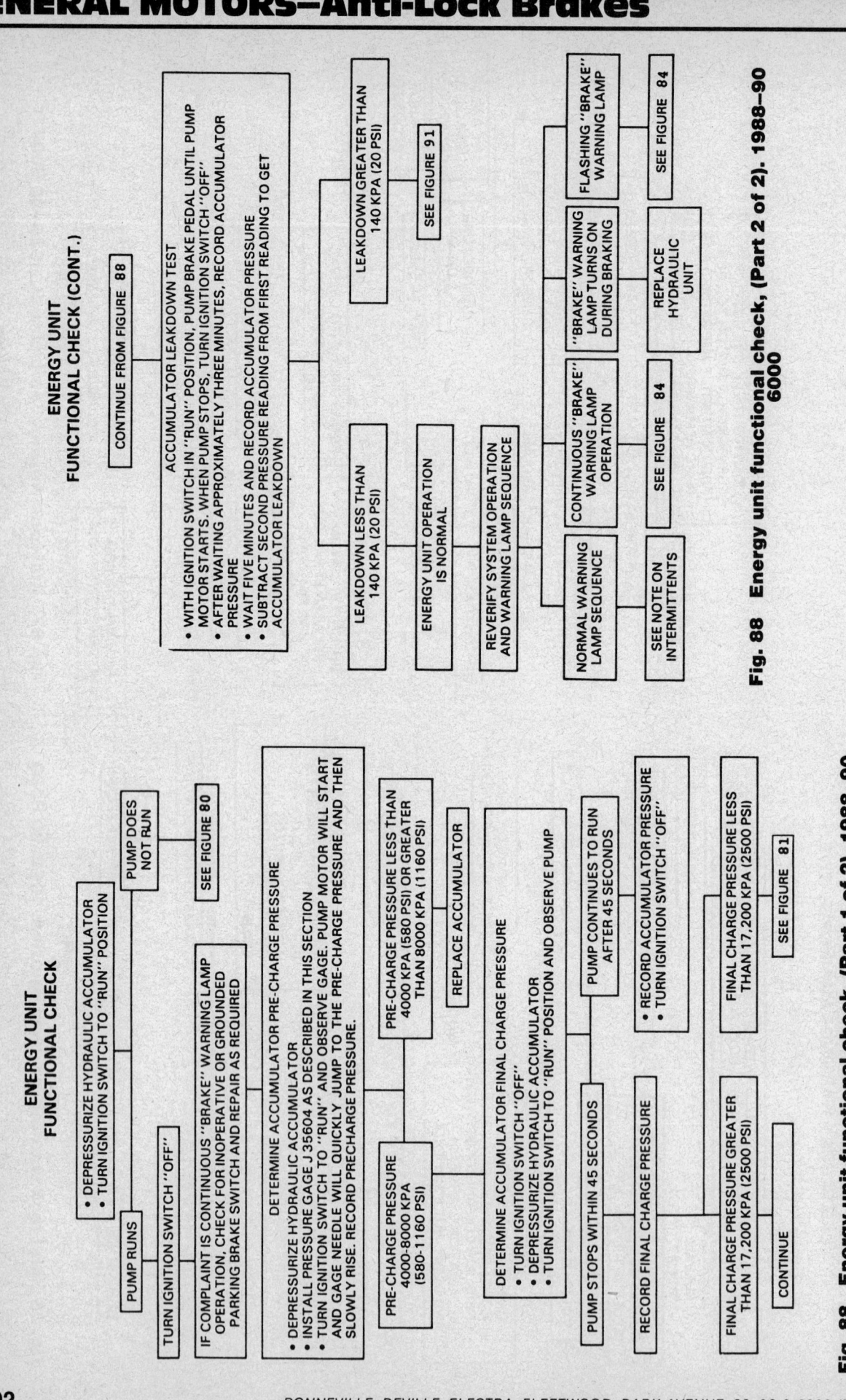

**ENERGY UNIT
FUNCTIONAL CHECK (CONT.)**

CONTINUE FROM FIGURE 88

ACCUMULATOR LEAKDOWN TEST
- WITH IGNITION SWITCH IN "RUN" POSITION, PUMP BRAKE PEDAL UNTIL PUMP MOTOR STARTS. WHEN PUMP STOPS, TURN IGNITION SWITCH "OFF"
- AFTER WAITING APPROXIMATELY THREE MINUTES, RECORD ACCUMULATOR PRESSURE
- WAIT FIVE MINUTES AND RECORD ACCUMULATOR PRESSURE
- SUBTRACT SECOND PRESSURE READING FROM FIRST READING TO GET ACCUMULATOR LEAKDOWN

LEAKDOWN GREATER THAN 140 KPA (20 PSI) → SEE FIGURE 91

LEAKDOWN LESS THAN 140 KPA (20 PSI)

ENERGY UNIT OPERATION IS NORMAL

REVERIFY SYSTEM OPERATION AND WARNING LAMP SEQUENCE

NORMAL WARNING LAMP SEQUENCE → SEE NOTE ON INTERMITTENTS

CONTINUOUS "BRAKE" WARNING LAMP OPERATION → SEE FIGURE 84

"BRAKE" WARNING LAMP TURNS ON DURING BRAKING → REPLACE HYDRAULIC UNIT

FLASHING "BRAKE" WARNING LAMP → SEE FIGURE 84

Fig. 88   Energy unit functional check, (Part 2 of 2). 1988–90 6000

**ENERGY UNIT
FUNCTIONAL CHECK**
- DEPRESSURIZE HYDRAULIC ACCUMULATOR
- TURN IGNITION SWITCH TO "RUN" POSITION

PUMP RUNS

PUMP DOES NOT RUN → SEE FIGURE 80

TURN IGNITION SWITCH "OFF"

IF COMPLAINT IS CONTINUOUS "BRAKE" WARNING LAMP OPERATION, CHECK FOR INOPERATIVE OR GROUNDED PARKING BRAKE SWITCH AND REPAIR AS REQUIRED

DETERMINE ACCUMULATOR PRE-CHARGE PRESSURE
- DEPRESSURIZE HYDRAULIC ACCUMULATOR
- INSTALL PRESSURE GAGE J 35604 AS DESCRIBED IN THIS SECTION
- TURN IGNITION SWITCH TO "RUN" AND OBSERVE GAGE. PUMP MOTOR WILL START AND GAGE NEEDLE WILL QUICKLY JUMP TO THE PRE-CHARGE PRESSURE AND THEN SLOWLY RISE. RECORD PRECHARGE PRESSURE.

PRE-CHARGE PRESSURE LESS THAN 4000 KPA (580 PSI) OR GREATER THAN 8000 KPA (1160 PSI) → REPLACE ACCUMULATOR

PRE-CHARGE PRESSURE 4000-8000 KPA (580-1160 PSI)

DETERMINE ACCUMULATOR FINAL CHARGE PRESSURE
- TURN IGNITION SWITCH "OFF"
- DEPRESSURIZE HYDRAULIC ACCUMULATOR
- TURN IGNITION SWITCH TO "RUN" POSITION AND OBSERVE PUMP

PUMP CONTINUES TO RUN AFTER 45 SECONDS
- RECORD ACCUMULATOR PRESSURE
- TURN IGNITION SWITCH "OFF"

FINAL CHARGE PRESSURE LESS THAN 17,200 KPA (2500 PSI) → SEE FIGURE 81

PUMP STOPS WITHIN 45 SECONDS

RECORD FINAL CHARGE PRESSURE

FINAL CHARGE PRESSURE GREATER THAN 17,200 KPA (2500 PSI)

CONTINUE

Fig. 88   Energy unit functional check, (Part 1 of 2). 1988–90 6000

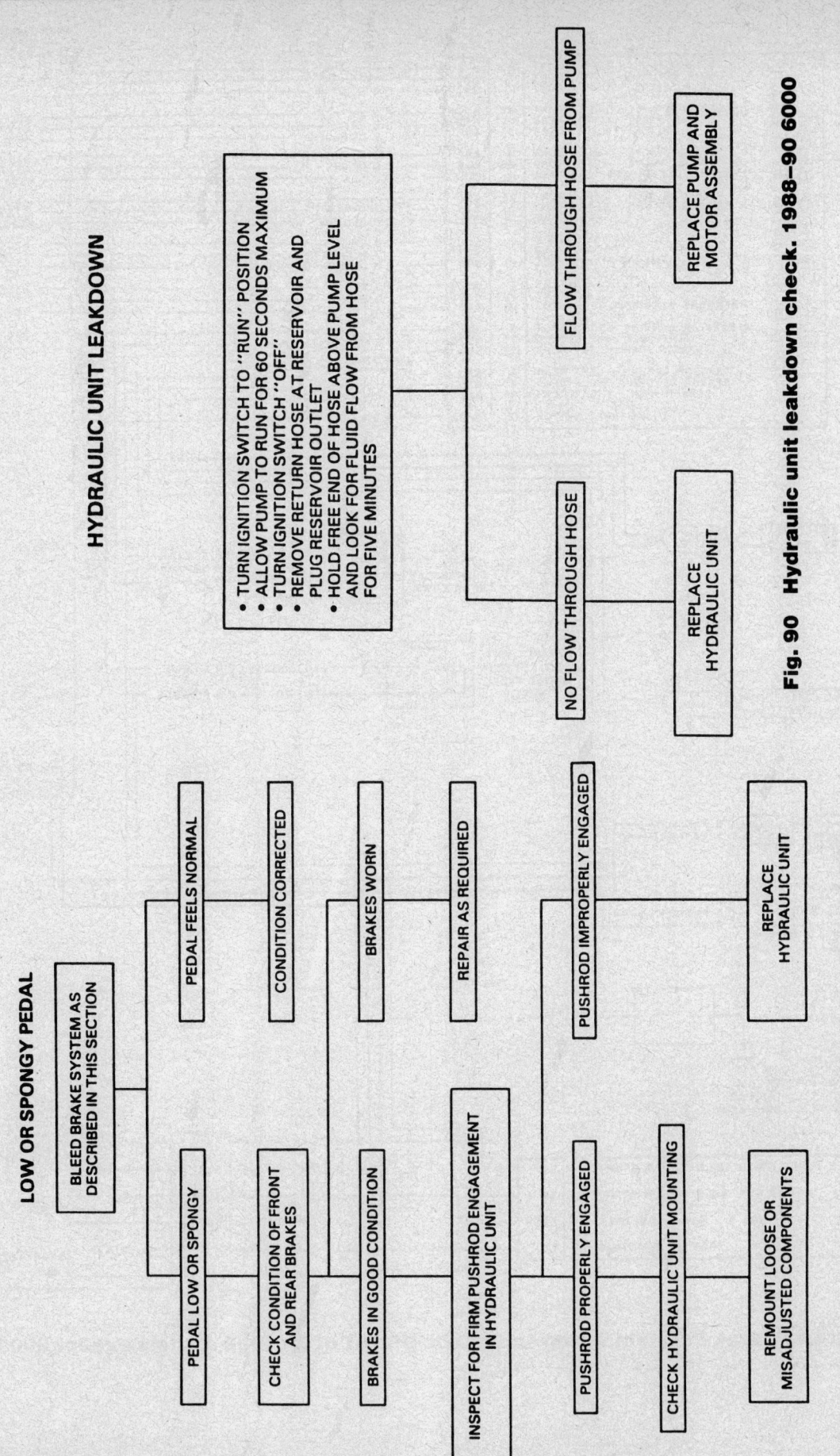

HYDRAULIC UNIT LEAKDOWN

- TURN IGNITION SWITCH TO "RUN" POSITION
- ALLOW PUMP TO RUN FOR 60 SECONDS MAXIMUM
- TURN IGNITION SWITCH "OFF"
- REMOVE RETURN HOSE AT RESERVOIR AND PLUG RESERVOIR OUTLET
- HOLD FREE END OF HOSE ABOVE PUMP LEVEL AND LOOK FOR FLUID FLOW FROM HOSE FOR FIVE MINUTES

FLOW THROUGH HOSE FROM PUMP → REPLACE PUMP AND MOTOR ASSEMBLY

NO FLOW THROUGH HOSE → REPLACE HYDRAULIC UNIT

Fig. 90 Hydraulic unit leakdown check. 1988–90 6000

LOW OR SPONGY PEDAL

BLEED BRAKE SYSTEM AS DESCRIBED IN THIS SECTION

PEDAL FEELS NORMAL → CONDITION CORRECTED

PEDAL LOW OR SPONGY → CHECK CONDITION OF FRONT AND REAR BRAKES

BRAKES WORN → REPAIR AS REQUIRED

BRAKES IN GOOD CONDITION → INSPECT FOR FIRM PUSHROD ENGAGEMENT IN HYDRAULIC UNIT

PUSHROD IMPROPERLY ENGAGED → REPLACE HYDRAULIC UNIT

PUSHROD PROPERLY ENGAGED → CHECK HYDRAULIC UNIT MOUNTING → REMOUNT LOOSE OR MISADJUSTED COMPONENTS

Fig. 89 Low or spongy pedal check. 1988–90 6000

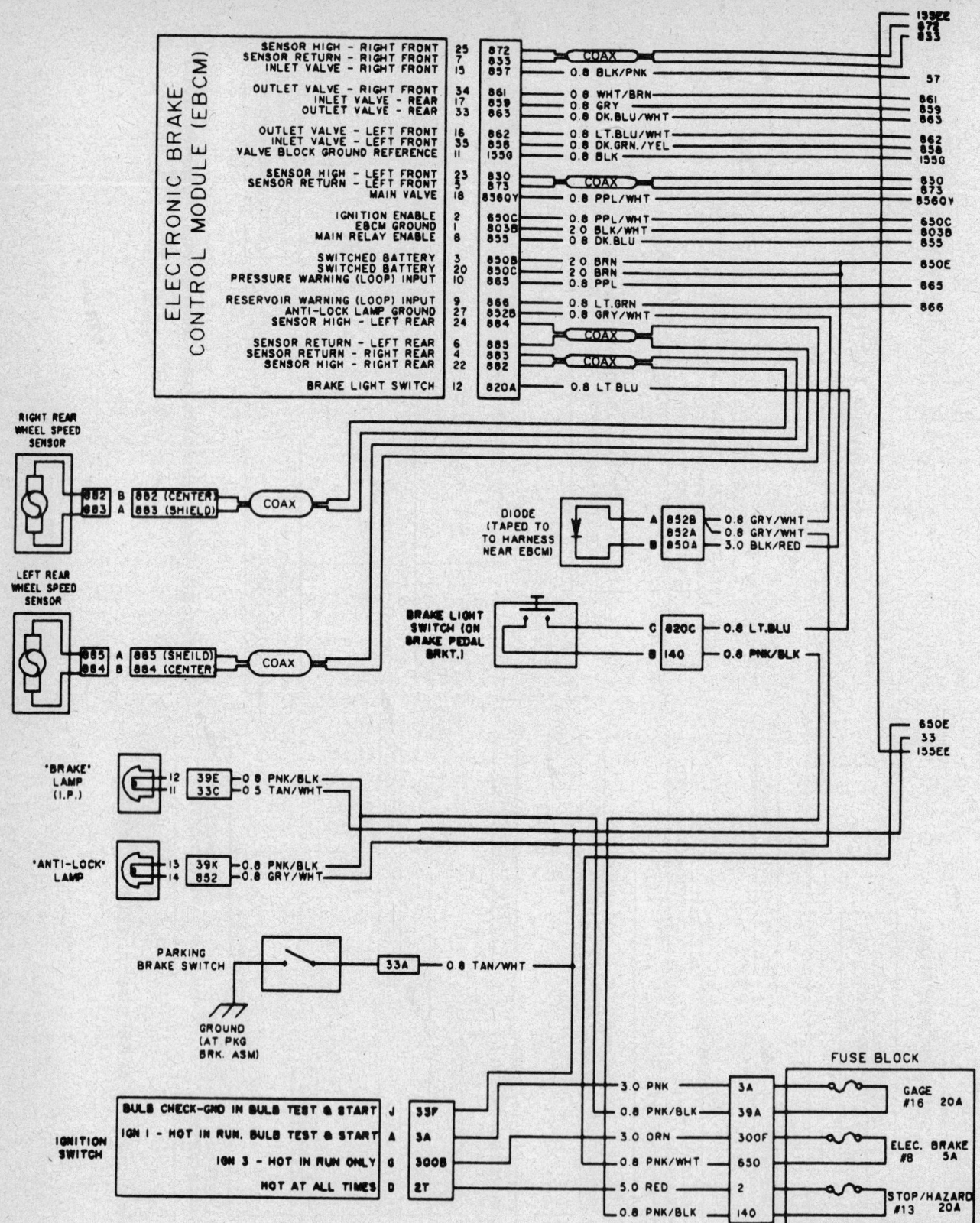

Fig. 91   Anti-Lock Brake system wiring schematic (Part 1 of 2). 1988 models except 6000

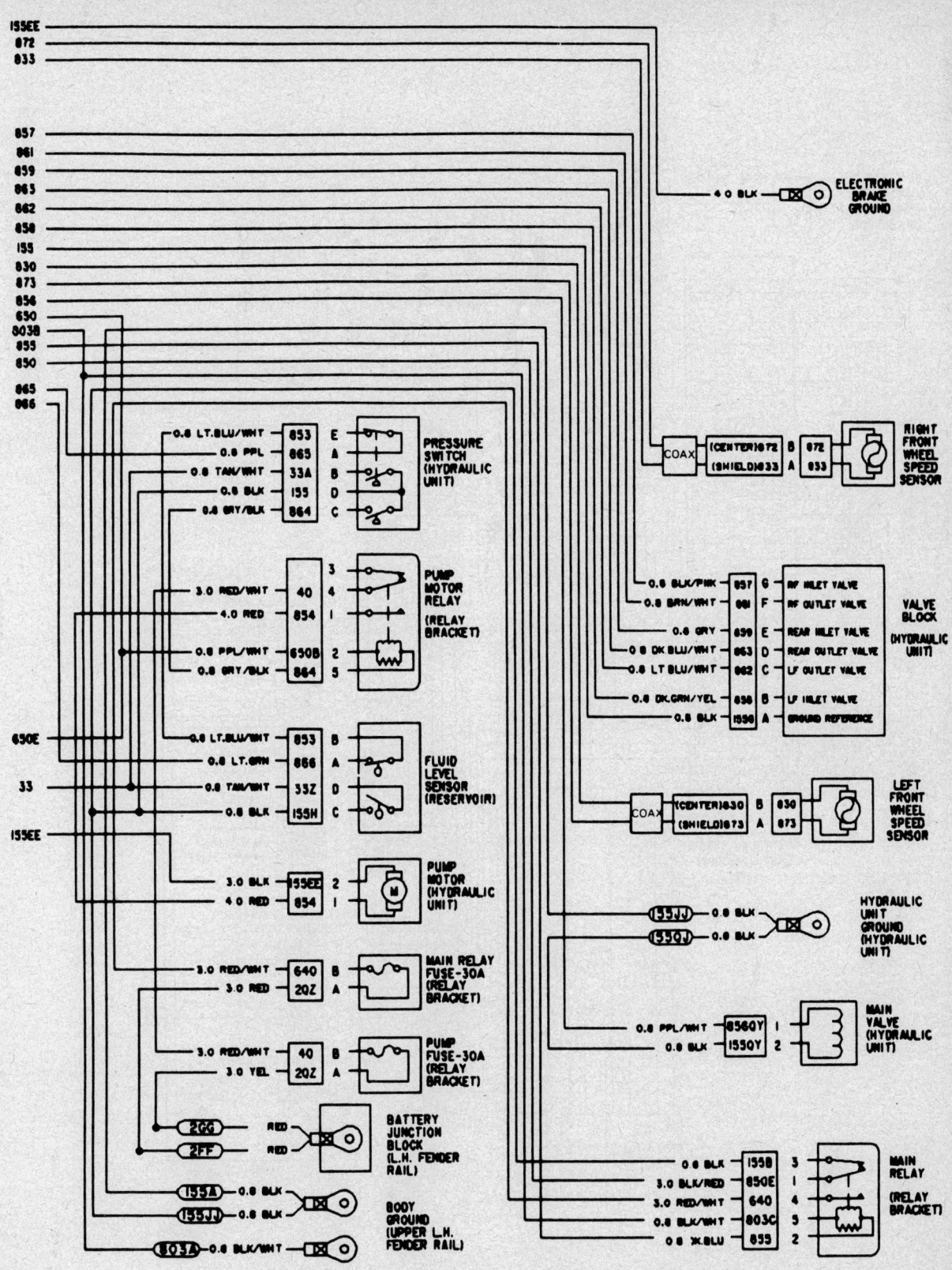

Fig. 91   Anti-Lock Brake system wiring schematic (Part 2 of 2). 1988 models except 6000

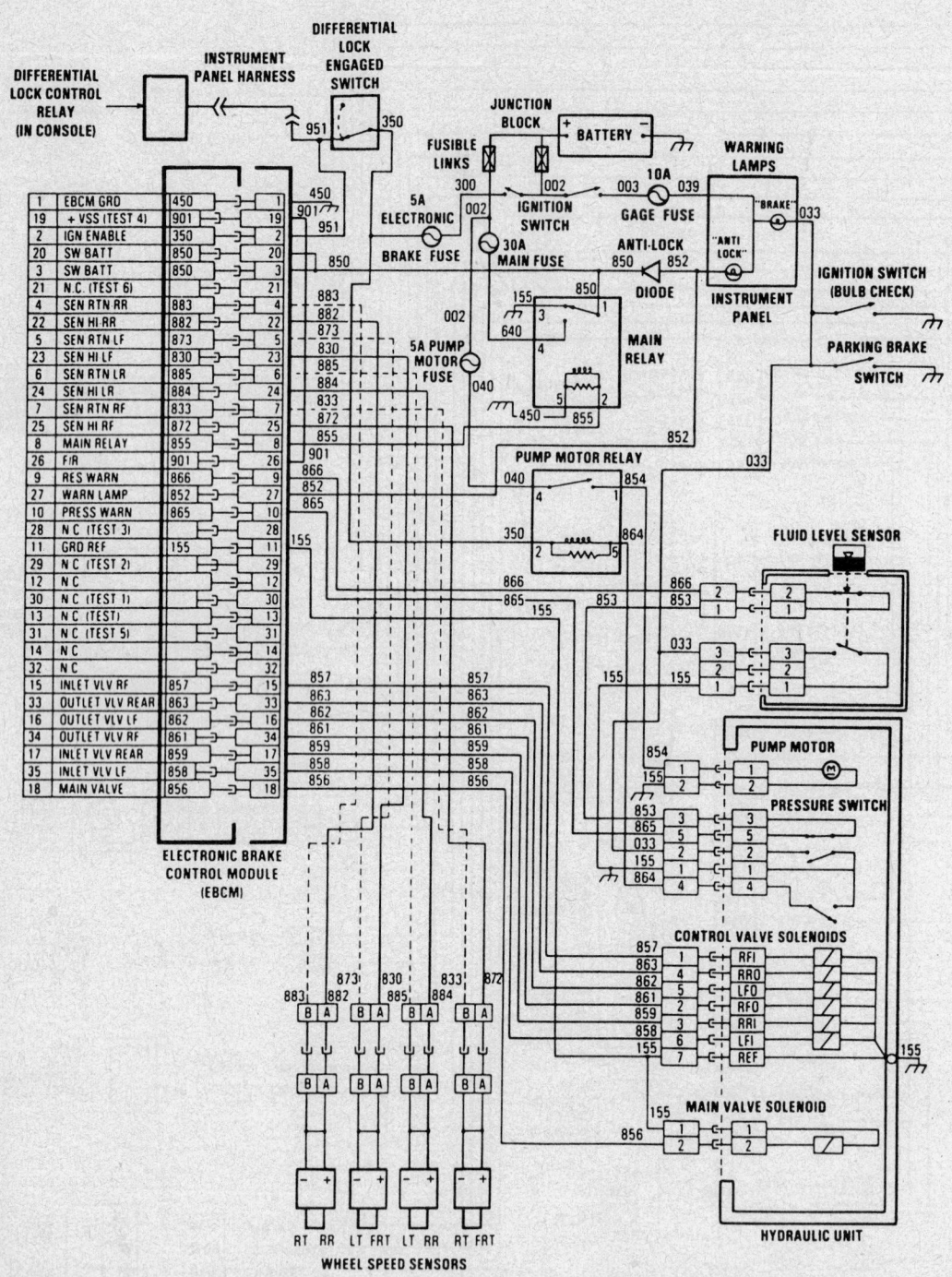

Fig. 92 Anti-Lock Brake system wiring schematic. 1988–90 6000

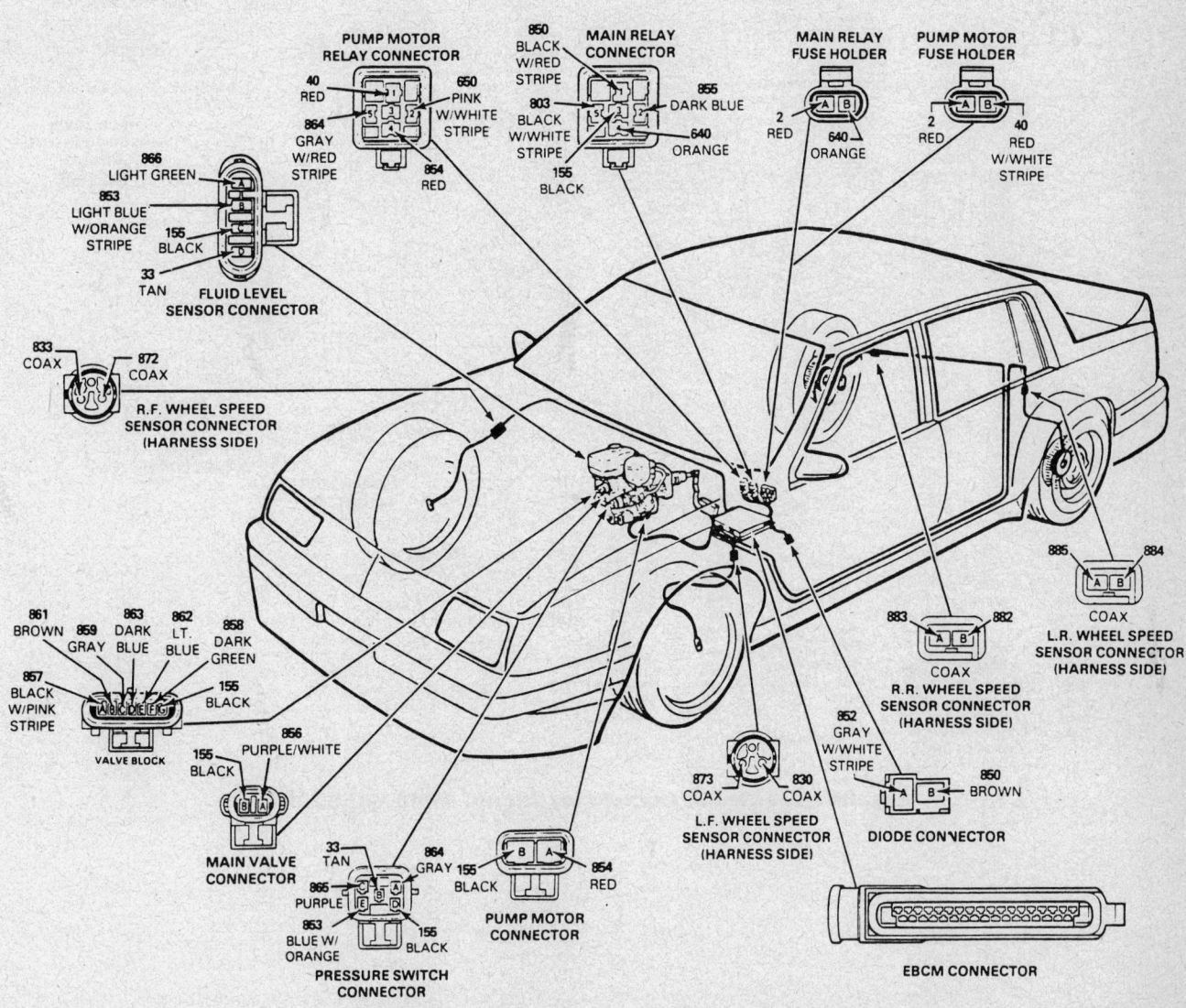

Fig. 93 Electrical connector faces. 1988 models ecept 6000

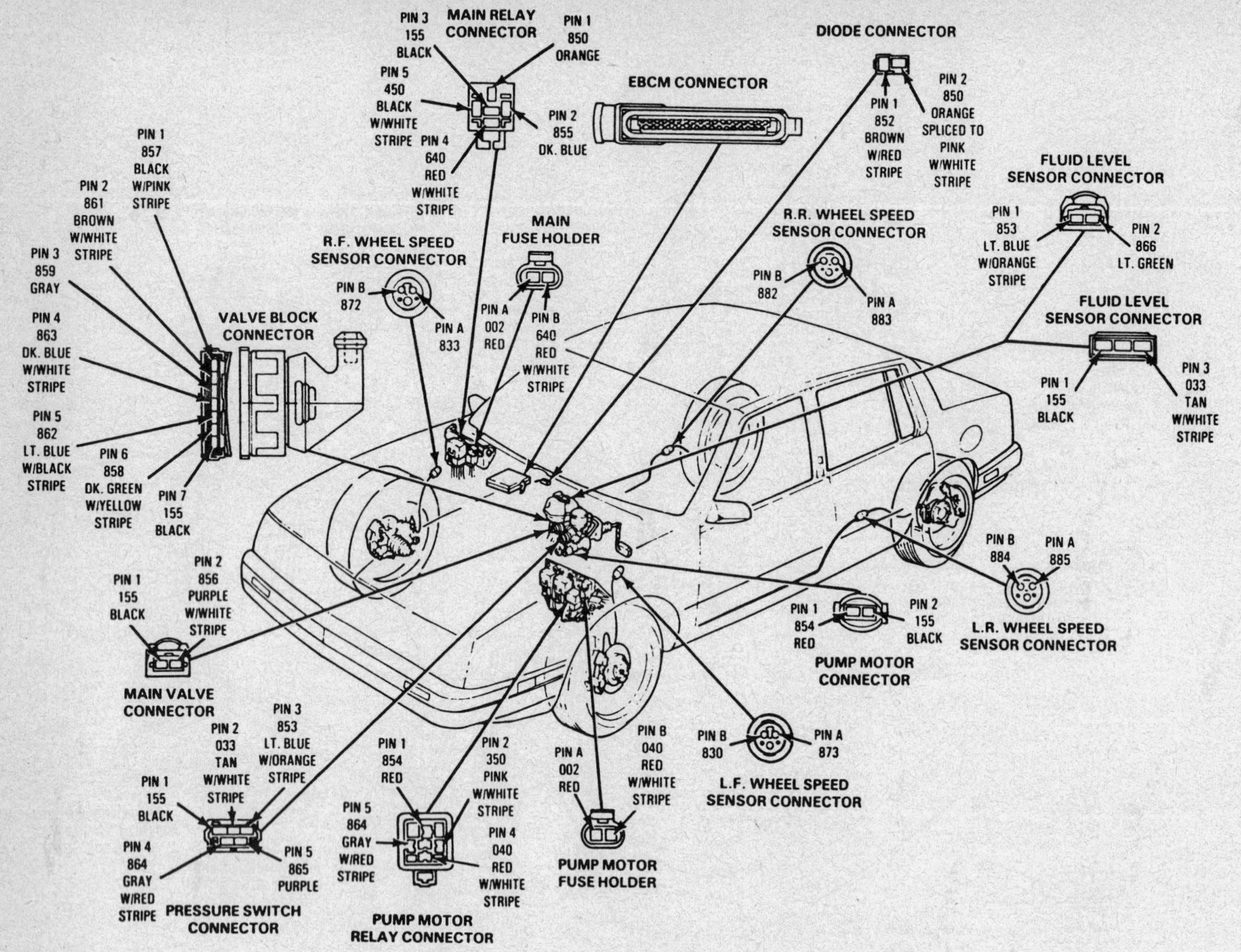

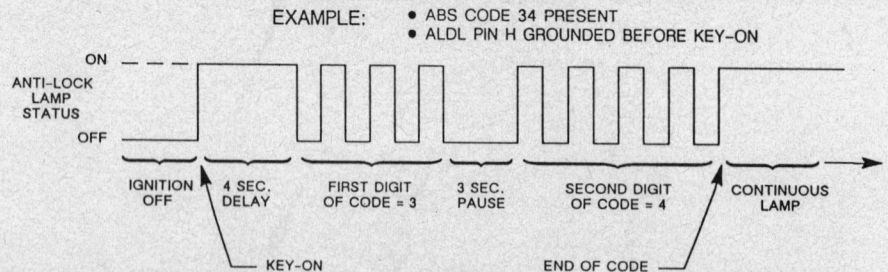

Fig. 94   Electrical connector faces. 1988–90 6000

ABS DIAGNOSTIC MODE

EXAMPLE:
- ABS CODE 34 PRESENT
- ALDL PIN H GROUNDED BEFORE KEY-ON

ANTI-LOCK LAMP STATUS

ON

OFF

| IGNITION OFF | 4 SEC. DELAY | FIRST DIGIT OF CODE = 3 | 3 SEC. PAUSE | SECOND DIGIT OF CODE = 4 | CONTINUOUS LAMP |

KEY-ON

END OF CODE

Fig. 95   ABS diagnostic code interpretation. 1989–90 models except 6000

ABS CODE INDEX

ABS CODE	SYSTEM	GO TO CHART	ABS CODE	SYSTEM	GO TO CHART
11	EBCM	A-1	45	2 SENSOR (LF)	A-13
12	EBCM	A-1	46	2 SENSORS (RF)	A-13
21	MAIN VALVE	A-2	47	2 SENSORS (REAR)	A-13
22	LF INLET VALVE	A-3	48	3 SENSORS	A-13
23	LF OUTLET VALVE	A-4	51	LF OUTLET VALVE	A-14
24	RF INLET VALVE	A-5	52	RF OUTLET VALVE	A-14
25	RF OUTLET VALVE	A-6	53	REAR OUTLET VALVE	A-14
26	REAR INLET VALVE	A-7	54	REAR OUTLET VALVE	A-14
27	REAR OUTLET VALVE	A-8	55	LF WSS	A-9
31	LF WSS	A-9	56	RF WSS	A-10
32	RF WSS	A-10	57	RR WSS	A-11
33	RR WSS	A-11	58	LR WSS	A-12
34	LR WSS	A-12	61	EBCM LOOP CKT	A-15
35	LF WSS	A-9	71	LF OUTLET VALVE	A-14
36	RF WSS	A-10	72	RF OUTLET VALVE	A-14
37	RR WSS	A-11	73	REAR OUTLET VALVE	A-14
38	LR WSS	A-12	74	REAR OUTLET VALVE	A-14
41	LF WSS	A-9	75	LF WSS	A-9
42	RF WSS	A-10	76	RF WSS	A-10
43	RR WSS	A-11	77	RR WSS	A-11
44	LR WSS	A-12	78	LR WSS	A-12

Fig. 97 ABS code index. 1989–90 models except 6000

ABS FUNCTIONAL CHECK

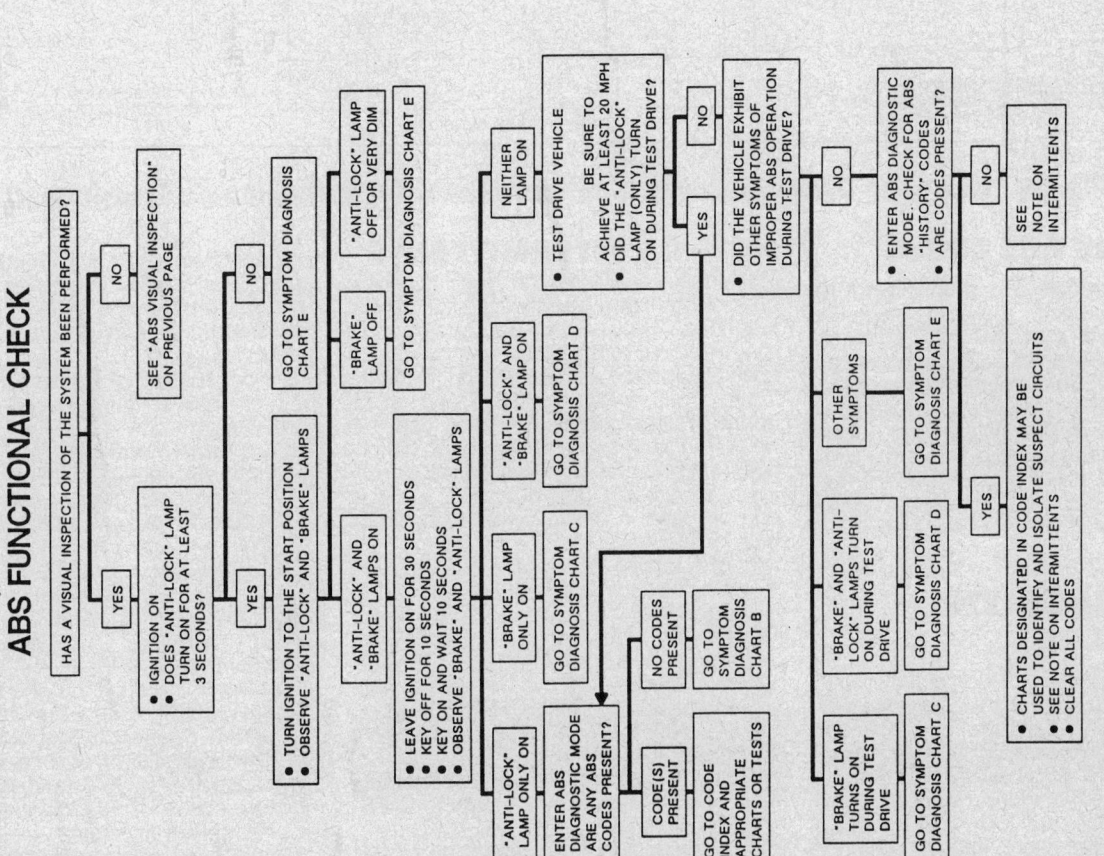

Fig. 96 ABS functional check. 1989–90 models except 6000

BONNEVILLE, DEVILLE, ELECTRA, FLEETWOOD, PARK AVENUE, 88, 98 & 6000 (TEVES TYPE)

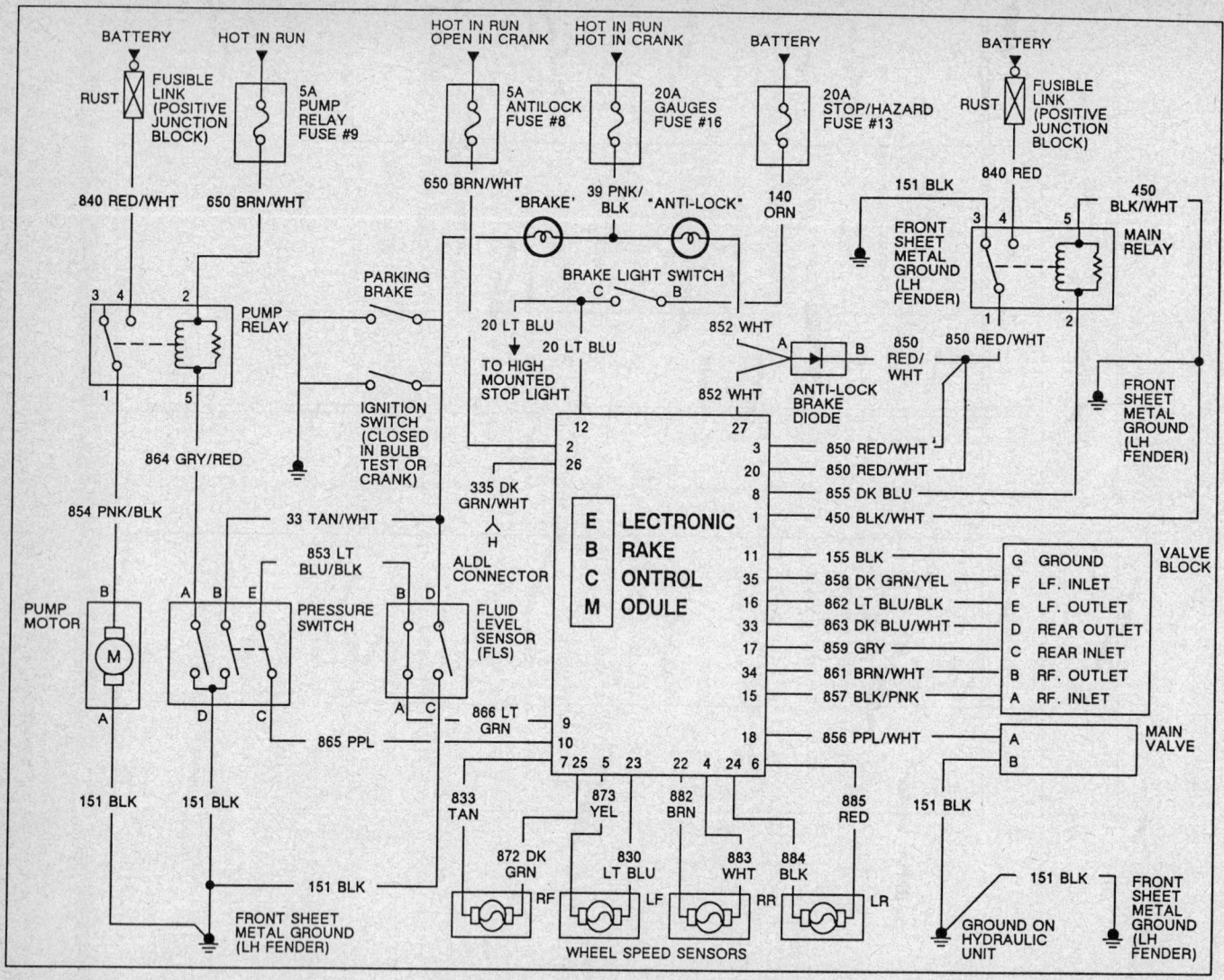

Fig. 98   Anti-Lock Brake system wiring schematic. 1989–90 models except 6000

CLEARING ABS CODES

The ABS trouble codes should not be cleared until repairs are completed. The EBCM will not allow the ABS codes to clear unless all codes have been read.

The ABS trouble codes are cleared by driving the vehicle at a speed greater than 18 mph. If the codes did not clear, repeat the read out procedure and drive the vehicle again at a speed greater than 18 mph. If codes do not clear, additional repairs may be required.

BASIC DIAGNOSTIC PROCEDURE

Diagnosis of the anti-lock brake system consists of the anti-lock pre-diagnosis inspection, anti-lock functional check and additional checks as specified by the functional check. All diagnosis should start with the anti-lock pre-diagnosis inspection and proceed to the anti-lock brake system (ABS), functional check, if the condition is not resolved by the visual inspection.

NOTE ON INTERMITTENTS

Intermittent failures in the anti-lock brake system may be difficult to accurately diagnose. The ABS trouble codes which may be stored by the EBCM are not specifically designated as "CURRENT" or "HISTORY" codes as are BCM and ECM codes. These codes, however, can be helpful in diagnosing intermittent conditions. If an intermittent condition is to be diagnosed, the ABS self-diagnostic system can be used in the following manner to help isolate the suspected circuit:

1. First, display and clear any ABS trouble codes which may be present in the EBCM.
2. Test drive the vehicle, attempting to repeat the failure condition.
3. After duplicating the condition, stop the vehicle and display any ABS trouble codes which may have been stored.
4. If no trouble codes were stored, it may become necessary to refer to "ABS Symptom Diagnosis."

If an intermittent fault cannot be otherwise diagnosed, the problem will most probably be caused by a defective electrical connection or wiring. When an intermittent problem is encountered, check questionable circuits and electrical connectors for the following:

1. Poor mating of connector halves or terminals not fully seated in connector body.
2. Improperly formed or damaged terminals. All connector terminals in the problem circuit should be carefully removed to increase contact tension.
3. Poor terminal wire connection.

The following conditions which could possibly cause intermittent operation of the BRAKE and ANTI-LOCK lamps are as follows:

1. Low system voltage — if low system voltage is detected at the EBCM, the ANTI-LOCK lamp will illuminate until normal system voltage is obtained.
2. Low brake fluid — low brake fluid will cause the BRAKE and ANTI-LOCK lamps to illuminate. When the fluid level sensor indicates an acceptable fluid level, normal system operation will resume.

CHART A-1
ABS CODES 11 AND 12

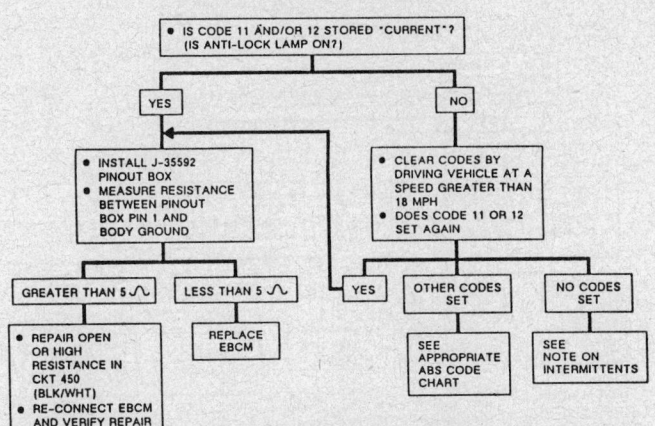

Fig. 99   Chart A-1, codes 11 & 12. 1989–90 models except 6000

3. Low accumulator pressure — low accumulator pressure will cause the BRAKE and ANTI-LOCK lamps to illuminate. When normal operating pressure is obtained, normal system operation will resume.
4. Any condition which results in interruption of power to the EBCM or hydraulic unit — main relay, pump motor relay, fuse and related wiring circuits.

SYSTEM VOLTAGE DURING DIAGNOSIS

Some diagnostic procedures require that the ignition switch remain On for extended periods of time. During this time, battery voltage may become low, causing erroneous voltage readings. If this situation occurs, connect a battery charger to the vehicle's electrical system, then apply a slow charge.

ABS PRE-DIAGNOSIS INSPECTION

Refer to **Fig. 6**, for anti-lock brake system (ABS), pre-diagnosis inspection procedure.

ABS FUNCTIONAL CHECK

Refer to **Fig. 96**, for anti-lock brake system (ABS), functional check procedure.

ABS TROUBLE CODE INDEX

Refer to **Fig. 97**, for anti-lock brake system trouble code index. When using the ABS trouble code index, "ABS Code," "System" and "Go To Chart" are referred to. Under "Go To Chart," you will find letters and numbers from A-1 to A-15 which are the actual diagnostic charts and can be found at the top of each individual diagnostic test chart.

ABS CIRCUIT DIAGRAM

Refer to **Fig. 98** for anti-lock brake system circuit diagram.

ABS TROUBLE CODE DIAGNOSIS

Refer to **Figs. 99 through 113**, for anti-lock brake system trouble code diagnostic procedures.

ABS SYMPTOM DIAGNOSIS

Refer to **Figs. 114 through 140**, for anti-lock brake system symptom diagnostic procedures.

SYSTEM SERVICE

On models equipped with Supplemental Inflatable Restraint (SIR) system, serious injury can result from unintended airbag deployment.

The SIR system is designed to retain sufficient voltage to deploy the airbag for a short time after power has been disconnected. To avoid serious injury, disarm the SIR as follows:
1. Turn ignition switch to Off position.
2. Remove SIR fuse from fuse panel.
3. Disconnect yellow two-way connector at base of steering column, if equipped, as follows:
   a. Remove lefthand sound insulator retaining screws and nuts.
   b. Remove courtesy lamp from sound insulator, then the sound insulator from vehicle.
   c. Remove Connector Position Assurance (CPA) pin, then disconnect yellow two-way connector at

CHART A-2
ABS CODE 21—MAIN VALVE

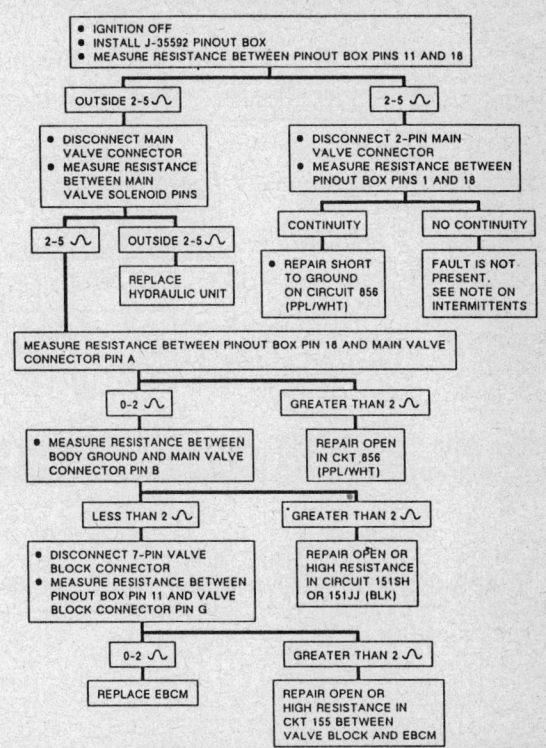

Fig. 100   Chart A-2, code 21 (main valve). 1989–90 models except 6000

base of steering column.
4. Wait at least 10 minutes before any further work is attempted. Serious injury may result from unintended airbag deployment if service is attempted immediately after SIR fuse is removed.
5. Reverse procedure to arm SIR system, noting the following:
   a. Turn ignition switch to On position.
   b. Observe INFALATABLE RESTRAINT indicator lamp.
   c. If lamp does not flash 7-9 times then remain Off, refer to "Passive Restraint Systems" for diagnosis.

DEPRESSURIZING HYDRAULIC ACCUMULATOR

Depressurize accumulator before performing any ABS service.
1. Disconnect battery ground cable or place ignition switch in the Off position.
2. Apply and release brake pedal a minimum of 20 times using approximately 50 lbs. of force on pedal. A noticeable change in pedal feel will occur when accumulator is completely discharged. **If battery negative cable was disconnected, reactivate Delco-Loc radios by turning ignition and radio to the On position, then pressing the Mute button on the steering wheel control.**

Continued on page 25-111

CHART A–3
ABS CODE 22–LEFT FRONT INLET VALVE

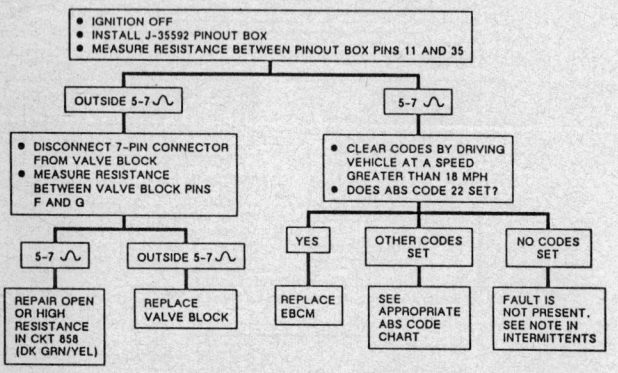

Fig. 101 Chart A-3, code 22 (left front inlet valve). 1989–90 models except 6000

CHART A–4
ABS CODE 23–LEFT FRONT OUTLET VALVE

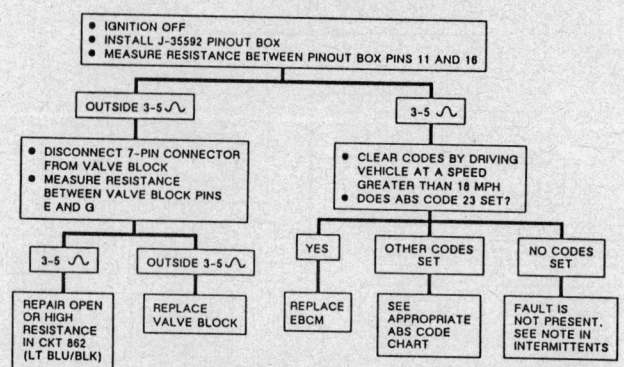

Fig. 102 Chart A-4, code 23 (left front outlet valve). 1989–90 models except 6000

CHART A–5
ABS CODE 24–RIGHT FRONT INLET VALVE

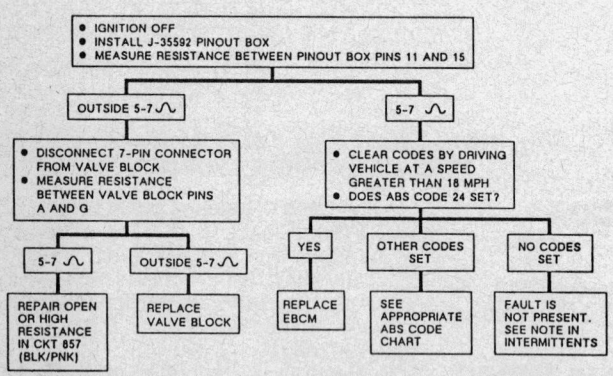

Fig. 103 Chart A-5, code 24 (right front inlet valve). 1989–90 models except 6000

CHART A–6
ABS CODE 25–RIGHT FRONT OUTLET VALVE

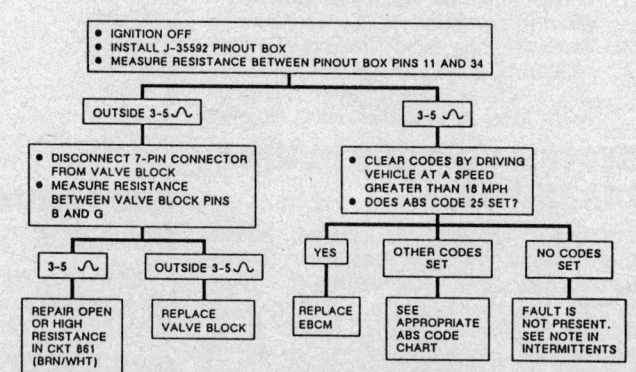

Fig. 104 Chart A-6, code 25 (right front outlet valve). 1989–90 models except 6000

CHART A–7
ABS CODE 26–REAR INLET VALVE

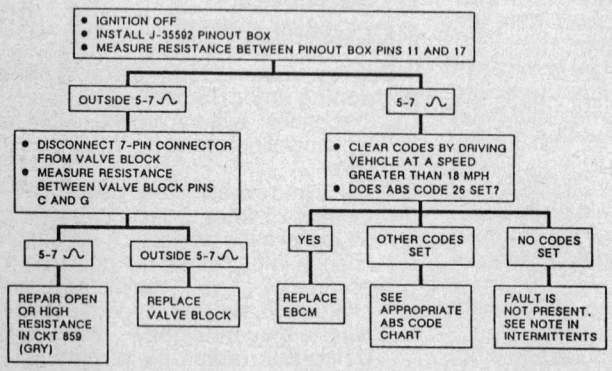

Fig. 105 Chart A-7, code 26 (rear inlet valve). 1989–90 models except 6000

CHART A–8
ABS CODE 27–REAR OUTLET VALVE

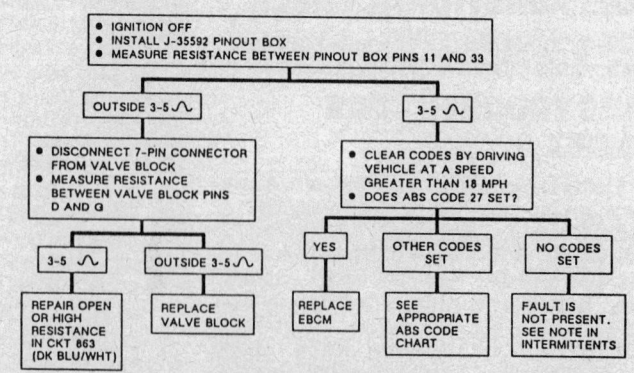

Fig. 106 Chart A-8, code 27 (rear outlet valve). 1989–90 models except 6000

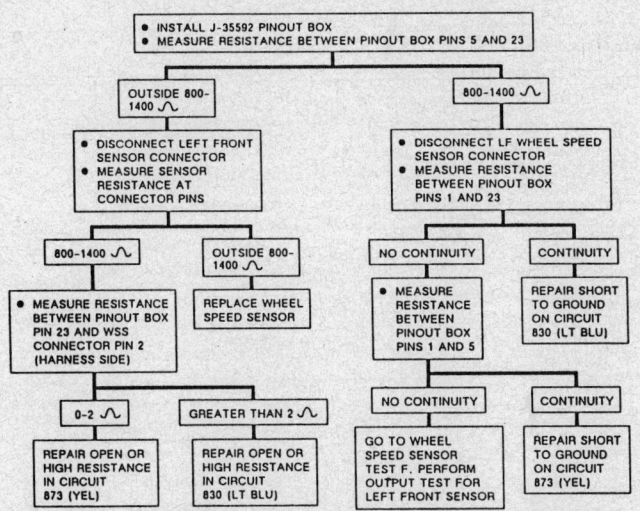

Fig. 107   Chart A-9, codes 31, 35, 41, 55 or 75 (left front wheel speed sensor). 1989–90 models except 6000

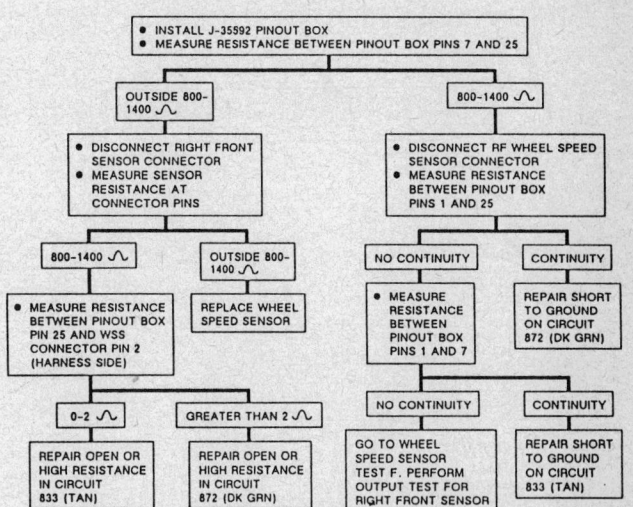

Fig. 108   Chart A-10, codes 32, 36, 42, 56 or 76 (right front wheel speed sensor). 1989–90 models except 6000

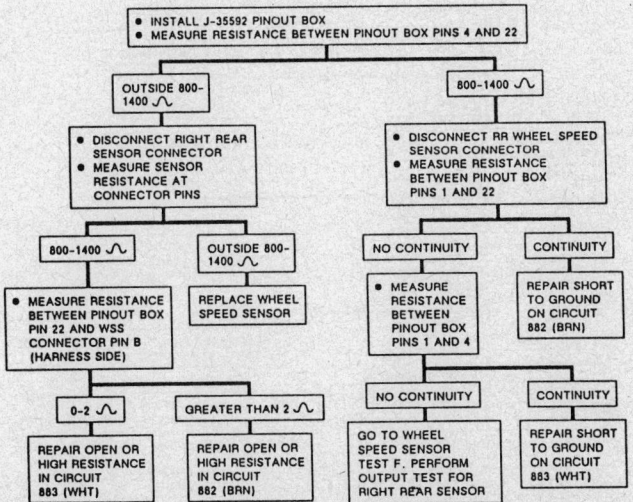

Fig. 109   Chart A-11, codes 33, 37, 43, 57 or 77 (right rear wheel speed sensor). 1989–90 models except 6000

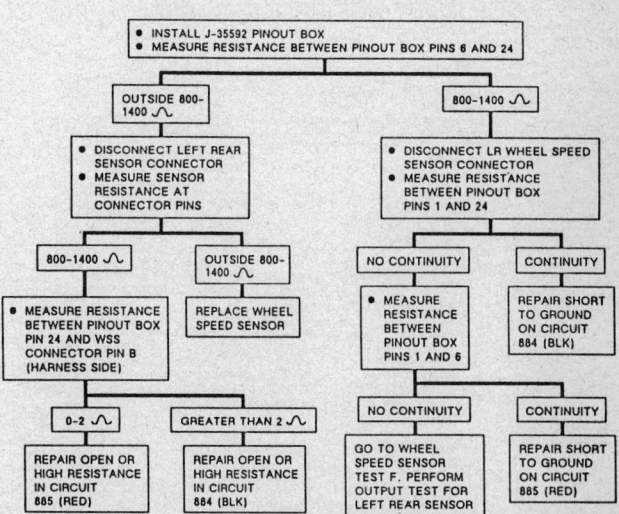

Fig. 110   Chart A-12, codes 34, 38, 44, 58 or 78 (left rear wheel speed sensor). 1989–90 models except 6000

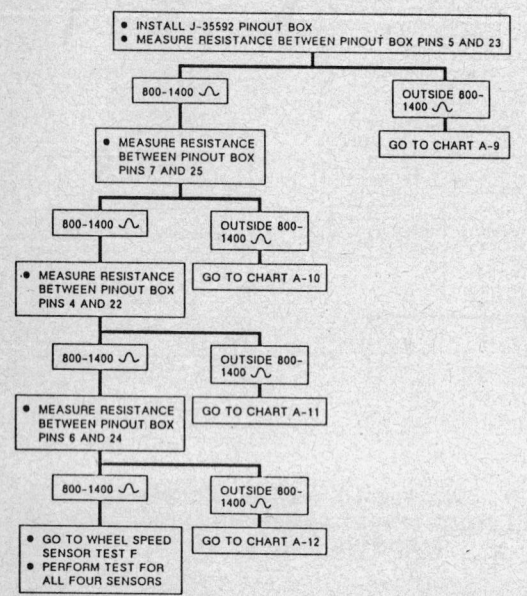

CHART A-13
ABS CODES 45, 46, 47 OR 48
MISSING WHEEL SPEED SENSOR SIGNALS

NOTE: THESE CODES (45, 46, 47 AND 48) INDICATE MORE THAN ONE WHEEL SPEED SENSOR WITH A MISSING SIGNAL

DRIVING THE FRONT WHEELS WITH THE ENGINE WHILE THE VEHICLE IS RAISED ON A HOIST (REAR WHEELS NOT TURNING) CAN CAUSE A CODE 47 TO SET

Fig. 111   Chart A-13, codes 45, 46, 47 or 48 (missing wheel speed sensor signals). 1989–90 models except 6000

CHART A-14
ABS CODES 51–54 AND 71–74
"PRESSURE REDUCTION" FAULT

NOTE: CODES 51–54 AND 71–74 INDICATE A CONDITION WHICH MAY BE ATTRIBUTABLE TO EITHER THE WHEEL SPEED SENSOR CIRCUIT OR THE OUTLET VALVE

FOR THESE CODES:	PERFORM THESE TESTS:
51 AND/OR 71	• GO TO CHART A-9 IF NO TROUBLE IS FOUND WHILE PERFORMING TESTS ON CHART A-9, DO NOT GO TO TEST F. INSTEAD, GO TO SOLENOID VALVE TEST G • PERFORM SOLENOID VALVE TEST FOR LEFT FRONT VALVES • IF NO TROUBLE IS FOUND, REPLACE EBCM
52 AND/OR 72	• GO TO CHART A-10 IF NO TROUBLE IS FOUND WHILE PERFORMING TESTS ON CHART A-10, DO NOT GO TO TEST F. INSTEAD, GO TO SOLENOID VALVE TEST G • PERFORM SOLENOID VALVE TEST FOR RIGHT FRONT VALVES • IF NO TROUBLE IS FOUND, REPLACE EBCM
53 AND/OR 73	• GO TO CHART A-11 IF NO TROUBLE IS FOUND WHILE PERFORMING TESTS ON CHART A-11, DO NOT GO TO TEST F. INSTEAD, GO TO SOLENOID VALVE TEST G • PERFORM SOLENOID VALVE TEST FOR REAR VALVES • IF NO TROUBLE IS FOUND, REPLACE EBCM
54 AND/OR 74	• GO TO CHART A-12 IF NO TROUBLE IS FOUND WHILE PERFORMING TESTS ON CHART A-12, DO NOT GO TO TEST F. INSTEAD, GO TO SOLENOID VALVE TEST G • PERFORM SOLENOID VALVE TEST FOR REAR VALVES • IF NO TROUBLE IS FOUND, REPLACE EBCM

Fig. 112   Chart A-14, codes 51–54 & 71–74 (pressure reduction fault). 1989–90 models except 6000

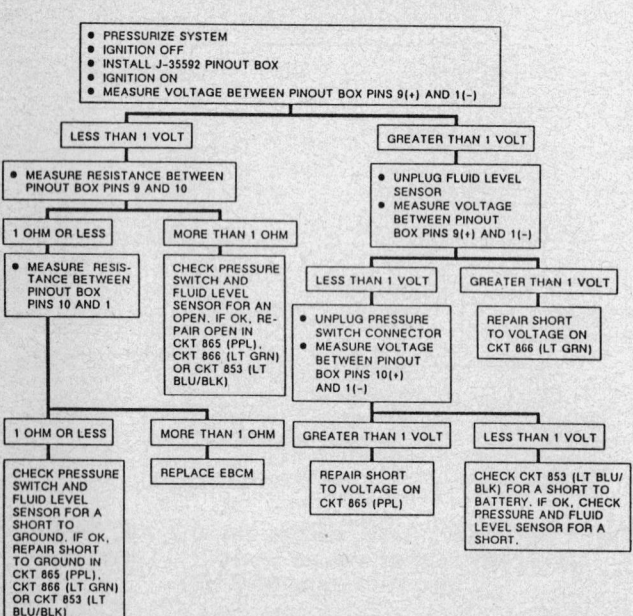

CHART A-15
ABS CODES 61–LOW FLUID/LOW PRESSURE
LOOP INPUT NOT PROCESSABLE

Fig. 113   Chart A-15, code 61 (low fluid/low pressure loop input not processable). 1989–90 models except 6000

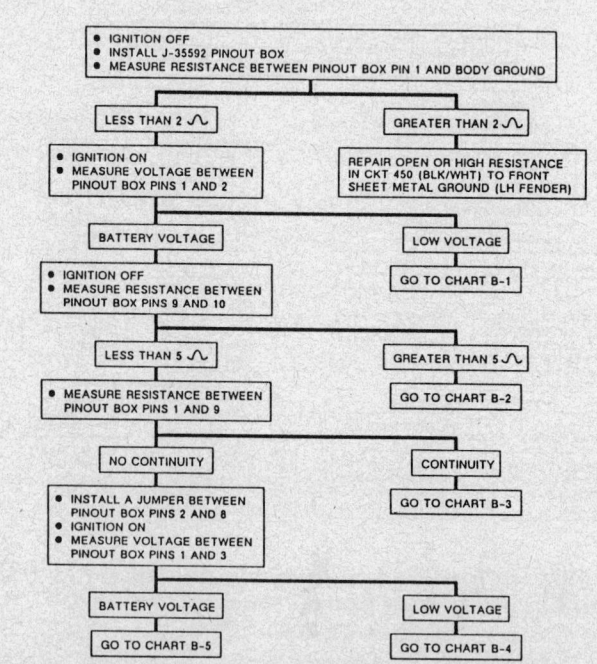

SYMPTOM DIAGNOSIS
CHART B
"ANTI-LOCK" LAMP ON AND NO ABS CODES PRESENT

Fig. 114   Chart B, symptom diagnosis (ANTI-LOCK lamp on & no codes present). 1989–90 models except 6000

BONNEVILLE, DEVILLE, ELECTRA, FLEETWOOD, PARK AVENUE, 88, 98 & 6000 (TEVES TYPE)

CHART B-1
IGNITION ENABLE CIRCUIT

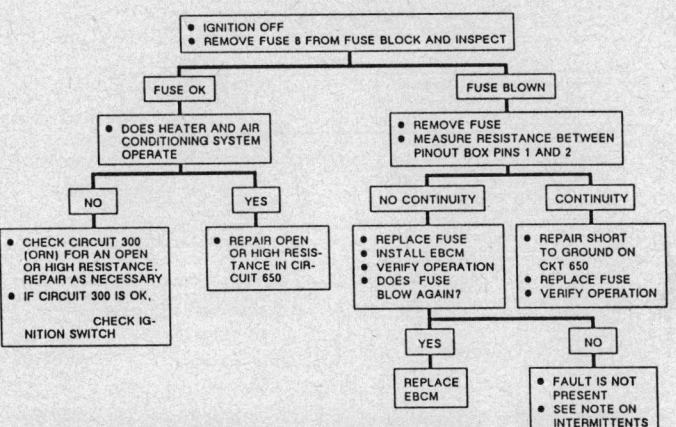

Fig. 115   Chart B-1, ignition enable circuit. 1989–90 models except 6000

CHART B-2
EBCM LOOP CIRCUIT OPEN

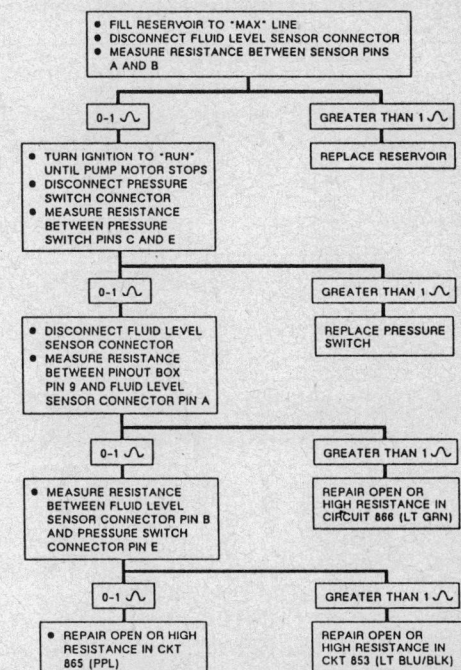

Fig. 116   Chart B-2, EBCM loop circuit open. 1989–90 models except 6000

CHART B-3
EBCM LOOP SHORT TO GROUND

Fig. 117   Chart B-3, EBCM loop short to ground. 1989–90 models except 6000

CHART B-4
MAIN RELAY CIRCUITS

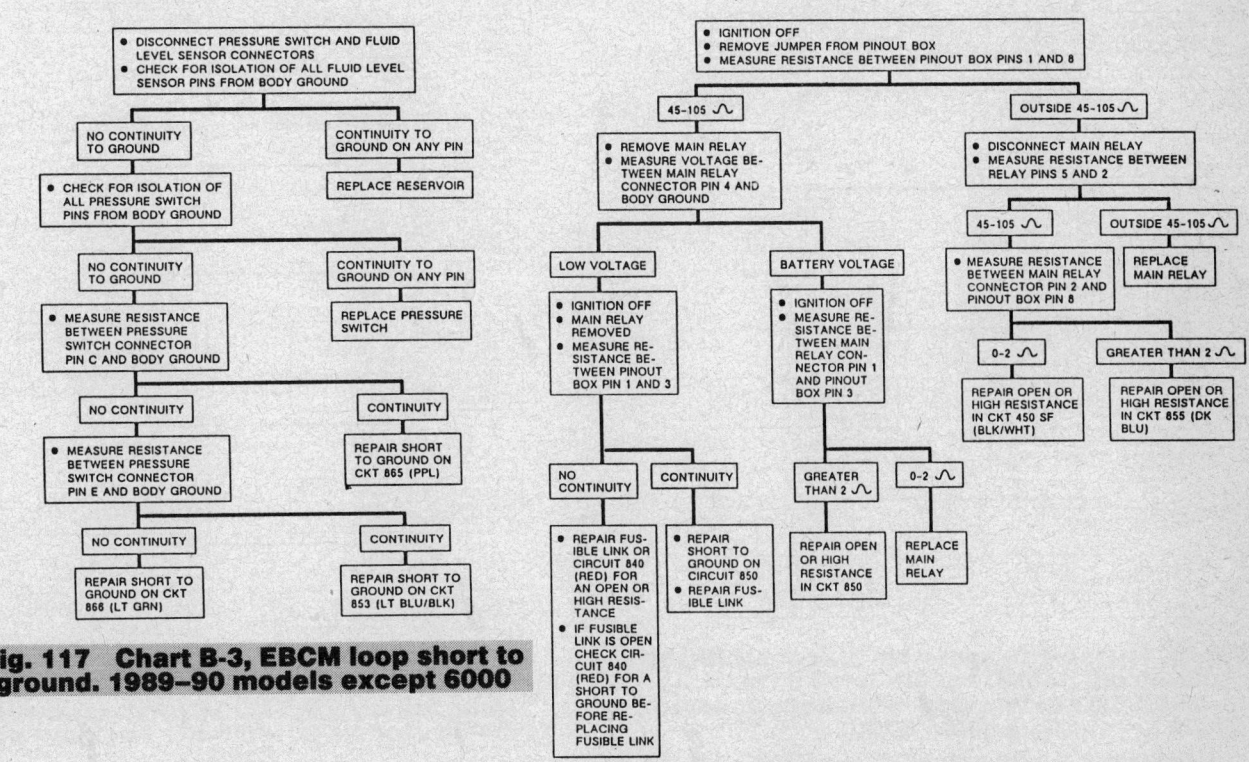

Fig. 118   Chart B-4, main relay circuits. 1989–90 models except 6000

CHART B-5
"ANTI-LOCK" LAMP CIRCUITS

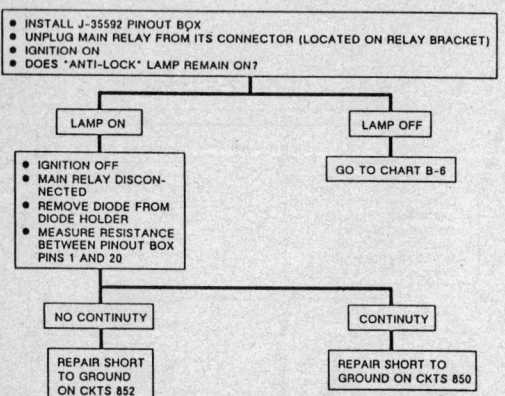

Fig. 119 Chart B-5, ANTI-LOCK lamp circuits. 1989–90 models except 6000

CHART B-6
MISCELLANEOUS EBCM INPUTS

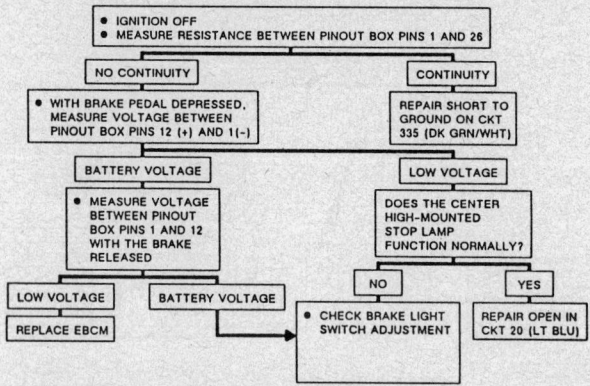

Fig. 120 Chart B-6, miscellaneous EBCM inputs. 1989–90 models except 6000

SYMPTOM DIAGNOSIS
CHART C
(WITHOUT Y67 REMINDER OPTION)
"BRAKE" LAMP ON (NO "ANTI-LOCK" LAMP OR ABS CODES)

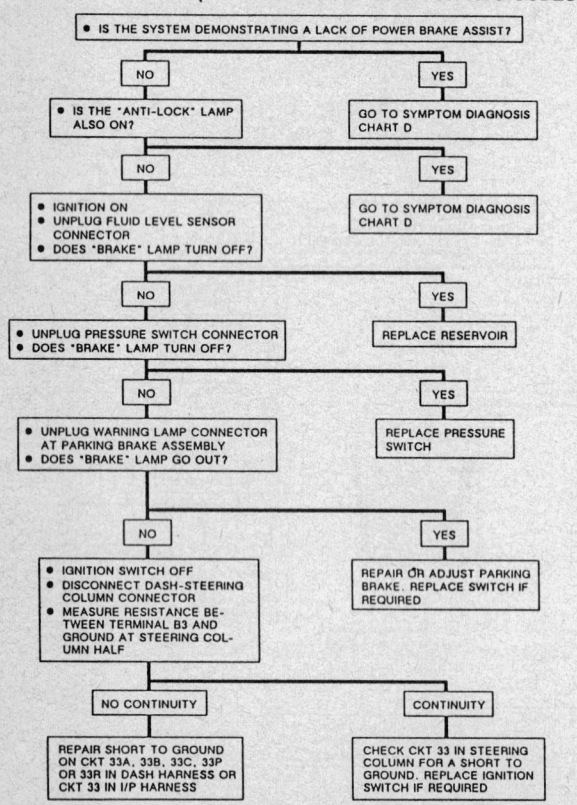

Fig. 121 Chart C, symptom diagnosis (BRAKE lamp on, no ANTI-LOCK lamp or codes). 1989–90 models less reminder package except 6000

SYMPTOM DIAGNOSIS
CHART C
(WITH Y67 REMINDER OPTION)
"BRAKE" LAMP ON (NO "ANTI-LOCK" LAMP OR ABS CODES)

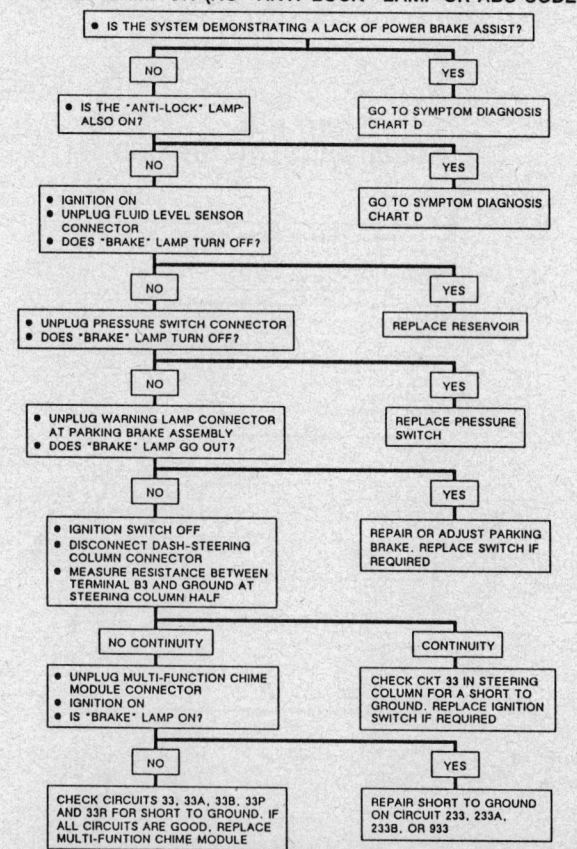

Fig. 122 Chart C, symptom diagnosis (BRAKE lamp on, no ANTI-LOCK lamp or codes). 1989–90 models w/reminder package except 6000

SYMPTOM DIAGNOSIS
CHART D
"BRAKE" AND "ANTI-LOCK" LAMPS ON

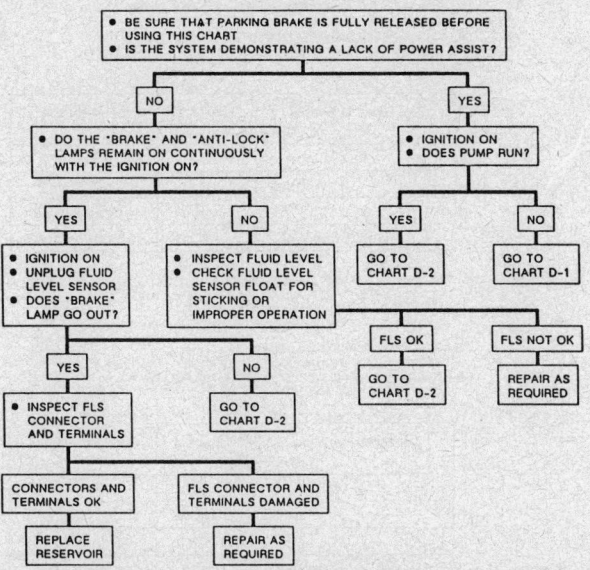

Fig. 123   Chart D, symptom diagnosis (BRAKE & ANTI-LOCK lamps on). 1989–90 models except 6000

CHART D-1
PUMP DOES NOT RUN

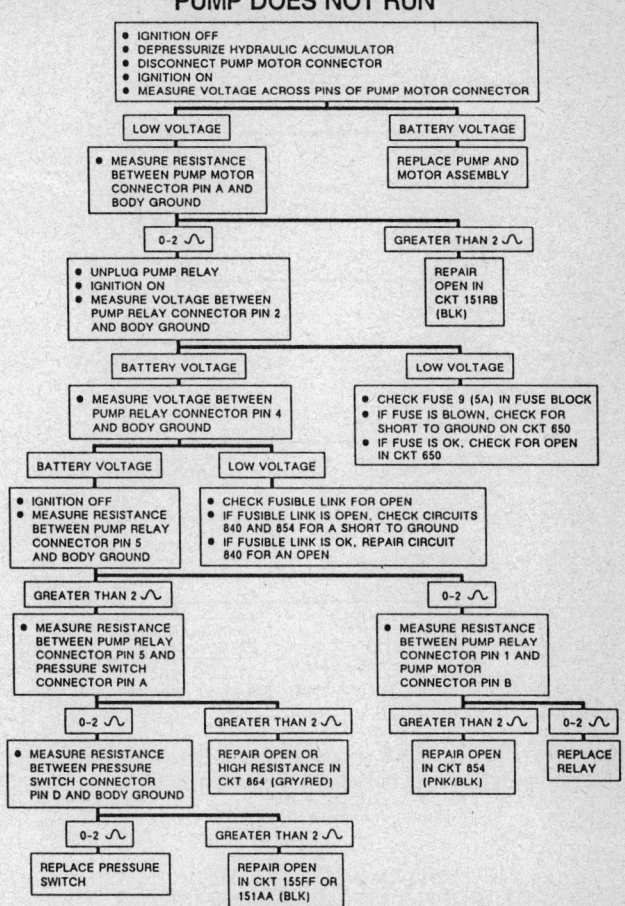

Fig. 124   Chart D-1, pump does not run. 1989–90 models except 6000

CHART D-2
HYDRAULIC UNIT FUNCTIONAL CHECK

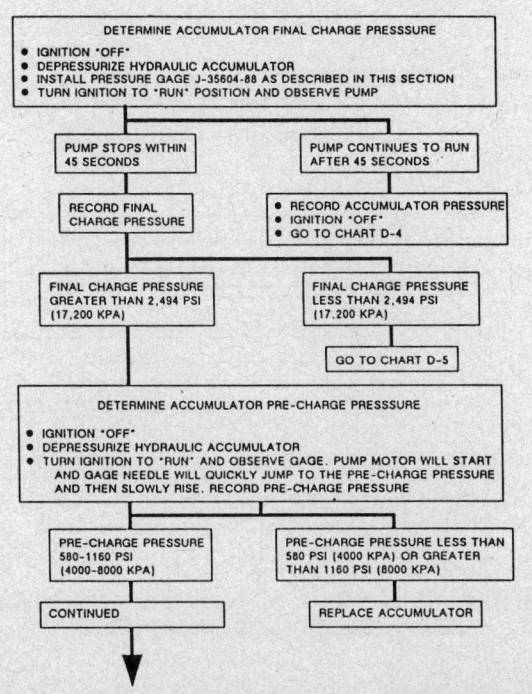

Fig. 125   Chart D-2, hydraulic unit functional check (Part 1 of 2). 1989–90 models except 6000

CHART D-2 (CONTINUED)
HYDRAULIC UNIT FUNCTIONAL CHECK

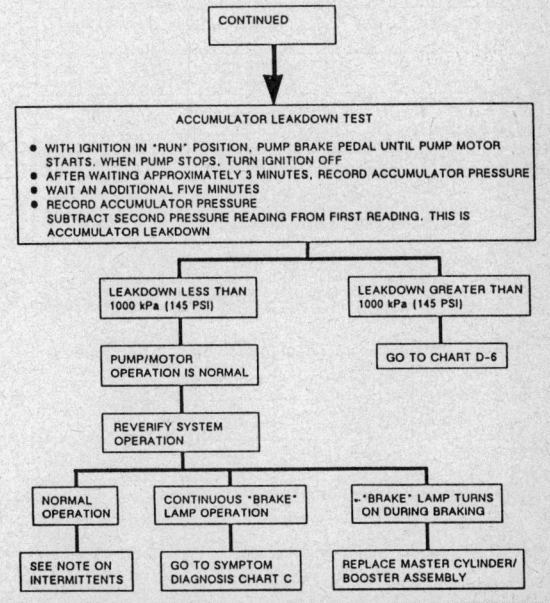

Fig. 125   Chart D-2, hydraulic unit functional check (Part 2 of 2). 1989–90 models except 6000

CHART D–4
EXTENDED PUMP OPERATION

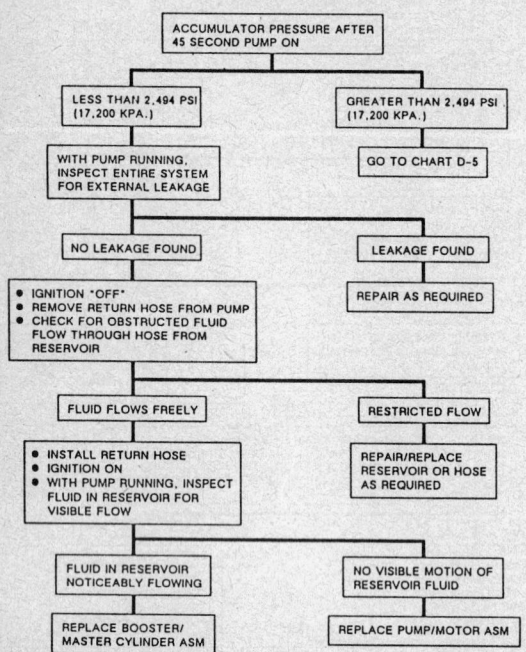

Fig. 126   Chart D-4, extended pump operation. 1989–90 models except 6000

CHART D–5
PRESSURE SWITCH PERFORMANCE

I. SWITCH STATUS - PRESSURIZED
- TURN IGNITION TO "RUN" UNTIL PUMP STOPS
- IGNITION "OFF" IF PUMP CONTINUES TO RUN AFTER 45 SECONDS, TURN IGNITION OFF AND PROCEED
- CHECK PRESSURE SWITCH PINS FOR THE FOLLOWING CONDITIONS USING VOM

MEASURE BETWEEN PINS	SCALE	SPECIFICATION
B, D	200	NO CONTINUITY
A, D	200	NO CONTINUITY
C, E	200	CONTINUITY
ALL PINS, BODY GROUND	200	NO CONTINUITY

IF ANY CONDITION IS NOT MET, REPLACE PRESSURE SWITCH AND VERIFY SYSTEM OPERATION

II. SWITCH STATUS - DEPRESSURIZED
- DEPRESSURIZE HYDRAULIC ACCUMULATOR
- CHECK PRESSURE SWITCH PINS FOR THE FOLLOWING CONDITIONS USING VOM

MEASURE BETWEEN PINS	SCALE	SPECIFICATION
B, D	200	CONTINUITY
A, D	200	CONTINUITY
C, E	200	NO CONTINUITY
ALL PINS, BODY GROUND	200	NO CONTINUITY

IF ANY CONDITION IS NOT MET, REPLACE PRESSURE SWITCH AND VERIFY SYSTEM OPERATION

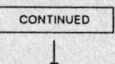

CONTINUED

Fig. 127   Chart D-5, pressure switch performance (Part 1 of 2). 1989–90 models except 6000

CHART D–5 (CONTINUED)
PRESSURE SWITCH PERFORMANCE

III. SWITCH STATUS - PRESSURIZED
- DEPRESSURIZE HYDRAULIC ACCUMULATOR
- INSTALL PRESSURE GAGE J-35604-88 AS DESCRIBED IN THIS SECTION
- CONNECT PRESSURE SWITCH CONNECTOR AND TURN IGNITION TO "RUN" UNTIL PUMP STOPS.
- USING VOM, MONITOR FOR CONTINUITY BETWEEN PRESSURE SWITCH PINS AS SHOWN BELOW WHILE SLOWLY BLEEDING OFF ACCUMULATOR PRESSURE BY PUMPING THE BRAKE PEDAL.
- PRESSURIZE SYSTEM BETWEEN EACH TEST BY RECONNECTING PRESSURE SWITCH AND TURNING IGNITION TO "RUN" UNTIL PUMP STOPS

MEASURE BETWEEN PINS	SCALE	SPECIFICATION
A, D	CONTINUITY SHOULD BE GAINED AT:	2,001-2,008 PSI (13,800-14,400 KPA)
B, D	CONTINUITY SHOULD BE GAINED AT:	1,465-1,552 PSI 10,103-10,703 KPA)
C, E	CONTINUITY SHOULD BE LOST AT:	1465-1552 PSI (10,103-10,703 KPA)

IF ANY CONDITION IS NOT MET, REPLACE PRESSURE SWITCH AND VERIFY SYSTEM OPERATION

- DEPRESSURIZE HYDRAULIC ACCUMULATOR
- WITH IGNITION OFF, CONNECT PRESSURE SWITCH CONNECTOR
- TURN IGNITION TO "RUN" AND OBSERVE GAGE, "ANTI-LOCK" LAMP, "BRAKE" LAMP AND PUMP MOTOR. EVENTS SHOULD OCCUR AT PRESSURES INDICATED IN CHART BELOW

EVENT	PRESSURE
"ANTI-LOCK" LAMP TURN OFF	1,937-2,037 PSI (13,358-14,048 KPA)
"BRAKE" LAMP TURN OFF	1,937-2,037 PSI (13,358-14,048 KPA)
PUMP MOTOR STOPS	2,494-2,755 PSI (17,200-19,00 KPA)

IF ANY CONDITION IS NOT MET, REPLACE PRESSURE SWITCH AND VERIFY SYSTEM OPERATION

Fig. 127   Chart D-5, pressure switch performance (Part 2 of 2). 1989–90 models except 6000

CHART D–6
HYDRAULIC UNIT LEAKDOWN

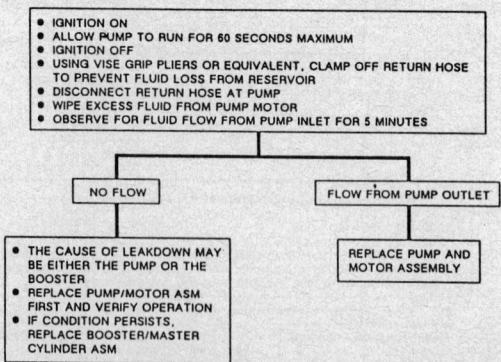

Fig. 128   Chart D-6, hydraulic unit leakdown. 1989–90 models except 6000

SYMPTOM DIAGNOSIS
CHART E

- ABS FUNCTIONAL CHECK MUST BE PERFORMED BEFORE USING THIS CHART

- IF ANY ABS TROUBLE CODES ARE SET, SEE APPROPRIATE TROUBLE CODE CHART

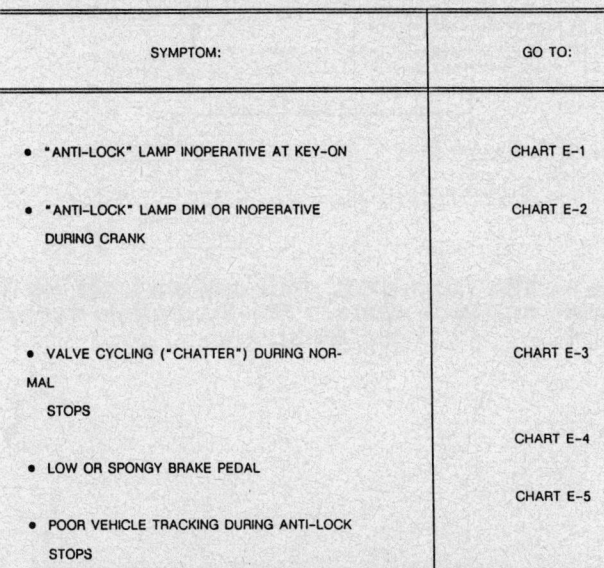

SYMPTOM:	GO TO:
• "ANTI-LOCK" LAMP INOPERATIVE AT KEY-ON	CHART E-1
• "ANTI-LOCK" LAMP DIM OR INOPERATIVE DURING CRANK	CHART E-2
• VALVE CYCLING ("CHATTER") DURING NORMAL STOPS	CHART E-3
	CHART E-4
• LOW OR SPONGY BRAKE PEDAL	
	CHART E-5
• POOR VEHICLE TRACKING DURING ANTI-LOCK STOPS	

Fig. 129   Chart E, symptom diagnosis. 1989–90 models except 6000

CHART E-1
"ANTI-LOCK" LAMP INOPERATIVE AT KEY-ON

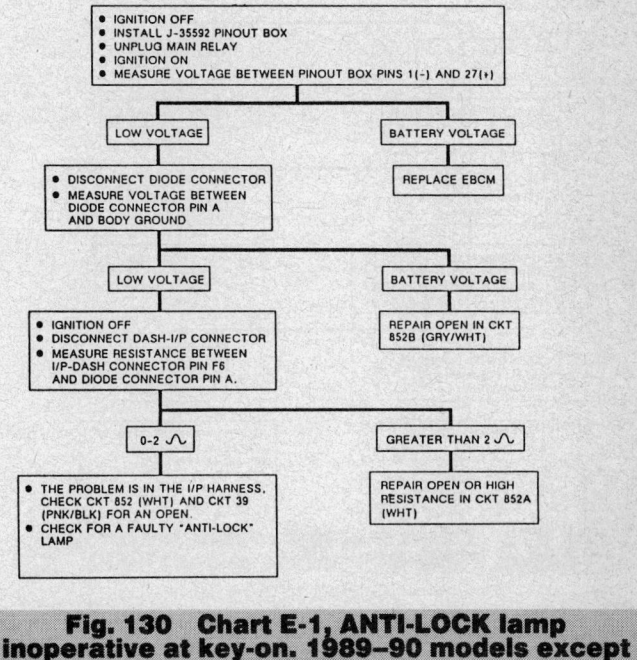

Fig. 130   Chart E-1, ANTI-LOCK lamp inoperative at key-on. 1989–90 models except 6000

CHART E-2
"ANTI-LOCK" LAMP DIM OR INOP DURING CRANK

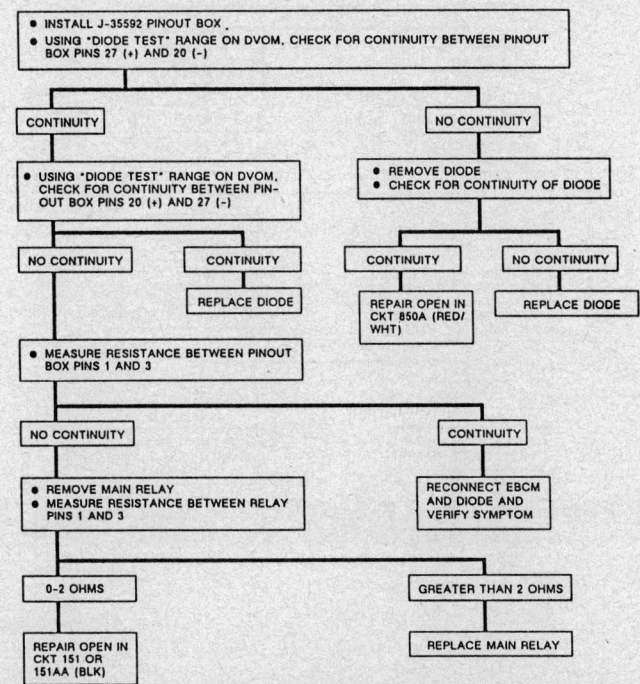

Fig. 131   Chart E-1, ANTI-LOCK lamp dim or inop during crank. 1989–90 models except 6000

CHART E-3
VALVE CYCLING ("CHATTER") DURING NORMAL STOPS

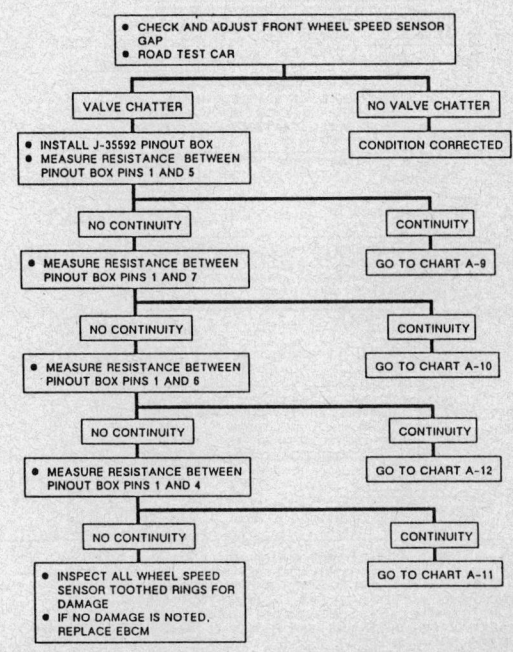

Fig. 132   Chart E-2, valve cycling (chatter) during normal stops. 1989–90 models except 6000

CHART E-4
LOW OR SPONGY BRAKE PEDAL

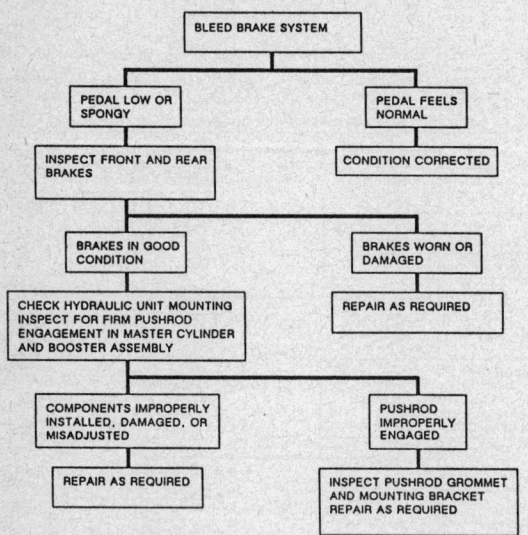

Fig. 133 Chart E-4, low or spongy brake pedal. 1989–90 models except 6000

CHART E-5
POOR VEHICLE TRACKING DURING ANTI-LOCK STOPS

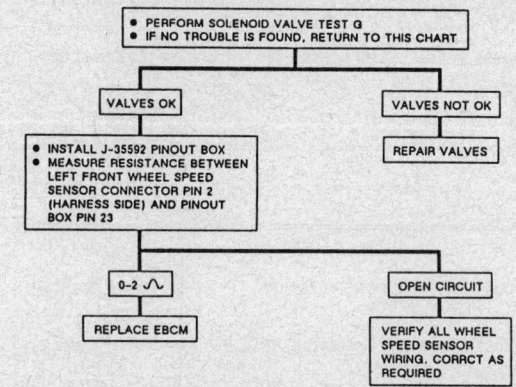

Fig. 134 Chart E-5, poor vehicle tracking during anti-lock stops. 1989–90 models except 6000

TEST F
WHEEL SPEED SENSOR OUTPUT

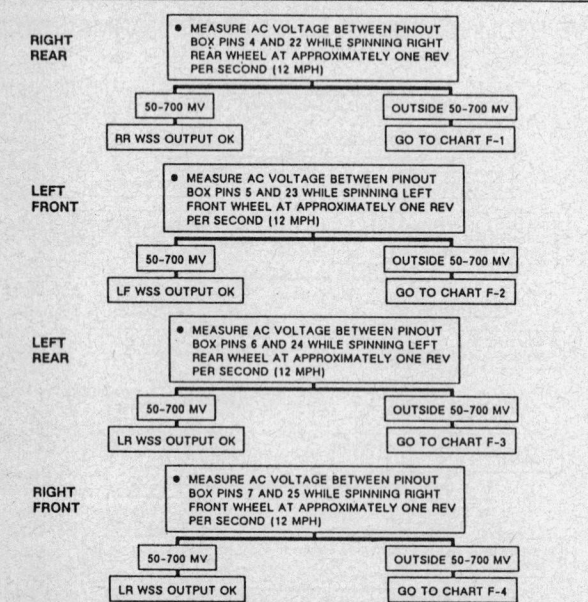

IF NO TROUBLE IS FOUND WITH WHEEL SPEED SENSOR OUTPUT, CONSIDER THAT:
- OUTPUT SHOULD NOT BE SIGNIFICANTLY DIFFERENT FROM LF TO RF AND LR TO RR
- FRONT WSS OUTPUT SHOULD BE SLIGHTLY HIGHER THAN REAR WSS OUTPUT
- IMPROPER OUTPUT MAY BE CAUSED BY MIS-ADJUSTED FRONT SENSOR
- WHEEL SPEED SENSOR CABLES SOMETIMES CAN INTERMITTENTLY GO OPEN, PARTICULARLY IN THE WHEELHOUSE AREA. MANIPULATE THE CABLES BY HAND WHEN INSPECTING FOR AN OPEN CIRCUIT
- TOOTHED SENSOR RINGS SHOULD ALSO BE INSPECTED FOR DAMAGE OR MISSING TEETH

Fig. 135 Chart F, wheel speed sensor output. 1989–90 models except 6000

CHART F-1
RIGHT REAR WSS OUTPUT

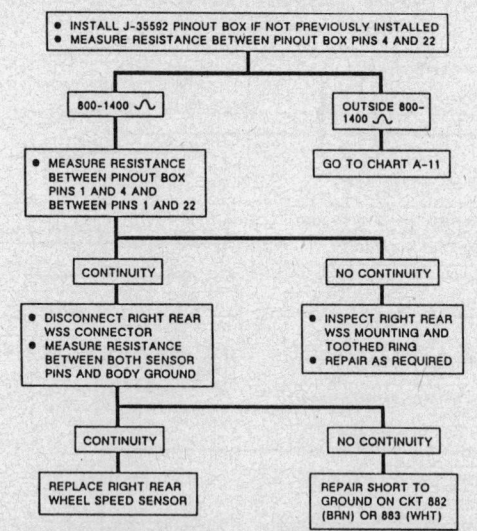

Fig. 136 Chart F-1, right rear WSS output. 1989–90 models except 6000

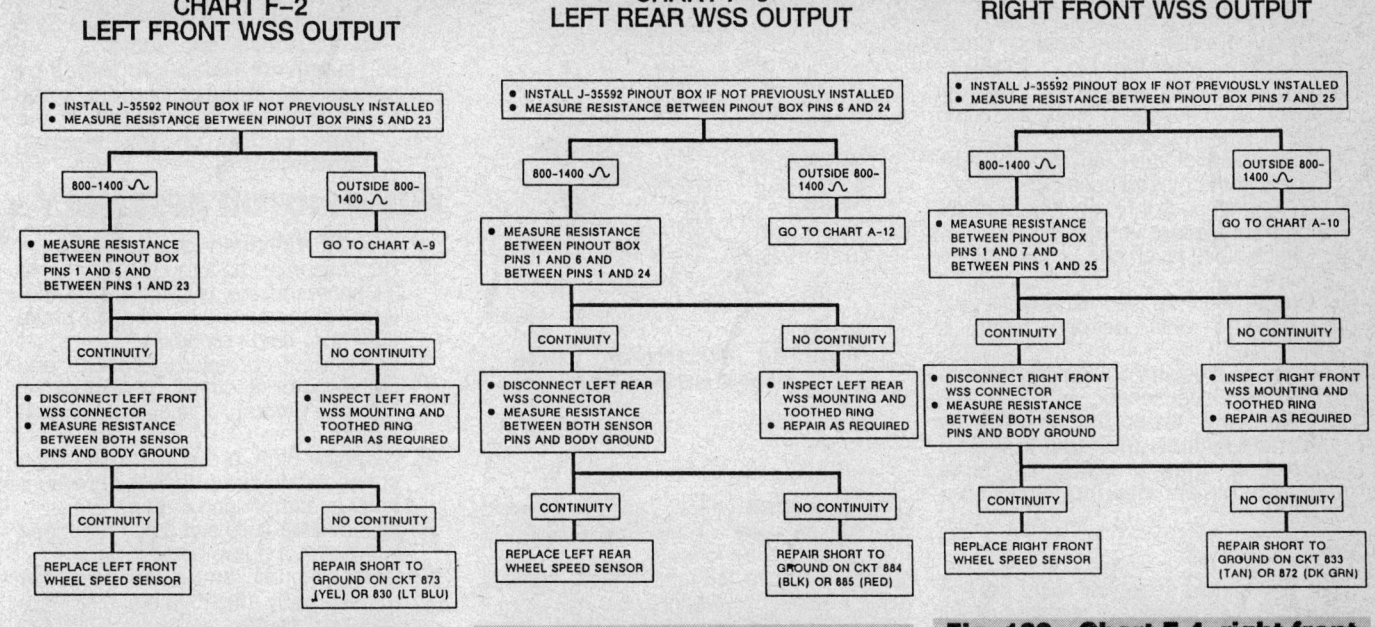

Fig. 137   Chart F-2, left front WSS output. 1989-90 models except 6000

Fig. 138   Chart F-3, left rear WSS output. 1989-90 models except 6000

Fig. 139   Chart F-4, right front WSS output. 1989-90 models except 6000

TEST G
SOLENOID VALVES

- THE FOLLOWING TEST MAY BE PERFORMED FOR INDIVIDUAL PAIRS OF SOLENOID VALVES (AS DIRECTED BY THE APPROPRIATE DIAGNOSTIC PROCEDURE) OR FOR ALL SENSORS AS A SYSTEM CHECK
- TO SET UP FOR TEST:
  - INSTALL J-35592
  - RAISE CAR SO THAT WHEELS CLEAR THE GROUND
  - AN ASSISTANT MAY BE REQUIRED TO SPIN THE WHEELS
- NOTICE: DO NOT LEAVE IGNITION ON FOR MORE THAN 30 SECONDS WITH JUMPER WIRES INSTALLED AS DESCRIBED BELOW. SOLENOID VALVE DAMAGE MAY RESULT

LEFT FRONT VALVES

- IGNITION OFF
- JUMPER PINOUT BOX PINS 2, 16 AND 35 TOGETHER
- APPLY MODERATE BRAKE PEDAL FORCE AND CHECK THAT THE LEFT FRONT WHEEL WILL NOT TURN

| WHEEL DOESN'T TURN | WHEEL TURNS |

- BRIEFLY TURN THE IGNITION ON WHILE STILL APPLYING PEDAL FORCE
- CHECK TO SEE IF WHEEL WILL NOW TURN

REPLACE VALVE BLOCK

WHEEL TURNS → LEFT FRONT VALVES OK

WHEEL DOESN'T TURN → REPLACE VALVE BLOCK

RIGHT FRONT VALVES

- IGNITION OFF
- JUMPER PINOUT BOX PINS 2, 15 AND 34 TOGETHER
- APPLY MODERATE BRAKE PEDAL FORCE AND CHECK THAT THE RIGHT FRONT WHEEL WILL NOT TURN

| WHEEL DOESN'T TURN | WHEEL TURNS |

- BRIEFLY TURN THE IGNITION ON WHILE STILL APPLYING PEDAL FORCE
- CHECK TO SEE IF WHEEL WILL NOW TURN

REPLACE VALVE BLOCK

WHEEL TURNS → RIGHT FRONT VALVES OK

WHEEL DOESN'T TURN → REPLACE VALVE BLOCK

REAR VALVES

- IGNITION OFF
- JUMPER PINOUT BOX PINS 2, 17 AND 33 TOGETHER
- APPLY MODERATE BRAKE PEDAL FORCE AND CHECK THAT EITHER REAR WHEEL WILL NOT TURN

| WHEEL DOESN'T TURN | WHEEL TURNS |

- BRIEFLY TURN THE IGNITION ON WHILE STILL APPLYING PEDAL FORCE
- CHECK TO SEE IF WHEEL WILL NOW TURN

REPLACE VALVE BLOCK

WHEEL TURNS → REAR VALVES OK

WHEEL DOESN'T TURN → REPLACE VALVE BLOCK

Fig. 140   Test G, solenoid valves. 1989-90 models except 6000

BRAKE SYSTEM FILLING

Ensure pump is not allowed to run for more than 60 seconds at one time. If pump must be run longer, allow pump to cool for several seconds between 60 second runs.
1. Depressurize accumulator, refer to ""Depressurizing Hydraulic Accumulator" procedure.
2. Fill reservoir to full mark using DOT 3 brake fluid or equivalent.

BRAKE SYSTEM BLEEDING
Manual Bleeding

The front hydraulic circuits may be manually bled in the same manner as conventional brakes. The rear brakes must be pressure bled according to the following procedure.

Pressure Bleeding

Only the rear brakes must be pressure bled. Front hydraulic circuits may be bled manually. To prevent air, moisture and other contaminants from entering system, only diaphragm type pressure bleeding equipment should be used.

Front Circuit

1. Disconnect battery ground cable, then depressurize hydraulic accumulator. See "Depressurizing Hydraulic Accumulator."
2. Disconnect fluid level sensor electrical connector, then remove sensor.
3. Install brake bleeder adapter tool No. J-35798 or equivalent, in place of sensor.
4. Attach diaphragm type brake bleeder tool No. J 29532 or equivalent, to fluid reservoir, then charge to 20 psi.
5. Raise and support vehicle. Attach a clear bleeder hose to a front bleeder

valve, then submerse the other end in a clear container partially filled with DOT 3 brake fluid.

6. Open bleeder valve, using brake bleeder wrench tool No. J 21472 or equivalent open end wrench, then allow fluid to flow from bleeder until no air is seen in brake fluid.
7. Close bleeder valve, ensuring bleeder seats in the closed position.
8. Repeat steps 5 through 7 on remaining front bleeder valve.
9. Check fluid level and adjust as required.
10. Check pedal for sponginess. Repeat procedure until desired pedal is achieved.
11. Remove bleeding equipment, then install fluid level sensor.
12. **Reactivate Delco-Loc radios by turning ignition and radio to the On position, then pressing the Mute button on the steering wheel control.**

Rear Circuit

Fill brake fluid reservoir with DOT 3 brake fluid. Keep reservoir at least half full during procedure.
1. Turn ignition switch to On position and allow system to charge. **Pump motor will stop when system is charged.**
2. Raise and support vehicle. Attach a clear bleeder hose to rear bleeder valve, then submerse the other end in a clear container partially filled with DOT 3 brake fluid.
3. Open bleeder valve using brake bleeder wrench tool No. J 21472 or equivalent open end wrench, then with ignition switch in On position, depress brake pedal for at least 10 seconds. **Do not allow pump to run more than 60 seconds at a time. If pump must be run longer than 60 seconds, allow pump to cool between 60 second runs.**
4. Allow fluid to flow from bleeder until no air is seen in brake fluid. Repeat step 3 if necessary.
5. Close bleeder valve, then repeat steps 2 through 4 on remaining rear bleeder valve.
6. Lower vehicle. Check reservoir fluid level and adjust as required.
7. Check pedal for sponginess. If condition exists, repeat procedure until desired pedal is achieved. **Do not move vehicle until a firm brake pedal is achieved.**

COMPONENT REPLACEMENT

On models equipped with Supplemental Inflatable Restraint (SIR) system, serious injury can result from unintended airbag deployment.

The SIR system is designed to retain sufficient voltage to deploy the airbag for a short time after power has been disconnected. To avoid serious injury, disarm the SIR as follows:
1. Turn ignition switch to Off position.
2. Remove SIR fuse from fuse panel.

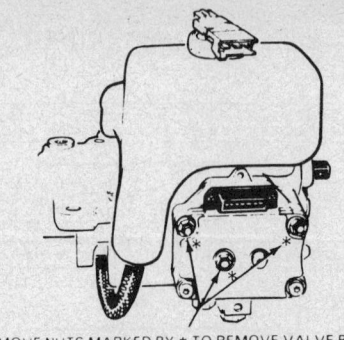

REMOVE NUTS MARKED BY ＊ TO REMOVE VALVE BLOCK

Fig. 141 Removing valve block assembly

3. Disconnect yellow two-way connector at base of steering column, if equipped, as follows:
   a. Remove lefthand sound insulator retaining screws and nuts.
   b. Remove courtesy lamp from sound insulator, then the sound insulator from vehicle.
   c. Remove Connector Position Assurance (CPA) pin, then disconnect yellow two-way connector at base of steering column.
4. Wait at least 10 minutes before any further work is attempted. Serious injury may result from unintended airbag deployment if service is attempted immediately after SIR fuse is removed.
5. Reverse procedure to arm SIR system, noting the following:
   a. Turn ignition switch to On position.
   b. Observe INFALATABLE RESTRAINT indicator lamp.
   c. If lamp does not flash 7-9 times then remain Off, refer to "Passive Restraint Systems" for diagnosis.

HYDRAULIC UNIT

1. Disconnect battery ground cable.
2. Depressurize accumulator, refer to ""Depressurizing Hydraulic Accumulator" procedure.
3. Disconnect all hydraulic unit electrical connectors, then remove all brake fluid from fluid reservoir.
4. Remove pump attaching bolt, then position energy unit aside to gain access to brake pipes.
5. Disconnect hydraulic lines to valve block. Use caution not to twist lines.
6. **On 6000 models,** remove line attaching hydraulic unit to combination valve.
7. **On all models,** disconnect push rod from brake pedal, then push dust boot forward, past hex on pushrod.
8. Separate pushrod halves, then remove hydraulic unit to pushrod attaching bolts.
9. Remove hydraulic unit from vehicle. **Front half of pushrod will remain locked into hydraulic unit.**
10. Reverse procedure to install, noting the following:

a. **Torque** support bracket attaching bolts to 37 ft. lbs.
b. Bleed brakes, refer to "Brake System Bleeding" procedure.
c. **Reactivate Delco-Loc radios by turning ignition and radio to the On position, then pressing the Mute button on the steering wheel control.**

PUMP MOTOR ASSEMBLY

1. Disconnect battery ground cable.
2. Depressurize accumulator, refer to ""Depressurizing Hydraulic Accumulator" procedure, then remove brake fluid from fluid reservoir.
3. Disconnect pressure switch and pump motor electrical connectors.
4. Remove hydraulic accumulator and O-ring.
5. Remove high pressure hose fitting connected to pump, then the pressure hose assembly and O-rings.
6. Remove wire clip and pull return hose fitting out of pump body.
7. Remove pump and motor assembly to main body attaching bolt and insulator grommets.
8. Remove pump and motor assembly by sliding off of locating pin.
9. Check insulators for damage or deterioration. Replace as required.
10. Reverse procedure to install. **Reactivate Delco-Loc radios by turning ignition and radio to the On position, then pressing the Mute button on the steering wheel control.**

VALVE BLOCK ASSEMBLY

1. Disconnect battery ground cable.
2. Depressurize accumulator, refer to ""Depressurizing Hydraulic Accumulator" procedure.
3. Remove hydraulic unit, then the three nuts and washers from valve block as shown in **Fig. 141.**
4. Remove valve block assembly and O-rings by sliding valve block off studs.
5. Reverse procedure to install. **Reactivate Delco-Loc radios by turning ignition and radio to the On position, then pressing the Mute button on the steering wheel control.**

PRESSURE/WARNING SWITCH

1. Disconnect battery ground cable.
2. Depressurize accumulator, refer to ""Depressurizing Hydraulic Accumulator" procedure.
3. Disconnect pressure switch electrical connector.
4. Remove pressure switch and O-ring using pressure switch socket tool No, J 35804-A or equivalent.
5. Reverse procedure to install, noting the following:
   a. Lubricate new O-ring with clean brake fluid.
   b. **Torque** pressure switch to 17 ft. lbs.
   c. Turn ignition switch to On position and ensure BRAKE light goes out within 60 seconds.
   d. **Reactivate Delco-Loc radios by**

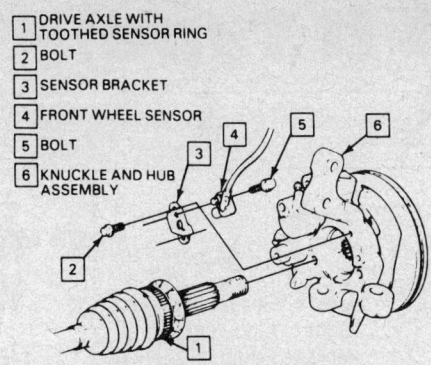

1 DRIVE AXLE WITH TOOTHED SENSOR RING
2 BOLT
3 SENSOR BRACKET
4 FRONT WHEEL SENSOR
5 BOLT
6 KNUCKLE AND HUB ASSEMBLY

Fig. 142   Front wheel sensor

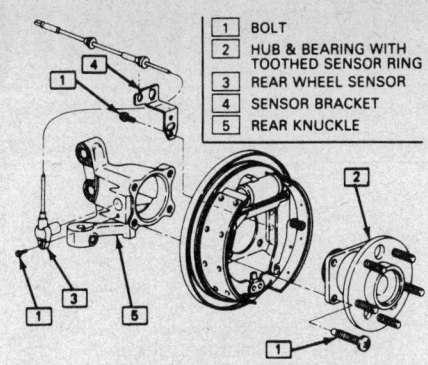

1 BOLT
2 HUB & BEARING WITH TOOTHED SENSOR RING
3 REAR WHEEL SENSOR
4 SENSOR BRACKET
5 REAR KNUCKLE

Fig. 143   Rear wheel sensor. Except 6000

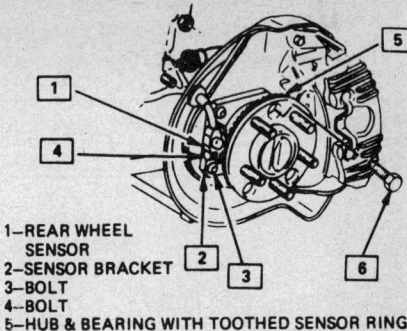

1—REAR WHEEL SENSOR
2—SENSOR BRACKET
3—BOLT
4—BOLT
5—HUB & BEARING WITH TOOTHED SENSOR RING
6—BOLT

Fig. 144   Rear wheel sensor. 1988 6000

turning ignition and radio to the On position, then pressing the Mute button on the steering wheel control.

HYDRAULIC ACCUMULATOR

1. Disconnect battery ground cable.
2. Depressurize accumulator, refer to ""Depressurizing Hydraulic Accumulator" procedure.
3. Remove accumulator and O-ring.
4. Reverse procedure to install, noting the following:
   a. Lubricate new O-ring with clean brake fluid.
   b. **Torque** accumulator to 17 ft. lbs.
   c. Turn ignition switch to On position and ensure BRAKE light goes out within 60 seconds.
   d. **Reactivate Delco-Loc radios by turning ignition and radio to the On position, then pressing the Mute button on the steering wheel control.**

FLUID RESERVOIR & SEALS

1. Disconnect battery ground cable.
2. Depressurize accumulator, refer to ""Depressurizing Hydraulic Accumulator" procedure.
3. Drain fluid reservoir, remove return hose, then drain brake fluid reservoir into a suitable container.
4. Remove fluid level sensor electrical connectors.
5. Remove reservoir-to-valve block mounting bracket attaching bolt.
6. Remove reservoir by carefully prying between master cylinder and reservoir.
7. Remove O-ring seals from hydraulic unit.
8. Reverse procedure to install, noting the following:
   a. Lubricate O-ring seals with clean DOT 3 brake fluid.
   b. **Torque** reservoir retaining bolt to 44 inch lbs.
   c. **Reactivate Delco-Loc radios by turning ignition and radio to the On position, then pressing the Mute button on the steering wheel control.**

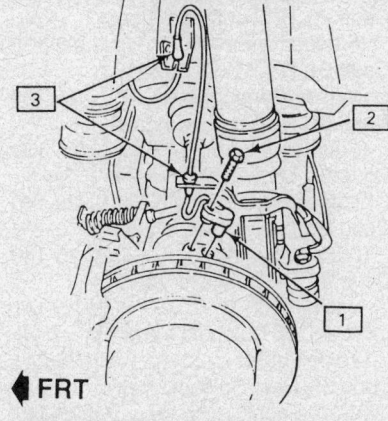

◄ FRT

1 – REAR WHEEL SPEED SENSOR
2 – MOUNTING BOLT
3 – GROMMET

Fig. 145   Rear wheel sensor. 1989–90 6000

WHEEL SENSOR

Front Wheel

1. Raise and support vehicle, then remove wheel.
2. Disconnect sensor electrical connector from wiring harness.
3. Remove sensor attaching bolts, **Fig. 142**, then the sensor.
4. Reverse procedure to install, noting the following:
   a. **On all models except 1989 6000, torque** sensor attaching bolt to 84 inch lbs. On 1989-90 6000 models, **torque** sensor attaching bolt to 53 inch lbs.
   b. If wheel sensor is reused, adjust air gap to .028 inches on 6000 models, or .040 inches on 1988 models except 6000 using a suitable feeler gauge. On all 1989-90 models except 6000, wheel sensor is automatically adjusted when installed. New sensors come equipped with a paper spacer which will properly gap the sensor when placed against speed sensor ring.
   c. **On 1989–90 6000 models, torque** sensor lock bolt to 19 inch lbs. On all other models, **torque** sensor lock bolt to 22 inch lbs.
   d. Ensure wire does not come in contact with suspension parts.

Rear Wheel

1. If the right rear sensor is to be removed, remove spare tire assembly, then fold back carpeting in corner of luggage compartment to gain access to sensor connector.
2. Disconnect sensor electrical connector from wiring harness.
3. Release the cable grommet, working the sensor cable and connector down through underbody.
4. Raise and support vehicle.
5. Remove rear wheel assembly.
6. **On all models except 6000,** proceed as follows:
   a. Remove grommet attaching screws.
   b. Remove sensor attaching bolts, **Fig. 143,** then the sensor.
7. **On 1988 6000 models,** proceed as follows:
   a. Remove caliper attaching bolts, then position caliper aside using wire. Use caution not to bend or twist fluid line.
   b. Remove rotor assembly.
   c. Remove sensor attaching bolts, **Fig. 144,** then the sensor.
8. **On 1989-90 6000 models,** proceed as follows:
   a. Remove sensor mounting bolt.
   b. Remove sensor, then the sensor cable and grommet, **Fig. 145.**
9. **On all models,** reverse procedure to install, noting the following:
   a. **On all 1988-90 models and 1988 6000 models, torque** sensor attaching bolt to 84 inch lbs. On 1989 6000 models, **torque** sensor attaching bolt to 75 inch lbs. On 1990 6000 models, **torque sensor attaching bolt to 80 inch lbs.**
   b. **On 6000 models,** if wheel sensor is reused, adjust air gap to .028 inches using a suitable feeler gauge. New sensors come equipped with a paper spacer which will properly gap the sensor when placed against speed sensor ring.
   c. **On all models except 6000,** wheel sensor is automatically adjusted when installed.
   d. **On 1988 6000 models, torque** caliper attaching bolts to 22 inch lbs., if equipped.
   e. Ensure wire does not come in contact with suspension parts.

NOTE: Wire Code Identification and Symbol Identification located in the front of this manual can be used as an aid when using wiring circuits found in this section.

INDEX

DESCRIPTION

The Bosch anti-lock brake II system (ABS II), **Fig. 1**, maintains vehicle steerablity, directional stability, and maximum deceleration under severe braking conditions. The ABS II performs this function by monitoring rotational speed and controlling line pressure of each vehicle wheel during a braking maneuver, to prevent the braked wheels from locking.

SYSTEM COMPONENTS

The ABS II consists of a modulator valve, control module, lateral acceleration switch, wheel speed sensors and toothed rings, fuse, wiring harness and relay.

MODULATOR VALVE

The modulator valve, **Fig. 2**, consists of three rapidly switching solenoid valves, two accumulator chambers (one for each brake circuit) and a return pump. One solenoid valve is assigned to each front wheel brake, the third is assigned to the rear wheel brakes. This system is known as a "Three-channel system."

The modulator valve receives its instructions from control module. The modular valve regulates brake fluid pressure based upon road conditions as interpreted

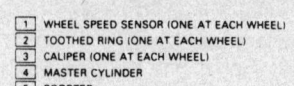

1	WHEEL SPEED SENSOR (ONE AT EACH WHEEL)	6	LATERAL ACCELERATION SWITCH
2	TOOTHED RING (ONE AT EACH WHEEL)	7	MODULE RELAY
3	CALIPER (ONE AT EACH WHEEL)	8	ANTILOCK WARNING LIGHT
4	MASTER CYLINDER	9	CONTROL MODULE
5	BOOSTER	10	MODULATOR VALVE

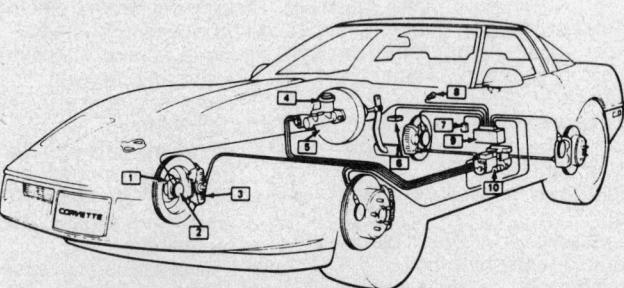

Fig. 1   Bosch anti-lock brake (ABS II) system

by the control module, regardless of master cylinder output pressure. **The modulator valve can maintain or reduce brake fluid pressure to the wheel calipers. However, the modulator valve can not increase the pressure above that sent by the master cylinder. The modulator valve alone can not apply the brakes.**

Two relays are mounted on top of modulator valve. These are the only replaceable parts of the modulator valve. The pump motor relay controls the return pump and the solenoid relay controls power supply to solenoid valves. Modulator valve is mounted in rear storage compartment located behind drivers seat. The modulator valve itself cannot be repaired and must be replaced as an assembly.

CONTROL MODULE

The control module consists of two printed circuit board plates. Resistors, diodes, transistors and large integrated circuits are mounted on one side of plates

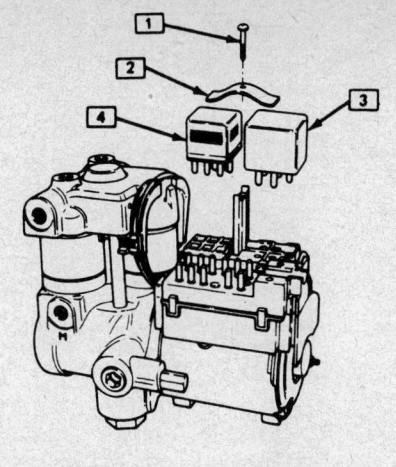

1	SCREW	3	PUMP MOTOR RELAY
2	RETAINER	4	SOLENOID RELAY

Fig. 2   Modulator valve

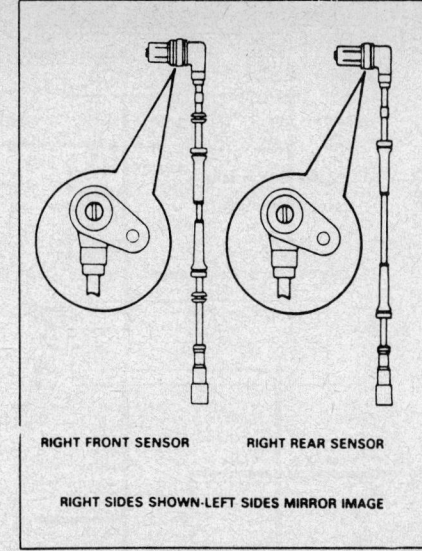

RIGHT FRONT SENSOR   RIGHT REAR SENSOR

RIGHT SIDES SHOWN-LEFT SIDES MIRROR IMAGE

Fig. 3   Wheel speed sensor

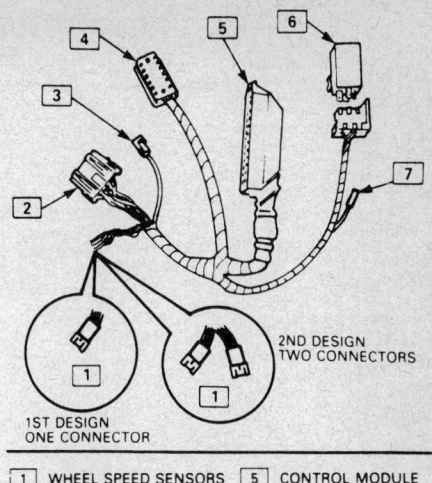

2ND DESIGN
TWO CONNECTORS

1ST DESIGN
ONE CONNECTOR

1	WHEEL SPEED SENSORS	5	CONTROL MODULE
2	BODY HARNESS	6	MODULE RELAY
3	BATTERY FEED	7	DIODE
4	MODULATOR VALVE		

Fig. 4   Wiring harness connector

and both sides have conductor paths. These integrated circuits (IC), contain thousands of transistors, resistors and diodes mounted on a single silicon chip. Plates are housed in control module and surrounded by light alloy casting.

Wheel acceleration, deceleration and slip values are calculated from electric signals, transmitted from wheel speed sensors, which are proportional to wheel speed. Electrical signals from this module produce commands for the hydraulic modulator valves.

The control module is located in rear storage compartment behind drivers seat. If control module is defective, it must be replaced as an assembly. **No attempt should be made to repair this module.**

LATERAL ACCELERATION SWITCH (ACCELEROMETER)

The lateral acceleration switch is made up of two mercury switches connected in series. They are used to detect if the vehicle is cornering faster than a predetermined curve speed. When this speed is exceeded, one of two switches opens up and sends a signal to control module.

The lateral acceleration switch is located under the A/C control head on the floor pan. This switch is not serviceable and should be replaced as an assembly.

WHEEL SPEED SENSORS

Rotational speed of each wheel is detected separately by an inductive wheel speed sensor, **Fig. 3**. Electrical signal sensed from the speed sensors are transmitted to control module.

In this system, front wheels are controlled individually and rear wheels together. Control of rear wheels works on the "Select Low" principle. "Select Low" means wheel with the greatest tendency to lock-up (lower tire to road friction

co-efficient), determines level of control.

Wheel speed sensors are installed in knuckles. Toothed rings are pressed onto front hub and bearing assemblies and rear drive shaft spindles. **The wheel speed sensors do not require adjustment.**

WIRING HARNESS, RELAY & FUSE

The ABS II system has its own wiring harness, located in rear storage compartment behind drivers seat. This harness is connected to the standard wiring harness. The wiring harness, **Fig. 4**, provides a path for inputs from the wheel speed sensors, lateral acceleration switch, power and stop light switch to control module and output signals from the control module to the modulator valve and warning lamps.

The module relay is installed in circuit between battery, fuse and control module. This relay protects the control module from possible excessive voltage spikes, due to a faulty alternator.

The fuse located in the main fuse panel labeled BRAKE, provides protection for main power feed circuit of the ABS electrical system. The GAGE fuse is also tied into the main power feed of the ABS.

OPERATION

When ignition switch is turned to On position, amber ANTI-LOCK warning lamp in the instrument panel illuminates. When engine is started, it goes out. If ABS warning light does not go out or comes on permanently while driving, it indicates a fault in ABS system.

When starting vehicle, the control module performs a functional check of electrical circuitry. The test cycle checks components of the monitoring circuit as well as the logic section. Test sample signals are sent to the control module, which checks whether or not the correct output signals are available.

Since the ABS system may not be used every day, there is an additional test which actually runs the modulator valve. Whenever ignition switch is turned to On position and vehicle reaches 4 mph, the test starts. Operation of the modular valve can be heard and felt, if the driver's foot is on the brake pedal. This test is performed once, each time the vehicle is started.

This system continuously monitors the following components: modulator valve, control module, lateral acceleration switch, wheel speed sensors, wiring harness and relays.

The control module constantly monitors its own supply voltage. If supply voltage drops below a predetermined value, ABS will be switched Off and the amber ANTI-LOCK lamp will come on. When supplied voltage returns to or exceeds the predetermined value, ANTI-LOCK lamp will go off. If a fault occurs in ABS, the ANTI-LOCK warning lamp comes on and ABS will be switched off. The system will remain off until vehicle is restarted at which time the functional check is repeated.

DIAGNOSIS
1988–89 Models

Refer to **Figs. 5 through 10,** during diagnostic procedures.

PRE-DIAGNOSIS INSPECTION

If a malfunction in the ABS system occurs, perform the following:
1. Ensure control module connector is securely connected.
2. Ensure that all ABS connectors are securely connected.
3. Check BRAKE and GAUGE for defective fuse.
4. If malfunction is still present after performing steps 1 through 3, refer to "System Check" procedure.

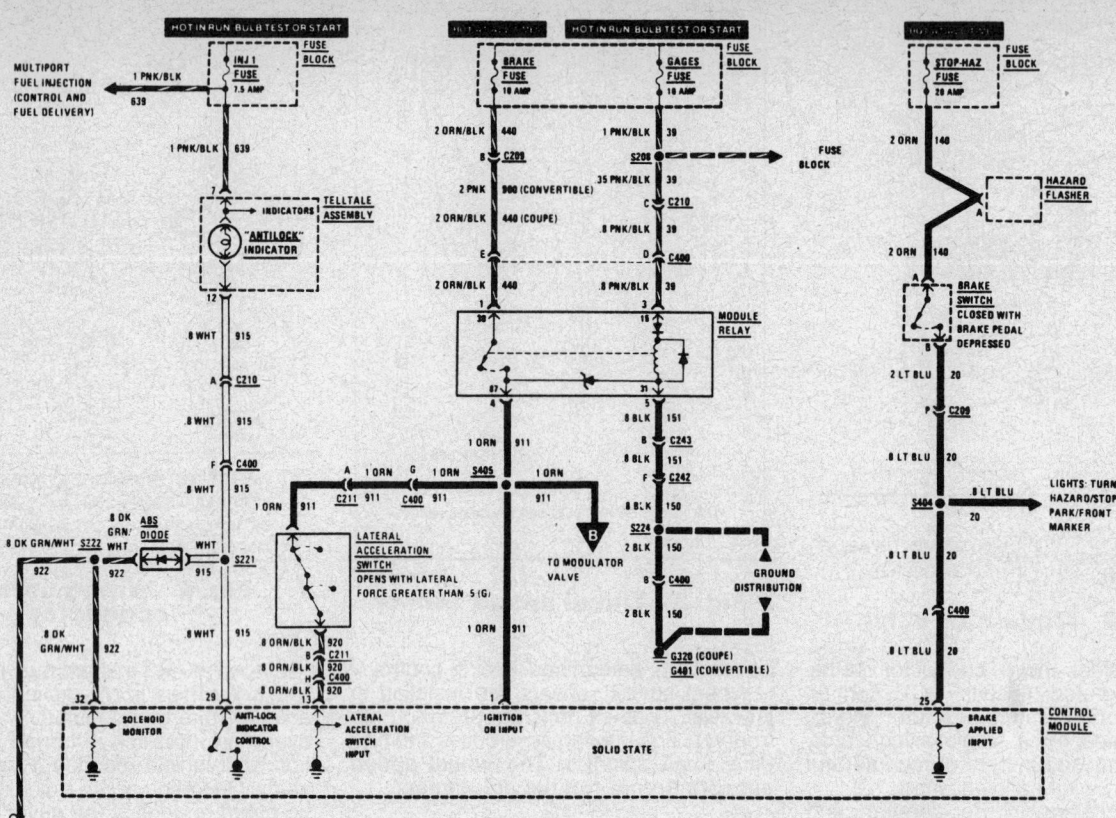

Fig. 5   Anti-lock brake system wiring schematic (Part 1 of 3). 1988

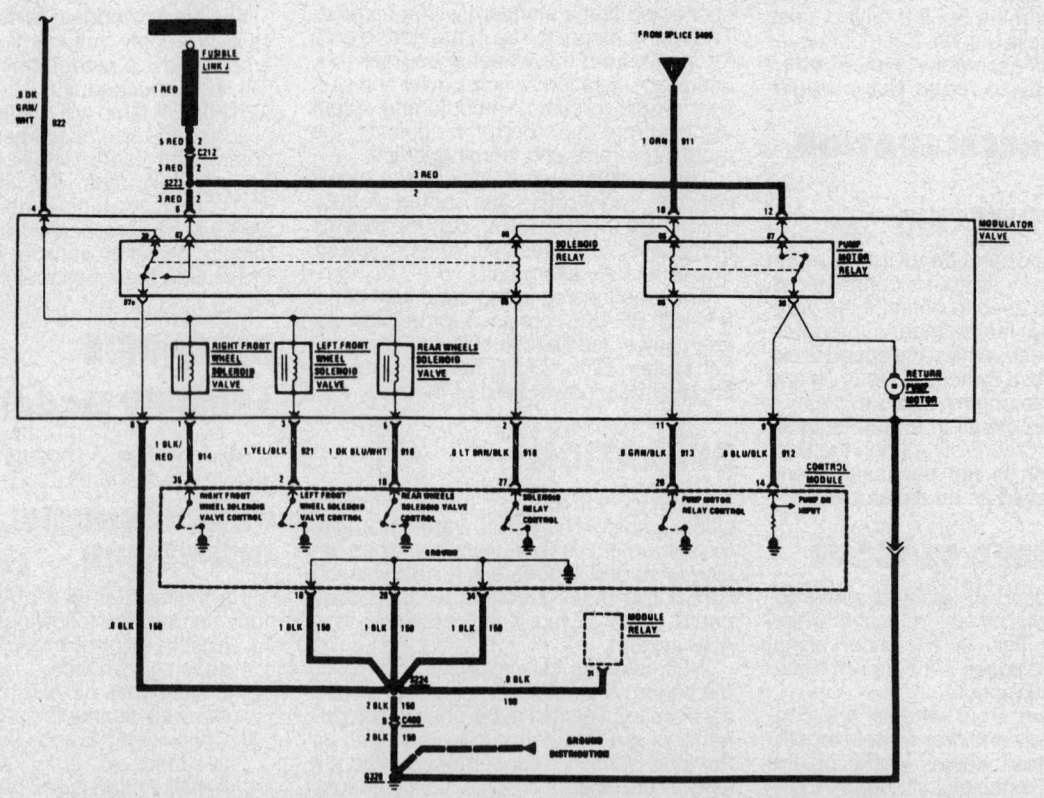

Fig. 5   Anti-lock brake system wiring schematic (Part 2 of 3). 1988

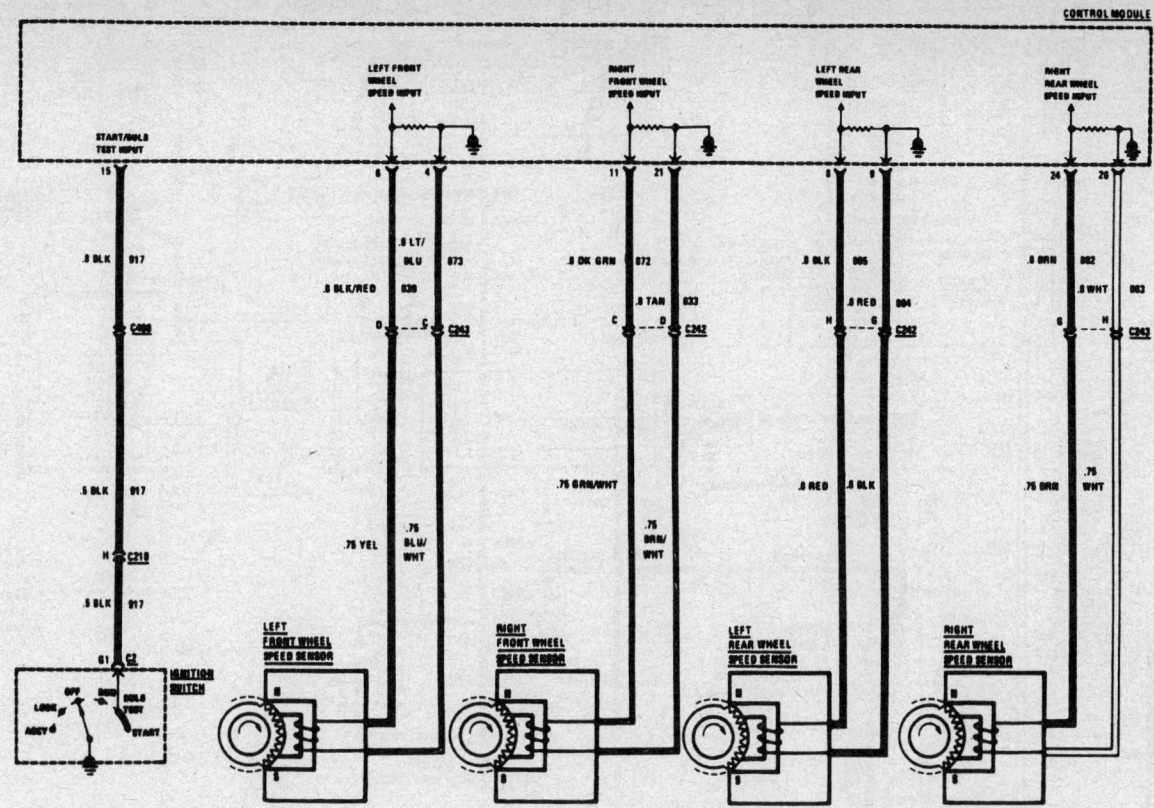

Fig. 5   Anti-lock brake system wiring schematic (Part 3 of 3). 1988

SYSTEM CHECK PROCEDURE

1. Release parking brake, then turn ignition switch to Run position. Amber ANTI-LOCK indicator lamp should light for several seconds.
2. Apply and release parking brake. Red BRAKE indicator lamp should light when parking brake is applied.
3. Start engine. ANTI-LOCK indicator lamp should remain illuminated during cranking.
4. Test drive vehicle at speeds between 20 and 30 mph. Use normal braking procedures to stop vehicle. Brake should operate smoothly and ANTI-LOCK indicator lamp should remain out.
5. Refer to "Diagnostic Procedure" if steps 1 through 4 are not satisfactory.

DIAGNOSTIC PROCEDURE

1. Turn ignition switch to Off position.
2. Disconnect ABS control module harness connector and connect it to ABS Tester tool No. J35890 or equivalent using the cable.
3. Follow manufacturers instructions for use of ABS Tester tool No. J35890-20 or equivalent.
4. Turn ignition switch to Run position to apply power to tester. Power-up messages will be displayed by tester in rapid sequence.

5. The ABS tester will display one or more messages. These messages are listed in SYMPTOM MESSAGE column of Symptom Directory chart, **Figs. 11 and 12**. Perform REPAIR ACTION as described in Symptom Directory chart by following pin-point tests, **Figs. 13 through 24**. Check tester manufacturer operating instructions for a description of test sequences and display messages.
6. After condition indicated by tester has been repaired, repeat entire test. This will reveal any other malfunction that may exist which has not been corrected.

1990 Models

On models equipped with Supplemental Inflatable Restraint (SIR) system, serious injury can result from unintended airbag deployment.

The SIR system is designed to retain sufficient voltage to deploy the airbag for a short time after power has been disconnected. To avoid serious injury, disarm the SIR as follows:

1. Turn ignition switch to Off position.
2. Remove Connector Position Assurance (CPA) pin, then disconnect yellow two-way connector at base of steering column.
3. Wait at least 10 minutes before any further work is attempted. Serious injury may result from unintended airbag deployment if service is attempted immediately after SIR fuse is removed.
4. Reverse procedure to arm SIR system, noting the following:
   a. Turn ignition switch to Run position.
   b. Observe INFL REST indicator lamp.
   c. If lamp does not illuminate for approximately 5 seconds then go out and remain remain Off for the next 100 seconds, refer to "Passive Restraint Systems" for diagnosis.

DESCRIPTION

The Electronic Brake Control Module (EBCM) monitors its own performance and certain input and output signals to determine if a system malfunction has occurred. Most ABS self-diagnostics are performed by the controller after the vehicle reaches 1.7 mph. For this reason, the vehicle must be road tested to check for malfunctions that will set fault codes.

The Built-In Test Equipment (BITE) test is performed once during each ignition cycle when the vehicle reaches 3-11 mph. The BITE test cycles each solenoid valve and the pump motor to test component operation. The EBCM also checks its own logic section and circuitry. If faults are detected during this test, the EBCM will set a code. The BITE test occurs once each ignition cycle as follows:

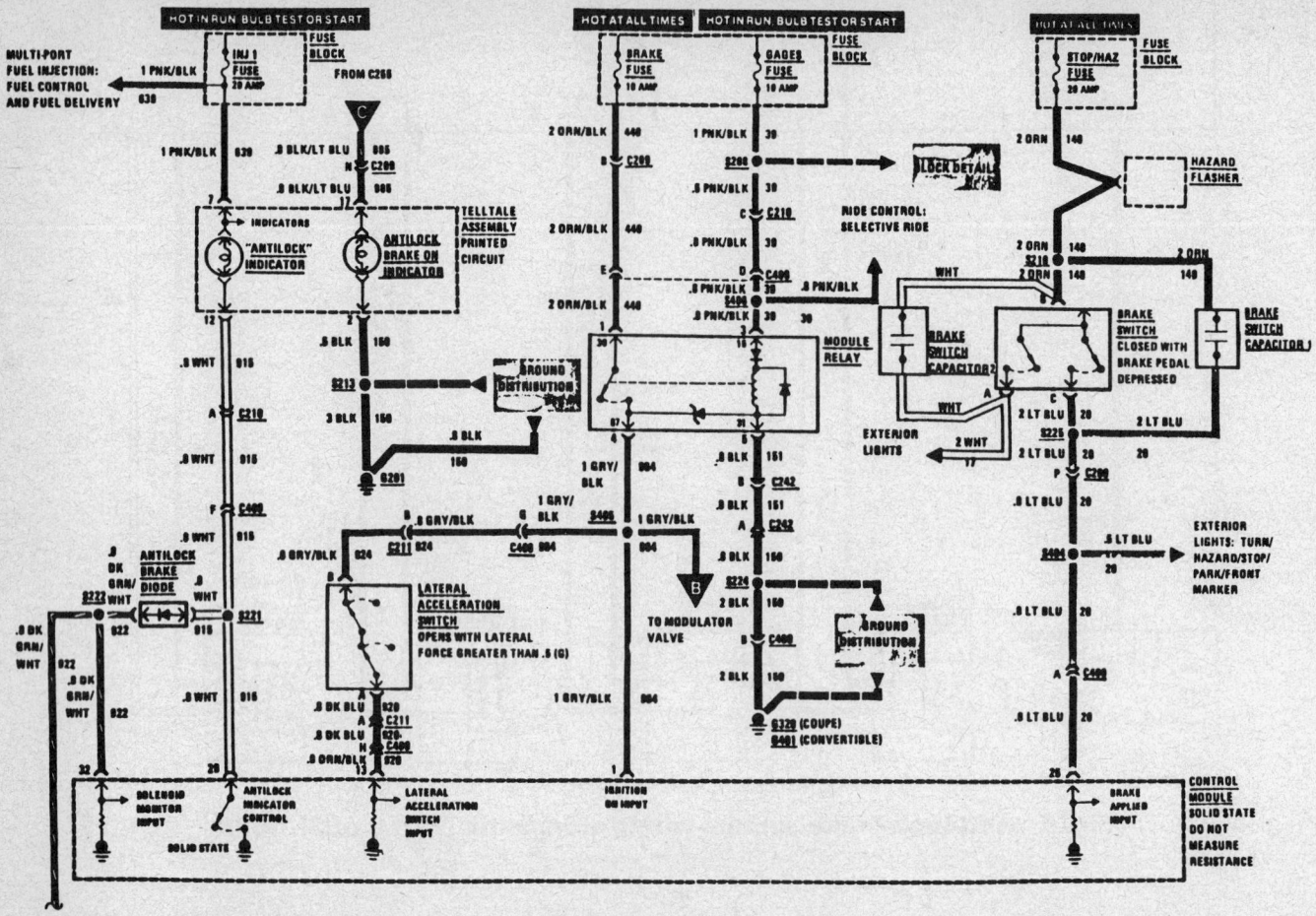

Fig. 6   Anti-lock brake system wiring schematic (Part 1 of 3). 1989

1. After receiving an Ignition On input, the EBCM grounds and activates the solenoid relay.
2. When the vehicle reaches 3-11 mph, the EBCM tests the solenoid valves and pump in the hydraulic modulator.
3. If the pump or solenoid valves fail to operate, the ABS will be disabled, a fault code will set and the SERVICE ABS indicator will illuminate.
4. When the EBCM receives a signal from any of the wheel speed sensors, it checks wheel speed sensor output. If any wheel speed sensor signal is missing, the ABS will be disabled, a fault code will set and the SERVICE ABS indicator will illuminate.

Once the vehicle is moving, the EBCM continuously monitors itself and the following components:

1. Modulator valves.
2. Wheel speed sensors.
3. Wiring harness and relays.
4. Battery voltage.

If battery voltage drops below approximately 9 volts, the ABS is disabled and the SERVICE ABS indicator will illuminate.

Each malfunction has an associated fault code, which is a two-digit number flashed over the SERVICE ABS lamp in the Driver Information Center (DIC). The system can store up to three fault code at once (in addition to Code 12). These codes may be either three separate fault codes, or three of the same codes if an intermittent condition occurs three times.

Some fault codes involving the solenoid valves and pump motor prevent the SERVICE ABS lamp from flashing. If one of these codes is present, the SERVICE ABS lamp will remain On and the system will be unable to enter the diagnostic display (flash codes) mode. In this case, the Tech 1 Diagnostic Computer tool No. 94-00101-A or equivalent must be used.

REQUIRED TEST EQUIPMENT

The following test equipment may be required during diagnostic procedures:

1. High Impedance Digital Multimeter tool No. J 34029-A or equivalent.
2. Pinout box tool No. J 35592 or equivalent.
3. Tech 1 Diagnostic Computer (with Bosch ABS ALDL Adapter) tool No. 94-00101-A or equivalent.

PRELIMINARY DIAGNOSTIC CHECKS

Refer to **Figs. 25 through 27**, during diagnostic procedures.

If a malfunction in the ABS system occurs, check the following before using the code diagnostic charts:

1. Check the STOP/HAZ, BRAKE, SIR and CLUSTER fuses.
2. Check fusible link J.
3. Ensure that all ABS connectors are securely connected.
4. Ensure control module connector is securely connected.
5. Check ABS system grounds.

ACCESSING FAULT CODES
Diagnostic Display Mode

To enable the diagnostic display mode, ground pin H of the ALDL connector, then turn the ignition On. The diagnostic display mode will remain enabled as long as pin H is grounded, serial data link communication has not been initiated and vehicle speed is less than 5 mph.

Approximately three seconds after ALDL pin H is grounded, the EBCM will begin the flash code sequence. The flash sequence will begin with Code 12 to signal the beginning of the fault code display. Each stored code will then be displayed three times. After all codes have been displayed, the sequence will repeat, starting with Code 12.

Some fault codes involving the solenoid valves and pump motor prevent the SERVICE ABS lamp from flashing. If one of these codes is present, the SERVICE ABS lamp will remain On and the system will be

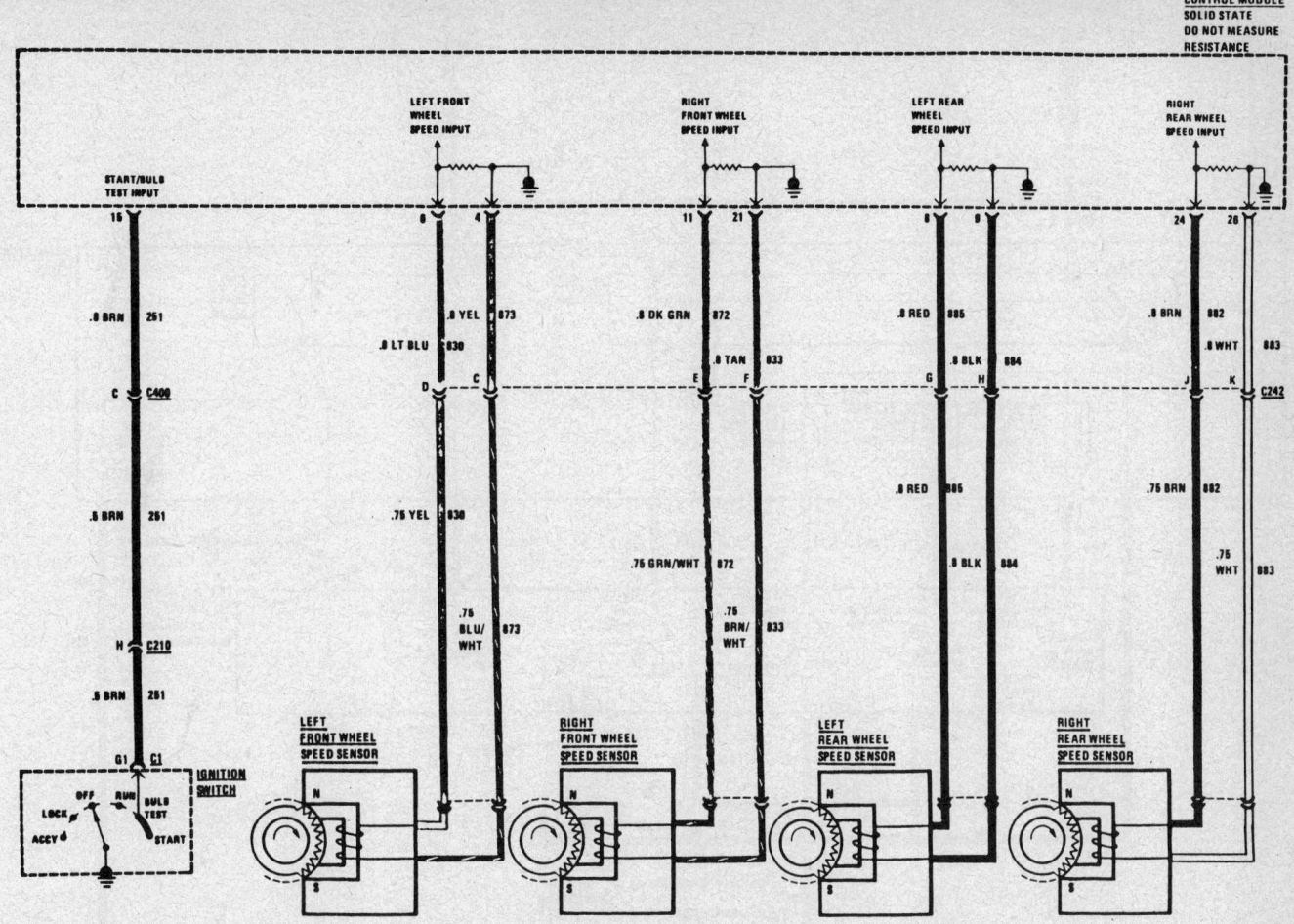

Fig. 6   Anti-lock brake system wiring schematic (Part 2 of 3). 1989

unable to enter the diagnostic display (flash codes) mode. In this case, the Tech 1 Diagnostic Computer must be used. Refer to procedure outlined under "Tech 1 Diagnostics."

CODE DEFINITION

Refer to **Fig. 28**, for code definition. Some codes can only be read through the ALDL connector using the Tech 1 Diagnostic Computer.

CODE DIAGNOSIS

Refer to **Figs. 29 through 45**, for fault code diagnostic procedures.

CLEARING CODES

Fault codes stored in the EBCM's memory can be erased in one of the three following ways:
1. Diagnostic Enable Line Procedure.
2. Tech 1 "Clear Codes" selection.
3. Ignition Cycle Default.
Whichever method is used, ensure to verify proper system operation and absence of fault codes when clearing procedure is completed.

The E'BCM will not allow codes to be cleared until all codes have been dis-

played. Codes cannot be cleared by disconnecting the EBCM, disconnecting battery cables or turning the ignition Off.

Diagnostic Enable Line Procedure

Clear codes using ALDL enable line (pin H) as follows:
1. Turn ignition Off.
2. Ground ALDL pin H.
3. Turn ignition On.
4. Wait for codes to begin flashing.
5. Unground pin H for at least one second, then ground pin H. This must be done three times within ten seconds.
6. Wait at least 15 seconds. Before turning ignition Off, verify that Code 12 is the only code being flashed. If not, codes have not been properly cleared. Repeat above procedure.

Tech 1 "Clear Codes" Procedure

Following tool manufacturer's instructions, select the appropriate menu, then select the "Clear Codes" function. Verify that codes are cleared by using Tech 1 to read codes. Refer to "Tech 1 Diagnostics" for procedure. If any codes other than Code 12 are present, codes were not cleared or a fault is still present.

Ignition Cycle Default

If the ignition is cycled 100 times without a particular fault reappearing, that particular fault code will be erased and the ignition cycle counter will be reset to zero.

TECH 1 DIAGNOSTICS

The Tech 1 has five test modes for diagnosing the ABS. The test modes are as follows:
1. Mode F0 - Data List: In this test mode, the Tech 1 continuously monitors wheel speed data and brake switch status.
2. Mode F1 - History Data: In this test mode, fault code history data is displayed. This data includes the number of ignition cycles since the fault code occurred and other information. Up to three fault codes are included in the ABS history data.
3. Mode F2 - Trouble Codes: In this test mode, trouble (fault) codes stored by the EBCM may be displayed or cleared.
4. Mode F3 - ABS Snapshot: In this test mode, the Tech 1 captures and records ABS data before and after a fault occurs.

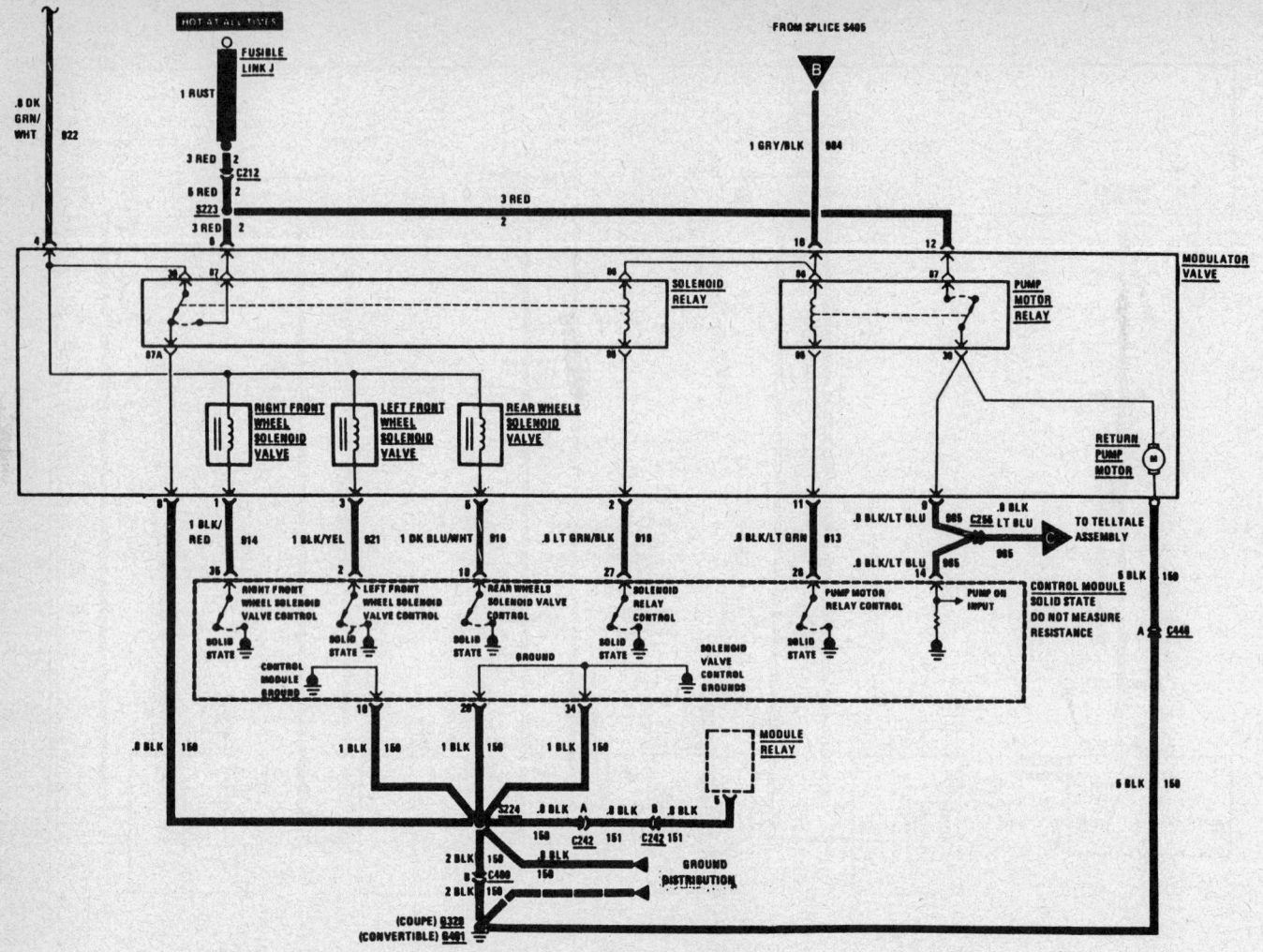

Fig. 6   Anti-lock brake system wiring schematic (Part 3 of 3). 1989

5. **Mode F4 - ABS Tests:** In this test mode, the Tech 1 performs hydraulic modulator functional tests to assist in problem isolation during diagnosis.

Mode F0: ABS Data List

The DATA LIST mode allows continuous monitoring of wheel speed data and brake switch status. When monitoring wheel speed data, the signals being sent from the wheel speed sensors to the EBCM are displayed. In this test mode, the vehicle can be driven while wheel speed data is displayed. The readings can be compared with vehicle speed to check for proper operation. Wheel speed signals can also be compared with each other to determine whether they are within specification.

If one wheel speed signal differs greatly from the other signals, improper operation of that sensor may be indicated. Intermittent wheel speed signals can be located in the DATA LIST mode by looking for signals that vary for no reason during vehicle operation.

In the DATA LIST mode, brake switch operation is displayed. With the brake pedal depressed, the Tech 1 screen reads ON, when the pedal is released, the screen reads OFF.

Mode F1: History Data

In the HISTORY DATA test mode, fault code history data is displayed. This data includes the number of ignition cycles since the fault occurred, brake switch status and ABS state when the fault occurred. Up to three codes are included in the ABS history data.

Mode F2: Trouble Codes

In the TROUBLE CODES test mode, ABS trouble (fault) codes stored by the EBCM are displayed. The EBCM can store up to three different codes. The Tech 1 can also clear stored codes when it is used in this test mode.

In addition to storing three trouble codes, the EBCM records when each code was set and ABS status when each code was set. Each code is accompanied by a brief description of what the code number represents.

After displaying the codes, the Tech 1 can be ordered to clear the codes. It will respond to the clear codes command by displaying one of the following screens:
1. ABS CODES CLEARED.
2. CODE CLEAR FAIL

In addition to storing fault codes, the EBCM stores other information about the codes that may aid in diagnosis. This function is called ENHANCED DIAGNOSTIC DATA. The Tech 1 can be ordered to display the following ENHANCED DIAGNOSTIC DATA:

1. **Brake Light Switch Status:** Indicates whether the brake light switch was On or Off when the code set.
2. **ABS State:** Indicates whether or not the anti-lock mode was engaged when the code set.
3. **Vehicle Speed:** Indicates vehicle speed when the code set.
4. **Ignition Cycles:** Indicates how many ignition cycles have occurred since the code set.

Mode F3: ABS Snapshot

The ABS SNAPSHOT mode mode will help isolate intermittent problems by capturing data before and after a trigger condition. This data can then be analyzed to determine the cause of the complaint. Three different trigger conditions can activate the ABS SNAPSHOT mode:
1. **Automatic Trigger:** When the snapshot mode is used with the automatic

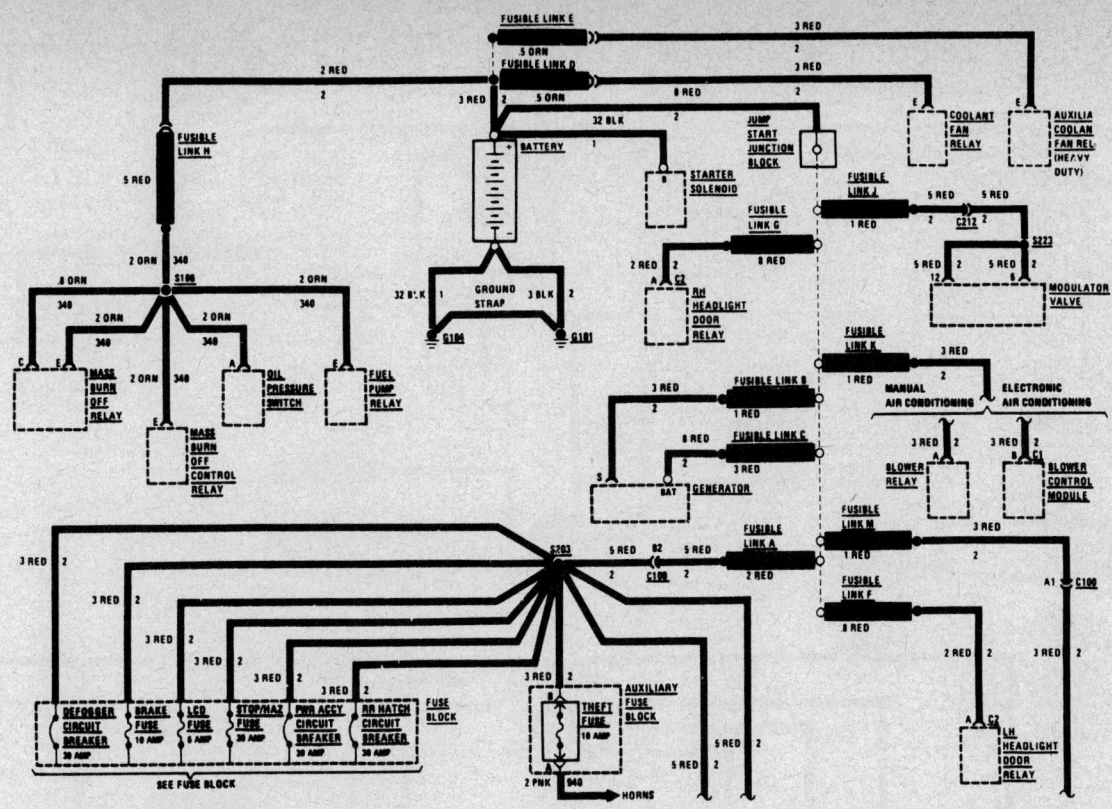

Fig. 7   Power distribution circuit (Part 1 of 2). 1988

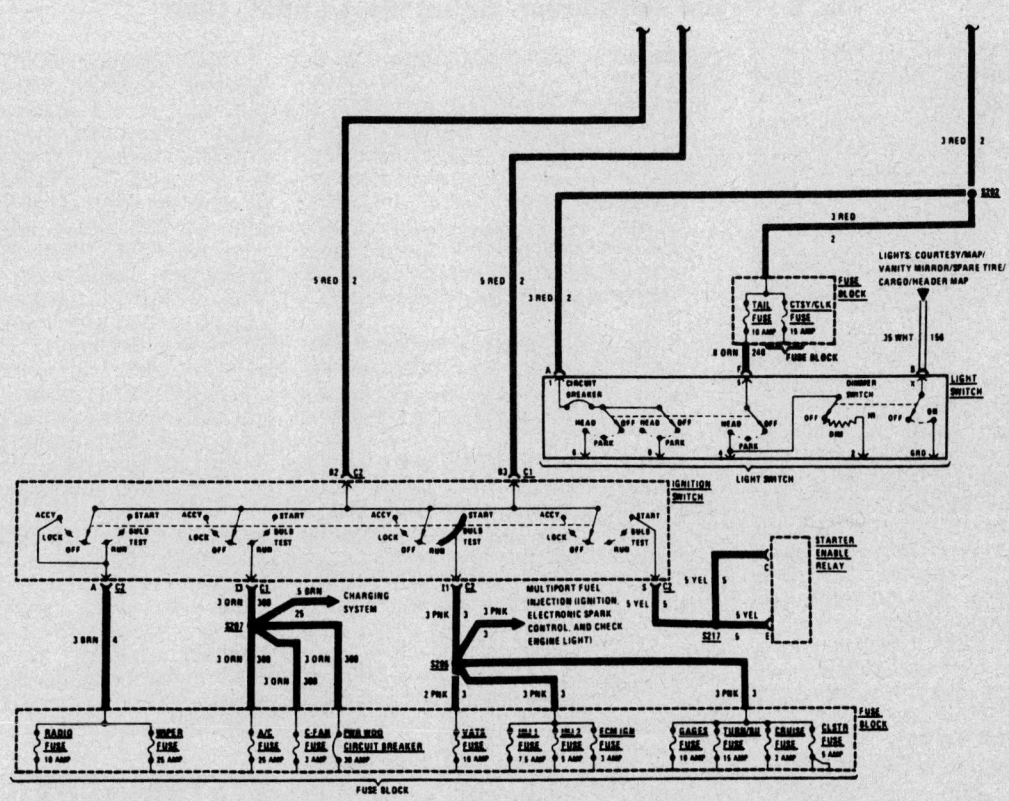

Fig. 7   Power distribution circuit (Part 2 of 2). 1988

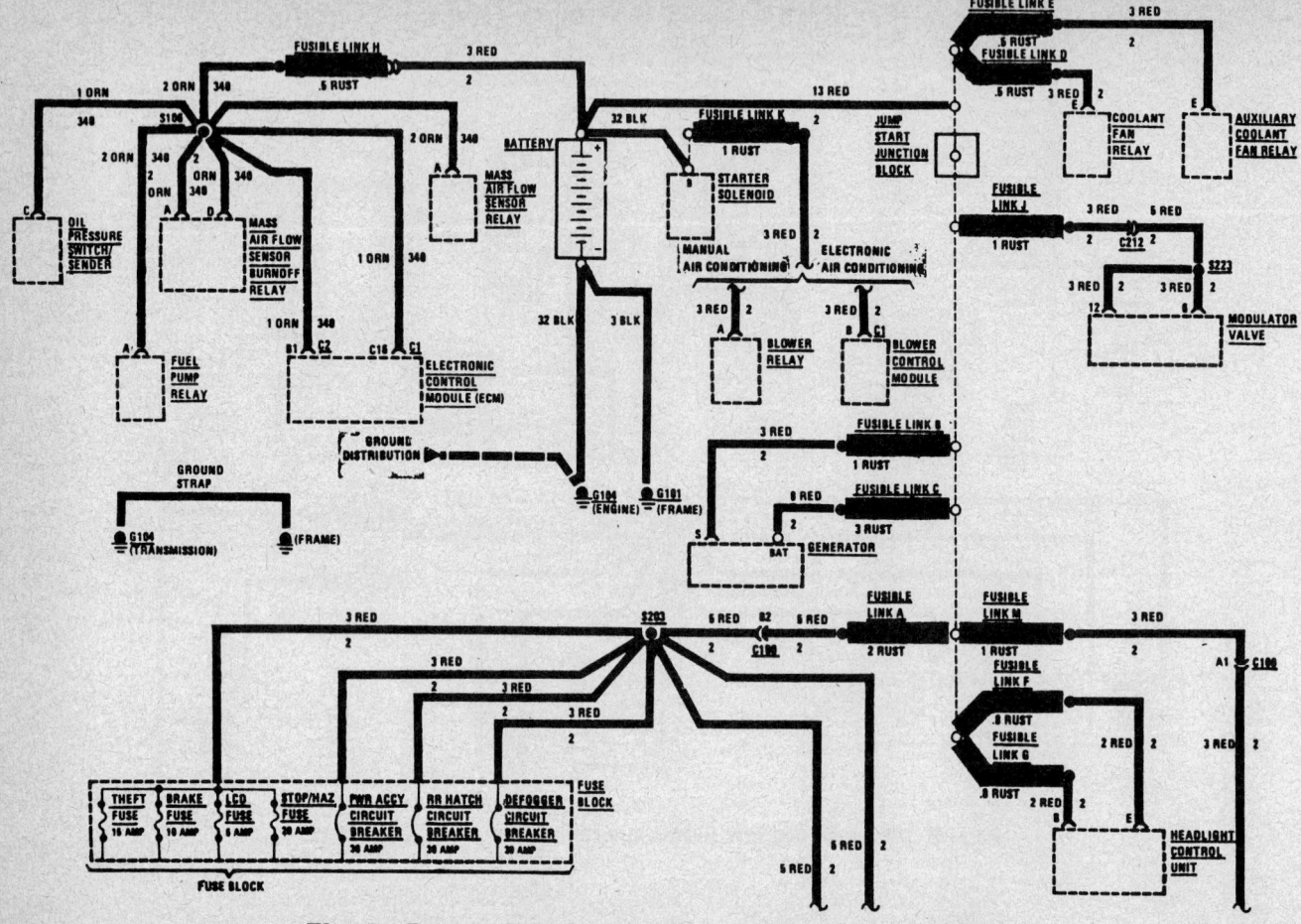

Fig. 8 Power distribution circuit (Part 1 of 2). 1989

trigger, the Tech 1 captures data which deviates from normal operation without setting a code.

2. ABS Code Set Trigger: Snapshot data can be captured by specifying an ABS code. When the Tech 1 is used with the code set trigger, it captures data immediately before and after the code setting.

3. Snapshot On Command: Snapshot data can be captured on command by pressing the Tech 1 ENTER key. When used with the command trigger, the Tech 1 continuously monitors data and waits for the ENTER command to begin storing data.

The snapshot can be set to capture data at the beginning, center or end of the data stream. Approximately 15 seconds of data are captured before the Tech 1 data buffer is full. If "Beginning" is selected, data occurring approximately 15 seconds before and up to the trigger point is captured. If "Center" is selected, data occurring approximately 8 seconds before through 8 seconds after the trigger point is captured. If "End" is selected, data occurring approximately 15 seconds after the trigger point is captured.

Mode F4: ABS Tests

The ABS TESTS mode performs functional tests on the ABS which help verify proper operation. In this mode, error conditions can be further identified by testing and observing the test results. In the ABS TESTS mode the following tests can be performed:

1. Solenoid Valve-Pressure Reduction: This test indicates whether specific solenoid valves in the hydraulic modulator release pressure to assigned wheel circuits.

2. Solenoid Valve-Pressure Hold: This test indicates whether specific solenoid valves in the hydraulic modulator hold pressure in assigned wheel circuits.

3. Static "BITE" Test: This test cycles each solenoid valve operates the pump motor briefly. The EBCM will store a fault code if the test conditions fail.

The PRESSURE REDUCE test activates a selected hydraulic wheel circuit valve, placing it in the pressure reduce position. Valve action can then be verified by checking the appropriate wheel for proper brake action. The Tech 1 will indicate whether the valve action was commanded properly. This test is used in conjunction with the PRESSURE HOLD test to completely check each solenoid valve. With an assistant, the pressure reduce test can be verified as follows:

1. Have an assistant apply the brakes.
2. Use Tech 1 to command the PRESSURE REDUCE mode.
3. Try to spin wheel being tested. It should spin due to the reduce command.

The PRESSURE HOLD test activates a selected hydraulic wheel circuit valve, placing it in the pressure hold position. Valve action can then be verified by checking the appropriate wheel for proper brake action. The Tech 1 will indicate whether the valve action was commanded properly. This test is used in conjunction with the PRESSURE REDUCE test to completely check each solenoid valve. With an assistant, the pressure reduce test can be verified as follows:

1. Spin wheel freely.
2. Use Tech 1 to command the PRESSURE HOLD mode.
3. Have an assistant apply the brakes.
4. Try to spin wheel being tested. It should spin due to the hold command, even if the brakes are applied.

The STATIC "BITE" test is performed automatically by the EBCM once during each ignition cycle when the vehicle speed reaches 3-11 mph. The Tech 1 will perform this test automatically the ABS TESTS mode. The BITE test cycles each solenoid valve and the pump motor to check component operation. If any error is detected during this test, the EBCM will set a code.

SYSTEM SERVICE

On models equipped with Supplemental Inflatable Restraint (SIR) sys-

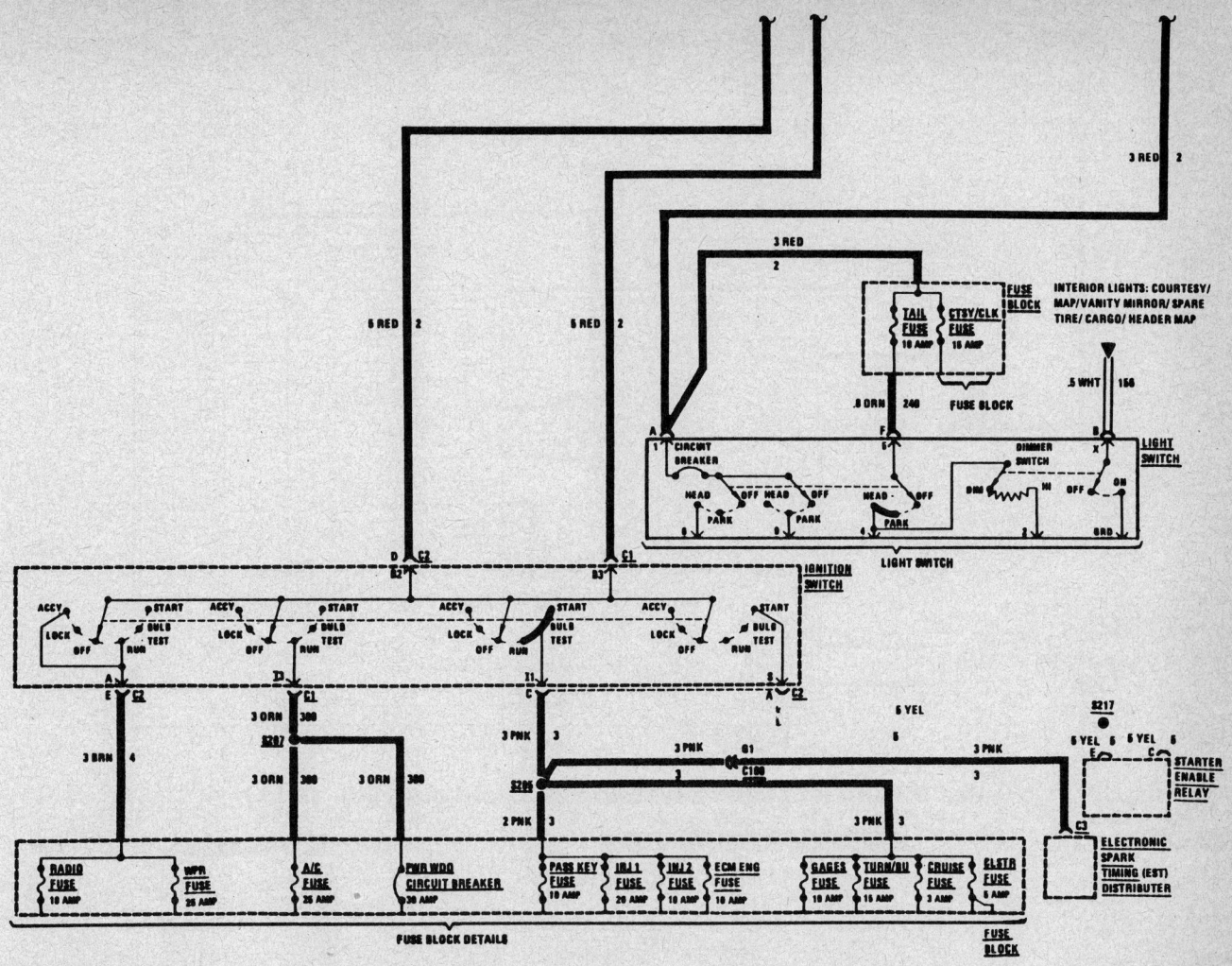

Fig. 8 Power distribution circuit (Part 2 of 2). 1989

PRECAUTIONS

tem, serious injury can result from unintended airbag deployment.

The SIR system is designed to retain sufficient voltage to deploy the airbag for a short time after power has been disconnected. To avoid serious injury, disarm the SIR as follows:

1. Turn ignition switch to Off position.
2. Remove Connector Position Assurance (CPA) pin, then disconnect yellow two-way connector at base of steering column.
3. Wait at least 10 minutes before any further work is attempted. Serious injury may result from unintended airbag deployment if service is attempted immediately after SIR fuse is removed.
4. Reverse procedure to arm SIR system, noting the following:
   a. Turn ignition switch to Run position.
   b. Observe INFL REST indicator lamp.
   c. If lamp does not illuminate for approximately 5 seconds then go out and remain remain Off for the next 100 seconds, refer to "Passive Restraint Systems" for diagnosis.

Before performing any service procedure on the ABS system, the following precautions should be followed:

1. The control module must be disconnected before performing any electric welding on these vehicles.
2. Use caution not to subject control module to a maximum heat of 203°F for brief periods, or a maximum of 184°F for longer than 2 hours.
3. After replacement of any ABS component, the entire ABS system should be tested.
4. Ensure inlet and outlet brake lines are properly routed.
5. Do not use a fast charger for starting engine.
6. Never disconnect battery from vehicle when engine is running.
7. Do not connect or disconnect control module electrical connector with ignition switch in On position. Ensure all harness connectors are securely connected.
8. No screws on the modulator valve should be loosened. If screws are loosened, it is no longer possible to get brake circuit leak-tight.

9. When replacing modulator valve, it should be removed through access panel in rear storage compartment. Ensure vehicle interior and exterior are protected to avoid damage from brake fluid spillage. Do not remove bottom of storage compartment to replace modulator valve.
10. Ensure rear storage compartment is wiped clean after replacing modulator valve.
11. Do not support suspension components by wheel speed sensor wires.
12. Wheel speed sensors are a tight fit into knuckle, but should be pushed in by hand. Do not hammer sensors into position.
13. Each replacement wheel speed sensor is identified with a white tag, located approximately 3/4 inch from neck of sensor, labeled L (left), or R (right).
14. Tire and wheel assemblies should be removed when replacing wheel speed sensors.
15. Wheel speed sensors should be given an anti-corrosion coating, No. 9981128 or equivalent, before installation to prevent corrosion. Do not use grease.

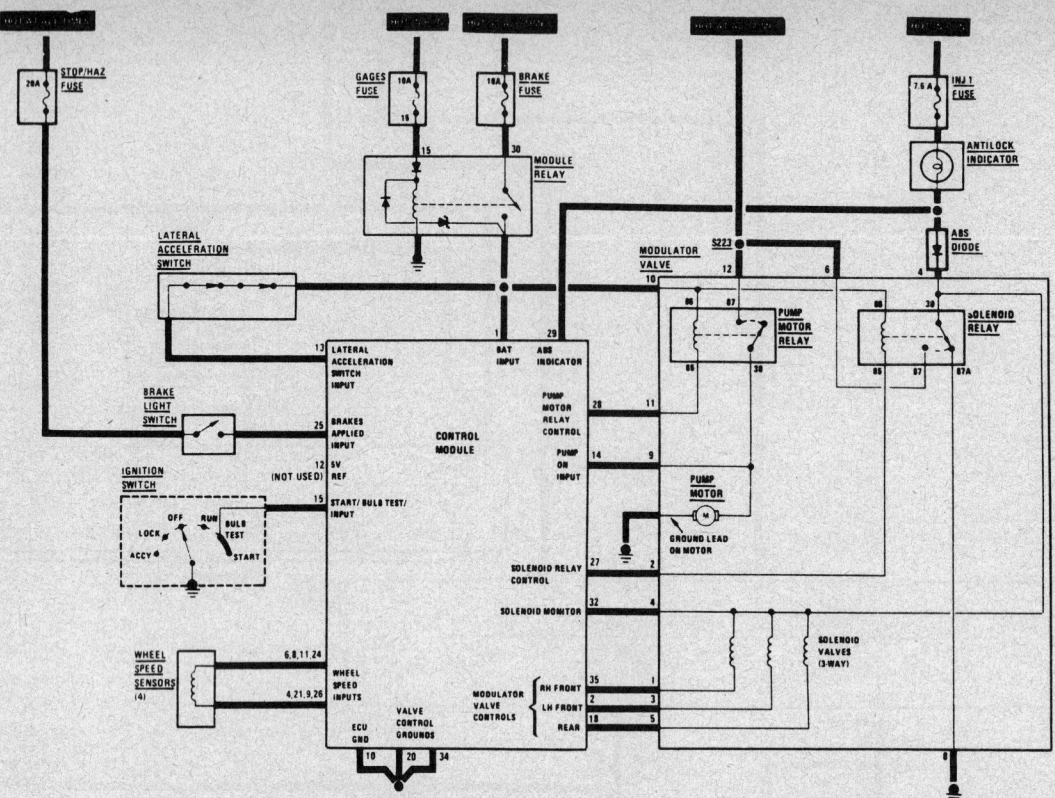

Fig. 9   Anti-lock brake system functional diagram. 1988

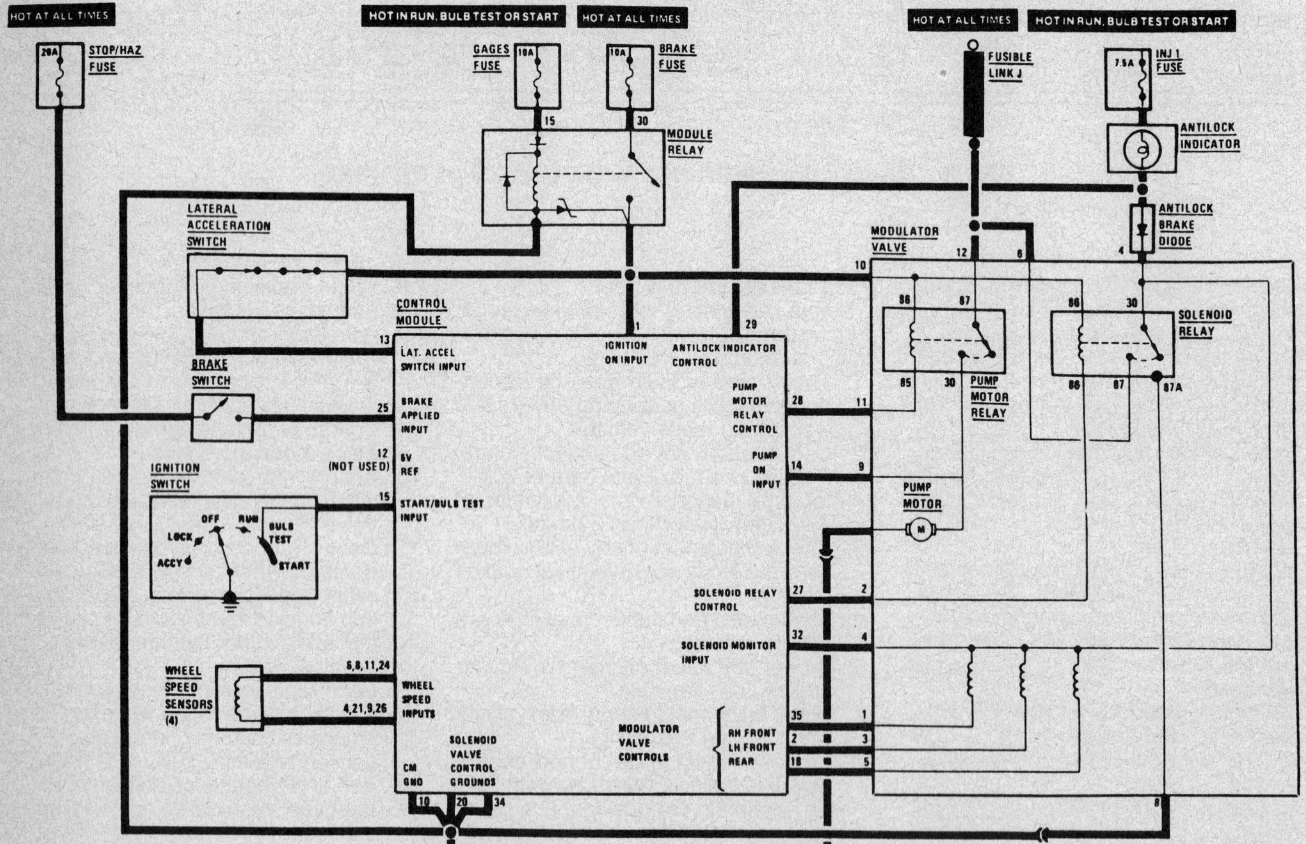

Fig. 10   Anti-lock brake system functional diagram. 1989

SYMPTOM MESSAGE	POSSIBLE CAUSE	REPAIR ACTION
No Power-up Messages	No Battery voltage to ABS Tester	Do Test A.
LOW BATTERY	Battery not fully charged	Charge Battery.
LF VALVE OPEN (Left Front Valve Open) (In Addition to LF VALVE OPEN, check for display of RF VALVE OPEN and REAR VALVE OPEN.	Open Circuit in Left Front Wheel Solenoid Valve	Do Test B: Solenoid Valve Resistance Test.
	Open Wire between Valve and Control Module	Check for open in YEL/BLK wire (921).
RF VALVE OPEN (Right Front Valve Open)	Open Circuit in Right Front Wheel Solenoid Valve	Do Test B: Solenoid Valve Resistance Test.
	Open Wire between Valve and Control Module	Check for open in DK BLU/WHT wire (916).
REAR VALVE OPEN	Open Circuit in Rear Wheel Solenoid Valve	Do Test B: Solenoid Valve Resistance Test.
	Open Wire between Valve and Control Module	Check for open in BLK/RED wire (914).
LF VALVE OPEN, RF VALVE OPEN, REAR VALVE OPEN	Open Solenoid Relay Contacts	Do Test C: Solenoid Relay Test.
	Open ground wire between Terminal 8 of the Modulator Valve and G320.	Check for open in BLK wire (150) to ground at G320.
CHK ABS DIODE	Open ABS Diode	Do Test D: ABS Diode Test.
	Open in circuit 915 or 922	Check for open in WHT wire (915) between ABS Diode and Splice S221, or DK GRN/WHT wire (922) between ABS Diode and Splice S222.
	Shorted ABS Diode	Do Test D: ABS Diode Test.
CHK CONT MOD GND (Check Control Module Ground)	Open in circuit 150 between the Control Module and the ground point on LH "B" Pillar	Check for open in BLK wire (150) from terminal 20 of the Control Module to terminal B of Connector C400.
		Check for open in BLK wire (150) from terminal 10 of the Control Module to terminal B of Connector C400.

Fig. 11 Anti-lock system symptom directory chart (Part 1 of 4). 1988

SYMPTOM MESSAGE	POSSIBLE CAUSE	REPAIR ACTION
CHK SYSTEM GND (Check System Ground)	Open circuit 150 between Control Module and ground point	Check for open in BLK wire (150) from terminal 34 of the Control Module to terminal B of Connector C400.
		Check for open in BLK wire (150) from terminal 20 of the Control Module to terminal B of Connector C400.
LAT ACCEL SW OPEN (Lateral Acceleration Switch Open)	Open Lateral Acceleration Switch (Switch should be closed)	Do Test E: Lateral Acceleration Switch Test.
	Open Connector at Lateral Acceleration Switch	Check that connector is firmly seated.
	Open circuit 919 or 920 connecting the Lateral Acceleration Switch and the Control Module	Check ORN wire (911) between terminal 1 of Control Module and Lateral Acceleration Switch.
		Check ORN/BLK wire (920) between terminal 13 of Control Module and Lateral Acceleration Switch.
CHK BRK LIGHT SW (Check Brake Light Switch)	Blown STOP/HAZ Fuse	Check operation of Hazard Flasher to check fuse.
	Condition may be due to inoperative, misaligned or permanently closed Brake Light Switch.	Check for proper operation of Stop Lights. If Stop Lights don't work, replace or realign Brake Switch.
	Open in circuit 20 between Brake Switch and Control Module	Check that Connectors C209 and C400 are properly mated.
		Check for an open in the LT BLU wire (20).
CHK IGNITION SW (Check Ignition Switch)	Ignition Switch not grounding terminal 15 at the Control Module in Bulb Test and Start	Check for proper operation of Ignition Switch in Bulb Test and Start. If switch does not operate, replace switch.
	Open in circuit 917 between Ignition Switch and Control Module	Check that connectors C210 and C400 are properly mated.
		Check for an open in the BLK wire (917).

Fig. 11 Anti-lock system symptom directory chart (Part 2 of 4). 1988

16. Use caution not to use silicone type brake fluid.

ON-VEHICLE SERVICE

When a diagnostic chart refers to removing, replacing or checking a component for proper mounting, refer to "Component Replacement."

After all diagnosis and repairs are completed, road test the vehicle to ensure proper ABS operation and that the SERVICE ABS light does not illuminate. If the Tech 1 was used for diagnosis, disconnect it from the ALDL connector and turn the ignition Off before road testing the vehicle. This is required to reset the EBCM, it is disabled during Tech 1 diagnostics and does not reset until serial data communication is stopped and ignition power is lost.

COMPONENT REPLACEMENT

On models equipped with Supplemental Inflatable Restraint (SIR) system, serious injury can result from unintended airbag deployment.

The SIR system is designed to retain sufficient voltage to deploy the airbag for a short time after power has been disconnected. To avoid serious injury, disarm the SIR as follows:

1. Turn ignition switch to Off position.
2. Remove Connector Position Assurance (CPA) pin, then disconnect yellow two-way connector at base of steering column.
3. Wait at least 10 minutes before any further work is attempted. Serious injury may result from unintended airbag deployment if service is attempted immediately after SIR fuse is removed.
4. Reverse procedure to arm SIR system, noting the following:
   a. Turn ignition switch to Run position.
   b. Observe INFL REST indicator lamp.
   c. If lamp does not illuminate for approximately 5 seconds then go out and remain remain Off for the next 100 seconds, refer to "Passive Restraint Systems" for diagnosis.

MODULATOR VALVE

Replace modulator valve through access in rear storage compartment.
1. Disconnect battery ground cable.
2. Remove storage tray and insulation.
3. Disconnect and remove entire ABS wiring harness from storage compartment.
4. Disconnect modulator valve ground from body wiring harness.
5. Disconnect five brake pipes from modulator valve, noting location for reassembly.
6. Remove three modulator valve to bracket attaching nuts, then the modulator valve, **Fig. 46**.
7. Reverse procedure to install, noting the following:
   a. **Torque** modulator valve to bracket attaching nuts to 7 ft. lbs.
   b. Remove shipping caps from modulator valve if necessary, then connect brake pipes. **Torque** brake pipes to 13 ft. lbs.
   c. Bleed brakes as necessary.

CONTROL MODULE

1. Disconnect battery ground cable.
2. Remove storage tray and insulation.
3. Disconnect control module electrical connector, then depress spring clip located under neck of compressor to remove module relay from control module bracket.
4. Remove two control module attaching bolts, then the control module, **Fig. 47**.
5. Reverse procedure to install. **Torque** control module mounting bolts to 22 inch lbs. Perform ABS system check.

LATERAL ACCELERATION SWITCH (ACCELEROMETER)
1988–89 Models

1. Disconnect battery ground cable.
2. Remove accessory trim plate attaching screws, then trim plate.
3. Remove console trim plate attaching screws, rotate trim plate, then disconnect lighter.
4. Remove A/C control head, then the lateral acceleration switch attaching bolts, **Fig. 48**.

SYMPTOM MESSAGE	POSSIBLE CAUSE	REPAIR ACTION
CHK LF SPD SENS (Check Left Front Speed Sensor)	Open Circuit in LF Wheel Speed Sensor	Do Test F.
CHK RF SPD SENS (Check Right Front Speed Sensor)	Open Circuit in RF Wheel Speed Sensor	Do Test F.
CHK LR SPD SENS (Check Left Rear Speed Sensor)	Open Circuit in LR Wheel Speed Sensor	Do Test F.
CHK RR SPD SENS (Check Right Rear Speed Sensor)	Open Circuit in RR Wheel Speed Sensor	Do Test F.
CHK ANTILOCK LT (Check Antilock Light)	Antilock Bulb burned out	Replace bulb.
	Connector pin not mated	Check that connectors C210 and C400 are securely mated.
	Open in circuit 915 or 639 between INJ 1 Fuse, Indicator and Control Module	Check PNK/BLK wire (639) and WHT wire (915) for an open.
CHK MOTOR RELAY	Pump Motor Relay not closing	Do Test G: Pump Motor Relay Test.
	Open circuit to Pump Motor Relay Coil or Pump ON input	Check for an open in the GRN/BLK wire (913).
		Check for open in the BLU/BLK wire (912)
CHK PUMP MOTOR	Pump Motor inoperative	Do Test G, Table 2.
	Open Ground Circuit from Pump Motor to ground	Check BLK wire (150) from case of Modulator Valve to Ground
		Check that connector C448 is mated correctly.
CHK SPD SENS CKT (Check Speed Sensor Circuit)	Damaged Wheel Speed Sensor	Check area of sensor for damage.

Fig. 11   Anti-lock system symptom directory chart (Part 3 of 4). 1988

SYMPTOM MESSAGE	POSSIBLE CAUSE	REPAIR ACTION
CHK SPD SENS CKT	Damaged Wheel Speed Sensor	Check area of sensor for damage
CHK TOOTHED WHL	Missing teeth in toothed wheel	Check toothed wheel for missing or damaged teeth.
	Misalignment of Wheel Speed Sensor	Check sensor for damage. Sensor should not contact toothed wheel
CHK VALVE RELAY	Open circuit to Solenoid Relay Coil or Solenoid Monitor Input	Check for an open in LT BRN/BLK (918) wire.
		Check for an open in DK GRN/WHT (922) wire between Modulator Valve Terminal 4 and Control Module Terminal 32
	Solenoid Relay inoperative	Do Test C: Solenoid Relay Test.
CHECK HYDRAULICS	Faulty Hydraulic Fluid Connection	Check that all Brake Fluid connections are tight and that no fluid is leaking.
	Solenoid Valve stuck in by-pass position	Replace Modulator Valve.
CHK HYDRA WIRING (Check Hydraulic Wiring)	Wiring to Modulator Valve or wiring inside Modulator Valve	Check that Modulator Valve harness connector is properly mated.
		Check that the Solenoid and Pump Motor relays are properly seated.

Fig. 11   Anti-lock system symptom directory chart (Part 4 of 4). 1988

5. Disconnect lateral acceleration switch electrical connector, then remove switch.
6. Reverse procedure to install. **Torque** lateral acceleration mounting bolts to 27 inch lbs. Perform ABS system check.

1990 Models

1. Disconnect battery ground cable.
2. Remove console trim plate attaching screws, then the console trim plate.
3. Remove radio assembly.
4. Remove lateral acceleration switch attaching screws, **Fig. 49.**
5. Disconnect lateral acceleration switch electrical connector, then remove switch.
6. Reverse procedure to install. **Torque** lateral acceleration mounting bolts to 15 inch lbs.

WHEEL SPEED SENSOR

1. Disconnect battery ground cable.
2. Raise and support vehicle, then remove tire and wheel assembly.
3. Remove sensor electrical connector from bracket, then disconnect sensor connector.
4. Remove sensor wire grommets from brackets, noting sensor wire routing for reassembly.
5. Remove sensor to knuckle attaching bolts, then the sensor, **Fig. 50.**
6. Reverse procedure to install, noting the following:
   a. Coat new wheel speed sensor with anti-corrosion compound No. 9981128, or equivalent prior to installation.
   b. Do not use hammer to install sensor.
   c. On 1988-89 models, torque sensor attaching bolts to 7 ft. lbs. On 1990 models, **torque** sensor attaching bolt to 89 inch. lbs.

WIRING HARNESS & MODULE RELAY

1. Disconnect battery ground cable.
2. Remove storage tray and insulation.
3. Disconnect control module harness connector by depressing spring clip located under neck of connector, **Figs. 51 and 52.**
4. Remove two screws from modulator valve harness retainer clip, then disconnect harness connector.
5. Disconnect battery feed (red), wire harness connector.
6. Disconnect wheel speed sensor connectors from wiring harness connector.
7. Remove module relay from control module bracket, then disconnect modular relay harness connector.
8. Remove wiring harness, noting routing for installation.
9. Reverse procedure to install. Ensure all connectors are securely connected.

SYMPTOM DIRECTORY

SYMPTOM MESSAGE	POSSIBLE CAUSE	REPAIR ACTION
No Power-up Messages	No Battery voltage to ABS Tester Open ABS Ground Circuit	Do Test A Repair Circuit (150) from Control Module Terminal 20 to Splice S224 (see schematic)
LOW BATTERY	Battery not fully charged	Charge Battery
LF VALVE OPEN (Left Front Valve Open) (In Addition to LF VALVE OPEN, check for display of RF VALVE OPEN and REAR VALVE OPEN,)	Open Circuit in Left Front Wheel Solenoid Valve Open Wire between Valve and Control Module	Do Test B Check for open in BLK/YEL (921) wire (see schematic)
RF VALVE OPEN (Right Front Valve Open)	Open Circuit in Right Front Wheel Solenoid Valve Open Wire between Valve and Control Module	Do Test B Check for open in BLK/RED (914) wire (see schematic)
REAR VALVE OPEN	Open Circuit in Rear Wheel Solenoid Valve Open Wire between Valve and Control Module	Do Test B Check for open in DK BLU/WHT (916) wire (see schematic)
LF VALVE OPEN, RF VALVE OPEN, REAR VALVE OPEN	Open Solenoid Relay Contacts Open ground wire between Terminal 8 of the Modulator Valve and G320	Do Test C (Table 3) Check for open in BLK (150) wire to ground (see schematic)
CHK ABS DIODE	Open or shorted Antilock Brake Diode Open in circuit 915 or 922	Do Test D Check for open in WHT (915) wire between Diode and Terminal 29, or DK GRN/WHT (922) wire between Antilock Brake Diode and Terminal 32 of Control Module (see schematic)
CHK CONT MOD GRN (Check Control Module ground)	Open in circuit 150 between the Control Module and the ground point (see schematic)	Check for open in BLK (150) wire from terminal 20 of the Control Module to Terminal B of Connector C400 Check for open in BLK (150) wire from Terminal 10 of the Control Module to Terminal B of Connector C400

Fig. 12   Anti-lock system symptom directory chart (Part 1 of 4).
1989

SYMPTOM DIRECTORY (Continued)

SYMPTOM MESSAGE	POSSIBLE CAUSE	REPAIR ACTION
CHK SYSTEM GND (Check System Ground)	Open circuit 150 between Control Module and ground point	Check for open in BLK (150) wire from Terminal 34 of the Control Module to Terminal B of Connector C400 (see schematic)
LAT ACCEL SW OPEN (Lateral Acceleration Switch Open)	Open Lateral Acceleration Switch (Switch should be closed)	Do Test E
	Open Connector at Lateral Acceleration Switch	Check that connector is firmly seated
	Open circuit 924, or 920 connecting the Lateral Acceleration Switch and the Control Module	Check GRY/BLK (984) wire between Terminal 1 of Control Module and Lateral Acceleration Switch (see schematic)
		Check ORN/BLK and DK BLU wires between Terminal 13 of Control Module and Lateral Acceleration Switch (see schematic)
CHK BRK LIGHT SW (Check Brake Light Switch)	Blown STOP/HAZ Fuse	Check operation of Hazard Flasher to check fuse
	Condition may be due to inoperative, misaligned or permanently closed Brake Light Switch	Check for proper operation of Stop Lights If Stop Lights don't work, replace or realign Brake Switch
	Open in circuit 20 between Brake Switch and Control Module	Check that Connectors C209 and C400 are properly mated
		Check for an open in the LT BLU (20) wire (see schematic)
CHK IGNITION SW (Check Ignition Switch)	Ignition Switch not grounding Terminal 15 at the Control Module in Bulb Test and Start	Check for proper operation of Ignition Switch in BULB TEST and START If switch does not operate, replace switch
	Open in circuit 251 between Ignition Switch and Control Module	Check that connectors C210 and C400 are properly mated
		Check for an open in the BRN (251) wire (see schematic)

Fig. 12 Anti-lock system symptom directory chart (Part 2 of 4).
1989

SYMPTOM MESSAGE	POSSIBLE CAUSE	REPAIR ACTION
CHK LF SPD SENS (Check Left Front Speed Sensor)	Open Circuit in LF Wheel Speed Sensor	Do Test F
CHK RF SPD SENS (Check Right Front Speed Sensor)	Open Circuit in RF Wheel Speed Sensor	Do Test F
CHK LR SPD SENS (Check Left Rear Speed Sensor)	Open Circuit in LR Wheel Speed Sensor	Do Test F
CHK RR SPD SENS (Check Right Rear Speed Sensor)	Open Circuit in RR Wheel Speed Sensor	Do Test F
CHK ANTILOCK LT (Check Antilock Light)	Antilock Indicator Bulb burned out	Replace bulb
	Connector pin not mated	Check that connectors C210 and C400 are securely mated
	Open in circuit 915 or 639 between INJ 1 Fuse, Indicator and Control Module	Check PNK/BLK (639) wire and WHT (915) wire for an open
CHK MOTOR RELAY	Pump Motor Relay not closing	Check for an open in the BLK/LT GRN (913) wire (see schematic)
	Open circuit to Pump Motor Relay Coil or Pump ON input	Check for open in the BLK/LT BLU (985) wire (see schematic) Do Test G
CHK PUMP MOTOR	Pump Motor inoperative	Do Test G (Table 2)
	Open Ground Circuit from Pump Motor to ground	Check BLK (150) wire from Return Pump Motor to Ground (see schematic) Check that connector C448 is mated correctly (see schematic)
CHK SPD SENS CKT (Check Speed Sensor Circuit)	Damaged Wheel Speed Sensor	Check area of sensor for damage

Fig. 12 Anti-lock system symptom directory chart (Part 3 of 4).
1989

CORVETTE (BOSCH ABS II TYPE)

SYMPTOM DIRECTORY (Continued)

SYMPTOM MESSAGE	POSSIBLE CAUSE	REPAIR ACTION
CHK TOOTHED WHL	Missing teeth in toothed wheel	Check toothed wheel for missing or damaged teeth Check sensor for damage. Sensor should not contact toothed wheel
CHK VALVE RELAY	Solenoid Relay inoperative	Do Test C Check for an open in LT GRN/BLK (918) wire (see schematic)
	Open circuit to Solenoid Relay Coil or Solenoid Monitor Input	Check for an open in DK GRN/WHT (922) wire between Modulator Valve Terminal 4 and Control Module Terminal 32 (see schematic)
CHK HYDRAULICS	Faulty Hydraulic Fluid Connection	Check that all Brake Fluid connections are tight and that no fluid is leaking
	Solenoid Valve stuck in by-pass position	Replace Modulator Valve
CHK HYDRA WIRING (Check Hydraulic Wiring)	Wiring to Modulator Valve or wiring inside Modulator Valve	Check that Modulator Valve harness connector is properly mated
		Check that the Solenoid and Pump Motor relays are properly seated

Note: Use J-35592 Pinout Box for all circuit checks. Do not probe ABS Harness Connector directly.

Fig. 12   Anti-lock system symptom directory chart (Part 4 of 4). 1989

A: MODULE RELAY TEST

Measure: VOLTAGE
At: MODULE RELAY CONNECTOR
(Disconnected)
Conditions:
• Ignition Switch: RUN

Measure Between	Correct Voltage	For Diagnosis
30 (ORN/BLK) & Ground	Battery	See 1.
15 (PNK/BLK) & Ground	Battery	See 2.
15 (PNK/BLK) & 31 (BLK)	Battery	See 3.
• Module Relay Connected		
87 (ORN) & 31 (BLK)	Battery	See 4

• If all voltages are correct, but Tester does not power-up check ORN (911) wire for an open.
1. Check Brake Fuse and ORN/BLK wire (440) for an open between Module Relay terminal 30 and Brake Fuse. If wire and Brake Fuse are good, refer to   Power Distribution.
2. Check Gages Fuse and PNK/BLK wire (39) for an open between Module Relay terminal 15 and Gages Fuse.
3. Check BLK wire (150) for an open between Module Relay terminal 31 and ground
4. Replace Module Relay.

Fig. 13   Module relay test. 1988

A: MODULE RELAY TEST

Measure: VOLTAGE
At: MODULE RELAY CONNECTOR
(Disconnected)
Conditions:
• Ignition Switch: RUN

Measure Between	Correct Voltage	For Diagnosis
30 (ORN/BLK) & Ground	Battery	See 1.
15 (PNK/BLK) & Ground	Battery	See 2.
15 (PNK/BLK) & 31 (BLK)	Battery	See 3.

• If all voltages are correct, but tester will not power-up, check the ORN wire (911) for an open. If ORN wire (911) is good, replace the Module Relay.
1. Check Brake Fuse and ORN/BLK wire (440) for an open between Module Relay terminal 30 and Brake Fuse. If wire and Brake Fuse are good, refer to Power Distribution.
2. Check Gages Fuse and PNK/BLK wire (39) for an open between Module Relay terminal 15 and Gages Fuse.
3. Check BLK wire (150) for an open between Module Relay terminal 31 and ground at ground G230.

Fig. 14   Module relay test. 1989

B: SOLENOID VALVE RESISTANCE TEST

Measure: RESISTANCE (200 ohm scale)
At: MODULATOR VALVE (Connector Disconnected)

Measure Between	Correct Resistance	For Diagnosis
1 & 4	0.8 to 1.5 ohms	See 1
3 & 4	0.8 to 1.5 ohms	See 1
5 & 4	0.8 to 1.5 ohms	See 1

• If the actual measured values of resistance differ by more than 0.1 ohms, replace the Modulator Valve.
• If measured values are correct, return to Symptom Directory.
1. Replace Modulator Valve.

Fig. 15   Solenoid valve resistance test. 1988–89

C: SOLENOID RELAY TEST (TABLE 1)

Measure: VOLTAGE
At: SOLENOID RELAY CONNECTOR
(Relay Disconnected)
Conditions:
• Ignition Switch: RUN

Measure Between	Correct Voltage	For Diagnosis
86 & Ground	Battery	See Table C2.
87 & Ground	Battery	See Table C2.

• If voltages are correct, go to Table C3.

Fig. 16   Solenoid relay test (Part 1 of 3). 1988

C: SOLENOID RELAY TEST (TABLE 3)

Measure: RESISTANCE
At: MODULATOR VALVE (Disconnected)
Conditions:
- Ignition Switch: OFF
- Solenoid Relay Disconnected
- Modulator Valve Connector Disconnected

Measure Between Sol. Relay Conn. & Mod. Valve Conn.	Correct Resistance	For Diagnosis
85 & 2	0 ohms	See 1.
30 & 4	0 ohms	See 1.
87A & 8	0 ohms	See 1.

- If voltages in Table C1 and resistances above are correct, but Solenoid Valves do not operate, replace the Solenoid Relay.
1. Replace Modulator Valve.

Fig. 16   Solenoid relay test (Part 2 of 3). 1988

C: SOLENOID RELAY TEST (TABLE 2)

Measure: VOLTAGE (20 Volt DC Scale)
At: MODULATOR VALVE HARNESS CONNECTOR (Disconnected)
Condition:
- Ignition Switch: RUN

Measure Between	Correct Voltage	For Diagnosis
6 (RED) & Ground	Battery	See 1
10 (GRY/ BLK) & Ground	Battery	See 2

- If voltages are correct, but were not present in Table 1, replace the Modulator Valve.
1. Check RED (2) wire for an open. If wire is good, check Fusible Link J (see schematic).
2. Check GRY/BLK (984) wire back to Module Relay for an open (see schematic).

Fig. 17   Solenoid relay test (Part 2 of 3). 1989

E: LATERAL ACCELERATION SWITCH

Measure: RESISTANCE (200 ohm Scale)
At: LATERAL ACCELERATION SWITCH (Disconnected)
Conditions:
- Ignition Switch: OFF
- Switch removed from vehicle

Measure Between	Correct Resistance	For Diagnosis
1 & 2	0 ohms	See 1.

- Tilt switch away from horizontal position while making measurement again.

Measure Between	Correct Resistance	For Diagnosis
1 & 2	OL	See 1.

- If both measurements are correct, Lateral Acceleration Switch is operating normally. Return to Symptom Directory.
1. If either measurement is incorrect, replace the Lateral Acceleration Switch.

Fig. 19   Lateral acceleration switch test. 1988

C: SOLENOID RELAY TEST (TABLE 2)

Measure: VOLTAGE
At: MODULATOR VALVE HARNESS CONNECTOR (Disconnected)
Conditions:
- Ignition Switch: RUN

Measure Between	Correct Voltage	For Diagnosis
6 (RED) & Ground	Battery	See 1.
10 (ORN) & Ground	Battery	See 2.

- If voltages are correct, but were not present in Table C1, replace the Modulator Valve.
1. Check RED wire (2) for an open. If wire is good, check Fusible Link J.
2. Check ORN wire (911) back to Module Relay for an open.

Fig. 16   Solenoid relay test (Part 3 of 3). 1988

C: SOLENOID RELAY TEST (TABLE 3)

Measure: RESISTANCE
At: MODULATOR VALVE (Disconnected)
Conditions:
- Ignition Switch: OFF
- Solenoid Relay: DISCONNECTED
- Modulator Valve Connector: DISCONNECTED

Measure Between Sol. Relay Conn. & Mod. Valve Conn.	Correct Resistance	For Diagnosis
85 & 2	0 Ohms	See 1
30 & 4	0 Ohms	See 1
87A & 8	0 Ohms	See 1

- If voltages in Table 1 and resistances above are correct but tester indicates Solenoid Valves are open, replace the Solenoid Relay.
1. Replace Modulator Valve.

Fig. 17   Solenoid relay test (Part 3 of 3). 1989

E: LATERAL ACCELERATION SWITCH

Measure: RESISTANCE
At: LATERAL ACCELERATION SWITCH (Disconnected)
Conditions:
- Ignition Switch: OFF
- Switch removed from vehicle
- Switch held in same relative position as when installed on vehicle

Measure Between	Correct Resistance	For Diagnosis
A & B	0 ohms	See 1

- Tilt switch away from horizontal position

Measure Between	Correct Resistance	For Diagnosis
A & B	OL	See 1

- If both measurements are correct, Lateral Acceleration Switch is operating normally. Return to Symptom Directory.
1. If either measurement is incorrect, replace the Lateral Acceleration Switch.

Fig. 20   Lateral acceleration switch. 1989

C: SOLENOID RELAY TEST (TABLE 1)

Measure: VOLTAGE (20 Volt DC Scale)
At: SOLENOID RELAY CONNECTOR (Relay Disconnected)
Condition:
- Ignition Switch: RUN

Measure Between	Correct Voltage	For Diagnosis
86 & Ground	Battery	See Table 2
87 & Ground	Battery	See Table 2

- If voltages are correct, go to Table 3.

Fig. 17   Solenoid relay test (Part 1 of 3). 1989

D: ABS DIODE TEST

Measure: DIODE CONTINUITY USING DIODE CHECK IN J34029 DIGITAL MULTIMETER
At: ABS DIODE (Disconnected)

Measure Between	Correct Result	For Diagnosis
1 & 2	0.4 to 0.6 Forward Direction	See 1.
	OL Reverse Direction	See 1.

- If results are correct, diode is operating normally.
1. If either check is incorrect, replace the ABS Diode.

Fig. 18   ABS diode test. 1988–89

F: WHEEL SPEED SENSOR TEST

Measure: RESISTANCE
At: ABS CONTROL MODULE CONNECTOR PINOUT BOX (Control Module Disconnected)
Conditions:
- Ignition Switch: OFF
- J35592 Pinout Box connected to Control Module Connector

Measure Between	Correct Resistance	For Diagnosis
4 (LT BLU) & 6 (BLK/RED)	900 to 1500 ohms	See 1.
11 (DK GRN) & 21 (TAN)	900 to 1500 ohms	See 2.
8 (BLK) & 9 (RED)	900 to 1500 ohms	See 3.
24 (BRN) & 26 (WHT)	900 to 1500 ohms	See 4.

Fig. 21   Wheel speed sensor test (Part 1 of 2). 1988

- Bend and gently pull on wheel speed sensor wires at the wheel and sensor connectors while measuring resistance to check for intermittent opens.
- Check that the individual resistances are within 100 ohms of each other. Replace any sensor having a resistance which differs more than this amount from any other sensor.
1. Check the Left Front Wheel Speed Sensor connector at the wheel to insure that it is properly mated. Check connector C243. Check sensor wires for opens. If all wiring is good and sensor resistance is incorrect, replace the sensor.
2. Check Right Front Wheel Speed Sensor connector at the wheel to insure that it is properly mated. Check connector C243. Check sensor wires for opens. If all wiring is good and sensor resistance is incorrect, replace the sensor.
3. Check Left Rear Wheel Speed Sensor connector at the wheel to insure that it is properly mated. Check connector C243. Check sensor wires for opens. If all wiring is good and sensor resistance is incorrect, replace the Wheel Speed Sensor.
4. Check Right Rear Wheel Speed Sensor connector at the wheel to insure that it is properly mated. Check connector C243. Check sensor wires for opens. If all wiring is good and sensor resistance is incorrect, replace the sensor.

Fig. 21 Wheel speed sensor test (Part 2 of 2). 1988

F: WHEEL SPEED SENSOR TEST

Measure: RESISTANCE
At: CONTROL MODULE CONNECTOR PINOUT BOX (Control Module Disconnected)
Conditions:
- Ignition Switch: OFF
- J35592 Pinout Box connected to Control Module Connector

Measure Between	Correct Resistance	For Diagnosis
4 (YEL) & 6 (LT BLU)	900 to 1500 ohms	See 1
11 (DK GRN) & 21 (TAN)	900 to 1500 ohms	See 2
9 (BLK) & 8 (RED)	900 to 1500 ohms	See 3
24 (BRN) & 26 (WHT)	900 to 1500 ohms	See 4

Fig. 22 Wheel speed sensor test (Part 1 of 2). 1989

- Bend and gently pull on wheel speed sensor wires at the wheel and sensor connectors while measuring resistance to check for intermittent opens.
- Check that the individual resistances are within 100 ohms of each other. Replace any sensor having a resistance which differs more than this amount from any other sensor.
1. Check the Left Front Wheel Speed Sensor connector at the wheel to insure that it is properly mated. Check connector C242. Check sensor wires for opens. If all wiring is good and sensor resistance is incorrect, replace the sensor.
2. Check Right Front Wheel Speed Sensor connector at the wheel to insure that it is properly mated. Check connector C242. Check sensor wires for opens. If all wiring is good and sensor resistance is incorrect, replace the sensor.
3. Check Left Rear Wheel Speed Sensor connector at the wheel to insure that it is properly mated. Check connector C242. Check sensor wires for opens. If all wiring is good and sensor resistance is incorrect, replace the sensor.
4. Check Right Rear Wheel Speed Sensor connector at the wheel to insure that it is properly mated. Check connector C242. Check sensor wires for opens. If all wiring is good and sensor resistance is incorrect, replace the sensor.

Fig. 22 Wheel speed sensor test (Part 2 of 2). 1989

G: PUMP MOTOR RELAY TEST (TABLE 1)

Measure: VOLTAGE (20 Volt Scale)
At: PUMP MOTOR RELAY CONNECTOR (Relay Disconnected)
Conditions:
- Ignition Switch: RUN

Measure Between	Correct Voltage	For Diagnosis
86 & Ground	Battery	See Table 2.
87 & Ground	Battery	See Table 2.

- If voltages are correct, proceed to Table 3.

Fig. 23 Pump motor relay test (Part 1 of 3). 1988

G: PUMP MOTOR RELAY TEST (TABLE 2)

Measure: RESISTANCE
At: MODULATOR VALVE HARNESS CONNECTOR (Disconnected)
Conditions
- Ignition Switch: RUN

Measure Between	Correct Voltage	For Diagnosis
10 (ORN) & Ground	Battery	See 1.
12 (RED) & Ground	Battery	See 2.

- If voltages are correct, but were not present in Table G1, replace the Modulator Valve.
1. Check the ORN (911) wire for an open back to the Module Relay. If wire is good, do Test A, Module Relay Test.
2. Check the RED (2) wire for an open between terminal 12 of the Modulator Valve and splice S223

Fig. 23 Pump motor relay test (Part 2 of 3). 1988

G: PUMP MOTOR RELAY TEST (TABLE 3)

Measure: RESISTANCE
At: MODULATOR VALVE (Disconnected)
- Ignition Switch: RUN

Measure Between	Correct Resistance	For Diagnosis
• Pump Motor Relay Connected		
10 & 11	Approx. 50 ohms	See 1.
• Pump Motor Relay Removed		
30 & 9	Less than 0.1 ohms	See 2
9 & Ground	Approx. 0.3 ohms	See 3.

- If all measurements are correct, but Pump Motor Relay does not operate, replace the Pump Motor Relay.
1. Check Pump Motor Relay Coil for an open. If relay coil is good, replace the Modulator Valve.
2. Replace Modulator Valve.
3. Check for an open in Return Pump Motor or BLK (150) wire to Ground
    If wire is good, replace the Modulator Valve.

Fig. 23 Pump motor relay test (Part 3 of 3). 1988

G: PUMP MOTOR RELAY TEST (TABLE 1)

Measure: VOLTAGE (20 Volt Scale)
At: PUMP MOTOR RELAY CONNECTOR (Relay Disconnected)
Condition:
- Ignition Switch: RUN

Measure Between	Correct Voltage	For Diagnosis
86 & Ground	Battery	See Table 2
87 & Ground	Battery	See Table 2

- If voltages are correct, proceed to Table 3

Fig. 24   Pump motor relay test (Part 1 of 3). 1989

G: PUMP MOTOR RELAY TEST (TABLE 2)

Measure: VOLTAGE
At: MODULATOR VALVE HARNESS CONNECTOR (Disconnected)
Condition:
- Ignition Switch: RUN

Measure Between	Correct Voltage	For Diagnosis
10 (GRY/BLK) & Ground	Battery	See 1
12 (RED) & Ground	Battery	See 2

- If voltages are correct but were not present in Table 1, replace the Modulator Valve.
1. Check the GRY/BLK (984) wire for an open back to the Module Relay (see schematic). If wire is good, do Test A.
2. Check the RED (2) wire for an open between Terminal 12 of the Modulator Valve and splice S223 (see schematic).

Fig. 24   Pump motor relay test (Part 2 of 3). 1989

G: PUMP MOTOR RELAY TEST (TABLE 3)

Measure: RESISTANCE
At: MODULATOR VALVE (Disconnected)
Condition:
- Ignition Switch: OFF

Measure Between	Correct Resistance	For Diagnosis
• Pump Motor Relay Connected		
10 & 11	Approx. 50 ohms	See 1
• Pump Motor Relay Removed		
30 & 9	Less than 0.1 ohms	See 2
9 & Ground	Approx. 0.3 ohms	See 3

- If all measurements are correct but Pump Motor Relay does not operate, replace the Pump Motor Relay.
1. Check Pump Motor Relay Coil for an open. If relay coil is good, replace the Modulator Valve.
2. Replace Modulator Valve.
3. Check for an open in Return Pump Motor or BLK (150) wire to Ground (see schematic). If wire is good, replace the Modulator Valve.

Fig. 24   Pump motor relay test (Part 3 of 3). 1989

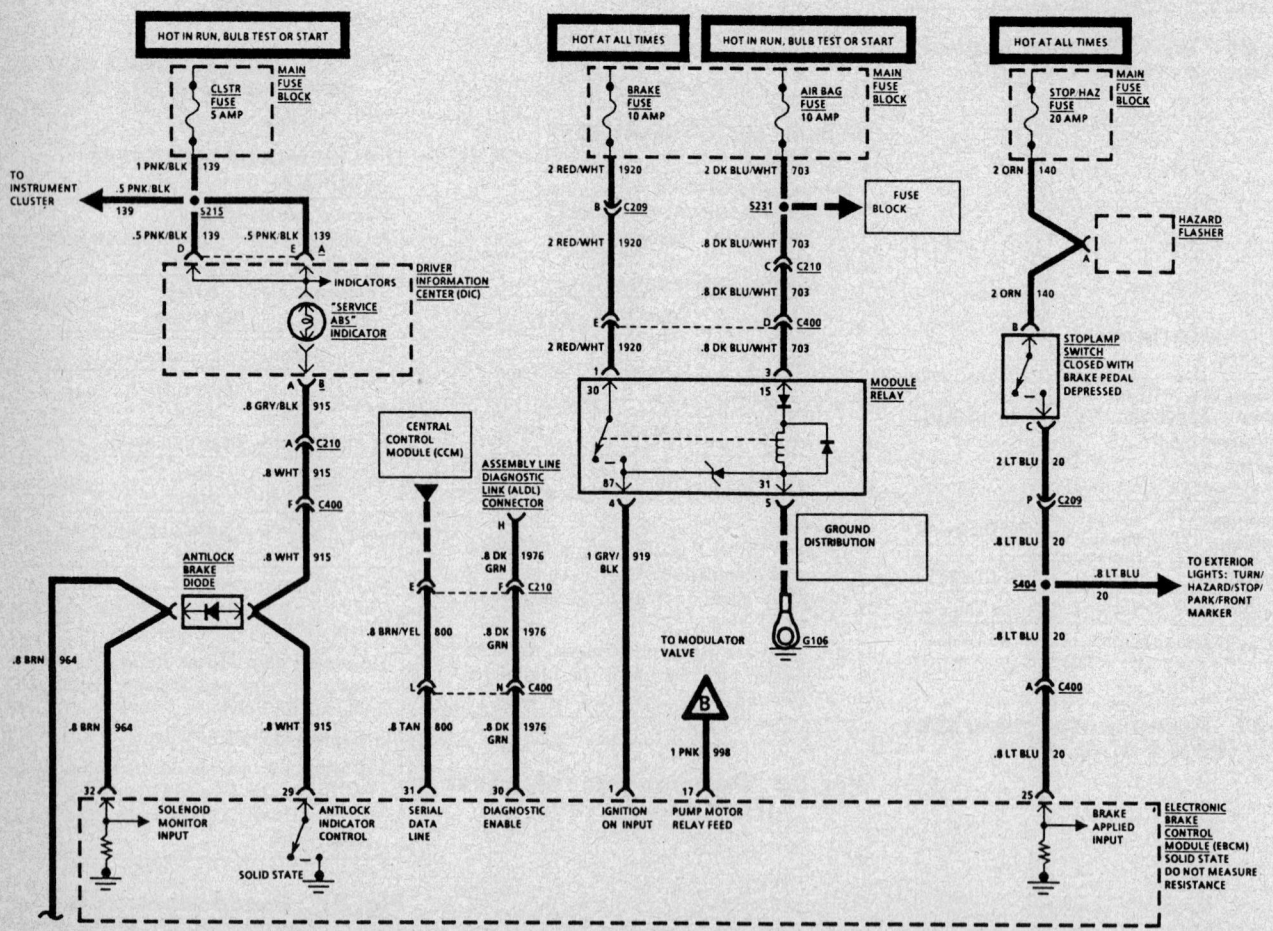

Fig. 25   Anti-lock brake system wiring schematic (Part 1 of 3). 1990

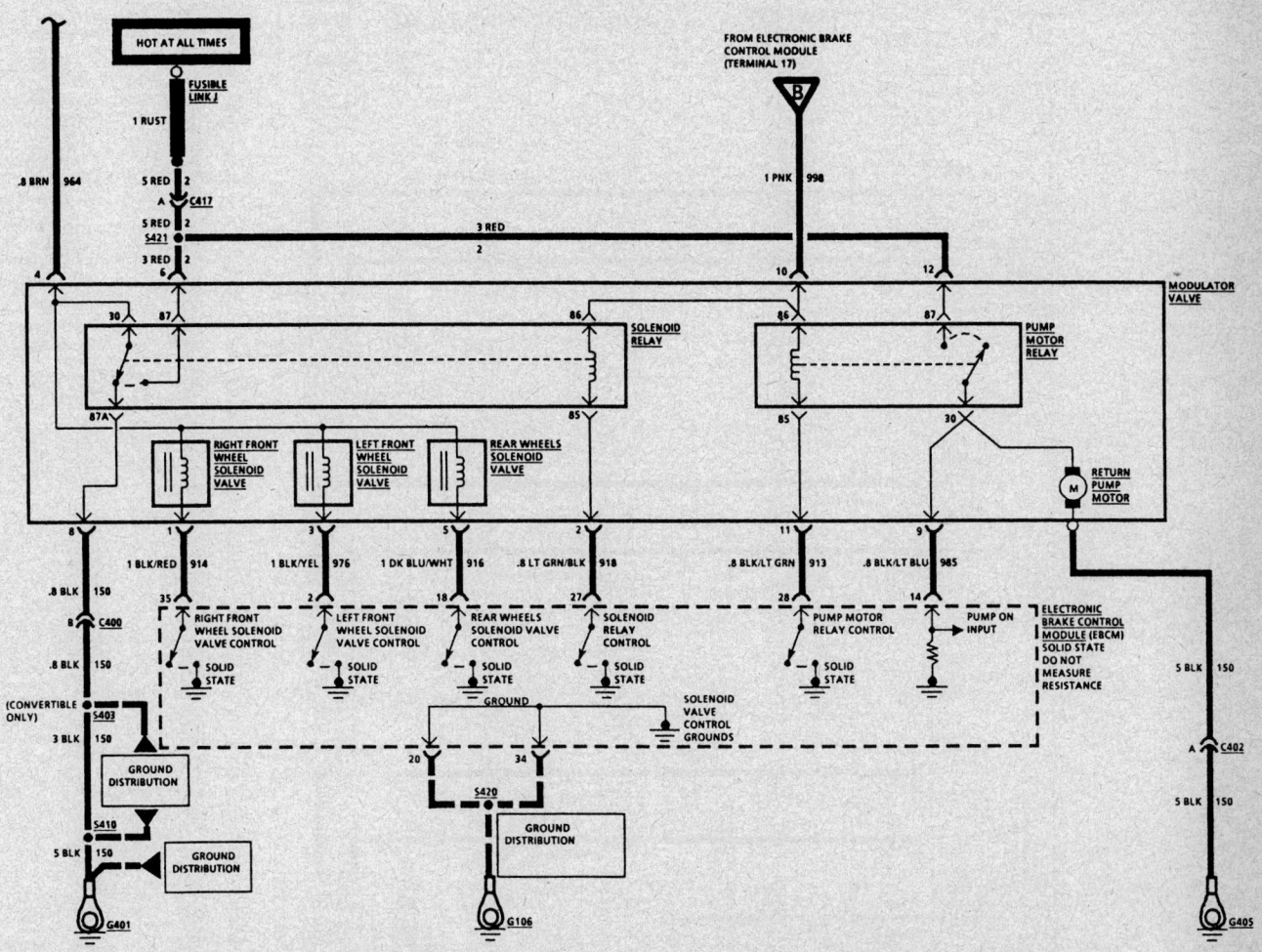

Fig. 25   Anti-lock brake system wiring schematic (Part 2 of 3). 1990

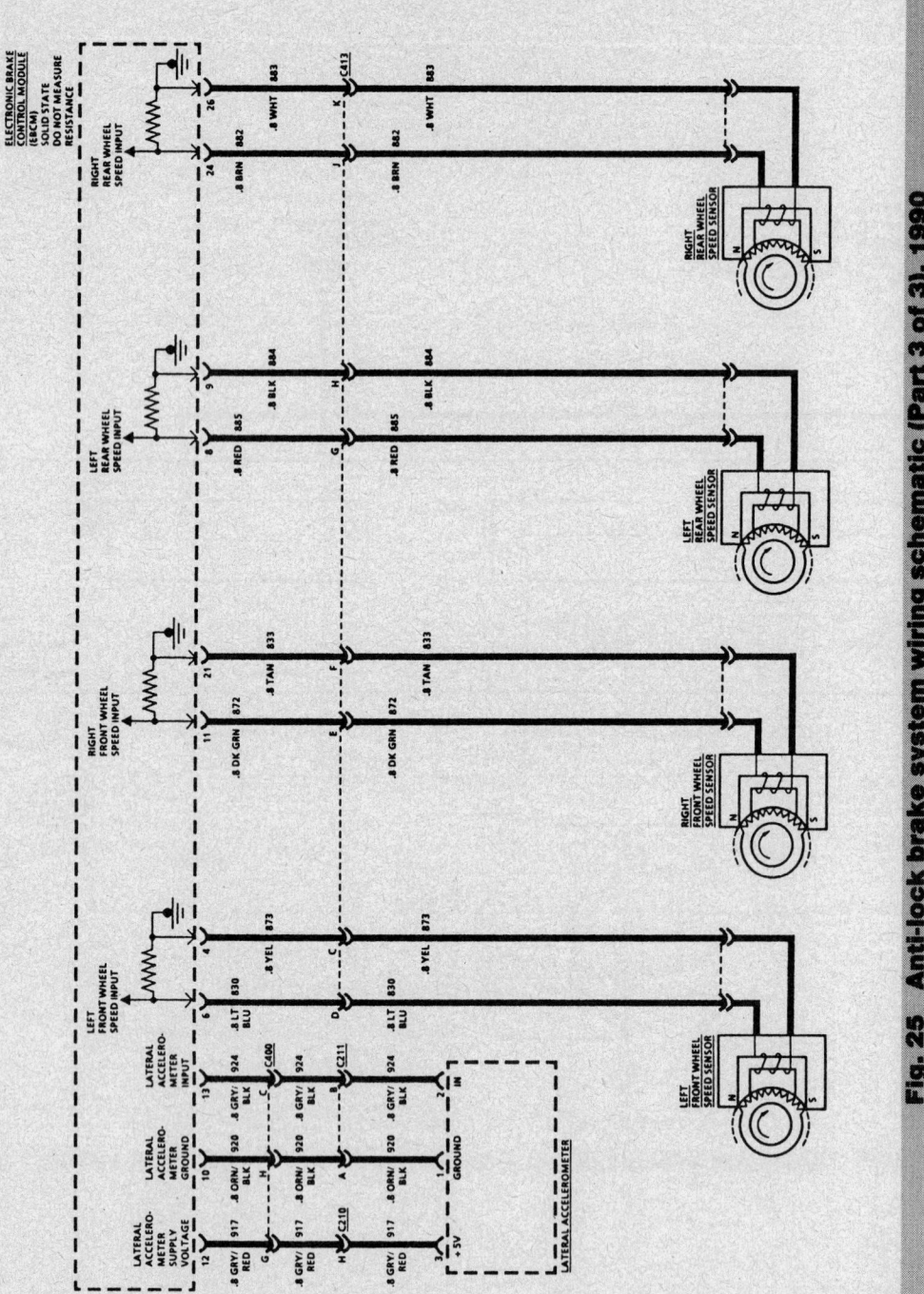

Fig. 25 Anti-lock brake system wiring schematic (Part 3 of 3). 1990

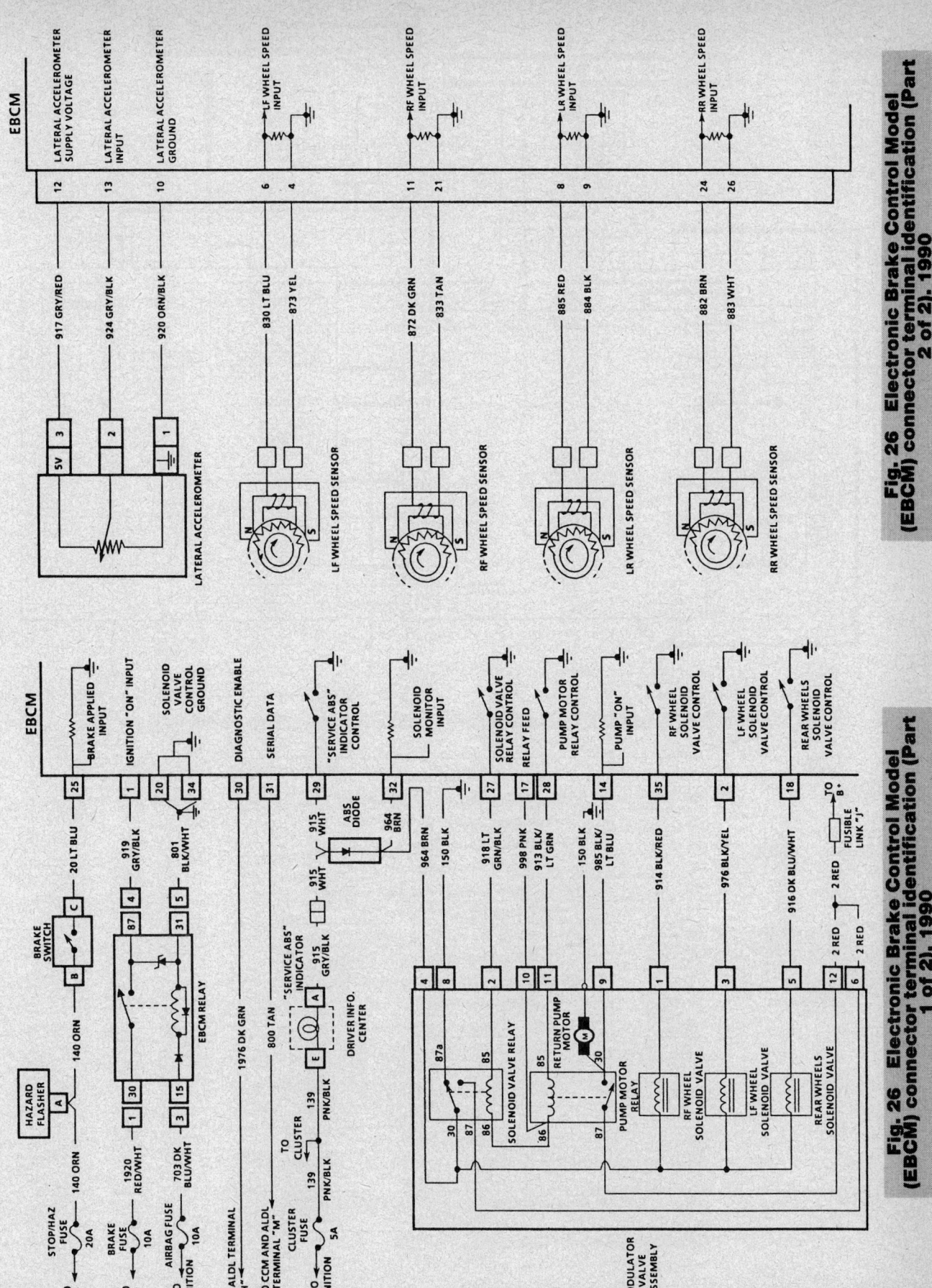

Fig. 26 Electronic Brake Control Model (EBCM) connector terminal identification (Part 2 of 2), 1990

Fig. 26 Electronic Brake Control Model (EBCM) connector terminal identification (Part 1 of 2), 1990

CORVETTE (BOSCH ABS II TYPE)

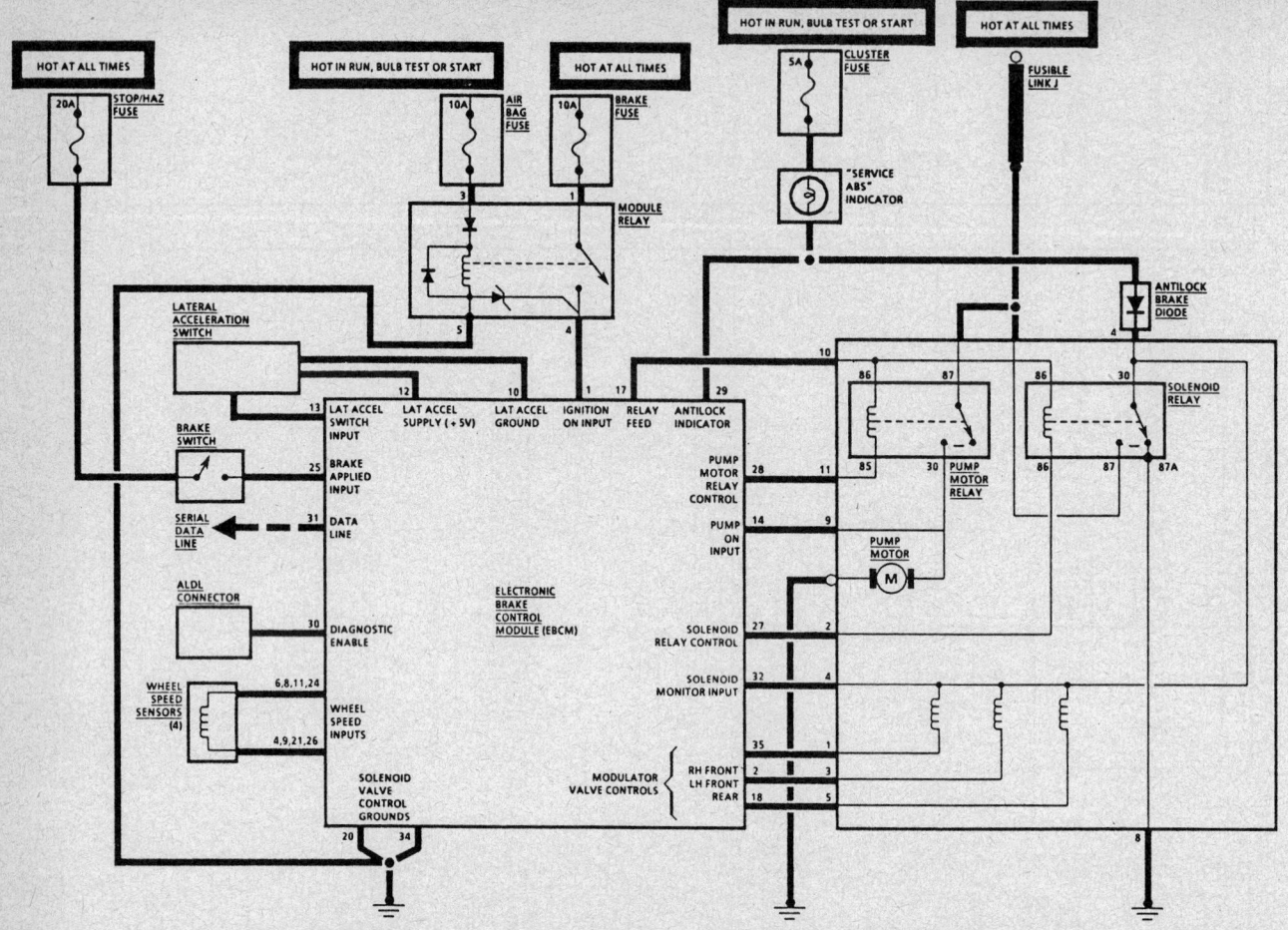

Fig. 27 Anti-lock brake system functional diagram. 1990

Code	Definition
12	Diagnostic System Operational
21	RF Wheel Speed Sensor Fault
22	RF Toothed Wheel Frequency Error
25	LF Wheel Speed Sensor Fault
26	LF Toothed Wheel Frequency Error
31	RR Wheel Speed Sensor Fault
32	RF Toothed Wheel Frequency Error
35	LR Wheel Speed Sensor Fault
36	LR Toothed Wheel Frequency Error
41①	RF Solenoid Valve Fault
45①	LF Solenoid Valve Fault
55①	Rear Solenoid Valve Fault
61①	Pump Motor Or Motor Relay Fault
63①	Solenoid Valve Relay Fault
71	EBCM Fault
72	Serial Data Link Fault
75	Lateral Accelerometer Fault (Short To B+ Or Ground Or Open Circuit
76	Lateral Accelerometer Fault (Signal Out Of Range Or Incorrect

①—Requires Tech 1 Diagnostic Computer.

Fig. 28 Code definition. 1990

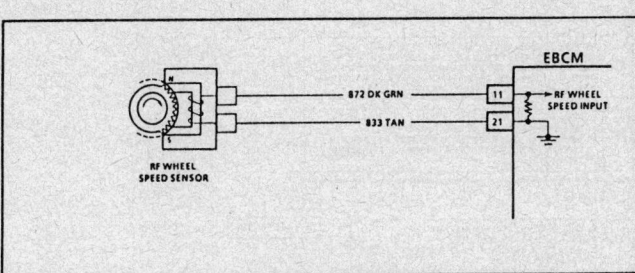

CODE 21
RF WHEEL SPEED SENSOR
(SENSOR FAULT)

Circuit Description:

The toothed wheel generates a voltage pulse as it moves past the sensor; each tooth-gap-tooth on the wheel generates these pulses. The frequency of these pulses is used by the EBCM to determine wheel speed. The amount of voltage generated in each pulse depends on the air gap between the sensor and the toothed wheel, and on wheel speed.

Code 21 is set if there is a loss of continuity in CKT 872 or 833 while the ignition is "ON," or if no signal is being produced by the wheel speed sensor at vehicle speeds of approximately 19 MPH or more.

Test Description: Numbers below refer to circled numbers on the diagnostic chart.

1. This test checks for a correct resistance reading of the sensor itself.
2. This test checks for a short between the wires for the RF wheel speed sensor.
3. This test checks for an open in the wires between the speed sensor and the EBCM.
4. This test checks for a short to ground in CKT 872.
5. This test checks for an intermittent in the RF wheel speed sensor circuitry. If no intermittent is found in the wiring, it may be in the sensor itself. Replace the sensor and road test the vehicle. If the code returns, replace the EBCM.

Diagnostic Aids:

Be sure speed sensor wiring is properly routed; this will help prevent false signals.

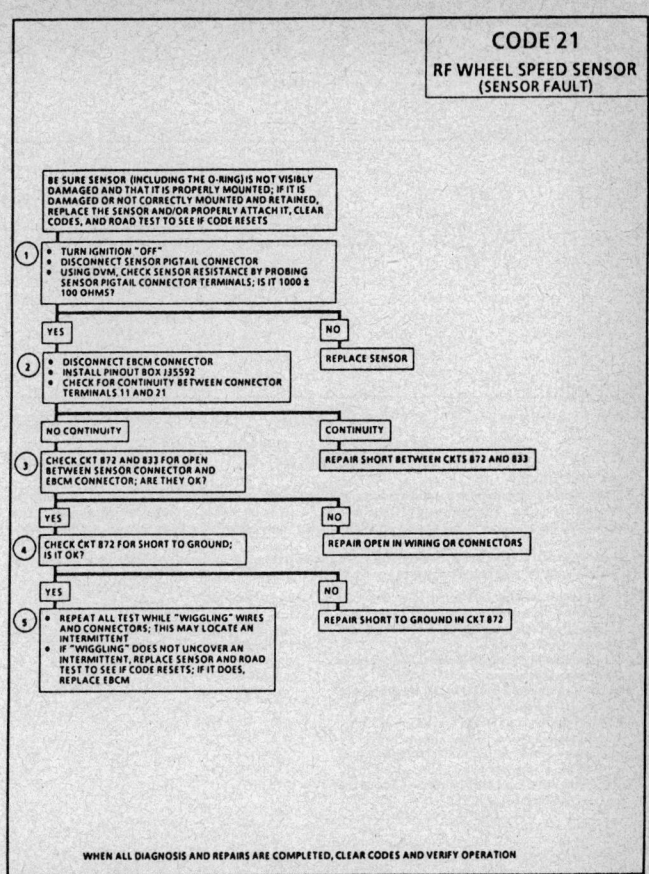

Fig. 29 Code 21, RF wheel speed sensor (sensor fault). 1990

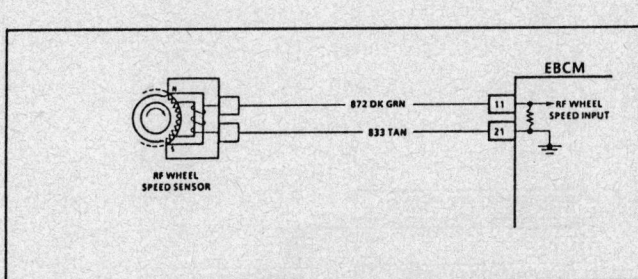

CODE 22
RF TOOTHED WHEEL
(FREQUENCY ERROR)

Circuit Description:

The toothed wheel generates a voltage pulse as it moves past the sensor; each tooth-gap-tooth on the wheel generates these pulses. The frequency of these pulses is used by the EBCM to determine wheel speed, and is determined by the number of teeth on the toothed wheel.

Code 22 will set if an incorrect number of teeth or damaged teeth are present on the toothed wheel. It may also set if the sensor-to-toothed-wheel air gap is incorrect.

Test Description: Numbers below refer to circled numbers on the diagnostic chart.

1. This test checks for a physical problem with the toothed wheel.
2. This test checks for proper mounting, which includes O-ring quality and position, and mounting torque.

Diagnostic Aids:

A worn hub/bearing assembly may cause this fault in extreme cases; the bearing play allows the sensor-to-toothed ring gap to change excessively.

Check for a buildup of foreign material in the gaps between teeth on the toothed wheel; this material may cause this error.

Also check the toothed wheel for any large grooves, gouges, marks, etc. that might influence the tooth's signal at the wheel speed sensor.

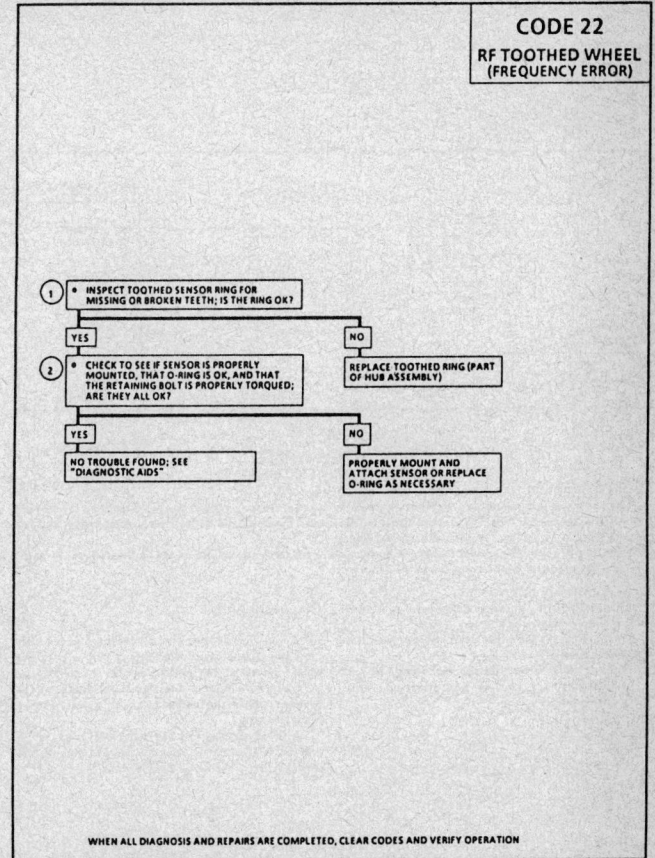

Fig. 30 Code 22, RF toothed wheel (frequency error). 1990

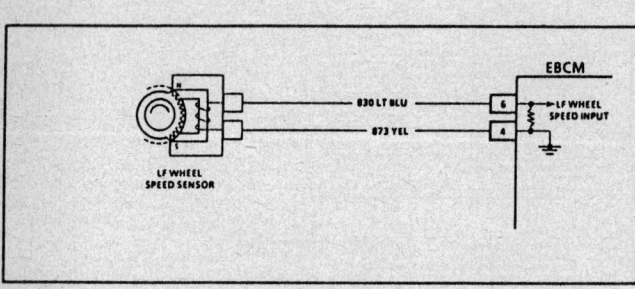

CODE 25
LF WHEEL SPEED SENSOR
(SENSOR FAULT)

Circuit Description:

The toothed wheel generates a voltage pulse as it moves past the sensor; each tooth-gap-tooth on the wheel generates these pulses. The frequency of these pulses is used by the EBCM to determine wheel speed. The amount of voltage generated in each pulse depends on the air gap between the sensor and the toothed wheel, and on wheel speed.

Code 25 is set if there is a loss of continuity in CKT 830 or 873 while the ignition is "ON," or if no signal is being produced by the wheel speed sensor at vehicle speeds of approximately 19 MPH or more.

Test Description: Numbers below refer to circled numbers on the diagnostic chart.

1. This test checks for a correct resistance reading of the sensor itself.
2. This test checks for a short between the wires for the LF wheel speed sensor.
3. This test checks for an open in the wires between the speed sensor and the EBCM.
4. This test checks for a short to ground in CKT 830.
5. This test checks for an intermittent in the LF wheel speed sensor circuitry. If no intermittent is found in the wiring, it may be in the sensor itself. Replace the sensor and road test the vehicle. If the code returns, replace the EBCM.

Diagnostic Aids:

Be sure speed sensor wiring is properly routed; this will help prevent false signals.

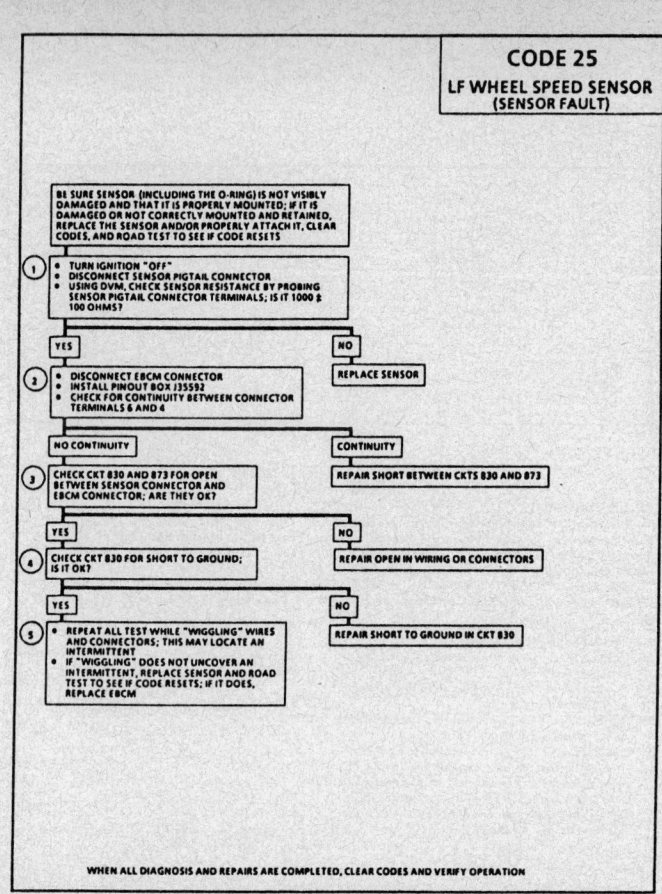

Fig. 31   Code 25, LF wheel speed sensor (sensor fault). 1990

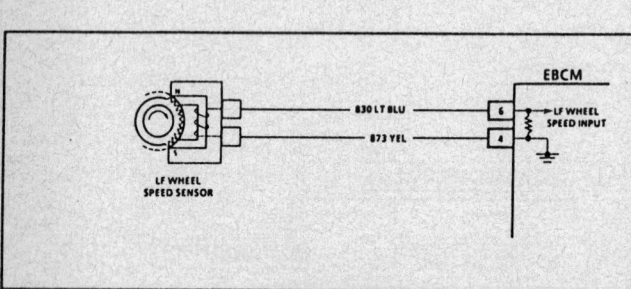

CODE 26
LF TOOTHED WHEEL
(FREQUENCY ERROR)

Circuit Description:

The toothed wheel generates a voltage pulse as it moves past the sensor; each tooth-gap-tooth on the wheel generates these pulses. The frequency of these pulses is used by the EBCM to determine wheel speed, and is determined by the number of teeth on the toothed wheel.

Code 26 will set if an incorrect number of teeth or damaged teeth are present on the toothed wheel. It may also set if the sensor-to-toothed-wheel air gap is incorrect.

Test Description: Numbers below refer to circled numbers on the diagnostic chart.

1. This test checks for a physical problem with the toothed wheel.
2. This test checks for proper mounting, which includes O-ring quality and position, and mounting torque.

Diagnostic Aids:

A worn hub/bearing assembly may cause this fault in extreme cases; the bearing play allows the sensor-to-toothed ring gap to change excessively.

Check for a buildup of foreign material in the gaps between teeth on the toothed wheel; this material may cause this error.

Also check the toothed wheel for any large grooves, gouges, marks, etc. that might influence the tooth's signal at the wheel speed sensor.

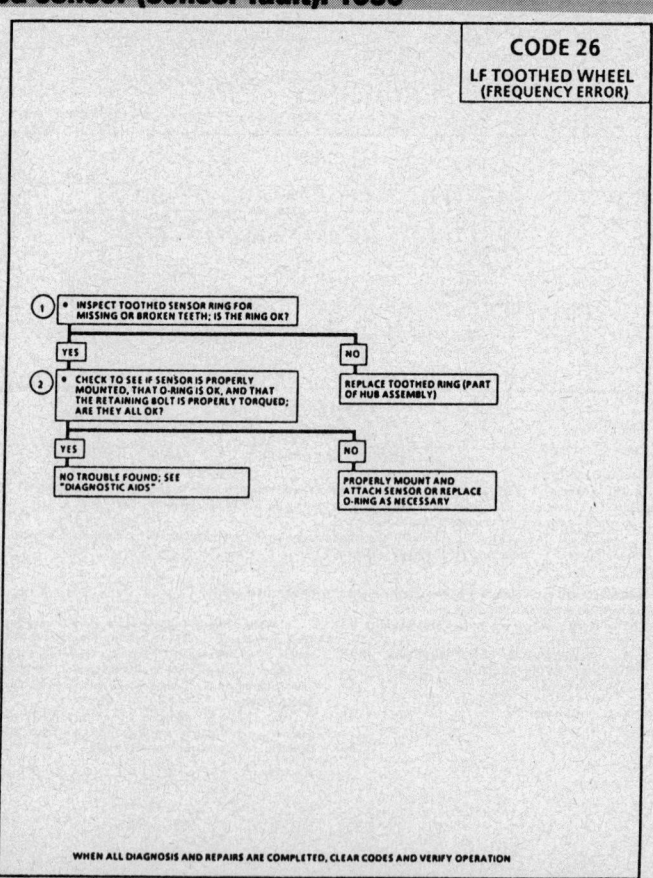

Fig. 32   Code 26, RF toothed wheel (frequency error). 1990

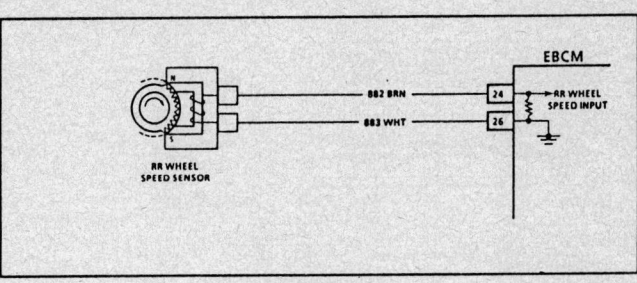

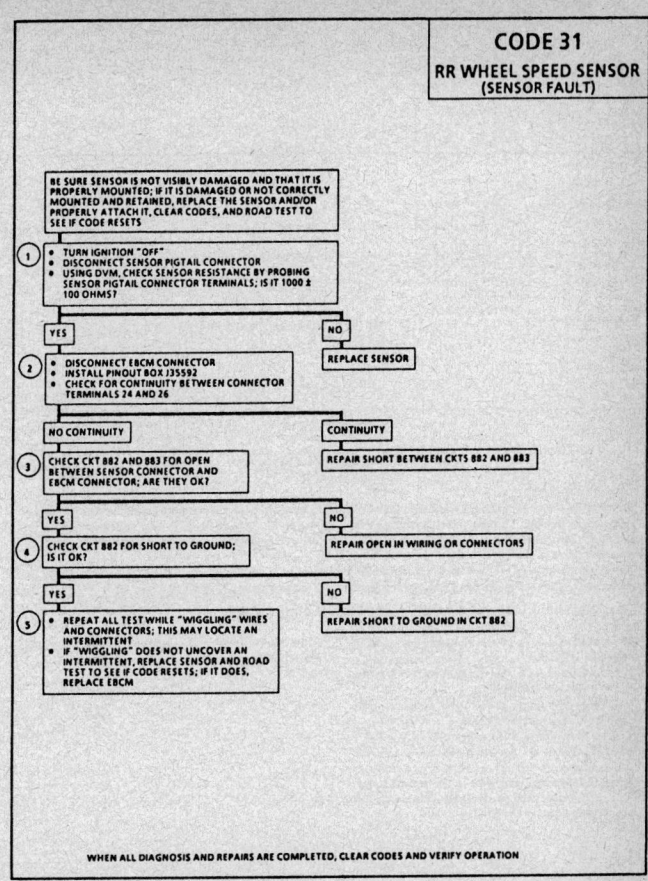

CODE 31
RR WHEEL SPEED SENSOR
(SENSOR FAULT)

Circuit Description:

The toothed wheel generates a voltage pulse as it moves past the sensor; each tooth-gap-tooth on the wheel generates these pulses. The frequency of these pulses is used by the EBCM to determine wheel speed. The amount of voltage generated in each pulse depends on the air gap between the sensor and the toothed wheel, and on wheel speed.

Code 31 is set if there is a loss of continuity in CKT 882 or 883 while the ignition is "ON," or if no signal is being produced by the wheel speed sensor at vehicle speeds of approximately 19 MPH or more.

Test Description: Numbers below refer to circled numbers on the diagnostic chart.

1. This test checks for a correct resistance reading of the sensor itself.
2. This test checks for a short between the wires for the RR wheel speed sensor.
3. This test checks for an open in the wires between the speed sensor and the EBCM.
4. This test checks for a short to ground in CKT 882.
5. This test checks for an intermittent in the RR wheel speed sensor circuitry. If no intermittent is found in the wiring, it may be in the sensor itself. Replace the sensor and road test the vehicle. If the code returns, replace the EBCM.

Diagnostic Aids:

Be sure speed sensor wiring is properly routed; this will help prevent false signals.

Fig. 33   Code 31, RR wheel speed sensor (sensor fault). 1990

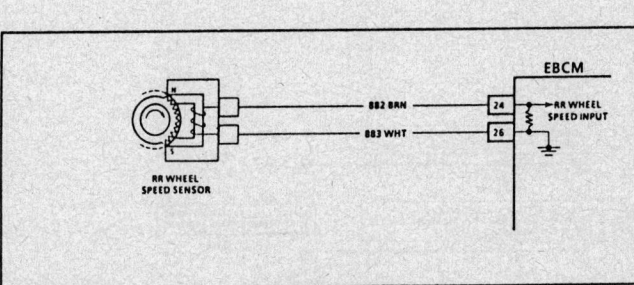

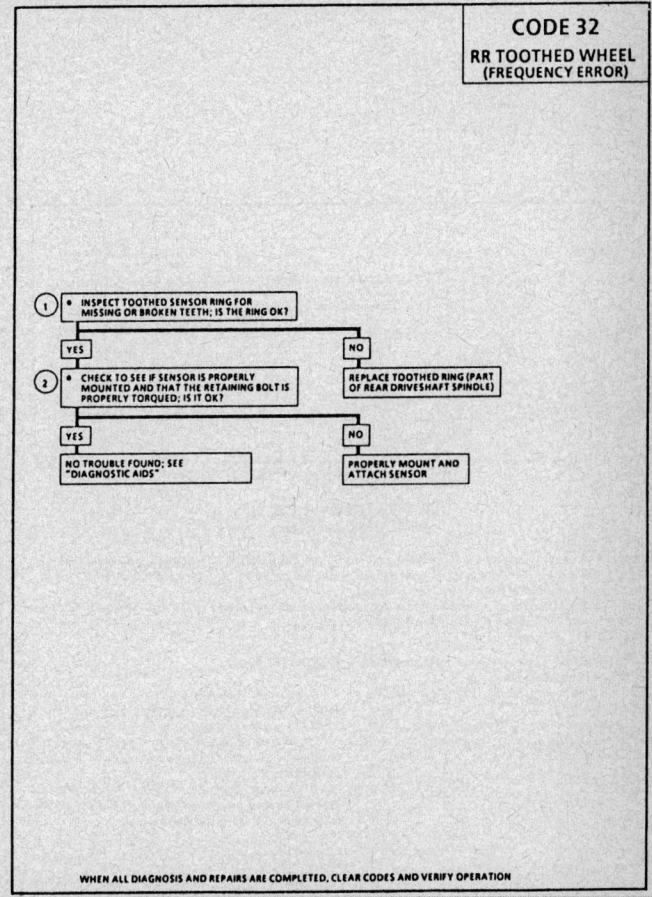

CODE 32
RR TOOTHED WHEEL
(FREQUENCY ERROR)

Circuit Description:

The toothed wheel generates a voltage pulse as it moves past the sensor; each tooth-gap-tooth on the wheel generates these pulses. The frequency of these pulses is used by the EBCM to determine wheel speed, and is determined by the number of teeth on the toothed wheel.

Code 32 will set if an incorrect number of teeth or damaged teeth are present on the toothed wheel. It may also set if the sensor-to-toothed-wheel air gap is incorrect.

Test Description: Numbers below refer to circled numbers on the diagnostic chart.

1. This test checks for a physical problem with the toothed wheel.
2. This test checks for proper mounting, which includes O-ring quality and position, and mounting torque.

Diagnostic Aids:

A worn hub/bearing assembly may cause this fault in extreme cases; the bearing play allows the sensor-to-toothed ring gap to change excessively.

Check for a buildup of foreign material in the gaps between teeth on the toothed wheel; this material may cause this error.

Also check the toothed wheel for any large grooves, gouges, marks, etc. that might influence the tooth's signal at the wheel speed sensor.

Fig. 34   Code 32, RR toothed wheel (frequency error). 1990

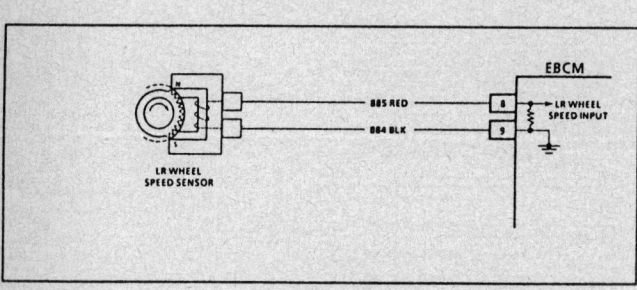

CODE 35
LR WHEEL SPEED SENSOR
(SENSOR FAULT)

Circuit Description:

The toothed wheel generates a voltage pulse as it moves past the sensor; each tooth-gap-tooth on the wheel generates these pulses. The frequency of these pulses is used by the EBCM to determine wheel speed. The amount of voltage generated in each pulse depends on the air gap between the sensor and the toothed wheel, and on wheel speed.

Code 35 is set if there is a loss of continuity in CKT 885 or 884 while the ignition is "ON," or if no signal is being produced by the wheel speed sensor at vehicle speeds of approximately 19 MPH or more.

Test Description: Numbers below refer to circled numbers on the diagnostic chart.

1. This test checks for a correct resistance reading of the sensor itself.
2. This test checks for a short between the wires for the LR wheel speed sensor.
3. This test checks for an open in the wires between the speed sensor and the EBCM.
4. This test checks for a short to ground in CKT 885.
5. This test checks for an intermittent in the LR wheel speed sensor circuitry. If no intermittent is found in the wiring, it may be in the sensor itself. Replace the sensor and road test the vehicle. If the code returns, replace the EBCM.

Diagnostic Aids:

Be sure speed sensor wiring is properly routed; this will help prevent false signals.

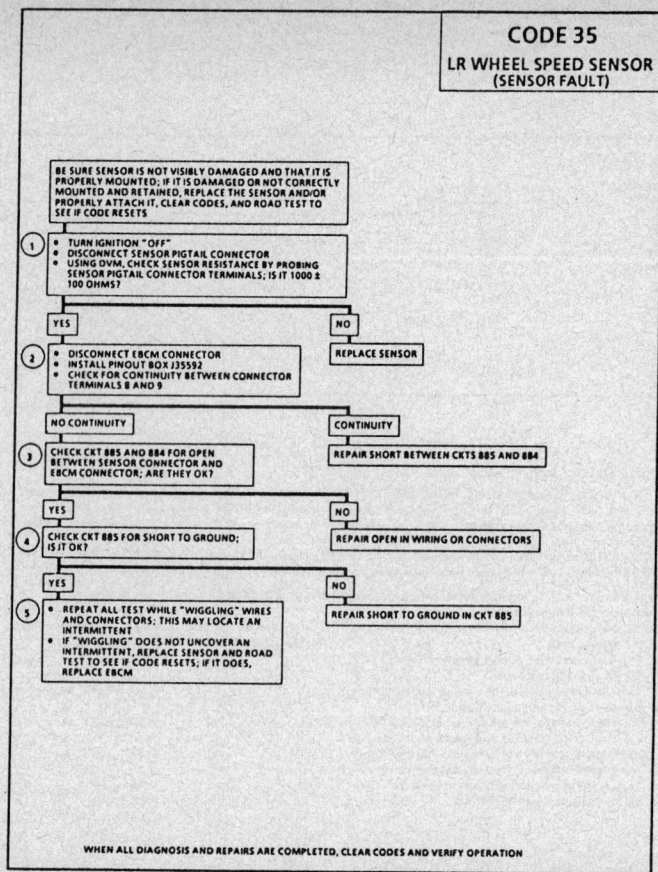

Fig. 35   Code 35, LR wheel speed sensor (sensor fault). 1990

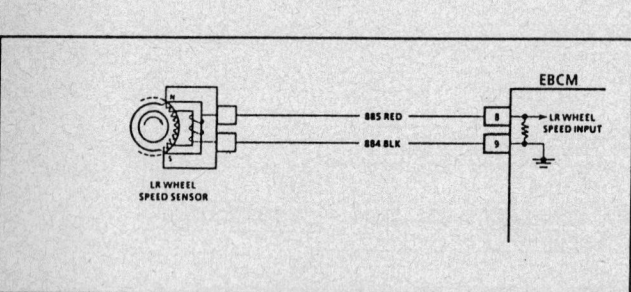

CODE 36
LR TOOTHED WHEEL
(FREQUENCY ERROR)

Circuit Description:

The toothed wheel generates a voltage pulse as it moves past the sensor; each tooth-gap-tooth on the wheel generates these pulses. The frequency of these pulses is used by the EBCM to determine wheel speed, and is determined by the number of teeth on the toothed wheel.

Code 36 will set if an incorrect number of teeth or damaged teeth are present on the toothed wheel. It may also be set if the sensor-to-toothed-wheel air gap is incorrect.

Test Description: Numbers below refer to the diagnostic chart

1. This test checks for a physical problem with the toothed wheel.
2. This test checks for proper mounting, which includes O-ring quality and position, and mounting torque.

Diagnostic Aids:

A worn hub/bearing assembly may cause this fault in extreme cases; the bearing play allows the sensor-to-toothed ring gap to change excessively.

Check for a buildup of foreign material in the gaps between teeth on the toothed wheel; this material may cause this error.

Also check the toothed wheel for any large grooves, gouges, marks, etc. that might influence the tooth's signal at the wheel speed sensor.

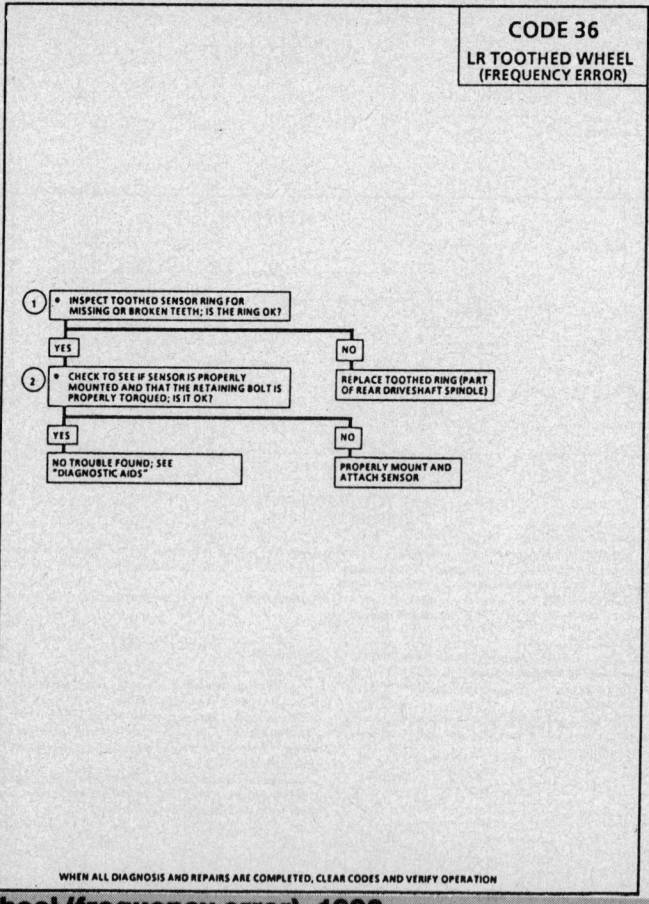

Fig. 36   Code 36, LR toothed wheel (frequency error). 1990

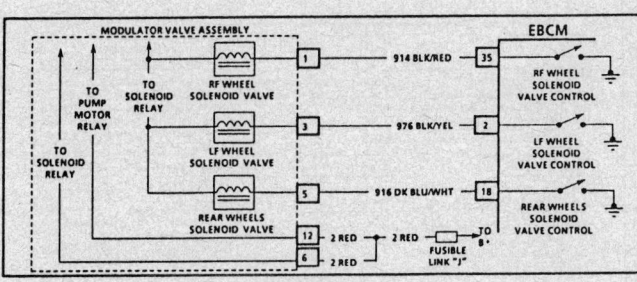

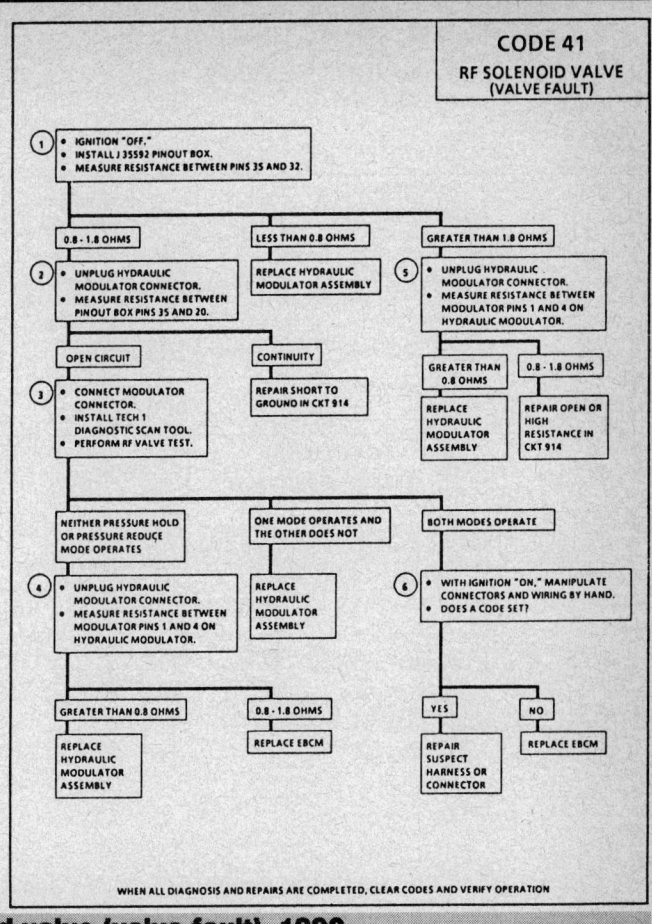

CODE 41
RF SOLENOID VALVE
(VALVE FAULT)

Circuit Description:
The wheel solenoid valve circuits are supplied with power from the battery when the ignition is "ON." The EBCM controls the valve functions by permitting one of three levels of current flow (0,2.5,5 amps).
If the EBCM senses a discrepancy such as an open or ground in the circuit, the valve relay will turn "OFF," the "SERVICE ABS" light will come on, and Code 41 will set.

Test Description: Numbers below refer to circled numbers on the diagnostic chart.
1. This test measures the resistance in the RF Solenoid Valve circuitry.
2. This test checks for a short to ground in CKT 914.
3. This test uses the Tech 1 Diagnostic Computer to check for proper RF Solenoid Valve operation.
4. This test determines if a problem found in Step 3 is due to the EBCM or the Hydraulic Modulator.

5. This test determines if a problem found in Step 1 is due to the Hydraulic Modulator or a problem in CKT 914.
6. This test determines if a problem found in Step 3 is due to an intermittent in the wiring and/or connectors, or a fault with the EBCM.

Fig. 37   Code 41, RF solenoid valve (valve fault). 1990

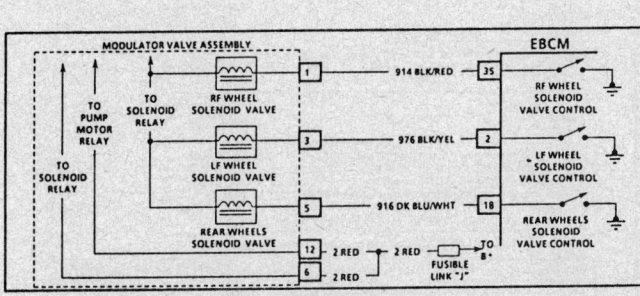

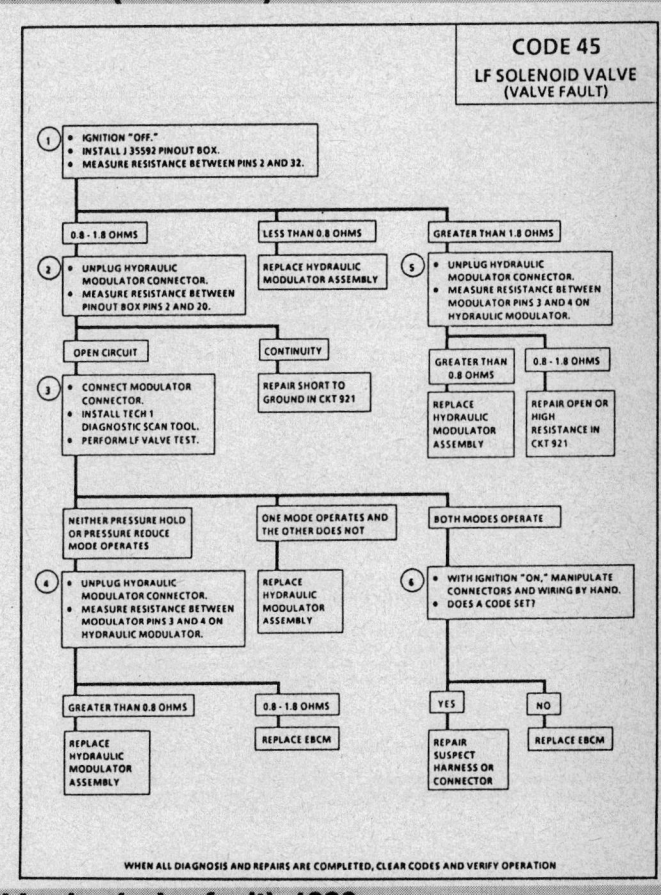

CODE 45
LF SOLENOID VALVE
(VALVE FAULT)

Circuit Description:
The wheel solenoid valve circuits are supplied with power from the battery when the ignition is "ON." The EBCM controls the valve functions by permitting one of three levels of current flow (0,2.5,5 amps).
If the EBCM senses a discrepancy such as an open or ground in the circuit, the valve relay will turn "OFF," the "SERVICE ABS" light will come on, and Code 45 will set.

Test Description: Numbers below refer to circled numbers on the diagnostic chart.
1. This test measures the resistance in the LF Solenoid Valve circuitry.
2. This test checks for a short to ground in CKT 921.
3. This test uses the Tech 1 Diagnostic Computer to check for proper LF Solenoid Valve operation.
4. This test determines if a problem found in Step 3 is due to the EBCM or the Hydraulic Modulator.

5. This test determines if a problem found in Step 1 is due to the Hydraulic Modulator or a problem in CKT 921.
6. This test determines if a problem found in Step 3 is due to an intermittent in the wiring and/or connectors, or a fault with the EBCM.

Fig. 38   Code 45, LF solenoid valve (valve fault). 1990

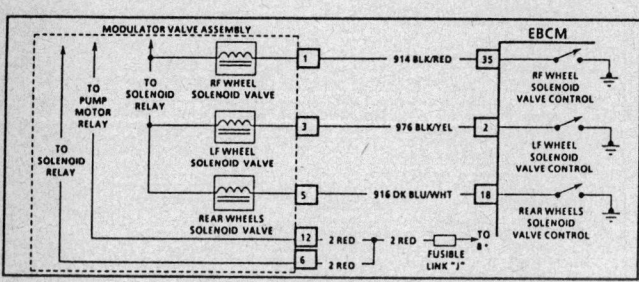

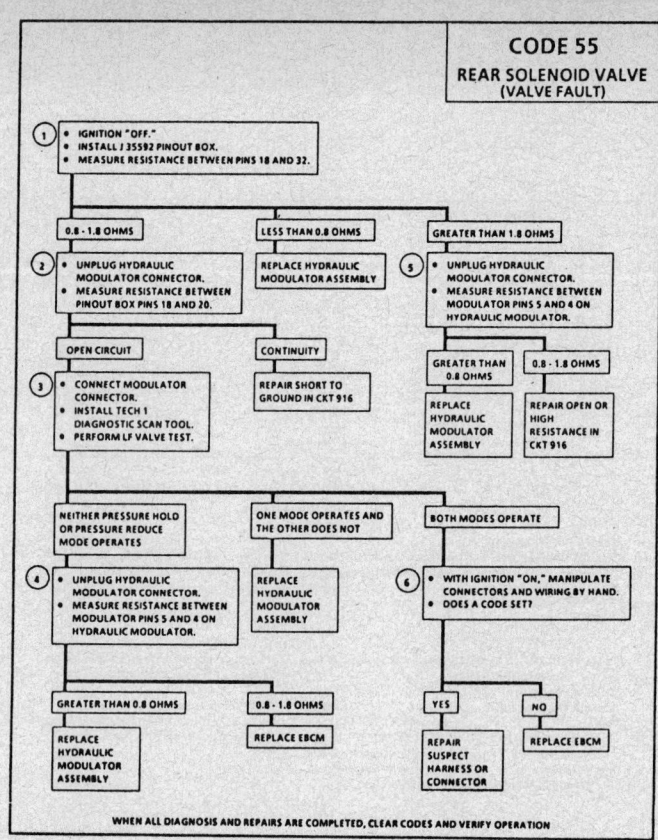

CODE 55
REAR SOLENOID VALVE
(VALVE FAULT)

Circuit Description:

The wheel solenoid valve circuits are supplied with power from the battery when the ignition is "ON." The EBCM controls the valve functions by permitting one of three levels of current flow (0,2.5,5 amps).

If the EBCM senses a discrepancy such as an open or ground in the circuit, the valve relay will turn "OFF," the "SERVICE ABS" light will come on, and Code 55 will set.

Test Description: Numbers below refer to circled numbers on the diagnostic chart.

1. This test measures the resistance in the Rear Solenoid Valve circuitry.
2. This test checks for a short to ground in CKT 916.
3. This test uses the Tech 1 Diagnostic Computer to check for proper Rear Solenoid Valve operation.
4. This test determines if a problem found in Step 3 is due to the EBCM or the Hydraulic Modulator.

5. This test determines if a problem found in Step 1 is due to the Hydraulic Modulator or a problem in CKT 916.
6. This test determines if a problem found in Step 3 is due to an intermittent in the wiring and/or connectors, or a fault with the EBCM.

Fig. 39 Code 55, Rear solenoid valve (valve fault). 1990

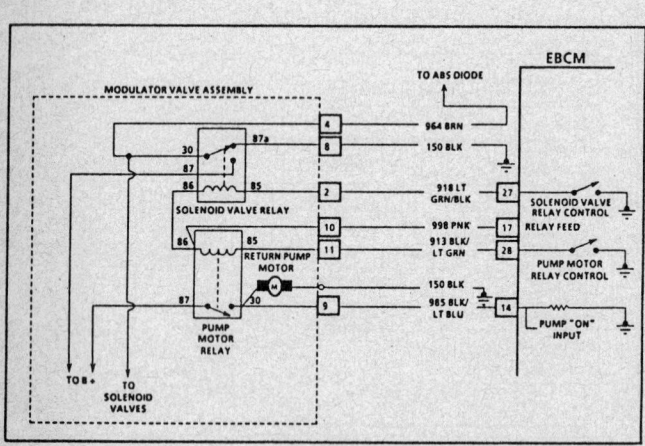

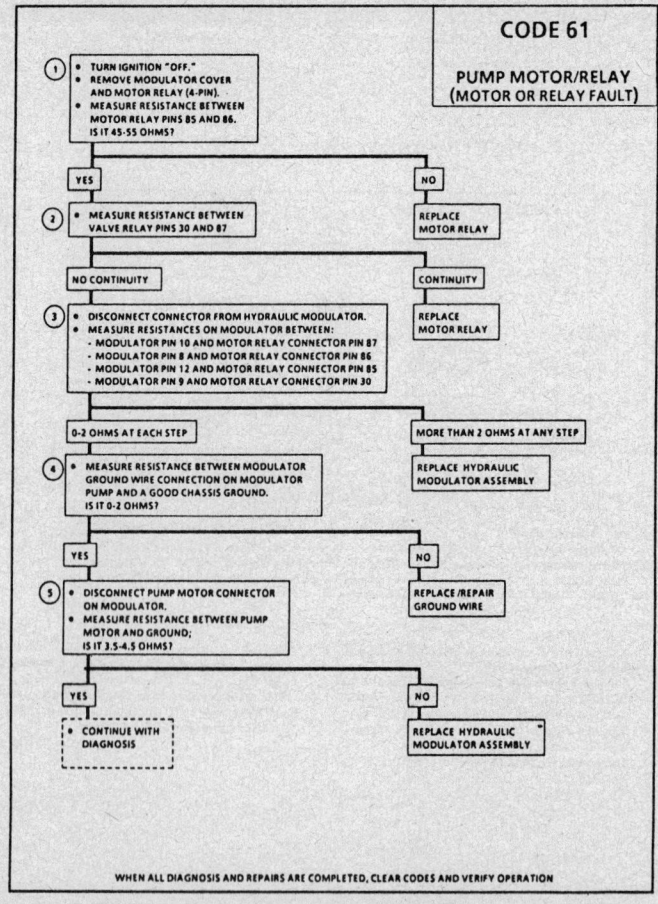

CODE 61
PUMP MOTOR/RELAY
(MOTOR OR RELAY FAULT)

Circuit Description:

When the pump motor relay is grounded by the EBCM, it provides B+ to operate the pump. Once the motor circuit is energized, a "Pump ON" signal is sent back to the EBCM to verify operation.

Code 61 will set if 12 volts is present at the pump motor without motor relay activation, or if 12 volts is NOT present at the pump motor within 60 milliseconds after the motor relay is activated.

Test Description: Numbers below refer to circled numbers on the diagnostic chart.

1. This checks the relay itself for correct resistance.
2. This checks the relay itself for being stuck closed.

3. These tests check for an open in the circuitry of the Hydraulic Modulator.
4. This test checks for a good ground.
5. This test checks the pump motor itself for correct resistance.

Fig. 40 Code 61, Pump motor/relay (motor or relay fault, Part 1 of 3). 1990

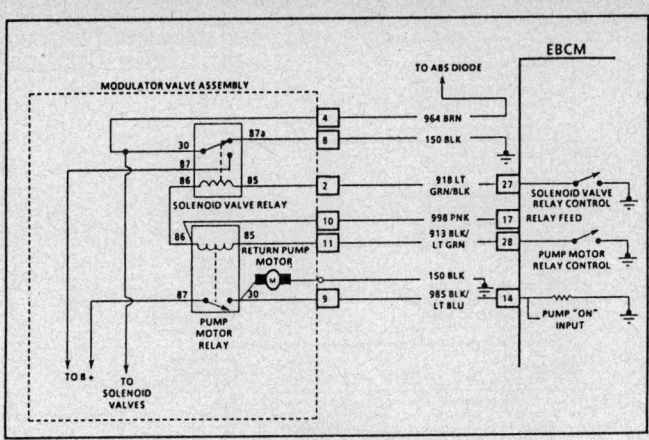

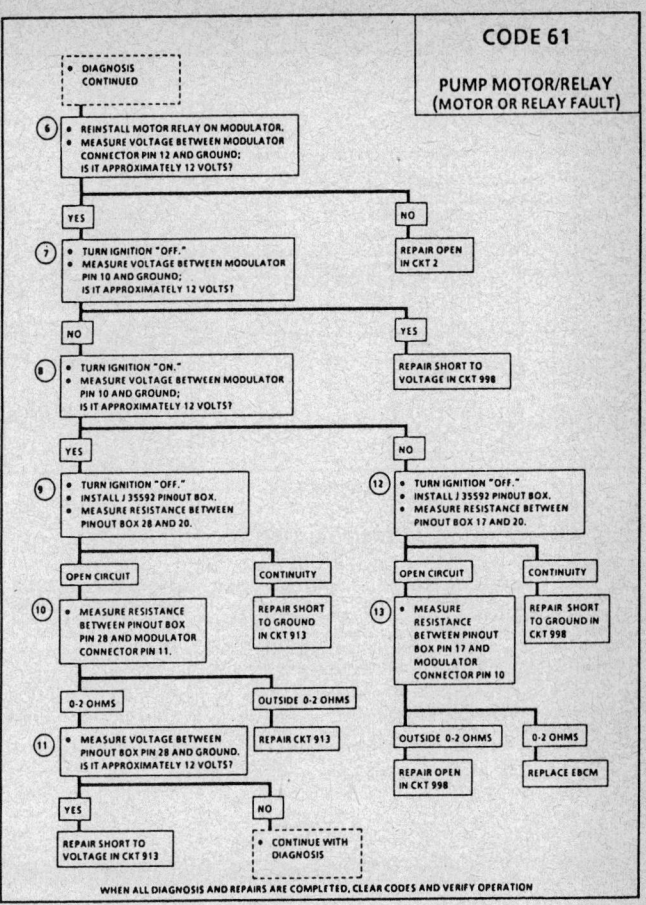

CODE 61

PUMP MOTOR/RELAY
(MOTOR OR RELAY FAULT)

Circuit Description:

When the pump motor relay is grounded by the EBCM, it provides B+ to operate the pump. Once the motor circuit is energized, a "Pump ON" signal is sent back to the EBCM to verify operation.

Code 61 will set if 12 volts is present at the pump motor without motor relay activation, or if 12 volts is NOT present at the pump motor within 60 milliseconds after the motor relay is activated.

Test Description: Numbers below refer to circled numbers on the diagnostic chart.

6. This test checks for battery voltage available to the pump motor relay.
7. This test checks for a short to battery in the Relay Feed circuit.
8. This test checks for a potential open or short to ground in CKT 998.
9. This test checks for a short to ground in CKT 913.
10. This test checks for an open in CKT 913.
11. This test checks for a short to B+ in CKT 913.
12. This test determines if a problem found in Step 8 is an open or a short to ground.
13. This test determines if a problem found in Step 12 is due to a problem in the circuit itself or a faulty EBCM.

Fig. 40   Code 61, Pump motor/relay (motor or relay fault, Part 2 of 3). 1990

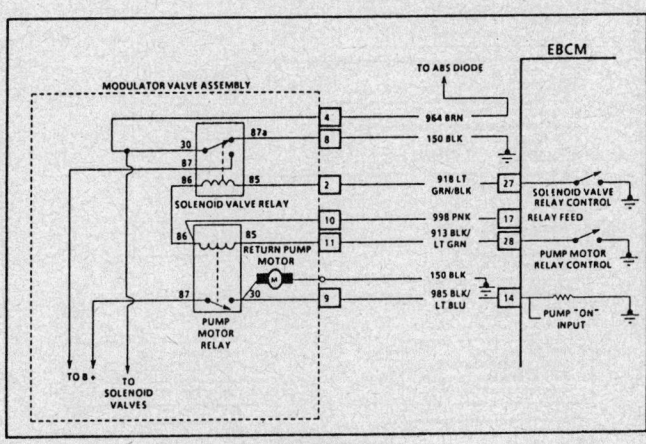

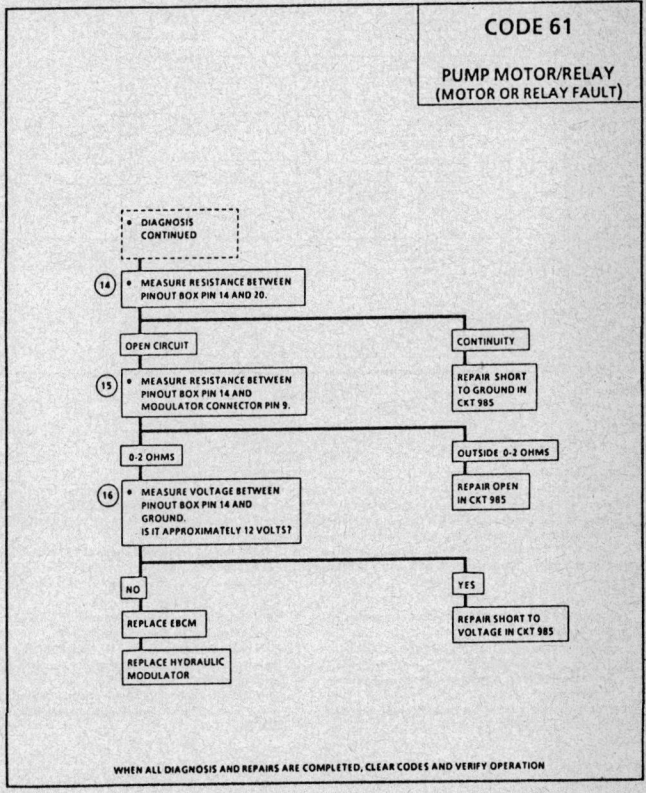

CODE 61

PUMP MOTOR/RELAY
(MOTOR OR RELAY FAULT)

Circuit Description:

When the pump motor relay is grounded by the EBCM, it provides B+ to operate the pump. Once the motor circuit is energized, a "Pump ON" signal is sent back to the EBCM to verify operation.

Code 61 will set if 12 volts is present at the pump motor without motor relay activation, or if 12 volts is NOT present at the pump motor within 60 milliseconds after the motor relay is activated.

Test Description: Numbers below refer to circled numbers on the diagnostic chart.

14. This test check for a short to ground in CKT 985.
15. This test checks for an open in CKT 985.
16. This test checks for a short to B+ in CKT 985.

Fig. 40   Code 61, Pump motor/relay (motor or relay fault, Part 3 of 3). 1990

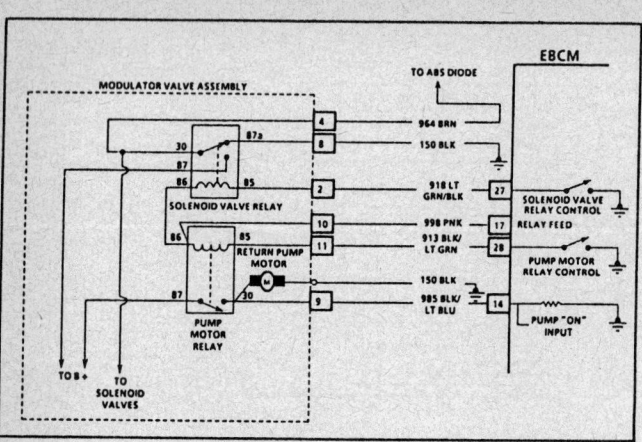

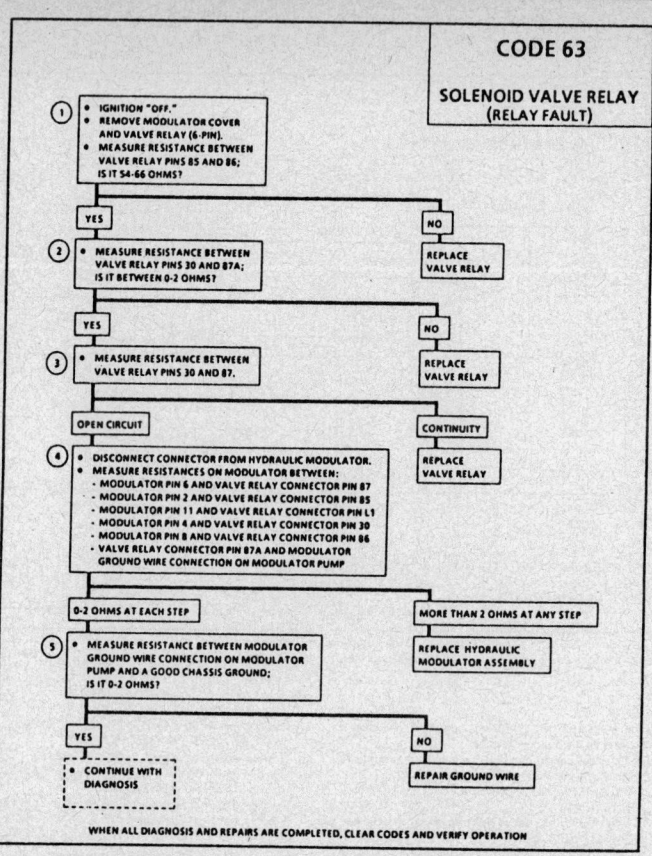

CODE 63

SOLENOID VALVE RELAY
(RELAY FAULT)

CODE 63

SOLENOID VALVE RELAY
(RELAY FAULT)

Circuit Description:

The solenoid valve relay circuit has 2 functions. When ABS is active, the relay provides voltage to actuate the three solenoid valves. However, the solenoid valves do not use this voltage unless the EBCM provides grounds. The second function of the solenoid valve relay circuit is to provide a ground path for illumination of the "SERVICE ABS" lamp if the solenoid relay loses power or ground.

Code 63 will set if the valve relay voltage falls to less than 5 volts, or if the relay feed line is at 12 volts when the EBCM is not requesting it to be; this would make the relay constantly "ON."

Test Description: Numbers below refer to circled numbers on the diagnostic chart.
1. This test checks the relay itself for correct resistance.
2. This test checks the relay itself for a bad internal switch.
3. This test checks the relay itself for being stuck closed to Pin 87.
4. This test checks for an open in the circuitry of the Hydraulic Modulator.
5. This test checks for a good ground.

Fig. 41   Code 63, Solenoid valve relay (relay fault, Part 1 of 3). 1990

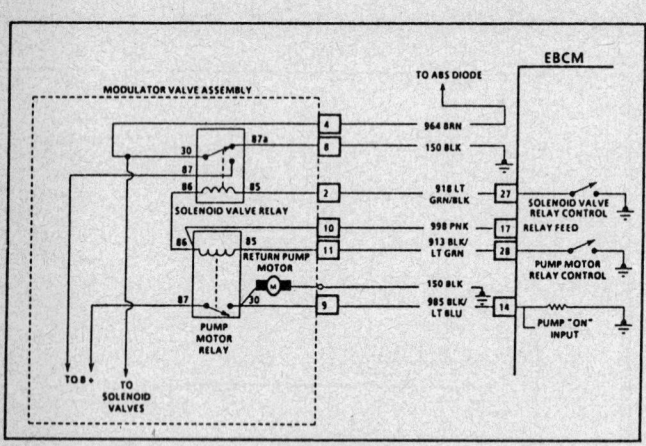

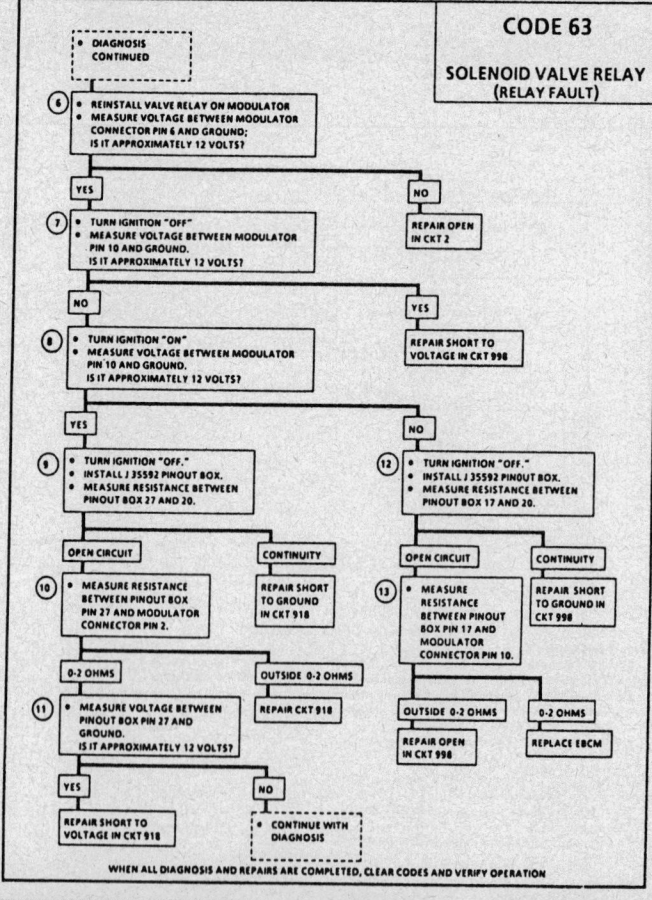

CODE 63

SOLENOID VALVE RELAY
(RELAY FAULT)

CODE 63

SOLENOID VALVE RELAY
(RELAY FAULT)

Circuit Description:

The solenoid valve relay circuit has 2 functions. When ABS is active, the relay provides voltage to actuate the three solenoid valves. However, the solenoid valves do not use this voltage unless the EBCM provides grounds. The second function of the solenoid valve relay circuit is to provide a ground path for illumination of the "SERVICE ABS" lamp if the solenoid relay loses power or ground.

Code 63 will set if the valve relay voltage falls to less than 5 volts, or if the relay feed line is at 12 volts when the EBCM is not requesting it to be; this would make the relay constantly "ON."

Test Description: Numbers below refer to circled numbers on the diagnostic chart.
6. This test checks for battery voltage available to the solenoid valve relay.
7. This test checks for a short to battery in the Relay Feed circuit.
8. This test checks for a potential open or short to ground in CKT 998.
9. This test checks for a short to ground in CKT 918.
10. This test checks for an open in CKT 918.
11. This test checks for a short to B + in CKT 918.
12. This test determines if a problem found in Step 8 is an open or a short to ground.
13. This test determines if a problem found in Step 12 is due to a problem in the circuit itself or a faulty EBCM.

Fig. 41   Code 63, Solenoid valve relay (relay fault, Part 2 of 3). 1990

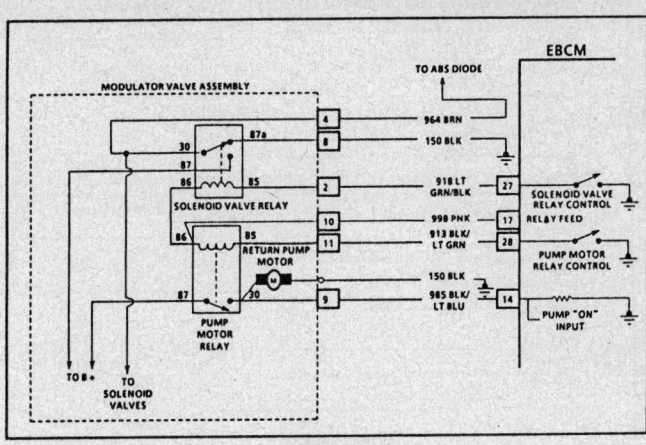

CODE 63

SOLENOID VALVE RELAY
(RELAY FAULT)

Circuit Description:
The solenoid valve relay circuit has 2 functions. When ABS is active, the relay provides voltage to actuate the three solenoid valves. However, the solenoid valves do not use this voltage unless the EBCM provides grounds. The second function of the solenoid valve relay circuit is to provide a ground path for illumination of the "SERVICE ABS" lamp if the solenoid relay loses power or ground.
Code 63 will be set if the valve relay voltage falls to less than 5 volts, or if the relay feed line is at 12 volts when the EBCM is not requesting it to be; this would make the relay constantly "ON."

Test Description: Numbers below refer to circled numbers on the diagnostic chart.
14. This test checks for a short to ground in CKT 964.
15. This test checks for an open in CKT 964.
16. This test checks for a short to B+ in CKT 964.

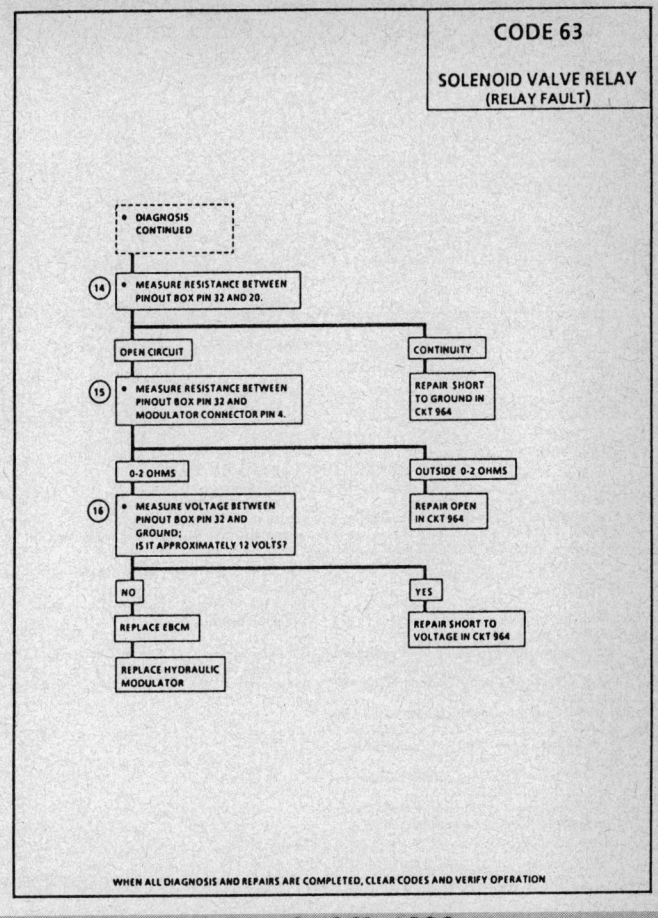

CODE 63

SOLENOID VALVE RELAY
(RELAY FAULT)

WHEN ALL DIAGNOSIS AND REPAIRS ARE COMPLETED, CLEAR CODES AND VERIFY OPERATION

Fig. 41   Code 63, Solenoid valve relay (relay fault, Part 3 of 3). 1990

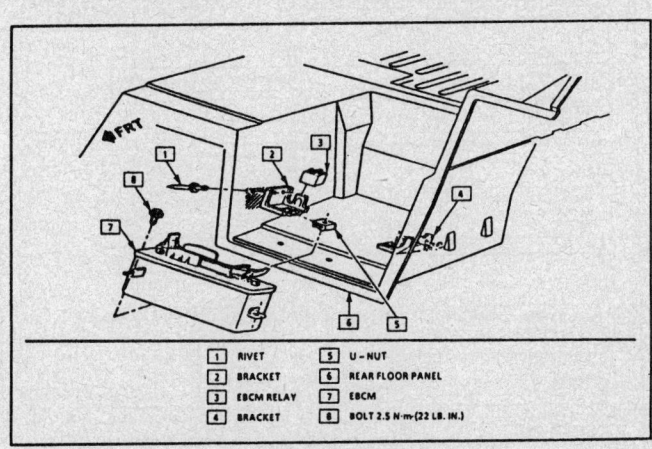

CODE 71

ELECTRONIC BRAKE CONTROL MODULE (EBCM)
(CONTROL MODULE FAULT)

1	RIVET	5	U – NUT
2	BRACKET	6	REAR FLOOR PANEL
3	EBCM RELAY	7	EBCM
4	BRACKET	8	BOLT 2.5 N·m (22 LB. IN.)

Circuit Description:
The EBCM performs various diagnostic checks on itself. If it finds a problem, Code 71 will set.

Test Description: Numbers below refer to circled numbers on the diagnostic chart.
1. This test checks to see if the minimum voltage for proper EBCM operation is available to the EBCM.
2. This test checks for good connections from the harness to the EBCM itself.
3. This test checks to see if the fault was false; if not, replace the EBCM.

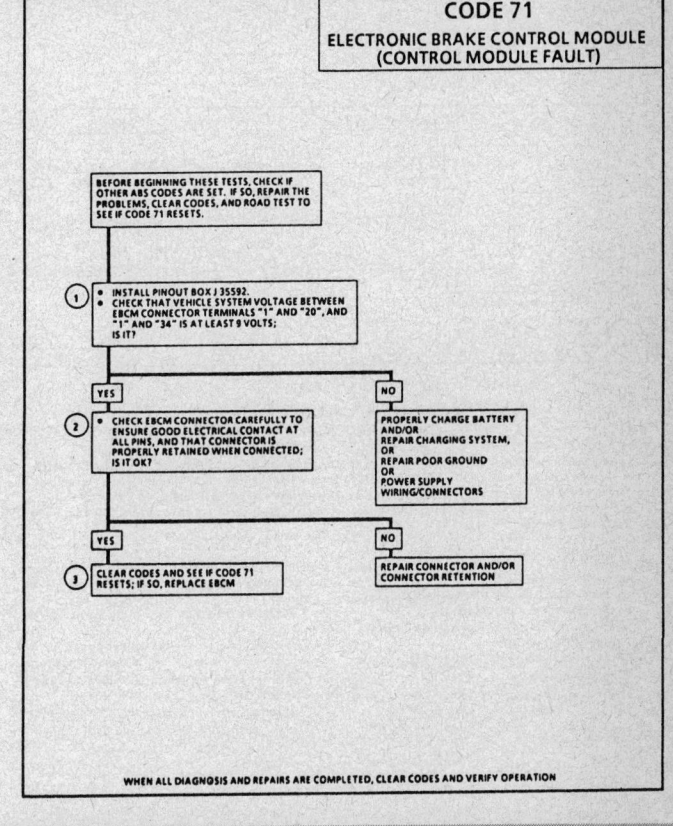

CODE 71

ELECTRONIC BRAKE CONTROL MODULE
(CONTROL MODULE FAULT)

WHEN ALL DIAGNOSIS AND REPAIRS ARE COMPLETED, CLEAR CODES AND VERIFY OPERATION

Fig. 42   Code 71, Electronic Brake Control Module (control module fault). 1990

CORVETTE (BOSCH ABS II TYPE)

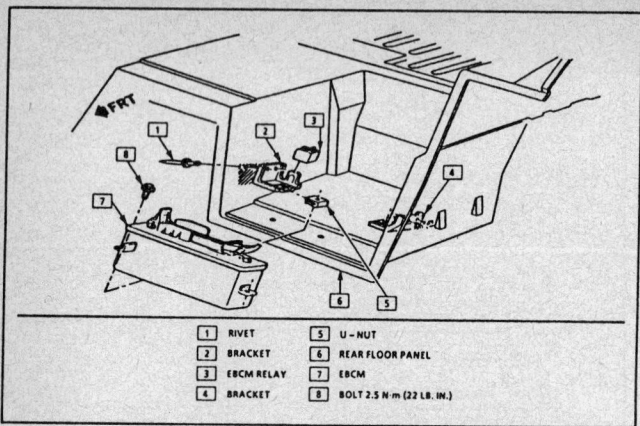

1	RIVET	5	U – NUT
2	BRACKET	6	REAR FLOOR PANEL
3	EBCM RELAY	7	EBCM
4	BRACKET	8	BOLT 2.5 N·m (22 LB. IN.)

CODE 72
ELECTRONIC BRAKE CONTROL MODULE (EBCM)
(SERIAL DATA LINE FAULT)

Circuit Description:

The Serial Data Link is an asynchronous link operating at 8192 bits per second.

Code 72 will set if the EBCM detects three consecutive serial data link messages that are ignored due to errors in transmission. The "SERVICE ABS" indicator will not be illuminated for this fault.

Test Description: Numbers below refer to the circled numbers on the diagnostic chart.

1. This test checks to see if the off-board device can communicate with the EBCM.
2. This test checks for a short to battery in the ABS serial data circuit.
3. This test checks for a short to ground in the ABS serial data circuit.
4. This test checks for an open in the ABS serial data circuit.
5. This test checks to see if the off-board device can communicate with the EBCM.
6. If the connections at the EBCM and ALDL connector are OK, replace the EBCM.

Diagnostic Aids:

The problem may be intermittent.. Try performing the tests shown while "wiggling" wiring and connectors; this can often cause the fault to appear.

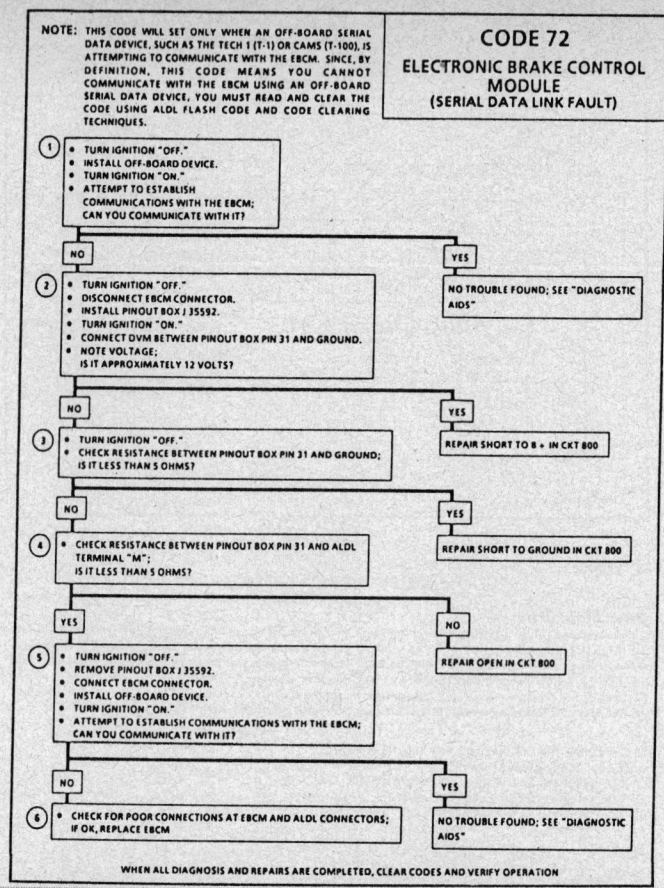

Fig. 43   Code 72, Electronic Brake Control Module (serial data link fault). 1990

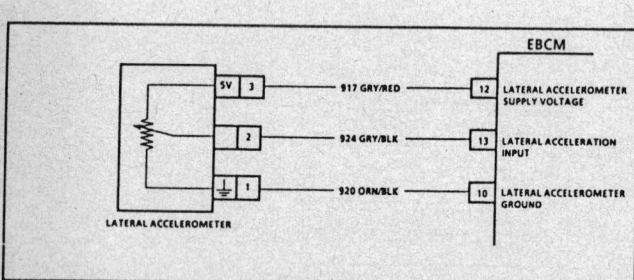

CODE 75
LATERAL ACCELEROMETER
(SHORT TO B + OR GROUND, OR OPEN CIRCUIT)

Circuit Description:

The lateral accelerometer circuit provides a signal to the EBCM which reflects the severity of a vehicle turn. This information is used by the EBCM to modify the control of the rear wheel brakes to help prevent loss of control in a turn due to light brake pedal application at speeds above 50 km/h (30 mph).

Code 75 will set if the EBCM senses the lateral accelerometer voltage to be out of its permissible range due to an electrical wiring fault.

Test Description: Numbers below refer to the circled numbers on the diagnostic chart.

1. This test checks to ensure good connections at the lateral accelerometer and the EBCM.
2. This test checks for a short to ground in the power supply and signal circuits.
3. This test checks for a short to battery in the signal and ground circuits.
4. This test checks for continuity in the power supply circuit through the accelerometer, and back to the EBCM.
5. This test checks for an open in the signal circuit wiring.
6. This test checks for correct voltage supply to the accelerometer from the EBCM. If it is OK, the EBCM must be incorrectly setting this code, and should be replaced.

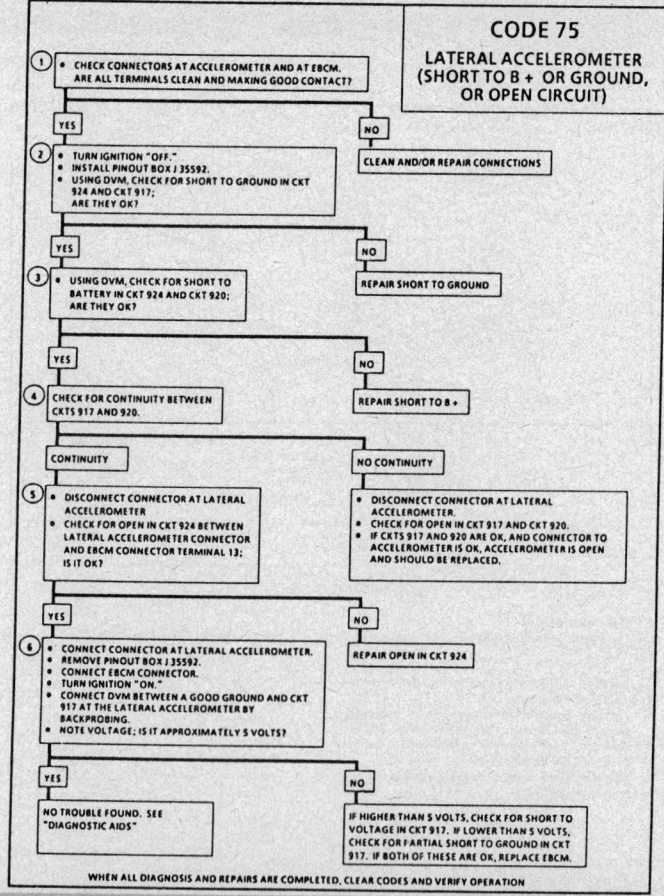

Fig. 44   Code 75, Lateral accelerometer (short to B+ or ground, or open circuit). 1990

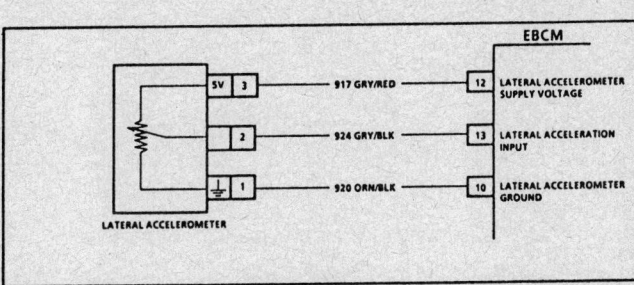

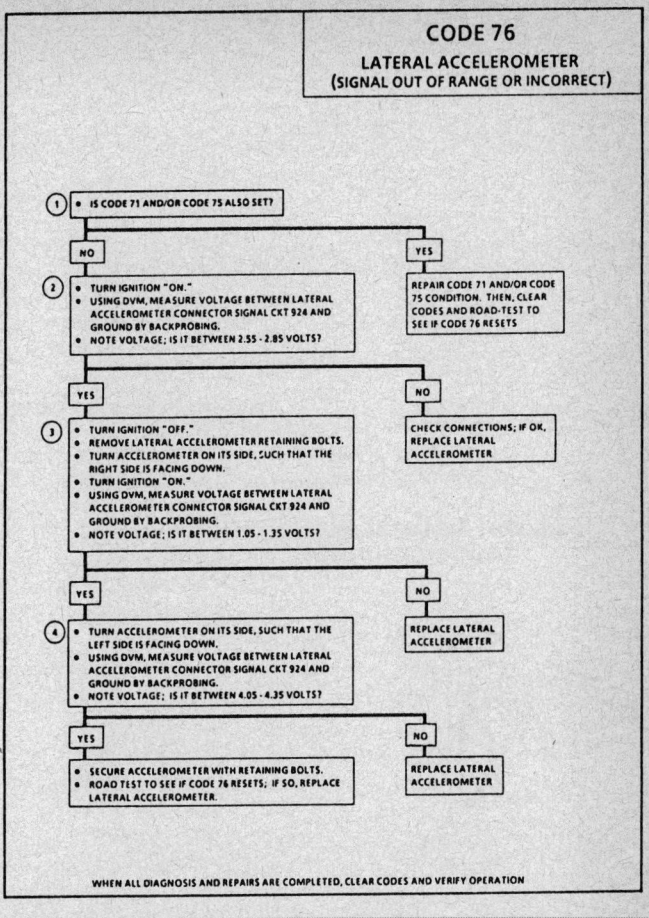

CODE 76
LATERAL ACCELEROMETER
(SIGNAL OUT OF RANGE OR INCORRECT)

Circuit Description:

The lateral accelerometer circuit provides a signal to the EBCM which reflects the severity of a vehicle turn. This information is used by the EBCM to modify the control of the rear wheel brakes to help prevent loss of control in a turn due light brake pedal application at speeds above 50 km/h (30 mph).

Code 76 will be set when the accelerometer signal is greater than 0.6g for 120 seconds or more.

Test Description: Numbers below refer to circled numbers on the diagnostic chart.
1. This test checks if another ABS system problem may be causing the Code 76.
2. This test checks for the appropriate accelerometer signal voltage at a 0g (no-turn) condition.
3. This test checks for the appropriate accelerometer signal voltage at a full-scale left hand turn. The full-scale left turn is simulated by the right side of the accelerometer being exposed to the 1g force of gravity.

4. This test checks for the appropriate accelerometer signal voltage at a full-scale right hand turn. The full-scale right turn is simulated by the left side of the accelerometer being exposed to the 1g force of gravity.

Fig. 45 Code 76, Lateral accelerometer (signal out of range or incorrect). 1990

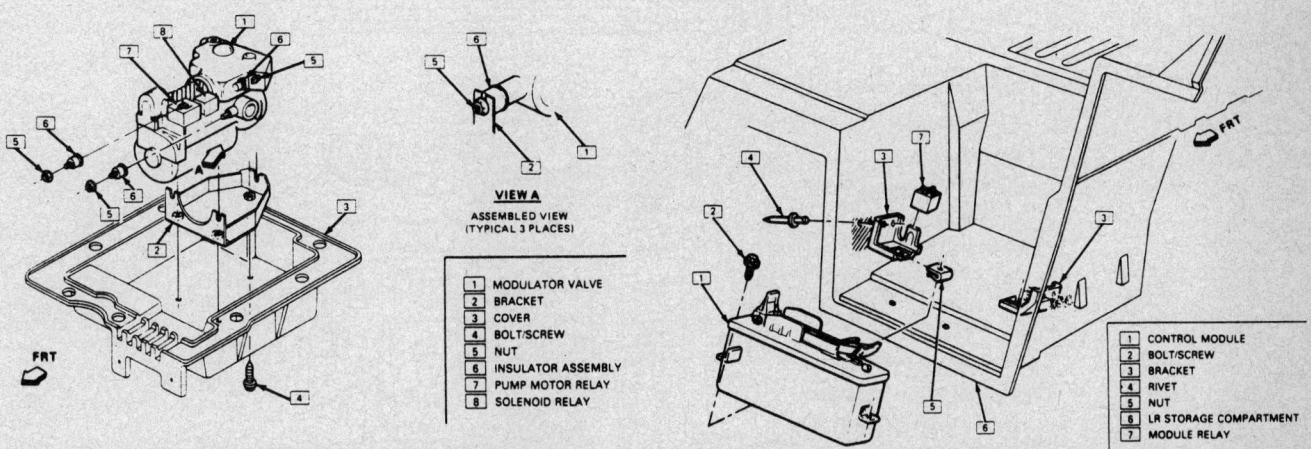

Fig. 46 Modulator valve location

Fig. 47 Control module location

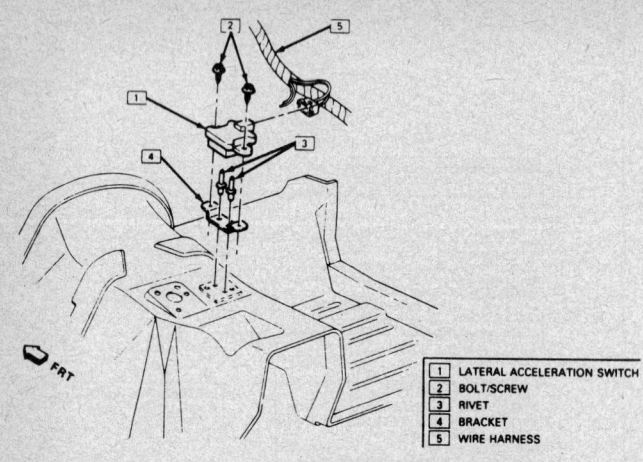

1	LATERAL ACCELERATION SWITCH
2	BOLT/SCREW
3	RIVET
4	BRACKET
5	WIRE HARNESS

Fig. 48 Lateral acceleration switch (accelerometer). 1988–89

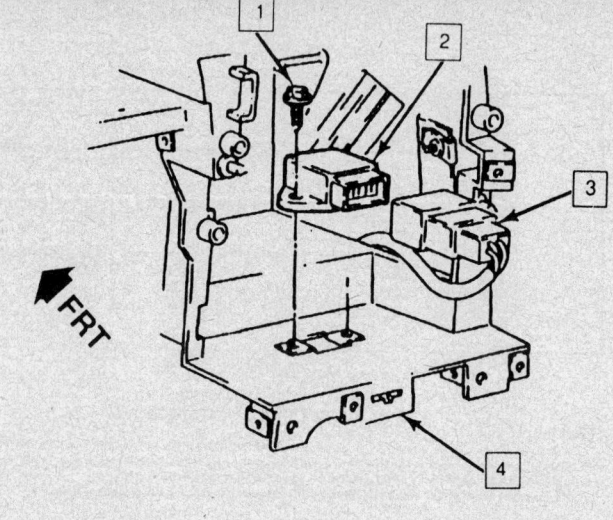

1	SCREW
2	ACCELEROMETER, LATERAL
3	CONNECTOR, ELECTRICAL
4	CARRIER ASSEMBLY, INSTRUMENT PANEL

Fig. 49 Lateral acceleration switch (accelerometer). 1990

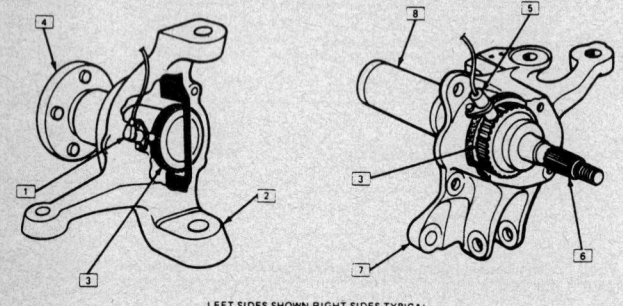

LEFT SIDES SHOWN RIGHT SIDES TYPICAL

1	FRONT SENSOR	5	REAR SENSOR
2	FRONT KNUCKLE	6	REAR DRIVE SHAFT SPINDLE
3	TOOTHED RING (PART OF 4 & 6)	7	REAR KNUCKLE
4	FRONT HUB & BEARING ASSEMBLY	8	REAR DRIVE SHAFT

Fig. 50 Wheel speed sensors

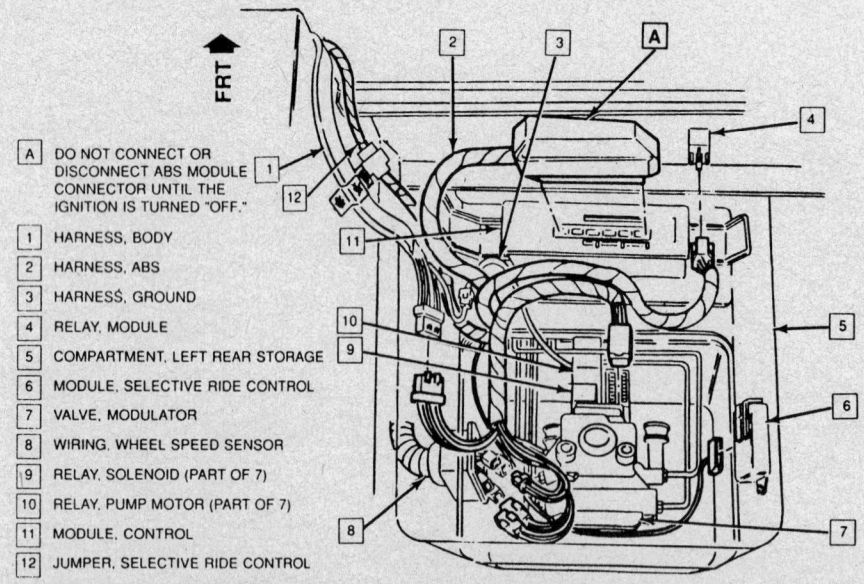

A	DO NOT CONNECT OR DISCONNECT ABS MODULE CONNECTOR UNTIL THE IGNITION IS TURNED "OFF."
1	HARNESS, BODY
2	HARNESS, ABS
3	HARNESS, GROUND
4	RELAY, MODULE
5	COMPARTMENT, LEFT REAR STORAGE
6	MODULE, SELECTIVE RIDE CONTROL
7	VALVE, MODULATOR
8	WIRING, WHEEL SPEED SENSOR
9	RELAY, SOLENOID (PART OF 7)
10	RELAY, PUMP MOTOR (PART OF 7)
11	MODULE, CONTROL
12	JUMPER, SELECTIVE RIDE CONTROL

Fig. 51 Wiring harness & relays. Models w/selective ride control

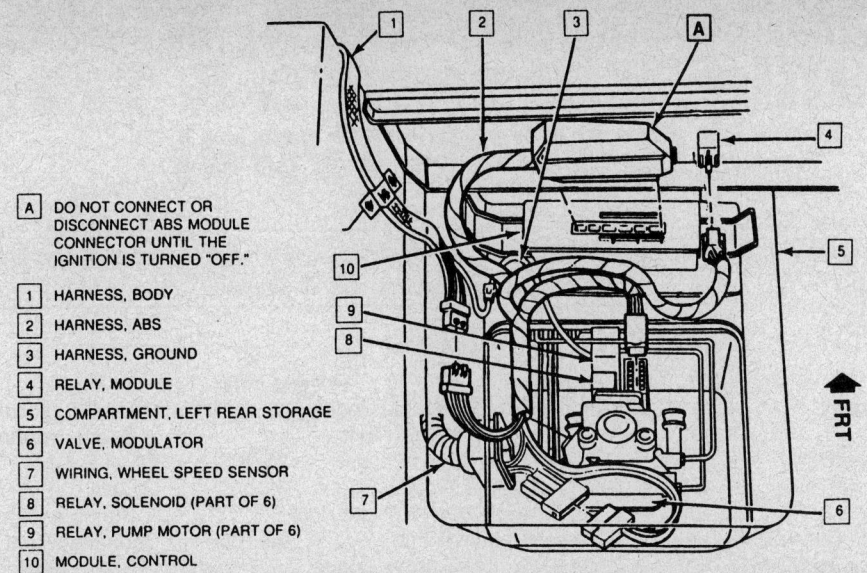

A DO NOT CONNECT OR
DISCONNECT ABS MODULE
CONNECTOR UNTIL THE
IGNITION IS TURNED "OFF."

1 HARNESS, BODY
2 HARNESS, ABS
3 HARNESS, GROUND
4 RELAY, MODULE
5 COMPARTMENT, LEFT REAR STORAGE
6 VALVE, MODULATOR
7 WIRING, WHEEL SPEED SENSOR
8 RELAY, SOLENOID (PART OF 6)
9 RELAY, PUMP MOTOR (PART OF 6)
10 MODULE, CONTROL

Fig. 52 Wiring harness & relays. Models less selective ride control

Eldorado, Reatta, Riviera, Seville, Toronado & Trofeo (Teves Type)

> **NOTE:** Wire Code Identification and Symbol Identification located in the front of this manual can be used as an aid when using wiring circuits found in this section.

INDEX

OPERATING PRECAUTIONS

Some of the following procedures require that hydraulic lines, hoses and fittings be disconnected for inspection of testing. This Teves brake system uses a hydraulic accumulator which, when completely charged, contains brake fluid under high pressure. Before disconnecting any hydraulic lines, hoses or fittings, ensure the accumulator is completely depressurized as described further on. Failure to depressurize the hydraulic accumulator may result in personal injury and/or damage to painted surfaces and/or the vehicle.

Certain components in the system are not intended to be serviced individually. Do not attempt to remove or disconnect certain system components, such as the hydraulic accumulator or valve block. Only those components with removal procedures should be serviced.

Torque bolts attaching the brake caliper mounting bracket to the front and rear knuckles must be replaced any time they are removed or become loose. Tightening or loosening the torque bolts, which use encapsulated thread locking compound, is not recommended. Failure to replace the brake caliper mounting bracket torque bolts, after they have been loosened or removed, may result in loosening of the caliper to knuckle assembly, causing reduced vehicle braking ability.

COMPUTER SYSTEM SERVICE PRECAUTIONS

This Teves anti-lock brake system interfaces directly with two control computers, the Electronic Brake Control Module (EBCM) and the Body Computer Module (BCM). These modules are designed to withstand normal current draws associated with vehicle operation. However, care must be taken to avoid overloading any of the EBCM or BCM circuits. During testing of opens or shorts, do not ground or apply voltage to any of the circuits unless instructed to do so by the appropriate diagnostic procedure. These circuits should only be tested with a high impedance multimeter (J-35029-A or equivalent), or special tools described further on. Power should never be removed or applied to any control module with the ignition switch in the On position. Before removing or connecting battery cables, fuses, or connectors, always turn the ignition switch to the Off position.

GENERAL SERVICE PRECAUTIONS

On models equipped with Supplemental Inflatable Restraint (SIR) system, serious injury can result from unintended airbag deployment.

The SIR system is designed to retain sufficient voltage to deploy the airbag for a short time after power has been disconnected. To avoid serious injury, disarm the SIR as follows:

1. Turn ignition switch to Off position.
2. Remove SIR fuse from fuse panel.
3. Disconnect yellow two-way connector at base of steering column as follows:
   a. Remove lower lefthand sound insulator retaining screws and nuts.
   b. Remove sound insulator from vehicle.
   c. Remove Connector Position Assurance (CPA) pin, then disconnect yellow two-way connector at base of steering column.
4. Wait at least 10 minutes before any further work is attempted. Serious injury may result from unintended airbag deployment if service is attempted immediately after SIR fuse is removed.
5. Reverse procedure to arm SIR system, noting the following:
   a. Turn ignition switch to On position.
   b. Observe INFALATABLE RESTRAINT indicator lamp.
   c. If lamp does not flash 7-9 times then remain Off, refer to "Passive Restraint Systems" for diagnosis.

If welding work is to be performed on the vehicle using an electric arc welder, the EBCM and valve block connectors should be disconnected before the welding operation begins. The EBCM and valve block connectors should never be connected or disconnected with the ignition switch in the On position. Some components of the anti-lock brake system are not serviceable separately and must be replaced as assemblies.

SYSTEM DESCRIPTION

The purpose of this Teves anti-lock brake system, is to prevent wheel lockup under heavy brake application.

The anti-lock function is desirable because a vehicle which is stopped without locking the wheels will normally stop in a shorter distance than a vehicle with locked wheels, while retaining directional stability and some steering capability. This allows the vehicle's operator to retain greater control of the vehicle during heavy brake application.

Major components of the anti-lock brake system include the electronic brake control module (EBCM), hydraulic unit, pump/motor assembly, wheel speed sensors and specific fuses and relays. Refer to **Figs. 1 through 5,** for system schematic and system component locations.

COMPONENT DESCRIPTION

HYDRAULIC UNIT

This anti-lock brake system uses an integral hydraulic unit which serves the purpose of booster and master cylinder. The hydraulic unit also includes the electrical and mechanical components required to modulate brake fluid pressure in each hydraulic circuit while in anti-lock mode.

BOOSTER/MASTER CYLINDER ASSEMBLY

The booster/master cylinder assembly contains the necessary valves and pistons to develop hydraulic pressure in the wheel circuits during brake application. Power brake assist is provided through the use of pressurized brake fluid supplied by the hydraulic accumulator.

VALVE BLOCK

The valve block is attached to the right side of the booster/master cylinder assembly and contains six hydraulic wheel circuit valves. The position of these valves is controlled by the electronic brake control module (EBCM). The valve block is serviceable separate from the booster/master cylinder assembly, but should not be disassembled. A seven pin electrical connector is used to make electrical connection from the valve block to the EBCM.

Wheel Circuit Valves

Two solenoid valves are used for each of the three hydraulic wheel circuits (left front, right front and rear). Each hydraulic circuit uses an inlet valve and an outlet valve. When these valves are used in combination, each hydraulic wheel circuit may be put into the pressure increase, pressure hold and pressure reduction mode during anti-lock mode. The position of each valve is determined by the EBCM, outlet valves are normally closed and inlet valves are normally open. Valve are activated when the EBCM switches 12 volts to the appropriate valve circuit. During normal driving and braking, the wheel circuit valves are not activated.

Ground Reference Line

A ground reference circuit is included at the 7 pin valve block connector. This circuit is used by the EBCM to verify that the hydraulic unit and valve block are grounded through their mounting on the front of the dash. If ground is lost at the hydraulic unit, anti-lock function would be disabled.

MAIN VALVE

The main valve is a two position valve which is also controlled by the EBCM. Except for test purposes, this valve is opened only during anti-lock mode. When the main valve is engaged, pressurized brake fluid from the booster servo circuit is directed into the master cylinder (front brake), circuits to prevent excessive pedal travel.

PRESSURE SWITCH

The pressure switch is mounted on the hydraulic unit pump/motor assembly and serves two major functions, including pump operation control and low pressure warning.

Pump Motor Control

The pressure switch will ground the pump motor relay coil circuit, causing the pump to run, if accumulator pressure drops below approximately 2030 psi. The switch will turn the pump motor off (by removing the relay coil circuit ground), at an accumulator pressure of approximately 2610 psi.

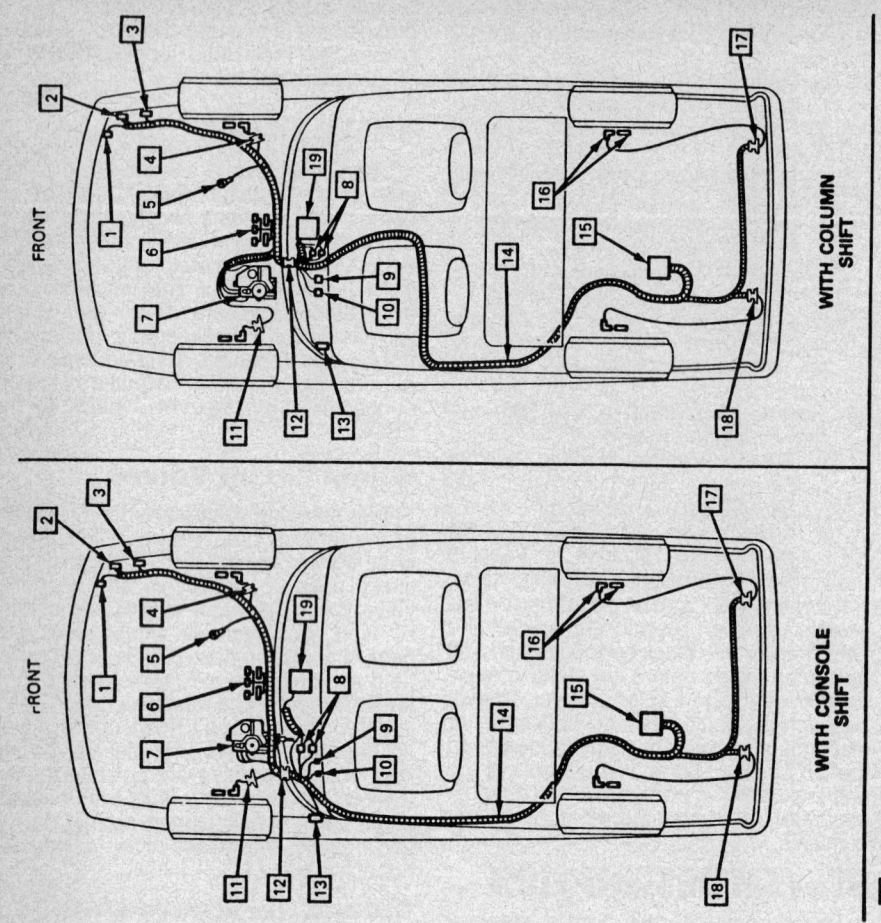

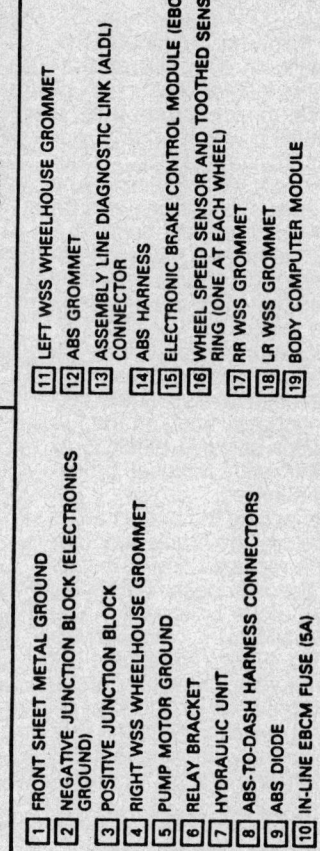

Component locations (top view)

WITH COLUMN SHIFT

WITH CONSOLE SHIFT

FRONT

11 LEFT WSS WHEELHOUSE GROMMET
12 ABS GROMMET
13 ASSEMBLY LINE DIAGNOSTIC LINK (ALDL) CONNECTOR
14 ABS HARNESS
15 ELECTRONIC BRAKE CONTROL MODULE (EBCM)
16 WHEEL SPEED SENSOR AND TOOTHED SENSOR RING (ONE AT EACH WHEEL)
17 RR WSS GROMMET
18 LR WSS GROMMET
19 BODY COMPUTER MODULE

1 FRONT SHEET METAL GROUND
2 NEGATIVE JUNCTION BLOCK (ELECTRONICS GROUND)
3 POSITIVE JUNCTION BLOCK
4 RIGHT WSS WHEELHOUSE GROMMET
5 PUMP MOTOR GROUND
6 RELAY BRACKET
7 HYDRAULIC UNIT
8 ABS-TO-DASH HARNESS CONNECTORS
9 ABS DIODE
10 IN-LINE EBCM FUSE (5A)

Fig. 2 Component locations (top view)

1 WHEEL SPEED SENSOR AND TOOTHED SENSOR RING (ONE AT EACH WHEEL)
2 CALIPER (ONE AT EACH WHEEL)
3 HYDRAULIC UNIT
4 RELAY BRACKET
5 PEDAL
6 REAR BRAKE PIPE
7 PROPORTIONER/TEE
8 ELECTRONIC BRAKE CONTROL MODULE (EBCM)

**Fig. 1 Anti-lock brake system (ABS).
Eldorado, Reatta, Riviera, Seville, Toronado & Trofeo**

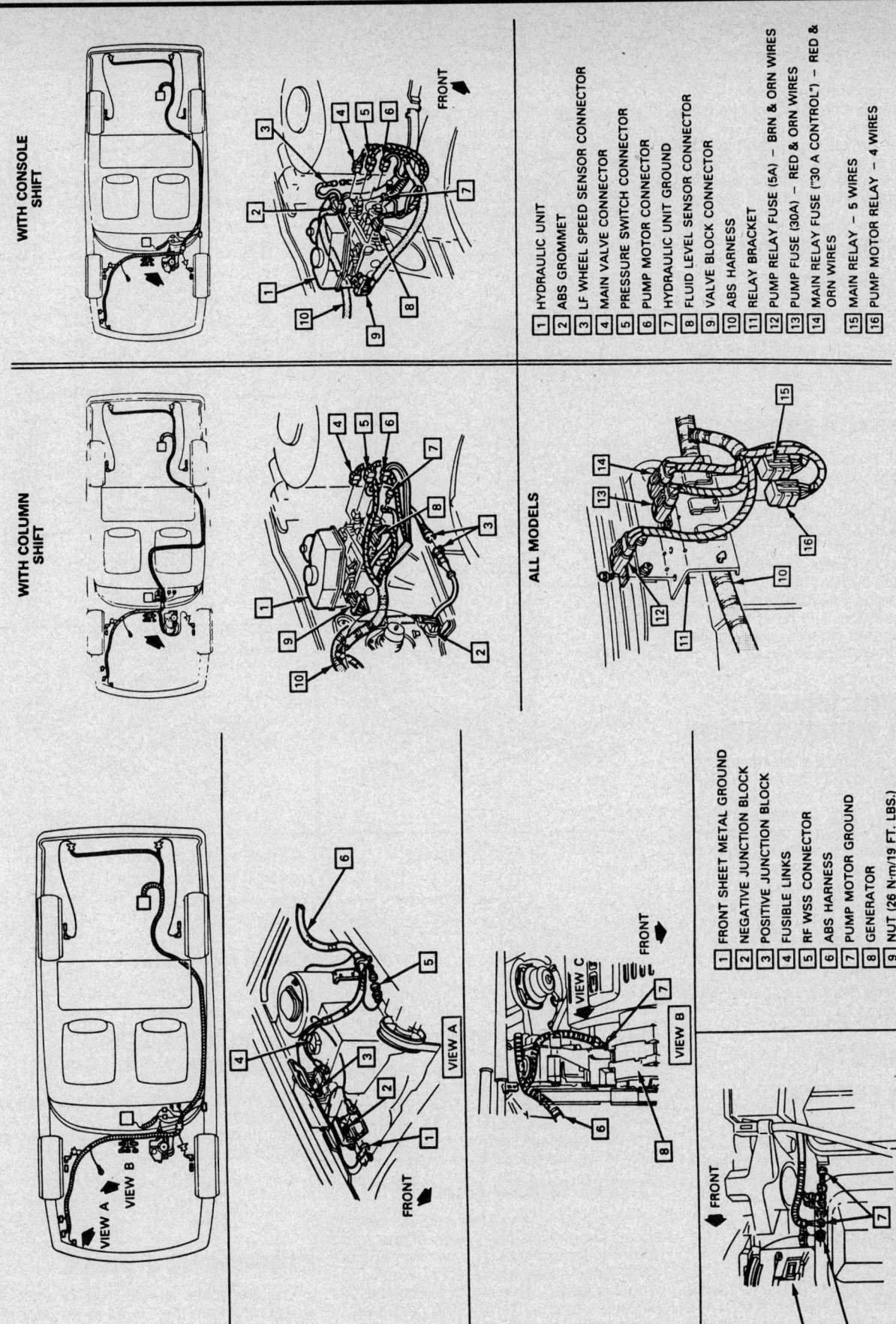

Fig. 3 Underhood component locations (Part 2 of 2)

1 HYDRAULIC UNIT
2 ABS GROMMET
3 LF WHEEL SPEED SENSOR CONNECTOR
4 MAIN VALVE CONNECTOR
5 PRESSURE SWITCH CONNECTOR
6 PUMP MOTOR CONNECTOR
7 HYDRAULIC UNIT GROUND
8 FLUID LEVEL SENSOR CONNECTOR
9 VALVE BLOCK CONNECTOR
10 ABS HARNESS
11 RELAY BRACKET
12 PUMP RELAY FUSE (5A) — BRN & ORN WIRES
13 PUMP FUSE (30A) — RED & ORN WIRES
14 MAIN RELAY FUSE ("30 A CONTROL") — RED & ORN WIRES
15 MAIN RELAY — 5 WIRES
16 PUMP MOTOR RELAY — 4 WIRES

Fig. 3 Underhood component locations (Part 1 of 2)

1 FRONT SHEET METAL GROUND
2 NEGATIVE JUNCTION BLOCK
3 POSITIVE JUNCTION BLOCK
4 FUSIBLE LINKS
5 RF WSS CONNECTOR
6 ABS HARNESS
7 PUMP MOTOR GROUND
8 GENERATOR
9 NUT (26 N·m/19 FT. LBS.)

Warning System Control

The pressure switch also contains two separate switches to provide warning in case of low accumulator pressure. One switch is normally closed and opens when accumulator pressure drops below 1500 psi. The other switch is part of the brake warning lamp circuit and consists of a normally open switch which also closes when accumulator pressure reaches 1500 psi.

FLUID LEVEL SENSOR

A fluid level sensor is included in the hydraulic unit reservoir. The sensor consists of a float with reed switch contacts which make up two switches. One switch is normally open and the other is normally closed. Both switches change position when low fluid is detected.

PUMP/MOTOR ASSEMBLY

An integral pump/motor assembly is used to provide pressurized brake fluid to the hydraulic unit accumulator. The pump/motor assembly is mounted on the left side of the hydraulic unit, with pressure and return hoses running to the booster inlet and reservoir. Pump operation is controlled using the pump motor relay, located on the underhood relay bracket near the center of the vehicle. The pump motor relay coil is powered whenever the ignition switch is in the RUN position.

ELECTRONIC BRAKE CONTROL MODULE (EBCM)

The EBCM is a small control computer, mounted inside the trunk on the left wheelhouse, which monitors system operation and controls anti-lock function when required. The EBCM relies on inputs from the wheel speed sensors and feedback from the hydraulic unit to determine if the anti-lock brake system is operating correctly and to determine when the anti-lock function is required. The EBCM has a self-diagnostic capability, including 42 trouble codes, which may be used in the event of a system malfunction. The EBCM can display these trouble codes by entering the ABS diagnostic mode.

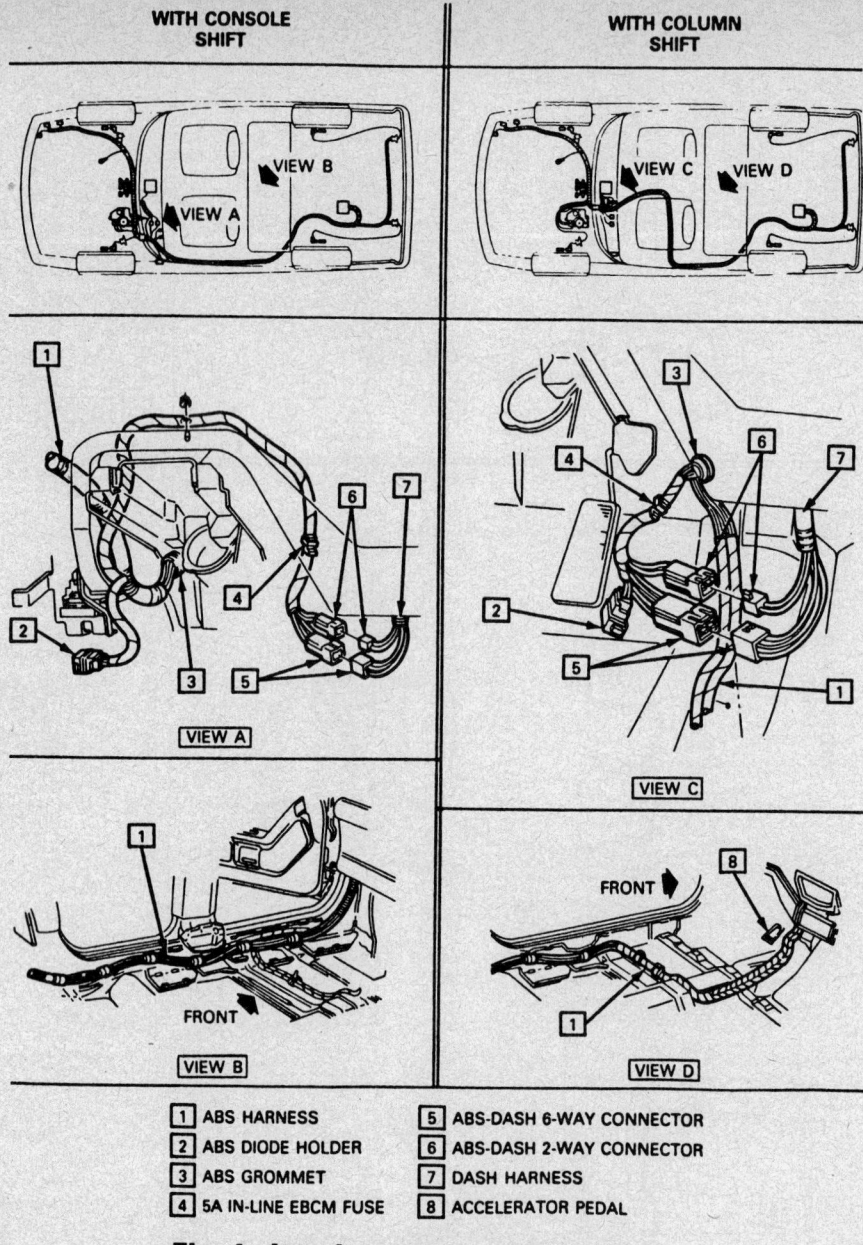

WITH CONSOLE SHIFT

WITH COLUMN SHIFT

VIEW B

VIEW A

VIEW C   VIEW D

1 ABS HARNESS	5 ABS-DASH 6-WAY CONNECTOR
2 ABS DIODE HOLDER	6 ABS-DASH 2-WAY CONNECTOR
3 ABS GROMMET	7 DASH HARNESS
4 5A IN-LINE EBCM FUSE	8 ACCELERATOR PEDAL

Fig. 4   Interior component locations

EBCM INPUTS

IGNITION ENABLE

The ignition enable input receives battery voltage whenever the ignition switch is in the RUN position. Upon receiving an ignition enable input, the EBCM begins its self-checks.

CRANK SENSE

A crank sense input is provide to the EBCM which goes high (12 volts), when the ignition switch is moved to the START position. When the crank sense input is high, the EBCM commands itself, internally, to shut off until engine start is completed.

BRAKE LIGHT SWITCH

The EBCM also receives a 12 volt signal from the brake light switch whenever the brake pedal is depressed. The brake light switch input alerts the EBCM when the brakes are applied and increases its sensitivity to wheel speed sensor inputs.

WHEEL SPEED SENSORS

The EBCM continuously receives wheel speed information from each of the four wheel speed sensors. The sensors one at each wheel, generate a signal when the wheel is turned. This signal is created by passing a toothed sensor ring past a stationary sensor which consists of a permanent magnet and coil. A specified air gap must be maintained between the sensor face and the toothed sensor ring.

LOW FLUID & LOW PRESSURE

The low brake fluid and low pressure inputs consist of a continuous loop circuit which runs through the fluid level sensor and the pressure switch.

DIAGNOSTIC ENABLE

The diagnostic enable input is a circuit which runs from the EBCM to the assembly line diagnostic link (ALDL), pin G on 1998 models or pin H on 1989-90 models. When this line is grounded, the EBCM enters the diagnostic mode.

ELDORADO, REATTA, RIVIERA, SEVILLE, TORONADO & TROFEO (TEVES TYPE)

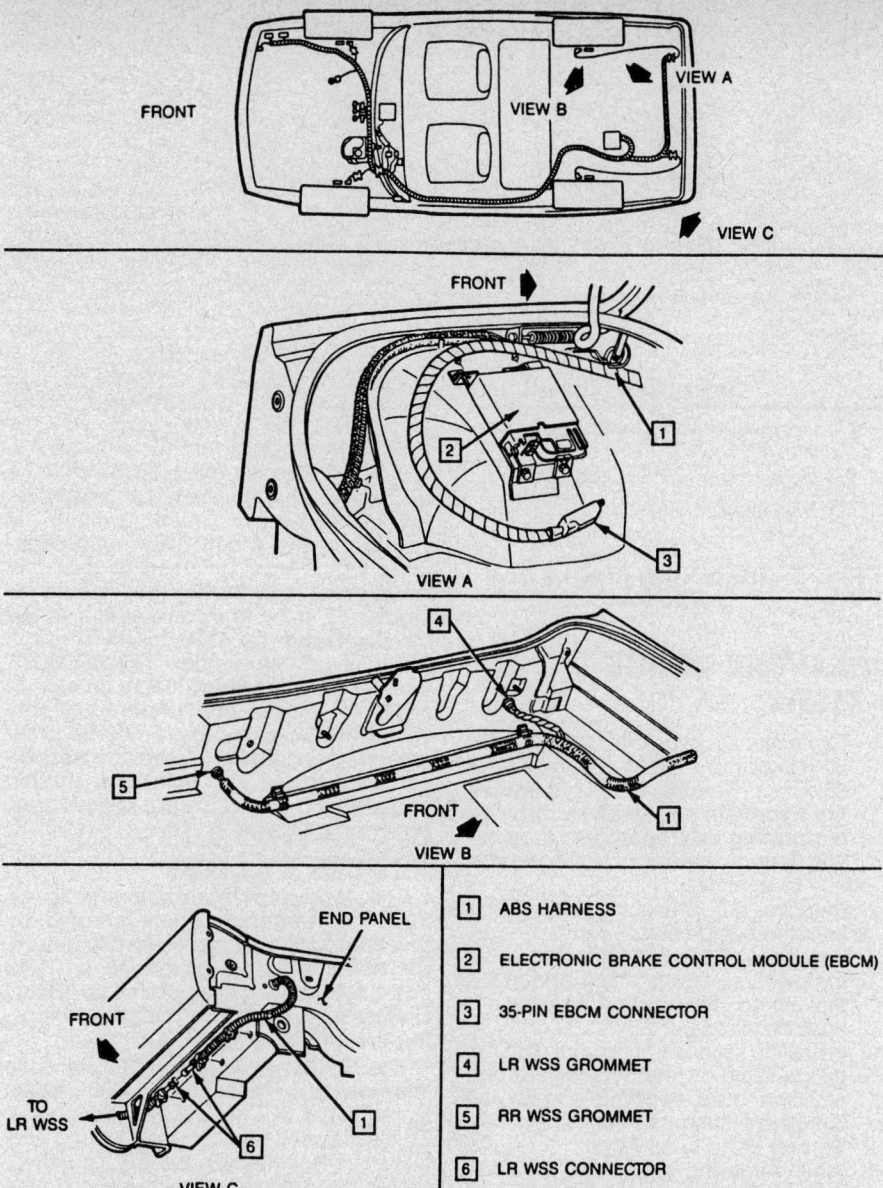

[1] ABS HARNESS

[2] ELECTRONIC BRAKE CONTROL MODULE (EBCM)

[3] 35-PIN EBCM CONNECTOR

[4] LR WSS GROMMET

[5] RR WSS GROMMET

[6] LR WSS CONNECTOR

Fig. 5 Luggage compartment component locations

EBCM OUTPUTS

MAIN RELAY ENABLE

The main relay provides switched battery power to the EBCM. Switched battery power is turned on only after the EBCM receives an ignition enable input signal. If the main relay is not energized, anti-lock braking is disabled. The EBCM energizes the main relay by providing 12 volts at the main relay enable output. The main relay is disabled if a fault in the anti-lock brake system is detected.

SOLENOID VALVES

Each brake circuit is equipped with two non-serviceable solenoid valves for fluid inlet and outlet. These valves are actuated by a 12 volt signal from the EBCM when in the anti-lock mode. The valves act individually or in combination to increase, hold or decrease pressure as required to prevent wheel lockup. During normal braking (not in anti-lock mode), no voltage is provided to the valves. The inlet valve is normally open and the outlet valve is normally closed.

MAIN VALVE SOLENOID

The main valve solenoid is located in the hydraulic unit and is switched on by the EBCM only when anti-lock braking is required. During anti-lock braking, the EBCM provides 12 volts to the main valve solenoid output.

ANTI-LOCK LAMP GROUND

When a fault in the anti-lock brake system is detected by the EBCM, the anti-lock lamp output is grounded, turning on the anti-lock lamp in the instrument panel cluster.

WARNING SYSTEM OPERATION

The anti-lock brake system uses three methods of notifying the driver of a system malfunction. These include a red "BRAKE" warning lamp and an "amber "ANTI-LOCK" warning lamp, both in the instrument panel cluster. Also included are three messages which may be displayed on the driver information center (DIC).

BRAKE WARNING LAMP

The brake warning lamp in the instrument panel cluster will illuminate to warn the driver of conditions in the brake system which may result in reduced braking ability as well as to notify the driver that the parking brake is applied or not completely released. The brake lamp is controlled by the body computer module (BCM).

ANTI-LOCK WARNING LAMP

The anti-lock warning lamp is located in the instrument panel cluster and will illuminate if a malfunction in the anti-lock brake system is detected by the electronic brake control module (EBCM). The anti-lock lamp is intended only to inform the driver that a condition has been detected which results in partial or total inhibit of the anti-lock function. If the anti-lock lamp is on, normal braking will full assist is still available.

DRIVER INFORMATION CENTER (DIC) MESSAGES

Three messages related to the brake system may be displayed on the driver information center (DIC), these include:
1. Brake Fluid Is Low. This message will be commanded by the BCM upon detection of low brake fluid by the fluid level sensor in the hydraulic unit reservoir. While displaying this message, the BCM will also turn on a warning chime which will sound for approximately 30 seconds (unless it is disabled by pressing the system monitor button).
2. Low Brake Pressure. This message is displayed when a low boost pressure condition has been detected in the hydraulic unit accumulator. In order for the BCM to command this message, the low pressure condition must exist for at least 50 seconds. When the BCM turns on the Low Brake Pressure message, it will also sound a warning chime for approximately 30 seconds (unless it is disabled by pressing the system monitor button).
3. Park Brake Is On. This message will notify the driver that the parking brake has not been released. This message will only occur when the car is shifted from Park or Neutral to Reverse or a Drive range.

Illumination of the Brake warning lamp may indicate reduced braking ability. Most conditions which cause the brake lamp to light will also cause the Anti-Lock lamp to light. Illumination of the Anti-Lock lamp without the Brake warning lamp on, indicates only that anti-lock braking is no longer available. Power assisted braking without anti-lock control is still available.

DEPRESSURIZING HYDRAULIC ACCUMULATOR

The anti-lock brake system pump/motor assembly will keep the hydraulic charged to a pressure between approximately 2000-2600 psi, anytime the ignition switch is in the RUN position. The pump/motor assembly cannot run if the ignition switch is off, or if either battery cable is disconnected. Disconnecting the pressure switch connector or the pump/motor connector from the hydraulic unit will also prevent the pump from operating. Unless otherwise specified, the hydraulic accumulator should be depressurized before working on any portion of the hydraulic system. The following procedure should be used to depressurize the hydraulic accumulator. To depressurize accumulator, proceed as follows:

1. With ignition switch turned to the Off position, pressure switch disconnected, pump motor connector disconnected or battery ground cable disconnected, pump the brake pedal a minimum of 25 times using approximately 50 lbs of force.
2. A noticeable change in pedal feel will occur then the accumulator is discharged.
3. When a definite increase in pedal effort is felt, stroke pedal a few additional times. This should remove all hydraulic pressure from the system.

REQUIRED TEST EQUIPMENT

PINOUT BOX J-35592

In order to prevent damage to the 35 pin EBCM connector, pinout box tool J-35592 or equivalent should be installed on the EBCM connector prior to probing any circuit with the digital multimeter. Do not probe the 35 pin EBCM connector without installing J-35592 pinout box. Damage to connector terminals may occur if the pinout box is not installed, resulting in incorrect system operation. Proceed as follows to install the J-35592 pinout box:

1. The ignition switch must be in the off position when installing or removing the 35 pin EBCM connector.
2. Open trunk and remove EBCM trim cover from the left wheelwell. The cover is retained by velcro tape.
3. Disconnect the 35 pin EBCM harness connector by depressing the connector locking plate and rotating the connector toward the front of the vehicle.
4. Inspect the 35 pin connector for damage. Connect J-35592 to the 35 pin connector, **Fig. 6.**

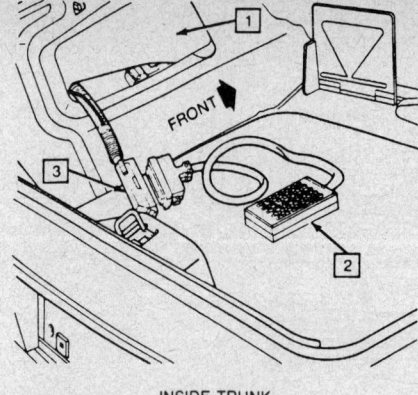

INSIDE TRUNK

1. ELECTRONIC BRAKE CONTROL MODULE (BENEATH CARPET TRIM)
2. J-35592 PINOUT BOX
3. 35-PIN EBCM CONNECTOR

Fig. 6 Installing pinout box J-35592

PRESSURE GAUGE J-35604

1. Depressurize hydraulic accumulator by pumping the brake a minimum of 25 times. **Failure to depressurize the hydraulic accumulator prior to performing this operation may result in personal injury and/or damage to vehicle.**
2. Remove the pressure hose fitting from the pump body.
3. Install one of the two O-ring seals on the pressure gauge fitting and insert the gauge fitting into the pressure hose coupling.
4. Install the second O-ring seal onto the gauge fitting on the underside of the pressure hose coupling and thread the gauge fitting into the pump body. **Torque** fitting to 15 ft. lbs.
5. When removing gauge and installing pressure fitting, inspect O-ring seals for cuts or damage. Replace any cut or damaged O-ring seals.

When removing pressure gauge and adapter, ensure that the hydraulic accumulator is depressurized.

ANTI-LOCK BRAKE SYSTEM SELF-DIAGNOSIS

On models equipped with Supplemental Inflatable Restraint (SIR) system, serious injury can result from unintended airbag deployment.

The SIR system is designed to retain sufficient voltage to deploy the airbag for a short time after power has been disconnected. To avoid serious injury, disarm the SIR as follows:

1. Turn ignition switch to Off position.
2. Remove SIR fuse from fuse panel.
3. Disconnect yellow two-way connector at base of steering column as follows:

a. Remove lower lefthand sound insulator retaining screws and nuts.
b. Remove sound insulator from vehicle.
c. Remove Connector Position Assurance (CPA) pin, then disconnect yellow two-way connector at base of steering column.
4. Wait at least 10 minutes before any further work is attempted. Serious injury may result from unintended airbag deployment if service is attempted immediately after SIR fuse is removed.
5. Reverse procedure to arm SIR system, noting the following:
a. Turn ignition switch to On position.
b. Observe INFALATABLE RESTRAINT indicator lamp.
c. If lamp does not flash 7-9 times then remain Off, refer to "Passive Restraint Systems" for diagnosis.

This anti-lock brake system is equipped with a self-diagnostic capability which may be used to assist in isolation of ABS faults. This feature includes 42 trouble codes which could be displayed by the EBCM through flashing of the amber "ANTI-LOCK" lamp in the instrument panel cluster. In order to access and understand any ABS trouble code which may be present, it is necessary to enter the ABS diagnostic mode and read the trouble codes using the following procedures.

DISPLAYING ABS TROUBLE CODES

The following information is to be used for reference when directed by the appropriate diagnostic procedure. Do not attempt to diagnose an ABS condition at this time. Refer to "Basic Diagnostic Procedure" before attempting diagnosis.

The EBCM will store any failure code into memory. These codes will remain stored in the EBCM until they are erased. To clear codes proceed to "Clearing ABS Codes." Disconnecting the EBCM, battery cables, or turning the ignition switch to the Off position, will not clear the trouble codes from memory.

READING ABS TROUBLE CODES

1. With ignition switch turned to the On position, allow pump/motor to charge the accumulator. If accumulator is discharged, the "BRAKE" and ""ANTI-LOCK" lamps will remain on for up to 30 seconds.
2. If the "ANTI-LOCK" lamp does not go off within 30 seconds, note that lamp did not go off, then proceed to step 3.
3. With ignition switch turned to the Off position, place a jumper wire between Assembly Line Diagnostic Link (ALDL), pins G on 1988 models, pin H, on 1989-90 models and A or between ALDL pin G, on 1988 models, pin H, on 1989-90 models and body ground, **Fig. 7.** The ALDL is located on the driver's side of the vehicle near the parking brake pedal assembly.
4. Turn ignition switch to the RUN posi-

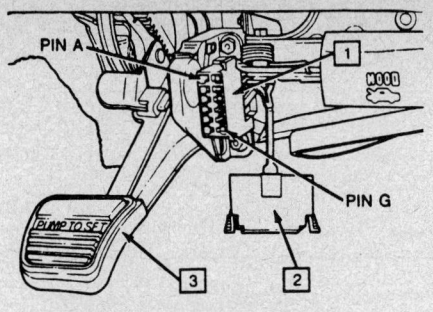

PLACE JUMPER BETWEEN PINS A AND G
(OR BETWEEN G AND GROUND) TO ENTER
ABS DIAGNOSTIC MODE

[1] ALDL CONNECTOR
[2] ALDL CONNECTOR COVER
[3] PARKING BRAKE PEDAL

Fig. 7   1988 ABS diagnostic enable, ALDL pin G (Part 1 of 3)

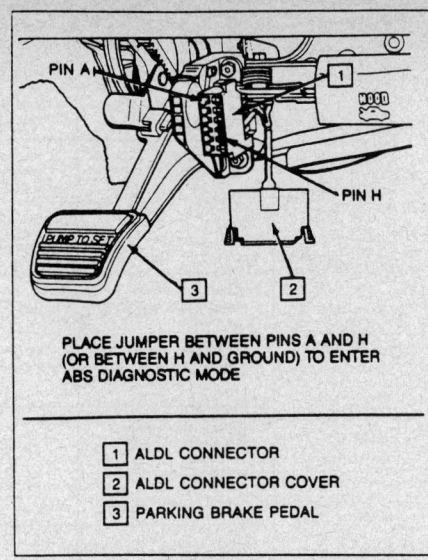

PLACE JUMPER BETWEEN PINS A AND H
(OR BETWEEN H AND GROUND) TO ENTER
ABS DIAGNOSTIC MODE

[1] ALDL CONNECTOR
[2] ALDL CONNECTOR COVER
[3] PARKING BRAKE PEDAL

Fig. 7   1989 ABS diagnostic enable, ALDL pin H (Part 2 of 3)

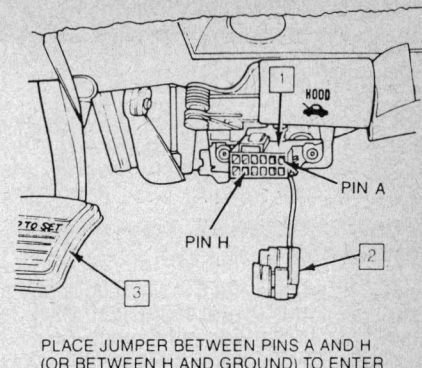

PLACE JUMPER BETWEEN PINS A AND H
(OR BETWEEN H AND GROUND) TO ENTER
ABS DIAGNOSTIC MODE

[1] ALDL CONNECTOR
[2] ALDL CONNECTOR COVER
[3] PARKING BRAKE PEDAL

Fig. 7   1990 ABS diagnostic enable, ALDL pin H (Part 3 of 3)

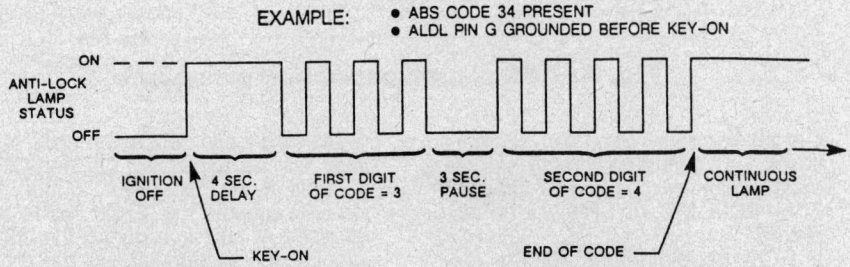

ABS DIAGNOSTIC MODE

EXAMPLE:
• ABS CODE 34 PRESENT
• ALDL PIN G GROUNDED BEFORE KEY-ON

ANTI-LOCK LAMP STATUS — ON / OFF

IGNITION OFF | 4 SEC. DELAY | FIRST DIGIT OF CODE = 3 | 3 SEC. PAUSE | SECOND DIGIT OF CODE = 4 | CONTINUOUS LAMP

KEY-ON   END OF CODE

Fig. 8   ABS diagnostic code interpretation

tion, then count the lamp flashes to identify the first digit. If the lamp turns on for four seconds, then turns off (and remains off), no trouble codes are present. Proceed to "ABS Functional Check," then proceed with diagnosis as directed. If the EBCM has stored any trouble codes, the "ANTI-LOCK" lamp will turn on for approximately four seconds and will then start flashing. These flashes represent the first digit of the trouble code.

5. Count lamp flashes for the second digit. The lamp will pause (remain off), for approximately three seconds after flashing the first digit. It will then flash the second digit of the trouble code. **When the ""ANTI-LOCK" lamp flashes the second digit of the trouble code, be careful to count only the number of times the lamp turns on and goes out. When the EBCM is done flashing the second digit, the "ANTI-LOCK" lamp will remain on. The last pulse, when the lamp remains on, should not be**

counted as a flash, Fig. 8.
6. Record trouble codes obtained.
7. Check for additional trouble codes. Without turning the ignition switch to the off position, disconnect the jumper wire from ALDL pin G on 1988 models, pin H, on 1989-90 models. Connect the jumper again to ALDL pin. If an additional code is present, the "ANTI-LOCK" lamp will begin flashing the first digit as described previously. Count lamp flashes for the first and second digits as was done for the first code. Record the additional trouble code if present.
8. Repeat steps 6 and 7, until no additional trouble codes are displayed. Up to seven trouble codes can be displayed. The "ANTI-LOCK" lamp will remain on continuously when all trouble codes have been displayed. ABS trouble codes cannot be cleared unless all codes have been displayed.
9. After recording all ABS codes, remove jumper from the ALDL, install ALDL cover, then proceed with the "ABS Functional Check."

HISTORY & CURRENT ABS CODES

The ABS trouble codes which may be stored by the EBCM are not specifically designated as current or history codes, as are BCM and ECM codes. The anti-lock lamp, may be used to assist in differentiating between current and history codes as follows:
1. If the anti-lock lamp is on before entering the ABS diagnostic mode, at least one of the stored codes is current.
2. If the anti-lock lamp is off before entering the ABS diagnostic mode, none of the stored codes are current.
3. If more than one ABS code is stored and the anti-lock lamp is on before diagnostic mode was entered, it is impossible to determine which is a current code and which is a history code.
4. If the Anti-Lock lamp remains on continuously throughout the diagnostic procedure, see symptom diagnosis information as directed by the "ABS Functional Check." If the anti-lock lamp does not come on at all, see symptom diagnosis information as directed by the "ABS Functional Check" as well.

CLEARING ABS CODES

The ABS trouble codes should not be cleared until repairs are completed. The EBCM will not allow the ABS codes to clear unless all codes have been read.

The ABS trouble codes are cleared by driving the vehicle at a speed greater than 18 mph. If the codes did not clear, repeat the read out procedure and drive the vehicle again at a speed greater than 18 mph. If codes do not clear, additional repairs may be required.

BODY COMPUTER MODULE (BCM) TROUBLE CODES & INPUT TESTS

The vehicle self-diagnostic system includes one BCM trouble code and three BCM input tests which involve the anti-lock brake system.

BCM Code B482, Low Brake Pressure

Code B482 will set if the hydraulic brake pressure input to the BCM (pin 2B1), is held low (at ground), continuously for 50 seconds. This BCM input will be pulled low by the ABS pressure switch in the event of low accumulator pressure. If code B482 sets, the low brake pressure message on the driver information center will be displayed.

BCM Input BI18, Brake Pressure

BCM Input test BI18 can be used to determine the status of the hydraulic brake pressure input at BCM pin 2B1. This input is normally held high (at battery voltage) and is pulled low (grounded), in the case of low brake pressure.

BCM Input BI21, Brake Fluid

BCM input test BI21 can be used to determine the status of the brake fluid level input at BCM pin 1C2. This input is normally held high (at battery voltage) and is pulled low (grounded), by the fluid level sensor in case of low brake fluid.

BCM Input BI22, Park Brake

BCM Input Test BI22 can be used to determine the status of the parking brake pedal switch input at BCM pin 1C5. This input is normally held high (at battery voltage) and is pulled low (grounded), by the parking brake pedal switch whenever the brake is applied.

ENTERING DIAGNOSTIC SERVICE MODE

The following information is to be used for reference when directed by the appropriate diagnostic procedure. Do not attempt to diagnosis an ABS condition starting here. The following procedure deals only with the aspects of entering the diagnostic service mode which are required for diagnosis of the anti-lock brake system.

1. Turn ignition switch to the On position. On CRT models, select the "Climate" screen by pressing the button in upper righthand corner.
2. **On non-CRT models,** press the Off and WARM buttons on the climate control panel simultaneously and hold until the segment check begins on the instrument panel cluster. On CRT models, touch Off and Warm pads simultaneously, until screen displays "Service Mode" configuration.
3. **On non-CRT models,** the segment check will cause the instrument panel cluster to illuminate and cycle all displays. The segment check takes approximately five seconds to complete.

ABS VISUAL INSPECTION		
ITEM	INSPECT FOR	CORRECTIVE ACTION
PARKING BRAKE	- FULL RELEASE - PROPER SWITCH FUNCTION IF NECESSARY, UNPLUG SWITCH CONNECTOR FROM PEDAL ASSEMBLY TO VERIFY - PROPER VACUUM RELEASE SYSTEM OPERATION	- OPERATE MANUAL RELEASE LEVER TO VERIFY RELEASE - ADJUST CABLE OR REPAIR RELEASE SYSTEM AS REQUIRED - REPAIR SWITCH AS REQUIRED
MAJOR COMPONENTS • BRAKE FLUID RESERVOIR • HYDRAULIC UNIT • PUMP/MOTOR ASSEMBLY	- LOW FLUID LEVEL - EXTERNAL LEAKS - PROPER ASSEMBLY	- ADD FLUID AS REQUIRED DETERMINE CAUSE OF FLUID LOSS AND REPAIR - REPAIR LEAKS AS REQUIRED - INSTALL OR POSITION COMPONENTS PROPERLY
FUSES-ON RELAY BRACKET • PUMP MOTOR RELAY FUSE (5A) • MAIN RELAY (CONTROL) FUSE (30A) • PUMP MOTOR FUSE (30A)	- BLOWN FUSE	- REPLACE FUSE - VERIFY OPERATION - INSPECT FOR CAUSE OF FUSE FAILURE
CONNECTORS UNDERHOOD • MAIN RELAY • PUMP MOTOR RELAY • PRESSURE SWITCH • PUMP MOTOR • MAIN VALVE • VALVE BLOCK • FLUID LEVEL SENSOR • LF AND RF WHEEL SPEED SENSORS REAR OF CAR • LR AND RR WHEEL SPEED SENSORS • ELECTRONIC BRAKE CONTROL MODULE	- PROPER ENGAGEMENT - LOOSE WIRES OR TERMINALS - CORRODED OR BROKEN EYELETS	- PROPERLY ENGAGE CONNECTOR - REPAIR AS REQUIRED

Fig. 9   ABS visual inspection procedure

4. **On all models,** after the segment check is completed, any trouble codes which have been stored by the ECM, BCM, IPC, or CRT will be displayed.
   a. ECM trouble codes will be displayed first. If no ECM trouble codes are present, the "NO ECM CODES" message will appear. ECM codes are prefixed with an E. ECM codes are not relevant to ABS diagnosis.
   b. BCM trouble codes will be displayed next. If no BCM trouble codes are present the "NO BCM CODES" message will appear. BCM codes are prefixed with a B. **BCM code B482 applies to ABS diagnosis.**
   c. CRT code will be displayed next. If no CRT codes are present, "No CRT Codes will appear. CRT codes ar prefixed with a C. CRT codes are not relevant to ABS diagnosis.
5. All codes will be accompanied by a "CURRENT" or "HISTORY" designation. History indicates that the failure was not present the last time the code was tested. Current indicates the fault still exists. If BCM codes B482 is present, note if it is designated current or history before proceeding with the diagnosis procedure.
6. **On non-CRT models,** if the "LO FAN" (down arrow), button on the climate control panel, or on CRT models, the "NO" pad is depressed at any time during the display of the ECM or BCM diagnostic codes, the code display will be bypassed. On non-CRT models, if the "BI-LEVEL" button, or on CRT models, the "END" pad is depressed at any time during the code display, the system will exit the diagnostic service mode and resume normal vehicle operation.
7. After the trouble codes have been displayed, the computer system allows one of two vehicle systems to be selected for testing, on non-CRT models, and one of four vehicle systems on CRT models. At this time, the driver information center displays the first available system as indicated by the ECM message. Three responses are possible:
   a. Bypass ECM system test is activated by pressing the "LO FAN" (down arrow), button, on non-CRT models, and the "NO" pad on CRT models. This should be done if ABS diagnosis is desired.
   b. Display trouble codes again by pressing the OFF button on non-CRT models, or the "LEVEL" pad on CRT models. This should be done if you need to review the code display.
   c. Exit diagnostic mode by pressing the "BI-LEV" button on non-CRT models, or the "END" button on CRT models. This will resume normal vehicle operation.
8. After bypassing the ECM test system, the climate control driver information center will display, the prompt BCM. This mode should be selected by de-

ABS FUNCTIONAL CHECK

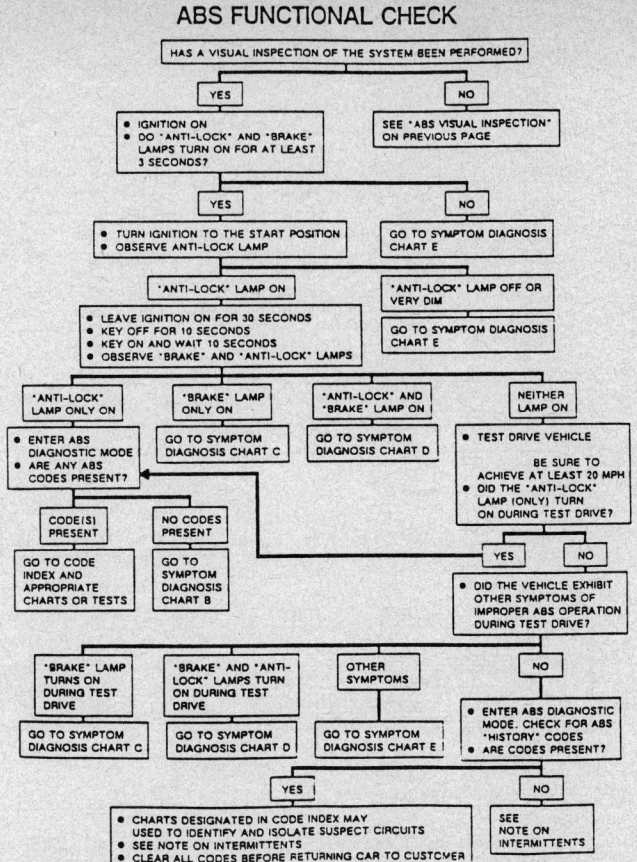

Fig. 10 ABS functional check procedure

pressing the "HI FAN" (up arrow), button on non-CRT models, or the "YES" pad on CRT models.

9. After entering BCM diagnostic mode. The anti-lock brake system inputs to the BCM can be monitored. The BCM input feature of diagnostic service mode is accessed as follows:
   a. After entering BCM diagnostic mode, the driver information center will display the prompt "BCM DATA." You should respond to this by pressing the "LO FAN" (down arrow), button on non-CRT models, or "NO" pad on CRT models.
   b. The driver information center will then display the prompt "BCM INPUTS." You should respond to this by pressing the "HI FAN" (up arrow), button on non-CRT models, or "YES" pad on CRT models. This will place the system in BCM input mode.
   c. The system will now show the status of selected BCM inputs, Inputs which are relevant to the anti-lock brake system include BI18, BI21 and BI22.
10. While in the input mode, the BCM can display the status of up to 18 different inputs. Each input is designated with an identifier such as BI21, meaning BCM input 21. In order to display a BCM input which is higher or lower in number than the one currently on the display, press the "HI FAN" (up arrow), button on non-CRT models, or the "YES" pad on CRT models, to in-

crement the display. On non-CRT models, press the "LO FAN" (down arrow), or the "NO" pad on CRT models, to lower the numbered display. Each of these input displays will appear in the same format. All displays are normally HI. A warning input to the BCM would appear as a LO status indication.
11. After evaluating the ABS inputs to the BCM in conjunction with the correct diagnostic procedures, exit diagnostic service mode by depressing the "BI-LEV" button on non-CRT models, or the "END" pad on CRT models. This will return the computer system to normal operation.

BASIC DIAGNOSTIC PROCEDURE

On models equipped with Supplemental Inflatable Restraint (SIR) system, serious injury can result from unintended airbag deployment.

The SIR system is designed to retain sufficient voltage to deploy the airbag for a short time after power has been disconnected. To avoid serious injury, disarm the SIR as follows:
1. Turn ignition switch to Off position.
2. Remove SIR fuse from fuse panel.
3. Disconnect yellow two-way connector at base of steering column as follows:

   a. Remove lower lefthand sound insulator retaining screws and nuts.
   b. Remove sound insulator from vehicle.
   c. Remove Connector Position Assurance (CPA) pin, then disconnect yellow two-way connector at base of steering column.
4. Wait at least 10 minutes before any further work is attempted. Serious injury may result from unintended airbag deployment if service is attempted immediately after SIR fuse is removed.
5. Reverse procedure to arm SIR system, noting the following:
   a. Turn ignition switch to On position.
   b. Observe INFALATABLE RESTRAINT indicator lamp.
   c. If lamp does not flash 7-9 times then remain Off, refer to "Passive Restraint Systems" for diagnosis.

Diagnosis of the anti-lock brake system consists of the anti-lock visual inspection, anti-lock functional check and additional checks as specified by the functional check. All diagnosis should start with the anti-lock visual inspection and proceed to the anti-lock brake system (ABS), functional check, if the condition is not resolved by the visual inspection.

NOTE ON INTERMITTENTS

Intermittent failures in the anti-lock brake system may be difficult to accurately diagnosis. The ABS trouble codes which may be stored by the EBCM are not specifically designated as "CURRENT" or "HISTORY" codes as are BCM and ECM codes. These codes, however, can be helpful in diagnosing intermittent conditions. If an intermittent condition is to be diagnosed, the ABS self-diagnostic system can be used in the following manner to help isolate the suspected circuit:
1. First, display and clear any ABS trouble codes which may be present in the EBCM.
2. Test drive the vehicle, attempting to repeat the failure condition.
3. After duplicating the condition, stop the vehicle and display any ABS trouble codes which may have been stored.
4. If no trouble codes were stored, it may become necessary to refer to "ABS Symptom Diagnosis."

SYSTEM VOLTAGE DURING DIAGNOSIS

Some diagnostic procedures require that the ignition switch remain On for extended periods of time. During this time, battery voltage may become low, causing erroneous voltage readings. If this situation occurs, connect a battery charger to the vehicle's electrical system, then apply a slow charge.

ABS VISUAL INSPECTION

Refer to **Fig. 9**, for anti-lock brake system (ABS), visual inspection procedure.

ABS FUNCTIONAL CHECK

Refer to **Fig. 10**, for anti-lock brake system (ABS), functional check procedure.

ELECTRICAL CONNECTOR IDENTIFICATION VIEWS

Refer to **Fig. 11**, for system and system component electrical connector identification views.

ABS TROUBLE CODE INDEX

Refer to **Fig. 12**, for anti-lock brake system trouble code index. **When using the ABS trouble code index, "ABS Code," "System" and "Go To Chart" are referred to. Under "Go To Chart," you will find letters and numbers from A-1 to A-15 which are the actual diagnostic charts that can be found at the top of each individual diagnostic test chart.**

ABS TROUBLE CODE DIAGNOSIS

Refer to **Figs. 13** through **27**, for anti-lock brake system trouble code diagnostic procedures.

ABS SYMPTOM DIAGNOSIS

Refer to **Figs. 28** through **57**, for anti-lock brake system symptom diagnostic procedures.

ABS WIRING CIRCUITS

Refer to **Fig. 58**, for anti-lock brake system wiring circuit diagrams.

SYSTEM SERVICE

On models equipped with Supplemental Inflatable Restraint (SIR) system, serious injury can result from unintended airbag deployment.

The SIR system is designed to retain sufficient voltage to deploy the airbag for a short time after power has been disconnected. To avoid serious injury, disarm the SIR as follows:
1. Turn ignition switch to Off position.
2. Remove SIR fuse from fuse panel.
3. Disconnect yellow two-way connector at base of steering column as follows:
   a. Remove lower lefthand sound insulator retaining screws and nuts.
   b. Remove sound insulator from vehicle.
   c. Remove Connector Position Assurance (CPA) pin, then disconnect yellow two-way connector at base of steering column.
4. Wait at least 10 minutes before any further work is attempted. Serious injury may result from unintended airbag deployment if service is attempted immediately after SIR fuse is removed.
5. Reverse procedure to arm SIR system, noting the following:
   a. Turn ignition switch to On position.
   b. Observe INFALATABLE RESTRAINT indicator lamp.
   c. If lamp does not flash 7-9 times then remain Off, refer to "Passive Restraint Systems" for diagnosis.

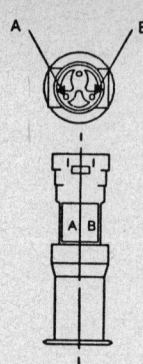

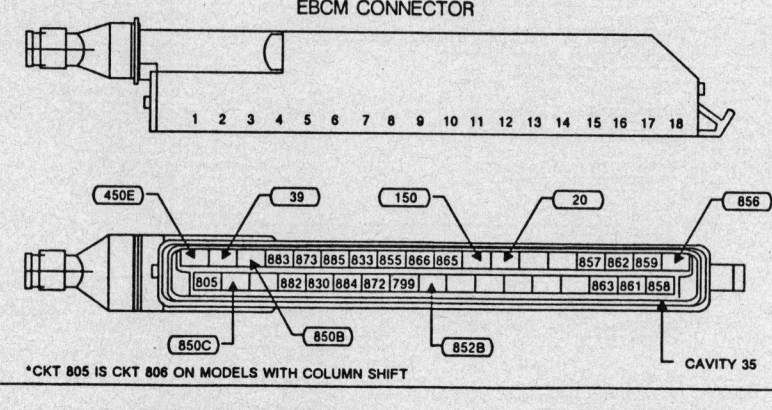

WHEEL SPEED SENSOR CONNECTOR

	PIN A	PIN B
RIGHT FRONT	833	872
LEFT FRONT	873	830
RIGHT REAR	883	882
LEFT REAR	885	884

EBCM CONNECTOR

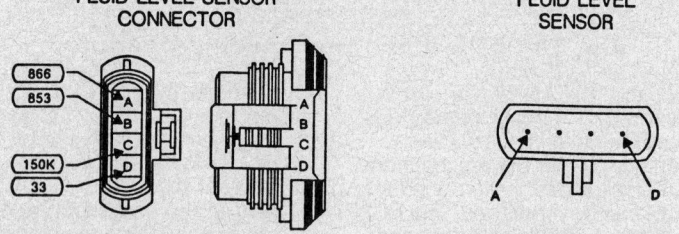

*CKT 805 IS CKT 806 ON MODELS WITH COLUMN SHIFT

FLUID LEVEL SENSOR CONNECTOR

FLUID LEVEL SENSOR

Fig. 11   ABS electrical connector views (Part 1 of 3)

HYDRAULIC UNIT, REPLACE

1. Disconnect battery ground cable.
2. Depressurize hydraulic accumulator by depressing brake pedal a minimum of 25 times. **A noticeable change in pedal resistance will be felt when accumulator is depressurized. Failure to depressurize accumulator may result in personal injury and/or damage to vehicle and painted surfaces.**
3. Label, then disconnect all electrical connectors from hydraulic unit.
4. Remove cross-car brace.
5. Remove pump bolt, then move pump/motor assembly to the side.
6. Disconnect three hydraulic lines from valve block. Use a back-up wrench to prevent pipes from twisting.
7. From inside the vehicle, disconnect pushrod from brake pedal.
8. Push dust boot past hex on pushrod, then separate push rod halves by unthreading.
9. Remove two hydraulic unit mounting bolts from the pushrod bracket, then the hydraulic unit, **Fig. 59**. The front half of the pushrod will remain locked in hydraulic unit.
10. Reverse procedure to install, noting the following:
    a. Use new hydraulic unit mounting bolts.
    b. Torque mounting bolts to 37 ft. lbs.

PRESSURE SWITCH, REPLACE

1. Disconnect battery ground cable and depressurize hydraulic accumulator Depressurize hydraulic accumulator by depressing brake pedal a minimum of 25 times. **A noticeable change in pedal resistance will be felt when accumulator is depressurized. Failure to depressurize accumulator may result in personal injury and/or damage to vehicle and painted surfaces.**

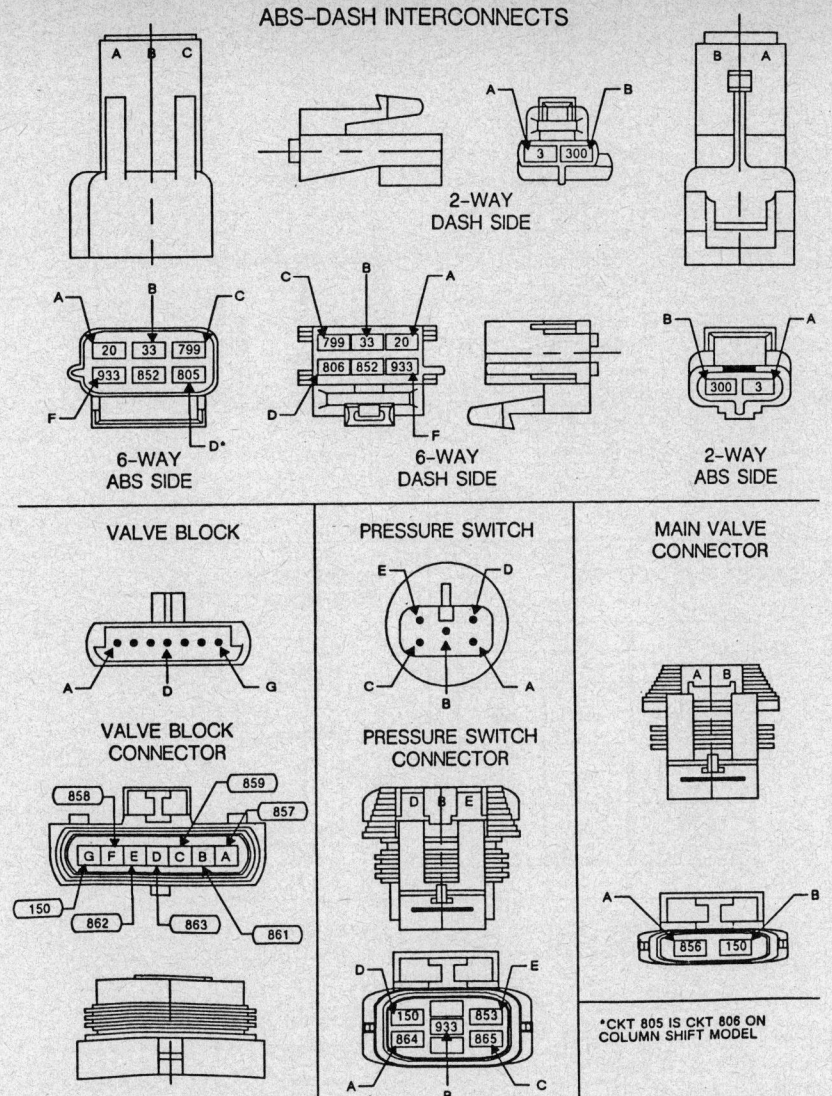

ABS–DASH INTERCONNECTS

2-WAY DASH SIDE

6-WAY ABS SIDE

6-WAY DASH SIDE

2-WAY ABS SIDE

VALVE BLOCK

VALVE BLOCK CONNECTOR

PRESSURE SWITCH

PRESSURE SWITCH CONNECTOR

MAIN VALVE CONNECTOR

*CKT 805 IS CKT 806 ON COLUMN SHIFT MODEL

Fig. 11   ABS electrical connector views (Part 2 of 3)

2. Disconnect electrical connector from pressure switch.
3. Using pressure switch socket tool No. J-35804 or equivalent, remove pressure switch and O-ring.
4. Reverse procedure to install, noting the following:
   a. Lubricate O-ring seal with clean brake fluid.
   b. **Torque** pressure switch to 15 ft. lbs.
   c. Turn ignition switch On. Allow system to pressurize. BRAKE lamp should go out within 30 seconds and pump motor should turn off within 40 seconds.
   d. Inspect for leaks.

HYDRAULIC ACCUMULATOR, REPLACE

1. Turn ignition switch to Off position

and disconnect battery ground cable.
2. Depressurize hydraulic accumulator by depressing brake pedal a minimum of 25 times. **A noticeable change in pedal resistance will be felt when accumulator is depressurized. Failure to depressurize accumulator may result in personal injury and/or damage to vehicle and painted surfaces.**
3. Remove accumulator and O-ring.
4. Reverse procedure to install, noting the following:
   a. Lubricate O-ring with clean brake fluid.
   b. **Torque** accumulator attaching bolts to 30 ft. lbs.
   c. Turn ignition switch On. Allow system to pressurize. BRAKE lamp should go out within 30 seconds and pump motor should turn off within 40 seconds.

PUMP & MOTOR ASSEMBLY, REPLACE

1. Disconnect battery ground cable.
2. Depressurize hydraulic accumulator by depressing brake pedal a minimum of 25 times. **A noticeable change in pedal resistance will be felt when accumulator is depressurized. Failure to depressurize accumulator may result in personal injury and/or damage to vehicle and painted surfaces.**
3. Disconnect electrical connectors from pressure switch and pump motor.
4. Pinch return hose to prevent fluid loss, then remove hydraulic accumulator.
5. Disconnect pressure hose from pump.
6. Remove pressure hose assembly and O-rings.
7. Remove wire clip which retains hose at pump body, then pull return hose fitting from pump body.
8. Remove pump mounting bolt, sleeve and insulator.
9. Remove pump and motor assembly from vehicle, by sliding pump from locating pin.
10. Reverse procedure to install, noting the following:
    a. **Torque** pressure pipe assembly-to-pump fittings to 9 ft. lbs.
    b. **Torque** accumulator attaching bolts to 30 ft. lbs.
    c. Turn ignition switch On. Allow system to pressurize. BRAKE lamp should go out within 30 seconds and pump motor should turn off within 40 seconds.

VALVE BLOCK ASSEMBLY, REPLACE

1. Disconnect battery ground cable.
2. Depressurize hydraulic accumulator by depressing brake pedal a minimum of 25 times. **A noticeable change in pedal resistance will be felt when accumulator is depressurized. Failure to depressurize accumulator may result in personal injury and/or damage to vehicle and painted surfaces.**
3. Remove fluid from reservoir.
4. Remove valve block assembly, **Fig. 60.**
5. Reverse procedure to install. Lubricate O-ring seals with clean brake fluid. **Torque** valve block mounting nuts to 18 ft. lbs.

FRONT WHEEL SPEED SENSOR, REPLACE

If the sensor mounting bracket bolts are loosened or removed, the sensor gap must be adjusted. If the sensor is removed without loosening or removing the mounting bracket bolts, it is not necessary to adjust sensor gap. If the wheel speed sensor is removed from the mounting bracket, the sensor must be coated with GM anti-corrosion compound 1052856, or equivalent.

1. Disconnect battery ground cable.

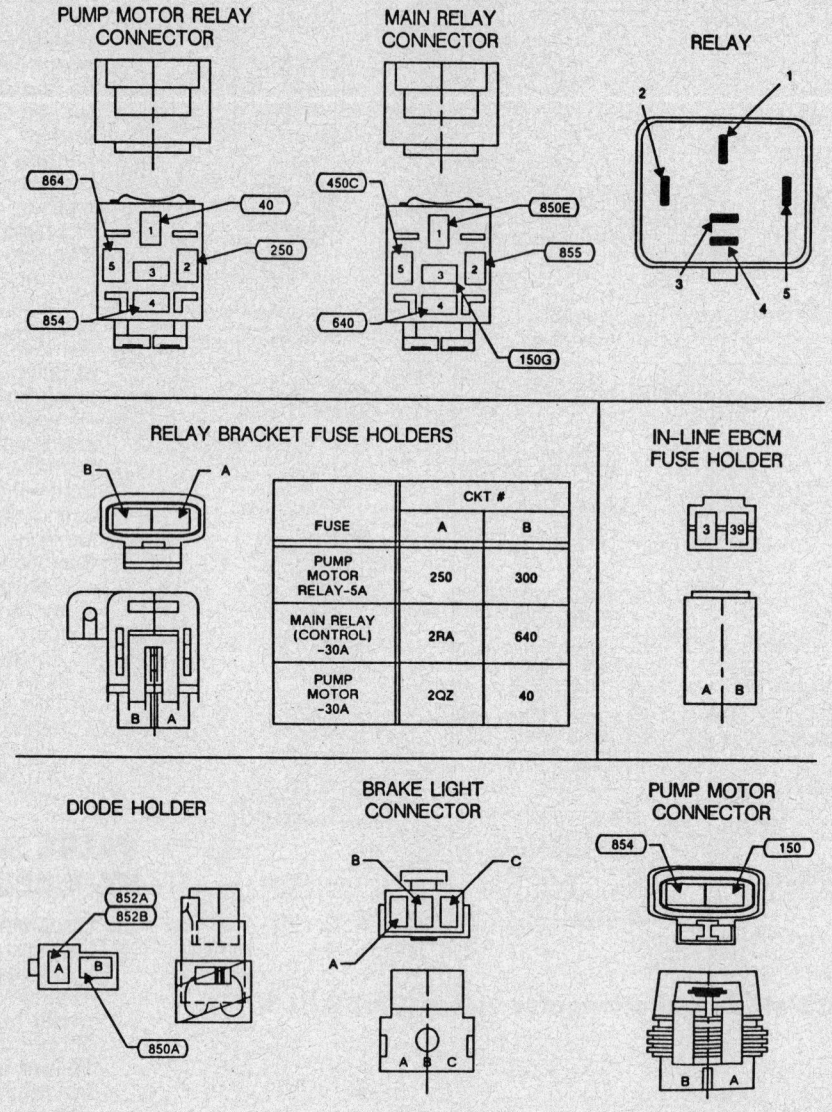

Fig. 11   ABS electrical connector views (Part 3 of 3)

2. Disconnect sensor electrical connector from underhood, near strut tower.
3. Raise and support vehicle.
4. Disconnect sensor cable grommet from wheelwell, then remove sensor cable from retaining brackets.
5. Remove sensor, or if necessary, remove mounting bracket and sensor assembly from vehicle, **Fig. 61.**
6. Reverse procedure to install. Adjust sensor as follows:
   a. Loosen front wheel speed sensor mounting bracket bolts so that bracket is snug to knuckle but can be moved by hand.
   b. Using a feeler gauge, adjust sensor (between the tip of the sensor and one of the teeth on the toothed sensor ring), to .020 inch by moving bracket.
   c. **Torque** mounting bracket bolts to 9 ft. lbs.
   d. After tightening, check sensor gap.

REAR TOOTHED SENSOR RING

The rear toothed sensor ring is an integral part of the hub and bearing assembly.

If the sensor ring requires replacement, the entire hub and bearing assembly must be replaced.

REAR WHEEL SPEED SENSOR, REPLACE

1. Disconnect battery ground cable.
2. Raise and support vehicle.
3. Disconnect electrical connector from sensor.
4. Remove sensor mounting bracket, then the sensor, **Fig. 62.**
5. Reverse procedure to install. **Torque** attaching bolts to 106 inch lbs.

ABS CODE INDEX					
ABS CODE	SYSTEM	GO TO CHART	ABS CODE	SYSTEM	GO TO CHART
11	EBCM	A-1	45	2 SENSOR (LF)	A-13
12	EBCM	A-1	46	2 SENSORS (RF)	A-13
21	MAIN VALVE	A-2	47	2 SENSORS (REAR)	A-13
22	LF INLET VALVE	A-3	48	3 SENSORS	A-13
23	LF OUTLET VALVE	A-4	51	LF OUTLET VALVE	A-14
24	RF INLET VALVE	A-5	52	RF OUTLET VALVE	A-14
25	RF OUTLET VALVE	A-6	53	REAR OUTLET VALVE	A-14
26	REAR INLET VALVE	A-7	54	REAR OUTLET VALVE	A-14
27	REAR OUTLET VALVE	A-8	55	LF WSS	A-9
31	LF WSS	A-9	56	RF WSS	A-10
32	RF WSS	A-10	57	RR WSS	A-11
33	RR WSS	A-11	58	LR WSS	A-12
34	LR WSS	A-12	61	EBCM LOOP CKT	A-15
35	LF WSS	A-9	71	LF OUTLET VALVE	A-14
36	RF WSS	A-10	72	RF OUTLET VALVE	A-14
37	RR WSS	A-11	73	REAR OUTLET VALVE	A-14
38	LR WSS	A-12	74	REAR OUTLET VALVE	A-14
41	LF WSS	A-9	75	LF WSS	A-9
42	RF WSS	A-10	76	RF WSS	A-10
43	RR WSS	A-11	77	RR WSS	A-11
44	LR WSS	A-12	78	LR WSS	A-12

Fig. 12   ABS trouble code index

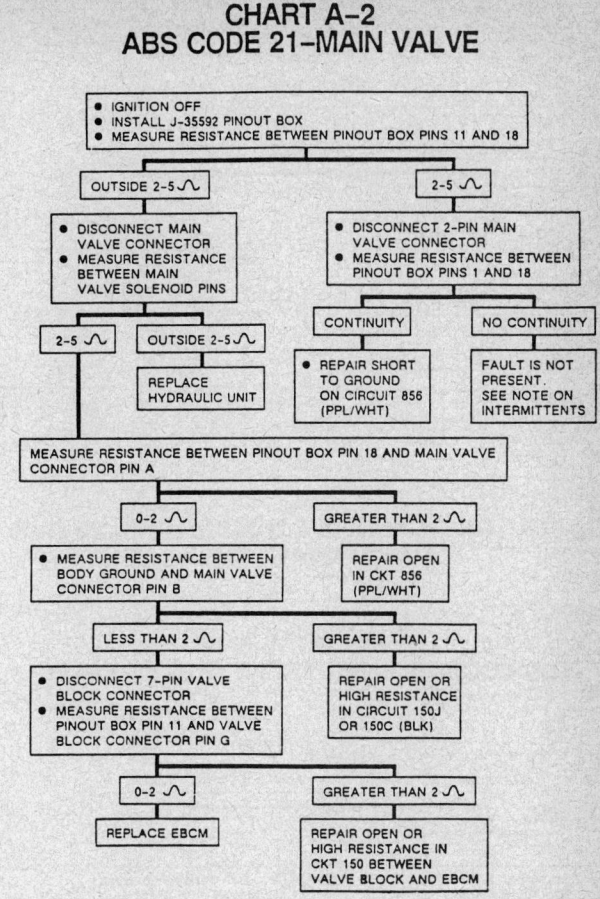

Fig. 14   Chart A-2, ABS trouble code 21 (main valve)

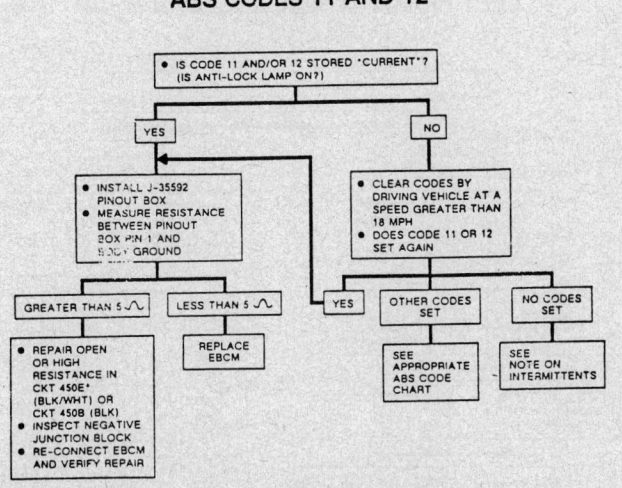

Fig. 13   Chart A-1, ABS trouble codes 11 & 12

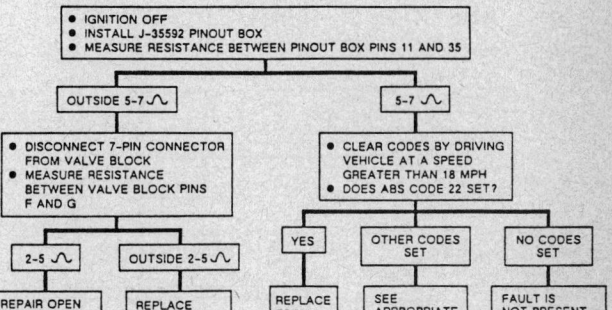

Fig. 15   Chart A-3, ABS trouble code 22 (left front inlet valve)

CHART A-4
ABS CODE 23–LEFT FRONT OUTLET VALVE

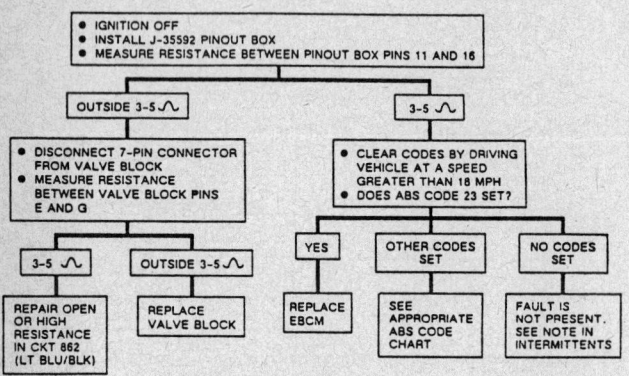

Fig. 16   Chart A-4, ABS trouble code 23 (left front outlet valve)

CHART A-5
ABS CODE 24–RIGHT FRONT INLET VALVE

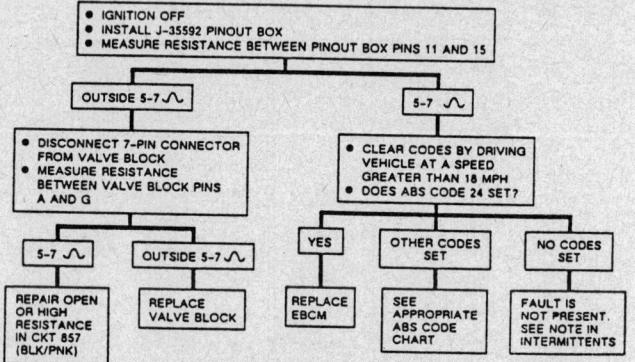

Fig. 17   Chart A-5, ABS trouble code 24 (right front inlet valve)

CHART A-6
ABS CODE 25–RIGHT FRONT OUTLET VALVE

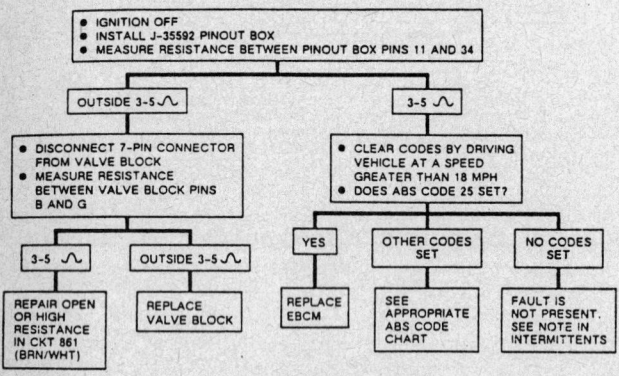

Fig. 18   Chart A-6, ABS trouble code 25 (right front outlet valve)

CHART A-7
ABS CODE 26–REAR INLET VALVE

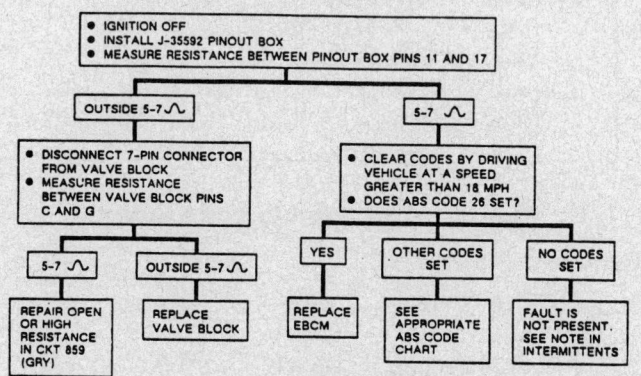

Fig. 19   Chart A-7, ABS trouble code 26 (rear inlet valve)

CHART A-8
ABS CODE 27–REAR OUTLET VALVE

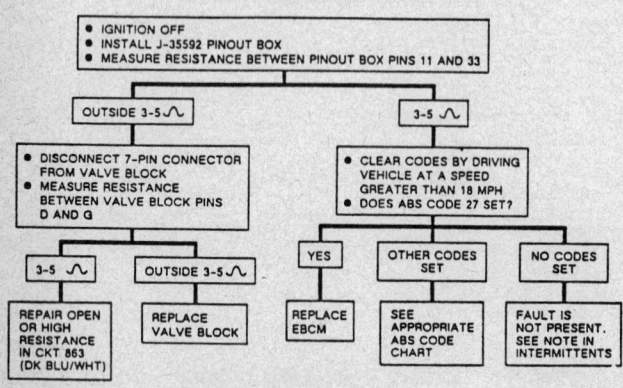

Fig. 20   Chart A-8, ABS trouble code 27 (rear outlet valve)

CHART A-9
ABS CODES 31, 35, 41, 55 OR 75
LEFT FRONT WHEEL SPEED SENSOR

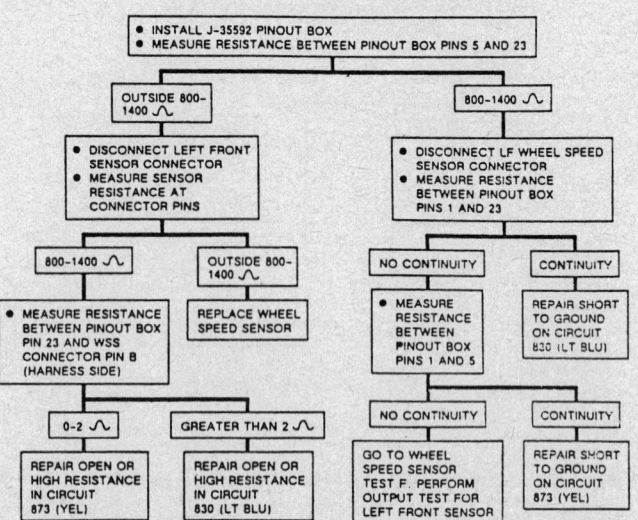

Fig. 21   Chart A-9, ABS trouble codes 31, 35, 41, 55 or 75 (left front wheel speed sensor)

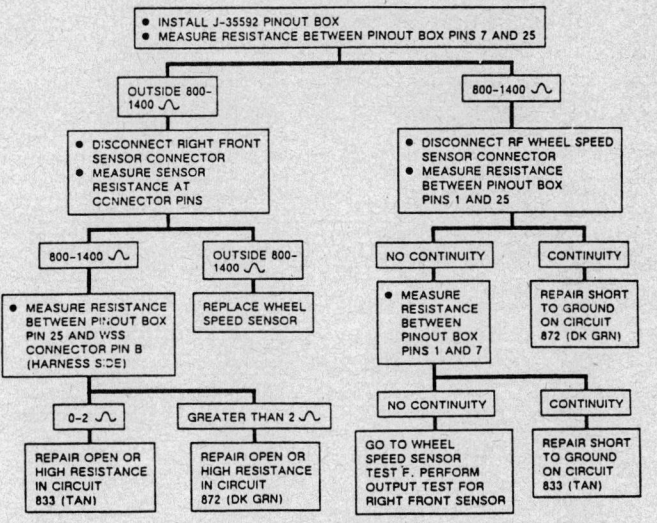

Fig. 22   Chart A-10, ABS trouble codes 32, 36, 42, 56 or 76 (right front wheel speed sensor)

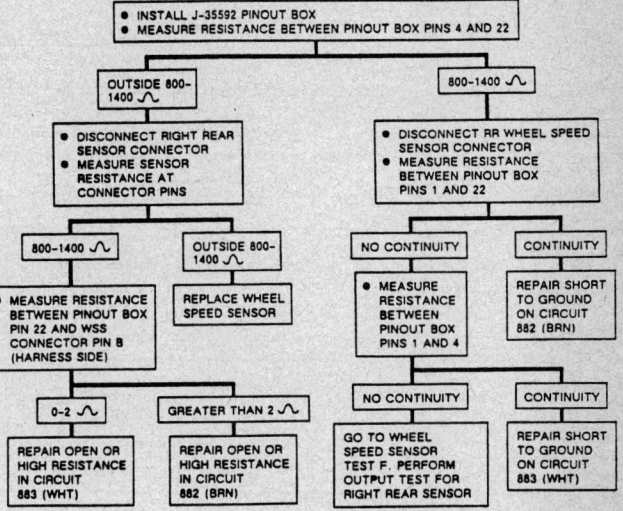

Fig. 23   Chart A-11, ABS trouble codes 33, 37, 43, 57 or 77 (right rear wheel speed sensor)

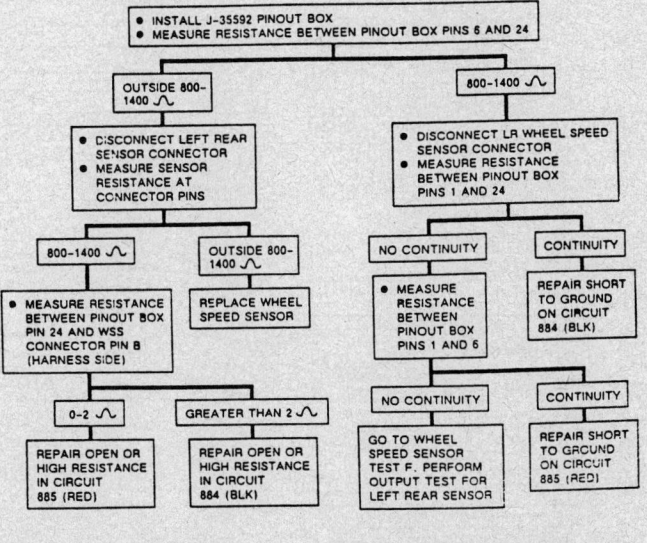

Fig. 24   Chart A-12, ABS trouble codes 34, 38, 44, 58 or 78 (left rear wheel speed sensor)

CHART A-13
ABS CODES 45, 46, 47 OR 48
MISSING WHEEL SPEED SENSOR SIGNALS

NOTE: THESE CODES (45, 46, 47 AND 48) INDICATE MORE THAN ONE WHEEL SPEED SENSOR WITH A MISSING SIGNAL

DRIVING THE FRONT WHEELS WITH THE ENGINE WHILE THE VEHICLE IS RAISED ON A HOIST (REAR WHEELS NOT TURNING) CAN CAUSE A CODE 47 TO SET

Fig. 25   Chart A-13, ABS trouble codes 45, 46, 47 or 48 (missing wheel speed sensor signals)

CHART A-14
ABS CODES 51–54 AND 71–74
"PRESSURE REDUCTION" FAULT

NOTE: CODES 51–54 AND 71–74 INDICATE A CONDITION WHICH MAY BE ATTRIBUTABLE TO EITHER THE WHEEL SPEED SENSOR CIRCUIT OR THE OUTLET VALVE

FOR THESE CODES:	PERFORM THESE TESTS:
51 AND/OR 71	• GO TO CHART A-9 IF NO TROUBLE IS FOUND WHILE PERFORMING TESTS ON CHART A-9, DO NOT GO TO TEST F. INSTEAD, GO TO SOLENOID VALVE TEST G • PERFORM SOLENOID VALVE TEST FOR LEFT FRONT VALVES • IF NO TROUBLE IS FOUND, REPLACE EBCM
52 AND/OR 72	• GO TO CHART A-10 IF NO TROUBLE IS FOUND WHILE PERFORMING TESTS ON CHART A-10, DO NOT GO TO TEST F. INSTEAD, GO TO SOLENOID VALVE TEST G • PERFORM SOLENOID VALVE TEST FOR RIGHT FRONT VALVES • IF NO TROUBLE IS FOUND, REPLACE EBCM
53 AND/OR 73	• GO TO CHART A-11 IF NO TROUBLE IS FOUND WHILE PERFORMING TESTS ON CHART A-11, DO NOT GO TO TEST F. INSTEAD, GO TO SOLENOID VALVE TEST G • PERFORM SOLENOID VALVE TEST FOR REAR VALVES • IF NO TROUBLE IS FOUND, REPLACE EBCM
54 AND/OR 74	• GO TO CHART A-12 IF NO TROUBLE IS FOUND WHILE PERFORMING TESTS ON CHART A-12, DO NOT GO TO TEST F. INSTEAD, GO TO SOLENOID VALVE TEST G • PERFORM SOLENOID VALVE TEST FOR REAR VALVES • IF NO TROUBLE IS FOUND, REPLACE EBCM

CHART A-15
ABS CODES 61-LOW FLUID/LOW PRESSURE
LOOP INPUT NOT PROCESSABLE

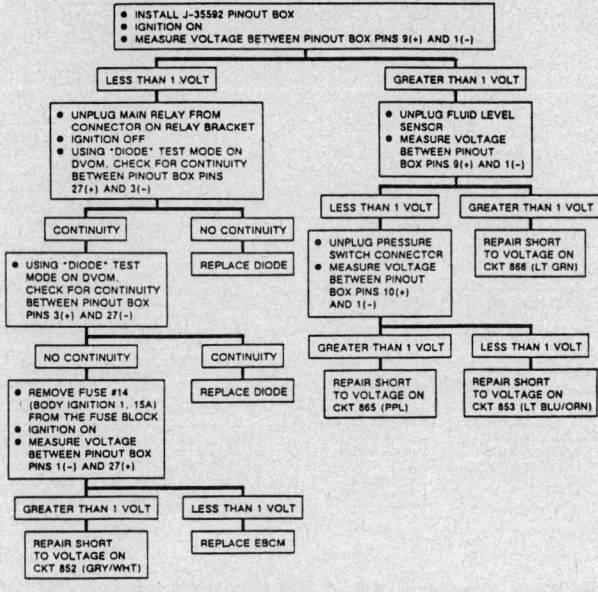

Fig. 26   Chart A-14, ABS trouble codes 51–54 & 71–74 (pressure reduction fault)

Fig. 27   Chart A-15, ABS trouble code 61 (low fluid/low pressure)

SYMPTOM DIAGNOSIS
CHART B
"ANTI–LOCK" LAMP ON AND NO ABS CODES PRESENT

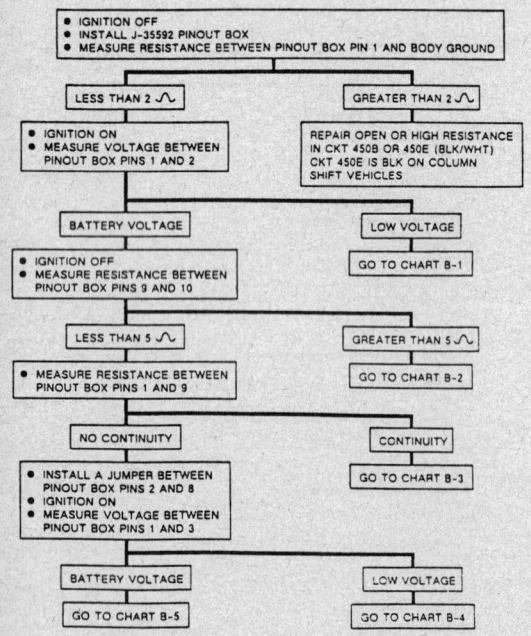

CHART B-1
IGNITION ENABLE CIRCUIT

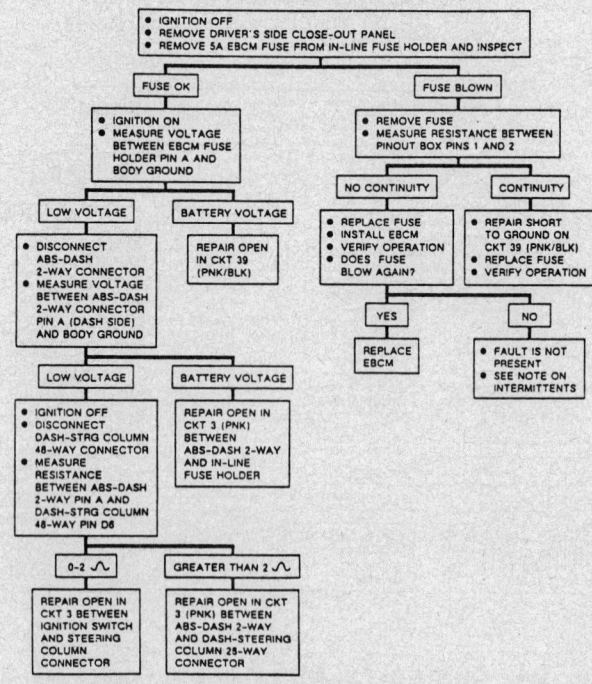

Fig. 28   Chart B, symptom diagnosis (anti-lock lamp on & no ABS codes)

Fig. 29   Chart B-1, ignition enable circuit

CHART B–2
EBCM LOOP CIRCUIT OPEN

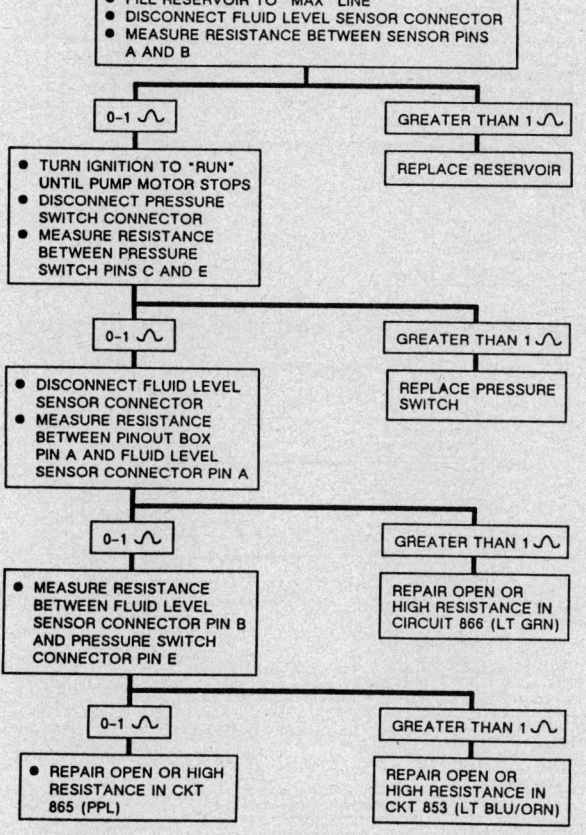

Fig. 30   Chart B-2, EBCM loop circuit open

CHART B–3
EBCM LOOP SHORT TO GROUND

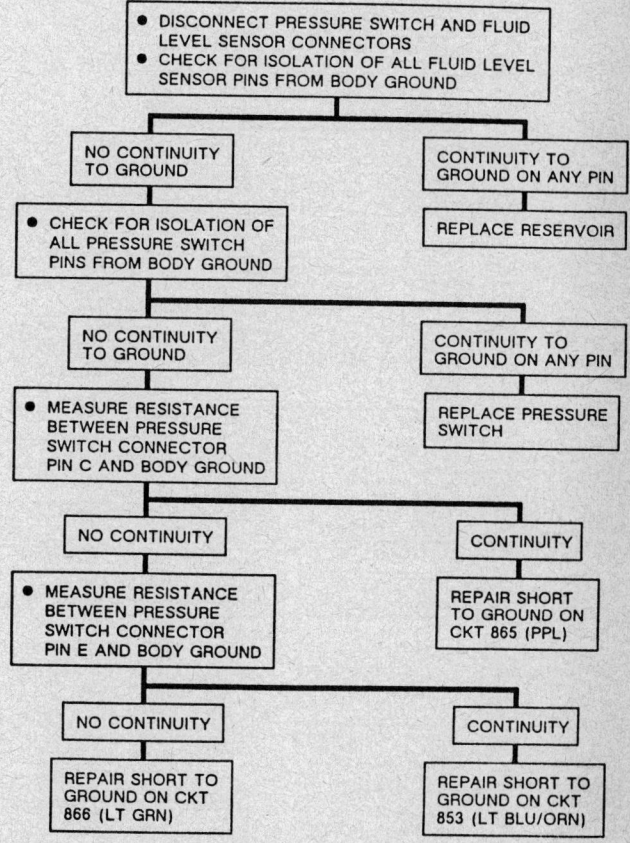

Fig. 31   Chart B-3, EBCM loop short to ground

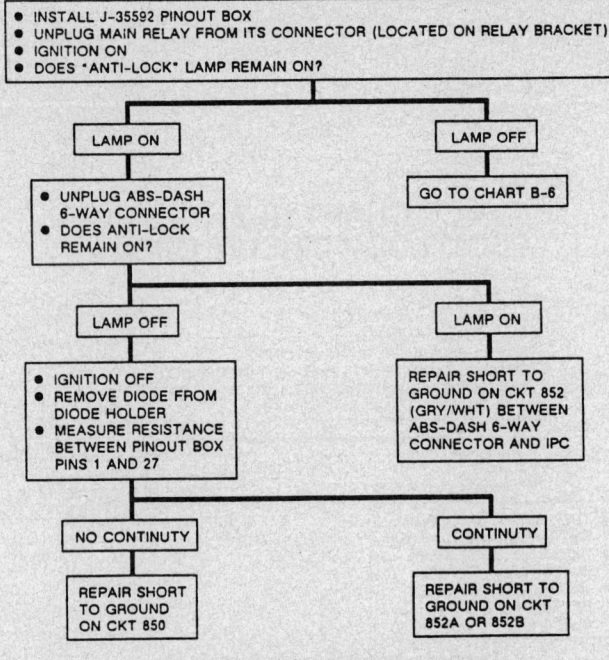

Fig. 33   Chart B-5, anti-lock lamp circuits

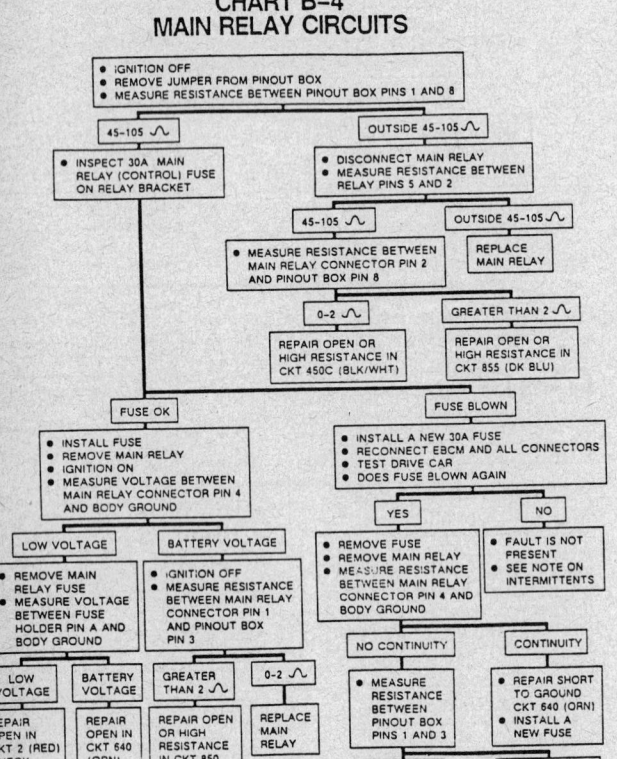

Fig. 32   Chart B-4, main relay circuits

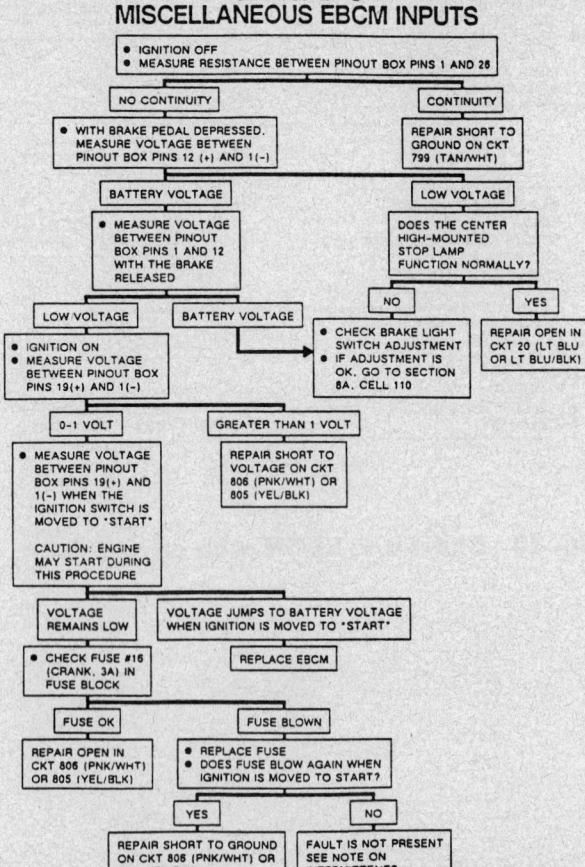

Fig. 34   Chart B-6, miscellaneous EBCM inputs

SYMPTOM DIAGNOSIS
CHART C
"BRAKE" LAMP ON AND NO ABS CODES PRESENT

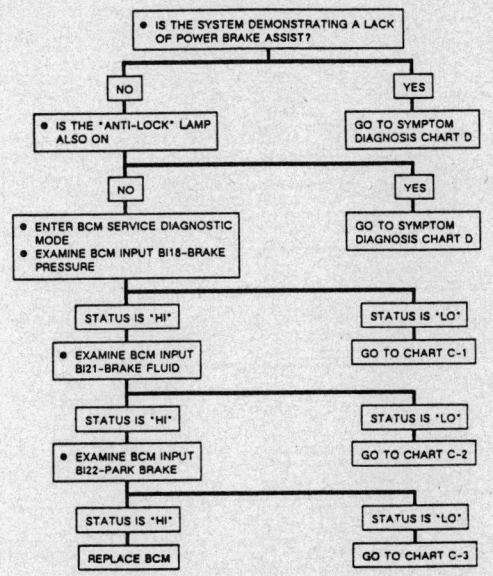

Fig. 35 Chart C, symptom diagnosis (brake lamp on & no ABS codes)

CHART C-1
BRAKE PRESSURE INPUT

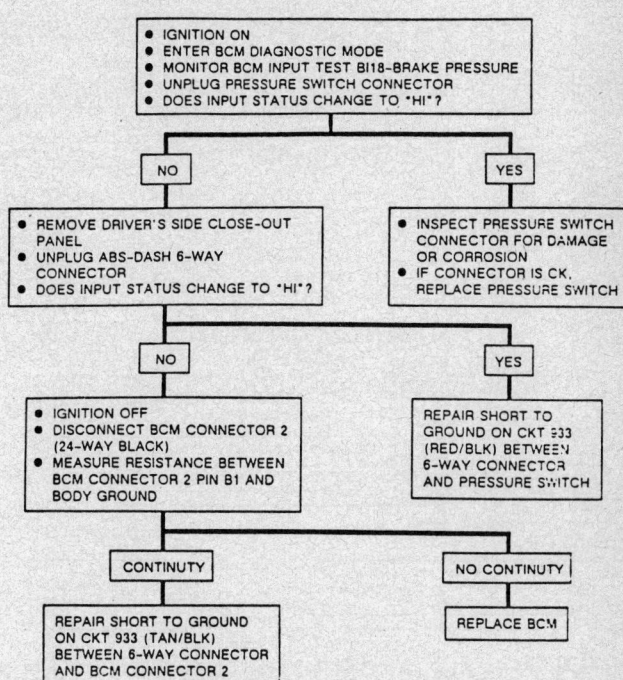

Fig. 36 Chart C-1, brake pressure input

CHART C-2
LOW BRAKE FLUID INPUT

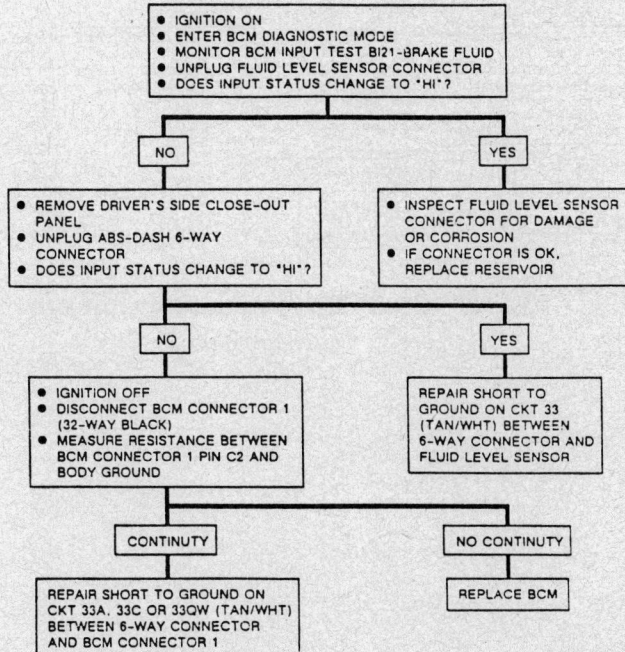

Fig. 37 Chart C-2, low brake fluid input

CHART C-3
PARKING BRAKE INPUT

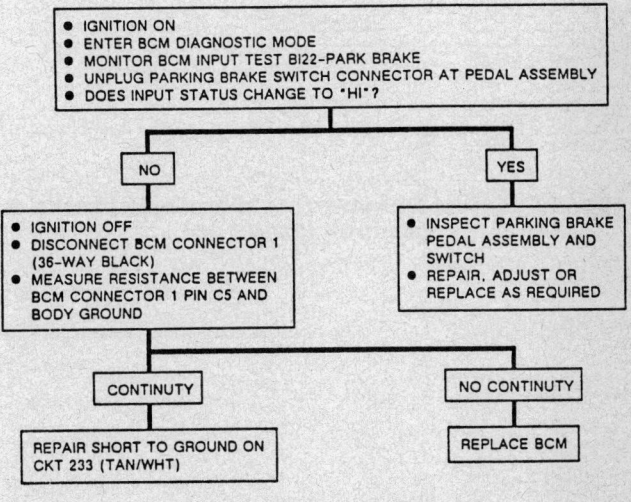

Fig. 38 Chart C-3, parking brake input

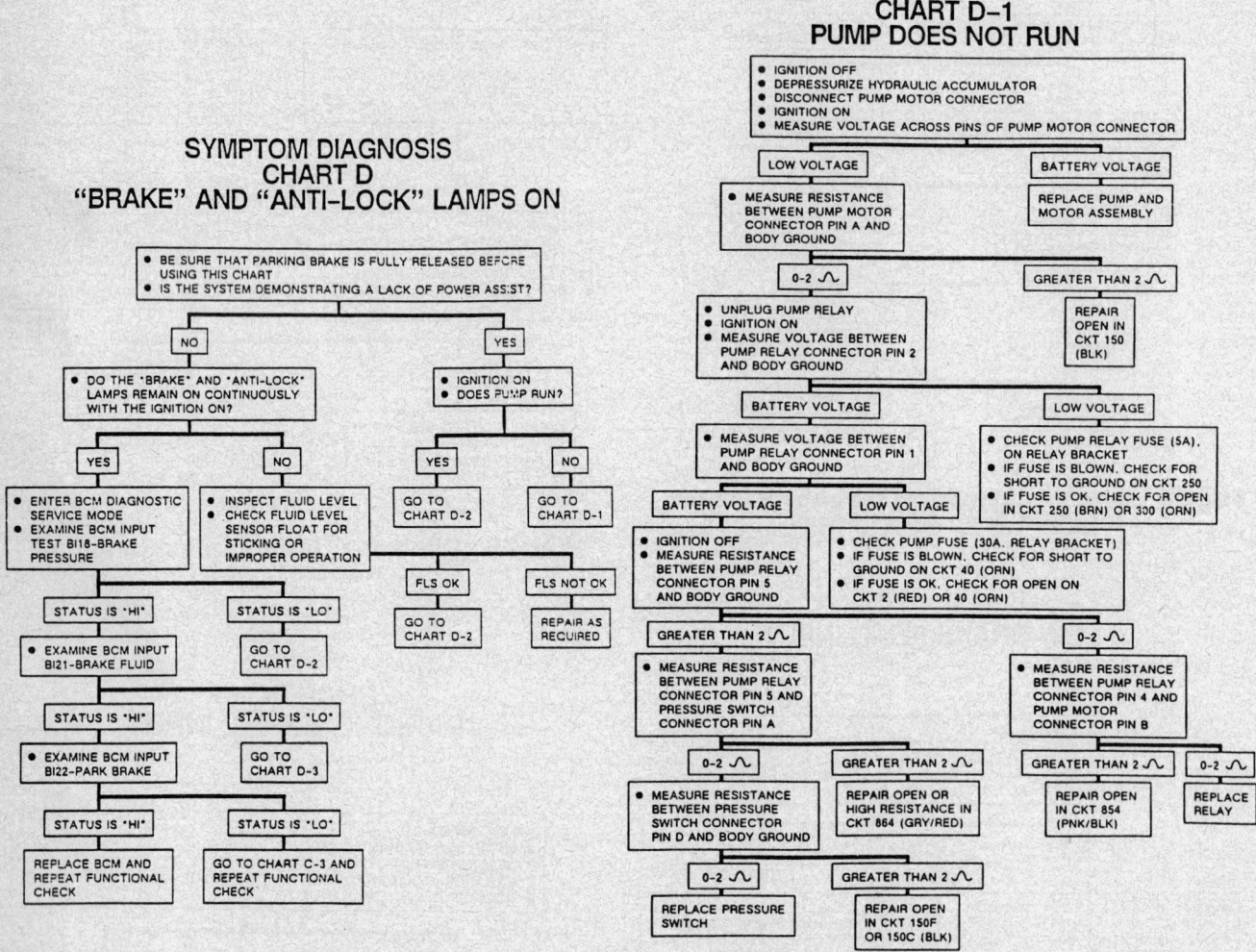

Fig. 39   Chart D, symptom diagnosis (brake & anti-lock lamps on)

Fig. 40   Chart D-1, pump does not run

CHART D–2
HYDRAULIC UNIT FUNCTIONAL CHECK

CHART D–2 (CONTINUED)
HYDRAULIC UNIT FUNCTIONAL CHECK

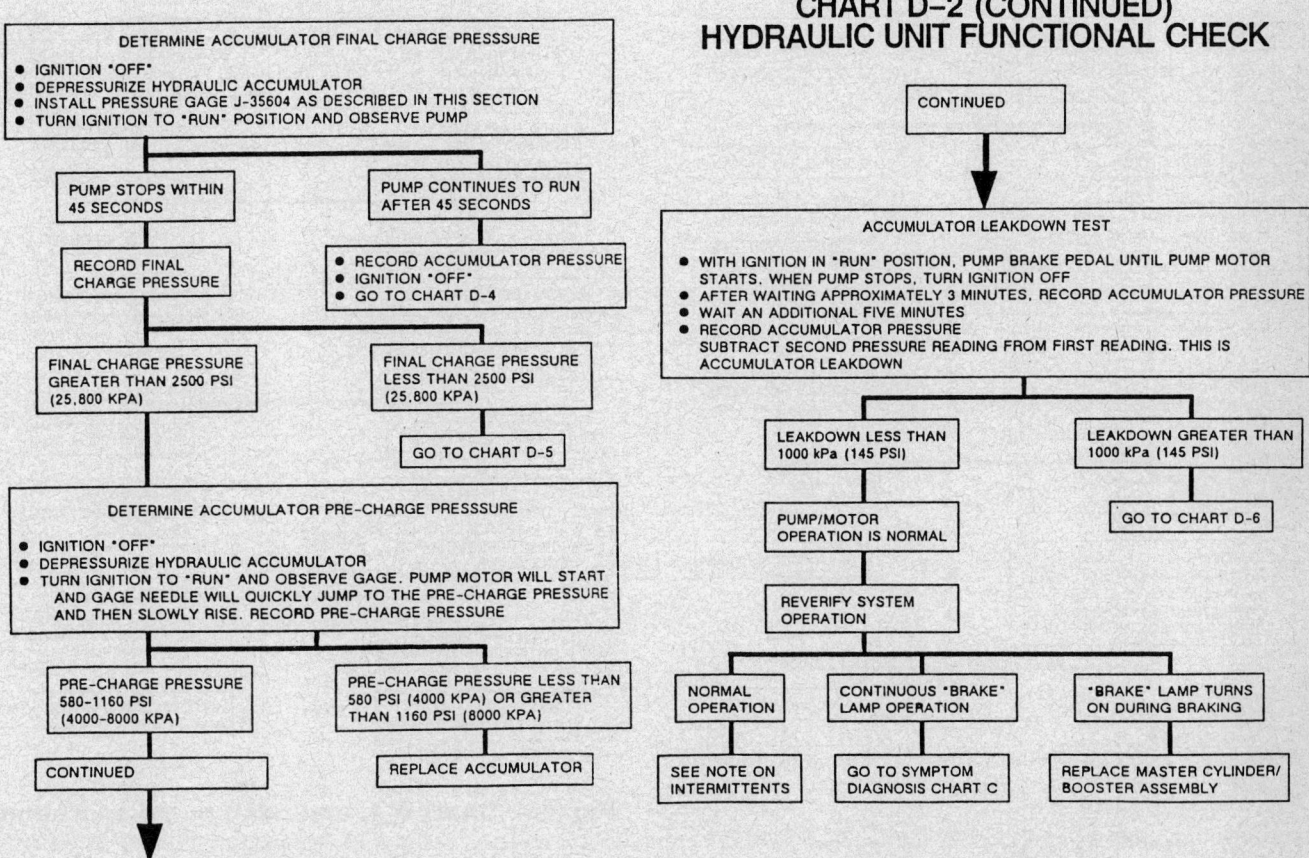

Fig. 41   Chart D-2, hydraulic unit functional check (Part 1 of 2)

Fig. 41   Chart D-2, hydraulic unit functional check (Part 2 of 2)

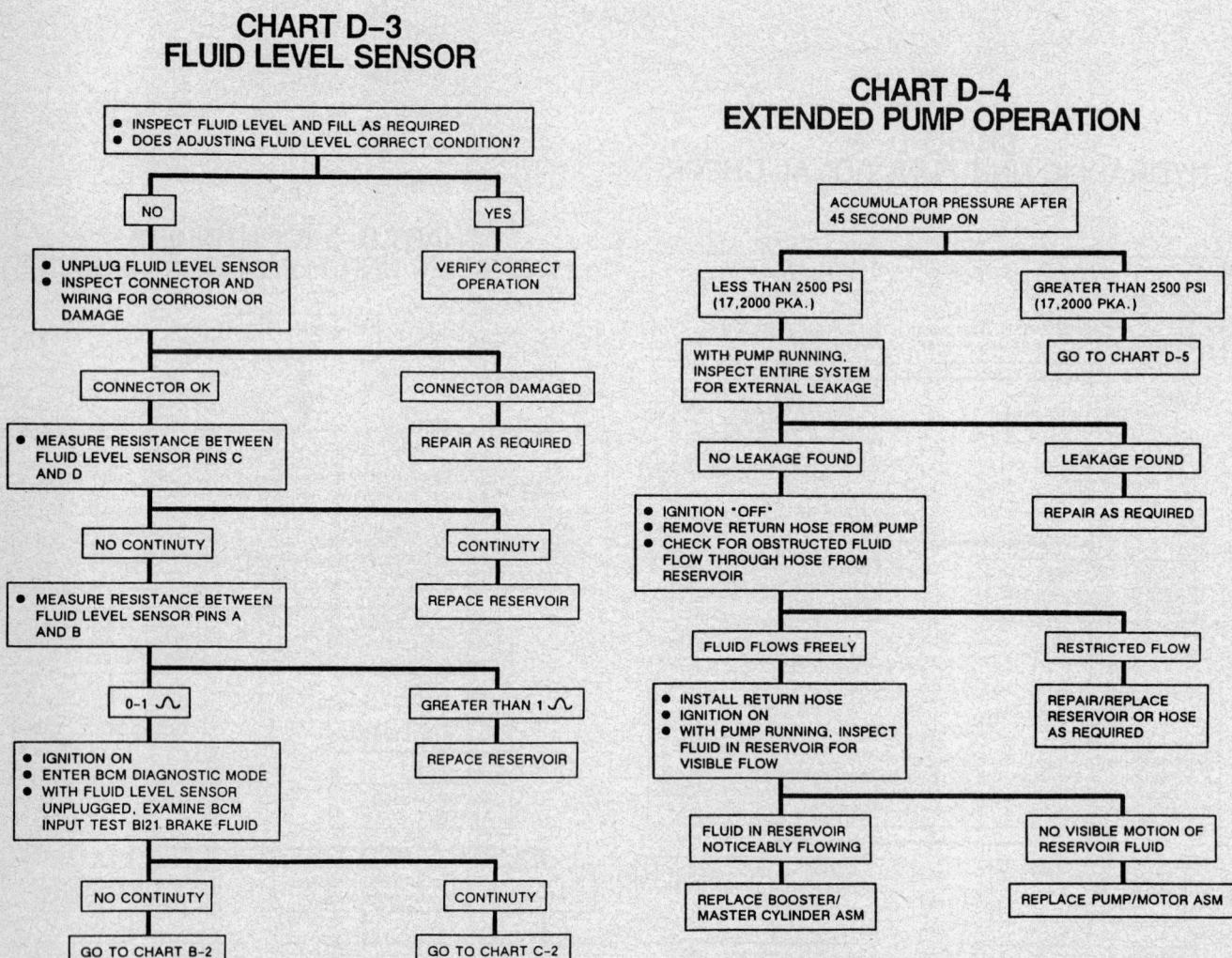

CHART D-3
FLUID LEVEL SENSOR

- INSPECT FLUID LEVEL AND FILL AS REQUIRED
- DOES ADJUSTING FLUID LEVEL CORRECT CONDITION?

NO →
- UNPLUG FLUID LEVEL SENSOR
- INSPECT CONNECTOR AND WIRING FOR CORROSION OR DAMAGE

YES → VERIFY CORRECT OPERATION

CONNECTOR OK
- MEASURE RESISTANCE BETWEEN FLUID LEVEL SENSOR PINS C AND D

CONNECTOR DAMAGED
REPAIR AS REQUIRED

NO CONTINUITY
- MEASURE RESISTANCE BETWEEN FLUID LEVEL SENSOR PINS A AND B

CONTINUITY
REPACE RESERVOIR

0-1 ∿
- IGNITION ON
- ENTER BCM DIAGNOSTIC MODE
- WITH FLUID LEVEL SENSOR UNPLUGGED, EXAMINE BCM INPUT TEST BI21 BRAKE FLUID

GREATER THAN 1 ∿
REPACE RESERVOIR

NO CONTINUITY
GO TO CHART B-2

CONTINUITY
GO TO CHART C-2

Fig. 42   Chart D-3, fluid level sensor

CHART D-4
EXTENDED PUMP OPERATION

ACCUMULATOR PRESSURE AFTER 45 SECOND PUMP ON

LESS THAN 2500 PSI (17,2000 PKA.)
WITH PUMP RUNNING, INSPECT ENTIRE SYSTEM FOR EXTERNAL LEAKAGE

GREATER THAN 2500 PSI (17,2000 PKA.)
GO TO CHART D-5

NO LEAKAGE FOUND
- IGNITION "OFF"
- REMOVE RETURN HOSE FROM PUMP
- CHECK FOR OBSTRUCTED FLUID FLOW THROUGH HOSE FROM RESERVOIR

LEAKAGE FOUND
REPAIR AS REQUIRED

FLUID FLOWS FREELY
- INSTALL RETURN HOSE
- IGNITION ON
- WITH PUMP RUNNING, INSPECT FLUID IN RESERVOIR FOR VISIBLE FLOW

RESTRICTED FLOW
REPAIR/REPLACE RESERVOIR OR HOSE AS REQUIRED

FLUID IN RESERVOIR NOTICEABLY FLOWING
REPLACE BOOSTER/MASTER CYLINDER ASM

NO VISIBLE MOTION OF RESERVOIR FLUID
REPLACE PUMP/MOTOR ASM

Fig. 43   Chart D-4, extended pump operation

ELDORADO, REATTA, RIVIERA, SEVILLE, TORONADO & TROFEO (TEVES TYPE)

CHART D-5
PRESSURE SWITCH PERFORMANCE

SWITCH STATUS - PRESSURIZED
- TURN IGNITION TO "RUN" UNTIL PUMP STOPS
- IGNITION "OFF"
  NOTE: IF PUMP CONTINUES TO RUN AFTER 45 SECONDS, TURN IGNITION OFF AND PROCEDE
- CHECK PRESSURE SWITCH PINS FOR THE FOLLOWING CONDITIONS USING VOM

MEASURE BETWEEN PINS	SCALE	SPECIFICATION
B, D	200Ω	NO CONTINUITY
A, D	200Ω	NO CONTINUITY
C, E	200Ω	CONTINUITY
ALL PINS, BODY GROUND	200Ω	NO CONTINUITY

IF ANY CONDITION IS NOT MET, REPLACE PRESSURE SWITCH AND VERIFY SYSTEM OPERATION

SWITCH STATUS - DEPRESSURIZED
- DEPRESSURIZE HYDRAULIC ACCUMULATOR
- CHECK PRESSURE SWITCH PINS FOR THE FOLLOWING CONDITIONS USING VOM

MEASURE BETWEEN PINS	SCALE	SPECIFICATION
B, D	200Ω	CONTINUITY
A, D	200Ω	CONTINUITY
C, E	200Ω	NO CONTINUITY
ALL PINS, BODY GROUND	200Ω	NO CONTINUITY

Fig. 44 Chart D-5, pressure switch performance (Part 1 of 2)

CHART D-5 (CONTINUED)
PRESSURE SWITCH PERFORMANCE

SWITCH STATUS - PRESSURIZED
- DEPRESSURIZE HYDRAULIC ACCUMULATOR
- INSTALL PRESSURE GAGE J-35604 AS DESCRIBED IN THIS SECTION
- CONNECT PRESSURE SWITCH CONNECTOR AND TURN IGNITION TO "RUN" UNTIL PUMP STOPS
- USING VOM, MONITOR FOR CONTINUITY BETWEEN PRESSURE SWITCH PINS AS SHOWN BELOW WHILE SLOWLY BLEEDING OFF ACCUMULATOR PRESSURE BY PUMPING THE BRAKE PEDAL.
- PRESSURIZE SYSTEM BETWEEN EACH TEST BY RECONNECTING PRESSURE SWITCH AND TURNING IGNITION TO "RUN" UNTIL PUMP STOPS

MEASURE BETWEEN PINS	SCALE	SPECIFICATION
A, D	CONTINUITY SHOULD BE GAINED AT:	1980-2080 PSI (13,650-14,350 KPA)
B, D	CONTINUITY SHOULD BE GAINED AT:	1500-1550 PSI 10,350-10,700 KPA)
C, E	CONTINUITY SHOULD BE GAINED AT:	1500-1550 PSI (10,350-10,700 KPA)

IF ANY CONDITION IS NOT MET, REPLACE PRESSURE SWITCH AND VERIFY SYSTEM OPERATION

- DEPRESSURIZE HYDRAULIC ACCUMULATOR
- WITH IGNITION OFF, CONNECT PRESSURE SWITCH CONNECTOR
- TURN IGNITION TO "RUN" AND OBSERVE GAGE, "ANTI-LOCK" LAMP, "BRAKE" LAMP AND PUMP MOTOR. EVENTS SHOULD OCCUR AT PRESSURES INDICATED IN CHART BELOW

EVENT	PRESSURE
"ANTI-LOCK" LAMP TURN OFF	1850-1950 PSI (12,750-13,450 KPA)
"BRAKE" LAMP TURN OFF	1850-1950 PSI (12,750-13,450 KPA)
PUMP MOTOR STOPS	2550-2670 PSI (17,580-18,400 KPA)

Fig. 44 Chart D-5, pressure switch performance (Part 2 of 2)

CHART D-6
HYDRAULIC UNIT LEAKDOWN

- IGNITION ON
- ALLOW PUMP TO RUN FOR 60 SECONDS MAXIMUM
- IGNITION OFF
- USING VICE GRIP PLIERS OR EQUIVALENT, CLAMP OFF RETURN HOSE TO PREVENT FLUID LOSS FROM RESERVOIR
- DISCONNECT RETURN HOSE AT PUMP
- WIPE EXCESS FLUID FROM PUMP MOTOR
- OBSERVE FOR FLUID FLOW FROM PUMP INLET FOR 5 MINUTES

NO FLOW
- THE CAUSE OF LEAKDOWN MAY BE EITHER THE PUMP OR THE BOOSTER
- REPLACE PUMP/MOTOR ASM FIRST AND VERIFY OPERATION
- IF CONDITION PERSISTS, REPLACE BOOSTER/MASTER CYLINDER ASM

FLOW FROM PUMP OUTLET

REPLACE PUMP AND MOTOR ASSEMBLY

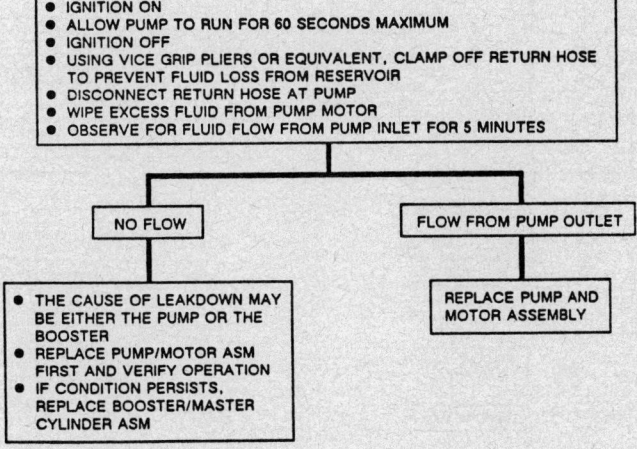

Fig. 45 Chart D-6, hydraulic unit leakdown

SYMPTOM DIAGNOSIS
CHART E

- ABS FUNCTIONAL CHECK MUST BE PERFORMED BEFORE USING THIS CHART

- IF ANY ABS TROUBLE CODES ARE SET, SEE APPROPRIATE TROUBLE CODE CHART

SYMPTOM:	GO TO:
• "ANTI-LOCK" LAMP INOPERATIVE AT KEY-ON	CHART E-1
• "ANTI-LOCK" LAMP DIM OR INOPERATIVE DURING START	CHART E-2
• VALVE CYCLING (CHATTER) DURING NORMAL STOPS	CHART E-3
• LOW OR SPONGY BRAKE PEDAL	CHART E-4
• POOR VEHICLE TRACKING DURING ANTI-LOCK STOPS	CHART E-5

Fig. 46   Chart E, symptom diagnosis

CHART E-1
"ANTI-LOCK" LAMP INOPERATIVE AT KEY-ON

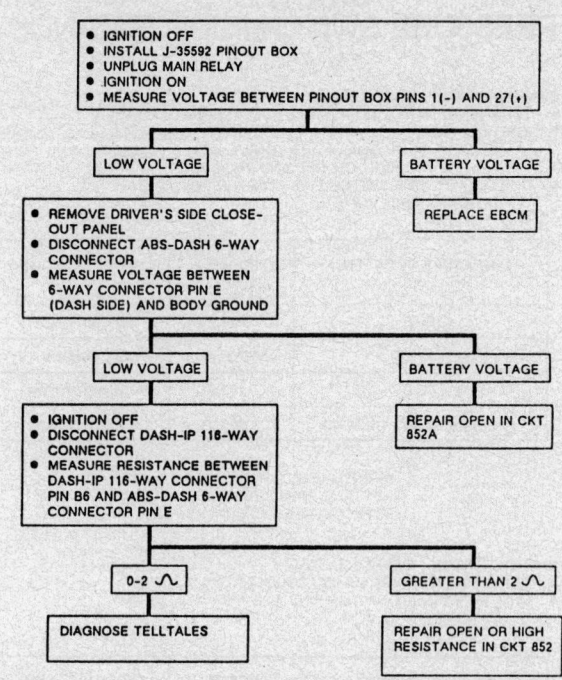

Fig. 47   Chart E-1, anti-lock lamp inoperative at key-on

CHART E-2
"ANTI-LOCK" LAMP DIM OR INOP DURING CRANK

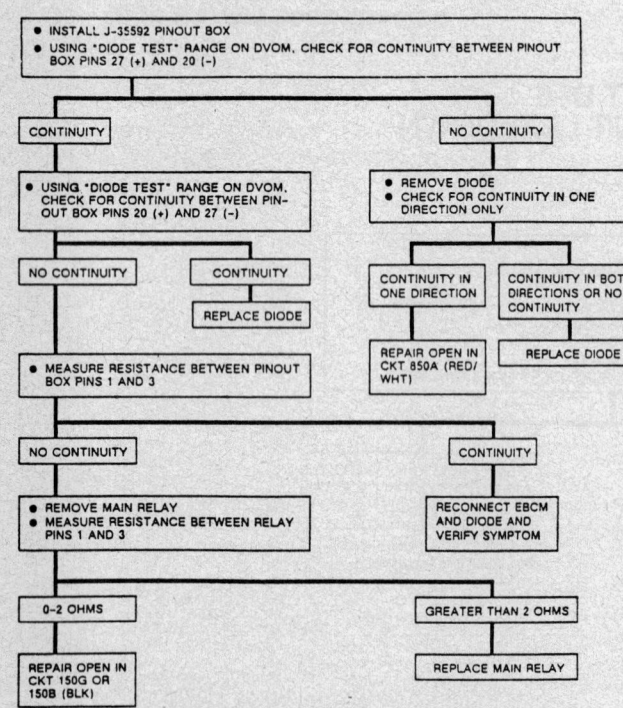

Fig. 48   Chart E-2, anti-lock lamp dim or inoperative during engine crank

CHART E-3
VALVE CYCLING (CHATTER) DURING NORMAL STOPS

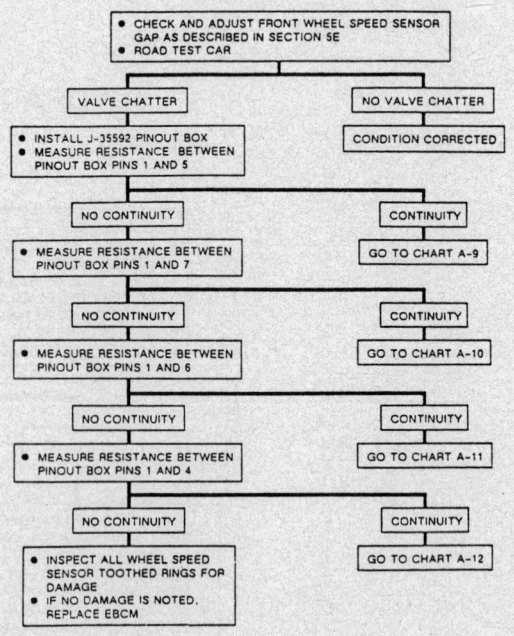

Fig. 49   Chart E-3, valve cycling (chatter) during normal stops

CHART E-5
POOR VEHICLE TRACKING DURING ANTI-LOCK STOPS

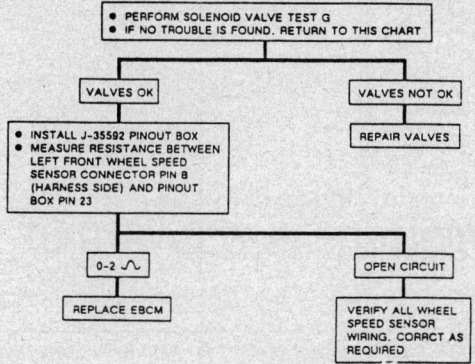

Fig. 51   Chart E-5, poor vehicle tracking during anti-lock stops

CHART E-4
LOW OR SPONGY PEDAL

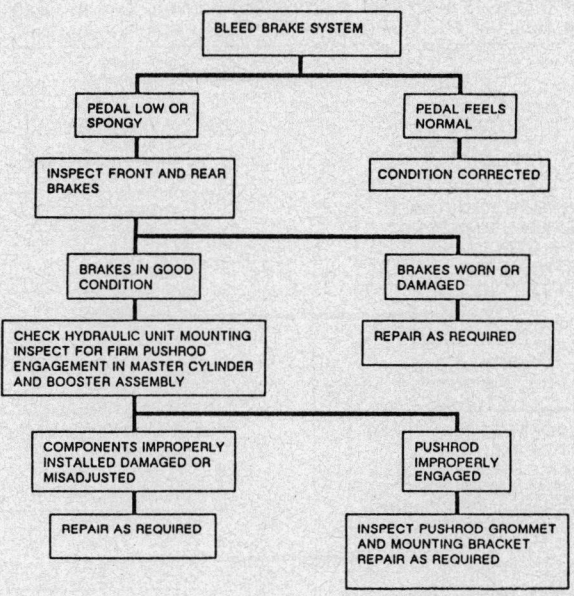

• IF CONDITION IS STILL NOT CORRECTED, REPLACE BOOSTER/MASTER CYLINDER ASM

Fig. 50   Chart E-4, low or spongy pedal

TEST F
WHEEL SPEED SENSOR OUTPUT

• THE FOLLOWING TEST MAY BE PERFORMED FOR INDIVIDUAL WHEEL SPEED SENSORS (AS DIRECTED BY THE APPROPRIATE DIAGNOSTIC PROCEDURE) OR FOR ALL SENSORS AS A SYSTEM CHECK

• TO SET UP FOR TEST:
  – INSTALL J-35592 PINOUT BOX
  – RAISE CAR SO THAT WHEELS CLEAR THE GROUND
  – AN ASSISTANT MAY BE REQUIRED TO SPIN THE WHEELS

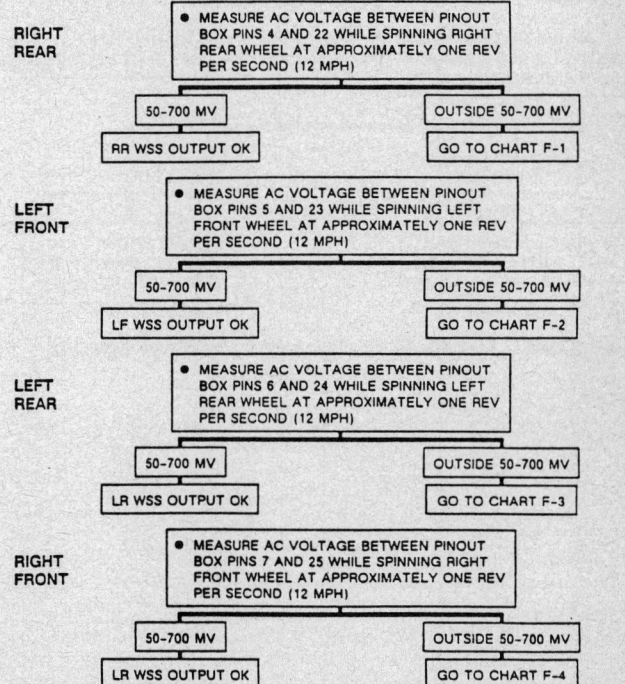

IF NO TROUBLE IS FOUND WITH WHEEL SPEED SENSOR OUTPUT, CONSIDER THAT:
• OUTPUT SHOULD NOT BE SIGNIFICANTLY DIFFERENT FROM LF TO RF AND LR TO RR
• FRONT WSS OUTPUT SHOULD BE SLIGHTLY HIGHER THAN REAR WSS OUTPUT
• IMPROPER OUTPUT MAY BE CAUSD BY MIS-ADJUSTED FRONT SENSOR
• WHEEL SPEED SENSOR CABLES SOMETIMES CAN INTERMITTENTLY GO OPEN, PARTICULARLY IN THE WHEELHOUSE AREA. MANIPULATE THE CABLES BY HAND WHEN INSPECTING FOR AN OPEN CIRCUIT
• TOOTHED SENSOR RINGS SHOULD ALSO BE INSPECTED FOR DAMAGE OR MISSING TEETH

Fig. 52   Test F, wheel speed sensor output

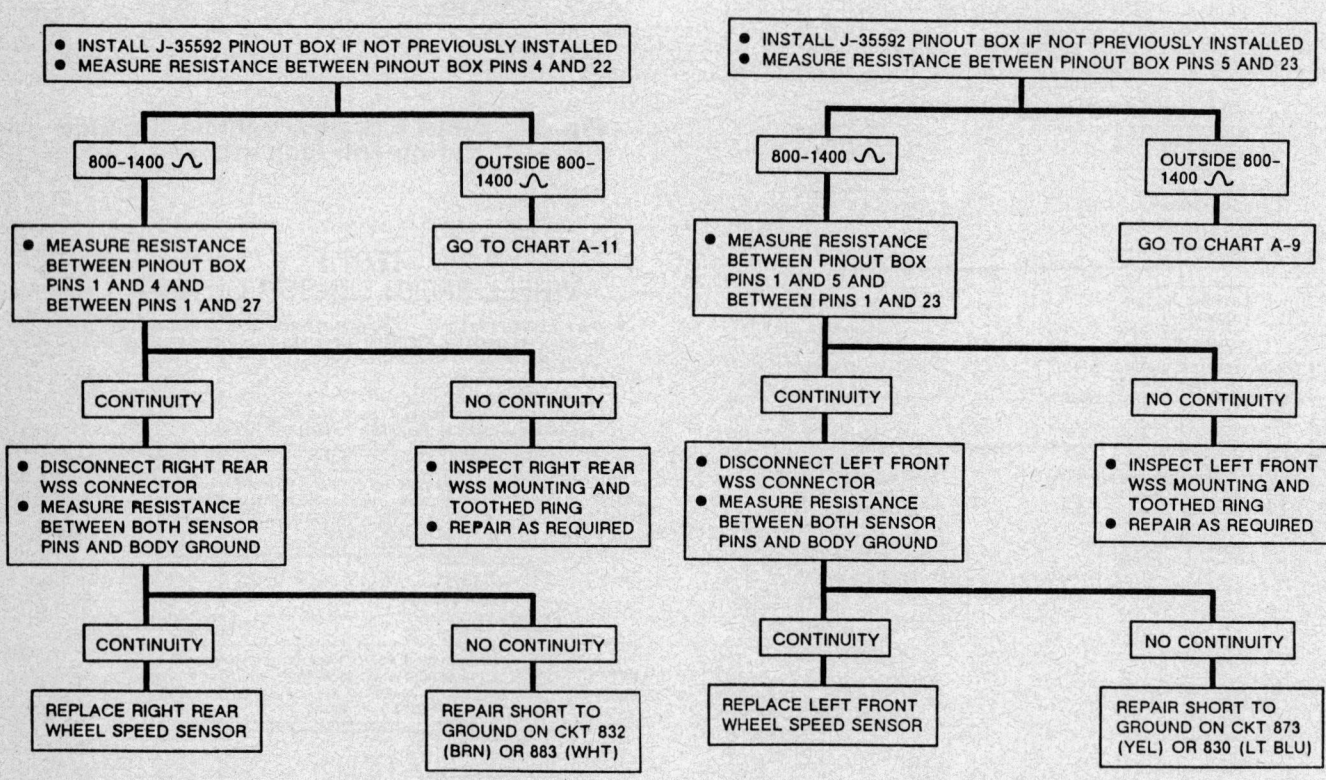

CHART F–1
RIGHT REAR WSS OUTPUT

- INSTALL J-35592 PINOUT BOX IF NOT PREVIOUSLY INSTALLED
- MEASURE RESISTANCE BETWEEN PINOUT BOX PINS 4 AND 22

800-1400

OUTSIDE 800-1400

- MEASURE RESISTANCE BETWEEN PINOUT BOX PINS 1 AND 4 AND BETWEEN PINS 1 AND 27

GO TO CHART A-11

CONTINUITY

NO CONTINUITY

- DISCONNECT RIGHT REAR WSS CONNECTOR
- MEASURE RESISTANCE BETWEEN BOTH SENSOR PINS AND BODY GROUND

- INSPECT RIGHT REAR WSS MOUNTING AND TOOTHED RING
- REPAIR AS REQUIRED

CONTINUITY

NO CONTINUITY

REPLACE RIGHT REAR WHEEL SPEED SENSOR

REPAIR SHORT TO GROUND ON CKT 832 (BRN) OR 883 (WHT)

Fig. 53   Chart F-1, right rear wheel speed sensor output

CHART F–2
LEFT FRONT WSS OUTPUT

- INSTALL J-35592 PINOUT BOX IF NOT PREVIOUSLY INSTALLED
- MEASURE RESISTANCE BETWEEN PINOUT BOX PINS 5 AND 23

800-1400

OUTSIDE 800-1400

- MEASURE RESISTANCE BETWEEN PINOUT BOX PINS 1 AND 5 AND BETWEEN PINS 1 AND 23

GO TO CHART A-9

CONTINUITY

NO CONTINUITY

- DISCONNECT LEFT FRONT WSS CONNECTOR
- MEASURE RESISTANCE BETWEEN BOTH SENSOR PINS AND BODY GROUND

- INSPECT LEFT FRONT WSS MOUNTING AND TOOTHED RING
- REPAIR AS REQUIRED

CONTINUITY

NO CONTINUITY

REPLACE LEFT FRONT WHEEL SPEED SENSOR

REPAIR SHORT TO GROUND ON CKT 873 (YEL) OR 830 (LT BLU)

Fig. 54   Chart F-2, left front wheel speed sensor output

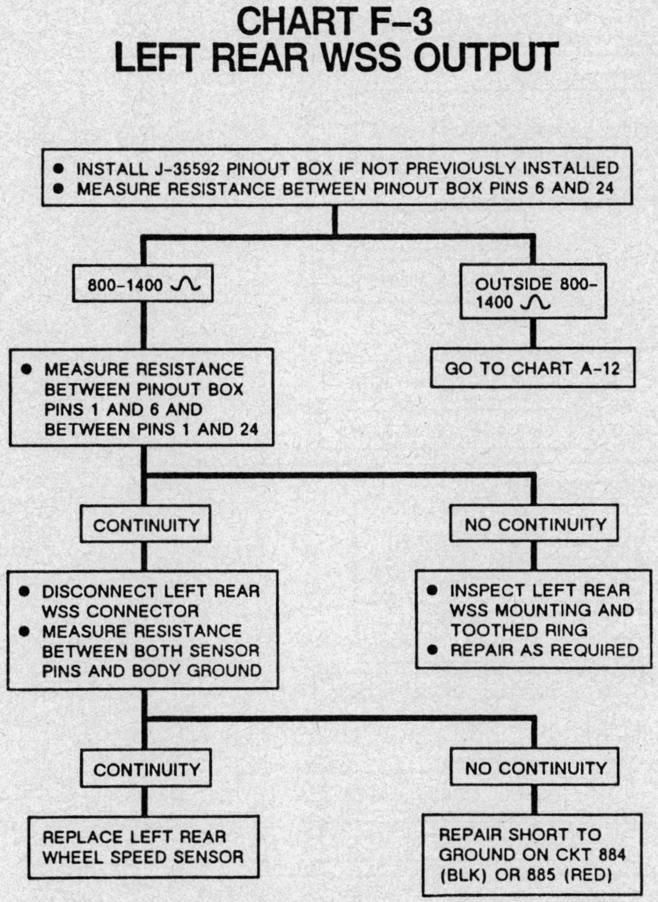

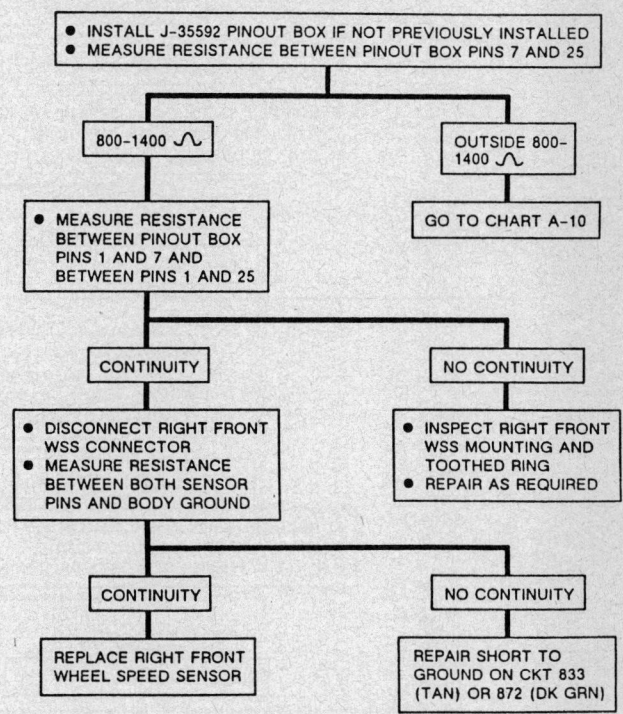

CHART F–3
LEFT REAR WSS OUTPUT

- INSTALL J-35592 PINOUT BOX IF NOT PREVIOUSLY INSTALLED
- MEASURE RESISTANCE BETWEEN PINOUT BOX PINS 6 AND 24

800–1400 ⏜

OUTSIDE 800–1400 ⏜

- MEASURE RESISTANCE BETWEEN PINOUT BOX PINS 1 AND 6 AND BETWEEN PINS 1 AND 24

GO TO CHART A-12

CONTINUITY

NO CONTINUITY

- DISCONNECT LEFT REAR WSS CONNECTOR
- MEASURE RESISTANCE BETWEEN BOTH SENSOR PINS AND BODY GROUND

- INSPECT LEFT REAR WSS MOUNTING AND TOOTHED RING
- REPAIR AS REQUIRED

CONTINUITY

NO CONTINUITY

REPLACE LEFT REAR WHEEL SPEED SENSOR

REPAIR SHORT TO GROUND ON CKT 884 (BLK) OR 885 (RED)

Fig. 55   Chart F-3, left rear wheel speed sensor output

CHART F–4
RIGHT FRONT WSS OUTPUT

- INSTALL J-35592 PINOUT BOX IF NOT PREVIOUSLY INSTALLED
- MEASURE RESISTANCE BETWEEN PINOUT BOX PINS 7 AND 25

800–1400 ⏜

OUTSIDE 800–1400 ⏜

- MEASURE RESISTANCE BETWEEN PINOUT BOX PINS 1 AND 7 AND BETWEEN PINS 1 AND 25

GO TO CHART A-10

CONTINUITY

NO CONTINUITY

- DISCONNECT RIGHT FRONT WSS CONNECTOR
- MEASURE RESISTANCE BETWEEN BOTH SENSOR PINS AND BODY GROUND

- INSPECT RIGHT FRONT WSS MOUNTING AND TOOTHED RING
- REPAIR AS REQUIRED

CONTINUITY

NO CONTINUITY

REPLACE RIGHT FRONT WHEEL SPEED SENSOR

REPAIR SHORT TO GROUND ON CKT 833 (TAN) OR 872 (DK GRN)

Fig. 56   Chart F-4, right front wheel speed sensor output

TEST G
SOLENOID VALVES

- THE FOLLOWING TEST MAY BE PERFORMED FOR INDIVIDUAL PAIRS OF SOLENOID VALVES (AS DIRECTED BY THE APPROPRIATE DIAGNOSTIC PROCEDURE) OR FOR ALL SENSORS AS A SYSTEM CHECK
- TO SET UP FOR TEST:
  – INSTALL J-35592
  – RAISE CAR SO THAT WHEELS CLEAR THE GROUND
  – AN ASSISTANT MAY BE REQUIRED TO SPIN THE WHEELS
- IMPORTANT: DO NOT LEAVE IGNITION ON FOR MORE THAN 30 SECONDS WITH JUMPER WIRES INSTALLED AS DESCRIBED BELOW. SOLENOID VALVE DAMAGE MAY RESULT

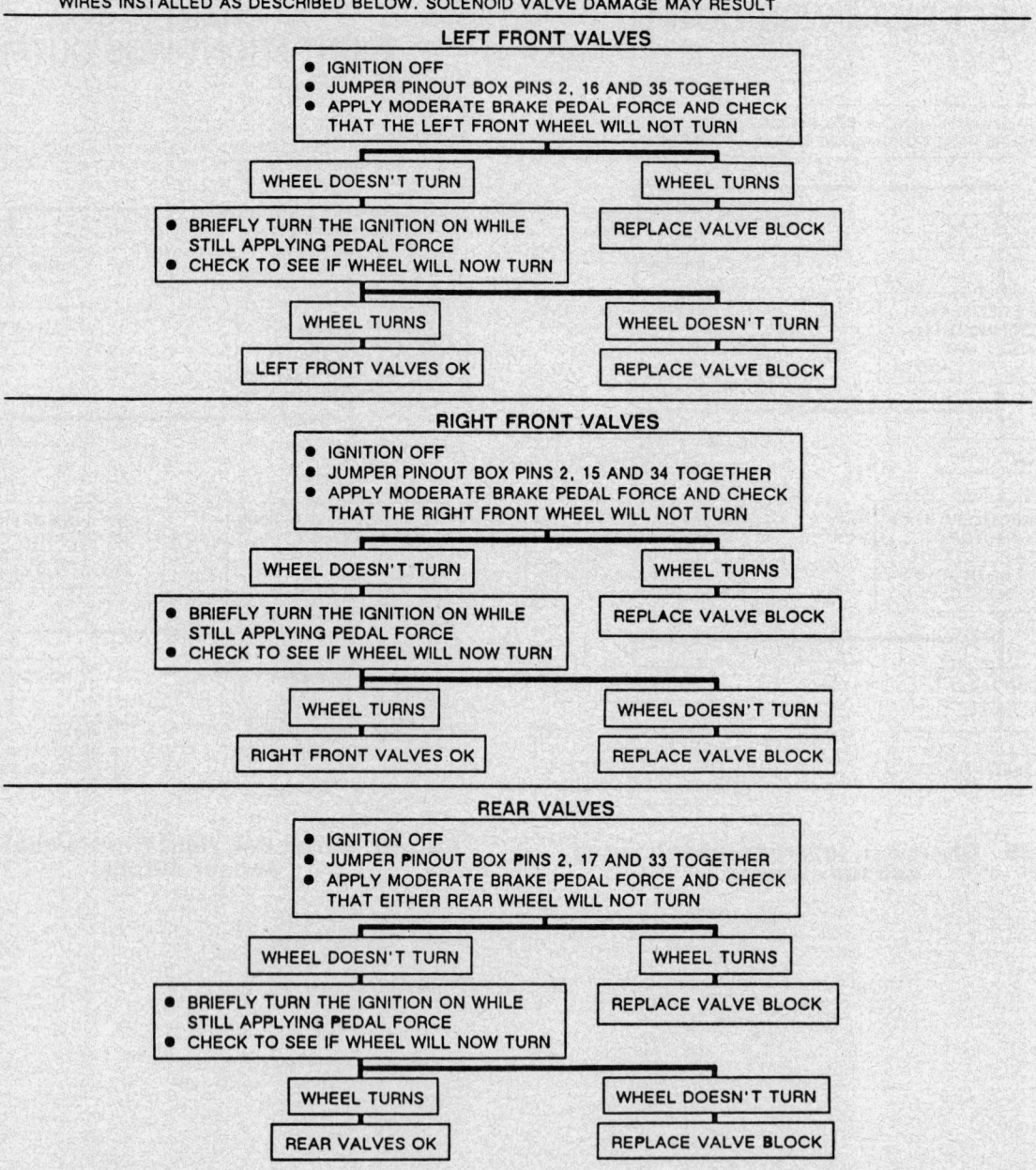

Fig. 57 Test G, symptom diagnosis (solenoid valves)

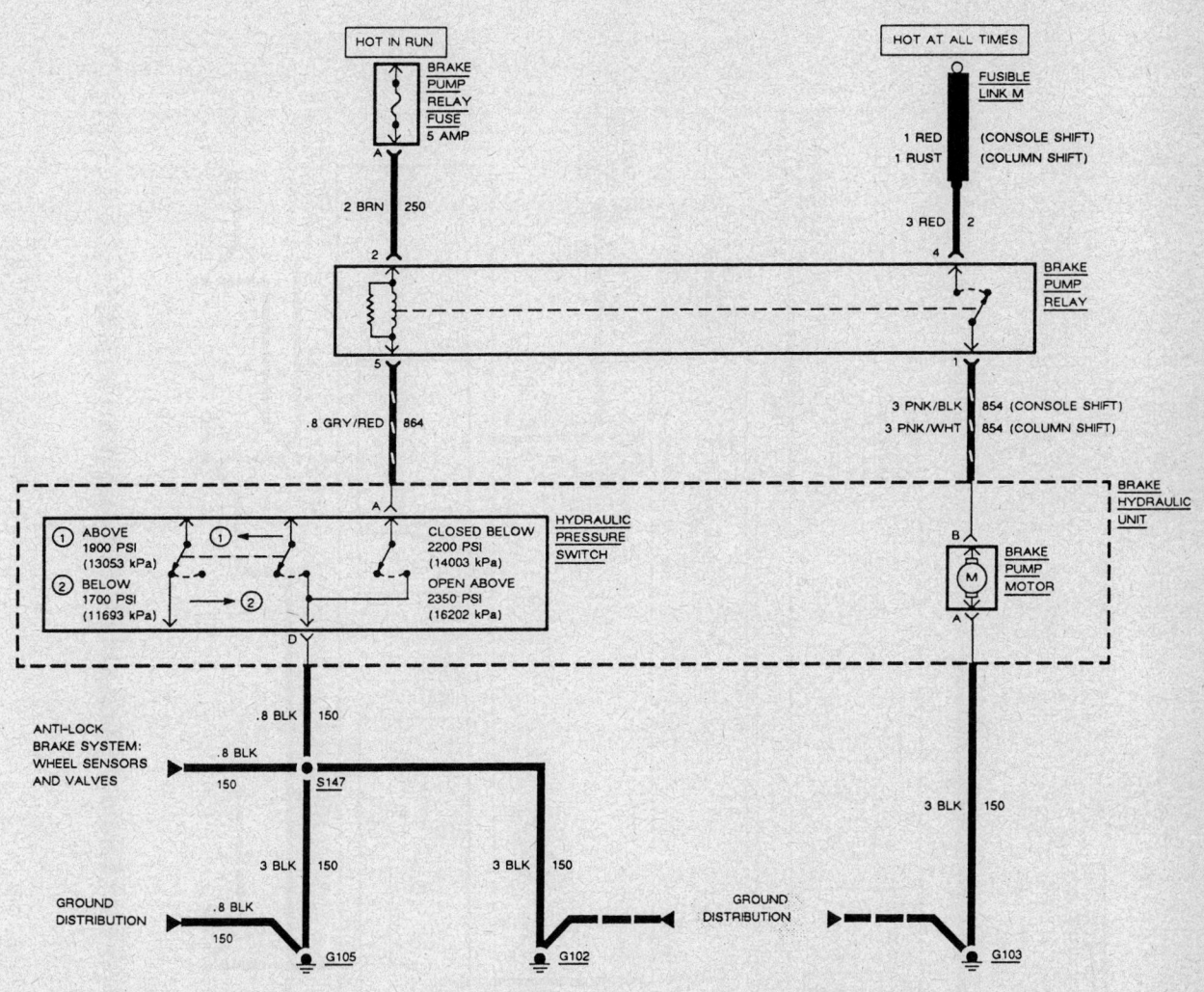

Fig. 58   Anti-lock brake system circuit diagram (Part 1 of 5)

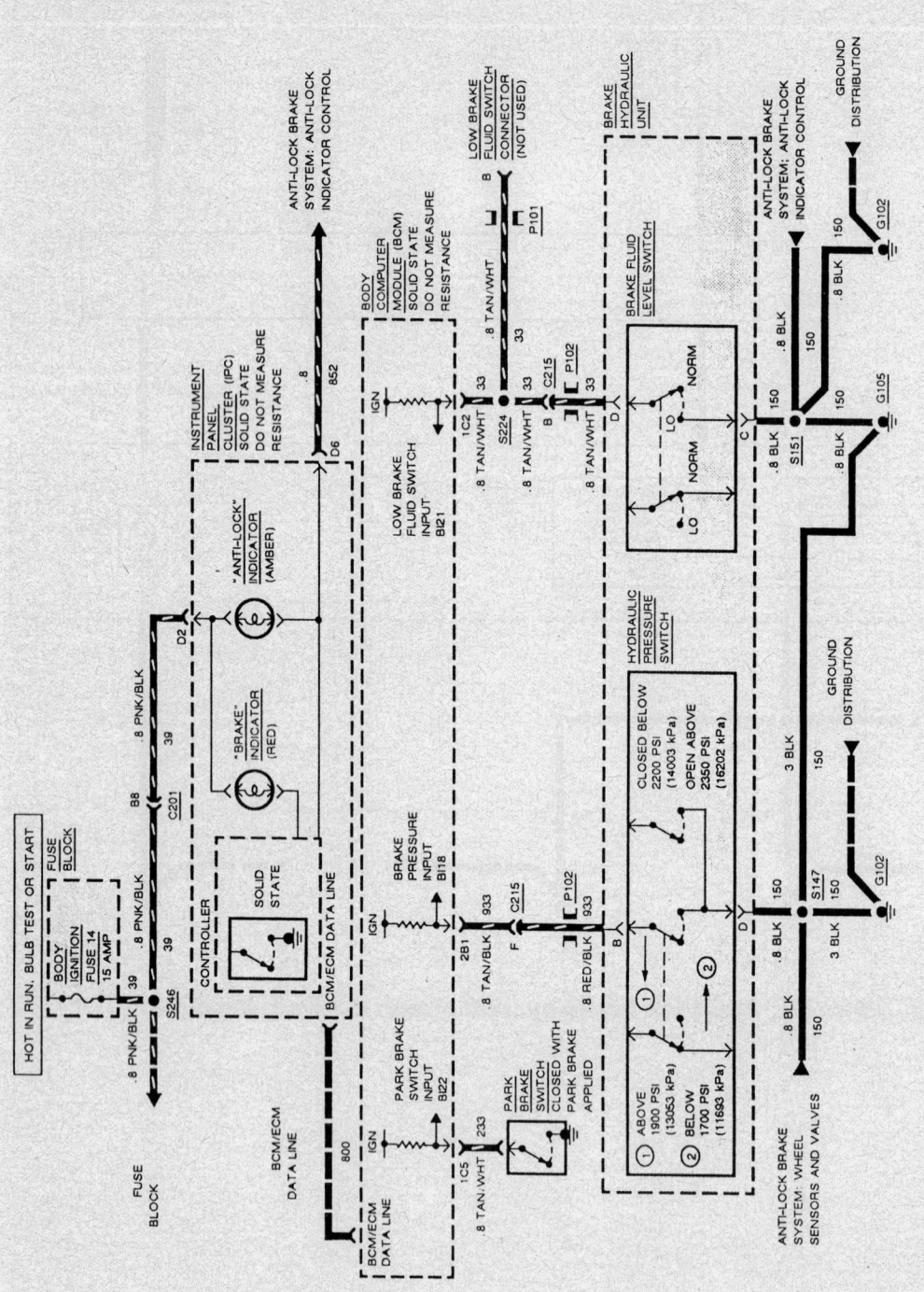

Fig. 58 Anti-lock brake system circuit diagram (Part 2 of 5)

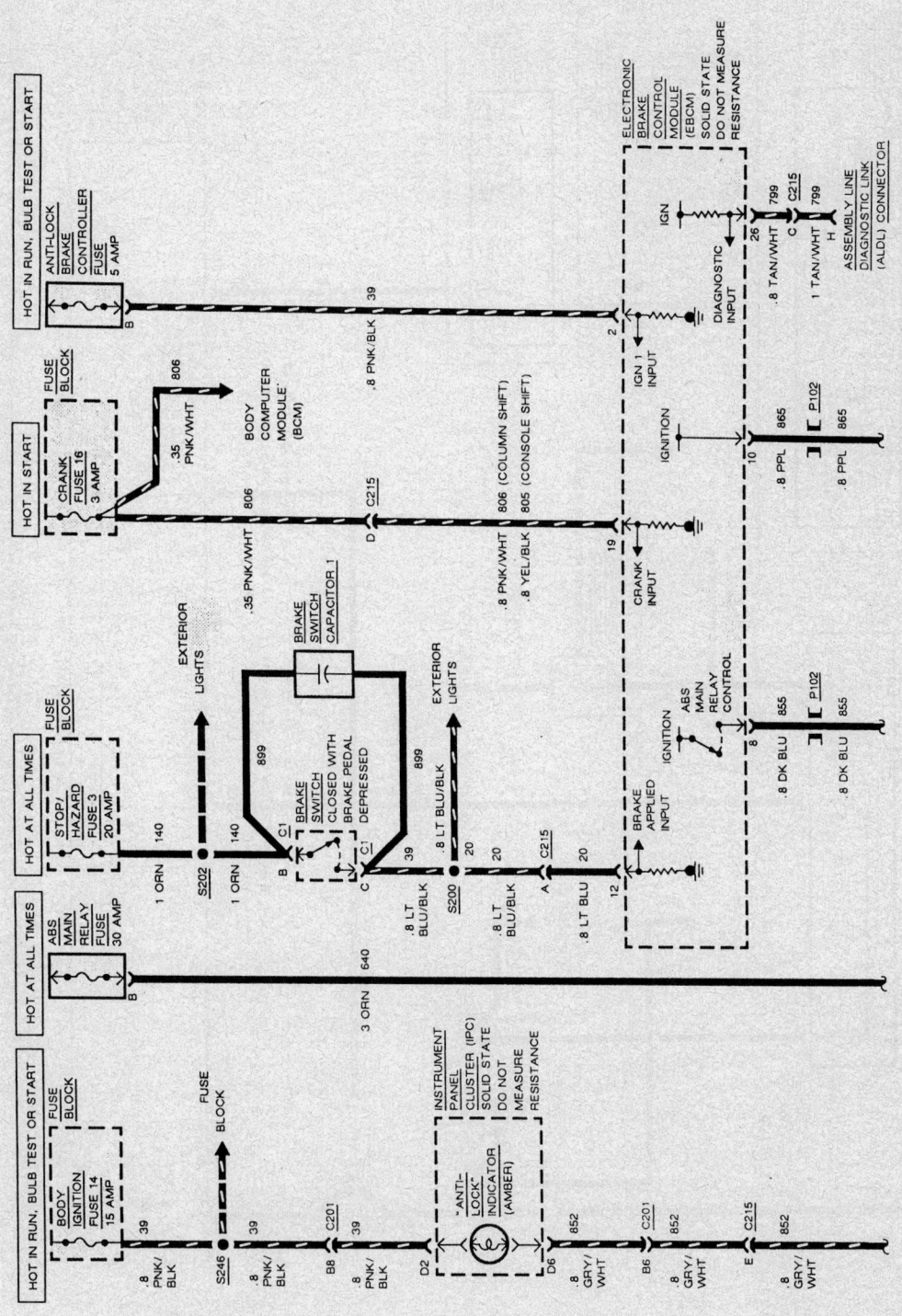

Fig. 58 Anti-lock brake system circuit diagram (Part 3 of 5)

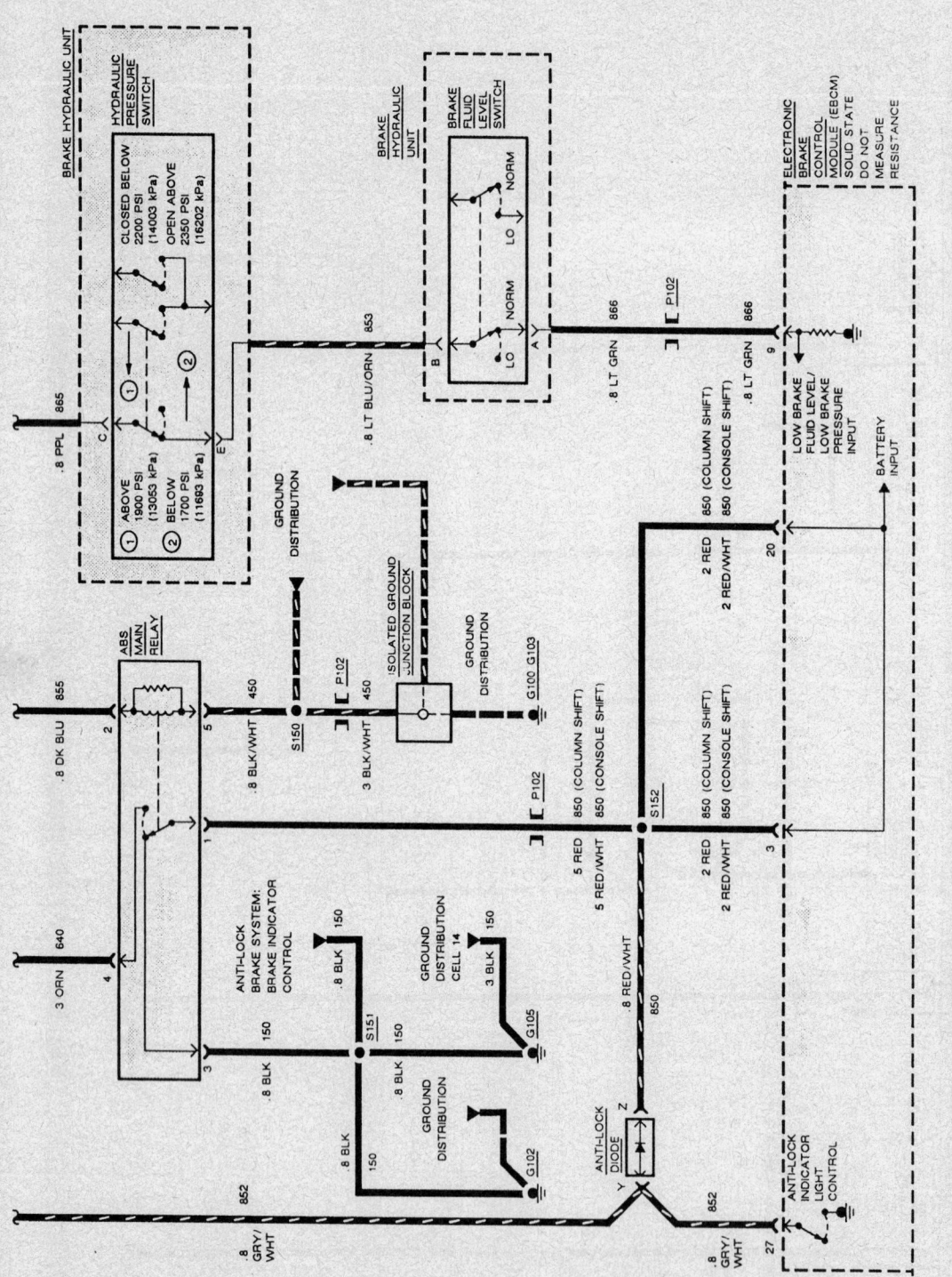

Fig. 58 Anti-lock brake system circuit diagram (Part 4 of 5)

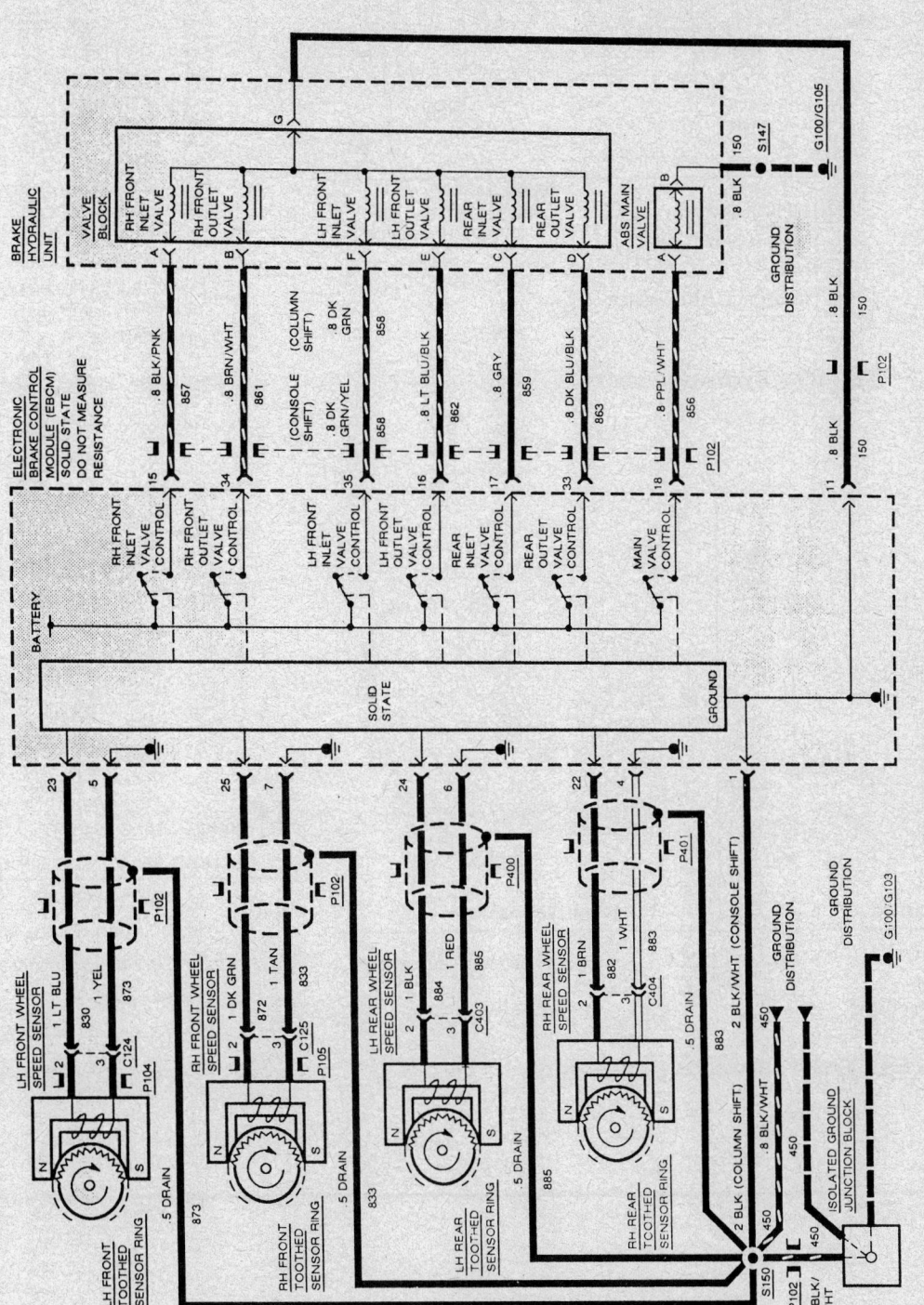

Fig. 58 Anti-lock brake system circuit diagram (Part 5 of 5)

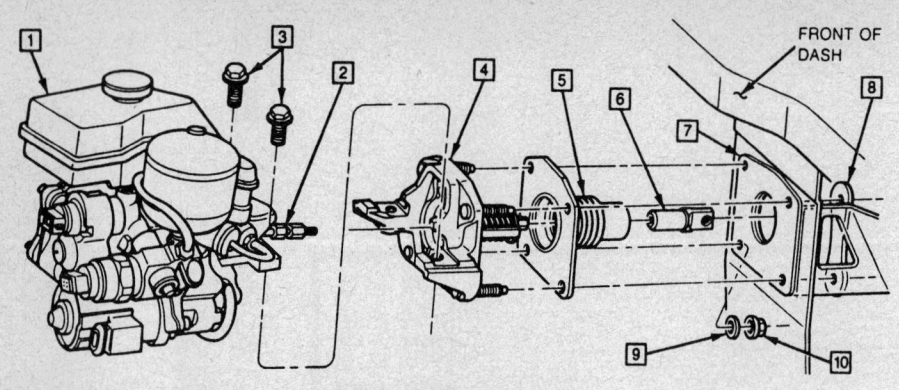

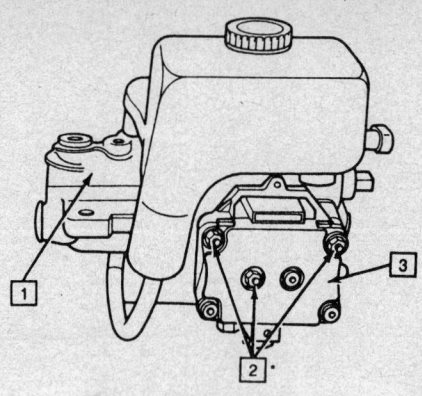

1	HYDRAULIC UNIT	5	RUBBER BOOT	9	WASHER - USED ON LOWER R.H. STUD ONLY
2	FRONT PUSHROD HALF	6	REAR PUSHROD HALF	10	NUTS - 4 REQ'D (20 N·m/15 LB.FT.)
3	MOUNTING BOLTS (50 N·m/37 LB.FT.)	7	GASKET		
4	PUSHROD BRACKET ASM.	8	REINFORCEMENT WASHER		

Fig. 59   Hydraulic unit

*REMOVE THESE NUTS ONLY TO REMOVE VALVE BLOCK

1	HYDRAULIC UNIT
2	VALVE BLOCK RETAINING NUTS (25 N·m /18 LB.FT..)
3	VALVE BLOCK

Fig. 60   Valve block

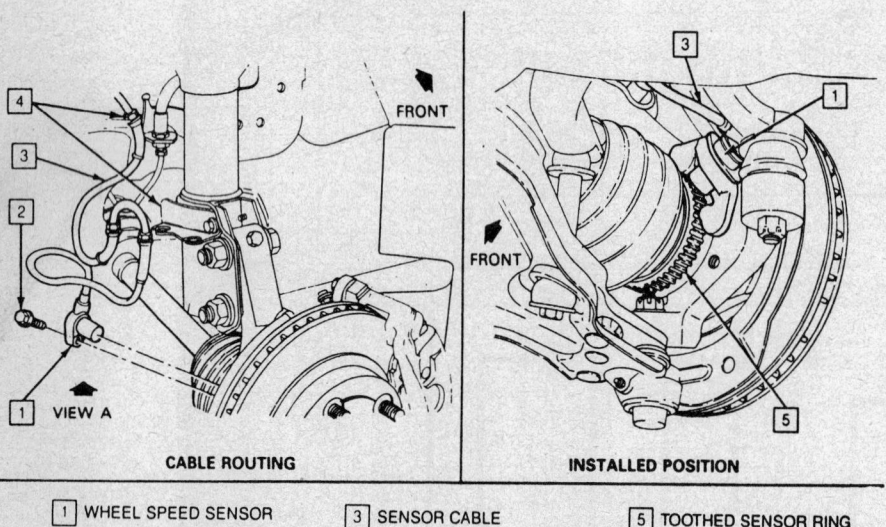

CABLE ROUTING

INSTALLED POSITION

1	WHEEL SPEED SENSOR	3	SENSOR CABLE	5	TOOTHED SENSOR RING
2	SENSOR MOUNTING BOLT (12 N·m/106 LB. IN.) - 2 REQ'D	4	CABLE RETAINER BRACKETS		

Fig. 61   Front wheel speed sensor

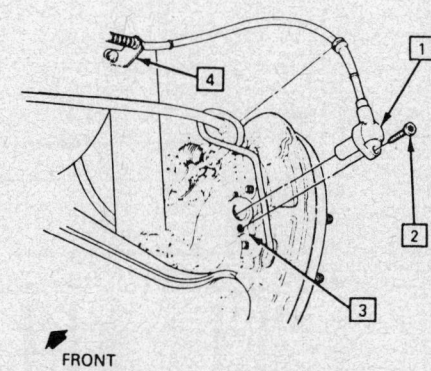

FRONT

RIGHT REAR – LEFT SIMILAR

1	WHEEL SPEED SENSOR
2	BOLT (12 N·m/106 LB. IN.)
3	SUSPENSION KNUCKLE
4	BRACKET

Fig. 62   Rear wheel speed sensors

REAR DRIVE AXLES

TABLE OF CONTENTS

Troubleshooting

INDEX

PRELIMINARY CHECKS

Before the rear axle is to be serviced, ensure the source of the problem is the rear axle itself and not from other sources such as noise from the tires, road surface, engine, transmission, wheel bearings, muffler or body parts. Perform the following procedures to check for other sources that could be mistaken for axle noise:

1. Ensure rear axle lubricant is at the correct level and type, then select a level asphalt road to reduce tire and body noise.
2. After vehicle has been driven far enough to warm lubricant, note at which speed the noise occurs then stop vehicle. With vehicle in neutral run engine slowly through the RPM range that the noise occurred to check if noise was caused by the exhaust or power train.
3. Check for tire noise by temporarily inflating all tires to approximately 50 psi for test purposes only. Drive vehicle on a level asphalt road and note if a change in noise occurs compared to noise while tires are inflated at normal pressure. After test is completed ensure tires are inflated to manufacture's specification.
4. Check the front and rear wheel bearings by lightly applying the brakes while keeping vehicle speed steady. If the noise diminishes, inspect front and rear wheel bearings by jacking up the front wheels, then spinning or shaking them to determine if bearings are loose. Replace if nescessary.
5. With vehicle jacked up, check for metal to metal contact between the spring and the spring opening in the frame, upper and lower control arm bushings and frame and axle housing brackets. Ensure there is no metal to metal contact between the floor of the body and the frame. Replace bushings or rubber insulators if necessary.

REAR AXLE NOISES

After noise has been determined to be in the axle and not from other sources, check for the specific type of axle noise as follows:

ROUGH GROWL OR GRATING

1. Faulty pinion or rear axle case side bearing.

CHATTER ON TURNS

1. Wrong lubricant in axle.
2. Clutch cones worn.

KNOCK AT LOW SPEEDS

1. Worn universal joint.
2. Side gear hub counterbore in the differential case worn oversize.

CLUNK WHILE ACCELERATING OR DECELERATING

1. Worn differential case.
2. Excessive clearance between the axle shaft and side gear splines.
3. Excessive clearance between side gear hub and counterbore in case.
4. Excessive drive pinion and ring gear backlash.
5. Worn pinion and side gear teeth.
6. Worn thrust washers.

CONSTANT SCRAPING NOISE AT LOW SPEEDS

1. Defective or worn pinion bearing.

CONSTANT WHINE WHILE DRIVING

1. Defective or worn ring and pinion gear.

GROAN IN FORWARD OR REVERSE

1. Wrong lubricant in axle.

WHINE LOUDER WHILE TURNING

1. Defective or worn axle side gear and/or pinion.

LIMITED SLIP AXLE OPERATION

On all models, improper operation is often indicated by clutch slipping or grabbing which produces a whirring or chattering noise. These noises do not always indicate an axle failure but could be from lack of proper lubrication or normal noise when axle clutchs are engaged during certain road conditions. Since the operational life of the limited slip unit is dependent on equal rotation of the wheels while driving straight ahead, it is important that there is no major difference in rear wheel tire size, air pressure or wear pattern, otherwise the vehicle may swerve during acceleration. If improper limited slip differential problems are not caused by the above, check for proper operation as follows:

AUBURN CONE TYPE DIFFERENTIAL

1. With parking brake released and automatic transmission in park or manual transmission in gear, raise both tires off the floor.
2. Remove hubcap or wheel disc and apply torque wrench and axle shaft puller tool No. J-21579 to either wheel. Measure torque required to rotate one wheel. The **torque** should be between 125 and 225 ft. lbs.

3. Place transmission in nuetral position, then lower one rear tire to the ground.
4. Measure torque required to rotate the raised wheel. **On full size wagons and Caprice sedan, torque** should be between 45 and 110 ft. lbs. **On Camaro models, torque** should be between 44 and 66 ft. lbs. and **on Monte Carlo models, torque** should be between 45 and 100 ft. lbs.
5. The differential case must be re-

placed as a unit if proper specifications are not obtained.

GM DISC TYPE DIFFERENTIAL

1. With automatic transmission in park and manual transmission in gear, raise rear of vehicle until one rear tire is off the ground.
2. Remove the rear tire and wheel assembly, then attach side hammer as-

sembly tool No. J-2619-01 and shaft remover tool No. J-2157 axle shaft flange and then inch-13 bolt into adapter.
3. Raise the other tire off the ground attach torque wrench to side hamm assembly tool No. J-2619-01, th measure torque required to rota axle shaft. If **torque** reading is les than 48 ft. lbs., remove and repair th differential unit.

Except Borg Warner Four Pinion Differential

INDEX

REMOVAL
DIFFERENTIAL ASSEMBLY
Except Corvette

1. Raise and support rear of vehicle, then loosen axle housing cover bolts and allow lubricant to drain into suitable container, **Fig. 1.**
2. Remove axle housing cover, then proceed as follows:
   a. Wipe excess lubricant from inside axle housing, then visually inspect parts for wear and/or damage.
   b. Rotate gears and check for roughness, indicating damaged bearings or gears.
   c. Install dial indicator on axle housing cover flange, then check and record ring gear to drive pinion backlash.
3. Remove rear axles and propeller shaft. Refer to "Rear Axle, Propeller Shaft & Brakes" for procedures.
4. If not previously marked, scribe reference marks on differential bearing bearing caps to be used during reassembly, then loosen bearing cap bolts.
5. Using suitable tool, pry differential case, bearing races and shims out of housing until loose in the bearing caps. Remove bearing races, then the differential assembly. Mark side cups and shims for reference during reassembly.

Corvette

1. Remove rear axle assembly. Refer to "Rear Axle, Propeller Shaft & Brakes" for procedure.

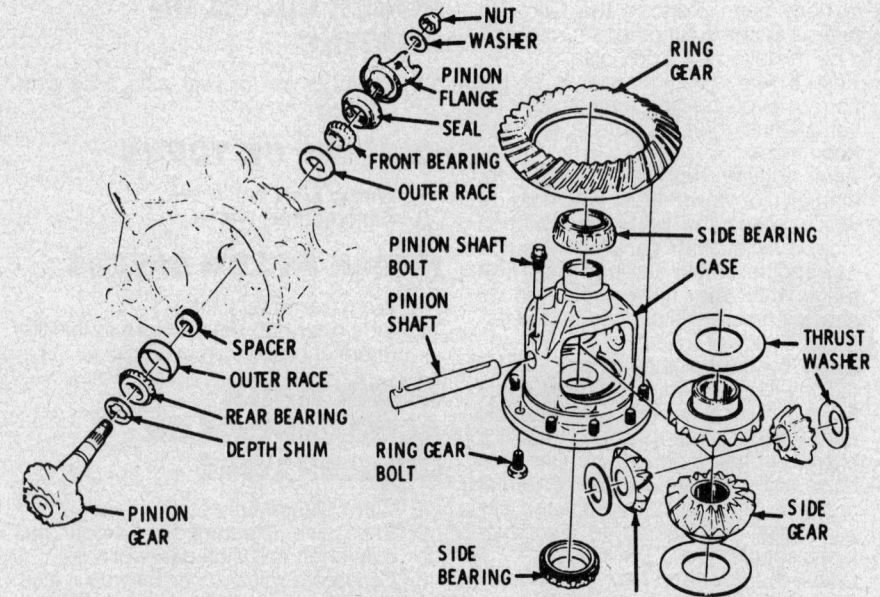

Fig. 1 Exploded view of rear axle assembly. Except Corvette

2. Remove axle housing cover and allow lubricant to drain.
3. Mount carrier assembly in a holding fixture, then remove snap rings retaining yoke shafts and the yoke shafts. Tag snap rings indicating which side they were removed from.
4. Remove bearing cap bolts, then the bearing caps. **When removing bearing caps, note matched letters**

stamped on caps and carrier. During reassembly, the caps must be installed in the exact position they were removed from.
5. Install spreader tool, J-24385-01, adapter, J-24385 and a dial indicator set, **Fig. 2.** Zero indicator and ensure indicator stylus contacts one side of housing opening.
6. While observing micrometer, spread

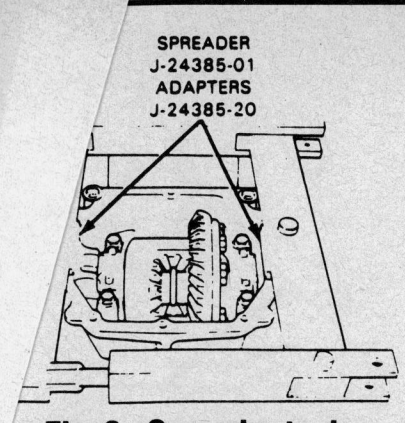

Fig. 2 Spreader tool installation. Corvette models

housing with tool. Do not spread housing more than 0.010 inch or distortion could result.
7. Using two pry bars, pry differential assembly upwards to remove. **Tag bearing cups and shims to indicate which side removed from.**
8. Remove spreader tool to prevent housing from taking a set.

DRIVE PINION

1. Scribe reference mark between drive pinion and driveshaft yoke, then hold yoke with suitable tool and remove pinion nut and yoke. **If yoke shows wear in the seal-to-flange contacting surface, the yoke should be replaced.**
2. Install original pinion nut a few turns on pinion shaft, then using hammer and drift, tap pinion shaft out of pinion housing. **Hold gear end of pinion shaft when removing to prevent it from falling from axle housing. On Corvette models, the pinion preload shims may stick to the pinion housing or the rear bearing during removal. These shims must be collected and kept together for use during reassembly.**
3. Remove and discard pinion nut and collapsible spacer.
4. If being replaced, remove front and rear bearing races from pinion housing using drift positioned in race slots and hammer.
5. If rear pinion bearing is being replaced, remove using arbor press and adapters. Measure and record thickness of shim which is found under rear bearing.

DIFFERENTIAL CASE OVERHAUL

STANDARD DIFFERENTIAL

1. If side carrier bearings are to be replaced, remove bearings using a bearing puller.
2. Remove differential pinion shaft lock bolt and the pinion shaft, **Fig. 1.**
3. Remove differential pinions and thrust washers, side gears and side gear

thrust washers, noting installation position for assembly. Keep thrust washers with respective gears.
4. Remove ring gear bolts, then the ring gear, driving ring gear from case using drift and hammer. **Ring gear bolts have left hand threads. Do not pry between ring gear and case, as mating surfaces will be damaged.**
5. Inspect components as outlined in "Cleaning and Inspection" and replace as needed.
6. Install thrust washers on side gears and mount side gears in case. **Lubricate all components with specified gear lubricant prior to assembly.**
7. Position one differential pinion (less thrust washer) between side gears and rotate gears until pinion is directly opposite case loading opening.
8. Install other pinion with pinion shaft holes aligned, then rotate side gears and ensure pinions align with shaft openings in case.
9. When pinions are properly aligned, rotate pinions toward loading opening just enough to allow thrust washer installation and install washers.
10. Align pinions with shaft opening in case, insert pinion shaft through case, install new lock bolt. It is not necessary to torque lock bolt at this time.
11. Ensure ring gear and case mating surfaces are clean and free from burrs, mount gear on case, install 2 new retaining bolts at opposite sides of gear and alternately tighten bolts to draw gear on case.
12. Install remaining ring gear bolts hand tight and ensure gear is squarely seated on case. **Always use new bolts of proper type when installing ring gear. Do not reuse old bolts.**
13. Alternately **torque** ring gear bolts to 80-90 ft. lbs.
14. Press side bearings onto case. If old bearings are reused, ensure bearings are installed in original position.

GM CORP. TYPE LIMITED SLIP DIFFERENTIAL

For ring gear removal and installation, refer to "Standard Differential."
1. Remove pinion shaft lock screw, then remove pinion shaft from case, **Fig. 3.**
2. Using a brass drift drive preload spring from case.
3. Remove pinion gears and washers, followed by the side gears.
4. Remove clutch plate guides and separate shims and clutch plates from side gears. Keep clutch plates in their original location in clutch pack.
5. Clean and inspect all parts and replace as required.
6. Apply recommended lubricant to clutch plates and discs.
7. Alternately position clutch plates on side gear, starting and ending with a clutch plate having external lugs.
8. Place spacer against plate having external lugs, then install shims. Make sure to install the same spacer and shims or an equal amount on the clutch pack for a starting point.

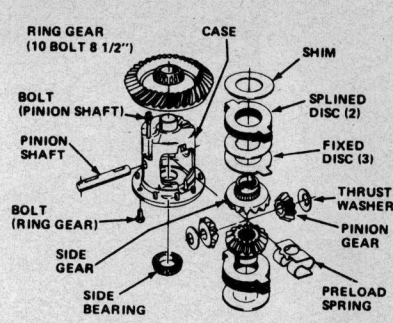

Fig. 3 Exploded view of GM Corp. type locking differential

9. Repeat foregoing procedure on other clutch pack.
10. Install one side gear with clutch pack and shims in case.
11. Position two pinion gears and thrust washers on side gear and install pinion shaft.
12. Compress clutch pack by inserting a screwdriver between side gear and pinion shaft.
13. Install dial indicator with contact button against pinion gear, **Fig. 4.**
14. Rotate pinion gear, clearance should be .001-.006 inch.
15. If clearance is more than .006 inch, add shims between clutch pack and case. If clearance is less .001 inch, remove shims. A .002 inch shim will change clearance about .001 inch. Recheck clearance after adding or subtracting shims.
16. Remove side gear and repeat procedure with opposite clutch on opposite side of case.
17. Remove pinion shaft, pinions and thrust washers.
18. Install remaining side gear and clutch pack with correct shims in case.
19. Place pinion gears on side gears and rotate into correct position, **Fig. 5.**
20. Install thrust washers behind pinion gears and align.
21. Insert pinion shaft into case, through thrust washer and part way into pinion gear. This will keep pinion gears aligned while driving preload spring into place.
22. Position preload spring as shown in **Fig. 6,** next to side gears and drive into place.
23. Push pinion shaft into position and align lock screw hole in shaft with hole in case. Install lock screw and **torque** to 20 ft. lbs.

TWO PINION CONE TYPE (BORG WARNER) LOCKING DIFFERENTIAL

For side gear removal, refer to "Standard Differential."
1. If removing ring gear, clamp case in a vise so jaws are 90° to pinion shaft holes and remove ten ring gear retaining bolts.
2. Partially install two bolts on opposite sides of ring gear.

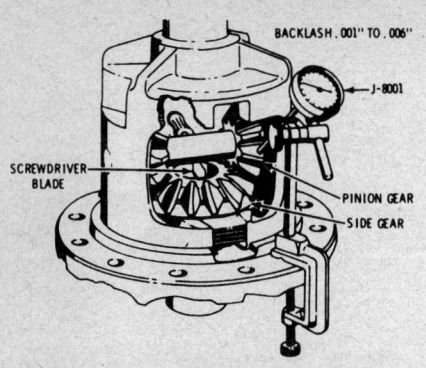

Fig. 4 Positioning dial indicator (typical)

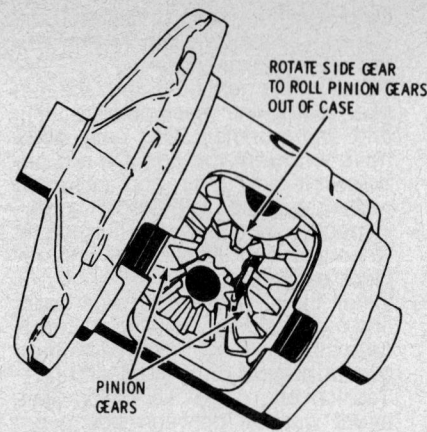

Fig. 5 Installing pinion gears

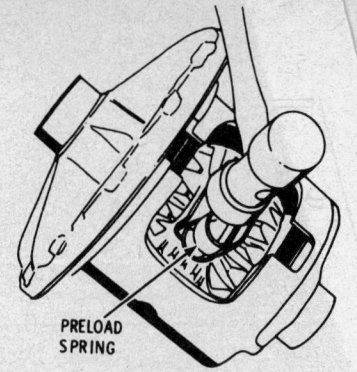

Fig. 6 Installing preload spring

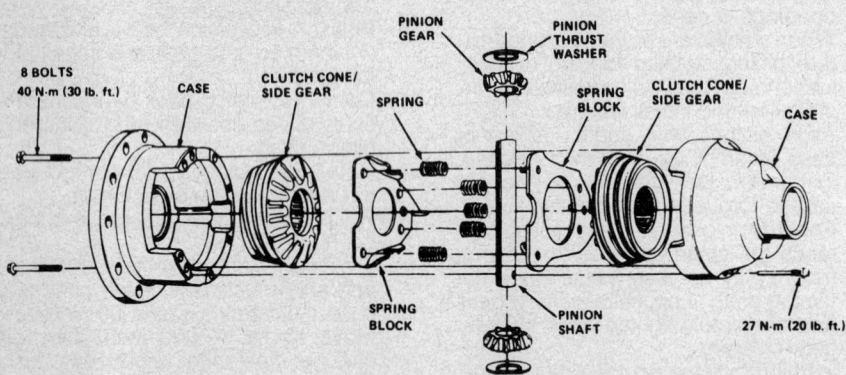

Fig. 7 Exploded view of 2 pinion cone type (Borg Warner) locking differential

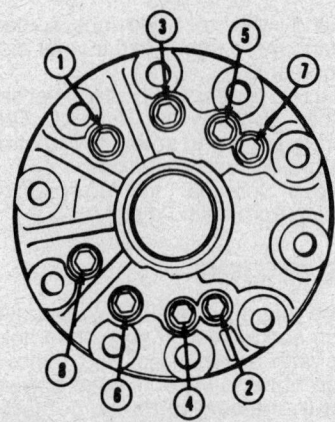

TIGHTEN BOLTS ONE TURN AT A TIME. THEN TORQUE TO 40 N·m (30 lb. ft.)

Fig. 8 Case bolt tightening sequence

3. Remove ring gear from case by alternately tapping on bolts. Do not pry between case and ring gear.
4. Remove differential case half attaching bolts, **Fig. 7.**
5. Lift cap half of case from flange half. Remove clutch cone/side gears, spring blocks, preload springs, pinion gears and shaft. Mark each clutch cone/side gear and pinion gear so they can be reinstalled in their original position.
6. Clean and inspect all parts and replace as necessary. Slight grooves or scratches, indicating passage of foreign material, are permissible and normal. If case or clutch cone/side gear are damaged, it is necessary to replace case assembly. All others parts are serviceable.
7. Install proper cone/gear assembly into position in cap half of case.
8. Place one spring block in position over gear face, in alignment with pinion gear shaft grooves. Install pinion shaft, pinion gears and thrust washers into cap half or differential case in such a manner that pinion shaft retaining dowel can be inserted through pinion gear shaft into differential case. Be certain that pinon gears are installed in their original location.
9. Insert five springs into spring block that is already installed in case, then

place second spring block over springs.
10. Install second cone/gear assembly face down on spring block so that gear will mesh with pinion gears.
11. Install flange half of differential case over cone, insert case bolts finger tight. Tighten bolts one turn at a time in sequence shown in **Fig. 8.** Then **torque** case bolts to 30 ft. lbs.
12. If ring gear was removed, position it so that holes line up with case holes.
13. Lubricate new attaching bolts with clean engine oil and install.
14. Tighten bolts evenly and alternately around the case. When all bolts are snug, **torque** evenly and alternately to 90 ft. lbs.

2 PINION CONE TYPE (AUBURN) DIFFERENTIAL

1. Remove case side bearings using tool J-22888.
2. Remove all but two opposite ring gear attaching bolts, then loosen the two remaining bolts.
3. Loosen ring gear by tapping on bolts, then remove ring gear from differential.
4. This limited slip rear axle case is not serviceable. If differential case is not

satisfactory, replace complete assembly.

DANA TRAC-LOK LIMITED SLIP DIFFERENTIAL

For side gear removal, refer to "Standard Differential."
1. Remove ring gear bolts, then using a brass drift tap gear from case, **Fig. 9.**
2. Remove cross pin retainers, then using punch and hammer, tap cross pin from case.
3. Assemble adapter plate from tool J-34174 into bottom side gear, then install threaded adapter plate into top side gear. Thread forcing screw into threaded adapter, and tighten until snug. This will force dished spacers to collapse and allow a loose condition in the case, **Fig. 10.**
4. Using a .020 inch feeler gauge, push out both pinion gear spherical washers, then back off forcing screw.
5. Using suitable tools, rotate case assembly until pinion gears can be removed. Remove pinion and differential gears, then the top side gear and clutch pack. **Keep stack of plates and discs in order they were removed from case.**
6. Remove retaining clips from plate tangs then separate plates and discs.

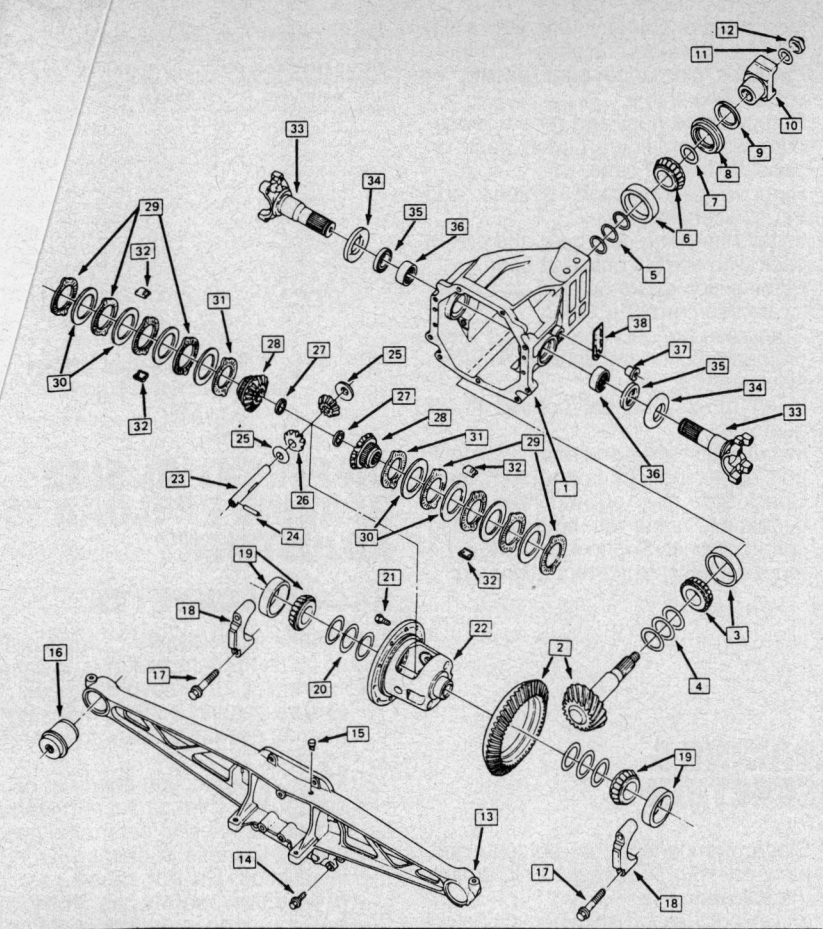

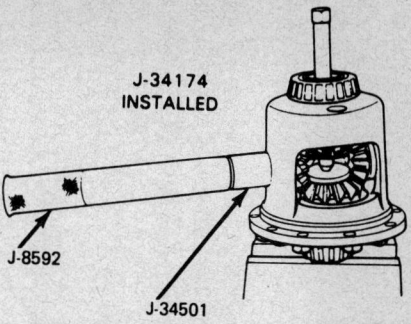

Fig. 10 Installing special tools

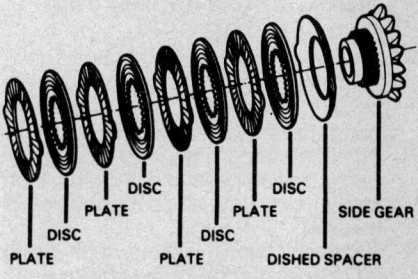

Fig. 11 Clutch plate arrangement. Dana Trac-Lok

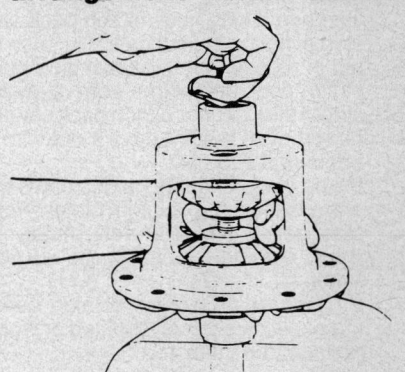

Fig. 12 Tool & pinion installation

1. CARRIER	15. VENT	29. CLUTCH PACK PLATES
2. RING AND PINION GEARS	16. BUSHING	30. CLUTCH PACK DISCS
3. INNER PINION BEARING AND CUP	17. SIDE BEARING BOLT	31. BELLEVILLE SPRING SPACER
4. PINION DEPTH SHIMS	18. SIDE BEARING CAP	32. CLUTCH PACK RETAINER CLIP
5. PINION BEARING PRELOAD SHIMS	19. SIDE BEARING AND CUP	33. YOKE (AXLE) SHAFT
6. OUTER PINION BEARING AND CUP	20. SIDE BEARING SHIMS	34. YOKE (AXLE) SEAL DUST SHIELD
7. OIL SLINGER	21. RING GEAR BOLT	35. YOKE (AXLE) SEAL
8. PINION YOKE SEAL	22. CASE	36. YOKE (AXLE) BEARING
9. PINION YOKE SEAL DUST SHIELD	23. PINION SHAFT	37. LUBRICANT FILLER PLUG
10. PINION YOKE	24. PINION SHAFT RETAINER	38. LUBRICANT IDENTIFICATION TAG
11. WASHER	25. THRUST WASHER	
12. PINION NUT	26. PINION GEAR	
13. CARRIER COVER BEAM	27. YOKE (AXLE)SHAFT SNAP RING RETAINER	
14. COVER BEAM BOLT	28. SIDE GEAR	

Fig. 9 Exploded view of Dana Trac-Lok limited slip differential. 1988–89 Corvette

Note position of plates and discs before disassembling.

7. Lubricate, then install dished spacer, discs and plates on side gear splines, **Fig. 11.** When lubricating parts during assembly always use special limited slip differential lubricant.
8. Install retaining clips on plate tangs, ensuring clips are completely seated on tangs.
9. Install side gear and clutch packs in case, ensuring retaining clips are properly seated in case recesses. Assemble adapter plate from tool J-34174 onto side gear, **Fig. 12.**
10. Install plates and discs on other differential gear and install in same manner.
11. Install threaded adapter plate into side gear. Thread forcing screw into threaded adapter, and tighten until snug. This will hold clutch packs in position.
12. Position pinion gears in case. Rotate

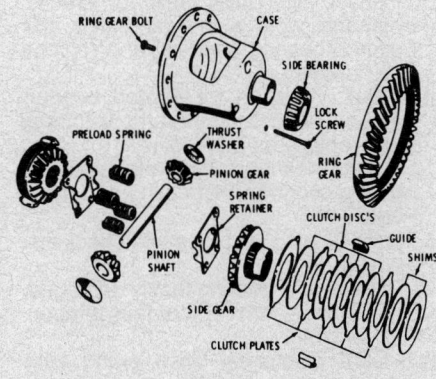

Fig. 13 Exploded view of Eaton limited slip differential

differential case with suitable tool until pinion gear holes align with case bores.

13. Lubricate and install spherical washers, using a screwdriver. **Ensure pinion gear and spherical washer holes are aligned with case bores.**
14. Remove tools, then lubricate and install cross pin shaft and install retainers.
15. Do not install ring gear at this time. The ring gear will be installed during Final Assembly & Backlash Adjustment.

EATON LIMITED SLIP DIFFERENTIAL

For ring gear and side gear removal, refer to "Standard Differential."

1. Remove pinion shaft lock screw and pull pinion shaft from case, **Fig. 13.**
2. Drive preload spring retainer and springs through observation hole in case only far enough to secure a C-clamp then install ¼ inch nut and

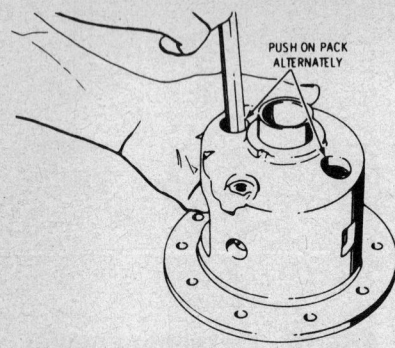

PUSH ON PACK ALTERNATELY

Fig. 14 Removing clutch pack. Eaton limited slip differential

bolt through each front spring.

3. Position spring pack in vise and remove ¼ inch bolts and C-clamp, then loosen vise until all spring tension is relieved.
4. Remove pinion washers, then using an axle shaft rotate case clockwise to remove first pinion gear. Rotate case counterclockwise and remove second pinion gear.
5. Remove a side gear, clutch pack and shims, noting shim location in case to aid in reassembly. Remove side gear clutch pack and shims from opposite side. If side gear or clutch pack cannot be removed readily, drive it out with a brass drift, **Fig. 14.**
6. Remove clutch plate guides and separate shims and clutch plates from side gears. **Keep clutch plates in their original location in clutch pack.**
7. If pinion shaft, pinions or side gears are excessively scored, pitted or worn, replace parts affected.
8. Inspect clutch plates for scored, worn, cracked or distorted condition. If any of these conditions exist, new clutch plates must be installed.
9. Alternately position clutch plates and discs on side gear, starting and ending with a plate having external lugs.
10. Install two clutch guides over clutch plate lugs.
11. Install same shims which were removed or an equal amount on clutch plate.
12. Repeat above steps on other clutch pack.
13. Install one side gear with clutch pack and shims in case.
14. Position two pinion gears and thrust washers on side gear and install pinion shaft.
15. Compress clutch pack by inserting a screwdriver or wedge between side gear and pinion shaft.
16. Install a dial indicator with contact button against pinion gear, **Fig. 4.**
17. Rotate pinion gear. Clearance should be .001 inch to .006 inch.
18. If clearance is more than .006 inch, add shims between clutch pack and case. If clearance is less than .001

inch, remove shims. A .002 inch shim will change clearance about .001 inch. Recheck clearance after adding or subtracting shims.
19. Remove side gear and repeat procedure with remaining clutch pack on opposite side of case.
20. Remove pinion shaft, pinions and thrust washers.
21. Install remaining side gear and clutch pack with correct shims in case.
22. Place pinion gears on side gears and rotate into correct position.
23. Compress preload springs and drive preload retainer and springs between side gears.
24. Insert thrust washers behind pinion gears.
25. Install pinion shaft and retain with lock bolt, tightening lock bolt to 20 ft. lbs.
26. Check side gear splined hole to be certain it is in line with hole in preload spring retainer. Spring retainer can be moved slightly to correct alignment.

CLEANING & INSPECTION

1. Clean components in solvent and blow dry with compressed air, noting the following:
   a. Do not use brush when cleaning bearings.
   b. Do not spin dry bearings, as bearings will be damaged.
   c. Lightly lubricate components after cleaning to retard corrosion.
   d. Keep all components in order to ensure proper assembly.
2. Inspect gears for cracks, chipped teeth, wear and scoring, and damaged bearing or mounting surfaces. Replace gears that are damaged or excessively worn. **Ring gear and pinion must be replaced as an assembly.**
3. Inspect differential case for cracks, damage, worn side gear bores and scored bearing surfaces and replace as needed.
4. Inspect housing for scored bearing mount surfaces, cracks and distortion, and replace as needed.
5. Inspect bearing rollers and races for pitting, scoring, overheating and damage.
6. Mate bearing with race and check operation.
7. Replace any bearing that is damaged, excessively worn or that fails to operate smoothly.
8. Mount differential case along with side bearings and ring gear in housing, and check run-out with side bearings adjusted for zero preload and a dial indicator positioned against machined edge of ring gear.
9. If run-out exceeds .003 inch, and gear cannot be positioned to eliminate run-out, ring gear and/or case should be replaced.

TOTAL THICKNESS OF BOTH PROD. SHIMS REMOVED		TOTAL THICKNESS OF SERVICE SHIMS TO BE USED AS A STARTING POINT	
10.57mm	.420″	1.52mm	.060″
10.92mm	.430″	1.78mm	.070″
11.18mm	.440″	2.03mm	.080″
11.43mm	.450″	2.29mm	.090″
11.68mm	.460″	2.54mm	.100″
11.94mm	.470″	2.79mm	.110″
12.19mm	.480″	3.05mm	.120″
12.45mm	.490″	3.30mm	.130″
12.70mm	.500″	3.56mm	.140″
12.95mm	.510″	3.81mm	.150″
13.21mm	.520″	4.06mm	.160″
13.46mm	.530″	4.32mm	.170″
13.97mm	.550″	4.83mm	.190″

4.32mm (.170″) SERVICE SPACER

Fig. 15 Service shim thickness chart

DIFFERENTIAL SIDE BEARING PRELOAD ADJUSTMENT

EXCEPT CORVETTE

On these models, side bearing preload should be set before pinion is installed. If pinion is installed, remove ring gear.

1. Ensure bearing bores in housing and bearing caps are clean and free from burrs.
2. Measure production shims or service spacer and shim packs removed during disassembly to determine approximate thickness of shims needed for installation. **Do not reuse cast iron production shims as they may break during installation. If service spacers and shims were previously installed, they can be reused.**
3. In addition to .170 inch service spacers for each side, refer to chart, **Fig. 15,** and select service shim thickness required based on measurements made in step 2.
4. Place outer races over side bearings, mount differential assembly in housing and insert service spacer between each bearing race and housing with chamfered edge against housing.
5. Install left bearing cap to retain case assembly and tighten bolts hand tight so that case can be moved while checking adjustments. **A bearing cap bolt can be installed in lower right bearing cap hole to prevent case from dropping while performing shim adjustments.**
6. Select one or two shims totaling thickness calculated in step 3 and insert shims between right bearing cap and service spacer.
7. Insert progressively larger feeler gauges between shim and service spacer until noticeable increase in drag can be felt, pushing gauge down until it contacts housing bore to obtain proper reading. **Rotate case while inserting gauges to ensure even readings.**
8. The gauge used just before additional drag is felt is correct thickness to obtain "zero preload." By starting with a thin gauge a sense of feel can be obtained for the original light drag caused by the weight of the case, al-

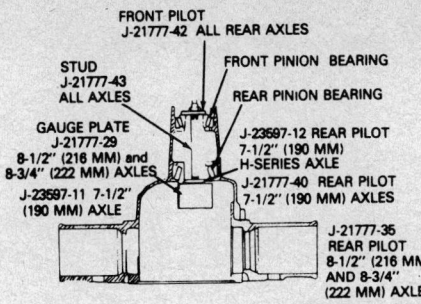

Fig. 16 Pinion gauge plate installation

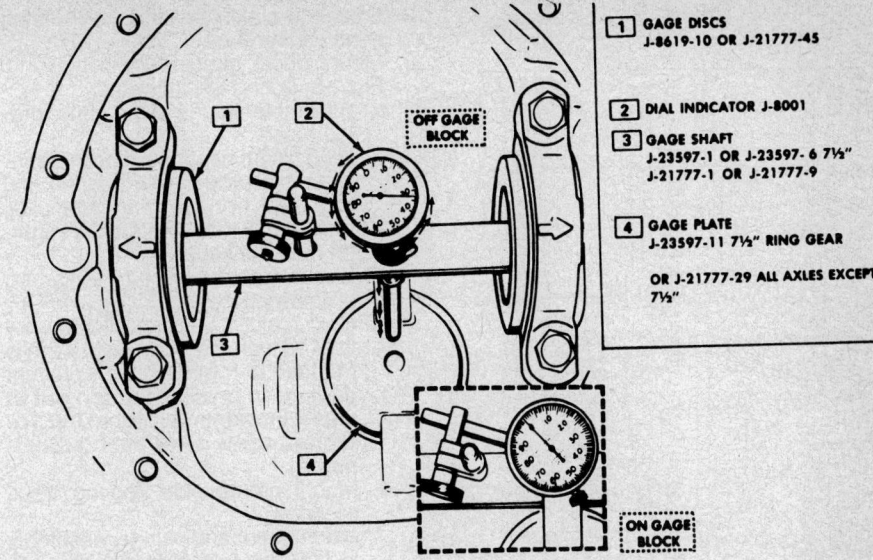

Fig. 17 Checking pinion depth

lowing the drag caused by the beginning of preload to be recognized. **It will be necessary to work case in and out and to the left in order to insert feeler gauges.**

9. When the proper gauge thickness has been determined to obtain zero preload, remove bearing cap, case assembly service spacers and shim pack.

10. Select 2 service shims of approximate equal thickness whose total thickness is equal to the thickness of the shims installed in step 6 plus the thickness of the feeler gauge used to obtain zero preload.

11. Shims selected during this procedure allow differential assembly to be installed at zero preload, the equivalent of a "slip-fit" in case, during backlash adjustment. Final preload is not added until backlash has been adjusted.

CORVETTE

This procedure is performed before the drive pinion or ring gear is installed. If yoke seals and bearings were removed, install then at this time.

1. Ensure bearing bores and caps are clean and free of burrs.
2. Install master differential bearings J-34170 on 7.874 inch axles or J-35505 on 8.5 inch axles.
3. Assemble case assembly into carrier. Mount dial indicator with plunger travel of at least .200 inch to supporting fixture with plunger on the flange face.
4. Force case assembly as far as possible in dial indicator direction. With force still applied to case, zero dial indicator.
5. While observing dial indicator movement, force differential case in opposite direction. Repeat this step until the same reading is obtained.
6. Record dial indicator reading. The reading will be used during "Final Assembly And Backlash Adjustment."
7. Remove differential case assembly from carrier.

DRIVE PINION INSTALLATION & ADJUSTMENT

EXCEPT CORVETTE
Pinion Depth Adjustment

1. Install pinion bearing races in housing using a suitable driver.
2. Lubricate pinion bearings and install bearings in races.
3. Mount depth gauging jig in housing, **Figs. 16**, noting the following:
   a. Assemble gauge plate onto preload stud.
   b. Hold pinion bearings in position, insert stud through rear bearing and pilot and front bearing and pilot, then install retaining nut and tighten nut until snug.
   c. Rotate tool to ensure bearings are properly seated.
   d. Hold preload stud and tighten nut until 20 inch lbs. of **torque**, which is required to rotate stud. To prevent damage to bearing, **tighten nut in small increments, checking rotating torque after each adjustment.**
   e. Mount side bearing discs on arbor, using step for disc that corresponds to base of housing.
   f. Mount arbor and plunger assembly in housing, ensuring side bearing discs are properly seated, install bearing caps and tighten cap bolts to prevent bearing discs from moving, **Fig. 17.**
4. Mount dial indicator on arbor stud with indicator contact button bearing against top of arbor plunger.
5. Preload indicator ³/₄ revolution and secure to arbor mounting stud in this position.
6. Place arbor plunger on gauge plate, rotating plate as needed so that plunger rests directly on button corresponding to ring gear size.
7. Slowly rock plunger rod back and forth across button while observing dial indicator.
8. At point on button where indicator registers greatest deflection, zero dial indicator. **Perform steps 7 and 8 several times to ensure correct setting.**
9. Once verified zero reading is obtained, swing plunger aside until it is clear of gauge plate button and record dial indicator reading. **Indicator will now read required pinion depth shim thickness for a "nominal" pinion.**
10. Inspect rear face of drive pinion to be installed for a pinion code number. This number indicates in thousandths of an inch necessary modification of pinion shim thickness obtained in step 9.
11. Select pinion depth adjusting shim as follows:
    a. If pinion is stamped with a plus (+) number, add that number of thousandths to dimension obtained in step 9.
    b. If pinion is stamped with a minus (−) number, subtract that many thousandths from dimension obtained in step 9.
    c. If pinion is not stamped with plus or minus number, dimension obtained in step 9 is correct shim thickness.
12. Remove gauging tools and pinion bearings from housing, noting installation position of bearings.

Pinion Installation

1. Install selected shim onto pinion shaft, lubricate rear pinion bearing with specified axle lubricant, then press rear bearing onto pinion using suitable spacers.

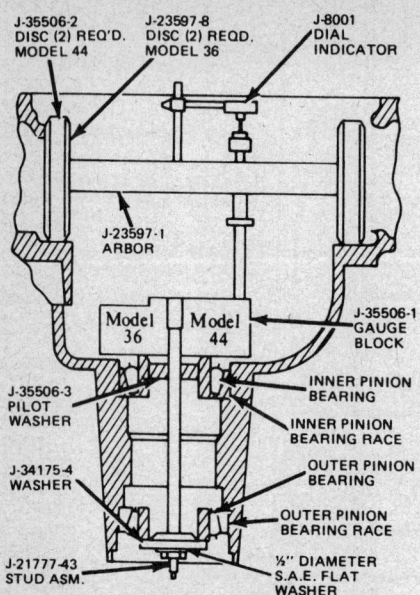

Fig. 18 Pinion depth gauge tool installation. Corvette

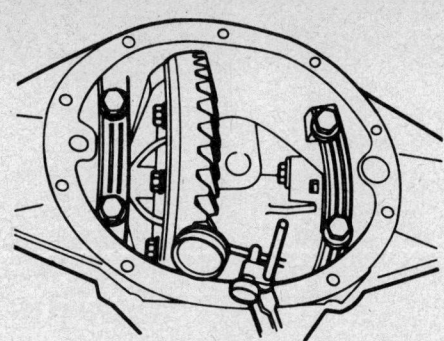

Fig. 19 Checking ring gear & pinion backlash

2. Install new collapsible spacer onto pinion shaft, then insert pinion assembly into housing.
3. Lubricate front pinion bearing, install bearing into housing and tap bearing over pinion shaft with a drift while assistant holds pinion in place. **Old pinion nut and a large washer can be used to seat front bearing on pinion, but care must be taken not to collapse spacer if this method is used.**
4. Install new pinion seal in housing, coat seal lips with grease, then mount driveshaft yoke on pinion shaft, lightly tapping yoke until several pinion shaft threads protrude from yoke.
5. Coat rear of pinion washer with suitable sealer, then install washer and new drive nut.
6. Hold drive shaft yoke with suitable tool, then alternately tighten pinion nut and rotate pinion until end play is reduced to zero.
7. When end play is reduced to zero, check pinion bearing preload using a torque wrench.
8. Continue tightening pinion nut in small increments until specified pinion bearing preload is obtained, rotating pinion and checking preload after each adjustment. **Exceeding preload specification will compress collapsible spacer too far, requiring replacement of spacer. If preload specification is exceeded, spacer must be replaced and adjustment procedure must be repeated. Do not loosen pinion nut to reduce preload.**

CORVETTE
Pinion Depth Adjustment

The standard setting for the drive pinion is 2.565 inches on 7.874 ring gear axles or 2.625 inches on 8.5 inch ring gear axles.
1. Install pinion bearing races in housing

using suitable driver.
2. Lubricate pinion bearings and install bearings in races.
3. Mount depth gauging jig in housing, **Fig. 18**, noting the following:
   a. Assemble gauge plate onto preload stud.
   b. Hold pinion bearings in position, insert stud through rear bearing and pilot and front bearing and pilot, then install retaining nut and tighten nut until snug.
   c. Rotate tool to ensure bearings are properly seated.
   d. Hold preload stud and tighten nut until 10 inch lbs. of **torque** which is required to rotate stud. To prevent damage to bearing, **tighten nut in small increments, checking rotating torque after each adjustment.**
   e. Mount proper side bearing discs on arbor.
   f. Mount arbor and plunger assembly in housing, ensuring side bearing discs are properly seated, install bearing caps and tighten cap bolts until a slight resistance is felt while rotating arbor.
4. Mount a dial indicator on arbor stud with indicator contact button bearing against top of arbor plunger.
5. Preload indicator ¾ revolution and secure to arbor mounting stud in this position.
6. Place arbor plunger on gauge plate, rotating plate as needed so that plunger rests directly on button corresponding to ring gear size.
7. Slowly rock plunger rod back and forth across button while observing dial indicator.
8. At point on button where indicator registers greatest deflection, zero dial indicator. **Perform steps 7 and 8 several times to ensure correct setting.**
9. Once verified zero reading is obtained, swing plunger aside until it is clear of gauge plate button and record dial indicator reading. **Indicator will now read required pinion depth shim thickness for a "nominal" pinion.**
10. Inspect rear face of drive pinion to be installed for a pinion code number. This number indicates in thousandths of an inch necessary modification of pinion shim thickness obtained in step 9.
11. Select pinion depth adjusting shim as follows:
    a. If pinion is stamped with a plus (+) number, add that number of thousandths to dimension obtained in step 9.
    b. If pinion is stamped with a minus (−) number, subtract that many thousandths from dimension obtained in step 9.
    c. If pinion is not stamped with plus or minus number, dimension obtained in step 9 is correct shim thickness.
12. Remove gauging tools and pinion bearings from housing, noting installation position of bearings.

Pinion Installation

1. Install correct pinion depth shim in axle housing bearing cup bore, then install inner bearing cup using a bearing installer.
2. Apply appropriate axle lubricant to inner and outer pinion bearings. Apply oil to pinion seal, then install with seal installer.
3. Assemble new pinion preload shim stack with thickness being the same as was removed, then place preload stack on pinion and install pinion, oil slinger and end yoke in axle housing. Use a wooden hammer to tap end yoke onto pinion splines.
4. Install pinion nut and washer. While holding end yoke, **torque** pinion nut to 200 ft. lbs.
5. Using an inch lbs. torque wrench, check rotating torque of pinion shaft. Pinion rotating **torque** should be 15-35 inch lbs. To increase preload, remove shims. To decrease preload, add shims.

FINAL ASSEMBLY & BACKLASH ADJUSTMENT
EXCEPT CORVETTE

1. Ensure pinion depth and bearing preload are properly adjusted.
2. Install differential case assembly and selected side bearing shims as outlined in "Differential Side Bearing Preload, Adjust."
3. Install bearing caps in proper position and **torque** cap bolts to 55-60 ft. lbs.
4. Rotate assembly to ensure bearings are properly seated.
5. Mount dial indicator on housing with plunger bearing against tooth on ring gear, **Fig. 19.** Use small contact button on indicator plunger so that contact can be made at heel end of tooth and position dial indicator with plunger in line with gear rotation and perpendicular to gear tooth.
6. Hold pinion stationary and rock ring gear back and forth while reading backlash on indicator.
7. Check backlash at 3 evenly spaced positions around ring gear and record readings. **If backlash varies by more**

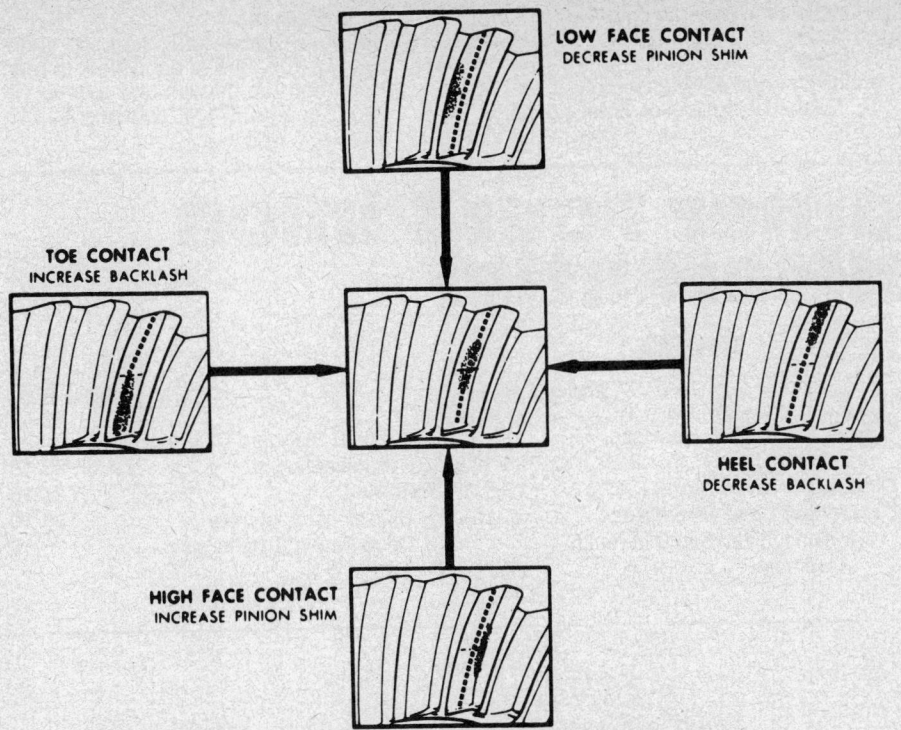

Fig. 20   Gear tooth contact pattern check

than .002 inch at any position, check ring gear installation and run-out, and correct as needed.

8. If backlash is not within specifications, remove differential case assembly and bearing shims keeping shims in order.

9. Backlash is adjusted by increasing thickness of one shim while decreasing thickness of opposite side shim by the same amount in order to maintain proper side bearing preload. Select shims to adjust backlash as follows:

   a. If backlash is excessive, increase thickness of shim on gear tooth side and decrease thickness of shim on opposite side by the same amount.

   b. If backlash is less than specified, decrease thickness of shim on gear tooth side while increasing thickness of opposite shim by the same amount. **Each .002 inch change in shim thickness alters backlash by .001 inch.**

10. Reinstall differential assembly, shims and bearing caps, **torque** bearing cap bolts to 55-60 ft. lbs., then recheck backlash and adjust as needed.

11. If side bearing preload was set to zero during side bearing preload adjustment, proceed as follows:

    a. Remove both bearing caps and shim packs, keeping shim packs in respective left or right positions.

    b. Select left side differential preload shim from specifications chart and insert shim between left bearing race and spacer, then install left bearing cap with bolts hand tight.

    c. Select right side differential preload shim from specifications chart and insert shim between right

bearing race and spacer using a soft faced hammer.

    d. Install right bearing cap and **torque** all cap bolts to 55-60 ft. lbs.

12. Ensure ring gear teeth are clean and free from oil, then coat both drive and coast side of each tooth with marking compound.

13. Apply braking force to "load" ring gear, then rotate driveshaft yoke with wrench so that ring gear rotates one full revolution in each direction. **Test made without "loading" gears will not yield satisfactory pattern, and excessive rotating of gears is not recommended.**

14. Compare gear tooth pattern with **Fig. 20**, and correct assembly adjustments as needed.

15. When proper gear tooth contact pattern has been obtained, clean marking compound from gears.

16. Install axles and driveshaft. Refer to "Rear Axle, Propeller Shaft & Brakes" for procedure.

17. Install rear cover using RTV or new gasket, then fill rear axle with appropriate lubricant. On models equipped with limited slip differential, add additive No. 1050428 or equivalent to rear axle lubricant.

CORVETTE

1. Ensure differential case flange is free of nicks and burrs, then install ring gear on case using new bolts. **Torque** attaching bolts to 75-85 ft. lbs. **Tighten bolts evenly so that ring gear will be properly seated on case.**

2. Install master differential bearings J-34170 on 7.874 inch axles or

J-35505 on 8.5 inch axles.

3. Assemble case assembly into carrier. Mount dial indicator to supporting fixture.

4. Force differential case away from pinion gear until completely seated against carrier cross bore face. With force still applied to case, place dial indicator plunger on a flat machined surface of differential case, if available, or on the head of a ring gear screw. Zero dial indicator.

5. Force ring gear to mesh with drive pinion. Rock gear slightly to ensure gear teeth are meshed and note dial indicator reading. Repeat procedure several times to ensure the reading is accurate. Ensure dial indicator reads zero each time the case is seated against cross bore face. The reading, .006 inch for preload and backlash adjustment will be the size of the shim pack between differential case and differential bearing on ring gear side.

6. Remove dial indicator, differential case and master bearings.

7. Assemble shim pack as determined in step 5 above to ring gear side hub, then install bearing cone.

8. Take measurement obtained during differential side bearing preload adjustment and subtract shim pack dimension determined in step 5 above. The resulting dimension should be .015-.020 inch on models with 7.874 inch axle or .008-.012 inch on models with 8.5 inch rear axle.

9. Assemble shim pack as determined in step 8 above to hub opposite ring gear, then install bearing cone.

10. Install spreader tool, J-24385-01, adapter, J-24385 and dial indicator set, **Fig. 2.** Zero indicator and ensure indicator stylus contacts one side of housing opening.

11. While observing micrometer, spread housing with tool. Do not spread housing more than 0.010 inch or distortion could result.

12. Assemble differential bearing cups on case, then install case in rear housing. If necessary, use a soft faced hammer to seat case in carrier cross bore.

13. Install bearing caps and bolts. Ensure letters stamped on caps correspond in position and direction with letters stamped in carrier. **Torque** bolts to 42-48 ft. lbs. on models with 7.874 inch rear axle or 58-68 ft. lbs. on models with 8.5 inch rear axle.

14. Check ring gear and pinion backlash at three equally spaced points with dial indicator. Backlash tolerance is .006-.009. Backlash cannot vary between points checked more than .001-.0015.

15. If backlash is excessive, move shims from side opposite ring gear to ring gear side, but do not change the combined total thickness of both shim packs.

16. If backlash is too small, move shims from ring gear side to side opposite ring gear, but do not change the combined total thickness of both shim packs.

17. Install inner yoke shafts into carrier,

then the shaft snap rings. Check axle shaft end play. If end play is not within .0005–.0085 inch, install thicker or narrower axle shaft snap ring as necessary.

18. Install axle housing cover with RTV or gasket to rear housing and install bolts.
19. Install rear axle assembly. Refer to "Rear Axle, Propeller Shaft & Brakes"

for procedure.
20. Add four ounces of limited slip additive No. 1052358 or equivalent to rear axle, then top off with rear axle lubricant No. 1052271 or equivalent.

Borg Warner Four Pinion Differential

INDEX

REMOVAL

DIFFERENTIAL ASSEMBLY

1. Raise and support rear of vehicle, then loosen axle housing cover bolts and allow lubricant to drain into a container.
2. Remove axle housing cover, then proceed as follows:
   a. Wipe excess lubricant from inside axle housing, then visually inspect parts for wear and/or damage.
   b. Rotate gears and check for roughness, indicating damaged bearings or gears.
   c. Install dial indicator on axle housing cover flange, then check and record ring gear to drive pinion backlash.
3. Remove rear axles and propeller shaft. Refer to "Rear Axle, Propeller Shaft & Brakes" section for procedures.
4. If not previously marked, scribe reference marks on differential bearing caps to be used during reassembly, then remove bearing cap attaching bolts and caps.
5. Remove differential assembly from carrier by putting a box wrench on ring gear bolt and rotating companion flange with suitable tool. When differential assembly is removed from carrier, shims will also come out. Mark shims for reference during reassembly.

DRIVE PINION & BEARINGS

1. Remove pinion nut and companion flange using tool J-8614-01 or equivalent.
2. Remove drive pinion gear through rear of carrier using a hammer.
3. Pry front seal out of carrier assembly, then remove bearing cone.
4. Remove rear pinion bearing using tool J-21493-B or equivalent and press.

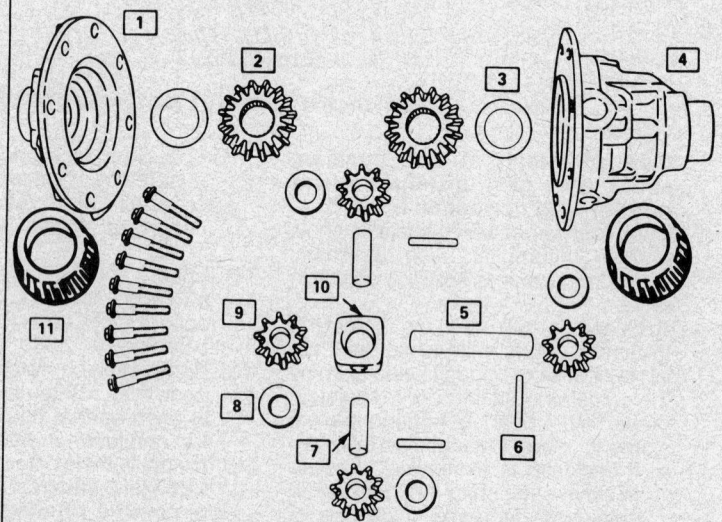

1—DIFF. CASE
2—SIDE GEAR (2)
3—THRUST WASHER (S. G.) (2)
4—DIFF. CASE
5—PINION CROSS SHAFT (1)
6—RETAINER PINS (3)
7—PINION SHAFT (SHORT) (2)
8—THRUST WASHERS (DIFF PINION) (4)
9—DIFF. PINIONS (4)
10—THRUST BLOCK (1)
11—SIDE CASE BEARINGS

Fig. 1 Exploded view of Borg Warner 4 pinion standard differential

5. Remove rear bearing cone from carrier using a punch.
6. Remove selective spacer washer.

DIFFERENTIAL CASE OVERHAUL

4 PINION STANDARD DIFFERENTIAL ASSEMBLY

1. Remove ring gear attaching bolts, then the ring gear from differential housing.
2. Drive out three differential pinion cross shaft retaining pins, **Fig. 1**, using a punch.
3. Drive three differential pinion shafts from housing using a punch. Remove long pinion shaft first.
4. Scribe alignment marks on differential case halves, then separate differential case halves by holding one side and

tapping against other side with a soft hammer.
5. Remove four differential pinions, side gears and thrust washers from housing.
6. Remove differential case bearings using tool J-22888-D or equivalent.
7. Inspect components as outlined in "Cleaning & Inspection" and replace as required.
8. Lubricate all gears and thrust washers with appropriate lubricant.
9. Install side gear thrust washers in differential case. Hold washers in position with grease.
10. Install side gear in large half of differential case.
11. Install thrust block in case, then drive long pinion cross shaft through case, pinion and thrust block bores. Align retainer pin hole with hole in case. **Use caution not to damage differential pinion thrust washers.**

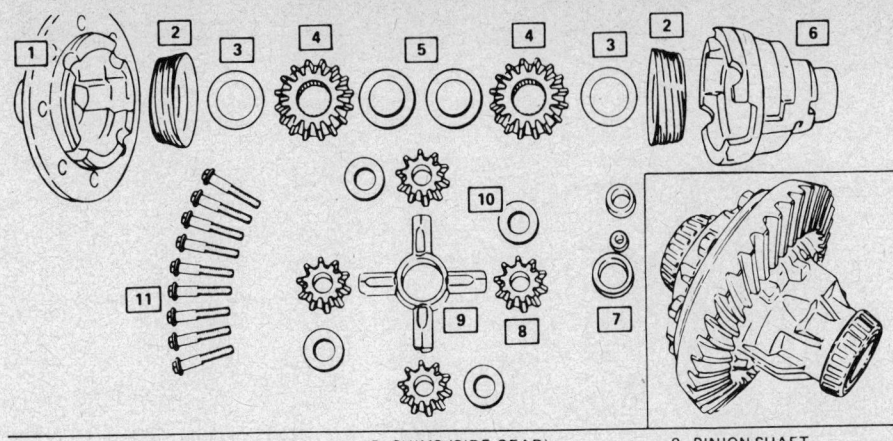

1—DIFF. CASE—FLANGE HALF

2—BRAKE CONES (2)

3—SPRING PLATES (2)

4—SIDE GEARS (2)

5—SHIMS (SIDE GEAR) (IF REQUIRED)

6—DIFF. CASE—CAP HALF

7—COMPRESSION SPRINGS

8—DIFF. PINIONS (4)

9—PINION SHAFT

10—THRUST WASHERS (DIFF. PINION) (4)

11—MOUNTING SCREWS (8)

Fig. 2 Exploded view of Borg Warner 4 pinion limited slip differential

12. Install two remaining pinions and thrust washers in large half of differential case. Drive two short pinion cross shafts through case, pinions and into thrust block bores. Align retainer pin hole with hole in case.
13. Install three cross shaft retaining pins through case and shafts. Ensure long cross shaft retaining pin extends 6 mm from case.
14. Install remaining side gear and thrust washer in small case half.
15. Install side gear through case bore, then align case halves on retaining pin. Rotate side gear to ensure gears are meshing.
16. Install ring gear and ring gear attaching bolts onto housing. **Torque** ring gear attaching bolts to 101 ft. lbs.
17. Press differential bearings on housing journals using tool J-21784 or equivalent.

4 PINION LIMITED SLIP DIFFERENTIAL ASSEMBLY

1. Remove ring gear attaching bolts, then the ring gear from differential housing.
2. Scribe alignment marks on differential case halves, then remove differential housing half attaching bolts and separate halves.
3. Scribe alignment marks on brake cones and shims, then remove pinion shaft, four differential pinions, thrust washer side gears, side gear shims if required, spring plates, compression springs and brake cones from housing, **Fig. 2**. Discard used compression springs.
4. Remove differential bearing using tool J-22888-D or equivalent.
5. Inspect components as outlined in "Cleaning & Inspection" and replace as required.
6. Install brake cones in case, then select correct side gear positioning shim

as follows:
   a. With brake cones fully seated, measure distance from case mating surface to flat surface on brake cone.
   b. If distance is 1.155-1.162 inches, no shims are required. If distance is 1.163-1.167 inches, .005 inch shim is required. If distance is 1.168-1.172 inches, .010 inch shim is required.
   c. Remove brake cones.
7. Apply suitable lubricant to both sides of pinion thrust washers, pinion bores and differential pinion shafts.
8. Install four pinions and spherical thrust washers.
9. Install brake cones, shims (if required) and side gear in cap half of differential case, then apply suitable lubricant to face of side gear. If cone or case is defective, they should be replaced as an assembly.
10. Install spring plate on side gear with convex side towards flange half.
11. Install differential pinion shaft, pinions and spherical thrust washers into cap half of differential case with pinions meshing with side gear.
12. Install three new concentric thrust washer springs through center of pinion shaft spider, then assemble second spring plate and spring with convex side toward springs.
13. Apply suitable lubricant to other side gear face, then install side gear shim, if required.
14. Install brake cone on spring plate.
15. Install flange half of case on top of assembly. Ensure oil channels are aligned.
16. Install two case attaching bolts 180° apart and tighten finger tight.
17. Align side gear and brake cone splines with axle shafts. Install clamp on one axle shaft so 3 inches extends beyond clamp.
18. Install differential housing on axle

shaft splines, flanged half first.
19. Install remaining axle shaft through cap side of differential case, aligning side gear and cone splines.
20. Install remaining case attaching bolts. **Torque** bolts to 29 ft. lbs.
21. Install ring gear and ring gear attaching bolts. **Torque** attaching bolts to 101 ft. lbs.
22. Install differential bearings using tool J-21784 or equivalent.

CLEANING & INSPECTION

1. Clean components in solvent and blow dry with compressed air, noting the following:
   a. Do not use brush when cleaning bearings.
   b. Do not "spin dry" bearings, as bearings will be damaged.
   c. Lightly lubricate components after cleaning to retard corrosion.
   d. Keep all components in order to ensure proper assembly.
2. Inspect gears for cracks, chipped teeth, wear and scoring, and damaged bearing or mounting surfaces. Replace gears that are damaged or excessively worn.
3. Inspect differential case for cracks, damage, worn side gear bores and scored bearing surfaces and replace as needed.
4. Inspect housing for scored bearing mount surfaces, cracks and distortion, and replace as needed.
5. Inspect bearing rollers and races for pitting, scoring, overheating and damage.
6. Mate bearing with race and check operation.
7. Replace any bearing that is damaged, excessively worn or that fails to operate smoothly.

ASSEMBLY
DIFFERENTIAL BEARING PRELOAD ADJUSTMENT

To adjust differential side bearing preload, change thickness of right and left shims equally so original backlash is not disturbed.
1. Ensure side bearing surfaces are clean and free of burrs.
2. Apply suitable lubricant to side bearings. **If original bearings are to be reused, original outer races should also be used.**
3. Install differential case in carrier, with bearing outer races in position.
4. Install left bearing cap and cap attaching bolts loosely so case may be moved during adjustment.
5. Measure original spacers and subtract .004 inch from each reading. Use caution not to interchange right and left spacers.
6. Select a service spacer for each side equal to thickness of original shim minus .004 inch, then install shim as shown in **Fig. 3**. Ensure flat edge of spacer faces against housing.

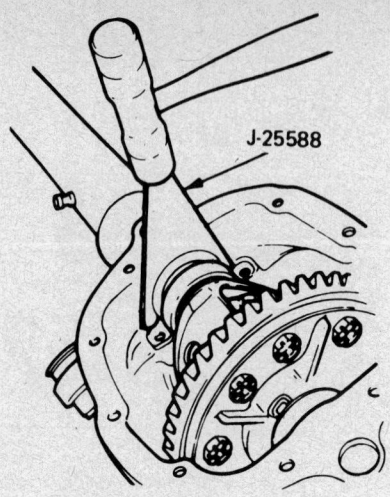

Fig. 3   Installing shims

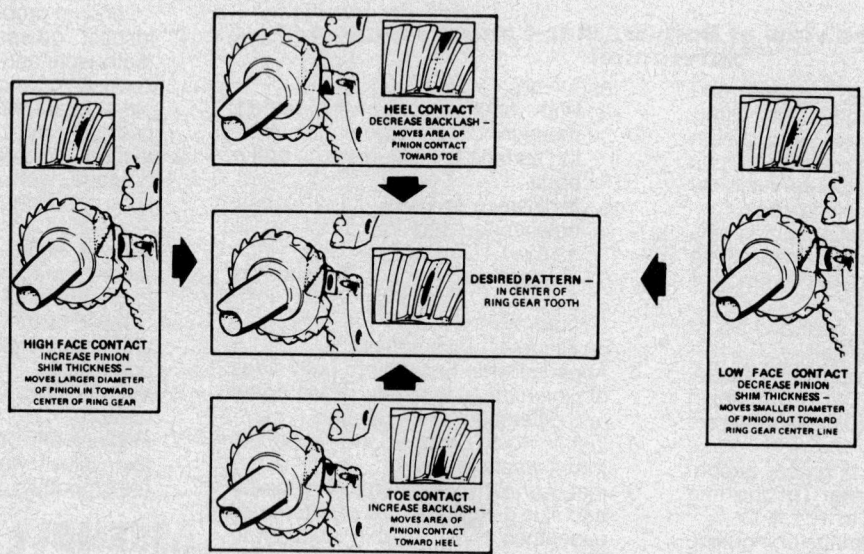

Fig. 4   Gear tooth contact pattern check

7. At this point, bearings should have no play and no drag (zero preload). If zero preload is not present, shims should be added or removed equally from both sides as necessary.
8. Check case for zero end play using a dial indicator. **If shim installation causes excessive pinion to ring gear clearance, select thinner left shim and add difference to right side. Keep total shim thickness at a value equal to that obtained in step 6.**
9. Install both bearing caps and cap attaching bolts. **Torque** bolts 40 ft. lbs.
10. If pinion was not removed, check backlash and tooth pattern as follows:
   a. Apply marking compound on ring gear teeth.
   b. Rotate drive pinion one revolution and check gear tooth contact pattern as shown on **Fig. 4.** Add or remove shims as required.

c. After backlash and tooth pattern operation has been completed, remove shim packs using caution not to mix them.
d. Select new shims for each side .004 inch thicker than those removed, then install each shim on its proper side. This additional thickness will ensure proper bearing preload.
e. Check total rotational torque. Total **torque** with differential case preloaded and pinion installed should be 16-29 inch lbs. if new bearings are installed or 10-16 inch lbs. if original bearings are installed.
f. If total rotational torque is not as specified, repeat steps 4 through 10.
11. If drive pinion was removed, remove differential case and shims, then proceed to "Drive Pinion & Bearing Shim Adjustment" procedure.

DRIVE PINION & BEARING SHIM ADJUSTMENT

1. Install front pinion bearing cup in carrier using tool J-7817 or equivalent.
2. Install spacer (E) into carrier bore, **Fig. 5.**
3. Slide rear pinion bearing and cap (F) onto thru bolt (D) and rear bearing into axle housing.
4. Install thru bolt (D), rear bearing and cap (F) into axle housing.
5. Assemble front bearing cone (A) and spacer (B) onto thru bolt.
6. Rotate nut and shaft while increasing torque on nut until a rotational **torque** of 15-22 inch lbs. is obtained. Rotate thru bolt back and forth when tightening nut to properly seat bearing.
7. Install discs on thru bolt assembly as shown in **Fig. 5.** Position carrier so

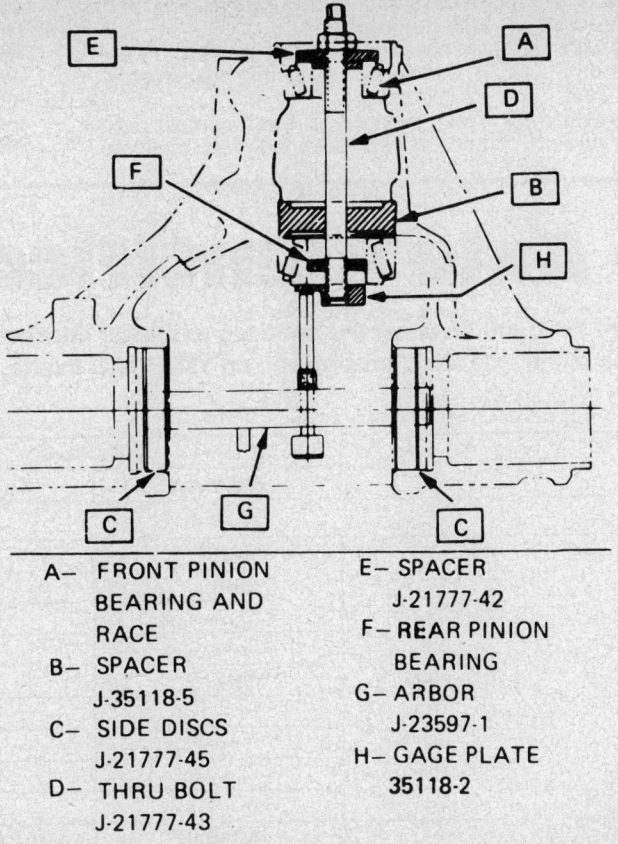

A— FRONT PINION
   BEARING AND
   RACE
B— SPACER
   J-35118-5
C— SIDE DISCS
   J-21777-45
D— THRU BOLT
   J-21777-43

E— SPACER
   J-21777-42
F— REAR PINION
   BEARING
G— ARBOR
   J-23597-1
H— GAGE PLATE
   35118-2

Fig. 5   Drive pinion & bearing shim adjustment

dial indicator contact rod is directly over gauging area of gauge plate J-35118-2. **Discs must be fully seated in side bearing bores.**

8. Install bearing caps over gauge shaft discs, then the cap attaching bolts. **torque** attaching bolts to 40 ft. lbs.
9. With dial indicator rod contacting gauging area of J-35118-2, rock gauge shaft back and forth until dial indicator measures the greatest deflection, then zero dial indicator.
10. Rotate gauge shaft until shaft does not contact gauge plate, then note measurement.
11. Select correct pinion shim as follows:
   a. If reusing production pinion, and pinion is marked with a "+," correct shim will have a thickness equal to gauge reading minus amount specified on pinion.
   b. If reusing production pinion, and pinion is marked with a "−," correct shim will have a thickness equal to gauge reading plus amount specified on pinion.
   c. If using a production or service pinion which has no marking, correct shim will have a thickness equal to gauge reading.
12. Install selected pinion shim into carrier, then press rear pinion bearing cup into carrier using tool J-5590 or equivalent.
13. Press rear pinion bearing onto pinion using a bearing installation tool, then install pinion in carrier.

14. Install collapsible spacer and front bearing onto pinion while supporting pinion under head.
15. Install oil seal, companion flange and new nut on pinion, then **torque** pinion nut to 12-25 inch lbs. if new bearings are used or 6-12 inch lbs. if original bearings are used while rotating pinion forwards to seat bearings.
16. If preload is excessive after tightening pinion nut, replace collapsible spacer and repeat steps 14 and 15.

FINAL ASSEMBLY & BACKLASH ADJUSTMENT

1. Ensure pinion depth and bearing preload are properly adjusted.
2. Install differential case assembly and selected side bearing shims as outlined in "Differential Bearing Preload Adjustment" procedure.
3. Rotate assembly to ensure bearings are properly seated.
4. Mount dial indicator on housing with indicator stem against tooth on ring gear. Use small contact button on indicator stem so that contact can be made at heel end of tooth and position dial indicator with stem in line with gear rotation and perpendicular to gear tooth.
5. Hold pinion stationary and rock ring gear back and forth while reading backlash on indicator.
6. Check backlash at 3 evenly spaced positions around ring gear and record readings. **If backlash varies by more than .002 inch at any position, check ring gear installation and run-out, and correct as needed.**
7. If backlash is not within .005-.009 inch, remove differential case assembly and bearing shims keeping shims in order.
8. Backlash is adjusted by increasing thickness of one shim while decreasing thickness of opposite side shim by the same amount in order to maintain proper side bearing preload. Select shims to adjust backlash as follows:
   a. If backlash is excessive, increase thickness of shim on gear tooth side and decrease thickness of shim on opposite side by the same amount.
   b. If backlash is less than specified, decrease thickness of shim on gear tooth side while increasing thickness of opposite shim by the same amount. **Each .002 inch change in shim thickness alters backlash by .001 inch.**
9. Reinstall differential assembly, shims and bearing caps, **torque** bearing cap bolts to 40 ft. lbs., then recheck backlash and adjust as needed.
10. Ensure ring gear teeth are clean and free from oil, then coat both drive and coast side of each tooth with marking

11. Apply braking force to "load" ring gear, then rotate driveshaft yoke with wrench so that ring gear rotates one full revolution in each direction. **Test made without "loading" gears will not yield satisfactory pattern, and** **excessive rotating of gears is not recommended.**

12. Compare gear tooth pattern with **Fig. 4**, and correct assembly adjustments as needed.

13. When proper gear tooth contact pattern has been obtained, clean marking compound from gears.

14. Install axles and driveshaft. Refer to "Rear Axle, Propeller Shaft & Brakes" section for procedure.

15. Install rear cover using new gasket, then fill rear axle with appropriate lubricant.

Drive Axle Identification

Axle identification numbers can be found on either the code tag or sticker attached to the axle housing cover or stamped on the right front section of the axle shaft housing and on 1988-89 Corvette, the axle I.D. is underneath the differential.

Model	Axle Code		Gear Ratio
	Standard	Limited Slip	
1988			
Camaro	6HP	6HE	2.73
	6HP①	6HE①	2.73
	—	6HT①	2.73
	—	4ET②	2.77
	6HK①	6HF①	3.08
	—	6HB①	3.08
	—	4EU②	3.27
	—	6HL①	3.42
	—	4EW②	3.45
Caprice	6GM①	6GA①	2.56
	6GN	6GB①	2.73
	6GS①	—	2.56
	6GT①	—	2.73
	6LG①	—	3.08
	6LJ①	—	3.08
	6LH①	—	3.23
Caprice Wagon	6YC①	—	2.93
	6YY①	—	3.08
	6YE①	—	3.23
Corvette	—	8YA①③	2.59
	—	8YB①③	2.73
	—	8YC①③	3.07
	—	8YH①④	3.07
Cutlass Supreme Classic	2AA①	2BA①	2.56
	2AC①	2BC①	3.08
Custom Cruiser	6YC①	—	2.93
	6YE①	—	3.23
Firebird	—	6HE①	
	6HP①	6HT①	2.73
	—	4ET②	2.77
	6HK①	6HF①	3.08
	—	6HB①	3.08
	—	3.27②	3.27
	6HL①	—	3.42
	—	4EW②	3.45
Fleetwood Brougham	6TE①	—	2.93
	6MC①	—	3.23
Monte Carlo	2AJ①	2BJ①	2.41
	2AC①	2BC①	3.08
	2TF①	2TH①	3.73

Continued
DRIVE AXLE IDENTIFICATION

DRIVE AXLE IDENTIFICATION—Continued

Model	Axle Code		Gear Ratio
	Standard	**Limited Slip**	
1989			
Camaro	6HP①	6HT①	2.73
	—	BET②	2.77
	6HK①	6HB/6HF①	3.08
	—	6HJ/6HQ①	3.23
	—	BEU②	3.27
	6HL①	—	3.42
	—	BEW②	3.45
Caprice	6GM①	6GA①	2.56
	6GS①	—	2.56
	6GN①	6GB①	2.73
	8LL/8LM①	8NC①	3.08
Caprice Wagon, Custom Cruiser, LeSabre Wagon, Safari	8YA①	8YH①	2.93
	8YG①	8YM①	3.23
Corvette	—	8YA①③	2.59
	—	8YB①③	2.73
	—	8YC①③	3.07
	—	8YW①④	3.33
	—	8YJ①④	3.54
Firebird	6HP	6HE/6HT①	2.73
	—	4ET②	2.77
	6HK①	6HF①	3.08
	—	6HJ/6HQ①	3.23
	—	BEU②	3.27
	6HL①	—	3.42
	—	BEW②	3.45
Fleetwood Brougham	6TE①	—	2.93
	6MC①	—	3.23
1990			
Camaro	8HP①	8HT/8RC①	2.73
	8HK①	8HB/8HF①	3.08
	—	2PM/2PN①	3.23
	—	9EQ②	3.27
	8HL①	—	3.42
	—	9ER②	3.45
Caprice	2GM①	2GA①	2.56
	2GN①	2GB①	2.73
	2LG①	2NA/2NC①	3.08
Caprice Wagon, Custom Cruiser & LeSabre Wagon	2YC①	2YH①	2.93
	2YE①	2YM①	3.23
Corvette	—	8YA①③	2.59
	—	8YB①③	2.73
	—	8YC①③	3.07
	—	8YW①④	3.33
	—	8YJ①④	3.45
	—	8YS①④	3.54
Firebird	8HP	8HE/8HT①	2.73
	—	4ET②	2.77
	8HK①	8HB/8HF①	3.08
	8HJ①	2PM①	3.23

Continued

DRIVE AXLE IDENTIFICATION—Continued

| Model | Axle Code | | Gear Ratio |
	Standard	Limited Slip	
Firebird (Con't.)	—	8EV/9EQ ②	3.27
	8HL ①	2PM ①	3.42
	—	8EW ②	3.45
Brougham	2TM ①	—	2.73
	2TE ①	—	2.93
	2MG ①	—	3.08

① —General Motors.
② —Borg-Warner.
③ —Corvette w/Automatic Transmission.
④ —Corvette w/Manual Transmission.

MANUAL STEERING GEARS

TABLE OF CONTENTS

Applications

Domestic General Motors Models & LeMans

Saginaw Rack & Pinion

Nova & Prizm

Toyota Rack & Pinion

Spectrum

Jidosha Kiki & Saginaw Rack & Pinion

Sprint & Metro

Suzuki Rack & Pinion

Jidosha Kiki Rack & Pinion

INDEX

DESCRIPTION

This rack and pinion steering system consists of two main components, the rack and the pinion. When the steering wheel is turned, motion is transmitted to the steering shaft, shaft joint and then the pinion. The pinion teeth mesh with the rack teeth and the motion is further transferred to the rack and changed to linear motion. The linear force is then transmitted through the tie rods and to the steering knuckles which steer the front wheels.

DISASSEMBLY

1. Place steering gear into a vise.
2. Remove tie rod end, **Fig. 1.**
3. Remove boot.
4. Using a suitable chisel, bend back staked portion of lock washer between inner tie rod and rack assembly.
5. Remove tie rod from rack.
6. Loosen adjusting plug nut, then remove spring and plunger.
7. Remove pinion seal and snap ring.
8. Rotate pinion gear shaft until pinion flat is parallel or aligned with rack assembly. Then carefully measure dimension A, **Fig. 2.** Record reading obtained. This relationship must be used for assembly.
9. Remove pinion assembly.
10. Pull rack from housing.

ASSEMBLY

1. Install rack into steering housing.
2. Carefully set rack to dimension A recorded previously. Install pinion, aligning flat parallel as shown in **Fig. 2.** Plus or minus 5 degrees from parallel is acceptable.
3. Install pinion retaining snap ring.
4. Lubricate, then install plunger, spring, adjusting plug and locknut.
5. **Torque** adjusting plug to 4 ft. lbs.
6. Back off adjusting nut up to 25 degrees.
7. Measure pinion shaft preload. Preload should be .4–.9 ft. lbs. If preload is not within specified limit, loosen locknut and adjust plug torque. When an acceptable preload is achieved, apply liquid thread lock to locknut and **torque** to 49 ft. lbs.
8. Install inner tie rod and a new locking washer on to rack end. **Torque** to 65 ft. lbs. Stake lock washer to the flat on the inner tie rod. Apply suitable grease to the inner surface of the small opening in the boot.
9. Install boot over inner tie rod.
10. Install tie rod nut and attach to tie rod end.
11. Adjust tie rod length L dimension as shown in **Fig. 3.** L dimension length should be 7.5 inches.
12. **Torque** tie rod locknut to 40 ft. lbs.
13. Install boot clamp and wire.

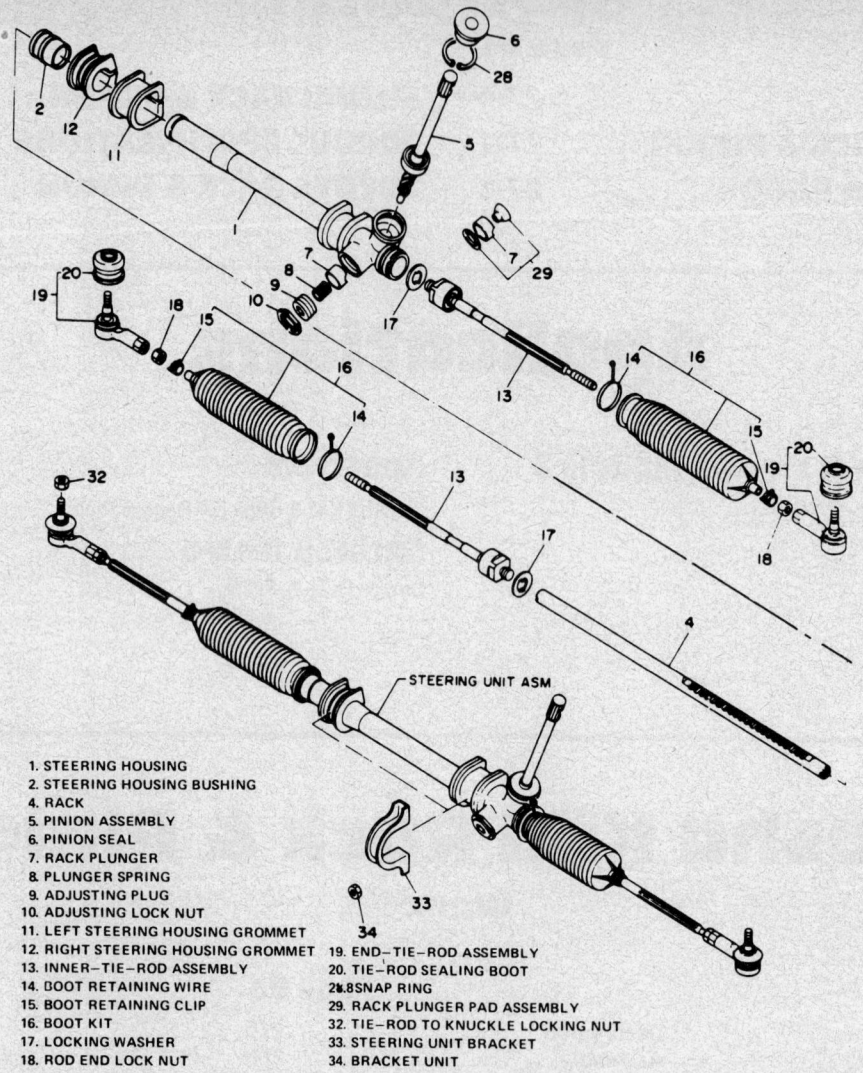

1. STEERING HOUSING
2. STEERING HOUSING BUSHING
4. RACK
5. PINION ASSEMBLY
6. PINION SEAL
7. RACK PLUNGER
8. PLUNGER SPRING
9. ADJUSTING PLUG
10. ADJUSTING LOCK NUT
11. LEFT STEERING HOUSING GROMMET
12. RIGHT STEERING HOUSING GROMMET
13. INNER–TIE–ROD ASSEMBLY
14. BOOT RETAINING WIRE
15. BOOT RETAINING CLIP
16. BOOT KIT
17. LOCKING WASHER
18. ROD END LOCK NUT
19. END–TIE–ROD ASSEMBLY
20. TIE–ROD SEALING BOOT
28. SNAP RING
29. RACK PLUNGER PAD ASSEMBLY
32. TIE–ROD TO KNUCKLE LOCKING NUT
33. STEERING UNIT BRACKET
34. BRACKET UNIT

Fig. 1   Disassembled view of manual steering gear assembly

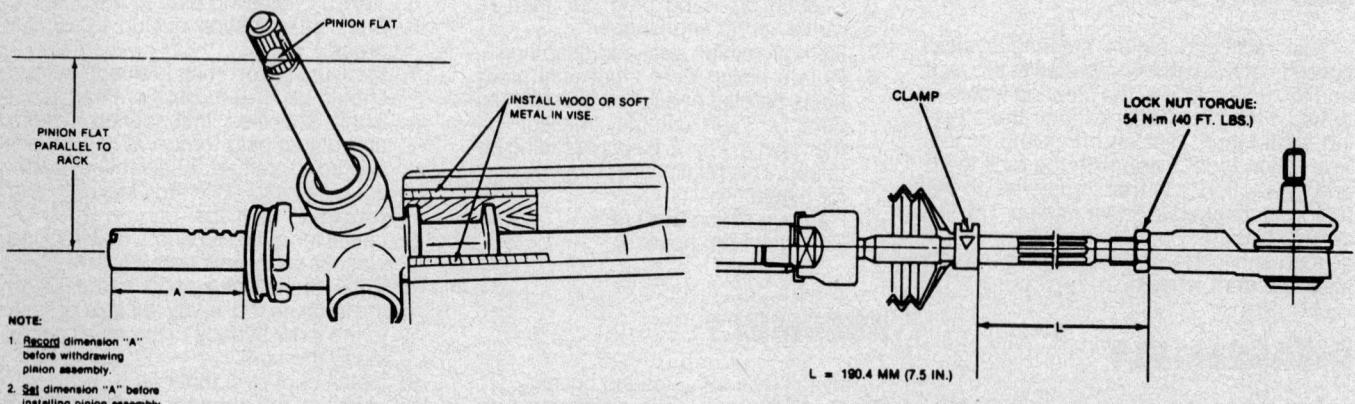

Fig. 2   Measuring & centering rack/pinion

Fig. 3   Checking tie rod end dimension

Saginaw Rack & Pinion

INDEX

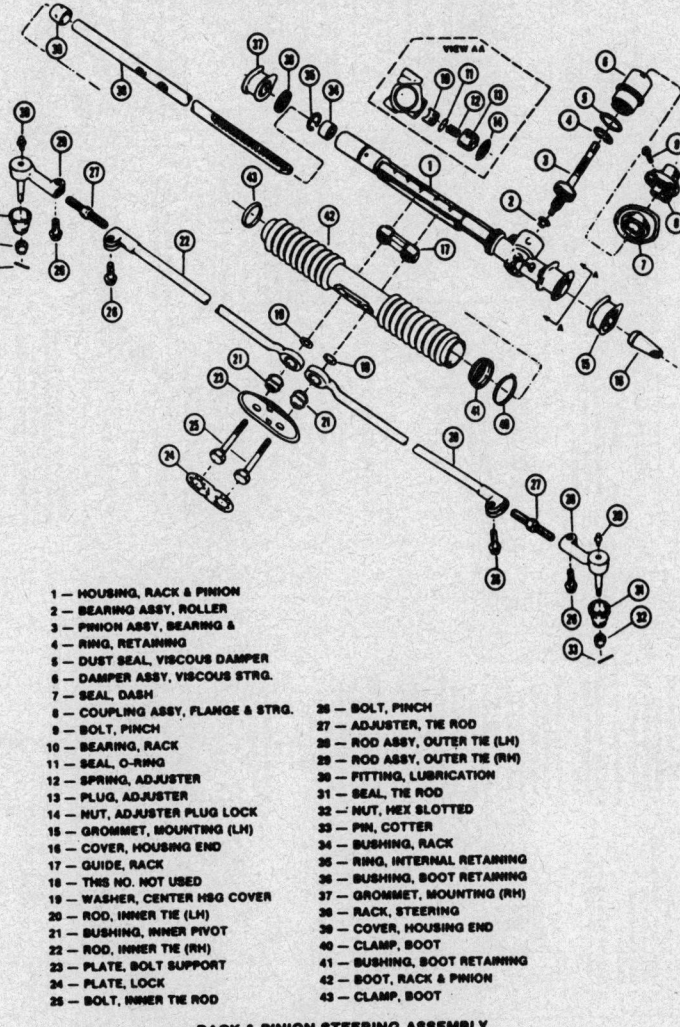

1 — HOUSING, RACK & PINION
2 — BEARING ASSY, ROLLER
3 — PINION ASSY, BEARING &
4 — RING, RETAINING
5 — DUST SEAL, VISCOUS DAMPER
6 — DAMPER ASSY, VISCOUS STRG.
7 — SEAL, DASH
8 — COUPLING ASSY, FLANGE & STRG.
9 — BOLT, PINCH
10 — BEARING, RACK
11 — SEAL, O-RING
12 — SPRING, ADJUSTER
13 — PLUG, ADJUSTER
14 — NUT, ADJUSTER PLUG LOCK
15 — GROMMET, MOUNTING (LH)
16 — COVER, HOUSING END
17 — GUIDE, RACK
18 — THIS NO. NOT USED
19 — WASHER, CENTER HSG COVER
20 — ROD, INNER TIE (LH)
21 — BUSHING, INNER PIVOT
22 — ROD, INNER TIE (RH)
23 — PLATE, BOLT SUPPORT
24 — PLATE, LOCK
25 — BOLT, INNER TIE ROD

26 — BOLT, PINCH
27 — ADJUSTER, TIE ROD
28 — ROD ASSY, OUTER TIE (LH)
29 — ROD ASSY, OUTER TIE (RH)
30 — FITTING, LUBRICATION
31 — SEAL, TIE ROD
32 — NUT, HEX SLOTTED
33 — PIN, COTTER
34 — BUSHING, RACK
35 — RING, INTERNAL RETAINING
36 — BUSHING, BOOT RETAINING
37 — GROMMET, MOUNTING (RH)
38 — RACK, STEERING
39 — COVER, HOUSING END
40 — CLAMP, BOOT
41 — BUSHING, BOOT RETAINING
42 — BOOT, RACK & PINION
43 — CLAMP, BOOT

RACK & PINION STEERING ASSEMBLY

**Fig. 1 Exploded view of Saginaw rack &
pinion steering gear. All models except Fiero**

DESCRIPTION

The rack and pinion steering system consists of two main components, the rack and the pinion. The motion of turning the steering wheel is transferred to the pinion. The rotary motion of the pinion is then transferred through the pinion teeth which mesh with teeth on the rack, which gives the rack linear motion. The linear motion is then transmitted through the inner and outer tie rods to the steering knuckles which turn the wheels.

SERVICE

ALL MODELS EXCEPT FIERO

Refer to **Figs. 1 and 2** for service proce-dures on this Saginaw rack and pinion steering gear.

Refer to the rear of this section for torque specifications.

FIERO

Refer to **Figs. 3 and 4** for service proce-dures on the Saginaw rack and pinion steering gear.

Refer to the rear of this section for torque specifications.

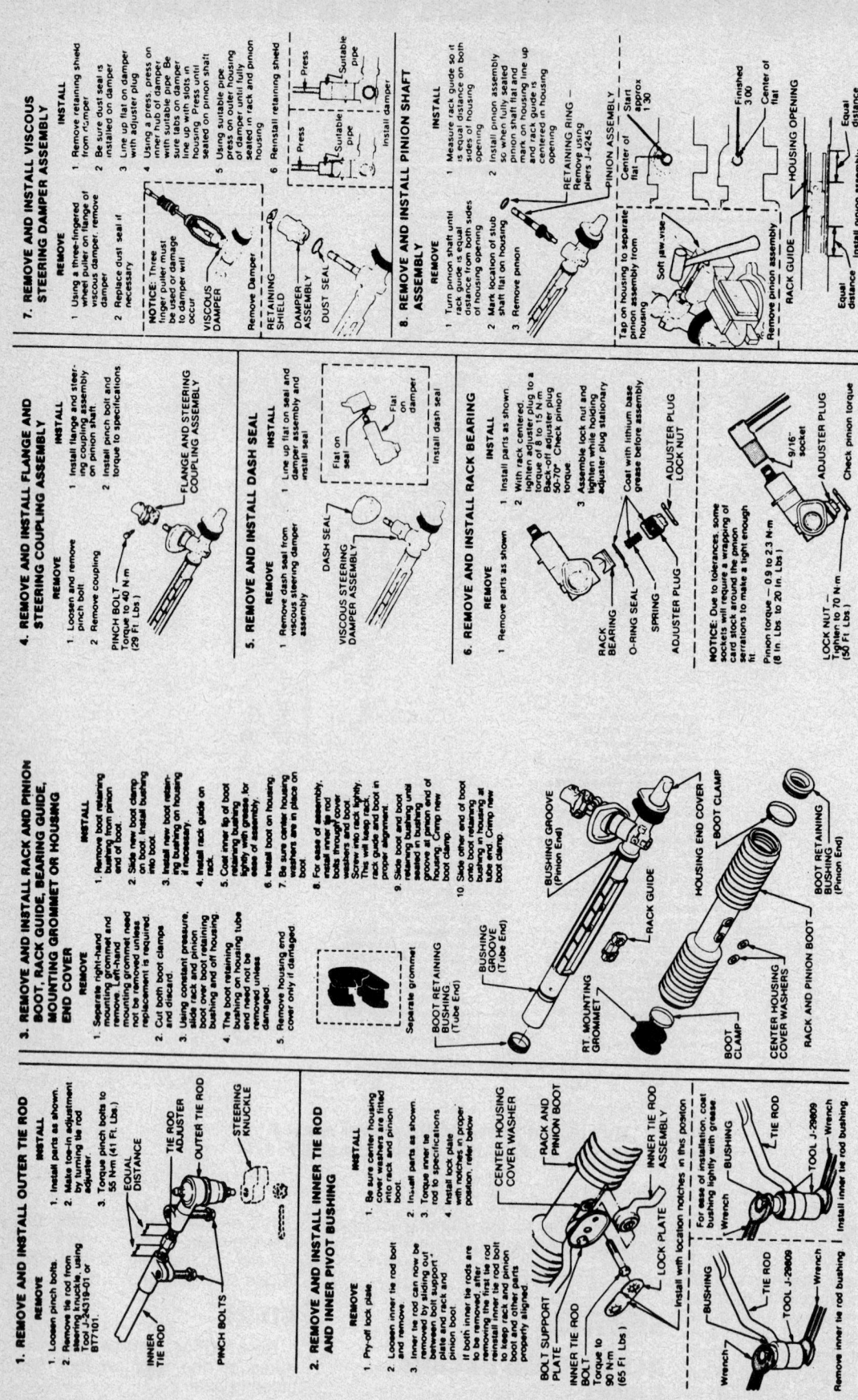

7. REMOVE AND INSTALL VISCOUS STEERING DAMPER ASSEMBLY

REMOVE

1. Using a three-fingered wheel puller on flange of viscous damper, remove damper
2. Replace dust seal if necessary

NOTICE: Three finger puller must be used or damage to damper will occur

Remove Damper

RETAINING SHIELD
DAMPER ASSEMBLY
DUST SEAL
VISCOUS DAMPER

INSTALL

1. Remove retaining shield from r/c amper
2. Be sure dust seal is installed on r/c amper
3. Line up flat on damper with adjuster plug
4. Using a press, press on inner hub of damper with suitable pipe Be sure to index damper line up with slots in housing Press until seated on rack and pinion shaft
5. Using suitable pipe press on outer housing of damper until fully seated on rack and pinion housing
6. Reinstall retaining shield

Press — Suitable pipe
Install damper

8. REMOVE AND INSTALL PINION SHAFT ASSEMBLY

REMOVE

1. Turn pinion shaft until rack guide is equal distance from both sides of housing opening
2. Mark location of stub shaft flat on housing
3. Remove pinion

Tap on housing to separate pinion assembly from housing

Soft jaw vise
Remove pinion assembly

INSTALL

1. Measure rack guide so it is equal distance on both sides of housing opening
2. Install pinion assembly so when fully seated pinion shaft flat and mark on housing line up and rack guide is centered in housing opening

RETAINING RING — Remove using pliers J-4245
PINION ASSEMBLY
Center of Start approx 130
Finished 3 00
Center of flat
RACK GUIDE — HOUSING OPENING
Equal distance — Equal distance
Install pinion assembly

Fig. 2 Saginaw rack & pinion steering gear service procedures (Part 2 of 3). All models except Fiero

---

4. REMOVE AND INSTALL FLANGE AND STEERING COUPLING ASSEMBLY

REMOVE

1. Loosen and remove pinch bolt
2. Remove coupling

PINCH BOLT
Torque to 40 N·m (29 Ft Lbs)

INSTALL

1. Install flange and steering coupling assembly on pinion shaft
2. Install pinch bolt and torque to specifications

FLANGE AND STEERING COUPLING ASSEMBLY

5. REMOVE AND INSTALL DASH SEAL

REMOVE

1. Remove dash seal from viscous steering damper assembly

DASH SEAL
VISCOUS STEERING DAMPER ASSEMBLY

INSTALL

1. Line up flat on seal and damper assembly and install seal

Flat on seal — Flat on damper
Install dash seal

6. REMOVE AND INSTALL RACK BEARING

REMOVE

1. Remove parts as shown

RACK BEARING
O-RING SEAL
SPRING
ADJUSTER PLUG

INSTALL

1. Install parts as shown
2. With rack centered, tighten adjuster plug to a torque of 8 to 15 N·m. Back-off of adjuster plug 50-70° Check pinion torque
3. Assemble lock nut and tighten while holding adjuster plug stationary

Coat with lithium base grease before assembly

ADJUSTER PLUG
LOCK NUT
9/16" socket
ADJUSTER PLUG — Check pinion torque

NOTICE: Due to tolerances, some sockets will require a wrapping of card stock around the pinion serrations to make a tight enough fit

Pinion torque — 0.9 to 2.3 N·m (8 In Lbs to 20 In Lbs)

LOCK NUT — Tighten to 70 N·m (50 Ft Lbs)

Fig. 2 Saginaw rack & pinion steering gear service procedures (Part 1 of 3). All models except Fiero

---

3. REMOVE AND INSTALL RACK AND PINION BOOT, RACK GUIDE, BEARING GUIDE, MOUNTING GROMMET OR HOUSING END COVER

REMOVE

1. Separate right-hand mounting grommet and remove. Left-hand mounting grommet need not be removed unless replacement is required.
2. Cut both boot clamps and discard.
3. Using constant pressure, slide rack and pinion boot over boot retaining bushing and off housing.
4. The boot retaining bushing on housing tube end need not be removed unless damaged.
5. Remove housing end cover only if damaged.

Separate grommet

BOOT RETAINING BUSHING (Tube End)

INSTALL

1. Remove boot retaining bushing from pinion end of boot.
2. Slide new boot clamp on boot. Install bushing into boot.
3. Install new boot retaining bushing in pinion end of boot.
4. Install rack guide on rack.
5. Coat inner tip of boot retaining bushing with grease for ease of assembly.
6. Install boot on housing.
7. Be sure center housing washers are in place on boot.
8. For ease of assembly, install inner and boot bolts through cover washers and into boot. Screw in loosely. This will keep rack guide in place and boot in proper alignment.
9. Slide boot and boot retaining bushing until seated in housing groove at pinion end of housing. Clamp new boot clamp.
10. Slide other end of boot onto boot retaining bushing in housing at tube end. Clamp new boot clamp.

Fig. 2 Saginaw rack & pinion steering gear service procedures (Part 1 of 3). All models except Fiero

BUSHING GROOVE (Pinion End)
RACK GUIDE
HOUSING END COVER
BOOT CLAMP
BOOT CLAMP
BOOT RETAINING BUSHING (Pinion End)
BUSHING GROOVE (Tube End)
RT. MOUNTING GROMMET
BOOT CLAMP
CENTER HOUSING COVER WASHERS
RACK AND PINION BOOT

---

1. REMOVE AND INSTALL OUTER TIE ROD

REMOVE

1. Loosen pinch bolts.
2. Remove tie rod from steering knuckle using Tool J-34418-01 or BT7101.

INNER TIE ROD
PINCH BOLTS

INSTALL

1. Install parts as shown.
2. Make toe-in adjustment by turning tie rod adjuster.
3. Torque pinch bolts to 55 N·m (41 Ft Lbs).

EQUAL DISTANCE
TIE ROD ADJUSTER
OUTER TIE ROD
STEERING KNUCKLE

2. REMOVE AND INSTALL INNER TIE ROD AND INNER PIVOT BUSHING

REMOVE

1. Pry-off lock plate.
2. Loosen inner tie rod and remove.
3. Inner tie rod can now be removed by sliding out between bolt support plate and rack and pinion boot. If both inner tie rods are to be removed, after removing the first tie rod reinstall inner tie rod bolt and nut to keep rack and pinion boot and other parts properly aligned.

BOLT SUPPORT PLATE
INNER TIE ROD BOLT
Torque to 90 N·m (65 Ft Lbs)
LOCK PLATE
BUSHING
TIE ROD
Wrench

INSTALL

1. Be sure center housing cover washers are lined into inner rack and pinion boot.
2. Install parts as shown.
3. Torque inner tie rod to specifications.
4. Install lock plate with notches in proper position, refer below

For ease of installation, coat bushing lightly with grease

Install with location notches in this position

CENTER HOUSING COVER WASHER
RACK AND PINION BOOT
INNER TIE ROD ASSEMBLY
BUSHING
TOOL J-29909 Wrench
TIE ROD
INNER TIE ROD
BUSHING
TOOL J-29909 Wrench
Remove inner tie rod bushing
Install inner tie rod bushing

Fig. 2 Saginaw rack & pinion steering gear service procedures (Part 1 of 3). All models except Fiero

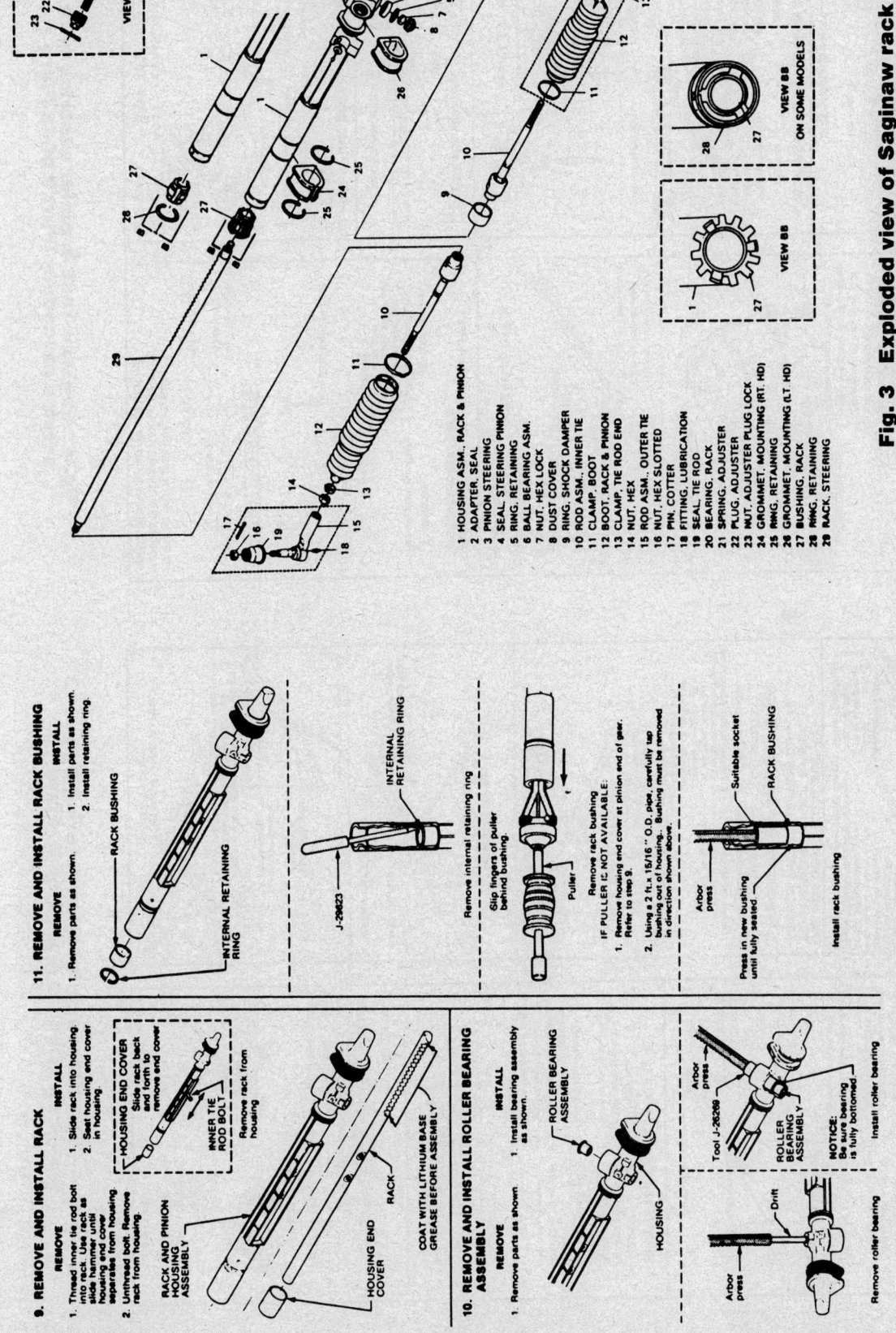

VIEW AA

VIEW BB ON SOME MODELS

VIEW BB

1 HOUSING ASM. RACK & PINION
2 ADAPTER, SEAL
3 PINION STEERING
4 SEAL, STEERING PINION
5 RING, RETAINING
6 BALL BEARING ASM.
7 NUT, HEX LOCK
8 DUST COVER
9 RING, SHOCK DAMPER
10 ROD ASM. INNER TIE
11 CLAMP, BOOT
12 BOOT, RACK & PINION
13 CLAMP, TIE ROD END
14 NUT, HEX
15 ROD ASM. OUTER TIE
16 NUT, HEX SLOTTED
17 PIN, COTTER
18 FITTING, LUBRICATION
19 SEAL, TIE ROD
20 BEARING, RACK
21 SPRING, ADJUSTER
22 PLUG, ADJUSTER
23 NUT, ADJUSTER PLUG LOCK
24 GROMMET, MOUNTING (RT. HD)
25 RING, RETAINING
26 GROMMET, MOUNTING (LT. HD)
27 BUSHING, RACK
28 RING, RETAINING
29 RACK, STEERING

Fig. 3 Exploded view of Saginaw rack & pinion steering gear. Fiero

---

8. REMOVE AND INSTALL RACK

REMOVE
1. Thread inner tie rod bolt into rack. Use rack as slide hammer until housing and cover separate from housing
2. Unthread bolt. Remove rack from housing

INSTALL
1. Slide rack into housing.
2. Seat housing end cover in housing

HOUSING END COVER
Slide rack back and turn to remove end and cover

INNER TIE ROD BOLT

RACK AND PINION HOUSING ASSEMBLY

COAT WITH LITHIUM BASE GREASE BEFORE ASSEMBLY

HOUSING END COVER

Remove rack from housing

RACK

10. REMOVE AND INSTALL ROLLER BEARING ASSEMBLY

REMOVE
1. Remove parts as shown.

INSTALL
1. Install bearing assembly as shown.

ROLLER BEARING ASSEMBLY

HOUSING

Tool J-28266

Arbor press

ROLLER BEARING ASSEMBLY

NOTICE: Be sure bearing is fully bottomed.

Install roller bearing

Remove roller bearing

Drift

Arbor press

11. REMOVE AND INSTALL RACK BUSHING

REMOVE
1. Remove parts as shown.

INSTALL
1. Install parts as shown.
2. Install retaining ring.

RACK BUSHING

INTERNAL RETAINING RING

Remove internal retaining ring

INTERNAL RETAINING RING

J-29623

Slip fingers of puller behind bushing

Puller

Remove rack bushing

IF PULLER IC IS NOT AVAILABLE:

1. Remove housing end cover at pinion end of gear. Refer to step 9.
2. Using a 2 ft. x 15/16" O.D. pipe, carefully tap bushing out of housing. Bushing must be removed in direction shown.

Suitable socket

RACK BUSHING

Arbor press

Press in new bushing until fully seated

Install rack bushing

Fig. 2 Saginaw rack & pinion steering gear service procedures (Part 3 of 3). All models except Fiero

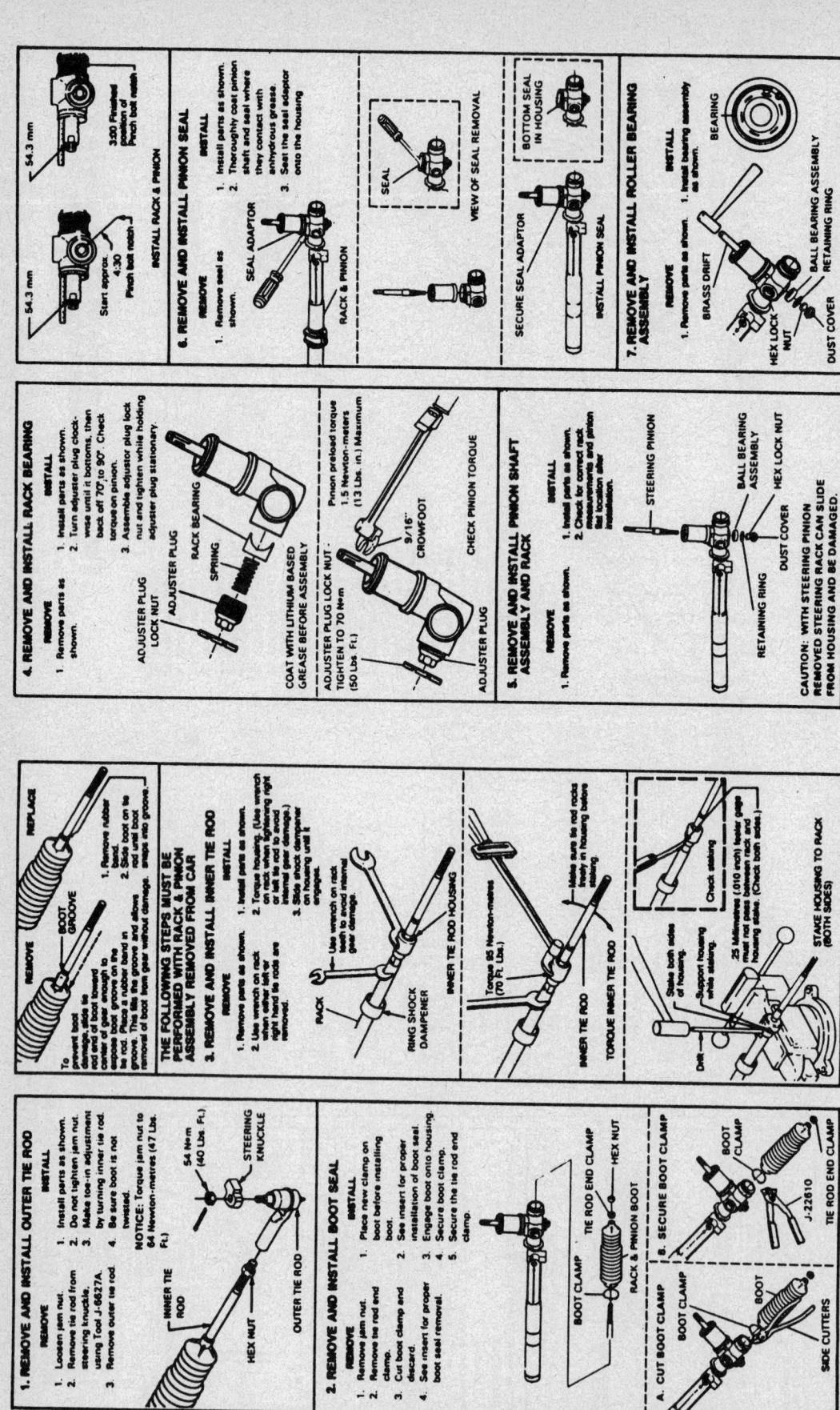

Fig. 4 Saginaw rack & pinion steering gear service procedure (Part 2 of 3). Fiero

Fig. 4 Saginaw rack & pinion steering gear service procedure (Part 1 of 3). Fiero

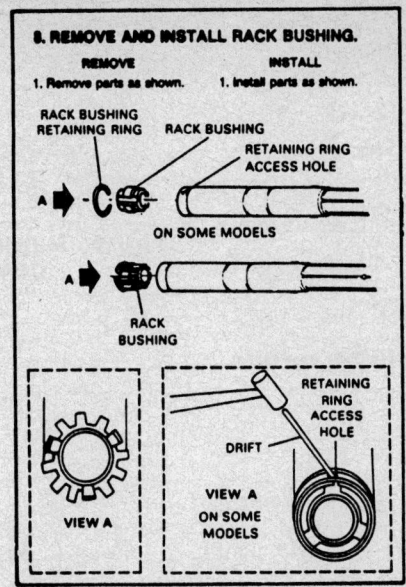

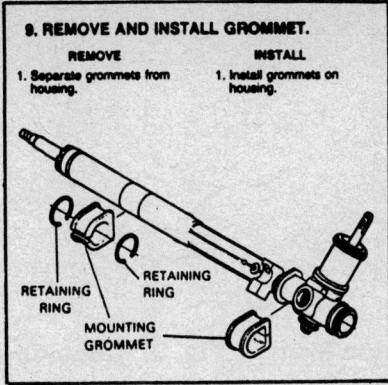

Fig. 4   Saginaw rack & pinion steering gear service procedure (Part 3 of 3). Fiero

Suzuki Rack & Pinion

INDEX

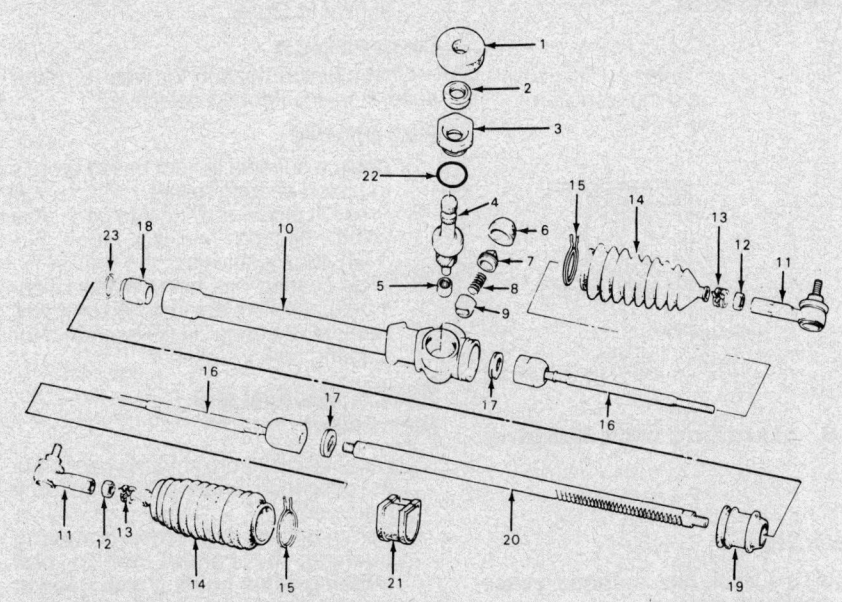

1. STEERING GEAR CASE PACKING
2. STEERING GEAR CASE OIL SEAL
3. PINION BEARING PLUG
4. STEERING PINION
5. STEERING PINION NEEDLE BEARING
6. RACK DAMPER SCREW CAP
7. RACK DAMPER SCREW
8. RACK PLUNGER SPRING

9. STEERING RACK PLUNGER
10. STEERING RACK HOUSING AND GEAR CASE
11. TIE-ROD END
12. TIE-ROD END LOCK NUT
13. RACK BOOT CLIP
14. BOOT
15. WIRE
16. STEERING TIE-ROD

17. TIE-ROD LOCK WASHER
18. STEERING RACK BUSHING
19. STEERING RACK SIDE MOUNT
20. STEERING RACK
21. STEERING PINION SIDE MOUNT
22. GEAR CASE SEAL
23. SNAP RING

Fig. 1   Manual rack & pinion steering assembly

STEERING GEAR SERVICE

Refer to **Fig. 1** when servicing steering gear assembly.

STEERING PINION

Removal

1. Remove rack damper screw cap and damper screw.
2. Remove rack plunger spring and rack plunger.
3. Remove steering gear case packing.
4. Using a 43 mm socket, remove pinion bearing plug with oil seal.
5. Tap on position shown in **Fig. 2** with a plastic hammer to separate pinion assembly from housing.

Inspection

1. Inspect pinion teeth for wear or damage.
2. Inspect oil seal for wear or damage.
3. Inspect plunger spring for deterioration and screw cap, screw and plunger for wear or damage.
4. Inspect gear case packing for damage. Replace all seals and any parts found defective.

Assembly

1. Apply grease to pinion teeth and gear

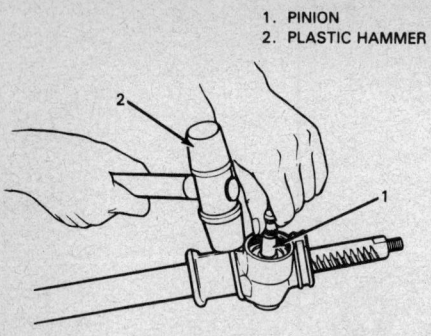

1. PINION
2. PLASTIC HAMMER

Fig. 2 Separating pinion from housing

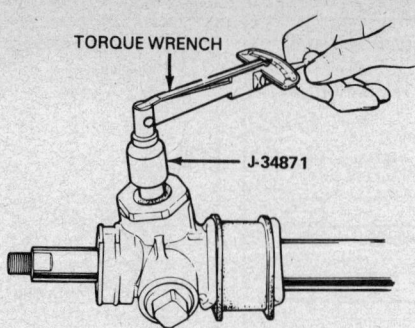

TORQUE WRENCH

J-34871

Fig. 3 Checking pinion torque

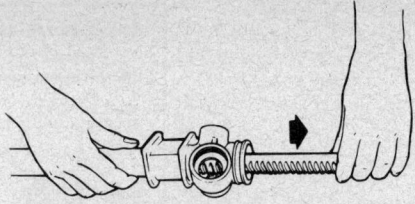

Fig. 4 Removing rack from gear case

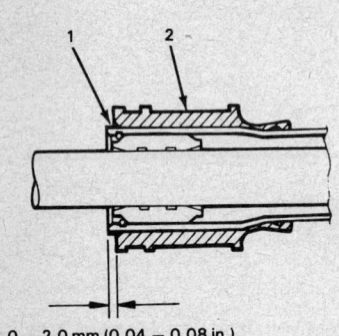

1. STEERING RACK HOUSING
2. RACK SIDE MOUNT

1.0 — 2.0 mm (0.04 — 0.08 in.)

Fig. 5 Ensuring that rack side mount is positioned

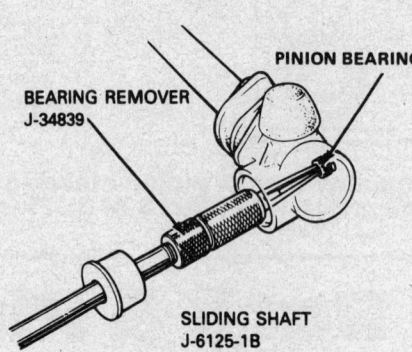

BEARING REMOVER J-34839

PINION BEARING

SLIDING SHAFT J-6125-1B

Fig. 6 Removing pinion bearing

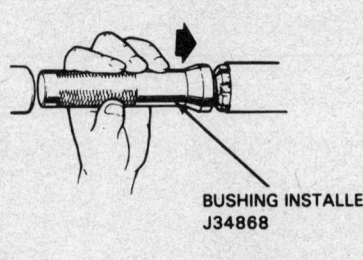

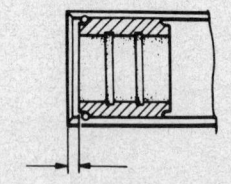

BUSHING INSTALLER J34868

1.0 — 2.0 mm (0.04 — 0.08 in.)

Fig. 8 Installing rack bushing

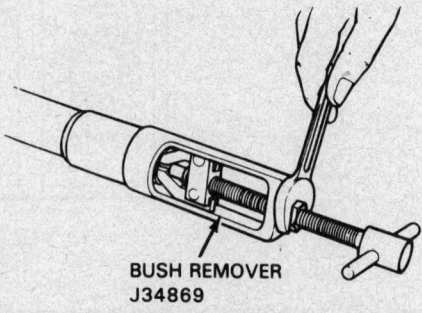

BUSH REMOVER J34869

Fig. 7 Removing rack bushing

---

case oil seal lip.
2. Install pinion assembly.
3. Install pinion case seal and bearing plug. **Torque** plug to 70. ft. lbs.
4. Install oil seal and gear case packing.
5. Install rack plunger, plunger spring and damper screw.
6. After tightening damper screw, back it off 90 degrees and check rotational torque of pinion. Pinion torque should be 9.6 inch lbs., **Fig. 3**.

STEERING RACK
Removal
1. Remove boot wires and clips. Slide boots toward tie rod end.
2. Unbend tie rod lock washers and remove tie rods. Mark left and right tie rods.
3. Remove rack plunger and pinion assembly as described under Steering Pinion.
4. Remove rack from gear case as shown in **Fig. 4**.

Inspection
1. Inspect steering rack for deflection and rack teeth for wear or damage. Rack deflection should not exceed .016 inch.

Assembly
1. Apply a suitable lithium based grease to rack teeth surface.
2. Install rack into steering gear case, in opposite direction of removal.
3. Install pinion assembly and plunger assembly as described under "Steering Rack" Removal.
4. Install boot to steering rack housing, ensuring that rack side mount is positioned as shown in **Fig. 5**.

5. Install tie rods as described under "Steering Rack."

PINION BEARING
Removal
1. Remove rack from steering gear case as described under "Steering Rack Removal."
2. Remove pinion bearing using tools Nos. J-34839 and J-6125-1B, as shown in **Fig. 6**.

Inspection
Check pinion bearing for wear or damages. Replace if found defective.

Assembly
1. Apply a suitable lithium based grease to pinion bearing rollers.
2. Press fit pinion bearing into gear case using bearing installer tool No. J-34840 or equivalent.
3. After bearing has been installed, ensure that rollers are installed properly.
4. Refer to "Steering Rack Assembly" for steering rack installation.

RACK BUSHING
Removal
1. Remove rack from steering gear case as described under "Steering Rack Removal."
2. Remove snap ring. **When removing bushing, be careful not to pull bushing while holding gear case in vise as the housing may come off gear case.**
3. Remove bushing from rack housing using tool J-34869 or equivalent, **Fig. 7**.

Inspection
Inspect bushing for wear or damage and replace if necessary.

Assembly

1. Apply a suitable lithium based grease to inner surface of bushing.
2. Using bushing installer tool

No.J-34868 or equivalent, install bushing into rack housing, ensuring bushing to housing clearance is as shown, **Fig. 8.**

3. Install snap ring.
4. Install steering rack assembly as described under Steering Rack Assembly.

Toyota Rack & Pinion

INDEX

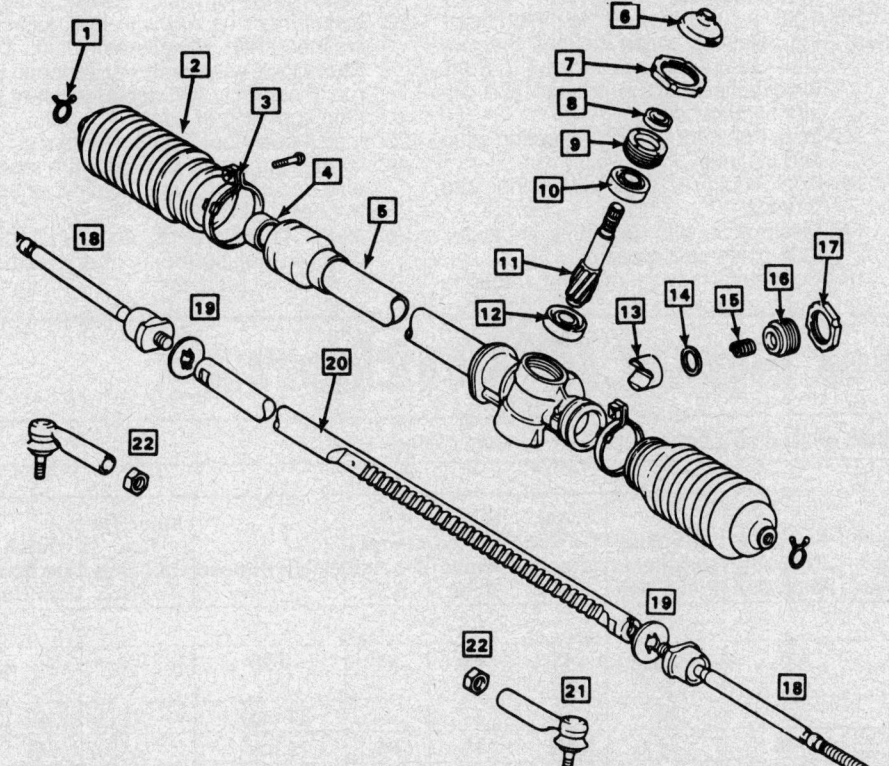

1. CLIP, BOOT
2. BOOT, STEERING GEAR RACK
3. CLAMP, BOOT
4. BUSHING, RACK
5. HOUSING, STEERING GEAR RACK
6. COVER, PINION DUST
7. NUT, LOCKING
8. SEAL, UPPER PINION
9. SCREW, PINION BEARING ADJUSTING
10. BEARING, PINION UPPER
11. PINION, STEERING
12. BEARING, PINION LOWER
13. GUIDE, RACK
14. SPACER, RACK GUIDE
15. SPRING, RACK GUIDE
16. CAP, RACK GUIDE SPRING
17. NUT, RACK GUIDE LOCKING
18. ROD, INNER TIE
19. WASHER, LOCKING
20. RACK, STEERING
21. ROD, OUTER TIE
22. NUT, TIE ROD LOCKING

Fig. 1   Exploded view of Toyota (Nova) rack & pinion steering gear

DESCRIPTION

This steering system converts rotary motion to linear motion as follows; when the steering wheel is turned, rotary motion is transferred to the steering shaft, shaft joint and rack pinion. The pinion teeth mesh with teeth on the rack and the rotary motion is transferred to the rack and changed to linear motion. The linear force is then transmitted through the tie rods and to the steering knuckles which steer the front wheels.

DISASSEMBLY

1. Clamp steering gear housing in a suit-

able vise, **Fig. 1.**
2. Remove tie rod ends after making alignment marks, then remove and discard boots.
3. Straighten staked portion of locking washer between inner tie rod and rack, then remove inner tie rods after marking left and right ends.
4. Using sockets No. J-35692 and J-25423 or equivalent, loosen rack guide spring cap locknut, then remove spring and rack guide.
5. Remove pinion bearing adjusting screw using wrench, tool No. J-35418 or equivalent, then the pinion with upper bearing, using care not to damage pinion serrations.

6. Pull rack fully from housing side and align pinion with notched portion of rack. Remove pinion and upper bearing as an assembly.
7. Remove rack from pinion side without turning it.

INSPECTION & ASSEMBLY

Refer to the rear of this section for torque specifications.
1. Check rack teeth and back for wear or damage, **Fig. 1.**
2. Ensure runout does not exceed .012 inch.
3. Inspect pinion bearings.

4. If necessary to replace pinion bearing, proceed as follows:
   a. Remove upper bearing using bearing puller, tool No. J-22888 or equivalent.
   b. Install new upper bearing using bearing installer, tool No. J35419 or equivalent.
5. If necessary to replace lower pinion bearing, proceed as follows:
   a. Tap housing to free bearing using a suitable mallet and drift.
   b. Install new bearing using bearing installer, tool No. J-35682 or equivalent, ensuring proper installation direction.
6. If necessary to replace rack bushing, proceed as follows:
   a. Remove rack bushing using puller, tool No. J-35420 or equivalent.
   b. Ensure tube hole is not blocked with grease.
   c. Install new rack bushing using bushing installer, tool No. J-35421 or equivalent, and a suitable press.
   d. Ensure edge surface of new bushing is even with surface of tool.
7. If necessary to replace pinion oil seal, proceed as follows:
   a. Drive out old seal with deep well socket.
   b. Drive new oil seal into place using seal installer, tool No. J 35433 or equivalent, until it protrudes .020

inch (.5 mm). **During assembly, coat all friction surfaces with molybdenum disulphide lithium base grease.**
8. Install rack into housing from pinion side. Position notched portion of rack so that pinion can be positioned inside.
9. Line up cutout portion of rack with pinion, then install pinion ensuring pinion end is securely positioned in lower bearing.
10. Apply liquid sealer to threads of pinion bearing adjusting screw. Install screw using suitable socket.
11. Align cutout portion of rack with pinion.
12. **Torque** pinion bearing adjusting screw using suitable socket to 3.2 inch lbs.
13. Loosen screw until turning torque is between 2 and 2.2 inch lbs.
14. Apply a suitable sealer to pinion bearing adjusting screw locknut, then install locknut. **Torque** locknut to 83 ft. lbs. Recheck pinion preload and adjust as necessary.
15. Install plunger, spring adjusting plug and locknut.
16. Apply liquid sealer to guide spring cap threads.
17. Mesh rack with pinion, then install rack guide spring cap.
18. Count total number of pinion rotations

possible, then return pinion half that amount to place pinion in neutral position.
19. Adjust total preload as follows:
   a. **Torque** rack guide spring cap to 18 ft. lbs.
   b. Return rack guide spring cap 25°.
   c. Measure total preload within one rotation from neutral position in both directions. Preload should be 6.9-11.3 inch lbs.
   d. If preload is insufficient. Retorque guide spring cap and return slightly less than 12°.
   e. If preload is excessive, return rack guide spring cap slightly.
20. Apply a suitable sealant to locknut threads and rack housing surface, then install locknut and **torque** to 51 ft. lbs.
21. Recheck total preload and adjust as necessary, then install new dust boot.
22. Install inner tie rod with new locking washer, then **torque** to 61 ft. lbs. Stake lock washer to flat of inner tie rod, then apply a suitable lubricant to small opening in boot.
23. Install new boot over inner tie rod.
24. Install clamps and clips with open ends facing outward to avoid damage to boots.
25. Install tie rod ends so marks are aligned. Adjust toe-in, then **torque** locknuts to 35 ft. lbs.

Torque Specifications

NOTE: All Specifications In Ft. Lbs. Unless Noted.

Year & Model	Adjuster Plug Locknut	Flange & Coupling Pinch Bolt	Coupling To Column Pinch Bolt	Inner Tie Rod Pinch Bolts	Outer Tie Rod Pinch Bolts	Inner Tie Rod Bolt	Pinion Preload ① ②	Inner Tie Rod Housing To Rack	Outer Tie Rod Jam Nut
1988									
Cavalier, Firenza, Skyhawk & Sunbird	50	29	34	41	41	65	8-20	—	—
Fiero	50	—	46	—	—	—	13 max.	70	50
LeMans	52	18	18	16	16	66	14 max.	—	44
Nova	83	26	26	—	—	—	2-2.9	61	41
Spectrum	49	—	—	—	40③	—	3-8	65	—
Sprint	70	18	18	—	33③	—	7 max.	63	32
1989									
Cavalier, Skyhawk & Sunbird	50	29	34	41	41	65	8-20	—	—
LeMans	52	18	18	16	16	66	14 max.	—	44
Metro	70	18	18	—	33③	—	7 max.	63	32
Spectrum	49	—	—	—	40③	—	3-8	65	—
Sprint	70	18	18	—	33③	—	7 max.	63	32
1990									
Cavalier & Sunbird	50	29	34	41	41	65	8-20	—	—
LeMans	52	18	18	16	16	66	14 max.	—	44
Metro	70	18	18	—	33③	—	7 max.	63	32
Sprint	70	18	18	—	33③	—	7 max.	63	32

①—Inch lbs.
②—Effort required to sustain input shaft rotation with gear filled with lubricant.
③—Locknut

POWER STEERING

NOTE: Automatic transmission fluid should not be used in these power steering systems. ATF is not compatible with the seals and hoses used in this system and will eventually cause damage. Also, power steering fluid must withstand very high pressure (about 1400 psi), whereas transmission fluid does not have the need to operate at these pressures. If ATF has been added to a power steering system as in an emergency situation, the system should be drained, flushed and refilled with power steering fluid as soon as possible to avoid damage.

TABLE OF CONTENTS

Applications

FRONT WHEEL DRIVE VEHICLES

Domestic Front Wheel Drive Vehicles & Le Mans

Saginaw Rack & Pinion

Nova

Toyota Rack & Pinion

Prizm

Toyota Rack & Pinion

Spectrum

Jidosha Kiki & Saginaw Rack & Pinion

Storm

Jidosha Kiki Rack & Pinion

REAR WHEEL DRIVE VEHICLES

Except Corvette

Saginaw Rotary Valve

Corvette

Saginaw Rack & Pinion

Power Steering Pumps

INDEX

CB SERIES PUMP
DISASSEMBLY

1. Disconnect battery ground cable, then remove power steering pump from vehicle. Refer to individual car chapters for procedures.
2. Remove union fitting with O-ring and the O-ring seal, **Fig. 1.**
3. Remove control valve assembly and flow control spring.
4. Protect driveshaft with shim stock and remove driveshaft seal by cutting with small chisel. Discard seal.
5. Remove return tube using tap, nut and washers, **Fig. 2,** as follows. **Plug return tube to prevent chips from entering pump.**
   a. Stack five 5/8 inch washers onto return tube.
   b. Run one 9/16 inch-12 nut midway up a 9/16 inch 12 tap.
   c. Install threaded end of tap into return tube until nut is positioned

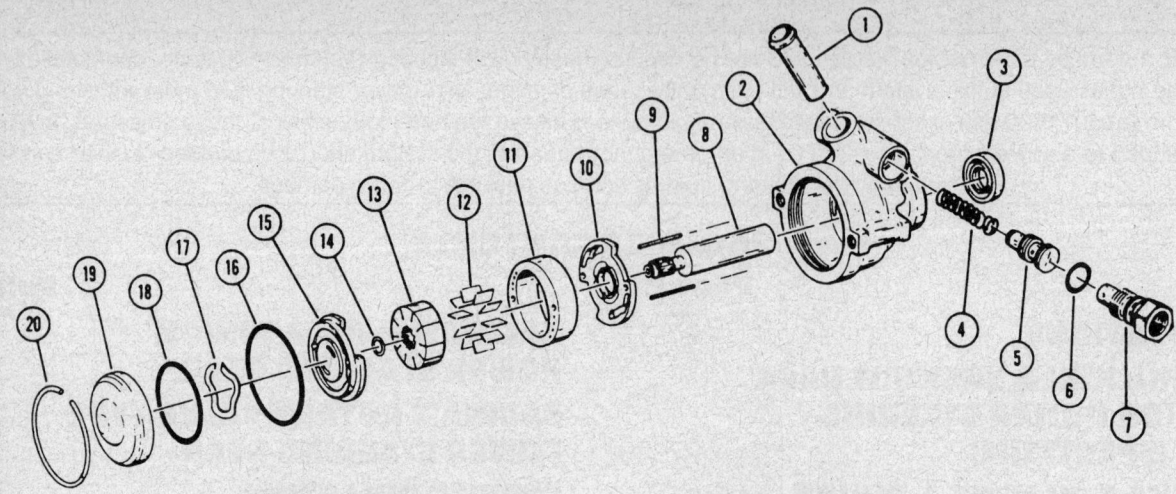

1-TUBE, RETURN
2-HOUSING ASM, HYD PUMP
3-SEAL, DRIVE SHAFT
4-SPRING, FLOW CONTROL
5-VALVE ASM, CONTROL
6-SEAL, O-RING
7-FITTING, O-RING UNION
8-SHAFT, DRIVE
9-PIN, PUMP RING DOWEL (2)
10-PLATE, THRUST

11-RING, PUMP
12-VANE (10)
13-ROTOR, PUMP
14-RING, SHAFT RETAINING
15-PLATE, PRESSURE
16-SEAL, O-RING
17-SPRING, PRESSURE PLATE
18-SEAL, O-RING
19-COVER, END
20-RING, RETAINING

Fig. 1   Exploded view of CB series power steering pump

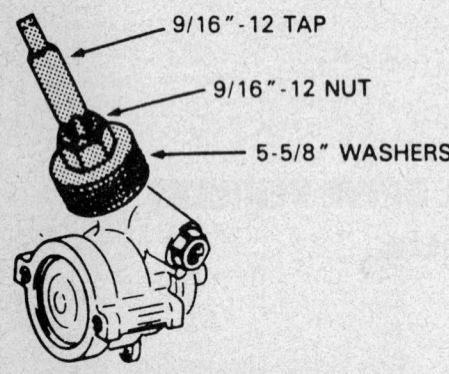

Fig. 2   Removing return tube. CB series power steering pump

against washers.
d. Using wrench, hold top stationary while turning nut clockwise.
6. Remove end cover retaining ring by inserting punch in access hole.
7. Gently push on driveshaft to assist in removing end cover, O-ring, pressure plate spring, pump ring, pump vanes and the driveshaft subassembly, consisting of pump rotor, thrust plate, driveshaft and shaft retaining ring.
8. Remove O-ring from housing.
9. Remove dowel pins, then the driveshaft seal if not previously removed.
10. Remove pressure plate, pressure plate spring and O-ring from end cover.
11. Remove shaft retaining ring from driveshaft, then the pump rotor and thrust plate.

INSPECTION

1. Clean all parts in power steering fluid, then dry thoroughly.
2. Inspect pump ring, vanes, thrust plate, pressure plate and driveshaft for scoring, pitting or chatter marks, replacing parts as necessary.

ASSEMBLY

1. Lubricate new driveshaft seal with power steering fluid and, using seal installer, tool No. J 7728 or equivalent, press driveshaft seal into pump housing.
2. Install pump ring dowel pins into housing.
3. Install thrust plate and pump rotor onto driveshaft, **Fig. 3**.
4. Install new shaft retaining ring onto driveshaft.
5. Install driveshaft subassembly into housing.
6. Install pump ring, with holes positioned correctly onto dowel pins, **Fig. 3**, in housing.
7. Install vanes into pump rotor.
8. Lubricate new O-ring (large) with power steering fluid and install O-ring into end cover.
9. Install pressure plate and pressure plate spring.
10. Lubricate new O-ring (small) and install O-ring into end cover.
11. Lubricate outer edge of end cover with power steering fluid and press end cover into housing.
12. Insert retaining ring into groove in housing, with ring opening near access hole opening.

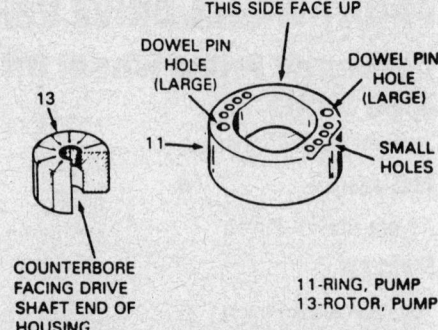

Fig. 3   Installing rotor and/or pump ring. CB series power steering pump

13. Remove plug and any chips, then coat end of new return tube with Loctite solvent 75559 and Loctite 290 adhesive, or equivalents, and press return tube into housing until bottomed.

JIDOSHA KIKI

This pump is only serviced as an assembly, except for relief valve and pulley.

PUMP REPLACEMENT

1. Place drain pan below pump, then remove pressure hose clamp.
2. Disconnect pressure and return hoses at pump.
3. Remove adjusting and pivot bolts, then remove drive belt.
4. Remove pump assembly and bracket.
5. Remove pulley using suitable puller.

POWER STEERING PUMP ASSEMBLY
(N SERIES-REMOTE RESERVOIR)
(P SERIES-SUBMERGED)

1-SHAFT, DRIVE
2-SEAL, DRIVE SHAFT
3-SEAL, O-RING (HOUSING)
4-HOUSING ASM., PUMP
5-SPRING, FLOW CONTROL
6-VALVE ASM., CONTROL
7-SEAL, O-RING (HOUSING)
8-SEAL, O-RING (PRESSURE & END PLATE)
9-PIN, DOWEL
10-PLATE, THRUST
11-ROTOR, PUMP
12-RING, SHAFT RETAINING

13-VANE, PUMP
14-RING, PUMP
15-PLATE, PRESSURE
16-SPRING, PRESSURE PLATE
17-PLATE, END
18-RING, END PLATE RETAINING
19-SEAL, O-RING (HOUSING TO STUD)
20-RESERVOIR ASM.
21-CAP ASM., RESERVOIR
22-STUD OR BOLT, PUMP MOUNTING
23-SEAL, O-RING (FITTING ASM.)
24-FITTING ASM. (CONNECTOR &)
25-MAGNET
26-RESERVOIR ASM.
27-HOUSING ASM., PUMP
28-TUBE, RETURN

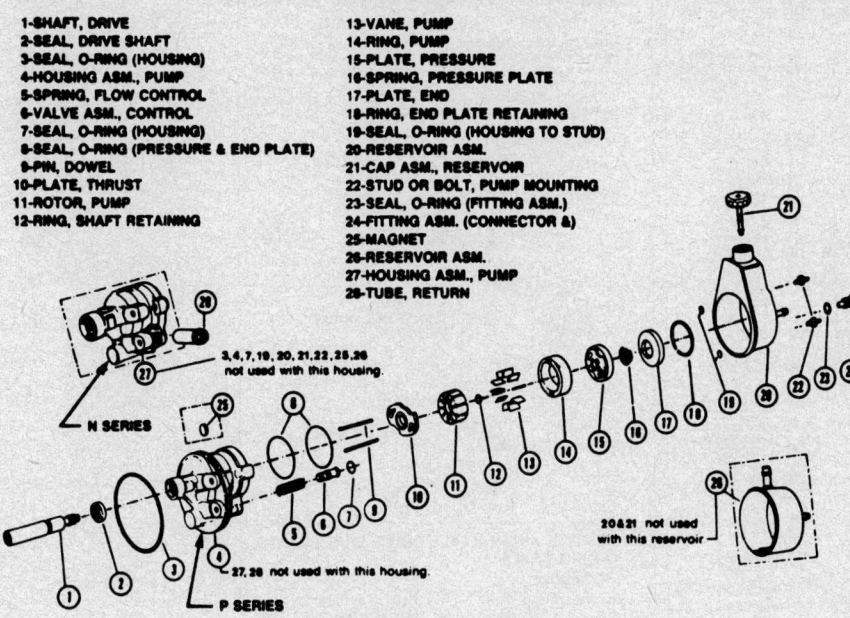

BENCH REPAIR INDEX
(N&P SERIES PUMP)

TO REMOVE	EXPLODED VIEW NO.	PERFORM STEPS
Drive Shaft Seal	2	1
Pump Reservoir	20 or 26	2
Control Valve Asm.	6	2-3
End Plate	17	3
Rotating Group	1-10-11-12-13-14-15	2-3-4
O-Ring Seals (Rotating Group) & Drive Shaft	2-8	2-3-4-5
Return Tube	28	6

Fig. 4 Power steering pump assembly overhaul (Part 1 of 2). N & P series

6. Reverse procedure to install. **Torque pressure hose to 20 ft. lbs.**

N & P SERIES PUMP

Refer to **Fig. 4** for service procedures on this power steering pump.

P SERIES L/RESERVOIR PUMP

Refer to **Fig. 5** for service procedures on this power steering pump.

TC SERIES PUMP

Refer to **Fig. 6** for service procedures on this power steering pump.

TOYOTA (NOVA) PUMP
DISASSEMBLY

1. Disconnect battery ground cable, then remove power steering pump from vehicle. Refer to individual car chapters for procedure.
2. Mount pump in suitable vise. **Do not over tighten vise as damage may result to pump.**
3. Remove pump reservoir tank attaching bolts, then the reservoir, bracket and O-ring, **Fig. 7.**
4. Remove pressure port union, then the valve and spring.
5. Using suitable snap ring pliers, remove flow control spring seat seal snap ring.
6. Using suitable bolt, remove flow control spring seat, then the spring.
7. Using two screwdrivers, remove rear housing snap ring, then the rear housing and wave washer.

8. Remove rear side plate, straight pins, vane plates and cam ring.
9. Using suitable soft faced hammer, tap out rotor assembly.
10. Using suitable screwdriver, pry snap ring from rotor shaft, then remove rotor and side plate from shaft. **Do not scratch rotor or shaft.**
11. Using screwdriver, pry front seal from housing.

INSPECTION

1. Using suitable caliper, measure rotor shaft and housing bushing to determine shaft to housing clearance. Standard clearance is .0004-.0012 inch (.01-.03 mm), with a maximum clearance of .0028 inch (.07 mm). If clearance exceeds specifications, replace pump assembly.
2. Measure rotor vanes as follows:
   a. Minimum rotor vane height, .319 inch (8.1 mm).
   b. Minimum rotor vane thickness, .0707 inch (1.797 mm).
   c. Minimum rotor vane length, .5901 inch (14.988 mm).
3. Using suitable feeler gauge, measure clearance between rotor groove and vane plate. Clearance should not exceed .0011 inch (.028 mm). If clearance exceeds specifications, replace pump plate and/or rotor as necessary. **When replacing pump plate and/or rotor assembly, ensure stamped number (1, 2, 3, 4 or blank) is the same.**
4. Inspect flow control as follows:
   a. Apply auto. trans. fluid to flow control valve, then ensure valve falls smoothly into valve hole under its own weight. Remove valve.
   b. While holding one side hole of flow control valve closed with finger pressure, apply compressed air to other flow control valve side hole. No air should be expelled from main port.
   c. If necessary, replace flow control valve. **When replacing flow control valve, ensure stamped letter (A, B, C, D, E or F) is the same.**
5. Measure flow control valve spring. Minimum length is 1.97 inch (50 mm). If not within specification, replace spring.

ASSEMBLY

1. Apply auto. trans. fluid to front seal, then install seal using 23 mm socket.
2. Apply auto. trans. fluid to replacement O-rings, then install O-rings on side plate. Position side plate on shaft, then place rotor onto shaft with mark facing upwards and install snap ring.
3. Apply auto. trans. fluid to front shaft seal, then install long pin into housing.
4. Using suitable soft faced hammer, tap in rotor assembly. **Use caution not to damage seals.**
5. Install short pin into housing, then the cam ring with mark facing outward.
6. Install rotor vanes into rotor with rounded end facing outward.
7. Apply auto. trans. fluid to O-ring, then

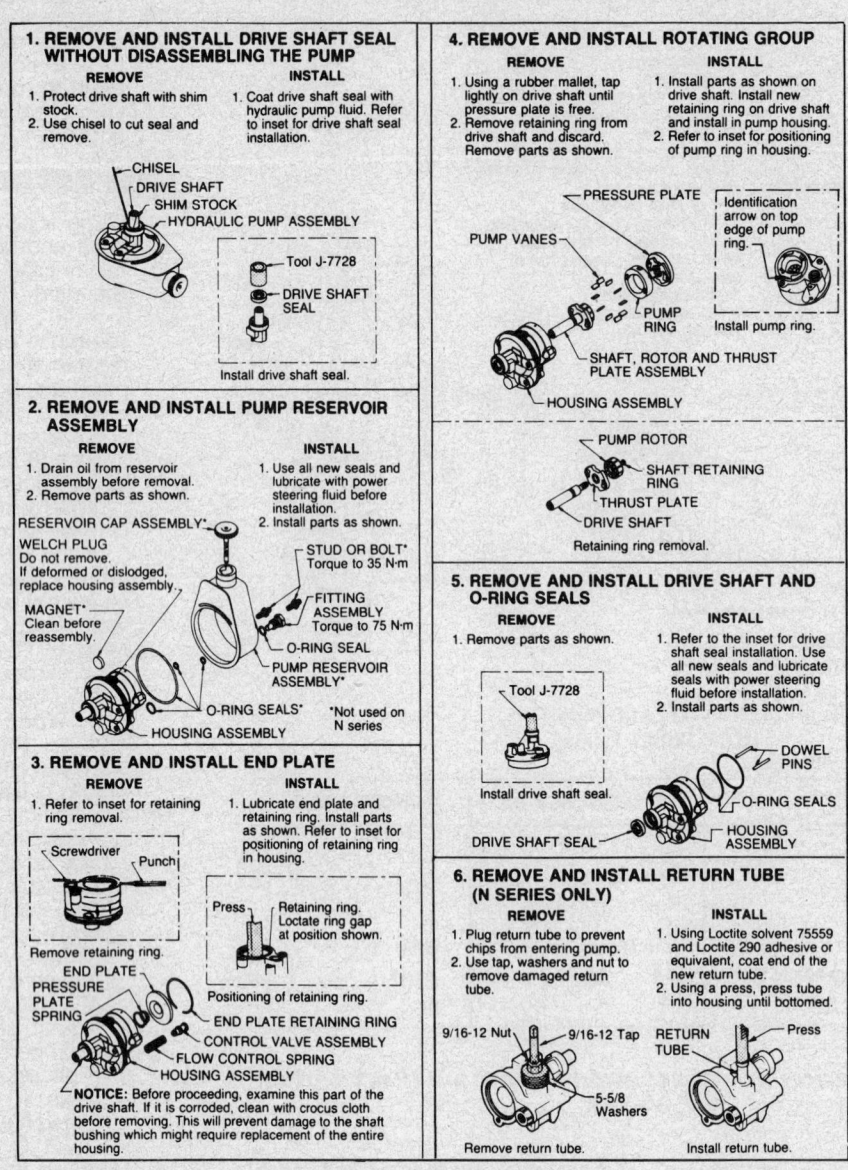

Fig. 4   Power steering pump assembly overhaul (Part 2 of 2). N & P series

install onto side plate. Install side plate in housing, aligning pins and holes during installation.

8. Apply auto. trans. fluid to O-ring, then install wave washer and O-ring in rear housing, then using soft faced hammer, tap rear housing into place and install snap ring. **Ensure shaft rotates smoothly.**

9. Temporarily install front pulley and measure pump shaft rotating torque. Rotating torque should be less than 2.4 inch lbs.

10. Apply auto. trans. fluid to spring seat, then install spring seat and snap ring.

11. Apply auto. trans. fluid to O-ring, then install flow control spring, valve, O-ring and pressure port union. **Torque** pressure port union to 51 ft. lbs.

12. Apply auto. trans. fluid to reservoir tank O-ring, then install O-ring and reservoir tank. **Torque** reservoir tank bracket attaching bolts to 9 ft. lbs.

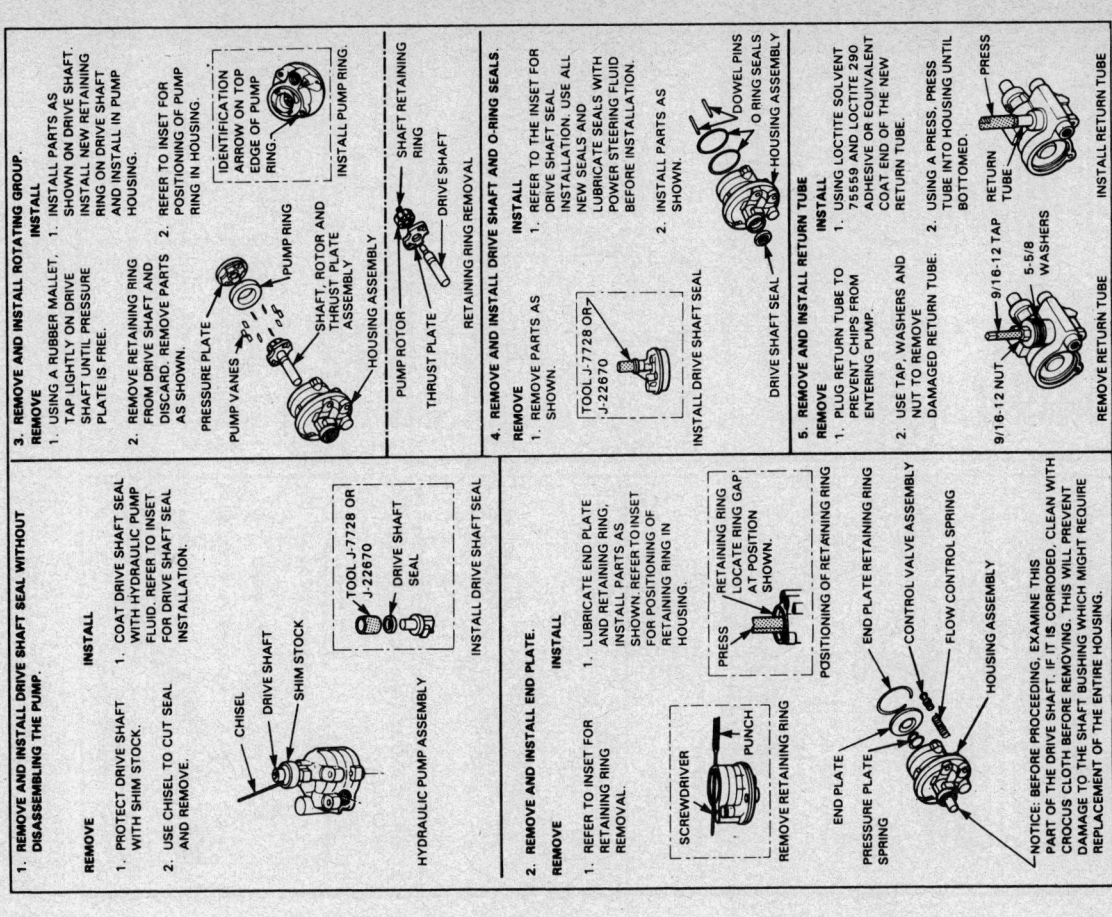

Fig. 5 Power steering pump assembly overhaul (Part 2 of 2). P series, L/reservoir

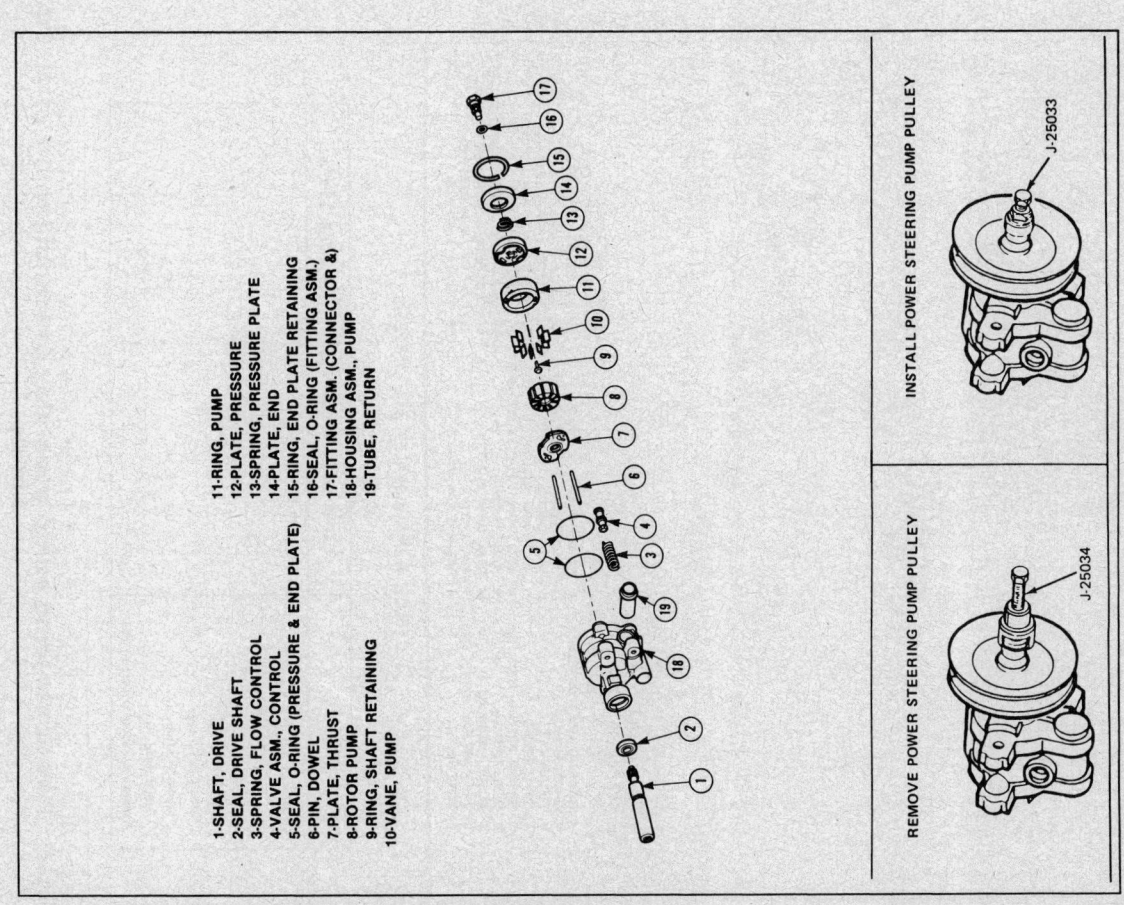

1-SHAFT, DRIVE
2-SEAL, DRIVE SHAFT
3-SPRING, FLOW CONTROL
4-VALVE ASM., CONTROL
5-SEAL, O-RING (PRESSURE & END PLATE)
6-PIN, DOWEL
7-PLATE, THRUST
8-ROTOR PUMP
9-RING, SHAFT RETAINING
10-VANE, PUMP

11-RING, PUMP
12-PLATE, PRESSURE
13-SPRING, PRESSURE PLATE
14-PLATE, END
15-RING, END PLATE RETAINING
16-SEAL, O-RING (FITTING ASM.)
17-FITTING ASM. (CONNECTOR &)
18-HOUSING ASM., PUMP
19-TUBE, RETURN

Fig. 5 Power steering pump assembly overhaul (Part 1 of 2). P series, L/reservoir

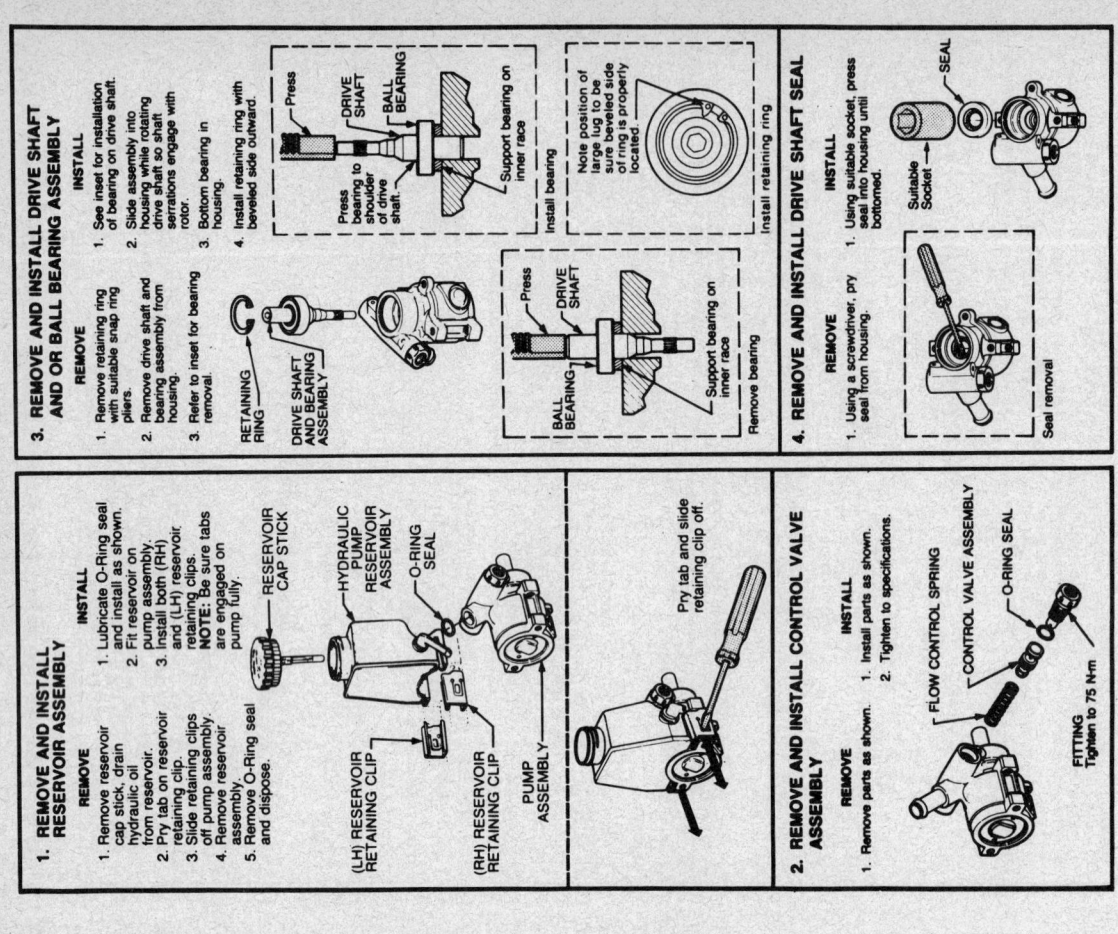

3. REMOVE AND INSTALL DRIVE SHAFT AND OR BALL BEARING ASSEMBLY

INSTALL
1. See inset for installation of bearing on drive shaft.
2. Slide assembly into housing while rotating drive shaft so shaft serrations engage with rotor.
3. Bottom bearing in housing.
4. Install retaining ring with beveled side outward.

Press bearing to shoulder of drive shaft.
DRIVE SHAFT
BALL BEARING
Support bearing on inner race

Note position of large lug to be sure beveled side of ring is properly located.
Install retaining ring

REMOVE
1. Remove retaining ring with suitable snap ring pliers.
2. Remove drive shaft and bearing assembly from housing.
3. Refer to inset for bearing removal.

RETAINING RING
DRIVE SHAFT AND BEARING ASSEMBLY

Press
DRIVE SHAFT
BALL BEARING
Support bearing on inner race
Remove bearing

4. REMOVE AND INSTALL DRIVE SHAFT SEAL

SEAL
Suitable Socket

INSTALL
1. Using suitable socket, press seal into housing until bottomed.

REMOVE
1. Using a screwdriver, pry seal from housing.

Seal removal

1. REMOVE AND INSTALL RESERVOIR ASSEMBLY

REMOVE
1. Remove reservoir cap stick, drain hydraulic oil from reservoir.
2. Pry tab on reservoir retaining clip.
3. Slide retaining clips off pump assembly.
4. Remove reservoir assembly.
5. Remove O-Ring seal and dispose.

INSTALL
1. Lubricate O-Ring seal and install as shown.
2. Fit reservoir on pump assembly.
3. Install both (RH) and (LH) reservoir retaining clips. **NOTE:** Be sure tabs are engaged on pump fully.

RESERVOIR CAP STICK
HYDRAULIC PUMP RESERVOIR ASSEMBLY
O-RING SEAL
(LH) RESERVOIR RETAINING CLIP
(RH) RESERVOIR RETAINING CLIP
PUMP ASSEMBLY

Pry tab and slide retaining clip off.

2. REMOVE AND INSTALL CONTROL VALVE ASSEMBLY

REMOVE
1. Remove parts as shown.

INSTALL
1. Install parts as shown.
2. Tighten to specifications.

FLOW CONTROL SPRING
CONTROL VALVE ASSEMBLY
O-RING SEAL
FITTING Tighten to 75 N·m

Fig. 6 Power steering pump assembly overhaul (Part 2 of 4). TC series

POWER STEERING PUMP ASSEMBLY (TC SERIES)

USED ON SOME MODELS

NOTE: Return tube (15) used in place of Reservoir Assembly (24) and related parts (25 thru 28).

1 - HOUSING ASM, HYD. PUMP
2 - SLEEVE ASM
3 - PIN, DOWEL
4 - SEAL, O-RING
5 - SPRING, PRESSURE PLATE
6 - SEAL, O-RING
7 - PLATE, PRESSURE
8 - PIN, PUMP RING DOWEL (2)
9 - VANE (10)
10 - ROTOR, PUMP
11 - RING, PUMP
12 - SEAL, O-RING
13 - PLATE ASM, THRUST
14 - RING, THRUST PLATE RETAINING
15 - TUBE, RETURN
16 - SEAL, DRIVE SHAFT
17 - SHAFT, DRIVE
18 - BEARING ASM, BALL
19 - RING, RETAINING
20 - SPRING, FLOW CONTROL
21 - VALVE ASM, CONTROL
22 - SEAL, O-RING
23 - FITTING, O-RING UNION
24 - RESERVOIR ASM, HYD. PUMP
25 - SEAL, O-RING
26 - CLIP, RESERVOIR RETAINING (LH)
27 - CLIP, RESERVOIR RETAINING (RH)
28 - CAPSTICK ASM, RESERVOIR
29 - BAFFLE, PUMP ASM.

BENCH REPAIR INDEX (TC SERIES)

TO REMOVE	EXPLODED VIEW NO.	PERFORM STEPS
Return Tube	15	7
Control Valve Asm.	21	2
Drive Shaft	17	3
Ball Bearing (Drive Shaft)	18	3
Drive Shaft Seal	16	3-4
Rotating Group	7-9-10-11-12-13	3&5
Sleeve Asm.	2	3-5-6
Hydraulic Pump Reservoir Asm.	24	1

Fig. 6 Power steering pump assembly overhaul (Part 1 of 4). TC series

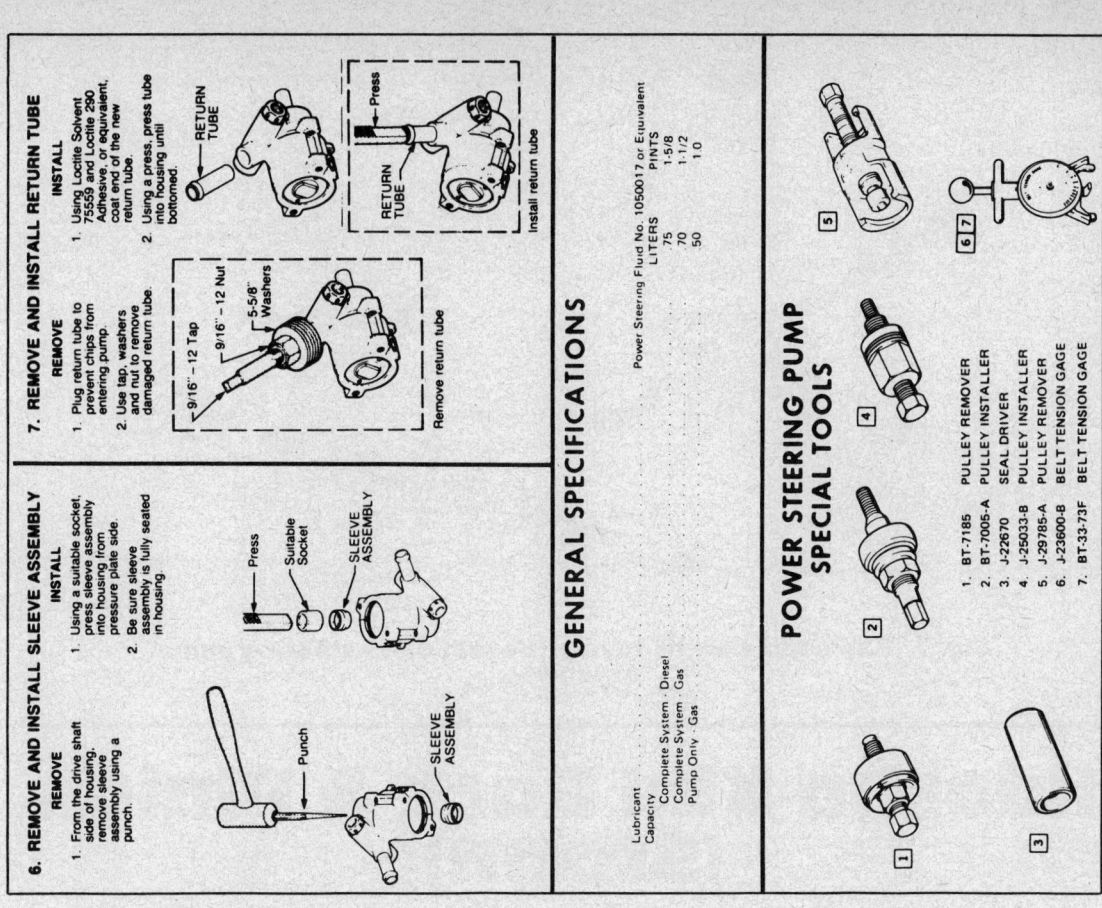

Fig. 6 Power steering pump assembly overhaul (Part 4 of 4). TC series

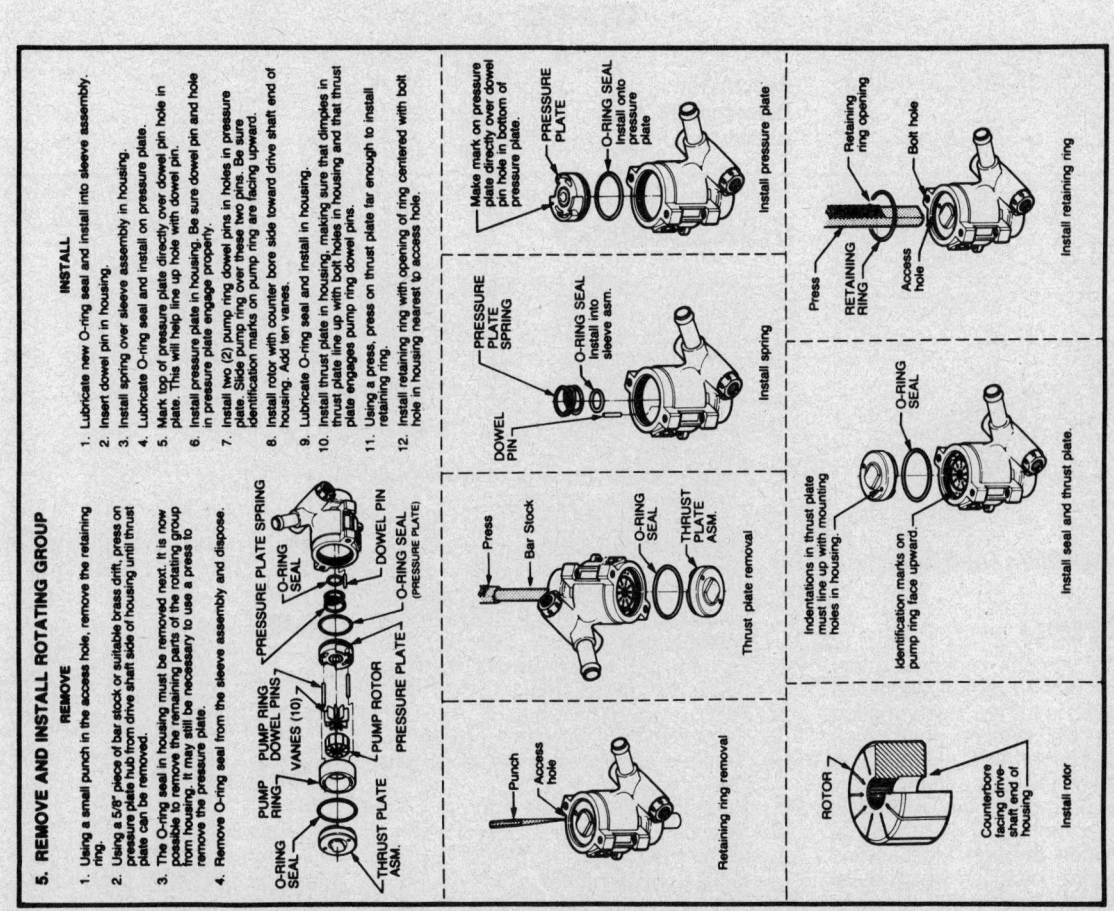

Fig. 6 Power steering pump assembly overhaul (Part 3 of 4). TC series

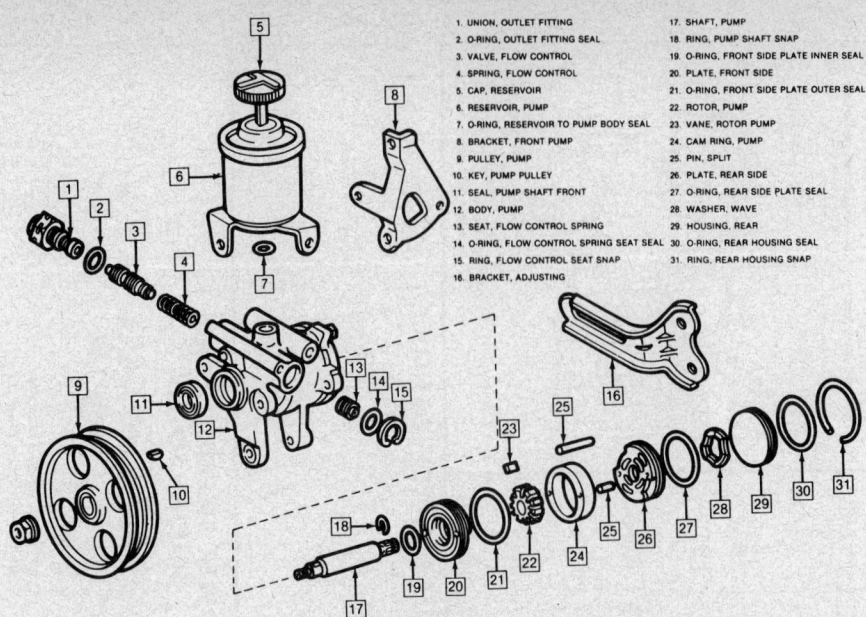

1. UNION, OUTLET FITTING
2. O-RING, OUTLET FITTING SEAL
3. VALVE, FLOW CONTROL
4. SPRING, FLOW CONTROL
5. CAP, RESERVOIR
6. RESERVOIR, PUMP
7. O-RING, RESERVOIR TO PUMP BODY SEAL
8. BRACKET, FRONT PUMP
9. PULLEY, PUMP
10. KEY, PUMP PULLEY
11. SEAL, PUMP SHAFT FRONT
12. BODY, PUMP
13. SEAT, FLOW CONTROL SPRING
14. O-RING, FLOW CONTROL SPRING SEAT SEAL
15. RING, FLOW CONTROL SEAT SNAP
16. BRACKET, ADJUSTING
17. SHAFT, PUMP
18. RING, PUMP SHAFT SNAP
19. O-RING, FRONT SIDE PLATE INNER SEAL
20. PLATE, FRONT SIDE
21. O-RING, FRONT SIDE PLATE OUTER SEAL
22. ROTOR, PUMP
23. VANE, ROTOR PUMP
24. CAM RING, PUMP
25. PIN, SPLIT
26. PLATE, REAR SIDE
27. O-RING, REAR SIDE PLATE SEAL
28. WASHER, WAVE
29. HOUSING, REAR
30. O-RING, REAR HOUSING SEAL
31. RING, REAR HOUSING SNAP

Fig. 7 Exploded view of Toyota (Nova) power steering pump assembly

Jidosha Kiki Rack & Pinion (Storm)

INDEX
Page No.

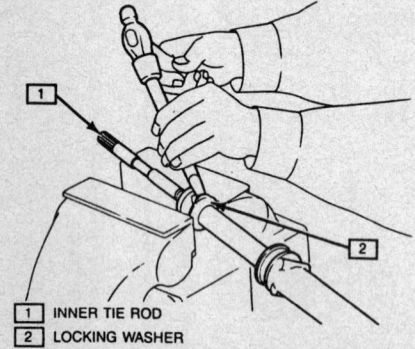

1 INNER TIE ROD
2 LOCKING WASHER

Fig. 1 Unstaking lock washer

DESCRIPTION

This steering system converts rotary motion to linear motion as follows; when the steering wheel is turned, rotary motion is transferred to the steering shaft, shaft joint and rack pinion. The pinion teeth mesh with teeth on the rack and the rotary motion is transferred to the rack and changed to linear motion. The linear force is then transmitted through the tie rods and to the steering knuckles which steer the front wheels.

DISASSEMBLY

1. Remove retaining ring and dust boot from rack.
2. Clamp steering gear in suitable vise.
3. Remove clamps from tie rod boots, then separate boots from rack and slide down tie rods.
4. Unstake locking washers between inner tie rods and rack, **Fig. 1.**
5. Remove right tie rod, then left tie rod assembly from rack, **Fig. 2.**
6. Loosen adjusting plug nut, then remove spring and rack plunger, **Fig. 3.**
7. Center rack and mark position of pinion valve. Rotate pinion gear until notch is parallel to rack, then carefully measure and record dimension "A", **Fig. 4.** This measurement **must** be used upon reassembly.
8. Remove valve plug, **Fig. 5.**
9. Remove pinion fixing nut, **Fig. 6.**
10. Remove pinion retaining snap ring, **Fig. 7.**
11. Remove rack from housing.
12. Remove inner rack seal and shock damper using inner rack seal remover tool No. 38304-5, **Fig. 8.**
13. Remove lower pinion bearing from

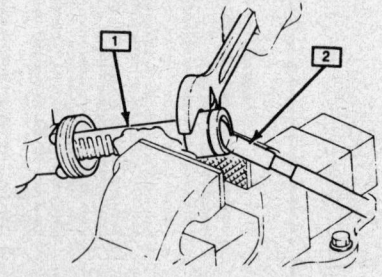

1 RACK GEAR
2 INNER TIE ROD

Fig. 2   Removing inner tie rod assembly

rack housing.
14. Remove bearing and seal from valve housing using lower pinion valve housing seal and bearing remover tool No. 38304-1, **Fig. 9.**

ASSEMBLY

1. Install inner rack seal onto rack seal ring installer, tool No. J 33997-3 using rack seal ring expander, tool No. J 33997-2.

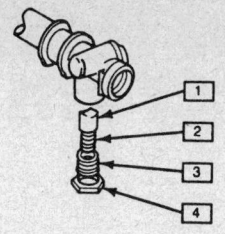

1 PLUNGER
2 SPRING
3 ADJUSTING PLUG
4 LOCK NUT

Fig. 3 Adjusting plug, spring and plunger assembly

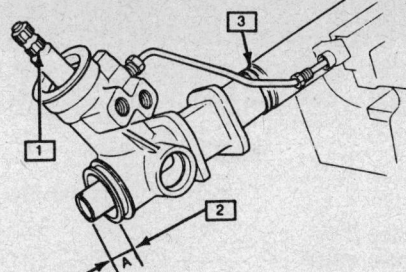

1 NOTCH ON SHAFT
2 DIMENSION "A"
3 RACK HOUSING

Fig. 4 Pinion shaft measurment location

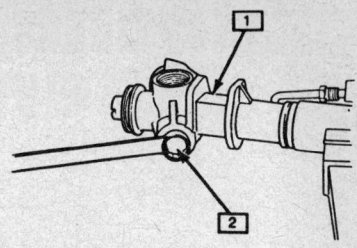

1 RACK HOUSING
2 VALVE PLUG

Fig. 5 Removing valve plug

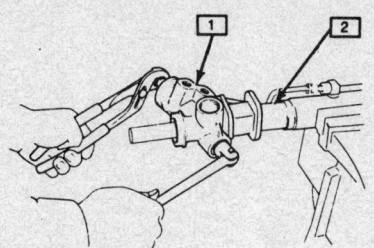

1 PINION HOUSING
2 RACK HOUSING

Fig. 6 Removing pinion fixing nut

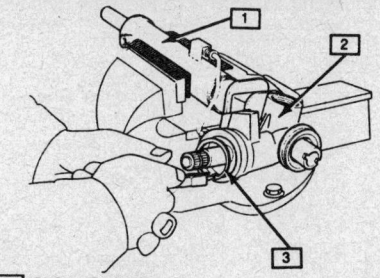

1 RACK HOUSING
2 PINION HOUSING
3 PINION RETAINING RING

Fig. 7 Removing retaining snap ring

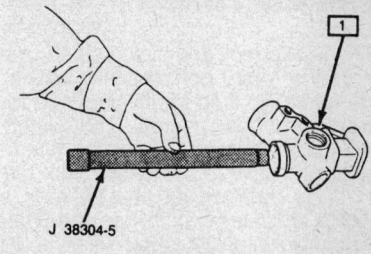

1 PINION VALVE HOUSING

Fig. 8 Removing inner rack seal and shock dampner

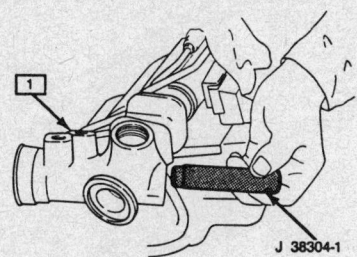

1 PINION VALVE HOUSING

Fig. 9 Removing pinion bearing

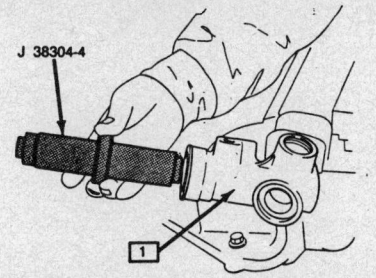

1 PINION VALVE HOUSING

Fig. 10 Installing pinion valve bearing and seal

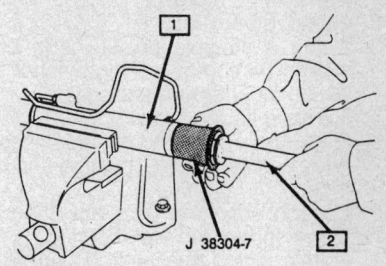

1 RACK HOUSING
2 RACK GEAR

Fig. 11 Installing inner rack seal

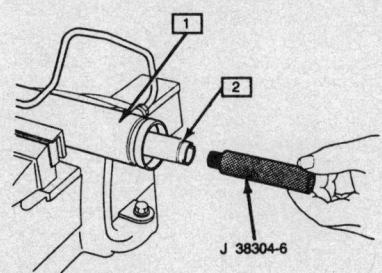

1 RACK HOUSING
2 RACK GEAR

Fig. 12 Seating inner rack seal

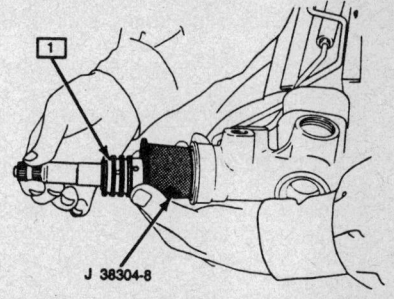

1 PINION VALVE ASSEMBLY

Fig. 13 Installing pinion valve assembly

3. Install rack into housing and seat inner rack seal using pack piston ring installer tool No. J 38304-7 and inner rack seal installer tool No. J 38304-6, **Figs. 11 and 12.**
4. Install seal holder on to housing, then retaining ring on seal holder.
5. Install pinion valve assembly into housing using pinion ring compressor tool No. 38304-8, **Fig. 13.**
6. Install lower bearing on pinion valve.
7. Install pinion fixing nut and **torque** to 29 ft. lbs.
8. Install pinion valve housing cap, then rack plunger and plunger plug. **Torque** rack plunger adjusting plug to 44 inch lbs. Back off plug, then **torque** to 44 inch lbs. Back off plug 26° then, tighten lock nut.
9. Install upper pinion valve seal, then retaining ring on upper pinion valve seal.
10. Install left tie rod assembly, then **torque** inner tie rod to 65 ft. lbs. and

2. Install upper bearing and seal into pinion valve housing using lower pinion valve housing seal and bearing installer tool No. J 38304-4, **Fig. 10.**

peen over stake washer. Install left tie rod boot.
11. Install right tie rod assembly, then **torque** inner tie rod to 65 ft. lbs. and peen over stake washer. Install right tie rod boot.

Jidosha Kiki & Saginaw Power Steering Gear (Spectrum)

INDEX

Page No.

DESCRIPTION

The power rack and pinion steering system has a rotary control valve which directs hydraulic fluid under pressure to either side of rack piston. The piston is attached to the rack. The piston uses hydraulic pressure to move the rack left or right. This then moves the tie rods and steering knuckles, which turn the wheels.

If hydraulic assist should fail, manual control is maintained; however, under these conditions, more steering effort is required.

DISASSEMBLY

1. Remove tie rod end.
2. Remove boot, **Fig. 1.**
3. Using a suitable chisel, bend back staked portion of locking washer between inner tie rod and rack.
4. Remove tie rod from rack.
5. Disconnect right and left pipe assemblies between valve housing and cylinder.
6. Loosen adjusting plug nut, then remove spring and rack bearing.
7. Rotate pinion gear until pinion flat is parallel or aligned to the rack assembly. Carefully measure dimension A, **Fig. 2.** Record reading. This relationship must be used for assembly.
8. Remove valve/pinion housing assembly.
9. Remove adjusting shims and retaining ring.
10. Withdraw rack assembly and seal holder together.
11. Remove inner rack seal and shock dampener.
12. Remove piston and O-ring seals from rack.
13. Remove valve assembly from housing.
14. Remove bearing and seal from valve housing.
15. Remove snap ring from spool end of valve assembly, then slide spool, seals and spacer. Do not remove Teflon seals.

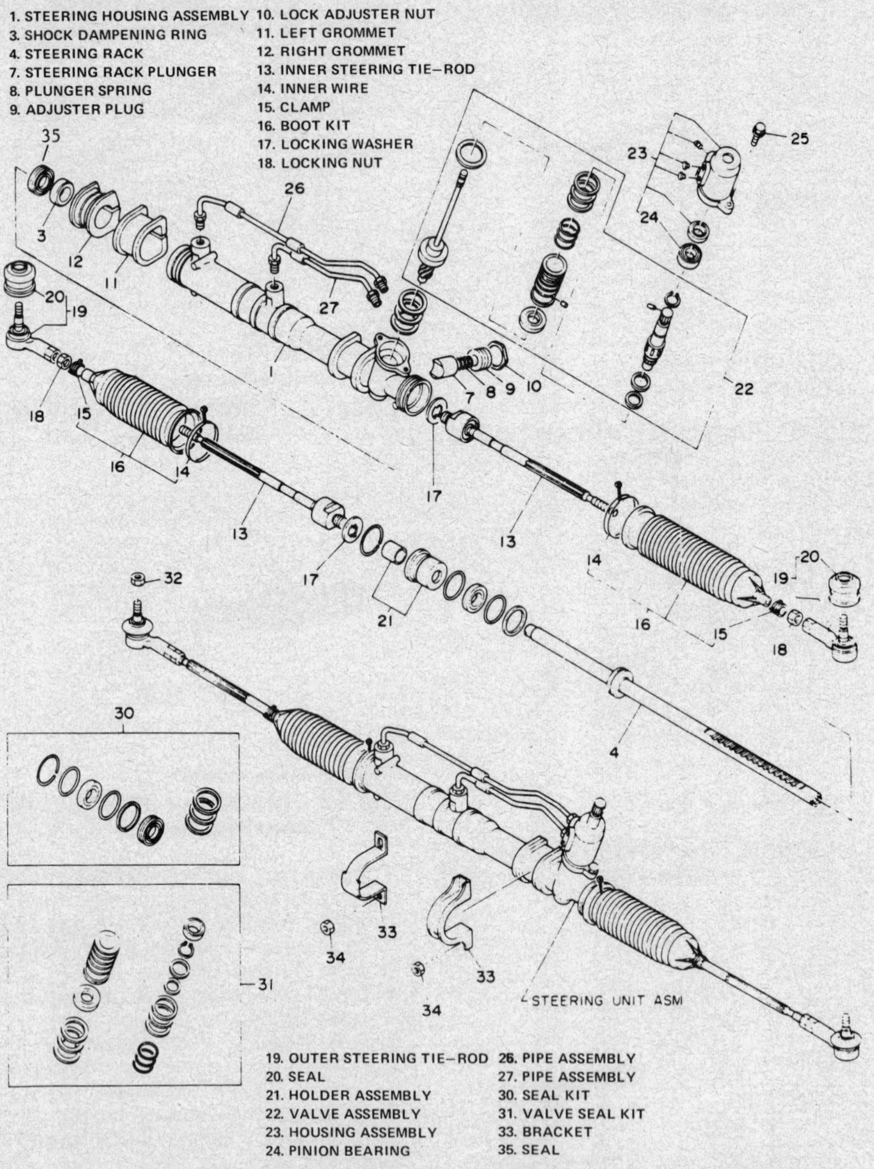

ASSEMBLY

1. Install spacer, then slide oil seal onto shaft.
2. Install valve spool.
3. Install snap ring on to shaft at spool.
4. Install upper bearing and seal into

1. STEERING HOUSING ASSEMBLY
3. SHOCK DAMPENING RING
4. STEERING RACK
7. STEERING RACK PLUNGER
8. PLUNGER SPRING
9. ADJUSTER PLUG
10. LOCK ADJUSTER NUT
11. LEFT GROMMET
12. RIGHT GROMMET
13. INNER STEERING TIE—ROD
14. INNER WIRE
15. CLAMP
16. BOOT KIT
17. LOCKING WASHER
18. LOCKING NUT

19. OUTER STEERING TIE—ROD
20. SEAL
21. HOLDER ASSEMBLY
22. VALVE ASSEMBLY
23. HOUSING ASSEMBLY
24. PINION BEARING
26. PIPE ASSEMBLY
27. PIPE ASSEMBLY
30. SEAL KIT
31. VALVE SEAL KIT
33. BRACKET
35. SEAL

Fig. 1 Exploded view of power steering gear assembly

valve housing, **Flat side of seal towards bearing.**
5. Before installing pinion/valve assembly into valve housing.
6. Place seal protector, tool No. J-33997-9 or equivalent, onto upper pinion shaft.
7. Install pinion/valve assembly into valve housing.
8. Install seal onto rack piston.
9. Lubricate rack gear surfaces. Install seal into seal holder with flat end of seal in first, then install seal holder.
10. Install shock damping ring.

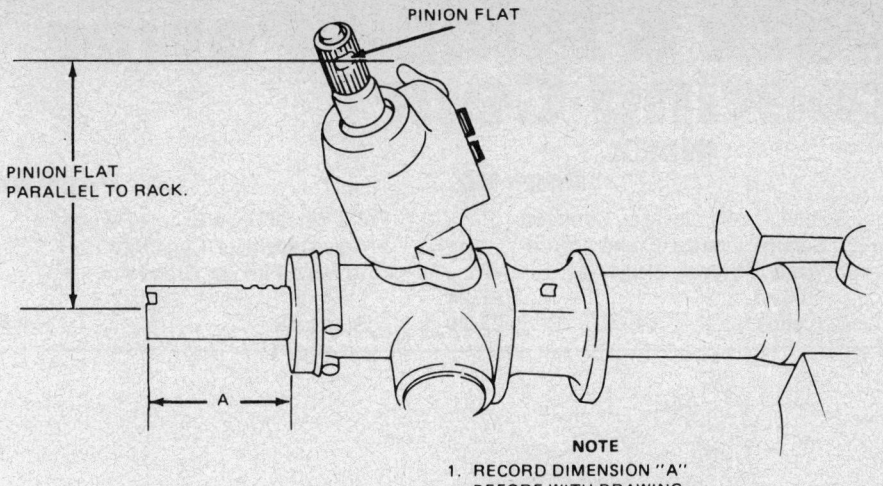

PINION FLAT

PINION FLAT PARALLEL TO RACK.

A

NOTE
1. RECORD DIMENSION "A" BEFORE WITH DRAWING THE PINION/VALVE ASSEMBLY
2. SET DIMENSION "A" BEFORE INSTALLING PINION/VALVE ASSEMBLY.

Fig. 2   Measuring & centering rack/pinion

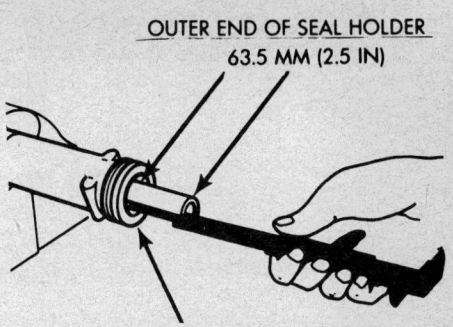

OUTER END OF SEAL HOLDER
63.5 MM (2.5 IN)

Fig. 3   Centering rack assembly

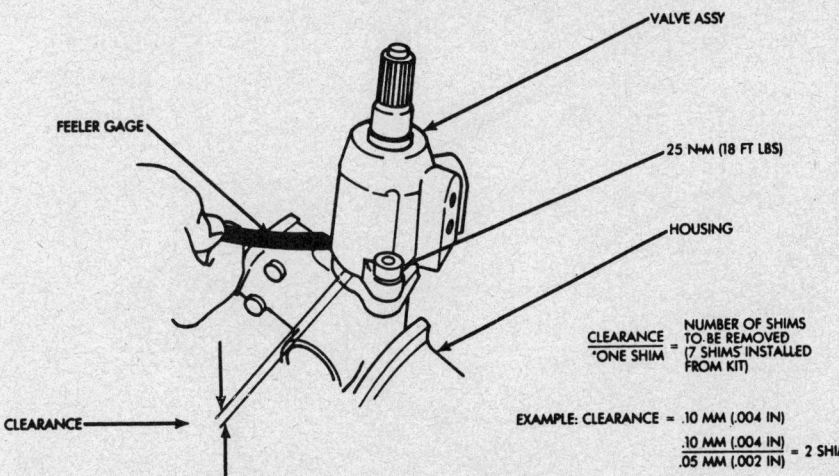

VALVE ASSY

25 N·M (18 FT LBS)

HOUSING

FEELER GAGE

CLEARANCE

$\dfrac{\text{CLEARANCE}}{\text{*ONE SHIM}}$ = NUMBER OF SHIMS TO BE REMOVED (7 SHIMS INSTALLED FROM KIT)

EXAMPLE: CLEARANCE = .10 MM (.004 IN)

$\dfrac{.10 \text{ MM } (.004 \text{ IN})}{.05 \text{ MM } (.002 \text{ IN})}$ = 2 SHIMS

Fig. 5   Checking clearance

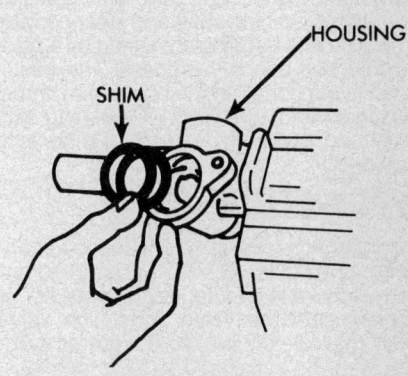

SHIM

HOUSING

Fig. 4   Installing adjusting shims

11. Install inner rack seal with flat end of seal facing away from rack piston.
12. Install rack assembly and push seal holder into housing.
13. Install retaining ring.
14. Move rack assembly into housing as far as it will go and measure distance between end of holder and tip of rack shaft. The seals are positioned correctly when dimension L is .39 inch (10 mm) or more.
15. If the valve assembly, valve housing, or any internal valve components, rack assembly or housing have been replaced, it is necessary to check and adjust the clearance between the valve assembly and housing. To check and adjust clearance, proceed as follows:
    a. Center rack assembly, then measure between end of seal holder and rack end. Distance should be 2.5 inches, **Fig. 3.**
    b. Lubricate pinion gear teeth and pinion ball bearings with suitable

grease.
    c. Using valve assembly repair kit, install all seven adjusting shims, **Fig. 4.**
    d. Install pinion/valve assembly into housing and carefully tighten the two bolts ¼ turn each until snug.
    e. Using a feeler gauge, measure clearance between the valve and gear housing, **Fig. 5. The purpose of step e is to reduce the clearance as close to zero as possible by removing shims. This minimizes endplay for the pinion gear assembly.**
    f. Using example shown in **Fig. 5** calculate, then remove the necessary shims. Install pinion and valve assembly following the procedure in step d. Again check clearance. Final clearance measurement obtained should be .002 inch or less.
    g. Carefully set rack to dimension A, recorded previously. Install pinion aligning flat parallel, as shown in

Fig. 2. Plus or minus 5 degrees from parallel is acceptable.
    h. When final clearance is obtained, use RTV sealer No. 1052366 or equivalent, to seal mating surfaces of valve and steering housing. **Torque** to 18 ft. lbs.
    i. Install rack plunger, spring, adjusting plug and locknut. **Torque** adjusting plug to 3.6 ft. lbs., loosen plug, then again **torque** to 3.6 ft. lbs. Back off plug 30 or 35 degrees, then tighten locknut.
    j. Check pinion shaft preload. Preload should be 4.1-2 ft. lbs. If preload is not as specified, loosen locknut and adjust plug torque. When an acceptable preload is obtained, apply liquid thread lock to locknut and **torque** nut to 49 ft. lbs.
16. Install right and left cylinder pipes. **Torque** fittings to 14 ft. lbs.
17. Install inner tie rod and new locking washer to rack end. **Torque** to 65 ft. lbs. Stake locking washer to the flat of inner tie rod. Apply grease to inner surface of small opening c boot.
18. Install boot over inner tie rod. Install boot clamp and wire. Use new boot, if necessary.
19. Install tie rod nut and attach tie rod end.
20. Adjust rod length L dimension to 7.5 inch.
21. **Torque** tie rod locking nut to 40 ft. lbs.

Saginaw Rack & Pinion Power Steering Gear
INDEX

DESCRIPTION

This power steering gear assembly, in-corporates an integral tube and housing, containing a pinion shaft and steering rack. The tube and housing are joined by a plas-tic injection-bonding process. The pinion shaft is supported in the housing by thrust bearings and bushings. A bushing and bulkhead assembly supports the steering in the tube.

OPERATION

A rotary-type valve body is used to con-trol the hydraulic steering assist. Fluid un-der pressure is directed to the gear hous-ing and into the valve body. The valve body then directs fluid to the power cylin-der.

A spool valve, connected to the stub shaft by a locating pin, rotates within the valve body. Fluid directional passages, machined into the spool valve, are aligned with fluid passages in the valve body as the spool valve rotates. Fluid is directed through these passages, into either side of the power cylinder through the externally mounted oil lines.

SERVICE PROCEDURES
FRONT WHEEL DRIVE EXCEPT BERETTA, CALAIS, CAVALIER, CIMARRON, CORSICA, FIRENZA, GRAND AM, LEMANS, SKYHAWK, SKYLARK & SUNBIRD

To prevent damage to the rack and pinion boot seal when removing it, the following should be noted. Slide the small end of the boot towards the rack until the groove is exposed. Place a small rubber band in the groove then, slide the small end of the boot over the rubber band and off the threaded end of the tie rod. This will prevent boot damage.

OUTER TIE ROD

1. Remove cotter pin, then hex slotted nut from outer tie rod assembly, **Figs. 1 and 2.**
2. Loosen jam nut, then remove outer tie rod from steering knuckle using steer-ing linkage remover tool No. J 24319-01.

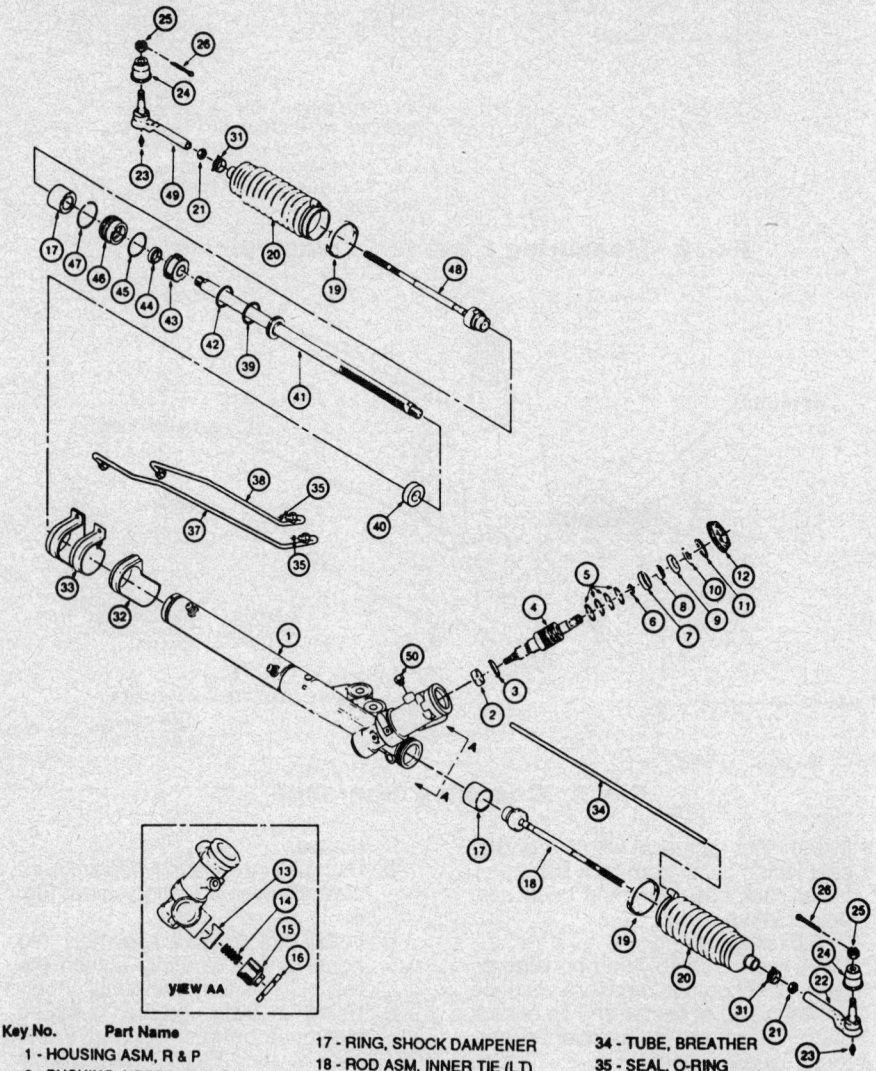

Key No.	Part Name
1	HOUSING ASM, R & P
2	BUSHING, UPPER PINION
3	SEAL, RACK & PINION
4	VALVE ASM, PINION &
5	RING, VALVE BODY
6	RING, RETAINING
7	ANNULUS, STUB SHAFT BEARING
8	BEARING ASM, NEEDLE
9	SEAL, STUB SHAFT
10	SEAL, STUB SHAFT DUST
11	RING, RETAINING
12	ADAPTER, SEAL
13	BEARING, RACK
14	SPRING, ADJUSTER
15	PLUG, ADJUSTER
16	NUT, ADJUSTER PLUG LOCK
17	RING, SHOCK DAMPENER
18	ROD ASM, INNER TIE (LT)
19	CLAMP, BOOT
20	BOOT, RACK & PINION
21	NUT, HEX JAM
22	ROD ASM, OUTER TIE (LT)
23	FITTING, LUBRICATION
24	SEAL, TIE ROD
25	NUT, HEXAGON SLOTTED
26	PIN, COTTER
27	BEARING ASM, BALL
28	RING, RETAINING
29	NUT, HEX LOCK
30	COVER, DUST
31	CLAMP, TIE ROD END
32	GROMMET, MOUNTING
33	BRACKET ASM, MOUNTING
34	TUBE, BREATHER
35	SEAL, O-RING
36	THIS NUMBER NOT USED
37	LINE ASM, CYLINDER (LT)
38	LINE ASM, CYLINDER (RT)
39	THIS NUMBER NOT USED
40	SEAL, INNER RACK
41	RACK ASM, PISTON & STEERING
42	RING PISTON
43	BULKHEAD, CYLINDER INNER
44	SEAL, RACK & PINION (BULKHEAD)
45	SEAL, O-RING
46	BULKHEAD, CYLINDER OUTER
47	RING, BULKHEAD RETAINING
48	ROD ASM, INNER TIE (RT)
49	ROD ASM, OUTER TIE (RT)
50	PLUG ASM, O-RING

Fig. 1 Exploded view, power rack & pinion assembly. Front wheel drive except Beretta, Calais, Cavalier, Cimarron, Corsica, Firenza, Grand Am, LeMans, Skyhawk, Skylark & Sunbird

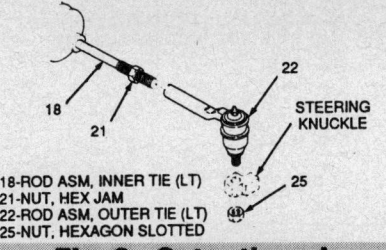

18-ROD ASM, INNER TIE (LT)
21-NUT, HEX JAM
22-ROD ASM, OUTER TIE (LT)
25-NUT, HEXAGON SLOTTED

Fig. 2   Outer tie rod replacement

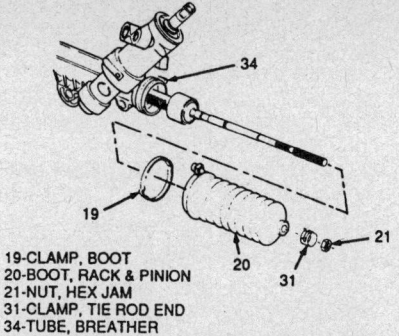

19-CLAMP, BOOT
20-BOOT, RACK & PINION
21-NUT, HEX JAM
31-CLAMP, TIE ROD END
34-TUBE, BREATHER

Fig. 3   Boot Replacement

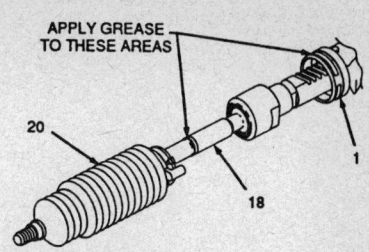

APPLY GREASE TO THESE AREAS

1-HOUSING ASM, R & P
18-ROD ASM, INNER TIE (LT)
20-BOOT, RACK & PINION

Fig. 4   Boot seal application

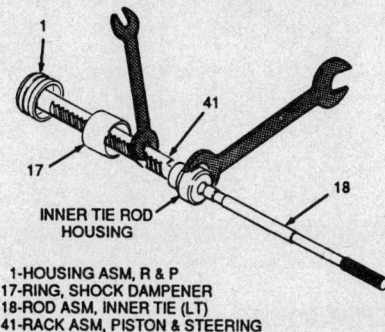

INNER TIE ROD HOUSING

1-HOUSING ASM, R & P
17-RING, SHOCK DAMPENER
18-ROD ASM, INNER TIE (LT)
41-RACK ASM, PISTON & STEERING

Fig. 5   Inner tie rod removal

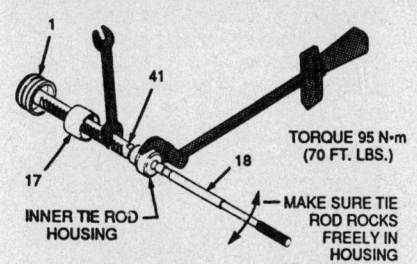

INNER TIE ROD HOUSING

TORQUE 95 N·m (70 FT. LBS.)

MAKE SURE TIE ROD ROCKS FREELY IN HOUSING BEFORE STAKING

1-HOUSING ASM, R & P
17-RING, SHOCK DAMPENER
18-ROD ASM, INNER TIE (LT)
41-RACK ASM, PISTON & STEERING

Fig. 6   Inner tie rod installation

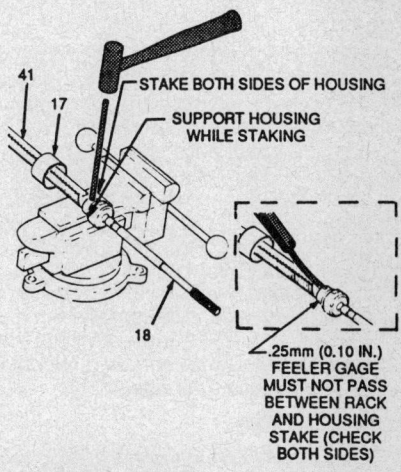

STAKE BOTH SIDES OF HOUSING
SUPPORT HOUSING WHILE STAKING

.25mm (0.10 IN.) FEELER GAGE MUST NOT PASS BETWEEN RACK AND HOUSING STAKE (CHECK BOTH SIDES)

17-RING, SHOCK DAMPENER
18-ROD ASM, INNER TIE (LT)
41-RACK ASM, PISTON & STEERING

Fig. 7   Inner tie rod staking procedure

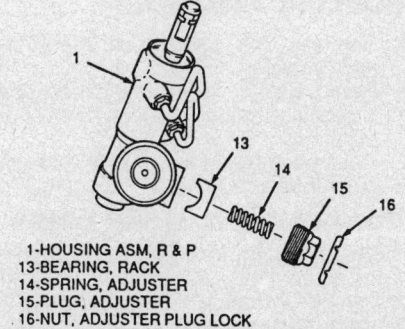

1-HOUSING ASM, R & P
13-BEARING, RACK
14-SPRING, ADJUSTER
15-PLUG, ADJUSTER
16-NUT, ADJUSTER PLUG LOCK

Fig. 8   Rack bearing removal

3. Remove outer tie rod from inner tie rod.
4. Reverse procedure to install, noting the following:
   a. **Torque** hex slotted nut to 35 ft. lbs. with a maximum of 50 ft. lbs. to install cotter pin.
   b. Adjust toe by turning inner tie rod.
   c. **Torque** jam nut against outer tie rod to 50 ft. lbs.

RACK & PINION BOOT & BREATHER TUBE
Removal
1. Remove outer tie rod.
2. Remove hex jam nut from inner tie rod assembly.
3. Remove tie rod end clamp, **Fig. 3**, then boot clamp with side cutters and discard.
4. Mark location of breather tube on housing before removing tube, then remove boot and breather tube.

Installation
1. Install new boot clamp onto boot.
2. Apply grease to inner tie rod or hous-

ing as shown in **Fig. 4**.
3. Align and install breather tube.
4. Install boot onto housing until seated in housing groove thang.
5. Position boot clamp on boot and crimp.
6. Position tie rod end clamp with pliers on boot.

INNER TIE ROD
Removal
1. Remove rack and pinion steering assembly from vehicle.
2. Remove outer tie rod from inner tie rod assembly, then rack and pinion boot.
3. Place wrench on flat of rack assembly and place wrench on flats of inner tie rod housing **Fig. 5**.
4. Rotate housing counterclockwise until inner tie rod separates from rack.

Installation
Rack must be held during inner tie rod installation to prevent internal gear damage.
1. Install inner tie rod on rack and **torque** to 70 ft. lbs., **Fig. 6**.
2. Support rack and housing of inner tie rod assembly, then stake **both** sides of inner tie rod housing to flats on rack, **Fig. 7**.
3. Check both stakes by inserting a .010 inch feeler gauge between rack and housing stake.
4. Slide shock damper over housing until it engages.
5. Install boot and rack outer tie rod, then rack and pinion assembly to vehicle.

RACK BEARING PRELOAD
Make adjustment with front wheels raised and steering wheel centered. Be sure to check returnability of steering wheel to center after adjustment.
1. Loosen lock nut, then turn adjuster plug clockwise until it bottoms in housing, then back off 50° to 70°.
2. **Torque** lock nut to 50 ft lbs while holding adjuster plug.

PINION & VALVE ASSEMBLY
Removal
1. Remove rack and pinion steering assembly from vehicle.
2. Remove adjuster plug lock nut from adjuster plug, **Fig. 8**.
3. Remove adjuster plug from housing, then adjuster spring and rack bearing.
4. Remove retaining ring from valve bore of housing, then dust cover, **Fig. 9**.
5. Holding stub shaft, remove hex lock nut from pinion and valve assembly. **Stub shaft must be held to prevent damage to pinion teeth.**
6. With rack centered, mark location of stub shaft notch on housing, then measure distance "A", as shown in **Fig. 10**.
7. Using a suitable press, press threaded

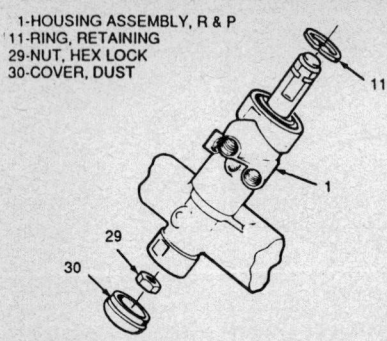

1-HOUSING ASSEMBLY, R & P
11-RING, RETAINING
29-NUT, HEX LOCK
30-COVER, DUST

Fig. 9   Retaining ring & lock nut removal

end of pinion until the pinion and valve assembly is almost removed. Mark a second location of stub shaft notch on housing. The second mark is used to position notch prior to reassembly.

8. Remove stub shaft dust seal, stub shaft seal, stub shaft bearing annulus assembly and pinion and valve assembly with retaining ring and valve body rings attached.

9. If necessary, remove valve body rings from pinion and valve assembly, then clean ring grooves. Inspect pinion and valve assembly for broken drive pin. If found, replace gear assembly.

Installation

1. If valve body rings are to be replaced, apply grease to ring grooves and rings. Install new rings, ensure split tabs are engaged and staggered, **Fig. 1.**

2. Place pinion and valve assembly into clear pinion and valve assembly ring protector tool No. 37090. Allow to set for at least three minutes.

3. Center rack in housing, refer to measurement "A" taken during disassembly.

4. Wipe housing bore clean and apply grease to valve housing bore. Inspect stub shaft bearing annulus for damage and ensure bearing is flush with annulus.

5. Align notch on valve stub shaft with second mark on housing made during disassembly.

6. Install pinion and valve assembly with spool shaft retaining ring and valve body rings installed into housing using clear pinion and valve assembly ring protector tool No. 37090 to prevent ring damage.

7. Install pinion and valve assembly onto rack using clear pinion and valve assembly ring protector tool No. J 37090 and pinion seal installer tool No. J 29822. **Do not hammer or use excessive force.**

8. Ensure notch in stub shaft and first mark on housing are lined up while rack is centered in housing. Refer to measurement "A" taken during disassembly.

9. Hold valve stub shaft and thread hex lock nut into pinion, then **torque** to 26 ft lbs. **If stub shaft is not held, damage to pinion teeth will result.**

10. Install dust cover onto housing.
11. Install stub shaft bearing annulus assembly onto valve stub shaft.
12. Place seal protector, tool No. J 29810 onto valve stub shaft, then apply a small quanity of grease between stub shaft seals.
13. Install stub shaft seal and stub shaft dust seal over protector and into housing.
14. Install retaining ring into groove in housing.
15. Lubricate stub shaft and dust seal area, then coat rack bearing, adjuster spring and adjuster plug with lithium grease and install in housing.
16. With rack centered in housing, turn adjuster plug clockwise until it bottoms in housing, then back off 50° to 70°. Check torque on pinion. Maximum pinion preload torque is 16 inch lbs.
17. Install adjuster plug lock nut to adjuster plug, then tighten firmly against housing while holding adjuster plug stationary.
18. Install rack and pinion assembly, then flush power steering system.

BERETTA, CALAIS, CAVALIER, CIMARRON, CORSICA, FIRENZA, GRAND AM, LEMANS, SKYHAWK, SKYLARK & SUNBIRD

OUTER TIE ROD

1. Remove cotter pin, then hex slotted nut from outer tie rod ball stud, **Fig. 11 and 12.**
2. Loosen outer tie rod pinch bolts, then separate outer tie rod from steering knuckle using steering linkage puller, tool No. J 24319-01 or equivalent.
3. Remove outer tie rod from tie rod adjuster.
4. Reverse procedure to install, noting the following:
   a. **On all models except LeMans, torque** hex slotted nut to 35 ft. lbs. **On LeMans models, torque** nut to 44 ft. lbs,. with a maximum of 50 ft. lbs. to install cotter pin.
   b. Adjust toe by turning tie rod adjuster.
   c. **Torque** pinch bolts to 15 ft. lbs.

INNER TIE ROD

1. Remove and dispose of lock plate from inner tie rod bolts, **Fig. 13.**
2. Remove inner tie rod bolt.
3. Slide out and remove inner tie rod between bolt support plate and rack and pinion boot. **If both inner tie rods are to be removed, after removing the first tie rod, reinstall bolt to keep rack and pinion and other parts aligned.**
4. Reverse procedure to install. Ensure center housing cover washers are fitted into rack and pinion boot. **Torque** inner tie rod bolts to 65 ft. lbs. and install new lock plate with notches in proper position over flats of inner tie rod bolts.

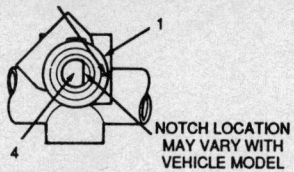

WITH RACK CENTERED MARK LOCATION OF STUB SHAFT NOTCH ON HOUSING

NOTCH LOCATION MAY VARY WITH VEHICLE MODEL

1-HOUSING ASM, R & P
4-VALVE ASM, PINION &

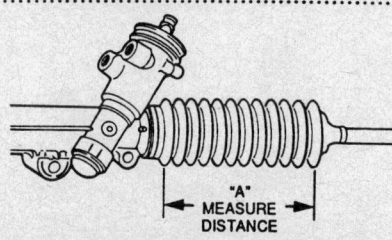

"A" MEASURE DISTANCE

Fig. 10   Housing reference mark

INNER PIVOT BUSHINGS

Refer to **Figs. 14 and 15,** for replacement procedure.

FLANGE & STEERING COUPLING ASSEMBLY

1. Remove rack and pinion assembly from vehicle.
2. Remove pinch bolt from flange and steering coupling assembly, then coupling, **Fig. 16.**
3. Reverse procedure to install. **Torque** pinch bolt to 29 ft. lbs.

HYDRAULIC CYLINDER LINES

Refer to **Fig. 11,** for replacement procedure. Ensure new O-rings are installed. **Torque** line fittings at valve end to 14 ft. lbs. and at cylinder end to 20 ft. lbs.

RACK GUIDE
Removal

1. Remove rack and pinion steering assembly from vehicle.
2. Remove and dispose lock plate from inner tie rod bolts, **Figs. 11 and 17.**
3. Remove inner tie rod bolts, bolt support plate, cylinder lines and inner tie rod assemblies.
4. Cut and remove mounting grommet and boot clamp.
5. Slide boot retaining bushing from rack and pinion boot, then boot assembly from rack and pinion housing.
6. Insert rack guide assembly from rod and rack assembly if necessary.

Installation

1. Slide boot retaining bushing from rack and pinion housing.
2. Slide new boot clamp on rack and pinion boot and install boot retaining bushing into rack and pinion boot.
3. Install rack guide on rack.
4. Coat inner lip of boot retaining bushing lightly with grease, then install boot on housing. Ensure that center housing cover washers are in place on boot.

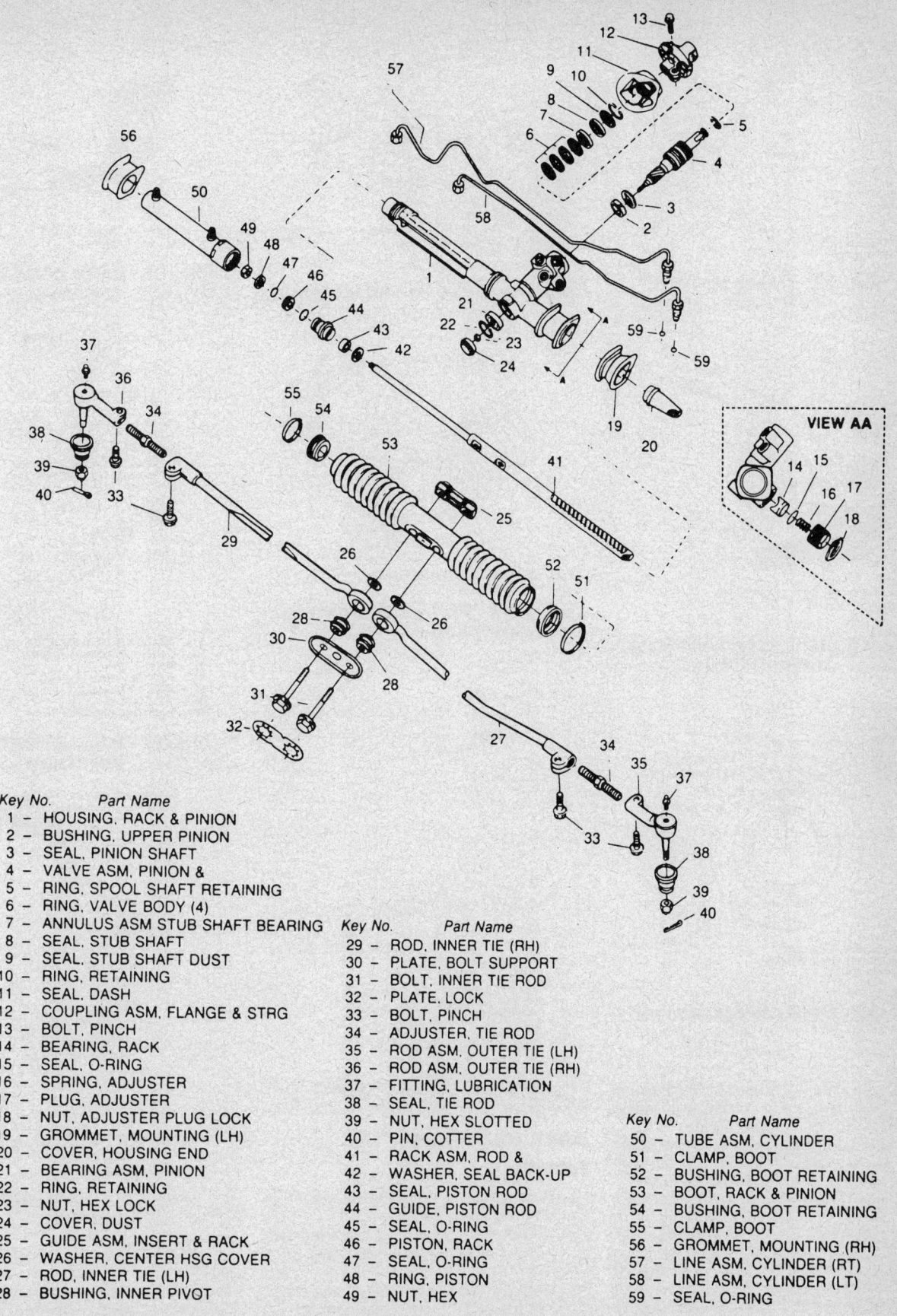

Key No.	Part Name
1	HOUSING, RACK & PINION
2	BUSHING, UPPER PINION
3	SEAL, PINION SHAFT
4	VALVE ASM, PINION &
5	RING, SPOOL SHAFT RETAINING
6	RING, VALVE BODY (4)
7	ANNULUS ASM STUB SHAFT BEARING
8	SEAL, STUB SHAFT
9	SEAL, STUB SHAFT DUST
10	RING, RETAINING
11	SEAL, DASH
12	COUPLING ASM, FLANGE & STRG
13	BOLT, PINCH
14	BEARING, RACK
15	SEAL, O-RING
16	SPRING, ADJUSTER
17	PLUG, ADJUSTER
18	NUT, ADJUSTER PLUG LOCK
19	GROMMET, MOUNTING (LH)
20	COVER, HOUSING END
21	BEARING ASM, PINION
22	RING, RETAINING
23	NUT, HEX LOCK
24	COVER, DUST
25	GUIDE ASM, INSERT & RACK
26	WASHER, CENTER HSG COVER
27	ROD, INNER TIE (LH)
28	BUSHING, INNER PIVOT

Key No.	Part Name
29	ROD, INNER TIE (RH)
30	PLATE, BOLT SUPPORT
31	BOLT, INNER TIE ROD
32	PLATE, LOCK
33	BOLT, PINCH
34	ADJUSTER, TIE ROD
35	ROD ASM, OUTER TIE (LH)
36	ROD ASM, OUTER TIE (RH)
37	FITTING, LUBRICATION
38	SEAL, TIE ROD
39	NUT, HEX SLOTTED
40	PIN, COTTER
41	RACK ASM, ROD &
42	WASHER, SEAL BACK-UP
43	SEAL, PISTON ROD
44	GUIDE, PISTON ROD
45	SEAL, O-RING
46	PISTON, RACK
47	SEAL, O-RING
48	RING, PISTON
49	NUT, HEX

Key No.	Part Name
50	TUBE ASM, CYLINDER
51	CLAMP, BOOT
52	BUSHING, BOOT RETAINING
53	BOOT, RACK & PINION
54	BUSHING, BOOT RETAINING
55	CLAMP, BOOT
56	GROMMET, MOUNTING (RH)
57	LINE ASM, CYLINDER (RT)
58	LINE ASM, CYLINDER (LT)
59	SEAL, O-RING

Fig. 11 Exploded view, power rack & pinion assembly. Beretta, Calais, Cavalier, Cimarron, Corsica, Firenza, Grand Am, LeMans, Skyhawk, Skylark & Sunbird

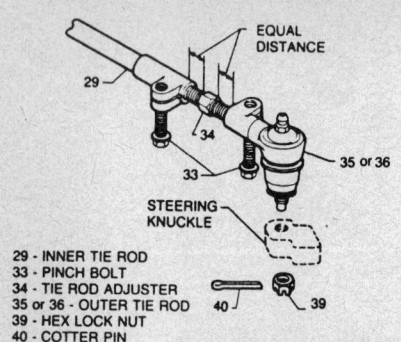

29 – INNER TIE ROD
33 – PINCH BOLT
34 – TIE ROD ADJUSTER
35 or 36 – OUTER TIE ROD
39 – HEX LOCK NUT
40 – COTTER PIN

Fig. 12   Outer tie rod assembly

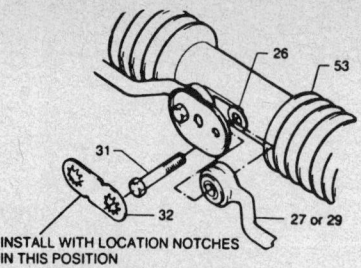

INSTALL WITH LOCATION NOTCHES IN THIS POSITION

26 – CENTER COVER HSG WASHER
27 OR 29 – INNER TIE ROD ASSEMBLY
31 – INNER TIE ROD BOLTS
32 – LOCK PLATE
53 – RACK & PINION BOOT

Fig. 13   Inner tie rod assembly

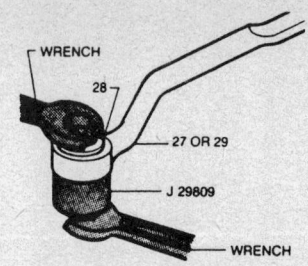

27 OR 29 – INNER TIE ROD
28 – PIVOT BUSHING

Fig. 14   Inner pivot bushing removal

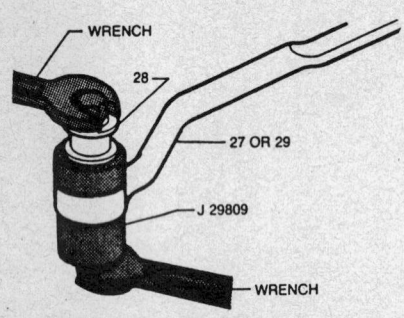

27 OR 29 – INNER TIE ROD ASSEMBLY
28 – PIVOT BUSHING

Fig. 15   Inner pivot bushing installation

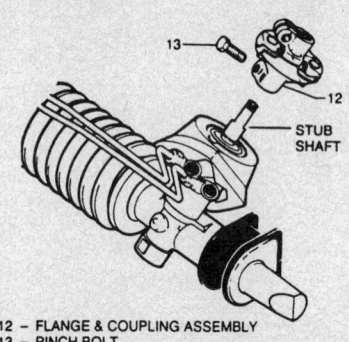

12 – FLANGE & COUPLING ASSEMBLY
13 – PINCH BOLT

Fig. 16   Flange & steering coupling assembly

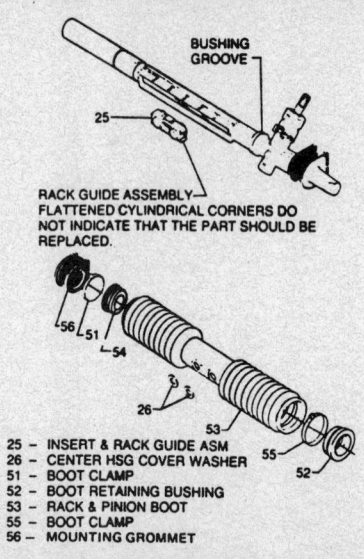

RACK GUIDE ASSEMBLY—FLATTENED CYLINDRICAL CORNERS DO NOT INDICATE THAT THE PART SHOULD BE REPLACED.

25 – INSERT & RACK GUIDE ASM
26 – CENTER HSG COVER WASHER
51 – BOOT CLAMP
52 – BOOT RETAINING BUSHING
53 – RACK & PINION BOOT
55 – BOOT CLAMP
56 – MOUNTING GROMMET

Fig. 17   Boot & rack guide assembly

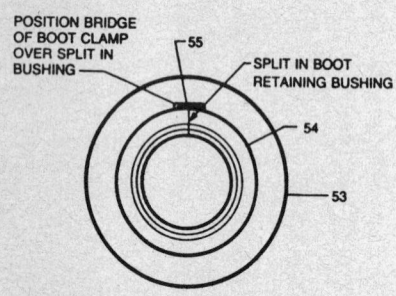

POSITION BRIDGE OF BOOT CLAMP OVER SPLIT IN BUSHING

SPLIT IN BOOT RETAINING BUSHING

53 – RACK AND PINION BOOT
54 – BOOT RETAINING BUSHING
55 – BOOT CLAMP

Fig. 18   Boot clamp position

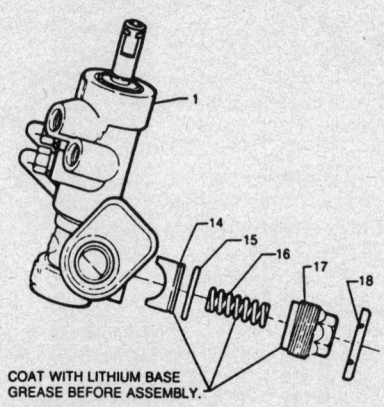

COAT WITH LITHIUM BASE GREASE BEFORE ASSEMBLY.

1 – HOUSING ASSEMBLY
14 – RACK BEARING
15 – O-RING SEAL
16 – ADJUSTER SPRING
17 – ADJUSTER PLUG
18 – ADJUSTER PLUG LOCK NUT

Fig. 19   Rack bearing assembly

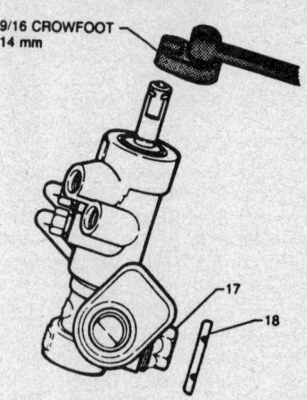

9/16 CROWFOOT 14 mm

17 – ADJUSTER PLUG
18 – ADJUSTER PLUG LOCK NUT

Fig. 20   Rack bearing adjustment

5. Install inner tie rod bolts bolts through cover washers and rack and pinion boot. Screw into rack lightly.
6. Slide boot and boot retaining bushing until seated in bushing groove in housing. Crimp new boot clamp.
7. Slide other end of boot into boot groove on cylinder end of housing.
8. Slide other end of boot into boot groove on cylinder end of housing and crimp new boot clamp. **Bridge of boot clamp must be crimped over split in boot retaining bushing to ensure proper sealing, Fig. 18.**
9. Install new lock plate with notches in proper position over flats of inner tie rod bolts.

RACK BEARINGS
Removal

1. Remove rack and pinion assembly from vehicle.
2. Remove adjuster plug nut from adjuster plug, then adjuster plug from housing, **Fig. 19.**
3. Remove adjuster spring and rack bearing with O-ring seal attached.

Installation

1. Coat parts with lithium grease, then install rack bearing with O-ring seal

adjuster spring and adjuster plug into housing.
2. With rack centered in housing, turn adjuster plug clockwise until it bottoms in housing, then back off 35° to 45° and check torque on pinion. Maximum pinion preload torque is 16 inch lbs.

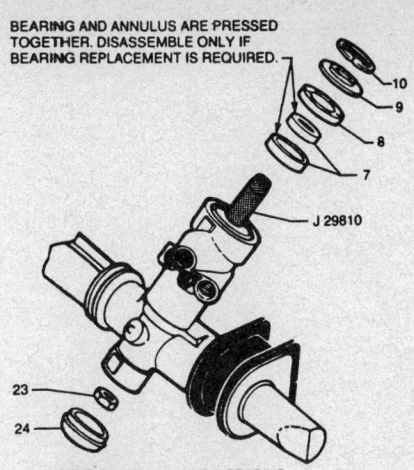

BEARING AND ANNULUS ARE PRESSED TOGETHER. DISASSEMBLE ONLY IF BEARING REPLACEMENT IS REQUIRED.

10
9
8
7
J 29810
23
24

7 – STUB SHAFT ANNULUS & BEARING
8 – STUB SHAFT SEAL
9 – STUB SHAFT DUST SEAL
10 – RETAINING RING
23 – HEX LOCK NUT
24 – DUST COVER

Fig. 21 Stub shaft seals & upper bearing assembly

3. Install lock nut to adjuster plug and tighten to 50 ft. lbs. while holding adjuster plug stationary, **Fig. 20**.

STUB SHAFT SEALS & UPPER BEARING
Removal

1. Remove rack and pinion assembly from vehicle.
2. Remove retaining ring, then dust cover, **Fig. 21**.
3. While holding stub shaft, remove lock nut from pinion. **If stub shaft is not held, damage to the pinion teeth will occur.**
4. Using a suitable press, press on threaded end of pinion until flush with ball bearing assembly. Complete removal of valve and pinion assembly is not required.
5. Remove stub shaft dust seal, stub shaft seal and stub shaft bearing annulus assembly from valve end of housing.

Installation

1. Install annulus assembly into gear.
2. Place seal protector, tool No. J 29810 onto stub shaft and install stub shaft seal and stub shaft dust seal over protector and into housing.
3. While holding the stub shaft firmly, seat the lock nut, **torque to 26 ft. lbs.**

PINION & VALVE ASSEMBLY
Removal

1. Turn stub shaft until rack guide is equal distance from both sides of housing opening, then mark location of stub shaft notch on housing, **Fig. 22**.
2. Using a suitable press, press on threaded end of pinion until it is possible to remove valve and pinion assembly from housing.
3. Replace valve body rings if necessary.

Installation

1. Install rack so it is centered in housing.

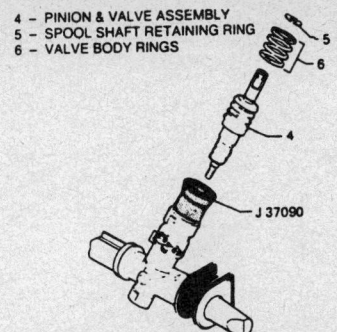

4 – PINION & VALVE ASSEMBLY
5 – SPOOL SHAFT RETAINING RING
6 – VALVE BODY RINGS

5
6
4
J 37090

Fig. 22 Pinion & valve assembly

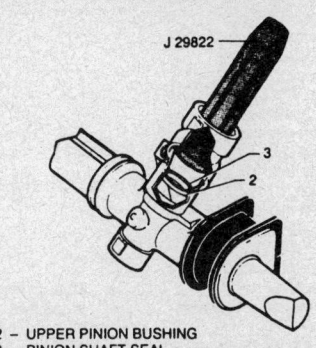

J 29822
3
2

2 – UPPER PINION BUSHING
3 – PINION SHAFT SEAL

Fig. 24 Pinion shaft seal & bushing removal

2. Using valve body ring protector, tool No. J 33057 to prevent damaging valve body rings, install valve and pinion assembly.
3. When pinion and valve assembly is fully seated, ensure notch in stub shaft and mark on housing line up, and the rack is centered in housing.

RACK BEARING PRELOAD
On Vehicle Adjustment

Make adjustment with front wheels raised and steering wheel centered. Be sure to check returnability of steering wheel to center after adjustment.

1. Loosen lock nut, then turn adjuster plug clockwise until it bottoms in housing, then back off 35° to 45°.
2. **Torque** lock nut to adjuster plug to 50 ft. lbs. while holding adjuster plug.

PINION BEARING ASSEMBLY

1. Remove bearing retainer ring, **Fig. 23**.
2. Using a drift or punch, gently tap on bearing until removed.
3. To install, use a suitable socket and press on outer race of bearing until firmly seated.
4. Install retaining ring.

UPPER PINION BUSHING & PINION SHAFT SEAL

1. Remove upper pinion bushing and seal with a hearty punch, and install new bushing, **Fig. 24**.
2. Using pinion seal installer, tool No. J 29822 seat new seal in housing with seal tip facing up.

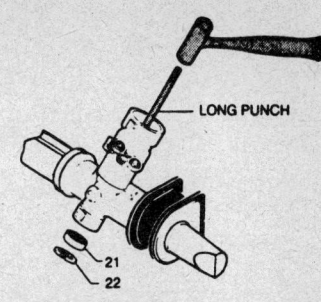

LONG PUNCH
21
22

21 – PINION BEARING ASSEMBLY
22 – RETAINING RING

Fig. 23 Pinion bearing assembly removal

BOOT OR RACK GUIDE

1. Cut off RH mounting grommet and boot clamps, **Fig. 11**.
2. Slide boot retaining bushing bushing from rack and pinion boot.
3. Slide boot assembly, consisting of rack and pinion boot, boot retaining bushing and center housing cover washers, captured in the rack and pinion boot, from rack and pinion housing.
4. Remove insert and rack guide assembly as necessary.
5. Slide boot retaining bushing from rack and pinion boot.
6. Slide new boot clamp onto rack and pinion boot.
7. Insert boot retaining bushing into rack and pinion boot.
8. Coat inner lip of boot retaining bushing lightly with suitable grease to facilitate assembly, then slide assembly onto housing assembly.
9. Ensure center housing cover washers are in place on rack and pinion boot.
10. For ease of assembly, insert inner tie rod bolt through center housing cover washers, insert and rack guide and lightly thread bolt into rod and rack assembly to keep components in proper alignment.
11. Place boot retaining bushing onto cylinder tube of rack and pinion assembly, then slide into end of rack and pinion boot.
12. Slide boot clamp over cylinder end of housing and position on rack and pinion boot.
13. Slide rack and pinion boot and boot retaining bushing until seated in bushing groove in housing.
14. Position boot clamp on rack and pinion boot and crimp clamp.
15. Position bridge of boot clamp over split in boot retaining bushing and crimp clamp. **Bridge of boot clamp must be crimped over split in boot retaining bushing to ensure proper sealing.**

ROD & RACK & CYLINDER TUBE ASSEMBLY

1. Remove dust cover from housing, **Fig. 11**.
2. While holding stub shaft, remove locknut from pinion.
3. With gear centered, mark location of stub shaft notch on housing to aid in

---

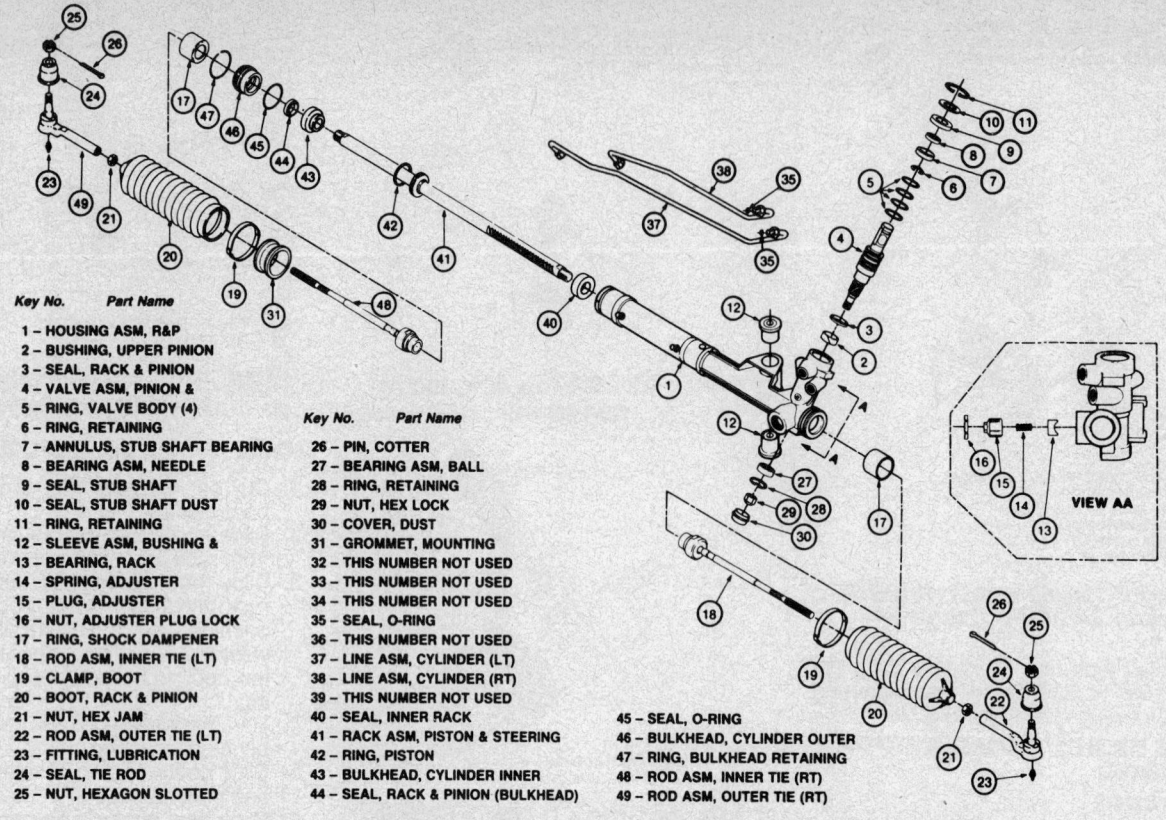

Key No.   Part Name

1 – HOUSING ASM, R&P
2 – BUSHING, UPPER PINION
3 – SEAL, RACK & PINION
4 – VALVE ASM, PINION &
5 – RING, VALVE BODY (4)
6 – RING, RETAINING
7 – ANNULUS, STUB SHAFT BEARING
8 – BEARING ASM, NEEDLE
9 – SEAL, STUB SHAFT
10 – SEAL, STUB SHAFT DUST
11 – RING, RETAINING
12 – SLEEVE ASM, BUSHING &
13 – BEARING, RACK
14 – SPRING, ADJUSTER
15 – PLUG, ADJUSTER
16 – NUT, ADJUSTER PLUG LOCK
17 – RING, SHOCK DAMPENER
18 – ROD ASM, INNER TIE (LT)
19 – CLAMP, BOOT
20 – BOOT, RACK & PINION
21 – NUT, HEX JAM
22 – ROD ASM, OUTER TIE (LT)
23 – FITTING, LUBRICATION
24 – SEAL, TIE ROD
25 – NUT, HEXAGON SLOTTED

Key No.   Part Name

26 – PIN, COTTER
27 – BEARING ASM, BALL
28 – RING, RETAINING
29 – NUT, HEX LOCK
30 – COVER, DUST
31 – GROMMET, MOUNTING
32 – THIS NUMBER NOT USED
33 – THIS NUMBER NOT USED
34 – THIS NUMBER NOT USED
35 – SEAL, O-RING
36 – THIS NUMBER NOT USED
37 – LINE ASM, CYLINDER (LT)
38 – LINE ASM, CYLINDER (RT)
39 – THIS NUMBER NOT USED
40 – SEAL, INNER RACK
41 – RACK ASM, PISTON & STEERING
42 – RING, PISTON
43 – BULKHEAD, CYLINDER INNER
44 – SEAL, RACK & PINION (BULKHEAD)

45 – SEAL, O-RING
46 – BULKHEAD, CYLINDER OUTER
47 – RING, BULKHEAD RETAINING
48 – ROD ASM, INNER TIE (RT)
49 – ROD ASM, OUTER TIE (RT)

VIEW AA

Fig. 25 Exploded view, power rack & pinion assembly. Corvette

proper installation of the pinion and valve assembly. **Using a press, press on threaded end of pinion until it is possible to remove the pinion and valve assembly from the housing.**

4. Remove stub shaft dust seal, stub shaft seal, stub shaft bearing annulus assembly, then the pinion and valve assembly with spool shaft retaining ring and valve body rings attached.
5. Using wrench, tool No. J 36343 or equivalent, remove cylinder tube assembly from housing. **Mark location of fittings on housing before removal.**
6. Remove piston rod guide rack from housing and disassemble as follows:
   a. Remove hex nut from rod and rack assembly.
   b. Remove rack piston, containing O-ring seal, and piston ring, piston rod guide assembly, consisting of piston rod guide, O-ring seal, piston rod seal and seal backup washer for rod and rack assembly.
   c. Remove O-ring seal and piston rod seal from from piston rod guide.
7. Remove retaining ring from housing.
8. Remove pinion bearing assembly from housing.
9. Remove pinion shaft seal and upper pinion bushing from housing.
10. Coat all seals with power steering fluid.
11. Install upper pinion bushing into valve bore in housing.

12. Using seal installer, tool No. J 29822 or equivalent, seat pinion shaft seal into housing.
13. Using suitable press, install pinion bearing assembly into housing.
14. Install retaining ring in groove in housing, positioning properly.
15. Assemble piston rod seal and O-ring seal to piston rod guide.
16. Assemble O-ring seal and piston ring to rack piston.
17. Slide seal backup washer, piston rod guide assembly and rack piston onto rod and rack assembly.
18. Install hex nut on rod and rack assembly, **on all models except LeMans torque** to 30 ft. lbs., **on LeMans models, torque** to 22 ft. lbs.
19. Slide piston rod guide assembly into housing.
20. Apply one small drop of Loctite 242 or equivalent in three equally spaced locations around the threaded portion of housing. **Be sure to use the Loctite 242 sparingly to ensure ease of removal of cylinder tube assembly if future repairs are necessary.**
21. Slide cylinder tube assembly over rack piston ring to housing, then, using torque wrench or equivalent, **torque to 82 ft. lbs. Be sure to align fittings on cylinder tube with mark on housing before tightening to ensure cylinder line installation.**
22. Assemble insert and rack guide assembly to rod and rack assembly in housing.

23. Center rack guide assembly in housing window opening.
24. Using protector tool, No. J 33057 or equivalent, install pinion and valve assembly, together with new valve body rings, and spool shaft retaining ring into housing. **When pinion and valve assembly is fully seated in housing, notch in stub shaft and mark on housing line up and insert and rack guide assembly is centered in window housing.**
25. While holding stub shaft, tighten locknut to 26 ft. lbs.
26. Install dust cover on housing.
27. Install stub shaft bearing annulus assembly onto stub shaft and slide into housing.
28. Place seal protector, tool No. J 29810 or equivalent onto stub shaft, then slide stub shaft seal and stub shaft dust seal over protector and into housing.
29. Install retaining ring into groove in housing.
30. Coat rack bearing, with O-ring seal attached, adjuster spring and the adjuster plug with lithium base grease and install in housing.
31. With rack centered in window in housing, turn adjuster plug clockwise until it bottoms in housing, then back off 50-70°. Check pinion preload torque, which should not exceed 16 inch lbs.
32. Install locknut on adjuster plug and **torque** to 50 ft. lbs. while holding adjuster plug stationary.

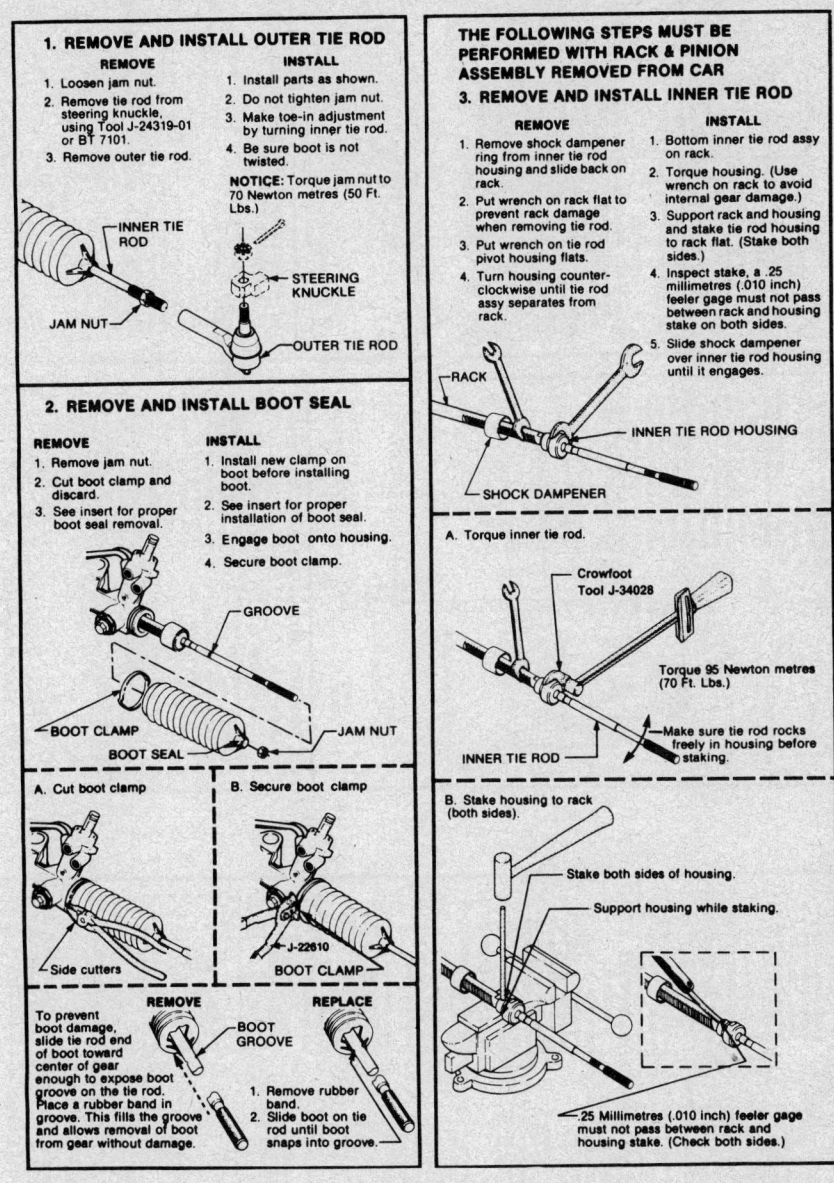

Fig. 26 Service procedures, power rack & pinion assembly (Part 1 of 3). Corvette

CORVETTE

For service procedures on this power rack and pinion steering gear assembly, refer to **Figs. 25 and 26.**

EXTERNAL LEAK CHECK

1. With engine off, wipe dry the entire power steering system.
2. Ensure fluid level is correct.
3. Start engine, then turn steering wheel from stop to stop a few times. Do not hold at stop for a long period.
4. Find the exact area of leak and repair as necessary, **Figs. 27 through 29.**

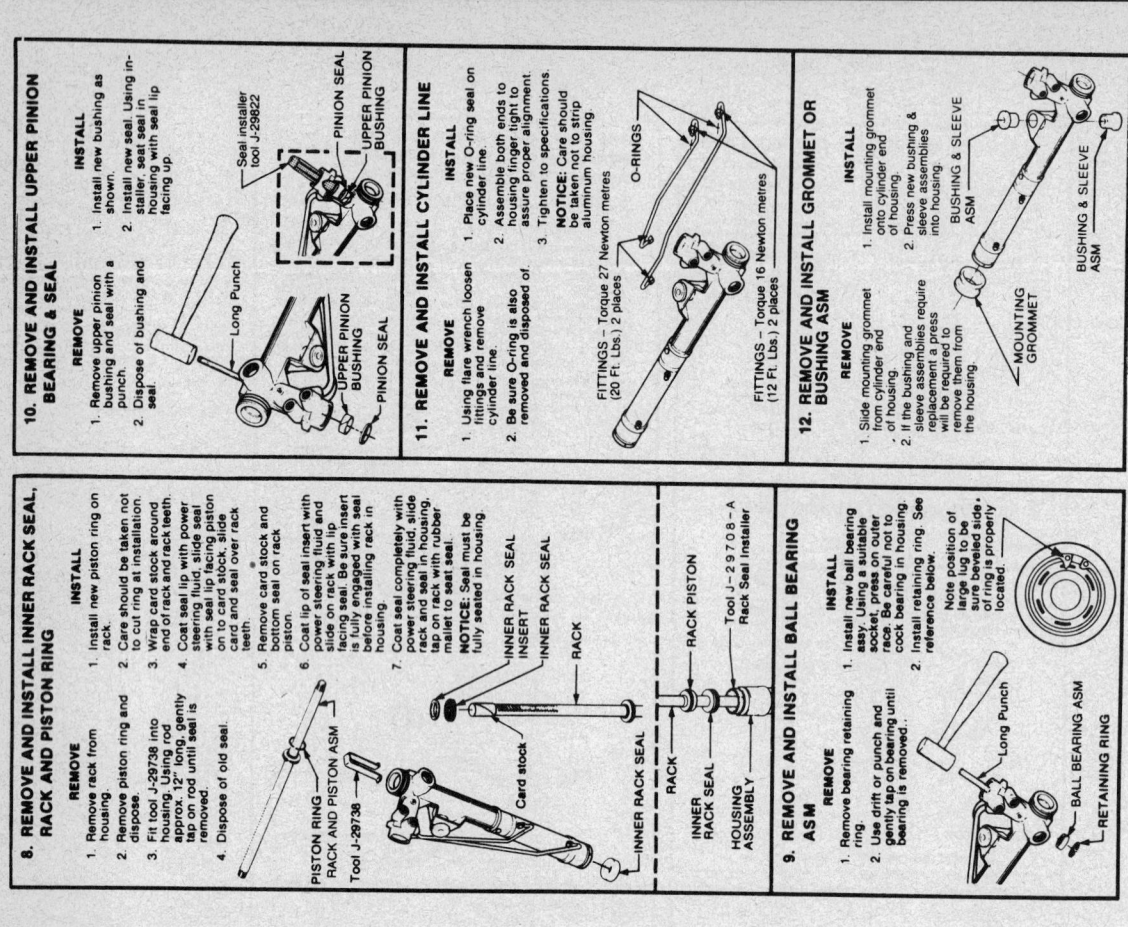

10. REMOVE AND INSTALL UPPER PINION BEARING & SEAL

REMOVE
1. Remove upper pinion bushing and seal with a punch.
2. Dispose of bushing and seal.

INSTALL
1. Install new bushing as shown.
2. Install new seal. Using installer seat seal in housing with seal lip facing up.

11. REMOVE AND INSTALL CYLINDER LINE

REMOVE
1. Using flare wrench loosen fittings and remove cylinder line.
2. Be sure O-ring is also removed and disposed of.

INSTALL
1. Place new O-ring seal on cylinder line.
2. Assemble both ends to housing finger tight to assure proper alignment.
3. Tighten to specifications.
NOTICE: Care should be taken not to strip aluminum housing.
FITTINGS – Torque 27 Newton metres (20 Ft. Lbs.) 2 places
FITTINGS – Torque 16 Newton metres (12 Ft. Lbs.) 2 places

12. REMOVE AND INSTALL GROMMET OR BUSHING ASM

REMOVE
1. Slide mounting grommet from cylinder end of housing.
2. If the bushing and sleeve assemblies require replacement a press will be required to remove them from the housing.

INSTALL
1. Install mounting grommet onto cylinder end of housing.
2. Press new bushing & sleeve assemblies into housing.

8. REMOVE AND INSTALL INNER RACK SEAL, RACK AND PISTON RING

REMOVE
1. Remove rack from housing.
2. Remove piston ring and dispose.
3. Fit tool J-29738 into housing. Using rod approx. 12" long, gently tap on rod until seal is removed.
4. Dispose of old seal.

INSTALL
1. Install new piston ring on rack.
2. Care should be taken not to cut ring at installation.
3. Wrap card stock around end of rack and rack teeth.
4. Coat seal lip with power steering fluid, slide seal with seal lip facing piston on to card stock, slide card and seal over rack teeth.
5. Remove card stock and bottom seal on rack piston.
6. Coat lip of seal insert with power steering fluid and slide on rack with lip facing seal. Be sure insert is fully engaged with seal before installing rack in housing.
7. Coat seal completely with power steering fluid, slide rack and install in housing, tap on rack with rubber mallet to seat seal.
NOTICE: Seal must be fully seated in housing.

9. REMOVE AND INSTALL BALL BEARING ASM

REMOVE
1. Remove bearing retaining ring.
2. Use drift or punch and gently tap on bearing until bearing is removed.

INSTALL
1. Install new ball bearing assy. Using a suitable socket, press on outer race. Be careful not to cock bearing in housing.
2. Install retaining ring. Note position of large lug to be sure beveled side of ring is properly located.

Fig. 26 Service procedures, power rack & pinion assembly (Part 3 of 3). Corvette

6. REMOVE AND INSTALL VALVE AND PINION ASM

REMOVE
1. Turn stub shaft until rack is equal distance on both sides of housing, with pinion fully engaged.
2. Mark location of stub bolt notch on housing.
3. USING A PRESS, press on threaded end of pinion until it is possible to remove valve and pinion assy.
4. Remove valve body rings if replacement is necessary.

INSTALL
1. Install new valve body rings if removed.
2. Care should be taken not to cut rings at installation.
3. Measure rack so that it's equal on both sides.
4. Use valve body ring protector, Tool J-33057 to prevent damaging valve body rings while installing valve and pinion assembly.
5. Install valve and pinion assembly so when fully seated, stub shaft pinch bolt notch will mark on housing then assy.
Before installing valve and pinion asm both ends of the rack should be equal in the housing.

Valve Body Ring Protector Tool J-33057
Pinch Bolt Notch
RETAINING RING
VALVE BODY RINGS
VALVE AND PINION ASM

7. REMOVE AND INSTALL BULKHEAD

REMOVE
1. Use punch in access hole to remove bulkhead retaining ring.
2. If only the bulkhead, bulkhead O-ring seal or rack seal are to be replaced. Loosen (LT) fitting and remove cylinder line.
3. Plug (LT) cylinder line hole at cylinder using a finger or plug.
4. Using a 9/16 crowfoot turn stub shaft. Move rack to the right forcing the bulkhead out of the housing. Use drain pan to catch hydraulic oil from assy.
5. If inner rack seal or piston ring are to be replaced, use rack to remove bulkhead instead of compressed air method.

INSTALL
1. Using crocus cloth remove burrs or sharp edges from retaining ring groove in housing. This must be done to ensure that the new O-ring seal is not damaged at assembly.
2. Install parts as shown.
3. Coat all seals with power steering fluid.
4. Slip bullet seal protector over end of rack and install bulkhead.
5. Make sure open end of retaining ring is approximately 13 millimeters (.50 inch) from access hole.
6. Retaining ring must be fully seated.
(Install Seal Using Seal Installer J-28527)

Rack Seal (Bulkhead) Removal
Retaining ring access hole
Pliers
Tool J-28478-A Bullet Seal Protector
CYLINDER INNER BULKHEAD
O-RING SEAL
CYLINDER OUTER BULKHEAD
BULKHEAD RETAINING RING
SHOCK DAMPENER
RACK SEAL (BULKHEAD)
CYLINDER OUTER BULKHEAD
RACK SEAL (BULKHEAD)

Fig. 26 Service procedures, power rack & pinion assembly (Part 2 of 3). Corvette

4. REMOVE AND INSTALL RACK BEARING

REMOVE
1. Loosen adjuster plug lock nut.
2. Turn adjuster plug counterclockwise until it separates from housing.
3. Remove parts as shown.

INSTALL
1. Install parts as shown.
2. Turn adjuster plug clockwise until it bottoms, then back off 50° to 70°. Check torque on pinion.
3. Assemble lock nut and tighten while holding adjuster plug stationary.

ADJUSTER PLUG LOCK NUT
SPRING
RACK BEARING
ADJUSTER PLUG
Coat with lithium base grease before assembly.
LOCK NUT — Torque to 70 Newton Metres (50 Ft. Lbs.)

5. REMOVE AND INSTALL STUB SHAFT SEALS

REMOVE
1. Remove retaining ring.
2. Remove dust cover.
3. While holding the stub shaft remove lock nut from pinion.
NOTICE: If stub shaft is not held, damage to the pinion teeth will occur.
4. USING A PRESS, press on threaded end of pinion until flush with ball bearing assy.
5. Complete removal of valve and pinion or assy is not necessary.

INSTALL
1. Install annulus assembly in gear.
2. Place seal protector Tool J-29810 on stub shaft and install stub shaft seals and dust cover.
3. While holding stub shaft firmly seat the lock nut. Torque to specifications.

LOCK NUT — Torque to 35 Newton metres (26 Ft. Lbs.) after lock nut has been firmly seated.

9/16" Crowfoot
Pinion preload torque 2.2 Newton Metres (19 in lbs) maximum

DUST COVER
RETAINING RING
STUB SHAFT DUST SEAL
STUB SHAFT SEAL
NEEDLE BEARING
STUB SHAFT BEARING ANNULUS
Seal Protector Tool J-29810

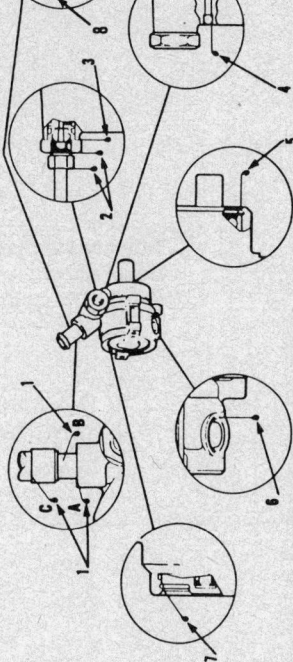

A IF SEEPAGE IS OBSERVED BETWEEN TORSION BAR AND STUB SHAFT, REPLACE THE VALVE ASSEMBLY (A).

B TORQUE HOSE FITTING TO 27 N·m (20 FT. LBS.). IF LEAKAGE PERSISTS, REPLACE "O" RING.

C TORQUE CYLINDER LINE FITTING TO 18 N·m (13 FT. LBS.). IF LEAKAGE PERSISTS, REPLACE BOTH "O" RINGS.

D IF SEEPAGE LEAK IS OBSERVED AT DRIVER SIDE OF HOUSING OPENING, REPLACE PINION SHAFT SEAL.

E IF LEAKAGE IS OBSERVED AT CYLINDER END AND SPURTS WHEN BOTTOMED IN LEFT TURN, REPLACE THE PISTON ROD GUIDE SEAL AND "O" RING SEAL.

Fig. 28 Power rack & pinion steering gear leak diagnosis. Front wheel drive except Beretta, Calais, Cavalier, Cimarron, Corsica, Firenza, Grand Am, LeMans, Skyhawk, Skylark & Sunbird

1. IF LEAKAGE IS OBSERVED AT (A), APPLY LOCTITE SAFETY SOLVENT AND LOCTITE 290 OR EQUIVALENT TO TUBE/ HOUSING CONNECTION. IF LEAKAGE IS FROM (B), REPLACE RETURN TUBE. IF LEAKAGE IS FROM (C), REPLACE HOSE OR CLAMP.
2. TORQUE FITTING TO 27 N·m (20 FT. LBS.). IF LEAKAGE PERSISTS, REPLACE "O" RING SEAL.
3. TORQUE FITTING TO 75 N·m (55 FT. LBS.) IF LEAKAGE PERSISTS, REPLACE "O" RING SEAL.
4. SEAT BALL IN HOUSING WITH BLUNT PUNCH. APPLY LOCTITE SAFETY SOLVENT AND LOCTITE 290 OR EQUIVALENT TO AREA.
5. REPLACE DRIVE SHAFT SEAL. MAKE CERTAIN THAT DRIVE SHAFT IS CLEAN AND FREE OF PITTING IN SEAL AREA.
6. SEAT PLUG IN HOUSING. APPLY LOCTITE SAFETY SOLVENT AND LOCTITE 290 OR EQUIVALENT TO AREA.
7. REPLACE "O" RING SEAL.
8. REPLACE RESERVOIR IF CRACKED OR DENTED
9. IF CAP LEAKS WITH CORRECT FLUID LEVEL, REPLACE CAP.

Fig. 29 Power steering pump leak diagnosis. Front wheel drive models w/rack & pinion steering

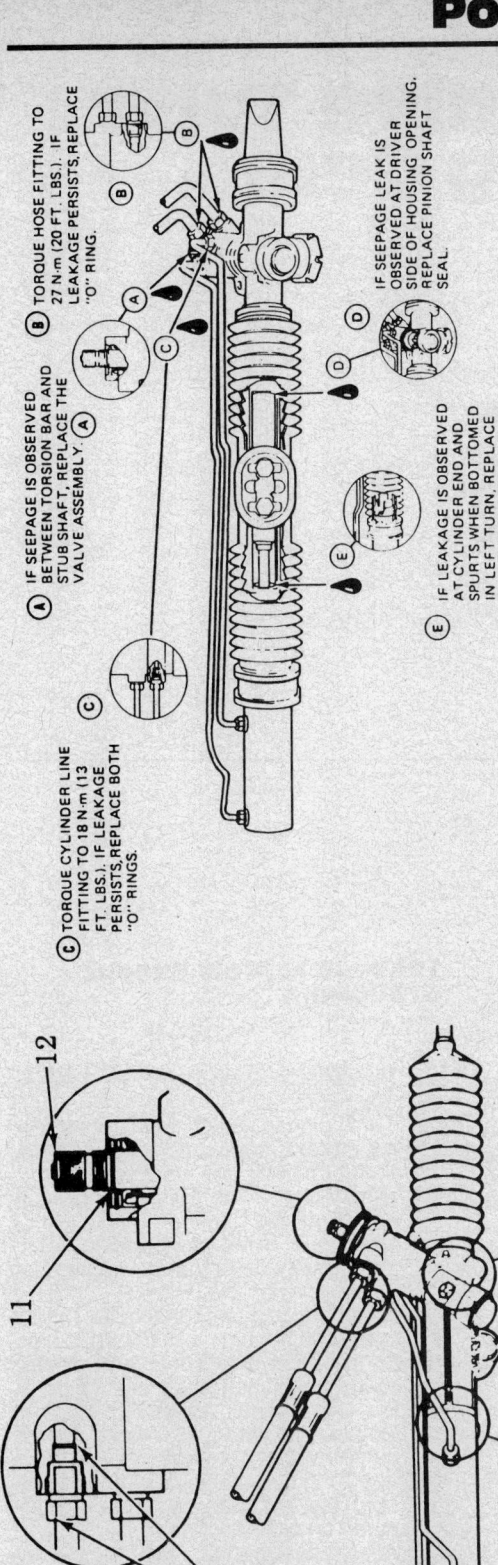

10 Torque fitting to 27 N·M (20 FT. LBS.). If leakage persists, replace "O" ring seal. If leakage is due to damaged threads, repair fitting nut or replace line as required. If housing threads are badly damaged, replace housing.

11 Replace dust and stub shaft seals.

12 If leakage is observed between torsion bar and stub shaft, replace the valve assembly.

13 If leakage is observed at driver side and is not affected by the direction of turn, replace pinion shaft seal.

14 If leakage is observed at the housing end and spurts when bottomed in left turn, replace inner rack seal.

15 Replace inner rack seal.

16 If leakage is observed at passenger side, it is necessary to remove bulkhead and replace both "O" ring seals and lip seal.

Fig. 27 Power rack & pinion steering gear leak diagnosis. Front wheel drive except Beretta, Calais, Cavalier, Cimarron, Corsica, Firenza, Grand Am, LeMans, Skyhawk, Skylark & Sunbird

Saginaw Rotary Valve Type Power Steering Gear

INDEX

DESCRIPTION

The Saginaw rotary valve steering gear incorporates a recirculating ball system in which steel balls act a rolling thread between a steering worm shaft and the rack piston.

SERVICE PROCEDURES

Whenever a part which forms a sealing surface for an O-ring is removed, the O-ring seal should also be removed and replaced with a new seal. Whenever one of the Pitman shaft or stub shaft seals are removed, all adjacent seals should be removed and replaced with new seals. Lubricate all new seals with power steering fluid to facilitate assembly.

For service procedures on this power rack and pinion steering gear assembly, refer to **Figs. 1 and 2.**

ADJUSTMENT SPECIFICATIONS

Adjustment of steering gear in the vehicle is not recommended because of the difficulty encountered in adjusting the worm thrust bearing preload and confirming the effects of the hydraulic fluid in the gear. Since a gear adjustment is made only as a correction and not a periodic adjustment, it is better to take the extra time and make the adjustment correctly the first time.

Since a handling stability complaint can be caused by improperly adjusted worm thrust bearings as well as an improper gear over-center adjustment, it is necessary that the steering gear assembly be removed from vehicle and both thrust bearing and over-center preload be checked and corrected as necessary. An in-vehicle check of steering gear will not show a thrust bearing adjustment error.

Valve assembly and seal drag should be 1-4 inch lbs. Thrust bearing preload should be 3-4 inch lbs. in excess of valve assembly and seal drag.

OVER CENTER ADJUSTMENT

1988 Models & Brougham

Refer to **Fig. 3,** for proper procedure. Over-center adjustment should be 5-11 inch lbs. (new gear) or 4-5 inch lbs. (used gear) in excess of combined thrust bearing preload.

1989–90 Models Except Brougham

1. Rotate stub shaft back and forth to drain fluid.
2. Turn pitman shaft adjuster screw counterclockwise until fully extended, then turn back one full turn, **Fig. 4.**
3. Rotate stub shaft from stop to stop and count the turns.
4. Starting at either stop, turn the stub shaft back one-half the total number of turns.
5. When the gear is centered, the flat on stub shaft should face upward and be parallel with side cover and master spline on pitman shaft should be in line with adjuster screw, **Fig. 5.**
6. Rotate stub shaft 45° each side of center using a torque wrench with handle in vertical position, **Fig. 6,** record the highest drag torque measured on or near center.
7. Adjust over-center drag torque by loosening adjuster locknut and turning the pitman shaft adjuster screw clockwise until correct drag torque is obtained. On new steering gears (under 400 miles) add 5-11 inch lbs. to previously measured worm bearing preload. Do not exceed total preload of 18 inch lbs. On used steering gears (400 miles or more) add 4-5 inch lbs. to previously measured worm bearing preload. Do not exceed total gear preload of 13 inch lbs.
8. Hold adjuster screw and **torque** adjuster locknut to 20 ft. lbs.

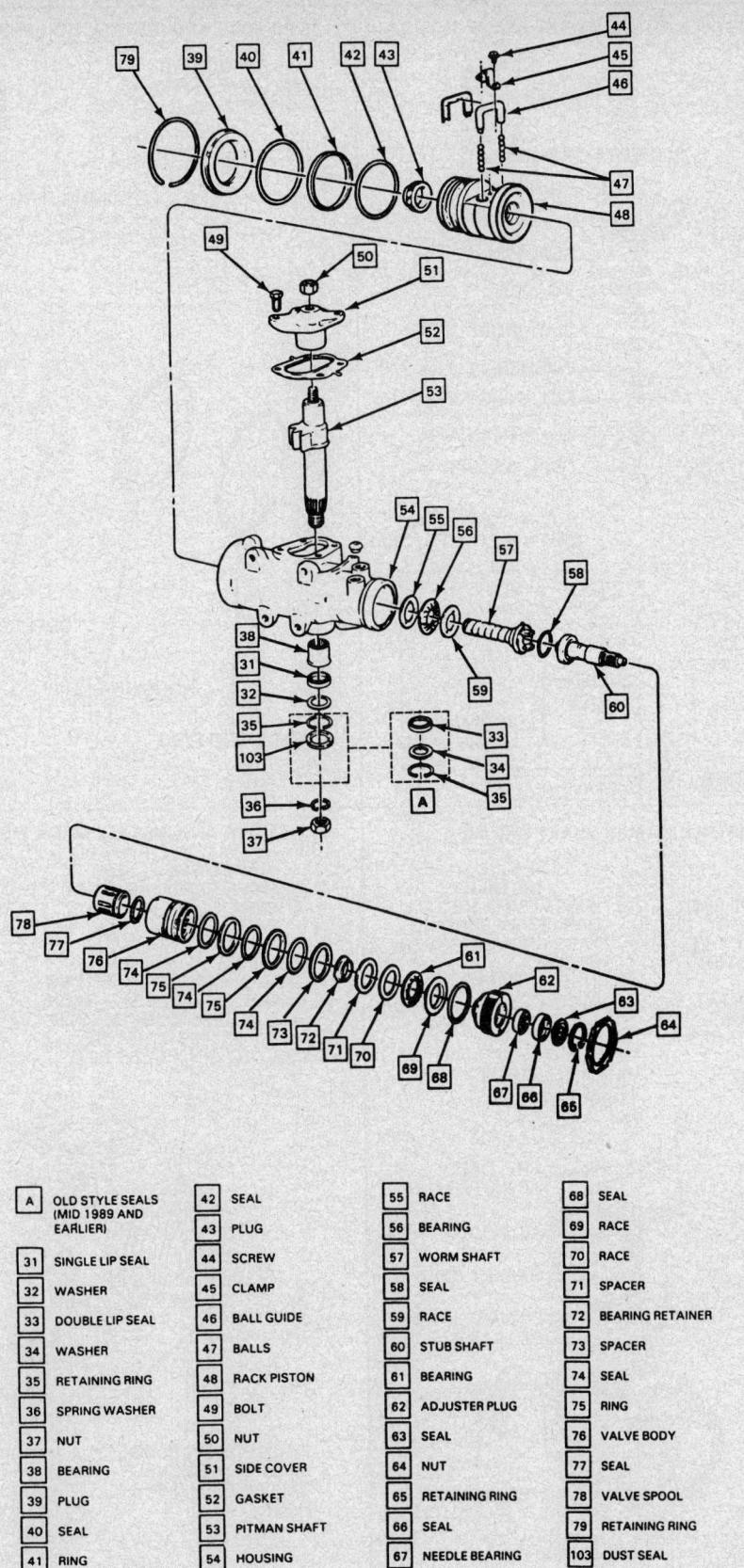

A	OLD STYLE SEALS (MID 1989 AND EARLIER)	42	SEAL	55	RACE	68	SEAL
31	SINGLE LIP SEAL	43	PLUG	56	BEARING	69	RACE
32	WASHER	44	SCREW	57	WORM SHAFT	70	RACE
33	DOUBLE LIP SEAL	45	CLAMP	58	SEAL	71	SPACER
34	WASHER	46	BALL GUIDE	59	RACE	72	BEARING RETAINER
35	RETAINING RING	47	BALLS	60	STUB SHAFT	73	SPACER
36	SPRING WASHER	48	RACK PISTON	61	BEARING	74	SEAL
37	NUT	49	BOLT	62	ADJUSTER PLUG	75	RING
38	BEARING	50	NUT	63	SEAL	76	VALVE BODY
39	PLUG	51	SIDE COVER	64	NUT	77	SEAL
40	SEAL	52	GASKET	65	RETAINING RING	78	VALVE SPOOL
41	RING	53	PITMAN SHAFT	66	SEAL	79	RETAINING RING
		54	HOUSING	67	NEEDLE BEARING	103	DUST SEAL

Fig. 1   Exploded view of Saginaw rotary valve type power steering gear

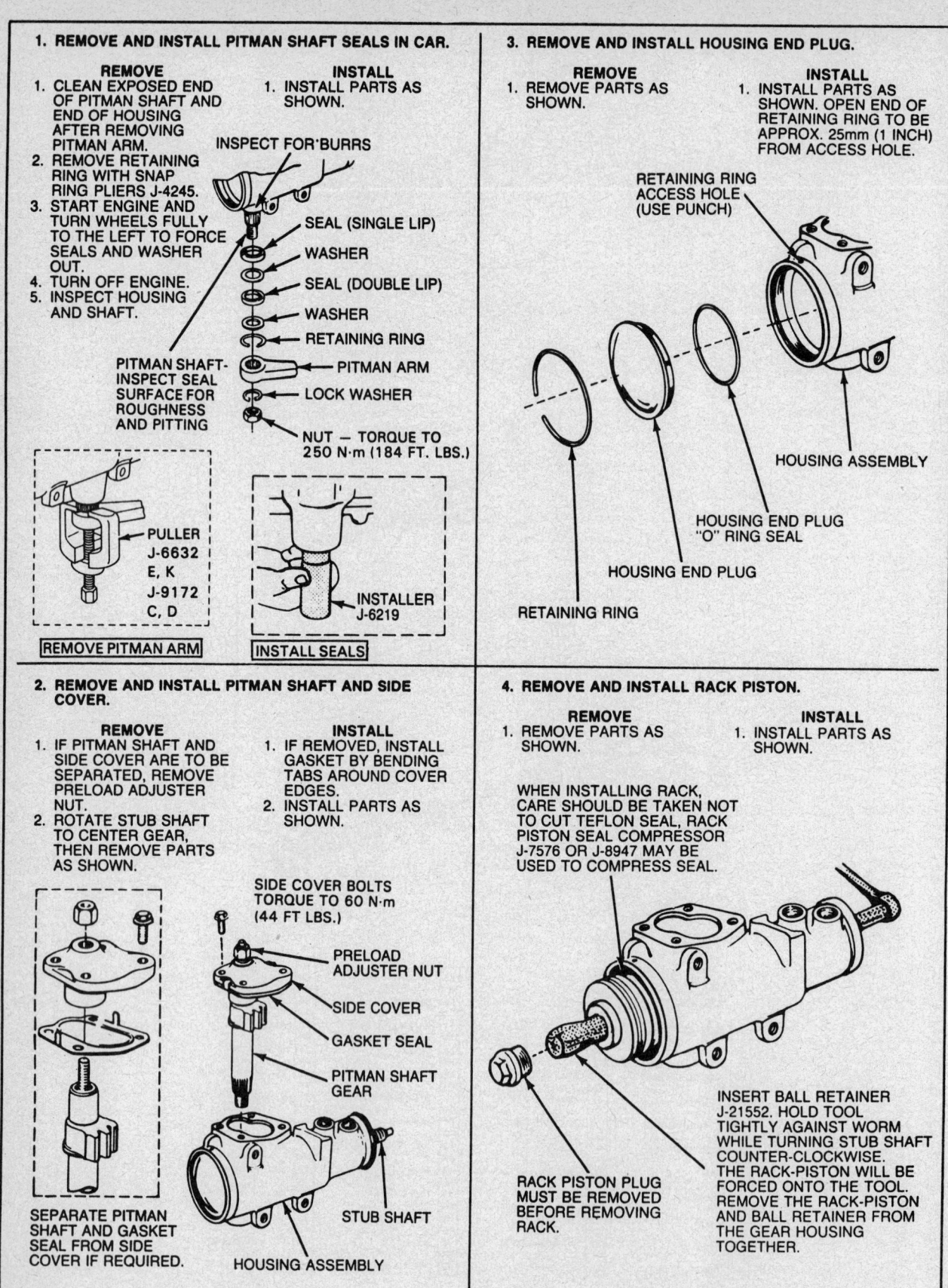

1. REMOVE AND INSTALL PITMAN SHAFT SEALS IN CAR.

REMOVE
1. CLEAN EXPOSED END OF PITMAN SHAFT AND END OF HOUSING AFTER REMOVING PITMAN ARM.
2. REMOVE RETAINING RING WITH SNAP RING PLIERS J-4245.
3. START ENGINE AND TURN WHEELS FULLY TO THE LEFT TO FORCE SEALS AND WASHER OUT.
4. TURN OFF ENGINE.
5. INSPECT HOUSING AND SHAFT.

INSTALL
1. INSTALL PARTS AS SHOWN.

INSPECT FOR BURRS
SEAL (SINGLE LIP)
WASHER
SEAL (DOUBLE LIP)
WASHER
RETAINING RING
PITMAN ARM
LOCK WASHER
NUT – TORQUE TO 250 N·m (184 FT. LBS.)

PITMAN SHAFT-INSPECT SEAL SURFACE FOR ROUGHNESS AND PITTING

PULLER J-6632 E, K J-9172 C, D

REMOVE PITMAN ARM

INSTALLER J-6219

INSTALL SEALS

2. REMOVE AND INSTALL PITMAN SHAFT AND SIDE COVER.

REMOVE
1. IF PITMAN SHAFT AND SIDE COVER ARE TO BE SEPARATED, REMOVE PRELOAD ADJUSTER NUT.
2. ROTATE STUB SHAFT TO CENTER GEAR, THEN REMOVE PARTS AS SHOWN.

INSTALL
1. IF REMOVED, INSTALL GASKET BY BENDING TABS AROUND COVER EDGES.
2. INSTALL PARTS AS SHOWN.

SIDE COVER BOLTS TORQUE TO 60 N·m (44 FT LBS.)
PRELOAD ADJUSTER NUT
SIDE COVER
GASKET SEAL
PITMAN SHAFT GEAR
STUB SHAFT
HOUSING ASSEMBLY

SEPARATE PITMAN SHAFT AND GASKET SEAL FROM SIDE COVER IF REQUIRED.

3. REMOVE AND INSTALL HOUSING END PLUG.

REMOVE
1. REMOVE PARTS AS SHOWN.

INSTALL
1. INSTALL PARTS AS SHOWN. OPEN END OF RETAINING RING TO BE APPROX. 25mm (1 INCH) FROM ACCESS HOLE.

RETAINING RING ACCESS HOLE (USE PUNCH)
HOUSING ASSEMBLY
HOUSING END PLUG "O" RING SEAL
HOUSING END PLUG
RETAINING RING

4. REMOVE AND INSTALL RACK PISTON.

REMOVE
1. REMOVE PARTS AS SHOWN.

INSTALL
1. INSTALL PARTS AS SHOWN.

WHEN INSTALLING RACK, CARE SHOULD BE TAKEN NOT TO CUT TEFLON SEAL, RACK PISTON SEAL COMPRESSOR J-7576 OR J-8947 MAY BE USED TO COMPRESS SEAL.

INSERT BALL RETAINER J-21552. HOLD TOOL TIGHTLY AGAINST WORM WHILE TURNING STUB SHAFT COUNTER-CLOCKWISE. THE RACK-PISTON WILL BE FORCED ONTO THE TOOL. REMOVE THE RACK-PISTON AND BALL RETAINER FROM THE GEAR HOUSING TOGETHER.

RACK PISTON PLUG MUST BE REMOVED BEFORE REMOVING RACK.

Fig. 2   Service procedures, Saginaw power steering gear (Part 1 of 4)

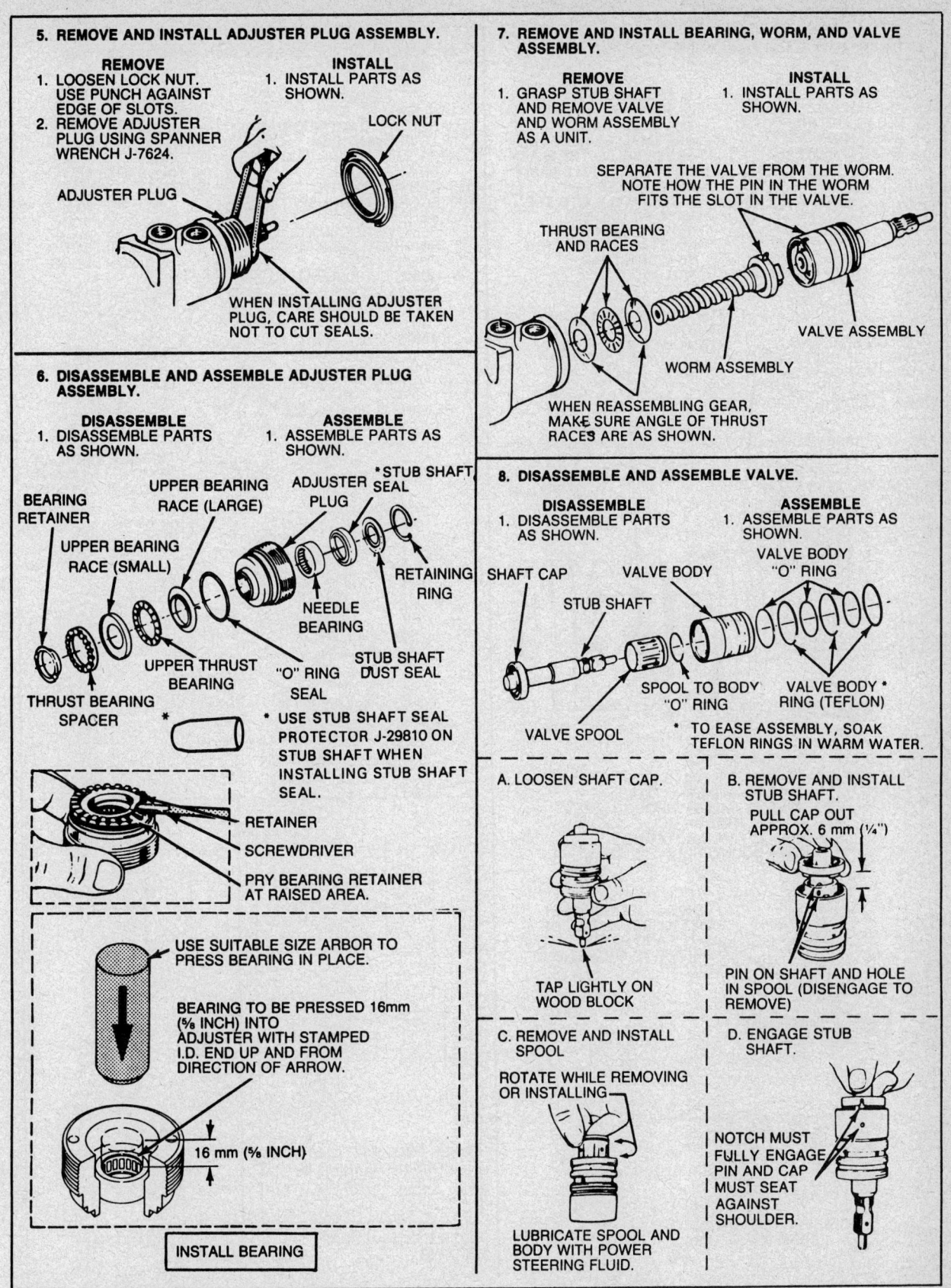

5. REMOVE AND INSTALL ADJUSTER PLUG ASSEMBLY.

REMOVE
1. LOOSEN LOCK NUT. USE PUNCH AGAINST EDGE OF SLOTS.
2. REMOVE ADJUSTER PLUG USING SPANNER WRENCH J-7624.

ADJUSTER PLUG

INSTALL
1. INSTALL PARTS AS SHOWN.

LOCK NUT

WHEN INSTALLING ADJUSTER PLUG, CARE SHOULD BE TAKEN NOT TO CUT SEALS.

6. DISASSEMBLE AND ASSEMBLE ADJUSTER PLUG ASSEMBLY.

DISASSEMBLE
1. DISASSEMBLE PARTS AS SHOWN.

ASSEMBLE
1. ASSEMBLE PARTS AS SHOWN.

BEARING RETAINER

UPPER BEARING RACE (LARGE)

UPPER BEARING RACE (SMALL)

ADJUSTER PLUG

*STUB SHAFT SEAL

RETAINING RING

NEEDLE BEARING

STUB SHAFT DUST SEAL

UPPER THRUST BEARING

"O" RING SEAL

THRUST BEARING SPACER *

* USE STUB SHAFT SEAL PROTECTOR J-29810 ON STUB SHAFT WHEN INSTALLING STUB SHAFT SEAL.

RETAINER
SCREWDRIVER
PRY BEARING RETAINER AT RAISED AREA.

USE SUITABLE SIZE ARBOR TO PRESS BEARING IN PLACE.

BEARING TO BE PRESSED 16mm (⅝ INCH) INTO ADJUSTER WITH STAMPED I.D. END UP AND FROM DIRECTION OF ARROW.

16 mm (⅝ INCH)

INSTALL BEARING

7. REMOVE AND INSTALL BEARING, WORM, AND VALVE ASSEMBLY.

REMOVE
1. GRASP STUB SHAFT AND REMOVE VALVE AND WORM ASSEMBLY AS A UNIT.

INSTALL
1. INSTALL PARTS AS SHOWN.

SEPARATE THE VALVE FROM THE WORM. NOTE HOW THE PIN IN THE WORM FITS THE SLOT IN THE VALVE.

THRUST BEARING AND RACES

VALVE ASSEMBLY

WORM ASSEMBLY

WHEN REASSEMBLING GEAR, MAKE SURE ANGLE OF THRUST RACES ARE AS SHOWN.

8. DISASSEMBLE AND ASSEMBLE VALVE.

DISASSEMBLE
1. DISASSEMBLE PARTS AS SHOWN.

SHAFT CAP

STUB SHAFT

VALVE SPOOL

ASSEMBLE
1. ASSEMBLE PARTS AS SHOWN.

VALVE BODY

VALVE BODY "O" RING

SPOOL TO BODY "O" RING

VALVE BODY * RING (TEFLON)

* TO EASE ASSEMBLY, SOAK TEFLON RINGS IN WARM WATER.

A. LOOSEN SHAFT CAP.

TAP LIGHTLY ON WOOD BLOCK

B. REMOVE AND INSTALL STUB SHAFT.

PULL CAP OUT APPROX. 6 mm (¼")

PIN ON SHAFT AND HOLE IN SPOOL (DISENGAGE TO REMOVE)

C. REMOVE AND INSTALL SPOOL

ROTATE WHILE REMOVING OR INSTALLING

LUBRICATE SPOOL AND BODY WITH POWER STEERING FLUID.

D. ENGAGE STUB SHAFT.

NOTCH MUST FULLY ENGAGE PIN AND CAP MUST SEAT AGAINST SHOULDER.

Fig. 2   Service procedures, Saginaw power steering gear (Part 2 of 4)

SAGINAW ROTARY VALVE TYPE POWER STEERING GEAR

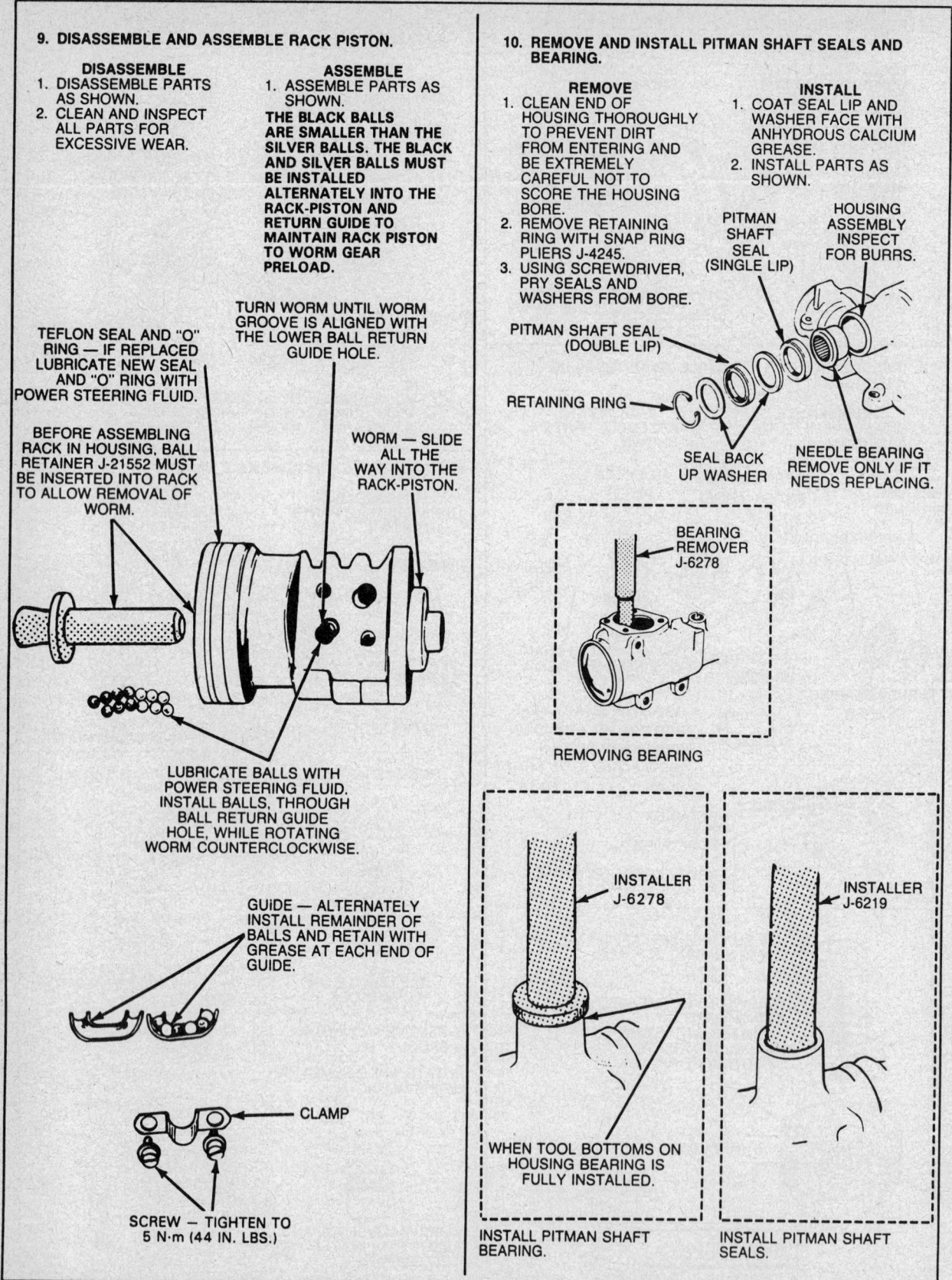

9. DISASSEMBLE AND ASSEMBLE RACK PISTON.

DISASSEMBLE
1. DISASSEMBLE PARTS AS SHOWN.
2. CLEAN AND INSPECT ALL PARTS FOR EXCESSIVE WEAR.

ASSEMBLE
1. ASSEMBLE PARTS AS SHOWN.
THE BLACK BALLS ARE SMALLER THAN THE SILVER BALLS. THE BLACK AND SILVER BALLS MUST BE INSTALLED ALTERNATELY INTO THE RACK-PISTON AND RETURN GUIDE TO MAINTAIN RACK PISTON TO WORM GEAR PRELOAD.

TURN WORM UNTIL WORM GROOVE IS ALIGNED WITH THE LOWER BALL RETURN GUIDE HOLE.

TEFLON SEAL AND "O" RING — IF REPLACED LUBRICATE NEW SEAL AND "O" RING WITH POWER STEERING FLUID.

BEFORE ASSEMBLING RACK IN HOUSING, BALL RETAINER J-21552 MUST BE INSERTED INTO RACK TO ALLOW REMOVAL OF WORM.

WORM — SLIDE ALL THE WAY INTO THE RACK-PISTON.

LUBRICATE BALLS WITH POWER STEERING FLUID. INSTALL BALLS, THROUGH BALL RETURN GUIDE HOLE, WHILE ROTATING WORM COUNTERCLOCKWISE.

GUIDE — ALTERNATELY INSTALL REMAINDER OF BALLS AND RETAIN WITH GREASE AT EACH END OF GUIDE.

CLAMP

SCREW — TIGHTEN TO 5 N·m (44 IN. LBS.)

10. REMOVE AND INSTALL PITMAN SHAFT SEALS AND BEARING.

REMOVE
1. CLEAN END OF HOUSING THOROUGHLY TO PREVENT DIRT FROM ENTERING AND BE EXTREMELY CAREFUL NOT TO SCORE THE HOUSING BORE.
2. REMOVE RETAINING RING WITH SNAP RING PLIERS J-4245.
3. USING SCREWDRIVER, PRY SEALS AND WASHERS FROM BORE.

INSTALL
1. COAT SEAL LIP AND WASHER FACE WITH ANHYDROUS CALCIUM GREASE.
2. INSTALL PARTS AS SHOWN.

PITMAN SHAFT SEAL (SINGLE LIP)

HOUSING ASSEMBLY INSPECT FOR BURRS.

PITMAN SHAFT SEAL (DOUBLE LIP)

RETAINING RING

SEAL BACK UP WASHER

NEEDLE BEARING REMOVE ONLY IF IT NEEDS REPLACING.

BEARING REMOVER J-6278

REMOVING BEARING

INSTALLER J-6278

WHEN TOOL BOTTOMS ON HOUSING BEARING IS FULLY INSTALLED.

INSTALL PITMAN SHAFT BEARING.

INSTALLER J-6219

INSTALL PITMAN SHAFT SEALS.

Fig. 2   Service procedures, Saginaw power steering gear (Part 3 of 4)

11. REMOVE AND INSTALL CHECK VALVE.

REMOVE	INSTALL
1. REMOVE PARTS AS SHOWN.	1. INSTALL PARTS AS SHOWN.

WITH SMALL SCREWDRIVER, PRY CHECK VALVE FROM HOUSING.

CARE SHOULD BE TAKEN NOT TO DAMAGE THREADS WHEN PRYING ON EDGE OF HOUSING.

REMOVE CHECK VALVE.

USING A PIECE OF 3⁄8 TUBING, 4 INCHES LONG, CAREFULLY DRIVE THE CHECK VALVE INTO THE HOUSING.

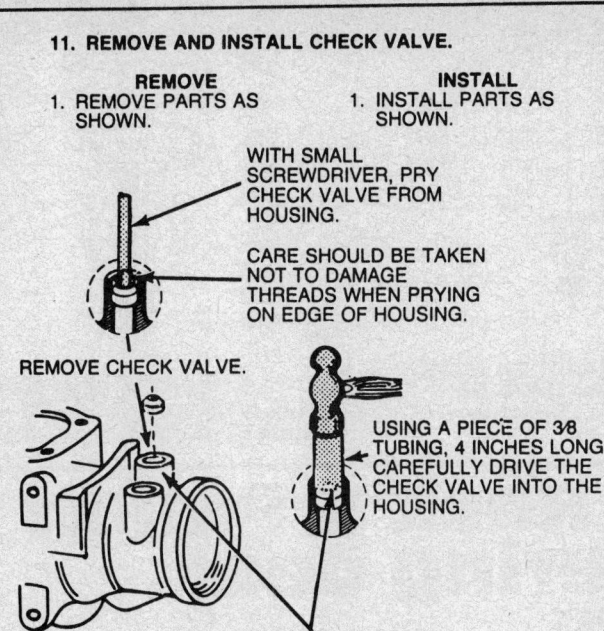

INSTALL CHECK VALVE.

12. ADJUST THRUST BEARING PRELOAD.

A. USING SPANNER WRENCH J-7624. TIGHTEN ADJUSTER PLUG UNTIL THRUST BEARING IS FIRMLY BOTTOMED, 27 N·m (20 FT. LBS.)

MARK HOUSING AND FACE OF ADJUSTER PLUG.

B. MEASURE BACK COUNTERCLOCKWISE 13mm (½") AND PLACE A SECOND MARK ON HOUSING.

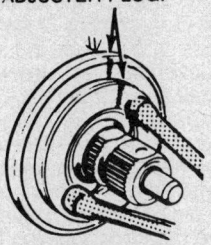

C. TURN ADJUSTER COUNTERCLOCKWISE UNTIL MARK ON FACE OF ADJUSTER LINES UP WITH SECOND MARK ON HOUSING.

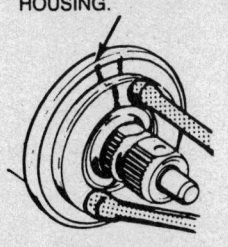

D. USING PUNCH IN NOTCH TIGHTEN LOCK NUT SECURELY. HOLD ADJUSTER PLUG TO MAINTAIN ALIGNMENT OF THE MARKS.

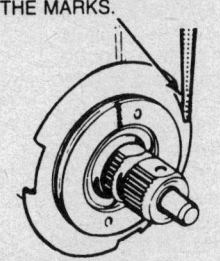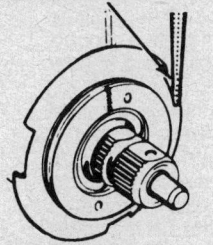

13. PITMAN SHAFT "OVER-CENTER" SECTOR ADJUSTMENT.

A.

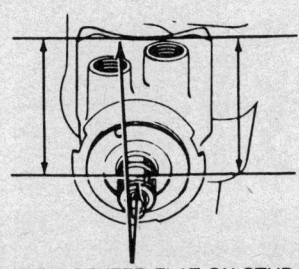

WHEN GEAR IS ON CENTER FLAT ON STUB SHAFT IS NORMALLY ON SAME SIDE AS, AND PARALLEL WITH, SIDE COVER.

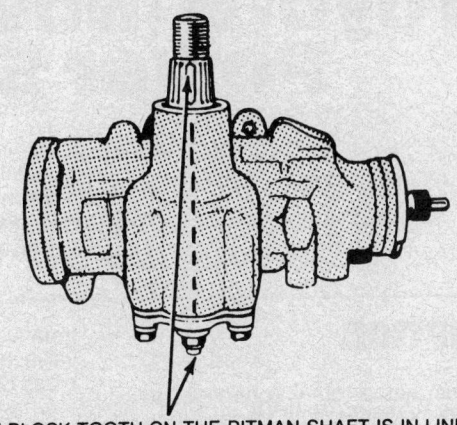

THE BLOCK TOOTH ON THE PITMAN SHAFT IS IN LINE WITH THE OVER-CENTER PRELOAD ADJUSTER.

B. BACK OFF PRELOAD ADJUSTER UNTIL IT STOPS, THEN TURN IT IN ONE FULL TURN.

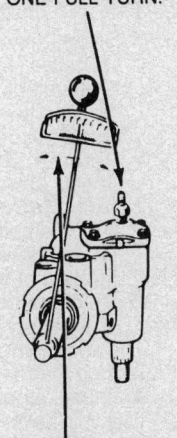

WITH GEAR AT CENTER OF TRAVEL, CHECK TORQUE TO TURN STUB SHAFT (READING #1).

C. TURN ADJUSTER IN UNTIL TORQUE TO TURN STUB SHAFT IS 0.6 TO 1.2 N·m (6 TO 11 IN. LBS.) MORE THAN READING #1.

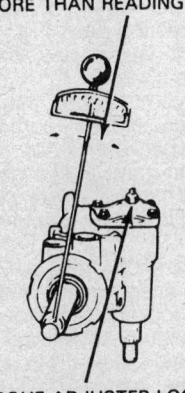

TORQUE ADJUSTER LOCK NUT TO 27 N·m (20 FT. LBS.)

PREVENT ADJUSTER SCREW FROM TURNING WHILE TORQUING LOCK NUT.

Fig. 2   Service procedures, Saginaw power steering gear (Part 4 of 4)

Fig. 3   Over center adjustment. 1988 models & Brougham

SAGINAW ROTARY VALVE TYPE POWER STEERING GEAR

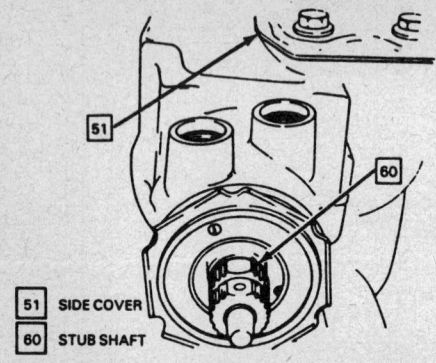

51 SIDE COVER
60 STUB SHAFT

Fig. 4 Aligning stub shaft. 1989–90 models except Brougham

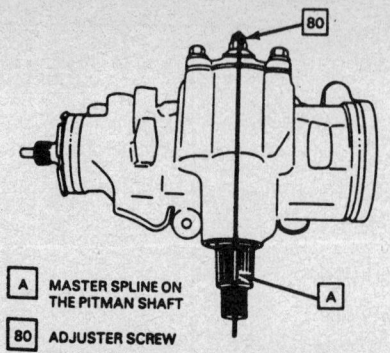

A MASTER SPLINE ON THE PITMAN SHAFT
80 ADJUSTER SCREW

Fig. 5 Aligning pitman shaft master spline. 1989–90 models except Brougham

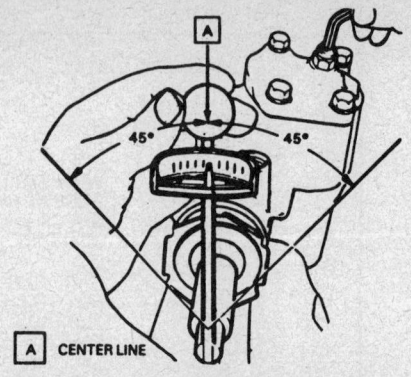

A CENTER LINE

Fig. 6 Checking over center rotational torque. 1989–90 models except Brougham

Toyota (Nova) Rack & Pinion Power Steering Gear

INDEX

DESCRIPTION

This system has a rotary control valve which directs hydraulic fluid under pressure to either side of rack piston. The piston is attached to the rack. The piston uses hydraulic pressure to move the rack left or right. This then moves the tie rods and steering knuckles, which turns the wheels.

DISASSEMBLY

1. Place steering gear, **Fig. 1**, in a suitable soft jawed vise, then remove pressure switch.
2. Remove tie rod ends, then the boots.
3. Straighten staked portion of lock washer between inner tie rod and rack, then remove tie rods from rack.
4. Remove right and left pipe assemblies between valve housing and cylinder.
5. Using wrench Nos. J-35692 and J-35423 or equivalent, remove adjusting plug locknut, cap and rack guide.
6. Remove dust cover and snap ring, then using socket No. J-35428 or equivalent, remove self locking nut from lower end of pinion gear.
7. Remove pinion assembly, then the upper bearing and oil seal.
8. Remove cylinder end stopper snap ring, then withdraw rack assembly, cylinder and stopper as an assembly.
9. Remove inner rack seal and spacer using drift, tool No. J-35434 or equivalent, then the pistons and O-ring seals from rack.
10. Using puller, tool No. J-35420 or equivalent, remove inner bushing

from valve housing, then the inner valve housing seal using a suitable brass drift.

INSPECTION & ASSEMBLY

1. Install inner bushings using bushing installer Nos. J-35695 and J-8092 or equivalent. **Bushing must be installed to a depth of 2.736 inch. If bushing is installed too far, it will deform. If bushing is not installed deep enough, it will interfere with the control valve pinion.**
2. Apply a suitable lubricant to valve and inner bushing, then ensure proper operation of valve and remove.
3. Remove piston and O-ring from rack, then apply a suitable lubricant. Install new O-ring, then expand new piston ring to ensure tight fit in piston groove.
4. Install inner cylinder seal and spacer as follows:
   a. Clean rack teeth, then wrap vinyl tape around rack teeth.
   b. Apply a suitable lubricant to cylinder bore and inner seal, then install inner cylinder seal and thin spacer onto rack. **Seal must be installed with lip end onto rack first followed by thin spacer.**
   c. Insert rack into cylinder, then tap end of rack with a suitable mallet to seat inner seal and spacer.
5. Apply a suitable lubricant to seal and

end stopper, then install outer cylinder seal spacer and end stopper, using drift, tool No. J-35425 or equivalent, as follows:
   a. Install seal with lip end into cylinder, followed by thick spacer.
   b. Install stopper until bottomed using drift No. J-35425 or equivalent.
   c. Stopper should be in far enough to expose snap ring groove.
   d. Install snap ring.
6. Test inner and outer seals using vacuum gauge. Apply $15\frac{3}{4}$ inch Hg for approximately 30 seconds. If vacuum does not hold, reinstall inner seals.
7. Install pinion control valve into housing, then the upper pinion bearing using bearing installer, tool No. J-35425 or equivalent.
8. Apply a suitable lubricant to seal, then install seal and snap ring.
9. Install dust cover.
10. Install spacer, lower bearing and new self locking nut onto pinion valve shaft, then **torque** lower nut to 43 ft. lbs., using socket No. J-35428 or equivalent, and a suitable torque wrench.
11. Apply a suitable sealant to threads of lower cap, then install cap and **torque** to 51 ft. lbs. Stake cap to housing.
12. Install rack guide seat, guide and spring, then apply a suitable sealant to guide cap. Install cap.
13. Install inner tie rods with claw washers, then **torque** to 61 ft. lbs. Stake locking washers, ensuring air bleed holes in rack are open.
14. Install rack boots and clips, ensuring clips are installed with loop facing away from boot. Apply a suitable lubri-

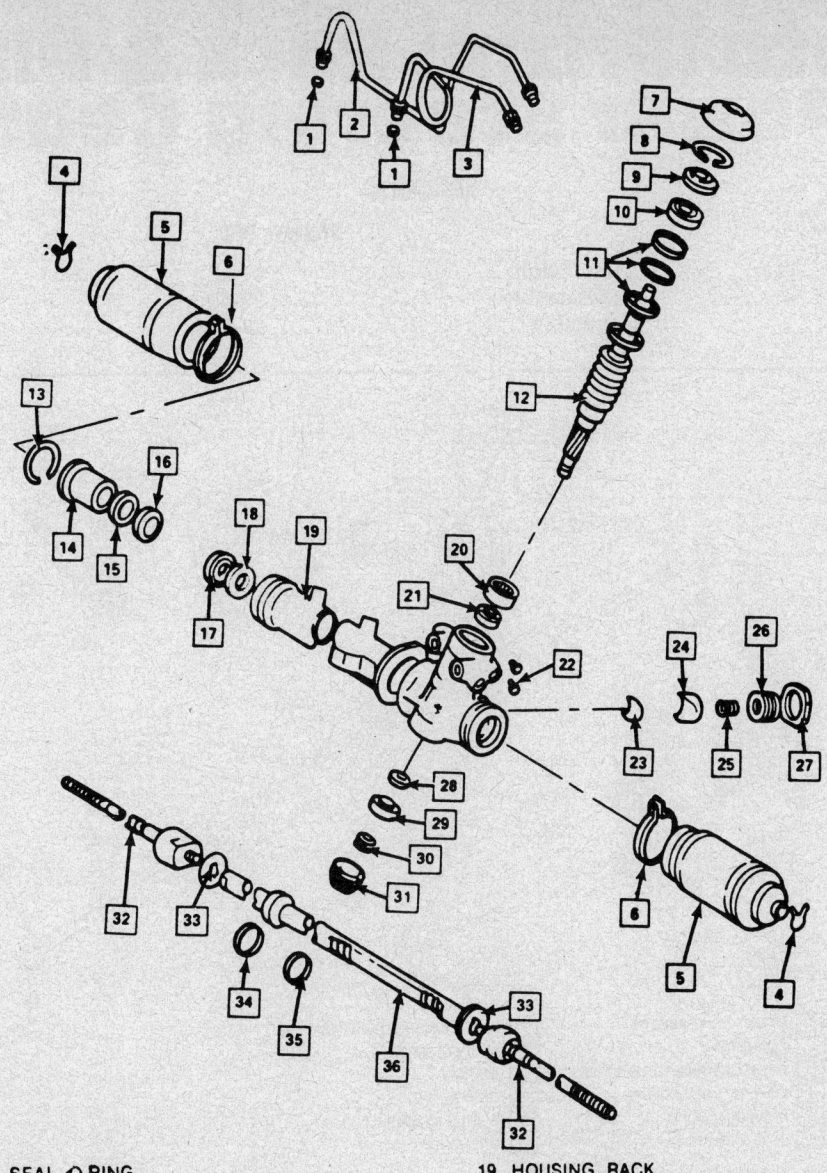

1. SEAL, O-RING
2. TUBE, PRESSURE · RIGHT SIDE
3. TUBE, PRESSURE · LEFT SIDE
4. CLIP, BOOT
5. BOOT, STEERING RACK
6. CLAMP, BOOT
7. COVER, PINION DUST
8. RING, SNAP
9. SEAL, PINION UPPER
10. BEARING, PINION UPPER
11. RING, CONTROL VALVE SEALING
12. VALVE/PINION ASSY., STEERING
13. RING, SNAP
14. STOPPER, CYLINDER END
15. SPACER, OUTER CYLINDER END (THICK)
16. SEAL, OUTER CYLINDER END
17. SEAL, INNER CYLINDER END
18. SPACER, INNER CYLINDER END (THIN)

19. HOUSING, RACK
20. BUSHING, LOWER PINION/VALVE
21. SEAL, PINION/VALVE
22. SEAT, UNION
23. **SEAT, RACK GUIDE**
24. GUIDE, RACK
25. SPRING RACK GUIDE
26. CAP, RACK GUIDE, SPRING
27. NUT, RACK GUIDE LOCKING
28. SPACER, VALVE/PINION LOWER
29. BEARING, VALVE/PINION LOWER
30. NUT, VALVE/PINION LOWER LOCKING
31. CAP, VALVE/PINION LOWER
32. END SUB-ASSY., BALL JOINT INNER
33. WASHER, CLAW LOCKING
34. RING, O-RING
35. RING, PISTON SEALING
36. RACK

Fig. 1 Toyota (Nova) power rack & pinion exploded view

cant to inside of boot at small end.
15. Install tie rods and align mating marks. Ensure distance between inner tie rod and outer tie rod ends are 1.890 inch (48 mm). **Torque** locking nut to 35 ft. lbs.
16. Install right and left pressure tubes, then **torque** to 18 ft. lbs.
17. Adjust total preload as follows:

a. Using socket, tool No. J-35423 or equivalent, and a suitable torque wrench, **torque** rack guide cap to 18 ft. lbs.
b. Back cap off 12 degrees, then move rack back and forth one or 2 times.
c. Check value of preload using a suitable torque wrench. Preload

should be 7-11 inch lbs.
d. Install locking nut after adjusting preload to specifications, then **torque** locknut to 33 ft. lbs.
e. Ensure final preload is 7-11 inch lbs. and readjust as necessary.
18. Apply a suitable sealer to pressure switch threads, then **torque** to 10 ft. lbs.

Toyota (Prizm) Rack & Pinion Power Steering Gear

INDEX

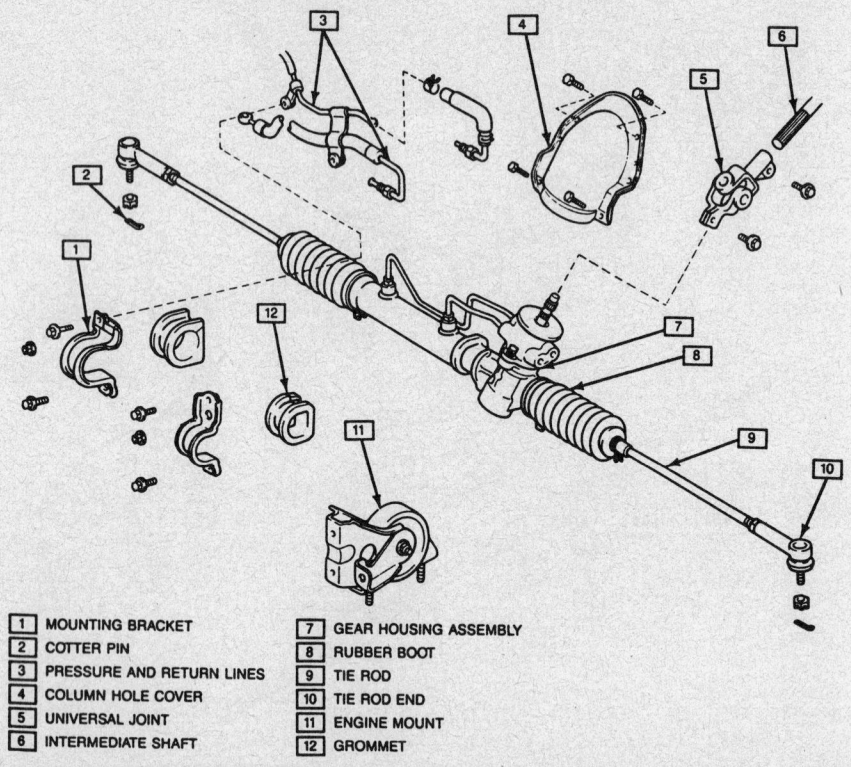

1	MOUNTING BRACKET	7	GEAR HOUSING ASSEMBLY
2	COTTER PIN	8	RUBBER BOOT
3	PRESSURE AND RETURN LINES	9	TIE ROD
4	COLUMN HOLE COVER	10	TIE ROD END
5	UNIVERSAL JOINT	11	ENGINE MOUNT
6	INTERMEDIATE SHAFT	12	GROMMET

Fig. 1   Toyota (Prizm) power rack & pinion steering gear assembly

DESCRIPTION

This steering system converts rotary motion to linear motion as follows; when the steering wheel is turned, rotary motion is transferred to the steering shaft, shaft joint and rack pinion. The pinion teeth mesh with teeth on the rack and the rotary motion is transferred to the rack and changed to linear motion. The linear force is then transmitted through the tie rods and to the steering knuckles which steer the front wheels.

DISASSEMBLY

The power steering gear is non-serviceable and therefore must be replaced as a unit. To remove the power steering gear proceed as follows:
1. Remove steering unit from vehicle and place in suitable vise, **Fig. 1.**
2. Remove power steering lines.
3. Scribe alignment mark on tie rod end and tie rod, then remove tie rod ends.
4. Remove rack boots, then bend back locking washer using appropriate punch or chisel and remove.
5. Using tie rod housing wrench, tool No. J 35414 and steering rack end wrench, tool No. J 35418, remove tie rod.
6. Remove dust cover, snap ring then, oil seal.

ASSEMBLY

1. Install a new upper oil seal, then install snap ring and dust cover.
2. Install a new claw washer, then using tie rod housing wrench, tool No. J 351414 and steering rack end wrench, tool No. J 35418 install tie rods and **torque** tie rods to 53 ft. lbs.
3. Install rubber rack boot, then screw lock nuts and tie rod ends onto the tie rods until match marks are aligned, **torque** lock nut to 41 ft. lbs.
4. Adjust toe-in, then **torque** lock nut to 41 ft. lbs.
5. Install power steering lines, **torque** nuts to 8 ft. lbs.
6. Install steering assembly into vehicle.

Torque Specifications

NOTE: All Specifications In Ft. Lbs. Unless Noted.

BERETTA, CALAIS, CAVALIER, CIMARRON, CORSICA, FIRENZA, GRAND AM, LEMANS, SKYHAWK, SKYLARK & SUNBIRD

Year	Adjuster Plug Locknut	Coupling To Stub Shaft	Coupling To Steering Column	Inner Tie Rod Bolts	Pinion Locknut	Pinion Preload	Power Steering Line Fittings	Rack & Pinion Mounting Clamp Nuts	Rod & Piston Assembly To Rack	Tie Rod End To Steering Knuckle Nut	Tie Rod Pinch Bolts
1988-90	50	37	34	65	26	16①	②	22	65	35	41

①—Inch lbs.
②—Valve end, 14 ft. lbs., cylinder end, 20 ft. lbs.

MODELS w/SAGINAW RACK & PINION POWER STEERING EXCEPT BERETTA, CALAIS, CAVALIER, CIMARRON, CORSICA, FIRENZA, GRAND AM, LEMANS, SKYHAWK, SKYLARK & SUNBIRD

Year	Adjuster Plug Locknut	Inner Tie Rod Housing To Rack	Intermediate Shaft Pinch Bolts	Outer Tie Rod Jam Nut	Pinion Locknut	Pinion Preload	Power Steering Line Fittings	Tie Rod Pinch Bolts
1988-90	50	70	35	30	26	16①	②	41

①—Inch lbs.
②—Valve end, 12 ft. lbs., cylinder end, 20 ft. lbs.

NOVA, PRIZM, SPECTRUM & STORM

Model	Adjuster Plug Locknut	Flange & Coupling Pinch Bolt	Coupling To Column Pinch Bolt	Inner Tie Rod Pinch Bolts	Outer Tie Rod Pinch Bolts	Inner Tie Rod Bolt	Pinion Preload①	Power Steering Line Fittings	Inner Tie Rod Housing To Rack	Outer Tie Rod Jam Nut
1988										
Nova	43	—	—	35	35	—	7-11	—	61	—
Spectrum	49	—	18	30	29	40	5–14.5	14	65	—
1989										
Prizm	—	—	34	53	33	—	—	8	—	41
Spectrum	49	—	18	30	29	40	5–14.5	14	65	—
1990										
Prizm	—	—	34	53	33	—	—	8	—	41
Storm	—	—	—	—	—	65	44	20	—	41

①—Inch lbs.

Service Bulletins

INDEX

IDENTIFYING RACK & PINION STEERING NOISES

All Models

When removing or installing any rack and pinion steering gear for service, be sure to inspect the intermediate steering shaft or steering coupling seal for cuts or tears which would allow noises to be transmitted into the passenger area.

All models are susceptible to having the power steering pump lines lay against other components which could transmit steering system noises into the car. Hoses should be inspected to be sure they are not touching any other components and creating the noise.

When diagnosing a growl, ground out, or rattle noise, there is a possibility that one of the cylinder lines of the gear could be grounding out on the heater case on the right side of the cowl. If this condition exists, bend pipe away from the contact area.

Grand Am & Sunbird

Check upper portion of steering coupling seal to be sure it is seated over the bushing or a noise path could be created. On 6000 and Bonneville models, check seal to be sure it is securely fastened to the cowl and lower column.

The center-take-off gears, also use a dash seal which must be properly indexed on the housing before the gear is installed. If the dash seal is improperly installed another noise path can be created. A mispositioned dash seal could also cause a condition of stiff steering.

POWER STEERING HOSE LINE CONNECTION FITTING LEAKS

All Models

Fitting **torque** specification is 20 ft. lbs. If a leak is experienced at the fitting area when properly tightened, this condition may be caused by a damaged fitting O-ring. Inspect the O-ring for damage, pipe end for cracks, fitting threads for damage, replace as necessary.

Do not exceed fitting torque specification. Additional torque will not increase O-ring sealing ability and may result in cracking the connection boss on aluminum gear housings. If a leak is experienced at the connection area with a new undamaged O-ring under correct torque, inspect housing boss for casting defects. A casting defect will require housing or short gear replacement.

POWER STEERING SHUDDER (RETURN HOSE & PIPE ASSEMBLY REPLACEMENT)

6000

Some 6000 models with 2.8L engines may exhibit a power steering shudder condition. This condition is apparent during low speed turning maneuvers and would be perceived as a vibration felt in the steering wheel.

Vehicles exhibiting this condition may be repaired by replacing existing power steering outlet hose and pipe assembly with new assembly No. 26017135.

POWER STEERING PUMP NOISE

1988 DeVille & Fleetwood

On models with standard suspension, power steering noise may be heard. This condition may be caused by the power steering pump. Replace the pump with a reduced flow pump No. 26012285. For proper replacement procedure refer to "Power Steering Pumps" section.

POWER STEERING PUMP NOISE & INCREASED STEERING EFFORT

1988 Electra, LeSabre, Riviera & Park Avenue

These models may experience increased steering effort during long duration and/or aggressive turns and noise may be heard even after bleeding. The noise can be corrected by installing a new type reservoir. This reservoir No. 26009846 has increased baffling and is 1/4 taller. To correct steering effort condition install a new flow control valve, O-ring union fitting, part No. 7840203. Refer to the proper replacement procedures in the "Power Steering Pumps" section

DASH PANEL SERVICE

INDEX

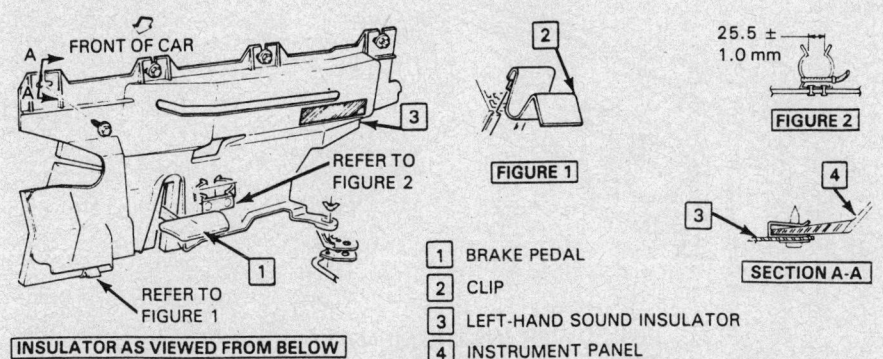

1 BRAKE PEDAL
2 CLIP
3 LEFT-HAND SOUND INSULATOR
4 INSTRUMENT PANEL

Fig. 1 Removing left side sound insulator. 1988–89 Fleetwood (RWD)

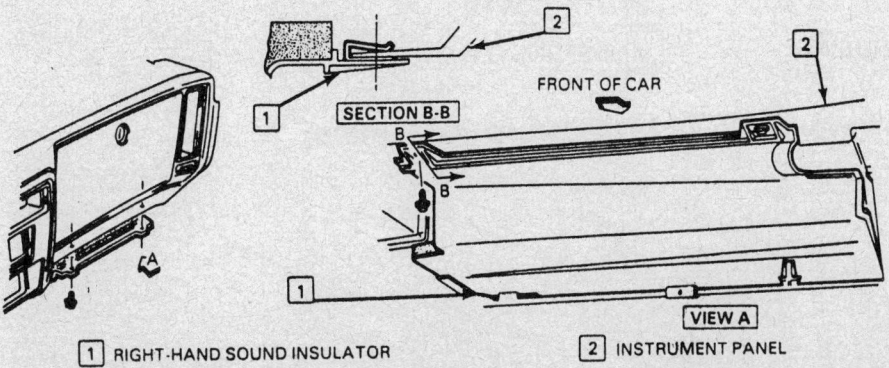

1 RIGHT-HAND SOUND INSULATOR
2 INSTRUMENT PANEL

Fig. 2 Removing right side sound insulator. 1988–89 Fleetwood (RWD)

1988–89 FLEETWOOD BROUGHAM (RWD)

1. Disconnect battery ground cable.
2. Remove left and right side sound insulators, **Figs. 1 and 2.**
3. Remove screw securing A/C left side outlet duct extension and remove duct.
4. Remove screw securing instrument panel top cover to left and right side of instrument panel, **Fig. 3.**
5. Remove top cover attaching screw through access hole located above the speedometer cluster trim plate.
6. Remove top cover attaching screw through access hole located in top of glove box liner.
7. Remove four cover attaching screws located at the ends of the defroster grilles.
8. Remove top cover by pulling panel rearward off the spring clips located near center of panel.
9. Remove radio knobs, anti-rattle springs, then the two hex nuts securing center trim plate to radio, **Fig. 4.**
10. Remove two center air conditioner outlet grilles, then remove screws behind each outlet.
11. Remove remaining trim plate attaching screws, then trim plate.
12. Remove two screws securing right side rear view mirror control head to the instrument panel.
13. Remove remote control cable from clips at glove box.
14. Remove screws and nuts securing steering column and rest on seat.
15. Disconnect guidematic and twilight sentinel outside wiring connectors.
16. Disconnect cruise control brake release switch, **Fig. 5.**
17. Disconnect stop light switch, then the rear defogger relay on top of accessory relay panel.
18. Disconnect dimmer switch, then all relays at relay convenience center.
19. Disconnect body connector at fuse block.
20. Disconnect aspirator hose at aspirator, then the vacuum harness at vacuum hose interconnect.
21. Disconnect electrical connector at A/C programmer.
22. Disconnect right side instrument panel ground screw.
23. Remove two screws attaching two halves of main instrument panel electrical connector, then separate connector.
24. Remove screw securing two halves of center bulkhead connector and disconnect.
25. Remove two screws securing inner half of center bulkhead to cowl and remove connector.
26. Remove right and left instrument panel side mounting screws.
27. Remove two screws securing upper steering column guide bracket to instrument panel and remove bracket.
28. Remove four screws securing instrument panel to cowl at base of windshield.

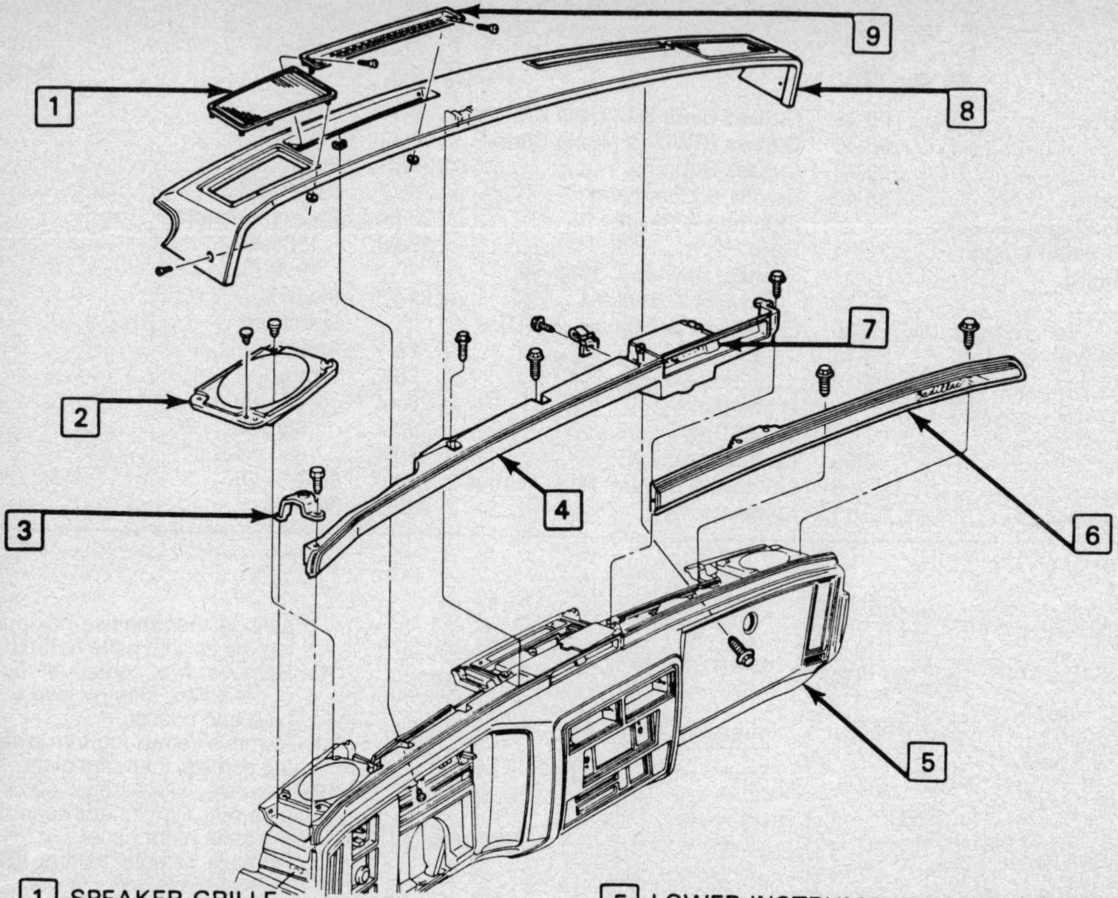

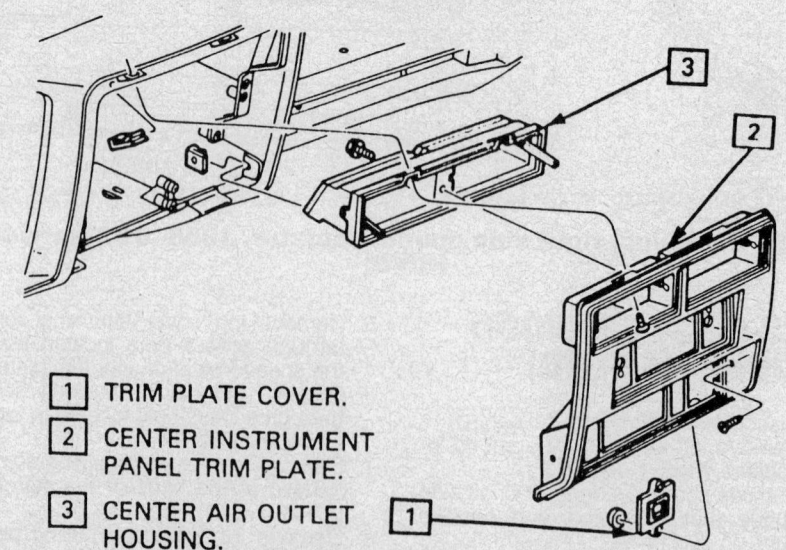

Fig. 3   I/P top cover removal. 1988–89 Brougham (RWD)

1	SPEAKER GRILLE
2	SPEAKER
3	PHOTOCELL HOLDER FOR TWILIGHT SENTINEL
4	LEFT-HAND TELLTALE HOUSING
5	LOWER INSTRUMENT PANEL ASSEMBLY
6	RIGHT-HAND APPLIQUE PLATE
7	FUEL GAGE
8	TOP COVER
9	DEFROSTER OUTLET GRILLE

29. Slide panel away from cowl and disconnect trunk release, switch speedometer, rear seat speakers and antenna.
30. Remove instrument panel from vehicle.
31. Reverse procedure to install.

1990 BROUGHAM

1. Disconnect battery ground cable.
2. Remove sound insulators, **Figs. 6 and 7.**
3. Remove screw securing left side A/C outlet duct extension and remove duct.
4. Remove two steering column cover retaining screws and lower cover.
5. Remove A/C left side outlet duct extension retaining screw, then the duct.
6. Remove instrument panel retaining screws at each end of instrument panel.

1 TRIM PLATE COVER.

2 CENTER INSTRUMENT PANEL TRIM PLATE.

3 CENTER AIR OUTLET HOUSING.

Fig. 4   Removing I/P center trim plate. 1988–89 Brougham (RWD)

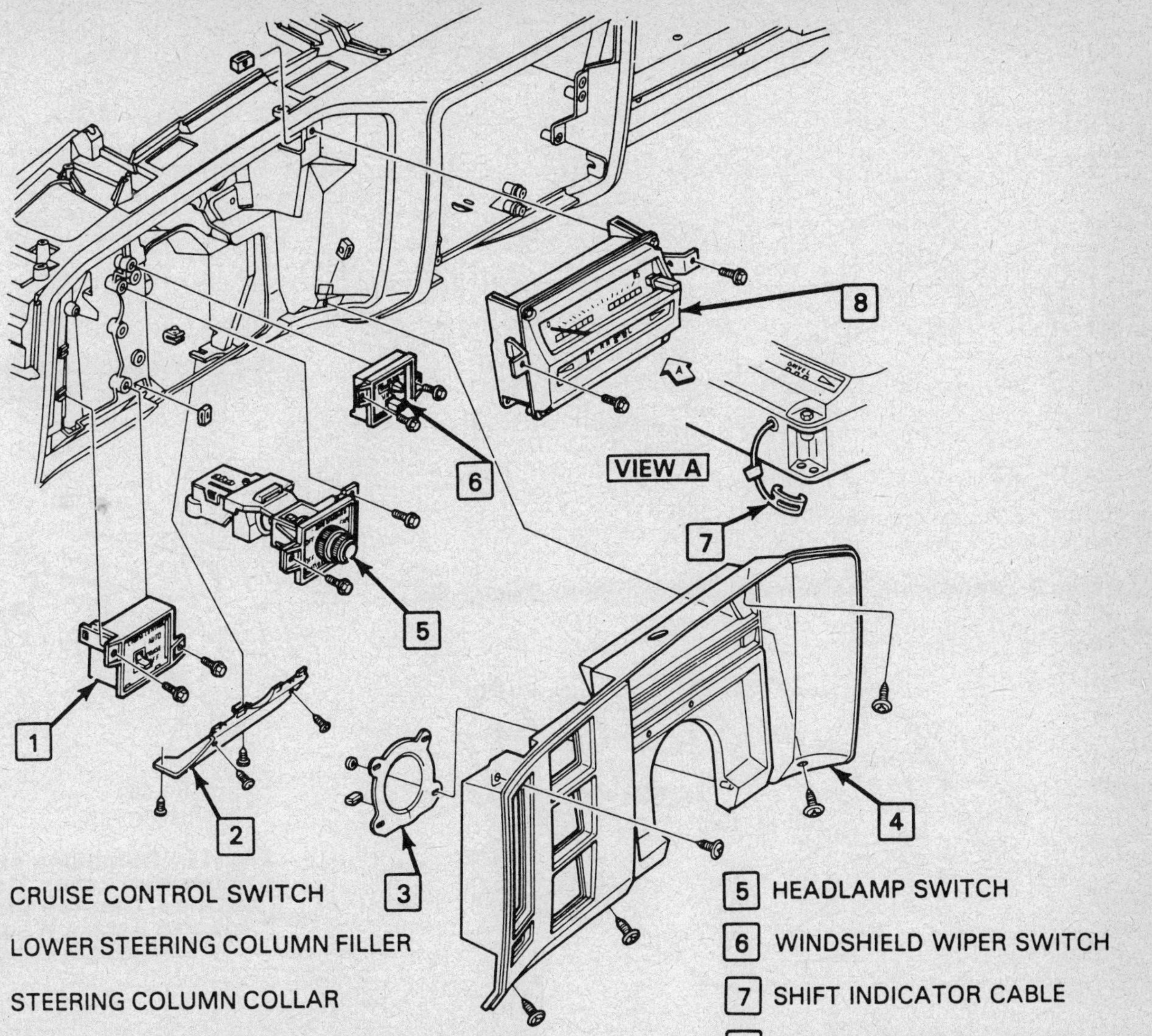

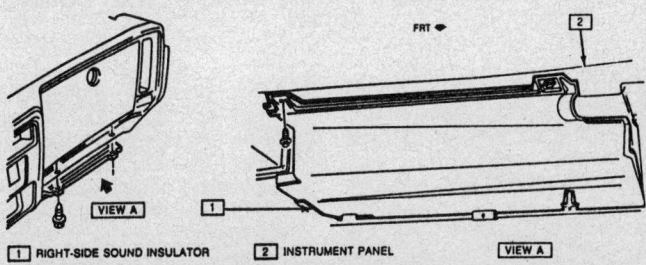

1	CRUISE CONTROL SWITCH	5	HEADLAMP SWITCH
2	LOWER STEERING COLUMN FILLER	6	WINDSHIELD WIPER SWITCH
3	STEERING COLUMN COLLAR	7	SHIFT INDICATOR CABLE
4	LEFT-HAND INSTRUMENT PANEL TRIM PLATE	8	SPEEDOMETER CLUSTER

Fig. 5 Exploded view of speedometer cluster & left side trim plate. 1988–89 Brougham (RWD)

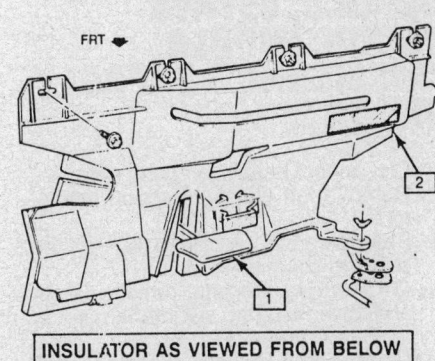

INSULATOR AS VIEWED FROM BELOW

| 1 | BRAKE PEDAL |
| 2 | LEFT-SIDE SOUND INSULATOR |

Fig. 6 Left side sound insulator. 1990 Brougham

7. Remove top cover attaching screw through access hole located in top of glove box liner.

| 1 | RIGHT-SIDE SOUND INSULATOR | 2 | INSTRUMENT PANEL | VIEW A |

Fig. 7 Right side sound insulator. 1990 Brougham

8. Remove four top cover to cowl retaining screws located in the defroster grilles.
9. Remove top cover by pulling panel up and out of retaining clips.
10. Using a 1/16 inch Allen wrench, loosen key on bottom of each center outlet grille directional knob, then remove knobs.
11. Remove four center trim panel retaining screws, then the trim panel.
12. Remove remaining grille directional knob.
13. Remove six trim panel retaining screws, then the trim panel.
14. Remove four instrument cluster retaining screws, **Fig. 8.**
15. Remove upper steering column mounting bolts and set column on front seat.
16. Remove two windshield wiper switch retaining screws.
17. Remove three headlamp switch to instrument panel retaining screws.

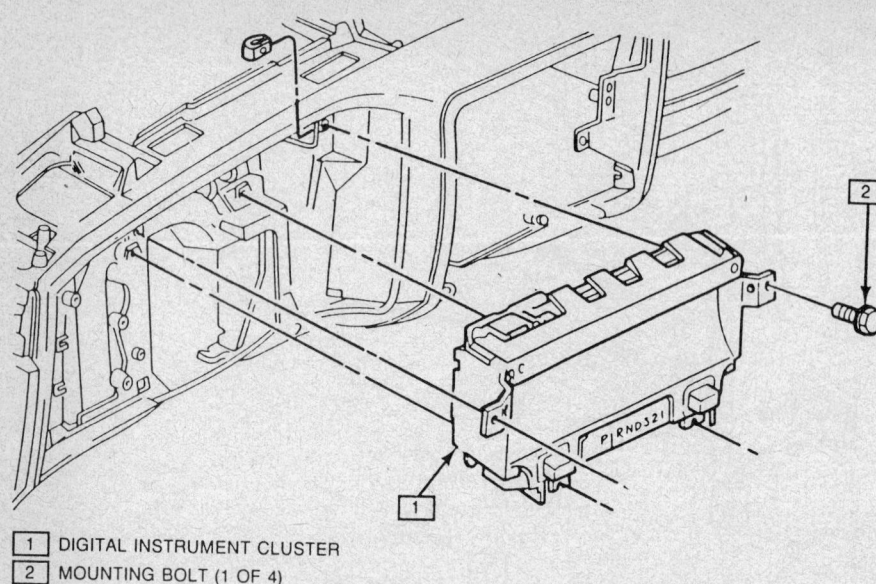

1. DIGITAL INSTRUMENT CLUSTER
2. MOUNTING BOLT (1 OF 4)

Fig. 8   Removing instrument cluster. 1990 Brougham

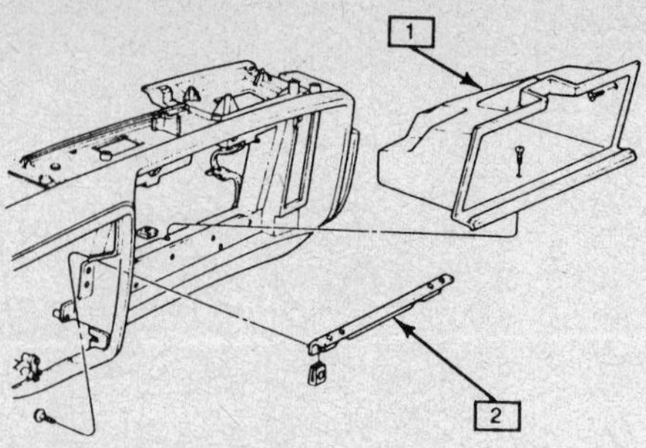

1. GLOVE BOX LINER
2. LINER BRACKET

Fig. 9   Removing glove box liner. 1990 Brougham

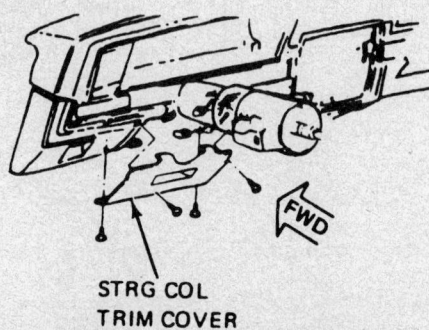

STRG COL
TRIM COVER

Fig. 11   Removing steering column trim cover. Delta 88, Caprice, Caprice Classic, Electra Estate Wagon & LeSabre Wagon

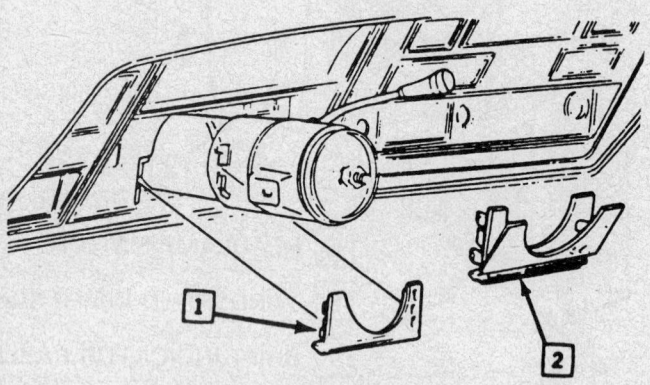

1. STEERING COLUMN TRIM COVER
2. TRIM COVER WITH GAGES

Fig. 10   Removing steering column trim cover. Safari

18. **On models equipped with cruise control,** remove two cruise control switch retaining screws, then slide switch forward.
19. Disconnect switch two piece electrical connector.
20. Remove twilight Sentinel wiring if equipped.
21. **On all models,** remove headlamp switch retaining nut, then the switch from housing.
22. Remove two 10mm mounting bolts and ground strap from chime mounting bracket.
23. Remove 10mm retaining nut from stud on bottom of radio chassis.
24. Pull chime module, bracket and chime wiring downwards, then position aside.
25. Disconnect antenna lead.
26. Pull radio chassis down and pivot towards front of car until connector end of chassis is horizontal with floorpan.

27. Disconnect (2) electrical connectors from side opposite coax cable.
28. Pull chassis out from behind instrument panel and disconnect three electrical connectors.
29. Remove two ECC head retaining screws.
30. Disconnect electrical connector from ECC head, then the EEC.
31. Remove right side mirror remote control retaining screws, then the remote control.
32. Remove three glove box liner retaining screws, **Fig. 9.**
33. Remove four glove box door retaining screws, then remove accessory relay bracket and position aside.
34. Remove four upper instrument panel retaining screws and two lower instrument panel retaining bolts.
35. Disconnect instrument panel electrical connectors.
36. Remove instrument panel.

37. Reverse procedure to install.

CAPRICE, ESTATE WAGON, IMPALA, PARISIÉNNE & SAFARI WAGON

1. Disconnect battery ground cable.
2. Remove left and right sound insulators.
3. Slide steering column collar up the steering column.
4. **On Pontiac models,** remove upper and lower steering column trim cover retaining screws, **Fig. 10.**
5. **On models except Pontiac,** pull steering column trim cover rearward to release clips, **Fig. 11.**
6. **On all models,** open left and right front doors to gain access to instrument panel pad side screws.
7. Remove instrument panel pad side retaining screws, **Fig. 12.**
8. Remove defogger grilles, then pad retaining screws inside defogger openings.
9. Remove retaining screws located un-

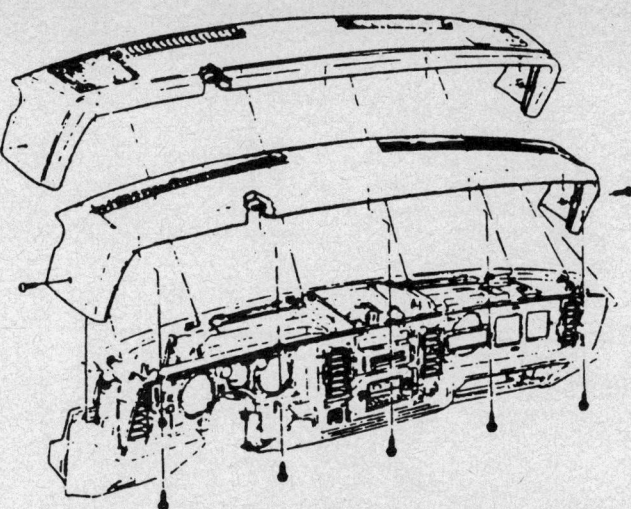

Fig. 12 I/P pad removal. Delta 88, Caprice, Caprice Classic, Electra Estate Wagon, LeSabre Wagon & Safari

derneath the front of the pad, then remove pad from instrument panel.

10. Split bulkhead connector by removing bolt and screws on the inside of the fuse block and pull harness free.
11. Remove nuts securing steering column, then disconnect shift indicator cable clip and all electrical connectors between steering column and instrument panel harness.
12. Lower the steering column, then disconnect brake release cable.
13. Remove Heater-A/C control head.
14. If equipped, remove the following connectors:
    a. Wire at switch for rear compartment release.
    b. Antenna lead and power antenna wire connector.
    c. Rear window defogger connector.
15. Disconnect speedometer cable at the split in the engine compartment, if a

two piece cable is used, or the transmission for slack.
16. Remove lower A/C duct by removing screw, then rotate duct out.
17. Remove instrument panel retaining nuts from top left and right sides of the panel, **Fig. 13.**
18. Remove instrument panel retaining screws from center support.
19. Remove panel retaining bolts from steering column support bracket.
20. Remove retaining screws from upper tie bar, then the screws from lower reinforcement.
21. Remove retaining bolts located in the steering column opening.
22. Disconnect speedometer cable from speedometer.
23. Remove instrument panel from support brackets.
24. Reverse procedure to install.

1988-89 CORVETTE

Refer to **Figs. 14 and 15,** when performing this procedure.
1. Disconnect battery ground cable.
2. Remove steering column tilt lever.
3. Remove headlamp switch knob.
4. Remove eight instrument panel courtesy trim plate screws and courtesy trim plate.
5. Remove five instrument panel accessory trim plate screws and accessory trim plate, **Fig. 16.**
6. **On models with automatic trans-**

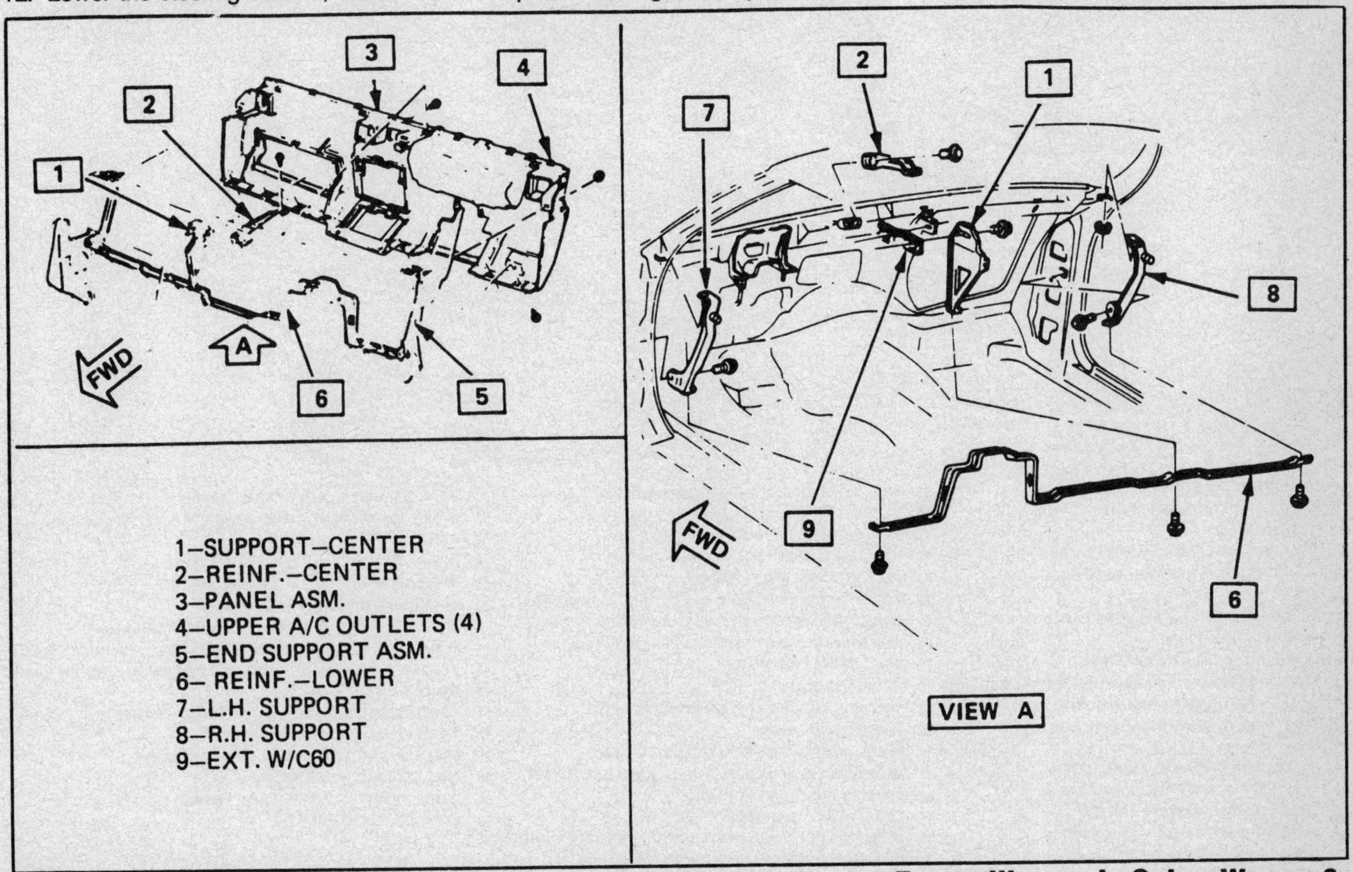

1–SUPPORT–CENTER
2–REINF.–CENTER
3–PANEL ASM.
4–UPPER A/C OUTLETS (4)
5–END SUPPORT ASM.
6– REINF.–LOWER
7–L.H. SUPPORT
8–R.H. SUPPORT
9–EXT. W/C60

VIEW A

Fig. 13 I/P removal. Delta 88, Caprice, Caprice Classic, Electra Estate Wagon, LeSabre Wagon & Safari

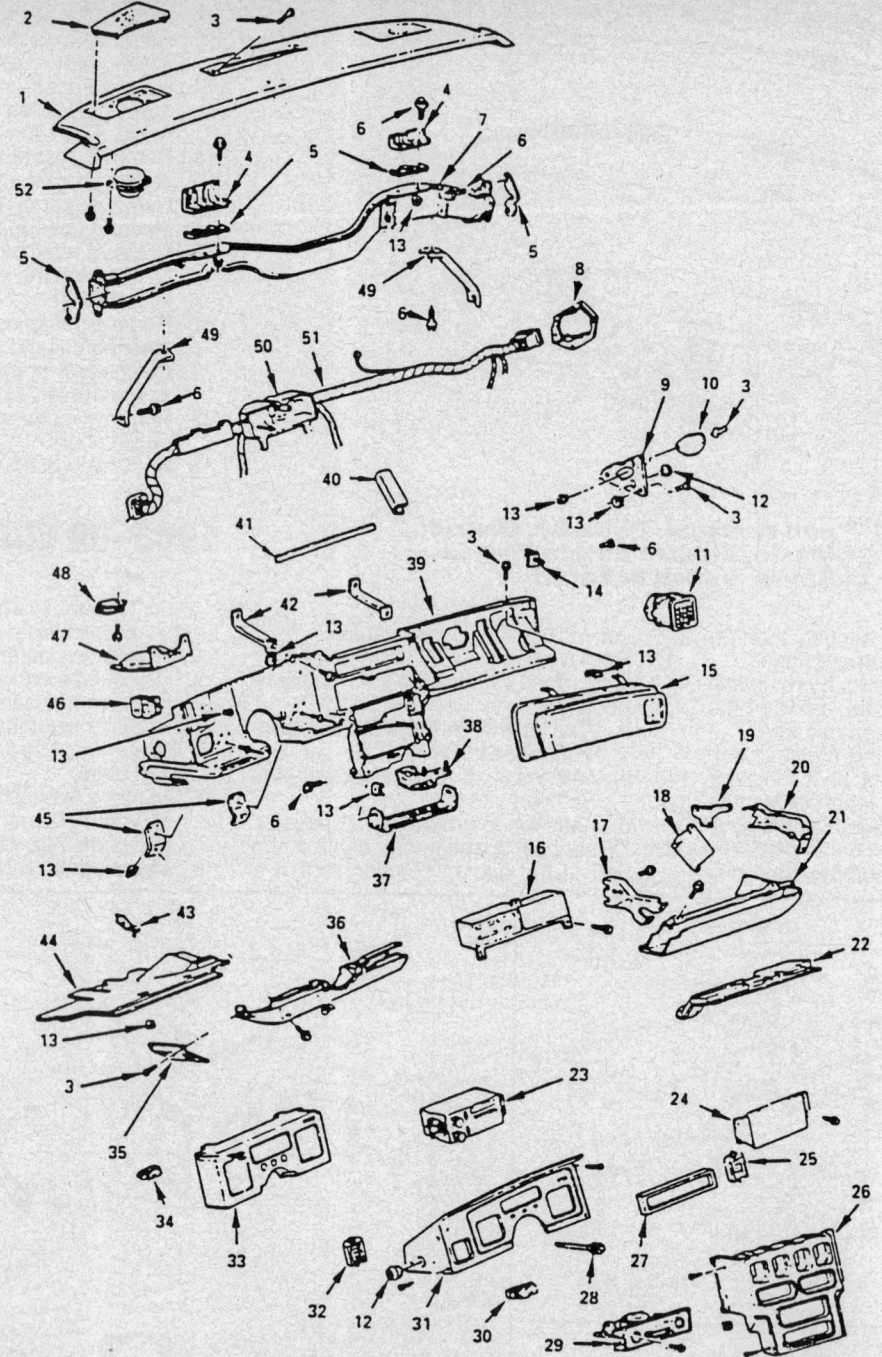

Fig. 14 Exploded view of I/P. 1988–89 Corvette

1 PAD, INSTRUMENT PANEL UPPER
2 GRILLE, RADIO FRONT SPEAKER
3 SCREW
4 BRACKET, WINDSHIELD INNER LOWER
5 SHIM, INSTRUMENT PANEL REINFORCEMENT
6 BOLT
7 REINFORCEMENT, INSTRUMENT PANEL
8 BRACKET, FUSE PANEL
9 PLATE, INSTRUMENT PANEL TRIM
10 COVER, INSTRUMENT PANEL FUSE BOX ACCESS HOLE
11 OUTLET, INSTRUMENT PANEL OUTER AIR
12 SEAL, SIDE WINDOW DEFROSTER DUCT
13 NUT
14 BRACKET, INSTRUMENT PANEL UPPER
15 PAD, INSTRUMENT PANEL CENTER TRIM
16 TELLTALE, INFORMATION CENTER
17 SUPPORT, INSTRUMENT PANEL CENTER
18 MODULE, THEFT DETERRENT

19 BRACKET, THEFT DETERRENT CONTROL
20 SUPPORT, INSTRUMENT PANEL OUTER
21 PAD, INSTRUMENT PANEL LOWER TRIM
22 INSULATOR, INSTRUMENT PANEL SOUND
23 RECEIVER ASSEMBLY, RADIO
24 COVER, RADIO OPENING
25 DEFLECTOR, AIR CONDITIONING AIR CONTROL OUTLET
26 PLATE, INSTRUMENT PANEL ACCESSORY TRIM
27 SEAL, CENTER AIR OUTLET
28 KNOB, HEADLAMP SWITCH
29 CONTROL, HEATER AND AIR CONDITIONING
30 SWITCH, FOG LAMP
31 PLATE, INSTRUMENT PANEL CLUSTER TRIM
32 DEFLECTOR, INSTRUMENT PANEL OUTER AIR OUTLET
33 CLUSTER, INSTRUMENT PANEL
34 LAMP, FRONT COURTESY
35 BEZEL, HOOD PRIMARY LATCH RELEASE CABLE HANDLE
36 PAD, INSTRUMENT PANEL LOWER TRIM

37 BRACKET, INSTRUMENT PANEL LOWER
38 PLATE, INSTRUMENT PANEL LOWER BRACKET STUD
39 PANEL, INSTRUMENT
40 INSULATOR, INSTRUMENT PANEL SOUND
41 INSULATOR, INSTRUMENT PANEL
42 BRACE, INSTRUMENT PANEL UPPER
43 BRACKET, INSTRUMENT PANEL SOUND INSULATOR
44 INSULATOR, INSTRUMENT PANEL SOUND
45 BRACKET, INSTRUMENT PANEL LOWER TRIM PAD OUTER
46 SWITCH, HEADLAMP
47 BRACKET, INSTRUMENT PANEL REINFORCEMENT
48 BRACKET, DIAGNOSTIC CONNECTOR
49 BRACE, INSTRUMENT PANEL REINFORCEMENT
50 BRACKET, MULTI-USE RELAY
51 HARNESS, INSTRUMENT PANEL WIRING
52 SPEAKER, RADIO FRONT

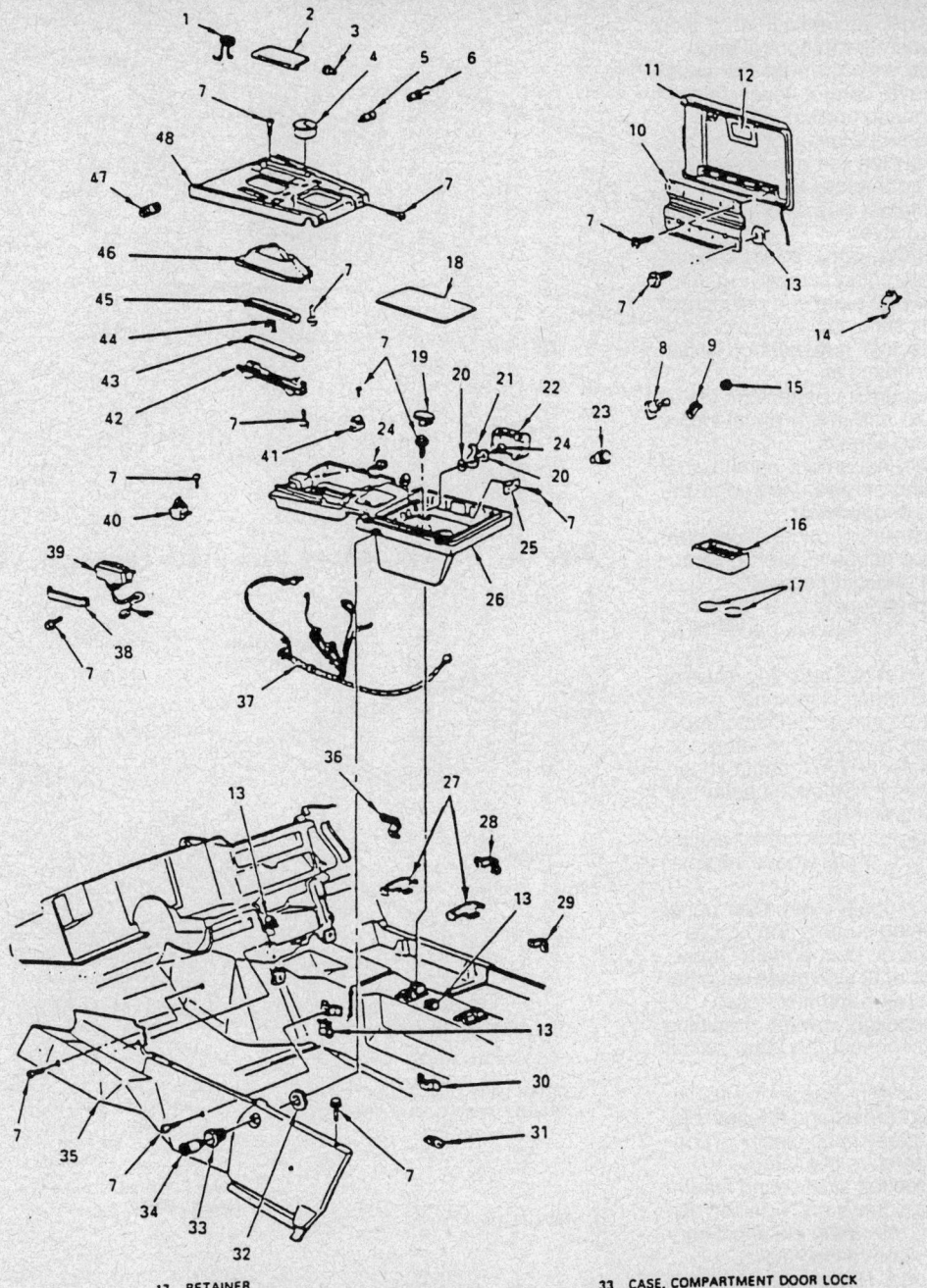

Fig. 15 Exploded view of floor console. 1988–89 Corvette

1 SPRING, CONSOLE TRIM PLATE	17 RETAINER	33 CASE, COMPARTMENT DOOR LOCK
2 COVER, ASH TRAY	18 COVER, FLOOR CONSOLE POCKET OPENING	34 LOCK UNIT, COMPARTMENT DOOR
3 BUSHING, ASH TRAY COVER	19 FILLER, FLOOR CONSOLE COMPARTMENT	35 PANEL, FLOOR CONSOLE SIDE TRIM
4 TRAY, ASH	20 WASHER, COMPARTMENT DOOR LOCK	36 BRACKET, FLOOR CONSOLE FRONT
5 HOUSING, CIGAR LIGHTER	21 LEVER, COMPARTMENT DOOR LOCK	37 HARNESS, FLOOR CONSOLE WIRING
6 ELEMENT, CIGAR LIGHTER	22 COVER, FLOOR CONSOLE DOOR LATCH OPENING	38 BRACKET, POWER SEAT ADJUSTER SWITCH
7 SCREW	23 SWITCH, REAR COMPARTMENT LID RELEASE	39 SWITCH, POWER SEAT ADJUSTER
8 CONTROL, OUTSIDE REARVIEW MIRROR REMOTE	24 BOLT	40 SWITCH, POWER WINDOW
9 RETAINER, POWER MIRROR CONTROL ESCUTCHEON	25 STRIKER, FLOOR COMPARTMENT DOOR	41 SWITCH, OUTSIDE REARVIEW MIRROR REMOTE CONTROL SELECTOR
10 HINGE, FLOOR CONSOLE DOOR	26 CONSOLE, FLOOR	42 HOUSING, TRANSMISSION CONTROL INDICATOR
11 DOOR, FLOOR CONSOLE	27 BRACKET, FLOOR CONSOLE	43 SHIELD, TRANSMISSION CONTROL INDICATOR OPENING
12 LAMP, FLOOR CONSOLE DOOR	28 BRACKET, FLOOR CONSOLE INTERMEDIATE FRONT-RH	44 INDICATOR, TRANSMISSION CONTROL
13 NUT	29 BRACKET, FLOOR CONSOLE INTERMEDIATE REAR-RH	45 DIAL, TRANSMISSION CONTROL INDICATOR
14 COVER, FLOOR CONSOLE COMPARTMENT LAMP	30 BRACKET, FLOOR CONSOLE INTERMEDIATE FRONT LH	46 BOOT, TRANSMISSION CONTROL LEVER UPPER
15 BEZEL, OUTSIDE REARVIEW MIRROR REMOTE CONTROL	31 BRACKET, FLOOR CONSOLE INTERMEDIATE REAR-LH	47 RETAINER, CIGAR LIGHTER
16 TRAY, FLOOR CONSOLE TAPE STORAGE	32 RETAINER, FLOOR COMPARTMENT DOOR LOCK CYLINDER	48 PANEL, FLOOR CONSOLE TRIM

mission, remove control lever knob and retainer assembly button by prying button upward.

7. Remove external retainer ring, then remove transmission control knob.

8. **On models with manual transmission,** remove control lever release button by prying upward.

9. Remove control lever pivot pin by prying upward, then remove lever knob by turning counterclockwise.

10. Remove retainer ring and finger grip from control lever.

11. **On all models,** remove four console trim plate attaching screws, **Fig. 17.**

12. Lift console trim plate and disconnect cigar lighter, shift indicator lamp socket and selective ride control switch electrical connectors.

13. Remove instrument panel fuse plate.

14. Remove six instrument panel upper pad attaching screws.

15. Remove two instrument panel upper pad attaching screws, located in the defroster duct openings.

16. Remove instrument panel upper pad.

17. Remove four gauge cluster to instrument panel attaching screws.

18. Disconnect gauge cluster electrical connectors, then remove gauge cluster.

19. Remove four radio retaining screws, pull radio to obtain clearance.

20. Disconnect electrical connectors and antenna lead, then remove radio.

21. Remove heater and A/C control head.

22. Remove three information center telltale attaching screws.

23. Disconnect information center electrical connectors, then remove information center.

24. Remove four upper instrument panel brace attaching screws and braces.

25. Remove right air duct and flex hose.

26. Remove two right side glass defroster attaching screws and flex hoses.

27. Remove headlight switch retaining nut, then disconnect fog lamp switch electrical connector.

28. Remove three right side sound insulator attaching screws and retainer, disconnect courtesy lamp electrical connector and remove insulator.

29. Remove three left side sound insulator attaching screws and retainer, disconnect courtesy lamp electrical connector and remove insulator.

30. Remove hood release handle trim piece.

31. Remove three left lower trim pad attaching screws, **Fig. 18.**

32. Remove two left lower trim pad attaching bolts, then remove trim pad.

33. Remove twelve instrument panel carrier attaching bolts, then disconnect fuse block from carrier.

34. Remove two left side defroster screws and flex hose.

35. Remove two steering column to carrier attaching bolts.

36. Remove two retainers and air conditioning center duct.

37. Remove multi-use relay bracket, then pull carrier rearward to obtain clearance.

38. Remove air conditioning left duct.

39. Remove two wiring harness retaining

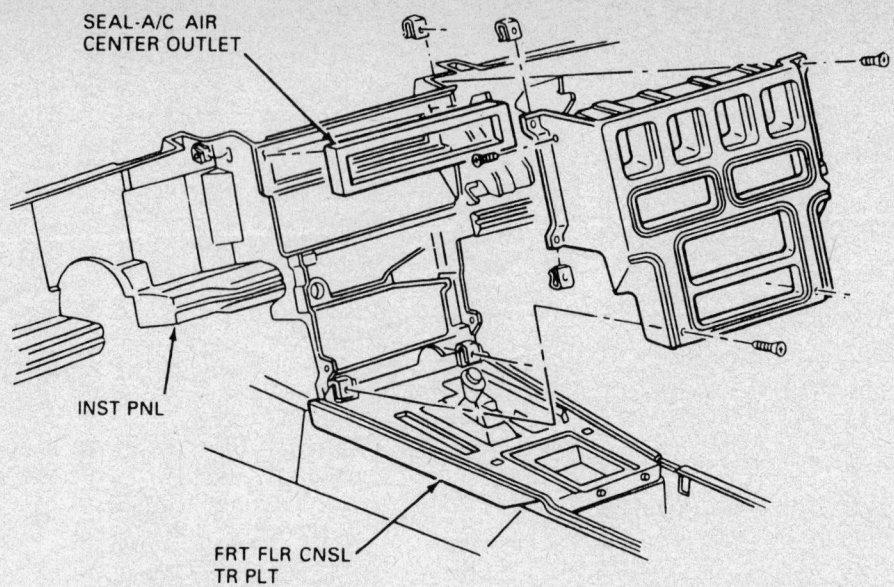

Fig. 16   I/P accessory trim plate removal. 1988–89 Corvette

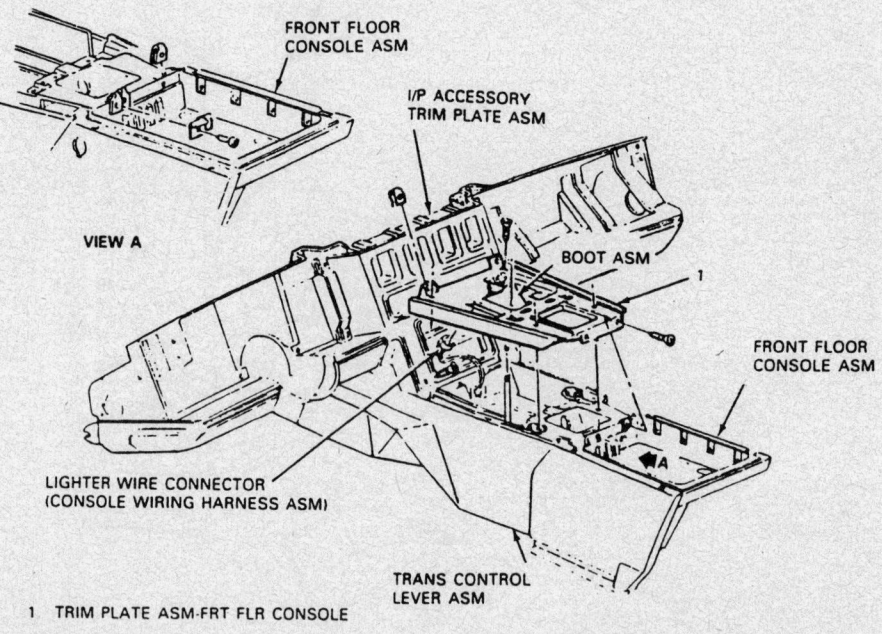

Fig. 17   Floor console trim plate removal. 1988–89 Corvette

screws and three clips.

40. Remove instrument panel left carrier support and two retaining nuts.

41. Disconnect theft deterrent controller, pass key module and LTPWS module.

42. Remove instrument panel carrier from the vehicle.

43. Reverse procedure to install.

1990 CORVETTE

The Diagnositc Energy Reserve Module (DERM) can maintain sufficient voltage to cause a deployment of the Supplemental Restraint System air bag for up to 10 minutes after disconnecting battery ground cable. Before performing service on the instrument panel wait 10 minutes to allow DERM voltage to drop after disconnecting battery.

1. Disconnect battery ground cable.

2. On models equipped with automatic transmission, remove shifter button, snap ring and shift knob, **Fig. 19.**

3. On models equipped with manual transmission, remove shifter button, setscrew and shift knob, **Fig. 20.**

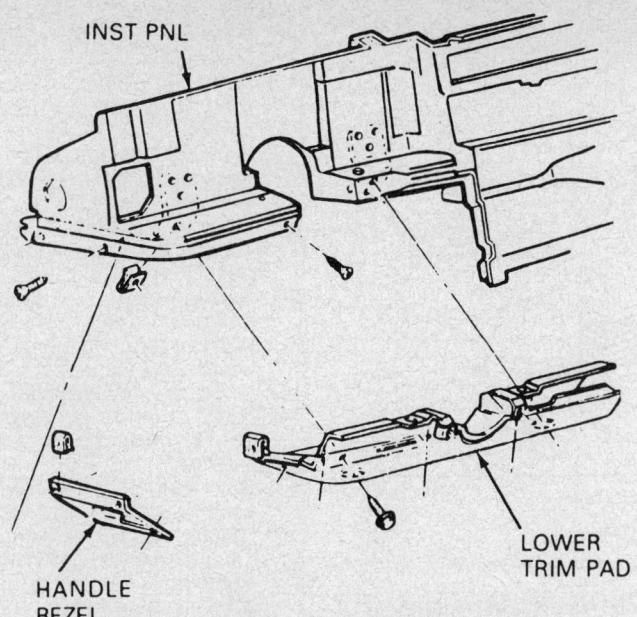

Fig. 18   I/P left lower trim pad removal. 1988–89 Corvette

Fig. 19   Automatic transmission shift knob removal. 1990 Corvette

1	CONTROL KNOB BUTTON
2	CONTROL KNOB BUTTON RETAINER
3	EXTERNAL RETAINER RING
4	CONTROL KNOB
5	CONTROL LEVER AND BRACKET
6	CONTROL LEVER UPPER BOOT

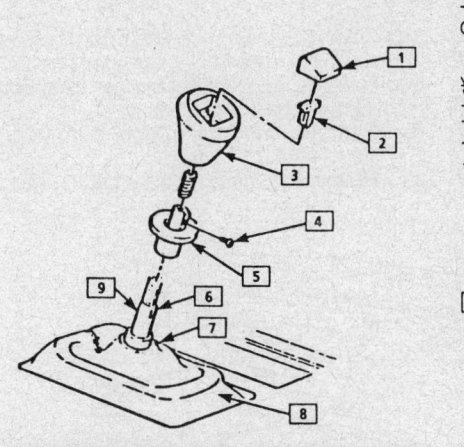

1	TRANS CONTROL LEVER BUTTON	6	SLOT
2	COTTER PIN	7	TRANS CONTROL LEVER BOOT
3	CONTROL LEVER KNOB	8	TRANS ASM
4	SOCKET SET SCREW (RING)	9	TRANS CONTROL LEVER
5	SHIFTER REVERSE INHIBITOR RING		

Fig. 20   Manual transmission shift knob removal. 1990 Corvette

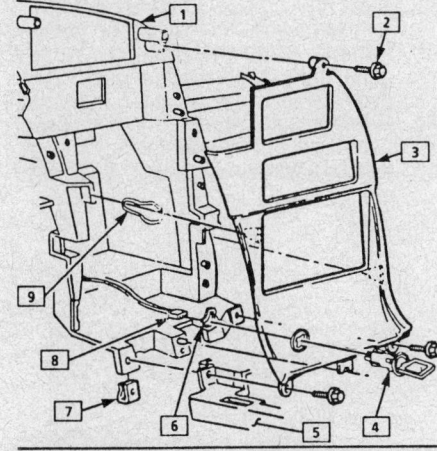

1	INSTRUMENT PANEL	6	RETAINER
2	BOLT/SCREW	7	U NUT
3	ACCESSORY TRIM PLATE (LT5 SHOWN)	8	I/P HARNESS TO VALET SWITCH
4	VALET PARKING SWITCH	9	SPRING CLIP
5	CONSOLE		

Fig. 21   Removing accessory trim plate. 1990 Corvette

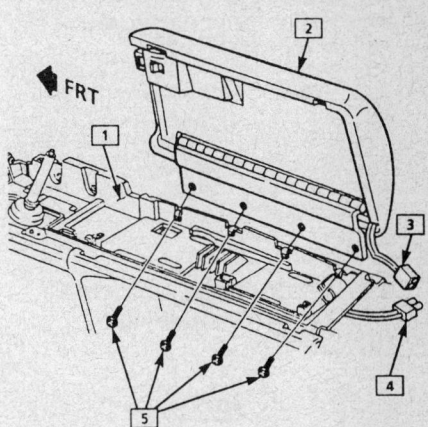

1	CONSOLE ASSEMBLY
2	CONSOLE DOOR ASSEMBLY
3	CONSOLE DOOR LAMP CONNECTOR
4	INSTRUMENT PANEL HARNESS CONNECTOR
5	SCREWS

Fig. 22   Removing console door. 1990 Corvette

4. **On all models,** remove front and rear accessory trim plate screws, **Fig. 21.**
5. Remove trim plate retaining screw under ashtray.
6. **On models equipped with automatic transmission,** remove instrument panel electrical connectors for lighter, rear hatch release and gear indicator lamp.
7. **On all models,** disconnect valet parking switch electrical connectors.
8. Remove trim plate.
9. Remove center air outlet deflector.
10. Remove accessory trim plate to instrument panel retaining screws.
11. Remove two driver information center

retaining bolts.
12. Disconnect light bulb socket electrical connectors from back of driver information center.
13. Remove two heater and air conditioning control assembly retaining screws.
14. Disconnect A/C control assembly electrical connector, then remove assembly from instrument panel.
15. Remove console door to console retaining screws, then disconnect console door lamp connector, **Fig. 22.**
16. Remove radio control to instrument panel retaining screws.
17. Pull radio control outward and discon-

nect electrical connectors.
18. Remove retainer securing lower LH trim panel to stud on steering column.
19. Remove LH trim panel to knee bolster and trim panel to instrument panel retaining screws.
20. Remove ALDL connector assembly retaining screw.
21. Disconnect courtesy lamp electrical connector.
22. Remove RH trim panel to trim panel support and instrument panel retaining screws.
23. Remove air distributor duct, **Fig. 23.**
24. Remove side panel to instrument panel retaining screws.

25. Move passenger seat to forward position.
26. Fold seatback forward to reveal floor pan studs and nuts.
27. Remove seat adjuster to floor retaining nuts.
28. **On driver's seat**, remove jack wheel wrench handle.
29. **On all models**, reposition seatback, slide seat rearward and remove seat adjuster covers.
30. Remove seat adjuster retaining nuts.
31. **On vehicles equipped with power seats**, remove seat cushion and cover by pushing down on the front of cushion and releasing retainer wire at front of cushion frame.
32. Disconnect electrical and pneumatic connectors.
33. **On all models**, remove seat assembly from vehicle.
34. Remove side trim panel to tunnel retaining screws.
35. Remove driver knee bolster inner and outer bracket retaining screws.
36. Remove lap air outlet and LH duct from lower duct assembly.
37. Remove right and left side window outlet duct to instrument panel retaining screw.
38. Remove passenger knee bolster outer bracket retaining clip.
39. Remove defogger outlet duct flex tube end from side window defog outlet duct.
40. Remove glove compartment lower hinge and latch retaining screws.
41. Remove glove compartment from upper trim pad.

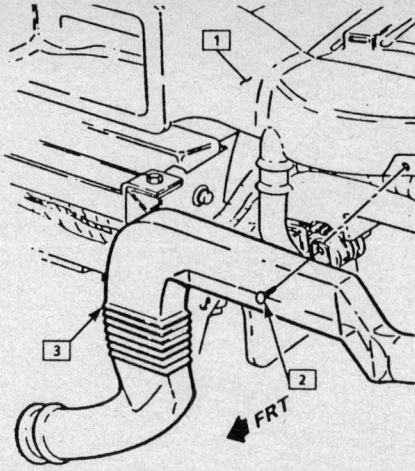

1	AIR DISTRIBUTOR DUCT
2	PUSH-ON RETAINER
3	SIDEWINDOW DEFOG OUTLET DUCT-LH

Fig. 23 Removing air distributor duct. 1990 Corvette

42. Disconnect glove compartment courtesy lamp switch electrical connector.
43. Remove windshield defogger nozzle grille then disconnect sunload temperature sensor electrical connector.
44. Remove upper trim pad to instrument panel and bulkhead retaining screws.
45. Remove steering column front support bolts.
46. Remove cluster bezel retaining screws.
47. Remove cluster retaining screws, then disconnect cluster electrical connector.
48. Remove headlamp, dimmer and accessory switch retaining screws on RH side of switch.
49. Remove switch plate retaining screws, then disconnect instrument panel harness electrical connectors.
50. Remove fuse box from instrument panel by drilling rivets securing fuse box to instrument panel.
51. Disconnect alarm module and low tire pressure module electrical connector.
52. Remove inside air temperature sensor to instrument panel retaining screws.
53. Remove lateral accelerometer assembly retaining screws.
54. Remove upper instrument panel reinforcement brace retaining screws.
55. Remove driver and passenger knee bolster outer bracket retaining nuts.
56. Remove driver and passenger knee bolster inner bracket retaining nuts on bulkhead and console bracket.
57. Remove two wiring harness retainers from rear of instrument panel (cluster area).
58. Remove three multi-use relay bracket retaining nuts from instrument panel.
59. Remove air distributor duct retaining screws, then the air duct.
60. Remove instrument panel from vehicle.
61. Reverse procedure to install.

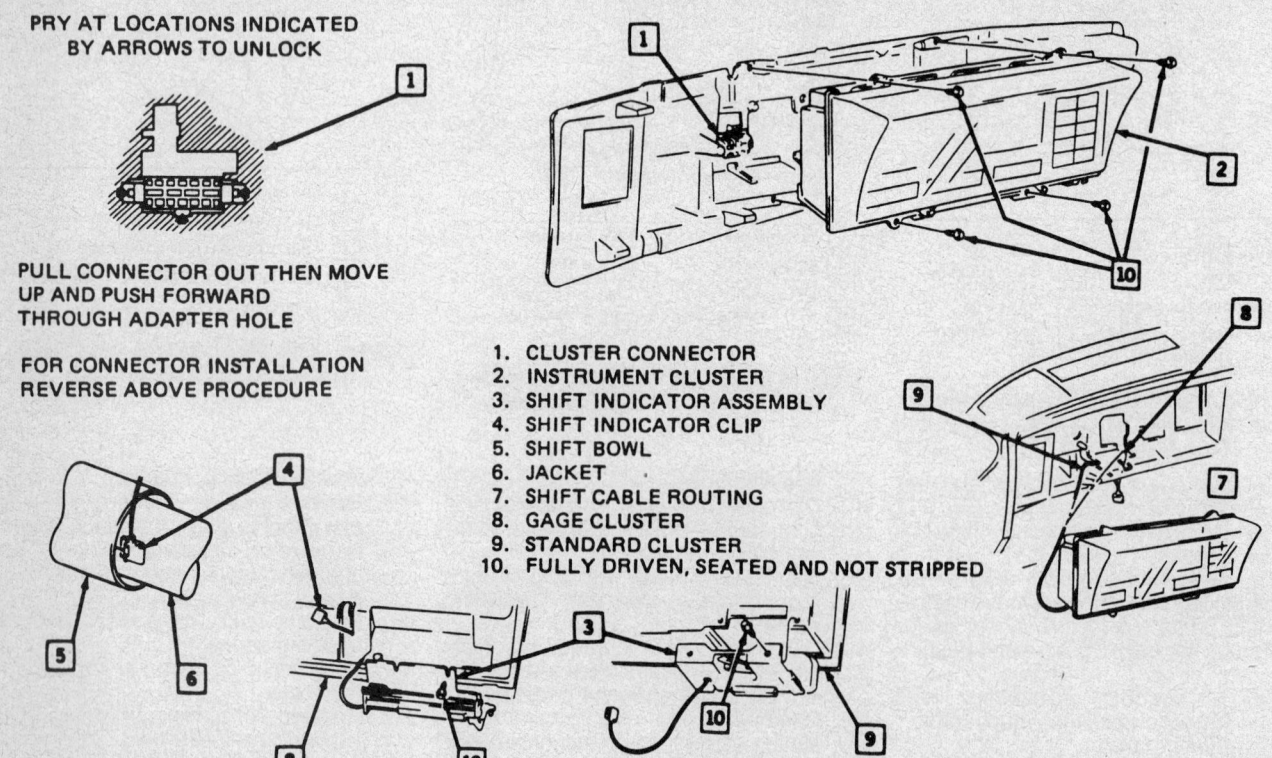

PRY AT LOCATIONS INDICATED BY ARROWS TO UNLOCK

PULL CONNECTOR OUT THEN MOVE UP AND PUSH FORWARD THROUGH ADAPTER HOLE

FOR CONNECTOR INSTALLATION REVERSE ABOVE PROCEDURE

1. CLUSTER CONNECTOR
2. INSTRUMENT CLUSTER
3. SHIFT INDICATOR ASSEMBLY
4. SHIFT INDICATOR CLIP
5. SHIFT BOWL
6. JACKET
7. SHIFT CABLE ROUTING
8. GAGE CLUSTER
9. STANDARD CLUSTER
10. FULLY DRIVEN, SEATED AND NOT STRIPPED

Fig. 24 Removing instrument cluster, connector & shift indicator. Cutlass Supreme & Monte Carlo

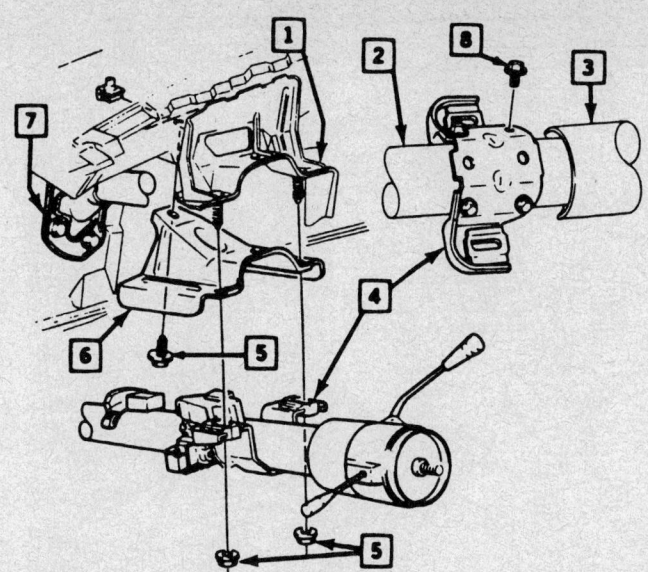

1. LOWER I.P. TIE BAR
2. JACKET
3. SHIFT BOWL
4. STEERING COLUMN SUPPORT
5. 27 N·m (20 LBS. FT.)
6. COLUMN GUIDE
7. TOE PLATE
8. 24 N·m (18 LBS. FT.)

Fig. 25 Removing steering column support. Cutlass Supreme & Monte Carlo

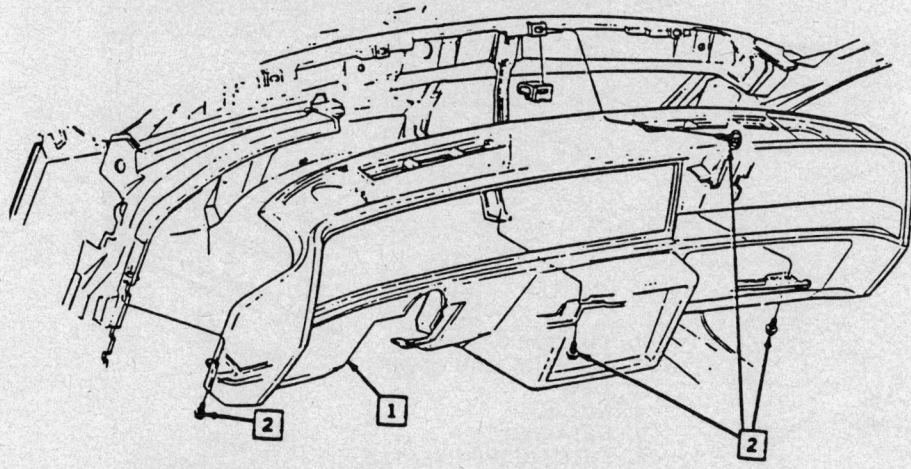

1. I.P. PAD
2. FULLY DRIVEN, SEATED AND NOT STRIPPED

Fig. 26 I/P pad removal. Cutlass Supreme & Monte Carlo

CUTLASS (RWD) & MONTE CARLO

1. Disconnect battery ground cable.
2. Remove instrument cluster pad assembly.
3. Remove steering column trim cover.
4. Disconnect shift indicator clip from steering column shift bowl, **Fig. 24.**
5. Remove four screws holding instrument cluster to panel adapter.
6. Pull instrument cluster rearward enough to reach behind it and disconnect speedometer cable.
7. Disconnect vehicle speed sensor and remove instrument cluster.
8. Disconnect remote control mirror cable from instrument panel pad.
9. Remove upper and lower steering column support bolts, and lower steering column, **Fig. 25.**
10. Remove toe plate, **Fig. 25.**
11. Disconnect brake release cable, and remove speaker grilles.
12. Disconnect wire connectors from steering column.
13. Disconnect chassis harness from engine harness at fuse block.
14. Remove two dash panel to fuse block attaching screws.
15. Remove four upper instrument panel pad attaching screws, **Fig. 26.**
16. Remove three lower instrument panel attaching screws.
17. Pull instrument panel outward enough to disconnect accessory wiring and vacuum lines necessary to remove panel, **Fig. 27.**
18. Remove instrument panel with wiring harness from the vehicle.
19. Reverse procedure to install.

CUSTOM CRUISER

1. Disconnect battery ground cable.
2. Remove screws attaching speaker grilles to instrument panel pad.
3. Disconnect electrical connectors, then remove speakers along with grilles.
4. With glove compartment open, remove compartment to instrument panel attaching screws.
5. Slide steering column collar up the steering column.
6. To remove steering column trim cover, pull back gently.
7. **On models equipped with a gauge cluster,** remove cluster as follows:
   a. Remove four gauge cluster to left trim panel attaching screws.
   b. Pull cluster out far enough to reach behind it and disconnect wiring terminals and both lamp sockets.
   c. Remove cluster from trim panel.
8. **On all models,** remove headlight switch knob by depressing the retaining clip with a small screwdriver while pulling on the knob.
9. Remove two screws attaching left side trim plate to cluster carrier.
10. Remove trim plate by pulling to disengage clips, **Fig. 28.**
11. Remove radio knobs, cigar lighter and rear window defogger knob.
12. Remove right side trim plate to carrier panel attaching screws, then remove trim plate, **Fig. 29.**
13. Remove screws attaching left side sound insulator to instrument panel, remove insulator, **Fig. 30.**
14. Remove screws attaching right side sound insulator to instrument panel, remove insulator, **Fig. 31.**
15. Remove ashtray and parking brake release cable at parking brake lever assembly.
16. Remove lower trim panel, **Fig. 32,** as follows:
   a. Remove eleven screws attaching lower trim panel to cluster carrier, **Fig. 33.**
   b. Remove lower tie bar, then the lower left and center air ducts.
   c. Remove ashtray retainer, then the ALCL connector.

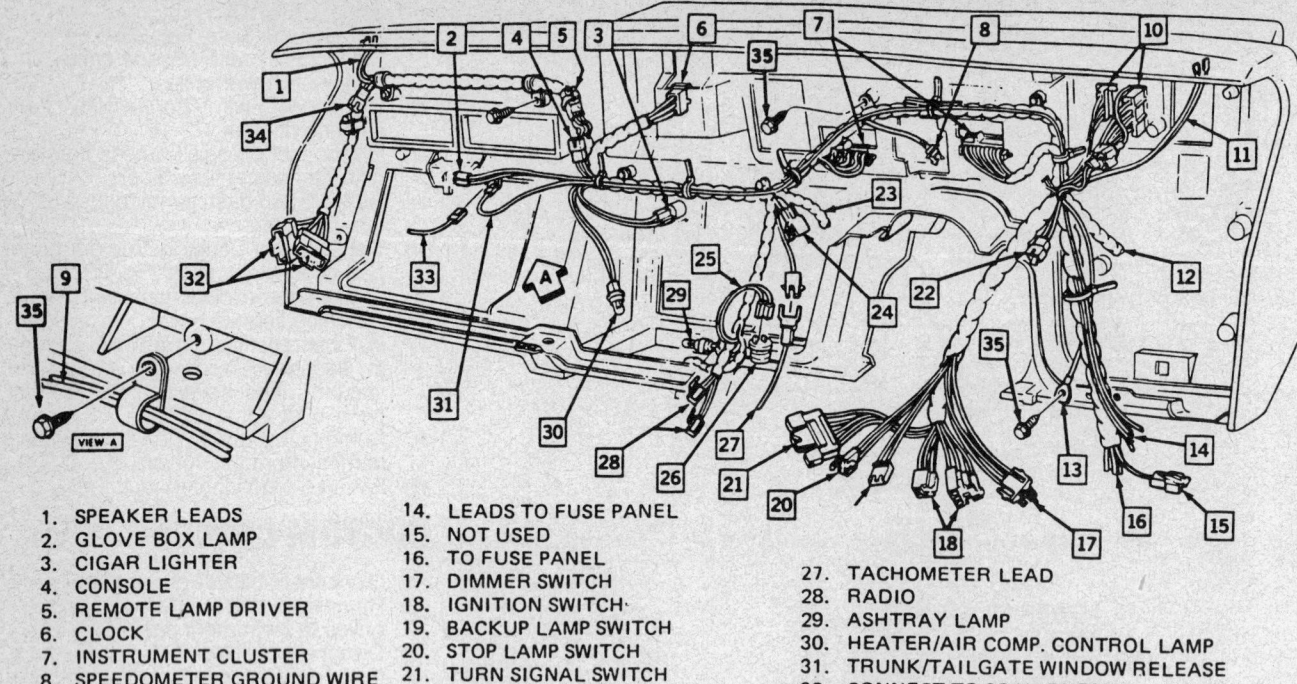

1. SPEAKER LEADS
2. GLOVE BOX LAMP
3. CIGAR LIGHTER
4. CONSOLE
5. REMOTE LAMP DRIVER
6. CLOCK
7. INSTRUMENT CLUSTER
8. SPEEDOMETER GROUND WIRE
9. GLOVE BOX LAMP LEADS
10. HEADLAMP SWITCH
11. SPEAKER LEADS
12. TO CONVENIENCE CENTER
13. I.P. HARNESS GROUND

14. LEADS TO FUSE PANEL
15. NOT USED
16. TO FUSE PANEL
17. DIMMER SWITCH
18. IGNITION SWITCH
19. BACKUP LAMP SWITCH
20. STOP LAMP SWITCH
21. TURN SIGNAL SWITCH
22. L.H. COURTESY LAMP
23. NOT USED
24. HEATER
25. TURN SIGNAL FLASHER LEAD
26. TURN SIGNAL FLASHER

27. TACHOMETER LEAD
28. RADIO
29. ASHTRAY LAMP
30. HEATER/AIR COMP. CONTROL LAMP
31. TRUNK/TAILGATE WINDOW RELEASE
32. CONNECT TO 3C HARNESS
33. TO TRUNK RELEASE SWITCH
34. R.H. COURTESY LAMP
35. FULLY DRIVEN, SEATED AND NOT STRIPPED

Fig. 27 I/P wiring. Cutlass Supreme & Monte Carlo

1. CLUSTER TRIM PLATE
2. FULLY DRIVEN, SEATED AND NOT STRIPPED
3. LEFT HAND TRIM PANEL

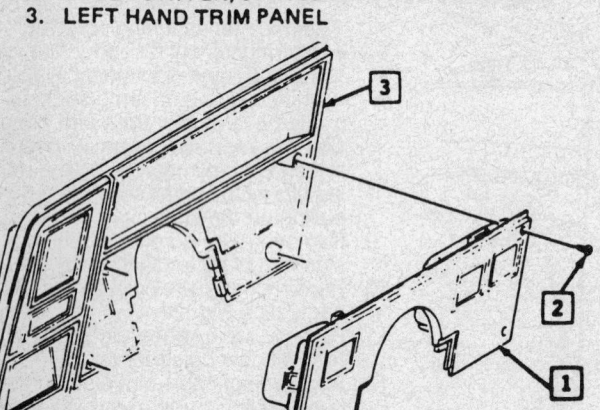

1. CLUSTER CARRIER
2. RT. HAND TRIM COVER
3. LENS
4. NUT
5. RETAINER
6. FULLY DRIVEN, SEATED AND NOT STRIPPED

Fig. 29 Removing right side trim plate. Custom Cruiser

Fig. 28 Removing left side trim plate. Custom Cruiser

d. Lower trim panel by sliding it rearward and downward.
e. Disconnect parking brake release cable from lower trim panel by depressing both locking tabs and pushing cable through mounting hole.
17. Remove thirteen screws attaching instrument panel pad to tie bars, then the pad.
18. Disconnect shift indicator cable clip from the shift bowl.

19. Remove two steering column supporting nuts, then lower column.
20. Remove two screws attaching cluster carrier to cruise module and reminder package mounting bracket.
21. Remove headlamp switch mounting bracket and rear window defogger switch.
22. Remove speedometer, then the shift indicator cable at the shift indicator.
23. Remove right side mirror control, heater and A/C control and rear win-

dow switch.
24. Remove radio mounting plate and screw attaching cluster carriage to radio mounting bracket.
25. Remove nine screws attaching cluster carrier to instrument panel supports.
26. Pull cluster carrier rearward far enough to reach behind it and disconnect circuit board wiring connector.
27. Remove three screws attaching center air duct to cluster carrier, then dis-

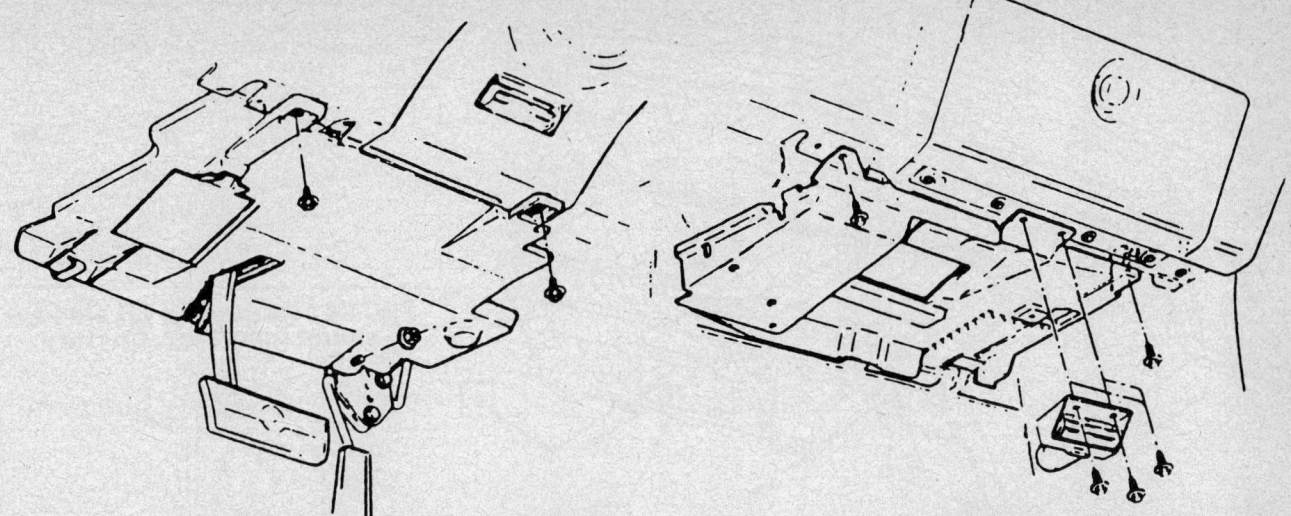

Fig. 30 Removing left side sound insulator. Custom Cruiser

Fig. 31 Removing right side sound insulator. Custom Cruiser

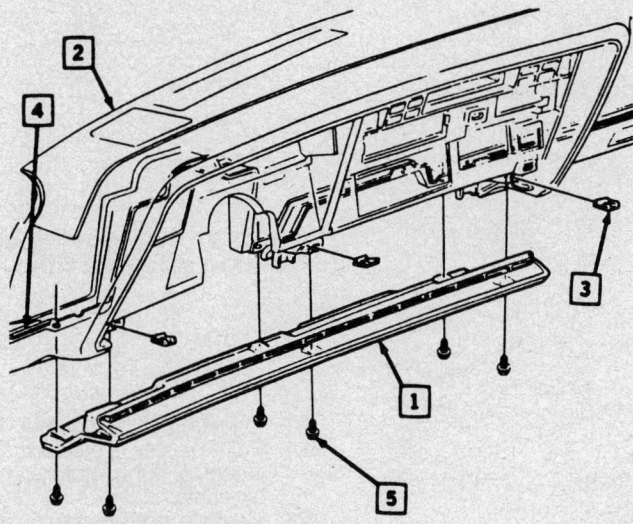

1. LOWER TRIM PANEL
2. INSTRUMENT PANEL
3. NUT
4. LOWER TIE BAR
5. FULLY DRIVEN, SEATED AND NOT STRIPPED

Fig. 32 Removing lower trim panel. Custom Cruiser

connect cluster connector.
28. Remove three screws attaching instrument panel wiring harness to the left side of cluster carrier.
29. Release retaining clips attaching instrument panel wiring harness to right side of cluster carrier.
30. Remove cluster carrier from vehicle.
31. Reverse procedure to install.

CENTURY
1. Disconnect battery ground cable.
2. Remove two screws from front of left side instrument panel sound insulator, **Fig. 34.**
3. Remove one bolt from rear left side and one nut from accelerator pedal

bracket, then pull left sound insulator straight forward to remove.
4. Remove three screws from front of right side sound insulator, **Fig. 35.**
5. Remove nut from right back side, then pull right side sound insulator straight forward to remove.
6. Remove two screws from instrument panel filler panel, **Fig. 36.**
7. Gently pull forward on left side trim cover to release hooks on front of lower instrument panel filler panel.
8. Disconnect lap vent hose and ALDL connector, then remove instrument panel filler.
9. Remove two screws from steering column opening filler, **Fig. 37.**

10. Lower steering column by removing shift indicator clip, then the three retaining bolts and one nut.
11. Disconnect electrical connectors at steering column and disconnect parking brake cable.
12. Disconnect instrument panel harness connectors to body connectors at junction block, **Fig. 38.**
13. Disconnect speaker connectors, A/C vacuum harness and temperature door cable.
14. Disconnect emission harness connectors, antenna cable and side window defroster hoses.
15. Disconnect speedometer cable from engine compartment split if a two piece cable is used, or from the transmission for slack.
16. Split bulk head connector by removing 1/4 inch bolt, then slide instrument panel side of connector out of clip.
17. Disconnect electrical connectors form windshield wiper motor, master brake cylinder and hood light.
18. Disconnect harness cowl connector, then feed harness through cowl.
19. Remove two screws, then pull speaker-defroster grille straight out.
20. Remove two nuts on both inner sides of steering column opening.
21. Remove three bolts on bottom side of instrument panel, then remove six screws in defroster area at top of instrument panel, **Fig. 39.**
22. Pull instrument panel forward and disconnect speedometer cable, then remove panel. **On vehicles equipped with digital instrument cluster,** the Vehicle Speed Sensor (VSS) buffer must be disconnected.
23. Reverse procedure to install.

CELEBRITY
1. Disconnect battery ground cable.
2. Remove instrument panel sound insulator, **Fig. 40.**
3. Remove courtesy lights, then left side speaker grille and speaker.
4. Remove left side instrument panel trim pad.

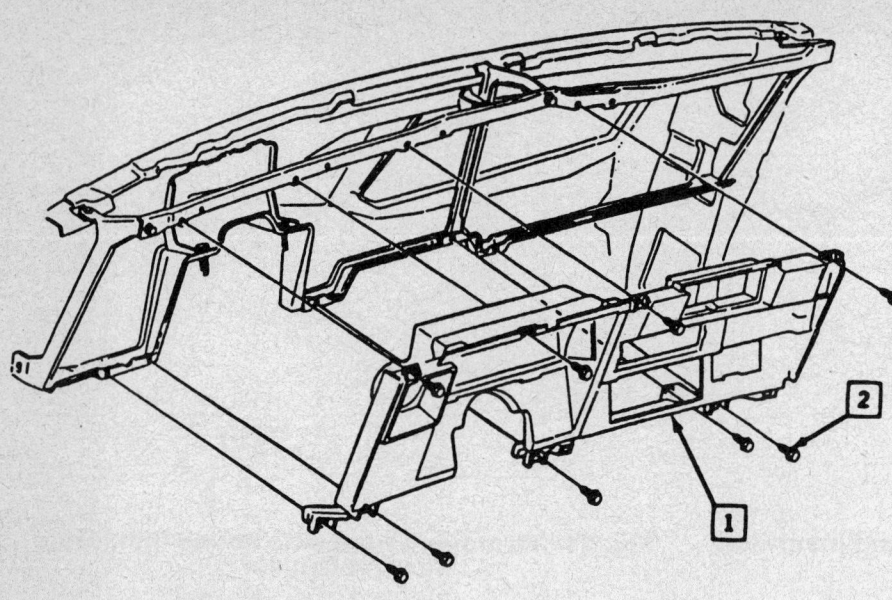

1. CLUSTER CARRIER
2. FULLY DRIVEN, SEATED AND NOT STRIPPED

Fig. 33   Removing cluster carrier. Custom Cruiser

Fig. 34   Removing LH side I/P sound insulator. Century

1	INSTRUMENT PNL
2	ACCELERATOR BRACKET
3	RT. HUSH PNL

Fig. 37   Removing steering column opening filler. Century

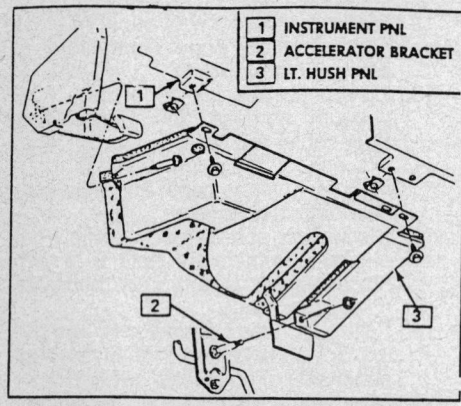

1	INSTRUMENT PNL
2	ACCELERATOR BRACKET
3	LT. HUSH PNL

Fig. 35   Removing RH side I/P sound insulator. Century

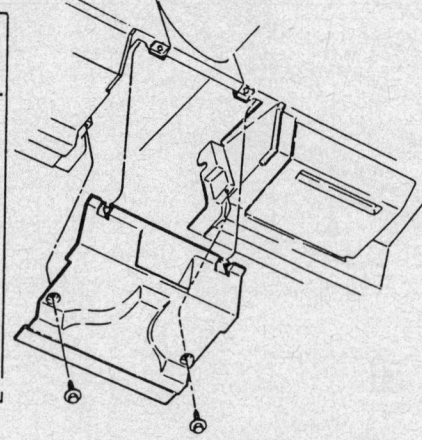

Fig. 36   Removing I/P filler panel. Century

5. Disconnect parking brake cable by unhooking it from actuator.
6. Open glove compartment and remove three screws holding glove compartment to hinge, **Fig. 41.**
7. Pull compartment rearward and disconnect electrical connectors.
8. Remove three screws attaching door hinge to instrument panel.
9. Remove right side speaker grille and speaker.
10. Remove two bolts attaching convenience center and lower convenience center.
11. Remove two attaching bolts at the ALDL connector and lower connector.
12. **On vehicles without A/C,** remove vent housing, **Fig. 42.**
13. **On all vehicles,** remove six steering column trim cover attaching screws.
14. Disconnect electrical connector to trunk/tailgate release switch and remove steering column trim cover, **Fig. 43.**
15. Remove the ashtray, then the three bolts attaching fuse block and lower

fuse block.
16. Remove headlight switch knob and rear window wiper/washer switch.
17. Remove lighter and lighter housing, then disconnect rear defogger switch electrical connector.
18. Remove four screws attaching radio to instrument panel, disconnect electrical connectors and remove radio.
19. Remove four screws attaching heater and A/C controller to instrument panel, disconnect electrical connector, vacuum harness and temperature control cable.
20. Remove ten screws attaching instrument cluster trim pad to instrument panel, **Fig. 44.**
21. Remove four nuts from under instrument panel and remove trim pad.
22. Disconnect shift indicator clip from under steering column shift bowl.
23. Remove six screws attaching cluster

to instrument panel, **Fig. 45.**
24. Pull cluster rearward, disconnect electrical connectors and speedometer cable.
25. Remove side window defogger grilles.
26. Remove four screws attaching instrument panel braces to steering column.
27. Remove two screws attaching instrument panel brace to heater case.
28. Remove two bolts holding steering column and lower steering column.
29. Remove screws attaching ventilation ducts to the instrument panel.
30. Remove screws attaching upper part of instrument panel to body, **Fig. 46.**
31. Remove two bolts and ground wires, one at each side of the instrument panel.
32. Push side defoggers and printed circuit through dash openings.
33. Pull instrument panel rearward, disconnect any remaining electrical connectors and remove instrument panel.
34. Reverse procedure to install.

6000

1. Disconnect battery ground cable.
2. Remove steering column filler and four screws to instrument panel pad, **Fig. 47.**
3. Remove right side trim plate, then one screw inside glove compartment.

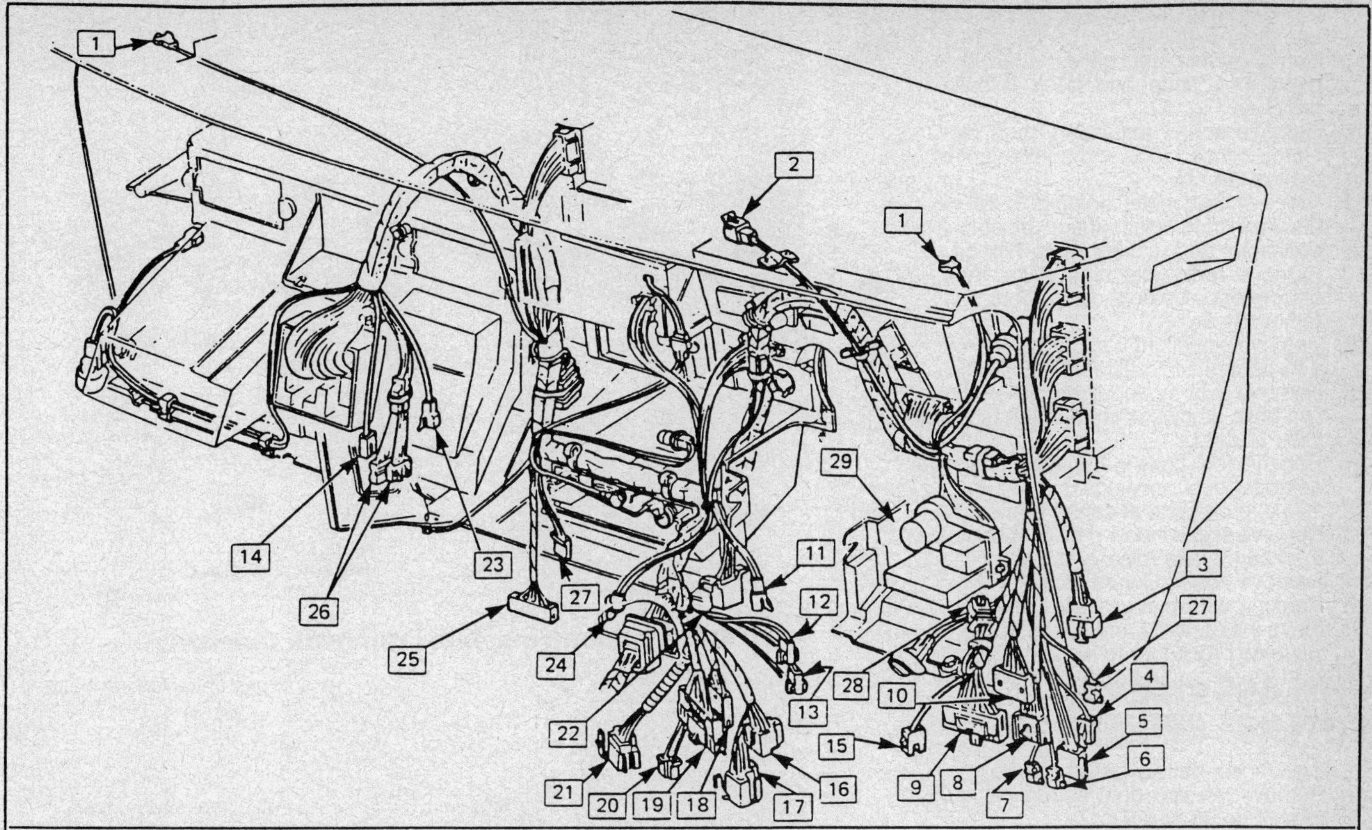

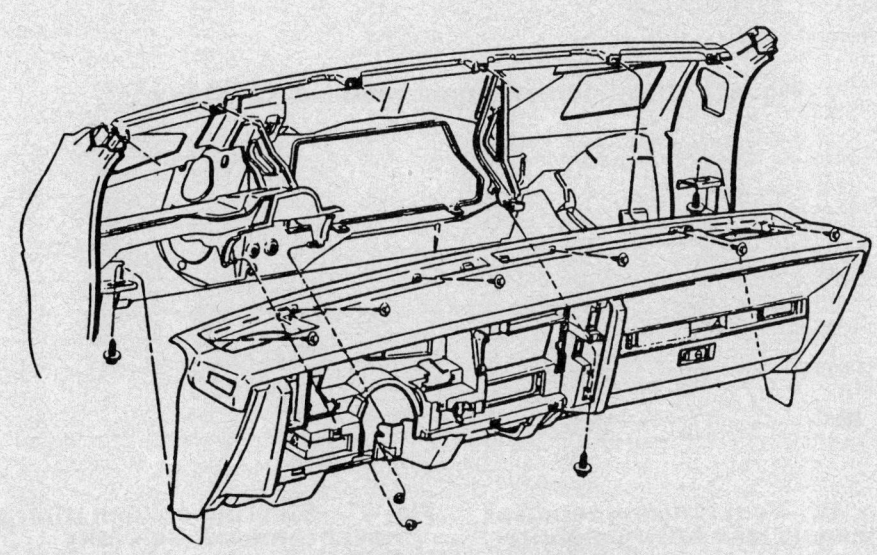

Fig. 38   I/P electrical connectors. Century

1	SPEAKER CONN.	11	CRUISE CONTROL CONN.	21	DIMMER SWITCH CONN.
2	TWILIGHT SENTINEL CONN.	12	BRAKE SWITCH CONN.	22	A.L.D.L. CONN.
3	THEFT DETERRENT CONN.	13	STOPLAMP SWITCH CONN.	23	HEATER/A/C CONN.
4	PARKING BRAKE CONN.	14	REAR RELEASE CONN (WAG)	24	HEATER/A/C LAMP
5	DOME & COURTESY CONN.	15	CONSOLE POWER FEED CONN	25	TWILIGHT SENTINEL CONN.
6	POWER SEAT CONN.	16	IGNITION CONN.	26	NB1 CONN.
7	POWER WINDOW CONN.	17	IGNITION CONN.	27	DEFOGGER CONN.
8	THEFT DETERRENT CONN.	18	WIPER/WASHER CONN.	28	HIGH LEVEL STOP LAMP CONN.
9	BODY CONN.	19	TURN SIGNAL CONN.	29	CONVENIENCE CENTER
10	THEFT DETERRENT CONN.	20	TURN SIGNAL CONN. (FLASHERS)		

Fig. 39   Removing I/P. Century

4. Using a small flat blade tool remove clips that hold right plate to pad.
5. Remove clips that hold left plate to pad.
6. Disconnect memory seat switch and fog light switch electrical connections, **Figs. 48 and 49.**
7. Remove two screws from right side cluster pad air outlet, and one screw from left side air outlet.
8. **On models with column shift,** disconnect shift indicator light, then rotate and pull out of indicator, **Fig. 50.**
9. **On all models,** remove cluster trim pad.
10. Remove A/C lower distributor duct or vent duct on vehicles without A/C, **Fig. 51.**
11. Remove distributor duct.
12. Remove eight screws that hold the instrument cluster to the instrument panel.
13. Pull cluster assembly carefully to the rear and disengage electrical connectors.

14. Using a small flat blade, carefully pry out speaker grilles.
15. Remove defroster grilles, then the glove box lamp and deck release switches, **Fig. 52.**
16. Remove sound insulation, then disconnect fuse block and convenience center, **Fig. 53.**
17. Remove four bolts holding ECM to bracket, then disconnect electrical connector and remove ECM, **Fig. 54.**
18. Remove radio attaching bolts, then disconnect electrical connectors and remove radio.
19. Remove headlight switch, heater nd A/C control and multi-function switch.
20. Remove ashtray and lighter, then the two bolts at lower right and left hinge pillar brackets.
21. Remove four bolts in the speaker and defroster duct openings.
22. Remove one bolt at center brace.
23. Remove side window defroster ducts, then park brake release cable.
24. Remove non A/C vent cables.
25. Remove wire harness clips, then remove instrument panel pad, **Fig. 55.**
26. Reverse procedure to install.

CUTLASS CIERA & CUTLASS CRUISER

1. Disconnect battery ground cable.
2. Remove left and right sound insulators, **Figs. 56 and 57.**
3. **On models with center console,** proceed as follows:
   a. Open armrest and remove cassette holder.
   b. Remove six screws, then lift compartment straight up.
   c. Remove ashtray, then two screws in ashtray opening.
   d. **On models with column shifter,** open center compartment and remove two screws at rear of center compartment.
   e. **On models with console shifter,** use a small screwdriver to pry off snap ring that holds shift knob in place. Remove shift knob and remove two screws at rear of shifter plate.
4. **On all models,** remove center compartment or shifter plate, **Fig. 58.**
5. Pull console trim plate rearward, then disconnect the electrical connectors to DIS, ashtray light and lighter.
6. Remove console trim plate, then remove two screws from console trim plate opening.
7. Remove upper console, **Fig. 59.**
8. Remove steering column collar by carefully prying rearward to release the five clips.
9. Remove outer air deflectors by pulling rearward.
10. Remove one bolt and one screw from deflector openings, then one bolt and one screw from steering column opening.
11. **On models with center console,** remove four bolts from ashtray trim cover. Remove ashtray trim cover and the two bolts holding accessory trim plate.
12. **On models less center console,** open ashtray and remove two bolts

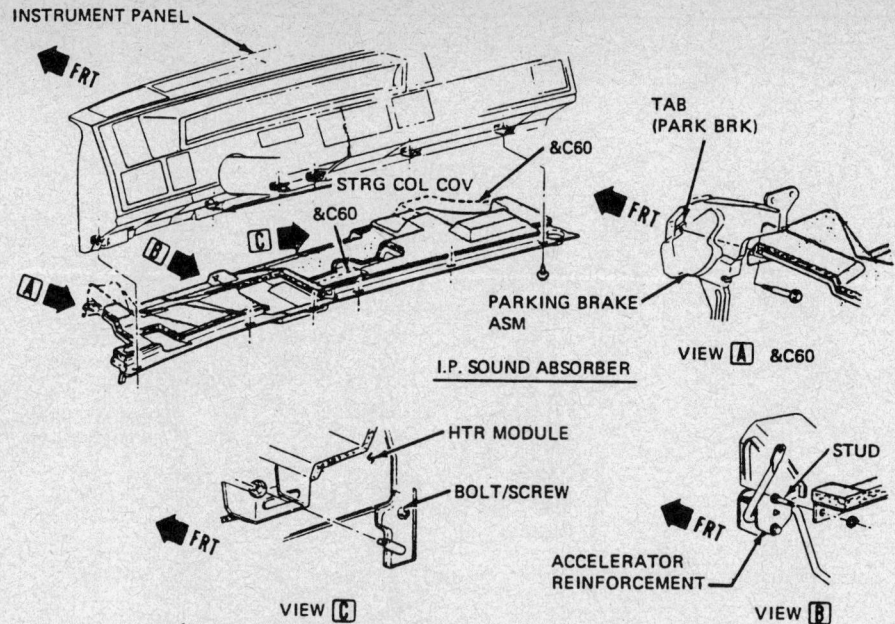

Fig. 40   I/P sound insulator removal. Celebrity

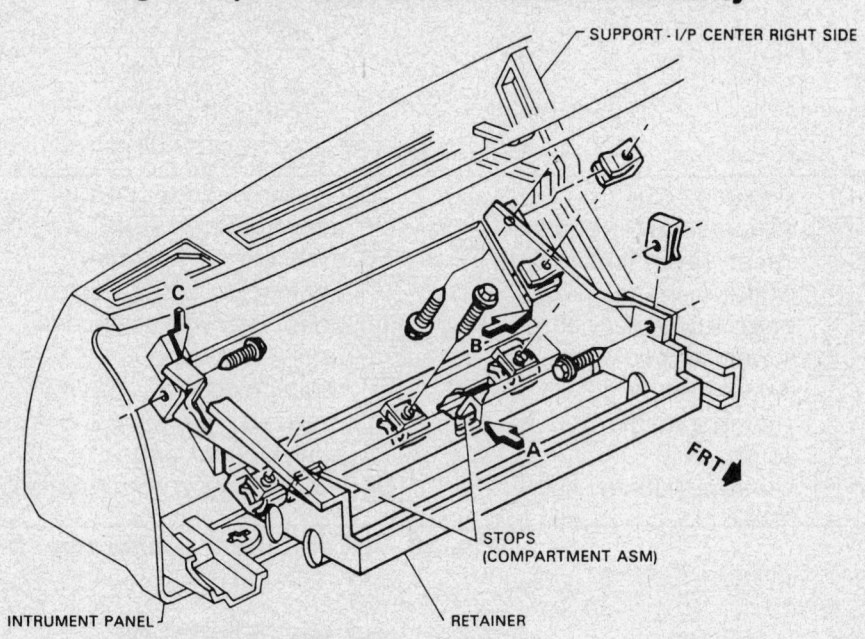

Fig. 41   Glove compartment removal. Celebrity

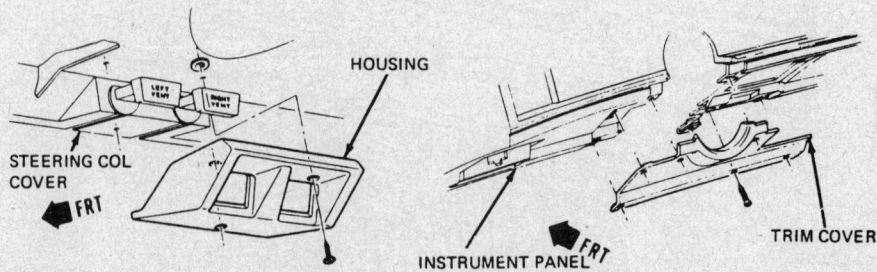

Fig. 42   Vent housing removal (models less A/C). Celebrity

Fig. 43   Steering column trim cover removal. Celebrity

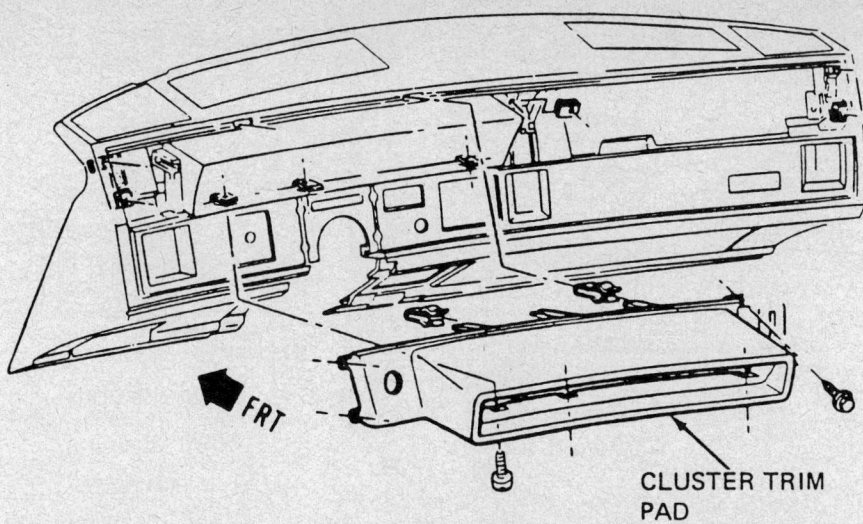

Fig. 44 Instrument cluster trim pad removal. Celebrity

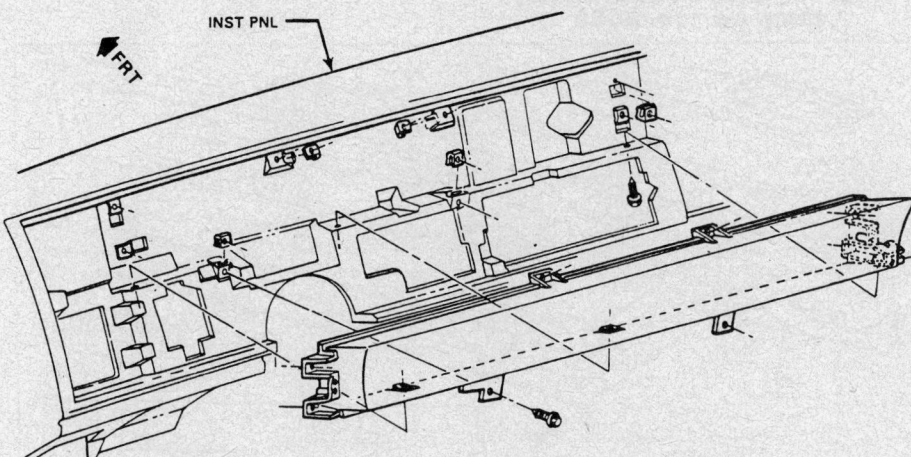

Fig. 45 Instrument cluster removal. Celebrity

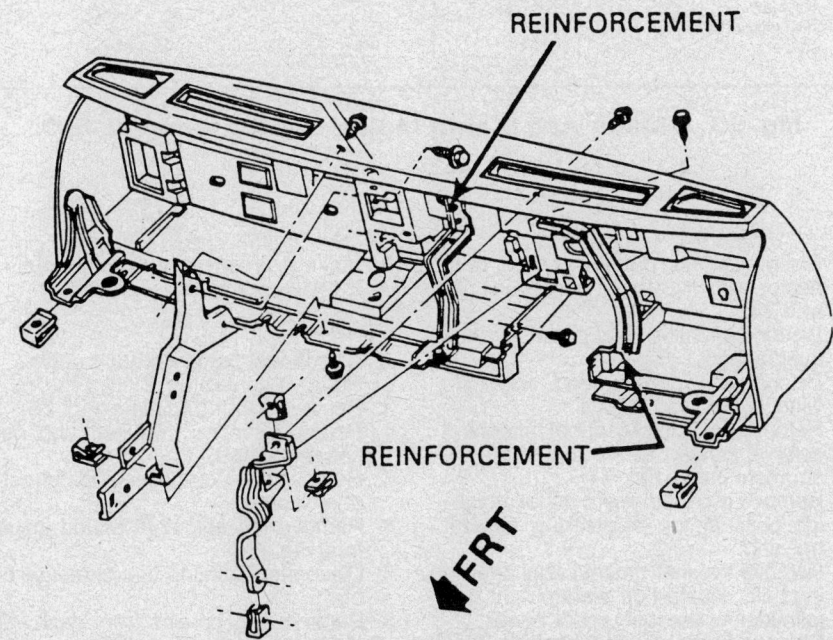

Fig. 46 I/P removal. Celebrity

holding accessory trim plate.

13. **On models with column shift,** move shift lever to the 1 position.
14. **On all models,** remove accessory trim panel by carefully pulling rearward to release clips, **Fig. 60.**
15. Remove torx screws from bottom and top of cluster trim plate, then remove trim plate, **Fig. 61.**
16. **On models with column shifter,** remove shift indicator clip from steering column shift bowl.
17. **On all models,** remove four bolts holding instrument cluster, pull cluster rearward and disconnect speedometer.
18. Remove speaker grilles by prying carefully.
19. Remove ventilation control assembly, **Fig. 62.**
20. Remove parking brake release handle, then side window defogger hoses from heater outlet.
21. Disconnect steering column wiring harness from the steering column.
22. Remove wiper motor to cowl attaching bolts, then disconnect bulkhead connector at cowl.
23. Remove lower instrument panel attaching bolts, then using a small screwdriver remove defroster grille by carefully prying upward.
24. Remove upper instrument panel attaching bolts, **Fig. 63,** then open engine compartment hood.
25. Remove clip in engine compartment holding instrument panel wiring harness to cowl.
26. Disconnect electrical connectors from wiring harness in engine compartment.
27. Pull wiring harness through cowl opening into passenger compartment.
28. Tilt instrument panel forward and disconnect remaining electrical connectors and remove instrument panel.
29. Reverse procedure to install.

DEVILLE & FLEETWOOD

The Diagnositc Energy Reserve Module (DERM) can maintain sufficient voltage to cause a deployment of the Supplemental Restraint System air bag for up to 10 minutes after disconnecting battery ground cable. Before performing service on the instrument panel wait 10 minutes to allow DERM voltage to drop after disconnecting battery.

Refer to **Fig. 64,** when performing this procedure.

1. Disconnect battery ground cable.
2. Remove right and left side sound insulators, **Fig. 65.**
3. Remove upper trim pad as shown in **Fig. 64.**
4. Remove lower steering column filler.
5. **On models equipped with Supplemental Inflatable Restraint (SIR) System, proceed as follows:**
   a. Remove fuse No. 3 from fuse panel.
   b. Disconnect position assurance (CPA) and yellow two-way (SIR) harness connector at base of steering column.
6. Remove steering column to support

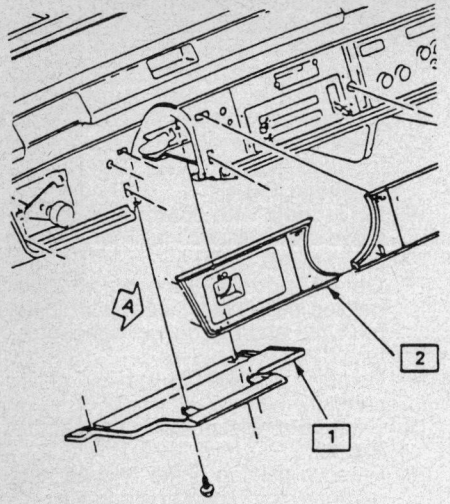

1—STEERING COLUMN
FILLER PANEL

2—IP TRIM L.H.

Fig. 47 Steering column filler panel removal. 6000

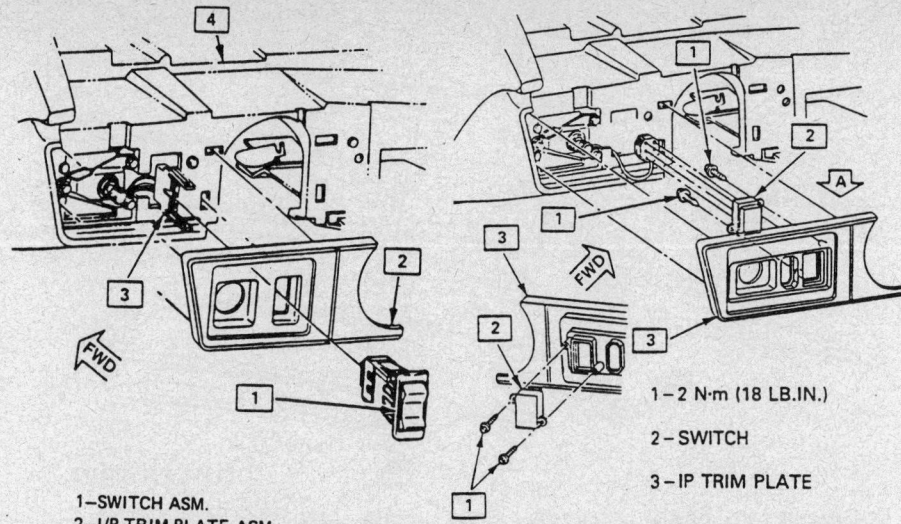

1—SWITCH ASM.
2—I/P TRIM PLATE ASM.
3—INST. PANEL WIRING HARN.
4—INSTRUMENT PANEL RETAINER

Fig. 48 Disconnecting fog lamp switch. 6000

1—2 N·m (18 LB.IN.)

2—SWITCH

3—IP TRIM PLATE

Fig. 49 Disconnecting memory seat switch. 6000

bracket attaching bolts, then lower steering column.
7. Remove lower instrument panel trim pad support.
8. Remove lower instrument panel brace retaining nut from accelerator pedal stud.
9. Disconnect electrical connectors between instrument panel and dash, then remove glove box switches, **Fig. 66.**
10. Remove instrument panel to dash attaching screws, **Fig. 67.**
11. Remove trim pad assembly.
12. Reverse procedure to install.

LESABRE & ELECTRA/PARK AVENUE

1. Disconnect battery ground cable.
2. Remove defroster grille and air outlet deflectors, **Fig. 68.**
3. Remove instrument panel accessory trim plates.
4. Remove ten instrument panel trim pad attaching screws, **Fig. 69.**
5. If vehicle is equipped with Twilight Sentinel, pop up photocell retainer, and remove photocell by turning counterclockwise.
6. Slide instrument panel trim pad out far enough to disconnect aspirator hose and electrical connector from in-car temperature sensor.
7. Remove instrument trim pad from vehicle.
8. Remove left and right side sound insulators, **Fig. 70.**
9. Remove steering column filler, **Fig. 71.**
10. Remove four steering column support bolts, then lower column.
11. Disconnect brake release cable from parking brake.

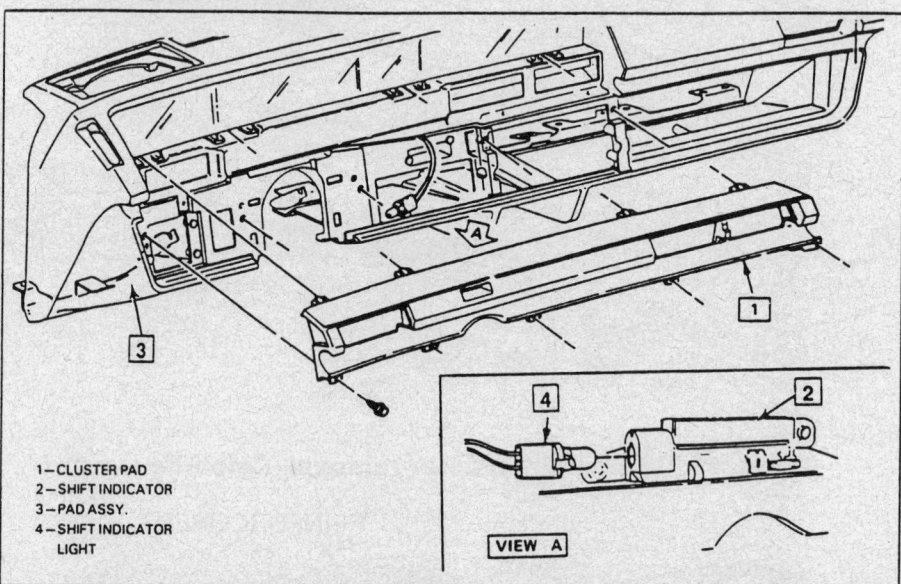

1—CLUSTER PAD
2—SHIFT INDICATOR
3—PAD ASSY.
4—SHIFT INDICATOR LIGHT

VIEW A

Fig. 50 Cluster pad & shift indicator light removal. 6000

12. Disconnect fuse panel and ALDL connector from instrument panel, **Figs. 72 and 73.**
13. Disconnect instrument panel harness interconnect.
14. Disconnect antenna lead and side window defogger hoses.
15. Remove instrument panel attaching screws, located at the top of the instrument panel, **Fig. 74.**
16. Remove two instrument panel attaching bolts at top of steering column opening.
17. Remove two instrument panel attaching bolts, located on bottom right and left sides of the instrument panel.
18. Remove two instrument panel to center support attaching bolts.
19. Pull instrument panel straight out.
20. Reverse procedure to install.

88 & 98

1. Disconnect battery ground cable.
2. Remove center trim plate, **Fig. 75.**
3. Remove lower trim plate, **Fig. 76.**
4. Remove screws from left and right speaker grilles.
5. Remove speaker grilles and defroster duct screen.
6. Remove left and right sound insulators, **Fig. 77.**
7. Disconnect parking brake release cable.
8. Remove two screws from dash wire electrical connectors between radio and steering column.

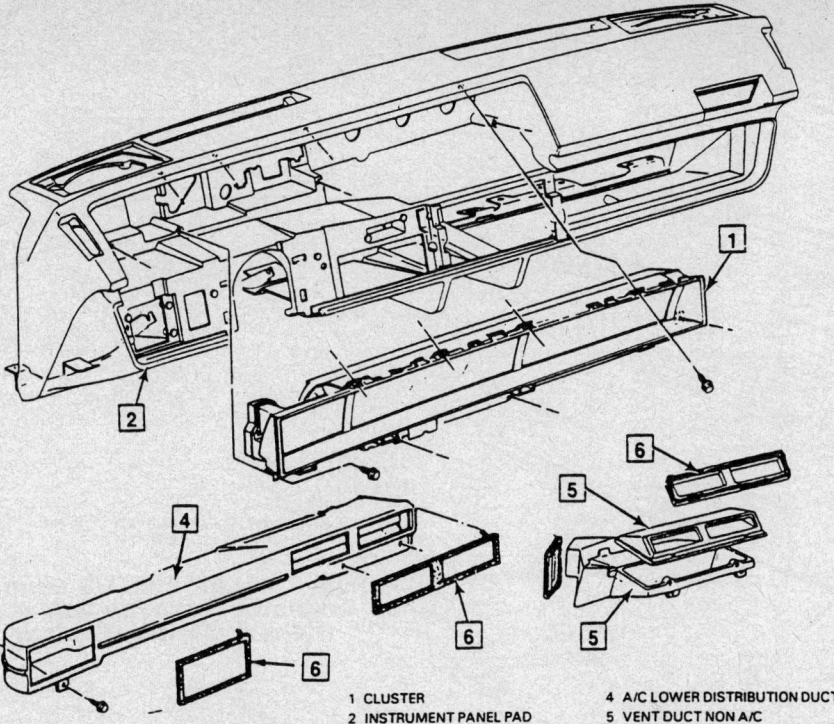

1 CLUSTER
2 INSTRUMENT PANEL PAD
4 A/C LOWER DISTRIBUTION DUCT
5 VENT DUCT NON A/C
6 SEALS

Fig. 51 Removing A/C & non A/C distribution ducts. 6000

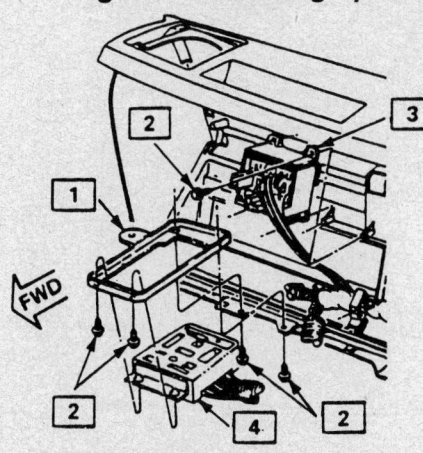

1 – BRACKET

2 – 1.5 N·m (13 LB.IN.)

3 – FUSE BLOCK

4 – CONVENIENCE CENTER

Fig. 53 Fuse block & convenience center mounting. 6000

9. Remove four steering column support bolts, disconnect shift indicator cable.
10. Lower steering column, and rest it on driver's seat.
11. Remove two ALDL connector attaching screws.
12. Remove two clips from steering column and pull forward and down.
13. Remove three bolts on lower rail of instrument panel.

14. Remove two instrument panel attaching bolts from brace directly above steering column opening, **Fig. 78.**
15. Remove two bolts in instrument panel bracket, behind instrument panel compartment opening.
16. Remove air sensor duct, lift upward on instrument panel and pull rearward. Disconnect two side window defogger hoses at distributor outlet.
17. Remove instrument panel assembly from vehicle.
18. Reverse procedure to install.

1988–89 TORONADO

1. Disconnect battery ground cable.
2. Remove left and right instrument panel sound insulators, **Fig. 79.**
3. Remove steering column trim cover, **Fig. 80.**
4. Remove mounting bolts and lower steering column.
5. Remove bolts attaching bottom of instrument panel to dash, **Fig. 81.**
6. Insert a small, flat blade at the inside edge of each side window defroster grille and pry out carefully, **Fig. 82.**
7. Remove screws attaching top of instrument panel pad to front of dash.
8. Disconnect bulkhead electrical connector.
9. Tilt instrument panel rearward and disconnect aspirator hose, fuse panel, fuel door and rear compartment release switch wires and antenna lead, **Fig. 83.**
10. Remove instrument panel pad.
11. Reverse procedure to install.

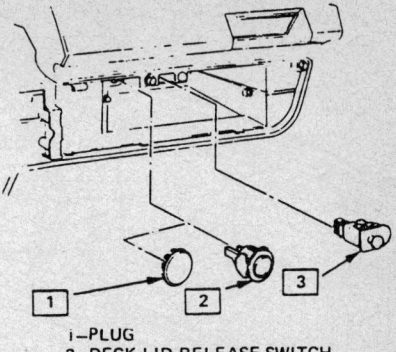

i–PLUG
2–DECK LID RELEASE SWITCH
3–GLOVEBOX LAMP SWITCH

Fig. 52 Glove box lamp switch & deck lid release switch removal. 6000

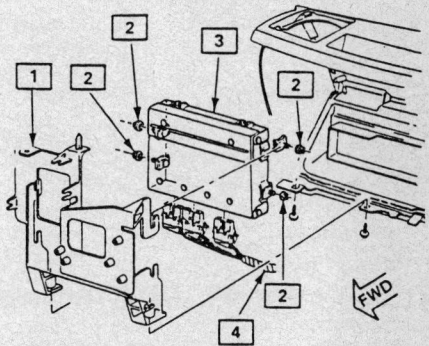

1 – MULTI-USE BRACKET

2 – 3 N·m (27 LB.IN.)

3 – ECM

4 – HARNESS ASSEMBLY

Fig. 54 Disconnecting & removing ECM. 6000

1990 TORNADO

The Diagnositc Energy Reserve Module (DERM) can maintain sufficient voltage to cause a deployment of the Supplemental Restraint System air bag for up to 10 minutes after disconnecting battery ground cable. Before performing service on the instrument panel wait 10 minutes to allow DERM voltage to drop after disconnecting battery.

On models equipped with Supplemental Inflatable Restraint (SIR) System, refer to steps 2 through 5 to disable system:
1. Disconnect battery ground cable.
2. Turn ignition to the Off position, then remove fuse No. 9 from fuse panel.
3. Remove four left side sound insulator retaining screws.
4. Disconnect courtesy lamp from panel and remove sound insulator from vehicle.
5. Disconnect position assurance (CPA) and yellow two-way (SIR) harness

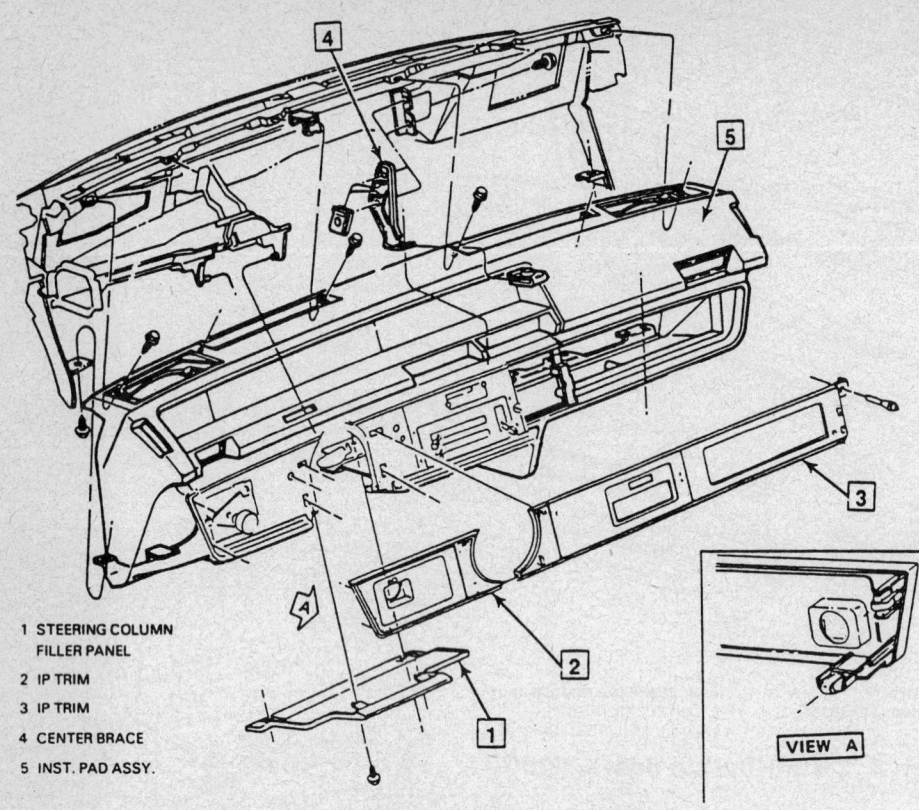

1 STEERING COLUMN
  FILLER PANEL
2 IP TRIM
3 IP TRIM
4 CENTER BRACE
5 INST. PAD ASSY.

Fig. 55   I/P & trim plate removal. 6000

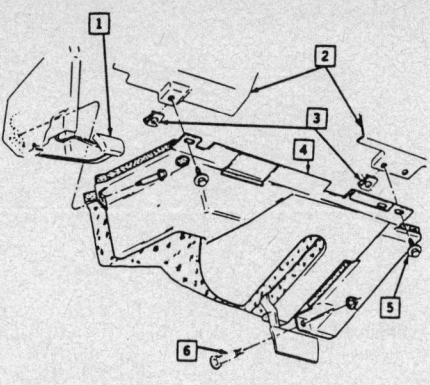

1. PARKING BRAKE
2. I.P. PAD
3. NUT
4. INSULATOR
5. FULLY DRIVEN, SEATED AND NOT STRIPPED
6. STUD ON ACCELERATOR SUPPORT

Fig. 56   Left side I/P sound insulator removal. Cutlass Ciera & Cutlass Cruiser

VIEW A

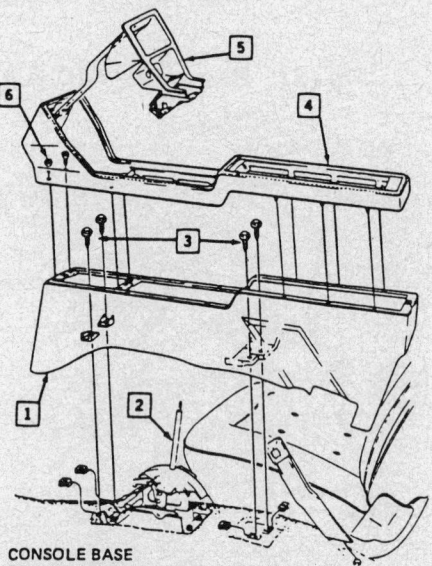

1. CONSOLE BASE
2. TRANSMISSION SHIFTER ASSEMBLY
3. 6 N·m (4 LBS. FT.)
4. PAD ASM.
5. COMPARTMENT ASM.
6. FULLY DRIVEN, SEATED AND NOT STRIPPED

Fig. 59   Upper console removal. Cutlass Ciera & Cutlass Cruiser

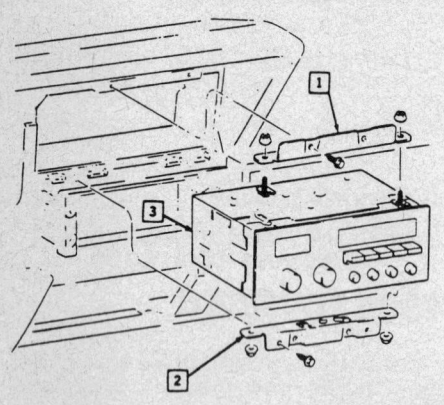

1. UPPER BRACKET
2. LOWER BRACKET
3. RADIO

Fig. 57   Right side I/P sound insulator removal. Cutlass Ciera & Cutlass Cruiser

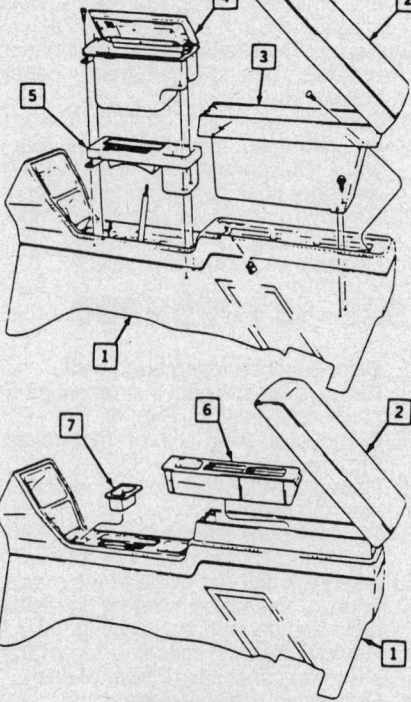

1. CONSOLE BASE
2. COMPARTMENT DOOR
3. COMPARTMENT
4. CENTER COMPARTMENT
5. SHIFTER PLATE
6. TAPE STORAGE
7. ASHTRAY

Fig. 58   Center console assembly. Cutlass Ciera & Cutlass Cruiser

connector at base of steering column, **Fig. 84.**
6. Remove four right side sound insulator retaining screws, **Fig. 85.**
7. Disconnect courtesy lamp from panel and remove sound insulator from vehicle.
8. Remove two knee bolster retaining screws, then remove bolster from vehicle, **Fig. 86.**
9. Remove four steering column rein-

forcement plate retaining screws, then remove plate from vehicle.
10. Remove instrument panel cluster trim plate retaining screws, then remove plate from vehicle, **Fig. 87.**
11. Remove right and left side switch assembly retaining screws, then disconnect switch assemblies from electrical connectors and remove from vehicle.
12. Remove instrument panel cluster retaining screws, then pull cluster outward disengaging electrical connector.
13. Remove electronic climate control head retaining screws, if equipped.

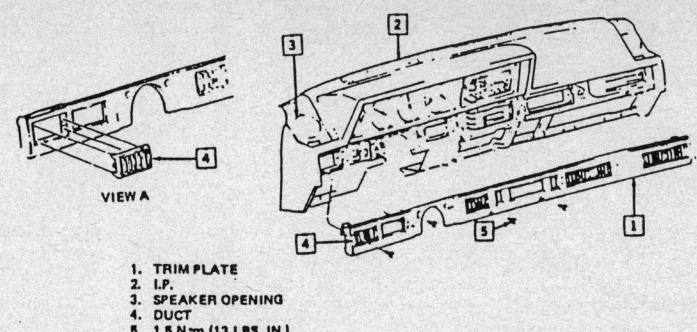

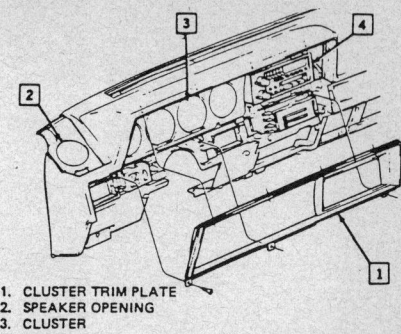

1. TRIM PLATE
2. I.P.
3. SPEAKER OPENING
4. DUCT
5. 1.5 N·m (13 LBS. IN.)

Fig. 60   Accessory trim plate removal. Cutlass Ciera & Cutlass Cruiser

1. CLUSTER TRIM PLATE
2. SPEAKER OPENING
3. CLUSTER
4. RADIO

Fig. 61   Cluster trim plate removal. Cutlass Ciera & Cutlass Cruiser

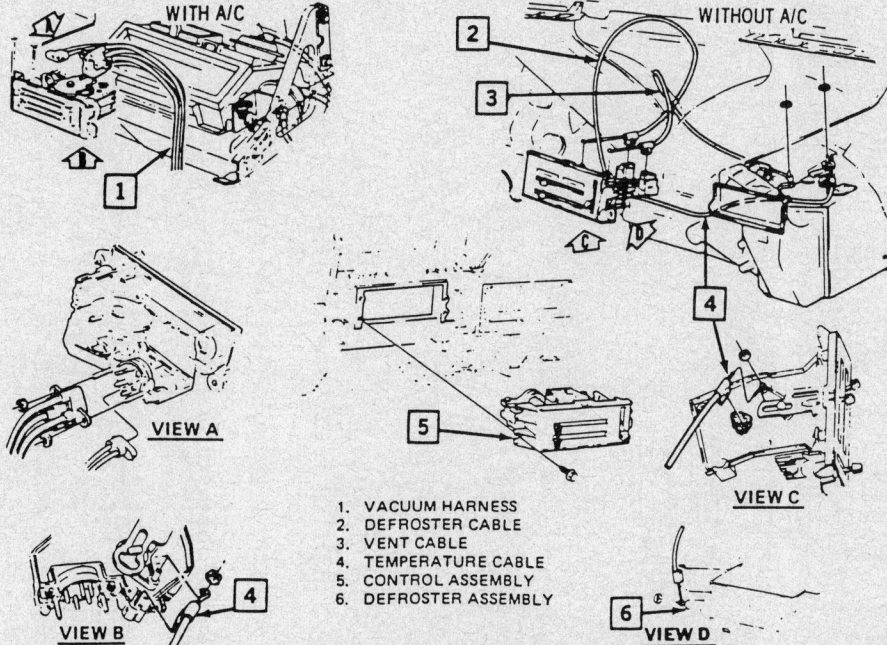

1. VACUUM HARNESS
2. DEFROSTER CABLE
3. VENT CABLE
4. TEMPERATURE CABLE
5. CONTROL ASSEMBLY
6. DEFROSTER ASSEMBLY

Fig. 62   Ventilation system control removal. Cutlass Ciera & Cutlass Cruiser

14. **On models equipped with integral radio unit,** proceed as follows:
   a. Remove radio/ECC retaining screws, **Fig. 88.**
   b. Remove radio bracket to radio retaining nuts.
   c. Disconnect radio electrical connectors and remove radio from vehicle.
15. **On models equipped with remote radio chassis,** proceed as follows:
   a. Open console storage tray and remove CD, cassette holder or phone handset if equipped, **Fig. 89.**
   b. Remove four T-15 Torx screws.
   c. Remove storage tray liner, then disconnect two seat control electrical connectors and handset connector if equipped.
   d. Open ashtray and remove cigar lighter and ashtray bucket.
   e. Pull console trim plate upward, then disconnect trim plate bulb and cigar lighter electrical connectors.
   f. Remove console trim plate from vehicle.
   g. Remove three 10mm chassis to CRTC bracket retaining nuts.
   h. Disconnect six remote chassis and one coax lead electrical connectors.
16. **On all models,** remove four driver information display to mounting bracket retaining bolts.
17. Disconnect driver information display electrical connector and remove from vehicle.
18. Remove center A/C deflector, then unsnap and remove defroster grille.
19. Remove upper and lower left instrument panel retaining screws.
20. Remove hood release assembly, remaining instrument panel retaining screws and center instrument panel brace.
21. Remove four inflator module retaining screws located on back of steering wheel assembly.
22. Remove position assurance (CPA) and coil assembly connector from inflator module.
23. Remove inflator module from vehicle. **When carrying a live inflator, en-**

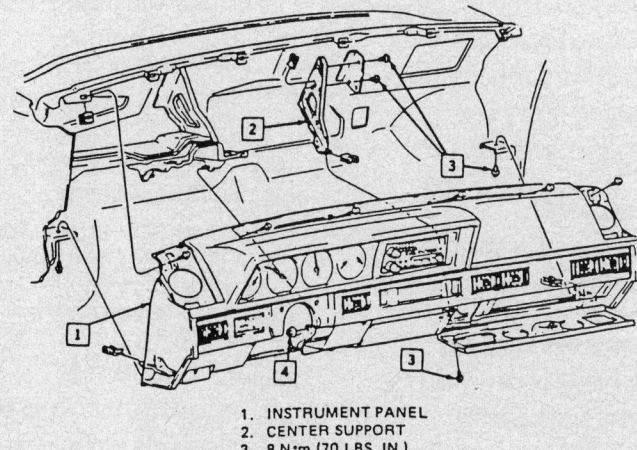

1. INSTRUMENT PANEL
2. CENTER SUPPORT
3. 8 N·m (70 LBS. IN.)
4. 9 N·m (80 LBS. IN.)

Fig. 63   I/P removal. Cutlass Ciera & Cutlass Cruiser

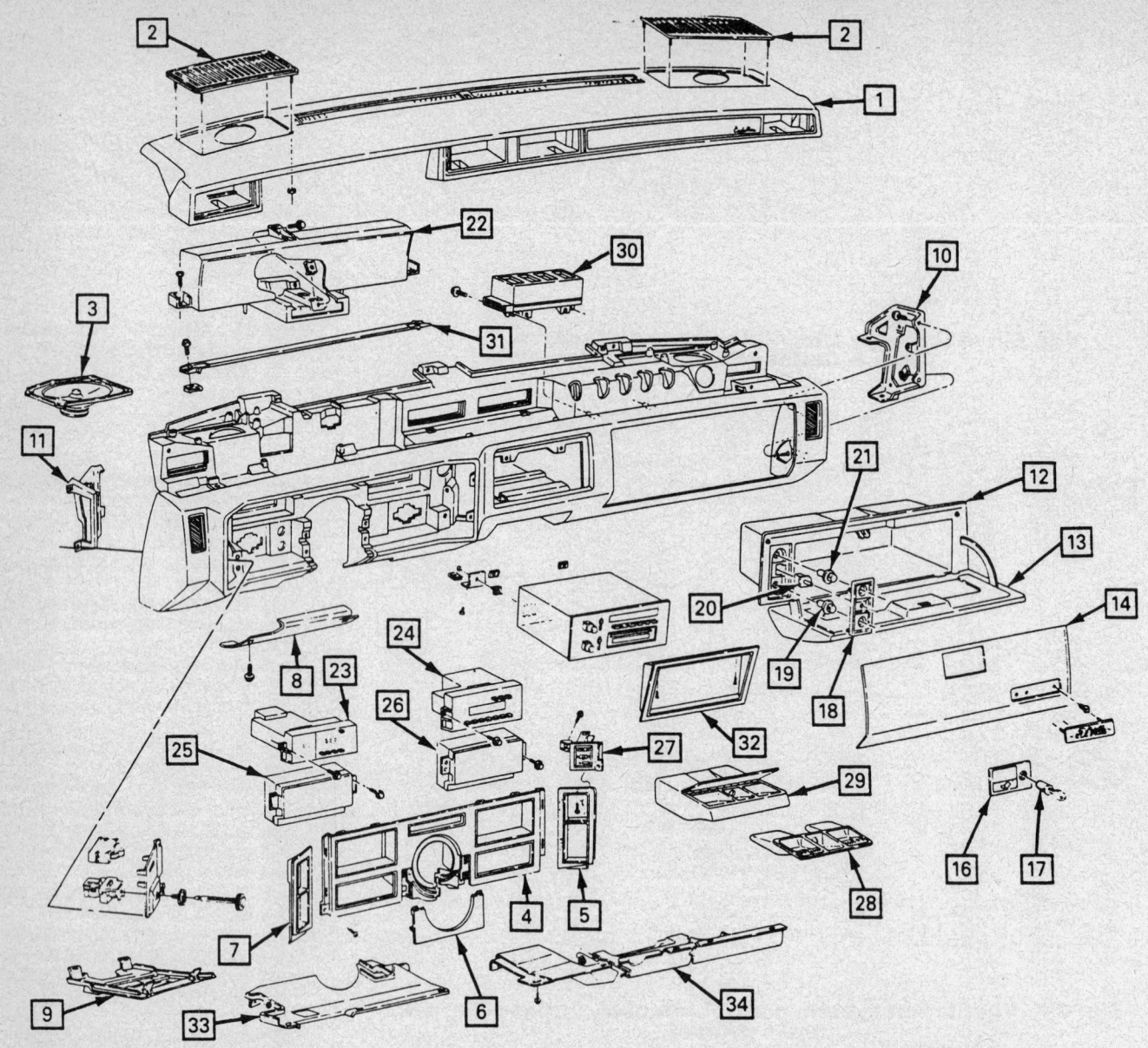

Fig. 64 Exploded view of I/P. DeVille & Fleetwood

1	PAD ASSEMBLY, INSTRUMENT PANEL (I/P) UPPER TRIM PAD
2	GRILLE, FRONT SPEAKER
3	SPEAKER
4	PLATE, I/P CLUSTER CENTER TRIM
5	PLATE, I/P CLUSTER RIGHT-HAND TRIM
6	FILLER, STEERING COLUMN OPENING UPPER
7	PLATE, I/P CLUSTER LEFT-HAND TRIM
8	FILLER, I/P STEERING COLUMN OPENING LOWER
9	COVER, FUSE PANEL ACCESS OPENING
10	BRACKET, I/P MOUNTING
11	BRACKET, HEADLIGHT SWITCH
12	BOX, GLOVE COMPARTMENT MODULE
13	PANEL, GLOVE BOX DOOR INNER
14	PANEL, GLOVE BOX DOOR OUTER
15	NAMEPLATE, GLOVE BOX
16	LATCH ASSEMBLY, GLOVE BOX
17	LOCK CYLINDER, GLOVE BOX LATCH ASSEMBLY
18	PLATE, GLOVE BOX SWITCHES
19	SWITCH, FUEL FILLER DOOR RELEASE
20	SWITCH, GLOVE BOX LIGHT
21	SWITCH, REAR DECK LID RELEASE
22	CLUSTER, SPEEDOMETER
23	DISPLAY, FUEL DATA CENTER
24	CONTROL, HEATER AND AIR CONDITIONER (A/C)
25	TELLTALE, LEFT-HAND INFORMATION CENTER
26	TELLTALE, RIGHT-HAND INFORMATION CENTER
27	SWITCH, CRUISE CONTROL ON-OFF
28	TRAY, ASH RECEPTACLE
29	HOUSING, ASHTRAY
30	ALARM, SEAT BELT WARNING, IGNITION KEY AND HEADLAMPS "ON" REMINDER
31	PLATE, I/P SPEEDOMETER CLUSTER
32	PLATE, RADIO TRIM
33	INSULATOR, LEFT-HAND SOUND
34	INSULATOR, RIGHT-HAND SOUND

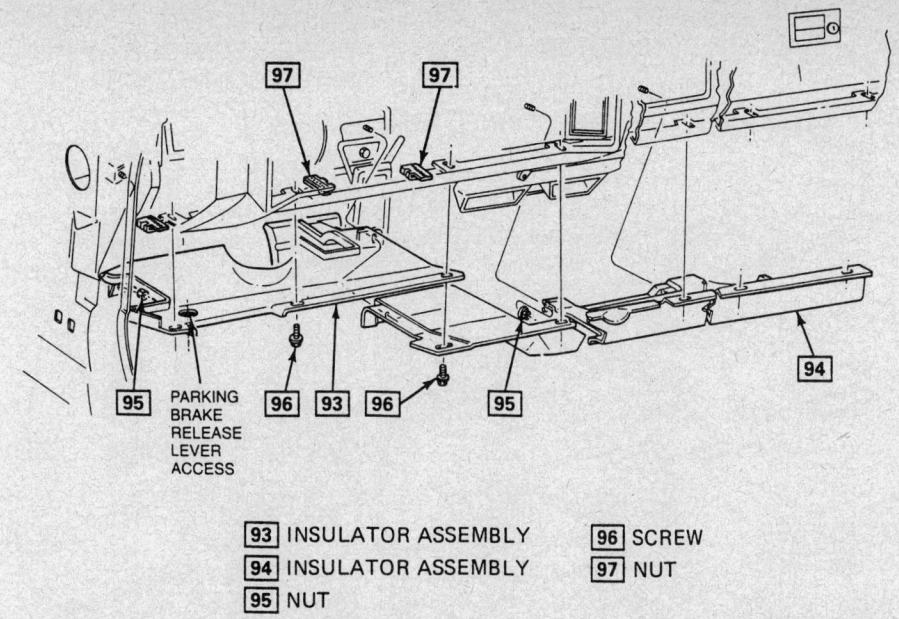

93 INSULATOR ASSEMBLY		96 SCREW	
94 INSULATOR ASSEMBLY		97 NUT	
95 NUT			

Fig. 65   Insulator sound panel removal. DeVille & Fleetwood

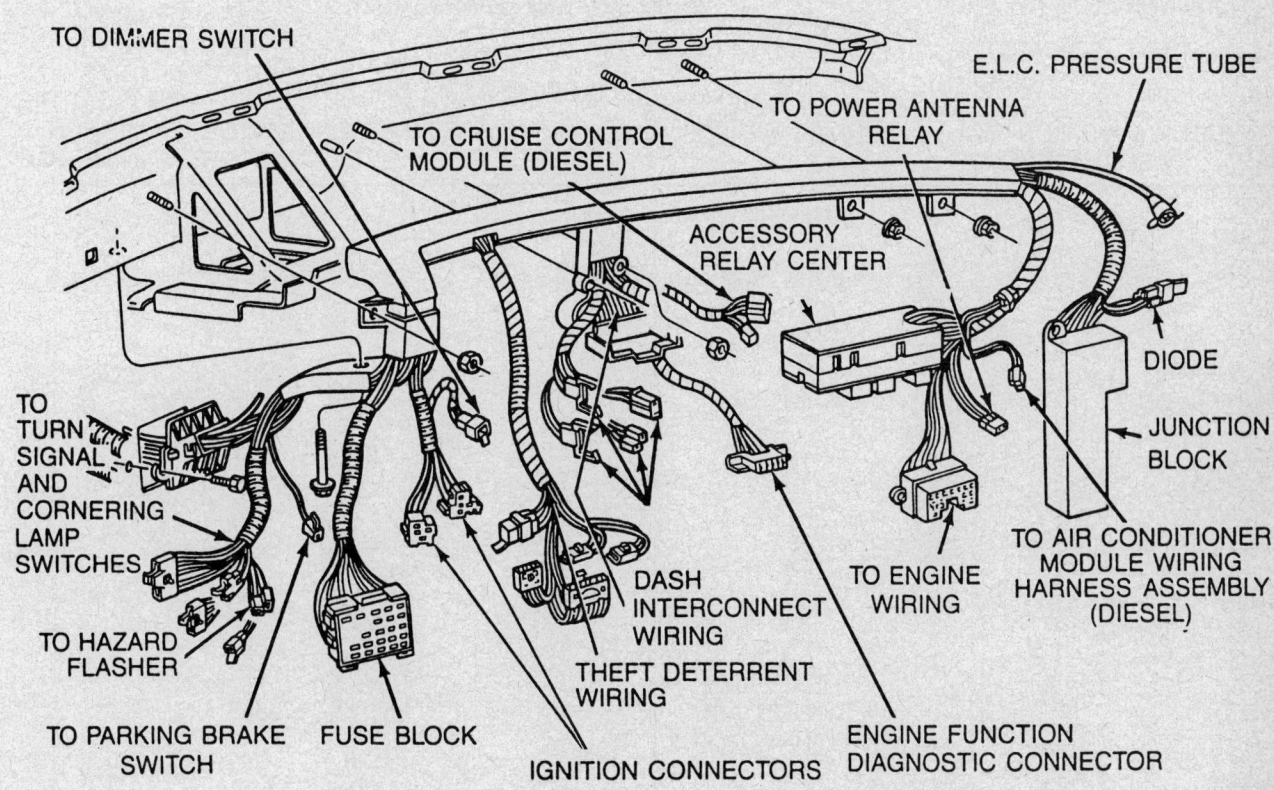

Fig. 66   I/P wiring & connectors (Part 1 of 2). DeVille & Fleetwood

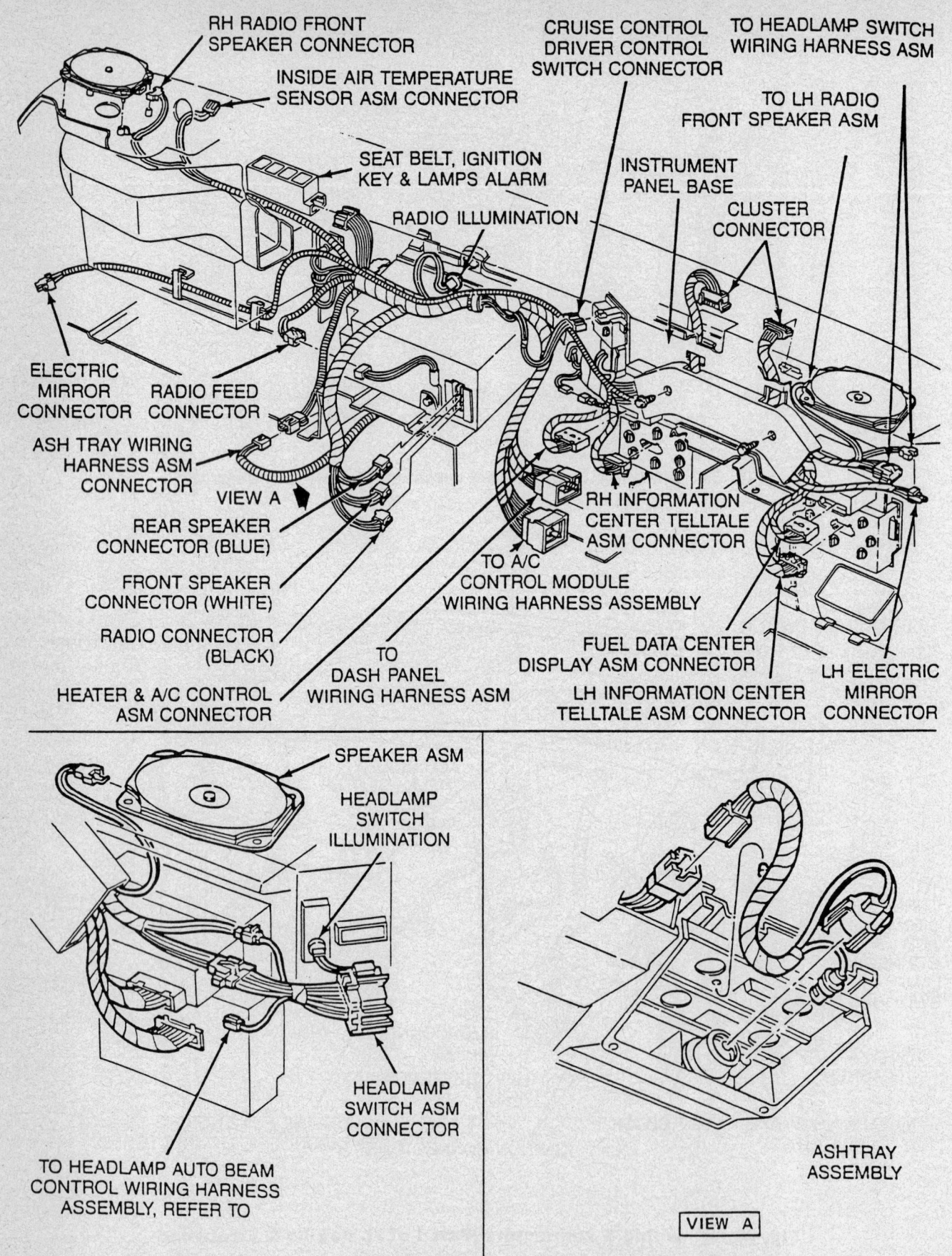

RH RADIO FRONT
SPEAKER CONNECTOR

INSIDE AIR TEMPERATURE
SENSOR ASM CONNECTOR

CRUISE CONTROL
DRIVER CONTROL
SWITCH CONNECTOR

TO HEADLAMP SWITCH
WIRING HARNESS ASM

SEAT BELT, IGNITION
KEY & LAMPS ALARM

RADIO ILLUMINATION

TO LH RADIO
FRONT SPEAKER ASM

INSTRUMENT
PANEL BASE

CLUSTER
CONNECTOR

ELECTRIC
MIRROR
CONNECTOR

RADIO FEED
CONNECTOR

ASH TRAY WIRING
HARNESS ASM
CONNECTOR

VIEW A

REAR SPEAKER
CONNECTOR (BLUE)

FRONT SPEAKER
CONNECTOR (WHITE)

RADIO CONNECTOR
(BLACK)

TO
DASH PANEL
WIRING HARNESS ASM

HEATER & A/C CONTROL
ASM CONNECTOR

RH INFORMATION
CENTER TELLTALE
ASM CONNECTOR

TO A/C
CONTROL MODULE
WIRING HARNESS ASSEMBLY

FUEL DATA CENTER
DISPLAY ASM CONNECTOR

LH INFORMATION CENTER
TELLTALE ASM CONNECTOR

LH ELECTRIC
MIRROR
CONNECTOR

SPEAKER ASM

HEADLAMP
SWITCH
ILLUMINATION

HEADLAMP
SWITCH ASM
CONNECTOR

TO HEADLAMP AUTO BEAM
CONTROL WIRING HARNESS
ASSEMBLY, REFER TO

ASHTRAY
ASSEMBLY

VIEW A

Fig. 66   I/P wiring & connectors (Part 2 of 2). DeVille & Fleetwood

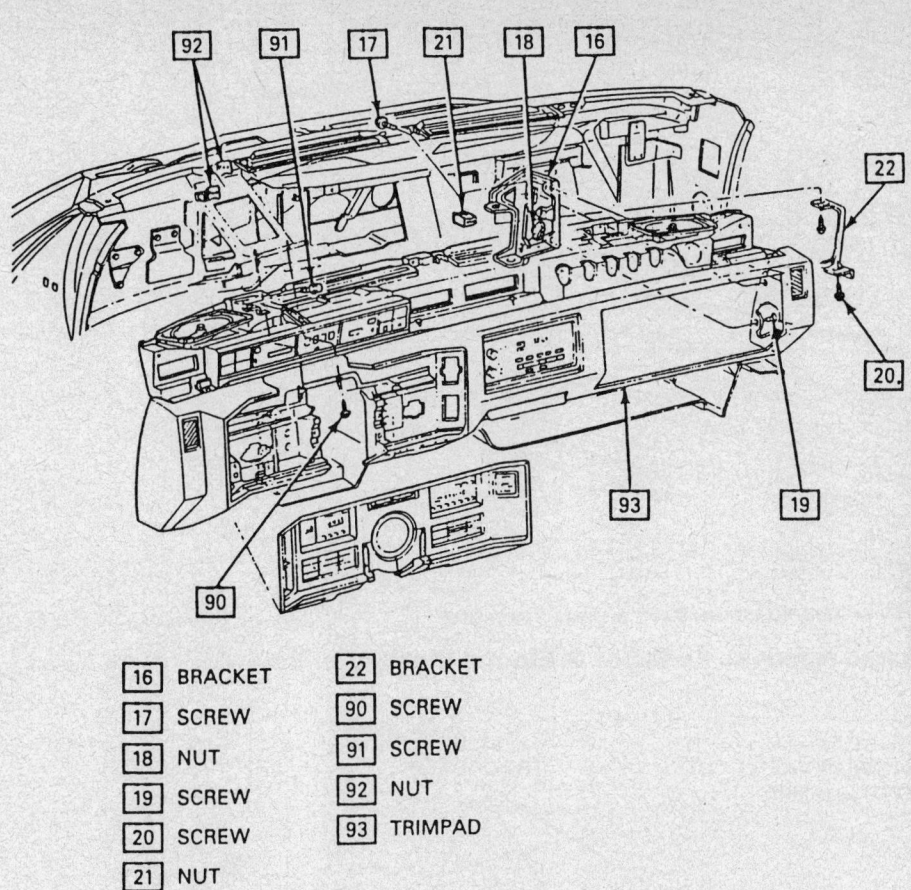

Fig. 67 I/P removal. DeVille & Fleetwood

16	BRACKET	22	BRACKET
17	SCREW	90	SCREW
18	NUT	91	SCREW
19	SCREW	92	NUT
20	SCREW	93	TRIMPAD
21	NUT		

sure the bag and trim cover are pointed away in case of accidental deployment. Do not carry inflator module by wires of connector on the underside of the module. In-case of accidental deployment, the bag will then deploy with minimal chance of injury. When placing a live inflator module on a bench or other surface, ensure the bag and trim cover faces in a upward direction. Never rest steering column assembly on the steering wheel with the inflator module face down and column vertical. This is necessary in case of accidental deployment. Otherwise, personal injury may result.

24. Remove horn contact by pushing slightly and twisting counterclockwise.
25. Remove glove box door and glove box unit retaining screws.
26. Remove lower right instrument panel retaining bolt.
27. Remove fuse box retaining screws.
28. Remove console assembly to floor retaining screws and nuts.
29. Disconnect console electrical connectors and remove console from vehicle.
30. Disconnect instrument panel electrical connectors, then remove instrument panel.
31. Reverse procedure to install.

1988–89 RIVIERA & REATTA

1. Remove three retaining screws from front of right sound insulator and four retaining screws from left side insulator, **Fig. 90**.

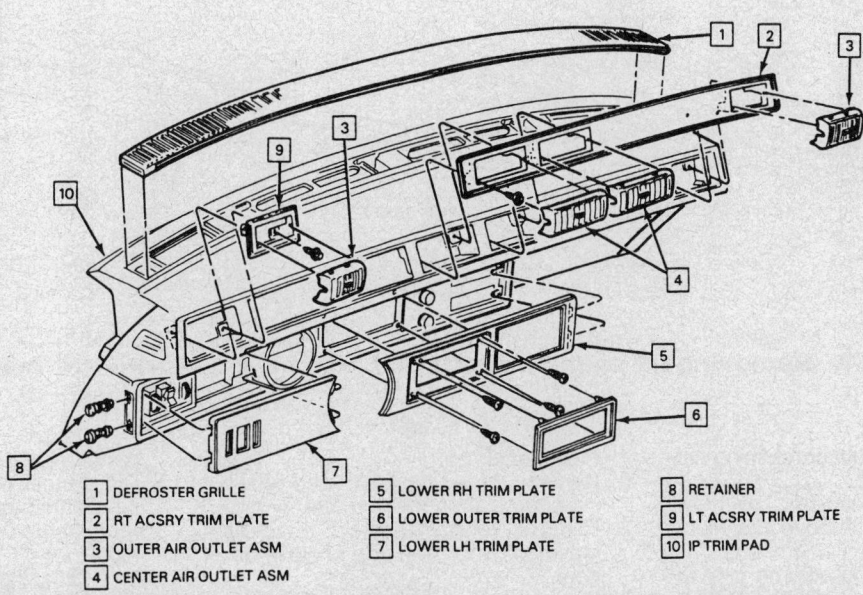

1	DEFROSTER GRILLE	5	LOWER RH TRIM PLATE	8	RETAINER
2	RT ACSRY TRIM PLATE	6	LOWER OUTER TRIM PLATE	9	LT ACSRY TRIM PLATE
3	OUTER AIR OUTLET ASM	7	LOWER LH TRIM PLATE	10	IP TRIM PAD
4	CENTER AIR OUTLET ASM				

Fig. 68 Exploded view of I/P trim pad. LeSabre & Electra/Park Avenue

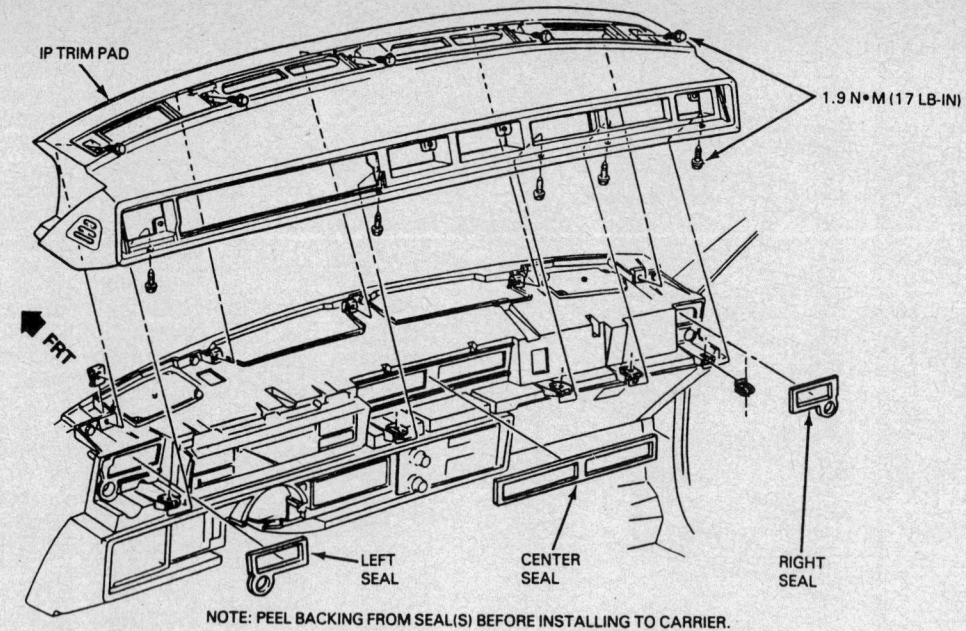

Fig. 69   I/P trim pad removal. LeSabre & Electra/Park Avenue

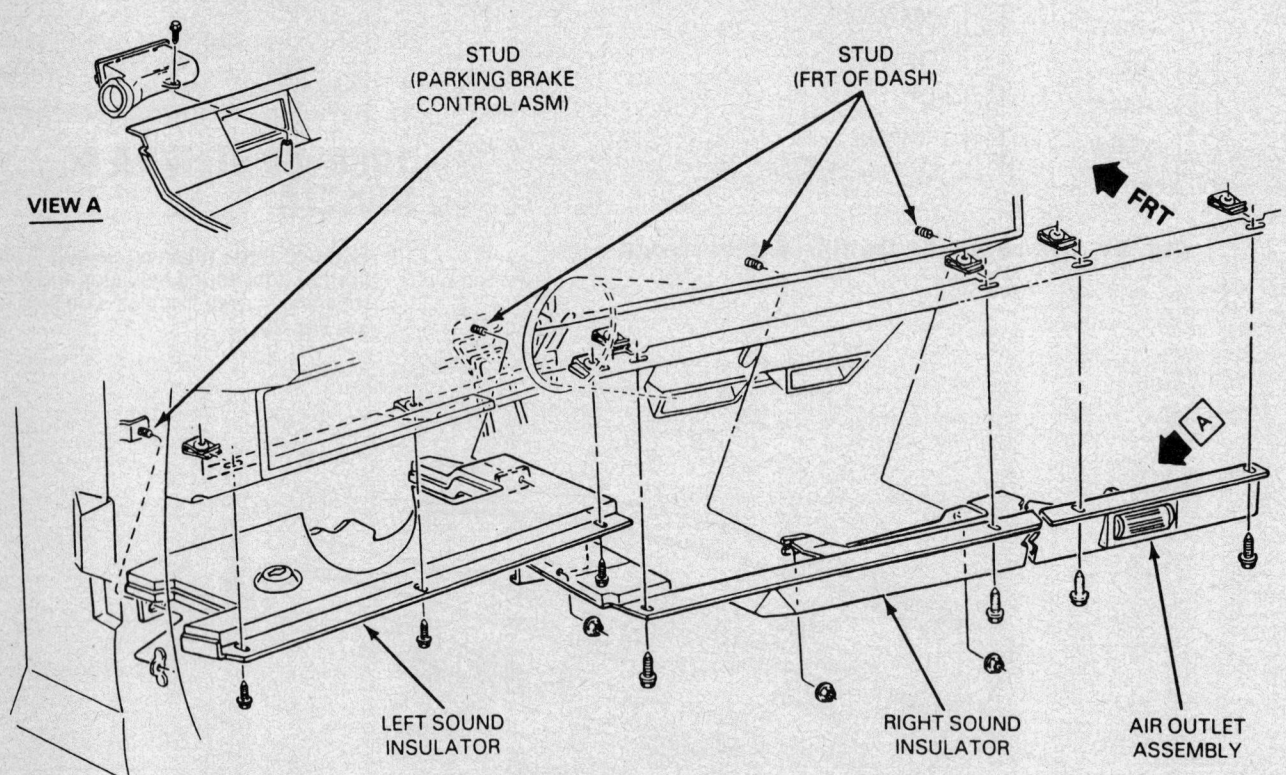

Fig. 70   Removing I/P sound insulators. LeSabre & Electra/Park Avenue

2. Remove sound insulator retaining nut from rear of insulator.

3. Remove sound insulator courtesy lamp sockets, then remove insulators from vehicle.

4. Remove six steering column filler to lower left instrument panel retaining screws, then the filler.

5. Gently pull defroster grille from instrument panel.

6. Remove three upper trim pad retaining screws, then the trim pad.

7. Remove retaining screw attaching glove box door limit arm to glove box door.

8. Remove four glove box door retaining screws.

9. Remove four glove box to instrument panel retaining screws.

10. Disconnect instrument panel electrical connectors, then remove instrument panel from vehicle, **Fig. 91.**

1990 RIVIERA & REATTA

The Diagnositc Energy Reserve Module

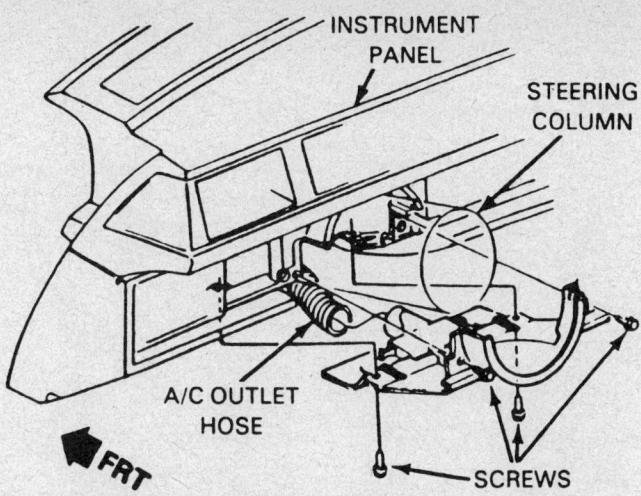

**Fig. 71 Steering column filler removal.
LeSabre & Electra/Park Avenue**

(DERM) can maintain sufficient voltage to cause a deployment of the Supplemental Restraint System air bag for up to 10 minutes after disconnecting battery ground cable. Before performing service on the instrument panel wait 10 minutes to allow DERM voltage to drop after disconnecting battery.

On models equipped with Supplemental Inflatable Restraint (SIR) System, refer to steps 2 through 5 to disable system:

1. Disconnect battery ground cable.
2. Turn ignition to the Off position, then remove fuse No. 14 from fuse panel.
3. Remove left side sound insulator retaining screws and nuts, **Fig. 92.**
4. Disconnect courtesy lamp from insulator panel and remove from vehicle.
5. Disconnect position assurance (CPA) and yellow two-way (SIR) harness connector at base of steering column, **Fig. 84.**
6. Remove instrument panel cluster trim plate retaining screws, then remove plate from vehicle, **Fig. 93.**
7. Remove center air duct assembly.
8. Remove 13 instrument panel cluster retaining screws, then pull cluster outward from instrument panel, **Fig. 94.**
9. Remove two headlamp switch to instrument panel retaining screws, then disconnect headlamp switch electrical connector and remove from vehicle.
10. Remove four electronic climate control head retaining screws, if equipped.
11. Remove climate control electrical connector then the climate control assembly.
12. **On models equipped with integral radio unit,** proceed as follows:
    a. Remove radio/ECC retaining screws, **Fig. 95.**
    b. Remove radio bracket to radio retaining nuts.
    c. Disconnect radio electrical connectors and remove radio from vehicle.
13. **On models equipped with cassette tape/compact disc,** remove holder from rear console storage compartment.
14. Remove two outer and three inner console trim plate retaining screws, then the trim plate.
15. **On models equipped with CD player,** proceed as follows:
    a. Remove CD trim plate from instrument panel.
    b. Disconnect two CD player electrical connectors accessed through ashtray, **Fig. 96.**

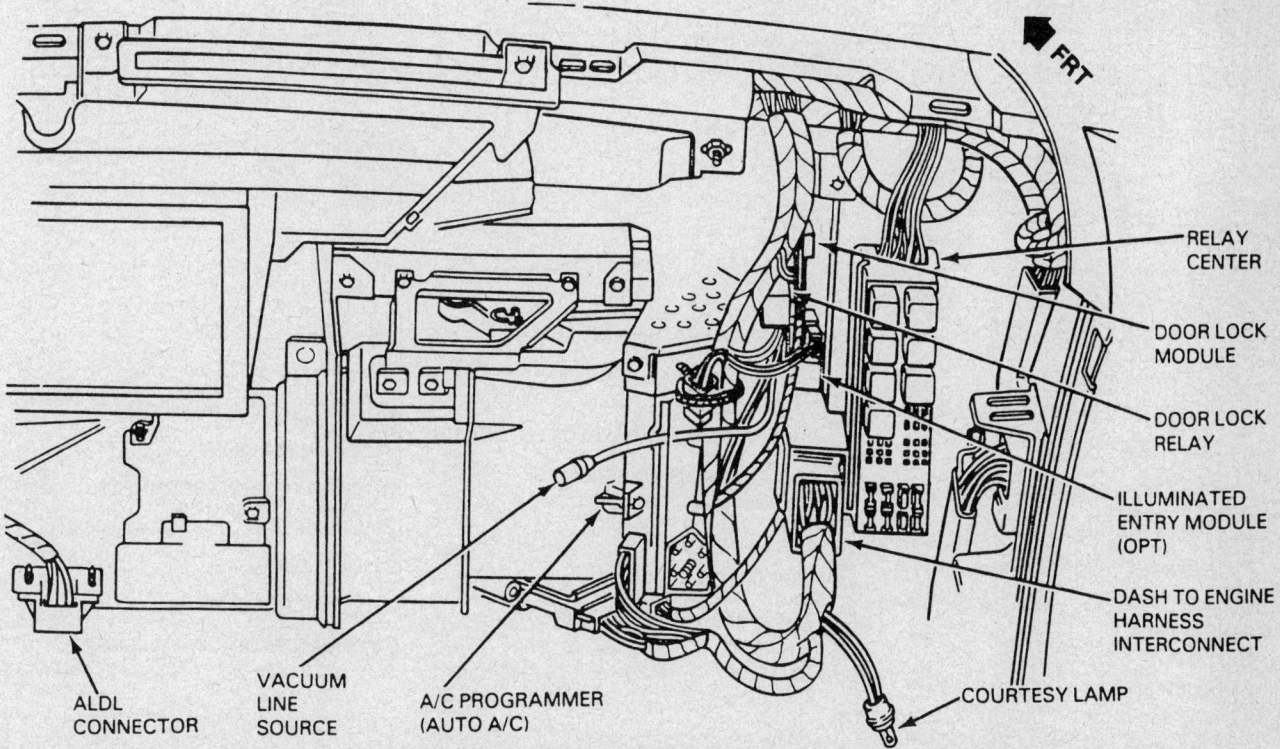

Fig. 72 I/P wiring (right side). LeSabre & Electra/Park Avenue

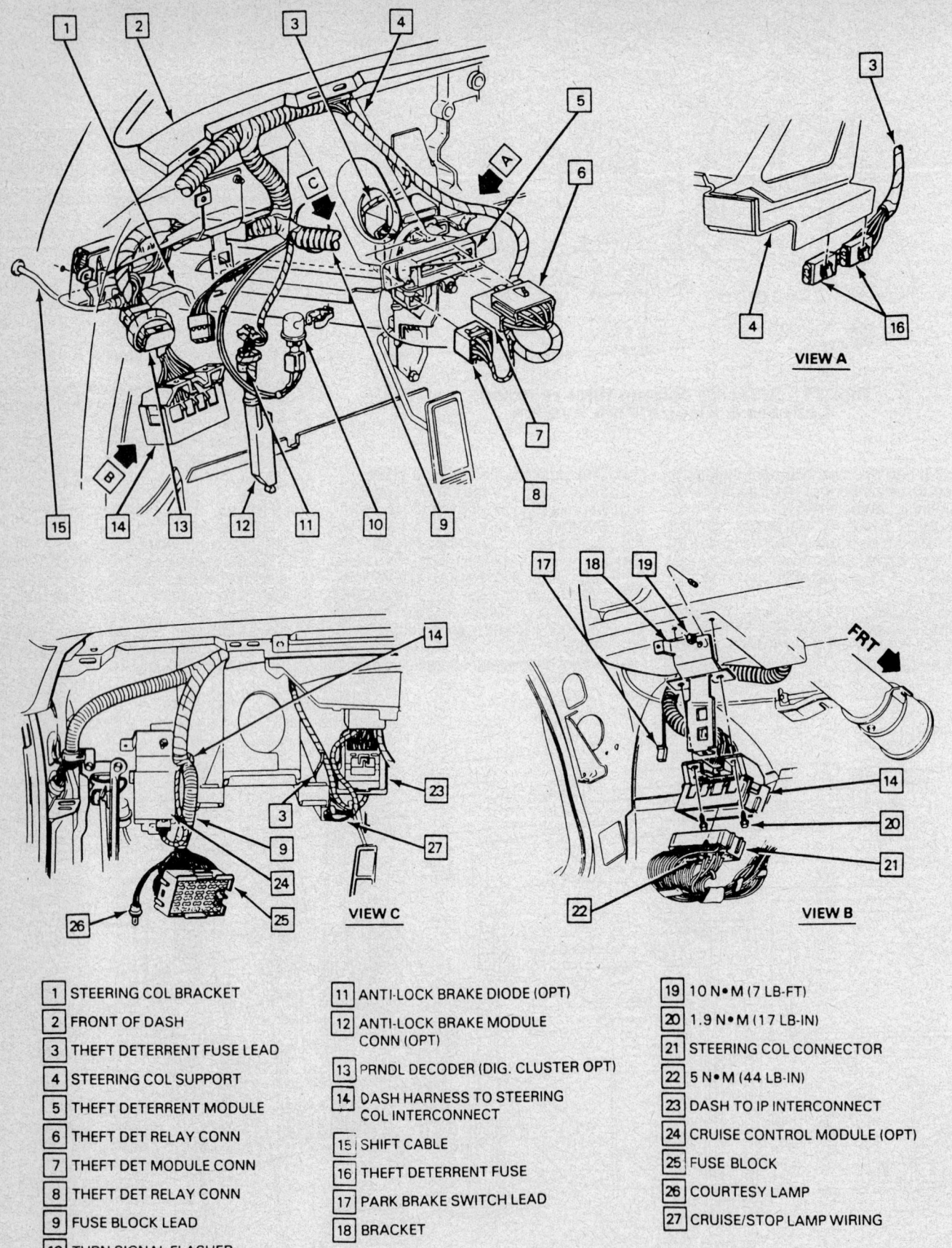

Fig. 73 I/P wiring (left side). LeSabre & Electra/Park Avenue

1 STEERING COL BRACKET	11 ANTI-LOCK BRAKE DIODE (OPT)	19 10 N•M (7 LB-FT)
2 FRONT OF DASH	12 ANTI-LOCK BRAKE MODULE CONN (OPT)	20 1.9 N•M (17 LB-IN)
3 THEFT DETERRENT FUSE LEAD	13 PRNDL DECODER (DIG. CLUSTER OPT)	21 STEERING COL CONNECTOR
4 STEERING COL SUPPORT	14 DASH HARNESS TO STEERING COL INTERCONNECT	22 5 N•M (44 LB-IN)
5 THEFT DETERRENT MODULE	15 SHIFT CABLE	23 DASH TO IP INTERCONNECT
6 THEFT DET RELAY CONN	16 THEFT DETERRENT FUSE	24 CRUISE CONTROL MODULE (OPT)
7 THEFT DET MODULE CONN	17 PARK BRAKE SWITCH LEAD	25 FUSE BLOCK
8 THEFT DET RELAY CONN	18 BRACKET	26 COURTESY LAMP
9 FUSE BLOCK LEAD		27 CRUISE/STOP LAMP WIRING
10 TURN SIGNAL FLASHER		

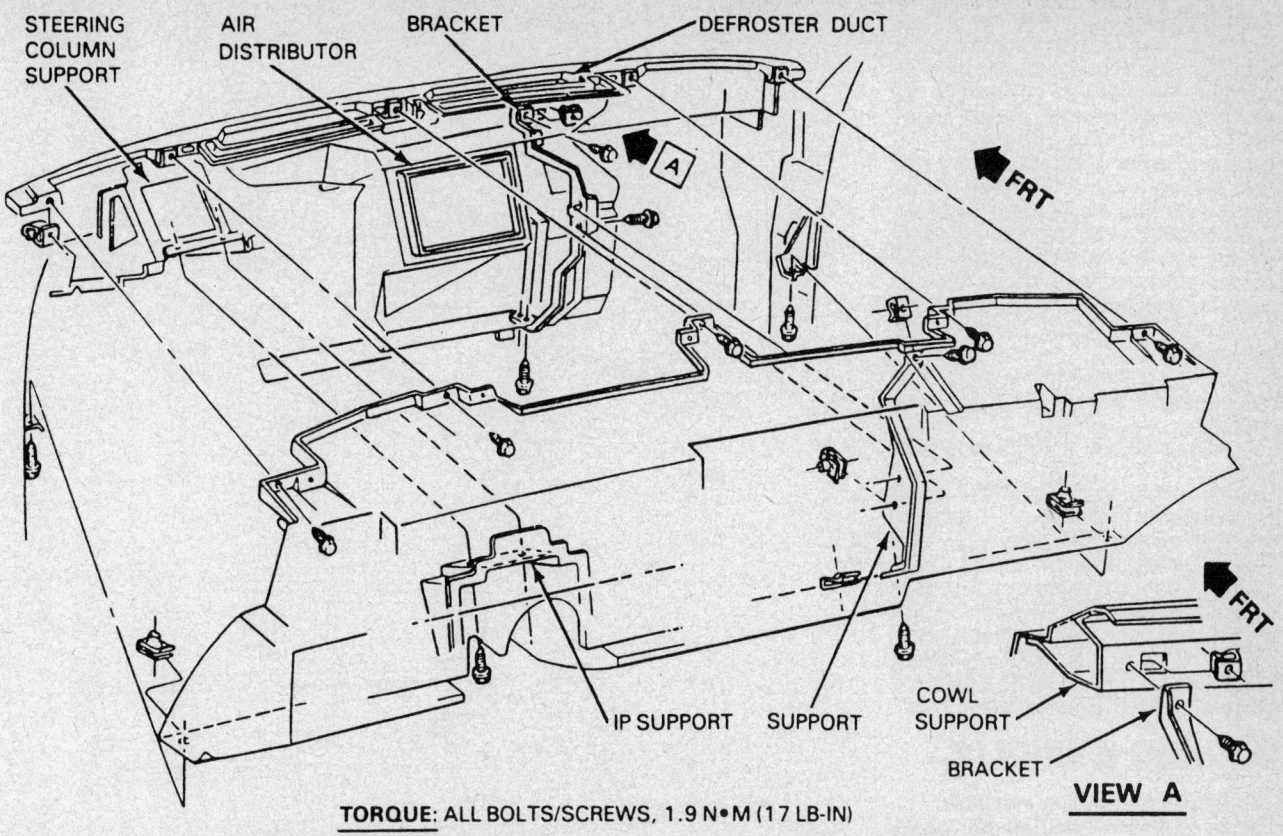

STEERING COLUMN SUPPORT AIR DISTRIBUTOR BRACKET DEFROSTER DUCT FRT

IP SUPPORT SUPPORT COWL SUPPORT BRACKET VIEW A FRT

TORQUE: ALL BOLTS/SCREWS, 1.9 N•M (17 LB-IN)

Fig. 74 I/P removal. LeSabre & Electra/Park Avenue

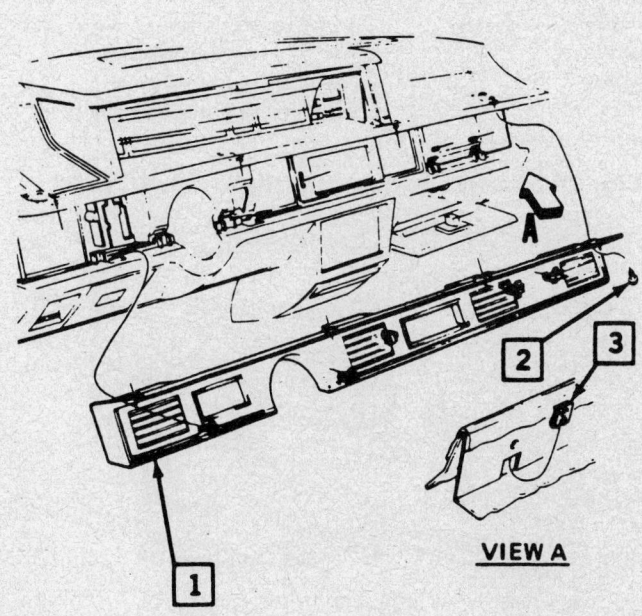

1. CENTER TRIM PLATE
2. FULLY DRIVEN, SEATED AND NOT STRIPPED
3. NUT

Fig. 75 Center trim plate removal. 88 & 98

c. Remove two T-15 Torx retaining screws to CD mounting bracket, then pull player and bracket forward.
d. Remove two 10mm bracket to CD retaining nuts.
16. **On all models,** remove two front storage compartment retaining screws, then the storage compartment.
17. Remove right side sound insulator retaining screws and nuts.
18. Disconnect courtesy lamp from panel and remove sound insulator from vehicle.
19. Remove six knee bolster retaining screws, then remove bolster from vehicle.
20. Remove four steering column reinforcement plate retaining screws, then remove plate from vehicle.
21. Remove glove box door and glove box unit retaining screws.
22. Remove three upper trim pad retaining screws, then pull trim pad up and out of retaining clips to remove from vehicle, **Fig. 97.**
23. Remove lower left side instrument panel retaining bolt.
24. Remove hood release retaining screws.
25. Remove two instrument panel brace retaining screws, then the brace.
26. Remove four inflator module retaining screws located on back of steering wheel assembly.
27. Remove inflator module from vehicle.

When carrying a live inflator, ensure the bag and trim cover are pointed away in case of accidental deployment. Do not carry inflator module by wires of connector on underside of module. When placing a live inflator module on a bench or other surface, ensure the bag and trim cover faces in a upward direction. Never rest steering column assembly on the steering wheel with the inflator module face down and column vertical. This is necessary in case of accidental deployment. Otherwise, personal injury may result.

28. Disconnect ignition wiring and multi-function switch electrical connectors.
29. Remove pinch bolt from intermediate shaft.
30. Remove upper and lower steering column support brackets, then remove steering column from vehicle.
31. Remove lower right instrument panel retaining bolt and three upper instrument panel retaining screws.
32. Disconnect instrument panel electrical connectors, then remove instrument panel from vehicle, **Fig. 98**.
33. Reverse procedure to install.

ELDORADO & SEVILLE

1. Disconnect battery ground cable.
2. Remove lower instrument panel sound insulators, **Fig. 99**.
3. Remove instrument panel steering column cover, **Fig. 100**.
4. Remove four bolts attaching steering column to support bracket.
5. Remove climate control driver information center, **Fig. 101**.
6. Remove dash to instrument panel interconnect.
7. Remove glove box box module, **Fig. 102**.
8. Remove fuse panel from glove box, **Fig. 103**.
9. Disconnect instrument panel compartment electrical connector.
10. Remove instrument panel reinforcement brace, **Fig. 104**.
11. Remove six instrument panel attaching screws, then remove instrument panel, **Fig. 104**.
12. Reverse procedure to install.

CIMARRON

1. Disconnect battery ground cable.
2. Remove right and left side hush panels and lower steering column trim cover, **Fig. 105**.
3. Remove glove box and door, **Fig. 106**.
4. Disconnect temperature control cable, then remove lower A/C duct.
5. Remove three steering column mounting bolts, then lower steering column.
6. Remove right side lower trim plate, and disconnect cigar lighter and accessory switches, **Fig. 107**.
7. Pull A/C control head out far enough to disconnect wiring and vacuum harnesses, then remove head.

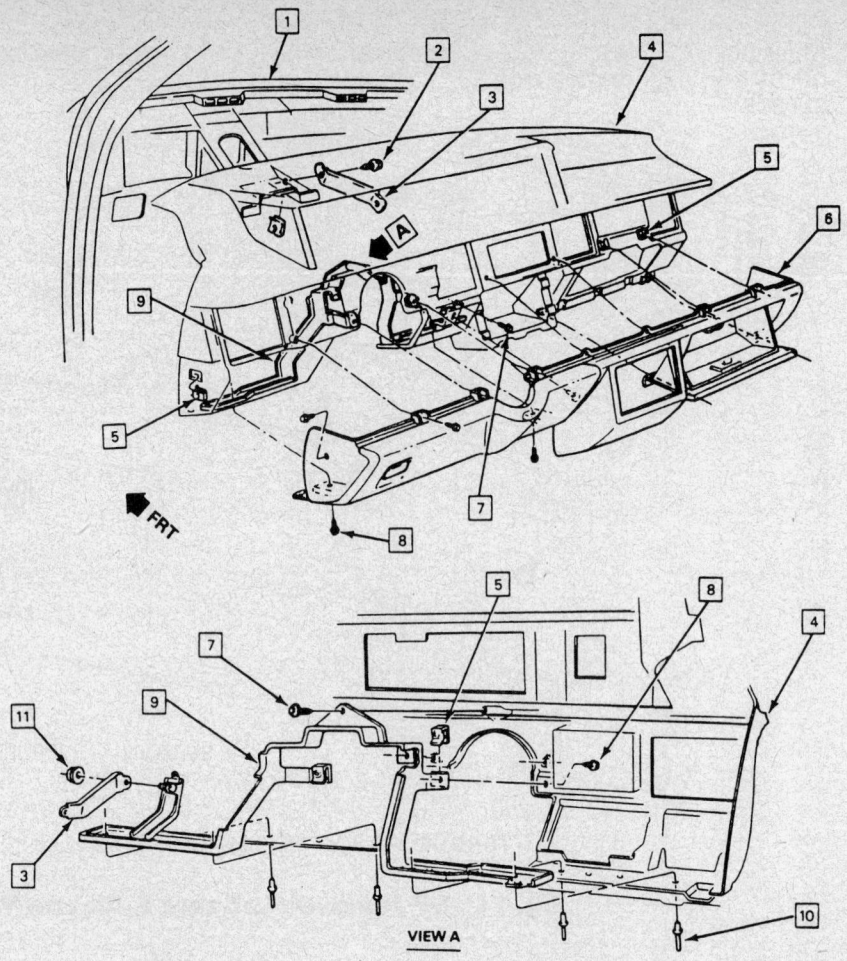

1. FRONT OF DASH	7. BOLT/SCREW; 1.4 N•M (12 LB-IN)
2. BOLT/SCREW; 5 N•M (53 LB-IN)	8. BOLT/SCREW; 1.9 N•M (17 LB-IN)
3. IP LOWER BRACE	9. IP LOWER TIE BAR ASM
4. IP ASSEMBLY	10. RIVET
5. NUT	11. NUT; 10 N•M (89 LB-IN)
6. IP LOWER TRIM PANEL ASM	

Fig. 76   Lower trim panel removal. 88 & 98

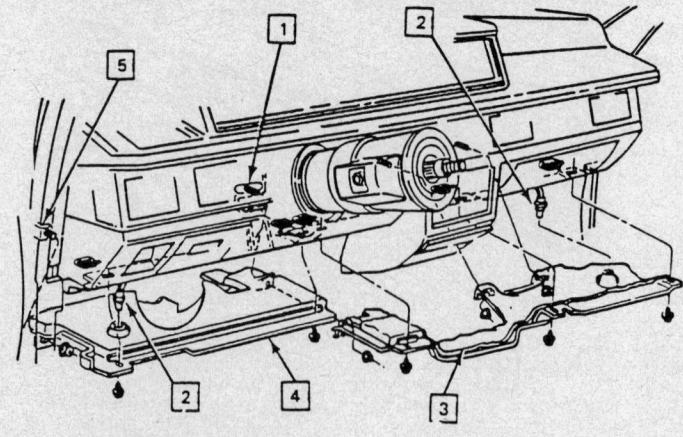

1. ACCELERATOR ASM BRACKET
2. COURTESY LIGHT
3. R. H. SOUND INSULATOR
4. L. H. SOUND INSULATOR
5. PARKING BRAKE ASM BRACKET

Fig. 77   I/P sound insulator removal. 88 & 98

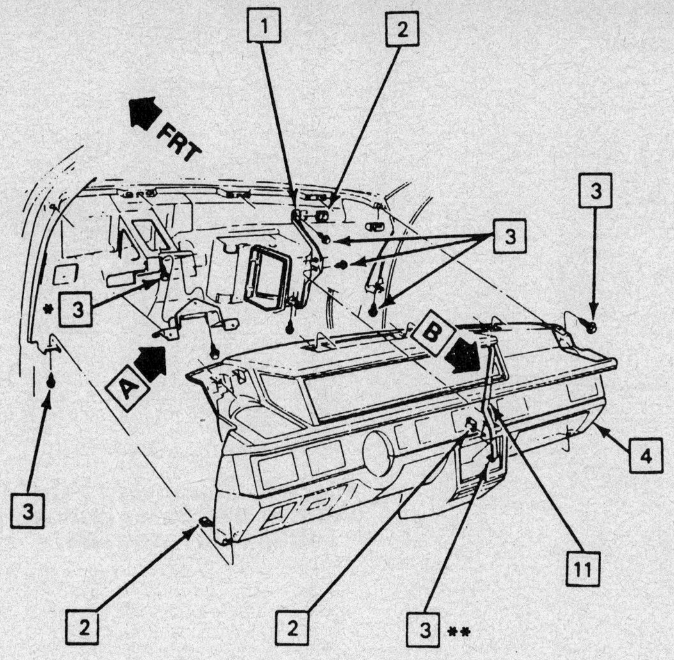

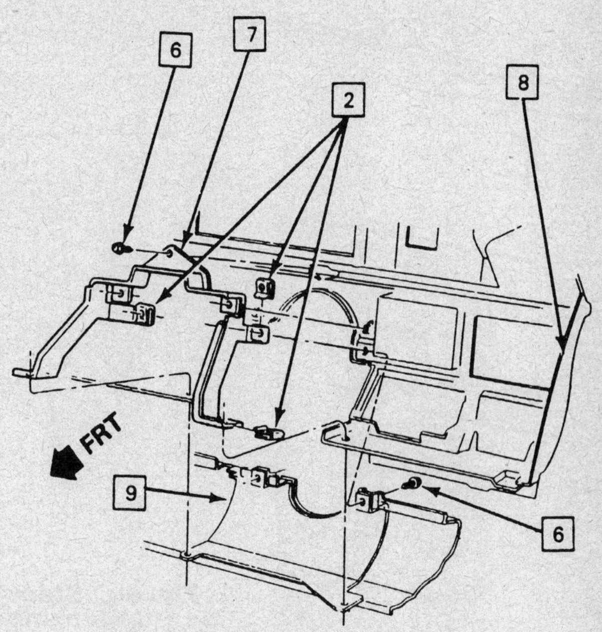

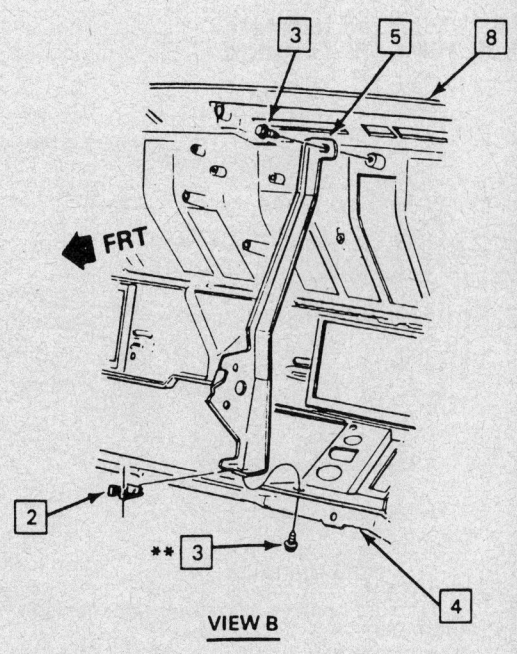

*LH BOLT/SCREW MUST BE PARTIALLY
DRIVEN INTO STEERING COL SUPPORT
BEFORE IP PAD ASM IS INSTALLED TO
DASH AND STEERING COL SUPPORT TO
SERVE AS CROSS-VEHICLE LOCATOR OF
IP.

**DO NOT FULLY DRIVE BOLT/SCREW UN-
TIL IP PAD IS INSTALLED IN CAR AND SUP-
PORT IS FASTENED TO IP CENTER
BRACKET.

1. IP CENTER BRACKET

2. NUT

3. 1.9 N•M (17LB-IN)

4. IP ASSEMBLY

5. SUPPORT

6. 1.9 N•M (17LB-IN)

7. IP LOWER TIE BAR

8. IP UPPER PAD ASM

9. REINFORCEMENT; P/O IP LOWER
   TRIM PANEL ASM

VIEW A

VIEW B

Fig. 78   Removing I/P assembly. 88 & 98

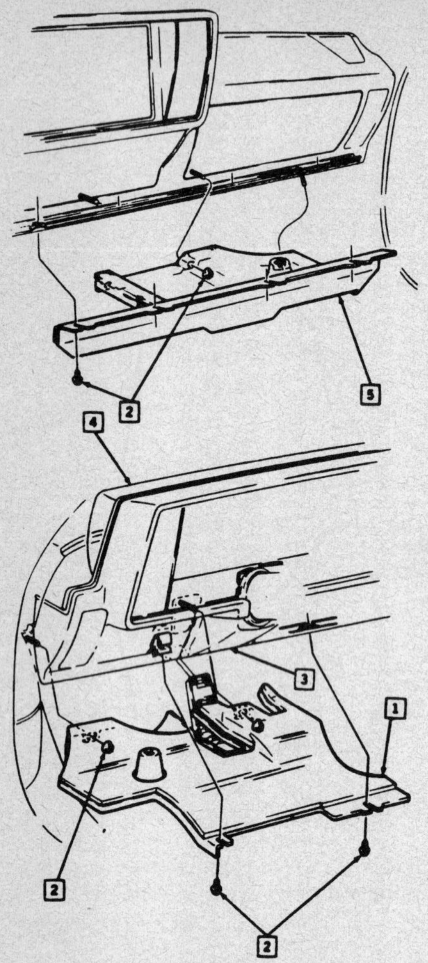

1. STEERING COLUMN FILLER AND COLLAR
2. FULLY DRIVEN, SEATED AND NOT STRIPPED
3. POSITION COLLAR AGAINST SURFACE OF MATING PARTS
4. STEERING COLUMN COLLAR

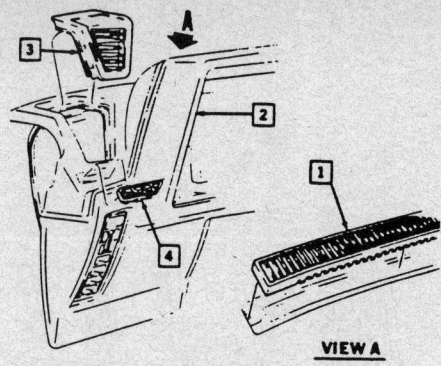

VIEW A

1. WINDSHIELD DEFROSTER NOZZLE GRILLE
2. INSTRUMENT PANEL
3. DEFLECTOR HOUSING
4. SIDE WINDOW OUTLET GRILLE

Fig. 82 Removing side window defroster grilles. 1988–89 Toronado

Fig. 80 Steering column trim cover removal. 1988–89 Toronado

1. L.H. SOUND INSULATOR
2. FULLY DRIVEN, SEATED AND NOT STRIPPED
3. STEERING COLUMN FILLER
4. I.P. ASSEMBLY
5. R.H. SOUND INSULATOR

Fig. 79 I/P sound insulator removal. 1988–89 Toronado

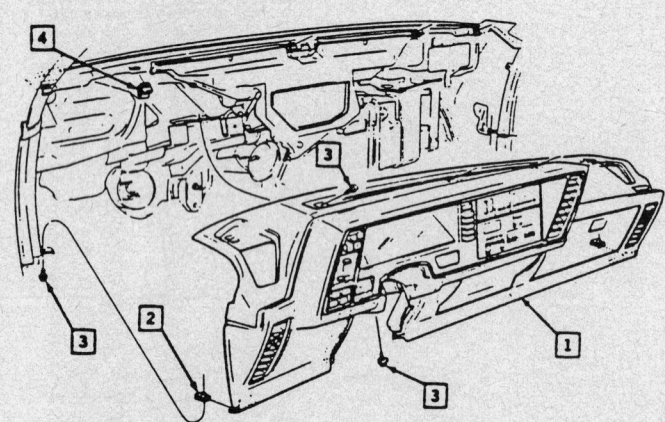

1. INSTRUMENT PANEL
2. NUT
3. FULLY DRIVEN, SEATED AND NOT STRIPPED
4. NUT

Fig. 81 I/P pad removal. 1988–89 Toronado

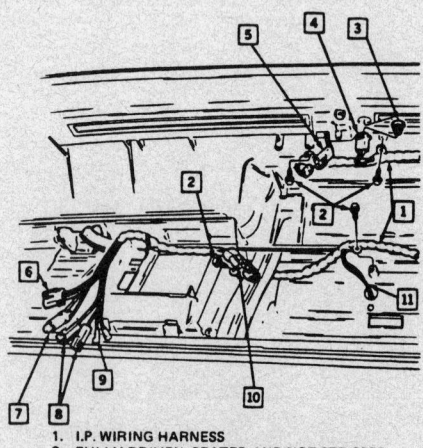

1. I.P. WIRING HARNESS
2. FULLY DRIVEN, SEATED AND NOT STRIPPED
3. PHOTO CELL SENSOR ASSEMBLY
4. TWILIGHT PHOTO SENSOR CONNECTOR
5. SUN SENSOR CONNECTOR
6. I.P. COMPARTMENT SWITCH CONNECTOR
7. I.P. COMPARTMENT LAMP
8. DECK LID CONNECTOR
9. FUEL FILLER DOOR CONNECTOR
10. AMBIENT AIR TEMP. SENSOR CONNECTOR
11. ASHTRAY LAMP AND CIGAR LIGHTER LEADS

Fig. 83 I/P wiring harness & connectors. 1988–89 Toronado

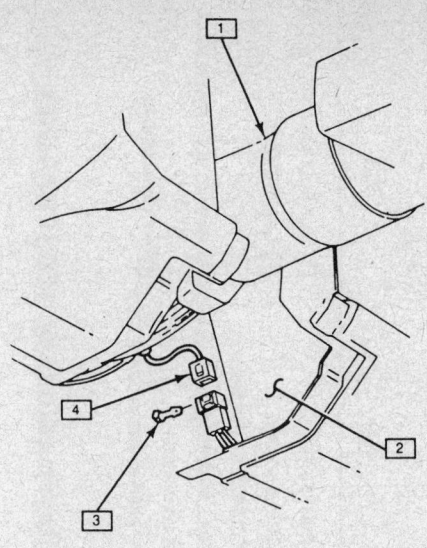

1	STEERING COLUMN ASSEMBLY
2	IP LOWER TIE BAR ASSEMBLY
3	CONNECTOR POSITION ASSURANCE (CPA)
4	YELLOW SIR HARNESS CONNECTOR

Fig. 84 Disconnecting two-way SIR harness connector. 1990 Toronado

8. Disconnect forward lamp harness and engine harness from bulkhead connector in engine compartment, then remove bulkhead connector from cowl.
9. Remove hood release handle, then unscrew cable retaining nut and push hood release cable through instrument panel.
10. Remove four upper instrument panel retaining screws located in defroster duct openings.
11. Remove screw securing twilight sentinel photocell.
12. Remove two lower corner instrument panel retaining nuts.
13. Remove screw attaching instrument panel to instrument panel brace located at left side of glove box opening.
14. Pull instrument panel assembly rearward enough to disconnect ignition switch, headlight dimmer switch and turn signal switch.
15. Disconnect all other electrical wiring, vacuum lines and radio antenna.
16. Remove instrument panel with wiring harness attached.
17. Reverse procedure to install.

FIRENZA, SKYHAWK, 1988–89 CAVALIER & SUNBIRD

1. Remove six screws attaching steering column trim cover to instrument panel.
2. Remove two screws attaching steering column trim cover to left hand in-

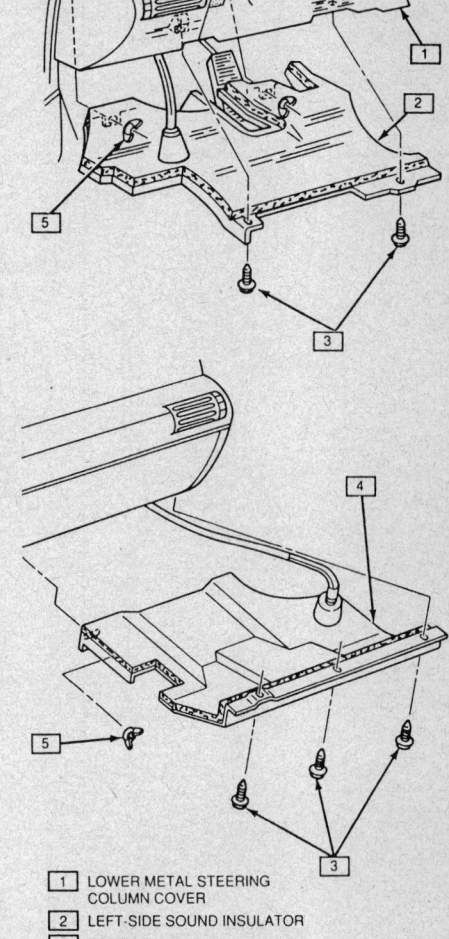

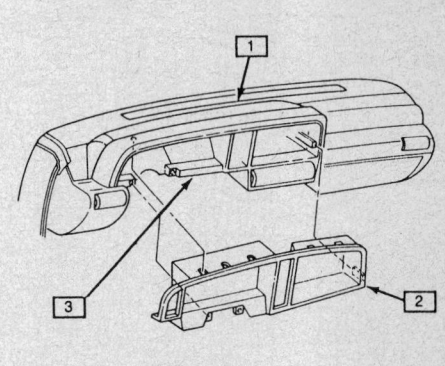

1	LOWER METAL STEERING COLUMN COVER
2	LEFT-SIDE SOUND INSULATOR
3	SCREWS
4	RIGHT-SIDE SOUND INSULATOR
5	WING NUTS

Fig. 85 Removing sound insulators. 1990 Toronado

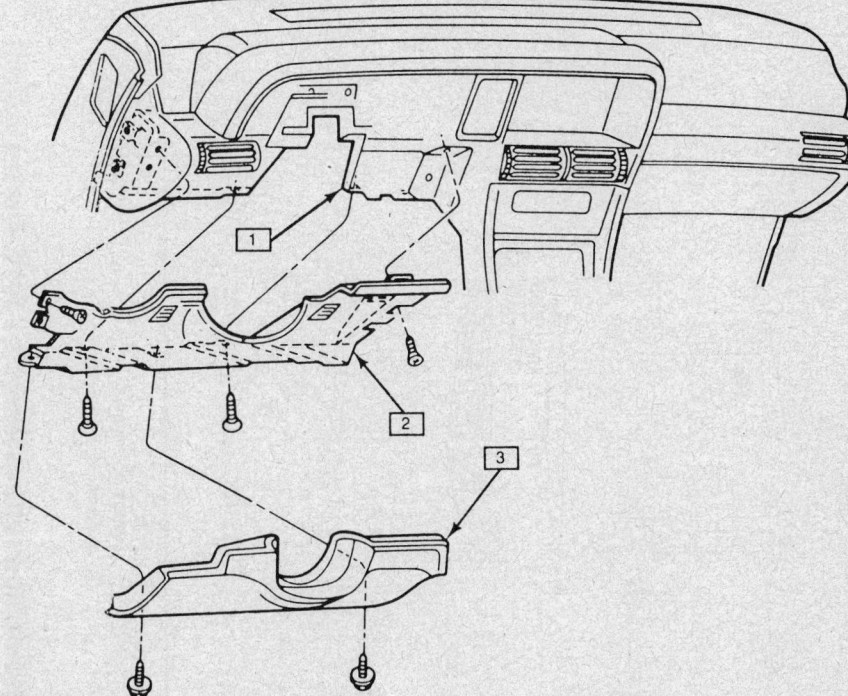

1	I/P PAD
2	I/P STEERING COLUMN REINFORCEMENT PLATE
3	KNEE BOLSTER

Fig. 86 Removing knee bolster. 1990 Toronado

1	I/P PAD
2	I/P CLUSTER TRIM PLATE
3	I/P CLUSTER HOUSING (CLUSTER REMOVED)

Fig. 87 Removing I/P cluster trim plate. 1990 Toronado

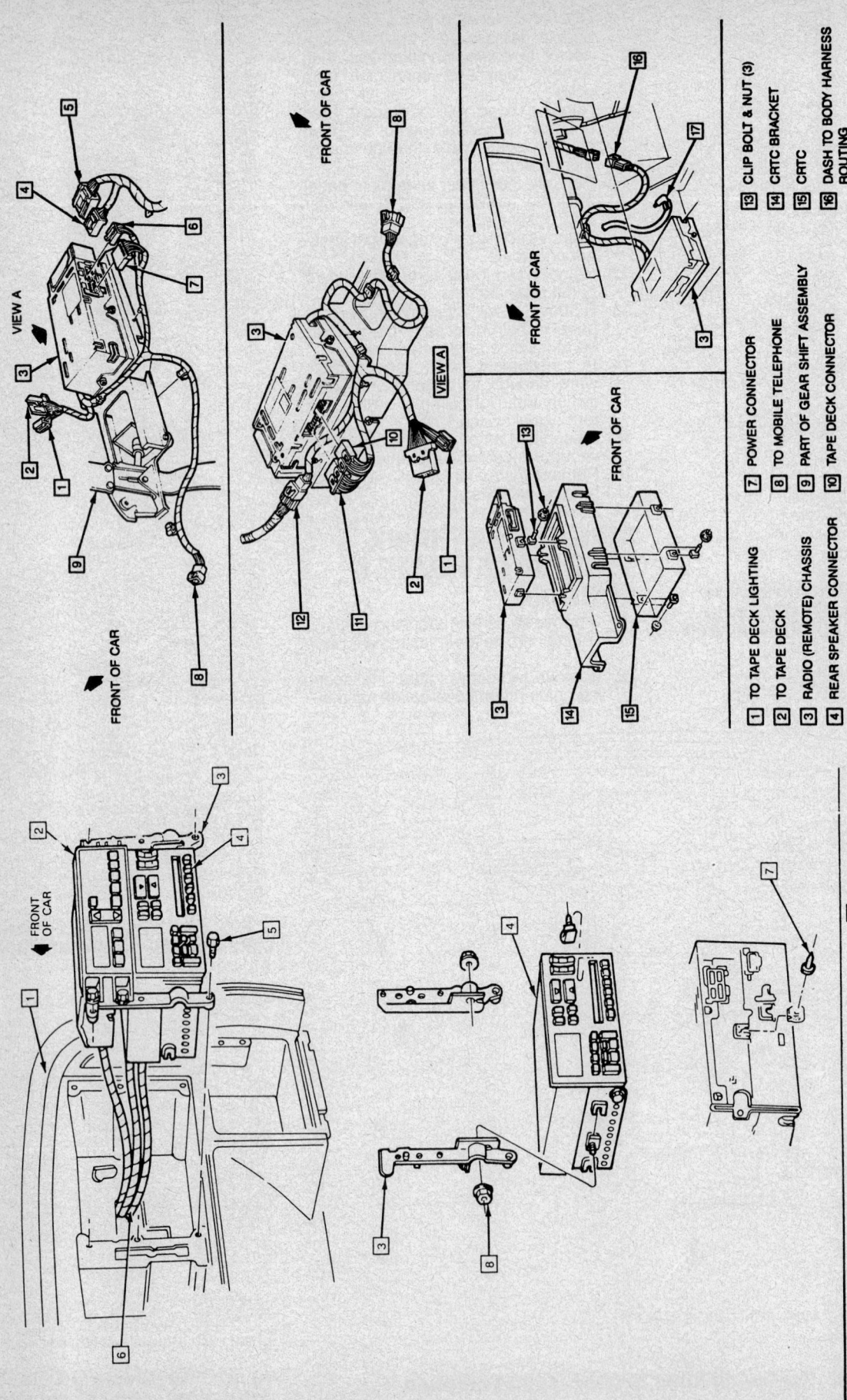

Fig. 88 Removing radio assembly. 1990 Toronado

1	INSTRUMENT PANEL	4	RADIO
2	ECC HEAD	5	MOUNTING SCREWS
3	MOUNTING BRACKET	6	ELECTRICAL CONNECTORS
		7	REAR LOCATING PIN
		8	BRACKET NUT

Fig. 89 Removing C/D player assembly. 1990 Toronado

1	TO TAPE DECK LIGHTING	7	POWER CONNECTOR	13	CLIP BOLT & NUT (3)
2	TO TAPE DECK	8	TO MOBILE TELEPHONE	14	CRTC BRACKET
3	RADIO (REMOTE) CHASSIS	9	PART OF GEAR SHIFT ASSEMBLY	15	CRTC
4	REAR SPEAKER CONNECTOR	10	TAPE DECK CONNECTOR	16	DASH TO BODY HARNESS ROUTING
5	FRONT SPEAKER CONNECTOR	11	E&C BUS CONNECTOR	17	ANTENNA LEAD-IN
6	TO PHONE AUDIO (WITH UZ3)	12	RADIO TO DASH HARNESS CONNECTOR		

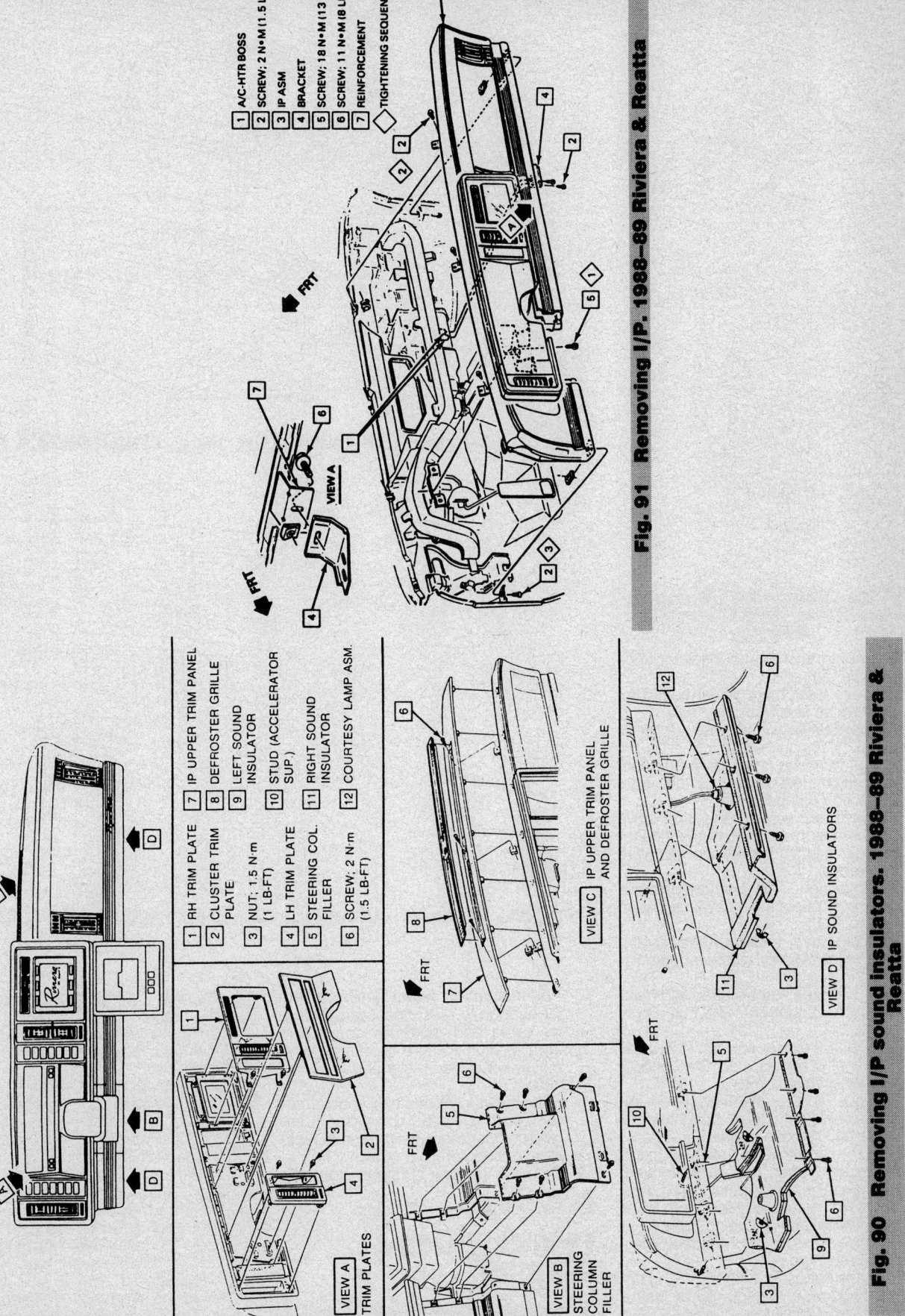

Key for Fig. 91:

1. A/C-HTR BOSS
2. SCREW: 2 N•M (1.5 LB-FT)
3. IP ASM
4. BRACKET
5. SCREW: 18 N•M (13 LB-FT)
6. SCREW: 11 N•M (8 LB-FT)
7. REINFORCEMENT
◇ TIGHTENING SEQUENCE

Fig. 91 Removing I/P. 1988–89 Riviera & Reatta

Key for Fig. 90:

1. RH TRIM PLATE
2. CLUSTER TRIM PLATE
3. NUT: 1.5 N•m (1 LB-FT)
4. LH TRIM PLATE
5. STEERING COL. FILLER
6. SCREW: 2 N•m (1.5 LB-FT)
7. IP UPPER TRIM PANEL
8. DEFROSTER GRILLE
9. LEFT SOUND INSULATOR
10. STUD (ACCELERATOR SUP.)
11. RIGHT SOUND INSULATOR
12. COURTESY LAMP ASM.

VIEW A TRIM PLATES

VIEW B STEERING COLUMN FILLER

VIEW C IP UPPER TRIM PANEL AND DEFROSTER GRILLE

VIEW D IP SOUND INSULATORS

Fig. 90 Removing I/P sound insulators. 1988–89 Riviera & Reatta

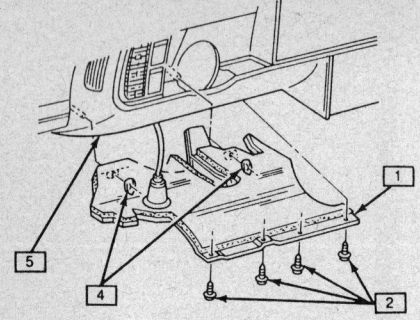

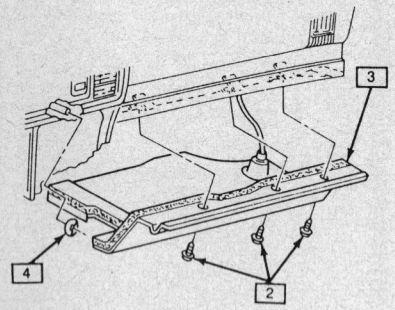

1. LEFT-SIDE SOUND INSULATOR
2. SCREWS
3. RIGHT-SIDE SOUND INSULATOR
4. WING NUTS
5. KNEE BOLSTER

Fig. 92 Removing I/P sound insulators. 1990 Riviera & Reatta

strument panel sound insulator, then remove trim cover.

3. Remove instrument panel sound insulators as shown in **Fig. 108.**
4. **On models with A/C,** remove heater outlet.
5. **On all models,** open glove box door and disconnect stop strap clip from glove box compartment.
6. Remove four screws attaching glove box compartment to instrument panel.
7. Pull glove box compartment rearward to remove.
8. Remove right side instrument panel trim cover attaching screws as shown in **Fig. 109.**
9. Pull trim cover rearward and disconnect all necessary electrical connectors.
10. Remove three screws attaching heater and A/C control to the instrument panel.
11. Pull control out far enough to disconnect control cables, electrical connectors and vacuum lines.
12. Remove screw attaching hood release cable handle to hood release cable and remove handle.
13. Unscrew nut holding cable to instrument panel, then pull cable forward through instrument panel to remove.
14. Remove two upper, and one lower steering column attaching bolts.
15. Remove two lower corner instrument panel retaining nuts.
16. Remove defroster grille by pulling upward and removing four upper instrument panel retaining screws.

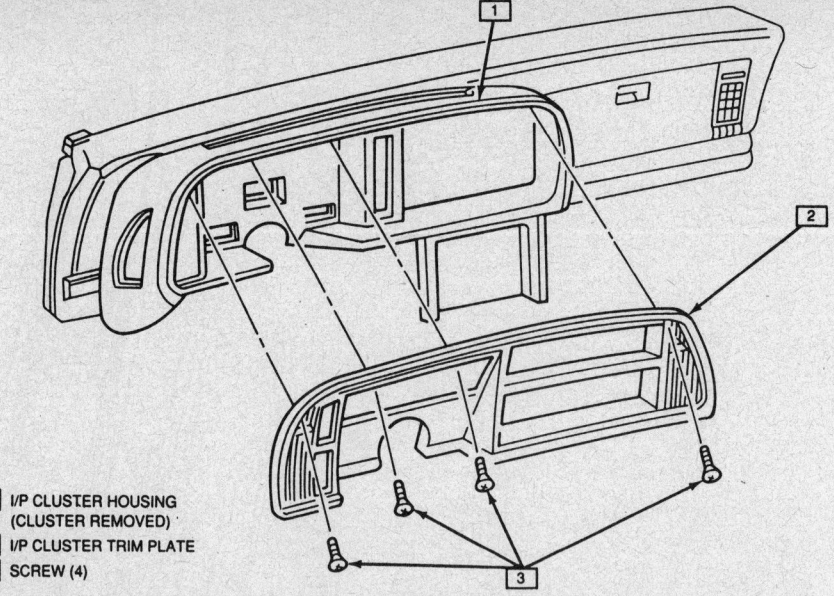

1. I/P CLUSTER HOUSING (CLUSTER REMOVED)
2. I/P CLUSTER TRIM PLATE
3. SCREW (4)

Fig. 93 Removing I/P cluster trim plate. 1990 Riviera & Reatta

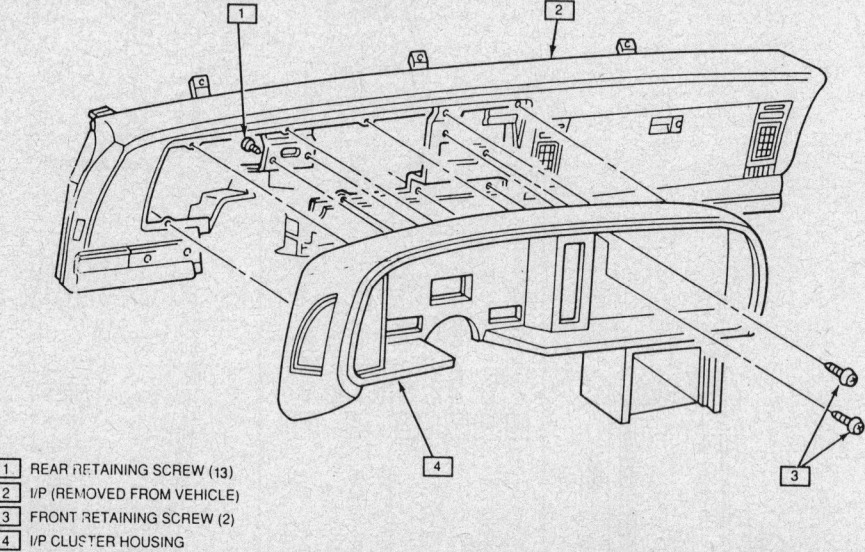

1. REAR RETAINING SCREW (13)
2. I/P (REMOVED FROM VEHICLE)
3. FRONT RETAINING SCREW (2)
4. I/P CLUSTER HOUSING

Fig. 94 Removing I/P cluster housing. 1990 Riviera & Reatta

17. Pull instrument panel assembly out far enough to disconnect speedometer cable and electrical connectors from ignition switch, headlamp dimmer switch and turn signal switch, **Fig. 110.**
18. Disconnect front end and engine harness from bulkhead connector in engine compartment, then remove bulkhead connector from cowl.
19. Remove instrument panel from the vehicle.
20. Reverse procedure to install.

1990 CAVALIER & SUNBIRD

1. Disconnect battery ground cable.

2. Remove right and left sound insulators, **Figs. 111 and 112.**
3. Lower steering column trim cover.
4. Remove instrument panel compartment door.
5. Remove lower A/C duct.
6. Remove three steering column retaining bolts, then lower steering column.
7. **On Z24 models,** remove console assembly as follows:
   a. Place transmission in the Neutral position and set parking brake.
   b. **On models with automatic transmission,** remove shifter knob horse shoe retaining clip.
   c. **On models with manual transmission,** remove shift knob set screw, then the shift knob.
   d. **On all models,** remove console

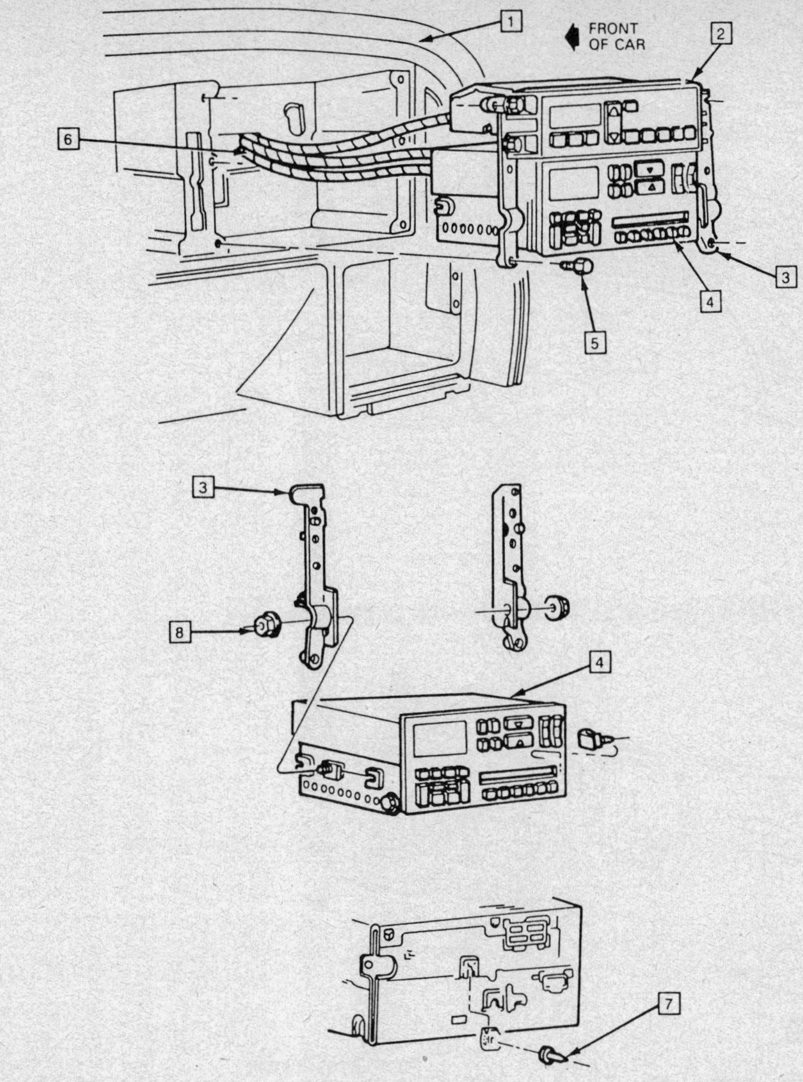

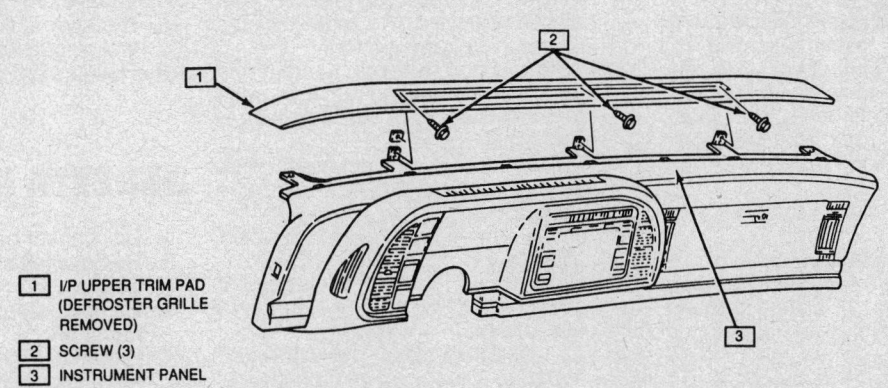

1	INSTRUMENT PANEL	4	RADIO	7	REAR LOCATING PIN
2	ECC HEAD	5	MOUNTING SCREWS	3	BRACKET NUT
3	MOUNTING BRACKET	6	ELECTRICAL CONNECTORS		

Fig. 95   Removing radio assembly. 1990 Riviera & Reatta

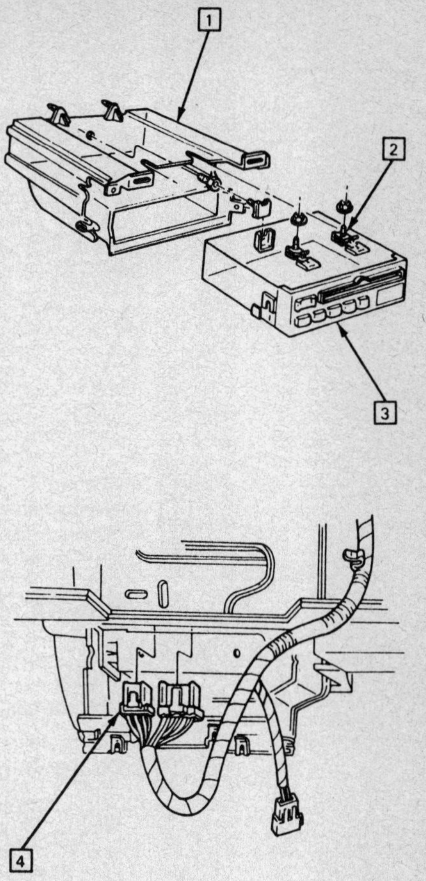

1	MOUNTING BRACKET
2	CLIP STUDS AND NUTS
3	REMOTE UNIT
4	ELECTRICAL CONNECTOR

Fig. 96   Removing CD player assembly. 1990 Riviera & Reatta

1	I/P UPPER TRIM PAD (DEFROSTER GRILLE REMOVED)
2	SCREW (3)
3	INSTRUMENT PANEL

Fig. 97   Removing I/P trim pad assembly. 1990 Riviera & Reatta

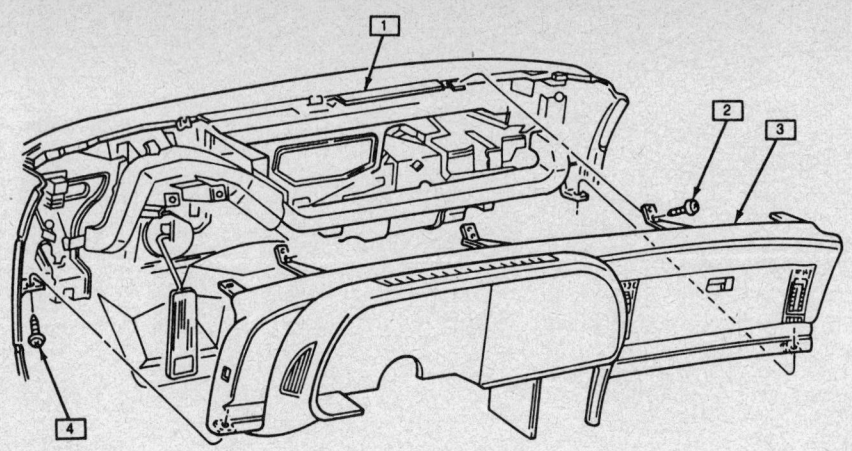

1. FRONT COWL
2. UPPER MOUNTING SCREWS
3. INSTRUMENT PANEL
4. LOWER MOUNTING BOLTS

Fig. 98   Removing I/P assembly. 1990 Riviera & Reatta

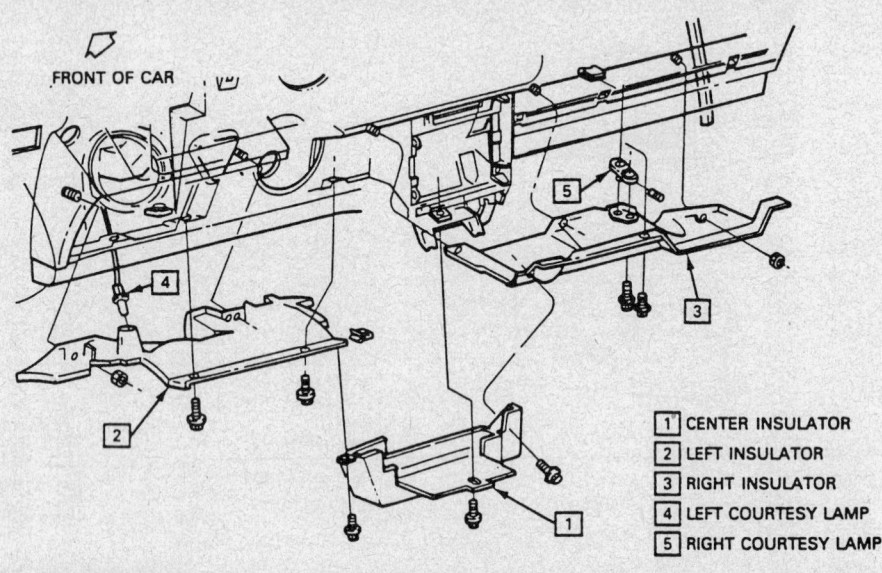

1. CENTER INSULATOR
2. LEFT INSULATOR
3. RIGHT INSULATOR
4. LEFT COURTESY LAMP
5. RIGHT COURTESY LAMP

Fig. 99   Removing I/P sound insulators. Eldorado & Seville

front trim plate.
  e. Remove two console to instrument panel bracket retaining screws.
  f. Remove rear console ashtray and two trim plate to retaining screws.
  g. Remove console upper trim plate.
  h. Remove two front and rear console to mounting bracket retaining screws.
  i. Remove console to wiring harness and radio.
  j. Remove console from vehicle.
8. On all models, remove right hand lower trim plate, **Fig. 113,** then disconnect cigar lighter and accessory switches.
9. Pull A/C control head out from I/P enough to disconnect wiring and vacuum harnesses, then remove head.
10. Disconnect forward lamp harness and engine harness from bulkhead connector in engine compartment, then

remove bulkhead connector from cowl by removing two retaining nuts in the engine compartment.
11. Remove hood release handle and hood release retaining nut, then push hood release cable through instrument panel.
12. Remove four upper instrument panel retaining screws located in defroster duct openings.
13. Remove two lower corner instrument panel retaining nuts, **Fig. 114.**
14. Remove one screw to instrument panel brace at left side of instrument panel compartment opening.
15. Pull instrument panel assembly out enough to disconnect ignition switch, headlight dimmer switch and turn signal switch electrical connectors.
16. Disconnect vacuum hoses and remaining electrical connectors.
17. Disconnect leads from instrument

panel to PRNDL and ashtray lamps.
18. Remove instrument panel assembly with wiring harness attached.
19. Reverse procedure to install.

BERETTA & CORSICA

1. Disconnect battery ground cable.
2. Remove left side sound insulator, **Fig. 115.**
3. Remove steering column trim cover, **Fig. 116.**
4. Remove three steering column mounting bolts, then lower steering column.
5. Disconnect electrical connectors from the steering column.
6. Remove two instrument cluster trim panel attaching screws.

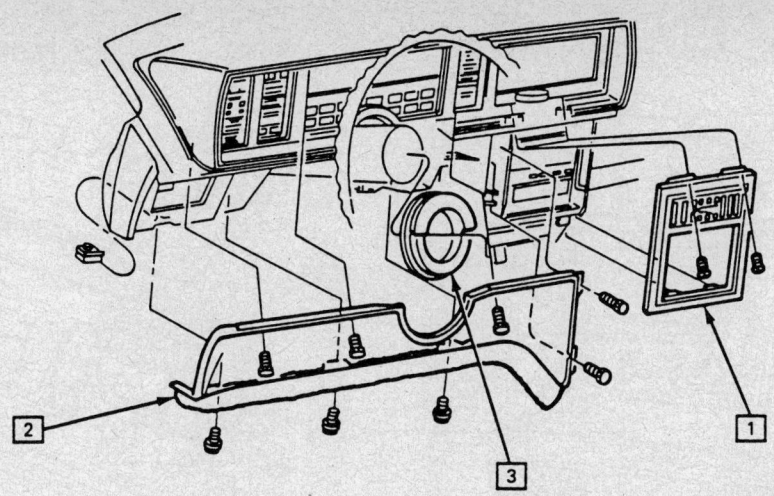

| 1 | CENTER TRIM PLATE | 2 | INSTRUMENT PANEL STEERING COLUMN COVER | 3 | COLLAR |

Fig. 100 Steering column cover removal. Eldorado & Seville

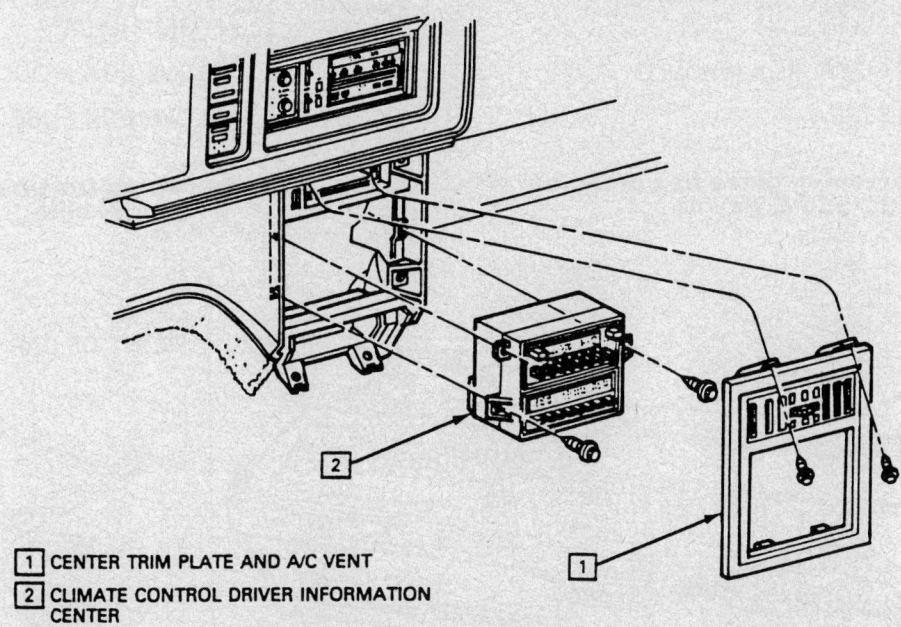

1 | CENTER TRIM PLATE AND A/C VENT
2 | CLIMATE CONTROL DRIVER INFORMATION CENTER

Fig. 101 Removing climate control driver information center. Eldorado & Seville

7. Disconnect electrical connectors from trim panel, then remove trim panel.
8. Remove four instrument cluster retaining screws, then the cluster.
9. **On Beretta models,** remove two accessory trim panel attaching screws, then pull on bottom of trim plate to release tabs at the top, **Fig. 117.**
10. **On Corsica models,** pull bottom of trim plate to release tabs at the top, **Fig. 118.**
11. Remove two accessory center attaching screws located at the top of the assembly.
12. Remove two screws from underside of the assembly, then pull assembly away outward.
13. **On models with A/C,** proceed as follows:
    a. Disconnect two clips from vacuum valve on right rear of assembly.
    b. Disconnect vacuum hose assembly from vacuum valve.
14. **On models less A/C,** remove two cables from control assembly.
15. **On all models,** disconnect antenna connector from right rear of sound system.
16. Disconnect electrical connectors from left rear of accessory center assembly, then remove assembly.
17. Remove right side sound insulator, **Fig. 119.**
18. Open glove compartment door and remove four compartment attaching screws, slide assembly outward.
19. Reaching through glove compartment opening, disconnect electrical connectors and antenna located behind right side of instrument panel.
20. Remove four instrument panel left side compartment to instrument panel attaching bolts, slide compartment outward.
21. Reaching through left side compartment opening, disconnect electrical connectors from fuse block.
22. Using a small screwdriver push in on defroster grille retaining clips, and remove grille.
23. Remove speaker covers by prying

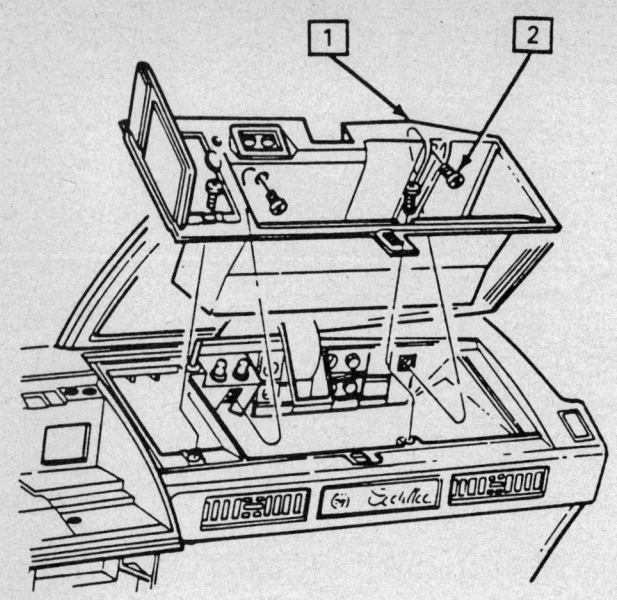

1 GLOVE BOX MODULE
2 SCREW

Fig. 102   Removing glove box module. Eldorado & Seville

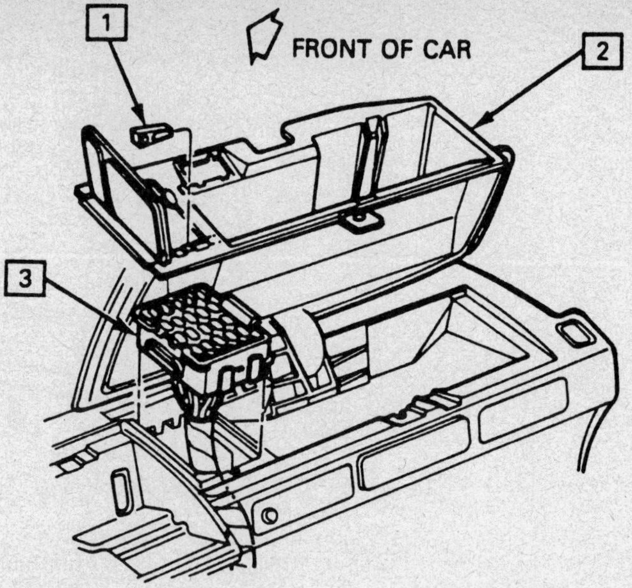

1 FUSE PULLER
2 GLOVE BOX MODULE
3 GLOVE BOX FUSE PANEL

Fig. 103   Removing fuse panel. Eldorado & Seville

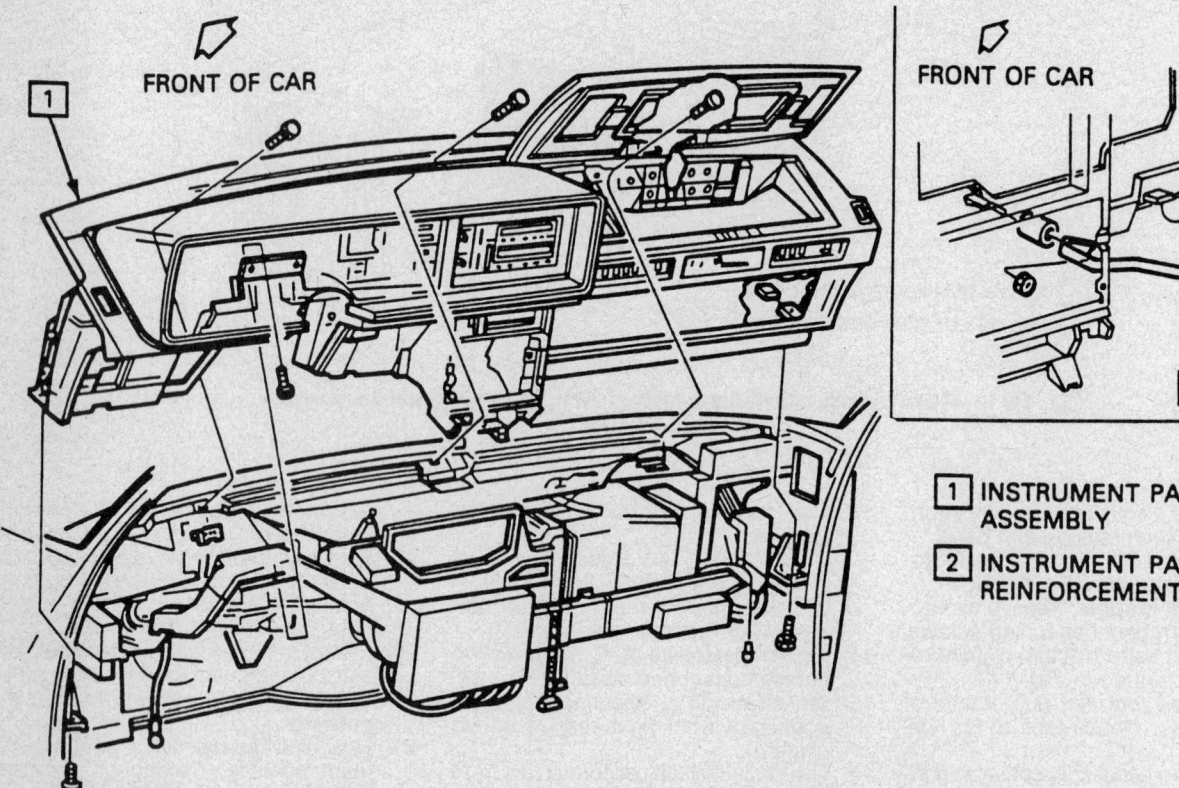

1 INSTRUMENT PANEL ASSEMBLY
2 INSTRUMENT PANEL REINFORCEMENT BRACE

Fig. 104   Removing I/P. Eldorado & Seville

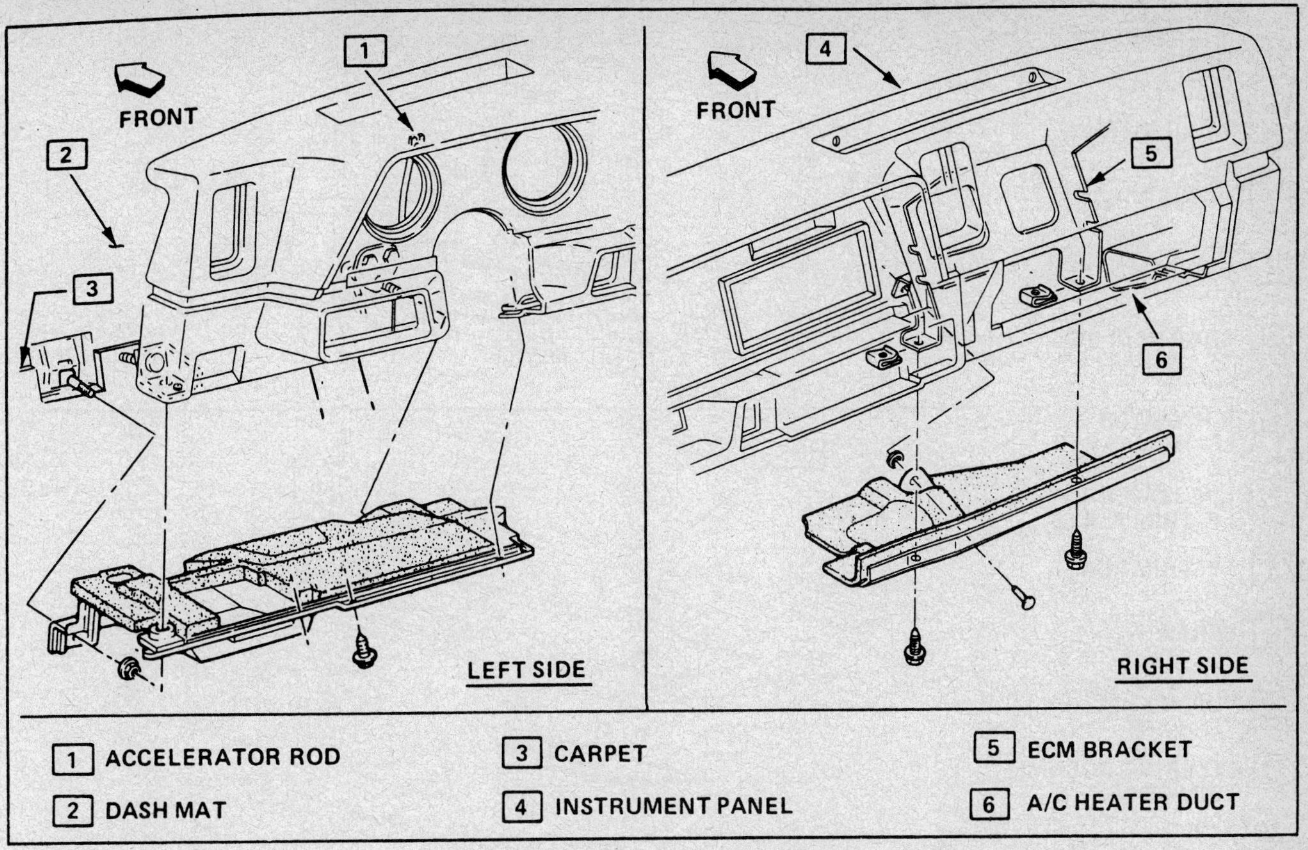

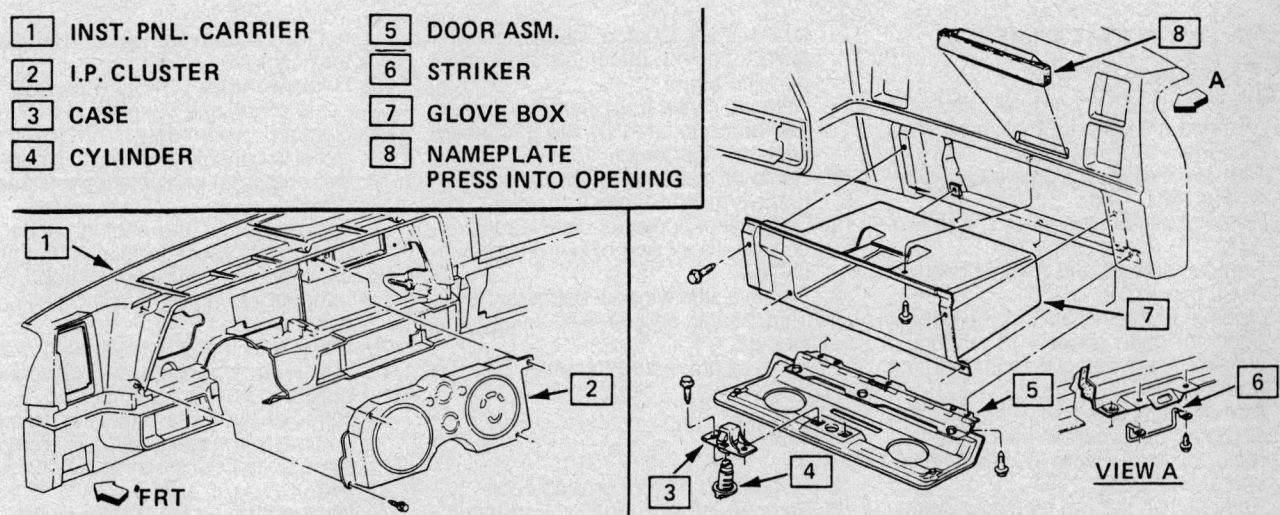

FRONT
1
2
3
4
5
6
LEFT SIDE
RIGHT SIDE
1 ACCELERATOR ROD
2 DASH MAT
3 CARPET
4 INSTRUMENT PANEL
5 ECM BRACKET
6 A/C HEATER DUCT

Fig. 105 Removing hush panels. Cimarron

1 INST. PNL. CARRIER
2 I.P. CLUSTER
3 CASE
4 CYLINDER
5 DOOR ASM.
6 STRIKER
7 GLOVE BOX
8 NAMEPLATE
PRESS INTO OPENING
A
FRT
VIEW A

Fig. 106 Cluster & glove box removal. Cimarron

two spring clips carefully with a small screwdriver.

24. Reaching under the instrument panel, remove cover from junction block.
25. Raise engine compartment hood and remove cover from junction block located on left side of cowl.
26. Remove two junction block retaining nuts, then the one bolt from center of junction block.
27. Reaching under the instrument panel, disconnect junction block from cowl.
28. Disconnect electrical connector from lower left side of heater module.
29. Remove two nuts holding wiring harness to cowl.
30. Remove four instrument panel attaching bolts from speaker and defroster openings, **Fig. 120.**
31. Remove two instrument panel attaching bolts located on the left and right sides of the instrument panel.
32. Remove instrument panel from the vehicle.

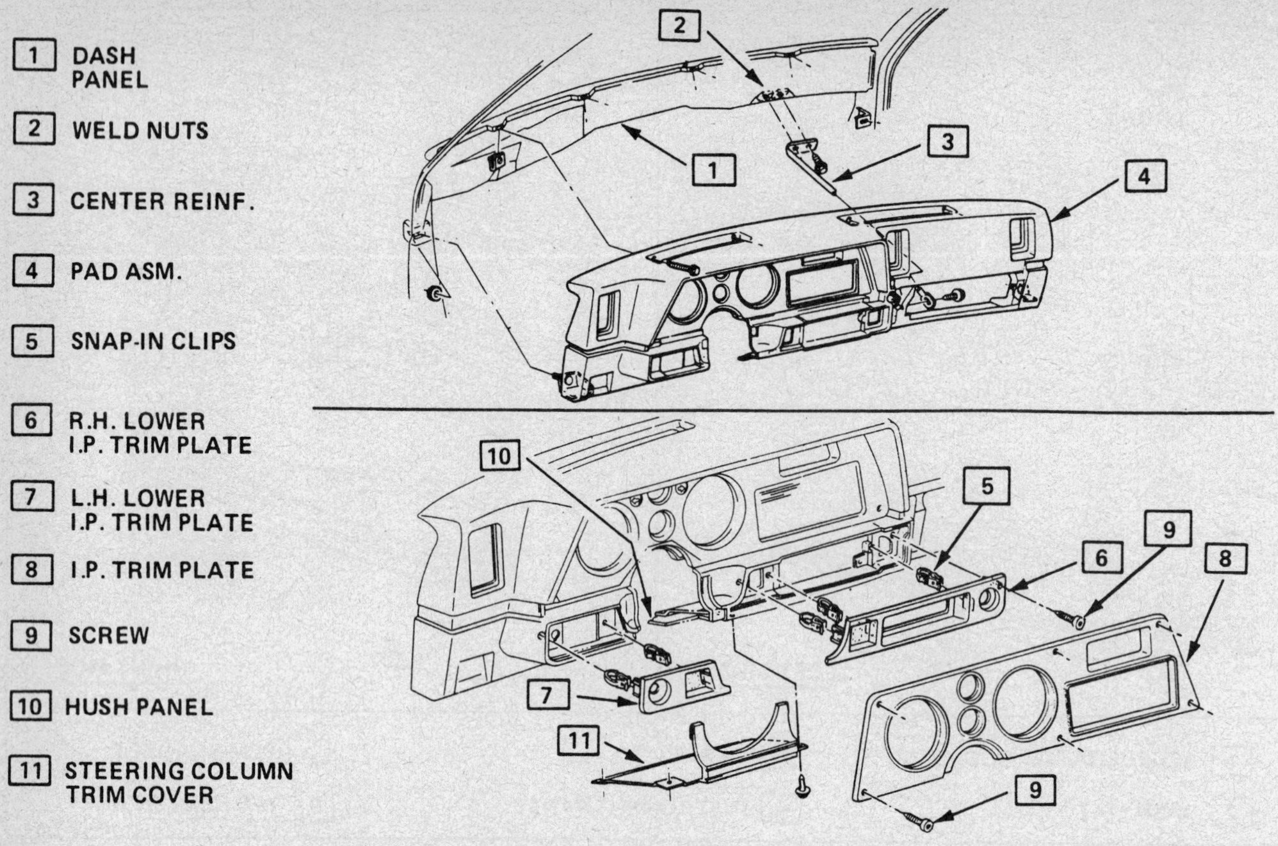

1. DASH PANEL
2. WELD NUTS
3. CENTER REINF.
4. PAD ASM.
5. SNAP-IN CLIPS
6. R.H. LOWER I.P. TRIM PLATE
7. L.H. LOWER I.P. TRIM PLATE
8. I.P. TRIM PLATE
9. SCREW
10. HUSH PANEL
11. STEERING COLUMN TRIM COVER

Fig. 107 I/P & trim plate removal. Cimarron

33. Reverse procedure to install.

SKYLARK

1. Disconnect battery ground cable.
2. Remove left and right sound insulators, **Figs. 121 and 122.**
3. Remove steering column opening filler, **Fig. 123.**
4. Remove center cluster trim plate, **Fig. 124.**
5. Remove screws and then disconnect ALCL connector.
6. Open instrument panel compartment door to gain access to attaching screws, then remove compartment from panel.
7. Remove right side trim plate, **Fig. 124.**
8. Remove lower center trim plate and radio, disconnecting electrical leads and antenna, **Fig. 125.**
9. Remove two screws attaching instrument panel to console bracket.
10. Remove two nuts from instrument panel to cowl, **Fig. 126.**
11. Loosen ¼ inch screws and unplug connector under instrument panel.
12. Open hood and disconnect bulkhead connector, **Fig. 127.**
13. Remove two nuts attaching steering column harness to cowl, **Fig. 128.**
14. Remove three steering column support attaching bolts.
15. Unplug high beam dimmer switch, ignition switch, turn signal, brake light, TCC, cruise and clutch start connectors.
16. Remove defroster grilles, then remove

four screws located inside defroster grille opening attaching instrument panel to top of cowl.
17. Remove screw from instrument panel pad brace located by the instrument panel compartment.
18. Remove instrument panel pad, then remove antenna lead from pad.
19. Disconnect body electrical lead located on the right side of instrument panel.
20. Remove side window defroster hoses from heater and or A/C evaporator module.
21. Reverse procedure to install.

CALAIS

1. Disconnect battery ground cable.
2. Remove left and right sound insulators, **Figs. 129 and 130.**
3. Remove steering column opening filler and cluster trim plate.
4. Remove screws, and then disconnect ALCL connector.
5. Open instrument panel compartment door, remove compartment attaching screws and then remove compartment.
6. Remove right side trim plate by pulling rearward, **Fig. 131.**
7. Remove lower center trim plate.
8. Remove heater and A/C controls, **Fig. 132.**
9. Pulling control head rearward, disconnect both illumination bulbs, blower switch connector, rotary switch con-

nector, vacuum harness and temperature cable.
10. Remove radio, disconnecting electrical and antenna connections.
11. Remove two screws from instrument panel to console bracket, then remove two nuts from instrument panel pad to cowl.
12. Loosen screw and unplug connector under instrument panel compartment.
13. Open engine compartment hood, then remove two nuts attaching bulkhead connector.
14. Using a ¼ inch socket loosen bolt of bulkhead connector, and disconnect bulkhead connector, **Fig. 133.**
15. Remove two nuts attaching steering column harness to cowl, then remove three bolts from steering column support.
16. Unplug high beam dimmer switch, ignition switch, turn signal, brake light, TCC, cruise and clutch start connectors, **Fig. 134.**
17. Remove defroster grilles, then remove four instrument panel to top of cowl attaching screws located in defroster grille opening.
18. Remove screw attaching instrument panel pad to brace located near instrument panel compartment, **Fig. 135.**
19. Pull instrument panel pad rearward and disconnect antenna lead and body electrical lead located on right side of instrument panel.
20. Disconnect side window defroster

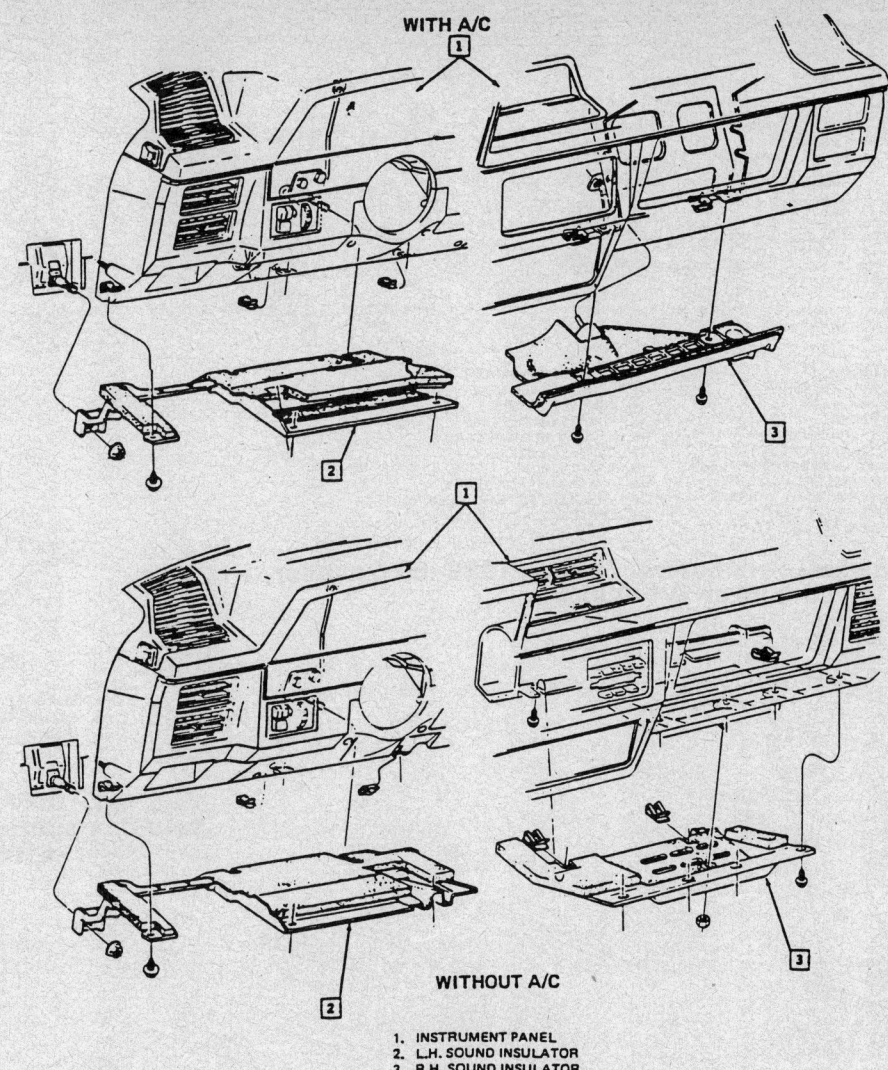

WITH A/C

WITHOUT A/C

1. INSTRUMENT PANEL
2. L.H. SOUND INSULATOR
3. R.H. SOUND INSULATOR

Fig. 108   I/P sound insulators removal. Firenza 1988–89 Cavalier, Skyhawk & Sunbird

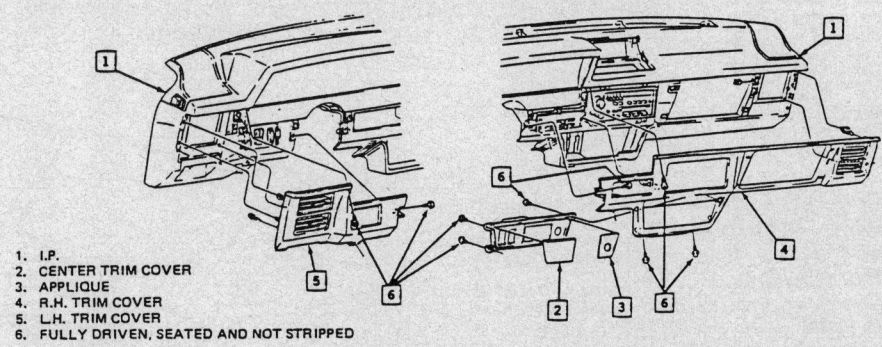

1. I.P.
2. CENTER TRIM COVER
3. APPLIQUE
4. R.H. TRIM COVER
5. L.H. TRIM COVER
6. FULLY DRIVEN, SEATED AND NOT STRIPPED

Fig. 109   Removing I/P trim covers. Firenza 1988–89 Cavalier, Skyhawk & Sunbird

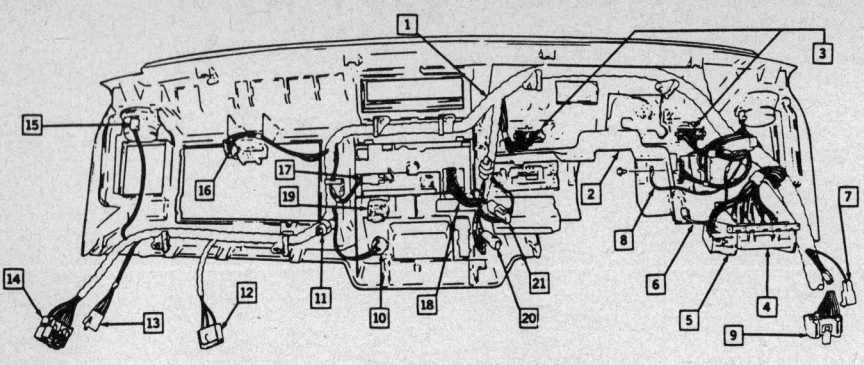

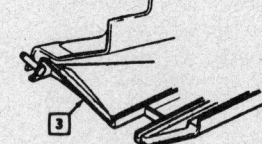

1. I.P. HARNESS
2. I.P. LOWER TIE BAR
3. CLUSTER LEADS
4. FUSE PANEL
5. A.L.D.L. CONNECTOR
6. TURN SIGNAL FLASHER LEAD
7. REAR WINDOW DEFOGGER LEAD
8. I.P. HARNESS GROUND WIRE
9. CONNECT TO BODY HARNESS
10. CIGAR LIGHTER LEAD
11. TAILGATE RELEASE LEAD
12. CONSOLE CONNECTOR
13. REAR SPEAKER LEAD
14. CONNECT TO ECM
15. R.H. SPEAKER LEADS
16. I.P. COMPARTMENT LEAD
17. DIGITAL CLOCK LEAD
18. RADIO WIRING
19. POWER ANTENNA RELAY
20. VEHICLE SPEED SENSOR LEAD
21. HEATER OR A/C LEAD

Fig. 110   I/P electrical connectors. Firenza 1988–89 Cavalier, Skyhawk & Sunbird

SECTION A-A

1. BRACKET, SOUND INSULATOR
2. A/C HEATER DUCT
3. INSULATOR
4. SCREW – 2 N·m (17 LBS. IN.)
5. NUT

Fig. 111   Removing right side sound insulator. 1990 Cavalier & Sunbird

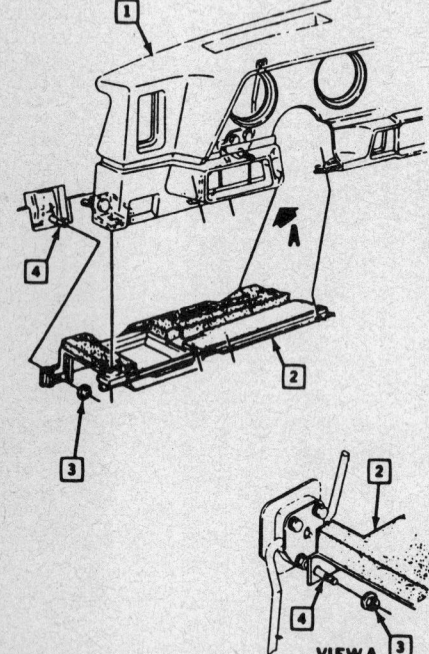

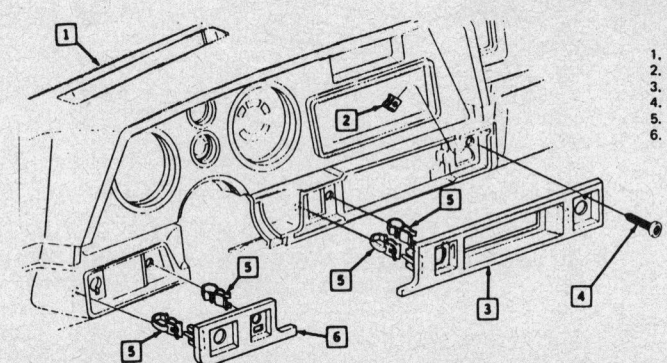

1. INSTRUMENT PANEL
2. NUT
3. PLATE ASM., RIGHT TRIM
4. SCREW – 1.9 N·m (17 LBS. IN.)
5. RETAINER
6. PLATE ASM., LEFT TRIM

Fig. 113   Removing lower trim plate assembly. 1990 Cavalier & Sunbird

VIEW A

1. INSTRUMENT PANEL
2. SOUND INSULATOR – LEFT SIDE
3. NUT – 1.4 N·m (12 LBS. IN.)
4. BOLT

Fig. 112   Removing left side sound insulator. 1990 Cavalier & Sunbird

hoses from heater and/or A/C module.
21. Reverse procedure to install.

GRAND AM

1. Disconnect battery ground cable.
2. Remove left side hush panel, steering column filler panel and right side hush panel, Fig. 136.
3. Remove instrument cluster trim plate.
4. Remove three bolts from steering column mounting bracket.

1. SCREW – 10 N·m (89 LBS. IN.)
2. INSTRUMENT PANEL
3. SCREW – 2 N·m (17 LBS. IN.)
4. SUPPORT, I.P. CENTER
5. NUT
6. SCREW – 1 N·m (12 LBS. IN.)
7. 10 N·m (89 LBS. IN.)
8. NUT

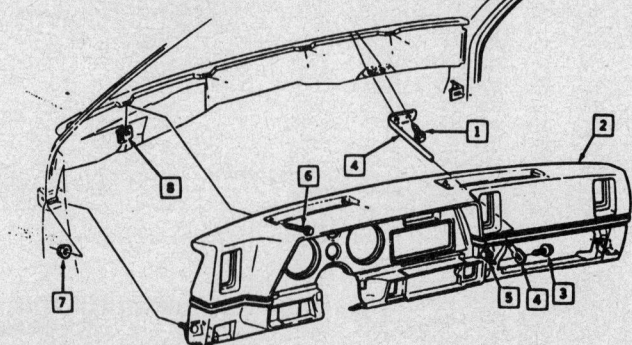

Fig. 114   I/P assembly. 1990 Cavalier & Sunbird

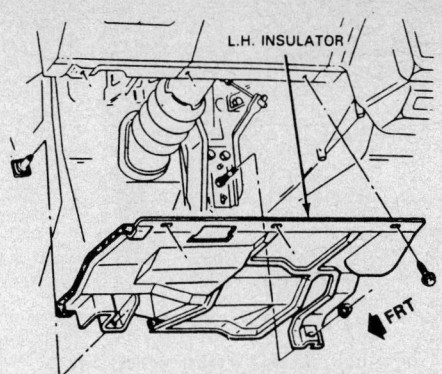

Fig. 115   Removing left side sound insulator. Beretta & Corsica

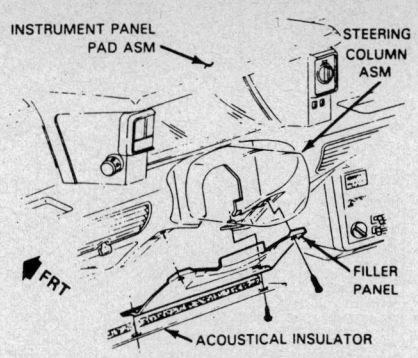

Fig. 116   Steering column trim cover removal. Beretta & Corsica

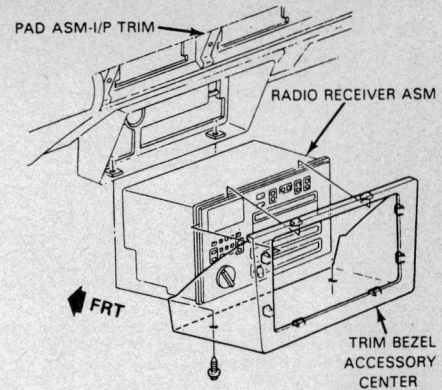

Fig. 117   Accessory center removal. Beretta

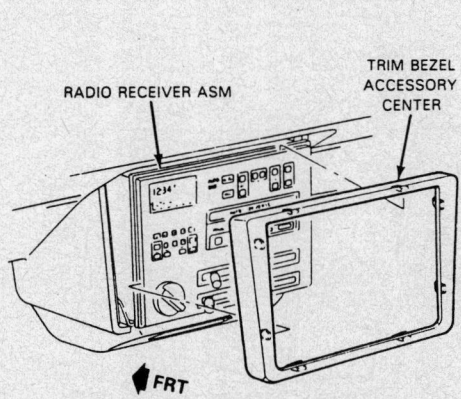

Fig. 118   Accessory center removal. Corsica

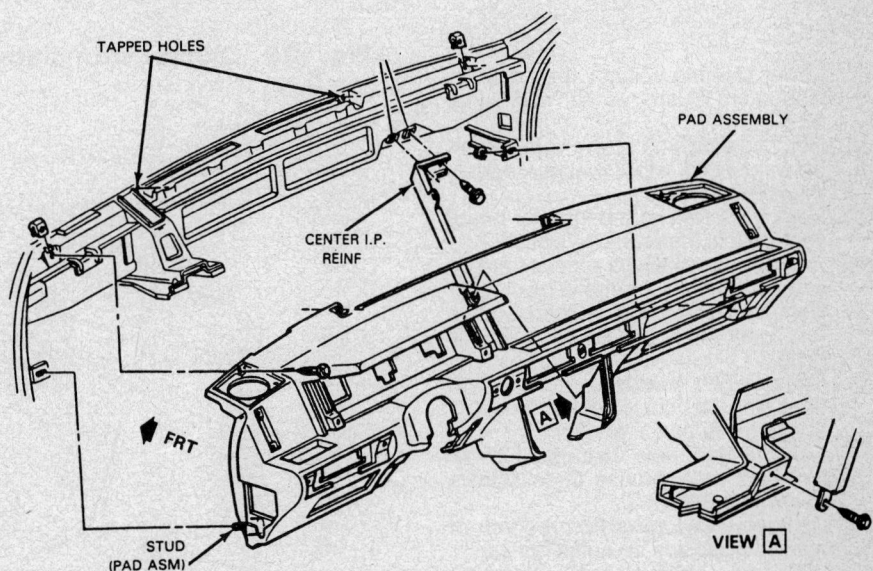

Fig. 120   I/P removal. Beretta & Corsica

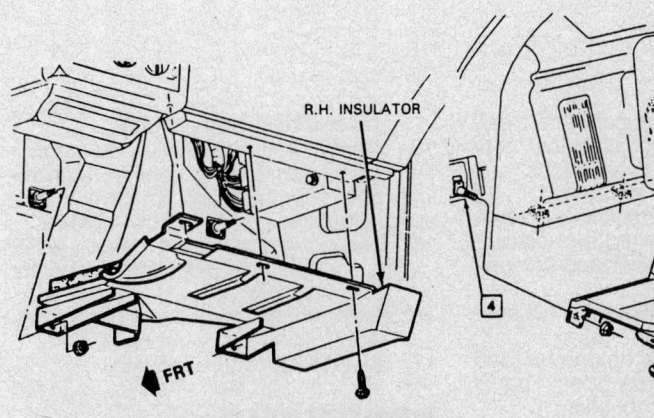

Fig. 119   Removing right side sound insulator. Beretta & Corsica

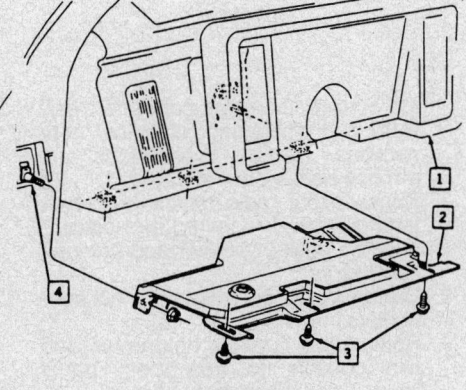

1. INSTRUMENT PANEL
2. INSULATOR ASM., LEFT
3. SCREW — FULLY DRIVEN, SEATED AND NOT STRIPPED
4. BOLT/STUD

Fig. 121   Removing left side I/P sound insulator. Skylark

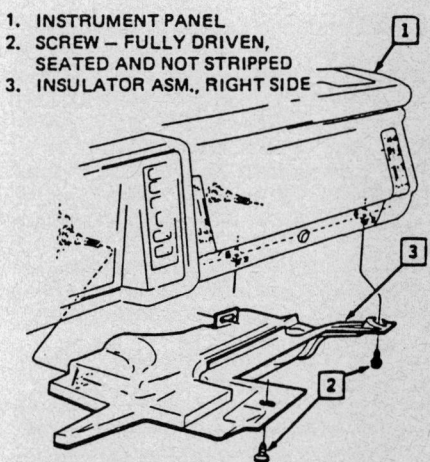

1. INSTRUMENT PANEL
2. SCREW — FULLY DRIVEN, SEATED AND NOT STRIPPED
3. INSULATOR ASM., RIGHT SIDE

Fig. 122   Removing right side I/P sound insulator. Skylark

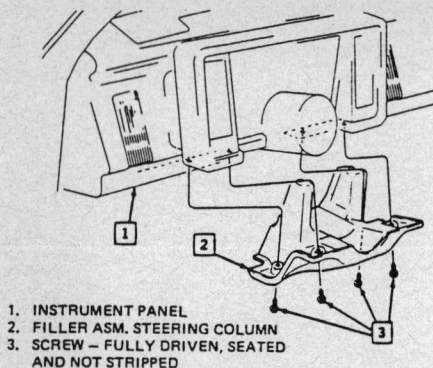

1. INSTRUMENT PANEL
2. FILLER ASM. STEERING COLUMN
3. SCREW – FULLY DRIVEN, SEATED AND NOT STRIPPED

Fig. 123 Removing steering column close out mounting. Skylark

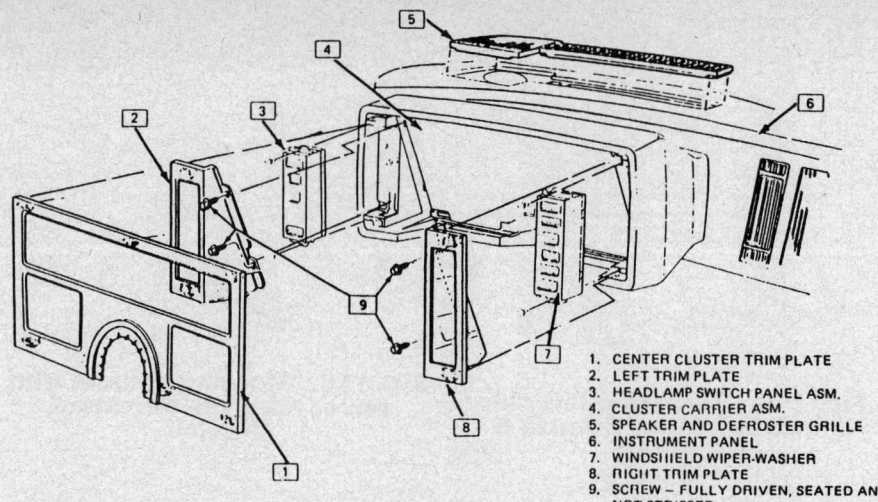

1. CENTER CLUSTER TRIM PLATE
2. LEFT TRIM PLATE
3. HEADLAMP SWITCH PANEL ASM.
4. CLUSTER CARRIER ASM.
5. SPEAKER AND DEFROSTER GRILLE
6. INSTRUMENT PANEL
7. WINDSHIELD WIPER-WASHER
8. RIGHT TRIM PLATE
9. SCREW – FULLY DRIVEN, SEATED AND NOT STRIPPED

Fig. 124   Cluster trim plate & switch pod removal. Skylark

5. Lower steering column, then remove instrument cluster as shown in **Fig. 137.**
6. Remove attaching screw from bottom of windshield wiper/washer switch, then remove switch.
7. Remove screw from bottom of headlight switch, then remove switch.
8. Remove two retaining screws from instrument panel pad above cluster.
9. Remove defroster grilles, then remove torx screws from under each defroster grille.
10. Remove two screws from bottom of right side instrument panel trim pad above glove box, **Fig. 138.**
11. Remove right side instrument panel trim pad, then remove three screws below trim pad.
12. Remove two screws from bottom of right and left side air outlet grilles.
13. With center grille staying in place, remove right and left air outlet grilles.
14. Disconnect right and left speaker wires, then remove instrument panel.
15. Reverse procedure to install.

CAMARO & FIREBIRD

The Diagnositc Energy Reserve Module (DERM) can maintain sufficient voltage to cause a deployment of the Supplemental Restraint System air bag for up to 10 minutes after disconnecting battery ground cable. Before performing service on the instrument panel wait 10 minutes to allow DERM voltage to drop after disconnecting battery.

On 1990 models equipped with Supplemental Inflatable Restraint (SIR) System, refer to steps 2 and 3 to disable system:
1. Disconnect battery ground cable.
2. Turn ignition to the Off position, then remove fuse No. 10 from fuse panel.
3. Disconnect position assurance (CPA) and yellow two-way (SIR) harness connector at base of steering column.
4. Remove shifter handle and seven shift gate trim plate attaching screws.
5. Remove radio and A/C heater controller trim plate.
6. Remove A/C heater controller attach-

1. RADIO CONTROL ASM.
2. BOLT/SCREW (3)
3. RETAINER – FULLY DRIVEN, SEATED AND NOT STRIPPED
4. BRACKET
5. NUT (2) – 6 N·m (50 LBS. IN.)
6. BOLT/SCREW – FULLY DRIVEN, SEATED AND NOT STRIPPED
7. CONSOLE ASM.

VIEW A

FRT

Fig. 125   Radio assembly removal. Skylark

ing screws, then pull controller rearward and disconnect electrical connections, vacuum connections and remove heater control cable.
7. Remove four radio retaining screws, then pull radio rearward and disconnect the power, speaker and antenna connectors.
8. Disconnect all console electrical connectors.
9. Remove six console hold down and two console to instrument panel screws and remove console.
10. Remove instrument panel trim pad and hush panels, **Figs. 139 through 142.**
11. Remove right and left lower instrument panel covers and trim plates, **Figs. 143 and 144.**
12. Remove six instrument cluster attachment screws, then pull cluster back and disconnect speedometer cable

and electrical connections.
13. Remove headlight switch assembly.
14. Lower the steering column, then remove five upper and six lower instrument panel carrier to cowl screws.
15. Disconnect instrument panel electrical harness at bulkhead connector and under dash.
16. Remove instrument panel carrier, **Fig. 145.**
17. Reverse procedure to install.

BONNEVILLE

1. Disconnect battery ground cable.
2. If equipped with tilt wheel steering, move wheel to the lowest position.
3. Move shift lever to the 1 position.
4. Pry lightly around perimeter of instrument panel trim plate, and remove trim plate, **Fig. 146.**

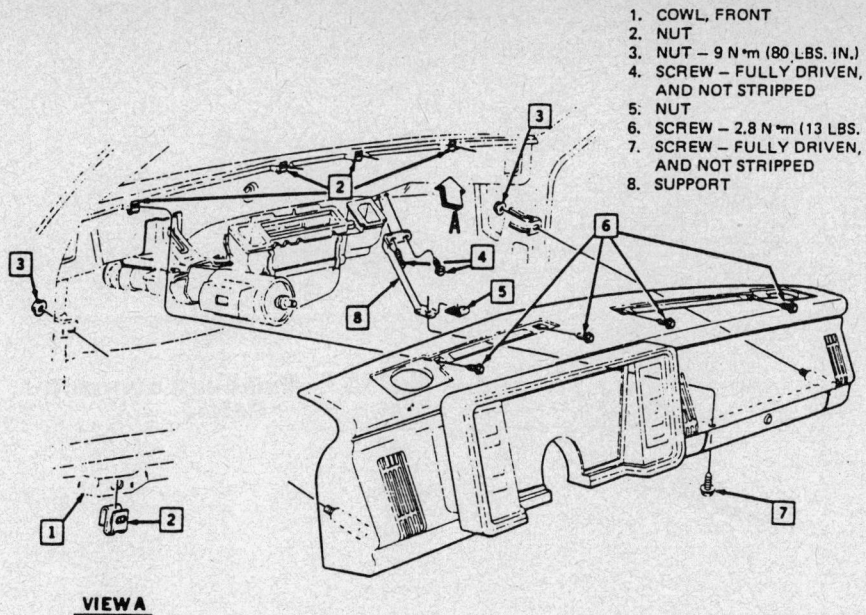

1. COWL, FRONT
2. NUT
3. NUT — 9 N·m (80 LBS. IN.)
4. SCREW — FULLY DRIVEN, SEATED AND NOT STRIPPED
5. NUT
6. SCREW — 2.8 N·m (13 LBS. IN.)
7. SCREW — FULLY DRIVEN, SEATED AND NOT STRIPPED
8. SUPPORT

Fig. 126   I/P pad removal. Skylark

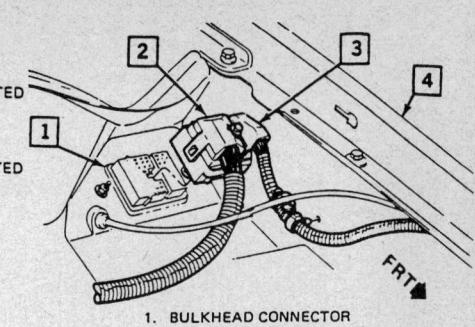

1. BULKHEAD CONNECTOR
2. ENGINE CONNECTOR
3. FORWARD LAMP CONNECTOR
4. LEFT FRONT FENDER

Fig. 127   Bulkhead connector. Skylark

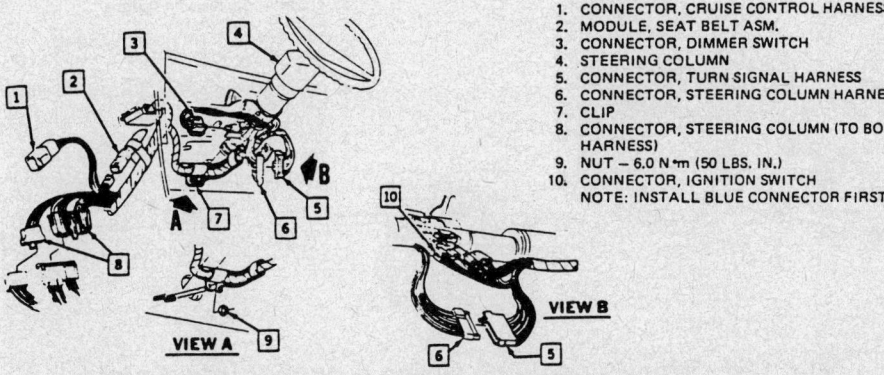

1. CONNECTOR, CRUISE CONTROL HARNESS
2. MODULE, SEAT BELT ASM.
3. CONNECTOR, DIMMER SWITCH
4. STEERING COLUMN
5. CONNECTOR, TURN SIGNAL HARNESS
6. CONNECTOR, STEERING COLUMN HARNESS
7. CLIP
8. CONNECTOR, STEERING COLUMN (TO BODY HARNESS)
9. NUT — 6.0 N·m (50 LBS. IN.)
10. CONNECTOR, IGNITION SWITCH
    NOTE: INSTALL BLUE CONNECTOR FIRST.

Fig. 128   Steering column wiring harness connectors. Skylark

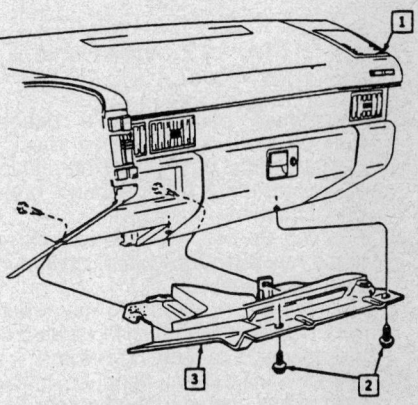

1. INSTRUMENT PANEL
2. SCREW — FULLY DRIVEN, SEATED AND NOT STRIPPED
3. INSULATOR ASM., RIGHT SIDE

Fig. 129   Left side I/P sound insulator removal. Calais

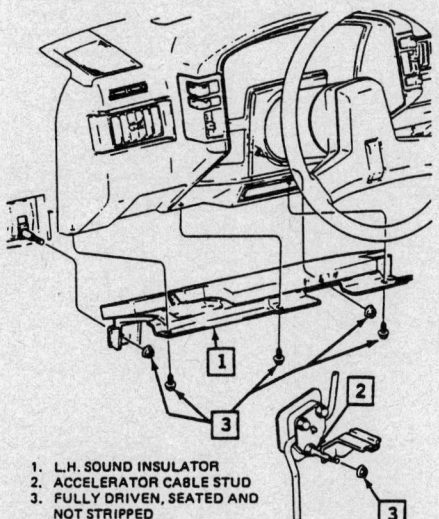

1. L.H. SOUND INSULATOR
2. ACCELERATOR CABLE STUD
3. FULLY DRIVEN, SEATED AND NOT STRIPPED

Fig. 130   Right side I/P sound insulator removal. Calais

5. Remove speaker, side defogger and defroster grilles by carefully prying around perimeter of grille.
6. Remove speaker retaining screws, disconnect electrical connectors, then remove speakers.
7. Remove instrument panel pad attaching screws, then the pad, **Fig. 147.**
8. Remove instrument cluster attaching screws, then disconnect the PRNDL indicator cable from steering column bowl and remove cluster.
9. Remove steering column filler and reinforcement panels, **Fig. 148.**
10. Remove electronic brake control module.
11. Remove left and right side hush panels, **Fig. 149.**
12. Remove headlamp/twilight sentinel/instrument panel dimmer control.
13. Remove radio and HVAC control unit.
14. Remove glove box/door assembly.
15. Reaching through glove box opening, disconnect deck lid, fuel door and glove box lamp switch electrical con-

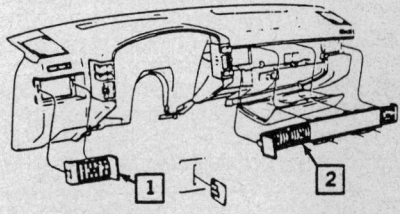

1. L.H. TRIM PLATE
2. R.H. TRIM PLATE

Fig. 131   Trim plate removal. Calais

nectors.
16. Disconnect electrical connector from instrument panel dimmer module.
17. Remove screws attaching ALDL connector to instrument panel.
18. Disconnect wires to cigarette lighter, then remove ashtray.
19. Remove screws attaching ashtray slide to instrument panel, unsnap ashtray lamp/socket assembly from slide and remove slide.

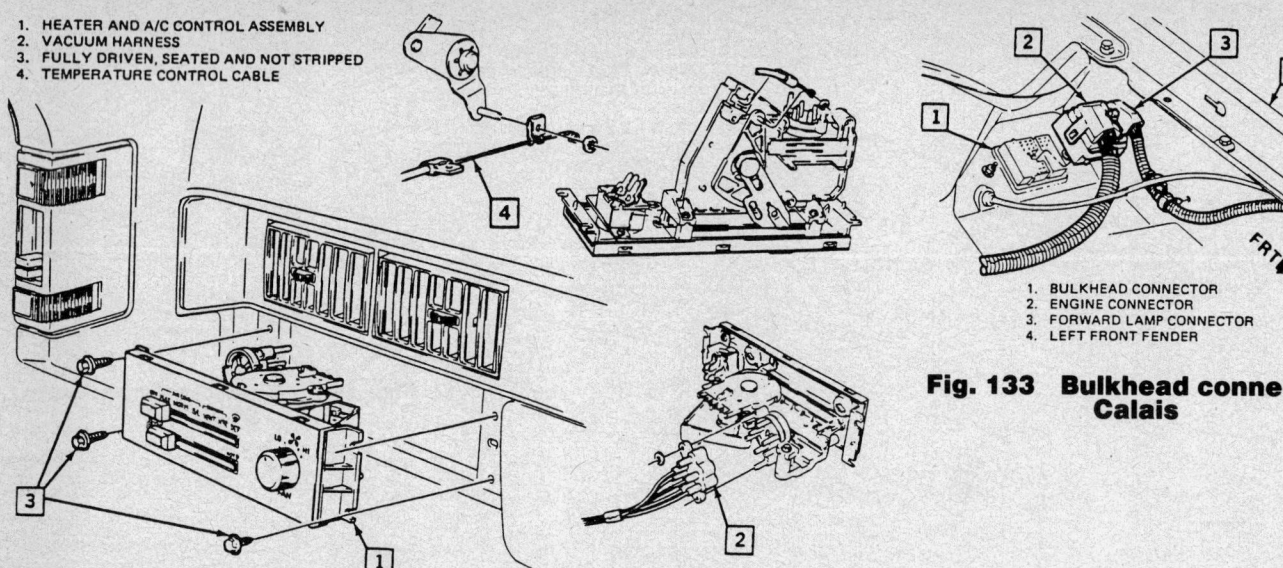

1. HEATER AND A/C CONTROL ASSEMBLY
2. VACUUM HARNESS
3. FULLY DRIVEN, SEATED AND NOT STRIPPED
4. TEMPERATURE CONTROL CABLE

Fig. 132   Heater & A/C control removal. Calais

1. BULKHEAD CONNECTOR
2. ENGINE CONNECTOR
3. FORWARD LAMP CONNECTOR
4. LEFT FRONT FENDER

Fig. 133   Bulkhead connector. Calais

20. Disconnect parking brake release handle cable from release mechanism on pedal assembly. Pop release cable grommet from parking brake pedal bracket.
21. Pushing up on lower fuse block release tab, push fuse panel behind instrument panel.
22. Remove screw attaching instrument panel to panel stiffener rod, located on the right side of steering column.
23. Remove instrument panel to instrument panel center support screw, **Fig. 150.**
24. Remove all other instrument panel attaching screws shown in **Fig. 150.**
25. Disengage cluster connectors from instrument panel by using a small screwdriver to push locking tangs from holes in instrument panel.
26. Slide wiring conduit just above steering column upward to disengage tabs from instrument panel, then push behind instrument panel.
27. Remove bolts holding steering column to column support.
28. Remove bolts holding metal instrument panel bracket to steering column support.
29. Disconnect side defogger hoses from instrument panel outlet connections.
30. Remove harness retaining clips from various points on metal instrument panel bracket, **Figs. 151 and 152.**
31. Remove instrument panel from vehicle.
32. Reverse procedure to install.

REGAL

Refer to **Fig. 153,** when performing this procedure.
1. Disconnect battery ground cable.
2. Remove speaker grilles by prying carefully at edge of grille.
3. Remove one instrument panel pad cover retaining screw from under each speaker grille, **Fig. 154.**

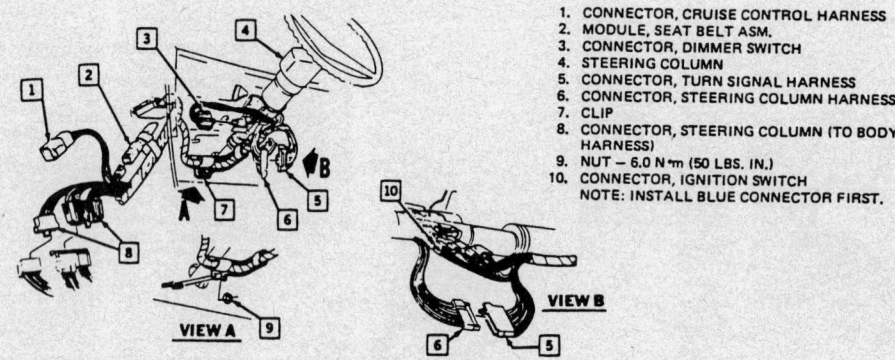

1. CONNECTOR, CRUISE CONTROL HARNESS
2. MODULE, SEAT BELT ASM.
3. CONNECTOR, DIMMER SWITCH
4. STEERING COLUMN
5. CONNECTOR, TURN SIGNAL HARNESS
6. CONNECTOR, STEERING COLUMN HARNESS
7. CLIP
8. CONNECTOR, STEERING COLUMN (TO BODY HARNESS)
9. NUT — 6.0 N·m (50 LBS. IN.)
10. CONNECTOR, IGNITION SWITCH
NOTE: INSTALL BLUE CONNECTOR FIRST.

Fig. 134   Steering column wiring & connectors. Calais

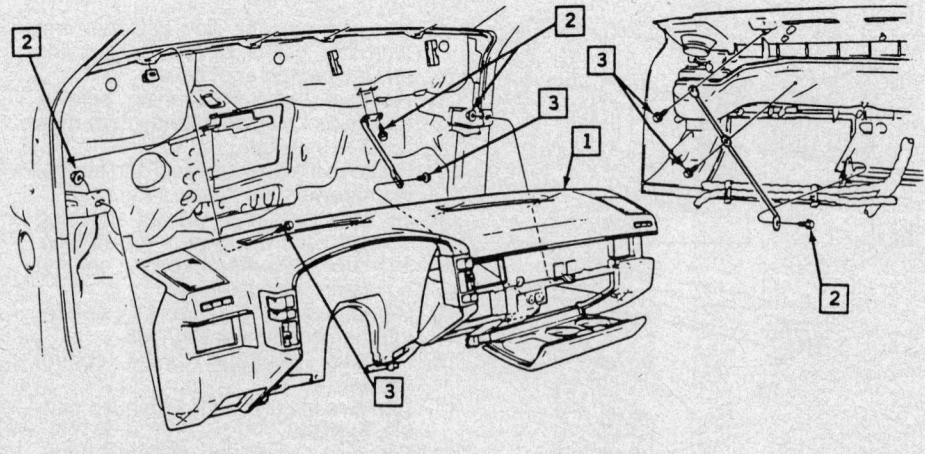

1. I.P. PAD
2. 10 N·m (88 LBS. IN.)
3. FULLY DRIVEN, SEATED AND NOT STRIPPED

Fig. 135   Instrument pad removal. Calais

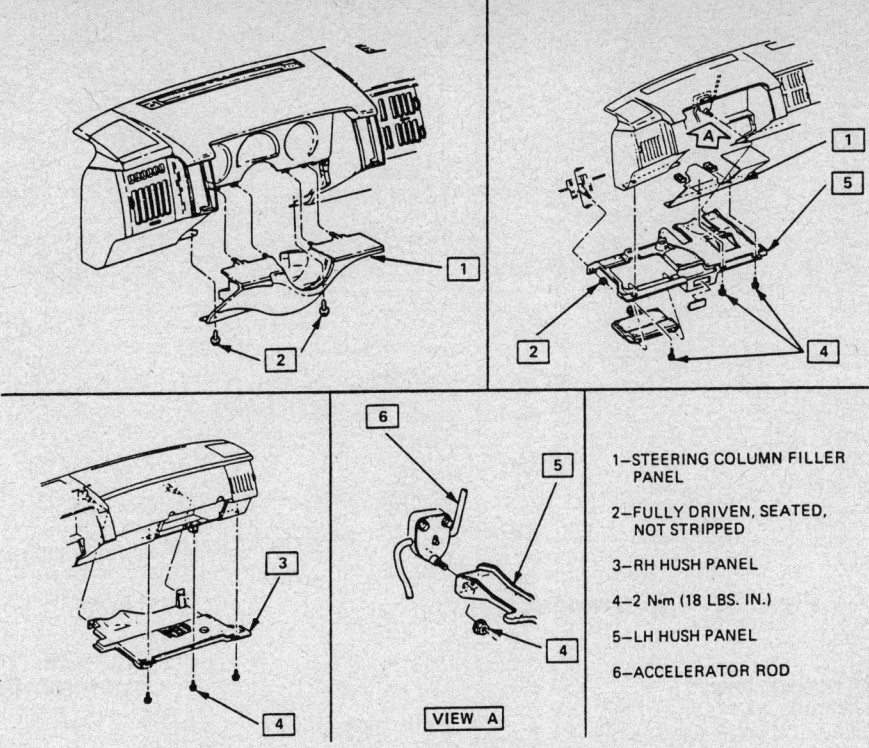

Fig. 136   I/P hush & trim panels. Grand Am

1—STEERING COLUMN FILLER PANEL

2—FULLY DRIVEN, SEATED, NOT STRIPPED

3—RH HUSH PANEL

4—2 N•m (18 LBS. IN.)

5—LH HUSH PANEL

6—ACCELERATOR ROD

VIEW A

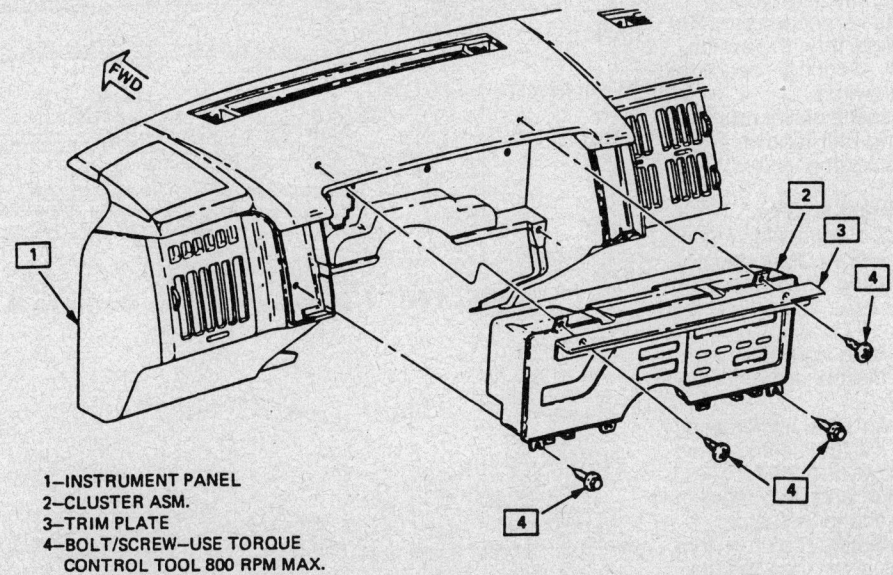

1—INSTRUMENT PANEL
2—CLUSTER ASM.
3—TRIM PLATE
4—BOLT/SCREW—USE TORQUE CONTROL TOOL 800 RPM MAX.

Fig. 137   Instrument cluster removal. Grand Am

4. Remove five screws under lower edge of instrument panel pad.
5. Remove pad by lifting front, pulling rearward to release, then lifting up and out.
6. Remove two speaker retaining bolts, then disconnect electrical connectors and remove speakers.
7. Remove one cluster trim plate retaining bolt on left side, then the trim plate.
8. Remove electrical connectors, then six cluster retaining bolts and the cluster.
9. With glove box open, remove gasket from around air outlet.
10. Remove two screws behind gasket, then open fuse block cover.
11. Remove two glove box retaining screws, located on the left side of glove box.
12. Disconnect electrical connector, then remove glove box.
13. Remove three bolts holding right side sound insulator.

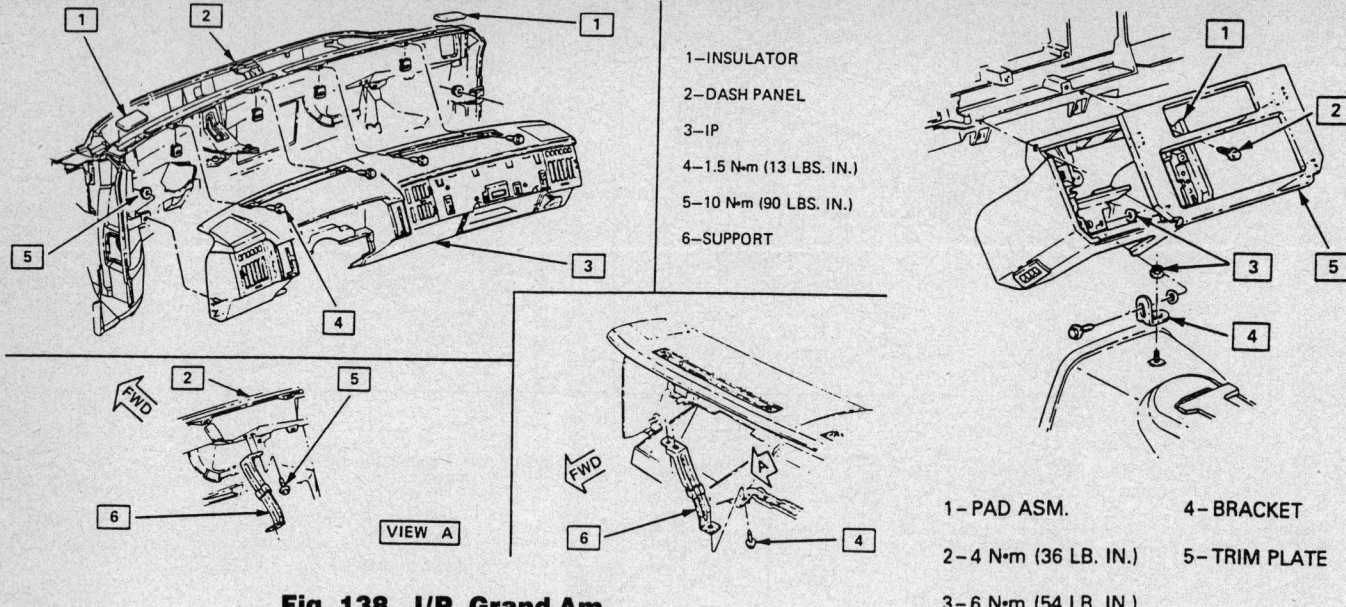

1—INSULATOR

2—DASH PANEL

3—IP

4—1.5 N·m (13 LBS. IN.)

5—10 N·m (90 LBS. IN.)

6—SUPPORT

VIEW A

Fig. 138   I/P. Grand Am

1—PAD ASM.   4—BRACKET

2—4 N·m (36 LB. IN.)   5—TRIM PLATE

3—6 N·m (54 LB. IN.)

Fig. 139   I/P lower trim pad removal. Camaro & Firebird

14. Remove insulator by pushing towards front of car, then pulling down.
15. Remove four ventilation control assembly retaining bolts, then the control assembly and connectors.
16. Remove bolts securing radio, then the radio and connectors, **Fig. 155.**
17. Remove bolts securing English/Metric switch, then the switch.
18. Remove bolts securing headlight switch, then the switch.
19. Remove four cassette player retaining bolts, then pulling unit rearward, disconnect electrical connectors, **Fig. 156.**
20. Remove ashtray and bracket.
21. Remove two ALDL connector retaining bolts, then lower ALDL connector.
22. Remove two parking brake retaining bolts, then lower lever and pull to the right.
23. Remove bolt holding right side courtesy light, then disconnect electrical connector.
24. Remove two radio receiver retaining bolts, then the receiver, electrical and antenna connectors, **Fig. 157.**
25. Remove one nut and two screws holding left side sound insulator.
26. Remove four steering column trim cover retaining screws, then the cover.
27. Remove four steering column retaining bolts, lower steering column.
28. Remove seven instrument panel carrier assembly retaining bolts, five at top and two at bottom.
29. Remove two carrier assembly retaining bolts, located above steering column.
30. Remove five carrier assembly to air duct attaching bolts.
31. Remove three conduit retaining nuts, two above glove compartment and one through cassette compartment opening.
32. Remove nine clips holding wiring harness.

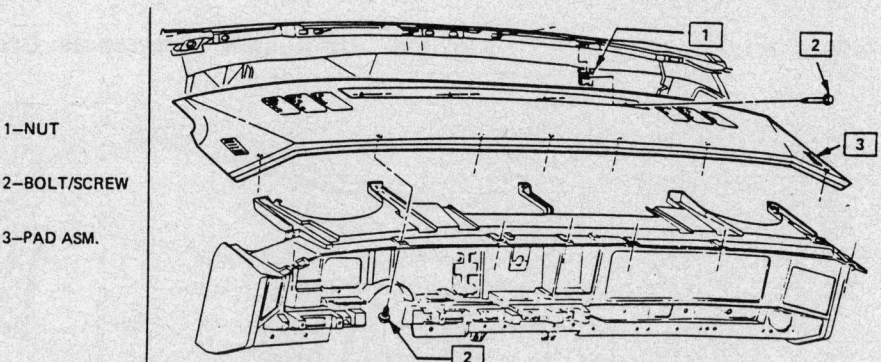

1—NUT

2—BOLT/SCREW

3—PAD ASM.

Fig. 140   I/P pad removal. Camaro & Firebird

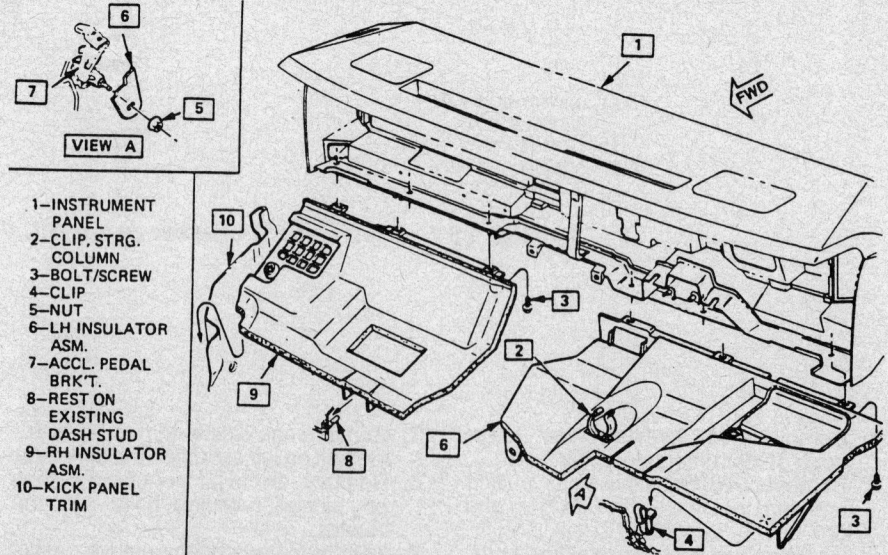

VIEW A

1—INSTRUMENT PANEL
2—CLIP, STRG. COLUMN
3—BOLT/SCREW
4—CLIP
5—NUT
6—LH INSULATOR ASM.
7—ACCL. PEDAL BRK'T.
8—REST ON EXISTING DASH STUD
9—RH INSULATOR ASM.
10—KICK PANEL TRIM

Fig. 141   I/P hush panel removal (with A/C). Camaro & Firebird

28-50

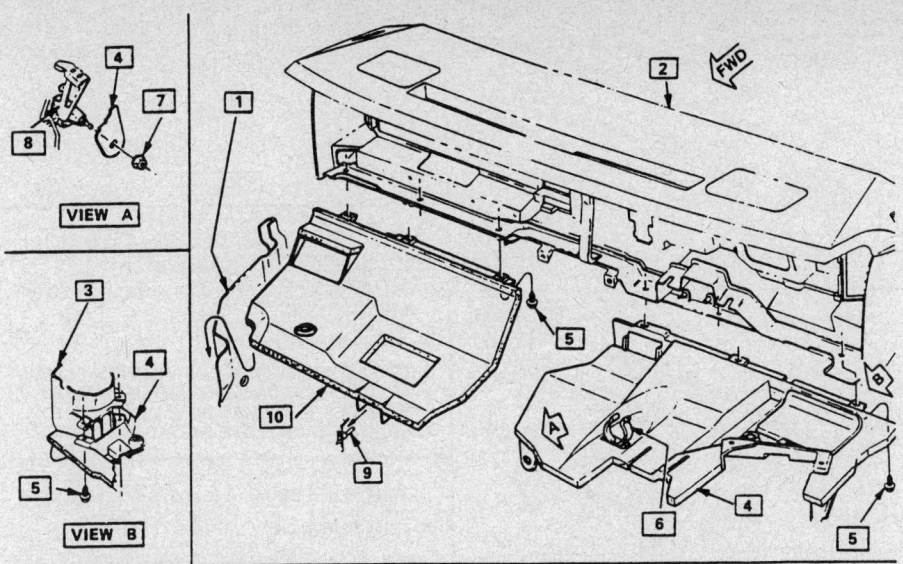

VIEW A

VIEW B

1—KICK PANEL TRIM

2—INSTRUMENT PANEL

3—LH VENT DUCT EXTENSION

4—LH INSULATOR ASM.

5—BOLT/SCREW

6—CLIP INTO STEERING COLUMN

7—NUT

8—ACCEL. PEDAL BRK'T.

9—REST ON EXISTING DASH STUD

10—RH INSULATOR ASM.

Fig. 142 I/P hush panel removal (less A/C). Camaro & Firebird

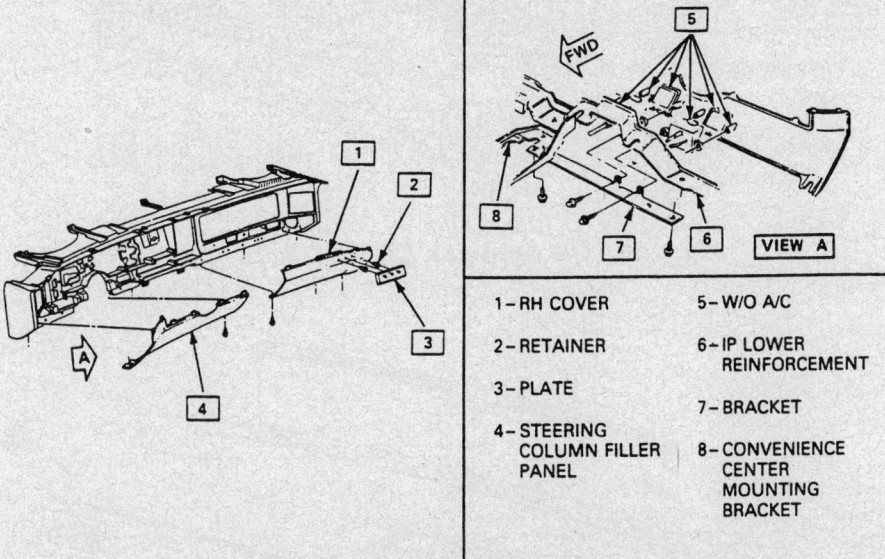

VIEW A

1— RH COVER

2— RETAINER

3— PLATE

4— STEERING COLUMN FILLER PANEL

5— W/O A/C

6— IP LOWER REINFORCEMENT

7— BRACKET

8— CONVENIENCE CENTER MOUNTING BRACKET

Fig. 143 Lower I/P cover removal. Camaro & Firebird

33. Remove instrument panel by pulling top out, then lifting panel up and out.
34. Reverse procedure to install.

CUTLASS SUPREME

Refer to **Fig. 158**, when performing this procedure.
1. Disconnect battery ground cable.
2. Open glove compartment door, then remove lower storage compartment by lifting it out.
3. Remove two screws inside glove compartment opening.
4. Remove defroster grille and deflector, **Fig. 159**.
5. Remove two instrument panel upper pad retaining screws, located in defroster grille opening.
6. Remove five instrument panel cluster trim plate attaching screws, **Fig. 160**.

7. Pull top of trim plate outward, then starting at one side of trim plate carefully pull bottom outward to release five spring clips.
8. Remove two screws at sides of instrument cluster opening.
9. Lift upper pad and disconnect electrical connector to glove compartment light, then remove upper pad.
10. Remove two screws attaching speakers to instrument panel.
11. Disconnect speaker electrical connectors, and remove speaker.
12. Remove radio assembly retaining screws, then pulling assembly rearward, disconnect antenna, speaker and electrical connectors.
13. Remove two screws holding left air outlet trim plate to instrument panel, **Fig. 161**.
14. Carefully pull at bottom of trim plate to release spring clips.
15. Disconnect electrical connector for headlight switch, and remove air outlet trim plate.
16. **On vehicles equipped with sport pod,** remove sport pod as follows:
    a. Remove two screws on bottom of assembly, **Fig. 162**.
    b. Remove three screws holding assembly to instrument panel.
    c. Pull assembly outward and disconnect electrical connector to lighter.
    d. Remove four screws holding filler to instrument panel.
17. **On vehicles not equipped with sport pod,** remove left center air outlet plate assembly as follows:
    a. Remove three screws holding left center air outlet assembly to instrument panel trim plate.
    b. Remove air outlet trim plate by pulling carefully at bottom of plate to release spring clips.
18. **On all models,** remove left and right instrument panel sound insulators.
19. Remove two screws holding ALDL connector to instrument panel.
20. Remove four steering column trim plate attaching screws, **Fig. 163**.
21. Pull trim cover rearward and disconnect trunk release electrical connector.
22. Remove two bolts at upper part of column and one bolt at lower part of column, then lower column.
23. Disconnect left and right courtesy light assemblies.
24. Remove two screws holding parking brake release handle to instrument panel.
25. Turn handle and remove it from instrument panel.
26. Remove three fuse block bracket to instrument panel attaching screws.
27. Remove seven screws holding main ventilation duct to the instrument panel.
28. Remove nut holding wiring harness clip to instrument panel.
29. Remove screw holding glove compartment light, then slide off bracket.
30. Remove two instrument panel attaching screws, located at lower left and right sides of panel.
31. Remove five instrument panel attach-

ing screws at top of instrument panel.
32. Remove two instrument panel attaching screws at steering column support.
33. Remove instrument panel from vehicle.
34. Reverse procedure to install.

GRAND PRIX

Refer to **Figs. 164 and 165,** when performing this procedure.
1. Disconnect battery ground cable.
2. Remove two instrument panel pad cover attaching screws at top of cluster trim plate, **Fig. 166.**
3. Remove two screws securing glove compartment hinges to instrument panel.
4. Holding door at the bottom, open door, then lift door up and out to release.
5. Remove three glove compartment attaching screws, located at the top of glove compartment.
6. Remove two screws securing plastic clips under the compartment.
7. Slide glove compartment out of instrument panel and disconnect electrical connectors to light and trunk release switch.
8. Remove one instrument panel pad cover attaching screw above glove compartment opening.
9. Lift front of pad and pull rearward to release clips.
10. Remove light switch assembly retaining screw, then remove assembly by carefully pulling out to release two spring clips at the top.
11. Remove windshield wiper/washer switch assembly retaining screw, then remove assembly by carefully pulling out to release two spring clips at the top.
12. Remove four cluster trim plate attaching screws, located inside switch openings.
13. Remove two cluster trim plate attaching screws from top of trim plate.
14. Remove two switch assembly connectors by sliding out of holders.
15. Remove two screws attaching clutch brake release lever, then disconnect linkage from brake assembly.
16. Remove two bolts securing ALDL connector, then lower connector.
17. Remove two left side sound insulator attaching screws, located on the rear edge of the insulator.
18. Remove one slide clip from front of insulator, then remove insulator.
19. Remove three attaching screws at the bottom of steering column cover, **Fig. 167.**
20. Remove cover by carefully pulling rearward to release it from the three clips at the top.
21. Remove two bolts at upper part of steering column.
22. Remove two bolts at lower part of column, then lower column.
23. Disconnect electrical connectors at steering column.
24. Remove two screws securing right side sound insulator, then remove insulator.

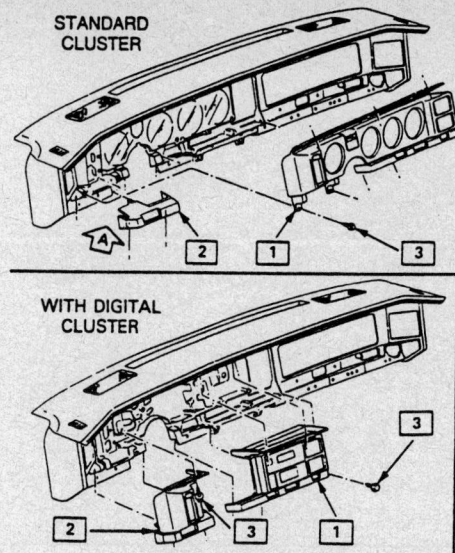
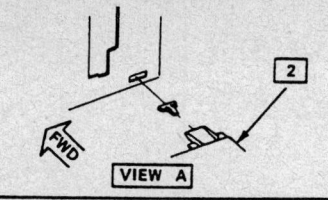

• WITH DIGITAL CLUSTER •
INSTALLATION PROCEDURE FOR LEFT & RIGHT HAND PLATE ASSEMBLIES

1 – POSITION BOSS ON PLATE ASSEMBLY OVER LOCATING PIN.
2 – ALIGN SCREW HOLES.
3 – INSTALL SCREWS, BEGINNING WITH SCREW LOCATIONS ALONG THE LOWER EDGE OF EACH PLATE. SECURE SCREWS ALONG TOP EDGE OF EACH PLATE LAST.

1 – TRIM PLATE (RH)   3 – 1.5 N•m (13 LB. IN.)
2 – TRIM PLATE (LH)

Fig. 144   I/P trim plate removal. Camaro & Firebird

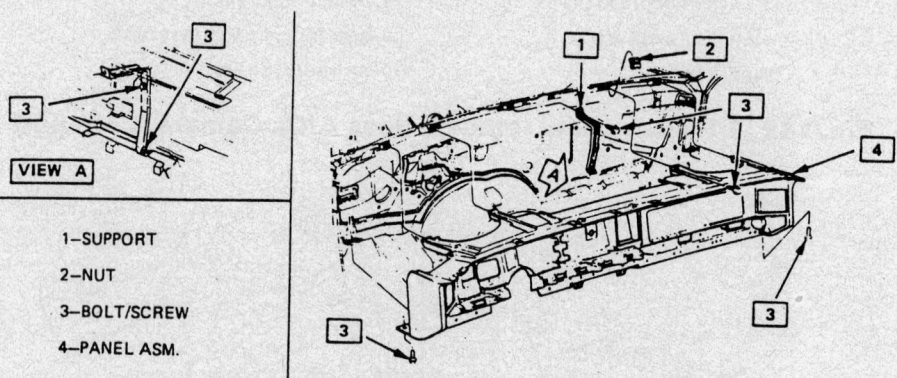

1 – SUPPORT
2 – NUT
3 – BOLT/SCREW
4 – PANEL ASM.

Fig. 145   I/P removal. Camaro & Firebird

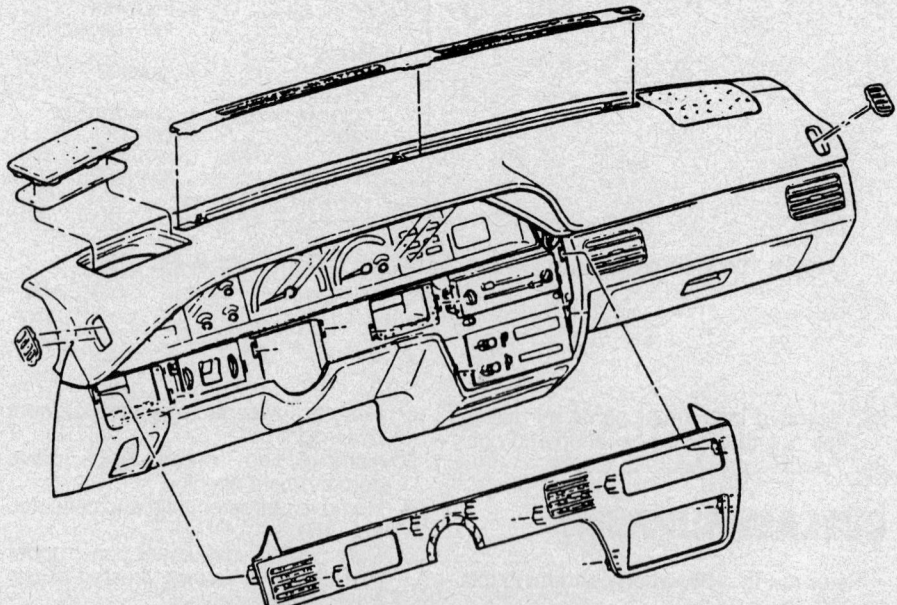

Fig. 146   I/P trim plate removal. Bonneville

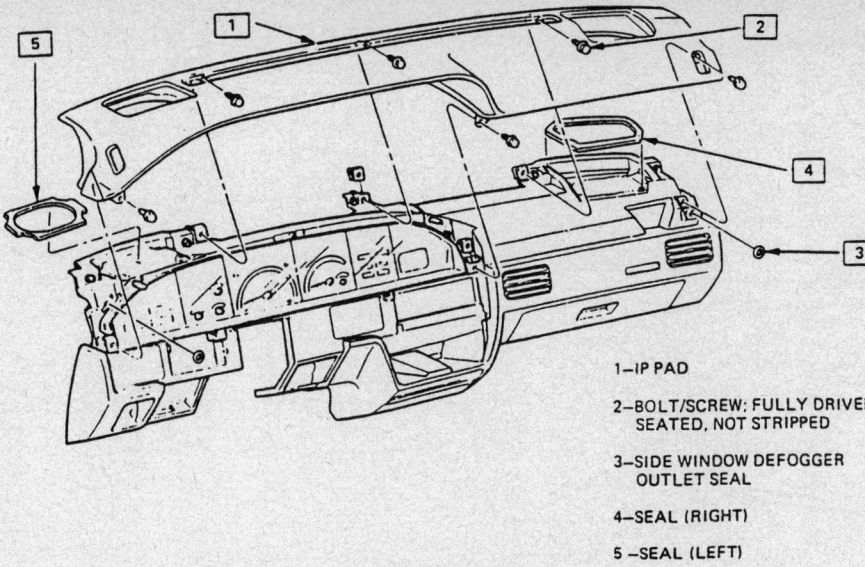

1—IP PAD

2—BOLT/SCREW; FULLY DRIVEN, SEATED, NOT STRIPPED

3—SIDE WINDOW DEFOGGER OUTLET SEAL

4—SEAL (RIGHT)

5—SEAL (LEFT)

Fig. 147   I/P pad removal. Bonneville

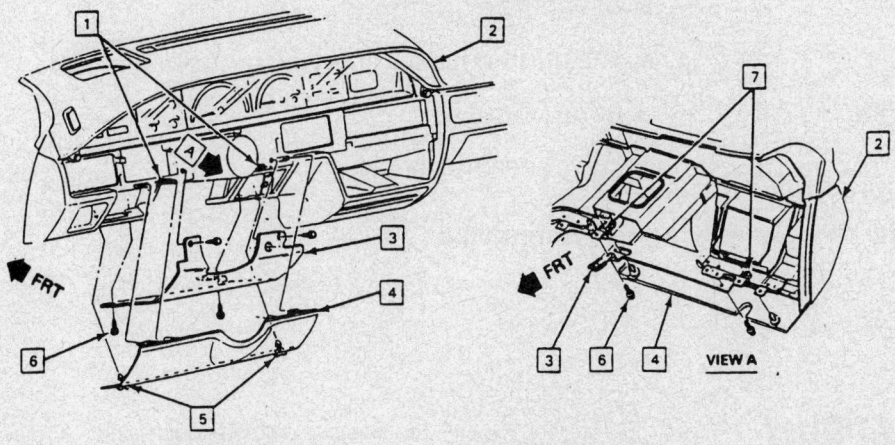

1 — LOCATOR PIN
2 — IP ASSEMBLY
3 — REINFORCEMENT, IP STRG COL OPENING FILLER
4 — STRG COL FILLER PANEL

5 — RETAINER; PUSH RETAINER THRU REINFORCEMENT AND RECEPTACLE IN IP TIE BAR AND TWIST TO FASTEN
6 — BOLT/SCREW; 1.4 N•M (12 LB-IN)
7 — RECEPTACLE, IP ASM

Fig. 148   Removing steering column filler & reinforcement panels. Bonneville

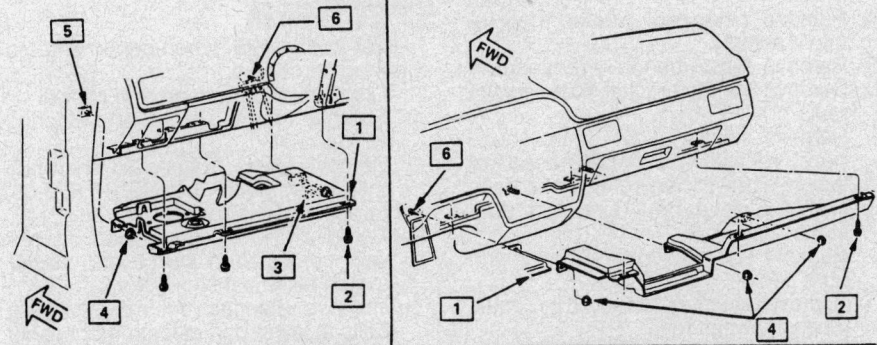

1—LEFT HUSH PANEL

2—BOLT/SCREW; 18 LB.IN./2 N•m

3—MOUNTING TAB OF RIGHT HUSH PANEL

4—NUT; 90 LB.IN./10 N•m

5—PARKING BRAKE STUD

6—ACCELERATOR PEDAL BRACKET STUD

Fig. 149   Removing I/P hush panels. Bonneville

25. Disconnect electrical connectors to fuse block.
26. Remove four bolts securing fuse block, and remove fuse block.
27. Disconnect electrical connector at HVAC assembly.
28. Remove two remote radio amplifier attaching screws, disconnect electrical connectors and remove amplifier.
29. Remove four radio trim plate attaching bolts, then trim plate.
30. Remove two ventilation control attaching screws, **Fig. 168**.
31. Pull control rearward, disconnect electrical connectors.
32. Remove two radio control attaching bolts, disconnect electrical connectors and remove radio control assembly.
33. Remove two cassette player attaching bolts, disconnect electrical connectors and remove cassette player assembly.
34. Remove two radio receiver retaining nuts, disconnect electrical connectors and antenna connector, remove radio receiver.
35. Remove four cluster retaining screws, lift cluster and disconnect electrical connector, remove cluster.
36. Remove four radio speaker retaining screws, and remove both speaker assemblies.
37. Remove seven screws securing ventilation duct to instrument panel, **Fig. 169**.
38. Remove three retaining nuts from wiring harness carrier.
39. Lift instrument panel carrier up and rearward then out through the passenger door.
40. Remove ventilation duct and wiring harness carrier as a unit.
41. Reverse procedure to install.

FIERO

1. Disconnect battery ground cable.
2. Disconnect hood release from instrument panel.
3. Remove Steering column cover.
4. Remove speaker grilles and speakers.
5. Remove instrument panel attaching screws.
6. Remove instrument panel service cover.
7. Remove front console trim plate, **Fig. 170**.
8. Remove front console pad assembly.
9. Remove remaining instrument panel reinforcement screws.
10. Remove instrument panel from vehicle, **Fig. 171**.
11. Reverse procedure to install.

NOVA

Refer to **Fig. 172**, when performing the following procedure.
1. Disconnect battery ground cable.
2. Remove steering wheel cover from center of steering wheel.
3. Remove screw at lower portion of the steering wheel pad and remove pad.
4. Remove steering wheel to steering shaft attaching nut and washer, then

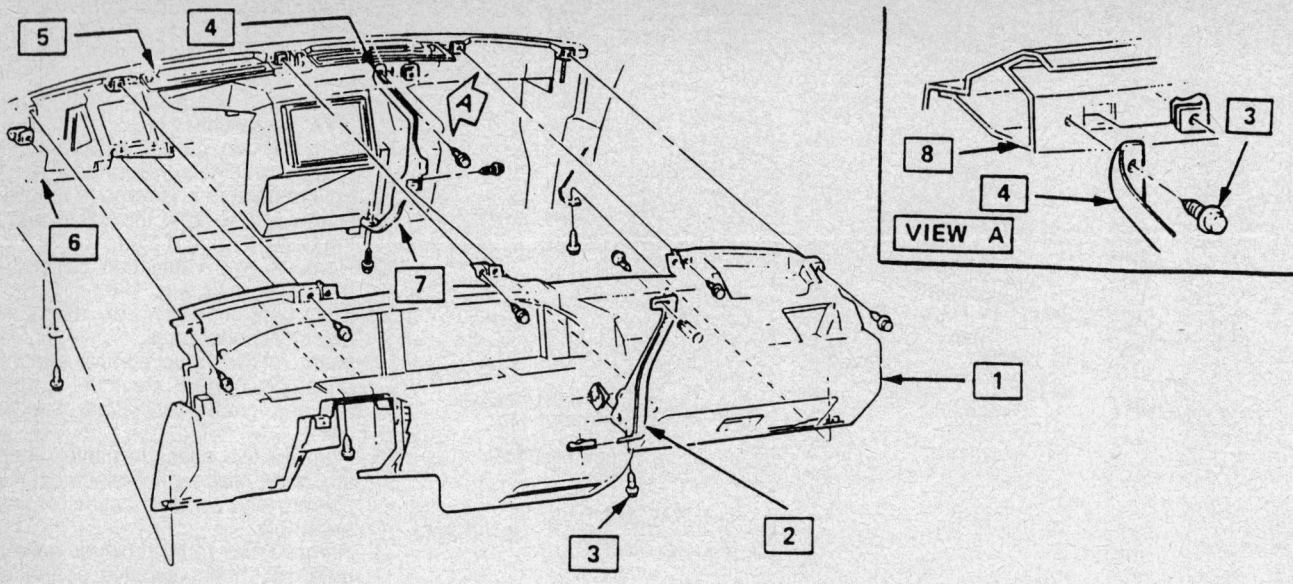

1—IP

2—IP CENTER SUPPORT

3—BOLT/SCREW; FULLY DRIVEN,
    SEATED, NOT STRIPPED

4—IP CENTER SUPPORT BRACKET

5—DEFROSTER DUCT

6—STEERING COLUMN SUPPORT (BODY)

7—HVAC MODULE

8—COWL SUPPORT (BODY)

Fig. 150 Removing I/P. Bonneville

using steering wheel puller to No. J-1859-03, remove steering wheel.

5. Remove left side speaker grille, then remove steering column lower trim cover.
6. Remove hood release lever.
7. Remove heater duct assembly.
8. Remove A/C registers, then remove four screws and meter hood.
9. Remove six screws attaching combination meter to instrument panel, pull meter rearward and disconnect speedometer cable and electrical connectors.
10. Remove end finish panel, then right side speaker grille.
11. Remove speaker bracket with speaker attached.
12. Remove glove compartment door with glove door reinforcement.
13. Remove glove compartment door lock striker.
14. Remove center cluster finish panel, then the radio assembly.
15. Remove lower center cluster finish panel.
16. Remove heater control panel attaching screws, then pull control rearward and disconnect vacuum and electrical connectors.
17. Remove side defroster nozzle, then remove instrument panel.
18. Reverse procedure to install.

SPRINT

Refer to **Figs. 173 and 174**, when performing the following procedure.
1. Disconnect battery ground cable.
2. Remove instrument panel bezel, then disconnect lamp switch and wiper switch connectors.
3. Remove lower steering column trim cover.
4. Remove instrument cluster, then remove ashtray.
5. Remove console and shifter knob.
6. Remove ashtray bracket, then remove radio.
7. Remove heater A/C control head bezel, remove two control head retaining screws then control head.
8. Remove glove box door and door striker.
9. Remove steering column cover and horn pad.
10. Remove steering wheel, then multi function switch lever.
11. Lower steering column, then remove hood release handle at retaining nut.
12. Disconnect hood release cable at handle and remove fuse block cover.
13. Remove screws covers at top of instrument panel, then remove instrument panel retaining screws.
14. Remove instrument panel disconnecting all harness connectors.

15. Remove defroster ducts, and A/C distribution ducts.
16. Remove all switches; cigar lighter, rear defogger, rear wiper/washer and disconnect all electrical connectors.
17. Remove illumination control, buzzer, wire harness, speakers and A/C vent outlets.
18. Reverse procedure to install.

SPECTRUM

Refer to **Fig. 175**, when performing the following procedure.
1. Disconnect battery ground cable.
2. Remove horn pad from steering wheel.
3. Remove steering wheel to shaft nut, then using puller tool No. J-1859-03, remove steering wheel.
4. Remove steering cowl, then disconnect combination switch and starter switch electrical connectors.
5. Remove steering column attaching bolts at lower part of instrument panel and pedal bracket.
6. Remove steering universal joint 2nd attaching bolt, then remove steering column assembly.
7. Remove glove box, then remove radio bracket.
8. Disconnect radio electrical connectors and antenna cable.
9. Remove ashtray, then remove heater

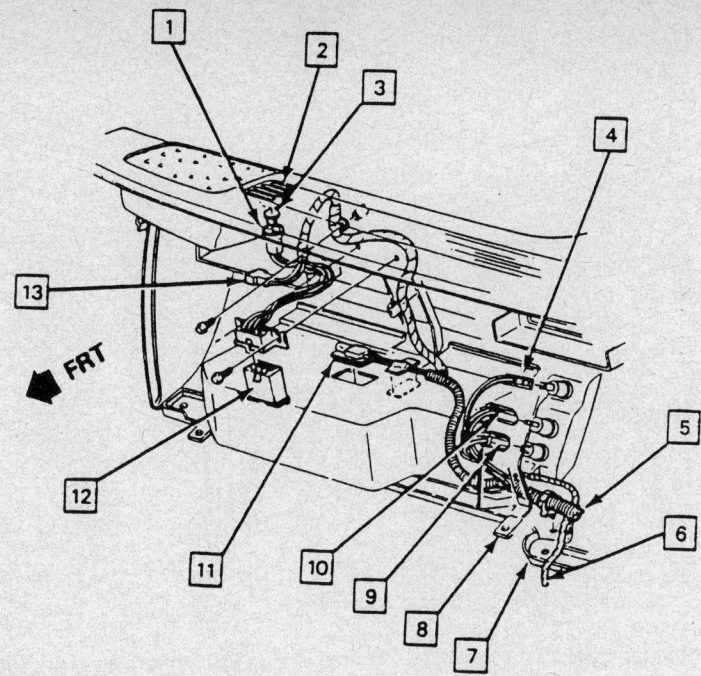

1 — TWILIGHT SENTINEL SENSOR LEAD
2 — DEFROSTER GRILLE
3 — TWILIGHT SENTINEL SENSOR
4 — FUEL FILLER DOOR SW CONN
5 — IP HARNESS
6 — ASHTRAY LIGHTER LEAD
7 — IP TIE BAR
8 — IP CENTER SUPPORT
9 — GLOVE BOX LAMP SW CONN
10 — DECK LID RELEASE SW CONN
11 — GLOVEBOX LAMP ASM
12 — SEATBELT ALARM ASM
13 — SPEAKER CONN

Fig. 151   I/P wiring right side. Bonneville

control lever knob.
10. Remove heater control panel attaching screws.
11. Remove meter hood attaching screws, then remove meter hood.
12. Disconnect wiper switch and lighting switch connectors.
13. Remove meter attaching screws, then pull meter rearward and disconnect electrical connectors.
14. Remove speedometer cable holder.
15. Remove fuse block attaching screws, then disconnect electrical connector from instrument panel to chassis, **Fig. 176.**
16. Disconnect heater control cable and electrical connectors.
17. Remove instrument panel screw covers, then remove instrument panel attaching screws.
18. Remove air duct to instrument panel attaching screws.
19. Pulling instrument panel rearward, disconnect clock and speaker connectors, and remove rheostat knob.
20. Remove rheostat assembly, clock assembly and speakers from instrument panel.
21. Reverse procedure to install.

LEMANS

1. Disconnect battery ground cable.
2. Remove horn pad and disconnect horn lead.
3. Remove nut and retainer, mark shaft and wheel for assembly reference.
4. Using steering wheel puller tool No. J-3651 or equivalent, remove steering wheel.
5. If necessary remove contact ring from steering wheel.
6. Using a pointed plastic tool, pry package panel out of console.
7. Remove two screws from under ashtray.
8. **On models with automatic transmission,** pull gear selector lever off. Pull out indicator strap from cover, then remove retaining clips and cover.
9. **On models with manual transmission,** remove shift knob, trim plate and boot.
10. **On all models,** remove front center console, **Fig. 177.**
11. Remove two attaching screws, then pull center back and out, **Fig. 178.**

12. Remove right side hush panel, **Fig. 179.**
13. Open glove box door and pry off two retaining straps.
14. Remove two screws attaching glove box to instrument panel pad.
15. Remove A/C or heater control.
16. Turning steering wheel to gain access to turn signal switch housing attaching screws, remove turn signal switch housing.
17. Remove instrument panel trim plate, then remove dimmer switch from trim plate.
18. While pressing down on speedometer cable retainer spring, pull out speedometer cable.
19. Remove instrument cluster attaching screws, pull cluster rearward and disconnect electrical connectors.
20. Remove cluster from instrument panel.
21. Remove instrument panel center section.
22. Remove air nozzles and air vents from instrument panel.
23. Remove fuse box, disconnect wiring harness from all switches and lamps.
24. Disconnect wiring harness from instrument panel.
25. Remove six instrument panel screw on panel and remove instrument panel.
26. Reverse procedure to install.

METRO

Refer to **Figs. 180 through 182,** when performing the following procedure.
1. Disconnect battery ground cable.
2. If equipped with center console, remove four attaching screws from the console box, **Fig. 183.**
3. Shift gear selector to the LOW position and gently pull outward at bottom of console box to disengage the two retaining pins.
4. Remove four attaching screws from cluster switch panel.
5. Disconnect front windshield wiper/washer switch and light/hazard flasher switch electrical connectors and remove cluster bezel and switch panel as an assembly.
6. Remove six attaching screws from cluster bezel and bezel from the switch panel.
7. Remove front wiper switch and light/hazard switch from the switch panel.
8. Remove four cluster housing mounting screws from the housing.
9. Disconnect two electrical connectors and speedometer cable from the rear of cluster housing.
10. Remove turn signal/dimmer switch.
11. Remove two mounting screws from heater control panel and disconnect blower switch electrical connector.
12. Remove hood latch release lever mounting screw and lever from instrument panel carrier assembly.
13. Remove two main instrument panel mounting screws from both the left and right sides of the main panel.
14. Remove four attaching screws from

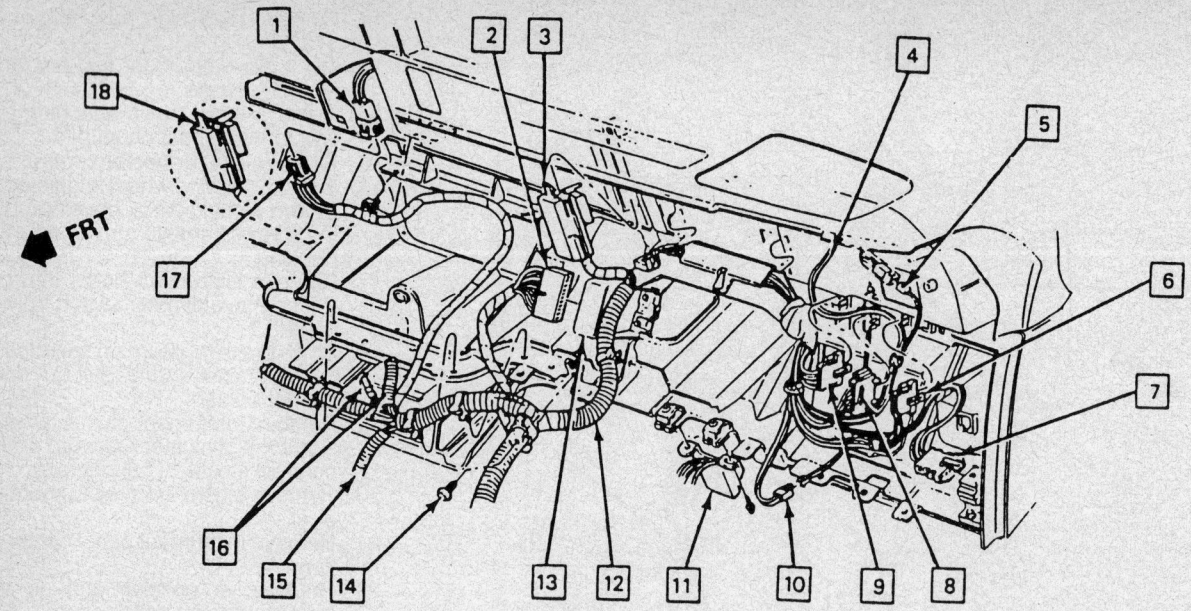

1 — CLUSTER CONN (P/O CLUSTER)
2 — TWILIGHT SENTINEL MODULE
      CONN
3 — CLUSTER CONN
4 — SPEAKER WIRING
5 — CLUSTER CONN (OPT)
6 — TWILIGHT SENTINEL SW CONN

7 — IP DIMMER CONN
8 — HEADLAMP SW CONN
9 — GAGE BRIGHTNESS SW CONN
10 — HDLP SW ILLUMINATION CONN.
11 — ALDL CONN
12 — IP WIRING HARNESS

13 — TWILIGHT SENTINEL MODULE
14 — BOLT/SCREW; 1.9 N•M (17 LB-IN)
15 — ASHTRAY WIRING
16 — RADIO WIRING
17 — CLUSTER CONN (OPT)
18 — CLUSTER CONN (OPT)

Fig. 152   I/P wiring left side. Bonneville

the instrument panel support member.
15. Remove two mounting screws from the heater control assembly.
16. Remove one attaching screw from rear of glove box upper panel.
17. Remove main instrument panel access cover and one attaching screw at each panel.
18. Remove both front speaker garnish covers, then remove one attaching screw at each speaker.
19. Remove two push pins from both left and right side kick panels and remove panels from vehicle.
20. Remove one attaching screw from instrument main panel behind each kick panel.
21. Disconnect both left and right side speaker connectors.
22. Disconnect all instrument panel switches; rheostat, rear wiper/washer, rear window defogger.
23. Disconnect instrument panel wiring harness from instrument panel carrier assembly.
24. Remove instrument panel carrier assembly from the vehicle.
25. Reverse procedure to install.

1990 LUMINA

1. Disconnect battery ground cable.
2. Remove instrument panel pad retaining screws under edge of instrument panel pad, **Fig. 184.**
3. Lift upward on front of pad assembly,

then pull rearward to release.
4. Remove speaker retaining bolts, then lift speaker and disconnect speaker electrical connectors.
5. Disconnect instrument cluster assembly electrical connectors, then remove cluster retaining screws, **Fig. 185.**
6. Remove glove compartment door.
7. Remove glove compartment assembly retaining screws.
8. Disconnect glove compartment electrical connector.
9. Remove glove compartment assembly.
10. Remove right side sound insulator retaining screws.
11. Push insulator toward front of vehicle then pull downward to remove.
12. Remove ventilation system control retaining bolts, **Fig. 186.**
13. Disconnect control assembly electrical connectors and remove from vehicle.
14. Remove radio retaining bolts, then disconnect electrical connectors and remove from vehicle.
15. Remove headlamp switch retaining screws, then disconnect switch electrical connector and remove from vehicle.
16. Remove ashtray, slide bracket retaining screws, then the bracket.
17. Remove ALDL cover.
18. Remove ALDL retaining screws then disconnect ALDL electrical connector.
19. Remove two parking brake release handle retaining screws then lower handle and pull to right to remove.

20. Disconnect fuse block electrical connectors.
21. Remove fuse block retaining screws, then the fuse block.
22. Remove left sound insulator and steering column trim panel.
23. Remove two upper and lower steering column support retaining bolts, then lower steering column.
24. Remove seven instrument panel carrier assembly retaining bolts, **Fig. 187.**
25. Remove carrier assembly from vehicle.
26. Reverse procedure to install.

PRIZM

Refer to **Fig. 188**, when performing the following procedure.
1. Disconnect battery ground cable.
2. Remove two steering wheel pad retaining bolts from back of steering wheel.
3. Remove steering wheel pad.
4. Disconnect horn switch electrical connector.
5. Remove steering wheel shaft nut.
6. Using steering wheel puller tool No. 1859-03 or equivalent, remove steering wheel.
7. Remove two hood release attaching screws lever.
8. Remove four lower left trim panel retaining screws, **Fig. 189.**
9. Disconnect speaker electrical connector, then remove A/C duct from lower A/C register, if equipped.

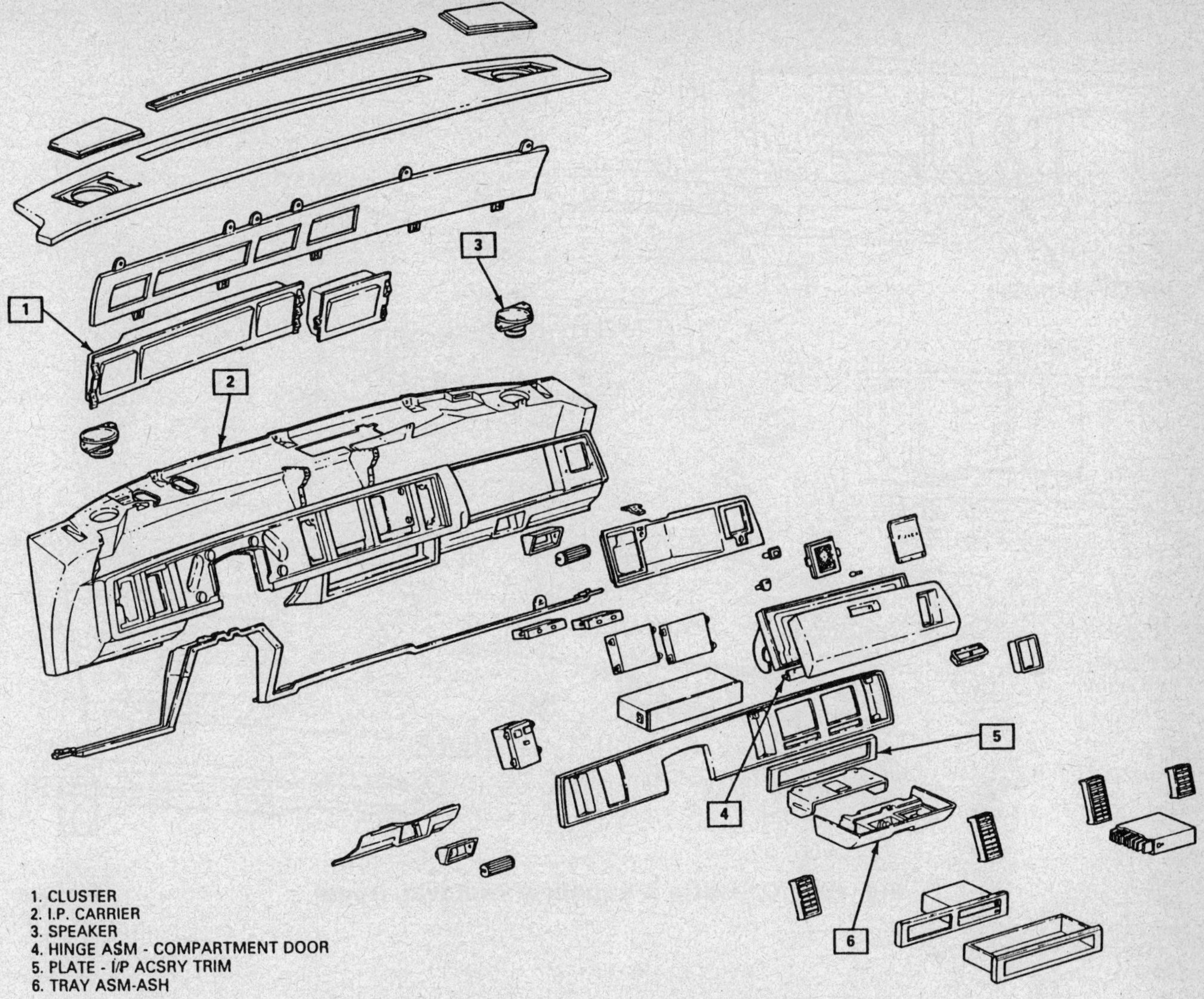

1. CLUSTER
2. I.P. CARRIER
3. SPEAKER
4. HINGE ASM - COMPARTMENT DOOR
5. PLATE - I/P ACSRY TRIM
6. TRAY ASM-ASH

Fig. 153   Exploded view of I/P assembly. Regal

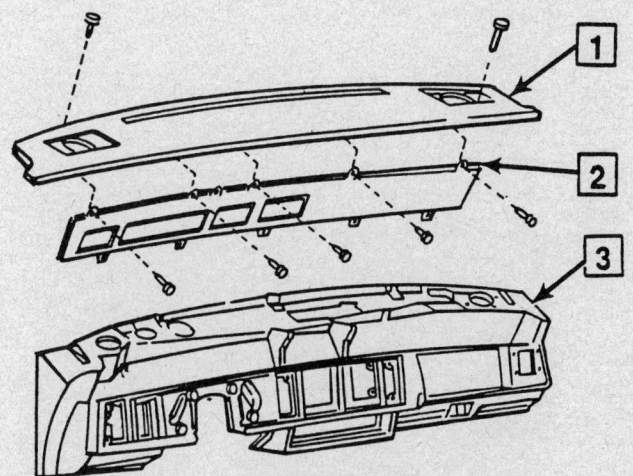

1- INSTRUMENT PANEL PAD
2- INSTRUMENT PANEL / CLUSTER BEZEL
3- INSTRUMENT PANEL CARRIER

Fig. 154   I/P pad removal. Regal

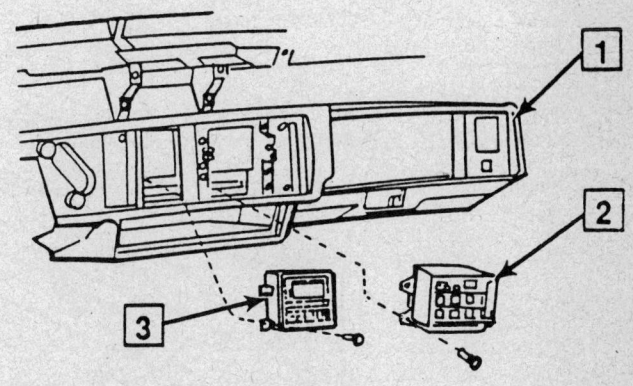

1- INSTRUMENT PANEL CARRIER
2- HEATER AND A/C CONTROL
3- RADIO CONTROL

Fig. 155   Removing radio control. Regal

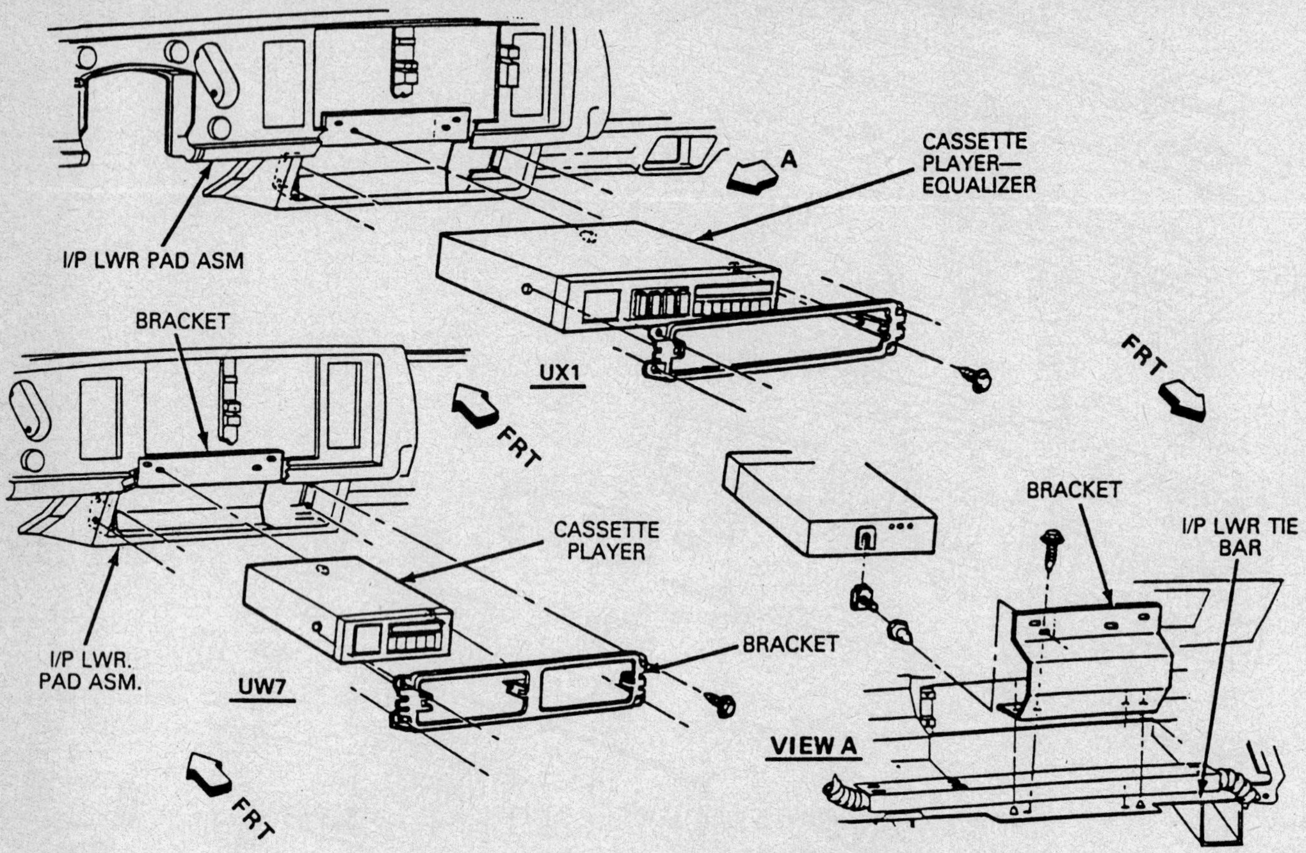

I/P LWR PAD ASM

CASSETTE PLAYER—EQUALIZER

A

BRACKET

UX1

FRT

I/P LWR. PAD ASM.

BRACKET

CASSETTE PLAYER

UW7

FRT

BRACKET

BRACKET

I/P LWR TIE BAR

VIEW A

FRT

Fig. 156 Cassette & equalizer removal. Regal

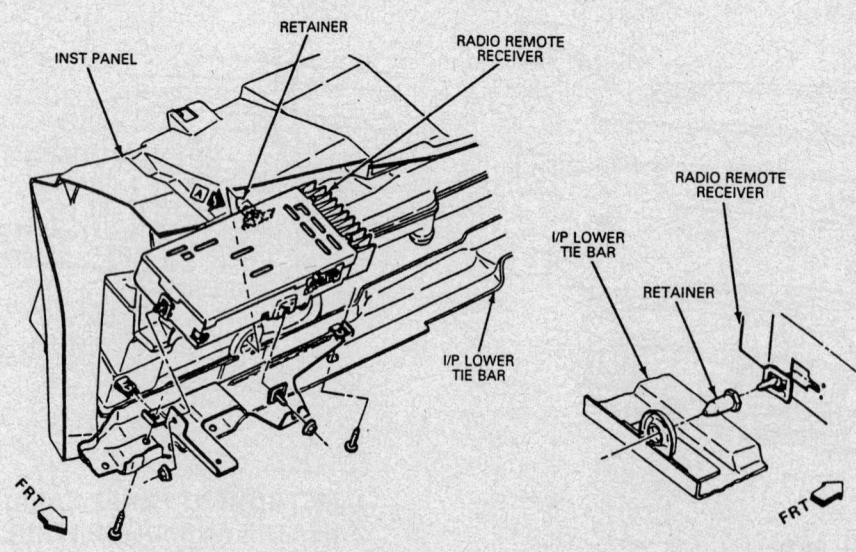

INST PANEL

RETAINER

RADIO REMOTE RECEIVER

RADIO REMOTE RECEIVER

I/P LOWER TIE BAR

RETAINER

I/P LOWER TIE BAR

FRT

FRT

Fig. 157 Radio remote receiver removal. Regal

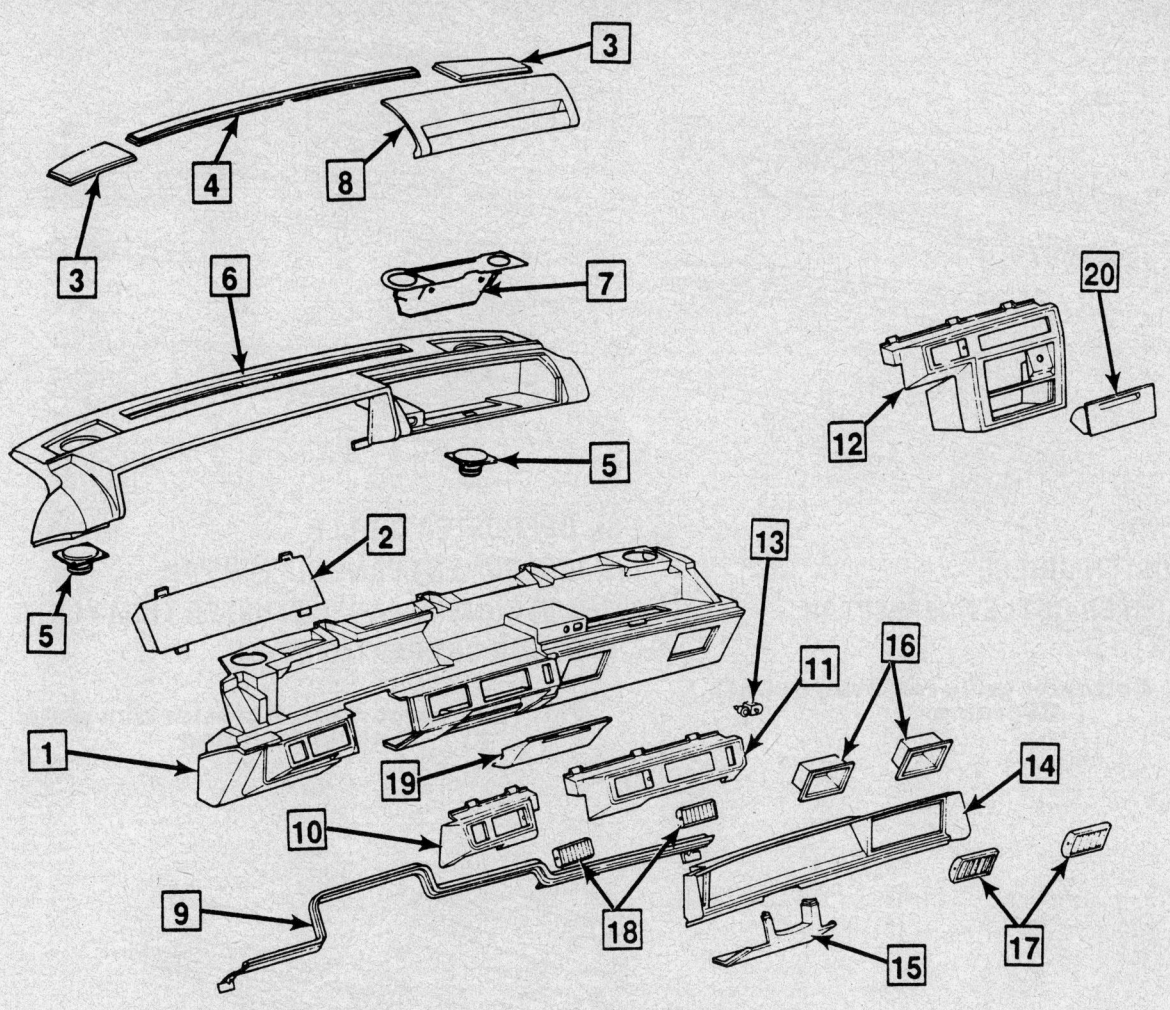

1- INSTRUMENT PANEL CARRIER
2- INSTRUMENT CLUSTER
3- SPEAKER COVERS
4- DEFROSTER GRILLE
5- SPEAKER
6- INSTRUMENT PANEL UPPER PAD
7- LOWER COMPARTMENT
8- COMPARTMENT DOOR (SPORT OPTION)
9- INSTRUMENT PANEL CARRIER TIE BAR
10- LEFT AIR OUTLET PLATE ASSEMBLY

11- LEFT CENTER AIR OUTLET PLATE ASSEMBLY
12- LEFT CENTER AIR OUTLET PLATE ASSEMBLY (SPORT OPTION)
13- SWITCH INSTRUMENT PANEL COMPARTMENT LIGHT
14- INSTRUMENT CLUSTER TRIM PLATE
15- STEERING COLUMN LOWER FILLER
16- RIGHT AND RIGHT CENTER AIR OUTLET HOUSING S
17- RIGHT AND RIGHT CENTER AIR OUTLET GRILLES
18- LEFT AND LEFT CENTER AIR OUTLET GRILLES
19- ASH TRAY
20- ASH TRAY (SPORT OPTION)

Fig. 158 Exploded view of I/P. Cutlass Supreme

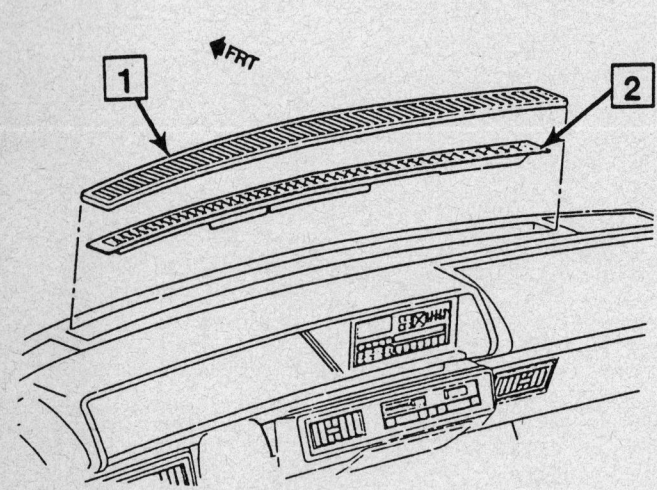

1- DEFROSTER GRILLE
2- DEFROSTER OUTLET DEFLECTOR

Fig. 159   Defroster grille removal. Cutlass Supreme

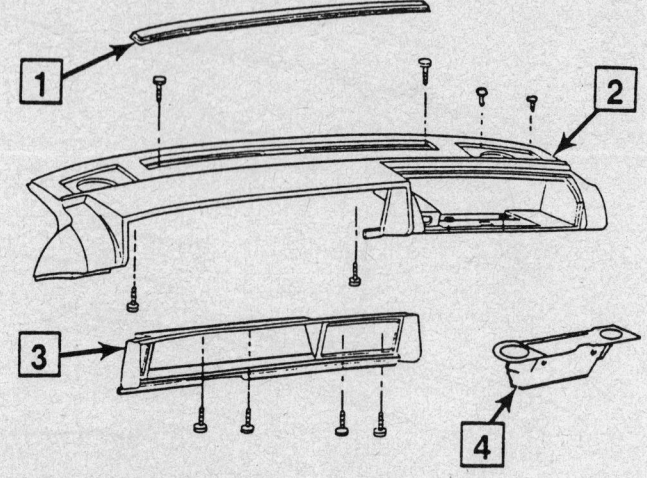

1- DEFROSTER GRILLE
2- INSTRUMENT PANEL UPPER PAD
3- INSTRUMENT PANEL CLUSTER TRIM PLATE
4- LOWER COMPARTMENT

Fig. 160   Removing I/P cluster trim plate. Cutlass Supreme

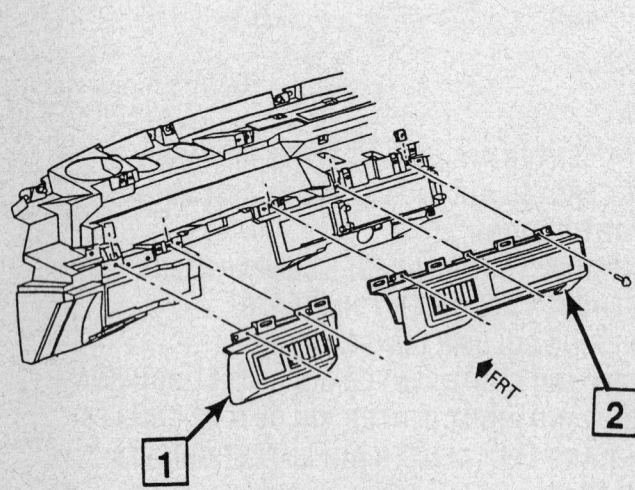

1- LEFT AIR OUTLET PLATE ASSEMBLY
2- LEFT CENTER AIR OUTLET PLATE ASSEMBLY

Fig. 161   Removing air outlet plate assemblies. Cutlass Supreme

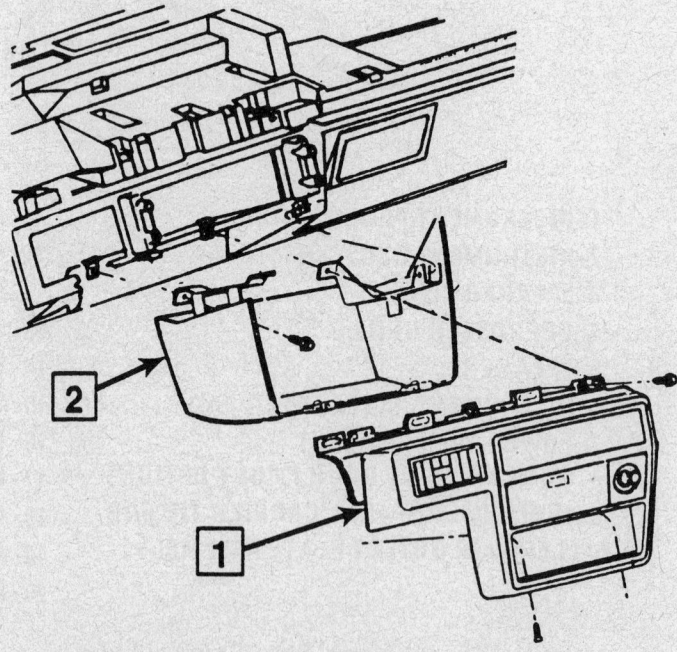

1- LEFT CENTER AIR OUTLET ASSEMBLY
2- FILLER

Fig. 162   Sport pod removal. Cutlass Supreme

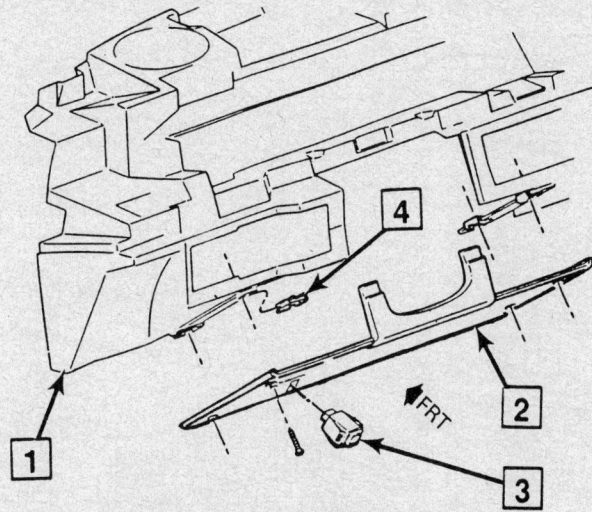

1- INSTRUMENT PANEL CARRIER
2- STEERING COLUMN LOWER FILLER
3- REAR COMPARTMENT LID RELEASE SWITCH
4- LID RELEASE SWITCH WIRE HARNESS CONNECTOF

**Fig. 163   Steering column trim plate removal.
Cutlass Supreme**

10. Remove seven steering column cover retaining screws.
11. Remove two trim bezel retaining screws, **Fig. 190.**
12. Disconnect control/defogger switch electrical connector.
13. Disconnect rear wiper/washer switch, if equipped.
14. Disconnect two electrical connectors and cigar lighter from trim bezel.
15. Remove trim bezel, then four cluster bezel retaining screws.
16. Disconnect hazard flasher and dimmer switch electrical connectors.
17. Remove four instrument cluster retaining screws, **Fig. 191.**
18. Disconnect speedometer cable and remaining electrical connectors from instrument cluster.
19. Remove instrument cluster.
20. Remove two cup holder retaining screws, then the cup holder.
21. Remove four radio retaining screws, then pull radio from console.
22. Disconnect two radio electrical connectors and antenna from radio.
23. Remove three glove box door scuff plate retaining screws.
24. Remove one side trim panel retaining screw, **Fig. 192.**
25. Remove cowl side trim, then five glove box and trim assembly retaining screws, **Fig. 193.**
26. Pull glove box out of trim assembly,

then disconnect speaker electrical connector.
27. Remove glove box and trim assembly.
28. Remove glove box retaining pins and glove box door from trim panel.
29. Remove four heater and A/C control unit retaining screws.
30. Remove remaining console retaining screws, then the console.
31. Remove five instrument panel retaining screws, **Fig. 194.**
32. Disconnect three instrument panel electrical connectors and one relay unit from left side of instrument panel.
33. Remove one electrical connector from right side of instrument panel, then disconnect defroster duct retainers and remove instrument panel.
34. Reverse procedure to install.

STORM

1. Disconnect battery ground cable. **After disconnecting battery, wait 10 minutes before proceeding with removal procedure. The Energy Reserve Module in the DERM may maintain SIR system voltage for a period after the battery is disconnected.**
2. Pull out on switch bezel, **Fig. 195,**

then disconnect electrical connectors and remove bezel.
3. Pull out on cigar lighter bezel, then disconnect cigar lighter electrical connector and remove bezel, **Fig. 195.**
4. Remove two hood release retaining screws, then disconnect hood release cable, **Fig. 196.**
5. Remove knee bezel retaining screws and nuts.
6. Remove two glove box hinge pins, then the glove box.
7. Remove front console mounting bracket.
8. Remove two meter hood hole covers, **Fig. 197.**
9. Remove four meter hood retaining screws.
10. Disconnect lighting and windshield wiper switch electrical connectors.
11. Remove meter hood and meter assembly.
12. Remove front cover hole covers, **Fig. 198.**
13. Remove three bolts and two screws from front cover assembly, then the front cover.
14. Remove four bolts, two screws and one nut attaching instrument panel assembly.
15. Remove electrical harness to instrument panel retaining clips.
16. Remove instrument panel assembly.
17. Reverse procedure to install.

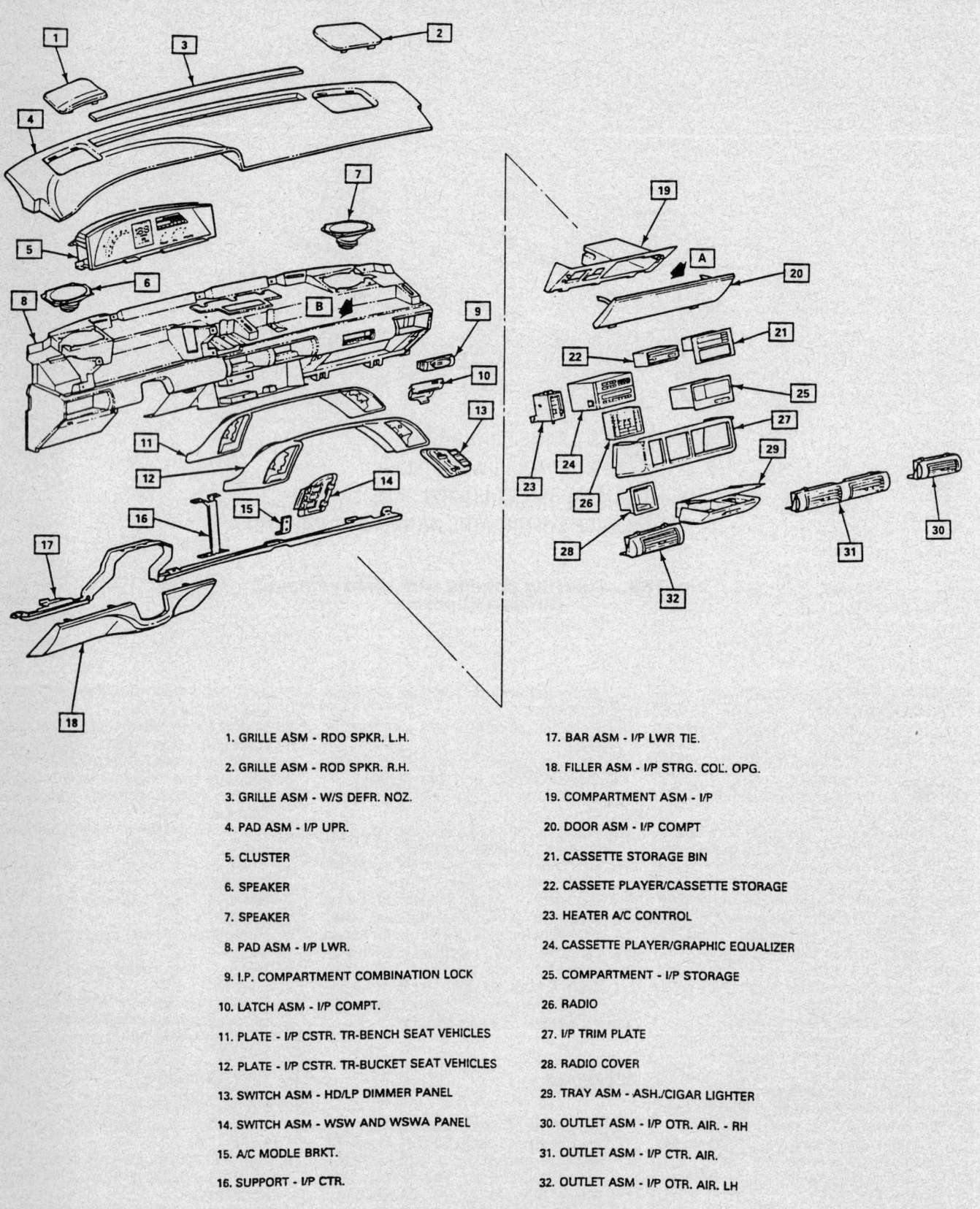

1. GRILLE ASM - RDO SPKR. L.H.

2. GRILLE ASM - ROD SPKR. R.H.

3. GRILLE ASM - W/S DEFR. NOZ.

4. PAD ASM - I/P UPR.

5. CLUSTER

6. SPEAKER

7. SPEAKER

8. PAD ASM - I/P LWR.

9. I.P. COMPARTMENT COMBINATION LOCK

10. LATCH ASM - I/P COMPT.

11. PLATE - I/P CSTR. TR-BENCH SEAT VEHICLES

12. PLATE - I/P CSTR. TR-BUCKET SEAT VEHICLES

13. SWITCH ASM - HD./LP DIMMER PANEL

14. SWITCH ASM - WSW AND WSWA PANEL

15. A/C MODLE BRKT.

16. SUPPORT - I/P CTR.

17. BAR ASM - I/P LWR TIE.

18. FILLER ASM - I/P STRG. COL. OPG.

19. COMPARTMENT ASM - I/P

20. DOOR ASM - I/P COMPT

21. CASSETTE STORAGE BIN

22. CASSETE PLAYER/CASSETTE STORAGE

23. HEATER A/C CONTROL

24. CASSETTE PLAYER/GRAPHIC EQUALIZER

25. COMPARTMENT - I/P STORAGE

26. RADIO

27. I/P TRIM PLATE

28. RADIO COVER

29. TRAY ASM - ASH./CIGAR LIGHTER

30. OUTLET ASM - I/P OTR. AIR. - RH

31. OUTLET ASM - I/P CTR. AIR.

32. OUTLET ASM - I/P OTR. AIR. LH

Fig. 164   Exploded view of I/P. Grand Prix

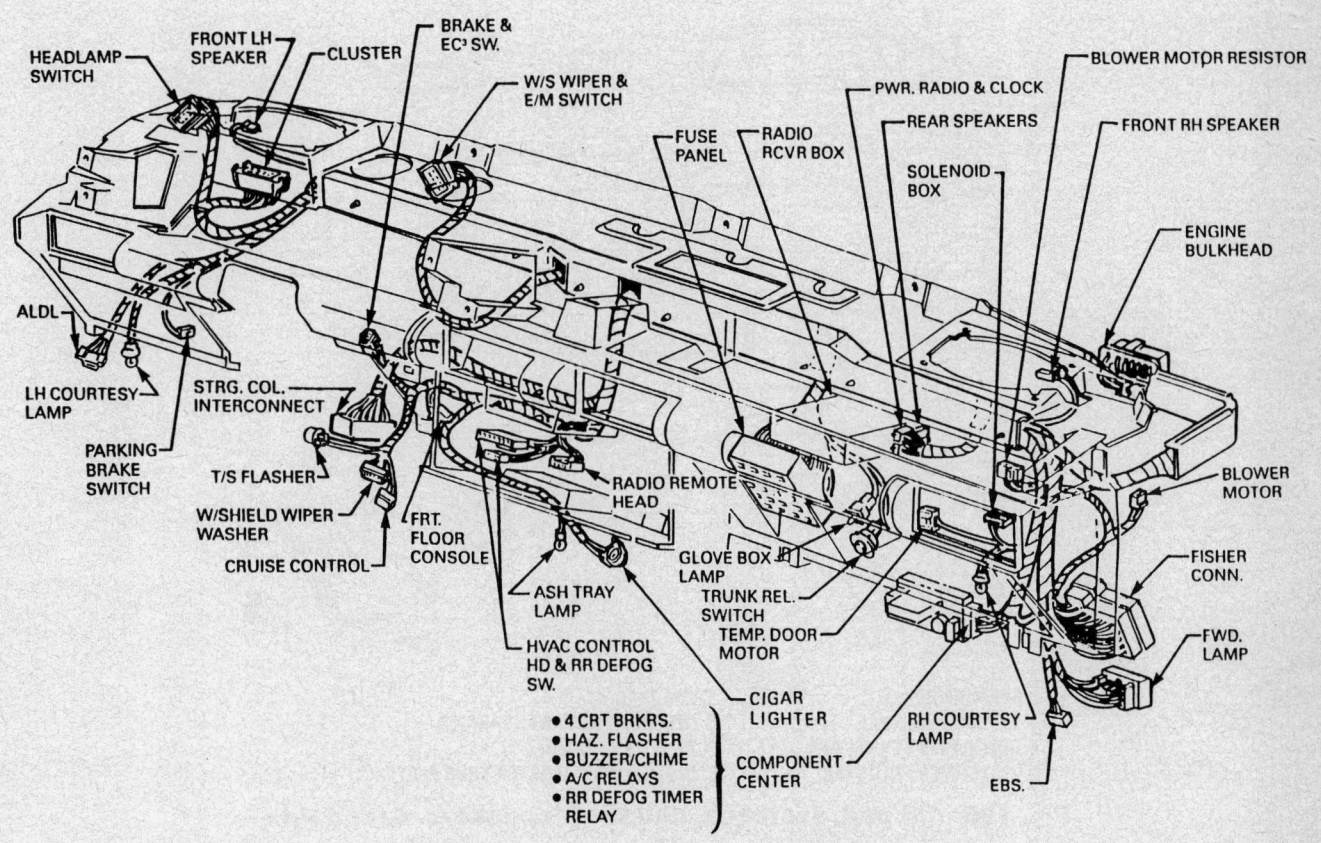

Fig. 165 I/P wiring. Grand Prix

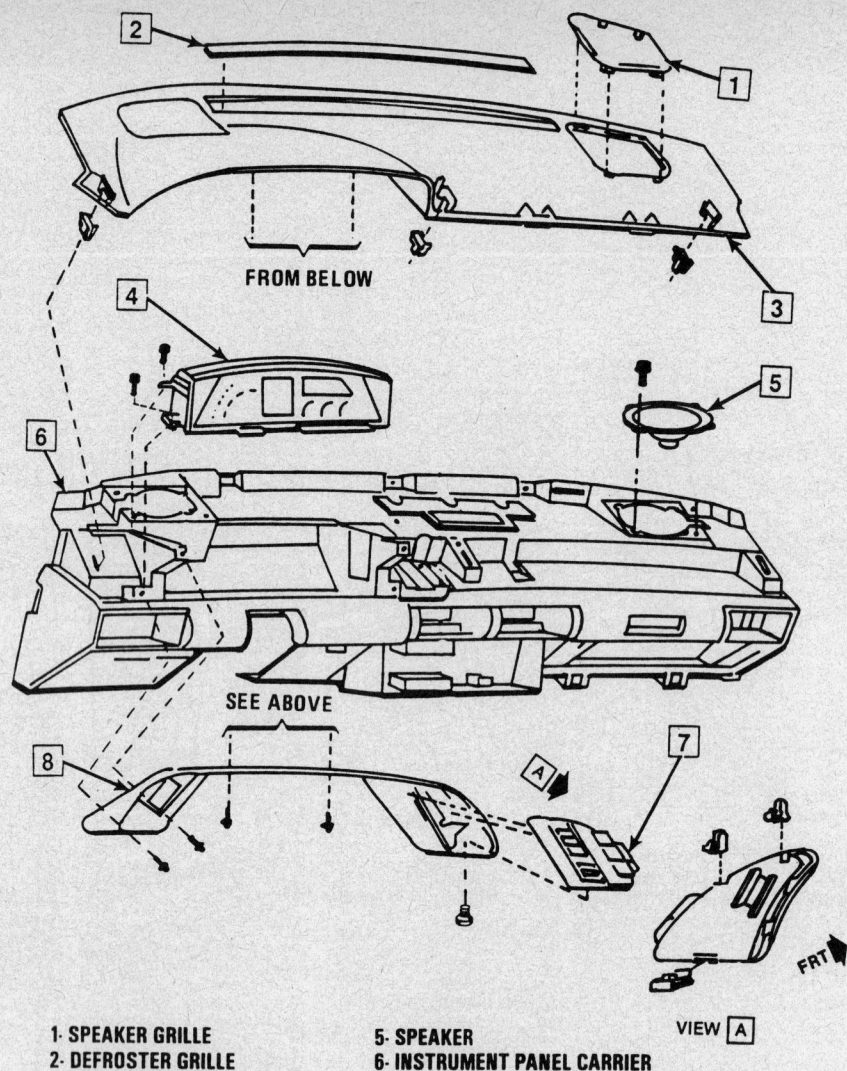

1- SPEAKER GRILLE
2- DEFROSTER GRILLE
3- INSTRUMENT PANEL PAD
4- INSTRUMENT CLUSTER
5- SPEAKER
6- INSTRUMENT PANEL CARRIER
7- SWITCH ASSEMBLY
8- INSTRUMENT CLUSTER TRIM PLATE

Fig. 166 I/P pad, switches, cluster & speakers. Grand Prix

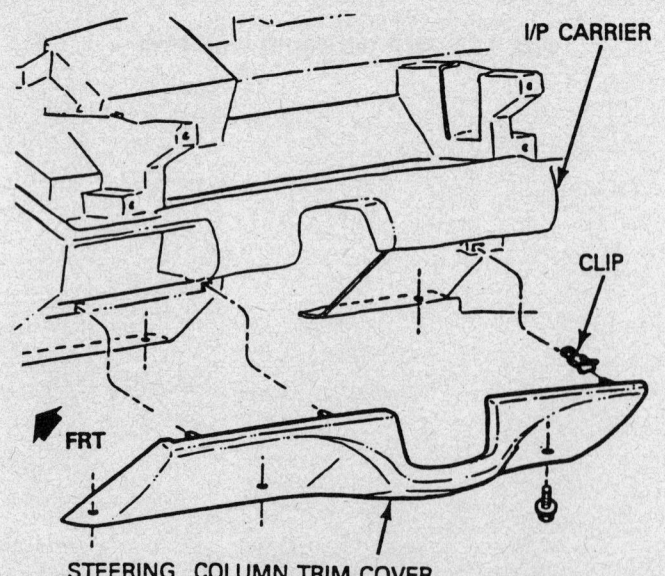

Fig. 167 Steering column trim cover removal. Grand Prix

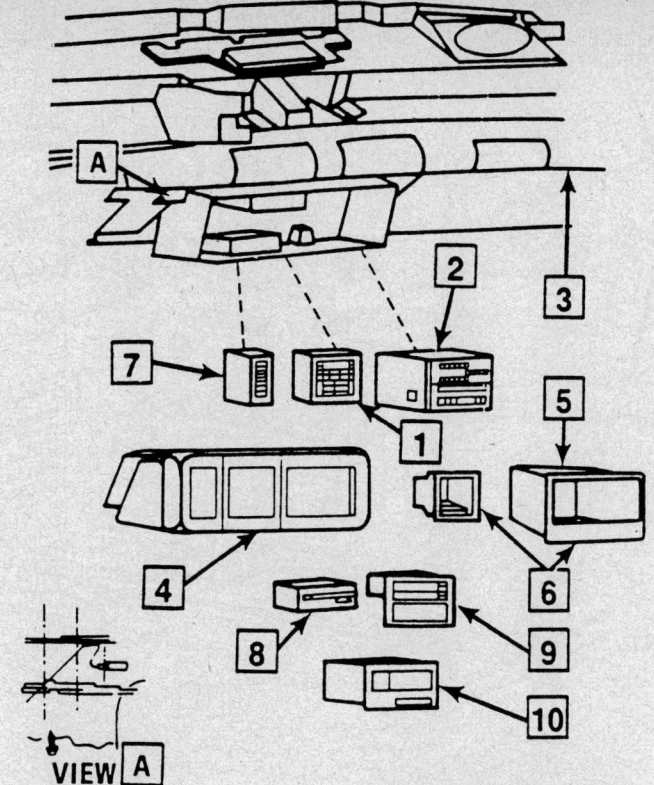

VIEW A

1- RADIO
2- CASSETTE
3- INSTRUMENT PANEL
CARRIER
4- INSTRUMENT PANEL
TRIM PLATE
5- STORAGE COMPT.
AVAILABLE W/O ITEM 2

6- STORAGE COMPT'S
AVAILABLE
W/O ITEMS 1 AND 2
7- A/C CONTROL UNIT
8- CASSETTE PLAYER
9- CASSETTE STORAGE
COMPARTMENT
10- INSTRUMENT PANEL
STORAGE
COMPARTMENT

**Fig. 168   Removing radio & ventilation
controls. 1988–89 Grand Prix (1990 similar)**

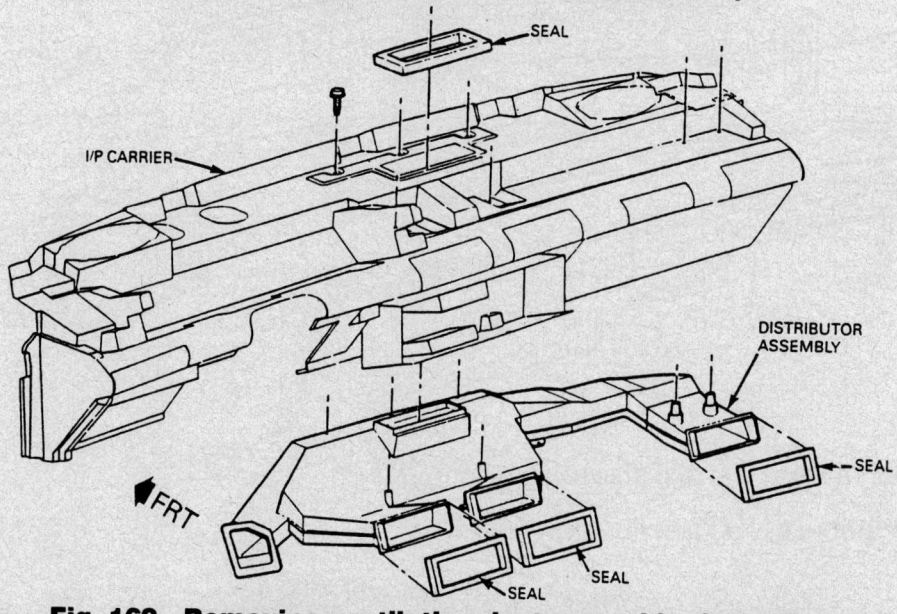

Fig. 169   Removing ventilation duct assembly. Grand Prix

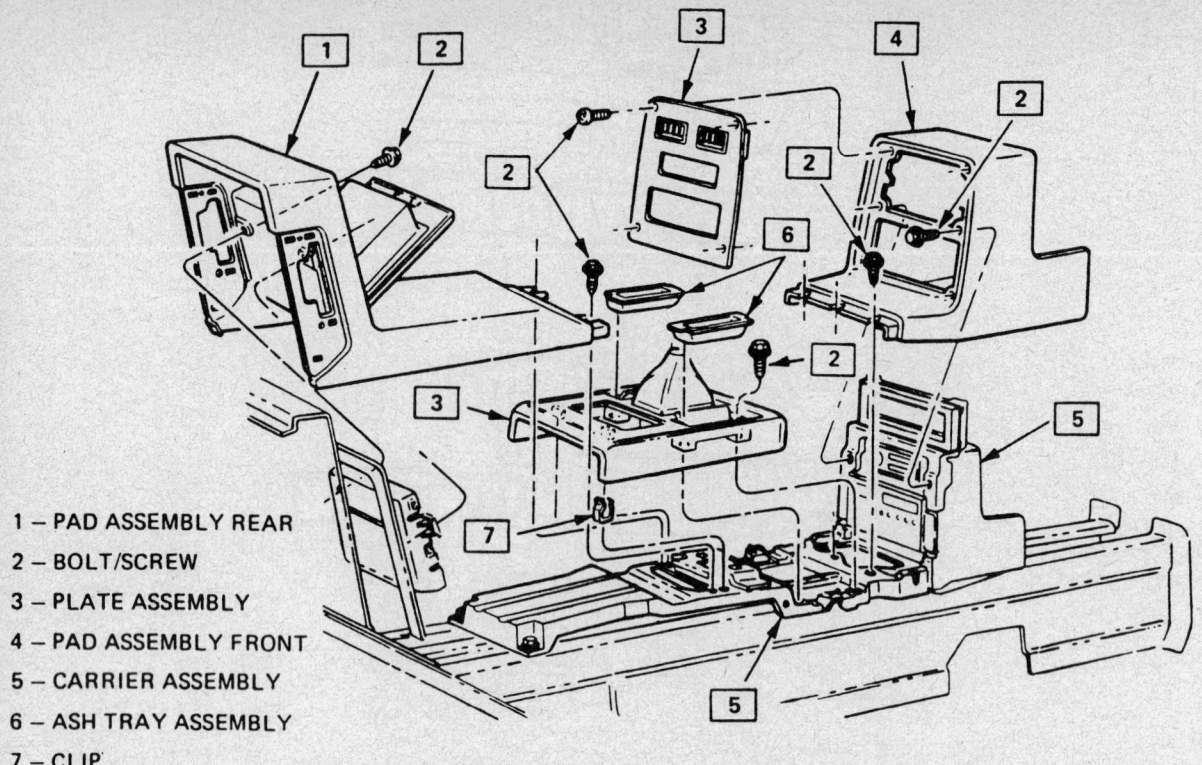

1 – PAD ASSEMBLY REAR
2 – BOLT/SCREW
3 – PLATE ASSEMBLY
4 – PAD ASSEMBLY FRONT
5 – CARRIER ASSEMBLY
6 – ASH TRAY ASSEMBLY
7 – CLIP

Fig. 170   Exploded view of console. Fiero

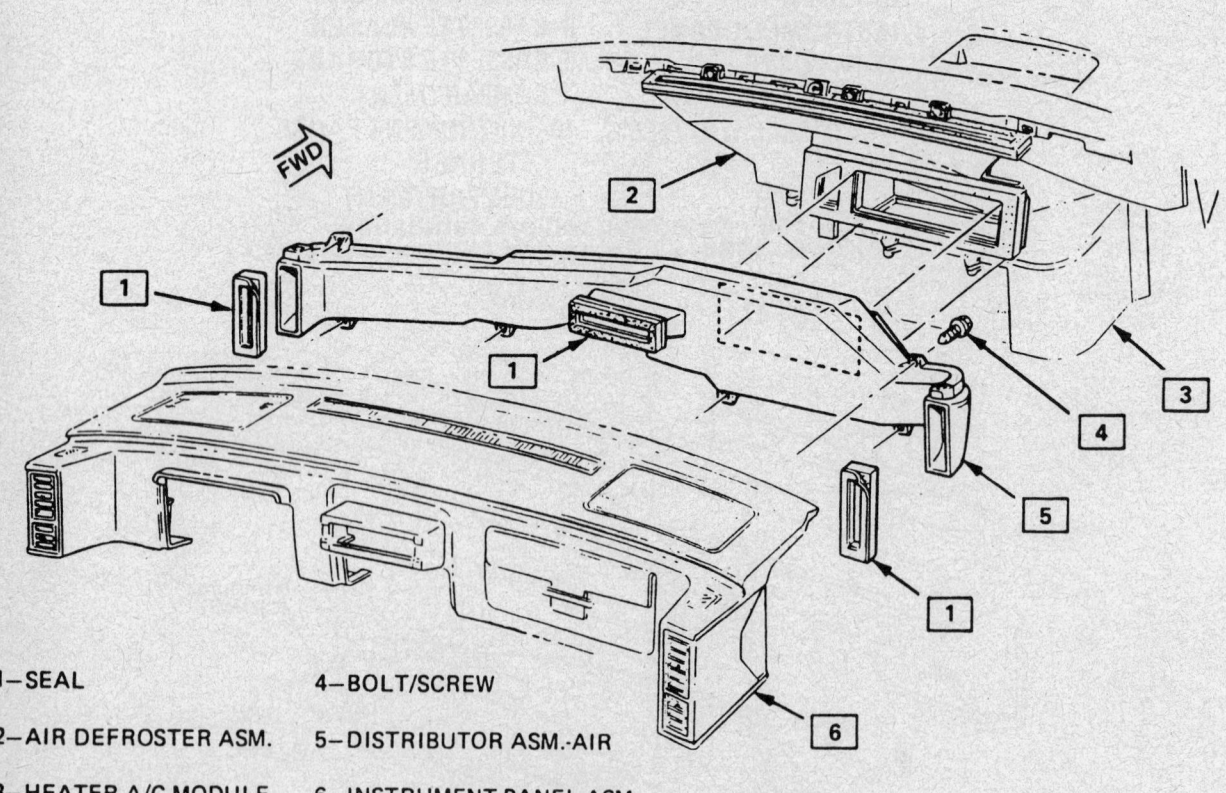

1—SEAL

2—AIR DEFROSTER ASM.

3—HEATER A/C MODULE

4—BOLT/SCREW

5—DISTRIBUTOR ASM.-AIR

6—INSTRUMENT PANEL ASM.

Fig. 171   I/P removal. Fiero

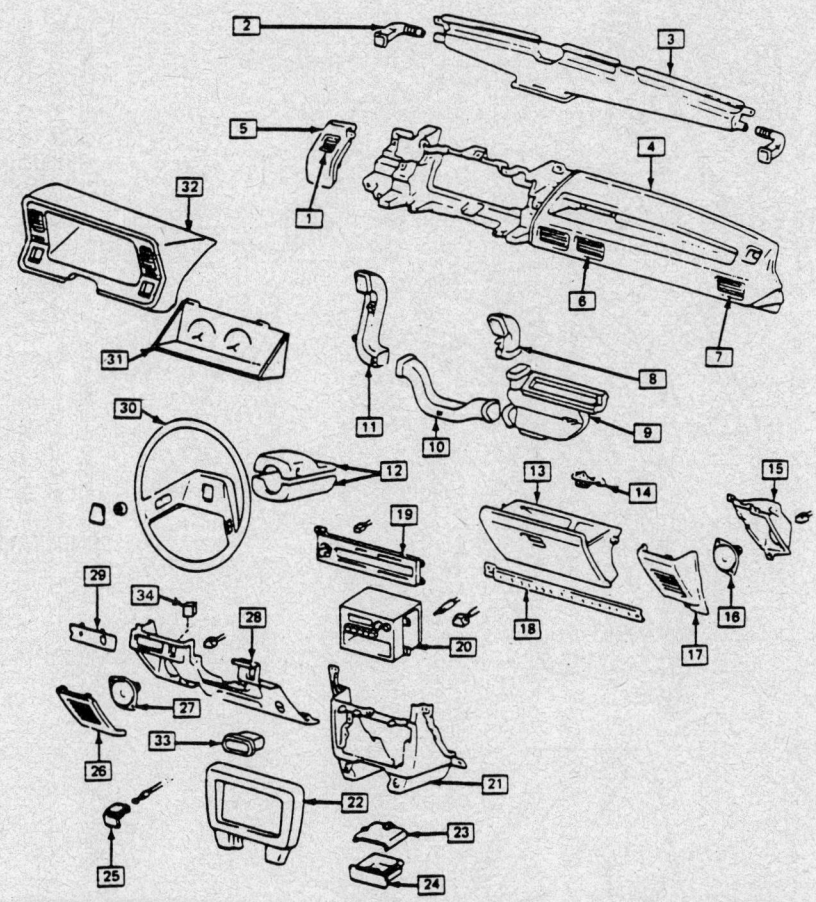

1	SIDE DEFROSTER NOZZLE	13	GLOVE COMPARTMENT DOOR	25	ENGINE HOOD RELEASE LEVER
2	SIDE DEFROSTER DUCT	14	DOOR LOCK STRIKER	26	NO. 1 SPEAKER PANEL
3	DEFROSTER NOZZLE	15	SPEAKER BRACKET	27	SPEAKER
4	SAFETY PAD	16	SPEAKER	28	LOWER FINISH PANEL
5	END FINISH PANEL	17	NO. 2 SPEAKER PANEL	29	FINISH PANEL
6	CENTER REGISTER	18	GLOVE DOOR REINFORCEMENT	30	STEERING WHEEL
7	SIDE REGISTER	19	HEATER CONTROL PANEL	31	COMBINATION METER
8	NO. 3 HEATER DUCT	20	RADIO	32	METER HOOD
9	DUCT	21	LOWER CENTER CLUSTER FINISH PANEL	33	LOWER REGISTER
10	NO. 2 HEATER DUCT	22	CENTER CLUSTER FINISH PANEL	34	ECT INDICATOR (A/T)
11	NO. 1 HEATER DUCT	23	RETAINER		
12	COLUMN HOUSING	24	ASH RECEPTACLE		

Fig. 172 I/P components. Nova

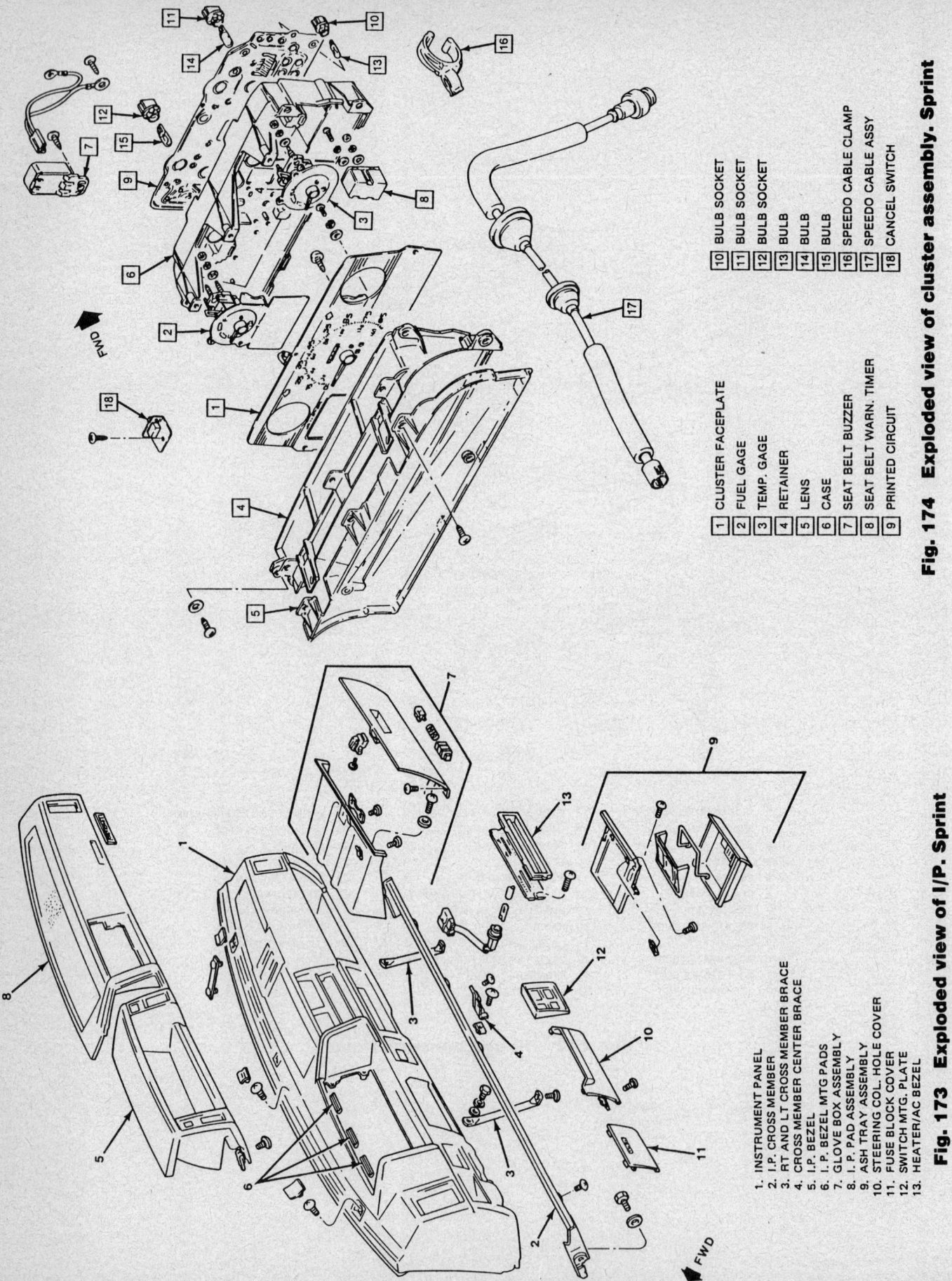

Fig. 174 Exploded view of cluster assembly. Sprint

1. CLUSTER FACEPLATE
2. FUEL GAGE
3. TEMP. GAGE
4. RETAINER
5. LENS
6. CASE
7. SEAT BELT BUZZER
8. SEAT BELT WARN. TIMER
9. PRINTED CIRCUIT
10. BULB SOCKET
11. BULB SOCKET
12. BULB SOCKET
13. BULB
14. BULB
15. BULB
16. SPEEDO CABLE CLAMP
17. SPEEDO CABLE ASSY
18. CANCEL SWITCH

Fig. 173 Exploded view of I/P. Sprint

1. INSTRUMENT PANEL
2. I.P. CROSS MEMBER
3. RT AND LT CROSS MEMBER BRACE
4. CROSS MEMBER CENTER BRACE
5. I.P. BEZEL
6. I.P. BEZEL MTG PADS
7. GLOVE BOX ASSEMBLY
8. I.P. PAD ASSEMBLY
9. ASH TRAY ASSEMBLY
10. STEERING COL. HOLE COVER
11. FUSE BLOCK COVER
12. SWITCH MTG. PLATE
13. HEATER/AC BEZEL

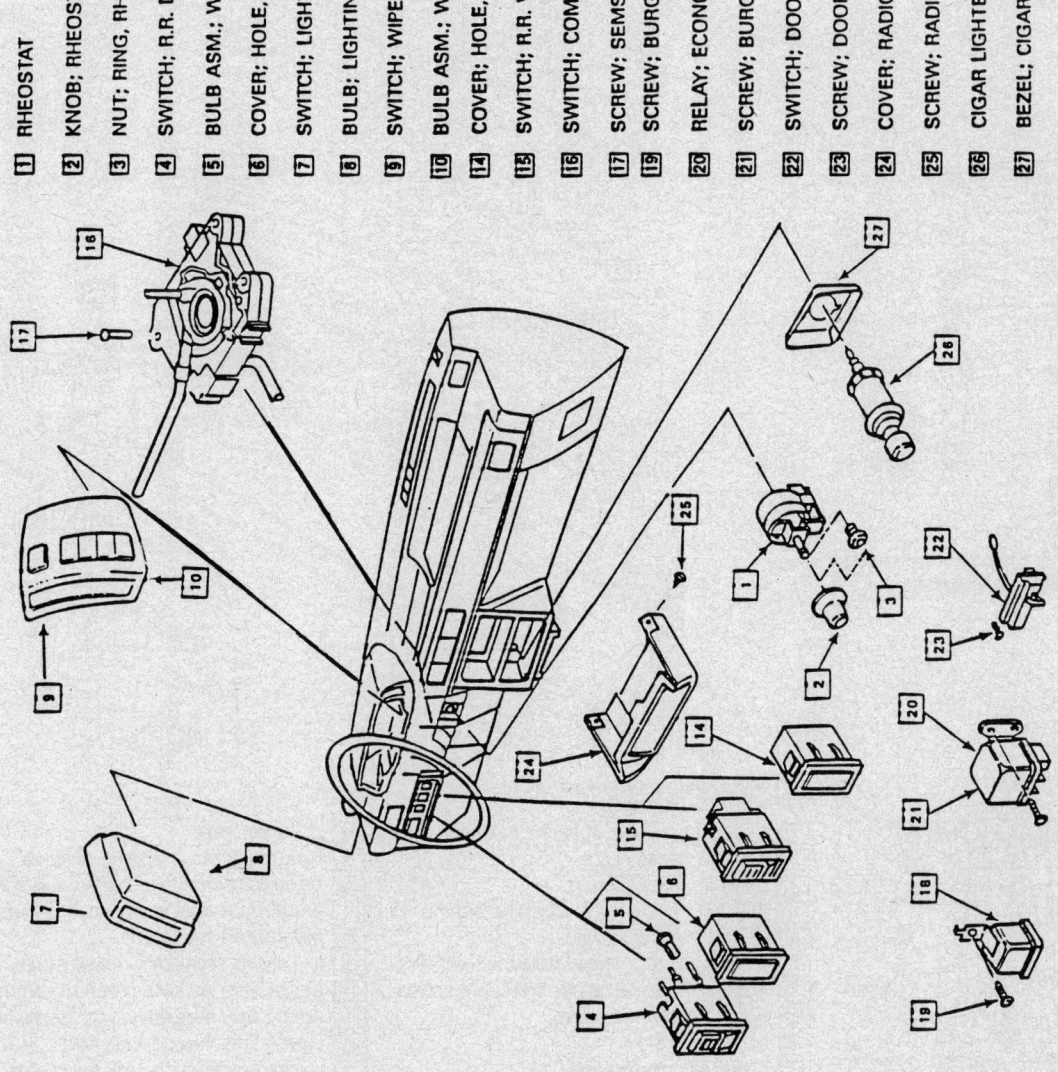

1. RHEOSTAT
2. KNOB: RHEOSTAT
3. NUT; RING, RHEOSTAT
4. SWITCH; R.R. DEFOGGER
5. BULB ASM.; W/SOCKET, R.R. DEFOGGER SW.
6. COVER; HOLE, SW., R.R. DEFOGGER
7. SWITCH; LIGHTING
8. BULB; LIGHTING SW.
9. SWITCH; WIPER AND WASHER
10. BULB ASM.; W/SOCKET, WIPER & WASHER SW.
14. COVER; HOLE, SW., R.R. WIPER
15. SWITCH; R.R. WIPER AND WASHER
16. SWITCH; COMB. W/PASSING
17. SCREW; SEMS, COMB. SW.
19. SCREW; BURG., BUZZER
20. RELAY; ECONOMY LIGHT
21. SCREW; BURG. RELAY
22. SWITCH; DOOR
23. SCREW; DOOR SW.
24. COVER; RADIO
25. SCREW; RADIO COVER
26. CIGAR LIGHTER ASM.
27. BEZEL; CIGAR LIGHTER

Fig. 175 I/P electrical components. Spectrum

Fig. 176   Disconnecting I/P electrical connector. Spectrum

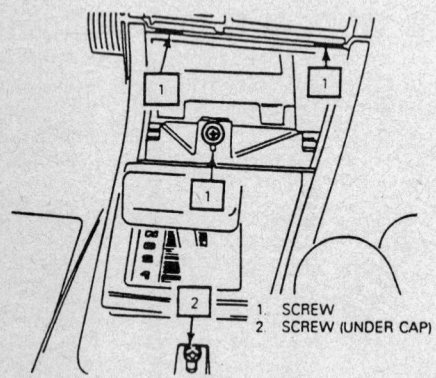

1. SCREW
2. SCREW (UNDER CAP)

Fig. 177   Front center console removal. LeMans

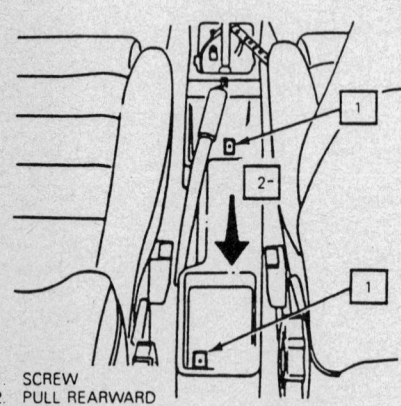

1. SCREW
2. PULL REARWARD

Fig. 178   Center console removal. LeMans

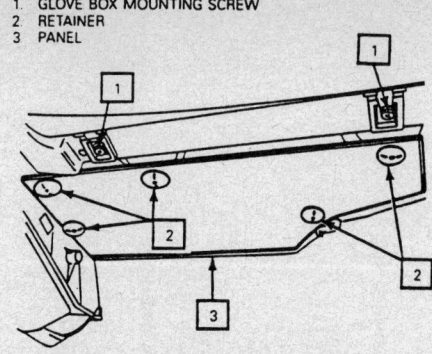

1. GLOVE BOX MOUNTING SCREW
2. RETAINER
3. PANEL

Fig. 179   Removing right side hush panel. LeMans

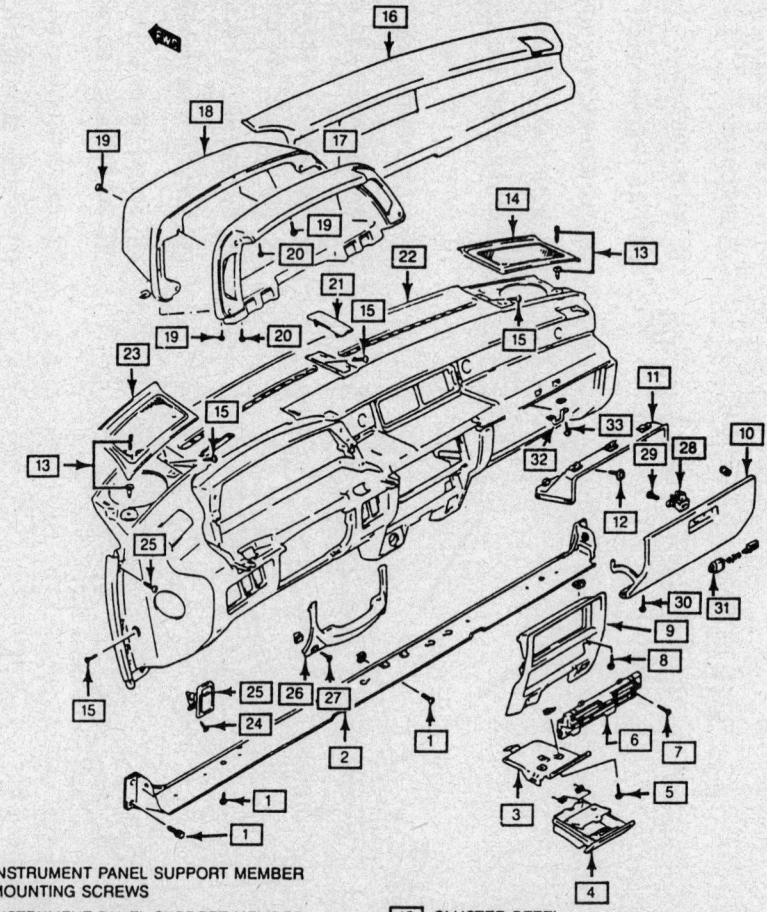

1	INSTRUMENT PANEL SUPPORT MEMBER MOUNTING SCREWS
2	INSTRUMENT PANEL SUPPORT MEMBER
3	ASHTRAY UPPER PLATE
4	ASHTRAY ASSEMBLY
5	ASHTRAY UPPER PLATE ATTACHING SCREW
6	HEATER CONTROL PANEL
7	HEATER CONTROL PANEL MOUNTING SCREW
8	INSTRUMENT PANEL BEZEL ATTACHING SCREW
9	INSTRUMENT PANEL BEZEL
10	GLOVE BOX DOOR
11	GLOVE BOX UPPER PANEL
12	GLOVE BOX UPPER PANEL ATTACHING SCREW
13	GARNISH COVER PUSH PINS
14	(RH) FRONT SPEAKER GARNISH COVER
15	INSTRUMENT MAIN PANEL ATTACHING SCREWS
16	INSTRUMENT PANEL PAD
17	CLUSTER SWITCH PANEL
18	CLUSTER BEZEL
19	CLUSTER BEZEL ATTACHING SCREWS
20	CLUSTER SWITCH PANEL ATTACHING SCREWS
21	INSTRUMENT MAIN PANEL ACCESS PANEL
22	INSTRUMENT MAIN PANEL
23	(LH) FRONT SPEAKER GARNISH PANEL
24	HOOD LATCH RELEASE LEVER MOUNTING SCREW
25	HOOD LATCH RELEASE LEVER ASSEMBLY
26	LOWER STEERING COLUMN PANEL
27	LOWER STEERING COLUMN PANEL ATTACHING SCREW
28	GLOVEBOX LATCH ASSEMBLY
29	GLOVEBOX LATCH ASSEMBLY ATTACHING SCREW
30	GLOVEBOX DOOR MOUNTING SCREW
31	GLOVEBOX LATCH BUTTON
32	GLOVEBOX STRIKER
33	GLOVEBOX STRIKER MOUNTING SCREW

Fig. 180   Exploded view of I/P. Metro

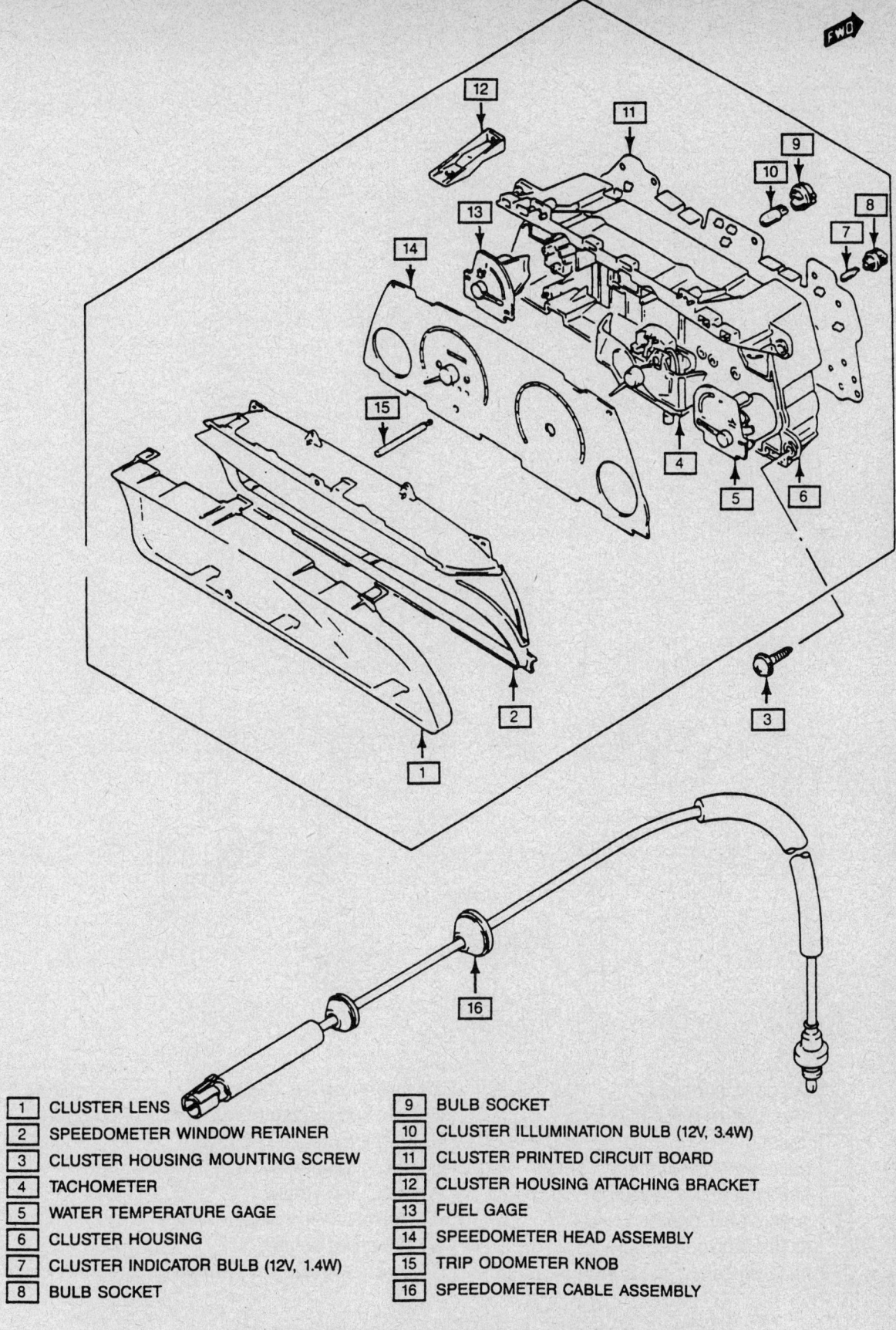

1	CLUSTER LENS	9	BULB SOCKET
2	SPEEDOMETER WINDOW RETAINER	10	CLUSTER ILLUMINATION BULB (12V, 3.4W)
3	CLUSTER HOUSING MOUNTING SCREW	11	CLUSTER PRINTED CIRCUIT BOARD
4	TACHOMETER	12	CLUSTER HOUSING ATTACHING BRACKET
5	WATER TEMPERATURE GAGE	13	FUEL GAGE
6	CLUSTER HOUSING	14	SPEEDOMETER HEAD ASSEMBLY
7	CLUSTER INDICATOR BULB (12V, 1.4W)	15	TRIP ODOMETER KNOB
8	BULB SOCKET	16	SPEEDOMETER CABLE ASSEMBLY

Fig. 181 Exploded view of cluster assembly. Metro

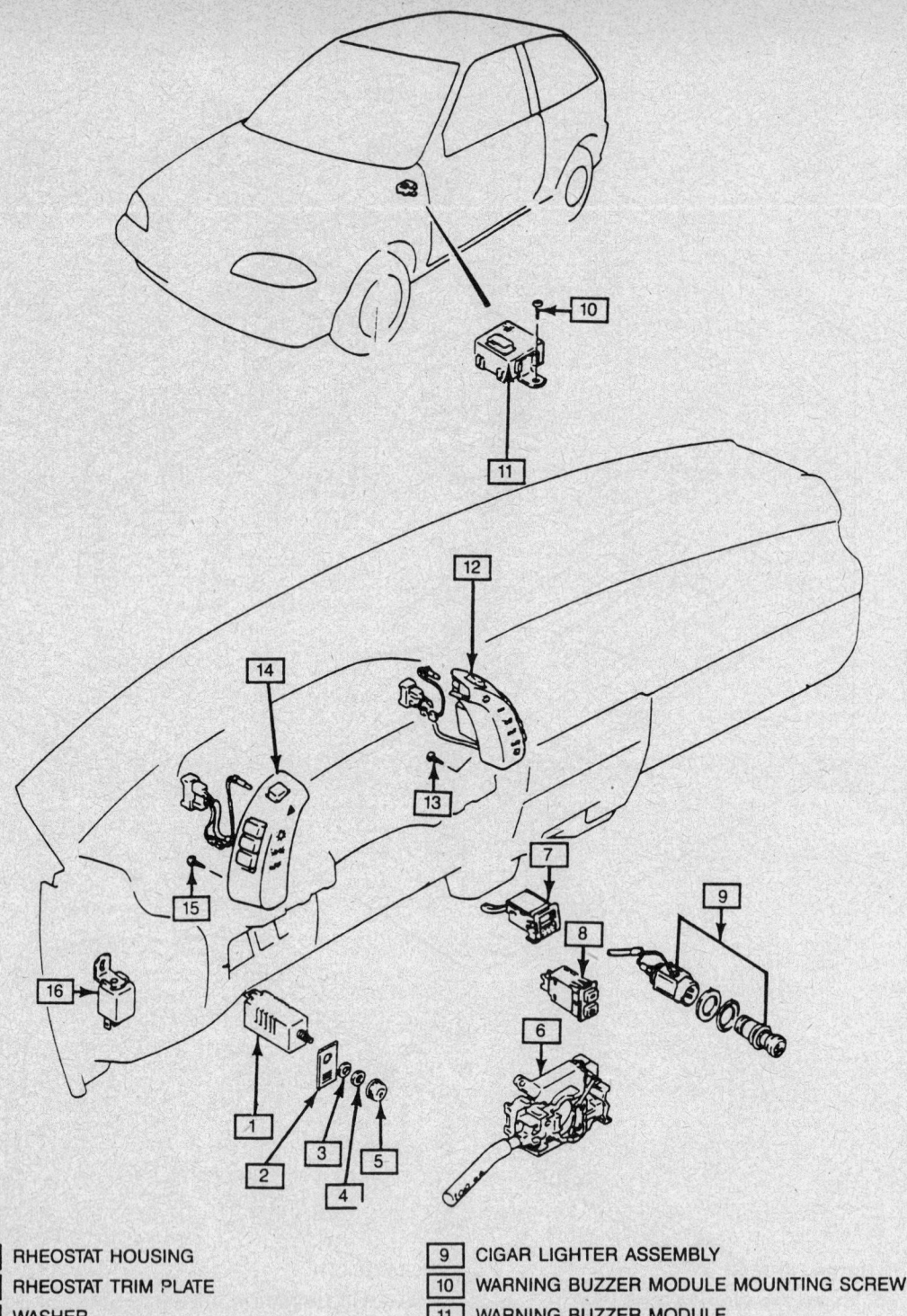

1	RHEOSTAT HOUSING	9	CIGAR LIGHTER ASSEMBLY
2	RHEOSTAT TRIM PLATE	10	WARNING BUZZER MODULE MOUNTING SCREW
3	WASHER	11	WARNING BUZZER MODULE
4	RHEOSTAT RETAINING NUT	12	FRONT WINDSHIELD WIPER SWITCH
5	RHEOSTAT ADJUSTING KNOB	13	ATTACHING SCREW
6	TURN SIGNAL/DIMMER SWITCH	14	LIGHT/HAZARD FLASHER SWITCH
7	REAR DEFOGGER SWITCH	15	ATTACHING SCREW
8	REAR WIPER/WASHER SWITCH	16	FLASHER (TURN AND HAZARD)

Fig. 182 I/P electrical components. Metro

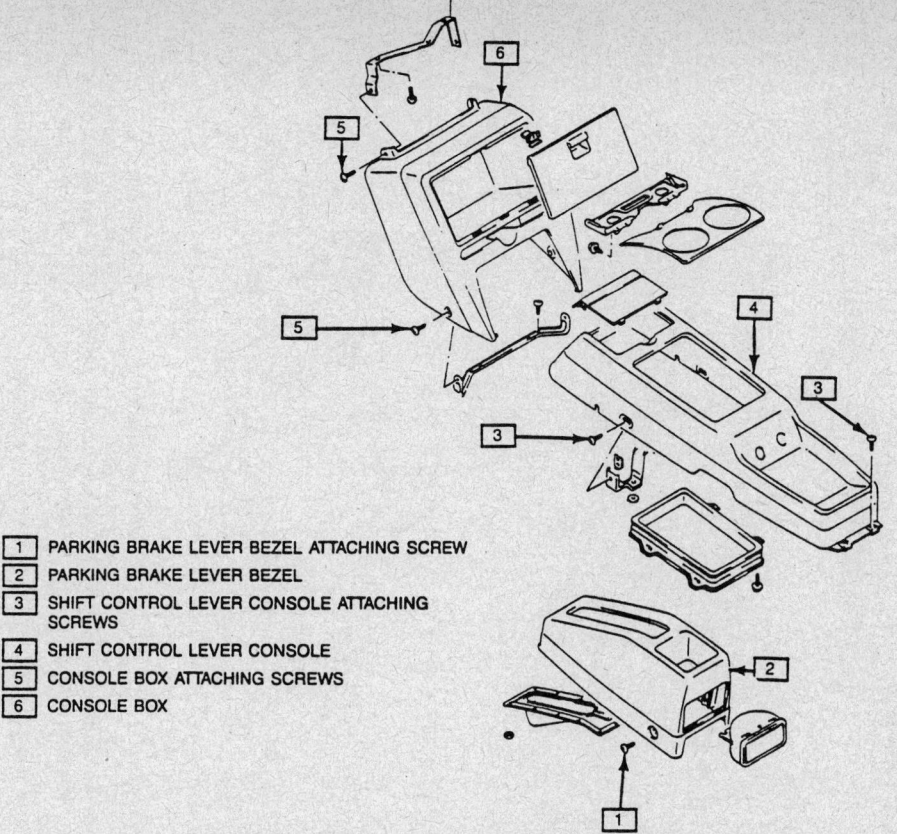

1. PARKING BRAKE LEVER BEZEL ATTACHING SCREW
2. PARKING BRAKE LEVER BEZEL
3. SHIFT CONTROL LEVER CONSOLE ATTACHING SCREWS
4. SHIFT CONTROL LEVER CONSOLE
5. CONSOLE BOX ATTACHING SCREWS
6. CONSOLE BOX

Fig. 183   Exploded view of console. Metro

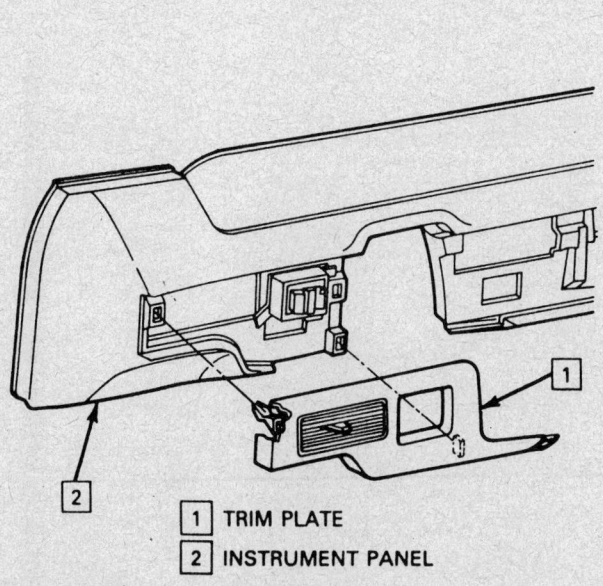

1. TRIM PLATE
2. INSTRUMENT PANEL

Fig. 184   Removing instrument panel pad. Lumina

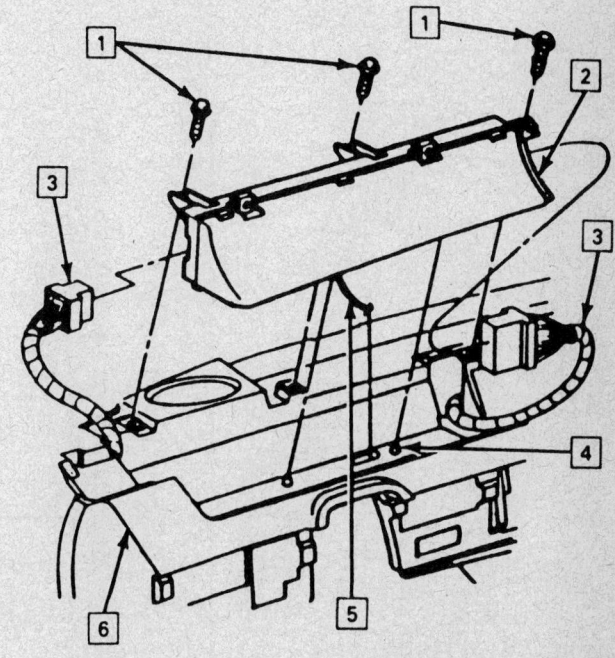

1. SCREWS
2. CLUSTER
3. CONNECTOR
4. LOCATING TAB
5. PRNDL CABLE
6. INSTRUMENT PANEL CARRIER

Fig. 185   Removing I/P cluster. Lumina

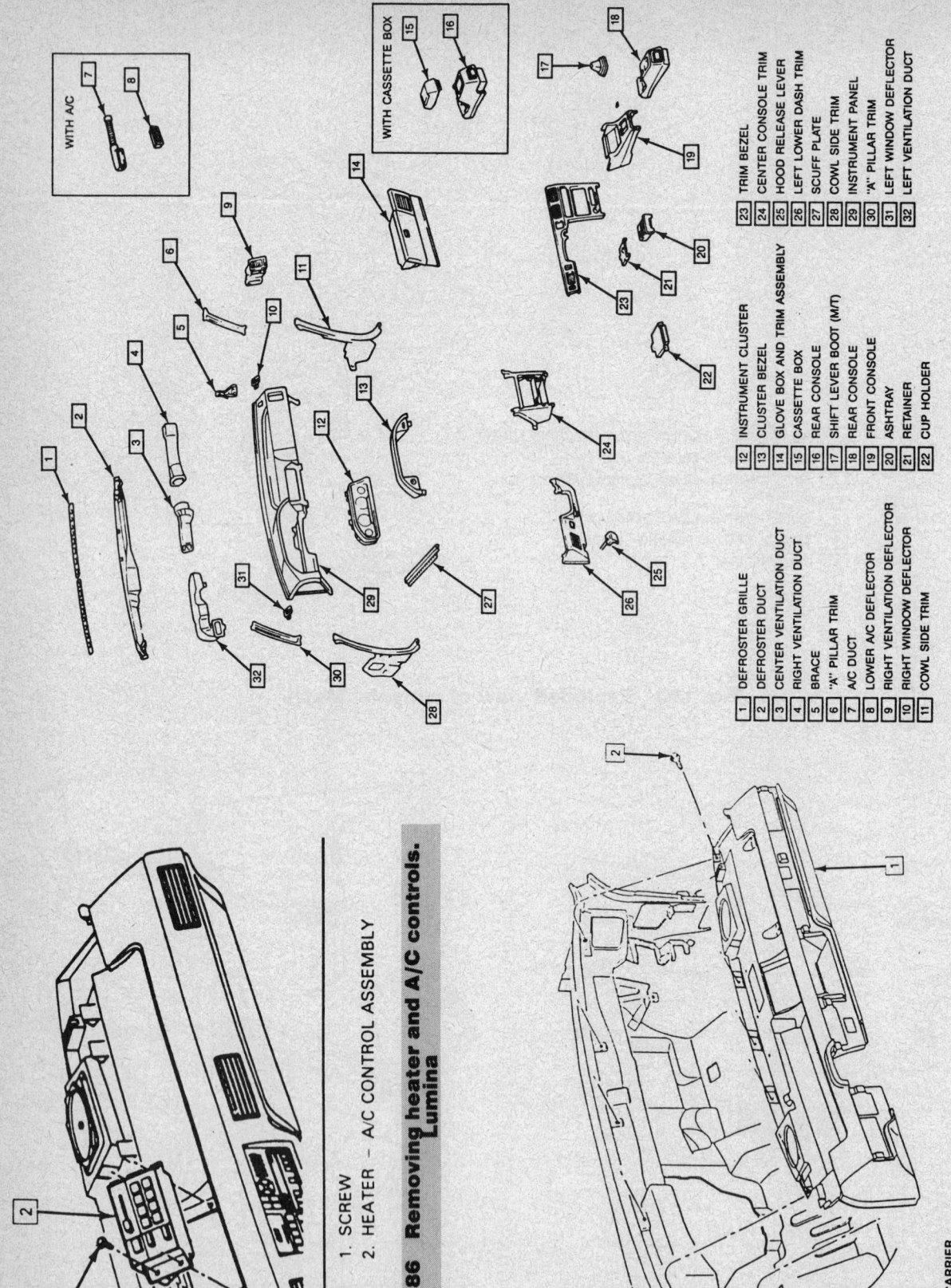

WITH A/C

WITH CASSETTE BOX

1	DEFROSTER GRILLE
2	DEFROSTER DUCT
3	CENTER VENTILATION DUCT
4	RIGHT VENTILATION DUCT
5	BRACE
6	"A" PILLAR TRIM
7	A/C DUCT
8	LOWER A/C DEFLECTOR
9	RIGHT VENTILATION DEFLECTOR
10	RIGHT WINDOW DEFLECTOR
11	COWL SIDE TRIM

12	INSTRUMENT CLUSTER
13	CLUSTER BEZEL
14	GLOVE BOX AND TRIM ASSEMBLY
15	CASSETTE BOX
16	REAR CONSOLE
17	SHIFT LEVER BOOT (M/T)
18	REAR CONSOLE
19	FRONT CONSOLE
20	ASHTRAY
21	RETAINER
22	CUP HOLDER

23	TRIM BEZEL
24	CENTER CONSOLE TRIM
25	HOOD RELEASE LEVER
26	LEFT LOWER DASH TRIM
27	SCUFF PLATE
28	COWL SIDE TRIM
29	INSTRUMENT PANEL
30	"A" PILLAR TRIM
31	LEFT WINDOW DEFLECTOR
32	LEFT VENTILATION DUCT

Fig. 188 Exploded view of I/P. Prizm

1. SCREW
2. HEATER – A/C CONTROL ASSEMBLY

Fig. 186 Removing heater and A/C controls. Lumina

1	INSTRUMENT PANEL CARRIER
2	10 N·m (89 LB. IN.)

Fig. 187 Removing I/P carrier assembly. Lumina

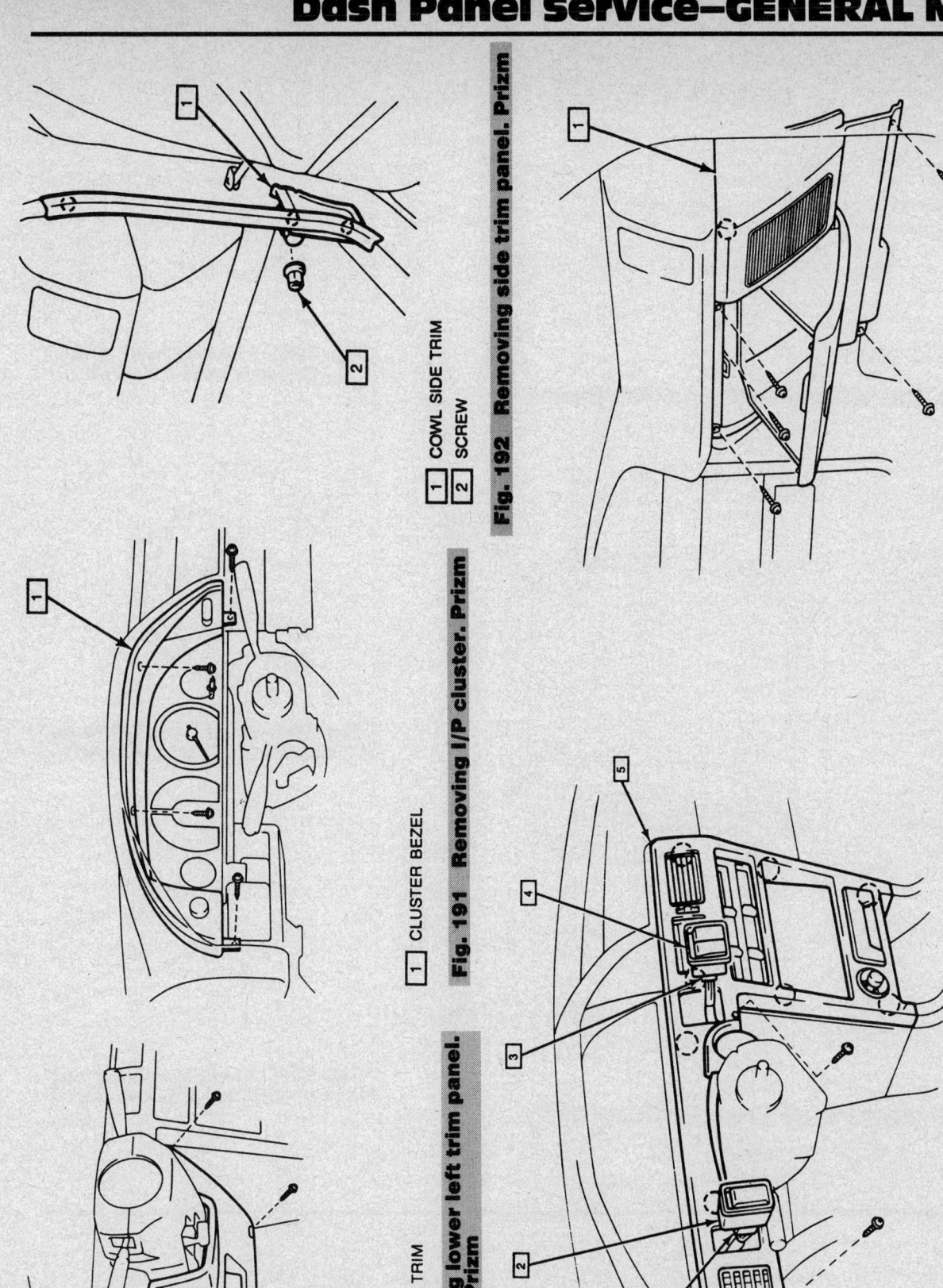

1 COWL SIDE TRIM
2 SCREW

Fig. 192 Removing side trim panel. Prizm

1 GLOVE BOX AND TRIM ASSEMBLY

Fig. 193 Removing glove box assembly. Prizm

1 CLUSTER BEZEL

Fig. 191 Removing I/P cluster. Prizm

1 LEFT LOWER DASH TRIM

Fig. 189 Removing lower left trim panel. Prizm

1 ELECTRICAL CONNECTOR
2 REAR WIPER-WASHER SWITCH
3 ELECTRICAL CONNECTOR
4 CRUISE CONTROL/DEFOGGER SWITCH
5 TRIM BEZEL

Fig. 190 Removing trim bezel. Prizm

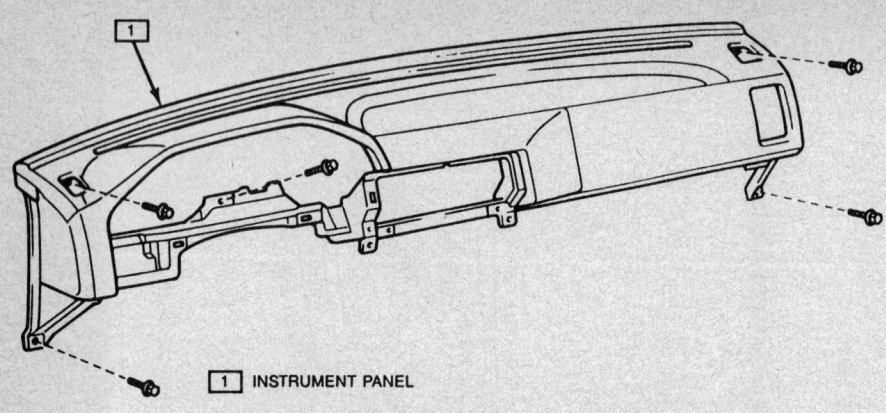

1 INSTRUMENT PANEL

Fig. 194   Removing I/P assembly. Prizm

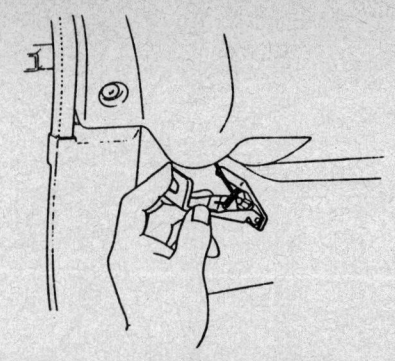

Fig. 196   Disconnecting hood release cable. Storm

1 METER HOOD
2 METER ASSEMBLY
3 FRONT COVER HOLE COVER
4 FRONT COVER
5 INSTRUMENT PANEL ASSEMBLY

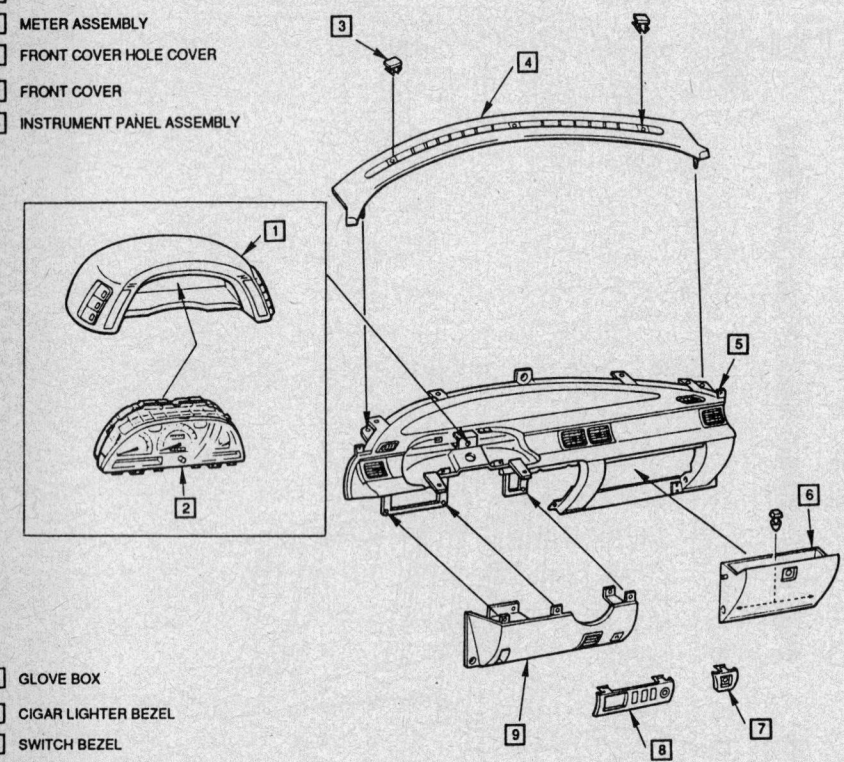

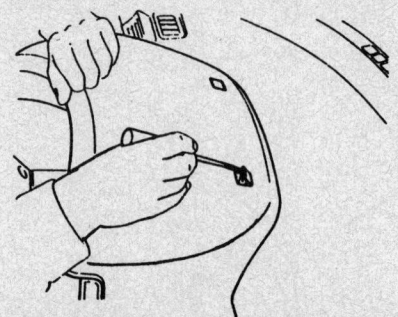

Fig. 197   Removing I/P hood retaining screws. Storm

6 GLOVE BOX
7 CIGAR LIGHTER BEZEL
8 SWITCH BEZEL
9 KNEE PAD ASSEMBLY

Fig. 195   I/P assembly. Storm

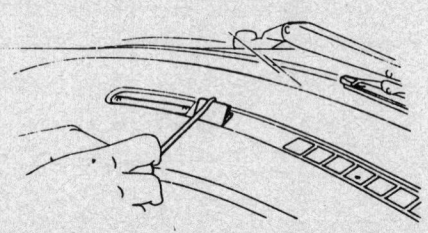

Fig. 198   Removing I/P front cover retaining screws. Storm

STEERING COLUMNS

INDEX

INDEX—Continued

When servicing collapsible steering columns, care should be exercised since they are extremely susceptible to damage. Dropping of or leaning on column or striking sharp blows on end of steering shaft or shift levers could loosen or shear plastic fasteners which maintain column rigidity.

It is important that only the specified screws, bolts and nuts be used during the mandatory reassembly sequence and torqued to specifications to insure proper breakaway action of column under impact. Avoid using excessively long bolts as they may prevent a portion of the steering column from collapsing under impact.

When removing or installing, steering wheel, ignition switch or lock, turn signal switch, adjusting transmission linkage, or installing and adjusting neutral-start or back-up light switch, refer to appropriate car chapter.

If a shift tube shows a sheared plastic injection, a new shift tube must be installed. If a steering shaft shows a sheared plastic, but it is not bent, it can be repaired by using a Service Steering Shaft Repair Kit part number 7810077. The kit contains instructions and dimensions for all steering columns. On some models, the attaching brackets will shear under impact and must also be replaced.

TROUBLESHOOTING

When troubleshooting steering columns, refer to **Figs. 1 and 2.**

STEERING COLUMN REPLACE

BUICK REAR WHEEL DRIVE MODELS

Removal

Wheels must be in a straight forward position and the key must be in the Lock position when removing or installing column to ensure proper alignment of components during installation.

1. Disconnect battery ground cable.
2. Remove bolt from intermediate shaft at lower end of column shaft.
3. Disconnect shift linkage from shift tube lever at lower end of steering column.
4. Remove steering wheel.
5. Remove left sound insulator and trim cap or lower trim panel.
6. Remove cover and seal attaching screws.
7. **On models equipped with column shift automatic transmission,** remove shift indicator cable clip from shift housing bowl.
8. **On all models,** remove two nuts from upper column support and lower column assembly. If shims are used, retain for use in installation.
9. Disconnect all wiring connectors from column and remove column from vehicle.
10. If necessary, remove column support bracket and column guide.

Installation

1. If column support bracket or column guide were removed, reinstall and **torque** column support bracket bolts to 22 ft. lbs. and column guide bolt to 18 ft. lbs.
2. Carefully place column into position in vehicle.
3. Connect all wiring to column.
4. Raise column and loosely install nuts, **Fig. 3.** Install shims, if removed.
5. Install cover and seal to dash panel and **torque** screws to 53 inch lbs.
6. Install intermediate shaft onto steering column shaft, then install clamp bolt and nut. **Torque** to 52 ft. lbs.
7. **Torque** steering column bracket nuts to 20 ft. lbs.
8. **On models equipped with column shift automatic transmission,** install shift indicator cable clip to shift housing bowl and adjust shift indicator if necessary.
9. **On all models,** connect shift linkage to shift tube lever at lower end of column.
10. Install trim cap or lower trim panel and left sound insulator.
11. Install steering wheel if removed.
12. Connect battery ground cable.
13. Adjust neutral safety switch and/or back-up light switch, if necessary.

BONNEVILLE, DEVILLE, ELECTRA, FLEETWOOD, LESABRE, 88 & 98
MODELS w/SUPPLEMENTAL INFLATABLE RESTRAINT (SIR)

Removal

Before removing the SIR steering column, **Fig. 4,** the wheels of the car must be straight and the column in the Lock position. **Care must be taken when handling column with a live inflator module. Never point bag deploy surface toward you, and never stand column on steering wheel. Accidental deployment in these positions may cause injury. Always face bag deploy surface toward open space to allow for unrestricted expansion.**

The (DERM) Diagnostic Energy Reserve Module, can maintain sufficient voltage to cause a deployment for up to 10 minutes after the ignition switch is turned to the Off position and the battery ground has been disconnected.

1. Remove the inflator module as follows:
   a. With the ignition switch in the Off position and the battery ground cable disconnected and taped, remove the SIR fuse (No. 3) from the fuse panel.
   b. Remove left side sound insulator.
   c. Disconnect the yellow two way harness connector at the base of steering column.
   d. Remove the Torx screws from the back of the steering wheel, then remove the inflator module from steering wheel.
   e. Remove the horn contact by pushing lightly and twisting counterclockwise.
   f. Disconnect the coil assembly connector from inflator module.
2. Snap out the instrument panel steering column trim plate.
3. Remove two screws retaining filler, then four bolt/screws from column reinforcement plate and the reinforcement plate.
4. Disconnect any necessary electrical connectors.
5. Disconnect shift control cable at actu-

ALL COLUMNS (NO MARK)
TILT COLUMN ONLY*

LOCK SYSTEM

Will Not Unlock
1. Shear flange on sector shaft collapsed.
2. Lock bolt damaged.
3. Damaged lock cylinder.
4. Damaged housing.
5. Damaged sector.
6. Damaged rack.

Will Not Lock
1. Lock bolt spring broken or defective.
2. Damaged sector.
3. Damaged lock cylinder
4. Burr on lock bolt.
5. Damaged housing.
6. Transmission linkage adjustment incorrect.
7. Damaged rack.
8. Interference between bowl and rack coupling*.
9. Ignition switch stuck.
10. Actuator rod restricted.

High Lock Effort
1. Lock cylinder damaged.
2. Ignition switch damaged.
3. Rack preload spring broken or deformed.
4. Burrs on sector, rack, housing, support or actuator rod coupling.
5. Bent sector shaft.
6. Damaged rack.
7. Extreme misalignment of housing to cover.*
8. Distorted coupling slot in rack.*
9. Bent actuator rod.
10. Ignition switch mounting bracket bent.
11. Improper shift linkage adjustment.

Will Stick In "Start"
1. Actuator rod deformed.
2. Check items under "High Lock Effort".

Key Cannot Be Removed In "Off-Lock"
1. Ignition switch is not set correctly.
2. Damaged lock cylinder.

Lock Cylinder Can Be Removed
1. Lock cylinder retaining screw missing.

COLUMN

Noise In Column
1. Intermediate shaft pinch bolt not tightened.
2. Column not correctly aligned.
3. Horn contact ring not lubricated.
4. Lack of grease on bearings.
5. Loose sight shields.*
6. Lower or upper steering shaft bearing worn or broken.
7. Shaft lock snap ring not seated.
8. Plastic spherical joint not lubricated.*

High Steering Shaft Effort
1. Column assembly misaligned.
2. Improperly installed or deformed dust seal.
3. Damaged upper or lower bearing.
4. Flash on I.D. of shift tube from plastic joint.
5. Tight intermediate steering shaft universal joint.

High Shift Effort (Automatic)
1. Column not aligned correctly in car.
2. Wave washer with burrs.*
3. Improperly installed dust seal.
4. Lack of grease on seal or bearing.
5. Improper screws used for ignition switch.
6. Burr on upper or lower end of shift tube.

Improper Transmission Shifting (Automatic Transmission)
1. Sheared shift tube joint or lower shift lever weld.
2. Improper transmission linkage adjustment.
3. Improper gate plate.

Lash In Mounted Column Assembly
1. IP to column upper and lower bracket mounting bolts loose.
2. Broken weld nuts on jacket.
3. IP upper bracket capsule sheared.
4. Loose shoes in housing.*
5. Loose tilt head pivot pins.*
6. Loose shoe lock pin in support.*
7. Loose support screws.
8. Column upper and lower bracket to jacket bolts loose.

Fig. 1 Steering column troubleshooting

ator, then remove four seal assembly mounting bolts, **Fig. 5.**
6. Remove bolt from upper knuckle of intermediate steering shaft, **Fig. 5.**
7. Remove nut and bolt holding lower brace assembly, then remove lower brace.
8. Remove remaining bracket bolts, then remove the lower support bracket.
9. Remove two column to upper support retaining bolts/screws, then the column.

Installation

1. Install lower support bracket to steering column, **Fig. 6.** Do not tighten fasteners at this time.
2. Install two bolts into upper support assembly, **Fig. 7.** Do not tighten completely.
3. Position steering column with lower support bracket slots over fasteners installed in step 2. Do not allow to hang freely and do not tighten fasten-

ers.
4. Install two bolts through steering column into upper support assembly, **Fig. 7,** but do not tighten.
5. Install upper knuckle of intermediate steering shaft on upper steering shaft. **Torque** bolt to 35 ft. lbs.
6. Install seal assembly and **torque** four bolts to 21 inch lbs.
7. Remove left bolt from lower support bracket, then install lower brace assembly. **Torque** bolts to 84 inch lbs.

8. **Torque** remaining lower brace and bracket bolts to 84 inch lbs. and upper support assembly bolts to 20 ft. lbs.
9. **Torque** two lower support bracket through bolts to 20 ft. lbs., then connect shift control cable and electrical connections.
10. Install steering wheel inflator module as follows:
   a. With ignition off, install horn contact, then connect coil assembly connector to inflator module.
   b. Push coil assembly lead wires into channel in lower right portion of steering wheel, then install inflator module in steering wheel.
   c. **Torque** screws holding inflator module to steering wheel to 25 inch lbs.
   d. Connect yellow two way SIR harness connector at base of steering column, then install left side sound insulator and No. 3 SIR fuse.
   e. Connect battery ground cable, then turn ignition to Run and verify inflatable restraint indicator lamp flashes seven to nine times and then turns off.
11. Install reinforcement plate and **torque** bolts to 17 inch lbs.
12. Install instrument panel column filler and trim plate.

MODELS LESS SUPPLEMENTAL INFLATABLE RESTRAINT (SIR)
Removal
1. Disconnect battery ground cable.
2. Remove left instrument panel sound insulator, trim pad and column trim collar.
3. Remove steering shaft to intermediate shaft connection.
4. Remove column bracket support bolts and nut.
5. Remove shift indicator cable.
6. Disconnect steering column wiring connectors.
7. Remove shift cable at actuator and housing.
8. Remove steering column from vehicle.

Installation
1. Position steering column in vehicle and install shift cable and housing, **Fig. 8.**
2. Connect steering column wiring connectors.
3. Install shift indicator cable.
4. Install steering column mounting bolts and nut, **Fig. 10,** and **torque** bolts to 20 ft. lbs.
5. Install intermediate shaft and upper pinch bolt, **Fig. 9,** and **torque** bolt to 35 ft. lbs.
6. Install left instrument panel sound insulator, trim pad and column trim collar.
7. Connect battery ground cable.

REATTA, RIVIERA & TORONADO
1990 MODELS W/SUPPLEMENTAL INFLATABLE RESTRAINT (SIR)
Removal
Before removing the SIR steering col-

ALL COLUMNS (NO MARK) TILT COLUMN ONLY*

Housing Scraping On Bowl
  1. Bowl bent or not concentric with hub.*

Steering Wheel Loose
  1. Excessive clearance between holes in support or housing and pivot pin diameters.*
  2. Defective or missing anti-lash spring in spheres.*
  3. Upper bearing not seated in housing.*
  4. Upper bearing inner race seal missing.*
  5. Loose support screws.
  6. Bearing proload spring missing or broken.*

Steering Wheel Loose (Every Other Tilt Position)
  1. Loose fit between shoe and shoe pivot pin.*
  2. Shoe not free in slot.*

Steering Column Not Locking In Any Tilt Position
  1. Shoe seized on its pivot pin.*
  2. Shoe grooves may have burrs or dirt.*
  3. Shoe lock spring weak or broken.*

Steering Wheel Fails To Return To Top Tilt Position
  1. Pivot pins are bound up.*
  2. Wheel tilt spring is defective.*
  3. Turn signal switch wires too tight.*

Noise When Tilting Column
  1. Upper tilt bumpers worn.*
  2. Tilt spring rubbing in housing.*

Miscellaneous
  1. Housing loose on jacket — will be noticed with ignition in "off-lock" and a torque applied to the steering wheel.

Fig. 2   Steering column troubleshooting

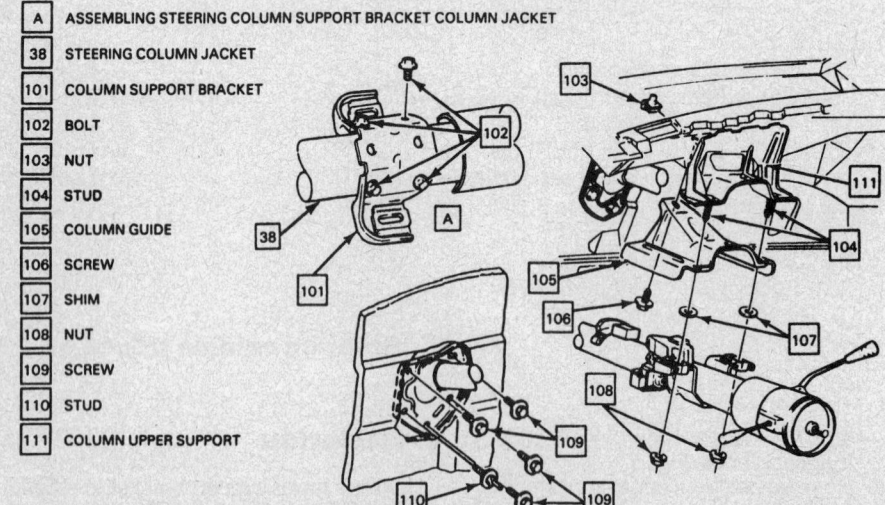

A	ASSEMBLING STEERING COLUMN SUPPORT BRACKET COLUMN JACKET
38	STEERING COLUMN JACKET
101	COLUMN SUPPORT BRACKET
102	BOLT
103	NUT
104	STUD
105	COLUMN GUIDE
106	SCREW
107	SHIM
108	NUT
109	SCREW
110	STUD
111	COLUMN UPPER SUPPORT

Fig. 3   Steering column installation (typical). Buick, Oldsmobile & Pontiac except Fiero rear wheel drive

umn, Fig. 4, the wheels of the car must be straight and the column in the Lock position. Care must be taken when handling column with a live inflator module. Never point bag deploy surface toward you, and never stand column on steering wheel. Accidental deployment in these positions may cause injury. Always face bag deploy surface toward open space to allow for unrestricted

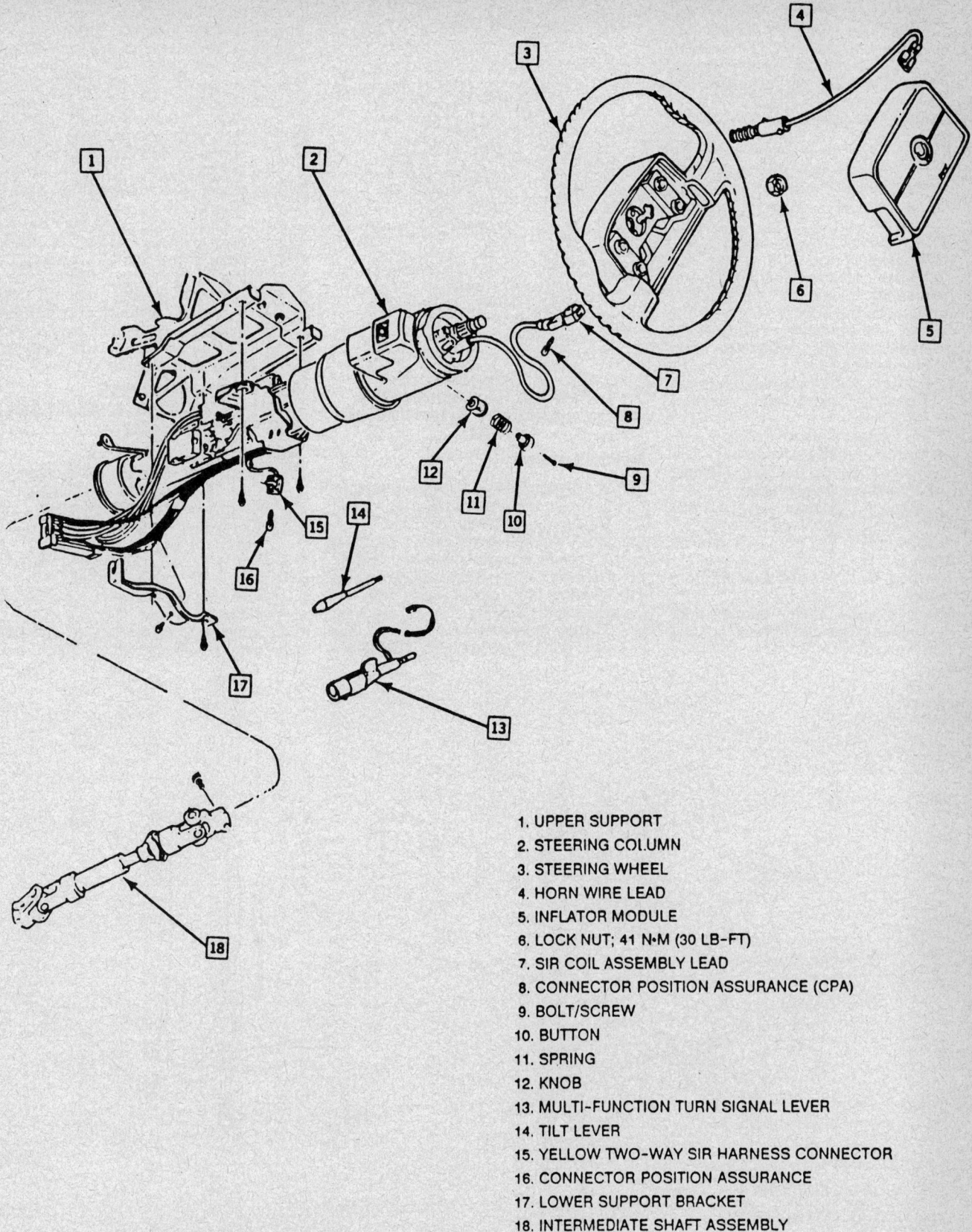

1. UPPER SUPPORT
2. STEERING COLUMN
3. STEERING WHEEL
4. HORN WIRE LEAD
5. INFLATOR MODULE
6. LOCK NUT; 41 N·M (30 LB-FT)
7. SIR COIL ASSEMBLY LEAD
8. CONNECTOR POSITION ASSURANCE (CPA)
9. BOLT/SCREW
10. BUTTON
11. SPRING
12. KNOB
13. MULTI-FUNCTION TURN SIGNAL LEVER
14. TILT LEVER
15. YELLOW TWO-WAY SIR HARNESS CONNECTOR
16. CONNECTOR POSITION ASSURANCE
17. LOWER SUPPORT BRACKET
18. INTERMEDIATE SHAFT ASSEMBLY

Fig. 4 Supplemental Inflatable Restraint (SIR) steering column exploded view

expansion.

The (DERM) Diagnostic Energy Reserve Module, can maintain sufficient voltage to cause a deployment for up to 10 minutes after the ignition switch is turned to the Off position and the battery ground has been disconnected.

1. Remove the inflator module as follows:
   a. With the ignition switch in the Off position and the battery ground cable disconnected and taped, remove the SIR fuse (No. 9) from the fuse panel.
   b. Remove left side sound insulator.
   c. Disconnect the yellow two way harness connector at the base of steering column.
   d. Remove the Torx screws from the back of the steering wheel, then remove the inflator module from steering wheel.
   e. Remove the horn contact by pushing lightly and twisting counterclockwise.
   f. Disconnect the coil assembly connector from inflator module.
2. Remove knee bolster and steering column reinforcement plate.
3. Disconnect ignition wiring and multi-function switch connectors.
4. Remove pinch bolt from intermediate shaft, **Fig. 5**.
5. Remove lower support bracket from vehicle.
6. Remove upper column support from instrument panel and remove column from vehicle.

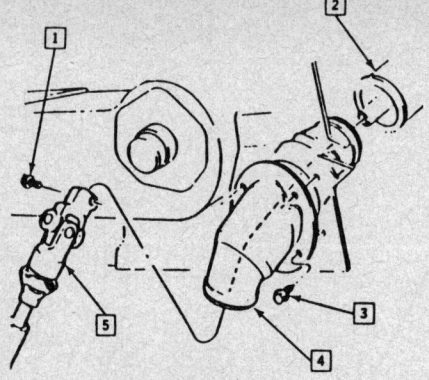

1. BOLT; 47 N•M (35 LB-FT)
2. STEERING COLUMN
3. SCREW (4); 2.4 N•M (21 LB-IN)
4. SEAL ASSEMBLY
5. INTERMEDIATE SHAFT ASSEMBLY

Fig. 5 Supplemental Inflatable Restraint (SIR) steering column intermediate shaft

Installation

1. Install column in vehicle and support at upper bracket with two bolts, **Fig. 11**, do not tighten at this time.
2. Install column lower support bracket in vehicle, do not tighten at this time.
3. Connect column intermediate shaft to steering rack, install pinch bolt and **torque** to 35 ft. lbs.
4. **Torque** upper and lower column support bolts to 20 ft. lbs. and lower bracket to column screws to 12 ft. lbs.
5. Connect ignition wiring and multi-function switch connectors.
6. Install knee bolster and column reinforcement plate.
7. Install steering wheel inflator module as follows:
   a. With ignition off, install horn contact, then connect coil assembly connector to inflator module.
   b. Install inflator module in steering wheel and **torque** screws to 27 inch lbs.
   c. Connect yellow two way SIR harness connector at base of steering column, then install left side sound insulator and No. 9 SIR fuse.
   d. Connect battery ground cable, then turn ignition to Run and verify inflatable restraint indicator lamp flashes seven to nine times and then turns off.

1989 MODELS LESS SUPPLEMENTAL INFLATABLE RESTRAINT (SIR)

Removal

1. Disconnect battery ground cable.
2. Remove lefthand sound insulator.
3. Disconnect column wiring connector.
4. Remove park lock cable from ignition switch.
5. Remove bolt connecting steering shaft to intermediate shaft.
6. Remove column lower mounting nut and bolt.
7. Remove column upper mounting bracket bolts, then the column.

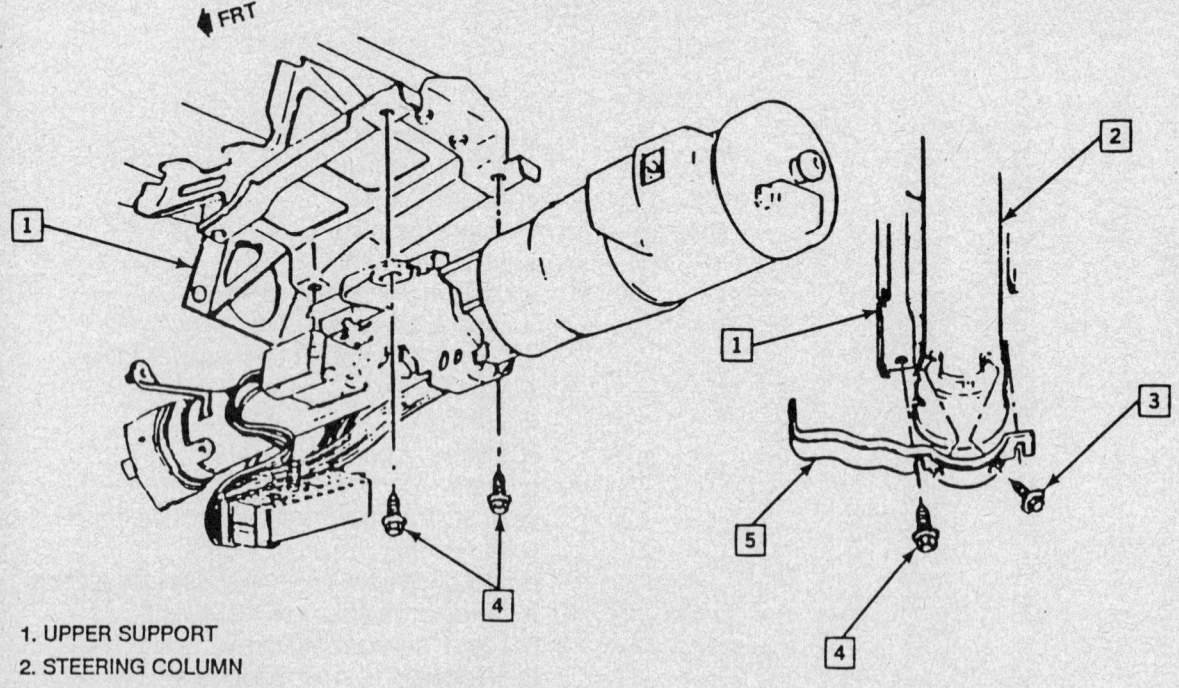

1. UPPER SUPPORT
2. STEERING COLUMN
3. BOLT; 9.5 N•M (84 LB-IN)
4. BOLT (4); 27 N•M (20 LB-FT)
5. LOWER SUPPORT BRACKET

Fig. 6 Supplemental Inflatable Restraint (SIR) steering column support brackets

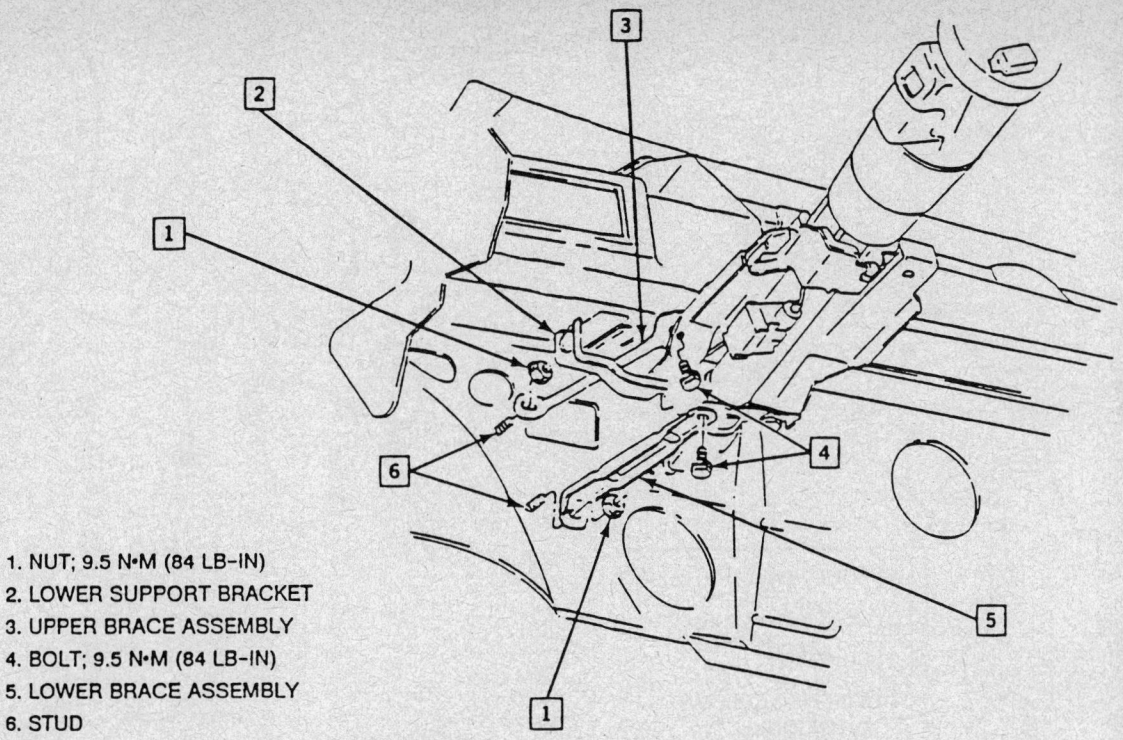

1. NUT; 9.5 N•M (84 LB-IN)
2. LOWER SUPPORT BRACKET
3. UPPER BRACE ASSEMBLY
4. BOLT; 9.5 N•M (84 LB-IN)
5. LOWER BRACE ASSEMBLY
6. STUD

Fig. 7   Supplemental Inflatable Restraint (SIR) steering column lower brackets

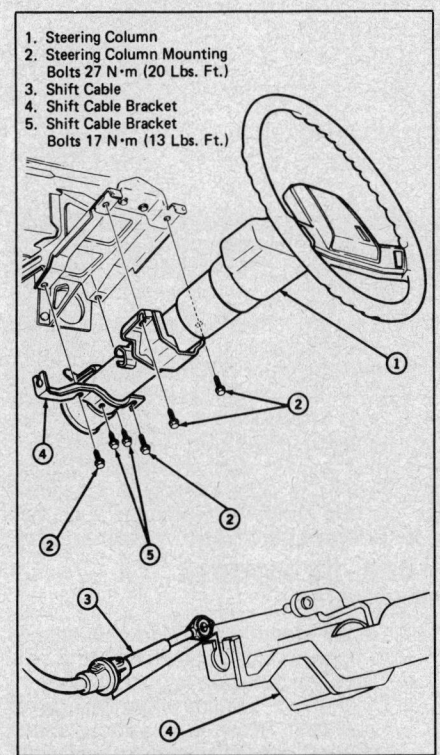

1. Steering Column
2. Steering Column Mounting Bolts 27 N•m (20 Lbs. Ft.)
3. Shift Cable
4. Shift Cable Bracket
5. Shift Cable Bracket Bolts 17 N•m (13 Lbs. Ft.)

Fig. 8   Steering column installation. Bonneville, DeVille, Electra, Fleetwood, LeSabre, 88 & 98

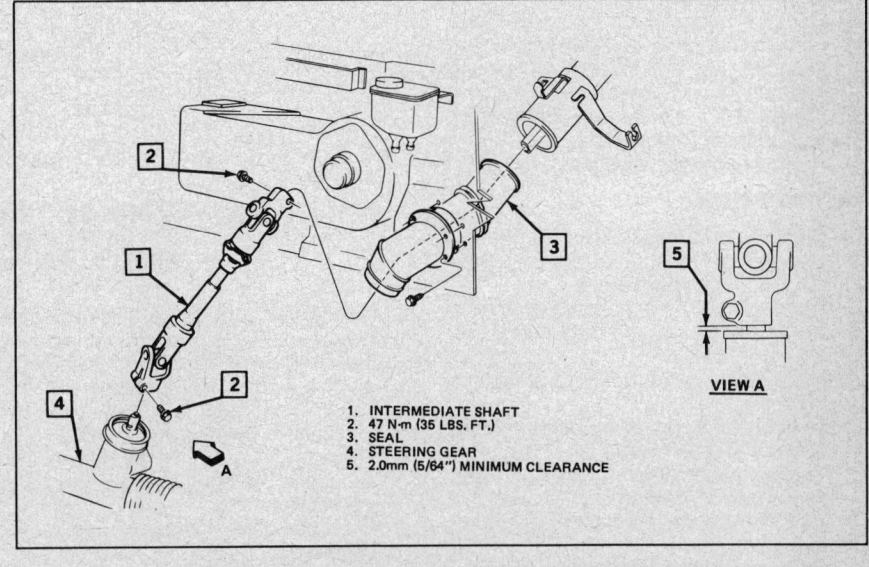

1. INTERMEDIATE SHAFT
2. 47 N•m (35 LBS. FT.)
3. SEAL
4. STEERING GEAR
5. 2.0mm (5/64") MINIMUM CLEARANCE

VIEW A

Fig. 9   Intermediate shaft & boot installation. Bonneville, DeVille, Electra, Fleetwood, LeSabre, 88 & 98

Installation

1. Install column assembly in vehicle and upper column bolts loosely, **Fig. 10.**
2. Install lower column nut and bolt loosely.
3. Install intermediate shaft coupling to column shaft and **torque** bolt to 35 ft. lbs.
4. **Torque** column mounting bolts to 20 ft. lbs.
5. Connect park lock cable to ignition switch.
6. Connect column wiring connector.
7. Install lefthand sound insulator, then connect battery ground cable.

1988 MODELS LESS SUPPLEMENTAL INFLATABLE RESTRAINT (SIR)

Removal

1. Disconnect battery ground cable.

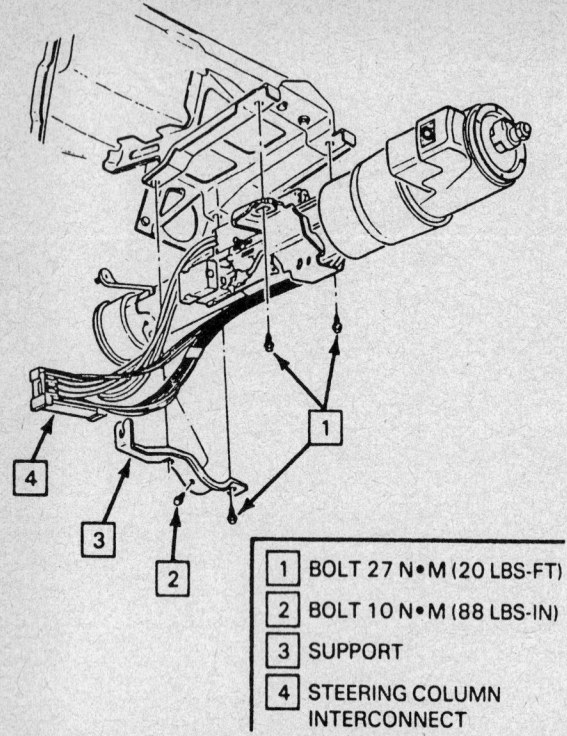

1 | BOLT 27 N•M (20 LBS-FT)
2 | BOLT 10 N•M (88 LBS-IN)
3 | SUPPORT
4 | STEERING COLUMN INTERCONNECT

Fig. 10 Steering column installation. 1988–89 Reatta, Riviera & Toronado (Eldorado & Seville similar)

2. Remove left sound insulator and column trim cover.
3. Remove upper pinch bolt and lower column mounting bolt and nut.
4. Remove upper mounting bracket bolts and wire harness protector.
5. Disconnect electrical connections and shift cable at column.
6. Remove column assembly.

Installation

1. Install column assembly, **Fig. 10.**
2. Connect shift cable at column, then the electrical connectors.
3. Install column wire harness protector.
4. Install lower column mounting bolt and nut loosely.
5. Install upper pinch bolt and **torque** to 35 ft. lbs.
6. Install column upper mounting bracket bolts and **torque** to 20 ft. lbs.
7. **Torque** lower column mounting bolt and nut to 25 ft. lbs.
8. Install left sound insulator and column trim cover.
9. Connect battery ground cable.

CADILLAC REAR WHEEL DRIVE MODELS
1990 MODELS
Removal

1. Disconnect battery ground cable.
2. Disconnect transmission linkage at lower shift lever.
3. Remove nut attaching intermediate shaft and column, then separate shaft from the column.
4. Remove column lower cover and lower fuse panel cover.
5. Remove lefthand A/C outlet duct.

6. Disconnect turn signal harness connector, park neutral switch, parking brake release hose and headlamp dimmer switch from column.
7. Remove clip retaining shift cable and loosen two upper support nuts.
8. Position carpet out of the way to gain access to the cowl insulator and seal fasteners.
9. Remove cowl insulator and cover seal.
10 Remove two upper column support nuts, then the column from vehicle.

Installation

1. Install column in vehicle and finger tighten upper mounting bracket nuts, **Fig. 12.**
2. Install nut securing column to the intermediate shaft and finger tighten.
3. Connect transmission linkage to lower shaft lever.
4. Connect shift cable and securing clip.
5. Install cowl seal and finger tighten nuts and bolts.
6. Connect turn signal harness, park neutral switch, parking brake release

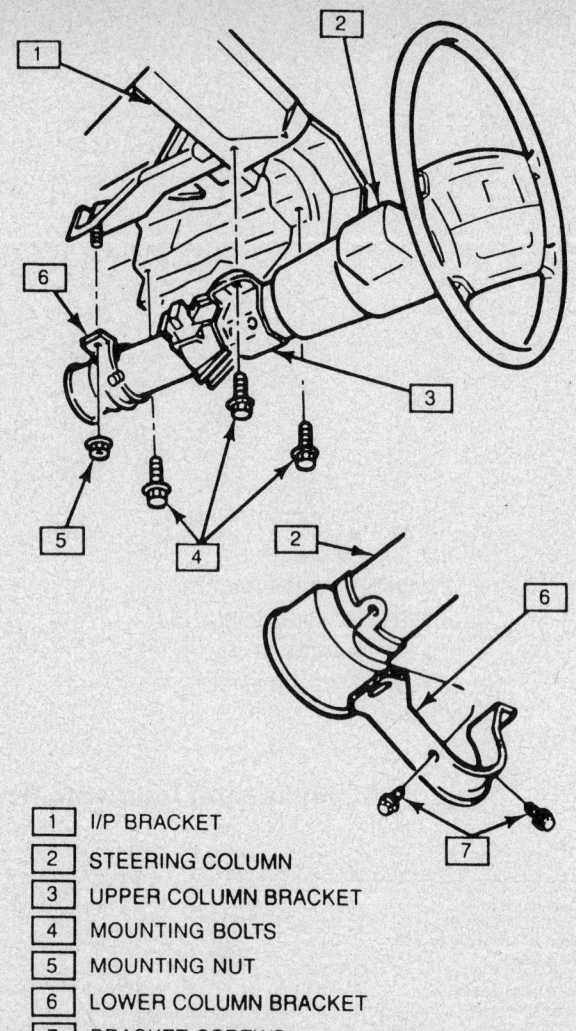

1 | I/P BRACKET
2 | STEERING COLUMN
3 | UPPER COLUMN BRACKET
4 | MOUNTING BOLTS
5 | MOUNTING NUT
6 | LOWER COLUMN BRACKET
7 | BRACKET SCREWS

Fig. 11 Supplemental Inflatable Restraint (SIR) steering column installation. 1990 Reatta, Riviera & Toronado (Eldorado & Seville similar)

hose and headlamp dimmer switch connectors.
7. **Torque** upper column bracket nuts to 20 ft. lbs., cowl cover seal nuts and bolts to 35 inch lbs. and column to intermediate shaft bolt to 52 ft. lbs.
8. Install cowl seal insulator, lefthand A/C outlet duct, lower fuse panel cover and steering column lower cover.
9. Connect battery ground cable.

1988–89 MODELS
Removal

1. Center steering wheel to gain access to upper coupling pinch bolt and nut.
2. Disconnect battery ground cable.
3. Disconnect transmission linkage at lower shift lever, then remove pinch bolt and separate intermediate shaft from spline.
4. Remove four screws attaching steering lower cover to instrument panel, then remove cover.
5. Disconnect turn signal wiring at connector. Also disconnect cruise control wiring at this time.
6. Remove screw attaching shift indica-

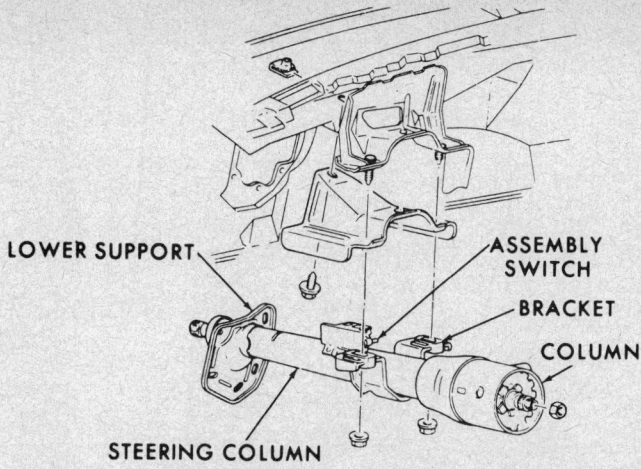

Fig. 12 Typical Steering column installation. Cadillac rear wheel drive models

tor cable to shift bowl.

7. Loosen two screws at steering column upper support, **Fig. 12**, and on Seville models, remove shims.
8. Move toe pan seal up on steering column as far as possible, then position carpet out of way to gain access to toe pan.
9. Remove five screws attaching toe pan bracket to toe pan.
10. Remove two nuts attaching upper column bracket to column support, then disconnect ignition and back-up light switch connectors and parking brake release hose. On models equipped with automatic door locks, disconnect wire connector.
11. Carefully pull steering column up and out of vehicle, using care not to damage column mounted switches or dash seal. If shaft binds on upper coupling, reattach column upper mounting bracket and pry shaft from coupling using a screwdriver.

Installation

1. Position toe pan seal on column, if removed.
2. Insert lower end of steering column through hole in toe pan and into flex coupling, aligning coupling and steering shaft flats. Use care not to damage lower shift lever or back-up light switch.
3. Connect ignition switch wire connector, then install two nuts to secure upper column bracket to column support. Do not tighten nuts at this time.
4. Connect back-up light and turn signal switch wire connector, parking brake release hose and automatic door lock and Cruise Control wiring harness, if equipped.
5. Install screw in toe plate locator hole, aligning toe plate to toe pan, then install four attaching screws and **torque** to 50 inch lbs.
6. Install toe pan insulator at column support.
7. Install carpet at lower column support, then position toe pan seal over carpet.
8. Tighten upper column mounting bracket to upper column support nuts to 20 ft. lbs.

9. Position shift pointer cable to shift bowl, then install attaching screw and check for proper alignment.
10. Install steering column lower cover.
11. Connect transmission linkage at lower shift lever.
12. Secure upper coupling to steering shaft. **Clearance between steering shaft and upper coupling should be 5/16 inch, otherwise damage to lower bearing may result. Torque** pinch bolt to 45 ft. lbs.
13. Connect battery ground cable.

ELDORADO & SEVILLE

1990 MODELS W/SUPPLEMENTAL INFLATABLE RESTRAINT (SIR)

Refer to "1988-90 Riviera, Toronado and Reatta" for procedures.

1988–89 MODELS LESS SUPPLEMENTAL INFLATABLE RESTRAINT (SIR)

Removal

1. Disconnect battery ground cable, then remove lefthand dash close-out panel.
2. Disconnect column electrical connector from lefthand grommet.
3. Disconnect park-lock cable from ignition switch.
4. Remove intermediate shaft bolt, then the upper and lower bracket bolts and remove column assembly from vehicle, **Fig. 10. The lower column bracket bolts must be removed first to prevent possible damage to the lower bearing casting.**

Installation

1. Position column assembly in vehicle and secure with mounting bolts and nut. **The upper column bracket bolts must be installed first to prevent possible damage to the lower bearing casting.**
2. Position intermediate shaft coupling, then **torque** shaft bolt to 35 ft. lbs. and column mounting bolts to 20 ft. lbs.
3. Reconnect park-lock cable to ignition

switch.
4. Reconnect column electrical connector to lefthand grommet.
5. Install dash close-out panel, then reconnect battery ground cable.

CHEVROLET REAR WHEEL DRIVE

REMOVAL

1990 Camaro W/Supplemental Inflatable Restraint (SIR)

Before removing the SIR steering column, **Fig. 13**, the wheels of the car must be straight and the column in the Lock position. Care must be taken when handling column with a live inflator module. Never point bag deploy surface toward you, and never stand column on steering wheel. Accidental deployment in these positions may cause injury. Always face bag deploy surface toward open space to allow for unrestricted expansion.

The (DERM) Diagnostic Energy Reserve Module, can maintain sufficient voltage to cause a deployment for up to 10 minutes after the ignition switch is turned to the Off position and the battery ground has been disconnected.

1. Remove the inflator module as follows:
   a. With the ignition switch in the Off position and the battery ground cable disconnected and taped, remove the SIR fuse from fuse panel.
   b. Remove left side sound insulator.
   c. Disconnect the yellow two way harness connector at the base of steering column.
   d. Remove the Torx screws from the back of the steering wheel, then remove the inflator module from steering wheel.
   e. Disconnect the coil assembly connector from inflator module.
2. Disconnect park lock cable from the ignition switch inhibitor.
3. Remove bolt and nut from upper intermediate shaft clamp.
4. Remove knee bolster and bracket and screws attaching toe pan cover to the cowl.
5. Disconnect electrical connectors and remove capsule nuts attaching column support bracket to the instrument panel.
6. Remove steering column from the vehicle.

1990 Corvette W/Supplemental Inflatable Restraint (SIR)

Before removing the SIR steering column, **Fig. 4**, the wheels of the car must be straight and the column in the Lock position. Care must be taken when handling column with a live inflator module. Never point bag deploy surface toward you, and never stand column on steering wheel. Accidental deployment in these positions may cause injury. Always face bag deploy surface toward open space to allow for unrestricted expansion.

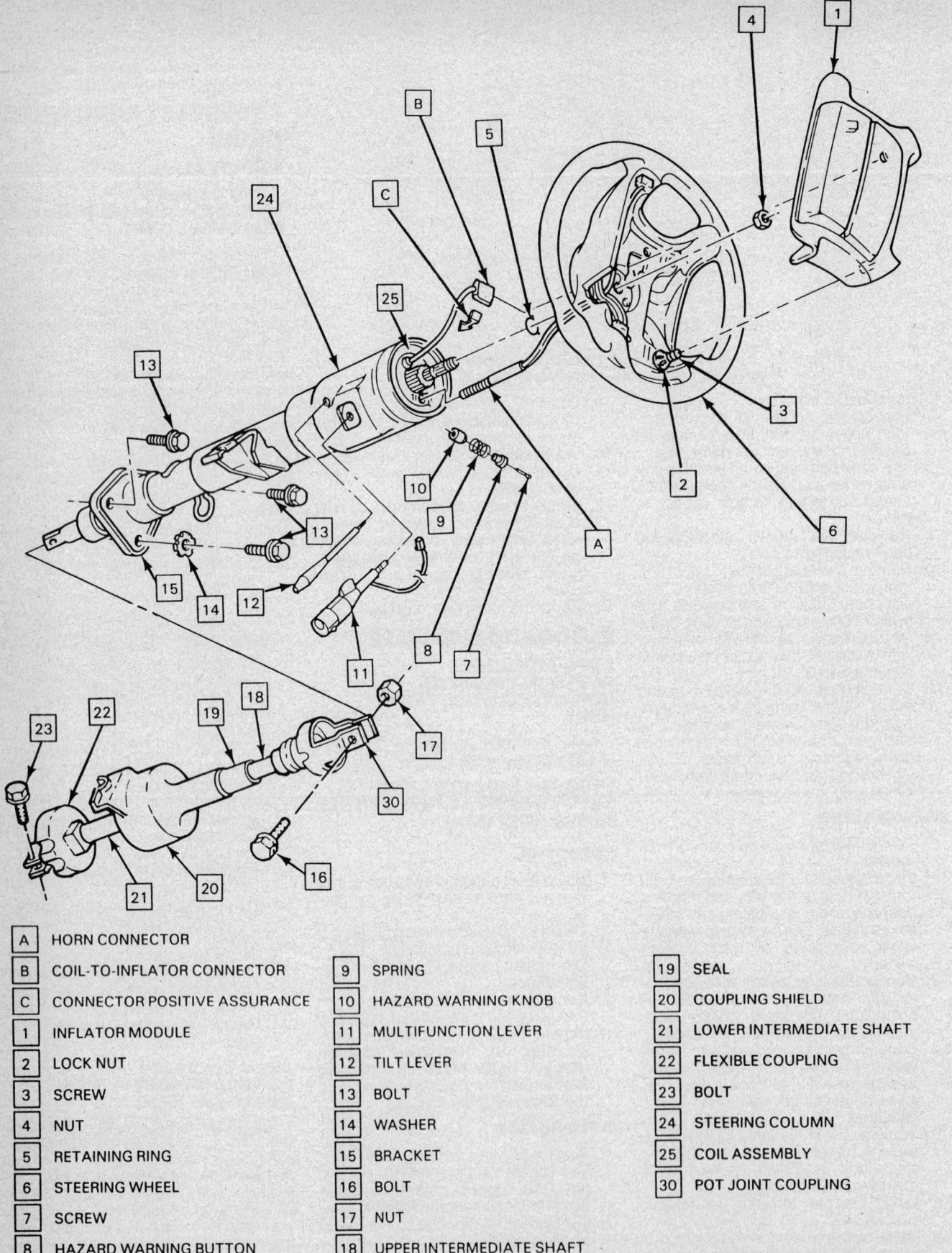

Fig. 13 Supplemental Inflatable Restraint (SIR) steering column removal. 1990 Camaro

A	HORN CONNECTOR
B	COIL-TO-INFLATOR CONNECTOR
C	CONNECTOR POSITIVE ASSURANCE
1	INFLATOR MODULE
2	LOCK NUT
3	SCREW
4	NUT
5	RETAINING RING
6	STEERING WHEEL
7	SCREW
8	HAZARD WARNING BUTTON

9	SPRING
10	HAZARD WARNING KNOB
11	MULTIFUNCTION LEVER
12	TILT LEVER
13	BOLT
14	WASHER
15	BRACKET
16	BOLT
17	NUT
18	UPPER INTERMEDIATE SHAFT

19	SEAL
20	COUPLING SHIELD
21	LOWER INTERMEDIATE SHAFT
22	FLEXIBLE COUPLING
23	BOLT
24	STEERING COLUMN
25	COIL ASSEMBLY
30	POT JOINT COUPLING

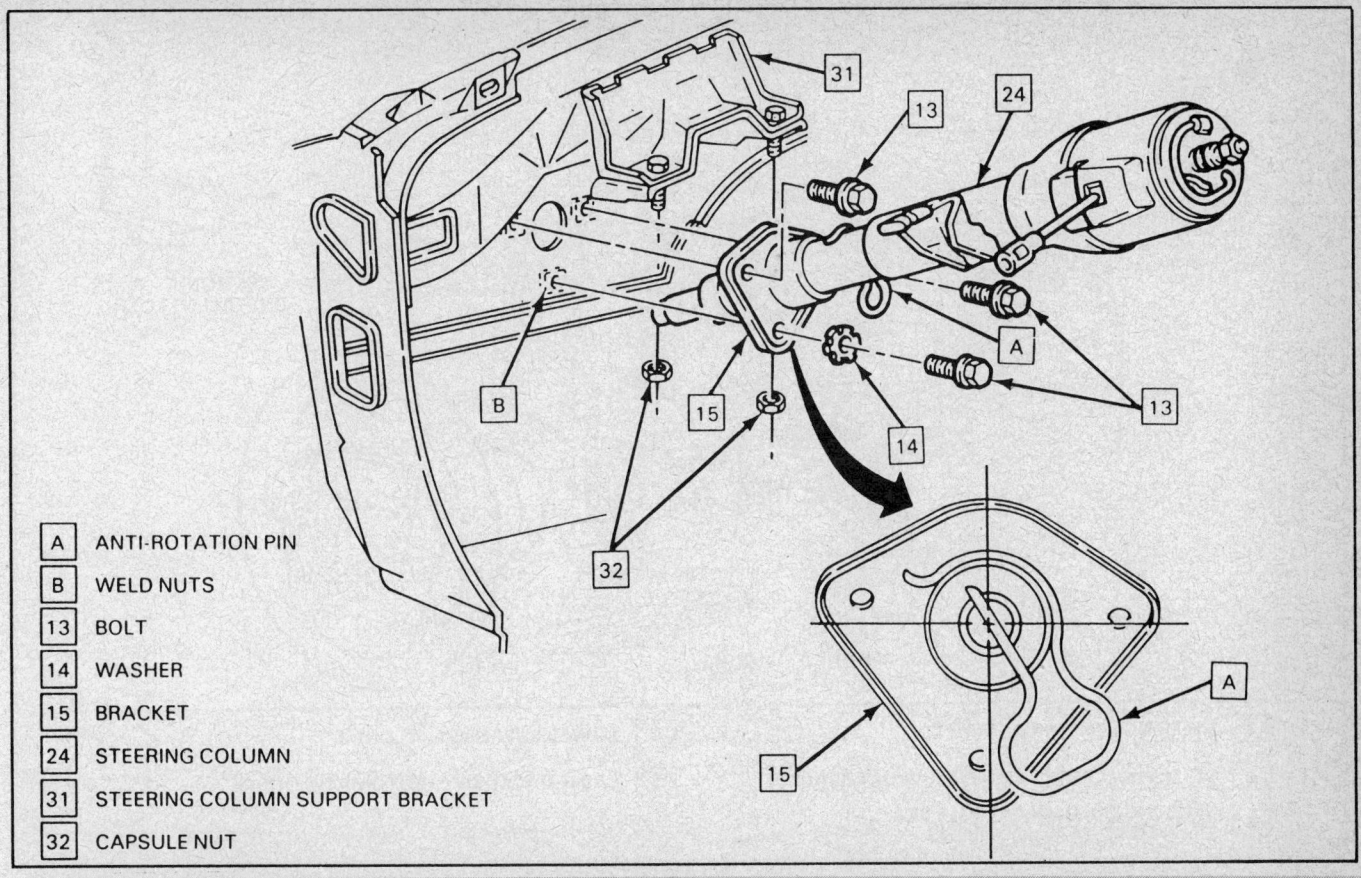

A	ANTI-ROTATION PIN
B	WELD NUTS
13	BOLT
14	WASHER
15	BRACKET
24	STEERING COLUMN
31	STEERING COLUMN SUPPORT BRACKET
32	CAPSULE NUT

Fig. 14 Supplemental Inflatable Restraint (SIR) steering column installation. 1990 Camaro

The (DERM) Diagnostic Energy Reserve Module, can maintain sufficient voltage to cause a deployment for up to 10 minutes after the ignition switch is turned to the Off position and the battery ground has been disconnected.

1. Remove the inflator module as follows:
   a. Turn the ignition switch to the Off position and disconnect and tape the battery ground cable.
   b. Remove left side sound insulator.
   c. Disconnect the yellow two way harness connector at the base of steering column.
   d. Install Load Tool No. J 37808 or equivalent by connecting "base of column" lead of tool.
   e. Remove the Torx screws from the back of the steering wheel, then remove the inflator module from steering wheel.
   f. Disconnect the coil assembly connector from inflator module.
2. Remove steering wheel retaining nut, steering wheel and disconnect horn connector.
3. Remove intermediate shaft upper bolt.
4. Disconnect the (ALDL) Assembly Line Diagnostic Link connector and lamp from the sound insulator and remove sound insulator.
5. Remove column housing cover end cap by pulling toward front of vehicle.
6. Disconnect harness connector and grommet and remove multi-function lever by pulling toward driver side door.
7. Remove driver's side knee bolster and tilt lever.
8. Remove nuts from lower support plate and capsule bolts from reinforcement assembly.
9. Disconnect electrical connectors from column.
10. Remove sound insulator to column lower support bracket and nuts from the accelerator pedal bracket.
11. Remove steering column from vehicle.

1988-89 Camaro, 1988-90 Caprice & 1988 Monte Carlo Less Supplemental Inflatable Restraint (SIR)

1. Disconnect battery ground cable.
2. Remove nut and bolt from upper intermediate shaft coupling, then separate coupling from lower end of steering column.
3. Disconnect shift linkage from lower shift lever.
4. Remove left sound insulator and lower column cover.
5. Remove cover and seal mounting screws.
6. Remove shift indicator clip from shift bowl, if equipped with column shift.
7. Remove the nuts from the column upper support and lower column.
8. Disconnect wiring from column, then remove column from vehicle.

1989 Corvette Less Supplemental Inflatable Restraint (SIR)

1. Disconnect battery ground cable, then remove the steering wheel as follows:
   a. Pull the horn button off steering wheel, then disconnect the horn button wire.
   b. Remove the telescope lever screws and shaft lock knob screw.
   c. Remove telescope adjustment lever, steering wheel nut retainer and nut.
   d. Remove steering wheel with puller tool No. J1859-03 or equivalent.
2. Remove intermediate shaft upper bolt, instrument panel sound insulator and lower trim pad from the left side of the instrument panel.
3. Disconnect the park lock cable from cable backdrive pin and cable bracket.
4. Disconnect electrical connectors from steering column.
5. Remove lower support plate attaching nuts, both capsule bolts and then the steering column from vehicle.

1988 Corvette Less Supplemental Inflatable Restraint (SIR)

1. Disconnect battery ground cable.
2. Remove pinch bolt from universal coupling.
3. Remove lower steering column attaching bolt and the two capsule bolts.

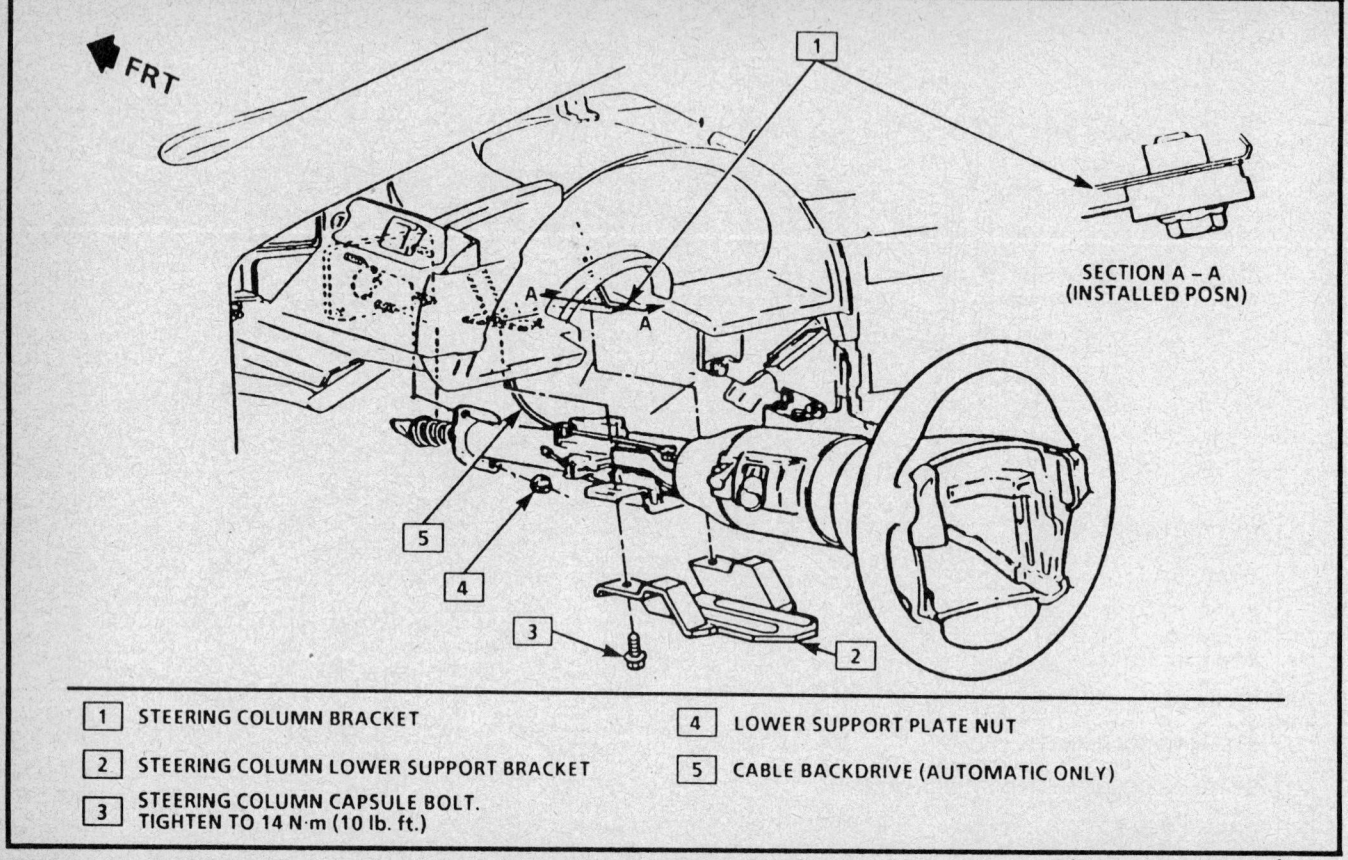

1	STEERING COLUMN BRACKET	**4**	LOWER SUPPORT PLATE NUT
2	STEERING COLUMN LOWER SUPPORT BRACKET	**5**	CABLE BACKDRIVE (AUTOMATIC ONLY)
3	STEERING COLUMN CAPSULE BOLT. TIGHTEN TO 14 N·m (10 lb. ft.)		

Fig. 15 Supplemental Inflatable Restraint (SIR) steering column installation. 1990 Corvette

4. Disconnect all electrical connectors from steering column.
5. Remove steering column assembly from vehicle.

INSTALLATION
1990 Camaro W/Supplemental Inflatable Restraint (SIR)

1. Install steering column into the vehicle, **Fig. 14** and connect the park lock cable to the ignition switch inhibitor.
2. Install the capsule nuts attaching the column support bracket to the instrument panel.
3. Install the bolt and nut to the clamp attaching the intermediate shaft to the steering column and **torque** to 44 ft. lbs.
4. Install screws attaching toe pan cover to the cowl and connect electrical connectors.
5. Install knee bolster and bracket and sound insulator panel.
6. Connect coil assembly to the inflator module, then install inflator module to the steering wheel and **torque** screws to 25 inch lbs.
7. Connect yellow two way harness at the base of the column.
8. Install left side sound insulator, SIR fuse into the fuse block and connect the battery ground cable.
9. Turn ignition switch to Run position and verify inflatable restraint indicator

lamp flashes seven to nine times and then turns off.

1990 Corvette W/Supplemental Inflatable Restraint (SIR)

1. Install steering column assembly in vehicle and insert lower steering shaft assembly into U-joint of intermediate shaft.
2. Install intermediate shaft upper bolt and loosely attach column and upper support plate to instrument panel reinforcement assembly with capsule bolts, **Fig. 15**.
3. Install cable backdrive on vehicles with automatic transmission, then loosely attach column nuts to support plate studs.
4. **Torque** intermediate shaft bolt to 26 ft. lbs., capsule bolts to 20 ft. lbs. and lower support plate nuts to 10 ft. lbs.
5. Connect electrical connectors to column and install driver's side knee bolster.
6. Install multi-function lever, harness and grommet, column housing cover end cap and tilt lever.
7. Align tilt lever tab into slot, with lever in Off position.
8. Install sound insulator bracket to column lower support and accelerator pedal bracket nuts. **Torque** accelerator pedal bracket nuts to 71 inch lbs.
9. Install steering wheel, retaining nut and connect horn connector.
10. Connect coil assembly to the inflator

module, then install inflator module to the steering wheel, using new screws and **torque** screws to 87 inch lbs.
11. Remove Load Tool No. J 37808.
12. Connect yellow two way harness at the base of the column.
13. Install left side sound insulator, ALDL and lamp connectors.
14. Connect battery ground cable and turn ignition switch to Run position and verify inflatable restraint indicator lamp flashes seven to nine times and then turns off.

1988–89 Camaro, 1989–90 Caprice And 1988 Monte Carlo Less Supplemental Inflatable Restraint (SIR)

1. Install steering column in vehicle, **Fig. 16.** and connect wiring.
2. Connect column to upper column support and finger tighten nuts.
3. Install cover and seal to dash panel and **torque** screws to 53 inch lbs.
4. Connect intermediate shaft to column shaft, install nut and bolt and **torque** to 52 ft. lbs.
5. Install shift indicator clip to the shift bowl, if equipped with column shift.
6. Install left sound insulator and lower column cover.
7. Connect shift linkage to lower shift lever and connect battery ground cable.

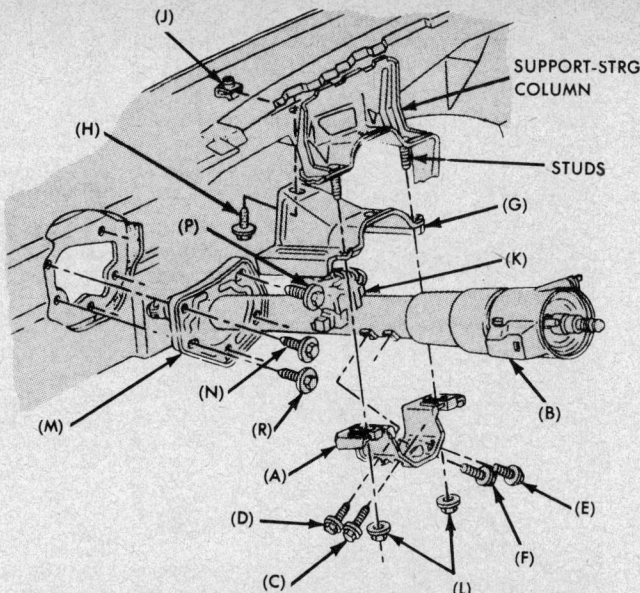

Fig. 16   Steering column installation. 1988 Monte Carlo, 1988–89 Camaro & 1988–90 Caprice

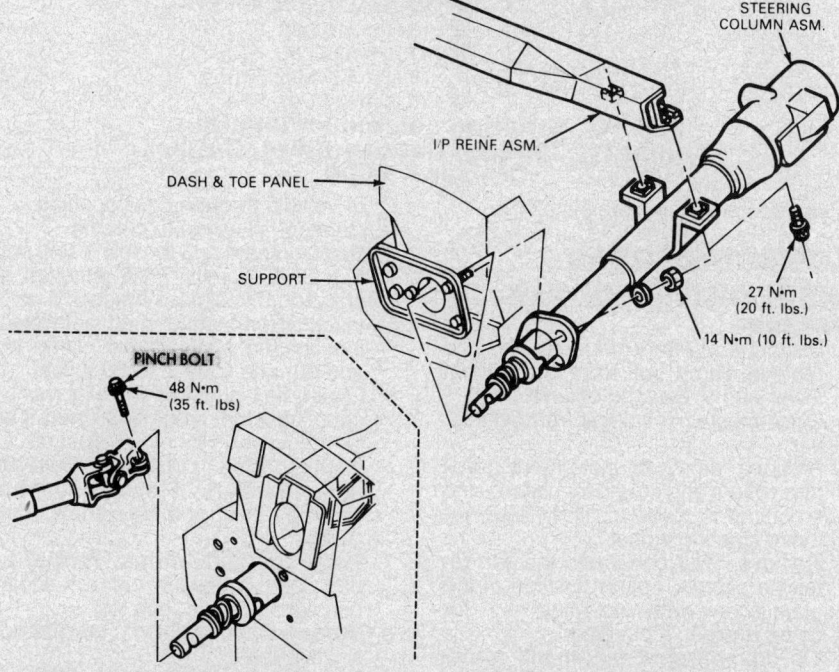

Fig. 17   Steering column installation. 1988–89 Corvette

1989 Corvette Less Supplemental Inflatable Restraint (SIR)

1. Install steering column in the vehicle and insert lower steering shaft assembly into the U-joint of the intermediate shaft, **Fig. 17.**
2. Loosely attach steering column to mounting studs on lower support plate and to instrument panel reinforcement assembly with capsule bolts.
3. **Torque** intermediate shaft upper bolt to 44 ft. lbs. and capsule bolts to 20 ft.

lbs.
4. Install and **torque** lower support plate attaching nuts to 10 ft. lbs.
5. Connect electrical connectors, then the park lock cable to cable backdrive and cable bracket.
6. Install instrument panel sound insulator and lower trim pad.
7. Connect horn contact spring and install steering wheel and nut and **torque** to 30 ft. lbs.
8. Install steering wheel nut retainer, telescope adjustment lever and shaft lock knob screw. **Torque** knob screw to 30 inch lbs.

9. Install telescope lever screws and **torque** to 40 inch lbs. Position lever as far to the right as possible while aligning screws.
10. Install horn button wire, horn cap, then connect battery ground cable.

1988 Corvette Less Supplemental Inflatable Restraint (SIR)

1. Position steering column in vehicle and guide column shaft into intermediate shaft U-joint, **Fig. 17.** Install bolt and **torque** to 46 ft. lbs.
2. Loosely attach column to studs on dash and toe panel with washers and nuts to instrument panel reinforcement assembly nuts. Torque nuts to specifications, **Fig. 15.**
3. Install pinch bolt to flex coupling and **torque** to 35 ft. lbs.
4. Connect all electrical connectors to columns, then reconnect battery ground cable.

NOVA
Removal

1. Disconnect battery ground cable, then remove steering wheel.
2. Remove instrument cluster lower finish panel, air duct and lower steering column cover.
3. Disconnect ignition switch, turn signal wiring connectors and remove combination switch with column upper cover.
4. Remove hole cover clamp screw, then remove pinch bolt from yoke.
5. Remove yoke from steering gear.
6. Remove lower column mounting bracket bolts.
7. Remove upper steering column to instrument panel attaching bolts.
8. Remove column assembly from vehicle.

Installation

1. Position column assembly under instrument panel and install upper and lower column bracket bolts hand tight.
2. Ensure column is properly aligned and **torque** mounting bolts to 19 ft. lbs.
3. Install intermediate shaft yoke joint and **torque** retaining bolts to 26 ft. lbs.
4. Reverse remaining procedure to complete installation.

CELEBRITY, CENTURY, CUTLASS CIERA, CUTLASS CRUISER & 6000
Removal

1. Disconnect battery ground cable.
2. Remove left instrument panel sound absorber, trim pad and column trim collar.
3. Remove bolt and disconnect column to intermediate shaft connection.
4. Remove column support bracket bolts and nut.
5. Disconnect shift indicator cable and electrical connectors.
6. Disconnect shift cable at actuator and

housing holder, then remove column assembly from vehicle.

Installation

1. Install column assembly in vehicle, **Fig. 18.**
2. Connect shift cable at actuator and housing holder, then the electrical connectors.
3. Connect shift indicator cable and install column bracket support bolts and nut.
4. Install intermediate shaft to column upper shaft pinch bolt and **torque** to 35 ft. lbs.
5. **Torque** column bracket support bolts and nut to 20 ft. lbs.
6. Install column trim collar, left instrument panel trim pad and sound insulator, then connect battery ground cable.

BERETTA & CORSICA

Refer to **Figs. 19 through 23** for steering column removal and installation procedures.

CALAIS, CAVALIER, CIMARRON, FIRENZA, GRAND AM, SKYHAWK, SKYLARK, SOMERSET REGAL & SUNBIRD

Removal

1. Disconnect battery ground cable and remove left instrument panel sound insulator, lower trim panel or duct assembly, and steering column collar, as equipped.
2. If column is to be disassembled, remove horn contact pad and steering wheel.
3. Push back seal to expose flexible coupling, **Fig. 24,** then remove coupling pinch bolt.
4. Remove lower column support bracket bolt, then the upper bracket to instrument panel support bolts and lower column.
5. Disconnect column electrical connectors and shift indicator cable, if equipped.
6. Disconnect shift cable at actuator and housing holder, then remove steering column.

Installation

1. Insert steering shaft into flexible coupling.
2. Connect shift cable to actuator and housing holder.
3. Connect column electrical connectors and shift indicator cable.
4. Raise column into position, then install upper and lower bracket mounting bolts hand tight.
5. Install flexible coupling pinch bolt and **torque** bolt to 29 ft. lbs.
6. Ensure steering shaft is centered in mast jacket, repositioning column as needed, then **torque** mounting bolts to 20 ft. lbs.
7. Adjust shift cable and shift indicator as needed, then reverse remaining

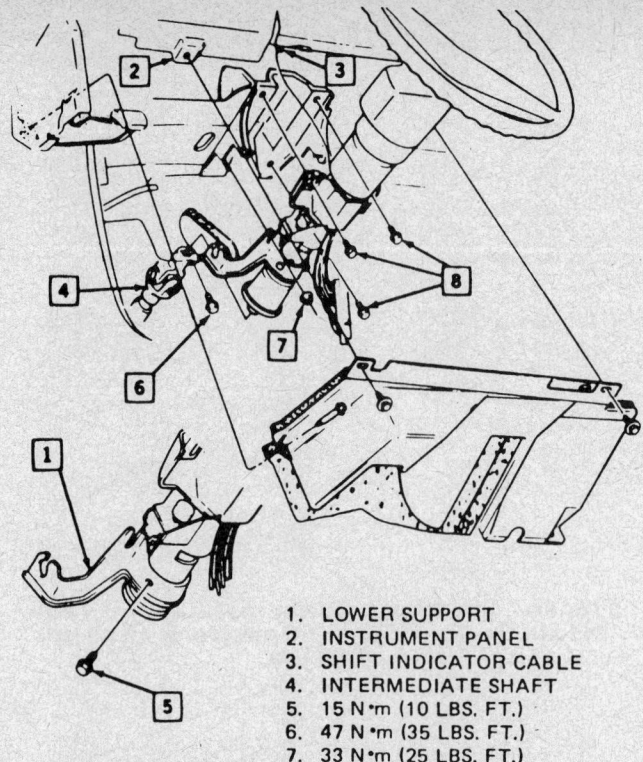

1. LOWER SUPPORT
2. INSTRUMENT PANEL
3. SHIFT INDICATOR CABLE
4. INTERMEDIATE SHAFT
5. 15 N·m (10 LBS. FT.)
6. 47 N·m (35 LBS. FT.)
7. 33 N·m (25 LBS. FT.)
8. 28 N·m (20 LBS. FT.)

Fig. 18   Steering column installation. Celebrity, Century, Cutlass Ciera, Cutlass Cruiser & 6000

procedure to complete installation.

OLDSMOBILE REAR WHEEL DRIVE MODELS

Removal

1. Disconnect battery ground cables and remove clamp bolt from coupling at lower end of steering column shaft.
2. Disconnect shift linkage from shift lever.
3. Remove left lower instrument panel trim covers and sound insulators, and if column is to be disassembled, remove steering wheel.
4. Remove lower cover and toe pan retaining screws, noting position of toe plate screw with mounting stud for cover retainer, if equipped.
5. **On column shift automatic transmission,** disconnect shift indicator cable from column shift bowl, **Fig. 25.**
6. Support column and remove upper bracket capsule retaining nuts, then lower column, noting installation position of shims, if used.
7. Disconnect column electrical connectors and remove steering column assembly. **If spacers are used, retain for use during installation.**
8. If necessary to remove intermediate shaft, remove cover, nut and bolt from clamp, then disconnect shaft from steering gear.

Installation

1. If intermediate shaft was removed, install intermediate shaft on steering gear shaft and **torque** nut to 30 ft. lbs.
2. Carefully position column from inside

of vehicle through cowl opening.
3. Connect all wiring to column.
4. Raise column and loosely install nuts, **Fig. 3.** If spacers were removed, install equal thickness on each side.
5. Install intermediate shaft onto steering column shaft. Install clamp bolt and nut and **torque** to 50 ft. lbs.
6. Check flex coupling for alignment. If coupling is not properly aligned, it will be necessary to move column assembly. **Flex coupling must be straight within 1/16 inch without bottoming intermediate shaft coupling.**
7. Install toe pan screws. **Torque** toe pan clamp bolts to 60 inch lbs. and toe pan screws to 45 inch lbs.
8. **Torque** steering column bracket nuts to 20 ft. lbs.
9. If equipped with column shift automatic transmission, connect and adjust shift indicator cable as shown in **Fig. 25.**
10. Check flex coupling and intermediate shaft for bottoming. If either is bottoming, it will be necessary to loosen toe pan clamp bolts and steering column bracket nuts, then lift upward and rearward on column assembly. **Torque** toe pan clamp bolts to 60 inch lbs. and steering column bracket nuts to 20 ft. lbs.
11. Install cover over toe pan and lower trim panel on instrument panel.
12. Install steering wheel if removed.
13. Install flex coupling shield, then connect battery ground cable.
14. Adjust neutral safety switch and or back-up light switch.

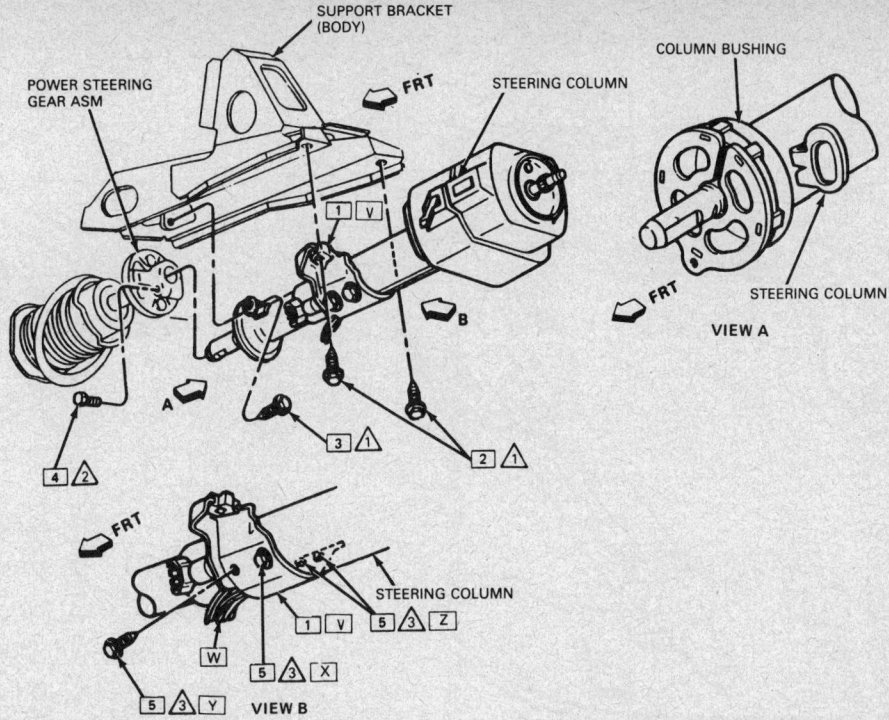

STEERING COLUMN INSTALLATION PROCEDURE:

1. PUSH CONVOLUTED SEAL Ⓐ BACK OVER RAG JOINT.
2. WITH STEERING SHAFT INSERTED INTO THE RAG COUPLING, RAISE COLUMN INTO POSITION AND LOOSE ASSEMBLE THE TWO CAPSULE BOLTS Ⓑ.
3. INSTALL AND TORQUE THE LOWER SHACKLE BOLT Ⓒ. THIS POSITIONS THE COLUMN IN THE FORE-AFT DIRECTION.
4. TORQUE THE TWO CAPSULE BOLTS Ⓑ.
5. INSTALL AND TORQUE COUPLING PINCH BOLT Ⓓ.
6.
7. PULL THE SEAL Ⓐ OVER THE END OF THE COLUMN.
   THE SEAL IS RETAINED BY THE LIP ON
   THE BUSHING.

NOTE: ELECTRICAL CONNECTIONS MAY BE MADE BEFORE THE COLUMN IS INSERTED INTO THE RAG COUPLING OR AFTER INSTALLATION OF THE THREE ATTACHING BOLTS. IN NO CASE SHOULD THE COLUMN BE SUPPORTED BY ONLY THE RAG JOINT.

TORQUE:

⚠1 27 N·m (20 FT. LBS.)
⚠2 40 N·m (29 FT. LBS.)
⚠3 30 N·m (22 FT. LBS.)

1	SUPPORT ASM
2	BOLT/SCREW
3	BOLT/SCREW
4	BOLT/SCREW
5	BOLT/SCREW

Ⓥ THERE MUST BE +5° LOCATION OF STEERING COLUMN SUPPORT BRACKET RELATIVE TO STEERING COLUMN.

Ⓦ WIRING HARNESS MUST BE ROUTED UNDER SUPPORT (AS SHOWN) TO PREVENT PINCHED OR CUT WIRES.

Ⓧ INSTALL THIS BOLT/SCREW 5 FIRST.

Ⓨ INSTALL THIS BOLT/SCREW 5 SECOND.

Ⓩ INSTALL THESE TWO BOLT/SCREWS 5 LAST.

Fig. 19   Steering column removal & installation. 1987–88 Beretta & Corsica

PONTIAC REAR WHEEL DRIVE MODELS EXCEPT FIERO

REMOVAL

1990 Firebird w/Supplemental Inflatable Restraint (SIR)

Refer to "Chevrolet Rear Wheel Drive, 1990 Camaro w/Supplemental Inflatable Restraint (SIR)" for procedures.

1988–89 Firebird & Safari Wagon

1. Disconnect battery ground cable and remove bolt securing upper intermediate shaft joint to steering shaft.
2. Disconnect shift linkage from shift lever.
3. Remove lower instrument panel trim covers, and if column is to be disassembled, the steering wheel.
4. Remove toe plate cover and toe plate mounting screws and clamp bolt, noting installation position for assembly.
5. **On column shift automatic transmission,** disconnect shift indicator cable from column shift bowl, **Fig. 25.**
6. Support column and remove two nuts from column upper support.
7. Lower column and disconnect electrical connections. **If spacers are used, retain for use during installation.**
8. Carefully remove column from vehicle.

Installation

1. Carefully position column from inside of vehicle through cowl opening.
2. Connect all wiring to column.
3. Raise column and loosely install nuts, **Fig. 3.** If shims were removed, install equal thickness on each side.
4. Install intermediate shaft onto steering column shaft. Install clamp bolt and nut and **torque** to 44 ft. lbs.
5. Check flex coupling for alignment. If coupling is not properly aligned, it will be necessary to move column assembly. Flex coupling must be straight within 1/16 inch without bottoming intermediate shaft coupling.
6. Install and **torque** toe pan screws in sequence shown in **Fig. 3,** to 53 inch lbs.
7. **Torque** steering column bracket nuts to 18 ft. lbs.
8. If equipped with column shift automatic transmission, connect and adjust shift indicator cable as shown in **Fig. 25.**
9. Check flex coupling and intermediate shaft for bottoming. If either is bottoming, it will be necessary to loosen pan bolts and steering column bracket nuts, then lift upward and rearward on column assembly. **Torque** toe pan bolts to 53 inch lbs. and steering column bracket nuts to 18 ft. lbs.
10. Install cover over toe pan and lower trim panel on instrument panel.

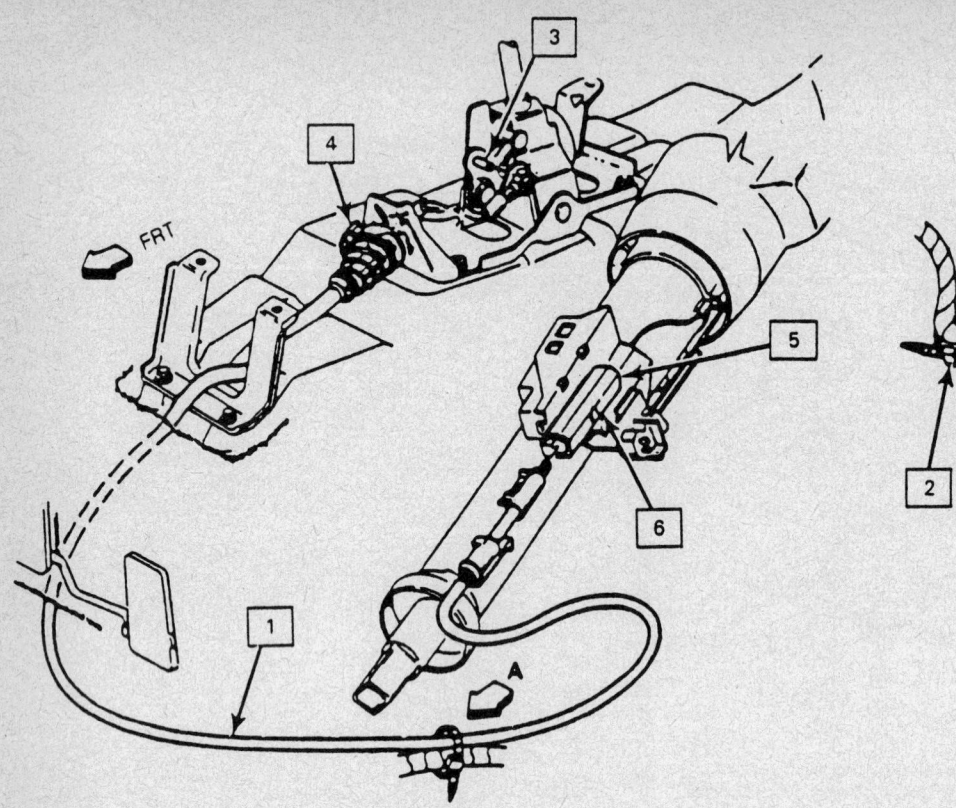
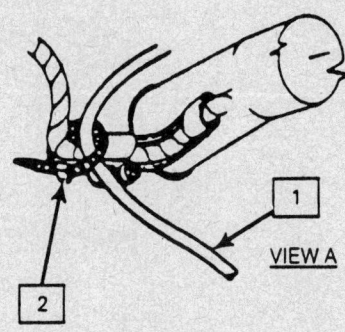

VIEW A

1. PARK LOCK CABLE
2. STRAP
3. PIN
4. LOCKING BUTTON
5. IGNITION SWITCH INHIBITOR
6. RELEASE SLOT

STEERING COLUMN REMOVAL PROCEDURE

1. REMOVE HORN COVER
2. REMOVE STEERING WHEEL
3. REMOVE STEERING COLUMN FILLER PANEL AND INSULATOR PANEL
4. DISCONNECT ALL ACCESSIBLE CONNECTORS
5. REMOVE THREE (3) MOUNT BOLTS
6. DISCONNECT IGNITION CONNECTOR
7. INSERT SMALL FLAT BLADE SCREW DRIVER INTO IGNITION INHIBITOR HOUSING AND DEPRESS TAB
8. PULL PARK LOCK CABLE OUT
9. REMOVE LOWER RAG JOINT PINCH BOLT

Fig. 20 Steering column removal. 1989 Beretta & Corsica

11. Install steering wheel if removed.
12. Install flex coupling shield, then connect battery ground cable.

FIERO
Removal

1. Disconnect battery ground cable.
2. Remove left instrument panel sound absorber, trim pad and column trim collar.
3. Remove bolt attaching steering column to intermediate shaft and separate.
4. Remove column support bracket support bolts and nut, then disconnect shift indicator cable.
5. Disconnect electrical connectors and

shift cable at actuator housing.
6. Remove column from vehicle.

Installation

1. Install steering column, then connect shift cable and housing.
2. Connect electrical connectors, then install shift indicator cable.
3. Install support bolts and nut, **Fig. 26.** and intermediate shaft upper bolt.
4. **Torque** upper support bolts to 20 ft. lbs. and intermediate shaft bolt to 39 ft. lbs.
5. Install instrument panel sound absorber, trim pad and column trim collar.
6. Connect battery ground cable.

CUTLASS SUPREME, GRAND PRIX, LUMINA & REGAL
Removal

1. On 1990 models, remove air cleaner.
2. **On all models**, disconnect battery ground cable, then remove steering wheel as necessary.
3. Remove left hand sound insulator and the trim panel below steering column.
4. Unlock steering column, then push top of intermediate shaft seal down for access to upper intermediate shaft coupling and upper coupling pinch bolt.

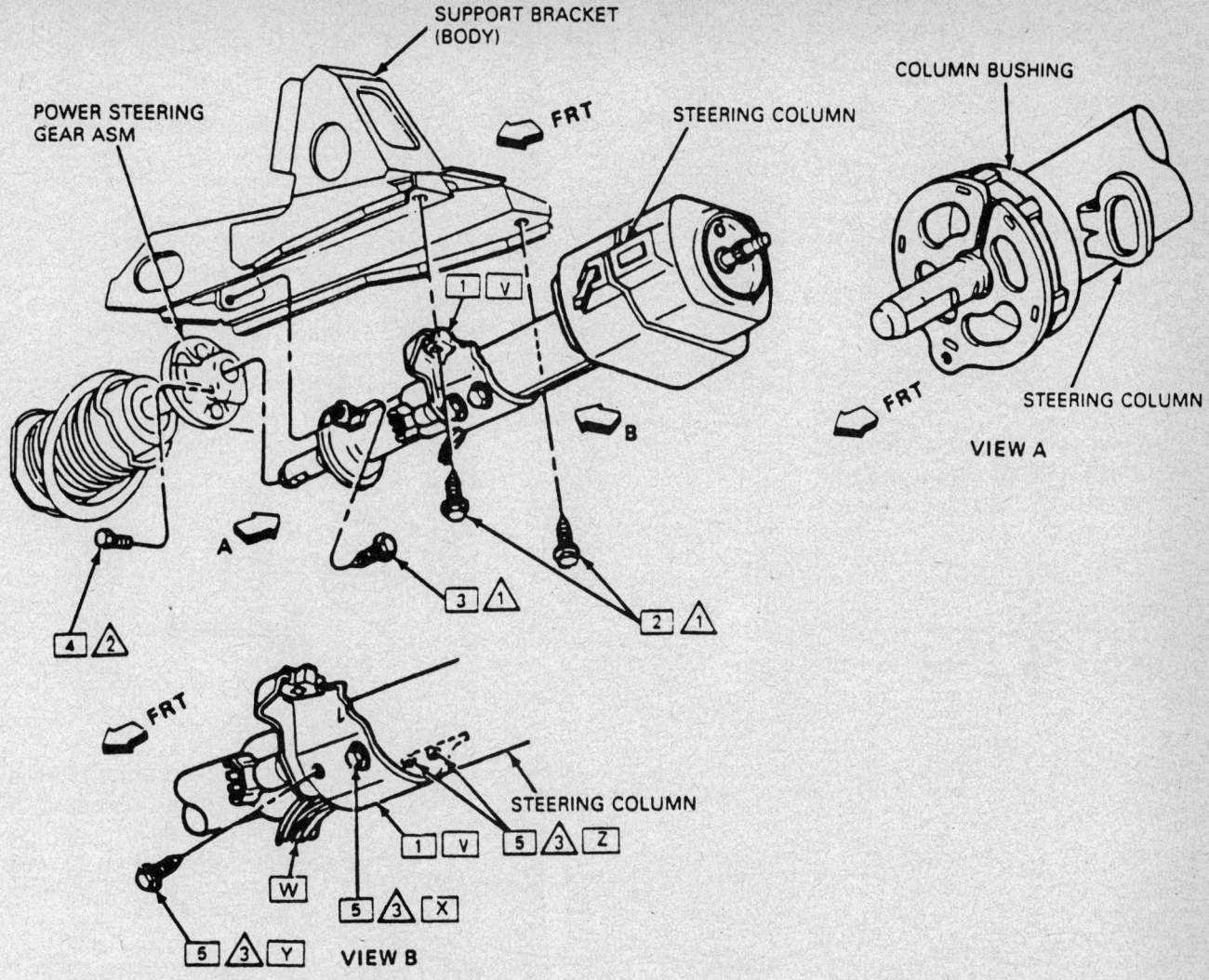

Fig. 21   Steering column installation. 1989 Beretta & Corsica

STEERING COLUMN INSTALLATION PROCEDURE:

1. PUSH CONVOLUTED SEAL Ⓐ BACK OVER RAG JOINT.

2. WITH STEERING SHAFT INSERTED INTO THE RAG COUPLING, RAISE COLUMN INTO POSITION AND LOOSE ASSEMBLE THE TWO CAPSULE BOLTS Ⓑ.

3. INSTALL AND TORQUE THE LOWER SHACKLE BOLT Ⓒ. THIS POSITIONS THE COLUMN IN THE FORE-AFT DIRECTION.

4. TORQUE THE TWO CAPSULE BOLTS Ⓑ.

5. INSTALL AND TORQUE COUPLING PINCH BOLT Ⓓ.

6

7. PULL THE SEAL Ⓐ OVER THE END OF THE COLUMN. THE SEAL IS RETAINED BY THE LIP ON THE BUSHING.

NOTE: ELECTRICAL CONNECTIONS MAY BE MADE BEFORE THE COLUMN IS INSERTED INTO THE RAG COUPLING OR AFTER INSTALLATION OF THE THREE ATTACHING BOLTS. IN NO CASE SHOULD THE COLUMN BE SUPPORTED BY ONLY THE RAG JOINT.

TORQUE:

△1 27 N·m (20 FT. LBS.)

△2 40 N·m (29 FT. LBS.)

△3 30 N·m (22 FT. LBS.)

☐	
1	SUPPORT ASM
2	BOLT/SCREW
3	BOLT/SCREW
4	BOLT/SCREW
5	BOLT/SCREW

Ⓥ THERE MUST BE +5° LOCATION OF STEERING COLUMN SUPPORT BRACKET RELATIVE TO STEERING COLUMN.

Ⓦ WIRING HARNESS MUST BE ROUTED UNDER SUPPORT (AS SHOWN) TO PREVENT PINCHED OR CUT WIRES.

Ⓧ INSTALL THIS BOLT SCREW ⑤ FIRST.

Ⓨ INSTALL THIS BOLT SCREW ⑤ SECOND.

Ⓩ INSTALL THESE TWO BOLT SCREWS ⑤ LAST.

- REMOVE IN NUMERICAL ORDER
- INSTALL IN REVERSE ORDER.

1 NEGATIVE BATTERY CABLE

2 STEERING WHEEL

3 STEERING COLUMN FILLER
   AND INSULATOR PANEL

9 PLACE IGNITION SWITCH IN
   RUN AND GEAR SELECTOR IN
   PARK

NOTE: ELECTRICAL CONNECTIONS
MAY BE MADE BEFORE THE
COLUMN IS INSERTED INTO THE
RAG COUPLING OR AFTER
INSTALLATION OF THE THREE
ATTACHING BOLTS. IN NO CASE
SHOULD THE COLUMN BE
SUPPORTED BY ONLY THE RAG
JOINT.

WIRING HARNESS MUST BE ROUTED
UNDER SUPPORT (AS SHOWN) TO
PREVENT PINCHED OR CUT WIRES.

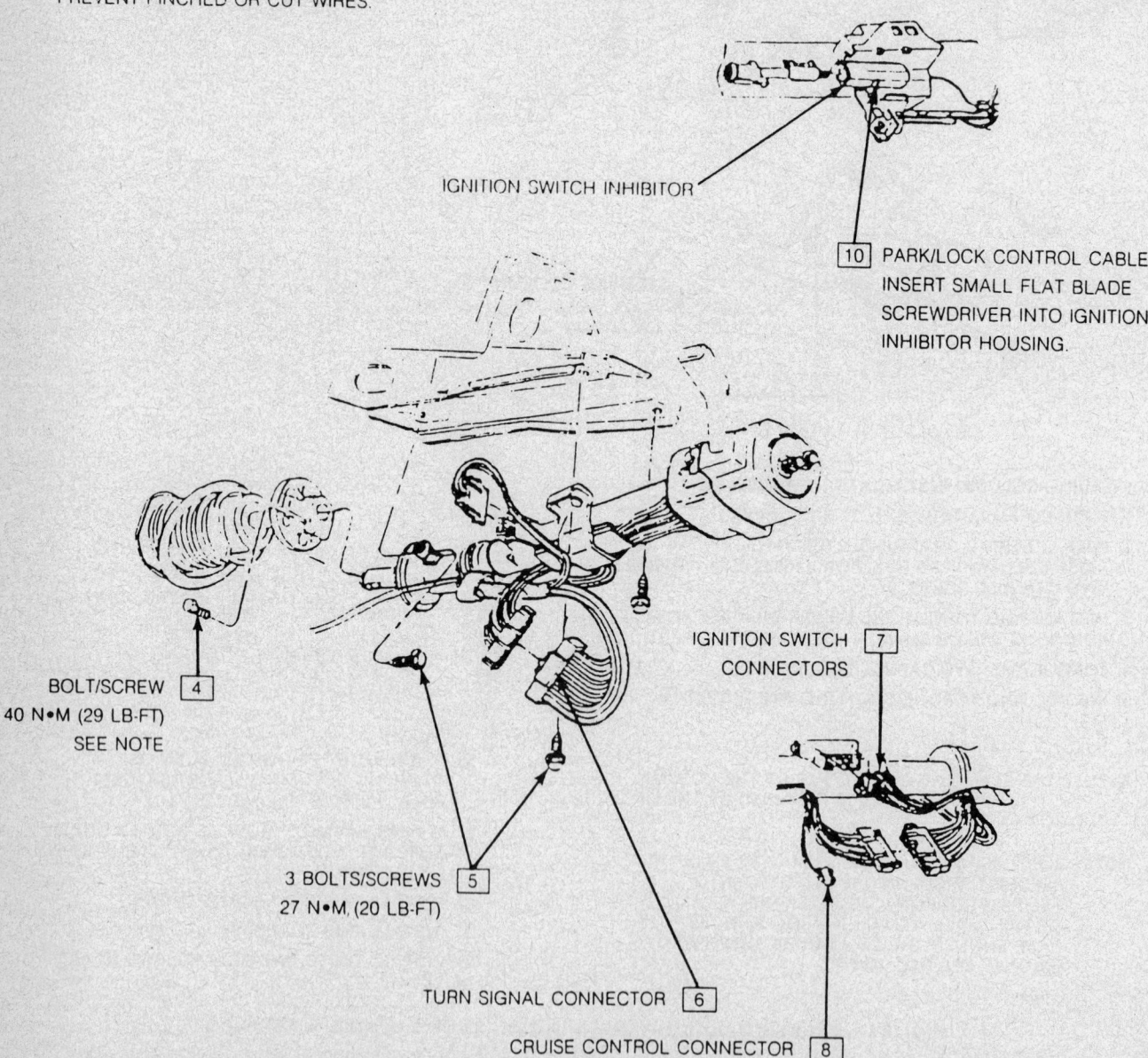

IGNITION SWITCH INHIBITOR

10 PARK/LOCK CONTROL CABLE
    INSERT SMALL FLAT BLADE
    SCREWDRIVER INTO IGNITION
    INHIBITOR HOUSING.

IGNITION SWITCH 7
CONNECTORS

BOLT/SCREW 4
40 N•M (29 LB-FT)
SEE NOTE

3 BOLTS/SCREWS 5
27 N•M (20 LB-FT)

TURN SIGNAL CONNECTOR 6

CRUISE CONTROL CONNECTOR 8

Fig. 22 Steering column removal & installation. 1990 Beretta & Corsica

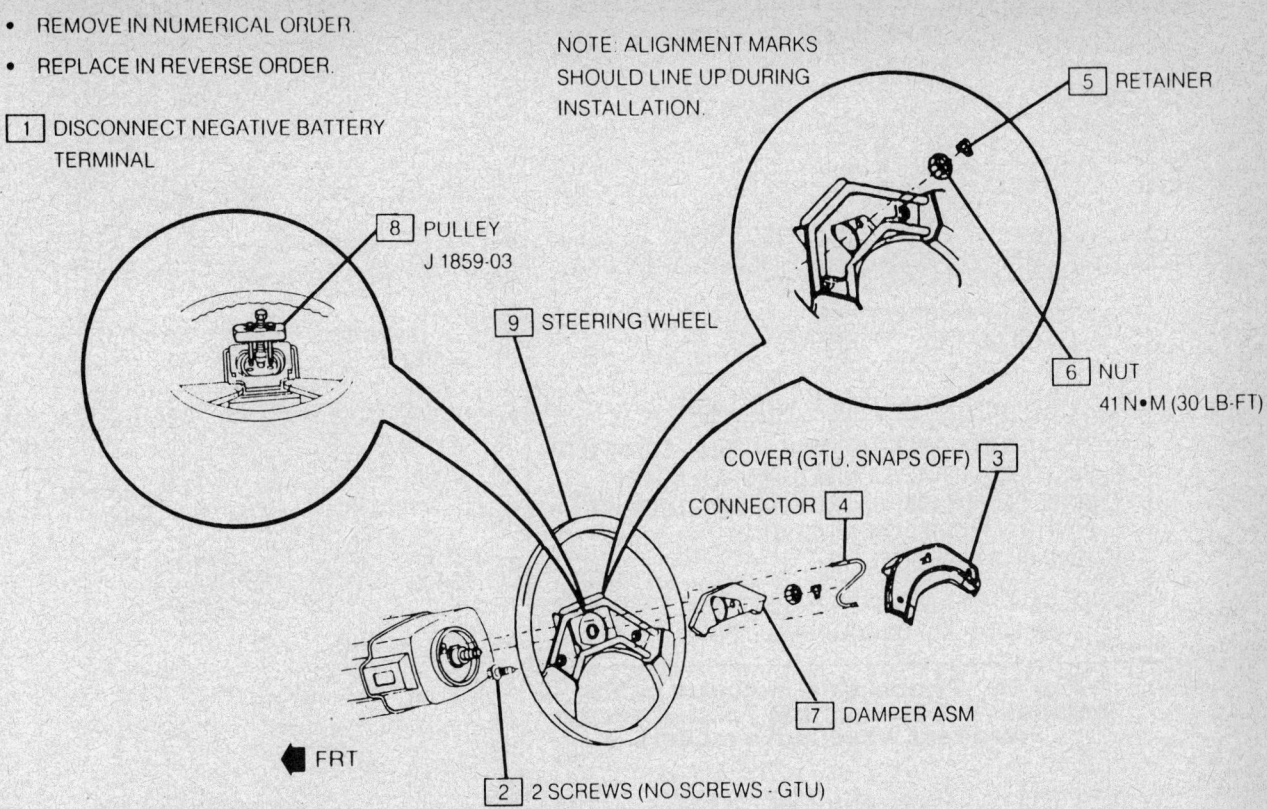

- REMOVE IN NUMERICAL ORDER.
- REPLACE IN REVERSE ORDER.

1 DISCONNECT NEGATIVE BATTERY TERMINAL

NOTE: ALIGNMENT MARKS SHOULD LINE UP DURING INSTALLATION.

5 RETAINER

8 PULLEY J 1859-03

9 STEERING WHEEL

6 NUT 41 N•M (30 LB-FT)

COVER (GTU, SNAPS OFF) 3

CONNECTOR 4

7 DAMPER ASM

FRT

2 2 SCREWS (NO SCREWS - GTU)

Fig. 23   Steering wheel removal & installation. 1990 Beretta & Corsica

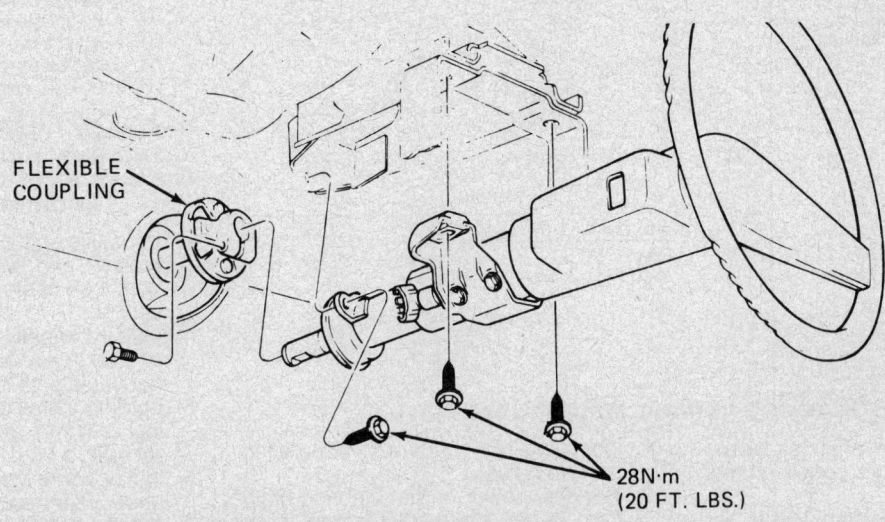

FLEXIBLE COUPLING

28N·m (20 FT. LBS.)

Fig. 24   Steering column installation.Calais, cavalier, Cimarron, Firenza, Grand Am, Skyhawk, Skylark, Somerset Regal & Sunbird.

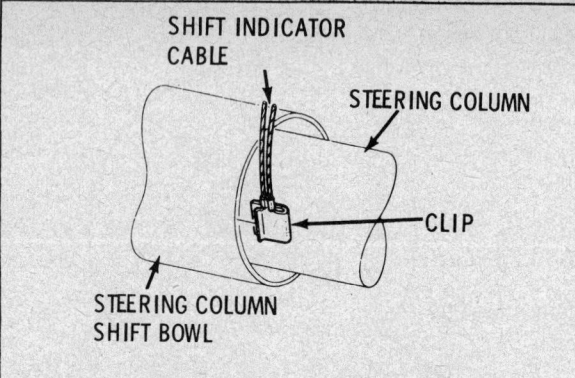

SHIFT INDICATOR CABLE

STEERING COLUMN

CLIP

STEERING COLUMN SHIFT BOWL

SHIFT INDICATOR ADJUSTMENT

1. STEERING COLUMN ATTACHMENT SHOULD BE COMPLETED.
2. POSITION SHIFT LEVER IN NEUTRAL GATE NOTCH.
3. GUIDE CLIP ON EDGE OF SHIFT BOWL TO CENTRALLY POSITION POINTER ON "N" (NEUTRAL).
4. PUSH CLIP ONTO BOWL.

NOTICE: CARE MUST BE TAKEN TO ASSURE THAT CABLE RESTS ON BOWL; NOT ON COLUMN JACKET.

Fig. 25 Typical shift indicator cable installation. Oldsmobile & Pontiac except Fiero rear wheel drive models.

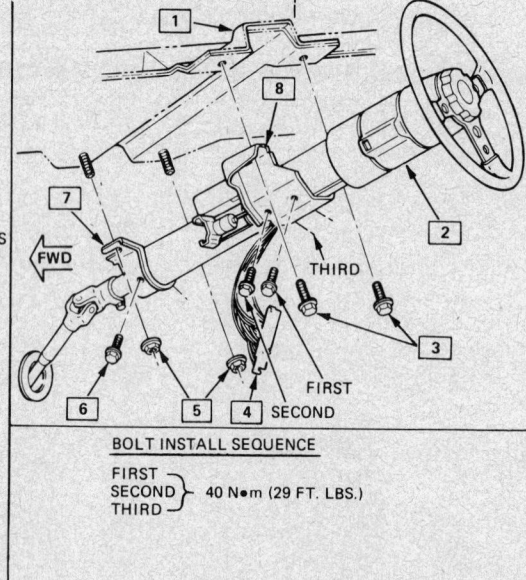

1—STEERING COLUMN SUPPORT

2—STEERING COLUMN

3—BOLT/SCREW 34 N•m (25 FT. LBS.)

4—WIRING HARNESS MUST BE ROUTED UNDER SUPPORT (AS SHOWN) TO PREVENT PINCHED OR CUT WIRES

5—NUT 34 N•m (25 FT. LBS.)

6—BOLT/SCREW 20 N•m (14 FT. LBS.) THIS SCREW MUST BE INSTALLED FIRST

7—SUPPORT LOWER

8—SUPPORT UPPER

BOLT INSTALL SEQUENCE

FIRST
SECOND } 40 N•m (29 FT. LBS.)
THIRD

Fig. 26 Steering column installation. Fiero

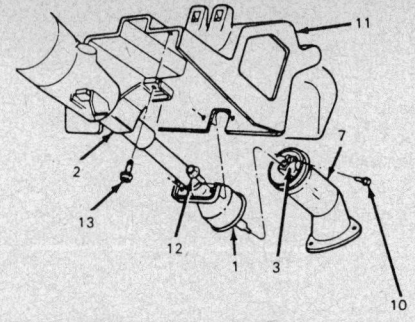

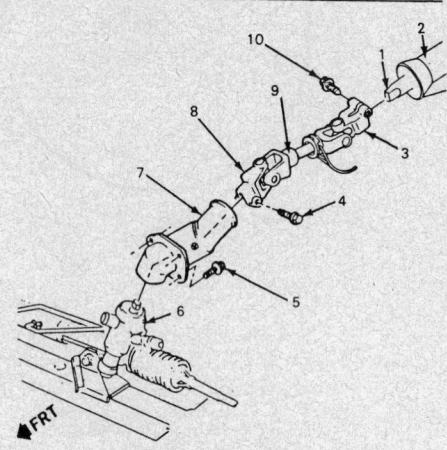

1 STEERING SHAFT-LOWER END
2 STEERING COLUMN ASSEMBLY
3 INTERMEDIATE SHAFT COUPLING-UPPER
4 PINCH BOLT-LOWER COUPLING
5 SCREW
6 STEERING GEAR
7 SEAL-INTERMEDIATE SHAFT
8 INTERMEDIATE SHAFT COUPLING-LOWER
9 INTERMEDIATE SHAFT
10 PINCH BOLT-UPPER COUPLING
11 BRACKET-BRAKE PEDAL
12 BOLT-LOWER STEERING COLUMN
13 BOLT-UPPER STEERING COLUMN

Fig. 27 Steering column removal and installation. Cutlass Supreme, Grand Prix, Lumina & Regal

5. Rotate intermediate shaft as necessary to remove upper coupling pinch bolt.
6. Disconnect shift indicator cable end and casing from steering column and transaxle shift lever, or park lock cable if equipped with floor shift.
7. Disconnect transaxle shift cable from ball stud on transaxle shift lever, then remove transaxle shift cable casing from steering column bracket by depressing two tabs.
8. Remove lower steering column attaching bolts, **Fig. 27**, then the upper steering column attaching bolts, and lower steering column to seat.
9. Disconnect electrical connector by loosening the screw and separating the two halves.
10. Withdraw lower end of steering shaft from upper intermediate shaft coupling and remove column. **It may be necessary to spread coupling clamp with a screwdriver to withdraw steering shaft.**

Installation

1. Install column back into vehicle and insert lower end of column shaft into upper intermediate shaft coupling.
2. Connect column electrical connector, tightening screw that draws the two halves together.
3. Connect transaxle shift cable and transaxle shift cable casing to column bracket and shift lever ball stud, or park lock cable if equipped with floor shift.
4. Install transaxle shift indicator cable end and casing and connect cable to transaxle shift lever.
5. Loosely install upper and lower steering column attaching bolts, then **torque** to 18 ft. lbs.
6. Install upper coupling pinch bolt into upper intermediate shaft coupling and **torque** to 35 ft. lbs.
7. Ensure clearance between lower shaft coupling and steering gear is at least .08 inch, then pull up intermediate shaft seal over lower column until it locks in place.
8. Install trim panel below steering column and the left hand sound insulator.
9. Install steering wheel, if removed, then connect battery ground cable and confirm proper operation of all steering column components and functions.
10. On 1990 models, install air cleaner.

NOTICE:
Once the steering column is removed from the car, the column is extremely susceptible to damage. Dropping the column assembly on its end could collapse the steering shaft or loosen the plastic injections which maintain column length. Leaning on the column assembly could cause the jacket to bend or deform. Any of the above damage could impair the column's collapsible design. If it is necessary to remove the steering wheel, use standard wheel puller. Under no condition should the end of the shaft be hammered upon as hammering could loosen the plastic injections which maintain column length.

REMOVAL

1) Disconnect negative battery cable.
2) Remove steering wheel.

3) Remove turn signal/dimmer switch.

4) Disconnect lead wires from ignition and ignition key warning switch electrical connector at junction/fusebox.
5) Pull off floor mat at the foot of steering shaft and remove steering joint cover.

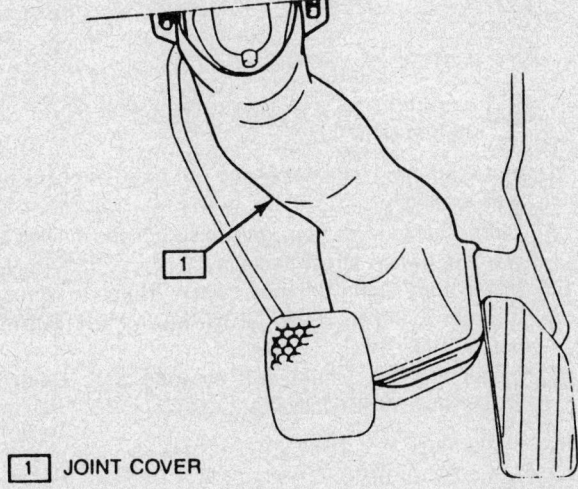

`1` JOINT COVER

6) Remove steering shaft joint upper side bolt.

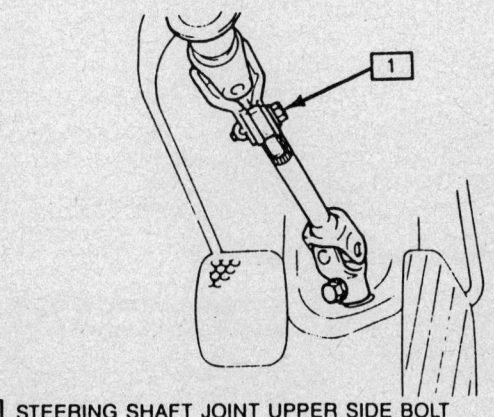

`1` STEERING SHAFT JOINT UPPER SIDE BOLT

7) Remove steering column mount nuts.

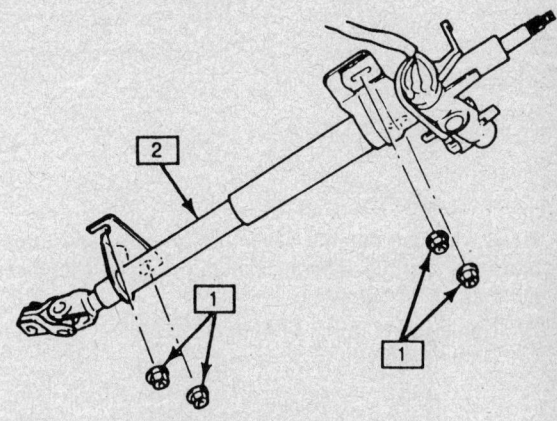

`1` STEERING COLUMN MOUNTING NUTS
`2` STEERING COLUMN

8) Remove steering column assembly.

NOTICE: Do not disassemble steering column assembly into column and shaft. If steering column or shaft is found defective, replace as an assembly.

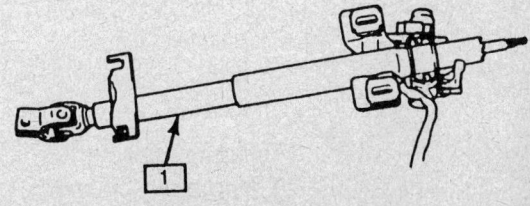

`1` STEERING COLUMN ASSEMBLY

Fig. 28 Steering column removal. Metro & Sprint

LEMANS
Removal

1. Disconnect battery ground cable.
2. Remove the turn signal/wiper switch lever as follows:

a. Remove lower instrument cluster trim.
b. Remove screws from upper cover panel by turning wheel 90° right or left for access.
c. Remove the three screws from the lower panel. Pull handle from the lock release lever and unscrew tilt lever, if so equipped.
d. Unclip switch from housing by pushing in on tab on either side of switch.

INSTALLATION

1) Align flat part "A" of lower joint shaft with bolt hole "B" of upper side joint as shown. Then insert upper side joint into lower joint shaft.

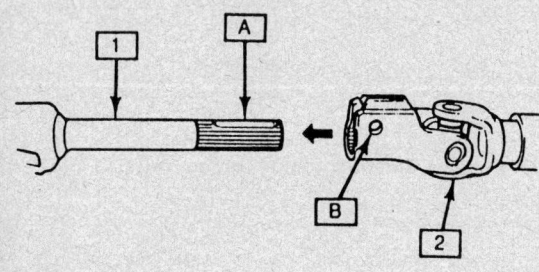

1 LOWER JOINT
2 UPPER JOINT

2) Install steering column assembly to lower and upper brackets. Torque steering column nuts to specifications as given below:

- Tighten nuts (a) to 14 N·m (10 lb.ft.).
- Tighten nuts (b) to 14 N·m (10 lb.ft.).

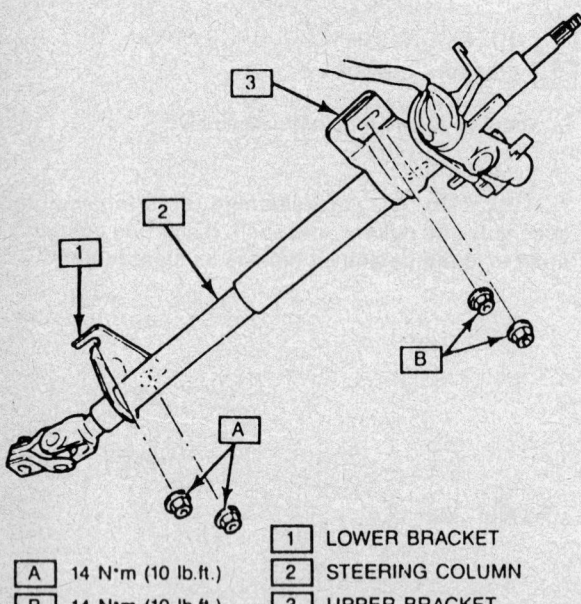

A	14 N·m (10 lb.ft.)	1	LOWER BRACKET
B	14 N·m (10 lb.ft.)	2	STEERING COLUMN
		3	UPPER BRACKET

3) Install bolt to steering shaft upper joint and tighten it to specified torque.

NOTICE: After tightening column nuts, steering shaft joint upper side bolt should be tightened.

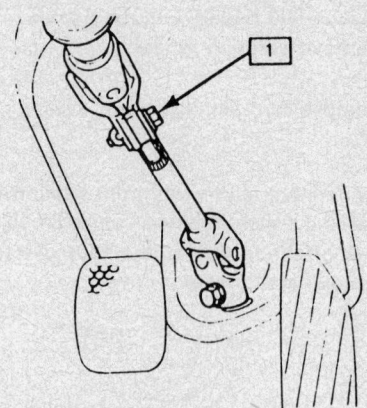

1 STEERING SHAFT JOINT UPPER SIDE BOLT
25 N·m (18 lb.ft.)

4) Install steering joint cover and put floor mat back as it was originally.
5) Connect lead wires from ignition switch and ignition key warning switch at connector.
6) Install turn signal/dimmer switch. Refer to steps 1 through 4 under TURN SIGNAL/DIMMER SWITCH INSTALLATION.
7) Install steering wheel and steering pad. Refer to STEERING WHEEL INSTALLATION.

Fig. 29 Steering column installation. Metro & Sprint

3. Disconnect wire harness and park lock actuation cable, if equipped.
4. Adjust steering to the straight ahead position, then remove pinch bolt from steering shaft flange.
5. Remove column jacket assembly lower mounting bolt from the instrument panel.
6. Remove shear plates below instrument panel as follows:
   a. Center punch the lefthand shear bolt, then drill a hole using a 1/8 inch bolt extractor bit.
   b. Install Drive No. 1411 bolt extractor or equivalent into hole and un-

screw shear bolt.
   c. Remove shear plates.
7. Guide column assembly out of shaft flange and remove from vehicle.

Installation

1. Guide steering shaft into steering shaft flange and provide support for column until shear bolts are fastened.
2. Loosely mount shear plates on instrument panel, then install column jacket assembly lower mounting bolt to instrument panel and pinch bolt in steering shaft flange.
3. **Torque** column jacket assembly low-

er mounting bolt to 12 ft. lbs. and shear bolt and self locking nut to 16 ft. lbs.
4. Draw steering shaft upwards until the stop reaches the steering shaft ball bearing and **torque** pinch bolt to 18 ft. lbs.
5. Slide alignment bushing out of column allowing bushing to remain on steering shaft.
6. Connect wiring harness and park lock actuation cable, if equipped.
7. Connect electrical connectors to turn signal/wiper switch, then clip switch back into housing.

REMOVAL

1) Disconnect negative battery cable.
2) Pull steering pad off and disconnect ground wire from inside of steering pad.
3) Remove steering wheel damper attaching screws and then steering wheel damper.
4) Remove steering shaft nut.
5) Scribe a line on the steering wheel and shaft to use as guide during reinstallation.
6) Remove steering wheel with special tool (A).

INSTALLATION

1) Install steering wheel onto shaft, using the alignment marks.
2) Install steering shaft nut and torque to 33 N·m (24.0 lb.ft.) as shown below.
3) Install steering wheel damper and damper attaching screws.

NOTICE: When installing steering wheel damper, be sure ground wire runs through center of damper and is not pinched underneath it.

4) Connect ground wire to inside of steering pad and press steering pad on.
5) Connect negative battery cable.

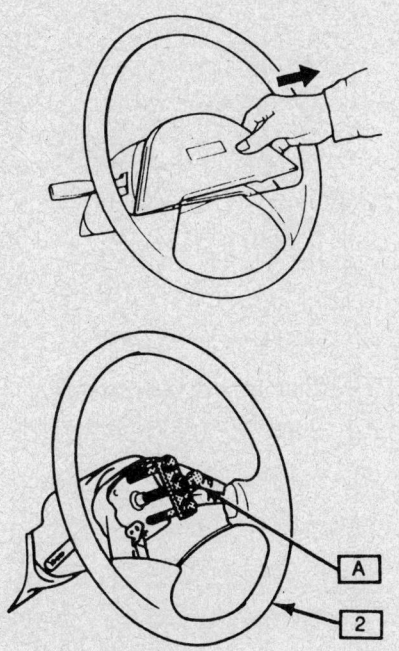

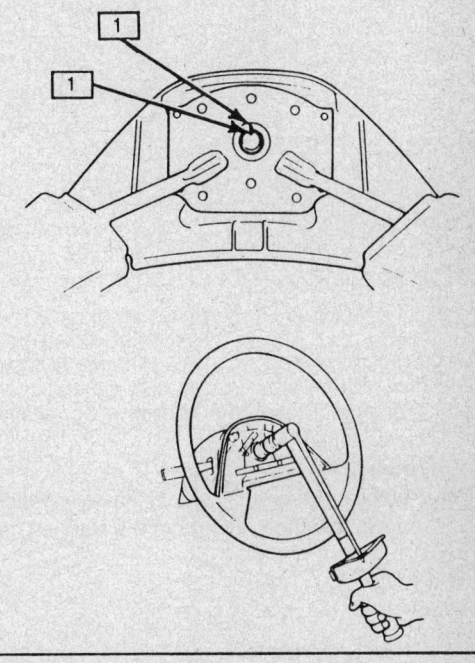

A	STEERING WHEEL REMOVER J1859-03
1	SCRIBE ALIGNMENT LINE
2	STEERING WHEEL

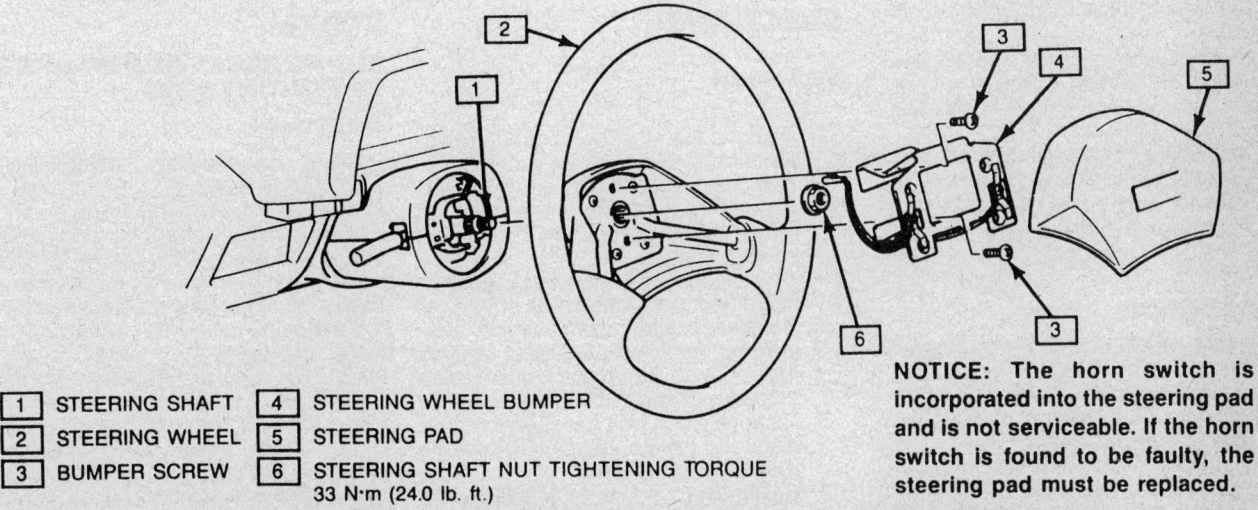

1	STEERING SHAFT	4	STEERING WHEEL BUMPER
2	STEERING WHEEL	5	STEERING PAD
3	BUMPER SCREW	6	STEERING SHAFT NUT TIGHTENING TORQUE 33 N·m (24.0 lb. ft.)

NOTICE: The horn switch is incorporated into the steering pad and is not serviceable. If the horn switch is found to be faulty, the steering pad must be replaced.

Fig. 30 Steering wheel removal & installation. Metro & Sprint

8. Install cover panels, lock release lever and tilt lever, if so equipped.
9. Install lower cluster trim, then connect battery ground cable.
10. Inspect steering for straight ahead po-sition.

METRO & SPRINT

Refer to **Figs. 28 through 31** for removal and installation procedures.

PRIZM
Removal

1. Disconnect battery ground cable.
2. Remove left side lower instrument fin-

REMOVAL

1) Disconnect negative battery cable.
2) Before removing this switch, remove steering wheel. Refer to STEERING WHEEL REMOVAL.
3) Remove column covers (under and lower).

INSTALLATION

1) Install turn signal/dimmer switch and three attaching screws to the steering column shaft.
2) Connect lead wire to turn signal/dimmer switch electrical connector.
3) Tighten wire bands.
4) Install column lower and under covers.
5) Install steering wheel and steering pad. Refer to STEERING WHEEL INSTALLATION.

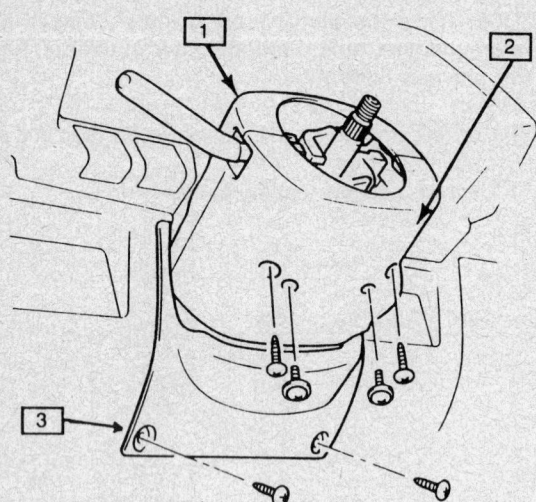

1	UPPER COVER
2	LOWER COVER
3	UNDER COVER

NOTE: MARKED WITH * ARE STANDARD SCREWS. ALL OTHERS ARE TAPPING SCREWS.

4) Disconnect lead wire from turn signal/dimmer switch electrical connector.
5) Loosen wire bands.
6) Remove three turn signal/dimmer switch attaching screws and the switch from the steering column shaft.

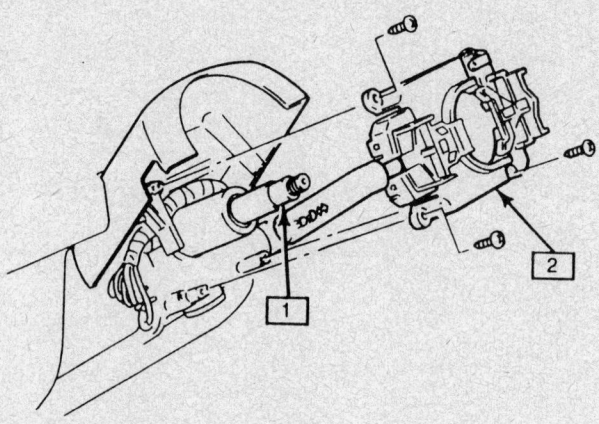

| 1 | STEERING COLUMN SHAFT |
| 2 | TURN SIGNAL/DIMMER SWITCH |

Fig. 31 Turn signal/dimmer switch removal & installation. Metro & Sprint

ish panel, upper and lower column covers.
3. Disconnect multi-function and ignition switch harnesses.
4. Disconnect park lock cable from lock cylinder housing.
5. Remove air intake filter assembly to gain access to column yoke and disconnect yoke from steering gear.
6. Remove lower column bolts, then upper column bolts and remove steering column.

Installation

1. Install steering column securing with upper and lower column bolts. **Torque** bolts to19 ft. lbs.
2. Connect shaft yoke to steering gear and **torque** bolt to 26 ft. lbs.
3. Install air intake filter assembly and connect multi-function and ignition switch harnesses.
4. Connect park lock cable to lock cylinder housing, then install upper and lower column covers.
5. Install left side lower instrument finish panel, then connect battery ground cable.

SPECTRUM

Removal

1. Remove the steering column protector nut and clip, then the protector.
2. Remove pinch bolt between the steering and intermediate shafts, then remove the lower column mounting bracket bolts.
3. Remove the upper steering column to instrument panel attaching bolts.
4. Remove column from vehicle. Disconnect park lock cable at ignition lock and, on automatic transmission models, remove cable bracket.
5. Remove pinch bolt between intermediate and pinion shafts, then remove the intermediate shaft.
6. Reverse procedure to install noting the following:
   a. **Torque** lower and upper steering column attaching bracket bolt to 11 ft. lbs. Pull column toward you as you tighten the upper bracket.
   b. **Torque** pinch bolts of intermediate shaft to 19 ft. lbs.

STORM

SUPPLEMENTAL INFLATABLE RESTRAINT (SIR)

Removal

Before removing the SIR steering column, the wheels of the car must be straight and the column in the Lock position. **Care must be taken when handling column with a live inflator module. Never point bag deploy surface toward you, and never stand column on steering wheel. Accidental deployment in these positions may cause injury. Always face bag deploy surface toward open space to allow for unrestricted expansion.**

The (DERM) Diagnostic Energy Reserve Module, can maintain sufficient voltage to cause a deployment for up to 10 minutes after the ignition switch is turned to the Off position and the battery ground has been disconnected.

1. Remove the inflator module as follows:
   a. With the ignition switch in the Off position and the battery ground ca-

Fig. 32 Servicing lock plate and/or cancelling cam

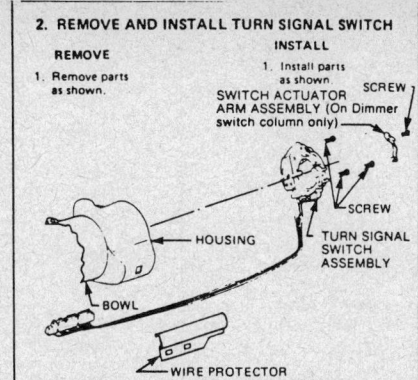

Fig. 33 Servicing turn signal switch

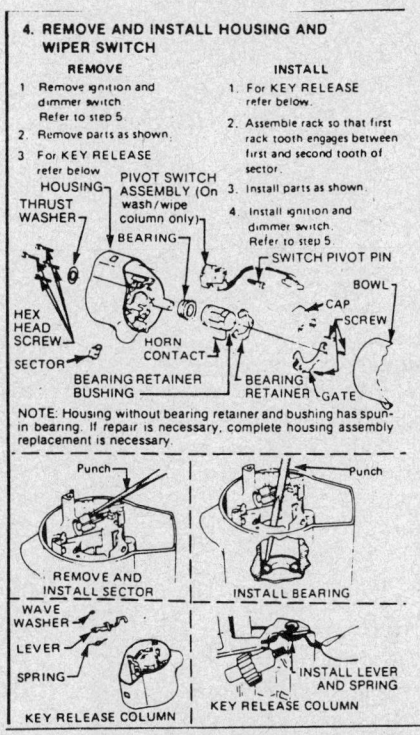

Fig. 35 Servicing housing & wiper switch

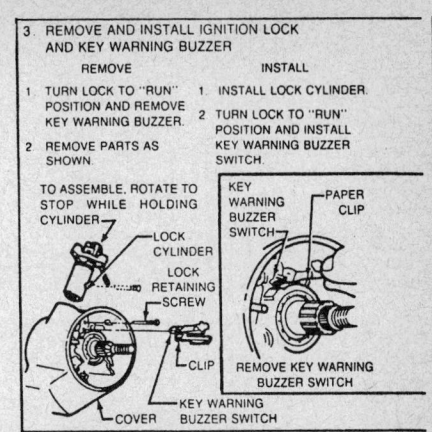

Fig. 34 Servicing ignition lock & key warning buzzer

ble disconnected and taped, remove the SIR fuse from the fuse panel.
   b. Remove left side sound insulator.
   c. Disconnect the yellow two way harness connector at the base of steering column.
   d. Remove the Torx screws from the back of the steering wheel, then remove the inflator module from steering wheel.
   e. Remove the horn contact by pushing lightly and twisting counterclockwise.
   f. Disconnect the coil assembly connector from inflator module.
2. Remove steering wheel retaining nut and wheel from column using No. J 1859-03 or equivalent steering wheel puller.
3. Remove lower switch panel and dash lighter panel.
4. Disconnect hood release cable and remove lap air deflector.
5. Remove left lower dash trim panel and upper column mounting bolts, then allow column to drop down.
6. Remove the two piece column cover and disconnect necessary electrical connectors.
7. Disconnect backdrive cable from ignition switch, then remove pinch bolt from column knuckle.
8. Remove the two nuts from the lower column mount, then the column from vehicle.

Installation

1. Install column assembly into vehicle and secure with retaining nuts on lower column mount. **Torque** retaining nuts to 18 ft. lbs.
2. Connect intermediate shaft to column and install pinch bolt. **Torque** pinch bolt to 30 ft. lbs.
3. Connect backdrive cable to ignition switch and necessary electrical connectors.
4. Install two piece column cover and upper column bolts. **Torque** bolts to 18 ft. lbs.
5. Install lower dash trim panel and lap air deflector.
6. Connect hood release cable, install lighter panel and lower switch panel.
7. Install steering wheel and retaining nut onto column and **torque** retaining nut to 25 ft. lbs.
8. Install steering wheel inflator module as follows:
   a. With ignition off, install horn contact, then connect coil assembly connector to inflator module.
   b. Push coil assembly lead wires into channel in lower right portion of steering wheel, then install inflator module in steering wheel.
   c. **Torque** screws holding inflator module to steering wheel to 25 inch lbs.
   d. Connect yellow two way SIR harness connector at base of steering column, then install left side sound insulator and SIR fuse.
   e. Connect battery ground cable, then turn ignition to Run and verify inflatable restraint indicator lamp flashes seven to nine times and then turns off.

STEERING COLUMN REPAIRS

1988 Cimarron, Cutlass Supreme (RWD), Fiero, Firenza & Monte Carlo; 1988–89 Brougham, Celebrity, Century, Cutlass Ciera, Cutlass Cruiser, Skyhawk, Toronado & 6000 & 1988–90 Cavalier, Cutlass Calais, Grand Am, Skylark, Somerset Regal & Sunbird

FIXED COLUMNS

When servicing these columns, refer to **Figs. 32** through **41**.

TILT COLUMNS

When servicing these steering columns, refer to **Figs. 42** through **54**.

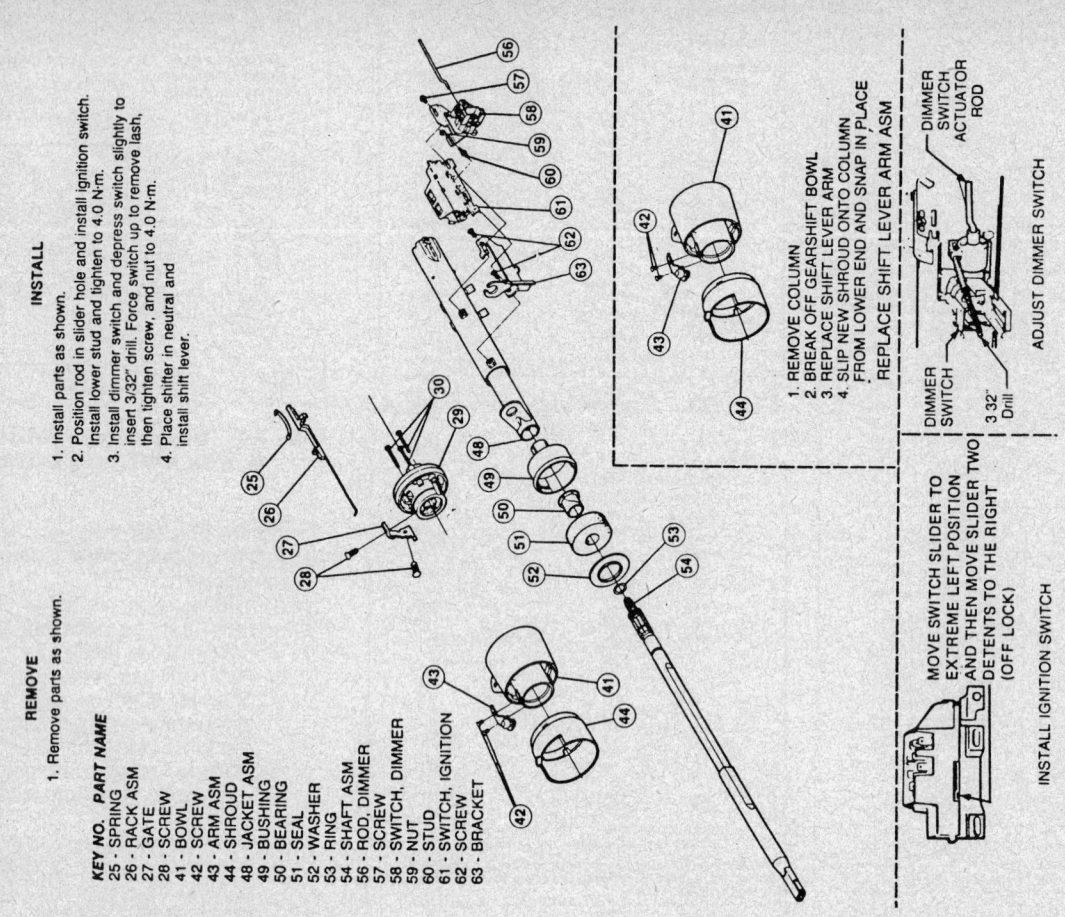

REMOVE

1. Remove parts as shown.

INSTALL

1. Install parts as shown.
2. Position rod in slider hole and install ignition switch. Install lower stud and tighten to 4.0 N·m.
3. Install dimmer switch and depress switch slightly to insert 3/32" drill. Force switch up to remove lash, then tighten screw, and nut to 4.0 N·m.
4. Place shifter in neutral and install shift lever.

KEY NO. PART NAME

25 – SPRING
26 – RACK ASM
27 – GATE
28 – SCREW
41 – BOWL
42 – SCREW
43 – ARM ASM
44 – SHROUD
48 – JACKET ASM
49 – BUSHING
50 – BEARING
51 – SEAL
52 – WASHER
53 – RING
54 – SHAFT ASM
56 – ROD, DIMMER
57 – SCREW
58 – SWITCH, DIMMER
59 – NUT
60 – STUD
61 – SWITCH, IGNITION
62 – SCREW
63 – BRACKET

1. REMOVE COLUMN
2. BREAK OFF GEARSHIFT BOWL
3. REPLACE SHIFT LEVER ARM
4. SLIP NEW SHROUD ONTO COLUMN FROM LOWER END AND SNAP IN PLACE

REPLACE SHIFT LEVER ARM ASM

MOVE SWITCH SLIDER TO EXTREME LEFT POSITION AND THEN MOVE SLIDER TWO DETENTS TO THE RIGHT (OFF LOCK)

INSTALL IGNITION SWITCH

ADJUST DIMMER SWITCH

DIMMER SWITCH

DIMMER SWITCH ACTUATOR ROD

3 32" Drill

Fig. 39 Servicing steering shaft, ignition & dimmer switch assembly, vehicles w/column shift automatic transmission.
1988 Cimarron, Cutlass Supreme (RWD), Fiero, Firenza & Monte Carlo; 1988–89 Celebrity, Century, Cutlass Ciera, Cutlass Cruiser, Skyhawk & 6000 & 1988–90 Cavalier, Cutlass Calais, Grand Am, Skylark, Somerset Regal & Sunbird w/standard column

---

5. REMOVE AND INSTALL IGNITION AND DIMMER SWITCH

REMOVE

1. Remove parts as shown.

INSTALL

1. Install parts as shown.
2. Position rod in slider hole and install ignition switch. Install lower stud and tighten to 4.0 N·m.
3. Install dimmer switch and depress switch slightly to insert 3/32" drill. Force switch up to remove lash, then tighten screw, and nut to 4.0 N·m.
4. Place shifter in neutral and install shift lever.

IGN SWITCH INHIBITOR HOUSING ASSEMBLY
SCREWS (2)
STUD
SCREW
PARK LOCK
NUT
IGNITION SWITCH ASSEMBLY
DIMMER SWITCH
STEERING COLUMN JACKET

MOVE SWITCH SLIDER TO EXTREME LEFT POSITION

BOWL LOWER BEARING
SHIFT BOWL SHROUD
SCREWS (KEY REL ONLY)
DIMMER SWITCH ACTUATOR ROD

• KEY RELEASE
  Leave slider at extreme left
• PARK LOCK
  Move slider one detent to the right (off lock)
• ALL OTHER COLUMNS
  Move slider two detents to the right (off unlock)

INSTALL IGNITION SWITCH

SWITCH RACK & ACTUATOR ASSEMBLY
RACK PRELOAD SPRING
SPRING THRUST WASHER
SPRING AND BOLT ASSEMBLY
UPPER SHIFT LEVER SPRING
GEAR SHIFT LEVER BOWL
DIMMER SWITCH ACTUATOR ROD
DIMMER SWITCH
ADJUST DIMMER SWITCH
3 32" Drill

Fig. 36 Servicing ignition & dimmer switch

---

6. REMOVE AND INSTALL LOWER STEERING SHAFT

REMOVE

1. Remove parts as shown.

INSTALL

1. Install parts as shown.

ON DISASSEMBLY, OBSERVE ALIGNMENT OF BOLT SLOT AND INDEX MARK. REASSEMBLE IN SAME MANNER.

BOWL & SHROUD ASSEMBLY
LOWER STEERING SHAFT ASSEMBLY
CENTERING SPHERE
JOINT PRELOAD SPRING
RACE AND UPPER SHAFT ASSEMBLY
INDEX MARK

Fig. 37 Servicing lower steering shaft assembly, vehicles w/standard column.

---

6. REMOVE AND INSTALL STEERING SHAFT AND SHIFT TUBE

REMOVE

1. Remove parts as shown.

INSTALL

1. Install parts as shown.
2. Refer to chart for manual transmission lever adjustment.

STEERING COLUMN JACKET
RETAINING RING
BACK-UP LIGHT SWITCH
SPRING THRUST WASHER
SHIFT TUBE RETURN SPRING
STEERING COLUMN HOLDING FIXTURE
J-23074

STEERING SHAFT ASSEMBLY
SHIFT TUBE ASSEMBLY (COLUMN SHIFT ONLY)

Rotate screw in direction of arrow until 2 & 3 shift lever is tight against shim. Tighten (3) screws to 10.2 N·m. Remove shim.

Install shim between second & third shift lever and lever spacer.
13mm SHIM
2 & 3 SHIFT LEVER

MANUAL TRANSMISSION SHIFT LEVER ADJUSTMENT

ADAPTER AND BEARING ASSEMBLY
BEARING RETAINER SCREWS
OPTIONAL
RETAINER
LOCKWASHER & SCREW ASM
SHIFT TUBE RETURN SPRING
RETAINER CLIP
LOWER BEARING ADAPTER
RETAINER BEARING ADAPTER
LOWER BEARING ADAPTER CLIP

MANUAL TRANSMISSION
SPACER LEVER
LOWER SHIFT LEVER
SUPPORT & ALIGNMENT PLATE
LEVER SPACER
BEARING ASSEMBLY

Fig. 38 Servicing steering shaft & shift tube

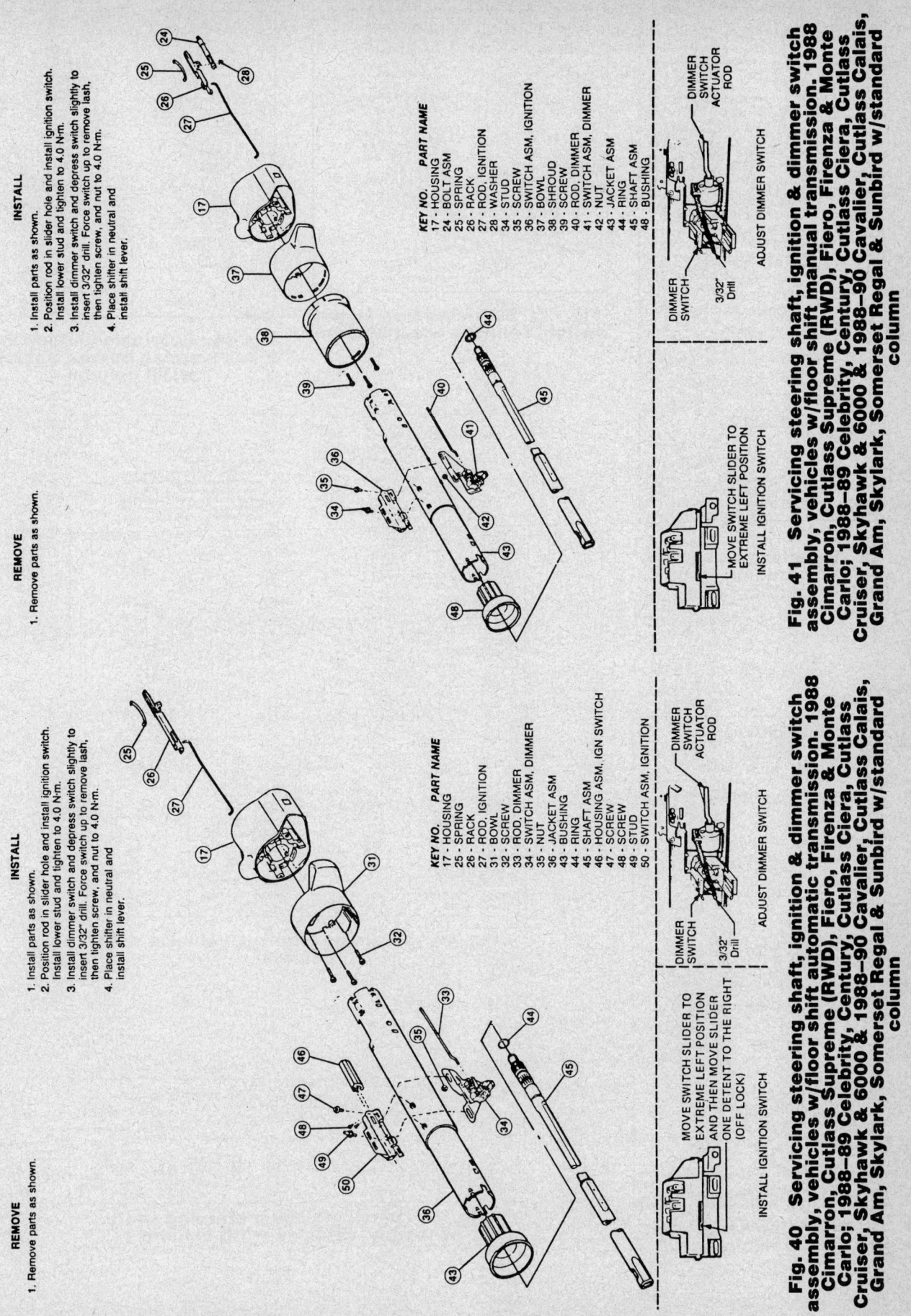

REMOVE

1. Remove parts as shown.

INSTALL

1. Install parts as shown.
2. Position rod in slider hole and install ignition switch. Install lower stud and tighten to 4.0 N·m.
3. Install dimmer switch and depress switch slightly to insert 3/32" drill. Force switch up to remove lash, then tighten screw, and nut to 4.0 N·m.
4. Place shifter in neutral and install shift lever.

KEY NO.   PART NAME

KEY NO.	PART NAME
17	HOUSING
24	BOLT ASM
25	SPRING
26	RACK
27	ROD, IGNITION
28	WASHER
34	STUD
35	SCREW
36	SWITCH ASM, IGNITION
37	BOWL
38	SHROUD
39	SCREW
40	ROD, DIMMER
41	SWITCH ASM, DIMMER
42	NUT
43	RING
44	JACKET ASM
45	SHAFT ASM
48	BUSHING

ADJUST DIMMER SWITCH

INSTALL IGNITION SWITCH

MOVE SWITCH SLIDER TO EXTREME LEFT POSITION

Fig. 41 Servicing steering shaft, ignition & dimmer switch assembly, vehicles w/floor shift manual transmission. 1988 Cimarron, Cutlass Supreme (RWD), Fiero, Firenza & Monte Carlo; 1988–89 Celebrity, Century, Cutlass Ciera, Cutlass Cruiser, Skyhawk & 6000 & 1988–90 Cavalier, Cutlass Calais, Grand Am, Skylark, Somerset Regal & Sunbird w/standard column

REMOVE

1. Remove parts as shown.

INSTALL

1. Install parts as shown.
2. Position rod in slider hole and install ignition switch. Install lower stud and tighten to 4.0 N·m.
3. Install dimmer switch and depress switch slightly to insert 3/32" drill. Force switch up to remove lash, then tighten screw, and nut to 4.0 N·m.
4. Place shifter in neutral and install shift lever.

KEY NO.	PART NAME
17	HOUSING
25	SPRING
26	RACK
27	ROD, IGNITION
31	BOWL
32	SCREW
33	ROD, DIMMER
34	SWITCH ASM, DIMMER
35	NUT
36	JACKET ASM
43	BUSHING
44	RING
45	SHAFT ASM
46	HOUSING ASM, IGN SWITCH
47	SCREW
48	SCREW
49	STUD
50	SWITCH ASM, IGNITION

ADJUST DIMMER SWITCH

INSTALL IGNITION SWITCH

MOVE SWITCH SLIDER TO EXTREME LEFT POSITION AND THEN MOVE SLIDER ONE DETENT TO THE RIGHT (OFF LOCK)

Fig. 40 Servicing steering shaft, ignition & dimmer switch assembly, vehicles w/floor shift automatic transmission. 1988 Cimarron, Cutlass Supreme (RWD), Fiero, Firenza & Monte Carlo; 1988–89 Celebrity, Century, Cutlass Ciera, Cutlass Cruiser, Skyhawk & 6000 & 1988–90 Cavalier, Cutlass Calais, Grand Am, Skylark, Somerset Regal & Sunbird w/standard column

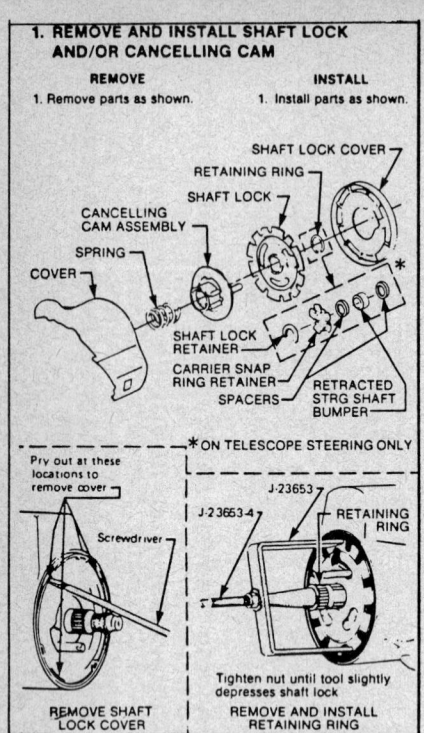

1. REMOVE AND INSTALL SHAFT LOCK AND/OR CANCELLING CAM

REMOVE	INSTALL
1. Remove parts as shown.	1. Install parts as shown.

SHAFT LOCK COVER
RETAINING RING
SHAFT LOCK
CANCELLING CAM ASSEMBLY
SPRING
COVER
SHAFT LOCK RETAINER
CARRIER SNAP RING RETAINER
SPACERS
RETRACTED STRG SHAFT BUMPER
*ON TELESCOPE STEERING ONLY

Pry out at these locations to remove cover
Screwdriver
J-23653
J-23653-4
RETAINING RING
Tighten nut until tool slightly depresses shaft lock

REMOVE SHAFT LOCK COVER

REMOVE AND INSTALL RETAINING RING

Fig. 42 Servicing shaft lock and/or cancelling cam, vehicles w/tilt column

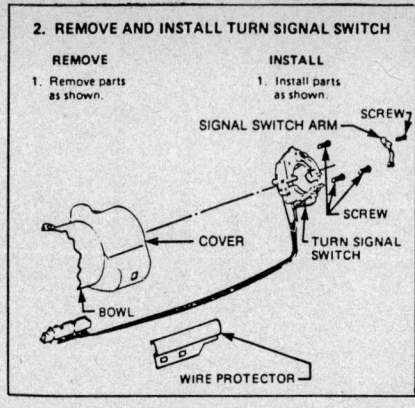

2. REMOVE AND INSTALL TURN SIGNAL SWITCH

REMOVE	INSTALL
1. Remove parts as shown.	1. Install parts as shown.

SIGNAL SWITCH ARM
SCREW
COVER
SCREW
TURN SIGNAL SWITCH
BOWL
WIRE PROTECTOR

Fig. 43 Servicing turn signal switch, vehicles w/tilt column

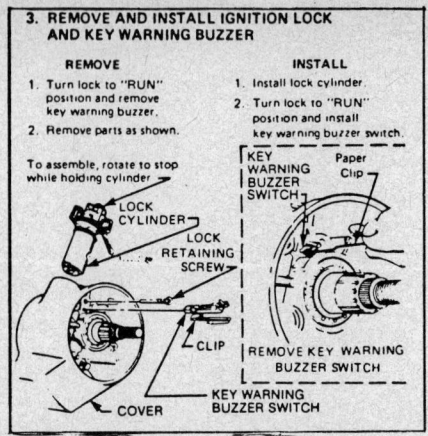

3. REMOVE AND INSTALL IGNITION LOCK AND KEY WARNING BUZZER

REMOVE	INSTALL
1. Turn lock to "RUN" position and remove key warning buzzer.	1. Install lock cylinder.
2. Remove parts as shown.	2. Turn lock to "RUN" position and install key warning buzzer switch.

To assemble, rotate to stop while holding cylinder.

KEY WARNING BUZZER SWITCH
Paper Clip
LOCK CYLINDER
LOCK RETAINING SCREW
CLIP
REMOVE KEY WARNING BUZZER SWITCH
COVER
KEY WARNING BUZZER SWITCH

Fig. 44 Servicing ignition lock & key warning buzzer, vehicles w/tilt column

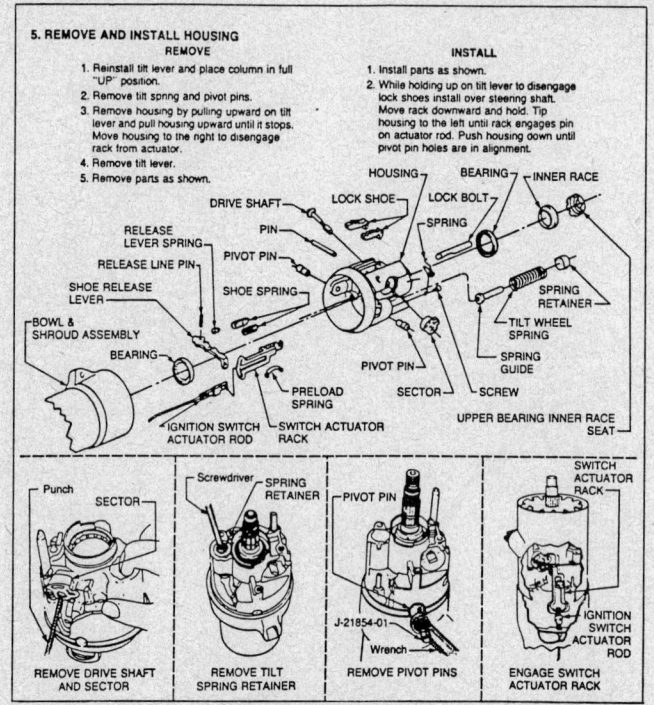

5. REMOVE AND INSTALL HOUSING

REMOVE
1. Reinstall tilt lever and place column in full "UP" position.
2. Remove tilt spring and pivot pins.
3. Remove housing by pulling upward on tilt lever and pull housing upward until it stops. Move housing to the right to disengage rack from actuator.
4. Remove tilt lever.
5. Remove parts as shown.

INSTALL
1. Install parts as shown.
2. While holding up on tilt lever to disengage lock shoes install shoes over steering shaft. Move rack downward and hold. Tip housing to the left until rack engages pin on actuator rod. Push housing down until pivot pin holes are in alignment.

DRIVE SHAFT
RELEASE LEVER SPRING
RELEASE LINE PIN
SHOE RELEASE LEVER
BOWL & SHROUD ASSEMBLY
BEARING
LOCK SHOE
PIN
PIVOT PIN
SHOE SPRING
IGNITION SWITCH ACTUATOR ROD
PRELOAD SPRING
SWITCH ACTUATOR RACK
HOUSING
BEARING
LOCK BOLT
SPRING
INNER RACE
SPRING RETAINER
TILT WHEEL SPRING
PIVOT PIN
SECTOR
SPRING GUIDE
SCREW
UPPER BEARING INNER RACE SEAT

Punch
SECTOR
REMOVE DRIVE SHAFT AND SECTOR

Screwdriver
SPRING RETAINER
REMOVE TILT SPRING RETAINER

PIVOT PIN
J-21854-01
Wrench
REMOVE PIVOT PINS

SWITCH ACTUATOR RACK
IGNITION SWITCH ACTUATOR ROD
ENGAGE SWITCH ACTUATOR RACK

Fig. 46 Servicing housing, vehicles w/tilt column

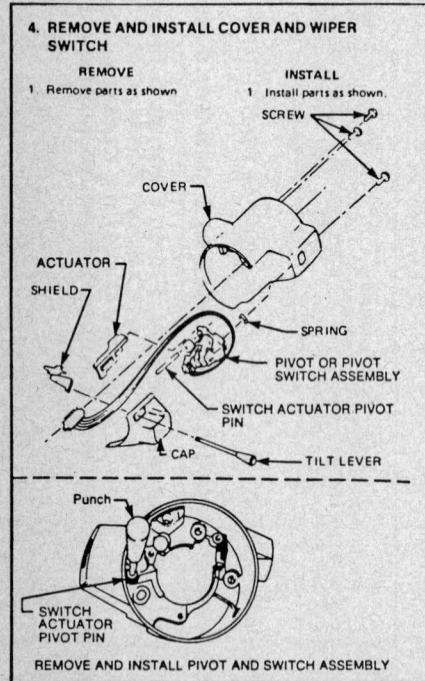

4. REMOVE AND INSTALL COVER AND WIPER SWITCH

REMOVE	INSTALL
1. Remove parts as shown.	1. Install parts as shown.

SCREW
COVER
ACTUATOR
SHIELD
SPRING
PIVOT OR PIVOT SWITCH ASSEMBLY
SWITCH ACTUATOR PIVOT PIN
CAP
TILT LEVER

Punch
SWITCH ACTUATOR PIVOT PIN
REMOVE AND INSTALL PIVOT AND SWITCH ASSEMBLY

Fig. 45 Servicing cover and wiper switch, vehicles w/tilt column

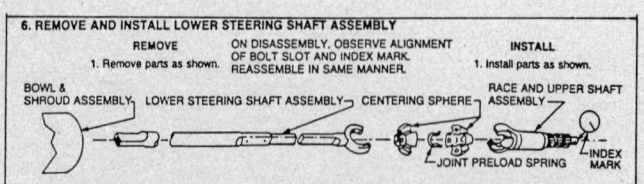

6. REMOVE AND INSTALL LOWER STEERING SHAFT ASSEMBLY

REMOVE
1. Remove parts as shown.

ON DISASSEMBLY, OBSERVE ALIGNMENT OF BOLT SLOT AND INDEX MARK. REASSEMBLE IN SAME MANNER.

INSTALL
1. Install parts as shown.

BOWL & SHROUD ASSEMBLY
LOWER STEERING SHAFT ASSEMBLY
CENTERING SPHERE
JOINT PRELOAD SPRING
RACE AND UPPER SHAFT ASSEMBLY
INDEX MARK

Fig. 47 Servicing lower steering shaft assembly, vehicles w/tilt column

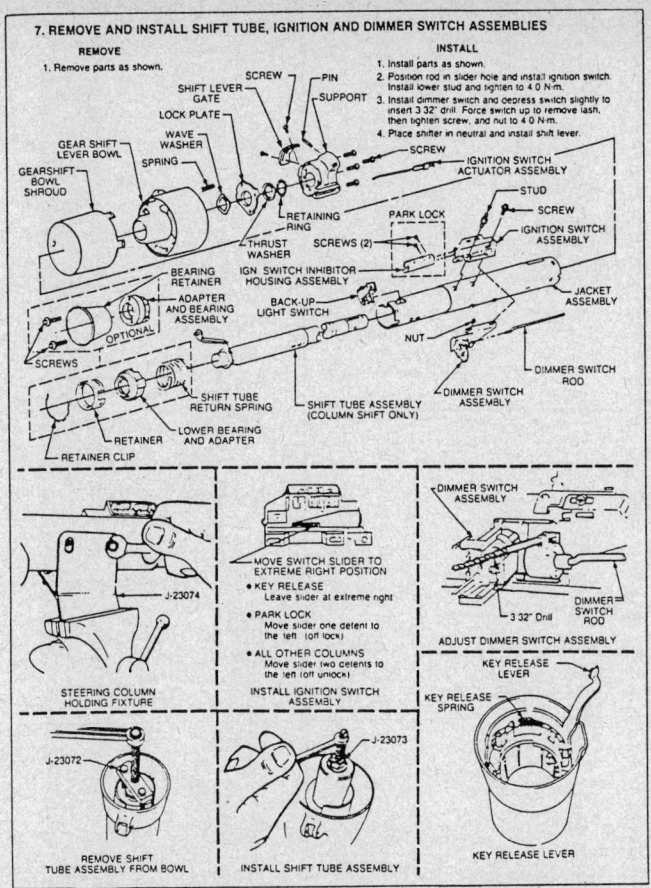

7. REMOVE AND INSTALL SHIFT TUBE, IGNITION AND DIMMER SWITCH ASSEMBLIES

REMOVE
1. Remove parts as shown.

INSTALL
1. Install parts as shown.
2. Position rod in slider hole and install ignition switch. Install lower stud and tighten to 4.0 N·m.
3. Install ignition switch and depress switch slightly to insert 3/32" drill. Force switch up to remove lash, then tighten screw, and nut to 4.0 N·m.
4. Place shifter in neutral and install shift lever.

REMOVE
1. Reinstall tilt lever and place column in full "UP" position.
2. Remove tilt spring and pivot pins.
3. Remove housing by pulling upward on tilt lever and pull housing upward until it stops. Move housing to the right to disengage rack from actuator.
4. Remove tilt lever.
5. Remove parts as shown.

INSTALL
1. Install parts as shown.
2. While holding up on tilt lever to disengage lock shoes install lock over steering shaft. Move rack downward and hold. Tip housing to the left until rack engages pin on actuator rod. Push housing down until pivot pin holes are in alignment.

Fig. 48 Servicing shift tube, ignition & dimmer switch assemblies, vehicles w/tilt column

Fig. 49 Servicing housing. 1988–89 Brougham & Toronado

d. When lever is in proper position, install lever retaining screw, **torquing** to 25 ft. lbs.
e. Install tension springs and grommets, then check tilt operation.

1988 Corvette

When servicing steering column, refer to Fig. 59.

1989 Corvette

When servicing steering column, refer to Fig. 60.

SHAFT LOCK, TURN SIGNAL CANCELLING CAM, UPPER BEARING SPRING, UPPER BEARING SEAT & INNER RACE

Disassembly

1. Remove steering wheel as follows:
   a. Disconnect battery ground cable, then remove horn cap from steering wheel by pulling.
   b. Disconnect horn button wire, then remove telescope lever screws and shaft lock knob screw.
   c. Remove telescope adjustment lever, steering wheel nut retainer and nut.
   d. Remove steering wheel with a puller.
2. Remove spacer, bumper, spacer and snap ring retainer (Nos. 2, 3, 4, and 5 in **Fig. 60**).
3. Remove shaft lock retainer using lock plate compressor to depress shaft lock.
4. Remove shaft lock and carrier assem-

Nova

DISASSEMBLY

1. Remove combination switch to column attaching screws, **Fig. 55.**
2. On tilt column, proceed as follows:
   a. Remove tension springs and grommets.
   b. Remove tilt lever. **Bolt has left-hand threads.**
   c. Remove adjusting nut and washer.
   d. Pull out lock bolt and remove column upper support.
   e. Remove lower column support.
3. **On all models,** Remove three screws and retainer from upper bracket.
4. Remove snap ring, insert key into ignition and release steering lock, then tap out tapered-head bolt with hammer and punch.
5. Remove upper bracket to column tube retaining bolts and separate the bracket.
6. Remove main shaft to column tube attaching bolts.
7. Remove shaft assembly.
8. Using pliers, remove thrust stopper snap ring.
9. Check steering lock mechanism for smooth operation and the upper bearing for smooth rotation.
10. If removal of upper bearing is necessary, tap out with screwdriver.

ASSEMBLY

1. If upper bearing was removed, pack new bearing with grease.
2. Using suitable tools, tap in new bearing.
3. Check lower stopper, replacing as necessary. Install stopper and snap ring on shaft, then apply molybdenum disulphide lithium grease to thrust stopper and install shaft assembly, aligning stopper with hole in column, **Fig. 56.**
4. **Torque** column to stopper attaching bolts to 9 ft. lbs.
5. Release steering lock and install upper bracket, then install attaching bolts, tightening until bolt head snaps off.
6. Install new upper bearing snap ring, then the upper bearing retainer.
7. **On tilt columns,** proceed as follows:
   a. Apply grease to bushings and O-rings and install lower support tube as shown, **Fig. 57.**
   b. Apply grease to surfaces as shown, **Fig. 58,** then install upper support and lock bolt. If there is any play in the adjusting support, snug up the adjusting nut.
   c. Install tilt lever. Move lever to loosen bracket to column bolt and adjust column height, then move lever to lock column into position. If lever is out of position, reposition

adjusting nut as shown, **Fig. 58.**

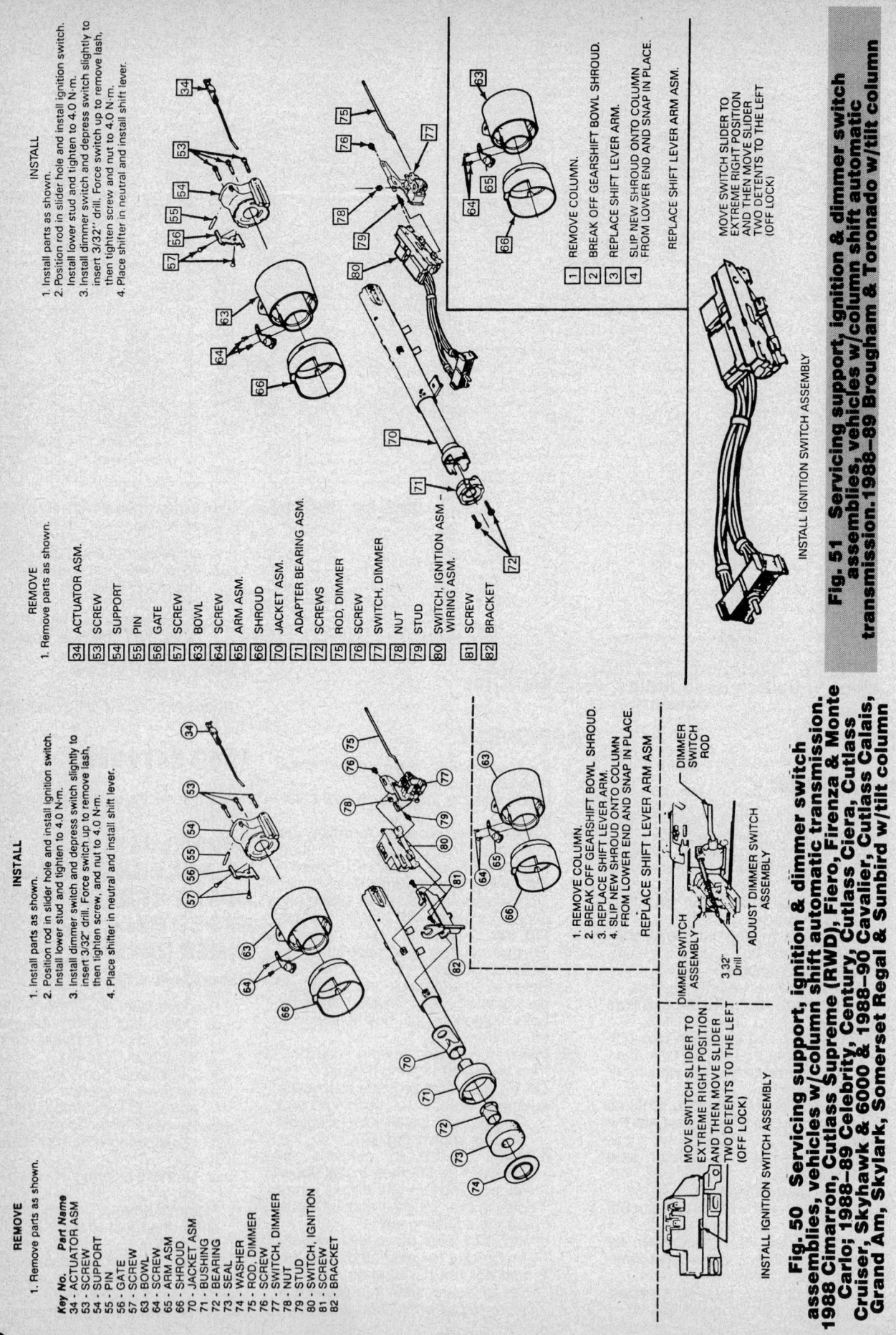

REMOVE

1. Remove parts as shown.

Key No.	Part Name
34	ACTUATOR ASM.
53	SCREW
54	SUPPORT
55	PIN
56	GATE
57	SCREW
63	BOWL
64	SCREW
65	ARM ASM.
66	SHROUD
70	JACKET ASM.
71	ADAPTER BEARING ASM.
72	SCREWS
75	ROD, DIMMER
76	SCREW
77	SWITCH, DIMMER
78	NUT
79	STUD
80	SWITCH, IGNITION ASM - WIRING ASM.
81	SCREW
82	BRACKET

INSTALL

1. Install parts as shown.
2. Position rod in slider hole and install ignition switch. Install lower stud and tighten to 4.0 N·m.
3. Install dimmer switch and depress switch slightly to insert 3/32" drill. Force switch up to remove lash, then tighten screw and nut to 4.0 N·m.
4. Place shifter in neutral and install shift lever.

1. REMOVE COLUMN.
2. BREAK OFF GEARSHIFT BOWL SHROUD.
3. REPLACE SHIFT LEVER ARM.
4. SLIP NEW SHROUD ONTO COLUMN FROM LOWER END AND SNAP IN PLACE.

REPLACE SHIFT LEVER ARM ASM.

MOVE SWITCH SLIDER TO EXTREME RIGHT POSITION AND THEN MOVE SLIDER TWO DETENTS TO THE LEFT (OFF LOCK)

INSTALL IGNITION SWITCH ASSEMBLY

Fig. 51 Servicing support, ignition & dimmer switch assemblies, vehicles w/column shift automatic transmission. 1988-89 Brougham & Toronado w/tilt column

REMOVE

1. Remove parts as shown.

Key No.	Part Name
34	ACTUATOR ASM
53	SCREW
54	SUPPORT
55	PIN
56	GATE
57	SCREW
63	BOWL
64	SCREW
65	ARM ASM
66	SHROUD
70	JACKET ASM
71	BUSHING
72	BEARING
73	SEAL
74	WASHER
75	ROD, DIMMER
76	SCREW
77	SWITCH, DIMMER
78	NUT
79	STUD
80	SWITCH, IGNITION
81	SCREW
82	BRACKET

INSTALL

1. Install parts as shown.
2. Position rod in slider hole and install ignition switch. Install lower stud and tighten to 4.0 N·m.
3. Install dimmer switch and depress switch slightly to insert 3/32" drill. Force switch up to remove lash, then tighten screw, and nut to 4.0 N·m.
4. Place shifter in neutral and install shift lever.

1. REMOVE COLUMN.
2. BREAK OFF GEARSHIFT BOWL SHROUD.
3. REPLACE SHIFT LEVER ARM.
4. SLIP NEW SHROUD ONTO COLUMN FROM LOWER END AND SNAP IN PLACE.

REPLACE SHIFT LEVER ARM ASM

DIMMER SWITCH ASSEMBLY

DIMMER SWITCH ROD

3 32" Drill

ADJUST DIMMER SWITCH ASSEMBLY

MOVE SWITCH SLIDER TO EXTREME RIGHT POSITION AND THEN MOVE SLIDER TWO DETENTS TO THE LEFT (OFF LOCK)

INSTALL IGNITION SWITCH ASSEMBLY

Fig. 50 Servicing support, ignition & dimmer switch assemblies, vehicles w/column shift automatic transmission. 1988 Cimarron, Cutlass Supreme (RWD), Fiero, Firenza & Monte Carlo; 1988-89 Celebrity, Century, Cutlass Ciera, Cutlass Cruiser, Skyhawk & 6000 1988-90 Cavalier, Cutlass Calais, Grand Am, Skylark, Somerset Regal & Sunbird w/tilt column

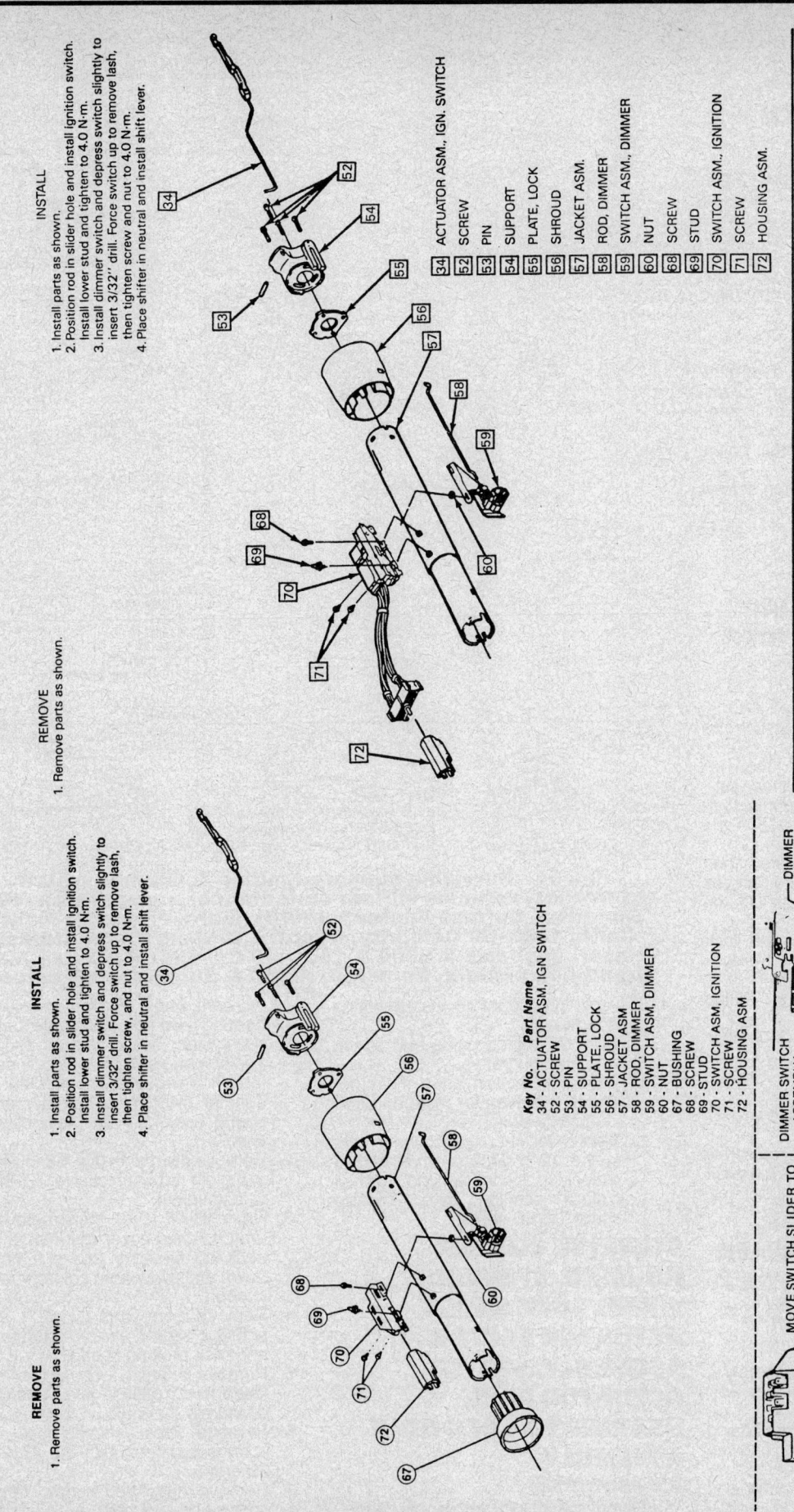

REMOVE

1. Remove parts as shown.

INSTALL

1. Install parts as shown.
2. Position rod in slider hole and install ignition switch. Install lower stud and tighten to 4.0 N·m.
3. Install dimmer switch and depress switch slightly to insert 3/32" drill. Force switch up to remove lash, then tighten screw, and nut to 4.0 N·m.
4. Place shifter in neutral and install shift lever.

REMOVE

1. Remove parts as shown.

INSTALL

1. Install parts as shown.
2. Position rod in slider hole and install ignition switch. Install lower stud and tighten to 4.0 N·m.
3. Install dimmer switch and depress switch slightly to insert 3/32" drill. Force switch up to remove lash, then tighten screw, and nut to 4.0 N·m.
4. Place shifter in neutral and install shift lever.

Key No.	Part Name
34	ACTUATOR ASM., IGN SWITCH
52	SCREW
53	PIN
54	SUPPORT
55	PLATE, LOCK
56	SHROUD
57	JACKET ASM
58	ROD, DIMMER
59	SWITCH ASM, DIMMER
60	NUT
67	BUSHING
68	SCREW
69	STUD
70	SWITCH ASM. IGNITION
71	SCREW
72	HOUSING ASM

Key No.	Part Name
34	ACTUATOR ASM., IGN. SWITCH
52	SCREW
53	PIN
54	SUPPORT
55	PLATE, LOCK
56	SHROUD
57	JACKET ASM.
58	ROD, DIMMER
59	SWITCH ASM., DIMMER
60	NUT
68	SCREW
69	STUD
70	SWITCH ASM. IGNITION
71	SCREW
72	HOUSING ASM.

DIMMER SWITCH ASSEMBLY

DIMMER SWITCH ROD

3/32" Drill

ADJUST DIMMER SWITCH ASSEMBLY

MOVE SWITCH SLIDER TO EXTREME RIGHT POSITION AND THEN MOVE SLIDER ONE DETENT TO THE LEFT (OFF LOCK)

INSTALL IGNITION SWITCH ASSEMBLY

MOVE SWITCH SLIDER TO EXTREME RIGHT POSITION AND THEN MOVE SLIDER TWO DETENTS TO THE LEFT (OFF LOCK)

INSTALL IGNITION SWITCH ASSEMBLY

Fig. 52 Servicing support, ignition & dimmer switch assemblies, vehicles w/floor shift automatic transmission. 1988 Cimarron, Cutlass Supreme (RWD), Fiero, Firenza & Monte Carlo; 1988-89 Celebrity, Century, Cutlass Ciera, Cutlass Cruiser, Skyhawk & 6000 & 1988-90 Cavalier, Cutlass Calais, Grand Am, Skylark, Somerset Regal & Sunbird w/tilt column

Fig. 53 Servicing support, ignition & dimmer switch assemblies, vehicles w/floor shift automatic transmission. 1988-89 Brougham & Toronado w/tilt column

bly, upper bearing spring, upper bearing seat and inner race.
5. Reverse procedure to install.

TURN SIGNAL SWITCH
Disassembly

1. Remove "Shaft Lock, Turn Signal Canceling Cam, Upper Bearing Spring, Upper Bearing Seat And Inner Race" as previously outlined.
2. Place turn signal lever to the right turn position, then remove screw and switch actuator pivot assembly (Nos. 11 and 44 in **Fig. 60**).
3. Remove the screws and the wiring protector (Nos. 10 and 45).
4. Remove turn signal switch, then gently pull wire harness through column housing shroud, column housing and lock housing cover.
5. Reverse procedure to install, noting the following:
   a. **Torque** turn signal switch screws (No. 10 in **Fig. 60**) to 27 inch lbs. and **torque** screw (No. 11) to 18 inch lbs.

BUZZER SWITCH ASSEMBLY & STEERING COLUMN LOCK CYLINDER SET
Disassembly

1. Remove the "Turn Signal Switch" as previously outlined.
2. Remove the hazard knob, then remove the key from lock cylinder set.
3. Remove buzzer switch and clip, then reinsert key in lock and place in the Lock position.
4. Remove the lock retaining screw, then disconnect lock cylinder wire harness and gently pull wire through column housing shroud.
5. Remove column housing and lock housing cover, then remove the lock cylinder set.
6. Reverse procedure to install, noting the following:
   a. Install cylinder wire harness through lock housing cover, column housing and column housing shroud first.
   b. **Torque** lock retaining screw to 27 inch lbs.
   c. Install lock cylinder and setscrew then place the key in the Run position.

LOCK HOUSING COVER, COVER END CAP, DIMMER SWITCH ROD ACTUATOR & TILT SPRING ASSEMBLY
Disassembly

1. Remove "Buzzer Switch Assembly & Steering Column Lock Cylinder Set" as previously outlined.
2. Remove cover screws, lock housing cover, tilt lever, cover housing end cap and dimmer switch rod actuator.
3. Remove spring retainer, spring and spring guide.

REMOVE
1. Remove parts as shown.

INSTALL
1. Install parts as shown.
2. Position rod in slider hole and install ignition switch. Install lower stud and tighten to 4.0 N·m.
3. Install dimmer switch and depress switch slightly to insert 3/32" drill. Force switch up to remove lash, then tighten screw, and nut to 4.0 N·m.
4. Place shifter in neutral and install shift lever.

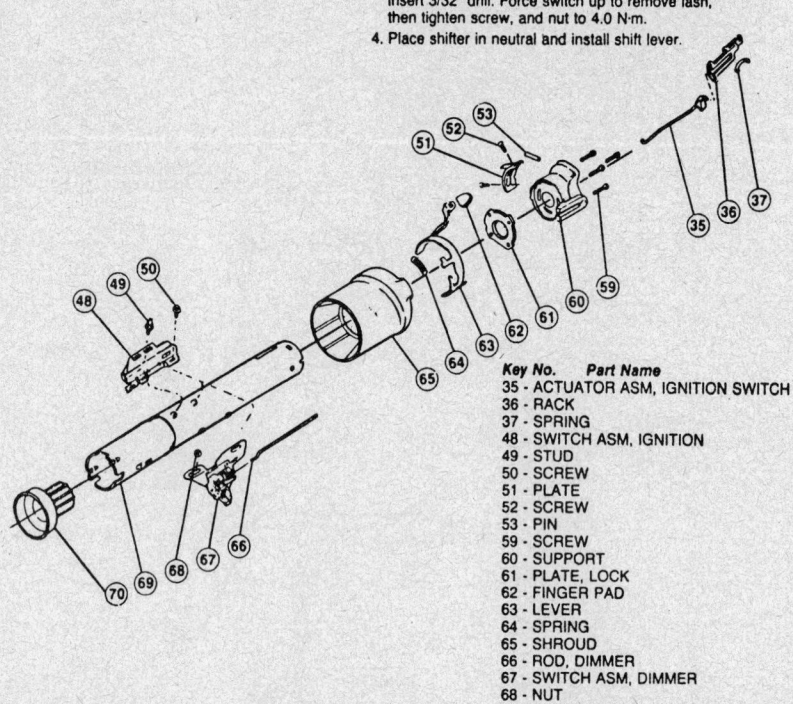

Key No.	Part Name
35	ACTUATOR ASM, IGNITION SWITCH
36	RACK
37	SPRING
48	SWITCH ASM, IGNITION
49	STUD
50	SCREW
51	PLATE
52	SCREW
53	PIN
59	SCREW
60	SUPPORT
61	PLATE, LOCK
62	FINGER PAD
63	LEVER
64	SPRING
65	SHROUD
66	ROD, DIMMER
67	SWITCH ASM, DIMMER
68	NUT
69	JACKET ASM
70	BUSHING

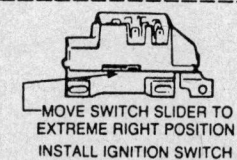

KEY RELEASE LEVER
KEY RELEASE SPRING
KEY RELEASE LEVER

MOVE SWITCH SLIDER TO EXTREME RIGHT POSITION
INSTALL IGNITION SWITCH

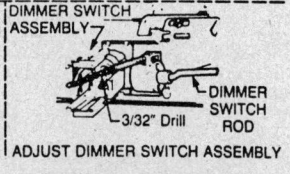

DIMMER SWITCH ASSEMBLY
3/32" Drill
DIMMER SWITCH ROD
ADJUST DIMMER SWITCH ASSEMBLY

Fig. 54 Servicing support, ignition & dimmer switch assemblies, vehicles w/floor shift manual transmission. 1988 Cimarron, Cutlass Supreme (RWD), Fiero, Firenza & Monte Carlo; 1988–89 Celebrity, Century, Cutlass Ciera, Cutlass Cruiser, Skyhawk & 6000 & 1988–90 Cavalier, Cutlass Calais, Grand Am, Skylark, Somerset Regal & Sunbird w/tilt column

4. Reverse procedure to install, noting the following:
   a. Coat the spring guide and spring with lithium grease.
   b. Ensure the bottom edge of dimmer switch rod actuator rests on bend in dimmer switch rod.
   c. Tighten lock housing cover screws in the 12 o'clock position first, 8 o'clock position second and 3 o'clock position third. **Torque** screws to 80 inch lbs.

STEERING COLUMN HOUSING, STEERING WHEEL LOCK SHOES, ACTUATOR SECTOR ASSEMBLY, SWITCH ACTUATOR RACK, BEARINGS & LOCK BOLT ASSEMBLY
Disassembly

1. Remove shaft lock, turn signal canceling cam, upper bearing spring, upper bearing seat and inner race; turn signal switch; buzzer switch assembly and steering column lock cylinder set; lock housing cover, cover end cap, dimmer switch rod actuator and tilt spring assembly as previously outlined.
2. Remove pivot pins (No. 38 in **Fig. 60**) using pin removal tool No. J21854-01 or equivalent.
3. Reinstall tilt lever, then remove column housing assembly (No. 37). Pull back on tilt lever and pull housing down and away from column housing support.
4. Remove drive shaft (No. 27), switch actuator sector, switch actuator rack and rack preload spring.
5. Remove release lever pin, shoe release lever, release lever spring and dowel pin (Nos. 32, 34, 31 and 28).
6. Remove lock shoes, lock shoe springs and bearings (Nos. 25, 26, 30, 22 and 33).
7. Remove hex head screw, lock bolt spring and lock bolt.

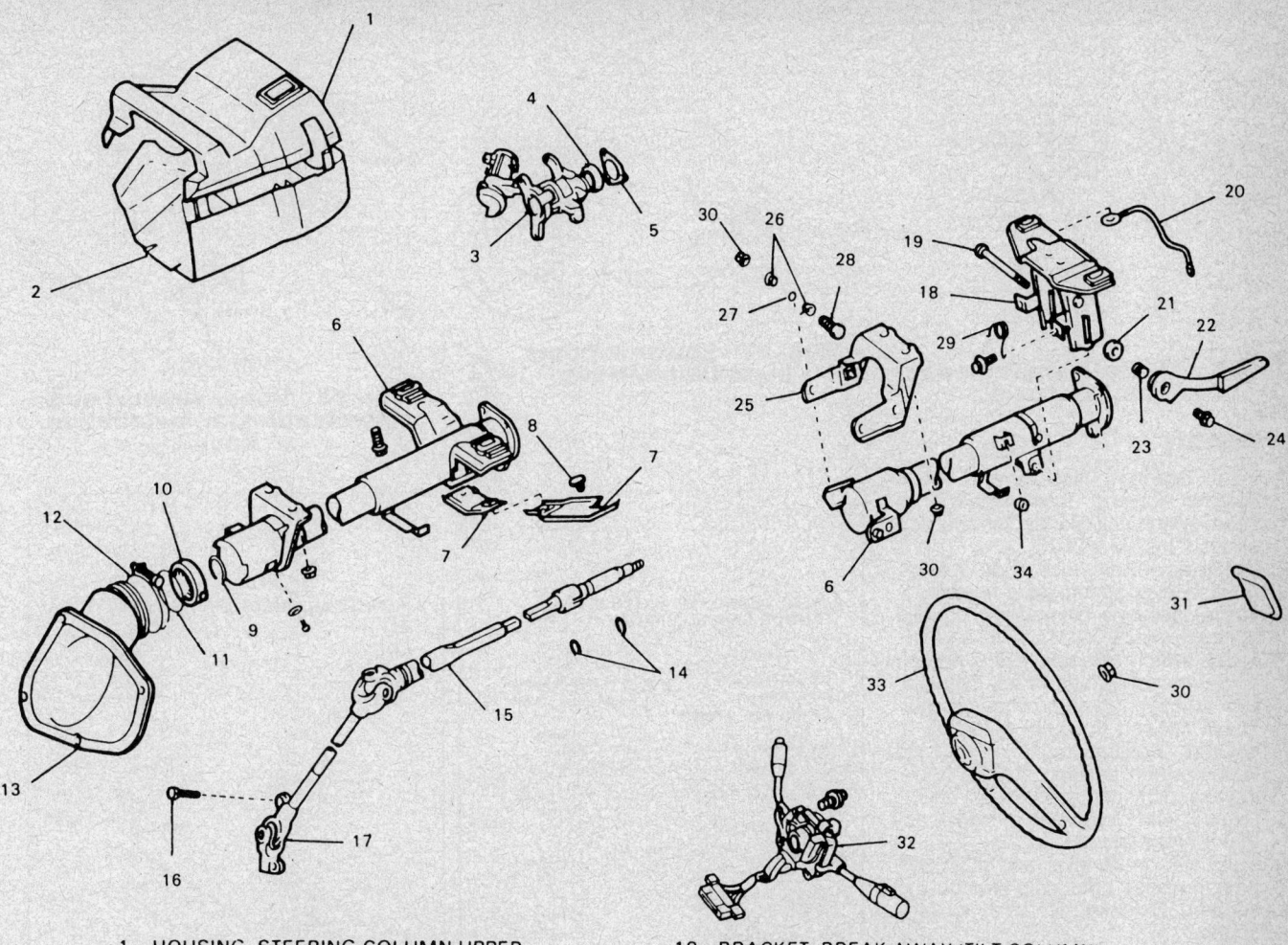

1 HOUSING, STEERING COLUMN UPPER	18 BRACKET, BREAK AWAY (TILT COLUMN)
2 HOUSING, STEERING COLUMN LOWER	19 BOLT, TILT LEVER LOCK (TILT COLUMN)
3 BRACKET ASSY., STEERING COLUMN UPPER	20 CABLE, COLUMN GROUND (TILT COLUMN)
4 BEARING, STEERING MAIN SHAFT	21 WASHER, PLATE (TILT COLUMN)
5 RETAINER, MAIN SHAFT BEARING	22 LEVER, TILT (TILT COLUMN)
6 TUBE ASSY., STEERING COLUMN	23 NUT, ADJUSTING (TILT COLUMN)
7 PROTECTOR, STEERING COLUMN (STANDARD)	24 BOLT, ADJUSTING LEVER (TILT COLUMN)
8 CUSHION, STEERING COLUMN PROTECTOR	25 SUPPORT, COLUMN LOWER (TILT COLUMN)
(STANDARD)	26 BUSHING, SUPPORT TO TUBE (TILT COLUMN)
9 RING, STEERING MAIN SHAFT BEARING SNAP	27 RING, O (TILT COLUMN)
10 STOPPER, STEERING SHAFT THRUST	28 BOLT, PAWL SET (TILT COLUMN)
11 RING, "O"	29 SPRING, TORSION (TILT COLUMN)
12 CLAMP, STEERING COLUMN HOLE COVER	30 NUT
13 COVER, STEERING COLUMN HOLE	31 PAD, STEERING WHEEL
14 RING, SHAFT SNAP	32 SWITCH, COMBINATION
15 SHAFT, ASSY STEERING MAIN	33 WHEEL, STEERING
16 BOLT, PINCH	34 GROMMET, RETURN SPRING
17 YOKE, STEERING SLIDING	

Fig. 55 Steering column exploded view. Nova

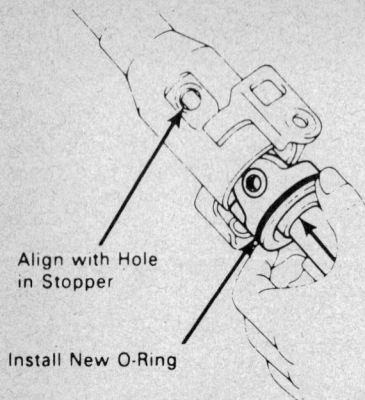

Fig. 56 Steering shaft stopper alignment. Nova

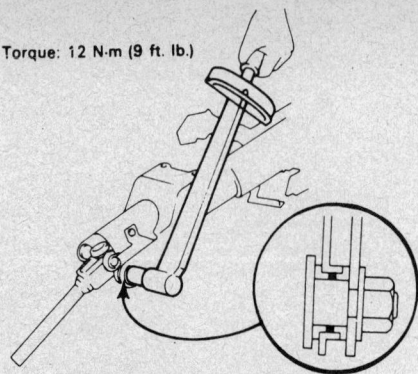

Fig. 57 Lower support installation. Nova

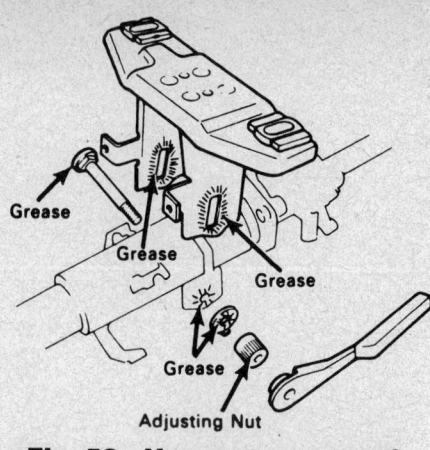

Fig. 58 Upper support and column adjuster installation. Nova

Assembly

1. Install bearings (Nos. 22 and 33) to column housing, then install drive shaft, switch actuator sector and lock shoes (Nos. 25 and 26).
2. Install dowel pin, lock shoe springs, release lever spring, shoe release lever, release lever pin and rack preload spring (Nos. 28, 30, 31, 34, 32 and 36).
3. Install switch actuator rack to switch actuator sector, then install lock bolt, lock bolt spring and hex head screw.
4. Install column housing assembly to column. Position column housing support, then position column housing assembly and align switch actuator rack with pin on end of switch actuator assembly.
5. Pull back on tilt lever and push column housing onto column housing support. Release tilt lever to lock shoes.
6. Remove tilt lever, then install pivot pins, spring guide and spring. Coat all parts with lithium grease.
7. Follow installation procedure from "Lock Housing Cover, Cover End Cap, Dimmer Switch Rod Actuator & Tilt Spring Assembly" to complete installation.

SHAFT ASSEMBLY, COLUMN HOUSING SUPPORT, IGNITION SWITCH, DIMMER SWITCH & LOWER BEARING ASSEMBLY

Disassembly

1. Follow removal procedure outlined under "Lock Housing Cover, Cover End Cap, Dimmer Switch Rod Actuator & Tilt Spring Assembly."
2. Remove pivot pins using pivot pin remover tool No. J21854-01 or equivalent, then reinstall tilt lever.
3. Remove column housing assembly. Pull back on tilt lever and pull housing down and away from column housing support.
4. Remove lower spring retainer, lower bearing spring, lower bearing seat and screws.

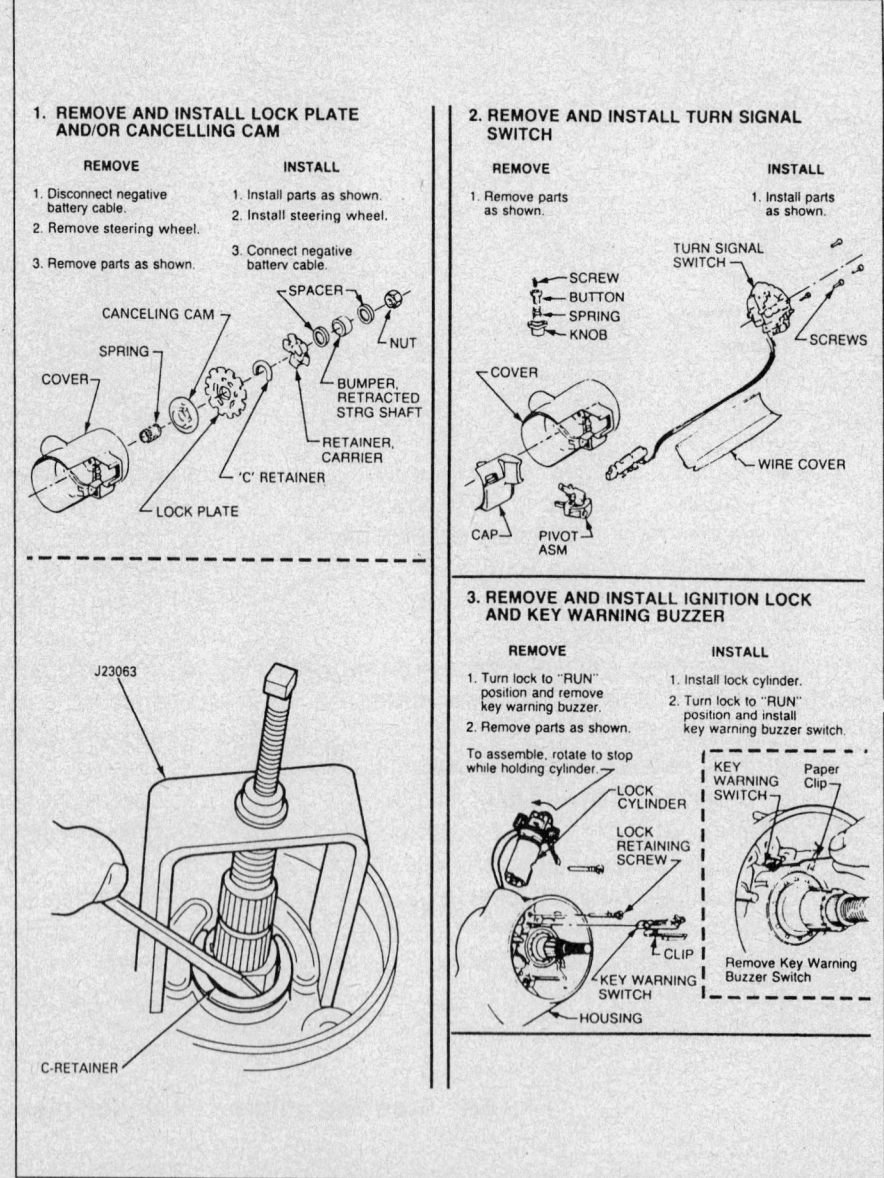

Fig. 59 Servicing steering column (Part 1 of 3). 1988 Corvette

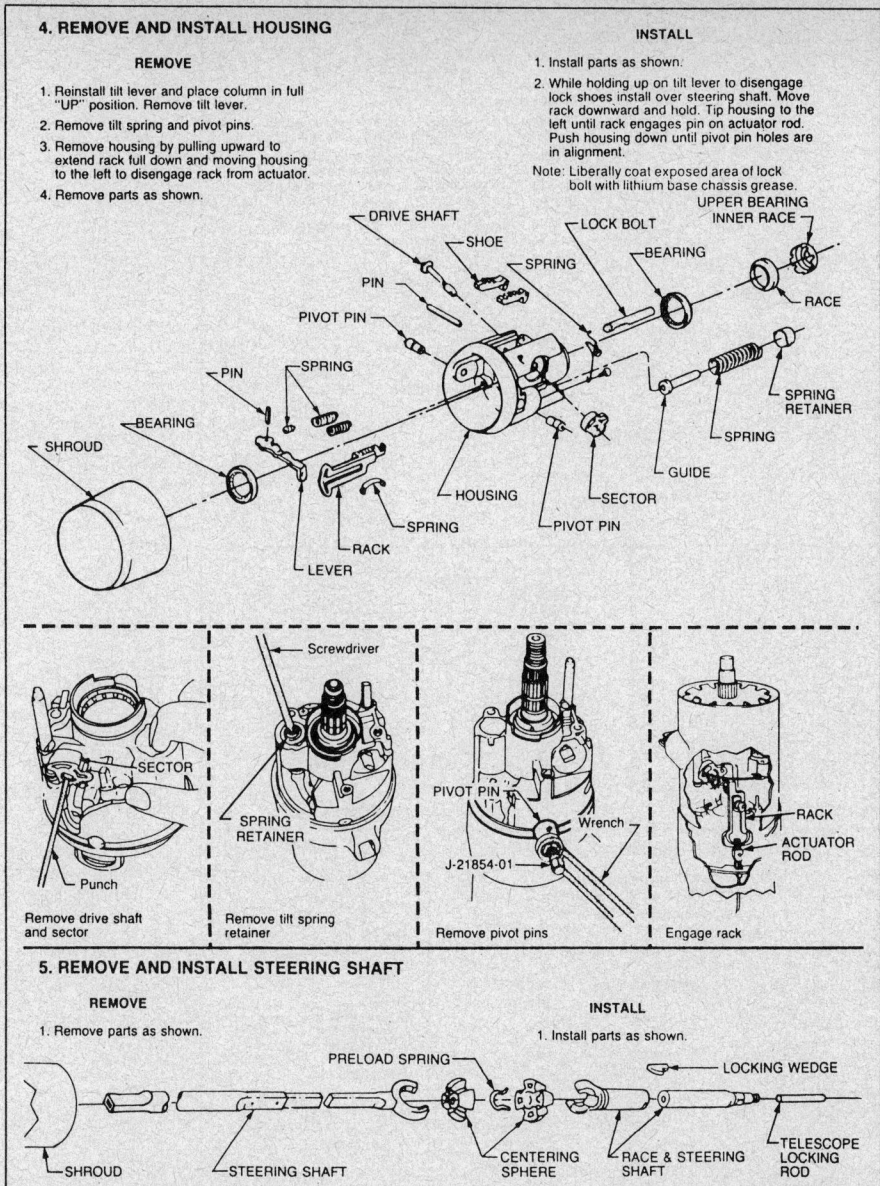

4. REMOVE AND INSTALL HOUSING

REMOVE

1. Reinstall tilt lever and place column in full "UP" position. Remove tilt lever.
2. Remove tilt spring and pivot pins.
3. Remove housing by pulling upward to extend rack full down and moving housing to the left to disengage rack from actuator.
4. Remove parts as shown.

INSTALL

1. Install parts as shown.
2. While holding up on tilt lever to disengage lock shoes install over steering shaft. Move rack downward and hold. Tip housing to the left until rack engages pin on actuator rod. Push housing down until pivot pin holes are in alignment.

Note: Liberally coat exposed area of lock bolt with lithium base chassis grease.

5. REMOVE AND INSTALL STEERING SHAFT

REMOVE

1. Remove parts as shown.

INSTALL

1. Install parts as shown.

Fig. 59 Servicing steering column (Part 2 of 3). 1988 Corvette

5. Remove adapter and lower bearing assembly.
6. Remove shaft assembly from column jacket assembly and check for accident damage.
7. Mark yoke assembly and lower steering shaft assembly to ensure proper assembly. Failure to assemble properly will cause steering wheel to be turned 180° out of position.
8. Remove yoke assembly from lower steering shaft assembly. Tilt 90° to each other and disengage.
9. Remove centering sphere from yoke assembly. Rotate sphere 90° and slip out.
10. Remove joint preload spring and screws, then the housing support assembly and dimmer switch rod.
11. Remove housing shroud, inhibitor cross pin, cable backdrive pin and spring.
12. Remove hex nut, then disconnect ground wire and cable bracket.
13. Remove dimmer switch, mounting stud, ignition switch and actuator rod assembly.

Assembly

1. Install housing shroud to jacket (No. 66).
2. Install dimmer switch rod to column housing support, then install housing support and screws.
3. **Torque** housing support screws to 80 inch lbs.
4. Install joint preload spring, then install centering sphere. Lubricate with lithium grease and slip into yoke assembly and rotate 90°.
5. Install yoke assembly to lower steering shaft assembly. Line up marks, then tilt assemblies 90° to each other.
6. Install steering shaft assembly (lubricated with lithium grease) to jacket assembly, then install inhibitor

cross pin, spring and cable backdrive pin to housing shroud.
7. Install actuator rod assembly to track in column housing support, then install ignition switch with mounting stud.
8. **Torque** dimmer and ignition switch mounting stud to 35 inch lbs., then install dimmer switch with hex head bolt (No. 63). **Torque** hex head bolt to 35 ft. lbs.
9. Install cable bracket and ground wire with hex nut (No. 74). **Torque** hex nut to 35 inch lbs.
10. Install lower adapter bearing assembly (No. 67) with inner surface lubricated with lithium grease, then install mounting screws and **torque** to 27 inch lbs.
11. Install lower bearing seat, spring and spring retainer (Nos. 69, 70 and 71).
12. Install column housing assembly to column. Position column housing support, then position column housing assembly and align switch actuator rack with pin on end of switch actuator assembly.
13. Pull back on tilt lever and push column housing onto column housing support. Release tilt lever to lock shoes.
14. Remove tilt lever, then install pivot pins, spring guide and spring. Coat all parts with lithium grease.
15. Follow installation procedure "Lock Housing Cover, Cover End Cap, Dimmer Switch Rod Actuator & Tilt Spring Assembly" to complete installation.

1988–89 Eldorado, Reatta, Riviera & Seville

Refer to **Figs. 61 and 62** for steering column component identification.

SHAFT LOCK, CANCELLING CAM & UPPER BEARING SPRING

This service can be performed without removing steering column from vehicle, after steering wheel has been removed.

Disassembly

1. **On Eldorado & Seville,** proceed as follows:
   a. Remove steering shaft bumper and carrier snap ring retainer.
   b. Install lock plate compressor screw J-23653-10 or equivalent. Lock plate compressor screw must be installed in upper steering shaft and **torqued** to 40 inch lbs. to keep shaft from telescoping.
2. **On all models,** using a suitable tool, slightly depress shaft lock plate, then remove shaft lock retainer from steering shaft.
3. Remove steering shaft lock plate, turn signal cancel cam assembly and the upper bearing spring. **Turn signal switch must be in "neutral" position to remove upper bearing spring.**

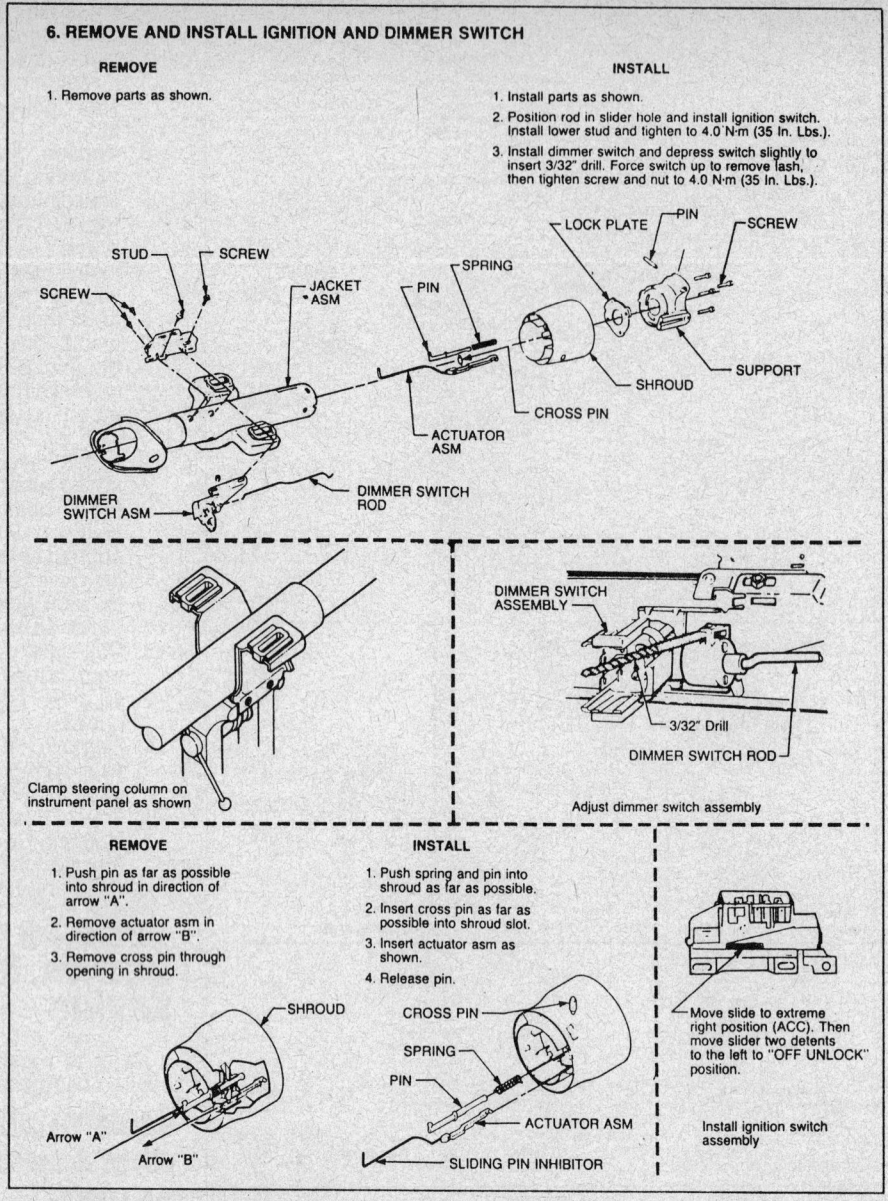

6. REMOVE AND INSTALL IGNITION AND DIMMER SWITCH

REMOVE

1. Remove parts as shown.

INSTALL

1. Install parts as shown.
2. Position rod in slider hole and install ignition switch. Install lower stud and tighten to 4.0 N·m (35 In. Lbs.).
3. Install dimmer switch and depress switch slightly to insert 3/32" drill. Force switch up to remove lash, then tighten screw and nut to 4.0 N·m (35 In. Lbs.).

Clamp steering column on instrument panel as shown

Adjust dimmer switch assembly

REMOVE

1. Push pin as far as possible into shroud in direction of arrow "A".
2. Remove actuator asm in direction of arrow "B".
3. Remove cross pin through opening in shroud.

INSTALL

1. Push spring and pin into shroud as far as possible.
2. Insert cross pin as far as possible into shroud slot.
3. Insert actuator asm as shown.
4. Release pin.

Move slide to extreme right position (ACC). Then move slider two detents to the left to "OFF UNLOCK" position.

Install ignition switch assembly

Fig. 59   Servicing steering column (Part 3 of 3). 1988 Corvette

Assembly

1. Install upper bearing spring, then the turn signal cancel cam assembly.
2. Install steering shaft lock plate, then compress shaft lock plate and install shaft lock retainer.
3. **On Eldorado and Seville,** install carrier snap ring assembly and the steering shaft bumper.

TURN SIGNAL SWITCH ASSEMBLY, BUZZER SWITCH ASSEMBLY & STEERING COLUMN LOCK CYLINDER SET

This service can be performed without removing steering column from vehicle, after steering wheel has been removed.

Disassembly

1. Remove shaft lock, cancelling cam and upper bearing spring as previously described.
2. Remove turn signal lever, positioning turn signal switch so that screws can be removed through opening in switch.
3. Remove turn signal switch attaching screws.
4. Remove wire protector and disconnect turn signal switch connector.
5. Disconnect buzzer switch wires from turn signal switch connector, **Fig. 63.**
6. Using a suitable tool, remove buzzer switch assembly.
7. Place lock cylinder in "accessory" position and remove lock retaining screw and the steering column lock cylinder set.
8. Remove turn signal switch assembly, gently pulling wire and connector through steering column housing shroud.

Assembly

1. Install turn signal connector through lock housing cover and steering column shroud.
2. Install steering column lock cylinder set while in "accessory" position.
3. Install lock retaining screw, **torquing** to 22 inch lbs.
4. Install buzzer switch, pushing switch down into its retaining bore until bottomed with plastic tab covering lock retaining screw.
5. Connect buzzer switch wires to turn signal switch connector. **Wire terminal retainer must be removed from service buzzer switch wire and discarded.**
6. Install wire connector retainer and connect turn signal switch connector, then install wire protector.
7. Install turn signal switch, positioning so that screws can be installed

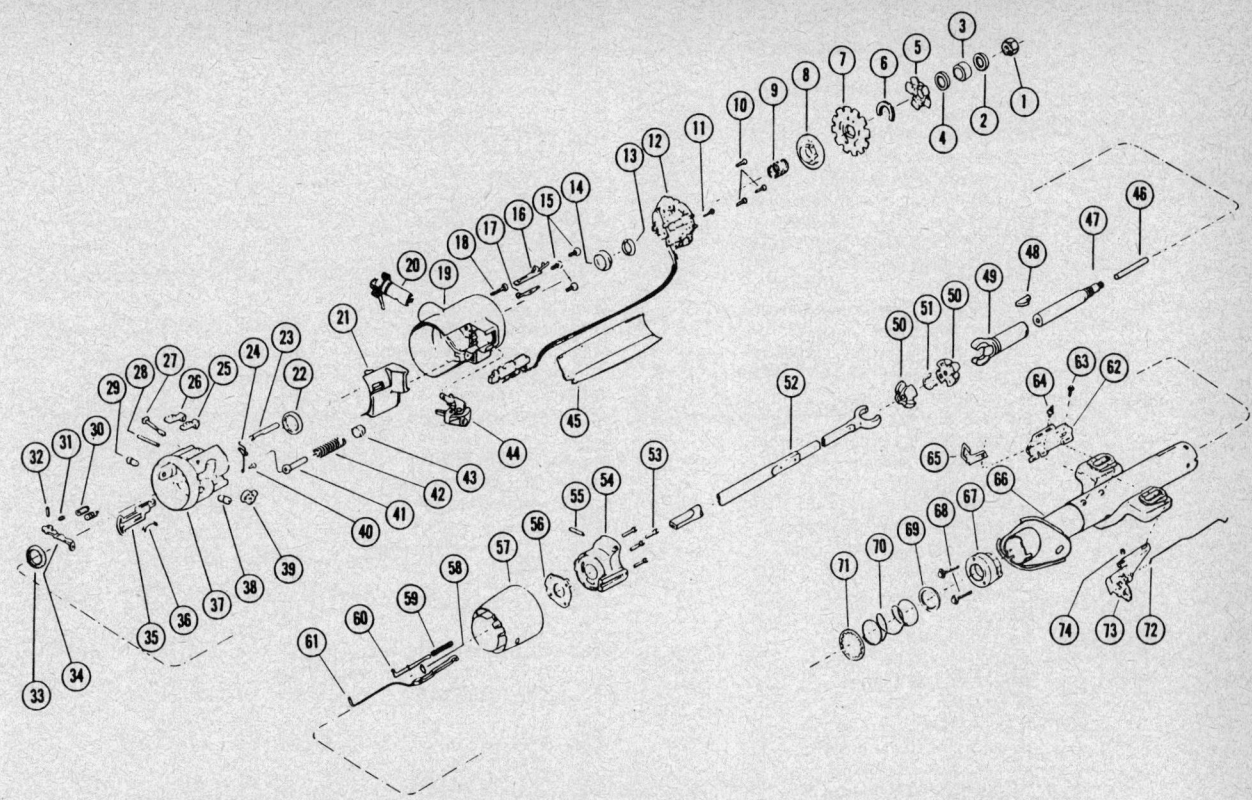

Fig. 60   Steering column exploded view (Part 1 of 2). 1989 Corvette

through openings in switch, and **torque** screws to 59 inch lbs.

8. Install turn signal lever, **torquing** screw to 53 inch lbs.

9. Install shaft lock, cancelling cam and upper bearing spring as previously described.

STEERING COLUMN HOUSING, SWITCH ACTUATOR RACK, STEERING WHEEL LOCK SHOES, BEARING ASSEMBLY & STEERING SHAFT ASSEMBLY

Disassembly

1. Perform steps 1 through 4 of "Disassembly" for "Turn Signal switch Assembly, Buzzer Switch Assembly & Steering Column Lock Cylinder Set."
2. Place lock cylinder set in "run" position, then remove buzzer switch assembly.
3. Place lock cylinder in "accessory" position, then remove lock retaining screw and the steering column lock cylinder set.
4. Remove tilt lever, then the lock housing cover retaining screws.
5. Remove lock housing cover together with turn signal and buzzer switch assemblies, gently pulling wires and connector through steering column housing shroud.

6. Remove upper bearing inner race seat and the inner race.
7. Install tilt lever and place column housing in full "up" position.
8. Remove spring retainer, spring and guide as an assembly by placing screwdriver in hole of spring retainer, pushing inward and turning counter-clockwise.
9. Using pivot pin tool No. J-21854-01 or equivalent, remove pivot pins, **Fig. 64.**
10. Remove steering column housing assembly by pulling back on tilt lever and moving housing up and to the right to disengage steering wheel lock shoes and switch actuator rack.
11. Remove spring and bolt assembly, then the switch actuator rack and rack preload spring.
12. Remove and discard bearing assemblies, using drift to drive out assemblies.
13. Remove release lever pin, then the shoe release lever and tilt lever.
14. Remove release lever spring, dowel pin, lock shoes and shoe springs.
15. Remove steering column from vehicle.
16. Remove bearing retainer, then the lower spring retainer, lower bearing spring and lower spring seat.
17. Remove attaching screws, then the adapter and bearing assembly.
18. Remove steering shaft from steering column jacket assembly.
19. Mark yoke assembly and lower steering shaft assembly, then disconnect yoke assembly from lower steering shaft assembly, tilting 90° to each other to disengage.

20. Remove centering sphere from yoke assembly, rotating sphere 90° and slipping out.
21. Remove joint preload spring.

Assembly

1. Install joint preload spring.
2. Lubricate centering sphere with lithium grease, then slip into yoke assembly and rotate 90°.
3. Connect yoke assembly to lower steering shaft assembly, by aligning marks made during disassembly and tilting assemblies 90° to each other.
4. Install steering shaft to steering column jacket assembly.
5. Install adapter and bearing assembly, **torquing** screws to 30 inch lbs.
6. Install lower bearing seat and lower bearing spring, then the lower spring retainer and bearing retainer.
7. Install steering column in vehicle.
8. Install steering column housing support assembly attaching screws, **torquing** to 47 inch lbs.
9. Lubricate shoe springs and lock shoes with lithium grease and install.
10. Install dowel pin.
11. Lubricate release lever spring with lithium grease and install.
12. Install shoe release lever and tilt lever, then the release lever pin.
13. Lubricate bearing assemblies with lithium grease, then, using 1 inch socket, press into housing until bottomed.
14. Install rack preload spring.
15. Lubricate gear teeth on switch actuator rack with lithium grease then in-

1	NUT, HEXAGON JAM	48	WEDGE, LOCKING
2	SPACER	49	YOKE ASSEMBLY, RACE AND STEERING SHAFT
3	BUMPER, RETRACTED STEERING SHAFT	50	SPHERE, CENTERING
4	SPACER	51	SPRING, JOINT PRELOAD
5	RETAINER, CARRIER SNAP RING	52	SHAFT ASSEMBLY, LOWER STEERING
6	RETAINER, SHAFT LOCK	53	SCREW, SUPPORT
7	LOCK, STEERING SHAFT	54	SUPPORT, STEERING COLUMN HOUSING
8	ASSEMBLY, CARRIER	55	PIN, DOWEL
9	SPRING, UPPER BEARING	56	PLATE, LOCK
10	SCREW, BINDING HEAD CROSS RECESS	57	SHROUD, COLUMN HOUSING
11	SCREW, ROUND WASHER HEAD	58	PIN, INHIBITOR CROSS
12	SWITCH ASSEMBLY, TURN SIGNAL	59	SPRING, CABLE BACKDRIVE PIN
13	SEAT, INNER RACE	60	PIN, CABLE BACKDRIVE
14	RACE, INNER	61	ACTUATOR ASSEMBLY, SWITCH
15	SCREW, OVAL HEAD CROSS RECESS	62	SWITCH ASSEMBLY, IGNITION
16	SWITCH ASSEMBLY, BUZZER	63	SCREW, WASHER HEAD
17	CLIP, BUZZER SWITCH RETAINING	64	STUD, DIMMER AND IGNITION SWITCH MOUNTING
18	SCREW, LOCK RETAINING	65	BRACKET, CABLE
19	COVER, LOCK HOUSING	66	JACKET ASSEMBLY, STEERING COLUMN
20	LOCK CYLINDER SET, STEERING COLUMN	67	BEARING ASSEMBLY, ADAPTER AND
21	CAP, LOCK HOUSING COVER END	68	SCREW, HEX WASHER HEAD TAPPING
22	ASSEMBLY, BEARING	69	SEAT, LOWER BEARING
23	BOLT, LOCK	70	SPRING, LOWER BEARING
24	SPRING, LOCK BOLT	71	RETAINER, LOWER SPRING
25	SHOE, STEERING WHEEL LOCK	72	ROD, DIMMER SWITCH
26	SHOE, STEERING WHEEL LOCK	73	SWITCH ASSEMBLY, DIMMER
27	SHAFT, DRIVE	74	NUT, HEX
28	PIN, DOWEL		
29	PIN, PIVOT		
30	SPRING, SHOE		
31	SPRING, RELEASE LEVER	101	SHAFT ASSEMBLY, STEERING
32	PIN, RELEASE LEVER	102	HOUSING ASSEMBLY, STEERING COLUMN
33	ASSEMBLY, BEARING	103	ASSEMBLY, SUPPORT
34	LEVER, SHOE RELEASE		
35	RACK, SWITCH ACTUATOR		
36	SPRING, RACK PRELOAD		
37	HOUSING, STEERING COLUMN		
38	PIN, PIVOT		
39	SECTOR, SWITCH ACTUATOR		
40	SCREW, HEX WASHER HEAD		
41	GUIDE, SPRING		
42	SPRING, WHEEL TILT		
43	RETAINER, SPRING		
44	PIVOT ASSEMBLY, SWITCH ACTUATOR		
45	PROTECTOR, WIRING		
46	ROD, TELESCOPE LOCKING		
47	SHAFT, UPPER STEERING		

Fig. 60   Steering column exploded view (Part 2 of 2). 1989 Corvette

stall switch actuator rack through opening in housing until it rests on preload spring.
16. Lubricate spring and bolt assembly with lithium grease, then install through hole in housing.
17. Grease housing support assembly where housing pivots, then install bolt assembly to rack.
18. Connect switch actuator rack to pin on ignition switch actuator assembly while assembled in housing.
19. Connect steering column housing to pin in steering column housing support assembly by pulling back on tilt lever on engage shoes, then push housing down until pivot pin holes are aligned and install pivot pins, lubricated with lithium grease, driving into position with punch.
20. Tilt housing to full "up" position.
21. Lubricate spring guide with lithium grease, then install spring guide, spring and retainer as an assembly into hole in housing, push retainer into housing with screwdriver and turn clockwise to lock in place.
22. Install inner race and upper bearing inner race seat, then remove tilt lever.
23. Insert wires and connector from turn signal switch and buzzer switch through lock housing cover and housing shroud, then install lock housing cover, **torquing** attaching screws to 89 inch lbs.
24. Install tilt lever.
25. Place lock cylinder in "accessory" position and install steering column lock cylinder set, then the retaining screw, **torquing** to 22 inch lbs.
26. Place lock cylinder set in "run" position and install buzzer switch by by pushing down into its retaining bore until bottomed with plastic tab covering lock retaining screw.
27. Connect turn signal switch connector, then perform steps 7 through 9 of "Assembly" for "Turn Signal Switch Assembly, Buzzer Switch Assembly & Steering Column Lock Cylinder Set."

IGNITION SWITCH ASSEMBLY & IGNITION SWITCH INHIBITOR

Disassembly

1. Place lock cylinder in "off lock" position.
2. Remove steering column instrument panel lower mounting nut and bolt, the upper mounting bolts, and gently lower steering column onto driver's seat.
3. Disconnect steering column wire assembly from ignition switch assembly.
4. Remove washer head screws, then the ignition switch assembly from the ignition switch actuator.
5. Remove pan head screws, then the ignition switch inhibitor housing assembly from the ignition switch assembly.
6. Using screwdriver, disconnect park lock cable from ignition switch inhibitor housing assembly, **Fig. 65.**

Assembly

1. Place ignition switch assembly and lock cylinder in "off lock" position.
2. Connect park lock cable to ignition switch inhibitor housing assembly.
3. Install ignition switch inhibitor housing assembly to ignition switch assembly.
4. Install pan head screws, **torquing** to 9 inch lbs.
5. Install ignition switch assembly to ignition switch actuator.
6. Install washer head screws, **torquing** to 35 inch lbs.

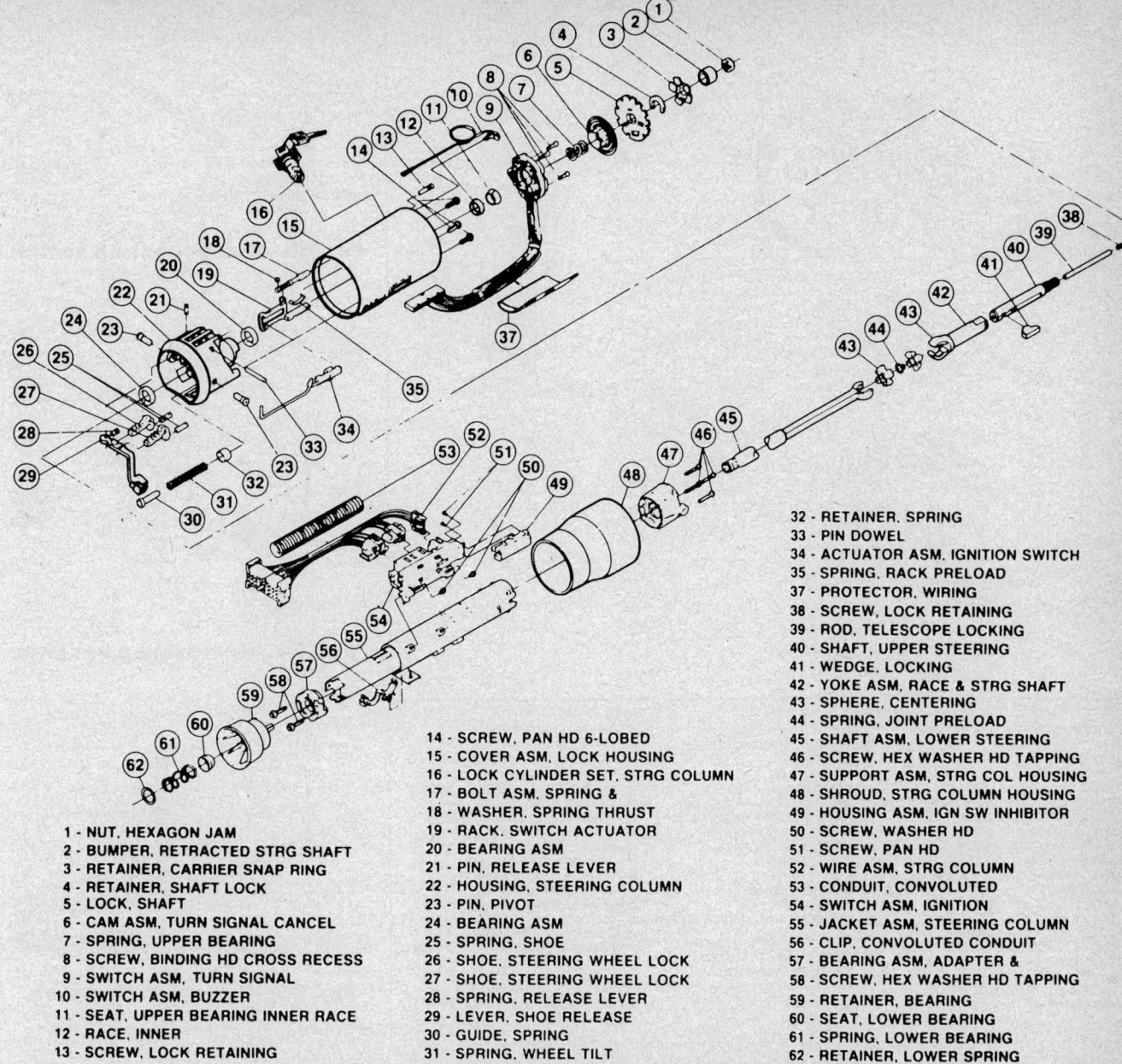

Fig. 61   Exploded view of steering column. 1988–89 Eldorado & Seville

1 - NUT, HEXAGON JAM
2 - BUMPER, RETRACTED STRG SHAFT
3 - RETAINER, CARRIER SNAP RING
4 - RETAINER, SHAFT LOCK
5 - LOCK, SHAFT
6 - CAM ASM, TURN SIGNAL CANCEL
7 - SPRING, UPPER BEARING
8 - SCREW, BINDING HD CROSS RECESS
9 - SWITCH ASM, TURN SIGNAL
10 - SWITCH ASM, BUZZER
11 - SEAT, UPPER BEARING INNER RACE
12 - RACE, INNER
13 - SCREW, LOCK RETAINING

14 - SCREW, PAN HD 6-LOBED
15 - COVER ASM, LOCK HOUSING
16 - LOCK CYLINDER SET, STRG COLUMN
17 - BOLT ASM, SPRING &
18 - WASHER, SPRING THRUST
19 - RACK. SWITCH ACTUATOR
20 - BEARING ASM
21 - PIN, RELEASE LEVER
22 - HOUSING, STEERING COLUMN
23 - PIN, PIVOT
24 - BEARING ASM
25 - SPRING, SHOE
26 - SHOE, STEERING WHEEL LOCK
27 - SHOE, STEERING WHEEL LOCK
28 - SPRING, RELEASE LEVER
29 - LEVER, SHOE RELEASE
30 - GUIDE, SPRING
31 - SPRING, WHEEL TILT

32 - RETAINER, SPRING
33 - PIN DOWEL
34 - ACTUATOR ASM, IGNITION SWITCH
35 - SPRING, RACK PRELOAD
37 - PROTECTOR, WIRING
38 - SCREW, LOCK RETAINING
39 - ROD, TELESCOPE LOCKING
40 - SHAFT, UPPER STEERING
41 - WEDGE, LOCKING
42 - YOKE ASM, RACE & STRG SHAFT
43 - SPHERE, CENTERING
44 - SPRING, JOINT PRELOAD
45 - SHAFT ASM, LOWER STEERING
46 - SCREW, HEX WASHER HD TAPPING
47 - SUPPORT ASM, STRG COL HOUSING
48 - SHROUD, STRG COLUMN HOUSING
49 - HOUSING ASM, IGN SW INHIBITOR
50 - SCREW, WASHER HD
51 - SCREW, PAN HD
52 - WIRE ASM, STRG COLUMN
53 - CONDUIT, CONVOLUTED
54 - SWITCH ASM, IGNITION
55 - JACKET ASM, STEERING COLUMN
56 - CLIP, CONVOLUTED CONDUIT
57 - BEARING ASM, ADAPTER &
58 - SCREW, HEX WASHER HD TAPPING
59 - RETAINER, BEARING
60 - SEAT, LOWER BEARING
61 - SPRING, LOWER BEARING
62 - RETAINER, LOWER SPRING

7. Connect steering column wire assembly to ignition switch assembly.
8. Raise steering column to instrument panel and loosely install upper column bracket bolts, then install and tighten lower column nuts and bolt.
9. Tighten upper bolts.

1988 Beretta & Corsica

FIXED COLUMN

Refer to **Fig. 66** for steering column component identification. All components of the steering column are sensitive to damage and must be handled carefully.

COLUMN BOWL CAP & SHIFT LEVER GATE (COLUMN SHIFT ONLY)

Disassembly

1. Remove steering wheel.
2. Position shift lever in Neutral position.
3. Remove column bowl cap attaching screws from back of steering column bowl, then the column bowl cap.
4. Remove shift lever gate attaching screws, then the gate.
5. Reverse procedure to install, noting the following:
   a. Apply Loctite No. 242 to shift lever gate attaching screws.
   b. **Torque** column bowl cap attaching screws to 27 inch lbs.

DIMMER SWITCH ACTUATOR PIVOT & TURN SIGNAL SWITCH

Disassembly

1. Remove steering wheel, then the turn signal cancel cam assembly.
2. Remove hazard warning knob attaching screw, then the hazard warning knob.
3. Position turn signal switch in such a way so column cover attaching screw and turn signal attaching screws are accessible.
4. Remove column cover attaching screw, then the column cover.
5. Remove dimmer switch actuator upper attaching screw, then the dimmer switch actuator.

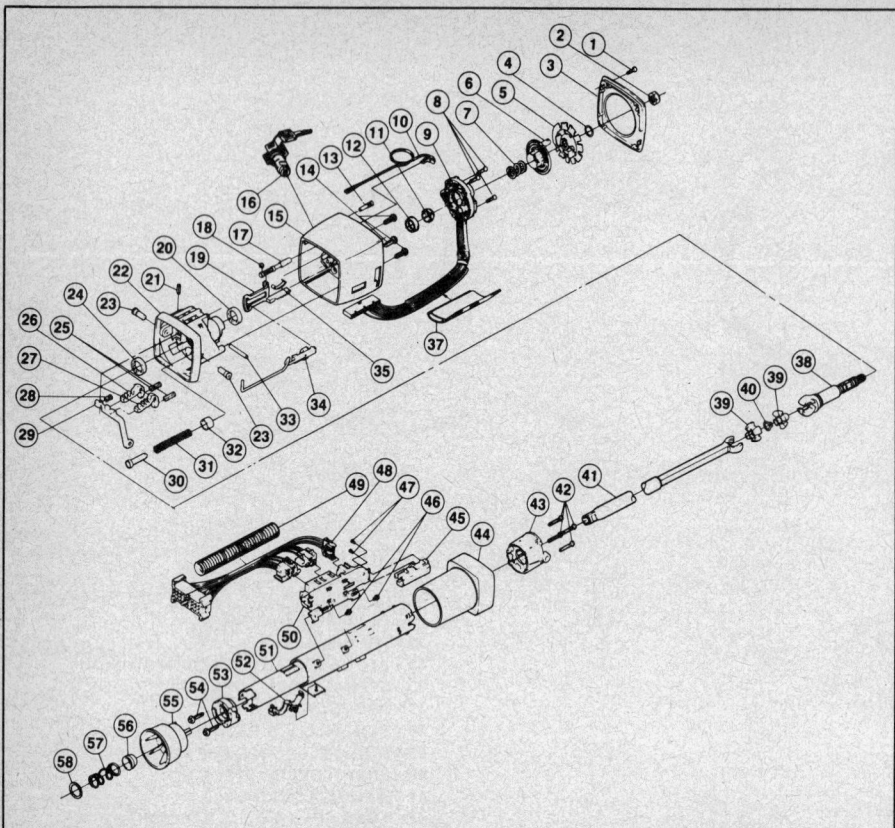

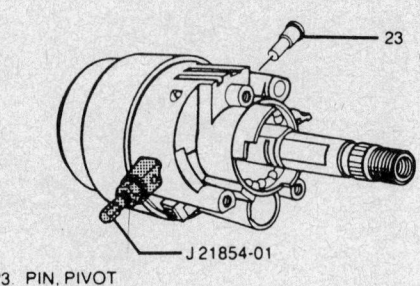

Fig. 63 Disconnecting switch wires

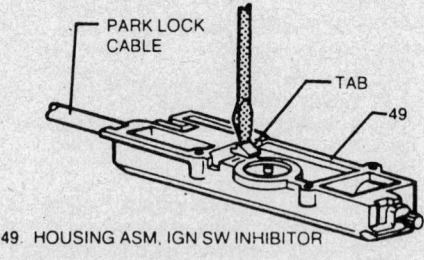

23 PIN, PIVOT

Fig. 64 Removing pivot pins

Key No.	Part Name	Key No.	Part Name	Key No.	Part Name
1	SCREW, BINDING HD CROSS RECESS	21	PIN, RELEASE LEVER	39	SPHERE, CENTERING
2	NUT, HEXAGON JAM	22	HOUSING, STEERING COLUMN	40	SPRING, JOINT PRELOAD
3	CAP, HOUSING COVER	23	PIN, PIVOT	41	SHAFT ASM, LOWER STEERING
4	RING, RETAINING	24	BEARING ASM	42	SCREW, HEX WASHER HD TAPPING
5	LOCK, SHAFT	25	SPRING, SHOE	43	SUPPORT ASM, STRG COL HOUSING
6	CAM ASM, TURN SIGNAL CANCEL	26	SHOE, STEERING WHEEL LOCK	44	SHROUD, STRG COLUMN HOUSING
7	SPRING, UPPER BEARING	27	SHOE, STEERING WHEEL LOCK	45	HOUSING ASM, IGN SW INHIBITOR
8	SCREW, BINDING HD CROSS RECESS	28	SPRING, RELEASE LEVER	46	SCREW, WASHER HD
9	SWITCH ASM, TURN SIGNAL	29	LEVER, SHOE RELEASE	47	SCREW, PAN HD
10	SWITCH ASM, BUZZER	30	GUIDE, SPRING	48	WIRE ASM, STRG COLUMN
11	SEAT, UPPER BEARING INNER RACE	31	SPRING, WHEEL TILT	49	CONDUIT, CONVOLUTED
12	RACE, INNER	32	RETAINER, SPRING	50	SWITCH ASM, IGNITION
13	SCREW, LOCK RETAINING	33	PIN DOWEL	51	JACKET ASM, STEERING COLUMN
14	SCREW, PAN HD 6-LOBED	34	ACTUATOR ASM, IGNITION SWITCH	52	CLIP, CONVOLUTED CONDUIT
15	COVER ASM, LOCK HOUSING			53	BEARING ASM, ADAPTER &
16	LOCK CYLINDER SET, STRG COLUMN	**Key No.**	**Part Name**	54	SCREW, HEX WASHER HD TAPPING
17	BOLT ASM, SPRING &	35	SPRING, RACK PRELOAD	55	RETAINER, BEARING
18	WASHER, SPRING THRUST	36	THIS NUMBER NOT USED	56	SEAT, LOWER BEARING
19	RACK, SWITCH ACTUATOR	37	PROTECTOR, WIRING	57	SPRING, LOWER BEARING
20	BEARING ASM	38	SHAFT ASM, RACE & UPPER	58	RETAINER, LOWER SPRING

Fig. 62 Exploded view of steering column. 1988–89 Reatta & Riviera

PARK LOCK CABLE

TAB

49 HOUSING ASM, IGN SW INHIBITOR

Fig. 65 Disconnecting park lock cable

6. Remove turn signal lever attaching screw from dimmer switch actuator, then remove lever. **On models equipped with cruise control, disconnect wire connector.**
7. Remove turn signal switch attaching screws.
8. Remove buzzer switch wires (light green and tan/black wires) from turn signal switch wiring connector using a suitable tool.
9. Remove turn signal switch.
10. Reverse procedure to install, noting the following:
    a. **Torque** turn signal switch attaching screws to 35 inch lbs.
    b. Attach light green buzzer switch wire to terminal F of turn signal switch wiring connector.
    c. Attach tan/black buzzer switch wire to terminal G of turn signal switch wiring connector.
    d. **Torque** turn signal lever attaching screw to 18 inch lbs.
    e. **Torque** dimmer switch actuator attaching screw to 20 inch lbs.
    f. **Torque** column cover attaching screw to 35 inch lbs.
    g. **Torque** hazard warning switch attaching screw to 7 inch lbs.
    h. **Torque** steering wheel attaching nut to 30 ft. lbs.

STEERING SHAFT ASSEMBLY, TURN SIGNAL SWITCH HOUSING & BEARING ASSEMBLY

Disassembly

1. Remove steering column from vehicle, then the steering wheel and the turn signal cancel cam assembly.

2. Remove hazard warning knob attaching screw, then the hazard warning knob.
3. Position turn signal switch in such a way so column cover attaching screw and turn signal attaching screws are accessible.
4. Remove column cover attaching screw, then the column cover.
5. Remove dimmer switch actuator upper attaching screw, then the dimmer switch actuator.
6. Remove turn signal lever attaching screw from dimmer switch actuator, then remove lever. **On models equipped with cruise control, disconnect wire connector.**
7. Remove turn signal switch attaching screws.
8. Remove buzzer switch wires (light green and tan/black wires) from turn signal switch wiring connector using a suitable tool.

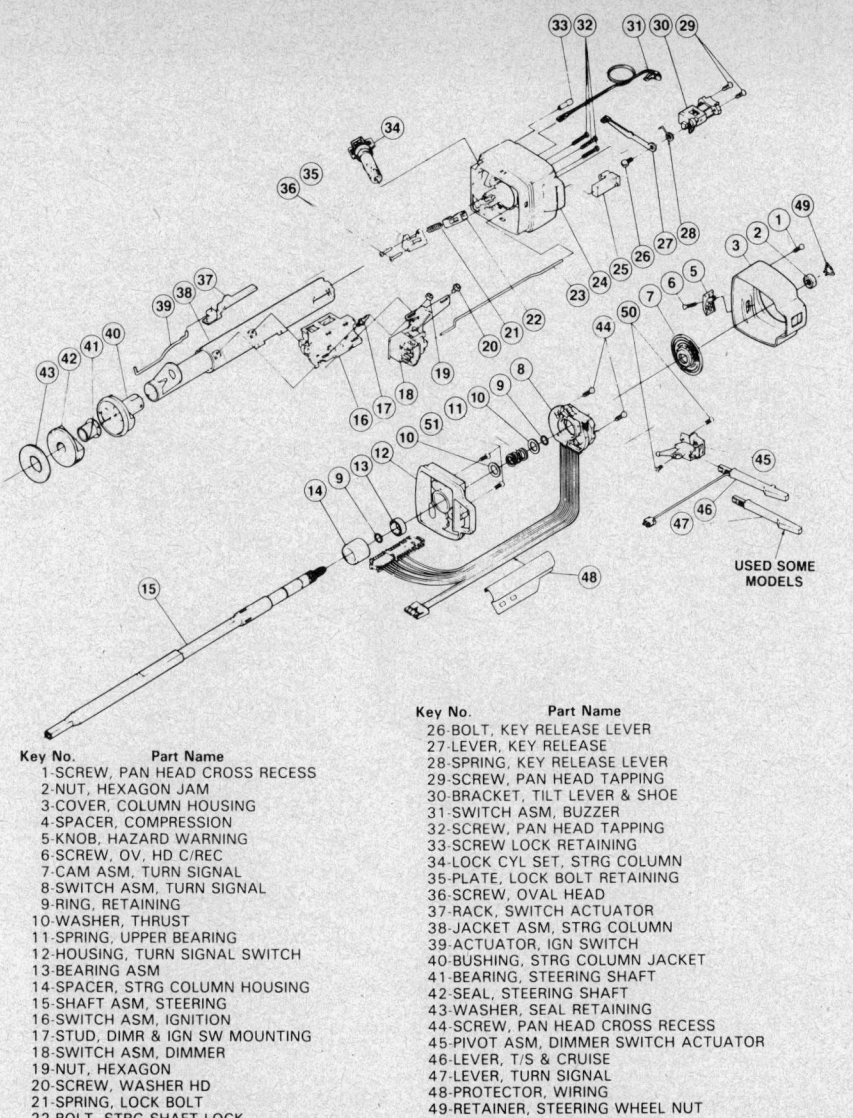

Fig. 66 Key release steering column exploded view, fixed column. 1988 Beretta & Corsica (similar to park lock column)

Key No.	Part Name
1	SCREW, PAN HEAD CROSS RECESS
2	NUT, HEXAGON JAM
3	COVER, COLUMN HOUSING
4	SPACER, COMPRESSION
5	KNOB, HAZARD WARNING
6	SCREW, OV. HD C/REC
7	CAM ASM, TURN SIGNAL
8	SWITCH ASM, TURN SIGNAL
9	RING, RETAINING
10	WASHER, THRUST
11	SPRING, UPPER BEARING
12	HOUSING, TURN SIGNAL SWITCH
13	BEARING ASM
14	SPACER, STRG COLUMN HOUSING
15	SHAFT ASM, STEERING
16	SWITCH ASM, IGNITION
17	STUD, DIMR & IGN SW MOUNTING
18	SWITCH ASM, DIMMER
19	NUT, HEXAGON
20	SCREW, WASHER HD
21	SPRING, LOCK BOLT
22	BOLT, STRG SHAFT LOCK
23	ROD, DIMMER SW ACTUATOR
24	BOWL, STEERING COLUMN
25	CAP, DIMMER SWITCH ROD
26	BOLT, KEY RELEASE LEVER
27	LEVER, KEY RELEASE
28	SPRING, KEY RELEASE LEVER
29	SCREW, PAN HEAD TAPPING
30	BRACKET, TILT LEVER & SHOE
31	SWITCH ASM, BUZZER
32	SCREW, PAN HEAD TAPPING
33	SCREW LOCK RETAINING
34	LOCK CYL SET, STRG COLUMN
35	PLATE, LOCK BOLT RETAINING
36	SCREW, OVAL HEAD
37	RACK, SWITCH ACTUATOR
38	JACKET ASM, STRG COLUMN
39	ACTUATOR, IGN SWITCH
40	BUSHING, STRG COLUMN JACKET
41	BEARING, STEERING SHAFT
42	SEAL, STEERING SHAFT
43	WASHER, SEAL RETAINING
44	SCREW, PAN HEAD CROSS RECESS
45	PIVOT ASM, DIMMER SWITCH ACTUATOR
46	LEVER, T/S & CRUISE
47	LEVER, TURN SIGNAL
48	PROTECTOR, WIRING
49	RETAINER, STEERING WHEEL NUT
50	SCREW, C/S TAPPING
51	SCREW, PAN HD 6-LOBED SOC TAP

9. Remove turn signal switch.
10. Place ignition switch in Run position.
11. Position flat of retaining ring over flat of steering shaft, then pry off retaining ring with screwdriver and discard.
12. Remove thrust washer, upper bearing spring washer and remaining thrust washer.
13. Remove steering shaft.
14. Remove turn signal switch housing attaching screws, then the turn signal switch housing.
15. Remove bearing using drift.
16. Reverse procedure to install, noting the following:
   a. Press bearing into housing with 1 inch (25 mm) socket until bearing is bottomed.
   b. **Torque** turn signal switch housing attaching screws to 88 inch lbs.
   c. Turn ignition switch to Run position, then install steering shaft from lower end of steering column until

shaft is bottomed against bearing. Shaft should extend 2.5 inches above highest point of turn signal switch housing. Turn ignition switch to Lock position to engage steering shaft lock bolt. Rotate steering shaft until it locks in place.
   d. Prior to installing new retainer ring over thrust washers and upper bearing spring, wrap a piece of 2 inch wide, .005 inch thick shim stock around steering shaft. Slide retainer ring over shaft to retainer ring groove, then using 2 screwdrivers, seat retainer ring in groove.
   e. **Torque** turn signal switch attaching screws to 35 inch lbs.
   f. Attach light green buzzer switch wire to terminal F of turn signal switch wiring connector.
   g. Attach tan/black buzzer switch wire to terminal G of turn signal switch wiring connector.

h. **Torque** turn signal lever attaching screw to 18 inch lbs.
i. **Torque** dimmer switch actuator attaching screw to 20 inch lbs.
j. **Torque** column cover attaching screw to 35 inch lbs.
k. **Torque** hazard warning switch attaching screw to 7 inch lbs.
l. **Torque** steering wheel attaching nut to 30 ft. lbs.

BUZZER SWITCH ASSEMBLY & STEERING COLUMN LOCK CYLINDER SET
Disassembly

1. Remove steering column from vehicle, then the steering wheel and the turn signal cancel cam assembly.
2. Remove hazard warning knob attaching screw, then the hazard warning knob.
3. Position turn signal switch in such a way so column cover attaching screw and turn signal attaching screws are accessible.
4. Remove column cover attaching screw, then the column cover.
5. Remove turn signal switch attaching screws.
6. Remove buzzer switch wires (light green and tan/black wires) from turn signal switch wiring connector.
7. Remove turn signal switch.
8. Place ignition switch in Run position.
9. Remove turn signal switch housing attaching screws.
10. Remove steering shaft and turn signal switch housing as an assembly.
11. Remove buzzer switch by using screwdriver to lift switch tab, then gently pull on wires.
12. Place ignition switch in Accessory position, then remove lock retaining screw and lock cylinder.
13. Reverse procedure to install, noting the following:
   a. Install lock cylinder set, then hold barrel of lock cylinder. Insert key and turn to accessory position. Install lock retaining screw and **torque** to 22 inch lbs.
   b. **Torque** turn signal switch housing attaching screws to 88 inch lbs.
   c. **Torque** turn signal switch attaching screws to 35 inch lbs.
   d. Attach light green buzzer switch wire to terminal F of turn signal switch wiring connector.
   e. Attach tan/black buzzer switch wire to terminal G of turn signal switch wiring connector.
   f. **Torque** turn signal lever attaching screw to 18 inch lbs.
   g. **Torque** dimmer switch actuator attaching screw to 20 inch lbs.
   h. **Torque** column cover attaching screw to 35 inch lbs.
   i. **Torque** hazard warning switch attaching screw to 7 inch lbs.
   j. **Torque** steering wheel attaching nut to 30 ft. lbs.

TILT COLUMN

Refer to **Fig. 67** for steering column component identification. All components of the steering column are sensitive to damage and must be handled carefully.

DIMMER SWITCH ACTUATOR PIVOT & TURN SIGNAL SWITCH

Disassembly

1. Remove steering wheel, then the turn signal cancel cam assembly.
2. Remove hazard warning knob attaching screw, then the hazard warning knob.
3. Position turn signal switch in such a way so column cover attaching screw and turn signal attaching screws are accessible.
4. Remove column cover attaching screw, then the column cover.
5. Remove dimmer switch actuator upper attaching screw, then the dimmer switch actuator.
6. Remove turn signal lever attaching screw from dimmer switch actuator, then remove lever. **On models equipped with cruise control, disconnect wire connector.**
7. Remove turn signal switch attaching screws.
8. Remove buzzer switch wires (light green and tan/black wires) from turn signal switch wiring connector.
9. Remove turn signal switch.
10. Reverse procedure to install, noting the following:
    a. **Torque** turn signal switch attaching screws to 35 inch lbs.
    b. Attach light green buzzer switch wire to terminal F of turn signal switch wiring connector.
    c. Attach tan/black buzzer switch wire to terminal G of turn signal switch wiring connector.
    d. **Torque** turn signal lever attaching screw to 18 inch lbs.
    e. **Torque** dimmer switch actuator attaching screw to 20 inch lbs.
    f. **Torque** column cover attaching screw to 35 inch lbs.
    g. **Torque** hazard warning switch attaching screw to 7 inch lbs.
    h. **Torque** steering wheel attaching nut to 30 ft. lbs.

WHEEL TILT SPRING, TILT & SHOE BRACKET, KEY RELEASE LEVER (IF EQUIPPED), BUZZER SWITCH ASSEMBLY, STEERING COLUMN LOCK CYLINDER SET & COLUMN TILT BUMPERS

Disassembly

1. Pull shoe release lever and tilt column upwards.
2. Remove steering column from vehicle.
3. Remove steering wheel, then the turn signal cancel cam assembly.
4. Remove hazard warning knob attaching screw, then the hazard warning knob.
5. Position turn signal switch in such a way so column cover attaching screw and turn signal attaching screws are accessible.
6. Remove column cover attaching screw, then the column cover.

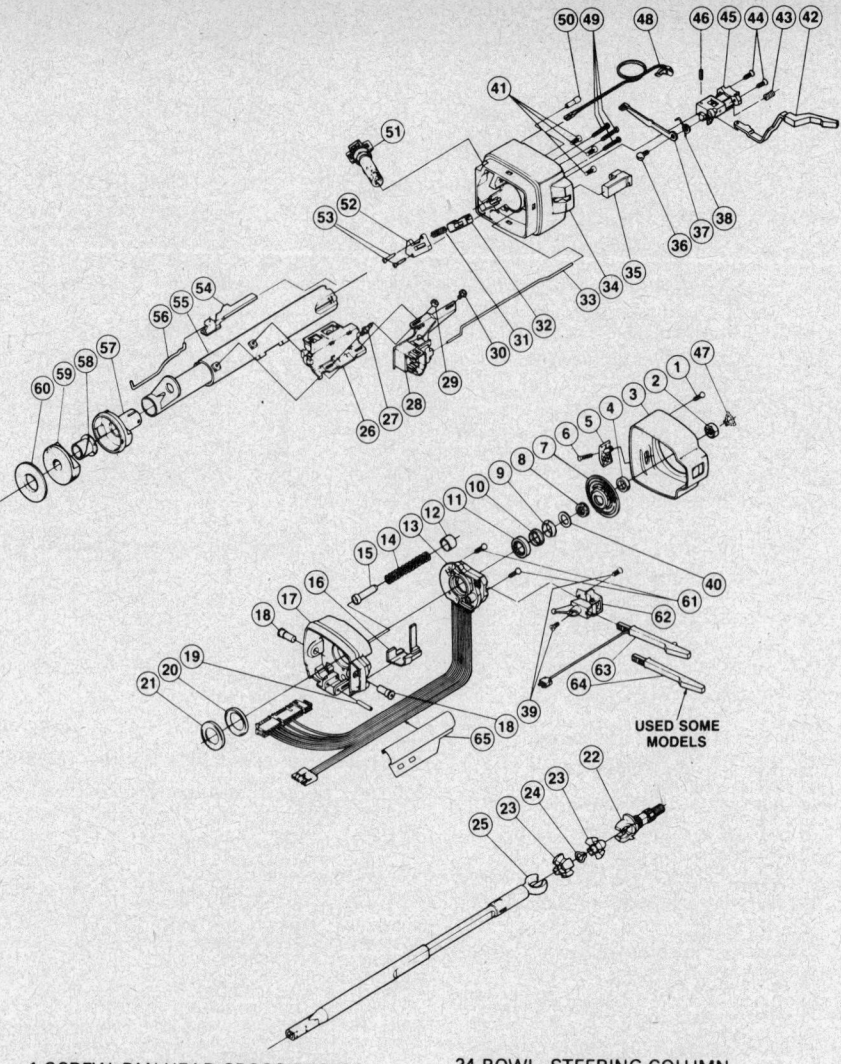

1-SCREW, PAN HEAD CROSS RECESS	34-BOWL, STEERING COLUMN
2-NUT, HEXAGON JAM	35-CAP, DIMMER SWITCH ROD
3-COVER, COLUMN HOUSING	36-BOLT, KEY RELEASE LEVER
4-SPACER, COMPRESSION	37-LEVER, KEY RELEASE
5-KNOB, HAZARD WARNING	38-SPRING, KEY RELEASE LEVER
6-SCREW, OV. HD. C/REC	39-SCREW, C/S TAPPING
7-CAM ASM, TURN SIG CANCEL	40-WASHER, FLAT
8-NUT, UPPER SHAFT BRG LOCK	41-BUMPER, COLUMN TILT
9-SEAT, UPPER BRG INNER RACE	42-LEVER, SHOE RELEASE
10-RACE, INNER	43-SPRING, RELEASE LEVER
11-BEARING ASM	44-SCREW, PAN HEAD CROSS RECESS
12-RETAINER, SPRING	45-BRACKET, TILT LEVER & SHOE
13-SWITCH ASM, TURN SIGNAL	46-PIN, RELEASE LEVER
14-SPRING, WHEEL TILT	47-RETAINER, STEERING WHEEL NUT
15-GUIDE, TILT SPRING	48-SWITCH ASM, BUZZER
16-CAP, HOUS SHOE PIN RETAINING	49-SCREW, PAN HEAD TAPPING
17-HOUSING, STEERING COLUMN	50-SCREW, LOCK RETAINING
18-PIN, PIVOT	51-LOCK CYL SET, STRG COLUMN
19-PIN, HOUSING SHOE LOCKING	52-PLATE, LOCK BOLT RETAINING
20-BEARING ASM, NEEDLE THRUST	53-SCREW, OVAL HEAD
21-RACE, BRG ASM-THRUST	54-RACK, SWITCH ACTUATOR
22-SHAFT, UPPER STEERING	55-JACKET ASM, STRG COLUMN
23-SPHERE, CENTERING	56-ACTUATORS, IGN SWITCH
24-SPRING, JOINT PRELOAD	57-BUSHING STRG COLUMN JACKET
25-SHAFT ASM, LOWER STEERING	58-BEARING, STEERING SHAFT
26-SWITCH ASM, IGNITION	59-SEAL, STEERING SHAFT
27-STUD, DIMR. & IGN SW MOUNTING	60-WASHER, SEAL RETAINING
28-SWITCH ASM, DIMMER	61-SCREW, PAN HEAD CROSS RECESS
29-NUT, HEXAGON	62-PIVOT ASM, DIMMER SWITCH ACTUATOR
30-SCREW, WASH HD	63-LEVER, T/S & CRUISE
31-SPRING, LOCK BOLT	64-LEVER, TURN SIGNAL
32-BOLT, STRG SHAFT LOCK	65-PROTECTOR. WIRING
33-ROD, DIMMER SW ACTUATOR	

Fig. 67 Key release steering column exploded view, tilt column. 1988 Beretta & Corsica (similar to park lock column)

7. Remove turn signal switch attaching screws.
8. Remove buzzer switch wires (light green and tan/black wires) from turn signal switch wiring connector.
9. Remove turn signal switch.
10. Insert a screwdriver into spring retainer square opening, then push down and turn left to release retainer and wheel tilt spring.
11. Remove spring retainer, tilt spring and tilt spring guide.
12. Remove shoe pin retaining cap.
13. Remove pivot pins using pivot pin remover tool No. J-21854-01.
14. Place ignition switch in Run position, then pull shoe release lever to release steering column housing.
15. Remove steering column housing and steering shaft as an assembly from steering column bowl.
16. Place ignition switch in Run position.
17. Remove buzzer switch by using a screwdriver to lift switch tab, then gently pull on wires.
18. Place ignition switch in Accessory position.
19. Remove lock retaining screw, then the lock cylinder.
20. **On models equipped with key release column,** proceed as follows:
    a. Remove key release lever bolt.
    b. Remove key release lever through slot in steering column bowl.
    c. Key release lever spring.
21. **On all models,** remove column tilt bumpers using vise grips.
22. Remove tilt lever and shoe bracket attaching screws, then the tilt lever and shoe bracket.
23. Using 3/16 inch drift, remove release lever pin.
24. Remove shoe release lever and release lever spring.
25. Reverse procedure to install, noting the following:
    a. Lubricate tilt bracket with lithium grease.
    b. **Torque** tilt lever and shoe bracket attaching screws to 32 inch lbs.
    c. When installing column lock cylinder set, hold lock cylinder barrel, then insert key and turn to Accessory position. Install attaching screw and **torque** to 22 inch lbs.
    d. When installing buzzer switch, turn ignition switch to Run position and push switch down until bottomed with plastic tab covering lock attaching screw.
    e. Lubricate pivot pins with lithium grease.
    f. **Torque** turn signal switch attaching screws to 35 inch lbs.
    g. Attach light green buzzer switch wire to terminal F of turn signal switch wiring connector.
    h. Attach tan/black buzzer switch wire to terminal G of turn signal switch wiring connector.
    i. **Torque** turn signal lever attaching screw to 18 inch lbs.
    j. **Torque** dimmer switch actuator attaching screw to 20 inch lbs.
    k. **Torque** column cover attaching screw to 35 inch lbs.
    l. **Torque** hazard warning switch at-

taching screw to 7 inch lbs.
    m. **Torque** steering wheel attaching nut to 30 ft. lbs.

UPPER & LOWER STEERING SHAFTS, STEERING COLUMN HOUSING, CENTERING SPHERE & BEARING ASSEMBLY

Disassembly

1. Pull shoe release lever and tilt column upwards.
2. Remove steering column from vehicle.
3. Remove steering wheel, then the turn signal cancel cam assembly.
4. Remove hazard warning knob attaching screw, then the hazard warning knob.
5. Position turn signal switch in such a way so column cover attaching screw and turn signal attaching screws are accessible.
6. Remove column cover attaching screw, then the column cover.
7. Remove turn signal switch attaching screws.
8. Remove buzzer switch wires (light green and tan/black wires) from turn signal switch wiring connector using tool.
9. Remove turn signal switch.
10. Insert a screwdriver into spring retainer square opening, then push down and turn left to release retainer and wheel tilt spring.
11. Remove spring retainer, tilt spring and tilt spring guide.
12. Remove shoe pin retaining cap.
13. Remove pivot pins using pivot pin remover tool No. J-21854-01.
14. Remove upper shaft bearing locknut, flat washer, upper bearing inner race seat and inner bearing.
15. Pull shoe release lever to release steering column housing and remove.
16. Remove bearing assembly using a drift and discard.
17. Remove thrust bearing and bearing assembly thrust race.
18. Place ignition switch in Run position, then remove upper and lower steering shafts.
19. Scribe alignment marks between upper and lower steering shafts, then position lower shaft 90° to upper shaft and separate them.
20. Remove centering sphere by rotating 90° to shaft and pulling out.
21. If necessary, separate sphere and remove preload spring.
22. Reverse procedure to install, noting the following:
    a. Apply lithium grease to centering sphere halves and sphere ends of steering shafts, tilt spring guides, thrust race and needle thrust bearing and pivot pins.
    b. Install upper and lower steering shaft with ignition switch in the Run position.
    c. Press bearing into housing with 1 1/2 inch socket until bottomed.
    d. Tighten bearing locknut until torque required to rotate steering shaft is 3 inch lbs.
    e. **Torque** turn signal switch attach-

ing screws to 35 inch lbs.
    f. Attach light green buzzer switch wire to terminal F of turn signal switch wiring connector.
    g. Attach tan/black buzzer switch wire to terminal G of turn signal switch wiring connector.
    h. Torque turn signal lever attaching screw to 18 inch lbs.
    i. Torque dimmer switch actuator attaching screw to 20 inch lbs.
    j. Torque column cover attaching screw to 35 inch lbs.
    k. Torque hazard warning switch attaching screw to 7 inch lbs.
    l. Torque steering wheel attaching nut to 30 ft. lbs.

1989–90 Beretta & Corsica

FIXED COLUMN

Refer to **Fig. 68** when servicing this steering column.

TURN SIGNAL CANCEL CAM ASSEMBLY, DIMMER SWITCH ACTUATOR PIVOT ASSEMBLY, TURN SIGNAL SWITCH ASSEMBLY, STEERING SHAFT ASSEMBLY, BEARING ASSEMBLY & JACKET BUSHING ASSEMBLY

Disassembly

1. Remove retainer and jam nut, then remove steering wheel, turn signal cancel cam assembly, hazard knob screw and knob.
2. Remove housing cover screw, column housing cover, actuator screw and dimmer switch actuator. If equipped with cruise control, disconnect wire connector.
3. Remove turn signal switch screws, then disconnect wires on buzzer switch assembly from turn signal connector with terminal remover tool No. J35689-A or equivalent. Wrap wire ends with tape to protect them.
4. Remove turn signal switch assembly, then remove standard steering column from the vehicle as previously outlined in this section.
5. Twist and pull jacket bushing assembly from lower end of bowl and jacket assembly.
6. Place lock cylinder in the Run position, then place opening in retaining ring over flat on steering shaft. Remove retaining ring with a screwdriver and discard.
7. Remove thrust washer, upper bearing spring and remaining washer, then remove steering shaft from lower end of jacket and bowl assembly.
8. Remove housing screws (No. 13 in **Fig. 68**), then remove steering column housing, housing spacer and bearing with drift. Discard bearing.
9. Reverse procedure to assemble noting the following:
    a. Lubricate bearing (No. 15) with lithium grease before pressing into place. Use a 1 1/2 inch socket to press bearing into place.
    b. **Torque** housing screws (No. 13) to 88 inch lbs.

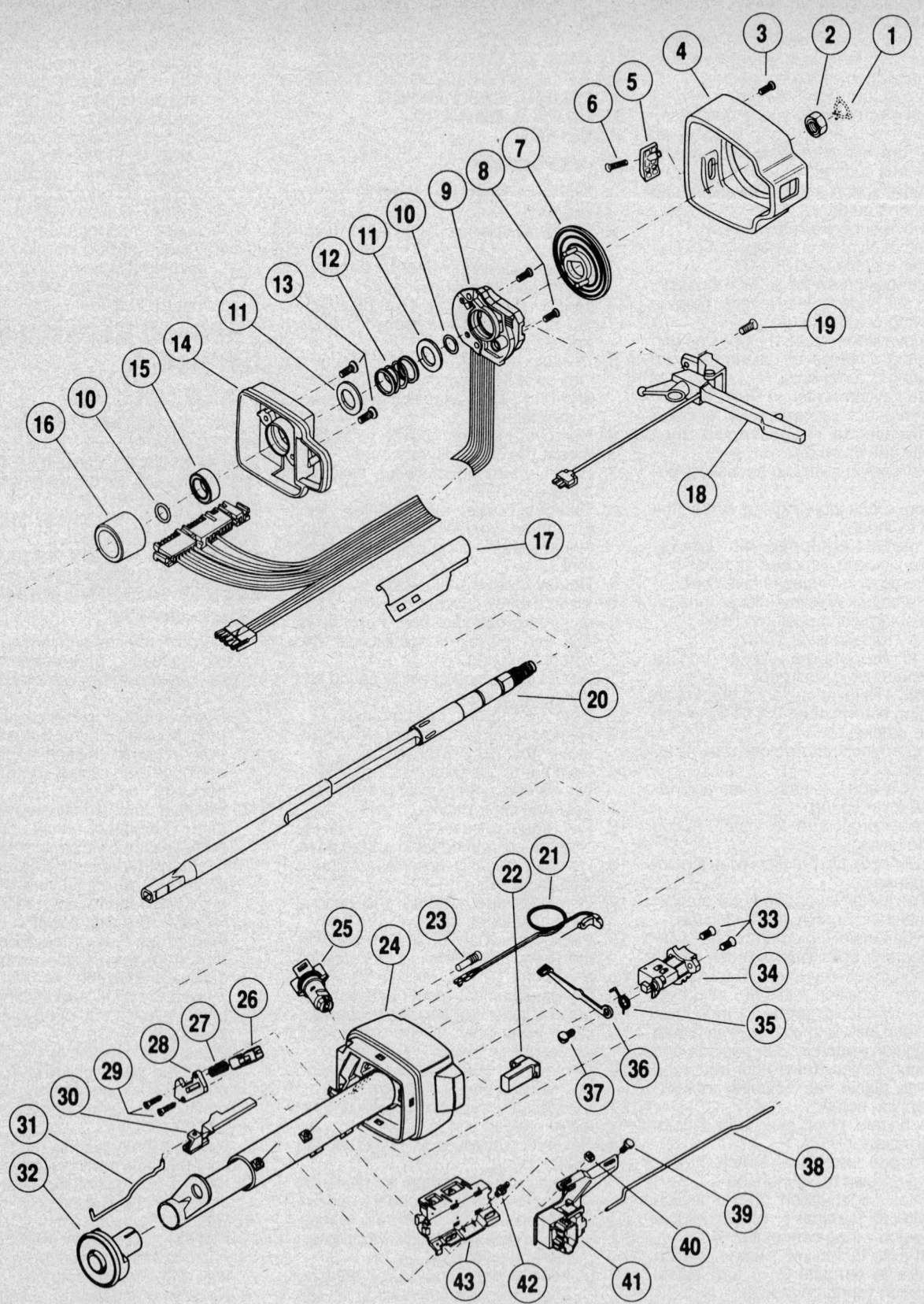

Fig. 68 Standard steering column exploded view (Part 1 of 2). 1989–90 Beretta & Corsica

Key No.	Part Name
1 -	RETAINER, STEERING WHEEL NUT
2 -	NUT, HEXAGON JAM
3 -	SCREW, PAN HEAD CROSS RECESS
4 -	COVER, COLUMN HOUSING
5 -	KNOB, HAZARD WARNING
6 -	SCREW, OV HD C/REC
7 -	CAM ASM, TURN SIG CANCEL
8 -	SCREW, PAN HEAD CROSS RECESS
9 -	SWITCH ASM, TURN SIGNAL
10 -	RING, RETAINING
11 -	WASHER, THRUST
12 -	SPRING, UPPER BEARING
13 -	SCREW, PAN HD 6-LOBED SOC TAP
14 -	HOUSING, TURN SIGNAL SWITCH
15 -	BEARING ASM
16 -	SPACER, STRG COLUMN HOUSING
17 -	PROTECTOR, WIRING
18 -	ACTUATOR ASM, DIMMER & T/S
19 -	SCREW, C/S TAPPING
20 -	SHAFT ASM, STEERING
21 -	SWITCH ASM, BUZZER
22 -	CAP, DIMMER SWITCH ROD
23 -	SCREW, LOCK RETAINING
24 -	BOWL & JACKET ASM, STRG COLUMN
25 -	LOCK CYL SET, STRG COLUMN
26 -	BOLT, STRG SHAFT LOCK
27 -	SPRING, LOCK BOLT
28 -	PLATE, LOCK BOLT RETAINING
29 -	SCREW, OVAL HEAD
30 -	RACK, SWITCH ACTUATOR
31 -	ACTUATOR, IGN SWITCH
32 -	BUSHING ASM, STRG COLUMN JACKET
33 -	SCREW, PAN HEAD TAPPING
34 -	BRACKET, TILT LEVER & SHOE
35 -	SPRING, KEY RELEASE LEVER (F/S, M/T ONLY)
36 -	LEVER, KEY RELEASE (F/S, M/T ONLY)
37 -	BOLT, KEY RELEASE LEVER (F/S, M/T ONLY)
38 -	ROD, DIMMER SW ACTUATOR
39 -	SCREW, WASHER HD
40 -	NUT, HEXAGON
41 -	SWITCH ASM, DIMMER
42 -	STUD, DIMR & IGN SW MOUNTING
43 -	SWITCH ASM, IGNITION

Fig. 68   Standard steering column exploded view (Part 2 of 2). 1989–90 Beretta & Corsica

c. Turn lock cylinder set to the Run position, then insert steering shaft into lower end of jacket and bowl assembly until shaft rests against bearing. **The shaft will extend 2½ inches beyond the highest surface of steering column housing when installed properly.**

d. Wrap a two inch wide piece of shim stock (.005 inch thick) around shaft and slip a new retaining ring (No. 10) up to thrust washer (No. 11). Use two long handled screwdrivers and push retaining ring until it seats in the retainer ring groove in shaft, **Fig. 69.** Discard shim stock.

e. Align tab on jacket bushing assembly with V-groove on lower end of bowl and jacket assembly and snap into position.

f. **Torque** turn signal switch screws to 35 inch lbs., actuator screw to 20 inch lbs. and housing cover screws to 35 inch lbs.

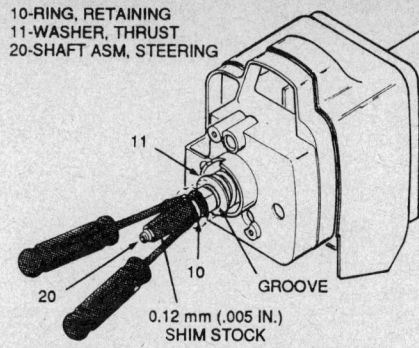

10-RING, RETAINING
11-WASHER, THRUST
20-SHAFT ASM, STEERING

11

20

10

GROOVE

0.12 mm (.005 IN.) SHIM STOCK

Fig. 69   Installing retaining ring. 1989–90 Beretta & Corsica

IGNITION & DIMMER SWITCH ASSEMBLY
Disassembly

1. With the ignition lock cylinder in the Off-Lock position, remove the dimmer switch assembly and ignition switch assembly.
2. Remove dimmer switch actuator rod from rod cap.
3. Reverse procedure to assemble noting the following:
   a. The ignition lock cylinder set must be in the Off-Lock position when installing.
   b. **Torque** ignition switch mounting stud to 35 inch lbs.
   c. When installing dimmer switch assembly on stud, install the hex nut and screw but do not tighten.
   d. Adjust dimmer switch by inserting a 3/32 inch drill bit into hole, **Fig. 70.** Push gently to remove all lash, then **torque** nut and screw to 35 inch lbs. and remove drill bit.

BUZZER SWITCH ASSEMBLY, STEERING COLUMN LOCK CYLINDER SET, SWITCH ACTUATOR RACK, STEERING SHAFT LOCK BOLT, TILT & SHOE BRACKET, KEY RELEASE LEVER, STEERING COLUMN BOWL & JACKET ASSEMBLY
Disassembly

1. Perform the disassembly steps outlined under "Turn Signal Cancel Cam Assembly, Dimmer Switch Actuator Pivot Assembly, Turn Signal Switch Assembly, Steering Shaft Assembly, Bearing Assembly & Jacket Bushing Assembly" and "Ignition & Dimmer Switch Assembly."
2. Place ignition lock cylinder in the Off-Lock position, then remove the key.
3. Remove the buzzer switch using a screwdriver to lift the tab, then pull gently on wires to remove.
4. Remove lock retaining screw and lock cylinder, then remove the retaining plate screws, switch actuator rack, ignition switch actuator rod and lock bolt retaining plate.

2.34 mm DIAMETER PIN (3/32" DRILL BIT)

DIMMER SWITCH ASSEMBLY

38

38-ROD, DIMMER SW ACTUATOR

Fig. 70   Adjusting dimmer switch. 1989–90 Beretta & Corsica

5. Remove steering shaft lock bolt and lock bolt spring. On models equipped with key release lever, proceed as follows:
   a. Remove key release lever bolt, then the lever through slot in bowl and jacket assembly.
   b. Remove key release lever spring.
6. On all models, remove tilt bracket screws, tilt lever and shoe bracket.
7. Remove rod cap where necessary, then remove bowl and jacket assembly.
8. Reverse procedure to install, noting the following:
   a. **Torque** tilt bracket screws to 32 inch lbs.
   b. **On models with key release lever,** install release lever spring, centered on boss, with loop end of spring facing up.
   c. Install key release lever through slot in column bowl and jacket assembly. Loop of spring must rest on lever.
9. **On all models** lubricate steering shaft lock bolt with lithium grease, then install steering bolt and lock bolt spring.
10. **Torque** lock bolt retaining plate screws to 27 inch lbs.
11. When installing key lock cylinder, insert key and turn cylinder to the Accessory position. **Torque** lock cylinder retaining screw to 27 inch lbs.
12. After securing lock cylinder with retaining screw, turn to the Start position while observing. The rack should extend as cylinder is turned to and from the Start position.
13. Place the lock cylinder in the Off-Lock position and remove the key, then install buzzer switch assembly and the rest of the components following assembly procedures as outlined under "Turn Signal Cancel Cam Assembly, Dimmer Switch Actuator Pivot Assembly, Turn Signal Switch Assembly, Steering Shaft Assembly, Bearing Assembly & Jacket Bushing Assembly" and "Ignition & Dimmer Switch Assembly."

TILT COLUMN

Refer to **Fig. 71** when servicing this steering column.

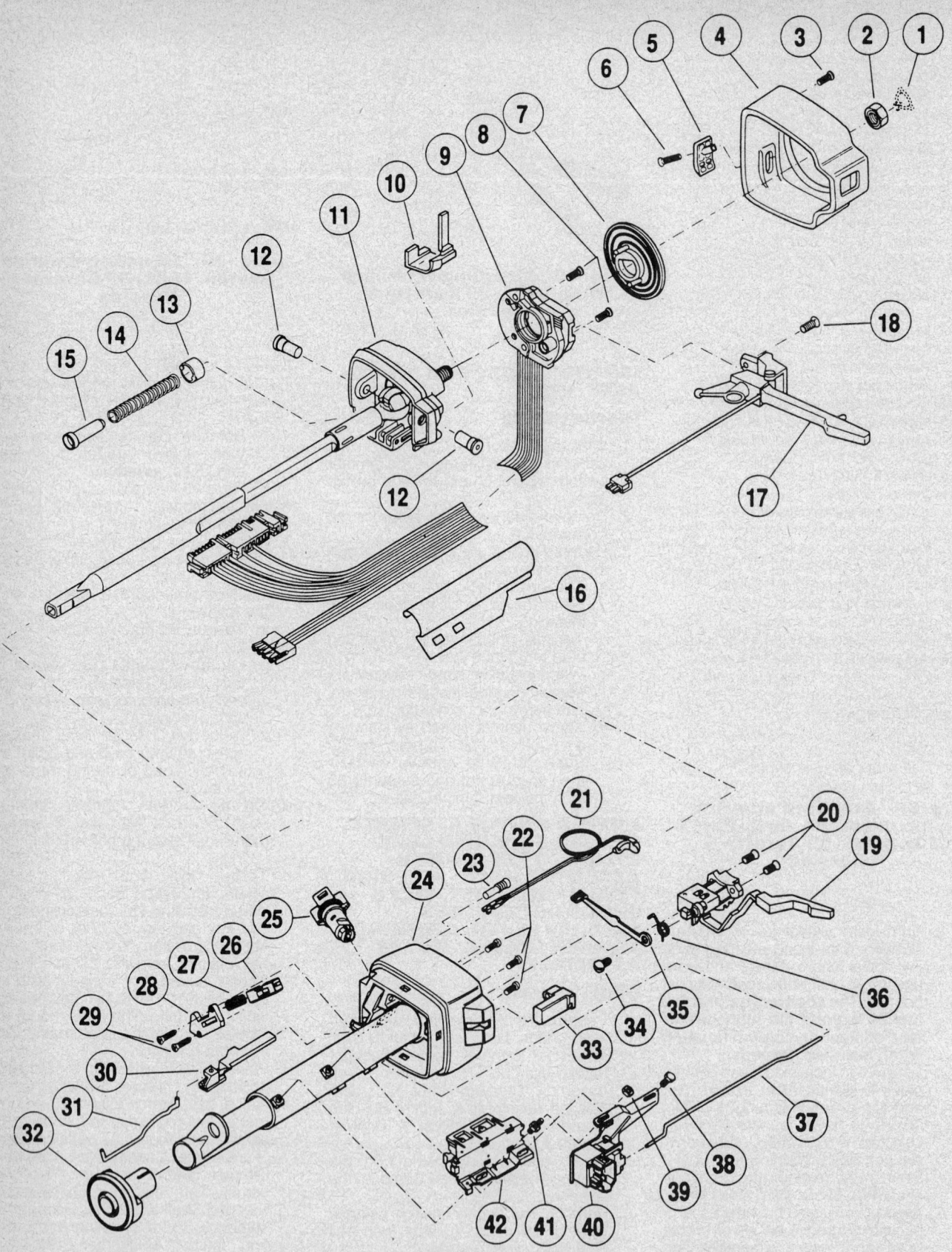

Fig. 71   Tilt steering column exploded view (Part 1 of 2). 1989–90 Beretta & Corsica

TURN SIGNAL CANCEL CAM ASSEMBLY, DIMMER SWITCH ACTUATOR PIVOT ASSEMBLY, TURN SIGNAL SWITCH ASSEMBLY, WHEEL TILT SPRING, SHAFT AND HOUSING ASSEMBLY & JACKET BUSHING ASSEMBLY

Disassembly

1. Remove retainer and jam nut, then remove steering wheel, turn signal cancel cam assembly, hazard knob screw and knob.
2. Remove housing cover screw, column housing cover, actuator screw and dimmer switch actuator. If equipped with cruise control, disconnect wire connector.
3. Remove turn signal switch screws, then disconnect wires on buzzer switch assembly from turn signal connector with terminal remover tool No. J35689-A or equivalent. Wrap wire ends with tape to protect them.
4. Remove turn signal switch assembly, then pull shoe release lever and tilt column all the way up, then insert a screwdriver into square opening in spring retainer, push down and turn to the left to release retainer and wheel tilt spring.
5. Remove spring retainer, tilt spring and tilt spring guide, then the shoe pin retaining cap.
6. Remove pivot pins with pin remover tool No. J21854-01 or equivalent, then place lock cylinder in the Run position.
7. Pull shoe release lever to release shaft and housing assembly, then remove shaft and housing assembly from column bowl and jacket assembly.
8. Twist and pull jacket bushing assembly from lower end of bowl and jacket assembly.
9. Reverse procedure to assemble noting the following:
   a. Align tab on jacket bushing assembly with V-groove on lower end of bowl and jacket assembly, then snap it into place.
   b. Place lock cylinder in the Run position and install shaft and housing assembly into bowl and jacket assembly while holding tilt lever in the Release position.
   c. Lubricate pivot pins with lithium grease then install flush with shaft and housing assembly.
   d. Pull shoe release lever and tilt column all the way up, then lubricate spring guide with lithium grease and install spring guide, spring and retainer.
   e. Insert screwdriver into square opening in spring retainer, push down and turn to the right to lock in place.
   f. Install turn signal switch assembly and position so turn signal switch screws and housing cover screws can be installed through openings in switch.
   g. **Torque** turn signal switch screws to 35 inch lbs.

Key No.   **Part Name**

1-RETAINER, STEERING WHEEL NUT
2-NUT, HEXAGON JAM
3-SCREW, PAN HEAD CROSS RECESS
4-COVER, COLUMN HOUSING
5-KNOB, HAZARD WARNING
6-SCREW, OV HD C/REC
7-CAM ASM, TURN SIG CANCEL
8-SCREW, PAN HEAD CROSS RECESS
9-SWITCH ASM, TURN SIGNAL
10-CAP, HSG SHOE PIN RETAINING
11-HOUSING ASM, SHAFT &
12-PIN, PIVOT
13-RETAINER, SPRING
14-SPRING, WHEEL TILT
15-GUIDE, TILT SPRING
16-PROTECTOR, WIRING
17-ACTUATOR ASM, DIMMER & T/S
18-SCREW, C/S TAPPING
19-BRACKET ASM, TILT LEVER & SHOE
20-SCREW, PAN HEAD CROSS RECESS
21-SWITCH ASM, BUZZER
22-BUMPER, COLUMN TILT
23-SCREW, LOCK RETAINING
24-BOWL & JACKET ASM, STRG COLUMN
25-LOCK CYL SET, STRG COLUMN
26-BOLT, STRG SHAFT LOCK
27-SPRING, LOCK BOLT
28-PLATE, LOCK BOLT RETAINING
29-SCREW, OVAL HEAD
30-RACK, SWITCH ACTUATOR
31-ACTUATORS, IGN SWITCH
32-BUSHING ASM, STRG COLUMN JACKET
33-CAP, DIMMER SWITCH ROD
34-BOLT, KEY RELEASE LEVER (F/S, M/T ONLY)
35-LEVER, KEY RELEASE (F/S, M/T ONLY)
36-SPRING, KEY RELEASE LEVER (F/S, M/T ONLY)
37-ROD, DIMMER SW ACTUATOR
38-SCREW, WASH HD
39-NUT HEXAGON
40-SWITCH ASM, DIMMER
41-STUD, DIMR & IGN SW MOUNTING
42-SWITCH ASM, IGNITION

Fig. 71 Tilt steering column exploded view (Part 2 of 2). 1989–90 Beretta & Corsica

    h. When connecting wires from buzzer switch to signal switch connector body, the light green wire mates with location F and the tan/black wire mates with location G.
    i. **Torque** actuator screw to 20 inch lbs. and housing cover screw to 35 inch lbs.

Ignition & Dimmer Switch Assembly

Refer to "Fixed Steering Column" portion of this section for procedure.

Buzzer Switch Assembly, Steering Column Lock Cylinder Set, Switch Actuator Rack, Steering Shaft Lock Bolt, Tilt & Shoe Bracket, Column Tilt Bumpers, Key Release Lever, Steering Column Bowl & Jacket Assembly

Refer to "Fixed Steering Column" portion of this section for procedure.

1988–89 Camaro & Firebird

Wheels of vehicle must be in straight ahead position, key must be in "lock" position and battery ground cable must be disconnected.

FIXED COLUMN w/KEY RELEASE, VEHICLES w/MANUAL TRANSMISSION

SHAFT LOCK, TURN SIGNAL CANCELLING CAM, UPPER BEARING SPRING, TURN SIGNAL SWITCH, BUZZER SWITCH & CYLINDER LOCK SET

Disassembly

1. Remove horn pad and disconnect electrical connectors, then remove retainer and jam nut, **Fig. 72.**
2. Remove steering wheel and cover.
3. Depress shaft lock with a suitable tool, then remove shaft lock retaining ring and shaft lock.
4. Remove turn signal cancelling cam, then the upper bearing spring.
5. Place turn signal in "right turn" position, then remove screw and crossover arm.
6. Remove turn signal lever.
7. Remove turn signal switch attaching screws and the switch, positioning out of way. If it is necessary to remove switch, remove wire harness protector and gently pull wire harness through column.
8. Remove key from lock cylinder set and remove buzzer switch and clip, then reinsert key.
9. Remove lock retaining screw and the lock cylinder set.

Assembly

1. Install lock cylinder set, then the lock retaining screw.
2. Place key in "run" position, then install clip and buzzer switch.
3. Install turn signal switch and attaching screws.
4. Lubricate crossover arm with lithium grease, then install arm and attaching screw.
5. Install upper bearing spring and turn signal cancelling cam, then the shaft lock.
6. Depress shaft lock with a suitable tool and install shaft lock retaining ring, then the cover.
7. Install steering wheel, then the jam nut and retainer.
8. Install turn signal lever and wire harness protector.
9. Install horn pad and attaching screws.

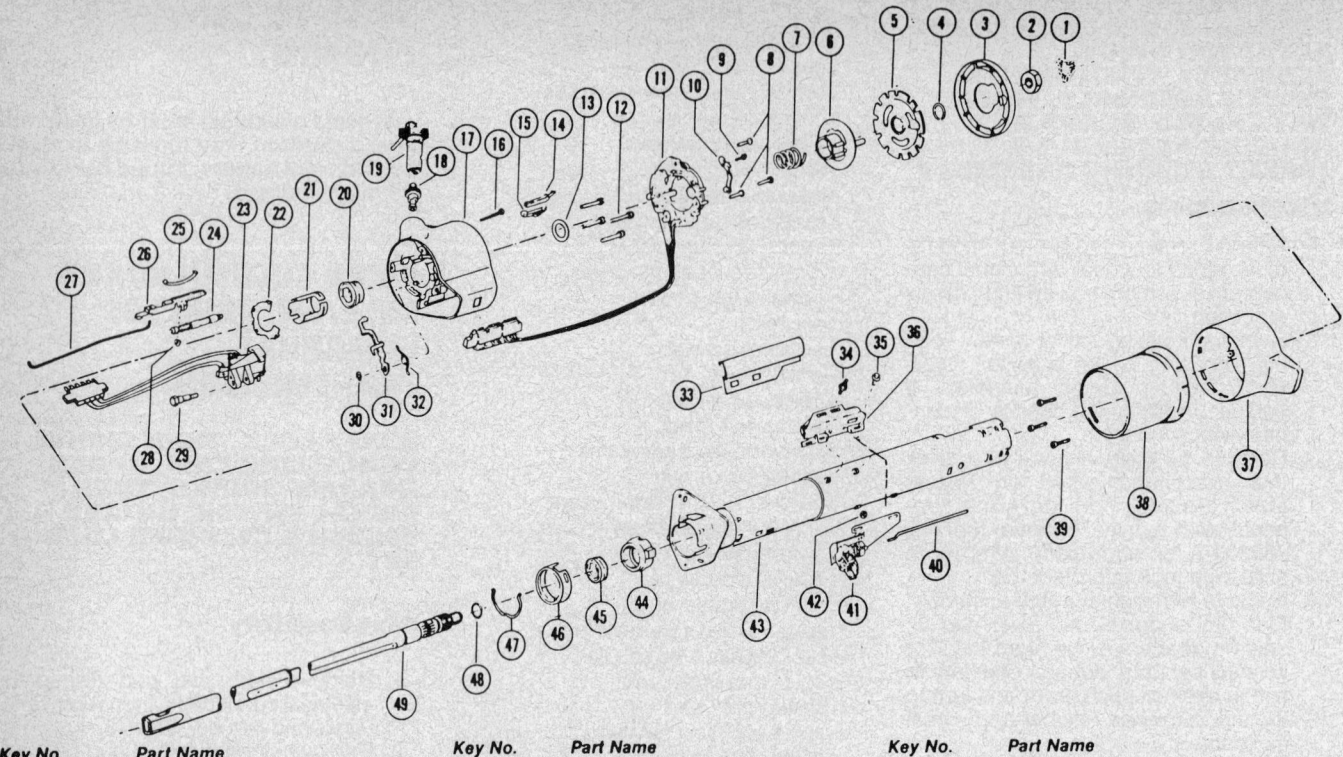

Fig. 72 Exploded view of fixed column with key release. 1988–89 Camaro & Firebird w/manual transmission

Key No.	Part Name
1 -	RETAINER
2 -	NUT, HEXAGON JAM
3 -	COVER, SHAFT LOCK
4 -	RING, RETAINING
5 -	LOCK, STEERING SHAFT
6 -	CAM ASM, TURN SIGNAL CANCELLING
7 -	SPRING, UPPER BEARING
8 -	SCREW, BINDING HEAD CROSS RECESS
9 -	SCREW, ROUND WASHER HEAD
10 -	ARM ASM, ACTUATOR SWITCH
11 -	SWITCH ASM, TURN SIGNAL
12 -	SCREW, HEX WASHER HEAD TAPPING
13 -	WASHER, THRUST
14 -	SWITCH ASM, BUZZER
15 -	CLIP, BUZZER SWITCH RETAINING
16 -	SCREW, LOCK RETAINING
17 -	HOUSING, STEERING COLUMN
18 -	SECTOR ASM, SWITCH ACTUATOR
19 -	LOCK CYLINDER SET, STEERING COLUMN
20 -	BEARING ASM
21 -	BUSHING, BEARING RETAINING
22 -	RETAINER, UPPER BEARING
23 -	SWITCH ASM, PIVOT &
24 -	BOLT ASM, SPRING &
25 -	SPRING, RACK PRELOAD

Key No.	Part Name
26 -	RACK, SWITCH ACTUATOR
27 -	ROD, SWITCH ACTUATOR
28 -	WASHER, SPRING THRUST
29 -	PIN, SWITCH ACTUATOR PIVOT
30 -	WASHER, WAVE
31 -	LEVER, KEY RELEASE
32 -	SPRING, KEY RELEASE
33 -	PROTECTOR, WIRING
34 -	STUD, DIMMER AND IGNITION SWITCH MOUNTING
35 -	SCREW, WASHER HEAD
36 -	SWITCH ASM, IGNITION
37 -	BOWL, FLOOR SHIFT
38 -	SHROUD, SHIFT BOWL
39 -	SCREW, BINDING HEAD CROSS RECESS
40 -	ROD, DIMMER SWITCH ACTUATOR
41 -	SWITCH ASM, DIMMER
42 -	NUT, HEXAGON
43 -	JACKET ASM, STEERING COLUMN
44 -	ADAPTER, LOWER BEARING
45 -	BEARING ASSEMBLY
46 -	RETAINER, BEARING ADAPTER
47 -	CLIP, LOWER BEARING ADAPTER
48 -	RING, RETAINING
49 -	SHAFT ASM, STEERING

Key No.	Part Name
	ASSEMBLIES
0 -	COLUMN ASM, E/A STEERING
101 -	BRACKET ASM, COLUMN DASH
	SERVICE KITS
201 -	HOUSING ASM SERVICE KIT, STEERING COLUMN
202 -	SHAFT REPAIR KIT, INJECTION STEERING
203 -	SECTOR SERVICE KIT, IGNITION SWITCH ACTUATOR

DIMMER SWITCH, IGNITION SWITCH, LOCK HOUSING, COVER SHROUD, KEY RELEASE LEVER, SWITCH ACTUATOR RACK, SWITCH ACTUATOR SEGMENT, LOCK BOLT, PIVOT & SWITCH ASSEMBLY & UPPER BEARING

Disassembly

1. Perform "Disassembly" of "Shaft Lock, Turn Signal Cancelling Cam, Upper Bearing Spring, Turn Signal Switch, Buzzer Switch & Cylinder Lock Set" as previously described.
2. Remove thrust washer and steering column housing mounting screws, then the ignition and dimmer switch mounting bolts.
3. Remove dimmer switch and dimmer switch rod, then the ignition switch mounting stud and ignition switch.
4. Remove lock housing cover and shroud assembly, then the shroud attaching screws.
5. Remove shroud from lock housing cover.
6. Remove upper bearing retainer and wave washer, then the key release lever and key release spring.
7. Remove switch actuator rod and rack assembly, then the lock bolt.
8. Remove switch actuator pivot pin, then the pivot and switch assembly.
9. Remove bearing retaining bushing

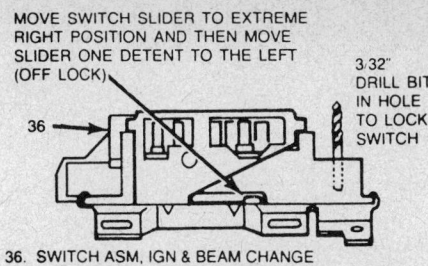

MOVE SWITCH SLIDER TO EXTREME RIGHT POSITION AND THEN MOVE SLIDER ONE DETENT TO THE LEFT (OFF LOCK)

36

3/32" DRILL BIT IN HOLE TO LOCK SWITCH

36. SWITCH ASM, IGN & BEAM CHANGE

Fig. 73 Adjusting ignition switch

and switch actuator segment, then the upper bearing.

Assembly

1. Install upper bearing, then the switch actuator segment and bearing retaining bushing.
2. Install pivot and switch assembly, then the switch actuator pivot pin.
3. Install lock bolt, then the switch actuator rod and rack assembly.
4. Install key release spring and key release lever, then the wave washer and upper bearing retainer.
5. Attach shroud to lock housing cover and install retaining screws.
6. Attach lock housing cover and shroud assembly to column and install attaching screws.
7. Install ignition switch and mounting stud, then adjust ignition switch, **Fig. 73.**
8. Install dimmer switch rod, dimmer switch and hex nut, then adjust dimmer switch, **Fig. 74.**
9. Install thrust washer.
10. Perform "Assembly" steps of "Shaft Lock, Turn Signal Cancelling Cam, Upper Bearing Spring, Turn Signal Switch, Buzzer Switch & Cylinder Lock Set" as previously described.

SHAFT & LOWER BEARING ASSEMBLY

Disassembly

1. Remove horn pad and disconnect electrical connectors, then remove retainer and jam nut.
2. Remove steering wheel and cover.
3. Remove steering column from vehicle as previously described.
4. Remove lower bearing adapter clip, then the retainer and bearing adapter.
5. Remove bearing assembly and lower bearing assembly, then the cover.
6. Depress shaft lock with a suitable tool, then remove shaft lock retaining ring.
7. Remove shaft lock, turn signal cancelling cam and upper bearing spring, then the shaft.

Assembly

1. Install shaft, then the upper bearing spring, turn signal cancelling cam and shaft lock.
2. Depress shaft lock with a suitable tool and install shaft lock retaining ring.

3. Install cover, then the lower bearing adapter.
4. Install lower bearing assembly, then the lower bearing adapter retainer and clip.
5. Install steering column.
6. Install steering wheel, then the jam nut and retainer.
7. Install turn signal lever and wire harness protector.
8. Install horn pad and attaching screws.

FIXED COLUMN, VEHICLES W/AUTOMATIC TRANSMISSION

SHAFT LOCK, TURN SIGNAL CANCELLING CAM, UPPER BEARING SPRING, SHAFT ASSEMBLY & LOWER BEARING ASSEMBLY

Disassembly

1. Remove horn pad and disconnect electrical connectors, then remove retainer and jam nut, **Fig. 75.**
2. Remove steering wheel.
3. If removing and/or repairing shaft assembly and/or lower bearing assembly, remove steering column from vehicle.
4. Using a suitable tool, depress shaft lock, then remove shaft lock retaining ring.
5. Remove shaft lock and cover, then the turn signal cancelling cam.
6. Remove upper bearing spring, then the shaft.
7. Remove lower bearing adapter clip and bearing adapter retainer, then the bearing assembly and lower bearing adapter.

Assembly

1. Install lower bearing adapter and bearing assembly, then the bearing adapter retainer and lower bearing adapter clip.
2. Install shaft assembly to column, then install bearing spring.
3. Install turn signal cancelling cam, then the shaft lock and cover.
4. Depress shaft lock and install shaft lock retaining ring.
5. Install steering column in vehicle, then install steering wheel, jam nut, retainer and horn pad.

DIMMER SWITCH, IGNITION SWITCH & DIMMER SWITCH ROD

Disassembly

1. Remove dimmer switch hex nut and ignition switch mounting bolt.
2. Remove dimmer switch and dimmer switch rod.
3. Remove ignition switch mounting stud and ignition switch.

Assembly

1. Place key in "lock" position.
2. Install ignition switch and mounting stud, then adjust ignition switch, **Fig. 76.**
3. Install dimmer switch rod and dimmer

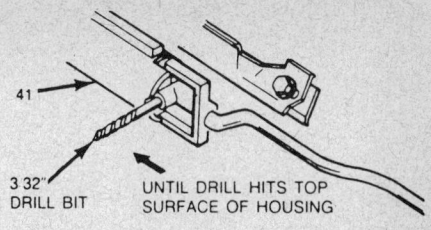

41

3/32" DRILL BIT

UNTIL DRILL HITS TOP SURFACE OF HOUSING

41. SWITCH, DIMMER

Fig. 74 Adjusting dimmer switch. 1988–89 Camaro & Firebird

switch, then adjust dimmer switch, Fig. 74.
4. Install hex nut and mounting bolt.

TURN SIGNAL SWITCH, BUZZER SWITCH & CYLINDER LOCK SET

Disassembly

1. Perform steps 1 through 5 of "Disassembly" for "Shaft Lock, Turn Signal Cancelling Cam, Upper Bearing Spring, Shaft Assembly & Lower Bearing Assembly."
2. Remove upper bearing spring.
3. Place turn signal in "right turn" position, then remove hazard knob.
4. Remove signal switch arm attaching screw and the arm.
5. Remove turn signal switch attaching screws and position switch out of way. If it is necessary to remove switch, remove clip and wire harness protector, then gently pull wire harness through column.
6. Remove key from lock cylinder and remove buzzer switch and clip, then the lock retaining bolt.
7. Reinsert key in lock cylinder, then remove lock cylinder set.

Assembly

1. Install lock cylinder set, then place key in "run" position and install lock retaining bolt.
2. Install clip and buzzer switch, then the turn signal switch and attaching screws.
3. Install signal switch arm and attaching screw, then the hazard knob.
4. Install upper bearing spring.
5. Perform steps 3 through 5 of "Assembly" for "Shaft Lock, Turn Signal Cancelling Cam, Upper bearing Spring, Shaft Assembly & Lower Bearing Assembly."

LOCK HOUSING COVER, SHROUD, UPPER BEARING, ACTUATOR ROD/RACK ASSEMBLY, LOCK BOLT & PIVOT & SWITCH ASSEMBLY

Disassembly

1. Perform steps 1 through 5 of "Disassembly" for "Shaft Lock, Turn Signal Cancelling Cam, Upper Bearing Spring, Shaft Assembly & Lower Bearing Assembly," then remove upper bearing spring.
2. Perform "Disassembly" steps for "Dimmer Switch, Ignition Switch &

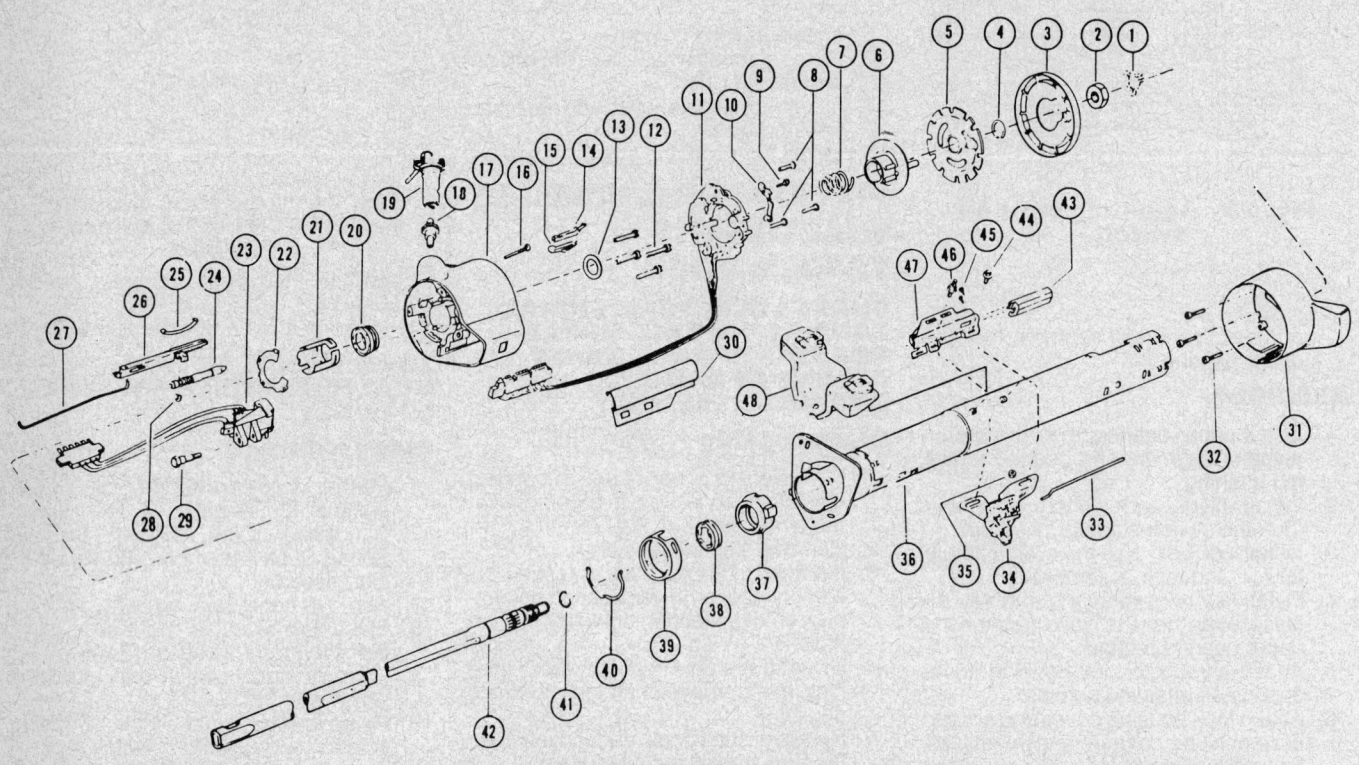

Key No.	Part Name
1 -	RETAINER
2 -	NUT, HEXAGON JAM
3 -	COVER, SHAFT LOCK
4 -	RING, RETAINING
5 -	LOCK, STEERING SHAFT
6 -	CAM ASM, TURN SIGNAL CANCELLING
7 -	SPRING, UPPER BEARING
8 -	SCREW, BINDING HEAD CROSS RECESS
9 -	SCREW, ROUND WASHER HEAD
10 -	ARM ASM, SWITCH ACTUATOR
11 -	SWITCH ASM, TURN SIGNAL
12 -	SCREW, HEX WASHER HEAD TAPPING
13 -	WASHER, THRUST
14 -	SWITCH ASM, BUZZER
15 -	CLIP, BUZZER SWITCH RETAINING
16 -	SCREW, LOCK RETAINING
17 -	HOUSING, STEERING COLUMN
18 -	SECTOR, SWITCH ACTUATOR
19 -	LOCK CYLINDER SET, STEERING COLUMN
20 -	BEARING ASM
21 -	BUSHING, BEARING RETAINING
22 -	RETAINER, UPPER BEARING
23 -	SWITCH ASM, PIVOT &
24 -	BOLT, LOCK
25 -	SPRING, RACK PRELOAD
26 -	RACK, SWITCH ACTUATOR
27 -	ROD, SWITCH ACTUATOR
28 -	WASHER, SPRING THRUST
29 -	PIN, SWITCH ACTUATOR PIVOT
30 -	PROTECTOR, WIRING

Key No.	Part Name
31 -	BOWL, FLOOR SHIFT
32 -	SCREW, BINDING HD CROSS RECESS
33 -	ROD, DIMMER SWITCH ACTUATOR
34 -	SWITCH ASM, DIMMER
35 -	NUT, HEXAGON
36 -	JACKET ASM, STEERING COLUMN
37 -	ADAPTER, LOWER BEARING
38 -	BEARING ASM
39 -	RETAINER, BEARING ADAPTER
40 -	CLIP, LOWER BEARING ADAPTER
41 -	RING, RETAINING
42 -	SHAFT ASM, STEERING
43 -	HOUSING ASM, IGN SWITCH
44 -	SCREW, WASHER HEAD
45 -	SCREW, PAN HD
46 -	STUD, DIMR & IGN SW MOUNTING
47 -	SWITCH ASM, IGNITION
48 -	BRACKET ASM, STRG. COL. SUPPORT

ASSEMBLIES

0 -	COLUMN ASM, E/A STEERING
101 -	BOLT ASM, SPRING &
102 -	BOWL ASM, GEARSHIFT LEVER
103 -	JACKET ASM, STEERING COLUMN
104 -	SWITCH ASM, COLUMN LOCK & IGN

SERVICE KITS

201 -	HOUSING ASM SERVICE KIT STEERING COLUMN
202 -	SECTOR SERVICE KIT, IGNITION SWITCH ACTUATOR
203 -	SHAFT REPAIR KIT INJ. STEERING

Fig. 75   Exploded view of fixed steering column. 1988–89 Camaro & Firebird w/automatic transmission

Dimmer Switch Rod" and "Turn Signal Switch, Buzzer Switch & Cylinder Lock Set."

3. Remove attaching screws, then the shroud bowl assembly and lock housing cover.
4. Remove attaching screws, then the lock housing cover and bowl.
5. Remove upper bearing retainer, then the actuator rod assembly and lock bolt.
6. Disconnect horn circuit contact and remove bearing retaining bushing.
7. Remove thrust washer and upper bearing, then the switch actuator pivot pin.
8. Remove pivot and switch assembly, then the actuator selector.

Assembly

1. Connect horn circuit contact and install bearing retaining bushing to lock housing cover.
2. Install pivot and switch assembly to lock housing cover, then install switch actuator pivot pin and the actuator selector.
3. Install lock bolts and actuator rod/rack assembly, then the upper bearing retainer.
4. Install bowl to lock housing cover, then the attaching screws.
5. Install cover assembly to column, then the attaching screws. Tighten screw in 12 o'clock position first, screw in 8 o'clock position second and screw in 4 o'clock position third, then **torque** screws, in same order, to 89 inch lbs.
6. Perform "Assembly" steps for "Turn Signal Switch, Buzzer Switch & Cylinder Lock Set," then for "Dimmer Switch, Ignition Switch & Dimmer Switch Rod."

TILT COLUMN w/ KEY RELEASE

SHAFT LOCK, TURN SIGNAL CANCELLING CAM, UPPER BEARING SPRING, UPPER BEARING SEAT, INNER RACE TURN SIGNAL SWITCH, BUZZER SWITCH & LOCK CYLINDER SET.

1. Remove horn pad and disconnect electrical connectors, then remove retainer and jam nut, **Figs. 77 and 78.**
2. Remove steering wheel.
3. Depress shaft lock using special tool No. J 23653-B or equivalent, then remove shaft lock retaining ring.
4. Remove shaft lock and shaft lock cover, then the turn signal cancelling cam.
5. Remove upper bearing spring and upper bearing seat, then the inner race.
6. Place turn signal in "right turn" position, then remove signal switch arm attaching screw and the arm.
7. Remove turn signal switch attaching screws and position switch out of way. If it is necessary to remove

MOVE SWITCH SLIDER TO EXTREME LEFT POSITION AND THEN MOVE SLIDER ONE DETENT TO THE RIGHT (OFF LOCK)

3/32" DRILL BIT IN HOLE TO LOCK SWITCH

47 — SWITCH ASM. IGN & BEAM CHANGE

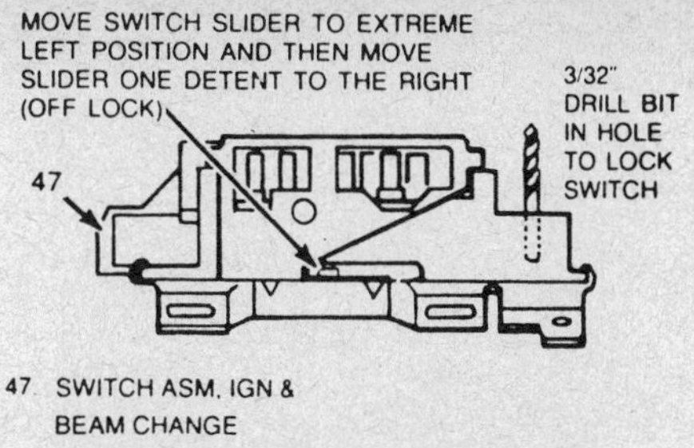

Fig. 76 Adjusting ignition switch. 1988–89 Camaro & Firebird w/fixed automatic transmission

switch, remove wiring protector and hazard knob, then gently pull wire harness through column housing shroud, column housing and lock housing cover.
8. Remove key from lock cylinder set and remove buzzer switch and clip, then reinsert key and place in "lock" position.
9. Remove lock retaining screw, then the lock cylinder set.
10. Reverse procedure to assemble noting the following:
   a. **Torque** lock cylinder retaining screw to 22 inch lbs.
   b. Turn key to the RUN position and install buzzer switch and clip.
   c. **Torque** turn signal switch screws to 30 inch lbs. and signal switch arm screw to 20 inch lbs.
   d. Depress shaft lock using special tool and install shaft lock retaining ring and shaft lock cover.

LOCK HOUSING COVER, COVER END CAP, PIVOT & SWITCH ASSEMBLY, DIMMER SWITCH ROD ACTUATOR & TILT SPRING ASSEMBLY

1. Perform ""Shaft Lock, Turn Signal Cancelling Cam, Upper Bearing Spring, Upper Bearing Seat, Inner Race Turn Signal Switch, Buzzer Switch & Lock Cylinder Set" procedure as previously described.
2. Remove lock housing cover retaining screws, then the cover and tilt release lever.
3. Remove housing cover end cap and dimmer switch rod actuator. On vehicles equipped with cruise control, disconnect cruise control connector and remove multifunction lever.
4. Gently pull pivot and switch assembly wire harness through column housing and column housing shroud.
5. Remove pivot pin, then the pivot and switch assembly.
6. Remove spring retainer, then the tilt spring and spring guide.
7. Reverse procedure to assemble noting the following:
   a. Before installing spring guide and tilt spring, coat spring with lithium grease.
   b. When installing dimmer switch rod

actuator, bottom edge of rod actuator should rest on bend in dimmer switch rod.

COLUMN HOUSING, LOCK SHOES, ACTUATOR SECTOR ASSEMBLY, SWITCH ACTUATOR RACK BEARINGS & LOCK BOLT ASSEMBLY

1. Perform "Shaft Lock, Turn Signal Cancelling Cam, Upper Bearing Spring, Upper Bearing Seat, Inner Race Turn Signal Switch & Lock Cylinder Set & Lock Housing Cover, Cover End Cap, Pivot & Switch Assembly, Dimmer Switch Rod Actuator & Tilt Spring Assembly" procedure as previously described.
2. Using pivot pin tool remover No. J-21854-01 or equivalent, remove pivot pins, **Fig. 64.**
3. Install tilt release lever, then remove column housing assembly by pulling back on tilt release lever and pulling housing down and away from column.
4. Remove drive shaft, then switch actuator sector.
5. Remove switch actuator rack and rack preload spring, then the release lever pin.
6. Remove shoe release lever, then the release lever spring.
7. Remove dowel pin, then the lock shoes and lock shoe springs.
8. Remove bearings, then the hex head bolt, lock bolt spring and lock bolt.
9. Reverse procedure to assemble noting the following:
   a. When installing column housing assembly, position column housing assembly and align switch actuator rack with pin on end of actuator rod.
   b. Pull back on tilt lever and push column housing assembly onto housing support assembly
   c. Release tilt lever to lock shoes and remove tilt lever.
   d. Lubricate pivot pins with lithium grease, then install pins.

SHAFT ASSEMBLY, COLUMN HOUSING SUPPORT SHIFT TUBE ASSEMBLY, IGNITION SWITCH, DIMMER SWITCH & LOWER BEARING ASSEMBLY

1. Perform "Shaft Lock, Turn Signal Cancelling Cam, Upper Bearing Spring, Upper Bearing Seat, Inner Race Turn Signal Switch & Lock Cylinder Set, Lock Housing Cover, Cover End Cap, Pivot & Switch Assembly, Dimmer Switch Rod Actuator & Tilt Spring Assembly & Column Housing, Lock Shoes, Actuator Sector Assembly, Switch Actuator Rack Bearings & Lock Bolt Assembly" procedure as previously described.
2. Remove bearing retainer, lower spring retainer and lower bearing spring.
3. Remove lower bearing seat, attaching screws and lower bearing.
4. Remove shaft assembly, then the lower shaft from the shaft assembly.

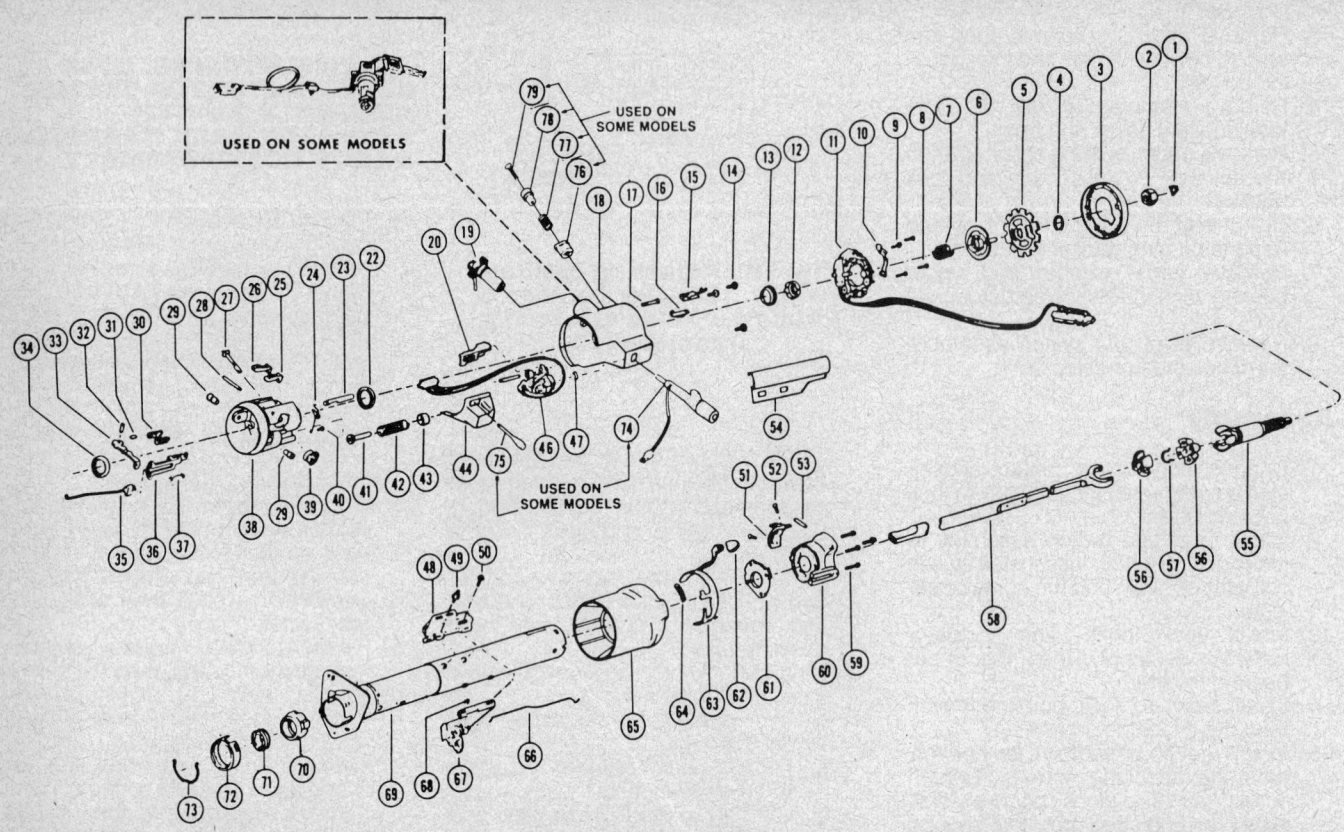

USED ON SOME MODELS

USED ON SOME MODELS

USED ON SOME MODELS

1 - RETAINER	35 - ACTUATOR ASM, IGNITION SWITCH	69 - JACKET ASM, STEERING COLUMN
2 - NUT, HEXAGON JAM	36 - RACK, SWITCH ACTUATOR	70 - ADAPTER, LOWER BEARING
3 - COVER, SHAFT LOCK	37 - SPRING, RACK PRELOAD	71 - BEARING ASM
4 - RING, RETAINING	38 - HOUSING, STEERING COLUMN	72 - RETAINER, BEARING ADAPTER
5 - LOCK, SHAFT	39 - SECTOR, SWITCH ACTUATOR	73 - CLIP, LOWER BEARING ADAPTER
6 - CAM ASM, TURN SIGNAL CANCELLING	40 - SCREW, HEX WASHER HEAD	74 - LEVER ASM, T/S MULTIFUNCTION
7 - SPRING, UPPER BEARING	41 - GUIDE, SPRING	75 - LEVER ASM, TILT RELEASE
8 - SCREW, BINDING HEAD CROSS RECESS	42 - SPRING, WHEEL TILT	76 - KNOB, HAZARD WARNING SWITCH
9 - SCREW, ROUND WASHER HEAD	43 - RETAINER, SPRING	77 - SPRING, HAZARD WARNING
10 - ARM ASM, SIGNAL SWITCH	44 - CAP, COLUMN HOUSING COVER END	78 - BUTTON, HAZARD WARNING
11 - SWITCH ASM, TURN SIGNAL	45 - PIN, SWITCH ACTUATOR PIVOT	79 - SCREW, OVAL HEAD
12 - SEAT, UPPER BEARING INNER RACE	46 - SWITCH ASM, PIVOT &	
13 - RACE, INNER	47 - SPRING, PIN PRELOAD	
14 - SCREW, PAN HEAD CROSS RECESS	48 - SWITCH ASM, IGNITION	
15 - SWITCH ASM, BUZZER	49 - STUD, DIMMER & IGNITION SWITCH MOUNTING	**ASSEMBLIES**
16 - CLIP, BUZZER SWITCH RETAINING	50 - SCREW, WASHER HEAD	
17 - SCREW, LOCK RETAINING	51 - PLATE, SHROUD RETAINING	0 - COLUMN ASM, E/A STEERING
18 - COVER, LOCK HOUSING	52 - SCREW, OVAL HEAD CROSS RECESS	101 - COVER ASM, LOCK HOUSING
19 - LOCK CYLINDER SET, STEERING COLUMN	53 - PIN, DOWEL	102 - HOUSING ASM, STEERING COLUMN
20 - ACTUATOR, DIMMER SWITCH ROD	54 - PROTECTOR, WIRING	103 - SHAFT ASM, STEERING
21 - THIS NUMBER NOT USED	55 - SHAFT ASM, RACE & UPPER	104 - SUPPORT ASM, STEERING COLUMN HOUSING
22 - BEARING ASM	56 - SPHERE, CENTERING	
23 - BOLT, LOCK	57 - SPRING, JOINT PRELOAD	
24 - SPRING, LOCK BOLT	58 - SHAFT ASM, LOWER STEERING	
25 - SHOE, STEERING WHEEL LOCK	59 - SCREW, SUPPORT	
26 - SHOE, STEERING WHEEL LOCK	60 - SUPPORT, STEERING COLUMN HOUSING	
27 - SHAFT, DRIVE	61 - PLATE, LOCK	
28 - PIN, DOWEL	62 - FINGER PAD, RELEASE LEVER	
29 - PIN, PIVOT	63 - LEVER, KEY RELEASE	
30 - SPRING, SHOE	64 - SPRING, KEY RELEASE	
31 - SPRING, RELEASE LEVER	65 - SHROUD, STEERING COLUMN HOUSING	
32 - PIN, RELEASE LEVER	66 - ROD, DIMMER SWITCH	
33 - LEVER, SHOE RELEASE	67 - SWITCH ASM, DIMMER	
34 - BEARING ASM	68 - NUT, HEXAGON	

Fig. 77   Exploded view key release tilt wheel steering column. 1988–89 Camaro & Firebird w/manual transmission

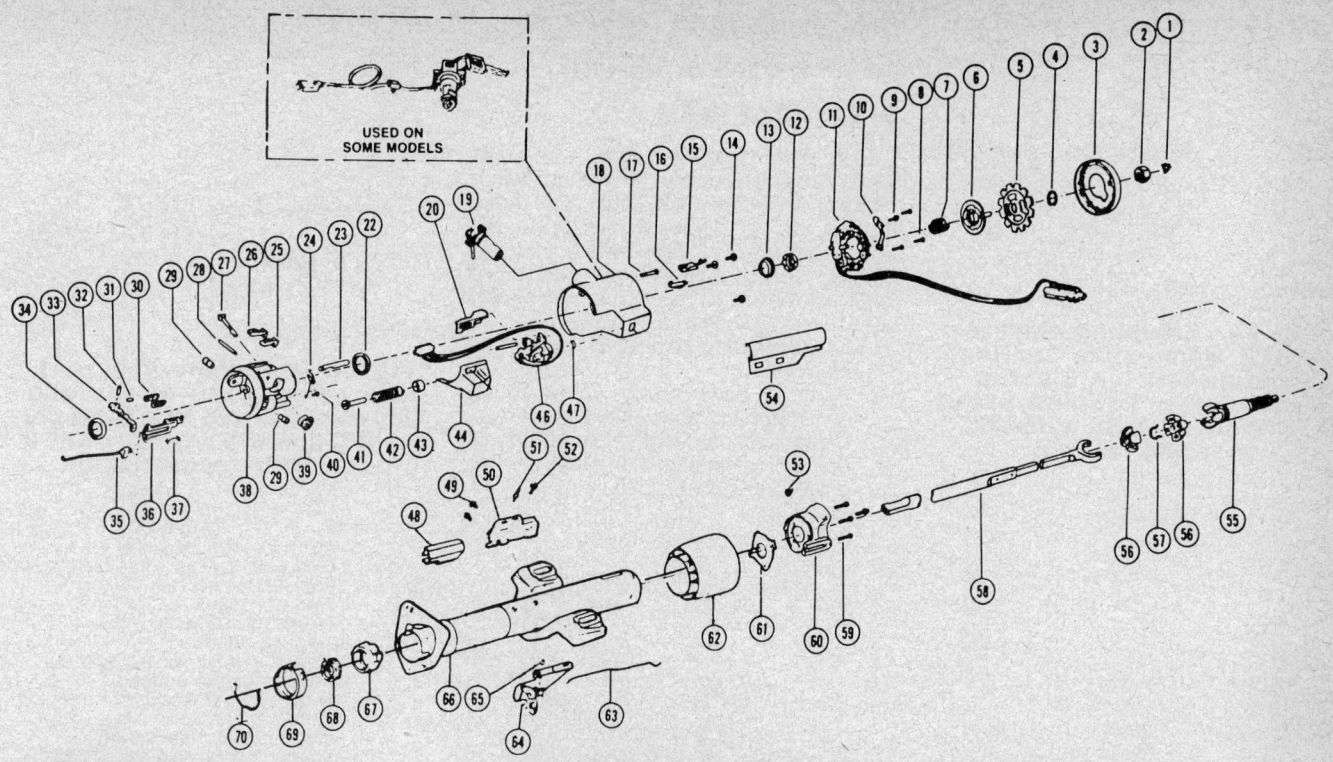

USED ON SOME MODELS

1 - RETAINER
2 - NUT, HEXAGON JAM
3 - COVER, SHAFT LOCK
4 - RING, RETAINING
5 - LOCK, SHAFT
6 - CAM ASM, TURN SIGNAL CANCELLING
7 - SPRING, UPPER BEARING
8 - SCREW, BINDING HEAD CROSS RECESS
9 - SCREW, ROUND WASHER HEAD
10 - ARM ASM, SIGNAL SWITCH
11 - SWITCH ASM, TURN SIGNAL
12 - SEAT, UPPER BEARING INNER RACE
13 - RACE, INNER
14 - SCREW, PAN HEAD CROSS RECESS
15 - SWITCH ASM, BUZZER
16 - CLIP, BUZZER SWITCH RETAINING
17 - SCREW, LOCK RETAINING
18 - COVER, LOCK HOUSING
19 - LOCK CYLINDER SET, STEERING COLUMN
20 - ACTUATOR, DIMMER SWITCH ROD
21 - THIS NUMBER NOT USED
22 - BEARING ASM
23 - BOLT, LOCK
24 - SPRING, LOCK BOLT
25 - SHOE, STEERING WHEEL LOCK
26 - SHOE, STEERING WHEEL LOCK
27 - SHAFT, DRIVE
28 - PIN, DOWEL
29 - PIN, PIVOT
30 - SPRING, SHOE
31 - SPRING, RELEASE LEVER
32 - PIN, RELEASE LEVER
33 - LEVER, SHOE RELEASE
34 - BEARING ASM

35 - ACTUATOR ASM, IGNITION SWITCH
36 - RACK, SWITCH ACTUATOR
37 - SPRING, RACK PRELOAD
38 - HOUSING, STEERING COLUMN
39 - SECTOR, SWITCH ACTUATOR
40 - SCREW, HEX WASHER HEAD
41 - GUIDE, SPRING
42 - SPRING, WHEEL TILT
43 - RETAINER, SPRING
44 - CAP, COLUMN HOUSING COVER END
45 - PIN, SWITCH ACTUATOR PIVOT
46 - SWITCH ASM, PIVOT &
47 - SPRING, PIN PRELOAD
48 - HOUSING, IGN SWITCH INHIBITOR
49 - SCREW, WASHER HEAD
50 - SWITCH, IGNITION
51 - SWITCH, PIVOT & PULSE
52 - SCREW, OVAL HEAD CROSS RECESS
53 - PIN, DOWEL
54 - PROTECTOR, WIRING
55 - SHAFT ASM, RACE & UPPER
56 - SPHERE, CENTERING
57 - SPRING, JOINT PRELOAD
58 - SHAFT ASM, LOWER STEERING
59 - SCREW, SUPPORT
60 - SUPPORT, STEERING COLUMN HOUSING
61 - PLATE, LOCK
62 - SHROUD, STEERING COLUMN HOUSING
63 - ROD, DIMMER SWITCH
64 - SWITCH ASM, DIMMER
65 - NUT, HEXAGON
66 - JACKET ASM, STEERING COLUMN
67 - ADAPTER, LOWER BEARING
68 - BEARING ASM

69 - RETAINER, BEARING ADAPTER
70 - CLIP, LOWER BEARING ADAPTER

ASSEMBLIES

0 - COLUMN ASM, E/A STEERING
101 - COVER ASM, LOCK HOUSING
102 - HOUSING ASM, STEERING COLUMN
103 - SHAFT ASM, STEERING
104 - SUPPORT ASM, STEERING COLUMN HOUSING

Fig. 78 Exploded view of tilt steering column. 1988–89 Camaro & Firebird w/automatic transmission

5. Remove sphere from upper shaft, then the preload spring from sphere.
6. Remove attaching screws, then the housing support assembly and dimmer switch rod.
7. Remove key release lever and spring, if equipped, then the hex nut and hex head bolt.
8. Remove dimmer switch, mounting stud and gear shift lever bowl.
9. Reverse procedure to assemble noting the following:
   a. **Torque** housing support assembly screws to 77 inch lbs.
   b. Install lower shaft to upper shaft with block tooth on shaft end of upper shaft at 12 o'clock position and notch at end of lower shaft at 4 o'clock position.
   c. Lubricate shaft assembly with lithium grease.

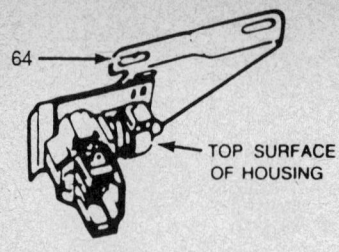

64 SWITCH, DIMMER

Fig. 79 Adjusting dimmer switch. Bonneville, Caprice, Custom Cruiser, Electra, Estate Wagon, LeSabre, Safari Wagon, 88 & 98 w/fixed steering column

1988 Cutlass Supreme, Grand Prix & Regal

FIXED COLUMN

Floor shift models equipped with automatic transmissions use an ignition switch inhibitor and park lock cable. On these models, the park lock cable must be disconnected from ignition switch inhibitor before steering column is removed from vehicle. When removal of steering column is necessary, proceed as follows:

1. Lower steering column to floor of vehicle.
2. Remove bowl shield screw, bowl shield nut and bowl shield.
3. Disconnect park lock cable from ignition switch inhibitor with small screwdriver or punch, **Fig. 80**.

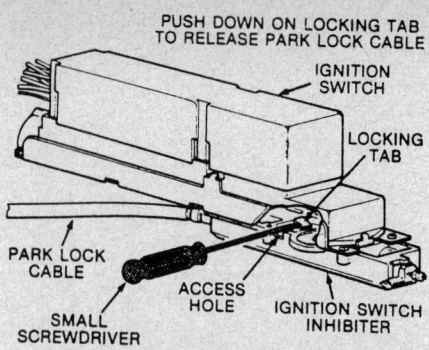

Fig. 80 Disconnecting park lock cable. 1988–90 Cutlass Supreme, Grand Prix & Regal & 1990 Lumina w/floor shift & automatic transmission

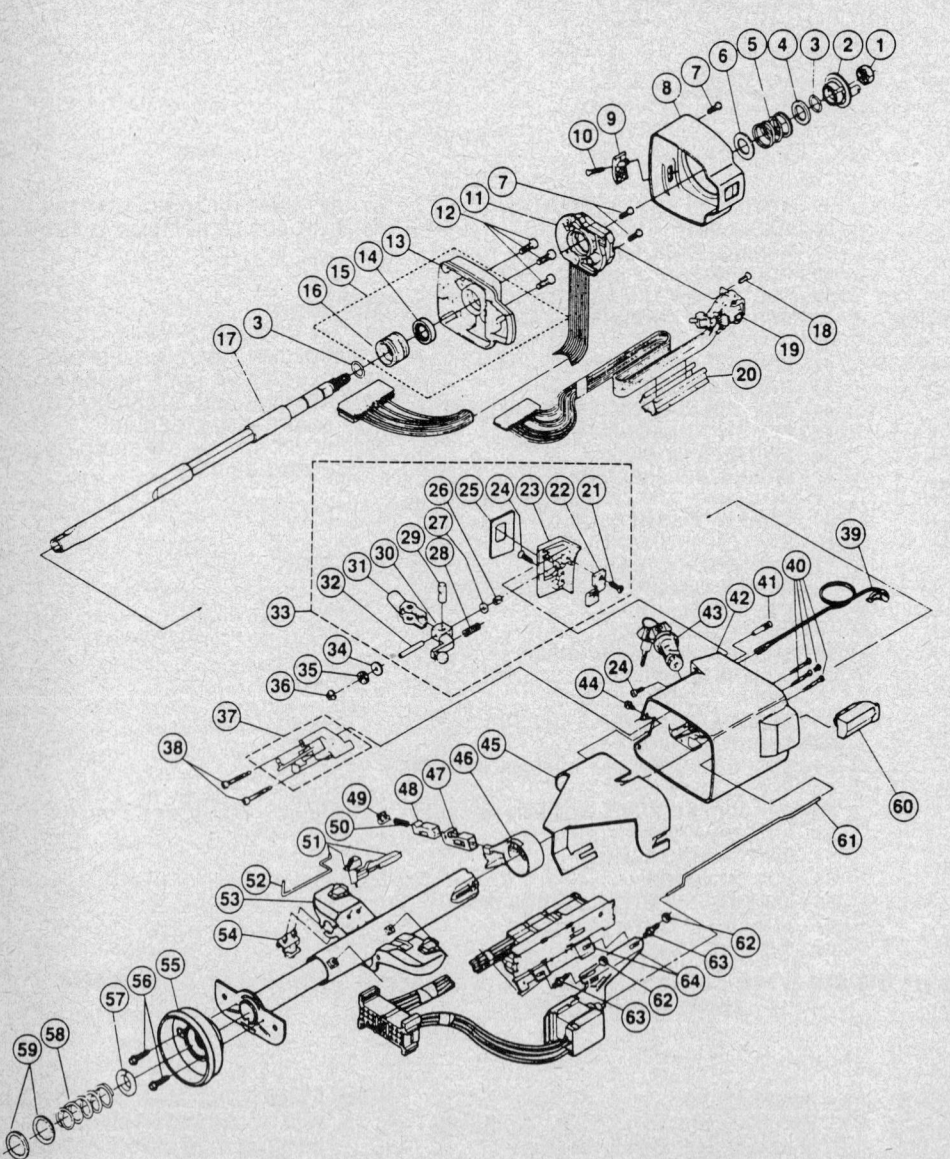

Key No.	Part No.
1	NUT, HEXAGON JAM (M14 x 1.5)
2	CAM ASM, SPACER & CANCELLING
3	RING, RETAINING
4	WASHER, THRUST
5	SPRING, UPPER BEARING
6	WASHER, THRUST
7	SCREW, PAN HD 6-LOBED SOC TAP
8	COVER, COLUMN HOUSING
9	KNOB, HAZARD WARNING
10	SCREW, OV HD C/REC (M3.5 x 1.27)
11	SWITCH, ASM, TURN SIGNAL
12	SCREW, PAN HD 6-LOBED SOC TAP
13	HOUSING, STEERING COLUMN
14	BEARING ASM
15	HOUSING ASM, STRG COLUMN
16	SPACER, STRG COLUMN HOUSING
17	SHAFT ASM, STEERING
18	SCR, OVL HD 6-LOBED SOC TAP
19	SWITCH ASM, PIVOT & PULSE
20	PROTECTOR, WIRING
21	SCREW, OVAL HD 6-LOBED SOC TAP
22	GATE, SHIFT LEVER
23	CAP, COLUMN BOWL
24	SCREW, OVAL HD 6-LOBED SOC TAP
25	SEAL, SHIFT LEVER
26	BUSHING, CAP ACTUATOR PIN
27	SPACER, SHIFT LEVER CLEVIS
28	SPRING, SHIFT LEVER
29	PIN, CABLE ARM ACTUATOR PIVOT
30	ACTUATOR ASM, CABLE LEVER
31	CLEVIS, SHIFT LEVER
32	PIN, SHIFT LEVER CLEVIS PIVOT
33	CAP ASM, SHIFT LEVER & BOWL
34	RACE, BRG ASM THRUST
35	BEARING ASM, NEEDLE THRUST
36	BUSHING, BOWL ACTUATOR PIN
37	ARM ASM, CABLE SHIFT
38	SCREW, OVAL HD 6-LOBED SOC TAP
39	SWITCH ASM, BUZZER
40	SCREW, PAN HEAD TAPPING
41	SCREW, LOCK RETAINING
42	BOWL, PAINTED
43	LOCK CYL SET, STRG COLUMN
44	SCREW, HEX WASHER HD TAPPING
45	SHIELD, BOWL
46	HOUSING, LOCK BOLT & SLEEVE
47	TUBE, LOCK BOLT RETAINING
48	BOLT, STRG SHAFT LOCK
49	CAP, LOCK BOLT SPRING RET
50	SPRING, LOCK BOLT
51	RACK, SWITCH ACTUATOR
52	ROD, IGNITION SWITCH
53	JACKET ASM, STRG COLUMN
54	ADJUSTER ASM, PRNDL
55	BEARING ASM, ADAPTER &
56	SCREW, HEX WASHER HD TAPPING
57	SEAT, LOWER BEARING
58	SPRING, LOWER BEARING
59	RETAINER, LOWER SPRING
60	CAP, DIMMER SWITCH ROD
61	ROD, DIMMER SW ACTUATOR
62	STUD DIMR & IGN SW MOUNTING
63	NUT, HEXAGON (#10-24)
64	SWITCH ASM, COLUMN LOCK & IGN

Fig. 81 Exploded view of fixed steering column. 1988 Cutlass Supreme, Grand Prix & Regal w/column shift

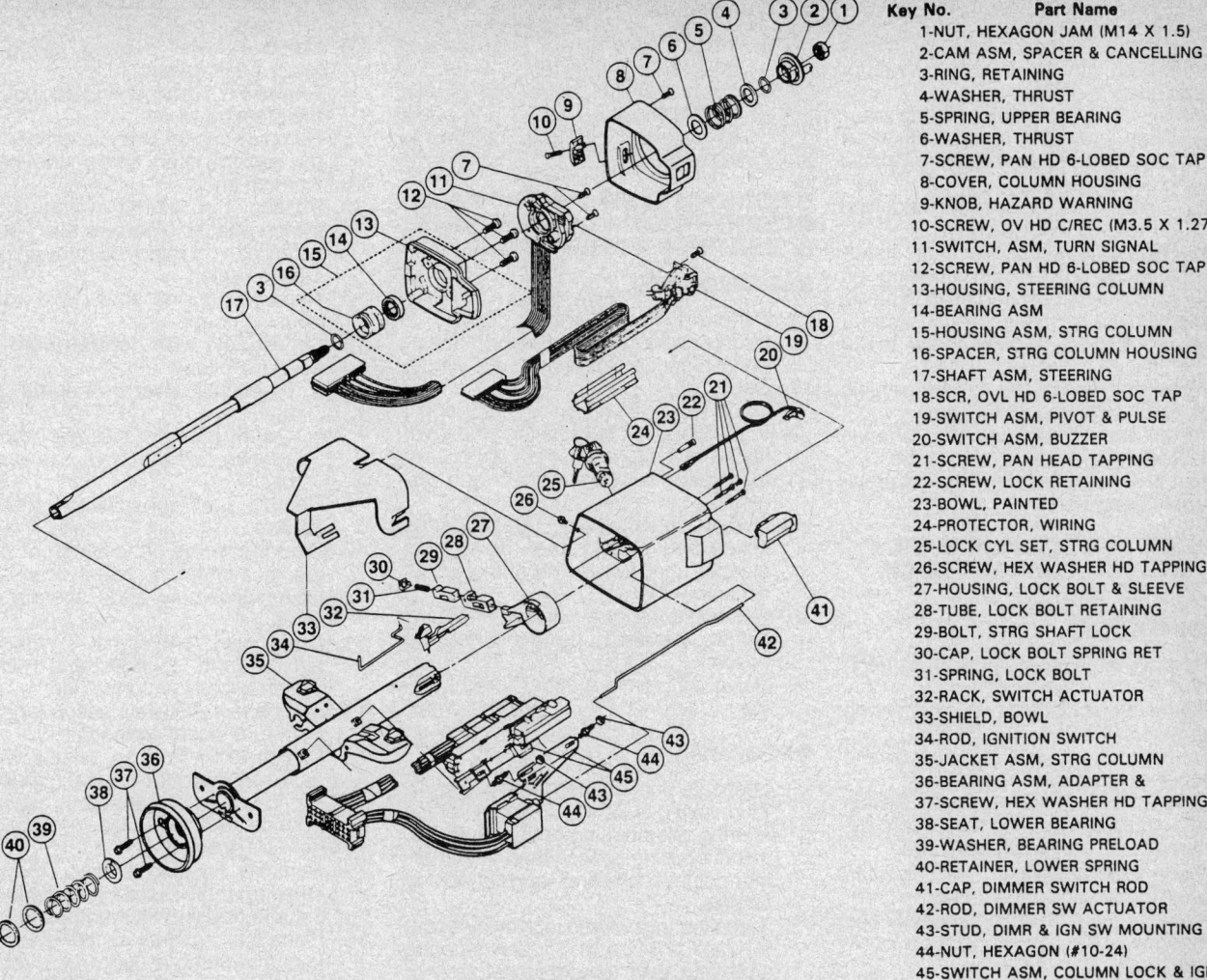

Key No.	Part Name
1	NUT, HEXAGON JAM (M14 X 1.5)
2	CAM ASM, SPACER & CANCELLING
3	RING, RETAINING
4	WASHER, THRUST
5	SPRING, UPPER BEARING
6	WASHER, THRUST
7	SCREW, PAN HD 6-LOBED SOC TAP
8	COVER, COLUMN HOUSING
9	KNOB, HAZARD WARNING
10	SCREW, OV HD C/REC (M3.5 X 1.27)
11	SWITCH, ASM, TURN SIGNAL
12	SCREW, PAN HD 6-LOBED SOC TAP
13	HOUSING, STEERING COLUMN
14	BEARING ASM
15	HOUSING ASM, STRG COLUMN
16	SPACER, STRG COLUMN HOUSING
17	SHAFT ASM, STEERING
18	SCR, OVL HD 6-LOBED SOC TAP
19	SWITCH ASM, PIVOT & PULSE
20	SWITCH ASM, BUZZER
21	SCREW, PAN HEAD TAPPING
22	SCREW, LOCK RETAINING
23	BOWL, PAINTED
24	PROTECTOR, WIRING
25	LOCK CYL SET, STRG COLUMN
26	SCREW, HEX WASHER HD TAPPING
27	HOUSING, LOCK BOLT & SLEEVE
28	TUBE, LOCK BOLT RETAINING
29	BOLT, STRG SHAFT LOCK
30	CAP, LOCK BOLT SPRING RET
31	SPRING, LOCK BOLT
32	RACK, SWITCH ACTUATOR
33	SHIELD, BOWL
34	ROD, IGNITION SWITCH
35	JACKET ASM, STRG COLUMN
36	BEARING ASM, ADAPTER &
37	SCREW, HEX WASHER HD TAPPING
38	SEAT, LOWER BEARING
39	WASHER, BEARING PRELOAD
40	RETAINER, LOWER SPRING
41	CAP, DIMMER SWITCH ROD
42	ROD, DIMMER SW ACTUATOR
43	STUD, DIMR & IGN SW MOUNTING
44	NUT, HEXAGON (#10-24)
45	SWITCH ASM, COLUMN LOCK & IGN

Fig. 82 Exploded view of fixed steering column. 1988 Cutlass Supreme, Grand Prix & Regal w/floor shift

COLUMN BOWL CAP & SHIFT LEVER GATE

Disassembly

1. Place shift lever in "neutral" position.
2. Remove bowl cap screws and the bowl cap assembly, **Figs. 81 and 82.**
3. Remove gate screw and shift lever gate.

Assembly

1. Install shift lever gate and gate screw. Apply loctite No. 242 or equivalent to screw threads and **torque** to 35 inch lbs.
2. Install bowl cap assembly. Position cable arm assembly so that plastic ball on end of actuator assembly can be inserted into its mating slot, move arm counterclockwise and slide extending clevis pivot pin into bowl actuator pin bushing.
3. Install bowl cap screws, torquing to 27 inch lbs.

TURN SIGNAL CANCEL CAM ASSEMBLY

Disassembly

1. Remove nut retainer and jam nut, then the steering wheel.
2. Remove turn signal cancel cam assembly.

Assembly

1. Lubricate bottom of turn signal cancel cam assembly with lithium grease and install assembly.
2. Install steering wheel.
3. Install jam nut, **torque** to 30 ft. lbs. and secure with nut retainer.

PIVOT & PULSE SWITCH ASSEMBLY & TURN SIGNAL SWITCH ASSEMBLY

Disassembly

1. Remove turn signal cancel cam assembly as previously described.
2. Remove hazard knob screw, then the hazard warning knob.
3. Remove housing screw, then the column housing cover.

4. Position turn signal switch so that attaching screws can be removed through openings, then remove housing screw and the column housing cover.
5. Remove pivot switch screw, then the pivot and pulse switch assembly.
6. Remove turn signal switch attaching screws.
7. Remove wiring protector from opening in instrument panel bracket on jacket assembly and separate from wires, then disconnect turn signal switch connector from ignition and dimmer switch assembly connector.
8. Remove 17 way secondary lock from turn signal connector, then disconnect wires on buzzer switch assembly from turn signal connector, **Fig. 63.**
9. Remove turn signal switch assembly from column.

Assembly

1. Install turn signal switch assembly and attaching screws, torquing to 35 inch lbs.
2. Attach wires from buzzer switch assembly to turn signal switch connector, then attach 17 way secondary

lock to turn signal connector and snap in place.

3. Connect turn signal connector to ignition and dimmer switch connector and snap in place.

4. Install wiring protector as follows:
   a. Wrap protector around all wires passing through instrument panel bracket opening.
   b. Close protector so that interlocking grooves engage.
   c. Slide wiring protector into instrument panel bracket opening on jacket assembly and snap in place.

5. Install pivot and pulse switch assembly, torquing attaching screw to 20 inch lbs.

6. Install column housing cover, torquing housing screw to 35 inch lbs.

7. Install hazard warning knob, torquing hazard knob screw to 7 inch lbs.

8. Install cancel cam assembly as previously described.

BUZZER SWITCH ASSEMBLY & STEERING COLUMN LOCK CYLINDER SET

Disassembly

1. Remove steering column from vehicle.

2. Remove and discard two lower spring retainers.

3. Remove lower bearing spring and lower bearing seat.

4. Disassemble "Pivot & Pulse Switch Assembly & Turn Signal Switch Assembly" as previously described.

5. Place lock cylinder in "run" position and remove housing screws.

6. Remove steering shaft assembly and steering column housing as a complete unit.

7. Place lock cylinder in "off-lock" position and remove key.

8. Remove buzzer switch by lifting switch tab with screwdriver and pulling gently on wires.

9. Remove lock retaining screw and lock cylinder.

Assembly

1. Install steering column lock cylinder set in "off-lock" position with key removed, torquing lock retaining screw to 22 inch lbs.

2. Install buzzer switch assembly, pushing switch down into retaining bore until bottomed, with plastic tab covering lock retaining screw.

3. Insert key and place lock cylinder in "run" position.

4. Install steering shaft and steering column housing as a unit, torquing housing screws to 88 inch lbs.

5. Assemble "Pivot & Pulse Switch Assembly & Turn Signal Switch Assembly" as previously described.

6. Install lower bearing seat and lower bearing spring.

7. Install two new lower spring retainers, compressing spring until retainers are positioned 1.14 inch (29 mm) from lower end of steering shaft.

8. On floor shift models equipped with an ignition switch inhibitor and park lock cable proceed as follows:

   a. Install bowl shield to column bowl and upper mounting stud.
   b. Install shield screw and nut and torque to 35 inch lbs.
   c. Install park lock cable into ignition switch inhibitor and snap in place as steering column is installed in vehicle.

STEERING SHAFT ASSEMBLY, STEERING COLUMN HOUSING & BEARING ASSEMBLIES

Disassembly

1. Perform "Disassembly" steps 1 through 4 for "Buzzer Switch Assembly & Steering Column Lock Cylinder Set."

2. Place lock cylinder in "run" position.

3. Place opening in retaining ring over flat on steering shaft, then pry out retaining ring with screwdriver and discard.

4. Remove thrust washer, upper bearing spring and washer, then disconnect steering shaft from lower end of jacket assembly.

5. Remove turn signal housing attaching screws, then the housing and housing spacer.

6. Using drift, remove and discard bearing.

Assembly

1. Lubricate bearing with lithium grease, then, using 1½ inch socket, press bearing into housing until bottomed.

2. Install housing spacer, then the steering column housing and attaching screws.

3. Turn steering column lock cylinder set to "run" position and insert steering shaft into lower end of jacket assembly until shaft rests against bearing. **When installed properly, the shaft will extend 2.5 inches beyond highest surface of steering column.**

4. Install thrust washer, upper bearing spring and thrust washer.

5. Wrap a two inch wide piece of .005 inch (.127 mm) shim stock around shaft and slip a new retaining ring up to thrust washer, then, using two long handled screwdrivers, push on retaining ring until it seats in retainer ring groove in shaft.

6. Install adapter and lower bearing assembly, torquing adapter screws to 30 inch lbs.

7. Install lower bearing seat and lower bearing spring.

8. Install two new lower spring retainers, compressing springs until retainers are positioned 1.14 inch (29 mm) from lower end of steering shaft.

9. Perform "Assembly" steps for "Pivot & Pulse Switch Assembly & Turn Signal Switch Assembly."

CABLE SHIFT ARM ASSEMBLY, SWITCH ACTUATOR RACK & STEERING SHAFT LOCK BOLT

Disassembly

1. Remove steering column from vehicle.

2. Remove and discard two lower spring retainers.

3. Remove lower bearing spring and lower bearing seat.

4. Remove nut retainer and jam nut, then the steering wheel.

5. Remove cancel cam assembly, then the hazard knob screw and hazard warning knob.

6. Position turn signal switch so that switch attaching screws and housing screw can be removed through openings in switch.

7. Remove housing screw and column housing cover.

8. **On models with column shift,** proceed as follows:
   a. Place shift lever in "neutral" position.
   b. **On all models,** remove bowl cap screws and the bowl cap assembly.

9. Remove turn signal switch attaching screws.

10. Remove wiring protector from opening in instrument panel bracket on jacket assembly and separate from wires.

11. Disconnect turn signal switch connector from ignition and dimmer switch assembly connector.

12. Disconnect 17 way secondary lock from turn signal connector.

13. Disconnect wires on buzzer switch assembly from turn signal connector.

14. Remove turn signal switch assembly from column, then place lock cylinder in "run" position.

15. Remove housing screws, then the steering shaft assembly and steering column housing as a complete unit.

16. Place lock cylinder in "off-lock" position and remove key, then remove buzzer switch by lifting switch tab with screwdriver and pulling gently on wires.

17. Remove lock retaining screw and lock cylinder, then the bowl shield screw, bowl shield nut and bowl shield.

18. Remove dimmer switch nut and upper mounting stud, then the dimmer switch.

19. Remove dimmer switch actuator rod and dimmer switch rod cap, then the lower mounting stud and dimmer and ignition switch assembly.

20. Remove column bowl screws, then the steering column bowl from steering column jacket assembly.

21. **On models with column shift,** remove shift arm screws, then the cable shift arm assembly from column bowl.

22. **On all models,** remove switch actuator rack and steering shaft lock bolt assembly from sleeve housing as follows:
    a. Move actuator rack down while manually retracting lock bolt and retainer tube.
    b. Raise sleeve housing and remove actuator rack.
    c. Remove lock bolt assembly.

23. Remove sleeve housing from jacket assembly.

Assembly

1. Install sleeve housing onto jacket assembly.

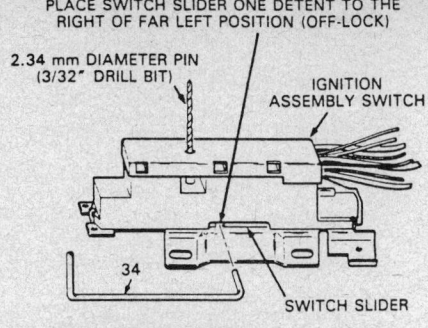

PLACE SWITCH SLIDER ONE DETENT TO THE RIGHT OF FAR LEFT POSITION (OFF-LOCK)

2.34 mm DIAMETER PIN (3/32" DRILL BIT)

IGNITION ASSEMBLY SWITCH

34

SWITCH SLIDER

34-ROD, IGNITION SWITCH

Fig. 83 Installing ignition switch & actuator

2. Lubricate steering shaft lock bolt with lithium grease and assemble as follows:
   a. Install lock bolt into retainer tube.
   b. Install spring into lock bolt.
   c. Install spring retainer cap into retainer tube and snap in place.
3. Install lock bolt assembly into sleeve housing.
4. Lubricate gear teeth on switch actuator rack with lithium grease and install ignition switch rod to actuator rack.
5. Install switch actuator rack into lock bolt assembly as follows:
   a. Raise sleeve housing while manually retracting lock bolt and retainer tube.
   b. Insert actuator rack through opening in lock bolt until it contacts bottom edge of sleeve housing.
6. **On models with column shift,** install cable shift arm assembly to column bowl, torquing shift arm screws to 27 inch lbs.
7. **On all models,** install steering column bowl to column jacket assembly, apply Loctite No. 242 or equivalent to column bowl screws and **torque** to 47 inch lbs.
8. Install steering column lock cylinder set as follows:
   a. Hold barrel of lock cylinder, insert key and turn counterclockwise to "accessory" position.
   b. Install lock set into lock opening in steering column bowl while holding rack against bottom of sleeve housing.
9. Install lock retaining screw, torquing to 27 inch lbs., then turn lock cylinder to "start" position and ensure rack extends and steering shaft lock bolt extends and retracts as lock is turned from start to lock.
10. Place lock cylinder set in "off-lock" position.
11. Place ignition switch slider in far left position and move back one detent to right, then insert 3/32 inch drill bit in adjustment hole on ignition switch to hold switch slider in proper position during installation, **Fig. 83.**
12. Install ignition switch to ignition rod, then the ignition switch to steering column jacket assembly with lower mounting stud, torquing to 35 inch lbs.

13. Remove adjustment tool from ignition switch.
14. Lubricate dimmer switch rod cap with lithium grease and install cap into column bowl.
15. Install dimmer switch actuator rod through hole in instrument panel bracket and into hole in dimmer switch rod cap, then the dimmer switch onto actuator rod.
16. Install dimmer switch assembly on lower mounting stud with dimmer switch nut and upper mounting stud, but do not tighten.
17. Adjust dimmer switch by inserting 3/32 inch drill bit and pushing dimmer switch against actuator rod to remove all lash, **Fig. 84.**
18. Torque dimmer switch nut and upper mounting stud to 35 inch lbs., then remove adjusting tool.
19. Install bowl shield to column bowl and upper mounting stud, torquing shield screw and bowl shield nut to 35 inch lbs.
20. **On models with column shift,** install shift lever and bowl cap assembly as follows:
    a. Position cable arm assembly so that plastic ball on end of actuator assembly can be inserted into its mating slot.
    b. Move arm counterclockwise and slide extending cable arm actuator pivot pin into cap actuator pin bushing.
    c. Install bowl cap screws, torquing to 27 inch lbs.
21. **On all models,** install buzzer switch assembly as follows:
    a. Place lock cylinder in "off-lock" position and remove key.
    b. Push switch down into its retaining bore until bottomed, with plastic tab covering lock retaining screw.
22. Insert key and place lock cylinder in "run" position, then install steering shaft and steering column housing as an assembly, torquing housing screws to 88 inch lbs.
23. Install turn signal switch assembly, torquing screws to 35 inch lbs.
24. Connect wires from buzzer switch assembly to turn signal switch connector.
25. Connect 17 way secondary lock to turn signal connector and snap in place, then connect turn signal connector to ignition and dimmer switch connector and snap in place.
26. Install wiring protector as follows:
    a. Wrap protector around all wires passing through instrument panel bracket opening.
    b. Close protector so that interlocking grooves engage.
    c. Slide wiring protector into instrument panel bracket opening on jacket assembly and snap in place.
27. Install column housing cover, torquing attaching screw to 35 inch lbs.
28. Install hazard warning knob, torquing attaching screw to 7 inch lbs.
29. Install turn signal cancel cam, then the steering wheel.
30. Install jam nut, torquing to 30 ft. lbs., and secure with nut retainer.

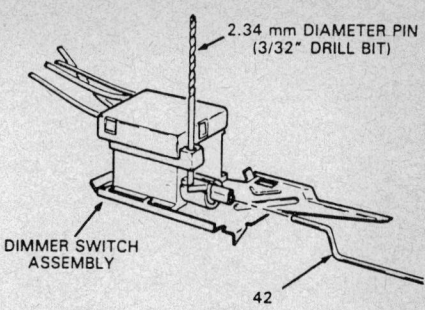

2.34 mm DIAMETER PIN (3/32" DRILL BIT)

DIMMER SWITCH ASSEMBLY

42

42-ROD, DIMMER SW ACTUATOR

Fig. 84 Adjusting dimmer switch. 1988–90 Cutlass Supreme, Grand Prix & Regal & 1990 Lumina

31. Install lower bearing seat and lower bearing spring, then two new lower spring retainers, compressing spring until retainers are positioned 1.14 inch (29 mm) from lower end of steering shaft.
32. **On models with floor shift and automatic transmission,** install park lock cable into ignition switch inhibitor and snap in place as steering column is installed in vehicle.

IGNITION & DIMMER SWITCH ASSEMBLY

Disassembly

1. Place shift lever in "Park" position on models with column shift, then, on all models, place lock cylinder in "off-lock" position, then remove steering column from vehicle.
2. Disconnect turn signal switch connector from ignition and dimmer switch assembly connector.
3. Remove bowl shield retaining screw and nut, then the shield.
4. Remove dimmer switch nut and upper mounting stud, then the dimmer switch.
5. Remove dimmer switch actuator rod.
6. Remove lower mounting stud, then the ignition switch from ignition switch actuator rod.

Assembly

Lock cylinder set must be in "off-lock" position when installing ignition switch to insure proper switch slider positioning.

1. Place ignition switch slider in far left position and move back one detent to right into "off-lock" position, then insert a 3/32 inch drill bit in adjustment hole on ignition switch to hold switch slider in proper position during installation, **Fig. 83.**
2. Install ignition switch to switch rod.
3. Install ignition switch to steering column jacket assembly with lower mounting stud, torquing to 35 inch lbs.
4. Remove adjustment tool from ignition switch, then install dimmer switch actuator rod through hole in instrument panel bracket and into hole in dimmer switch rod cap.
5. Install dimmer switch assembly on lower mounting stud with dimmer

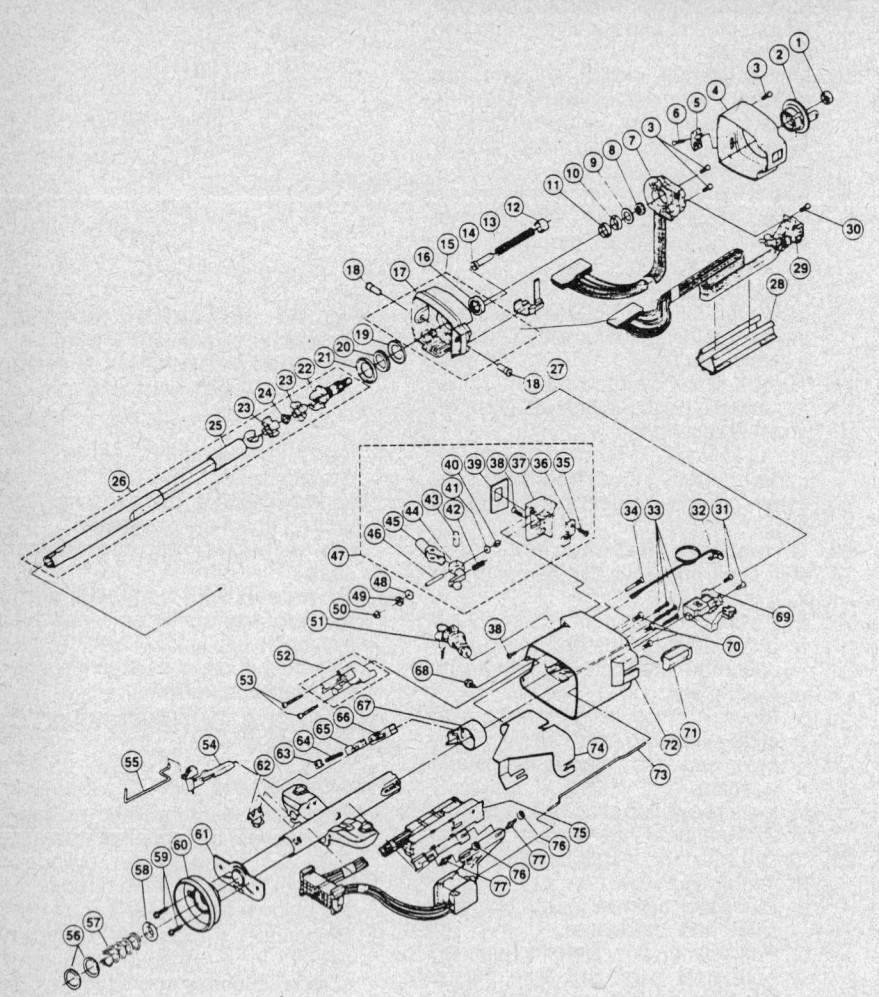

Key No.	Part Name
1	NUT, HEXAGON JAM (M14X1.5)
2	CAM ASM, SPACER & CANCELLING
3	SCREW, PAN HD 6-LOBED SOC TAP
4	COVER, COLUMN HOUSING
5	KNOB, HAZARD WARNING
6	SCREW, OV HD C/REC (M3.5X1.27)
7	SWITCH ASM, TURN SIGNAL
8	NUT, UPPER SHAFT BRG LOCK
9	WASHER, FLAT
10	SEAT, INNER RACE
11	RACE, INNER
12	RETAINER, SPRING
13	SPRING, WHEEL TILT
14	GUIDE, TILT SPRING
15	HOUSING ASM, STRG COLUMN
16	BEARING ASM
17	HOUSING, STRG COLUMN
18	PIN, PIVOT
19	WASHER, THRUST
20	BEARING ASM, NEEDLE THRUST
21	RACE, THRUST BEARING ASM
22	SHAFT, UPPER STEERING
23	SPHERE, CENTERING
24	SPRING, JOINT PRELOAD
25	SHAFT ASM, LOWER STRG
26	SHAFT ASM, STEERING
27	CAP, HSG SHOE PIN RETAINER
28	PROTECTOR, WIRING
29	SWITCH ASM, PIVOT & PULSE
30	SCR, OVL HD 6-LOBED SOC TAP
31	SCR, OVL HD 6-LOBED SOC TAP
32	BUZZER SWITCH ASM
33	SCREW, PAN HEAD TAPPING
34	SCREW, LOCK RETAINING
35	SCREW, OVAL HD 6-LOBED SOC TAP
36	GATE, SHIFT LEVER
37	CAP, COLUMN BOWL
38	SCREW, OVAL HD 6-LOBED SOC TAP
39	SEAL, SHIFT LEVER
40	BUSHING, CAP ACTUATOR PIN
41	SPACER, SHIFT LEVER CLEVIS
42	SPRING, SHIFT LEVER
43	PIN, CABLE ARM ACTUATOR PIVOT
44	ACTUATOR ASM, CABLE LEVER
45	CLEVIS, SHIFT LEVER
46	PIN, SHIFT LEVER CLEVIS PIVOT
47	CAP ASM, SHIFT LEVER & BOWL
48	RACE, BRG ASM THRUST
49	BEARING ASM, NEEDLE THRUST
50	BUSHING, BOWL ACTUATOR PIN
51	LOCK CYL SET, STRG COLUMN
52	ARM ASM, CABLE SHIFT
53	SCREW, OVAL HD 6-LOBED SOC TAP
54	RACK, SWITCH ACTUATOR
55	ROD, IGNITION SWITCH
56	RETAINER, LOWER SPRING
57	SPRING, LOWER BEARING
58	SEAT, LOWER BEARING
59	SCREW, HEX WASHER HD TAPPING
60	BEARING ASM, ADAPTER &
61	JACKET ASM, STRG COLUMN
62	ADJUSTER ASM, PRNDL
63	CAP, LOCK BOLT SPRING RET
64	SPRING, LOCK BOLT
65	BOLT, STRG SHAFT LOCK
66	TUBE, LOCK BOLT RETAINER
67	HOUSING, LOCK BOLT & SLEEVE
68	SCREW, HEX WASHER HD TAPPING
69	BRACKET ASM, TILT LEVER &
70	BUMPER, COLUMN TILT
71	CAP, DIMMER SWITCH ROD
72	BOWL, STRG COLUMN (PAINTED)
73	ROD, DIMMER SW ACTUATOR
74	SHIELD, BOWL
75	SWITCH ASM, IGNITION
76	NUT, HEXAGON (#10-24)
77	STUD, DIMR & IGN SW MOUNTING

Fig. 85 Exploded view of tilt steering column. 1988 Cutlass Supreme, Grand Prix & Regal w/column shift

switch nut and upper mounting stud, but do not tighten.

6. Adjust dimmer switch by inserting a 3/32 inch drill bit and pushing switch against actuator rod to remove all lash, **Fig. 84**, then **torque** dimmer switch nut and upper mounting stud to 35 inch lbs.

7. Remove adjustment tool from dimmer switch, then install bowl shield to column bowl and upper mounting stud, torquing attaching screw and nut to 35 inch lbs.

8. Connect turn signal switch connector to ignition and dimmer switch assembly connector and snap into place.

9. **On models with floor shift and automatic transmission,** install park lock cable into ignition switch inhibitor and snap in place as steering column is installed in vehicle.

TILT COLUMN

Floor shift models equipped with automatic transmissions use an ignition switch inhibitor and park lock cable. On these models, the park lock cable must be disconnected from ignition switch inhibitor before steering column is removed from vehicle. When removal of steering column is necessary, proceed as follows:

1. Lower steering column to floor of vehicle.
2. Remove bowl shield screw, bowl shield nut and bowl shield.
3. Disconnect park lock cable from ignition switch inhibitor with small screwdriver or punch, **Fig. 80.**

COLUMN BOWL CAP & SHIFT LEVER GATE
Disassembly

1. Place column in "0" tilt position and the shift lever in "Neutral position.
2. Remove bowl cap screws and the bowl cap assembly, **Figs. 85 and 86.**
3. Remove gate screw and the shift lever gate.

Assembly

1. Install shift lever gate, then apply Loctite No. 242 or equivalent to threads of gate screw and **torque** to 35 inch lbs.
2. Install bowl cap assembly. Position cable arm assembly so that plastic ball on end of actuator can be inserted into its mating slot, then move arm counterclockwise and slide the extending clevis pivot pin into bowl actuator pin bushing.
3. Torque bowl cap screws to 27 inch lbs.

TURN SIGNAL CANCEL CAM ASSEMBLY
Disassembly

1. Remove nut retainer and jam nut.
2. Remove steering wheel.
3. Remove turn signal cancel cam assembly.

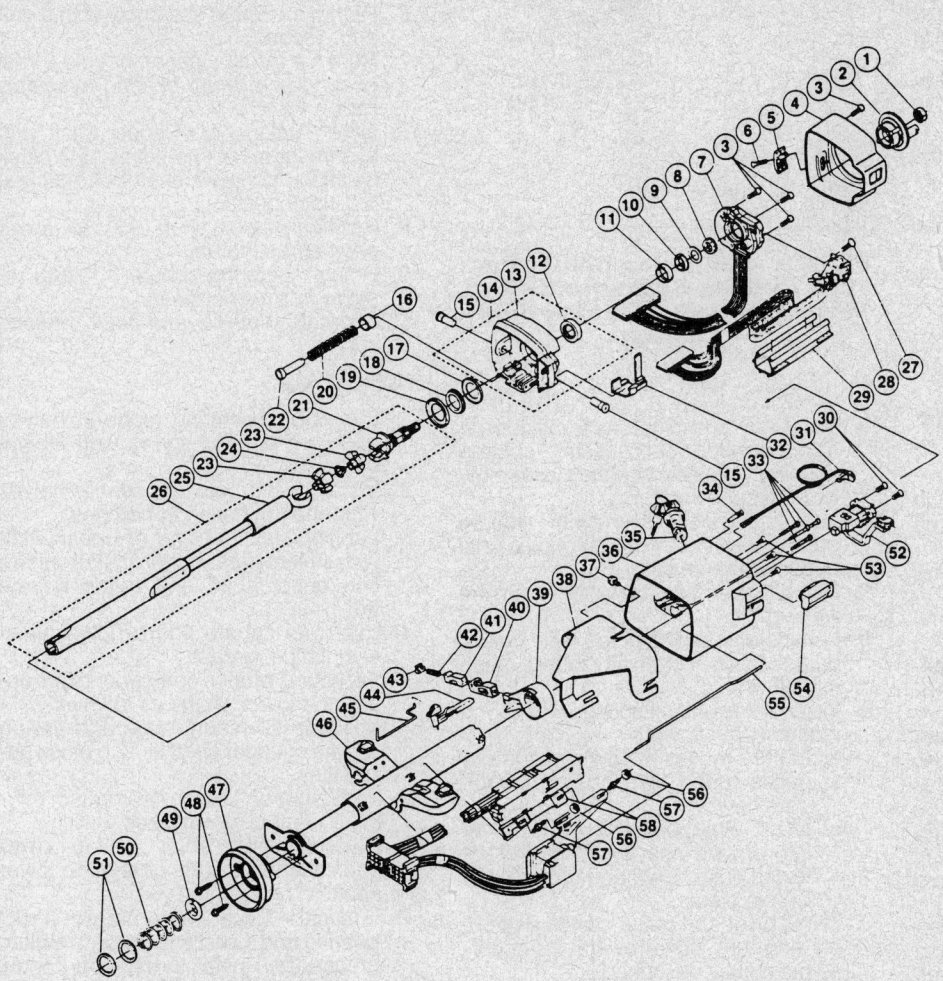

Key No.	Part Name
1	NUT, HEXAGON JAM (M14X1.5)
2	CAM ASM, SPACER & CANCELLING
3	SCREW, PAN HD 6-LOBED SOC TAP
4	COVER, COLUMN HOUSING
5	KNOB, HAZARD WARNING
6	SCREW, OV HD C/REC (M3.5X1.27)
7	SWITCH ASM, TURN SIGNAL
8	NUT, UPPER SHAFT BRG LOCK
9	WASHER, FLAT
10	SEAT, INNER RACE
11	RACE, INNER
12	BEARING ASM
13	HOUSING, STRG COLUMN
14	HOUSING ASM, STRG COLUMN
15	PIN, PIVOT
16	RETAINER, SPRING
17	WASHER, THRUST
18	BEARING ASM, NEEDLE THRUST
19	RACE, THRUST BEARING ASM
20	SPRING, WHEEL TILT
21	SHAFT, UPPER STEERING
22	GUIDE, TILT SPRING
23	SPHERE, CENTERING
24	SPRING, JOINT PRELOAD
25	SHAFT ASM, LOWER STRG
26	SHAFT ASM, STEERING
27	SCR, OVL HD 6-LOBED SOC TAP
28	SWITCH ASM, PIVOT & PULSE
29	PROTECTOR, WIRING
30	SCR, OVL HD 6-LOBED SOC TAP
31	SWITCH ASM, BUZZER
32	CAP, HSG SHOE PIN RETAINER
33	SCREW, PAN HEAD TAPPING
34	SCREW, LOCK RETAINING
35	LOCK CYL SET, STRG COLUMN
36	BOWL, STRG COLUMN
37	SCREW, HEX WASHER HD TAPPING
38	SHIELD, BOWL
39	HOUSING, LOCK BOLT & SLEEVE
40	TUBE, LOCK BOLT RETAINER
41	BOLT, STRG SHAFT LOCK
42	SPRING, LOCK BOLT
43	CAP, LOCK BOLT SPRING RET
44	RACK, SWITCH ACTUATOR
45	ROD, IGNITION SWITCH
46	JACKET ASM, STRG COLUMN
47	BEARING ASM, ADAPTER &
48	SCREW, HEX WASHER HD TAPPING
49	SEAT, LOWER BEARING
50	SPRING, LOWER BEARING
51	RETAINER, LOWER SPRING
52	BRACKET ASM, TILT LEVER &
53	BUMPER, COLUMN TILT
54	CAP, DIMMER SWITCH ROD
55	ROD, DIMMER SW ACTUATOR
56	NUT, HEXAGON (#10-24)
57	STUD, DIMR & IGN SW MOUNTING
58	SWITCH ASM, IGNITION

Fig. 86   Exploded view of tilt steering column. 1988 Cutlass Supreme, Grand Prix & Regal w/floor shift

Assembly

1. Lubricate bottom side of cancel cam with lithium grease and install turn signal cancel cam assembly.
2. Install steering wheel.
3. Install jam nut, torquing to 30 ft. lbs., and secure with nut retainer.

PIVOT & PULSE SWITCH ASSEMBLY & TURN SIGNAL SWITCH ASSEMBLY

Disassembly

1. Remove turn signal cancel cam assembly as previously described.
2. Remove hazard knob screw and the hazard warning knob.
3. Position turn signal switch so that turn signal switch screws and housing screw can be removed through openings in switch.
4. Remove housing screw and column housing cover, then he shoe pin retainer cap, pivot switch screw and the pivot and pulse switch assembly.
5. Remove turn signal switch attaching screws.
6. Remove wiring protector from opening in instrument panel bracket on jacket assembly and separate from wires.
7. Disconnect turn signal switch connector from ignition and dimmer switch assembly connector and the 17 way secondary lock from turn signal connector.
8. Disconnect wires on buzzer switch assembly from turn signal connector, **Fig. 63.**
9. Remove turn signal switch assembly from column.

Assembly

1. Install turn signal switch, positioning switch so that turn signal switch screws and housing screw can be installed through openings in switch.
2. Install turn signal switch attaching screws torquing to 35 inch lbs.
3. Connect wires from buzzer switch assembly to turn signal switch assembly.
4. Connect 17 way secondary lock to turn signal connector, then the turn signal switch connector to ignition and dimmer switch connector, and snap in place.
5. Install wiring protector as follows:
   a. Wrap protector around all wires

passing through instrument panel bracket opening.

b. Close protector so that interlocking grooves engage.

c. Slide wire protector into instrument panel bracket opening on jacket assembly and snap into place.

6. Install pivot and pulse switch assembly, torquing pivot switch screw to to 20 inch lbs.

7. Install shoe pin retainer cap, then the column housing cover, torquing housing screw to 35 inch lbs.

8. Install housing warning knob, torquing hazard knob screw to 7 inch lbs.

9. Install turn signal cancel cam assembly as previously described.

WHEEL TILT SPRING, TILT LEVER & BRACKET ASSEMBLY, BUZZER SWITCH ASSEMBLY, STEERING COLUMN LOCK CYLINDER SET & COLUMN TILT BUMPERS

Disassembly

1. Pull tilt lever and tilt column all the way up, then remove steering column from vehicle.

2. Remove and discard two lower spring retainers.

3. Remove lower bearing spring and lower bearing seat.

4. Remove pivot and pulse switch assembly and turn signal switch assembly as previously described.

5. Insert Phillips head screwdriver into square opening in spring retainer, push down and turn left to release retainer and wheel tilt spring.

6. Remove spring retainer, tilt spring and tilt spring guide.

7. Using pivot pin remover tool, remove two pivot pins, **Fig. 87.**

8. Place lock cylinder in "run" position and pull tilt lever to release steering column housing, then remove column housing and steering shaft assembly from steering column housing as a complete unit.

9. Place lock cylinder in "off-lock" position and remove key, then remove buzzer switch, using screwdriver to lift switch tab, and pull gently on wires.

10. Remove lock retaining screw and the lock cylinder.

11. Using suitable tool, remove column tilt bumpers. If bumper is broken off, use a 7/32 inch drill bit to remove remaining piece of bumper.

12. Remove tilt bracket screws and the tilt lever and bracket assembly.

Assembly

1. Lubricate tilt bracket with lithium grease, then install tilt lever and bracket assembly into column bowl, torquing tilt bracket screws to 32 inch lbs.

2. Install three tilt bumpers into column bowl until bottomed.

3. Install steering column lock cylinder set in "off-lock" position with key removed, torquing lock retaining screw to 22 inch lbs.

4. Install buzzer switch assembly, pushing switch down into retaining bore until bottomed, with plastic tab covering lock retaining screw.

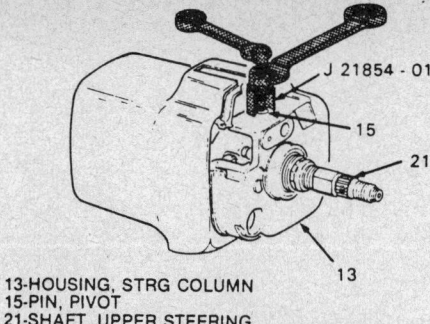

13-HOUSING, STRG COLUMN
15-PIN, PIVOT
21-SHAFT, UPPER STEERING

Fig. 87 Removing pivot pins. 1988 Cutlass Supreme, Grand Prix & Regal w/tilt steering column

5. Insert key and place lock cylinder in "run" position, then install column housing and steering shaft assembly as a complete unit.

6. Lubricate pivot pins with lithium grease, then install two pivot pins until bottomed in housing.

7. Pull tilt lever and tilt column all the way up.

8. Lubricate tilt spring guide with lithium grease, then install tilt spring guide into tilt spring.

9. Install guide and tilt spring, with spring retainer, as follows:

a. Ensure recess in spring guide engages round locating tab in column bowl.

b. Insert Phillips head screwdriver into square opening in spring retainer, push down and turn right to lock in place.

10. Install pivot and pulse switch assembly and turn signal switch assembly as previously described.

11. Install lower bearing seat and lower bearing spring.

12. Install two lower spring retainers, compressing spring until retainers are positioned 1.14 inch (29 mm) from lower end of steering shaft.

13. **On models with floor shift and automatic transmission,** proceed as follows:

a. Install bowl shield to column bowl and upper mounting stud.

b. Install bowl shield screw and bowl shield nut, torquing to 35 inch lbs.

c. Insert park lock cable into ignition switch inhibitor and snap in place as steering column is installed in vehicle.

STEERING SHAFT ASSEMBLY, STEERING COLUMN, HOUSING, CENTERING SPHERE & BEARING ASSEMBLIES

Disassembly

1. Perform "Removal" steps 1 through 8 for "Wheel Tilt Spring, Tilt Lever & Bracket Assembly, Buzzer Switch Assembly, Steering column Lock Cylinder Set & Column Tilt Bumpers."

2. Place column housing in a holding fixture.

3. Remove upper shaft bearing lock nut.

4. Remove flat washer, upper bearing inner race seat and the inner race.

5. Remove column housing.

6. Remove bearing assembly with a drift and discard.

7. Remove thrust washer, needle thrust bearing and thrust bearing assembly race.

8. Note relationship of upper shaft with alignment mark and flat at 12 o'clock position and lower shaft bolt notch at 4 o'clock position.

9. Position upper shaft 90° to lower shaft and separate.

10. Rotate centering sphere 90° and remove from upper shaft.

11. Separate sphere and joint preload spring.

Assembly

1. Lubricate centering sphere halves and joint preload spring with lithium grease.

2. Install spring between sphere halves with ends of spring in notches.

3. Lubricate sphere end of upper shaft with lithium grease, then install sphere into upper shaft and rotate sphere 90°.

4. Lubricate sphere end of lower shaft with lithium grease.

5. To insure proper operation, align upper and lower shafts as follows:

a. Place alignment mark and flat on end of upper shaft at 12 o'clock position.

b. Ensure bolt notch near end of lower shaft is at 4 o'clock position.

6. Position upper shaft 90° to lower shaft, then install upper shaft to lower shaft and straighten.

7. Lubricate thrust race, needle thrust bearing and thrust washer with lithium grease, then install thrust race, needle thrust bearing and thrust washer.

8. Lubricate bearing with lithium grease, then press bearing into column housing, using 1 1/2 inch socket, until bottomed.

9. Install column housing to upper shaft, then install inner race, inner race seat and flat washer.

10. Install upper shaft bearing lock nut as follows:

a. Place column housing and steering shaft assembly in a holding fixture.

b. Tighten lock nut until **torque** required to rotate shaft is 3 inch lbs.

11. Place lock cylinder in "run" position and install column housing and steering shaft assembly into column bowl.

12. Lubricate pivot pins with lithium grease and install two pivot pins until bottomed in housing.

13. Install adapter and lower bearing assembly, torquing adapter screws to 30 inch lbs.

14. Install lower bearing spring and lower bearing seat.

15. Install two new lower spring retainers, compressing spring until retainers are positioned 1.14 inch (29 mm) from lower end of steering shaft.

16. Perform "Assembly" steps 7 through 10 for "Wheel Tilt Spring, Tilt Lever &

Bracket Assembly, Buzzer Switch Assembly, Steering Column Lock Cylinder Set & Column Tilt Bumpers."

17. **On models with floor shift and automatic transmission**, proceed as follows:
    a. Install bowl shield to column bowl and upper mounting stud.
    b. Install bowl shield screw and bowl shield nut, torquing to 35 inch lbs.
    c. Insert park lock cable into ignition switch inhibitor and snap in place as steering column is installed in vehicle.

CABLE SHIFT ARM ASSEMBLY, SWITCH ACTUATOR RACK & STEERING SHAFT LOCK BOLT

Disassembly

1. Place column in "0" tilt position, then remove steering column from vehicle.
2. Remove turn signal cancel cam assembly as previously described, then the hazard knob screw and hazard warning knob.
3. Position turn signal switch so that turn signal switch screws and housing screw can be removed through openings in switch.
4. Remove housing screw and column housing cover, then the shoe pin retainer cap.
5. **On models with column shift**, place shift lever in "Neutral" position and remove bowl cap screws and the bowl cap assembly.
6. **On all models**, perform "Removal" steps 5 through 9 for "Pivot & Pulse Switch Assembly & Turn Signal Switch Assembly.
7. **On models with column shift**, pull tilt lever and tilt column all the way up.
8. **On all models**, perform "Disassembly" steps 5 through 10 for "Wheel Tilt Spring, Tilt Lever & Bracket Assembly, Buzzer Switch Assembly, Steering Column Lock Cylinder Set & Column Tilt Bumpers."
9. Remove bowl shield screw, bowl shield nut and bowl shield.
10. Remove dimmer switch nut and upper mounting stud, then the dimmer switch.
11. Remove dimmer switch actuator rod and dimmer switch rod cap, then the lower mounting stud.
12. Remove dimmer and ignition switch assembly.
13. Remove column bowl screws, then the steering column bowl from steering column jacket assembly.
14. **On models with column shift**, remove shift arm screws, then the cable shift arm assembly from column bowl.
15. **On all models**, remove switch actuator rack and steering shaft lock bolt assembly as follows:
    a. Move actuator rack down while manually retracting lock bolt and retainer tube.
    b. Raise sleeve housing and remove actuator rack.
    c. Remove lock bolt assembly.
16. Remove sleeve housing from jacket assembly.

Assembly

1. Install sleeve housing onto jacket assembly.
2. Lubricate steering shaft lock bolt with lithium grease and assemble as follows:
    a. Install lock bolt into retainer tube.
    b. Install spring onto lock bolt.
    c. Install spring retainer cap into retainer tube and snap in place.
3. Install lock bolt assembly into sleeve housing.
4. Lubricate gear teeth on switch actuator rack with lithium grease and install ignition switch rod to actuator rack.
5. Install switch actuator rack into lock bolt assembly as follows:
    a. Raise sleeve housing while manually retracting lock bolt and retainer tube.
    b. Insert actuator rack through opening in lock bolt until it contacts bottom edge of sleeve housing.
6. **On models with column shift**, install cable shift arm assembly to column bowl, torquing shift arm screws to 27 inch lbs.
7. **On all models**, install steering column bowl to column jacket assembly, apply Loctite No. 242 or equivalent to threads of column bowl screws and **torque** screws to 47 inch lbs.
8. Install steering column lock cylinder set by holding barrel of lock cylinder, inserting key and turning counterclockwise to "accessory" position and installing lock set into lock opening in steering column bowl while holding rack against bottom of sleeve housing.
9. Install lock retaining screw, torquing to 27 inch lbs., then turn lock cylinder to "start" position and ensure rack extends and steering shaft lock bolt extends and retracts as the lock is turned from start to lock.
10. Place lock cylinder set in "off-lock" position.
11. Place ignition switch slider in far left position and move back one detent to right, then insert a 3/32 inch drill bit in adjustment hole on ignition switch to hold switch slider in proper position during installation, **Fig. 83.**
12. Install ignition switch to switch rod.
13. Install ignition switch to steering column jacket assembly with lower mounting stud, torquing to 35 inch lbs., then remove adjustment tool from ignition switch.
14. Lubricate dimmer switch rod cap with lithium grease, then install cap into column bowl.
15. Install dimmer switch actuator rod through hole in instrument panel bracket and into hole in dimmer switch rod cap.
16. Install dimmer switch assembly onto actuator rod.
17. Install dimmer switch assembly on lower mounting stud with dimmer switch nut and upper mounting stud, but do not tighten.
18. Adjust dimmer switch by inserting a 3/32 inch drill bit and pushing dimmer switch against actuator rod to remove

all lash, then **torque** dimmer switch nut and upper mounting stud to 35 inch lbs. and remove adjustment tool.
19. Install bowl shield to column bowl and upper mounting stud, torquing screw and nut to 35 inch lbs.
20. **On models with column shift**, install shift lever and bowl cap assembly as follows:
    a. Position cable arm assembly so that plastic ball on end of actuator can be inserted into its mating slot.
    b. Move arm counterclockwise and slide the extending cable arm actuator pivot pin into cap actuator pin bushing.
    c. Install bowl cap screws, torquing to 27 inch lbs.
21. **On all models**, perform "Assembly" steps 5 through 9 for "Wheel Tilt Spring, Tilt Lever & Bracket Assembly, Buzzer Switch Assembly, Steering Column Lock Cylinder Set & Column Tilt Bumpers."
22. Perform "Installation" steps for "Pivot & Pulse Switch Assembly & Turn Signal Switch Assembly."
23. Install lower bearing seat and lower bearing spring.
24. Install two new lower spring retainers, then compress spring until retainers are positioned 1.14 inch (29 mm) from lower end of steering shaft.
25. **On models with floor shift and automatic transmission**, proceed as follows:
    a. Install bowl shield to column bowl and upper mounting stud.
    b. Install bowl shield screw and bowl shield nut, torquing to 35 inch lbs.
    c. Insert park lock cable into ignition switch inhibitor and snap in place as steering column is installed in vehicle.

Ignition & Dimmer Switch Assembly

Refer to procedure for fixed column.

1989–90 Cutlass Supreme, Grand Prix & Regal & 1990 Lumina

FIXED COLUMN

Refer to **Fig. 88.** when servicing this column.

Floor shift models equipped with automatic transmission use an ignition switch inhibitor and park lock cable. On these models, the park lock cable must be disconnected from ignition switch inhibitor before steering column is removed from vehicle. When removal of steering column is necessary, proceed as follows:
1. Lower steering column to floor of vehicle.
2. Remove shield or other upper column housing.
3. Turn column lock cylinder to the On position.
4. Disconnect park lock cable from ignition switch inhibitor with small screwdriver or punch, **Fig. 80.**

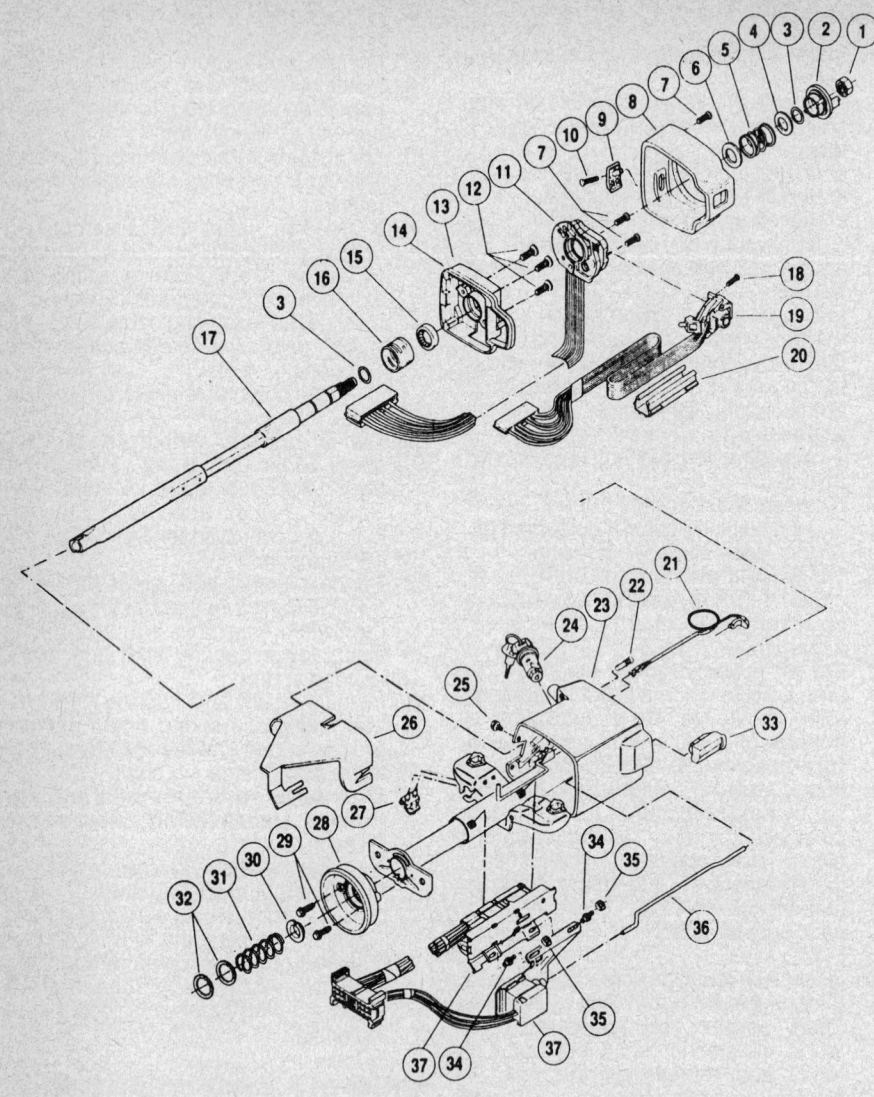

5-SPRING, UPPER BEARING

6-WASHER, THRUST

7-SCREW, PAN HD 6-LOBED SOC TAP

8-COVER, COLUMN HOUSING

9-KNOB, HAZARD WARNING

10-SCREW, OV HD C/REC (M3.5X1.27)

11-SWITCH ASM, TURN SIGNAL

12-SCREW, PAN HD 6-LOBED SOC TAP

13-HOUSING ASM, STRG COLUMN

14-HOUSING, STEERING COLUMN

15-BEARING ASM

16-SPACER, STRG COLUMN HOUSING

17-SHAFT ASM, STEERING

18-SCR, OVL HD 6-LOBED SOC TAP

19-SWITCH ASM, PIVOT & PULSE

20-PROTECTOR, WIRING

21-SWITCH ASM, BUZZER

22-SCREW, LOCK RETAINING

23-BOWL ASM, JACKET &

24-LOCK CYL SET, STRG COLUMN

25-SCREW, HEX WASHER HD TAPPING

26-SHIELD, BOWL

27-ADJUSTER ASM, PRNDL

28-BEARING ASM, ADAPTER &

29-SCREW, HEX WASHER HD TAPPING

30-SEAT, LOWER BEARING

31-SPRING, LOWER BEARING

32-RETAINER, LOWER SPRING

33-CAP, DIMMER SWITCH ROD

34-STUD DIMR & IGN SW MOUNTING

35-NUT, HEXAGON (#10-24)

36-ROD, DIMMER SW ACTUATOR

37-SWITCH ASM, COLUMN LOCK & IGN

Key No.	Part Name
1-NUT, HEXAGON JAM (M14X1.5)	3-RING, RETAINING
2-CAM ASM, SPACER & CANCELLING	4-WASHER, THRUST

Fig. 88   Exploded view of fixed steering column. 1989–90 Cutlass Supreme, Grand Prix & Regal & 1990 Lumina

TURN SIGNAL CANCEL CAM ASSEMBLY, PIVOT & PULSE SWITCH ASSEMBLY & TURN SIGNAL SWITCH ASSEMBLY
Disassembly

1. Remove nut retainer, jam nut and steering wheel.
2. Remove turn signal cancel cam assembly, hazard knob screw and hazard warning knob.
3. Position turn signal switch so that signal switch screws and housing cover screw can be removed through openings in switch.
4. Remove housing cover screw and column housing cover.
5. Disconnect wiring protector from opening in instrument panel bracket on jacket and bowl assembly and separate from wires.
6. Disconnect pivot and pulse switch connector from ignition and dimmer switch.
7. Remove pivot switch screw and pivot and pulse switch assembly.
8. Remove turn signal switch screws and disconnect turn signal switch connector from ignition and dimmer switch assembly connector.
9. Remove seventeen-way lock from turn signal connector and disconnect wires on alarm or buzzer assembly from turn signal connector with special tool No. J 35689-A or equivalent, **Fig. 63.** Wrap wire ends with tape to protect during removal and installation.
10. Remove turn signal switch assembly from column.

Assembly

1. Install turn signal switch assembly and **torque** screws to 35 inch lbs.
2. Connect wires from alarm or buzzer assembly to turn signal switch connector.
3. Install seventeen-way secondary lock to turn signal connector and snap in place.
4. Connect turn signal switch connector to ignition and dimmer switch connector and snap in place.
5. Install pivot and pulse switch assembly and **torque** screw to 18 inch lbs.
6. Connect pivot switch connector to ignition and dimmer switch connector and snap in place.
7. Install wiring protector as follows:
   a. Wrap protector around all wires passing through instrument panel bracket opening.
   b. Close protector so that interlocking grooves engage and slide protector into instrument panel bracket opening on jacket and bowl assembly and snap in place.

8. Install column housing cover and **torque** screw to 35 inch lbs.
9. Install hazard warning knob and **torque** screw to 9 inch lbs.
10. Lubricate bottom side of cancel cam with lithium grease and install turn signal cancel cam assembly.
11. Install steering wheel and jam nut, **torque** jam nut to 30 inch lbs. and secure with nut retainer.

STEERING SHAFT ASSEMBLY, STEERING COLUMN HOUSING, BEARING ASSEMBLIES, ALARM ASSEMBLY & STEERING COLUMN LOCK CYLINDER.

Disassembly

1. Remove turn signal cancel cam assembly, pivot & pulse switch assembly & turn signal switch assembly as previously described.
2. Remove two lower spring retainers and discard.
3. Remove lower bearing spring and lower bearing seat.
4. Remove adapter screws, adapter and lower bearing assembly.
5. Turn lock cylinder to the Run position.
6. Place opening in retaining ring over flat on steering shaf, then remove retaining ring with a screwdriver and discard.
7. Remove thrust washer, upper bearing spring and washer.
8. Remove steering shaft from lower end of jacket and bowl assembly.
9. Remove housing screws and column housing.
10. Remove housing spacer and bearing with drift and discard.
11. Turn lock cylinder to the Off-Lock position and remove key.
12. Remove alarm assembly by lifting alarm tab with a screwdriver and gently pulling wires to remove.
13. Remove lock retaining screw and lock cylinder.
14. Remove rod cap from dimmer switch rod and jacket and bowl assembly.

Assembly

1. Install rod cap into jacket and bowl assembly.
2. Install lock cylinder and **torque** retaining retaining screw to 27 inch lbs.
3. Install alarm assembly by pushing down into retaining bore until bottomed with plastic tab covering lock retaining screw.
4. Lubricate bearing with lithium grease and press into housing with a 1½ inch socket until bottomed.
5. Install housing spacer and column housing and **torque** screw to 88 inch lbs.
6. Turn lock cylinder to the Run position and insert steering shaft into the lower end of jacket and bowl assembly until shaft rests against bearing. The shaft will extend 2½ inches beyond the highest surface of column housing when installed properly.
7. Install thrust washer, upper bearing spring and thrust washer.
8. Wrap a two inch wide piece of shim

stock .005 inch, around the shaft and slip a new retaining ring up to the thrust washer. Use two long handled screwdrivers and push on retaining ring until it seats in the retainer ring groove in shaft. Discard shim stock.
9. Install adapter and lower bearing assembly and **torque** adapter screws to 27 inch lbs.
10. Install lower bearing seat and lower bearing spring.
11. Install two new lower spring retainers and compress spring until retainers are positioned 1.14 inch from lower end of steering shaft.
12. Perform assembly steps for turn signal cancel cam assembly, pivot & pulse switch assembly & turn signal switch assembly as previously described.

IGNITION & DIMMER SWITCH ASSEMBLY

Disassembly

1. Place shift lever in the Park position and lock cylinder in the Off position.
2. Remove steering column from vehicle.
3. Disconnect turn signal switch and pivot and pulse switch connectors from ignition and dimmer switch assembly connector.
4. Remove bowl shield screw and nut and remove bowl shield.
5. Remove dimmer and ignition switch assembly as follows:
   a. Remove dimmer switch nut, upper mounting stud, then dimmer switch.
   b. Remove lower mounting stud and ignition switch from ignition switch actuator rod.
6. Remove dimmer switch actuator rod from rod cap.

Assembly

1. Place the ignition switch slider in the far left position and move back one detent to the right, Off-Lock position. **Fig. 83.**
2. Insert a $^3/_{32}$ inch drill bit into the adjustment hole on ignition switch to hold switch slider in proper position during installation.
3. Install ignition switch to switch rod.
4. Install ignition switch to jacket and bowl assembly with lower mounting stud and **torque** stud to 35 inch lbs.
5. Remove drill bit from ignition switch and install dimmer switch actuator rod, tab first, through hole in instrument panel bracket and hole in dimmer switch rod cap.
6. Tab on rod must engage wide slot in rod cap and snap in place.
7. Install dimmer switch onto actuator rod and dimmer switch assembly on lower mounting stud with dimmer switch nut and upper mounting stud.
8. Adjust dimmer switch by inserting a $^3/_{32}$ inch drill bit through hole in switch and push switch against actuator rod to remove all lash. **Fig. 84.**
9. **Torque** dimmer switch nut and upper mounting stud to 35 inch lbs.
10. Install shield screw and bowl shield

nut and **torque** shield screw to 53 inch lbs. and bowl shield nut to 35 inch lbs.
11. Connect turn signal switch and pivot and pulse switch connectors to ignition and dimmer switch connector and snap in place.

TILT COLUMN

Refer to **Fig. 89.** when servicing this column.

Floor shift models equipped with automatic transmission use an ignition switch inhibitor and park lock cable. On these models, the park lock cable must be disconnected from ignition switch inhibitor before steering column is removed from vehicle. When removal of steering column is necessary, proceed as follows:

1. Lower steering column to floor of vehicle.
2. Remove shield or other upper column housing.
3. Turn column lock cylinder to the On position.
4. Disconnect park lock cable from ignition switch inhibitor with small screwdriver or punch, **Fig. 80.**

TURN SIGNAL CANCEL CAM ASSEMBLY, PIVOT & PULSE SWITCH ASSEMBLY & TURN SIGNAL SWITCH ASSEMBLY

Disassembly

1. Remove nut retainer, jam nut and steering wheel.
2. Remove turn signal cancel cam assembly, hazard knob screw and hazard warning knob.
3. Position turn signal switch so that signal switch screws and housing cover screw can be removed through openings in switch.
4. Remove housing cover screw and column housing cover.
5. Disconnect wiring protector from opening in instrument panel bracket on jacket and bowl assembly and separate from wires.
6. Disconnect pivot and pulse switch connector from ignition and dimmer switch.
7. Remove pivot switch screw and pivot and pulse switch assembly.
8. Remove turn signal switch screws and disconnect turn signal switch connector from ignition and dimmer switch assembly connector.
9. Remove seventeen-way lock from turn signal connector and disconnect wires on alarm or buzzer assembly from turn signal connector with special tool No. J 35689-A or equivalent, **Fig. 63.** Wrap wire ends with tape to protect during removal and installation.
10. Remove turn signal switch assembly from column.

Assembly

1. Install turn signal switch assembly and **torque** screws to 35 inch lbs.
2. Connect wires from alarm or buzzer assembly to turn signal switch connector.
3. Install seventeen-way secondary lock to turn signal connector and snap in place.

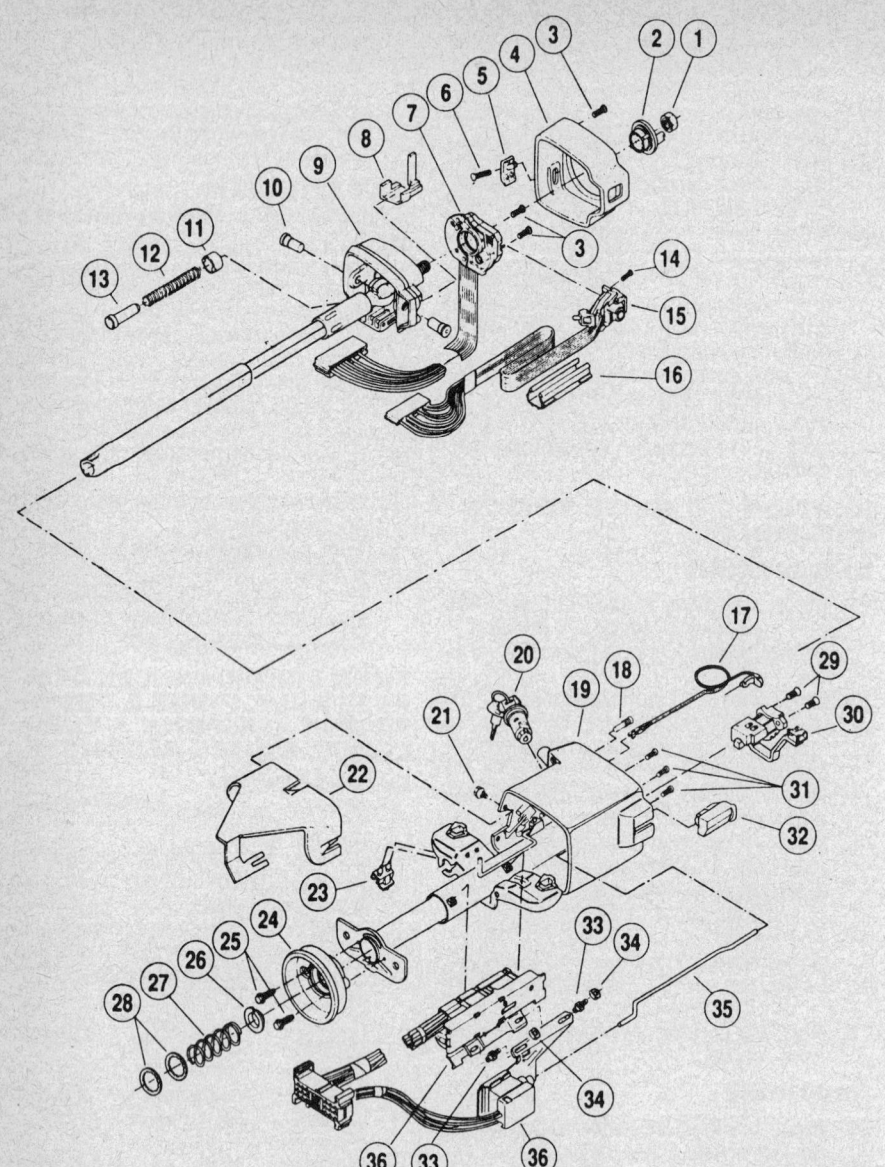

Key No.	Part Name
1	NUT, HEXAGON JAM (M14X1.5)
2	CAM ASM, SPACER & CANCELLING
3	SCREW, PAN HD 6 - LOBED SOC TAP
4	COVER, COLUMN HOUSING
5	KNOB, HAZARD WARNING
6	SCREW, OV HD C/REC (M3.5X1.27)
7	SWITCH ASM, TURN SIGNAL
8	CAP, HSG SHOE PIN RETAINER
9	HOUSING ASM, SHAFT &
10	PIN, PIVOT
11	RETAINER, SPRING
12	SPRING, WHEEL TILT
13	GUIDE, TILT SPRING
14	SCR, OVL HD 6 - LOBED SOC TAP
15	SWITCH ASM, PIVOT & PULSE
16	PROTECTOR, WIRING
17	BUZZER SWITCH ASM
18	SCREW, LOCK RETAINING
19	BOWL ASM, JACKET &
20	LOCK CYL SET, STRG COLUMN
21	SCREW, HEX WASHER HD TAPPING
22	SHIELD, BOWL
23	ADJUSTER ASM, PRNDL
24	BEARING ASM, ADAPTER &
25	SCREW, HEX WASHER HD TAPPING
26	SEAT, LOWER BEARING
27	SPRING, LOWER BEARING
28	RETAINER, LOWER SPRING
29	SCR, OVL HD 6 - LOBED SOC TAP
30	BRACKET ASM, TILT LEVER &
31	BUMPER, COLUMN TILT
32	CAP, DIMMER SWITCH ROD
33	STUD, DIMR & IGN SW MOUNTING
34	NUT, HEXAGON (#10 - 24)
35	ROD, DIMMER SW ACTUATOR
36	SWITCH ASM, IGNITION

Fig. 89   Exploded view of tilt steering column. 1989–90 Cutlass Supreme, Grand Prix & Regal & 1990 Lumina

4. Connect turn signal switch connector to ignition and dimmer switch connector and snap in place.
5. Install pivot and pulse switch assembly and **torque** screw to 18 inch lbs.
6. Connect pivot switch connector to ignition and dimmer switch connector and snap in place.
7. Install wiring protector as follows:
   a. Wrap protector around all wires passing through instrument panel bracket opening.
   b. Close protector so that interlocking grooves engage and slide protector into instrument panel bracket opening on jacket and bowl assembly and snap in place.
8. Install column housing cover and **torque** screw to 35 inch lbs.
9. Install hazard warning knob and **torque** screw to 9 inch lbs.
10. Lubricate bottom side of cancel cam

with lithium grease and install turn signal cancel cam assembly.
11. Install steering wheel and jam nut, **torque** jam nut to 30 inch lbs. and secure with nut retainer.

TILT LEVER & BRACKET ASSEMBLY, WHEEL TILT SPRING, LOWER BEARING ASSEMBLY, STEERING SHAFT & HOUSING ASSEMBLY, ALARM ASSEMBLY, STEERING COLUMN LOCK CYLINDER, COLUMN TILT BUMPERS & JACKET & BOWL ASSEMBLY

Disassembly

1. Remove turn signal cancel cam assembly, pivot & pulse switch assembly & turn signal switch assembly as previously described.

2. Pull tilt lever and tilt column all the way up.
3. Insert phillips tip screwdriver into square opening in spring retainer, push down and turn left to release retainer and wheel tilt spring.
4. Remove spring retainer, tilt spring and tilt spring guide.
5. Remove two lower spring retainers and discard.
6. Remove lower bearing spring and lower bearing seat.
7. Remove adapter screws, adapter and lower bearing assembly.
8. Remove two pivot pins from shaft and housing assembly with special tool No. J 21854-01 or equivalent.
9. Turn lock cylinder to the Run position and pull tilt lever to release shaft and housing assembly.
10. Remove shaft and housing assembly from jacket and bowl assembly.

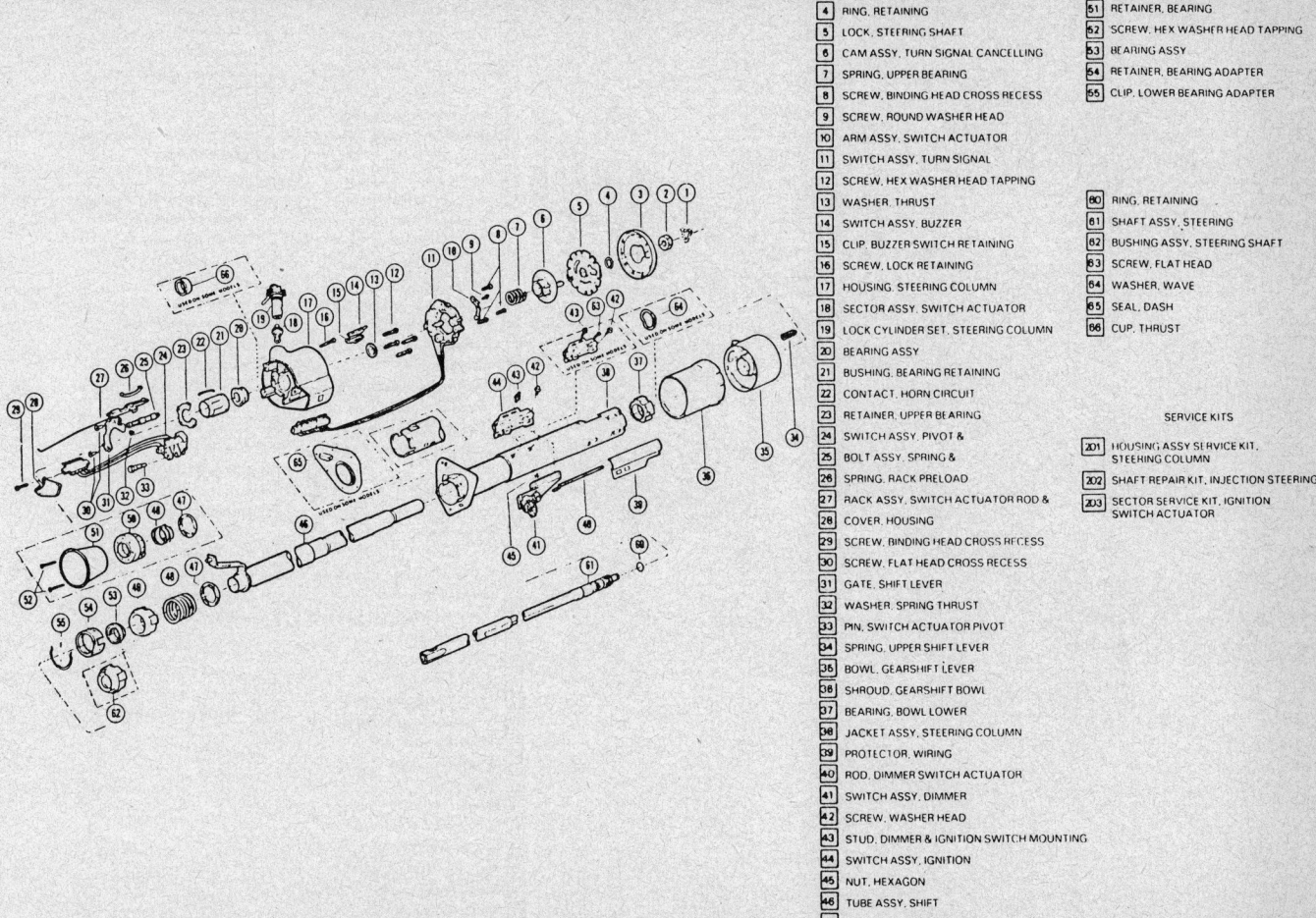

1	RETAINER	48	SPRING, SHIFT TUBE RETURN
2	NUT, HEXAGON	49	ADAPTER, LOWER BEARING
3	COVER, SHAFT LOCK	50	BEARING ASSY, ADAPTER &
4	RING, RETAINING	51	RETAINER, BEARING
5	LOCK, STEERING SHAFT	52	SCREW, HEX WASHER HEAD TAPPING
6	CAM ASSY, TURN SIGNAL CANCELLING	53	BEARING ASSY
7	SPRING, UPPER BEARING	54	RETAINER, BEARING ADAPTER
8	SCREW, BINDING HEAD CROSS RECESS	55	CLIP, LOWER BEARING ADAPTER
9	SCREW, ROUND WASHER HEAD		
10	ARM ASSY, SWITCH ACTUATOR		
11	SWITCH ASSY, TURN SIGNAL		
12	SCREW, HEX WASHER HEAD TAPPING		
13	WASHER, THRUST	60	RING, RETAINING
14	SWITCH ASSY, BUZZER	61	SHAFT ASSY, STEERING
15	CLIP, BUZZER SWITCH RETAINING	62	BUSHING ASSY, STEERING SHAFT
16	SCREW, LOCK RETAINING	63	SCREW, FLAT HEAD
17	HOUSING, STEERING COLUMN	64	WASHER, WAVE
18	SECTOR ASSY, SWITCH ACTUATOR	65	SEAL, DASH
19	LOCK CYLINDER SET, STEERING COLUMN	66	CUP, THRUST
20	BEARING ASSY		
21	BUSHING, BEARING RETAINING		
22	CONTACT, HORN CIRCUIT		SERVICE KITS
23	RETAINER, UPPER BEARING		
24	SWITCH ASSY, PIVOT &	201	HOUSING ASSY SERVICE KIT, STEERING COLUMN
25	BOLT ASSY, SPRING &	202	SHAFT REPAIR KIT, INJECTION STEERING
26	SPRING, RACK PRELOAD	203	SECTOR SERVICE KIT, IGNITION SWITCH ACTUATOR
27	RACK ASSY, SWITCH ACTUATOR ROD &		
28	COVER, HOUSING		
29	SCREW, BINDING HEAD CROSS RECESS		
30	SCREW, FLAT HEAD CROSS RECESS		
31	GATE, SHIFT LEVER		
32	WASHER, SPRING THRUST		
33	PIN, SWITCH ACTUATOR PIVOT		
34	SPRING, UPPER SHIFT LEVER		
35	BOWL, GEARSHIFT LEVER		
36	SHROUD, GEARSHIFT BOWL		
37	BEARING, BOWL LOWER		
38	JACKET ASSY, STEERING COLUMN		
39	PROTECTOR, WIRING		
40	ROD, DIMMER SWITCH ACTUATOR		
41	SWITCH ASSY, DIMMER		
42	SCREW, WASHER HEAD		
43	STUD, DIMMER & IGNITION SWITCH MOUNTING		
44	SWITCH ASSY, IGNITION		
45	NUT, HEXAGON		
46	TUBE ASSY, SHIFT		
47	WASHER, SPRING THRUST		

Fig. 90 Exploded view of fixed steering column. Bonneville, Caprice, Custom Cruiser, Electra, Estate Wagon, LeSabre, Safari Wagon, 88 & 98

11. Turn lock cylinder to the Off-Lock position and remove key.
12. Remove alarm assembly by lifting alarm tab with a screwdriver and gently pulling wires to remove.
13. Remove lock retaining screw and lock cylinder.
14. Remove column tilt bumpers with vise grips. If bumper is broken off use a 7/32 inch drill bit to remove remaining piece of bumper.
15. Remove tilt bracket screws and tilt lever and bracket assembly.
16. Remove rod cap from dimmer switch rod and jacket and bowl assembly.

Assembly

1. Install rod cap into jacket and bowl assembly.
2. Install tilt lever and bracket assembly into jacket and bowl assembly and **torque** tilt bracket screws to 35 inch lbs.
3. Install three tilt bumpers into jacket and bowl assembly until bottomed.
4. Install column lock cylinder and **torque** screw to 27 inch lbs.
5. Install alarm assembly by pushing down into retaining bore until bottomed with plastic tab covering lock

retaining screw.
6. Insert key and turn lock cylinder to the Run position.
7. Install shaft and housing assembly.
8. Lubricate pivot pins with lithium grease and install into pivot holes in shaft and housing assembly until bottomed.
9. Pull tilt lever and tilt column all the way up.
10. Lubricate tilt spring guide with lithium grease and install tilt spring guide into tilt spring.
11. Install guide and tilt spring with spring retainer as follows:
    a. Ensure that recess in spring guide engages round locating tab in jacket and bowl assembly.
    b. Insert phillips tip screwdriver into square opening in spring retainer, push down and turn right to lock in place.
12. Install adapter and lower bearing assembly and **torque** adapter screws to 27 inch lbs.
13. Install lower bearing seat and lower bearing spring.
14. Install two new lower spring retainers and compress spring until retainers are positioned 1.14 inch from lower end of steering shaft.

15. Perform assembly steps for turn signal cancel cam assembly, pivot & pulse switch assembly & turn signal switch assembly as previously described.

Ignition & Dimmer Switch Assembly

Refer to procedure for fixed column.

Bonneville, Caprice, Custom Cruiser, Electra, Estate Wagon, LeSabre, Safari Wagon, 88 & 98

FIXED COLUMN

SHAFT LOCK, TURN SIGNAL CANCELLING CAM, UPPER BEARING SPRING, TURN SWITCH ACTUATOR, BUZZER SWITCH & LOCK CYLINDER SET

Disassembly

Wheels of vehicle must be in straight ahead position. Failure to do so may cause

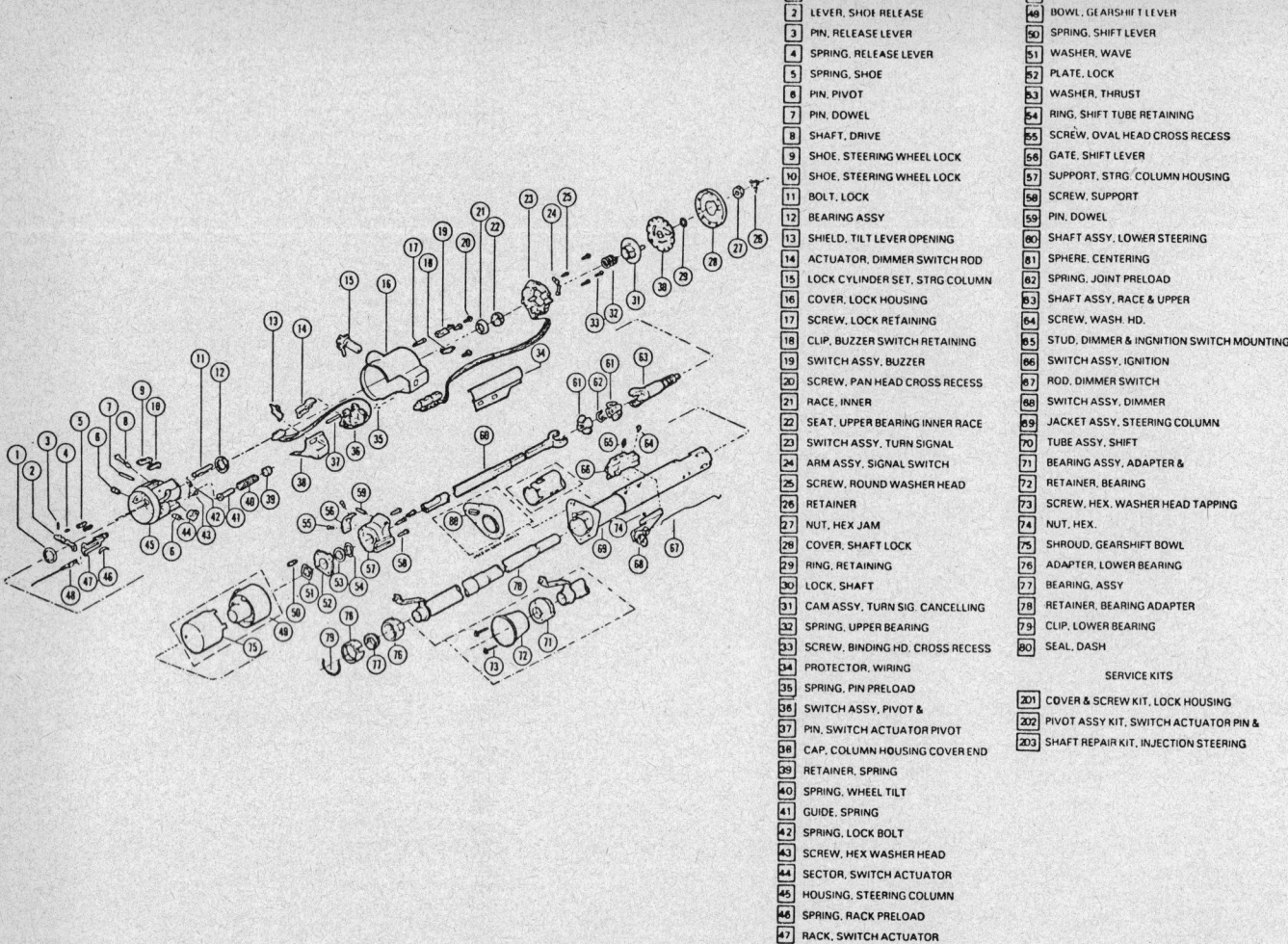

1	BEARING ASSY	48	ACTUATOR ASSY, IGNITION SWITCH
2	LEVER, SHOE RELEASE	49	BOWL, GEARSHIFT LEVER
3	PIN, RELEASE LEVER	50	SPRING, SHIFT LEVER
4	SPRING, RELEASE LEVER	51	WASHER, WAVE
5	SPRING, SHOE	52	PLATE, LOCK
6	PIN, PIVOT	53	WASHER, THRUST
7	PIN, DOWEL	54	RING, SHIFT TUBE RETAINING
8	SHAFT, DRIVE	55	SCREW, OVAL HEAD CROSS RECESS
9	SHOE, STEERING WHEEL LOCK	56	GATE, SHIFT LEVER
10	SHOE, STEERING WHEEL LOCK	57	SUPPORT, STRG. COLUMN HOUSING
11	BOLT, LOCK	58	SCREW, SUPPORT
12	BEARING ASSY	59	PIN, DOWEL
13	SHIELD, TILT LEVER OPENING	60	SHAFT ASSY, LOWER STEERING
14	ACTUATOR, DIMMER SWITCH ROD	61	SPHERE, CENTERING
15	LOCK CYLINDER SET, STRG COLUMN	62	SPRING, JOINT PRELOAD
16	COVER, LOCK HOUSING	63	SHAFT ASSY, RACE & UPPER
17	SCREW, LOCK RETAINING	64	SCREW, WASH. HD.
18	CLIP, BUZZER SWITCH RETAINING	65	STUD, DIMMER & IGNITION SWITCH MOUNTING
19	SWITCH ASSY, BUZZER	66	SWITCH ASSY, IGNITION
20	SCREW, PAN HEAD CROSS RECESS	67	ROD, DIMMER SWITCH
21	RACE, INNER	68	SWITCH ASSY, DIMMER
22	SEAT, UPPER BEARING INNER RACE	69	JACKET ASSY, STEERING COLUMN
23	SWITCH ASSY, TURN SIGNAL	70	TUBE ASSY, SHIFT
24	ARM ASSY, SIGNAL SWITCH	71	BEARING ASSY, ADAPTER &
25	SCREW, ROUND WASHER HEAD	72	RETAINER, BEARING
26	RETAINER	73	SCREW, HEX. WASHER HEAD TAPPING
27	NUT, HEX JAM	74	NUT, HEX.
28	COVER, SHAFT LOCK	75	SHROUD, GEARSHIFT BOWL
29	RING, RETAINING	76	ADAPTER, LOWER BEARING
30	LOCK, SHAFT	77	BEARING, ASSY
31	CAM ASSY, TURN SIG. CANCELLING	78	RETAINER, BEARING ADAPTER
32	SPRING, UPPER BEARING	79	CLIP, LOWER BEARING
33	SCREW, BINDING HD. CROSS RECESS	80	SEAL, DASH
34	PROTECTOR, WIRING		
35	SPRING, PIN PRELOAD		SERVICE KITS
36	SWITCH ASSY, PIVOT &	201	COVER & SCREW KIT, LOCK HOUSING
37	PIN, SWITCH ACTUATOR PIVOT	202	PIVOT ASSY KIT, SWITCH ACTUATOR PIN &
38	CAP, COLUMN HOUSING COVER END	203	SHAFT REPAIR KIT, INJECTION STEERING
39	RETAINER, SPRING		
40	SPRING, WHEEL TILT		
41	GUIDE, SPRING		
42	SPRING, LOCK BOLT		
43	SCREW, HEX WASHER HEAD		
44	SECTOR, SWITCH ACTUATOR		
45	HOUSING, STEERING COLUMN		
46	SPRING, RACK PRELOAD		
47	RACK, SWITCH ACTUATOR		

Fig. 91 Exploded view of tilt steering column. Bonneville, Caprice, Custom Cruiser, Electra, Estate Wagon, LeSabre, Safari Wagon, 88 & 98

improper alignment of some components during installation, resulting in column malfunction.

1. Place key in "lock" position.
2. Remove screws from back of steering wheel and horn pad, disconnecting horn lead from cam tower.
3. Remove retainer and hex nut, **Fig. 90**, then remove the steering wheel.
4. Depress shaft lock, then remove shaft lock retaining ring.
5. Remove shaft lock and shaft lock cover, then the turn signal cancelling cam.
6. Remove upper bearing spring, then the thrust washer.
7. Place turn signal in right turn position.
8. Remove switch actuator arm attaching screw and the arm, then the turn signal switch attaching screws, positioning switch out of way. If it is necessary to remove switch, remove wiring protector and hazard knob, then gently pull wire harness through gearshift lever bowl shroud and steering column housing.
9. Remove key from lock cylinder set and remove buzzer switch and clip, then reinsert key in lock cylinder set and turn to "lock" position.
10. Remove lock cylinder retaining screw and the lock cylinder set.

Assembly

1. Install lock cylinder set, torquing retaining screw to 22 inch lbs.
2. Place key in "run" position and install buzzer switch and clip.
3. Route turn signal switch wiring harness through steering column housing, gearshift bowl shroud and gearshift lever bowl and secure switch, torquing retaining screws to 22 inch lbs.
4. Install switch actuator arm, torquing attaching screw to 18 inch lbs.
5. Install thrust washer, then the upper bearing spring.
6. Install turn signal cancelling cam, then the shaft lock.
7. Depress shaft lock, then install shaft lock retaining ring.
8. Install steering wheel, then the hex nut and retainer.
9. Install horn pad and wiring protector.

STEERING COLUMN HOUSING, COVER END CAP, PIVOT & SWITCH ASSEMBLY, SWITCH ACTUATOR ROD/RACK, UPPER BEARING, DIMMER SWITCH & IGNITION SWITCH

Disassembly

1. Perform "Disassembly" steps for "Shaft Lock, Turn Signal Cancelling Cam, Upper Bearing Spring, Turn Switch Actuator, Buzzer Switch & Lock Cylinder Set."
2. Remove steering column housing and dimmer switch attaching screws and the dimmer switch hex nut, then the dimmer switch and mounting stud.
3. **On models equipped with cruise control**, unplug connector from base plate and remove multifunction lever.
4. **On all models**, remove ignition switch, then the dimmer switch rod.
5. Remove steering column housing, then the shift lever gate attaching screws and the shift lever gate.
6. Remove switch actuator rod and rack assembly, lock bolt assembly and spring thrust washer.
7. Remove switch actuator sector, then the upper bearing retainer.
8. Remove bearing retaining bushing and horn circuit contact, then the bearing assembly.
9. Remove housing cover attaching screw and cover, then the switch actuator pivot pin and pivot and switch assembly.

Assembly

1. Install pivot and switch assembly to

steering column housing, then install switch actuator pivot pin.

2. Install housing cover and screw, then the bearing assembly.

3. Install bearing retaining bushing and horn circuit contact, then the switch actuator sector.

4. Install switch actuator rod and rack assembly and lock bolt assembly, then the shift lever gate and attaching screws.

5. **On models equipped with cruise control,** plug multifunction lever connector and cruise control wire on wash/wipe switch together and mount on base plate, then install multifunction lever.

6. **On all models,** install upper bearing retainer, then the steering column housing with attaching screws. Tighten screw in 12 o'clock position first, screw in 8 o'clock position second and screw in 4 o'clock position third, torquing to 80 inch lbs.

7. Install ignition switch and mounting stud, then adjust ignition switch, **Fig. 83.**

8. Install dimmer switch rod, then the dimmer switch and hex nut.

9. Adjust dimmer switch, **Fig. 79.**

10. Install dimmer switch attaching screw.

11. Perform "Assembly" steps for "Shaft Lock, Turn Signal Cancelling Cam, Upper Bearing Spring, Turn Switch Actuator, Buzzer Switch & Lock Cylinder Set."

SHAFT & LOWER BEARING ASSEMBLY, GEARSHIFT LEVER BOWL SWITCH TUBE ASSEMBLY & LOWER BOWL BEARING

Disassembly

1. Remove screws from back of steering wheel and horn pad, disconnecting horn lead from cam tower.

2. Remove retainer and hex nut, then remove the steering wheel.

3. Remove steering column from vehicle.

4. Perform "Disassembly" steps 4 through 10 for "Shaft Lock, Turn Signal Cancelling Cam, Upper Bearing Spring, Turn Switch Actuator, Buzzer Switch & Lock Cylinder Set."

5. Perform "Disassembly" steps for "Steering Column Housing, Cover End Cap, Pivot & Switch Assembly, Switch Actuator Rod Rack, Upper Bearing, Dimmer Switch & Ignition Switch."

6. Remove lower bearing adapter clip, then the bearing adapter retainer.

7. Remove bearing assembly, then the lower bearing adapter.

8. Remove shift tube return spring and spring thrust washer, then the gear shift lever bowl and shroud.

9. Remove shift tube assembly, then the wave washer.

10. Remove lower bowl bearing.

Assembly

1. Install lower bowl bearing to jacket assembly.

2. Install wave washer, then the shift tube assembly.

3. Install gearshift lever bowl and shroud, then the shift tube return spring and spring thrust washer.

4. Install lower bearing adapter, then the bearing assembly.

5. Install bearing adapter retainer, then the lower bearing adapter clip.

6. Perform "Assembly" steps for "Steering Column Housing, Cover End Cap, Pivot & Switch Assembly, Switch Actuator Rod Rack, Upper Bearing, Dimmer Switch & Ignition Switch."

7. Install steering column in vehicle.

8. Perform "Assembly" steps for "Shaft Lock, Turn Signal Cancelling Cam, Upper Bearing Spring, Turn Switch Actuator, Buzzer Switch & Lock Cylinder Set."

TILT COLUMN

SHAFT LOCK, TURN SIGNAL CANCELLING CAM, UPPER BEARING SPRING, UPPER BEARING SEAT, INNER RACE, TURN SIGNAL SWITCH, BUZZER SWITCH & LOCK CYLINDER SET

Disassembly

Wheels of vehicle must be in straight ahead position. Failure to do so may cause improper alignment of some components during installation, resulting in column malfunction. Refer to **Fig. 91** for parts identification.

1. Place key in "lock" position.

2. Disconnect battery ground cable.

3. Remove screws from back of steering wheel and horn pad, disconnecting horn lead from cam tower.

4. Remove retainer and jam nut, then, using tool J-1859-03 or equivalent, the steering wheel.

5. Using tool J-23653-A or equivalent, depress shaft lock, then remove shaft lock retaining ring.

6. Remove shaft lock and shaft lock cover, then the turn signal cancelling cam.

7. Remove upper bearing spring, then the upper bearing seat.

8. Remove inner race.

9. Place turn signal in "right turn" position, then remove signal switch arm attaching screw and the arm.

10. Remove turn signal switch attaching screws and position switch out of way. If it is necessary to remove switch, remove wiring harness protector and hazard knob, then gently pull wire harness through gear shift lever bowl, column housing and lock housing cover.

11. Remove key from cylinder lock, and remove buzzer switch and clip, then reinsert key in cylinder lock and turn to "lock" position.

12. Remove lock retaining screw and lock cylinder set.

Assembly

1. Install lock cylinder set, torquing retaining screw to 26 inch lbs.

2. Place key in "run" position, then install buzzer switch and clip.

3. Route turn signal switch wiring harness through lock housing cover, column housing and gear shift lever bowl, then secure switch, torquing retaining screws to 26 inch lbs.

4. Install signal switch arm, torquing retaining screw to 18 inch lbs.

5. Install hazard knob, then the inner race.

6. Install upper bearing seat, then the upper bearing spring.

7. Install turn signal cancelling cam, then the shaft lock.

8. Depress shaft lock, then install shaft lock retaining ring.

9. Install steering wheel, then the jam nut and retainer.

10. Install horn pad, then the wiring harness protector.

11. Connect battery ground cable.

LOCK HOUSING COVER, COVER END CAP, PIVOT & SWITCH ASSEMBLY, DIMMER SWITCH ROD ACTUATOR & TILT SPRING ASSEMBLY

Disassembly

1. Perform "Disassembly" steps for "Shaft Lock, Turn Signal Cancelling Cam, Upper Bearing Spring, Upper Bearing Seat, Inner Race, Turn Signal Switch, Buzzer Switch & Lock Cylinder Set."

2. Remove lock housing cover attaching screws and cover, then the tilt lever.

3. Remove cover housing end cap and the dimmer switch rod actuator.

4. **On vehicles equipped with cruise control,** unplug cruise control connector and remove multifunction lever.

5. **On all models,** gently pull pivot switch wiring harness through column housing and gear shift lever bowl.

6. Remove pivot pin, then the pivot and switch assembly.

7. Remove spring retainer, then the spring and spring guide.

Assembly

1. Coat spring guide and spring with lithium grease and install, then install spring retainer.

2. Install pivot and switch assembly, then the pivot pin.

3. Route pivot and switch assembly wiring harness through gear shift lever bowl and column housing.

4. Install dimmer switch rod actuator, then the gear shift lever bowl, ensuring bottom edge of dimmer switch rod actuator rests on bend in dimmer switch rod.

5. Install cover housing end cap.

6. **On vehicles equipped with cruise control,** plug in cruise control connector and install multifunction lever.

7. **On all models,** Install lock housing cover. Tighten screw in 12 o'clock position first, screw in 8 o'clock position second and screw in 4 o'clock position third, then **torque** in same order to 89 inch lbs.

8. Perform "Assembly" steps for "Shaft Lock, Turn Signal Cancelling Cam, Upper Bearing Spring, Upper Bearing

Seat, Inner Race, Turn Signal Switch, Buzzer Switch & Lock Cylinder Set."

COLUMN HOUSING, LOCK SHOES, ACTUATOR SECTOR ASSEMBLY, SWITCH ACTUATOR RACK, BEARINGS & LOCK BOLT ASSEMBLY

Disassembly

1. Perform "Disassembly" steps for "Shaft Lock, Turn Signal Cancelling Cam, Upper Bearing Spring, Upper Bearing Seat, Inner Race, Turn Signal Switch, Buzzer Switch & Lock Cylinder Set."
2. Perform "Disassembly" steps for "Lock Housing Cover, Cover End Cap, Pivot & Switch Assembly, Dimmer Switch Rod Actuator & Tilt Spring Assembly."
3. Using pivot pin remover tool No. J-21854-01 or equivalent, remove pivot pins, **Fig. 64.**
4. Reinstall tilt lever.
5. Remove column housing assembly by pulling back on tilt lever and pulling housing down and away from column.
6. Remove drive shaft, then the switch actuator sector.
7. Remove switch actuator rack and rack preload spring, then the release lever pin and release lever.
8. Remove release lever spring, then the dowel pin.
9. Remove lock shoes and lock shoe springs, then the bearings.
10. Remove hex head bolt, then the lock bolt spring and lock bolt.

Assembly

1. Install bearings to column housing, then install drive shaft.
2. Install actuator sector, then the lock shoes.
3. Install dowel pin, then the lock shoe springs.
4. Install release lever spring, then the release lever.
5. Install release lever pin, then the rack preload spring.
6. Install switch actuator rack to actuator sector.
7. Install lock bolt and lock bolt spring, then the hex head bolt.
8. Install column housing assembly to column as follows:
   a. Position column housing assembly and align switch actuator rack with pin on end of actuator rod.
   b. Pull back on tilt lever, pushing column housing assembly onto column housing support assembly.
   c. Release tilt lever to lock shoes.
9. Remove tilt lever.
10. Lubricate pivot pins with lithium grease and install them.
11. Perform "Assembly" steps for "Lock Housing Cover, Cover End Cap, Pivot & Switch Assembly, Dimmer Switch Rod Actuator & Tilt Spring Assembly."
12. Perform "Assembly" steps for "Shaft Lock, Turn Signal Cancelling Cam, Upper Bearing Spring, Upper Bearing Seat, Inner Race, Turn Signal Switch, Buzzer Switch & Lock Cylinder Set."

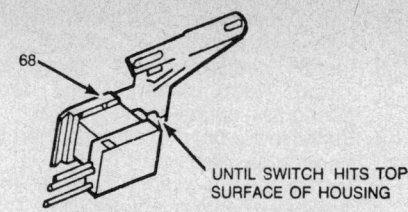

UNTIL SWITCH HITS TOP SURFACE OF HOUSING

68. SWITCH, DIMMER

Fig. 92   Adjusting dimmer switch. Bonneville, Caprice, Custom Cruiser, Electra, Estate Wagon, LeSabre, Safari Wagon, 88 & 98 w/tilt column

SHAFT ASSEMBLY, COLUMN HOUSING SUPPORT, SHIFT TUBE ASSEMBLY, IGNITION SWITCH, DIMMER SWITCH & LOWER BEARING ASSEMBLY

Disassembly

1. Perform "Disassembly" steps for "Shaft Lock, Turn Signal Cancelling Cam, Upper Bearing Spring, Upper Bearing Seat, Inner Race, Turn Signal Switch, Buzzer Switch & Lock Cylinder Set."
2. Perform "Disassembly" steps for "Lock Housing Cover, Cover End Cap, Pivot & Switch Assembly, Dimmer Switch Rod Actuator & Tilt Spring Assembly."
3. Perform "Disassembly" steps for "Column Housing, Lock Shoes, Actuator Sector Assembly, Switch Actuator Rack, Bearings & Lock Bolt Assembly."
4. Remove steering column from vehicle.
5. Remove bearing retainer, then the attaching screws and the lower bearing.
6. Remove shaft assembly then disconnect lower shaft.
7. Remove sphere from upper shaft, then the retainer clip from the sphere.
8. Remove housing support assembly attaching screws, then the housing support assembly and dimmer switch rod.
9. Remove hex nut and hex head bolt, then the dimmer switch and mounting stud.
10. Remove gear shift bowl.

Assembly

1. Install gear shift lever bowl to jacket, then the dimmer switch rod to housing support.
2. Install housing support assembly, torquing attaching screws to 80 inch lbs.
3. Install actuator rod assembly to track in housing support.
4. Install ignition switch and mounting stud, then adjust switch, **Fig. 83.**
5. Install retaining clip and sphere to upper shaft.
6. Install lower shaft to upper shaft with block tooth on shaft lower end of upper shaft at 12 o'clock position and notch at end of lower shaft at 4 o'clock position.
7. Lubricate shaft assembly with lithium grease and install to column.

8. Install column housing assembly to column.
9. Position column assembly and align switch actuator rack with pin on end of actuator rod.
10. Pull back on tilt lever, pushing column housing assembly onto column housing support assembly.
11. Release tilt lever to lock shoes, then remove tilt lever.
12. Lubricate inner surface of lower bearing with lithium grease, then install bearing and retaining screws.
13. Install bearing retainer.
14. Install dimmer switch, hex nut and hex head bolt, then adjust dimmer switch, **Fig. 92.**
15. Install steering column to instrument panel.
16. Install tilt lever.
17. Perform "Assembly" steps for "Column Housing, Lock Shoes, Actuator Sector Assembly, Switch Actuator Rack, Bearings & Lock Bolt Assembly."
18. Perform "Assembly" steps for "Lock Housing Cover, Cover End Cap, Pivot & Switch Assembly, Dimmer Switch Rod Actuator & Tilt Spring Assembly."
19. Perform "Assembly" steps for "Shaft Lock, Turn Signal Cancelling Cam, Upper Bearing Spring, Upper Bearing Seat, Inner Race, Turn Signal Switch, Buzzer Switch & Lock Cylinder Set."

1988–89 DeVille & Fleetwood
TILT & TELESCOPING COLUMN

Refer to **Fig. 93.** when servicing this column.

SHAFT LOCK, TURN SIGNAL CANCELLING CAM, UPPER BEARING SPRING, UPPER BEARING SEAT, INNER RACE, TURN SIGNAL SWITCH, BUZZER SWITCH & LOCK CYLINDER SET

Disassembly

1. Disconnect battery ground cable.
2. Remove horn pad, disconnecting horn lead from cam tower and remove retainer, jam nut and steering wheel.
3. Remove shaft lock retainer, bumper, spacer and snap ring retainer using special tool No. J 23653-A to depress shaft lock.
4. Remove shaft lock and turn signal cancelling cam.
5. Remove upper bearing spring, upper bearing seat and inner race.
6. Turn signal to "right turn" position and remove screw and signal switch arm.
7. Remove screws and turn signal switch, harness protector, hazard knob and pull wire harness through gear shift lever bowl, column housing and lock housing cover.
8. Remove key from cylinder lock, then buzzer switch and clip.
9. Install key in cylinder lock and turn to Lock position.
10. Remove lock retaining screw and lock cylinder set.

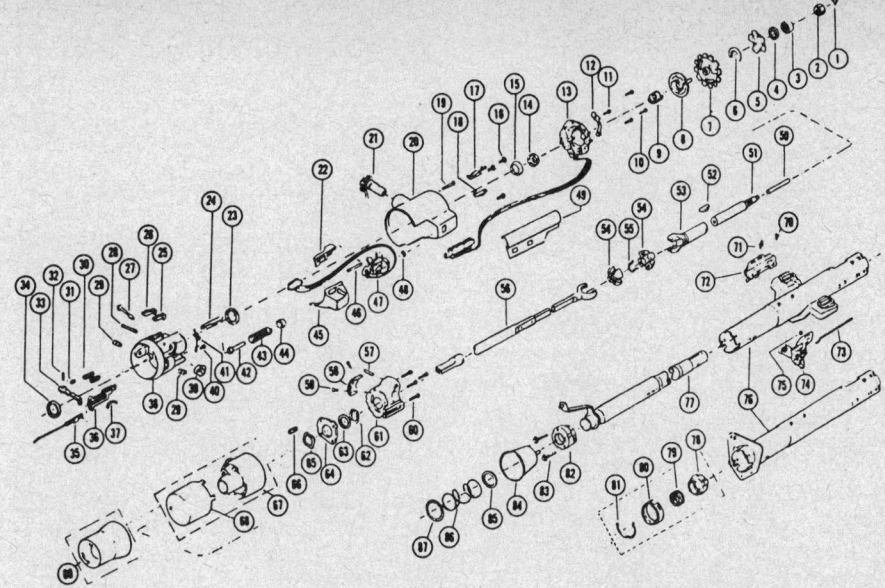

Key No.   Part Name

1 - RETAINER
2 - NUT, HEX JAM
3 - BUMPER, RETRACTED STRG SHAFT
4 - SPACER
5 - RETAINER, CARRIER SNAP RING
6 - RETAINER, SHAFT LOCK
7 - LOCK, STEERING SHAFT
8 - CAM ASM, TURN SIG. CANCELLING
9 - SPRING, UPPER BEARING
10 - SCREW, BINDING HD CROSS RECESS
11 - SCREW, ROUND WASHER HEAD
12 - ARM ASM, SIGNAL SWITCH
13 - SWITCH ASM, TURN SIGNAL
14 - SEAT, UPPER BEARING INNER RACE
15 - RACE, INNER
16 - SCREW, PAN HEAD CROSS RECESS
17 - SWITCH ASM, BUZZER
18 - CLIP, BUZZER SWITCH RETAINING
19 - SCREW, LOCK RETAINING
20 - COVER, LOCK HOUSING
21 - LOCK CYLINDER SET, STRG COLUMN
22 - ACTUATOR, DIMMER SWITCH ROD
23 - BEARING ASM
24 - BOLT, LOCK
25 - SHOE, STEERING WHEEL LOCK
26 - SHOE, STEERING WHEEL LOCK
27 - SHAFT, DRIVE
28 - PIN, DOWEL
29 - PIN, PIVOT
30 - SPRING, SHOE
31 - SPRING, RELEASE LEVER
32 - PIN, RELEASE LEVER
33 - LEVER, SHOE RELEASE

34 - BEARING, ASM
35 - ACTUATOR ASM, IGNITION SWITCH
36 - RACK, SWITCH ACTUATOR
37 - SPRING, RACK PRELOAD
38 - HOUSING, STEERING COLUMN
39 - SECTOR, SWITCH ACTUATOR
40 - SCREW, HEX WASHER HEAD
41 - SPRING, LOCK BOLT
42 - GUIDE, SPRING
43 - SPRING, WHEEL TILT
44 - RETAINER, SPRING
45 - CAP, COLUMN HOUSING COVER END
46 - PIN, SWITCH ACTUATOR PIVOT
47 - SWITCH ASM, PIVOT &
48 - SPRING, PIN PRELOAD
49 - PROTECTOR, WIRING
50 - ROD, TELESCOPE LOCKING
51 - SHAFT, UPPER STEERING
52 - WEDGE, LOCKING
53 - YOKE ASM, RACE & STEERING SHAFT
54 - SPHERE, CENTERING
55 - SPRING, JOINT PRELOAD
56 - SHAFT ASM, LOWER STEERING
57 - PIN, DOWEL
58 - GATE, SHIFT LEVER
59 - SCREW, OVAL HEAD CROSS RECESS
60 - SCREW, SUPPORT
61 - SUPPORT, STRG COLUMN HOUSING
62 - RING, SHIFT TUBE RETAINING
63 - WASHER, THRUST
64 - PLATE, LOCK
65 - WASHER, THRUST
66 - SPRING, SHIFT LEVER

67 - BOWL, GEARSHIFT LEVER
68 - SHROUD, GEARSHIFT BOWL
69 - COVER ASM
70 - SCREW, WASHER HD
71 - STUD, DIMMER & IGNITION
72 - SWITCH ASM, IGNITION SWITCH MOUNTING
73 - ROD, DIMMER SWITCH
74 - SWITCH ASM, DIMMER
75 - NUT, HEX
76 - JACKET ASM, STEERING COLUMN
77 - TUBE ASM, SHIFT
78 - ADAPTER, LOWER BEARING
79 - BEARING, ASM
80 - RETAINER, BEARING ADAPTER
81 - CLIP, LOWER BEARING
82 - BEARING ASM, ADAPTER &
83 - SCREW, HEX WASHER HEAD TAPPING
84 - RETAINER, BEARING
85 - SEAT, LOWER BEARING
86 - SPRING, LOWER BEARING
87 - RETAINER, LOWER SPRING
0 - COLUMN ASM, E/A STRG
101 - SHAFT ASM, STEERING
102 - HOUSING ASM, STEERING
103 - SUPPORT ASM, STEERING COLUMN HOUSING
104 - COVER SERV ASM, LOCK HOUSING
SERVICE KITS
201 - PARTS SERVICE KIT, TILT COL UPPER
202 - RACK SERVICE KIT, COLUMN SECTOR &
203 - SPHERE SERV KIT, TILT COLUMN
204 - SWITCH ASM SERV KIT, PIVOT &

Fig. 93   Exploded view of tilt & telescoping steering column. 1988–89 DeVille & Fleetwood

Assembly

1. Install lock cylinder set and **torque** screw to 26 inch lbs.
2. Turn key to the Run position and install buzzer switch and clip.
3. Connect turn signal switch wire harness through lock housing cover, column housing and gear shift lever bowl, installing wiring protector.
4. Install turn signal switch and **torque** screws to 26 inch lbs.
5. Install signal switch arm and **torque** to 18 inch lbs.
6. Install hazard knob, inner race, upper bearing seat, upper bearing spring and turn signal cancelling cam.
7. Install shaft lock and retainer using special tool No. J 23653-A to depress shaft lock.
8. Install steering wheel, jam nut and retainer.
9. Connect horn lead, then install horn pad and connect battery ground cable.

LOCK HOUSING COVER, COVER END CAP, PIVOT & SWITCH ASSEMBLY, DIMMER SWITCH ROD ACTUATOR & TILT SPRING ASSEMBLY

Disassembly

1. Remove shaft lock, turn signal cancelling cam, upper bearing spring, upper bearing seat, inner race, turn signal switch, buzzer switch & lock cylinder set as previously described.
2. Remove cover screws, lock housing cover and tilt lever.
3. Remove cover housing end cap and dimmer switch rod actuator.
4. **On models equipped with cruise control,** disconnect cruise control connector and remove multifunction lever.
5. **On all models,** disconnect and pull pivot switch harness through column housing and gear shift lever bowl.

6. Remove pivot pin, pivot and switch assembly.
7. Remove spring retainer, spring and spring guide.

Assembly

1. Install spring guide and spring coated with lithium grease, then spring retainer.
2. Install pivot switch harness through gear shift lever bowl and column housing, pivot and switch assembly and pivot pin.
3. Install dimmer switch rod actuator, bottom edge of actuator should rest on bend in dimmer switch rod, then cover housing end cap.
4. **On models equipped with cruise control,** connect cruise control connector and install multifunction lever.
5. **On all models, torque** screws for the lock housing cover to 89 inch lbs. Tightening the screw in the 12 o'clock position first, then the 8 o'clock position second and the 4 o'clock position last.
6. Perform assembly steps for shaft lock, turn signal cancelling cam, upper bearing spring, upper bearing seat, inner race, turn signal switch, buzzer switch & lock cylinder set as previously described.

COLUMN HOUSING, LOCK SHOES, ACTUATOR SECTOR ASSEMBLY, SWITCH ACTUATOR RACK, BEARINGS & LOCK BOLT ASSEMBLY

Disassembly

1. Remove shaft lock, turn signal cancelling cam, upper bearing spring, upper bearing seat, inner race, turn signal switch, buzzer switch & lock set, lock housing cover, cover end cap, pivot & switch assembly, dimmer switch rod actuator & tilt spring assembly as previously described.
2. Remove pivot pins using special tool No. J 21854-01 or equivalent, **Fig. 64.**
3. Install tilt lever and remove column housing assembly by pulling back on tilt lever and pulling housing down and away from column.
4. Remove drive shaft, switch actuator sector, switch actuator rack and rack preload spring.
5. Remove release lever pin, shoe release lever and release lever spring.
6. Remove dowel pin, lock shoes and lock shoe springs.
7. Remove bearings, hex head bolt, lock bolt spring and lock bolt.

Assembly

1. Install bearings to column housing, then drive shaft and switch actuator sector.
2. Install lock shoes, dowel pin and lock shoe springs.
3. Install release lever spring, shoe release lever and release lever pin.
4. Install rack preload spring and switch actuator rack to actuator sector.
5. Install lock bolt, lock bolt spring and hex head bolt.
6. Install column housing assembly to column. Position column housing assembly and align switch actuator rack

with pin on end of actuator rod. Pull back on tilt lever, pushing column housing assembly onto column housing support assembly. Release tilt lever to lock shoes.

7. Remove tilt lever and install pivot pins lubricated with lithium grease.
8. Perform assembly steps for shaft lock, turn signal cancelling cam, upper bearing spring, upper bearing seat, inner race, turn signal switch, buzzer switch & lock cylinder set, lock housing cover, cover end cap, pivot & switch assembly, dimmer switch rod actuator & tilt spring assembly as previously described.

SHAFT ASSEMBLY, COLUMN HOUSING SUPPORT, SHIFT TUBE ASSEMBLY, IGNITION SWITCH, DIMMER SWITCH & LOWER BEARING ASSEMBLY

Disassembly

1. Remove shaft lock, turn signal cancelling cam, upper bearing spring, upper bearing seat, inner race, turn signal switch, buzzer switch & lock cylinder set, lock housing cover, cover end cap, pivot & switch assembly, dimmer switch rod actuator & tilt spring, column housing, lock shoes, actuator sector assembly, switch actuator rack, bearings & lock bolt assembly assembly as previously described.
2. Remove steering column from vehicle.
3. Remove bearing clip, bearing retainer, lower bearing and lower bearing adapter.
4. Remove shaft assembly and check for accident damage.
5. Remove lower shaft, sphere from shaft assembly, and retainer clip from sphere.
6. Remove screws, housing support assembly and dimmer switch rod.
7. Remove hex nut and bolt, dimmer switch and mounting stud.
8. Remove ignition switch, and actuator rod assembly.
9. Remove shift tube retaining ring, thrust washer and gear shift lever spring.
10. Remove shift tube using special tool No. J 23072 or equivalent.
11. Remove lock plate, wave washer and gear shift lever bowl.

Assembly

1. Install gear shift lever spring to gear shift lever bowl and gear shift lever bowl to shift tube bracket.
2. Install wave washer lubricated with lithium grease and lock plate.
3. Install shift tube using special tool No. J 23073 or equivalent.
4. Install thrust washer and shift tube retaining ring.
5. Install dimmer switch rod to housing support.
6. Install housing support assembly and **torque** screws to 80 inch lbs.
7. Install actuator rod assembly to track in housing support, retaining clip and sphere to shaft assembly.
8. Install lower shaft to shaft assembly.

1	SPRING SHOE
2	PIVOT PIN
3	DOWEL PIN
4	DRIVE SHAFT
5	STEERING WHEEL LOCK SHOE
6	LOCK BOLT SPRING
7	LOCK BOLT
8	BEARING
9	SWITCH ACTUATOR PIVOT PIN
10	DIMMER SWITCH ROD ACTUATOR
11	SWITCH ACTUATOR PIVOT
12	PIN PRELOAD
13	TILT LEVER OPENING SHIELD
14	LOCK CYLINDER
15	LOCK CYLINDER COVER
16	BUZZER RETAINER CLIP
17	BUZZER SWITCH
18	INNER RACE
19	INNER RACE SEAT
20	TURN SIGNAL SWITCH
21	SIGNAL SWITCH ARM ASSEMBLY
22	UPPER BEARING SPRING
23	CARRIER ASSEMBLY
24	STEERING SHAFT LOCK
25	SHAFT LOCK RETAINER
26	CARRIER SNAP RING RETAINER
27	RETRACTED SHAFT BUMPER
28	SHAFT NUT
29	SPACERS
30	WIRE PROTECTOR
31	COLUMN HOUSING END CAP
32	SPRING RETAINER
33	WHEEL TILT SPRING
34	SPRING GUIDE
35	SWITCH ACTUATOR SECTOR
36	PIVOT PIN
37	STEERING COLUMN HOUSING
38	RACK PRELOAD SPRING
39	SWITCH ACTUATOR RACK
40	IGNITION SWITCH ACTUATOR
41	SHOE RELEASE LEVER
42	BEARING
43	GEARSHIFT BOWL SHROUD
44	GEARSHIFT LEVER BOWL
45	LIFT LEVER SPRING
46	SHIFT TUBE RETAINING RING
47	SHIFT LEVER GATE
48	DOWEL PIN
49	COLUMN SUPPORT
50	LOWER STEERING SHAFT
51	CENTERING SPHERE
52	JOINT PRELOAD SPRING
53	RACE & STEERING YOKE
54	LOCKING WEDGE
55	UPPER STEERING SHAFT
56	TELESCOPE LOCKING ROD
57	SCREWS
58	IGNITION SWITCH ASSEMBLY
59	BEARING
60	LOWER BEARING ADAPTER
61	BEARING ADAPTER RETAINER
62	SNAP RING
63	WASHER
64	LOCK PLATE
65	WAVE WASHER
66	SHIFT TUBE
67	COWL SEAL
68	STEERING COLUMN JACKET
69	DIMMER SWITCH
70	DIMMER SWITCH ROD

Fig. 94 Exploded view of tilt/telescopic steering column. 1990 Brougham

Block tooth on shaft lower end of shaft assembly at 12 o'clock position; notch at end of lower shaft at 4 o'clock position.

9. Install shaft assembly lubricated with lithium grease, to column.
10. Perform assembly steps for shaft lock, turn signal cancelling cam, upper bearing spring, upper bearing seat, inner race, turn signal switch, buzzer switch & lock cylinder set, lock housing cover, cover end cap, pivot & switch assembly, dimmer switch rod actuator & tilt spring assembly, column housing, lock shoes, actuator sector assembly, switch actuator rack, bearings & lock bolt assembly as previously described.
11. Install lower bearing adapter and bearing. Lubricate inner bearing surface with lithium grease.
12. Install lower bearing retainer, lower bearing clip, dimmer switch, hex nut and bolt.

13. Install ignition switch and mounting stud.
14. Install column in vehicle and connect battery ground cable.

1990 Brougham

TILT/TELESCOPIC COLUMN

Refer to **Fig. 94.** when servicing this column.

Disassembly

1. Disconnect battery ground cable, then remove column from vehicle.
2. Turn ignition switch to the Run position.
3. Remove horn pad, switch and horn connector.
4. Remove three small bolts and unscrew telescoping adjuster from shaft.
5. Remove telescoping lever from column, nut from steering column shaft

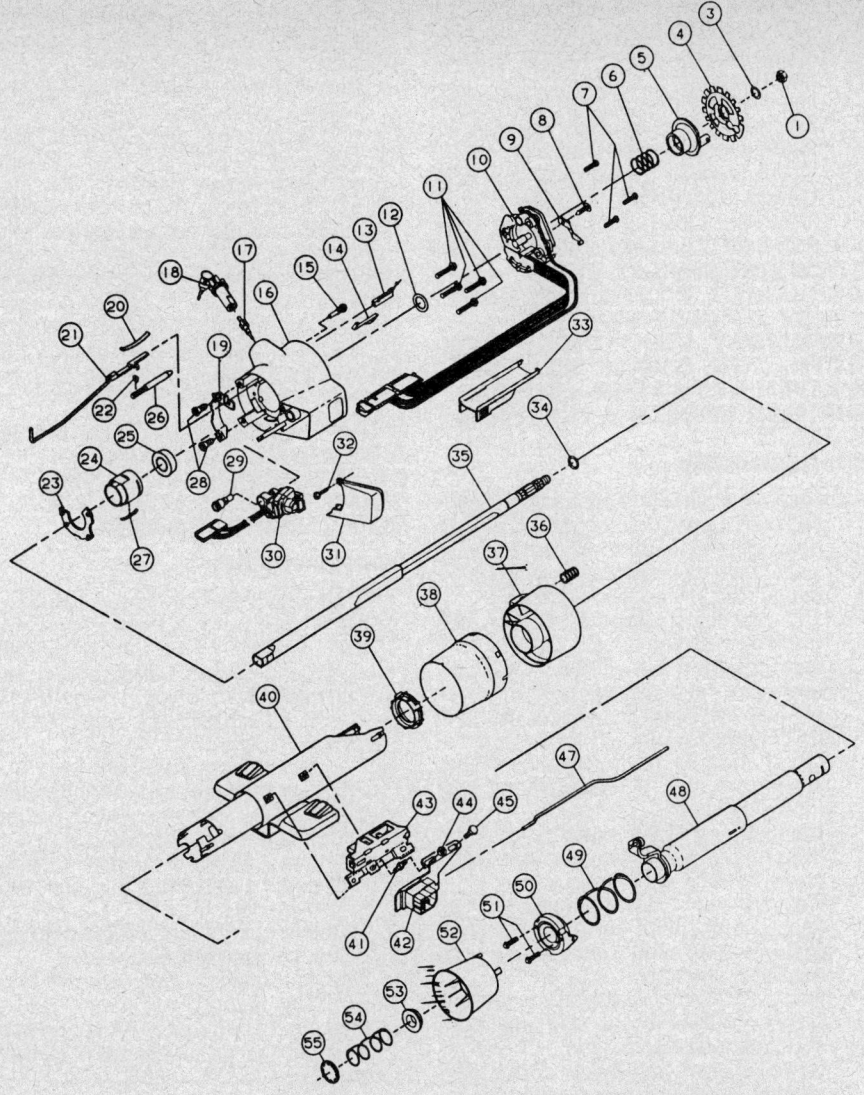

and steering wheel.
6. Remove key warning buzzer and retaining clip.
7. Remove lock cylinder retaining screw inside lock housing column cover and lock cylinder from column.
8. Remove hazard switch, tilt column lever and turn signal/cruise control lever.
9. Remove lock housing column cover, lower column cover and fuse panel cover.
10. Disconnect harness connector, then remove wiring protector and multifunction turn signal switch from column.
11. Install tilt lever and place column in the full up position.
12. Remove upper bearing seat, inner race and bearing.
13. Remove tilt spring retainer, spring and guide.
14. Use a punch to remove drive shaft and sector.
15. Remove pivot pins using special tool No. J 21854-01 or equivalent, **Fig. 64.**
16. Tilt housing by pulling upward on tilt lever and pulling housing upward until it stops. Move housing to the right to disengage rack from actuator.
17. Remove race and upper shaft assembly from lower shaft at centering sphere.
18. Remove gearshift lever, gate and column support.
19. Remove lock plate, retaining ring and washers.
20. Remove shift tube from shift bowl using special tool No. J 23072 or equivalent.
21. Remove lower bearing and retainer.

Assembly

1. Install lower bearing and retainer.
2. Install gear shift tube to bowl using special tool No. J 23073-01 or equivalent.
3. Install lock plate, retaining ring and washers.
4. Install column support, gearshift lever and gate.
5. Install race and upper shaft assembly to lower shaft at centering sphere.
6. Install tilt housing and new pivot pins.
7. Install drive shaft and sector.
8. Install tilt spring, retainer and guide.
9. Install upper bearing, seat and inner race.
10. Install multifunction switch to column, wiring protector and connect harness connector.
11. Install fuse panel, lower column and lock housing column covers.
12. Install hazard switch, turn signal/cruise control and tilt column levers to column.
13. Install lock cylinder and retaining screw to column.
14. Install key warning buzzer and retaining clip.
15. Install steering wheel to column shaft and **torque** nut to 35 ft. lbs.
16. Install telescope locking lever on shaft and telescope adjuster.
17. Position locking lever and bolts along the marks made by the bolts when

1 NUT, HEXAGON LOCKING (M14 × 1.5)	20 SPRING, RACK PRELOAD	38 SHROUD, GEARSHIFT BOWL
3 RING, RETAINING	21 ACTUATOR ASM, IGNITION SWITCH	39 BEARING, BOWL LOWER
4 LOCK, SHAFT	22 WASHER, SPRING THRUST	40 JACKET ASM, STRG COL
5 CAM ASM, TURN SIG CANCELLING	23 RETAINER, UPPER BEARING	41 STUD, DIMR & IGN SW MOUNTING
6 SPRING, UPPER BEARING	24 BUSHING, BEARING RETAINING	42 SWITCH ASM, DIMMER
7 SCREW, BINDING HD CROSS RECESS	25 BEARING ASM	43 SWITCH ASM, IGNITION
8 SCREW, RD WASH HD (M4.2 × 1.41)	26 BOLT ASM, SPRING &	44 NUT, HEXAGON (#10-24 × .25)
9 ARM, SIGNAL SWITCH	27 CONTACT, HORN CIRCUIT	45 SCREW, WASH HD (#10-24 × .25)
10 SWITCH ASM, TURN SIGNAL	28 SCREW, FLAT HEAD CROSS RECESS	47 ROD, DIMMER SWITCH
11 SCREW, HEX WASHER HD TAPPING	29 PIN, SWITCH ACTUATOR PIVOT	48 TUBE ASM, SHIFT
12 WASHER, THRUST	30 SWITCH ASM, PIVOT & (PULSE)	49 SPRING, LOWER BEARING
13 SWITCH ASM, BUZZER	31 CAP, COL HSG COVER END	50 BEARING ASM, ADAPTER &
14 CLIP, BUZZER SWITCH RETAINING	32 SCREW, BINDING HEAD CROSS RECESS	51 SCREW, HEX WASHER HD TAPPING
15 SCREW, LOCK RETAINING	33 PROTECTOR, WIRING	52 RETAINER, BEARING & SEAL
16 COVER ASM, LOCK HOUSING	34 RING, RETAINING	53 SEAT, LOWER BEARING
17 SECTOR, SWITCH ACTUATOR	35 SHAFT ASM, STEERING COLUMN	54 SPRING, SHIFT TUBE RETURN
18 LOCK CYLINDER SET, STRG COLUMN	36 SPRING, UPPER SHIFT LEVER	55 RETAINER, LOWER SPRING
19 GATE, SHIFT LEVER	37 BOWL, GEARSHIFT LEVER	

Fig. 95 Exploded view of fixed steering column. 1990 Celebrity, Century, Cutlass Ciera, Cutlass Cruiser & 6000

18. tightened, **torque** bolts to 35 inch lbs.
18. Check operation of telescoping lever for proper release and tightening within the lever's range of motion. Ensure that the wheel is free to telescope when the lever is all the way to the left and securely locked when lever is all the way to the right. If necessary adjust using the slotted locking lever bolt holes.
19. Install horn contact wire and horn pad assembly, then connect battery ground cable.

1990 Celebrity, Century, Cutlass Ciera, Cutlass Cruiser & 6000
FIXED COLUMN

Refer to **Fig. 95.** when servicing this column.

SHAFT LOCK, TURN SIGNAL CANCELLING CAM, UPPER BEARING SPRING, UPPER BEARING SEAT, INNER RACE, TURN SIGNAL SWITCH, ALARM ASSEMBLY & LOCK CYLINDER SET

Disassembly

1. Disconnect battery ground cable.
2. Gently pull up on horn pad to remove.
3. Disconnect horn lead by gently pushing down on lead and turning to the left, spring will then come out of cancelling cam tower.
4. Remove retainer, nut and steering wheel.
5. Remove shaft lock retaining ring using special tool No. J 23653-C or equivalent to depress shaft lock.
6. Remove shaft lock, turn signal cancelling cam, upper bearing spring and thrust washer.
7. Move turn signal to the "right turn" position.
8. Remove multi-function lever, screw and switch actuator arm.
9. Remove screws, hazard knob assembly and turn signal switch.
10. Remove wiring protector and gently pull harness through gearshift lever bowl, gearshift lever bowl shroud and lock cover assembly housing.
11. Remove key from lock cylinder and alarm assembly and clip.
12. Reinstall key and turn to the Lock position, remove lock retaining screw, then lock cylinder set.

Assembly

1. Install lock cylinder set and retaining screw and **torque** to 30 inch lbs.
2. Install key and turn to the Run position.
3. Install alarm assembly and clip.
4. Install turn signal switch harness through lock housing cover assembly, gearshift lever bowl and gearshift bowl shroud and connect.
5. Install turn signal switch and screws and **torque** to 35 inch lbs.
6. Install wiring protector, switch actuator arm and screw and **torque** to 20 inch lbs.
7. Install hazard knob assembly, multi-function lever, thrust washer, upper bearing spring and turn signal cancelling cam.
8. Install shaft lock and shaft lock retaining ring using special tool No. J 23653-C to depress shaft lock.
9. Install steering wheel and nut and **torque** to 30 ft. lbs.
10. Install horn lead and pad, then connect battery ground cable.

LOCK HOUSING COVER ASSEMBLY, COVER END CAP, PIVOT & PULSE SWITCH ASSEMBLY, IGNITION SWITCH ACTUATOR, UPPER BEARING, SWITCH ACTUATOR SECTOR, DIMMER SWITCH & IGNITION SWITCH

Disassembly

1. Remove shaft lock, turn signal cancelling cam, upper bearing spring, upper bearing seat, inner race, turn signal switch, alarm assembly & lock cylinder set as previously described.
2. **On models equipped with cruise control**, remove housing cover end cap, disconnect multi-function lever connector and gently pull through shroud, bowl and cover and remove multi-function lever.
3. **On all models**, remove washer head screw, hex nut, dimmer switch and mounting stud.
4. Remove ignition switch, dimmer switch rod, cover screws and lock cover housing assembly.
5. Remove upper bearing retainer and gently pull pivot switch harness through gear shift bowl shroud and gear shift lever bowl.
6. Remove binding head cross recess screw, housing cover end cap and switch actuator pivot pin.
7. Remove pivot and pulse switch assembly, flat head cross recess screws and shift lever gate.
8. Remove ignition switch actuator assembly, spring and lock bolt assembly, spring thrust washer and rack preload spring.
9. Remove bearing retaining bushing and horn circuit contact.
10. Remove bearing assembly and switch actuator sector.

Assembly

1. Install switch actuator sector and bearing assembly.
2. Install bearing retaining bushing, horn circuit contact and rack preload spring.
3. Install ignition switch actuator assembly, spring and lock bolt assembly and spring thrust washer.
4. Install shift lever gate and **torque** screws to 44 inch lbs.
5. Install pivot and pulse switch assembly and switch actuator pivot pin.
6. **On models equipped with cruise control**, gently pull connector through cover assembly, bowl, and shroud and connect, then install multi-function lever.
7. **On all models**, install housing cover end cap and screw and **torque** screw to 18 inch lbs.

8. Gently pull pivot switch harness through bowl and shroud and connect.
9. Install upper bearing retainer, lock housing cover assembly and screws and **torque** screws to 97 inch lbs.
10. Install ignition switch and mounting stud and **torque** to 36 inch lbs.
11. Install dimmer switch rod, dimmer switch and hex nut and **torque** to 36 inch lbs.
12. Perform assembly steps for shaft lock, turn signal cancelling cam, upper bearing spring, upper bearing seat, inner race, turn signal switch, alarm assembly & lock cylinder set as previously described.

SHAFT ASSEMBLY, ADAPTER & BEARING ASSEMBLY, GEARSHIFT LEVER BOWL, SHIFT TUBE ASSEMBLY & BOWL LOWER BEARING

Disassembly

1. Disconnect battery ground cable.
2. Gently pull up on horn pad to remove and disconnect horn lead by pushing down and turning left to remove from cancelling cam tower.
3. Remove retainer, nut and steering wheel.
4. Remove column from vehicle.
5. Remove bearing and seal retainer, lower spring retainer, lower bearing spring and lower bearing seat.
6. Remove hex head screws, adapter and bearing assembly and shift tube return spring.
7. Remove column shaft assembly and check for accident damage.
8. Remove retaining ring, gearshift lever bowl and shroud.
9. Remove upper shift lever spring from bowl, shift tube assembly and bowl lower bearing.

Assembly

1. Install lower bowl bearing to jacket assembly and upper shift lever spring to bowl.
2. Install shift tube assembly, gearshift lever bowl and shroud.
3. Install shift tube return spring, adapter and bearing assembly, lubricating inner surface with lithium grease.
4. Install screws and **torque** to 27 inch lbs.
5. Install lower bearing seat, lower bearing spring, bearing and seal retainer.
6. Install steering wheel and **torque** nut to 30 ft. lbs.
7. Install retainer, horn lead and pad and connect battery ground cable.

TILT COLUMN

Refer to **Fig. 96.** when servicing this column.

Shaft Lock, Turn Signal Cancelling Cam, Upper Bearing Spring, Upper Bearing Seat, Inner Race, Turn Signal Switch, Alarm Assembly & Lock Cylinder Set

Refer to "Fixed Column" for procedures.

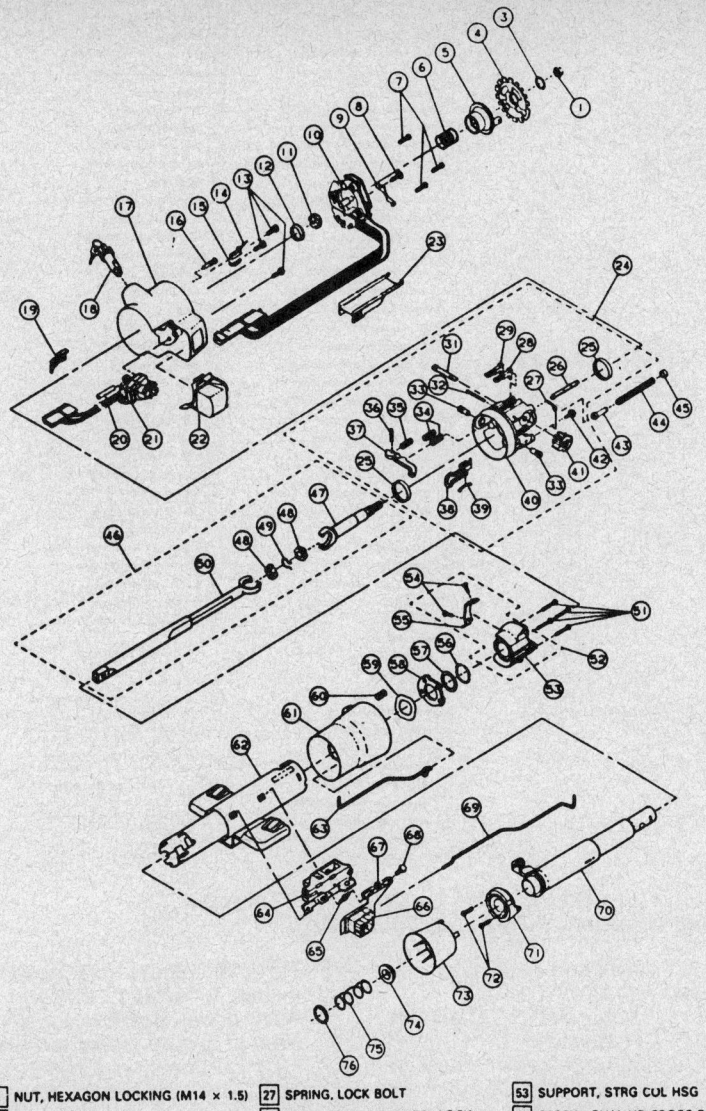

LOCK HOUSING COVER, COVER END CAP, PIVOT & PULSE SWITCH ASSEMBLY, DIMMER SWITCH ROD ACTUATOR & TILT SPRING ASSEMBLY

Disassembly

1. Remove shaft lock, turn signal cancelling cam, upper bearing spring, upper bearing seat, inner race, turn signal switch, alarm assembly & lock cylinder set as previously described.
2. **On models equipped with cruise control**, remove housing cover end cap, unplug connector and gently pull through bowl assembly, then remove multi-function lever.
3. **On all models**, remove cover screws and lock housing cover assembly.
4. Remove tilt lever, cover end cap and dimmer switch rod actuator.
5. Gently pull pivot switch harness through bowl assembly and column housing.
6. Remove pivot pin, pivot and pulse switch assembly, spring retainer, spring and spring guide.

Assembly

1. Install spring guide and spring coated with lithium grease.
2. Install spring retainer, pivot and pulse switch assembly and pivot pin.
3. Feed pivot and pulse switch assembly harness through column housing and bowl assembly and connect.
4. Install dimmer switch rod actuator to cover end cap.
5. Install cover end cap to lock housing cover assembly. Bottom edge of dimmer switch rod actuator should rest on bend in dimmer switch rod.
6. Install lock housing cover assembly.
7. **On models equipped with cruise control**, gently pull connector through column housing and bowl assembly and connect, then install multi-function lever.
8. **On all models**, install lock housing cover assembly screws and **torque** to 80 inch lbs. Screw in the 12 o'clock position first, 8 o'clock position second and the 4 o'clock position last.
9. Perform assembly steps for shaft lock, turn signal cancelling cam, upper bearing spring, upper bearing seat, inner race, turn signal switch, alarm assembly & lock cylinder set as previously described.

COLUMN HOUSING, LOCK SHOES, ACTUATOR SECTOR ASSEMBLY, SWITCH ACTUATOR RACK, BEARINGS & LOCK BOLT ASSEMBLY

Disassembly

1. Remove shaft lock, turn signal cancelling cam, upper bearing spring, upper bearing seat, inner race, turn signal switch, alarm assembly & lock cylinder set, lock housing cover, cover end cap, pivot & pulse switch assembly, dimmer switch rod actuator & tilt spring assembly as previously described.
2. Remove pivot pins using special tool

1	NUT, HEXAGON LOCKING (M14 × 1.5)	27	SPRING, LOCK BOLT
3	RING, RETAINING	28	SHOE, STEERING WHEEL LOCK
4	LOCK, SHAFT	29	SHOE, STEERING WHEEL LOCK
5	CAM ASM, TURN SIG CANCELLING	31	SHAFT, DRIVE
6	SPRING, UPPER BEARING	32	PIN, DOWEL
7	SCREW, BINDING HD CROSS RECESS	33	PIN, PIVOT
8	SCREW, RD WASH HD (M4.2 × 1.41)	34	SPRING, SHOE
9	ARM, SIGNAL SWITCH	35	SPRING, RELEASE LEVER
10	SWITCH ASM, TURN SIGNAL	36	PIN, RELEASE LEVER
11	SEAT, UPPER BEARING INNER RACE	37	LEVER, SHOE RELEASE
12	RACE, INNER	38	RACK, SWITCH ACTUATOR
13	SCREW, PAN HD 6-LOBED SOC TAP	39	SPRING, RACK PRELOAD
14	SWITCH ASM, BUZZER	40	HOUSING, STRG COLUMN
15	CLIP, BUZZER SWITCH RETAINING	41	SECTOR, SWITCH ACTUATOR
16	SCREW, LOCK RETAINING	42	SCREW, HEX WASHER HEAD
17	COVER ASM, LOCK HOUSING	43	GUIDE, SPRING
18	LOCK CYLINDER SET, STRG COLUMN	44	SPRING, WHEEL TILT
19	ACTUATOR, DIMMER SWITCH ROD	45	RETAINER, SPRING
20	PIN, SWITCH ACTUATOR PIVOT	46	SHAFT ASM, STEERING COLUMN
21	SWITCH ASM, PIVOT & (PULSE)	47	SHAFT ASM, RACE & UPPER
22	CAP, COL HSG COVER END	48	SPHERE, CENTERING
23	PROTECTOR, WIRING	49	SPRING, JOINT PRELOAD
24	HOUSING ASM, STRG COLUMN	50	SHAFT ASM, LOWER STEERING
25	BEARING ASM	51	SCREW, SUPPORT
26	BOLT, LOCK	52	SUPPORT ASM, STRG COL HSG

53	SUPPORT, STRG COL HSG
54	SCREW, OVAL HD CROSS RECESS
55	GATE, SHIFT LEVER
56	RING, SHIFT TUBE RETAINING
57	WASHER, THRUST
58	PLATE, LOCK
59	WASHER, WAVE
60	SPRING, SHIFT LEVER
61	BOWL ASM, GEARSHIFT LEVER
62	JACKET ASM, STRG COL
63	ACTUATOR ASM, IGNITION SWITCH
64	SWITCH ASM, IGNITION
65	STUD, DIMR & IGN SW MOUNTING
66	SWITCH ASM, DIMMER
67	NUT, HEXAGON (#10-24 × .25)
68	SCREW, WASH HD (#10-24 × .25)
69	ROD, DIMMER SWITCH
70	TUBE ASM, SHIFT
71	BEARING ASM, ADAPTER &
72	SCREW, HEX WASHER HD TAPPING
73	RETAINER, BEARING & SEAL
74	SEAT, LOWER BEARING
75	SPRING, LOWER BEARING
76	RETAINER, LOWER SPRING

Fig. 96   Exploded view of tilt steering column. 1990 Celebrity, Century, Cutlass Ciera, Cutlass Cruiser & 6000

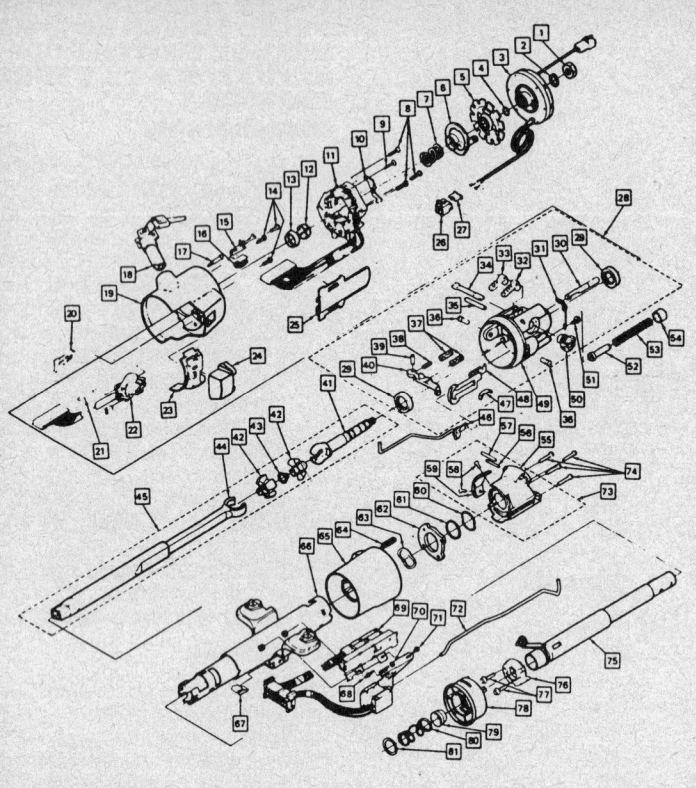

1	NUT, HEXAGON LOCKING (M14 X 1.5)
2	RING, RETAINING
3	COIL ASM, INFL RESTRAINT
4	RING, RETAINING
5	LOCK, SHAFT
6	CAM ASM, TURN SIG CANCELLING
7	SPRING, UPPER BEARING
8	SCREW, BINDING HD CROSS RECESS
9	SCREW, RD WASH. HD (M4.2 X 1.41)
10	ARM, SIGNAL SWITCH
11	SWITCH ASM, TURN SIGNAL
12	SEAT, UPPER BEARING INNER RACE
13	RACE INNER
14	SCREW, PAN HD 6-LOBED SOC TAP
15	SWITCH ASM, BUZZER
16	CLIP, BUZZER SWITCH RETAINING
17	SCREW, LOCK RETAINING
18	LOCK CYLINDER SET, STRG COLUMN
19	COVER, LOCK HOUSING
20	ACTUATOR, DIMMER SWITCH ROD
21	PIN, SWITCH ACTUATOR PIVOT
22	SWITCH ASM, PIVOT & PULSE
23	BASE PLATE, COL HSG COVER END
24	CAP, COL HSG COVER END
25	PROTECTOR, WIRING
26	CONNECTOR ASM, BODY
27	TERMINAL, POS ASSURANCE
28	HOUSING ASM, STRG COLUMN
29	BEARING ASM
30	BOLT, LOCK
31	SPRING, LOCK BOLT
32	SHOE, STEERING WHEEL LOCK
33	SHOE, STEERING WHEEL LOCK
34	SHAFT, DRIVE
35	PIN, DOWEL
36	PIN, PIVOT
37	SPRING, SHOE
38	SPRING, RELEASE LEVER
39	PIN, RELEASE LEVER
40	LEVER, SHOE RELEASE
41	SHAFT ASM, RACE & UPPER
42	SPHERE, CENTERING
43	SPRING, JOINT PRELOAD
44	SHAFT ASM, LOWER STEERING
45	SHAFT ASM, STEERING
46	ACTUATOR ASM, IGNITION SWITCH
47	SPRING, RACK PRELOAD
48	RACK, SWITCH ACTUATOR
49	HOUSING, STRG COLUMN
50	SECTOR, SWITCH ACTUATOR
51	SCREW, HEX. WASHER HEAD
52	GUIDE, SPRING
53	SPRING WHEEL TILT
54	RETAINER, SPRING
55	SUPPORT, STRG COL HSG
56	PIN, DOWEL (SECONDARY)
57	PIN, DOWEL
58	SCREW, OVAL HEAD CROSS RECESS
59	GATE, SHIFT LEVER
60	RING, SHIFT TUBE RETAINING
61	WASHER, THRUST
62	PLATE, LOCK
63	WASHER, WAVE
64	SPRING, SHIFT LEVER
65	BOWL ASM, GEAR SHIFT LEVER
66	JACKET ASM, STRG. COL.
67	SPRING, RETAINER
68	STUD, DIMR & IGN SW MOUNTING
69	SWITCH ASM IGN & BEAM CHANGE
70	NUT, HEXAGON (#10-24 X .25)
71	SCREW, WASH. HD (#10-24 X .25)
72	ROD, DIMMER SWITCH
73	SUPPORT ASM, STRG COL HSG
74	SCREW, SUPPORT
75	TUBE ASM, SHIFT
76	BEARING ASM, ADAPTER
77	SCREW, HEX WASHER HD TAPPING
78	RETAINER, BEARING & SEAL
79	SEAT, LOWER BEARING
80	SPRING, LOWER BEARING
81	RETAINER, LOWER SPRING

SERVICE KITS

201	SWITCH ASM SERVICE KIT, PIVOT & INCLUDES: 21, & 22
202	RACK SERV KIT, COLUMN SELECTOR & INCLUDES: 13, 29, 31, 48, 50, & 51
203	SPRING SERV KIT, TILT COLUMN INCLUDES: 12, 13, 52, 53, & 54
204	COIL SERV KIT, INFL RESTRAINT INCLUDES: 2, 3, 26, & 27
205	COVER & SCR SERV KIT, LOCK HSG. INCLUDES: 17, & 19
206	SPHERE SERV KIT, TILT COLUMN INCLUDES: 42, & 43

Fig. 97 Exploded view of Supplemental Inflatable Restraint (SIR) steering column. 1988–90 88 & 98

No. J 21854-01 or equivalent, **Fig. 64.**

3. Reinstall tilt lever and remove column housing by pulling back on tilt lever and pulling housing down and away from column.
4. Remove drive shaft, switch actuator sector, switch actuator rack and rack preload spring.
5. Remove release lever pin, shoe release lever and release lever spring.
6. Remove dowel pin, lock shoes, shoe springs and bearing assembly.
7. Remove hex head screw, lock bolt spring and lock bolt.

Assembly

1. Install bearing assembly to column housing.
2. Install drive shaft, switch actuator sector and lock shoes.
3. Install dowel pin, shoe springs and release lever spring.
4. Install shoe release lever, release lever pin and rack preload spring.
5. Install switch actuator rack to switch actuator sector.
6. Install lock bolt, lock bolt spring and hex head screw. **Torque** screw to 37 inch lbs.
7. Install column housing to column. Position column housing and align switch actuator rack with pin on end of actuator assembly. pull back on tilt lever, pushing column housing onto column housing support assembly. Release tilt lever to lock shoes onto dowel pins.

8. Remove tilt lever and install pivot pins lubricated with lithium grease.
9. Perform assembly steps for shaft lock, turn signal cancelling cam, upper bearing spring, upper bearing seat, inner race, turn signal switch, alarm assembly & lock cylinder set, lock housing cover, cover end cap, pivot & pulse switch assembly, dimmer switch rod actuator & tilt spring assembly as previously described.

SHAFT ASSEMBLY, COLUMN HOUSING SUPPORT, SHIFT TUBE ASSEMBLY, IGNITION SWITCH, DIMMER SWITCH & LOWER BEARING ASSEMBLY

Disassembly

1. Remove shaft lock, turn signal cancelling cam, upper bearing spring, upper bearing seat, inner race, turn signal switch, alarm assembly & lock cylinder set, lock housing cover, cover end cap, pivot & pulse switch assembly, dimmer switch rod actuator & tilt spring assembly, column housing, lock shoes, actuator sector assembly, switch actuator rack, bearings & lock bolt assembly as previously described.
2. Remove column from vehicle.
3. Remove bearing and seal retainer, lower spring retainer, lower bearing spring and lower bearing seat.
4. Remove hex head screws, adapter and bearing assembly.

5. Remove column shaft assembly and inspect for accident damage.
6. Mark upper and lower shaft assemblies to ensure proper assembly.
7. Remove upper shaft assembly, lower shaft assembly. Tilt 90° to each other and disengage.
8. Remove centering sphere from upper shaft assembly. Rotate sphere 90° and slip out.
9. Remove joint preload spring from centering sphere.
10. Remove screws, column housing support assembly and dimmer switch rod from steering column jacket assembly.
11. Remove rod from column housing support assembly and screws and shift lever gate from support assembly.
12. Remove hex nut, screw, dimmer switch assembly and mounting stud.
13. Remove ignition switch assembly and switch actuator assembly.
14. Remove switch actuator assembly from switch assembly.
15. Remove shift tube retaining ring, thrust washer and shift lever spring.
16. Remove shift tube using special tool No. J 23072 or equivalent.
17. Remove lock plate, wave washer and gearshift lever bowl.

Assembly

1. Install shift lever spring to gear shift lever bowl and gear shift lever bowl to shift tube jacket.

2. Install wave washer lubricated with lithium grease and lock plate.
3. Install shift tube using special tool No. J 23073 or equivalent.
4. Install thrust washer and shift tube retaining ring.
5. Install gate and screws to support assembly and **torque** screws to 27 inch lbs.
6. Install dimmer switch rod to support assembly.
7. Install column support assembly and **torque** screws to 80 inch lbs.
8. Install actuator assembly to track in housing support assembly.
9. Install joint preload spring to centering sphere.
10. Lubricate centering sphere with lithium grease and slip into upper shaft assembly and rotate 90°.
11. Ensure marks made on upper and lower shaft assemblies line up after assembly.
12. Install upper shaft assembly to lower shaft assembly, line up marks and tilt assemblies 90° to each other.
13. Install column shaft assembly lubricated with lithium grease to jacket assembly.
14. Perform assembly steps for shaft lock, turn signal cancelling cam, upper bearing spring, upper bearing seat, inner race, turn signal switch, alarm assembly & lock cylinder set, lock housing cover, cover end cap, pivot & pulse switch assembly, dimmer switch rod actuator & tilt spring assembly, column housing, lock shoes, actuator sector assembly, switch actuator rack, bearings & lock bolt assembly as previously described.
15. Install adapter and bearing assembly and lubricate inner surface with lithium grease.
16. Install screws and **torque** to 27 inch lbs.
17. Install lower bearing seat, lower bearing spring, lower spring retainer, bearing and seal retainer.
18. Install ignition switch assembly and mounting stud and **torque** to 36 inch lbs.
19. Install dimmer switch assembly, screw and nut and **torque** to 36 inch lbs.
20. Install column into vehicle.

1988–90 88 & 98, 1989–90 DeVille & Fleetwood & 1990 Camaro, Corvette, Eldorado, Firebird, Reatta, Riviera, Seville & Toronado Models w/Supplemental Inflatable Restraint (SIR)

Before removing the SIR steering column, the wheels of the car must be straight and the column in the Lock position. Care must be taken when handling column with a live inflator module. Never point bag deploy surface toward you, and never stand column on steering wheel. Accidental deployment in these positions may cause injury. Always face bag deploy surface toward open space to allow for unrestricted expansion.

The (DERM) Diagnostic Energy Reserve Module, can maintain sufficient voltage to cause a deployment for up to 10 minutes after the ignition switch is turned to the Off position and the battery ground has been disconnected.

COIL ASSEMBLY, SHAFT LOCK, TURN SIGNAL CANCELLING CAM, UPPER BEARING SPRING, UPPER BEARING SEAT, INNER RACE TURN SIGNAL SWITCH, BUZZER SWITCH & LOCK CYLINDER SET

Refer to **Figs. 97 through 103.** when servicing this column.

Disassembly

Wheels of vehicle must be in straight ahead position and key must be in Lock position.

1. Remove screws from back of steering wheel.
2. Remove restraint module from steering wheel.
3. Remove coil assembly plug from restraint module, then the horn contact from column.
4. Remove hexagon locking nut, then, using tool J-1859-03 or equivalent, the steering wheel.
5. Remove steering wheel shroud.
6. Remove lock screw from boss HOME position on coil assembly to CENTER LOCK position on coil assembly, **Fig. 104.**
7. Remove coil assembly retaining ring.
8. Remove coil assembly off shaft end, allowing coil to hang freely.
9. Using tool J-23653-A or equivalent, depress shaft lock, then remove shaft lock retaining ring.
10. Remove shaft lock, then the turn signal cancelling cam.
11. Remove upper bearing spring, then the upper bearing seat.
12. Remove inner race, then place turn signal in Right Turn position.
13. Remove signal switch arm attaching screw and the arm, then the turn signal switch attaching screws.
14. Remove hazard knob, then position turn signal switch out of way. If removal of switch is necessary, remove retainer spring and wiring protector, then gently pull wire harness through gear shift lever bowl, column housing and lock housing cover.
15. Remove coil assembly, if necessary, as follows:
    a. Disconnect POS assurance terminal, and, using tool J-35689-A or equivalent, disconnect wires from body connector assembly, **Fig. 105.**
    b. Tape wire ends, then gently pull wire through gear shift lever bowl, column housing, and lock housing cover.
16. Remove key from cylinder lock and remove buzzer switch and clip, then reinstall key in cylinder lock and place key in Lock position.
17. Remove lock retaining screw and lock cylinder set.

Assembly

Ensure all fasteners are securely seated before applying required torque.

1. Install lock cylinder set, **torquing** lock retaining screw to 26 inch lbs.
2. Place key in Run position, then install buzzer switch and clip.
3. Route turn signal switch wiring harness through lock housing cover, column housing and gear shift lever bowl.
4. Route coil assembly wire through lock housing cover, column housing and gear shift lever bowl and allow coil to hang freely.
5. Install turn signal switch, **torquing** attaching screws to 26 inch lbs.
6. Install wiring protector and retaining spring.
7. Install signal switch arm, **torquing** retaining screw to 18 inch lbs.
8. Install hazard knob, then the inner race.
9. Install upper bearing seat, then the upper bearing spring.
10. Install turn signal cancelling cam, then the shaft lock.
11. Using tool J-23653-A or equivalent to depress shaft lock, install shaft lock retaining ring, aligning to block tooth on shaft.
12. Ensure coil assembly hub is centered, **Fig. 106. The coil assembly will become uncentered if the column is separated from the steering gear and is allowed to rotate, or the coil is removed from the column without first locking in position with locking screw.**
13. Install coil assembly, using horn tower on cancel cam on inner ring and projections on outer ring for alignment, then the coil assembly retaining ring. **Move lock screw from CENTER LOCK position to HOME position on coil assembly.**
14. Install steering wheel and steering wheel shroud, then the hexagon locking nut.
15. Install coil assembly plug to air bag module and the horn contact into column.
16. Install steering wheel module to steering wheel.
17. Using tool J-35689-A or equivalent, connect wires to connector body assembly and install POS assurance terminal, **Fig. 107.**
18. Install screws to back of steering column, then connect battery ground cable.

Continued on page 29-82

Key
No.   Part Name

50—GUIDE, SPRING
51—SPRING, WHEEL TILT
52—RETAINER, SPRING
55—SHAFT ASM, STEERING COLUMN
56—SHAFT ASM, RACE & UPPER
57—SPHERE, CENTERING
58—SPRING, JOINT PRELOAD
59—SHAFT ASM, LOWER STEERING
61—SCREW, SUPPORT
62—SUPPORT ASM, STRG COL HSG
63—SUPPORT, STRG COL HSG
64—SCREW, OVAL HD CROSS RECESS
65—GATE, SHIFT LEVER
66—RING, SHIFT TUBE RETAINING
67—WASHER, THRUST
68—PLATE, LOCK
69—WASHER, WAVE
70—SPRING, SHIFT LEVER
71—BOWL ASM, GEARSHIFT LEVER
72—JACKET ASM, STRG COL
76—ACTUATOR ASM, IGNITION SWITCH
77—ROD, DIMMER SWITCH
78—SCREW, WASH HD (#10-24 X .25)
79—NUT, HEXAGON (#10-24 X .25)
80—SWITCH ASM, DIMR & IGNITION
81—STUD, DIMR & IGN SW MOUNTING
86—TUBE ASM, SHIFT
87—BEARING ASM, ADAPTER &
88—SCREW, HEX WASHER HD TAPPING
89—RETAINER, BEARING & SEAL
90—SEAT, LOWER BEARING
91—SPRING, LOWER BEARING
92—RETAINER, LOWER SPRING

Service Kits

201—RACK SERV KIT, COLUMN SECTOR &
    —INCLUDES: 14,31,33,44,47,48
202—SPRING SERV KIT, TILT COLUMN
    —INCLUDES: 13,14,39,50,51,52
203—COIL SERV KIT, INFL RESTRAINT
    —INCLUDES: 3,4,27
204—SPHERE SERV KIT, TILT COLUMN
    —INCLUDES: 57,58

Key
No.   Part Name

1—NUT, HEXAGON LOCKING (M14X1.5)
2—RING, RETAINING
3—COIL ASM, INFL RESTRAINT
4—WASHER, WAVE
5—RING, RETAINING
6—LOCK, SHAFT
7—CAM ASM, TURN SIG CANCELLING
8—SPRING, UPPER BEARING
9—SCREW, BINDING HD CROSS RECESS
10—SCREW, RD WASH HD (M4.2X1.41)
11—ARM, SIGNAL SWITCH
12—SWITCH ASM, TURN SIGNAL
13—SEAT, UPPER BEARING INNER RACE
14—RACE, INNER
15—SCREW, PAN HD 6-LOBED SOC TAP
16—SWITCH ASM, BUZZER
17—CLIP, BUZZER SWITCH RETAINING
18—SCREW, LOCK RETAINING
19—COVER ASM, LOCK HOUSING
20—LOCK CYLINDER SET, STRG COLUMN
21—ACTUATOR, DIMMER SWITCH ROD
22—PIN, SWITCH ACTUATOR PIVOT
23—SWITCH ASM, PIVOT & (PULSE)
25—CAP, COL HSG COVER END
26—PROTECTOR, WIRING
27—SHROUD, CONNECTOR
30—HOUSING ASM, STRG COLUMN
31—BEARING ASM
32—BOLT, LOCK
33—SPRING, LOCK BOLT
34—SHOE, STEERING WHEEL LOCK
35—SHOE, STEERING WHEEL LOCK
36—SHIELD, WIRE ABRASION
37—SHAFT, DRIVE
38—PIN, DOWEL
39—PIN, PIVOT
40—SPRING, SHOE
41—SPRING, RELEASE LEVER
42—PIN, RELEASE LEVER
43—LEVER, SHOE RELEASE
44—RACK, SWITCH ACTUATOR
45—SPRING, RACK PRELOAD
46—HOUSING, STRG COLUMN
47—SECTOR, SWITCH ACTUATOR
48—SCREW, HEX WASHER HEAD

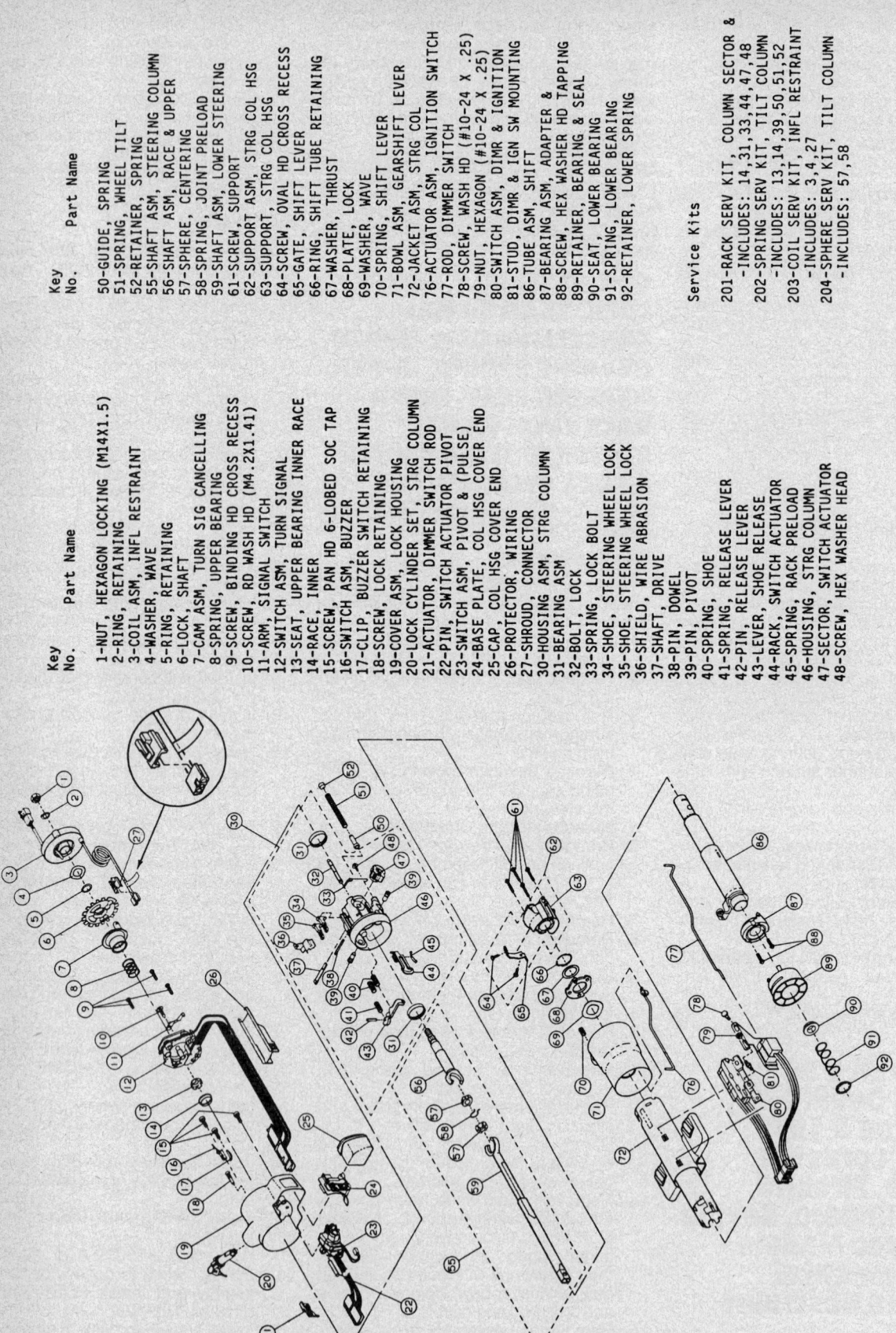

Fig. 98 Exploded view of Supplemental Inflatable Restraint (SIR) steering column. 1989-90 DeVille & Fleetwood

38	DOWEL PIN
39	PIVOT PIN
40	SHOE SPRING
41	RELEASE LEVER SPRING
42	RELEASE LEVER PIN
43	SHOE RELEASE LEVER
44	SWITCH ACTUATOR RACK
45	RACK PRELOAD SPRING
46	STEERING COLUMN HOUSING
47	SWITCH ACTUATOR SECTOR
48	SCREW
50	SPRING GUIDE
51	WHEEL TILT SPRING
52	SPRING RETAINER
55	STEERING COLUMN SHAFT
56	RACE AND UPPER SHAFT
57	CENTERING SPHERE
58	JOINT PRELOAD SPRING
59	LOWER STEERING SHAFT
61	SCREW
62	STEERING COLUMN HOUSING SUPPORT
71	STEERING COLUMN HOUSING SHROUD
72	STEERING COLUMN JACKET
73	LOWER BEARING ADAPTER
74	BEARING
75	BEARING ADAPTER RETAINER
76	LOWER BEARING CLIP
80	IGNITION SWITCH ACTUATOR
81	DIMMER SWITCH ROD
82	SCREW
83	NUT
84	IGNITION SWITCH
85	DIMMER AND IGNITION SWITCH MOUNTING STUD
86	DIMMER SWITCH

1	HEXAGON LOCKING NUT
2	RETAINING RING
3	COIL ASSEMBLY
4	WAVE WASHER
5	RETAINING RING
6	SHAFT LOCK
7	TURN SIGNAL CANCELLING CAM
8	UPPER BEARING SPRING
9	SCREW
10	SCREW
11	SIGNAL SWITCH ARM
12	TURN SIGNAL SWITCH
13	UPPER BEARING INNER RACE SEAT
14	INNER RACE
15	SCREW
16	BUZZER SWITCH
17	BUZZER SWITCH RETAINING CLIP
18	LOCK RETAINING SCREW
19	LOCK HOUSING COVER
20	VATS LOCK CYLINDER SET
21	DIMMER SWITCH ROD ACTUATOR
22	SWITCH ACTUATOR PIVOT PIN
23	PIVOT AND PULSE SWITCH
24	HOUSING COVER END BASE PLATE
25	HOUSING COVER END CAP
26	WIRING PROTECTOR
27	CONNECTOR SHROUD
30	STEERING COLUMN HOUSING
31	BEARING
32	LOCK BOLT
33	LOCK BOLT SPRING
34	STEERING WHEEL LOCK SHOE
35	STEERING WHEEL LOCK SHOE
36	WIRE ABRASION SHIELD
37	DRIVE SHAFT

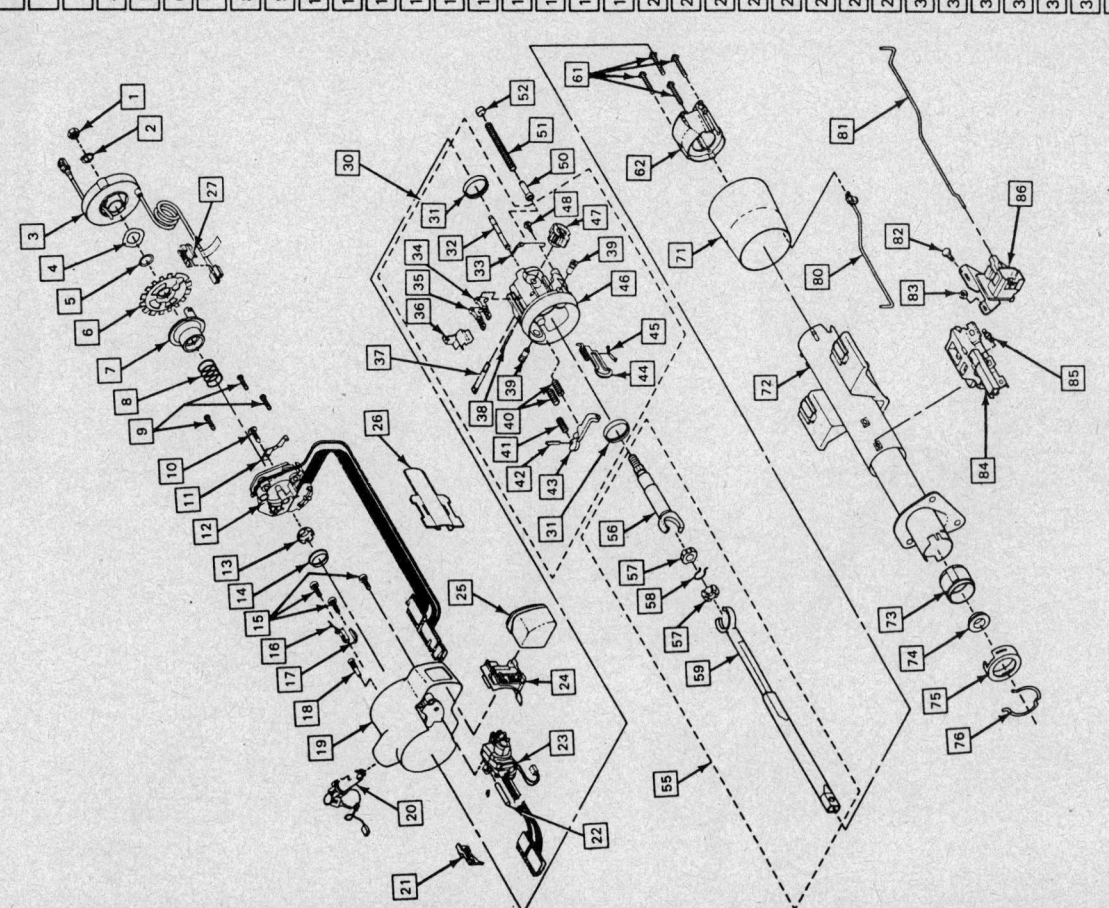

Fig. 99 Exploded view of Supplemental Inflatable Restraint (SIR) steering column. 1990 Camaro

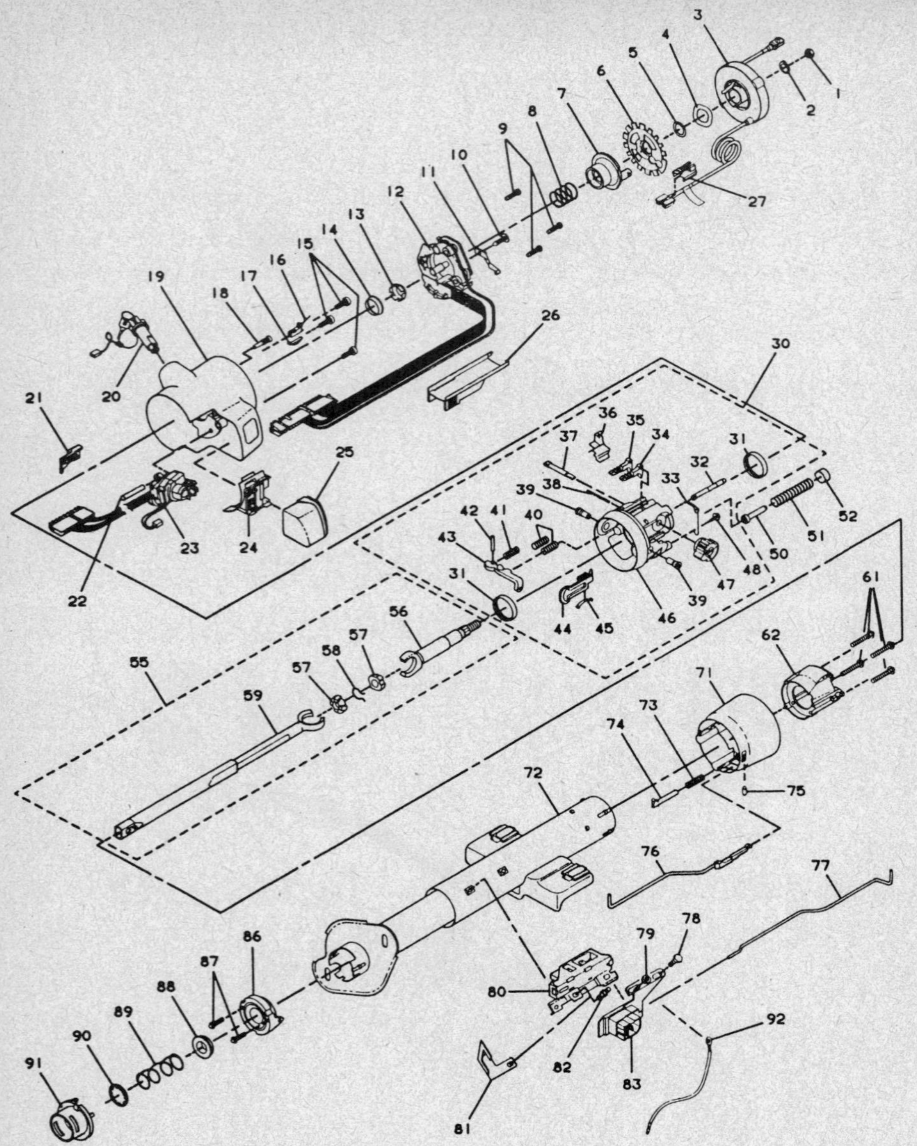

Key No.   Part Name

50-GUIDE, SPRING
51-SPRING, WHEEL TILT
52-RETAINER, SPRING
55-SHAFT ASM, STEERING COLUMN
56-SHAFT ASM, RACE & UPPER
57-SPHERE, CENTERING
58-SPRING, JOINT PRELOAD
59-SHAFT ASM, LOWER STEERING
61-SCREW, SUPPORT
62-SUPPORT ASM, STRG COL HSG
71-SHROUD, STRG COLUMN HOUSING
72-JACKET ASM, STRG COL
73-SPRING, CABLE BACKDRIVE PIN
74-PIN, CABLE BACKDRIVE
75-PIN, INHIBITOR
76-ACTUATOR ASM, IGNITION SWITCH
77-ROD, DIMMER SWITCH
78-SCREW, WASH HD (#10-24 X .25)
79-NUT, HEXAGON (#10-24 X .25)
80-SWITCH ASM, IGNITION
81-BRACKET, CABLE
82-STUD, DIMR & IGN SW MOUNTING
83-SWITCH ASM, DIMMER
86-BEARING ASM, ADAPTER &
87-SCREW, HEX WASHER HD TAPPING
88-SEAT, LOWER BEARING
89-SPRING, LOWER BEARING
90-RETAINER, LOWER SPRING
91-RETAINER (NON-SERVICEABLE)
92-WIRING ASM, HORN PAD GROUND

Service Kits

201-RACK SERV KIT, COLUMN SECTOR &
  -INCLUDES: 14,31,33,44,47,48
202-SPRING SERV KIT, TILT COLUMN
  -INCLUDES: 13,14,39,50,51,52
203-COIL SERV KIT, INFL RESTRAINT
  -INCLUDES: 3,4,27
204-SPHERE SERV KIT, TILT COLUMN
  -INCLUDES: 57,58

Key No.   Part Name

1-NUT, HEXAGON LOCKING (M14X1.5)
2-RING, RETAINING
3-COIL ASM, INFL RESTRAINT
4-WASHER, WAVE
5-RING, RETAINING
6-LOCK, SHAFT
7-CAM ASM, TURN SIG CANCELLING
8-SPRING, UPPER BEARING
9-SCREW, BINDING HD CROSS RECESS
10-SCREW, RD WASH HD (M4.2X1.41)
11-ARM, SIGNAL SWITCH
12-SWITCH ASM, TURN SIGNAL
13-SEAT, UPPER BEARING INNER RACE
14-RACE, INNER
15-SCREW, PAN HD 6-LOBED SOC TAP
16-SWITCH ASM, BUZZER
17-CLIP, BUZZER SWITCH RETAINING
18-SCREW, LOCK RETAINING
19-COVER ASM, LOCK HOUSING
20-LOCK CYLINDER SET, STRG COLUMN
  VATS
21-ACTUATOR, DIMMER SWITCH ROD
22-PIVOT, SWITCH ACTUATOR PIVOT
23-SWITCH ASM, PIVOT & (PULSE)
24-BASE PLATE, COL HSG COVER END
25-CAP, COL HSG COVER END
26-PROTECTOR, WIRING
27-SHROUD, CONNECTOR
30-HOUSING ASM, STRG COLUMN
31-BEARING ASM
32-BOLT, LOCK
33-SPRING, LOCK BOLT
34-SHOE, STEERING WHEEL LOCK
35-SHOE, STEERING WHEEL LOCK
36-SHIELD, WIRE ABRASION
37-SHAFT, DRIVE
38-PIN, DOWEL
39-PIN, PIVOT
40-SPRING, SHOE
41-SPRING, RELEASE LEVER
42-PIN, RELEASE LEVER
43-LEVER, SHOE RELEASE
44-RACK, SWITCH ACTUATOR
45-SPRING, RACK PRELOAD
46-HOUSING, STRG COLUMN
47-SECTOR, SWITCH ACTUATOR
48-SCREW, HEX WASHER HEAD

Fig. 100 Exploded view of Supplemental Inflatable Restraint (SIR) steering column. 1990 Corvette

Key No.	Part Name
50	GUIDE, SPRING
51	SPRING, WHEEL TILT
52	RETAINER, SPRING
55	SHAFT ASM, STEERING COLUMN
56	SHAFT ASM, RACE & UPPER
57	SPHERE, CENTERING
58	SPRING, JOINT PRELOAD
59	SHAFT ASM, LOWER STEERING
61	SCREW, SUPPORT
62	SUPPORT ASM, STRG COL HSG
71	SHROUD, STRG COLUMN HOUSING
72	JACKET ASM, STRG COL
79	CLIP, CONVOLUTED CONDUIT
80	CONDUIT, CONVOLUTED
81	SWITCH ASM, IGNITION
82	SCREW, WASH HD (#10-24 X .25)
83	ACTUATOR ASM, IGNITION SWITCH
91	BEARING ASM, ADAPTER &
93	SCREW, HEX WASHER HD TAPPING
94	RETAINER, BEARING & SEAL
95	SEAT, LOWER BEARING
96	SPRING, LOWER BEARING
97	RETAINER, LOWER SPRING

Service Kits

Key No.	Part Name
201	RACK SERV KIT, COLUMN SECTOR &
	-INCLUDES: 14,31,44
202	SPRING SERV KIT, TILT COLUMN
	-INCLUDES: 13,14,39,50,51,52
203	COIL SERV KIT, INFL RESTRAINT
	-INCLUDES: 3,4,28
204	SPHERE SERV KIT, TILT COLUMN
	-INCLUDES: 57,58

Key No.	Part Name
1	NUT, HEXAGON LOCKING (M14X1.5)
2	RING, RETAINING
3	COIL ASM, INFL RESTRAINT
4	WASHER, WAVE
5	RING, RETAINING
6	LOCK, SHAFT
7	CAM ASM, TURN SIG CANCELLING
8	SPRING, UPPER BEARING
9	SCREW, BINDING HD CROSS RECESS
12	SWITCH ASM, TURN SIGNAL
13	SEAT, UPPER BEARING INNER RACE
14	RACE, INNER
15	SCREW, PAN HD 6-LOBED SOC TAP
16	SWITCH ASM, BUZZER
18	SCREW, LOCK RETAINING
19	COVER ASM, LOCK HOUSING
20	LOCK CYLINDER SET, STRG COLUMN PASS KEY
26	PROTECTOR, WIRING
28	SHROUD, CONNECTOR
30	HOUSING ASM, STRG COLUMN
31	BEARING ASM
32	BOLT, LOCK
34	SHOE, STEERING WHEEL LOCK
35	SHOE, STEERING WHEEL LOCK
36	SHIELD, WIRE ABRASION
38	PIN, DOWEL
39	PIN, PIVOT
40	SPRING, SHOE
41	SPRING, RELEASE LEVER
42	PIN, RELEASE LEVER
43	LEVER, SHOE RELEASE
44	RACK, SWITCH ACTUATOR
45	SPRING, RACK PRELOAD
46	HOUSING, STRG COLUMN
48	WASHER, SPRING THRUST

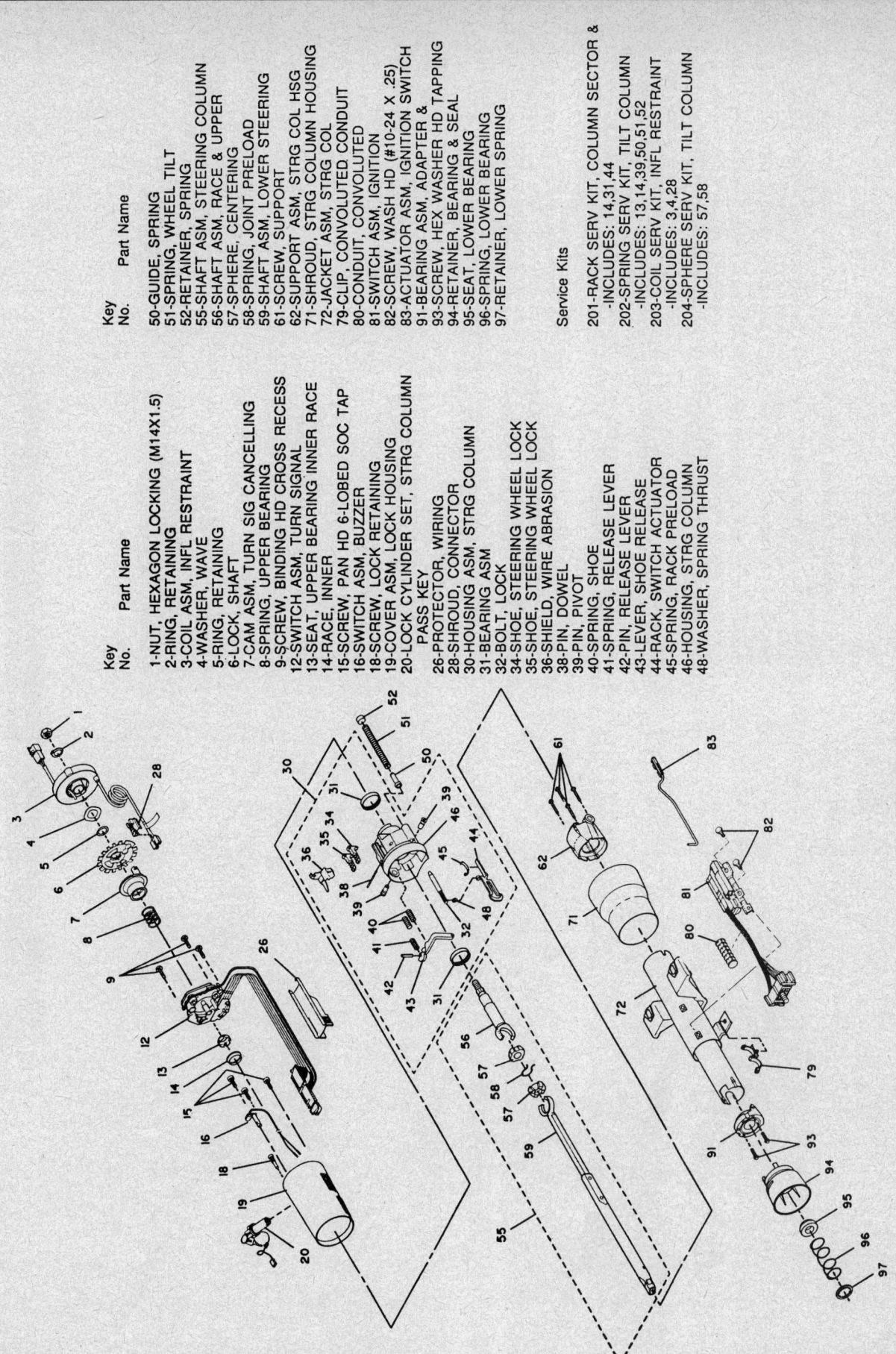

Fig. 101 Exploded view of Supplemental Inflatable Restraint (SIR) steering column. 1990 Eldorado & Seville

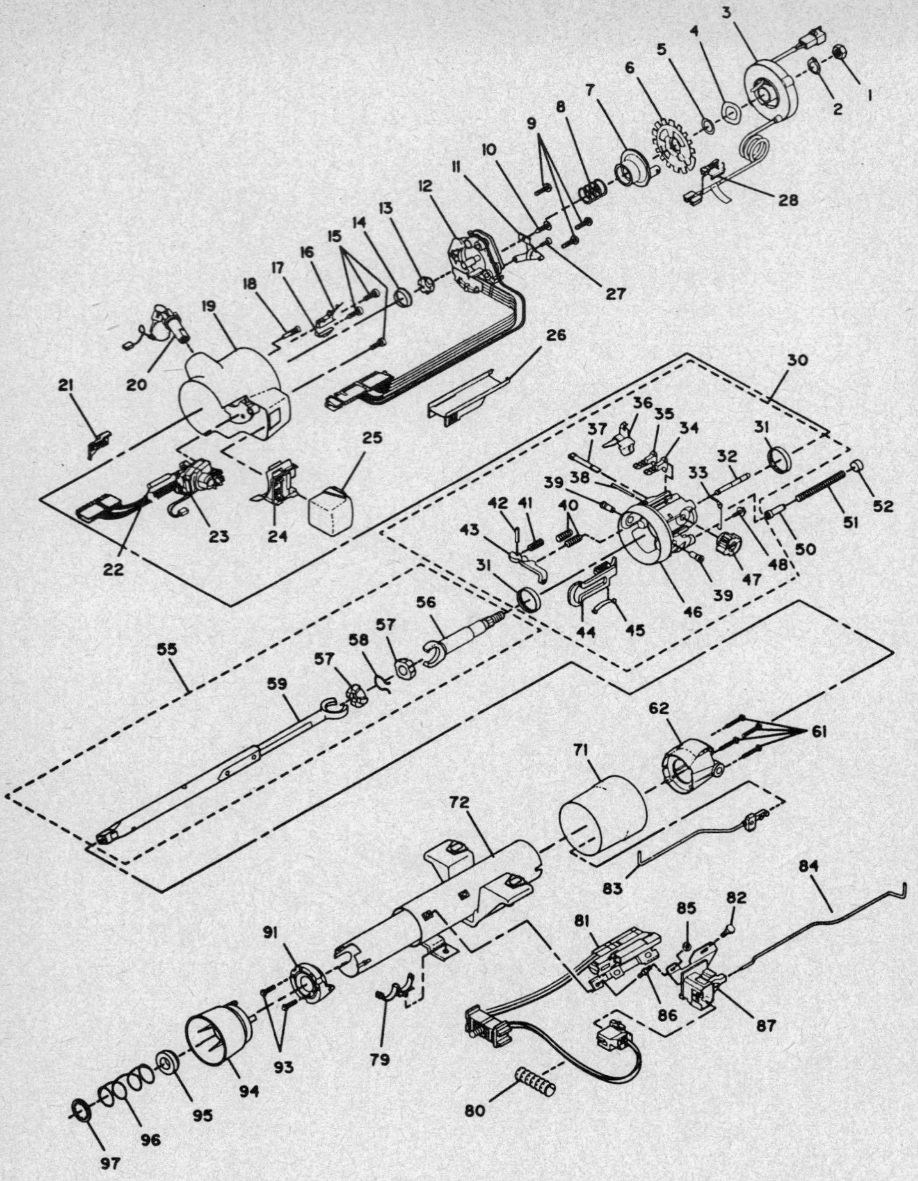

Key No. — Part Name

Key No.	Part Name
1	NUT, HEXAGON LOCKING (M14X1.5)
2	RING, RETAINING
3	COIL ASM, INFL RESTRAINT
4	WASHER, WAVE
5	RING, RETAINING
6	LOCK, SHAFT
7	CAM ASM, TURN SIG CANCELLING
8	SPRING, UPPER BEARING
9	SCREW, BINDING HD CROSS RECESS
10	SCREW, RD WASH HD (M4.2X1.41)
11	RACE, INNER
12	SWITCH ASM, TURN SIGNAL
13	SEAT, UPPER BEARING INNER RACE
14	RACE, INNER
15	SCREW, PAN HD 6-LOBED SOC TAP
16	SWITCH ASM, BUZZER
17	CLIP, BUZZER SWITCH RETAINING
18	SCREW, LOCK RETAINING
19	COVER ASM, LOCK HOUSING
20	LOCK CYLINDER SET, STRG COLUMN PASS KEY
21	ACTUATOR, DIMMER SWITCH ROD
22	PIN, SWITCH ACTUATOR PIVOT
23	SWITCH ASM, PIVOT & (PULSE)
24	BASE PLATE, COL HSG COVER END
25	CAP, COL HSG COVER END
26	PROTECTOR, WIRING
27	SCREW, FLT HD TAPPING
28	SHROUD, CONNECTOR
30	HOUSING ASM, STRG COLUMN
31	BEARING ASM
32	BOLT, LOCK
33	SPRING, LOCK BOLT
34	SHOE, STEERING WHEEL LOCK
35	SHOE, STEERING WHEEL LOCK
36	SHIELD, WIRE ABRASION
37	SHAFT, DRIVE
38	PIN, DOWEL
39	PIN, PIVOT
40	SPRING, SHOE
41	SPRING, RELEASE LEVER
42	PIN, RELEASE LEVER
43	LEVER, SHOE RELEASE
44	RACK, SWITCH ACTUATOR
45	SPRING, RACK PRELOAD
46	HOUSING, STRG COLUMN
47	SECTOR, SWITCH ACTUATOR
48	SCREW, HEX WASHER HEAD
50	GUIDE, SPRING
51	SPRING, WHEEL TILT
52	RETAINER, SPRING
55	SHAFT ASM, STEERING COLUMN
56	SHAFT ASM, RACE & UPPER
57	SPHERE, CENTERING
58	SPHERE, JOINT PRELOAD
59	SHAFT ASM, LOWER STEERING
61	SCREW, SUPPORT
62	SUPPORT ASM, STRG COL HSG
71	SHROUD, STRG COLUMN HOUSING
72	JACKET ASM, STRG COL
79	CLIP, CONVOLUTED CONDUIT
80	CONDUIT, CONVOLUTED
81	SWITCH ASM, IGNITION
82	SCREW, WASH HD (#10-24 X .25)
83	ACTUATOR ASM, IGNITION SWITCH
84	ROD, DIMMER SWITCH
85	NUT, HEXAGON (#10-24 X .25)
86	STUD, DIMR & IGN SW MOUNTING
87	SWITCH ASM, DIMMER
91	BEARING ASM, ADAPTER &
93	SCREW, HEX WASHER HD TAPPING
94	RETAINER, BEARING & SEAL
95	SEAT, LOWER BEARING
96	SPRING, LOWER BEARING
97	RETAINER, LOWER SPRING

Service Kits

Key No.	Part Name
201	RACK SERV KIT, COLUMN SECTOR &
	—INCLUDES: 14,31,33,44,47,48
202	SPRING SERV KIT, TILT COLUMN
	—INCLUDES: 13,14,39,50,51,52
203	COIL SERV KIT, INFL RESTRAINT
	—INCLUDES: 3,4,28
204	SPHERE SERV KIT, TILT COLUMN
	—INCLUDES: 57,58

Fig. 102 Exploded view of Supplemental Inflatable Restraint (SIR) steering column. 1990 Reatta & Riviera

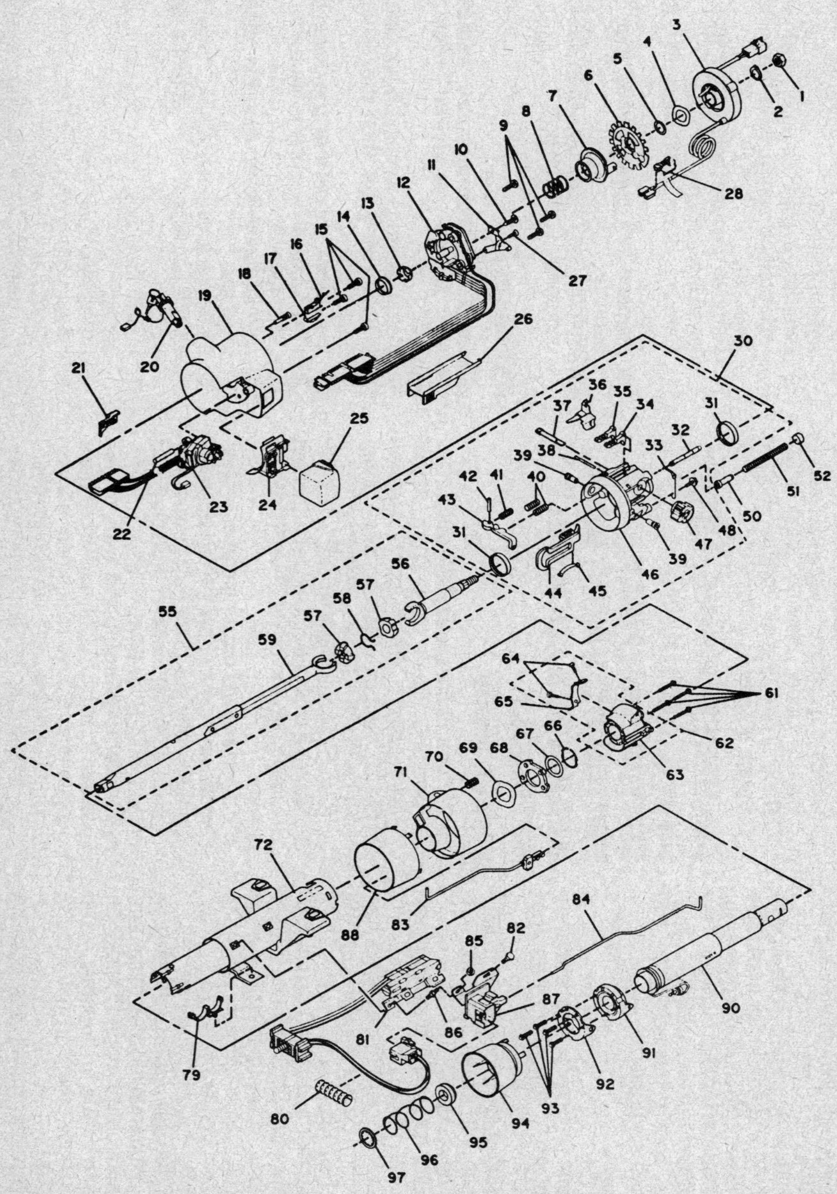

Key No. / Part Name

1-NUT, HEXAGON LOCKING (M14X1.5)
2-RING, RETAINING
3-COIL ASM, INFL RESTRAINT
4-WASHER, WAVE
5-RING, RETAINING
6-LOCK, SHAFT
7-CAM ASM, TURN SIG CANCELLING
8-SPRING, UPPER BEARING
9-SCREW, BINDING HD CROSS RECESS
10-SCREW, RD WASH HD (M4.2X1.41)
11-ARM, SIGNAL SWITCH
12-SWITCH ASM, TURN SIGNAL
13-SEAT, UPPER BEARING INNER RACE
14-RACE, INNER
15-SCREW, PAN HD 6-LOBED SOC TAP
16-SWITCH ASM, BUZZER
17-CLIP, BUZZER SWITCH RETAINING
18-SCREW, LOCK RETAINING
19-COVER ASM, LOCK HOUSING
20-LOCK CYLINDER SET, STRG COLUMN
   PASS KEY
21-ACTUATOR, DIMMER SWITCH ROD
22-PIN, SWITCH ACTUATOR PIVOT
23-SWITCH ASM, PIVOT & (PULSE)
24-BASE PLATE, COL HSG COVER END
25-CAP, COL HSG COVER END
26-PROTECTOR, WIRING
27-SCREW, FLT HD TAPPING
28-SHROUD, CONNECTOR
30-HOUSING ASM, STRG COLUMN
31-BEARING ASM
32-BOLT, LOCK
33-SPRING, LOCK BOLT
34-SHOE, STEERING WHEEL LOCK
35-SHOE, STEERING WHEEL LOCK
36-SHIELD, WIRE ABRASION
37-SHAFT, DRIVE
38-PIN, DOWEL
39-PIN, PIVOT
40-SPRING, SHOE
41-SPRING, RELEASE LEVER
42-PIN, RELEASE LEVER
43-LEVER, SHOE RELEASE
44-RACK, SWITCH ACTUATOR
45-SPRING, RACK PRELOAD
46-HOUSING, STRG COLUMN
47-SECTOR, SWITCH ACTUATOR
48-SCREW, HEX WASHER HEAD
50-GUIDE, SPRING
51-SPRING, WHEEL TILT
52-RETAINER, SPRING

Key No. / Part Name

55-SHAFT ASM, STEERING COLUMN
56-SHAFT ASM, RACE & UPPER
57-SPHERE, CENTERING
58-SPRING, JOINT PRELOAD
59-SHAFT ASM, LOWER STEERING
61-SCREW, SUPPORT
62-SUPPORT ASM, STRG COL HSG
63-SUPPORT, STRG COL HSG
64-SCREW, OVAL HD CROSS RECESS
65-GATE, SHIFT LEVER
66-RING, SHIFT TUBE RETAINING
67-WASHER, THRUST
68-PLATE, LOCK
69-WASHER, WAVE
70-SPRING, SHIFT LEVER
71-BOWL, GEARSHIFT LEVER
72-JACKET ASM, STRG COL
79-CLIP, CONVOLUTED CONDUIT
80-CONDUIT, CONVOLUTED
81-SWITCH ASM, IGNITION
82-SCREW, WASH HD (#10-24 X .25)
83-ACTUATOR ASM, IGNITION SWITCH
84-ROD, DIMMER SWITCH
85-NUT, HEXAGON (#10-24 X .25)
86-STUD, DIMR & IGN SW MOUNTING
87-SWITCH ASM, DIMMER
88-SHROUD, GEARSHIFT BOWL
90-TUBE ASM, SHIFT
91-BEARING ASM, ADAPTER &
92-CUP, LOWER BEARING
93-SCREW, HEX WASHER HD TAPPING
94-RETAINER, BEARING & SEAL
95-SEAT, LOWER BEARING
96-SPRING, LOWER BEARING
97-RETAINER, LOWER SPRING

Service Kits

201-RACK SERV KIT, COLUMN SECTOR &
   -INCLUDES: 14,31,33,44,47,48
202-SPRING SERV KIT, TILT COLUMN
   -INCLUDES: 13,14,39,50,51,52
203-COIL SERV KIT, INFL RESTRAINT
   -INCLUDES: 3,4,28
204-SPHERE SERV KIT, TILT COLUMN
   -INCLUDES: 57,58

Fig. 103 Exploded view of Supplemental Inflatable Restraint (SIR) steering column. 1990 Toronado

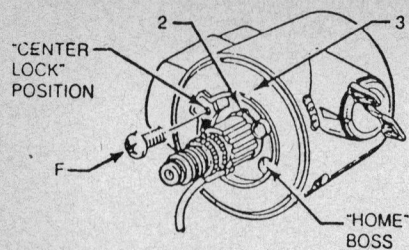

2. RING, RETAINING
3. COIL ASM, INFL RESTRAINT
F. LOCK SCREW

Fig. 104 Locking coil assembly, Supplemental Inflatable Restraint (SIR) system

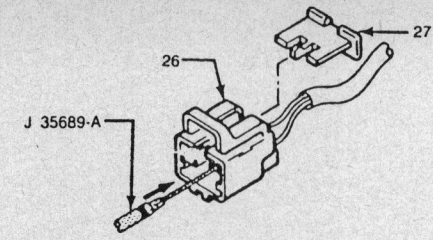

26. CONNECTOR ASM, BODY
27. TERMINAL, POS ASSURANCE

Fig. 105 Disassembling connector body, Supplemental Inflatable Restraint (SIR) system

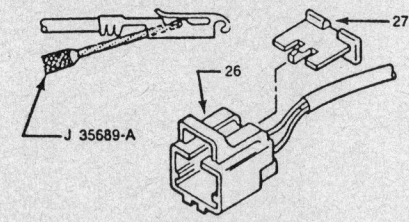

26. CONNECTOR ASM, BODY
27. TERMINAL, POS ASSURANCE

Fig. 107 Assembling connector body, Supplemental Inflatable Restraint (SIR) system

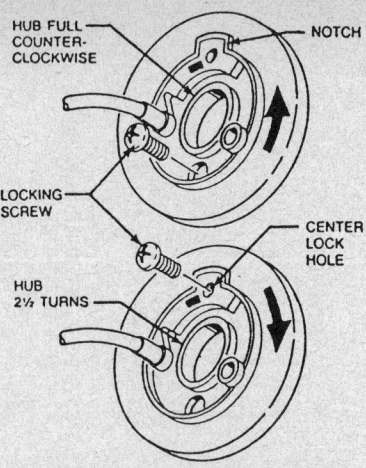

Fig. 106 Centering coil assembly, Supplemental Inflatable Restraint (SIR) system

LOCK HOUSING COVER, COVER END CAP, PIVOT & SWITCH ASSEMBLY, DIMMER SWITCH ROD ACTUATOR & TILT SPRING ASSEMBLY

Disassembly

1. Perform "Disassembly" steps for "Coil Assembly, Shaft Lock, Turn Signal Cancelling Cam, Upper Bearing Spring, Upper Bearing Seat, Inner Race Turn Signal Switch, Buzzer Switch & Lock Cylinder Set."
2. Remove lock housing cover attaching screws and the cover, then the tilt lever.
3. Remove cover housing end cap, base plate, and dimmer switch rod actuator, then gently pull pivot switch wiring harness through column housing and gear shift lever bowl.
4. **On vehicles equipped with cruise control,** unplug connector from base plate and remove multifunction lever.
5. **On all models,** remove pivot pin, then the pivot and switch assembly.
6. Remove spring retainer, then the spring and spring guide.

Assembly

Ensure all fasteners are securely seated before applying required torque.

1. Coat spring guide and spring with lithium grease and install them, then install spring retainer.
2. Install pivot and pulse switch assembly, then the pivot pin.
3. Route lock housing cover wire harness through gear shift lever bowl and column housing.
4. Install dimmer switch rod actuator to base plate, then the base plate to gear shift lever bowl, ensuring bottom edge of dimmer switch rod actuator rests on bend in dimmer switch rod.
5. Install cover housing end cap.
6. **On vehicles equipped with cruise control,** plug multifunction lever connector and cruise control wires on wipe/wash switch together and mount on base plate and install multifunction lever.
7. **On all models,** install lock housing

cover. Tighten screw in 12 o'clock position first, screw in 8 o'clock position second and screw in 4 o'clock position third, then **torque** screws to 89 inch lbs. in same order.

8. Perform "Assembly" steps for "Coil Assembly, Shaft Lock, Turn Signal Cancelling Cam, Upper Bearing Spring, Upper Bearing Seat, Inner Race Turn Signal Switch, Buzzer Switch & Lock Cylinder Set."

COLUMN HOUSING, LOCK SHOES, ACTUATOR SECTOR ASSEMBLY, SWITCH ACTUATOR RACK, BEARINGS & LOCK BOLT ASSEMBLY

Disassembly

1. Perform "Disassembly" steps for "Coil Assembly, Shaft Lock, Turn Signal Cancelling Cam, Upper Bearing Spring, Upper Bearing Seat, Inner Race Turn Signal Switch, Buzzer Switch & Lock Cylinder Set."
2. Remove lock housing cover attaching screws and the cover, then the tilt lever.
3. Remove cover housing end cap, base plate and dimmer switch rod actuator, then gently pull pivot switch wire harness through column housing and gear shift lever bowl.
4. **On vehicles equipped with cruise control,** unplug connector from base plate and remove multifunction lever.
5. **On all models,** remove spring retainer, then the spring and spring guide.

Perform the following steps to center coil assembly:

A. Remove coil assembly (3) from column
B. Lock screw to boss "Home" position, allowing hub to rotate
C. Hold coil assembly housing in one hand with steering wheel connector up
D. Rotate coil hub counterclockwise until it stops. Turn coil over to inspect coil position through the clear bottom. The coil ribbon should be wound up snug against center hub.
E. Rotate coil hub clockwise approximately two and a half (2½) turns until "Center Lock" hole is even with the notch in coil housing
F. Hold hub in position while installing lock screw to "Center Lock" hole

6. Using tool J-21854-01 or equivalent, remove pivot pins, **Fig. 64,** then reinstall tilt lever.
7. Remove column housing assembly by pulling back on tilt lever and pulling housing down and away from column.
8. Remove drive shaft, then the switch actuator sector.
9. Remove switch actuator rack and rack preload spring, then the release lever pin.
10. Remove release lever, then the release lever spring.
11. Remove dowel pin, then the lock shoes.
12. Remove lock shoe springs, then the bearings.
13. Remove hex head bolt, then the lock bolt spring and lock bolt.

Assembly

Ensure all fasteners are securely seated before applying required torque.

1. Install bearings to column housing.
2. Install drive shaft, then the actuator sector.
3. Install lock shoes, then the dowel pin.
4. Install lock shoe springs, then the release lever spring.
5. Install release lever, then the release lever pin.
6. Install rack preload spring, then the switch actuator rack to actuator sector.
7. Install lock bolt, then the lock bolt spring.
8. Install hex head bolt.
9. Install column housing assembly to column as follows:
   a. Position column housing assembly

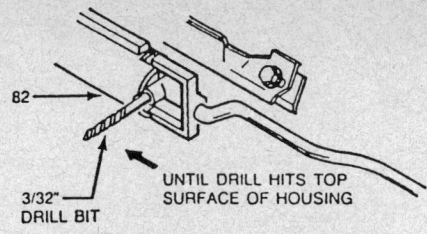

82. SWITCH, DIMMER

Fig. 108 Adjusting dimmer switch, Supplemental Inflatable Restraint (SIR) system

and align switch actuator rack with pin on end of actuator rod.

b. Pull back on tilt lever, pushing column housing assembly onto column housing support assembly, then release tilt lever to lock shoes.

10. Remove tilt lever.
11. Lubricate pivot pins with lithium grease and install them.
12. Perform "Assembly" steps for "Lock Housing Cover, Cover End Cap, Pivot & Switch Assembly, Dimmer Switch Rod Actuator & Tilt Spring Assembly" and "Coil Assembly, Shaft Lock, Turn Signal Cancelling Cam, Upper Bearing Spring, Upper Bearing Seat, Inner Race Turn Signal Switch, Buzzer Switch & Lock Cylinder Set."

SHAFT ASSEMBLY, COLUMN HOUSING SUPPORT, SHIFT TUBE ASSEMBLY, IGNITION SWITCH, DIMMER SWITCH & LOWER BEARING ASSEMBLY

Disassembly

1. Perform "Disassembly" steps for "Coil Assembly, Shaft Lock, Turn Signal Cancelling Cam, Upper Bearing Spring, Upper Bearing Seat, Inner Race Turn Signal Switch, Buzzer Switch & Lock Cylinder Set."
2. Remove lock housing cover attaching screws and the cover, then the tilt lever.
3. Remove cover housing end cap, base plate and dimmer switch rod actuator, then gently pull pivot switch wire harness through column housing and gear shift lever bowl.
4. **On vehicles equipped with cruise control,** unplug connector from base plate and remove multifunction lever.
5. **On all models,** remove spring retainer, then the spring and spring guide.
6. Using tool J-21854-01 or equivalent, remove pivot pins, **Fig. 64,** then reinstall tilt lever.
7. Remove column housing assembly by pulling back on tilt lever and pulling housing down and away from column.
8. Remove steering column from vehicle. **Once steering column is removed from vehicle, the column is extremely susceptible to damage.**

Dropping column assembly on its end could collapse steering shaft or loosen plastic injections that maintain column rigidity. Leaning on column assembly may cause jacket to bend or deform. Any of the above damage may impair column's collapsible design. If it is necessary to remove steering wheel, use only the specified steering wheel puller. Under no conditions should end of shaft be hammered on because hammering could loosen plastic injections that maintain column rigidity.

9. Remove bearing retainer, then the spring retainer.
10. Remove lower bearing spring, then the lower bearing seat.
11. Remove screws and lower bearing, then the shaft assembly. Check for accident damage.
12. Remove lower shaft.
13. Remove sphere from shaft assembly, then the retainer clip from sphere.
14. Remove housing support assembly retaining screws, then the housing support assembly and dimmer switch rod.
15. Remove hex nut and hex head bolt, then the dimmer switch and mounting stud.
16. Remove ignition switch and actuator rod assembly, then the shift tube retaining ring.
17. Remove thrust washer, then the gear shift lever spring.
18. Using tool J-23072 or equivalent, remove shift tube.
19. Remove lock plate and wave washer, then the gear shift lever bowl.

Assembly

Ensure all fasteners are securely seated before applying required torque.

1. Install gear shift lever spring to gear shift lever bowl, then the gear shift lever bowl to the shift tube jacket.
2. Lubricate wave washer with lithium grease and install it.
3. Install lock plate, then, using tool J-23073-1-2-3 or equivalent, the shift tube.
4. Install thrust washer, then the shift tube retaining ring.
5. Install dimmer switch rod to housing support.
6. Install housing support assembly, **torquing** attaching bolts to 79 inch lbs.
7. Install actuator rod assembly to track in housing support.
8. Install retaining clip and sphere to shaft assembly.
9. Install lower shaft to shaft assembly with block tooth on shaft end of shaft assembly at 12 o'clock position and notch at lower end of shaft at 4 o'clock position.
10. Lubricate shaft assembly with lithium grease and install to column.
11. Perform "Assembly" steps for "Column Housing, Lock Shoes, Actuator Sector Assembly, Switch Actuator Rack, Bearings & Lock Bolt Assembly," "Lock Housing Cover, Cover End Cap, Pivot & Switch Assembly, Dimmer Switch Rod Actuator & Tilt Spring

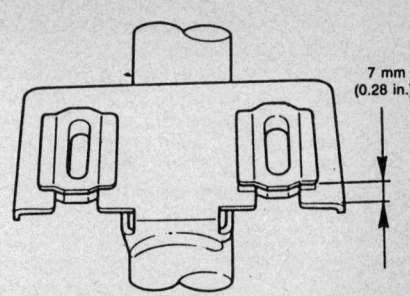

7 mm (0.28 in.)

Fig. 109 Checking slide block. 1990 Storm

Assembly" and "Coil Assembly, Shaft Lock, Turn Signal Cancelling Cam, Upper Bearing Spring, Upper Bearing Seat, Inner Race Turn Signal Switch, Buzzer Switch & Lock Cylinder Set."

12. Lubricate inner surface of lower bearing with lithium grease, then install lower bearing and screws.
13. Install lower bearing seat, then the lower bearing spring.
14. Install spring retainer, then the bearing retainer.
15. Install dimmer switch, hex nut and hex head bolt, then adjust dimmer switch, **Fig. 108.**
16. Install ignition switch and mounting stud, then adjust ignition switch, **Fig. 73.**
17. Install column to vehicle instrument panel.

Storm w/Supplemental Inflatable Restraint (SIR)

Before removing the SIR steering column, the wheels of the car must be straight and the column in the Lock position. **Care must be taken when handling column with a live inflator module. Never point bag deploy surface toward you, and never stand column on steering wheel. Accidental deployment in these positions may cause injury. Always face bag deploy surface toward open space to allow for unrestricted expansion.**

The (DERM) Diagnostic Energy Reserve Module, can maintain sufficient voltage to cause a deployment for up to 10 minutes after the ignition switch is turned to the Off position and the battery ground has been disconnected.

DISASSEMBLY

1. Remove the inflator module as follows:
   a. With the ignition switch in the Off position and the battery ground cable disconnected and taped, remove the SIR fuse (No. 3) from the fuse panel.
   b. Disconnect the orange 3-way connector at the base of the steering column.
2. Remove the SIR module screws and the SIR module.

3. Remove steering wheel retaining nut and steering wheel.
4. Remove horn switch screws and horn switch, rear steering wheel cover screws and rear cover.
5. Remove lower switch panel, dash lighter panel and hood release panel.
6. Remove lap air deflector and left lower dash trim panel.
7. Remove upper steering column mounting bolts and drop column down.
8. Remove two piece steering column cover, then disconnect coil assembly wiring harness from turn signal switch.
9. Remove four screws and coil assembly from turn signal switch.
10. Remove turn signal switch, then snap ring and spacer collar from steering shaft.
11. Remove ignition switch, then steering shaft from steering column.
12. Remove back drive cable and guide.
13. Inspect steering column for damage as follows:
   a. Check upper column tube bearing for abnormal noise or rotation difficulty, replace as necessary.
   b. Check slide block on steering column bracket assembly. Block be within .28 inch from the slots insert edge. **Fig. 109**. If measurement is not within specifications, replace column.

ASSEMBLY

1. Install guide onto column, then ignition switch.
2. Install steering shaft into column, then install collar and snap ring onto column.
3. Install turn signal switch onto column, then four screws and coil assembly onto turn signal switch.
4. Connect coil assembly wiring harness into turn signal switch.
5. Install two piece steering column cover, then install steering column and steering column mounting bolts and **torque** to 18 ft.lbs..
6. Install left lower dash trim panel and lap air deflector.
7. Install hood release panel, dash lighter panel and lower switch panel.
8. Install rear steering wheel cover, then connect horn contact switches into wheel.
9. Install steering wheel and retaining nut, **torque** nut to 25 ft. lbs.
10. Install SIR module and SIR module screws, **torque** screws to 44 inch lbs.
11. Connect the orange 3-way connector at the base of the steering column.
12. With the ignition switch in the Off position, install the SIR fuse (No. 3) in the fuse panel and connect the battery ground cable.
13. Turn the ignition switch to the Run position and make sure the "Inflatable Restraint" light flashes 7 to 9 times and then goes out.

Spectrum

Refer to **Fig. 110.** when servicing this steering column.

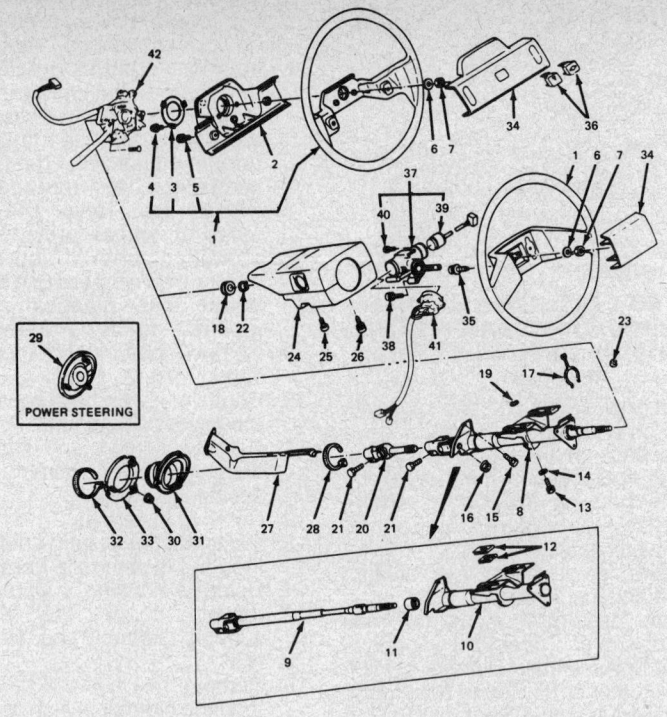

1. Wheel Asm., Steering	22. Ring, Snap
2. Cover, Lower Steering Wheel	23. Washer, LK Column to Shaft
3. Ring, Horn Contact	24. Cover Set, Steering Cowl, Upper and Lower
4. Screw, Contact Ring	25. Screw, Steering Cover
5. Screw, Lower Cover	26. Screw, Tap, Steering Cover
6. Washer, PL, Steering Wheel to Shaft	27. Protector, Column Shaft
7. Nut, Steering Wheel to Shaft	28. Clip, Protector to Column
8. Column Asm., Steering Shaft	29. Seal, Power Steering Unit
9. Shaft, Steering	30. Nut, Steering Unit Seal
10. Column, Steering	31. Boot, Rubber Steering Unit
11. Bush, Steering Column	32. Clip, Boot
12. Plate, Coating, Steering Column	33. Plate, Boot, Steering Unit
13. Bolt, Steering Column to Instrument Panel	34. Shroud Asm., Pad, Steering Wheel
14. Washer, PL Steering Column to Instrument Panel	35. Screw, Steering Wheel Shroud
15. Bolt, SEMS, Steering Column to BC Pedal Mtg	36. Mark, Steering Wheel (Emblem)
16. Nut, Column to Pedal Mtg	37. Lock Asm., Steering
17. Clip, Steering Column	38. Bolt, SEMS, Steering Lock
18. Cushion, Rubber	39. Switch, Ignition Starter
19. Washer, LK, Steering Column to Instrument Panel	40. Screw, Ignition Switch to Steering Lock
20. Shaft, Steering Intermediate	41. Switch, Ignition
21. Bolt, Column to Shaft	42. Switch, Turn Signal

Fig. 110 Steering column exploded view. Spectrum

1. Remove turn signal switch, then insert key into ignition and move to the On position. Lock bar should be pulled all the way in as key is turned.
2. Remove the steering shaft snap ring and rubber cushion.
3. Remove lock assembly to steering column attaching screws, then remove the lock arm.
4. Pull shaft from column.
5. Inspect for worn or damaged parts and replace as necessary.
6. Reverse procedure to assemble noting the following:
   a. Turn the ignition lock to the On position when installing.
   b. Ensure snap ring is seated securely.

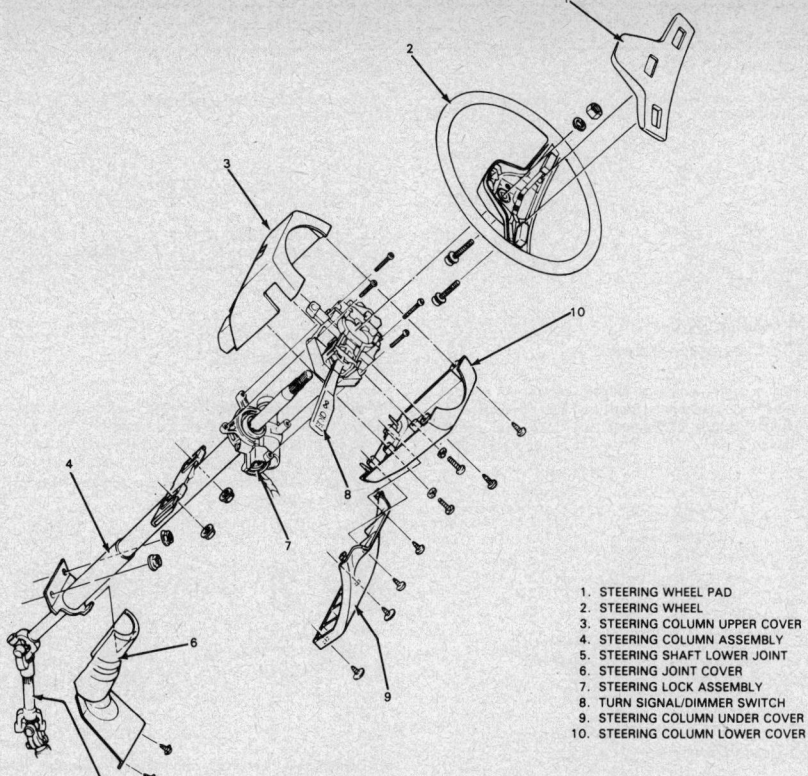

1. STEERING WHEEL PAD
2. STEERING WHEEL
3. STEERING COLUMN UPPER COVER
4. STEERING COLUMN ASSEMBLY
5. STEERING SHAFT LOWER JOINT
6. STEERING JOINT COVER
7. STEERING LOCK ASSEMBLY
8. TURN SIGNAL/DIMMER SWITCH
9. STEERING COLUMN UNDER COVER
10. STEERING COLUMN LOWER COVER

Fig. 111 Steering column exploded view. Sprint

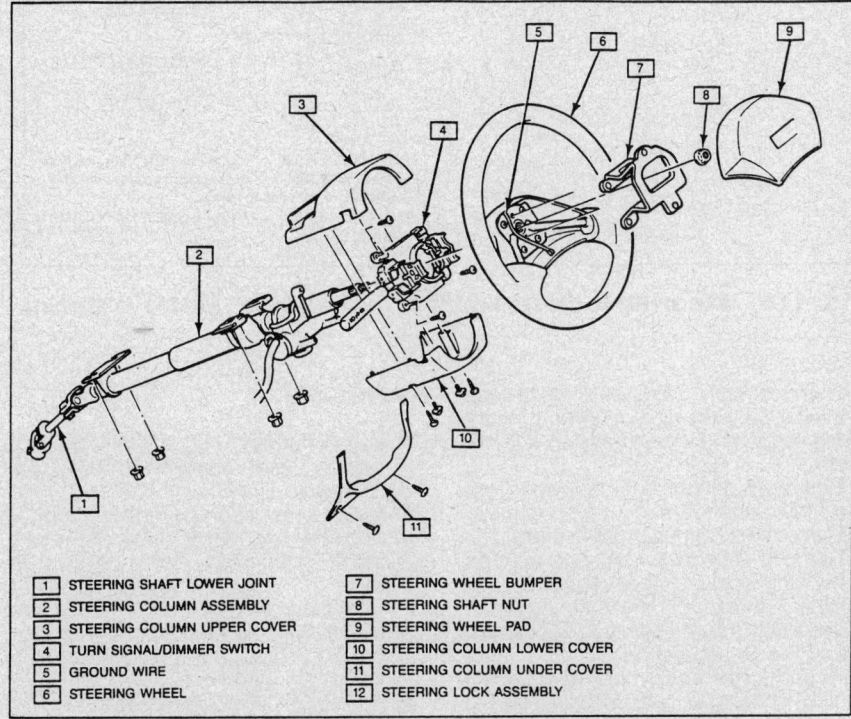

1	STEERING SHAFT LOWER JOINT	7	STEERING WHEEL BUMPER
2	STEERING COLUMN ASSEMBLY	8	STEERING SHAFT NUT
3	STEERING COLUMN UPPER COVER	9	STEERING WHEEL PAD
4	TURN SIGNAL/DIMMER SWITCH	10	STEERING COLUMN LOWER COVER
5	GROUND WIRE	11	STEERING COLUMN UNDER COVER
6	STEERING WHEEL	12	STEERING LOCK ASSEMBLY

Fig. 112 Steering column exploded view. Metro

Metro & Sprint

Refer to **Figs. 28 through 31 and 111 through 114** when servicing this steering column.

Lemans
FIXED COLUMN

Refer to **Fig. 115** when servicing this column.

TURN SIGNAL SWITCH HOUSING ASSEMBLY, STEERING SHAFT ASSEMBLY, STEERING COLUMN HOUSING & IGNITION SWITCH HOUSING ASSEMBLY

Disassembly

1. Disconnect battery ground cable and remove steering wheel horn cap and horn leads.
2. Remove nut, retainer and steering wheel, then unclip contact ring from wheel if necessary.
3. Remove steering column as previously described in Steering Column, Replace section.
4. Remove alignment bushing from lower end of shaft assembly, then upper steering shaft spring.
5. Remove thrust washer, washer head tap screws and turn signal switch housing assembly.
6. Turn lock cylinder to the Run position and remove steering shaft from lower end of jacket assembly.
7. Remove shear bolts, shear bolt washers and ignition switch housing as follows:
   a. Drill off head of shear bolts down to shear bolt washers with a 1/4 inch drill bit.
   b. Separate washers and switch housing from column housing.
   c. Remove threaded end of shear bolts from ignition switch housing using vise grips.
8. Remove lock cylinder from ignition switch housing, ignition switch retaining screw and ignition switch assembly.
9. Remove shear bolts and column housing as follows:
   a. Drill off head of shear bolts with a 5/16 inch drill bit.
   b. Separate column housing from jacket assembly.
   c. Remove threaded end of shear bolts from Jacket assembly using vise grips.

Assembly

1. Install column housing to jacket assembly using "new" shear bolts and **torque** until bolt head separates from body, approximately 11 ft. lbs.
2. Install ignition switch to ignition switch housing ensuring retaining pin engages ear on ignition switch. Ensure that the tab on the lock cylinder shaft and the slotted opening on the ignition switch are in alignment, the lock cylinder and ignition switch must be in the Run position prior to installation.
3. Install lock cylinder into ignition switch housing.
4. Install ignition switch housing to column housing using "new" shear bolts and washers and **torque** until bolt head separates from body, approximately 15 ft. lbs.
5. Turn lock cylinder to the Run position and install steering shaft assembly into lower end of jacket assembly until bottomed.
6. Turn lock cylinder to the Off-Lock position and remove key.

7. Rotate steering shaft until lock bolt engages and locks steering shaft in position.
8. Install signal switch housing to steering column housing with washer head tap screws and **torque** to 30 inch lbs.
9. Install alignment bushing over lower end of steering shaft and into lower end of jacket assembly.
10. Install steering column in car, refer to Steering Column, Replace section.
11. Install thrust washer and upper steering shaft spring on steering shaft.
12. Install contact ring if necessary, steering wheel, retainer and nut and **torque** nut to 13 ft. lbs.
13. Install horn leads and cap, then connect battery ground cable.

TILT COLUMN

Refer to **Fig. 116** when servicing this column.

TURN SIGNAL SWITCH HOUSING ASSEMBLY, STEERING SHAFT ASSEMBLY, STEERING COLUMN HOUSING & IGNITION SWITCH HOUSING ASSEMBLY

Disassembly

1. Disconnect battery ground cable and remove steering wheel horn cap and horn leads.
2. Remove nut, retainer and steering wheel, then unclip contact ring from wheel if necessary.
3. Remove steering column as previously described in Steering Column, Replace section.
4. Remove alignment bushing from lower end of shaft assembly, then cancelling cam spring from upper end of shaft assembly.
5. Remove washer head tap screws and signal switch housing assembly.
6. Compress spring retainer and upper bearing spring with special tools No. J 36667 and J 23653-A or equivalent.
7. Remove retaining ring, spring retainer, upper bearing spring, inner race seat and inner race.
8. Pull tilt lever and tilt column all the way up.
9. Insert a phillips tip screwdriver into square opening in spring retainer, push down and turn left to release retainer and tilt spring.
10. Remove spring retainer and tilt spring.
11. Remove two pivot pins using special tool No. J 21854-01 or equivalent.
12. Turn lock cylinder to the Run position and pull tilt lever to release column housing from housing support.
13. Remove shear bolts, shear bolt washers and ignition switch housing from column housing as follows:
    a. Drill off head of shear bolts down to shear bolt washers with a 1/4 inch drill bit.
    b. Separate washers and switch housing from column housing.
    c. Remove threaded end of shear bolts from ignition switch housing using vise grips.

14. Remove lock cylinder from ignition switch housing, ignition switch retaining screw and ignition switch assembly.
15. Remove steering shaft assembly from housing support.
16. Remove tilt bumpers using pliers.
17. Remove support screws and support housing from jacket assembly.
18. When necessary, the steering shaft assembly may be serviced as follows:
    a. Prior to separation of upper shaft and lower shaft, note relationship of upper shaft with lock bolt slot at 12 o'clock position and lower shaft pinch bolt groove at 7 o'clock position. Refer to this orientation for proper reassembly.
    b. Position upper shaft 90° to lower shaft and separate.
    c. Rotate centering sphere 90° and remove from upper shaft.
    d. Separate sphere halves and joint preload spring.

---

5. REMOVE AND INSTALL STEERING LOCK

REMOVAL

1) Remove steering column. Refer to STEERING COLUMN REMOVAL.

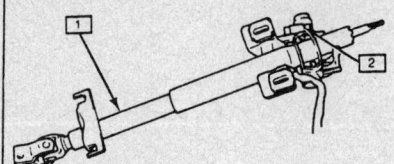

1. STEERING COLUMN
2. IGNITION SWITCH ASSEMBLY

2) Using center punch as shown, loosen and remove steering lock mounting bolts. Use care not to damage aluminum part of steering lock body with center punch.

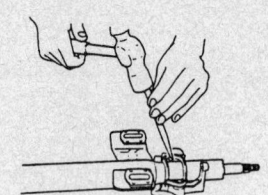

1. CENTER PUNCH (WITH SHARP POINT)
2. IGNITION SWITCH MOUNTING BOLTS

3) Turn ignition key to "ACC" or "ON" position and remove ignition switch assembly from steering column.

INSTALLATION

1) Position oblong hole of steering shaft in the center of hole in column.

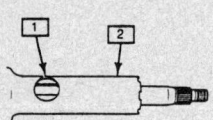

1. STEERING SHAFT
2. STEERING COLUMN

2) Turn ignition key to "ACC" or "ON" position and install ignition switch assembly onto column.
3) Now turn ignition key to "LOCK" position and pull it out.
4) Align hub on ignition switch assembly with oblong hole of steering shaft and rotate shaft to ensure that steering shaft is locked.

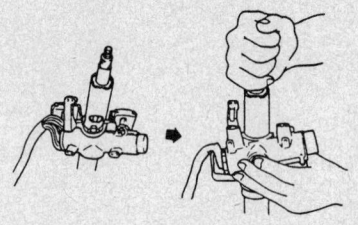

5) Tighten two new bolts until head of each bolt is broken off.

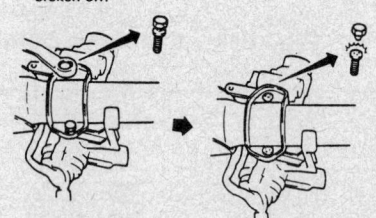

6) Turn ignition key to "ACC' or "ON" position and check to be sure that steering shaft rotates smoothly. Also check for lock operation.
7) Install steering column. Refer to STEERING COLUMN INSTALLATION.

Fig. 113 Steering lock removal & installation. Metro & Sprint

Assembly

1. Install housing support to jacket assembly with support screws and **torque** to 12 ft.lbs.
2. Install tilt bumpers to housing support and snap into place, then install steering shaft assembly into support housing.
3. Lubricate bearings in column housing with lithium grease and install column housing onto shaft assembly and housing support.
4. Lubricate pivot pins with lithium grease and install until bottomed in housing.
5. **Pivot pins must be staked to housing after installation. Stake each pin at three equally spaced locations.**
6. Pull tilt lever and tilt column all the way up.
7. Lubricate tilt spring with lithium grease and install tilt spring with

6. REMOVE AND INSTALL STEERING SHAFT LOWER JOINT

REMOVAL

1) Set front wheels in the straightforward state and remove steering shaft joint cover.
2) Remove steering shaft joint bolts.

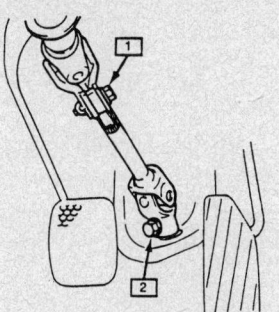

1 STEERING SHAFT JOINT UPPER SIDE BOLT
2 STEERING SHAFT JOINT LOWER SIDE BOLT

INSTALLATION

1) Align flat part of lower joint shaft with bolt hole of upper joint as shown. Then insert lower joint shaft into upper joint.

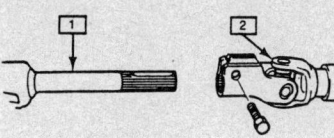

1 LOWER JOINT ASSEMBLY
2 UPPER JOINT ASSEMBLY

2) Be sure that front wheels and steering wheel are in straightforward state and insert lower joint into steering pinion shaft.
3) If steering column nuts were loosened in removal, torque lower bracket nuts to below specification first:

N·m	lb. ft.
14	10

And then torque upper bracket nuts to specification:

N·m	lb. ft.
14	10

4) Torque steering shaft joint bolts to specification:

N·m	lb. ft.
25	18

5) Install steering shaft joint cover.

6. REMOVE AND INSTALL HORN RELAY

REMOVAL

1) Disconnect negative battery cable.
2) Disconnect horn relay electrical connector.
3) Remove horn relay from mounting bracket, located near the front of the main fusebox.

INSTALLATION

1) Horn relay to mounting bracket.
2) Connect horn relay electrical connector.
3) Connect negative battery cable.
4) Verify proper horn relay operation.

Fig. 114 Steering shaft lower joint & horn relay removal & installation. Metro & Sprint

spring retainer as follows:
a. Make sure that spring engages locating tab on support housing.
b. Insert a phillips tip screwdriver into square opening in spring retainer, push down and turn right to lock in place.
8. Install ignition switch to ignition switch housing ensuring retaining pin engages ear on ignition switch. **Ensure that the tab on the lock cylinder shaft and the slotted opening on the ignition switch are in alignment, the lock cylinder and ignition switch must be in the Run position prior to installation.**
9. Install ignition switch retaining screw and hand tighten, approximately 2.7 inch lbs. of **torque**.
10. Install lock cylinder into ignition switch housing.
11. Install ignition switch housing to column housing using "new" shear bolts

and washers and **torque** until bolt head separates from body, approximately 15 ft. lbs.
12. Turn lock cylinder to the Off-Lock position and remove key.
13. Rotate steering shaft assembly until lock bolt engages and locks steering shaft into position.
14. Install inner race, inner race seat, upper bearing spring and spring retainer.
15. Compress retainer and spring with special tools No. J 26667 and J 23653-A or equivalent.
16. Install retaining ring in groove on upper shaft.
17. Install signal switch housing to steering column housing with washer head tap screws and **torque** to 30 inch lbs.
18. Install alignment bushing over lower end of steering shaft and into lower end of jacket assembly.
19. Install steering column as previously described in Steering Column, Re-

place section.
20. Install cancelling cam spring on steering shaft.
21. Install contact ring if necessary, steering wheel, retainer and nut and **torque** nut to 13 ft. lbs.
22. Install horn leads and cap, then connect battery ground cable.

STEERING SHAFT ASSEMBLY
Disassembly

1. When necessary, the steering shaft assembly may be serviced as follows:
   a. Prior to separation of upper shaft and lower shaft, note relationship of upper shaft with lock bolt slot at 12 o'clock position and lower shaft pinch bolt groove at 7 o'clock position. Refer to this orientation for proper reassembly.
   b. Position upper shaft 90° to lower shaft and separate.
   c. Rotate centering sphere 90° and remove from upper shaft.
   d. Separate sphere halves and joint preload spring.

Assembly

1. Lubricate centering sphere halves and joint preload spring with lithium grease and install spring between sphere halves with ends of spring in notches.
2. Lubricate sphere end of upper and lower shaft with lithium grease and install sphere into upper shaft and rotate sphere 90°
3. To ensure proper operation, align upper shaft and lower shaft by placing lock bolt slot on upper shaft at 12 o'clock position and pinch bolt groove near end of lower shaft at 7 o'clock position.
4. Position upper shaft 90° to lower shaft and install upper shaft to lower shaft and straighten.

Prizm
FIXED COLUMN

Refer to **Fig. 117** when servicing this column.

Disassembly

1. Disconnect battery ground cable.
2. Remove steering wheel pad, horn switch connector, shaft nut and steering wheel.
3. Remove steering column as previously described in Steering Column, Replace section.
4. Secure column assembly into a vise, making sure not to damage column.
5. Remove lock cylinder housing as follows:
   a. Using a centering punch, mark the center of the tapered-head bolts securing the lock cylinder housing.
   b. Using a .12-.16 inch drill bit, drill into the bolts then remove with a suitable bolt extractor.
6. Remove main shaft as follows:
   a. Using snap ring pliers, remove upper snap ring.
   b. Remove shaft from column tube, then snap ring from shaft.

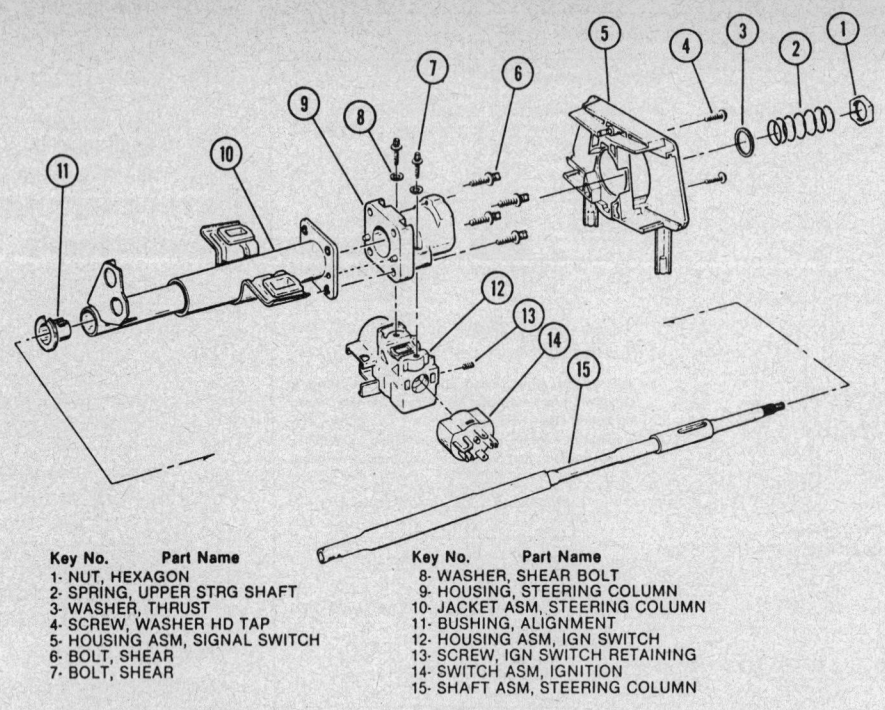

Key No.	Part Name	Key No.	Part Name
1-	NUT, HEXAGON	8-	WASHER, SHEAR BOLT
2-	SPRING, UPPER STRG SHAFT	9-	HOUSING, STEERING COLUMN
3-	WASHER, THRUST	10-	JACKET ASM, STEERING COLUMN
4-	SCREW, WASHER HD TAP	11-	BUSHING, ALIGNMENT
5-	HOUSING ASM, SIGNAL SWITCH	12-	HOUSING ASM, IGN SWITCH
6-	BOLT, SHEAR	13-	SCREW, IGN SWITCH RETAINING
7-	BOLT, SHEAR	14-	SWITCH ASM, IGNITION
		15-	SHAFT ASM, STEERING COLUMN

Fig. 115 Exploded view of fixed steering column. LeMans

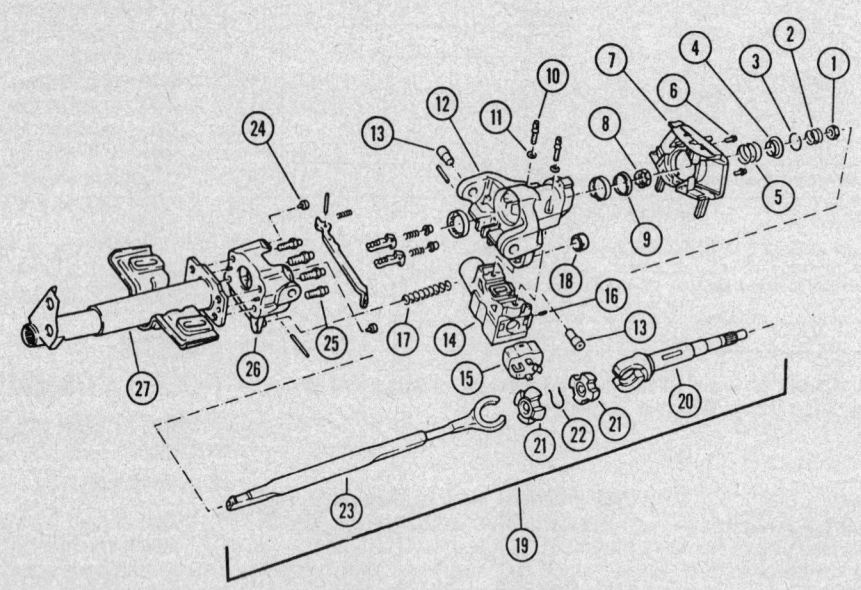

Key No.	Part Name	Key No.	Part Name
1-	NUT, HEXAGON	15-	SWITCH ASM, IGNITION
2-	SPRING, CANCELLING CAM	16-	SCREW, IGN SWITCH RETAINING
3-	RING, RETAINING	17-	SPRING, WHEEL TILT
4-	RETAINER, SPRING	18-	RETAINER, SPRING
5-	SPRING, UPPER BEARING	19-	SHAFT ASM, STEERING
6-	SCREW, HEX WASHER HD TAP	20-	SHAFT ASM, RACE & UPPER
7-	HOUSING ASM, SIGNAL SWITCH	21-	SPHERE, CENTERING
8-	SEAT, INNER RACE	22-	SPRING, JOINT PRELOAD
9-	RACE, INNER	23-	SHAFT ASM, LOWER STEERING
10-	BOLT, SHEAR	24-	BUMPER, TILT
11-	WASHER, SHEAR BOLT	25-	SCREW, SUPPORT
12-	HOUSING ASM, STEERING COLUMN	26-	SUPPORT, STRG COLUMN HOUSING
13-	PIN, PIVOT	27-	JACKET ASM, STEERING COLUMN
14-	HOUSING ASM, IGN SWITCH		

Fig. 116 Exploded view of tilt steering column. LeMans

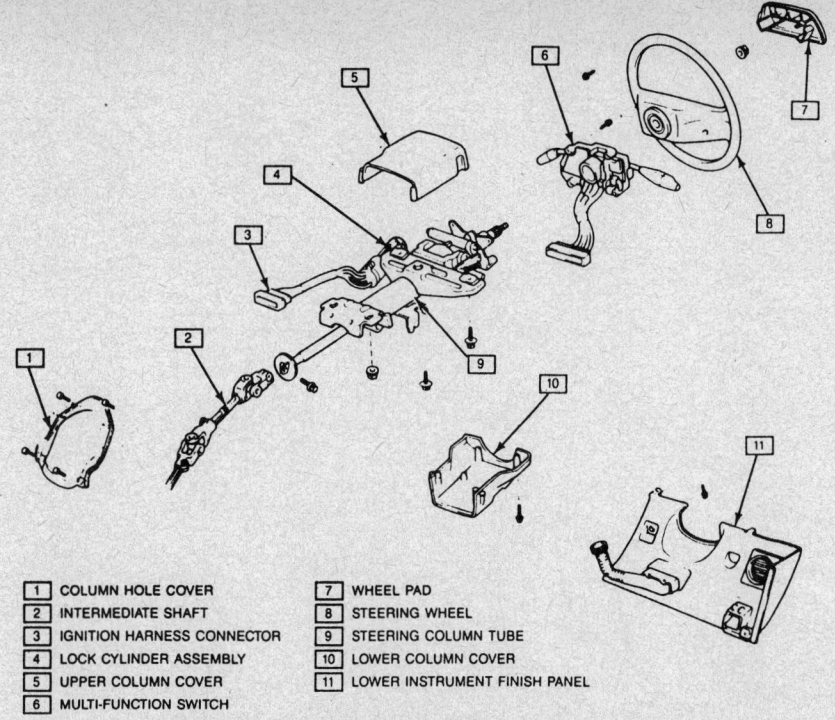

1 COLUMN HOLE COVER	7 WHEEL PAD
2 INTERMEDIATE SHAFT	8 STEERING WHEEL
3 IGNITION HARNESS CONNECTOR	9 STEERING COLUMN TUBE
4 LOCK CYLINDER ASSEMBLY	10 LOWER COLUMN COVER
5 UPPER COLUMN COVER	11 LOWER INSTRUMENT FINISH PANEL
6 MULTI-FUNCTION SWITCH	

Fig. 117 Exploded view of fixed steering column. Prizm

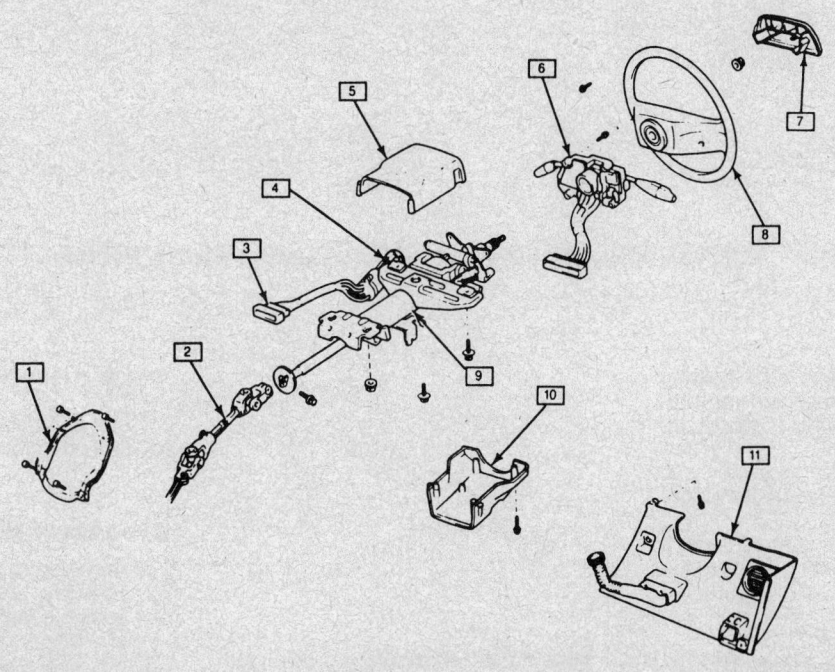

1 COLUMN HOLE COVER	7 WHEEL PAD
2 INTERMEDIATE SHAFT	8 STEERING WHEEL
3 IGNITION HARNESS CONNECTOR	9 STEERING COLUMN TUBE
4 LOCK CYLINDER ASSEMBLY	10 LOWER COLUMN COVER
5 UPPER COLUMN COVER	11 LOWER INSTRUMENT FINISH PANEL
6 MULTI-FUNCTION SWITCH	

Fig. 118 Exploded view of tilt steering column. Prizm

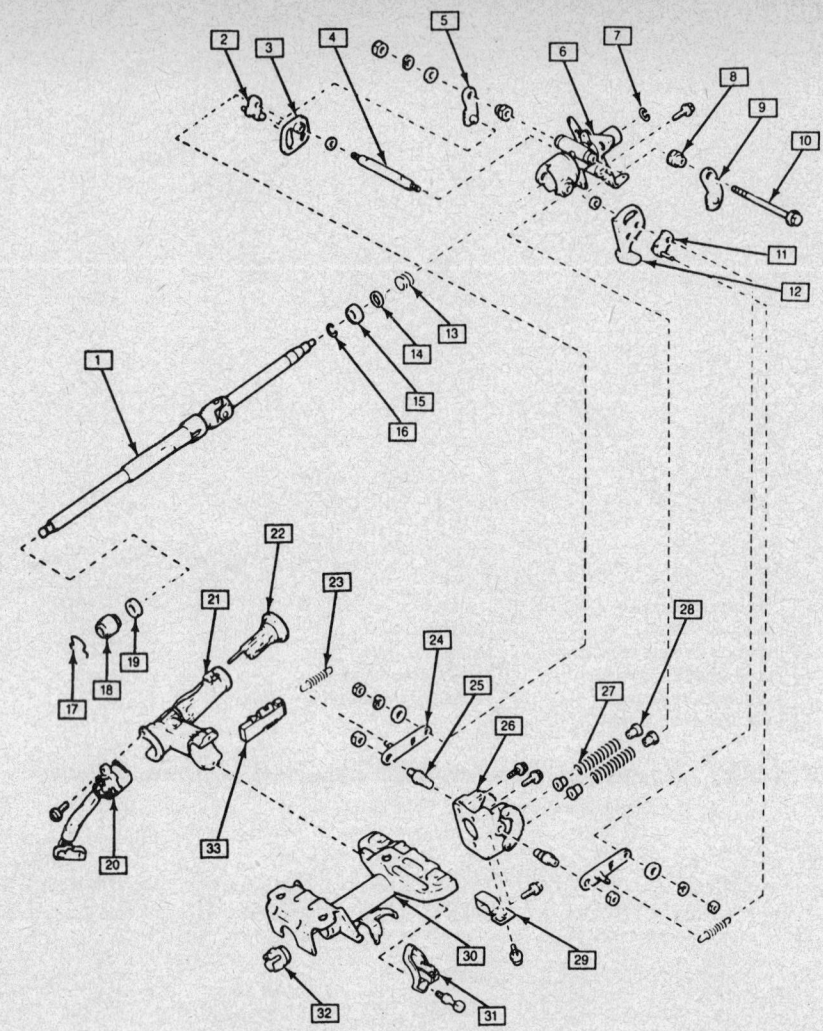

Fig. 119 Exploded view of tilt steering shaft. Prizm

7. Remove upper column tube bearing and check for abnormal noise or rotation difficulty. If bearing is faulty, replace.
8. Remove lock cylinder assembly and check for proper operation. If cylinder is faulty, replace.
9. Remove column tube bushing using a screwdriver, inspect for damage and replace if necessary.

Assembly

1. Install column tube bushing, then upper column tube bearing.
2. Install main shaft into column tube as follows:
   a. Using snap ring pliers, install snap ring in the inside groove of the main shaft.
   b. Insert main shaft into tube.
   c. Using snap ring pliers, connect shaft snap ring to column.
3. Install lock cylinder assembly.
4. Install lock cylinder housing onto column with "new" tapered-head bolts and **torque** bolts until the bolt heads break off.

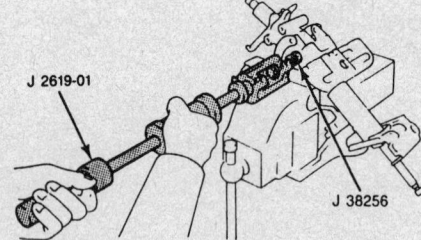

J 2619-01

J 38256

Fig. 120   Removing pivot bolts. Prizm

5. Install column assembly as described in Steering Column, Replace section.
6. Install steering wheel and nut, **torque** bolt to 25 ft. lbs.
7. Install horn switch connector and horn pad, then connect battery ground cable.

TILT COLUMN

Refer to **Figs. 118 and 119** when servicing this column.

Disassembly

1. Disconnect battery ground cable.
2. Remove steering wheel pad, horn switch connector, shaft nut and steering wheel.
3. Remove steering column as previously described in Steering Column, Replace section.
4. Secure column assembly into a vise, making sure not to damage column.
5. Remove lock cylinder housing as follows:
   a. Using a centering punch, mark the center of the tapered-head bolts securing the lock cylinder housing
   b. Using a .12-.16 inch drill bit, drill into the bolts then remove with a suitable bolt extractor.
6. Remove two tension springs, then two bolts, two bushings and two compres-

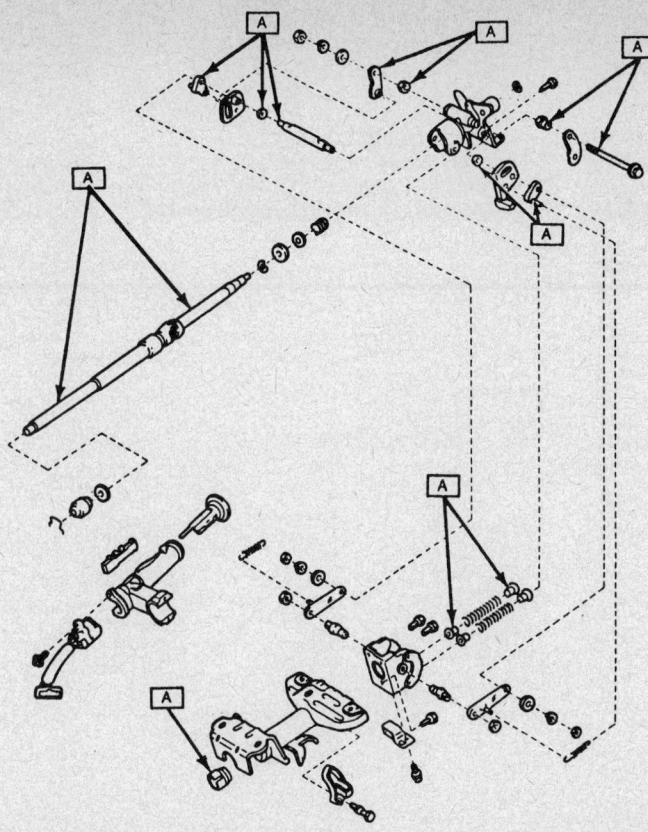

Fig. 121   Tilt steering column grease points. Prizm

sion springs.
7. Remove tilt levers retainers, then tilt pawls, two nuts and bolts and separate two pawls from collars.
8. Remove two pawl stoppers, then remove tilt lever, tilt sub-lever and lever lock bolt.
9. Remove lower column tube.
10. Remove column pivot bolts using special tools No. J 38256 or equivalent pivot bolt remover and a J 2619-01 or equivalent slide hammer, **Fig. 120.**
11. Separate upper and lower columns.
12. Remove main shaft as follows;
    a. Using special tool No. J 38364 or equivalent spring compressor, compress main shaft spring.
    b. Remove shaft snap ring with snap ring pliers.
    c. Separate main shaft from column.
    d. Remove thrust collar and bearing.
    e. Remove snap ring from shaft using snap ring pliers.
13. Remove wiring harness clamp, then steering support
14. Remove snap ring from lower column tube using snap ring pliers, then remove main shaft collar.
15. Inspect lock cylinder assembly to ensure that lock mechanism operates properly. Replace if necessary.
16. Remove column tube bushing with a

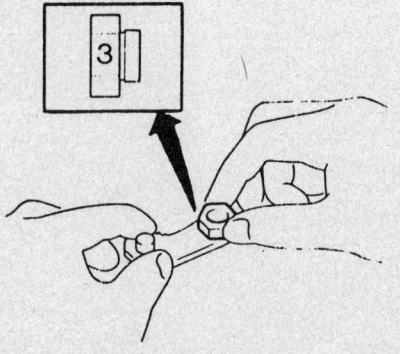

TILT LEVER SIDE	TILT SUB LEVER SIDE	OUTER DIAMETER
1	5	11.504–11.514 mm (0.4529–0.4533")
2	6	11.499–11.509 mm (0.4527–0.4531")
3	7	11.494–11.504 mm (0.4525–0.4529")
4	8	11.488–11.498 mm (0.4523–0.4527")

Fig. 122   Selecting correct collars. Prizm

screwdriver and inspect for damage or unusual wear. Replace if necessary.

Assembly

Prior to assembly of steering column, apply GM 1050109 or equivalent grease to all parts indicated in **Fig. 121**
1. Install column tube bushing, then steering support to lower column.
2. **Torque** steering support to lower column bolts to 14 ft. lbs.
3. Install main shaft to column tube as follows:
   a. Using snap ring pliers, install snap ring.
   b. Install main shaft, bearing, collar and spring.
   c. Using special tool No. J 38364 or equivalent spring compressor, compress main shaft spring and install a "new" snap ring with snap ring pliers.
4. Install wire harness clamp to column.
5. Install main shaft with upper and lower columns.
6. **Select the proper pivot bolts to match the upper column. If the column is marked with a number 1 on the side, select a grooveless bolt; if the upper column is marked with a number 2, select a grooved bolt. When one bolt has been selected, choose its opposite for the other side as both sides are different.**
7. Install pivot bolts, driving in with a hammer.

8. Install tilt lever lock bolt, tilt lever and sub lever.
9. Select collars for tilt pawl, **Fig. 122**
10. Insert collars into tilt pawls and install temporarily.
11. Engage tilt lever side pawls at the center of the ratchet and **torque** pawl nut to 70 inch lbs.
12. Install two tilt levers and **torque** tilt lever retainer forward nuts to 70 inch lbs. and retainer rearward nuts to 89 inch lbs.
13. Install two compression springs with bushings in each end and **torque** spring bolts to 70 inch lbs.
14. Install two tension springs.
15. Install lock cylinder housing onto column with "new" tapered-head bolts and **torque** bolts until the bolt heads break off.
16. Install column assembly as described in Steering Column, Replace section.
17. Install steering wheel and nut, **torque** bolt to 25 ft. lbs.
18. Install horn switch connector and horn pad, then connect battery ground cable.

TABLE OF CONTENTS

Supplemental Inflatable Restraint System

INDEX

Continued

INDEX —Continued

DESCRIPTION

The Supplemental Inflatable Restraint System (SIR), is intended as a supplement to the driver's seat belt.

The supplemental inflatable restraint deploys for the driver when the vehicle is involved in a front end accident of sufficient force, up to 30 degrees off the centerline of the vehicle. Restraint is provided by an inflatable cushion stored in the steering wheel module.

On 1988-90 Delta 88 and 1989-90 98, three sensors, **Fig. 1,** control system deployment. They are the forward sensor (1), the passenger compartment sensor (2) and the arming sensor (3).

These sensors initiate restraint inflation when a change in the vehicle's velocity is sufficient to indicate that an accident is occurring.

The complete supplemental inflatable restraint system, **Fig. 2,** consists of the following major components:

1. SIR control module (passenger compartment sensor)
2. Forward sensor

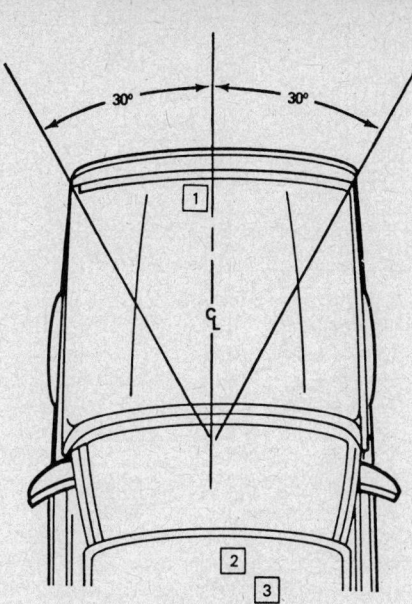

Fig. 1 Inflatable restraint sensor locations

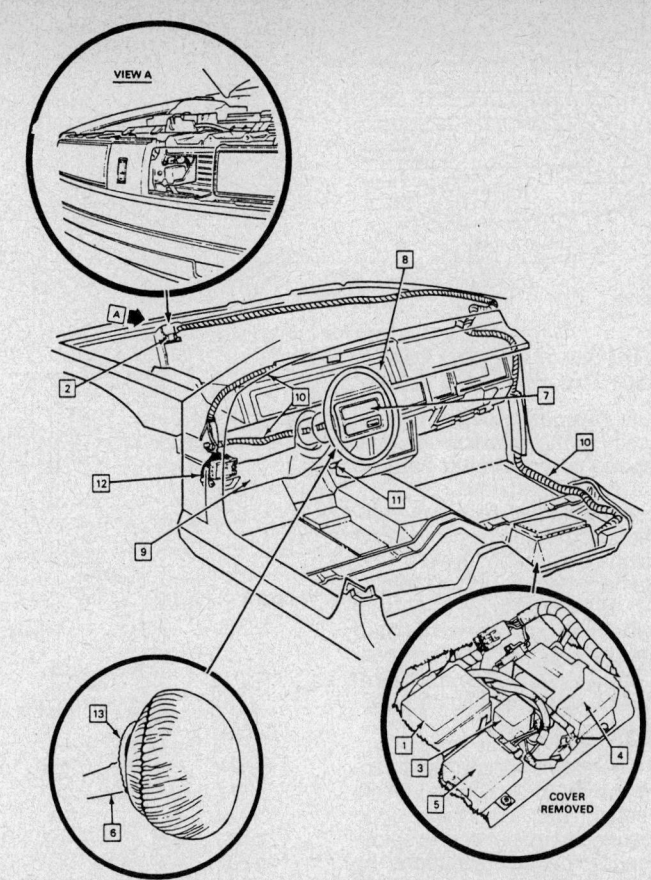

Fig. 2 Inflatable restraint system component locations. 88 & 98

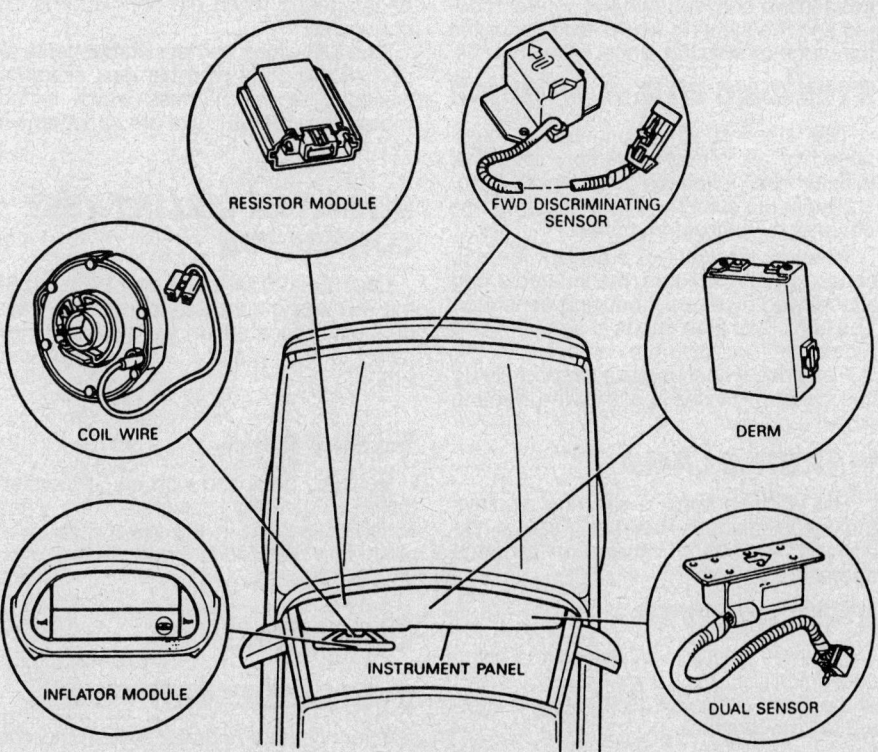

Fig. 3 Inflatable restraint system component locations. Except 88 & 98

3. Arming sensor
4. Power supply
5. Energy reserve module
6. Steering column and coil assembly
7. Steering wheel module
8. Warning lamp
9. Knee bolster
10. SIR harness (part of body harness assembly)
11. Test connector
12. Fuse panel
13. Steering wheel

On 1989 Deville/Fleetwood and all 1990 models, the main components of the SIR system are the Deployment Loop and the Diagnostic Energy Reserve Module (DERM), **Fig. 3.** The Arming Sensor, Coil Assembly, Inflator Module and Discriminating Sensors make up the deployment loop. The main function of the deployment loop is to supply current through the Inflator Module in the steering wheel which will cause deployment of the air bag in the event of an accident severe enough to warrant deployment.

SUPPLEMENTAL INFLATABLE RESTRAINT CONTROL MODULE (PASSENGER COMPARTMENT SENSOR)

On 1988-90 Delta 88 and 1989-90 98, the SIR control module contains the passenger compartment sensor and the inflatable restraint system diagnostics. The SIR

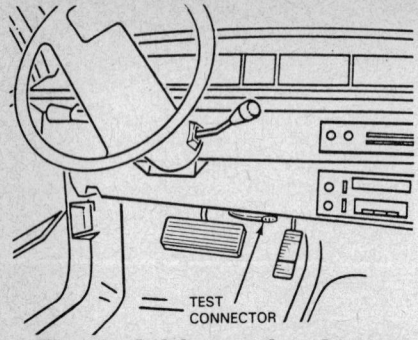

Fig. 4   Initiator circuit test connector location. 88 & 98

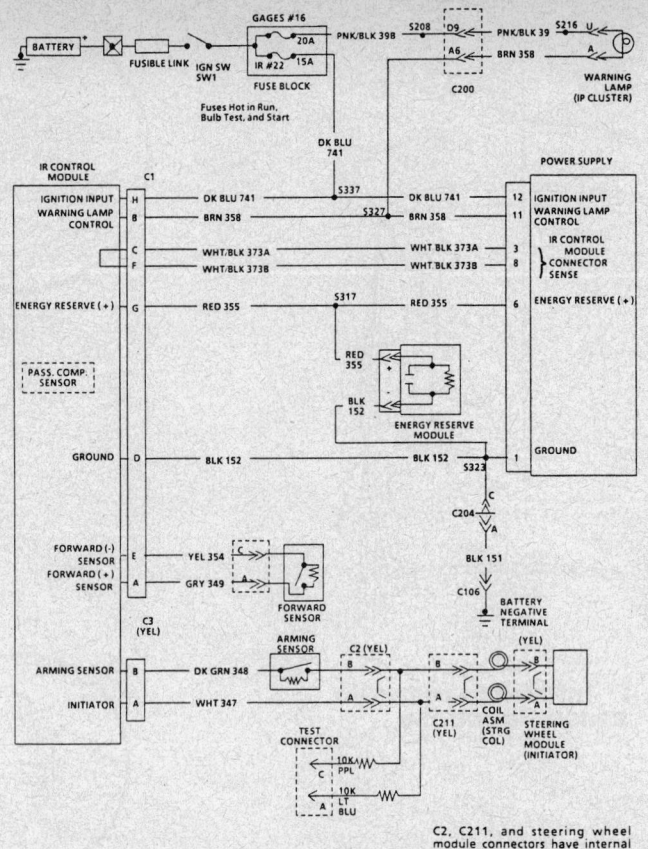

Fig. 5   Inflatable restraint system wiring circuit. 88 & 98

control module diagnostic system monitors the accuracy of the inflatable restraint sensing components and wiring harness and controls the warning lamp.

The SIR control module monitors vehicle deceleration and combines this information with signals from the forward sensor to determine whether deployment is necessary. An electrical pulse is sent to the steering wheel module when a forward sensor closure, or a signal from the passenger compartment sensor, and an arming sensor closure occur simultaneously.

FORWARD SENSOR

The forward sensor is mechanically actuated and responds to a drop in vehicle speed. This sensor has a normally open switch, and distinguishes between deployment and non-deployment situations by means of a preset calibration which allows the sensor to close only with sufficient impact force. If an accident occurs, the contacts of the forward sensor close, completing an electrical circuit. If the contacts of the forward sensor close simultaneously with the contacts of the arming sensor, deployment occurs.

ARMING SENSOR

This sensor is a normally open mechanical switch that closes during deceleration encountered in an accident. The arming sensor is wired in series with the steering wheel module and provides backup to the other sensors. A parallel resistor in the arming sensor permits a small amount of current to flow through the initiator circuit for diagnostic purposes.

POWER SUPPLY

The power supply provides an increased voltage to the inflatable restraint system to guarantee deployment for low voltage conditions, perform limited internal diagnostics and monitor the reliability of the inflatable restraint harness at the 8 terminal connector.

ENERGY RESERVE MODULE

This module provides sufficient electrical energy to guarantee restraint deployment even if vehicle's battery is damaged or disconnected during deployment.

STEERING COLUMN & COIL ASSEMBLY

This system uses a collapsible steering column that incorporates a coil assembly which provides a continuous electrical connection between the SIR control module and the steering wheel module for the full range of steering wheel rotation.

STEERING WHEEL MODULE

The steering wheel module is composed of an inflator assembly, electrical initiator and inflatable bag which is installed in the steering wheel hub area and covered by a vinyl trim cover.

When an accident of sufficient force is sensed by the sensors, the inflatable bag is deployed by a gas producing generator. The trim cover then opens at seams which rupture as the system is deployed.

A steering wheel designed especially for this system provides space for the steering wheel module.

WARNING LAMP

The warning lamp is red and displays the words Inflatable Restraint. Refer to "Diagnosis" for further information on lamp operation.

KNEE BOLSTER

The knee bolster is an energy absorbing pad which controls the forward movement of the driver during an accident by restricting leg movement.

SIR WIRING HARNESS

This wiring harness interconnects the system components. The initiator circuit has special yellow shorting bar connectors which help prevent accidental deployment or tampering when the connector is disconnected.

The SIR wiring harness components are part of the body wire harness assembly. Sections of the harness which include more than one SIR wire are wrapped with yellow tape.

INITIATOR CIRCUIT TEST CONNECTOR

On 1988-90 Delta 88 and 1989-90 98, the SIR wiring harness incorporates a test connector located under the instrument panel to the right of the steering column, Fig. 4.

FUSE PANEL

Vehicles equipped with an SIR system have a specially designed fuse panel which is located in the lower instrument panel trim pad and is hinged to swing out for easy access.

DIAGNOSIS

SYSTEM DESCRIPTION

The inflatable restraint system incorporates a built in diagnostic system that monitors the system's electrical circuits. This system, through the warning lamp, indicates to the driver that the system is either operating properly or in need of service.

The warning lamp, located on the instrument panel, illuminates when the ignition switch is first turned on, then goes off after 5-15 seconds if the system is operating properly. If the warning lamp does not illuminate or illuminates for less than 5 seconds when the ignition switch is first turned on, or remains illuminated after 15 seconds, or comes on while the vehicle is being driven, the system needs immediate service.

The inflatable restraint system diagnostic procedures are divided into two categories.

1. Tests for when the inflatable restraint warning lamp does not illuminate (Never-On) when the ignition system is turned to Run or Start.
2. Tests for when the inflatable restraint system warning lamp remains on continuously (full brilliance or dimly) when the ignition switch is turned to Run or Start, or comes on when vehicle is being driven.

If warning lamp is continuously on, never on, comes on when the vehicle is being driven or on for less than 5 seconds, refer to "Inflatable Restraint Diagnostic Procedures" to locate problems.

Refer to **Figs. 5 through 67,** for SIR system wiring schematics and diagnosis charts, and **Figs. 68 through 157,** for system trouble code identification, when locating problems in the inflatable restraint system. Multiple problems may lead to a combination of conditions, each of which must be checked separately.

Before connecting tester J-26884 into system, check all wiring harness connectors to ensure problem is not caused by an improperly engaged connector, and check the SIR fuse.

Do not attempt to repair the following, as these components are serviced only by replacement.

1. Forward sensor
2. Arming sensor
3. Power supply
4. Energy reserve module
5. SIR control module
6. Coil assembly
7. Steering wheel module

The inflatable restraint system tester J-36884 is a special purpose tester designed to be used only with the 1988-90 Delta 88 and 1989-90 98. The tester is used to determine whether or not a specific component or the entire system is functioning correctly.

To avoid accidental deployment when diagnosing the inflatable restraint system, do not use electrical test equipment, such as battery or A/C powered voltmeter, ohmmeter, etc., or any type of electrical equipment other than specified. Do not use a non-powered probe type tester. Use of any other test equipment may result in personal injury.

INFLATABLE RESTRAINT DIAGNOSTIC PROCEDURES

Use this diagnostic sequence to locate the source of problems in the inflatable restraint system. A malfunction in the system is indicated when the Inflatable Restraint warning lamp is never on or is on for less

than 5 seconds after the ignition is on, is on continuously or comes on while the vehicle is being driven.

1. With ignition switch in Off position, disconnect and tape negative terminal of battery. **Wait 15 seconds before continuing diagnosis.**
2. Connect 8 pin connectors of tester J-36884 to mating 8 pin connectors at the SIR system control center, **Fig. 158.**
3. Connect 2 pin connectors of tester J-36884 to mating 2 pin connectors of SIR system control center.
4. Connect 3 pin connectors of tester J-36884 to test connector of SIR system located to right side of steering column behind knee bolster.
5. Reconnect negative battery terminal.
6. Connect battery leads of tester J-36884 to battery terminals, routing leads through passenger window.
7. Follow "Diagnostic Tester Sequence," **Fig. 159,** to locate source of problem.
8. After diagnosing problem, proceed as follows:
   a. Turn ignition switch to Off position.
   b. Disconnect and tape negative battery terminal. **Wait 15 seconds before continuing.**
   c. Repair system as instructed by diagnostic charts, **Figs. 11 through 67.**
   d. Reconnect system and repeat "Diagnostic Tester Sequence" to confirm proper operation of inflatable restraint system.

SERVICE PRECAUTIONS

Safe handling of steering wheel module requires adhering to following procedures for both live and deployed steering wheel modules.

Always wear safety glasses when servicing an inflatable restraint system vehicle and when handling a steering wheel module.

HANDLING SENSORS

Be careful when handling a sensor. This also pertains to the SIR control module which contains the passenger compartment sensor.

Never strike or jar a sensor in such a way that may cause deployment.

All sensors, the SIR system control module and the SIR control center mounting plate bolts must be carefully torqued to ensure proper operation.

Before servicing SIR system, wait 10 minutes after disconnecting battery voltage before servicing SIR system. This prevents accidental deployment and possible injury.

LIVE (UNDEPLOYED) MODULES

When carrying a live steering wheel module, be sure the bag and trim cover are pointed away from you.

When placing the steering wheel module on a bench or other surface, always face the bag and trim cover up, away from the surface.

DEPLOYED MODULES

Safety precautions must be observed when handling a deployed module because the air bag may contain deposits of sodium hydroxide.

Always wear safety glasses and gloves when handling a deployed module, and wash hands with mild soap and water afterward.

SHIPPING & STORAGE

The transportation of inflatable restraint modules not installed is regulated by the Hazardous Material regulations of the U. S. Department of Transportation and many state governments. Special procedures may be required for transportation. It is therefore recommended that repair shops and/or dealers check with the hazardous material section of their respective state police authority for shipping regulations.

For interstate shipment, the U. S. Department of Transportation classifies a inflatable restraint module not installed, as a flammable solid under a special exemption process. The module should always be stored and/or shipped in the approved container in which it was purchased. This container should be marked "Flammable Solid, n.o.s., UN 1325, DOT-E 8236" and labeled with a specified white and red flammable solid label. Each shipping location must have a copy of the exemption on file and a shipping paper must be included with each shipment and must identify the module as "Flammable Solid, n.o.s., UN 1325, DOT-E 8236." Handling, storage and transportation of the module should be in accordance with the exemption and the requirements for a DOT flammable solid. Do not expose the module to heat, open flame, impact, friction or electrical discharge.

REQUIRED REPLACEMENTS FOLLOWING AN ACCIDENT

When the steering wheel module is replaced due to deployment, both the SIR control module and the arming sensor must also be replaced. Any SIR system components, harness or brackets damaged or bent in an accident must be replaced. Inspect steering column and knee bolster for damage.

Do not attempt to repair steering column coil assembly, forward sensor, arming sensor, power supply, SIR control module, steering wheel module or energy reserve module, as these are serviced by replacement only.

Before servicing SIR system, wait 10 minutes after disconnecting battery voltage before continuing.

If vehicle is equipped with passenger power seat, do not connect seat power feed harness to SIR control module terminal connector.

Continued on page 30-83

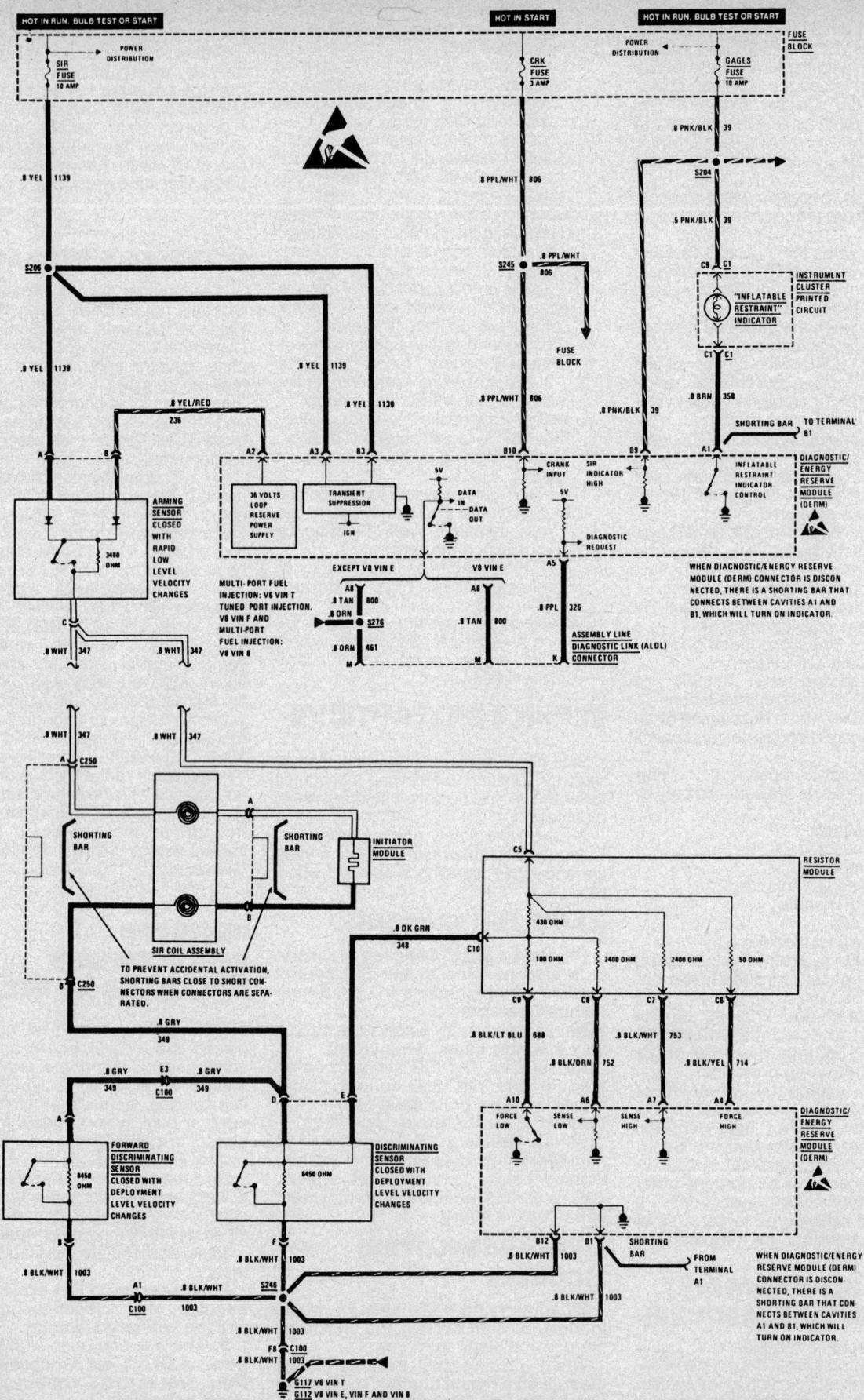

Fig. 6   Inflatable restraint system wiring circuit. Camaro & Firebird

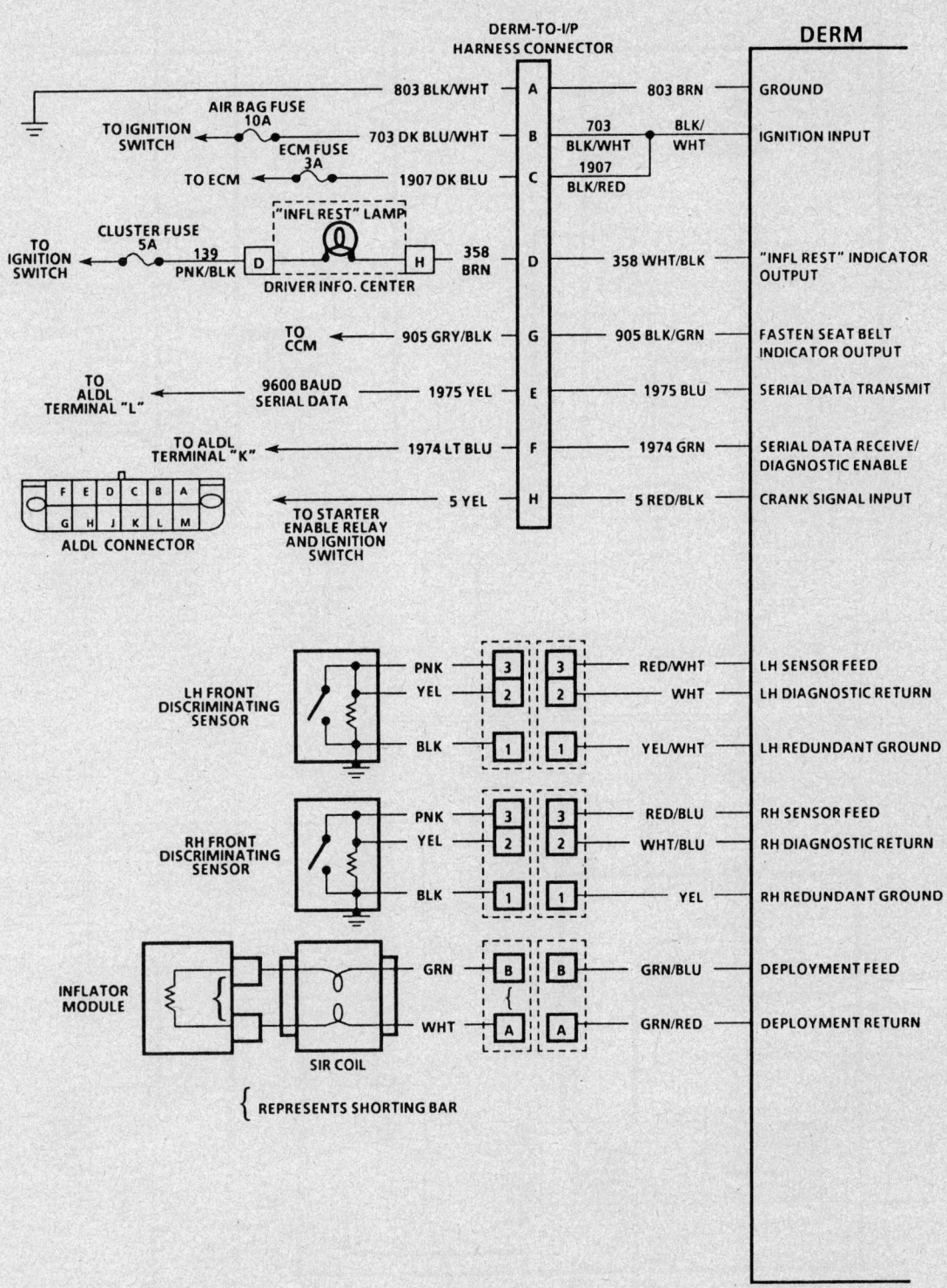

Fig. 7 Inflatable restraint system wiring circuit. Corvette

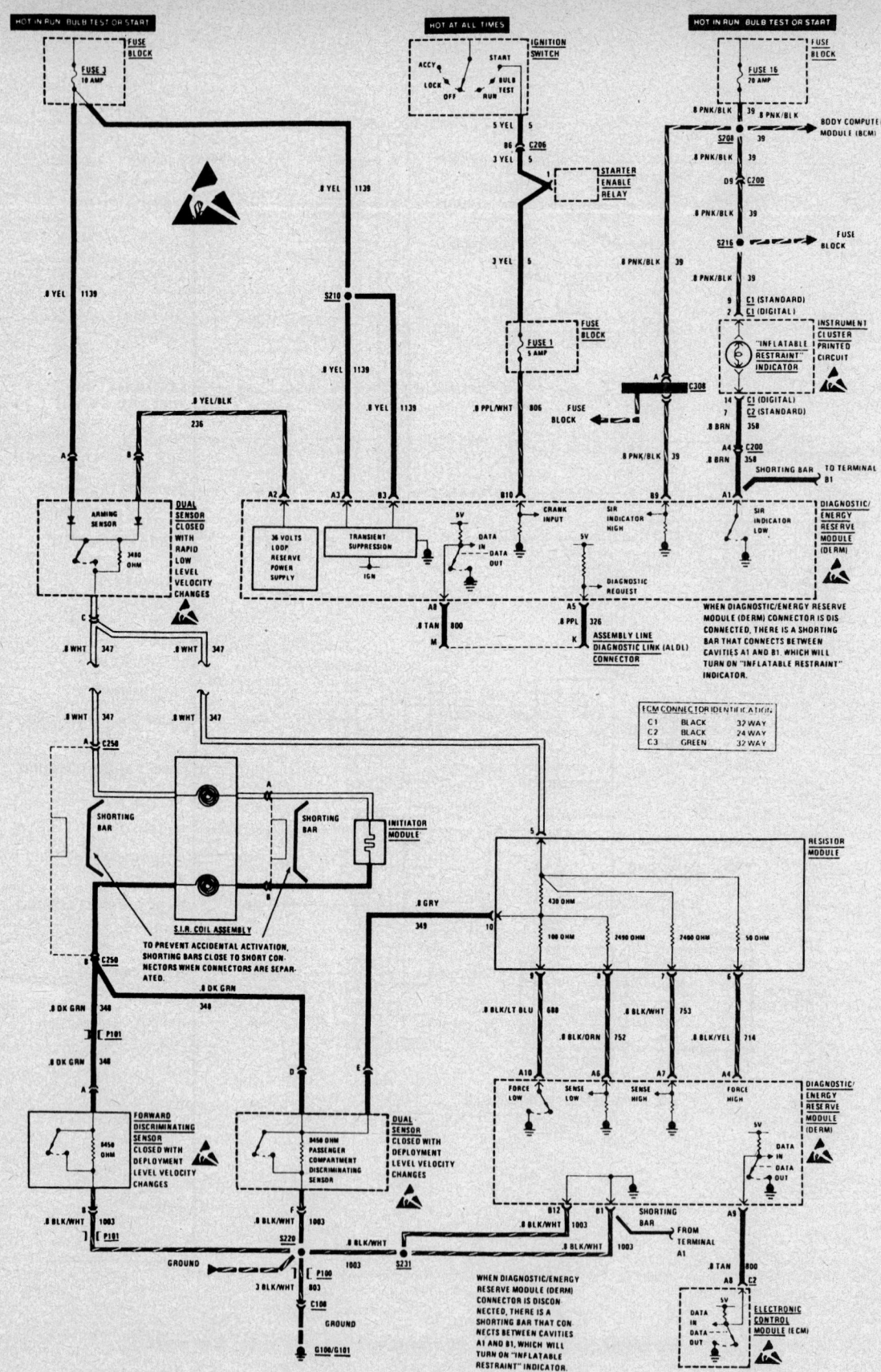

Fig. 8 Inflatable restraint system wiring circuit. Deville & Fleetwood

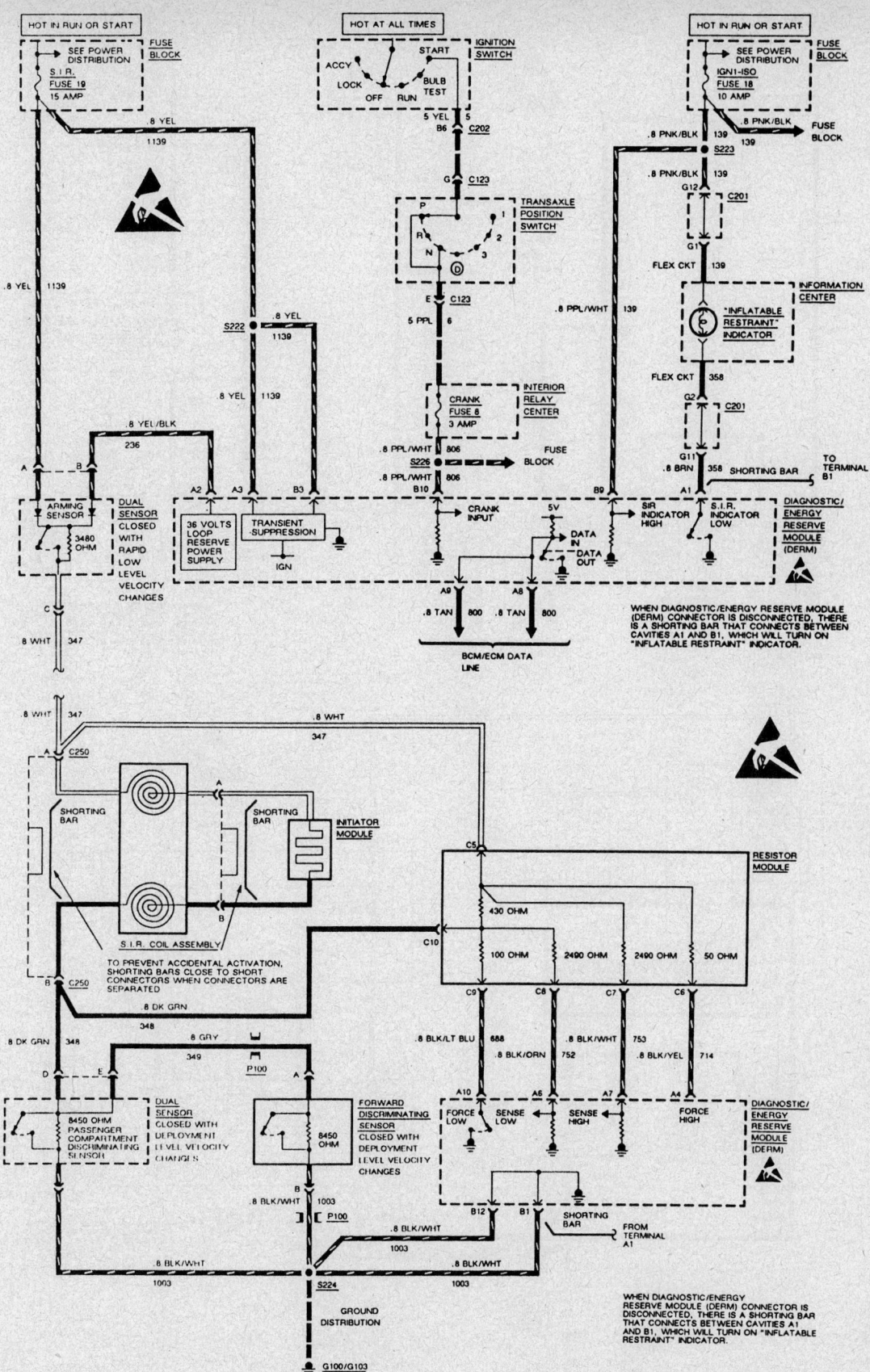

Fig. 9 Inflatable restraint system wiring circuit. Eldorado & Seville

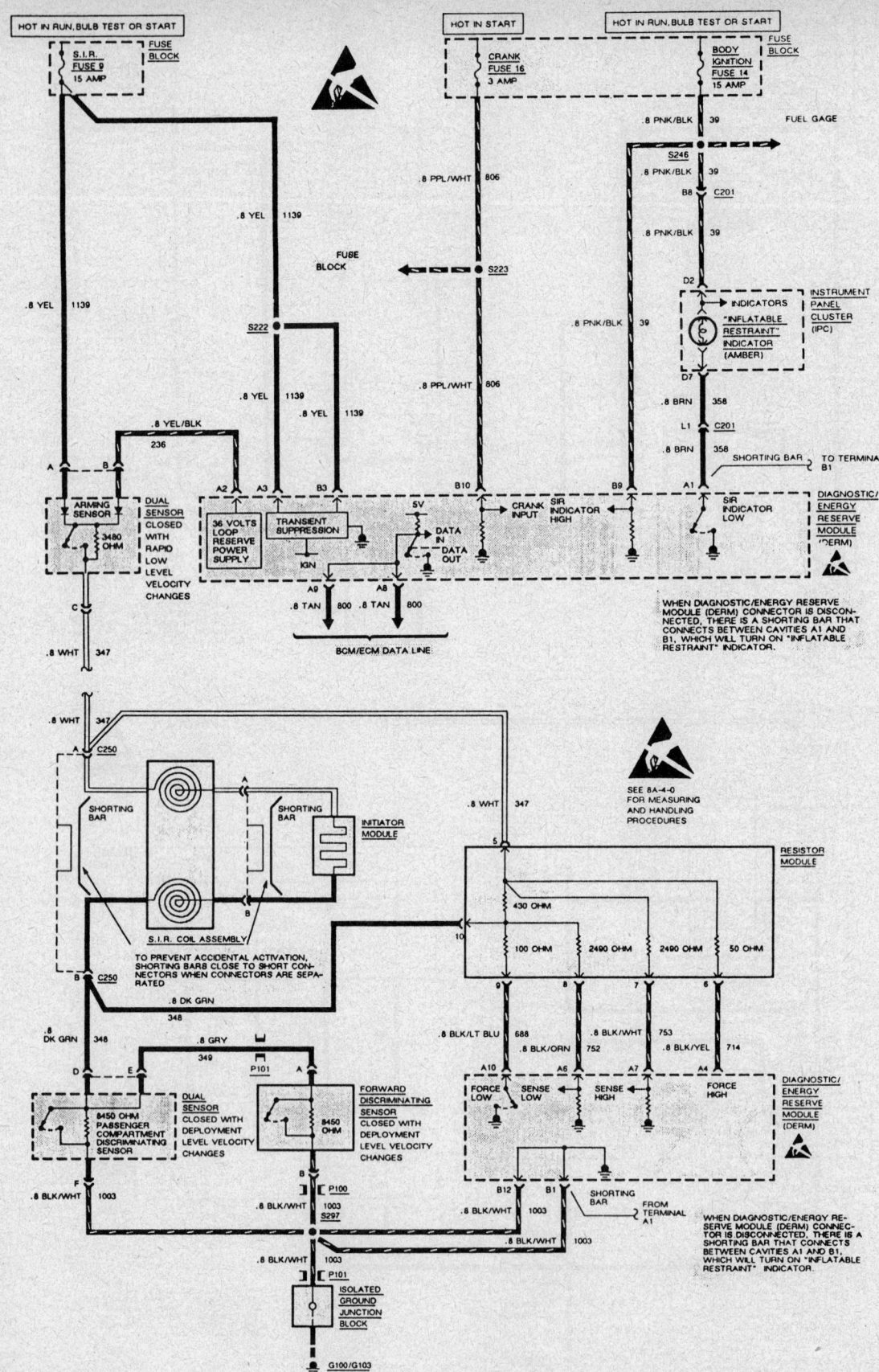

Fig. 10 Inflatable restraint system wiring circuit. Riviera & Reatta

CAUTION:

To avoid deployment when troubleshooting the SIR system, do not use electrical test equipment such as test lights, battery powered or A/C powered voltmeter, ohmmeter, etc., or any type of electrical equipment other than those specified in this manual. Instructions in this manual must be followed carefully, otherwise personal injury may result.

SIR DIAGNOSTIC SYSTEM CHECK

The diagnostic procedures used in this section are designed to find and repair SIR problems. To get the best results, it is important to utilize the diagnostic charts and follow the sequence listed below.

A. PERFORM THE "SIR DIAGNOSTIC SYSTEM CHECK".

The "SIR Diagnostic System Check" should be the starting point of any SIR diagnostics. The "SIR Diagnostic System Check" checks for proper "INFLATABLE RESTRAINT" indicator operation and checks for SIR trouble codes.

B. REFER TO THE PROPER DIAGNOSTIC CHART AS DIRECTED BY THE "SIR DIAGNOSTIC SYSTEM CHECK".

The "SIR Diagnostic System Check" will lead you to the correct chart to diagnose any SIR problems. Bypassing these procedures may result in extended diagnostic time.

C. REPEAT THE "SIR DIAGNOSTIC SYSTEM CHECK" AFTER ANY REPAIR OR DIAGNOSTIC PROCEDURES HAVE BEEN PERFORMED.

Performing the "SIR Diagnostic System Check" after all repair or diagnostic procedures will assure that the repair has been made correctly and that no other conditions exist.

Description:

When the ignition switch is first turned "ON", system voltage is applied through the SIR FUSE to the DERM at the "Ignition 1" input and through GAGES FUSE to the DERM at the "SIR Indicator Low" and "SIR Indicator High" inputs. The DERM responds by blinking the "INFLATABLE RESTRAINT" indicator 7 to 9 times.

When the engine is being cranked system voltage is applied to the DERM at the "CRANK" input. The DERM grounds the lamp circuit until system voltage is removed from the "CRANK" input. This results in a steady "INFLATABLE RESTRAINT" indicator during cranking.

After cranking the DERM will again blink the "INFLATABLE RESTRAINT" indicator 7 to 9 times.

Notes on Fault Tree:

1) The "INFLATABLE RESTRAINT" indicator should blink 7 to 9 times as the ignition is just turned on. If the indicator does not respond use Chart C or D to diagnose the indicator malfunction.

2) As the engine is "Cranked" the "INFLATABLE RESTRAINT" indicator should remain on steady. If the indicator does not respond use Chart E to diagnose the malfunction.

3) The "INFLATABLE RESTRAINT" indicator has completed the "Bulb Check" and remains on indicating a current code has been detected. At this point a "Scan Tool" or the "INFLATABLE RESTRAINT" indicator can be used to diagnose the malfunction. For "Flash Code" diagnosis use Chart B.

4) After "Cranking" the engine the "INFLATABLE RESTRAINT" indicator should blink 7 to 9 times and then go out. If the indicator begins to flash a Code 12, there is a system fault. Use Chart F to diagnose the malfunction.

5) The "INFLATABLE RESTRAINT" indicator has completed the "Bulb Check" and is indicating no current codes exist.

6) Record all codes (both History and Current) onto the repair order. If there are no codes (History or Current) record this fact onto the repair order. No further diagnosis is required. If the scan tool indicates that no data is being received from the DERM, then the data link will require repair.

7) If multiple codes are displayed (History or Current). The order that the codes are diagnosed is very important. Refer to the recommended charts.

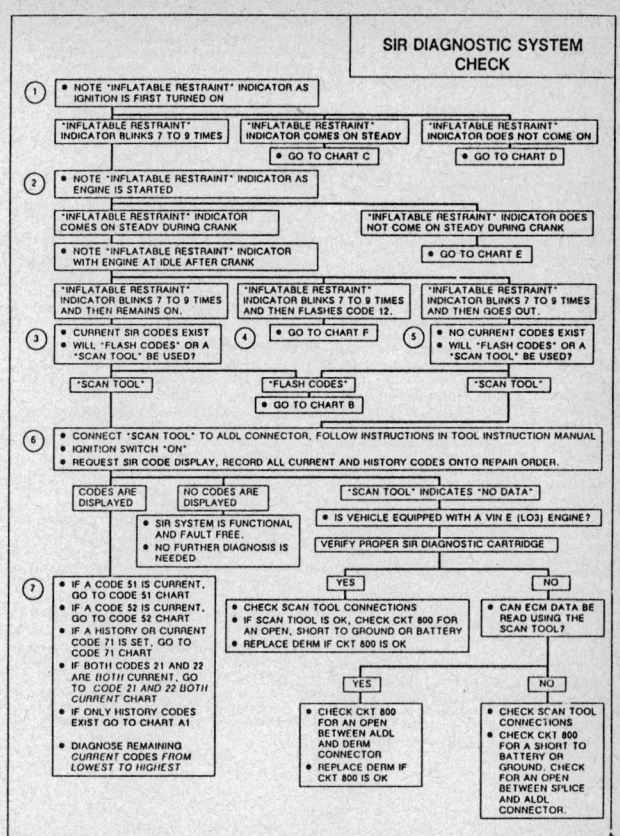

Fig. 11 SIR diagnostic system check. Camaro & Firebird

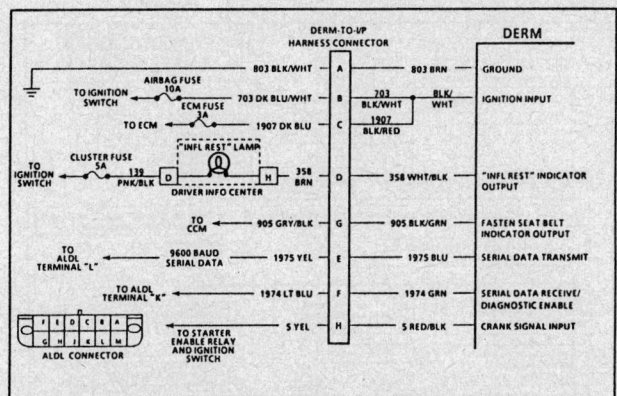

SIR DIAGNOSTIC SYSTEM CHECK

Circuit Description:

When the ignition switch is first turned "ON," system voltage is applied through the AIRBAG fuse to the IGNITION INPUT and through the CLUSTER fuse to the "INFL REST" indicator. The DERM feeds system power through the ECM fuse to the ECM. Therefore, the ECM can only receive power if the DERM is properly connected to the I/P harness and the AIRBAG fuse is not blown.

When power is applied to the DERM it responds by illuminating the "INFL REST" indicator for five seconds if no fault codes have been stored. If the DERM has fault codes in memory, it illuminates both the "INFL REST" and Fasten Seatbelt indicators continuously. The DERM has an internal lamp driver for the "INFL REST" indicator. The FASTEN SEATBELT output of the DERM is connected to the CCM which actually drives the Fasten Seatbelt indicator.

When the engine is being cranked, system voltage is applied to the DERM at the CRANK SIGNAL INPUT. If no fault codes are stored and system power is removed from the CRANK SIGNAL INPUT, the DERM will reset and again illuminate the "INFL REST" indicator for 5 seconds.

Test Description: Numbers below refer to circled numbers on the diagnostic chart.

1. This test checks the status of the "INFL REST" indicator. The "INFL REST" indicator should illuminate for 5 seconds and go "OFF".

2. This test verifies that any fault codes which have been cleared do not still exist. If a fault exists but no codes are in memory when the DERM is powered up, the "INFL REST" indicator will illuminate for 5 seconds and then go out. The DERM will then perform tests on all circuits, which may take up to 100 seconds to recognize a fault. If a fault is detected, the DERM will illuminate both the "INFL REST" and "FASTEN SEATBELT" indicators and store the fault code in memory.

3. This test checks the CRANK SIGNAL INPUT. As the engine is "cranked," system voltage is applied to the CRANK SIGNAL INPUT of the DERM. If no fault codes are in memory, the DERM will reset after the CRANK SIGNAL INPUT goes low. The DERM responds by illuminating the "INFL REST" indicator for 5 seconds after reset. If the indicator does not respond correctly, refer to CHART C to diagnose the CRANK SIGNAL INPUT malfunction.

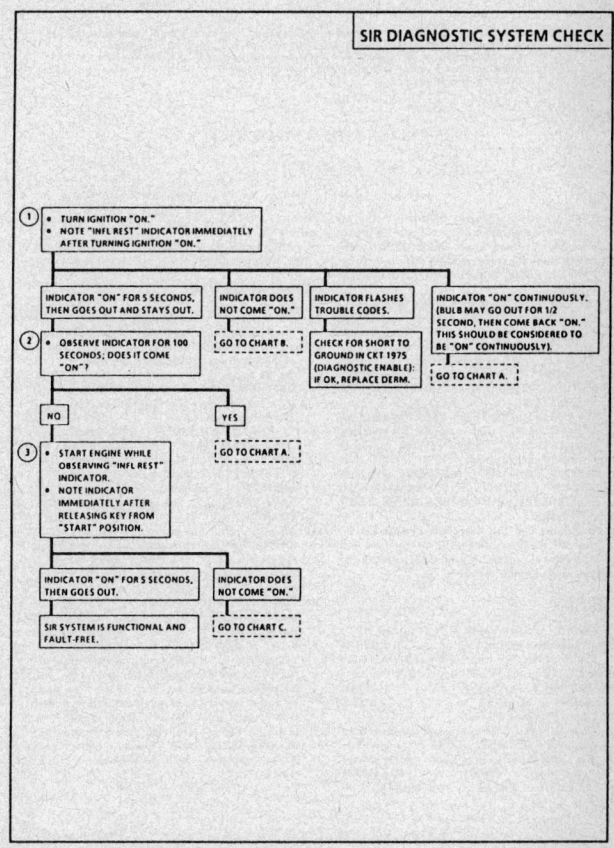

Fig. 12 SIR diagnostic system check. Corvette

CAUTION: To avoid deployment when troubleshooting the SIR system, do not use electrical test equipment such as battery powered or A/C powered voltmeter, ohmmeter, etc., or any type of electrical equipment other than those specified in this manual. Do not use a non-powered probe type tester. Instructions in this manual must be followed carefully, otherwise personal injury may result.

SIR DIAGNOSTIC SYSTEM CHECK

The diagnostic procedures used in this section are designed to aid in finding and repairing SIR problems. Outlined below are the steps to find and repair SIR problems quickly and effectively. Not carefully following these procedures may result in extended diagnostic time, incorrect diagnosis and incorrect part replacements.

A. PERFORM THE "SIR DIAGNOSTIC SYSTEM CHECK".

The "SIR Diagnostic System Check" should be the starting point of any SIR diagnostics. The "SIR Diagnostic System Check" checks for proper "INFLATABLE RESTRAINT" indicator operation and checks for SIR trouble codes.

B. REFER TO THE PROPER DIAGNOSTIC CHART AS DIRECTED BY THE "SIR DIAGNOSTIC SYSTEM CHECK".

The "SIR Diagnostic System Check" will lead you to the correct chart to diagnose SIR problems. Bypassing these procedures may result in extended diagnostic time, incorrect diagnosis and incorrect part replacements.

C. REPEAT THE "SIR DIAGNOSTIC SYSTEM CHECK" AFTER ANY REPAIR OR DIAGNOSTIC PROCEDURES HAVE BEEN PERFORMED.

Performing the "SIR Diagnostic System Check" after all repair or diagnostic procedures will assure that the repair has been made correctly and that no other conditions exist.

Description:

When the ignition switch is first turned "ON", system voltage is applied through the fuse #19 to the DERM at the "IGNITION 1" input and through fuse #18 to the DERM at the "SIR Indicator Low" and "SIR Indicator High" inputs. The DERM responds by blinking the "INFLATABLE RESTRAINT" indicator 7 to 9 times.

When the engine is being cranked system voltage is applied to the DERM at the "CRANK" input. The DERM grounds the lamp circuit until system voltage is removed from the "CRANK" input. This results in a steady "INFLATABLE RESTRAINT" indicator during cranking.

After cranking the DERM will again blink the "INFLATABLE RESTRAINT" indicator 7 to 9 times.

Notes on Fault Tree:

1) The "INFLATABLE RESTRAINT" indicator should blink 7 to 9 times as the ignition is just turned on.

2) As the engine is "Cranked" the "INFLATABLE RESTRAINT" indicator should remain on steady. If the indicator does not respond use Chart D to diagnose the malfunction.

3) The "INFLATABLE RESTRAINT" indicator has completed the "Bulb Check" and remains on indicating a current code has been detected.

4) The "INFLATABLE RESTRAINT" indicator has completed the "Bulb Check" and goes out, indicating no current codes exist.

5) Record all codes (both History and Current) onto the repair order.

6) If there are no codes (History or Current) record this fact onto the repair order. No further diagnosis is required.

7) If the Driver Information Center indicates that no SIR data is being received from the DERM, then the Data Link will require diagnosis.

8) Codes are displayed (History or Current). The order that the codes are diagnosed is very important. Refer to the recommended charts.

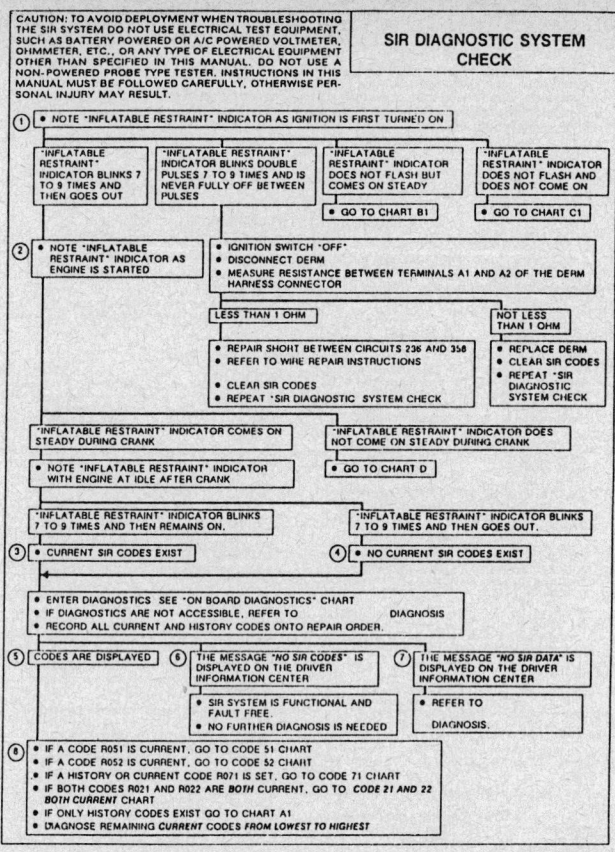

Fig. 13   SIR diagnostic system check. Deville, Eldorado, Fleetwood, Seville, Toronado & Trofeo

---

CAUTION: To avoid deployment when troubleshooting the SIR system, do not use electrical test equipment such as test lights, battery powered or A/C powered voltmeter, ohmmeter, etc., or any type of electrical equipment other than those specified in this manual. Instructions in this manual must be followed carefully, otherwise personal injury may result.

SIR DIAGNOSTIC SYSTEM CHECK

The diagnostic procedures used in this section are designed to find and repair SIR problems. To get the best results, it is important to utilize the diagnostic charts and follow the sequence listed below.

A. PERFORM THE "SIR DIAGNOSTIC SYSTEM CHECK".

The "SIR Diagnostic System Check" should be the starting point of any SIR diagnostics. The "SIR Diagnostic System Check" checks for proper "INFLATABLE RESTRAINT" indicator operation and checks for SIR trouble codes.

B. REFER TO THE PROPER DIAGNOSTIC CHART AS DIRECTED BY THE "SIR DIAGNOSTIC SYSTEM CHECK".

The "SIR Diagnostic System Check" will lead you to the correct chart to diagnose any SIR problems. Bypassing these procedures may result in extended diagnostic time.

C. REPEAT THE "SIR DIAGNOSTIC SYSTEM CHECK" AFTER ANY REPAIR OR DIAGNOSTIC PROCEDURES HAVE BEEN PERFORMED.

Performing the "SIR Diagnostic System Check" after all repair or diagnostic procedures will assure that the repair has been made correctly and that no other conditions exist.

Description:

When the ignition switch is first turned "ON", system voltage is applied through the SIR FUSE to the DERM at the "IGNITION 1" input and through GAGES FUSE to the DERM at the "SIR Indicator Low" and "SIR Indicator High" inputs. The DERM responds by blinking the "INFLATABLE RESTRAINT" indicator 7 times.

When the engine is being cranked system voltage is applied to the DERM at the "CRANK" input. The DERM grounds the lamp circuit until system voltage is removed from the "CRANK" input. The DERM grounds the lamp circuit until system voltage is removed from the "CRANK" input. This results in a steady "INFLATABLE RESTRAINT" indicator during cranking.

After cranking the DERM will again blink the "INFLATABLE RESTRAINT" indicator 7 times.

Notes on Fault Tree:

1. The "INFLATABLE RESTRAINT" indicator should bring 7 times as the ignition is just turned on. If the indicator does not respond use CHART C or D to diagnose the indicator malfunction.

2. As the engine is "Cranked" the "INFLATABLE RESTRAINT" indicator should remain on steady. If the indicator does not respond use CHART E to diagnose the malfunction.

3. The "INFLATABLE RESTRAINT" indicator has completed the "Bulb Check" and remains on indicating a current code has been detected. At this point a "Scan" tool or the "INFLATABLE RESTRAINT" indicator can be used to diagnose the malfunction. For "Flash Code" diagnosis use CHART B.

4. After "Cranking" the engine the "INFLATABLE RESTRAINT" indicator should blink 7 to 9 times and then go out. If the indicator begins to flash a Code 12, there is a system fault. Use CHART F to diagnose the malfunction.

5. The "INFLATABLE RESTRAINT" indicator has completed the "Bulb Check" and is indicating no current codes exist.

6. Record all codes (both History and Current) onto the repair order. If there are no codes (History or Current) record this fact onto the repair order. No further diagnosis is required. If the scan tool indicates that no data is being received from the DERM, then the data link will require diagnosis.

7. If multiple codes are displayed (History or Current). The order that the codes are diagnosed is very important. Refer to the recommended charts.

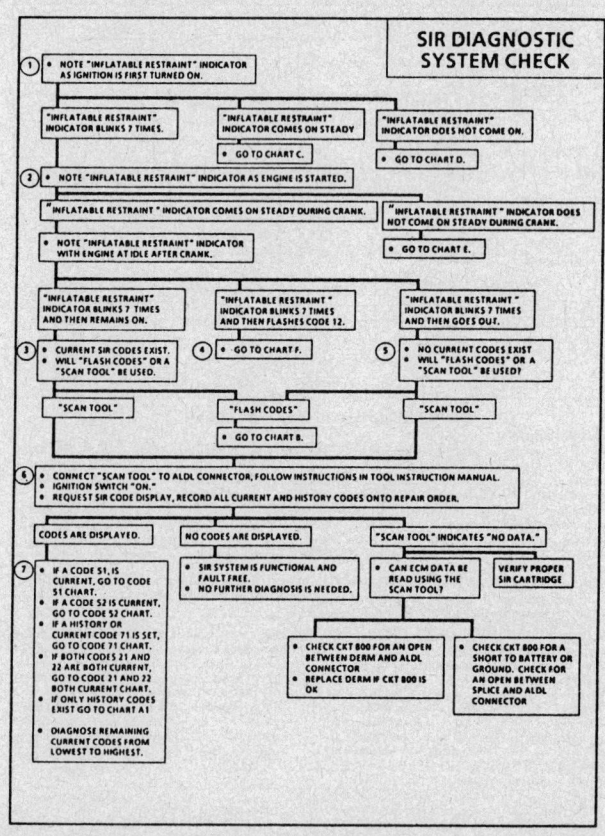

Fig. 14   SIR diagnostic system check. Storm

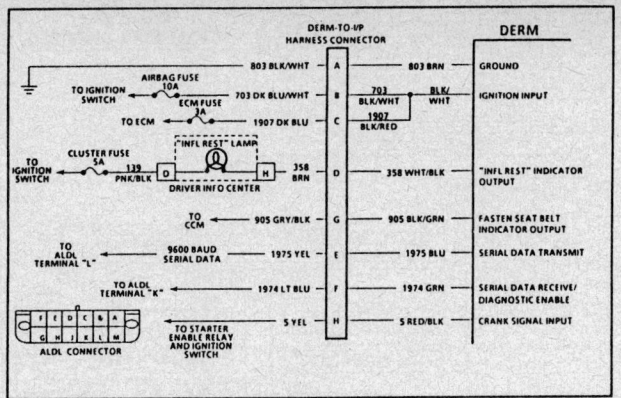

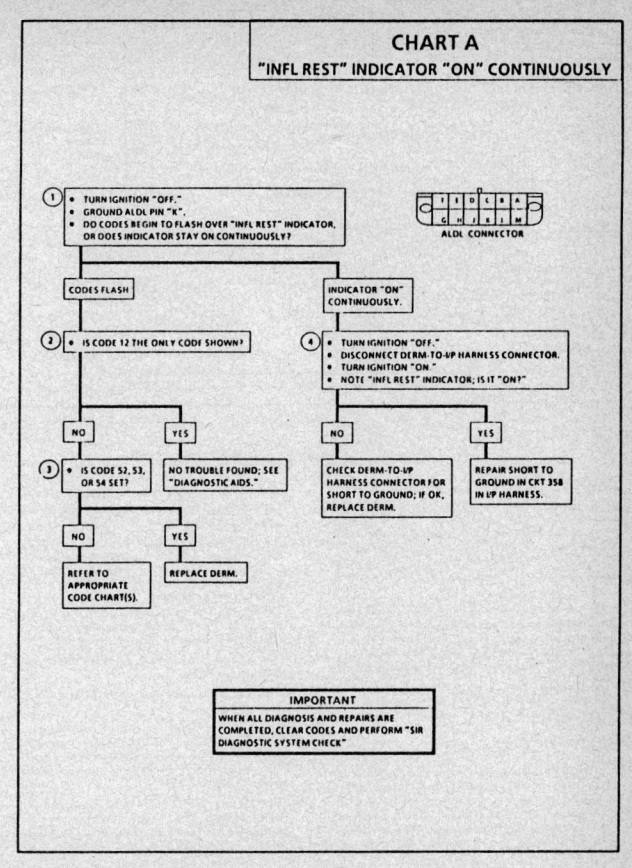

CHART A
"INFL REST" INDICATOR "ON" CONTINUOUSLY

Circuit Description:

When power is applied to the DERM, it responds by illuminating the "INFL REST" indicator for five seconds if no fault codes have been stored. If the DERM has fault codes in memory, it illuminates both the "INFL REST" and Fasten Seatbelt indicators continuously. The DERM has an internal lamp driver for the "INFL REST" indicator. The FASTEN SEATBELT output of the DERM is connected to the Central Control Module (CCM) which actually drives the Fasten Seatbelt indicator.

When the engine is being cranked, system voltage is applied to the DERM at the CRANK SIGNAL INPUT. If no fault codes are stored and system power is removed from the CRANK SIGNAL INPUT, the DERM will reset and again illuminate the "INFL REST" indicator for 5 seconds.

Test Description: Numbers below refer to circled numbers on the diagnostic chart.

1. This test checks for a problem in the indicator circuit. If the "INFL REST" indicator is "ON" continuously, there is a short to ground in CKT 358.
2. This test checks for stored fault codes.
3. Codes 52, 53 and 54 cannot be cleared and will cause the indicator lamp to stay "ON" continuously.
4. This test determines whether a short to ground in CKT 358, which was found in Test 1, is in the I/P harness or in the DERM harness. If the short is in the DERM harness itself, or in the DERM, the DERM must be replaced.

Diagnostic Aids:

The Fasten Seat Belt indicator will stay "ON" continuously when an SIR failure code has been set.

If power is applied to the SIR system while any component is not properly connected, an additional failure code will be set for the disconnected SIR component.

IMPORTANT

WHEN ALL DIAGNOSIS AND REPAIRS ARE COMPLETED, CLEAR CODES AND PERFORM "SIR DIAGNOSTIC SYSTEM CHECK"

Fig. 15 Diagnostic chart A. Corvette

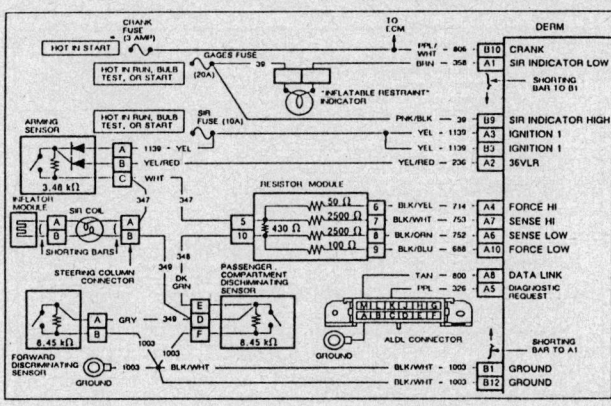

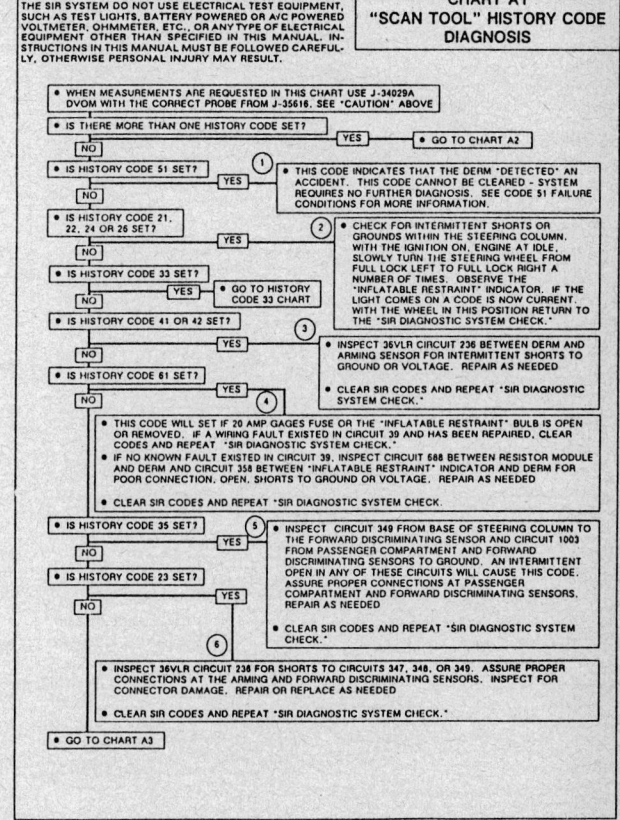

CHART A1
"SCAN TOOL" HISTORY CODE DIAGNOSIS

Description:

When the Ignition Switch is first turned "ON" system voltage is applied through GAGES FUSE to "SIR Indicator High" (B9) and to the "INFLATABLE RESTRAINT" Indicator Lamp which is connected to "SIR Indicator Low" (A1). SIR FUSE also applies system voltage to the "Ignition 1" inputs (A3 and B3). The DERM responds by blinking the "INFLATABLE RESTRAINT" indicator 7 to 9 times.

When the engine is being cranked system voltage is applied to the DERM at the "CRANK" input. The DERM grounds the lamp circuit until system voltage is removed from the "CRANK" input. This results in a steady "INFLATABLE RESTRAINT" indicator during cranking.

After cranking the DERM will again blink the "INFLATABLE RESTRAINT" indicator 7 to 9 times.

Notes on Fault Tree:

1) The DERM determines that the Arming Sensor is closed when system voltage or more is present at the "Sense Hi" input, and it determines that a

Discriminating sensor in closed when it notes low voltage at the "Sense Low" input. There are some faults that "look" like an accident to the DERM, and therefore record a code 51. History Code 51 therefore is not proof that the vehicle was in an accident.

2) Checks for intermittent electrical conditions within the steering column.

3) Checks for intermittent shorts in the 36VLR wiring (circuit 236).

4) Checks for misinstalled GAGES FUSE and "INFLATABLE RESTRAINT" Indicator bulb or uncleared code 61 after a completed wiring repair on circuit 39. Also checks for intermittent faults in circuits 688 and 358.

5) Checks for intermittent opens in the ground path of the deployment loop between the base of the steering column and both discriminating sensors (circuit 349-both branches).

6) Checks for intermittent wiring shorts between 36VLR circuit 236 and circuits 347, 348 and 349 of the SIR wiring harness.

Fig. 16 Diagnostic chart A1. Camaro & Firebird

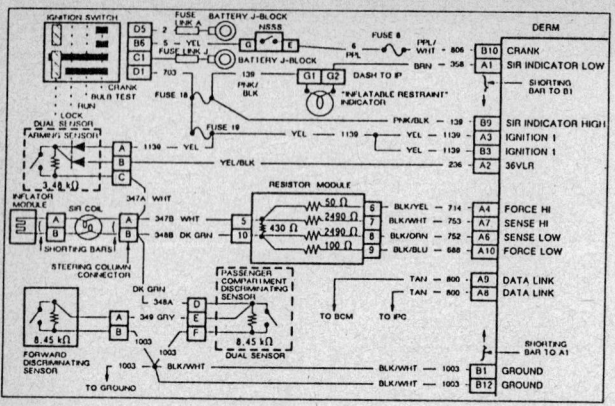

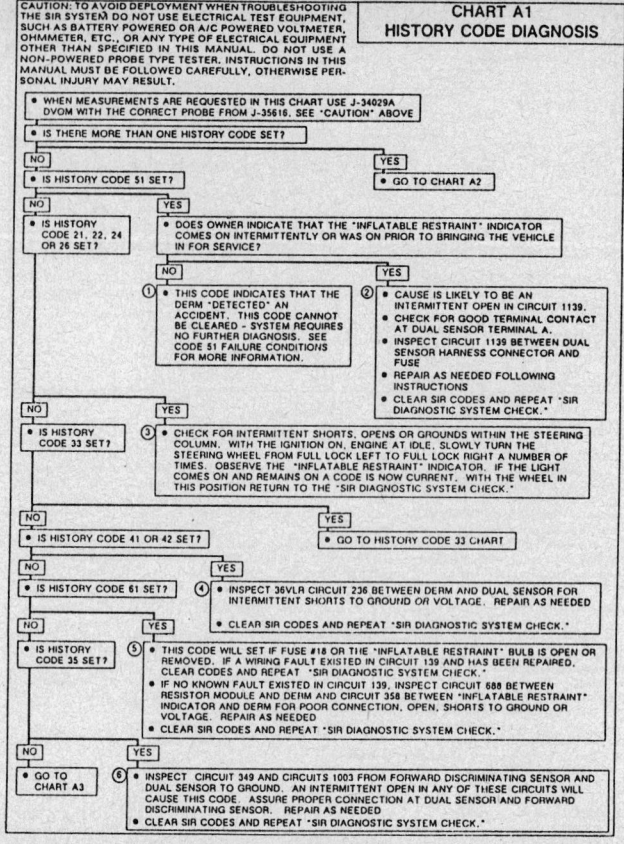

CHART A1
HISTORY CODE DIAGNOSIS

CHART A1
HISTORY CODE DIAGNOSIS

When the Ignition Switch is first turned "ON" system voltage is applied through fuse #18 to "SIR Indicator High" (B9) and to the "INFLATABLE RESTRAINT" Indicator Lamp which is connected to "SIR Indicator Low" (A1). Fuse #19 also applies system voltage to the "IGNITION 1" inputs (A3 and B3). The DERM responds by blinking the "INFLATABLE RESTRAINT" indicator 7 to 9 times.

When the engine is being cranked system voltage is applied to the DERM at the "CRANK" input. The DERM grounds the lamp circuit until system voltage is removed from the "CRANK" input. This results in a steady "INFLATABLE RESTRAINT" indicator during cranking.

After cranking the DERM will again blink the "INFLATABLE RESTRAINT" indicator 7 to 9 times.

Notes on Fault Tree:

1) The DERM determines that the Arming Sensor is closed when system voltage or more is present at the "Sense Hi" input, and it determines that a Discriminating sensor is closed when it notes low voltage at the "Sense Low" input. There are some faults that may "look" like an accident to the

DERM, and therefore record a code 51. History Code 51 therefore is not proof that the vehicle was in an accident.

2) If a history code 51 is set, history code 34 will not set. Therefore, any conditions which may cause a current code 34 to set will not set a history code 34 if a history code 51 is set. If the "INFLATABLE RESTRAINT" indicator alerts the owner intermittently of a current code and no corresponding history codes are set, the most likely cause is an intermittent open in circuit 1139.

3) Checks for intermittent electrical conditions within the steering column.

4) Checks for intermittent shorts in the 36VLR wiring (circuit 236).

5) Checks for burned or misinstalled fuse #18 and "INFLATABLE RESTRAINT" Indicator bulb or uncleared code 61 after a completed wiring repair on circuit 139. Also checks for intermittent faults in circuits 688 and 358.

6) Checks for intermittent opens in the ground path of the deployment loop between the base of the steering column and both discriminating sensors (circuits 349 and 1003).

Fig. 17 Diagnostic chart A1. Deville, Fleetwood, Eldorado, Seville, Riviera, Reatta, Toronado & Trofeo

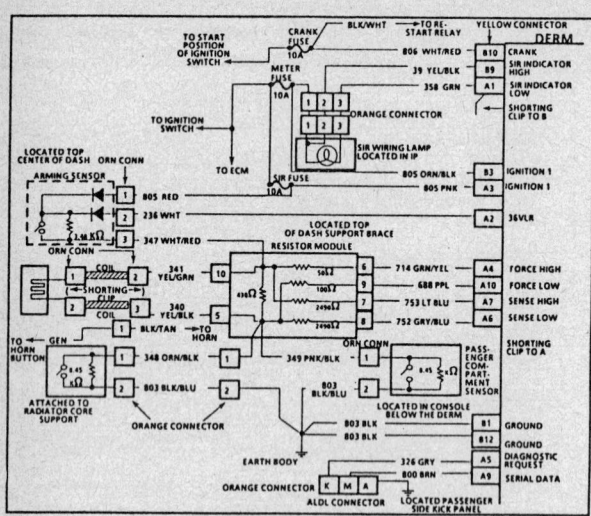

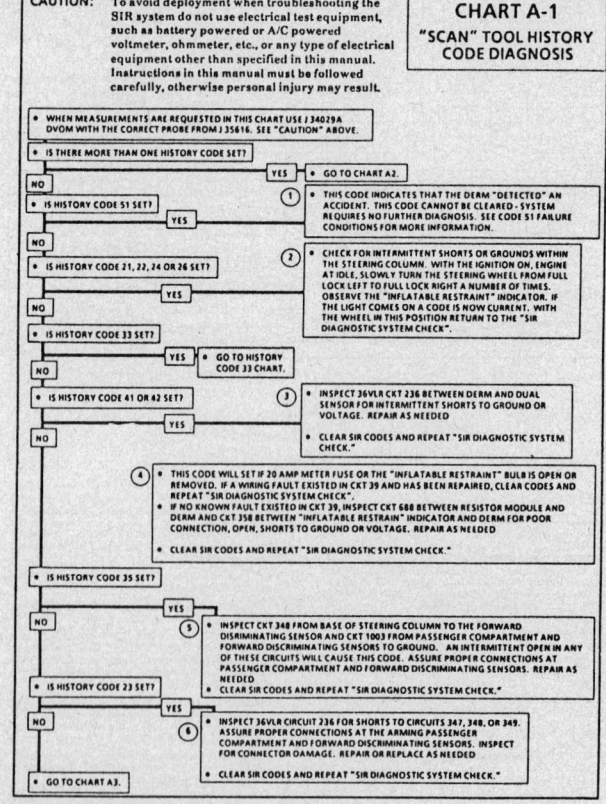

CAUTION: To avoid deployment when troubleshooting the SIR system do not use electrical test equipment, such as battery powered or A/C powered voltmeter, ohmmeter, etc., or any type of electrical equipment other than specified in this manual. Instructions in this manual must be followed carefully, otherwise personal injury may result.

CHART A-1
"SCAN" TOOL HISTORY CODE DIAGNOSIS

CHART A-1
"SCAN" TOOL HISTORY CODE DIAGNOSIS

Description:

When the Ignition Switch is first turned "ON" system voltage is applied through METER FUSE to "SIR Indicator High" (B9) and to the "INFLATABLE RESTRAINT" Indicator Lamp which is connected to "SIR Indicator Low" (A1). SIR FUSE also applies system voltage to the "Ignition 1" inputs (A3 and B3). The DERM responds by blinking the "INFLATABLE RESTRAINT" indicator 7 times.

When the engine is being cranked system voltage is applied to the DERM at the "CRANK" input. The DERM grounds the lamp circuit until system voltage is removed from the "CRANK" input. This results in a steady "INFLATABLE RESTRAINT" indicator during cranking.

After cranking the DERM will again blink the "INFLATABLE RESTRAINT" indicator 7 times.

Notes on Fault Tree:

1. The DERM determines that the Arming Sensor is closed when system voltage or more is present at the "Sense Hi" input, and it determines that a Discriminating sensor is closed when it notes low

voltage at the "Sense Low" input. There are some faults that may "look" like an accident to the DERM, and therefore record a Code 51. History Code 51 therefore is not proof that the vehicle was in an accident.

2. Checks for intermittent electrical conditions within the steering column.

3. Checks for intermittent shorts in the 36VLR wiring (CKT 236).

4. Checks for misinstalled GAGES FUSE and "INFLATABLE RESTRAINT" Indicator bulb or uncleared Code 61 after a completed wiring repair on CKT 39. Also checks for intermittent faults in CKTs 688 and 358.

5. Checks for intermittent opens in the ground path of the deployment loop between the base of the steering column and both discriminating sensors (CKT 348–both branches).

6. Checks for intermittent wiring shorts between 36VLR circuit 236 and circuits 347, 348 and of the SIR wiring harness.

Fig. 18 Diagnostic chart A1. Storm

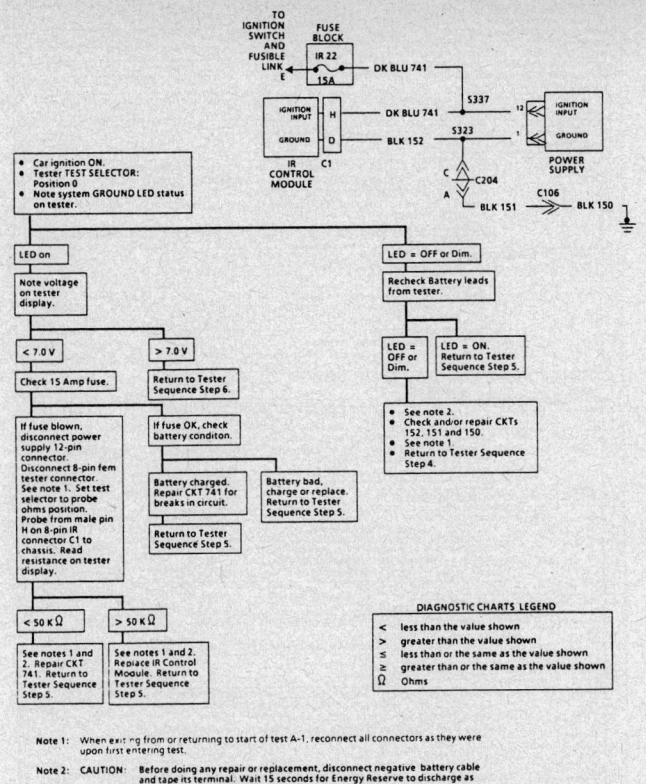

Fig. 19 Diagnostic chart, Test A-1. 88 & 98

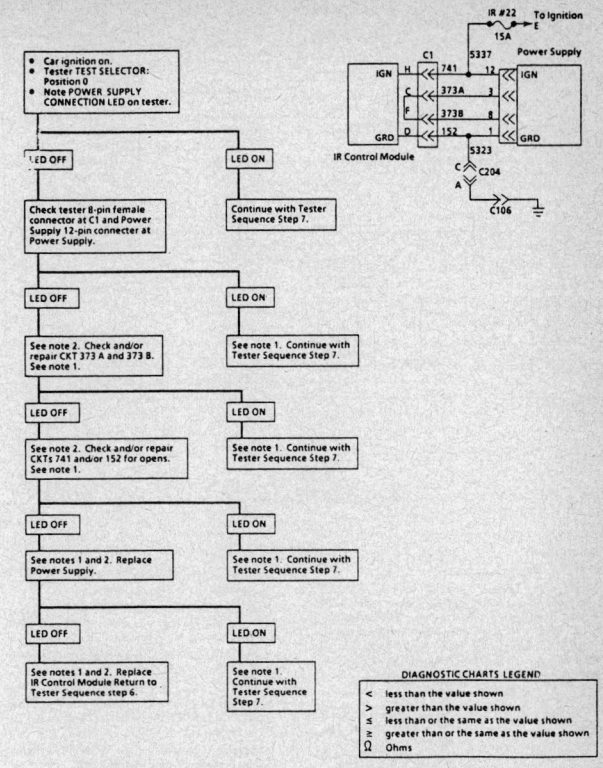

Fig. 20 Diagnostic chart, Test A-2. 88 & 98

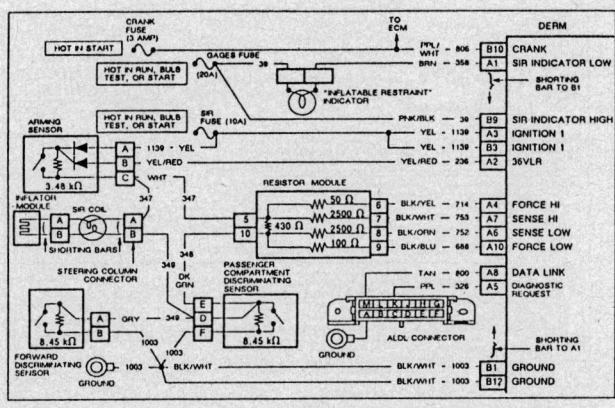

CHART A2
"SCAN TOOL" HISTORY CODE DIAGNOSIS

Description:

When the Ignition Switch is first turned "ON" system voltage is applied through GAGES FUSE to "SIR Indicator High" (B9) and to the "INFLATABLE RESTRAINT" Indicator Lamp which is connected to "SIR Indicator Low" (A1). SIR FUSE also applies system voltage to the "Ignition 1" inputs (A3 and B3). The DERM responds by blinking the "INFLATABLE RESTRAINT" indicator 7 to 9 times.

When the engine is being cranked system voltage is applied to the DERM at the "CRANK" input. The DERM grounds the lamp circuit until voltage is removed from the "CRANK" input. This results in a steady "INFLATABLE RESTRAINT" indicator during cranking.

After cranking the DERM will again blink the "INFLATABLE RESTRAINT" indicator 7 to 9 times.

Notes on Fault Tree:

1) Checks for intermittent shorts to system voltage in the 36VLR wiring (circuit 236).
2) Checks for intermittent shorts to ground in the 36VLR wiring (circuit 236).
3) Checks for intermittent open in the 36VLR wiring (circuit 236).
4) Checks for intermittent open in the Force Hi and Force Low wiring (circuits 714 and 688).
5) Checks for intermittent opens or shorts to ground in the Sense Low wiring (circuit 752).
6) Checks for shorts to system voltage in the deployment loop (circuits 347 and 349) or in the diagnostic circuits (circuits 347, 348, 688, 714, 752 and 753).
7) Checks for shorts between circuit 236 and 347, 348, or 349.

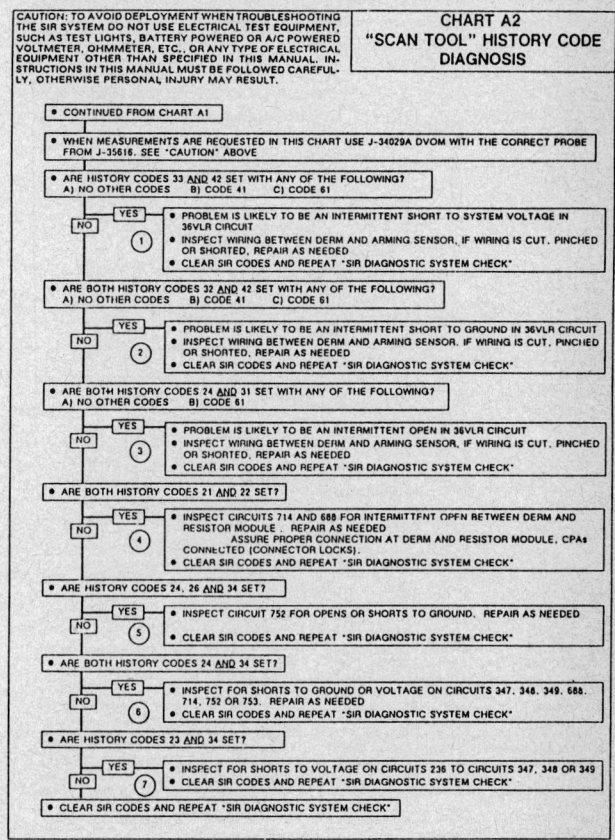

Fig. 21 Diagnostic chart A2. Camaro & Firebird

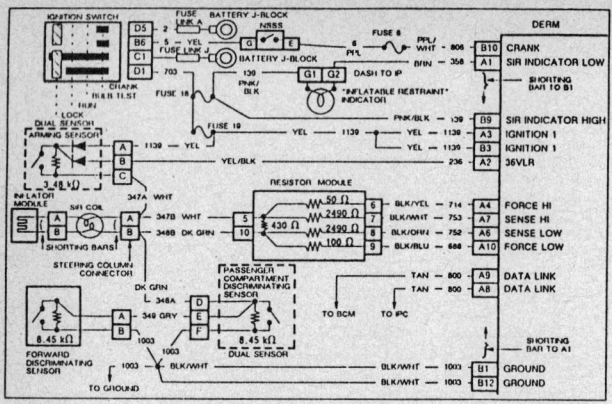

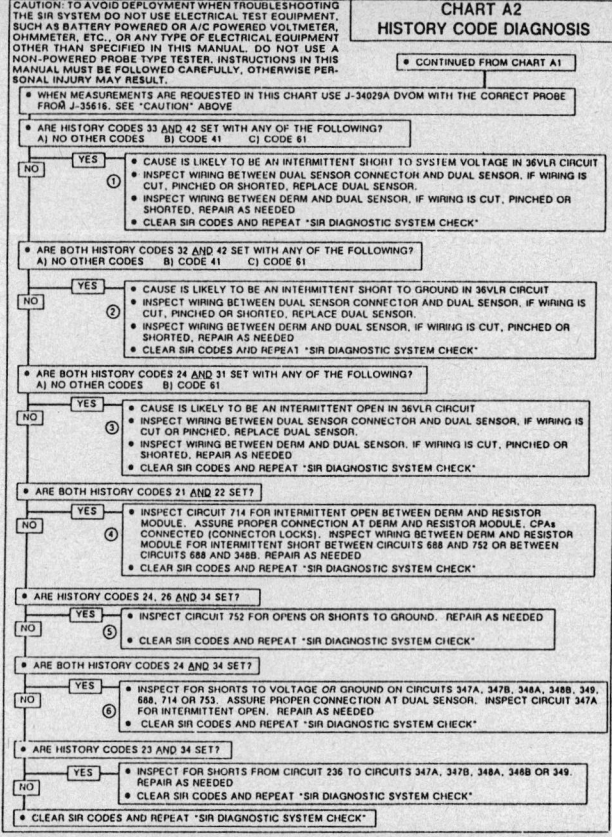

CAUTION: TO AVOID DEPLOYMENT WHEN TROUBLESHOOTING THE SIR SYSTEM DO NOT USE ELECTRICAL TEST EQUIPMENT, SUCH AS BATTERY POWERED OR A/C POWERED VOLTMETER, OHMMETER, ETC., OR ANY TYPE OF ELECTRICAL EQUIPMENT OTHER THAN SPECIFIED IN THIS MANUAL. DO NOT USE A NON-POWERED PROBE TYPE TESTER. INSTRUCTIONS IN THIS MANUAL MUST BE FOLLOWED CAREFULLY, OTHERWISE PERSONAL INJURY MAY RESULT.

CHART A2
HISTORY CODE DIAGNOSIS

CHART A2
HISTORY CODE DIAGNOSIS

Description:

When the Ignition Switch is first turned "ON" system voltage is applied through fuse #18 to "SIR Indicator High" (B9) and to the "INFLATABLE RESTRAINT" Indicator Lamp which is connected to "SIR Indicator Low" (A1). Fuse #19 also applies system voltage to the "IGNITION 1" inputs (A3 and B3). The DERM responds by blinking the "INFLATABLE RESTRAINT" indicator 7 to 9 times.

When the engine is being cranked system voltage is applied to the DERM at the "CRANK" input. The DERM grounds the lamp circuit until system voltage is removed from the "CRANK" input. This results in a steady "INFLATABLE RESTRAINT" indicator during cranking.

After cranking the DERM will again blink the "INFLATABLE RESTRAINT" indicator 7 to 9 times.

Notes on Fault Tree:

1) Checks for intermittent shorts to system voltage in the 36VLR wiring (circuit 236).
2) Checks for intermittent shorts in the 36VLR wiring (circuit 236) to ground or to DERM supplied ground thru the lamp driver.
3) Checks for intermittent open in the 36VLR wiring (circuit 236).
4) Checks for intermittent open in the Force Hi wiring (circuit 714) and for intermittent shorts from Force Low (circuit 688) to Sense Low (circuit 752) or to circuit 348.
5) Checks for intermittent opens or shorts to ground in the Sense Low wiring (circuit 752).
6) Checks for shorts to ground in the deployment loop (circuits 347 and 348) or shorts to ground in the diagnostic circuits (circuits 688, 714 and 753). Also checks for intermittent open in circuit 347A.

Fig. 22   Diagnostic chart A2. Deville, Fleetwood, Eldorado, Seville, Riviera, Reatta, Toronado & Trofeo

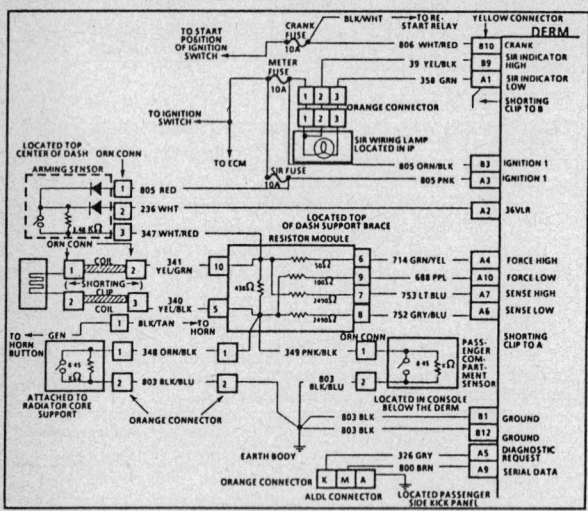

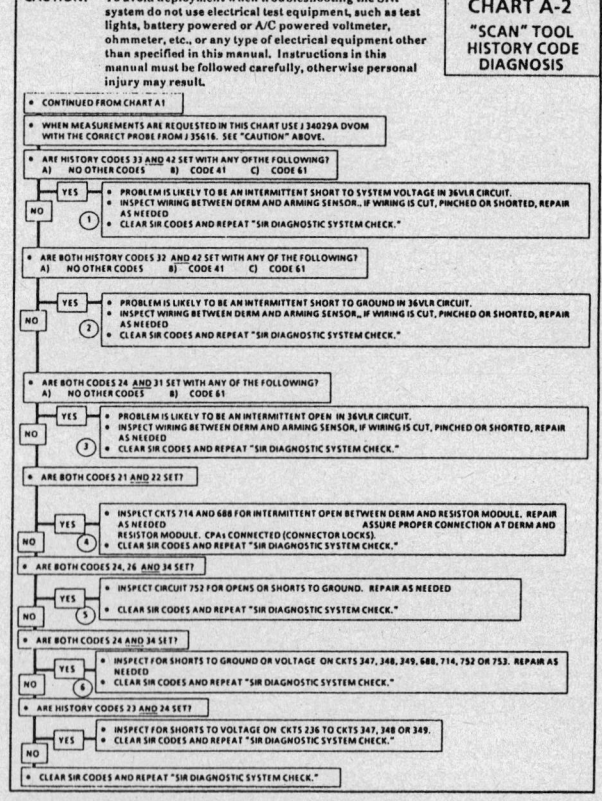

CAUTION: To avoid deployment when troubleshooting the SIR system do not use electrical test equipment, such as test lights, battery powered or A/C powered voltmeter, ohmmeter, etc., or any type of electrical equipment other than specified in this manual. Instructions in this manual must be followed carefully, otherwise personal injury may result.

CHART A-2
"SCAN" TOOL HISTORY CODE DIAGNOSIS

CHART A-2
"SCAN" TOOL HISTORY CODE DIAGNOSIS

Description:

When the Ignition Switch is first turned "ON" system voltage is applied through METER FUSE 16 to "SIR Indicator High" (B9) and to the "INFLATABLE RESTRAINT" Indicator Lamp which is connected to "SIR Indicator Low" (A1). Fuse 3 also applies system voltage to the "IGNITION 1" inputs (A3 and B3). The DERM responds by blinking the "INFLATABLE RESTRAINT" indicator 7 times.

When the engine is being cranked system voltage is applied to the DERM at the "CRANK" input. The DERM grounds the lamp circuit until system voltage is removed from the "CRANK" input. This results in a steady "INFLATABLE RESTRAINT" indicator during cranking.

After cranking the DERM will again blink the "INFLATABLE RESTRAINT" indicator 7 times.

Notes on Fault Tree:

1. Checks for intermittent shorts to system voltage in the 36VLR wiring (CKT 236).
2. Checks for intermittent shorts to ground in the 36VLR wiring (CKT 236).
3. Checks for intermittent open in the 36VLR wiring (CKT 236).
4. Checks for intermittent open in the Force Hi and Force Low wiring (CKT 714 and 688).
5. Checks for intermittent opens or shorts to ground in the Sense Low wiring (CKT 752).
6. Checks for shorts to system voltage in the deployment loop (CKT 347 and 349) or in the diagnostic circuits (CKT 347, 348, 688, 714, 752 and 753).
7. Checks for shorts between circuit 236 and 347, 348, or 349.

Fig. 23   Diagnostic chart A2. Storm

SUPPLEMENTAL INFLATABLE RESTRAINT SYSTEM

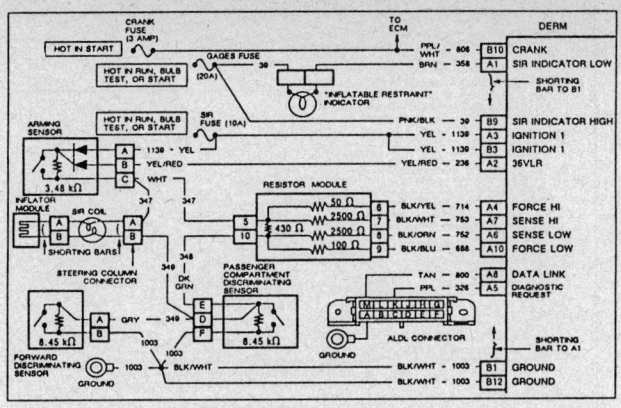

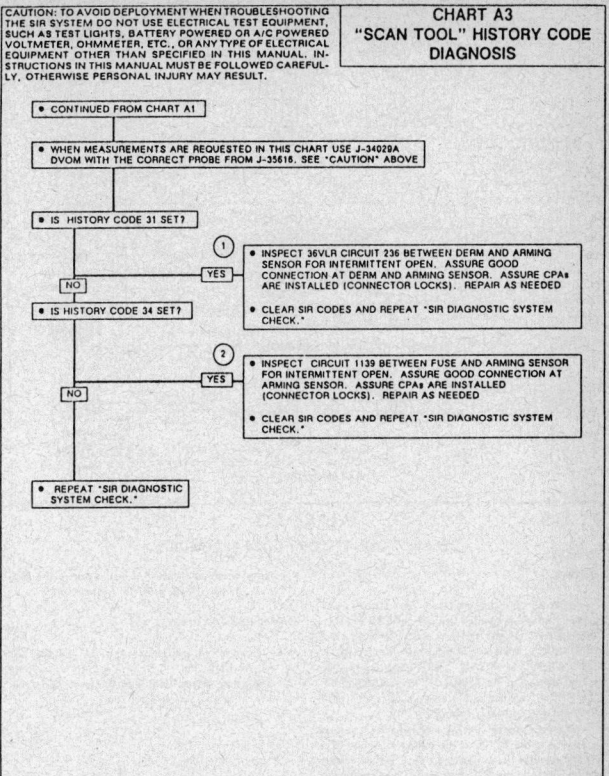

CHART A3
"SCAN TOOL" HISTORY CODE DIAGNOSIS

Description:

When the Ignition Switch is first turned "ON" system voltage is applied through GAGES FUSE to "SIR Indicator High" (B9) and to the "INFLATABLE RESTRAINT" Indicator Lamp which is connected to "SIR Indicator Low" (A1). SIR FUSE also applies system voltage to the "Ignition 1" inputs (A3 and B3). The DERM responds by blinking the "INFLATABLE RESTRAINT" indicator 7 to 9 times.

When the engine is being cranked system voltage is applied to the DERM at the "CRANK" input. The DERM grounds the lamp circuit until system voltage is

removed from the "CRANK" input. This results in a steady "INFLATABLE RESTRAINT" indicator during cranking.

After cranking the DERM will again blink the "INFLATABLE RESTRAINT" indicator 7 to 9 times.

Notes on Fault Tree:

1) Checks for intermittent opens in the 36VLR wiring (circuit 236).
2) Checks for intermittent open between fuse 3 and the arming sensor (circuit 1139).

Fig. 24   Diagnostic chart A3. Camaro & Firebird

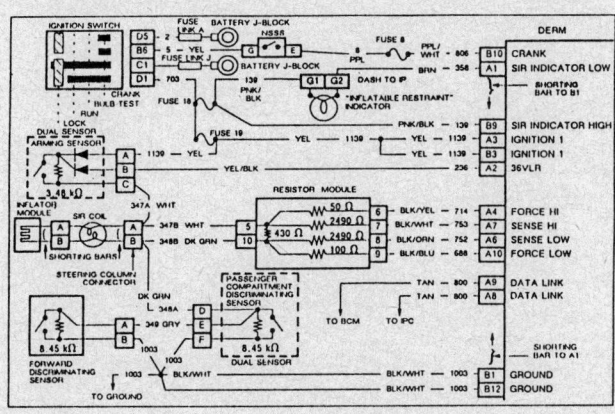

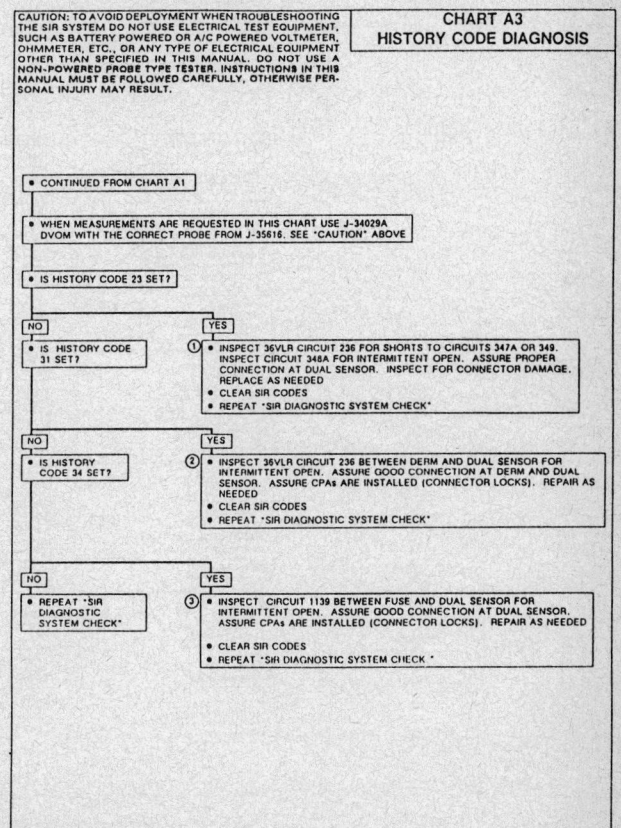

CHART A3
HISTORY CODE DIAGNOSIS

Description:

When the Ignition Switch is first turned "ON" system voltage is applied through fuse #18 to "SIR Indicator High" (B9) and to the "INFLATABLE RESTRAINT" Indicator Lamp which is connected to "SIR Indicator Low" (A1). Fuse #19 also applies system voltage to the "IGNITION 1" inputs (A3 and B3). The DERM responds by blinking the "INFLATABLE RESTRAINT" indicator 7 to 9 times.

When the engine is being cranked system voltage is applied to the DERM at the "CRANK" input. The DERM grounds the lamp circuit until system voltage is removed from the "CRANK" input. This results in a steady "INFLATABLE RESTRAINT" indicator during cranking.

After cranking the DERM will again blink the "INFLATABLE RESTRAINT" indicator 7 to 9 times.

Notes on Fault Tree:

1) Checks for intermittent wiring shorts between 36VLR (circuit 236) and circuits 347A, 347B, 348A, 348B and 349 of the SIR wiring harness. Also checks for intermittent open in circuit 348A.
2) Checks for intermittent opens in the 36VLR wiring (circuit 236).
3) Checks for intermittent open between fuse #19 and the arming sensor (circuit 1139).

Fig. 25   Diagnostic chart A3. Deville, Fleetwood, Eldorado, Seville, Riviera, Reatta, Toronado & Trofeo

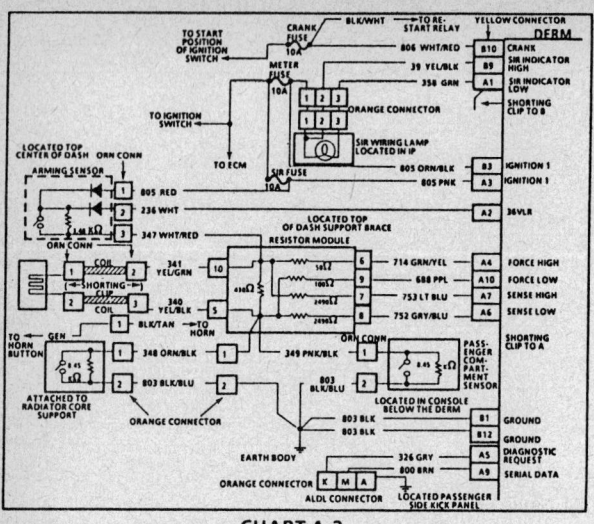

CHART A-3
"SCAN" TOOL HISTORY CODE DIAGNOSIS

Description:

When the Ignition Switch is first turned "ON" system voltage is applied through METER FUSE to "SIR Indicator High" (B9) and to the "INFLATABLE RESTRAINT" Indicator Lamp which is connected to "SIR Indicator Low" (A1). SIR FUSE also applies system voltage to the "Ignition 1" inputs (A3 and B3). The DERM responds by blinking the "INFLATABLE RESTRAINT" indicator 7 times.

When the engine is being cranked system voltage is applied to the DERM at the "CRANK" input. The DERM grounds the lamp circuit until system voltage is removed from the "CRANK" input. This results in a steady "INFLATABLE RESTRAINT" indicator during cranking.

After cranking the DERM will again blink the "INFLATABLE RESTRAINT" indicator 7 times.

Notes on Fault Tree:

1. Checks for intermittent opens in the 36VLR wiring (CKT 236).
2. Checks for intermittent open between SIR fuse and the arming sensor (CKT 805).

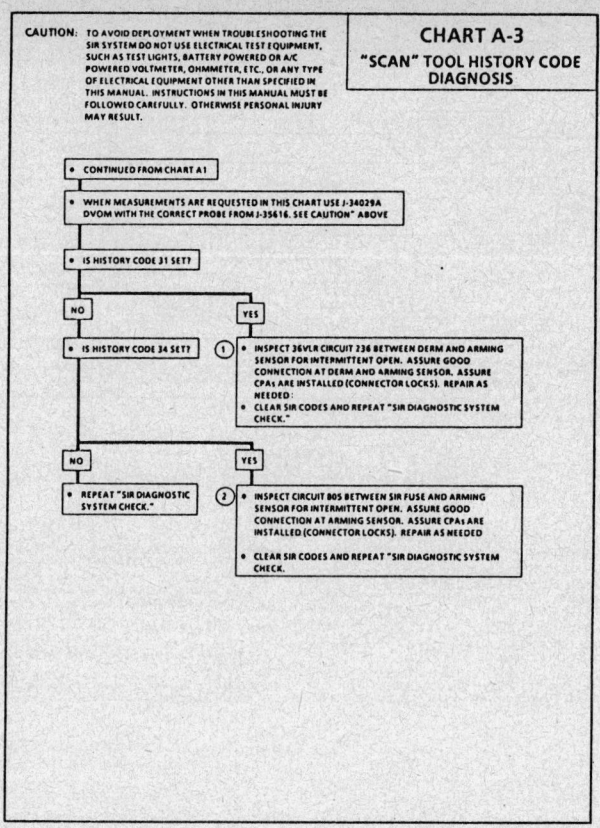

CHART A-3
"SCAN" TOOL HISTORY CODE DIAGNOSIS

CAUTION: TO AVOID DEPLOYMENT WHEN TROUBLESHOOTING THE SIR SYSTEM DO NOT USE ELECTRICAL TEST EQUIPMENT, SUCH AS TEST LIGHTS, BATTERY POWERED OR A/C POWERED VOLTMETER, OHMMETER, ETC., OR ANY TYPE OF ELECTRICAL EQUIPMENT OTHER THAN SPECIFIED IN THIS MANUAL. INSTRUCTIONS IN THIS MANUAL MUST BE FOLLOWED CAREFULLY. OTHERWISE PERSONAL INJURY MAY RESULT.

Fig. 26 Diagnostic chart A3. Storm

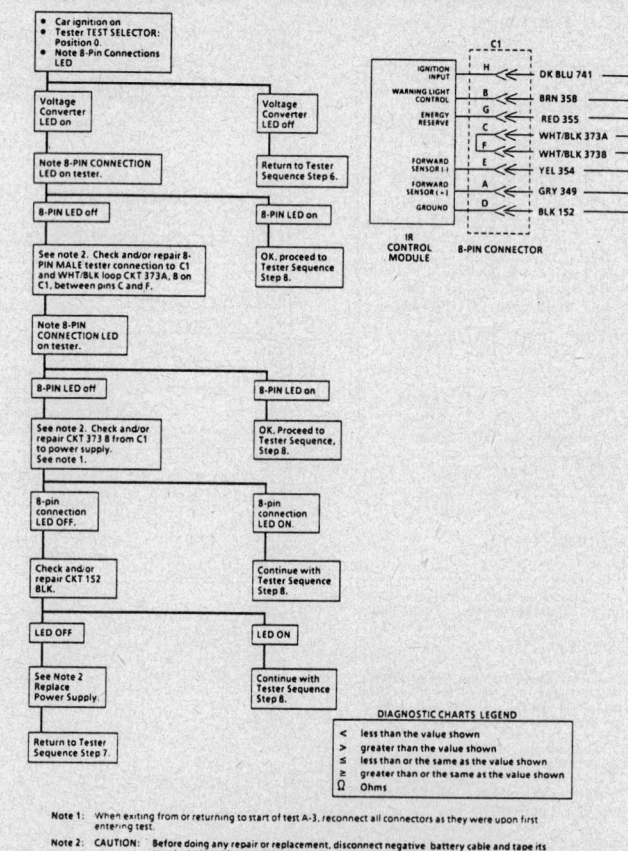

DIAGNOSTIC CHARTS LEGEND

<	less than the value shown
>	greater than the value shown
≤	less than or the same as the value shown
≥	greater than or the same as the value shown
Ω	Ohms

Note 1: When exiting from or returning to start of test A-3, reconnect all connectors as they were upon first entering test.

Note 2: CAUTION: Before doing any repair or replacement, disconnect negative battery cable and tape its terminal. Wait 15 seconds for Energy Reserve to discharge as personal injury could result.

Fig. 27 Diagnostic chart, Test A-3. 88 & 98

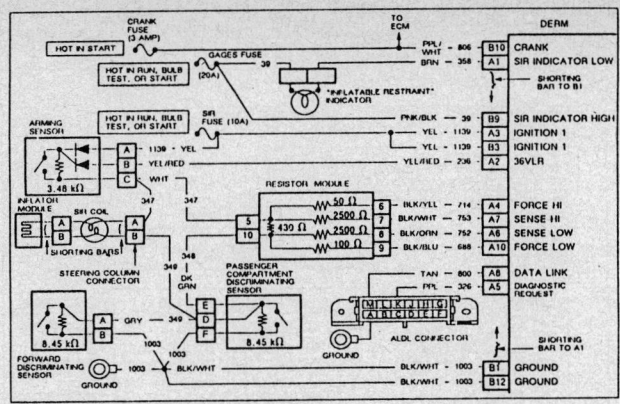

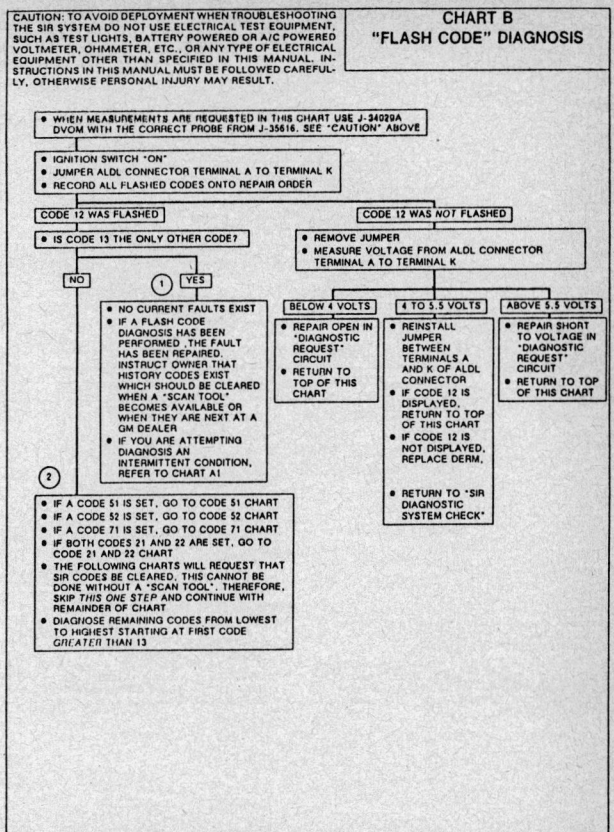

CHART B
"FLASH CODE" DIAGNOSIS

Fig. 28   Diagnostic chart B. Camaro & Firebird

Description:

When the Ignition Switch is first turned "ON" system voltage is applied through GAGES FUSE to "SIR Indicator High" (B9) and to the "INFLATABLE RESTRAINT" Indicator Lamp which is connected to "SIR Indicator Low" (A1). SIR FUSE also applies system voltage to the "Ignition 1" inputs (A3 and B3). The DERM responds by blinking the "INFLATABLE RESTRAINT" indicator 7 to 9 times.

When the engine is being cranked system voltage is applied to the DERM at the "CRANK" input. The DERM grounds the lamp circuit until system voltage is removed from the "CRANK" input. This results in a steady "INFLATABLE RESTRAINT" indicator during cranking.

After cranking the DERM will again blink the "INFLATABLE RESTRAINT" indicator 7 to 9 times.

Notes on Fault Tree:

1) If flash codes have been used to diagnose and repair a fault, the code(s) diagnosed and repaired will still appear as history codes only. The only way to clear history codes is with a "scan tool".

2) Where diagnostic charts request the clearing of SIR codes, the step is to be skipped since codes cannot be cleared through flash code diagnostics.

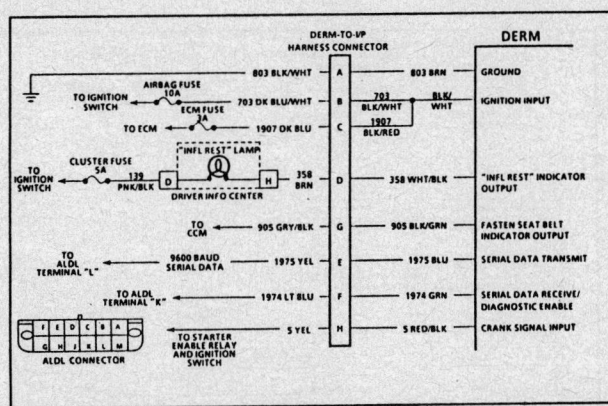

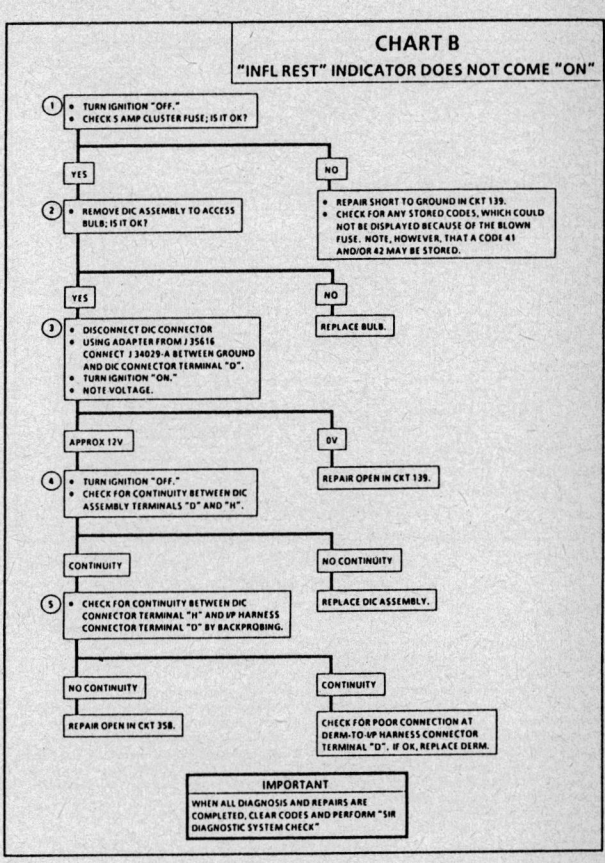

CHART B
"INFL REST" INDICATOR DOES NOT COME "ON"

Circuit Description:

When power is applied to the DERM, it responds by illuminating the "INFL REST" indicator for five seconds if no fault codes have been stored. If the DERM has fault codes in memory, it illuminates both the "INFL REST" and Fasten Seatbelt indicators continuously. The DERM has an internal lamp driver for the "INFL REST" indicator. The FASTEN SEATBELT output of the DERM is connected to the Central Control Module (CCM) which actually drives the Fasten Seatbelt indicator.

When the engine is being cranked, system voltage is applied to the DERM at the CRANK SIGNAL INPUT. If no fault codes are stored and system voltage is removed from the CRANK SIGNAL INPUT, the DERM will reset and again illuminate the "INFL REST" indicator for 5 seconds.

Test Description: Numbers below refer to circled numbers on the diagnostic chart.

1. This checks if power is available to illuminate the indicator lamp.
2. This checks if the bulb is good.
3. This test checks for an open in CKT 139.
4. This test checks for an open in the indicator circuit internal to the Driver Information Center (DIC).
5. This test checks for an open in CKT 358 in the I/P harness.

Diagnostic Aids:

The Fasten Seat Belt indicator will stay "ON" continuously when an SIR failure code has been set.

If power is applied to the SIR system while any component is not properly connected, an additional failure code will be set for the disconnected SIR component.

Fig. 29   Diagnostic chart B. Corvette

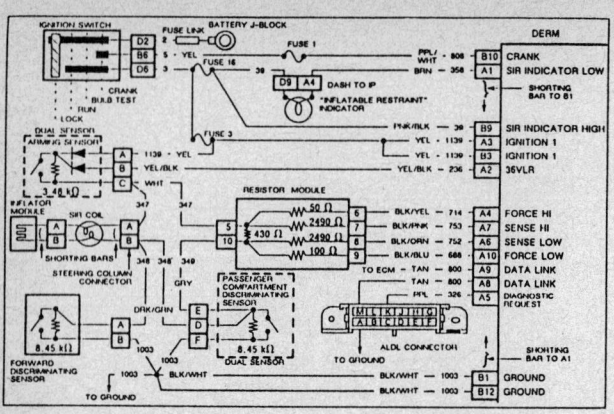

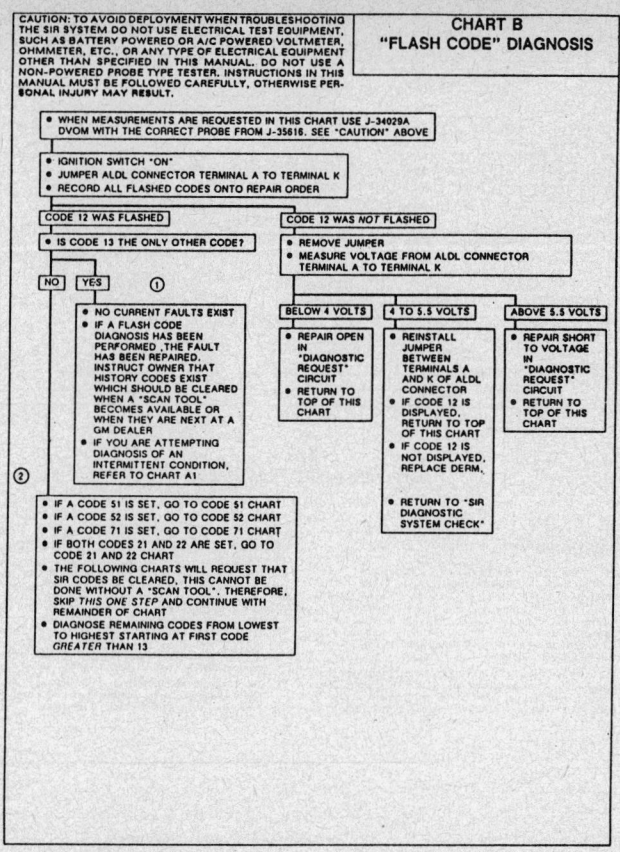

CHART B
"FLASH CODE" DIAGNOSIS

Description:

When the Ignition Switch is first turned "ON" system voltage is applied through fuse #16 to "SIR Indicator High" (B9) and to the "INFLATABLE RESTRAINT" Indicator Lamp which is connected to "SIR Indicator Low" (A1). Fuse #3 also applies system voltage to the "IGNITION 1" inputs (A3 and B3). The DERM responds by blinking the "INFLATABLE RESTRAINT" indicator 7 to 9 times.

When the engine is being cranked system voltage is applied to the DERM at the "CRANK" input. The DERM grounds the lamp circuit until system voltage is removed from the "CRANK" input. This results in a steady "INFLATABLE RESTRAINT" indicator during cranking.

After cranking the DERM will again blink the "INFLATABLE RESTRAINT" indicator 7 to 9 times.

Notes on Fault Tree:

1) If flash codes have been used to diagnose and repair a fault, the code(s) diagnosed and repaired will still appear as history codes only. The only way to clear history codes is with a "scan tool".

2) Where diagnostic charts request the clearing of SIR codes, the step is to be skipped since codes cannot be cleared through flash code diagnostics.

Fig. 30   Diagnostic chart B. Deville & Fleetwood

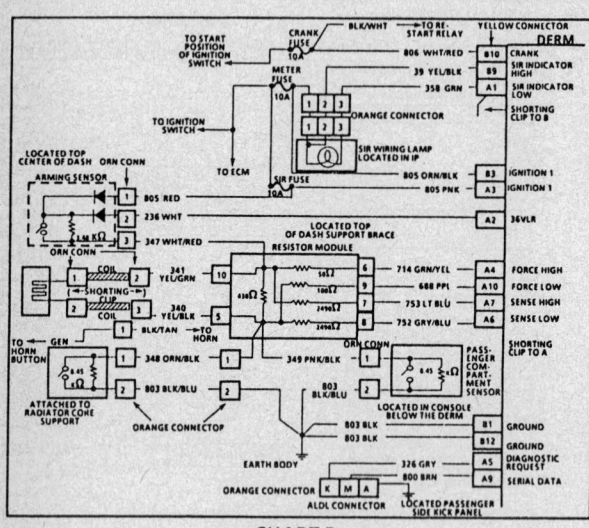

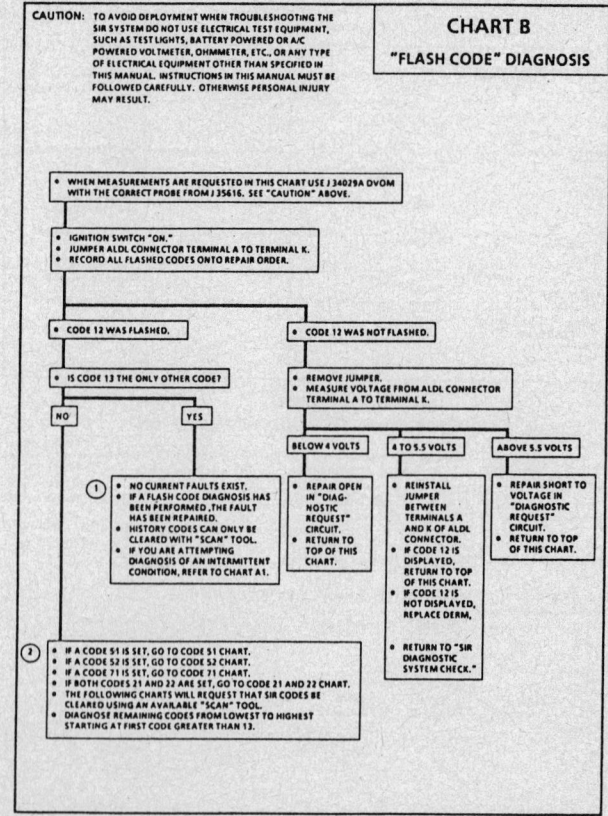

CHART B
"FLASH CODE" DIAGNOSIS

Description:

When the Ignition Switch is first turned "ON" system voltage is applied through METER FUSE to "SIR Indicator High" (B9) and to the "INFLATABLE RESTRAINT" Indicator Lamp which is connected to "SIR Indicator Low" (A1). SIR Fuse 3 also applies system voltage to the "Ignition 1" inputs (A3 and B3). The DERM responds by blinking the "INFLATABLE RESTRAINT" indicator 7 times.

When the engine is being cranked system voltage is applied to the DERM at the "CRANK" input. The DERM grounds the lamp circuit until system voltage is removed from the "CRANK" input. This results in a steady "INFLATABLE RESTRAINT" indicator during cranking.

After cranking the DERM will again blink the "INFLATABLE RESTRAINT" indicator 7 times.

Notes on Fault Tree:

1. If flash codes have been used to diagnose and repair a fault, the code(s) diagnosed and repaired will still appear as history codes only. The only way to clear history codes is with a "Scan" tool.

2. Where diagnostic charts request the clearing of SIR codes, the step is to be skipped since codes cannot be cleared through flash code diagnostics.

Fig. 31   Diagnostic chart B. Storm

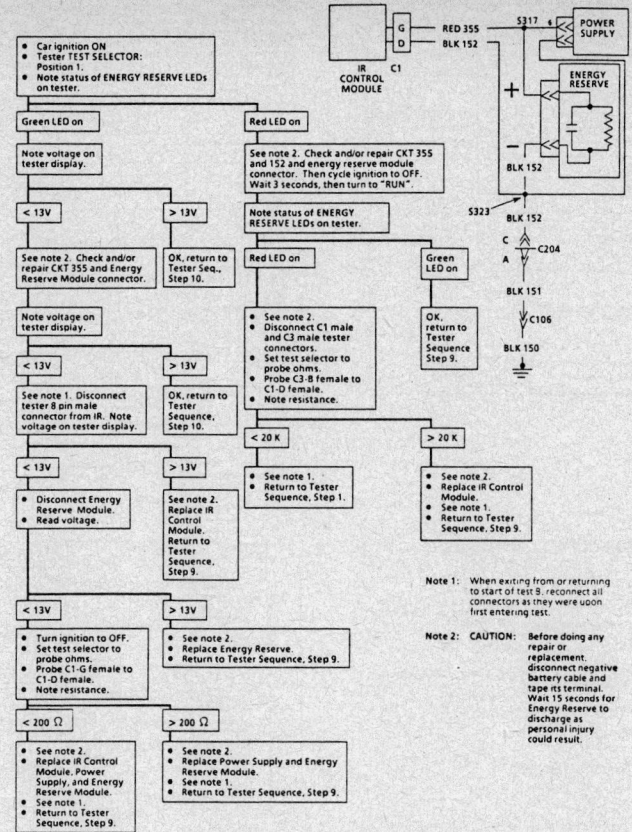

Fig. 32 Diagnostic chart, Test B. 88 & 98

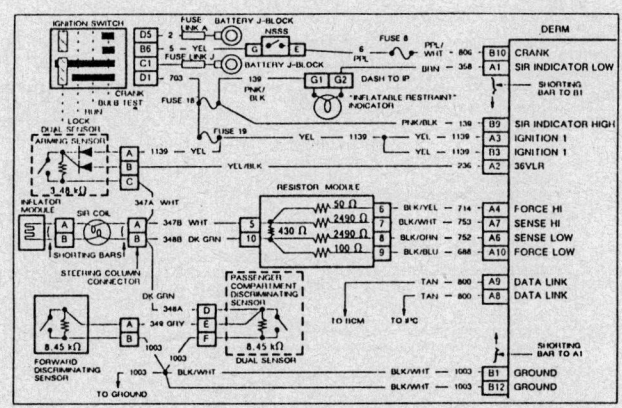

CHART B1
"INFLATABLE RESTRAINT" INDICATOR COMES ON STEADY

Description:

When the Ignition Switch is first turned "ON" system voltage is applied through fuse #18 to "SIR Indicator High" (B9) and to the "INFLATABLE RESTRAINT" Indicator Lamp which is connected to "SIR Indicator Low" (A1). Fuse #19 also applies system voltage to the "IGNITION 1" inputs (A3 and B3). The DERM responds by blinking the "INFLATABLE RESTRAINT" indicator 7 to 9 times.

The purpose of the Shorting Bar is to turn the "INFLATABLE RESTRAINT" Indicator Lamp ON should the DERM become disconnected.

When the engine is being cranked system voltage is applied to the DERM at the "CRANK" input. The DERM grounds the lamp circuit until system voltage is removed from the "CRANK" input. This results in a steady "INFLATABLE RESTRAINT" indicator during cranking.

After cranking the DERM will again blink the "INFLATABLE RESTRAINT" indicator 7 to 9 times.

Notes on Fault Tree:

1) An open SIR Fuse would result in a loss of "IGNITION 1" voltage at the DERM. The DERM will respond by grounding the lamp circuit ("SIR Indicator Low") whenever the Ignition Switch is "ON".

2) Checks for a short to ground in the "IGNITION 1" circuits or the DERM.

3) Checks if short to ground is in the DERM or the "IGNITION 1" circuits.

4) If the DERM and the SIR harness connector are disconnected the shorting bar between terminals A1 and B1 of the harness connector will ground the lamp circuit.

5) Checks for short in the DERM wiring harness.

6) Checks for short to voltage in the "CRANK" circuit.

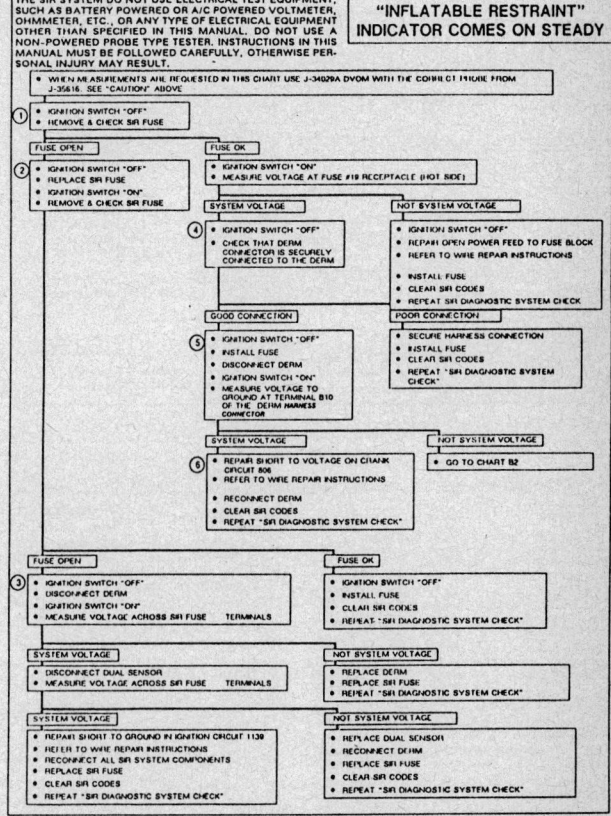

Fig. 33 Diagnostic chart B1. Eldorado, Seville, Toronado & Trofeo

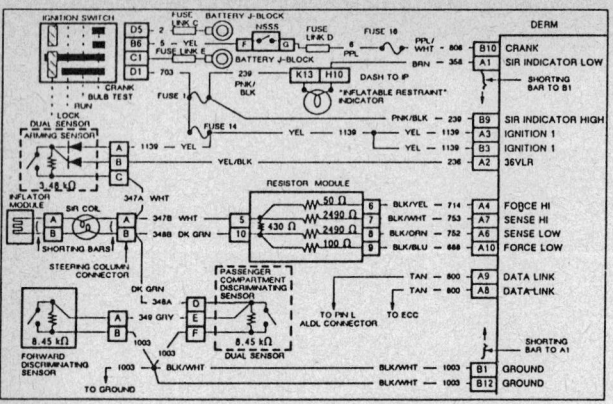

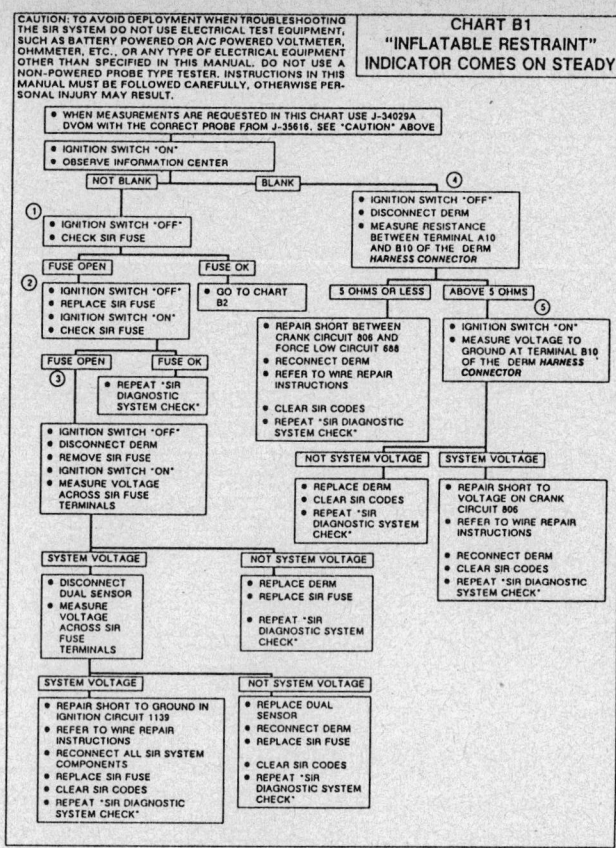

CHART B1

"INFLATABLE RESTRAINT" INDICATOR COMES ON STEADY

Description:

When the Ignition Switch is first turned "ON" system voltage is applied through fuse #1 to "SIR Indicator High" (B9) and to the "INFLATABLE RESTRAINT" Indicator Lamp which is connected to "SIR Indicator Low" (A1). Fuse #14 also applies system voltage to the "Ignition 1" inputs (A3 and B3). The DERM responds by blinking the "INFLATABLE RESTRAINT" indicator 7 to 9 times.

The purpose of the Shorting Bar is to turn the "INFLATABLE RESTRAINT" Indicator Lamp ON should the DERM become disconnected.

When the engine is being cranked system voltage is applied to the DERM at the "CRANK" input. The DERM grounds the lamp circuit until system voltage is removed from the "CRANK" input. This results in a steady "INFLATABLE RESTRAINT" indicator during cranking.

After cranking the DERM will again blink the "INFLATABLE RESTRAINT" indicator 7 to 9 times.

Notes on Fault Tree:

1) An open SIR Fuse would result in a loss of Ignition 1 voltage at the DERM. The DERM will respond by grounding the lamp circuit ("SIR Indicator Low") whenever the Ignition Switch is "ON".
2) Checks for a short to ground in the "Ignition 1" circuits or the DERM.
3) Checks if short to ground is in the DERM or the "Ignition 1" circuits.
4) Checks for short in DERM wiring harness.
5) Checks for short to voltage in "CRANK" circuit.

Fig. 34   Diagnostic chart B1. Riviera & Reatta

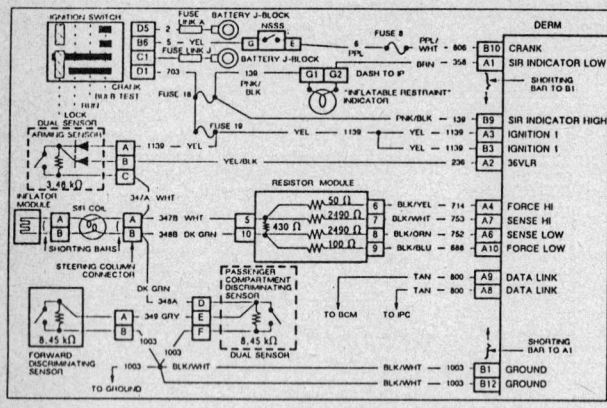

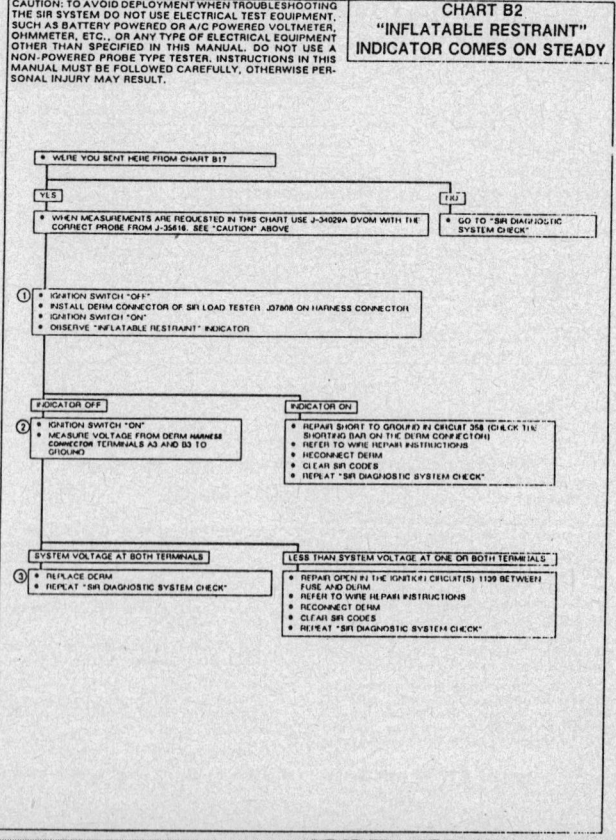

CHART B2

"INFLATABLE RESTRAINT" INDICATOR COMES ON STEADY

Description:

When the Ignition Switch is first turned "ON" system voltage is applied through fuse #18 to "SIR Indicator High" (B9) and to the "INFLATABLE RESTRAINT" Indicator Lamp which is connected to "SIR Indicator Low" (A1). Fuse #19 also applies system voltage to the "IGNITION 1" inputs (A3 and B3). The DERM responds by blinking the "INFLATABLE RESTRAINT" indicator 7 to 9 times.

The purpose of the Shorting Bar is to turn the "INFLATABLE RESTRAINT" Indicator Lamp ON should the DERM become disconnected.

When the engine is being cranked system voltage is applied to the DERM at the "CRANK" input. The DERM grounds the lamp circuit until system voltage is removed from the "CRANK" input. This results in a steady "INFLATABLE RESTRAINT" indicator during cranking.

After cranking the DERM will again blink the "INFLATABLE RESTRAINT" indicator 7 to 9 times.

Notes on Fault Tree:

1) Checks if there is a short to ground on the low side of the lamp circuit external of the DERM. The SIR Load Tool prevents the shorting bar in the DERM connector from grounding the lamp circuit.
2) Checks for "IGNITION 1" voltage at the DERM. If the "IGNITION 1" circuits are open the DERM will ground the lamp circuit whenever the Ignition Switch is "ON" (if the "SIR Indicator High" circuit is good).
3) Checks for a short to system voltage in the "Crank" circuit.

Fig. 35   Diagnostic chart B2. Eldorado, Seville, Riviera, Reatta, Toronado & Trofeo

SUPPLEMENTAL INFLATABLE RESTRAINT SYSTEM

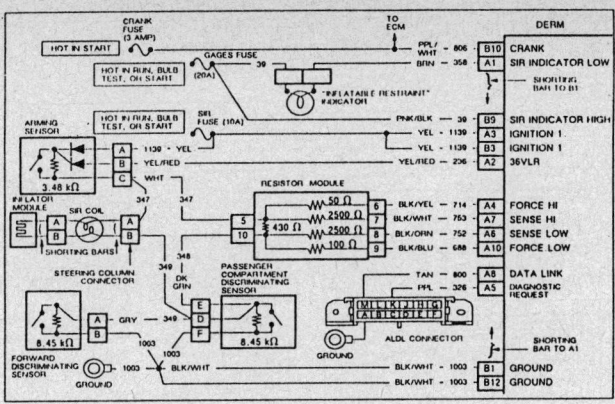

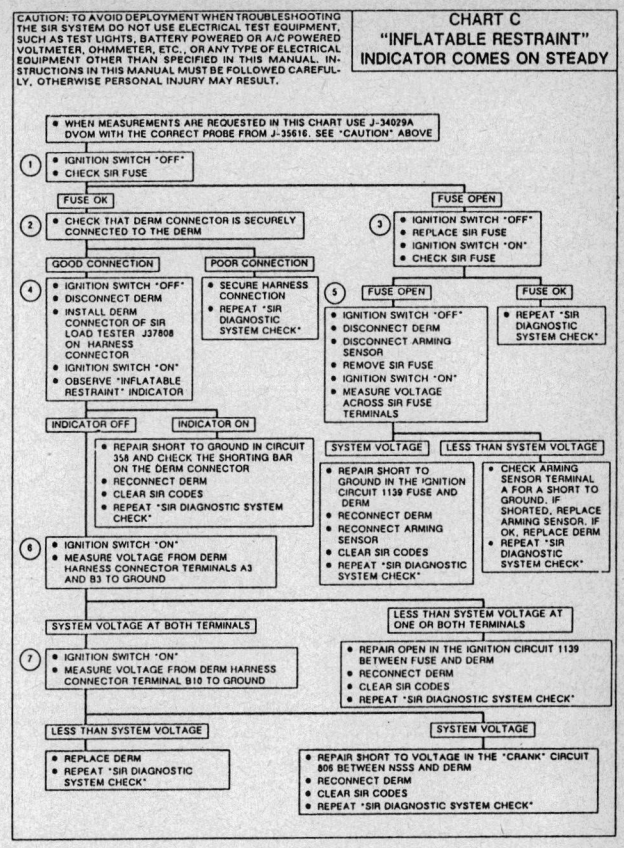

CHART C

"INFLATABLE RESTRAINT" INDICATOR COMES ON STEADY

Description:

When the Ignition Switch is first turned "ON" system voltage is applied through the GAGES FUSE to "SIR Indicator High" (B9) and to the "INFLATABLE RESTRAINT" Indicator Lamp which is connected to "SIR Indicator Low" (A1). SIR FUSE also applies system voltage to the "Ignition 1" inputs (A3 and B3). The DERM responds by blinking the "INFLATABLE RESTRAINT" indicator 7 to 9 times.

The purpose of the Shorting Bar is to turn the "INFLATABLE RESTRAINT" Indicator Lamp ON should the DERM become disconnected.

When the engine is being cranked system voltage is applied to the DERM at the "CRANK" input. The DERM grounds the lamp circuit until system voltage is removed from the "CRANK" input. This results in a steady "INFLATABLE RESTRAINT" indicator during cranking.

After cranking the DERM will again blink the "INFLATABLE RESTRAINT" indicator 7 to 9 times.

Notes on Fault Tree:

1) An open SIR Fuse would result in a loss of Ignition I voltage at the DERM. The DERM will respond by grounding the lamp circuit ("SIR Indicator Low") whenever the Ignition Switch is "ON".

2) If the DERM and the SIR harness connector are disconnected the shorting bar between terminals A1 and B1 of the harness connector will ground the lamp circuit.

3) Checks for a short to ground in the "Ignition 1" circuits or the DERM.

4) Checks if there is a short to ground on the low side of the lamp circuit external of the DERM. The SIR Load Tool prevents the shorting bar in the DERM connector from grounding the lamp circuit.

5) Checks if short to ground is in the DERM or the "Ignition 1" circuits.

6) Checks for Ignition 1 voltage at the DERM. If the "Ignition 1" circuits are open the DERM will ground the lamp circuit whenever the Ignition Switch is "ON" (if the "SIR Indicator High" circuit is good).

7) Checks for a short to system voltage in the "Crank" circuit.

Fig. 36   Diagnostic chart C. Camaro & Firebird

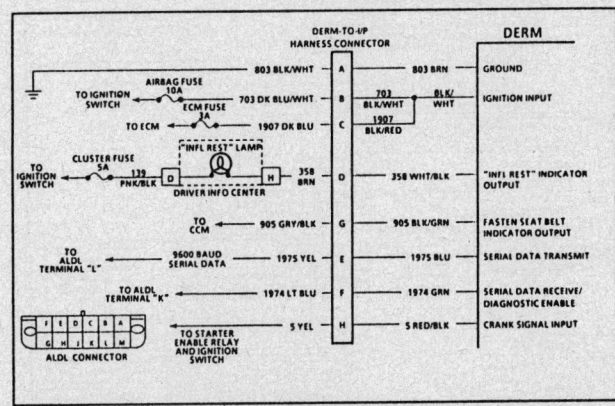

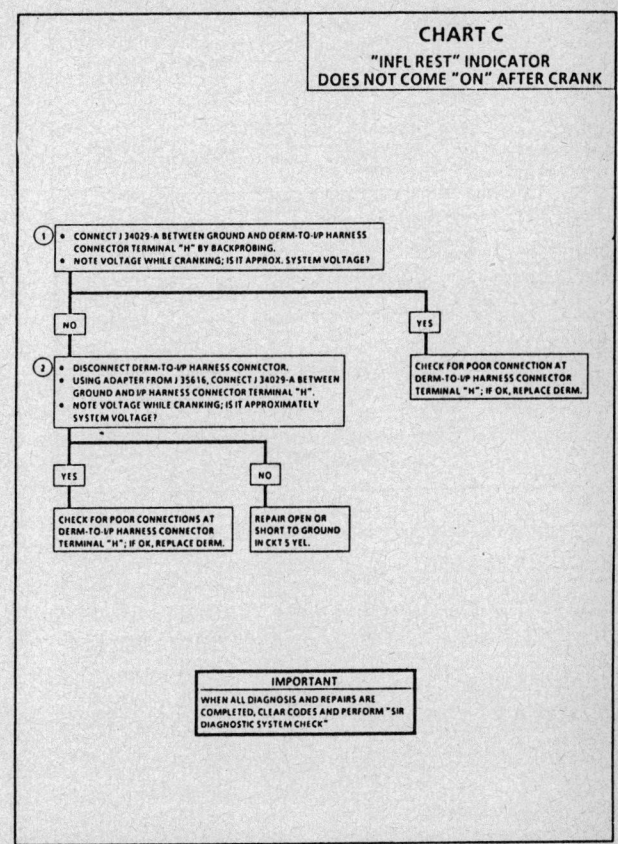

CHART C

"INFL REST" INDICATOR DOES NOT COME "ON" AFTER CRANK

Circuit Description:

When power is applied to the DERM, it responds by illuminating the "INFL REST" indicator for five seconds if no fault codes have been stored. If the DERM has fault codes in memory, it illuminates both the "INFL REST" and Fasten Seatbelt indicators continuously. The DERM has an internal lamp driver for the "INFL REST" indicator. The FASTEN SEATBELT output of the DERM is connected to the Central Control Module (CCM) which actually drives the Fasten Seatbelt indicator.

When the engine is being cranked, system voltage is applied to the DERM at the CRANK SIGNAL INPUT. If no fault codes are stored and system power is removed from the CRANK SIGNAL INPUT, the DERM will reset and again illuminate the "INFL REST" indicator for 5 seconds.

Test Description: Numbers below refer to circled numbers on the diagnostic chart.

1. This test checks to see if the "CRANK" signal voltage is getting to the I/P harness-to-DERM harness connector.

2. This test checks to see if the DERM or the I/P harness CKT 5 is at fault.

Diagnostic Aids:

The Fasten Seat Belt indicator will stay "ON" continuously when an SIR failure code has been set.

If power is applied to the SIR system while any component is not properly connected, an additional failure code will be set for the disconnected SIR component.

Fig. 37   Diagnostic chart C. Corvette

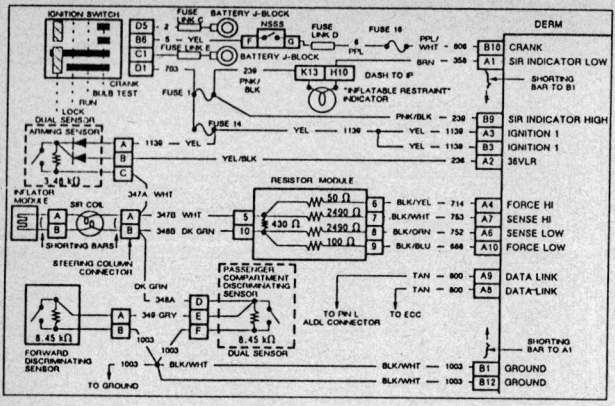

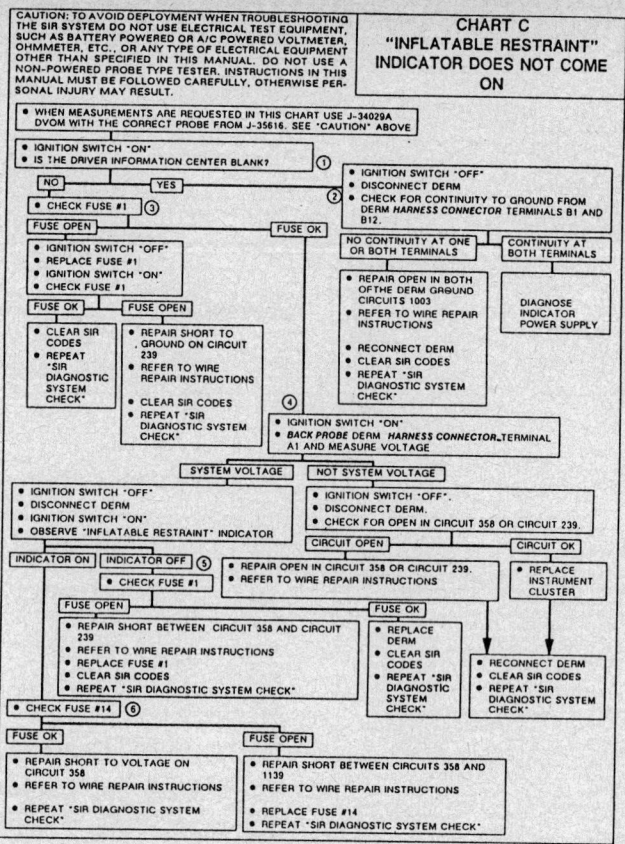

CHART C
"INFLATABLE RESTRAINT" INDICATOR DOES NOT COME ON

Fig. 38   Diagnostic chart C, Riviera & Reatta

CHART C
"INFLATABLE RESTRAINT" INDICATOR DOES NOT COME ON

Description:

When the Ignition Switch is first turned "ON" system voltage is applied through fuse #1 to "SIR Indicator High" (B9) and to the "INFLATABLE RESTRAINT" Indicator Lamp which is connected to "SIR Indicator Low" (A1). fuse #14 also applies system voltage to the "Ignition 1" inputs (A3 and B3). The DERM responds by blinking the "INFLATABLE RESTRAINT" indicator 7 to 9 times.

When the engine is being cranked system voltage is applied through the DERM at the "CRANK" input. The DERM grounds the lamp circuit until system voltage is removed from the "CRANK" input. This results in a steady "INFLATABLE RESTRAINT" indicator during cranking.

After cranking the DERM will again blink the "INFLATABLE RESTRAINT" indicator 7 to 9 times if the Ignition Switch is "ON".

Notes on Fault Tree:

1) Checks if high side (power side) of the lamp circuit is fault free. This circuit powers the Information Center. If the Information center is operative, then the power supply to the "Inflatable Restraint" indicator is not suspect.
2) Checks for an open in the lamp circuit or in the "Inflatable Restraint" bulb.
3) Checks fuse #1 which is in the high side (power side) of the lamp circuit.
4) Checks for an open ground.
5) After the DERM is disconnected, the shorting bar supplies a ground to terminal A1 of the DERM Harness. A short to system voltage via circuit 239 will burn fuse #1.
6) After the DERM is disconnected, the shorting bar supplies a ground to terminal A1 of the DERM Harness. A short to system voltage via circuit 1139 will burn fuse #14.

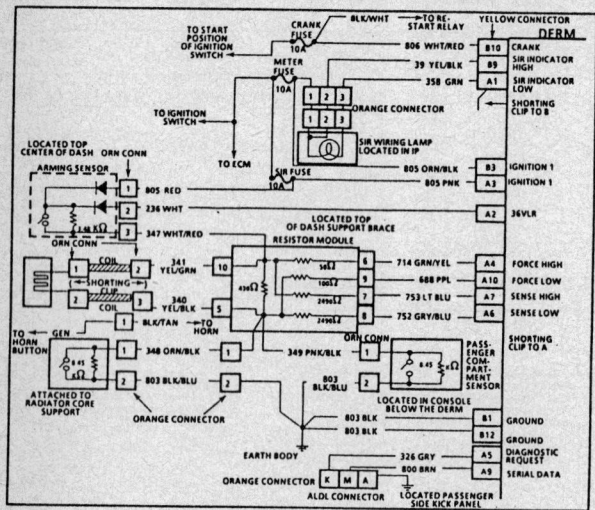

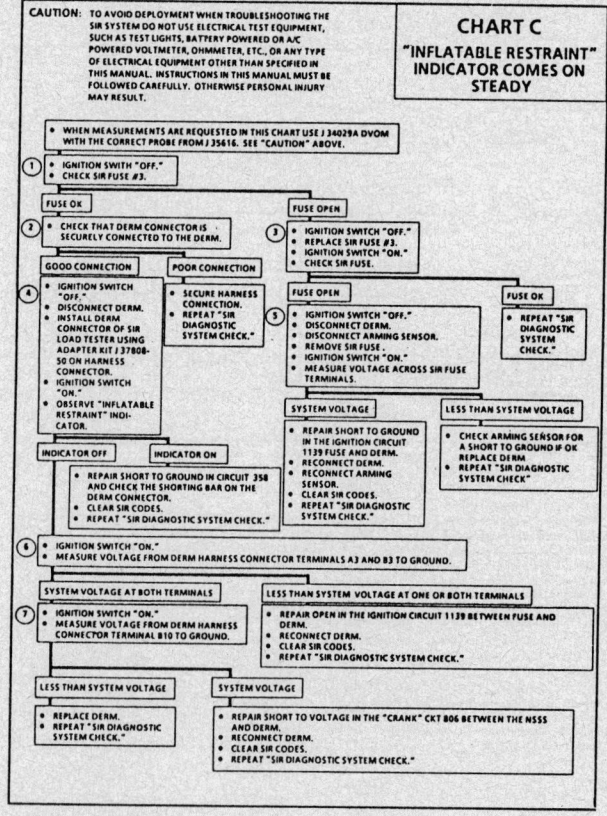

CHART C
"INFLATABLE RESTRAINT" INDICATOR COMES ON STEADY

Fig. 39   Diagnostic chart C, Storm

CHART C
"INFLATABLE RESTRAINT" INDICATOR COMES ON STEADY

Description:

When the Ignition Switch is first turned "ON" system voltage is applied through the METER FUSE to "SIR Indicator High" (B9) and to the "INFLATABLE RESTRAINT" Indicator Lamp which is connected to "SIR Indicator Low" (A1). SIR FUSE also applies system voltage to the "Ignition 1" inputs (A3 and B3). The DERM responds by blinking the "INFLATABLE RESTRAINT" indicator 7 times.

The purpose of the Shorting Bar is to turn the "INFLATABLE RESTRAINT" Indicator Lamp "ON" should the DERM become disconnected.

When the engine is being cranked system voltage is applied to the DERM at the "CRANK" input. The DERM grounds the lamp circuit until system voltage is removed from the "CRANK" input. This results in a steady "INFLATABLE RESTRAINT" indicator during cranking.

After cranking the DERM will again blink the "INFLATABLE RESTRAINT" indicator 7 times.

Notes on Fault Tree:

1. An open SIR Fuse would result in a loss of Ignition 1 voltage at the DERM. The DERM will respond by grounding the lamp circuit ("SIR Indicator Low") whenever the Ignition Switch is "ON".
2. If the DERM and the SIR harness connector are disconnected the shorting bar between terminals "A1" and "B1" of the harness connector will ground the lamp circuit.
3. Checks for a short to ground in the "Ignition 1" circuits or the DERM.
4. Checks if there is a short to ground on the low side of the lamp circuit external of the DERM. The SIR Load Tool prevents the shorting bar in the DERM connector from grounding the lamp circuit.
5. Checks if short to ground is in the DERM on the "Ignition 1" circuits.
6. Checks for Ignition 1 voltage at the DERM. If the "Ignition 1" circuits are open the DERM will ground the lamp circuit whenever the Ignition Switch is "ON" if the "SIR Indicator High" circuit is good.
7. Checks for a short to system voltage in the "Crank" circuit.

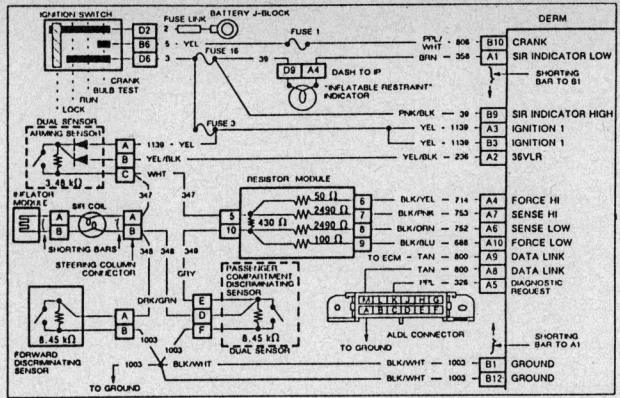

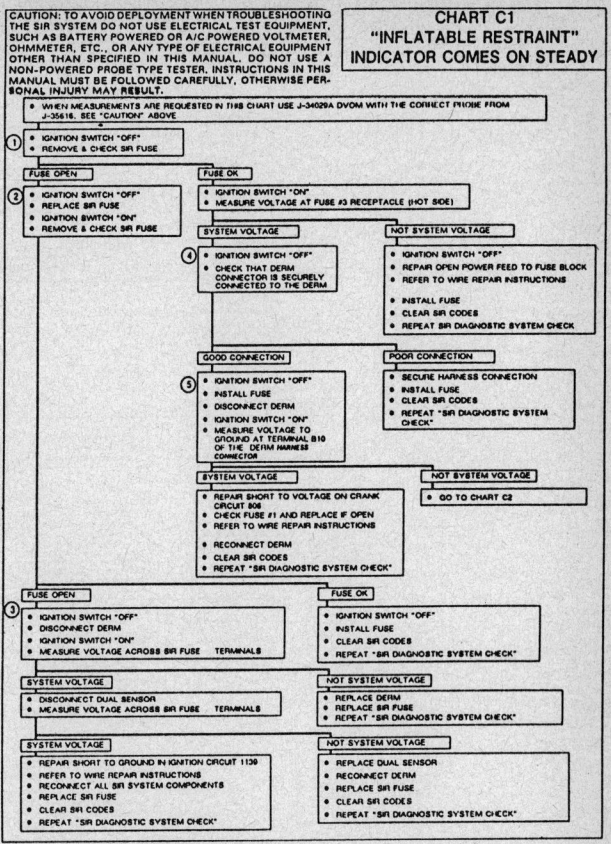

CHART C1
"INFLATABLE RESTRAINT" INDICATOR COMES ON STEADY

Description:

When the Ignition Switch is first turned "ON" system voltage is applied through fuse #16 to "SIR Indicator High" (B9) and to the "INFLATABLE RESTRAINT" Indicator Lamp which is connected to "SIR Indicator Low" (A1). Fuse #3 also applies system voltage to the "IGNITION 1" inputs (A3 and B3). The DERM responds by blinking the "INFLATABLE RESTRAINT" indicator 7 to 9 times.

The purpose of the Shorting Bar is to turn the "INFLATABLE RESTRAINT" Indicator Lamp ON should the DERM become disconnected.

When the engine is being cranked system voltage is applied to the DERM at the "CRANK" input. The DERM grounds the lamp circuit until system voltage is removed from the "CRANK" input. This results in a steady "INFLATABLE RESTRAINT" indicator during

cranking.

After cranking the DERM will again blink the "INFLATABLE RESTRAINT" indicator 7 to 9 times.

Notes on Fault Tree:

1) An open SIR fuse would result in a loss of "IGNITION 1" voltage at the DERM. The DERM will respond by grounding the lamp circuit ("SIR Indicator Low") whenever the Ignition Switch is "ON".

2) Checks for a short to ground in the "IGNITION 1" circuits or the DERM.

3) Checks if short to ground is in the DERM or the "IGNITION 1" circuits.

4) If the DERM and the SIR harness connector are disconnected the shorting bar between terminals A1 and B1 of the harness connector will ground the lamp circuit.

5) Checks for short to voltage in the "CRANK" circuit.

Fig. 40   Diagnostic chart C1. Deville & Fleetwood

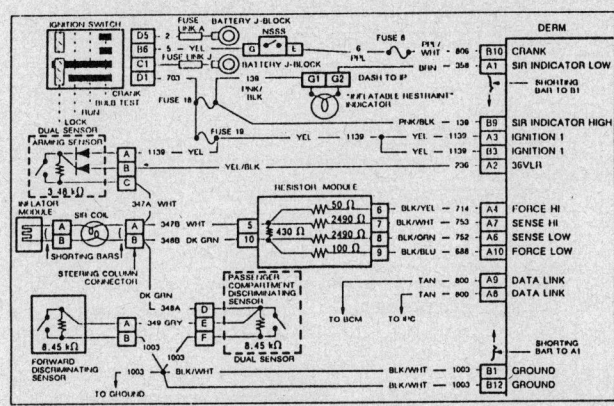

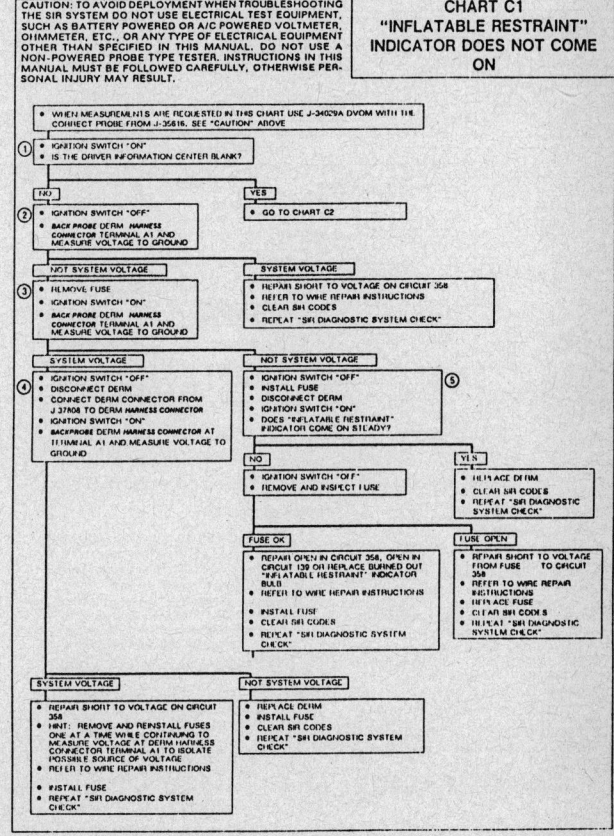

CHART C1
"INFLATABLE RESTRAINT" INDICATOR DOES NOT COME ON

Description:

When the Ignition Switch is first turned "ON" system voltage is applied through fuse #18 to "SIR Indicator High" (B9) and to the "INFLATABLE RESTRAINT" Indicator Lamp which is connected to "SIR Indicator Low" (A1). Fuse #19 also applies system voltage to the "IGNITION 1" inputs (A3 and B3). The DERM responds by blinking the "INFLATABLE RESTRAINT" indicator 7 to 9 times.

When the engine is being cranked system voltage is applied to the DERM at the "CRANK" input. The DERM grounds the lamp circuit until system voltage is removed from the "CRANK" input. This results in a steady "INFLATABLE RESTRAINT" indicator during cranking.

After cranking the DERM will again blink the "INFLATABLE RESTRAINT" indicator 7 to 9 times if the Ignition Switch is "ON".

Notes on Fault Tree:

1) Checks if high side (power side) of the lamp circuit is fault free and if DERM ground is present. These circuits affect proper operation of the Information Center. If the Information center is operative, then the power supply to the "INFLATABLE RESTRAINT" indicator and DERM ground is not suspect.

2) Checks for short to system voltage (hot at all times).

3) Checks for short to system voltage (hot with ignition switch "ON").

4) Determines if short to system voltage (hot with ignition switch "ON") is internal to DERM.

5) Determines if open circuit is internal to DERM.

Fig. 41   Diagnostic chart C1. Eldorado, Seville, Toronado & Trofeo

SUPPLEMENTAL INFLATABLE RESTRAINT SYSTEM

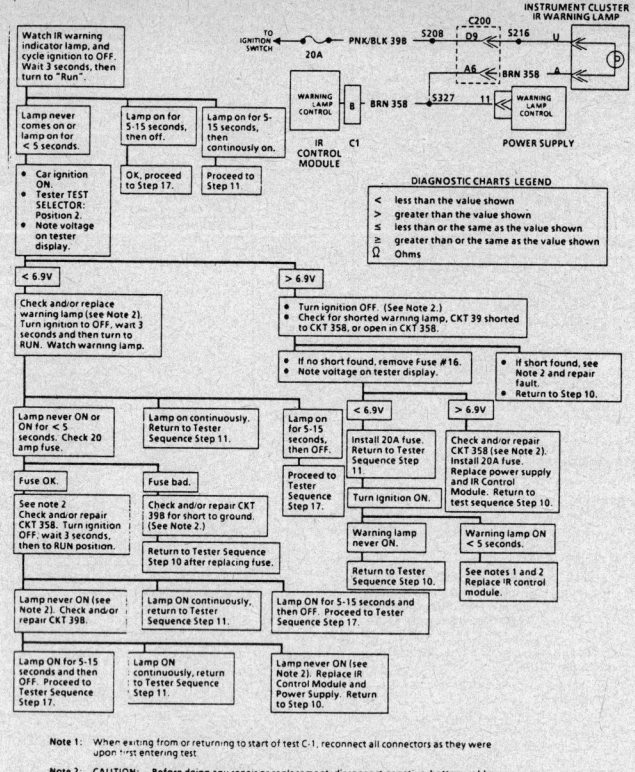

Diagnostic Charts Legend

<	less than the value shown
>	greater than the value shown
≤	less than or the same as the value shown
≥	greater than or the same as the value shown
Ω	Ohms

Note 1: When exiting from or returning to start of test C-1, reconnect all connectors as they were upon first entering test

Note 2: CAUTION: Before doing any repair or replacement, disconnect negative battery cable and tape its terminal. Wait 15 seconds for Energy Reserve to discharge as personal injury could result.

Fig. 42   Diagnostic chart, Test C-1. 88 & 98

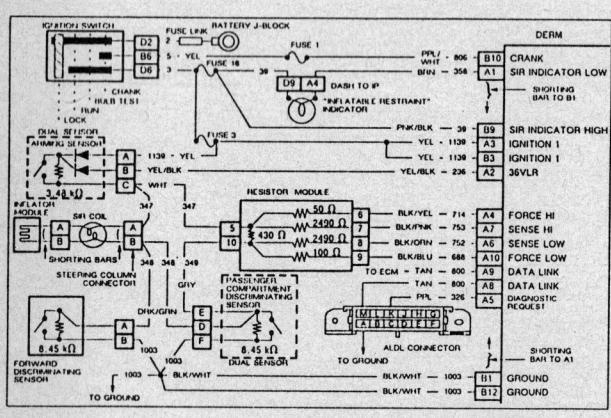

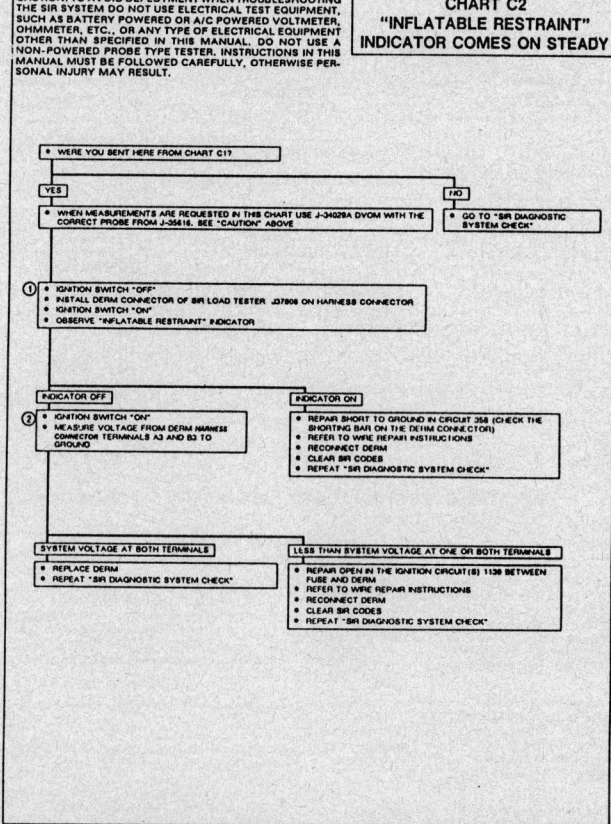

CHART C2

"INFLATABLE RESTRAINT" INDICATOR COMES ON STEADY

Description:

When the Ignition Switch is first turned "ON" system voltage is applied through fuse #16 to "SIR Indicator High" (B9) and to the "INFLATABLE RESTRAINT" Indicator Lamp which is connected to "SIR Indicator Low" (A1). Fuse #3 also applies system voltage to the "IGNITION 1" inputs (A3 and B3). The DERM responds by blinking the "INFLATABLE RESTRAINT" indicator 7 to 9 times.

The purpose of the Shorting Bar is to turn the "INFLATABLE RESTRAINT" Indicator Lamp ON should the DERM become disconnected.

When the engine is being cranked system voltage is applied to the DERM at the "CRANK" input. The DERM grounds the lamp circuit until system voltage is removed from the "CRANK" input. This results in a steady "INFLATABLE RESTRAINT" indicator during cranking.

After cranking the DERM will again blink the "INFLATABLE RESTRAINT" indicator 7 to 9 times.

Notes on Fault Tree:

1) Checks if there is a short to ground on the low side of the lamp circuit external of the DERM. The SIR Load Tool prevents the shorting bar in the DERM connector from grounding the lamp circuit.

2) Checks for "IGNITION 1" voltage at the DERM. If the "IGNITION 1" circuits are open the DERM will ground the lamp circuit whenever the Ignition Switch is "ON" (if the "SIR Indicator High" circuit is good).

Fig. 43   Diagnostic chart C2. Deville & Fleetwood

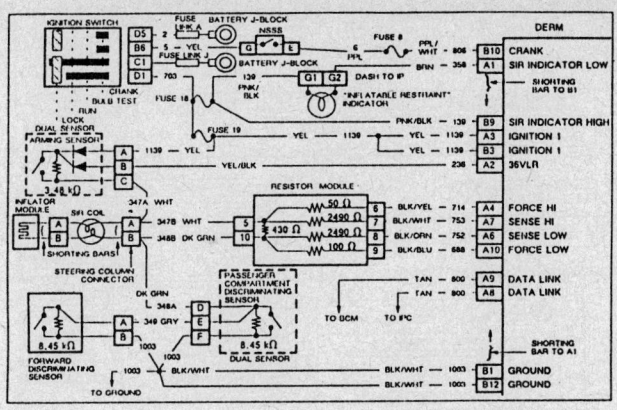

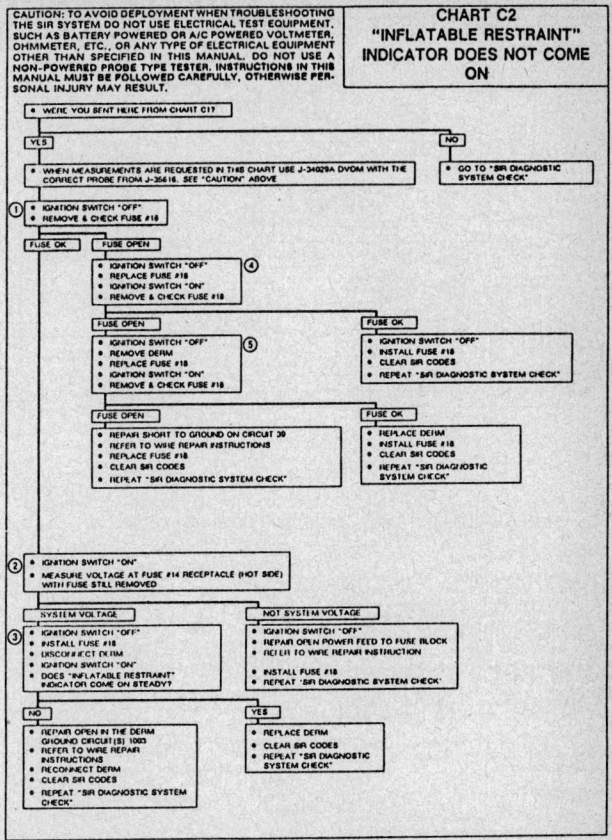

CHART C2
"INFLATABLE RESTRAINT"
INDICATOR DOES NOT COME ON

CHART C2

"INFLATABLE RESTRAINT" INDICATOR DOES NOT COME ON

Description:

When the Ignition Switch is first turned "ON" system voltage is applied through fuse #18 to "SIR Indicator High" (B9) and to the "INFLATABLE RESTRAINT" Indicator Lamp which is connected to "SIR Indicator Low" (A1). Fuse #19 also applies system voltage to the "IGNITION 1" inputs (A3 and B3). The DERM responds by blinking the "INFLATABLE RESTRAINT" indicator 7 to 9 times.

When the engine is being cranked system voltage is applied to the DERM at the "CRANK" input. The DERM grounds the lamp circuit until system voltage is removed from the "CRANK" input. This results in a steady "INFLATABLE RESTRAINT" indicator during cranking.

After cranking the DERM will again blink the "INFLATABLE RESTRAINT" indicator 7 to 9 times if the Ignition Switch is "ON".

Notes on Fault Tree:

1) Determines if fuse #18 which feeds the "INFLATABLE RESTRAINT" indicator lamp is blown.

2) Checks if fuse block at fuse #18 receptacle has voltage.

3) Determines if loss of DERM ground is in wiring harness or internal to DERM.

4) Determines if fault causing fuse #18 to blow is current.

5) Determines if fault causing fuse #18 to blow is in wiring harness or internal to DERM.

Fig. 44 Diagnostic chart C2. Eldorado, Seville, Toronado & Trofeo

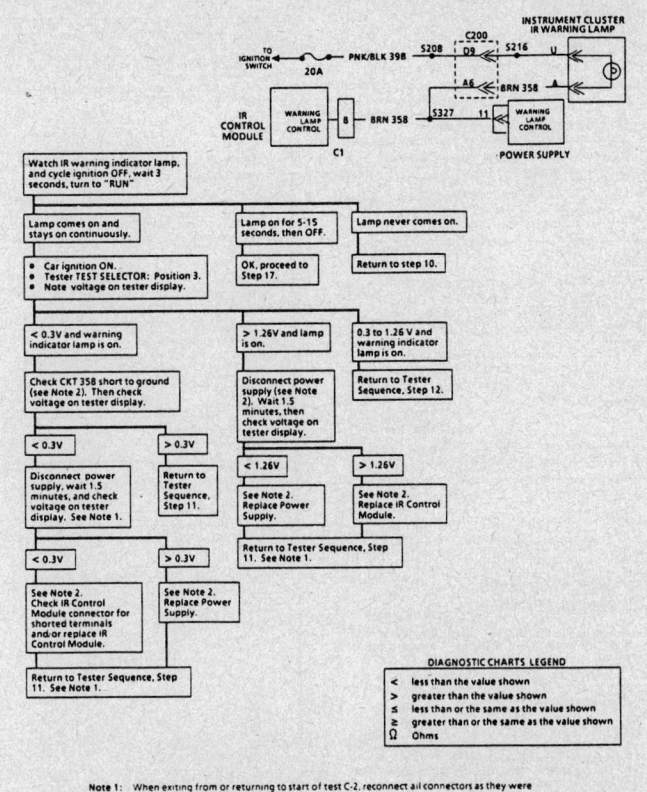

DIAGNOSTIC CHARTS LEGEND

<	less than the value shown
>	greater than the value shown
≤	less than or the same as the value shown
≥	greater than or the same as the value shown
Ω	Ohms

Note 1: When exiting from or returning to start of test C-2, reconnect all connectors as they were upon first entering test.

Note 2: CAUTION: Before doing any repair or replacement, disconnect negative battery cable and tape its terminal. Wait 15 seconds for Energy Reserve to discharge as personal injury could result.

Fig. 45 Diagnostic chart, Test C-2. 88 & 98

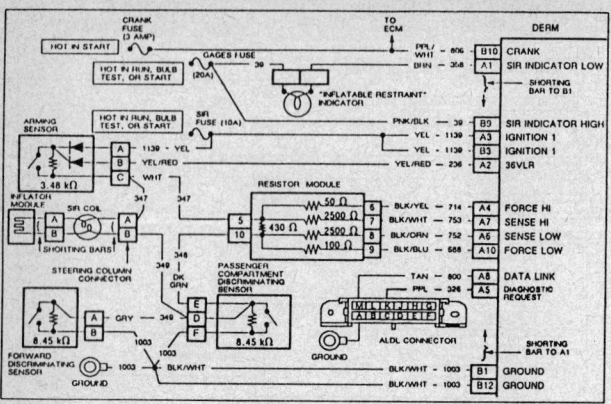

CHART D

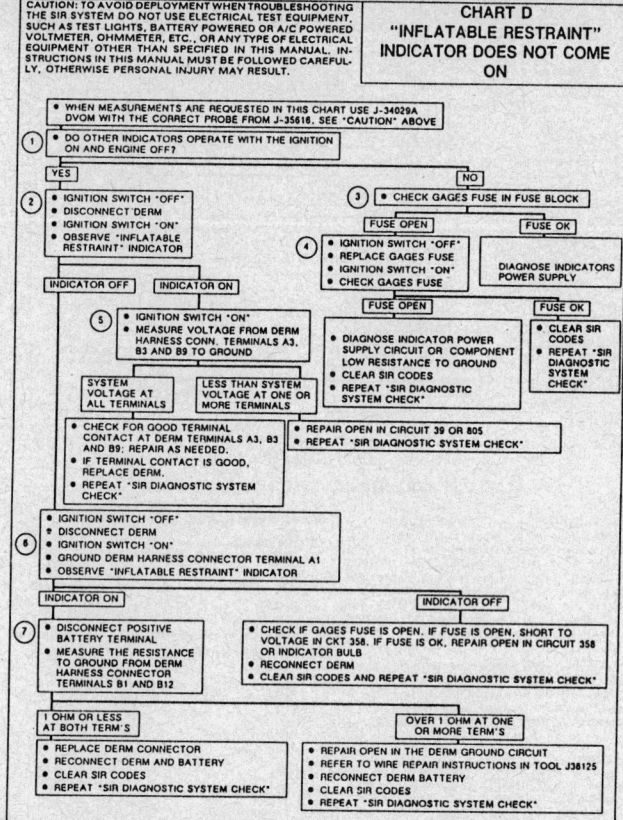

"INFLATABLE RESTRAINT" INDICATOR DOES NOT COME ON

Description:

When the Ignition Switch is first turned "ON" system voltage is applied through the SIR FUSE and GAGES FUSE to the DERM at the "SIR Indicator Low", "SIR Indicator High" and the "Ignition 1" inputs. The DERM responds by blinking the "INFLATABLE RESTRAINT" indicator 7 to 9 times with a lamp driver at the "SIR Indicator Low" input.

When the engine is being cranked system voltage is applied to the DERM at the "CRANK" input. The DERM grounds the lamp circuit until system voltage is removed from the "CRANK" input. This results in a steady "INFLATABLE RESTRAINT" indicator during cranking.

After cranking the DERM will again blink the "INFLATABLE RESTRAINT" indicator 7 to 9 times if the Ignition Switch is "ON".

Notes on Fault Tree:

1) Checks if high side (power side) of the lamp circuit is good. This circuit powers a number of indicators within the indicators cluster (such as the "Service Engine Soon" and "Oil" indicators). If these other indicators are operative, then the power supply to the "Inflatable Restraint" indicator is not suspect.

2) When the DERM is disconnected the shorting bar between terminals A1 and B1 of the DERM harness connector should ground the lamp circuit. If the indicator does not come on the ground circuits, Indicator circuit on the shorting bar are suspect. If the indicator comes on the DERM or the "SIR Indicator High" and the "Ignition 1" circuits are suspect.

3) Checks Fuse 16 which is in the high side (power side) of the lamp circuit.

4) Checks for a short to ground in Fuse 16 circuits.

5) Checks for system voltage at the "Ignition 1" and "SIR Indicator High" inputs at the DERM.

6) Checks if the lamp circuit external to the DERM is good.

7) Checks if the ground circuits to the DERM are good.

Fig. 46 Diagnostic chart D. Camaro & Firebird

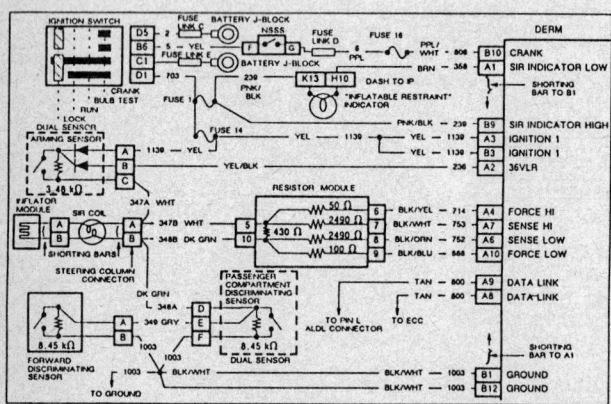

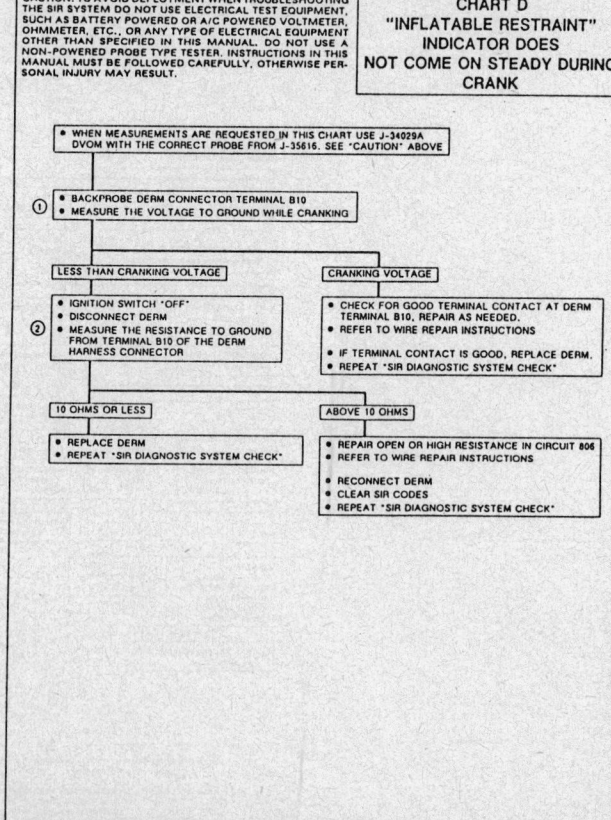

"INFLATABLE RESTRAINT" INDICATOR DOES NOT COME ON STEADY DURING CRANK

Description:

When the Ignition Switch is first turned "ON" system voltage is applied through fuse #1 to "SIR Indicator High" (B9) and to the "INFLATABLE RESTRAINT" Indicator Lamp which is connected to ("SIR Indicator Low" (A1). fuse #14 also applies system voltage to the "Ignition 1" inputs (A3 and B3). The DERM responds by blinking the "INFLATABLE RESTRAINT" indicator 7 to 9 times.

When the engine is being cranked system voltage is applied to the DERM at the "CRANK" input. The DERM grounds the lamp circuit until system voltage is removed from the "CRANK" input. This results in a steady "INFLATABLE RESTRAINT" indicator during cranking.

After cranking the DERM will again blink the "INFLATABLE RESTRAINT" indicator 7 to 9 times if the Ignition Switch is "ON".

Notes on Fault Tree:

1) Checks for system voltage at the "CRANK" input of the DERM during cranking.

2) Checks for the "CRANK" circuit for an open or high resistance.

Fig. 47 Diagnostic chart D. Riviera & Reatta

SUPPLEMENTAL INFLATABLE RESTRAINT SYSTEM

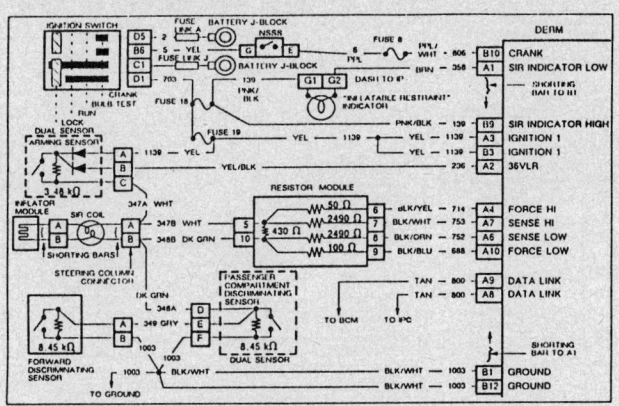

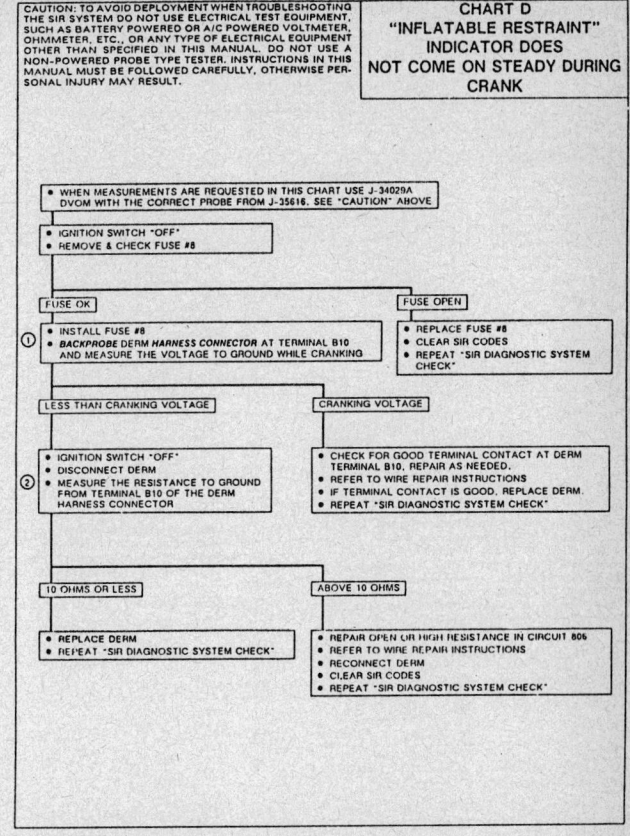

CHART D
"INFLATABLE RESTRAINT" INDICATOR DOES NOT COME ON STEADY DURING CRANK

CAUTION: TO AVOID DEPLOYMENT WHEN TROUBLESHOOTING THE SIR SYSTEM DO NOT USE ELECTRICAL TEST EQUIPMENT, SUCH AS BATTERY POWERED OR A/C POWERED VOLTMETER, OHMMETER, ETC., OR ANY TYPE OF ELECTRICAL EQUIPMENT OTHER THAN SPECIFIED IN THIS MANUAL. DO NOT USE A NON-POWERED PROBE TYPE TESTER. INSTRUCTIONS IN THIS MANUAL MUST BE FOLLOWED CAREFULLY, OTHERWISE PERSONAL INJURY MAY RESULT.

CHART D
"INFLATABLE RESTRAINT" INDICATOR DOES NOT COME ON STEADY DURING CRANK

Description:

When the Ignition Switch is first turned "ON" system voltage is applied through fuse #18 to "SIR Indicator High" (B9) and to the "INFLATABLE RESTRAINT" Indicator Lamp which is connected to "SIR Indicator Low" (A1). Fuse #19 also applies system voltage to the "IGNITION 1" inputs (A3 and B3). The DERM responds by blinking the "INFLATABLE RESTRAINT" indicator 7 to 9 times.

When the engine is being cranked system voltage is applied to the DERM at the "CRANK" input. The DERM grounds the lamp circuit until system voltage is removed from the "CRANK" input. This results in a steady "INFLATABLE RESTRAINT" indicator during cranking.

After cranking the DERM will again blink the "INFLATABLE RESTRAINT" indicator 7 to 9 times if the Ignition Switch is "ON".

Notes on Fault Tree:

1) Checks for system voltage at the "CRANK" input of the DERM during cranking.
2) Checks for the "CRANK" circuit for an open or high resistance.

Fig. 48   Diagnostic chart D. Eldorado, Seville, Toronado & Trofeo

---

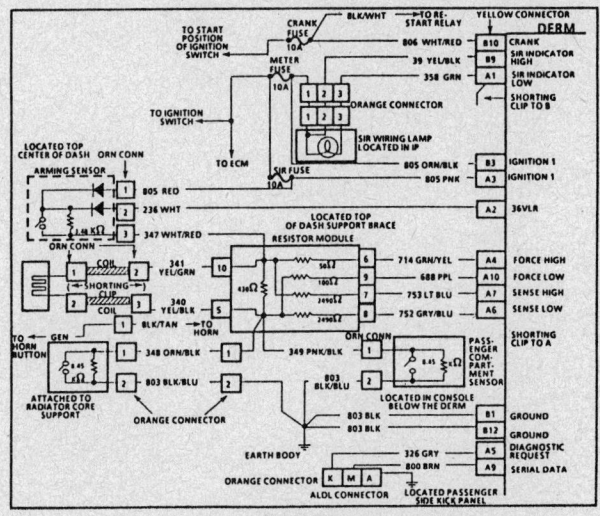

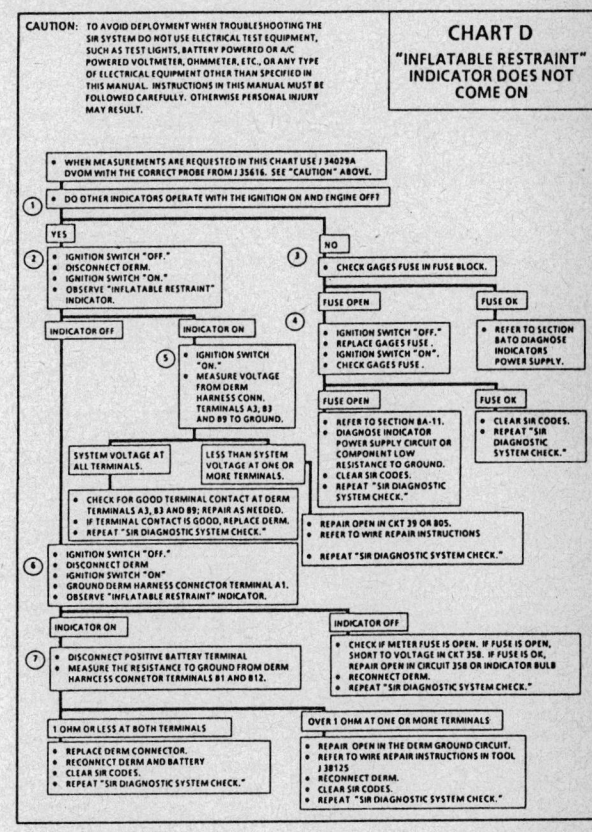

CHART D
"INFLATABLE RESTRAINT" INDICATOR DOES NOT COME ON

CAUTION: TO AVOID DEPLOYMENT WHEN TROUBLESHOOTING THE SIR SYSTEM DO NOT USE ELECTRICAL TEST EQUIPMENT, SUCH AS TEST LIGHTS, BATTERY POWERED OR A/C POWERED VOLTMETER, OHMMETER, ETC., OR ANY TYPE OF ELECTRICAL EQUIPMENT OTHER THAN SPECIFIED IN THIS MANUAL. INSTRUCTIONS IN THIS MANUAL MUST BE FOLLOWED CAREFULLY. OTHERWISE PERSONAL INJURY MAY RESULT.

CHART D
"INFLATABLE RESTRAINT" INDICATOR DOES NOT COME ON

Description:

When the Ignition Switch is first turned "ON" system voltage is applied through the SIR FUSE and METER FUSE to the DERM at the "SIR Indicator Low", "SIR Indicator High" and the "Ignition 1" inputs. The DERM responds by blinking the "INFLATABLE RESTRAINT" indicator 7 times with a lamp driver at the "SIR Indicator Low" input.

When the engine is being cranked system voltage is applied to the DERM at the "CRANK" input. The DERM grounds the lamp circuit until system voltage is removed from the "CRANK" input. This results in a steady "INFLATABLE RESTRAINT" indicator during cranking.

After cranking the DERM will again blink "INFLATABLE RESTRAINT" indicator 7 times if the Ignition Switch is "ON".

Notes on Fault Tree:

1. Checks if high side (power side) of the lamp circuit is good. This circuit powers a number of indicators

within the indicators cluster (such as the "Service Engine Soon" and "Oil" indicators). If these other indicators are operative, then the power supply to the "Inflatable Restraint" indicator is not suspect.
2. When the DERM is disconnected the shorting bar between terminals "A1" and "B1" of the DERM harness connector should ground the lamp circuit. If the indicator does not come on the ground circuits, Indicator circuit or the shorting bar are suspect. If the indicator comes on the DERM or the "SIR Indicator High" and the "Ignition 1" circuits are suspect.
3. Checks Meter Fuse which is in the high side (power side) of the lamp circuit.
4. Checks for a short to ground in Meter Fuse circuits.
5. Checks for system voltage at the "Ignition 1" and "SIR Indicator High" inputs at the DERM.
6. Checks if the lamp circuit external to the DERM is good.
7. Checks if the ground circuits to the DERM are good.

Fig. 49   Diagnostic chart D. Storm

GENERAL MOTORS—Passive Restraint Systems

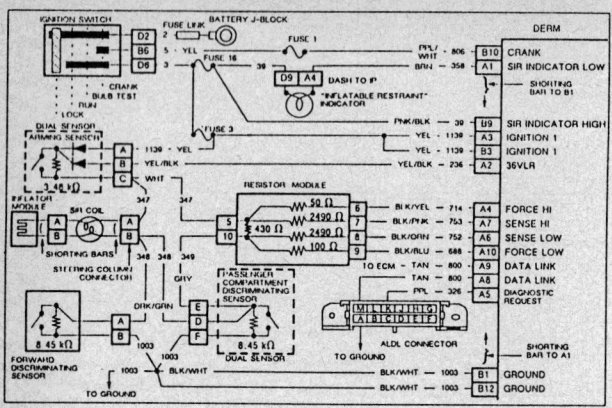

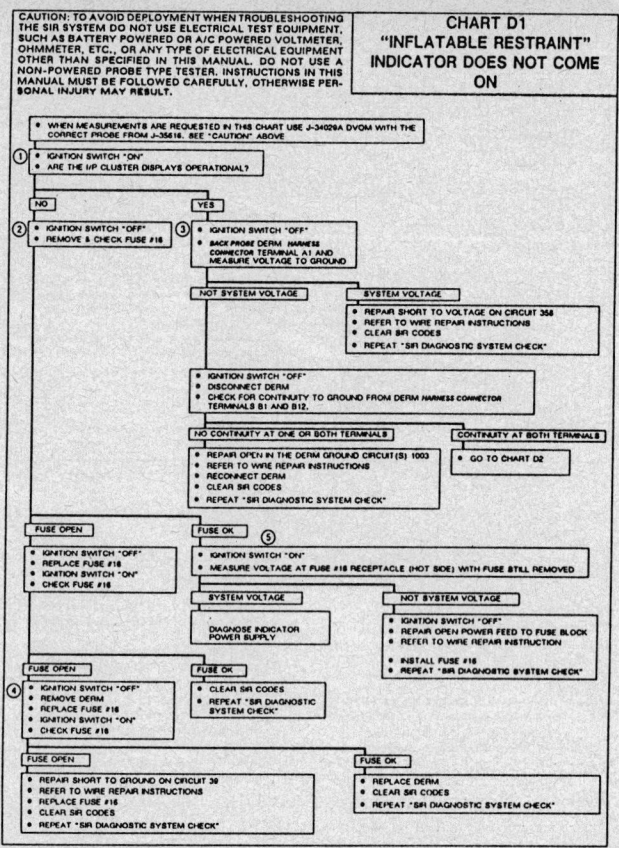

CHART D1

"INFLATABLE RESTRAINT" INDICATOR DOES NOT COME ON

Description:

When the Ignition Switch is first turned "ON" system voltage is applied through fuse #16 to "SIR Indicator High" (B9) and to the "INFLATABLE RESTRAINT" Indicator Lamp which is connected to "SIR Indicator Low" (A1). Fuse #3 also applies voltage to the "IGNITION 1" inputs (A3 and B3). The DERM responds by blinking the "INFLATABLE RESTRAINT" indicator 7 to 9 times.

When the engine is being cranked system voltage is applied to the DERM at the "CRANK" input. The DERM grounds the lamp circuit until system voltage is removed from the "CRANK" input. This results in a steady "INFLATABLE RESTRAINT" indicator during cranking.

After cranking the DERM will again blink the "INFLATABLE RESTRAINT" indicator 7 to 9 times if the Ignition Switch is "ON".

Notes on Fault Tree:

1) Checks if high side (power side) of the lamp circuit is fault free. This circuit powers the IP cluster. If the IP cluster is operative, then the power supply to the "INFLATABLE RESTRAINT" indicator is not suspect.
2) Checks fuse #16 which is in the high side (power side) of the lamp circuit.
3) Checks for short to voltage on circuit 358.
4) Checks for short to ground via wiring harness or DERM.
5) Checks for power supply fault.

Fig. 50   Diagnostic chart D1. Deville & Fleetwood

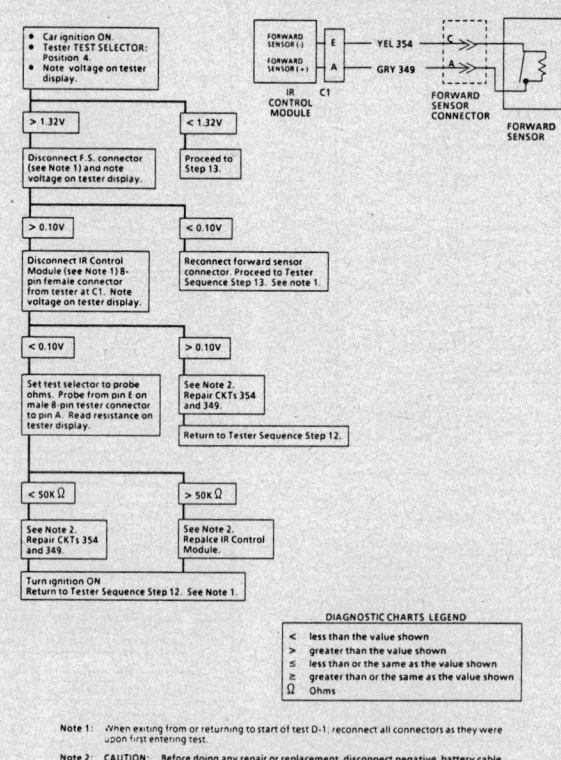

Fig. 51   Diagnostic chart, Test D-1. 88 & 98

SUPPLEMENTAL INFLATABLE RESTRAINT SYSTEM

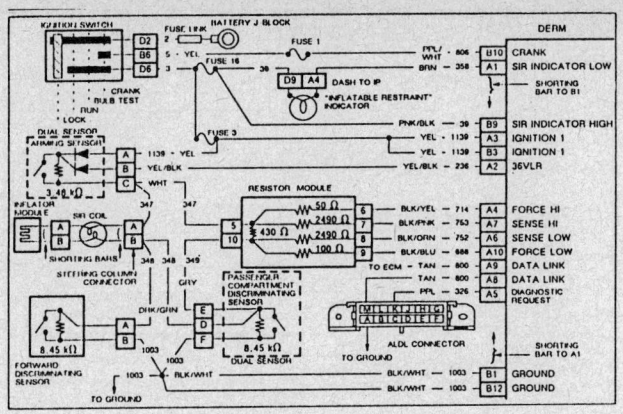

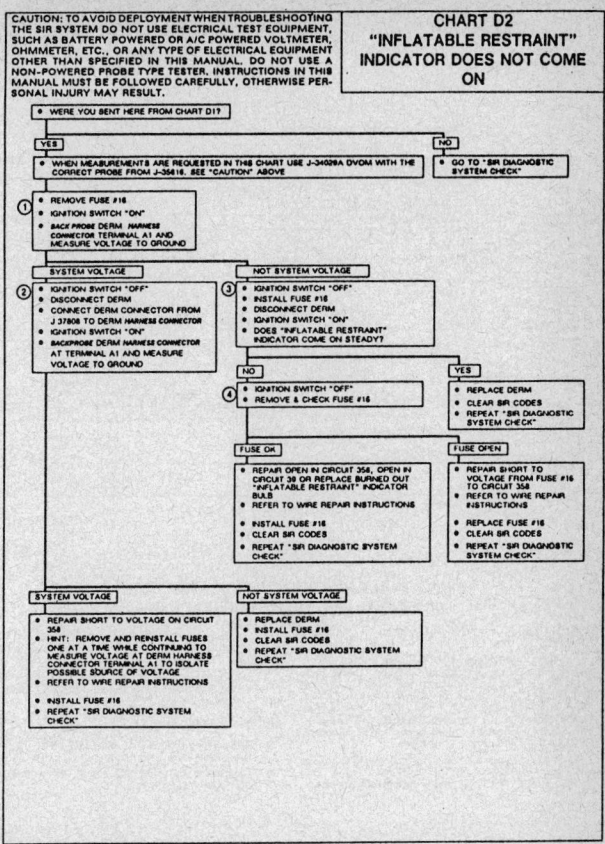

CAUTION: TO AVOID DEPLOYMENT WHEN TROUBLESHOOTING THE SIR SYSTEM DO NOT USE ELECTRICAL TEST EQUIPMENT, SUCH AS BATTERY POWERED OR A/C POWERED VOLTMETER, OHMMETER, ETC., OR ANY TYPE OF ELECTRICAL EQUIPMENT OTHER THAN SPECIFIED IN THIS MANUAL. DO NOT USE A NON-POWERED PROBE TYPE TESTER. INSTRUCTIONS IN THIS MANUAL MUST BE FOLLOWED CAREFULLY, OTHERWISE PERSONAL INJURY MAY RESULT.

CHART D2
"INFLATABLE RESTRAINT" INDICATOR DOES NOT COME ON

Description:

When the Ignition Switch is first turned "ON" system voltage is applied through fuse #16 to "SIR Indicator High" (B9) and to the "INFLATABLE RESTRAINT" Indicator Lamp which is connected to "SIR Indicator Low" (A1). Fuse #3 also applies system voltage to the "IGNITION 1" inputs (A3 and B3). The DERM responds by blinking the "INFLATABLE RESTRAINT" indicator 7 to 9 times.

When the engine is being cranked system voltage is applied to the DERM at the "CRANK" input. The DERM grounds the lamp circuit until system voltage is removed from the "CRANK" input. This results in a steady "INFLATABLE RESTRAINT" indicator during cranking.

After cranking the DERM will again blink the "INFLATABLE RESTRAINT" indicator 7 to 9 times if the Ignition Switch is "ON".

Notes on Fault Tree:

1) Determines if a short to voltage via an ignition fed source exists.

2) After the DERM is disconnected, the shorting bar normally supplies a ground to terminal A1 of the DERM harness. When the DERM connector from J 37808 is substituted in place of the DERM, the shorting bar which supplies the ground to terminal A1 is not allowed to close. Thus, circuit 358 is isolated from both ground and the DERM so that an accurate voltage measurement can be made.

3) Checks if DERM is defective.

4) Checks if a short to voltage or open circuit exists on circuit 358. Also checks for burned out lamp.

Fig. 52   Diagnostic chart D2. Deville & Fleetwood

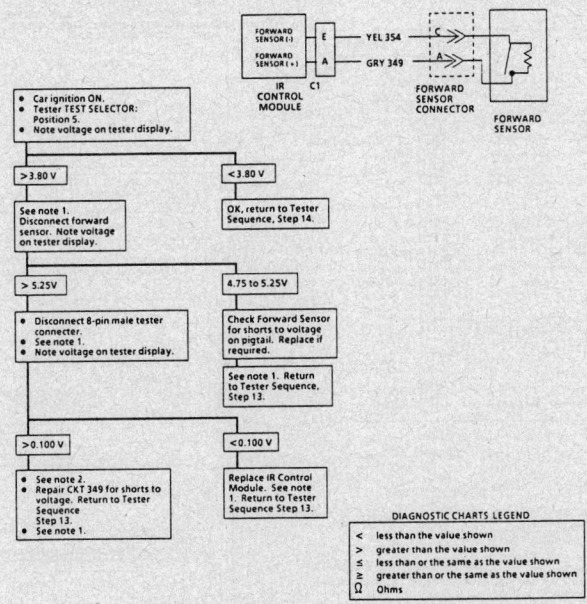

DIAGNOSTIC CHARTS LEGEND

<	less than the value shown
>	greater than the value shown
≤	less than or the same as the value shown
≥	greater than or the same as the value shown
Ω	Ohms

Note 1:   When exiting from or returning to start of test D-2, reconnect all connectors as they were upon first entering test.

Note 2:   CAUTION: Before doing any repair or replacement, disconnect negative battery cable and tape its terminal. Wait 15 seconds for Energy Reserve to discharge as personal injury could result.

Fig. 53   Diagnostic chart, Test D-2. 88 & 98

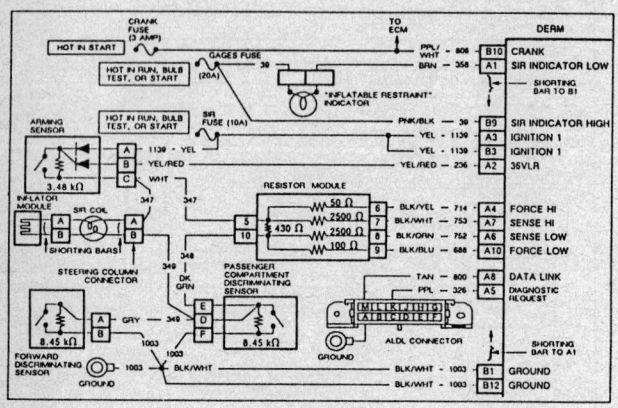

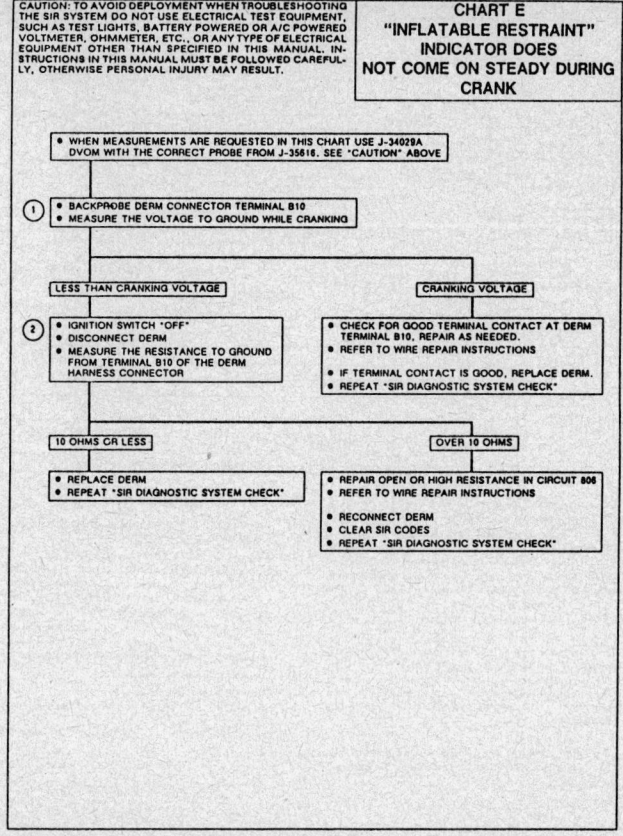

CHART E

"INFLATABLE RESTRAINT" INDICATOR DOES NOT COME ON STEADY DURING CRANK

Description:

When the Ignition Switch is first turned "ON" system voltage is applied through GAGES FUSE to "SIR Indicator High" (B9) and to the "INFLATABLE RESTRAINT" Indicator Lamp which is connected to ("SIR Indicator Low" (A1). SIR FUSE also applies system voltage to the "Ignition 1" inputs (A3 and B3). The DERM responds by blinking the "INFLATABLE RESTRAINT" indicator 7 to 9 times.

When the engine is being cranked system voltage is applied to the DERM at the "CRANK" input. The DERM grounds the lamp circuit until system voltage is removed from the "CRANK" input. This results in a steady "INFLATABLE RESTRAINT" indicator during cranking.

After cranking the DERM will again blink the "INFLATABLE RESTRAINT" indicator 7 to 9 times if the Ignition Switch is "ON".

Notes on Fault Tree:

1) Checks for system voltage at the "CRANK" input of the DERM during cranking.
2) Checks for the "CRANK" circuit for an open or high resistance.

Fig. 54   Diagnostic chart E. Camaro & Firebird

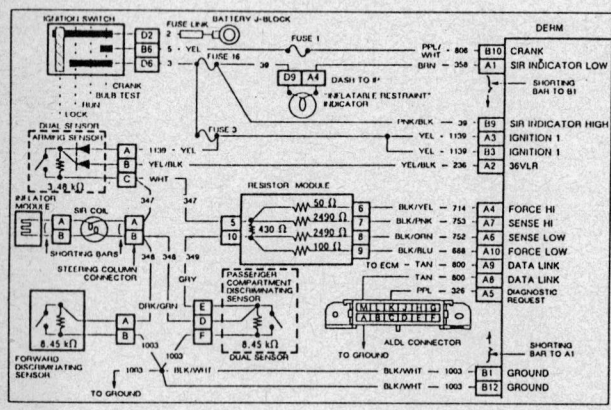

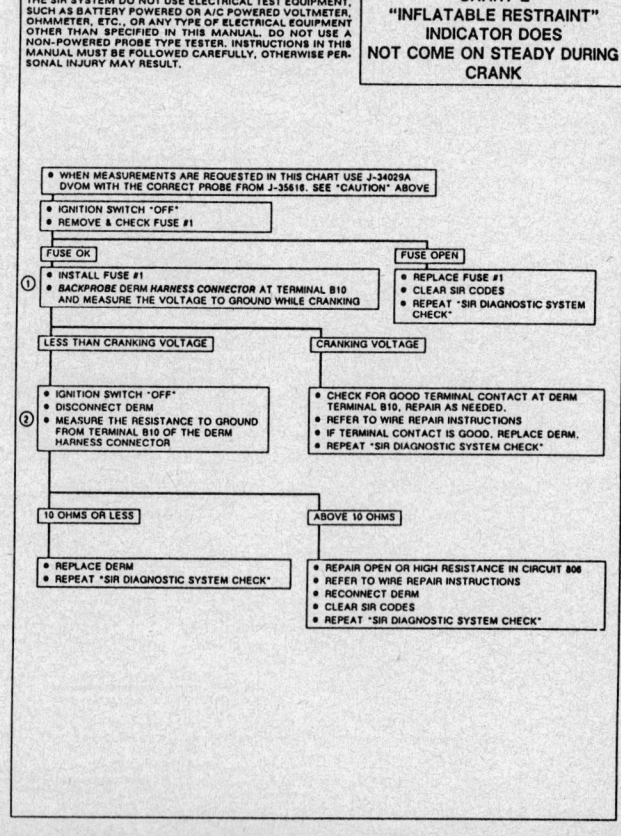

CHART E

"INFLATABLE RESTRAINT" INDICATOR DOES NOT COME ON STEADY DURING CRANK

Description:

When the Ignition Switch is first turned "ON" system voltage is applied through fuse #16 to "SIR Indicator High" (B9) and to the "INFLATABLE RESTRAINT" Indicator Lamp which is connected to "SIR Indicator Low" (A1). Fuse #3 also applies system voltage to the "IGNITION 1" inputs (A3 and B3). The DERM responds by blinking the "INFLATABLE RESTRAINT" indicator 7 to 9 times.

When the engine is being cranked system voltage is applied to the DERM at the "CRANK" input. The DERM grounds the lamp circuit until system voltage is removed from the "CRANK" input. This results in a steady "INFLATABLE RESTRAINT" indicator during cranking.

After cranking the DERM will again blink the "INFLATABLE RESTRAINT" indicator 7 to 9 times if the Ignition Switch is "ON".

Notes on Fault Tree:

1) Checks for system voltage at the "CRANK" input of the DERM during cranking.
2) Checks for the "CRANK" circuit for an open or high resistance.

Fig. 55   Diagnostic chart E. Deville & Fleetwood

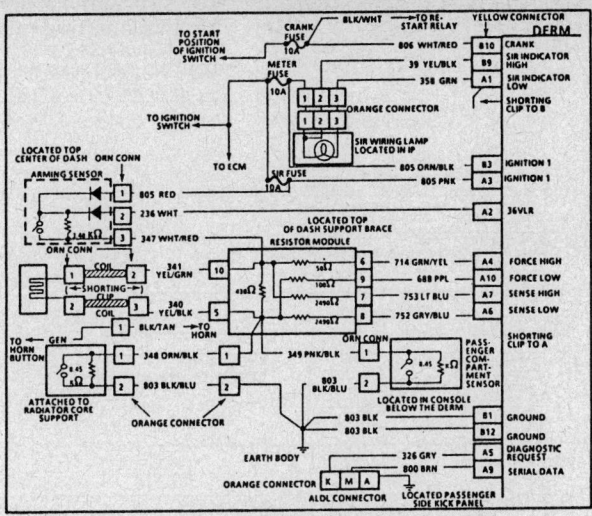

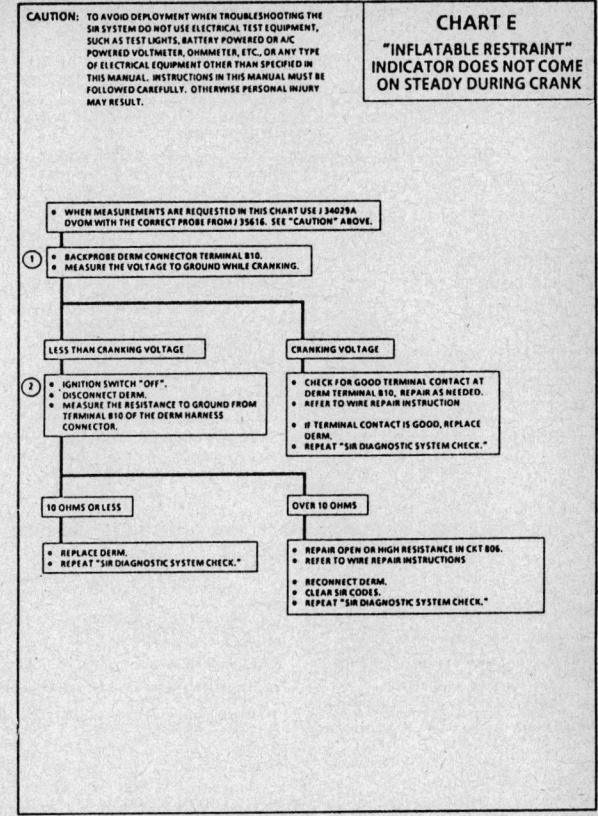

CAUTION: TO AVOID DEPLOYMENT WHEN TROUBLESHOOTING THE SIR SYSTEM DO NOT USE ELECTRICAL TEST EQUIPMENT, SUCH AS TEST LIGHTS, BATTERY POWERED OR A/C POWERED VOLTMETER, OHMMETER, ETC., OR ANY TYPE OF ELECTRICAL EQUIPMENT OTHER THAN SPECIFIED IN THIS MANUAL. INSTRUCTIONS IN THIS MANUAL MUST BE FOLLOWED CAREFULLY. OTHERWISE PERSONAL INJURY MAY RESULT.

CHART E
"INFLATABLE RESTRAINT"
INDICATOR DOES NOT COME
ON STEADY DURING CRANK

CHART E
"INFLATABLE RESTRAINT" INDICATOR DOES NOT COME ON STEADY DURING CRANK

Description:

When the Ignition Switch is first turned "ON" system voltage is applied through METER FUSE to "SIR Indicator High" (B9) and to the "INFLATABLE RESTRAINT" Indicator Lamp which is connected to "SIR Indicator Low" (A1). Fuse 3 also applies system voltage to the "Ignition 1" inputs (A3 and B3). The DERM responds by blinking the "INFLATABLE RESTRAINT" indicator 7 times.

When the engine is being cranked system voltage is applied to the DERM at the "CRANK" input. The DERM grounds the lamp circuit until system voltage is removed from the "CRANK" input. This results in a steady "INFLATABLE RESTRAINT" indicator during cranking.

After cranking the DERM will again blink "INFLATABLE RESTRAINT" indicator 7 times if the Ignition Switch is "ON".

Notes on Fault Tree:

1. Checks for system voltage at the "CRANK" input of the DERM during cranking.
2. Checks for the "CRANK" circuit for an open or high resistance.

Fig. 56   Diagnostic chart E. Storm

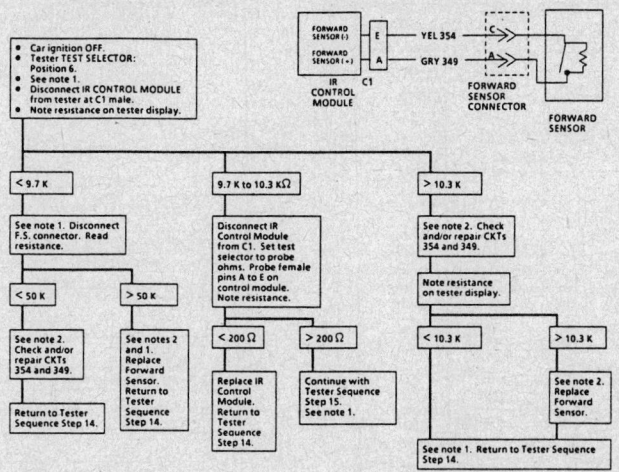

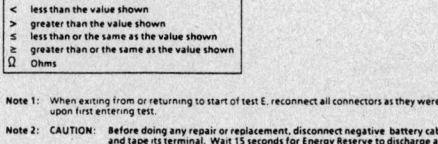

DIAGNOSTIC CHARTS LEGEND

<	less than the value shown
>	greater than the value shown
≤	less than or the same as the value shown
≥	greater than or the same as the value shown
Ω	Ohms

Note 1:   When exiting from or returning to start of test E, reconnect all connectors as they were upon first entering test.

Note 2:   CAUTION: Before doing any repair or replacement, disconnect negative battery cable and tape its terminal. Wait 15 seconds for Energy Reserve to discharge as personal injury could result.

Fig. 57   Diagnostic chart, Test E. 88 & 98

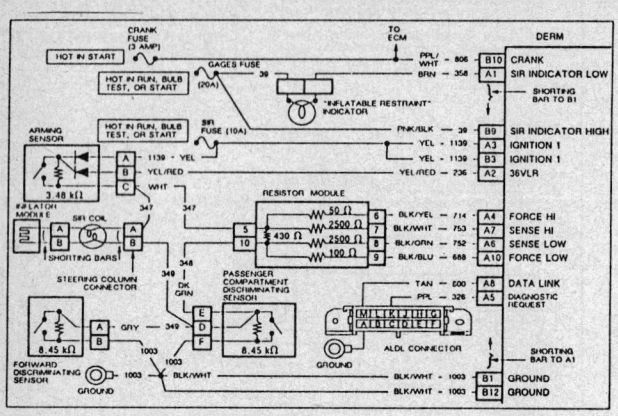

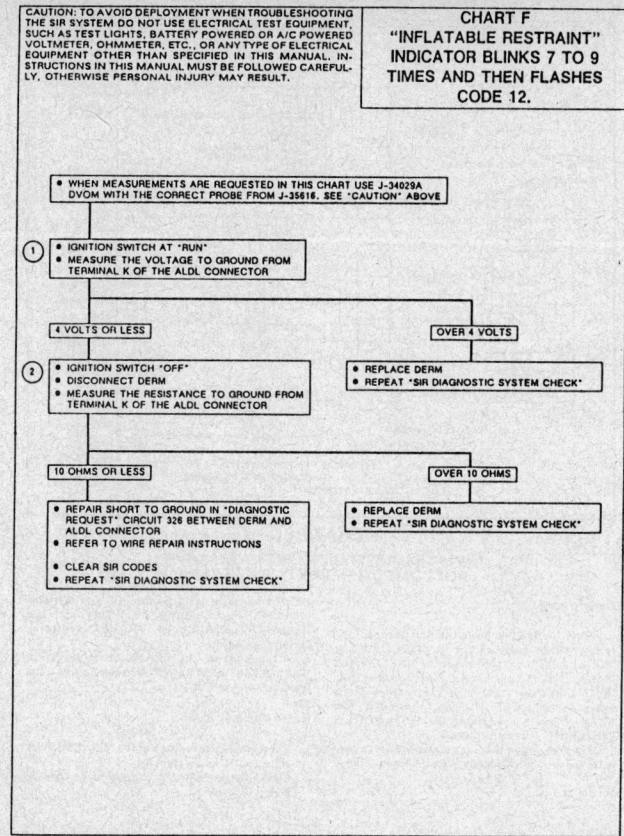

CHART F

"INFLATABLE RESTRAINT" INDICATOR BLINKS 7 TO 9 TIMES AND THEN FLASHES CODE 12.

Description:

When the Ignition Switch is first turned "ON" system voltage is applied through GAGES FUSE to "SIR Indicator High" (B9) and to the "INFLATABLE RESTRAINT" Indicator Lamp which is connected to "SIR Indicator Low" (A1). SIR FUSE also applies system voltage to the "Ignition I" inputs (A3 and B3). The DERM responds by blinking the "INFLATABLE RESTRAINT" indicator 7 to 9 times.

When the engine is being cranked system voltage is applied to the DERM at the "CRANK" input. The DERM grounds the lamp circuit until system voltage is

removed from the "CRANK" input. This results in a steady "INFLATABLE RESTRAINT" indicator during cranking.

After cranking the DERM will again blink the "INFLATABLE RESTRAINT" indicator 7 to 9 times if the Ignition Switch is "ON."

Notes on Fault Tree:

1) Checks the "Diagnostic Request" circuit for voltage at the ALDL connector.

2) Checks if short to ground is in the "Diagnostic Request" circuit or the DERM.

Fig. 58 Diagnostic chart F. Camaro & Firebird

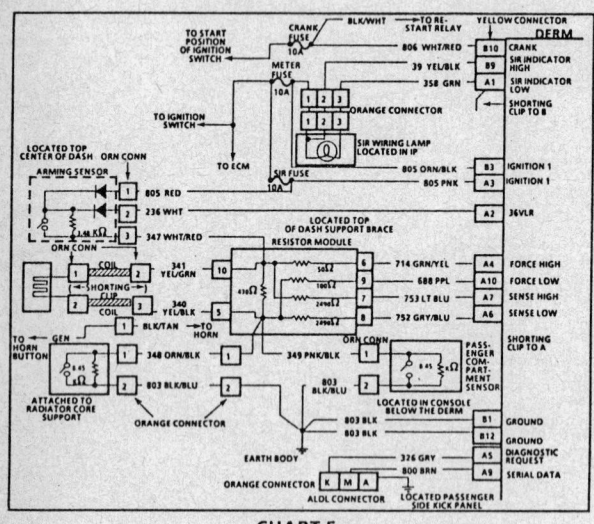

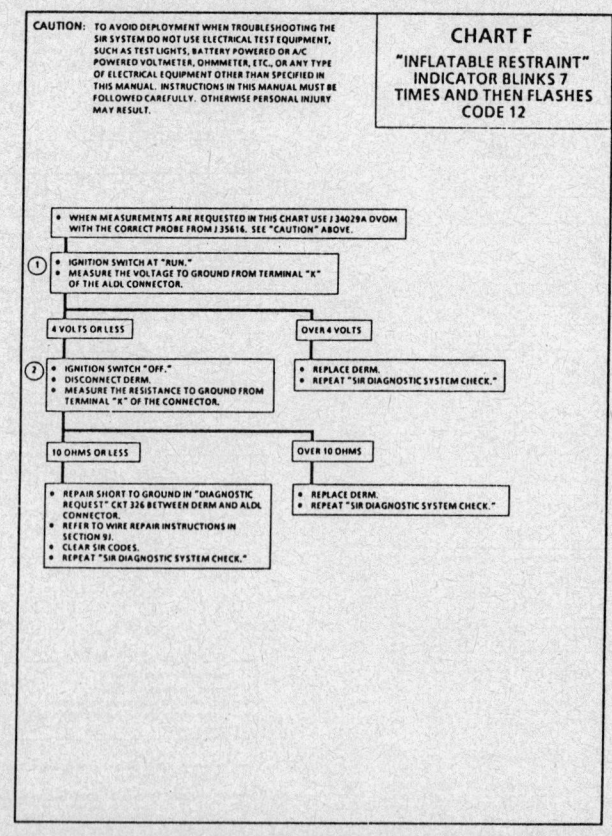

CHART F

"INFLATABLE RESTRAINT" INDICATOR BLINKS 7 TIMES AND THEN FLASHES CODE 12

Description:

When the Ignition Switch is first turned "ON" system voltage is applied through METER FUSE to "SIR Indicator High" (B9) and to the "INFLATABLE RESTRAINT" Indicator Lamp which is connected to "SIR Indicator Low" (A1). SIR FUSE also applies system voltage to the "Ignition I" inputs (A3 and B3). The DERM responds by blinking the "INFLATABLE RESTRAINT" indicator 7 times.

When the engine is being cranked system voltage is applied to the DERM at the "CRANK" input. The DERM grounds the lamp circuit until system voltage

is removed from the "CRANK" input. This results in a steady "INFLATABLE RESTRAINT" indicator during cranking.

After cranking the DERM will again blink "INFLATABLE RESTRAINT" indicator 7 times if the Ignition Switch is "ON."

Notes on Fault Tree:

1. Checks the "Diagnostic Request" circuit for voltage at the ALDL connector.

2. Checks if short to ground is in the "Diagnostic Request" circuit or the DERM.

Fig. 59 Diagnostic chart F. Storm

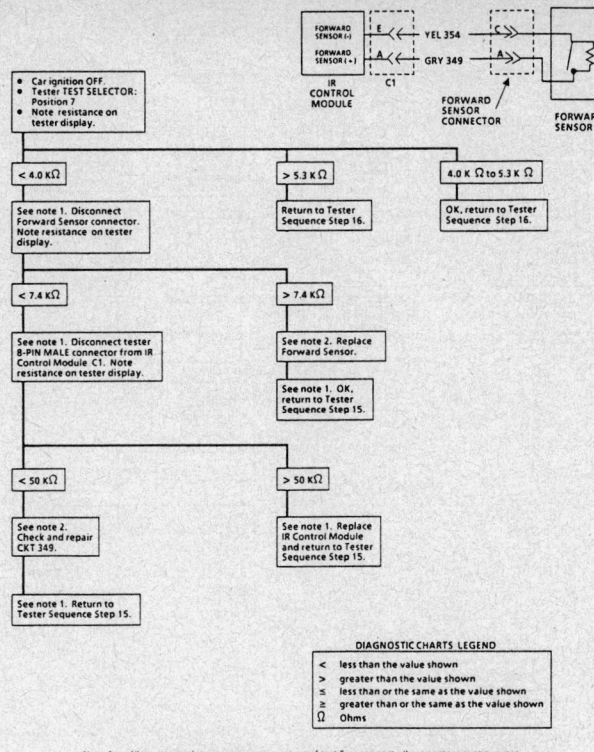

Fig. 60 Diagnostic chart F. 88 & 98

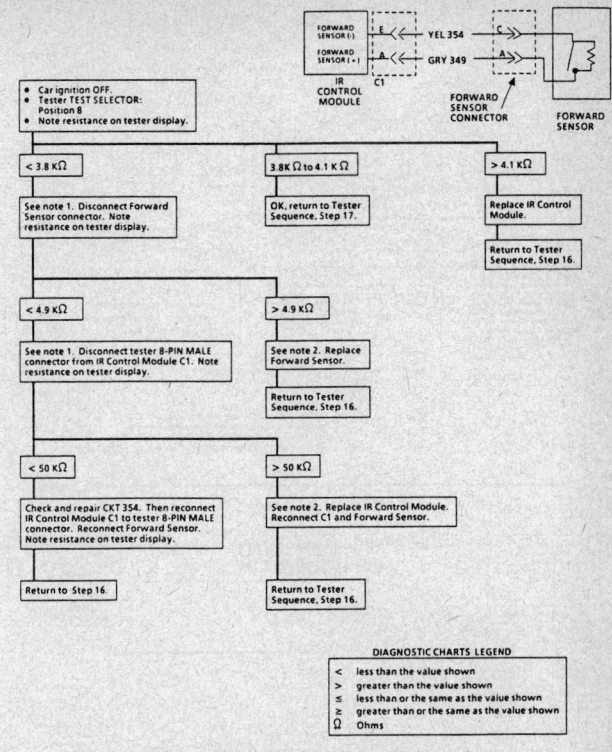

Fig. 61 Diagnostic chart G (Forward sensor low side shorts to ground). 88 & 98

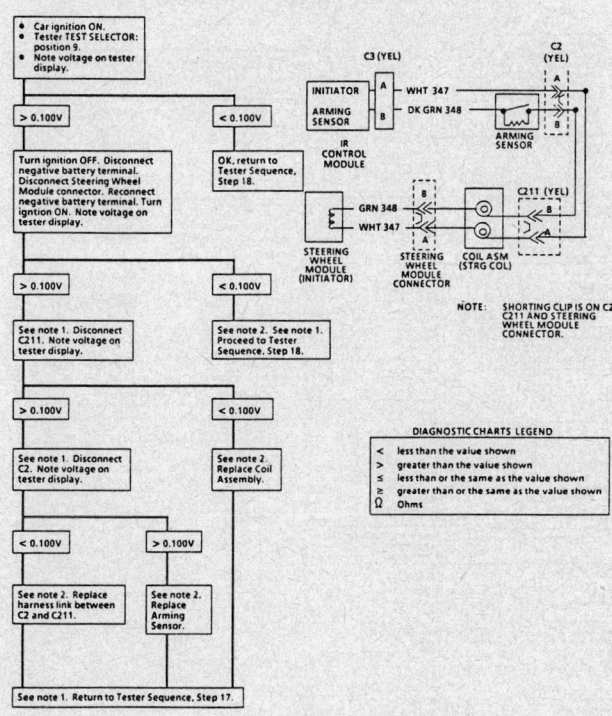

Fig. 62 Diagnostic chart H-1 (Steering wheel module high side shorts to voltage). 88 & 98

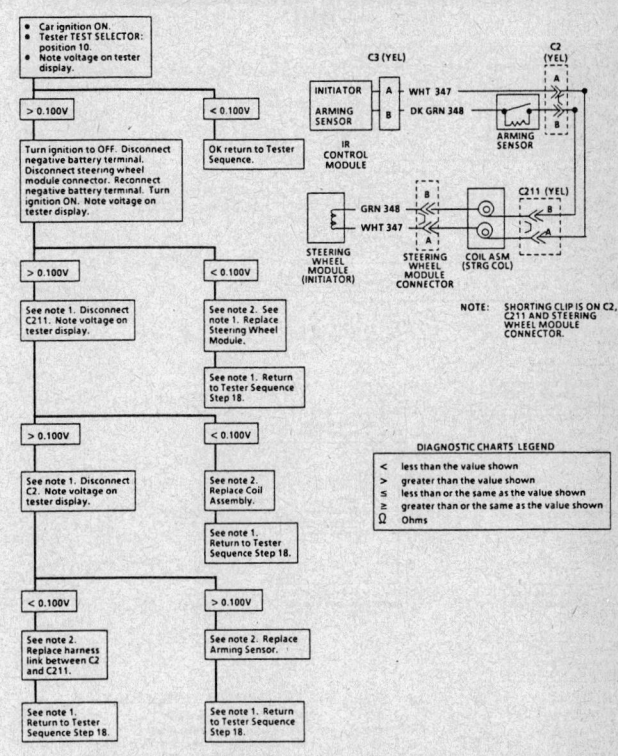

Fig. 63 Diagnostic chart H-2 (Steering wheel module low side shorts to voltage). 88 & 98

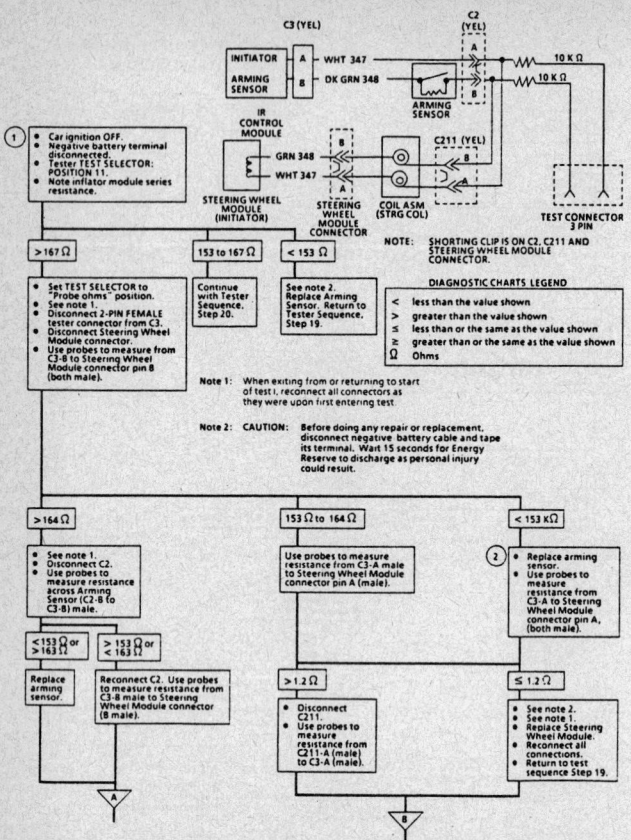

Fig. 64 Diagnostic chart I (Part 1 of 2). Steering wheel module series resistance (88 & 98)

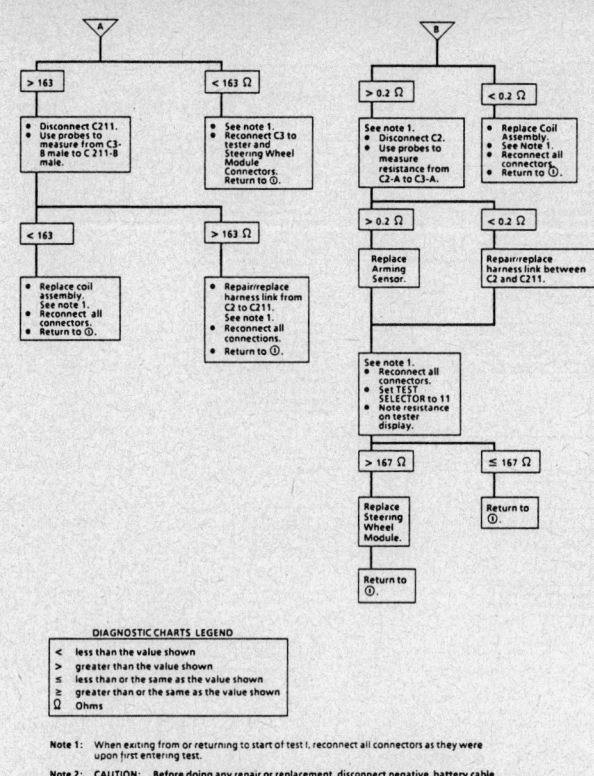

Fig. 64 Diagnostic chart I (Part 2 of 2). Steering wheel module series resistance (88 & 98)

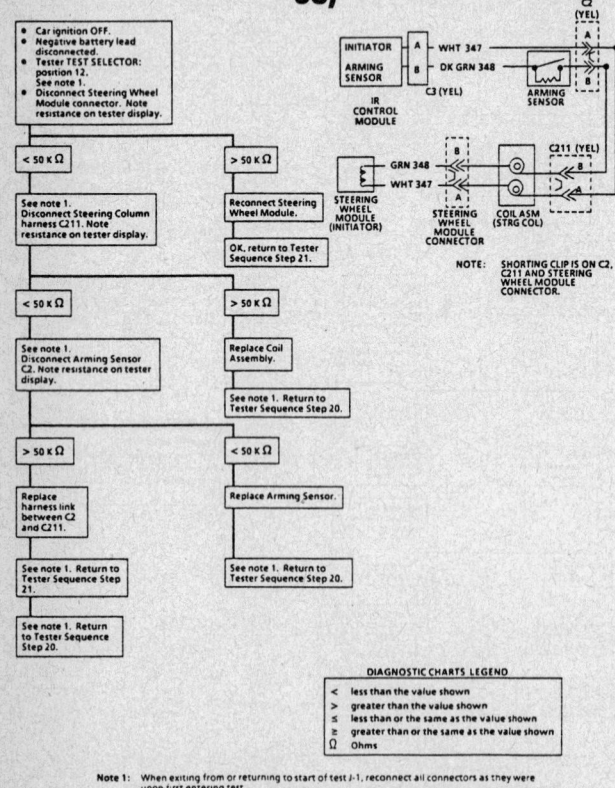

Fig. 65 Diagnostic chart J-1. Steering wheel module low side shorts to ground (88 & 98)

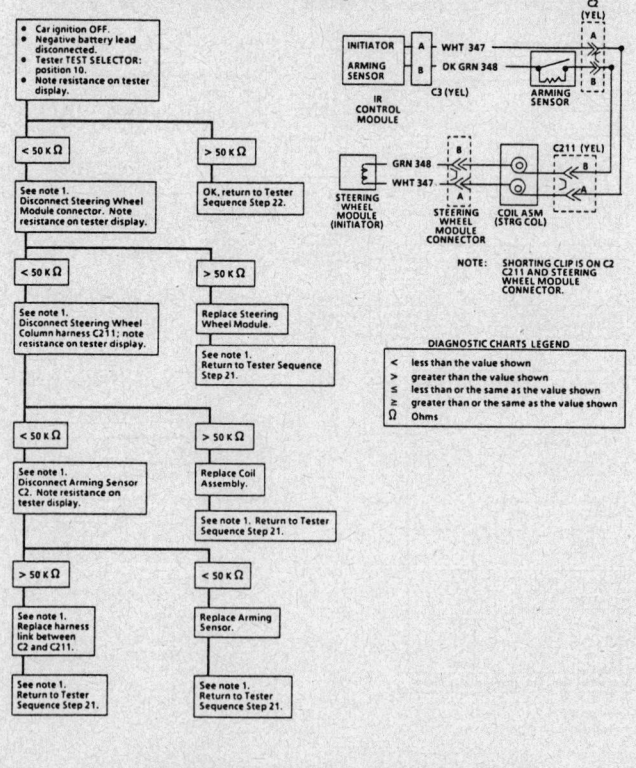

Fig. 66 Diagnostic chart J-2. Steering wheel module low side shorts to ground (88 & 98)

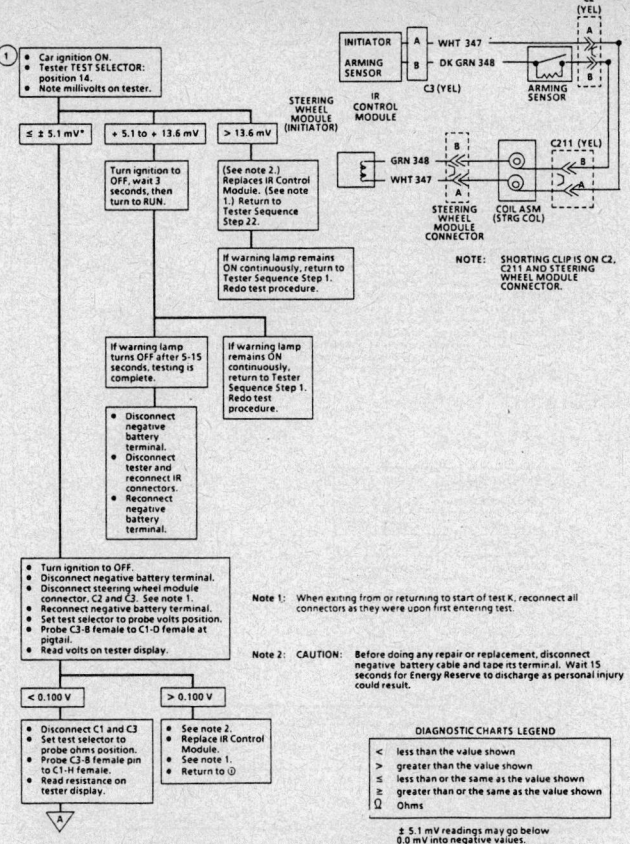

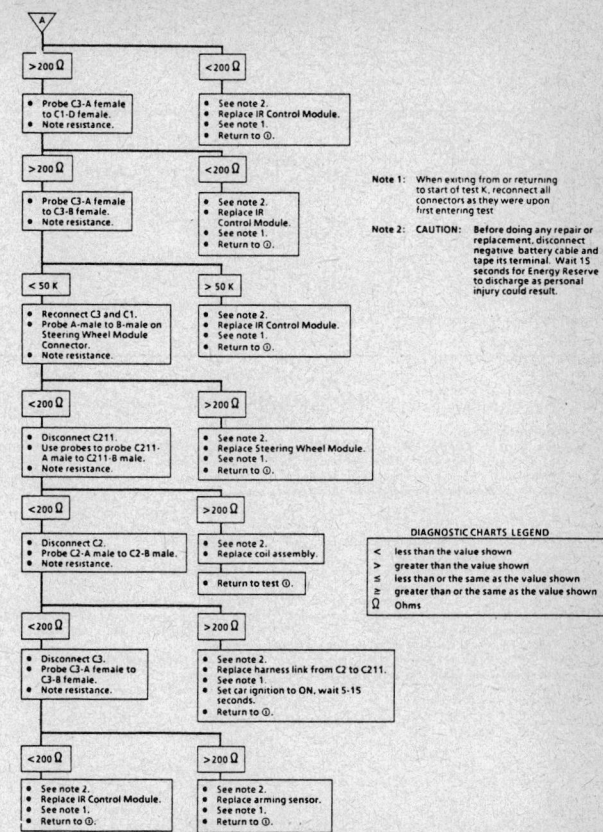

Fig. 67 Diagnostic chart K (Part 1 of 2). Steering wheel module shorts (88 & 98)

Fig. 67 Diagnostic chart K (Part 2 of 2). Steering wheel module shorts (88 & 98)

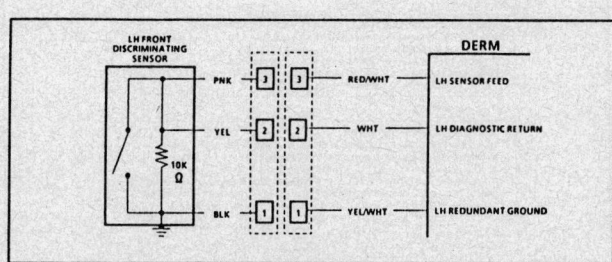

CODE 14
FRONT SENSOR #1 (LH)
(CIRCUIT SHORTED TO GROUND)

Circuit Description:

In an accident of sufficient force, the Front Discriminating Sensor switch closes, providing a path to ground for the deployment loop current. The sensor contains additional circuitry, used by the DERM for diagnostics.

If the DERM measures less than a certain resistance value between either the sensor feed line and ground or the diagnostic return line and ground, Code 14 will set.

Test Description: Numbers below refer to circled numbers on the diagnostic chart.

1. This step is essential to ensure that the ground between the sensor case and the frame rail is in good condition.
2. This test checks to see if the sensor and its wiring are within correct specifications. If the sensor and wiring check out as OK, the fault must be in the DERM or its wiring.

Diagnostic Aids:

The Fasten Seat Belt indicator will stay "ON" continuously when an SIR failure code has been set.

If power is applied to the SIR system while any component is not properly connected, an additional failure code will be set for the disconnected SIR component.

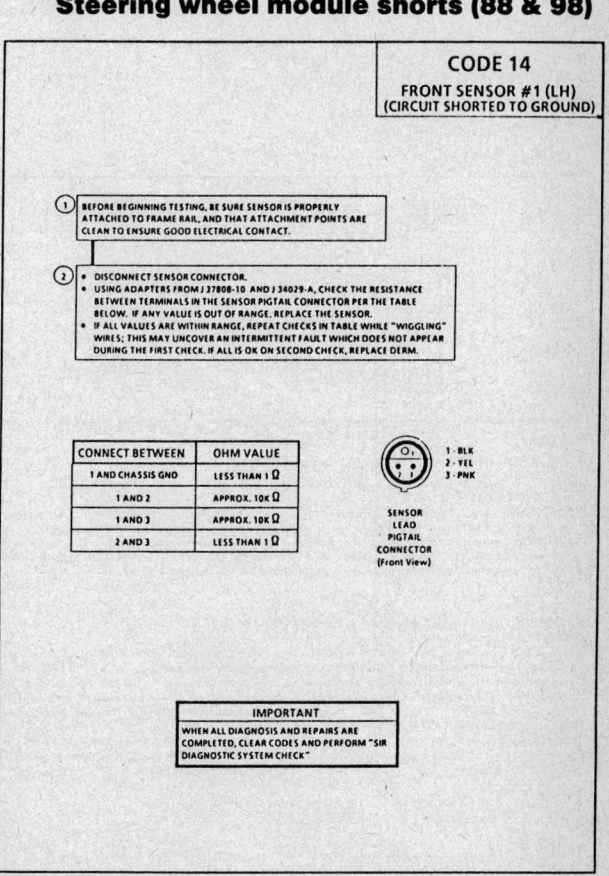

Fig. 68 Code 14 diagnosis. Corvette

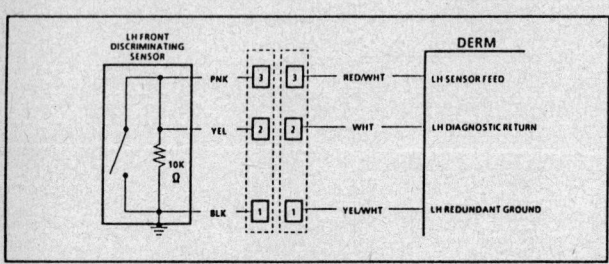

CODE 15
FRONT SENSOR #1 (LH)
(OPEN CIRCUIT)

Circuit Description:

In an accident of sufficient force, the Front Discriminating Sensor switch closes, providing a path to ground for the deployment loop current. The sensor contains additional circuitry, used by the DERM for diagnostics.

If the DERM measures more than a certain resistance value between either the sensor feed line and ground or the diagnostic return line and ground, Code 15 will set.

Test Description: Numbers below refer to circled numbers on the diagnostic chart.

1. This step is essential to ensure that the ground between the sensor case and the frame rail is in good condition. It is also necessary because a simple loose or disconnected sensor connection could cause this fault.
2. This test checks to see if the sensor and its wiring are within correct specifications. If the sensor and wiring check out as OK, the fault must be in the DERM or its wiring.

Diagnostic Aids:

The Fasten Seat Belt indicator will stay "ON" continuously when an SIR failure code has been set.

If power is applied to the SIR system while any component is not properly connected, an additional failure code will be set for the disconnected SIR component.

If a Code 15 has set, a Code 16 may also be set.

Severe corrosion under the sensor mounting bracket may cause a Code 15.

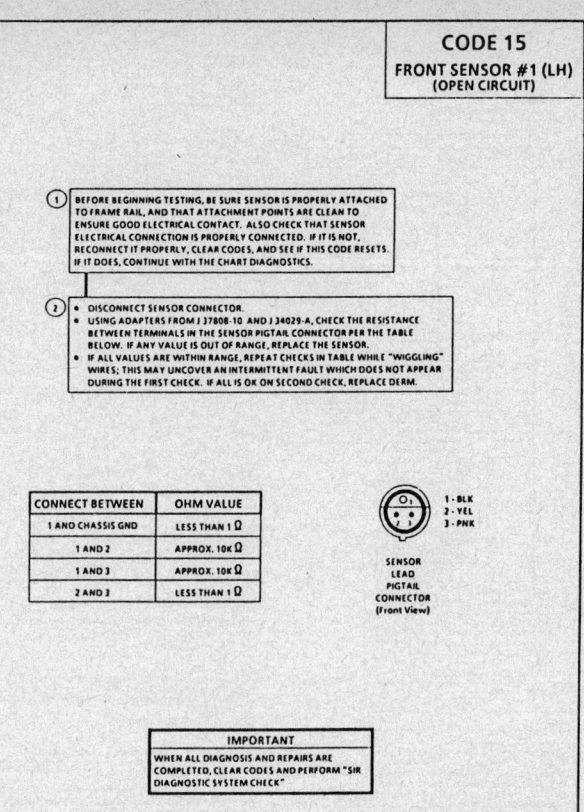

CODE 15
FRONT SENSOR #1 (LH)
(OPEN CIRCUIT)

① BEFORE BEGINNING TESTING, BE SURE SENSOR IS PROPERLY ATTACHED TO FRAME RAIL, AND THAT ATTACHMENT POINTS ARE CLEAN TO ENSURE GOOD ELECTRICAL CONTACT. ALSO CHECK THAT SENSOR ELECTRICAL CONNECTION IS PROPERLY CONNECTED. IF IT IS NOT, RECONNECT IT PROPERLY, CLEAR CODES, AND SEE IF THIS CODE RESETS. IF IT DOES, CONTINUE WITH THE CHART DIAGNOSTICS.

② • DISCONNECT SENSOR CONNECTOR.
• USING ADAPTERS FROM J 37808-10 AND J 34029-A, CHECK THE RESISTANCE BETWEEN TERMINALS IN THE SENSOR PIGTAIL CONNECTOR PER THE TABLE BELOW. IF ANY VALUE IS OUT OF RANGE, REPLACE THE SENSOR.
• IF ALL VALUES ARE WITHIN RANGE, REPEAT CHECKS IN TABLE WHILE "WIGGLING" WIRES; THIS MAY UNCOVER AN INTERMITTENT FAULT WHICH DOES NOT APPEAR DURING THE FIRST CHECK. IF ALL IS OK ON SECOND CHECK, REPLACE DERM.

CONNECT BETWEEN	OHM VALUE
1 AND CHASSIS GND	LESS THAN 1 Ω
1 AND 2	APPROX. 10K Ω
1 AND 3	APPROX. 10K Ω
2 AND 3	LESS THAN 1 Ω

1 - BLK
2 - YEL
3 - PNK

SENSOR LEAD PIGTAIL CONNECTOR (Front View)

IMPORTANT
WHEN ALL DIAGNOSIS AND REPAIRS ARE COMPLETED, CLEAR CODES AND PERFORM "SIR DIAGNOSTIC SYSTEM CHECK"

Fig. 69   Code 15 diagnosis. Corvette

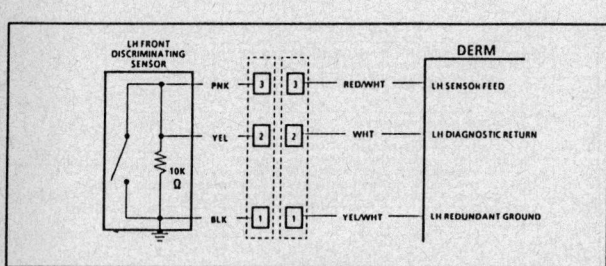

CODE 16
FRONT SENSOR #1 (LH)
(SENSOR FAULT)

Circuit Description:

In an accident of sufficient force, the Front Discriminating Sensor switch closes, providing a path to ground for the deployment loop current. The sensor contains additional circuitry, used by the DERM for diagnostics.

If the DERM measures more than a certain resistance value between the redundant ground circuit and the DERM's own ground, Code 16 will set. This code will also set if the DERM measures less than a certain resistance between the sensor feed circuit and B + or the diagnostic return circuit and B +.

Test Description: Numbers below refer to circled numbers on the diagnostic chart.

1. This step is essential to ensure that the ground between the sensor case and the frame rail is in good condition. It is also necessary because a simple loose or disconnected sensor connection could cause this fault.
2. This test checks to see if the sensor and its wiring are within correct specifications. If the sensor and wiring check out as OK, the fault must be in the DERM or its wiring.

Diagnostic Aids:

The Fasten Seat Belt indicator will stay "ON" continuously when an SIR failure code has been set.

If power is applied to the SIR system while any component is not properly connected, an additional failure code will be set for the disconnected SIR component.

If a Code 16 has set, a Code 15 may also be set.

Severe corrosion under the sensor mounting bracket may cause a Code 16.

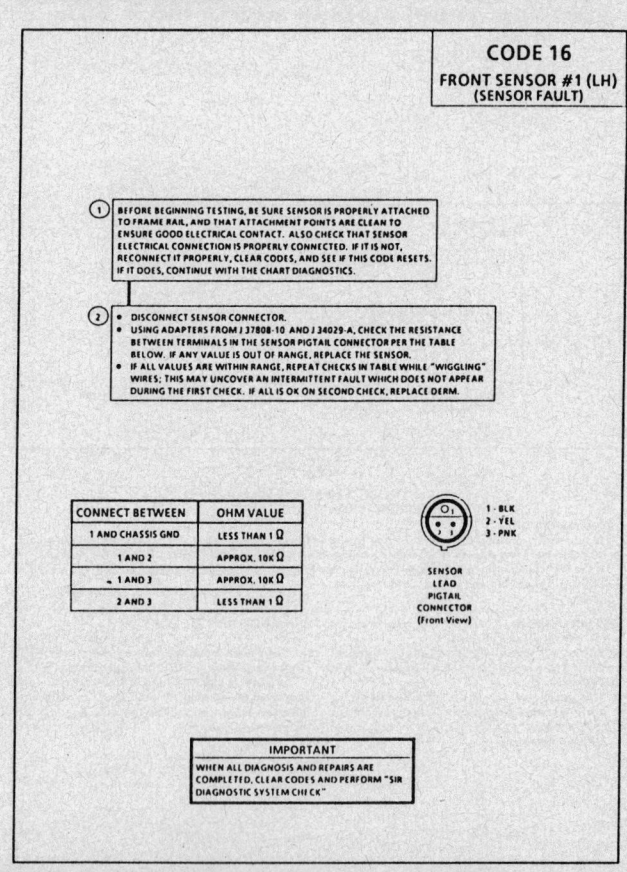

CODE 16
FRONT SENSOR #1 (LH)
(SENSOR FAULT)

① BEFORE BEGINNING TESTING, BE SURE SENSOR IS PROPERLY ATTACHED TO FRAME RAIL, AND THAT ATTACHMENT POINTS ARE CLEAN TO ENSURE GOOD ELECTRICAL CONTACT. ALSO CHECK THAT SENSOR ELECTRICAL CONNECTION IS PROPERLY CONNECTED. IF IT IS NOT, RECONNECT IT PROPERLY, CLEAR CODES, AND SEE IF THIS CODE RESETS. IF IT DOES, CONTINUE WITH THE CHART DIAGNOSTICS.

② • DISCONNECT SENSOR CONNECTOR.
• USING ADAPTERS FROM J 37808-10 AND J 34029-A, CHECK THE RESISTANCE BETWEEN TERMINALS IN THE SENSOR PIGTAIL CONNECTOR PER THE TABLE BELOW. IF ANY VALUE IS OUT OF RANGE, REPLACE THE SENSOR.
• IF ALL VALUES ARE WITHIN RANGE, REPEAT CHECKS IN TABLE WHILE "WIGGLING" WIRES; THIS MAY UNCOVER AN INTERMITTENT FAULT WHICH DOES NOT APPEAR DURING THE FIRST CHECK. IF ALL IS OK ON SECOND CHECK, REPLACE DERM.

CONNECT BETWEEN	OHM VALUE
1 AND CHASSIS GND	LESS THAN 1 Ω
1 AND 2	APPROX. 10K Ω
1 AND 3	APPROX. 10K Ω
2 AND 3	LESS THAN 1 Ω

1 - BLK
2 - YEL
3 - PNK

SENSOR LEAD PIGTAIL CONNECTOR (Front View)

IMPORTANT
WHEN ALL DIAGNOSIS AND REPAIRS ARE COMPLETED, CLEAR CODES AND PERFORM "SIR DIAGNOSTIC SYSTEM CHECK"

Fig. 70   Code 16 diagnosis. Corvette

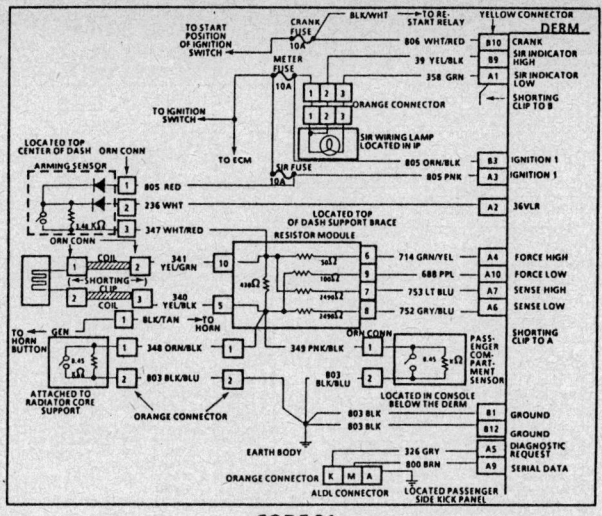

CODE 21
STEERING COLUMN RESISTANCE TOO HIGH

Test Conditions:

Tested once each ignition cycle during the "Steering Column Resistance Test" if: 1) No faults are detected during "Turn-ON", 2) No faults are detected during "Continuous Monitoring" for 1 second; 3) No Crank signal present.

Failure Conditions:

Code 21 will set if the combined resistance of the Inflator Module, SIR Coil, harness wiring and connector terminal contact in the steering column is greater than a specified value.

Conditions To Clear:

Current Code 21 will be cleared each time the Ignition Switch is turned "OFF".

Action Taken:

DERM turns "ON" the "INFLATABLE RESTRAINT" indicator lamp.

Description:

The DERM injects a current of 75 milliamperes through the steering column from the Force Hi output

terminal "A4" to the Force Low input terminal "A10". By monitoring the voltage at the Sense Hi input terminal "A7" and the Sense Low input terminal "A6" the DERM calculates the combined resistance of the Inflator Module, SIR Coil, harness wiring (CKTs 347, 348 and 349) and connector terminal contact in the steering column. Code 21 will set if the resistance is greater than 4.37 ohms value or the 1000hm resistors within the Resistor Module is shorted.

Notes on Fault Tree:

1. Checks if fault is in steering column. The SIR Load Tester simulates the resistance of good steering column wiring and components.
2. Determines if fault is in Inflator Module or in the SIR Coil. The SIR Load Tester simulates the resistance of a good Inflator Module.
3. Checks if 100 ohm resistor in the Resistor Module is shorted.
4. Checks the Resistor Module for internal shorts.
5. Checks the resistance of circuits between the Resistor Module and the DERM.
6. Checks for harness shorts between Force Hi and Sense Hi.
7. Checks for Sense Hi shorted to voltage.

Fig. 71   Code 21 diagnosis. Storm

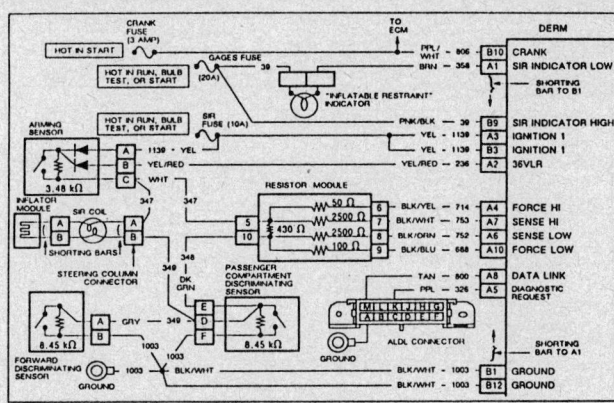

CODE 21 (CHART 1)

STEERING COLUMN RESISTANCE TOO HIGH

Test Conditions:

Tested once each ignition cycle during the "Steering Column Resistance Test" if: 1) No faults are detected during "Turn-on", 2) No faults are detected during "Continuous Monitoring" for 1 second; 3) No Crank signal present.

Failure Conditions:

Code 21 will set if the combined resistance of the Inflator Module, SIR Coil, harness wiring and connector terminal contact in the steering column is greater than a specified value.

Conditions To Clear:

Current Code 21 will be cleared each time the Ignition Switch is turned OFF.

Action Taken:

DERM turns ON the "INFLATABLE RESTRAINT" indicator lamp.

Description:

The DERM injects a current of 75 milliamperes through the steering column from the Force Hi output

(terminal A4) to the Force Low input (terminal A10). By monitoring the voltage at the Sense Hi input (terminal A7) and the Sense Low input (terminal A6) the DERM calculates the combined resistance of the Inflator Module, SIR Coil, harness wiring (circuits 347, 348 and 349) and connector terminal contact in the steering column. Code 21 will set if the resistance is greater than a specified value or the 100 ohm resistors within the Resistor Module is shorted.

Notes on Fault Tree:

1) Checks if fault is in steering column. The SIR Load Tester simulates the resistance of good steering column wiring and components.
2) Determines if fault is in Inflator Module or in the SIR Coil. The SIR Load Tester simulates the resistance of a good Inflator Module.
3) Checks if 100 ohm resistor in the Resistor Module is shorted.
4) Checks the Resistor Module for internal shorts.
5) Checks the resistance of circuits between the Resistor Module and the DERM.
6) Checks for harness shorts between Force Hi and Sense Hi.
7) Checks for Sense Hi shorted to voltage.

Fig. 72   Code 21 chart 1 diagnosis. Camaro & Firebird

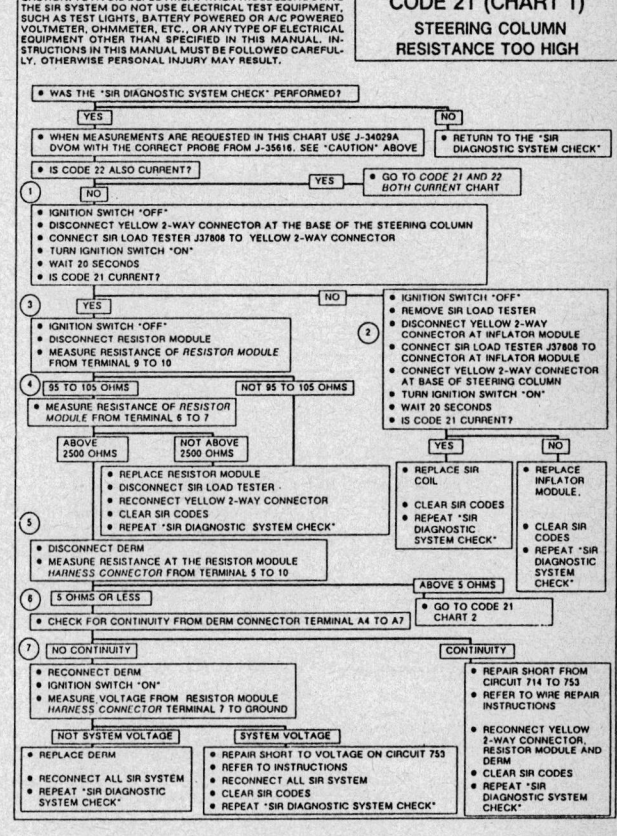

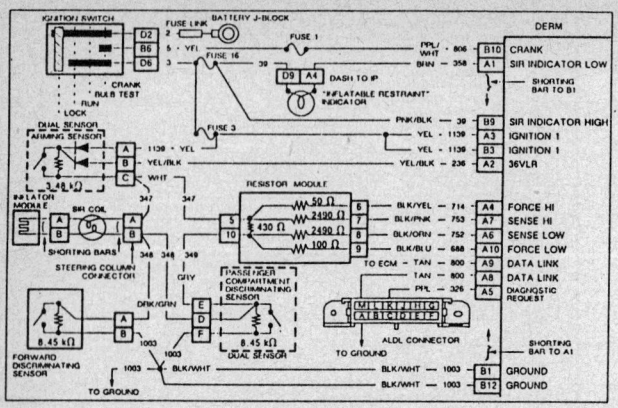

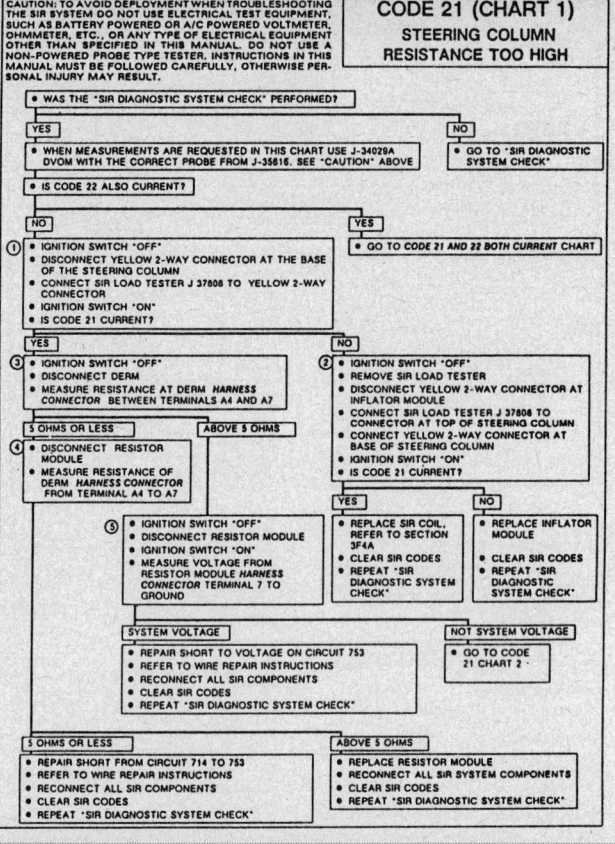

CODE 21 (CHART 1)

STEERING COLUMN RESISTANCE TOO HIGH

Test Conditions:

Tested once each ignition cycle during the "Steering Column Resistance Test" if: 1) No faults are detected during "Turn–on"; 2) No faults are detected during "Continuous Monitoring" for 1 second; 3) No Crank signal present.

Failure Conditions:

Code 21 will set if the combined resistance of the Inflator Module, SIR Coil, harness wiring and connector terminal contact in the steering column is greater than a specified value.

Conditions To Clear:

Current Code 21 will be cleared each time the Ignition Switch is turned OFF and the fault is corrected.

Action Taken:

DERM turns ON the "INFLATABLE RESTRAINT" indicator lamp.

Description:

The DERM injects a current of 75 milliamperes through the steering column from the Force Hi output

(terminal A4) to the Force Low input (terminal A10). By monitoring the voltage at the Sense Hi input (terminal A7) and the Sense Low input (terminal A6) the DERM calculates the combined resistance of the Inflator Module, SIR Coil, harness wiring (circuits 347, 348 or 349) and connector terminal contact in the steering column. Code 21 will be set if the resistance is greater than a specified value or the 100 ohm resistor within the Resistor Module is shorted.

Notes on Fault Tree:

1) Checks if fault is in steering column. The SIR Load Tester simulates the resistance of good steering column wiring and components.

2) Determines if fault is in Inflator Module or in the SIR Coil. The SIR Load Tester simulates the resistance of a good Inflator Module.

3) Checks for short in harness or Resistor Module.

4) Determines if short is in harness or Resistor Module.

5) Checks for short to voltage on circuit 753.

Fig. 73   Code 21 chart 1 diagnosis. Deville & Fleetwood

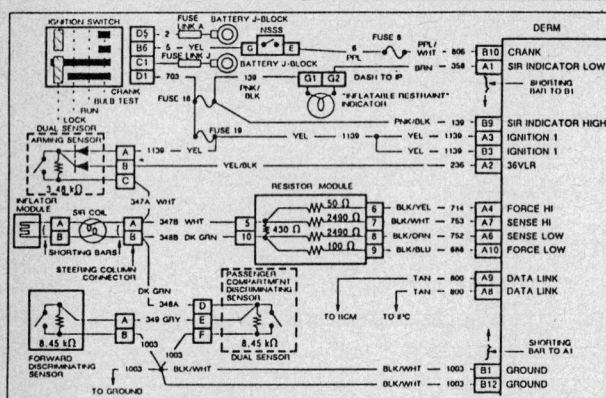

CODE 21 (CHART 1)

STEERING COLUMN RESISTANCE TOO HIGH

Test Conditions:

Tested once each ignition cycle during the "Steering Column Resistance Test" if: 1) No faults are detected during "Turn–on"; 2) No faults are detected during "Continuous Monitoring" for 1 second; 3) No Crank signal present.

Failure Conditions:

Code 21 will set if the combined resistance of the Inflator Module, SIR Coil, harness wiring and connector terminal contact in the steering column is greater than a specified value.

Conditions To Clear:

Current Code 21 will be cleared each time the Ignition Switch is turned OFF and the fault is corrected.

Action Taken:

Description:

The DERM injects a current of 75 milliamperes through the steering column from the Force Hi output

(terminal A4) to the Force Low input (terminal A10). By monitoring the voltage at the Sense Hi input (terminal A7) and the Sense Low input (terminal A6) the DERM calculates the combined resistance of the Inflator Module, SIR Coil, harness wiring (circuits 347A, 348A) and connector terminal contact in the steering column. Code 21 will set if the resistance is greater than a specified value or the 100 ohm resistors within the Resistor Module is shorted.

Notes on Fault Tree:

1) Checks if fault is in steering column. The SIR Load Tester simulates the resistance of good steering column wiring and components.

2) Determines if fault is in Inflator Module or in the SIR Coil. The SIR Load Tester simulates the resistance of a good Inflator Module.

3) Checks for short in harness or Resistor Module.

4) Determines if short is in harness or Resistor Module.

Fig. 74   Code 21 chart 1 diagnosis. Eldorado, Seville, Toronado & Trofeo

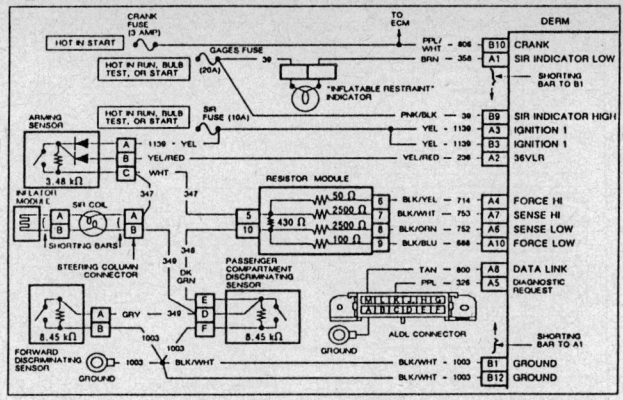

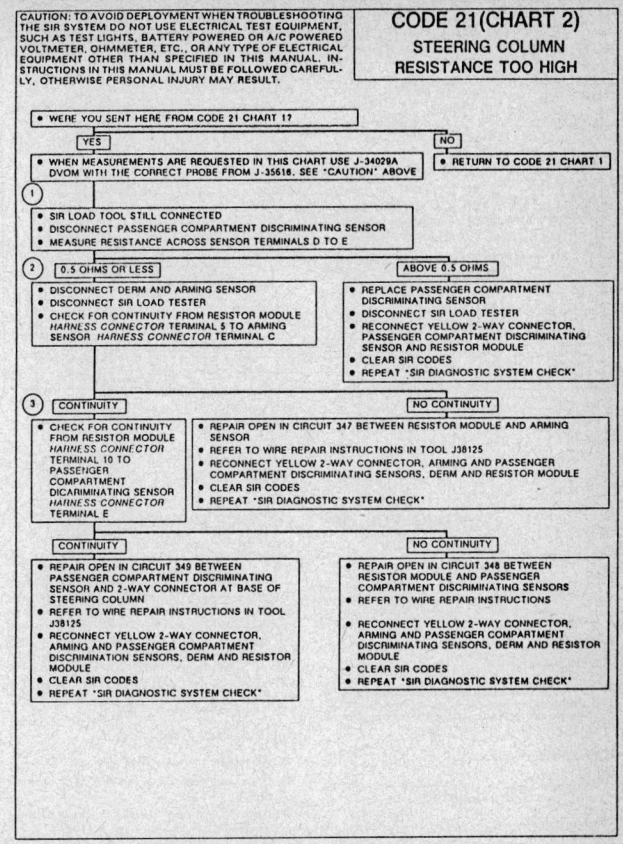

CAUTION: TO AVOID DEPLOYMENT WHEN TROUBLESHOOTING THE SIR SYSTEM DO NOT USE ELECTRICAL TEST EQUIPMENT, SUCH AS TEST LIGHTS, BATTERY POWERED OR A/C POWERED VOLTMETER, OHMMETER, ETC., OR ANY TYPE OF ELECTRICAL EQUIPMENT OTHER THAN SPECIFIED IN THIS MANUAL. IN-STRUCTIONS IN THIS MANUAL MUST BE FOLLOWED CAREFULLY, OTHERWISE PERSONAL INJURY MAY RESULT.

CODE 21 (CHART 2)
STEERING COLUMN RESISTANCE TOO HIGH

CODE 21 (CHART 2)

STEERING COLUMN RESISTANCE TOO HIGH

Test Conditions:

Tested once each ignition cycle during the "Steering Column Resistance Test" if: 1) No faults are detected during "Turn-on"; 2) No faults are detected during "Continuous Monitoring" for 1 second; 3) No Crank signal present.

Failure Conditions:

Code 21 will set if the combined resistance of the Inflator Module, SIR Coil, harness wiring and connector terminal contact in the steering column is greater than a specified value.

Conditions To Clear:

Current Code 21 will be cleared each time the Ignition Switch is turned OFF.

Action Taken:

DERM turns ON the "INFLATABLE RESTRAINT" indicator lamp.

Description:

The DERM injects a current of 75 milliamperes through the steering column from the Force Hi output (terminal A4) to the Force Low input (terminal A10). By monitoring the voltage at the Sense Hi input (terminal A7) and the Sense Low input (terminal A6) the DERM calculates the combined resistance of the Inflator Module, SIR Coil, harness wiring (circuits 347, 348 and 349) and connector terminal contact in the steering column. Code 21 will set if the resistance is greater than a specified value or the 100 ohm resistors within the Resistor Module is shorted.

Notes on Fault Tree:

1) Checks for resistance in Passenger Compartment Discriminating Sensor Dual Sensor between terminals D and E.

2) Checks for an open in circuit 347 between the Resistor Module and the Arming Sensor.

3) Checks for an open in circuit 348 between the Resistor Module and the Passenger Compartment Discriminating Sensor.

Fig. 75   Code 21 chart 2 diagnosis. Camaro & Firebird

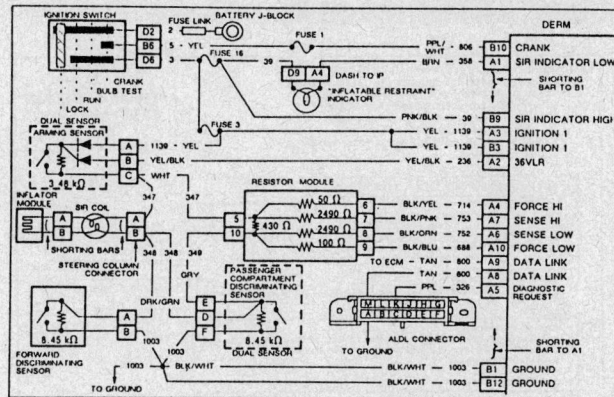

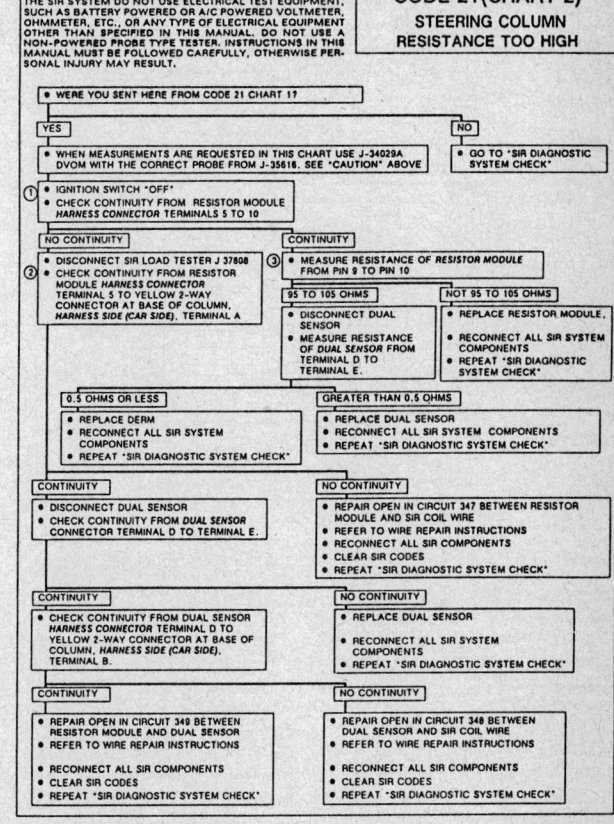

CAUTION: TO AVOID DEPLOYMENT WHEN TROUBLESHOOTING THE SIR SYSTEM DO NOT USE ELECTRICAL TEST EQUIPMENT, SUCH AS BATTERY POWERED OR A/C POWERED VOLTMETER, OHMMETER, ETC., OR ANY TYPE OF ELECTRICAL EQUIPMENT OTHER THAN SPECIFIED IN THIS MANUAL. DO NOT USE A NON-POWERED PROBE TYPE TESTER. INSTRUCTIONS IN THIS MANUAL MUST BE FOLLOWED CAREFULLY, OTHERWISE PERSONAL INJURY MAY RESULT.

CODE 21 (CHART 2)
STEERING COLUMN RESISTANCE TOO HIGH

CODE 21 (CHART 2)

STEERING COLUMN RESISTANCE TOO HIGH

Test Conditions:

Tested once each ignition cycle during the "Steering Column Resistance Test" if: 1) No faults are detected during "Turn-on"; 2) No faults are detected during "Continuous Monitoring" for 1 second; 3) No Crank signal present.

Failure Conditions:

Code 21 will set if the combined resistance of the Inflator Module, SIR Coil, harness wiring and connector terminal contact in the steering column is greater than a specified value.

Conditions To Clear:

Current Code 21 will be cleared each time the Ignition Switch is turned OFF and the fault is corrected.

Action Taken:

DERM turns ON the "INFLATABLE RESTRAINT" indicator lamp.

Description:

The DERM injects a current of 75 milliamperes through the steering column from the Force Hi output (terminal A4) to the Force Low input (terminal A10). By monitoring the voltage at the Sense Hi input (terminal A7) and the Sense Low input (terminal A6) the DERM calculates the combined resistance of the Inflator Module, SIR Coil, harness wiring (circuits 347, 348 or 349) and connector terminal contact in the steering column. Code 21 will set if the resistance is greater than a specified value or the 100 ohm resistor within the Resistor Module is shorted.

Notes on Fault Tree:

1) Checks for open circuit in circuit 347, 348, 349 or Dual Sensor.

2) Determines if open circuit is in circuit 347.

3) Checks 100 ohm resistor in resistor module.

Fig. 76   Code 21 chart 2 diagnosis. Deville & Fleetwood

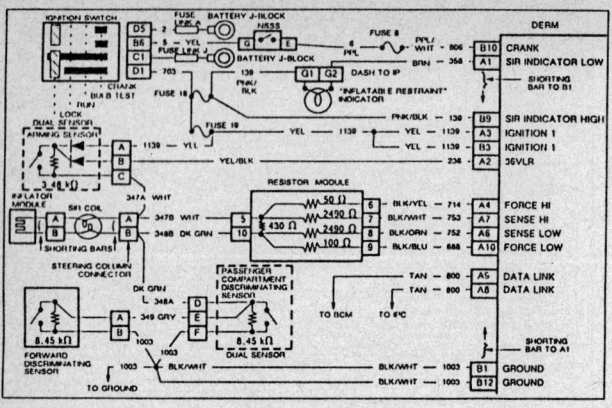

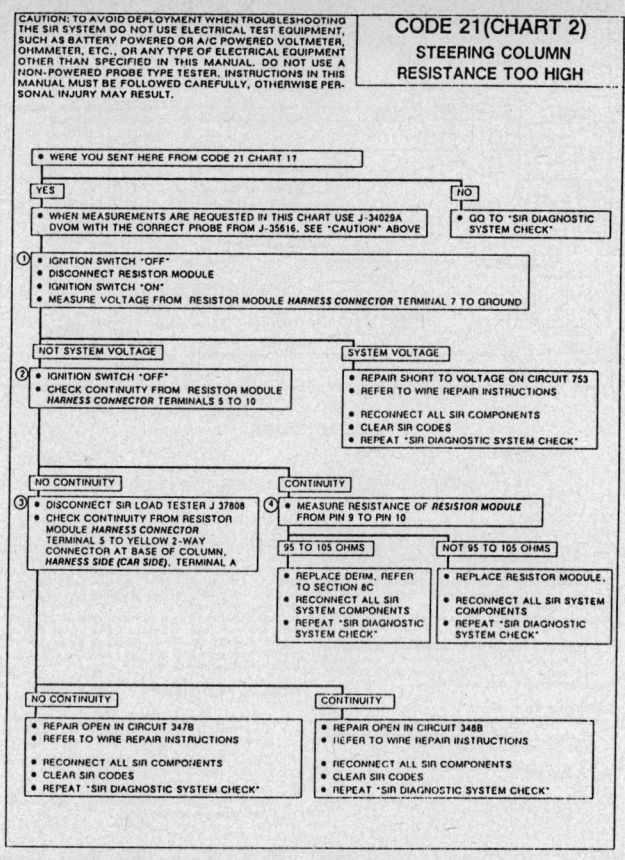

CODE 21 (CHART 2)

STEERING COLUMN RESISTANCE TOO HIGH

Test Conditions:

Tested once each ignition cycle during the "Steering Column Resistance Test" if: 1) No faults are detected during "Turn-on"; 2) No faults are detected during "Continuous Monitoring" for 1 second; 3) No Crank signal present.

Failure Conditions:

Code 21 will set if the combined resistance of the Inflator Module, SIR Coil, harness wiring and connector terminal contact in the steering column is greater than a specified value.

Conditions To Clear:

Current Code 21 will be cleared each time the Ignition Switch is turned OFF.

Action Taken:

DERM turns ON the "INFLATABLE RESTRAINT" indicator lamp.

Description:

The DERM injects a current of 75 milliamperes through the steering column from the Force Hi output (terminal A4) to the Force Low input (terminal A10). By monitoring the voltage at the Sense Hi input (terminal A7) and the Sense Low input (terminal A6) the DERM calculates the combined resistance of the Inflator Module, SIR Coil and connector terminal contact in the steering column. Code 21 will set if the resistance is greater than a specified value or the 100 ohm resistor within the Resistor Module is shorted.

Notes on Fault Tree:

1) Checks for short to voltage on circuit 753.

2) Checks for open circuit in circuit 347B or circuit 348B.

3) Determines if open circuit is in circuit 347B or circuit 348B.

4) Checks 100 ohm resistor in resistor module.

Fig. 77   Code 21 chart 2 diagnosis. Eldorado, Seville, Toronado & Trofeo

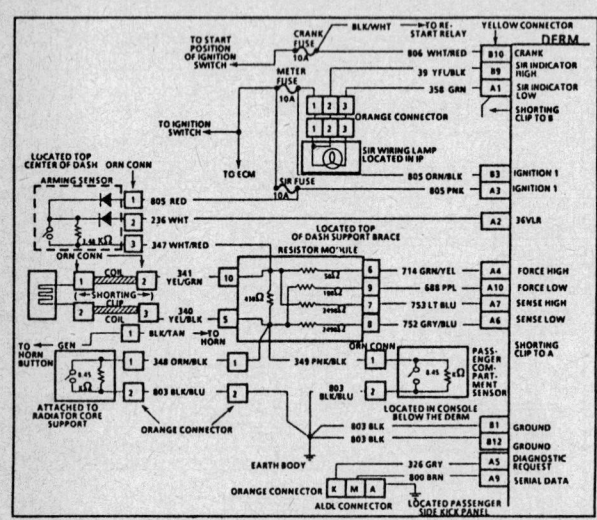

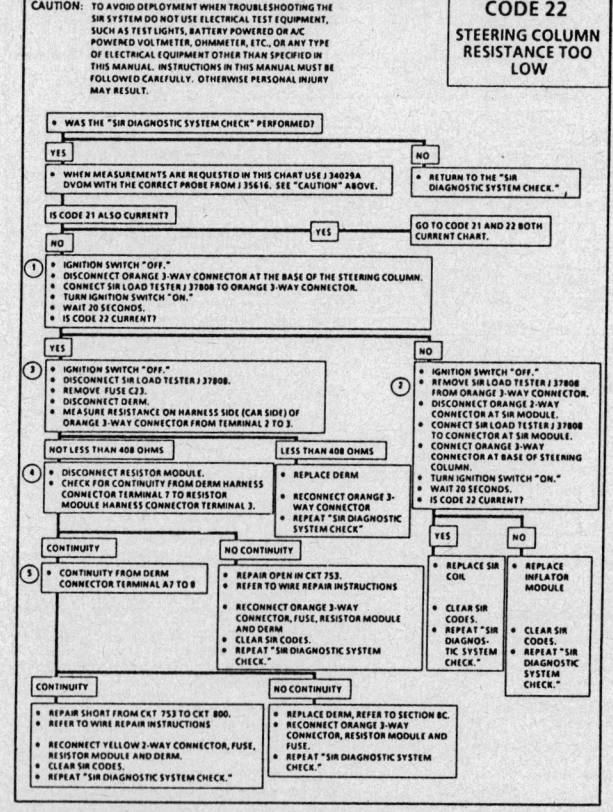

CODE 22

STEERING COLUMN RESISTANCE TOO LOW

Test Conditions:

Tested once each ignition cycle during the "Steering Column Resistance Test" if: 1) No faults are detected during "Turn-On"; 2) No faults are detected during "Continuous Monitoring" for 1 second; 3) No Crank signal present.

Failure Conditions:

Code 22 will set if the combined resistance of the Inflator Module, SIR Coil, harness wiring and connector contact in the steering column is greater than a specified value.

Conditions To Clear:

Current Code 22 will be cleared each time the Ignition Switch is turned OFF.

Action Taken:

DERM turns "ON" the "INFLATABLE RESTRAINT" indicator lamp.

Description:

The DERM injects a current of 75 milliamperes through the steering column from the Force Hi output

terminal "A4" to the Force Low input terminal "A10" by monitoring the voltage at the Sense Hi input terminal "A7" and the Sense Low input terminal "A6" the DERM calculates the combined resistance of the Inflator Module, SIR Coil harness wiring (CKTs 347, 348 and 349) and connector terminal contact in the steering column. Code 22 will set if:
- The steering column resistance is less than a specified value.
- The 430 ohm resistor in the Resistor Module is shorted.
- The resistance of the 100 ohm resistor in the Resistor Module is too high.
- The high side of the deployment loop is shorted to the low side of the deployment loop.

Notes on Fault Tree:

1. Checks if fault is in steering column. The SIR Load Tester J 37808 simulates the resistance of good steering column wiring and components.
2. Determines if fault is in Inflator Module or in the SIR Coil. The SIR Load Tester J 37808 simulates the resistance of a good Inflator Module. Use adapter kit J 37808-50.
3. Determines if fault is on deployment loop side or DERM side of resistor module.
4. Checks for open in Sense Hi (circuit 753).
5. Checks for an open or shorted Resistor Module.

Fig. 78   Code 22 diagnosis. Storm

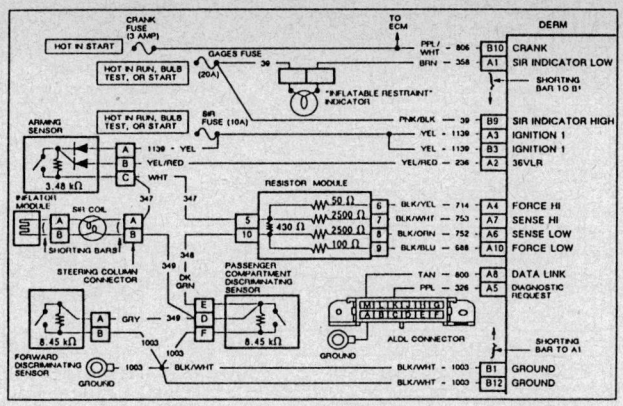

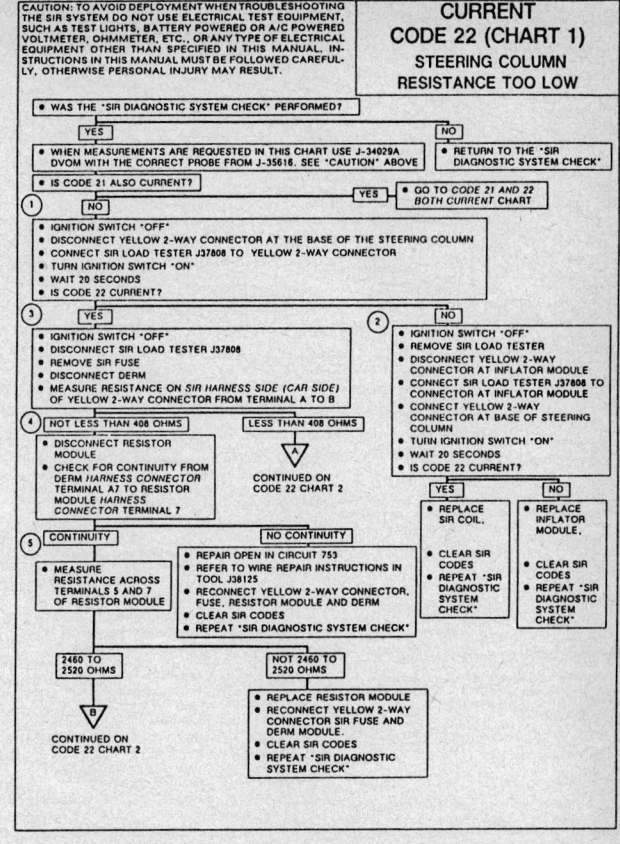

CURRENT CODE 22 (CHART 1) STEERING COLUMN RESISTANCE TOO LOW

CODE 22 (CHART 1)

STEERING COLUMN RESISTANCE TOO LOW

Test Conditions:

Tested once each ignition cycle during the "Steering Column Resistance Test" if: 1) No faults are detected during "Turn-on"; 2) No faults are detected during "Continuous Monitoring" for 1 second; 3) No Crank signal present.

Failure Conditions:

Code 22 will set if the combined resistance of the Inflator Module, SIR Coil, harness wiring and connector terminal contact in the steering column is less than a specified value.

Conditions To Clear:

Current Code 22 will be cleared each time the Ignition Switch is turned OFF.

Action Taken:

DERM turns on the "INFLATABLE RESTRAINT" indicator lamp.

Description:

The DERM injects a current of 75 milliamperes through the steering column from the Force Hi output

(terminal A4) to the Force Low input (terminal A10). By monitoring the voltage at the Sense Hi input (terminal A7) and the Sense Low input (terminal A6) the DERM calculates the combined resistance of the Inflator Module, SIR Coil and connector terminal contact in the steering column. Code 22 will set if:
- The steering column resistance is less than a specified value.
- The 430 ohm resistor in the Resistor Module is shorted.
- The resistance of the 100 ohm resistor in the Resistor Module is too high.
- The high side of the deployment loop is shorted to the low side of the deployment loop.

Notes on Fault Tree:
1) Checks if fault is in steering column. The SIR Load Tester J37808 simulates the resistance of good steering column wiring and components.
2) Determines if fault is in Inflator Module or in the SIR Coil. The SIR Load Tester J37808 simulates the resistance of a good Inflator Module.
3) Determines if fault is on deployment loop side or DERM side of resistor module.
4) Checks for open in Sense Hi (circuit 753)
5) Checks for an open or shorted Resistor Module.

Fig. 79   Code 22 chart 1 diagnosis. Camaro & Firebird

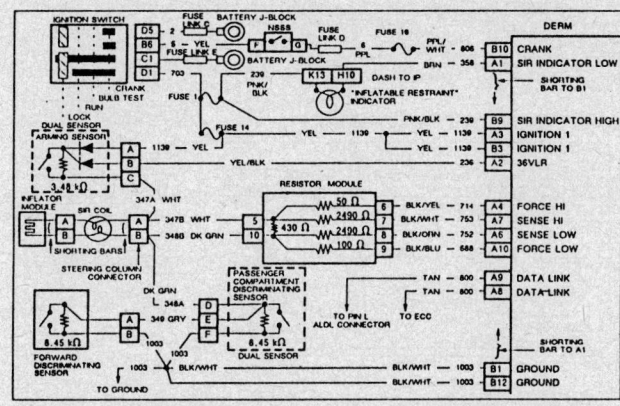

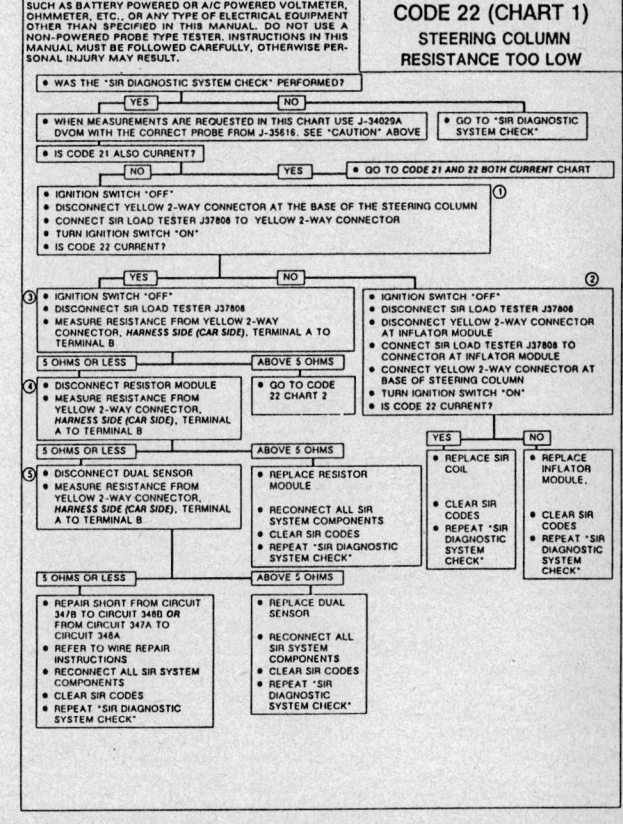

CODE 22 (CHART 1) STEERING COLUMN RESISTANCE TOO LOW

CODE 22 (CHART 1)

STEERING COLUMN RESISTANCE TOO LOW

Test Conditions:

Tested once each ignition cycle during the "Steering Column Resistance Test" if: 1) No faults are detected during "Turn-on"; 2) No faults are detected during "Continuous Monitoring" for 1 second; 3) No Crank signal present.

Failure Conditions:

Code 22 will set if the combined resistance of the Inflator Module, SIR Coil, harness wiring and connector terminal contact in the steering column is less than a specified value.

Conditions To Clear:

Current Code 22 will be cleared each time the Ignition Switch is turned OFF.

Action Taken:

DERM turns on the "INFLATABLE RESTRAINT" indicator lamp.

Description:

The DERM injects a current of 75 milliamperes through the steering column from the Force Hi output

(terminal A4) to the Force Low input (terminal A10). By monitoring the voltage at the Sense Hi input (terminal A7) and the Sense Low input (terminal A6) the DERM calculates the combined resistance of the Inflator Module, SIR Coil and connector terminal contact in the steering column. Code 22 will set if:
- The steering column resistance is less than a specified value.
- The 430 ohm resistor in the Resistor Module is shorted.
- The resistance of the 100 ohm resistor in the Resistor Module is too high.
- The high side of the deployment loop is shorted to the low side of the deployment loop.

Notes on Fault Tree:
1) Checks if fault is in steering column. The SIR Load Tester J37808 simulates the resistance of good steering column wiring and components.
2) Checks if fault is in Inflator Module or in the SIR Coil. The SIR Load Tester J37808 simulates the resistance of a good Inflator Module.
3) Checks if fault is on deployment loop side or DERM side of resistor module.
4) Checks if the 430 ohm resistor in the Resistor Module is shorted.
5) Checks if fault is in Dual Sensor or in wiring harness.

Fig. 80   Code 22 chart 1 diagnosis. Riviera & Reatta

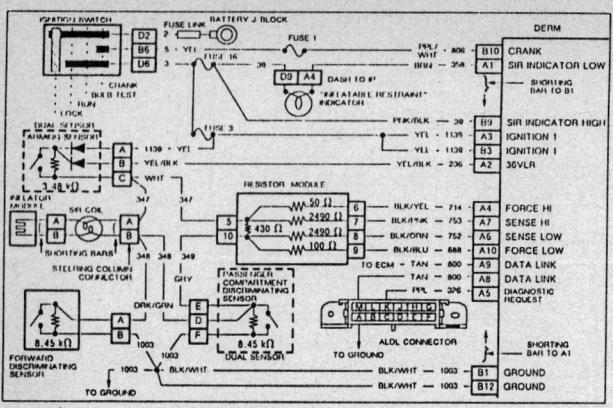

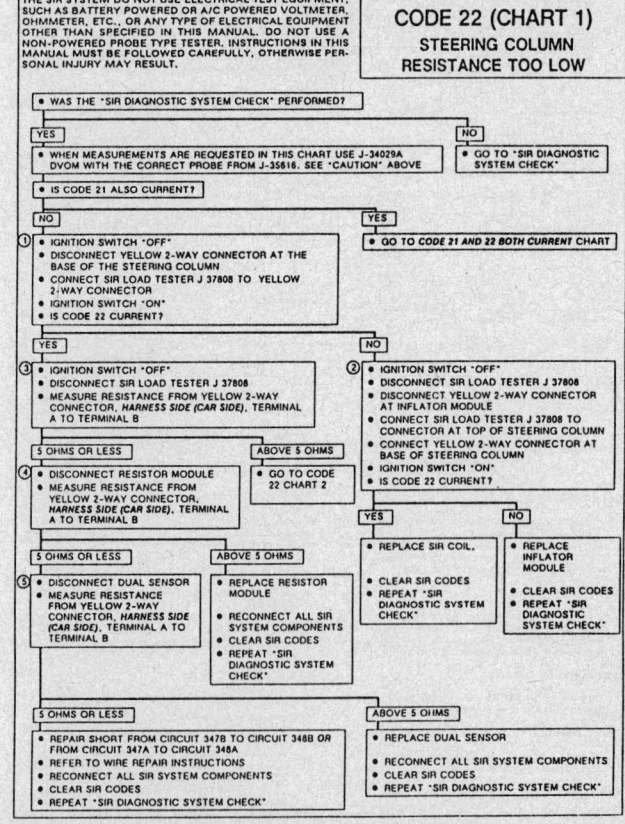

CODE 22 (CHART 1)
STEERING COLUMN RESISTANCE TOO LOW

Test Conditions:

Tested once each ignition cycle during the "Steering Column Resistance Test" if: 1) No faults are detected during "Turn-on"; 2) No faults are detected during "Continuous Monitoring" for 1 second; 3) No Crank signal present.

Failure Conditions:

Code 22 will set if the combined resistance of the Inflator Module, SIR Coil, harness wiring and connector terminal contact in the steering column is less than a specified value.

Conditions To Clear:

Current Code 22 will be cleared each time the Ignition Switch is turned OFF.

Action Taken:

DERM turns on the "INFLATABLE RESTRAINT" indicator lamp.

Description:

The DERM injects a current of 75 milliamperes through the steering column from the Force Hi output (terminal A4) to the Force Low input (terminal A10). By monitoring the voltage at the Sense Hi input (terminal

A7) and the Sense Low input (terminal A6) the DERM calculates the combined resistance of the Inflator Module, SIR Coil and connector terminal contact in the steering column. Code 22 will set if:

- The steering column resistance is less than a specified value.
- The 430 ohm resistor in the Resistor Module is shorted.
- The resistance of the 100 ohm resistor in the Resistor Module is too high.
- The high side of the deployment loop is shorted to the low side of the deployment loop.

Notes on Fault Tree:

1) Checks if fault is in steering column. The SIR Load Tester J 37808 simulates the resistance of good steering column wiring and components.

2) Checks if fault is in Inflator Module or in the SIR Coil. The SIR Load Tester J 37808 simulates the resistance of a good Inflator Module.

3) Checks if fault is on deployment loop side or DERM side of resistor module.

4) Checks if the 430 ohm resistor in the Resistor Module is shorted.

5) Checks if fault is in Dual Sensor or in wiring harness.

Fig. 81   Code 22 chart 1 diagnosis. Deville & Fleetwood

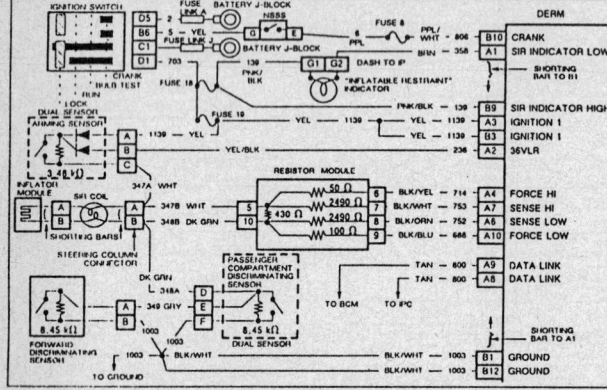

CODE 22 (CHART 1)
STEERING COLUMN RESISTANCE TOO LOW

Test Conditions:

Tested once each ignition cycle during the "Steering Column Resistance Test" if: 1) No faults are detected during "Turn-on"; 2) No faults are detected during "Continuous Monitoring" for 1 second; 3) No Crank signal present.

Failure Conditions:

Code 22 will set if the combined resistance of the Inflator Module, SIR Coil, harness wiring and connector terminal contact in the steering column is less than a specified value.

Conditions To Clear:

Current Code 22 will be cleared each time the Ignition Switch is turned OFF.

Action Taken:

DERM turns on the "INFLATABLE RESTRAINT" indicator lamp.

Description:

The DERM injects a current of 75 milliamperes through the steering column from the Force Hi output (terminal A4) to the Force Low input (terminal A10). By monitoring the voltage at the Sense Hi input (terminal

A7) and the Sense Low input (terminal A6) the DERM calculates the combined resistance of the Inflator Module, SIR Coil and connector terminal contact in the steering column. Code 22 will set if:

- The steering column resistance is less than a specified value.
- The 430 ohm resistor in the Resistor Module is shorted.
- The resistance of the 100 ohm resistor in the Resistor Module is too high.
- The high side of the deployment loop is shorted to the low side of the deployment loop.

Notes on Fault Tree:

1) Checks if fault is in steering column. The SIR Load Tester J 37808 simulates the resistance of good steering column wiring and components.

2) Checks if fault is in Inflator Module or in the SIR Coil. The SIR Load Tester J 37808 simulates the resistance of a good Inflator Module.

3) Checks if fault is on deployment loop side or DERM side of resistor module.

4) Checks if the 430 ohm resistor in the Resistor Module is shorted.

5) Checks if fault is in Dual Sensor or in wiring harness.

Fig. 82   Code 22 chart 1 diagnosis. Eldorado, Seville, Toronado & Trofeo

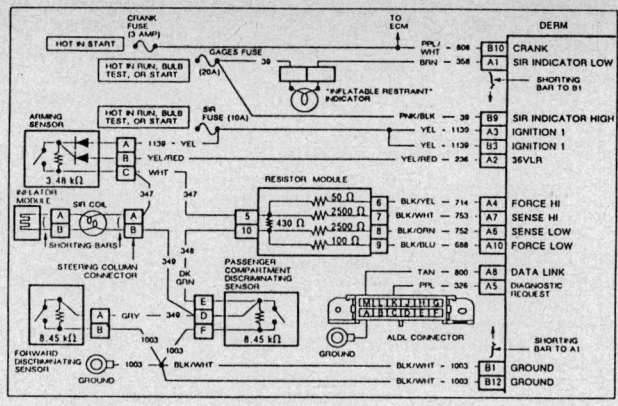

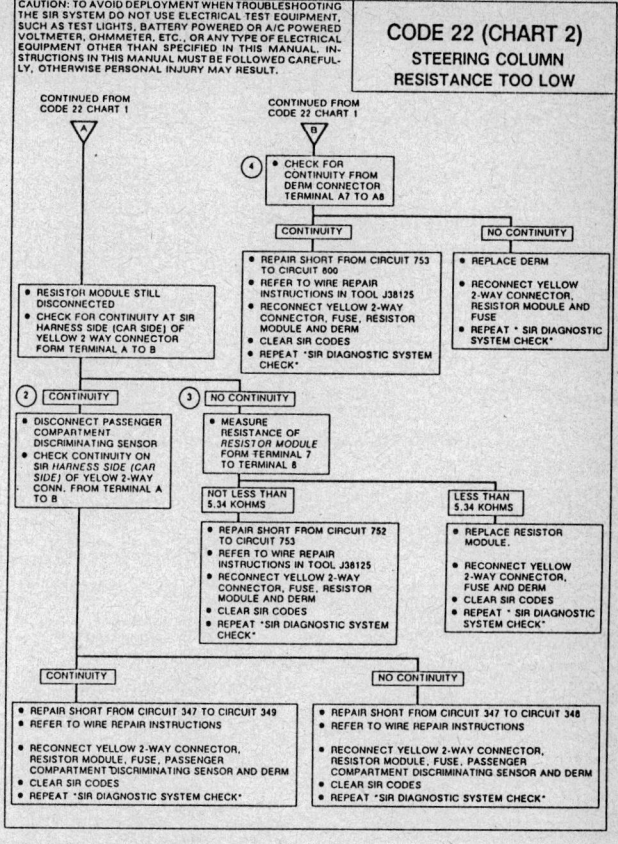

CODE 22 (CHART 2)

STEERING COLUMN RESISTANCE TOO LOW

Test Conditions:

Tested once each ignition cycle during the "Steering Column Resistance Test" if: 1) No faults are detected during "Turn-on"; 2) No faults are detected during "Continuous Monitoring" for 1 second; 3) No Crank signal present.

Failure Conditions:

Code 22 will set if the combined resistance of the Inflator Module, SIR Coil, harness wiring and connector terminal contact in the steering column is less than a specified value ohms.

Conditions To Clear:

Current Code 22 will be cleared each time the Ignition Switch is turned OFF.

Action Taken:

DERM turns on the "INFLATABLE RESTRAINT" indicator lamp.

Description:

The DERM injects a current of 75 milliamperes through the steering column from the Force Hi output

(terminal A4) to the Force Low input (terminal A10). By monitoring the voltage at the Sense Hi input (terminal A7) and the Sense Low input (terminal A6) the DERM calculates the combined resistance of the Inflator Module, SIR Coil, harness wiring (circuits 347, 348 and 349) and connector terminal contact in the steering column. Code 22 will set if:
- The steering column resistance is less than a specified value ohms.
- The 430 ohm resistor in the Resistor Module is shorted.
- The resistance of the 100 ohm resistor in the Resistor Module is too high.
- The high side of the deployment loop is shorted to the low side of the deployment loop.

Notes on Fault Tree:

1) Determines if a short exists in wiring from resistor module to steering column or from resistor module to DERM.
2) Determines if short is with circuit 348 or circuit 349.
3) Determines if resistor module is defective or if Sense Hi wiring is shorted to Sense Low wiring.
4) Checks for short between Sense HI and Data line.

Fig. 83 Code 22 chart 2 diagnosis. Camaro & Firebird

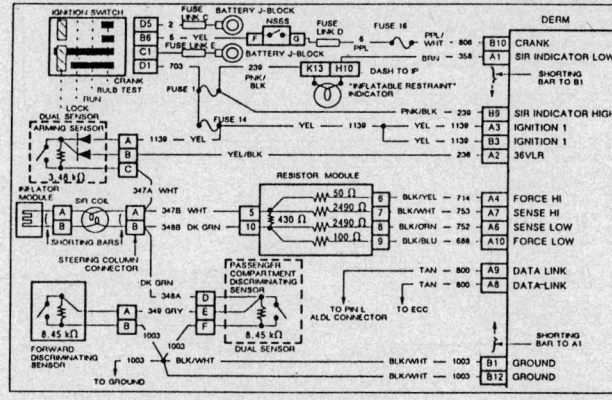

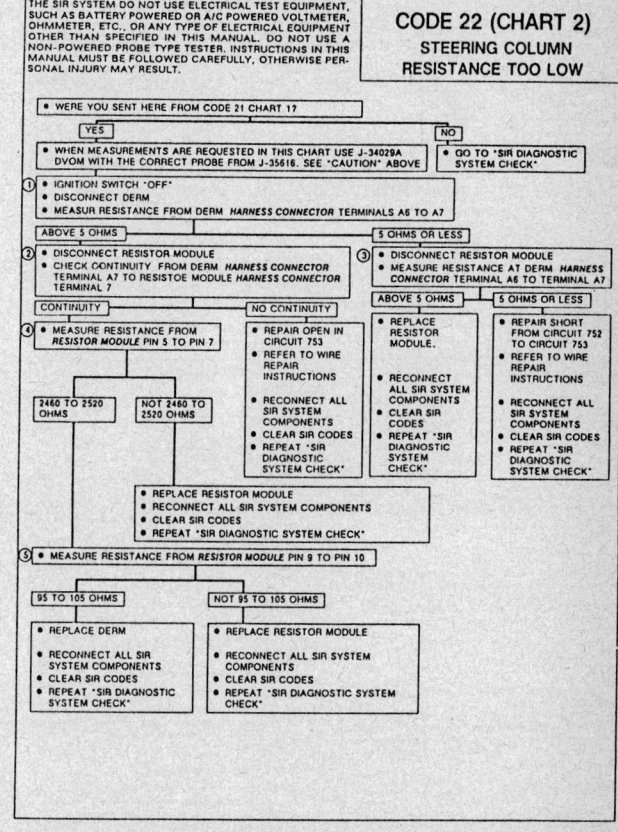

CODE 22 (CHART 2)

STEERING COLUMN RESISTANCE TOO LOW

Test Conditions:

Tested once each ignition cycle during the "Steering Column Resistance Test" if: 1) No faults are detected during "Turn-on"; 2) No faults are detected during "Continuous Monitoring" for 1 second; 3) No Crank signal present.

Failure Conditions:

Code 22 will set if the combined resistance of the Inflator Module, SIR Coil, harness wiring and connector terminal contact in the steering column is less than a specified value ohms.

Conditions To Clear:

Current Code 22 will be cleared each time the Ignition Switch is turned OFF.

Action Taken:

DERM turns on the "INFLATABLE RESTRAINT" indicator lamp.

Description:

The DERM injects a current of 75 milliamperes through the steering column from the Force Hi output

(terminal A4) to the Force Low input (terminal A10). By monitoring the voltage at the Sense Hi input (terminal A7) and the Sense Low input (terminal A6) the DERM calculates the combined resistance of the Inflator Module, SIR Coil and connector terminal contact in the steering column. Code 22 will set if:
- The steering column resistance is less than a specified value ohms.
- The 430 ohm resistor in the Resistor Module is shorted.
- The resistance of the 100 ohm resistor in the Resistor Module is too high.
- The high side of the deployment loop is shorted to the low side of the deployment loop.

Notes on Fault Tree:

1) Checks if a short exists in Resistor Module or in wiring from Resistor Module to DERM.
2) Checks if an open circuit exists in the Sense High circuit (Circuit 753).
3) Checks if short causing fault is in the Resistor Module or in the wiring harness.
4) Checks if the 2490 ohm resistor in the Resistor Module is defective.
5) Checks if the 100 ohm resistor in the Resistor Module is defective.

Fig. 84 Code 22 chart 2 diagnosis. Riviera & Reatta

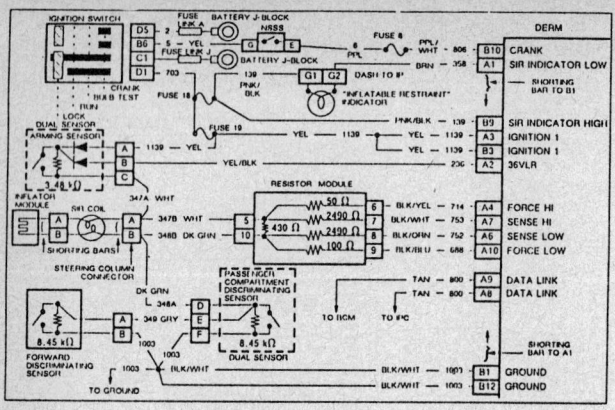

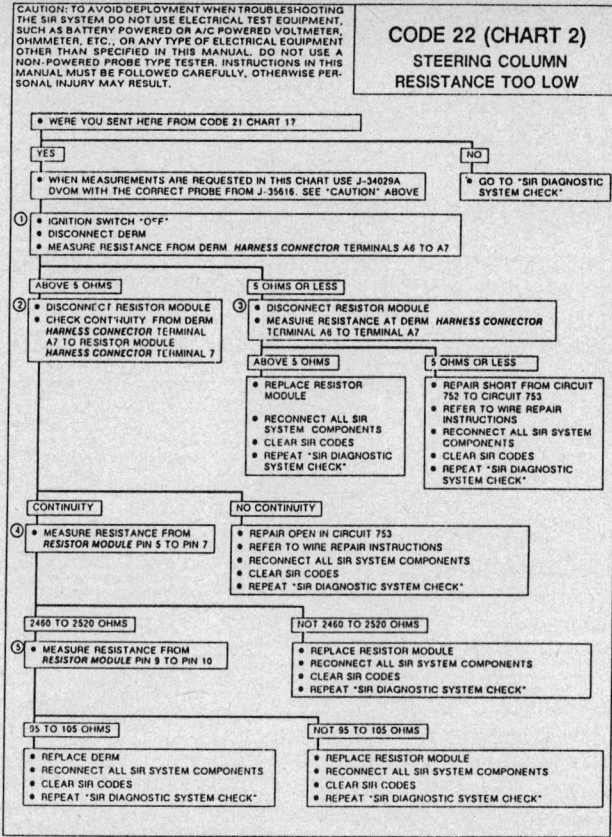

CODE 22 (CHART 2)

STEERING COLUMN RESISTANCE TOO LOW

Test Conditions:

Tested once each ignition cycle during the "Steering Column Resistance Test" if: 1) No faults are detected during "Turn-on"; 2) No faults are detected during "Continuous Monitoring" for 1 second; 3) No Crank signal present.

Failure Conditions:

Code 22 will be set if the combined resistance of the Inflator Module, SIR Coil, harness wiring and connector terminal contact in the steering column is less than a specified value ohms.

Conditions To Clear:

Current Code 22 will be cleared each time the Ignition Switch is turned OFF.

Action Taken:

DERM turns on the "INFLATABLE RESTRAINT" indicator lamp.

Description:

The DERM injects a current of 75 milliamperes through the steering column from the Force Hi output (terminal A4) to the Force Low input (terminal A10). By monitoring the voltage at the Sense Hi input (terminal A7) and the Sense Low input (terminal A6) the DERM

calculates the combined resistance of the Inflator Module, SIR Coil and connector terminal contact in the steering column. Code 22 will set if:

- The steering column resistance is less than a specified value.
- The 430 ohm resistor in the Resistor Module is shorted.
- The resistance of the 100 ohm resistor in the Resistor Module is too high.
- The high side of the deployment loop is shorted to the low side of the deployment loop.

Notes on Fault Tree:

1) Checks if a short exists in Resistor Module or in wiring from Resistor Module to DERM.
2) Checks if an open circuit exists in the Sense High circuit (Circuit 753).
3) Checks if short causing fault is in the Resistor Module or in the wiring harness.
4) Checks if the 2490 ohm resistor in the Resistor Module is defective.
5) Checks if the 100 ohm resistor in the Resistor Module is defective.

Fig. 85   Code 22 chart 2 diagnosis. Deville, Fleetwood, Eldorado, Seville, Toronado & Trofeo

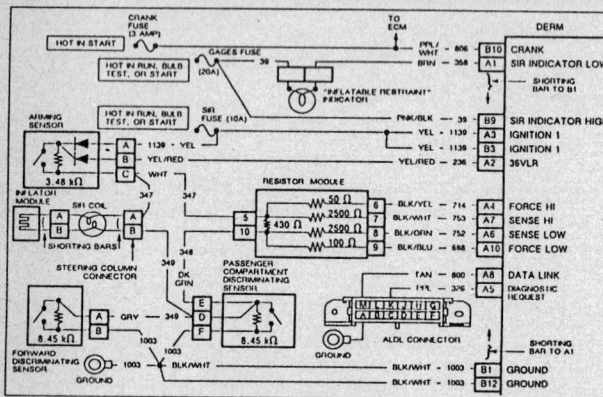

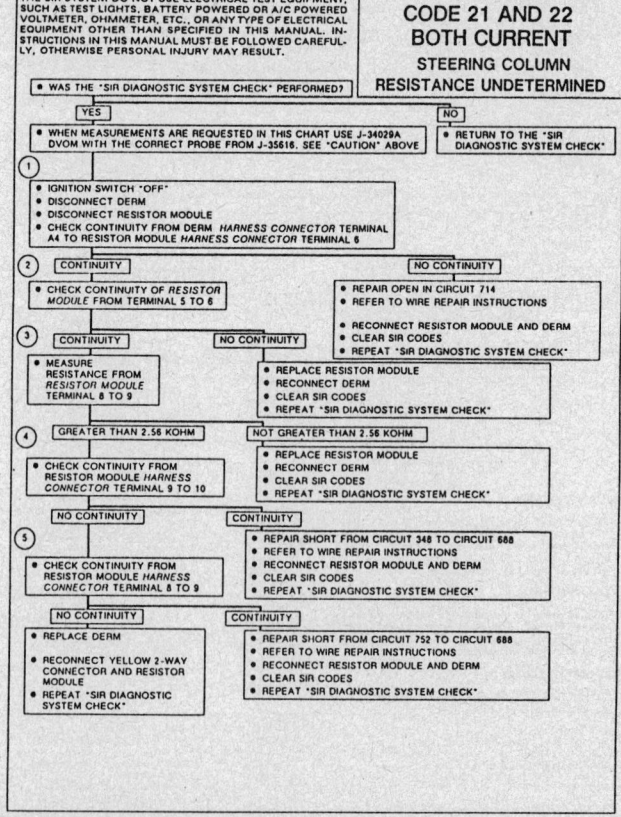

CODE 21 AND 22 BOTH CURRENT

STEERING COLUMN RESISTANCE UNDETERMINED

Test Conditions:

Tested once each ignition cycle during the "Steering Column Resistance Test" if: 1) No faults are detected during "Turn-on"; 2) No faults are detected during "Continuous Monitoring" for 1 second; 3) No Crank signal present.

Failure Conditions:

Code 21 and 22 will set if the voltage at the Sense Low input (terminal A6) is less than 5 volts during the first portion of the steering column resistance test. This will occur when the Force Hi output (terminal A4) is open and results in an undetermined steering column resistance.

Conditions To Clear:

Current Code 21 and 22 will be cleared each time the Ignition Switch is turned OFF.

Action Taken:

DERM turns on the "INFLATABLE RESTRAINT" indicator lamp.

Description:

The DERM injects a current of 75 milliamperes through the steering column from the Force Hi output (terminal A4) to the Force Low input (terminal A10). By monitoring the voltage at the Sense Hi input (terminal A7) and the Sense Low input (terminal A6) the DERM calculates the combined resistance of the Inflator Module, SIR Coil, harness wiring and connector terminal contact in the steering column. Codes 22 and 21 will set if the Force Hi output (terminal A4) is open.

Notes on Fault Tree:

1) Checks for open in Force Hi wiring.
2) Checks for open 50 ohm resistor in resistor module.
3) Checks for proper values in resistor module.
4) Checks for short in resistor module wiring harness.
5) Checks for short in resistor module wiring harness.

Fig. 86   Code 21 & 22 (both current) diagnosis. Camaro & Firebird

SUPPLEMENTAL INFLATABLE RESTRAINT SYSTEM

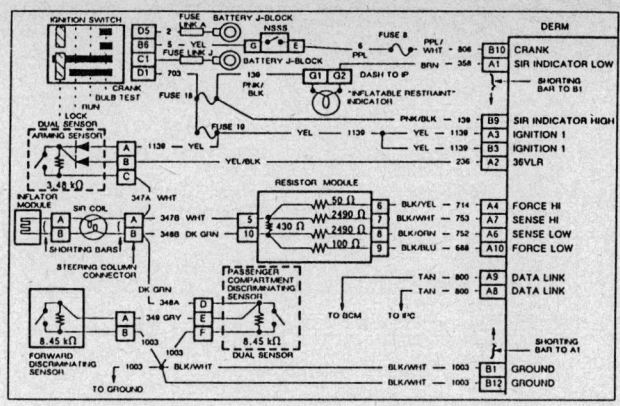

CODE 21 AND 22
BOTH CURRENT
STEERING COLUMN
RESISTANCE UNDETERMINED

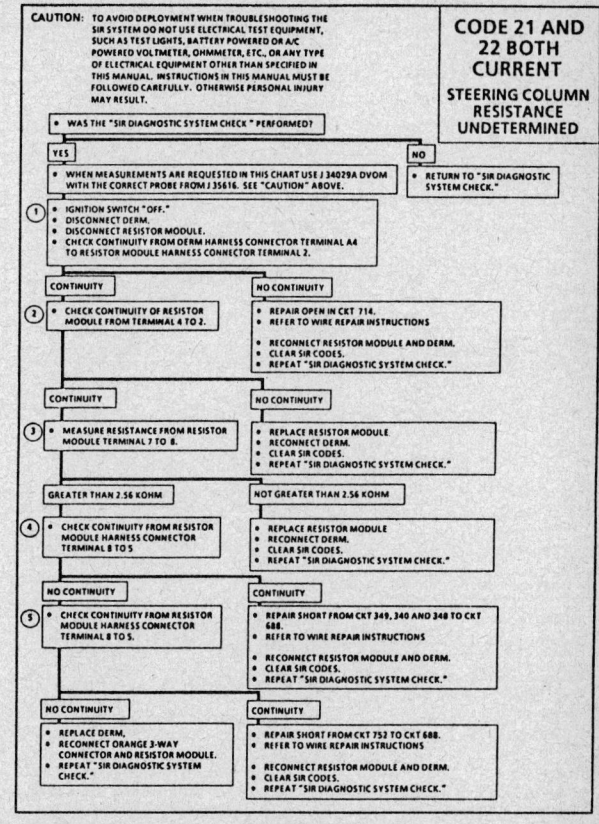

CODE 21 AND 22 BOTH CURRENT
STEERING COLUMN RESISTANCE UNDETERMINED

Test Conditions:

Tested once each ignition cycle during the "Steering Column Resistance Test" if: 1) No faults are detected during "Turn-on"; 2) No faults are detected during "Continuous Monitoring" for 1 second; 3) No Crank signal present.

Failure Conditions:

Code 21 and 22 will set if the voltage at the Sense Low input (terminal A6) is less than 5 volts during the first portion of the steering column resistance test. This will occur when the Force Hi output (terminal A4) is open and results in an undetermined steering column resistance.

Conditions To Clear:

Current Code 21 and 22 will be cleared each time the Ignition Switch is turned OFF.

Action Taken:

DERM turns on the "INFLATABLE RESTRAINT" indicator lamp.

Description:

The DERM injects a current of 75 milliamperes through the steering column from the Force Hi output (terminal A4) to the Force Low input (terminal A10). By monitoring the voltage at the Sense Hi input (terminal A7) and the Sense Low input (terminal A6) the DERM calculates the combined resistance of the Inflator Module, SIR Coil and connector terminal contact in the steering column. Codes 21 and 22 will set if the Force Hi output (terminal A4) is open.

Notes on Fault Tree:

1) Checks for open in Force Hi wiring.
2) Checks for open 50 ohm resistor in resistor module.
3) Checks for proper values in resistor module.
4) Checks for short in resistor module wiring harness.
5) Checks for short in resistor module wiring harness.

Fig. 87 Code 21 & 22 (both current) diagnosis. Deville, Fleetwood, Eldorado, Seville, Riviera, Reatta, Toronado & Trofeo

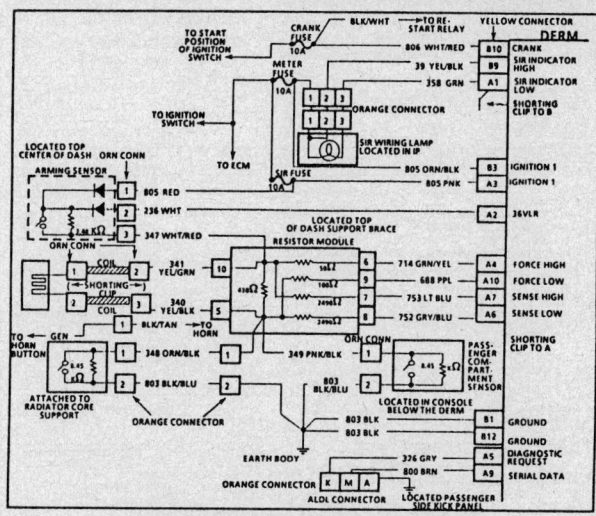

CODE 21 AND 22 BOTH CURRENT
STEERING COLUMN RESISTANCE UNDETERMINED

Test Conditions:

Tested once each ignition cycle during the "Steering Column Resistance Test" if: 1) No faults are detected during "Turn-ON"; 2) No faults are detected during "Continuous Monitoring" for 1 second; 3) No Crank signal present.

Failure Conditions:

Code 21 and 22 will set if the voltage at the Sense Low input terminal "A6" is less than 5 volts during the first portion of the steering column resistance test. This will occur when the Force Hi output terminal "A4" is open and results in an undetermined steering column resistance.

Conditions To Clear:

Current Code 21 and 22 will be cleared each time the Ignition Switch is turned "OFF."

Action Taken:

DERM turns "ON" the "INFLATABLE RESTRAINT" indicator lamp.

Description:

The DERM injects a current of 75 milliamperes through the steering column from the Force Hi output terminal "A4" to the Force Low input terminal "A10." By monitoring the voltage at the Sense Hi input terminal "A7" and the Sense Low input terminal "A6" the DERM calculates the combined resistance of the Inflator Module, SIR Coil, harness wiring and connector terminal contact in the steering column. Code 22 and 21 will set if the Force Hi output terminal "A4" is open.

Notes on Fault Tree:

1. Checks for opening Force Hi wiring.
2. Checks for open 50 ohm resistor in resistor module.
3. Checks for proper values in resistor module.
4. Checks for short in resistor module wiring harness.
5. Checks for short in resistor module wiring harness.

Fig. 88 Code 21 & 22 (both current) diagnosis. Storm

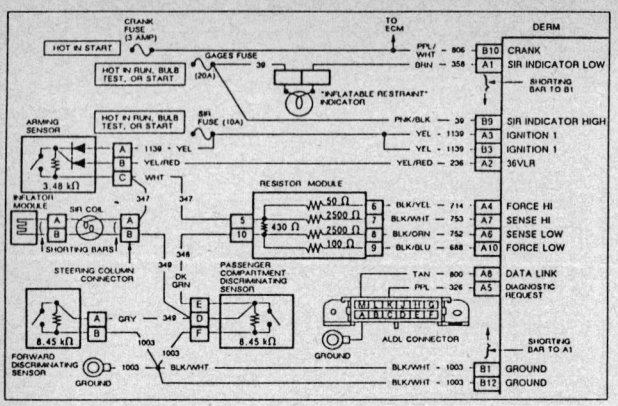

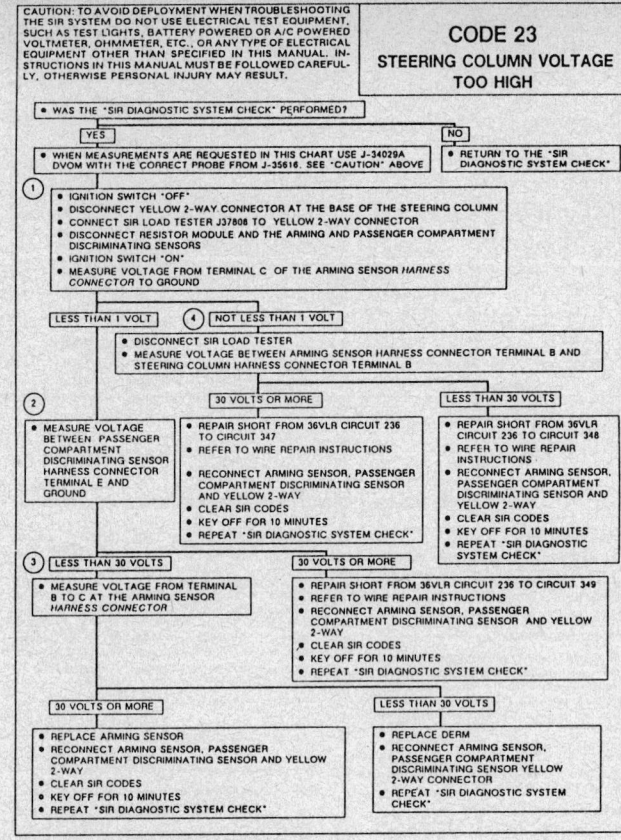

CODE 23

STEERING COLUMN VOLTAGE TOO HIGH

Test Condition:

Tested every 100 milliseconds during "Continuous Monitoring".

Failure Conditions:

Code 23 will set if the voltage at the Sense Low input (terminal A6) is greater than 78% of 36VLR output voltage for 500 milliseconds.

Conditions To Clear:

Current Code 23 will clear if the voltage at the Sense Low input (terminal A6) is between 41% and 61% of 36VLR output voltage for 500 milliseconds (5 consecutive "Continuous Monitoring" cycles) after Code 23 has been set.

Action Taken:

DERM turns on the "INFLATABLE RESTRAINT" indicator lamp.

Description:

Code 23 is set when the voltage at the Sense Low input (terminal A6) is greater than 78% of 36VLR output

voltage for 500 milliseconds during the "Continuous Monitoring" tests performed by the DERM. The "Continuous Monitoring" tests are performed by the DERM after the initial "Turn-on" tests are completed and are performed every 100 milliseconds while Ignition 1 voltage is present at the DERM. The "Coninuous Monitoring" tests check the continuity of the deployment loop from the 36VLR output of the DERM through the Arming Sensor, Inflator Module and the Discriminating Sensors to ground. Code 23 indicates a shorted Arming Sensor, shorted harness, or open grounds on both Discriminating Sensors.

Notes on Fault Tree:

1) Checks the 36VLR circuit for a short to the high side of the steering column (circuit 347).

2) Checks if the ground circuits on both Discriminating Sensors are open.

3) Checks the 36VLR circuit for a short to the low side of the steering column (circuit 348).

4) Checks the 36VLR circuit for a short to the low side of the steering column (circuit 349).

Fig. 89   Code 23 diagnosis. Camaro & Firebird

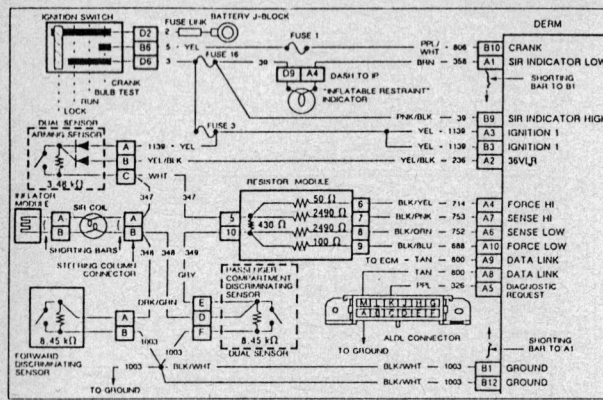

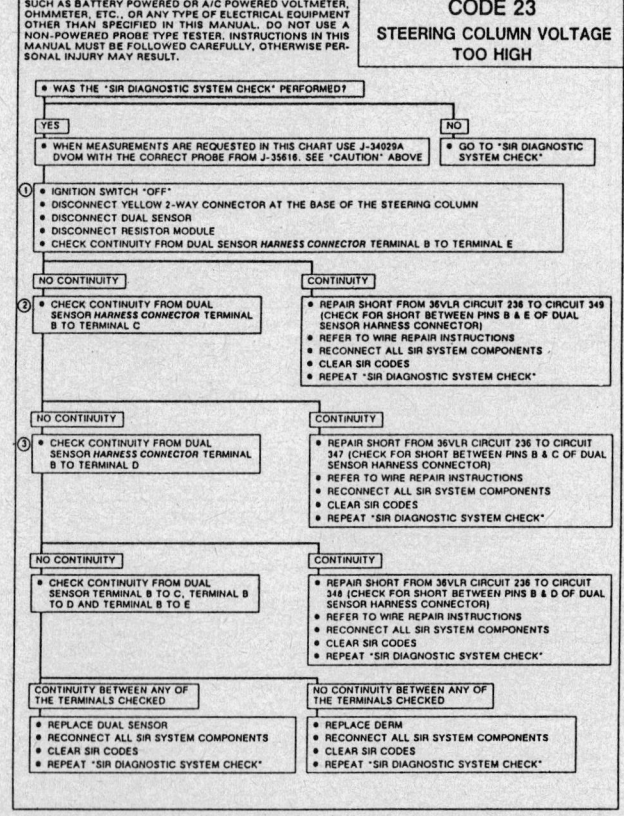

CODE 23

STEERING COLUMN VOLTAGE TOO HIGH

Test Condition:

Tested every 100 milliseconds during "Continuous Monitoring".

Failure Conditions:

Code 23 will set if the voltage at the Sense Low input (terminal A6) is greater than 78% of 36VLR output voltage for 500 milliseconds.

Conditions To Clear:

Current Code 23 will clear if the voltage at the Sense Low input (terminal A6) is between 41% and 61% of 36VLR output voltage for 500 milliseconds (5 consecutive "Continuous Monitoring" cycles) after Code 23 has been set.

Action Taken:

DERM turns on the "INFLATABLE RESTRAINT" indicator lamp.

Description:

Code 23 is set when the voltage at the Sense Low input (terminal A6) is greater than 78% of 36VLR output

voltage for 500 milliseconds during the "Continuous Monitoring" tests performed by the DERM. The "Continuous Monitoring" tests are performed by the DERM after the initial "Turn-on" tests are completed and are performed every 100 milliseconds while "IGNITION 1" voltage is present at the DERM. The "Continuous Monitoring" tests check the continuity of the deployment loop from the 36VLR output of the DERM through the Arming Sensor, Inflator Module and the Discriminating Sensors to ground. Code 23 indicates a shorted Arming Sensor, shorted harness, or open ground path on both Discriminating Sensors.

Notes on Fault Tree:

1) Checks the 36VLR circuit for a short to the low side of the steering column (circuit 349).

2) Checks the 36VLR circuit for a short to the high side of the steering column (circuit 347).

3) Checks the 36VLR circuit for a short to the low side of the steering column (circuit 348).

Fig. 90   Code 23 diagnosis. Deville & Fleetwood

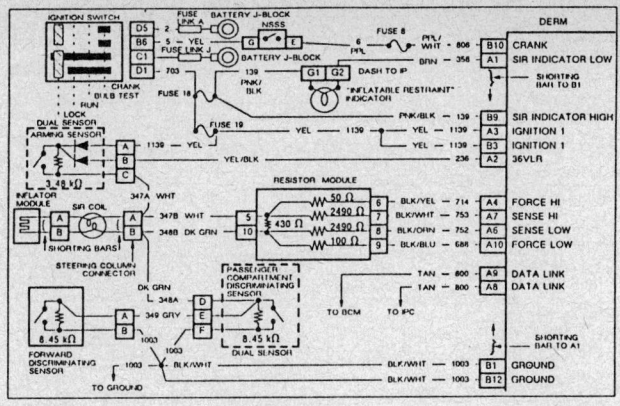

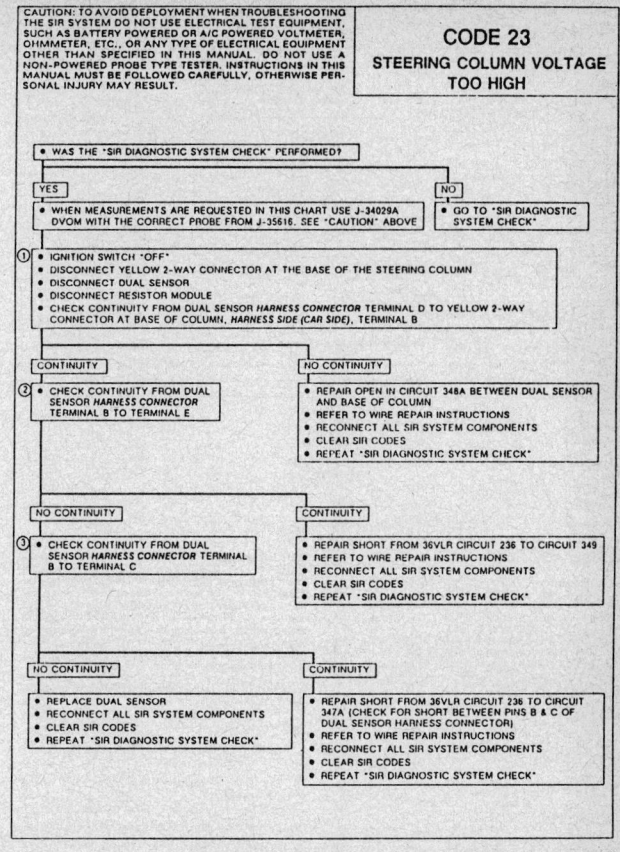

CODE 23
STEERING COLUMN VOLTAGE TOO HIGH

CODE 23
STEERING COLUMN VOLTAGE TOO HIGH

Test Condition:

Tested every 100 milliseconds during "Continuous Monitoring".

Failure Conditions:

Code 23 will set if the voltage at the Sense Low input (terminal A6) is greater than 78% of 36VLR output voltage for 500 milliseconds.

Conditions To Clear:

Current Code 23 will clear if the voltage at the Sense Low input (terminal A6) is between 41% and 61% of 36VLR output voltage for 500 milliseconds (5 consecutive "Continuous Monitoring" cycles) after Code 23 has been set.

Action Taken:

DERM turns on the "INFLATABLE RESTRAINT" indicator lamp.

Description:

Code 23 is set when the voltage at the Sense Low input (terminal A6) is greater than 78% of 36VLR output voltage for 500 milliseconds during the "Continuous Monitoring" tests performed by the DERM. The "Continuous Monitoring" tests are performed by the DERM after the initial "Turn-on" tests are completed and are performed every 100 milliseconds while "IGNITION 1" voltage is present at the DERM. The "Continuous Monitoring" tests check the continuity of the deployment loop from the 36VLR output of the DERM through the Arming Sensor, Inflator Module and the Discriminating Sensors to ground. Code 23 indicates a shorted Arming Sensor, shorted harness, or open ground path on both Discriminating Sensors.

Notes on Fault Tree:

1) Checks circuit 348A for an open circuit..

2) Checks the 36VLR circuit for a short to the low side of the steering column (circuit 349).

3) Checks the 36VLR circuit for a short to the high side of the steering column (circuit 347A).

Fig. 91 Code 23 diagnosis. Eldorado, Seville, Riviera, Reatta, Toronado & Trofeo

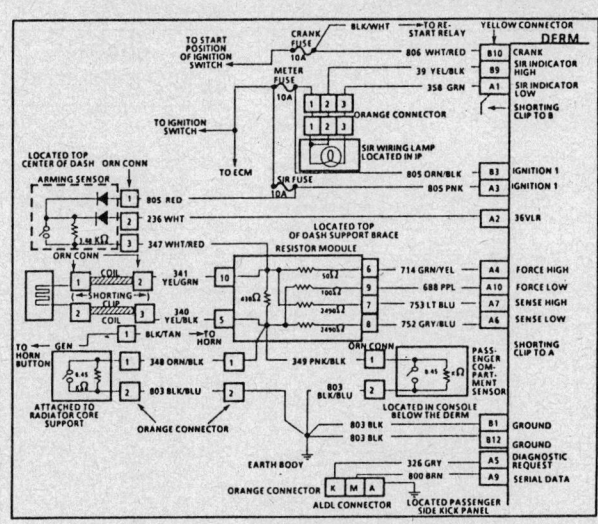

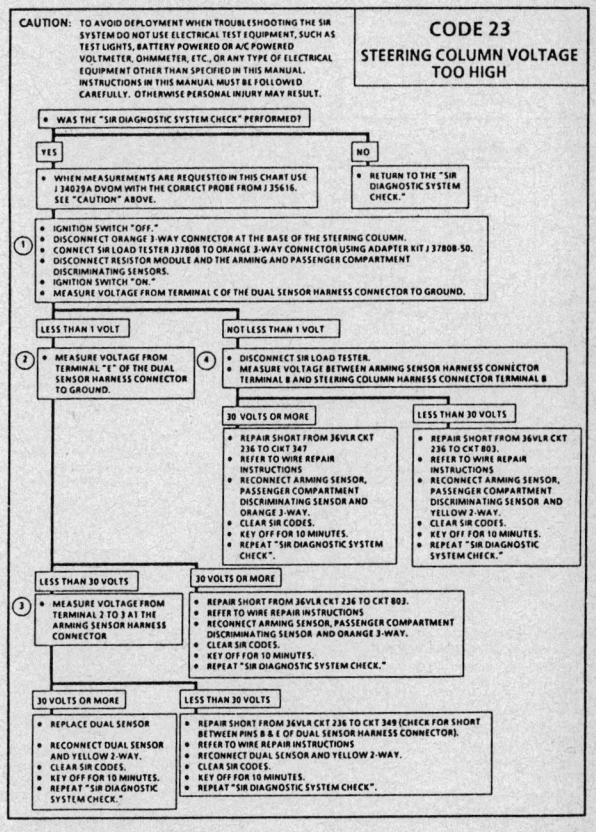

CODE 23
STEERING COLUMN VOLTAGE TOO HIGH

CODE 23
STEERING COLUMN VOLTAGE TOO HIGH

Test Conditions:
Tested every 100 milliseconds during "Continuous Monitoring".

Failure Conditions:
Code 23 will set if the voltage at the Sense Low input terminal "A6" is greater than 78% of 36VLR output voltage for 55 milliseconds

Conditions To Clear:
Current Code 23 will clear if the voltage at the Sense Low input terminal "A6" is between 41% and 61% of 36VLR output voltage for 500 milliseconds (5 consecutive "Continuous Monitoring" cycles) after Code 23 has been set.

Action Taken:
DERM turns "ON" the "INFLATABLE RESTRAINT" indicator lamp.

Description:
Code 23 is set when the voltage at the Sense Low input terminal "A6" is greater than 78% of 36VLR output voltage for 500 milliseconds during the "Continuous Monitoring" tests performed by the DERM. The "Continuous Monitoring" tests are performed by the DERM after the initial "Turn-ON" tests are completed and are performed every 100 milliseconds while Ignition 1 voltage is present at the DERM. The "Continuous Monitoring" tests check the continuity of the deployment loop from the 36VLR output of the DERM through the Arming Sensor, Inflator Module and the Discriminating Sensors to ground. Code 23 indicates a shorted Arming Sensor, shorted harness, or open grounds on both Discriminating Sensors.

Notes on Fault Tree:
1. Checks the 36VLR circuit for a short to the high side of the steering column (CKT 347).
2. Checks if the ground circuits on both Discriminating Sensors are open.
3. Checks the 36VLR circuit for a short to the low side of the steering column (CKT 349).
4. Checks the 36VLR circuit for a short to the low side of the steering column (CKT 348).

Fig. 92 Code 23 diagnosis. Storm

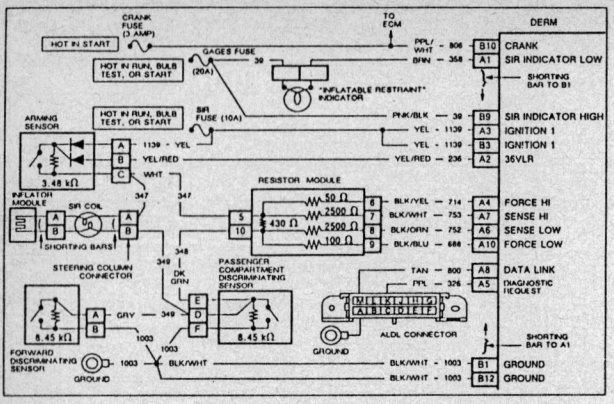

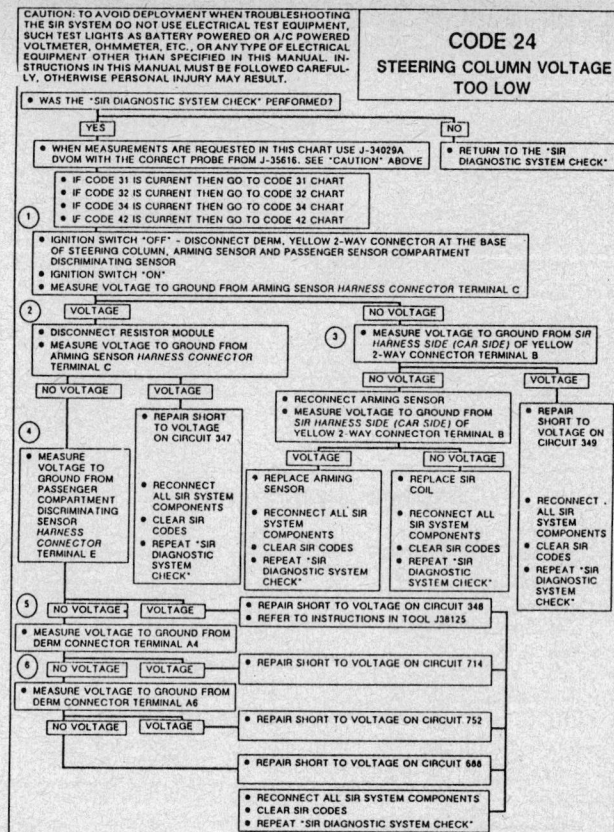

CODE 24

STEERING COLUMN VOLTAGE TOO LOW

Test Condition:

Tested every 100 milliseconds during "Continuous Monitoring".

Failure Conditions:

Code 24 will set if the voltage at the Sense Low input (terminal A6) is between 0% and 41% of 36VLR output voltage for 500 milliseconds.

Conditions To Clear:

Code 24 will clear if the voltage at the Sense Low input (terminal A6) is between 41% and 61% of 36VLR output voltage for 500 milliseconds.

Action Taken:

DERM turns on the "INFLATABLE RESTRAINT" indicator lamp.

Description:

Code 24 is set when the voltage at the Sense Low input (terminal A6) is between 0% and 41% of 36VLR output voltage for 500 milliseconds during the "Continuous Monitoring" tests performed by the DERM.

The "Continuous Monitoring" tests are performed by the DERM after the initial "Turn-on" tests are completed and are performed every 100 milliseconds while Ignition 1 voltage is present at the DERM. The "Continuous Monitoring" tests check the continuity of the deployment loop from the 36VLR output of the DERM through the Arming Sensor, Inflator Module and the Discriminating Sensors to ground. Code 24 will set if the Arming Sensor resistance is too high or open, the Discriminating Sensor resistance is too low or shorted, the "Force Hi", "Sense Hi", "Sense Low" or "Force Low" circuits are shorted to ground or system voltage, the high side of the deployment loop is shorted to the low side.

Notes on Fault Tree:

1) Determines if fault is short to voltage on circuit 349, SIR coil or Dual Sensor.
2) Determines if fault is short to voltage on circuit 347.
3) Determines if fault is short to voltage on circuit 349 or if fault is defective SIR coil or Dual Sensor.
4) Determines if fault is short to voltage on circuit 348.
5) Determines if fault is short to voltage on circuit 714.
6) Determines if fault is short to voltage on circuit 752 or 688.

Fig. 93 Code 24 diagnosis. Camaro & Firebird

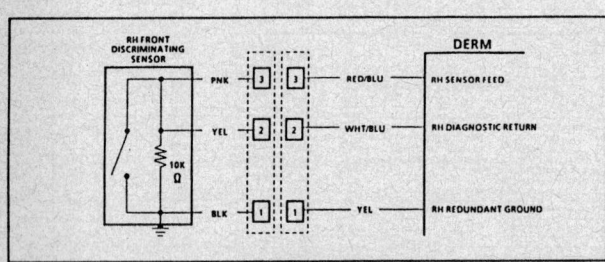

CODE 24

FRONT SENSOR #2 (RH)
(CIRCUIT SHORTED TO GROUND)

Circuit Description:

In an accident of sufficient force, the Front Discriminating Sensor switch closes, providing a path to ground for the deployment loop current. The sensor contains additional circuitry, used by the DERM for diagnostics.

If the DERM measures less than a certain resistance value between either the sensor feed line and ground or the diagnostic return line and ground, Code 24 will set.

Test Description: Numbers below refer to circled numbers on the diagnostic chart.

1. This step is essential to ensure that the ground between the sensor case and the frame rail is in good condition.
2. This test checks to see if the sensor and its wiring are within correct specifications. If the sensor and wiring check out as OK, the fault must be in the DERM or its wiring.

Diagnostic Aids:

The Fasten Seat Belt indicator will stay "ON" continuously when an SIR failure code has been set.

If power is applied to the SIR system while any component is not properly connected, an additional failure code will be set for the disconnected SIR component.

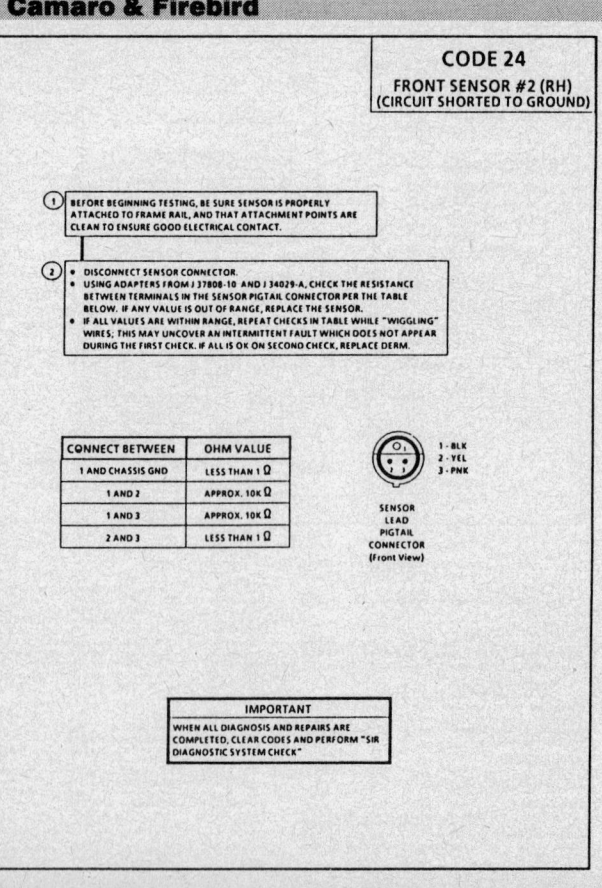

Fig. 94 Code 24 diagnosis. Corvette

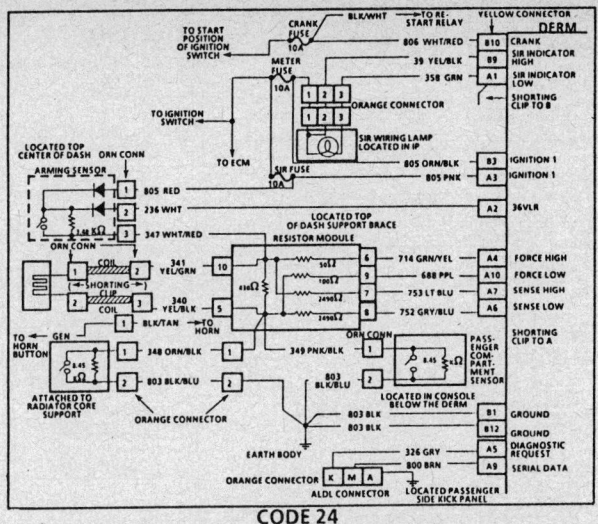

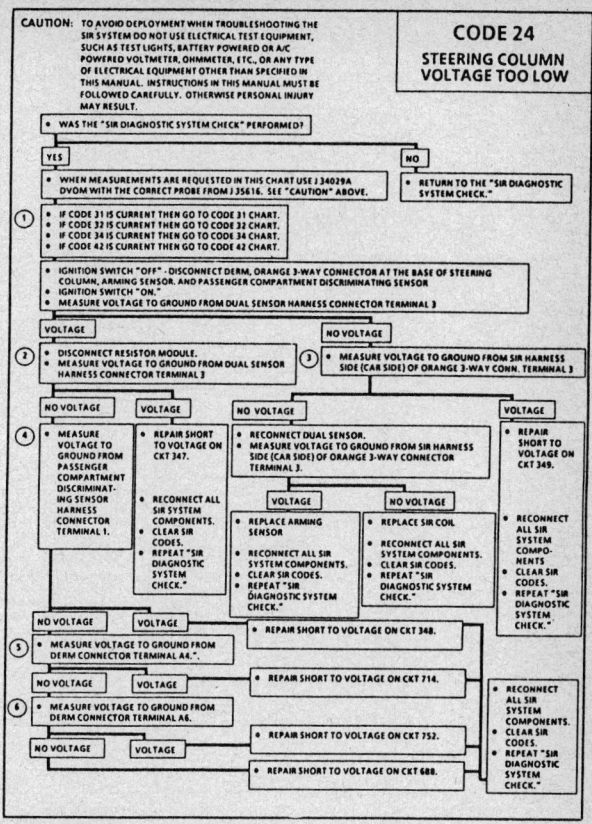

CODE 24
STEERING COLUMN VOLTAGE TOO LOW

Test Conditions:

Tested every 100 milliseconds during "Continuous Monitoring".

Failure Conditions:

Code 24 will set if the voltage at the Sense Low input terminal A6 is between 0% and 41% of 36 VLR output voltage for 500 milliseconds.

Conditions To Clear:

Code 24 will clear if the voltage at the Sense Low input terminal A6 is between 41% and 61% of 36VLR output voltage for 500 milliseconds.

Action Taken:

DERM turns "ON" the "INFLATABLE RESTRAINT" indicator lamp.

Description:

Code 24 is set when the voltage at the Sense Low input TERMINAL A6 is between 0% and 41% of 36VLR output voltage for 500 milliseconds during the "Continuous Monitoring" tests performed by the DERM. The "Continuous Monitoring" tests are performed by the DERM after the initial "Turn-ON" tests are completed and are performed every 100 milliseconds while ignition 1 voltage is present at the DERM. The "Continuous Monitoring" tests check the continuity of the deployment loop from the 36VLR output of the DERM through the Arming Sensor Inflator Module and the Discriminating Sensors to ground. Code 24 will set if the Arming Sensor resistance is too high or open, the Discriminating Sensor resistance is too low or shorted, the "Force Hi", "Sense Hi", "Sense Low" or "Force Low" circuits are shorted to ground or system voltage, the high side of the deployment loop is shorted to the low side.

Notes on Fault Tree:

1. Determines if fault is short to voltage on CKT 340 or 349 SIR coil or Dual Sensor.
2. Determines if fault is short to voltage on CKT 347.
3. Determines if fault is short to voltage on CKT 348 or if fault is defective SIR coil or Dual Sensor.
4. Determines if fault is short to voltage on CKT 349.
5. Determines if fault is short to voltage on CKT 714.
6. Determines if fault is short to voltage on CKT 752 or 688.

Fig. 95   Code 24 diagnosis. Storm

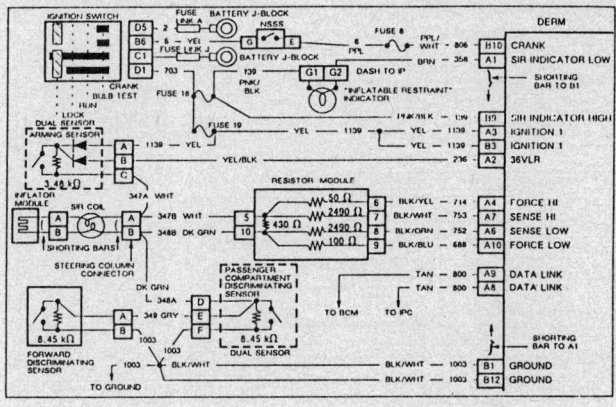

CODE 24 (CHART 1)
STEERING COLUMN VOLTAGE TOO LOW

Test Condition:

Tested every 100 milliseconds during "Continuous Monitoring".

Failure Conditions:

Code 24 will set if the voltage at the Sense Low input (terminal A6) is between 0% and 41% of 36VLR output voltage for 500 milliseconds.

Conditions To Clear:

Code 24 will clear if the voltage at the Sense Low input (terminal A6) is between 41% and 61% of 36VLR output voltage for 500 milliseconds.

Action Taken:

DERM turns on the "INFLATABLE RESTRAINT" indicator lamp.

Description:

Code 24 is set when the voltage at the Sense Low input (terminal A6) is between 0% and 41% of 36VLR output voltage for 500 milliseconds during the "Continuous Monitoring" tests performed by the DERM.

The "Continuous Monitoring" tests are performed by the DERM after the initial "Turn-on" tests are completed and are performed every 100 milliseconds while "IGNITION 1" voltage is present at the DERM. The "Continuous Monitoring" tests check the continuity of the deployment loop from the 36VLR output of the DERM through the Arming Sensor, Inflator Module and the Discriminating Sensors to ground. Code 24 will set if the Arming Sensor resistance is too high or open, the Discriminating Sensor resistance is too low or shorted, the "Force Hi", "Sense Hi", "Sense Low" or "Force Low" circuits are shorted to ground or system voltage, the high side of the deployment loop is shorted to the low side.

Notes on Fault Tree:

1) Checks if fault is in Steering Column.

2) Checks if fault is a short to voltage on high side of the Steering Column. If no short to voltage is detected, 36VLR voltage will be measured. **36VLR is not system voltage.**

3) Checks if fault is in Coil Wire or Inflator Module.

4) Checks if fault is a short to voltage in wiring harness or Dual Sensor.

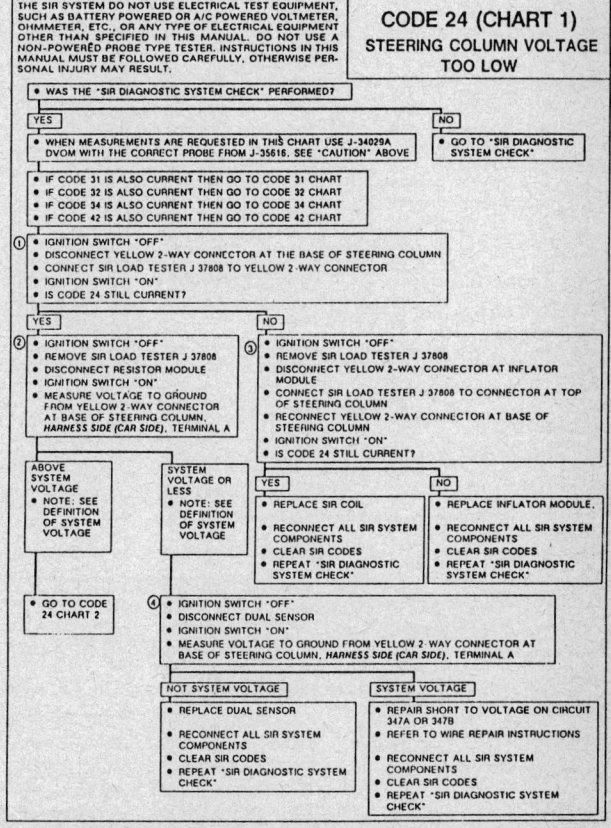

Fig. 96   Code 24 chart 1 diagnosis. Deville, Fleetwood, Eldorado, Seville, Riviera, Reatta, Toronado & Trofeo

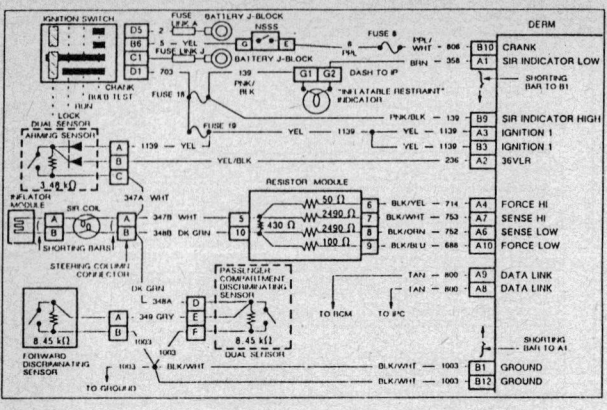

CODE 24 (CHART 2)
STEERING COLUMN VOLTAGE TOO LOW

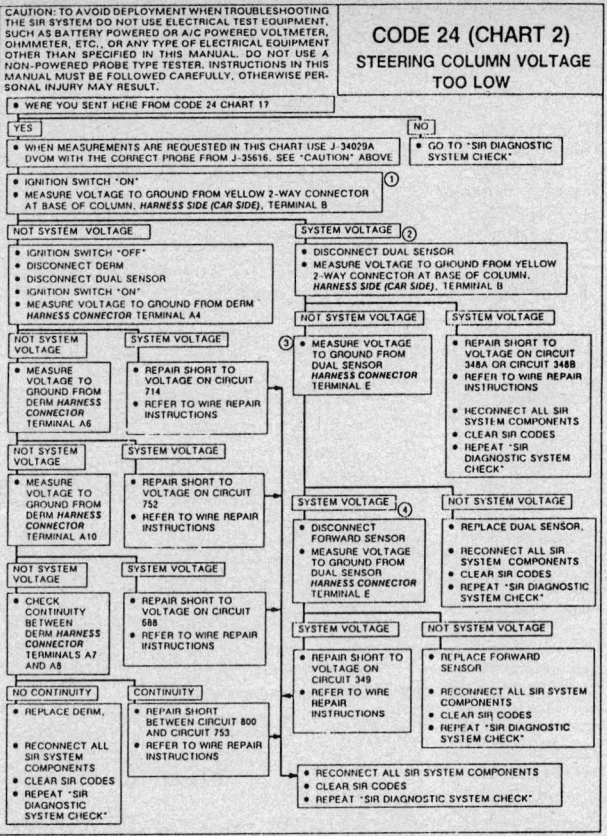

Fig. 97   Code 24 chart 2 diagnosis. Deville, Fleetwood, Eldorado, Seville, Riviera, Reatta, Toronado & Trofeo

CODE 24 (CHART 2)
STEERING COLUMN VOLTAGE TOO LOW

Test Condition:

Tested every 100 milliseconds during "Continuous Monitoring".

Failure Conditions:

Code 24 will set if the voltage at the *Sense Low* input (terminal A6) is between 0% and 41% of 36VLR output voltage for 500 milliseconds.

Conditions To Clear:

Code 24 will clear if the voltage at the *Sense Low* input (terminal A6) is between 41% and 61% of 36VLR output voltage for 500 milliseconds.

Action Taken:

DERM turns on the "INFLATABLE RESTRAINT" indicator lamp.

Description:

Code 24 is set when the voltage at the *Sense Low* input (terminal A6) is between 0% and 41% of 36VLR output voltage for 500 milliseconds during the "Continuous Monitoring" tests performed by the DERM.

The "Continuous Monitoring" tests are performed by the DERM after the initial "Turn-on" tests are completed and are performed every 100 milliseconds while "IGNITION 1" voltage is present at the DERM. The "Continuous Monitoring" tests check the continuity of the deployment loop from the 36VLR output of the DERM through the Arming Sensor, Inflator Module and the Discriminating Sensors to ground. Code 24 will set if the Arming Sensor resistance is too high or open, the Discriminating Sensor resistance is too low or open, the "Force Hi", "Sense Hi", "Sense Low" or "Force Low" circuits are shorted to ground or system voltage, the high side of the deployment loop is shorted to the low side.

Notes on Fault Tree:

1) Checks if fault is present on low side of the Steering Column circuits or in the circuits between the DERM and Resistor Module.

2) Checks if fault is a short to voltage on circuits 348A or 348B.

3) Checks if fault is in the Dual Sensor.

4) Determines if fault is in the Forward Sensor or in circuit 349.

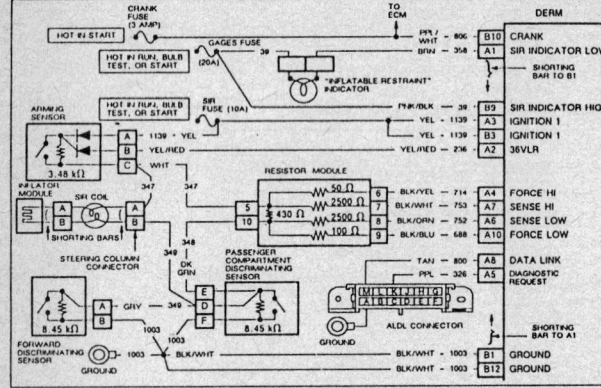

CODE 25
SHORT TO BATTERY IN STEERING COLUMN

Test Conditions:

Tested once each ignition cycle during the "Steering Column Resistance Test" if: 1) No faults are detected during "Turn-on"; 2) No faults are detected during "Continuous Monitoring" for 1 second; 3) No Crank signal present.

Failure Conditions:

Code 25 will set if the voltage at the *Sense Low* Input (terminal A6) is equal to Ignition 1 voltage (± 2 volts) during the first portion of the Steering Column Resistance Test.

Conditions To Clear:

Current Code 25 will be cleared each time the Ignition Switch is turned OFF.

Action Taken:

DERM turns on the "INFLATABLE RESTRAINT" indicator lamp.

Description:

The DERM grounds the Force Low input (terminal A10) and then monitors the voltage at the Sense Low input (terminal A6). If the voltage is greater than 3 volts Code 25 will set. Code 25 is an indication of a short to system voltage in the steering column, Dual Sensor, or associated wiring. Additionally, this code can be set if the actual resistance of the 100 ohm resistor within the Resistor Module is too high or is open.

Notes on Fault Tree:

1) Determines if fault is short to voltage on circuit 349, SIR coil or Dual Sensor.

2) Determines if fault is short to voltage on circuit 347.

3) Determines if fault is short to voltage on circuit 349 or if fault is defective SIR coil or Dual Sensor.

4) Determines if fault is short to voltage on circuit 348.

5) Determines if fault is short to voltage on circuit 714.

6) Determines if fault is short to voltage on circuit 752 or 688.

Fig. 98   Code 25 diagnosis. Camaro & Firebird

SUPPLEMENTAL INFLATABLE RESTRAINT SYSTEM

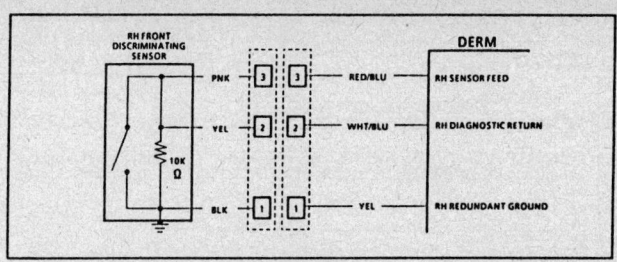

CODE 25
FRONT SENSOR #2 (RH)
(OPEN CIRCUIT)

Circuit Description:

In an accident of sufficient force, the Front Discriminating Sensor switch closes, providing a path to ground for the deployment loop current. The sensor contains additional circuitry, used by the DERM for diagnostics.

If the DERM measures more than a certain resistance value between either the sensor feed line and ground or the diagnostic return line and ground, Code 25 will set.

Test Description: Numbers below refer to circled numbers on the diagnostic chart.

1. This step is essential to ensure that the ground between the sensor case and the frame rail is in good condition. It is also necessary because a simple loose or disconnected sensor connection could cause this fault.
2. This test checks to see if the sensor and its wiring are within correct specifications. If the sensor and wiring check out as OK, the fault must be in the DERM or its wiring.

Diagnostic Aids:

The Fasten Seat Belt indicator will stay "ON" continuously when an SIR failure code has been set.

If power is applied to the SIR system while any component is not properly connected, an additional failure code will be set for the disconnected SIR component.

If a Code 25 has set, a Code 26 may also be set.

Severe corrosion under the sensor mounting bracket may cause a Code 25.

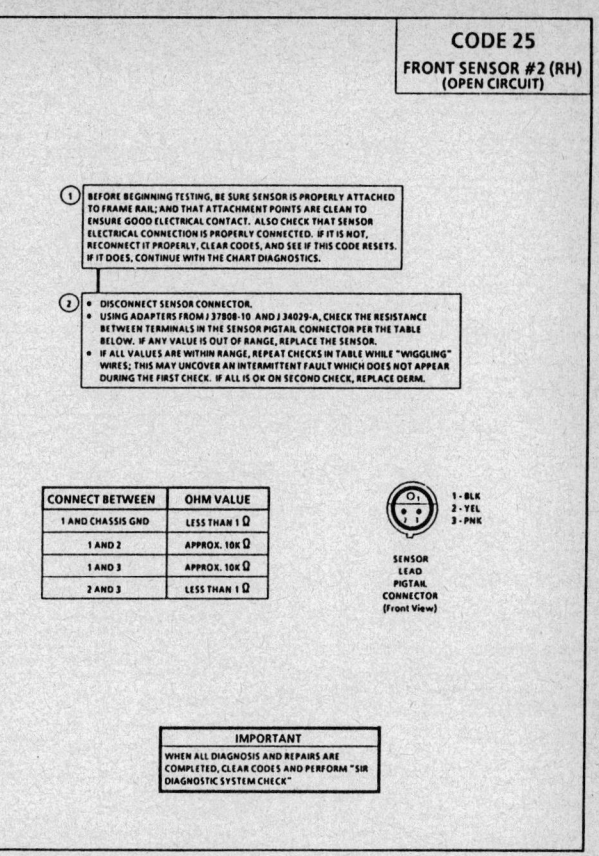

CODE 25
FRONT SENSOR #2 (RH)
(OPEN CIRCUIT)

① BEFORE BEGINNING TESTING, BE SURE SENSOR IS PROPERLY ATTACHED TO FRAME RAIL; AND THAT ATTACHMENT POINTS ARE CLEAN TO ENSURE GOOD ELECTRICAL CONTACT. ALSO CHECK THAT SENSOR ELECTRICAL CONNECTION IS PROPERLY CONNECTED. IF IT IS NOT, RECONNECT IT PROPERLY, CLEAR CODES, AND SEE IF THIS CODE RESETS. IF IT DOES, CONTINUE WITH THE CHART DIAGNOSTICS.

② • DISCONNECT SENSOR CONNECTOR.
• USING ADAPTERS FROM J 37808-10 AND J 34029-A, CHECK THE RESISTANCE BETWEEN TERMINALS IN THE SENSOR PIGTAIL CONNECTOR PER THE TABLE BELOW. IF ANY VALUE IS OUT OF RANGE, REPLACE THE SENSOR.
• IF ALL VALUES ARE WITHIN RANGE, REPEAT CHECKS IN TABLE WHILE "WIGGLING" WIRES; THIS MAY UNCOVER AN INTERMITTENT FAULT WHICH DOES NOT APPEAR DURING THE FIRST CHECK. IF ALL IS OK ON SECOND CHECK, REPLACE DERM.

CONNECT BETWEEN	OHM VALUE
1 AND CHASSIS GND	LESS THAN 1 Ω
1 AND 2	APPROX. 10K Ω
1 AND 3	APPROX. 10K Ω
2 AND 3	LESS THAN 1 Ω

1 - BLK
2 - YEL
3 - PNK

SENSOR LEAD PIGTAIL CONNECTOR (Front View)

IMPORTANT

WHEN ALL DIAGNOSIS AND REPAIRS ARE COMPLETED, CLEAR CODES AND PERFORM "SIR DIAGNOSTIC SYSTEM CHECK"

Fig. 99   Code 25 diagnosis. Corvette

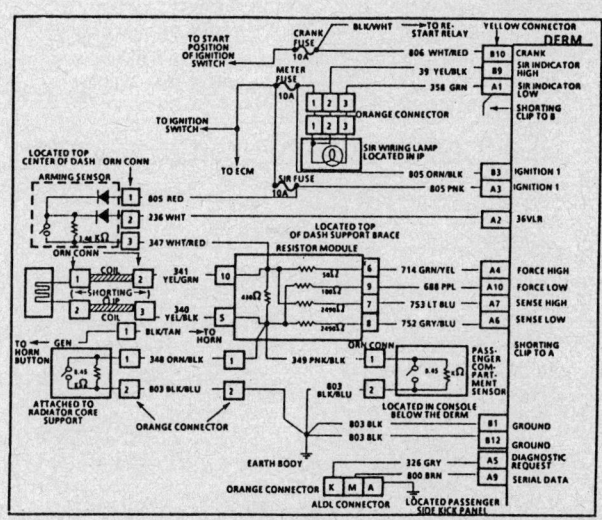

CODE 25
SHORT TO BATTERY IN STEERING COLUMN

Test Conditions:

Tested once each ignition cycle during the "Steering Column Resistance Test" if: 1) No faults are detected during "Turn-ON", 2) No faults are detected during "Continuous Monitoring" for 1 second; 3) No Crank signal present.

Failure Conditions:

Code 25 will set if the voltage at the Sense Low Input terminal "A6" is equal to Ignition 1 voltage (± 2 volts) during the first portion of the Steering Column Resistance Test.

Conditions To Clear:

Current Code 25 will be cleared each time the Ignition Switch is turned "OFF."

Action Taken:

DERM turns "ON" the "INFLATABLE RESTRAINT" indicator lamp.

Description:

The DERM grounds the Force Low input terminal "A10" and then monitors the voltage at the Sense Low input terminal "A6." If the voltage is greater than 3 volts Code 25 will set. Code 25 is an indication of a short to system voltage in the steering column, Dual Sensor, or associated wiring. Additionally, this code can be set if the actual resistance of the 100 ohm resistor within the Resistor Module is too high or is open.

Notes on Fault Tree:

1. Determines if fault is short to voltage on CKT 340, SIR coil or Dual Sensor.
2. Determines if fault is short to voltage on CKT 347.
3. Determines if fault is short to voltage on CKT 340 or if a fault is defective SIR coil or Dual Sensor.
4. Determines if fault is short to voltage on CKT 348.
5. Determines if fault is short to voltage on CKT 714.
6. Determines if fault is short to voltage on CKT 752 or 688.

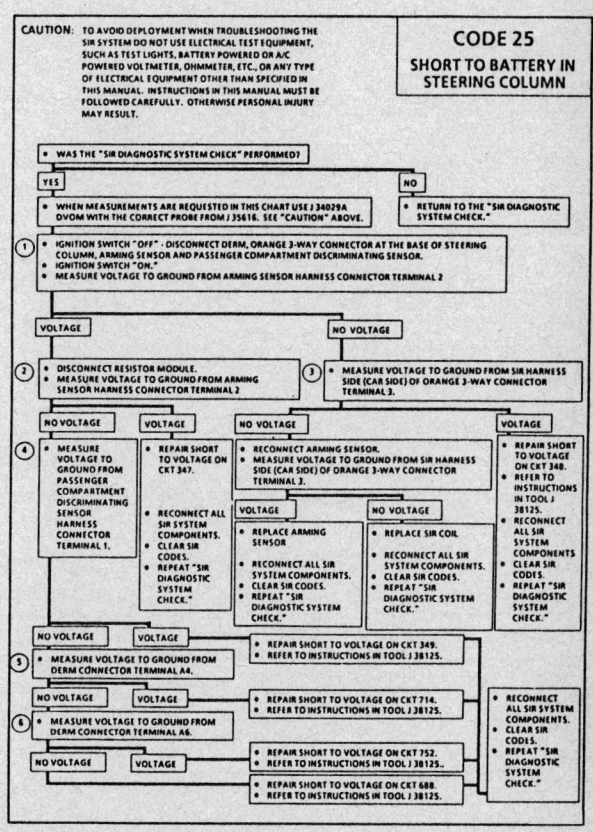

CODE 25
SHORT TO BATTERY IN STEERING COLUMN

CAUTION: TO AVOID DEPLOYMENT WHEN TROUBLESHOOTING THE SIR SYSTEM DO NOT USE ELECTRICAL TEST EQUIPMENT, SUCH AS TEST LIGHTS, BATTERY POWERED OR A/C POWERED VOLTMETER, OHMMETER, ETC., OR ANY TYPE OF ELECTRICAL EQUIPMENT OTHER THAN SPECIFIED IN THIS MANUAL. INSTRUCTIONS IN THIS MANUAL MUST BE FOLLOWED CAREFULLY. OTHERWISE PERSONAL INJURY MAY RESULT.

Fig. 100   Code 25 diagnosis. Storm

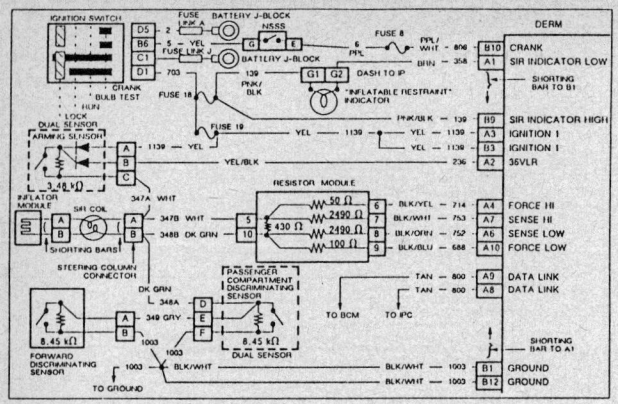

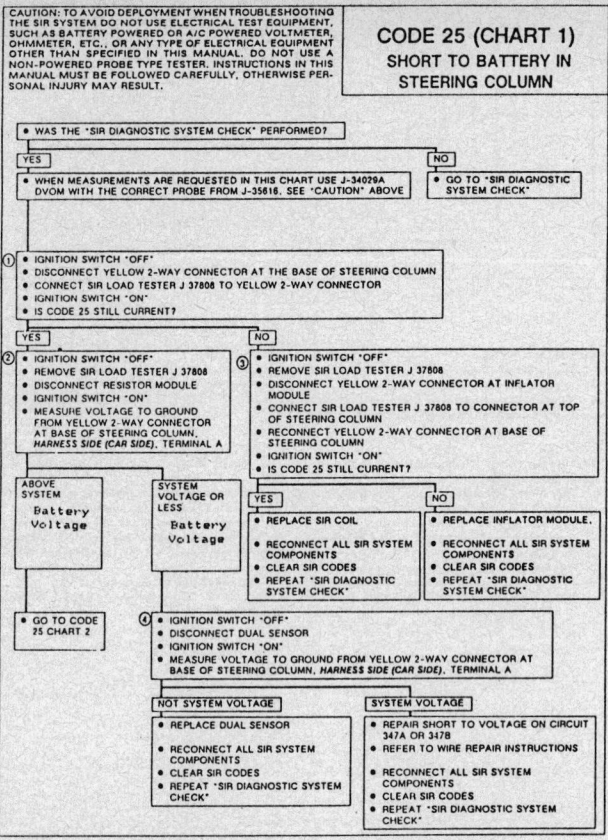

CAUTION: TO AVOID DEPLOYMENT WHEN TROUBLESHOOTING THE SIR SYSTEM DO NOT USE ELECTRICAL TEST EQUIPMENT, SUCH AS BATTERY POWERED OR A/C POWERED VOLTMETER, OHMMETER, ETC., OR ANY TYPE OF ELECTRICAL EQUIPMENT OTHER THAN SPECIFIED IN THIS MANUAL. DO NOT USE A NON-POWERED PROBE TYPE TESTER. INSTRUCTIONS IN THIS MANUAL MUST BE FOLLOWED CAREFULLY, OTHERWISE PERSONAL INJURY MAY RESULT.

CODE 25 (CHART 1)
SHORT TO BATTERY IN STEERING COLUMN

CODE 25 (CHART 1)
SHORT TO BATTERY IN STEERING COLUMN

Test Conditions:

Tested once each ignition cycle during the "Steering Column Resistance Test" if: 1) No faults are detected during "Turn-on"; 2) No faults are detected during "Continuous Monitoring" for 1 second; 3) No Crank signal present.

Failure Conditions:

Code 25 will set if the voltage at the Sense Low Input (terminal A6) is equal to "IGNITION 1" voltage (± 2 volts) during the first portion of the Steering Column Resistance Test.

Conditions To Clear:

Current Code 25 will be cleared each time the Ignition Switch is turned OFF.

Action Taken:

DERM turns on the "INFLATABLE RESTRAINT" indicator lamp.

Description:

The DERM grounds the Force Low input (terminal A10) and then monitors the voltage at the Sense Low input (terminal A6). If the voltage is greater than 3 volts Code 25 will set. Code 25 is an indication of a short to system voltage in the steering column, Dual Sensor, or associated wiring. Additionally, this code can be set if the actual resistance of the 100 ohm resistor within the Resistor Module is too high or is open.

Notes on Fault Tree:

1) Checks if fault is in Steering Column.
2) Checks if fault is a short to voltage on high side of the Steering Column. If no short to voltage is detected, 36VLR voltage will be measured. **36VLR is not system voltage.**
3) Checks if fault is in Coil Wire or Inflator Module.
4) Checks if fault is a short to voltage in wiring harness or Dual Sensor.

Fig. 101   Code 25 chart 1 diagnosis. Deville, Fleetwood, Eldorado, Seville, Riviera, Reatta, Toronado & Trofeo

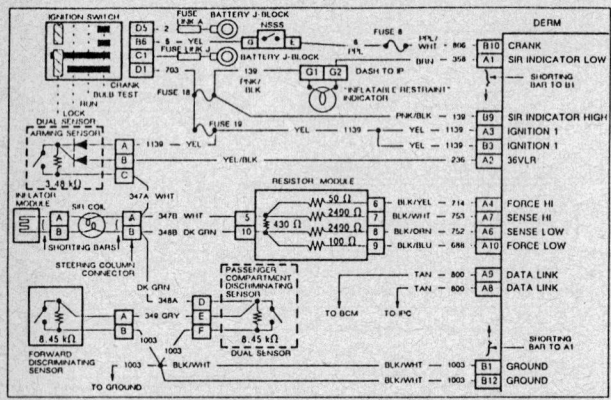

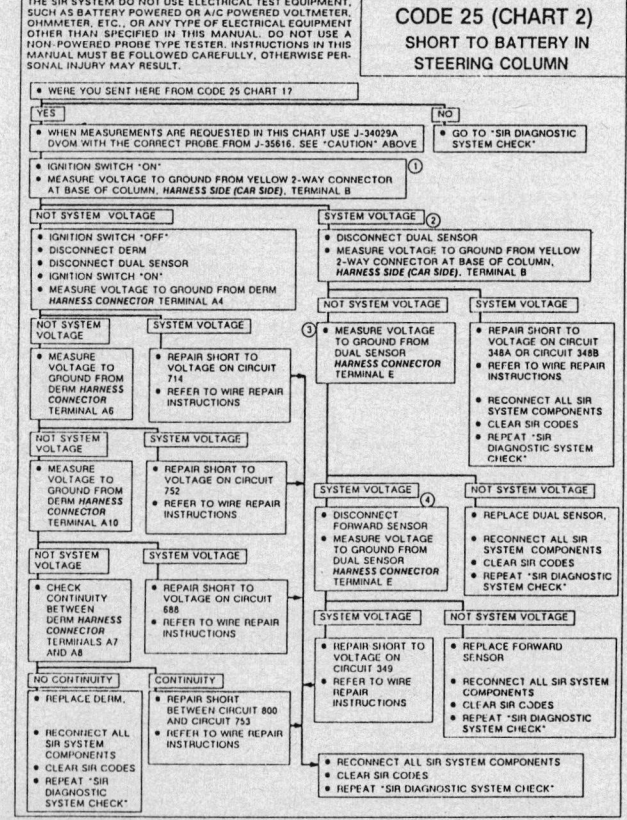

CAUTION: TO AVOID DEPLOYMENT WHEN TROUBLESHOOTING THE SIR SYSTEM DO NOT USE ELECTRICAL TEST EQUIPMENT, SUCH AS BATTERY POWERED OR A/C POWERED VOLTMETER, OHMMETER, ETC., OR ANY TYPE OF ELECTRICAL EQUIPMENT OTHER THAN SPECIFIED IN THIS MANUAL. DO NOT USE A NON-POWERED PROBE TYPE TESTER. INSTRUCTIONS IN THIS MANUAL MUST BE FOLLOWED CAREFULLY, OTHERWISE PERSONAL INJURY MAY RESULT.

CODE 25 (CHART 2)
SHORT TO BATTERY IN STEERING COLUMN

CODE 25 (CHART 2)
SHORT TO BATTERY IN STEERING COLUMN

Test Conditions:

Tested once each ignition cycle during the "Steering Column Resistance Test" if: 1) No faults are detected during "Turn-on"; 2) No faults are detected during "Continuous Monitoring" for 1 second; 3) No Crank signal present.

Failure Conditions:

Code 25 will set if the voltage at the Sense Low Input (terminal A6) is equal to "IGNITION 1" voltage (± 2 volts) during the first portion of the Steering Column Resistance Test.

Conditions To Clear:

Current Code 25 will be cleared each time the Ignition Switch is turned OFF.

Action Taken:

DERM turns on the "INFLATABLE RESTRAINT" indicator lamp.

Description:

The DERM grounds the Force Low input (terminal A10) and then monitors the voltage at the Sense Low input (terminal A6). If the voltage is greater than 3 volts Code 25 will set. Code 25 is an indication of a short to system voltage in the steering column, Dual Sensor, or associated wiring. Additionally, this code can be set if the actual resistance of the 100 ohm resistor within the Resistor Module is too high or is open.

Notes on Fault Tree:

1) Checks if fault is present on low side of the Steering Column circuits or in the circuits between the DERM and Resistor Module.
2) Checks if fault is a short to voltage on circuits 348A or 348B.
3) Checks if fault is in the Dual Sensor.
4) Determines if fault is in the Forward Sensor or in circuit 349.

Fig. 102   Code 25 chart 2 diagnosis. Deville, Fleetwood, Eldorado, Seville, Riviera, Reatta, Toronado & Trofeo

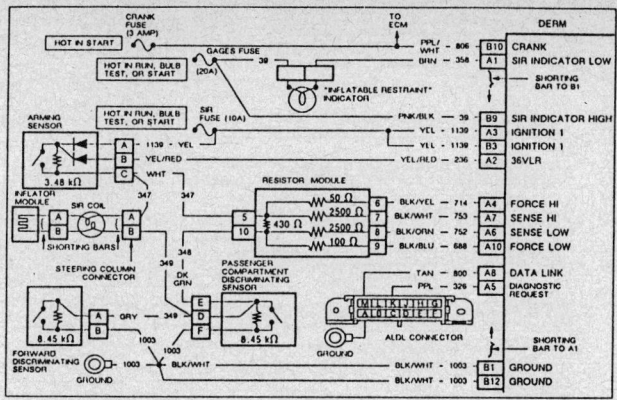

CODE 26

OPEN IN STEERING COLUMN

Test Condition:

Tested every 100 milliseconds during "Continuous Monitoring".

Failure Conditions:

Code 26 will set if the voltage at the Sense Hi input (terminal A7) minus the voltage at the Sense Low input (terminal A6) is greater than 0.45 volts for 500 milliseconds.

Conditions To Clear:

Current Code 26 will clear if the voltage at the Sense Hi input (terminal A7) minus the voltage at the Sense Low input (terminal A6) is greater than 0 volts but less than 0.40 volts for 500 milliseconds after Code 26 has been set.

Action taken:

DERM turns on the "INFLATABLE RESTRAINT" indicator lamp.

Description:

If there is an open in the SIR Coil, Inflator Module or wiring in the steering column the resistance between the Sense Hi input (terminal A7) and the Sense Low input (terminal A6) increases. This increased resistance causes a larger voltage drop from the Sense Hi input to the Sense Low input, across the 430 ohm resistor in the Resistor Module. The increase in voltage between the Sense Hi input and the Sense Low input is sensed by the DERM during the "Continuous Monitoring" Tests and Code 26 is set.

Notes on Fault Tree:

1) Checks if fault is in the steering column. The SIR load tester J37808 simulates the resistance of good steering column wiring and components.
2) Checks if fault is in the Inflator Module or the SIR Coil.
3) Checks if fault is in resistor module.
4) Checks if fault is in Dual Sensor.
5) Checks if fault is in circuit 347 or 348.

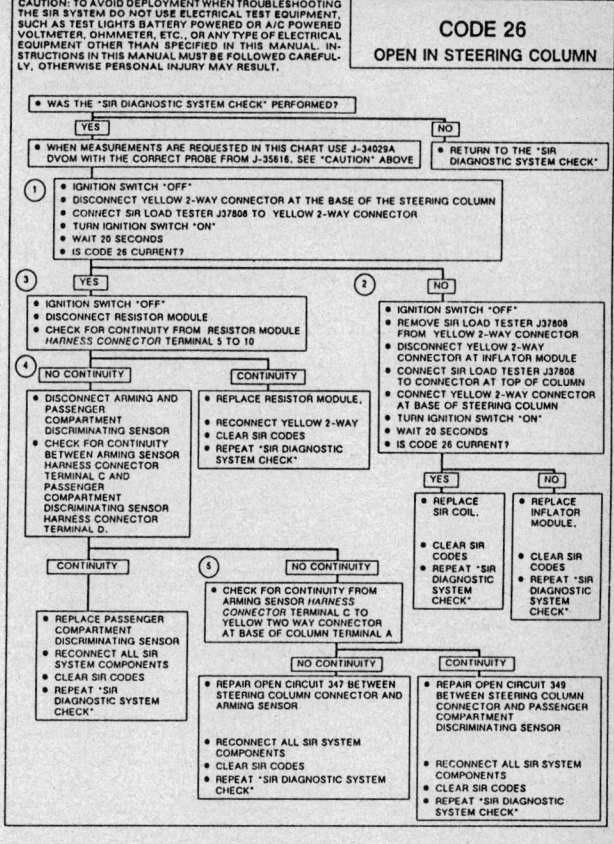

Fig. 103   Code 26 diagnosis. Camaro & Firebird

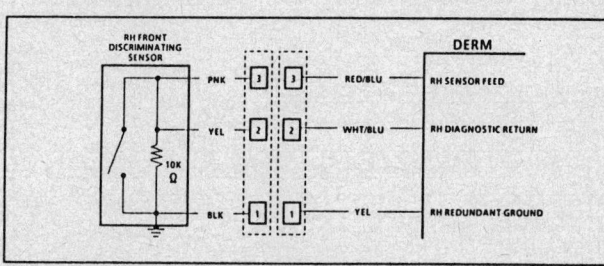

CODE 26

FRONT SENSOR #2 (RH)
(SENSOR FAULT)

Circuit Description:

In an accident of sufficient force, the Front Discriminating Sensor switch closes, providing a path to ground for the deployment loop current. The sensor contains additional circuitry, used by the DERM for diagnostics.

If the DERM measures more than a certain resistance value between the redundant ground circuit and the DERM's own ground, Code 26 will set. This code will also set if the DERM measures less than a certain resistance between the sensor feed circuit and B + or the diagnostic return circuit and B +.

Test Description: Numbers below refer to circled numbers on the diagnostic chart.

1. This step is essential to ensure that the ground between the sensor case and the frame rail is in good condition. It is also necessary because a simple loose or disconnected sensor connection could cause this fault.
2. This test checks to see if the sensor and its wiring are within correct specifications. If the sensor and wiring check out as OK, the fault must be in the DERM or its wiring.

Diagnostic Aids:

The Fasten Seat Belt indicator will stay "ON" continuously when an SIR failure code has been set.

If power is applied to the SIR system while any component is not properly connected, an additional failure code will be set for the disconnected SIR component.

If a Code 26 has set, a Code 25 may also be set.

Severe corrosion under the sensor mounting bracket may cause a Code 26.

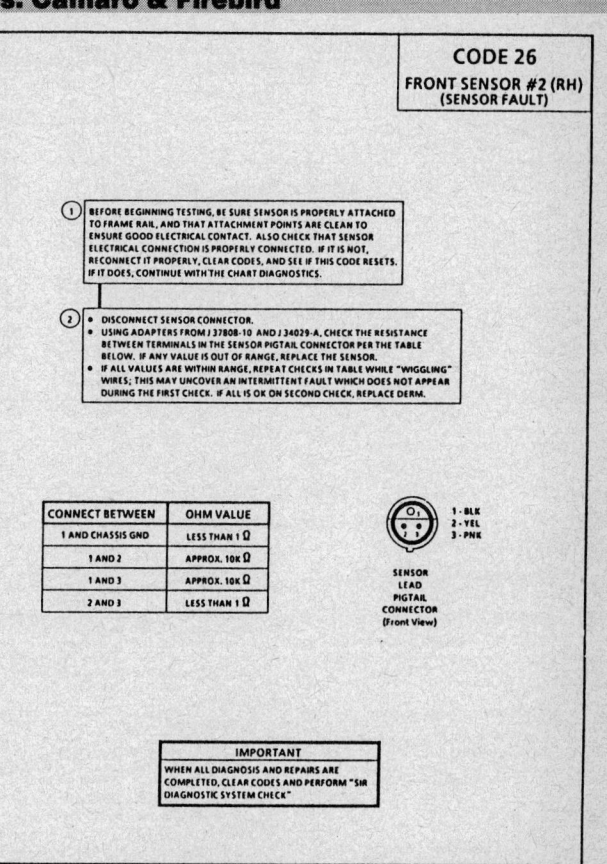

Fig. 104   Code 26 diagnosis. Corvette

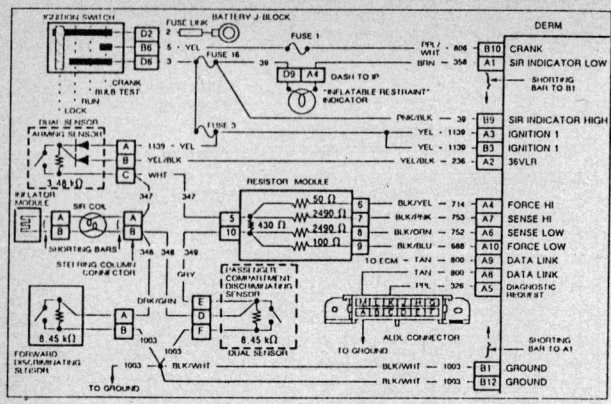

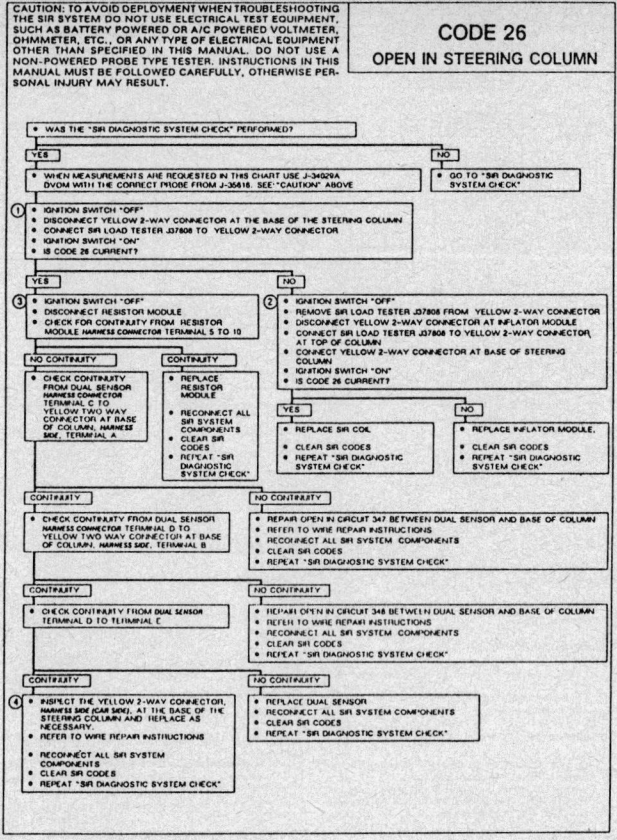

CODE 24 (CHART 1)
STEERING COLUMN VOLTAGE TOO LOW

Test Condition:

Tested every 100 milliseconds during "Continuous Monitoring".

Failure Conditions:

Code 24 will set if the voltage at the Sense Low input (terminal A6) is between 0% and 41% of 36VLR output voltage for 500 milliseconds.

Conditions To Clear:

Code 24 will clear if the voltage at the Sense Low input (terminal A6) is between 41% and 61% of 36VLR output voltage for 500 milliseconds.

Action Taken:

DERM turns on the "INFLATABLE RESTRAINT" indicator lamp.

Description:

Code 24 is set when the voltage at the Sense Low input (terminal A6) is between 0% and 41% of 36VLR output voltage for 500 milliseconds during the "Continuous Monitoring" tests performed by the DERM.

The "Continuous Monitoring" tests are performed by the DERM after the initial "Turn-on" tests are completed and are performed every 100 milliseconds while "IGNITION 1" voltage is present at the DERM. The "Continuous Monitoring" tests check the continuity of the deployment loop from the 36VLR output of the DERM through the Arming Sensor, Inflator Module and the Discriminating Sensors to ground. Code 24 will set if the Arming Sensor resistance is too high or open, the Discriminating Sensor resistance is too low or shorted, the "Force Hi", "Sense Hi", "Sense Low" or "Force Low" circuits are shorted to ground or system voltage, the high side of the deployment loop is shorted to the low side.

Notes on Fault Tree:

1) Checks if fault is in Steering Column.
2) Checks if fault is a short to voltage on high side of the Steering Column. If no short to voltage is detected, 36VLR voltage will be measured. **36VLR is not system voltage.**
3) Checks if fault is in Coil Wire or Inflator Module.
4) Checks if fault is a short to voltage in wiring harness or Dual Sensor.

Fig. 105 Code 26 diagnosis. Deville & Fleetwood

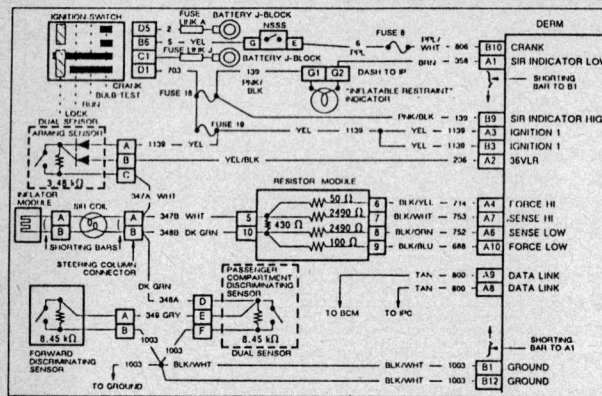

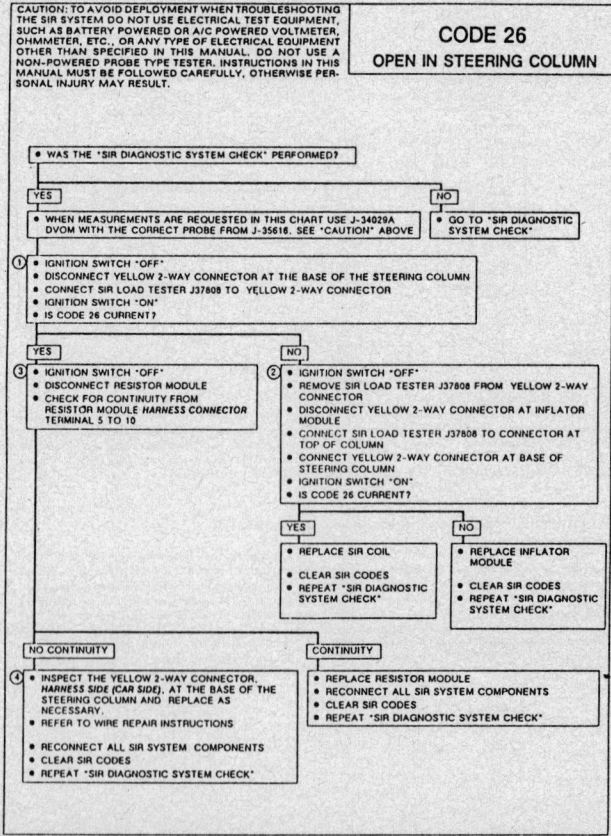

CODE 26
OPEN IN STEERING COLUMN

Test Condition:

Tested every 100 milliseconds during "Continuous Monitoring".

Failure Conditions:

Code 26 will set if the voltage at the Sense Hi input (terminal A7) minus the voltage at the Sense Low input (terminal A6) is greater than 0.45 volts for 500 milliseconds.

Conditions To Clear:

Current Code 26 will clear if the voltage at the Sense Hi input (terminal A7) minus the voltage at the Sense Low input (terminal A6) is greater than 0 volts but less than 0.40 volts for 500 milliseconds after Code 26 has been set.

Action taken:

DERM turns on the "INFLATABLE RESTRAINT" indicator lamp.

Description:

If there is an open in the SIR Coil, Inflator Module or wiring in the steering column the resistance between the Sense Hi input (terminal A7) and the Sense Low input (terminal A6) increases. This increased resistance causes a larger voltage drop from the Sense Hi input to the Sense Low input, across the 430 ohm resistor in the Resistor Module. The increase in voltage between the Sense Hi input and the Sense Low input is sensed by the DERM during the "Continuous Monitoring" Tests and Code 26 is set.

Notes on Fault Tree:

1) Checks if fault is in the Steering Column.
2) Checks if fault is in the Inflator Module or the SIR Coil.
3) Checks if fault is in the Resistor Module or in the terminal contacts at the base of the Steering Column.
4) Checks for defective connector at the wiring harness.

Fig. 106 Code 26 diagnosis. Eldorado, Seville, Riviera, Reatta, Toronado & Trofeo

SUPPLEMENTAL INFLATABLE RESTRAINT SYSTEM

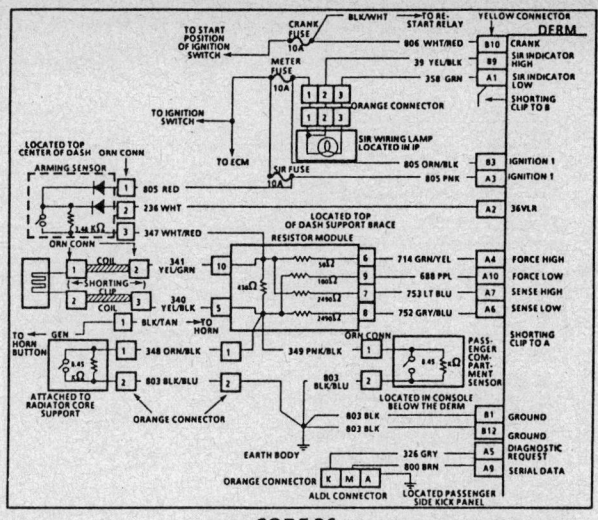

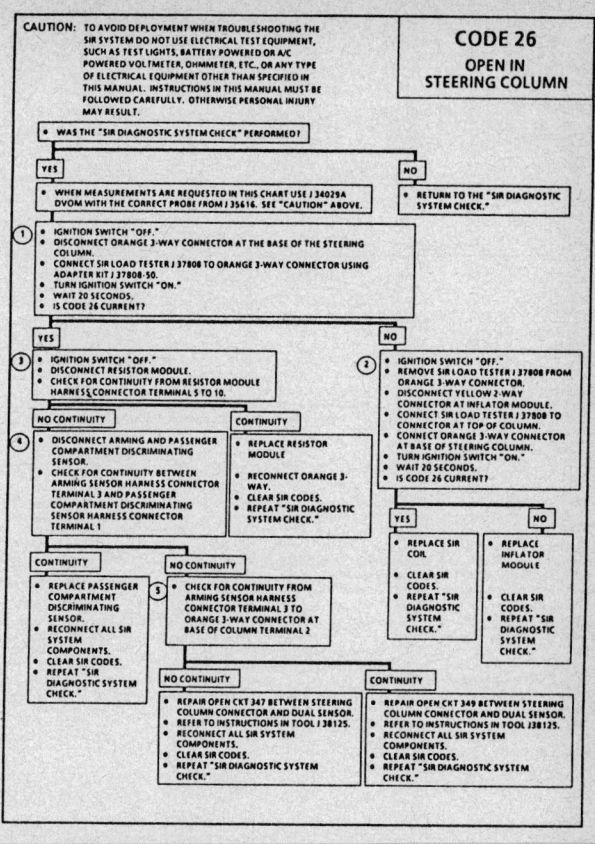

CODE 26

OPEN IN STEERING COLUMN

Test Conditions:

Tested every 100 milliseconds during "Continuous Monitoring".

Failure Conditions:

Code 26 will set if the voltage at the Sense IIi input terminal "A7" minus the voltage at the Sense Low input terminal "A6" is greater than 0.45 volts for 500 milliseconds.

Conditions To Clear:

Current Code 26 will clear if the voltage at the Sense IIi input terminal "A7" minus the voltage at the Sense Low input terminal "A6" is greater than 0 volts but less than 0.40 volts for 500 milliseconds after Code 26 has been set.

Action Taken:

DERM turns "ON" the "INFLATABLE RESTRAINT" indicator lamp.

Description:

If there is an open in the SIR Coil, Inflator Module or wiring in the steering column the resistance between the Sense IIi input terminal "A7" and the Sense Low input terminal "A6" increases. This increased resistance causes a larger voltage drop from the Sense IIi input to the Sense Low input, across the 430 ohm resistor in the Resistor Module. The increase in voltage between the Sense IIi input and the Sense Low input is sensed by the DERM during the "Continuous Monitoring" Tests and Code 26 is set.

Notes on Fault Tree:

1. Checks if fault is in the steering column. The SIR load tester J 37808 simulates the resistance of good steering column wiring and components.
2. Checks if fault is in the Inflator Module or the SIR Coil.
3. Checks if fault is in resistor module.
4. Checks if fault is in Dual Sensor.
5. Checks if fault is in CKT 347 or 348.

Fig. 107   Code 26 diagnosis. Storm

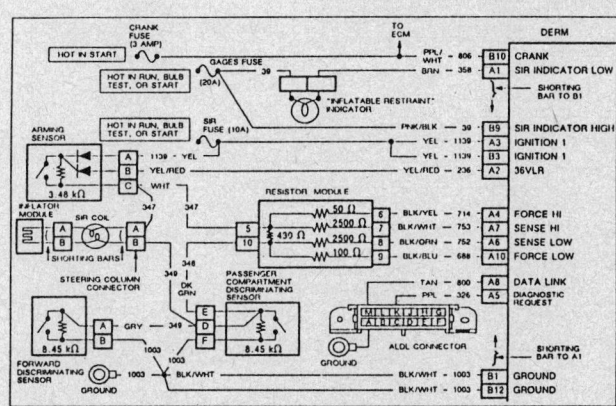

CODE 31

OPEN 36VLR TO DEPLOYMENT LOOP

Test Condition:

Tested every 100 milliseconds during "Continuous Monitoring".

Failure Conditions:

Code 31 will set if: 1) The Voltage at the Sense Low input (terminal A6) is between 28% and 59% of Ignition 1 output voltage for 700 milliseconds; 2) Code 42 is not set.

Conditions To Clear:

Current Code 31 will clear if the voltage at the Sense Low input (terminal A6) is between 41% and 61% of 36VLR output voltage for 500 milliseconds.

Action taken:

DERM turns on the "INFLATABLE RESTRAINT" indicator lamp.

Description:

The voltage at the Sense Low input (terminal A6) is between 41% and 61% of 36VLR output voltage when 36VLR output of the DERM is functional. Should the circuit open between the 36VLR output and the Arming Sensor, Ignition 1 voltage will be supplying the deployment loop. The voltage at the Sense Low input (terminal A6) will decrease due to the decrease in the supply voltage and Code 31 will set after 700 milliseconds (if Code 42 is not set). Code 31 indicates an open in the wiring between the 36VLR output of the DERM and the Arming Sensor, an open diode in the Arming Sensor or a problem with Sense High or Sense Low circuits.

Notes on Fault Tree:

1. Checks if the fault is in the 36VLR Circuit between the DERM and the Arming Sensor or if the fault is in the Arming Sensor.

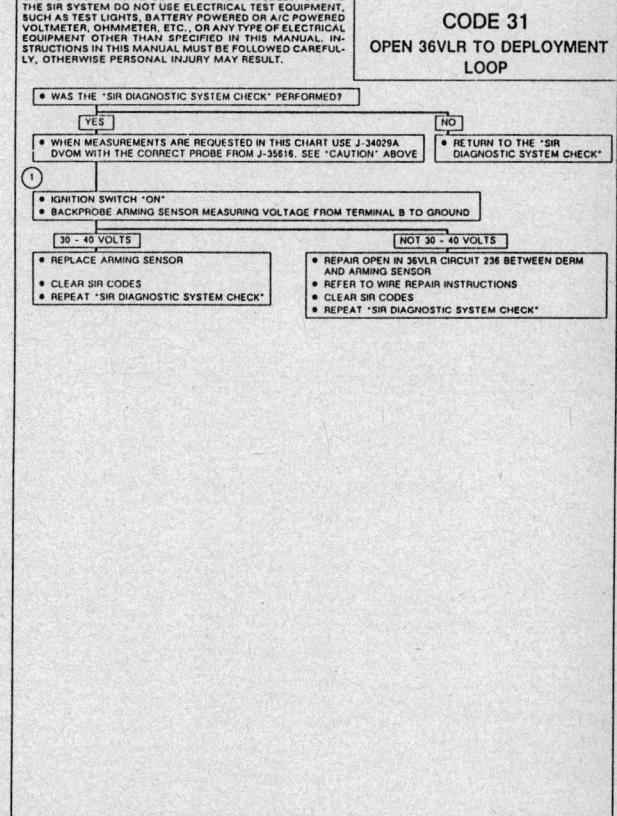

Fig. 108   Code 31 diagnosis. Camaro & Firebird

SUPPLEMENTAL INFLATABLE RESTRAINT SYSTEM

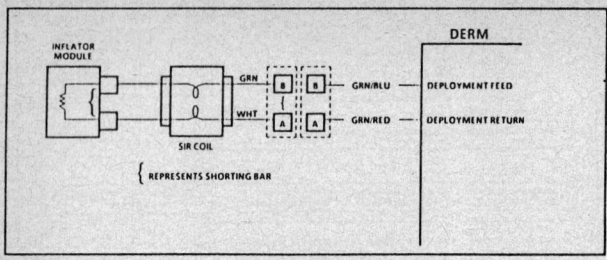

CODE 31
INFLATOR SQUIB
(CURRENT LEAKAGE TO BATTERY)

Circuit Description:

The Inflator Squib circuit provides the current path to ignite the gas generating material inside the Inflator Module. The squib itself is a resistive element which heats up very quickly when an appropriate current is applied. The SIR Coil Assembly allows rotation of the steering wheel while maintaining continuous contact of the deployment loop through the Inflator Module.

If the DERM measures a resistance that is less than a specified value, but not a "hard" short circuit between either the deployment feed circuit and B + or the deployment return circuit and B + , this code will set.

Test Description: Numbers below refer to circled numbers on the diagnostic chart.
1. This test determines if the fault is within the steering column. This is done by electrically mimicking the steering column SIR electrical components with the J 37808 Load Tool, clearing codes, and checking to see if the code resets. If it does, the fault is not in the steering column; if it does not, further checking of steering column SIR components is required.
2. This indicates that the faulty portion of the circuit lies in the steering column.
3. This indicates that the code clearing procedure required in Step 1 was not properly completed.
4. This indicates that the fault is still present. If this condition occurs a second time, after repeating the procedure in Step 1, replace the DERM.
5. This test replaces the Inflator Module with the Load Tool. If the code does not come back, the Inflator Module is the cause of the fault and must be replaced. If the code does come back, the SIR Coil Assembly and/or its wiring is the cause of the fault.

6. This indicates that everything checks OK at this time. Since the code was set, however, the fault has occurred before; the fault is intermittent.
7. This indicates that the fault is in the SIR Coil Assembly.

Diagnostic Aids:

The Fasten Seat Belt indicator will stay "ON" continuously when an SIR failure code has been set.

If power is applied to the SIR system while any component is not properly connected, an additional failure code will be set for the disconnected SIR component.

The problem may be intermittent. Try performing the tests shown while "wiggling" wiring and connectors; this can often cause the fault to appear.

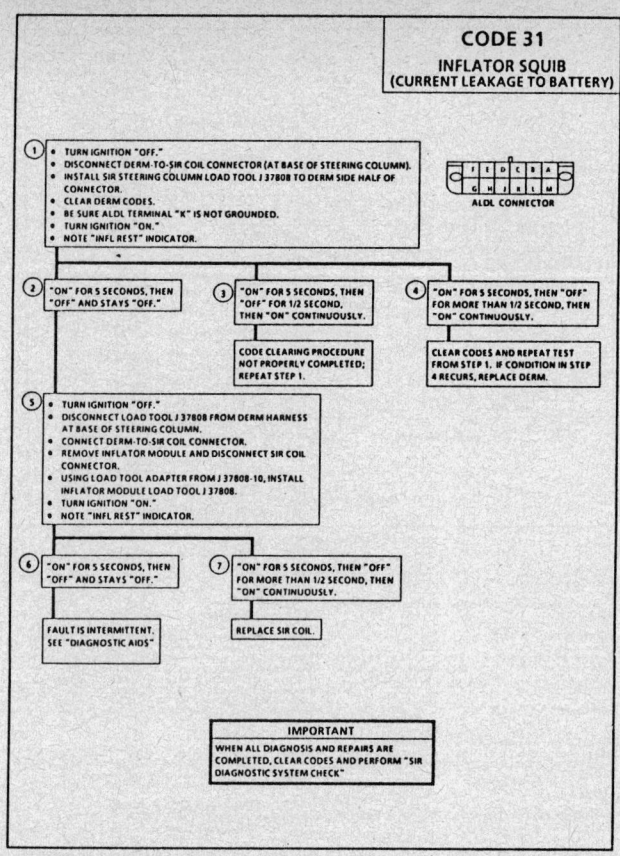

Fig. 109 Code 31 diagnosis. Corvette

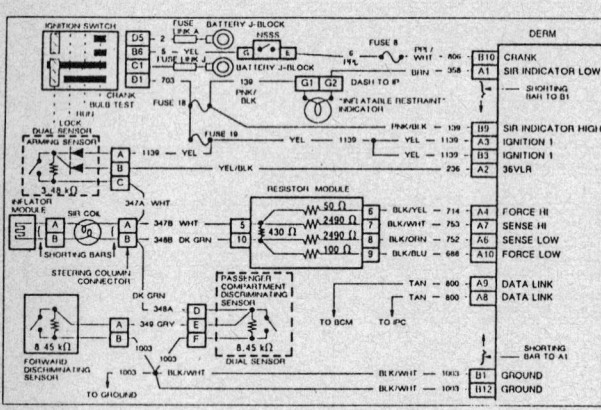

CODE 31
OPEN 36VLR TO DEPLOYMENT LOOP

Test Condition:

Tested every 100 milliseconds during "Continuous Monitoring".

Failure Conditions:

Code 31 will set if: 1) The Voltage at the Sense Low input (terminal A6) is between 28% and 59% of Ignition 1 output voltage for 700 milliseconds; 2) Code 42 *is not* set.

Conditions To Clear:

Current Code 31 will clear if the voltage at the Sense Low input (terminal A6) is between 41% and 61% of 36VLR output voltage for 500 milliseconds.

Action taken:

DERM turns on the "INFLATABLE RESTRAINT" indicator lamp.

Description:

The voltage at the Sense Low input (terminal A6) is between 41% and 61% of 36VLR output voltage when 36VLR output of the DERM is functional. Should the circuit open between the 36VLR output and the Arming Sensor, "IGNITION 1" voltage will be supplying the deployment loop. The voltage at the Sense Low input (terminal A6) will decrease due to the decrease in the supply voltage and Code 31 will set after 700 milliseconds (if Code 42 is not set). Code 31 indicates an open in the wiring between the 36VLR output of the DERM and the Arming Sensor, an open diode in the Arming Sensor or a problem with Sense High or Sense Low circuits.

Notes on Fault Tree:

1) Checks if the fault is in the 36VLR Circuit between the DERM and the Dual Sensor or if the fault is in the Dual Sensor.

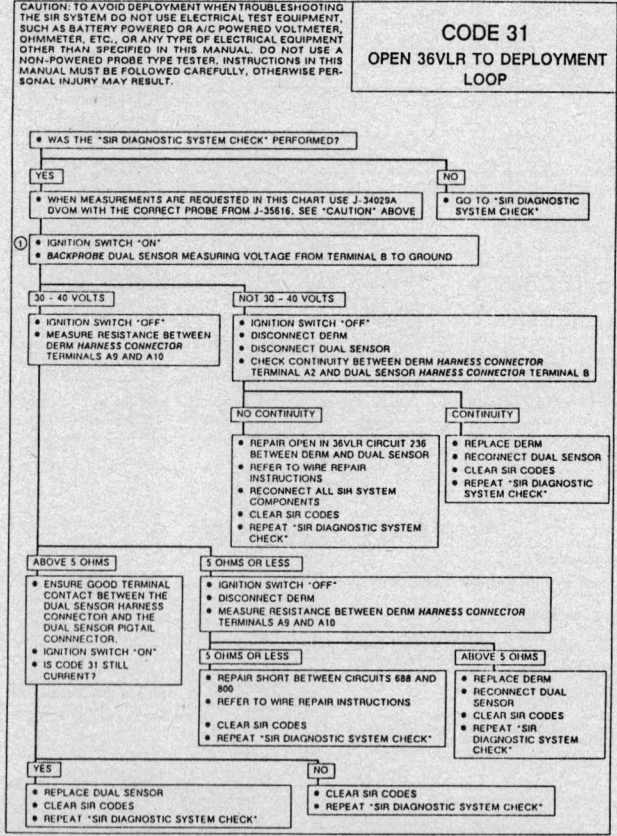

Fig. 110 Code 31 diagnosis. Deville, Fleetwood, Eldorado, Seville, Toronado & Trofeo

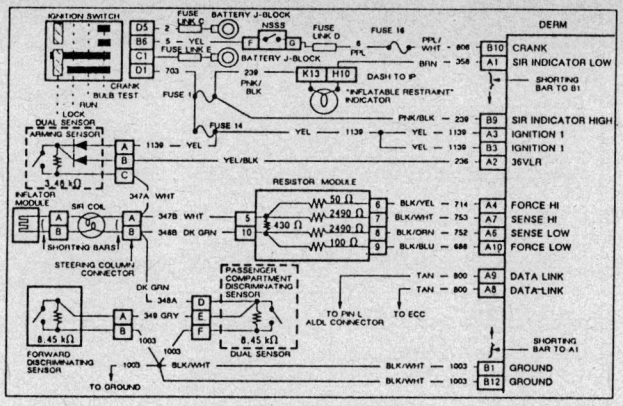

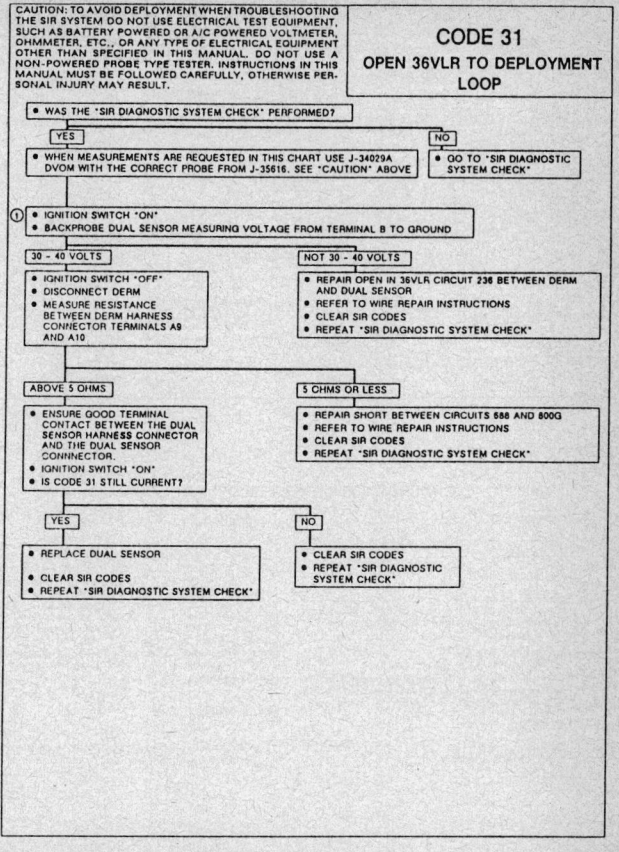

CODE 31

OPEN 36VLR TO DEPLOYMENT LOOP

Test Condition:

Tested every 100 milliseconds during "Continuous Monitoring".

Failure Conditions:

Code 31 will set if: 1) The Voltage at the Sense Low input (terminal A6) is between 28% and 59% of Ignition 1 output voltage for 700 milliseconds; 2) Code 42 is not set.

Conditions To Clear:

Current Code 31 will clear if the voltage at the Sense Low input (terminal A6) is between 41% and 61% of 36VLR output voltage for 500 milliseconds.

Action taken:

DERM turns on the "INFLATABLE RESTRAINT" indicator lamp.

Description:

The voltage at the Sense Low input (terminal A6) is between 41% and 61% of 36VLR output voltage when 36VLR output of the DERM is functional. Should the circuit open between the 36VLR output and the Arming Sensor, Ignition 1 voltage will be supplying the deployment loop. The voltage at the Sense Low input (terminal A6) will decrease due to the decrease in the supply voltage and Code 31 will set after 700 milliseconds (if Code 42 is not set). Code 31 indicates an open in the wiring between the 36VLR output of the DERM and the Arming Sensor, an open diode in the Arming Sensor or a problem with Sense High or Sense Low circuits.

Notes on Fault Tree:

1) Checks if the fault is in the 36VLR Circuit between the DERM and the Dual Sensor or if the fault is in the Dual Sensor.

Fig. 111   Code 31 diagnosis. Riviera & Reatta

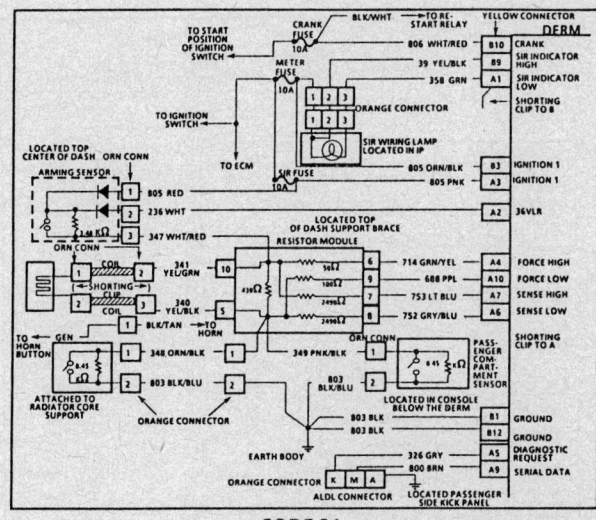

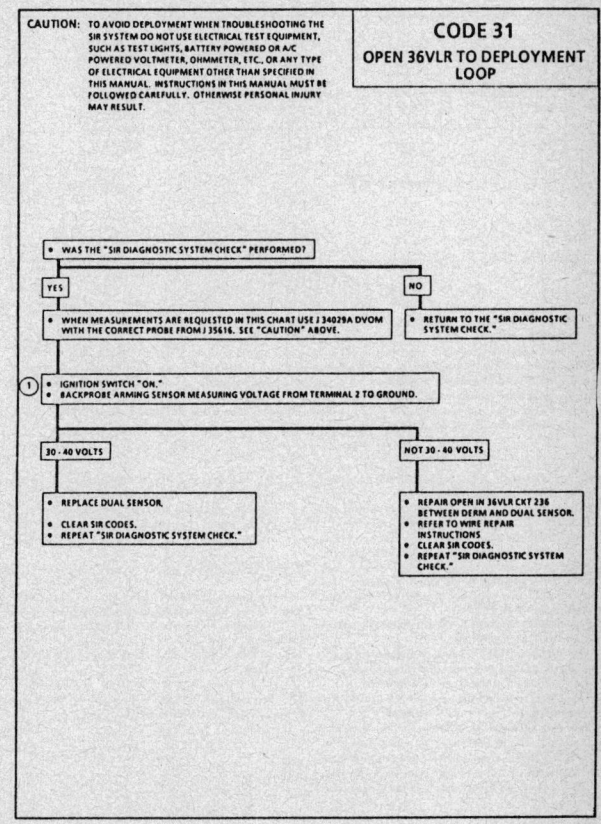

CODE 31

OPEN 36VLR TO DEPLOYMENT LOOP

Test Conditions:

Tested every 100 milliseconds during "Continuous Monitoring".

Failure Conditions:

Code 31 will set if: 1) The Voltage at the Sense Low input (terminal A6) is between 28% and 59% of Ignition 1 output voltage for 700 milliseconds; 2) Code 42 is not set.

Conditions To Clear:

Current Code 31 will clear if the voltage at the Sense Low input (terminal A6) is between 41% and 61% of 36VLR output voltage for 500 milliseconds.

Action Taken:

DERM turns "ON" the "INFLATABLE RESTRAINT" indicator lamp.

Description:

The voltage at the Sense Low input terminal "A6" is between 41% and 61% of 36VLR output voltage when 36VLR output of the DERM is functional. Should the circuit open between the 36VLR output and the Arming Sensor, Ignition 1 voltage will be supplying the deployment loop. The voltage at the Sense Low input terminal "A6" will decrease due to the decrease in the supply voltage and Code 31 will set after 700 milliseconds (if Code 42 is not set). Code 31 indicates an open in the wiring between the 36VLR output of the DERM and the Arming Sensor, an open diode in the Arming Sensor or a problem with Sense High or Sense Low circuits.

Notes on Fault Tree:

1. Checks if the fault is in the 36VLR Circuit between the DERM and the Dual Sensor or if the fault is in the Dual Sensor.

Fig. 112   Code 31 diagnosis. Storm

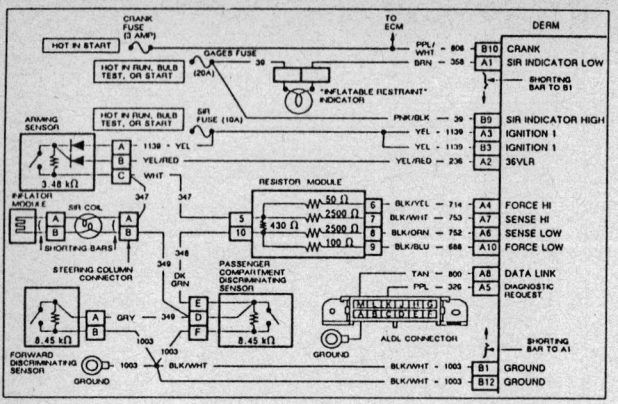

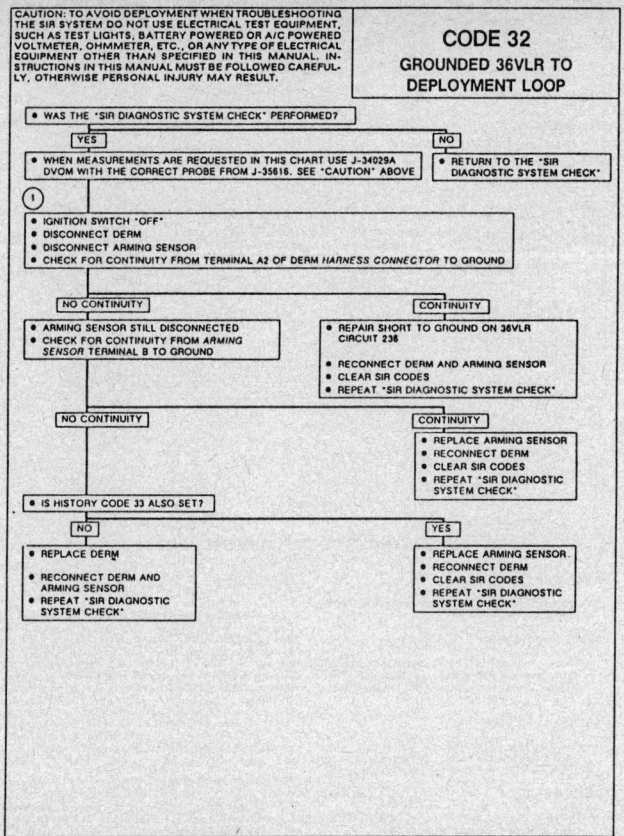

CAUTION: TO AVOID DEPLOYMENT WHEN TROUBLESHOOTING THE SIR SYSTEM DO NOT USE ELECTRICAL TEST EQUIPMENT, SUCH AS TEST LIGHTS, BATTERY POWERED OR A/C POWERED VOLTMETER, OHMMETER, ETC., OR ANY TYPE OF ELECTRICAL EQUIPMENT OTHER THAN SPECIFIED IN THIS MANUAL. INSTRUCTIONS IN THIS MANUAL MUST BE FOLLOWED CAREFULLY, OTHERWISE PERSONAL INJURY MAY RESULT.

CODE 32

GROUNDED 36VLR TO DEPLOYMENT LOOP

Test Condition:

Tested every 100 milliseconds during "Continuous Monitoring".

Failure Conditions:

Code 32 will set if: 1) The voltage at the Sense Low input (terminal A6) is between 28% and 59% of Ignition 1 output voltage for 700 milliseconds; 2) Code 42 is set.

Conditions To Clear:

Current Code 32 will clear if the voltage at the Sense Low input (terminal A6) is between 41% and 61% of 36VLR output voltage for 500 milliseconds.

Action taken:

DERM turns on the "INFLATABLE RESTRAINT" indicator lamp.

Description:

The voltage at the Sense Low input (terminal A6) is between 41% and 61% of 36VLR output voltage when 36VLR output of the DERM is charged. Should the circuit short to ground between the 36VLR output and the Arming Sensor, Ignition 1 voltage will be supplying the deployment loop. The voltage at the Sense Low input (terminal A6) will decrease due to the decrease in the supply voltage and Code 32 will set after 700 milliseconds. Code 32 indicates a short to ground in the wiring between the 36VLR output of the DERM and the Arming Sensor.

Notes on Fault Tree:

1) Checks for a short to ground in the 36 VLR circuit between the DERM and the Arming Sensor.

Fig. 113   Code 32 diagnosis. Camaro & Firebird

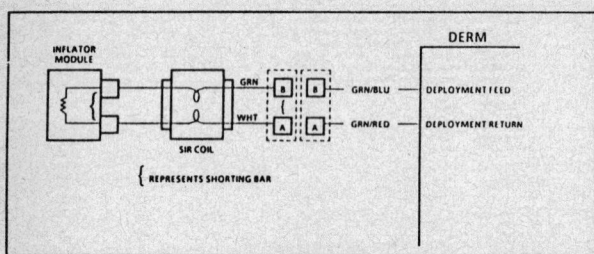

CODE 32

INFLATOR SQUIB
(CURRENT SHORTED TO BATTERY VOLTAGE)

Circuit Description:

The Inflator Squib circuit provides the current path to ignite the gas-generating material inside the Inflator Module. The squib itself is a resistive element which heats up very quickly when an appropriate current is applied. The SIR Coil Assembly allows rotation of the steering wheel while maintaining continuous contact of the deployment loop through the Inflator Module.

If the DERM measures less than a certain resistance value between the deployment feed circuit and B+ or the deployment return circuit and B+, this code will set.

Test Description: Numbers below refer to circled numbers on the diagnostic chart.

1. This test determines if the fault is within the steering column. This is done by electrically mimicking the steering column SIR electrical components with the J 37808 Load Tool, clearing codes, and checking to see if the code resets. If it does, the fault is not in the steering column; if it does not, further checking of steering column SIR components is required.
2. This indicates that the faulty portion of the circuit lies in the steering column.
3. This indicates that the code clearing procedures required in Step 1 was not properly completed.
4. This indicates that the fault is still present. If this condition occurs a second time, after repeating the procedure in Step 1, replace the DERM.
5. This test replaces the Inflator Module with the Load Tool. If the code does not come back, the Inflator Module is the cause of the fault and must be replaced. If the code does come back, the SIR Coil Assembly and/or its wiring is the cause of the fault.

6. This indicates that everything checks OK at this time. Since the code was set, however, the fault has occurred before; the fault is intermittent.
7. This indicates that the fault is in the SIR Coil Assembly.

Diagnostic Aids:

The Fasten Seat Belt indicator will stay "ON" continuously when an SIR failure code has been set.

If power is applied to the SIR system while any component is not properly connected, an additional failure code will be set for the disconnected SIR component.

The problem may be intermittent. Try performing the tests shown while "wiggling" wiring and connectors; this can often cause the fault to appear.

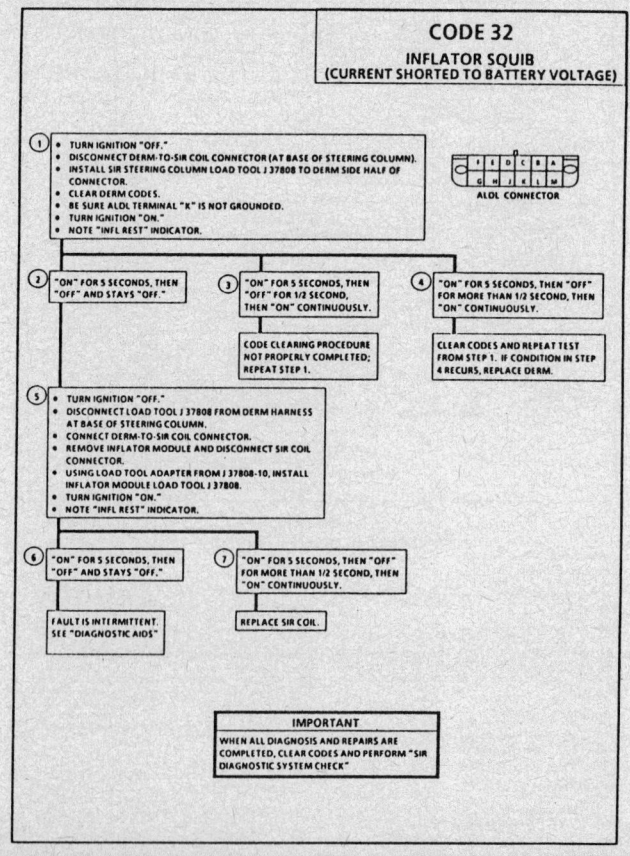

CODE 32

INFLATOR SQUIB
(CURRENT SHORTED TO BATTERY VOLTAGE)

Fig. 114   Code 32 diagnosis. Corvette

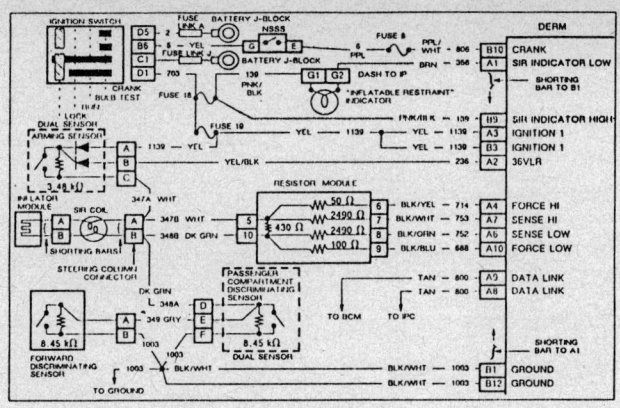

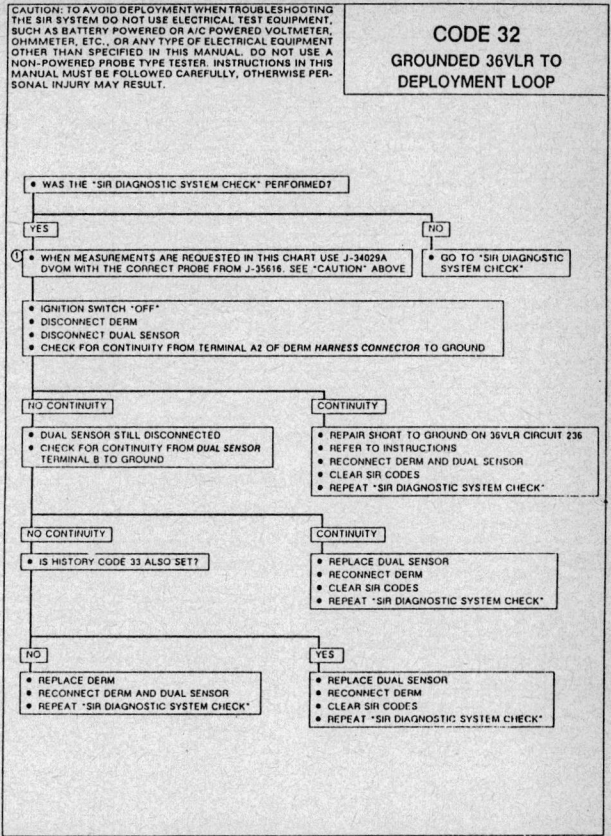

CODE 32
GROUNDED 36VLR TO DEPLOYMENT LOOP

Test Condition:

Tested every 100 milliseconds during "Continuous Monitoring".

Failure Conditions:

Code 32 will set if: 1) The voltage at the Sense Low input (terminal A6) is between 28% and 59% of Ignition 1 output voltage for 700 milliseconds; 2) Code 42 is set.

Conditions To Clear:

Current Code 32 will clear if the voltage at the Sense Low input (terminal A6) is between 41% and 61% of 36VLR output voltage for 500 milliseconds.

Action taken:

DERM turns on the "INFLATABLE RESTRAINT" indicator lamp.

Description:

The voltage at the Sense Low input (terminal A6) is between 41% and 61% of 36VLR output voltage when 36VLR output of the DERM is charged. Should the circuit short to ground between the 36VLR output and the Arming Sensor, "IGNITION 1" voltage will be supplying the deployment loop. The voltage at the Sense Low input (terminal A6) will decrease due to the decrease in the supply voltage and Code 32 will set after 700 milliseconds. Code 32 indicates a short to ground in the wiring between the 36VLR output of the DERM and the Arming Sensor.

Notes on Fault Tree:

1) Checks for a short to ground in the 36 VLR circuit between the DERM and the Dual Sensor.

Fig. 115   Code 32 diagnosis. Deville, Fleetwood, Eldorado, Seville, Riviera, Reatta, Toronado & Trofeo

---

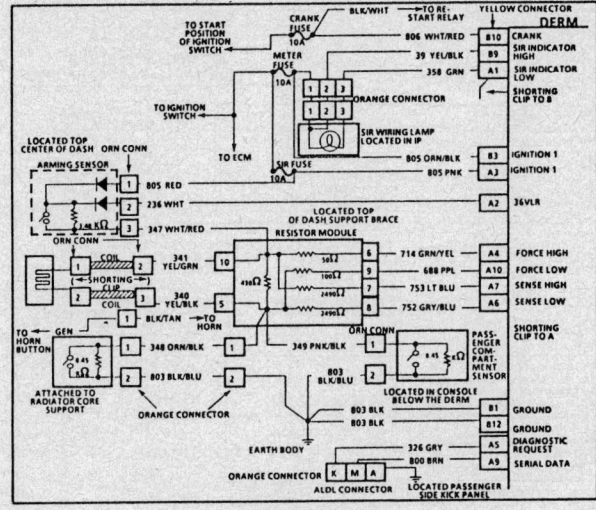

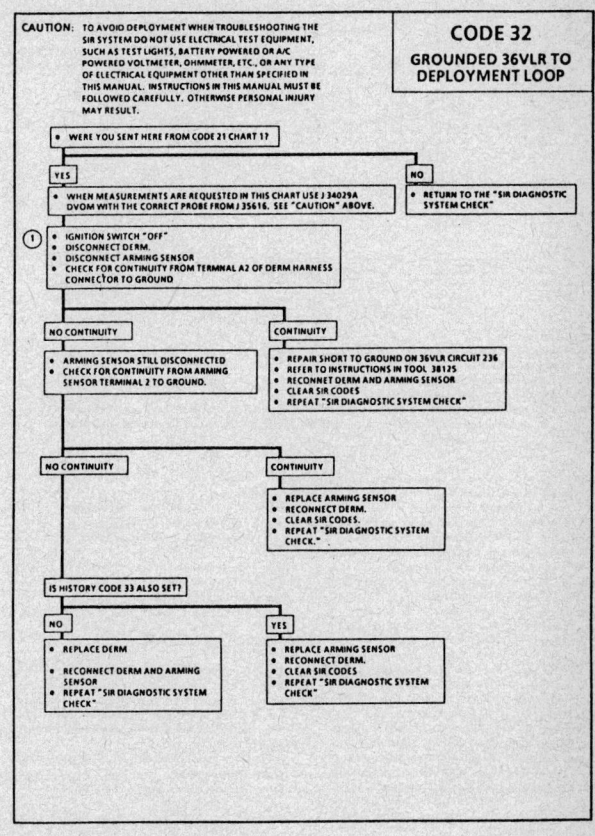

CODE 32
GROUNDED 36VLR TO DEPLOYMENT LOOP

Test Conditions:

Tested every 100 milliseconds during "Continuous Monitoring".

Failure Conditions:

Code 32 will set if: 1) The voltage at the Sense Low input terminal "A6" is between 28% and 59% of Ignition 1 output voltage for 700 milliseconds; 2) Code 42 is set.

Conditions To Clear:

Current Code 32 will clear if the voltage at the Sense Low input terminal "A6" is between 41% and 61% of 36VLR output voltage for 500 milliseconds.

Action Taken:

DERM turns "ON" the "INFLATABLE RESTRAINT" indicator lamp.

Description:

The voltage at the Sense Low input terminal "A6" is between 41% and 61% of 36VLR output voltage when 36VLR output of the DERM is charged. Should the circuit short to ground between the 36VLR output and the Arming Sensor, Ignition 1 voltage will be supplying the deployment loop. The voltage at the Sense Low input terminal "A6" will decrease due to the decrease supply voltage and Code 32 will set after 700 milliseconds. Code 32 indicates a short to ground in the wiring between the 36VLR output of the DERM and the Arming Sensor.

Notes on Fault Tree:

1. Checks for a short to ground in the 36VLR circuit between the DERM and the Arming Sensor.

Fig. 116   Code 32 diagnosis. Storm

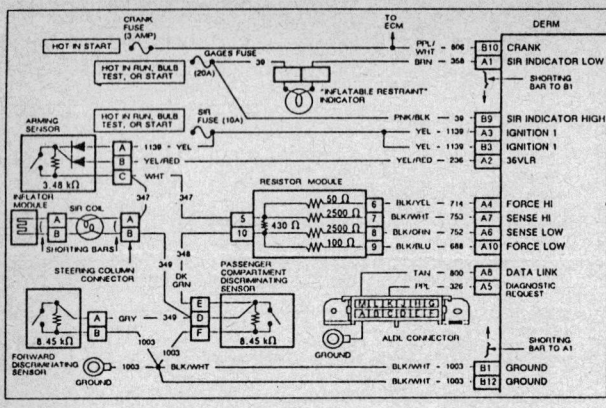

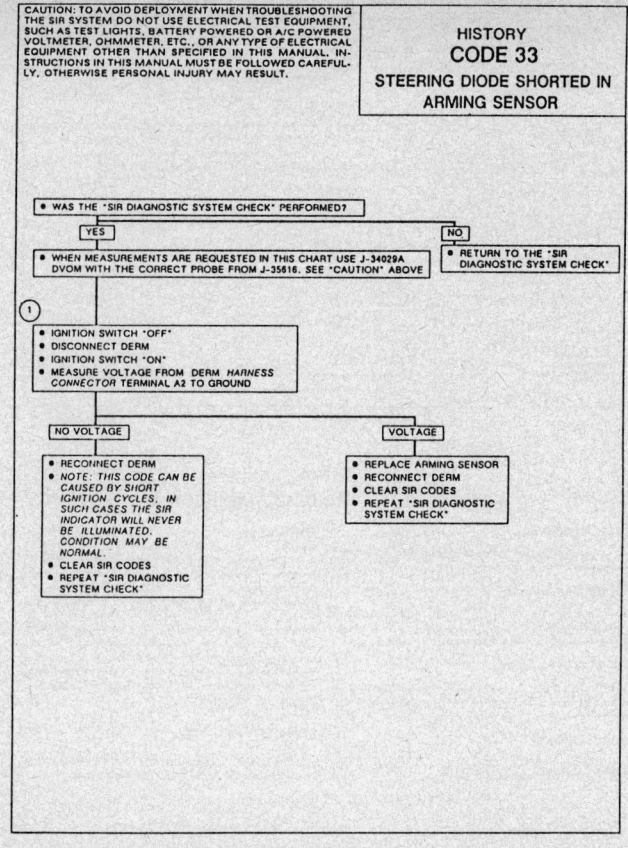

HISTORY CODE 33

STEERING DIODE SHORTED IN ARMING SENSOR

Test Condition:

Tested once during each ignition cycle at "Turn-on".

Failure Conditions:

History Code 33 will set if the voltage at the 36VLR output of the DERM (terminal A2) is equal to the Ignition 1 voltage (±2 volts) within the first 500 milliseconds after the ignition is turned on, three ignition cycles in a row.

Conditions To Clear:

History Code 33 will remain as a History Code until codes are cleared with a scan tool.

Action taken:

DERM will not turn on "INFLATABLE RESTRAINT" indicator lamp.

Description:

At "Turn-on" the DERM monitors the voltage at the 36VLR output (terminal A2) before this output begins to charge. If the diode in the Arming Sensor connected to Ignition 1 is shorted, Ignition 1 voltage will be present at the 36VLR output (terminal A2) as soon as the ignition is turned on. If the DERM detects this Ignition voltage (±2 volts) three ignition cycles in a row History Code 33 will be set.

Notes on Fault Tree:

1) Checks if diode on 36VLR circuit in the Arming Sensor is shorted.

Fig. 117   Code 33 diagnosis. Camaro & Firebird

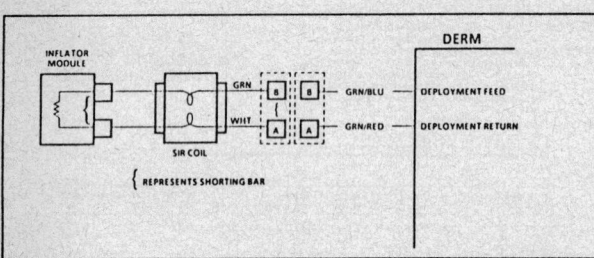

CODE 33

INFLATOR SQUIB
(CURRENT LEAKAGE TO GROUND)

Circuit Description:

The Inflator Squib circuit provides the current path to ignite the gas-generating material inside the Inflator Module. The squib itself is a resistive element which heats up very quickly when an appropriate current is applied. The SIR Coil Assembly allows rotation of the steering wheel while maintaining continuous contact of the deployment loop through the Inflator Module.

If the DERM measures a resistance that is less than a specified value, but not a "hard" short circuit, between either the deployment feed circuit and ground or the deployment return circuit and ground, this code will set.

Test Description: Numbers below refer to circled numbers on the diagnostic chart.

1. This test determines if the fault is within the steering column. This is done by electrically mimicking the steering column SIR electrical components with the J 37808 Load Tool, clearing codes, and checking to see if the code resets. If it does, the fault is not in the steering column; if it does not, further checking of steering column SIR components is required.

2. This indicates that the faulty portion of the circuit lies in the steering column.

3. This indicates that the code clearing procedures required in Step 1 was not properly completed.

4. This indicates that the fault is still present. If this condition occurs a second time, after repeating the procedure in Step 1, replace the DERM.

5. This test replaces the Inflator Module with the Load Tool. If the code does not come back, the Inflator Module is the cause of the fault and must be replaced. If the code does come back, the SIR Coil Assembly and/or its wiring is the cause of the fault.

6. This indicates that everything checks OK at this time.

7. This indicates that the fault is in the SIR Coil Assembly.

8. This test puts the Inflator Module back in the circuit to verify whether or not it is faulty.

9. This indicates that everything checks OK at this time.

10. This indicates that the fault returned to the system when the Inflator Module was reinstalled. Therefore, the Inflator Module is faulty and should be replaced.

Diagnostic Aids:

The Fasten Seat Belt indicator will stay "ON" continuously when an SIR failure code has been set.

If power is applied to the SIR system while any component is not properly connected, an additional failure code will be set for the disconnected SIR component.

The problem may be intermittent. Try performing the tests shown while "wiggling" wiring and connectors; this can often cause the fault to appear.

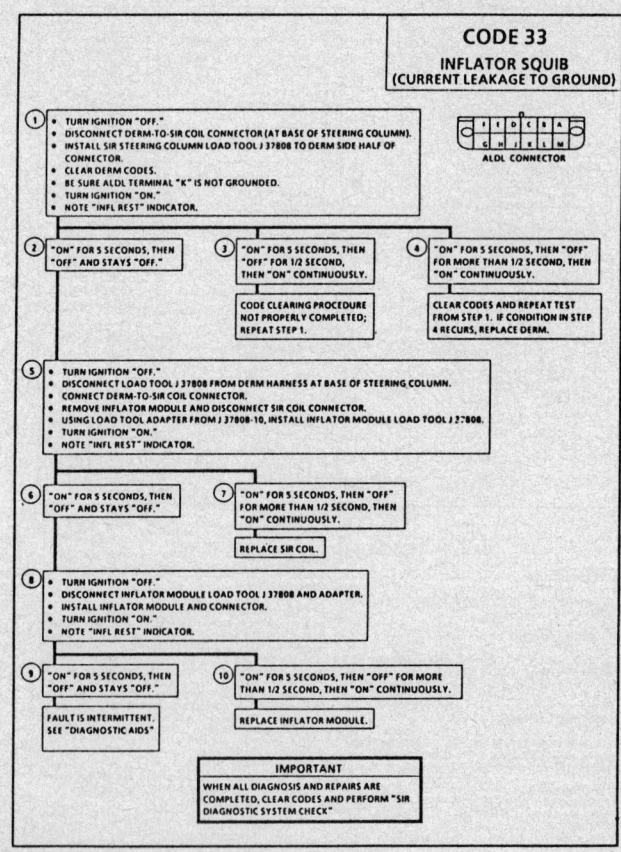

Fig. 118   Code 33 diagnosis. Corvette

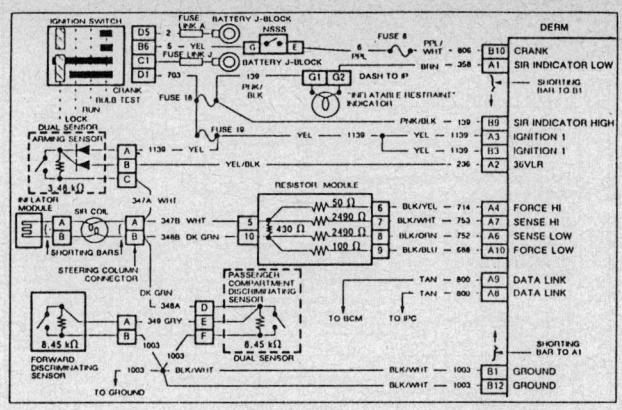

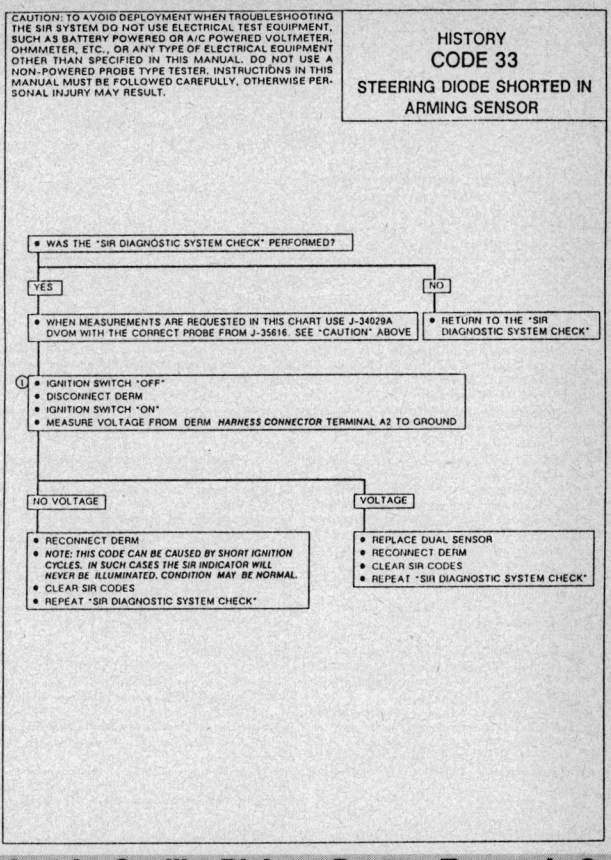

HISTORY CODE 33
STEERING DIODE SHORTED IN ARMING SENSOR

Test Condition:

Tested once during each ignition cycle at "Turn-on".

Failure Conditions:

History Code 33 will be set if the voltage at the 36VLR output of the DERM (terminal A2) is equal to the "IGNITION 1" voltage (±2 volts) within the first 500 milliseconds after the ignition is turned on, three ignition cycles in a row.

Note: History code 33 **will not** set if a history code 51 is set.

Conditions To Clear:

History Code 33 will remain as a History Code until codes are cleared with a scan tool.

Action taken:

DERM will **not** turn on "INFLATABLE RESTRAINT" indicator lamp.

Description:

At "Turn-on" the DERM monitors the voltage at the 36VLR output (terminal A2) before this output begins to charge. If the diode in the Arming Sensor connected to terminal B (circuit 236) is shorted, "IGNITION 1" voltage will be present at the 36VLR output (terminal A2) as soon as the ignition is turned on. If the DERM detects this Ignition voltage (±2 volts) three ignition cycles in a row, History Code 33 will be set.

Notes on Fault Tree:

1) Checks if diode on 36VLR circuit in the Dual Sensor is shorted.

Fig. 119   Code 33 diagnosis. Deville, Fleetwood, Eldorado, Seville, Riviera, Reatta, Toronado & Trofeo

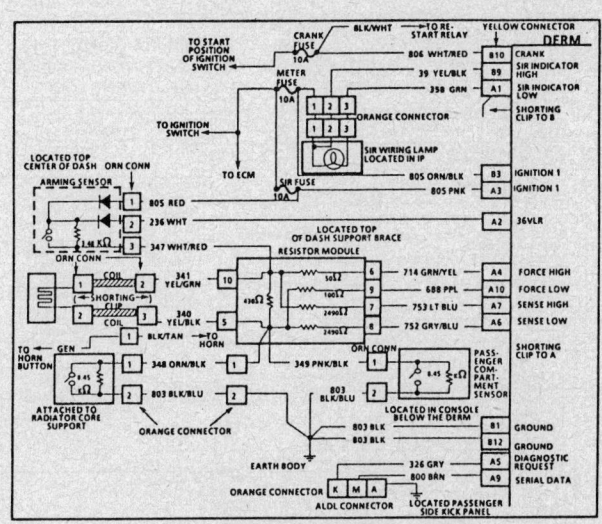

HISTORY CODE 33
STEERING DIODE SHORTED IN ARMING SENSOR

Test Conditions:

Tested once during each ignition cycle at "Turn-ON".

Failure Conditions:

History Code 33 will set if the voltage at the 36VLR output of the DERM terminal "A2" is equal to the Ignition 1 voltage (± 2 volts) within the first 500 milliseconds after the ignition is turned on, three ignition cycles in a row.

Conditions To Clear:

History Code 33 will remain as a History Code until codes are cleared with a scan tool.

Action Taken:

DERM will not turn "ON" "INFLATABLE RESTRAINT" indicator lamp.

Description:

At "Turn-ON" the DERM monitors the voltage at the 36VLR output terminal "A2" before this output begins to charge. If the diode in the Arming Sensor connected to Ignition 1 is shorted, Ignition 1 voltage will be present at the 36VLR output terminal "A2" as soon as the ignition is turned "ON". If the DERM detects this Ignition voltage (± 2 volts) three ignition cycles in a row History Code 33 will be set.

Notes on Fault Tree:

1. Checks if diode on 36VLR circuit in the Arming Sensor is shorted.

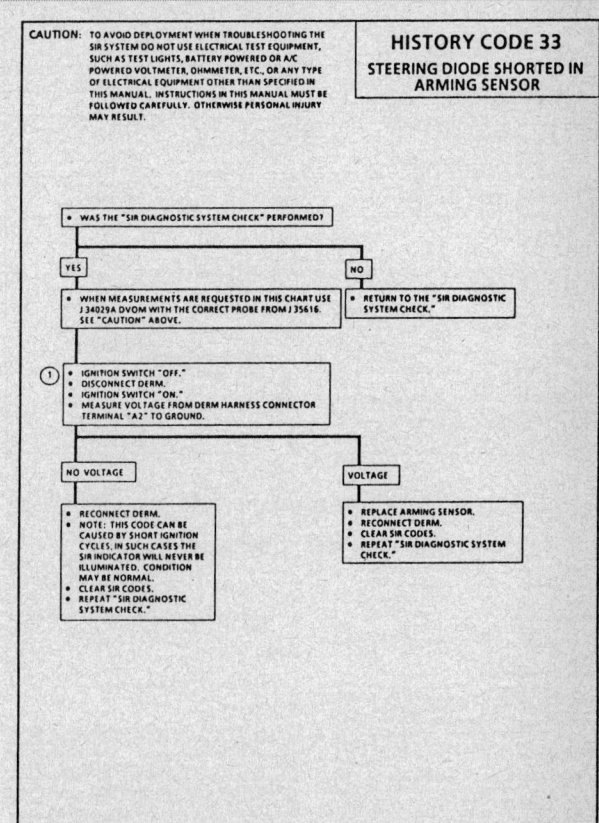

Fig. 120   Code 33 diagnosis. Storm

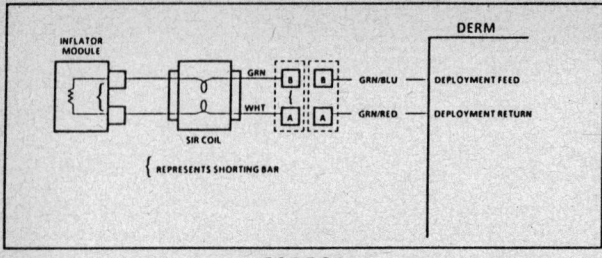

CODE 34
INFLATOR SQUIB
(CURRENT SHORTED TO GROUND)

Circuit Description:

The Inflator Squib circuit provides the current path to ignite the gas generating material inside the Inflator Module. The squib itself is a resistive element which heats up very quickly when an appropriate current is applied. The SIR Coil Assembly allows rotation of the steering wheel while maintaining continuous contact of the deployment loop through the Inflator Module.

If the DERM measures less than a certain resistance value between the deployment feed circuit and ground or the deployment return circuit and ground, this code will set.

Test Description: Numbers below refer to circled numbers on the diagnostic chart.

1. This test determines if the fault is within the steering column. This is done by electrically mimicking the steering column SIR electrical components with the J 37808 Load Tool, clearing codes, and checking to see if the code resets. If it does, the fault is not in the steering column; if it does not, further checking of steering column SIR components is required.
2. This indicates that the faulty portion of the circuit lies in the steering column.
3. This indicates that the code clearing procedures required in Step 1 was not properly completed.
4. This indicates that the fault is still present. If this condition occurs a second time, after repeating the procedure in Step 1, replace the DERM.
5. This test replaces the Inflator Module with the Load Tool. If the code does not come back, the Inflator Module is the cause of the fault and must be replaced. If the code does come back, the SIR Coil Assembly and/or its wiring is the cause of the fault.

6. This indicates that everything checks OK at this time.
7. This indicates that the fault is in the SIR Coil Assembly.
8. This test puts the Inflator Module back in the circuit to verify whether or not it is faulty.
9. This indicates that everything checks OK at this time.
10. This indicates that the fault returned to the system when the Inflator Module was reinstalled. Therefore, the Inflator Module is faulty and should be replaced.

Diagnostic Aids:

The Fasten Seat Belt indicator will stay "ON" continuously when an SIR failure code has been set.

If power is applied to the SIR system while any component is not properly connected, an additional failure code will be set for the disconnected SIR component.

The problem may be intermittent. Try performing the tests shown while "wiggling" wiring and connectors; this can often cause the fault to appear.

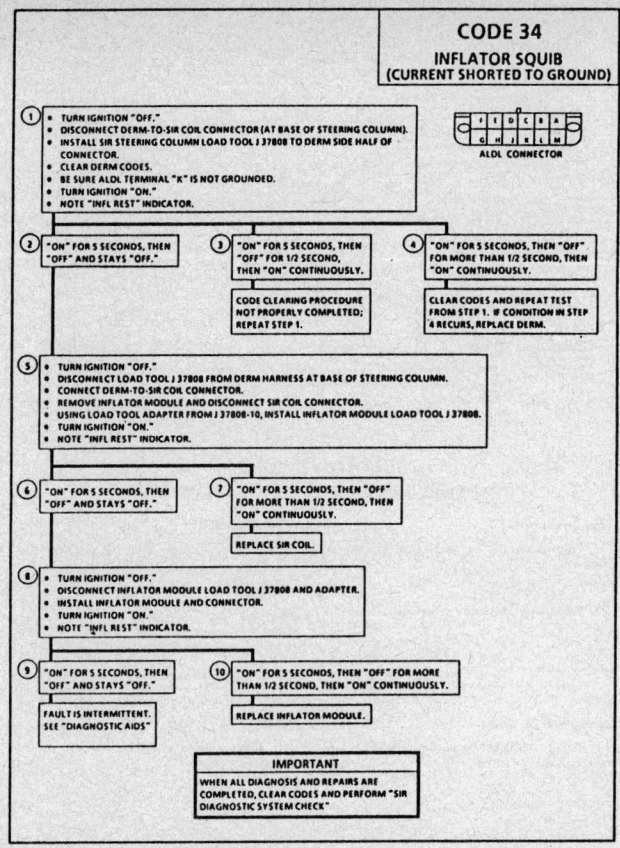

Fig. 121   Code 34 diagnosis. Corvette

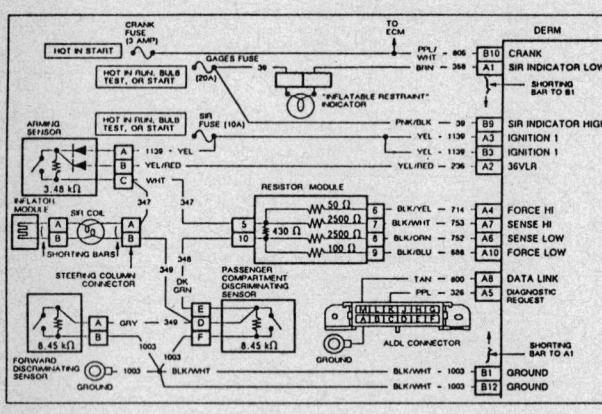

CODE 34 CHART 1

OPEN IN IGNITION 1 FEED TO DEPLOYMENT LOOP

Test Condition:

Tested once during each ignition cycle at "Turn-on".

Failure Conditions:

Code 34 will set if the voltage at the Sense Low input (terminal A6) is less than 28% of Ignition 1 output voltage for 500 milliseconds and 36VLR is less than Ignition 1 output voltage at "Turn-on".

Conditions To Clear:

To clear code 34, the ignition must be off long enough to assure the 36 VLR supply voltage has fully discharged. Once 36 VLR is discharged, the DERM will again check the failure conditions upon key on. If the failure conditions are not present (no failure indicated) then, and only then, will current code 34 be cleared.

Action taken:

DERM turns on the "INFLATABLE RESTRAINT" indicator lamp.

Description:

At "Turn-on" the DERM monitors the voltage at the Sense Low input (terminal A6) for 500 milliseconds. The DERM expects the voltage to be between 28% and 59% of Ignition 1 voltage before the 36VLR output is charged. If Ignition 1 circuit from the SIR fuse to the Arming Sensor is open or the Ignition 1 diode in the Arming Sensor is open the voltage at the Sense Low input (terminal A6) will be less than 4.6 volts and Code 34 will set.

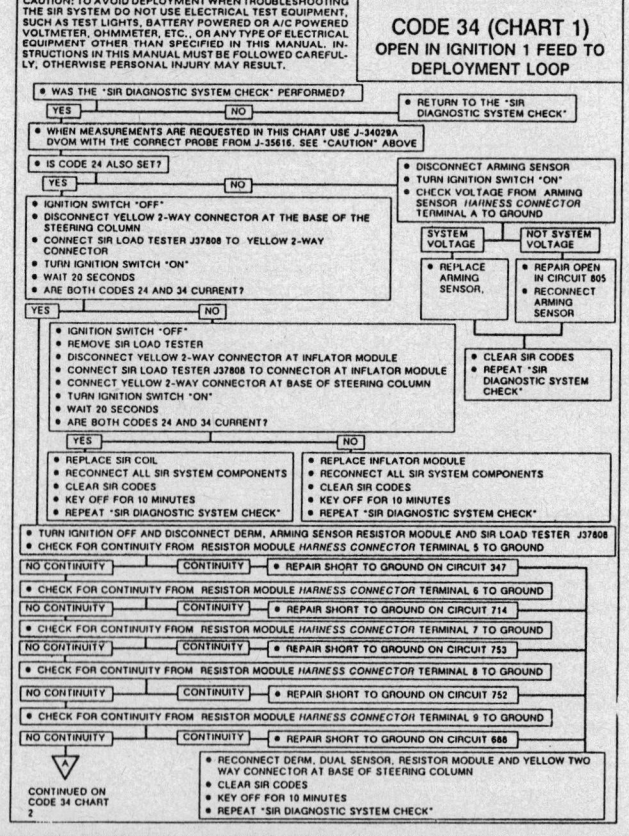

Fig. 122   Code 34 chart 1 diagnosis. Camaro & Firebird

SUPPLEMENTAL INFLATABLE RESTRAINT SYSTEM

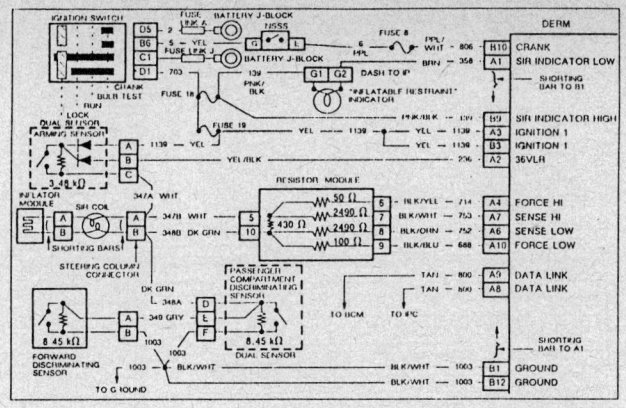

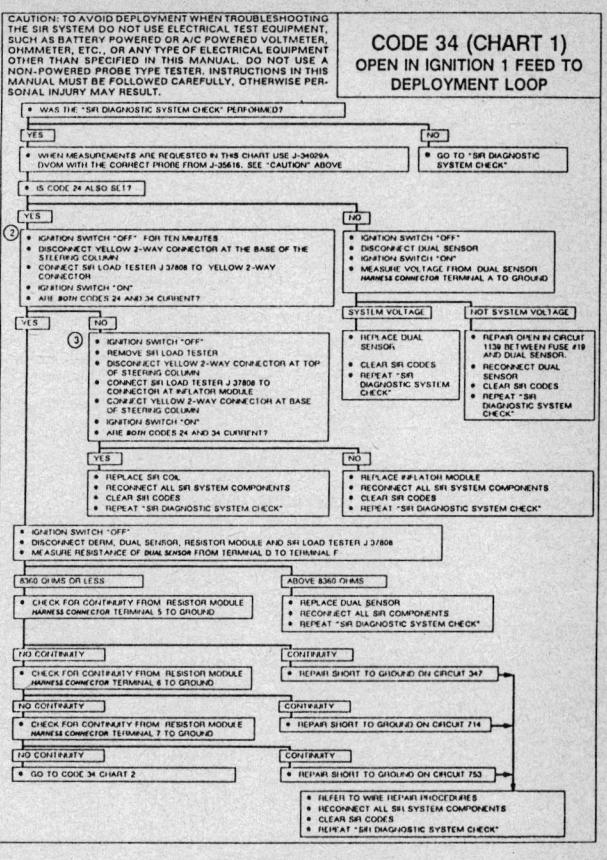

CODE 34 (CHART 1)
OPEN IN IGNITION 1 FEED TO
DEPLOYMENT LOOP

CODE 34 CHART 1

OPEN IN IGNITION 1 FEED TO DEPLOYMENT LOOP

Test Condition:

Tested once during each ignition cycle at "Turn-on".

Failure Conditions:

Code 34 will set if the voltage at the Sense Low input (terminal A6) is less than 28% of "IGNITION 1" output voltage for 500 milliseconds and 36VLR is less than "IGNITION 1" output voltage at "Turn-on".

Note: History code 34 _will not_ set if a history code 51 is set.

Conditions To Clear:

To clear code 34, the ignition must be off long enough to assure the 36VLR supply voltage has fully discharged. A wait of ten minutes after the ignition "OFF" is usually sufficient to allow the 36VLR to discharge. Once 36 VLR is discharged, the DERM will again check the failure conditions upon key on. If the failure conditions are not present (no failure indicated) then _current code 34_ will be cleared.

Action taken:

DERM turns on the "INFLATABLE RESTRAINT" indicator lamp.

Description:

At "Turn-on" the DERM monitors the voltage at the Sense Low input (terminal A6) for 500 milliseconds. The DERM expects the voltage to be between 28% and 59% of "IGNITION 1" voltage before the 36VLR output is charged. If "IGNITION 1" circuit from the SIR fuse to the Dual Sensor is open or the "IGNITION 1" diode in the Arming Sensor is open the voltage at the Sense Low input (terminal A6) will be less than 4.6 volts and Code 34 will set.

Notes on Fault Tree:

1) Checks if fault is in Dual Sensor or circuit 1139.

2) Checks if fault is in Steering Column.

3) Determines if fault is in SIR Coil or Inflator Module.

Fig. 123   Code 34 chart 1 diagnosis. Deville, Fleetwood, Eldorado, Seville, Riviera, Reatta, Toronado & Trofeo

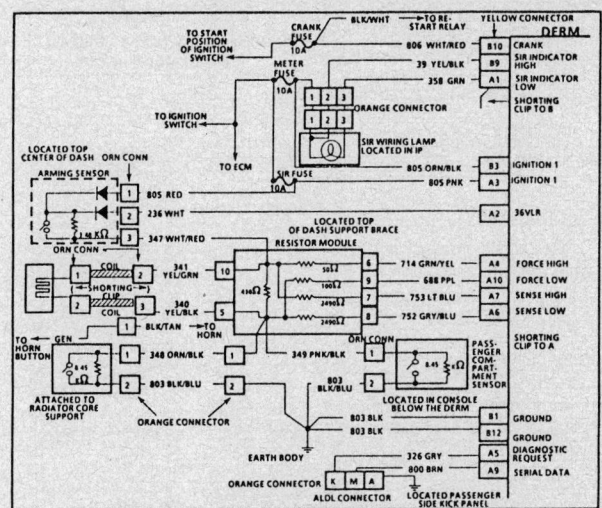

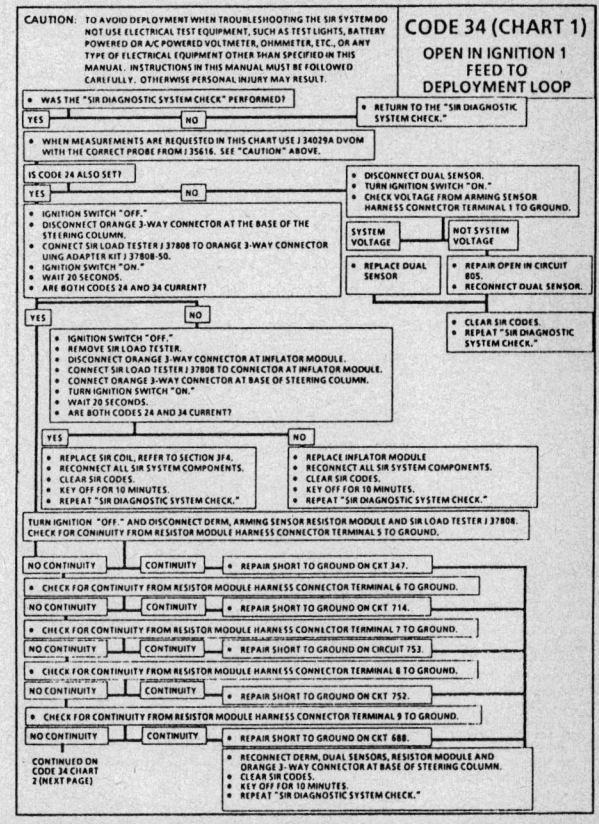

CODE 34 (CHART 1)
OPEN IN IGNITION 1
FEED TO
DEPLOYMENT LOOP

CODE 34 CHART 1

OPEN IN IGNITION 1 FEED TO DEPLOYMENT LOOP

Test Conditions:

Tested once during each ignition cycle at "Turn-ON".

Failure Conditions:

Code 34 will set if the voltage at the Sense Low input terminal "A6" is less than 28% of Ignition 1 output voltage for 500 milliseconds and 36VLR is less than Ignition 1 output voltage at "Turn-ON".

Conditions To Clear:

To clear Code 34, the ignition must be "OFF" long enough to assure the 36VLR supply voltage has fully discharged. Once 36VLR is discharged, the DERM will again check the failure conditions upon key "ON". If the failure conditions are not present (no failure indicated) then, and only then, will current Code 34 be cleared.

Action Taken:

DERM will not turn "ON" "INFLATABLE RESTRAINT" indicator lamp.

Description:

At "Turn-ON" the DERM monitors the voltage at the Sense Low input terminal "A6" for 500 milliseconds. The DERM expects the voltage to be between 28% and 59% of Ignition 1 voltage before the 36VLR output is charged. If Ignition 1 circuit from the SIR fuse to the Dual Sensor is open or the Ignition 1 diode in the Arming Sensor is open the voltage at the Sense Low input terminal "A6" will be less than 4.6 volts and Code 34 will set.

Fig. 124   Code 34 chart 1 diagnosis. Storm

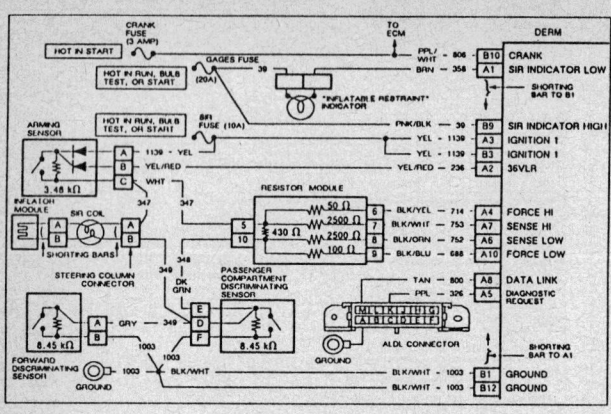

CODE 34 CHART 2

OPEN IN IGNITION 1 FEED TO DEPLOYMENT LOOP

Test Condition:

Tested once during each ignition cycle at "Turn-on".

Failure Conditions:

Code 34 will be set if the voltage at the Sense Low input (terminal A6) is less than 28% of Ignition 1 output voltage for 500 milliseconds and 36VLR is less than Ignition 1 output voltage at "Turn-on".

Conditions To Clear:

To clear code 34, the ignition must be off long enough to assure the 36VLR supply voltage has fully discharged. Once 36 VLR is discharged, the DERM will again check the failure conditions upon key on. If the failure conditions are not present (no

failure indicated) then, and only then, will current code 34 be cleared.

Action taken:

DERM turns on the "INFLATABLE RESTRAINT" indicator lamp.

Description:

At "Turn-on" the DERM monitors the voltage at the Sense Low input (terminal A6) for 500 milliseconds. The DERM expects the voltage to be between 28% and 59% of Ignition 1 voltage before the 36VLR output is charged. If Ignition 1 circuit from the SIR fuse to the Arming Sensor is open or the Ignition 1 diode in the Arming Sensor is open the voltage at the Sense Low input (terminal A6) will be less than 4.6 volts and Code 34 will set.

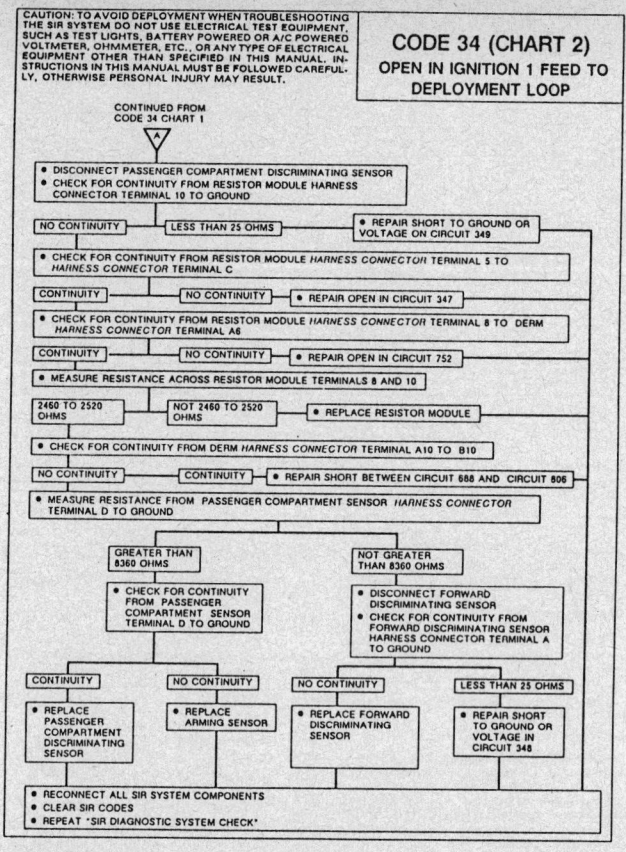

Fig. 125   Code 34 chart 2 diagnosis. Camaro & Firebird

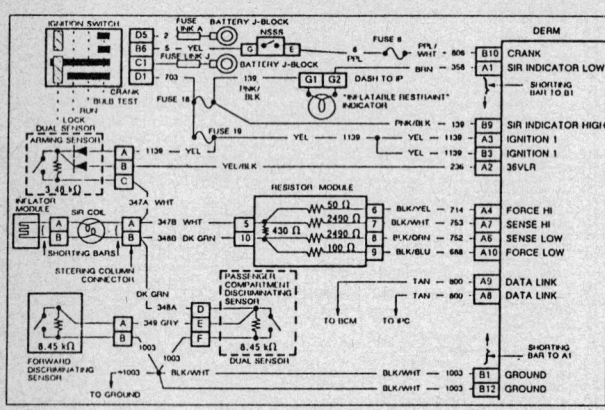

CODE 34 CHART 2

OPEN IN IGNITION 1 FEED TO DEPLOYMENT LOOP

Test Condition:

Tested once during each ignition cycle at "Turn-on".

Failure Conditions:

Code 34 will set if the voltage at the Sense Low input (terminal A6) is less than 28% of "IGNITION 1" output voltage for 500 milliseconds and 36VLR is less than "IGNITION 1" output voltage at "Turn-on".

Conditions To Clear:

To clear code 34, the ignition must be off long enough to assure the 36VLR supply voltage has fully discharged. A wait of ten minutes with the ignition "OFF" is usually sufficient to allow the 36 VLR to discharge. Once 36 VLR is discharged, the DERM will again check the failure conditions upon key on. If the failure conditions are not present (no failure indicated) then *current code 34* will be cleared.

Action taken:

DERM turns on the "INFLATABLE RESTRAINT" indicator lamp.

Description:

At "Turn-on" the DERM monitors the voltage at the Sense Low input for 500 milliseconds. The DERM expects the voltage to be between 28% and 59% of "IGNITION 1" voltage before the 36VLR output is charged. If "IGNITION 1" circuit from the SIR fuse to the Dual Sensor is open or the "IGNITION 1" diode in the Arming Sensor is open the voltage at the Sense Low input (terminal A6) will be less than 4.6 volts and Code 34 will set.

Notes on Fault Tree:

1) Determines if fault is in Forward Sensor or a short to ground on circuit 349 between Forward Sensor and Dual Sensor.

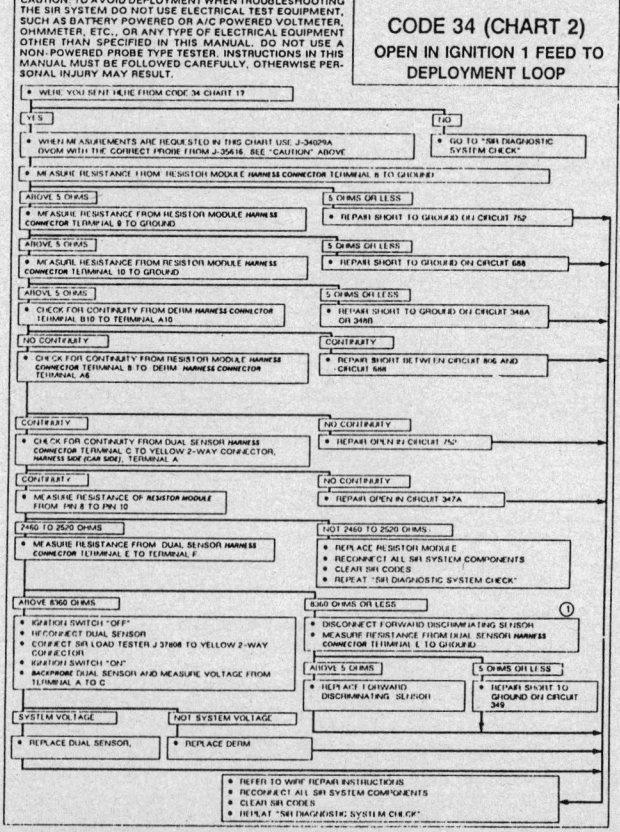

Fig. 126   Code 34 chart 2 diagnosis. Deville, Fleetwood, Eldorado, Seville, Riviera, Reatta, Toronado & Trofeo

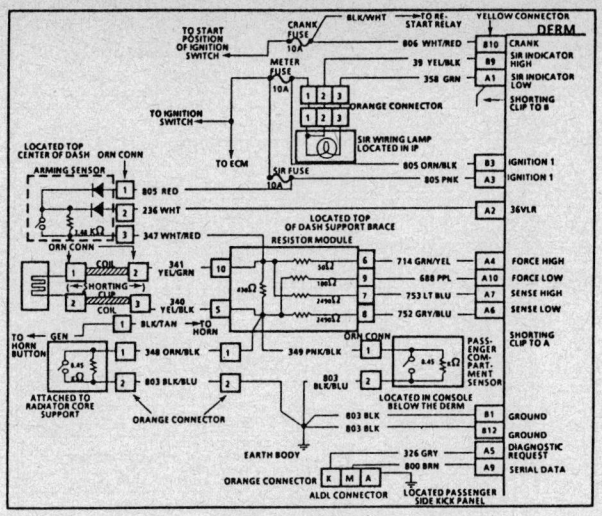

CODE 34 CHART 2
OPEN IN IGNITION 1 FEED TO DEPLOYMENT LOOP

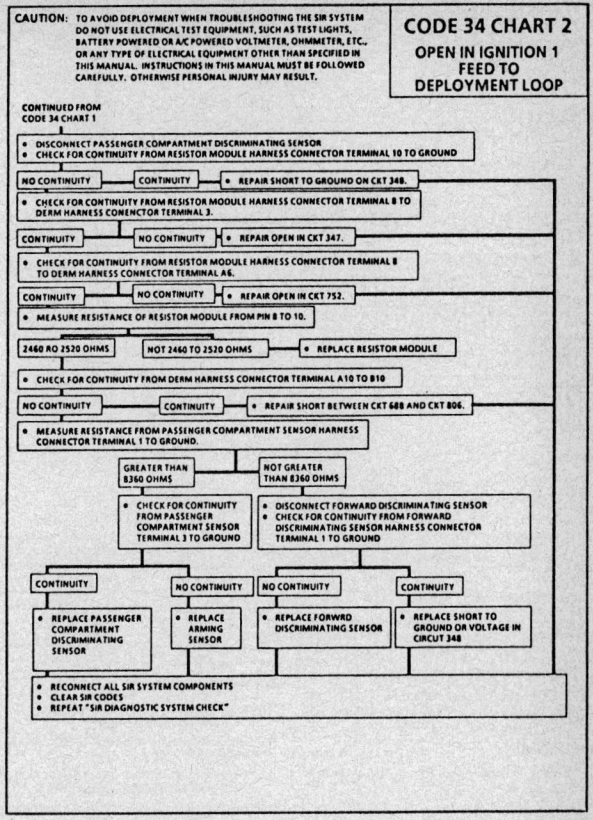

Fig. 127 Code 34 chart 2 diagnosis. Storm

Test Conditions:

Tested once during each ignition cycle at "Turn-ON."

Failure Conditions:

Code 34 will set if the voltage at the Sense Low input terminal "A6" is less than 28% of Ignition 1 output voltage for 500 milliseconds and 36VLR is less than Ignition 1 output voltage at "Turn-ON."

Conditions To Clear:

To clear Code 34, the ignition must be "OFF" long enough to assure the 36VLR supply voltage has fully discharged. Once 36VLR is discharged, the DERM will again check the failure conditions upon key "ON." If the failure conditions are not present (no failure indicated) then, and only then, will current Code 34 be cleared.

Action Taken:

DERM will not turn "ON" "INFLATABLE RESTRAINT" indicator lamp.

Description:

At "Turn-ON" the DERM monitors the voltage at the Sense Low input terminal "A6" for 500 milliseconds. The DERM expects the voltage to be between 28% and 59% of Ignition 1 voltage before the 36VLR output is charged. If Ignition 1 circuit from the SIR fuse to the Arming Sensor is open or the Ignition 1 diode in the Arming Sensor is open the voltage at the Sense Low input terminal "A6" will be less than 4.6 volts and Code 34 will set.

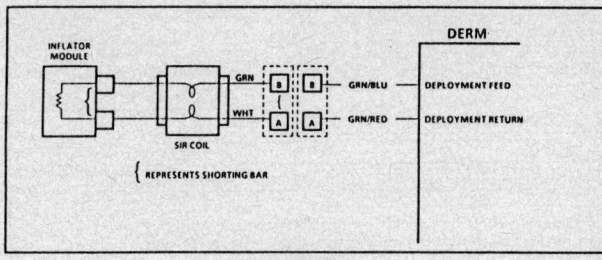

CODE 35
INFLATOR SQUIB
(OPEN CIRCUIT)

NOTE: If ignition is turned "ON," while DERM-to-SIR Coil Harness is disconnected and Load Tool J 37808 is NOT connected, this code will set.

Circuit Description:

The Inflator Squib circuit provides the current path to ignite the gas-generating material inside the Inflator Module. The squib itself is a resistive element which heats up very quickly when an appropriate current is applied. The SIR Coil Assembly allows rotation of the steering wheel while maintaining continuous contact of the deployment loop through the Inflator Module.

If the DERM measures infinite resistance (open circuit) in the Inflator Squib circuit, this code will set.

Test Description: Numbers below refer to circled numbers on the diagnostic chart.

1. This test determines if the fault is within the steering column. This is done by electrically mimicking the steering column SIR electrical components with the J 37808 Load Tool, clearing codes, and checking to see if the code resets. If it does, the fault is not in the steering column; if it does not, further checking of steering column SIR components is required.

2. This indicates that the faulty portion of the circuit lies in the steering column.

3. This indicates that the code clearing procedure required in Step 1 was not properly completed.

4. This indicates that the fault is still present. If the connections to the Load Tool and the tool itself check OK, clear the codes and repeat the testing described in Step 1. If this condition occurs a second time, after repeating the procedure in Step 1, replace the DERM.

5. This test replaces the Inflator Module with the Load Tool. If the code does not come back, the Inflator Module is the cause of the fault and must be replaced. If the code does come back, the SIR Coil Assembly and/or its wiring is the cause of the fault.

6. This indicates that everything checks OK at this time. Since the code was set, however, the fault has occurred before; the fault is intermittent.

7. This indicates that the fault is still present. If the connections to the Load Tool and the tool itself check OK, the SIR Coil Assembly and/or its wiring is the cause of the fault.

8. This test puts the Inflator Module back in the circuit to verify whether or not it is faulty.

9. This indicates that everything checks OK at this time.

10. This indicates that the fault returned to the system when the Inflator Module was reinstalled. Therefore, the Inflator Module is faulty and should be replaced.

Diagnostic Aids:

The Fasten Seat Belt indicator will stay "ON" continuously when an SIR failure code has been set.

If power is applied to the SIR system while any component is not properly connected, an additional failure code will be set for the disconnected SIR component.

The problem may be intermittent. Try performing the tests shown while "wiggling" wiring and connectors; this can often cause the fault to appear.

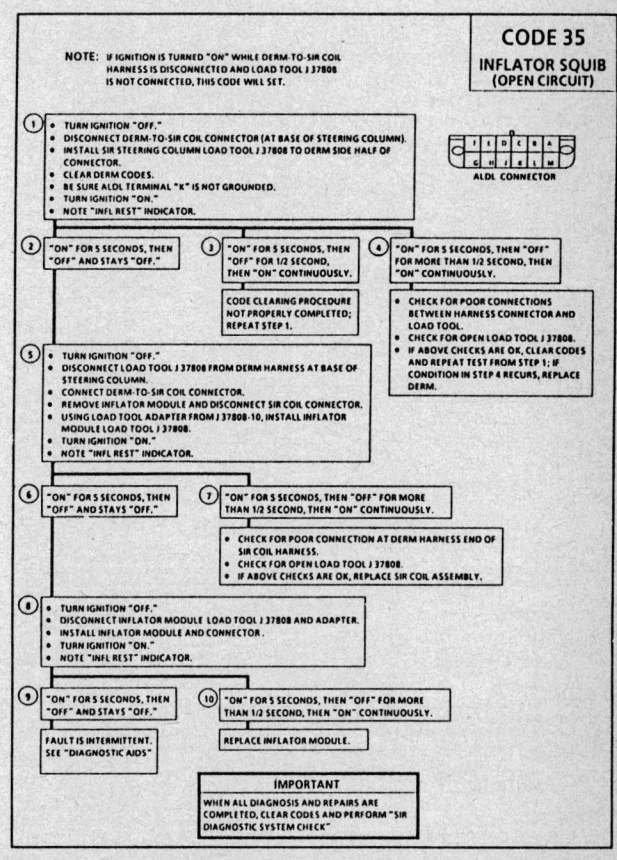

Fig. 128 Code 35 diagnosis. Corvette

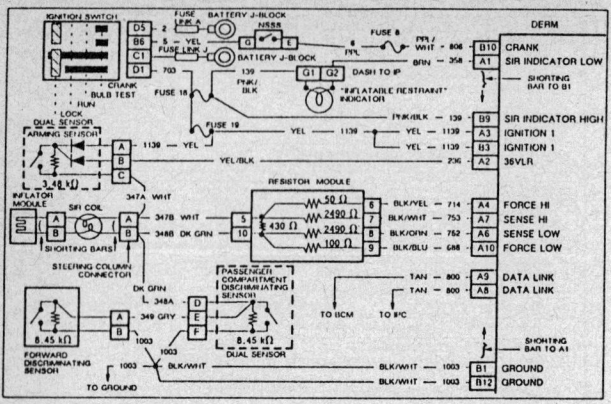

CODE 35

DISCRIMINATING SENSOR OPEN

Test Condition:

Tested every 100 milliseconds during "Continuous Monitoring".

Failure Conditions:

Code 35 will set if the voltage at the Sense Low input (terminal A6) is between 61% and 78% of 36VLR output voltage for 500 milliseconds.

Conditions To Clear:

Current Code 35 will clear if the voltage at the Sense Low input (terminal A6) is between 41% and 61% of 36VLR output voltage for 500 milliseconds.

Action taken:

DERM turns on the "INFLATABLE RESTRAINT" indicator lamp.

Description:

Code 35 is set when the voltage the Sense Low input (terminal A6) is between 61% and 78% of 36VL.R

output voltage for 500 milliseconds during the "Continuous Monitoring" tests performed by the DERM. The "Continuous Monitoring" tests are performed by the DERM after the initial "Turn-on" tests are completed and are performed every 100 milliseconds while "IGNITION 1" voltage is present at the DERM. If one of the Discriminating Sensors is open the voltage at the Sense Low input will increase due to the increase in resistance of the Discriminating Sensor section of the deployment loop and Code 35 will set.

Notes on Fault Tree:

1) Checks the resistance and ground path of the Forward Discriminating Sensor.
2) Determines if fault is in the Forward Discriminating Sensor.
3) Determines if fault is in the Dual Sensor or in the Dual Sensor Ground Path (circuit 1003)..
4) Determines if fault is an open circuit in the Forward Sensor Ground path (circuit 1003) or an open circuit in the harness between the Dual Sensor and the Forward Sensor (circuit 349).

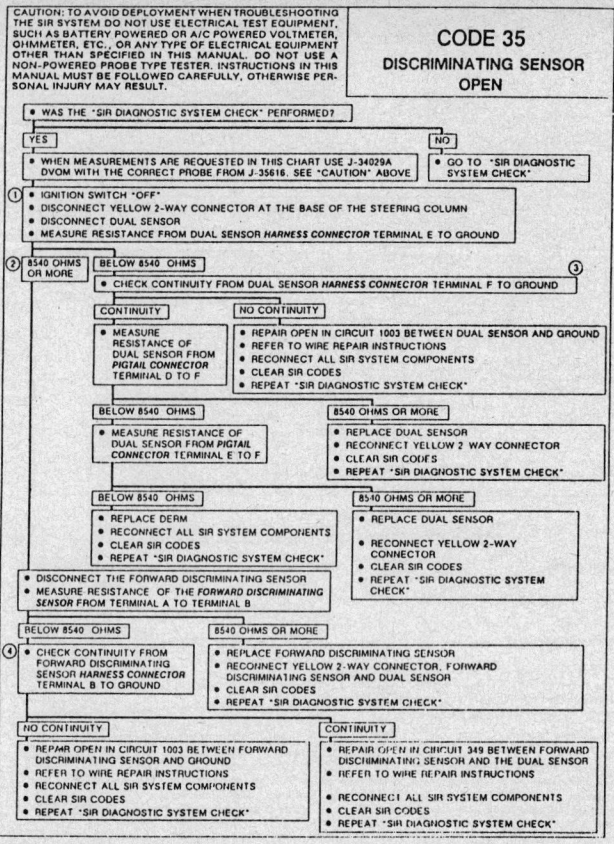

Fig. 129   Code 35 diagnosis. Deville, Fleetwood, Eldorado, Seville, Toronado & Trofeo

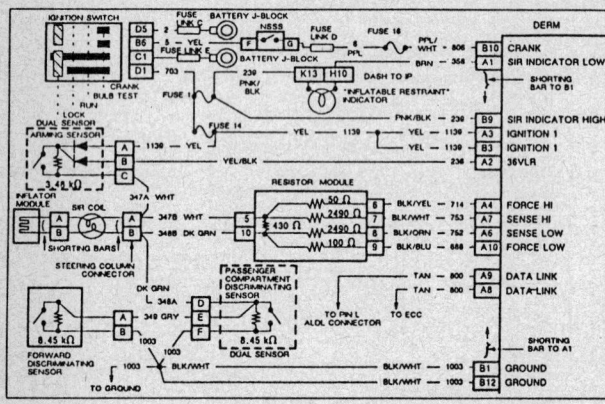

CODE 35

DISCRIMINATING SENSOR OPEN

Test Condition:

Tested every 100 milliseconds during "Continuous Monitoring".

Failure Conditions:

Code 35 will set if the voltage at the Sense Low input (terminal A6) is between 61% and 78% of 36VLR output voltage for 500 milliseconds.

Conditions To Clear:

Current Code 35 will clear if the voltage at the Sense Low input (terminal A6) is between 41% and 61% of 36VLR output voltage for 500 milliseconds.

Action taken:

DERM turns on the "INFLATABLE RESTRAINT" indicator lamp.

Description:

Code 35 is set when the voltage the Sense Low input (terminal A6) is between 61% and 78% of 36VLR

output voltage for 500 milliseconds during the "Continuous Monitoring" tests performed by the DERM. The "Continuous Monitoring" tests are performed by the DERM after the initial "Turn-on" tests are completed and are performed every 100 milliseconds while Ignition 1 voltage is present at the DERM. If one of the Discriminating Sensors is open the voltage at the Sense Low input will increase due to the increase in resistance of the Discriminating Sensor section of the deployment loop and Code 35 will set.

Notes on Fault Tree:

1) Checks the resistance and ground path of the Forward Discriminating Sensor.
2) Determines if fault is in the Forward Discriminating Sensor.
3) Determines if fault is in the Dual Sensor or in the Dual Sensor ground path (circuit 1003).
4) Determines if fault is an open circuit in the Forward Discriminating Sensor ground path (circuit 1003) or an open circuit in the harness between the Dual Sensor and the Forward Sensor (circuit 349).

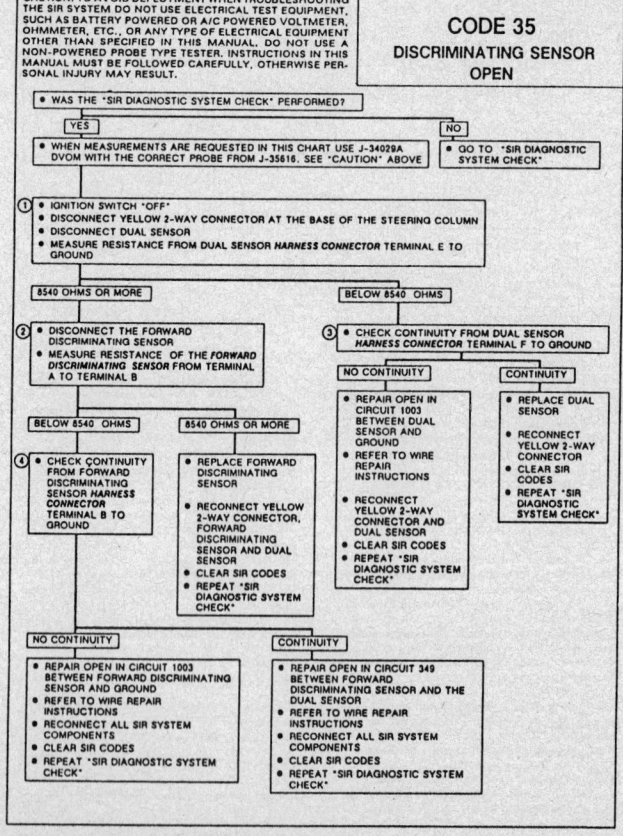

Fig. 130   Code 35 diagnosis. Riviera & Reatta

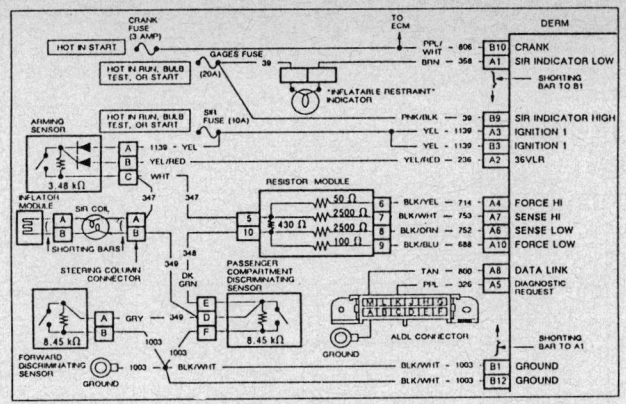

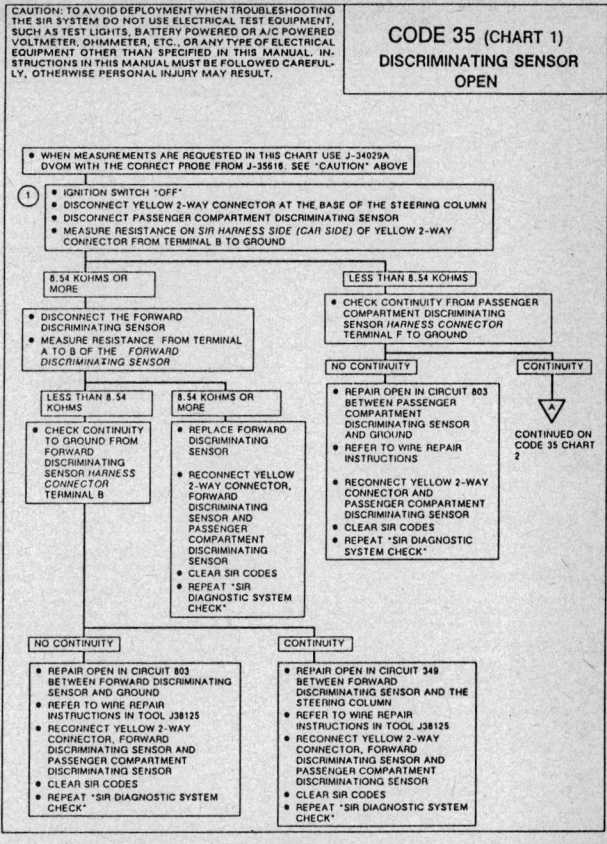

CODE 35 CHART 1
DISCRIMINATING SENSOR OPEN

Test Condition:

Tested every 100 milliseconds during "Continuous Monitoring".

Failure Conditions:

Code 35 will set if the voltage at the Sense Low input (terminal A6) is between 61% and 78% of 36VLR output voltage for 500 milliseconds.

Conditions To Clear:

Current Code 35 will clear if the voltage at the Sense Low input (terminal A6) is between 41% and 61% of 36VLR output voltage for 500 milliseconds.

Action taken:

DERM turns on the "INFLATABLE RESTRAINT" indicator lamp.

Description:

Code 35 is set when the voltage the Sense Low input (terminal A6) is between 61% and 78% of 36VLR output voltage for 500 milliseconds during the "Continuous Monitoring" tests performed by the DERM. The "Continuous Monitoring" tests are performed by the DERM after the initial "Turn-on" tests are completed and are performed every 100 milliseconds while Ignition 1 voltage is present at the DERM. If one of the Discriminating Sensors is open the voltage at the Sense Low input will increase due to the increase in the resistance of the Discriminating Sensor section of the deployment loop and Code 35 will set.

Notes on Fault Tree:

1) Checks the resistance of the Forward Discriminating Sensor.

Fig. 131   Code 35 chart 1 diagnosis. Camaro & Firebird

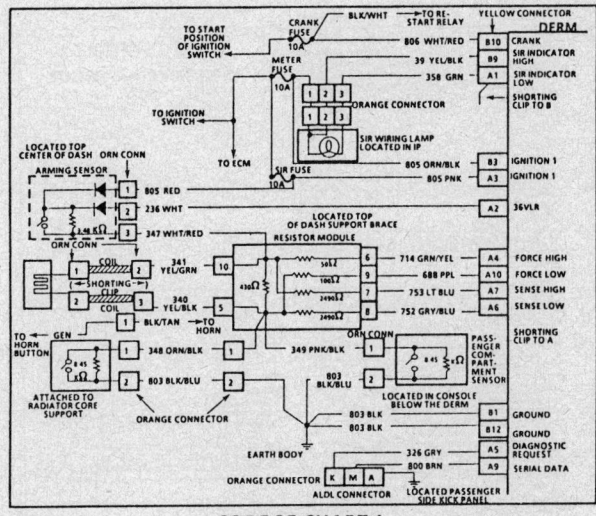

CODE 35 CHART 1
DISCRIMINATING SENSOR OPEN

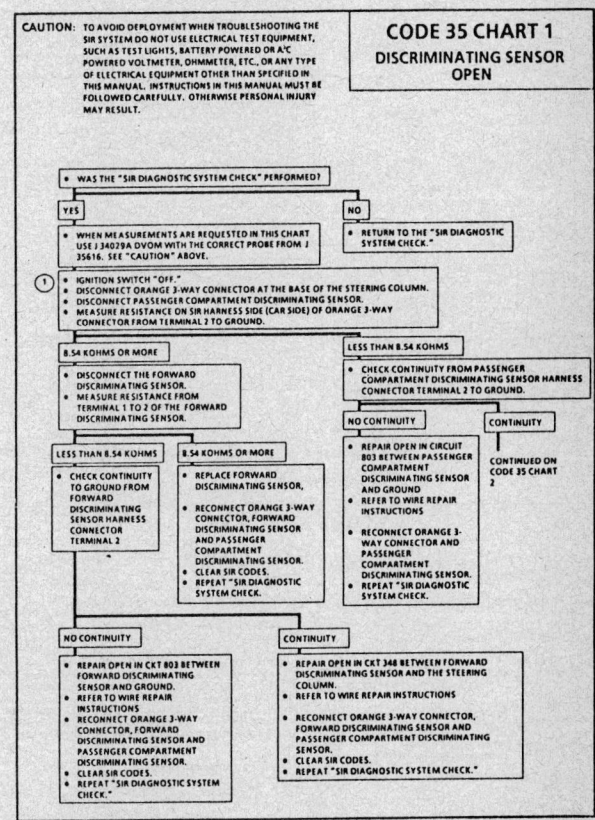

Test Conditions:

Tested every 100 milliseconds during "Continuous Monitoring".

Failure Conditions:

Code 35 will set if the voltage at the Sense Low input terminal "A6" is between 61% and 78% of 36VLR output voltage for 500 milliseconds.

Conditions To Clear:

Current Code 35 will clear if the voltage at the Sense Low input terminal "A6" is between 41% and 61% of 36VLR output voltage for 500 milliseconds.

Action Taken:

DERM will not turn "ON" "INFLATABLE RESTRAINT" indicator lamp.

Description:

Code 35 is set when the voltage the Sense Low input terminal "A6" is between 61% and 78% of 36VLR output voltage for 500 milliseconds during the "Continuous Monitoring" tests performed by the DERM. The "Continuous Monitoring" tests are performed by the DERM after the initial "Turn-ON" tests are completed and are performed every 100 milliseconds while Ignition 1 voltage is present at the DERM. If one of the Discriminating Sensors is open the voltage at the Sense Low input will increase due to the increase in the resistance of the Discriminating Sensor section of the deployment loop and Code 35 will set.

Notes on Fault Tree:

1. Checks the resistance of the Forward Discriminating Sensor.

Fig. 132   Code 35 chart 1 diagnosis. Storm

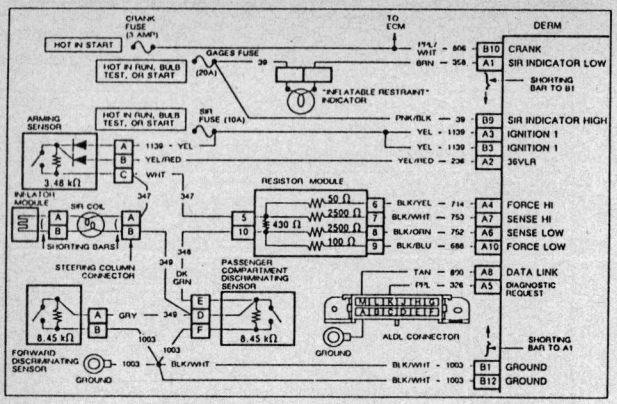

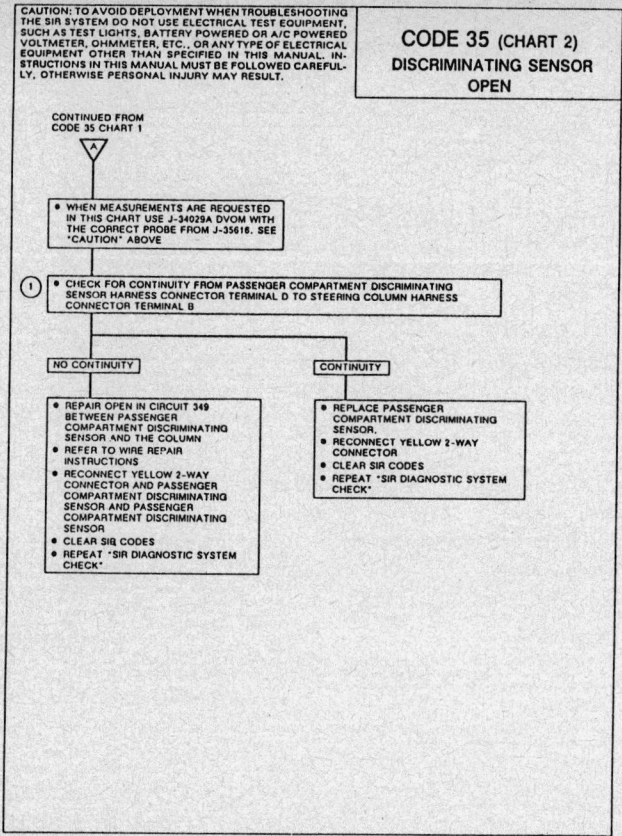

CODE 35 CHART 2

DISCRIMINATING SENSOR OPEN

Test Condition:

Tested every 100 milliseconds during "Continuous Monitoring".

Failure Conditions:

Code 35 will set if the voltage at the Sense Low input (terminal A6) is between 61% and 78% of 36VLR output voltage for 500 milliseconds.

Conditions to Clear:

Current Code 35 will clear if the voltage at the Sense Low input (terminal A6) is between 41% and 61% of 36VLR output voltage for 500 milliseconds.

Action taken:

DERM turns on the "INFLATABLE RESTRAINT" indicator lamp.

Description:

Code 35 is set when the voltage the Sense Low input (terminal A6) is between 61% and 78% of 36VLR output voltage for 500 milliseconds during the "Continuous Monitoring" tests performed by the DERM. The "Continuous Monitoring" tests are performed by the DERM after the initial "Turn-on" tests are completed and are performed every 100 milliseconds while Ignition 1 voltage is present at the DERM. If one of the Discriminating Sensors is open the voltage at the Sense Low input will increase due to the increase in the resistance of the Discriminating Sensor section of the deployment loop and Code 35 will set.

Notes on Fault Tree:

1) Checks for continuity in circuit 349.

Fig. 133   Code 35 chart 2 diagnosis. Camaro & Firebird

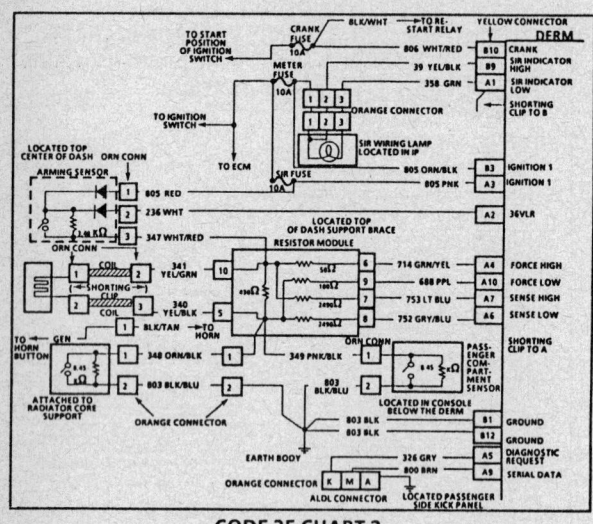

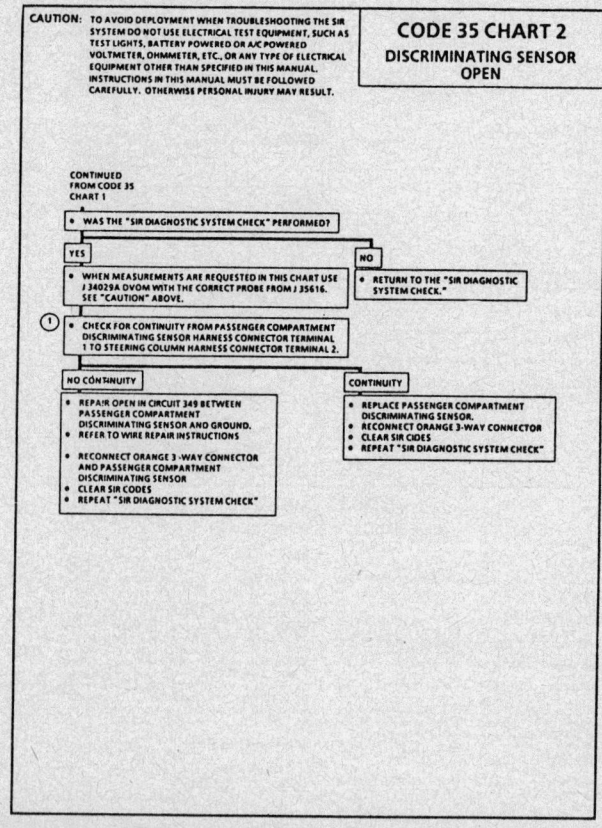

CODE 35 CHART 2

DISCRIMINATING SENSOR OPEN

Test Conditions:

Tested every 100 milliseconds during "Continuous Monitoring".

Failure Conditions:

Code 35 will set if the voltage at the Sense Low input terminal "A6" is between 61% and 78% of 36VLR output voltage for 500 milliseconds.

Conditions To Clear:

Current Code 35 will clear if the voltage at the Sense Low input terminal "A6" is between 41% and 61% of 36VLR output voltage for 500 milliseconds.

Action Taken:

DERM will not turn "ON" "INFLATABLE RESTRAINT" indicator lamp.

Description:

Code 35 is set when the voltage the Sense Low input terminal "A6" is between 61% and 78% of 36VLR output voltage for 500 milliseconds during the "Continuous Monitoring" tests performed by the DERM. The "Continuous Monitoring" tests are performed by the DERM after the initial "Turn-ON" tests are completed and are performed every 100 milliseconds while Ignition 1 voltage is present at the DERM. If one of the Discriminating Sensors is open the voltage at the Sense Low input will increase due to the increase in the resistance of the Discriminating Sensor section of the deployment loop and Code 35 will set.

Notes on Fault Tree:

1. Checks for continuity in circuit 349.

Fig. 134   Code 35 chart 2 diagnosis. Storm

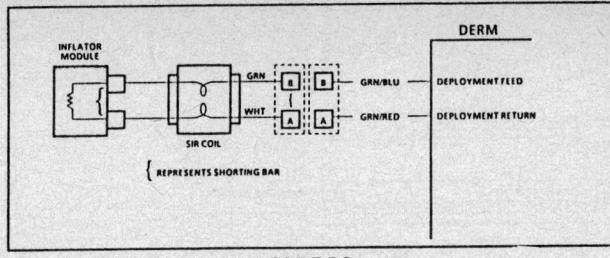

CODE 36
INFLATOR SQUIB
(SQUIB FAULT)

Circuit Description:

The Inflator Squib circuit provides the current path to ignite the gas-generating material inside the Inflator Module. The squib itself is a resistive element which heats up very quickly when an appropriate current is applied. The SIR Coil Assembly allows rotation of the steering wheel while maintaining continuous contact of the deployment loop through the Inflator Module.

If the DERM measures a resistance out of a specified range in the Inflator Squib circuit, this code will set.

Test Description: Numbers below refer to circled numbers on the diagnostic chart.

1. This test determines if the fault is within the steering column. This is done by electrically mimicking the steering column SIR electrical components with the J 37808 Load Tool, clearing codes, and checking to see if the code resets. If it does, the fault is not in the steering column; if it does not, further checking of steering column SIR components is required.

2. This indicates that the faulty portion of the circuit lies in the steering column.

3. This indicates that the code clearing procedures required in Step 1 was not properly completed.

4. This indicates that the fault is still present. If the connection to the Load Tool checks OK, and there is no short between the GRN/BLU and GRN/RED wires, clear codes and repeat Step 1. If this condition occurs a second time, after repeating the procedure described in Step 1, replace the DERM.

5. This test replaces the Inflator Module with the Load Tool. If the code does not come back, the Inflator Module is the cause of the fault and must be replaced. If the code does come back, the SIR Coil Assembly and/or its wiring is the cause of the fault.

6. This indicates that everything checks OK at this time. Since the code was set, however, the fault has occurred before; the fault is intermittent.

7. This indicates that the fault is still present. If the connections to the Load Tool are OK, and the connector shorting bar is not damaged, the SIR Coil Assembly is the cause of the fault and should be replaced.

8. This test puts the Inflator Module back in the circuit to verify whether or not it is faulty.

9. This indicates that everything checks OK at this time.

10. This indicates that the fault returned to the system when the Inflator Module was reinstalled. Therefore, the Inflator Module is faulty and should be replaced.

Diagnostic Aids:

The Fasten Seat Belt indicator will stay "ON" continuously when an SIR failure code has been set.

If power is applied to the SIR system while any component is not properly connected, an additional failure code will be set for the disconnected SIR component.

The problem may be intermittent. Try performing the tests shown while "wiggling" wiring and connectors; this can often cause the fault to appear.

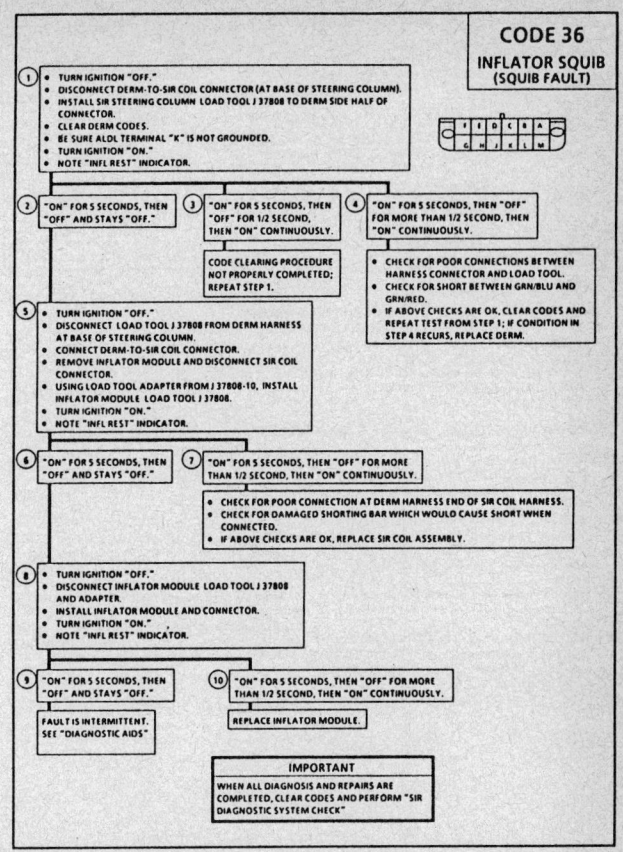

Fig. 135   Code 36 diagnosis. Corvette

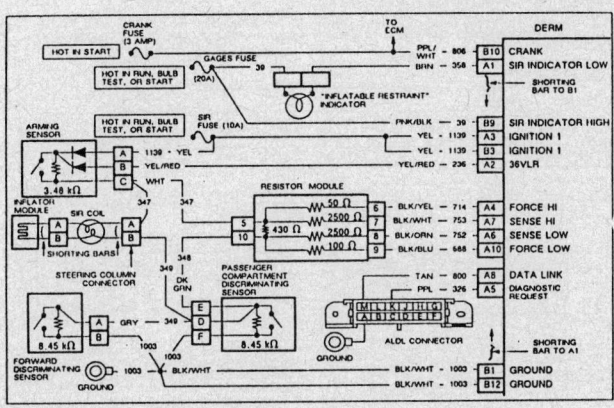

CODE 41

ENERGY RESERVE VOLTAGE CHARGING FAILURE

Test Condition:

Tested once during each ignition cycle at "Turn-on".

Failure Conditions:

Code 41 will be set if the 36VLR output of the DERM has not reached at least 28.4 volts within 7 seconds after Ignition 1 voltage is applied to the DERM.

Conditions To Clear:

Current Code 41 will be cleared each time the Ignition Switch is turned OFF.

Action taken:

DERM turns on the "INFLATABLE RESTRAINT" indicator lamp.

Description:

The DERM measures the deployment loop energy reserve voltage (36VLR) and checks that it has reached at least 28.4 volts within 7 seconds after Ignition 1 voltage is applied to the DERM. Code 41 indicates an internal fault in the DERM or a resistive short to ground in the 36VLR circuit to the Arming Sensor.

Notes on Fault Tree:

1) Checks for a resistive short to ground in the 36VLR circuit between the DERM and the Arming Sensor.

2) Checks for a short to system voltage on 36VLR circuit.

3) Checks for a open in the DERM or in circuit 236.

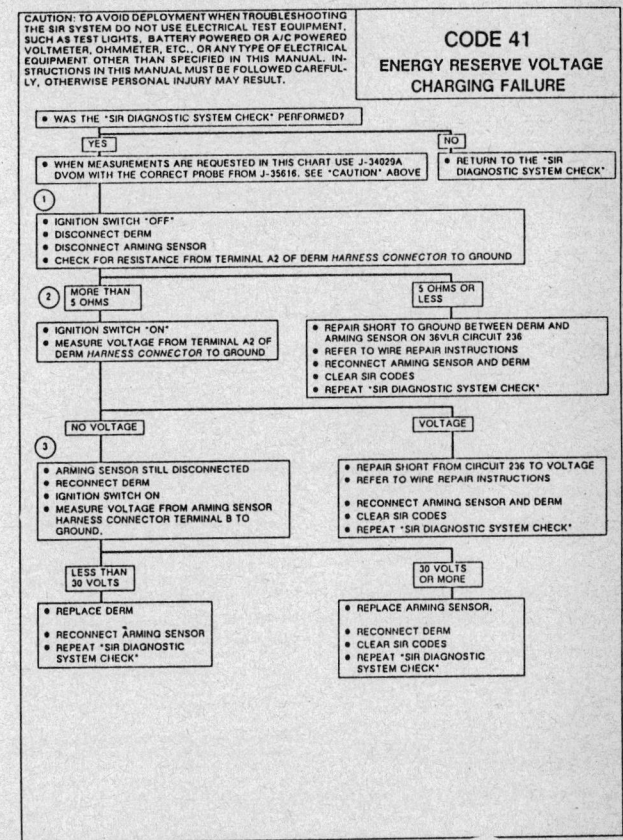

Fig. 136   Code 41 diagnosis. Camaro & Firebird

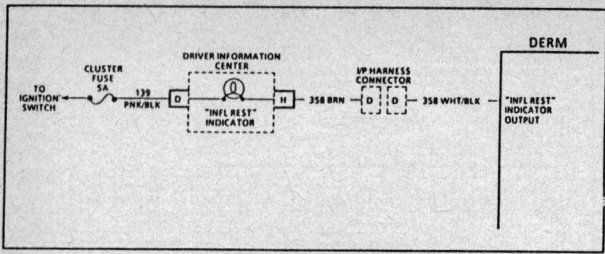

CODE 41
INDICATOR LAMP CIRCUIT
(CIRCUIT SHORTED TO BATTERY OR GROUND)

Circuit Description:

The power for the "INFL REST" indicator lamp circuit is provided by the 5A Cluster Fuse. Under the appropriate conditions, the DERM grounds the circuit, illuminating the bulb.

If the DERM senses CKT 358 to be high or low when it is expecting to see the opposite state, this code will set.

Test Description: Numbers below refer to circled numbers on the diagnostic chart.

1. This test checks to see if the Cluster Fuse, which powers the "INFL REST" indicator circuit, is OK or burned out. If blown, repair the short to ground in CKT 139.
2. This test helps to determine if the code is a result of a short to ground or a short to B+.
3. This test checks for a ground source in the circuit other than the intended ground through the DERM.
4. This test checks for a short to B+ in the vehicle side of the circuit, as opposed to the DERM side of the circuit.
5. This test checks if the short is possibly in the connectors. If the connectors check OK but the code resets, the fault must lie within the DERM and/or its wiring.

6. This test determines if the short to B+ is in the CKT 358 wiring to the DIC or in the DIC itself.
7. This test determines if the DERM and/or its wiring are the cause of the fault.

Diagnostic Aids:

The Fasten Seat Belt indicator will stay "ON" continuously when an SIR failure code has been set.

If power is applied to the SIR system while any component is not properly connected, an additional failure code will be set for the disconnected SIR component.

The problem may be intermittent. Try performing the tests shown while "wiggling" wiring and connectors; this can often cause the fault to appear.

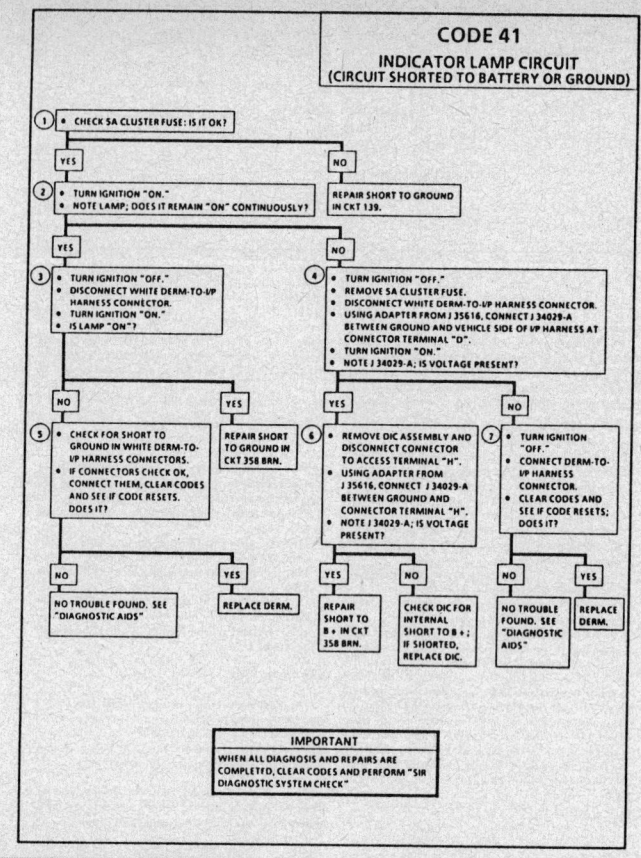

Fig. 137   Code 41 diagnosis. Corvette

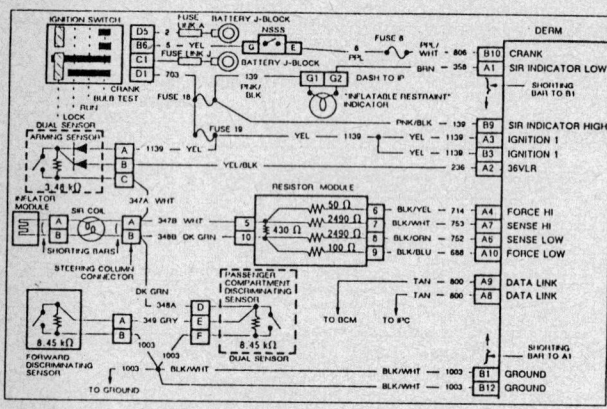

CODE 41
ENERGY RESERVE VOLTAGE CHARGING FAILURE

Test Condition:

Tested once during each ignition cycle at "Turn-on".

Failure Conditions:

Code 41 will set if the 36VLR output of the DERM has not reached at least 28.4 volts within 7 seconds after "IGNITION 1" voltage is applied to the DERM.

Conditions To Clear:

Current Code 41 will be cleared each time the Ignition Switch is turned OFF.

Action taken:

DERM turns on the "INFLATABLE RESTRAINT" indicator lamp.

Description:

The DERM measures the deployment loop energy reserve voltage (36VLR) and checks that it has reached at least 28.4 volts within 7 seconds after "IGNITION 1" voltage is applied to the DERM. Code 41 indicates an internal fault in the DERM or a resistive short to ground in the 36VLR circuit to the Arming Sensor.

Notes on Fault Tree:

1) Checks for a resistive short to ground in the 36VLR circuit between the DERM and the Dual Sensor.
2) Checks for a short to system voltage on 36VLR circuit.
3) Checks for a resistive short to ground within the Dual Sensor.
4) Checks for shorted diode in Dual Sensor. If the resistance value of the 3.48k ohm resistor can be read on a meter, this indicates a shorted diode.

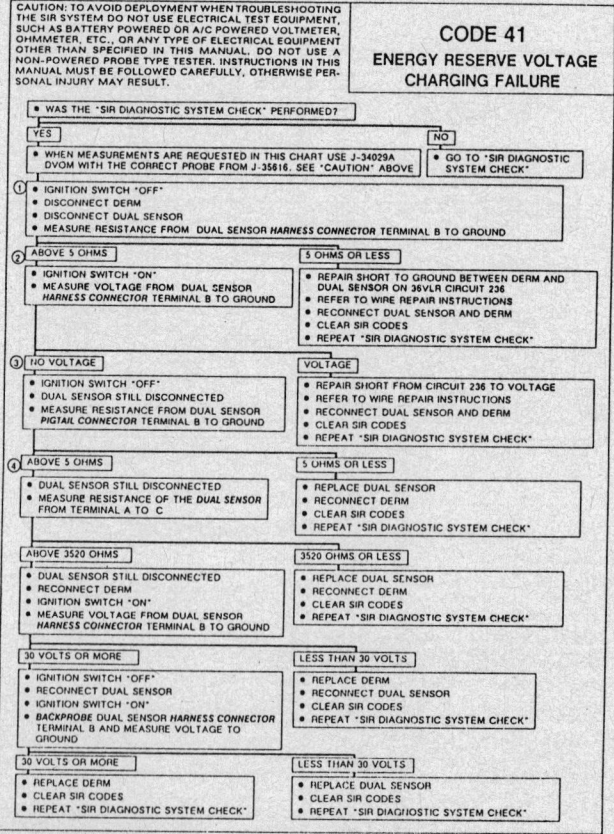

Fig. 138   Code 41 diagnosis. Deville, Fleetwood, Eldorado, Seville, Toronado & Trofeo

SUPPLEMENTAL INFLATABLE RESTRAINT SYSTEM

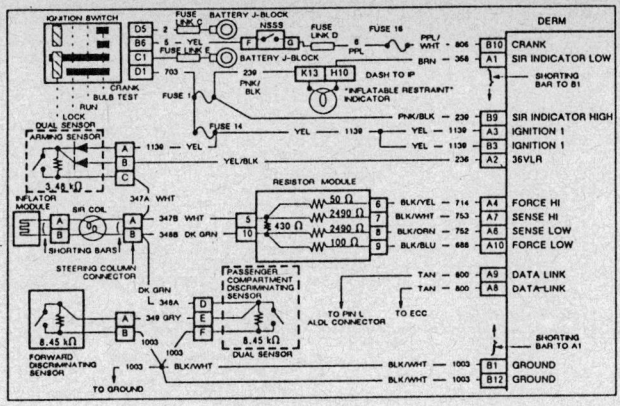

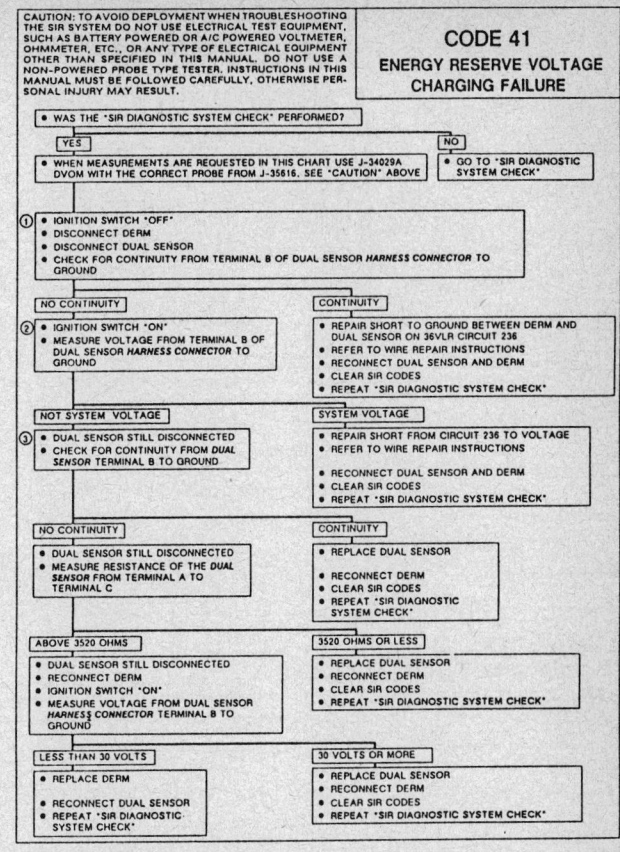

CODE 41

ENERGY RESERVE VOLTAGE CHARGING FAILURE

Test Condition:

Tested once during each ignition cycle at "Turn-on".

Failure Conditions:

Code 41 will set if the 36VLR output of the DERM has not reached at least 28.4 volts within 7 seconds after Ignition 1 voltage is applied to the DERM.

Conditions To Clear:

Current Code 41 will be cleared each time the Ignition Switch is turned OFF.

Action taken:

DERM turns on the "INFLATABLE RESTRAINT" indicator lamp.

Description:

The DERM measures the deployment loop energy reserve voltage (36VLR) and checks that it has reached at least 28.4 volts within 7 seconds after Ignition 1 voltage is applied to the DERM. Code 41 indicates an internal fault in the DERM or a resistive short to ground in the 36VLR circuit to the Arming Sensor.

Notes on Fault Tree:

1) Checks for a resistive short to ground in the 36VLR circuit between the DERM and the Dual Sensor.
2) Checks for a short to system voltage on 36VLR circuit.
3) Checks for a resistive short to ground within the Dual Sensor.

Fig. 139   Code 41 diagnosis. Riviera & Reatta

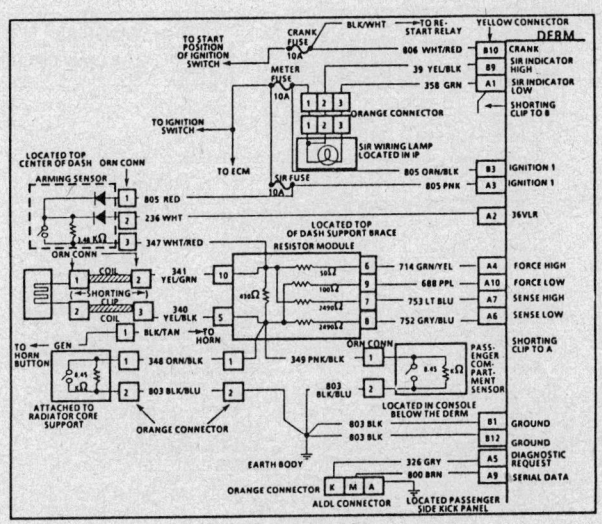

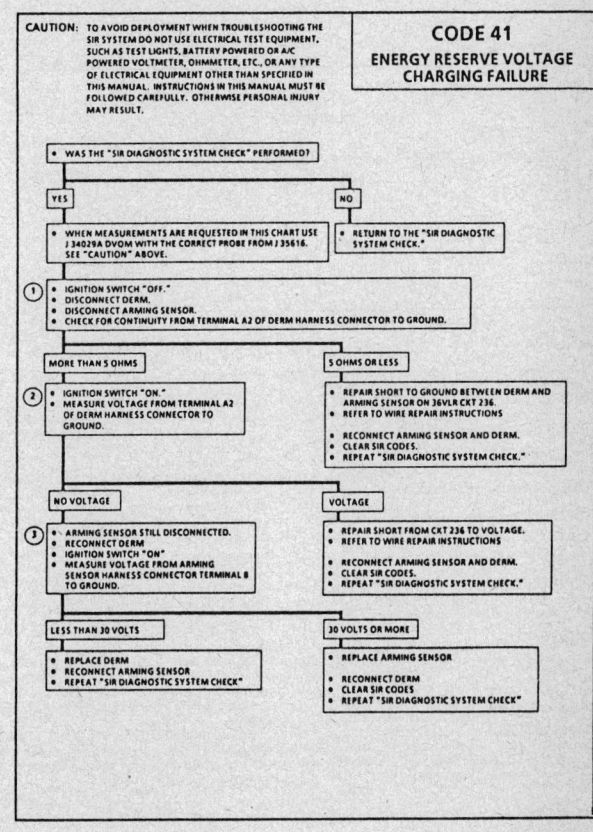

CODE 41

ENERGY RESERVE VOLTAGE CHARGING FAILURE

Test Conditions:

Tested once during each ignition cycle at "Turn-ON".

Failure Conditions:

Code 41 will set if the 36VLR output of the DERM has not reached at least 28.4 volts within 7 seconds after Ignition 1 voltage is applied to the DERM.

Conditions To Clear:

Current Code 41 will be cleared each time the Ignition Switch is turned "OFF."

Action Taken:

DERM turns "ON" the "INFLATABLE RESTRAINT" indicator lamp.

Description:

The DERM measures the deployment loop energy reserve voltage (36VLR) and checks that it has reached at least 28.4 volts within 7 seconds after Ignition 1 voltage is applied to the DERM. Code 41 indicates an internal fault in the DERM or a resistive short to ground in the 36VLR circuit to the Arming Sensor.

Notes on Fault Tree:

1. Checks for a resistive short to ground in the 36VLR circuit between the DERM and the Arming Sensor.
2. Checks for a short to system voltage on 36VLR circuit.
3. Checks for an open in the DERM or in circuit 236.

Fig. 140   Code 41 diagnosis. Storm

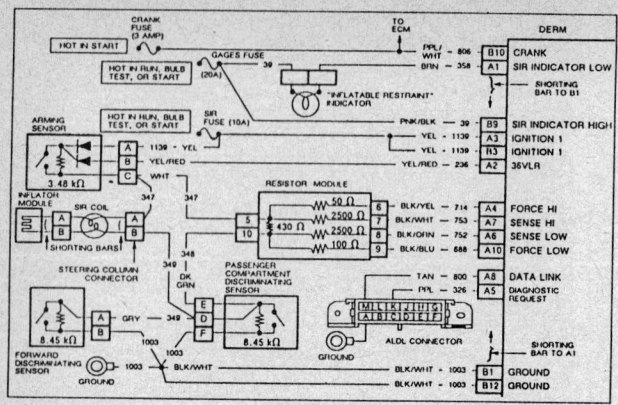

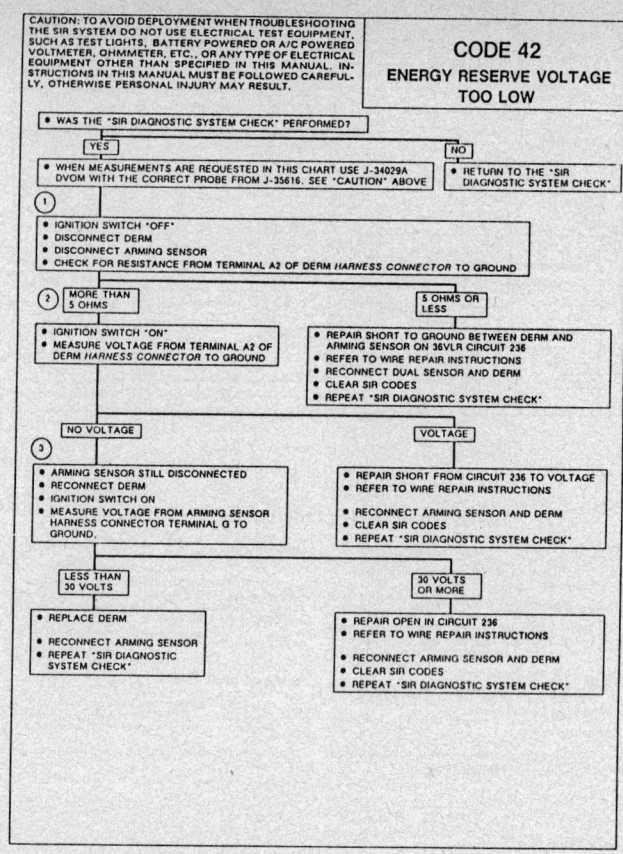

CODE 42

ENERGY RESERVE VOLTAGE TOO LOW

Test Condition:

Tested every 100 milliseconds during "Continuous Monitoring".

Failure Conditions:

Code 42 will be set if the deployment loop energy reserve voltage (36VLR) is less than 28.4 volts for 500 milliseconds.

Conditions To Clear:

Code 42 will clear if the deployment energy reserve voltage (36VLR) is greater than 28.4 volts for 500 milliseconds after Code 42 has set.

Action taken:

DERM turns on the "INFLATABLE RESTRAINT" indicator lamp.

Description:

The DERM measures the deployment loop energy reserve voltage (36VLR) and checks that it remains above 28.4 volts at all times after the initial charging of the reserve is completed (see Code 41). Code 42 indicates an internal fault in the DERM or a resistive short to ground in the 36VLR circuit to the Arming Sensor.

Notes on Fault Tree:

1) Checks for a resistive short to ground in the 36VLR circuit between the DERM and the Arming Sensor.
2) Checks for a short to system voltage on 36VLR circuit.
3) Checks for a open in the DERM or in circuit 236.

Fig. 141   Code 42 diagnosis. Camaro & Firebird

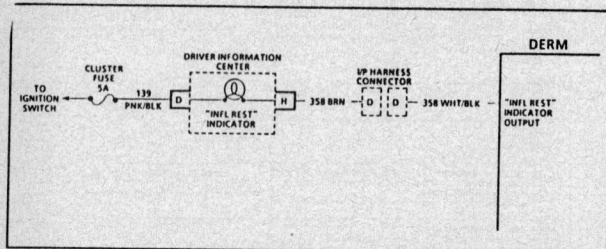

CODE 42

INDICATOR LAMP CIRCUIT
(OPEN CIRCUIT)

NOTE: If ignition is turned "ON" when Cluster Fuse is removed or blown, this code will set. Also, an intermittent open in the "INFL REST" indicator circuit or a disconnected DIC connector will set this code.

Circuit Description:

The power for the "INFL REST" indicator lamp circuit is provided by the 5A Cluster Fuse. Under the appropriate conditions, the DERM grounds the circuit, illuminating the bulb.

The DERM periodically checks resistance of the "INFL REST" indicator lamp circuit. If the resistance is above a specified resistance value, this code will set.

Test Description: Numbers below refer to circled numbers on the diagnostic chart.

1. This test checks to see if the Cluster Fuse, which powers the "INFL REST" indicator circuit, is OK or burned out. If blown, repair the short to ground in CKT 139.
2. This test checks if the bulb itself is burned out, causing an open, or if the bulb socket is cracked or loose.
3. This test checks if CKT 139 is open.
4. This test checks to see if the DIC itself is open in the "INFL REST" portion of its circuits.
5. This test checks for an open in CKT 358. If there is no open and the connection at the DERM-to-I/P harness connector is OK, the fault must lie with the DERM and/or its wiring.

Diagnostic Aids:

If the Fasten Seatbelt Indicator is "ON," but the "INFL REST" indicator is not, this fault may be the cause.

If any of the connections in the "INFL REST" Indicator Circuit are intermittent, a Code 42 will be set and will remain set even if the problem no longer exists. To check for intermittents, repeat the tests in the diagnostic chart while "wiggling" the wiring, connectors, bulb socket, etc.; this may cause the fault to appear.

If power is applied to the SIR system while any component is not properly connected, an additional failure code will be set for the disconnected SIR component.

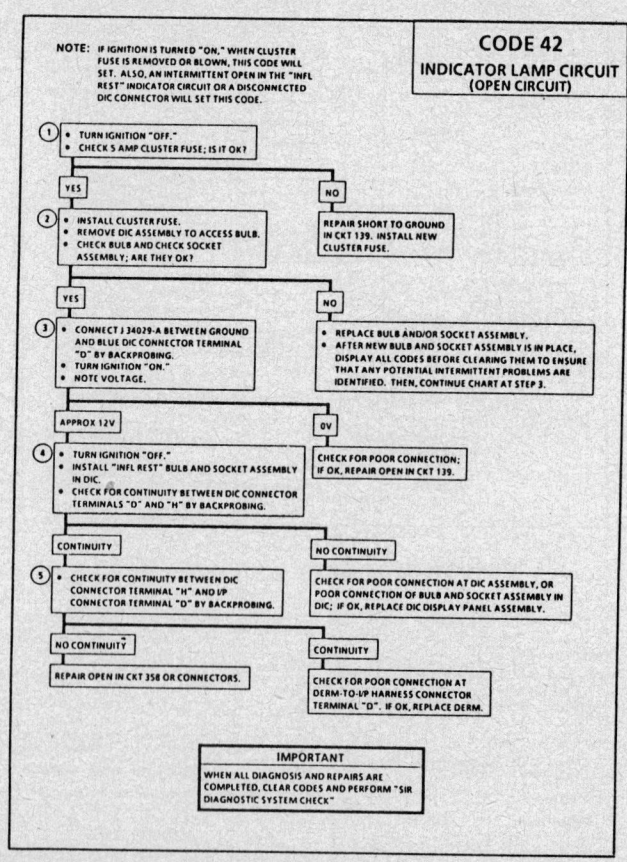

Fig. 142   Code 42 diagnosis. Corvette

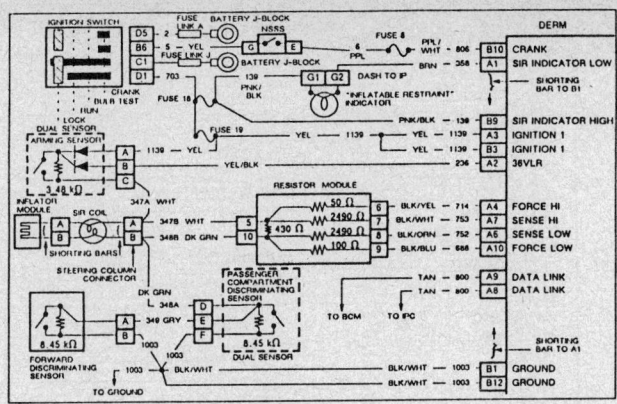

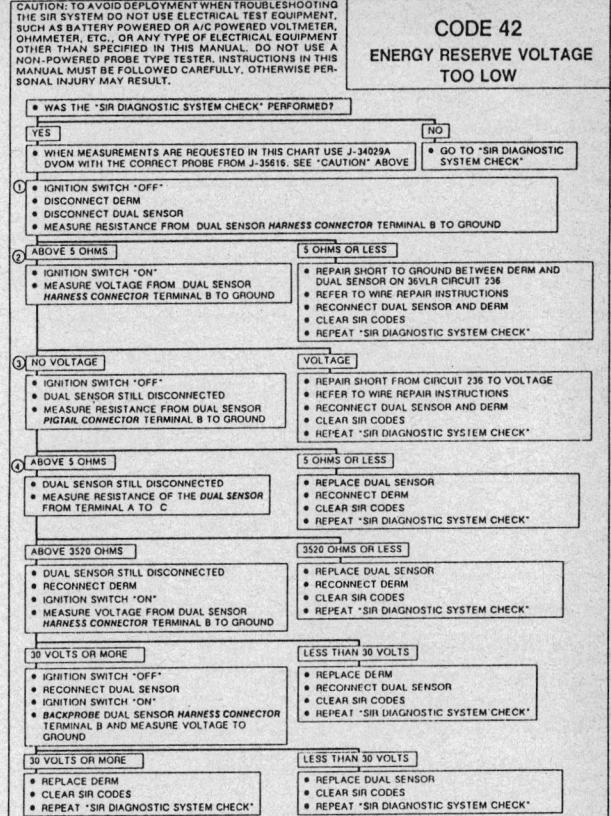

CAUTION: TO AVOID DEPLOYMENT WHEN TROUBLESHOOTING THE SIR SYSTEM DO NOT USE ELECTRICAL TEST EQUIPMENT, SUCH AS BATTERY POWERED OR A/C POWERED VOLTMETER, OHMMETER, ETC., OR ANY TYPE OF ELECTRICAL EQUIPMENT OTHER THAN SPECIFIED IN THIS MANUAL. DO NOT USE A NON-POWERED PROBE TYPE TESTER. INSTRUCTIONS IN THIS MANUAL MUST BE FOLLOWED CAREFULLY, OTHERWISE PERSONAL INJURY MAY RESULT.

CODE 42
ENERGY RESERVE VOLTAGE TOO LOW

CODE 42

ENERGY RESERVE VOLTAGE TOO LOW

Test Condition:

Tested every 100 milliseconds during "Continuous Monitoring".

Failure Conditions:

Code 42 will set if the deployment loop energy reserve voltage (36VLR) is less than 28.4 volts for 500 milliseconds.

Conditions To Clear:

Code 42 will clear if the deployment energy reserve voltage (36VLR) is greater than 28.4 volts for 500 milliseconds after Code 42 has set.

Action taken:

DERM turns on the "INFLATABLE RESTRAINT" indicator lamp.

Description:

The DERM measures the deployment loop energy reserve voltage (36VLR) and checks that it remains above 28.4 volts at all times after the initial charging of the reserve is completed (see Code 41). Code 42 indicates an internal fault in the DERM or a resistive short to ground in the 36VLR circuit to the Arming Sensor.

Notes on Fault Tree:

1) Checks for a resistive short to ground in the 36VLR circuit between the DERM and the Dual Sensor.
2) Checks for a short to system voltage on 36VLR circuit.
3) Checks for a resistive short to ground within the Dual Sensor.
4) Checks for shorted diode on dual sensor. If the resistance value of the 3.48k ohm resistor can be read on a meter, this indicates a shorted diode.

Fig. 143   Code 42 diagnosis. Deville, Fleetwood, Eldorado, Seville, Toronado & Trofeo

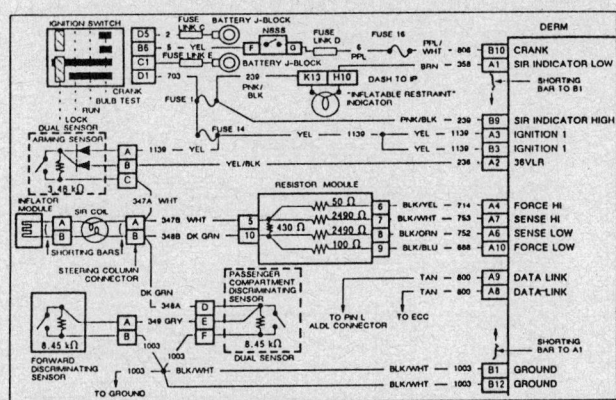

CAUTION: TO AVOID DEPLOYMENT WHEN TROUBLESHOOTING THE SIR SYSTEM DO NOT USE ELECTRICAL TEST EQUIPMENT, SUCH AS BATTERY POWERED OR A/C POWERED VOLTMETER, OHMMETER, ETC., OR ANY TYPE OF ELECTRICAL EQUIPMENT OTHER THAN SPECIFIED IN THIS MANUAL. DO NOT USE A NON-POWERED PROBE TYPE TESTER. INSTRUCTIONS IN THIS MANUAL MUST BE FOLLOWED CAREFULLY, OTHERWISE PERSONAL INJURY MAY RESULT.

CODE 42
ENERGY RESERVE VOLTAGE TOO LOW

CODE 42

ENERGY RESERVE VOLTAGE TOO LOW

Test Condition:

Tested every 100 milliseconds during "Continuous Monitoring".

Failure Conditions:

Code 42 will set if the deployment loop energy reserve voltage (36VLR) is less than 28.4 volts for 500 milliseconds.

Conditions To Clear:

Code 42 will clear if the deployment energy reserve voltage (36VLR) is greater than 28.4 volts for 500 milliseconds after Code 42 has set.

Action taken:

DERM turns on the "INFLATABLE RESTRAINT" indicator lamp.

Description:

The DERM measures the deployment loop energy reserve voltage (36VLR) and checks that it remains above 28.4 volts at all times after the initial charging of the reserve is completed (see Code 41). Code 42 indicates an internal fault in the DFRM or a resistive short to ground in the 36VLR circuit to the Arming Sensor.

Notes on Fault Tree:

1) Checks for a resistive short to ground in the 36VLR circuit between the DERM and the Dual Sensor.
2) Checks for a short to system voltage on 36VLR circuit.
3) Checks for a resistive short to ground within the Dual Sensor.
4) Checks for shorted diode in Dual Sensor.
5) Checks if the fault is internal to the DERM.

Fig. 144   Code 42 diagnosis. Riviera & Reatta

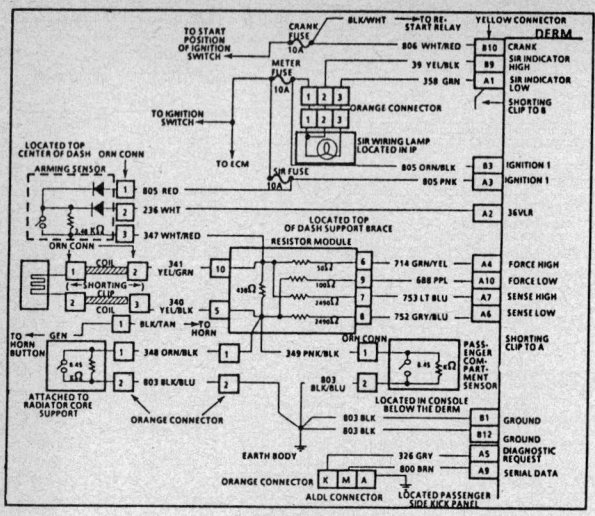

CODE 42
ENERGY RESERVE VOLTAGE TOO LOW

Test Conditions:

Tested every 100 milliseconds during "Continuous Monitoring".

Failure Conditions:

Code 42 will set if the deployment loop energy reserve voltage (36VLR) is less than 28.4 volts for 500 milliseconds.

Conditions To Clear:

Code 42 will clear if the deployment energy reserve voltage is greater than 28.4 volts for 500 milliseconds after Code 42 has set.

Action Taken:

DERM will not turn "ON" the "INFLATABLE RESTRAINT" indicator lamp.

Description:

The DERM measures the deployment loop energy reserve voltage (36VLR) and checks that it remains above 28.4 volts at all times after the initial charging of the reserve is completed (see Code 41). Code 42 indicates an internal fault in the DERM or a resistive short to ground in the 36VLR circuit to the Arming Sensor.

Notes on Fault Tree:

1. Checks for a resistive short to ground in the 36VLR circuit between the DERM and the Dual Sensor.
2. Checks for a short to system voltage on 36VLR circuit.
3. Checks for a resistive short to ground within the Dual Sensor.

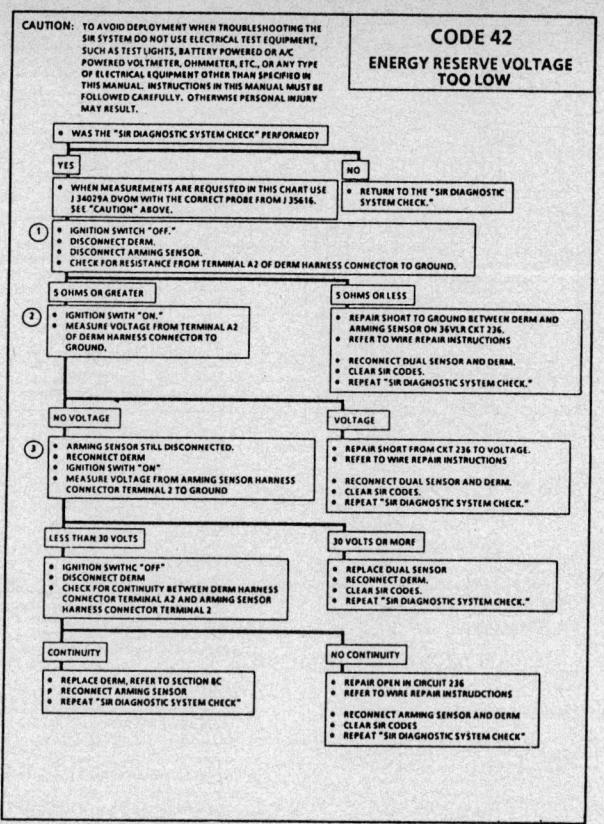

CODE 42
ENERGY RESERVE VOLTAGE TOO LOW

Fig. 145   Code 42 diagnosis. Storm

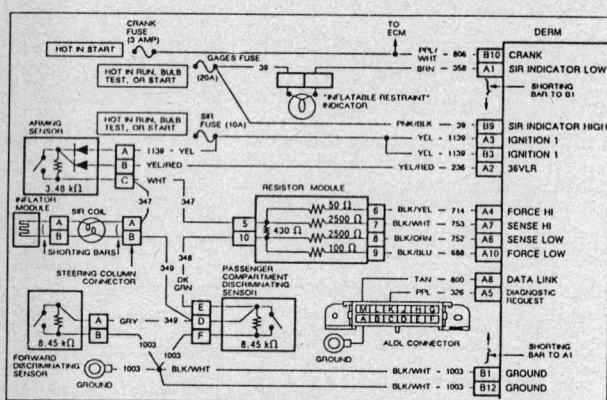

CURRENT CODE 51
ACCIDENT DETECTED

Test Condition:

DERM energy reserve voltage OK.

Failure Conditions:

Current Code 51 will set if the DERM senses that both the Arming Sensor and at least one of the Discriminating Sensors are closed simultaneously.

Conditions To Clear:

Current Code 51 can be cleared using a scan tool clear codes command. *History Code 51 will remain in the DERM thereafter.*

Action taken:

DERM turns on the "INFLATABLE RESTRAINT" indicator until current Code 51 is cleared.

Description:

The DERM determines that the Arming Sensor is closed when system voltage or more is present at the "Sense Hi" input, and it determines that a Discriminating sensor in closed when it notes low voltage at the "Sense Low" input. There are some faults that may "look" like an accident to the DERM, and therefore record a code 51. History Code 51 therefore is not proof that the vehicle was in an accident.

Notes On Fault Tree:

1) Incorrect diagnosis will occur if the SIR Diagnostic System Check is not performed

2) If a Code 51 is current without signs of frontal impact and no deployment, then the code has set falsely and the DERM should be replaced.

3) History Code 51 cannot be cleared because the event of both the arming sensor and discriminating sensor being closed simultaneously is permanently stored in the EEPROM of the DERM.

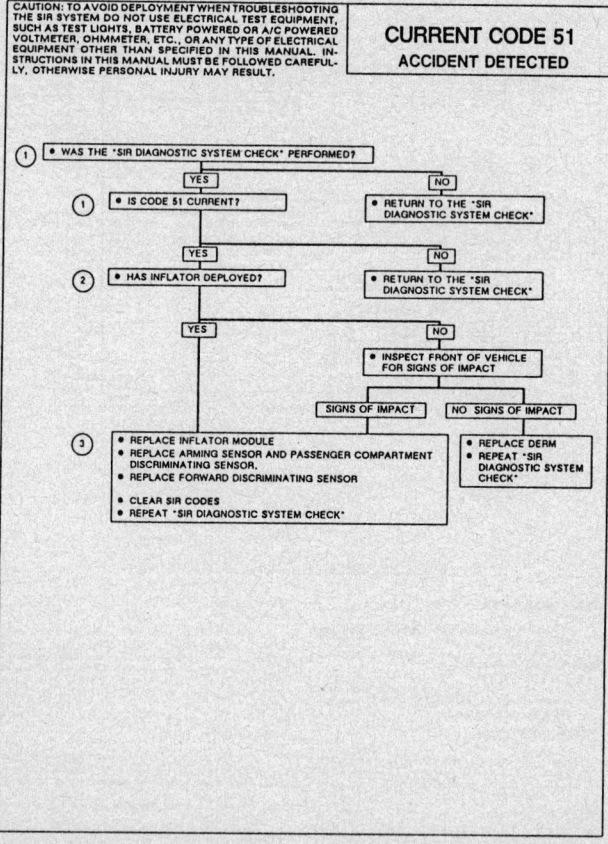

CURRENT CODE 51
ACCIDENT DETECTED

Fig. 146   Code 51 diagnosis. Camaro & Firebird

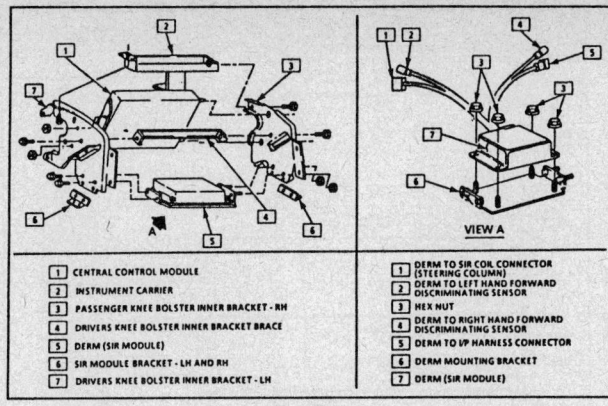

CODE 51

1	CENTRAL CONTROL MODULE
2	INSTRUMENT CARRIER
3	PASSENGER KNEE BOLSTER INNER BRACKET - RH
4	DRIVERS KNEE BOLSTER INNER BRACKET BRACE
5	DERM (SIR MODULE)
6	SIR MODULE BRACKET - LH AND RH
7	DRIVERS KNEE BOLSTER INNER BRACKET - LH

1	DERM TO SIR COIL CONNECTOR (STEERING COLUMN)
2	DERM TO LEFT HAND FORWARD DISCRIMINATING SENSOR
3	HEX NUT
4	DERM TO RIGHT HAND FORWARD DISCRIMINATING SENSOR
5	DERM TO I/P HARNESS CONNECTOR
6	DERM MOUNTING BRACKET
7	DERM (SIR MODULE)

CODE 51
DIAGNOSTIC UNIT FAULTY

Circuit Description:

The DERM performs numerous checks on its internal components and circuits. If it discovers a problem in these areas, this code will set.

Test Description: Numbers below refer to circled numbers on the diagnostic chart.

1. This test checks to see if any codes other than 51 are set. If so, the conditions causing those conditions should be repaired before clearing codes and checking for a Code 51 reset.

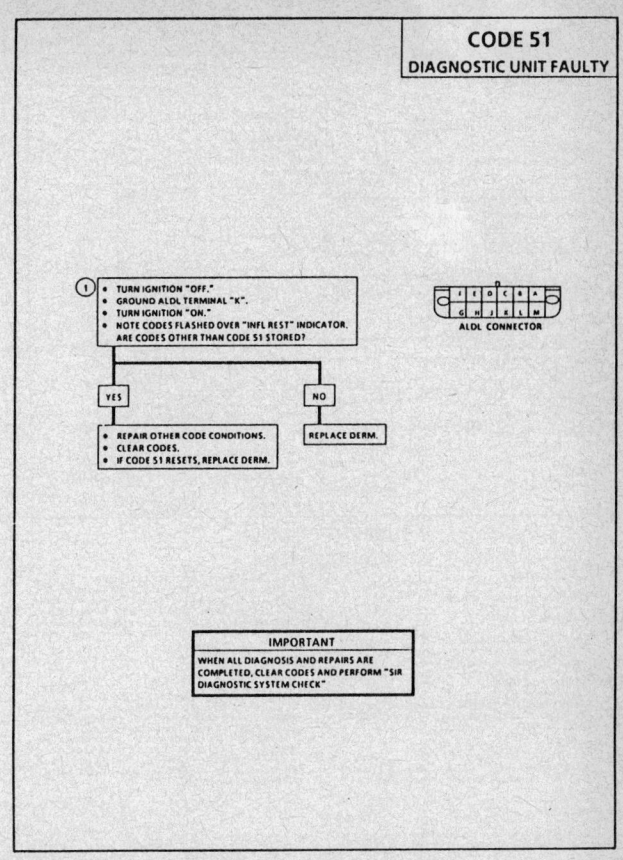

Fig. 147 Code 51 diagnosis. Corvette

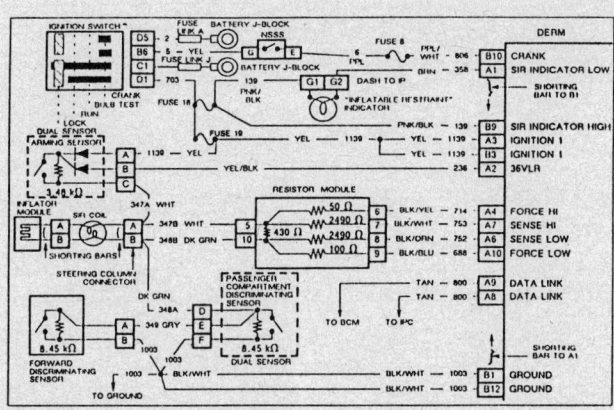

CURRENT CODE 51
ACCIDENT DETECTED

Test Condition:

DERM energy reserve voltage OK.

Failure Conditions:

Current Code 51 will set if the DERM senses that both the Arming Sensor and at least one of the Discriminating Sensors are closed simultaneously.

Conditions To Clear:

Current Code 51 can be cleared using a scan tool clear codes command. *History Code 51 will remain in the DERM thereafter.*

Action taken:

DERM turns on the "INFLATABLE RESTRAINT" indicator until current Code 51 is cleared.

Description:

The DERM determines that the Arming Sensor is closed when system voltage or more is present at the

"Sense Hi" input, and it determines that a Discriminating sensor is closed when it notes low voltage at the "Sense Low" input. There are some faults that may "look" like an accident to the DERM, and therefore record a code 51. History Code 51 therefore is not proof that the vehicle was in an accident.

Notes On Fault Tree:

1) Incorrect diagnosis will occur if the SIR Diagnostic System Check is not performed.

2) If a Code 51 is current without signs of frontal impact and no deployment, then the code has set falsely and the DERM should be replaced.

3) *History Code 51 cannot be cleared* because the event of both the arming sensor and discriminating sensor being closed simultaneously is permanently stored in the EEPROM of the DERM.

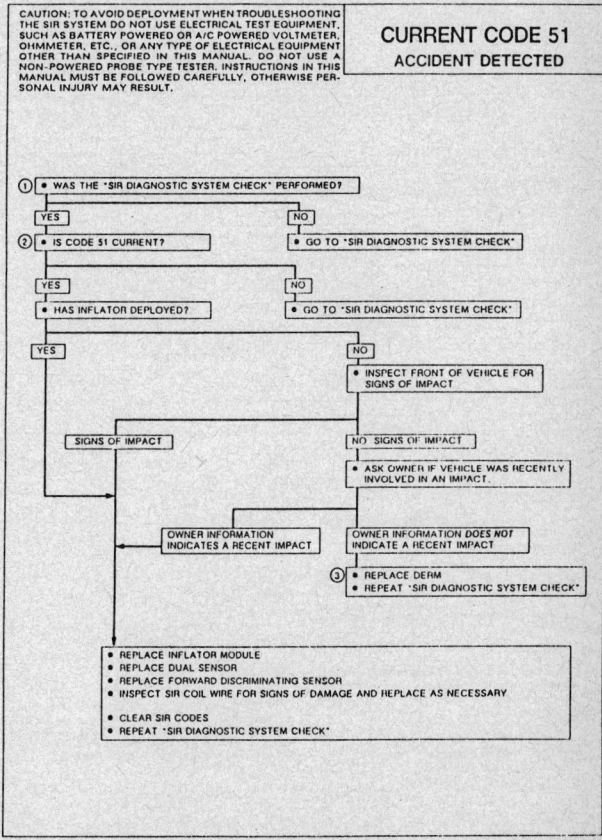

Fig. 148 Code 51 diagnosis. Deville, Fleetwood, Eldorado, Seville, Riviera, Reatta, Toronado & Trofeo

SUPPLEMENTAL INFLATABLE RESTRAINT SYSTEM

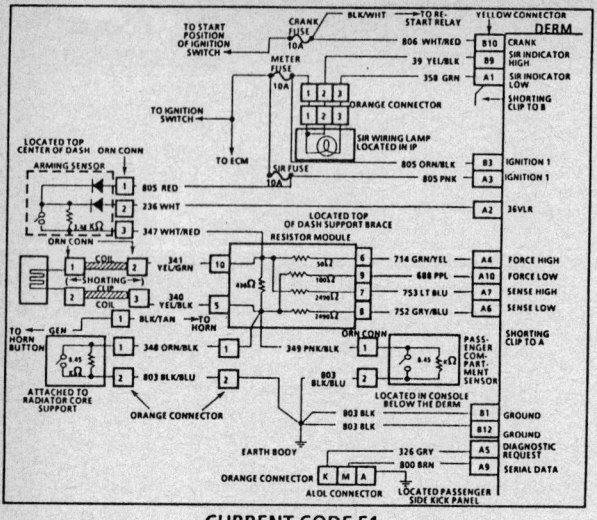

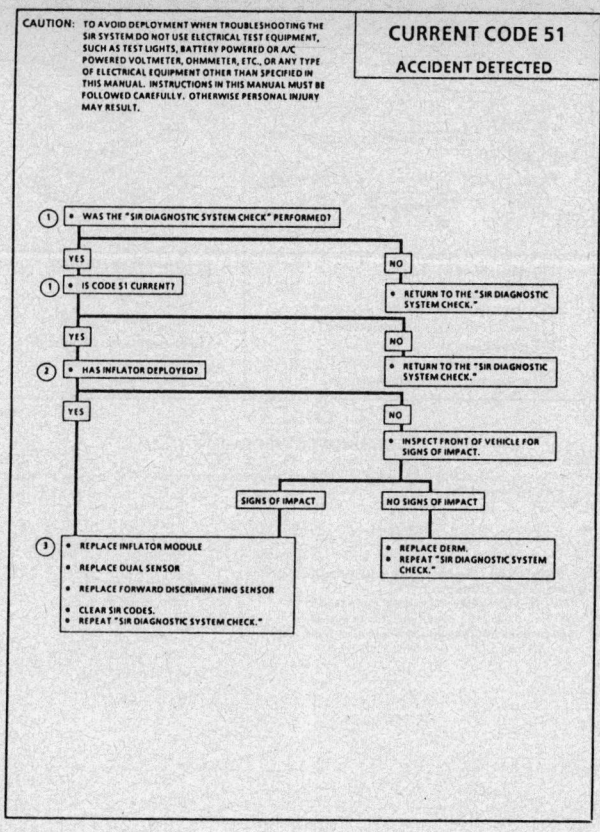

CURRENT CODE 51

ACCIDENT DETECTED

Test Conditions:

DERM energy reserve voltage OK.

Failure Conditions:

Current Code 51 will set if the DERM senses that both the Arming Sensor and at least one of the Discriminating Sensors are closed simultaneously.

Conditions To Clear:

Current Code 51 can be cleared using a "Scan" tool clear codes command. History Code 51 will remain in the DERM thereafter.

Action Taken:

DERM turns "ON" the "INFLATABLE RESTRAINT" indicator until current Code 51 is cleared.

Description:

The DERM determines that the Arming Sensor is closed when system voltage or more is present at the "Sense Hi" input, and it determines that a Discriminating sensor is closed when it notes low voltage at the "Sense Low" input. There are some faults that may "look" like an accident to the DERM, and therefore record a Code 51. History Code 51 therefore is not proof that the vehicle was in an accident.

Notes on Fault Tree:

1. Incorrect diagnosis will occur if the SIR Diagnostic System Check is not performed.
2. If a Code 51 is current without signs of frontal impact and no deployment, then the code has set falsely and the DERM should be replaced.
3. History Code 51 cannot be cleared because the event of both the arming sensor and discriminating sensor being closed simultaneously is permanently stored in the EEPROM of the DERM.

Fig. 149   Code 51 diagnosis. Storm

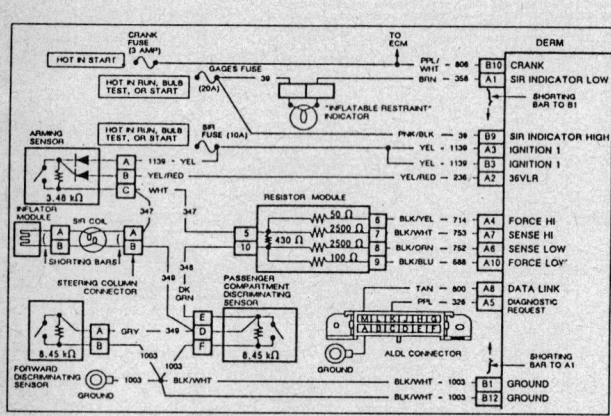

CODE 52

EEPROM ACCIDENT DATA AREA FULL

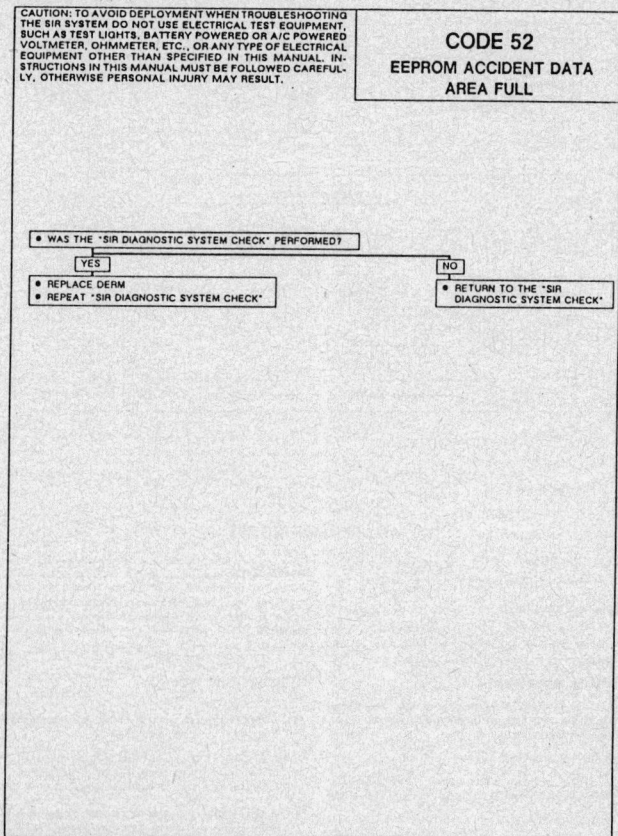

Test Condition:

Tested every 100 milliseconds during "Continuous Monitoring".

Failure Conditions:

Code 52 will be set when the EEPROM area reserved for accident data in the DERM is detected to be full during "Continuous Monitoring" for 100 milliseconds.

Conditions To Clear:

This code cannot be cleared.

Action taken:

"INFLATABLE RESTRAINT" indicator is turned on during all future Ignition cycles.

Description:

When there is a vehicle accident of sufficient magnitude to set Code 51, the DERM stores accident information in the EEPROM. Code 52 is set when the EEPROM has stored 4 simultaneously closed arming and discriminating sensor events (Code 51 settings).

Fig. 150   Code 52 diagnosis. Camaro & Firebird

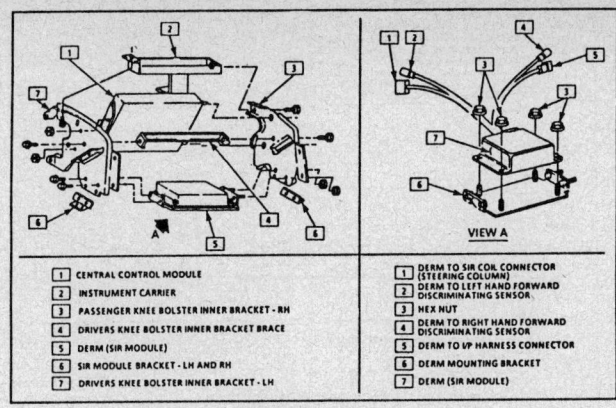

Key (left diagram):
1. CENTRAL CONTROL MODULE
2. INSTRUMENT CARRIER
3. PASSENGER KNEE BOLSTER INNER BRACKET - RH
4. DRIVERS KNEE BOLSTER INNER BRACKET BRACE
5. DERM (SIR MODULE)
6. SIR MODULE BRACKET - LH AND RH
7. DRIVERS KNEE BOLSTER INNER BRACKET - LH

Key (right diagram, VIEW A):
1. DERM TO SIR COIL CONNECTOR (STEERING COLUMN)
2. DERM TO LEFT HAND FORWARD DISCRIMINATING SENSOR
3. HEX NUT
4. DERM TO RIGHT HAND FORWARD DISCRIMINATING SENSOR
5. DERM TO VP HARNESS CONNECTOR
6. DERM MOUNTING BRACKET
7. DERM (SIR MODULE)

CODES 52, 53, 54
(FIRING SEQUENCE CONFIRMATION SET)
(FIRING CURRENT CONFIRMATION SET)
(SQUIB CURRENT HAS FLOWED)

Circuit Description:

These codes are set when the DERM senses an accident situation. During an accident, the DERM monitors the deployment loop and its operating conditions.

Code 52 sets when the DERM senses that the arming sensor and at least one front discriminating sensor have closed.

When the DERM recognizes that a Code 52 condition exists and the microprocessor switches from system diagnostic monitoring to accident data recording, Code 53 is set.

Code 54 sets when the DERM senses that the current to fire the squib has flowed through the deployment loop.

These codes cannot be cleared and render the DERM inoperative; the DERM must be replaced.

Test Description: Numbers below refer to circled numbers on the diagnostic chart.
1. If the vehicle was in an accident, there are specific steps which must be followed.
2. If the vehicle was not in an accident but these codes are set, it is possible that other system faults contributed to setting these codes. For this reason, find and repair any other code-setting conditions before replacing the DERM.

3. This refers to the correct instructions for SIR system work after a deployment accident.

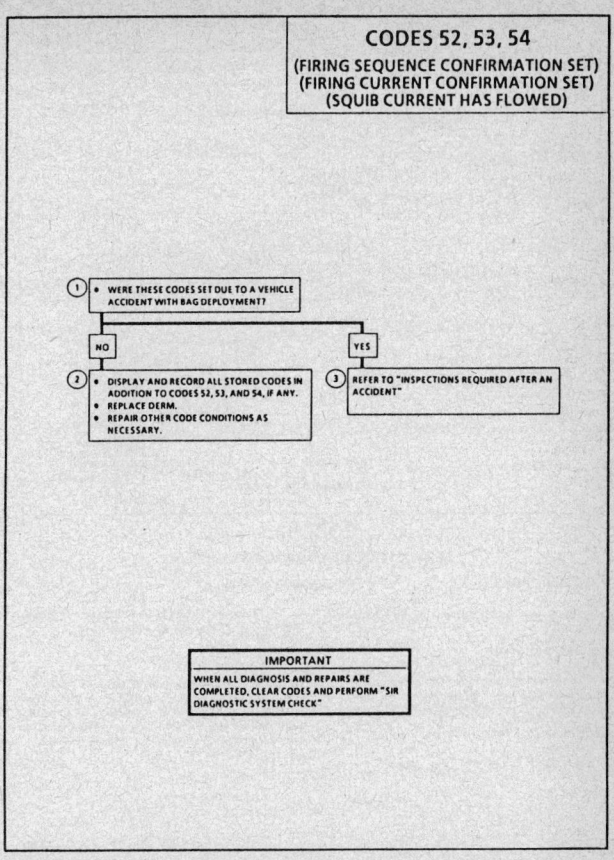

CODES 52, 53, 54
(FIRING SEQUENCE CONFIRMATION SET)
(FIRING CURRENT CONFIRMATION SET)
(SQUIB CURRENT HAS FLOWED)

1. WERE THESE CODES SET DUE TO A VEHICLE ACCIDENT WITH BAG DEPLOYMENT?

   NO → 2. DISPLAY AND RECORD ALL STORED CODES IN ADDITION TO CODES 52, 53, AND 54, IF ANY.
   • REPLACE DERM.
   • REPAIR OTHER CODE CONDITIONS AS NECESSARY.

   YES → 3. REFER TO "INSPECTIONS REQUIRED AFTER AN ACCIDENT"

IMPORTANT

WHEN ALL DIAGNOSIS AND REPAIRS ARE COMPLETED, CLEAR CODES AND PERFORM "SIR DIAGNOSTIC SYSTEM CHECK"

Fig. 151   Code 52, 53 & 54 diagnosis. Corvette

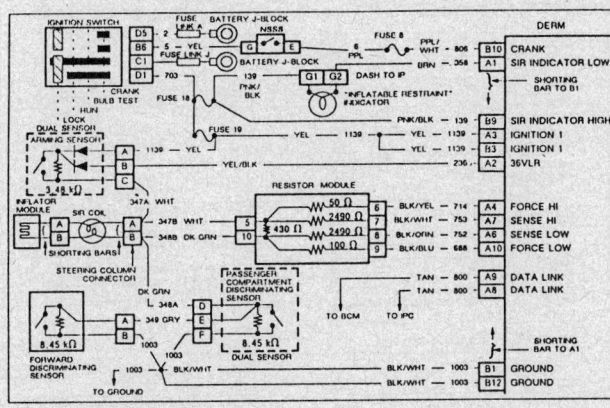

CODE 52
EEPROM ACCIDENT DATA AREA FULL

Test Condition:

Tested every 100 milliseconds during "Continuous Monitoring".

Failure Conditions:

Code 52 will set when the EEPROM area reserved for accident data in the DERM is detected to be full during "Continuous Monitoring" for 100 milliseconds.

Conditions To Clear:

This code cannot be cleared.

Action taken:

"INFLATABLE RESTRAINT" indicator is turned on during all future Ignition cycles.

Description:

When there is a vehicle accident of sufficient magnitude to set Code 51, the DERM stores accident information in the EEPROM. Code 52 is set when the EEPROM has stored 4 simultaneously closed arming and discriminating sensor events (Code 51 settings).

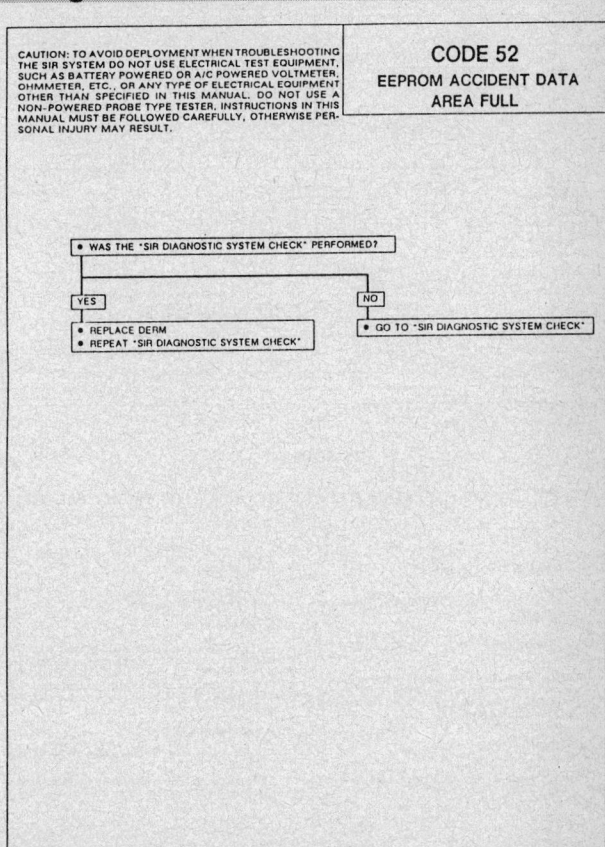

CAUTION: TO AVOID DEPLOYMENT WHEN TROUBLESHOOTING THE SIR SYSTEM DO NOT USE ELECTRICAL TEST EQUIPMENT, SUCH AS BATTERY POWERED OR A/C POWERED VOLTMETER, OHMMETER, ETC., OR ANY TYPE OF ELECTRICAL EQUIPMENT OTHER THAN SPECIFIED IN THIS MANUAL. DO NOT USE A NON-POWERED PROBE TYPE TESTER. INSTRUCTIONS IN THIS MANUAL MUST BE FOLLOWED CAREFULLY, OTHERWISE PERSONAL INJURY MAY RESULT.

CODE 52
EEPROM ACCIDENT DATA AREA FULL

• WAS THE "SIR DIAGNOSTIC SYSTEM CHECK" PERFORMED?

   YES → • REPLACE DERM
   • REPEAT "SIR DIAGNOSTIC SYSTEM CHECK"

   NO → • GO TO "SIR DIAGNOSTIC SYSTEM CHECK"

Fig. 152   Code 52 diagnosis. Deville, Fleetwood, Eldorado, Seville, Riviera, Reatta, Toronado & Trofeo

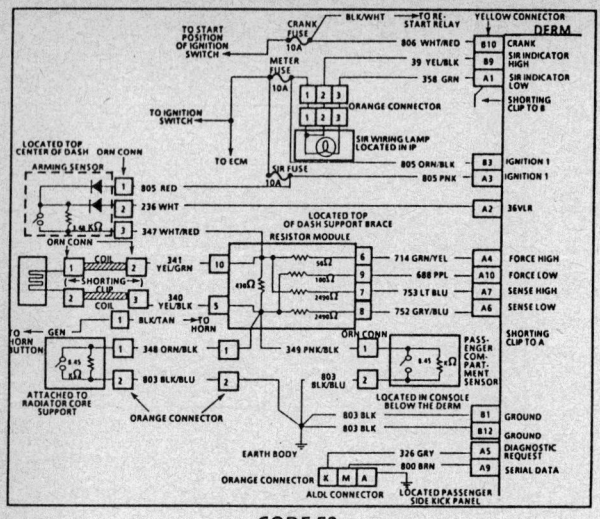

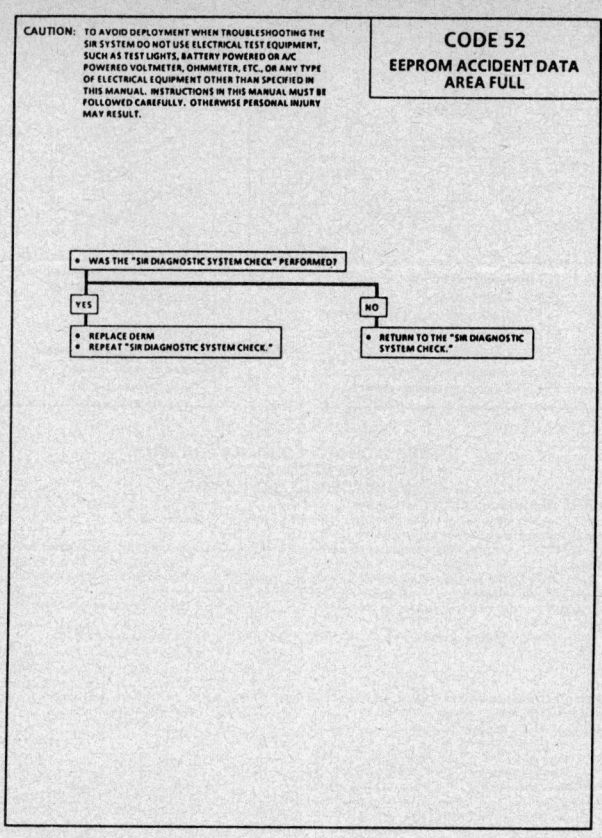

CODE 52
EEPROM ACCIDENT DATA AREA FULL

Test Conditions:

Tested every 100 milliseconds during "Continuous Monitoring".

Failure Conditions:

Code 52 will set when the EEPROM area reserved for accident data in the DERM is detected to be full during "Continuous Monitoring" for 100 milliseconds.

Conditions To Clear:

This code cannot be cleared.

Action Taken:

"INFLATABLE RESTRAINT" indicator is turned "ON" during all future Ignition cycles.

Description:

When there is a vehicle accident of sufficient magnitude to set Code 51, the DERM stores accident information in the EEPROM. Code 52 is set when the EEPROM has stored 4 simultaneously closed arming and discriminating sensor events (Code 51 settings).

Fig. 153   Code 52 diagnosis. Storm

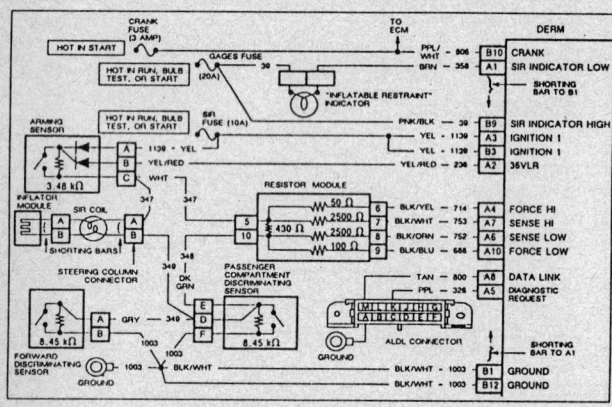

CODE 61
FORCE LOW OR "INFLATABLE RESTRAINT" INDICATOR CIRCUIT FAILURE

Test Conditions:

Tested every 100 milliseconds during "Continuous Monitoring".

Failure Conditions:

Code 61 will set if: 1) Voltage at Sense Low input is greater than 8 volts; 2) Feedback from ground driver (QDM) does not agree with the commanded state for 500 milliseconds.

Conditions To Clear:

Current Code 61 will be cleared each time the Ignition Switch is turned OFF.

Action taken:

DERM attempts to turn on the "INFLATABLE RESTRAINT" indicator.

Description:

The DERM monitors the ground driver output by comparing the output state to the processor commanded state. Code 61 will set when the commanded state does not match the output state of the ground driver. A possible cause for a Code 61 an open or short to ground in the Forced Low circuit.

Notes on Fault Tree:

1) Checks for an open 100 ohm resistor in the Resistor Module.

2) Checks for an open between the Resistor Module and the DERM on the Force Low circuit.

Fig. 154   Code 61 diagnosis. Camaro & Firebird

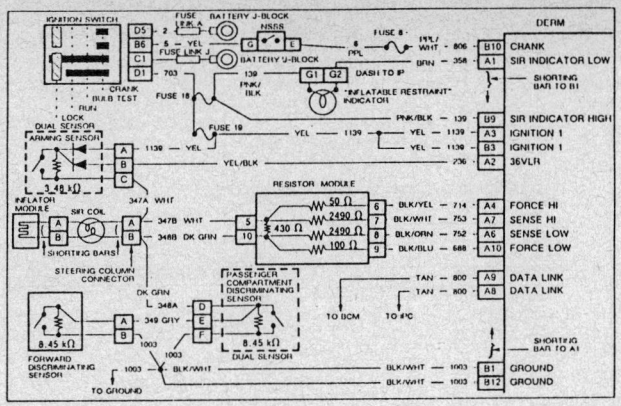

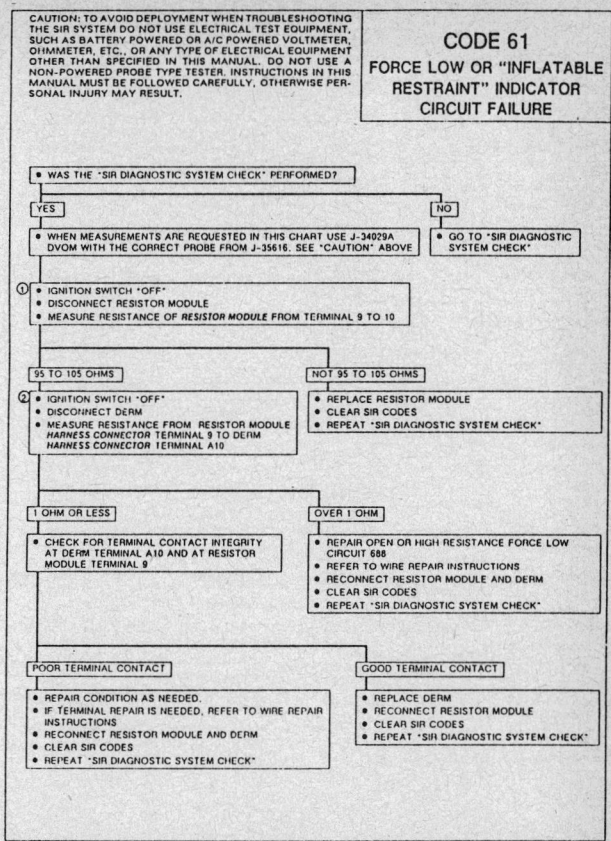

CODE 61
FORCE LOW OR "INFLATABLE RESTRAINT" INDICATOR CIRCUIT FAILURE

CODE 61

FORCE LOW OR "INFLATABLE RESTRAINT" INDICATOR CIRCUIT FAILURE

Test Conditions:

Tested every 100 milliseconds during "Continuous Monitoring".

Failure Conditions:

Code 61 will set if: 1) Voltage at Sense Low input is greater than 8 volts; 2) Feedback from ground driver (QDM) does not agree with the commanded state for 500 milliseconds.

Conditions To Clear:

Current Code 61 will be cleared each time the Ignition Switch is turned OFF.

Action taken:

DERM attempts to turn on the "INFLATABLE RESTRAINT" indicator.

Description:

The DERM monitors the ground driver output by comparing the output state to the processor commanded state. Code 61 will set when the commanded state does not match the output state of the ground driver. A possible cause for a Code 61 an open or short to ground in the Forced Low circuit.

Notes on Fault Tree:

1) Checks for an open 100 ohm resistor in the Resistor Module.

2) Checks for an open between the Resistor Module and the DERM on the Force Low circuit.

Fig. 155   Code 61 diagnosis. Deville, Fleetwood, Eldorado, Seville, Riviera, Reatta, Toronado & Trofeo

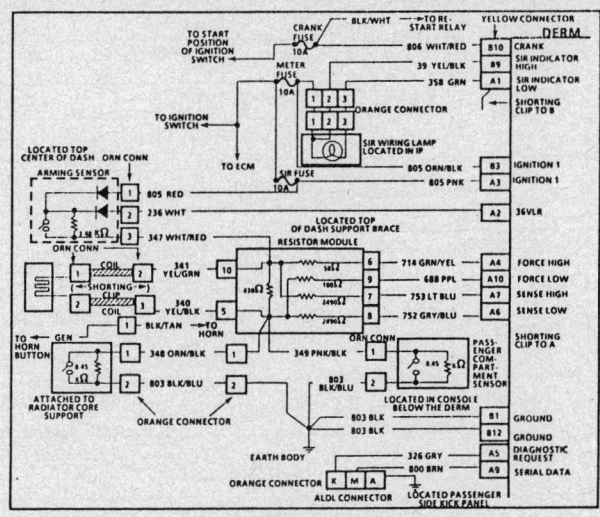

CODE 61

FORCE LOW OR "INFLATABLE RESTRAINT" INDICATOR CIRCUIT FAILURE

Test Conditions:

Tested every 100 milliseconds during "Continuous Monitoring".

Failure Condition's:

Code 61 will set if: 1) Voltage at Sense Low input is greater than 8 volts; 2) Feedback from ground driver (QDM) does not agree with the commanded state for 500 milliseconds.

Conditions To Clear:

Current Code 61 will be cleared each time the Ignition Switch is turned "OFF."

Action Taken:

DERM attempts to turn "ON" the "INFLATABLE RESTRAINT" indicator.

Description:

The DERM monitors the ground driver output by comparing the output state to the processor commanded state. Code 61 will set when the commanded state does not match the output state of the ground driver. A possible cause for a Code 61 an open or short to ground in the Forced Low circuit.

Notes on Fault Tree:

1. Checks for an open 100 ohm resistor in the Resistor Module.

2. Checks for an open between the Resistor Module and the DERM on the Force Low circuit.

Fig. 156   Code 61 diagnosis. Storm

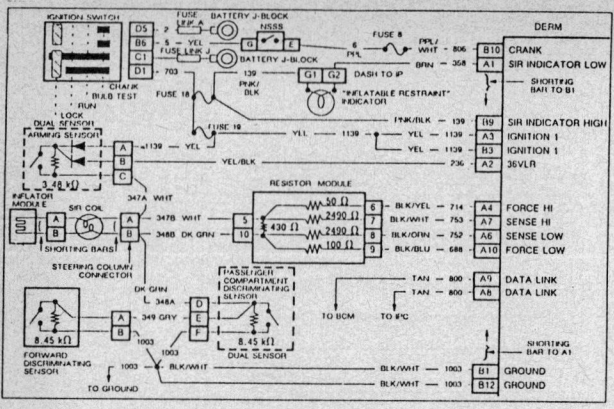

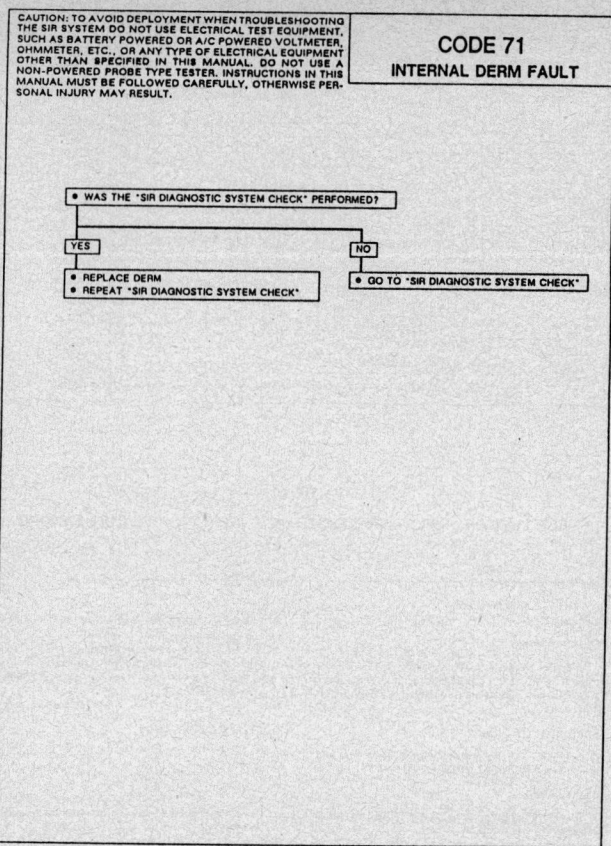

CODE 71
INTERNAL DERM FAULT

CAUTION: TO AVOID DEPLOYMENT WHEN TROUBLESHOOTING THE SIR SYSTEM DO NOT USE ELECTRICAL TEST EQUIPMENT, SUCH AS BATTERY POWERED OR A/C POWERED VOLTMETER, OHMMETER, ETC., OR ANY TYPE OF ELECTRICAL EQUIPMENT OTHER THAN SPECIFIED IN THIS MANUAL. DO NOT USE A NON-POWERED PROBE TYPE TESTER. INSTRUCTIONS IN THIS MANUAL MUST BE FOLLOWED CAREFULLY, OTHERWISE PERSONAL INJURY MAY RESULT.

- WAS THE "SIR DIAGNOSTIC SYSTEM CHECK" PERFORMED?

YES — NO

- REPLACE DERM
- REPEAT "SIR DIAGNOSTIC SYSTEM CHECK"

- GO TO "SIR DIAGNOSTIC SYSTEM CHECK"

CODE 71
INTERNAL DERM FAULT

Test Conditions:

Tested during "Turn-on" and every 100 milliseconds during "Continuous Monitoring".

Failure Conditions:

Code 71 is set when an internal DERM fault is detected during "Turn-on" or "Continuous Monitoring".

Conditions To Clear:

Current Code 71 will clear if no internal DERM faults are detected for 500 milliseconds.

Action taken:

DERM turns on the "INFLATABLE RESTRAINT" indicator.

Description:

Code 71 is an internal DERM fault and will set if any of the following conditions are detected:

1) DERM power supply reserve voltage charge or discharge time failure.
2) DERM power supply reserve voltage less than 13.0 volts or greater than 19.6 volts for 500 milliseconds.
3) DERM is unable to read from or write to EEPROM.
4) 36VLR is greater than 44.0 volts for 500 milliseconds.

Fig. 157   Code 71 diagnosis. Deville, Fleetwood, Eldorado, Seville, Riviera, Reatta, Toronado & Trofeo

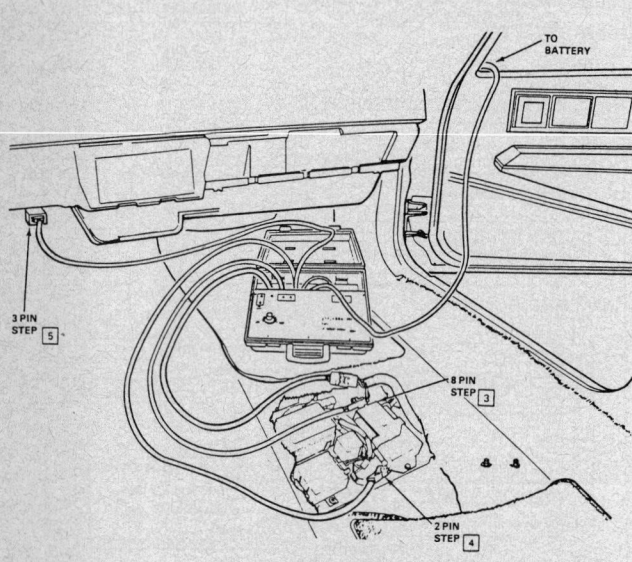

Fig. 158   Connecting inflatable restraint tester J-36884

STEP	SELECTOR POSITION	NORMAL VALUE	ABNORMAL VALUE
1	CAL. VOLTS	1.20 to 1.26 V	See Tester Service procedure.
2	CAL. OHMS	0.97 to 1.03 K	See Tester Service procedure.
3	0	Turn Ignition ON Turn Headlights ON "System Ground Affirm" Green LED = ON	(Green LED = OFF or Faint) Test A-1
4		Turn Ignition "OFF" wait 3 seconds then turn Ignition to "RUN". Wait 5-15 seconds to allow for warning lamp to turn off. If lamp turns off, after 5 to 15 seconds, continue with Step 17. If warning lamp is *never* on, on for less than 5 seconds, or remains on continuously, continue with Step 5.	
5	0	7 to 16 V	Test A-1
6	0	"Voltage Converter" Connections Green LED = ON	Test A-2
7	0	"8 Pin" Connections Green LED = ON	Test A-3
8	1	"Energy Reserve" Green LED = ON Red LED = OFF	Test B
9	1	13 V minimum	Test B
10	Cycle Ignition to OFF, wait 3 seconds, then to "RUN" 2	Warning lamp ON for 5-15 seconds then lamp turns off.	(Warning lamp *Never* ON, or ON for less than 5 seconds) Test C-1 Warning lamp on continuously, Step 11.
11	3 same as step 10	Same as Step 10 "Normal Value" condition	Test C-2 (Warning lamp *Continuously* ON)
12	4	< 1.32 V	Test D-1
13	5	< 3.80 V	Test D-2
14	Turn Ignition to "OFF" 6	5.40 K to 5.80 K	Test E

Fig. 159   Diagnostic Tester Sequence chart (Part 1 of 2). 88 & 98

STEP	SELECTOR POSITION	NORMAL VALUE	ABNORMAL VALUE
15	7 IGN. "OFF"	4.00 K to 5.30 K	Test F
16	8 IGN. "OFF"	3.83 K to 4.06 K	Test G
17	Turn Ignition to "RUN". Ignition remains in "RUN" and warning lamp indicator is ignored for Steps 17-18.		
	9	0.100 V Maximum	Test H-1
18	10 IGN. "RUN"	0.100 V Maximum	Test H-2
19	Turn Ignition "OFF". Disconnect Negative Battery Cable. Connect Black Tester Clamp to Negative Battery Terminal (Steps 19-21).		
	11	153 to 167 Ω	Test I
20	12 IGN. "OFF"	50 K to "0 L". (over limit)	Test J-1
21	13 IGN. "OFF"	50 K to "0 L". (over limit)	Test J-2
22	Ignition "OFF". Disconnect 2 pin and 8 pin connectors of tester from 2 pin and 8 pin connectors of system on mounting plate. Connect 2 pin and 8 pin mating connectors on mounting plate. (Leave 3 pin connector of tester connected to Test Connector. Reconnect Battery Negative Cable. Reconnect negative battery terminal and tester battery leads. Turn ignition to "RUN". Wait 15 seconds.		
23	14	5.9 mV to 13.6 mV	Test K
24	If Warning Lamp continues to operate improperly (ON less than 5 seconds or more than 15 seconds) after Ignition is cycled from "OFF" to "RUN", and all tests (Steps 1-24) displayed readings within NORMAL limits, replace IR Control Module. If Lamp still operates improperly, perform Diagnostic Procedure again.		

Fig. 159 Diagnostic Tester Sequence chart (Part 2 of 2). 88 & 98

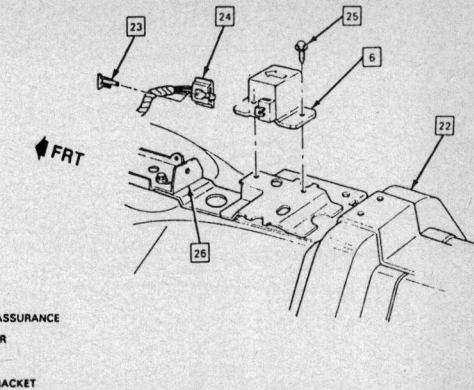

6	ARMING SENSOR
22	FLOOR TUNNEL
23	CONNECTOR POSITION ASSURANCE
24	ELECTRICAL CONNECTOR
25	BOLT
26	CONSOLE MOUNTING BRACKET

Fig. 160 Removing arming sensor. Camaro & Firebird

ON-VEHICLE SERVICE

INFLATABLE RESTRAINT SYSTEM CONTROL MODULE, REPLACE

88 & 98

Removal

Handle SIR control module carefully to avoid damaging passenger compartment sensor.
1. Place ignition switch in Lock position.
2. Disconnect and tape end of negative battery cable, then wait 10 minutes.
3. Remove front seat (passenger seat only if independent).
4. Bend up carpet retention tabs, then roll back carpet to expose passenger compartment sensing system cover.
5. Remove screws securing cover, then the cover.
6. Disconnect sensor connector from harness assembly and the arming sensor connector.
7. Remove SIR control module attaching nuts and the module. **Use care when handling a sensor. Never jar or strike the module in a manner which may cause deployment. Never apply voltage to a sensor when it is not rigidly attached to vehicle.**

Installation

1. Install SIR control module with arrow pointing toward front of vehicle.
2. Install module attaching bolts, **torquing to 88 inch lbs.**
3. Connect sensing connector to harness assembly, and the arming sensor.
4. Install sensor connector retaining pins.

5. Install sensing system cover to bracket, ensuring attaching screws are fully driven, seated and not stripped.
6. Install carpet in position and bend down carpet retention tabs.
7. Install front seat, then connect negative battery cable.
8. Use tester J-36884 to verify proper voltage at SIR test connector, **Fig. 4,** by performing steps 22 and 23 of "Diagnostic Tester Sequence."

ARMING SENSOR, REPLACE

88 & 98

Removal

1. Place ignition switch in Lock position.
2. Disconnect and tape end of negative battery cable, then wait 10 minutes.
3. Remove front seat (passenger seat only if independent).
4. Bend up carpet retention tabs, then roll back carpet to expose passenger compartment sensing system cover.
5. Remove screws securing cover, then the cover.
6. Disconnect arming sensor connectors and remove retaining pins.
7. Remove arming sensor attaching nuts and the sensor.

Installation

1. Install arming sensor with arrow pointing toward front of vehicle, **torquing** attaching nuts to 88 inch lbs.
2. Connect arming sensor connector.
3. Install sensor connector retaining pins.
4. Install sensing system cover to bracket, ensuring attaching screws are fully driven, seated and not stripped.
5. Install carpet in position and bend down carpet retention tabs.

6. Install front seat, then connect negative battery cable.
7. Use tester J-36884 to verify proper voltage at SIR test connector, **Fig. 4,** by performing steps 22 and 23 of "Diagnostic Tester Sequence."

CAMARO & FIREBIRD

Removal

1. Disconnect battery ground cable.
2. Remove SIR fuse from fuse block.
3. Remove left side sound insulator.
4. Remove CPA and disconnect yellow two-way SIR harness connector at base of steering column.
5. Remove knee bolster, refer to "Knee Bolster, Replace."
6. Remove upper console.
7. Remove arming sensor retaining bolts, then disconnect arming sensor electrical connector and remove arming sensor, **Fig. 160.**

Installation

1. Install arming sensor with arrow pointing toward front of vehicle, **torquing** retaining bolts to 25 inch lbs.
2. Install CPA and connect arming sensor electrical connectors.
3. Install upper console.
4. Install knee bolster, refer to "Knee Bolster, Replace."
5. Connect yellow two-way SIR harness connector at base of steering column.
6. Install left side sound insulator.
7. Install SIR fuse and connect battery ground cable.
8. Turn ignition switch to the On position and verify the "Inflatable Restraint" indicator flashes 7 to 9 times then turns Off. If indicator does not respond, refer to "Diagnosis."

DEVILLE & FLEETWOOD

Removal

1. Disconnect battery ground cable.
2. Remove DERM, refer to "Diagnostic Energy Reserve Module (DERM) Replace."
3. Remove arming sensor connector retaining nut.
4. Remove two Body Computer Module (BCM) retaining nuts.

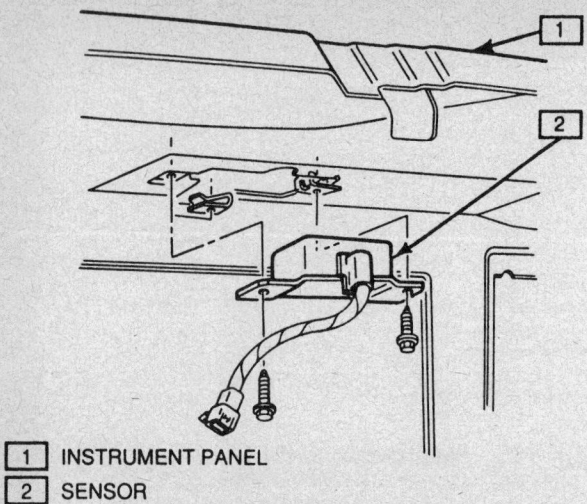

1 INSTRUMENT PANEL
2 SENSOR

Fig. 161   Removing arming sensor. Riviera, Reatta, Toronado & Trofeo

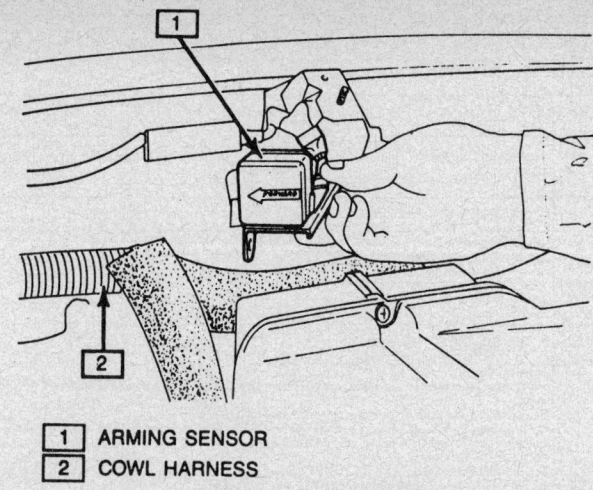

1 ARMING SENSOR
2 COWL HARNESS

Fig. 162   Removing arming sensor. Storm

5. Remove three DERM/BCM bracket retaining screws.
6. Remove two arming sensor retaining screws and nuts.
7. Rotate rear of sensor while pulling up to disengage arming sensor.

Installation

1. Install arming sensor with arrow pointing toward front of vehicle. **Ensure to engage front flange of sensor into spring clip on bracket.**
2. Install two sensor retaining bolts and **torque** to 84 inch lbs.
3. Install BCM module.
4. Install three DERM/BCM bracket retaining screws.
5. Install two BCM retaining nuts and **torque** to 84 inch lbs.
6. Connect sensor electrical connector and install CPA.
7. Install resistor module retaining nut and **torque** to 84 inch lbs.
8. Install sensor connector retaining nut and **torque** to 84 inch lbs.
9. Install DERM, refer to "Diagnostic Energy Reserve Module (DERM) Replace."
10. Connect battery ground cable.
11. Turn ignition switch to the On position and verify the "Inflatable Restraint" indicator flashes 7 to 9 times then turns Off. If indicator does not respond, refer to "Diagnosis."

RIVIERA, REATTA, TORONADO & TROFEO
Removal

1. **On all models,** disconnect battery ground cable.
2. **On Riviera & Reatta models,** remove SIR fuse No. 14 from fuse box.
3. **On Toronado & Trofeo models,** remove SIR fuse No. 9 from fuse box.
4. **On Riviera & Reatta models,** remove left side sound insulator.
5. **On all models,** remove CPA and disconnect yellow two-way SIR harness

electrical connector at base of steering column.
6. **On Reatta models,** remove body computer module.
7. **On all models,** remove glove box assembly and engine control module.
8. Position sound insulation aside from cowl.
9. Disconnect arming sensor electrical connector.
10. Using tool No. 000-T27H, remove two tamper resistant arming sensor retaining bolts, then the sensor, **Fig. 161.**

Installation

1. **On all models,** using tool No. 000-T27H, install two tamper resistant arming sensor retaining bolts.
2. Connect arming sensor electrical connector.
3. Position sound insulation.
4. Install glove box assembly and engine control module.
5. **On Reatta models,** install body computer module.
6. **On all models,** install CPA and disconnect yellow two-way SIR harness electrical connector at base of steering column.
7. **On Riviera & Reatta models,** install left side sound insulator.
8. **On Toronado & Trofeo models,** install SIR fuse No. 9 from fuse box.
9. **On Riviera & Reatta models,** install SIR fuse No. 14 from fuse box.
10. **On all models,** connect battery ground cable.

ELDORADO & SEVILLE
Removal

1. Disconnect battery ground cable.
2. Remove SIR fuse No. 19 from fuse box.
3. Remove sound insulator.
4. Remove CPA and disconnect yellow two-way SIR harness electrical connector at base of steering column.

5. Remove four glove box unit retaining screws, then the glove box.
6. Remove two body computer module (BCM) retaining nuts.
7. Disconnect BCM electrical connectors.
8. Remove BCM from mounting bracket.
9. Remove CPA and disconnect arming sensor electrical connector.
10. Remove two sensor retaining bolts, then the sensor, **Fig. 161.**

Installation

1. Install sensor in vehicle with arrow pointing toward front of vehicle.
2. Install two sensor retaining bolts and **torque** to 98 inch lbs.
3. Connect arming sensor electrical connector and connector CPA.
4. Install BCM in mounting bracket.
5. Connect BCM electrical connectors.
6. Install two body computer module (BCM) retaining nuts.
7. Install glove box unit and glove box retaining screws.
8. Connect yellow two-way SIR harness electrical connector and install connector CPA at base of steering column.
9. Install sound insulator.
10. Install SIR fuse No. 19 and connect battery ground cable.

STORM
Removal

1. Disconnect battery ground cable.
2. Remove SIR fuse No. 3 from fuse panel.
3. Disconnect orange three-way connector at base of steering column.
4. Remove instrument panel assembly.
5. Remove two arming sensor retaining bolts, then disconnect sensor electrical connector, **Fig. 162.**
6. Remove sensor from vehicle.

Installation

1. Position arming sensor, then install two arming sensor retaining bolts. **Torque** bolts to 62 inch lbs.

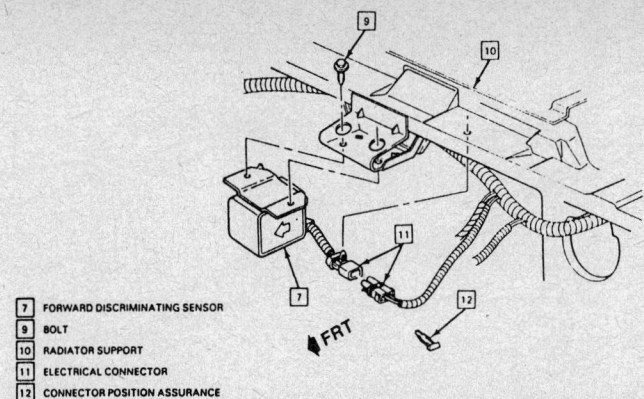

7 FORWARD DISCRIMINATING SENSOR
9 BOLT
10 RADIATOR SUPPORT
11 ELECTRICAL CONNECTOR
12 CONNECTOR POSITION ASSURANCE

Fig. 163   Removing forward sensor. Camaro & Firebird

2. Install instrument panel assembly.
3. Connect orange three-way connector at base of steering column.
4. Install SIR fuse No. 3.
5. Connect battery ground cable.
6. Turn ignition switch to the On position and verify the "Inflatable Restraint" indicator flashes 7 to 9 times then turns Off. If indicator does not respond, refer to "Diagnosis."

POWER SUPPLY, REPLACE

88 & 98
Removal

1. Place ignition switch in Lock position.
2. Disconnect and tape end of negative battery cable, then wait 15 seconds.
3. Remove front seat (passenger seat only if independent).
4. Bend up carpet retention tabs, then roll back carpet to expose passenger compartment sensing system cover.
5. Remove screws securing cover, then the cover.
6. remove two screws on side of power supply, then the connector retainer bracket.
7. Disconnect power supply connector from harness assembly.
8. remove screw attaching power supply to bracket, then the power supply.

Installation

1. Install power supply, securing to mounting bracket with one screw.
2. Connect power supply connector to harness assembly.
3. Install power supply connector retainer bracket, securing with two screws.
4. Install sensing system cover to bracket, ensuring attaching screws are fully driven, seated and not stripped.
5. Install carpet in position and bend down carpet retention tabs.
6. Install front seat, then connect negative battery cable.
7. Use tester J-36884 to verify proper voltage at SIR test connector, **Fig. 4,** by performing steps 22 and 23 of "Diagnostic Tester Sequence."

ENERGY RESERVE MODULE, REPLACE

88 & 98
Removal

1. Place ignition switch in Lock position.
2. Disconnect and tape end of negative battery cable, then wait 15 seconds.
3. Remove front seat (passenger seat only if independent).
4. Bend up carpet retention tabs, then roll back carpet to expose passenger compartment sensing system cover.
5. Remove screws securing cover, then the cover.
6. Remove screws securing energy reserve module to bracket.
7. Disconnect energy reserve module connector from harness assembly. **Wiggle connector when removing from module, do not attempt to pry up lock tabs on connector.**
8. Remove energy reserve module.

Installation

1. Install energy reserve module, securing to bracket with screws.
2. Connect energy reserve module connector to harness assembly.
3. Install sensing system cover to bracket, ensuring attaching screws are fully driven, seated and not stripped.
4. Install carpet in position and bend down carpet retention tabs.
5. Install front seat, then connect negative battery cable.
6. Use tester J-36884 to verify proper voltage at SIR test connector, **Fig. 4,** by performing steps 22 and 23 of "Diagnostic Tester Sequence."

SIR CONTROL CENTER MOUNTING BRACKET, REPLACE

88 & 98
Removal

1. Place ignition switch in Lock position.
2. Disconnect and tape end of negative battery cable, then wait 15 seconds.
3. Remove front seat (passenger seat only if independent).

4. Bend up carpet retention tabs, then roll back carpet to expose passenger compartment sensing system cover.
5. Remove screws securing cover, then the cover.
6. Remove screws and nuts securing modules to mounting bracket.
7. Disconnect electrical connectors at all modules.
8. Remove screws holding mounting bracket to numbers 2 and 3 bars and remove mounting bracket.

Installation

1. Align mounting bracket screw holes and drive three forward screws and right rear screw into U nuts, **torquing** to 88 inch lbs., then secure self tapping left rear screw and **torque** to 44 inch lbs. **Proper orientation and rigid attachment of the sensors and brackets to the vehicle is critical for proper functioning of the SIR sensors.**
2. Connect electrical connectors to modules and secure modules to mounting bracket with screws and nuts previously removed.
3. Use tester J-36884 to verify proper voltage at SIR test connector, **Fig. 4,** by performing steps 22 and 23 of "Diagnostic Tester Sequence."
4. Reverse "Removal" steps 2 through 5 to complete installation.

FORWARD SENSOR, REPLACE

88 & 98
Removal

1. Place ignition switch in Lock position.
2. Disconnect and tape negative battery terminal, then wait 15 seconds.
3. Remove driver's side grille attaching screws, then the grille.
4. Remove forward sensor connector retaining pin and disconnect connector.
5. Remove fasteners securing forward sensor to bracket.
6. Remove forward sensor.

Installation

1. Install forward sensor to bracket, **torquing** fasteners to 62 inch lbs.
2. Connect connector and install connector retaining pin.
3. Install grille, securing with attaching screws.
4. Connect negative battery cable.

CAMARO & FIREBIRD
Removal

1. Disconnect battery ground cable.
2. Remove SIR fuse from fuse block.
3. Remove left side sound insulator.
4. Remove CPA and disconnect yellow two-way SIR harness connector at base of steering column.
5. Remove air cleaner, then raise and support vehicle.
6. Remove radiator air upper baffle.
7. Remove CPA and disconnect Forward Discriminating Sensor electrical connector behind radiator support.

8. Remove forward discrimination sensor retaining bolts, then the sensor, **Fig. 163.**

Installation

1. Install forward discriminating sensor with arrow pointing towards front of vehicle **torquing** bolts to 25 inch lbs.
2. Connect sensor electrical connector and and connector position assurance behind radiator support.
3. Install radiator air upper baffle.
4. Lower vehicle and install air cleaner.
5. Install CPA and connect yellow two-way SIR electrical harness connector at base of steering column.
6. Install left side sound insulator.
7. Install SIR fuse and connect battery ground cable.
8. Turn ignition switch to the On position and verify the "Inflatable Restraint" indicator flashes 7 to 9 times then turns Off. If indicator does not respond, refer to "Diagnosis."

DEVILLE & FLEETWOOD
Removal

1. Disconnect battery ground cable.
2. Remove SIR fuse No. 3 from fuse panel.
3. Remove left and right sound insulators.
4. Remove CPA and disconnect yellow two-way SIR electrical connector at base of steering column.
5. Raise hood and remove left and right side headlamp filler panels.
6. Remove six grille retaining screws, then the grille.
7. Remove CPA and disconnect sensor electrical connectors from left fender in engine compartment.
8. Snap open six pigtail conduit clip and remove sensor pigtail.
9. Remove two sensor retaining bolts, then the sensor, **Fig. 164.**

Installation

1. Install sensor with arrow pointing toward front of vehicle.
2. Install two sensor retaining bolts and **torque** to 62 inch lbs.
3. Connect sensor electrical connectors and install CPA.
4. Install sensor pigtail into six conduit retaining clips.
5. Position grille and install six grille retaining screws.
6. Connect yellow two-way harness electrical connectors and install CPA at base of steering column.
7. Install left and right sound insulators.
8. Install SIR fuse No. 3 and connect battery ground cable.
9. Turn ignition switch to the On position and verify the "Inflatable Restraint" indicator flashes 7 to 9 times then turns Off. If indicator does not respond, refer to "Diagnosis."

ELDORADO, SEVILLE, RIVIERA, REATTA, TORONADO & TROFEO
Removal

1. **On all models,** disconnect battery ground cable.

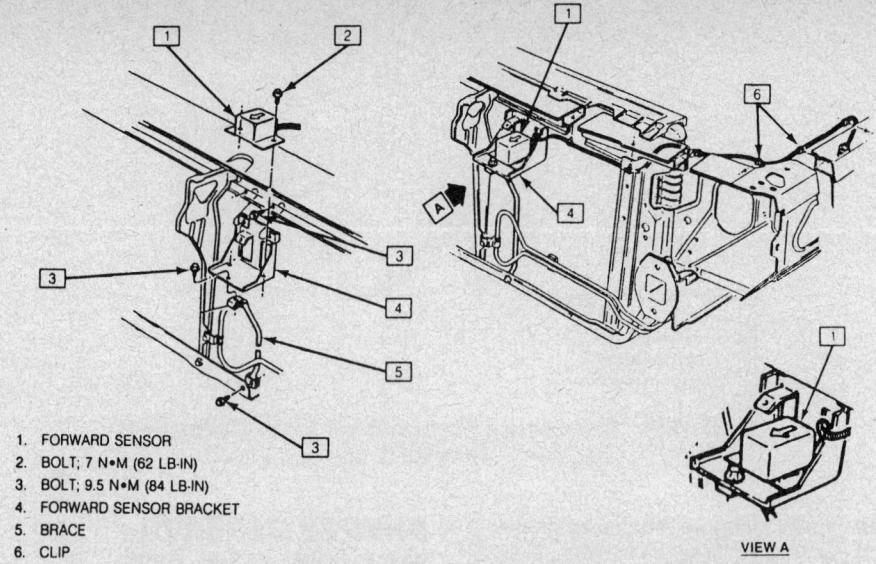

1. FORWARD SENSOR
2. BOLT; 7 N•M (62 LB-IN)
3. BOLT; 9.5 N•M (84 LB-IN)
4. FORWARD SENSOR BRACKET
5. BRACE
6. CLIP

VIEW A

Fig. 164   Removing forward sensor. Deville & Fleetwood

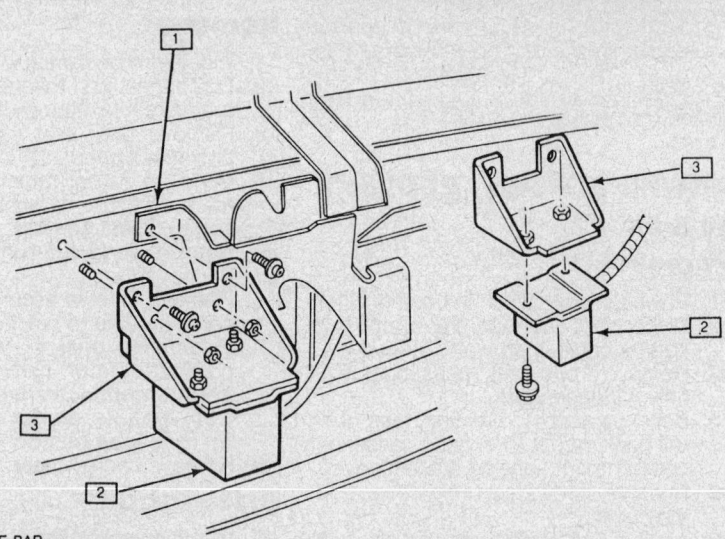

1. RADIATOR TIE BAR
2. FORWARD DISCRIMINATING SENSOR
3. SENSOR BRACKET ASSEMBLY

Fig. 165   Removing forward sensor. Eldorado, Seville, Riviera, Reatta, Toronado & Trofeo

2. **On Riviera, Reatta, Toronado and Trofeo models,** remove SIR fuse No. 14, **on Eldorado and Seville models,** remove SIR fuse No. 19.
3. **On all models,** remove left sound insulator.
4. Remove CPA and disconnect yellow two-way SIR harness electrical connector at base of steering column.
5. Remove three plastic radiator cover retaining screws.
6. Remove four plastic radiator cover retaining clips, then the cover.
7. Disconnect sensor electrical connector.
8. Using tool No. 000-T27H tamper resistant torx insert bit, remove two tamper resistant retaining bolts.
9. Remove sensor from vehicle, pulling

sensor wire harness through core support, **Fig. 165.**

Installation

1. Install sensor into vehicle with arrow pointing toward front of vehicle.
2. Install two tamper resistant retaining bolts. **Torque** bolts to 98 inch lbs.
3. Route sensor harness through radiator support bracket.
4. Connect forward sensor electrical connector.
5. Install radiator cover and four retaining clips.
6. Connect yellow two-way SIR harness electrical connector and install CPA at base of steering column.
7. Install left sound insulator.
8. Install SIR fuse and connect battery

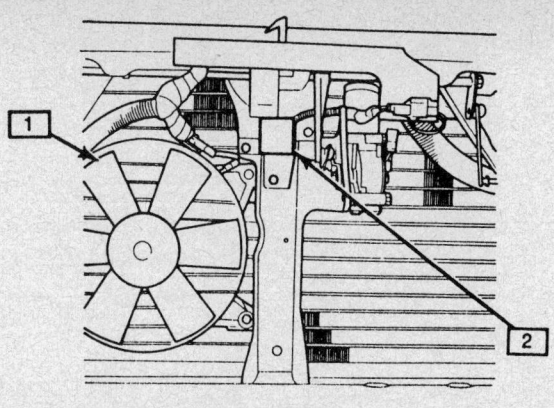

1 ENGINE COOLING FAN
2 FORWARD SENSOR

Fig. 166 Removing forward sensor. Storm

ground cable.
9. Turn ignition switch to the On position and verify the "Inflatable Restraint" indicator flashes 7 to 9 times then turns Off. If indicator does not respond, refer to "Diagnosis."

STORM
Removal

1. Disconnect battery ground cable.
2. Remove SIR fuse No. 3 from fuse panel.
3. Disconnect orange three-way connector at base of steering column.
4. Remove two sensor retaining bolts, then disconnect sensor electrical connector and remove from vehicle, Fig. 166.

Installation

1. Position sensor in vehicle with arrow point toward front of vehicle.
2. Connect sensor electrical connector.
3. Install two sensor retaining bolts, **torque** bolts to 62 inch lbs.
4. Connect orange three-way connector at base of steering column.
5. Install SIR fuse No. 3.
6. Connect battery ground cable.
7. Turn ignition switch to the On position and verify the "Inflatable Restraint" indicator flashes 7 to 9 times then turns Off. If indicator does not respond, refer to "Diagnosis."

LEFT FORWARD SENSOR, REPLACE
CORVETTE
Removal

1. Disconnect battery ground cable.
2. Remove left sound insulator.
3. Remove CPA and disconnect yellow two-way SIR connector at base of steering column.
4. Remove battery, ECM and ECM support.
5. Remove sensor mounting bolts then disconnect sensor electrical connector and remove from vehicle.

Installation

1. Position sensor in vehicle with arrow pointing toward front of vehicle.
2. Install sensor front retaining bolt and **torque** to 19 ft. lbs.
3. Install sensor rear retaining bolt and **torque** to 125 inch lbs.
4. Connect sensor electrical connector.
5. Install ECM, ECM support and battery.
6. Connect yellow two-way connector and install CPA at base of steering column.
7. Install left sound insulator.
8. Connect battery ground cable, then perform SIR Diagnosis System Check as outlined in "Diagnosis."

RIGHT FORWARD SENSOR, REPLACE
CORVETTE
Removal

1. Disconnect battery ground cable.
2. Remove left sound insulator.
3. Remove CPA and disconnect yellow two-way SIR connector at base of steering column.
4. Remove right side front fender gill panel retaining bolts, then the fender.
5. Peel back rear portion of wheelwell to hood seal.
6. Remove right side lower wheelwell retaining bolts, then the wheelwell.
7. Remove two front windshield washer reservoir retaining bolts, then loosen remaining washer reservoir bolt.
8. Rotate reservoir to access sensor.
9. Remove sensor retaining bolts, then disconnect sensor electrical connector.

Installation

1. Position forward sensor with arrow pointing toward front of vehicle.
2. Install sensor front retaining bolt and **torque** to 19 ft. lbs.
3. Install sensor rear retaining bolt and **torque** to 125 inch lbs.
4. Connect sensor electrical connector,

then install and **torque** washer reservoir retaining bolts to 54 inch lbs.
5. Reposition wheelwell to hood seal, then install fender and gill panel.
6. Install six rocker panel retaining screws.
7. Connect yellow two-way SIR electrical connector and install CPA at base of steering column.
8. Install left sound insulator.
9. Connect battery ground cable, then perform SIR Diagnosis System Check as outlined in "Diagnosis."

FORWARD SENSOR BRACKET ASSEMBLY, REPLACE
88 & 98
Removal

1. Remove forward sensor as previously described.
2. Remove bolt securing bracket to upper radiator tie bar, then the bolt securing brace to lower radiator tie bar.
3. Remove bracket from brace.

Installation

1. Install bracket to brace, **torquing** to 88 inch lbs.
2. Install bracket to upper radiator tie bar, **torquing** attaching bolts to 88 inch lbs.
3. Install bracket to lower radiator tie bar, **torquing** attaching bolts to 88 inch lbs.
4. Install forward sensor as previously described.

KNEE BOLSTER, REPLACE
88 & 98
Removal

1. Place ignition switch in lock position.
2. Disconnect and tape negative battery cable, then wait 15 seconds.
3. Remove trim pad between instrument panel and lower trim panel.
4. Remove screws along top of instrument panel lower trim panel.
5. Remove screws from left end of lower trim panel.
6. Remove screws from bottom of lower trim panel.
7. Disconnect electrical connectors as necessary to remove panel.

Installation

1. Connect electrical connectors.
2. Install lower trim pad, securing with screws along bottom edge.
3. Install screw through left end of lower trim panel.
4. Install screws in top of lower trim panel.
5. Install trim panel between lower trim panel and instrument panel.
6. Connect negative battery cable.

CAMARO & FIREBIRD
Removal

1. Place ignition switch in lock position.
2. Disconnect and tape battery ground cable.

3. Remove knee bolster retaining screw covers.
4. Remove knee bolster retaining screws and nuts, **Fig. 167.**

Installation

1. Position knee bolster and install retaining screws and nuts.
2. Install retaining screw covers and connect battery ground cable.

CORVETTE
Removal

1. Disconnect battery ground cable.
2. Remove lower and side trim panels.
3. Remove two knee bolster retaining bolts.
4. Remove knee bolster inner and outer bracket retaining screws.
5. Disconnect lap air outlet duct from lower duct assembly.

Installation

1. Connect lower duct assembly to lap air outlet duct.
2. Install inner and outer bracket retaining screws.
3. Install knee bolster inner retaining bolts and **torque** to 115 inch lbs.
4. Install knee bolster outer retaining bolts and **torque** to 17 inch lbs.
5. Install lower and side trim panels.
6. Connect battery ground cable.

DEVILLE & FLEETWOOD
Removal

1. Disconnect battery ground cable.
2. Remove instrument panel trim panel.
3. Remove two twilight sentinel bracket retaining screws.
4. Remove two fuse block bracket retaining screws.
5. Remove two knee bolster tie bar retaining screws, **Fig. 168.**
6. Remove left side instrument panel retaining bolt.

Installation.

1. Install left side instrument panel retaining bolt.
2. Install two knee bolster tie bar retaining screws.
3. Install two fuse block bracket retaining screws.
4. Install two twilight sentinel bracket retaining screws.
5. Install instrument panel trim panel.
6. Connect battery ground cable.

RIVIERA & REATTA
Removal

1. Disconnect battery ground cable.
2. Remove instrument panel trim plate.
3. Remove front and rear console assemblies.
4. Remove six knee bolster retaining screws, then the knee bolster, **Fig. 169.**

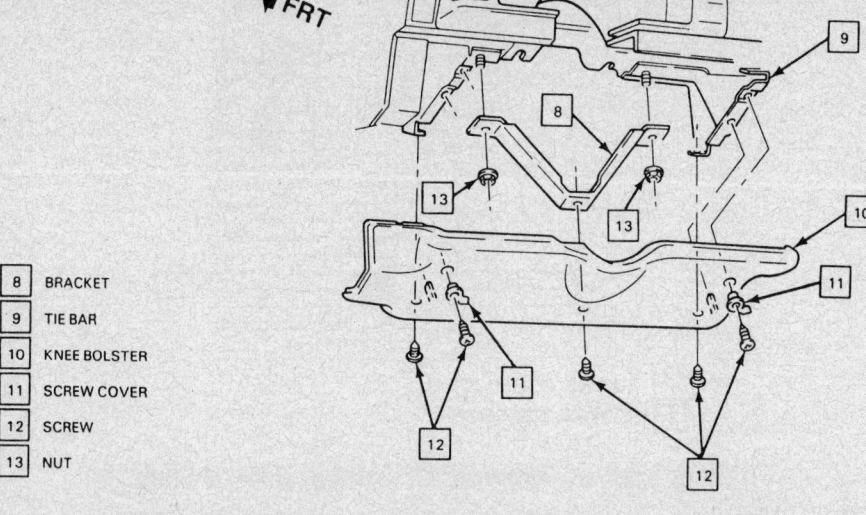

↑FRT

8	BRACKET
9	TIE BAR
10	KNEE BOLSTER
11	SCREW COVER
12	SCREW
13	NUT

Fig. 167 Removing knee bolster. Camaro & Firebird

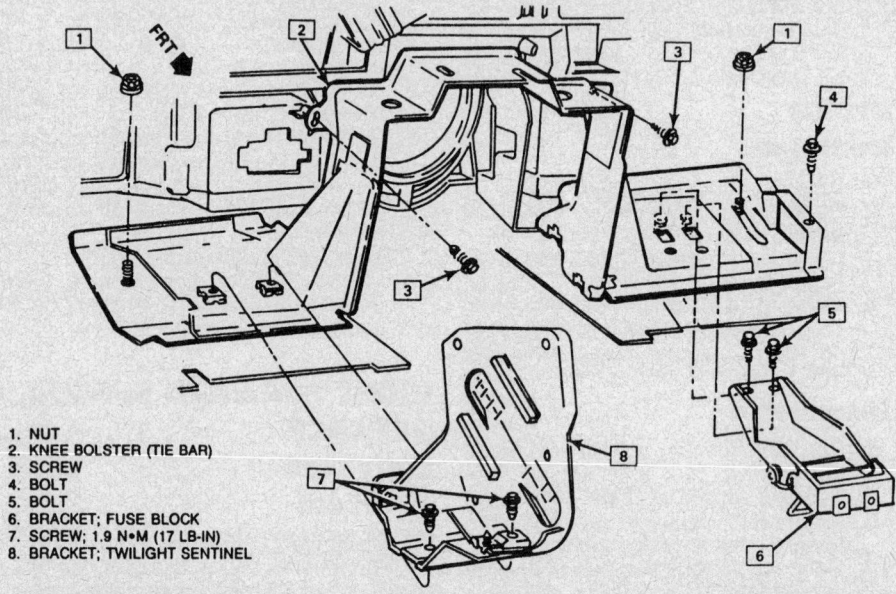

1. NUT
2. KNEE BOLSTER (TIE BAR)
3. SCREW
4. BOLT
5. BOLT
6. BRACKET; FUSE BLOCK
7. SCREW; 1.9 N•M (17 LB-IN)
8. BRACKET; TWILIGHT SENTINEL

Fig. 168 Removing knee bolster. Deville & Fleetwood

Installation

1. Position knee bolster in vehicle and install six retaining screws.
2. Install front and rear console assemblies.
3. Install instrument panel trim plate.
4. Connect battery ground cable.

STORM
Removal

1. Disconnect battery ground cable.
2. Remove SIR fuse No. 3 from fuse panel.
3. Disconnect orange three-way connector at base of steering column.
4. Remove left lower switch and dash lighter panel assemblies.

5. Remove knee bolster.

Installation

1. Install knee bolster.
2. Install lower left switch and dash lighter panel assemblies.
3. Install hood release handle.
4. Connect orange three-way connector at base of steering column.
5. Install SIR fuse No. 3.
6. Connect battery ground cable.
7. Turn ignition switch to the On position and verify the "Inflatable Restraint" indicator flashes 7 to 9 times then turns Off. If indicator does not respond, refer to "Diagnosis."

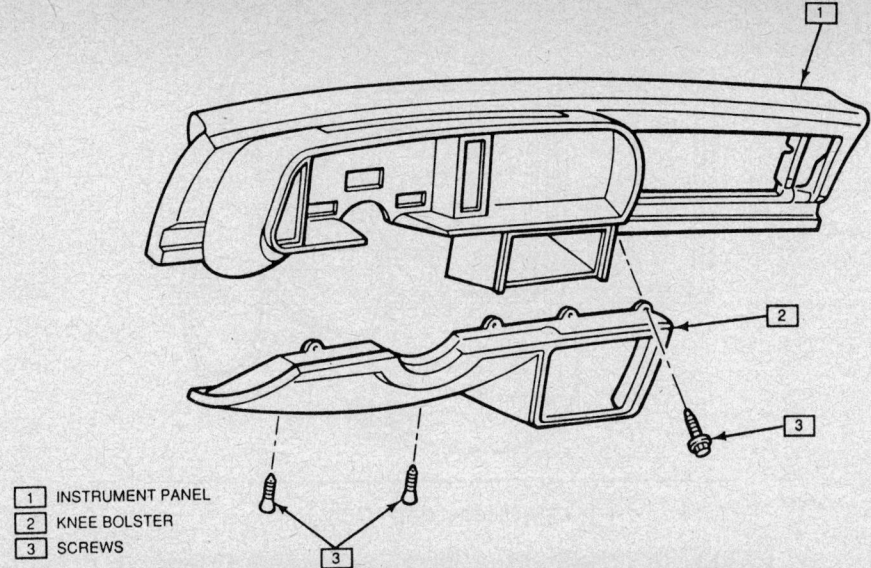

Fig. 169 Removing knee bolster. Riviera & Reatta

1	INSTRUMENT PANEL
2	KNEE BOLSTER
3	SCREWS

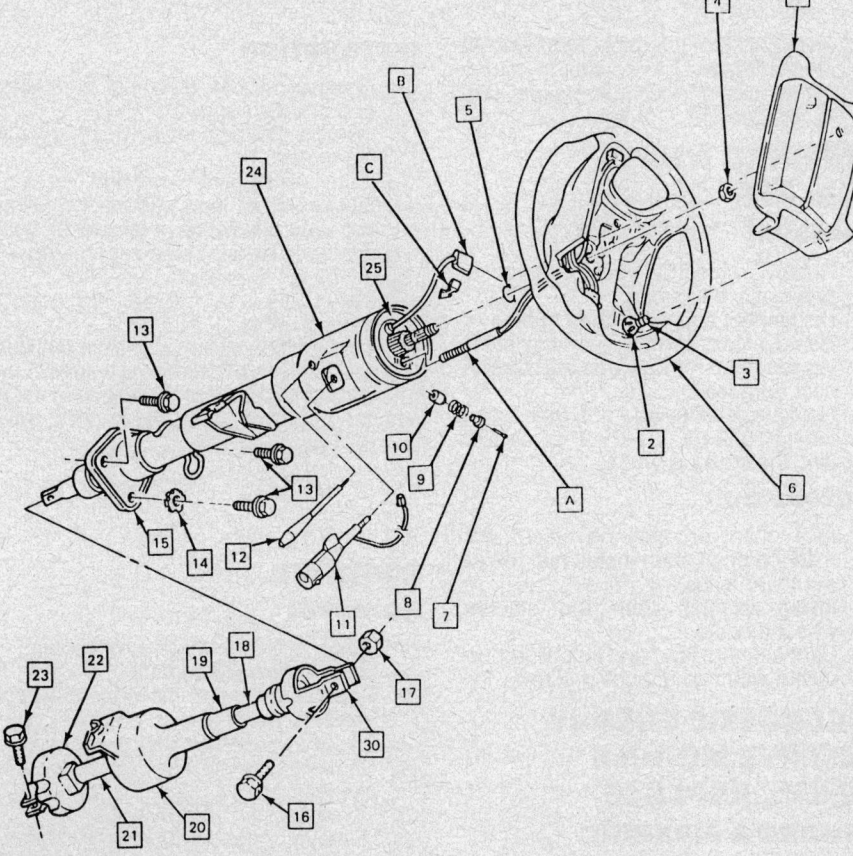

Fig. 170 Removing inflator module. Camaro & Firebird

A	HORN CONNECTOR			
B	COIL-TO-INFLATOR CONNECTOR	9	SPRING	19	SEAL
C	CONNECTOR POSITIVE ASSURANCE	10	HAZARD WARNING KNOB	20	COUPLING SHIELD
1	INFLATOR MODULE	11	MULTIFUNCTION LEVER	21	LOWER INTERMEDIATE SHAFT
2	LOCK NUT	12	TILT LEVER	22	FLEXIBLE COUPLING
3	SCREW	13	BOLT	23	BOLT
4	NUT	14	WASHER	24	STEERING COLUMN
5	RETAINING RING	15	BRACKET	25	COIL ASSEMBLY
6	STEERING WHEEL	16	BOLT	30	POT JOINT COUPLING
7	SCREW	17	NUT		
8	HAZARD WARNING BUTTON	18	UPPER INTERMEDIATE SHAFT		

INFLATOR MODULE, REPLACE

88 & 98

1. Always wear safety glasses and gloves.
2. Wash hands wild mild soap and water after handling a deployed module.

Removal

1. Turn ignition to Lock position.
2. Disconnect and tape battery ground cable.
3. Remove three of the four module to steering column attaching screws from back side of steering wheel.
4. While supporting module with one hand, remove fourth screw and disconnect the module connector, then tape the connector.
5. Disconnect horn lead.

Installation

1. While holding module with one hand, connect module connector and horn lead.
2. Place module in position and secure with one screw.
3. Install three remaining screws, ensuring all attaching bolts are fully driven, seated and not stripped.
4. Remove tape and connect battery ground cable.

CAMARO & FIREBIRD
Removal

1. Disconnect battery ground cable.
2. Remove SIR fuse from fuse block.
3. Remove left sound insulator.
4. Remove CPA and disconnect yellow two-way SIR harness at base of steering column.
5. Remove module retaining screws and nuts from back of steering wheel assembly.
6. Remove inflator module from steering column, **Fig. 170**.
7. Remove CPA and disconnect coil assembly electrical connector from inflator module.

Installation

1. Connect coil assembly electrical connector to inflator module electrical connectors and install CPA.
2. Install inflator module in steering wheel assembly.
3. Install module retaining screws and nuts. **Torque** screws to 25 inch lbs.
4. Connect yellow two-way SIR harness connector and connector position assurance electrical connectors.
5. Install left sound insulator.
6. Install SIR fuse and connect battery ground cable.
7. Turn ignition switch to the On position and verify the "Inflatable Restraint" indicator flashes 7 to 9 times then turns Off. If indicator does not respond, refer to "Diagnosis."

CORVETTE
Removal

1. Disconnect battery ground cable.
2. Remove left sound insulator.
3. Remove CPA and disconnect yellow two-way SIR harness at base of steering column.
4. Install SIR Load Tool J 37808, "Base of Column" lead of tool, **Fig. 171.**
5. Remove module retaining screws and nuts from back of steering wheel assembly.
6. Remove inflator module from steering column.
7. Disconnect coil assembly electrical from inflator module.

Installation

1. Connect coil assembly electrical connector to inflator module.
2. Install inflator module in steering wheel.
3. Install new inflator module retaining screws and **torque** to 87 inch lbs.
4. Remove Lead tool J 37808 then connect yellow two-way SIR harness electrical connector and install CPA at base of steering column.
5. Install left sound insulator.
6. Connect battery ground cable, then perform SIR Diagnosis System Check as outlined in "Diagnosis."

DEVILLE & FLEETWOOD
Removal

1. Disconnect battery ground cable.
2. Turn ignition switch to the Off position.
3. Remove SIR fuse No. 3 from fuse panel.
4. Remove left sound insulator.
5. Remove CPA and disconnect yellow two-way SIR harness electrical connector at base of steering column.
6. Using a No. 30 Torx driver or equivalent, remove inflator module retaining screws from back of steering column.
7. Remove inflator module from steering wheel.
8. Slightly push while twisting horn contact and remove from inflator module.
9. Remove CPA and disconnect coil assembly electrical connector from inflator module.

Installation

1. Install horn contact.
2. Connect coil assembly electrical connector and install CPA.
3. Push coil assembly lead wires into channel in lower right portion of steering wheel.
4. Install inflator module into steering wheel.
5. Install inflator module retaining screws and **torque** to 25 inch lbs.
6. Connect yellow two-way SIR harness electrical connector and install CPA at base of steering column.
7. Install left sound insulator.
8. Install SIR fuse No. 3 and connect battery ground cable.
9. Turn ignition switch to the On position

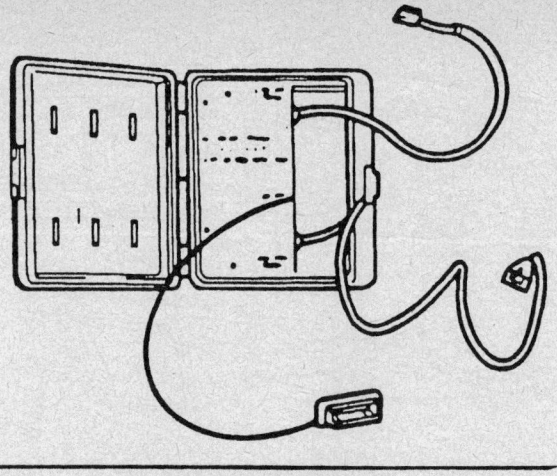

☐1☐ J 37808 - SIR LOAD TOOL

Fig. 171   Installing SIR Load Tool J 37808. Corvette

and verify the "Inflatable Restraint" indicator flashes 7 to 9 times then turns Off. If indicator does not respond, refer to "Diagnosis."

STEERING WHEEL, REPLACE
Removal

1. Remove steering wheel module as previously described.
2. Disconnect battery ground cable.
3. Remove two screws securing steering pad, then remove pad and disconnect horn lead.
4. Remove retainer and nut, then, using tool J-1859-03, BT-61-9 or equivalent, the steering wheel.

Installation

1. Align mark on steering wheel with mark on shaft, then install nut, **torquing** to 30 ft. lbs.
2. Install retainer, then the steering wheel module.
3. Connect horn lead and install pad, securing with two attaching screws.

DIAGNOSTIC ENERGY RESERVE MODULE (DERM), REPLACE
CAMARO & FIREBIRD
Removal

1. Disconnect battery ground cable.
2. Remove SIR fuse from fuse block.
3. Remove left side sound insulator.
4. Remove CPA and disconnect yellow two-way SIR harness at base of steering column.
5. Remove instrument panel pad.
6. Remove side window defogger duct and retaining screws.
7. Remove Derm upper and lower retaining screws, **Fig. 172.**
8. Unlatch orange lock and disconnect DERM electrical connector.

Installation

1. Connect DERM electrical connector and orange connector lock.
2. Install upper and lower DERM retaining screws.
3. Install instrument panel pad.
4. Install CPA and connect yellow two-way Sir harness electrical connector at base of steering column.
5. Install left side sound insulator.
6. Install SIR fuse and connect battery ground cable.
7. Turn ignition switch to the On position and verify the "Inflatable Restraint" indicator flashes 7 to 9 times then turns Off. If indicator does not respond, refer to "Diagnosis."

CORVETTE
Removal

1. Disconnect battery ground cable.
2. Remove lower trim panel.
3. Remove CPA and disconnect yellow two-way SIR harness electrical connector at base of steering column.
4. Remove console and accessory trim plates.
5. Remove radio control head.
6. Remove upper two side trim panel retaining screws, then flip panel down to access DERM.
7. Remove knee bolster, refer to "Knee Bolster, Replace."
8. Remove four SIR module brackets.
9. Remove passenger side seat.
10. Remove side trim panel to access DERM.
11. Remove driver's inner knee bolster bracket, then two nuts on right side of instrument panel bracket retaining DERM mounting bracket.
12. Remove LH forward sensor connector from retaining clip, then disconnect sensor electrical connector.

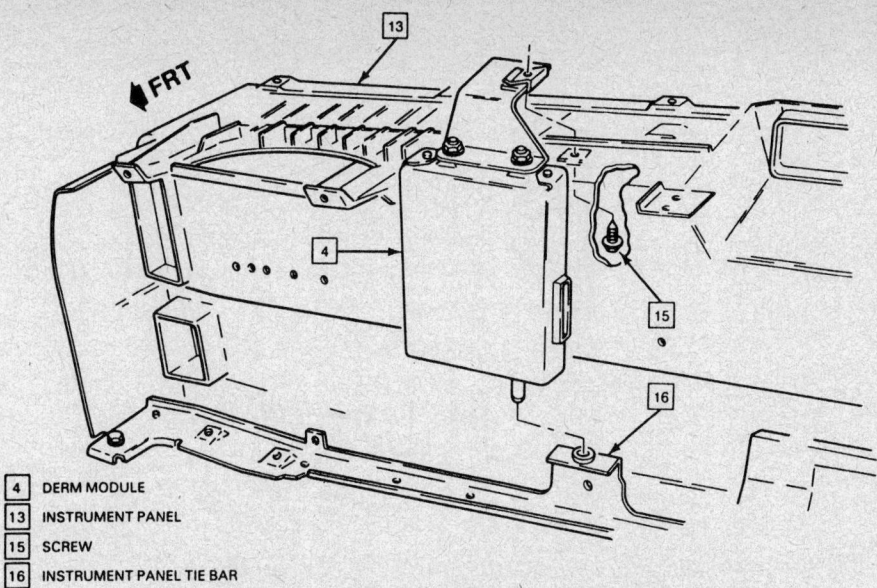

4 DERM MODULE
13 INSTRUMENT PANEL
15 SCREW
16 INSTRUMENT PANEL TIE BAR

Fig. 172 Removing the diagnostic energy reserve module. Camaro & Firebird

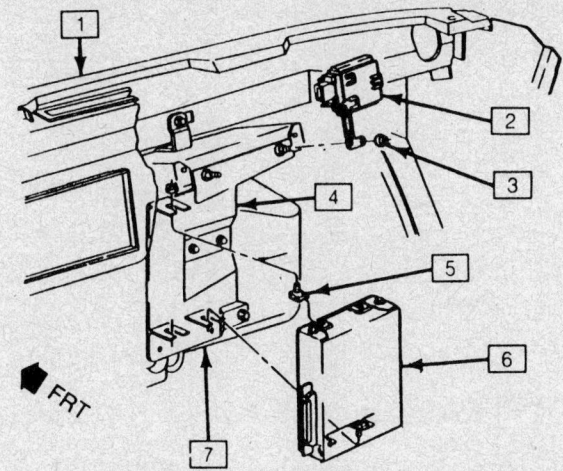

1. DASH

2. RESISTOR MODULE

3. NUT; 4 N•M (30 LB-FT)

4. BCM/DERM BRACKET

5. BOLT/SCREW

6. DIAGNOSTIC ENERGY RESERVE MODULE

Fig. 173 Removing the diagnostic energy reserve module. Deville & Fleetwood

13. Cut DERM side of LH sensor lead at least 6 inches from sensor connector, then remove RH forward sensor connector from retaining clip and disconnect sensor electrical connector.
14. Disconnect DERM to instrument panel harness.
15. Remove DERM from vehicle.

Installation
1. Install DERM to instrument panel.
2. Route RH sensor lead and DERM to instrument panel harness.

3. Connect instrument panel harness and install CPA.
4. Install DERM mounting bracket to passenger knee bolster inner bracket retaining nuts. **Torque** retaining nuts to 116 inch lbs.
5. Connect RH sensor electrical connector, then clip connection into retaining clip.
6. Route LH DERM to sensor lead above steering column support bracket, then position harness behind support bracket lip.

7. Using tie straps, secure LH sensor harness to large instrument panel wiring bundle. Secure on both sides of steering column.
8. Connect DERM-to-sensor harness to LH sensor connector, then install connector in retaining clip.
9. Install driver's inner knee bolster bracket. **Torque** bracket fasteners to 116 inch lbs.
10. Install side trim panel and passenger side seat.
11. Install SIR module bracket. **Torque** retaining bolts to 116 inch lbs.
12. Install knee bolster, refer to "Knee Bolster, Replace."
13. Flip side trim panel into position and install retaining screws.
14. Install radio control head, accessory trim plate and console trim plate.
15. Connect yellow two-way SIR electrical connector and install CPA at base of steering column.
16. Install lower trim panel.
17. Connect battery ground cable.
18. Perform SIR Diagnostic System Check as outlined in "Diagnosis."

DEVILLE & FLEETWOOD
Removal
1. Disconnect battery ground cable.
2. Remove SIR fuse No. 3 from fuse panel.
3. Remove left and right sound insulators.
4. Remove CPA and disconnect yellow two-way SIR electrical connector at base of steering column.
5. Remove glove box module.
6. Loosen three DERM retaining nuts.
7. Unlatch orange connector lock then disconnect DERM electrical connector and remove DERM, **Fig. 173.**

Installation
1. Position DERM and **torque** retaining nuts to 35 inch lbs.
2. Connect DERM electrical connector and latch orange connector lock.
3. Install glove box module.
4. Connect yellow two-way harness electrical connector and install CPA at base of steering column.
5. Install left and right sound insulators.
6. Install SIR fuse No. 3 and connect battery ground cable.
7. Turn ignition switch to the On position and verify the "Inflatable Restraint" indicator flashes 7 to 9 times then turns Off. If indicator does not respond, refer to "Diagnosis."

RIVIERA, REATTA & TORONADO & TROFEO
Removal
1. On **all models**, disconnect battery ground cable.
2. **On Riviera and Reatta models**, remove SIR fuse No. 14.

3. **On Toronado and Trofeo models,** remove SIR fuse No. 9.
4. **On all models,** remove left side sound insulator.
5. Remove CPA and disconnect yellow two-way SIR harness electrical connector at base of steering column.
6. Disconnect DERM electrical connector.
7. Loosen three DERM retaining nuts to the right of steering column.
8. Remove DERM from vehicle, **Fig. 174.**

Installation

1. Position DERM in vehicle and install three DERM retaining nuts.
2. Connect DERM electrical connector.
3. Connect yellow SIR harness electrical connector and install CPA at base of steering column.
4. Install left sound insulator.
5. Install SIR fuse and connect battery ground cable.
6. Turn ignition switch to the On position and verify the "Inflatable Restraint" indicator flashes 7 to 9 times then turns Off. If indicator does not respond, refer to "Diagnosis."

ELDORADO & SEVILLE
Removal

1. Disconnect battery ground cable.
2. Remove SIR fuse No. 19 from fuse panel.
3. Remove sound insulator.
4. Remove CPA and disconnect yellow SIR harness electrical connector at base of steering column.
5. Disconnect DERM electrical connector, **Fig. 174.**
6. Loosen three DERM retaining nuts located to the right of steering column.
7. Remove DERM from vehicle.

Installation

1. Install DERM in vehicle and tighten three retaining nuts located to the right of steering column.
2. . Connect DERM electrical connector, **Fig. 174.**
4. Connect yellow SIR harness electrical connector and install CPA at base of steering column.
5. Install sound insulator.
6. Connect battery ground cable.

STORM
Removal

1. Disconnect battery ground cable.
2. Remove SIR fuse No. 3 from fuse panel.
3. Disconnect orange three-way connector at base of steering column.
4. Remove front bezel and console side panels.
5. Disconnect DERM electrical connector.
6. Remove two DERM retaining bolts, then the DERM, **Fig. 175.**

Installation

1. Position DERM in vehicle and install two retaining bolts, **torque** bolts to 62 inch lbs.

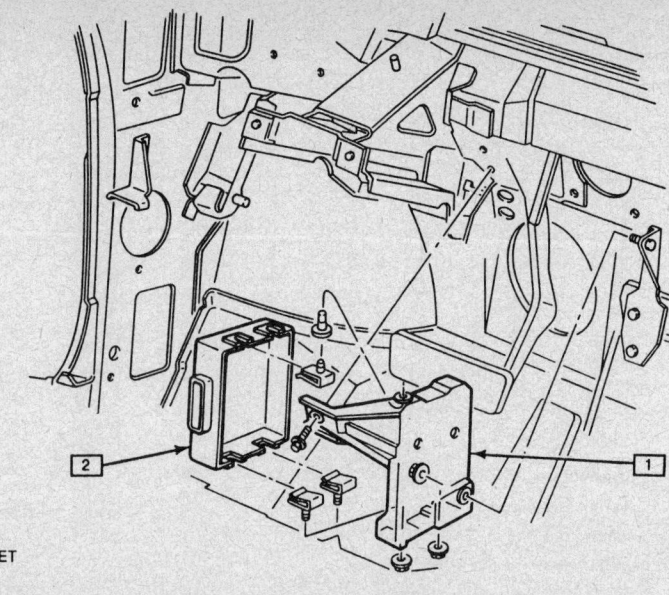

1 MOUNTING BRACKET
2 DERM

Fig. 174   Removing the diagnostic energy reserve module. Riviera, Reatta, Toronado & Trofeo

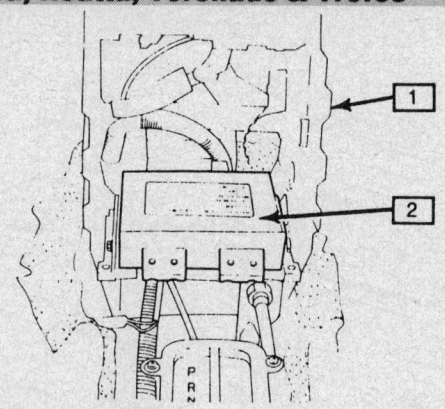

1 CONSOLE BRACKET
2 DERM

Fig. 175   Removing the diagnostic energy reserve module. Storm

2. Connect DERM electrical connector.
3. Install front bezel and console side panels.
4. Connect orange three-way connector at base of steering column.
5. Install SIR fuse No. 3.
6. Connect battery ground cable.

RESISTOR MODULE, REPLACE
CAMARO & FIREBIRD
Removal

1. Disconnect battery ground cable.
2. Remove SIR fuse from fuse block.
3. Remove left side sound insulator.
4. Remove CPA and disconnect yellow two-way Sir harness at base of steering column.
5. Remove knee bolster, refer to "Knee Bolster, Replace."
6. Unsnap resistor module from left side tie bar, **Fig. 176,** then remove CPA

and disconnect module electrical connector.

Installation

1. Connect module electrical connector and install CPA.
2. Snap resistor module to left side tie bar.
3. Install knee bolster, refer to "Knee Bolster, Replace."
4. Connect yellow two-way SIR harness electrical connector at base of steering column.
5. Install left side sound insulator, refer to "Instrument Panel Service."
6. Install SIR fuse and connect battery ground cable.
7. Turn ignition switch to the On position and verify the "Inflatable Restraint" indicator flashes 7 to 9 times then turns Off. If indicator does not respond, refer to "Diagnosis."

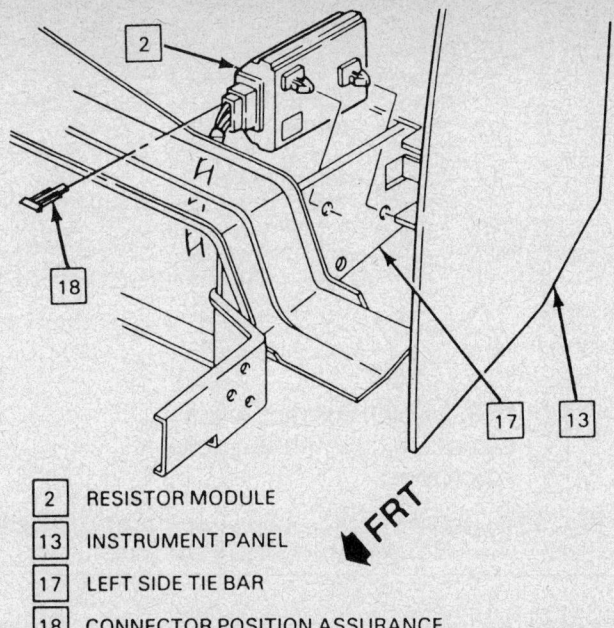

2 RESISTOR MODULE

13 INSTRUMENT PANEL

17 LEFT SIDE TIE BAR

18 CONNECTOR POSITION ASSURANCE

Fig. 176 Removing resistor module. Camaro & Firebird

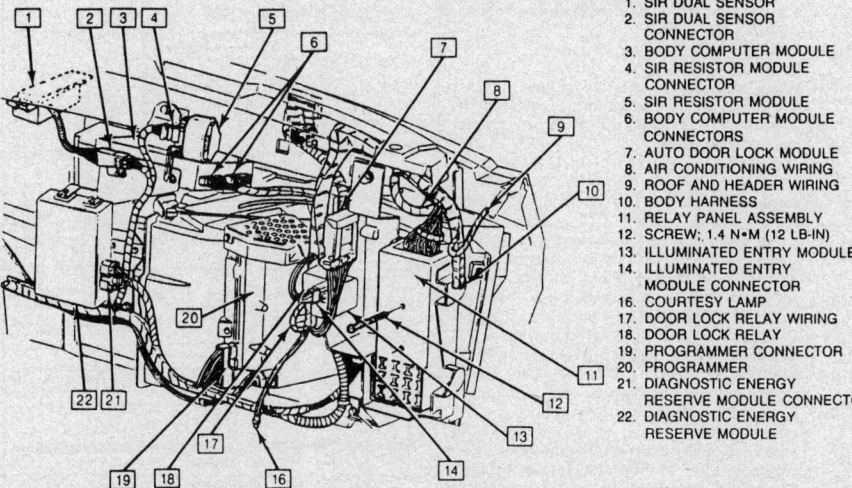

1. SIR DUAL SENSOR
2. SIR DUAL SENSOR CONNECTOR
3. BODY COMPUTER MODULE
4. SIR RESISTOR MODULE CONNECTOR
5. SIR RESISTOR MODULE
6. BODY COMPUTER MODULE CONNECTORS
7. AUTO DOOR LOCK MODULE
8. AIR CONDITIONING WIRING
9. ROOF AND HEADER WIRING
10. BODY HARNESS
11. RELAY PANEL ASSEMBLY
12. SCREW; 1.4 N•M (12 LB-IN)
13. ILLUMINATED ENTRY MODULE
14. ILLUMINATED ENTRY MODULE CONNECTOR
16. COURTESY LAMP
17. DOOR LOCK RELAY WIRING
18. DOOR LOCK RELAY
19. PROGRAMMER CONNECTOR
20. PROGRAMMER
21. DIAGNOSTIC ENERGY RESERVE MODULE CONNECTOR
22. DIAGNOSTIC ENERGY RESERVE MODULE

Fig. 177 Removing resistor module. Deville & Fleetwood

DEVILLE & FLEETWOOD
Removal

1. Disconnect battery ground cable.
2. Remove SIR fuse No. 3 from fuse panel.
3. Remove left and right sound insulators.
4. Remove CPA and disconnect yellow two-way SIR electrical connector at base of steering column.
5. Remove glove box module.
6. Remove CPA, then disconnect resistor module electrical connector and remove module, Fig. 177.

Installation

1. Install resistor module.
2. Connect module electrical connector and install CPA.
3. Install glove box module.
4. Connect yellow two-way SIR harness electrical and install CPA at base of steering column.
5. Install left and right side sound insulators.
6. Install SIR fuse No. 3 and connect battery ground cable.
7. Turn ignition switch to the On position and verify the "Inflatable Restraint" indicator flashes 7 to 9 times then turns Off. If indicator does not respond, refer to "Diagnosis."

ELDORADO & SEVILLE
Removal

1. Disconnect battery ground cable.
2. Remove SIR fuse No. 19 from fuse panel.

3. Remove sound insulator.
4. Remove CPA and disconnect yellow two-way SIR electrical connector at base of steering column.
5. Remove two center trim plate retaining screws, then the plate.
6. Remove knee bolster, refer to "Knee Bolster Replace."
7. Remove four instrument panel steering column reinforcement plate retaining screws.
8. Remove hood release lever, then unsnap module from bracket behind left side of instrument panel.
9. Remove CPA, then disconnect module electrical connector.
10. Remove module form vehicle.

Installation

1. Install resistor module to bracket.
2. Connect module electrical connector and install CPA.
3. Install hood release lever.
4. Install four instrument panel steering column reinforcement plate retaining screws.
5. Install knee bolster, refer to "Knee Bolster Replace."
6. Install center trim plate.
7. Connect yellow two-way SIR electrical connector and install CPA at base of steering column.
8. Install sound insulator.
9. Install SIR fuse No. 19 and connect battery ground cable.

STORM
Removal

1. Disconnect battery ground cable.
2. Remove SIR fuse No. 3 from fuse panel.
3. Disconnect orange three-way connector at base of steering column.
4. Remove dash pad assembly.
5. Remove module retaining clip, then disconnect module electrical connector and remove from vehicle.

Installation

1. Install module in module retaining clip, then connect module electrical connector.
2. Install dash pad assembly.
3. Connect orange three-way connector at base of steering column.
4. Install SIR fuse No. 3.
5. Connect battery ground cable.
6. Turn ignition switch to the On position and verify the "Inflatable Restraint" indicator flashes 7 to 9 times then turns Off. If indicator does not respond, refer to "Diagnosis."

SIR COIL ASSEMBLY, REPLACE
CAMARO & FIREBIRD

Refer to "Steering Wheel Module Replace."

EXCEPT CAMARO & FIREBIRD

Refer to "Steering Column Repairs" in "Steering Column" section.

PASSENGER COMPARTMENT SENSOR
CAMARO & FIREBIRD
Removal

1. Disconnect battery ground cable.
2. Remove SIR fuse from fuse block.
3. Remove left side sound insulator.
4. Remove CPA and disconnect yellow two-way Sir harness electrical connector at base of steering column.
5. Remove knee bolster, refer to "Knee Bolster, Replace."
6. Remove console.
7. Remove heater air distribution duct.
8. Remove CPA and disconnect passenger compartment discriminating sensor electrical connector.
9. Remove sensor retaining bolts, then the sensor.

Installation

1. Install sensor with arrow pointing toward front of vehicle, **torquing** bolts to 25 inch lbs.
2. Connect sensor and connector position assurance electrical connectors.
3. Install heater air distributor duct.
4. Install console.
5. Install knee bolster, refer to "Knee Bolster, Replace."
6. Connect yellow two-way SIR harness electrical connector and install CPA at base of steering column.
7. Install left side sound insulator.
8. Install SIR fuse and connect battery ground cable.
9. Turn ignition switch to the On position and verify the "Inflatable Restraint" indicator flashes 7 to 9 times then turns Off. If indicator does not respond, refer to "Diagnosis."

STORM
Removal

1. Disconnect battery ground cable.
2. Remove SIR fuse No. 3 from fuse panel.

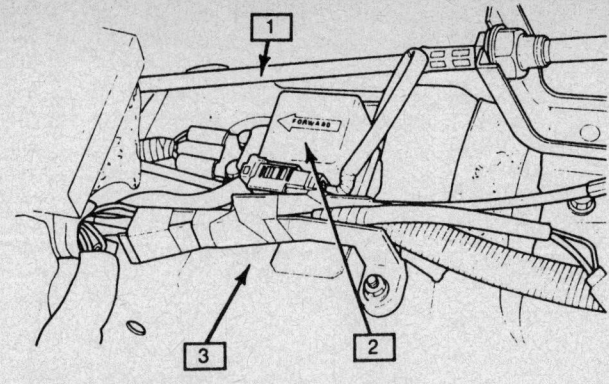

1	TRANSMISSION CONTROL CABLE
2	PASSENGER COMPARTMENT SENSOR
3	FLOOR PANEL

Fig. 178 Removing passenger compartment sensor. Storm

CHECKING STEERING COLUMN FOR ACCIDENT DAMAGE

NOTICE: Cars involved in accidents resulting in frame damage, major body or sheet metal damage, or where the steering column has been inpacted may also have a damaged or misaligned steering column.

CHECKING PROCEDURE

1. Check capsules on steering column bracket assembly; all should be within 1.59 mm from the bottom of the slots. (View A) If not, bracket should be replaced.
2. Check contact surface "A". (View B) The bolt-head must not contact surface "A" or shear load would be increased. If contact is made, replace bracket.
3. On cars with automatic transmission and column shift, check operation of the shift lever. If you are able to move lever to "Park" position without raising lever, it is an indication that the upper shift tube plastic bearing is broken.
4. Check for jacket collapse by measuring the distance from end of bearing assembly to the lower edge of upper jacket. (refer to View C for dimensions.) If jacket dimensions are not within specifications a NEW jacket must be installed and shift tube and steering shaft visually inspected for sheared injected plastic. If shift tube shows sheared plastic a NEW shift tube must be installed. (View D) If steering shaft shows sheared plastic and is not bent, it can be repaired by using a Service Steering Shaft Repair Package. Parts Book (View E)

5. Any frame damage that could cause a bent steering shaft must have steering shaft runout checked in the following manner: Remove intermediate shaft. Hold ruler against lower end of steering shaft and have steering wheel rotated. Runout must not exceed 1.59 mm. Dial indicator may be used instead of a ruler.

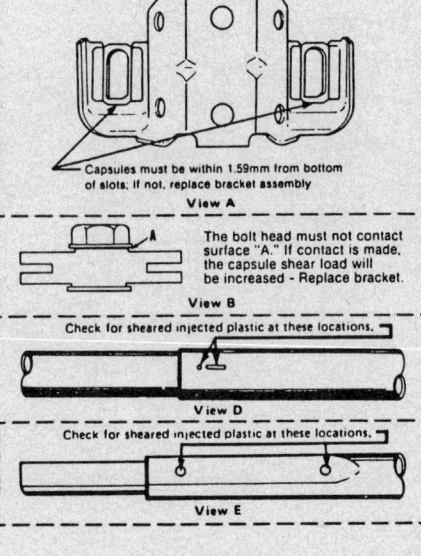

Capsules must be within 1.59mm from bottom of slots; if not, replace bracket assembly

View A

The bolt head must not contact surface "A." If contact is made, the capsule shear load will be increased - Replace bracket.

View B

Check for sheared injected plastic at these locations.

View D

Check for sheared injected plastic at these locations.

View E

METHOD TO DETERMINE COLUMN COLLAPSE
MEASURE DISTANCE BETWEEN ARROWS OF PROPER ILLUSTRATION.

127.21 mm

Fig. 179 Checking steering column for accident damage

3. Disconnect orange three-way connector at base of steering column.
4. Remove two sensor mounting bolts, **Fig. 178**, then disconnect sensor electrical connector and remove from vehicle.

Installation

1. Position sensor in vehicle with arrow pointing toward front of vehicle.
2. Connect sensor electrical connector.
3. Install two sensor retaining bolts, **torque** bolts to 62 inch lbs.
4. Connect orange three-way connector at base of steering column.
5. Install SIR fuse No. 3.
6. Connect battery ground cable.
7. Turn ignition switch to the On position and verify the "Inflatable Restraint" indicator flashes 7 to 9 times then turns Off. If indicator does not respond, refer to "Diagnosis."

CHECKING COLUMN FOR ACCIDENT DAMAGE

Vehicles involved in accidents resulting in frame damage, major body or sheet metal damage, or where the steering column has been impacted, may also have a damaged or misaligned steering column. To check steering column for accident damage, refer to **Fig. 179**.

WIRING REPAIR

Special wiring repair procedures have been developed for use on the Supplemental Inflatable Restraint systems due to the sensitive nature of the circuitry.

Tool No. J-38125 Terminal Repair Kit contains special sealed splices for use in repairing SIR system wiring. A special crimping tool, heat torch and instruction manual for these splices are also included.

The critical features of the sealed splices are a special heat shrink sleeve with sealing adhesive to produce an environmentally sealed splice and a cross hatched core crimp to provide necessary contact integrity for th sensitive low energy circuits.

SIR CONNECTOR BODY & TERMINAL REPAIR

If any connector or terminal in the SIR wire harness, except pigtail, is damaged the component should be repaired using one of the connector repair assembly packs. These kits include an instruction sheet and sealed splices which will be necessary to splice the new wires, connector and terminals to the harness.

If individual terminals are damaged on the DERM or resistor module, repair using the DERM/resistor terminal repair assembly pack. If individual terminals are damaged on any other SIR connection, the entire connection should be replaced using the appropriate repair assembly pack.

SIR PIGTAIL REPAIR

If the wiring pigtail is damaged, the entire component should be replaced.

SIR WIRE REPAIR

If any wire except the pigtail is damaged, the wire should be repaired by splicing in a new section of wire of the same gauge size. The sealed splices and crimping tool from J-38125 must be used for these splices.

PARTS DISPOSAL
STEERING WHEEL MODULE (DEPLOYED & REMOVED FROM VEHICLE)

When a deployed module has been remove from a vehicle, it may be disposed of with any other scrap material. Handle with gloves and safety glasses and wash hands after handling. **The steering wheel module must be deactivated prior to disposal. The module contains explosive material. Failure to deactivate before disposing may result in personal injury.**

UNDEPLOYED STEERING WHEEL MODULE (IN VEHICLE)

If any vehicle equipped with supplemental inflatable restraint system must be scrapped, deploy steering wheel module as follows:

1. Place ignition switch in Off position.
2. Disconnect and tape negative battery cable, then wait 15 seconds before proceeding.
3. Ensure steering wheel module is secured to steering wheel and that their is nobody in vehicle, and remove all loose objects from front seat.
4. Disconnect lower steering column connector and remove shorting clip from connector.
5. Splice two wires, at least 20 feet long, into steering wheel module circuit wiring at base of steering column.
6. Stretch wires away from vehicle to their full length.
7. Apply 12 volts across wires to deploy module. **Do not touch steering wheel module area for 20 minutes, due to heat generated by deployment.**

Automatic Safety Belt System

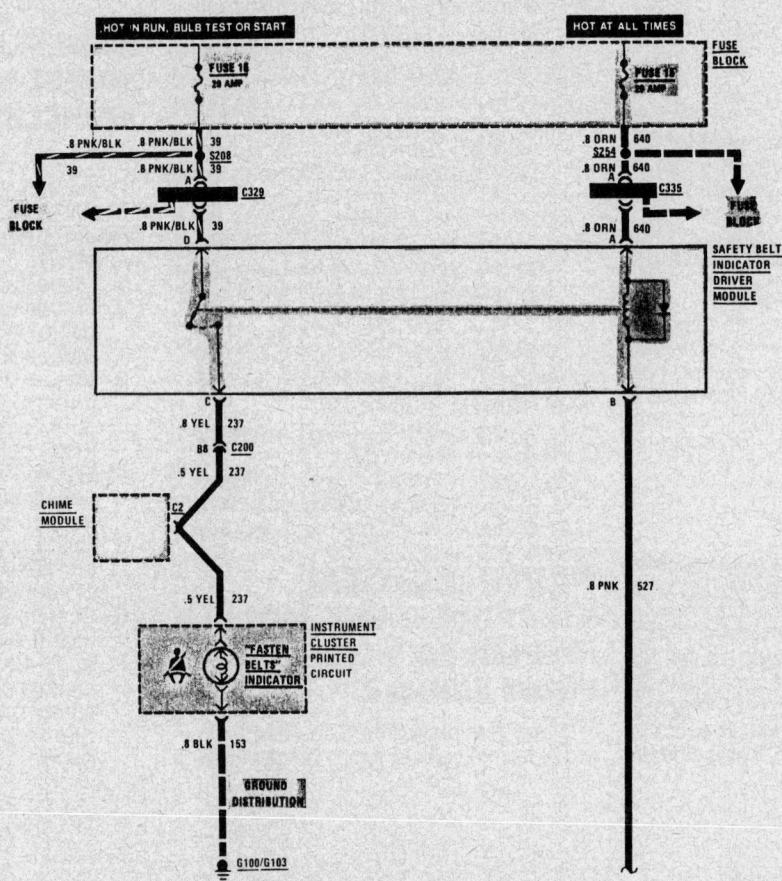

Fig. 1 Automatic safety belt schematic (Part 1 of 2)

DESCRIPTION

The automatic safety belt utilizes an upper-torso belt, a lap belt and two retractor assemblies mounted to each front door. The belt assemblies are permanently buckled to fixed hasps mounted near the vehicle's central console.

When a front door is opened, the corresponding safety belt retractor switch is closed and battery voltage is applied to the Safety Belt Shoulder and Lap Retractor Solenoids through the Safety Belt Indicator Driver Module, **Fig. 1.** The Lap Retractor Solenoids are energized and restrain the safety belt retractor lock pendulums.

The operation of the Retractor Switch results in a voltage across the Safety Belt Indicator Driver Module, which serves as a relay for the Fasten Belts Indicator. The voltage energizes the coil and closes the contacts which apply battery voltage from Fuse 16 to the Indicator. The diode in the Safety Belt Indicator Driver Module limits the voltage across the coil so that there will be sufficient voltage to operate the solenoids.

When the door is closed, the corresponding Safety Belt Retractor Switch is opened. The Time Delay Module keeps the solenoids energized for approximately one second after the Safety Belt Retractor Switch is opened. The Safety Belt Indicator Driver Module and Retractor Solenoids then de-energize. The indicator light goes out and the Safety Belt Retractors are then allowed to lock up in the event of sudden deceleration.

Voltage is applied at all times to terminal A of the Safety Belt Indicator Driver Module. Voltage is also applied to terminal D when the ignition switch is on Run, Bulb Test or Start.

DIAGNOSIS & TESTING

1. If safety belts prevent both front doors from opening freely, refer to **Fig. 2,** "Safety Belt Indicator Driver Module Test."
2. If safety belts prevent one front door from opening freely and Fasten Belts Indicator does not light when door is opened with the ignition switch in Run, refer to **Fig. 3,** "Safety Belt Retractor Switch Test."
3. If safety belts prevent one front door from opening freely and Fasten Belts indicator lights when door is opened with the ignition switch in Run, refer to **Fig. 4,** "Safety Belt Retractor Solenoid Test."
4. Fasten Belts indicator does not come on when a front door is open with the ignition switch in Run, but doors operate normally, refer to **Fig. 5,**' "Fasten Belts Indicator Test."
5. Fasten Belts indicator is on continuously with ignition switch in Run and doors closed and front doors can open freely, refer to **Fig. 6,** "Indicator Short Test."

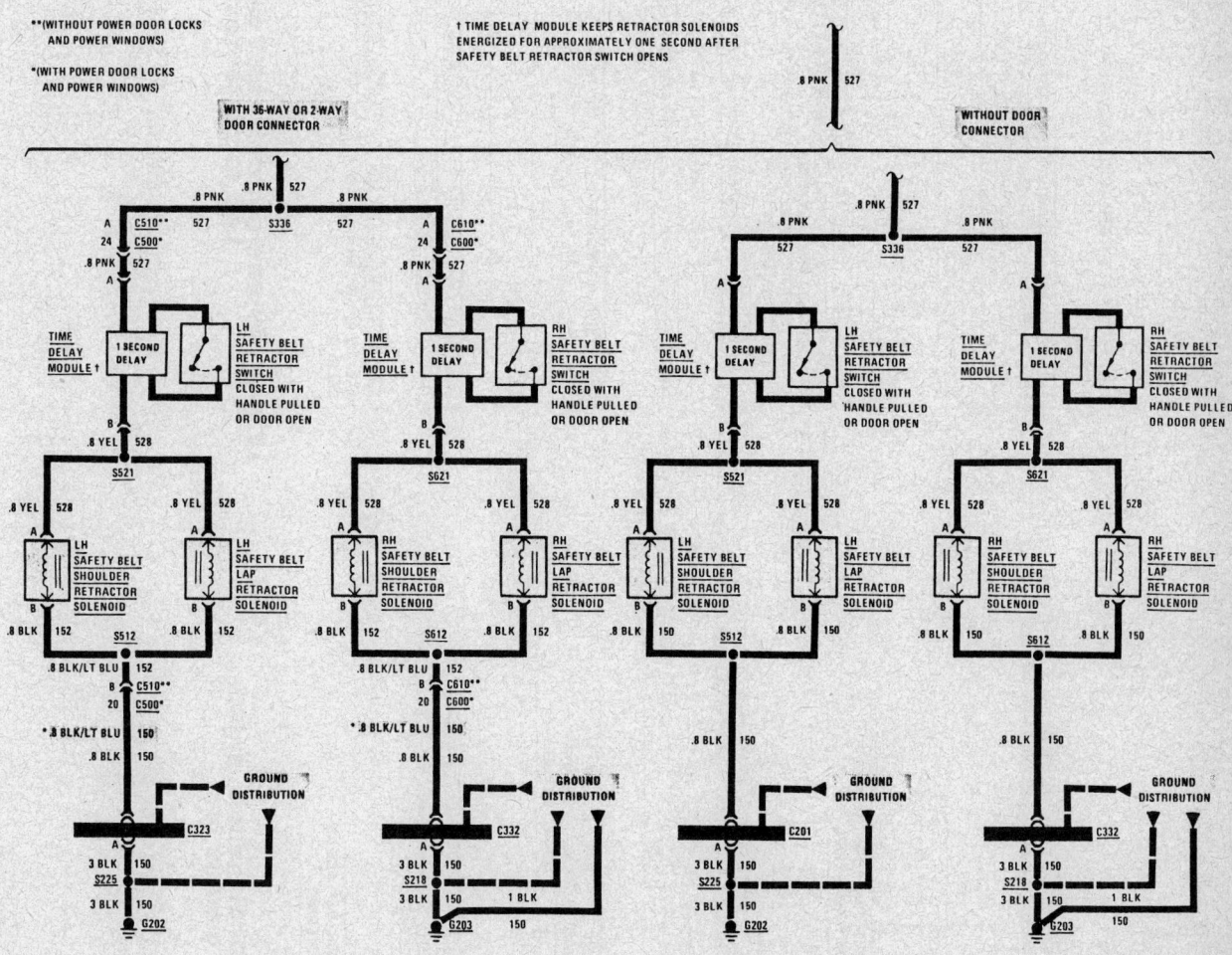

Fig. 1 Automatic safety belt schematic (Part 2 of 2)

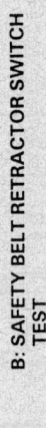

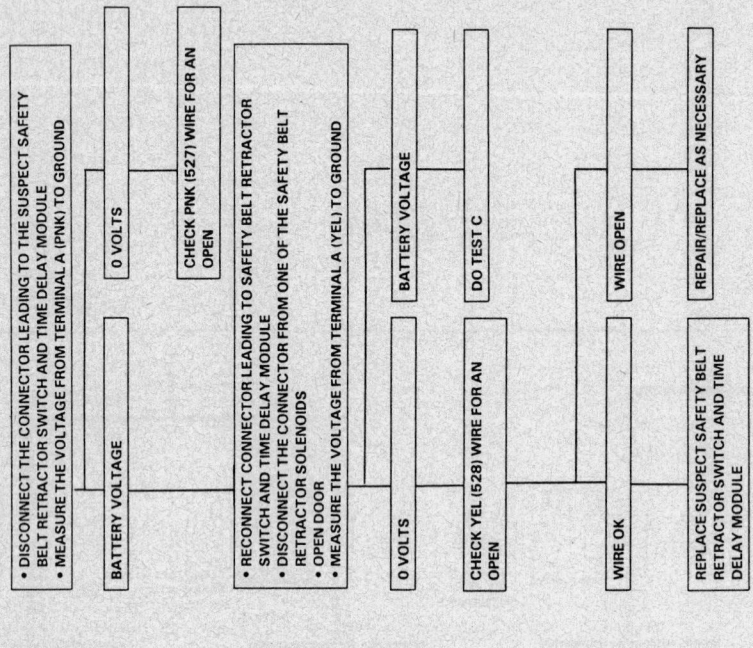

Fig. 3 Automatic safety belt diagnosis, safety belt retractor test

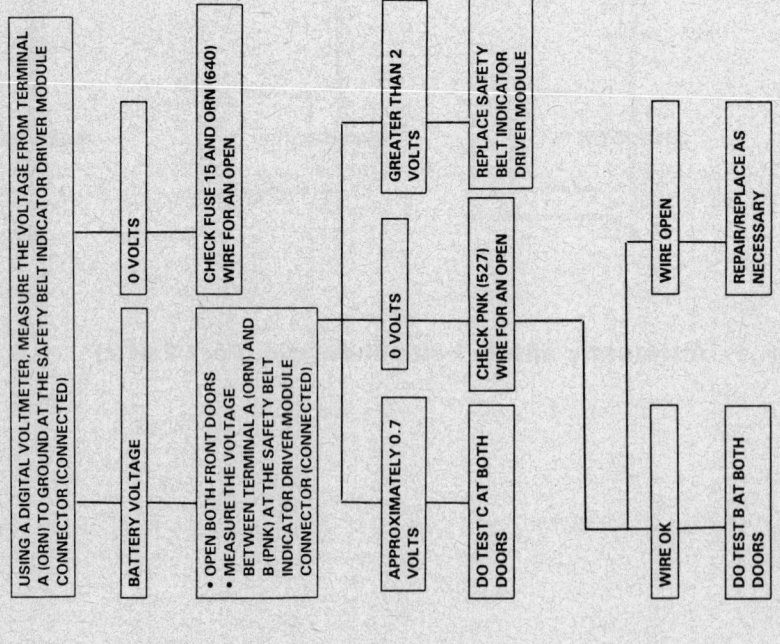

Fig. 2 Automatic safety belt diagnosis, safety belt indicator driver module test

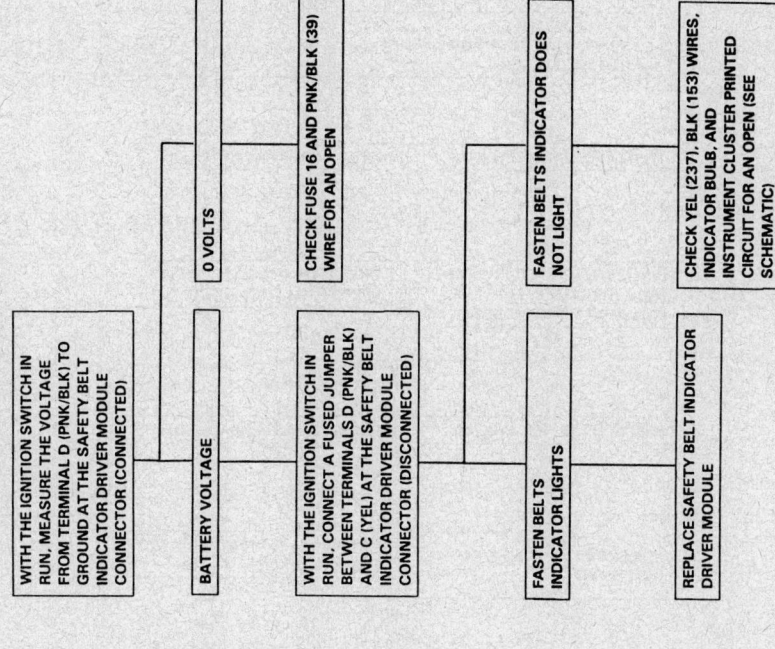

Fig. 5 Automatic safety belt diagnosis, fasten belts indicator test

D: FASTEN BELTS INDICATOR TEST

WITH THE IGNITION SWITCH IN RUN, MEASURE THE VOLTAGE FROM TERMINAL D (PNK/BLK) TO GROUND AT THE SAFETY BELT INDICATOR DRIVER MODULE CONNECTOR (CONNECTED)

- BATTERY VOLTAGE
- 0 VOLTS → CHECK FUSE 16 AND PNK/BLK (39) WIRE FOR AN OPEN

WITH THE IGNITION SWITCH IN RUN, CONNECT A FUSED JUMPER BETWEEN TERMINALS D (PNK/BLK) AND C (YEL) AT THE SAFETY BELT INDICATOR DRIVER MODULE CONNECTOR (DISCONNECTED)

- FASTEN BELTS INDICATOR LIGHTS → REPLACE SAFETY BELT INDICATOR DRIVER MODULE
- FASTEN BELTS INDICATOR DOES NOT LIGHT → CHECK YEL (237), BLK (153) WIRES, INDICATOR BULB, AND INSTRUMENT CLUSTER PRINTED CIRCUIT FOR AN OPEN (SEE SCHEMATIC)

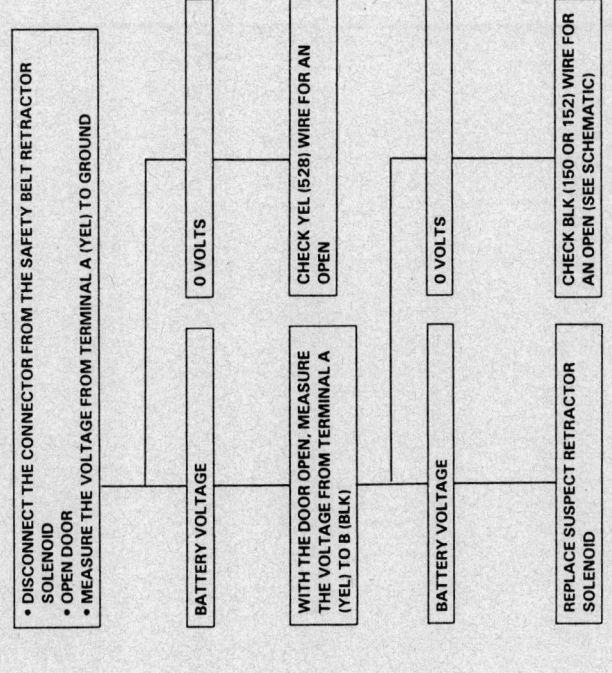

Fig. 4 Automatic safety belt diagnosis, safety belt retractor solenoid test

C: SAFETY BELT RETRACTOR SOLENOID TEST

Note: DO TEST C AT BOTH RETRACTOR SOLENOIDS AT THE SUSPECT DOOR(S)

- DISCONNECT THE CONNECTOR FROM THE SAFETY BELT RETRACTOR SOLENOID
- OPEN DOOR
- MEASURE THE VOLTAGE FROM TERMINAL A (YEL) TO GROUND

- BATTERY VOLTAGE
- 0 VOLTS → CHECK YEL (528) WIRE FOR AN OPEN

WITH THE DOOR OPEN, MEASURE THE VOLTAGE FROM TERMINAL A (YEL) TO B (BLK)

- BATTERY VOLTAGE → REPLACE SUSPECT RETRACTOR SOLENOID
- 0 VOLTS → CHECK BLK (150 OR 152) WIRE FOR AN OPEN (SEE SCHEMATIC)

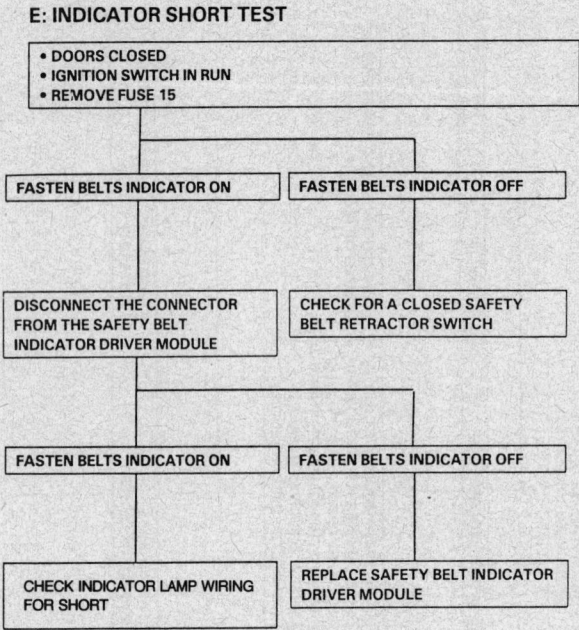

Fig. 6 Automatic safety belt diagnosis, indicator short test

ELECTRONIC LEVEL CONTROLS (ELC)

INDEX

DESCRIPTION

The Electronic Level Control (ELC) system adjusts rear trim height in response to changes in vehicle loading. This system consists of an air compressor assembly, air dryer, exhaust solenoid, compressor relay, height sensor, air adjustable shocks and air tubing. The compressor is activated when the ignition is On and weight is added to the vehicle. The exhaust solenoid is connected directly to the positive side of the battery, allowing the system to exhaust when the ignition is Off and excess weight is removed.

SYSTEM COMPONENTS

COMPRESSOR

This assembly is a single-piston air pump powered by a 12 volt DC permanent magnet motor. The compressor head casting contains intake and exhaust valves plus a solenoid-operated exhaust valve which releases air from the system when energized. The compressor on Celebrity, Pontiac 6000 models is mounted under the body on the rear left side of the vehicle. On Bonneville, Brougham, Delta 88 & 98, DeVille, Fleetwood and full size station wagons the compressor is located on the left side of the engine compartment. On Eldorado, Riviera, Seville, Toronado models the compressor is located at the top of the rear suspension support.

AIR DRYER

The air dryer, attached to the compressor outlet, performs two system functions. The dryer contains a dry chemical that absorbs moisture from the air before it is delivered to the shocks. Moisture is removed from the chemical and returned to the air when system is being exhausted. The air dryer also contains a valving arrangement that maintains a minimum air pressure of 7-14 psi in the shocks.

EXHAUST SOLENOID

The exhaust solenoid is located in the compressor head assembly and provides two functions. The solenoid exhausts air from the system when energized by the height sensor. It also acts as a blow-off valve to limit maximum pressure output of the compressor.

COMPRESSOR RELAY

The compressor relay is controlled by the height sensor and completes the 12 volt circuit to the compressor.

HEIGHT SENSOR

The height sensor controls two circuits, compressor relay coil ground circuit and exhaust solenoid coil ground circuit. To prevent energizing the compressor relay and exhaust solenoid circuits during normal ride motions, the sensor circuit provides a predetermined delay before the ground circuit is completed.

The sensor electronically limits compressor run time and exhaust solenoid energized time. This limit function is necessary to prevent continuous compressor operation in case of a system leak or continuous exhaust solenoid operation. This timer is reset whenever the ignition is turned Off and On, or height sensor exhaust or compressor signal changes.

The height sensor is mounted to the body frame in the rear of the vehicle. The sensor actuator arm is attached to the control arm by a short link.

AIR ADJUSTABLE SHOCKS

The shocks are constructed with a rubber-like sleeve attached to the dust tube and reservoir. This sleeve forms a flexible chamber which will extend the shock when air pressure is increased. In order to maintain proper operation and reliability, a minimum pressure of 7-14 psi must be maintained in the system at all times.

SYSTEM OPERATION

When a load is added to the vehicle, the body is moved down causing the height sensor arm to rotate upward. This movement activates the internal timing circuit which, after a predetermined delay of 8-15 seconds, grounds pin No. 3, thus completing the compressor relay circuit to ground. When the relay circuit is energized, the cir-cuit to the compressor is complete, allowing the compressor to send pressurized air to the shocks.

As the shocks inflate, the vehicle body moves upward, causing the sensor arm to rotate downward. Once the body reaches its original height, the sensor opens the compressor relay circuit and shuts the compressor Off.

When excess load is removed from the rear of the vehicle, the body rises upward, which causes the sensor arm to rotate downward. This movement activates the internal timing circuit which, after a predetermined delay of 8-15 seconds, allows the sensor to complete the exhaust solenoid circuit to ground. With the solenoid energized, air exhausts from the shocks back through the air dryer and exhaust solenoid valve.

As the vehicle body lowers, the height sensor arm is rotated upward until the vehicle reaches its original height. When this height is reached, the sensor opens the exhaust solenoid circuit which prevents air from escaping.

The height sensor position is checked when the ignition is turned On. If the height sensor indicates that it is not necessary to raise or lower the vehicle, the internal timer circuit is activated. After 40 seconds, the compressor will run for four seconds. This ensures the shocks are filled with the proper residual pressure (7-14 psi). If weight is added or removed from the vehicle during this 40 second delay, the air replenishment cycle will be overridden and the vehicle will raise or lower after normal delay.

DIAGNOSIS & TESTING

When diagnostic procedures require that vehicle be raised on a hoist, it is important that the rear axle assembly remains in the normal trim height position at all times. When a frame contact hoist is used, two additional jack stands should be used to support the rear axle or control arms in the normal trim height position.

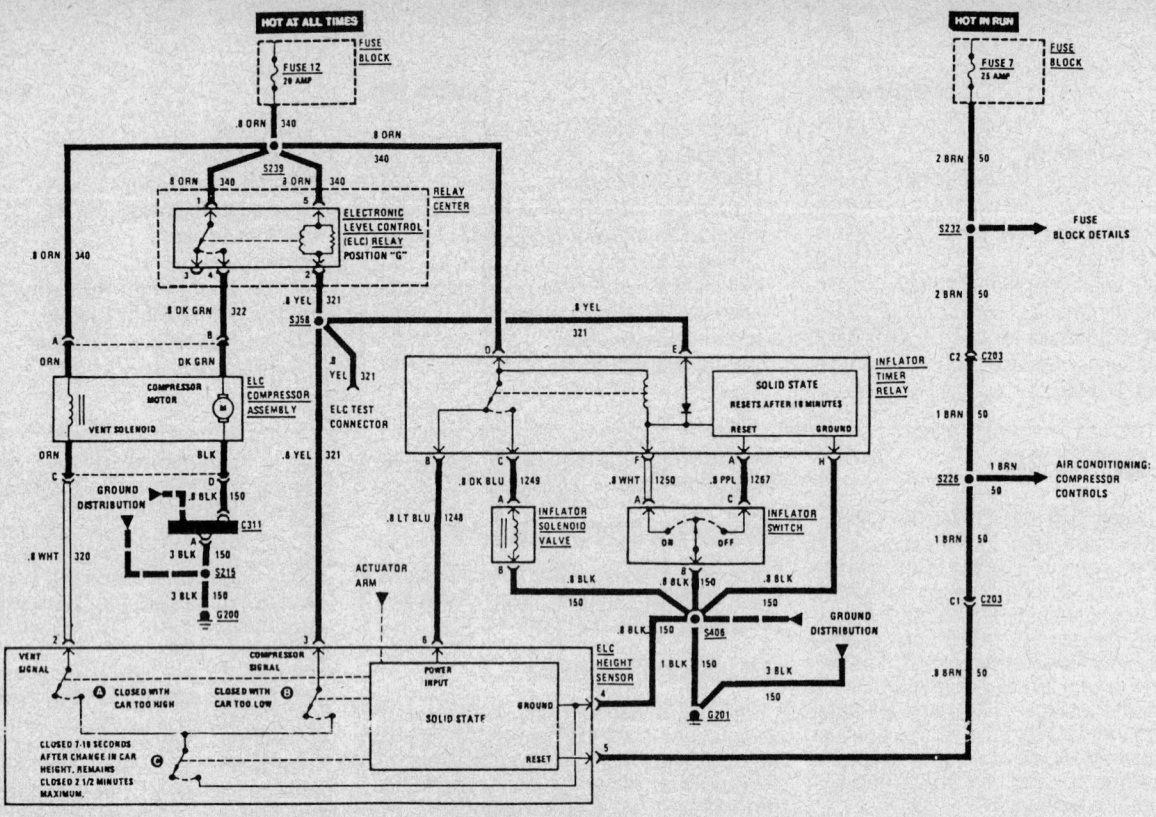

Fig. 1   ELC wiring diagram. Bonneville

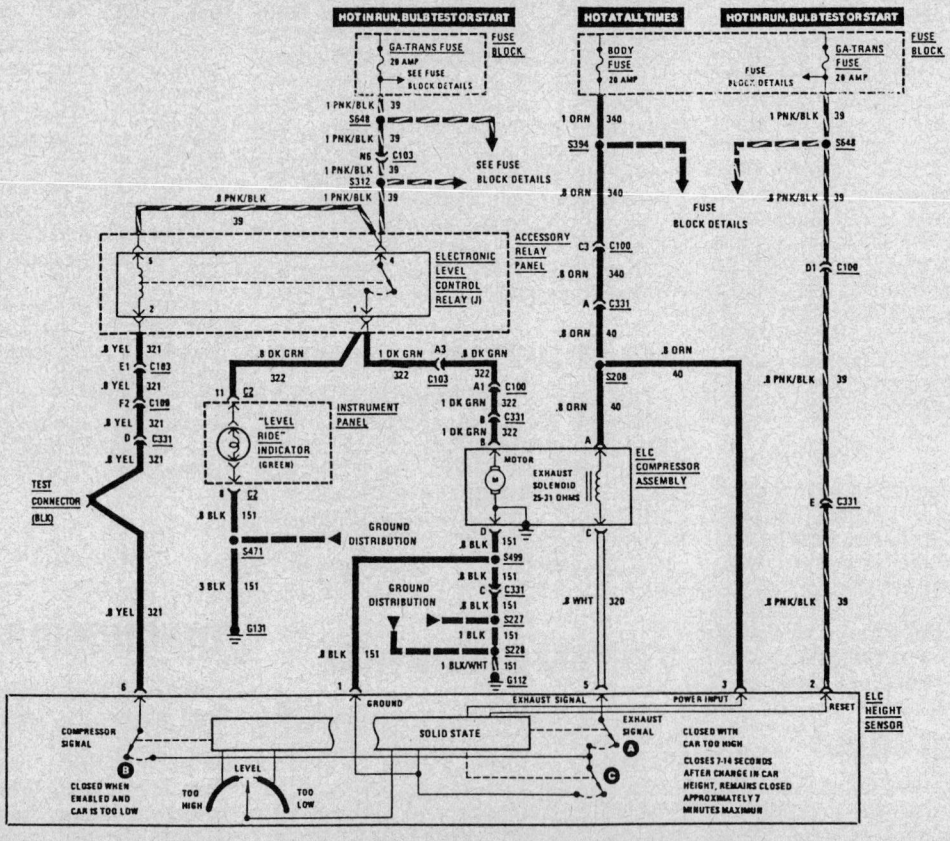

Fig. 2   ELC wiring diagram. Brougham

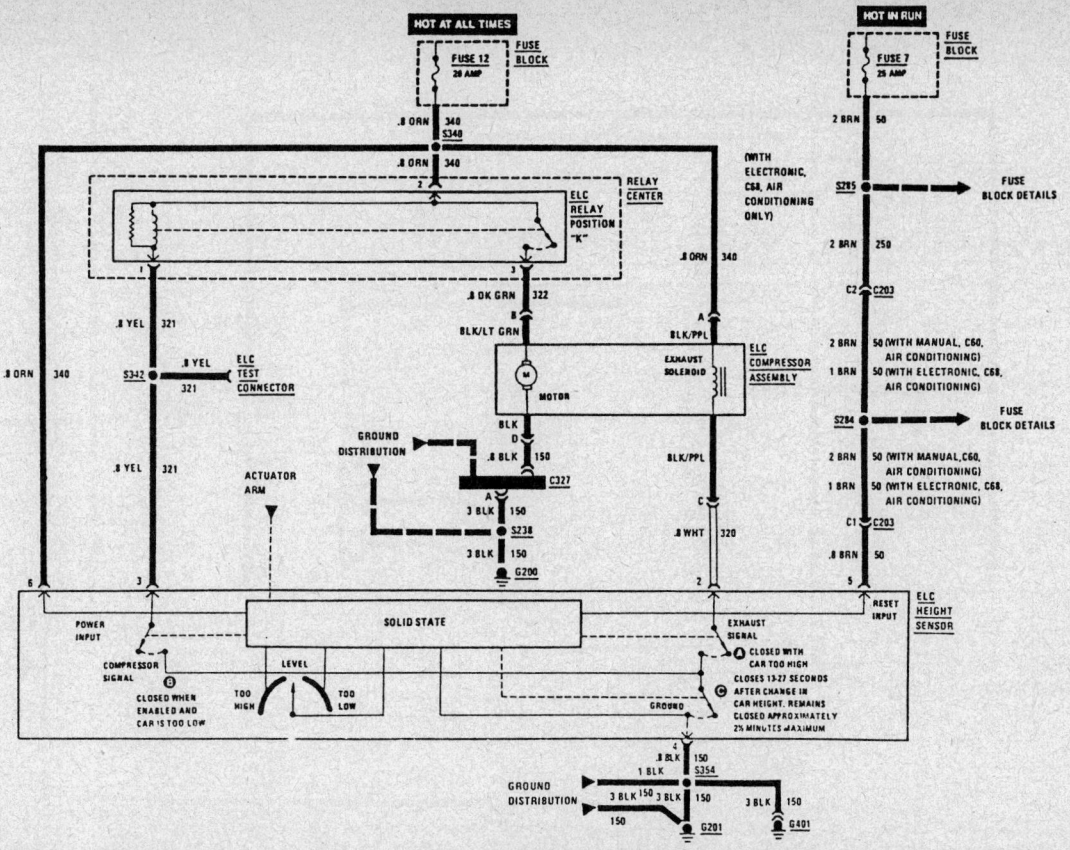

Fig. 3   ELC wiring diagram. Electra, LeSabre & Park Avenue

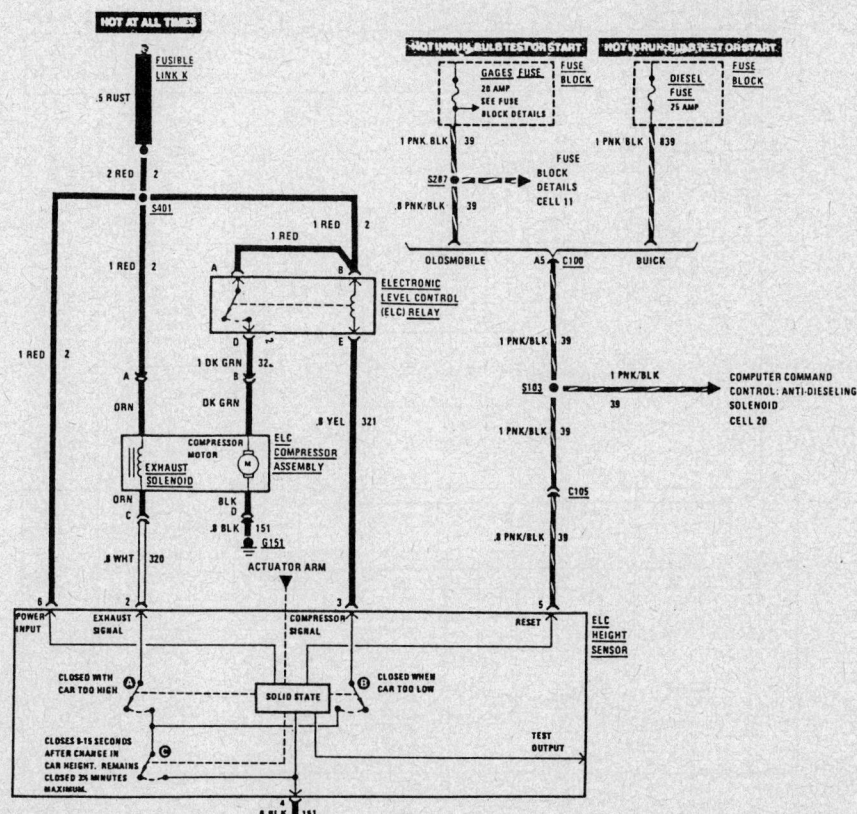

Fig. 4   ELC wiring diagram. Estate Wagon, Custom Cruiser, Safari & LeSabre Wagons

ELECTRICAL DIAGNOSIS

If ELC system is inoperative, check fuse in the fuse block.

Refer to ELC wiring circuits, **Figs. 1 through 10**, ELC system check **Fig. 11**, ELC compressor diagnosis, **Fig. 12** and diagnostic charts, **Figs. 13 through 18**, when performing electrical diagnosis on the ELC system.

RESIDUAL AIR CHECK

1. Remove air line from dryer fitting and attach air line from pressure gauge tool No. J 22124-A or equivalent to dryer fitting as shown in **Fig. 19**.
2. Disconnect electrical connection to pump and jumper 12 volt dark green wire terminal to run compressor. Pump should run until a pressure of 100 psi is reached.
3. Disconnect wiring from compressor exhaust solenoid and jumper 12 volt to one terminal and ground the other terminal to the exhaust system.
4. Air should be exhausted from the system until gauge indicates 7-14 psi.

COMPRESSOR/DRYER PERFORMANCE TEST

1. Disconnect wiring from compressor motor and exhaust solenoid terminals.
2. Disconnect existing pressure line from dryer and attach pressure gauge

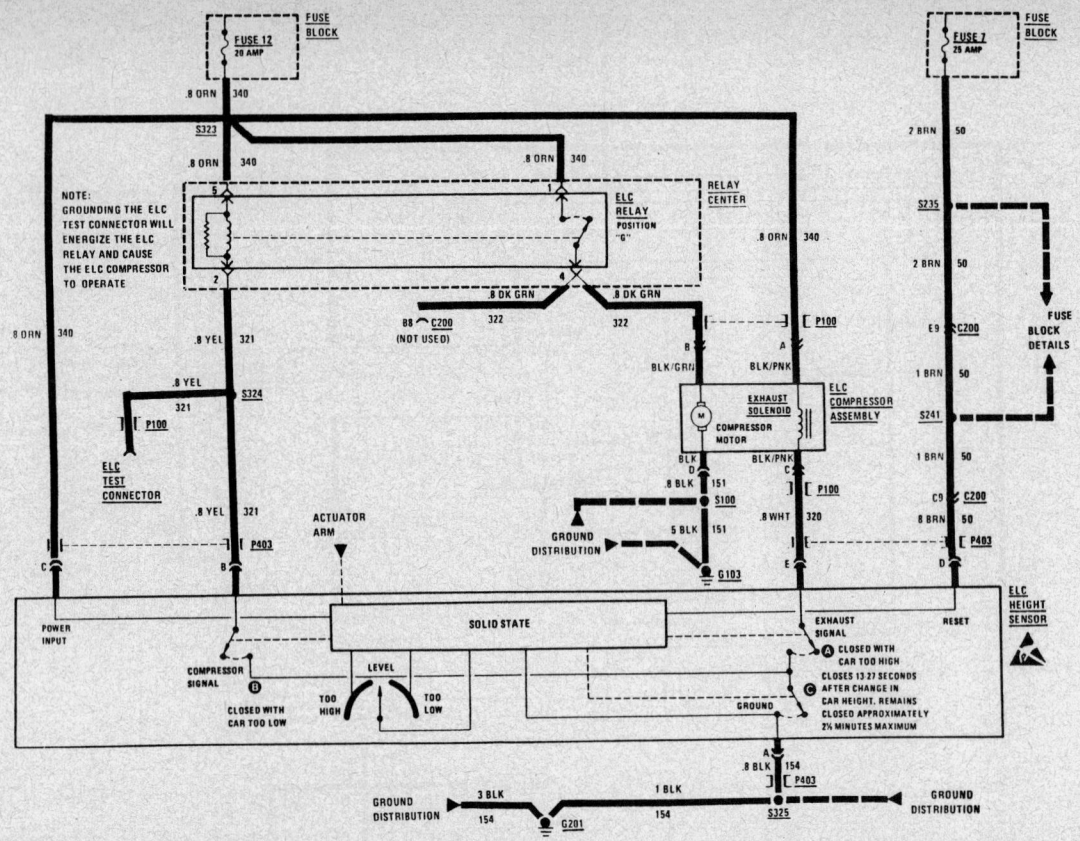

Fig. 5   ELC wiring diagram. DeVille & Fleetwood

tool No. J 22124-A or equivalent to dryer fitting.

3. Connect an ammeter to 12 volt source and to compressor.
4. Operate compressor and note the following:
   a. Current draw should not exceed 14 amps.
   b. When gauge reads at least 100 psi, turn compressor Off by disconnecting power supply and observe if pressure leaks down. Compressor should not leak below 90 psi. If compressor is permitted to run until it reaches maximum output pressure of 180 psi, the solenoid exhaust valve will act as a relief valve. The resulting leak down when compressor is shut off will indicate a false leak.
   c. Refer to chart shown in **Fig. 20** if compressor fails to meet specification.
   d. If performance is satisfactory, install compressor and connect wiring and air lines.

ELC SYSTEM LEAK TEST

1. Tee pressure gauge tool No. J 22124-A into ELC system between dryer assembly and pressure regulator valve. Install so that shut-off valve is on the compressor side of gauge.
2. With shutoff valve open, apply service air pressure through service valve on gauge until gauge reads 100 psi.

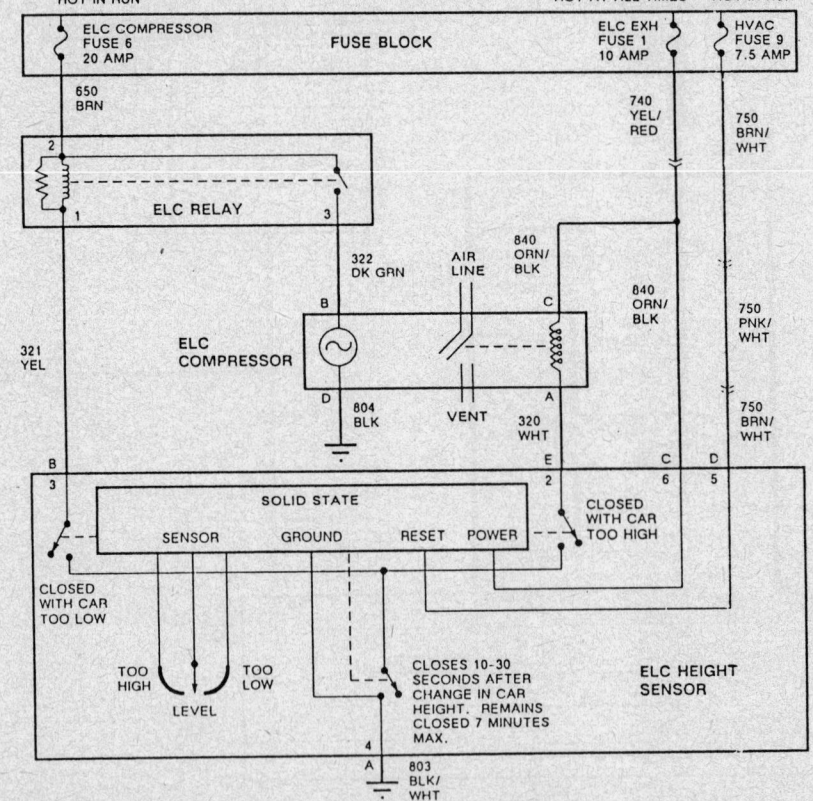

Fig. 6   ELC wiring diagram. Eldorado & Seville

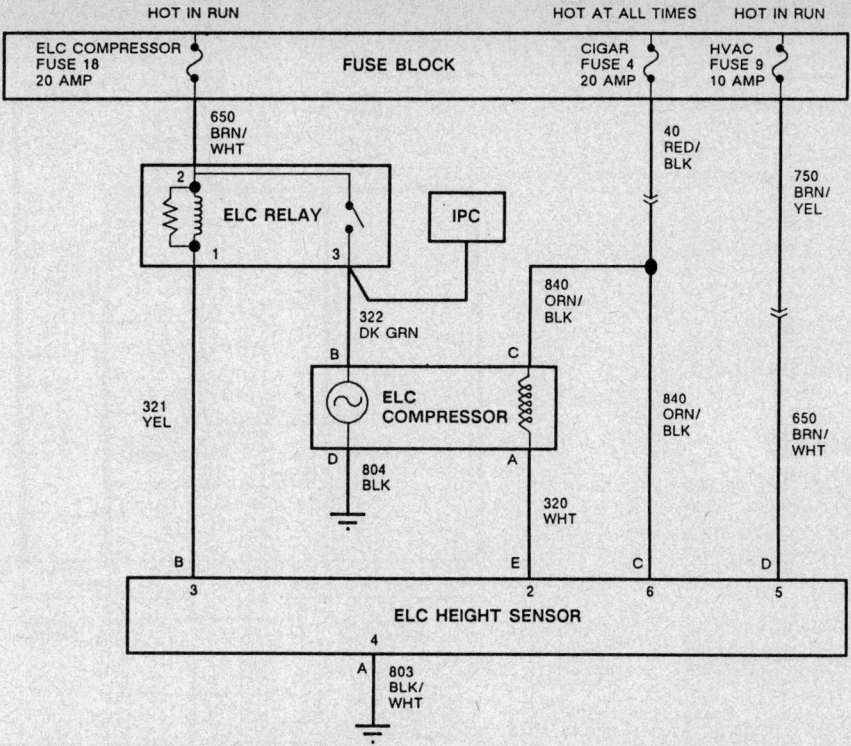

Fig. 7   ELC wiring diagram. Riviera & Toronado

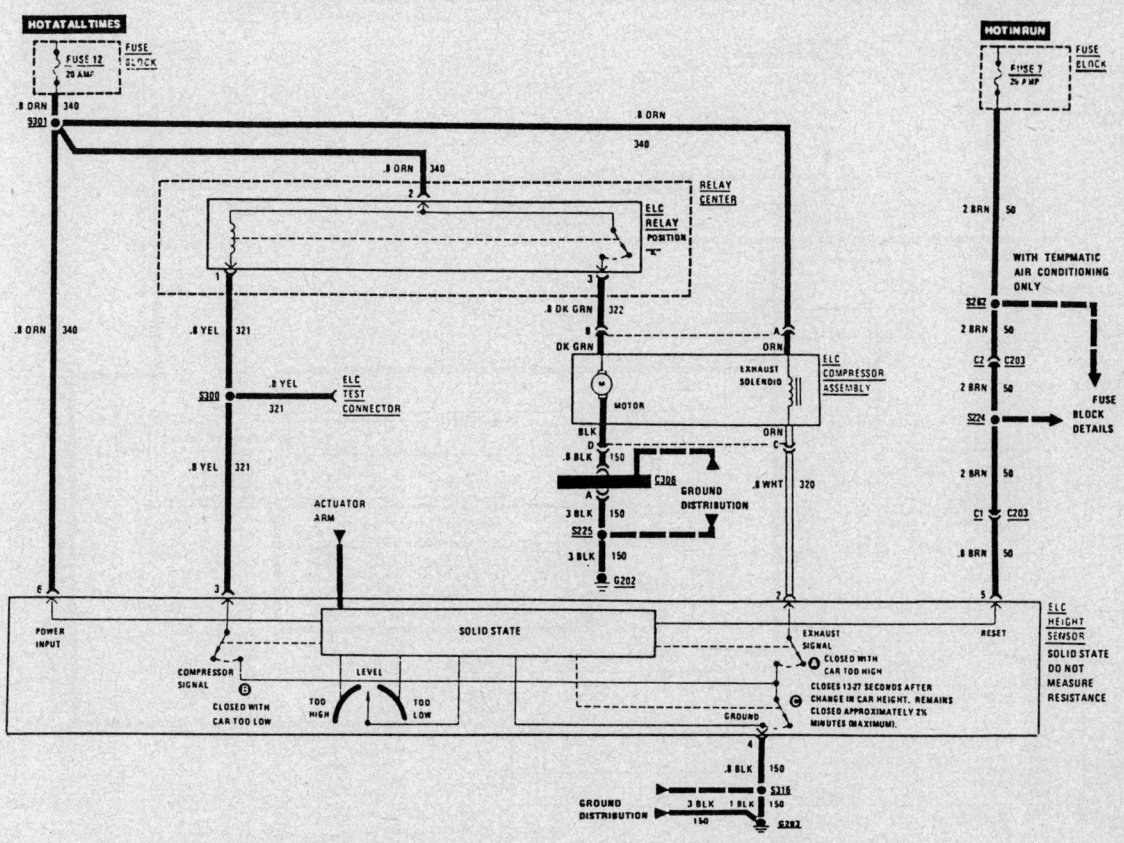

Fig. 8   ELC wiring diagram. Delta 88 & 98

3. If leak is indicated, close shutoff valve and continue to observe for pressure drop. Closing valve isolates the compressor from the rest of the system.
4. If gauge pressure continues to drop, leak is external to the compressor. Leak test all connections with soap and water or suitable leak test solution.
5. If gauge pressure does not continue to drop, leak is in the compressor. Refer to **Fig. 21** to check compressor for leaks.
6. If pressure builds up rapidly but vehicle does not raise, check for pinched air lines and stuck or binding shocks.

HEIGHT SENSOR OPERATIONAL CHECK

1. Turn ignition Off, then On. This will reset height sensor timer circuits.
2. Raise vehicle on hoist. Ensure rear wheels or axle housing are supported and that vehicle is at proper trim height.
3. Disconnect link from height sensor arm, then ensure sensor wiring and harness ground are connected properly.
4. Move sensor arm upward. There should be a delay of 8–15 seconds before compressor turns on and shocks start to inflate. As soon as shocks start to fill, stop compressor by moving sensor arm down.
5. Move sensor arm down below posi-

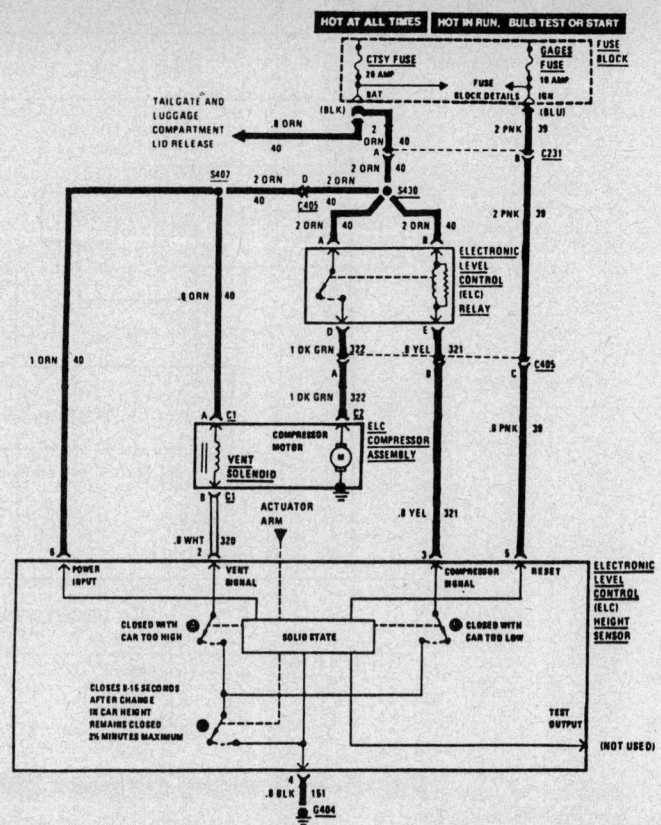

Fig. 9 ELC wiring diagram. 6000 except STE

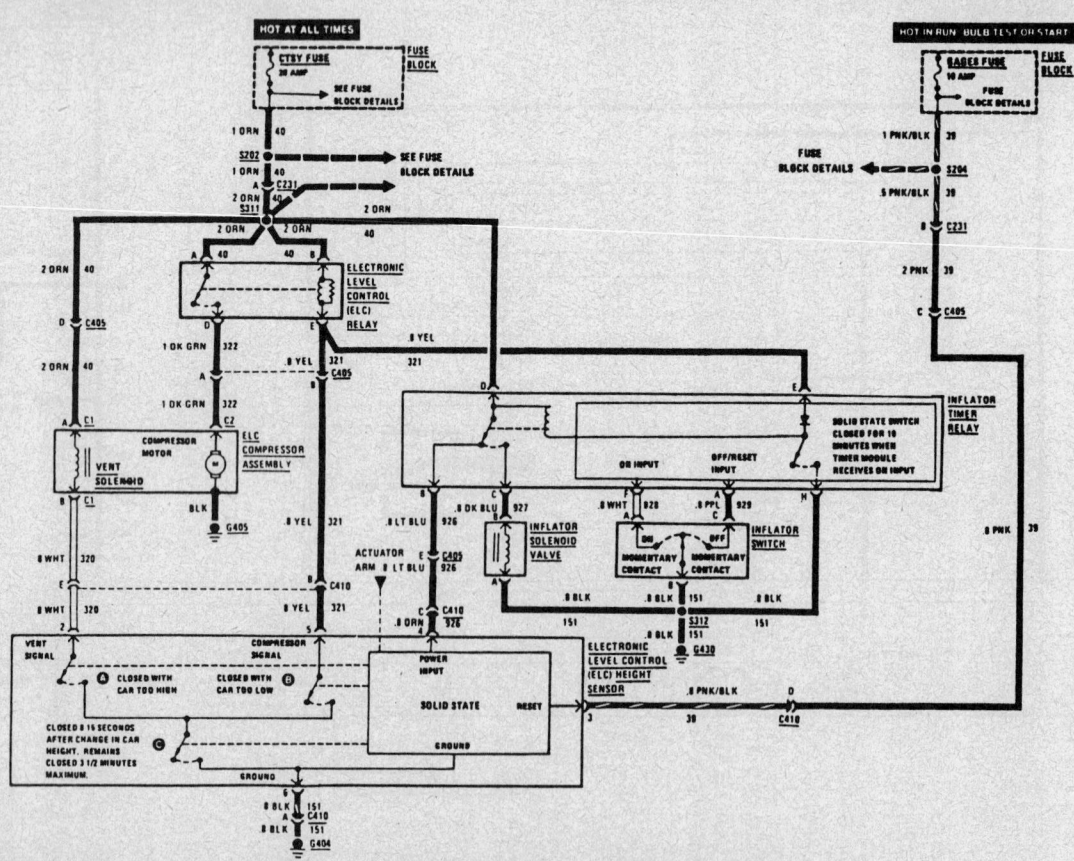

Fig. 10 ELC wiring diagram. 6000 STE

ELC SYSTEM CHECK

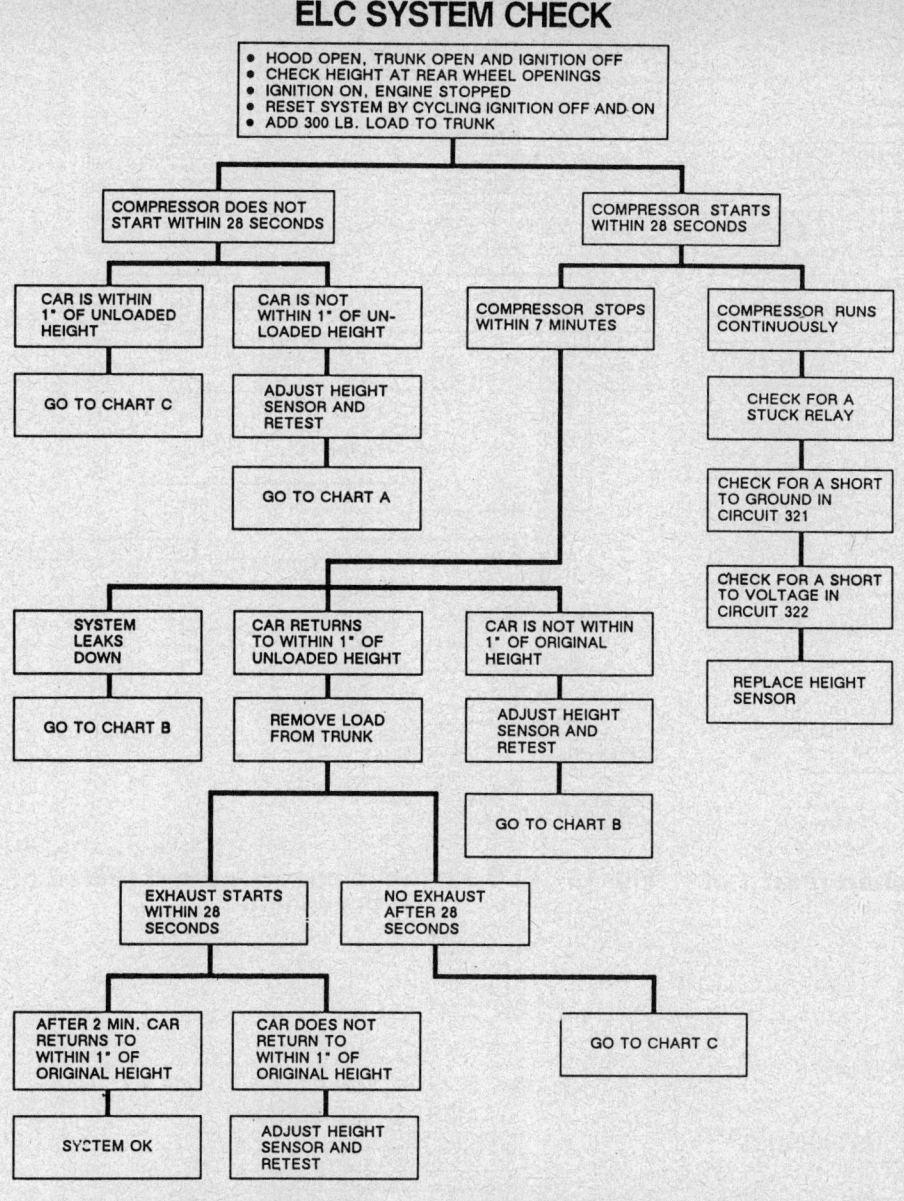

Fig. 11   Electronic level control system check

ELC COMPRESSOR DIAGNOSIS	
CONDITION	CORRECTION
COMPRESSOR RUNS BUT CURRENT DRAW EXCEEDS 10.0 AMPS	REPLACE MOTOR–CYLINDER ASSEMBLY.
COMPRESSOR INOPERATIVE	REMOVE MOTOR END HOUSING AND PERFORM COMPRESSOR MOTOR INSPECTION. IF NO DEFECT IS FOUND, REPLACE MOTOR–CYLINDER ASSEMBLY.
PRESSURE BUILD UP OK BUT LEAKS DOWN BELOW 60 PSI BEFORE HOLDING STEADY. (DOESN'T GO TO 0 PSI).	REPLACE HEAD ASSEMBLY.
PRESSURE LEAKS DOWN TO 0 PSI.	PERFORM COMPRESSOR / DRIER LEAK TEST AND MAKE CORRECTIONS AS REQUIRED.
PRESSURE BUILD UP LESS THAN 80 PSI.	PERFORM COMPRESSOR / DRIER LEAK TEST. IF NO LEAK IS FOUND, REPLACE MOTOR–CYLINDER ASSEMBLY.

Fig. 12   ELC compressor diagnosis

dryer by revolving spring clip 90° while holding connector end and removing tube assembly.
5. Disconnect electrical connector from compressor pigtail harness.
6. Remove three compressor mounting screws, then the compressor.
7. Remove three compressor mounting bracket screws, then the bracket.
8. If replacing compressor assembly, remove dryer and dryer bracket.
9. Reverse procedure to install, noting the following:
   a. **Torque** dryer bracket attaching screws to 20 inch lbs.
   b. **Torque** mounting bracket attaching screws to 35 inch lbs.
   c. **Torque** compressor mounting screws to 35 inch lbs.
   d. After connecting battery ground cable, cycle ignition switch, then test system operation, looking for air leaks at dryer.

AIR DRYER, REPLACE

1. Remove compressor as described in "Shield, Compressor & Bracket, Replace."
2. Rotate dryer retainer spring 90° and pull dryer and O-ring out of compressor head assembly, **Fig. 23.**
3. Reverse procedure to install.

COMPRESSOR HEAD ASSEMBLY, REPLACE

1. Remove air dryer assembly as described in "Air Dryer, Replace."
2. Remove three compressor head mounting bolts and head assembly,

tion where compressor stopped. There should be a delay of 8-15 seconds before shocks start to deflate and vehicle lowers.

SERVICE & ADJUSTMENTS

When repair or adjustment procedures require that vehicle be raised on a hoist, it is important that the rear axle assembly remains in the normal trim height position at all times. When a frame contact hoist is used, two additional jack stands should be used to support the rear axle or control arms in the normal trim height position.

HEIGHT SENSOR, ADJUST

The link should be properly attached to the sensor arm and track bar, when making this adjustment.
1. Loosen lock bolt that secures metal arm to height sensor plastic arm, **Fig. 22.**
2. To raise vehicle trim height, move plastic arm upward and tighten lock bolt.
3. To lower vehicle trim height, follow step 1 and move plastic arm down.
4. If adjustment cannot be made, check for correct sensor.

SHIELD, COMPRESSOR & BRACKET, REPLACE

1. Disconnect battery ground cable.
2. Raise and support vehicle.
3. Remove compressor shield, if equipped, then deflate system.
4. Disconnect high pressure line at air

ELC SYSTEM CHECK

- HOOD OPEN, TRUNK OPEN AND IGNITION OFF
- CHECK HEIGHT AT REAR WHEEL OPENINGS
- IGNITION ON, ENGINE STOPPED
- RESET SYSTEM BY CYCLING IGNITION OFF AND ON
- ADD 300 LB. LOAD TO TRUNK

COMPRESSOR DOES NOT START WITHIN 28 SECONDS
- CAR IS WITHIN 1" OF UNLOADED HEIGHT → GO TO CHART C
- CAR IS NOT WITHIN 1" OF UNLOADED HEIGHT → ADJUST HEIGHT SENSOR AND RETEST → GO TO CHART A
  - SYSTEM LEAKS DOWN → GO TO CHART B
  - CAR RETURNS TO WITHIN 1" OF UNLOADED HEIGHT → REMOVE LOAD FROM TRUNK
    - EXHAUST STARTS WITHIN 28 SECONDS
      - AFTER 2 MIN. CAR RETURNS TO WITHIN 1" OF ORIGINAL HEIGHT → SYSTEM OK
      - CAR DOES NOT RETURN TO WITHIN 1" OF ORIGINAL HEIGHT → ADJUST HEIGHT SENSOR AND RETEST
    - NO EXHAUST AFTER 28 SECONDS → GO TO CHART C
  - CAR IS NOT WITHIN 1" OF ORIGINAL HEIGHT → ADJUST HEIGHT SENSOR AND RETEST → GO TO CHART B

COMPRESSOR STARTS WITHIN 28 SECONDS
- COMPRESSOR STOPS WITHIN 7 MINUTES
- COMPRESSOR RUNS CONTINUOUSLY → CHECK FOR A STUCK RELAY → CHECK FOR A SHORT TO GROUND IN CIRCUIT 321 → CHECK FOR A SHORT TO VOLTAGE IN CIRCUIT 322 → REPLACE HEIGHT SENSOR

Fig. 13 ELC system diagnostic chart (Part 1 of 5). Brougham

CHART A – COMPRESSOR DOES NOT OPERATE

- IGNITION ON
- GROUND ELC TEST CONNECTOR

COMPRESSOR DOES NOT RUN
- REMOVE ELC RELAY
- CHECK FOR BATTERY VOLTAGE AT PIN 4 AND 5 OF RELAY CAVITY
  - BATTERY VOLTAGE → JUMPER PINS 1 AND 4 OF ELC RELAY CAVITY
  - 0 VOLTS → CHECK "GA – TRANS" FUSE
    - OK → REPAIR OPEN IN CIRCUIT 39
    - NOT OK → REPLACE FUSE
  - COMPRESSOR DOES NOT RUN
    - DISCONNECT COMPRESSOR HARNESS CONNECTOR
    - APPLY 12 VOLTS TO PIN 8 GROUND PIN D
      - COMPRESSOR DOES NOT RUN → REPLACE MOTOR AND HOUSING ASSEMBLY
      - COMPRESSOR RUNS → CHECK FOR OPEN IN CIRCUIT 322 OR 151
  - COMPRESSOR RUNS → CHECK FOR OPEN IN CIRCUIT 321 → REPLACE ELC RELAY

COMPRESSOR RUNS
- DISCONNECT HEIGHT SENSOR HARNESS CONNECTOR
- JUMPER PINS A AND F
  - COMPRESSOR DOES NOT RUN → CHECK FOR OPEN IN CIRCUIT 321 OR 151
  - COMPRESSOR RUNS → GO TO CHART D

Fig. 13 ELC system diagnostic chart (Part 2 of 5). Brougham

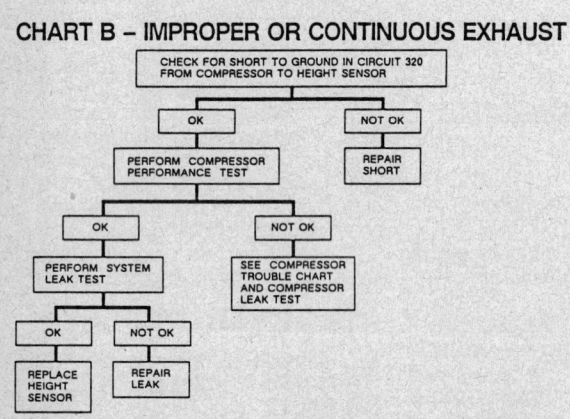

CHART B – IMPROPER OR CONTINUOUS EXHAUST

CHECK FOR SHORT TO GROUND IN CIRCUIT 320 FROM COMPRESSOR TO HEIGHT SENSOR
- OK → PERFORM COMPRESSOR PERFORMANCE TEST
  - OK → PERFORM SYSTEM LEAK TEST
    - OK → REPLACE HEIGHT SENSOR
    - NOT OK → REPAIR LEAK
  - NOT OK → SEE COMPRESSOR TROUBLE CHART AND COMPRESSOR LEAK TEST
- NOT OK → REPAIR SHORT

Fig. 13 ELC system diagnostic chart (Part 3 of 5). Brougham

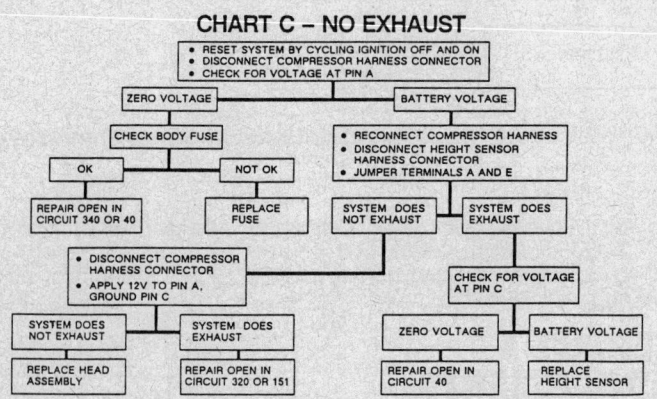

CHART C – NO EXHAUST

- RESET SYSTEM BY CYCLING IGNITION OFF AND ON
- DISCONNECT COMPRESSOR HARNESS CONNECTOR
- CHECK FOR VOLTAGE AT PIN A
  - ZERO VOLTAGE → CHECK BODY FUSE
    - OK → REPAIR OPEN IN CIRCUIT 340 OR 40
    - NOT OK → REPLACE FUSE
    - DISCONNECT COMPRESSOR HARNESS CONNECTOR
    - APPLY 12V TO PIN A, GROUND PIN C
      - SYSTEM DOES NOT EXHAUST → REPLACE HEAD ASSEMBLY
      - SYSTEM DOES EXHAUST → REPAIR OPEN IN CIRCUIT 320 OR 151
  - BATTERY VOLTAGE
    - RECONNECT COMPRESSOR HARNESS
    - DISCONNECT HEIGHT SENSOR HARNESS CONNECTOR
    - JUMPER TERMINALS A AND E
      - SYSTEM DOES NOT EXHAUST
      - SYSTEM DOES EXHAUST → CHECK FOR VOLTAGE AT PIN C
        - ZERO VOLTAGE → REPAIR OPEN IN CIRCUIT 40
        - BATTERY VOLTAGE → REPLACE HEIGHT SENSOR

Fig. 13 ELC system diagnostic chart (Part 4 of 5). Brougham

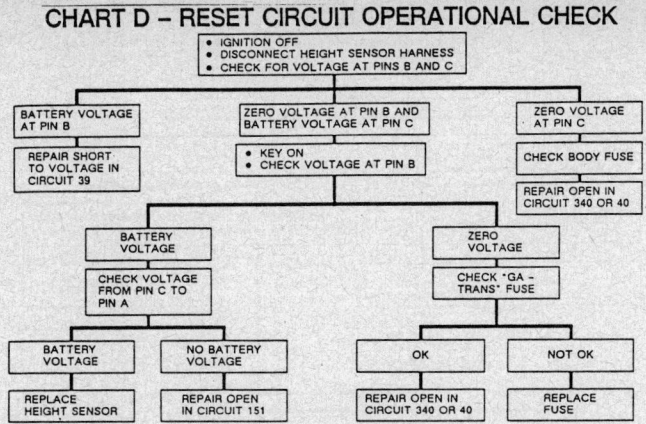

Fig. 13 ELC system diagnostic chart (Part 5 of 5). Brougham

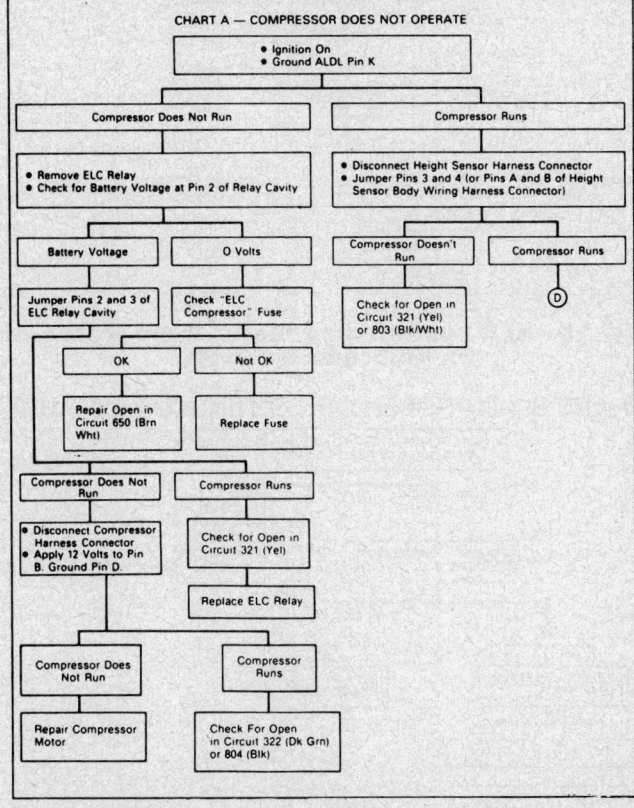

Fig. 14 ELC system diagnostic chart (Part 2 of 5). DeVille, Fleetwood, Toronado & all Buick models

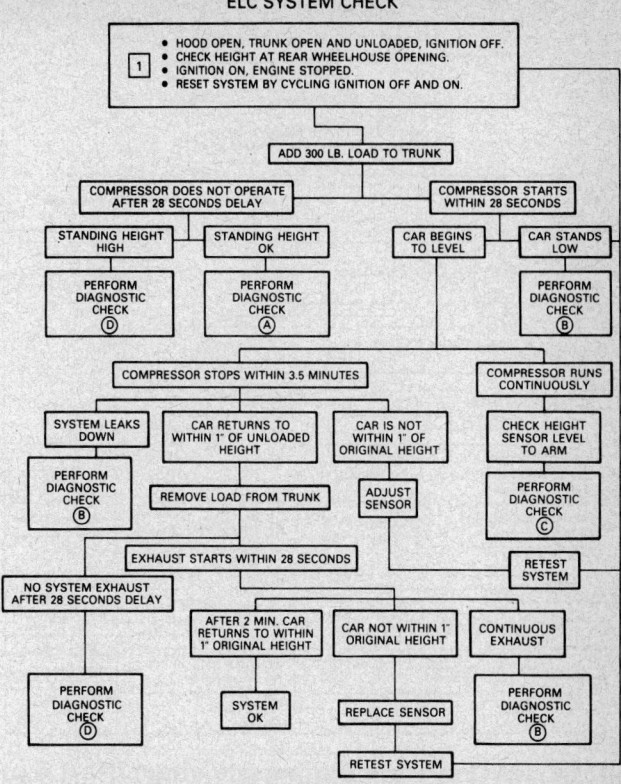

Fig. 14 ELC system diagnostic chart (Part 1 of 5). DeVille, Fleetwood, Toronado & all Buick models

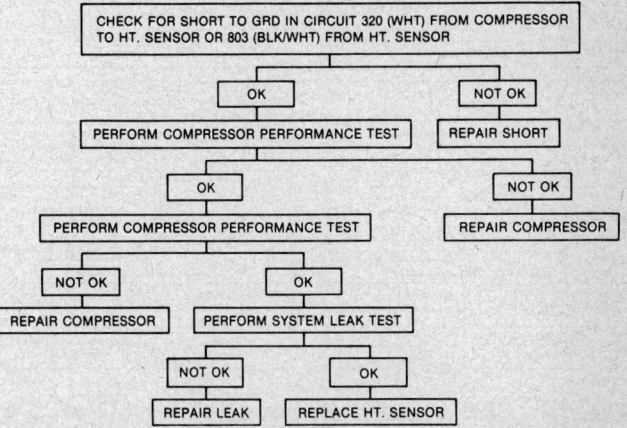

Fig. 14 ELC system diagnostic chart (Part 3 of 5). DeVille, Fleetwood, Toronado & all Buick models

Fig. 24.

3. Reverse procedure to install, using a new O-ring and **torqing** head mounting bolts to 35 inch lbs.

SOLENOID VALVE ASSEMBLY, REPLACE

If solenoid valve assembly requires replacement, it should be replaced with compressor head assembly. Refer to "Compressor Head Assembly, Replace."

HEIGHT SENSOR & BRACKET, REPLACE

1. Disconnect battery ground cable.
2. Raise and support vehicle.
3. Disconnect harness from sensor electrical connector by squeezing oval sides of the connector lock to release locking tabs.
4. Remove link from height sensor arm, then remove sensor mounting screws

or nuts and the sensor.

5. Remove sensor mounting bracket to underbody attaching screws and remove bracket.
6. Reverse procedure to install, noting the following:
   a. **Torque** sensor and sensor mounting bracket screws to 35 inch lbs.
   b. When connecting harness to sensor electrical connector, push connector into sensor plug until sloped shoulder on rear edge of boss is

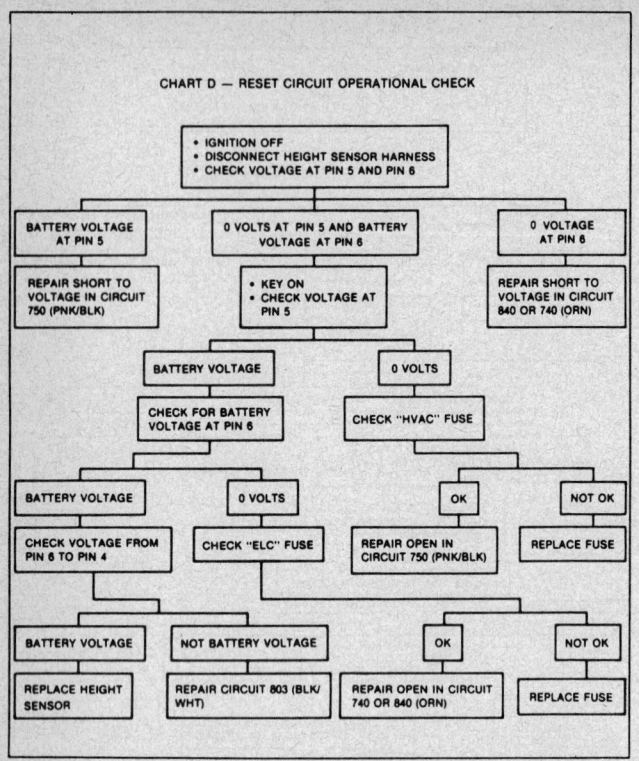

Fig. 14   ELC system diagnostic chart (Part 4 of 5). DeVille, Fleetwood, Toronado & all Buick models

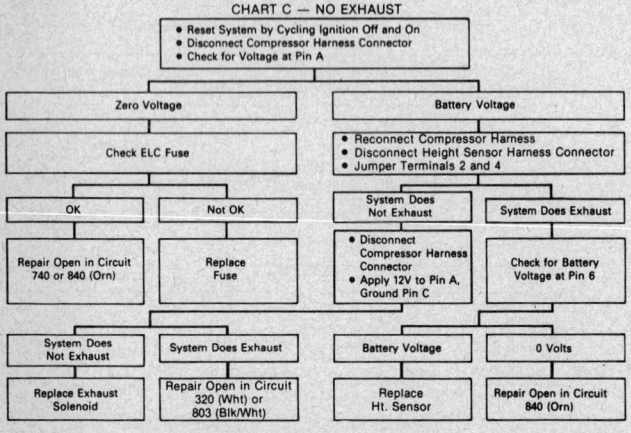

Fig. 14   ELC system diagnostic chart (Part 5 of 5). DeVille, Fleetwood, Toronado & all Buick models

Fig. 15   ELC system diagnostic chart (Part 1 of 5). Eldorado & Seville

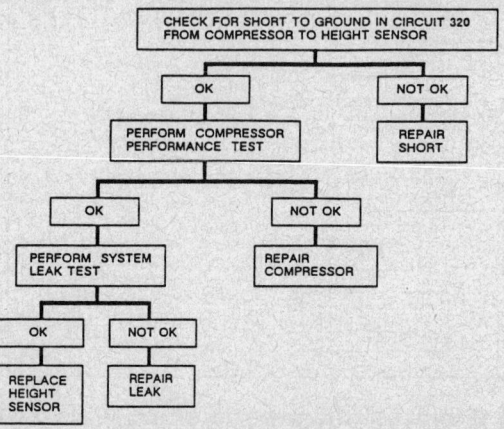

Fig. 15   ELC system diagnostic chart (Part 3 of 5). Eldorado & Seville

visible in plug slot. Push oval connector lock onto plug until its two locking tabs snap over shoulder of sensor plug.

c. Perform height sensor operational check and adjustment procedure as described in "Height Sensor Operational Check" and "Height Sensor, Adjustment."

AIR COMPRESSOR SERVICE

Disassembly

1. Remove the seven compressor cover screws, then the compressor cover and gasket, **Fig. 25**.
2. Remove head and solenoid assembly.
3. Remove two filters, exhaust valve, spring and air dryer O-ring from head assembly.
4. Remove solenoid from head by lifting slightly and sliding to the dryer outlet side.
5. Remove O-ring from solenoid assembly.
6. Remove head gasket from cylinder assembly.
7. Remove four mounting bracket screws, then the bracket and gasket. Note position of ground wire for installation.

Assembly

1. Install gasket and mounting bracket, then the ground wire and screws.

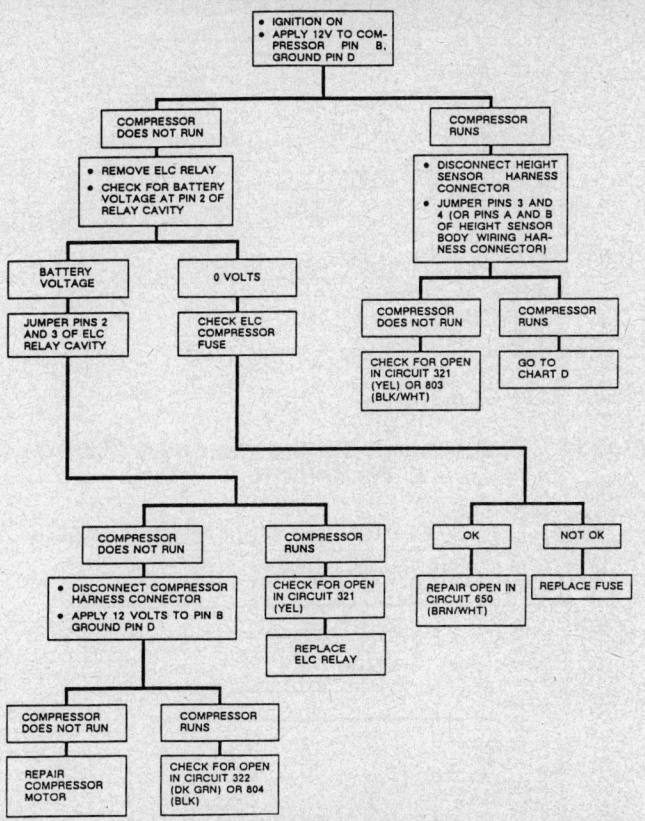

Fig. 15 ELC system diagnostic chart (Part 2 of 5). Eldorado & Seville

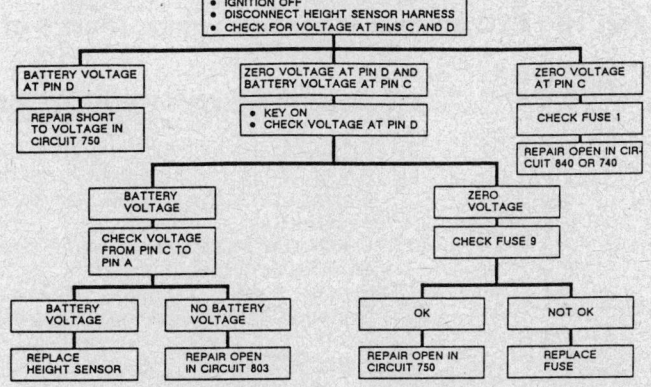

Fig. 15 ELC system diagnostic chart (Part 5 of 5). Eldorado & Seville

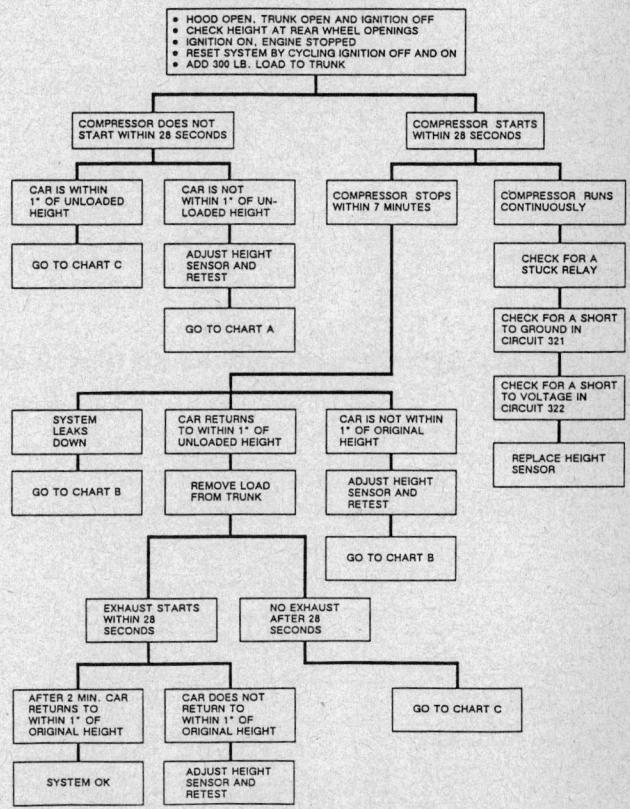

Fig. 15 ELC system diagnostic chart (Part 4 of 5). Eldorado & Seville

Fig. 16 ELC system diagnostic chart (Part 1 of 5). Riviera

Torque screws to 13 ft. lbs.
2. Install head gasket on cylinder assembly.
3. Install O-ring on solenoid assembly, then the solenoid in the head with valve opposite air dryer outlet.
4. Install two filters, exhaust valve and spring on head assembly.
5. Install gasket and cover on head assembly, then four short cover screws.
6. Install head and cover assembly to cylinder assembly using three long screws. **Torque** all seven screws in sequence, **Fig. 26**, to 36 inch lbs.
7. Install air dryer O-ring on compressor.

STRUT AIR BLADDER, REPLACE

Removal

1. Remove strut from vehicle.
2. Scribe alignment marks between upper mount and outer tube.
3. Clamp strut in a suitable vise using wooden blocks.
4. Remove upper mount from strut, **Fig. 27.**
5. Cut and remove outer clamp with a hacksaw, **Fig. 28.**
6. Cut air bladder from outer tube and

slide the inner tube upward.
7. Remove O-ring from inside top of outer tube, **Fig. 29.**
8. Cut and remove inner clamp with a hacksaw, **Fig. 30.**
9. Remove air bladder from inner tube.

Installation

1. Lubricate new O-ring and O-ring groove with silcone lubricant. Install O-ring in groove, **Fig. 29.**
2. Apply silcone lubricant to inside top of new air bladder and the entire outside of air bladder, **Fig. 31.**
3. Fold bottom of air bladder before in-

CHART A – COMPRESSOR DOES NOT OPERATE

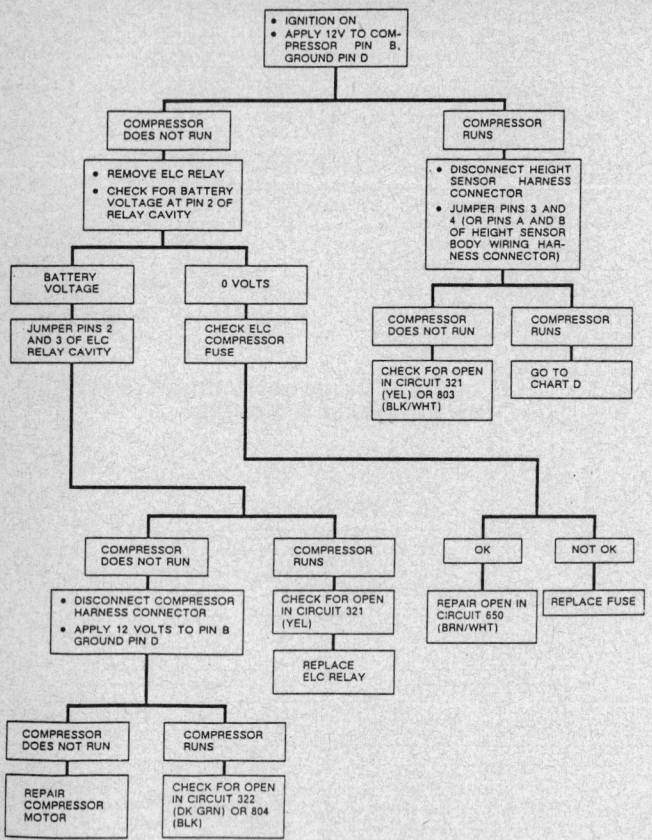

Fig. 16 ELC system diagnostic chart (Part 2 of 5). Riviera

CHART C – NO EXHAUST

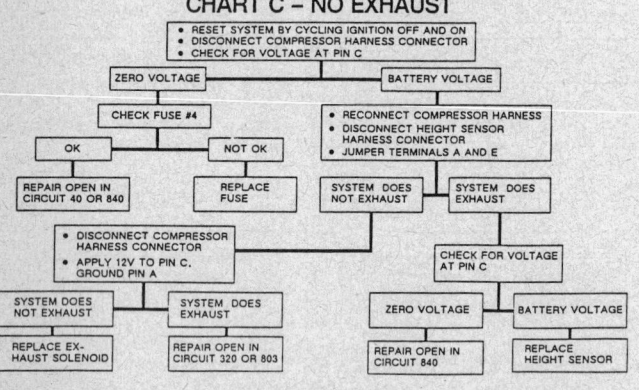

Fig. 16 ELC system diagnostic chart (Part 4 of 5). Riviera

CHART B – IMPROPER OR CONTINUOUS EXHAUST

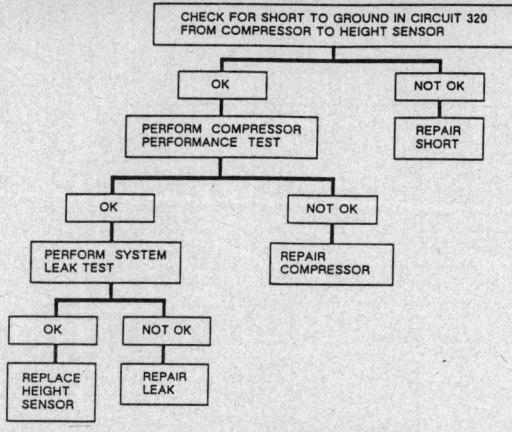

Fig. 16 ELC system diagnostic chart (Part 3 of 5). Riviera

CHART D – RESET CIRCUIT OPERATIONAL CHECK

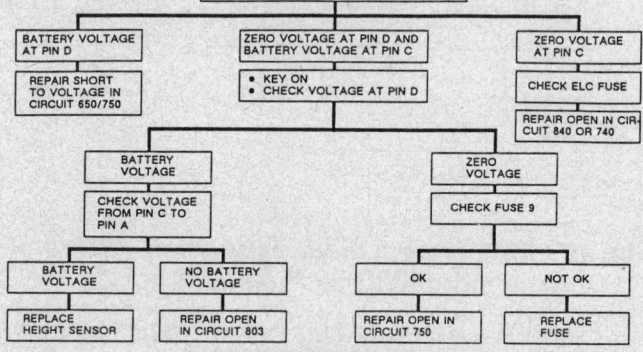

Fig. 16 ELC system diagnostic chart (Part 5 of 5). Riviera

properly positioned with the bottom strut mount, **Fig. 33.**

9. Apply silicone lubricant to outer tube.
10. Install air bladder over outer tube by folding upward over tube and push over tube.
11. Install and tighten hose clamp over grooved area of air bladder.
12. Support strut and partially inflate air bladder. Check for leaks with soap solution.
13. Install strut into vehicle.

VEHICLE TRIM HEIGHT CHECK

BUICK, OLDSMOBILE & PONTIAC

Trim heights are checked with tires at recommended pressure, fuel tank at capacity, front seat in rear position, no passengers and trunk empty, except for spare tire and jack.

Refer to **Figs. 34 through 40** for trim height measurements.

CADILLAC

Refer to **Figs. 41 through 44** for trim height measurements.

stallation on inner tube. Place air bladder over inner tube, continuing to fold bladder from the bottom up. Position top of air bladder as shown in **Fig. 32. Do not use tools to fold air bladder as damage may occur, causing air leakage.**
4. Place inner clamp in position as shown in **Fig. 32.** Tighten clamp with tool J-34649.
5. Fold bottom of air bladder upward and fold top of 4 inch section downward.
6. Apply silicone lubricant to polished diameter of inner shaft tube.
7. Place outer tube over air bladder and push downward against folded portion of bladder. **The outer tube must be completely seated over shaft.**
8. Install upper mount onto strut, aligning marks made during disassembly, and torque nut to 74 ft.lbs. **The upper mount and tube air fitting must be**

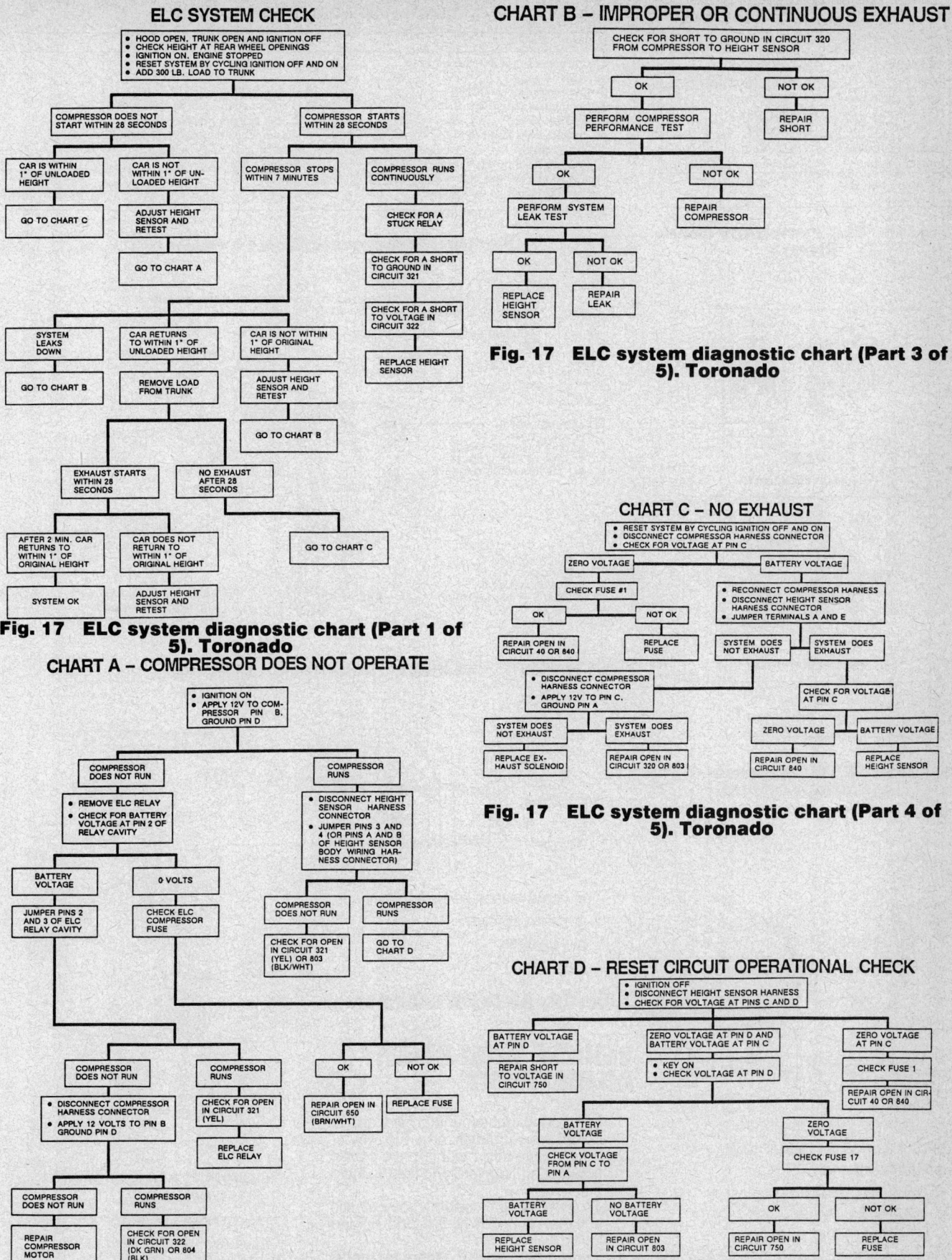

ELC SYSTEM CHECK

Fig. 17   ELC system diagnostic chart (Part 1 of 5). Toronado

CHART A – COMPRESSOR DOES NOT OPERATE

Fig. 17   ELC system diagnostic chart (Part 2 of 5). Toronado

CHART B – IMPROPER OR CONTINUOUS EXHAUST

Fig. 17   ELC system diagnostic chart (Part 3 of 5). Toronado

CHART C – NO EXHAUST

Fig. 17   ELC system diagnostic chart (Part 4 of 5). Toronado

CHART D – RESET CIRCUIT OPERATIONAL CHECK

Fig. 17   ELC system diagnostic chart (Part 5 of 5). Toronado

Symptoms	Components To Test
Compressor does not run	Electronic Level Control Compressor Assembly, ELC Relay
System does not vent	ELC Control Assembly Vent Solenoid
Compressor runs continuously	ELC Control Assembly, ELC Relay
System vents continuously	ELC Control Assembly

Fig. 18   ELC symptoms chart. Riviera

COMPRESSOR/DRYER TROUBLE CHART

MALFUNCTION	CORRECTION
1. Compressor runs but current draw exceeds 14 amps.	1. Replace compressor.
2. Compressor inoperative	2. Replace compressor.
3. Compressor output less than 758 kPa (110 psi)	3. Perform compressor/dryer leak test, if no leak is found, replace compressor.
4. Pressure leaks down to 0 kPa (0 psi)	4. Perform compressor/dryer leak test, and make corrections as required.
5. Pressure build up ok, but leaks down below 60 kPa (90 psi) before holding steady. (Does not go to 0 psi.)	5. Replace head assembly

Fig. 20   Compressor/Dryer trouble chart

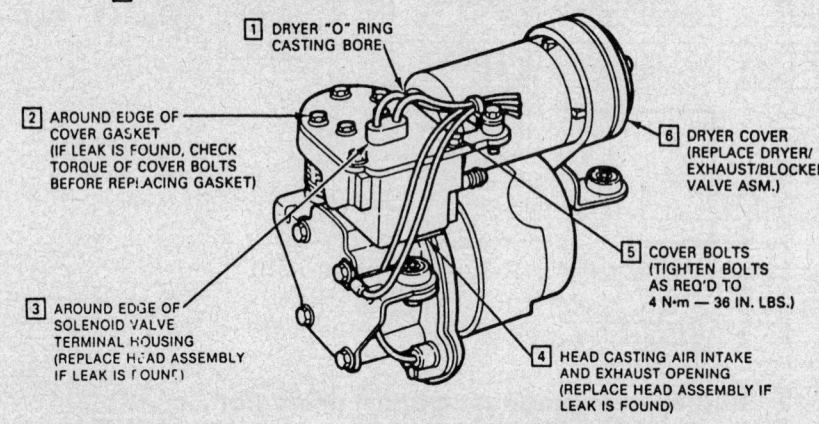

1. ATTACH PRESSURE GAGE J-22124-A TO DRYER, FIGURE 3D-28 AND RUN COMPRESSOR/DRYER ASSEMBLY TO 100 PSI THRU THE GAGE FILL-VALVE.

2. USING SOAP BUBBLE SOLUTION, CHECK ITEMS CALLED OUT BELOW:

1. DRYER "O" RING CASTING BORE
2. AROUND EDGE OF COVER GASKET (IF LEAK IS FOUND, CHECK TORQUE OF COVER BOLTS BEFORE REPLACING GASKET)
3. AROUND EDGE OF SOLENOID VALVE TERMINAL HOUSING (REPLACE HEAD ASSEMBLY IF LEAK IS FOUND)
4. HEAD CASTING AIR INTAKE AND EXHAUST OPENING (REPLACE HEAD ASSEMBLY IF LEAK IS FOUND)
5. COVER BOLTS (TIGHTEN BOLTS AS REQ'D TO 4 N·m — 36 IN. LBS.)
6. DRYER COVER (REPLACE DRYER/EXHAUST/BLOCKER VALVE ASM.)

Fig. 21   Compressor leak test

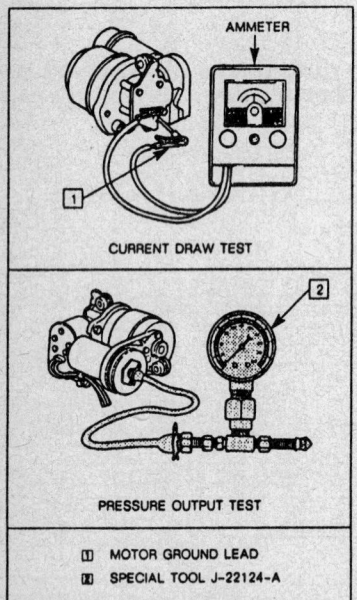

CURRENT DRAW TEST

PRESSURE OUTPUT TEST

1. MOTOR GROUND LEAD
2. SPECIAL TOOL J-22124-A

Fig. 19   Compressor performance test

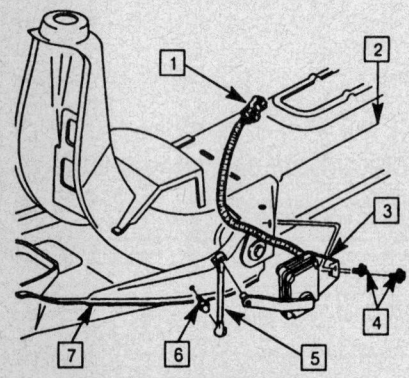

1. HEIGHT SENSOR CONNECTOR
2. SUSPENSION SUPPORT ASSEMBLY
3. HEIGHT SENSOR
4. MOUNTING SCREWS (5 N.m / 46 IN. LBS.)
5. HEIGHT SENSOR LINK
6. STUD (7 N.m / 62 IN. LBS.)
7. CONTROL ARM

Fig. 22   Height sensor

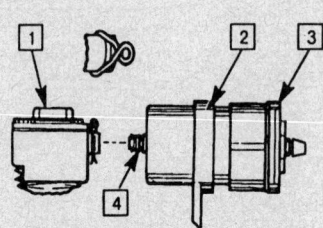

1. COMPRESSOR HEAD ASSEMBLY
2. DRIER BRACKET
3. AIR DRIER
4. O'RING

Fig. 23   Air dryer assembly

VEHICLE TRIM HEIGHT ADJUSTMENT

1. Loosen locknut securing metal arm to height sensor plastic arm, **Fig. 45.**
2. To increase trim height, move plastic actuator arm upward and tighten locknut.
3. To decrease trim height, move plastic actuator arm downward and tighten locknut.
4. If proper adjustment cannot be made, ensure correct height sensor is installed.

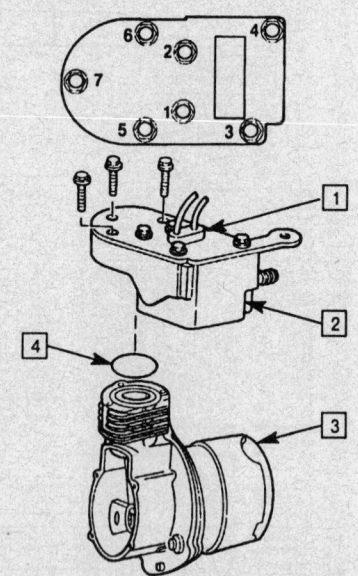

1. EXHAUST SOLENOID CONNECTOR
2. HEAD ASSEMBLY
3. CYLINDER AND MOTOR ASSEMBLY
4. CYLINDER HEAD O'RING

Fig. 24   Compressor head assembly

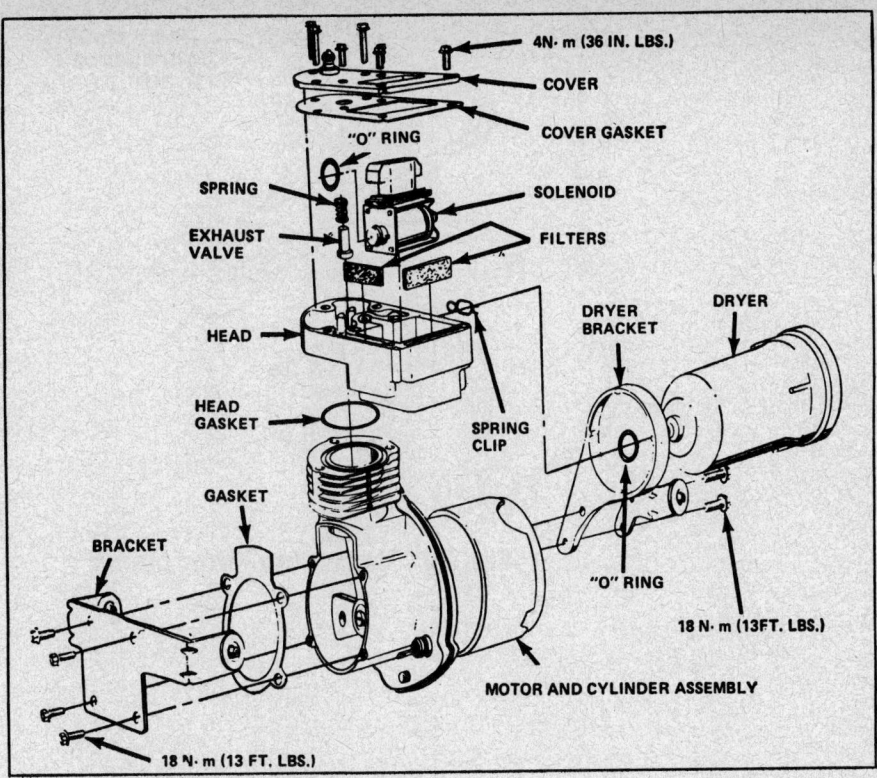

Fig. 25 Disassembled view of air compressor

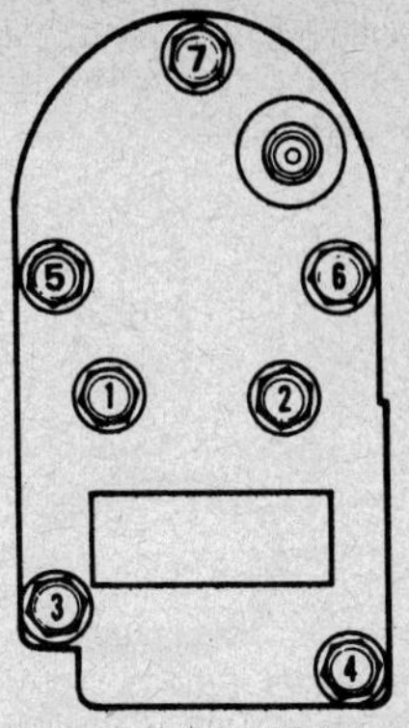

TORQUE BOLTS TO 4 N·m
(36 IN. LBS.) PER SEQUENCE

Fig. 26 Air compressor head tightening sequence

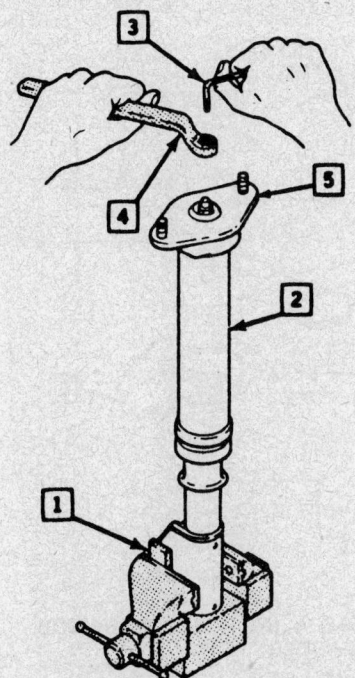

1. VISE WITH 3/16" SHIMS
2. STRUT
3. HOLD NUMBER 50 TORX
4. TURN 12 PT. BOX WRENCH
5. UPPER MOUNT

Fig. 27 Removing upper strut mount

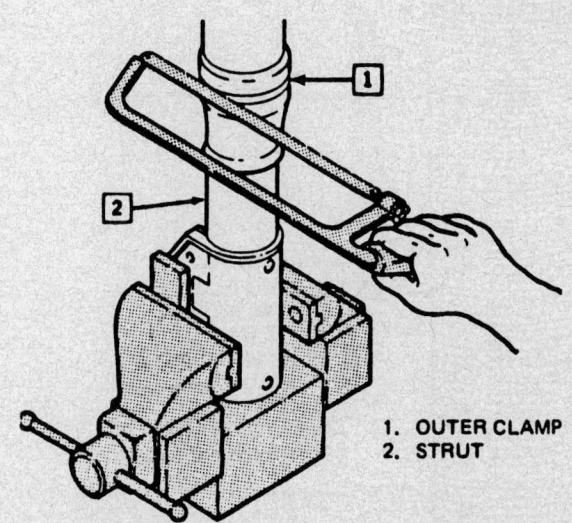

1. OUTER CLAMP
2. STRUT

Fig. 28 Removing outer clamp

1. OUTER TUBE
2. "O" RING – LUBRICATE WITH SILICONE
3. "O" RING GROVE

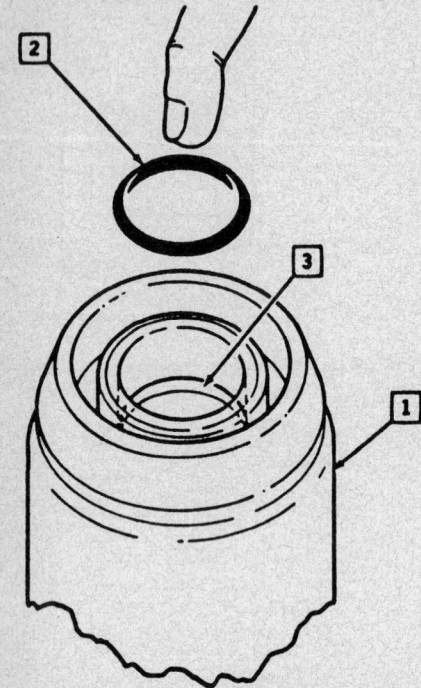

Fig. 29   O-ring replacement

1. INNER CLAMP
2. AIR BLADDER
3. STRUT

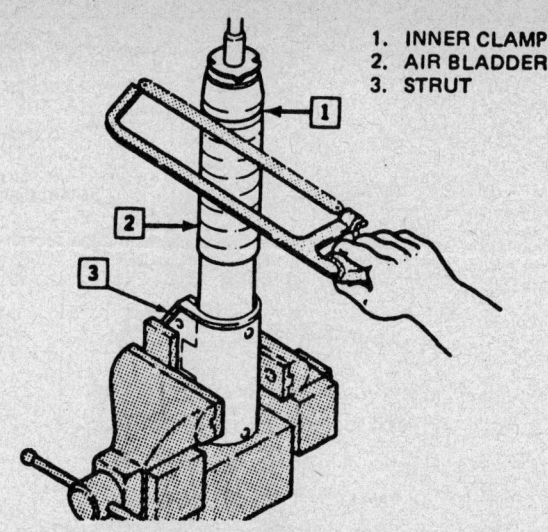

Fig. 30   Removing inner clamp

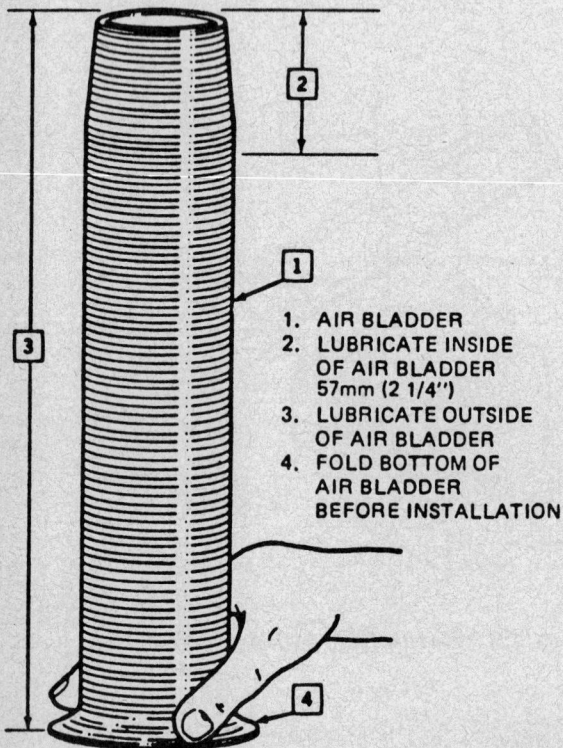

1. AIR BLADDER
2. LUBRICATE INSIDE OF AIR BLADDER 57mm (2 1/4")
3. LUBRICATE OUTSIDE OF AIR BLADDER
4. FOLD BOTTOM OF AIR BLADDER BEFORE INSTALLATION

Fig. 31   Replacing air bladder

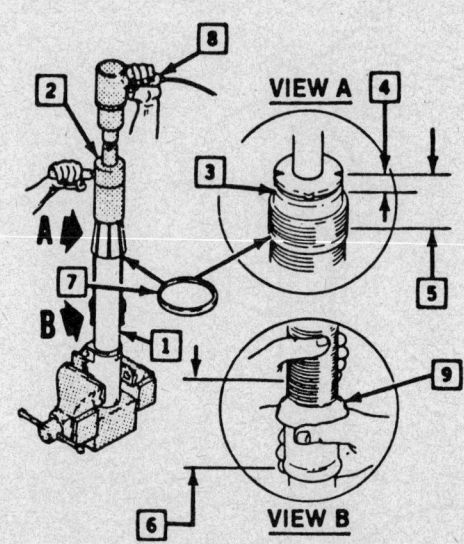

1. STRUT
2. J 34649 SEALING RING COMPRESSOR
3. AIR BLADDER
4. 6mm (1/4")
5. 44mm (1 3/4")
6. 102mm (4")
7. INNER CLAMP
8. IMPACT WRENCH
9. SECOND FOLD DOWN

Fig. 32   Inner clamp & air bladder position

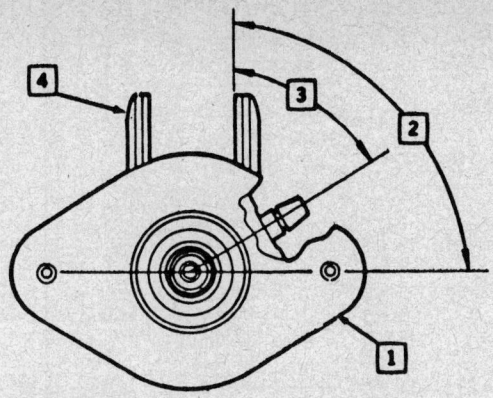

1. UPPER MOUNT
2. 90° ±2°
3. 58° ±2°
4. STRUT TO KNUCKLE MOUNT

Fig. 33 Air fitting position

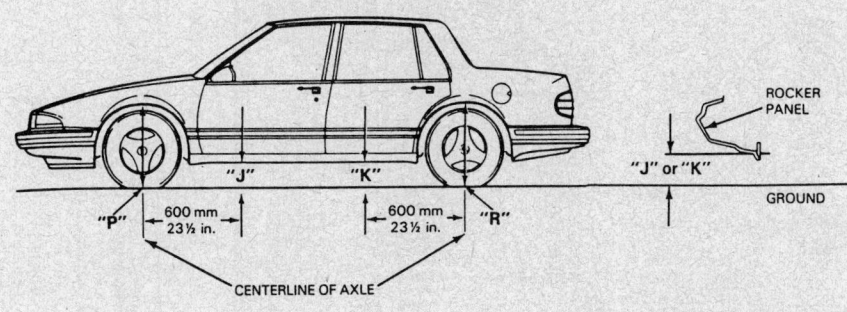

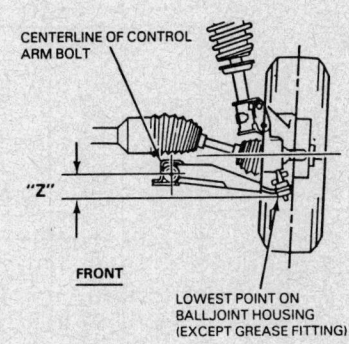

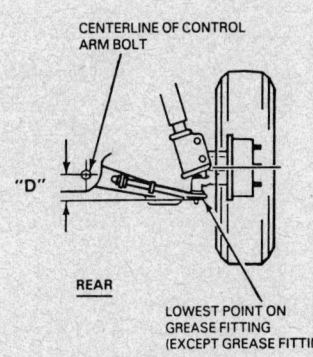

TRIM HEIGHT CHECK PROCEDURE

1. VEHICLE MUST BE ON LEVEL GROUND.

2. TIRES MUST BE INFLATED TO PROPER PRESSURE.

3. FUEL TANK SHOULD BE FULL.

4. NO PASSENGERS OR ADDED WEIGHT SHOULD BE IN THE VEHICLE. THE TRUNK MUST BE EMPTY EXCEPT FOR THE SPARE TIRE AND JACK.

5. PLACE THE FRONT SEAT IN THE REAR POSITION.

6. IGNITION SWITCH ON TO ACTIVATE ELECTRONIC LEVEL CONTROL (ELC). (IF EQUIPPED)

7. "BOUNCE" THE CAR THREE TIMES AT THE FRONT AND REAR TO NORMALIZE THE SUSPENSION.

8. MEASURE FROM THE LOWEST POINT ON THE BALLJOINT HOUSING TO CONTROL ARM BOLT CENTERLINE AT "D" AND "Z" POSITIONS. (SEE ILLUSTRATIONS ABOVE)

9. MEASURE FROM KNOWN LEVEL FLOOR TO ROCKER PANEL AT "J" AND "K" POSITIONS. EXCEPT SSE MODELS.

10. MEASURE FROM KNOWN LEVEL FLOOR TO THE WHEEL OPENING AT "P" AND "R" POSITIONS.

MAXIMUM VARIATION SIDE TO SIDE & FRONT TO REAR IS 19MM (¾ IN)

LOAD CONDITIONS — COOLANT TO
CAPACITY AND FULL TANK OF FUEL

"Z"	"D"	"P"	"R"	"J"	"K"
55-75 mm	70-90 mm	708-728 mm	710-730 mm	231-251 mm	231-251 mm
$2\frac{5}{32}$-$2\frac{61}{64}$ in.	$2\frac{3}{4}$-$3\frac{35}{64}$ in.	$27\frac{57}{64}$-$28\frac{21}{32}$ in.	$27\frac{61}{64}$-$28\frac{3}{4}$ in.	$9\frac{3}{32}$-$9\frac{7}{8}$ in.	$9\frac{3}{32}$-$9\frac{7}{8}$ in.

Fig. 34   Vehicle trim height measurements. Bonneville

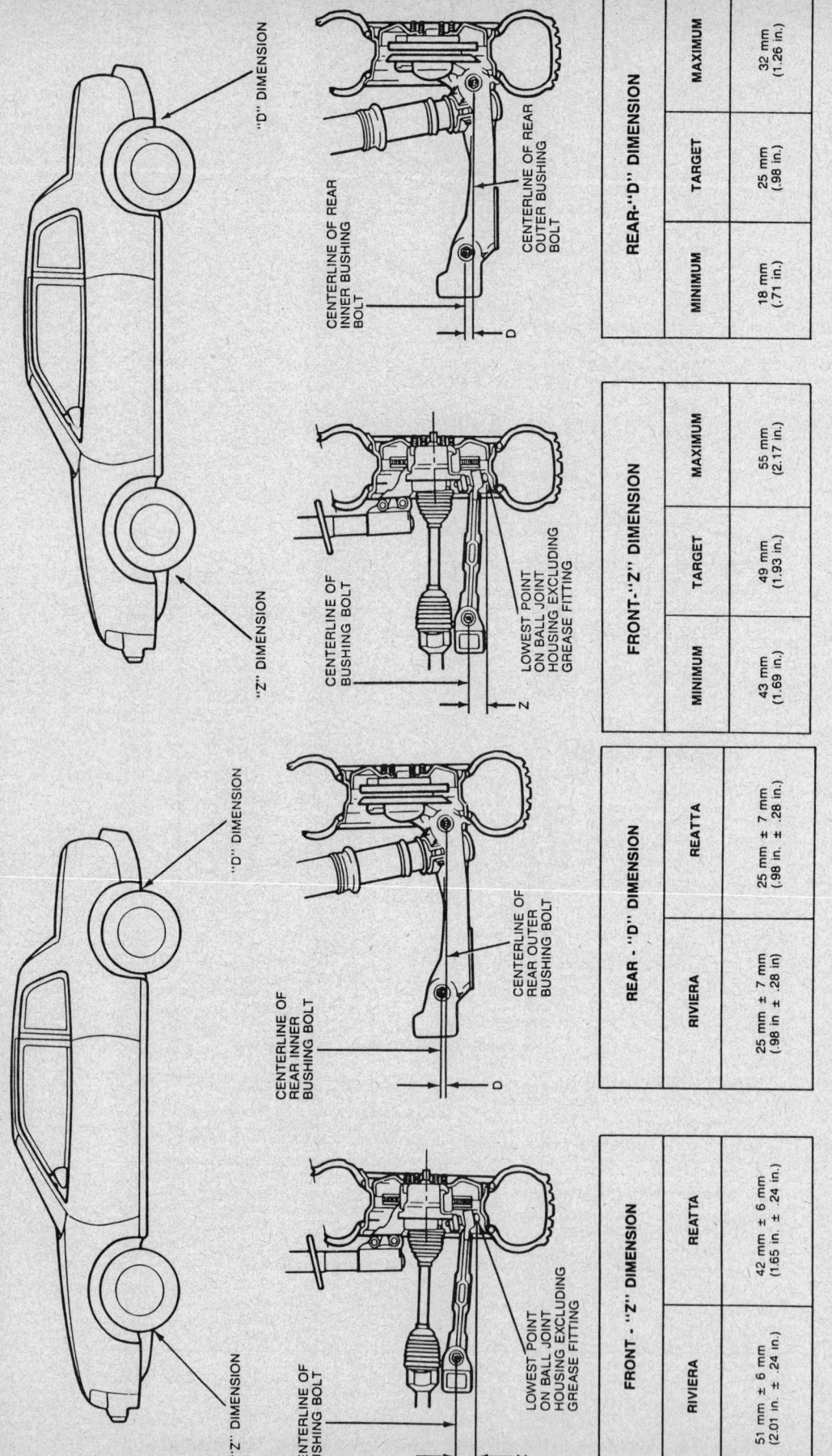

REAR-"D" DIMENSION

MINIMUM	TARGET	MAXIMUM
18 mm (.71 in.)	25 mm (.98 in.)	32 mm (1.26 in.)

FRONT-"Z" DIMENSION

MINIMUM	TARGET	MAXIMUM
43 mm (1.69 in.)	49 mm (1.93 in.)	55 mm (2.17 in.)

DIMENSIONS SHOWN ABOVE ARE FOR VEHICLE WITH CORRECT TIRE PRESSURE, FULL TANK OF FUEL, PROPERLY OPERATING ELC SYSTEM AND NO PASSENGERS OR ADDED WEIGHT IN CAR.

Fig. 36 Vehicle trim height measurements. Toronado

REAR - "D" DIMENSION

RIVIERA	REATTA
25 mm ± 7 mm (.98 in ± .28 in)	25 mm ± 7 mm (.98 in. ± .28 in.)

FRONT - "Z" DIMENSION

RIVIERA	REATTA
51 mm ± 6 mm (2.01 in. ± .24 in.)	42 mm ± 6 mm (1.65 in. ± .24 in.)

DIMENSIONS SHOWN ABOVE ARE FOR VEHICLE WITH CORRECT TIRE PRESSURE, FULL TANK OF FUEL, PROPERLY OPERATING ELC SYSTEM AND NO PASSENGERS OR ADDED WEIGHT IN CAR.

Fig. 35 Vehicle trim height measurements. Riviera

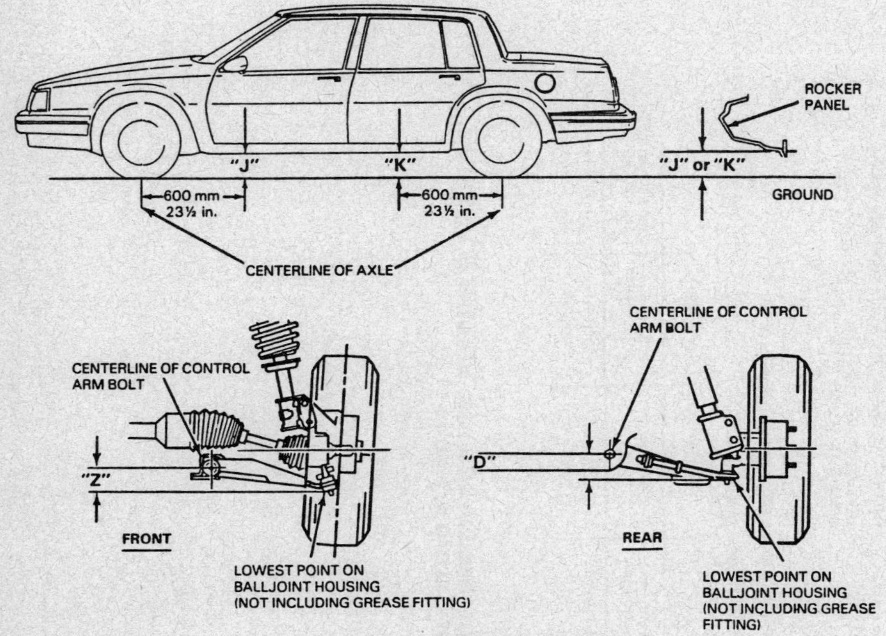

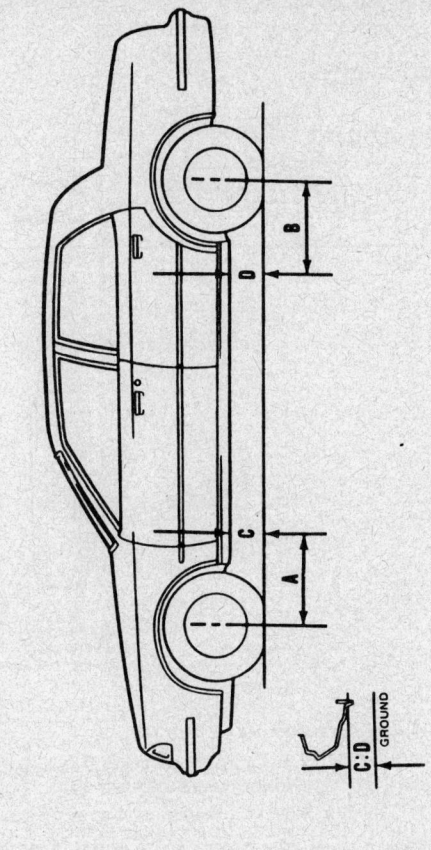

Trim heights checked with correct tire pressures, fuel tank full or equivalent weight in the trunk. No passengers or added weight in car. Front seat in rear position. Trunk must be empty except for spare tire and jack or simulated fuel load. Measure from known level floor to rocker panel with steering wheel in the centered position.

C & D DIMENSION

Lift center of front bumper up approximately 38 mm (1-1/2") and let vehicle settle gently. Repeat two more times, then measure "C" dimension. Push center of bumper down 38 mm (1-1/2") and let vehicle settle gently. Repeat two more times, then measure "C" dimension. The "C" dimension is an average of the high and low measurements. Repeat procedure on the rear bumper for the "D" dimension.

MAXIMUM VARIATION SIDE TO SIDE AND FRONT TO REAR IS 19 mm (3/4")

VIEW	A	B	C	D
Cutlass Supreme	623 mm (24-17/32")	532 mm (20-15/16")	255 mm (10")	255 mm (10")
Custom Cruiser	745 mm (29-21/64")	475 mm (18-11/16")	267 mm (10-1/2")	271 mm (10-5/8")

Fig. 38 Vehicle trim height measurements. Custom Cruiser

TRIM HEIGHT CHECK PROCEDURE

1. VEHICLE MUST BE ON LEVEL GROUND.
2. TIRES MUST BE INFLATED TO PROPER PRESSURE.
3. FUEL TANK SHOULD BE FULL.
4. NO PASSENGERS OR ADDED WEIGHT SHOULD BE IN THE VEHICLE. THE TRUNK MUST BE EMPTY EXCEPT FOR THE SPARE TIRE AND JACK.
5. PLACE THE FRONT SEAT IN THE REAR POSITION.
6. IGNITION SWITCH ON TO ACTIVATE ELECTRONIC LEVEL CONTROL (ELC).
7. "BOUNCE" THE CAR THREE TIMES AT THE FRONT AND REAR TO NORMALIZE THE SUSPENSION.
8. MEASURE FROM KNOWN LEVEL FLOOR TO ROCKER PANEL AT "J" AND "K" POSITIONS.
9. MEASURE FROM THE LOWEST POINT ON BALLJOINT HOUSING TO CONTROL ARM BOLT CENTERLINE AT "D" AND "Z" POSITIONS. (SEE ILLUSTRATIONS ABOVE.)

LOAD CONDITIONS — COOLANT TO CAPACITY AND FULL TANK OF FUEL

CARLINE	"Z"	"D"	"J"	"K"
C	56-76 mm 2³⁄₁₆-3 in.	70-90 mm 2¾-3⁹⁄₃₂ in.	228-248 mm 8³¹⁄₃₂-9⁹⁄₃₂ in.	230-250 mm 9ⁱ⁄₁₆-9⁷⁄₃₂ in.
H	50-70 mm 1³¹⁄₃₂-2¾ in.	77-97 mm 3¹⁄₃₂-3⅞ in.	229-249 mm 9¹⁄₃₂-9⅞ in.	236-256 mm 9⁹⁄₃₂-10⁵⁄₃₂ in.

MAXIMUM VARIATION SIDE TO SIDE & FRONT TO REAR IS 19 mm (¾ in.)

Fig. 37 Vehicle trim height measurements. Oldsmobile 88 & 98

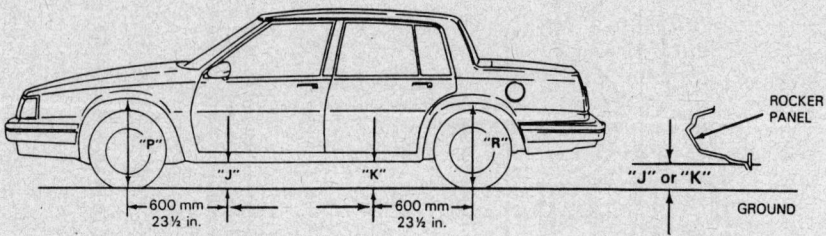

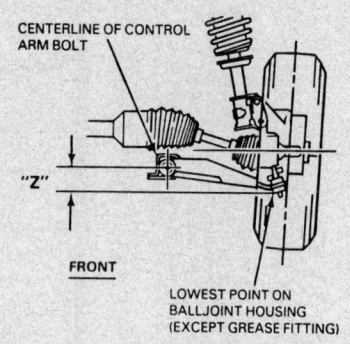

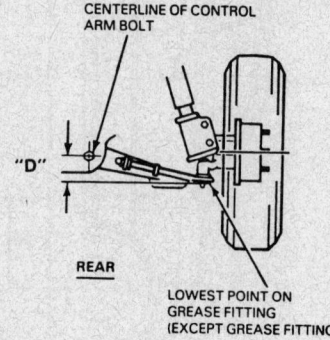

TRIM HEIGHT CHECK PROCEDURE

1. VEHICLE MUST BE ON LEVEL GROUND.

2. TIRES MUST BE INFLATED TO PROPER PRESSURE.

3. FUEL TANK SHOULD BE FULL.

4. NO PASSENGERS OR ADDED WEIGHT SHOULD BE IN THE VEHICLE. THE TRUNK MUST BE EMPTY EXCEPT FOR THE SPARE TIRE AND JACK.

5. PLACE THE FRONT SEAT IN THE REAR POSITION.

6. IGNITION SWITCH ON TO ACTIVATE ELECTRONIC LEVEL CONTROL (ELC). (IF EQUIPPED)

7. "BOUNCE" THE CAR THREE TIMES AT THE FRONT AND REAR TO NORMALIZE THE SUSPENSION.

8. MEASURE FROM THE LOWEST POINT ON THE BALLJOINT HOUSING TO CONTROL ARM BOLT CENTERLINE AT "D" AND "Z" POSITIONS. (SEE ILLUSTRATIONS ABOVE)

9. MEASURE FROM KNOWN LEVEL FLOOR TO ROCKER PANEL AT "J" AND "K" POSITIONS. EXCEPT SSE MODELS.

10. MEASURE FROM KNOWN LEVEL FLOOR TO THE WHEEL OPENING AT "P" AND "R" POSITIONS.

MAXIMUM VARIATION SIDE TO SIDE & FRONT TO REAR IS 19MM (¾ IN)

LOAD CONDITIONS — COOLANT TO CAPACITY AND FULL TANK OF FUEL

	"Z"	"D"	"P"	"R"	"J"	"K"
C	56-76 mm 2¹³⁄₆₄-3 in.	70-90 mm 2¾-3³⁵⁄₆₄ in.	699-719 mm 27½-28⁹⁄₁₆ in.	691-711 mm 27¹³⁄₁₆-28 in.	228-248 mm 8³¹⁄₃₂-9⁴⁵⁄₆₄ in.	230-250 mm 9³⁄₆₄-9²⁷⁄₃₂ in.
H	50-70 mm 1³¹⁄₃₂-2¾ in.	77-97 mm 3¹⁄₃₂-3¹³⁄₁₆ in.	699-719 mm 27½-28⁹⁄₁₆ in.	699-719 mm 27½-28⁹⁄₁₆ in.	229-249 mm 9⁴⁄₆₄-9⁷⁄₁₆ in.	236-256 mm 9¹⁹⁄₆₄-10⁴⁄₆₄ in.

Fig. 39 Vehicle trim height measurements. Electra & LeSabre except Estate Wagons

TRIM HEIGHTS (@ CURB WEIGHT)

The following procedure should be followed before making any trim height measurement:

1. "Z" "J" & "P" DIMENSIONS
   a. Lift vehicle up approximately 1-1/2" at the front bumper and gently remove hands allowing vehicle to settle on its own. Repeat this lifting operation twice for a total of three times. Measure the "Z" "J" & "P" heights in the settled position after the third lift.

   b. Push vehicle down approximately 1-1/2" at the front bumper and gently remove hands allowing vehicle to settle on its own. Repeat this pushing down operation twice for a total of 3 times. Measure the "Z", "J" & "P" heights in the settled position after the third push

   c. The true "Z", "J" & "P" height is the average of (a) and (b) for each side.

2. "D" "K" & R DIMENSIONS
   NOTE: Follow the same pattern as stated above for the "Z" "J" & "P" dimensions when measuring the "D" "K" & R dimensions except: Lift and push on the rear bumper.

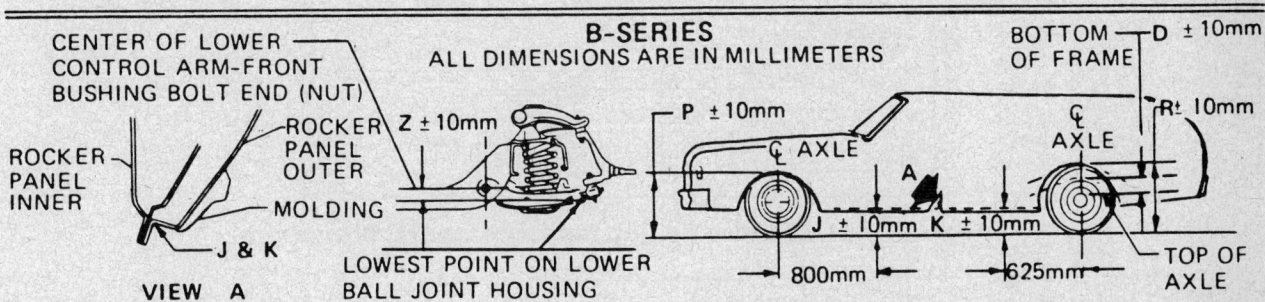

CURB WEIGHT—VEHICLE IS BUILT TO PARTS LIST SPECIFICATIONS INCLUDING COOLANT TO CAPACITY AND FULL TANK OF GASOLINE.
ALL DIMENSIONS ARE VERTICAL TO GROUND.

MODEL	TIRE	J	K	P	R	Z	D
WAGON	P225-75	268.0	271.0	731.0	734.0	48.0	124.0
DIMENSIONS GIVEN ARE IN MILLIMETERS/1mm 0.039 INCH							

Fig. 40   Vehicle trim height measurements. Electra & LeSabre Estate Wagons

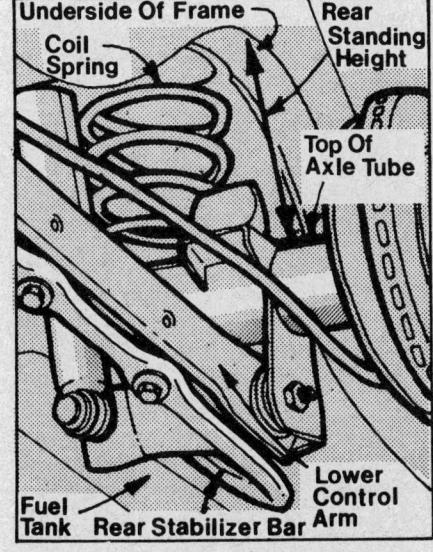

Fig. 41   Vehicle trim height measurements. Brougham

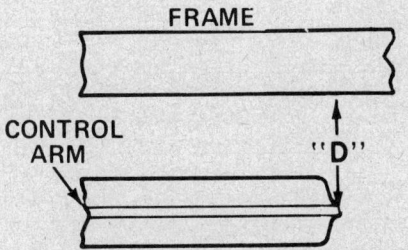

Fig. 42   Vehicle trim height measurement points. Eldorado & Seville

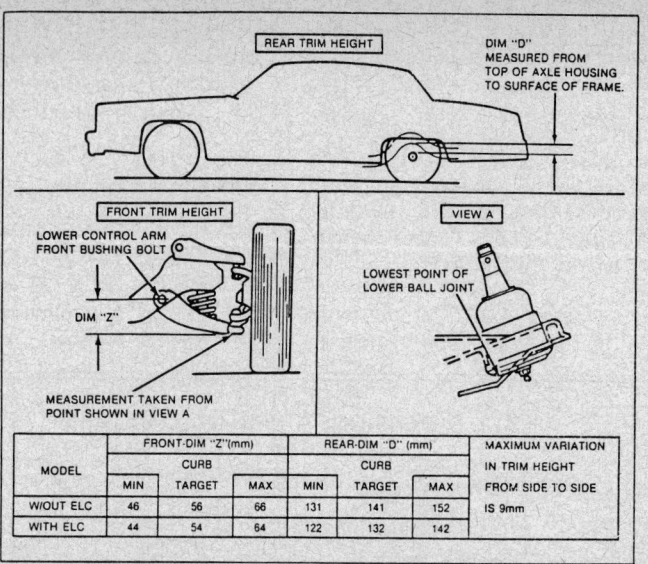

MODEL	FRONT-DIM "Z"(mm) CURB			REAR-DIM "D" (mm) CURB			MAXIMUM VARIATION IN TRIM HEIGHT FROM SIDE TO SIDE IS 9mm
	MIN	TARGET	MAX	MIN	TARGET	MAX	
W/OUT ELC	46	56	66	131	141	152	
WITH ELC	44	54	64	122	132	142	

Fig. 43 Vehicle trim height measurements. Brougham

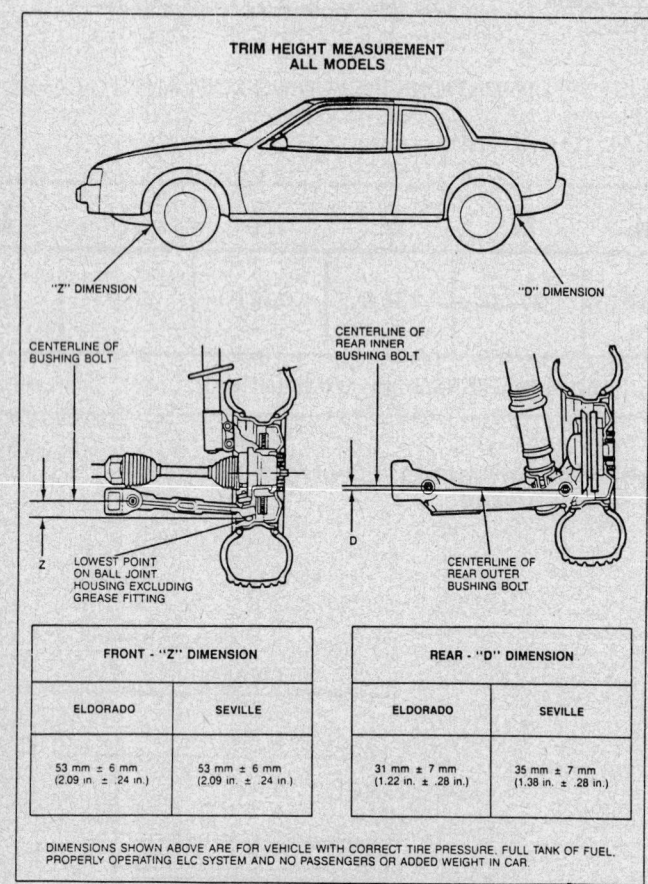

FRONT - "Z" DIMENSION		REAR - "D" DIMENSION	
ELDORADO	SEVILLE	ELDORADO	SEVILLE
53 mm ± 6 mm (2.09 in. ± .24 in.)	53 mm ± 6 mm (2.09 in. ± .24 in.)	31 mm ± 7 mm (1.22 in. ± .28 in.)	35 mm ± 7 mm (1.38 in. ± .28 in.)

DIMENSIONS SHOWN ABOVE ARE FOR VEHICLE WITH CORRECT TIRE PRESSURE, FULL TANK OF FUEL, PROPERLY OPERATING ELC SYSTEM AND NO PASSENGERS OR ADDED WEIGHT IN CAR.

Fig. 44 Vehicle trim height measurements. Eldorado & Seville

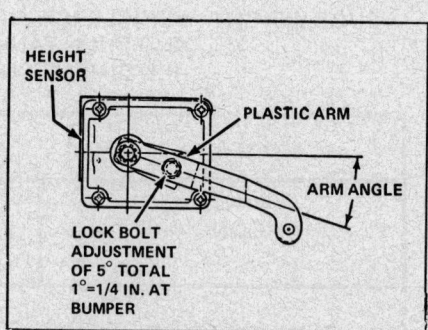

Fig. 45 Vehicle trim height adjustment

SELECTIVE RIDE CONTROL

INDEX

SYMPTOM TABLE

SYMPTOM	PROCEDURE
Codes 13, 14, 21, 22	Chart #1
Codes 31, 32, 33, 34	Chart #2
Codes 41, 42, 43 (See Note 1 below)	Chart #3
Code 23 (See Note 2 below)	Chart #4
Cannot read codes	Chart #5

CODE DEFINITION

- Code 12 – Start of code sequence
- Code 13 – Left Rear time out
- Code 14 – Right Front time out
- Code 21 – Left Front time out
- Code 22 – Right Rear time out
- Code 23 – Loss of vehicle speed signal (See Note 2 below)
- Code 31 – Left Front out of position
- Code 32 – Right Front out of position
- Code 33 – Left Rear out of position
- Code 34 – Right Rear out of position
- Code 41 – Selective Ride Control Switch short to "B+"
- Code 42 – Selective Ride Control Switch open contacts (See Note 1 below)
- Code 43 – Selective Ride Control Switch open circuit

Note 1:

Code 42 will set if the Selective Ride Control Switch is not properly positioned in one of the three detent positions.

Note 2:

Code 23 will set if the Ignition Switch is cycled "ON/OFF" three times without driving vehicle. The "Service Ride Control" Indicator will turn "OFF" once the vehicle has been driven if the system is OK, but the code will remain as a history code and should be cleared to avoid future misdiagnosis.

Fig. 1   Selective Ride symptom table

SYSTEM DIAGNOSIS

Selective Ride trouble codes may be read with the vehicle stopped by grounding terminal "C" of the Assembly Line Diagnostic Link (ALDL). Observe the "Service Ride Control" indicator with the ignition switch in "Run." The trouble codes are comprised of two digits. A digit is read by counting the number of flashes that occur within a half second of each other. The second digit will appear about one second after the first digit has gone.

Each code will repeat three times before the next code begins with a three second pause between codes. The entire trouble code sequence will reappear as long as terminal "C" is grounded. The trouble code display begins by showing code 12 three times, marking the beginning of the sequence.

If the diagnostic mode cannot be entered (no codes appear, not even 12), refer to **Fig. 1.**

When the diagnosis is complete and any necessary repairs have been made, the trouble codes must be cleared to prevent further misdiagnosis. To clear the system, ground pin "C" of the ALDL connector for two seconds and repeat the procedure twice for a total of three groundings.

Diagnose the Selective Ride problem by reading the trouble codes stored in the Selective Ride Control Module. After reading the codes, refer to the Symptom Table and **Figs. 2 through 8,** for system diagnosis and repair.

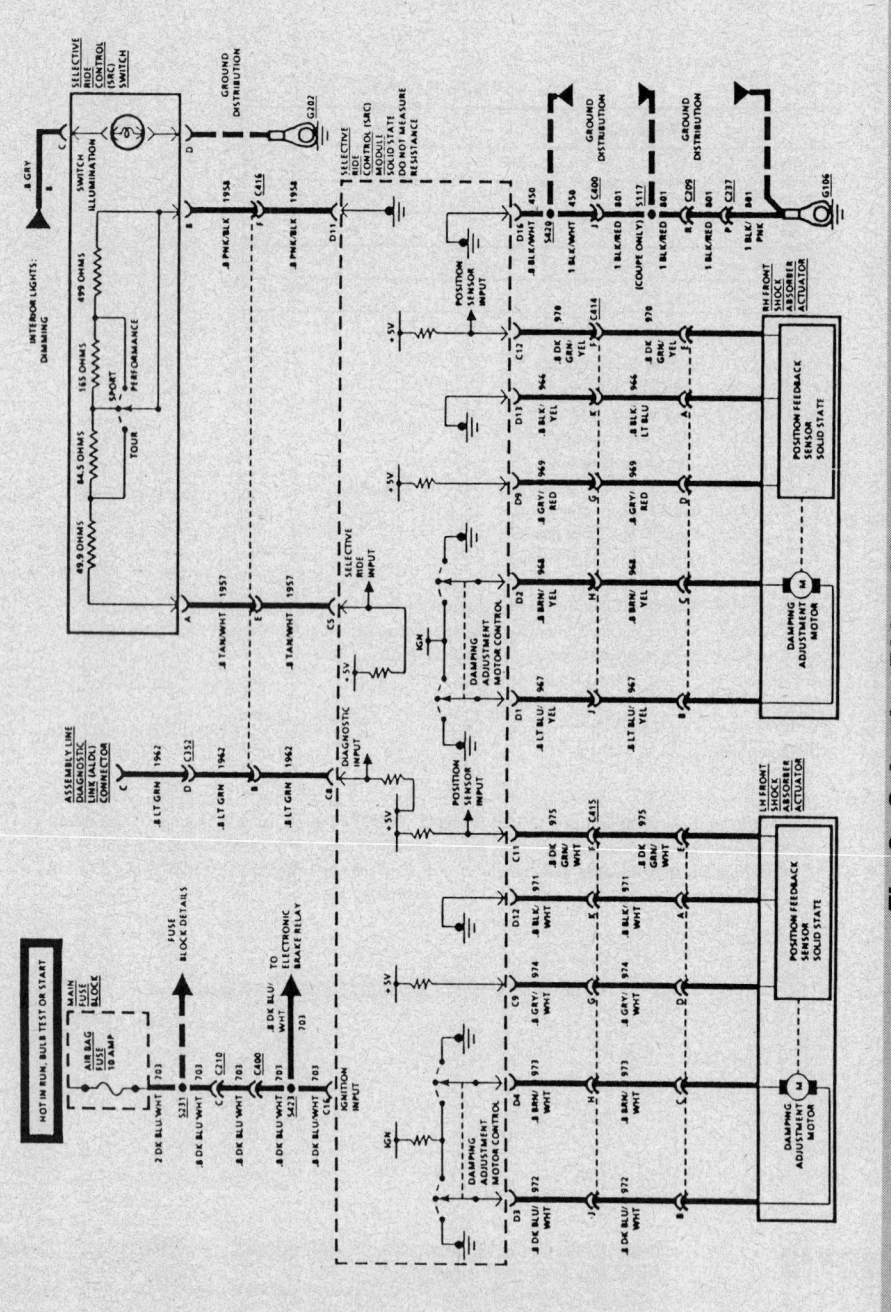

Fig. 2 Selective Ride wiring diagram

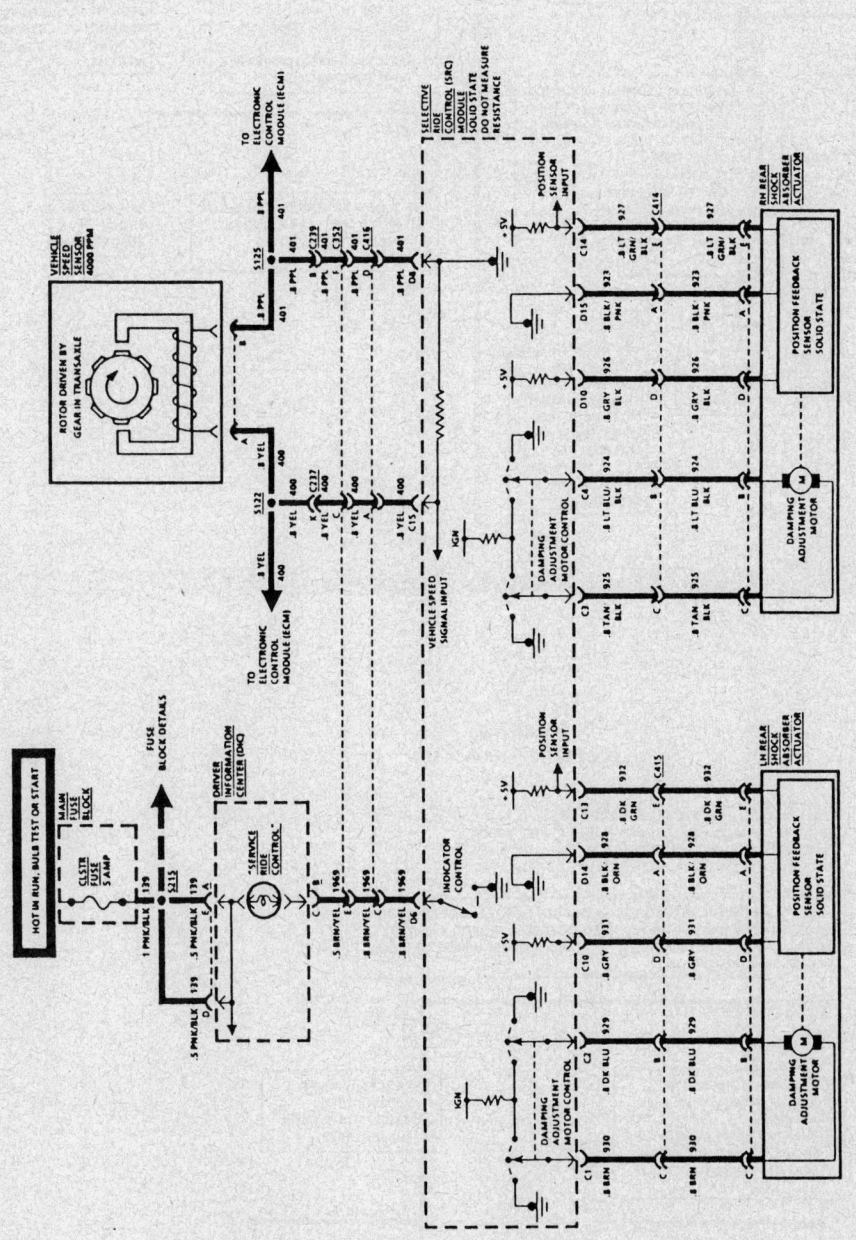

Fig. 3 Selective Ride wiring diagram

CHART #1
CODES 13, 14, 21 OR 22 SET

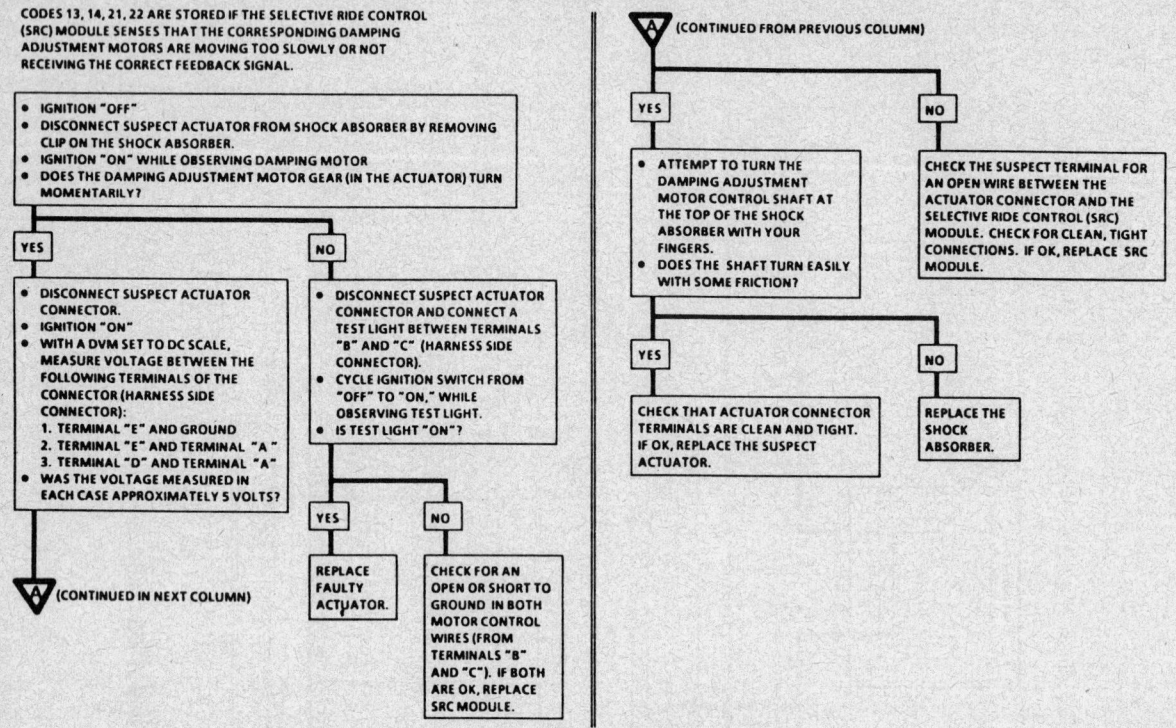

CODES 13, 14, 21, 22 ARE STORED IF THE SELECTIVE RIDE CONTROL (SRC) MODULE SENSES THAT THE CORRESPONDING DAMPING ADJUSTMENT MOTORS ARE MOVING TOO SLOWLY OR NOT RECEIVING THE CORRECT FEEDBACK SIGNAL.

- IGNITION "OFF"
- DISCONNECT SUSPECT ACTUATOR FROM SHOCK ABSORBER BY REMOVING CLIP ON THE SHOCK ABSORBER.
- IGNITION "ON" WHILE OBSERVING DAMPING MOTOR
- DOES THE DAMPING ADJUSTMENT MOTOR GEAR (IN THE ACTUATOR) TURN MOMENTARILY?

YES
- DISCONNECT SUSPECT ACTUATOR CONNECTOR.
- IGNITION "ON"
- WITH A DVM SET TO DC SCALE, MEASURE VOLTAGE BETWEEN THE FOLLOWING TERMINALS OF THE CONNECTOR (HARNESS SIDE CONNECTOR):
  1. TERMINAL "E" AND GROUND
  2. TERMINAL "E" AND TERMINAL "A"
  3. TERMINAL "D" AND TERMINAL "A"
- WAS THE VOLTAGE MEASURED IN EACH CASE APPROXIMATELY 5 VOLTS?

A (CONTINUED IN NEXT COLUMN)

NO
- DISCONNECT SUSPECT ACTUATOR CONNECTOR AND CONNECT A TEST LIGHT BETWEEN TERMINALS "B" AND "C" (HARNESS SIDE CONNECTOR).
- CYCLE IGNITION SWITCH FROM "OFF" TO "ON," WHILE OBSERVING TEST LIGHT.
- IS TEST LIGHT "ON"?

YES
REPLACE FAULTY ACTUATOR.

NO
CHECK FOR AN OPEN OR SHORT TO GROUND IN BOTH MOTOR CONTROL WIRES (FROM TERMINALS "B" AND "C"). IF BOTH ARE OK, REPLACE SRC MODULE.

A (CONTINUED FROM PREVIOUS COLUMN)

YES
- ATTEMPT TO TURN THE DAMPING ADJUSTMENT MOTOR CONTROL SHAFT AT THE TOP OF THE SHOCK ABSORBER WITH YOUR FINGERS.
- DOES THE SHAFT TURN EASILY WITH SOME FRICTION?

NO
CHECK THE SUSPECT TERMINAL FOR AN OPEN WIRE BETWEEN THE ACTUATOR CONNECTOR AND THE SELECTIVE RIDE CONTROL (SRC) MODULE. CHECK FOR CLEAN, TIGHT CONNECTIONS. IF OK, REPLACE SRC MODULE.

YES
CHECK THAT ACTUATOR CONNECTOR TERMINALS ARE CLEAN AND TIGHT. IF OK, REPLACE THE SUSPECT ACTUATOR.

NO
REPLACE THE SHOCK ABSORBER.

Fig. 4   Selective Ride diagnosis chart 1

CHART #2
CODES 31, 32, 33 OR 34 SET

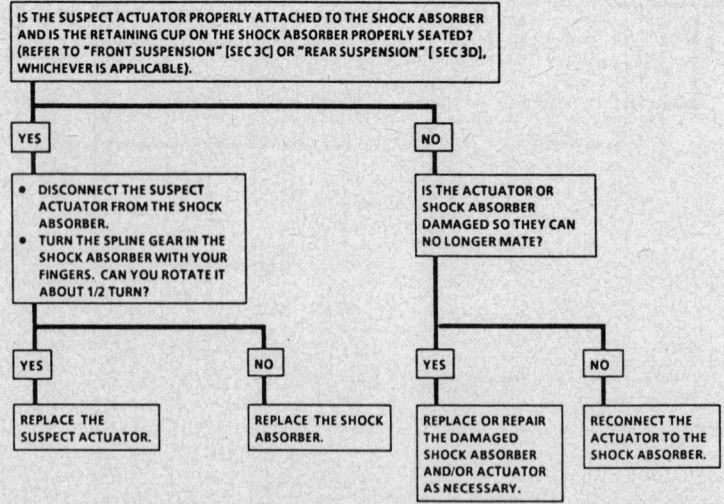

CODES 31, 32, 33 OR 34 ARE STORED IF THE SELECTIVE RIDE CONTROL (SRC) MODULE SENSES THAT THE CORRESPONDING DAMPING ADJUSTMENT MOTOR HAS NOT FOUND THE END STOP POSITION ON THE SHOCK ABSORBER DURING INITIALIZATION.

IS THE SUSPECT ACTUATOR PROPERLY ATTACHED TO THE SHOCK ABSORBER AND IS THE RETAINING CUP ON THE SHOCK ABSORBER PROPERLY SEATED? (REFER TO "FRONT SUSPENSION" [SEC 3C] OR "REAR SUSPENSION" [SEC 3D], WHICHEVER IS APPLICABLE).

YES
- DISCONNECT THE SUSPECT ACTUATOR FROM THE SHOCK ABSORBER.
- TURN THE SPLINE GEAR IN THE SHOCK ABSORBER WITH YOUR FINGERS. CAN YOU ROTATE IT ABOUT 1/2 TURN?

NO
IS THE ACTUATOR OR SHOCK ABSORBER DAMAGED SO THEY CAN NO LONGER MATE?

YES
REPLACE THE SUSPECT ACTUATOR.

NO
REPLACE THE SHOCK ABSORBER.

YES
REPLACE OR REPAIR THE DAMAGED SHOCK ABSORBER AND/OR ACTUATOR AS NECESSARY.

NO
RECONNECT THE ACTUATOR TO THE SHOCK ABSORBER.

Fig. 5   Selective Ride diagnosis chart 2

CHART #3
CODES 41, 42 OR 43 SET

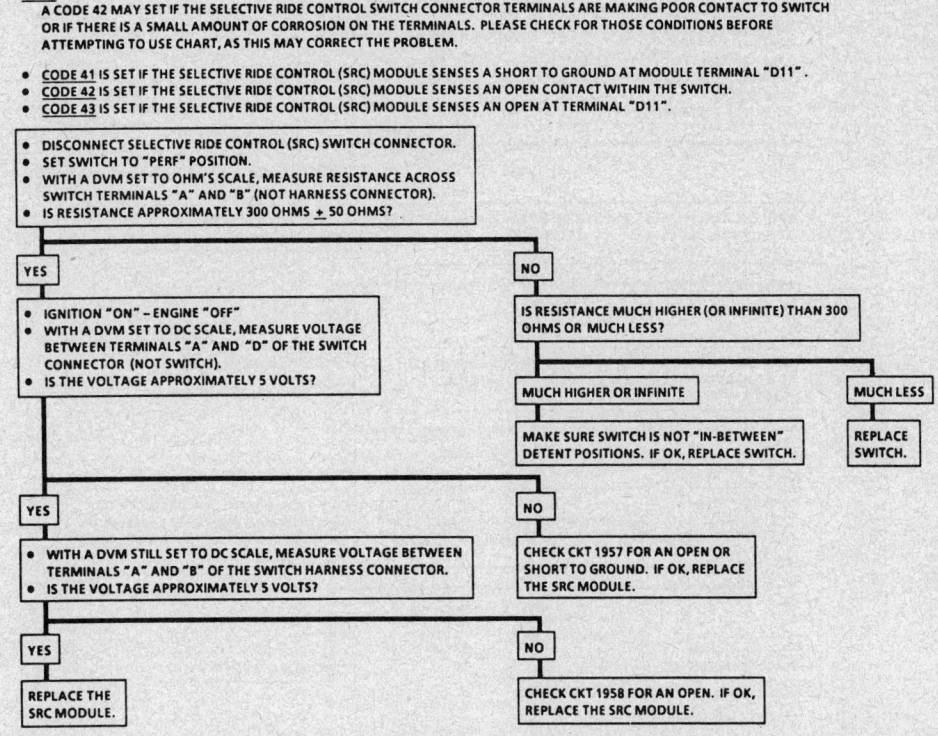

NOTE:
A CODE 42 MAY SET IF THE SELECTIVE RIDE CONTROL SWITCH CONNECTOR TERMINALS ARE MAKING POOR CONTACT TO SWITCH OR IF THERE IS A SMALL AMOUNT OF CORROSION ON THE TERMINALS. PLEASE CHECK FOR THOSE CONDITIONS BEFORE ATTEMPTING TO USE CHART, AS THIS MAY CORRECT THE PROBLEM.

- CODE 41 IS SET IF THE SELECTIVE RIDE CONTROL (SRC) MODULE SENSES A SHORT TO GROUND AT MODULE TERMINAL "D11".
- CODE 42 IS SET IF THE SELECTIVE RIDE CONTROL (SRC) MODULE SENSES AN OPEN CONTACT WITHIN THE SWITCH.
- CODE 43 IS SET IF THE SELECTIVE RIDE CONTROL (SRC) MODULE SENSES AN OPEN AT TERMINAL "D11".

Fig. 6   Selective Ride diagnosis chart 3

CHART #4
CODE 23
LOSS OF VEHICLE SPEED

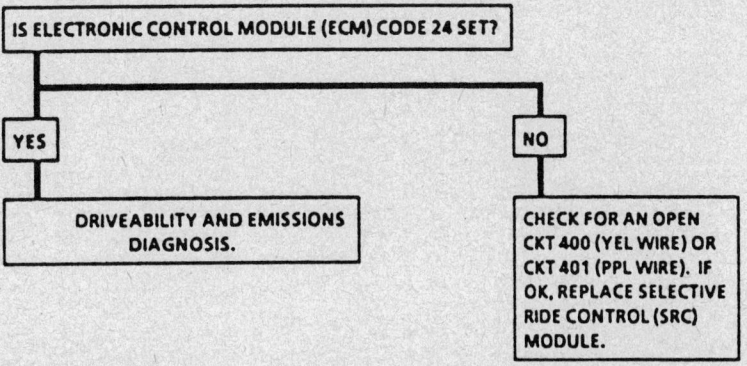

NOTE:
CODE 23 WILL SET IF THE IGNITION SWITCH IS CYCLED "ON" AND "OFF" THREE TIMES WITHOUT DRIVING THE VEHICLE. SYSTEM IS WORKING NORMALLY IF THE "SERVICE RIDE CONTROL" INDICATOR TURNS "OFF" AFTER DRIVING VEHICLE. CODE 23 WILL REMAIN AS A HISTORY CODE, AND SHOULD BE CLEARED TO PREVENT FUTURE MISDIAGNOSIS.

Fig. 7   Selective Ride diagnosis chart 4

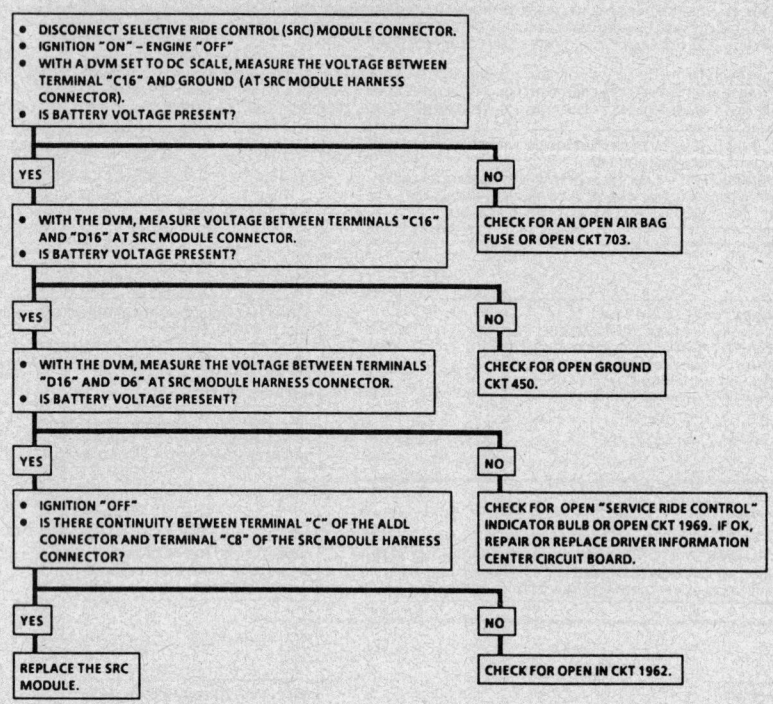

CHART #5
TROUBLE CODES CANNOT BE READ

- DISCONNECT SELECTIVE RIDE CONTROL (SRC) MODULE CONNECTOR.
- IGNITION "ON" – ENGINE "OFF"
- WITH A DVM SET TO DC SCALE, MEASURE THE VOLTAGE BETWEEN TERMINAL "C16" AND GROUND (AT SRC MODULE HARNESS CONNECTOR).
- IS BATTERY VOLTAGE PRESENT?

YES
- WITH THE DVM, MEASURE VOLTAGE BETWEEN TERMINALS "C16" AND "D16" AT SRC MODULE CONNECTOR.
- IS BATTERY VOLTAGE PRESENT?

NO
CHECK FOR AN OPEN AIR BAG FUSE OR OPEN CKT 703.

YES
- WITH THE DVM, MEASURE THE VOLTAGE BETWEEN TERMINALS "D16" AND "D6" AT SRC MODULE HARNESS CONNECTOR.
- IS BATTERY VOLTAGE PRESENT?

NO
CHECK FOR OPEN GROUND CKT 450.

YES
- IGNITION "OFF"
- IS THERE CONTINUITY BETWEEN TERMINAL "C" OF THE ALDL CONNECTOR AND TERMINAL "C8" OF THE SRC MODULE HARNESS CONNECTOR?

NO
CHECK FOR OPEN "SERVICE RIDE CONTROL" INDICATOR BULB OR OPEN CKT 1969. IF OK, REPAIR OR REPLACE DRIVER INFORMATION CENTER CIRCUIT BOARD.

YES
REPLACE THE SRC MODULE.

NO
CHECK FOR OPEN IN CKT 1962.

Fig. 8   Selective Ride diagnosis chart 5

WIPER MOTORS

INDEX

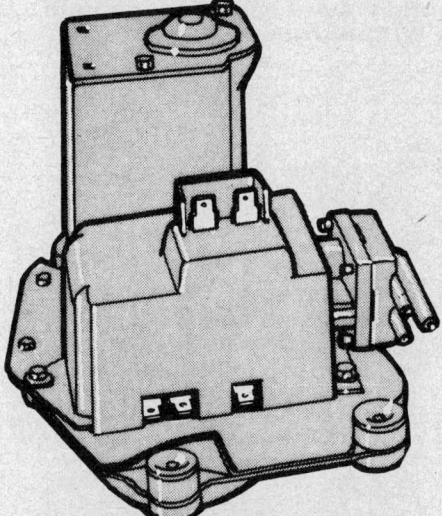

Fig. 1 Compound wound rectangular windshield wiper motor. Shown w/washer pump installed

WINDSHIELD WIPER MOTOR

A compound wound type wiper motor is used on all rear wheel drive models except Fiero, Camaro and Firebird, 1988 Grand Prix and Monte Carlo, 1988 Cutlass Supreme Classic. Motor speeds on this type motor are determined by varying current flow through the motor shunt field. Two different compound wound motors are used, depending upon application. A rectangular positive park motor is used on Cavalier, and a round motor is used on models with depressed park wipers.

A permanent magnet type motor is used on Fiero, Camaro and Firebird, 1988 Grand Prix and Monte Carlo, 1988 Cutlass Supreme Classic and front wheel drive models 1988 Nova & 1989-90 Prizm. Permanent magnet motors have three brushes, common, low and high speed. Motor

speeds are determined by completing the circuit to the low or high speed brush, while the common brush is used at both speeds.

There are two types of windshield wiper motor parking, non-depressed and depressed. Depressed park refers to the extra travel to lower the wipers below the hood line. Non-depressed refers to windshield wipers being visible on the windshield glass in the park position.

A two speed wiper motor is used on Prizm, Storm & Nova.

Description & Operation

Windshield wiper operation is controlled by a dash or steering column mounted switch. The wiper feed circuit is protected by a fuse which is located in the fuse block on most models, or in an inline fuse holder on some models with pulse wipers. A circuit breaker, integral with the motor brush holder, protects the motor against overload. Pulse wipers, available on most models, use a variable resistor, a pulse control module, and/or a modified wiper motor to provide a delay wipe mode.

COMPOUND WOUND MOTOR
RECTANGULAR MOTOR

The rectangular motor, **Fig. 1**, consists of an armature, brush plate assembly, field coils and a housing which is attached to a gear housing. The motor electrical connections, park switch, and on some models a washer pump are also mounted on the gear box. A gear on the commutator end of the armature drives an intermediate gear and pinion assembly, which in turn drives the output shaft. A crank arm on the output shaft operates wipers through a pivot link (transmission) assembly.

When ignition is on, battery voltage is supplied to motor terminal 2, **Fig. 2**. Current flows through the series field to a

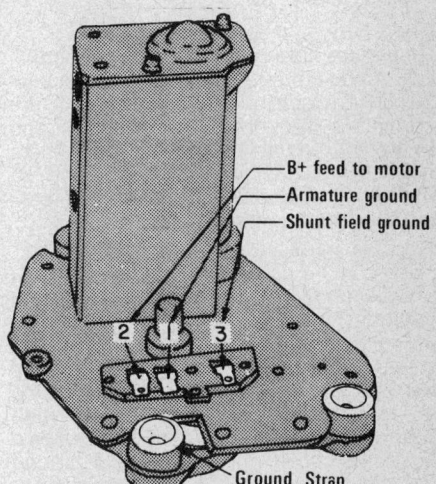

Fig. 2 Windshield wiper motor electrical connections. Compound wound rectangular motor

splice where it is divided, and part passes through the armature and part through the shunt field. The armature and shunt field circuits are completed to ground through the wiper switch, with motor speeds determined by resistance in the shunt field ground path.

Standard (Non-Pulse) Wiper Operation

Placing wiper switch in low position grounds motor terminals 1 and 3, **Fig. 2**, at the wiper switch. Shunt field current flows directly to ground through terminal 3, armature current flows to ground through terminal 1 and the motor runs at low speed. Placing wiper switch in high position grounds terminal 1, but terminal 3 remains open. Armature current flows directly to ground through terminal 1, shunt field current flows to ground through a resistor connected between terminals 1 and 3, and the motor runs at high speed due to the weakened shunt field.

When wiper switch is turned off, and

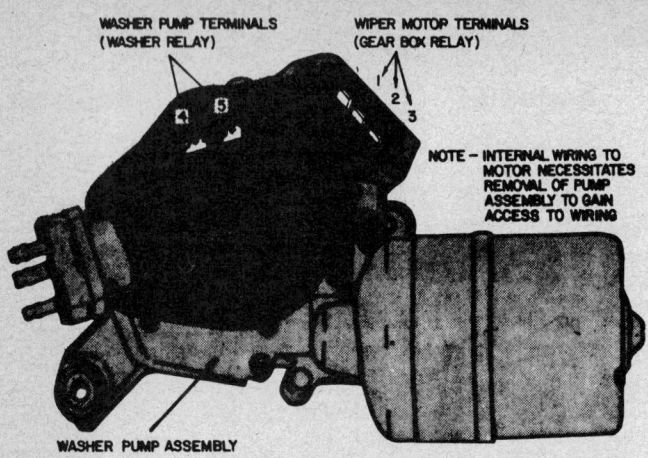

Fig. 3 Compound wound round windshield wiper motor

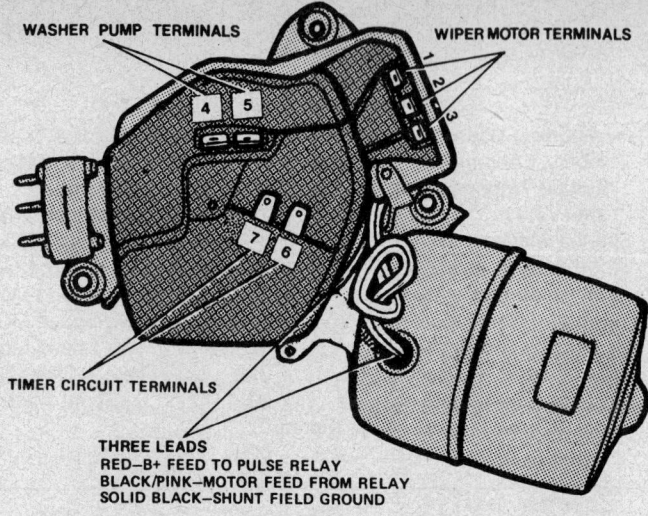

Fig. 4 Compound wound round windshield wiper motor w/modified pulse system

wipers are not in park position, terminal 1 is grounded through the closed motor park switch contacts. Terminals 1 and 3 are connected through the wiper switch, and the motor runs at low speed. When wipers reach their lowest point of travel, a cam on the motor output shaft opens the park switch, and the motor stops.

Pulse Wiper Operation

On models with pulse wipers, a pulse control module provides a delay wipe mode through the low speed circuit. When wiper control is in delay position, battery voltage is supplied to a capacitor in the module through a variable resistor. When the capacitor is fully charged, it activates a switching circuit which provides a ground to begin wiper operation. As the motor operates, park switch contacts close, the capacitor discharges, and the motor ground is maintained through the park switch. When wipers complete their cycle, the park switch opens and the capacitor begins to recharge. Delay between wipe cycles is determined by a variable resistor, which controls charging current to the capacitor. Higher resistance produces a longer delay.

ROUND MOTOR

The 4 or 4½ inch long, round motor assembly consists of an armature, field coil and end cap assembly, and a brush plate which fits over the armature and is connected to the field coils. The motor assembly is attached to a gear box housing which also provides a mount for the washer pump. A worm gear on the armature commutator end drives the output shaft at a 90° angle through a drive gear and pawl assembly.

The gear box assembly contains a magnet switch, relay and terminal board assembly (gear box relay) which provides electrical connections and controls current flow through the motor. On standard (non-pulse) motors, **Fig. 3,** the two motor leads to the gear box relay are concealed and routed through a cavity in the gear housing. On pulse type motors, **Figs. 4 and 5,** the two motor leads to the gear box relay, and the feed wire to the pulse relay are exposed. Both standard and pulse mo-

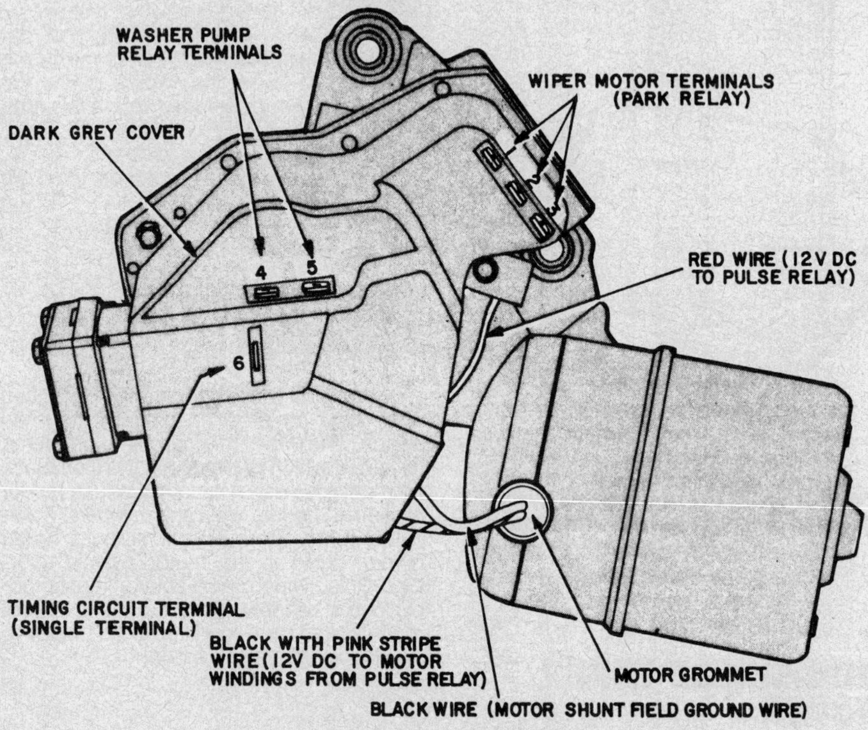

Fig. 5 Compound wound round windshield wiper motor w/multiplex pulse system

tors used on Corvette have an additional ground lead to ground the motor housing to the wiper switch.

Standard (Non-Pulse) Wiper Operation

When ignition is on, battery voltage is supplied to gear box relay terminal 2, **Fig. 3.** When terminal 1 is grounded, relay contacts close and current is supplied to the motor. Current flows through the series field to a splice where it is divided, and part passes through the armature to the motor housing ground, and part through the

shunt field. Motor speeds are determined by the amount of current flowing through the shunt field.

Placing wiper switch in low position grounds gear box relay terminals 1 and 3. The relay contacts close, shunt field current flows directly to ground at the switch through terminal 3, and the motor runs at low speed. Placing wiper switch in high, or medium position on Cadillac, grounds relay terminal 1, but terminal 3 remains open. Shunt field current flows to ground through a 20 ohm resistor connected between terminals 1 and 3, and the motor runs at a

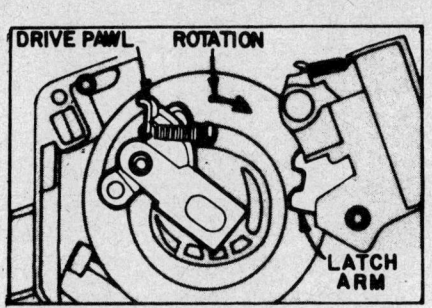

Fig. 6   Gear box relay and drive gear assembly, shown out of park position. Compound wound round windshield wiper motor

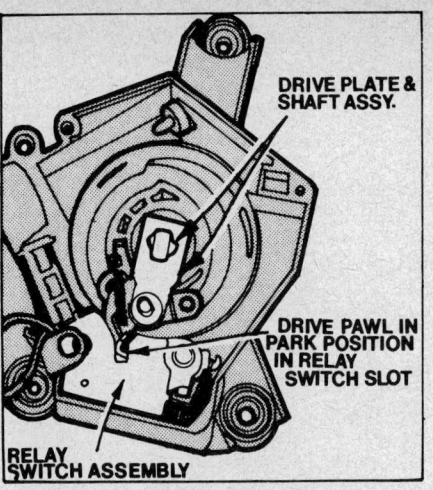

Fig. 7   Gear box relay and drive gear assembly, shown in park position. Compound wound round windshield wiper motor

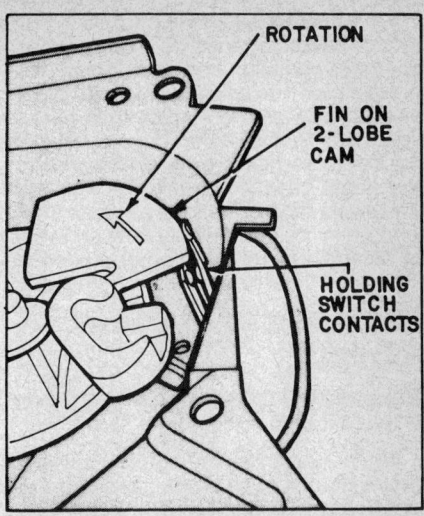

Fig. 8   Pulse wiper system holding switch. Compound wound round windshield wiper motor

PARK   HI SPEED

LO SPEED

NO LOAD CURRENT DRAW @ 12V.

LO SPEED — 2.5 AMPS MAX
HI SPEED — 5.0 AMPS MAX

CRANK ARM ROTATION — CCW
— (LOOKING AT ARM)

Fig. 9   Permanent magnet non-depressed park type windshield wiper motor

higher speed due to the weakened shunt field. Medium speed on Cadillac models results from a 13 ohm resistor in the wiper switch, wired parallel with the gear box relay resistor, which produces approximately 8 ohms resistance in the shunt field circuit.

Placing wiper switch in off position opens the circuit to the gear box relay magnet switch. This allows a spring loaded arm to move into the path of the output gear drive pawl, **Fig. 6,** while relay contacts remain closed. The shunt field is grounded through the wiper switch and the motor operates at low speed, allowing the gear mechanism to park the wipers and stop the motor.

As the output gear rotates, the drive pawl engages the latch arm on the gear box relay, and the output gear is unlocked from the drive pawl, lock pawl and drive plate. Since the output shaft and gear shaft are off center, continuing rotation causes a cam action which moves the drive pawl into a slot in the gear box relay and allows wipers to move below their lowest point of normal travel. The drive pawl pushes the

latch arm against the gear box relay contacts, opening the contacts and stopping the motor in park position, **Fig. 7.**

Multiplex Pulse Wiper Operation

Models with pulse wiper use a motor similar to the one used on standard systems, but with modifications to provide a delay wipe mode. The multiplex system, while similar to earlier pulse wipe systems, uses an integrated circuit timer and the voltage feed to the wiper switch has been eliminated. In addition to standard wiper system components, the multiplex system uses a variable resistor in the wiper switch, a pulse relay and holding switch mounted in the washer pump, and a timer circuit. The timer, consisting of a capacitor and integrated circuit, is mounted on a circuit board in the washer pump or contained in a separate module.

The gear box relay functions in a similar manner on both standard and multiplex systems. However, on pulse systems the gear box relay supplies voltage to the pulse relay, current to the motor windings is controlled by the pulse relay, and voltage is supplied to the timer circuit from motor terminal 2. In all switch positions except delay, the gear box relay, pulse relay and timer capacitor circuits are completed directly to ground through the wiper switch. This deactivates the timer circuit and allows the motor to operate as outlined in "Standard (Non-Pulse) Wiper Operation."

Placing wiper switch in delay position grounds gear box relay terminals 1 (relay) and 3 (shunt field), and the timer capacitor is partially grounded through the variable resistor, allowing it to charge at a controlled rate. When the timer capacitor is fully charged it activates the integrated circuit. The integrated circuit completes the pulse relay ground circuit, and current flows through the motor windings.

As the motor begins to operate, holding switch contacts close, the capacitor discharges partially, and the pulse relay ground is maintained by the holding switch. As wipers complete their cycle, a fin on the washer pump drive cam opens the holding switch, **Fig. 8**, wipers stop and the timer capacitor begins to recharge. This cycle repeats as long as wiper switch is in delay position. Delay between wipes is determined by varying resistance between the timer capacitor and ground.

PERMANENT MAGNET MOTOR

Standard (Non-Pulse) Wiper Operation

When ignition is on, battery voltage is supplied to the common brush through motor terminal 1, **Fig. 9**. Placing wiper switch in low or high position completes the ground circuit to motor terminal 2 (low) or 3 (high) at the switch, and the motor runs at the selected speed. When the wiper switch is turned off, park switch terminal 5 is grounded at the wiper switch. Park switch terminal 4 is connected to the low speed terminal through the wiring harness, and the closed park switch allows motor to continue running. When wipers reach their lowest point of travel, a cam on the output gear opens the park switch, and the motor stops.

Pulse Wiper Operation

In addition to standard wiper system components, models with pulse wipers use a variable resistor in the wiper switch and a control module connected between the motor and switch to provide a delay wipe mode. Current flow between the wiper motor and switch passes through the pulse control module, and the wiper switch is grounded through the module. However, when wiper switch is in low or high position, the pulse module does not affect system operation.

When the wiper switch is in delay position, battery voltage is applied to the control module timer through the motor low speed circuit, and the timer is partially grounded through the variable resistor. When the timer capacitor is fully charged, the low speed circuit is completed to ground at the module, starting the wipe cycle. As motor begins to operate, the park switch closes, the timer capacitor discharges, and the low speed circuit is grounded through the park switch. When wipers complete their cycle, the park switch opens, the motor stops, and the timer capacitor begins to recharge.

This cycle repeats as long as the wiper switch is in delay position. Delay between wipe cycles is determined by varying resistance between the timer capacitor and ground.

NON-DEPRESSED PARK

Wiper motor internal components, including permanent magnet fields, armature, brush holder and gear train, are enclosed in a die cast aluminum housing with a plastic cover, **Fig. 10**. The brush holder contains a circuit breaker and park

switch as well as common, low and high speed brushes, and it is located at the gear box end of the motor.

The common brush is connected to ground through the wiper motor ground strap. Battery voltage is supplied to the wiper switch and motor park switch fixed contacts through a fuse in the fuse block. Motor speeds are determined by supplying voltage through the wiper switch to the low or high speed motor brush, and when wiper switch is in off position, voltage supplied to the motor park switch allows wipers to park at the bottom of their travel. Pulse wiper operation, if equipped, is controlled by a variable resistor in the wiper switch and by a pulse module connected between the wiper motor and switch.

Standard (Non-Pulse) Wiper Operation

When ignition is on, battery voltage is supplied to low and high speed contacts in the wiper switch and to motor terminal 4, **Fig. 10**. Placing wiper switch in low or high position completes the feed circuit to motor terminal 2 (low speed brush) or terminal 1 (high speed brush), **Fig. 10**. Current flows through the armature to ground through the common brush, and the motor runs at the selected speed.

Placing wiper switch in off position connects the motor low speed brush to park switch terminal 3, **Fig. 10**. Current flows through the closed park switch contacts, allowing the motor to run at low speed. When wipers reach their lowest point of travel, a cam on the motor output shaft opens the park switch through an actuating lever, and the motor stops.

Pulse Wiper Operation

In addition to standard wiper system components, models with pulse wipers use a pulse control module and a wiper switch with a variable resistor and additional contacts to control pulse module operation. Current flow between the wiper motor and switch, and battery voltage to the switch pass through the pulse control module. However, when the wiper switch is in off, low or high position, the module does not affect system operation.

When the wiper switch is in delay position, voltage is supplied to the pulse module timer through the variable resistor. When the timer circuit becomes fully charged, the timer switch closes, and voltage is supplied to the motor through a second delay terminal in the wiper switch. As the motor begins to operate, the park switch closes, the timer switch opens, and voltage is supplied to the motor through a third delay contact which is linked to the park switch in the wiper switch. When wipers complete their cycle, the park switch opens, the motor stops, and the timer begins to recharge.

This cycle repeats as long as wiper switch is in delay position. Delay period is controlled by varying resistance in the pulse module timer feed circuit.

DEPRESSED PARK MOTOR

Wiper motor assembly consists of a permanent magnet wiper motor with either an integral flex-vane washer pump mounted in the cover, or with a washer pump remotely mounted in the washer tank, **Figs.**

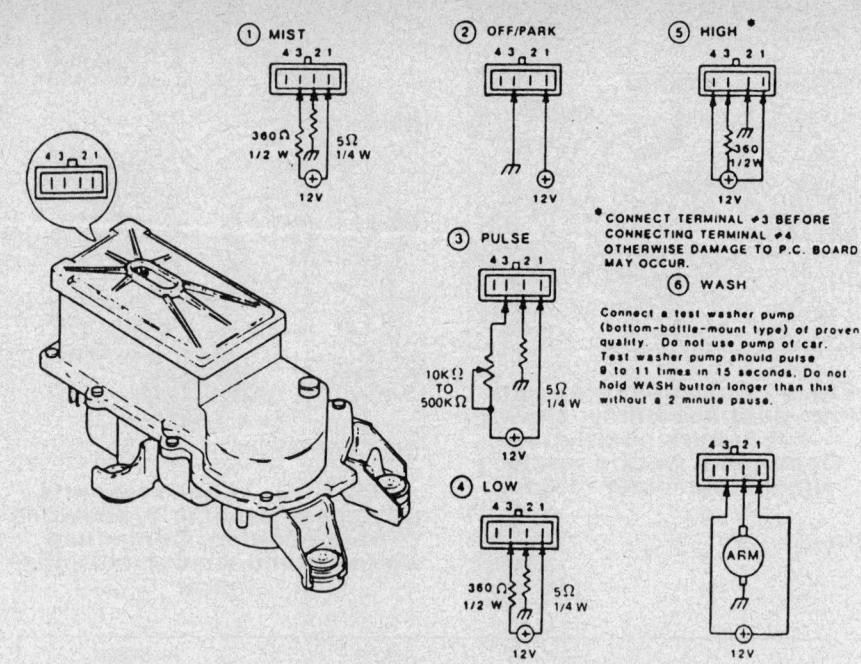

Fig. 10   Permanent magnet non-depressed park type windshield wiper motor. (Note: The harness connector may be labeled D-C-B-A instead of 1-2-3-4)

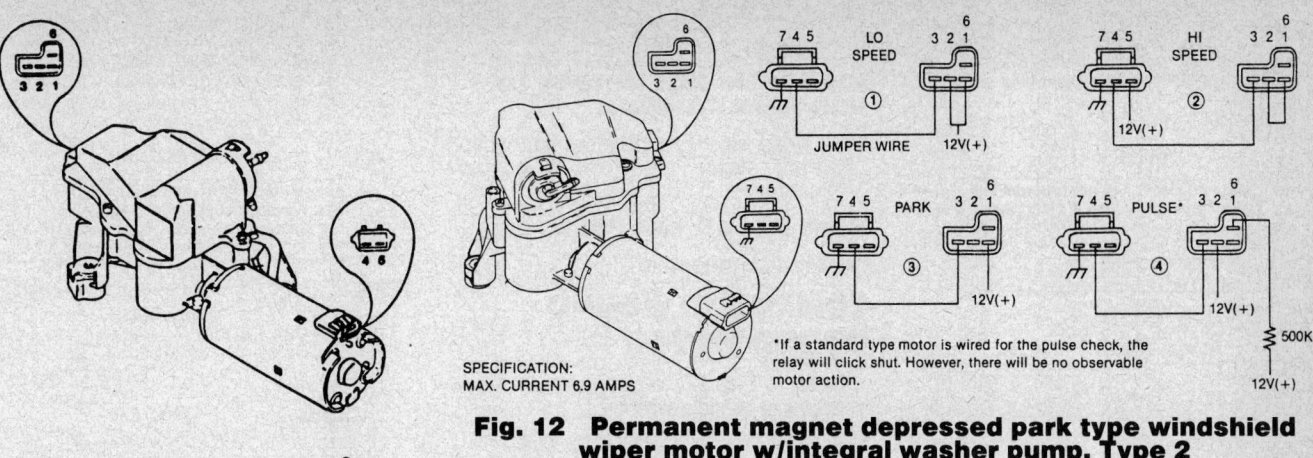

SPECIFICATION:
MAX. CURRENT 6.9 AMPS

*If a standard type motor is wired for the pulse check, the relay will click shut. However, there will be no observable motor action.

Fig. 12   Permanent magnet depressed park type windshield wiper motor w/integral washer pump. Type 2

LOW SPEED
12V(+)

HI SPEED
12V(+)

PARK
12V(+)

PULSE
500K
12V(+)

Fig. 11   Permanent magnet depressed park type windshield wiper motor w/integral washer pump. Type 1

11 through 14. Depending upon the type control switch used and whether an optional control board is included in the motor cover, the system can serve as either a standard or pulse type wiper. The timing functions along with the program and demand wash functions are controlled by a printed circuit board permanently attached to the wiper cover.

Standard (Non-Pulse) Wiper Operation

Moving the multi-function lever to low or high speed position completes the respective brush circuit to 12 volt terminal at the multi-function lever and motor runs at that speed.

An instantaneous wipe can be obtained by moving the multi-function lever to mist position. A continuous wipe will be performed if the button is held.

Pulse Wiper Operation

The multi-function lever in the DELAY mode can be turned from a minimum to a maximum position. Turning the control knob from minimum to maximum position varies the amount of time wiper will delay between each wipe. Delay ranges between 0-12 seconds depending on knob position. Minimum delay or 0 seconds between wipes provides equivalent of low speed continuous operation.

Moving the multi-function lever to low or high speed position completes the respective brush circuit to 12 volt terminal at the multi-function lever and motor runs at that speed.

Moving the multi-function lever to pulse mode operates the motor intermittently and delay can be varied by moving switch back and forth in the delay mode.

An instantaneous wipe can be obtained by moving the multi-function lever to mist position. A continuous wipe will be performed if the button is held.

TWO & THREE SPEED MOTOR (SPRINT, METRO)

Standard (Non-Pulse) Wiper Operation

When the wiper switch is on low, battery voltage is applied to the wiper motor through the blue wire. When the wiper switch is in high, battery voltage is applied directly to motor through the blue/red wire to the high speed brushes.

When the wiper switch is turned off, the run/park switch in the wiper motor is still in the Run position. Voltage is still applied to the wiper motor at the low speed brushes through the run/park switch, blue/white and blue wires.

Pulse Wiper Operation

When the wiper switch is in the delay position, a shunt is applied to two of the inputs at the pulse wiper relay, by section A of wiper switch **Fig. 15**, to start the pulse operation. The pulse wiper relay momentarily supplies battery voltage to section C of wiper switch **Fig. 15**, to run the wiper motor. The wiper blades make one sweep and reach park, the park/run switch opens. The wiper blades remain in park until the pulse wiper relay supplies battery voltage to start another sweep. The delay time between sweeps is determined by circuits in the pulse wiper relay.

Troubleshooting

COMPOUND WOUND RECTANGULAR MOTOR

On models with pulse wipers, check system operation with pulse control module removed. If problem is eliminated, pulse control is defective. Refer to **Fig. 16**, to check wiper motor independent of vehicle wiring.

Wiper Inoperative or Intermittent

1. Blown fuse.
2. Open circuit in feed wire (No. 2 terminal on wiper motor).
3. Loose mounting of wiper switch.
4. Open circuit in wire to wiper switch (No. 1 terminal on wiper motor).
5. Defective wiper switch.
6. Broken or damaged gear train.
7. Poor solder connections at terminal board.
8. Poor splice joints at brush plate.
9. Binding or damaged motor brushes.
10. Open circuit in armature or series field.

Motor Will Not Shut Off

1. Grounded wire between motor terminal 1 and wiper switch.
2. Defective motor park switch.
3. Grounded leads between motor terminal board and brush holder.
4. Grounded shunt field.

NOTE: THE FOLLOWING PROCEDURES ASSUME THAT THE TECHNICIAN HAS CHECKED THE FOLLOWING:
1. CONTINUITY OF ALL HARNESS WIRES
2. WIPER MOTOR TO DASH MOUNTING SCREWS TIGHT
3. FUSES

WIPER MOTOR

CHECK FOR MOTOR OPERATION BEFORE REMOVING FROM VEHICLE. DISCONNECT ALL WIRING FROM WIPER AND PERFORM THE FOLLOWING CHECKS IN THIS ORDER:

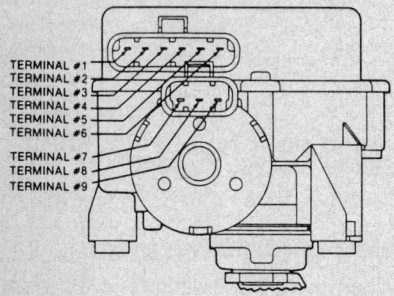

TERMINAL #1
TERMINAL #2
TERMINAL #3
TERMINAL #4
TERMINAL #5
TERMINAL #6
TERMINAL #7
TERMINAL #8
TERMINAL #9

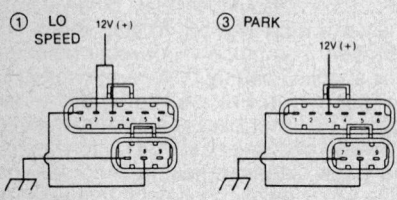

① LO SPEED   12V (+)

③ PARK   12V (+)

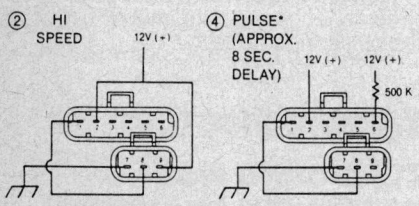

② HI SPEED   12V (+)

④ PULSE* (APPROX. 8 SEC. DELAY)   12V (+)   12V (+)   500 K

IF WIPER MOTOR FUNCTIONS IN ALL MODES, GO TO WIPER/WASHER SWITCH CHECK CHART.

*IF A STANDARD TYPE MOTOR IS WIRED FOR THE PULSE CHECK, THE PARK RELAY WILL CLICK SHUT BUT THERE WILL BE NO OBSERVABLE MOTOR ACTION.

Fig. 13   Permanent magnet depressed park type windshield wiper motor w/remote washer pump. 1988–89 Type 1

Motor Operates At Low Speed Only

1. Defective wiper switch.
2. Grounded wire between motor terminal 3 and wiper switch.
3. Grounded black wire between motor terminal board and shunt field or grounded shunt field.

Motor Runs At High Speed Only

1. Defective wiper switch.
2. Open circuit between motor terminal 3 and wiper switch.
3. Open circuit in black wire between

motor terminal board and shunt field, or open shunt field.

Blades Do Not Return to Full Park Position

1. Loose wiper ground strap connection.
2. Park switch defective or contacts dirty.

High Speed Too Fast

1. Resistor defective.

COMPOUND WOUND ROUND MOTOR

Refer to **Fig. 17**, to operate motor independent of vehicle wiring.

WIPER INOPERATIVE OR INTERMITTENT

1. Open lead wire from wiper terminal No. 1 to wiper switch.
2. Wiper switch not securely mounted.
3. Wiper switch defective.
4. Defective gear box relay.
5. Defective pulse relay or timer, if equipped.
6. Open motor ground.
7. Open series field, armature or circuit breaker.
8. Sticking or damaged motor brushes.
9. Poor connections at gear box relay.
10. Binding relay switch latch arm.

MOTOR WILL NOT SHUT OFF Crank Arm Rotates 360°

1. Grounded wire between terminal 1 on gear box relay and wiper switch.
2. Corroded terminals at switch or motor.
3. Defective wiper switch.
4. Grounded gear box relay coil.
5. Gear box relay latch arm binding, or spring missing.
6. Defective washer pump relay or override switch.
7. Loose or defective pulse timer, if equipped.

Crank Arm Moves In & Out of Park Position

1. Open wire between gear box relay terminal 3 and wiper switch.
2. Defective wiper switch.
3. Defective gear box relay.
4. Drive pawl spring disconnected.
5. Open shunt field.

MOTOR OPERATES AT HIGH SPEED ONLY

1. Open wire between gear box relay terminal 3 and wiper switch.
2. Defective wiper switch.
3. Open shunt field, or open wire between gear box relay and shunt field.

MOTOR OPERATES AT LOW SPEED ONLY (OPERATES PROPERLY IN DELAY & SHUTS OFF PROPERLY)

1. Grounded wire between gear box relay terminal 3 and wiper switch.
2. Defective wiper switch.
3. Grounded wire between shunt field and gear box relay, or grounded shunt field.
4. Shorted armature.

NOTE: THE FOLLOWING PROCEDURES ASSUME THAT THE TECHNICIAN HAS CHECKED THE FOLLOWING:
1. CONTINUITY OF ALL HARNESS WIRES
2. WIPER MOTOR TO DASH MOUNTING SCREWS TIGHT
3. FUSES

WIPER MOTOR

CHECK FOR MOTOR OPERATION BEFORE REMOVING FROM VEHICLE. DISCONNECT ALL WIRING FROM WIPER AND PERFORM THE FOLLOWING CHECKS IN THIS ORDER:

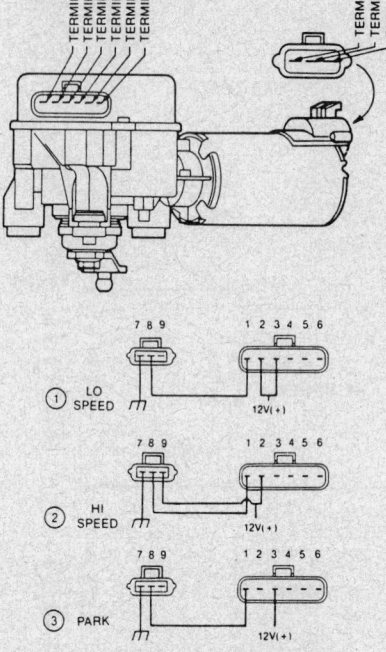

TERMINAL #1
TERMINAL #2
TERMINAL #3
TERMINAL #4
TERMINAL #5
TERMINAL #6
TERMINAL #7
TERMINAL #8
TERMINAL #9

① LO SPEED   7 8 9   1 2 3 4 5 6   12V (+)

② HI SPEED   7 8 9   1 2 3 4 5 6   12V (+)

③ PARK   7 8 9   1 2 3 4 5 6   12V (+)

④ PULSE*   7 8 9   1 2 3 4 5 6   500 K   12V (+)   12V (+)

IF WIPER MOTOR FUNCTIONS IN ALL MODES, GO TO WIPER/WASHER SWITCH CHECK CHART.

*IF A STANDARD TYPE MOTOR IS WIRED FOR THE PULSE CHECK, THE PARK RELAY WILL CLICK SHUT BUT THERE WILL BE NO OBSERVABLE MOTOR ACTION.

Fig. 14   Permanent magnet depressed park type windshield wiper motor w/remote washer pump. Type 2

MOTOR INOPERATIVE IN DELAY POSITION

1. Defective pulse timer.
2. Defective wiper switch.
3. Open between wiper switch and pulse timer.

WIPERS RUN CONTINUOUSLY IN DELAY POSITION

1. Grounded wire between pulse timer and wiper switch.
2. Defective wiper switch.
3. Defective pulse timer.
4. Defective pulse relay.
5. Fused holding switch contacts, or broken cam on washer pump.

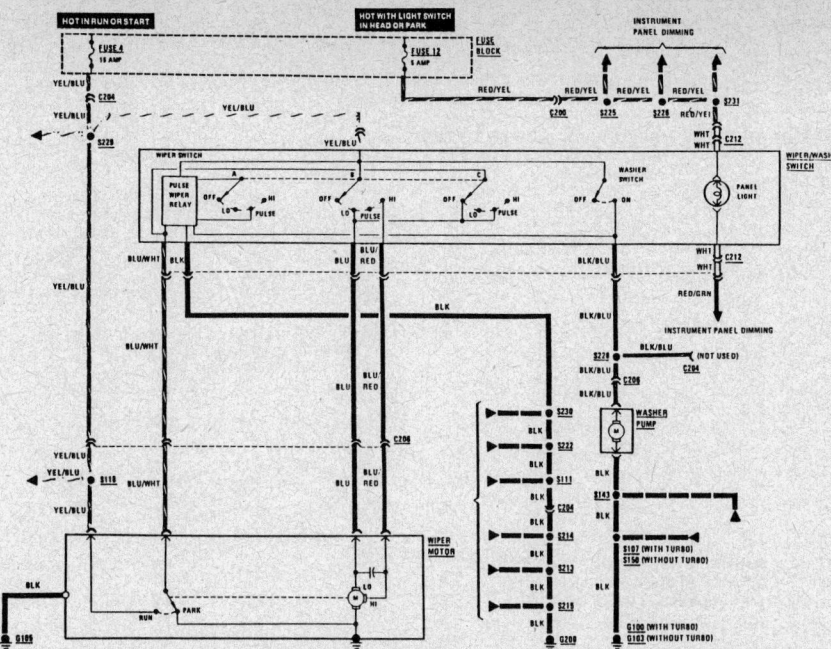

Fig. 15 Wiring Diagram, w/pulse (Sprint & Metro)

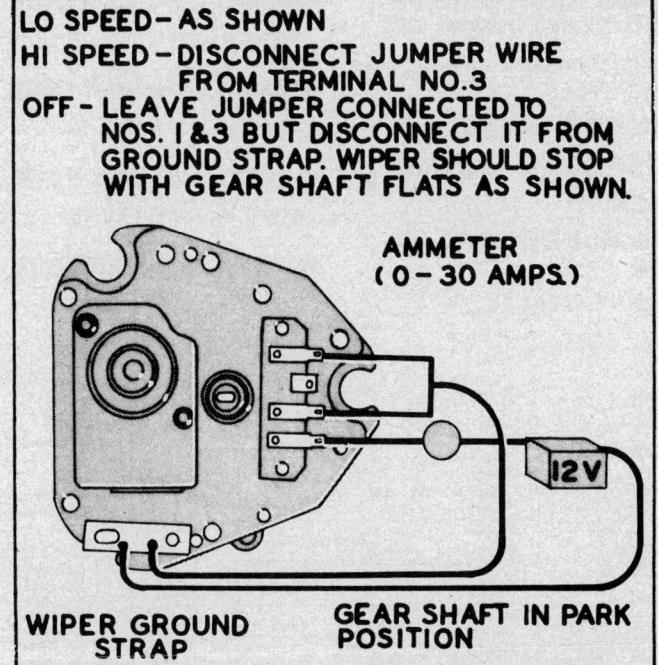

LO SPEED – AS SHOWN
HI SPEED – DISCONNECT JUMPER WIRE
FROM TERMINAL NO. 3
OFF – LEAVE JUMPER CONNECTED TO
NOS. 1 & 3 BUT DISCONNECT IT FROM
GROUND STRAP. WIPER SHOULD STOP
WITH GEAR SHAFT FLATS AS SHOWN.

AMMETER
(0 – 30 AMPS.)

12V

WIPER GROUND
STRAP

GEAR SHAFT IN PARK
POSITION

Fig. 16 Connections to operate compound wound rectangular wiper motor independent of vehicle wiring

HI SPEED IN MED POSITION (CADILLAC ONLY)

1. Open medium speed resistor.

WIPER STOPS AT RANDOM (CRANK ARM STOPS ROTATING IMMEDIATELY AND DOES NOT RETURN TO FULL PARK POSITION)

1. Relay switch contacts dirty or broken.

INTERMITTENT OPERATION

1. Defective circuit breaker (weak).
2. Circuit breaker tripping because of shorted armature and/or fields causing motor to draw excessive current.

NO APPARENT TROUBLE ON BENCH TEST BUT FAILS OCCASIONALLY ON CAR

1. Armature endplay tight.

---

2. Gear assembly endplay tight.
3. Loose solder or weld joints.

PERMANENT MAGNET MOTOR

On models with pulse wipers, disconnect pulse control module and connect motor and switch harness electrical connectors together, then recheck system. If problem is corrected, module is defective. Refer to **Figs. 9 through 14** to operate motor independent of vehicle wiring.

NON DEPRESSED PARK
Motor Inoperative

1. Open in feed circuit to wiper switch.
2. Binding or damaged motor brushes or defective armature.
3. Poor ground at motor.
4. Open connector between motor and switch.

Motor Will Not Shut Off

1. Defective wiper switch.
2. Binding park switch actuator or defective park switch.

Wipers Do Not Return To Park Position

1. Open in feed circuit to park switch terminal 4.
2. Defective wiper switch.
3. Binding park switch actuator or defective park switch.

Wipers Run Continuously In Delay Position

1. Defective pulse module.
2. Defective motor park switch.
3. Defective wiper switch.

DEPRESSED PARK MOTOR
Wiper System Inoperative

1. Defective cover board.
2. Defective motor.

Wiper Won't Shut Off

1. Defective cover board.
2. Defective park switch.

Blades Cycle In & Out of Park

1. Defective park switch.

Wiper Has High Speed Only & Won't Delay

1. Defective cover board.
2. Defective motor.
3. Defective Park switch.

Wiper Inoperative In Delay

1. Defective cover board.

Wiper Has Low Speed Only

1. Defective motor.

Wiper Intermittent

1. Defective motor.
2. Gear train damaged.

TWO SPEED MOTOR (1988 NOVA & 1989–90 PRIZM)

Wipers Do Not Operate Or Return To Parked Position

1. TURN fuse blown.
2. Faulty wiper motor.
3. Faulty wiper switch.
4. Faulty wiring or ground.

Wipers Do Not Operate In "INT" Position

1. Faulty wiper switch.
2. Faulty wiper motor.
3. Faulty wiring or ground.

TWO SPEED MOTOR (SPECTRUM)

Poor Wiping Action

1. Defective blade(s).
2. Distorted wiper link, or worn joint.

Sluggish Wiping Action

1. Poor ground or connections.
2. Resistance increased due to twisting of link. Check operation of link motor disconnected.
3. Defective motor.

Wiper Circuit Inoperative

1. Blown fuse.
2. Poorly connected or broken wiring.
3. Defective switch.
4. Defective motor.

Motor Continues To Run With Switch Off

1. Cam plate insulator defective. Motor continues to operate when switch leads are disconnected at connector.
2. Defective switch.

LO SPEED – AS SHOWN
(TERMINALS 1 AND 3 CONNECTED TO GROUND)

HI SPEED – DISCONNECT JUMPER FROM TERMINAL 3
(TERMINAL 1 REMAINS CONNECTED TO GROUND)

PARK OR SHUT OFF – RECONNECT JUMPER TO TERMINAL 3 BUT DISCONNECT FROM TERMINAL 1

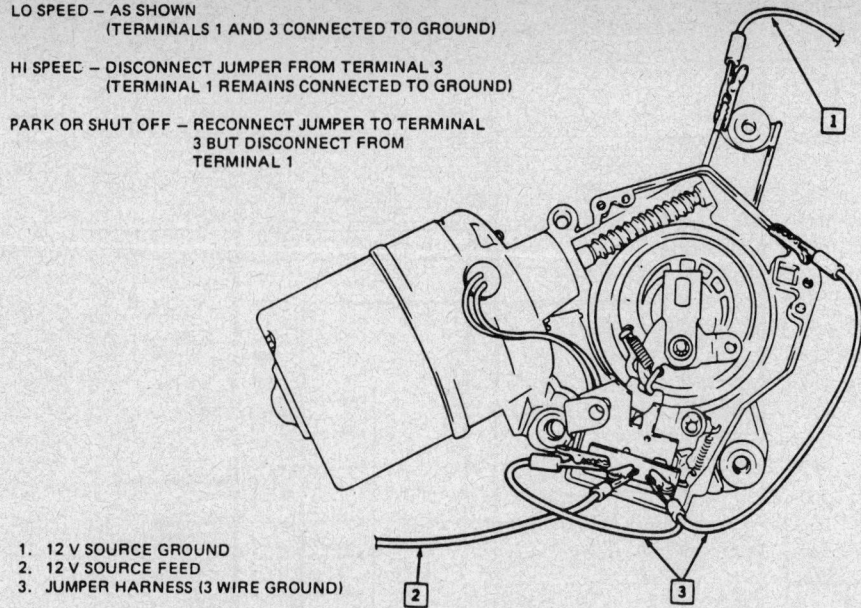

1. 12 V SOURCE GROUND
2. 12 V SOURCE FEED
3. JUMPER HARNESS (3 WIRE GROUND)

Fig. 17   Connections to operate compound wound round wiper motor independent of vehicle wiring

Motor Stops Immediately When Switch Is Turned Off

1. Self parking points defective.
2. Defective switch.

TWO & THREE SPEED MOTOR (SPRINT, METRO)

LESS PULSE

Wipers Do Not Operate In Any Mode

Refer to test A & C **Fig. 18**.

Wipers Operate Only In Low

Refer to test C **Fig. 18**.

Wipers Operate Only In High

Refer to test C **Fig. 18**.

Wipers Will Not Park

Refer to test B **Fig. 18**.

Wipers Will Not Shut Off

Refer to test C **Fig. 18**.

A: WIPER/WASHER SWITCH BATTERY VOLTAGE TEST

Measure: VOLTAGE
At: WIPER/WASHER SWITCH HARNESS CONNECTOR (Disconnected)
Condition:
• Ignition Switch: RUN

Measure Between	Correct Voltage	For Diagnosis
YEL/BLU & Ground	Battery	See 1

• If voltage is correct, do Test C.
1. Check Fuse 4 and YEL/BLU wire for an open.

B: WIPER/WASHER SWITCH RESISTANCE TEST

Measure: RESISTANCE
At: HARNESS CONNECTOR C206 (Disconnected)
Conditions:
• Ignition Switch: OFF
• Wiper Switch: OFF

Measure Between	Correct Resistance	For Diagnosis
BLU/WHT & BLU	Less than 0.5 ohms	See 1

• If resistance is correct, remove Wiper Motor for repair.

1. Replace Wiper/Washer Switch.

C: WIPER MOTOR INPUT VOLTAGE TEST

Measure: VOLTAGE
At: WIPER MOTOR HARNESS CONNECTOR (Disconnected)
Conditions:
• Ignition Switch: RUN
• Wiper Switch: LO

Measure Between	Correct Voltage	For Diagnosis
BLU & Ground	Battery	See 1

• Wiper Switch: HI

BLU/RED & Ground	Battery	See 2

• Wiper Switch: OFF, LO & HI

YEL/BLU & Ground	Battery	See 3

• If all voltages are correct, remove the Wiper Motor for repair.

1. Check BLU wire for an open. If wire is OK, replace the Wiper/Washer Switch.
2. Check BLU/RED wire for an open. If wire is OK, replace the Wiper/Washer Switch.
3. Check YEL/BLU wire for an open. If wire is OK, check Fuse 4.

A: WIPER/WASHER SWITCH BATTERY VOLTAGE TEST

Measure: VOLTAGE
At: WIPER/WASHER SWITCH CONNECTOR (Disconnected)
Conditions:
• Ignition Switch: RUN
• Light Switch: PARK

Measure Between	Correct Voltage	For Diagnosis
YEL/BLU & BLK	Battery	See 1
YEL/BLU & BLK	Battery	See 2
RED/YEL & Ground	Battery	See 3
RED/YEL & RED/GRN	Battery	See 4

• If voltages are correct but wipers do not operate, do Test B. If Panel Light does not light, check for an open RED/YEL or RED/GRN wire to the Panel Light.

1. Check Fuse 4 and YEL/BLU wire for an open or short to ground.
2. Check the BLK wire for an open.
3. Check the RED/YEL wire for an open or short to ground.
4. Check RED/GRN wire for an open.

B: WIPER/WASHER SWITCH CONTINUITY TEST

Measure: RESISTANCE
At: WIPER MOTOR CONNECTOR (Disconnected)
Conditions:
• Ignition Switch: OFF
• Negative Battery Terminal: DISCONNECTED
• Wiper Switch: OFF & PULSE

Measure Between	Correct Resistance	For Diagnosis
BLU/WHT & BLU	Less than 0.5 ohm	See 1

• Wiper Switch: LO

YEL/BLU & BLU	Less than 0.5 ohm	See 2

• Wiper Switch: HI

YEL/BLU & BLU/RED	Less than 0.5 ohm	See 3

• If resistances are correct but Wiper Motor does not operate normally, remove Wiper Motor for repair.

1. Check the BLU/WHT and BLU wires for an open. If wires are good, replace the Wiper/Washer Switch.
2. Check the YEL/BLU wire for an open. If wire is good, replace the Wiper/Washer Switch.
3. Check the BLU/RED wire for an open. If wire is good, replace the Wiper/Washer Switch.

Fig. 18   Troubleshooting procedures (less pulse)

Fig. 19   Troubleshooting procedures (pulse)

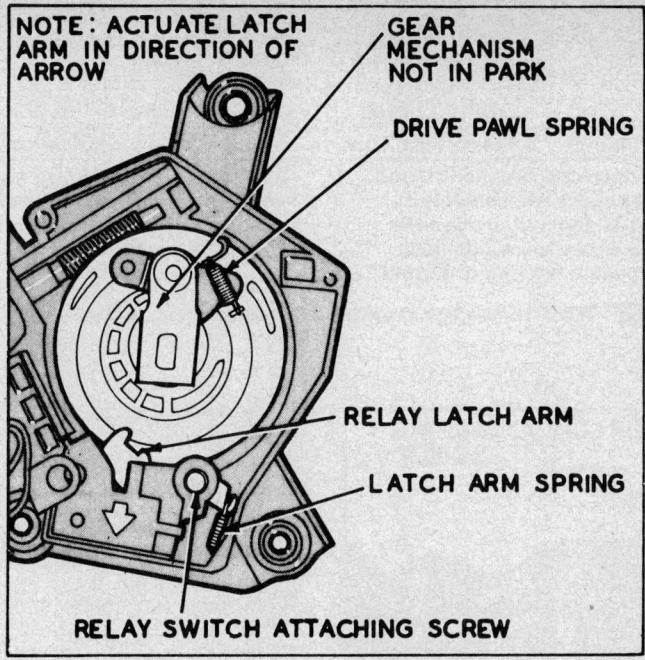

NOTE: ACTUATE LATCH ARM IN DIRECTION OF ARROW

GEAR MECHANISM NOT IN PARK

DRIVE PAWL SPRING

RELAY LATCH ARM

LATCH ARM SPRING

RELAY SWITCH ATTACHING SCREW

Fig. 20 Gear box relay & drive gear assembly inspection

PULSE

Wipers Do Not Operate In Any Mode

Refer to test A & B **Fig. 19.**

Wipers Operate Only In Low

Refer to test B **Fig. 19.**

Wipers Operate Only In High

Refer to test B **Fig. 19.**

Wipers Will Not Park

Refer to test B **Fig. 19.**

Pulse (Delay) Mode Does Not Operate

1. Check black wire to wiper/washer switch for open, if satisfactory replace wiper/washer switch.

Diagnosis & Testing

COMPOUND WOUND RECTANGULAR MOTOR

On models with pulse wipers, disconnect electrical connectors to pulse control module and connect switch and motor harnesses together. If problem is corrected, pulse control is defective.
1. Inspect wiring harness for breaks, loose or improper connections, and repair as needed.
2. Ensure motor and switch are securely mounted and properly grounded, and repair as needed.
3. Turn ignition on and operate wipers in all switch positions, then place wiper switch in off position with wipers at top of their travel.

4. If motor fails to operate, disconnect electrical connector to motor and check for battery voltage at terminal 2 in connector, **Fig. 2,** using a test lamp.
5. If lamp fails to light, check and repair feed circuit.
6. If lamp lights, operate motor independent of vehicle wiring as shown in **Fig. 17.** If motor fails to operate, repeat test with linkage disconnected.
7. If motor still fails to operate, repair or replace as needed. If motor operates, repair linkage.
8. If motor operates properly in step 6, check continuity of wiring between motor and switch. If wiring is satisfactory, replace switch.
9. If motor will not shut off, or if blades do not park when switch is placed in off position, check for defective park switch or open motor ground and repair as needed.
10. If motor operates properly in all other positions, but will not operate in delay mode, proceed as follows:
    a. Check feed circuit to pulse control and repair as needed.
    b. Check continuity of red and black wires between pulse control and wiper switch, and repair as needed.
    c. If feed circuit and wiring are satisfactory, replace pulse control.

COMPOUND WOUND ROUND MOTOR

On models with pulse wipers, refer to "Multiplex Wiper System" for testing procedures.

WIPER INOPERATIVE

1. Remove washer pump to gain access

to relay switch and terminal board assembly.
2. Connect 12 volt source to wiper, feed side to center terminal, ground side to gear housing, **Fig. 17.** Do not connect jumper to terminal 1 and 3.
3. To determine if relay coil is open, connect test lamp to wiper terminal No. 1. Test lamp should light.
4. Test relay switch as follows:
    a. If gear mechanism is in full park position insert a small screwdriver into the switch slot (between the drive pawl and the relay latch arm) and push relay latch arm downward and toward the relay coil in direction of the arrow, **Fig. 7.** Next, remove washer pump assembly and probe (penetrate insulation) black lead with pink tracer with 12 volt tester.
    b. If test lamp lights but motor doesn't run, proceed to step 5.
    c. If test lamp doesn't light, relay switch and terminal board are defective.
5. Disassemble motor section and check the following:
    a. Hung brush.
    b. Solder connections at brush holders.
    c. Splice joints at field coil connections to leads.
    d. Open armature.
    e. Circuit breaker ground connection on field lamination.
    f. Visually inspect the circuit breaker for dirty or burned contacts or solder connections.

WIPER WILL NOT SHUT OFF

Crank Arm Rotates 360 Degrees

1. Observe if relay latch arm spring is connected properly, **Fig. 20.**
2. Manually operate latch arm to check it for possible binding condition.
3. If items in 1 and 2 check out, connect power source to wiper and connect jumper wire from terminal No. 3 to wiper housing. DO NOT make any connections from terminal No. 1. Wiper motor should start to run as soon as connections are made. If this happens and wiper motor continues to run, the coil is internally grounded and the relay switch and terminal board assembly should be replaced.

Wiper Recycles

Crank arm oscillates in a somewhat horizontal plane and is accompanied by a loud knock with each revolution of the gear.
1. Check that drive pawl and relay latch arm springs are properly connected, **Fig. 20.**
2. Check wiper for LO speed operation, **Fig. 17.** If wiper has HI speed only, check the following items:
    a. Solder joint at No. 3 wiper terminal.
    b. Splice joint-field coil crossover splice.
    c. Splice joint-black lead to field coil.
3. Check relay switch and terminal board as follows:

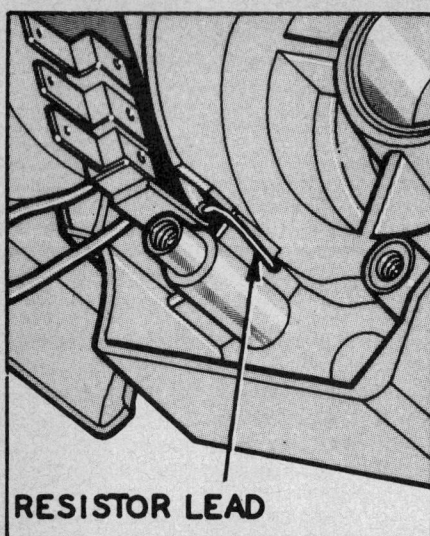

RESISTOR LEAD

Fig. 21 Gear box relay terminal board resistor

Current Draw (Amps)							
		No Load		On Car Dry W/S ①			Shunt Field Resistance
Car	Year	Low	High	Low	High	Stall	
All	1988-90	4.0 Max.	3.5 Max.	—	—	12 Max.	—

①—Current draw specifications listed for on-car check are subject to fluctuations depending upon the condition of blades, windshield, battery, engine running or turned off. The figures shown are only a guide and reflect the average current draw throughout a complete wiping stroke.

Fig. 22 Round wiper motor current draw specifications

a. Remove washer pump assembly to get at black with pink stripe wire. Ground 12 volt test lamp to wiper housing and probe (penetrate insulation) black with pink stripe wire with 12 volt tester.

b. Connect positive side of power source to terminal No. 2 and negative side to motor case. Install jumper wire from terminal No. 1 to motor case. Observe if test light goes out once for each revolution of gear or if light glows steadily. If light glows steadily, relay switch contacts are not opening and switch is defective. If light goes out each time drive pawl moves into relay switch slot, relay switch is functioning correctly.

WIPER HAS ONE SPEED, LO

1. Check for grounded condition in the internal black lead that connects to wiper terminal No. 3.
2. Disassemble motor section of wiper and check for grounded shunt field coil.

WIPER HAS EXCESSIVE SPEED IN HI BUT LO SPEED IS NORMAL

1. Check for open 20 ohm resistor and the resistor ground connection, **Fig. 21**.

INTERMITTENT OPERATION

1. Check solder connections at relay switch and terminal board.
2. Connect wiper to operate in LO speed, **Fig. 17**. Connect ammeter (range 0-30 amps) in feed wire circuit to wiper and observe current draw. Allow motor to run until it becomes hot; see Specification Chart, **Fig. 22**.
   a. If current draw is normal and wiper cycles on and off, a weak circuit breaker is indicated. Replace brush plate assembly.

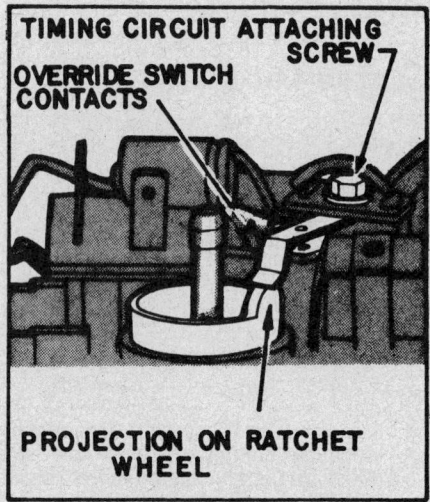

TIMING CIRCUIT ATTACHING SCREW
OVERRIDE SWITCH CONTACTS
PROJECTION ON RATCHET WHEEL

Fig. 23 Ratchet wheel and override switch assembly

b. If current draw exceeds specification, proceed to Steps 3, 4 and 5.
3. Adjust armature end play and recheck current draw.
4. Adjust gear assembly end play and recheck current draw.
5. If adjustments in steps 3 and 4 fail to correct excessive current draw condition, disassemble motor section of wiper and check armature on growler for shorted or grounded condition.

MULTIPLEX WIPER SYSTEM

WIPERS INOPERATIVE

1. Turn ignition on and, with wiper switch off, ground 12 volt test lamp and touch probe to wiper terminal No. 2, **Fig. 5.**.
2. If lamp fails to light, proceed as follows:
   a. Check wiper system fuse and replace if needed.
   b. If fuse blows again, check for short in wire to terminal Nos. 2 and 5, or the motor for high amperage draw.
   c. If fuse is satisfactory, repair open in feed circuit between fuse block and wiper motor.
3. If lamp lights in step 1, touch probe to

wiper terminal No. 1.
4. If wipers run, check for open circuit in wire between terminal No. 1 and wiper switch and, if wire is satisfactory, check wiper switch.
5. If wipers do not run, Place wiper switch in LO position and touch probe to terminal No. 6.
6. If wipers run, check for open circuit in wire between terminal No. 6 and wiper switch and, if wire is satisfactory, check wiper switch.
7. If wipers do not run, remove washer pump cover and reattach wiring to wiper.
8. With wiper in LO position, ground 12 volt test lamp and touch probe to terminal of red wire at pulse relay.
9. If lamp does not illuminate, proceed as follows:
   a. Check connection to No. 1 wiper terminal.
   b. Check for open in red wire.
   c. Replace park relay.
10. If lamp illuminates, touch probe to terminal of orange wire at pulse relay.
11. If wipers run, replace timing circuit board assembly.
12. If wipers do not run, touch probe to terminal of pink/black stripe wire at pulse relay.
13. If lamp illuminates, repair wiper motor.
14. If lamp does not illuminate, replace pulse relay.

WIPERS WILL NOT SHUT OFF, BLADES OPERATE IN NORMAL WIPE PATTERN

1. Operate wipers with switch in delay position.
2. If wipers operate properly in delay position, proceed as follows:
   a. Place wiper switch in off position, disconnect electrical connector to gear box relay, and connect test lamp between terminals 1 and 2 in connector, **Fig. 5**.
   b. If lamp lights, check for grounded wire between motor and switch or defective switch, and repair as needed.
   c. If lamp does not light, remove washer pump and inspect park relay spring, **Fig. 20**. If spring is properly installed, replace park relay.
3. If wipers do not operate properly in de-

lay position, proceed as follows:

a. Place wiper switch in off position, then turn ignition off and on.

b. If wipers park properly, check condition and adjustment of holding switch, and repair as needed.

c. If holding switch is satisfactory, replace pulse timer assembly.

d. If wipers do not shut off, inspect override switch contacts, **Fig. 23.**

e. If switch contacts are held open by ratchet wheel, check for grounded blue wire and repair as needed.

f. If override switch contacts are not held open, check for loose or defective pulse timer or improperly adjusted override switch.

MOTOR OPERATES AT LOW SPEED ONLY (OPERATES PROPERLY IN DELAY & PARKS PROPERLY)

1. With ignition on and wiper switch in high position, disconnect electrical connector to gear box relay, **Fig. 5,** and connect test lamp between terminals 2 and 3 in connector.

2. If lamp does not illuminate, repair wiper motor. Check for ground in shunt field.

3. If lamp illuminates, check for grounded wire between No. 3 wiper terminal and the wiper switch and, if satisfactory, check for defective wiper switch.

MOTOR OPERATES AT HIGH SPEED ONLY (WILL NOT DELAY BETWEEN WIPES)

1. Check for proper terminal contact at wiper motor connector terminal No. 3 and, if satisfactory, connect jumper wire from terminal No. 3 to ground, with wiring still connected to wiper motor.

2. If condition is still present, remove motor and check for open in shunt field.

3. If wiper has low speed and shuts off satisfactorily, check for open in lead between terminal No. 3 and wiper switch and, if satisfactory, check for defective wiper switch.

BLADES CYCLE IN & OUT OF PARK POSITION WHEN WIPER IS SHUT OFF

1. If wiper has both low and high speed, replace park relay.

2. If wiper has high speed only, check for proper terminal contact at wiper motor connector terminal No. 3.

3. If contact is satisfactory, with wiring still connected to wiper motor, connect a jumper wire from No. 3 terminal to ground.

4. If condition is still present, remove motor and check for open in shunt field.

5. If wiper has low speed and shuts off satisfactorily, check for open in lead between terminal No. 3 and wiper switch and, if satisfactory, check for defective wiper switch.

MOTOR INOPERATIVE IN DELAY MODE (WIPERS FUNCTION IN LOW OR HIGH SPEED)

1. Disconnect wire from No. 6 terminal and, with wiper switch in mid-delay, connect one lead of ohmmeter to to wire from terminal No. 6 and other lead to ground and set ohmmeter to megaohm scale.

2. If there is no resistance shown, replace wiper switch.

3. If there is resistance shown, replace timing circuit assembly.

WIPERS RUN CONTINUOUSLY IN DELAY MODE (WILL NOT DELAY BETWEEN WIPES)

1. With ignition switch on, operate wipers in low, medium and high speeds and check whether wipers shut off properly.

2. If wiper has high speed only, refer to "Motor Operates At High Speed Only (Will Not Delay Between Wipes)."

3. If wipers will not shut off, refer to "Wipers Will Not Shut Off, Blades Operate In Normal Wipe Pattern."

4. If wipers operate properly, but do not delay between wipes, ensure wiper switch is adjusted to mid-delay position and wipers are operating, then disconnect lead from terminal No. 6.

5. If wipers stop, check for grounded circuit between terminal No. 6 and wiper switch and, if satisfactory, replace wiper switch.

6. If wipers continue to run, remove washer pump cover and reconnect all wiring to wiper motor.

7. With wipers running continuously in delay mode, disconnect lead to timing circuit from pulse relay.

8. If wipers stop, replace timing circuit assembly.

9. If wipers continue to operate, replace pulse relay.

INTERMITTENT OPERATION—BLADES STOP RANDOMLY DURING OPERATION

1. Remove wiper system fuse and connect ammeter across fuse terminals.

2. Operate wipers at low speed while observing current draw on meter. **Readings will fluctuate.**

3. If lowest reading is 5-6.5 amps, replace circuit breaker and brush plate assembly.

4. If lowest reading exceeds 6.5 amps, replace wiper blades and repeat test.

5. If lowest reading still exceeds 6.5 amps, disconnect linkage from motor and repeat test.

6. If current draw is less than 6.5 amps, repair binding linkage. If current draw exceeds 6.5 amps, repair or replace motor.

PERMANENT MAGNET MOTOR

On models with pulse wipers, disconnect electrical connectors to pulse module and connect switch and motor harnesses together. If problem is corrected, pulse module is defective.

NON-DEPRESSED PARK Windshield Wipers Inoperative

1. Rotate wiper switch to high speed position, then connect test lamp between motor terminal No. 1 and ground, **Fig. 10.**

2. If lamp does not light, check fuse and replace if necessary. If fuse is satisfactory, check for open circuit in feed wire between motor and fuse block.

3. If fuse is blown, check for short circuit in motor or wiring to control switch.

4. If lamp lights, rotate wiper switch to low position and connect jumper wire between motor and ground.

5. If motor operates, check ground circuit and repair as necessary. If motor does not operate, repair or replace motor as necessary.

Motor Operates But Wiper Blades Do Not

1. Check to ensure wiper linkage is not binding and that linkage is connected to crank arm.

2. If linkage is satisfactory, motor gear mechanism is defective. Repair or replace motor as necessary.

Wiper Blades Stop At Random Position On Windshield

1. Remove wiper fuse, then connect ammeter across fuse block terminals. Operate wipers on dry windshield.

2. Ammeter reading will fluctuate. If reading remains below 5 amps, replace brush holder.

3. If reading is greater than 5 amps, disconnect wiper linkage at crank arm and perform test over. If reading is now less than 5 amps, check for binding linkage and replace wiper blades.

4. If lowest reading still exceeds 5 amps, repair or replace motor.

Motor Inoperative At Low Or High Speed

1. Disconnect electrical connector to wiper motor.

2. If motor operates at high speed, connect battery voltage to low speed terminal 2, **Fig. 10.** If motor operates at low speed, connect battery voltage to high speed terminal 1, **Fig. 10.**

3. If motor operates at affected speed, check continuity of wiring between motor and switch. If wiring is satisfactory, switch is defective.

4. If motor fails to operate in affected speed, repair or replace motor.

Motor Operates At One Speed In Both High & Low Switch Positions

1. Disconnect electrical connector to wiper motor and alternately connect battery voltage to motor low and high speed terminals, **Fig. 10.**

2. If motor runs at both low and high speeds, check continuity of wiring between motor and wiper switch. If wiring is satisfactory, wiper switch is defective.

3. If motor operates at one speed in both

test positions, check for short between high and low speed motor brushes and repair as needed.

Motor Inoperative In Delay Mode

1. Disconnect wiper switch electrical connector at pulse control module and connect ohmmeter between brown and dark green wire terminals in connector.
2. Meter readings should be approximately 50 ohms with switch in minimum delay position to 500,000 ohms with switch in maximum delay position.
3. If readings are as specified, pulse control module is defective. If readings are not as specified, wiper switch is defective.

Motor Will Not Shut Off

1. Disconnect electrical connector to wiper motor.
2. Connect jumper wire between motor terminals 2 and 3, and apply battery voltage to terminal 4, **Fig. 10.**
3. If motor runs to park position and stops, control switch is defective.
4. If motor does not park properly, check for defective park switch, brush holder or park switch actuator.

Wipers Stop But Do Not Return To Park

1. Rotate wiper switch to off position, disconnect wiper motor electrical connector and connect jumper wire between motor terminals 2 and 3. Connect 12 volt power source to terminal 4, **Fig. 10.**
2. If wipers do not return to park position, check park switch actuator and brush holder inside motor and repair or replace as necessary.
3. If wipers return to park position, connect wiper motor electrical connector and check current between terminals 2 and 3 using test lamp.
4. If lamp lights, check for open circuit in white wire between terminal 4 and fuse block. If lamp does not light, check for open circuit in orange wire between terminal 3 and control switch.
5. If wiring has continuity, replace control switch.

Wipers Park Above Normal Position

1. Rotate wiper switch to off position, disconnect wiper motor electrical connector and check continuity between motor terminal 3 and ground using test lamp.
2. If lamp lights, check crank arm and linkage for proper installation. If lamp does not light repair or replace motor as necessary.

DEPRESSED PARK MOTOR W/INTEGRAL WASHER PUMP

Wiper Motor Inoperative

1. Turn ignition switch on and wiper switch off and connect test lamp lead to ground on vehicle and backprobe

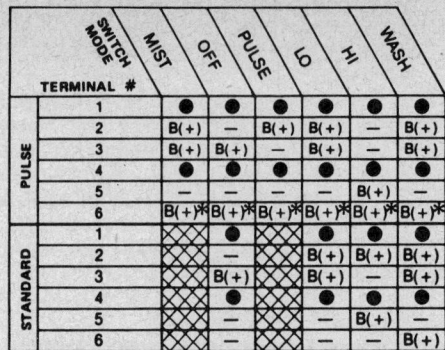

SWITCH MODE	TERMINAL #	MIST	OFF	PULSE	LO	HI	WASH
PULSE	1	●	●	●	●	●	●
	2	B(+)	—	B(+)	B(+)	—	B(+)
	3	B(+)	B(+)	—	B(+)	—	B(+)
	4	●	●	●	●	●	●
	5	—	—	—	—	B(+)	—
	6	B(+)✳	B(+)✳	B(+)✳	B(+)✳	B(+)✳	B(+)✳
STANDARD	1	▨	●	▨	●	●	●
	2	▨	—	▨	B(+)	B(+)	B(+)
	3	▨	B(+)	▨	B(+)	—	B(+)
	4	▨	●	▨	●	●	●
	5	▨	—	▨	—	B(+)	—
	6	▨	—	▨	—	—	B(+)

NOTE

All voltage readings taken with respect to vehicle ground.

● = Continuity between terminals 1 and 4

To use Wiper/Washer Switch Check chart, probe terminals 1 thru 6 with digital voltmeter and wiper switch in various positions.

✳Voltage might be slightly less than source (B+) voltage.

Fig. 24   Wiper switch continuity chart. Models w/permanent magnet, depressed park type motor & integral washer pump, Type 1

terminal 3.
2. If lamp does not illuminate, check fuse.
3. If fuse is satisfactory, locate and repair open circuit from fuse block to wiper motor.
4. If fuse is blown, replace it.
5. If fuse blows again, unplug motor and replace fuse.
6. If fuse blows again, check for grounded condition in wire to terminal No. 3.
7. If fuse does not blow again, check for high amperage of motor. Lowest current draw on dry glass should not exceed 6.5 amps.
8. If lamp illuminated in step 1, connect test lamp lead to ground at wiper motor case and backprobe terminal 3.
9. If lamp does not illuminate, check both motor ground connections.
10. If lamp illuminates, set wiper switch to LO, connect test lamp lead to ground at wiper motor case and backprobe terminal 3.
11. If lamp does not illuminate, repair open from wiper switch to motor.
12. If lamp illuminates, backprobe terminal 1.
13. If lamp does not illuminate, replace park switch.
14. If lamp illuminates, backprobe terminal 4.
15. If lamp does not illuminate, repair open between terminal Nos. 1 and 4 in wiring harness.
16. If lamp illuminates, check armature, circuit breaker, circuit breaker ground and brushes.

Intermittent Wiper Operation In Pulse, LO or HI Modes

1. Remove wiper fuse and connect 0-30 amp ammeter between fuse block terminals, set wiper to LO and note lowest current draw while wiper is running on dry glass. (Current draw will fluctuate).
2. If current draw is less than 3.5 amps, proceed as follows:
   a. Check motor grounds.
   b. Check brush plate assembly for restricted brush to commutator contact.
   c. Check circuit breaker for intermittent open.
   d. Check armature for open circuit.

3. If current draw exceeds 6.5 amps, replace wiper blade elements and repeat test.
4. If current draw still exceeds 6.5 amps, disconnect wiper linkage from wiper motor crank arm and repeat test.
5. If current draw is now less than 6.5 amps, repair or replace wiper transmission linkage as necessary.
6. If current draw still exceeds 6.5 amps, replace wiper motor.

Wiper Will Not Park

1. Turn ignition switch on and wiper switch off, connect test lamp lead to ground at wiper motor case and backprobe terminal 2.
2. If lamp illuminates, disconnect 4 terminal connector and probe terminal 2. If lamp remains on, perform wiper switch continuity check. If lamp goes off, replace cover.
3. If lamp does not illuminate, remove wiper cover and reconnect motor without cover, then switch motor from LO to OFF and note whether park switch latch arm is in position to catch drive pawl.
4. If latch arm is not in proper position, replace park switch.
5. If latch arm is in proper position, check if drive pawl is bent.
6. If drive pawl is bent, replace it.
7. If drive pawl is not bent, check shaft endplay. If drive pawl overrides latch, replace shaft assembly.

No Delay Or Continuous In Delay (Wipers Okay In Low Or High Speed)

1. Connect voltmeter between terminal 6 and ground at motor case and vary delay from minimum time to maximum time. Voltage should vary from maximum to minimum.
2. If voltage does not vary, perform wiper switch continuity check.
3. If voltage varies, turn ignition switch on and set wiper switch to minimum delay, then connect test lamp lead to ground at motor case and backprobe terminal 2.
4. If lamp does not illuminate, perform wiper switch continuity check.
5. If lamp illuminates, backprobe terminal No. 1.

SWITCH MODE TERMINAL #		MIST	OFF	PULSE	LO	HI	WASH
PULSE	1	C	C	C	C	C	C
	2	B (+)	—	B (+)	B (+)	—	B (+)
	3	B (+)	B (+)	—	B (+)	—	B (+)
	4	C	C	C	C	C	C
	5	—	—	—	—	B (+)	—
	6	B (+)*	B (+)*	B (+)*	B (+)*	B (+)*	B (+)*
	7	GROUND	GROUND	GROUND	GROUND	GROUND	GROUND
STANDARD	1		C		C	C	C
	2		—		B (+)	B (+)	B (+)
	3		B (+)		B (+)	—	B (+)
	4		C		C	C	C
	5		—		—	B (+)	—
	6		—		—	—	B (+)
	7		GROUND		GROUND	GROUND	GROUND

NOTE

All voltage readings taken with respect to vehicle ground.

C - Continuity between terminals 1 and 4.

To use Wiper-Washer Switch Check Chart, probe terminals 1 thru 7 with digital voltmeter and wiper switch in various positions.

*Voltage might be slightly less than source (B+) voltage.

Fig. 25 Wiper switch continuity chart. Models w/permanent magnet, depressed park type motor & integral washer pump, Type 2

6. If lamp illuminates, replace cover.
7. If lamp does not illuminate, remove cover and check whether park switch pulse terminals are touching pads on circuit board. It they are, replace cover. Otherwise, replace spring contacts.

No LO Mode

1. Set wiper switch to LO, connect test lamp lead to ground at motor case and backprobe terminal 2.
2. If lamp does not illuminate, repair open from wiper switch to motor.
3. If lamp illuminates, backprobe terminal 1.
4. If lamp does not illuminate, replace park switch.
5. If lamp illuminates, backprobe terminal No. 4.
6. If lamp does not illuminate, repair open between terminal Nos. 1 and 4 in wiring harness.
7. If lamp illuminates, check armature, circuit breaker, circuit breaker ground and brushes.

Blades Cycle In & Out Of Park Position When Wiper Is Off

1. Check whether motor operates in LO.
2. If not, refer to (No LO Mode.)
3. If motor operates in LO, replace park switch.

Wiper Switch Continuity Test

1. Disconnect electrical connectors from wiper motor, **Figs. 11 and 12.**
2. Check switch continuity using suitable voltmeter or continuity tester. Continuity should exist at various switch positions between terminals shown in **Figs. 24 and 25** and ground.

DEPRESSED PARK MOTOR W/REMOTE WASHER PUMP
Wiper Motor Inoperative

1. Turn ignition switch on and wiper off, then connect test light lead to ground on vehicle and probe harness terminal No. 3.
2. If light illuminates, proceed as follows:
   a. Connect test light lead to ground at wiper motor case and probe harness terminal No. 3.
   b. If light does not illuminate, check both motor ground connections.
   c. If light illuminates, place wiper switch in LO position, connect test light lead to ground at wiper motor case and probe harness terminal No. 2.
   d. If light does not illuminate, locate and repair open from wiper switch to motor.
   e. If light illuminates, check continuity between terminal Nos. 1 and 8.
   f. If there is no continuity, locate and repair open between terminal Nos. 1 and 8 in wiring harness.
   g. If there is continuity, check armature, circuit breaker, circuit breaker ground and brushes.
3. If light does not illuminate, proceed as follows:
   a. Check fuse.
   b. If fuse is not blown, locate and repair open in circuit from fuse block to wiper motor.
   c. If fuse is blown, replace it.
   d. If fuse blows again, unplug motor and replace fuse.
   e. If fuse blows again, check for grounded condition in wire to terminal No. 3.
   f. If fuse does not blow, check for

high amperage at motor. Lowest current draw on dry glass should not exceed 6.5 amps.

g. Move switch to LO position. If fuse does not blow, repeat step f.
h. If fuse blows, check resistance from terminal No. 2 to ground.
i. If resistance is not 20-25 ohms, replace park switch.

Intermittent Wiper Operation In Pulse, LO Or HI Modes

1. Remove wiper fuse and connect a 0-30 amp ammeter across fuse block terminals, then operate wiper in LO and observe lowest current draw while wiper is running on dry glass. (Current draw will fluctuate).
2. If lowest current draw is less than 3.5 amps, proceed as follows:
   a. Check motor grounds.
   b. Check brush plate assembly for restricted brush to commutator contact.
   c. Check circuit breaker for intermittent open.
   d. Check armature for open circuit.
3. If lowest current draw exceeds 6.5 amps, replace wiper blade elements and repeat test.
4. If lowest current draw still exceeds 6.5 amps, disconnect wiper linkage from wiper motor crank arm and repeat test.
5. If lowest current draw is now less than 6.5 amps, replace or repair wiper transmission (linkage) as necessary.
6. If lowest current draw still exceeds 6.5 amps, replace wiper motor.

Wiper Will Not Park

1. Turn ignition on and wiper off and probe harness terminal No. 2.
2. If light illuminates, refer to wiper switch continuity test.
3. If light does not illuminate, remove wiper cover, reconnect motor without cover, switch motor from LO to OFF and check whether park switch latch arm is in position to catch drive pawl.
4. If arm is not in proper position, replace park switch or, on pulse models, the cover assembly.
5. If arm is in proper position, check whether drive pawl is bent.
6. If drive pawl is bent, replace it. Otherwise, check shaft endplay. If drive pawl overrides latch, replace shaft assembly.

No Delay Or Continuous In Delay (Motor Operates In LO & HI)

1. With voltmeter connected to terminal No. 6 and grounded at motor case, vary delay mode from minimum delay time to maximum delay time. Voltage should vary from maximum to minimum.
2. If voltage does not vary, refer to wiper switch continuity test.
3. If voltage varies, turn ignition switch on and set wiper switch on minimum delay, then connect test light lead to ground at wiper motor case and probe harness terminal No. 2.

SWITCH MODE TERMINAL #	MIST	OFF	PULSE	LO	HI †	WASH
PULSE 1	C	C	C	C	C	C
2	B(+)	—	B(+)	B(+)	—	*B(+)
3	B(+)	B(+)	—	B(+)	—	*B(+)
4	—	—	—	—	—	—
5	—	—	—	—	—	—
6	10-12V	10-12V	10-12V	10-12V	10-12V	B(+)
7	GROUND	GROUND	GROUND	GROUND	GROUND	GROUND
8	C	C	C	C	C	C
9	—	—	—	—	B(+)	—
STANDARD 1		C		C	C	C
2		—		B(+)	—	*B(+)
3		B(+)		B(+)	—	*B(+)
4		—		—	—	—
5		—		—	—	—
6		—		—	—	B(+)
7		GROUND		GROUND	GROUND	GROUND
8		C		C	C	C
9		—		—	B(+)	—

C = CONTINUITY   † TERMINALS #2 & #3 CONNECTED TOGETHER.   *EXCEPT ON HI.

Fig. 26   Wiper switch continuity chart. 1988 models w/permanent magnet, depressed park type motor & remote washer pump

NO. COLOR OF SIZE TERMINAL POSITION	5 0.5B	2 —	1 0.5LgW	9 0.5LgY	4 0.85LB	6 0.85L	7 0.85RG	8 0.5GR
	E	—	LO	HI	WASH	B	ILLUMI	
OFF								
LO	o—		—o					
HI	o—			—o				
WASHER					o—	—o		

Fig. 27   Wiper switch continuity chart. Spectrum

4. If light does not illuminate, refer to wiper switch continuity test.
5. If light illuminates, remove cover and check whether park switch pulse terminals are touching pads on circuit board. If so, replace cover. Otherwise, replace spring contacts.

No LO Mode

1. With wiper switch on LO, connect test light lead to ground at wiper motor case and probe harness terminal No. 2.
2. If light does not illuminate, locate and repair open from wiper switch to motor.
3. If light illuminates, probe harness terminal No. 3.
4. If light does not illuminate, locate and repair open circuit from switch to motor.
5. If light illuminates, reconnect harness plug to cover and probe harness terminal No. 8.
6. If light illuminates, check armature, circuit breaker, circuit breaker ground and brushes.
7. If light does not illuminate, locate and repair open between terminal Nos. 1 and 8 in wiring harness.
8. If there is continuity between terminal Nos. 1 and 8, check continuity between terminal Nos. 1 and 3 of park switch.
9. If there is no continuity between terminal Nos. 1 and 3, replace park switch.

No HI Mode Or Blades Cycle In & Out Of Park With Switch In HI

1. With dash switch on HI, connect test light lead to ground and probe harness terminal No. 9.
2. If light does not illuminate, locate and repair open in circuit from wiper switch to motor.
3. If light illuminates, check continuity between terminal Nos. 2 and 3.

4. If there is no continuity, refer to wiper switch continuity test.
5. If there is continuity, check for continuity between terminal Nos. 1 and 8.
6. If there is no continuity, locate and repair open between terminal Nos. 1 and 8 in wiring harness.
7. If there is continuity, check armature, circuit breaker, circuit breaker ground and brushes.

Blades Cycle In & Out Of Park Position When Wiper Is Off

1. Check whether motor operates in LO.
2. If not, refer to (No LO Mode).
3. If motor operates in LO, replace park switch. **Problem may also be caused by bent drive pawl or excessive output shaft end play.**

Wiper Switch Continuity Test

1. Disconnect electrical connectors from wiper motor, **Figs. 12 through 14.**
2. Check switch continuity using suitable voltmeter or continuity tester. Continuity should exist at various switch positions between terminals shown in **Fig. 26** and ground.

TWO SPEED MOTOR (1988 NOVA)

Testing Switch

1. Inspect wiper and washer switch continuity, replacing switch as necessary.
2. Turn INT switch to minimum position.
3. Connect positive lead from battery to terminal +B and the negative lead from battery to terminal Ew.
4. Connect positive lead from battery to terminal +1 and negative lead from voltmeter to terminal Ew, then turn wiper switch to INT position and ensure battery voltage is available.

TWO SPEED MOTOR (SPECTRUM)

Testing Switch

Inspect wiper and washer switch for continuity, refer to **Fig. 27**, for switch connections.

TWO & THREE SPEED MOTOR (SPRINT, METRO)

Wiper Switch Test

Inspect wiper and washer switch for continuity, refer to **Figs. 28 & 29**, for switch connections.

WIPER MOTOR TEST

Low Speed Test

1. Using 12 volt battery, connect positive terminal to blue terminal on motor, and negative terminal to black lead wire **Fig. 30**.
2. Motor should rotate at 45 to 55 rpm.

High Speed Test

1. Using 12 volt battery, connect positive terminal to blue/red terminal on motor, and negative terminal to black lead wire **Fig. 30**.
2. Motor should rotate at 68 to 78 rpm.

Park Operation Test

1. Use 12 volt battery, connect positive terminal to yellow/blue terminal on motor, and negative terminal to black lead wire **Fig. 30**.
2. Using a jumper short the blue/white and blue terminals to each other.
3. Check whether motor shaft stops at a given position. **This position must conform to the start position.**
4. Repeat step 2 to confirm that shaft stops at the same position.

Checking Brush and Commutator

1. Check continuity between blue terminal and black lead wire.
2. If continuity is poor, check brush to commutator contact area.
3. If contact area is fouled, use suitable solvent to clean area. **When surface is coarse or burnt, use sandpaper to polish surface smooth.**
4. If necessary, replace brushes. **Replace brushes as a set.**

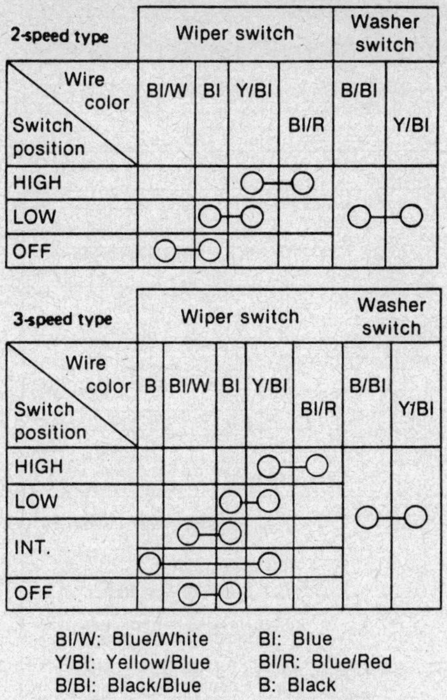

2-speed type	Wiper switch				Washer switch	
Wire color / Switch position	BI/W	BI	Y/BI	BI/R	B/BI	Y/BI
HIGH			◯—◯			
LOW		◯—◯—◯			◯—◯	
OFF	◯—◯					

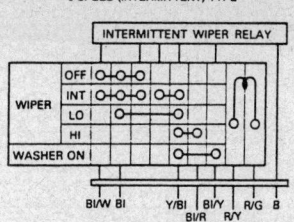

Fig. 29 Wiper switch continuity chart. Metro

3-speed type	Wiper switch					Washer switch	
Wire color / Switch position	B	BI/W	BI	Y/BI	BI/R	B/BI	Y/BI
HIGH				◯—◯			
LOW			◯—◯—◯			◯—◯	
INT.	◯—◯—◯		◯—◯				
OFF		◯—◯					

BI/W: Blue/White BI: Blue
Y/BI: Yellow/Blue BI/R: Blue/Red
B/BI: Black/Blue B: Black

Fig. 28 Wiper switch continuity chart. Sprint

Intermittent Wiper Relay Test

1. Disconnect wiper/washer switch connector.
2. Using 12 volt battery, connect positive terminal to black terminal on connector, and negative terminal to yellow/blue terminal on connector **Fig. 31.**
3. Turn intermittent switch to OFF position, If an operating sound is heard from relay, it is operating properly. If no sound is heard, replace relay.

TWO SPEED MOTOR (STORM)

Refer to **Fig. 32,** for complete system diagnosis.

Wiper Switch Test

Inspect wiper and washer switch for continuity, refer to **Figs. 33 and 34,** for switch connections.

WIPER MOTOR TEST
Low Speed Test

1. Using 12 volt battery, connect positive terminal to "LO" terminal on motor, and negative terminal to wiper motor body **Fig. 35.**
2. Motor should rotate at 45 to 55 rpm.

High Speed Test

1. Using 12 volt battery, connect positive terminal to "HI" terminal on motor, and

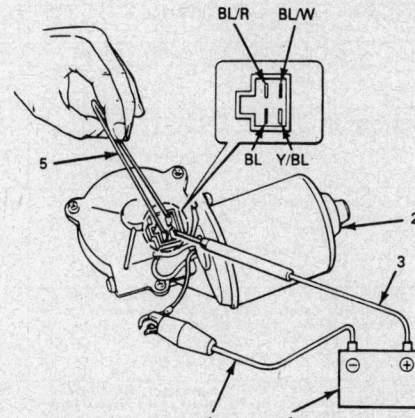

1. BATTERY
2. WIPER MOTOR
3. (+)-YELLOW/BLUE LEAD
4. (−)-BLACK LEAD
5. JUMPER

BL/R : BLUE/RED
BL/W : BLUE/WHITE
BL : BLUE
Y/BL : YELLOW/BLUE

Fig. 30 Connections to operate two and three speed wiper motor independent of vehicle wiring

negative terminal to wiper motor body **Fig. 35.**
2. Motor should rotate at 69 to 83 rpm.

Park Operation Test

1. Use 12 volt battery, connect positive terminal to "Park" terminal on motor, and negative terminal to wiper motor body **Fig. 35.**
2. Operate wiper motor at high speed.
3. Check whether motor shaft stops at a given position. **This position must conform to the start position.**
4. Repeat step 2 to confirm that shaft stops at the same position.

TWO SPEED MOTOR (PRIZM)

Wiper Switch Test

Inspect wiper/washer switch for continuity, refer to **Fig. 36,** for switch connections.

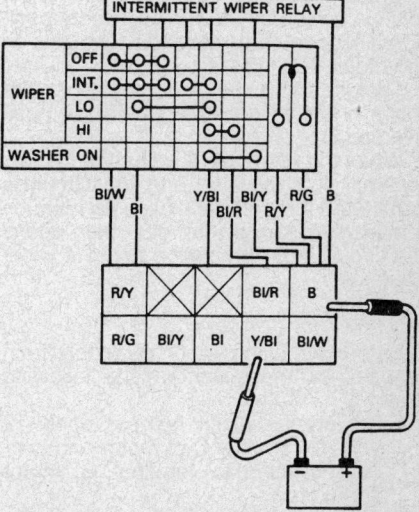

Fig. 31 Intermittent wiper relay test connections. Sprint & Metro

WIPER MOTOR TEST
Low Speed Test

1. Using 12 volt battery, connect positive terminal to terminal 2 on motor, and negative terminal to wiper motor body **Fig. 37.**
2. Motor should rotate at 45 to 55 rpm.

High Speed Test

1. Using 12 volt battery, connect positive terminal to terminal 1 on motor, and negative terminal to wiper motor body **Fig. 38.**
2. Motor should rotate at 69 to 83 rpm.

Park Operation Test

1. Use 12 volt battery, connect positive terminal to terminal 2 on motor, and negative terminal to wiper motor body **Fig. 39.**
2. Operate wiper motor at low speed.
3. Check whether motor shaft stops at a given position. **Time this disconnection so that wipers stop in any position other than their rest position.**
4. Install jumper wire between terminals 2 and 3, **Fig. 40.**

5. Connect battery positive lead to terminal 4.
6. Check that wiper motor stops running at rest position. If wiper motor operation is not as specified, replace motor.

REAR WINDOW WIPER

1988 FIRENZA & SKYHAWK WAGON

Description & Operation

These vehicles use a one speed, 12 volt, DC permanent magnet motor attached to a bracket, **Fig. 41.** The motor drives a linkage that in turn connects to a wiper pivot that provides an oscillating output to the arms and blades.

The wiper system operates only with the ignition switch in Run or Accessory position. There are three electrical terminals on the motor, **Fig. 42.**

Terminals B and C are utilized as the motor is in the Run mode where C is positive and B is ground.

When the wiper switch is turned to OFF, terminal A is positive and the circuit is completed through the closed park switch terminals. A cam on the gear then opens the circuit at Park position and the wiper shuts off.

Diagnosis

Before removing wiper assembly from rear compartment, perform the following tests:

1. Disconnect wiring harness apply 12 volts to terminal C of motor and connect ground to terminal B. Motor should run.
2. To test for proper Park operation, apply 12 volts to terminal A and connect ground to terminal B. The wiper motor should go into Park position and shut off.
3. If results are correct in steps 1 and 2, the problem is in the wiring harness or switch. After checking all wires for continuity and ensuring fuses are satisfactory, check switch by turning ignition switch on and probing connector to dash switch. Results should be as shown, **Fig. 43,** with respect to vehicle ground.

CELEBRITY, CENTURY, CUTLASS CRUISER & 6000 WAGONS

Description & Operation

These vehicles use a one speed, 12 volt, DC permanent magnet motor, **Fig. 44.** The motor drives a gear box which in turn drives a wiper pivot that provides an oscillating output to the arm and blade.

The system operates only with the ignition in Run position, but will park if the ignition is turned off.

There are three electrical terminals on the motor, **Fig. 45.** Terminals A, B and C are used when the motor is in Run mode. A and C are positive and B is ground.

When wiper switch is set to OFF, only motor terminals A and B are used, with A being positive and the circuit being completed through the closed park switch terminals. A cam on the gear then opens at Park position and the wiper shuts off.

The autopark module supplies power to the rear wiper motor to allow the wiper arm to park if the ignition switch is turned off while the wiper is operating.

Diagnosis

Before removing wiper assembly from vehicle, perform the following:

1. Disconnect wiring harness and apply 12 volts to motor terminals A and C and connect ground to terminal B. The motor should run.
2. To test for proper parking, apply 12 volts to terminal A and connect ground to terminal B. The wiper should park and shut off.

SYSTEM DIAGNOSIS

WIPER/WASHER		DIAGNOSTIC CHART A	
	TEST	RESULT	ACTION
A1.	Turn ignition switch to "ON." Press Wash button.	WASHER PUMP operates.	GO TO A2.
		WASHER PUMP does not operate.	GO TO A5.
		WASHER PUMP continues to operate after Wash button has been released.	GO TO A9.
A2.	Press and release "OFF/MIST" button.	Wipers complete 1 full sweep.	GO TO A3.
		Wipers do not sweep.	GO TO A10.
		Wipers do not complete 1 full sweep.	GO TO A13.
		Wipers sweep more than once.	GO TO A16.
A3.	Press "LO" button.	Wipers sweep at low speed.	GO TO A4.
		Wipers do not sweep.	Replace WIPER/WASHER SWITCH.
		Wipers sweep at high speed.	GO TO A18.
A4.	Press "HI" button.	Wipers sweep at high speed.	All systems diagnosed in this cell are functioning normally.
		Wipers do not sweep.	GO TO A20.
		Wipers sweep at low speed.	GO TO A16.
A5.	Disconnect WASHER PUMP connector. Connect a digital multimeter from cavity 2 to chassis ground. Measure resistance.	More than 0.3 ohms.	Repair BLK ground wire between WASHER PUMP and G103.
		Less than 0.3 ohms.	GO TO A6.
A6.	Connect a test lamp from WASHER PUMP connector cavity 1 to chassis ground. Press Wash button.	Test lamp lights.	Replace WASHER PUMP.
		Test lamp does not light.	GO TO A7.
A7.	Backprobe WINDSHIELD WIPER/WASHER SWITCH connector with a test lamp from cavity 4 to chassis ground. Press Wash button.	Test lamp lights.	Repair open in BLU/YEL wire between WINDSHIELD WIPER/WASHER SWITCH and WASHER PUMP.
		Test lamp does not light.	GO TO A8.
A8.	Backprobe WINDSHIELD WIPER/WASHER SWITCH connector with a test lamp from cavity 3 to chassis ground.	Test lamp lights.	Replace WINDSHIELD WIPER/WASHER SWITCH.
		Test lamp does not light.	Repair open in BLU wire between WINDSHIELD WIPER/WASHER SWITCH and FUSE BLOCK.
A9.	Disconnect WINDSHIELD WIPER/WASHER SWITCH connector.	WASHER PUMP continues to operate.	Repair short to voltage in BLU/YEL wire between WINDSHIELD WIPER/WASHER SWITCH and WASHER PUMP.
		WASHER PUMP stops.	Replace WINDSHIELD WIPER/WASHER SWITCH.
A10.	Disconnect WINDSHIELD WIPER/WASHER SWITCH connector. Connect a digital multimeter from cavity 8 to chassis ground. Measure resistance.	More than 0.3 ohms.	Repair BLK ground wire between WINDSHIELD WIPER/WASHER SWITCH and G201.
		Less than 0.3 ohms.	Reconnect WINDSHIELD WIPER/WASHER SWITCH connector and GO TO A11.
A11.	Disconnect WIPER MOTOR connector. Connect a digital multimeter from cavity 2 to chassis ground. Measure resistance while pressing "OFF/MIST" button.	Less than 0.3 ohms.	Replace WIPER MOTOR.
		More than 0.3 ohms.	GO TO A12.
A12.	Backprobe WINDSHIELD WIPER/WASHER SWITCH connector with a digital multimeter from cavity 7 to chassis ground. Measure resistance while pressing "OFF/MIST" button.	Less than 0.3 ohms.	Repair open in PNK/YEL wire between WINDSHIELD WIPER/WASHER SWITCH and WIPER MOTOR.
		More than 0.3 ohms.	Replace WINDSHIELD WIPER/WASHER SWITCH.
A13.	Disconnect WIPER MOTOR connector. Connect a digital multimeter from cavity 4 to chassis ground. Measure resistance.	More than 0.3 ohms.	Repair BLK ground wire between WIPER MOTOR and G102.
		Less than 0.3 ohms.	GO TO A14.
A14.	Connect a digital multimeter between WIPER MOTOR connector cavities 2 and 5. Measure resistance.	Less than 0.3 ohms.	Replace WIPER MOTOR.
		More than 0.3 ohms.	GO TO A15.
A15.	Disconnect WINDSHIELD WIPER/WASHER SWITCH connector. Connect a digital multimeter from WINDSHIELD WIPER/WASHER SWITCH connector cavity 5 to WIPER MOTOR connector cavity 5. Measure resistance.	More than 0.3 ohms.	Repair open in BLU/GRN wire between WINDSHIELD WIPER/WASHER SWITCH and WIPER MOTOR.
		Less than 0.3 ohms.	Replace WINDSHIELD WIPER/WASHER SWITCH.
A16.	Disconnect WIPER MOTOR connector. Connect a digital multimeter from cavity 2 to chassis ground. Measure resistance.	More than 0.3 ohms.	Replace WIPER MOTOR.
		Less than 0.3 ohms.	GO TO A17.
A17.	Disconnect WINDSHIELD WIPER/WASHER SWITCH connector. Connect a digital multimeter from cavity 7 to chassis ground. Measure resistance.	Less than 0.3 ohms.	Repair short to ground in PNK/YEL wire between WINDSHIELD WIPER/WASHER SWITCH and WIPER MOTOR.
		More than 0.3 ohms.	Replace WINDSHIELD WIPER/WASHER SWITCH.
A18.	Disconnect WIPER MOTOR connector. Connect a digital multimeter from cavity 1 to chassis ground. Measure resistance.	More than 0.3 ohms.	Replace WIPER MOTOR.
		Less than 0.3 ohms.	GO TO A19.
A19.	Disconnect WINDSHIELD WIPER/WASHER SWITCH connector. Connect a digital multimeter from cavity 6 to chassis ground. Measure resistance.	Less than 0.3 ohms.	Repair short to ground in BLU/WHT wire between WINDSHIELD WIPER/WASHER SWITCH and WIPER MOTOR.
		More than 0.3 ohms.	Replace WINDSHIELD WIPER/WASHER SWITCH.
A20.	Disconnect WIPER MOTOR connector. Connect a digital multimeter from cavity 1 to chassis ground. Measure resistance.	Less than 0.3 ohms.	Replace WIPER MOTOR.
		More than 0.3 ohms.	GO TO A21.
A21.	Backprobe WINDSHIELD WIPER/WASHER SWITCH connector with a digital multimeter from cavity 6 to chassis ground. Measure resistance.	Less than 0.3 ohms.	Repair open in BLU/WHT wire between WINDSHIELD WIPER/WASHER SWITCH and WIPER MOTOR.
		More than 0.3 ohms.	Replace WINDSHIELD WIPER/WASHER SWITCH.

Fig. 32   System diagnosis chart. Storm

pleted through the closed park switch terminals. A cam on the gear then opens at Park position and the wiper shuts off.

NO.	3	4	6	7	8	9	1	2
SWITCH POSITION								
(wiper)		o——o						
HI			o——	——o				
LO				o——o			
INT					o——o		
MIST					o——o		
OFF								
							ILLUMINATION (m)	

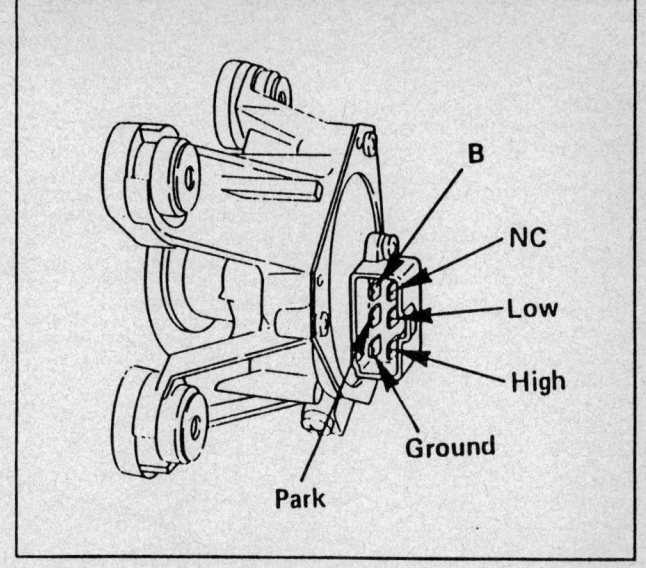

Fig. 33 Wiper switch continuity chart. Storm

Fig. 35 Windshield wiper connections. Storm

NO.	3	4	5	6	7	8	9	1	2
SWITCH POSITION									
(wiper)	o——o								
HI				o——o					
LO				o——o					
INT			o——o		o——o				
MIST					o——o				
OFF			o——o						
							ILLUMINATION (m)		

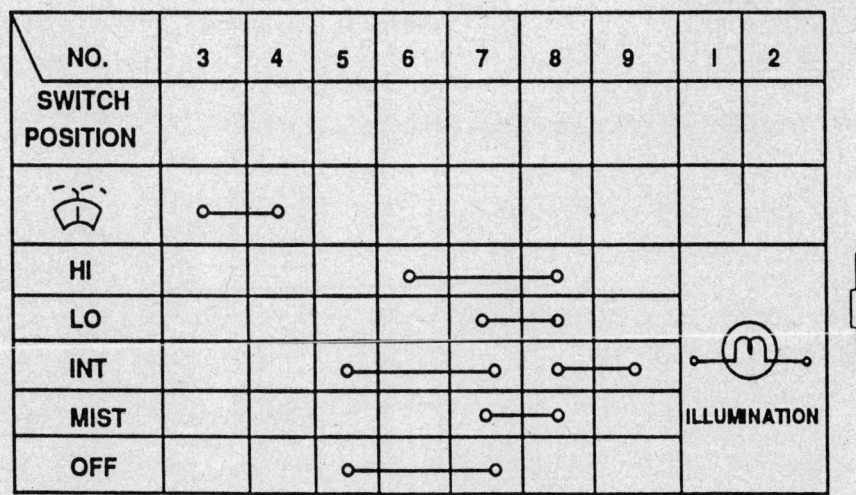

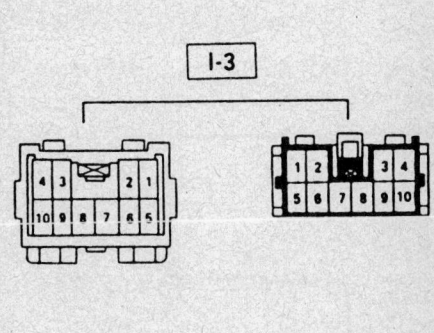

I-3

Fig. 34 Windshield wiper cable continuity chart. Storm

3. If results are correct in steps 1 and 2, the problem is in the wiring harness or switch. After checking all wires for continuity and ensuring fuses are satisfactory, check switch by turning ignition switch on and probing connector to dash switch. Results should be as shown, **Fig. 46**, with respect to vehicle ground.

SPRINT & METRO
Description

These vehicles use a one speed type motor and are equipped with a separate type washer pump provided on the front windshield washer tank.

Diagnosis

1. Using 12 volt battery, connect positive terminal to orange terminal of motor, and negative terminal to black lead wire **Fig. 47**.

2. Motor should rotate between 47 to 57 (38 to 46 on 1989 models) RPM.
3. Testing park operation as follows:
   a. Using 12 volt battery, connect positive terminal to yellow (yellow/blue on 1989 models) terminal of motor and negative terminal to black lead wire.
   b. Use a jumper to short orange and blue/green terminals to each other.
   c. Motor should shut off. Repeat step "B" several times to verify that motor stops in same position each time.
4. Check brush and commutator as follows:
   a. Check orange terminal to black lead wire for continuity. If no continuity, check brush and commutator area for proper contact condition. **If fouled clean area, if surface is coarse or burned, polish area with sandpaper.**

STORM
Description

These vehicles use a one speed type motor and are equipped with a separate type washer pump and reservoir located behind rear end trim panel.

DIAGNOSIS

Using a digital multimeter, take measurements and compare the results to the specifications in **Fig. 48**. If the motor does not operate as specified, replace motor.
1. Connect battery positive lead to terminal 2, **Fig. 49**.
2. Connect battery negative lead to wiper motor body.
3. If wiper motor does not operate as specified in **Fig. 48**, replace motor.

Park Position Inspection

1. Connect battery positive lead to terminal 2, **Fig. 49**.

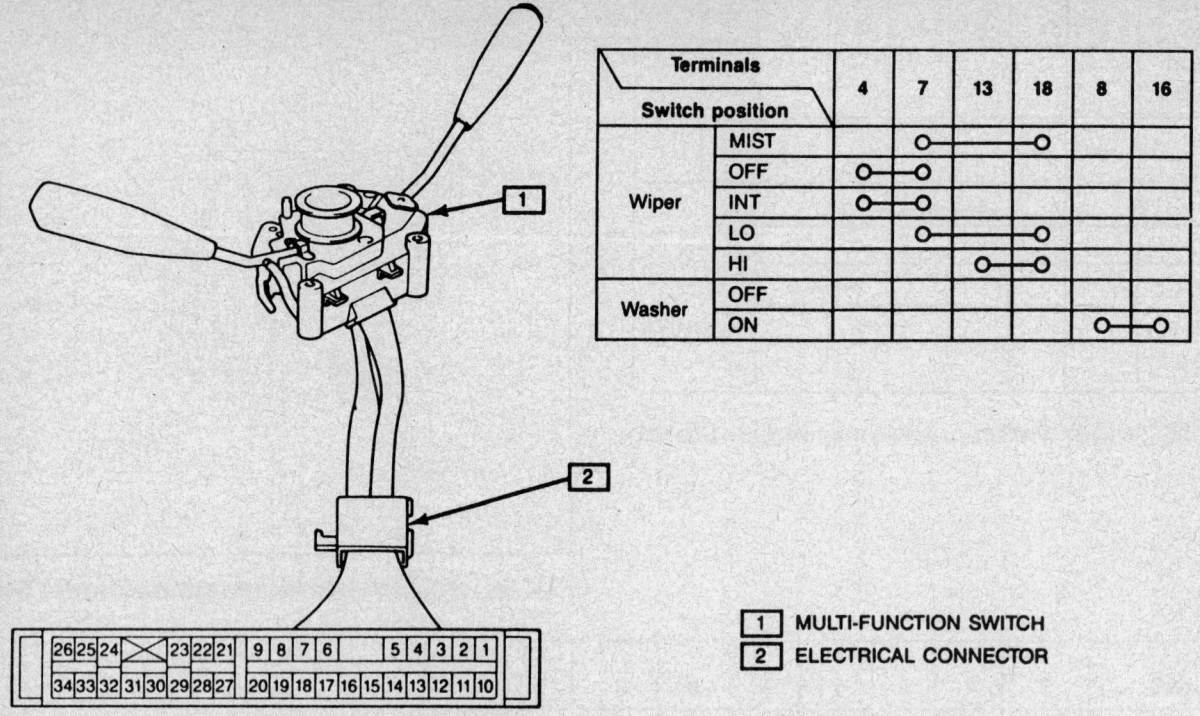

Terminals		4	7	13	18	8	16
Switch position							
Wiper	MIST		○		○		
	OFF	○	○				
	INT	○	○				
	LO		○		○		
	HI			○	○		
Washer	OFF						
	ON					○	○

1	MULTI-FUNCTION SWITCH
2	ELECTRICAL CONNECTOR

Fig. 36   Windshield wiper switch. Prizm

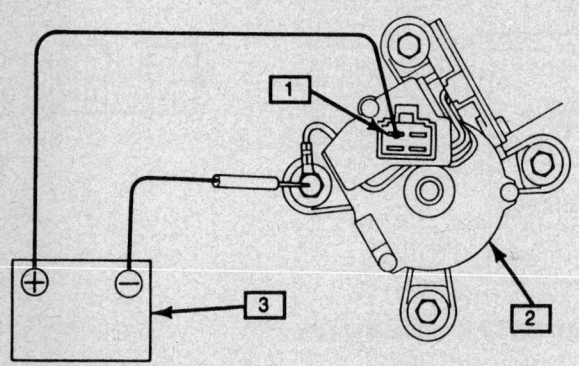

1	TERMINAL 2
2	WIPER MOTOR
3	BATTERY

Fig. 37   Windshield wiper "Low" speed operation. Prizm

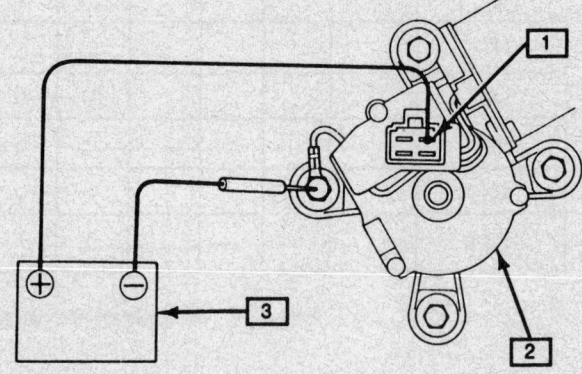

1	TERMINAL 1
2	WIPER MOTOR
3	BATTERY

Fig. 38   Windshield wiper "High" speed operation. Prizm

2. Connect battery negative lead to wiper motor body.
3. Remove battery positive lead from terminal 2. Time this disconnection so that the wiper stops in any position other than "Park" position.
4. If operation does not end in the "Park" position, replace wiper motor.

PRIZM
Description

These vehicles use a one speed type motor.

DIAGNOSIS
Switch Test

Using a digital multimeter, perform continuity tests in **Fig. 50.** If the continuity is not as specified, replace switch.

Motor Test

1. Connect battery positive lead to terminal 2, **Fig. 51.**
2. Connect battery negative lead to wiper motor body.
3. If wiper motor does not operate, replace motor.

Park Position Inspection

1. Connect battery positive lead to terminal 1, install jumper between terminals 2 and 3, **Fig. 52.**
2. Connect battery negative lead to wiper motor body.
3. If operation does not end in the "Park" position, replace wiper motor.

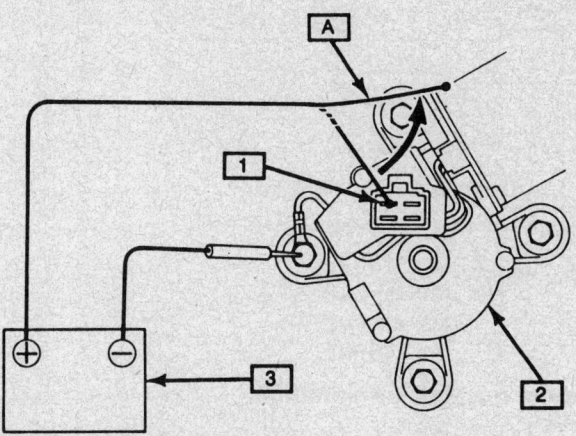

A	DISCONNECT TERMINAL 2
1	TERMINAL 2
2	WIPER MOTOR
3	BATTERY

Fig. 39 Windshield wiper terminal 2. Prizm

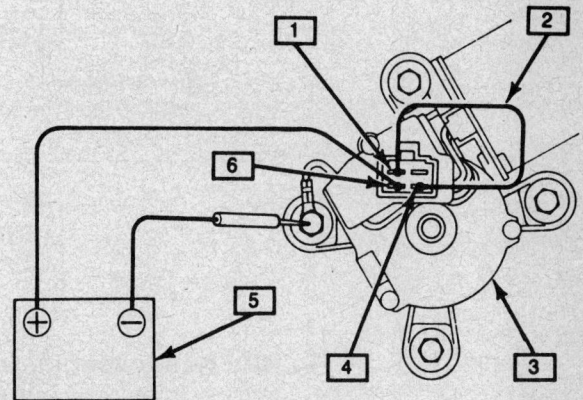

1	TERMINAL 2	4	TERMINAL 3
2	JUMPER WIRE	5	BATTERY
3	WIPER MOTOR	6	TERMINAL 4

Fig. 40 Windshield wiper "Park" operation. Prizm

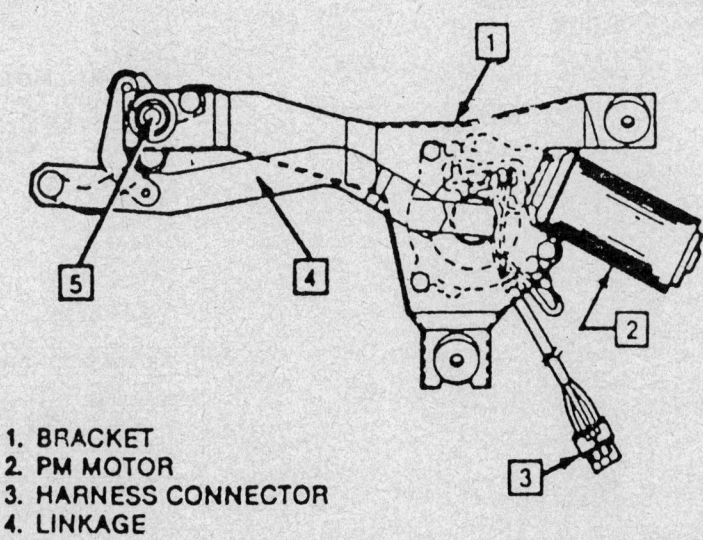

1. BRACKET
2. PM MOTOR
3. HARNESS CONNECTOR
4. LINKAGE
5. PIVOT

Fig. 41 Rear wiper motor assembly. 1988 Firenza & Skyhawk wagons

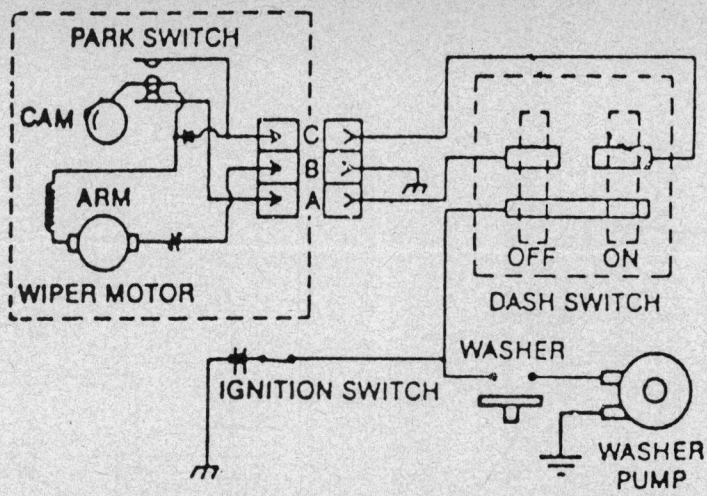

Fig. 42   Rear wiper motor wiring schematic. 1988 Firenza & Skyhawk wagons

REAR WINDOW WIPER SWITCH CHECK		
TERMINAL	SWITCH MODE	
	OFF	ON
A	B(+)	0V
B	Ground	Ground
C	0V	B(+)

Fig. 43   Rear window wiper switch test chart. 1988 Firenza & Skyhawk wagons

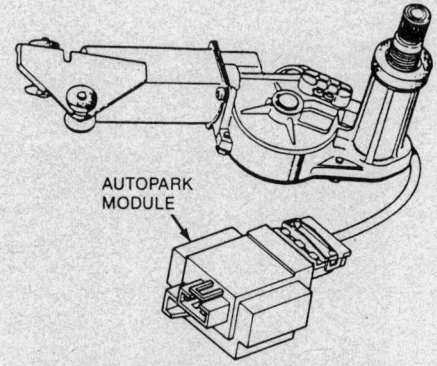

Fig. 44   Rear wiper motor assembly. Celebrity, Century, Cutlass Cruiser & 6000 wagons

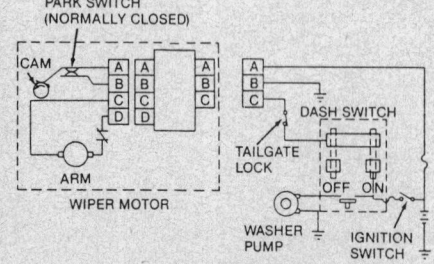

Fig. 45   Rear wiper motor wiring schematic. Celebrity, Century, Cutlass Cruiser & 6000 wagons

REAR WINDOW WIPER SWITCH CHECK		
TERMINAL	SWITCH MODE	
	OFF	ON
A	B(+)	0V
B	0V	B(+)
C	GROUND	GROUND
D	0V	B(+)

Fig. 46   Rear window wiper switch test chart. Celebrity, Century, Cutlass Cruiser & 6000 wagons

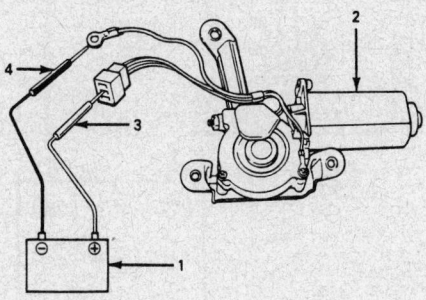

1. BATTERY
2. WIPER MOTOR
3. BATTERY (+) TERMINAL-TO-ORANGE TERMINAL
   CONNECTION
4. BATTERY (−) TERMINAL-TO-BLACK CORD
   CONNECTION

Fig. 47   Connections to operate rear wiper motor independent of vehicle wiring

REAR WIPER MOTOR	SPECIFICATIONS
RATED VOLTAGE	12V
OPERATING VOLTAGE	10-15V
STARTING VOLTAGE	8V
TESTING VOLTAGE	13.5V
CURRENT AT 10 KG-CM LOAD AT 15 KG-CM LOAD	2.0A OR LESS 2.5A OR LESS
STALL CURRENT	9A OR LESS
INSULATION RESISTANCE	1MΩ (MINIMUM)
SPEED (AT 10 KG-CM LOAD)	34-44 RPM

Fig. 48   Rear wiper motor specifications. Storm

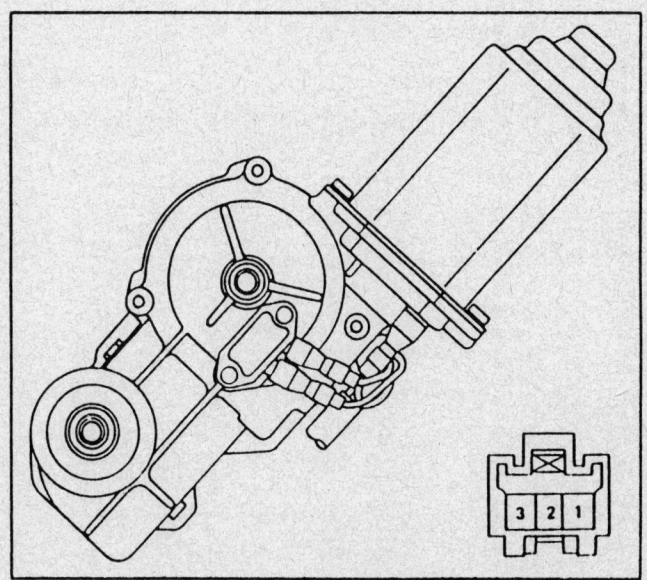

Fig. 49   Rear wiper motor connections. Storm

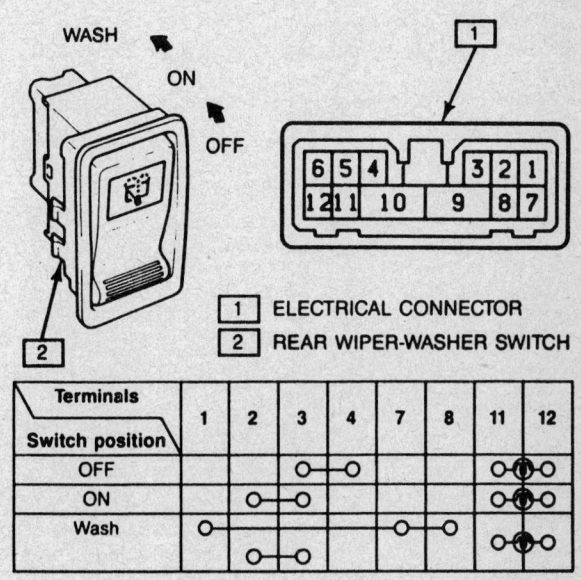

1   ELECTRICAL CONNECTOR
2   REAR WIPER-WASHER SWITCH

Terminals Switch position	1	2	3	4	7	8	11	12
OFF			○	○			○	○
ON		○	○				○	○
Wash	○				○	○	○	○
		○	○				○	○

Fig. 50   Rear wiper switch connections. Prizm

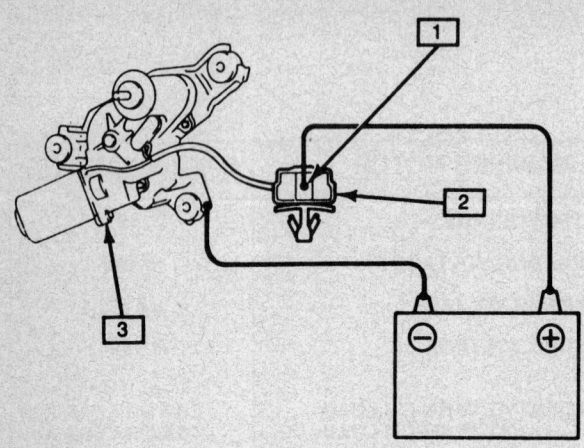

1 TERMINAL 2
2 ELECTRICAL CONNECTOR
3 REAR WIPER MOTOR

Fig. 51   Rear wiper motor connections. Prizm

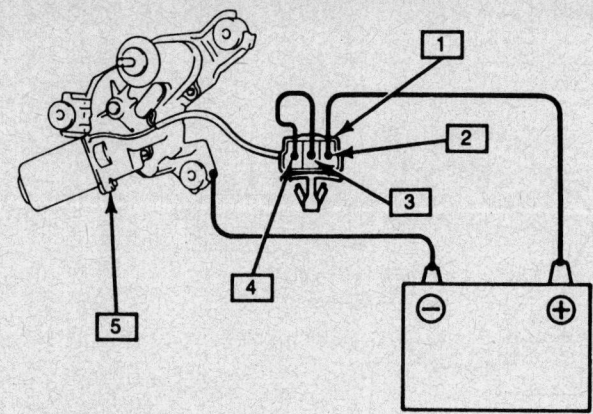

1 ELECTRICAL CONNECTOR
2 TERMINAL 1
3 TERMINAL 2
4 TERMINAL 3
5 REAR WIPER MOTOR

Fig. 52   Rear wiper "Park" connections. Prizm

SPEED CONTROL SYSTEMS

NOTE: Wire Code Identification and Symbol Identification located in the front of this manual can be used as an aid when using wiring circuits found in this section.

TABLE OF CONTENTS

Applications

TYPE 1

Cadillac Except Cimarron

TYPE 2

1988
  Cadillac Cimarron
1988-89
  Buick Except:
    Cavalier w/2.0L VIN 1 Engine
    Skyhawk
  Chevrolet Except:
    Beretta w/2.0L VIN 1 Engine
    Corsica w/2.0L VIN 1 Engine
    Nova, Spectrum & Sprint
  Oldsmobile Except:
    Firenza
1988-90
  Buick Except:
    Century w/2.5L VIN R Engine
    Reatta
    Riviera
    Skylark w/2.5L VIN U Engine
  Chevrolet Except:
    Celebrity w/2.5L VIN R Engine
  Oldsmobile Except:
    Calais w/2.5L VIN U Engine
    Ciera w/2.5L VIN R Engine
    Toronado

Pontiac Except:
  Fiero w/2.5L VIN R Engine
  Grand Am w/2.5L VIN U Engine
  Sunbird w/2.0L VIN K Engine
  6000 w/2.5L VIN R Engine
1990
  Chevrolet Except:
    Beretta w/2.2L VIN G Engine
    Cavalier w/2.2L VIN G Engine
    Corsica w/2.2L VIN G Engine
  Oldsmobile Except:
    Trofeo

TYPE 3

1988-90
  Reatta
  Riviera
  Toronado
1990
  Trofeo

TYPE 4

1988-89
  Buick:
    Cavalier w/2.0L VIN 1 Engine
    Skyhawk
  Chevrolet:
    Beretta w/2.0L VIN 1 Engine
    Corsica w/2.0L VIN 1 Engine
  Oldsmobile:
    Firenza

1988-90
  Buick:
    Century w/2.5L VIN R Engine
    Skylark w/2.5L VIN U Engine
  Chevrolet:
    Celebrity w/2.5L VIN R Engine
  Oldsmobile:
    Calais w/2.5L VIN U Engine
    Ciera w/2.5L VIN R Engine
  Pontiac:
    Fiero w/2.5L VIN R Engine
    Grand Am w/2.5L VIN U Engine
    Sunbird w/2.0L VIN K Engine
    6000 w/2.5L VIN R Engine
1990
  Chevrolet:
    Beretta w/2.2L VIN G Engine
    Cavalier w/2.2L VIN G Engine
    Corsica w/2.2L VIN G Engine

TYPE 5

Chevrolet Nova
Geo Prizm

TYPE 6

1988
  Sprint
1988-89
  Spectrum

NOTE: Wire Code Identification and Symbol Identification located in the front of this manual can be used as an aid when using wiring circuits found in this section.

INDEX

DESCRIPTION & OPERATION

This Cruise Control System utilizes either manifold vacuum or a vacuum pump to activate the throttle power unit or servo. Throttle position is changed when the servo unit diaphragm receives varying levels of vacuum, controlled by a solenoid valve. The solenoid valve modulates the vacuum signal to the servo in response to commands from the electronic controller. The electronic controller monitors signals from the engagement and instrument panel switches, electric brake release switch, and the speed sensor. The speed sensor, located at the rear of the speedometer cluster, signals vehicle speed to the controller. These signals are used by the controller to activate the solenoid valve, regulating the level of vacuum to the servo diaphragm. This system uses two brake release switches. An electric brake re-

lease, mounted on the brake pedal support, turns the system Off and vents the servo diaphragm to the atmosphere through the solenoid valve. A second brake release switch, a vacuum release valve also located on the brake pedal support, vents the servo unit to the atmosphere.

ELECTRONIC CONTROLLER

The ECM or BCM receives input signals from the cruise control engagement switches, instrument panel switch, brake release switch, drive switch and speed sensor.

On models equipped with DFI or PFI, the ECM or BCM also receives engine control signals. The ECM then processes these signals and transmits a command signal to the solenoid valve, regulating vacuum to the servo unit diaphragm. On some diesel engine equipped models, the cruise control module receives signals from the

cruise engagement switch, instrument panel switch, electric brake release switch and speed sensor. The cruise control module then processes this information and transmits command signals to the vacuum control solenoid valve to provide necessary vacuum to the system and signals to the servo unit solenoid valve to control vehicle speed.

SPEED SENSOR

The speed sensor is mounted in the transaxle. A magnet rotates near a coil, producing voltage pulses in the coil. As speed increases, so do the number of voltage pulses per second.

The speed sensor buffer takes the sensor/voltage pulses from the sensor and uses them to close two solid state output switches. Each output terminal is switched to ground at a rate that is proportional to the speed of the car. The speedometer and the ECM are switched at 4000 pulses per mile. **The output switches in the speed sensor are solid state. Self-powered test lights or ohmmeters should not be used to test them. Do not measure the resistance at the outputs of the buffer.**

VACUUM CONTROL VALVE

The vacuum control valve operates in response to a signal from the BCM, ECM or electronic controller and opens when the system is engaged. When the valve is opened, vacuum is available to the servo unit solenoid valve to regulate the servo unit. When the cruise control is disengaged, the vacuum control valve is closed.

SERVO UNIT SOLENOID VALVE

The solenoid valve modulates the vacuum signal to the servo unit in response to commands from the BCM, ECM or electronic controller in order for the throttle to be in proper position for desired cruise speed.

SERVO UNIT

The servo unit is essentially a vacuum activated variable diaphragm. It positions the throttle when the system is in operation through a bead chain actuator, combination chain and cable actuator or rod actuator depending on model of vehicle.

To operate the servo unit, a controlled vacuum provided by the servo unit solenoid valve is applied to the servo diaphragm, drawing the diaphragm inward, pulling the actuator to operate the throttle.

BRAKE RELEASE SWITCHES

The Cruise Control system utilizes an electrical brake release switch and a vacuum release valve.

The electric brake release switch cuts off the voltage supplied through the instrument panel switch to the electronic controller when the brake pedal is depressed. The vacuum release valve operates after the electric release switch disengages. It serves as a back-up release system and opens a port that vents the servo unit to atmospheric pressure, allowing the throttle to return to the idle position.

INSTRUMENT PANEL SWITCH

This instrument panel mounted switch provides electrical power to the cruise control system. When switch is in Off position, the system cannot be engaged. When switch is in On-Auto position, the amber light next to the words Cruise Control is lit and system may be engaged with the switch located on the turn signal lever at any speed above 25 mph. When system is engaged, a green light is illuminated adjacent to the word Auto.

ENGAGEMENT SWITCH OPERATION, CRUISE MODE

The turn signal lever mounted engagement switch has several modes of operation. With the switch in the On-Auto position, the engagement switch operates as follows:

Switch In Fully Released Position

1. System not operational.
2. System has been engaged previously. The electronic controller is supplying control voltage to the servo unit solenoid valve. The servo unit solenoid valve regulates vacuum to the servo unit which maintains throttle position for desired speed.

Push Button Depressed And Held

After using accelerator pedal to obtain desired speed, the operator can then momentarily depress the push button switch. The electronic controller will provide a control voltage to the servo unit solenoid valve and apply the required vacuum to the servo unit to maintain set speed. When a decrease in speed is desired, the operator may depress and hold the push button with no accelerator pedal pressure. The electronic controller then signals the servo unit solenoid valve to vent the servo unit to atmosphere, closing the throttle. When push button is released, vehicle will cruise at new desired speed.

Slide Lever Actuation

This switch allows the operator to resume a previously set speed after braking or accelerating. Depressing and releasing the slide switch above 25 mph, will accelerate vehicle until previously set speed is reached. If operator desires to advance speed from set speed, actuating and holding slide switch will accelerate vehicle until slide switch is released. Vehicle will now maintain new set speed.

SET/COAST BUTTON SWITCH

This switch has two positions, Normal and Depressed.

Set Position

With vehicle speed above approximately 25 mph and instrument panel switch in On position, pressing and releasing set/coast button will cause the cruise speed to be set at speed vehicle was travelling at when button was released, ± 1 mph. The system will cruise until either the instrument panel switch is moved to Off position, the ignition switch is turned off and/or the set/coast button is pushed in fully and held. Depressing the brake pedal releases the cruise, but not the resume capability.

Coast (Trim) Position

Cruise speed can be changed with the set/coast switch fully depressed. Cruise speed can be increased by accelerating to desired cruise speed, then fully depressing and releasing switch. When switch is released, a new cruise speed is set. To decrease cruise speed, fully depress and hold switch, then decelerate to desired cruise speed and release switch.

Tap Down Position

The cruise speed can be decreased in 1 mph increments by tapping the set/coast switch. With cruise control engaged and operating, quickly depress and release or tap switch. Each tap of switch will decrease cruise speed 1 mph to a maximum 10 mph decrease in cruise speed. This feature can be used to lower the cruise speed below the 25 mph minimum setting to as low as 16 mph.

RESUME/ACCEL SWITCH

This switch has two positions. When switch is **momentarily** moved toward the R/A position after braking, cruise control operation will be returned to last set speed.

If switch is held in R/A position for more than 1 second, the system reverts to the Accel mode. To accelerate vehicle, move switch to R/A position and hold until vehicle reaches desired increased speed. When switch is released, speed vehicle has accelerated to becomes new cruise speed. In order to use Accel mode, the cruise instrument panel switch must be in On position and vehicle speed must be above 25 mph.

Tap Up Position

This feature allows the cruise speed to be increased in 1 mph increments up to 10 mph by quickly pressing switch toward R/A position and quickly releasing switch.

SERVICE PRECAUTIONS

Before performing any diagnosis or repair procedures, temporarily disable the Supplemental Inflatable Restraint (SIR) system. Failure to do so may result in possible air bag deployment or personal injury. Disable SIR system as follows:

1. Turn ignition switch to Off position.
2. Remove SIR fuse.
3. Disconnect SIR electrical harness connector, at base of steering column.
4. Reverse procedure to reconnect, ensure "Inflatable Restraint" indicator flashes 7 to 9 times to indicate proper SIR operation.

On vehicles equipped with ABS brake system, the hydraulic accumulator, when fully charged contains brake fluid at high pressure. Before disconnecting any lines, hoses or fittings, ensure accumulator is full depressurized. Failure to do so may result in personal injury.

To depressurize the hydraulic accumulator, turn the ignition to the Off position or disconnect negative battery cable, pump brake pedal a minimum of 40 times at approximately 50 lbs. of force. A noticeable change in pedal feel will occur when accumulator is fully discharged.

TROUBLESHOOTING

PRELIMINARY CHECKS

Brougham

1. Apply vacuum to cruise control servo

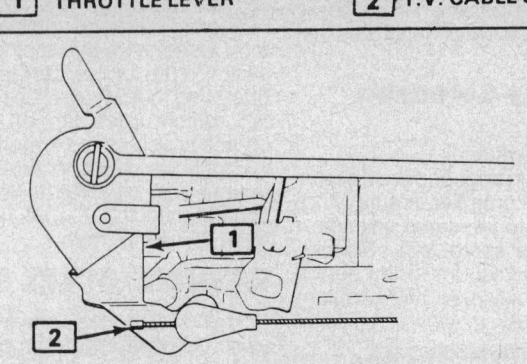

1 THROTTLE LEVER   2 T.V. CABLE STUCK

Fig. 1 Linkage adjustment. Brougham

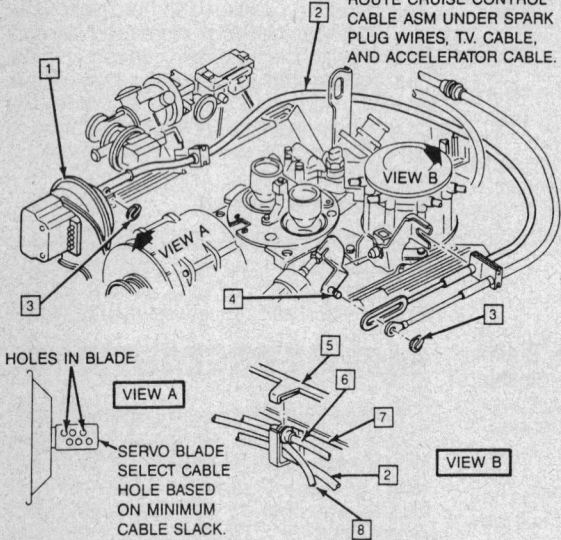

ROUTE CRUISE CONTROL CABLE ASM UNDER SPARK PLUG WIRES, T.V. CABLE, AND ACCELERATOR CABLE.

HOLES IN BLADE

VIEW A

SERVO BLADE SELECT CABLE HOLE BASED ON MINIMUM CABLE SLACK.

VIEW B

CABLE ADJUSTMENT
1. WITH ENGINE OFF (ISC) IDLE SPEED MOTOR MUST BE RETRACTED UNTIL THE THROTTLE LEVER IS CLEAR OF THE ISC PLUNGER. REFER TO SECTION 6E FOR PROCEDURE.
2. ATTACH CABLE ASM. TO THROTTLE LEVER AND SELECT THE CABLE HOLE ON SERVO BLADE BASED ON MINIMUM CABLE SLACK. (SEE VIEW B).

1 CRUISE CONTROL SERVO
2 CRUISE CONTROL CABLE ASM
3 RETAINER
4 THROTTLE LEVER
5 COVER AIR CLEANER ASM
6 ACCELERATOR CABLE
7 HOUSING
8 THROTTLE VALVE CABLE

Fig. 3 T.V. cable adjustment. Seville, Eldorado, DeVille & Fleetwood

1. SERVO ASSEMBLY
2. ROD ASSEMBLY
3. RETAINER

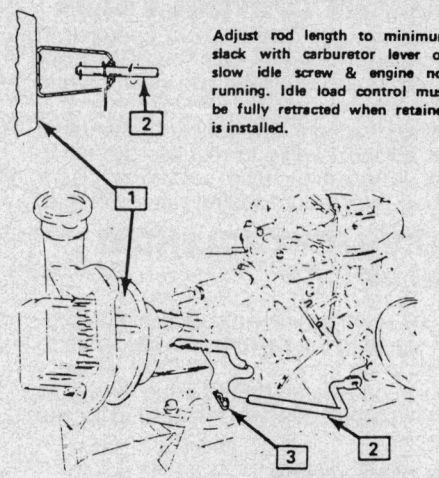

Adjust rod length to minimum slack with carburetor lever on slow idle screw & engine not running. Idle load control must be fully retracted when retainer is installed.

Fig. 2 Servo adjustment. Brougham

at 3 inch Hg increments to a maximum of 21 inch Hg to test vacuum hoses for leaks, kinks or restrictions, repairing or replacing as necessary.
2. Visually inspect cruise control wire and ground connections.
3. If speedometer does not work, check vehicle speed sensor.
4. Check cruise control fuse.
5. Check cruise control servo linkage for restrictions or kinks.
6. If tap-up and tap-down functions are the only fault in system, replace cruise control module.
7. If cruise control system loses speed while engaged, proceed as follows:
   a. Check throttle valve cable, adjust if necessary, **Fig. 1.**
   b. Check cruise control servo linkage, adjust if necessary, **Fig. 2**
8. If cruise control system surges while engaged, proceed as follows:
   a. Check for adequate vacuum source.
   b. Check cruise control servo vent valve for leaks.
   c. Check speedometer driven gear for chips or wear.
9. **On 1988-89 models,** check resistance between grounds G131 and G250. On 1990 models with 5.0L VIN Y engine, check resistance between grounds G202 and G102. On 1990 models with 5.7L VIN 7 engine, check resistance between ground G202 and G203. If resistance is greater than .1 ohm, clean and tighten both grounds and the negative battery cable. If ground circuit is suspect, add ground strap between engine block and bulkhead.

DeVille & Fleetwood

1. With throttle in hot idle position, check cruise servo and throttle linkage for minimum slack.
2. Inspect vacuum hoses for leaks, kinks or restrictions, repairing or replacing as necessary.
3. Visually inspect cruise control wire and ground connections.
4. If cruise On indicator or cruise control panel light do not light, on 1988-89 models, check 155 black, wire for open, on 1990 models, check 803 black/white, wire for open.

5. With cruise control engaged, if cruise On indicator does not light, check bulb. If bulb is good, replace cruise control switch.
6. **On 1988-89 models,** if cruise "Engaged" indicator does not light, ground terminal D4 connector C1 of ECM. If indicator works, check ECM for terminal contact. If contact is good, replace ECM. When grounded, if indicator does not light, check bulb and wiring.
7. **On 1990 models,** if cruise "Engaged" indicator does not light, check stored diagnostic codes. Ground BCM terminal A1 connector C1, if indicator does not light, check bulb and wiring. If indicator works, check BCM for terminal contact. If contact is good, replace BCM.

Seville & Eldorado

1. Check cruise fuse 8 for proper operation by observing the battery no charge indicator, with ignition switch in run and engine off
2. Check transaxle position switch by observing the PRNDL display.
3. Check vacuum hoses for leaks, kinks, and other restrictions.
4. Check cruise control servo linkage. If necessary to adjust, refer to **Fig. 3** for procedure.

ROAD TEST

Perform the following road test and note system operation. If a cause for the observed malfunction cannot be determined by following troubleshooting procedures, proceed to "System Diagnosis."

DeVille & Fleetwood

1. Place instrument panel switch in Off position. While operating vehicle at 50 mph push engagement switch button

on turn signal lever and release. System should remain inoperative.

2. Place instrument panel switch in On-AUTO position. Amber light should come on.

3. Engage system by momentarily pushing turn signal engagement switch button and releasing at 50 mph, remove foot from accelerator. Green light should come on when button is released and system is engaged. Vehicle should maintain set speed of 50 mph. Note amount, if any, by which vehicle speed differs from 50 mph speed when engaged. This is called lock-in error and can be corrected by turning screw on the servo unit solenoid valve towards the S position, reducing actual engagement speed. Turning the screw towards the F position, increases actual engagement speed.

4. Push switch and hold. Vehicle should accelerate at a controlled rate. Release switch to engage system at cruise speed of approximately 55 mph. System should now be set at a new speed and maintain set speed.

5. Depress brake pedal approximately 1/2 inch. Green light should go out confirming action of electric brake release switch and vehicle should start to reduce speed. Allow vehicle to decelerate to 45 mph.

6. Momentarily depress switch and release. Vehicle should accelerate at a controlled rate and resume previously set speed of 55 mph and maintain that speed. Green light should come on when switch is released.

7. Push switch in and hold. Green light should go out. Coast to 50 mph.

8. Release switch to engage system at 50 mph. Green light should come on and vehicle should maintain that set speed.

Brougham

Perform road test with cruise control switch on and vehicle speed above 25 mph.

1. Place engagement switch in Set/Coast position, then release it. Cruise engage indicator should light and vehicle should maintain speed.

2. Hold engage switch in Set/Coast position. Vehicle should coast at a slower speed.

3. Release Set/Coast switch. Cruise control should engage and hold a slower speed above 25 mph.

4. Place engage switch in Resume/Accel position and hold it there. Vehicle should accelerate.

5. Release engage switch. Vehicle should hold new faster speed.

6. Tap brake pedal. Vehicle should coast slower.

7. Place engage switch in Resume/Accel position momentarily. Vehicle should accelerate to former set speed.

8. While cruising, accelerate, then remove foot from accelerator pedal. Vehicle should coast back to set speed.

9. While cruising, tap engage switch to Resume/Accel position. Vehicle

speed should increase with each tap up to ten taps.

10. While cruising, tap engage switch to Set/Coast position. Vehicle speed should decrease 1 mph for each tap down to 25 mph.

11. Place cruise control switch in Off position. Cruise control should turn off.

Eldorado & Seville

Perform road test with cruise switch in On position and vehicle speed above 25 mph.

1. Momentarily depress set/coast switch in steering wheel pad and ensure vehicle maintains speed.

2. Hold set/coast switch in with foot off accelerator and ensure vehicle coasts down to a lower speed.

3. Release set/coast switch and ensure cruise control engages and holds slower speed if speed is greater than 25 mph.

4. Slide and hold resume/accelerate switch in and ensure vehicle accelerates.

5. Release resume/accelerate switch and ensure vehicle holds new, faster speed.

6. Tap brake pedal and ensure vehicle coasts.

7. Slide resume/accelerate switch and ensure vehicle accelerates to speed set before tapping of brake pedal.

8. Tap set/coast switch and ensure vehicle speed decreases 1 mph for each tap.

9. Tap resume/accelerate switch and ensure vehicle speed increases 1 mph for each tap.

10. Slide cruise switch in righthand switch assembly to Off position and ensure cruise control releases to manual operation.

SYSTEM DIAGNOSIS & TESTING

Before performing any diagnostic or repair procedures, temporarily disable the Supplemental Inflatable Restraint (SIR) system. Failure to do so may result in possible air bag deployment or personal injury. Disable SIR system as follows:

1. Turn ignition switch to OFF position.
2. Remove SIR fuse 3.
3. Disconnect yellow SIR electrical harness connector, at base of steering column.
4. Reverse procedure to reconnect, ensure "Inflatable Restraint" indicator flashes 7 to 9 times to indicate proper SIR operation.

On vehicles equipped with ABS brake system, the hydraulic accumulator, when fully charged contains brake fluid at high pressure. Before disconnecting any lines, hoses or fittings, ensure accumulator is full depressurized. Failure to do so may result in personal injury.

To depressurize the hydraulic accumulator, turn the ignition to the Off position or disconnect negative battery cable, pump brake pedal a minimum of 40 times at approximately 50 lbs. of

force. A noticeable change in pedal feel will occur when accumulator is fully discharged.

DeVille & Fleetwood SELF-DIAGNOSTIC SYSTEM

In the process of controlling the various subsystems, the ECM and BCM continually monitor operating conditions for possible malfunctions. By comparing system conditions against standard operating limits certain circuits and component malfunctions can be detected. A two digit numerical code is stored in the computer memory when a problem is detected by this self diagnostic system.

If the ECM diagnostics detect a fault, the cruise control system will be inhibited for the entire ignition cycle. The faults that may inhibit the cruise control system are as follows::

1. Fault with vehicle speed sensor or throttle position sensor circuit.
2. Cruise control requested above 90 mph.
3. A rapid rise in RPM's.
4. Difference between vehicle speed and set speed is too high.
5. Transaxle is shifted to neutral position.
6. ECM detects battery voltage either too high or too low.
7. Acceleration is too high.
8. Coolant temperature is too high.

Codes other than described may be stored in the control module memory and displayed when the system is accessed to diagnose cruise control malfunctions. It may be necessary to identify and diagnose the failures caused by these additional codes in order to ensure proper system operation. For complete diagnosis of the system, refer to the "Fuel Injection Section" in the MOTOR's Auto Engine Tune Up & Electronic Manual.

Intermittent Problem Diagnosis

Trouble codes displayed during the first pass of ECM diagnostic codes, but not the second pass, are considered intermittent. Intermittent trouble codes are those that the ECM previously determined to be faulty but later tested good. If the code is intermittent, most charts will refer to a special note. **Do not bypass the charts when checking intermittent conditions.** Failure to check an intermittent condition may result in replacement of good components.

Many intermittent problems are caused by poor electrical connections. Diagnosis should start with visual and physical inspection of connectors which are related with the code.

Entering Self-Diagnostic Mode

1. Turn ignition switch on.
2. Simultaneously depress the Off and Warmer buttons on the climate control panel and hold buttons until all display panel segments are illuminated which indicates the beginning of the diagnostic readout. The purpose of illuminating the two display panels is to ensure that all segments are

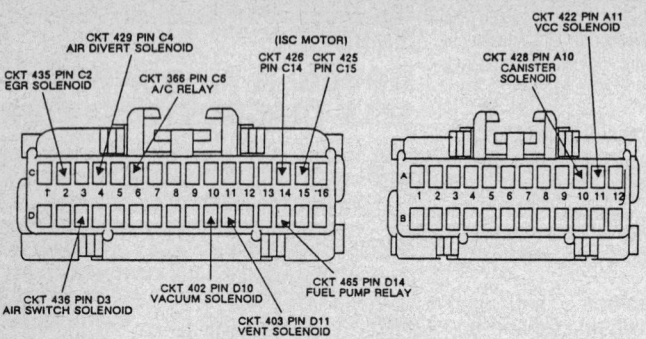

Fig. 4   ECM connector pin location. 1988-89 DeVille & Fleetwood

working. If any segments are are in-operative, the affected display panel must be replaced.

3. After the display segment check is completed, any stored trouble code will be displayed on the data center. These two-digit codes will be displayed with a prefix of either E or F to designate which computer sensed the malfunction. If a trouble code is displayed, or if the self-diagnostics system cannot be accessed, a defect has been sensed in the vehicle's electronic control system. To diagnose these malfunctions, refer to the "Fuel Injection Section" in the MOTOR's Auto Engine Tune Up & Electronics manual.

4. After all codes are displayed or if no trouble codes are stored, the code .7.0 will appear on the display.

Code .7.0

Code .7.0 is a decision point. When this code is displayed, the diagnostic feature relevant to the current malfunction can be selected. The two diagnostic modes relevant to cruise control diagnosis, ECM switch tests and ECM output cycling, are detailed below.

Clearing Trouble Codes

The trouble codes stored in the system memory can be cleared to aid in diagnosing intermittent conditions. To clear codes, proceed as follows:

1. Enter diagnostic mode as outlined.
2. To clear engine control module (ECM) codes, simultaneously depress the Off and HI buttons on the climate control panel and hold the buttons until the code E.0.0 is displayed.
3. To clear body control module (BCM) codes, simultaneously depress the Off and LO buttons on the climate control panel and hold until the code F.0.0 is displayed.
4. After E.0.0 and F.0.0 are displayed, the code .7.0 will be displayed. With this code displayed, turn off ignition and leave ignition off for at least 10 seconds before re-entering the diagnostic mode.

Exiting Self-Diagnostic Mode

To exit the self-diagnostic mode, de-press the AUTO button on the climate control panel or turn of ignition for at least 10 seconds.

ECM SWITCH TEST SERIES

To perform the switch test series, the engine must be running and the code .7.0 must be displayed on the data center panel. To begin the test sequence, depress and release the brake pedal, and the test will begin as soon as the display changes from code .7.0 to code E.7.1. If the code does not change, check brake switch feed to the ECM and check for defective ECM **Figs. 4 through 7.**

The ECM will display a code for each switch, in sequence, and if the switch does not operate properly, the ECM will store the code as a trouble code. In addition, the appropriate switch must be cycled within 10 seconds after its code is displayed or the ECM will store a trouble code associated with that switch. Perform switch tests as follows:

1. When performing the following tests, refer to wiring diagrams and connector points on **Figs. 8 through 11.**
2. With code E.7.1 displayed, depress and release brake pedal again to test cruise control brake switch circuit.
3. With code E.7.2 displayed, depress accelerator pedal from idle position to open throttle, then slowly release pedal. As throttle is moved the ECM tests throttle switch for proper operation.
4. **On 1990 models,** with code 7.3 displayed, operate the transmission in 3rd gear to test 3rd gear pressure switch.
5. **On 1988-89 models,** with code E.7.4 displayed, move transmission selec-

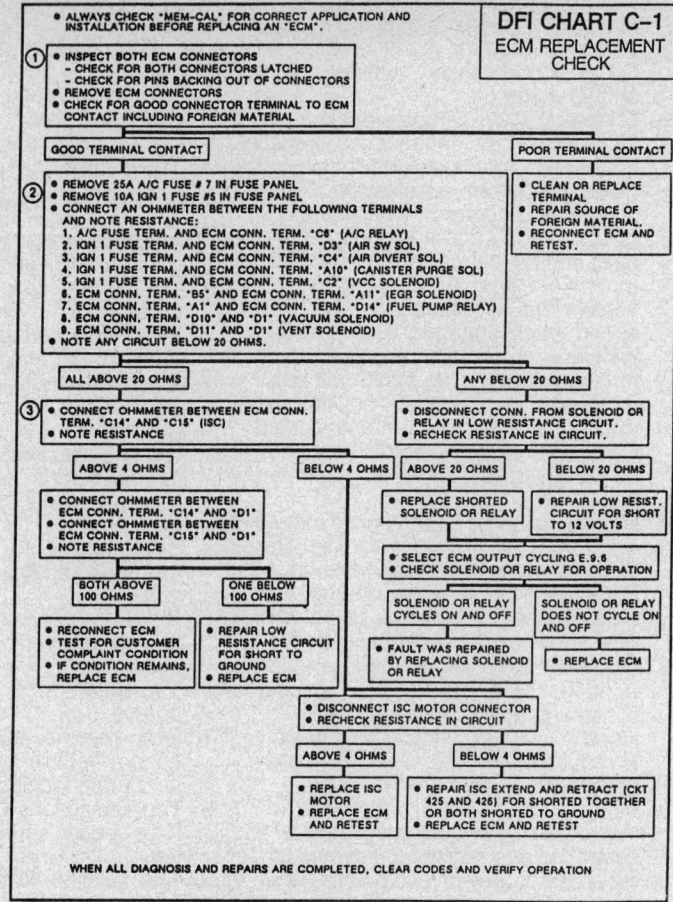

Fig. 5   ECM replacement check. 1988-89 DeVille & Fleetwood

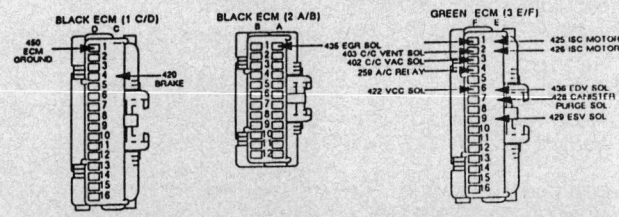

Fig. 6   ECM connector pin location. 1990 DeVille, Eldorado, Fleetwood & Seville

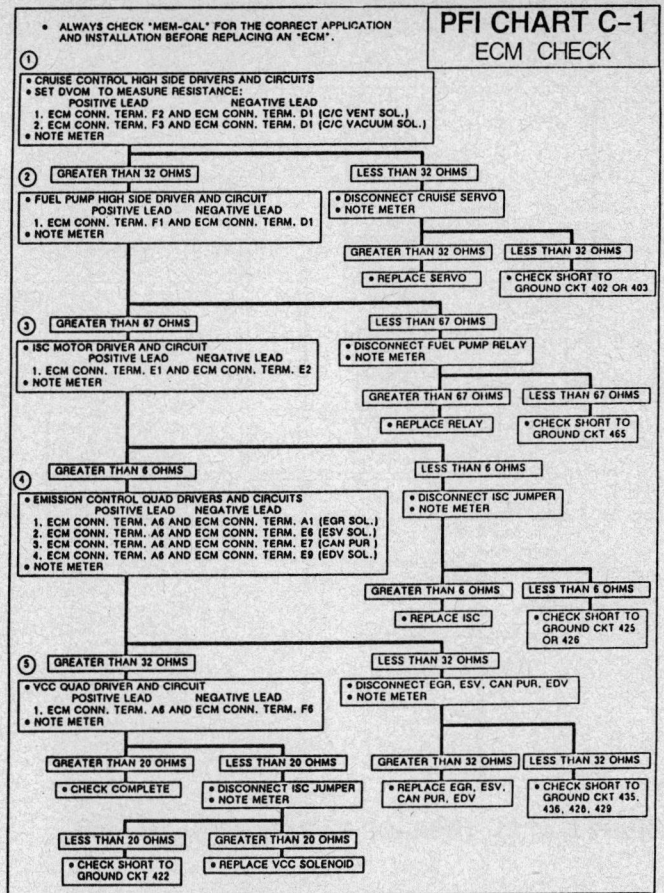

Fig. 7   ECM replacement check. 1990 DeVille, Eldorado, Fleetwood & Seville

tor into reverse, then neutral to test operation of park/neutral switch.

6. **On all models,** with code E.7.5 displayed, turn cruise control instrument panel switch from off to on, then back to off to test operation of switch. Refer to **Fig. 12 and 13** for further testing procedure. For intermittent codes proceed as follows:

a. The amber cruise-on indicator can be used to monitor the cruise dash switch status. Turn dash switch on and wiggle wiring and connectors. If switch or circuit from the fuse to switch are open, the amber light will blink out.

b. If cruise fuse blows intermittently, turn switch on, then wiggle wiring, connectors and cruise steering column switch. If circuit becomes grounded, fuse will blow.

7. With code E.7.6 displayed and with instrument panel cruise control switch on, depress and release set/coast button to test set/coast button operation. Refer to **Fig. 14 and 15** for further testing procedure. For intermittent codes proceed as follows:

a. Turn cruise dash switch to on and backprobe ECM B4 with a voltmeter to ground. B4 should show 12 volts with set/coast depressed and 0 volts with switch released. While observing meter, cycle switch and wiggle wiring and connectors.

8. With code E.7.7 displayed and with instrument panel cruise control switch on, depress and release re-

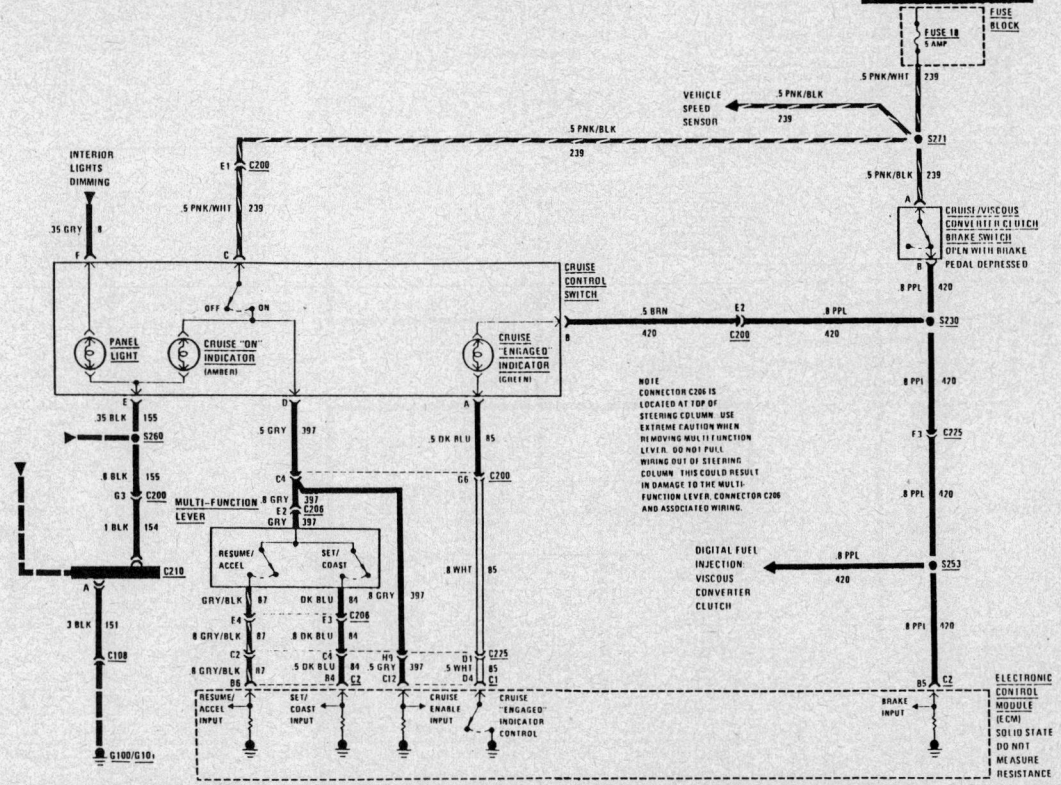

Fig. 8   Wiring diagram (Part 1 of 2). 1988–89 DeVille & Fleetwood

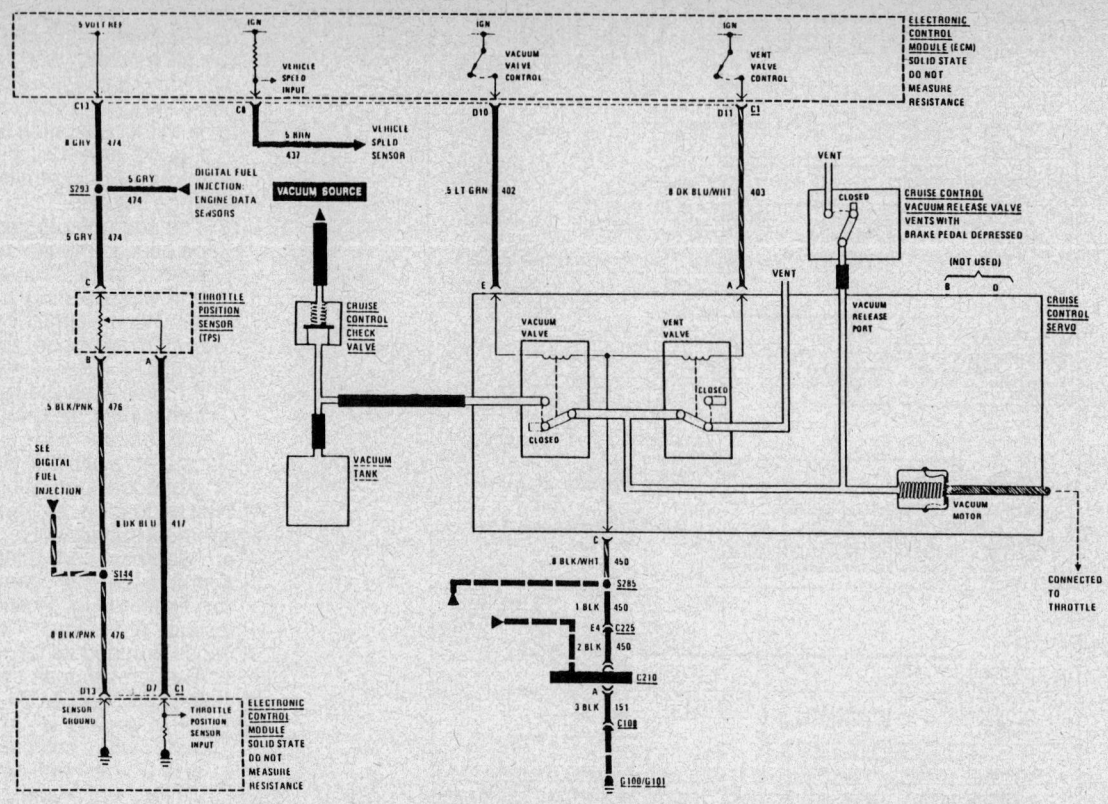

Fig. 8   Wiring diagram (Part 2 of 2). 1988–89 DeVille & Fleetwood

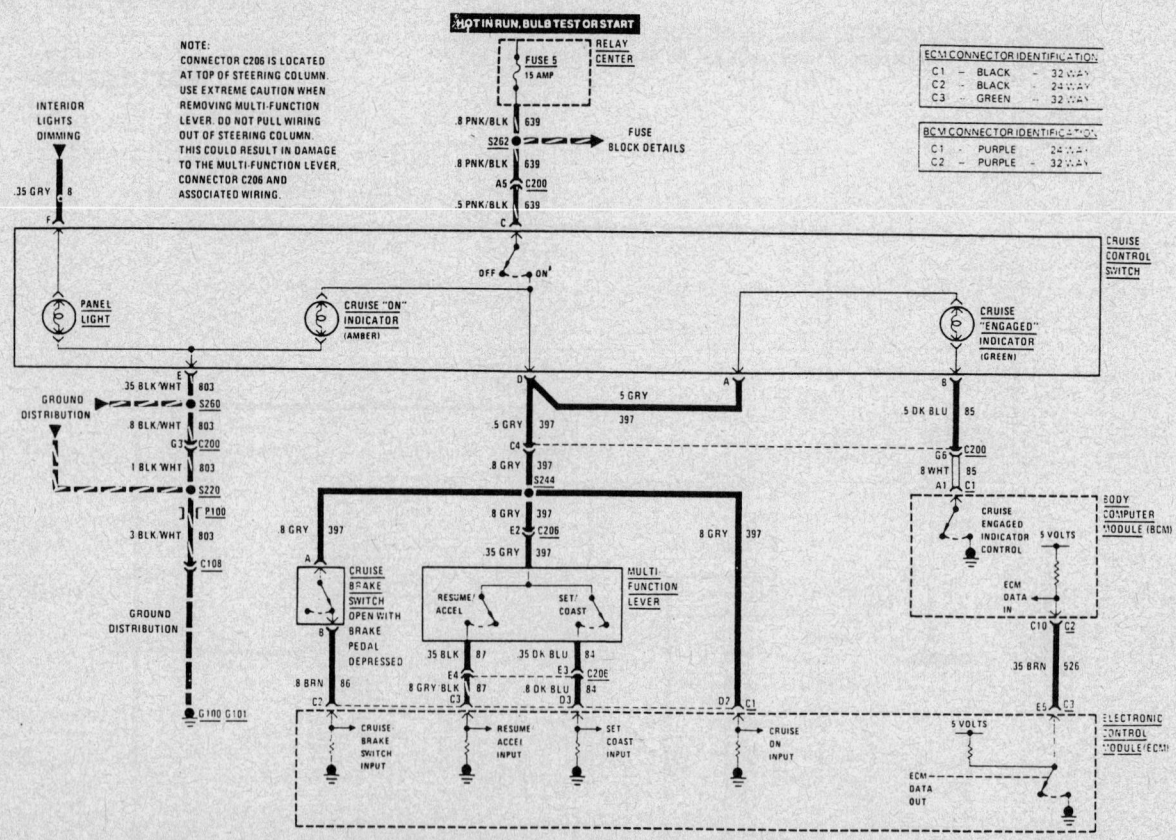

Fig. 9   Wiring diagram (Part 1 of 2). 1990 DeVille & Fleetwood

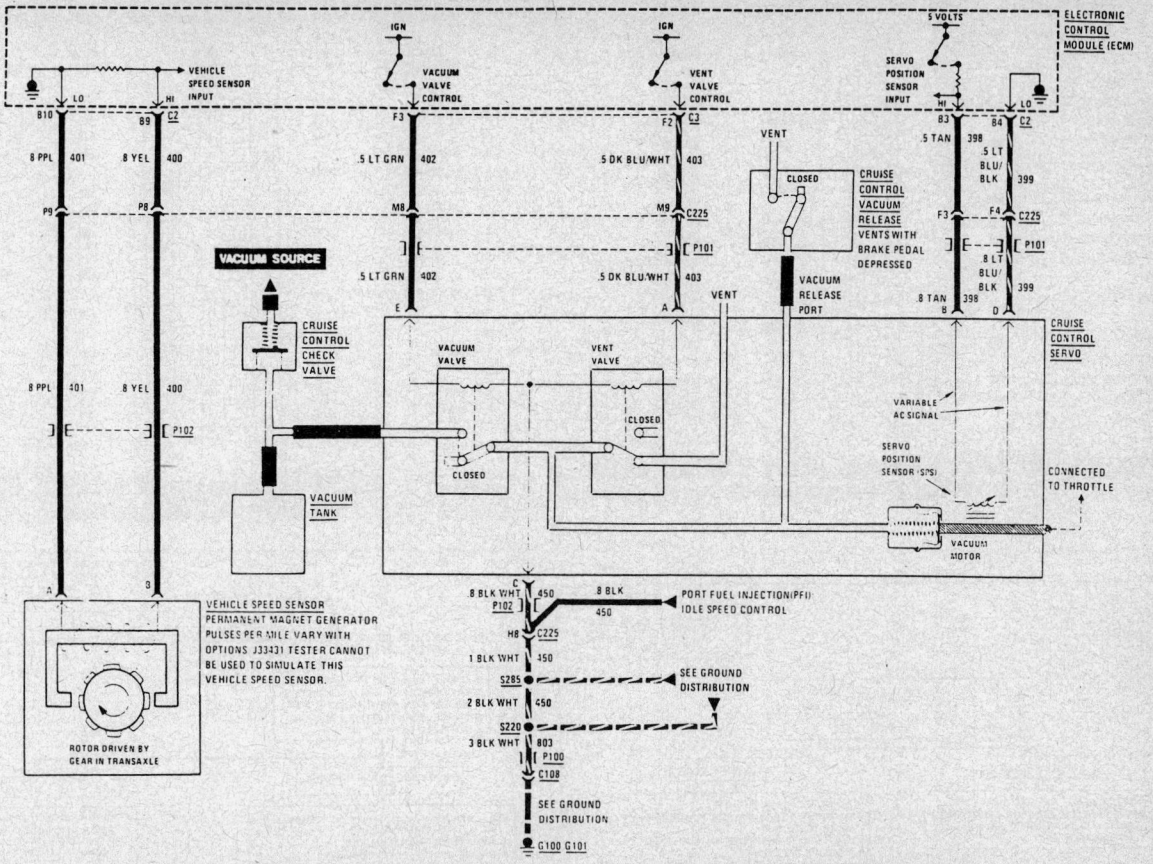

Fig. 9   Wiring diagram (Part 2 of 2). 1990 DeVille & Fleetwood

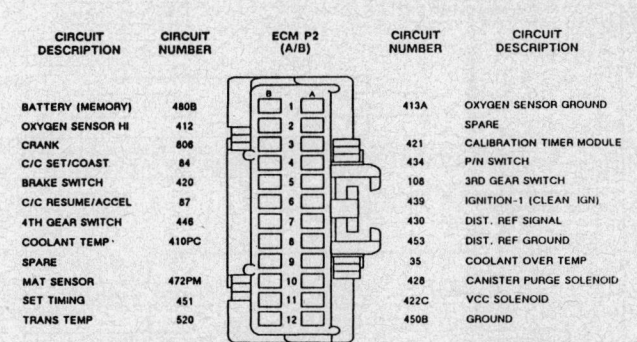

CIRCUIT DESCRIPTION	CIRCUIT NUMBER	ECM P2 (A/B)	CIRCUIT NUMBER	CIRCUIT DESCRIPTION
BATTERY (MEMORY)	480B	1	413A	OXYGEN SENSOR GROUND
OXYGEN SENSOR HI	412	2		SPARE
CRANK	806	3	421	CALIBRATION TIMER MODULE
C/C SET/COAST	84	4	434	P/N SWITCH
BRAKE SWITCH	420	5	108	3RD GEAR SWITCH
C/C RESUME/ACCEL	87	6	439	IGNITION-1 (CLEAN IGN)
4TH GEAR SWITCH	446	7	430	DIST. REF SIGNAL
COOLANT TEMP	410PC	8	453	DIST. REF GROUND
SPARE		9	35	COOLANT OVER TEMP
MAT SENSOR	472PM	10	428	CANISTER PURGE SOLENOID
SET TIMING	451	11	422C	VCC SOLENOID
TRANS TEMP	520	12	450B	GROUND

Fig. 10   ECM connector (Part 1 of 2). 1988–89 DeVille & Fleetwood

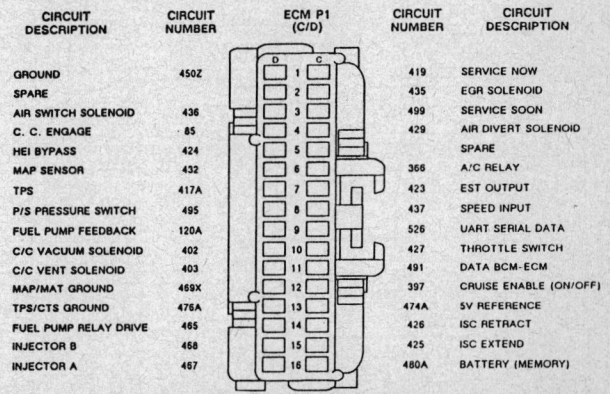

CIRCUIT DESCRIPTION	CIRCUIT NUMBER	ECM P1 (C/D)	CIRCUIT NUMBER	CIRCUIT DESCRIPTION
GROUND	450Z	D 1 C	419	SERVICE NOW
SPARE		2	435	EGR SOLENOID
AIR SWITCH SOLENOID	436	3	499	SERVICE SOON
C. C. ENGAGE	85	4	429	AIR DIVERT SOLENOID
HEI BYPASS	424	5		SPARE
MAP SENSOR	432	6	366	A/C RELAY
TPS	417A	7	423	EST OUTPUT
P/S PRESSURE SWITCH	495	8	437	SPEED INPUT
FUEL PUMP FEEDBACK	120A	9	526	UART SERIAL DATA
C/C VACUUM SOLENOID	402	10	427	THROTTLE SWITCH
C/C VENT SOLENOID	403	11	491	DATA BCM-ECM
MAP/MAT GROUND	469X	12	397	CRUISE ENABLE (ON/OFF)
TPS/CTS GROUND	476A	13	474A	5V REFERENCE
FUEL PUMP RELAY DRIVE	465	14	426	ISC RETRACT
INJECTOR B	468	15	425	ISC EXTEND
INJECTOR A	467	16	480A	BATTERY (MEMORY)

Fig. 10   ECM connector (Part 2 of 2). 1988–89 DeVille & Fleetwood

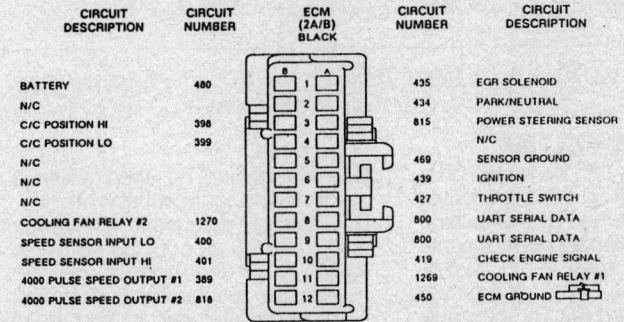

CIRCUIT DESCRIPTION	CIRCUIT NUMBER	ECM (2A/B) BLACK	CIRCUIT NUMBER	CIRCUIT DESCRIPTION
BATTERY	480	1	435	EGR SOLENOID
N/C		2	434	PARK/NEUTRAL
C/C POSITION HI	398	3	815	POWER STEERING SENSOR
C/C POSITION LO	399	4		N/C
N/C		5	469	SENSOR GROUND
N/C		6	439	IGNITION
N/C		7	427	THROTTLE SWITCH
COOLING FAN RELAY #2	1270	8	800	UART SERIAL DATA
SPEED SENSOR INPUT LO	400	9	800	UART SERIAL DATA
SPEED SENSOR INPUT HI	401	10	419	CHECK ENGINE SIGNAL
4000 PULSE SPEED OUTPUT #1	389	11	1269	COOLING FAN RELAY #1
4000 PULSE SPEED OUTPUT #2	818	12	450	ECM GROUND

☐ SINGLE CAVITY METRI PAK CONNECTOR

Fig. 11   ECM connector (Part 1 of 3). 1990 DeVille & Fleetwood

sume/acceleration switch to test operation of switch. Refer to **Fig. 16 and 17** for further testing procedure. For intermittent codes proceed as follows:

a. Turn cruise dash switch to on and backprobe ECM B6 with a voltmeter to ground. B6 should show 12 volts with resume/acceleration switch depressed and 0 volts with switch released. While observing meter, cycle switch and wiggle wiring and connectors.

9. With code E.7.8 displayed, turn steering wheel to full lock in both directions, then return wheel to straight ahead position to test power steering pressure switch operation.

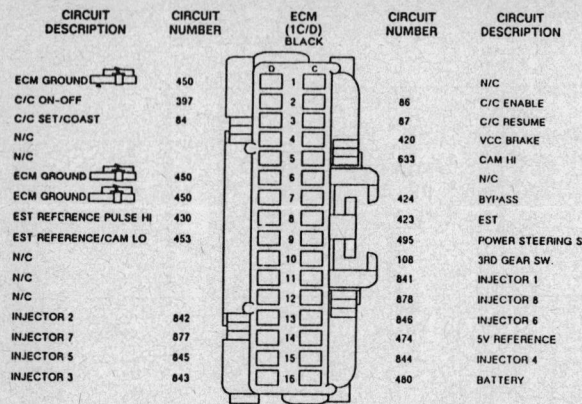

CIRCUIT DESCRIPTION	CIRCUIT NUMBER	ECM (1C/D) BLACK	CIRCUIT NUMBER	CIRCUIT DESCRIPTION
ECM GROUND	450	D C 1		N/C
C/C ON-OFF	397	2	86	C/C ENABLE
C/C SET/COAST	84	3	87	C/C RESUME
N/C		4	420	VCC BRAKE
N/C		5	633	CAM HI
ECM GROUND	450	6		N/C
ECM GROUND	450	7	424	BYPASS
EST REFERENCE PULSE HI	430	8	423	EST
EST REFERENCE/CAM LO	453	9	495	POWER STEERING SW.
N/C		10	108	3RD GEAR SW.
N/C		11	841	INJECTOR 1
N/C		12	878	INJECTOR 8
INJECTOR 2	842	13	846	INJECTOR 6
INJECTOR 7	877	14	474	5V REFERENCE
INJECTOR 5	845	15	844	INJECTOR 4
INJECTOR 3	843	16	480	BATTERY

Fig. 11 ECM connector (Part 2 of 3). 1990 DeVille & Fleetwood

NOTE: THE TPA STRAIN RELIEVERS IN THIS CONNECTOR WILL BE MARKED AS C AND D

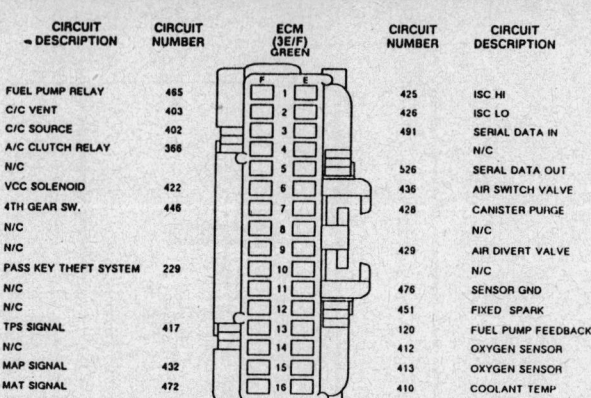

CIRCUIT DESCRIPTION	CIRCUIT NUMBER	ECM (3E/F) GREEN	CIRCUIT NUMBER	CIRCUIT DESCRIPTION
FUEL PUMP RELAY	465	F E 1	425	ISC HI
C/C VENT	403	2	426	ISC LO
C/C SOURCE	402	3	491	SERIAL DATA IN
A/C CLUTCH RELAY	366	4		N/C
N/C		5	526	SERIAL DATA OUT
VCC SOLENOID	422	6	436	AIR SWITCH VALVE
4TH GEAR SW.	446	7	428	CANISTER PURGE
N/C		8		N/C
N/C		9	429	AIR DIVERT VALVE
PASS KEY THEFT SYSTEM	229	10		N/C
N/C		11	476	SENSOR GND
N/C		12	451	FIXED SPARK
TPS SIGNAL	417	13	120	FUEL PUMP FEEDBACK
N/C		14	412	OXYGEN SENSOR
MAP SIGNAL	432	15	413	OXYGEN SENSOR
MAT SIGNAL	472	16	410	COOLANT TEMP

Fig. 11 ECM connector (Part 3 of 3). 1990 DeVille & Fleetwood

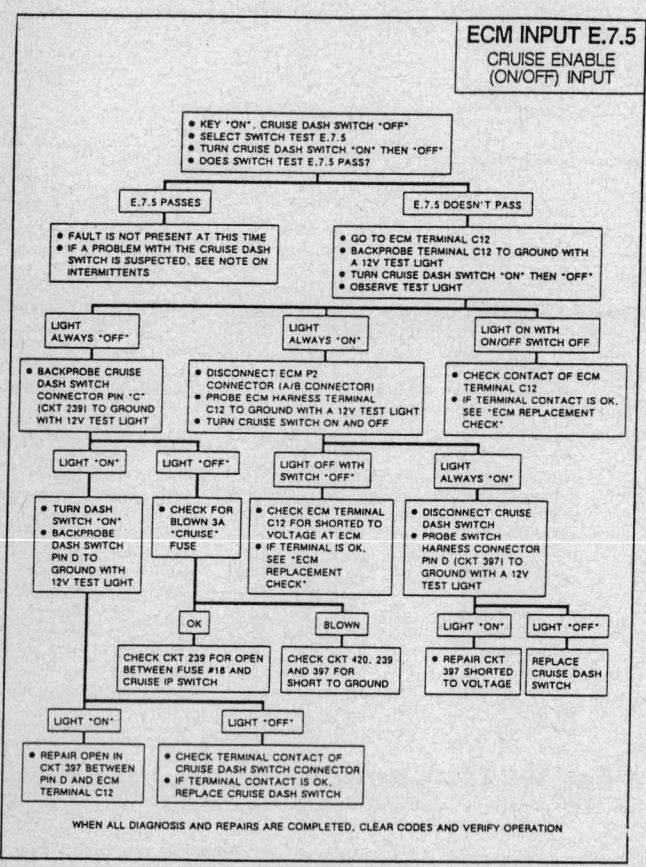

Fig. 12 ECM input test E7.5. 1988–89 DeVille & Fleetwood

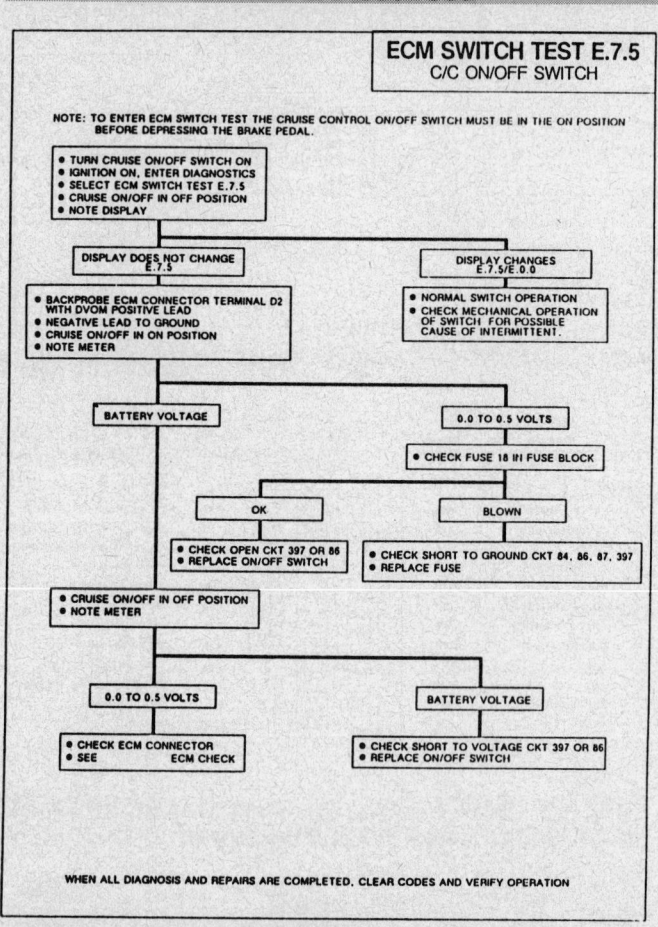

Fig. 13 ECM input test E7.5. 1990 DeVille & Fleetwood

10. When the switch tests are completed, the ECM will go back and display codes for switches which did not test properly.

11. Check circuit between each switch that failed and the ECM, test switches individually, repair as needed, then clear trouble codes and retest system.

12. If malfunction persists, refer to "Fuel Injection Section" in the MOTOR Auto Engine Tune Up & Electronics manual.

ECM OUTPUT CYCLING

ECM output cycling can be tested after code E.9.5 is displayed on the data center. Code E.9.5 can be reached by depressing the HI button on the climate control panel when code .7.0 is displayed. The ECM output cycling mode, code E.9.6, will then cycle ECM outputs on and off. To enter output cycling mode, proceed as follows:

1. With engine running, turn instrument panel cruise control switch to ON position to allow cruise control outputs to cycle.

2. Turn ignition off, then within 2 seconds turn ignition back on.

3. Enter self-diagnostic mode and obtain code E.9.5 as outlined above.

4. **On 1988-89 models,** depress and release accelerator pedal (open and close throttle switch) and the display code E.9.6 should appear. If not, check throttle switch signal as outlined.

5. The cruise power solenoid should cycle on and off rapidly, and the cruise

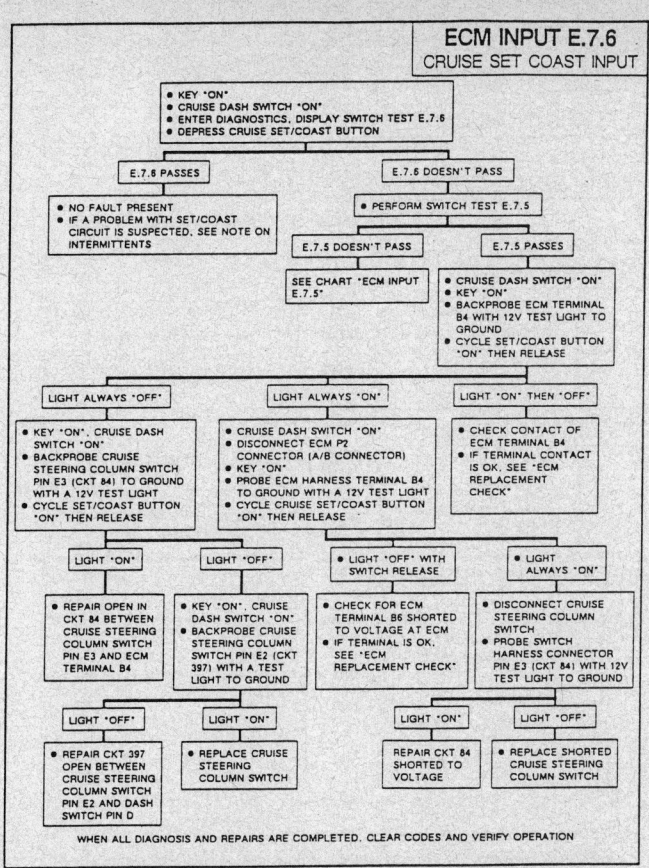

Fig. 14   ECM input test E7.6. 1988–89 DeVille & Fleetwood

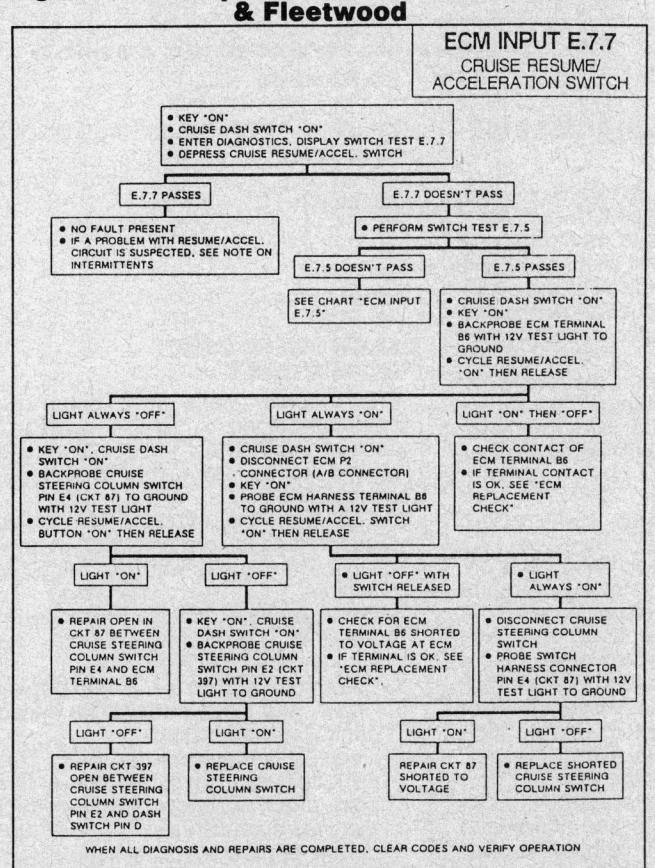

Fig. 16   ECM input test E7.7. 1988–89 DeVille & Fleetwood

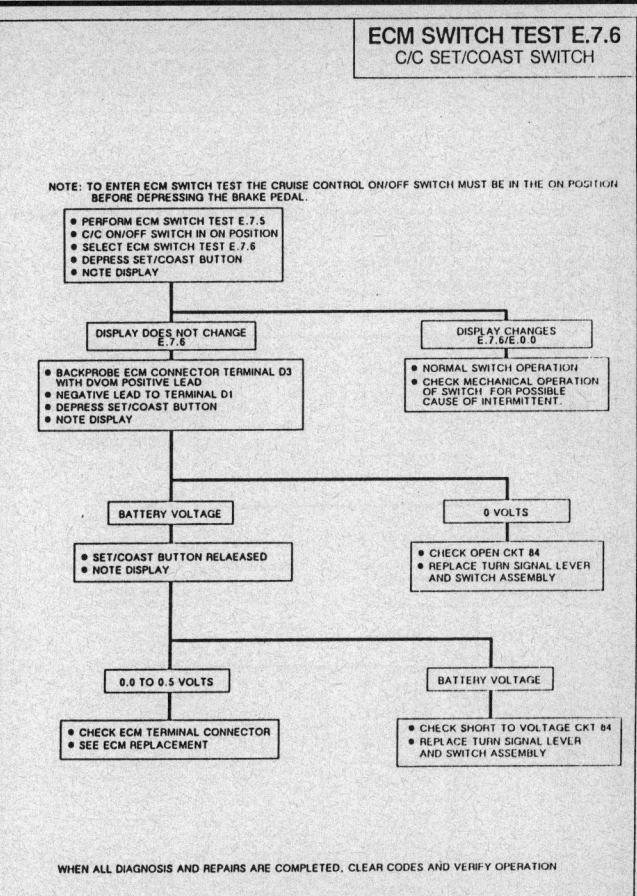

Fig. 15   ECM input test E7.6. 1990 DeVille & Fleetwood

vacuum valve should cycle on and off every 3 seconds.
6. The output cycling mode will stop automatically after 2 minutes and the display code will return to E.9.5
7. **On 1990 models,** depress LO button on the climate control panel to initiate cycling mode, then E1.2 and E9.6 will be displayed.
8. Every 3 seconds devices will be cycled.
9. Depress HI button on climate control panel to advance device testing and depress LO button to return to E0.0 (cycle none).
10. **On all models,** if the system fails to operate as outlined, check wiring between effected component and ECM, test components individually, repair as needed, then clear trouble codes and repeat test. If malfunction persists, refer to "Fuel Injection Section" in the MOTOR's Auto Engine Tune Up & Electronics manual.

Eldorado & Seville

Before performing any diagnosis or repair procedures, temporarily disable the Supplemental Inflatable Restraint (SIR) system. Failure to do so may result in possible air bag deployment or personal injury. Disable SIR system as follows:
1. Turn ignition switch to Off position.
2. Remove SIR fuse 3.
3. Disconnect yellow SIR electrical har-

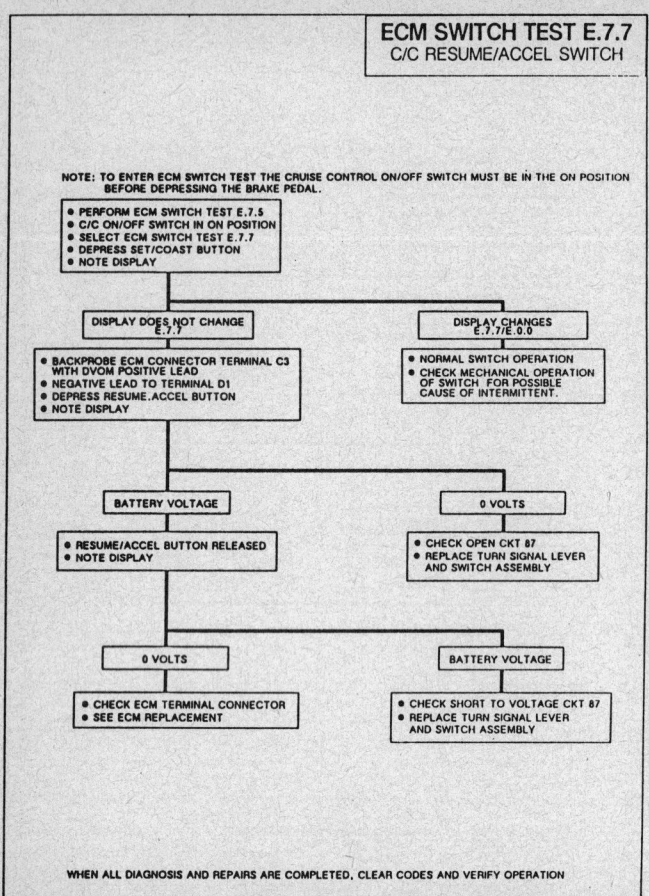

Fig. 17 ECM input test E7.7. 1990 DeVille & Fleetwood

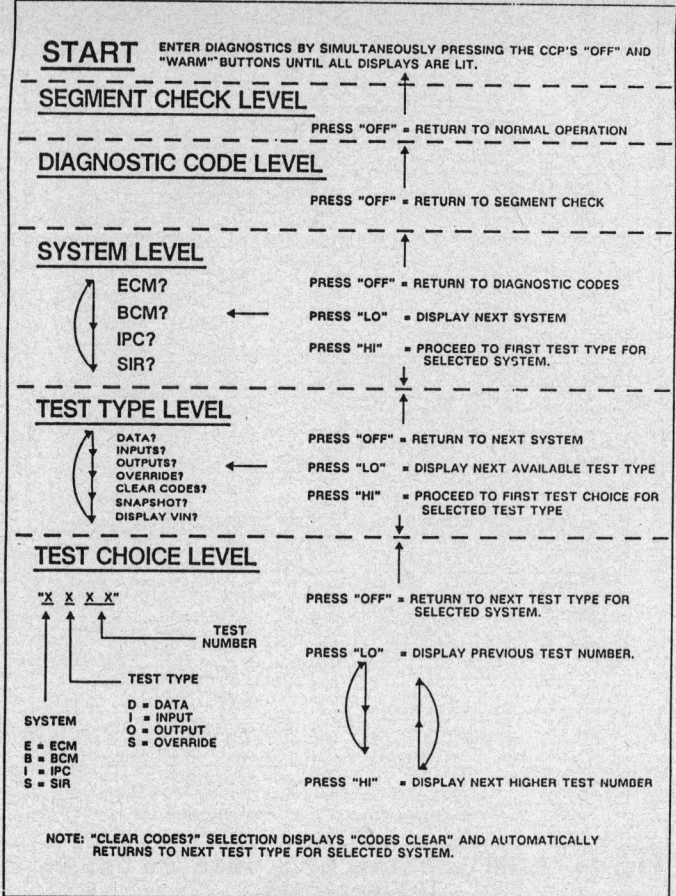

Fig. 18 Operating service mode. Seville & Eldorado

ness connector, at base of steering column.

4. Reverse procedure to reconnect, ensure "Inflatable Restraint" indicator flashes 7 to 9 times to indicate proper SIR operation.

On vehicles equipped with ABS brake system, the hydraulic accumulator, when fully charged contains brake fluid at high pressure. Before disconnecting any lines, hoses or fittings, ensure accumulator is full depressurized. Failure to do so may result in personal injury.

To depressurize the hydraulic accumulator, turn the ignition to the Off position or disconnect negative battery cable, pump brake pedal a minimum of 40 times at approximately 50 lbs. of force. A noticeable change in pedal feel will occur when accumulator is fully discharged.

SELF-DIAGNOSTIC SYSTEM

In the process of controlling the various subsystems, the ECM and BCM continually monitor operating conditions for possible malfunctions. By comparing system conditions against standard operating limits certain circuits and component malfunctions can be detected. A three digit numerical code is stored in the computer memory when a problem is detected by this self diagnostic system.

ENTERING SELF-DIAGNOSTIC MODE

To enter diagnostic service mode, turn ignition on, then depress Off and Warm buttons on the climate control panel (CCP). Hold buttons until all display panel segments illuminate, indicating the beginning of diagnostic readout. The two display panels must be illuminated, except for turn signal lights, to ensure all segments are operating. **Do not attempt diagnosis unless all segments appear, as an improper diagnosis may result.** If any segments are inoperative, the display panel must be replaced.

ACCESSING CODES

After the diagnostic service mode is entered, any trouble codes stored in the computer memory will be displayed, **Fig. 18**. ECM codes will be displayed first, then BCM codes. Codes will also be accompanied by Current or History. History indicates the failure was not present the last time the code was tested. Current indicates the fault still exists. At any time during the display of trouble codes the Low button on the CCP is depressed, the display of codes will be bypassed. At any time during the display of trouble codes the Reset/Recall button on the DIC is depressed, the system will exit diagnostic service mode and go back to normal vehicle oper-

ation. Refer to **Fig. 19**, for the following trouble codes:
Code EO60
Code EO63
Code EO64
Code EO65
Code EO66
Code EO67
Code E068

DIAGNOSTIC TEST PROCEDURES

After trouble codes have been displayed, the diagnostic service mode can be used to further test the speed control system. To do so, refer to **Fig. 18**, and proceed as follows:

1. Following the display of trouble codes, the first available system level will be displayed, which is the ECM system.
2. On all models, depress Hi button on the CCP. This will display "Data," the first available test type.
3. Press Lo button on the CCP to display "Input," the test type level for speed control system testing.
4. Depress Hi button on the CCP. This will displayed the first test type. At this point, press Hi button until the correct test type appears as listed below under the applicable model year.
5. To display the previous test, press Lo button. To return to previous test type, press Off.

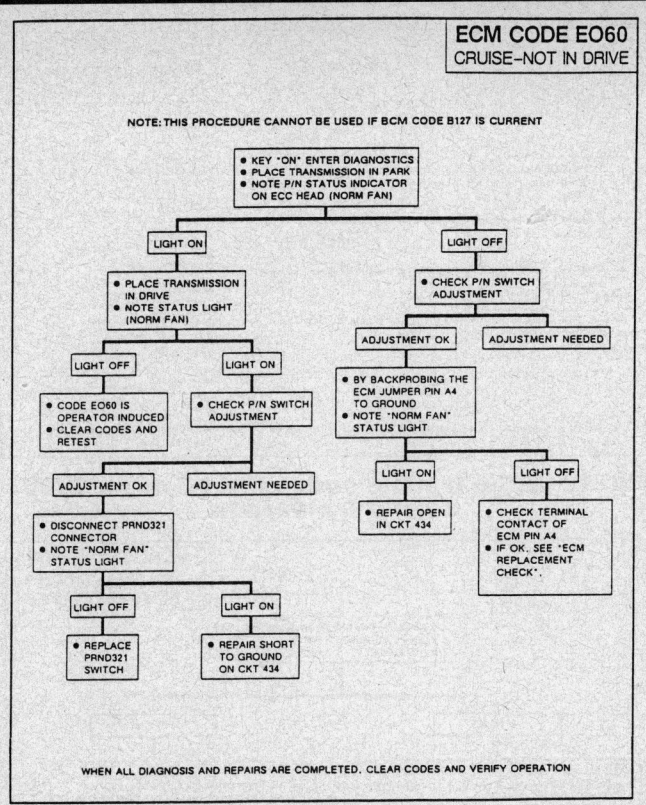

Fig. 19   ECM trouble code (Part 1 of 7). 1988–89 Seville & Eldorado

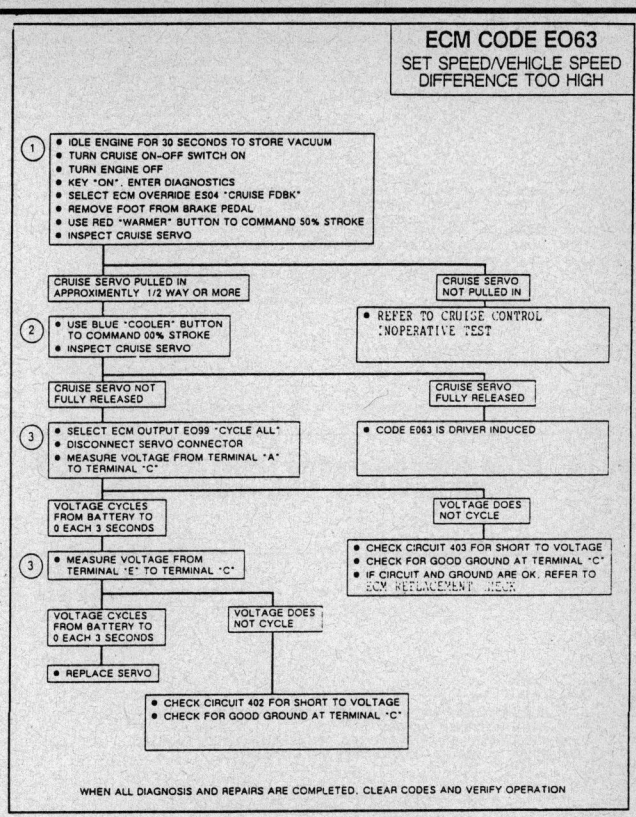

Fig. 19   ECM trouble codes (Part 2 of 7). 1988–89 Seville & Eldorado

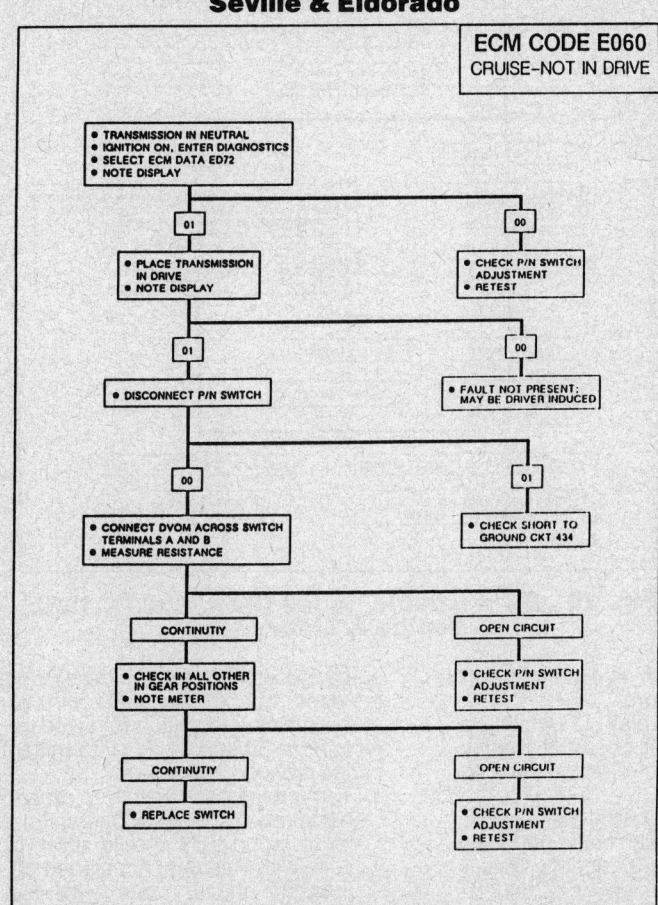

Fig. 19   ECM trouble codes (Part 1 of 7). 1990 Seville & Eldorado

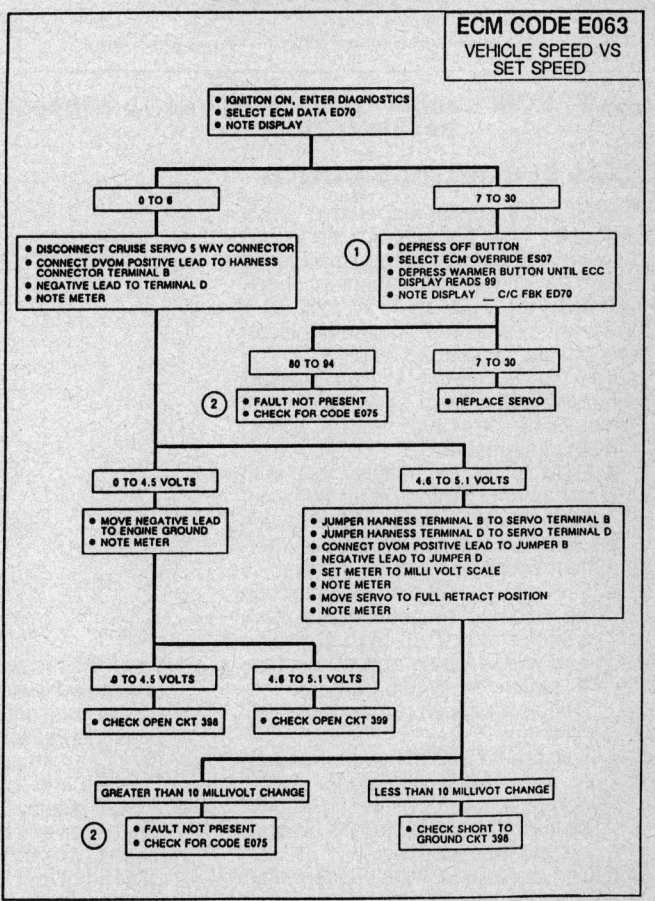

Fig. 19   ECM trouble codes (Part 2 of 7). 1990 Seville & Eldorado

TYPE 1

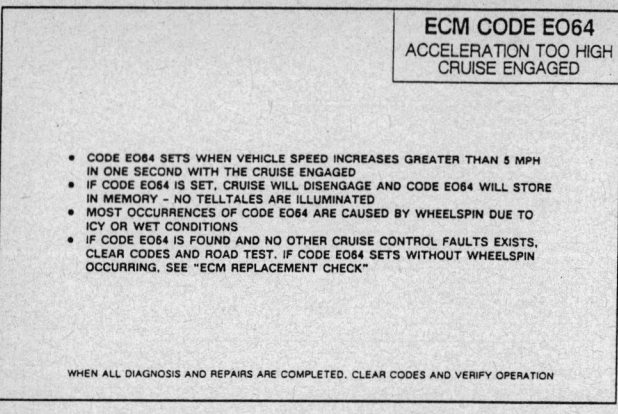

ECM CODE E064
ACCELERATION TOO HIGH
CRUISE ENGAGED

- CODE E064 SETS WHEN VEHICLE SPEED INCREASES GREATER THAN 5 MPH IN ONE SECOND WITH THE CRUISE ENGAGED
- IF CODE E064 IS SET, CRUISE WILL DISENGAGE AND CODE E064 WILL STORE IN MEMORY - NO TELLTALES ARE ILLUMINATED
- MOST OCCURRENCES OF CODE E064 ARE CAUSED BY WHEELSPIN DUE TO ICY OR WET CONDITIONS
- IF CODE E064 IS FOUND AND NO OTHER CRUISE CONTROL FAULTS EXISTS, CLEAR CODES AND ROAD TEST. IF CODE E064 SETS WITHOUT WHEELSPIN OCCURRING, SEE "ECM REPLACEMENT CHECK"

WHEN ALL DIAGNOSIS AND REPAIRS ARE COMPLETED, CLEAR CODES AND VERIFY OPERATION

Fig. 19   ECM trouble codes (Part 3 of 7). 1988–89 Seville & Eldorado

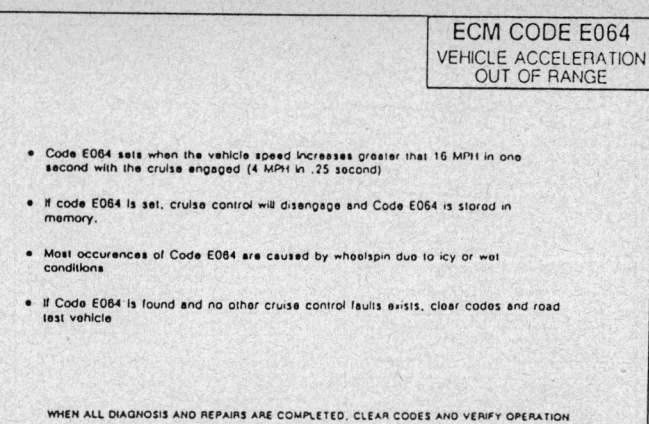

ECM CODE E064
VEHICLE ACCELERATION
OUT OF RANGE

- Code E064 sets when the vehicle speed increases greater than 16 MPH in one second with the cruise engaged (4 MPH in .25 second)
- If code E064 is set, cruise control will disengage and Code E064 is stored in memory.
- Most occurences of Code E064 are caused by wheelspin due to icy or wet conditions
- If Code E064 is found and no other cruise control faults exists, clear codes and road test vehicle

WHEN ALL DIAGNOSIS AND REPAIRS ARE COMPLETED, CLEAR CODES AND VERIFY OPERATION

Fig. 19   ECM trouble codes (Part 3 of 7). 1990 Seville & Eldorado

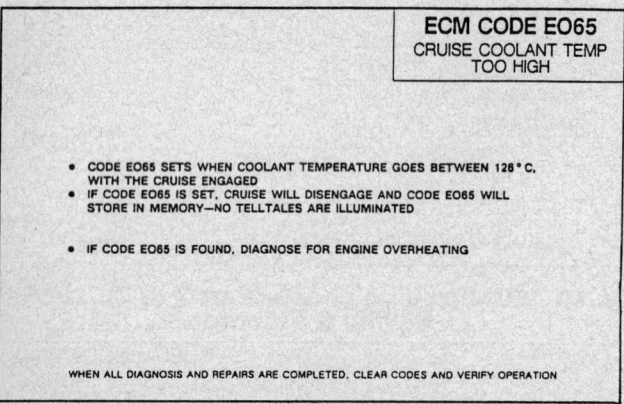

ECM CODE E065
CRUISE COOLANT TEMP
TOO HIGH

- CODE E065 SETS WHEN COOLANT TEMPERATURE GOES BETWEEN 126°C. WITH THE CRUISE ENGAGED
- IF CODE E065 IS SET, CRUISE WILL DISENGAGE AND CODE E065 WILL STORE IN MEMORY—NO TELLTALES ARE ILLUMINATED
- IF CODE E065 IS FOUND, DIAGNOSE FOR ENGINE OVERHEATING

WHEN ALL DIAGNOSIS AND REPAIRS ARE COMPLETED, CLEAR CODES AND VERIFY OPERATION

Fig. 19   ECM trouble codes (Part 4 of 7). 1988–89 Seville & Eldorado

Cruise Control Inoperative

If cruise control is inoperative, enter ECM "Input" tests and perform the following, referring to wiring diagram on **Figs. 20 through 23**, and ECM replacement check, if necessary, on **Figs. 6, 7, 24 and 25**. If cruise system does function, but indicator does not light, proceed to step 13.

1. With ignition switch in Run position, on 1988-89 models, select ECM input test EI79, on 1990 models, select ECM input test E182.
2. If ECM does not display LO with cruise control switch off, or does not display Hi with cruise control switch on, refer to **Figs. 26 and 27**. For intermittent codes proceed as follows:
   a. The amber cruise on indicator can be used to monitor cruise dash switch status. Turn dash switch on and wiggle wiring and connectors. If switch or circuit from fuse to switch are open, amber light will blink out.
   b. If cruise 3A fuse blows intermittently, turn switch on, wiggle wiring, connectors, cruise steering column switch. If circuit becomes grounded, the fuse will blow.
3. If ECM displays LO with cruise switch on and displays HI with cruise switch on, on 1988-89 models select ECM input test EI71, on 1990 models, select input test E170, on all models,

turn ignition switch to Run position and cruise switch on.
4. If ECM does not display LO with brake pedal depressed, or does not display HI with brake pedal released, refer to **Figs. 28 and 29**.
5. If ECM displays LO with brake pedal depressed and HI with brake pedal released, on 1988-89 models, select ECM input test EI81, on 1990 models, select ECM input test E184, on all models turn ignition switch to Run position and cruise control on.
6. If ECM does not display HI with Re-

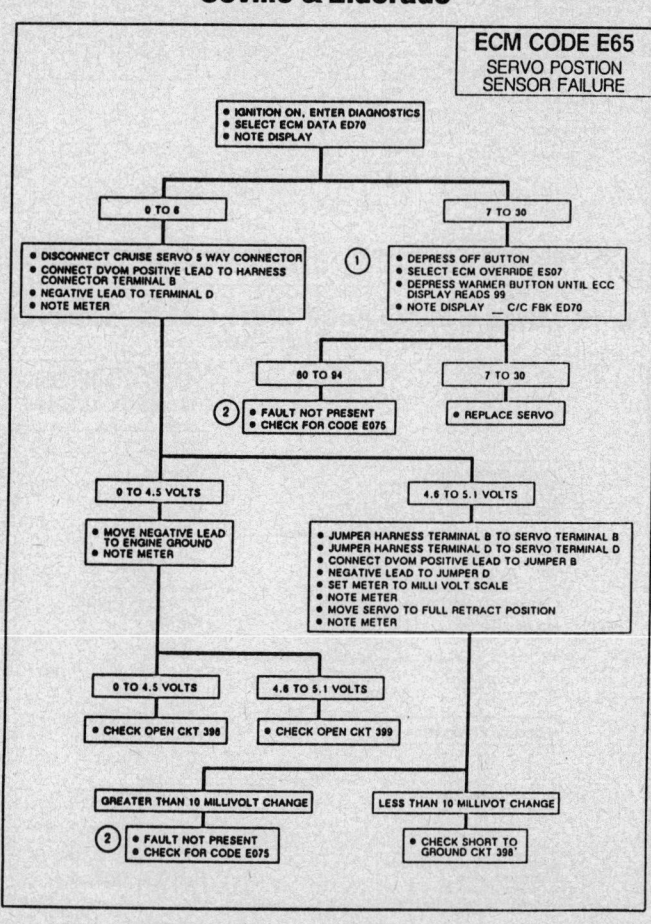

ECM CODE E65
SERVO POSTION
SENSOR FAILURE

- IGNITION ON, ENTER DIAGNOSTICS
- SELECT ECM DATA ED70
- NOTE DISPLAY

0 TO 6 →
- DISCONNECT CRUISE SERVO 5 WAY CONNECTOR
- CONNECT DVOM POSITIVE LEAD TO HARNESS CONNECTOR TERMINAL B
- NEGATIVE LEAD TO TERMINAL D
- NOTE METER

7 TO 30 → ①
- DEPRESS OFF BUTTON
- SELECT ECM OVERRIDE ES07
- DEPRESS WARMER BUTTON UNTIL ECC DISPLAY READS 99
- NOTE DISPLAY __ C/C FBK ED70

80 TO 94 → ②
- FAULT NOT PRESENT
- CHECK FOR CODE E075

7 TO 30 →
- REPLACE SERVO

0 TO 4.5 VOLTS →
- MOVE NEGATIVE LEAD TO ENGINE GROUND
- NOTE METER

4.6 TO 5.1 VOLTS →
- JUMPER HARNESS TERMINAL B TO SERVO TERMINAL B
- JUMPER HARNESS TERMINAL D TO SERVO TERMINAL D
- CONNECT DVOM POSITIVE LEAD TO JUMPER B
- NEGATIVE LEAD TO JUMPER D
- SET METER TO MILLI VOLT SCALE
- NOTE METER
- MOVE SERVO TO FULL RETRACT POSITION
- NOTE METER

0 TO 4.5 VOLTS →
- CHECK OPEN CKT 398

4.6 TO 5.1 VOLTS →
- CHECK OPEN CKT 399

GREATER THAN 10 MILLIVOLT CHANGE → ②
- FAULT NOT PRESENT
- CHECK FOR CODE E075

LESS THAN 10 MILLIVOT CHANGE →
- CHECK SHORT TO GROUND CKT 398

Fig. 19   ECM trouble codes (Part 4 of 7). 1990 Seville & Eldorado

sume/Accelerate switch depressed, or does not display LO with resume/accelerate switch released, refer to **Figs. 30 and 31**. For intermittent codes proceed as follows:
   a. Turn cruise dash switch to on and backprobe ECM B6 with a voltmeter to ground, B6 should show 12 volts with Resume/Accelerate depressed and 0 volts with Resume/Accelerate released. Cycle switch while observing the meter, wiggle wiring and connectors.
7. If ECM displays HI with re-

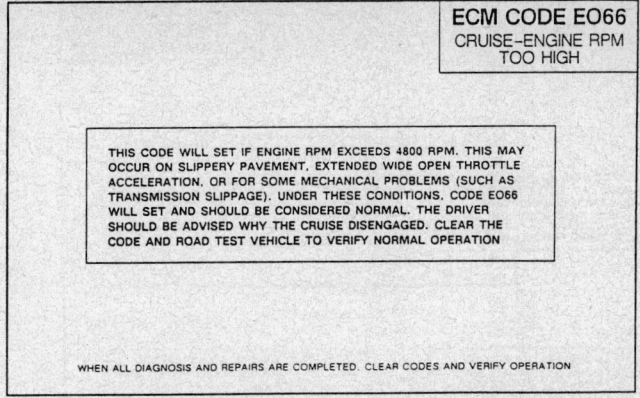

ECM CODE EO66
CRUISE–ENGINE RPM
TOO HIGH

THIS CODE WILL SET IF ENGINE RPM EXCEEDS 4800 RPM. THIS MAY OCCUR ON SLIPPERY PAVEMENT, EXTENDED WIDE OPEN THROTTLE ACCELERATION, OR FOR SOME MECHANICAL PROBLEMS (SUCH AS TRANSMISSION SLIPPAGE). UNDER THESE CONDITIONS, CODE EO66 WILL SET AND SHOULD BE CONSIDERED NORMAL. THE DRIVER SHOULD BE ADVISED WHY THE CRUISE DISENGAGED. CLEAR THE CODE AND ROAD TEST VEHICLE TO VERIFY NORMAL OPERATION

WHEN ALL DIAGNOSIS AND REPAIRS ARE COMPLETED, CLEAR CODES AND VERIFY OPERATION

Fig. 19 ECM trouble codes (Part 5 of 7). 1988–90 Seville & Eldorado

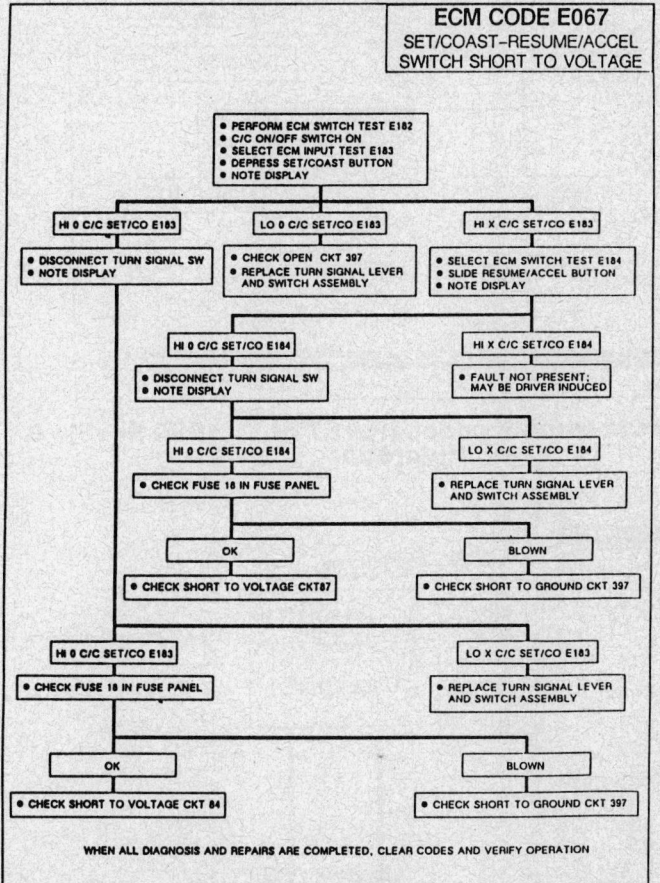

Fig. 19 ECM trouble codes (Part 6 of 7). 1990 Seville & Eldorado

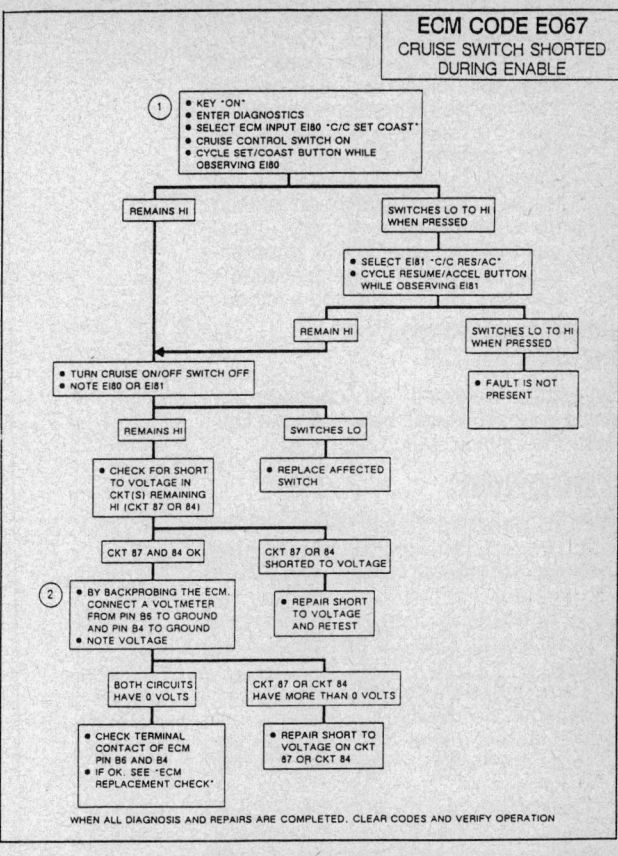

Fig. 19 ECM trouble codes (Part 6 of 7). 1988–89 Seville & Eldorado

sume/accelerate switch depressed and displays LO with resume accelerate switch released, on 1988-89 models, select ECM input test EI80, on 1990 models, select ECM input test E183, on all models, turn ignition switch to Run position and cruise switch on.

8. If ECM does not display HI with resume/accelerate switch depressed, or does not display LO with resume/accelerate switch released, refer to **Figs. 32 and 33.** For intermittent codes proceed as follows:
   a. Turn cruise dash switch to on and backprobe ECM B4 with a voltmeter to ground. B4 should show 12 volts with resume/accelerate depressed and 0 volts with resume/accelerate released. Cycle switch while observing meter, wiggle wiring and connectors.

9. If ECM displays HI when resume/accelerate switch is depressed and displays LO when resume/accelerate switch is released, run engine for 2 minutes, then turn engine off and select ECM override test ES04.

10. Vary override from 0 to 99, then to 0 again.

11. If cruise control servo does not pull fully in and then release, check vacuum source and hoses for leaks, kinks or restrictions and check servo linkage for mechanical binding, then replace cruise control servo as necessary.

12. If cruise control servo pulls fully in and then releases, replace ECM.

13. If cruise On indicator does not light, but cruise system does function, proceed as follows:
    a. Remove right switch assembly and connect test lamp between connector terminals B4 and BC1.
    b. If lamp illuminates, on 1988 models replace cruise on/off switch. On 1989-90 models replace, right switch assembly.
    c. If lamp does not illuminate, check flex circuit 804, repairing as necessary.

CLEARING CODES

The trouble codes stored in the system memory can be cleared to aid in diagnosing intermittent conditions. To clear codes, proceed as follows:

1. Enter diagnostic service mode as outlined.
2. Follow steps 1 and 2 under "Diagnostic Test Procedures."
3. Depress LO button on the CCP until clear codes is displayed.
4. Depress HI button on the CCP, this

will start the erasing process. **Note the following.**

a. Selection of the clear codes test type will result in the message clear codes being displayed along with the selected system name. This message will appear for 3 seconds to indicate that all stored trouble codes have been erased from that system's memory. After 3 seconds the display will automatically return to the next available test type for the selected system.

EXITING DIAGNOSTIC SERVICE MODE

To exit the diagnostic service mode, depress the Reset/Recall button on the DIC or turn the ignition switch off.

Brougham

Before performing any diagnosis or repair procedures, temporarily disable the Supplemental Inflatable Restraint (SIR) system. Failure to do so may result in possible air bag deployment or personal injury. Disable SIR system as follows:

1. Turn ignition switch to Off position.
2. Remove SIR fuse 3.
3. Disconnect yellow SIR electrical harness connector, at base of steering column.
4. Reverse procedure to reconnect, ensure "Inflatable Restraint" indicator flashes 7 to 9 times to indicate proper SIR operation.

On vehicles equipped with ABS brake system, the hydraulic accumula-

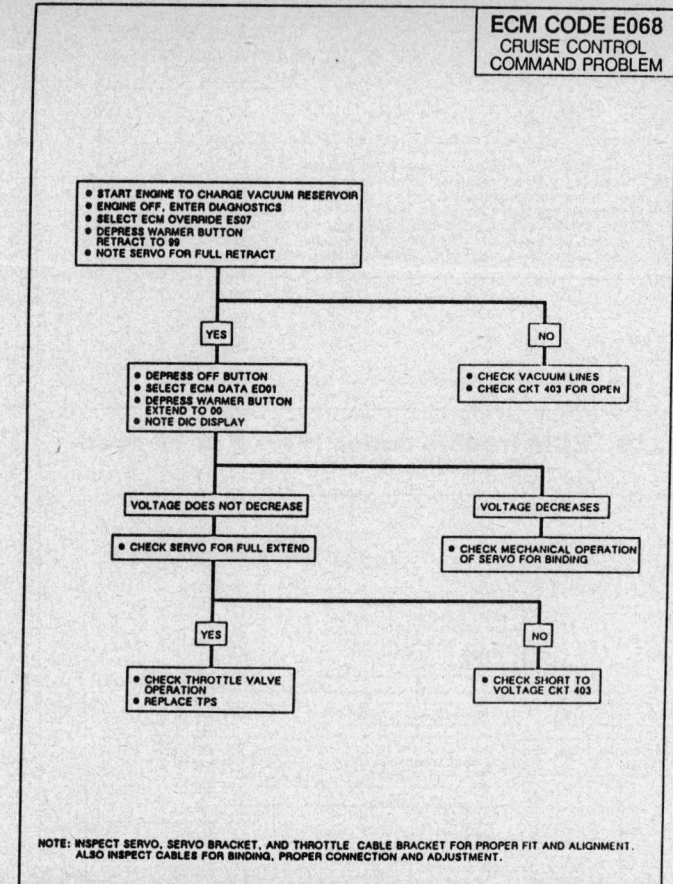

Fig. 19 ECM trouble codes (Part 7 of 7). 1990 Seville & Eldorado

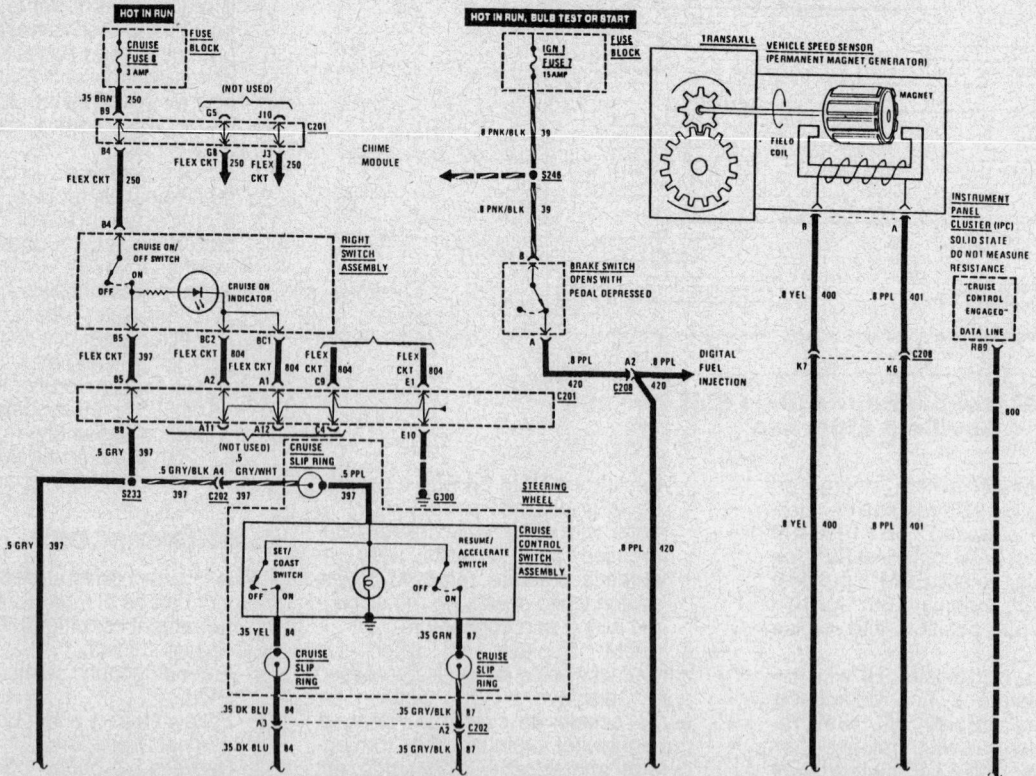

Fig. 20 Wiring diagram (Part 1 of 3). 1988–89 Seville & Eldorado

TYPE 1

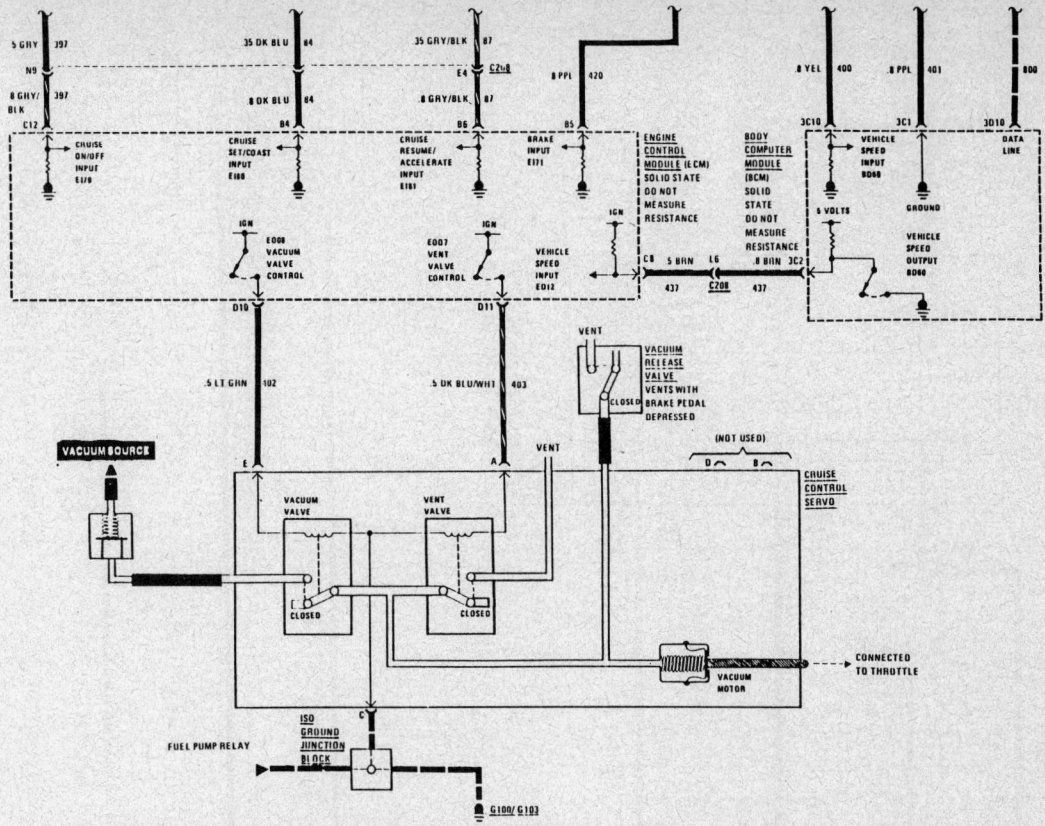

Fig. 20 Wiring diagram (Part 2 of 3). 1988–89 Seville & Eldorado

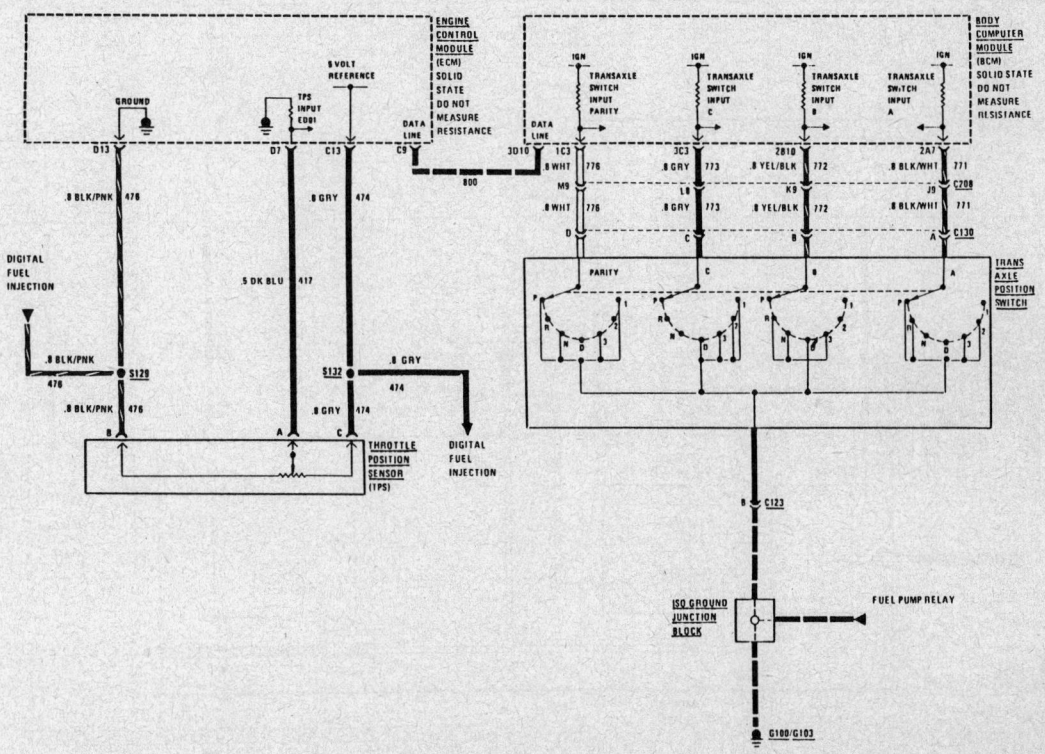

Fig. 20 Wiring diagram (Part 3 of 3). 1988–89 Seville & Eldorado

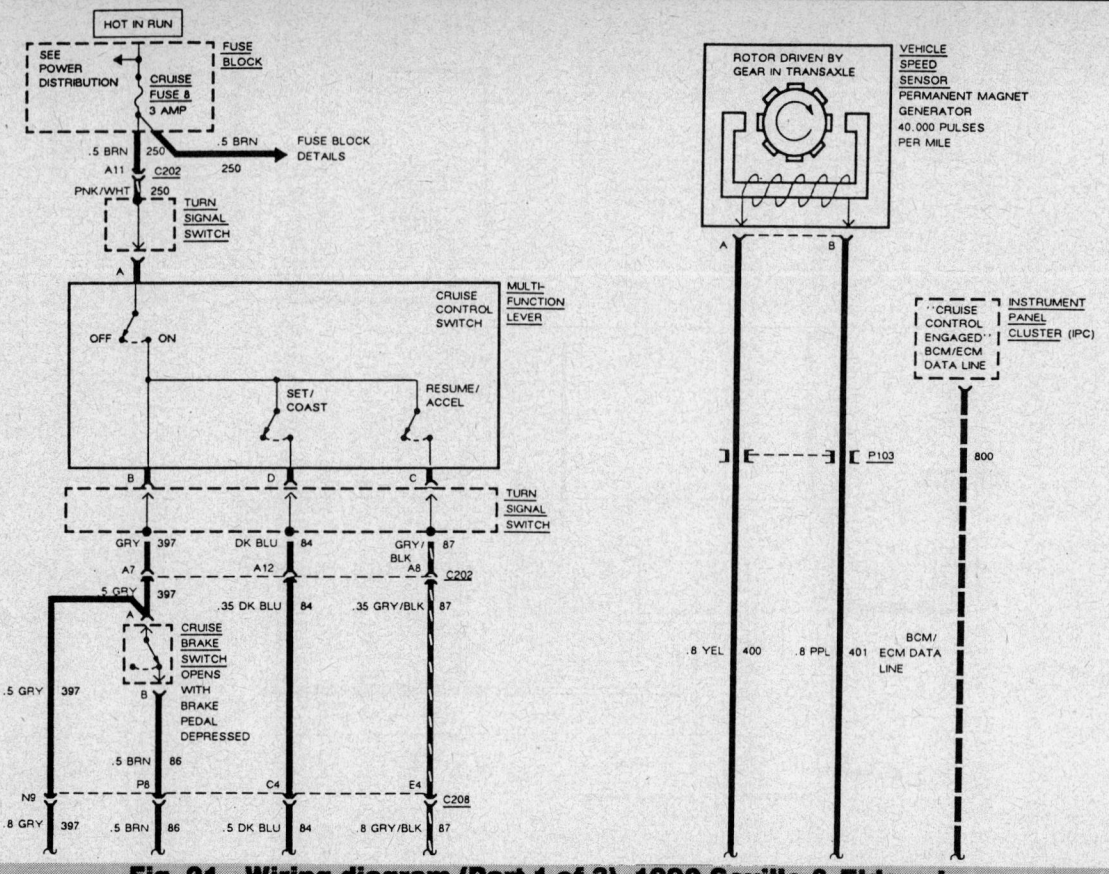

Fig. 21   Wiring diagram (Part 1 of 3). 1990 Seville & Eldorado

Fig. 21   Wiring diagram (Part 2 of 3). 1990 Seville & Eldorado

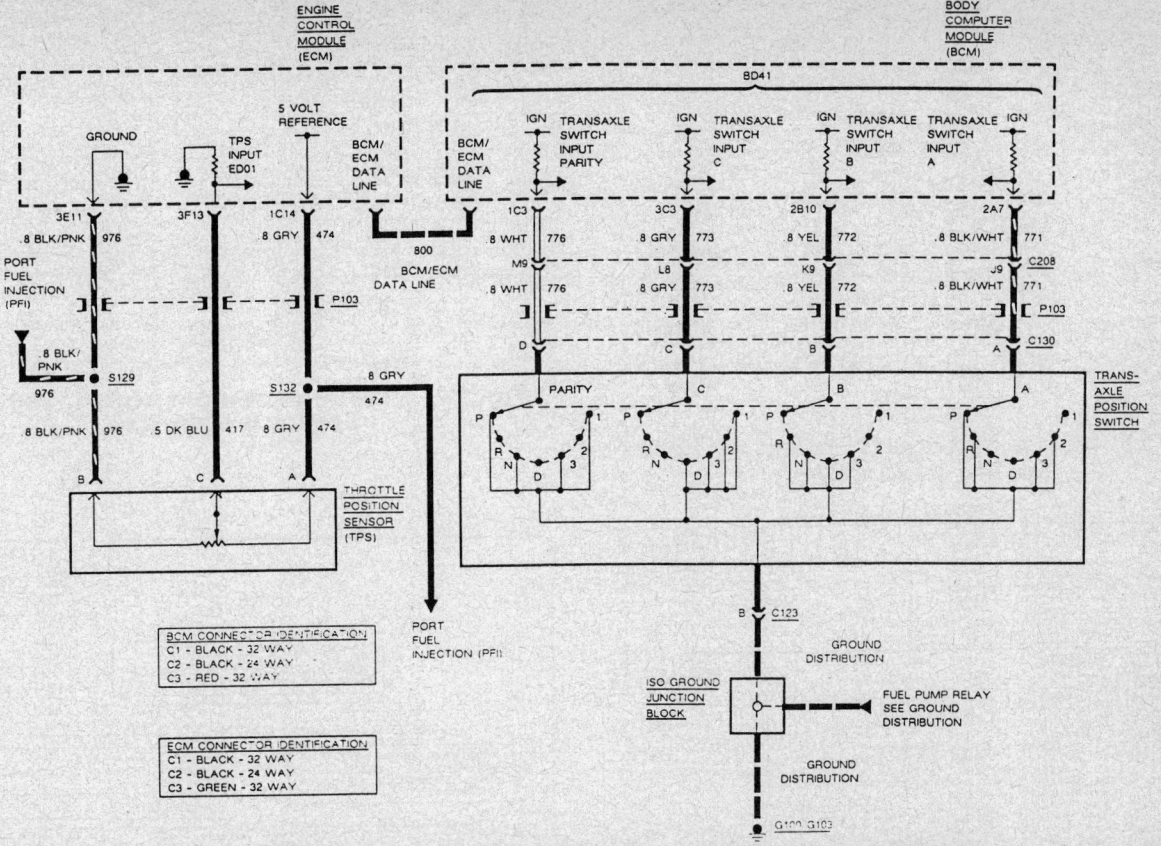

Fig. 21   Wiring diagram (Part 3 of 3). 1990 Seville & Eldorado

CIRCUIT DESCRIPTION	CIRCUIT NUMBER	ECM J1 (A/B)	CIRCUIT NUMBER	CIRCUIT DESCRIPTION
BATTERY (MEMORY)	480B	1	413B	O₂ SENSOR GROUND
O₂ SENSOR SIGNAL	412	2	229	PASS KEY ENABLE
CRANK	806B	3	434	P/N INPUT
CRUISE CONTROL SET/COAST	84	4	438	3RD GEAR INPUT
BRAKE SWITCH	420A	5	439	IGNITION-1
CRUISE CONTROL RESUME/ACCL.	87	6	430BS	DIST. REF. HI
4TH GEAR INPUT	446	7	453F	DIST. REF. LO
COOLANT SIGNAL	410PC	8		
MAT SIGNAL	472PM	9	428	CANISTER PURGE SOL
SET TIMING	451	10	422B	VCC SOLENOID
TRANS. TEMP.	520SK	11	450B	GROUND
		12		

Fig. 22   ECM connector (Part 1 of 2). 1988–89 Seville & Eldorado

CIRCUIT DESCRIPTION	CIRCUIT NUMBER	ECM J2 (C/D)	CIRCUIT NUMBER	CIRCUIT DESCRIPTION
GROUND	450A	1	325	ENG CONTROL SYSTEM
		2	435	EGR SOLENOID
AIR SWITCH SOLENOID	436	3	429	AIR DIVERT SOLENOID
BY PASS	424	4		
MAP SIGNAL	432	5	900	A/C RELAY
TPS SIGNAL	417A	6	423	EST OUTPUT
P/S PRESSURE SWITCH	495	7	437	SPEED INPUT 2km
FUEL PUMP FEEDBACK	120B	8	800H	UART
CRUISE CONTROL VACUUM	402	9	427	THROTTLE SWITCH
CRUISE CONTROL VENT	403	10		
MAP/MAT GROUND	476A	11	397	CRUISE CONTROL ON/OFF
TPS/CTS GROUND	476B	12	474A	TPS/MAP 5V REFERENCE
FUEL PUMP RELAY DRIVE	465	13	426BX	ISC RETRACT
INJECTOR A	468	14	425BX	ISC EXTEND
INJECTOR B	467	15	480A	BATTERY (MEMORY)
		16		

Fig. 22   ECM connector (Part 2 of 2). 1988–89 Seville & Eldorado

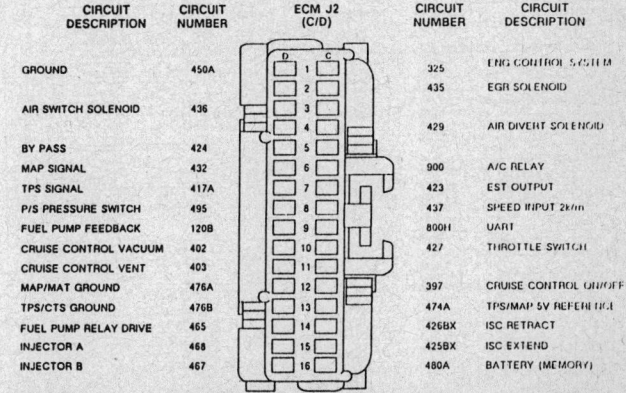

CIRCUIT DESCRIPTION	CIRCUIT NUMBER	ECM (2A/B) BLACK	CIRCUIT NUMBER	CIRCUIT DESCRIPTION
BATTERY	480	1	435	EGR SOLENOID
N/C		2	434	PARK/NEUTRAL
C/C POSITION HI	398	3	815	POWER STEERING SW.
C/C POSITION LO	399	4		N/C
N/C		5	476A	SENSOR GROUND
LEFT O₂ SENSOR	413	6	339	IGNITION
LEFT O₂ SENSOR	912	7	427	THROTTLE SWITCH
COOLING FAN RELAY #2	536	8	800	UART SERIAL DATA OUT
SPEED SENSOR INPUT LO	401	9	800	UART SERIAL DATA IN
SPEED SENSOR INPUT HI	400	10	325	CHECK ENGINE SIGNAL
4000 PULSE SPEED OUTPUT #1	817	11	535	COOLING FAN RELAY #1
N/C	818	12	450	ECM GROUND

Fig. 23   ECM connector (Part 1 of 3). 1990 Seville & Eldorado

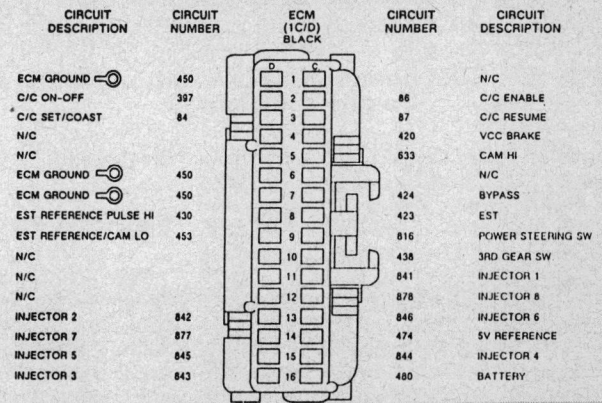

CIRCUIT DESCRIPTION	CIRCUIT NUMBER	ECM (1C/D) BLACK	CIRCUIT NUMBER	CIRCUIT DESCRIPTION
ECM GROUND	450	1		N/C
C/C ON-OFF	397	2	86	C/C ENABLE
C/C SET/COAST	84	3	87	C/C RESUME
N/C		4	420	VCC BRAKE
N/C		5	633	CAM HI
ECM GROUND	450	6		N/C
ECM GROUND	450	7	424	BYPASS
EST REFERENCE PULSE HI	430	8	423	EST
EST REFERENCE/CAM LO	453	9	816	POWER STEERING SW
N/C		10	438	3RD GEAR SW
N/C		11	841	INJECTOR 1
N/C		12	878	INJECTOR 8
INJECTOR 2	842	13	846	INJECTOR 6
INJECTOR 7	877	14	474	5V REFERENCE
INJECTOR 5	845	15	844	INJECTOR 4
INJECTOR 3	843	16	480	BATTERY

Fig. 23   ECM connector (Part 2 of 3). 1990 Seville & Eldorado

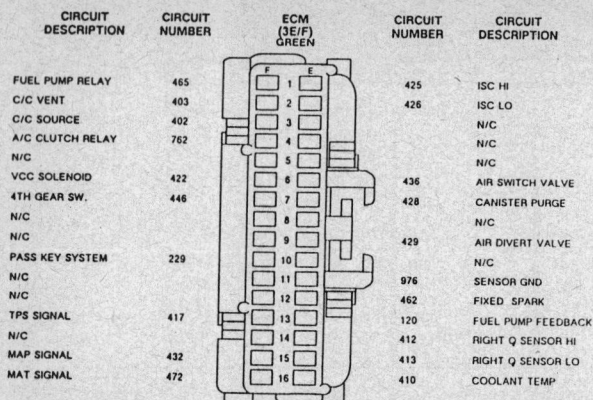

CIRCUIT DESCRIPTION	CIRCUIT NUMBER	ECM (3E/F) GREEN	CIRCUIT NUMBER	CIRCUIT DESCRIPTION
FUEL PUMP RELAY	465	F E 1	425	ISC HI
C/C VENT	403	2	426	ISC LO
C/C SOURCE	402	3		N/C
A/C CLUTCH RELAY	762	4		N/C
N/C		5		N/C
VCC SOLENOID	422	6	436	AIR SWITCH VALVE
4TH GEAR SW.	446	7	428	CANISTER PURGE
N/C		8		N/C
N/C		9	429	AIR DIVERT VALVE
PASS KEY SYSTEM	229	10		N/C
N/C		11	976	SENSOR GND
N/C		12	462	FIXED SPARK
TPS SIGNAL	417	13	120	FUEL PUMP FEEDBACK
N/C		14	412	RIGHT Q SENSOR HI
MAP SIGNAL	432	15	413	RIGHT Q SENSOR LO
MAT SIGNAL	472	16	410	COOLANT TEMP

Fig. 23 ECM connector (Part 3 of 3). 1990 Seville & Eldorado

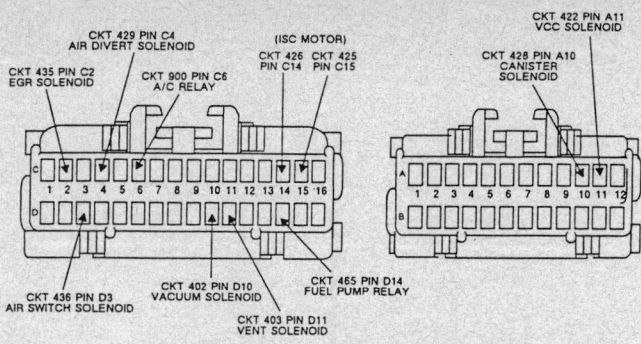

Fig. 24 ECM replacement check. 1988–89 Seville & Eldorado

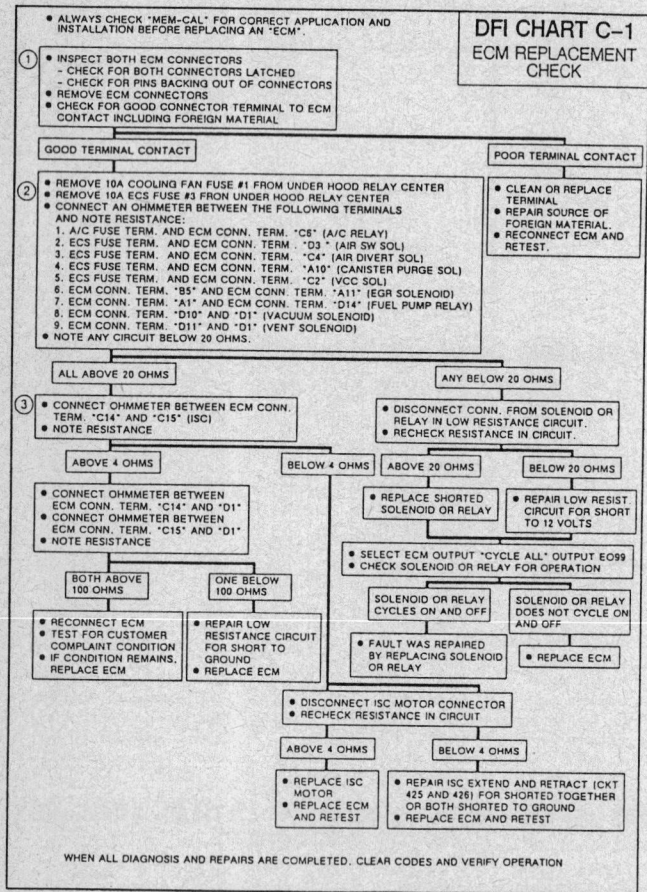

Fig. 25 ECM connector pin location. 1988–89 Seville & Eldorado

Fig. 26 ECM input test E179. 1988–89 Seville & Eldorado

tor, when fully charged contains brake fluid at high pressure. Before disconnecting any lines, hoses or fittings, ensure accumulator is full depressurized. Failure to do so may result in personal injury.

To depressurize the hydraulic accumulator, turn the ignition to the Off position or disconnect negative battery cable, pump brake pedal a minimum of 40 times at approximately 50 lbs. of force. A noticeable change in pedal feel will occur when accumulator is fully

discharged.

TEST PROCEDURES

When performing the following tests, refer wiring diagrams **Figs. 34 and 35**, and connector pin locations **Figs. 36 and 37**, noting the following:

1. Disconnect cruise control module connector and perform tests as outlined in diagnostic charts.
2. Do not put engage switch in Re-

sume/Accel while engine is running and jumpers are connected.

Refer to **Figs. 38 and 43**, for test procedures.

ELECTRICAL TESTING

Before proceeding with electrical tests on, ensure all test equipment such as test lights and voltmeters are in good working order, inspect cruise control fuse and replace as necessary, inspect all vacuum hoses for leaks and check for adequate system vacuum.

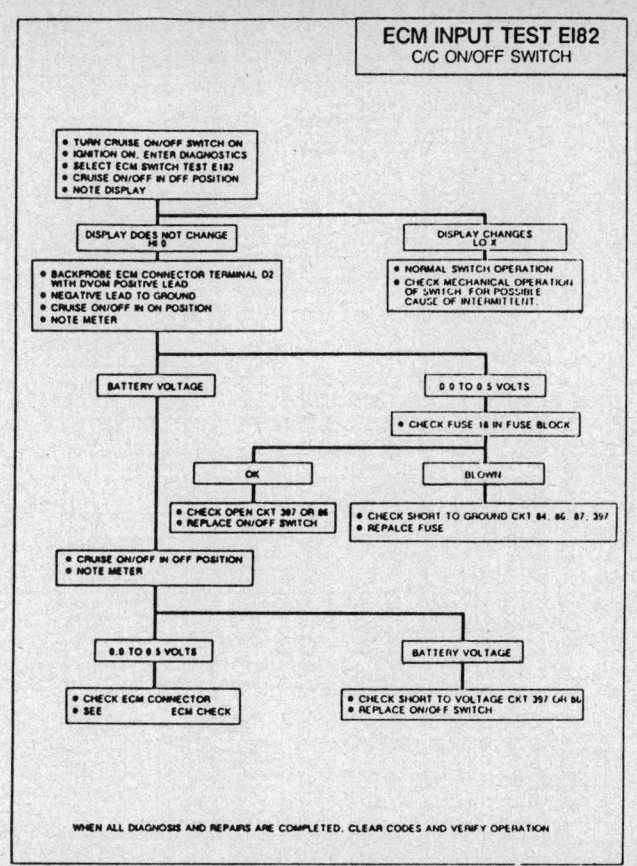

Fig. 27 ECM input test E182. 1990 Seville & Eldorado

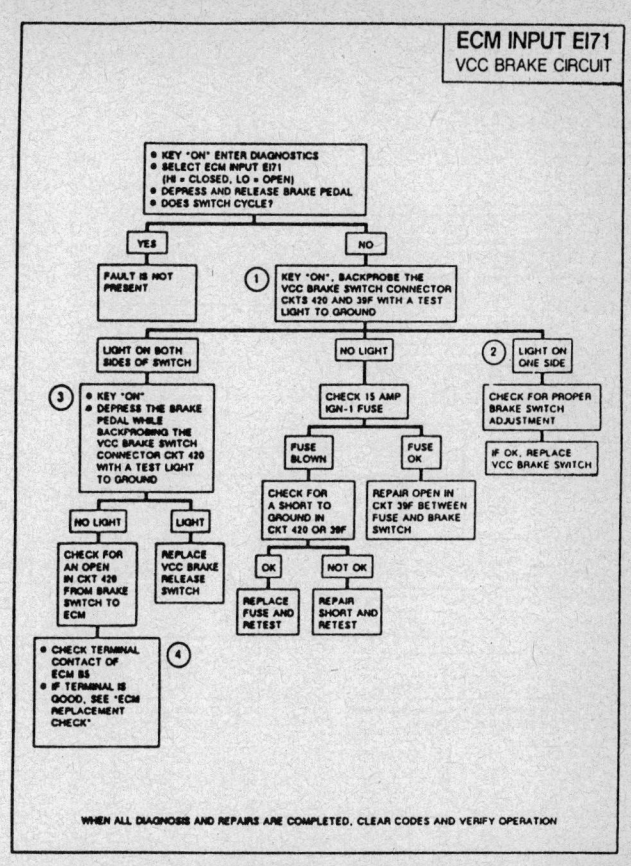

Fig. 28 ECM input test E171. 1988–89 Seville & Eldorado

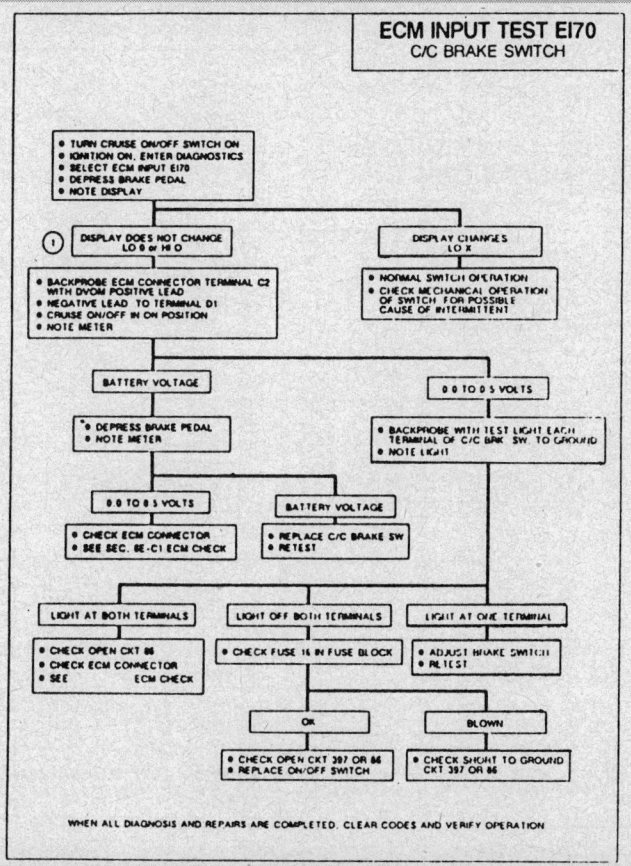

Fig. 29 ECM input test E170. 1990 Seville & Eldorado

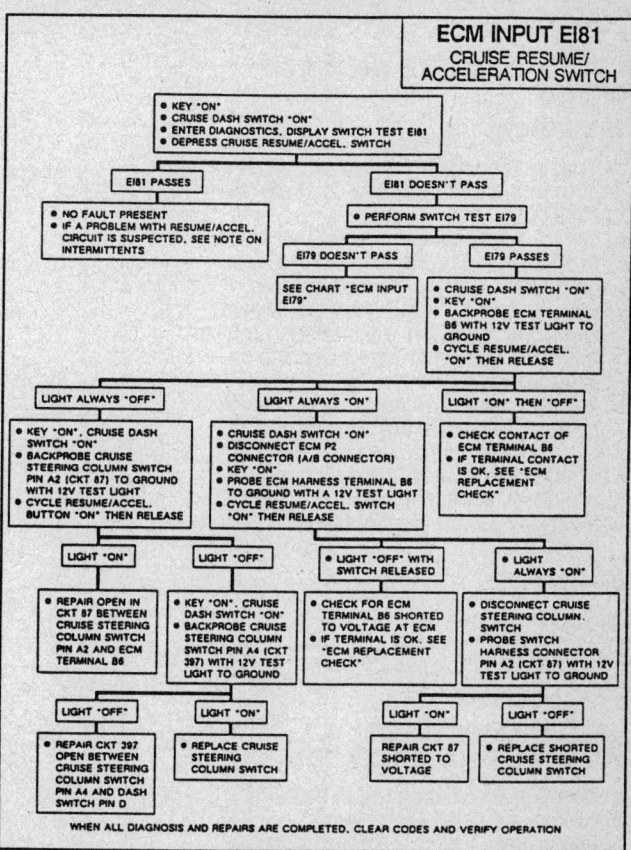

Fig. 30 ECM input test E181. 1988–89 Seville & Eldorado

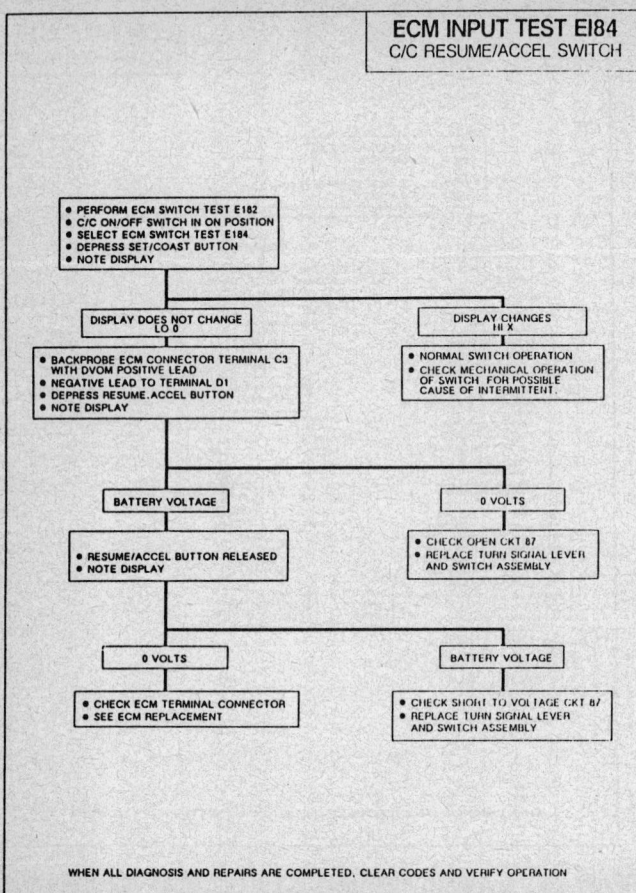

Fig. 31   ECM input test E184. 1990 Seville & Eldorado

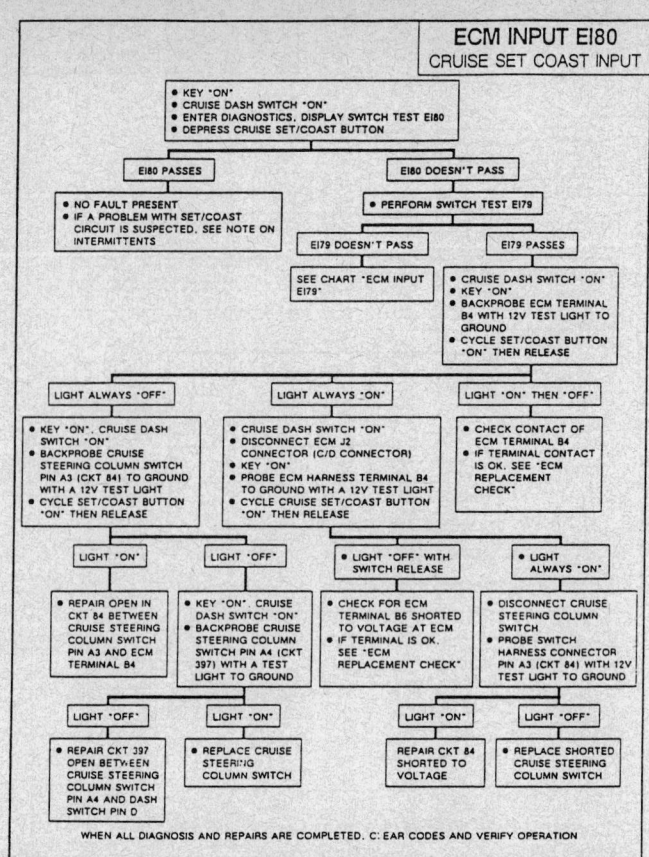

Fig. 32   ECM input test E180. 1988–89 Seville & Eldorado

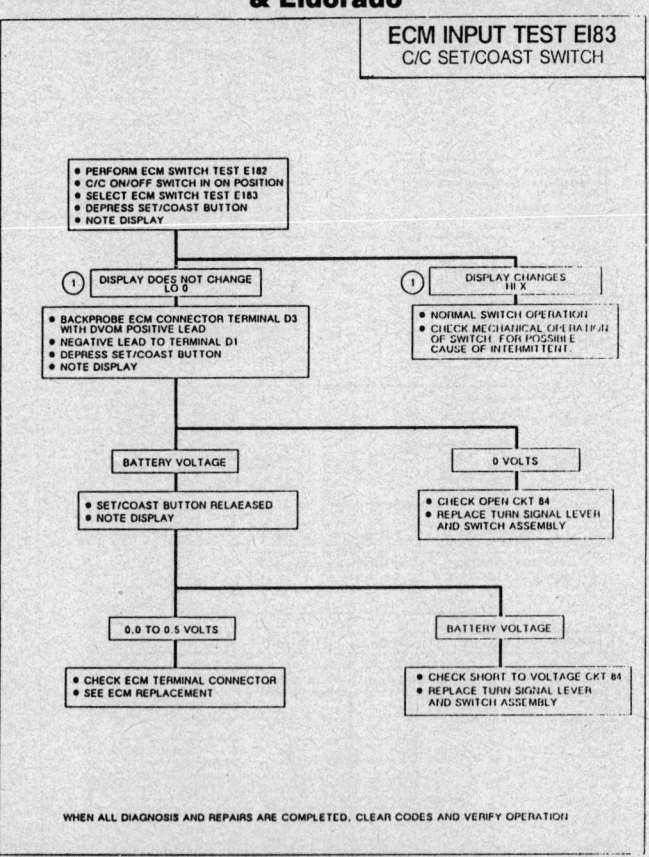

Fig. 33   ECM input test E183. 1990 Seville & Eldorado

ELECTRIC BRAKE RELEASE SWITCH

On Vehicle

1. Turn ignition to On position and the instrument panel switch to On-Auto position.
2. Connect test light to suitable ground.
3. Probe brown wire at brake switch connector. Lamp should illuminate.
4. With probe still attached to brown wire, check switch adjustment. Light should go out when brake pedal is depressed 1/8-1/2 inch.
5. If lamp did not illuminate in step 3, probe wire in adjacent connector cavity.
6. If lamp illuminates, adjust or replace switch as necessary.
7. If lamp does not illuminate, repair wiring to switch.

Off Vehicle

Using self powered test lamp, lamp should be off with switch plunger extended, and should illuminate with switch plunger fully depressed.

INSTRUMENT PANEL & ENGAGEMENT SWITCHES

1. Turn ignition switch to On position.
2. Connect test light to ground.
3. Probe three terminals of turn signal lever cruise harness connector with instrument panel switch in both Off and

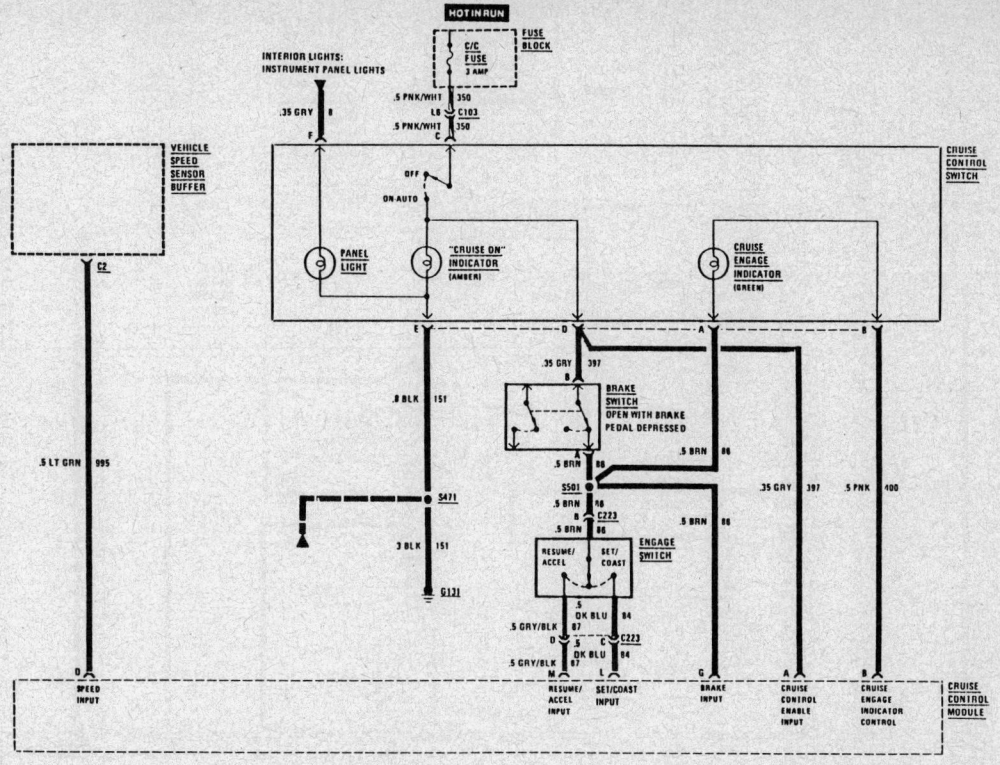

Fig. 34   Wiring diagram (Part 1 of 2). 1988–89 Brougham

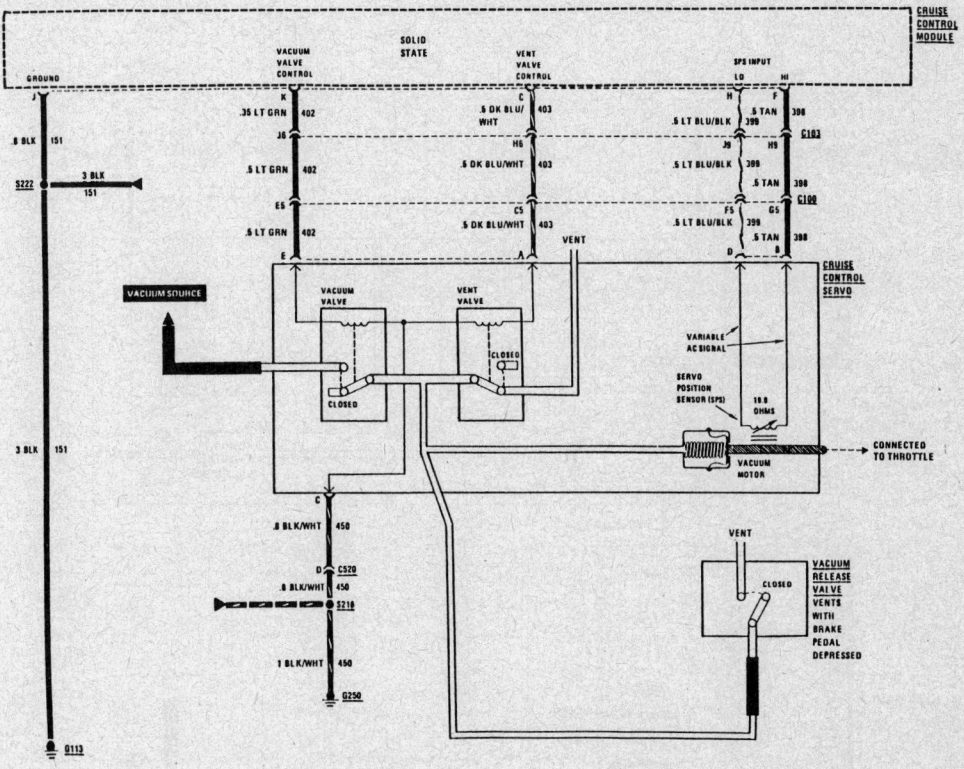

Fig. 34   Wiring diagram (Part 2 of 2). 1988–89 Brougham

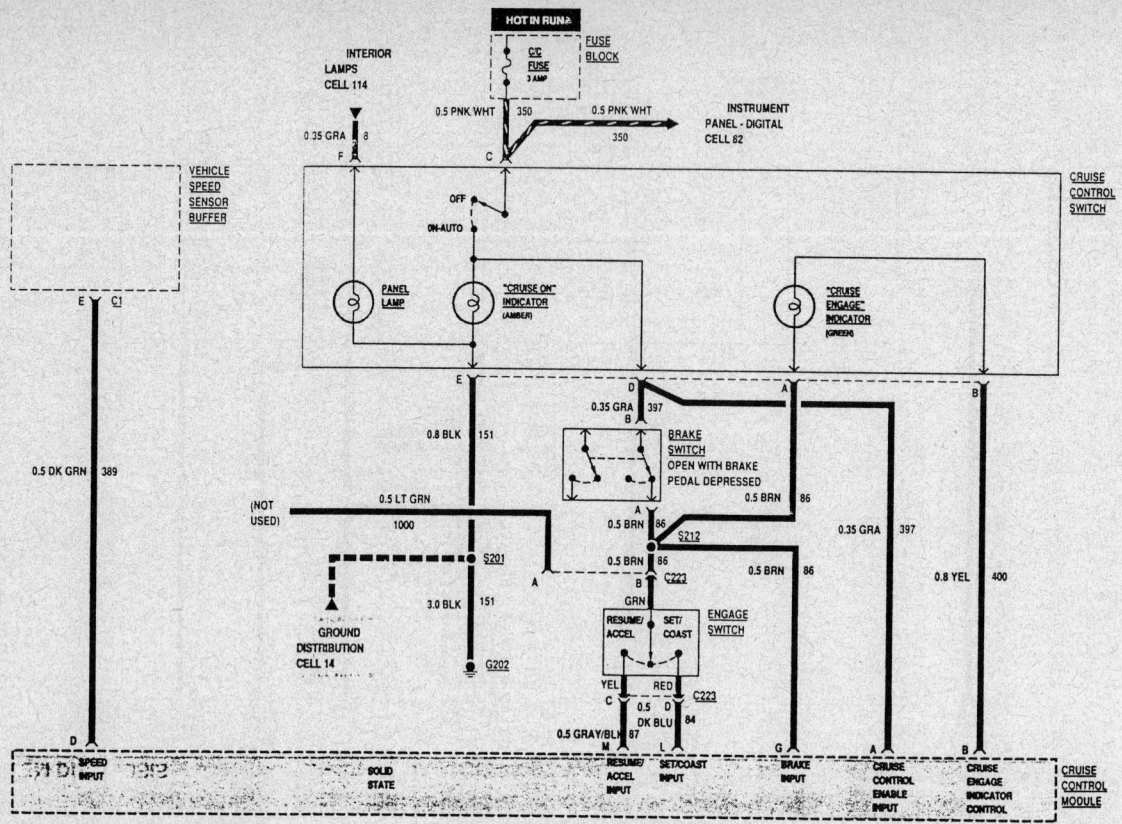

Fig. 35 Wiring diagram (Part 1 of 2). 1990 Brougham

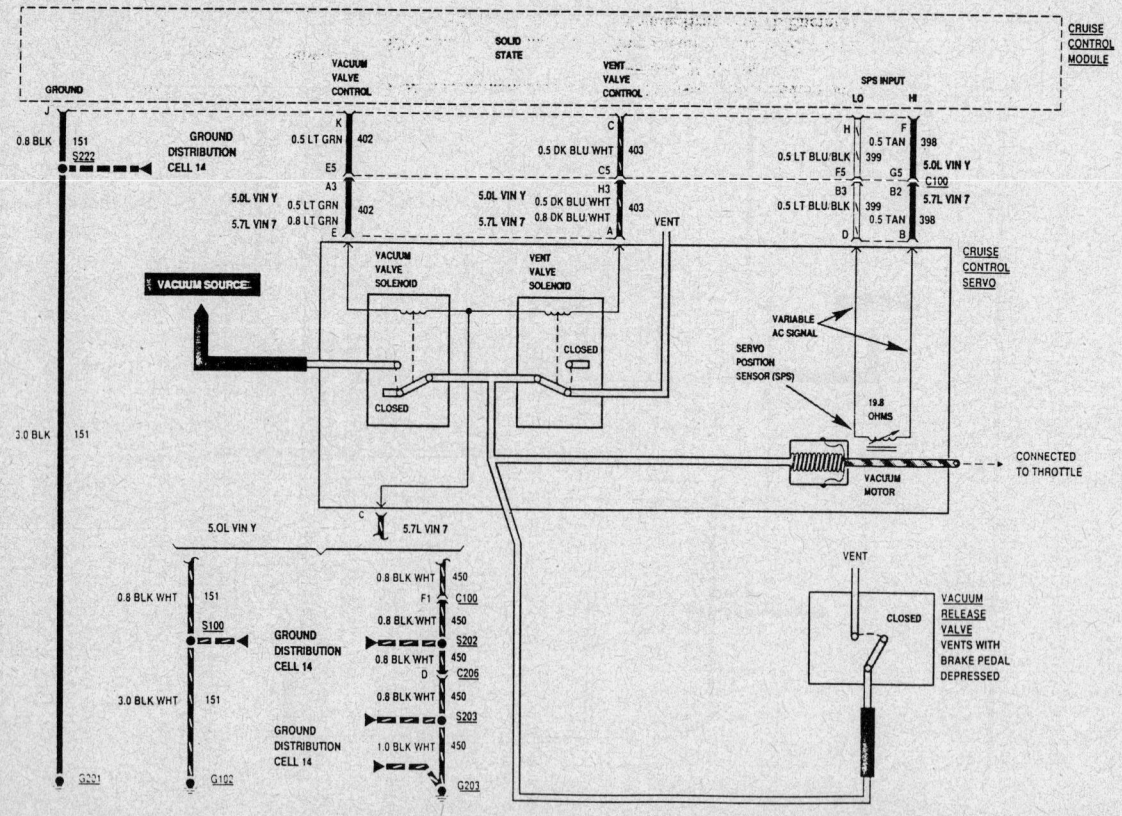

Fig. 35 Wiring diagram (Part 2 of 2). 1990 Brougham

WIRING DETAIL LEGEND

CAVITY	CIRCUIT NO.	WIRE COLOR	CIRCUIT
A	397	GRY	Cruise Control Switch (Cruise Control Enable)
B	400	PNK	Cruise Engage Indicator
C	403	DK BLU/WHT	Cruise Control Servo (Vent Control)
D	995	LT GRN	Vehicle Speed Sensor Buffer
E	NOT USED		
F	398	TAN	Cruise Control Servo (AC Signal)
G	86	BRN	Brake Input
H	399	LT BLU/BLK	Cruise Control Servo (AC Signal)
J	151	BLK	Ground Distribution
K	402	LT GRN	Cruise Control Servo (Vacuum Control)
L	84	DK BLU/WHT	Engage Switch (Set/Coast)
M	87	GRY/BLK	Engage Switch (Resume/Accel)

Fig. 36 Control module connector pin locations. 1988–89 Brougham

WIRING DETAIL LEGEND

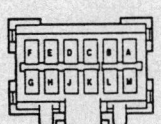

PRINTED CIRCUIT (EDGEBOARD-ECM)
BLK12034125

CAVITY	CIRCUIT NO.	WIRE COLOR	CIRCUIT
A	397	GRA	Cruise Control Switch (Cruise Control Enable)
B	400	YEL	Cruise Engage Indicator
C	403	DK BLU/WHT	Cruise Control Servo (Vent Control)
D	389	DK GRN	Vehicle Speed Sensor Buffer
E	NOT USED		
F	398	TAN	Cruise Control Servo (A/C Signal)
G	86	BRN	Brake Input
H	399	LT BLU/BLK	Cruise Control Servo (A/C Signal)
J	151	BLK	Ground Distribution
K	402	LT GRN	Cruise Control Servo (Vacuum Control)
L	84	DK BLU/WHT	Engage Switch (Set/Coast)
M	87	GRA/BLK	Engage Switch (Resume/Accel)

Fig. 37 Control module connector pin locations. 1990 Brougham

On-Auto positions. With switch in Off position, there should be no power at any terminal. With switch in On-Auto position, test lamp should illuminate at B cavity. and amber indicator should light.

4. Probe cavity D and depress Set/Coast switch. Lamp should illuminate.
5. Probe cavity C and depress Resume/Accel switch. Lamp should illuminate.
6. If results are satisfactory in step 3, but lamp does not illuminate in step 4 or 5, replace turn signal lever engagement switch.

AMBER ON LAMP INOPERATIVE OR MALFUNCTIONING

1. Turn ignition switch to On position.
2. Place instrument panel switch in On-Auto position.
3. If amber On switch does not illuminate, check for burned out lamp, open ground wire, open connector, inoperative switch, blown fuse or printed circuit.
4. Place instrument panel switch in Off position.
5. If amber On light illuminates, check for shorted leads or inoperative switch.

GREEN CRUISE LAMP INOPERATIVE OR MALFUNCTIONING

1. If road test indicates that system controls speed, but green indicator light is not illuminated, check for burned out lamp or open in pink wire of cavity B between switch connector and controller connector.
2. Turn ignition switch to On position and place instrument panel switch in On-Auto position, then ground cavity B in controller connector. If green lamp illuminates, replace controller.
3. If green indicator remains on when system is not controlling speed, check for short in harness between switch and controller connector and, if there is no short, replace controller.
4. Ensure amber light is illuminated to confirm power supply.

ENGAGE SWITCH & HARNESS

1. Disconnect turn lever engage switch from harness.
2. Using ohmmeter, test turn lever engage switch as follows:
   a. Place engage switch in released position. There should be no continuity between any two terminals.
   b. Depress engage switch slide. There should be continuity only between yellow and green wire terminals.

c. Depress engage switch push button. There should be continuity only between green and red wire terminals.
3. If results are not correct in steps a, b or c, replace engagement switch and harness.
4. Connect one lead of ohmmeter to steering column mounting bracket and check each terminal. If any terminal indicates continuity, replace lever and harness.

COMPONENT REPLACEMENT

SERVO UNIT
Brougham

1. Disconnect electrical connector and vacuum hoses.
2. Disconnect throttle cable, throttle actuating chain or actuating rod from servo unit.
3. Remove screws securing servo unit and servo unit solenoid valve assembly to mounting bracket.
4. Reverse procedure to install. **Torque** servo unit mounting bracket screws 10-15 inch lbs.

1988–89 DeVille & Fleetwood

1. Remove air cleaner assembly.
2. Disconnect servo unit electrical connectors.
3. Disconnect servo unit vacuum hoses.
4. Disconnect servo cable to servo unit attaching clips.
5. Remove servo unit attaching screws.
6. Reverse procedure to install. **Torque** servo unit attaching screws to 18 inch lbs.

1990 DeVille & Fleetwood

Refer to **Fig. 44**, for replacement procedure.

Eldorado & Seville

1. Disconnect electrical connector from

servo unit.

2. Disconnect throttle cable or throttle actuator rod from servo unit.
3. Remove vacuum hoses from servo unit.
4. Remove screws securing servo unit to mounting bracket.
5. Reverse procedure to install. **Torque** servo unit mounting bracket screws 11-15 inch lbs.

ELECTRIC BRAKE RELEASE SWITCH & VACUUM DUMP VALVE

Electric Brake Release Switch

An inoperative switch must be replaced. Install new switch and adjust as described under "Brake Release Switch Adjustment" previously outlined.

Vacuum Dump Valve

An inoperative switch must be replaced. Install new switch and adjust as described under "Vacuum Release Valve" previously outlined.

ENGAGEMENT SWITCH

The engagement switch cannot be serviced. The complete turn signal lever must be replaced as an assembly.

1. Disconnect battery ground cable.
2. Remove steering column lower cover and remove tape securing wire to column.
3. Disconnect cruise control switch connector and attach a suitable piece of wire to switch connector.
4. Remove turn signal lever by pulling it out of the detent retaining clip inside the steering column. **On some models, it may be necessary to remove steering wheel.**
5. Pull harness up gently so guide wire can be used to install new unit.
6. Reverse procedure to install.

SPEED SENSOR & HARNESS

Access to the speed sensor and harness assembly is gained by partially removing the speedometer cluster and disconnecting the electrical connector at the cluster and electronic controller ends of the harness. Refer to "Instrument Cluster, Replace" for partial removal of the speedometer cluster.

BUFFER AMPLIFIER

Brougham

1. Disconnect battery ground cable, then remove speedometer cluster. Refer to "Instrument Cluster, Replace" in individual car chapter for partial removal procedure.
2. Cut retaining strap holding buffer amplifier.
3. Disconnect electrical connectors and remove buffer amplifier.
4. Reverse procedure to install.

CRUISE CONTROL SYMPTOM CHART

TEST	RESULT	ACTION
Perform Cruise Control System Check.	"CRUISE ON" Indicator lit with CRUISE CONTROL SWITCH "OFF."	EXIT TO TEST A1 IN CHART A.
	"CRUISE ON" Indicator not lit with CRUISE CONTROL SWITCH "ON."	EXIT TO TEST A3 IN CHART A.
	"SET/RESUME" functions do not operate.	EXIT TO TEST A4 IN CHART A.
	Cruise Control re-engages after braking.	EXIT TO TEST A5 IN CHART A.
	"CRUISE ENGAGE" Indicator comes on but Cruise Control System does not operate.	EXIT TO TEST A6 IN CHART A.

Fig. 38   Cruise control symptom chart. 1990 Brougham

CRUISE CONTROL — DIAGNOSTIC CHART A

FOR USE WITH DIGITAL MULTI-METER ONLY
DISCONNECT CRUISE CONTROL MODULE CONNECTOR BEFORE PERFORMING DIAGNOSIS.

	TEST	RESULT	ACTION
A1.	IGNITION SWITCH in RUN. CRUISE CONTROL SWITCH OFF. Measure voltage from CRUISE CONTROL MODULE connector cavity A to J.	Battery Voltage.	EXIT TO TEST C1 IN CHART C.
		0 Volts.	GO TO A2.
A2.	IGNITION SWITCH in RUN. CRUISE CONTROL SWITCH OFF. Measure voltage from CRUISE CONTROL MODULE connector cavity M to J.	Battery Voltage.	EXIT TO TEST C1 IN CHART C.
		0 Volts.	GO TO A3.
A3.	IGNITION SWITCH in RUN. CRUISE CONTROL SWITCH ON. Measure voltage from CRUISE CONTROL MODULE connector cavity A to J.	0 Volts.	EXIT TO TEST C2 IN CHART C.
		Battery Voltage.	GO TO A4.
A4.	IGNITION SWITCH in RUN. CRUISE CONTROL SWITCH ON. Measure voltage from CRUISE CONTROL MODULE connector cavity G to J.	0 Volts.	EXIT TO TEST C5 IN CHART C.
		Battery Voltage.	GO TO A5.
A5.	IGNITION SWITCH in RUN. CRUISE CONTROL SWITCH ON. Measure voltage from CRUISE CONTROL MODULE connector cavity G to J with Brake Pedal pressed.	Battery Voltage.	EXIT TO TEST C23 IN CHART C.
		0 Volts.	GO TO A6.
A6.	IGNITION SWITCH in RUN. CRUISE CONTROL SWITCH ON. Measure resistance from CRUISE CONTROL MODULE connector cavity C to J.	Less than 30 Ohms.	EXIT TO TEST C7 IN CHART C.
		More than 55 Ohms.	EXIT TO TEST C8 IN CHART C.
		30 to 55 Ohms.	GO TO A7.
A7.	IGNITION SWITCH in RUN. CRUISE CONTROL SWITCH ON. Measure resistance from CRUISE CONTROL MODULE connector cavity K to J.	Less than 30 Ohms.	EXIT TO TEST C9 IN CHART C.
		More than 55 Ohms.	EXIT TO TEST C10 IN CHART C.
		30 to 55 Ohms.	GO TO A8.
A8.	IGNITION SWITCH in RUN. CRUISE CONTROL SWITCH ON. Measure resistance from CRUISE CONTROL MODULE connector cavity F to H.	Less than 15 Ohms.	EXIT TO TEST C11 IN CHART C.
		More than 25 Ohms.	EXIT TO TEST C12 IN CHART C.
		15 to 25 Ohms.	GO TO A9.
A9.	IGNITION SWITCH in RUN. CRUISE CONTROL SWITCH ON. Measure voltage from CRUISE CONTROL MODULE connector cavity M to J.	Battery Voltage.	EXIT TO TEST C13 IN CHART C.
		0 Volts.	GO TO A10.
A10.	IGNITION SWITCH in RUN. CRUISE CONTROL SWITCH ON. Measure voltage from CRUISE CONTROL MODULE connector cavity L to J.	Battery Voltage.	EXIT TO TEST C14 IN CHART C.
		0 Volts.	GO TO A11.

Fig. 39   Diagnostic procedure, A (Part 1 of 2). 1988–89 Brougham

CRUISE CONTROL — DIAGNOSTIC CHART A (CONT'D)

	TEST	RESULT	ACTION
A11.	IGNITION SWITCH in RUN. CRUISE CONTROL SWITCH ON. PRESS SET SWITCH. Measure voltage from CRUISE CONTROL MODULE connector cavity L to J.	0 Volts.	EXIT TO TEST C15 IN CHART C.
		Battery Voltage.	GO TO A12.
A12.	IGNITION SWITCH in RUN. CRUISE CONTROL SWITCH ON. PRESS SET SWITCH. Measure resistance from CRUISE CONTROL MODULE connector cavity K to J.	Less than 30 Ohms.	EXIT TO TEST C9 IN CHART C.
		More than 55 Ohms.	EXIT TO TEST C10 IN CHART C.
		30 to 55 Ohms.	GO TO A13.
A13.	IGNITION SWITCH in RUN. CRUISE CONTROL SWITCH ON. ENGAGE SWITCH in R/A. Measure voltage from CRUISE CONTROL MODULE connector cavity A to J.	0 Volts.	EXIT TO TEST C2 IN CHART C.
		Battery Voltage.	GO TO A14.
A14.	IGNITION SWITCH in RUN. CRUISE CONTROL SWITCH ON. ENGAGE SWITCH in R/A. Measure voltage from CRUISE CONTROL MODULE connector cavity M to J.	0 Volts.	EXIT TO TEST C17 IN CHART C.
		Battery Voltage.	GO TO A15.
A15.	IGNITION SWITCH in RUN. CRUISE CONTROL SWITCH ON. Lift vehicle's rear wheels. Place gearshift in NEUTRAL. Manually rotate drive wheel. Measure voltage from CRUISE CONTROL MODULE connector cavity A to D.	Voltage DOES NOT vary between approximately 7 Volts and Battery Voltage.	EXIT TO TEST C19 IN CHART C.
		Voltage varies between approximately 7 Volts and Battery Voltage.	GO TO A16.
A16.	Run engine for at least one minute and turn it off. Connect a fused jumper from CRUISE CONTROL MODULE connector cavities C to M and from cavities K to L. Turn IGNITION SWITCH to RUN and CRUISE CONTROL SWITCH to ON. Hold ENGAGE SWITCH in R/A. Press and release SET SWITCH.	Vacuum DOES NOT hold servo at wide open throttle position.	EXIT TO TEST C20 IN CHART C.
		Vacuum holds servo at wide open throttle position.	GO TO A17.
A17.	IGNITION SWITCH OFF. CRUISE CONTROL SWITCH OFF. Measure resistance from CRUISE CONTROL MODULE connector cavity F to J.	Less than infinity. (NOT OPEN)	EXIT TO TEST C22 IN CHART C.
		Infinity. (OPEN)	GO TO A18.
A18.	IGNITION SWITCH OFF. CRUISE CONTROL SWITCH OFF. Measure resistance from CRUISE CONTROL MODULE connector cavity F to H.	Less than 15 Ohms.	EXIT TO TEST C11 IN CHART C.
		More than 25 Ohms.	EXIT TO TEST C12 IN CHART C.
		15 to 25 Ohms.	Replace CRUISE CONTROL MODULE and retest.

Fig. 39   Diagnostic procedure, A (Part 2 of 2). 1988–89 Brougham

CONTROLLER

Brougham

1. Remove radio.
2. Disconnect cruise module electrical connectors.
3. Remove control module attaching screws to right of steering column, then remove module.
4. Reverse procedure to install.

CRUISE CONTROL	DIAGNOSTIC CHART A	
	FOR USE WITH A MULTIMETER ONLY	
	DISCONNECT CRUISE CONTROL MODULE CONNECTOR BEFORE PERFORMING DIAGNOSIS	
	TEST	RESULT	ACTION
A1.	IGNITION SWITCH in "RUN." CRUISE CONTROL SWITCH "OFF." Measure voltage from CRUISE CONTROL MODULE connector cavity A to J.	Battery voltage.	EXIT TO TEST C1 IN CHART C.
		0 volts	GO TO A2.
A2.	IGNITION SWITCH in "RUN." CRUISE CONTROL SWITCH "OFF." Measure voltage from CRUISE CONTROL MODULE connector M to J.	Battery voltage.	EXIT TO TEST C1 IN CHART C.
		0 volts.	GO TO A3.
A3.	IGNITION SWITCH in "RUN." CRUISE CONTROL SWITCH "ON." Measure voltage from CRUISE CONTROL MODULE connector cavity A to J.	0 volts.	EXIT TO TEST C2 IN CHART C.
		Battery voltage.	GO TO A4.

Fig. 40   Diagnostic procedure, A (Part 1 of 3). 1990 Brougham

CRUISE CONTROL	DIAGNOSTIC CHART A (CONT'D)	
	TEST	RESULT	ACTION
A4.	IGNITION SWITCH in "RUN." CRUISE CONTROL SWITCH "ON." Measure voltage from CRUISE CONTROL MODULE connector cavity G to J.	0 volts.	EXIT TO TEST C5 IN CHART C.
		Battery voltage.	GO TO A5.
A5.	IGNITION SWITCH in "RUN." CRUISE CONTROL SWITCH "ON." Measure voltage from CRUISE CONTROL MODULE connector cavity G to J with brake pedal pressed.	Battery voltage.	EXIT TO TEST C23 IN CHART C.
		0 volts.	GO TO A6.
A6.	IGNITION SWITCH in "RUN." CRUISE CONTROL SWITCH "ON." Measure resistance from CRUISE CONTROL MODULE connector cavity C to J.	Less than 30 ohms.	EXIT TO TEST C7 IN CHART C.
		More than 55 ohms.	EXIT TO TEST C8 IN CHART C.
		30 to 55 ohms.	GO TO A7.
A7.	IGNITION SWITCH in "RUN." CRUISE CONTROL SWITCH "ON." Measure resistance from CRUISE CONTROL MODULE connector cavity K to J.	Less than 30 ohms.	EXIT TO TEST C9 IN CHART C.
		More than 55 ohms.	EXIT TO TEST C10 IN CHART C.
		30 to 55 ohms.	GO TO A8.
A8.	IGNITION SWITCH in "RUN." CRUISE CONTROL SWITCH "ON." Measure resistance from CRUISE CONTROL MODULE connector cavity F to H.	Less than 15 ohms.	EXIT TO TEST C11 IN CHART C.
		More than 25 ohms.	EXIT TO TEST C12 IN CHART C.
		15 to 25 ohms.	GO TO A9.
A9.	IGNITION SWITCH in "RUN." CRUISE CONTROL SWITCH "ON." Measure voltage from CRUISE CONTROL MODULE connector cavity M to J.	Battery voltage.	EXIT TO TEST C13 IN CHART C.
		0 volts.	GO TO A10.
A10.	IGNITION SWITCH in "RUN." CRUISE CONTROL SWITCH "ON." Measure voltage from CRUISE CONTROL MODULE connector cavity L to J.	Battery voltage.	EXIT TO TEST C14 IN CHART C.
		0 volts.	GO TO A11.
A11.	IGNITION SWITCH in "RUN." Press SET SWITCH. Measure voltage from CRUISE CONTROL MODULE connector cavity L to J.	0 volts.	EXIT TO TEST C15 IN CHART C.
		Momentary battery voltage with switch pressed.	GO TO A12.
A12.	IGNITION SWITCH in "RUN." CRUISE CONTROL SWITCH "ON." ENGAGE SWITCH in "RESUME/ACCEL." Measure voltage from CRUISE CONTROL MODULE connector cavity M to J.	0 volts.	EXIT TO TEST C17 IN CHART C.
		Momentary battery voltage with switch pressed.	GO TO A13.

Fig. 40   Diagnostic procedure, A (Part 2 of 3). 1990 Brougham

CRUISE CONTROL	DIAGNOSTIC CHART A (CONT'D)	
	TEST	RESULT	ACTION
A13.	IGNITION SWITCH in "RUN." CRUISE CONTROL "ON." Lift vehicle's rear wheels. Place gearshift in NEUTRAL. Manually rotate drive wheel. Measure voltage from CRUISE CONTROL MODULE connector cavity A to D.	Voltage DOES NOT vary between approximately 7 volts and battery voltage.	EXIT TO TEST C19 IN CHART C.
		Voltage varies between approximately 7 volts and battery voltage.	GO TO A14.
A14.	Run engine for at least one minute and turn it "OFF." Connect a fused jumper from CRUISE CONTROL MODULE connector cavity C to M and cavity K to L. Turn IGNITION SWITCH to RUN and CRUISE CONTROL SWITCH to "ON." Hold ENGAGE SWITCH in "RESUME/ACCEL." Press and release SET SWITCH.	Vacuum DOES NOT hold servo at wide open throttle position.	EXIT TO TEST C20 IN CHART C.
		Vacuum holds servo at wide open throttle position.	GO TO A15.
A15.	IGNITION SWITCH "OFF." CRUISE CONTROL SWITCH "OFF." Measure resistance from CRUISE CONTROL MODULE connector cavity F to J.	Less than infinity (NOT OPEN).	EXIT TO TEST C22 IN CHART C.
		Infinity (OPEN).	GO TO A16.
A16.	IGNITION SWITCH "OFF." CRUISE CONTROL SWITCH "OFF." Measure resistance from CRUISE CONTROL MODULE connector cavity F to H.	Less than 15 ohms.	EXIT TO TEST C11 IN CHART C.
		More than 25 ohms.	EXIT TO TEST C12 IN CHART C.
		15 to 25 ohms.	Replace CRUISE CONTROL MODULE and perform System Check.

Fig. 40   Diagnostic procedure, A (Part 3 of 3). 1990 Brougham

CRUISE CONTROL	DIAGNOSTIC CHART B	
	FOR USE WITH CRUISE CONTROL QUICK/CHECKER ONLY	
	TEST	RESULT	ACTION
B1.	IGNITION SWITCH in "OFF." CRUISE CONTROL SWITCH "OFF."	Any Quick-Checker lamp comes on.	EXIT TO TEST C1 IN CHART C.
		All Quick-Checker lamps are off.	GO TO B2.
B2.	IGNITION SWITCH in "RUN." CRUISE CONTROL SWITCH "ON."	"ON/OFF" lamp is off.	EXIT TO TEST C2 IN CHART C.
		"BRK" lamp is off.	EXIT TO TEST C5 IN CHART C.
		"VENT" lamp is off.	EXIT TO TEST A6 IN CHART C.
		"VAC" lamp is off.	EXIT TO TEST A7 IN CHART C.
		"SPS" lamp is off.	EXIT TO TEST A8 IN CHART C.
		"SC/RA" lamp is on.	EXIT TO TESTS C13 AND C14 IN CHART C.
		"ON/OFF" lamp on, "BRAKE" lamp on, "LAMP" lamp on, "SPS" lamp on, "VAC" lamp on, "VENT" lamp on, "SC/RA" lamp off, and "VAC SHORT" lamp off.	GO TO B3.
B3.	IGNITION SWITCH in "RUN." CRUISE CONTROL SWITCH "ON." Press "SET/COAST" button.	"SC/RA" lamp off and "VAC" lamp on.	EXIT TO TEST C15 IN CHART C.
		"VAC SHORT" lamp on.	EXIT TO TEST A7 IN CHART C.
		"SC/RA" lamp on, "VAC" lamp off, and "VAC SHORT" lamp is off.	GO TO B4.
B4.	IGNITION SWITCH in "RUN." CRUISE CONTROL SWITCH "ON." ENGAGE SWITCH in "RESUME/ACCEL."	"SC/RA" lamp off and "VENT" lamp on.	EXIT TO TEST C17 IN CHART C.
		"VENT SHORT" lamp on.	EXIT TO TEST A6 IN CHART C.
		"SC/RA" lamp on, "VENT" lamp off, and "VENT SHORT" lamp is off.	GO TO B5.

Fig. 41   Diagnostic procedure, B (Part 1 of 2). 1990 Brougham

DeVille & Fleetwood

1. Remove steering column lower cover.
2. Disconnect electrical connectors from controller.
3. Remove screws securing controller to steering column lower cover.
4. Reverse procedure to install.

Eldorado & Seville

1. Disconnect battery ground cable.
2. Remove lower instrument panel cover.
3. Unclip relay panel from twilight sentinel amplifier and cruise control controller mounting bracket, located to the left of the steering column.
4. Remove screws securing controller mounting bracket to instrument panel assembly.
5. Lower mounting bracket and disconnect electrical connectors from cruise control controller.
6. Remove screws securing controller to mounting bracket and remove controller.
7. Reverse procedure to install.

SERVO UNIT SOLENOID VALVE

1. Remove screw securing solenoid valve to servo unit.
2. Disconnect vacuum hose and electrical connector and pull solenoid valve away from the servo unit.
3. Reverse procedure to install.

VACUUM CONTROL SOLENOID VALVE

1. Disconnect one electrical connector and two vacuum hoses from valve.
2. Remove screw securing valve to servo unit mounting bracket on front of dash bracket.
3. Reverse procedure to install.

SPEED CONTROL, ADJUST

CABLE OR ROD ADJUSTMENT

On fuel injected models, a cable is used in this system. The servo unit positions the throttle linkage through the use of a cable. To adjust this cable turn engine to the "Off" position. Retract idle speed control (ISC) motor plunger, **throttle lever must not touch ISC plunger.** Connect cruise control cable to servo hole blade, **Fig. 3,** that allows minimum slack.

On carbureated models, a rod assembly is used to control cruise control speed. Adjustment is made with engine Off, carburetor lever on slow idle screw and Idle Load Control (ILC), fully retracted. Adjust rod length to obtain the least amount of slack, **Fig. 2.**

BRAKE RELEASE SWITCH ADJUSTMENT

With brake pedal depressed, push cruise control/stoplight switch fully into re-

CRUISE CONTROL		DIAGNOSTIC CHART B (CONT'D)	
	TEST	RESULT	ACTION
B5.	IGNITION SWITCH in "RUN." CRUISE CONTROL SWITCH "ON." Lift vehicle's drive wheels. Place gearshift in "NEUTRAL." Manually rotate drive wheel.	"VSS" lamp DOES NOT flash on and off.	EXIT TO TEST C19 IN CHART C.
		"VSS" lamp flashes on and off.	GO TO B6.
B6.	Run engine for one minute and then turn it off. Turn IGNITION SWITCH to "RUN." Hold ENGAGE SWITCH in "RESUME/ACCEL." Press "SET/COAST" button.	Vacuum DOES NOT pull SERVO to wide open throttle position.	EXIT TO TEST C20 IN CHART C.
		Vacuum pulls SERVO to wide open throttle position.	EXIT TO TEST A16 IN CHART A.

Fig. 41   Diagnostic procedure, B (Part 2 of 2). 1990 Brougham

CRUISE CONTROL		DIAGNOSTIC CHART C	
	TEST	RESULT	ACTION
C1.	Check for shorts to voltage in wires to cavities G, A, M, and L of the CRUISE CONTROL MODULE connector.	Short found.	Repair/replace defective wiring.
		No short found.	Replace CRUISE CONTROL SWITCH.
C2.	Connect a Digital Ohmmeter between CRUISE CONTROL MODULE connector cavity J and chassis ground.	More than 0.03 Ohms.	Repair/replace BLK (151) wire.
		Less than 0.03 Ohms.	GO TO C3.
C3.	Backprobe CRUISE CONTROL SWITCH connector cavity C and measure voltage to chassis ground with a Digital Multi-meter.	0 Volts.	Repair/replace PNK/WHT (350) wire.
		Battery Voltage.	GO TO C4.
C4.	Backprobe CRUISE CONTROL SWITCH connector cavity D and measure voltage to chassis ground with a Digital Multi-meter.	0 Volts.	Replace CRUISE CONTROL SWITCH.
		Battery Voltage.	Repair/replace GRY (397) wire.
C5.	Backprobe BRAKE SWITCH connector cavity B and measure voltage to chassis ground with a Digital Voltmeter.	0 Volts.	GO TO C2.
		Battery Voltage.	GO TO C6.
C6.	Backprobe BRAKE SWITCH connector cavity A and measure voltage to chassis ground with a Digital Voltmeter.	0 Volts.	Replace BRAKE SWITCH.
		Battery Voltage.	Repair/replace BRN (85) wire.
C7.	Disconnect CRUISE CONTROL SERVO connector and measure resistance between terminals A and C of the SERVO.	Less than 30 Ohms.	Replace CRUISE CONTROL SERVO.
		30 to 55 Ohms.	Repair short to ground in DK BLU/WHT (403) wire.
C8.	Disconnect CRUISE CONTROL SERVO connector and measure resistance between terminals A and C of the SERVO.	More than 55 Ohms.	Replace CRUISE CONTROL SERVO.
		30 to 55 Ohms.	Repair open in DK BLU/WHT (403), BLK/WHT (450), or BLK (151) wire.
C9.	Disconnect CRUISE CONTROL SERVO connector and measure resistance between terminals E and C of the SERVO.	Less than 30 Ohms.	Replace CRUISE CONTROL SERVO.
		30 to 55 Ohms.	Repair short to ground in LT GRN (402) wire.
C10.	Disconnect CRUISE CONTROL SERVO connector and measure resistance between terminals A and C of the SERVO.	More than 55 Ohms.	Replace CRUISE CONTROL SERVO.
		30 to 55 Ohms.	Repair open in LT GRN (402), BLK/WHT (450), or BLK (151) wire.
C11.	Disconnect CRUISE CONTROL SERVO connector and measure resistance between terminals B and D of the SERVO.	Less than 15 Ohms.	Replace CRUISE CONTROL SERVO.
		15 to 25 Ohms.	Repair short to ground in TAN (398) wire.
C12.	Disconnect CRUISE CONTROL SERVO connector and measure resistance between terminals B and D of the SERVO.	More than 25 Ohms.	Replace CRUISE CONTROL SERVO.
		15 to 25 Ohms.	Repair open in TAN (398) or LT BLU/BLK (399) wire.

Fig. 42   Diagnostic procedure, C (Part 1 of 2). 1988–89 Brougham

CRUISE CONTROL		DIAGNOSTIC CHART C (CONT'D)	
	TEST	RESULT	ACTION
C13.	Backprobe connector C223 cavity D and measure voltage to chassis ground with a Digital Voltmeter.	Battery Voltage.	Replace ENGAGE SWITCH.
		0 Volts.	Repair short to voltage in GRY/BLK (87) or BLK (151) wire.
C14.	Backprobe connector C223 cavity C and measure voltage to chassis ground with a Digital Voltmeter.	Battery Voltage.	Replace ENGAGE SWITCH.
		0 Volts.	Repair short to voltage in DK BLU (84) or BLK (151) wire.
C15.	Backprobe connector C223 cavity B with a Digital Voltmeter. Press Set Switch and measure voltage to chassis ground.	0 Volts.	GO TO C5.
		Battery Voltage.	GO TO C16.
C16.	Backprobe connector C223 cavity C with a Digital Voltmeter. Press Set Switch and measure voltage to chassis ground.	0 Volts.	Replace ENGAGE SWITCH.
		Battery Voltage.	Repair open in DK BLU (84) wire.
C17.	Backprobe connector C223 cavity B with a Digital Voltmeter.	0 Volts.	GO TO C5.
		Battery Voltage.	GO TO C18.
C18.	Backprobe connector C223 cavity D with a Digital Voltmeter. Hold ENGAGE SWITCH in R/A and measure voltage to chassis ground.	0 Volts.	Replace ENGAGE SWITCH.
		Battery Voltage.	Repair open in GRY/BLK (87) wire.
C19.	Connect a Digital Voltmeter between C/C FUSE and CRUISE CONTROL MODULE cavity D. Measure voltage while manually rotating drive wheel.	Voltage DOES NOT vary between approximately 7 Volts and Battery Voltage.	Vehicle speed sensor/circuit malfunction.
		Voltage varies between approximately 7 Volts and Battery Voltage.	GO TO C2.
C20.	Check the vacuum source and all vacuum lines for blockage and leaks.	Blockage or leak discovered.	Repair vacuum system as necessary.
		No blockage or leaks found.	GO TO C21.
C21.	Plug the VACUUM RELEASE VALVE and repeat TEST B15 in CHART B.	Vacuum DOES NOT hold servo at wide open throttle position.	Replace CRUISE CONTROL SERVO.
		Vacuum holds servo wide open throttle position.	Replace VACUUM RELEASE VALVE.
C22.	Disconnect CRUISE CONTROL SERVO connector. Measure resistance from CRUISE CONTROL MODULE connector cavity F to J.	Infinity.	Replace CRUISE CONTROL SERVO.
		Less than infinity.	Repair short to ground in TAN (398) wire.
C23.	Disconnect BRAKE SWITCH connector. Turn IGNITION SWITCH to RUN. Measure voltage from BRAKE SWITCH connector cavity A to chassis ground.	Battery Voltage.	Repair short to voltage in BRN (86) wire.
		0 Volts.	Replace BRAKE SWITCH.

Fig. 42   Diagnostic procedure, C (Part 2 of 2). 1988–89 Brougham

CRUISE CONTROL		DIAGNOSTIC CHART C	
	TEST	RESULT	ACTION
C1.	Check for shorts to voltage in wires to cavities G, A, M, and L of the CRUISE CONTROL MODULE CONNECTOR.	Short found.	Repair/replace defective wiring.
		No short found.	Replace CRUISE CONTROL SWITCH.
C2.	Connect a digital multimeter between CRUISE CONTROL MODULE connector cavity J and chassis ground. Measure resistance.	More than 0.3 ohms.	Repair/replace BLK (151) wire.
		Less than 0.3 ohms.	GO TO C3.
C3.	Backprobe CRUISE CONTROL SWITCH connector cavity C and measure voltage to chassis ground with a digital multimeter.	0 volts.	Repair PNK/WHT (350) wire.
		Battery voltage.	GO TO C4.
C4.	Backprobe CRUISE CONTROL SWITCH connector cavity D and measure voltage to chassis ground with a digital multimeter.	0 volts.	Replace CRUISE CONTROL SWITCH.
		Battery voltage.	Repair/replace GRA (397) wire.
C5.	Backprobe BRAKE SWITCH connector cavity B and measure voltage to chassis ground with a digital multimeter.	0 volts.	GO TO C2.
		Battery voltage.	GO TO C6.
C6.	Backprobe BRAKE SWITCH connector cavity A and measure voltage to chassis ground with a digital multimeter.	0 volts.	Replace BRAKE SWITCH.
		Battery voltage.	Repair/replace BRN (86) wire.

Fig. 43   Diagnostic procedure, C (Part 1 of 4). 1990 Brougham

CRUISE CONTROL		DIAGNOSTIC CHART C (CONT'D)	
	TEST	RESULT	ACTION
C7.	Disconnect CRUISE CONTROL SERVO connector and measure resistance between terminals A and C of the SERVO.	Less than 30 ohms.	Replace CRUISE CONTROL SERVO.
		30 to 55 ohms.	Repair short to ground in DK BLU/WHT (403) wire.
C8.	Disconnect CRUISE CONTROL SERVO connector and measure resistance between terminals A and C of the SERVO.	More than 55 ohms.	Replace CRUISE CONTROL SERVO.
		30 to 55 ohms.	Repair open in DK BLU/WHT (403), BLK/WHT (450), or BLK (151) wire.
C9.	Disconnect CRUISE CONTROL SERVO connector and measure resistance between terminals E and C of the SERVO.	Less than 30 ohms.	Replace CRUISE CONTROL SERVO.
		30 to 55 ohms.	Repair short to ground in LT GRN (402) wire.
C10.	Disconnect CRUISE CONTROL SERVO connector and measure resistance between terminals E and C of the SERVO.	More than 55 ohms.	Replace CRUISE CONTROL SERVO.
		30 to 55 ohms.	Repair open in LT GRN (402), BLK/WHT (450), or BLK (151) wire.
C11.	Disconnect CRUISE CONTROL SERVO connector and measure resistance between terminals B and D of the SERVO.	Less than 15 ohms.	Replace CRUISE CONTROL SERVO.
		15 to 25 ohms.	Repair short to ground in TAN (398) or LT BLU/BLK (399) wire.
C12.	Disconnect CRUISE CONTROL SERVO connector and measure resistance between terminals B and D of the SERVO.	More than 25 ohms.	Replace CRUISE CONTROL SERVO.
		15 to 25 ohms.	Repair open in TAN (398) or LT BLU/BLK (399) wire.
C13.	Backprobe connector C223 cavity C and measure voltage to chassis ground with a digital multimeter.	Battery voltage.	Replace ENGAGE SWITCH.
		0 volts.	Repair short to voltage in GRA/BLK (87) wire.

Fig. 43   Diagnostic procedure, C (Part 2 of 4). 1990 Brougham

CRUISE CONTROL		DIAGNOSTIC CHART C (CONT'D)	
	TEST	RESULT	ACTION
C14.	Backprobe connector C223 cavity D and measure voltage to chassis ground with a digital multimeter.	Battery voltage.	Replace ENGAGE SWITCH.
		0 volts.	Repair short to voltage in DK BLU (84) wire or BLK (151) wire.
C15.	Backprobe connector C223 cavity B and measure voltage to chassis ground with a digital multimeter.	0 volts.	GO TO C5.
		Battery voltage.	GO TO C16.
C16.	Backprobe connector C223 cavity D with a digital multimeter. Press "SET/COAST" button and measure voltage.	0 volts.	Replace ENGAGE SWITCH.
		Battery voltage.	Repair open in DK/BLU (84) wire.
C17.	Backprobe connector C223 cavity B and measure voltage to chassis ground with a digital multimeter.	0 volts.	GO TO C5.
		Battery voltage.	GO TO C18.
C18.	Backprobe connector C223 cavity C with a digital multimeter. Hold ENGAGE SWITCH in "RESUME/ACCEL" and measure voltage to chassis ground.	0 volts.	Replace ENGAGE SWITCH.
		Battery voltage.	Repair open in GRA/BLK (87) wire.
C19.	Connect a digital multimeter between C/C FUSE and CRUISE CONTROL MODULE connector cavity D. Measure voltage while manually rotating drive wheel.	Voltage DOES NOT vary between approximately 7 volts and battery voltage.	See Cell 33 for Vehicle Speed Sensor System Diagnosis.
		Voltage varies between approximately 7 volts and battery voltage.	GO TO C2.
C20.	Check the vacuum source and all vacuum lines for blockage and leaks.	Blockage or leak discovered.	Repair Vacuum System as necessary.
		No blockage or leaks found.	GO TO C21.
C21.	Plug the VACUUM RELEASE VALVE. Run engine for one minute and then turn it off. Turn IGNITION SWITCH to "RUN." Hold ENGAGE SWITCH in "RESUME/ACCEL." Press and release "SET/COAST" button.	Vacuum DOES NOT hold SERVO at wide open throttle position.	Replace CRUISE CONTROL SERVO.
		Vacuum holds SERVO at wide open throttle position	Replace VACUUM RELEASE VALVE.

Fig. 43   Diagnostic procedure, C (Part 3 of 4). 1990 Brougham

CRUISE CONTROL		DIAGNOSTIC CHART C (CONT'D)	
	TEST	RESULT	ACTION
C22.	Disconnect CRUISE CONTROL SERVO connector. Measure resistance from CRUISE CONTROL MODULE connector cavity F to J.	Infinity.	Replace CRUISE CONTROL SERVO.
		Less than infinity.	Repair short to ground in TAN (398) wire.
C23.	Disconnect BRAKE SWITCH connector. Turn IGNITION SWITCH to "RUN." Measure voltage from BRAKE SWITCH connector cavity A to chassis ground.	Battery voltage.	Repair short to battery voltage in BRN (86) wire.
		0 volts.	Replace BRAKE SWITCH.

Fig. 43   Diagnostic procedure, C (Part 4 of 4). 1990 Brougham

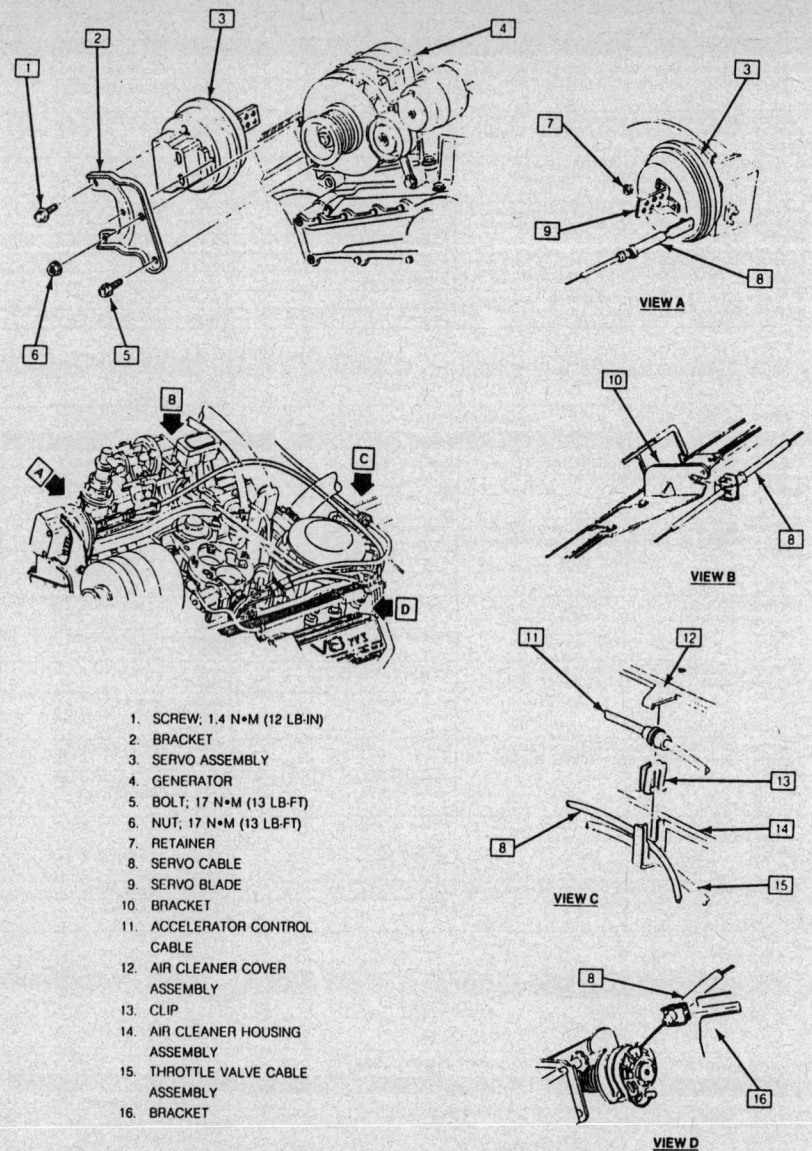

1. SCREW; 1.4 N•M (12 LB-IN)
2. BRACKET
3. SERVO ASSEMBLY
4. GENERATOR
5. BOLT; 17 N•M (13 LB-FT)
6. NUT; 17 N•M (13 LB-FT)
7. RETAINER
8. SERVO CABLE
9. SERVO BLADE
10. BRACKET
11. ACCELERATOR CONTROL CABLE
12. AIR CLEANER COVER ASSEMBLY
13. CLIP
14. AIR CLEANER HOUSING ASSEMBLY
15. THROTTLE VALVE CABLE ASSEMBLY
16. BRACKET

Fig. 44 Cruise control servo. 1990 DeVille & Fleetwood

tainer, then pull brake pedal fully back to rest position. Switch will back out of retainer and adjust automatically. **On vehicles equipped with anti-lock brakes,** release brake pedal and allow to come to rest. Brake release switch contacts should open at 1/8-1/2 inch pedal travel, measured at centerline of brake pedal pad. Actuation of stop lamp contact is 3/16 after cruise control contact opens.

VACUUM RELEASE VALVE ADJUSTMENT

With brake pedal depressed, push vacuum valve switch all the way into the retaining clip. Pull the brake pedal to the stop to automatically adjust the valve. **On vehicle equipped with anti-lock brakes,** release pedal and allow to come to rest. Vacuum dump valve assembly should open at 1-15/16 inch pedal travel, measured at centerline of brake pedal pad.

Type 2

NOTE: Wire Code Identification and Symbol Identification located in the front of this manual can be used as an aid when using wiring circuits found in this section.

INDEX

DESCRIPTION & OPERATION

This system consists of a mode control assembly, electronic controller (module), Vehicle Speed Sensor (VSS) buffer amplifier, servo unit, and release switches and valves. The servo unit maintains vehicle speed (throttle position) by trapping vacuum in its diaphragm chamber at servo positions determined by the control module. The module monitors mode control switch position, signals from the VSS buffer amplifier, servo position and release switch operation, then operates vacuum valves within the servo unit to control servo operation and vehicle speed. The module also contains a speed limiting function which prevents system operation at speeds below approximately 25 mph.

The mode control assembly consists of a 3 position slide-type switch and a set/coast switch button. To operate the system, the slide switch must be in on position and vehicle speed must be above 25 mph. The system is engaged at the desired speed by fully depressing, then releasing the set/coast button. Cruise speed can be increased from the set position by accelerating vehicle to desired speed, then pressing and releasing button. In order to decrease speed, the set/coast button is held in the fully-depressed position (disengaging system), then released when

the desired speed is reached. The system can be disengaged at any time by depressing the brake or clutch pedal, or by moving the slide switch to off position.

If the system is disengaged by depressing the brake or clutch pedal, the last set speed will be retained in the module memory until the slide switch or ignition switch is moved to off position. Momentarily moving the slide switch to the resume/accel. position will cause the vehicle to accelerate to the last set speed and maintain that speed. If the slide switch is held in the resume/accel. position, the vehicle will continue to accelerate until the switch is released. When the switch is released, the speed that the vehicle accelerated to becomes the new set speed.

The slide switch also allows a tap-up function to increase cruise set speed in 1 mph increments. With the cruise control engaged and operating, tapping-up is done by pressing the slide switch to the resume position, then quickly releasing it. This procedure can be repeated 10 times before the system must be reset to a new speed in the conventional manner.

SYSTEM COMPONENTS
Speed Sensor

On models with conventional instrument panels, a speedometer frame mounted optic head is used to pick up light reflected by a speedometer cable mounted blade. The

reflected light is produced by a light emitting diode (L.E.D.). As the speedometer cable mounted blade enters the L.E.D. light beam, the light is reflected into the optic head. From there, the light enters a photocell in the optic head and produces a low power speed signal. This signal is sent to a buffer for amplification and conditioning, then to the controller.

On models with electronic speedometers or electronic instrumentation, a transmission mounted speed sensor is used. This sensor utilizes a permanent magnet (PM) to generate vehicle speed information to the controller. Some models use a buffer amplifier to modify the sensor output.

Cruise Control Module

The module interprets the position of the servo, the position of the control switches and the output of the speed sensor. In response to these inputs, the module electrically signals the opening or closing of the vent and vacuum solenoid valves in the servo.

The module is mounted on the dash support bracket at the right side of the steering column, but is integral with the ECM on some models with certain engines.

Vacuum Release Valve

The vacuum release valve provides an additional vent to atmosphere for the servo unit when the brake pedal is held in the depressed position. The venting is spring actuated and occurs within the free travel of the brake pedal arm.

Combination Vacuum Release Valve/Converter Clutch Switch

This combination valve and switch is used on vehicles equipped with a lock-up torque converter. The vacuum release valve portion operates identically to the release valve previously described. At the same time, the converter clutch switch contacts open and the locking clutch mechanism in the transmission is disengaged.

Combination Cruise/Stop Light Switch

A separately mounted vacuum release valve is used with this combination switch. When the brake pedal is depressed, the switch resets the cruise function to a non-cruise condition and illuminates the brake lights. Two sets of electrical contacts are used in the switch: one to operate the stop lights, and the other to operate the cruise release function.

Clutch Switch

The clutch switch is used on vehicles equipped with manual transmission. When the clutch pedal is depressed, the cruise function is disconnected and will remain so after the pedal is released.

Servo Unit

The servo unit, **Fig. 1**, operates the throttle in response to signals from the electronic controller.

During a steady speed cruise condition, both vacuum and vent valves are closed or sealed. The servo holds a constant vacuum on the diaphragm and places no flow requirements on the vacuum source.

During vehicle deceleration, the vacuum solenoid is energized by the controller to open vacuum valve to vacuum source. Throttle angle is increased by increased vacuum level in the servo, and the vent remains closed.

During vehicle acceleration, the vent solenoid is de-energized by the controller to open the vent valve to atmosphere. This reduces vacuum in the servo and allows throttle return spring to decrease throttle angle while the vacuum valve remains closed.

SERVICE PRECAUTIONS

Before performing any diagnosis or repair procedures, temporarily disable the Supplemental Inflatable Restraint (SIR) system. Failure to do so may result in possible air bag deployment or personal injury. Disable SIR system as follows:
1. Turn ignition switch to Off position.
2. Remove SIR fuse.
3. Disconnect SIR electrical harness connector, at base of steering column.
4. Reverse procedure to reconnect, ensure "Inflatable Restraint" indicator flashes 7 to 9 times to indicate proper SIR operation.

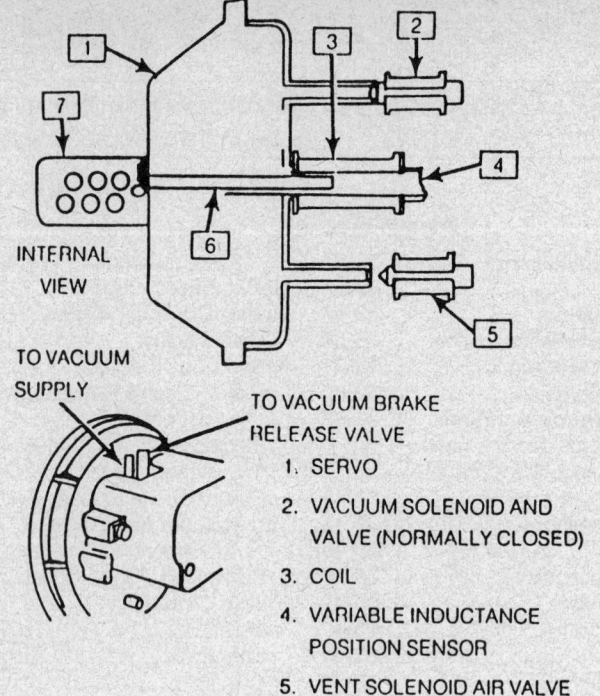

INTERNAL VIEW

TO VACUUM SUPPLY

TO VACUUM BRAKE RELEASE VALVE
1. SERVO
2. VACUUM SOLENOID AND VALVE (NORMALLY CLOSED)
3. COIL
4. VARIABLE INDUCTANCE POSITION SENSOR
5. VENT SOLENOID AIR VALVE (NORMALLY OPEN)
6. STEEL CORE
7. SERVO BLADE

Fig. 1 Servo unit

On vehicles equipped with ABS brake system, the hydraulic accumulator, when fully charged contains brake fluid at high pressure. Before disconnecting any lines, hoses or fittings, ensure accumulator is full depressurized. Failure to do so may result in personal injury.

To depressurize the hydraulic accumulator, turn the ignition to the Off position or disconnect negative battery cable, pump brake pedal a minimum of 40 times at approximately 50 lbs. of force. A noticeable change in pedal feel will occur when accumulator is fully discharged.

DIAGNOSIS & TROUBLESHOOTING

1988–90 Models Except Corvette, Cutlass Supreme, Electra, Grand Prix, LeSabre, Lumina, Park Avenue, Regal, 88 & 98

TROUBLESHOOTING
Except 1988 Cimarron

1. Check vacuum hoses for leaks, kinks and restrictions, and the cruise control servo linkage for proper slack.

2. If system works except for tap-up and tap-down functions, replace cruise control module.

1988 Cimarron

1. Check radio fuse by operating radio.
2. Ensure grounds G114 and G100 are clean and tight.
3. Check vacuum hoses for leaks, kinks and restrictions and check cruise control servo linkage.
4. If system works except for tap-up and tap-down functions, replace cruise control servo.

ROAD TEST

1. Drive vehicle at speed greater than 25 mph, place cruise switch in On position and depress set button at end of multi-function lever. Cruise indicator should illuminate and vehicle should maintain speed.
2. With foot off accelerator, hold set button in. Vehicle should coast at a slower speed.
3. Release set button. If new speed is greater than 25 mph, cruise control should engage and hold slower speed.
4. Slide cruise switch to Resume/Accel position and hold it there. Vehicle should accelerate.
5. Release cruise switch back to On position. Vehicle should hold new, faster speed.
6. Tap brake pedal. Vehicle should coast slower and cruise indicator should go out.

Connect: QUICK CHECKER or DIGITAL METER
At: CRUISE CONTROL MODULE CONNECTOR (Disconnected)
Condition:
• Ignition Switch: RUN

Test	Action	With Quick Checker, Correct Response	Without Quick Checker, Using a Digital Meter			For Different Result, Do Test
			Meter Range	Connector Terminals	Correct Response	
1	Cruise Switch OFF	LAMP light on	20 VDC	B & J	Battery voltage	Q
		All the lights off	20 VDC	A & J	0 volts	A
			20 VDC	M & J	0 volts	
2	Cruise Switch ON	ON/OFF light on	20 VDC	A & J	Battery voltage	B
		BRK light on	20 VDC	G & J	Battery voltage	C
		VENT light on	200 ohms	C & J	30 to 55 ohms	D
		VAC light on	200 ohms	K & J	30 to 55 ohms	E
		SPS light on	200 ohms	F & H	15 to 25 ohms	F
		RA light on	20 VDC	M & J	0 volts	A
		SC light on	20 VDC	L & J	0 volts	A

Fig. 2 Cruise control system diagnostic chart (Part 1 of 2). 1988–89 Century & Electra & LeSabre Estate Wagon

Test	Action	With Quick Checker, Correct Response	Without Quick Checker, Using a Digital Meter			For Different Result, Do Test
			Meter Range	Connector Terminals	Correct Result	
3	Cruise Switch ON, Set Switch pressed	SC light on	20 VDC	L & J	Battery voltage	G
		VAC & SHORT lights off	200 ohms	K & J	30 to 55 ohms	H
4	Cruise Switch in R/A	ON/OFF light on	20 VDC	A & J	Battery voltage	B
		RA light on	20 VDC	M & J	Battery voltage	I
		VENT & SHORT lights off	200 ohms	C & J	30 to 55 ohms	J
5	Cruise Switch ON, drive wheels turned by hand	VSS light flashes on and off	20 VDC	A & D	Pulses between approximately battery voltage and less than 7 volts	K, L
6	Run engine for one minute, then turn it off. With Ignition Switch in RUN and holding Cruise Switch in R/A, press and release Set Switch	Vacuum holds the servo at wide open throttle position	Connect fused jumper from C to M and from K to L, before operating switches		Vacuum holds the servo at wide open throttle position	M
7	Quick Checker not connected		200 ohms	F & J	Over range	N
8	Quick Checker not connected		200 ohms	F & H	15 to 25 ohms	O

• If all results are correct, do Test P.

Fig. 2 Cruise control system diagnostic chart (Part 2 of 2). 1988–89 Century & Electra & LeSabre Estate Wagon

Connect: QUICK CHECKER or DIGITAL METER
At: CRUISE CONTROL MODULE CONNECTOR (Disconnected)
Condition:
• Ignition Switch: RUN

Test	Action	With Quick Checker, Correct Response	Without Quick Checker, Using a Digital Meter			For Different Result, Do Test
			Meter Range	Connector Terminals	Correct Response	
1	Cruise Switch OFF	—	200 ohms	J & Ground	0 ohms	B
		LAMP light on	20 VDC	B & J	Battery voltage	Q
		All the lights off	20 VDC	A & J	0 volts	A
			20 VDC	M & J	0 volts	
2	Cruise Switch ON	ON/OFF light on	20 VDC	A & J	Battery voltage	B
		BRK light on	20 VDC	G & J	Battery voltage	C
		VENT light on	200 ohms	C & J	30 to 55 ohms	D
		VAC light on	200 ohms	K & J	30 to 55 ohms	E
		SPS light on	200 ohms	F & H	15 to 25 ohms	F
		RA light off	20 VDC	M & J	0 volts	A
		SC light off	20 VDC	L & J	0 volts	A

Fig. 3 Cruise control system diagnostic chart (Part 1 of 2). 1990 Century

Test	Action	With Quick Checker, Correct Response	Without Quick Checker, Using a Digital Meter			For Different Result, Do Test
			Meter Range	Connector Terminals	Correct Result	
3	Cruise Switch ON, Set Switch pressed	SC light on	20 VDC	L & J	Battery voltage	G
		VAC & SHORT lights off	200 ohms	K & J	30 to 55 ohms	H
4	Cruise Switch in R-A	ON/OFF light on	20 VDC	A & J	Battery voltage	B
		RA light on	20 VDC	M & J	Battery voltage	I
		VENT & SHORT lights off	200 ohms	C & J	30 to 55 ohms	J
5	Cruise Switch ON, drive wheels turned by hand	VSS light flashes on and off	20 VDC	A & D	Pulses between approximately battery voltage and less than 7 volts	K, L
6	Run engine for one minute, then turn it off. With Ignition Switch in RUN and holding Cruise Switch in R/A, press Set Switch, wait for Servo to pull in, and release Set Switch	Vacuum holds the servo all the way in	Connect fused jumper from C to M and from K to L, before operating switches		Vacuum holds the servo all the way in	M
7	Quick Checker not connected		200 ohms	F & J	Over range	N
8	Quick Checker not connected		200 ohms	F & H	15 to 25 ohms	O

• If all of the responses were correct, do Test P.

Fig. 3 Cruise control system diagnosis chart (Part 2 of 2). 1990 Century

Connect: QUICK CHECKER (J-34185, SPECMO QC-3 OR EQUIVALENT) or VOLT-OHMMETER
At: CRUISE CONTROL MODULE CONNECTOR (Disconnected)
Conditions:
• Ignition Switch: RUN
• Test with Quick Checker (J-34185 or equivalent) or Digital Meter

Test	Condition	With Quick Checker, Correct Response	Without Quick Checker, Using a Digital Meter			For Different Response, Do Test
			Meter Range	Connector Terminals	Correct Response	
1	Cruise Switch OFF		200 ohms	J & Ground	0 ohms	B
		All Lights Off	20 VDC	A & J	0 volts	A
			20 VDC	M & J	0 volts	
2	Cruise Switch ON	ON/OFF Light On	20 VDC	A & J	Battery voltage	B
		BRK Light On	20 VDC	G & J	Battery voltage	C
		VENT Light On	200 ohms	C & J	30 to 55 ohms	D
		VAC Light On	200 ohms	K & J	30 to 55 ohms	E
		SPS Light On	200 ohms	F & H	15 to 25 ohms	F
		RA Light Off	20 VDC	M & J	0 volts	A
		SC Light Off	20 VDC	L & J	0 volts	A
3	Cruise Switch ON, Set Switch pressed	SC Light On	20 VDC	L & J	Battery voltage	G
		VAC & SHORT Lights Off	200 ohms	K & J	30 to 55 ohms	H
4	Cruise Switch in R/A	ON/OFF Light On	20 VDC	A & J	Battery voltage	B
		RA Light On	20 VDC	M & J	Battery voltage	I
		VENT & SHORT Lights Off	200 ohms	C & J	30 to 55 ohms	J

Fig. 4 Cruise control system diagnostic chart (Part 1 of 2). 1988–89 Bonneville, Calais, Camaro, Caprice, Cavalier, Celebrity, Ciera, Custom Cruiser, Cutlass Supreme Classic, Fiero, Firebird, Firenza, Grand Am, Monte Carlo, Skyhawk, Sunbird, & 6000

Test	Condition	With Quick Checker, Correct Response	Without Quick Checker, Using a Digital Meter			For Different Result, Do Test
			Meter Range	Connector Terminals	Correct Response	
3	Cruise Switch ON, Set Switch pressed	SC light on	20 VDC	L & J	Battery voltage	G
		VAC & SHORT lights off	200 ohms	K & J	30 to 55 ohms	H
4	Cruise Switch in R-A	ON/OFF light on	20 VDC	A & J	Battery voltage	B
		RA light on	20 VDC	M & J	Battery voltage	I
		VENT & SHORT lights off	200 ohms	C & J	30 to 55 ohms	J
5	Cruise Switch ON, drive wheels turned by hand	VSS Light flashes On and Off	20 VDC	A & D	Pulses between approximately battery voltage and less than 7 volts	K, L
6	Run engine for one minute, then turn it off. With Ignition Switch in RUN and holding Cruise Switch in R/A, press Set Switch, wait for Servo to pull in, and release Set Switch	Vacuum holds the servo all the way in	Connect fused jumper from C to M and from K to L, before operating switches		Vacuum holds the servo all the way in	M
7	Quick Checker not connected		200 ohms	F & J	Over range	N
8	Quick Checker not connected		200 ohms	F & H	15 to 25 ohms	O

• If all of the responses were correct, do Test P.

Fig. 4 Cruise control system diagnostic chart (Part 2 of 2). 1988–89 Bonneville, Calais, Camaro, Caprice, Cavalier, Celebrity, Ciera, Custom Cruiser, Cutlass Supreme Classic, Fiero, Firebird, Firenza, Grand Am, Monte Carlo, Skyhawk, Sunbird, & 6000

7. Slide cruise control switch momentarily to Resume/Accel position. Cruise indicator should illuminate and vehicle should accelerate to former set speed.
8. While cruising, accelerate, then remove foot from accelerator pedal. Vehicle should coast back to set speed.
9. While cruising, tap cruise switch to Resume/Accel position. Vehicle speed should decrease 1 mph for each tap up to ten.
10. While cruising, tap set button. Vehicle speed should decrease 1 mph for each tap down to 25 mph.
11. Slide cruise control switch to Off position. Cruise control should turn off and cruise indicator should go out.

SYSTEM DIAGNOSIS

Perform tests as shown, **Figs. 2 through 8.** If results are other than specified, perform designated test. **Do not press set switch and Resume/Accel position of cruise switch at same time while engine is running. If quick checker displays a short light, release switches immediately.**

When performing the following tests refer to wiring diagram and control module pin connectors **Figs. 9 through 14,** for basic outlines.

TEST A

Except Beretta & Corsica

1. Check for shorts to voltage in wires to terminals A, G, L and M of cruise control module.
2. If wires are satisfactory, replace multi-function lever.

Beretta & Corsica

1. **On 1988 models,** check for short to voltage in wires to terminals A (gray wire) H (gray/black wire) and J (dark blue wire) of cruise control module.
2. **On 1989-90 models,** check for short to voltage in wires to terminals A (gray wire) G (dark green wire) L (dark blue wire) and M (gray black wire) of cruise control module.
3. **On all models,** if wires are satisfactory, check multi-function lever and cruise control switches for a short, replacing as necessary.

TEST B

1988 Cavalier, Celebrity, Ciera, Cimarron, Firenza, Skyhawk, Sunbird & 6000

1. Check gages, radio, and rad fuses, as equipped .
2. Ensure terminal J of cruise control module is grounded.
3. Disconnect connector C235 and check for battery voltage at terminal A (brown/white wire) with ignition in Run position. If battery voltage is not available on 6000, check yellow wire (circuit 43) or brown/white wire (circuit 141). If battery voltage is not available on Cavalier, Celebrity, Cimarron, Firenza or Sunbird, check brown/white wire (circuit 141). If battery voltage is not available on Ciera, check pink/black wire (circuit 39) on 3.8L engine, or brown/white wire (circuit 141) on 2.8L engine, and yellow wire (circuit 43). If battery voltage is not available on Skyhawk, check pink/black wire (circuit 39) and brown/white wire (circuit 141).
4. Check continuity between terminals A (blue wire) and B (green wire) of connector C235 with cruise switch in On position. If there is no continuity, replace multi-function lever.

Connect: QUICK CHECKER (J34185, SPECMO QC-3 OR EQUIVALENT) or DIGITAL MULTI-METER
At: CRUISE CONTROL MODULE CONNECTOR (Disconnected)
Condition:
- Ignition Switch: RUN

TEST	Condition	With Quick Checker, Correct Response	Meter Range	Connector Terminals	Correct Response	For Different Response, Do Test
1	Cruise Switch OFF	—	200 ohms	J & Ground	0 ohms	B
	All Lights OFF		20 VDC	A & J	0 volts	A
			20 VDC	M & J	0 volts	A
2	Cruise Switch ON	ON/OFF Light On	20 VDC	A & J	Battery voltage	B
		BRK Light On	20 VDC	G & J	Battery voltage	C
		VENT Light On	200 ohms	C & J	30 to 55 ohms	D
		VAC Light On	200 ohms	K & J	30 to 55 ohms	E
		SPS Light On	200 ohms	F & H	15 to 25 ohms	F
		RA Light On	20 VDC	M & J	0 volts	A
		SC Light Off	20 VDC	L & J	0 volts	A

Fig. 5   Cruise control system diagnosis chart (Part 1 of 4). 1990 Bonneville, Calais, Camaro, Caprice, Cavalier, Celebrity, Ciera, Custom Cruiser, Cutlass Supreme, Estate Wagon, Firebird, Grand Am, Grand Prix, Sunbird & 6000

Test	Action	With Quick Checker, Correct Response	Meter Range	Connector Terminals	Correct Result	For Different Result, Do Test
3	Cruise Switch ON, Set Switch pressed	SC light on	20 VDC	L & J	Battery voltage	G
		VAC & SHORT lights off	200 ohms	K & J	30 to 55 ohms	H
4	Cruise Switch in R-A	ON/OFF light on	20 VDC	A & J	Battery voltage	B
		RA light on	20 VDC	M & J	Battery voltage	I
		VENT & SHORT lights off	200 ohms	C & J	30 to 55 ohms	J
5	Cruise Switch ON, drive wheels turned by hand	VSS light flashes on and off	20 VDC	A & D	Pulses between approximately battery voltage and less than 7 volts	K, L
6	Run engine for one minute, then turn it off. With Ignition Switch in RUN and holding Cruise Switch in R/A, press Set Switch, wait for Servo to pull in, and release Set Switch.	Vacuum holds the servo all the way in	Connect fused jumper from C to M and from K to L before operating switches		Vacuum holds the servo all the way in	M
7	Quick Checker not connected		200 ohms	F & J	Over range	N
8	Quick Checker not connected		200 ohms	F & H	15 to 25 ohms	O

• If all results are correct, do Test P.

Fig. 5   Cruise control system diagnosis chart (Part 2 of 4). 1990 Bonneville, Calais, Cavalier, Celebrity, Cutlass Supreme, Grand Am, Grand Prix, Sunbird & 6000

Connect: QUICK CHECKER (J-34185, SPECMO QC-3 OR EQUIVALENT) or DIGITAL VOLTMETER
At: CRUISE CONTROL MODULE CONNECTOR (Disconnected)
Conditions:
- Ignition Switch: RUN

Check	Condition	With Quick Checker, Correct Response	Meter Range	Connector Terminals	Correct Response	For Different Response, Do Test
1	Cruise Switch OFF	—	200 ohms	L & Ground	0 ohms	B
	All Lights off		20 VDC	A & L	0 volts	A
			20 VDC	H & L	0 volts	A
2	Cruise Switch ON	ON/OFF Light On	20 VDC	A & L	Battery voltage	B
		BRK Light On	20 VDC	M & L	Battery voltage	C
		VENT Light On	200 ohms	C & L	30 to 55 ohms	D
		VAC Light On	200 ohms	K & L	30 to 55 ohms	E
		SPS Light On	200 ohms	F & H	15 to 25 ohms	F
		RA Light Off	20 VDC	H & L	0 volts	A
		SC Light Off	20 VDC	J & L	0 volts	A

Fig. 6   Cruise control system diagnostic chart (Part 1 of 2). 1988–89 Beretta & Corsica

Test	Condition	With Quick Checker, Correct Response	Meter Range	Connector Terminals	Correct Response	For Different Response, Do Test
3	Cruise Switch ON, Set Switch pressed	SC Light On	20 VDC	L & J	Battery voltage	G
		VAC & SHORT Lights Off	200 ohms	K & J	30 to 55 ohms	H
4	Cruise Switch in R/A	ON/OFF Light On	20 VDC	A & J	Battery voltage	A
		RA Light On	20 VDC	M & J	Battery voltage	I
		VENT & SHORT Lights Off	200 ohms	C & J	30 to 55 ohms	J
5	Cruise Switch ON, drive wheels turned by hand	VSS Light flashes On and Off	20 VDC	A & D	Pulses between approximately battery voltage and less than 7 volts	K, L
6	Run engine for one minute, then turn it off. With Ignition Switch in RUN, and holding Cruise Switch in R/A, press Set Switch, wait for Servo to pull in and release Set Switch.	Vacuum holds the servo all the way in	Connect fused jumper from C to M and from K to L before operating switches		Vacuum holds the servo all the way in	M
7	Quick Checker not connected		200 ohms	F & J	Over range	N

• If all the responses were correct, do Test O.

Fig. 5   Cruise control system diagnosis chart (Part 3 of 4). 1990 Camaro & Firebird

Test	Condition	With Quick Checker, Correct Response	Meter Range	Connector Terminals	Correct Response	For Different Response, Do Test
3	Cruise Switch ON, Set/Coast Switch pressed	SC Light On	20 VDC	J & L	Battery voltage	G
		VAC & SHORT Lights Off	200 ohms	K & L	30 to 55 ohms	H
4	Resume/Accel Switch pressed	ON/OFF Light On	20 VDC	A & L	Battery voltage	A
		RA Light On	20 VDC	H & L	Battery voltage	I
		VENT & SHORT Lights Off	200 ohms	C & L	30 to 55 ohms	J
5	Cruise Switch ON, drive wheels turned by hand	VSS Light flashes On and Off	20 VDC	A & D	Pulses between approximately battery voltage and less than 7 volts	K, L
6	Run engine for one minute, then turn it off. With Ignition Switch in RUN, and hold Resume/Accel, press Set/Coast Switch, wait for Servo to pull in and release Set/Coast Switch	Vacuum holds the servo all the way in	Connect fused jumper from C to H and from K to J before operating switches		Vacuum holds the servo all the way in	M
7	Quick Checker not connected		200 ohms	F & L	Over range	N

• If all the responses were correct, do Test O.

Fig. 5   Cruise control system diagnosis chart (Part 4 of 4). 1990 Caprice, Ciera, Custom Cruiser & Estate Wagon

Connect: QUICK CHECKER (J-34185, SPECMO QC-3 OR EQUIVALENT) or DIGITAL METER
At: CRUISE CONTROL MODULE CONNECTOR (Disconnected)
Condition:
- Ignition Switch: RUN

Test	Condition	With Quick Checker, Correct Response	Meter Range	Connector Terminals	Correct Response	For Different Response, Do Test
1	Cruise Switch OFF	—	200 ohms	J & Ground	0 ohms	B
	All lights off		20 VDC	A & J	0 volts	A
			20 VDC	M & J	0 volts	A
2	Cruise Switch ON	ON/OFF Light on	20 VDC	A & J	Battery voltage	B
		BRK Light on	20 VDC	G & J	Battery voltage	C
		VENT Light on	200 ohms	C & J	30 to 55 ohms	D
		VAC Light on	200 ohms	K & J	30 to 55 ohms	E
		SPS Light on	200 ohms	F & H	15 to 25 ohms	F
		R/A Light off	20 VDC	M & J	0 volts	A
		SC Light off	20 VDC	J & J	0 volts	A

Fig. 7   Cruise control system diagnosis chart (Part 1 of 2). 1990 Beretta & Corsica

Test	Condition	With Quick Checker, Correct Response	Meter Range	Connector Terminals	Correct Response	For Different Response, Do Test
3	Cruise Switch ON, Set Coast Switch pressed	SC Light on	20 VDC	J & L	Battery voltage	G
		VAC & SHORT Lights off	200 ohms	K & J	30 to 55 ohms	H
4	Resume Accel Switch pressed	ON/OFF Light on	20 VDC	A & J	Battery voltage	B
		R/A Light on	20 VDC	M & J	Battery voltage	I
		VENT & SHORT Lights off	200 ohms	C & J	30 to 55 ohms	J
5	Cruise Switch ON, drive wheels turned by hand	VSS Light Flashes On and Off	20 VDC	A & D	Pulses between approximately battery voltage and less than 4 volts	K, L
6	Run engine for one minute, then turn it off. With Ignition Switch in RUN, press and hold Resume/Accel, press Set/Coast Switch, wait for Servo to pull in and release Set/Coast Switch	Vacuum holds the servo all the way in	Connect fused jumper from C to M and from K to L before operating switches		Vacuum holds the servo all the way in	M
7	Quick Checker not connected		200 ohms	F & J	Over range	N

• If all of the responses are correct, do Test O.

Fig. 7   Cruise control system diagnosis chart (Part 2 of 2). 1990 Beretta & Corsica

Connect: QUICK CHECK (J-34185, SPECMO QC-3 OR EQUIVALENT) OR DIGITAL VOLTMETER
At: CRUISE CONTROL MODULE CONNECTOR (Disconnected)
Condition:
- Ignition Switch: RUN

Test	Condition	With Quick Checker, Correct Response	Meter Range	Connector Terminals	Correct Response	For Different Response, Do Test
1	Cruise Switch: OFF	—	200 ohms	J & Ground	0 ohms	B
	All Lights Off		20 VDC	A & J	0 volts	A
			20 VDC	M & J	0 volts	A
	(Digital Cluster Only)	LAMP Light On	20 VDC	B & J	Battery voltage	O
2	Cruise Switch: ON	ON/OFF Light On	20 VDC	A & J	Battery voltage	B
		BRK Light On	20 VDC	G & J	Battery voltage	C
		VENT Light On	200 ohms	C & J	30 to 55 ohms	D
		VAC Light On	200 ohms	K & J	30 to 55 ohms	E
		SPS Light On	200 ohms	F & H	15 to 25 ohms	F
		RA Light Off	20 VDC	M & J	0 volts	A
		SC Light Off	20 VDC	L & J	0 volts	A
3	Cruise Switch ON Set Switch pressed	SC Light On	20 VDC	L & J	Battery voltage	G
		VAC & SHORT Lights Off	200 ohms	K & J	30 to 55 Ohms	H
4	Cruise Switch in R/A	ON/OFF Light ON	20 VDC	A & J	Battery voltage	B
		RA Light On	20 VDC	M & J	Battery voltage	I
		VENT & SHORT Lights Off	200 ohms	C & J	30 to 55 ohms	J
5	Cruise Switch ON, drive wheels turned by hand	VSS Light flashes On and Off	20 VDC	A & D	Pulses between approximately battery voltage and less than 7 volts	K, L
6	Run engine for one minute, then turn it off. With Ignition Switch in RUN, and holding Cruise Switch in R/A, press Set Switch, wait for Servo to pull in and release Set Switch	Vacuum holds the servo all the way in	Connect fused jumpers from C to M and from K to L before operating switches		Vacuum holds the servo all the way in	M
7	Quick Checker not connected	—	200 ohms	F & J	Over range	N

• If all the responses were correct, replace the Cruise Control Module and check for proper operation.

Fig. 8   Cruise control system diagnostic chart. Skylark & 1988 Cimarron & 1989–90 Lemans

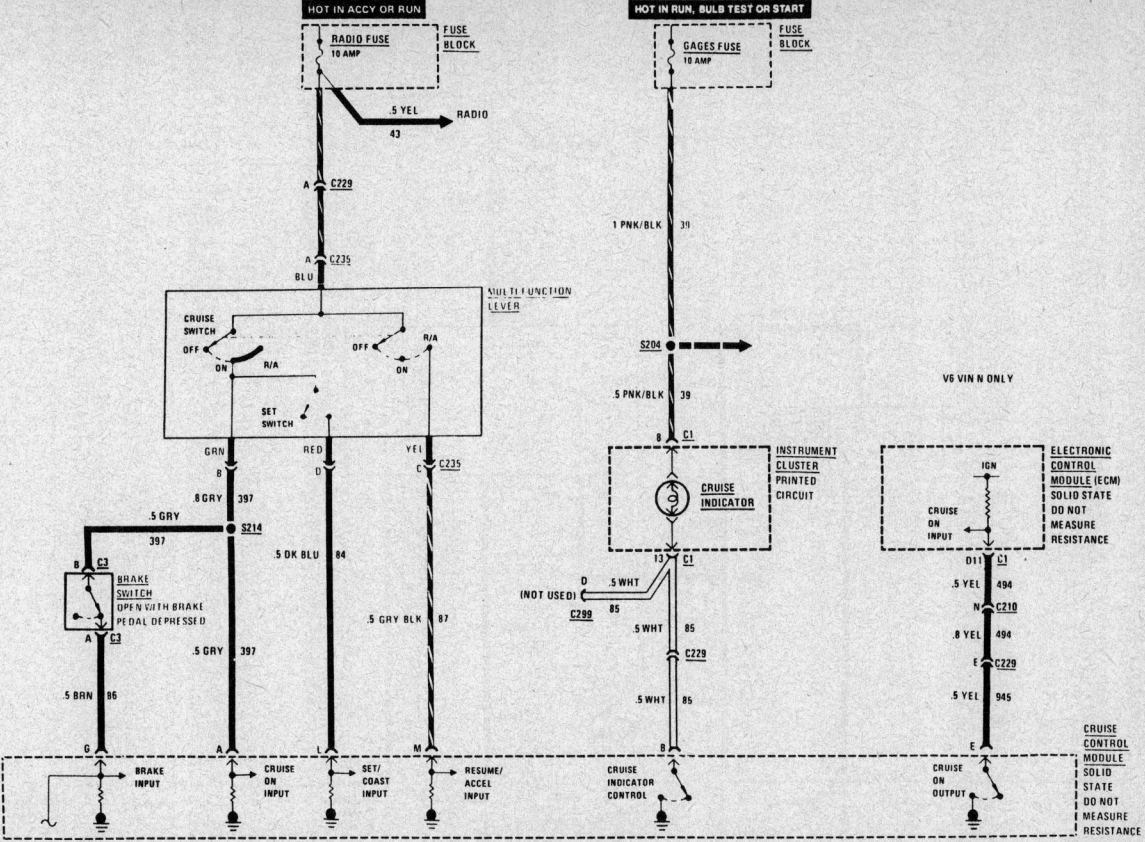

Fig. 9 Typical cruise control wiring diagram, (Part 1 of 2). 1988–89 Century, Electra, LeSabre & Estate Wagon

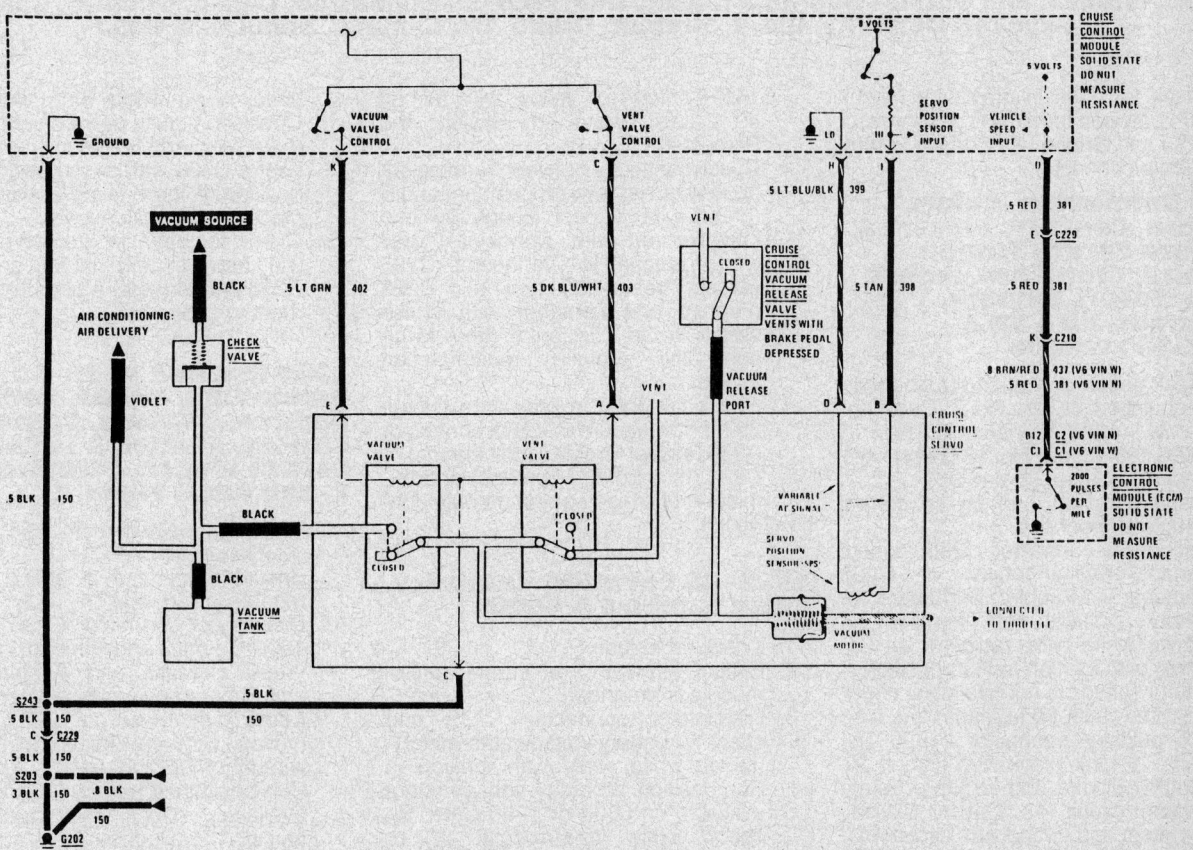

Fig. 9 Typical cruise control wiring diagram, (Part 2 of 2). 1988–89 Century, Electra, LeSabre & Estate Wagon

TYPE 2

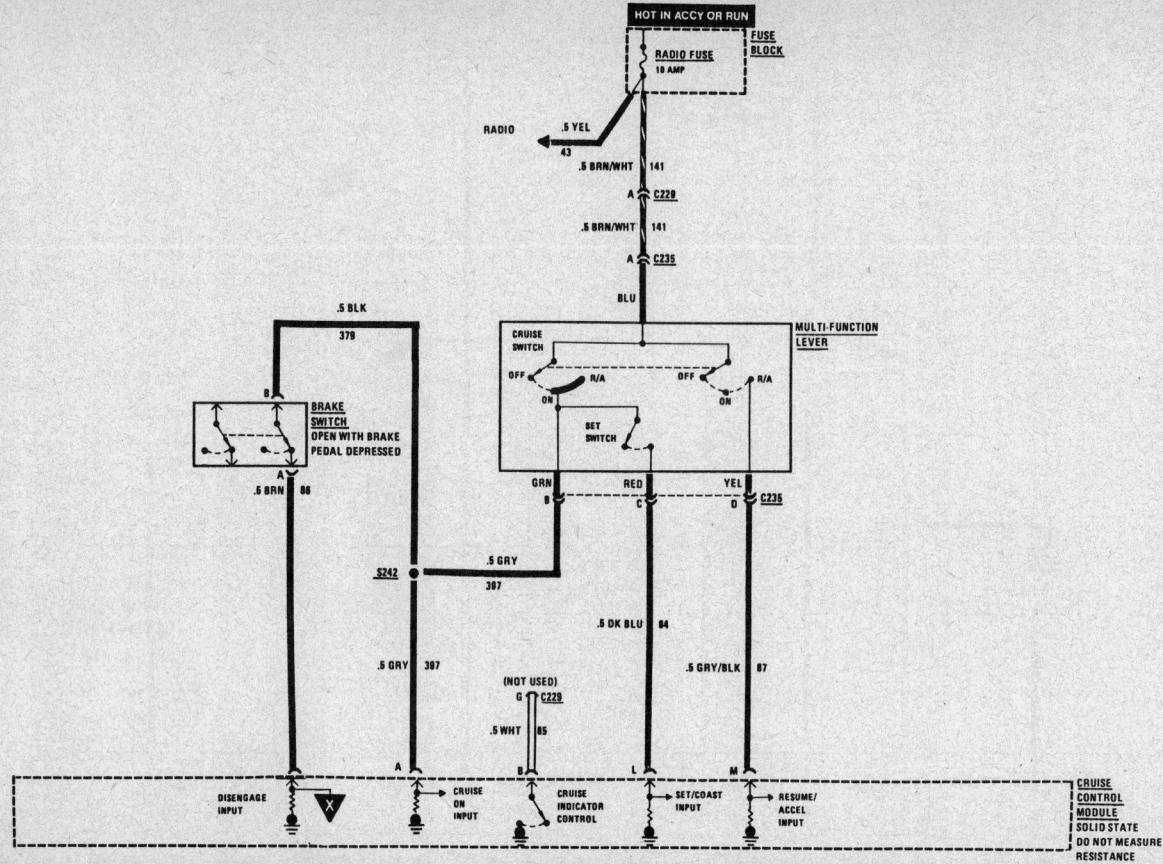

Fig. 10 Typical cruise control wiring diagram, (Part 1 of 2). 1988–89 Monte Carlo, Skyhawk, Fiero, Firenza, and Cutlass Supreme Classic and 1988–90 Bonneville, Calais, Camaro, Caprice, Cavalier, Celebrity, Ciera, Firebird, Grand Am, Lemans, Sunbird, & 6000

5. Check for open in gray wire (circuit 397) between terminal B of connector C235 and terminal A of cruise control module connector.

1988 Bonneville, Calais, Camaro, Century, Electra & LeSabre Estate Wagon, Firebird, Grand Am, Monte Carlo, Safari, Skylark, Somerset, 88 & 98 & 1989–90 Lemans

1. Check gages, cruise, and radio fuses, as equipped, or fuse No. 7 (Calais) or No. 15 (1989 Lemans) or No. 13 (1990 Lemans) or No. 18 (Bonneville, Electra, LeSabre, 88 and 98).
2. Ensure terminal J of cruise control module is grounded.
3. Disconnect connector C235 (except Lemans and Firebird) or C223 (Lemans and Firebird) and check for battery voltage at terminal A (brown/white wire, red wire on Lemans) with ignition in Run position. If battery voltage is not available, check red wire (1989-90 Lemans) and fuse box auxilary connector (1990 Lemans) or pink/black wire (circuit 39, Century, Electra and LeSabre Estate Wagon; circuit 43, Calais, Skylark, Somerset and Grand Am; circuit 141, Caprice, Monte Carlo and Safari; circuit 239, Bonneville, Camaro and Firebird) and brown/white wire (circuit

141, Century) or yellow wire (circuit 43, Calais, Grand Am, Skylark and Somerset).
4. Check continuity between terminals A (blue wire, red wire on Lemans) and B (green wire, except Bonneville and Lemans; red wire, Bonneville; gray wire, Lemans) of connector C235 (except Firebird and Lemans) or C223 (Firebird and Lemans) with cruise switch in On position. If there is no continuity, replace multi-function switch.
5. Check for open in gray wire (circuit 397) between terminal B of connector C235 (except Firebird and Lemans) or C223 (Firebird and Lemans) and terminal A of cruise control module connector.

1989–90 Cavalier, Celebrity, Ciera, Sunbird & 6000

1. Check radio fuse.
2. Ensure terminal J of cruise control module is grounded.
3. Disconnect connector C235 and check for battery voltage at terminal A (brown/white wire) with ignition in Run position. If battery voltage is not available on 6000 or 1990 Celebrity, check yellow wire (circuit 43) or brown/white wire (circuit 141). If battery voltage is not available on Cavalier, Ciera, Sunbird or 1989 Celebrity

check brown/white wire (circuit 141).
4. Check continuity between terminals A (blue wire) and B (green wire) of connector C235 with cruise switch in On position. If there is no continuity, replace multi-function lever.
5. Check for open in gray wire (circuit 397) between terminal B of connector C235 and terminal A of cruise control module connector.

1989 Safari & 1989–90 Bonneville, Calais, Camaro, Caprice, Century, Custom Cruiser, Electra & LeSabre Estate Wagon, Firebird, Grand Am & Skylark

1. Check gages and radio fuses, or No. 18 (Bonneville).
2. Ensure terminal J of cruise control module is grounded.
3. Disconnect connector C235 (except 1990 Camaro and Firebird) or C211 (1990 Camaro and Firebird) and check for battery voltage at terminal A (brown/white wire on 1989 Century) (yellow wire on Calais) (pink/black wire all other models) with ignition in Run position. If battery voltage is not available, check pink/black wire (circuit 141, Caprice, Electra and LeSabre Estate Wagon, Safari, and Custom Cruiser; circuit 43, Skylark and Grand Am; circuit 239, Bonneville; cir-

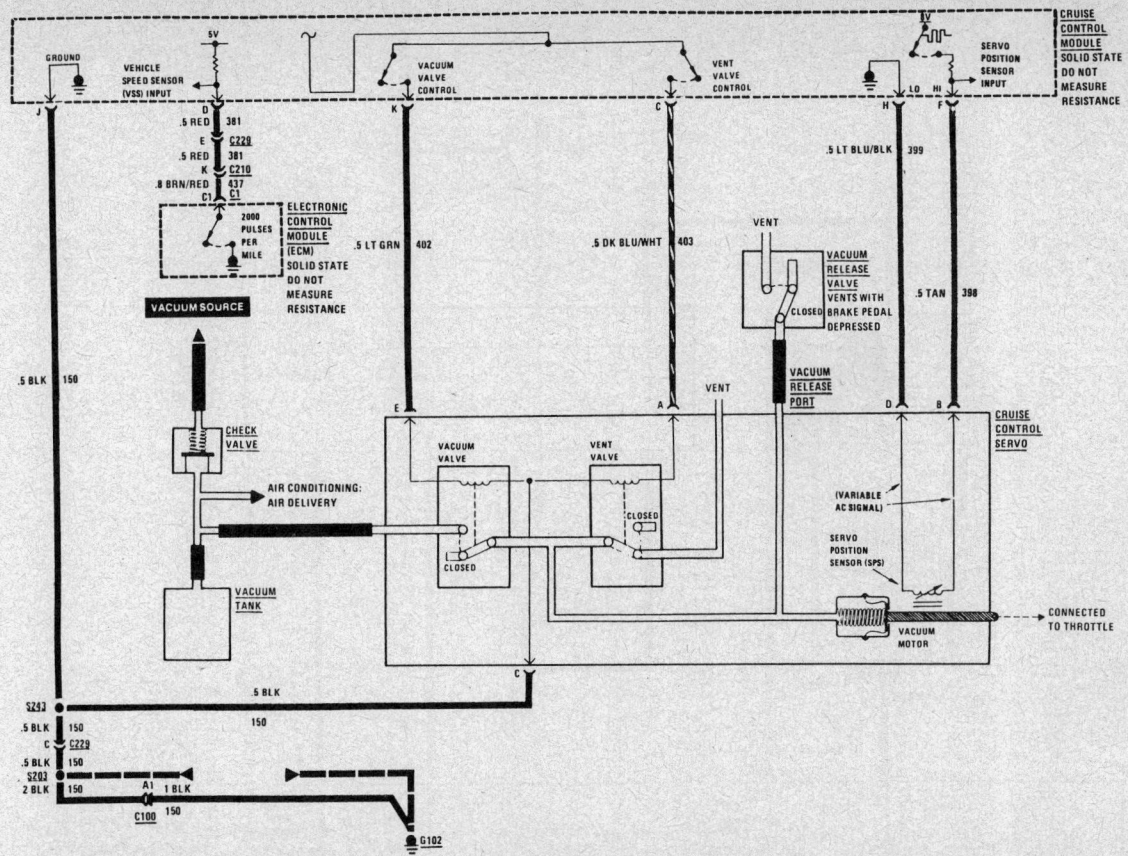

Fig. 10 Typical cruise control wiring diagram, (Part 2 of 2). 1988–89 Cutlass Supreme Classic, Fiero, Firenza, Monte Carlo, Skyhawk and 1988–90 Bonneville, Calais, Camaro, Caprice, Cavalier, Celebrity, Ciera, Firebird, Grand Am, Lemans, Sunbird, & 6000

cuit 39 Camaro, Firebird and 1990 Century) and brown/white wire (circuit 141, 1989 Century) or yellow wire (circuit 43, Calais, Grand Am, and Skylark).
4. Check continuity between terminals A (blue wire) and B (green wire, except Bonneville; red wire, Bonneville) of connector C235 (except 1990 Camaro and Firebird) or C211 (1990 Camaro and Firebird) with cruise switch in On position. If there is no continuity, replace multi-function lever.
5. Check for open in gray wire (circuit 397) between terminal B (except 1990 Camaro and Firebird) or terminal L (1990 Camaro and Firebird) of connector C235 (except 1990 Camaro and Firebird) or C211 (1990 Camaro and Firebird) and terminal A of cruise control module connector.

1988–90 Beretta & Corsica

1. Check fuse No. 14.
2. Ensure terminal L (J on 1989-90 models) (black wire) of cruise control module is grounded.
3. Disconnect connector C235 and check for battery voltage at terminal A (brown/white wire) of harness half with ignition switch in Run position. If battery voltage is not available, check brown/white wire (circuit 141) for an open.

4. Check continuity between terminals A (blue wire, brown wire on 1989-90 models) and C (green wire, gray wire on 1989-90 models) of pin half of connector C235 with cruise switch in On position. If there is no continuity, check multi-function lever and cruise control switches for an open, replacing as necessary.
5. Check for an open in gray wire (circuit 397) between terminal C of connector C235 and terminal A of cruise control module connector.

TEST C

1. Check for open in brake or clutch switch.
2. **On 1988 Custom Cruiser, Electra and LeSabre Estate Wagon, Skylark and Somerset and 1989 Celebrity and 1988–90 Bonneville, Century and Ciera,** check for open in brown/white wire (circuit 86) to terminal G of cruise control module.
3. **On 1988 Celebrity and 6000,** check for open in brown/white wire (circuit 86) or purple wire (circuit 986).
4. **On 1989-90 Skylark and 6000 and 1990 Celebrity,** check for open in brown/white (circuit 86).
5. **On Firenza and 1988-90 Cavalier and Sunbird,** check for open in brown wire (circuit 86) and brown/white wire (circuit 986).

6. **On Skyhawk,** check for open in brown wire (circuit 86) brown/white wire (circuit 986) and gray wire (circuit 397).
7. **On Beretta and Corsica,** check brown wire (circuit 86) and tan wire (circuit 986, 1988) and dark green wire (1989-90) for an open.
8. **On 1988 Cutlass Supreme Classic and 1988-90 Calais and Grand Am,** check for open in brown/white wire (circuit 86) or gray wire (circuit 986).
9. **On Camaro and Firebird,** check for an open in brown wire (circuit 86) gray/white wire (circuit 987, 1988-90 Firebird and 1990 Camaro) or gray wire (circuit 397).
10. **On 1988 Monte Carlo and 1988-89 Safari and 1988-90 Caprice and 1989-90 Custom Cruiser and Estate Wagon,** check for open in gray/black wire (circuit 87) to terminal G of cruise control module.
11. **On Fiero,** check for open in brown wire (circuit 86) gray wire (circuit 397) or yellow wire (circuit 918).
12. **On Cimarron,** check for open in brown wire (circuits 86 and 986) and brown/white wire (circuit 986).
13. **On Lemans,** check for open in gray and gray/black wires between the cruise control module, brake switch and clutch switch.

TEST D

1. If measurement is less than 30 ohms,

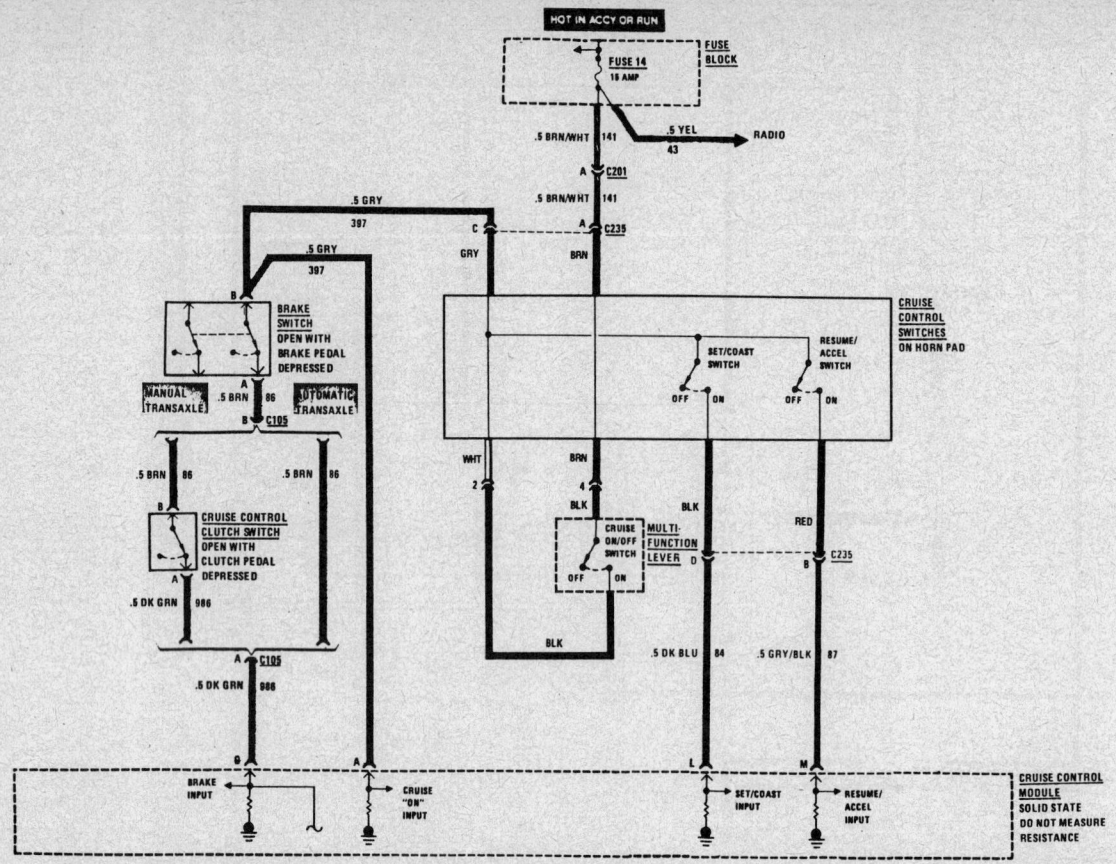

Fig. 11   Typical cruise control wiring diagram, (Part 1 of 2). Beretta & Corsica

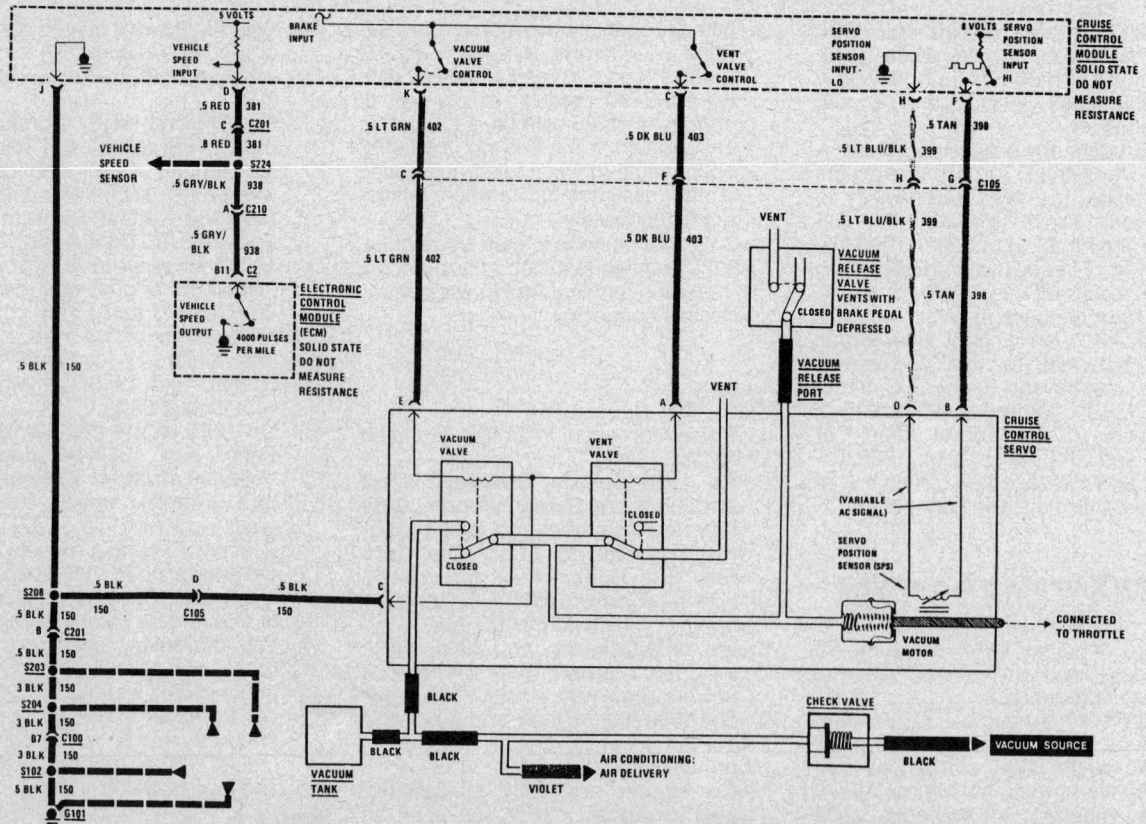

Fig. 11   Typical cruise control wiring diagram, (Part 2 of 2). Beretta & Corsica

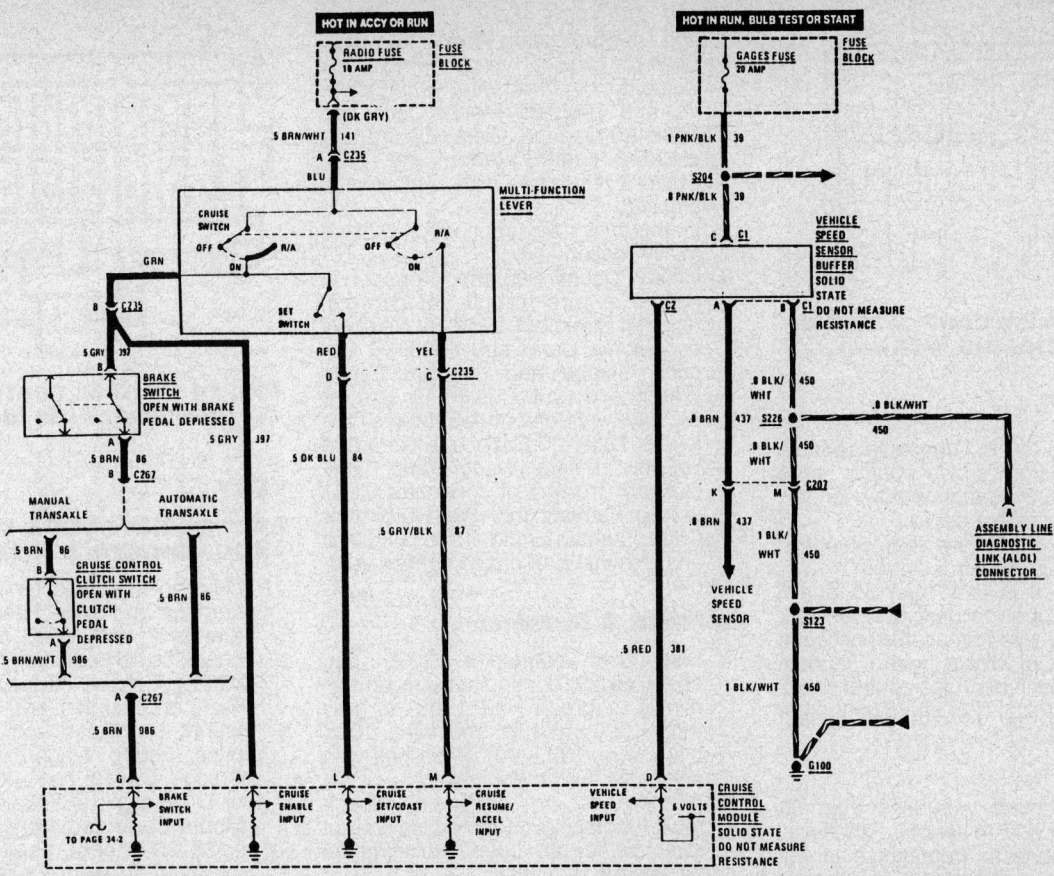

Fig. 12   Typical cruise control wiring diagram, (Part 1 of 2). Skylark & 1988 Cimarron

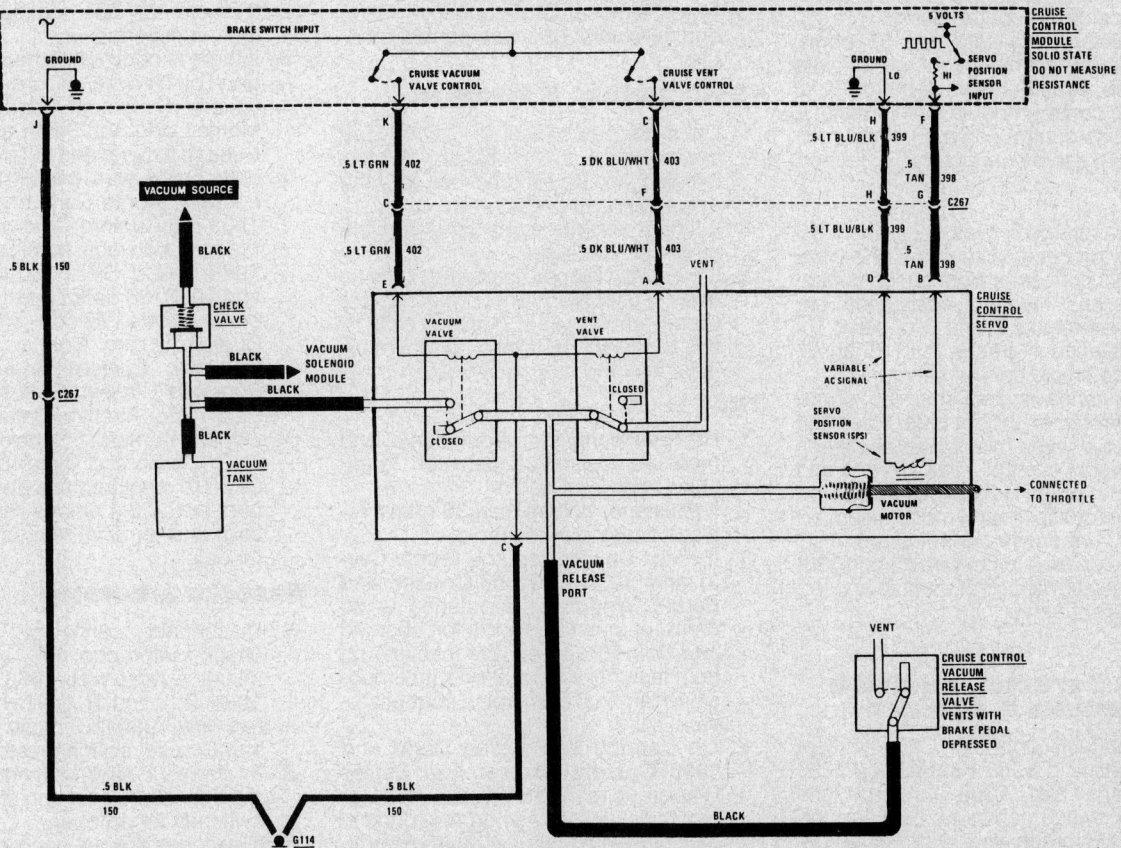

Fig. 12   Typical cruise control wiring diagram, (Part 2 of 2). Skylark & 1988 Cimarron

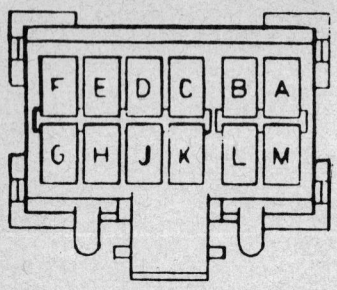

Fig. 13 Cruise control module connector pin location

proceed to test J. Otherwise, remove connector from cruise control servo and measure resistance between terminals A and C of servo.

2. If resistance is greater than 55 ohms, replace cruise control servo.

3. If resistance is less than 55 ohms, check for open in dark blue or dark blue/white wire (circuit 403) between terminal C of cruise control module and terminal A of cruise control servo. Ensure terminal C of servo connector is grounded.

TEST E

1. If measurement was less than 30 ohms, proceed to test H. Otherwise, remove connector from cruise control servo and measure resistance between terminals E and C of servo.

2. If resistance is greater than 55 ohms, replace cruise control servo.

3. If resistance is less than 55 ohms, check for open in light green wire (circuit 402) between terminal K of cruise control module and terminal E of cruise control servo. Ensure terminal C of servo connector is grounded.

TEST F

1. If measurement was less than 15 ohms, proceed to test N. Otherwise, remove connector from cruise control servo and measure resistance between terminals B and D of servo.

2. If resistance is greater than 25 ohms, replace cruise control servo.

3. If resistance is less than 25 ohms, check for open in light blue/black and light blue wires (circuit 399) between terminal H (except 1988 Beretta and Corsica) or N (1988 Beretta and Corsica) of cruise control module and terminal D of cruise control servo. Also, check for open in tan wire (circuit 398) between terminal F of module and terminal B of servo.

TEST G
Except Beretta, Corsica & 1990 Camaro & Firebird

1. Disconnect connector C235 (except Lemans and 1988 Firebird) or C223 (Lemans and 1988 Firebird) and check switch continuity between terminals B (green wire, gray wire on Lemans) and D (red wire, except 1988-89 Celebrity and Monte Carlo

and 1988-90 Caprice, Ciera, Electra and LeSabre Estate Wagon and 1990 Custom Cruiser; yellow wire, 1988 Celebrity) or C (red wire, 1989 Celebrity and 1988-89 Monte Carlo and 1988-90 Caprice, Ciera, Electra and LeSabre Estate Wagon and 1990 Custom Cruiser) with set switch pressed.

2. If there is no continuity, replace multi-function lever.

3. If there is continuity, check for open in dark blue wire (circuit 84) between terminal D (except 1988-89 Celebrity and Monte Carlo and 1988-90 Caprice, Electra and LeSabre Estate Wagon and 1990 Custom Cruiser) or C (1988-89 Celebrity and Monte Carlo and 1988-90 Caprice, Electra and LeSabre Estate Wagon and 1990 Custom Cruiser) of connector C235 (except Lemans and 1988 Firebird) or C223 (Lemans and 1988 Firebird) and terminal L of cruise control module.

Beretta & Corsica

1. Disconnect connector C235 and check switch continuity between terminals C (green wire, 1988-89 gray wire, 1990) and D (red wire, 1988 black wire, 1989-90) of pin half with set/coast switch depressed.

2. If there is no continuity, check multi-function lever and cruise control switches for an open, replacing as necessary.

3. If switches are not open, check for an open in dark blue wire (circuit 84) between terminal D of connector C235 and terminal J of cruise control module.

1990 Camaro & Firebird

1. Disconnect connector C211 and check switch continuity between terminals L and K of the pin half with the set switch pressed.

2. If there is no continuity, replace multi-function lever.

3. If the switch is not open, check for an open in dark blue wire (circuit 84) between terminal K of connector C211 and terminal L of cruise control module.

TEST H

1. Remove connector from servo and measure resistance between terminals C and E of servo.

2. If resistance is less than 30 ohms, replace cruise control servo.

3. **Except On Caprice and Monte Carlo and 1990 Custom Cruiser and Estate Wagon,** if resistance is 30 ohms or greater, check for short to ground in light green wire (circuit 402) from terminal K of cruise control module to terminal E of cruise control servo.

4. **On Caprice and Monte Carlo and 1990 Custom Cruiser and Estate Wagon,** if resistance is 30 ohms or greater, check for a short to ground in dark blue wire (circuit 403) from terminal C of cruise control module and terminal A of cruise control servo.

Fig. 14 Cruise control module connector pin location

TEST I
Except Beretta & Corsica & 1990 Camaro & Firebird

1. Disconnect connector C235 (except Lemans and 1988 Firebird) or C223 (Lemans and 1988 Firebird) and check switch continuity between terminals A and C (except 1988 Calais, Ciera and Monte Carlo and 1989 Celebrity and Safari and 1988-90 Caprice, Estate Wagon and 1989-90 Custom Cruiser and 1990 Grand Am) or D (except 1988 Calais, Ciera and Monte Carlo and 1989 Celebrity and 1988-90 Caprice, Estate Wagon and 1989-90 Custom Cruiser and 1990 Grand Am) with cruise switch in Resume/Accel position.

2. If there is no continuity, replace multi-function lever.

3. If there is continuity, check for open in gray/black wire or gray/white wire (circuit 87, except Caprice, Lemans, Monte Carlo, and Safari, and 1989-90 Custom Cruiser and Estate Wagon) or dark green wire (circuit 83, Caprice, Lemans, Monte Carlo and Safari and 1989-90 Custom Cruiser and Estate Wagon) between terminal C (except 1988 Calais, Ciera and Monte Carlo and 1988-89 Safari and 1988-90 Caprice, Estate Wagon and 1989-90 Custom Cruiser Bonneville, Cavalier, Celebrity, Custom Cruiser, Cutlass Supreme Classic, Grand Am, Grand Prix, Fiero, Firenza, Safari, Skyhawk, Skylark, Somerset, Sunbird and 6000) or D (Calais and Ciera) of connector C235 (except Lemans and 1988 Firebird) or C223 (Lemans and 1988 Firebird) and terminal M of cruise control module.

Beretta & Corsica

1. Disconnect connector C235 and check switch continuity between terminals A (blue wire, 1988 brown wire, 1989-90) and B (yellow wire, 1988 red wire, 1989-90) of pin half with resume/accel switch pressed.

2. If there is no continuity, check multi-function lever and cruise control switches for an open.

3. If switches are not open, check for an open in gray/black wire (circuit 87) between terminal B of connector

C235 and terminal B (1988) or terminal M (1989-90) of cruise control module.

1990 Camaro & Firebird

1. Disconnect C211 and check switch continuity between terminals M and J of the pin half with the cruise switch in resume/accel position.
2. If there is no continuity, replace multi-function lever.
3. If the switch does not open, check for open in gray/black wire (circuit 87), between terminal J of connector C211 and terminal M of cruise control module.

TEST J

1. Remove connector from cruise control servo and measure resistance between terminals A and C of servo.
2. If resistance is less than 30 ohms, replace cruise control servo.
3. If resistance is 30 ohms or greater, check for short to ground in dark blue/white wire or dark blue wire (circuit 403) from terminal C of cruise control module to terminal A of cruise control servo.

TEST K

If VSS light does not illuminate, or voltage between terminals A and D remains less than 7 volts (except 1990 Beretta, Cavalier, Corsica and Grand Am) or less than 4 volts (1990 Beretta, Cavalier, Corsica and Grand Am) check for open in red wire (circuit 381) brown or brown/red wire (circuit 437) gray/black wire (circuit 938) yellow wire (circuit 400) or green/white or dark green wire (circuit 389) from vehicle speed sensor buffer or ECM.

TEST L

If VSS light does not go off or battery voltage remains between terminals A and D, check for short to ground on red wire (circuit 381) brown or brown/red wire (circuit 437) gray/black wire (circuit 938) yellow wire (circuit 400) or green/white or dark green wire (circuit 389) from vehicle speed sensor buffer or ECM.

TEST M

Except Fiero

1. Check for blocked or leaking vacuum source. If vacuum source is satisfactory, plug vacuum release port and repeat test 6, **Figs. 2 through 8.**
2. If vacuum now holds throttle open, repair or replace vacuum release valve or the hose to the valve.
3. If test still fails, replace cruise control servo.

Fiero

1. Disconnect vacuum release solenoid connector, turn ignition switch to Accessory position and connect test lamp as follows:
   a. Connect between terminal A (purple wire) and ground. If lamp does not illuminate, check cruise brake switch and adjust as necessary and check yellow/black, light green/black and purple wires (circuit 943) for an open.

   b. Connect between terminals A (purple wire) and B (black wire). If light does not illuminate, check black wire (circuit 150) for an open.
2. If lamp illuminated in steps a and b, proceed as follows:
   a. Check for blocked or leaking vacuum source and, if vacuum source is satisfactory, plug vacuum release port and repeat test 6, **Figs. 4 and 5.**
   b. If vacuum now holds throttle open, repair or replace vacuum release solenoid valve or the hose to it.
   c. If test still fails, replace cruise control servo.

TEST N

Except 1988 Skylark

1. Disconnect cruise control servo connector and repeat test 7, **Figs. 2 through 8.**
2. If resistance is now over range, replace cruise control servo.
3. If resistance is still low, repair short in tan wire (circuit 398, except 1988 Celebrity) or black/white wire (circuit 398, 1988 Celebrity) from terminal F of cruise control module to terminal B of cruise control servo.

1988 Skylark

1. Disconnect cruise control servo connector and measure resistance between terminals B and D of cruise control servo connector.
2. If resistance is now over range, replace cruise control servo.
3. If resistance is still low, check for short in wire from terminal F (tan wire) of cruise control module to terminal B of cruise control servo or from terminal H (light blue/black and light blue wires) of cruise control module to terminal D of cruise control servo.

TEST O,

Except Beretta, Cimarron, Corsica, 1988-89 Skylark, 1989 Camaro

If all other tests in **Figs. 2 through 7** were satisfactory, replace cruise control servo.

Beretta & Corsica

1. Check resistance between grounds G100 and G101.
2. If resistance exceeds .1 ohm, clean and tighten both grounds and the negative battery cable. If ground circuit is suspect, add a ground strap between engine block and bulkhead.
3. If resistance is less than .1 ohm, replace cruise control module and check for normal operation.

1988-89 Skylark

1. With cruise control module disconnected, connect a fused jumper between terminal B (white or tan/white wire) and ground and turn ignition switch to Run position.
2. If indicator lights, check that terminal J of cruise control module connector is grounded and, if terminal J is grounded, replace cruise control module.

3. If indicator does not light, check gages fuse, cruise indicator bulb, instrument cluster printed circuit and related wiring, repairing or replacing as necessary. If no problem is found, replace cruise control module.

1989-90 Camaro

1. Check resistance between grounds G118 (VIN S and E) or G112 (VIN F and 8), G323 and G102.
2. If resistance is more than .1 ohm, clean and tighten both grounds and negative battery cable. If ground circuit is suspect, add a ground strap between engine block and bulkhead.
3. If resistance is less than .1 ohm, replace cruise control module and check for normal operation.

TEST P, 1988

Calais, Celebrity, Century, Ciera, Custom Cruiser, Cutlass Supreme, Cutlass Supreme Classic, Grand Am, & 6000

1. **On models w/2.8L engine,** check resistance between grounds G202 and G112. If resistance exceeds .1 ohm, clean and tighten both grounds and the negative battery cable. If ground circuit is suspect, add a ground strap between engine block and bulkhead.
2. **On all models,** connect a new cruise control module and check for normal operation and, if cruise control operates normally, leave new module in permanently.

Caprice, Electra & LeSabre Estate Wagon, Grand Prix & Monte Carlo

1. Check resistance between grounds G102 and G250. If resistance exceeds .1 ohm, clean and tighten both grounds and negative battery cable. If ground circuit is suspect on Century, add a ground strap between engine block and bulkhead.
2. Connect a new cruise control model and check for normal operation and, if operation is normal, leave new module in permanently.

Bonneville, Electra, LeSabre, 88 & 98

1. Check resistance between grounds G101 and G104. If resistance exceeds .1 ohm, clean and tighten both grounds and negative battery cable. If ground circuit is suspect, add a ground strap between engine block and bulkhead.
2. Connect a new cruise control model and check for normal operation and, if operation is normal, leave new module in permanently.

Regal

1. Check resistance between grounds G100 and G121. If resistance exceeds .1 ohm, clean and tighten both grounds and negative battery cable. If ground circuit is suspect, add a ground strap between engine block and bulkhead.
2. Connect a new cruise control model

and check for normal operation and, if operation is normal, leave new module in permanently.

Skyhawk

1. Check resistance between grounds G111 and G114. If resistance exceeds .1 ohm, clean and tighten both grounds and negative battery cable. If ground circuit is suspect, add a ground strap between engine block and bulkhead.
2. Connect a new cruise control model and check for normal operation and, if operation is normal, leave new module in permanently.

Cavalier, Firenza & Sunbird

1. Check resistance between grounds G100 and G114. If resistance exceeds .1 ohm, clean and tighten both grounds and negative battery cable. If ground circuit is suspect, add a ground strap between engine block and bulkhead.
2. Connect a new cruise control model and check for normal operation and, if operation is normal, leave new module in permanently.

Camaro & Firebird

1. Check resistance between grounds G103 and G112 (V8 VIN H engine) or G118 (except V8 VIN H engine). If resistance exceeds .1 ohm, clean and tighten both grounds and the negative battery cable. If ground circuit is suspect, add a ground strap between engine block and bulkhead.
2. Connect a new cruise control module and check for normal operation and, if operation is normal, leave new module in permanently.

Skylark

1. Check resistance between grounds G100 and G114. If resistance exceeds .1 ohm, clean and tighten both grounds and negative battery cable. If ground circuit is suspect, add a ground strap between engine block and bulkhead.
2. Connect a new cruise control model and check for normal operation and, if operation is normal, leave new module in permanently.

Fiero

1. Check resistance between grounds G202 and G504. If resistance exceeds .1 ohm, clean and tighten both grounds and negative battery cable. If ground circuit is suspect, add a ground strap between engine block and bulkhead.
2. Connect a new cruise control model and check for normal operation and, if operation is normal, leave new module in permanently.

Safari

1. Check resistance between grounds G102 and G110. If resistance exceeds .1 ohm, clean and tighten both grounds and negative battery cable. If ground circuit is suspect, add a

ground strap between engine block and bulkhead.
2. Connect a new cruise control model and check for normal operation and, if operation is normal, leave new module in permanently.

TEST P, 1989–90

1989 Celebrity & 1989–90 Century & Ciera

1. Connect a new cruise control module and check for normal operation.
2. If cruise control operates normally, leave new module in permanently.
3. If cruise control does not operate normally a malfunction in computer control system is indicated.

1989 Safari & 1989–90 Caprice, Estate Wagon & Custom Cruiser

1. Check resistance between grounds G102 and G250 (V8 VIN Y) or G102 and G251 (V6 VIN Z, V8 VIN E).
2. If resistance is more than .1 ohm, clean and tighten both grounds and negative battery cable. If ground circuit is suspect, add ground strap between engine block and bulkhead.
3. Connect new cruise control module and check for normal operation. If cruise control operates normally, leave new module in permanently.
4. If cruise control does not operate normally a malfunction in computer control system is indicated.

TEST Q

1988 Century, Electra, Electra & LeSabre Estate Wagon, LeSabre, Regal, Skylark & Somerset

1. Check gages (Century, Regal, Skylark and Somerset) or cruise (Electra & LeSabre Estate Wagon) fuse, or fuse No. 18 (Electra) or No. 16 (LeSabre).
2. Check cruise indicator bulb.
3. Check connections and wiring to indicator for an open.
4. Ensure terminal J of cruise control module connector is grounded.
5. **On LeSabre**, if cruise indicator light stays on when cruise control is not engaged, check white wire (circuit 85) for a short to ground.

1989–90 Century

1. Check gages fuse.
2. Check cruise indicator bulb and instrument cluster printed circuit.
3. Check pink/black wire (circuit 39) and white wire (circuit 85) to instrument cluster for an open.
4. If all checks are satisfactory, replace cruise control module.

1988–89 Corvette

TROUBLESHOOTING

1. If tap-up and tap-down functions are the only faults in system, replace instrument cluster.
2. Check vacuum hoses for leaks, kinks or restrictions.

3. Check for minimum slack in cruise control servo throttle linkage.
4. Visually inspect cruise control wire and ground connectors.
5. Test cruise, LCD and Cluster fuses with a fuse tester.
6. If speedometer does not work, check vehicle speed sensor.

ROAD TEST

1. Drive vehicle at speed greater than 25 mph, place cruise switch in On position and depress set button at end of multi-function lever. Cruise indicator should illuminate and vehicle should maintain speed.
2. With foot off accelerator, hold set button in. Vehicle should coast at a slower speed.
3. Release set button. If new speed is greater than 25 mph, cruise control should engage and hold slower speed.
4. Slide cruise switch to Resume/Accel position and hold it there. Vehicle should accelerate.
5. Release cruise switch back to On position. Vehicle should hold new, faster speed.
6. Tap brake pedal. Vehicle should coast slower and cruise indicator should go out.
7. Slide cruise control switch momentarily to Resume/Accel position. Cruise indicator should illuminate and vehicle should accelerate to former set speed.
8. While cruising, accelerate, then remove foot from accelerator pedal. Vehicle should coast back to set speed.
9. While cruising, tap cruise switch to Resume/Accel position. Vehicle speed should decrease 1 mph for each tap up to ten.
10. While cruising, tap set button. Vehicle speed should decrease 1 mph for each tap down to 25 mph.
11. Slide cruise control switch to Off position. Cruise control should turn off and cruise indicator should go out.

SYSTEM DIAGNOSIS

When performing the following tests, refer to wiring diagram **Figs. 15 and 16.**
1. Disconnect instrument cluster connector, turn ignition switch to Run position and cruise switch to Off position and measure voltage between terminals as follows:
   a. Measure between terminal D5 (orange wire) and ground. If battery voltage is not available, check LCD fuse and orange wire (circuit 840) for an open.
   b. Measure between terminal C7 (gray/white wire) and ground. If battery voltage is not available, replace multi-function lever.
   c. Place cruise switch in On position.
   d. Measure between terminal C7 (gray/white wire) and ground. If battery voltage is not available, check cruise fuse, cruise switch, pink/black wire (circuit 539) and gray/white wire (circuit 397) for an open.

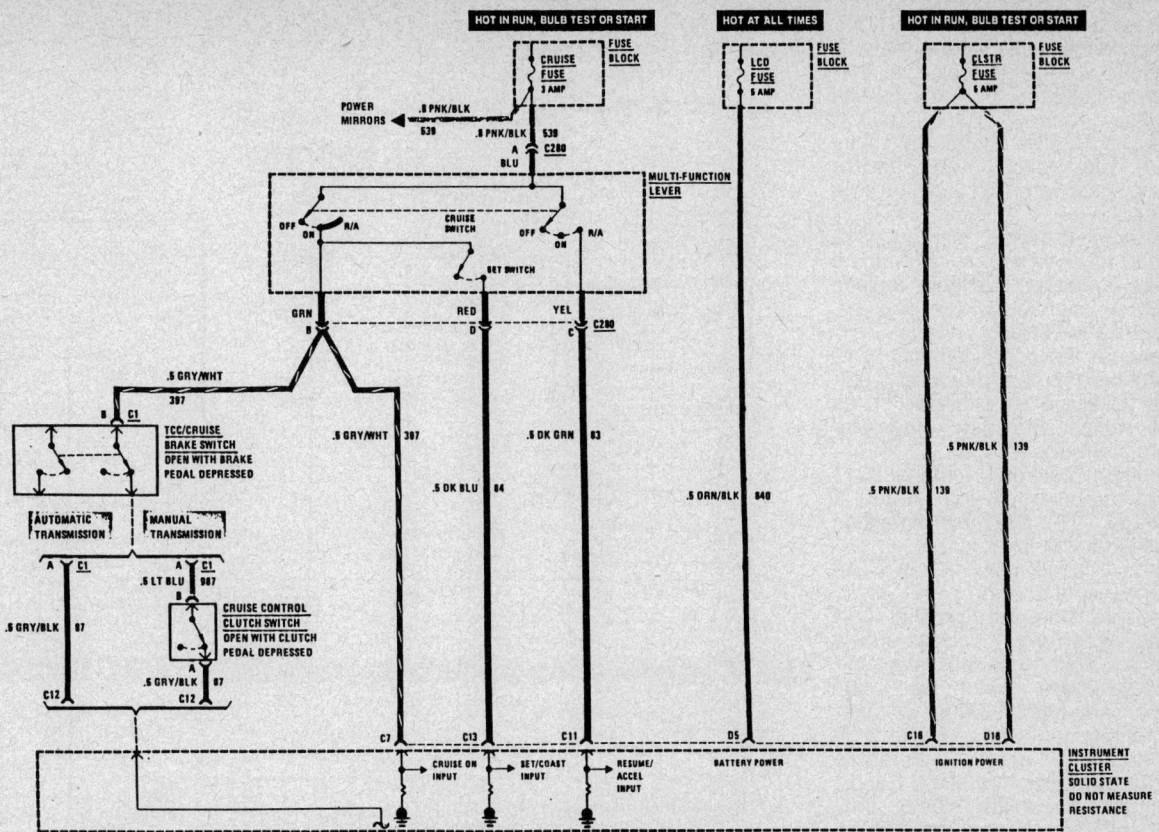

Fig. 15   Cruise control wiring diagram, (Part 1 of 2). 1988–89 Corvette

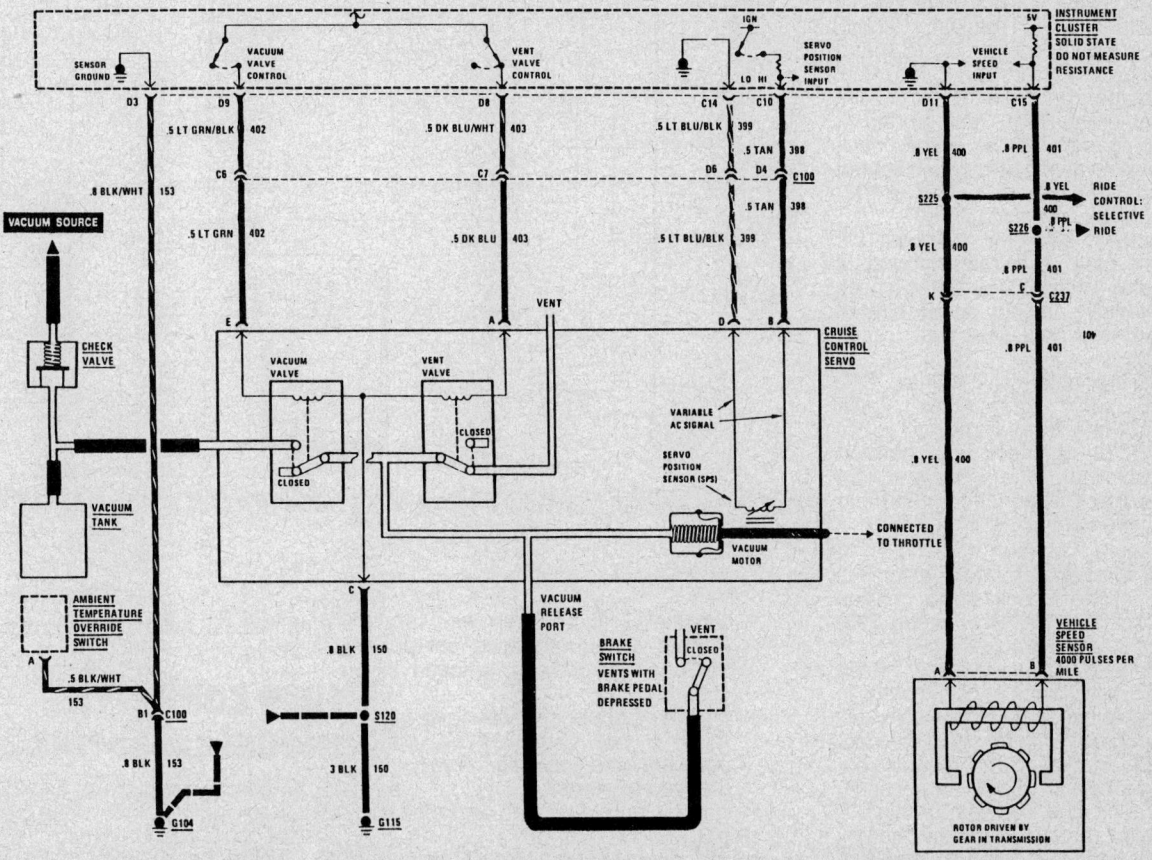

Fig. 15   Cruise control wiring diagram, (Part 2 of 2). 1988–89 Corvette

e. Measure between terminal C12 (gray/black wire) and ground. If battery voltage is not available, check TCC/cruise brake switch, cruise control clutch switch, gray/white wire (circuit 397) light blue wire (circuit 987) and/or gray/black wire (circuit 87) for an open.

f. Measure between terminal C13 (dark blue wire) and ground. If there is voltage available, replace multi-function lever.

g. Depress set switch.

h. Measure between terminal C13 (dark blue wire) and ground. If battery voltage is not available, check set switch and dark blue wire (circuit 84) for an open.

i. Measure between terminal C11 (dark green wire) and ground. If voltage is available, replace multi-function lever.

j. Place cruise switch in Resume/Accel position.

k. Measure between terminal C11 (dark green wire) and ground. If battery voltage is not available, check cruise switch and dark green wire (circuit 83) for an open.

2. If battery voltage was available in steps a, b, d, e, h and k and there was no voltage available in steps f and i, disconnect instrument cluster connector and measure resistance as follows:

a. Measure between terminal D3 (black/white wire) and ground. If resistance is shown, check black/white wire (circuit 153) and black wire (circuit 150) for an open.

b. Measure between terminal D9 (light green wire) and ground. If reading is not 30-55 ohms, check vacuum valve coil in cruise control servo, light green wire (circuit 402) and black wire (circuit 150).

c. Measure between terminal D8 (dark blue wire) and ground. If reading is not 30-55 ohms, check vent valve coil in cruise control servo and dark blue wire (circuit 403).

d. Measure between terminals C10 (tan wire) and C14 (dark blue/white wire). If reading is not 15-30 ohms, check servo position sensor, dark blue/white and light blue/black wires (circuit 399) and tan wire (circuit 398).

e. Measure between terminal C10 (tan wire) and ground. If reading is not infinite, check servo position sensor and tan wire (circuit 398) for a short to ground.

3. If reading was 0 ohms in step a, 30-55 ohms in steps b and c, 15-30 ohms in step d and infinite ohms in step e, disconnect cruise control servo connector and connect fused jumper between terminal C (black wire) of servo and ground and between terminal A (dark blue wire) of servo and battery and run engine for 1 minute, then turn engine off.

a. Connect fused jumper between

terminal E (light green wire) and battery. If vacuum does not pull servo all the way in, proceed to step 4.

b. Remove jumper from between terminal E and battery. If vacuum does not hold servo all the way in, proceed to step 4.

4. Plug vacuum release port and repeat step 3.

5. If vacuum now holds servo all the way in, repair or replace brake switch or the hose to it.

6. If test still fails, replace cruise control servo.

1990 CORVETTE
TROUBLESHOOTING

1. Check for open cruise fuse.
2. Check for vacuum leaks in cruise control servo vacuum lines.
3. Check cruise control cable for looseness, binding, and connection at throttle body.

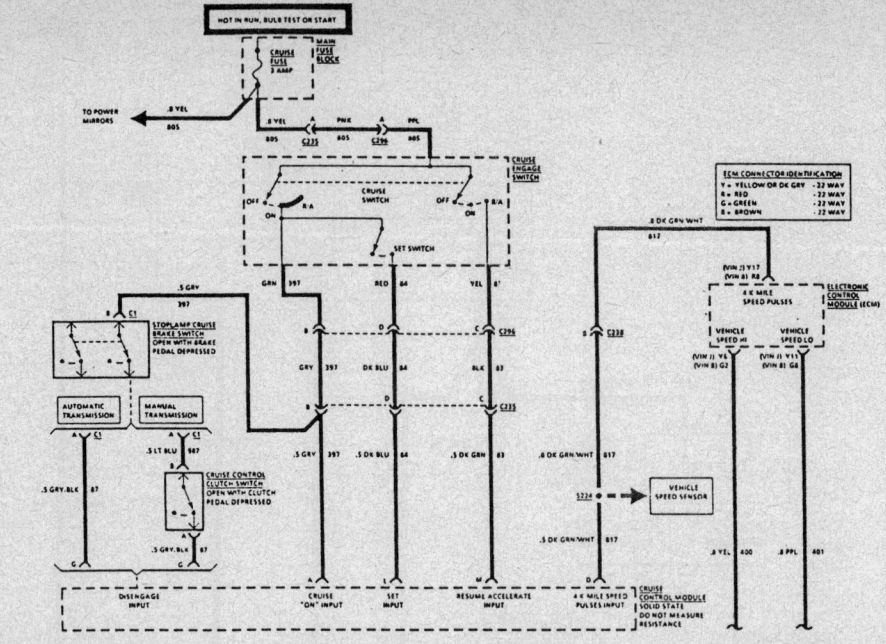

Fig. 16   Cruise control wiring diagram, (Part 1 of 2). 1990 Corvette

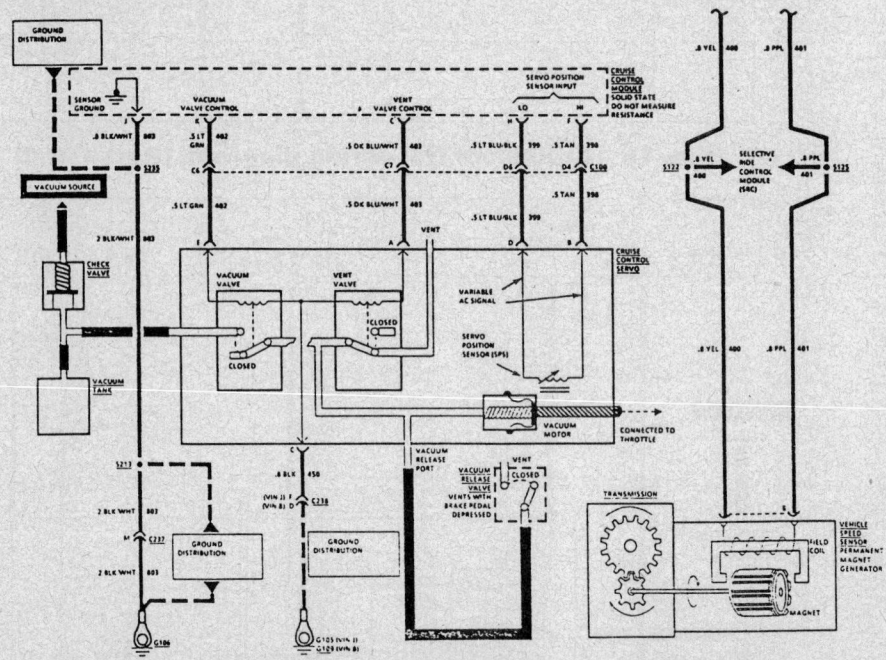

Fig. 16   Cruise control wiring diagram, (Part 2 of 2). 1990 Corvette

SYMPTOM	PROCEDURE
Cruise will not engage.	Chart #1
Cruise will not maintain set speed or cruise surges.	Chart #2
Does not resume, accelerate or tap up	Chart #3

Fig. 17 Cruise control symptom chart. 1990 Corvette

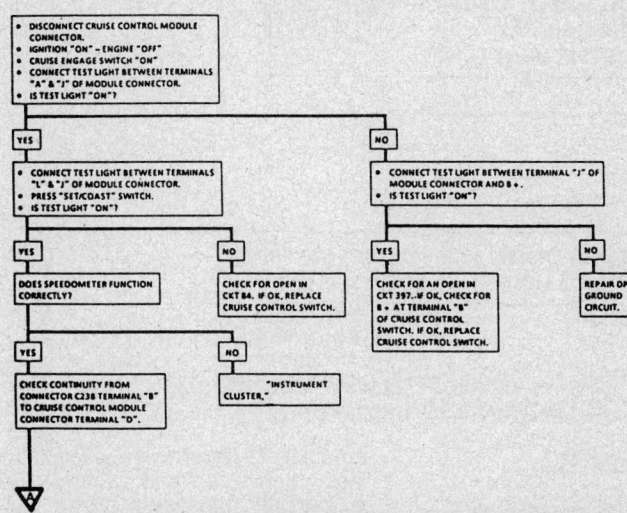

CHART #1
CRUISE WILL NOT ENGAGE

Fig. 18 Cruise control system diagnosis; Chart 1 (Part 1 of 3). 1990 Corvette

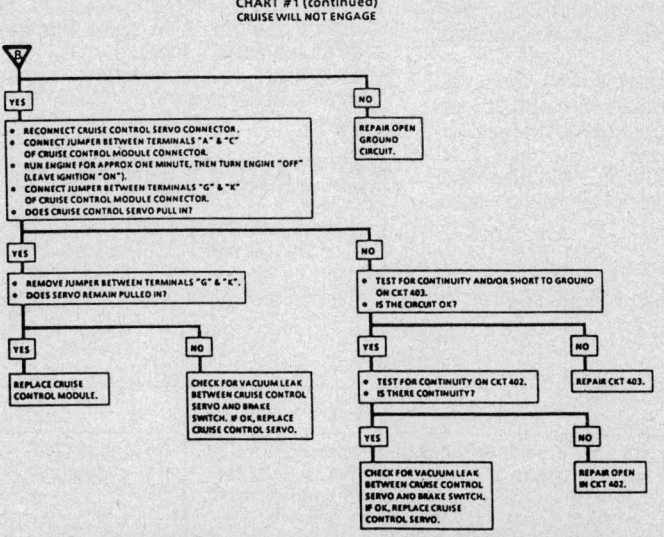

CHART #1 (continued)
CRUISE WILL NOT ENGAGE

Fig. 18 Cruise control system diagnosis; Chart 1 (Part 3 of 3). 1990 Corvette

4. Ensure proper terminal mating at connectors, then check for corrosion or bent terminals.

SYSTEM DIAGNOSIS

Refer to **Figs. 18 through 20**, for symptom and system diagnosis.

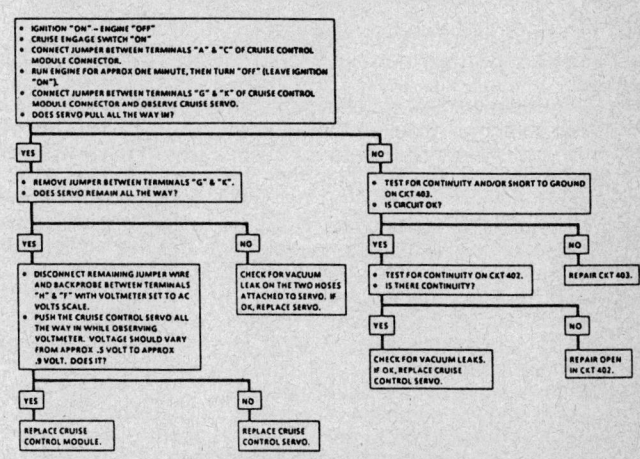

Fig. 18 Cruise control system diagnosis; Chart 1 (Part 2 of 3). 1990 Corvette

CHART #2
CRUISE WILL NOT MAINTAIN SET SPEED OR CRUISE SURGES

Fig. 19 Cruise control system diagnosis; Chart 2. 1990 Corvette

and/or restrictions.
2. Check cruise control servo linkage for proper slack.
3. If system works except for tap-up and tap-down functions, replace cruise control module.
4. If cruise indicator does not light, disconnect cruise control module connector and ground white wire (circuit 85). If cruise indicator lights, cruise control module is defective. If cruise indicator does not light, check fuse No. 16, pink/black wire (circuit 39) white wire (circuit 85) instrument cluster printed circuit and the cruise indicator bulb, repairing or replacing as necessary.

1989–90 Electra, LeSabre & Park Avenue

For troubleshooting and system diagnostic procedures, refer to **Figs. 21 through 25**. NOTE: On **Fig. 25** E1 circuit is a pink/black wire on 1990 models.

Cutlass Supreme, Electra, Grand Prix, LeSabre, Lumina, Park Avenue, Regal, 88 & 98

TROUBLESHOOTING
1988 Electra & LeSabre
1. Check vacuum hoses for leaks, kinks

Cutlass Supreme, Grand Prix, Regal, 88 & 98

1. Check vacuum hoses for leaks, kinks and/or restrictions.
2. Check cruise control servo linkage for proper slack.
3. If system works except for tap-up and tap-down functions, replace cruise control module.

ROAD TEST

1. Drive vehicle at speed greater than 25 mph, place cruise switch in On position and depress set button at end of multi-function lever. Cruise indicator should illuminate and vehicle should maintain speed.
2. With foot off accelerator, hold set button in. Vehicle should coast at a slower speed.
3. Release set button. If new speed is greater than 25 mph, cruise control should engage and hold slower speed.
4. Slide cruise switch to Resume/Accel position and hold it there. Vehicle should accelerate.
5. Release cruise switch back to On position. Vehicle should hold new, faster speed.
6. Tap brake pedal. Vehicle should coast slower and cruise indicator should go out.
7. Slide cruise control switch momentarily to Resume/Accel position. Cruise indicator should illuminate and vehicle should accelerate to former set speed.
8. While cruising, accelerate, then remove foot from accelerator pedal. Vehicle should coast back to set speed.
9. While cruising, tap cruise switch to Resume/Accel position. Vehicle speed should decrease 1 mph for each tap up to ten.
10. While cruising, tap set button. Vehicle speed should decrease 1 mph for each tap down to 25 mph.
11. Slide cruise control switch to Off position. Cruise control should turn off and cruise indicator should go out.

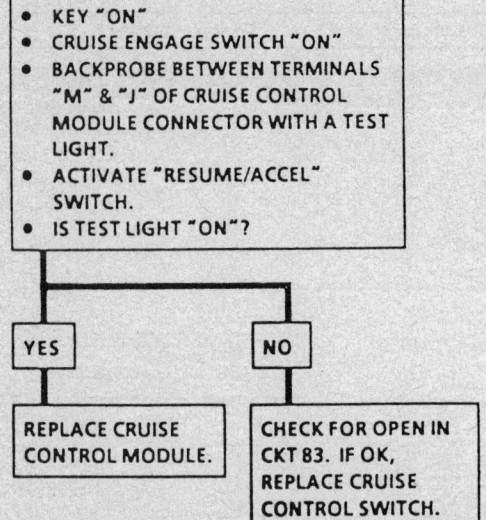

CHART #3
DOES NOT RESUME, ACCELERATE OR TAP-UP

- KEY "ON"
- CRUISE ENGAGE SWITCH "ON"
- BACKPROBE BETWEEN TERMINALS "M" & "J" OF CRUISE CONTROL MODULE CONNECTOR WITH A TEST LIGHT.
- ACTIVATE "RESUME/ACCEL" SWITCH.
- IS TEST LIGHT "ON"?

YES → REPLACE CRUISE CONTROL MODULE.

NO → CHECK FOR OPEN IN CKT 83. IF OK, REPLACE CRUISE CONTROL SWITCH.

Fig. 20   Cruise control system diagnosis; Chart 3. 1990 Corvette

SYSTEM DIAGNOSIS

Perform tests in diagnostic chart, **Figs. 5 and 26 through 30.** If results are incorrect perform designated test. **Do not press both the set switch and Resume/Accel position of cruise switch at same time with engine running. If quick checker displays a short light, release switches immediately.**

When performing the following tests, refer to **Figs. 13, 14 and 31 through 36.** for wiring diagram and control module pin locations.

For system diagnosis on 1989 Electra & LeSabre, refer to "Troubleshooting" section.

TEST A

1. Check for shorts to voltage in wires to terminals G (brown wire, except Cutlass Supreme and Grand Prix w/manual transaxle; brown/white wire, Cutlass Supreme and Grand Prix w/manual transaxle) A (gray wire) M (gray/black wire) and L (dark blue wire) of cruise control module. On 1990 Grand Prix and Cutlass Supreme use only A, M, and L terminals of cruise control module.
2. If wires are satisfactory, replace multi-function lever.

TEST B
1988 Electra & LeSabre & 1988–90 88 & 98

1. Check fuse No. 18.
2. Ensure terminal J of cruise control module is grounded.
3. Disconnect connector C202 (88 and

SYMPTOM	DIAGNOSIS				
	If a quick checker is available, do Cruise Control Module Test A. If a quick checker is not available, do Cruise Control Module Test B.	Replace Cruise Control Module.	Check for binding servo linkage or throttle linkage. Check vacuum lines for leaks or blockage.	Check YEL (494) wire to ECM for an open or short to ground.	Do Cruise Control Vacuum Test C.
All or some cruise control functions do not operate.	• Do 2nd	• Do 3rd	• Do 1st		
No tap up or tap down operation, otherwise system OK.		•			
Vehicle surges with cruise control engaged.	• Do 2nd	• Do 5th	• Do 1st	• Do 3rd	• Do 4th

Fig. 21   Troubleshooting procedure. 1989–90 Electra & LeSabre

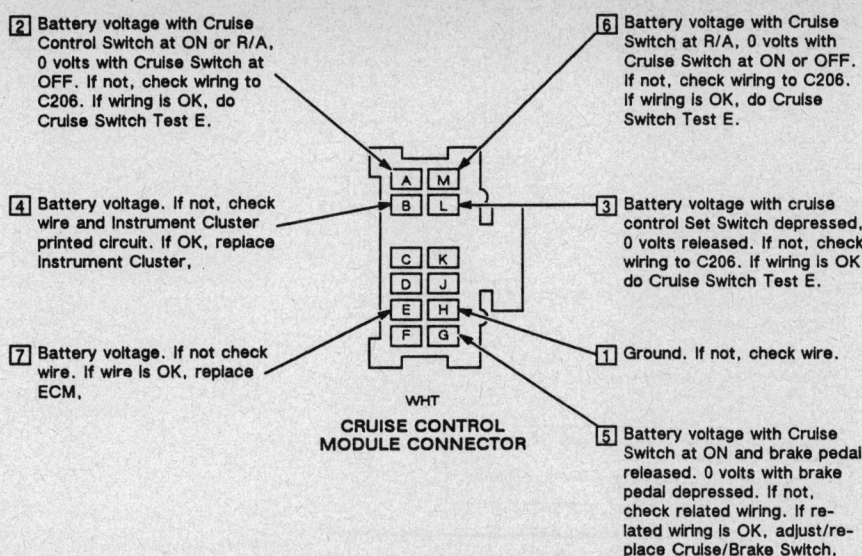

2 Battery voltage with Cruise Control Switch at ON or R/A, 0 volts with Cruise Switch at OFF. If not, check wiring to C206. If wiring is OK, do Cruise Switch Test E.

4 Battery voltage. If not, check wire and Instrument Cluster printed circuit. If OK, replace Instrument Cluster.

7 Battery voltage. If not check wire. If wire is OK, replace ECM.

6 Battery voltage with Cruise Control Switch at R/A, 0 volts with Cruise Switch at ON or OFF. If not, check wiring to C206. If wiring is OK, do Cruise Switch Test E.

3 Battery voltage with cruise control Set Switch depressed, 0 volts released. If not, check wiring to C206. If wiring is OK, do Cruise Switch Test E.

1 Ground. If not, check wire.

5 Battery voltage with Cruise Switch at ON and brake pedal released. 0 volts with brake pedal depressed. If not, check related wiring. If related wiring is OK, adjust/replace Cruise/Brake Switch.

WHT
CRUISE CONTROL
MODULE CONNECTOR

Fig. 22 Cruise control system diagnosis; Test B (Part 1 of 3). 1989–90 Electra & LeSabre

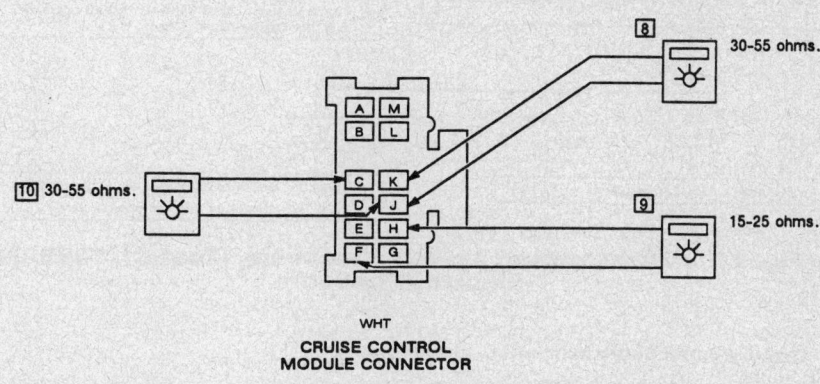

8 30-55 ohms.

10 30-55 ohms.

9 15-25 ohms.

WHT
CRUISE CONTROL
MODULE CONNECTOR

- If any measurement is not correct, check related wiring to Cruise Control Servo. If wiring is OK, replace Cruise Control Servo.

Fig. 22 Cruise control system diagnosis; Test B (Part 2 of 3). 1989–90 Electra & LeSabre

- Cruise Switch: ON
- Raise car and slowly turn drive wheels by hand.

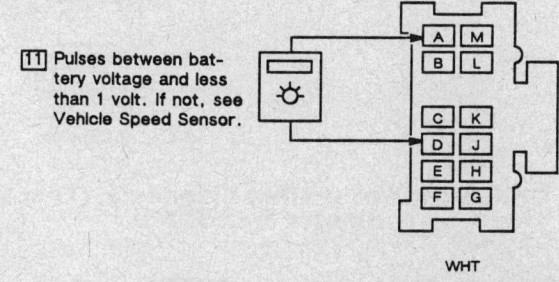

11 Pulses between battery voltage and less than 1 volt. If not, see Vehicle Speed Sensor.

WHT
CRUISE CONTROL
MODULE CONNECTOR

Fig. 22 Cruise control system diagnosis; Test B (Part 3 of 3). 1989–90 Electra & LeSabre

98) or C206 (Electra and LeSabre) and check for battery voltage at terminal E1 (pink/black wire) with ignition switch in Run position. If battery voltage is not available, check pink/black wire (circuit 239).

4. Check continuity between terminals E1 (pink wire) and E2 (gray wire) of connector C202 (88 and 98) or C206 (Electra and Lesabre) with cruise switch in On position. If there is no continuity, replace multi-function lever.

5. Check for an open in gray wire (circuit 397) between terminal E2 of connector C202 (88 and 98) or C206 (Electra and LeSabre) and terminal A of cruise control module connector.

Cutlass Supreme, Grand Prix, Lumina & Regal

1. Check instrument cluster.
2. Ensure terminal J of cruise control module connector is grounded.
3. Disconnect connector C202 and check for battery voltage at terminal E12 (pink/black wire) of female half with ignition switch in Run position. If battery voltage is not available, check pink/black wire (circuit 750).
4. Check continuity between terminals E1 (gray wire) and E12 (pink/black wire) of male half of connector C202 with cruise switch in On position. If there is no continuity, replace multi-function lever.
5. Check for open in gray/white wire (circuit 397) between terminal E1 of connector C202 and terminal A of cruise control module connector.

TEST C

1988 Electra & LeSabre & 1988–90 88 & 98

1. Check for open in cruise/brake switch.
2. Check for open in brown wire (circuit 86) and gray wire (circuit 397).

Regal

1. Check for open in brake switch.
2. Check for open in brown wire (circuit 86) to terminal G of cruise control module, or in gray wire (circuit 397).

1988 Cutlass Supreme

1. Check for open brake or clutch switch.
2. Check for open in brown wire (circuit 86) or brown/white wire (circuit 986) to terminal G of cruise control module, or in the gray/white wire (circuit 397).

Grand Prix & 1989–90 Cutlass Supreme & 1990 Lumina

1. Check for open in brake switch or clutch switch.
2. Check for open in brown wire (circuit 86) brown/white wire (circuit 379) or gray wire (circuit 397).

TEST D

1. If measurement was less than 30 ohms, proceed to test J. Otherwise, remove connector from cruise control servo and measure resistance between terminals A and C of servo.

2. If resistance is greater than 55 ohms, replace cruise control servo.

3. If resistance is less than 55 ohms, check for open in dark blue/white wire (circuit 403, Electra, LeSabre, Lumina, 88 and 98 and 1990 Cutlass Supreme) or dark blue wire (circuit 403, Grand Prix and Regal and 1988-89 Cutlass Supreme) between terminal C of cruise control module and terminal A of cruise control servo. Ensure terminal C of cruise control servo connector is grounded.

TEST E

1. If measurement is less than 30 ohms, proceed to test H. Otherwise, remove connector from cruise control servo and measure resistance between terminals E and C of cruise control servo.

2. If resistance is greater than 55 ohms, replace cruise control servo.

3. If resistance is less than 55 ohms, check for open in light green wire (circuit 402) between terminal K of cruise control module and terminal E of cruise control servo. Ensure terminal C of cruise control servo connector is grounded.

TEST F

1. If measurement is less than 15 ohms, proceed to test N. Otherwise, remove connector from cruise control servo and measure resistance between terminals B and D of cruise control servo.

2. If resistance is greater than 25 ohms, replace cruise control servo.

3. If resistance is less than 25 ohms, check for open in light blue/black wire (circuit 399, Except 1988-89 Grand Prix) or gray wire (circuit 399, 1988-89 Grand Prix) between terminal H of cruise control module and terminal D of cruise control servo. Also, check for open in tan wire (circuit 398) between terminal F of cruise control module and terminal B of cruise control servo.

TEST G

1988 Electra & LeSabre & 1988-90 88 & 98

1. Disconnect connector C202 (88 and 98) or C206 (Electra and LeSabre) and check switch continuity between terminals E2 (gray wire) and E3 (dark blue wire) with set switch depressed.

2. If there is no continuity, replace multi-function lever.

3. If there is continuity, check for open in dark blue wire (circuit 84) between terminal E3 of connector C202 (88 and 98) or C206 (Electra and LeSabre) and terminal L of cruise control module.

Cutlass Supreme, Grand Prix, Lumina & Regal

1. Disconnect connector C202 and check switch continuity between terminals E1 (gray wire) and E2 (dark blue wire) of male (female on Regal) half with set switch depressed.

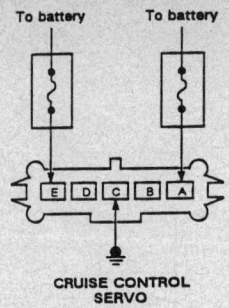

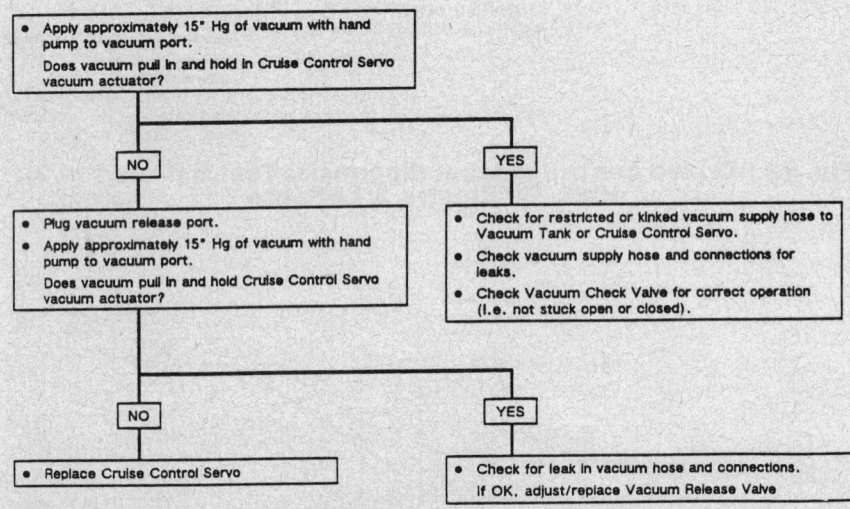

Fig. 23 Cruise control system diagnosis, (Test C). 1989-90 Electra & LeSabre

- **Cruise Control Servo connector: disconnected**
- **If any measurement is incorrect, replace Cruise Control Servo.**

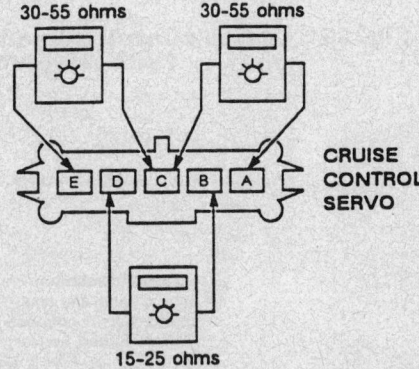

Fig. 24 Cruise control system diagnosis, (Test D). 1989-90 Electra & LeSabre

2. If there is no continuity, replace multi-function lever.

3. If there is continuity, check for open in dark blue wire (circuit 84) between terminal E2 of connector C202 and terminal L of cruise control module.

TEST H

1. Remove connector from cruise control servo and measure resistance between terminals C and E of cruise control servo connector.

- Remove connector C206 from mounting bracket. Separate connector and measure resistance at steering column half.
- X indicates continuity. O indicates open.
- If any measurement is incorrect, check steering column wiring and Multi-Function Lever connector. If OK, replace Multi-Function Lever.

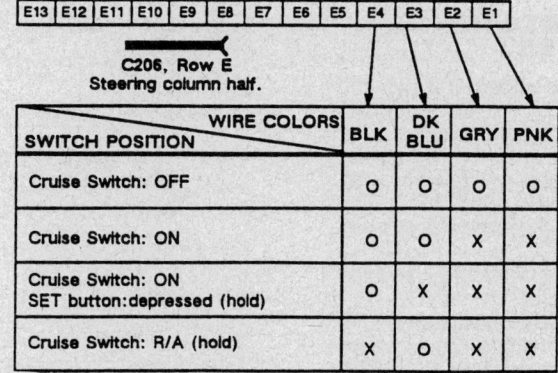

| E13 | E12 | E11 | E10 | E9 | E8 | E7 | E6 | E5 | E4 | E3 | E2 | E1 |

C206, Row E
Steering column half.

SWITCH POSITION / WIRE COLORS	BLK	DK BLU	GRY	PNK
Cruise Switch: OFF	O	O	O	O
Cruise Switch: ON	O	O	X	X
Cruise Switch: ON SET button: depressed (hold)	O	X	X	X
Cruise Switch: R/A (hold)	X	O	X	X

Fig. 25   Cruise control system diagnosis, (Test E). 1989–90 Electra & LeSabre

Connect: QUICK CHECKER OR DIGITAL METER
At: CRUISE CONTROL MODULE CONNECTOR (Disconnected)
Condition:
• Ignition Switch: RUN

Check	Action	With Quick Checker, Correct Response	Meter Range	Connector Terminals	Correct Result	For Different Result, Do Test
1	Cruise Switch OFF		200 ohms	J & Ground	0 ohms	Repair BLK/WHT (150) Ground wire
		All Lights Off	20 VDC	A & J	0 volts	A
			20 VDC	M & J	0 volts	A
2	Cruise Switch ON	ON/OFF Light On	20 VDC	A & J	Battery voltage	B
		BRK Light On	20 VDC	G & J	Battery voltage	C
		VENT Light On	200 ohms	C & J	30 to 55 ohms	D
		VAC Light On	200 ohms	K & J	30 to 55 ohms	E
		SPS Light On	200 ohms	F & H	15 to 25 ohms	F
		RA Light Off	20 VDC	M & J	0 volts	A
		SC Light Off	20 VDC	L & J	0 volts	A
3	Cruise Switch ON Set Switch pressed	SC Light On	20 VDC	L & J	Battery voltage	G
		VAC & SHORT Lights On	200 ohms	K & J	30 to 55 ohms	H
4	Cruise Switch in R/A	ON/OFF Light On	20 VDC	A & J	Battery voltage	B
		RA Light On	20 VDC	M & J	Battery voltage	I
		VENT & SHORT Lights Off	200 ohms	C & J	30 to 55 ohms	J
5	Cruise Switch ON, drive wheels turned by hand	VSS Light flashes On and Off	20 VDC	A & D	Pulses between approximately battery voltage and less than 7 volts	K, L
6	Run engine for one minute, then turn it off. With Ignition Switch in RUN and holding Cruise Switch in R/A, press Set Switch, wait for Servo to pull in, and release Set Switch.	Vacuum holds the servo all the way in	Connect fused jumpers from C to M and from K to L before operating switches	Vacuum holds the servo all the way in	M
7	Quick Checker not connected		200 ohms	F & J	Over range	N
8	Quick Checker not connected		200 ohms	F & H	15 to 25 ohms	F

• If all results are correct, replace Cruise Control Module and check for normal operation.

Fig. 26   Cruise control system diagnostic chart. 1988 Electra, LeSabre, 1988–89 88 and 98

Connect: QUICK CHECKER OR DIGITAL METER
At: CRUISE CONTROL MODULE CONNECTOR (Disconnected)
Conditions:
• Ignition Switch: RUN

Check	Action	With Quick Checker, Correct Response	Meter Range	Connector Terminals	Correct Result	For Different Result, Do Test
1	Cruise Switch OFF		200 ohms	J & Ground	0 ohms	B
		All lights off	20 VDC	A & J, L & J M & J, G & J	0 volts	A
2	Cruise Switch ON	ON/OFF light on	20 VDC	A & J	Battery voltage	B
		BRK light on	20 VDC	G & J	Battery voltage	C
		VENT light on	200 ohms	C & J	30 to 55 ohms	D
		VAC light on	200 ohms	K & J	30 to 55 ohms	E
		SPS light on	200 ohms	F & H	15 to 25 ohms	F
		RA light off	20 VDC	M & J	0 volts	A
		SC light off	20 VDC	L & J	0 volts	A
3	Cruise Switch ON, Set Switch pressed and held	SC light on	20 VDC	L & J	Battery voltage	G
		VAC & SHORT lights on	200 ohms	K & J	30 to 55 ohms	H
4	Cruise Switch in R/A	ON/OFF light on	20 VDC	A & J	Battery voltage	B
		RA light on	20 VDC	M & J	Battery voltage	I
		VENT & SHORT lights off	200 ohms	C & J	30 to 55 ohms	J
5	Cruise Switch ON, drive wheels turned by hand	VSS light flashes on and off	20 VDC	A & D	Pulses between approximately battery voltage and less than 1 volt	K, L
6	Run engine for one minute, then turn it off. With Ignition Switch in RUN and holding Cruise Switch in R/A, press Set Switch, wait for servo to pull in, and release Set Switch	Vacuum holds the servo all the way in	Connect fused jumper from C to M and from K to L, then follow instructions in Action column	Vacuum holds the servo all the way in	M
7	Quick Checker not connected		200 ohms	F & J	Over range	N
8	Quick Checker not connected		200 ohms	F & H	15 to 25 ohms	F

• If all results are correct, replace Cruise Control Module and check for normal operation.

Fig. 27   Cruise control system diagnosis chart. 1990 88 & 98

Connect: QUICK CHECKER (J-34185, SPECMO OC-3 OR EQUIVALENT) or VOLT-OHMETER
At: CRUISE CONTROL MODULE CONNECTOR (Disconnected)
Conditions:
• Ignition Switch: RUN
• Test with Quick Checker (J-34185 or equivalent) or Digital Meter

Test	Condition	With Quick Checker, Correct Response	Meter Range	Connector Terminals	Connector Response	For Different Response, Do Test
1	Cruise Switch OFF	Lamp Light On	20 VDC	N & J	Battery Voltage	O
		All Other Lights Off	20 VDC	A & J	0 volts	A
			20 VDC	M & J	0 volts	A
2	Cruise Switch ON	ON/OFF Light On	20 VDC	A & J	Battery Voltage	B
		BRK Light On	20 VDC	G & J	Battery Voltage	C
		VENT Light On	200 ohms	C & J	30 to 55 ohms	D
		VAC Light On	200 ohms	K & J	30 to 55 ohms	E
		SPS Light On	200 ohms	F & H	15 to 25 ohms	F
		RA Light Off	20 VDC	M & J	0 volts	A
		SC Light Off	20 VDC	L & J	0 volts	A
3	Cruise Switch ON, Set Switch pressed	SC Light On	20 VDC	L & J	Battery Voltage	G
		VAC & SHORT Lights Off	200 ohms	K & J	30 to 55 ohms	H

Fig. 28   Cruise control system diagnostic chart (Part 1 of 2). Regal

Test	Condition	With Quick Checker, Correct Response	Meter Range	Connector Terminals	Connector Response	For Different Response, Do Test
4	Cruise Switch in R/A	ON/OFF Light On	20 VDC	A & J	Battery Voltage	A
		RA Light On	20 VDC	M & J	Battery Voltage	I
		VENT & SHORT Lights On	200 ohms	C & J	30 to 55 ohms	J
5	Cruise Switch ON, drive wheels turned by hand	VSS Light flashes On and Off	20 VDC	A & D	Pulses between battery voltage and less than 7 volts	K, L
6	Run engine for one minute, then turn it off. With Ignition Switch in RUN, and holding Cruise Switch in R/A, press Set Switch, wait for Servo to pull in and release Set Switch	Vacuum holds the servo all the way in	Connect fused jumper from C to M and from K to L before operating switches	Vacuum holds the servo all the way in	M
7	Quick Checker not connected		200 ohms	F & J	Over range	N

• If all responses were correct, connect a new Cruise Control Module. Check for proper operation.

Fig. 28   Cruise control system diagnostic chart (Part 2 of 2). Regal

2. If resistance is less than 30 ohms, replace cruise control servo.

3. If resistance is 30 ohms or greater, check for short to ground in light green wire (circuit 402) between terminal K of cruise control module and terminal E of cruise control servo.

TEST I

1988 Electra & LeSabre & 1988–90 88 & 98

1. Disconnect connector C202 (88 and 98) or C206 (Electra and LeSabre) and check switch continuity between terminals E1 (pink wire, 1988–89 88 and 98) or E1 (pink/black wire, 1990 88 and 98) and E4 (black wire) with cruise switch in Resume/Accel position.
2. If there is no continuity, replace multi-function lever.
3. If there is continuity, check for open in gray/black wire (circuit 87) between terminal E4 of connector C202 (88 and 98) or C206 (Electra and Lesabre) and terminal M of cruise control module.

Cutlass Supreme, Grand Prix, Lumina & Regal

1. Disconnect connector C202 and check cruise switch continuity between terminals E12 (pink/black wire) and E13 (gray/black wire) of male half of connector C202 with cruise switch in Resume/Accel position.
2. If there is no continuity, replace multi-function lever.
3. If there is continuity, check for open in gray/black wire (circuit 87) between terminal E13 of connector C202 and terminal M of cruise control module.

TEST J

1. Remove connector from cruise control servo and measure resistance between terminals A and C of cruise control servo.
2. If resistance is less than 30 ohms, replace cruise control servo.
3. If resistance is 30 ohms or greater, check for short to ground in dark blue/white wire (circuit 403, Electra, LeSabre, 88 and 98 and 1990 Regal) or dark blue wire (circuit 403, Cutlass Supreme, Grand Prix and Lumina and 1988-89 Regal) from terminal C of cruise control module to terminal A of cruise control servo.

TEST K

1988 Electra & LeSabre & 1988–90 88 & 98

If VSS light does not illuminate, or voltage between terminals A and D remains less than 7 volts on 1989-90 models (1 volt on 1989-90 models) check for open in red wire (circuit 381) of vehicle speed sensor buffer.

Cutlass Supreme, Grand Prix, Lumina & Regal

1. If speedometer is not working, check vehicle speed sensor.
2. If voltage between terminals A and D of cruise control module remains less

Fig. 29 Cruise control system diagnostic chart (Part 1 of 2). 1988–89 Grand Prix & 1990 Lumina

Fig. 29 Cruise control system diagnostic chart (Part 2 of 2). 1988–89 Grand Prix & 1990 Lumina

Fig. 30 Cruise control system diagnostic chart. 1988–89 Cutlass Supreme

than 7 volts, check for open in dark green wire (circuit 389).

TEST L

1988 Electra & LeSabre & 1988–90 88 & 98

If VSS light does not go off or battery voltage remains between terminals A and D, check for short to ground in red wire (circuit 381) of vehicle speed sensor buffer.

Cutlass Supreme, Grand Prix, Lumina & Regal

1. If speedometer is not working, check vehicle speed sensor.
2. If battery voltage remains between terminals A and D of transaxle assembly, check for short to ground in dark green wire (circuit 389).

TEST M

1. Check for blocked or leaking vacuum source and, if vacuum source is satisfactory, plug vacuum release port and repeat test 6, Figs. 5 and 26 through 30.
2. If vacuum now holds throttle wide open, repair or replace vacuum release valve or hose to valve.
3. If test still fails, replace cruise control servo.

TEST N

1. Disconnect cruise control servo connector and repeat test 7, Figs. 5 and 26 through 30.
2. If resistance is now over range, replace cruise control servo.
3. If resistance is still low, check for short

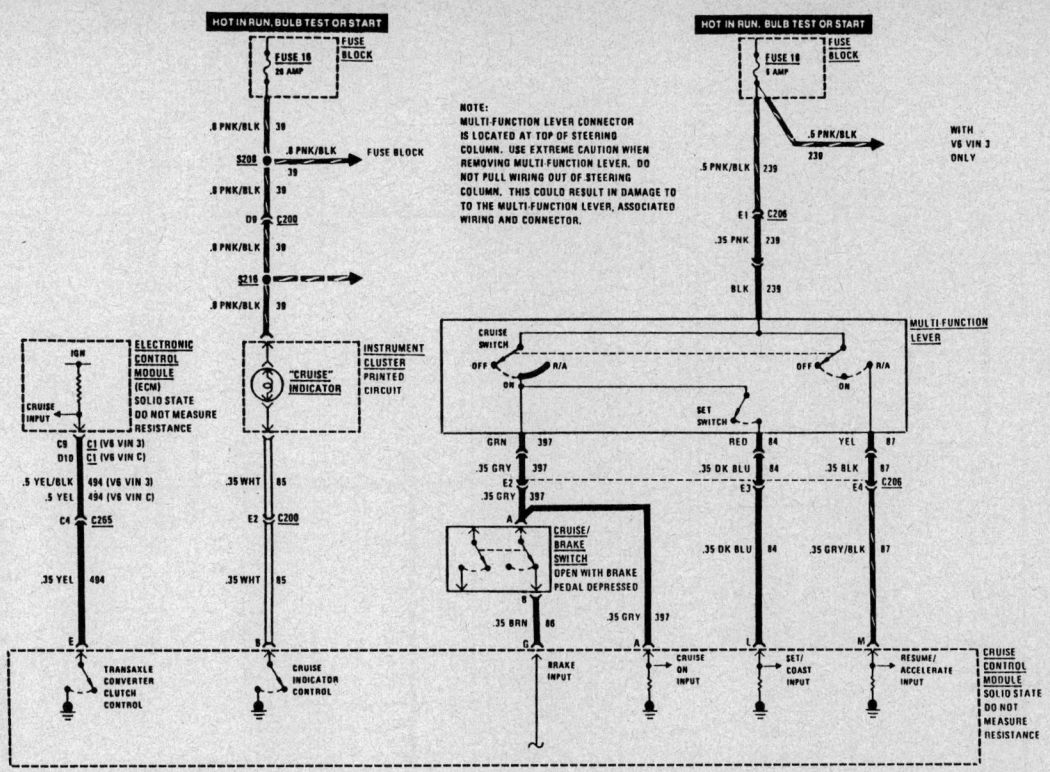

Fig. 31   Cruise control wiring diagram, (Part 1 of 2). 1988 Electra & LeSabre

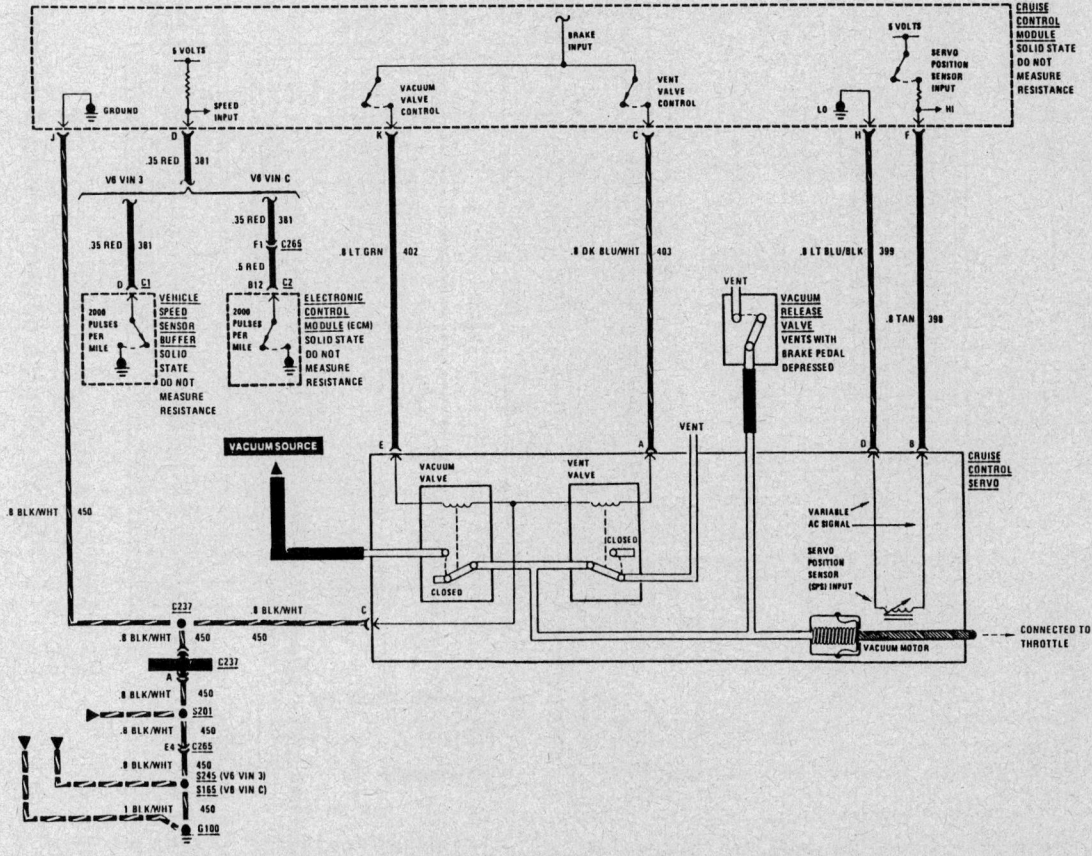

Fig. 31   Cruise control wiring diagram, (Part 2 of 2). 1988 Electra & LeSabre

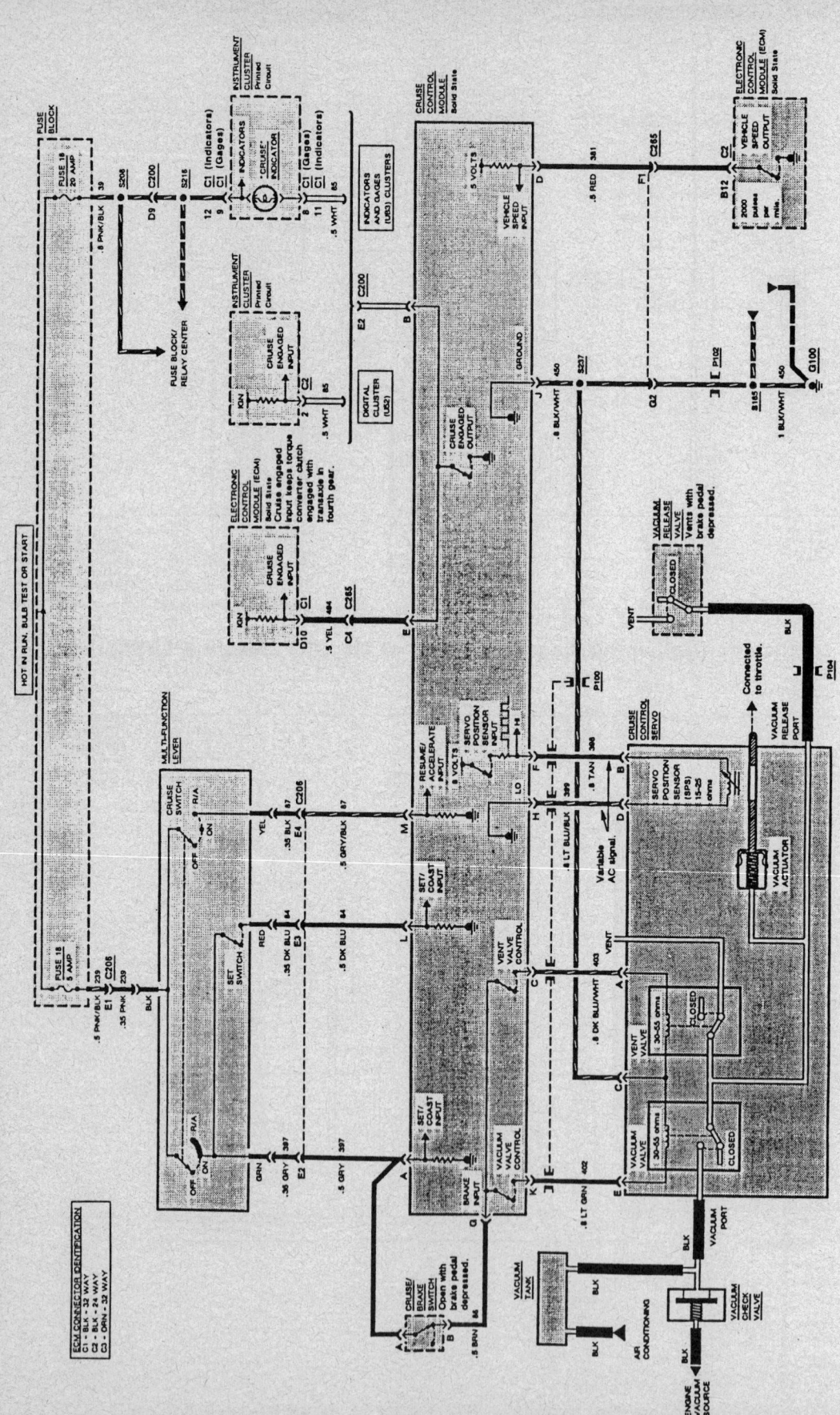

Fig. 32 Cruise control wiring diagram. 1989–90 Electra & LeSabre

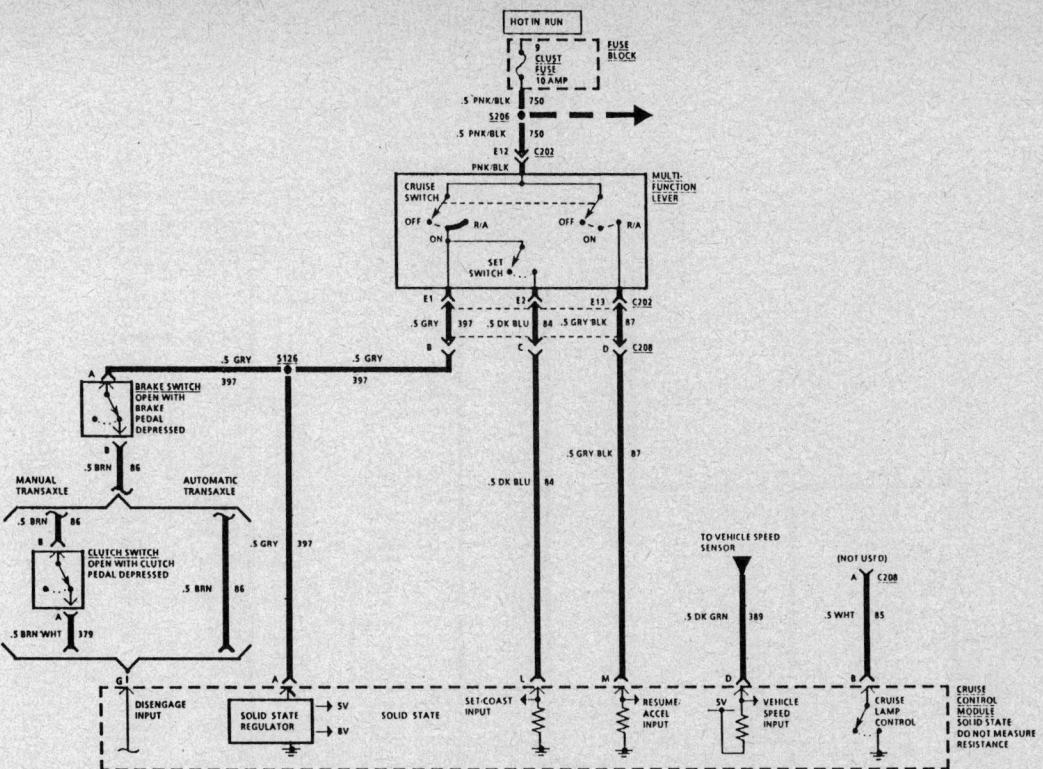

Fig. 33 Cruise control wiring diagram, (Part 1 of 2). 1988–90 Cutlass Supreme & Grand Prix & 1990 Lumina

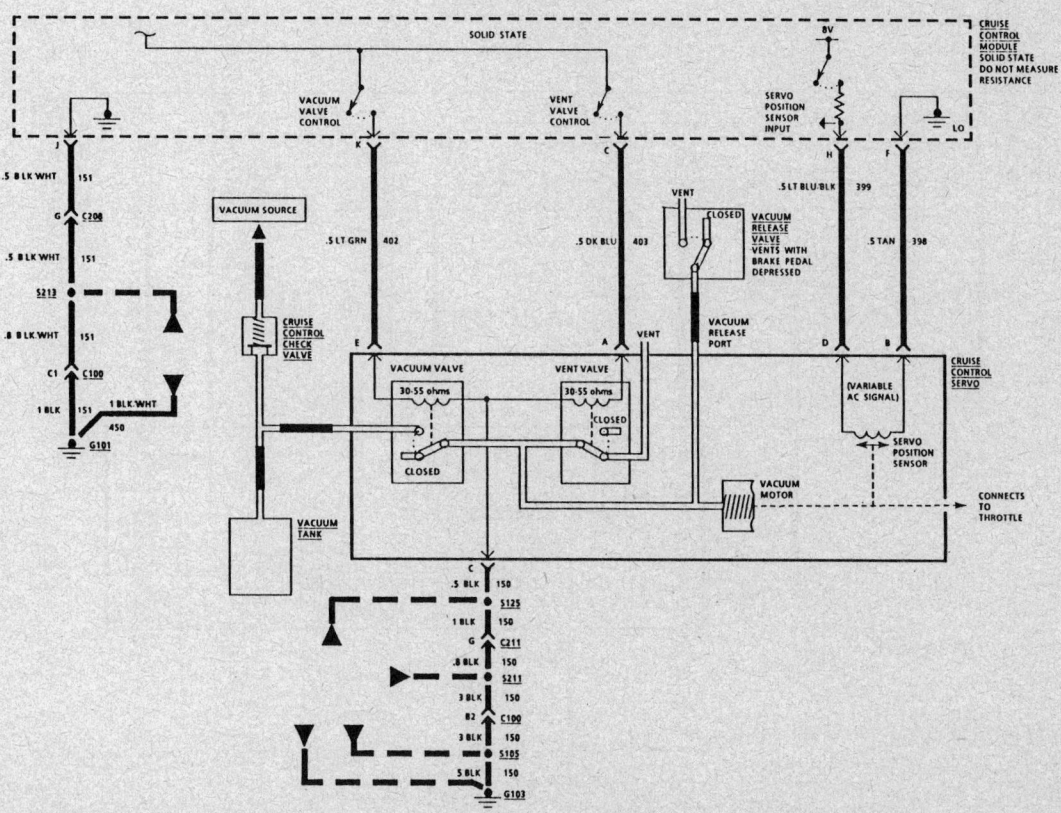

Fig. 33 Cruise control wiring diagram, (Part 2 of 2). 1988–90 Cutlass Supreme & Grand Prix & 1990 Lumina

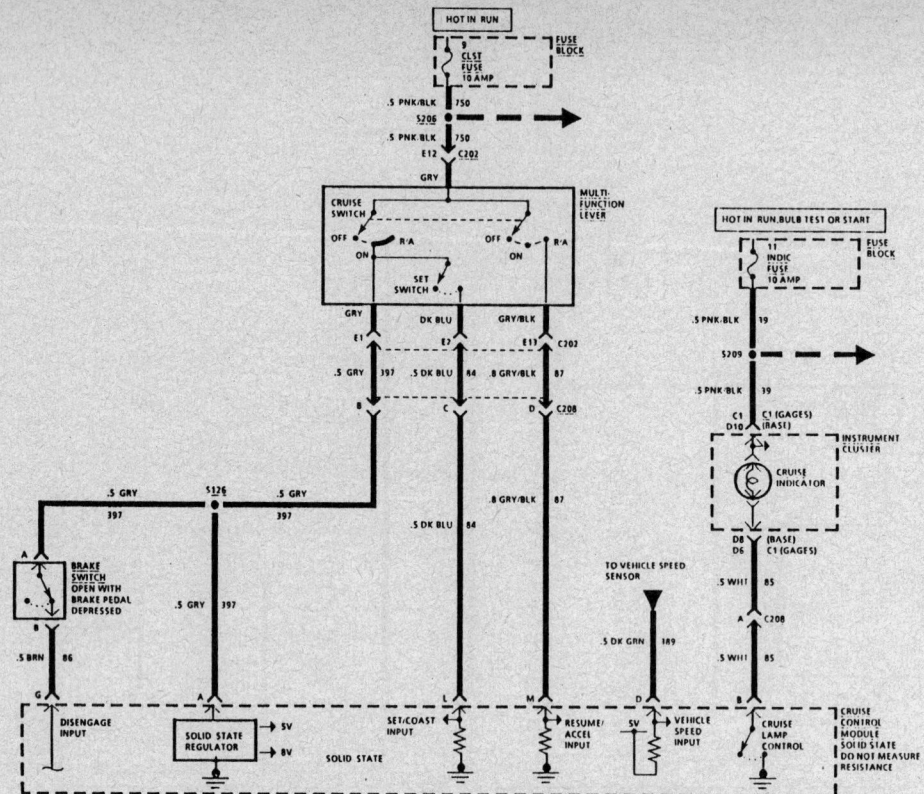

Fig. 34   Cruise control wiring diagram, (Part 1 of 2). Regal

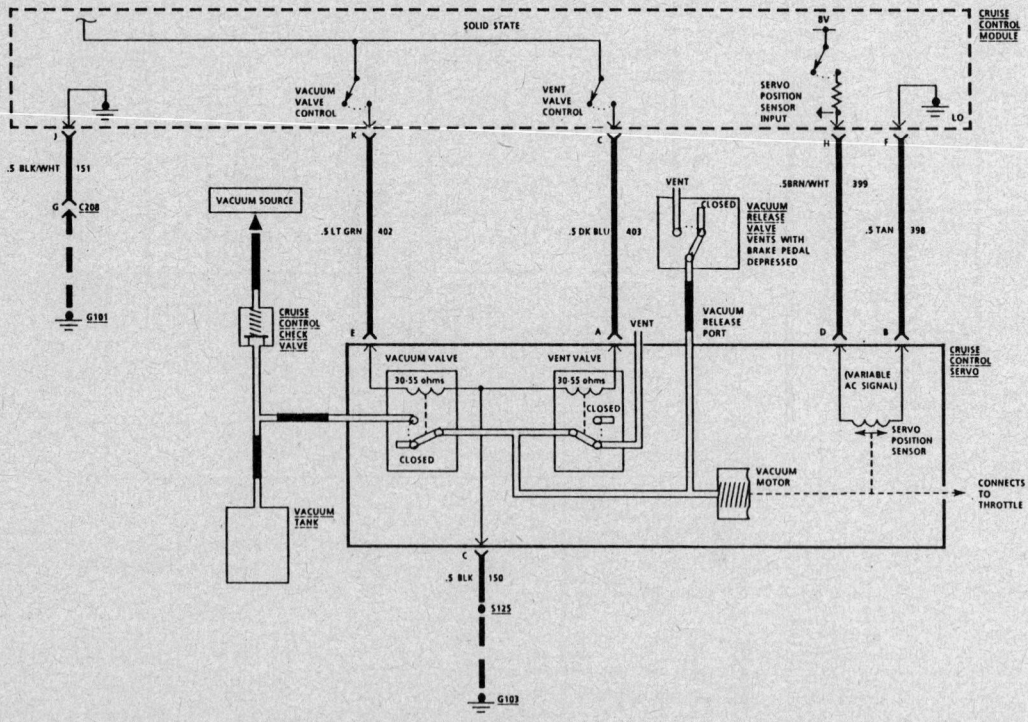

Fig. 34   Cruise control wiring diagram, (Part 2 of 2). Regal

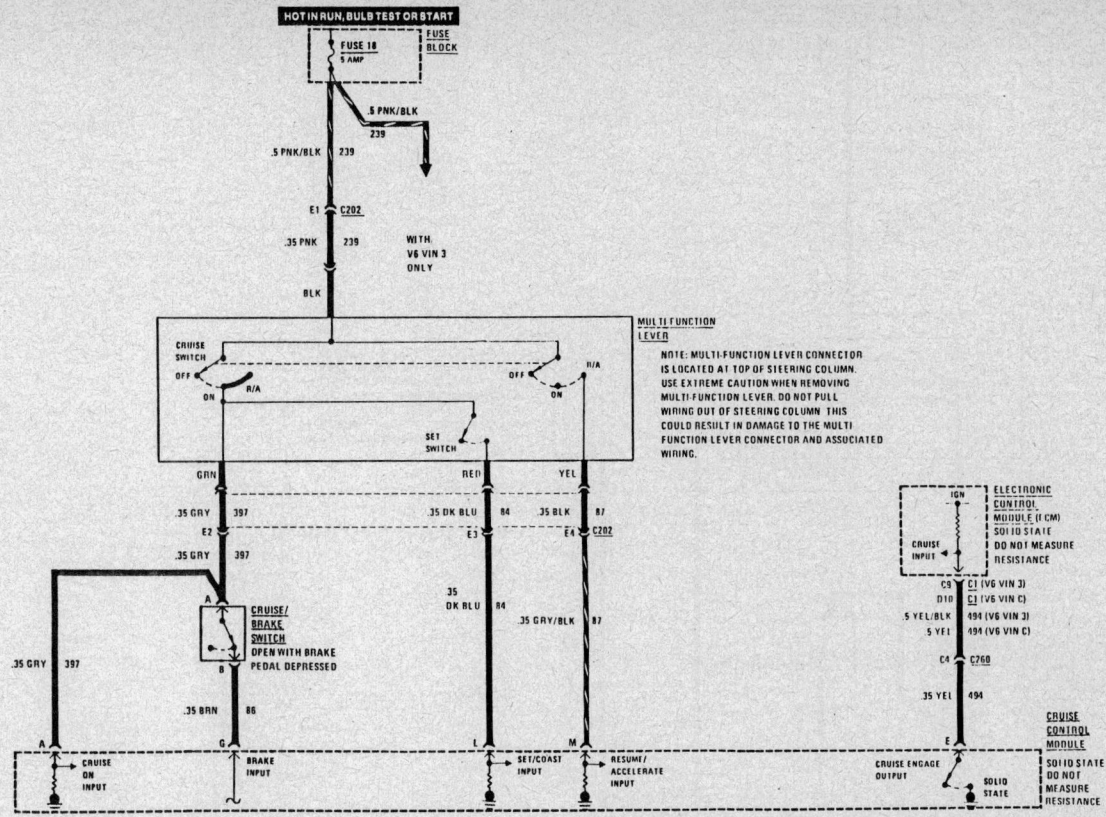

Fig. 35   Cruise control wiring diagram, (Part 1 of 2). 1988 88 & 98

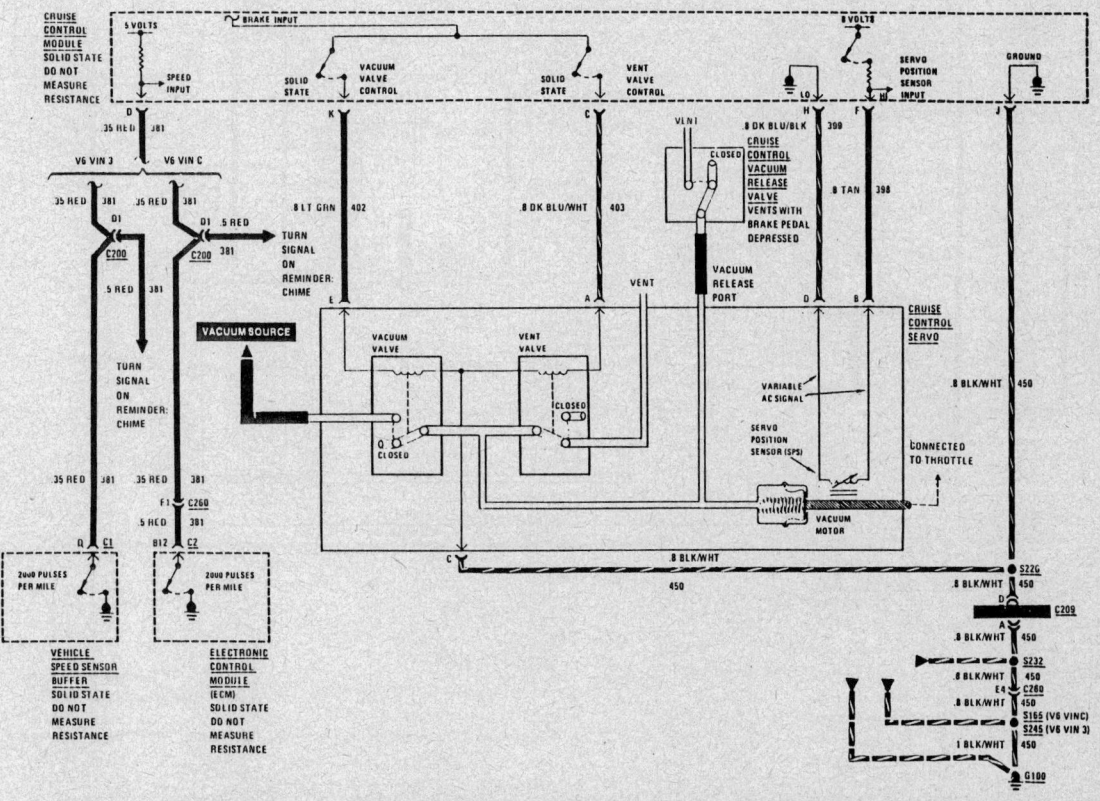

Fig. 35   Cruise control wiring diagram, (Part 2 of 2). 1988 88 & 98

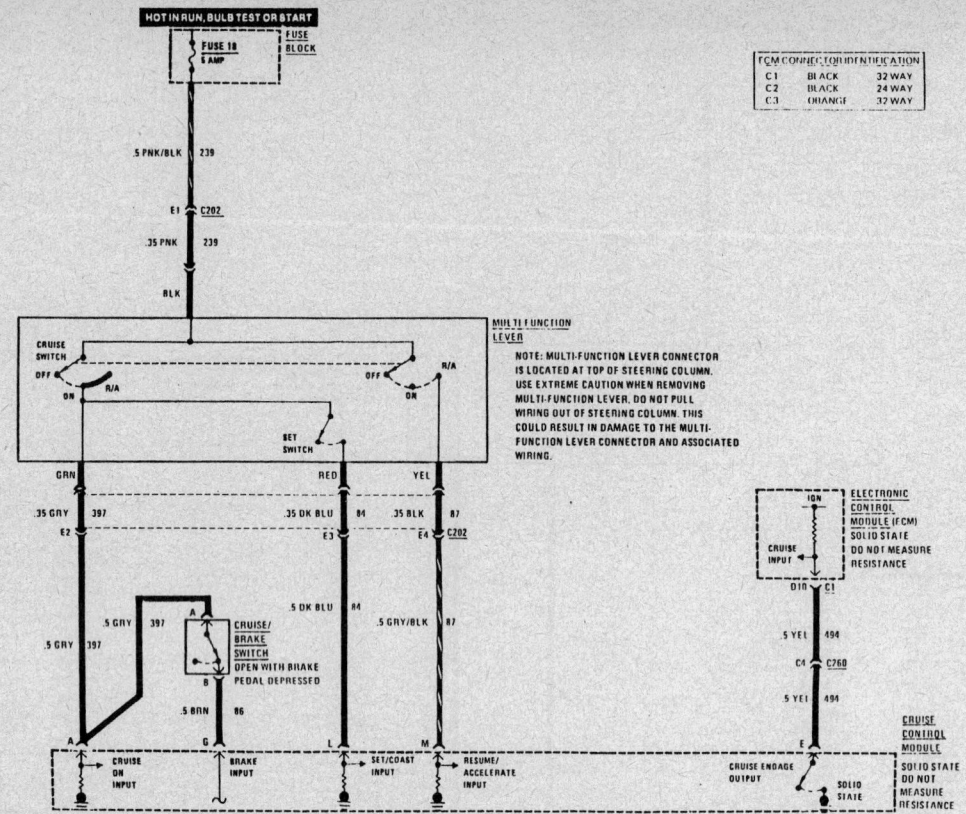

Fig. 36 Cruise control wiring diagram, (Part 1 of 2). 1989–90 88 & 98

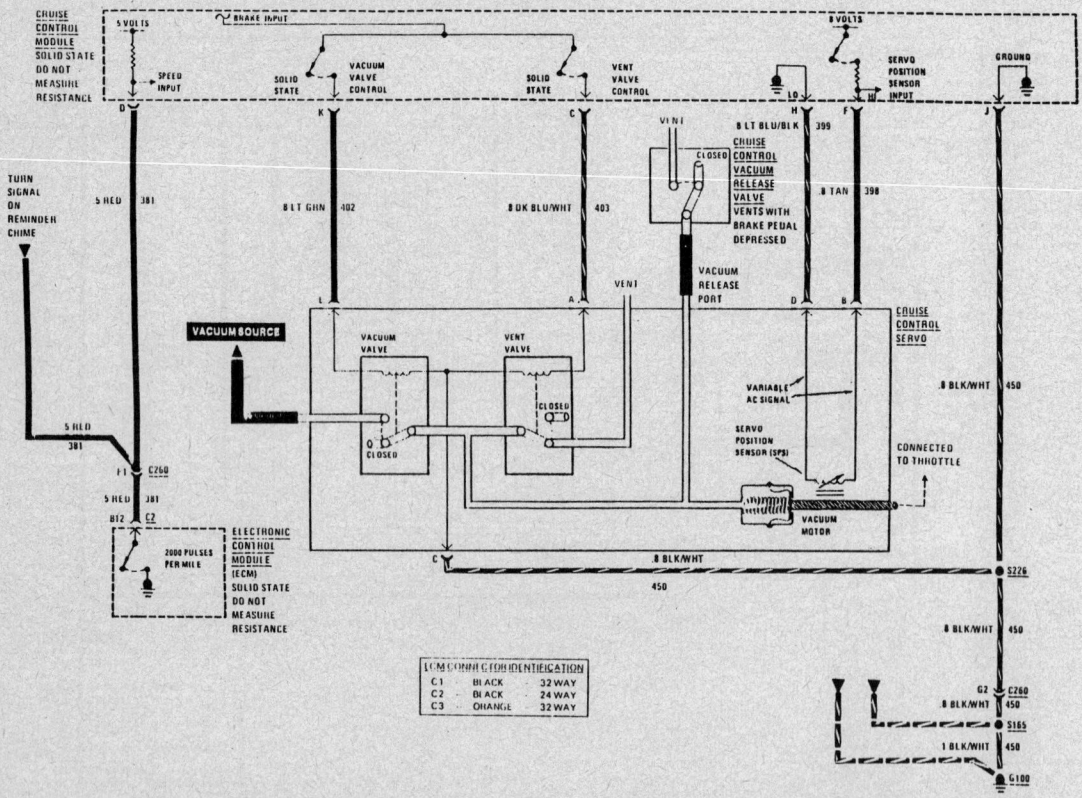

Fig. 36 Cruise control wiring diagram, (Part 2 of 2). 1989–90 88 & 98

in tan wire (circuit 398) from terminal F of cruise control module to terminal B of cruise control servo.

1989–90 Cutlass Supreme and 1990 Grand Prix, Lumina & Regal

1. Disconnect cruise control servo connector and repeat test 7, **Figs. 5 and 26 through 30.**
2. If resistance is now over range, replace cruise control servo.
3. If resistance is still low, repair short in wire from terminal H of cruise control module to terminal D of cruise control servo.

TEST O

Regal

1. Check fuse No. 11.
2. Check connectors and wiring to indicator for an open.
3. Ensure terminal J of cruise control module connector is grounded.
4. Check cruise indicator bulb.

1988 Cutlass Supreme

If all other test results were satisfactory, replace cruise control servo.

TEST P

1988 Cutlass Supreme

Connect a new cruise control module and check system for normal operation and, if system operates normally, leave new module in permanently.

COMPONENT TESTING

ELECTRIC BRAKE RELEASE SWITCH

1. Turn ignition switch to On position.
2. Connect test light to ground.
3. Probe brown wire at brake switch connector. Lamp should illuminate.
4. Check switch adjustment, with probe still at brown wire, depressing brake pedal 1/8-1/2 inch. Light should go out.
5. If lamp did not illuminate in step 3, probe wire in adjacent connector cavity. If lamp illuminates, adjust or replace switch as necessary. If light does not illuminate, check wiring to switch.

COMPONENT REPLACEMENT

SERVO UNIT

1. Disconnect servo assembly electrical

connector.
2. Disconnect vacuum hoses.
3. Disconnect actuating chain, cable or rod from servo assembly.
4. Remove servo assembly and servo unit solenoid valve assembly to mounting bracket attaching screws, then remove servo assembly.
5. Reverse procedure to install. **Torque** servo assembly to bracket attaching screws to 14-18 inch lbs.

SPEED CONTROLS ADJUST

CABLE, ADJUST

1. Ensure cable assembly in cable and servo bracket.
2. Pull servo assembly cable and toward servo without moving throttle body lever.
3. If one of the holes in the servo tab aligns with cable pin, connect pin to tab with retainer.
4. If tab hole does not align with pin, move cable from servo assembly until next closest tab hole lines up, then connect pin to tab with retainer. **Do not stretch cable to make adjustment, as the engine will not be able to return to idle.**

SERVO ROD, ADJUST

1. Ensure engine high idle speed is properly adjusted, turn off engine, the set carburetor choke to hot idle position.
2. Remove servo rod retainer, then adjust rod and install retainer in hole which provides some clearance between retainer and servo bushing. Clearance must not exceed width of one hole.

BEAD CHAIN, ADJUST

1. Ensure engine high idle speed is properly adjusted, turn off engine, the set carburetor choke to hot idle position.
2. Check slack in chain by disconnecting swivel from ball stud and holding chain taunt at ball stud. Center of swivel should extend 1/8 inch beyond center of ball stud.
3. To adjust ball chain slack, remove retainer from swivel and chain assembly, then place chain into swivel cavities which permits chain to have slight slack.
4. Install retainer over swivel and ball stud.

ELECTRIC & VACUUM RELEASE SWITCHES, ADJUST

1. With brake pedal fully depressed, insert switch into retainer until valve seats fully.
2. **On vehicles equipped with anti-lock brakes,** release brake pedal and allow to come to rest.
3. **On models less ABS brakes,** pull brake pedal rearward against pedal stop until clicking sounds are no longer heard.
4. Release brake pedal, then repeat step 2 and ensure clicking is not present.

ELECTRIC BRAKE RELEASE SWITCH & VACUUM RELEASE VALVE ADJUSTMENT

The switch assembly and valve assembly cannot be adjusted until brake booster push rod is assembled to brake pedal assembly. Adjustment is as follows:
1. Depress brake pedal and switch assembly and valve assembly into their proper retaining clips until fully seated.
2. **On vehicles equipped with anti-lock brakes,** release brake pedal and allow to come to rest.
3. **On models less anti-lock brakes,** slowly pull pedal back to its fully retracted position. The switch assembly and valve assembly will move within their retainers to their adjusted position.
4. The following brake pedal travel distances may be used to check for a properly adjusted cruise control and stop lamp switch assembly and vacuum release valve assembly.
   a. Cruise control switch contacts must open at 1/8-1/2 inch pedal travel, measured at centerline of brake pedal pad. **Nominal actuation of stop lamp contacts is 3/16 inch after cruise control contacts open.**
   b. Vacuum release valve assembly must open at 11/16-15/16 inches pedal travel, measured at centerline of brake pedal pad.

CLUTCH ELECTRIC RELEASE SWITCH ADJUSTMENT

1. Ensure clutch release switch is fully seated in retainer.
2. Pull clutch pedal pad upward. **Do not exert an upward force on the clutch pedal of more than 20 lbs, or damage to clutch master cylinder retaining ring may result.**

Type 3

INDEX

DESCRIPTION

This system is basically the same as Type 2, excepting the fact that on this type the function of the cruise control module is performed by the BCM.

ROAD TEST

1. Drive vehicle at speed greater than 25 mph, place cruise switch in On position and depress set button at end of multi-function lever. Cruise indicator should illuminate and vehicle should maintain speed.
2. With foot off accelerator, hold set button in. Vehicle should coast at a slower speed.
3. Release set button. If new speed is greater than 25 mph, cruise control should engage and hold slower speed.
4. Slide cruise switch to Resume/Accel position and hold it there. Vehicle should accelerate.
5. Release cruise switch back to On position. Vehicle should hold new, faster speed.
6. Tap brake pedal. Vehicle should coast slower and cruise indicator should go out.
7. Slide cruise control switch momentarily to Resume/Accel position. Cruise indicator should illuminate and vehicle should accelerate to former set speed.
8. While cruising, accelerate, then remove foot from accelerator pedal. Vehicle should coast back to set speed.
9. While cruising, tap cruise switch to

Resume/Accel position. Vehicle speed should decrease 1 mph for each tap up to ten.
10. While cruising, tap set button. Vehicle speed should decrease 1 mph for each tap down to 25 mph.
11. Slide cruise control switch to Off position. Cruise control should turn off and cruise indicator should go out.

SERVICE PRECAUTIONS

Before performing any diagnosis or repair procedures, temporarily disable the Supplemental Inflatable Restraint (SIR) system. Failure to do so may result in possible air bag deployment or personal injury. Disable SIR system as follows:
1. Turn ignition switch to Off position.
2. Remove SIR fuse.
3. Disconnect SIR electrical harness connector, at base of steering column.
4. Reverse procedure to reconnect, ensure "Inflatable Restraint" indicator flashes 7 to 9 times to indicate proper SIR operation.

On vehicles equipped with ABS brake system, the hydraulic accumulator, when fully charged contains brake fluid at high pressure. Before disconnecting any lines, hoses or fittings, ensure accumulator is full depressurized. Failure to do so may result in personal injury.

To depressurize the hydraulic accumulator, turn the ignition to the Off position or disconnect negative battery cable, pump brake pedal a minimum of 40 times at approximately 50 lbs. of force. A noticeable change in pedal feel will occur when accumulator is fully discharged.

SYSTEM DIAGNOSIS

The operation of the cruise control system is integral with the Body Control Module (BCM). The BCM monitors the cruise control system and other systems by comparing the actual operating conditions to standard values stored in memory. When certain system malfunctions are detected, a three digit trouble code is stored in the BCM memory. These trouble codes can be displayed to aid in system diagnosis. In this manner, the speed control system can be diagnosed by accessing fault codes, if they exist, that pertain to the speed control system.

Codes other than those described below may be stored in the BCM memory and displayed when the system is accessed to diagnose cruise control malfunctions. It may be necessary to diagnose these codes and identify the non-speed control related failure in order to ensure proper speed control system operation. For further diagnosis of other systems related to the BCM, refer to MOTOR's "Auto Engine Tune Up & Electronic Manual."

ENTERING DIAGNOSTIC SERVICE MODE

Toronado & Trofeo

To enter into diagnostic service mode, turn ignition on, then depress Off and

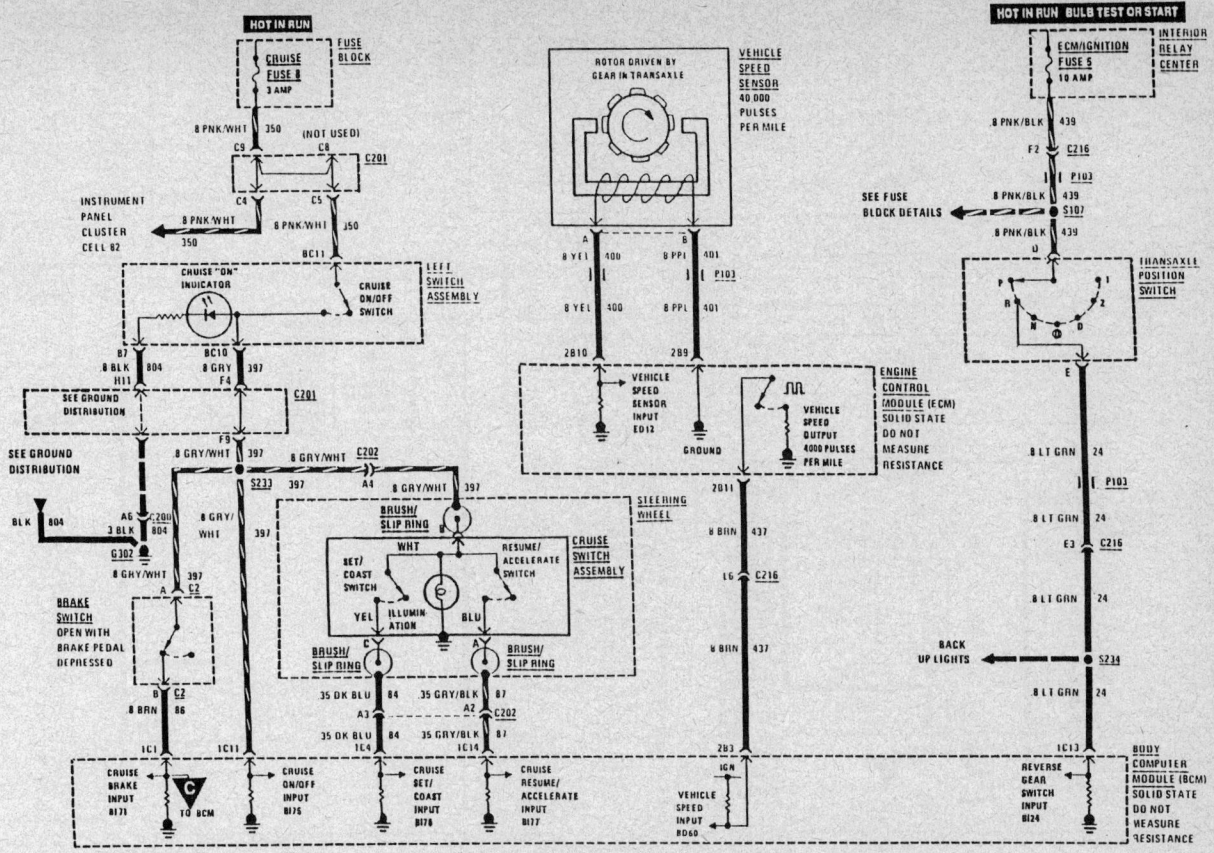

Fig. 1   Cruise control wiring diagram (Part 1 of 4). 1988 Riviera

Warm buttons on the Electronic Comfort Control panel (EEC) simultaneously. **On models equipped with color CRT, depress the Off hardkey and the Warm softkey.** Hold buttons or keys until a segment check is displayed on the Instrument Panel Cluster (IPC) and the EEC.

Reatta & Riviera

On 1988-89 models, to enter the diagnostic service mode, turn ignition on, then depress Off and Warm pads on the CRT's Climate Control page simultaneously. Hold until a double beep is heard or a page entitled Service Mode is displayed.

On 1990 models, to enter the diagnostic service mode, turn ignition on, then depress Off and Temp Up pads on the Electronic Climate Control Panel (ECCP) simultaneously. Hold until all display segments have been lite.

Operating vehicle in diagnostic service mode for extended time periods without the engine running will cause the battery to run down and possibly relate false diagnostic information. To ensure proper operation do not operate in diagnostic service mode for longer than 1/2 hour.

ACCESSING CODES

After diagnostic service mode is entered, any trouble codes stored in computer memory will be displayed. ECM codes will be displayed first, then BCM codes (ECM codes are prefixed with an E, BCM codes with an B, IPC codes with an I and

SIR codes with an R). On 1988-89 Reatta and Riviera and 1989 Toronado, codes will be accompanied by Current or History. History indicates the failure was not present the last time the code was tested and Current indicates the fault still exists. On Toronado and Trofeo models, if at any time during the display of trouble codes the Lo fan button is pressed, the display of codes will be bypassed. Also on Toronado and Trofeo models, any time the Bi-Lev button is pressed, the BCM will exit diagnostic service mode and return to normal vehicle operation. On Reatta & Riviera models, if at any time during display of trouble codes the No pad is touched, the display of codes will be bypassed; any time the End or Level pad is touched, the CRT will exit diagnostic service mode and return to normal vehicle operation. On all models, refer to wiring diagram and connector pin locations, **Figs. 1 through 8,** and proceed to the applicable code diagnosis as follows:

Code B660

This code was designed to prevent cruise control operation when vehicle is not in a forward gear. Refer to **Figs. 9 and 11** for diagnosis. If the code is intermittent, the code may have been set if the operator placed the gear selector into neutral when the cruise control was engaged. This will cause the cruise to drop out until it is re-engaged. Also, check PRNDD21 adjustment and or for looseness in the switch mounting or connections, as this could also cause an intermittent signal to the BCM.

Code B663/B664

Refer to **Fig. 12** for diagnosis. If code is intermittent, check vacuum source and brake release vacuum lines for proper connections or slow leaks. If the vehicle speed exceeds 30 mph over the engaged cruise control speed this code may be set.

Code B667

Refer to **Fig. 13** for diagnosis. If code is intermittent, wiggle related wiring while observing BCM inputs BI76 and BI77. If the failure is induced, the reading will jump from Lo to Hi with switch off.

Code B671

Refer to **Fig. 14** for diagnosis. If code is intermittent, wiggle related wiring while observing BCM data BD70. If failure is induced, the reading will jump from its normal value to a reading below 3%.

Code B672

Refer to **Fig. 15** for diagnosis. If code is intermittent, wiggle wiring while in the output function BO01 and listen for the solenoid to cycle, or stop cycling. This will have to be done slowly, as this function cycles the solenoid on and off every 3 seconds. **Ensure intermittent condition can be induced a few times. NOTE: On 1990 models, circuit 151 is now circuit 804.** On 1990 Reatta and Riviera, if measured resistance between terminals A and C is below 25 ohms, replace both the servo unit and the BCM.

Continued on page 33-71

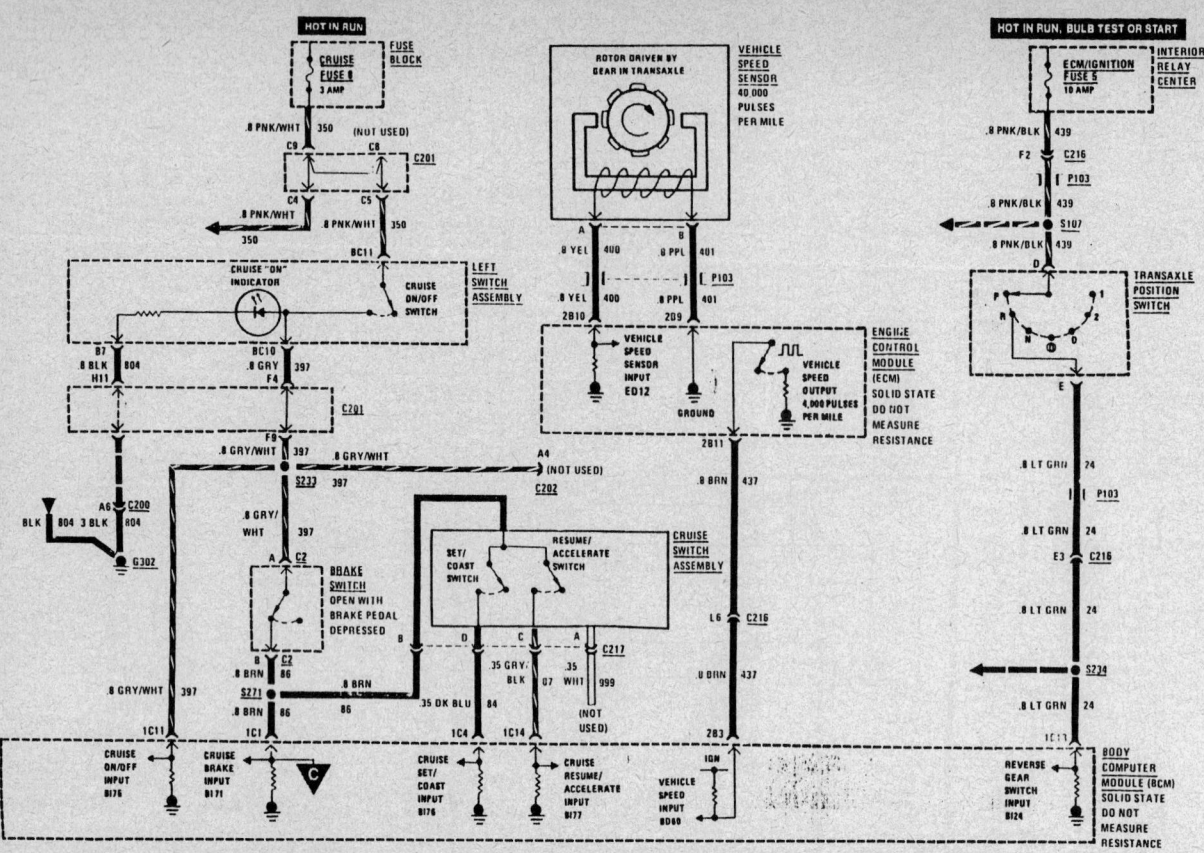

Fig. 1 Cruise control wiring diagram (Part 2 of 4). 1988 Reatta

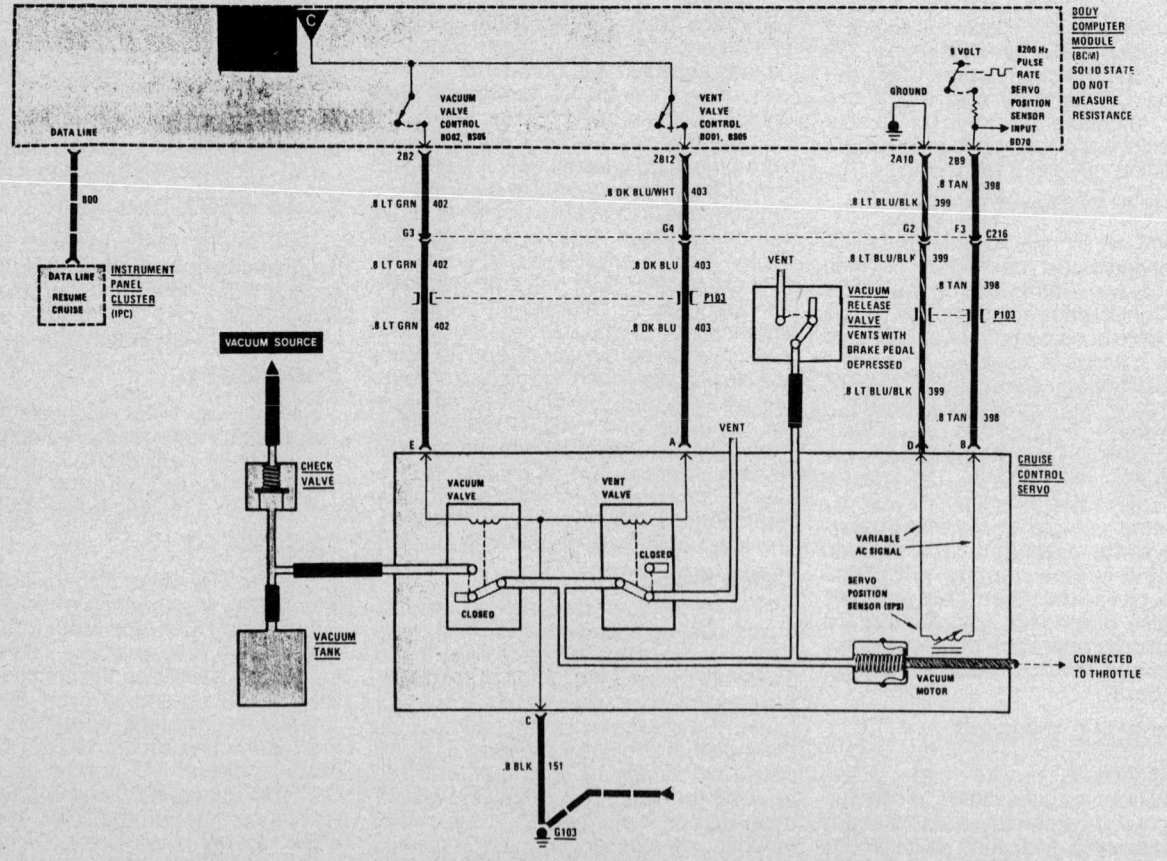

Fig. 1 Cruise control wiring diagram (Part 3 of 4). 1988 Reatta & Riviera

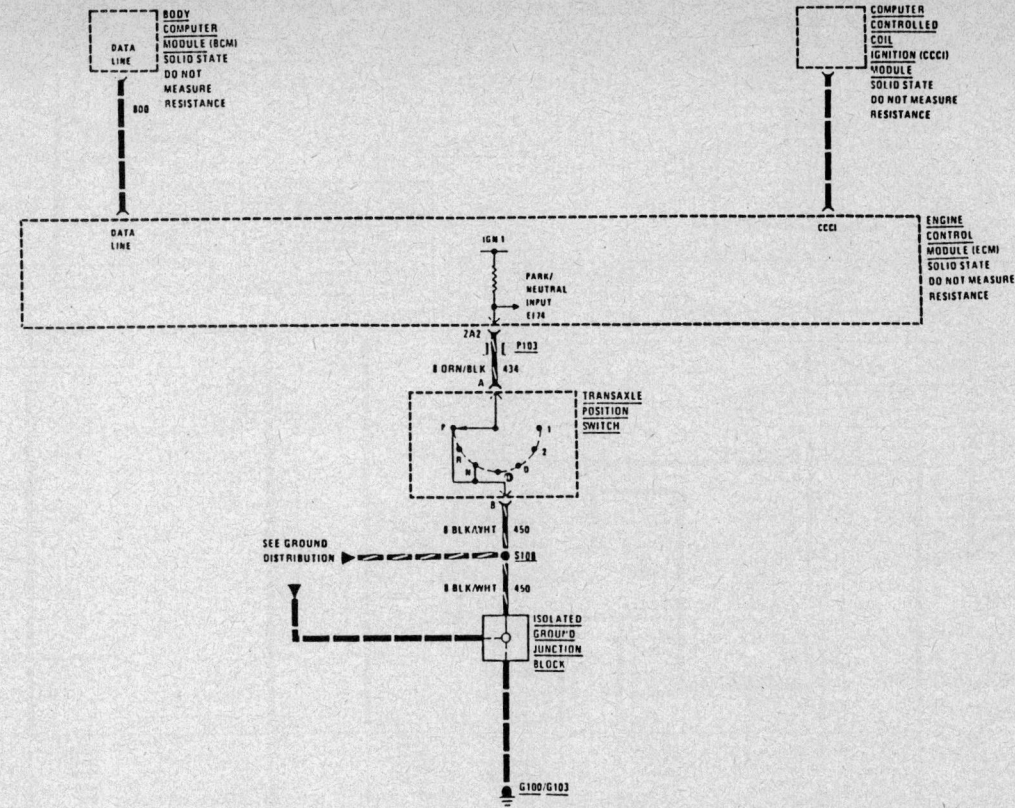

Fig. 1 Cruise control wiring diagram (Part 4 of 4). 1988 Reatta & Riviera

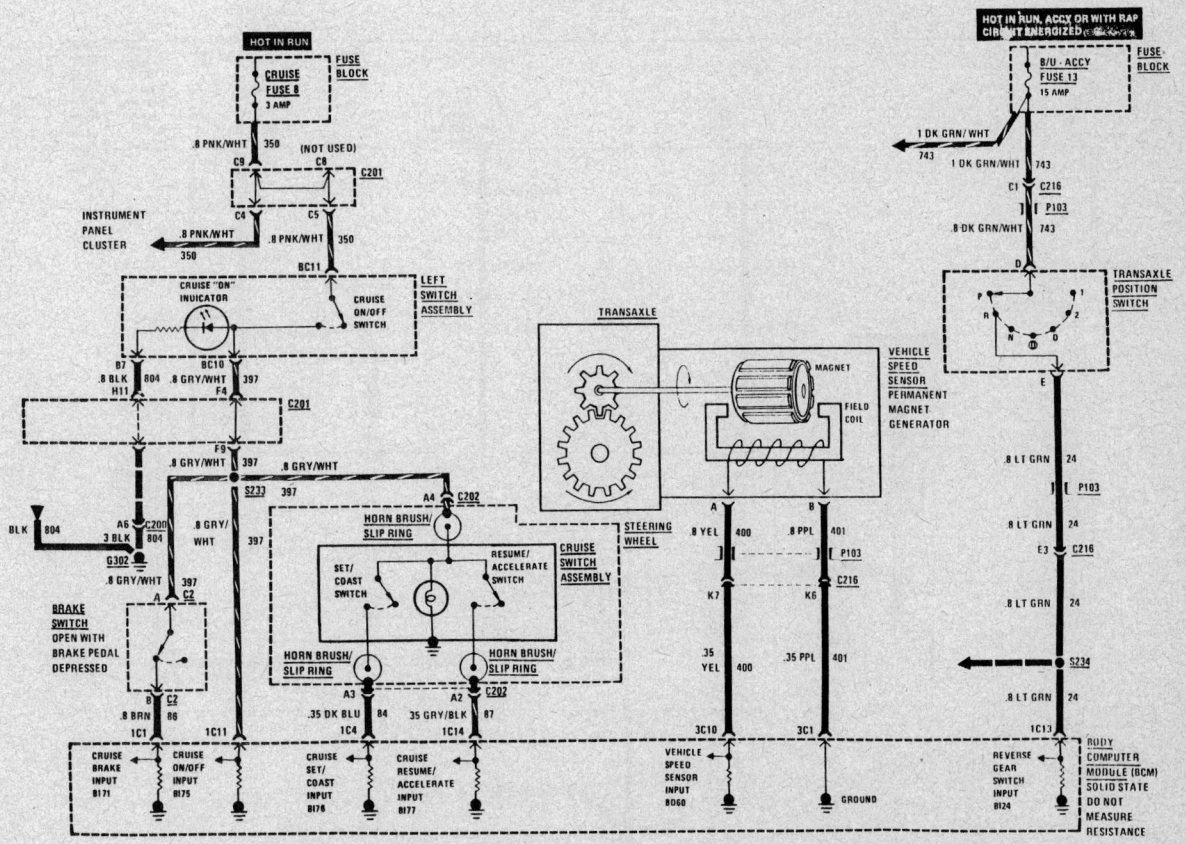

Fig. 2 Cruise control wiring diagram (Part 1 of 4). 1989 Riviera

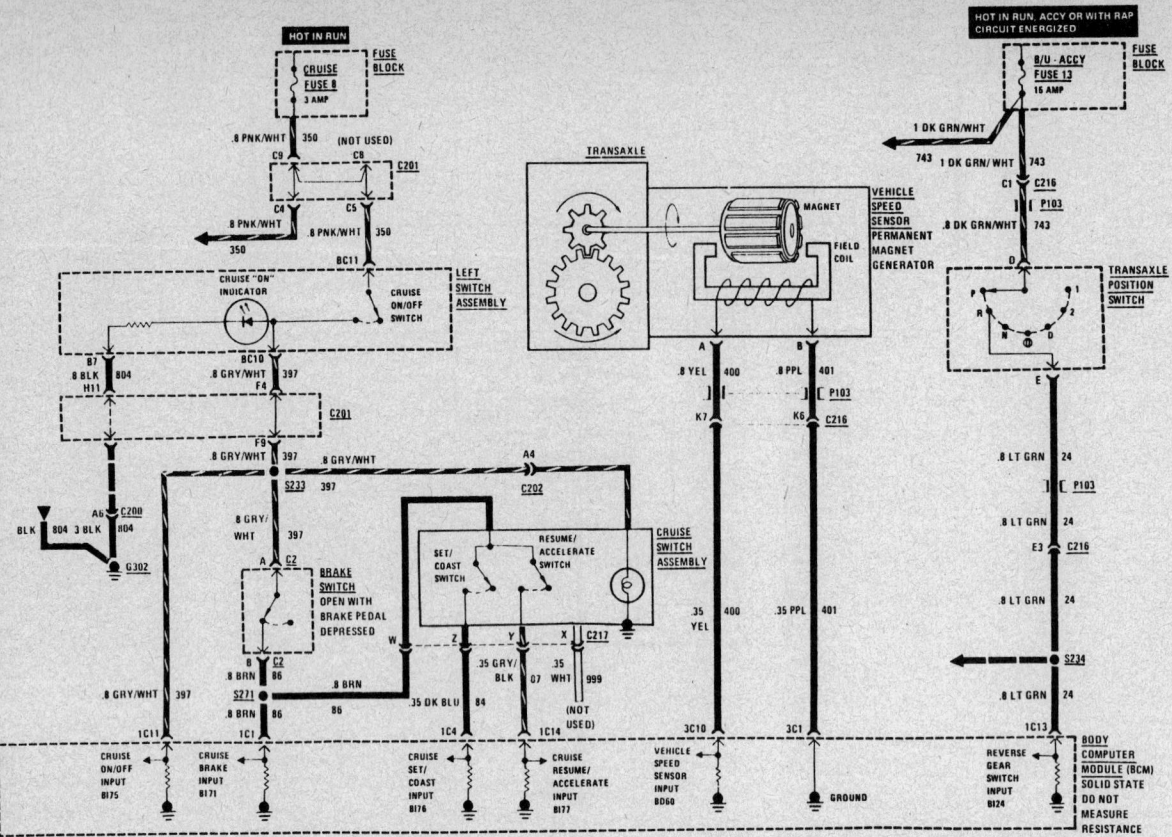

Fig. 2 Cruise control wiring diagram (Part 2 of 4). 1989 Reatta

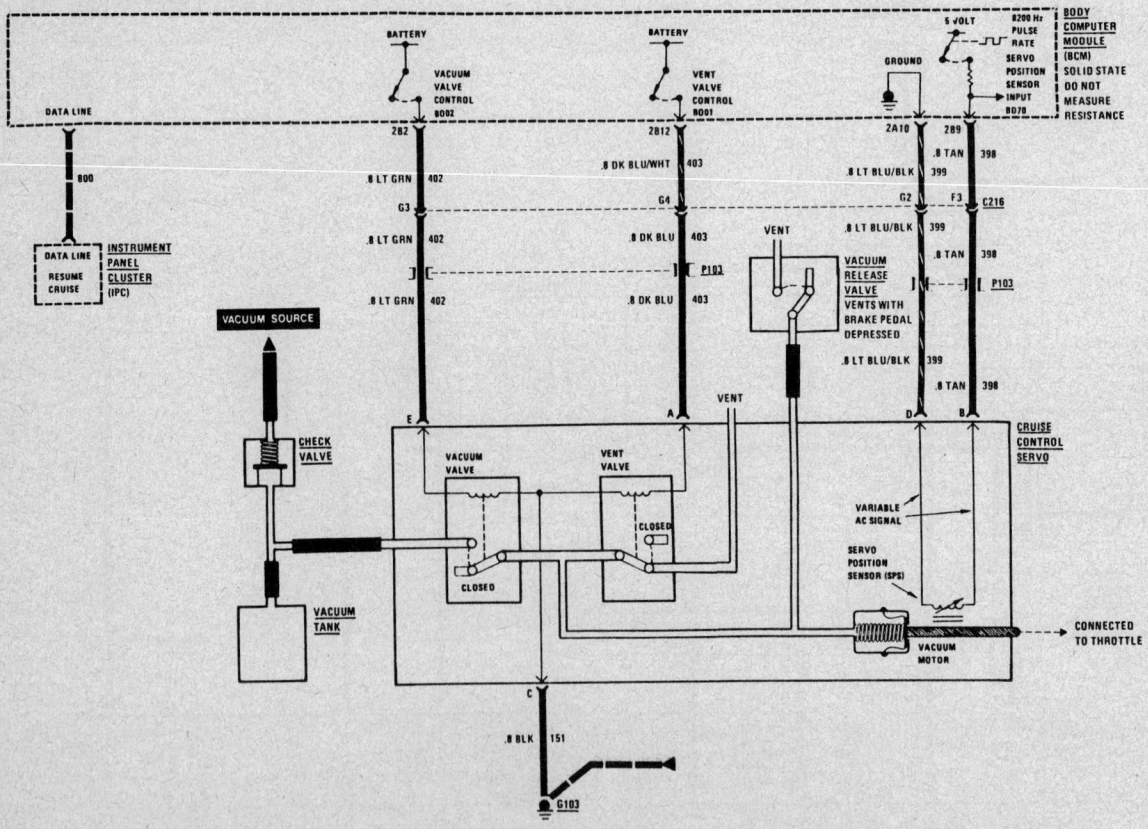

Fig. 2 Cruise control wiring diagram (Part 3 of 4). 1989 Reatta & Riviera

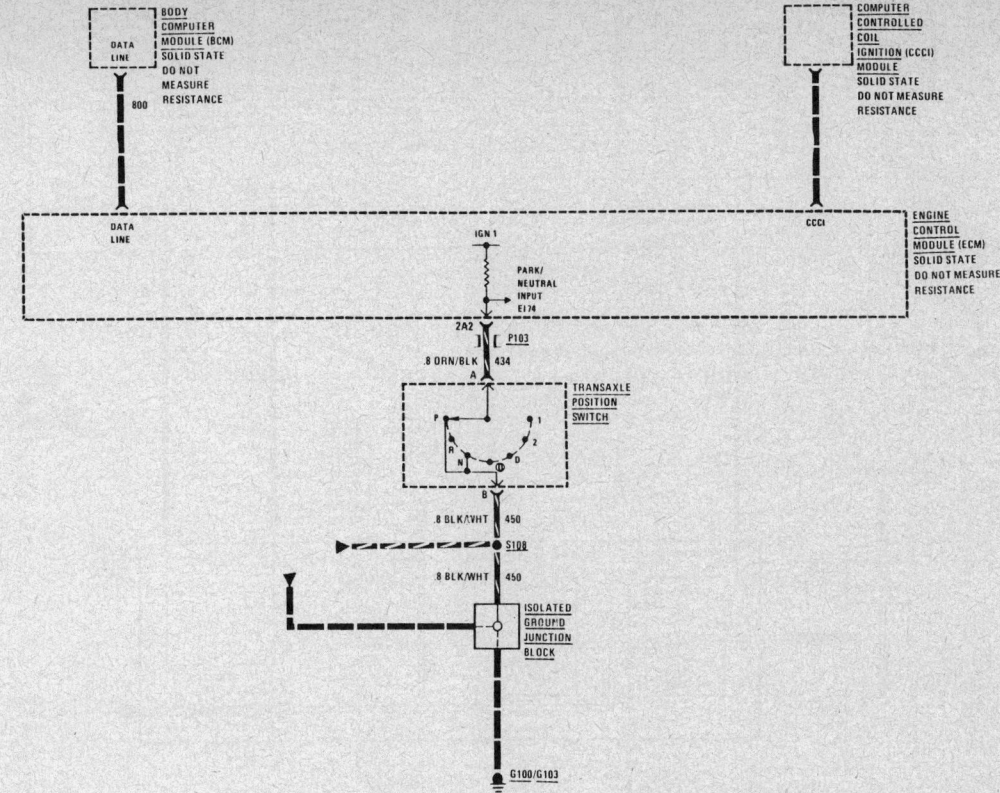

Fig. 2   Cruise control wiring diagram (Part 4 of 4). 1989 Reatta & Riviera

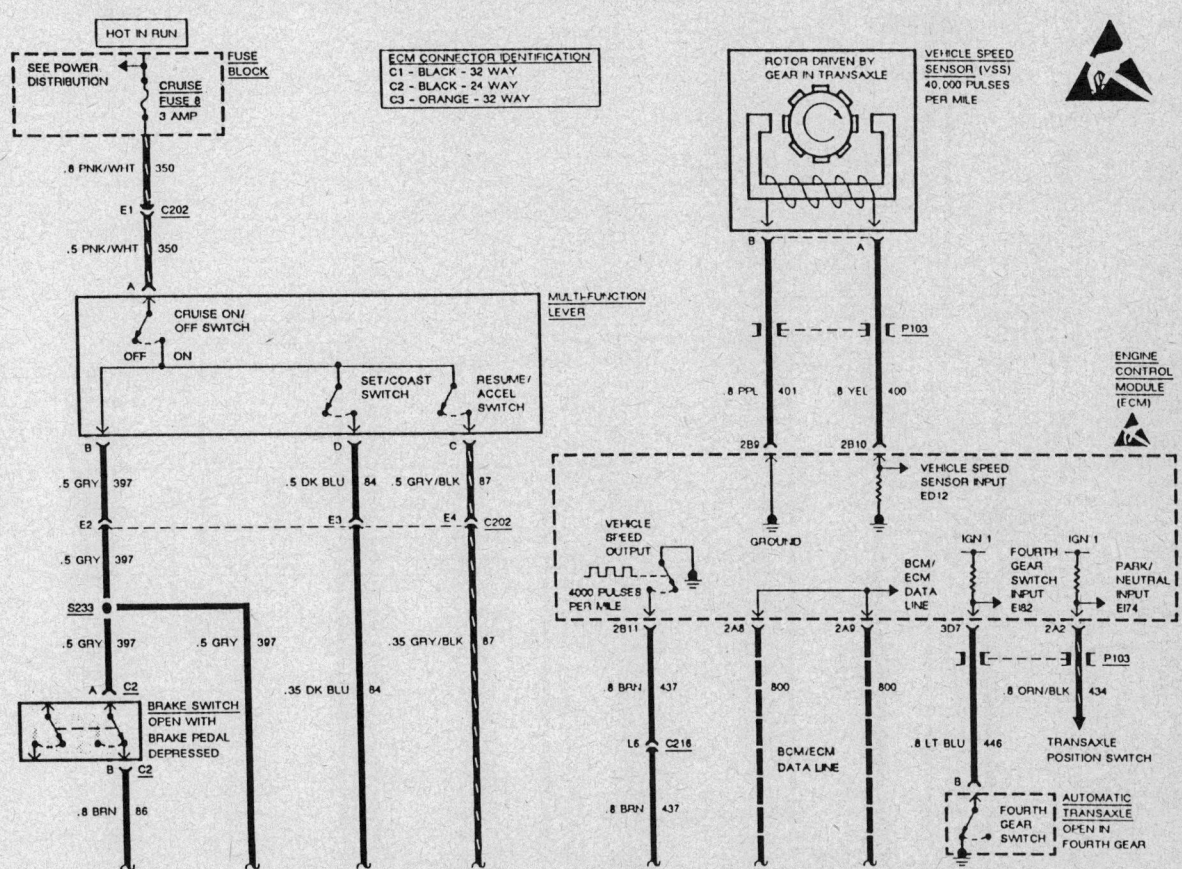

Fig. 3   Cruise control wiring diagram (Part 1 of 2). 1990 Reatta & Riviera

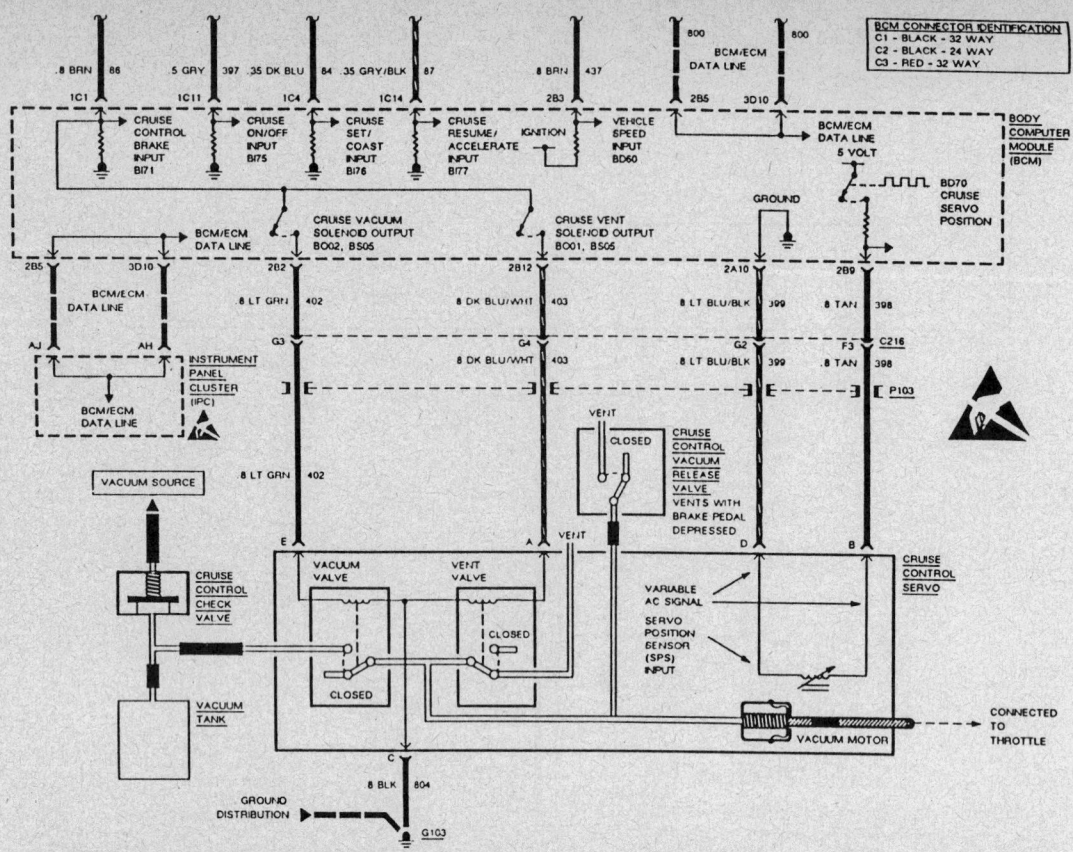

Fig. 3   Cruise control wiring diagram (Part 2 of 2). 1990 Reatta & Riviera

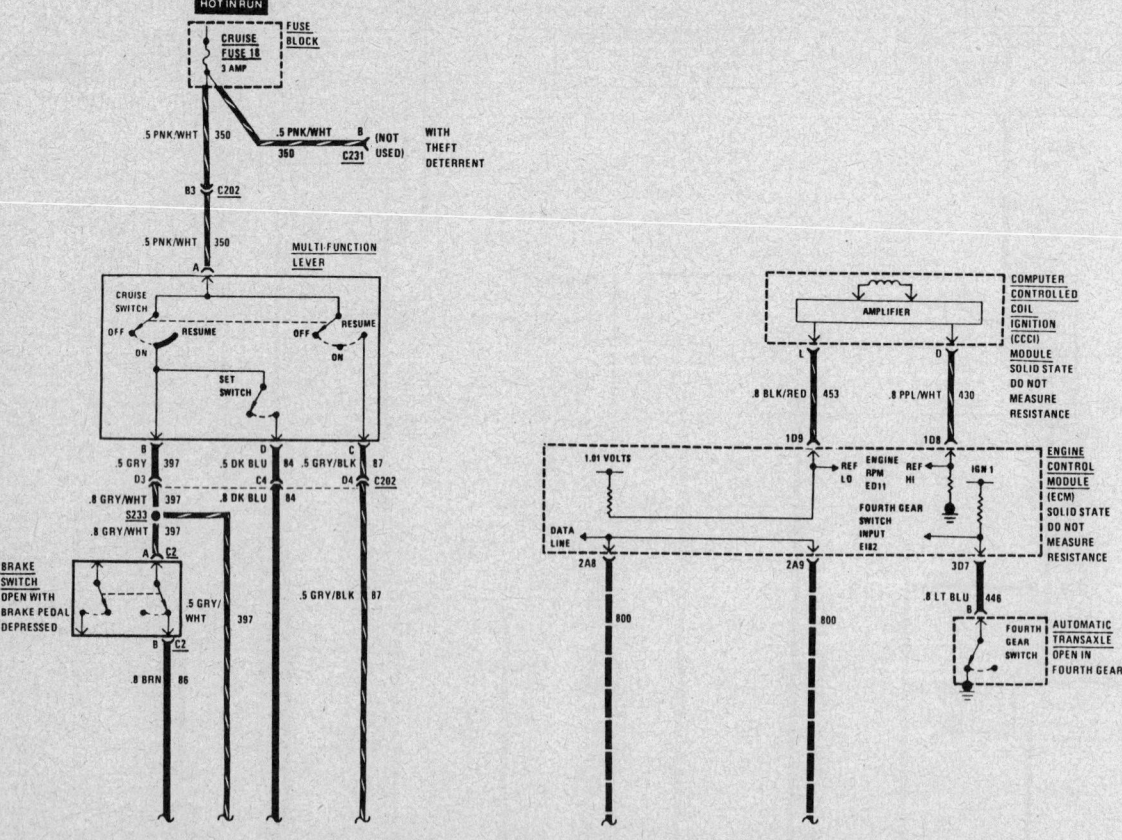

Fig. 4   Cruise control wiring diagram (Part 1 of 3). 1988 Toronado

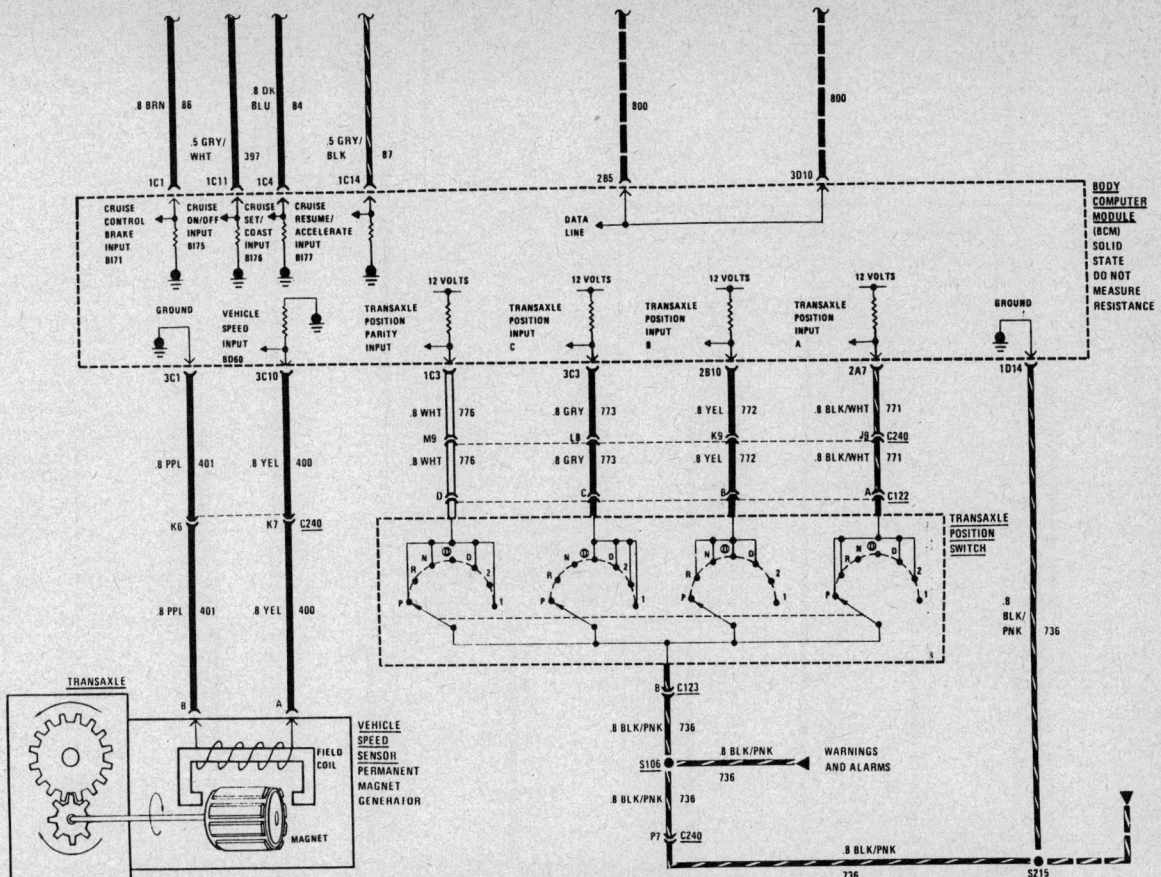

Fig. 4   Cruise control wiring diagram (Part 2 of 3). 1988 Toronado

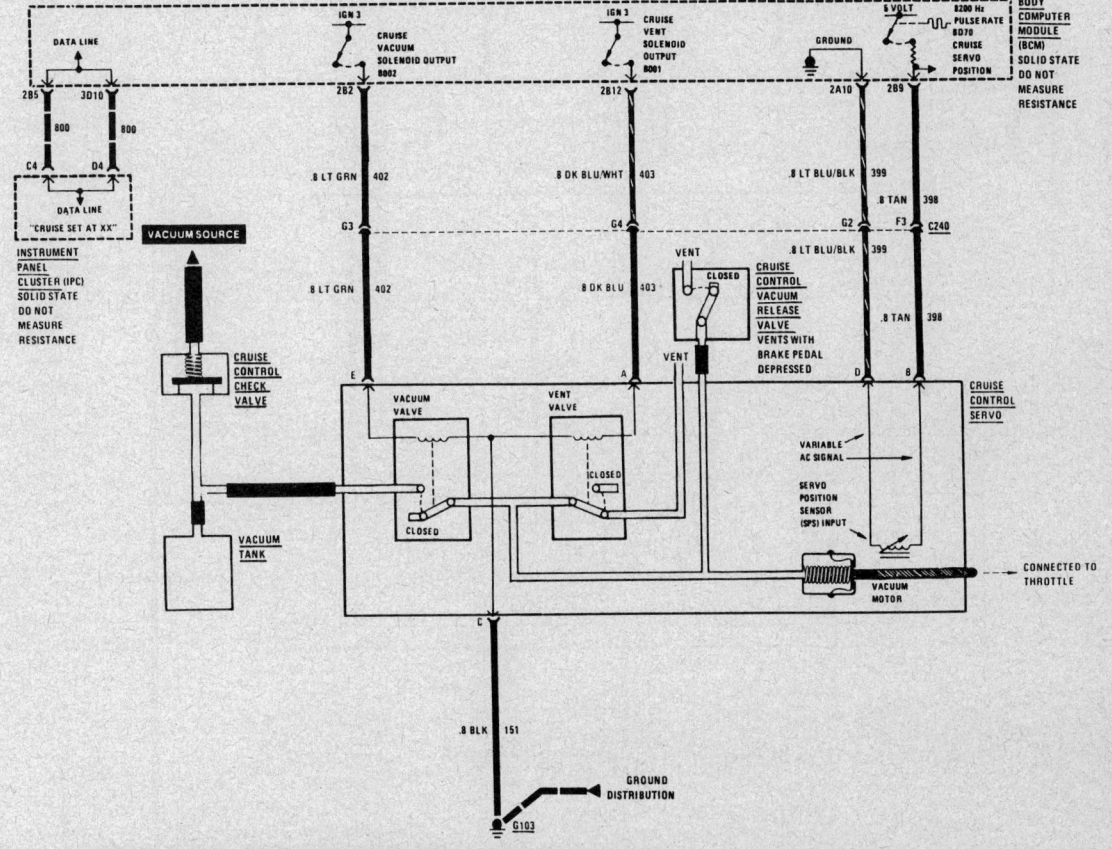

Fig. 4   Cruise control wiring diagram (Part 3 of 3). 1988 Toronado

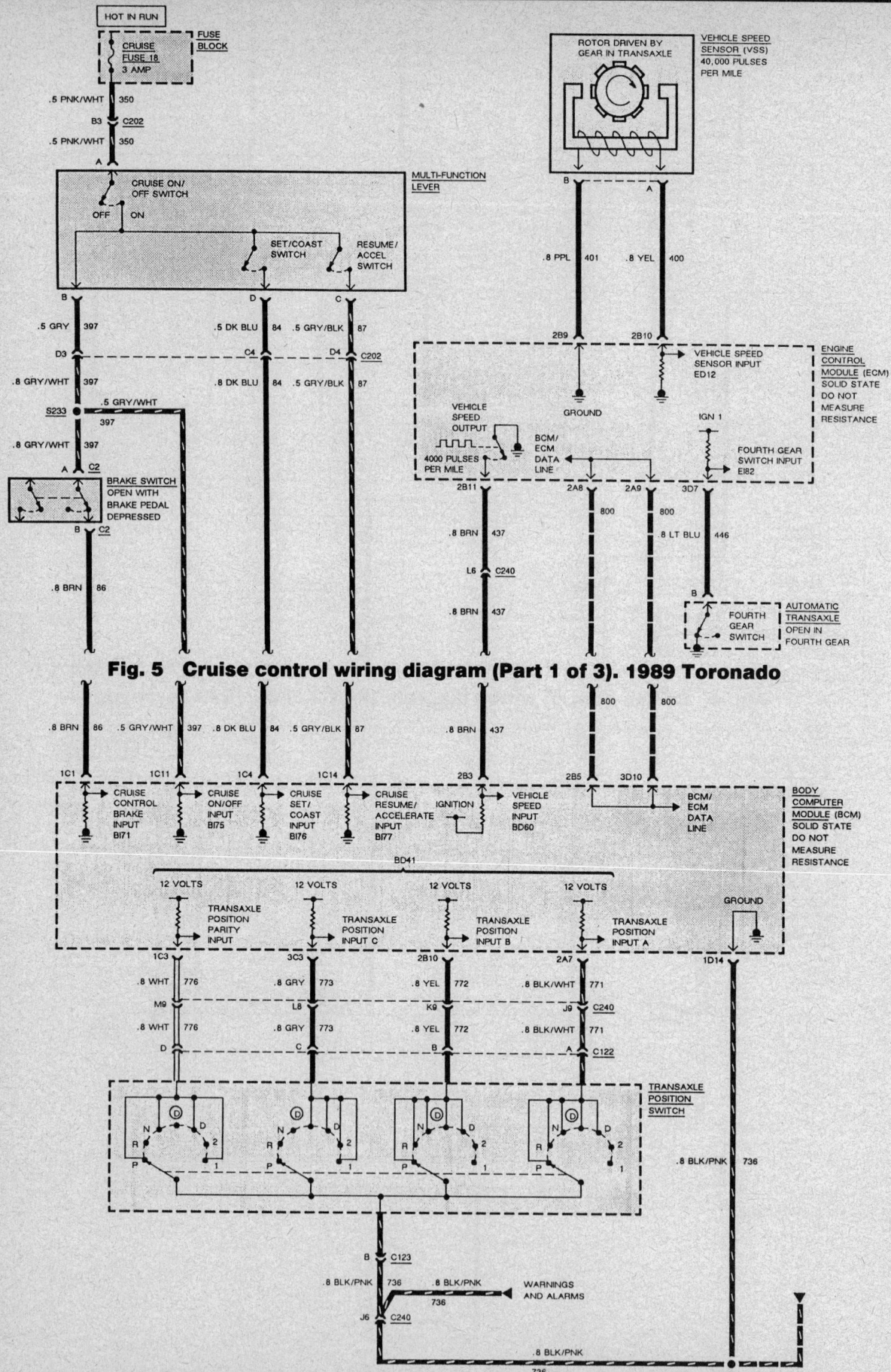

Fig. 5   Cruise control wiring diagram (Part 1 of 3). 1989 Toronado

Fig. 5   Cruise control wiring diagram (Part 2 of 3). 1989 Toronado

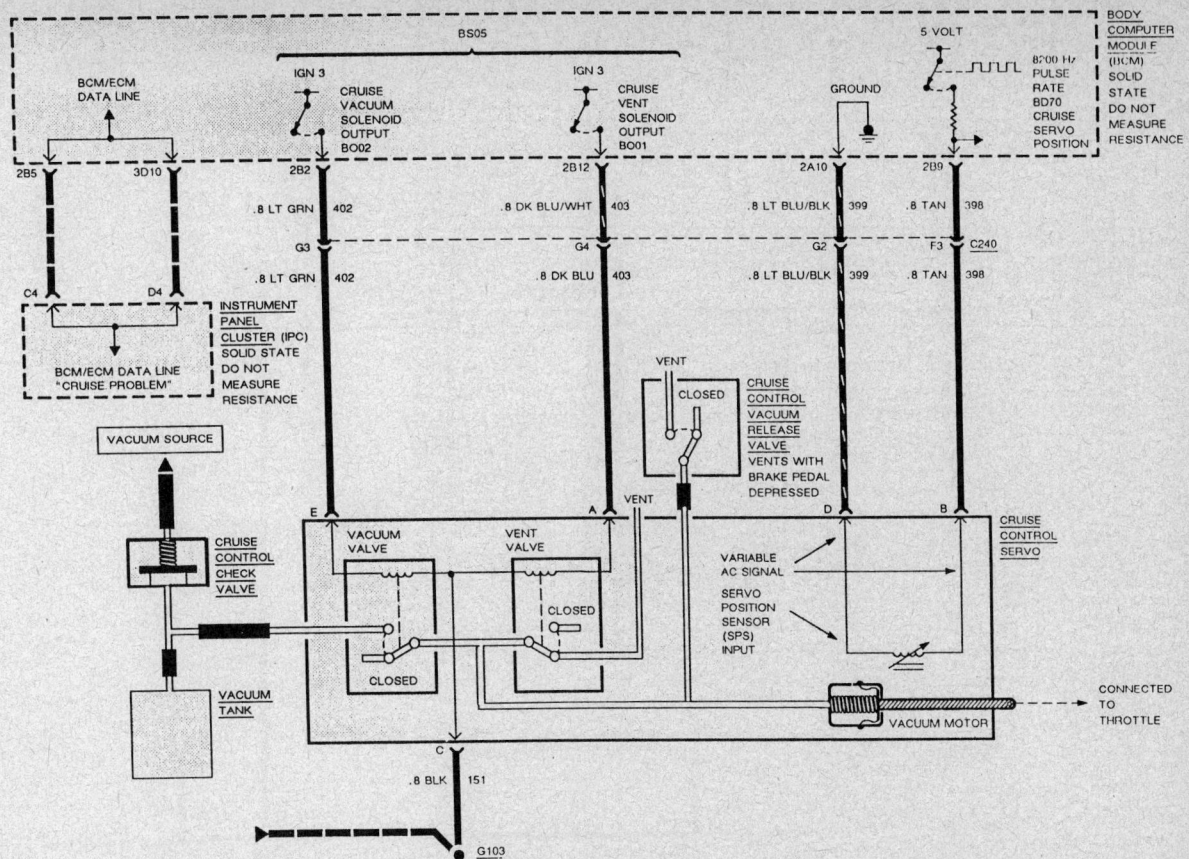

Fig. 5 Cruise control wiring diagram (Part 3 of 3). 1989 Toronado

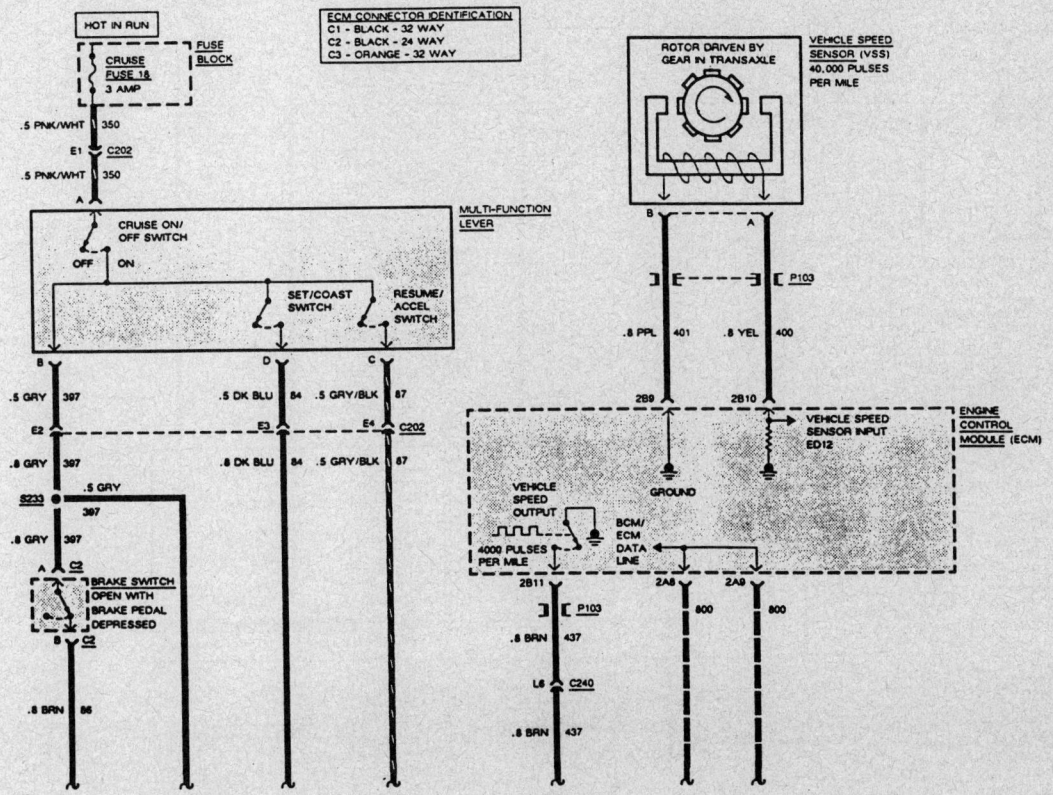

Fig. 6 Cruise control wiring diagram (Part 1 of 3). 1990 Toronado & Trofeo

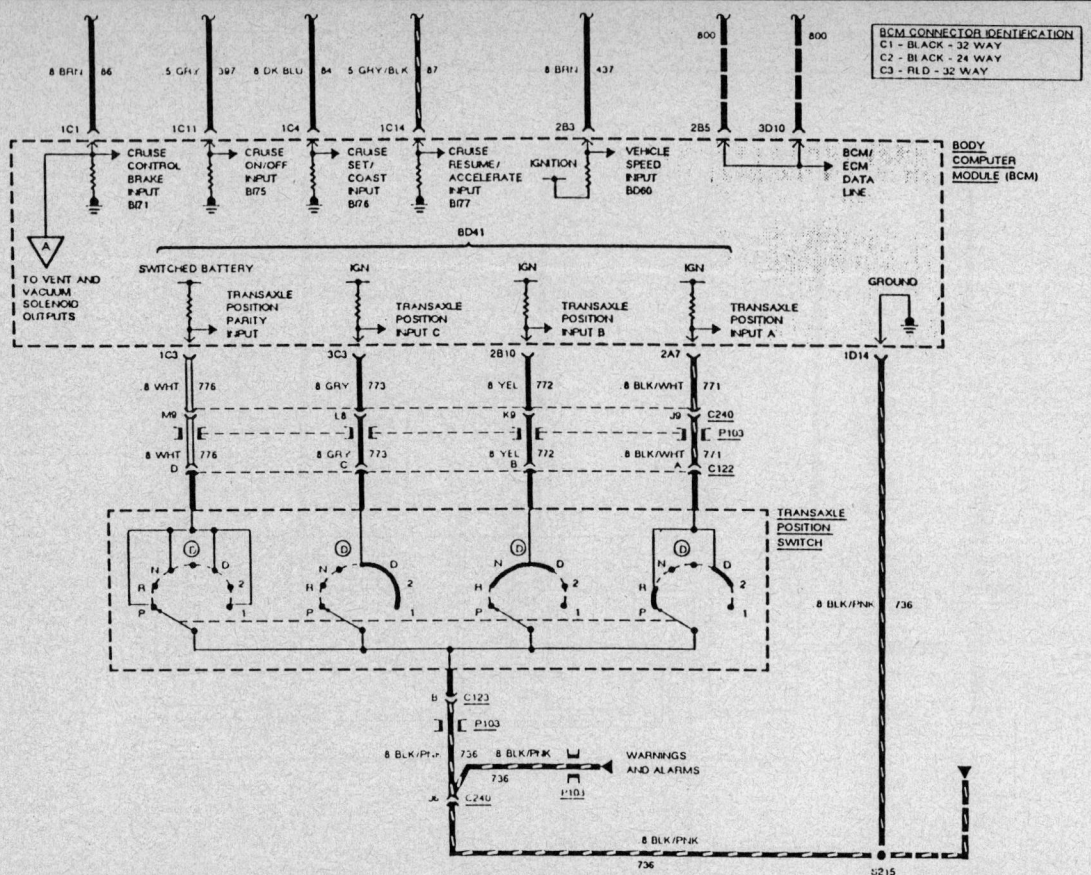

Fig. 6   Cruise control wiring diagram (Part 2 of 3). 1990 Toronado & Trofeo

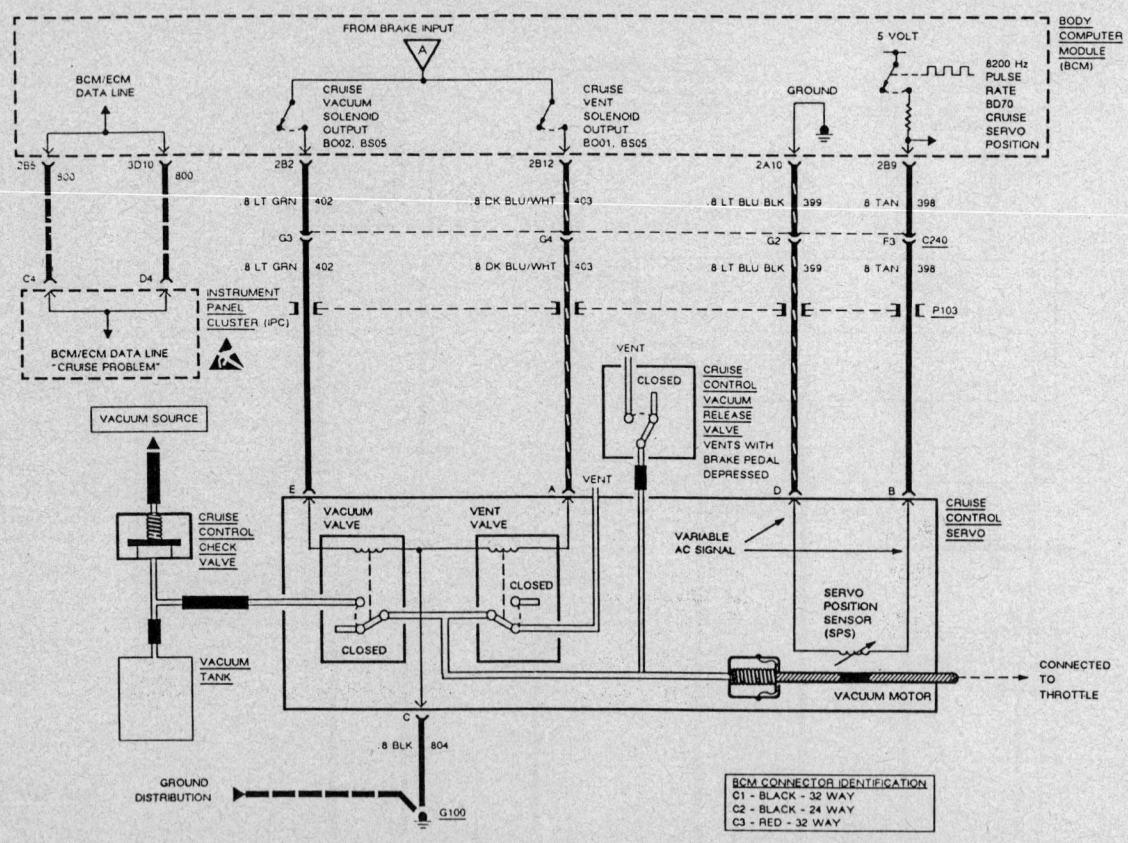

Fig. 6   Cruise control wiring diagram (Part 3 of 3). 1990 Toronado & Trofeo

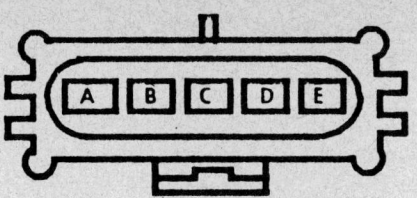

Fig. 7 Control servo connector pin locations

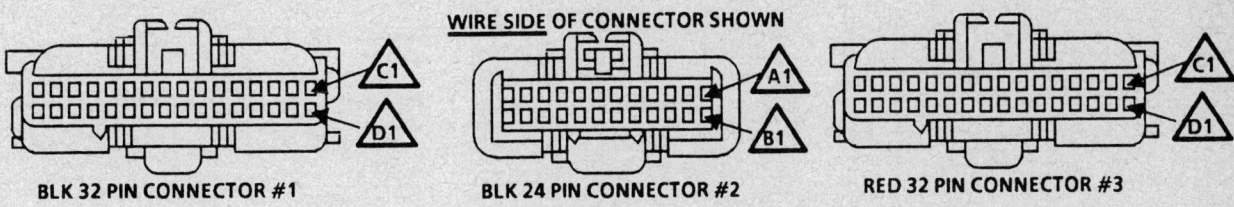

WIRE SIDE OF CONNECTOR SHOWN

BLK 32 PIN CONNECTOR #1   BLK 24 PIN CONNECTOR #2   RED 32 PIN CONNECTOR #3

Fig. 8 BCM connector pin locations

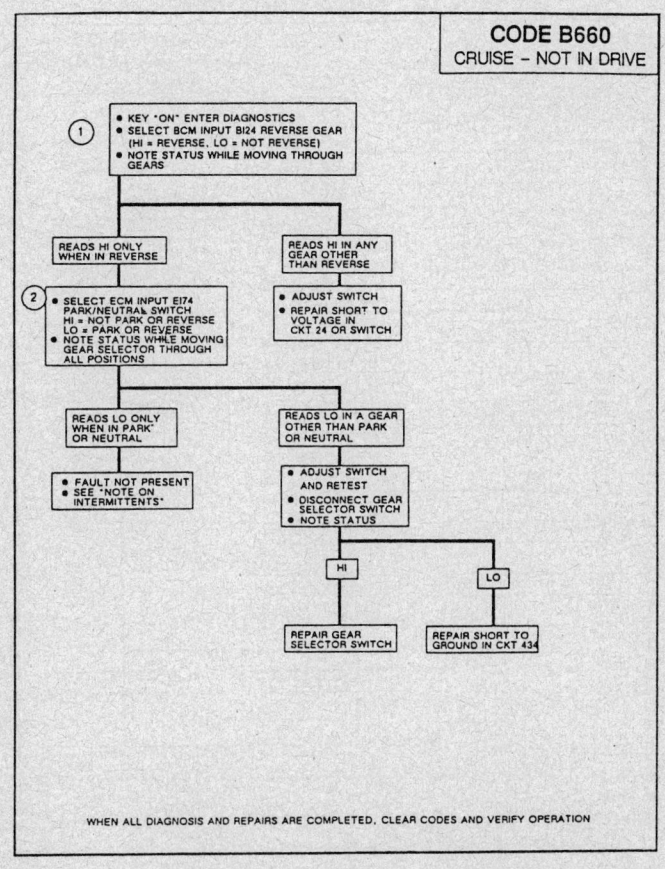

Fig. 9 Code B660. 1988–89 Reatta & Riviera

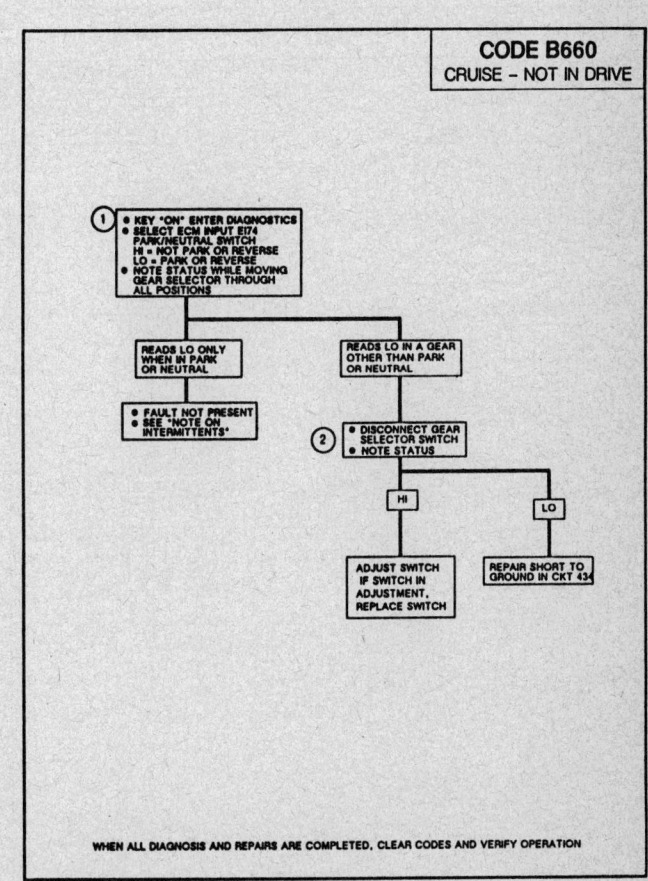

Fig. 10 Code B660. 1990 Reatta & Riviera

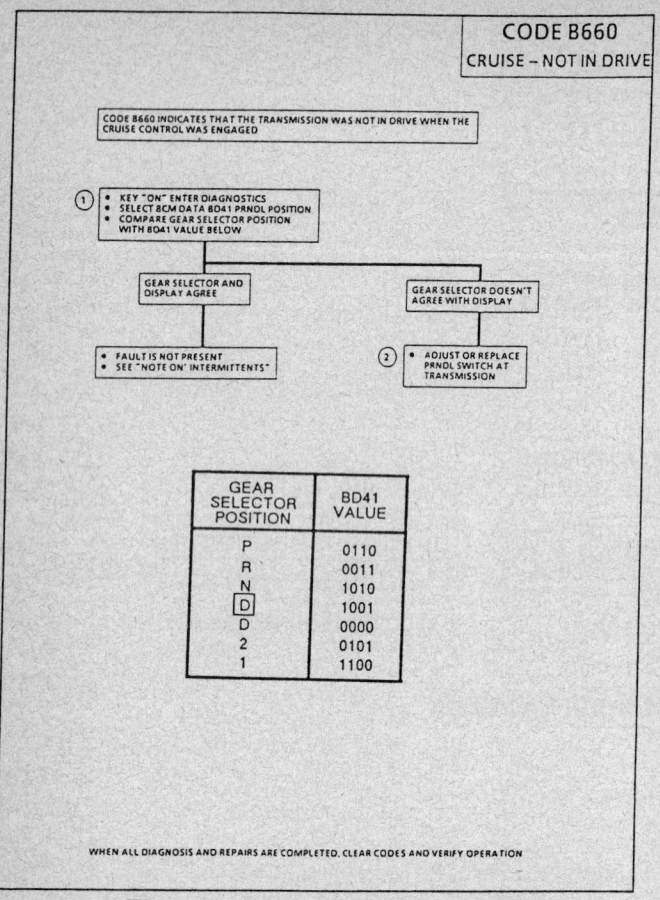

Fig. 11   Code B660. Toronado

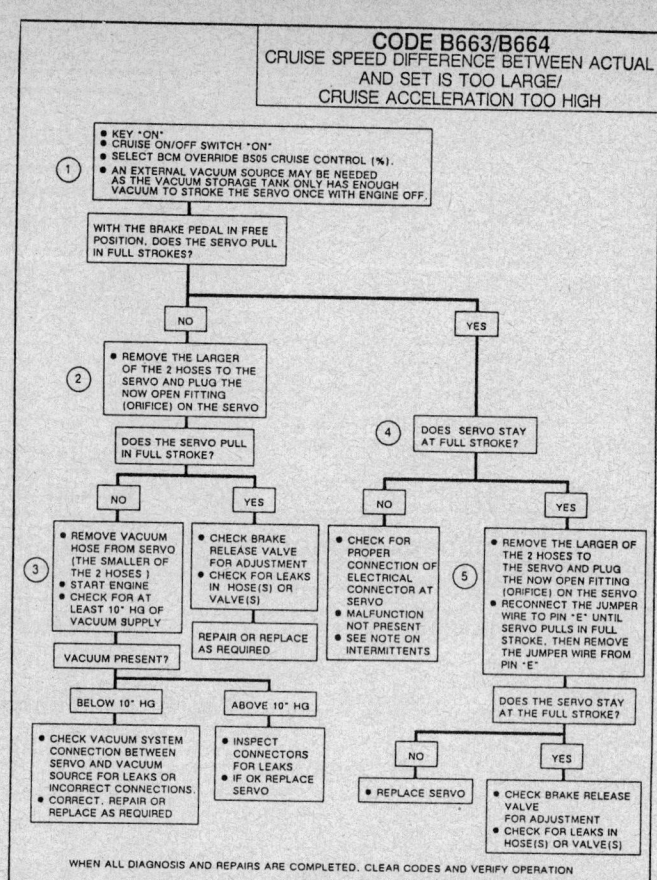

Fig. 12   Code B663/B664

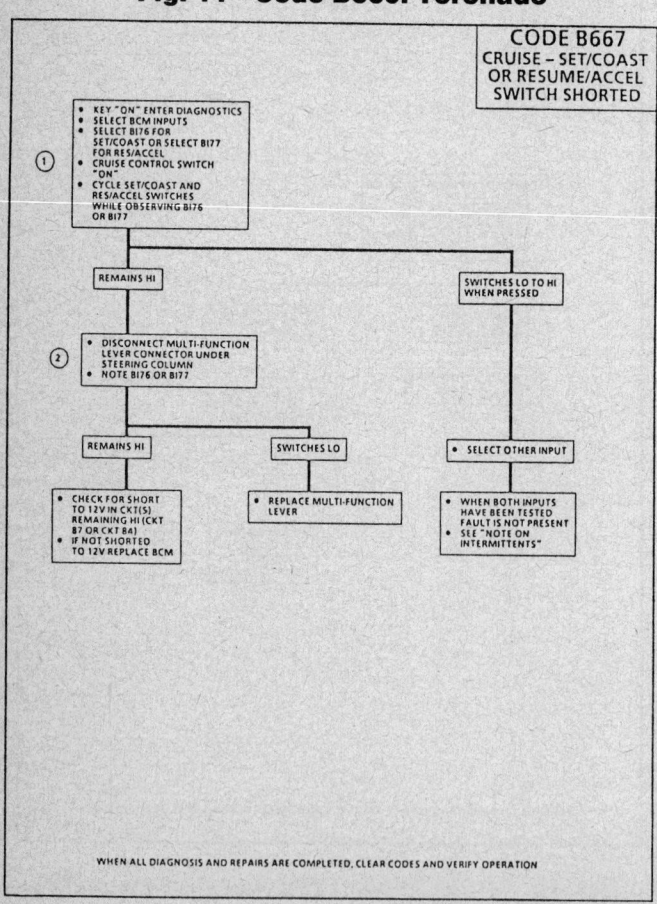

Fig. 13   Code B667

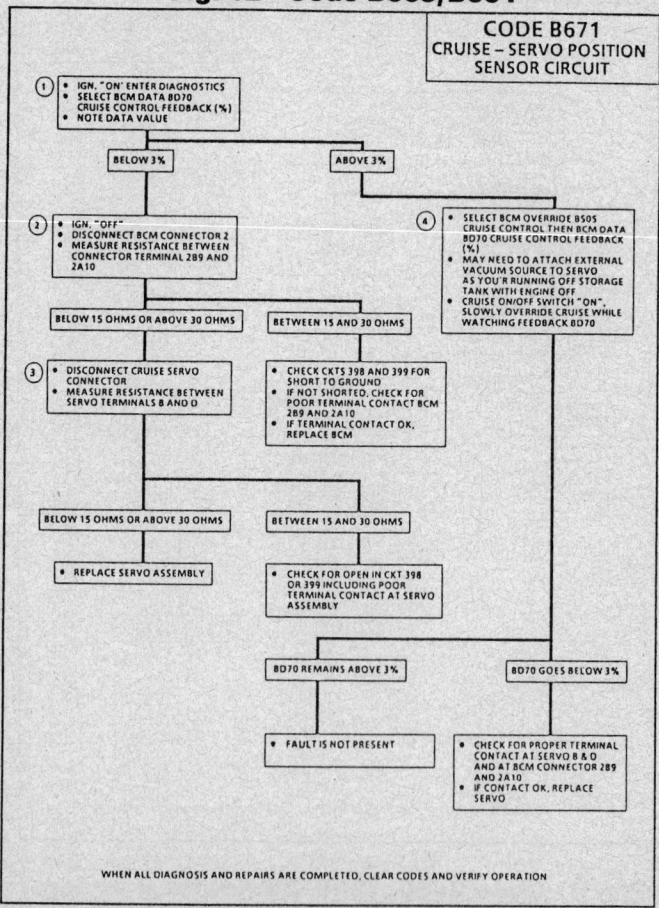

Fig. 14   Code B671

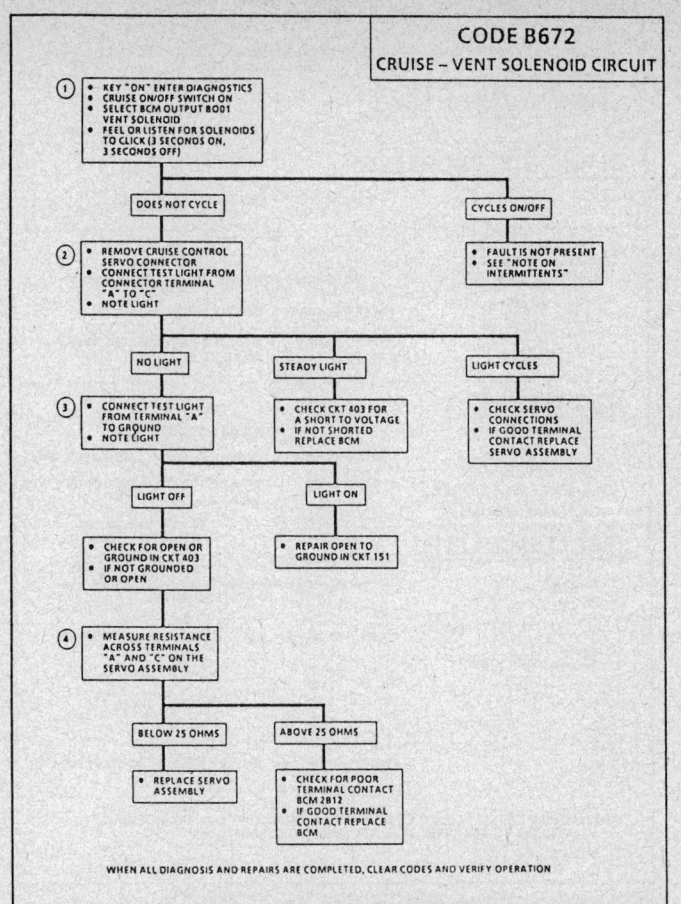

Fig. 15   Code B672

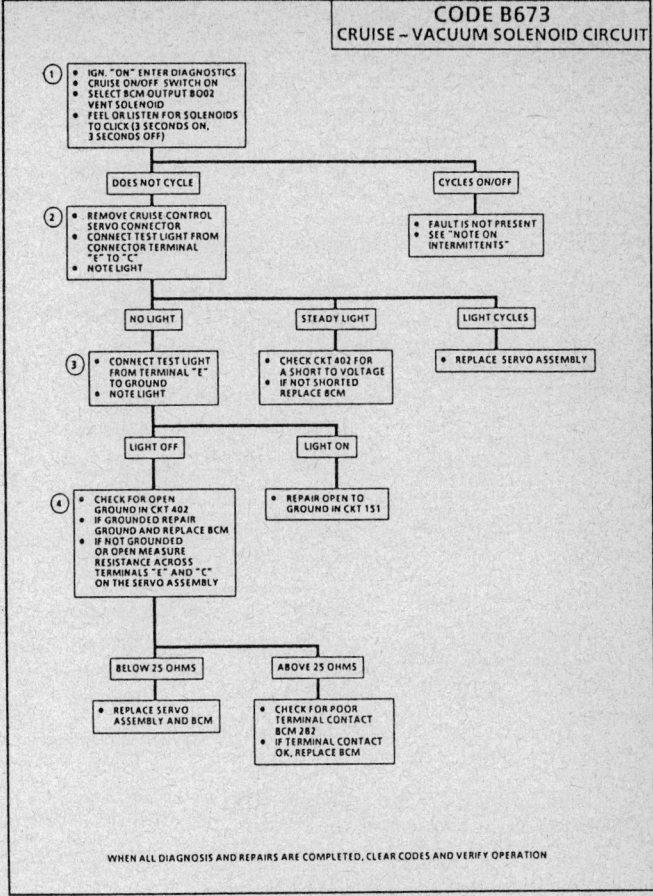

Fig. 16   Code B673

Fig. 17   Entering diagnostic service mode. 1988–89 Reatta & Riviera

Code B673

Refer to **Fig. 16** for diagnosis. If code is intermittent, wiggle wiring while in the output function BO02 and listen for the solenoid to cycle, or stop cycling. This will have to be done slowly, as this function cycles the solenoid on and off every 3 seconds. **Ensure intermittent condition can be induced a few times. NOTE: On 1990 models, circuit 151 is now circuit 804.**

DIAGNOSTIC TEST PROCEDURES

After trouble codes have been displayed, the diagnostic service mode can be used to test the speed control system by referring to **Figs. 17 through 20** and performing the following:

1. **On models less CRT,** proceed as follows:

   a. Following the display of trouble codes, the first available system level will be displayed, which is the ECM. On 1988-89 models, depress Lo fan button (secondary display) to enter into BCM system. On 1990 models, depress fan down button to enter BCM system. This will display the first available test type.

   b. **On 1988-89 models,** depress Hi fan button (secondary display). On 1990 models, depress fan up button. This will display the first available test type.

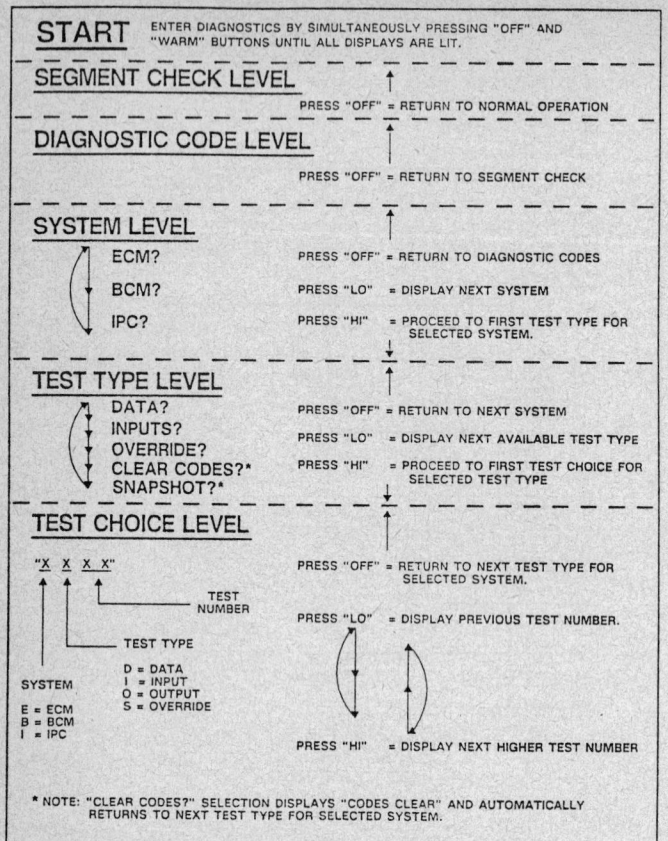

Fig. 18 Entering diagnostic service mode. 1988–89 Toronado less CRT

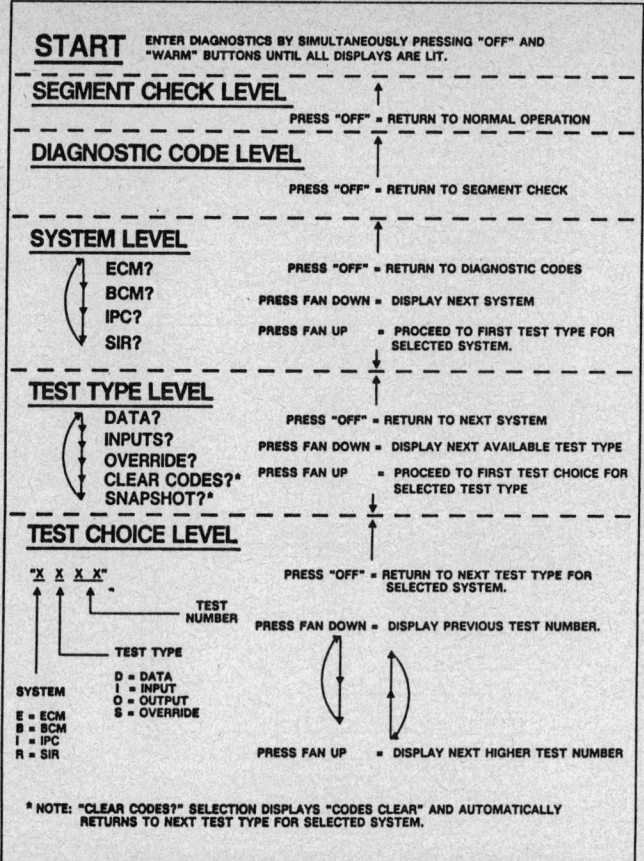

Fig. 19 Entering diagnostic service mode. 1990 models less CRT

c. **On 1988-89 models,** press Lo fan button (secondary display), on 1990 models, depress fan down button to change the display to "Inputs," the test level required for speed control system testing.

d. **On 1988-89 models,** depress Hi fan button (secondary display) and on 1990 models, depress fan up button. This will display the first test type. At this point, press Hi button until the correct test type appears as listed below under the applicable model and year.

2. **On models with CRT,** proceed as follows:

a. Following the display of trouble codes, the first available system level will be displayed, which is the ECM. Depress No button on secondary display to enter into BCM system.

b. Depress Yes button on secondary display. This will display the first available test type.

c. Press No button on secondary display to change the display to "Inputs," the test level required for speed control system testing.

d. Depress Yes button on secondary display. This will display the first test type. At this point, press Yes button until the correct test type appears as listed below under the applicable model and year.

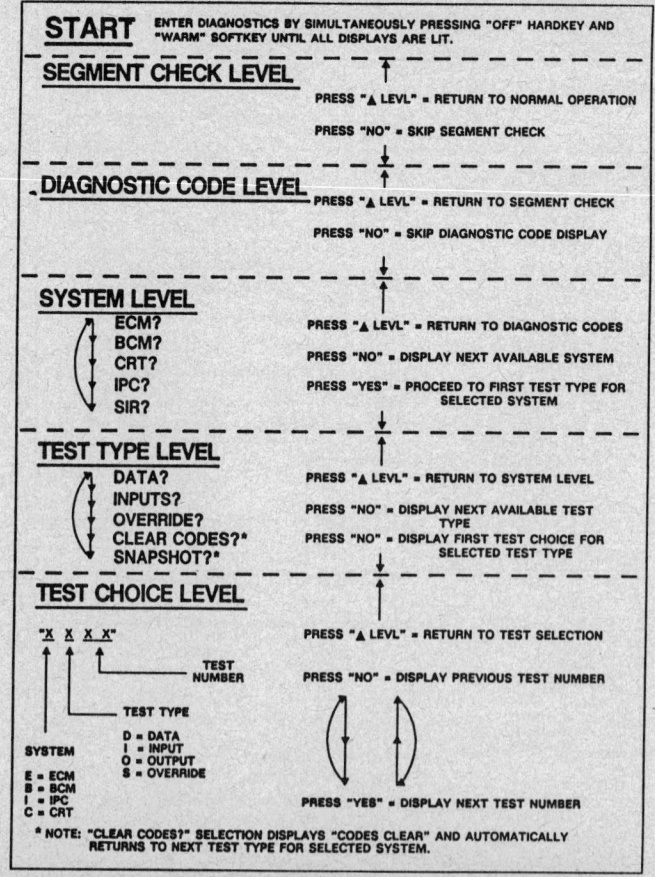

Fig. 20 Entering diagnostic service mode. Toronado w/CRT

Toronado & Trofeo

When performing the following tests, refer to applicable wiring diagram and connector pin locations, **Figs. 1 through 8.**

1. Enter BCM diagnostics, turn ignition switch to Run position, select BCM input BI75 and operate cruise switch.
2. If BCM BI75 display reads Lo with cruise switch on, proceed as follows:
   a. Check fuse No. 18.
   b. Disconnect multi-function lever connector and, using test lamp, check for voltage at terminal A (pink/white wire). If there is no voltage check pink/white wire (circuit 350) for open.
   c. Connect fused jumper between terminals A (pink/white wire) and B (gray wire) of multi-function lever. If display reads Hi, replace multi-function lever.
   d. If display reads Lo, reconnect multi-function lever connector and, with cruise switch on, backprobe BCM terminal 1C11 (gray/white wire) with a test lamp to ground.
   e. If lamp does not illuminate, on 1988-89 models, check gray/white wire (circuit 397) for open. On 1990 models, check gray wire (circuit 397) for open.
   f. If lamp illuminates, check contact terminal 1C11 and, if terminal is satisfactory, replace BCM.
3. If BI75 display reads Hi with cruise switch off, proceed as follows:
   a. Disconnect multi-function lever. If display reads Lo, replace multi-function lever.
   b. If display reads Hi, check gray wire (circuit 397) or, on 1990 models, check brown wire (circuit 86) for short to battery and, if wire is satisfactory, replace BCM.
4. If BCM BI75 displays Lo with cruise switch off and Hi with cruise switch on, turn ignition switch to Run position, place cruise control switch in On position, select BCM input BI71 and operate brake pedal.
5. If BI71 displays Lo with cruise switch in On position and brake pedal released, proceed as follows:
   a. Connect test lamp between terminal A (gray/white wire) of connector C2 of brake switch and ground. If lamp illuminates proceed to step c.
   b. If lamp does not illuminate, backprobe terminal B (gray wire) of multi-function lever. If lamp illuminates, check gray and gray/white wires (circuit 397) for an open. If lamp does not illuminate, repeat test.
   c. If lamp illuminated in step a, on 1988-89 models, connect jumper wire between terminals A (gray/white wire) and B (brown wire) of brake switch. On 1990 models, connect jumper wire between terminals A (gray wire) and B (brown wire) of brake switch. On all models, if display reads Hi, check brake switch adjustment and, if adjustment is correct, replace brake switch.

d. If display reads Lo, backprobe BCM terminal 1C1 (brown wire) with a test lamp to ground. If lamp does not illuminate, check brown wire (circuit 86) for an open. If lamp illuminates, check BCM terminal contact 1C1 and, if terminal is satisfactory, replace BCM.
6. If BI71 displays Hi with cruise switch in On position and brake pedal depressed, disconnect brake switch.
7. If display reads Lo, adjust or replace brake switch.
8. If display reads Hi, check brown wire (circuit 86) for short to battery and, if short is not found, replace BCM.
9. If BCM BI71 display reads Lo with cruise switch on and brake pedal depressed, and reads Hi with cruise switch on and brake pedal released, turn ignition switch to Run position, place cruise switch in On position, select BCM input BI76 and operate set switch.
10. If B176 display reads Lo with cruise switch on and set switch depressed, proceed as follows:
    a. Check fuse No. 18
    b. Disconnect multi-function lever connector and, using test lamp, check for voltage at terminal A (pink/white wire). If there is no voltage, check pink/white wire (circuit 350).
    c. Connect jumper wire between terminals A (pink/white wire) and D (dark blue wire) of multi-function lever. If display reads Hi, replace multi-function lever.
    d. If display reads Lo, reconnect multi-function lever connector and, with cruise switch on and set switch depressed, connect test lamp to ground and backprobe BCM connector 1C4 (dark blue wire). If lamp does not illuminate, repair dark blue wire (circuit 84). If lamp illuminates, check BCM terminal contact 1C4 and, if contact is satisfactory, replace BCM.
11. If B176 display reads Hi with cruise switch on and set switch released, disconnect multi-function switch connector.
12. If display reads Lo, replace multi-function lever.
13. If display reads Hi, check dark blue wire (circuit 84) for short to battery and, if short is not found, replace BCM.
14. If BCM BI76 display reads Lo with cruise switch on and set switch released and reads Hi with cruise switch on and set switch depressed, turn ignition switch to Run position, select BCM input BI77 and operate cruise switch.
15. If BI77 display reads Lo with cruise switch on and resume switch depressed, proceed as follows:
    a. Check fuse No. 18.
    b. Disconnect multi-function lever connector and, using test lamp, check for voltage at terminal A (pink/white wire). If there is no voltage check pink/white wire (circuit 350).
    c. Connect jumper wire between ter-

minals A (pink/white wire) and C (gray/black wire) of multi-function lever. If display reads Hi, replace multi-function lever.
    d. If display reads Lo, reconnect multi-function lever connector and, with cruise switch on and resume switch depressed, connect test lamp to ground and backprobe BCM connector 1C14 (gray/black wire). If lamp does not illuminate, repair gray/black wire (circuit 87). If lamp illuminates, replace BCM.
16. **On 1988-89 models,** if B177 display reads Hi with cruise switch on and resume switch released, disconnect multi-function lever connector.
17. If display reads Lo, replace multi-function lever.
18. If display reads Hi, check gray/black wire (circuit 87) for short to battery and, if wire is satisfactory, replace BCM.
19. **On 1990 models,** if display reads Hi, with cruise switch on, refer to test B667, **Fig. 13,** for procedure.
20. **On all models,** if BCM BI77 display reads Lo with cruise switch off, or with cruise switch on and resume switch released, and reads Hi with cruise switch on and resume switch depressed, enter BCM output BO01 and place cruise switch in On position. BCM BO01 display and vent valve solenoid should both cycle. (a clicking should be heard as relay cycles).
21. If vent valve does not cycle (no clicking is heard) refer to code B672, **Fig. 15.**
22. If vent valve cycles (clicking is heard) enter BCM output BO02 and place cruise switch in On position. BCM BO02 and vacuum valve solenoid should both cycle. (Clicking noise should be heard as relay cycles).
23. If vacuum valve solenoid does not cycle (clicking noise is not heard) refer to code B673, **Fig. 16.**
24. If vacuum valve solenoid cycles (clicking noise is heard) start engine and run for 2 minutes, turn engine off, turn ignition switch to Run position and select BCM override BS05.
25. With override cycling from 0 to 99 and back to 0, cruise control servo should pull fully in and then release. If so, replace BCM.
26. If cruise control servo does not pull fully in and then release, check vacuum source and hoses for leaks, kinks and/or restrictions and check cruise control servo for mechanical binding.
27. If vacuum and mechanism are satisfactory, replace cruise control servo.

Reatta & Riviera

When performing the following tests, refer to applicable wiring diagrams and connector pin locations, **Figs. 1 through 8.**

1. Turn ignition switch to Run position, enter BCM diagnostics, select BCM input test BI75 and operate cruise switch.
2. If BI75 displays Hi with cruise switch off, proceed as follows:
   a. Disconnect multi-function lever harness electrical connector.

b. If display reads Lo, replace multi-function lever.

c. If display reads Hi, reconnect multi-function lever assembly, and backprobe BCM terminal 1C11 (gray/white wire) to ground with voltmeter.

d. If battery voltage is present, on 1988—89 models, check gray/white wire (circuit 397) for short to battery. On 1990 models, check gray wire (circuit 397) or brown wire (circuit 86) for short to battery.

e. **On all models**, if battery voltage is not available, on 1988-89 models, check BCM terminal 1C11 (gray/white wire) for a good and clean connection and, on 1990 models, check BCM terminal 1C11 (gray wire) for a good and clean connection then, on all models, if terminal is satisfactory, replace BCM.

3. If BI75 displays Lo with cruise switch on, proceed as follows:

a. Check fuse No. 8.

b. If fuse is not blown, proceed to step h.

c. If fuse is blown, place cruise switch in Off position and replace fuse No. 8.

d. If fuse blows, check pink/white wire (circuit 350) for short to ground.

e. If fuse does not blow, hold brake pedal in depressed position and place cruise switch in On position.

f. If fuse blows, check gray/white wire (circuit 397) for short to ground.

g. If fuse does not blow, proceed to step 4.

h. If fuse did not blow in step b, disconnect multi-function lever assembly and connect a test lamp between terminal BC11 (pink/white wire) and ground.

i. If lamp does not illuminate, check pink/white wire (circuit 350) for an open.

j. If lamp illuminates, on 1988-89 models, connect fused jumper between terminals BC11 (pink/white wire) and BC10 (gray/white wire) of multi-function lever assembly. On 1990 models, connect fused jumper between terminals A (pink/white wire) and B (gray wire) of multi-function lever assembly.

k. **On all models**, if display reads Hi, replace multi-function lever assembly.

l. If display reads Lo, reconnect multi-function lever assembly, place cruise switch in On position and backprobe BCM terminal 1C11 (gray/white wire) to ground with a voltmeter.

m. If battery voltage is not available, on 1988-89 models, check gray/white wire (circuit 397) for an open. On 1990 models, check gray wire (circuit 397) for an open.

n. O all models, if battery voltage is available, check BCM terminal 1C11 (gray/white wire) for good terminal contact and, if contact is

good, replace BCM.

4. If BCM display reads Hi with cruise switch on and Lo with cruise switch off, place ignition switch in Run position, place cruise switch in On position, enter BCM diagnostics, select BCM input test BI71 and operate brake pedal.

5. If BI71 displays Hi with brake pedal depressed, proceed as follows:

a. Remove brake switch connector C2.

b. If display reads Lo, check brake switch adjustment and, if adjustment is satisfactory, replace brake switch.

c. If display reads Hi, disconnect BCM and connect voltmeter between BCM terminal 1C1 (brown wire) and ground.

d. If battery voltage is available, check brown wire (circuit 86) for short to battery.

e. If battery voltage is not available, check BCM terminal 1C1 (brown wire) for a good clean connection and, if connection is good, replace BCM.

6. **On 1988-89 models**, if BI71 displays Lo with brake pedal released, proceed as follows:

a. Check fuse No. 8.

b. If fuse is blown, disconnect BCM and replace fuse No. 8.

c. If fuse does not blow, check BCM terminal 1C1 (brown wire) for a good and clean connection and, if connection is good, replace BCM.

d. If fuse blows disconnect brake switch connector C2, replace fuse No. 8 and connect test lamp between terminals A (gray/white wire) and B (brown wire).

e. If lamp does not illuminate, replace brake switch.

f. If lamp illuminates, check brown wire (circuit 86) for a short to ground.

g. If fuse is not blown in step a, remove brake switch connector C2 and connect test lamp between terminal A (gray/white wire) and ground.

h. If lamp does not illuminate, check gray/white wire (circuit 397) between splice S233 and brake switch for open.

i. If lamp illuminates, connect terminals A (gray/white wire) and B (brown wire) of brake switch connector with a fused jumper.

j. If display reads Hi, replace brake switch.

k. If display reads Lo, reconnect brake switch connector and backprobe BCM terminal 1C1 (brown wire) to ground with a voltmeter.

l. If battery voltage is available, check brown wire (circuit 86) for an open.

m. If battery voltage is available, check BCM terminal 1C1 (brown wire) for good terminal contact and, if contact is good, replace BCM.

7. **On 1990 models,** if B171 displays Lo with cruise switch on and brake released, proceed as follows:

a. Connect a fused jumper wire between terminal A (gray wire) and terminal B (brown wire) of brake switch connector.

b. If display reads Hi, ensure proper brake switch adjustment. I adjustment is good, replace brake switch.

c. If display reads Lo, with jumper wire still connected, back probe BCM terminal 1C1.

d. If test lamp does not light, check brown wire (circuit 86) for open.

e. If test lamp lights, check BCM terminal contact. If terminal contact is good, replace BCM.

8. **On all models,** if BCM display reads Lo with brake pedal depressed and Hi with brake pedal released, turn ignition switch to Run position, place cruise switch in On position, enter BCM diagnostics, select BCM input test BI76 and operate set/coast switch.

9. If BI76 displays Hi with set/coast switch released refer to code B667, **Fig. 13.**

10. **On 1988-89 Riviera,** if BI76 displays Lo with set/coast switch depressed, proceed as follows. **If cruise On indicator does not illuminate, repeat test.**

a. Disconnect cruise switch assembly and connect test lamp between gray/white wire terminal connector and ground.

b. If lamp does not illuminate, check gray/white wire (circuit 397) between splice S233 and cruise switch assembly.

c. If lamp illuminates, connect test lamp between gray/white wire terminal and dark blue wire terminal of cruise switch assembly.

d. If display reads Hi, replace cruise switch assembly.

e. If display reads LO, reconnect cruise switch assembly and backprobe BCM terminal 1C4 (dark blue wire) to ground with a test lamp while depressing set/coast switch.

f. If lamp does not illuminate, check dark blue wire (circuit 84).

g. If lamp illuminates, check BCM terminal 1C4 (dark blue wire) for good terminal contact and, if contact is good, replace BCM.

11. **On 1988-89 Reatta,** if BI76 displays Lo with set/coast switch depressed, perform steps 4 through 6, then proceed as follows:

a. Disconnect C217 and connect test lamp between terminal W (brown wire) and terminal Z (dark blue wire).

b. If lamp does not illuminate, check brown wire (circuit 86) between splice S271 and connector C217.

c. If lamp illuminates, connect test lamp between terminal W (brown wire) and terminal Z (dark blue wire).

d. If display reads Hi, replace cruise switch assembly.

e. If display reads Lo, reconnect connector C217 and backprobe BCM terminal 1C4 (dark blue wire) with test lamp while depressing set/coast switch.

f. If lamp does not illuminate, check dark blue wire (circuit 84).

g. If lamp illuminates, check BCM terminal 1C4 (dark blue wire) for good terminal contact and, if contact is good, replace BCM.

12. **On 1990 Reatta and Riviera**, if B176 displays Lo with cruise switch on and set switch depressed, proceed as follows:

a. Connect fused jumper wire between terminal A (pink/white wire) and terminal D (dark blue wire) at multi-function lever connector.

b. If display reads Hi, replace multi-function lever if terminal contact is good.

c. If display reads Lo, reconnect multi-function lever connector, then with cruise switch on and set switch depressed, connect test lamp to ground and backprobe BCM terminal 1C4.

d. If test lamp does not light, check dark blue wire (circuit 84) for open.

e. If test lamp lights, check BCM terminal connector 1C4, if contact is good, replace BCM.

13. **On all models**, if BCM display reads HI with set/coast switch depressed and Lo with set/coast switch released, turn ignition switch to Run position, place cruise switch in On position, enter BCM diagnostics, select BCM input test BI77 and operate resume/accel switch.

14. If BI77 displays Hi with resume/accel switch released, refer to code B667, **Fig. 13.**

15. **On 1988-89 Riviera**, if BI77 displays Lo with resume/accel switch depressed, proceed as follows. **If cruise On indicator does not illuminate, repeat test.**

a. Disconnect cruise switch assembly and connect test lamp between gray/white wire terminal connector and ground.

b. If lamp does not illuminate, check gray/white wire (circuit 397) between splice S233 and cruise switch assembly.

c. If lamp illuminates, connect test lamp between gray/white and gray/black wire terminals of cruise switch assembly.

d. If display reads Hi, replace cruise switch assembly.

e. If display reads Lo, reconnect cruise switch assembly and backprobe BCM terminal 1C14 (gray/black wire) to ground with a test lamp while depressing resume/accel switch.

f. If lamp does not illuminate, check gray/black wire (circuit 87).

g. If lamp illuminates, check BCM terminal 1C14 (gray/black wire) for good terminal contact and, if contact is good, replace BCM.

16. **On 1988-89 Reatta**, if BI77 displays Lo with resume/accel switch depressed, proceed as follows. **Before proceeding, perform steps 4 through 6.**

a. Disconnect connector C217 and connect a test lamp between terminal W (brown wire) and ground.

b. If lamp does not illuminate, check brown wire (circuit 86) between splice S271 and connector C217.

c. If lamp illuminates, connect test lamp between terminals W (brown wire) and Y (gray/black wire).

d. If display reads Hi, replace cruise switch assembly.

e. If display reads Lo, reconnect connector C217 and backprobe BCM terminal 1C14 (gray/black wire) to ground while depressing resume/accel switch.

f. If lamp does not illuminate, check gray/black wire (circuit 87).

g. If lamp illuminates, check BCM terminal 1C14 (gray/black wire) for good terminal contact and, if contact is good, replace BCM.

17. **On 1990 models**, if B177 displays Lo with cruise switch on and resume switch depressed, proceed as follows:

a. Ensure steps 1 through 4 of this procedure are verified.

b. Connect fused jumper wire between multi-function lever connector terminals A and C.

c. If display reads Hi, replace multi-function lever.

d. If display reads Lo, reconnect multi-function lever, with cruise switch on and resume switch depressed, connect test lamp to ground and backprobe BCM connector 1C14.

e. If test lamp does not light, check gray/black wire (circuit 87) for open.

f. If test lamp lights, check BCM connector 1C14. If contact is good, replace BCM.

18. **On all models**, if BCM displays Hi with resume/accel switch depressed and Lo with resume/accel press released, enter BCM diagnostics and select BCM output test BO01.

19. With ignition switch in Run position and cruise switch in On position, BCM display and vent valve solenoid should both cycle. (A clicking noise should be heard at vent valve solenoid).

20. If vent valve solenoid does not cycle (clicking noise is not heard) refer to code B672, **Fig. 15.**

21. If vent valve solenoid cycles (clicking noise is heard) enter BCM diagnostics and select BCM output test BO02.

22. With ignition switch in Run position and cruise switch in On position, BCM display and vacuum valve solenoid should both cycle.

23. If vacuum valve solenoid does not cycle, refer to code B673.

24. If vacuum valve cycles, start engine and run for 2 minutes, turn engine off, turn ignition switch to Run position, enter BCM diagnostics and select BCM override test BS05.

25. Vary override cycle from 0 to 99 and back to 0.

26. If cruise control servo pulls fully in and then releases, replace BCM.

27. If cruise control servo does not pull all the way in and then release, check vacuum source and hoses for leaks, kinks or restrictions and check cruise control servo for mechanical binding. If vacuum source and hoses are satisfactory and there is no binding, replace cruise control servo.

CLEARING CODES

1. Enter diagnostic service mode as outlined previously.

2. **On models less CRT**, follow steps 1A and 1B under "Diagnostic Test Procedures." On models with CRT, follow steps 2A and 2B under "Diagnostic Test Procedures."

3. **On models less CRT**, on 1988-89 models, depress Lo fan button (secondary display) until "clear codes" is displayed, then depress Hi fan button (secondary display). On 1990 models, depress fan down until "clear codes" is displayed, then depress fan up button. On all models, this will start the erasing process.

4. **On models with CRT**, depress No button on secondary display, until "clear codes" is displayed, then depress Yes button on secondary display. This will start the erasing process.

5. **On all models**, the "clear codes" message will will end after 3 seconds, indicating that all stored trouble codes have been erased from that system's memory. After 3 seconds the display will automatically return to the next available test type for the selected system.

EXITING DIAGNOSTIC SERVICE MODE

Toronado & Trofeo Less CRT

To exit the diagnostic service mode, depress Bi-Level button on ECC or turn ignition switch off.

Toronado & Trofeo w/CRT

To exit the diagnostic service mode, depress RTN button on the CRT or turn ignition switch off.

Reatta & Riviera

To exit the diagnostic service mode, on 1988-89 models, depress Level button until the Service Mode page disappears or turn ignition switch off. On 1990 models, depress Bi-Level button until the Service Mode page disappears or turn ignition switch off.

COMPONENT TESTING

Before performing any diagnosis or repair procedures, temporarily disable the Supplemental Inflatable Restraint (SIR) system. Failure to do so may result in possible air bag deployment or personal injury. Disable SIR system as follows:

1. Turn ignition switch to Off position.
2. Remove SIR fuse.
3. Disconnect SIR electrical harness connector, at base of steering column.
4. Reverse procedure to reconnect, en-

sure "Inflatable Restraint" indicator flashes 7 to 9 times to indicate proper SIR operation.

ELECTRIC BRAKE RELEASE SWITCH

1. Turn ignition switch to On position.
2. Connect test light to ground.
3. Probe brown wire at brake switch connector. Lamp should illuminate.
4. Check switch adjustment, with probe still at brown wire, depressing brake pedal 1/8-1/2 inch. Light should go out.
5. If light did not illuminate in step 3, probe wire in adjacent connector cavity. If lamp illuminates, adjust or replace switch as necessary. If light does not illuminate, check wiring to switch.

VACUUM BRAKE RELEASE SWITCH

An inoperative valve must be replaced. Ensure vacuum hose to switch is firmly connected and that it is not cracked or deteriorated. Vacuum source and hoses should be checked for improper routing, leaks, kinks or restrictions.

COMPONENT REPLACEMENT

SERVO UNIT

1. Disconnect electrical connector and vacuum hoses.
2. Disconnect throttle actuating chain, cable or rod from servo unit.
3. Remove 3 screws retaining servo unit and servo unit solenoid valve assembly to mounting bracket and remove servo.
4. Reverse procedure to install. **Torque** servo unit to mounting bracket attaching screws to 10-15 inch lbs.

ENGAGEMENT SWITCH

The cruise control engagement switch is part of the multi-function lever, which must be replaced as an assembly. Refer to individual car chapter.

SPEED CONTROLS
ADJUST

CABLE ADJUSTMENT

Adjust cruise control cable to minimum slack as follows:
1. Ensure throttle lever is in idle position with engine off.
2. Pull servo assembly end of cable toward servo blade.
3. If hole in servo blade is aligned with cable pin, install pin in that hole and install retainer.
4. If hole does not align with pin, install pin in next hole away from servo assembly. **Do not stretch cable.**

ELECTRIC BRAKE RELEASE SWITCH & VACUUM RELEASE VALVE ADJUSTMENT

The switch assembly and valve assembly cannot be adjusted until brake booster push rod is assembled to brake pedal assembly. Adjustment is as follows:
1. Depress brake pedal and switch assembly and valve assembly into their proper retaining clips until fully seated.
2. **On vehicles equipped with anti-lock brakes,** release brake pedal and allow to come to rest.
3. **On vehicles less ABS brakes,** slowly pull pedal back to its fully retracted position. The switch assembly and valve assembly will move within their retainers to their adjusted position.
4. **On all models,** the following brake pedal travel distances may be used to check for a properly adjusted cruise control and stop lamp switch assembly and vacuum release valve assembly.
   a. Cruise control switch contacts must open at 1/8-1/2 inch pedal travel, measured at centerline of brake pedal pad. **Nominal actuation of stop lamp contacts is 3/16 inch after cruise control contacts open.**
   b. Vacuum release valve assembly must open at 1 1/16-1 5/16 inches pedal travel, measured at centerline of brake pedal pad.

Type 4

NOTE: Wire Code Identification and Symbol Identification located in the front of this manual can be used as an aid when using wiring circuits found in this section.

INDEX

DESCRIPTION

This system is basically the same as Type 2, except on this type the function of the cruise control module is performed by the ECM.

ROAD TEST

1. Drive vehicle at speed greater than 25 mph, place cruise switch in On position and depress set button at end of multi-function lever. Cruise indicator should illuminate and vehicle should maintain speed.
2. With foot off accelerator, hold set button in. Vehicle should coast at a slower speed.
3. Release set button. If new speed is greater than 25 mph, cruise control should engage and hold slower speed.
4. Slide cruise switch to Resume/Accel position and hold it there. Vehicle should accelerate.
5. Release cruise switch back to On position. Vehicle should hold new, faster speed.
6. Tap brake pedal. Vehicle should coast slower and cruise indicator should go out.
7. Slide cruise control switch momentarily to Resume/Accel position. Cruise indicator should illuminate and vehicle should accelerate to former set speed.
8. While cruising, accelerate, then remove foot from accelerator pedal. Vehicle should coast back to set speed.
9. While cruising, tap cruise switch to Resume/Accel position. Vehicle speed should decrease 1 mph for each tap up to ten.

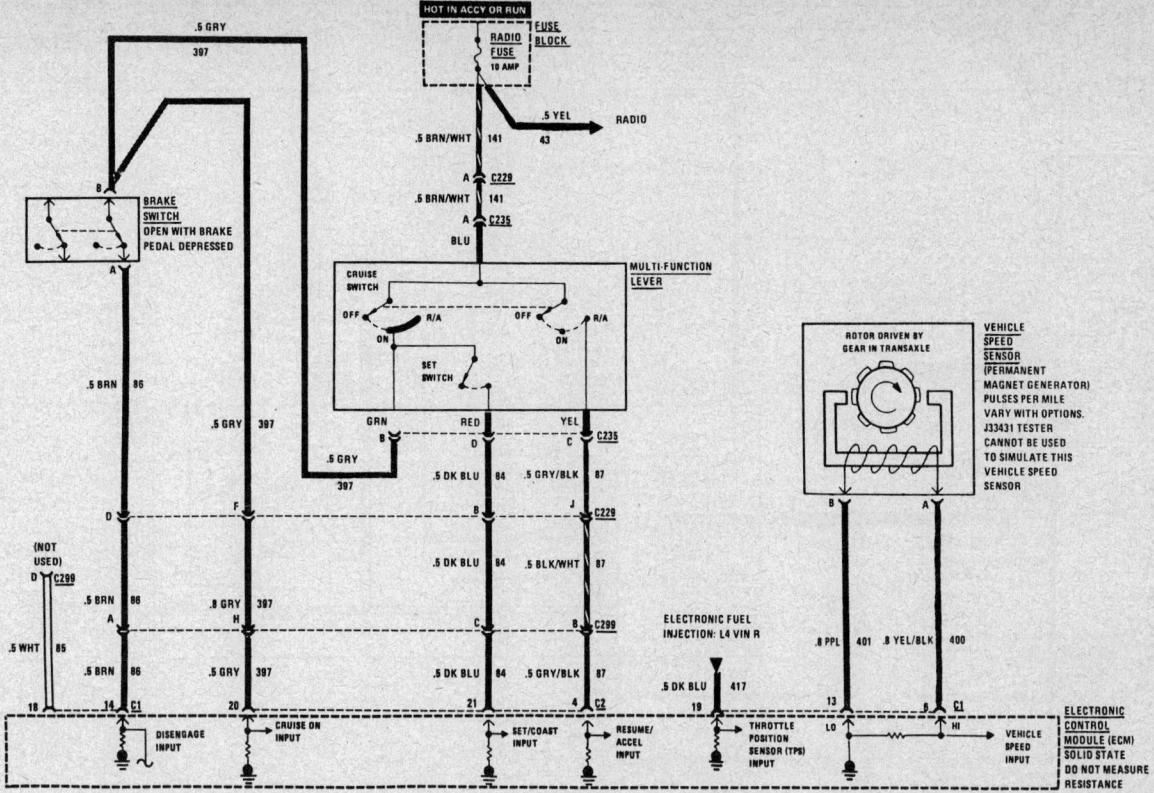

Fig. 1   Typical cruise control wiring diagram (Part 1 of 2). Celebrity

10. While cruising, tap set button. Vehicle speed should decrease 1 mph for each tap down to 25 mph.
11. Slide cruise control switch to Off position. Cruise control should turn off and cruise indicator should go out.

SERVICE PRECAUTIONS

Before performing any diagnosis or repair procedures, temporarily disable the Supplemental Inflatable Restraint (SIR) system. Failure to do so may result in possible air bag deployment or personal injury. Disable SIR system as follows:
1. Turn ignition switch to Off position.
2. Remove SIR fuse.
3. Disconnect SIR electrical harness connector, at base of steering column.
4. Reverse procedure to reconnect, ensure "Inflatable Restraint" indicator flashes 7 to 9 times to indicate proper SIR operation.

On vehicles equipped with ABS brake system, the hydraulic accumulator, when fully charged contains brake fluid at high pressure. Before disconnecting any lines, hoses or fittings, ensure accumulator is full depressurized. Failure to do so may result in personal injury.

To depressurize the hydraulic accumulator, turn the ignition to the Off position or disconnect negative battery cable, pump brake pedal a minimum of 40 times at approximately 50 lbs. of force. A noticeable change in pedal feel will occur when accumulator is fully discharged.

DIAGNOSIS & TESTING

6000, CELEBRITY & 1988 CENTURY & SUNBIRD

If cruise control does not work properly, refer to "Cruise System Test." If cruise indicator does not work properly, but all other cruise functions work properly, refer to "Cruise Indicator Test."

When performing the following tests, refer to wiring diagrams and connector pin locations, **Figs. 1 through 4.**.

Cruise System Test

1. Turn ignition switch to Run position, place cruise switch in On position and connect test lamp to connector C235 **Fig. 4,** as follows:
   a. Connect between terminal A (brown/white wire) and ground. If lamp does not illuminate On 6000, Celebrity or Century check Gages or Radio fuse, pink/black wire (circuit 39), yellow wire (circuit 43, 6000 and 1990 Celebrity) and brown/white wire (circuit 141) for an open. If lamp does not illuminate on Sunbird, check radio fuse and brown/white wire (circuit 141) for an open.
   b. Connect between terminal B (gray wire) and ground. If lamp does not illuminate, replace multi-function lever.
   c. Place cruise switch in Resume/Accel position.
   d. Connect between terminal B (gray wire) and ground. If lamp does not illuminate, replace multi-function lever.
   e. **On 1988 6000 or Celebrity models,** connect between terminal D (gray/black wire) and ground. On all other models, connect between terminal C (gray/black wire) and ground. On all models, if lamp does not illuminate, replace multi-function lever.
   f. Release cruise switch to On position.
   g. **On 1988 6000 or Celebrity models,** connect between terminal D (gray/black wire) and ground. On all other models, connect between terminal C (gray/black wire) and ground. On all models, if lamp illuminates, replace multi-function lever.
   h. **On 1988 6000 or Celebrity models,** connect between terminal C (dark blue wire) and ground. On all other models, connect between terminal D (dark blue wire) and ground. On all models, if lamp illuminates, replace multi-function lever.
   i. Press set switch and on 1988 6000 or Celebrity models, connect between terminal C (dark blue wire) and ground. On all other models, connect between terminal D (dark blue wire) and ground. On all models, if lamp does not illuminate, replace multi-function lever.
2. If lamp illuminated in steps a, b, d, e, and i, and did not illuminate in steps g

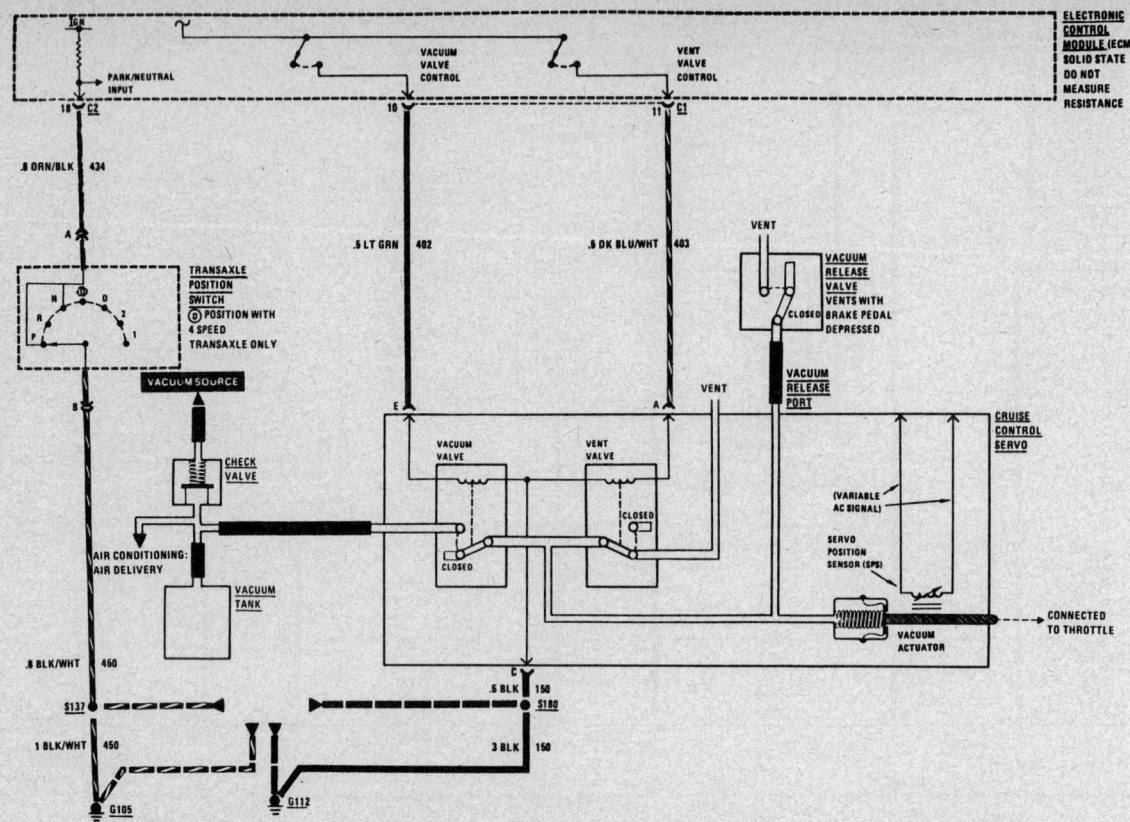

Fig. 1   Typical cruise control wiring diagram (Part 2 of 2). Celebrity

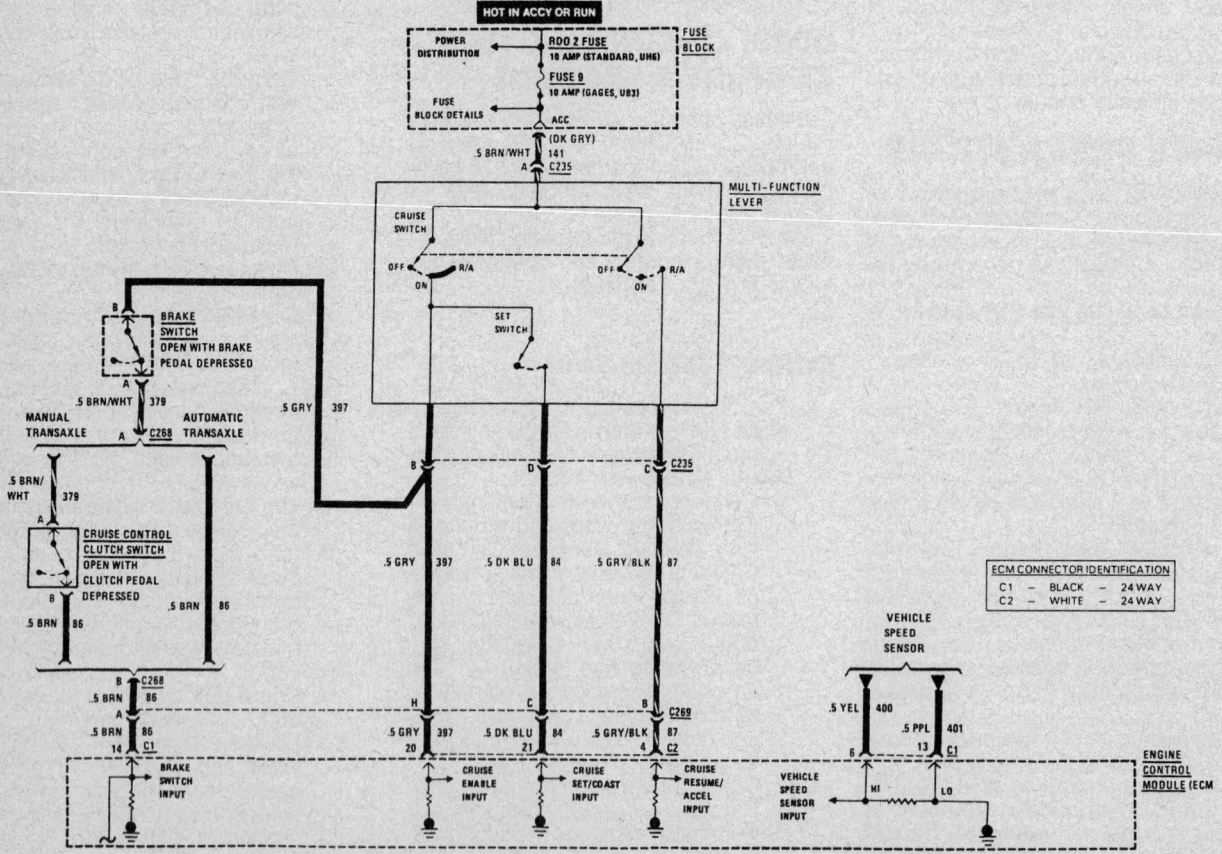

Fig. 2   Typical cruise control wiring diagram (Part 1 of 2). Cavalier

TYPE 4

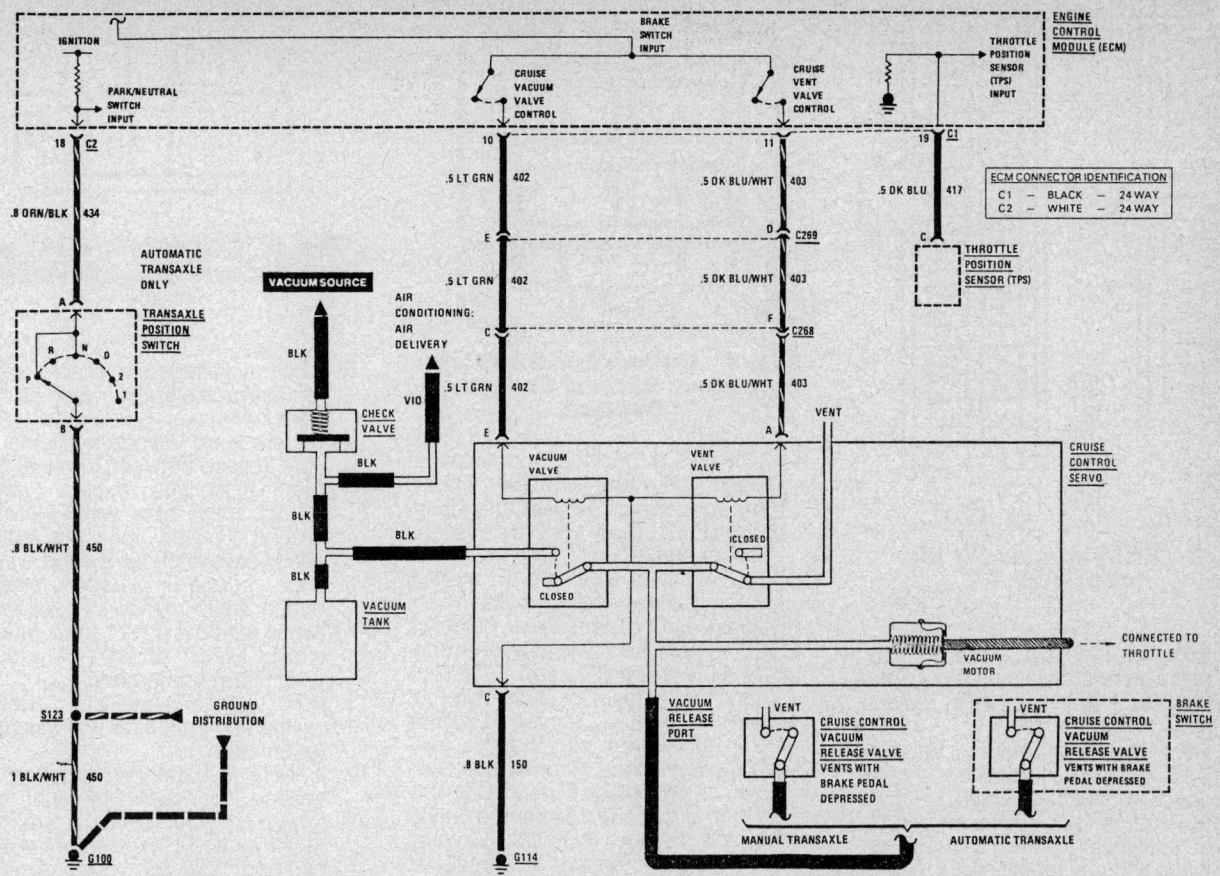

Fig. 2 Typical cruise control wiring diagram (Part 2 of 2). Cavalier

and h, turn off ignition, disconnect ECM connectors C1 and C2 **Fig. 3**, turn ignition switch to Run position, place cruise control switch in On position and measure voltage between terminals as follows:

a. Measure between terminal C2/20 (gray wire) and ground. If battery voltage is not available, check gray wire (circuit 397) for an open.

b. Measure between terminal C1/14 (brown wire, 6000, Celebrity and Century; brown/white wire, Sunbird) and ground. If battery voltage is not available on 6000, Celebrity or Century, check brake switch, adjusting as necessary, and check brown wire (circuit 86) for an open. If battery voltage is not available on Sunbird, check brake and clutch switches, adjusting as necessary and check gray wire (circuit 397) brown wire (circuit 86) and brown/white wire (circuit 986) for an open.

c. Press set switch and measure between terminal C2/21 (dark blue wire) and ground. If battery voltage is not available, check dark blue wire, circuit 84) for an open.

d. Release set switch, place cruise switch in Resume/Accel position and measure between terminal C2/4 (gray/black wire) and ground. If battery voltage is not available, check gray black wire

(circuit 87) for an open.

e. **On 1988 Century models,** release cruise switch to On position, turn drive wheels by hand and measure between terminals C2/20 (gray wire) and C2/3 (red wire). If voltage reading does not pulse between approximately battery voltage and less than 7 volts, check red wire (circuit 381) and brown wire (circuit 437) and, if wires are satisfactory, check vehicle speed sensor.

3. If battery voltage is available in steps a through d, and voltage pulses approximately battery voltage and less than 7 volts in step e, disconnect ECM connectors C1 and C2 **Fig. 3,** and measure resistance as follows:

a. Measure between terminal C1/10 and ground. If resistance is not 30-55 ohms, check cruise control servo, light green wire (circuit 402) and black wire (circuit 150).

b. Measure between terminal C1/11 (dark blue/white wire) and ground. If resistance is not 30-55 ohms, check cruise control servo and dark blue/white wire (circuit 403).

c. **On vehicles with automatic transaxle,** place gearshift in Neutral and measure between terminal C2/18 (orange/black wire, 6000, Celebrity and Century; white wire, Sunbird) and ground. If resistance is not 0 ohms on 6000, Celebrity or

Century, check automatic transaxle selector switch and orange/black wire (circuit 434) for an open. If resistance is not 0 ohms on Sunbird, check transaxle mounted neutral start switch and white wire (circuit 434) for an open.

d. Place gearshift in Drive and measure between terminal C2/18 (orange/black wire, 6000, Celebrity and Century; white wire, Sunbird) and ground. If reading is not infinity on 6000, Celebrity or Century, check automatic transaxle selector switch and orange/black wire (circuit 434) for a short to ground. If reading is not infinity on Sunbird, check transaxle mounted neutral start switch and white wire (circuit 434) for a short to ground.

4. If resistance was 30-55 ohms in steps a and b, 0 ohms in step c and infinite ohms in step d, disconnect cruise control servo, jumper terminal C of servo to ground, jumper terminal A of servo to battery, run engine for 1 minute then turn off and proceed as follows:

a. Connect fused jumper between terminal E of cruise control servo and ground. If vacuum does not pull servo all the way in, check for blocked or leaking vacuum source and, if vacuum source is satisfactory, plug vacuum release port and repeat step 4. If vacuum now pulls

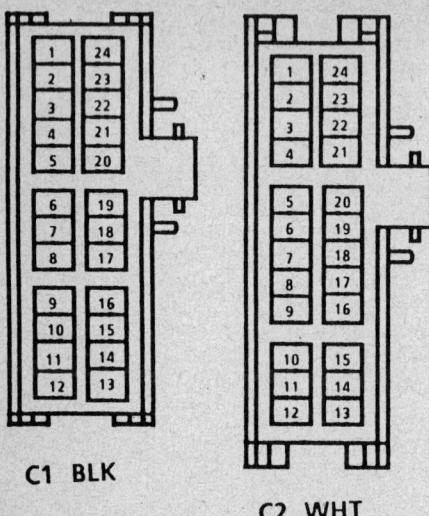

C1 BLK

C2 WHT

Fig. 3   ECM connector pin locations

Fig. 4   Connector C235 pin locations. Except Beretta & Corsica

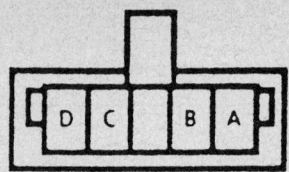

Fig. 5   Connector C235 pin locations. Beretta & Corsica

servo all the way in, repair or replace vacuum release valve or the hose to it. If test still fails, replace cruise control servo.

b. Remove fused jumper. If vacuum does not hold servo all the way in, check for blocked or leaking vacuum source and, if vacuum source is satisfactory, plug vacuum release port and repeat step 4. If vacuum now holds servo all the way in, repair or replace vacuum release valve or the hose to it. If test still fails, replace cruise control servo.

c. If vacuum pulls servo all the way in in step a and holds servo all the way in in step b, replace ECM.

Cruise Indicator Test

1. Disconnect ECM connector C1 **Fig. 3**, turn ignition switch to Run position and connect fused jumper between terminal 18 (white wire) and ground.
2. If cruise indicator lights, replace ECM.
3. If cruise indicator does not light, check bulb and wiring.

BERETTA, CALAIS, CAVALIER, CIERA, CORSICA, FIERO, FIRENZA, GRAND AM, SKYHAWK & SKYLARK & 1989–90 CENTURY & SUNBIRD

1. With ignition off, disconnect ECM connectors C1 and C2, **Fig. 3**, then turn ignition switch to Run position, place cruise control in Off position and measure voltage between terminal C2/20 (gray wire, except Beretta and Corsica) or C1/20 (gray wire, Beretta and Corsica) and ground.
2. If battery voltage is available, replace multi-function lever.
3. If no voltage is available, place cruise

switch in On position and measure voltage between terminal C2/20 (gray wire, except Beretta and Corsica) or C1/20 (gray wire, Beretta and Corsica) and ground.

4. If no voltage is available on models except Beretta and Corsica, check Radio (Century, Ciera, Fiero, Skyhawk and Firenza) Rad (Cavalier and Sunbird) ECM 4 Cyl (Skylark) ECM Rlys (Grand Am) fuse or fuse No. 18 (Calais) check cruise switch, brown/white wire (circuit 141, Cavalier, Century, Ciera, Firenza and Skyhawk) or pink/black wire, (circuit 430, Skylark; circuit 439, Calais and Grand Am) and gray wire (circuit 397, except 1988-89 Ciera) or yellow wire (circuit 43, Fiero and 1988-89 Ciera) for an open. If no voltage is available on Beretta and Corsica, check brown/white wire (circuit 141) and gray wire (circuit 397) multi-function lever and cruise control switches for an open.

5. If battery voltage is available, measure voltage between terminal C1/14 (brown wire, except Fiero) or C2/14 (brown wire, Fiero) and ground.

6. If no voltage is available, on Beretta, Calais, Cavalier, Century, Ciera, Corsica, Firenza, Grand Am or Skyhawk, check brake switch, cruise control clutch switch (except Ciera) gray wire (circuit 986, except Beretta and Corsica) or tan wire (circuit 986, 1988-89 Beretta and Corsica) or dark green wire (circuit 986, 1990 Beretta and Corsica) and brown wires (circuits 86 and 986, Cavalier, Skyhawk and Sunbird) brown and brown/white wires (circuit 86, Calais and Grand Am; circuits 86 and 986, Firenza) or brown wires (circuit 86, Beretta, Century, Ciera and Corsica) for an open. If no voltage is available on Skylark, check cruise switch and gray/white and gray/red wires (circuit 87) for an open. If no voltage is available on Fiero, check brake switch, cruise control clutch switch, gray wire (circuit 397) and brown wire (circuit 86) or yellow wire (circuit 918) for an open.

7. If battery voltage is available, depress brake pedal while measuring voltage between terminal C1/14 (brown wire, except Fiero) or C2/14 (brown wire, Fiero) and ground.

8. If battery voltage is available, adjust or replace cruise brake switch as necessary.

9. If there is no voltage available, measure voltage between terminal C2/21 (dark blue wire, except Fiero) or C1/21 (dark blue wire, Fiero) and ground. If battery voltage is available, check set switch for a short.

10. If no voltage is available, press set button while measuring voltage between terminal C2/21 (dark blue wire, except Fiero) or C1/21 (dark blue wire, Fiero) and ground.

11. If no voltage is available, check set switch and dark blue wire (circuit 84) for an open.

12. If there is battery voltage, measure voltage between terminal C2/4 (gray/red wire, Skylark, Grand Am, Skyhawk and 1989 Century and Sunbird and 1988-89 Calais; gray/black wire, Beretta, Cavalier, Ciera, Corsica, Firenza and 1990 Calais, Century, and Sunbird) or C1/4 (black wire, Fiero) and ground.

13. If battery voltage is available, check cruise switch for short.

14. If no voltage is available, hold cruise switch in Resume/Accel position while measuring voltage between terminal C2/4 (gray/red wire, Grand Am, Skyhawk and Skylark 1989 Century and Sunbird and 1988-89 Calais; gray/black wire, Beretta, Cavalier, Ciera, Corsica and Firenza and 1990 Calais, Century and Sunbird) or C1/4 (black wire, Fiero) and ground.

15. If no voltage is available, check cruise switch and gray/red and gray/white wires (circuit 87, Grand Am, Skyhawk and Skylark and 1988-89 Calais) gray/white and gray/black wires (circuit 87, 1990 Calais) gray/black wires (circuit 87, Beretta, Cavalier, Century, Ciera, Corsica, Firenza and Sunbird) or gray/black and black wires (circuit 87, Fiero) for an open.

16. If battery voltage is available on vehicles with automatic transaxle, place shift lever in D position and measure continuity between terminal C2/18 (orange/black wire, except Fiero) or C1/18 (orange/black wire, Fiero) and ground.

17. If reading is infinite ohms, check transaxle position switch and orange/black wire (circuit 434) for a short to ground.

18. If reading is 0 ohms, or there was battery voltage available in step 14 on vehicle with manual transaxle, mea-

sure resistance between terminal C1/10 (light green wire, except Fiero) or C2/14 (light green wire, Fiero) and ground. Disconnect negative battery cable before measuring resistance on Ciera, Century, Skylark, Sunbird and 1989-90 Grand Am.

19. If resistance is less than 30 ohms, check for short to ground in light green wire (circuit 402) or in cruise control servo.

20. If resistance is greater than 55 ohms, check for open in cruise control servo, light green wire (circuit 402) or black wire (circuit 150).

21. If resistance is 30-55 ohms, measure resistance between terminal C1/11 (dark blue/white wire, except Fiero and Beretta and Corsica), (dark blue wire, Beretta and Corsica) or C2/11 (dark blue wire, Fiero) and ground.

22. If resistance is less than 30 ohms, check for short to ground in dark blue/white and, on Beretta, Corsica and Fiero dark blue wire (circuit 403) or in cruise control servo.

23. If resistance is greater than 55 ohms, check for open in cruise control servo or dark blue/white wire and, on Beretta, Corsica and Fiero, dark blue wire (circuit 403).

24. If resistance is 30-55 ohms, proceed as follows:
    a. Reconnect ECM and, on Century, Ciera, Skylark, Sunbird and 1989-90 Grand Am, the negative battery cable.
    b. Remove connector from cruise control servo.
    c. Jumper terminal C of cruise control servo to ground.
    d. Jumper terminal A of cruise control servo to battery.
    e. Run engine for 1 minute, then turn engine off.
    f. Jumper terminal E of servo to battery.

25. If vacuum does not pull servo in, proceed as follows:
    a. Check for blocked or leaking vacuum source, repairing as necessary.
    b. If vacuum source is satisfactory, remove jumper from terminal E of servo and proceed to step 27.

26. If vacuum pulls servo all the way in, proceed as follows:
    a. Remove jumper from terminal E of servo.
    b. If vacuum holds servo all the way in, replace ECM.
    c. If vacuum does not hold servo all the way in, proceed to step 27.

27. Plug vacuum release port, run engine for 1 minute, turn engine off and jumper terminal E of servo to battery.

28. If vacuum does not pull servo in, replace cruise control servo.

29. If vacuum pulls servo all the way in, remove jumper from terminal E of servo.

30. If vacuum does not hold servo all the

way in, replace cruise control servo.

31. If vacuum holds servo all the way in, repair or replace cruise control vacuum release valve or the hose to it.

COMPONENT TESTING

ELECTRIC BRAKE RELEASE SWITCH

Refer to "Diagnosis and Testing" for electric brake release switch testing procedure.

VACUUM BRAKE RELEASE SWITCH

An inoperative valve must be replaced. Ensure vacuum hose to switch is firmly connected and that it is not cracked or deteriorated. Vacuum source and hoses should be checked for improper routing, leaks, kinks or restrictions.

COMPONENT REPLACEMENT

Before performing any diagnosis or repair procedures, temporarily disable the Supplemental Inflatable Restraint (SIR) system. Failure to do so may result in possible air bag deployment or personal injury. Disable SIR system as follows:
1. Turn ignition switch to OFF position.
2. Remove SIR fuse.
3. Disconnect SIR electrical harness connector, at base of steering column.
4. Reverse procedure to reconnect, ensure "Inflatable Restraint" indicator flashes 7 to 9 times to indicate proper SIR operation.

SERVO UNIT

1. Disconnect servo unit electrical connector and vacuum hoses.
2. Disconnect throttle actuating chain, cable or rod from servo unit.
3. Remove servo unit and servo unit solenoid valve assembly to mounting bracket attaching screws, then remove servo unit.

ENGAGEMENT SWITCH

The cruise control engagement switch is part of the multi-function lever, which must be replaced as an assembly. Refer to individual car chapter.

SPEED CONTROLS ADJUST

MODELS w/TBI

Adjust cable as follows:
1. Assemble cable in cable bracket and servo bracket.

2. Rotate TBI lever so its stud engages hole in cable end.
3. Assemble cable to TBI lever stud with retainer, then release TBI cable.
4. Pull servo end of cable toward servo without moving TBI lever.
5. If a hole in servo tab aligns with cable pin, connect pin to tab with retainer.
6. If a tab hole does not align with pin, move cable away from servo until next closest tab hole aligns with pin, then connect pin to tab with retainer. **Do not stretch cable to make a particular tab hole connect to pin.**

MODELS LESS TBI

Adjust cable as follows. Accelerator cable must be installed before cruise control cable.
1. With cruise cable attached at engine bracket and servo bracket, insert cable slug in cruise pulley slot.
2. Pull servo end of cable toward servo without moving idler pulley.
3. If one of six holes in servo assembly tab aligns with cable pin, connect pin to tab with retainer.
4. If a tab hole does not align with pin, move cable away from servo assembly until next closest tab hole aligns and connect pin to tab with retainer. **Do not stretch cable to make a particular hole connect to pin.**

VACUUM RELEASE VALVE

Switch assembly and valve assembly cannot be adjusted until brake booster push rod is assembled to brake pedal assembly. Adjustment is as follows:
1. Depress brake pedal and switch assembly and valve assembly into their proper retaining clips until fully seated.
2. **On vehicles equipped with anti-lock brakes,** release brake pedal and allow to come to rest.
3. **On models less ABS brakes,** slowly pull pedal back to its fully retracted position. The switch assembly and valve assembly will move within their retainers to their adjusted position.
4. The following brake pedal travel distances may be used to check for a properly adjusted cruise control and stop lamp switch assembly and vacuum release valve assembly.
    a. Cruise control switch contacts must open at $1/8$-$1/2$ inch pedal travel, measured at centerline of brake pedal pad. **Nominal actuation of stop lamp contacts is $3/16$ inch after cruise control contacts open.**
    b. Vacuum release valve assembly must open at $1\,1/16$-$1\,5/16$ inches pedal travel, measured at centerline of brake pedal pad.

NOTE: Wire Code Identification and Symbol Identification located in the front of this manual can be used as an aid when using wiring circuits found in this section.

INDEX

DESCRIPTION

This system automatically adjusts the opening of the engine throttle valve so that a selected vehicle speed can be maintained during favorable driving conditions. When system is engaged, the vehicle maintains a constant speed regardless of terrain.

OPERATION

SETTING DESIRED SPEED

Turn main switch to On position. The indicator lamp will illuminate. Depress accelerator pedal to obtain desired speed above 25 mph. Turn control switch downward toward Set (Coast), then release it. This will set the system at the speed the vehicle was moving at when the switch was released.

TEMPORARY ACCELERATION

Accelerate by depressing accelerator pedal. When accelerator pedal is released, the vehicle will automatically slow to the preset speed.

RESETTING AT A HIGHER SPEED

Turn control switch upward toward Resume (Accel). The vehicle speed will keep increasing until the control switch is released. Release control switch when desired speed is reached. **On vehicles with automatic transmission, overdrive is released during acceleration and is restored when the control switch is released.**

RESETTING AT LOWER SPEED

Turn control switch downward toward Set (Coast). The vehicle speed will continue decreasing until control switch is released. Release control switch at desired speed.

CANCELLING THE PRESET SPEED

Once the preset speed has been set, it may be cancelled by doing any of the following:
1. Depress brake pedal.
2. Depress clutch pedal (vehicles with manual transmission).
3. Place shift lever at Neutral position (vehicles with automatic transmission).
4. Slightly pull the parking brake lever.
5. Turn main switch to Off position.

RESUMING THE PRESET SPEED

Automatic cruising is only temporarily cancelled by steps 1 through 4 under Cancelling The Preset Speed if vehicle has not decelerated to below 25 mph. The preset speed will be resumed when the control switch is turned upward toward Resume (Accel).

TROUBLESHOOTING

1. Refer to chart, **Figs. 1 and 2.**
2. If instructed to read a type A code on 1988 models with 4A-GE engine, refer to **Fig. 3** and proceed as follows:
   a. Turn ignition switch on.
   b. Turn set/coast switch on.
   c. Push main switch on.
   d. Turn set/coast switch off.
   e. Meet conditions listed in chart. **Checking of No. 4 code is done with front of vehicle raised and supported and with engine idling.**
   f. Read diagnostic code on main switch indicator. If there is no indication code, refer to Diagnosis.
3. If instructed to read type B code on 1988 models, refer to **Fig. 4** and proceed as follows:
   a. If, while driving with cruise control on, the system is cancelled by a malfunction in either the actuator or the speed sensor, the main switch indicator will blink 5 times.
   b. While driving at a speed of no more than 10 mph, press set/coast

Symptom	Inspection area	Result	Refer to procedure
Cruise control does not operate.	(a) Inspect type A codes.	No. 1 NO	B
		No. 2 NO	C
		No. 3 NO	J
		No. 4 NO	F to I
		No. 5 NO	E
		No. 6 NO	E
	(b) Inspect type B codes.	11	D
		21	E
		23	D, E
		31	C
		33	B, C
	(c) All codes are normal.	—	A, D, E
Vehicle speed does not decrease when coast switch turned on.	Inspect No. 1 of type A code.	OK	D
		NO	B
Vehicle speed does not fluctuate when set switch turned on.			
Vehicle speed does not accelerate when accel switch turned on.	Inspect No. 2 of type A code.	OK	D
		NO	C
Vehicle speed does not return to memorized speed when resume switch turned on.			
Setting speed deviates on high side.	—	—	D, E
Setting speed deviates on low side.			
Setting speed does not cancel when brake pedal depressed.	Inspect No. 4 of type A code.	OK	D
		NO	F
Setting speed does not cancel when parking brake pulled up.	Inspec. No. 4 of type A code.	OK	D
		NO	G
Setting speed does not cancel when clutch pedal depressed (M/T only).	Inspect No. 4 of type A code.	OK	D
		NO	H
Setting speed does not cancel when shifted to "N" range (A/T only).	Inspect No. 4 of type A code.	OK	D
		NO	I
Speed can be set below about 40 km/h (25 mph).	Inspect No. 5 of type A code. Inspect No. 6 of type A code.	OK	D
		NO	E
Cruise control will not disengage even about 40 km/h (25 mph).			
Return and acceleration response is sluggish.	Inspect No. 3 of type A code.	OK	D
		NO	J
A short period after the O/D cut, (Approx. within 14 seconds) the O/D will resume. (4A-GE Engine)	—	—	K

Fig. 1 Cruise control system troubleshooting chart. Nova

Symptom	Read	Result	Circuits
• Cruise control switch indicator blinks five times or • Cruise control system does not set or • Cruise control system does not operate.	Type B Codes	11	• Actuator • Cruise Control Module
		21	• Speed Sensor • Cruise Control Module
		23	• Check speedometer cable operation • Actuator • Speed Sensor • Vacuum Pump and Hose • Vacuum Switch • Cruise Control Module
		31	• Engage Switch • Cruise Control Module
		33	• Engage Switch • Cruise Control Module
	Type A Code 5	No Code	• Speed Sensor • Cruise Control Module
		OK	• Cruise Control Switch • Engage Switch • Stoplamp Switch • Clutch or Neutral Start Switch • Parking Brake Switch • Check speedometer cable operation • Actuator • Cruise Control Module • Vacuum Hose and Brake Fluid
Setting speed deviated on high or low speed.	Type A Code 3	OK	• Check speedometer cable operation • Speed Sensor • Vacuum Pump • Vacuum Switch • Actuator • Cruise Control Module
		No Code	• Speed Sensor
Vehicle speed fluctuates when control switch is turned to "SET/COAST."			• Speed Sensor • Check speedometer cable operation • Actuator • Cruise Control Module
Setting speed does not cancel when the brake pedal is depressed.	Type A Code 4	OK	• Actuator • Stoplamp Switch • Cruise Control Module
		No Code	• Stoplamp Switch • Cruise Control Module
Setting speed does not cancel when the parking brake is applied.	Type A Code 4	OK	• Actuator • Cruise Control Module
		No Code	• Parking Brake Switch • Cruise Control Module

Fig. 2 Cruise control system troubleshooting chart (Part 1 of 2). Prizm

Symptom	Read	Result	Inspect these Circuits
Setting speed does not cancel when shifted to "N" range (A/T).	Type A Code 4	OK	• Actuator • Cruise Control Module
		No Code	• Neutral Start Switch • Cruise Control Module
Setting speed does not cancel when the clutch pedal is depressed. (M/T)	Type A Code 4	OK	• Actuator • Cruise Control Module
		No Code	• Clutch Switch • Cruise Control Module
Vehicle speed does not decrease when the engage switch is turned to "SET/COAST."	Type A Code 1	OK	• Actuator • Check speedometer cable operation • Cruise Control Module
		No Code	• Engage Switch • Cruise Control Module
Vehicle does not accelerate when the engage switch is turned to "RESUME/ACCEL."	Type A Code 2	OK	• Actuator • Check speedometer cable operation • Cruise Control Module
		No Code	• Engage Switch • Cruise Control Module
Vehicle speed does not return to set speed when engage switch is turned to "RESUME/ACCEL."	Type A Code 2	OK	• Actuator • Check speedometer cable operation • Cruise Control Module
		No Code	• Engage Switch • Cruise Control Module
Speed can be set below approximately 30 Km/hr (19 mph)	Type A Code 5	OK	• Actuator • Cruise Control Module
		No Code	• Speed Sensor • Cruise Control Module
Cruise control will not disengage at approximately 30 Km/hr (19 mph)	Type A Code 5	OK	• Actuator • Cruise Control Module
		No Code	• Speed Sensor • Check speedometer cable operation • Cruise Control Module
Acceleration is sluggish when the engage switch is turned to "RESUME/ACCEL."	Type A Code 3	OK	• Check speedometer cable operation • Vacuum Pump • Actuator • Cruise Control Module • Check Vacuum Hose
		No Code	• Vacuum Switch • Vacuum Pump

Fig. 2 Cruise control system troubleshooting chart (Part 2 of 2). Prizm

No.	Conditions	Indicator code	Diagnosis
1	Set/coast switch on	ON / OFF — 0.25S 1.0S 0.25S	Set/coast switch circuit is normal.
2	Resume/accel switch on	ON / OFF	Resume/accel switch circuit is normal.
3	Vacuum switch on	ON / OFF	Vacuum switch circuit is normal.
4	Each cancel switch on (Stop light switch, Parking brake switch, Clutch switch, Neutral start switch)	ON / OFF	Each cancel switch circuit is normal.
5	Drive 40 km/h (25 mph) or over	ON / OFF	Speed sensor circuit is normal.
6	Drive 30 km/h (19 mph) or below	ON / OFF	Speed sensor circuit is normal.

Fig. 3 Type A code chart

switch three times within two seconds. **In order to save diagnostic code(s) when a malfunction has occurred, always inspect with ignition and main switches on. Should the power be cut, the di-**agnostic code(s) will be erased from the computer memory.
c. Read diagnostic code on main switch indicator. **Indicator codes appear in order beginning with No. 11. Indication is stopped** when vehicle speed exceeds 10 mph. If there is no indication code, refer to Diagnosis.

DIAGNOSIS

If referred to specific procedure on Nova models, refer to **Figs. 5 through 15**, referring to **Figs. 16 and 17** as necessary. If referred to a specific procedure on Prizm models, refer to **Figs. 18 through 27**, referring to **Figs. 28 and 29** as necessary.

Continued on page 33-93

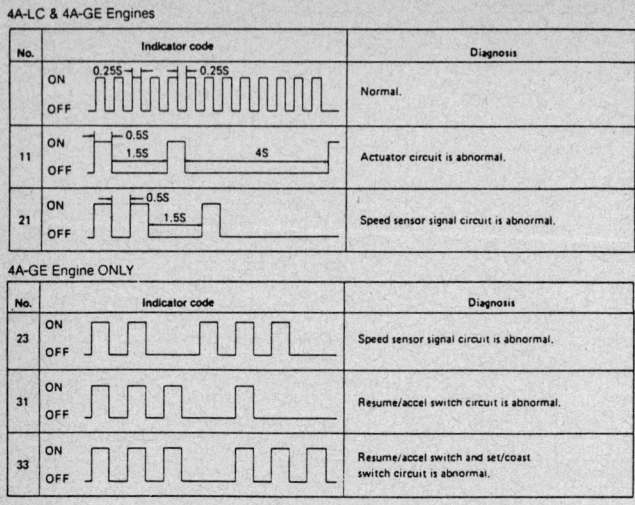

Fig. 4 Type B code chart

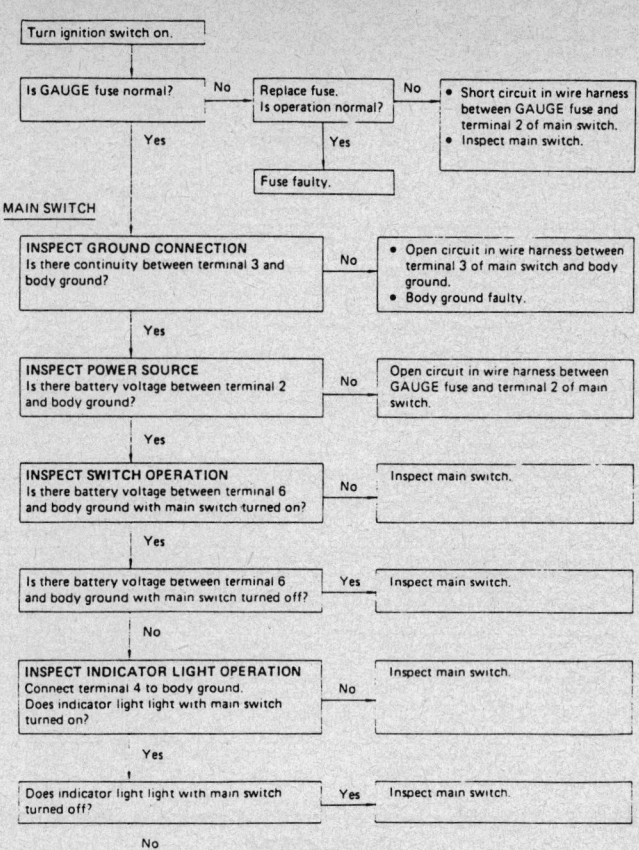

Fig. 5 Procedure A (Part 1 of 2). Nova

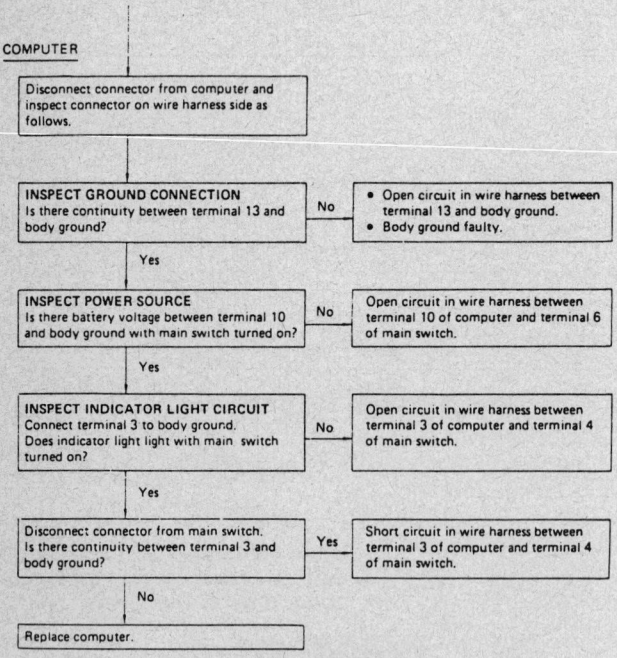

Fig. 5 Procedure A (Part 2 of 2). Nova

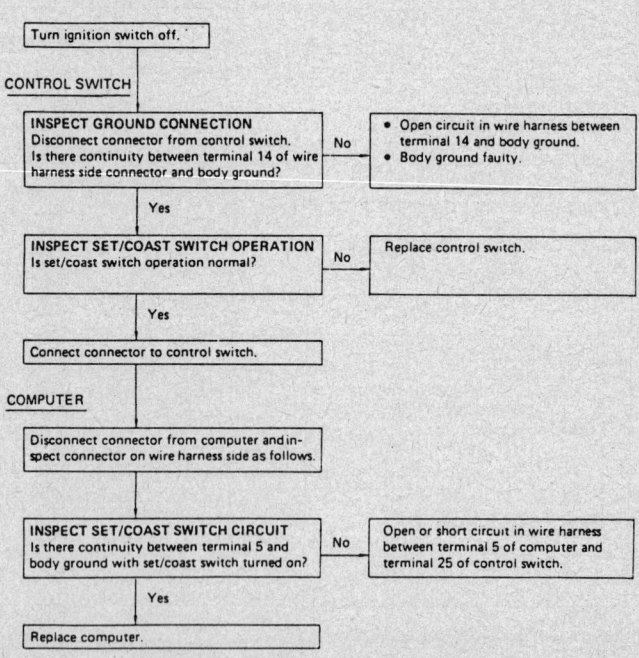

Fig. 6 Procedure B. Nova

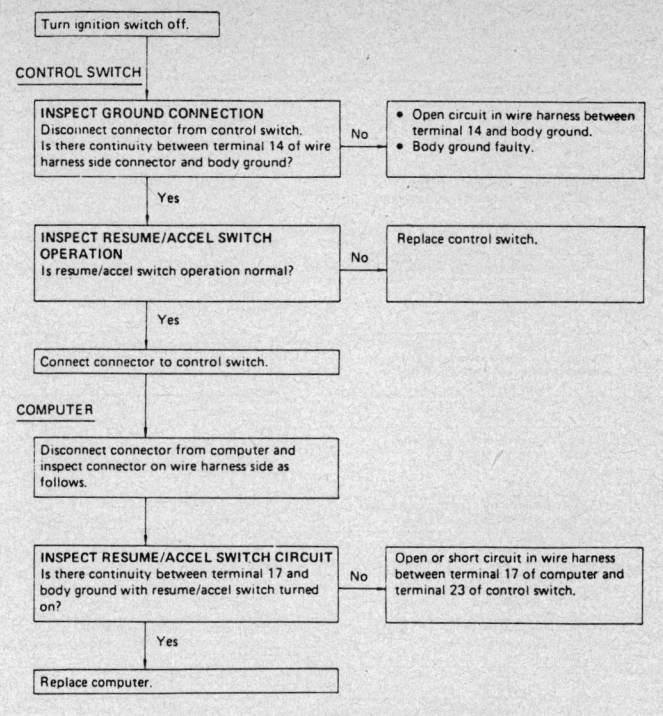

Fig. 7   Procedure C. Nova

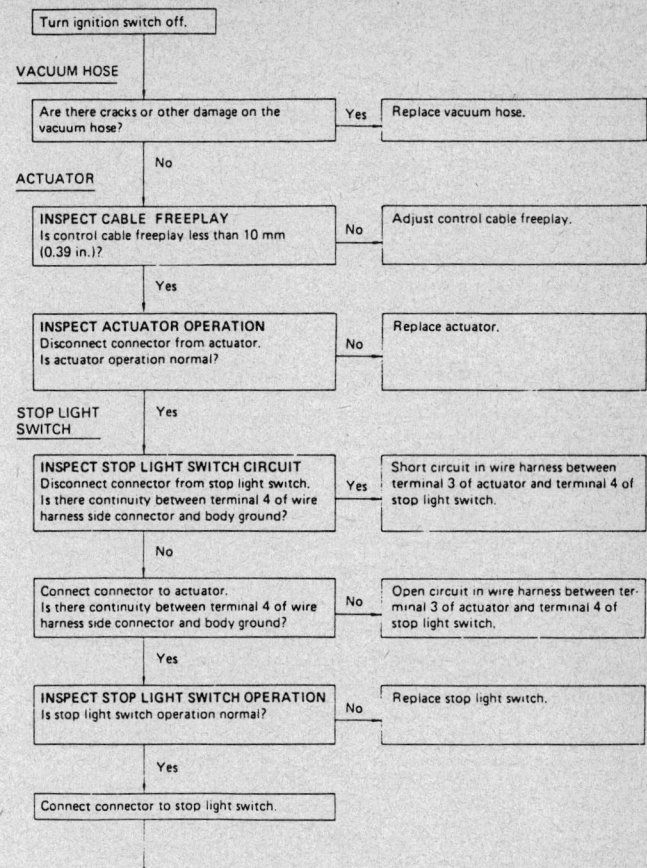

Fig. 8   Procedure D (Part 1 of 2). Nova

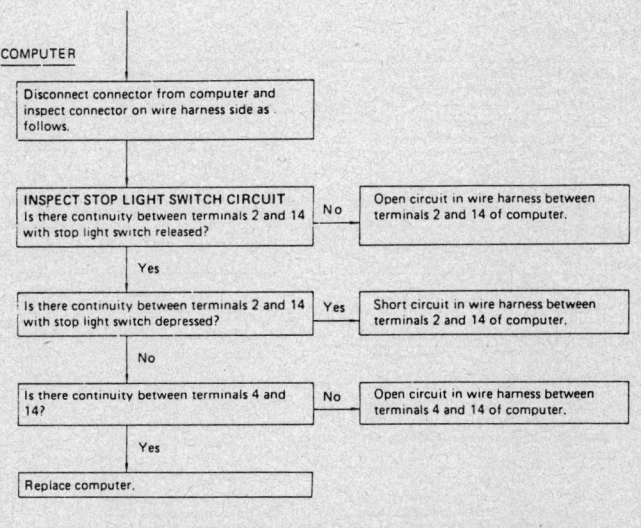

Fig. 8   Procedure D (Part 2 of 2). Nova

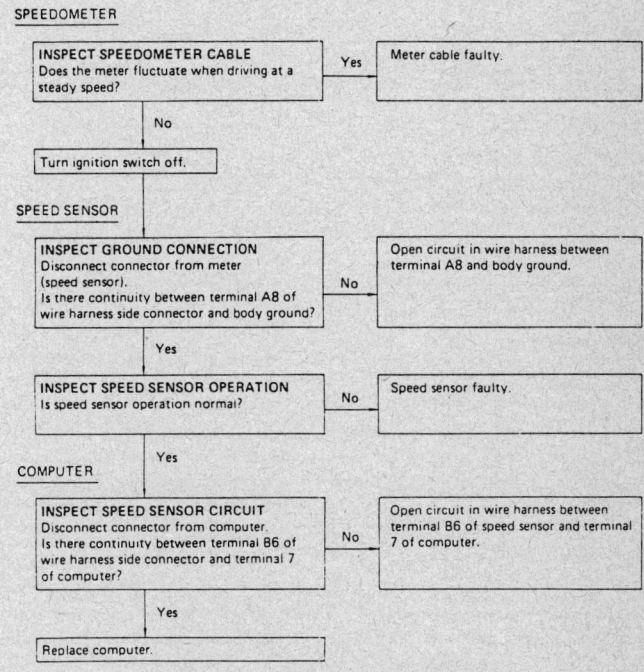

Fig. 9   Procedure E. Nova

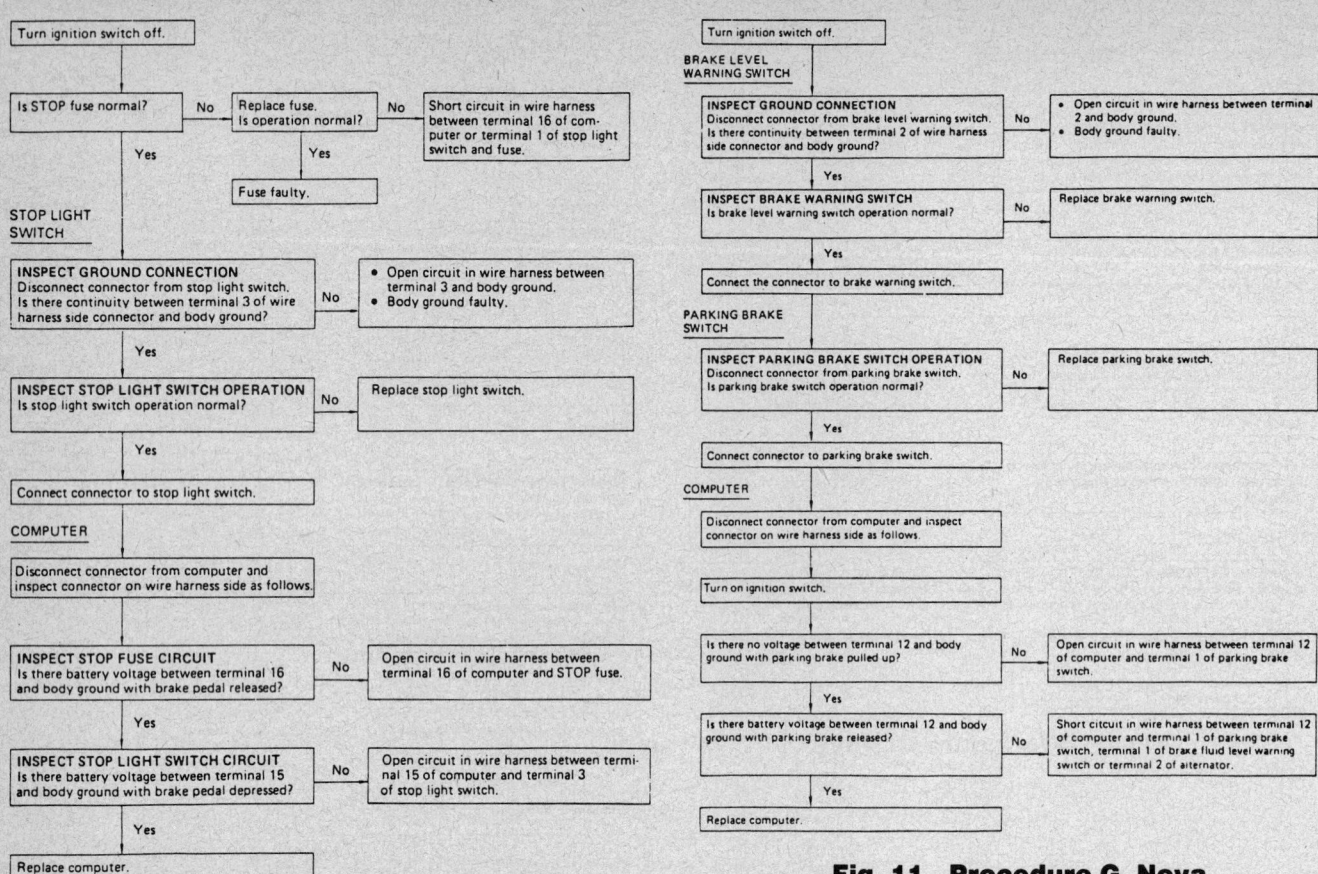

Fig. 10   Procedure F. Nova

Fig. 11   Procedure G. Nova

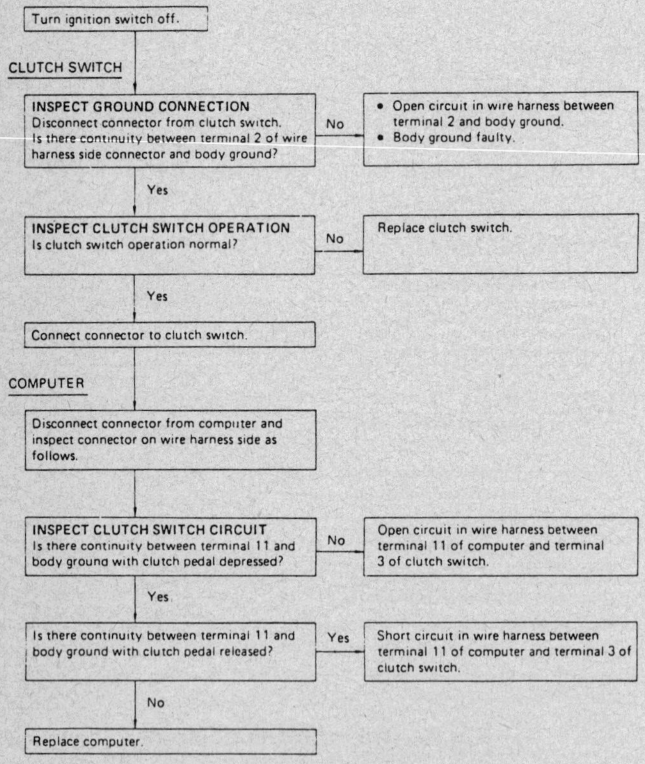

Fig. 12   Procedure H. Nova

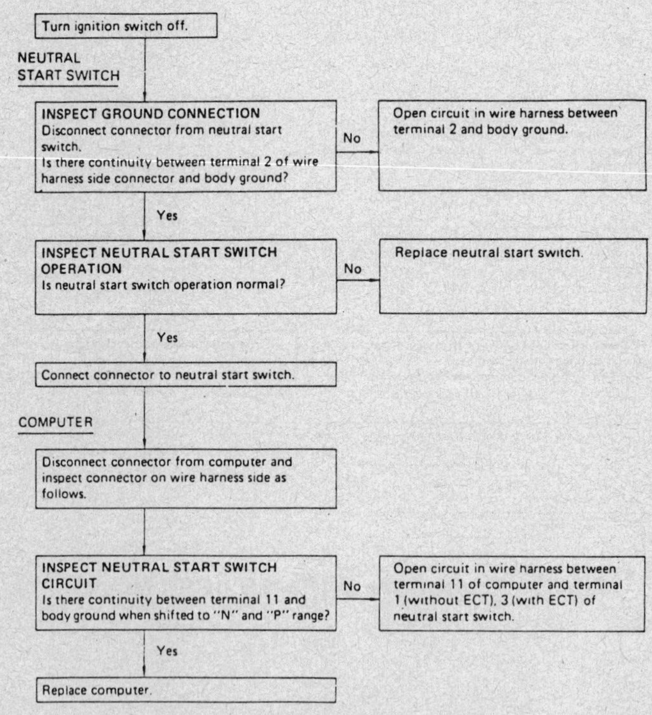

Fig. 13   Procedure I. Nova

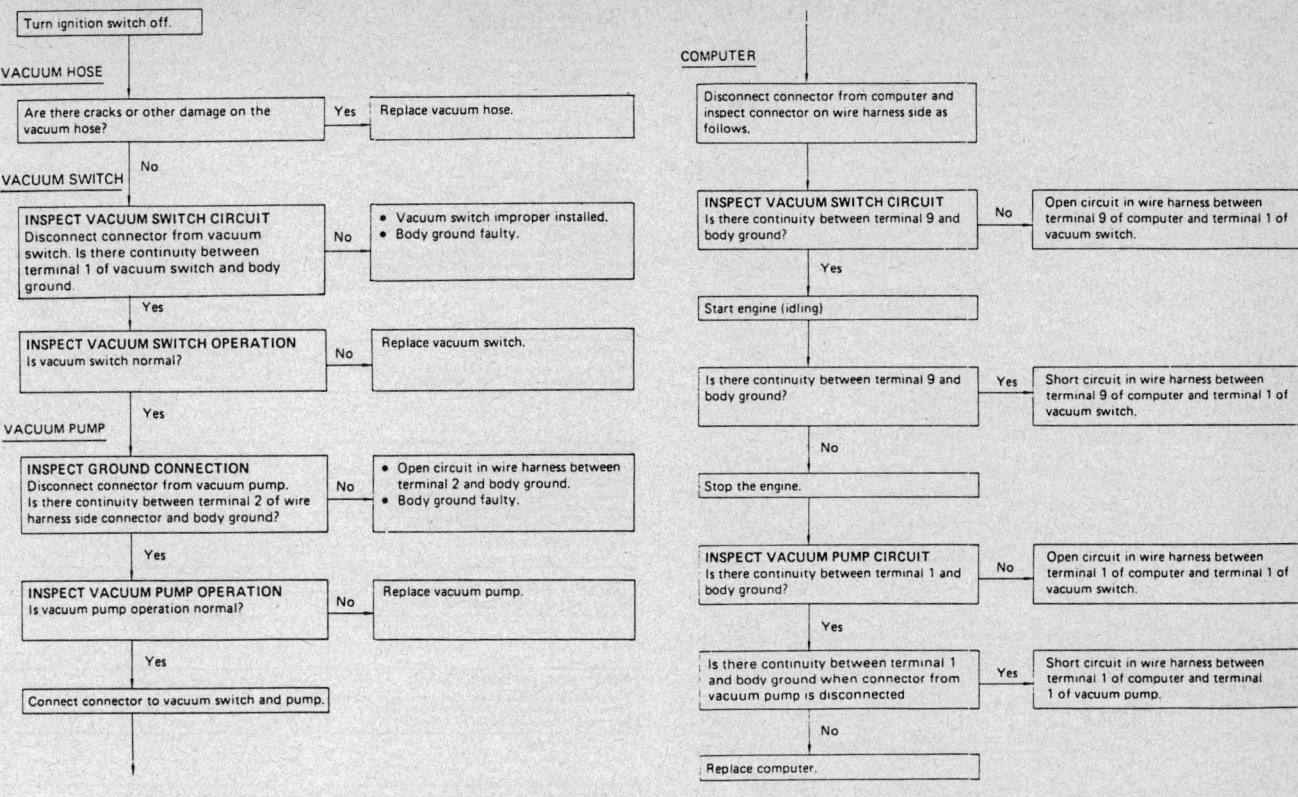

Fig. 14   Procedure J (Part 1 of 2). Nova

Fig. 14   Procedure J (Part 2 of 2). Nova

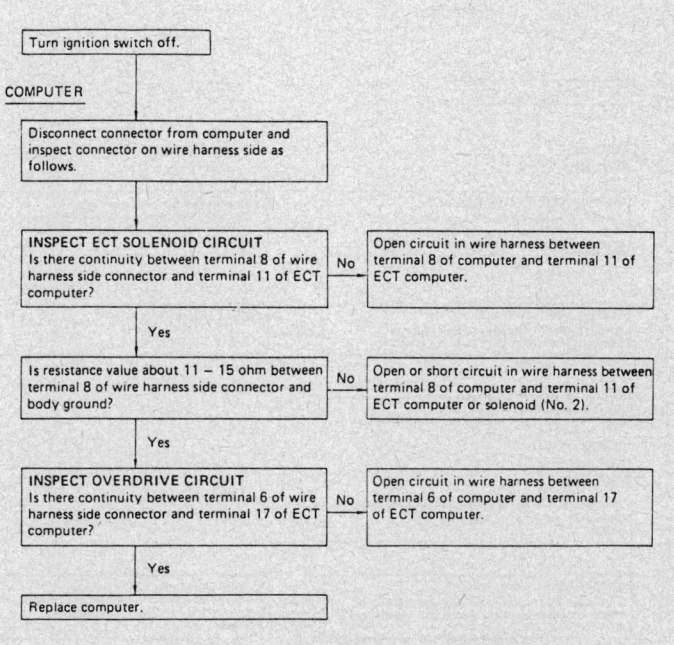

Fig. 15   Procedure K. Nova

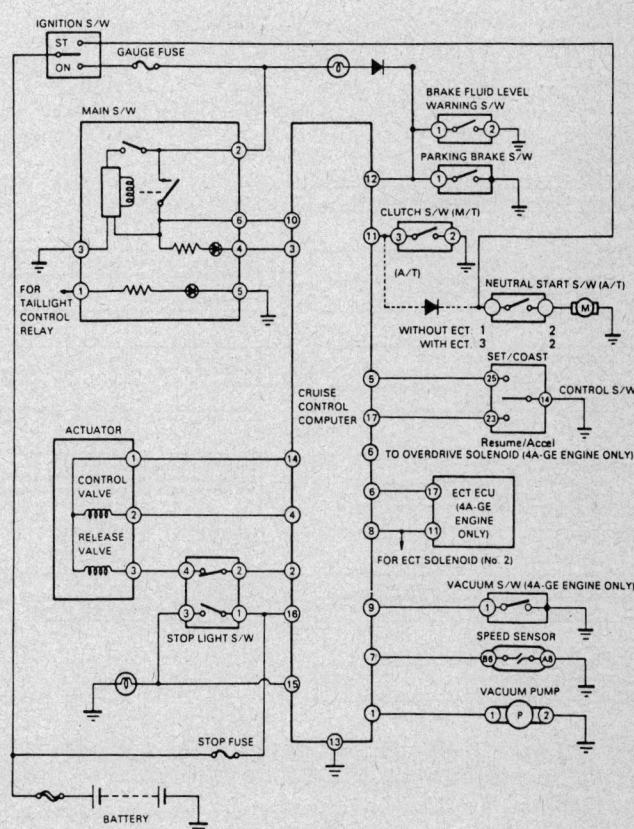

Fig. 16   Cruise control system wiring diagram. Nova

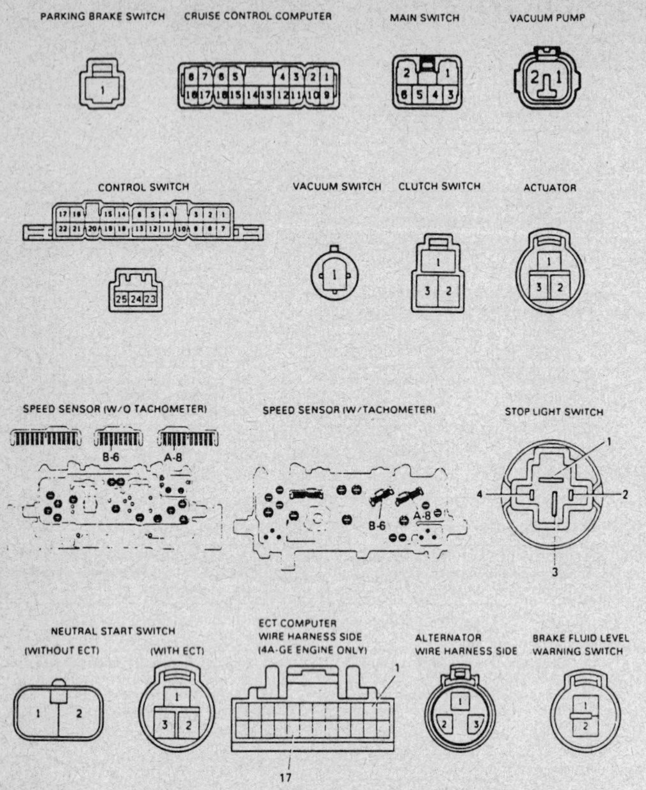

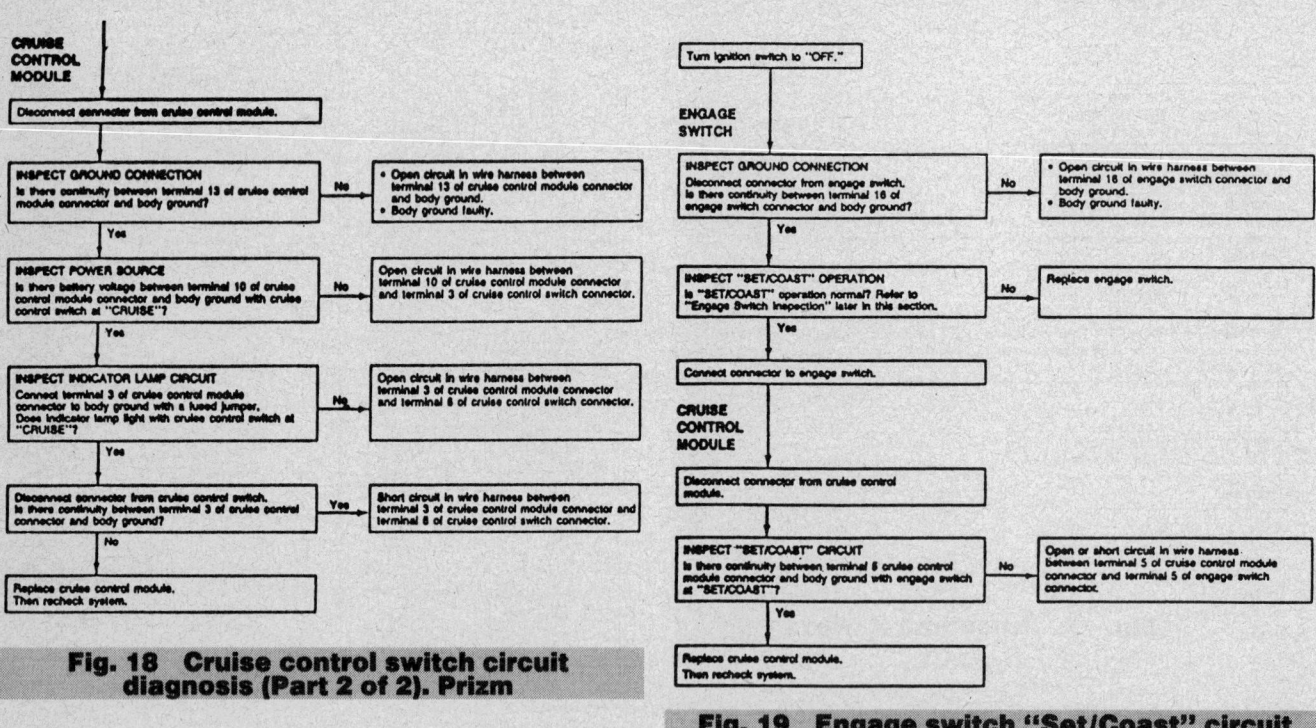

PARKING BRAKE SWITCH | **CRUISE CONTROL COMPUTER** | **MAIN SWITCH** | **VACUUM PUMP**

CONTROL SWITCH | **VACUUM SWITCH** | **CLUTCH SWITCH** | **ACTUATOR**

SPEED SENSOR (W/O TACHOMETER) | **SPEED SENSOR (W/TACHOMETER)** | **STOP LIGHT SWITCH**

NEUTRAL START SWITCH (WITHOUT ECT) | **(WITH ECT)** | **ECT COMPUTER WIRE HARNESS SIDE (4A-GE ENGINE ONLY)** | **ALTERNATOR WIRE HARNESS SIDE** | **BRAKE FLUID LEVEL WARNING SWITCH**

Fig. 17 Cruise control system connector terminal identification. Nova

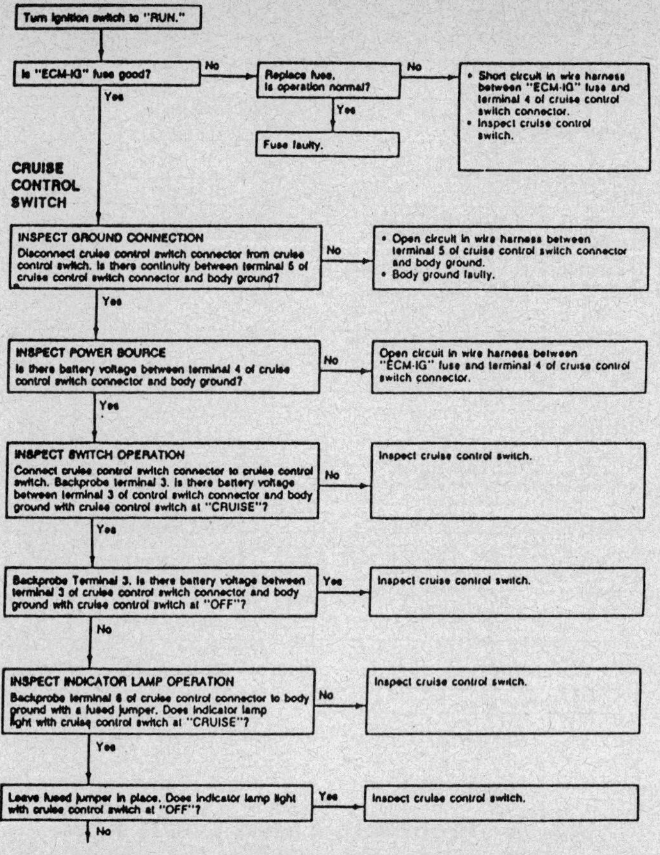

Turn ignition switch to "RUN."

Is "ECM-IG" fuse good? → No → Replace fuse. Is operation normal? → No → • Short circuit in wire harness between "ECM-IG" fuse and terminal 4 of cruise control switch connector. • Inspect cruise control switch.

Yes → Fuse faulty.

CRUISE CONTROL SWITCH

INSPECT GROUND CONNECTION
Disconnect cruise control switch connector from cruise control switch. Is there continuity between terminal 5 of cruise control switch connector and body ground? → No → • Open circuit in wire harness between terminal 5 of cruise control switch connector and body ground. • Body ground faulty.

Yes

INSPECT POWER SOURCE
Is there battery voltage between terminal 4 of cruise control switch connector and body ground? → No → Open circuit in wire harness between "ECM-IG" fuse and terminal 4 of cruise control switch connector.

Yes

INSPECT SWITCH OPERATION
Connect cruise control switch connector to cruise control switch. Backprobe terminal 3. Is there battery voltage between terminal 3 of control switch connector and body ground with cruise control switch at "CRUISE"? → No → Inspect cruise control switch.

Yes

Backprobe Terminal 3. Is there battery voltage between terminal 3 of cruise control switch connector and body ground with cruise control switch at "OFF"? → Yes → Inspect cruise control switch.

No

INSPECT INDICATOR LAMP OPERATION
Backprobe terminal 6 of cruise control switch connector to body ground with a fused jumper. Does indicator lamp light with cruise control switch at "CRUISE"? → No → Inspect cruise control switch.

Yes

Leave fused jumper in place. Does indicator lamp light with cruise control switch at "OFF"? → Yes → Inspect cruise control switch.

No

Fig. 18 Cruise control switch circuit diagnosis (Part 1 of 2). Prizm

---

CRUISE CONTROL MODULE

Disconnect connector from cruise control module.

INSPECT GROUND CONNECTION
Is there continuity between terminal 13 of cruise control module connector and body ground? → No → • Open circuit in wire harness between terminal 13 of cruise control module connector and body ground. • Body ground faulty.

Yes

INSPECT POWER SOURCE
Is there battery voltage between terminal 10 of cruise control module connector and body ground with cruise control switch at "CRUISE"? → No → Open circuit in wire harness between terminal 10 of cruise control module connector and terminal 3 of cruise control switch connector.

Yes

INSPECT INDICATOR LAMP CIRCUIT
Connect terminal 3 of cruise control module connector to body ground with a fused jumper. Does indicator lamp light with cruise control switch at "CRUISE"? → No → Open circuit in wire harness between terminal 3 of cruise control module connector and terminal 6 of cruise control switch connector.

Yes

Disconnect connector from cruise control switch. Is there continuity between terminal 3 of cruise control connector and body ground? → Yes → Short circuit in wire harness between terminal 3 of cruise control module connector and terminal 6 of cruise control switch connector.

No

Replace cruise control module. Then recheck system.

Fig. 18 Cruise control switch circuit diagnosis (Part 2 of 2). Prizm

---

Turn ignition switch to "OFF."

ENGAGE SWITCH

INSPECT GROUND CONNECTION
Disconnect connector from engage switch. Is there continuity between terminal 16 of engage switch connector and body ground? → No → • Open circuit in wire harness between terminal 16 of engage switch connector and body ground. • Body ground faulty.

Yes

INSPECT "SET/COAST" OPERATION
Is "SET/COAST" operation normal? Refer to "Engage Switch Inspection" later in this section. → No → Replace engage switch.

Yes

Connect connector to engage switch.

CRUISE CONTROL MODULE

Disconnect connector from cruise control module.

INSPECT "SET/COAST" CIRCUIT
Is there continuity between terminal 5 of cruise control module connector and body ground with engage switch at "SET/COAST"? → No → Open or short circuit in wire harness between terminal 5 of cruise control module connector and terminal 5 of engage switch connector.

Yes

Replace cruise control module. Then recheck system.

Fig. 19 Engage switch "Set/Coast" circuit diagnosis. Prizm

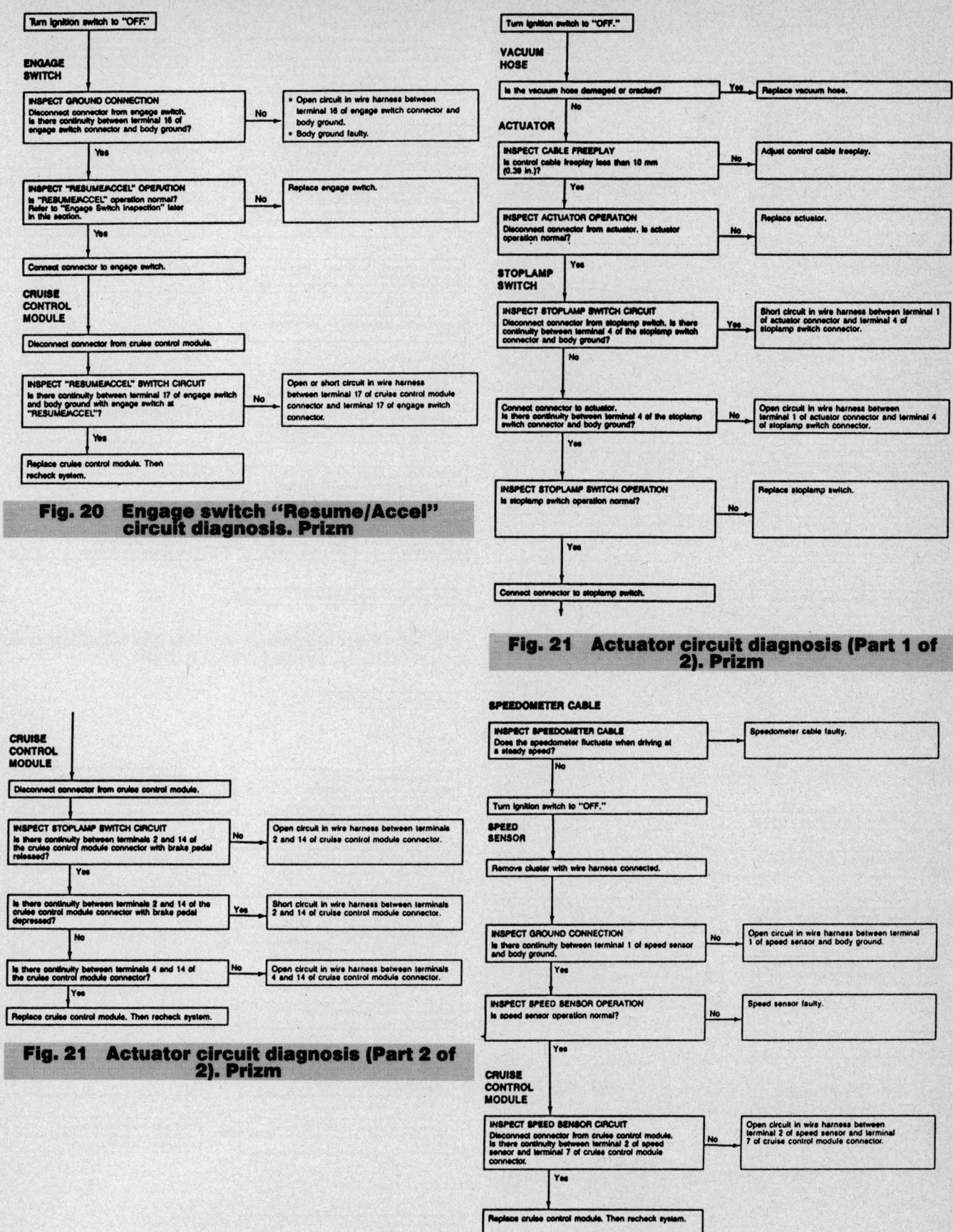

Fig. 20 Engage switch "Resume/Accel" circuit diagnosis. Prizm

Fig. 21 Actuator circuit diagnosis (Part 1 of 2). Prizm

Fig. 21 Actuator circuit diagnosis (Part 2 of 2). Prizm

Fig. 22 Speed sensor circuit diagnosis. Prizm

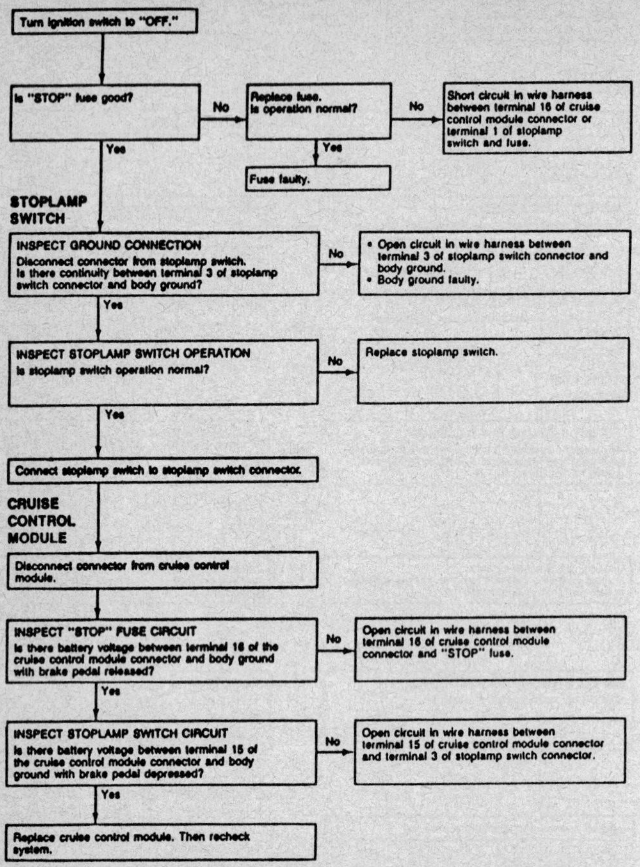

Fig. 23 — Stoplamp switch circuit diagnosis. Prizm

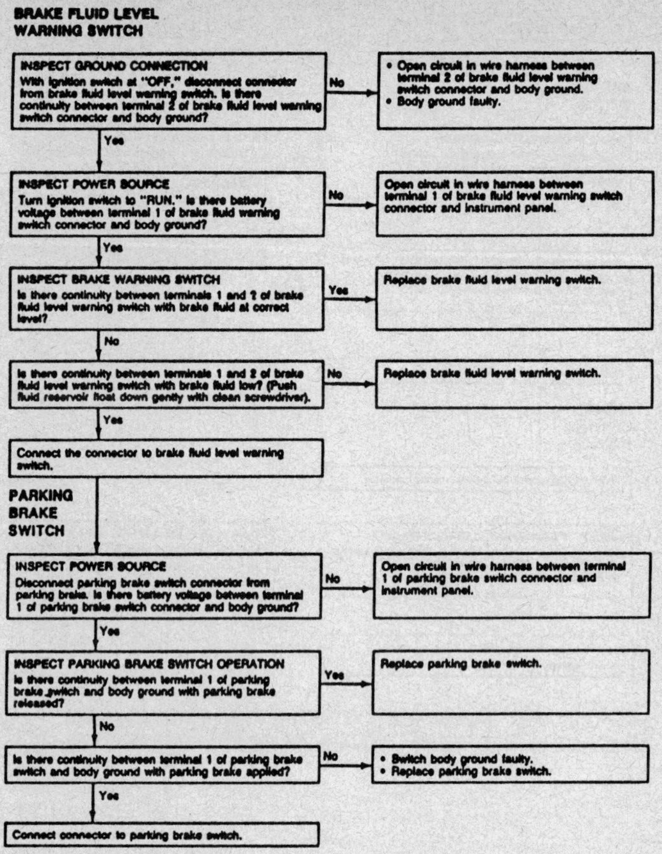

Turn ignition switch to "OFF."

→ Is "STOP" fuse good? — No → Replace fuse. Is operation normal? — No → Short circuit in wire harness between terminal 16 of cruise control module connector or terminal 1 of stoplamp switch and fuse.

Is operation normal? — Yes → Fuse faulty.

"STOP" fuse good? — Yes

STOPLAMP SWITCH

INSPECT GROUND CONNECTION
Disconnect connector from stoplamp switch. Is there continuity between terminal 3 of stoplamp switch connector and body ground? — No → • Open circuit in wire harness between terminal 3 of stoplamp switch connector and body ground. • Body ground faulty.

Yes ↓

INSPECT STOPLAMP SWITCH OPERATION
Is stoplamp switch operation normal? — No → Replace stoplamp switch.

Yes ↓

Connect stoplamp switch to stoplamp switch connector.

CRUISE CONTROL MODULE

Disconnect connector from cruise control module.

INSPECT "STOP" FUSE CIRCUIT
Is there battery voltage between terminal 16 of the cruise control module connector and body ground with brake pedal released? — No → Open circuit in wire harness between terminal 16 of cruise control module connector and "STOP" fuse.

Yes ↓

INSPECT STOPLAMP SWITCH CIRCUIT
Is there battery voltage between terminal 15 of the cruise control module connector and body ground with brake pedal depressed? — No → Open circuit in wire harness between terminal 15 of cruise control module connector and terminal 3 of stoplamp switch connector.

Yes ↓

Replace cruise control module. Then recheck system.

BRAKE FLUID LEVEL WARNING SWITCH

INSPECT GROUND CONNECTION
With ignition switch at "OFF," disconnect connector from brake fluid level warning switch. Is there continuity between terminal 2 of brake fluid level warning switch connector and body ground? — No → • Open circuit in wire harness between terminal 2 of brake fluid level warning switch connector and body ground. • Body ground faulty.

Yes ↓

INSPECT POWER SOURCE
Turn ignition switch to "RUN." Is there battery voltage between terminal 1 of brake fluid warning switch connector and body ground? — No → Open circuit in wire harness between terminal 1 of brake fluid level warning switch connector and instrument panel.

Yes ↓

INSPECT BRAKE WARNING SWITCH
Is there continuity between terminals 1 and 2 of brake fluid level warning switch with brake fluid at correct level? — Yes → Replace brake fluid level warning switch.

No ↓

Is there continuity between terminals 1 and 2 of brake fluid level warning switch with brake fluid low? (Push fluid reservoir float down gently with clean screwdriver.) — No → Replace brake fluid level warning switch.

Yes ↓

Connect the connector to brake fluid level warning switch.

PARKING BRAKE SWITCH

INSPECT POWER SOURCE
Disconnect parking brake switch connector from parking brake. Is there battery voltage between terminal 1 of parking brake switch connector and body ground? — No → Open circuit in wire harness between terminal 1 of parking brake switch connector and instrument panel.

Yes ↓

INSPECT PARKING BRAKE SWITCH OPERATION
Is there continuity between terminal 1 of parking brake switch and body ground with parking brake released? — Yes → Replace parking brake switch.

No ↓

Is there continuity between terminal 1 of parking brake switch and body ground with parking brake applied? — No → • Switch body ground faulty. • Replace parking brake switch.

Yes ↓

Connect connector to parking brake switch.

Fig. 24 — Parking brake switch circuit diagnosis (Part 1 of 2). Prizm

---

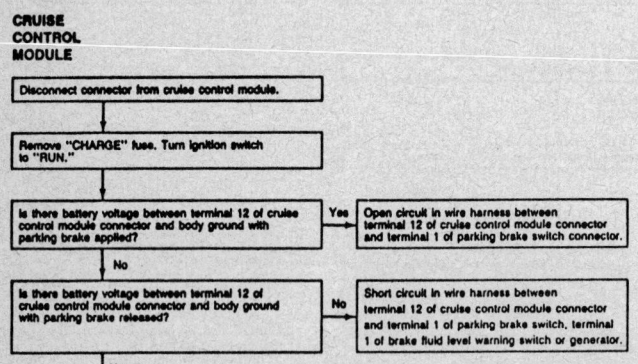

CRUISE CONTROL MODULE

Disconnect connector from cruise control module.

Remove "CHARGE" fuse. Turn ignition switch to "RUN."

Is there battery voltage between terminal 12 of cruise control module connector and body ground with parking brake applied? — Yes → Open circuit in wire harness between terminal 12 of cruise control module connector and terminal 1 of parking brake switch connector.

No ↓

Is there battery voltage between terminal 12 of cruise control module connector and body ground with parking brake released? — No → Short circuit in wire harness between terminal 12 of cruise control module connector and terminal 1 of parking brake switch, terminal 1 of brake fluid level warning switch or generator.

Yes ↓

Replace cruise control module. Then recheck system.

Fig. 24 — Parking brake switch circuit diagnosis (Part 2 of 2). Prizm

---

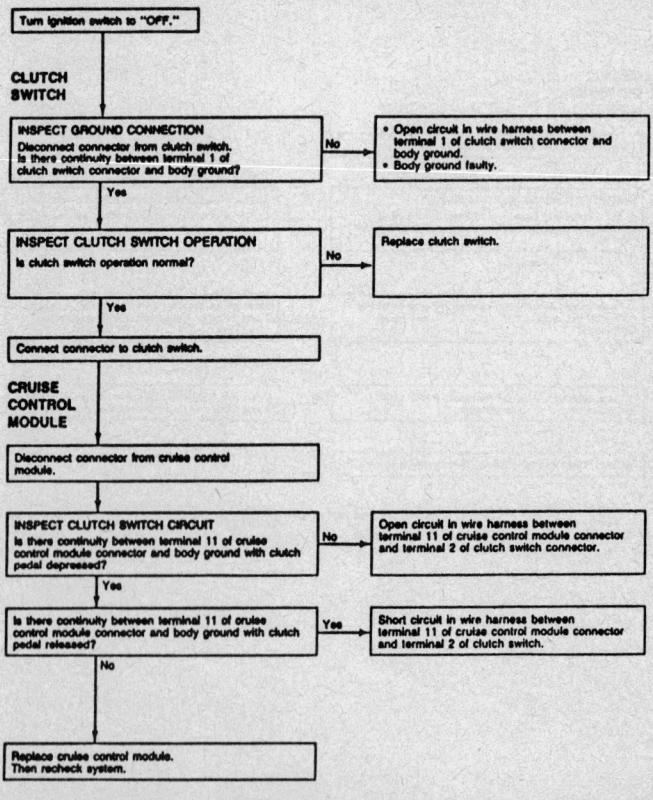

Turn ignition switch to "OFF."

CLUTCH SWITCH

INSPECT GROUND CONNECTION
Disconnect connector from clutch switch. Is there continuity between terminal 1 of clutch switch connector and body ground? — No → • Open circuit in wire harness between terminal 1 of clutch switch connector and body ground. • Body ground faulty.

Yes ↓

INSPECT CLUTCH SWITCH OPERATION
Is clutch switch operation normal? — No → Replace clutch switch.

Yes ↓

Connect connector to clutch switch.

CRUISE CONTROL MODULE

Disconnect connector from cruise control module.

INSPECT CLUTCH SWITCH CIRCUIT
Is there continuity between terminal 11 of cruise control module connector and body ground with clutch pedal depressed? — No → Open circuit in wire harness between terminal 11 of cruise control module connector and terminal 2 of clutch switch connector.

Yes ↓

Is there continuity between terminal 11 of cruise control module connector and body ground with clutch pedal released? — Yes → Short circuit in wire harness between terminal 11 of cruise control module connector and terminal 2 of clutch switch.

No ↓

Replace cruise control module. Then recheck system.

Fig. 25 — Clutch switch circuit diagnosis. Prizm

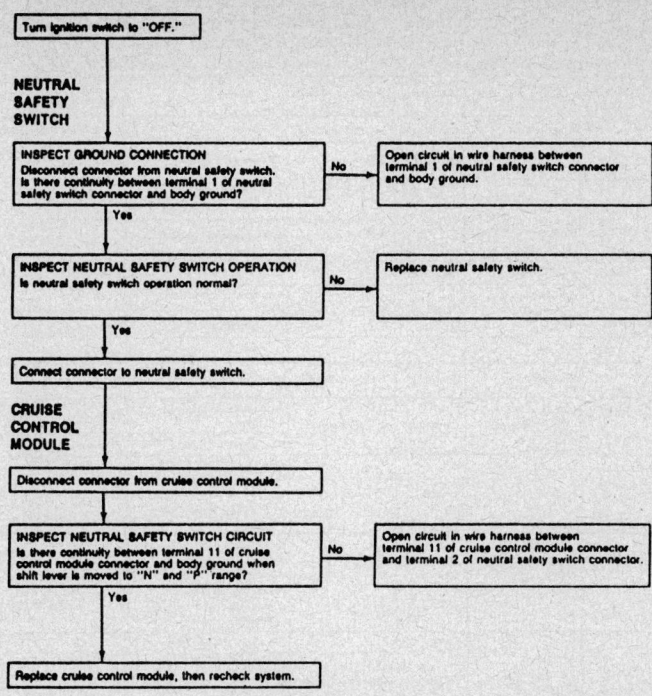

Fig. 26 Neutral safety switch circuit diagnosis. Prizm

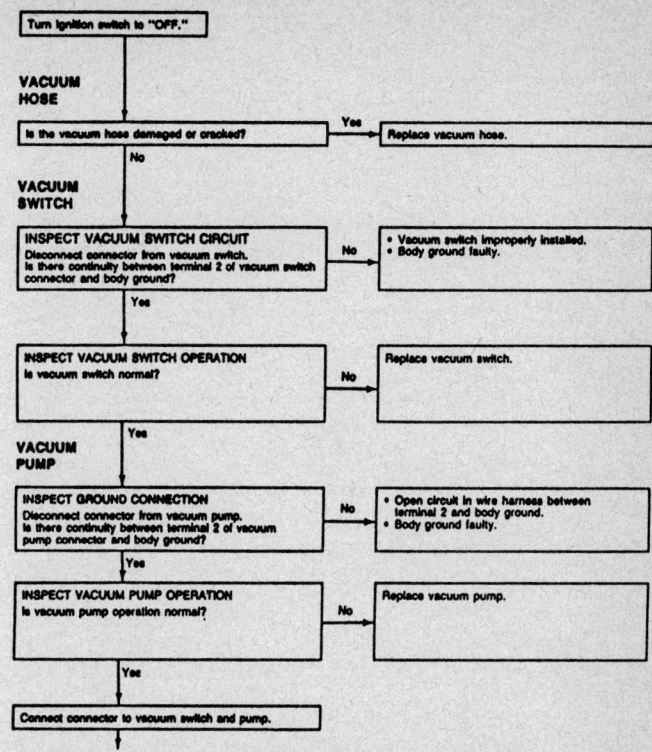

Fig. 27 Vacuum circuit diagnosis (Part 1 of 2). Prizm

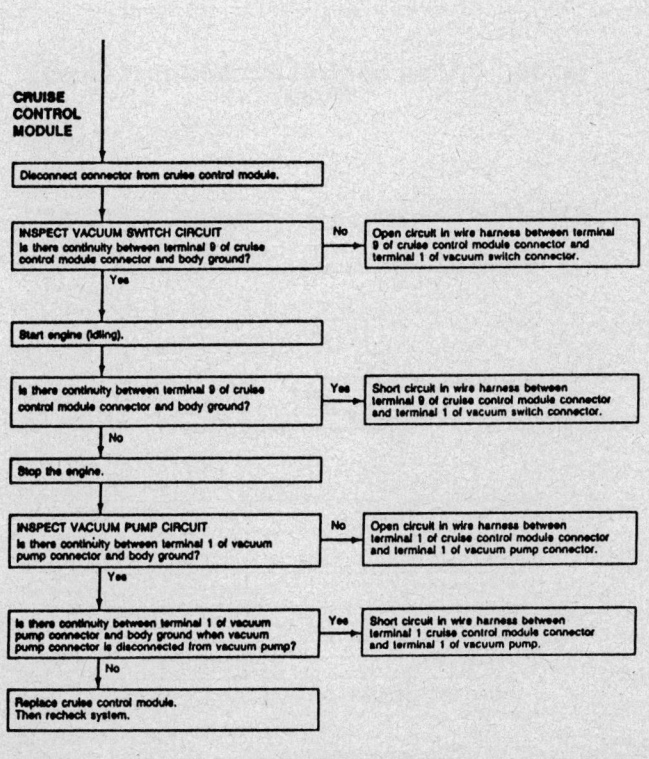

Fig. 27 Vacuum circuit diagnosis (Part 2 of 2). Prizm

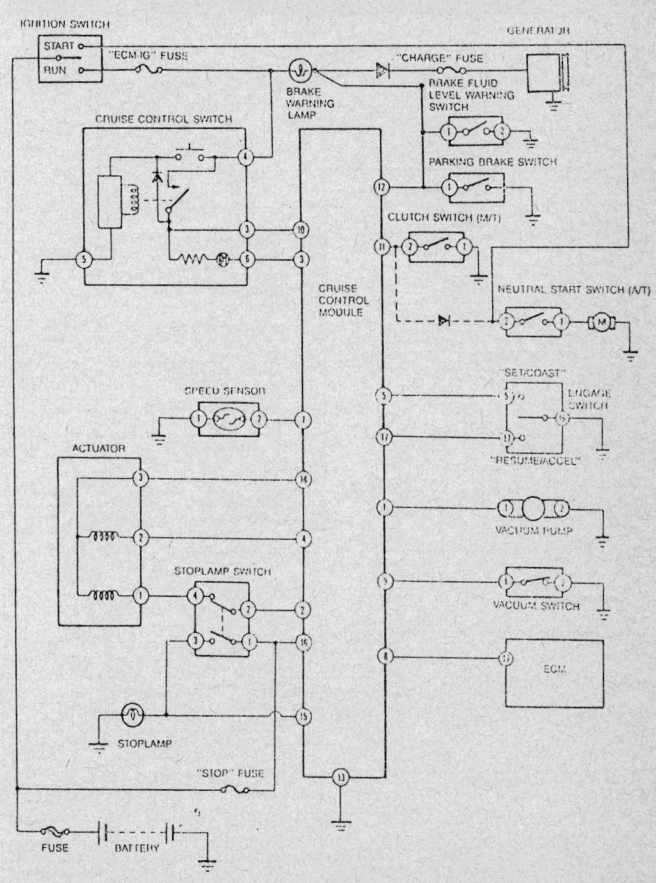

Fig. 28 Cruise control system wiring diagram. Prizm

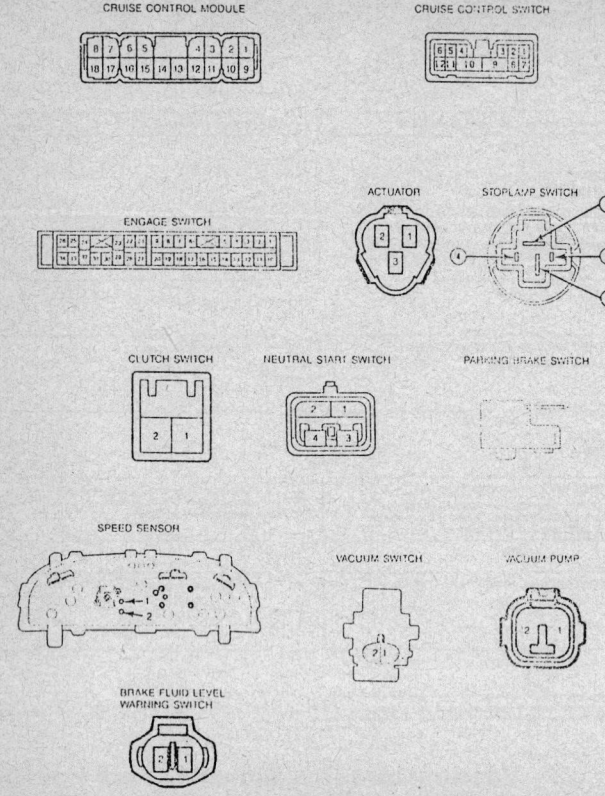

Fig. 29 Cruise control system connector terminal identification. Prizm

Cruise Control Computer Circuit
INSPECTION OF COMPUTER CIRCUIT

Disconnect the computer and inspect the connector on the wire harness side as shown in the chart below.

Terminal	Connection or Measure item	Check item	Tester connection	Condition	Voltage or Resistance value
1	Vacuum Pump	Continuity	1 — Body ground	—	Continuity
2	Stop Light Switch and Release Valve	Resistance	2 — 14	Brake pedal returned	About 68 Ω
3	Main Switch (Indicator Circuit)	Voltage	3 — Body ground	Turn ignition switch and main switch on	Battery voltage
				Turn ignition switch and or main switch off	No voltage
4	Control Valve	Resistance	4 — 14	—	About 30 Ω
5	Control Switch (set/coast)	Continuity	5 — Body ground	Turn set coast switch on	Continuity
				Turn set coast switch off	No continuity
6	OD relay	—	—	—	—
7	Speed Sensor	Continuity	7 — Body ground	Vehicle moving slowly	1 pulse each 40 cm (15.75 in.)
9	Vacuum Switch	Continuity	9 — Body ground	Apply vacuum approx. 170 mmHg	No continuity
				No vacuum.	Continuity
10	Main Switch	Voltage	10 — Body ground	Turn ignition switch and main switch on	Battery voltage
				Turn ignition switch and or main switch off	No voltage
11	Clutch Switch (M T) or Neutral Start Switch (A T)	Continuity	11 — Body ground	Clutch pedal depressed or shifted into "N" range	Continuity
				Clutch pedal returned or shifted into any range except "N" range	No continuity
12	Parking Brake Switch	Voltage	12 — Body ground	Remove CHARGE fuse and ignition switch on with parking brake pulled up	No voltage
				Remove CHARGE fuse and ignition switch on with parking brake released	Battery voltage
13	Body Ground	Continuity	13 — Body ground	—	Continuity
14	Release Valve and Control Valve	—	—	—	—
15	Stop Light Switch	Voltage	15 — Body ground	Brake pedal depressed	Battery voltage
				Brake pedal returned	No voltage
16	STOP Fuse	Voltage	16 — Body ground	—	Battery voltage
17	Control Switch (resume-accel)	Continuity	17 — Body ground	Turn resume accel switch on	Continuity
				Turn resume accel switch off	No continuity

Fig. 30 Cruise control module test chart. Nova

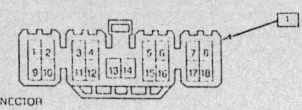

[1] CRUISE CONTROL MODULE CONNECTOR (WIRE HARNESS SIDE)

Connection or measure item	Check for	Tester connection	Condition	Specified value
"STOP" Fuse	Voltage	16–Body ground		Battery voltage
Stoplamp Switch	Voltage	15–16	Brake pedal depressed	No voltage
			Brake pedal released	Battery voltage
Stoplamp Switch (Release Valve)	Resistance	2–14	Brake pedal released	Approx. 68 ohms
Control Valve	Resistance	4–14	—	Approx. 30 ohms
Cruise Control Switch	Voltage	10–Body ground	Turn ignition switch to "RUN" and cruise control switch to "CRUISE"	Battery voltage
			Turn ignition switch to "RUN" and cruise control switch to "OFF"	No voltage
Cruise Control Switch (indicator circuit)	Voltage	3–Body ground	Turn ignition switch to "RUN" and cruise control switch to "CRUISE"	Battery voltage
			Turn ignition switch to "RUN" and cruise control switch to "OFF"	No voltage
Engage Switch "SET/COAST"	Continuity	5–Body ground	Turn "SET/COAST" on	Continuity
			Turn "SET/COAST" off	No continuity
Engage Switch "RESUME/ACCEL"	Continuity	17–Body ground	Turn "RESUME/ACCEL" on	Continuity
			Turn "RESUME/ACCEL" off	No continuity
Speed Sensor	Continuity	7–Body ground	Vehicle moving slowly	1 pulse each 40 cm (15.75 in.)
Clutch Switch (M/T) or Neutral Start Switch (A/T)	Continuity	11–Body ground	Clutch pedal depressed or shifted into "N" range	Continuity
			Clutch pedal released or shifted into any range except "N" and "P" range	No continuity
Parking Brake Switch	Voltage	12–Body ground	Remove "CHARGE" fuse. Turn ignition switch to "RUN" with parking brake applied.	No voltage
			Remove "CHARGE" fuse and turn ignition switch to "RUN" with parking brake lever released.	Battery voltage
Vacuum Switch	Continuity	9–Body ground	Apply vacuum approx.170 mmHg (6.69 in. Hg, 22.7 kPa)	No continuity
			No vacuum.	Continuity
Vacuum Pump	Continuity	1–Body ground	—	Continuity
Body Ground	Continuity	13–Body ground	—	Continuity

Fig. 31 Cruise control module test chart. Prizm

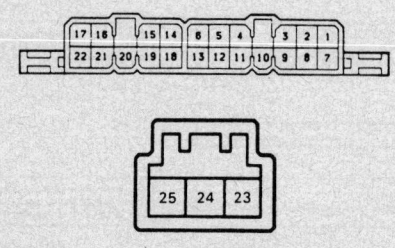

INSPECT THE SWITCH CONTINUITY BETWEEN TERMINALS.

SWITCH POSITION	TERMINAL 14	23	25
RESUME ACCEL	o—	—o	
OFF			
SET COAST	o—		—o

IF CONTINUITY IS NOT AS SPECIFIED, REPLACE THE SWITCH.

Fig. 32 Testing control switch. Nova

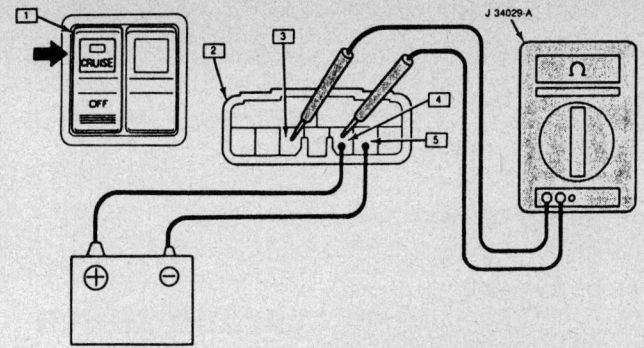

Fig. 33   Testing cruise control switch. Prizm

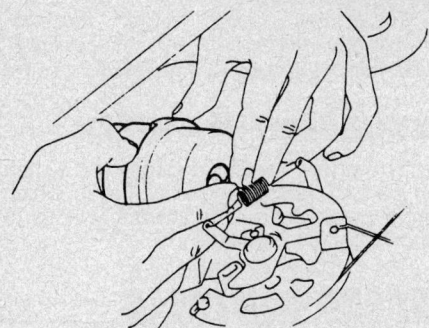

Fig. 35   Checking control cable freeplay. Nova

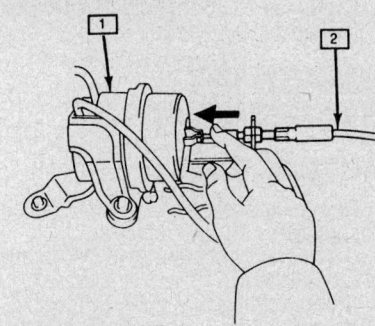

1 ACTUATOR
2 CONTROL CABLE

Fig. 36   Checking control cable freeplay. Prizm

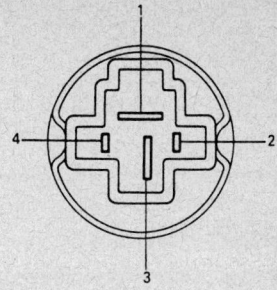

Inspect the switch continuity between terminals.

Terminal Brake pedal position	1	3	2	4
Brake pedal depressed	o——	——o		
Brake pedal returned			o——	——o

If continuity is not as specified, replace the switch.

Fig. 34   Testing stop light switch

COMPONENT TESTING

CRUISE CONTROL MODULE

Refer to **Figs. 30 and 31** to test cruise control module.

MAIN SWITCH

1988

1. Connect positive lead from battery to terminal 2 and the negative lead to terminal 3.
2. Check that there is continuity between terminals 2 and 6 with main switch turned on.
3. Check that there is no continuity between terminals 2 and 6 with main switch turned off.
4. If there was no continuity in step 2 and/or there was continuity in step 3, replace switch.

CRUISE CONTROL SWITCH

To test control switch, refer to **Figs. 32 and 33.**

CLUTCH SWITCH

Nova

1. Check that there is continuity between terminals 2 and 3 with clutch pedal depressed.
2. Check that there is no continuity between terminals 2 and 3 with clutch pedal released.

3. If there is no continuity in step 1 and/or there is continuity in step 2, replace switch.

Prizm

1. Disconnect clutch switch electrical connector.
2. Connect digital multimeter, J34029-A, or equivalent, to clutch switch terminals 1 and 2.
3. With clutch pedal depressed, ensure continuity.
4. With clutch pedal released, ensure no continuity.
5. If results are not as indicated, replace clutch switch.

SPEED SENSOR

Refer to procedure E, **Figs. 9 and 22,** to test speed sensor.

STOP LIGHT SWITCH

Refer to **Fig. 34** to test stop light switch.

PARKING BRAKE SWITCH

1. **On 1989-90 models,** disconnect parking brake switch electrical connectors.
2. **On all models,** ensure continuity between terminals with parking brake engaged.
3. No continuity should be indicated between terminals with parking brake returned.

4. If results are not as indicated, replace parking brake switch.

ACTUATOR

1988 NOVA

1. Ensure control cable freeplay is less than .39 inch, **Figs. 35 and 36,** adjusting as necessary.
2. Using an ohmmeter, measure resistance values between terminals.
3. If resistance is not approximately 30 ohms between terminals 1 and 2, and approximately 68 ohms between terminals 1 and 3, replace actuator.
4. Connect positive lead from battery to terminals 2 and 3 and the negative lead to terminal 1.
5. Slowly apply vacuum from 0 to 11.8 inches Hg and check that control cable can be pulled smoothly.
6. With vacuum stabilized, ensure control cable does not return.
7. Disconnect terminal 2 or 3 and ensure control cable returns to its original position and the vacuum returns to 0.

PRIZM

1. Ensure control cable freeplay is less than .39 inch, **Figs. 35 and 36,** adjusting as necessary.
2. Using a digital multimeter, J43029-A, or equivalent, measure resistance values between terminals 2 and 3, then measure resistance between terminals 1 and 3.
3. If resistance is not approximately 30 ohms between terminals 2 and 3, and approximately 68 ohms between terminals 1 and 3, replace actuator.
4. Disconnect actuator electrical connector.
5. Connect positive lead from battery to terminals 1 and 2 and the negative lead to terminal 3.
6. Using a hand held vacuum pump, J23738-A, or equivalent, slowly apply

vacuum from 0 to 11.8 inches Hg, ensuring control cable can be pulled smoothly.
7. Disconnect terminal 1 and 2, then check control cable returns to original position, and vacuum returns to 0 inches Hg.
8. If results are not as indicated, replace actuator.

VACUUM PUMP

1. Connect a hand held vacuum pump, J23738-A, or equivalent, to actuator side of vacuum pump.
2. Connect positive battery terminal to terminal 1 of vacuum pump.
3. Connect negative battery lead to terminal 2.
4. Ensure vacuum of 7.87 inches Hg or above.
5. If results are not as indicated, replace vacuum pump.

VACUUM SWITCH

1. **On 1988 models,** ensure no continuity between vacuum switch terminal and body with vacuum of 6.30 to 7.08 inches Hg applied.
2. **On 1989-90 models,** ensure no continuity between vacuum switch terminal 1 and 2 with vacuum of 6.30 to 7.08 inches Hg applied.
3. **On all models,** ensure no continuity between terminals with no vacuum applied.
4. If results are not as indicated, replace switch.

NEUTRAL SAFETY SWITCH
1988 NOVA

1. **On models equipped with ECT,** ensure continuity between terminals 2

and 3 with switch in "P" and "N" position.
2. **On models less ECT,** ensure continuity between terminals 1 and 2 with switch in "P" and "N" position.
3. **On all models,** if results are not as indicated, replace neutral safety switch.

PRIZM

1. Disconnect neutral safety switch electrical connector.
2. Connect a digital multimeter, J34029-A, or equivalent, to neutral safety switch terminals 1 and 2, then test continuity with switch in "P" and "N" position.
3. Ensure continuity between terminals 3 and 4 with switch in "R" position.
4. If results are not as indicated, replace neutral safety switch.

COMPONENT REPLACEMENT
CONTROL CABLE

1. Remove actuator cover attaching screws.
2. Disconnect control cable from actuator assembly.
3. Remove left lower dash trim panel.
4. Remove inner cable plate attaching nuts.
5. Remove outer cable plate attaching bolt.
6. Remove control cable from cable plate, then remove cable.
7. Reverse procedure to install.

ACTUATOR

1. Remove actuator electrical connector, then remove vacuum hose.
2. Remove actuator cover attaching screws, then remove cover.

3. Remove control cable as outlined previously.
4. Remove actuator attaching nuts.
5. Reverse procedure to install.

VACUUM PUMP

1. Disconnect vacuum pump electrical connector.
2. Disconnect vacuum hoses.
3. Remove vacuum pump attaching bolts, then remove vacuum pump.
4. Reverse procedure to install.

VACUUM SWITCH

1. Disconnect vacuum switch electrical connector.
2. Disconnect vacuum switch vacuum hose.
3. Unscrew vacuum switch, then remove vacuum switch.
4. Reverse procedure to install.

ENGAGEMENT SWITCH

The cruise control engagement switch is part of the multi-function lever, which must be replaced as an assembly. Refer to individual car chapter.

SPEED CONTROLS
ADJUST

This system utilizes the actuator cable for adjustment. Check that the cables are properly installed. Measure the cable stroke to where the throttle valve begins to open. If the cable stroke is not approximately .39 inches with a slight amount of freeplay, adjustment is required. Loosen cable tightening nut and carefully position cable forward until specification is met. **Do not stretch cable.**

Type 6

INDEX

DESCRIPTION & OPERATION

This cruise system is an electronic control system. The major components are the mode control switches, electronic module, servo unit, speed sensor, and wiring harness. Throttle actuation is accomplished by an electrically operated servo motor attached by cable to the vehicle's throttle linkage. The module also contains a speed limiting function which prevents system operation at speed below approximately 25 mph.

The mode control assembly consists of a 3 position slide-type switch and a set/coast button. To operate the system, the slide switch must be in On position and vehicle speed must be above 25 mph. The system is engaged at the desired speed by fully depressing, then releasing the set/coast button. Cruise speed can be increased from the set position by holding slider in Resume/Accel position, vehicle accelerates at a controlled rate until slider is released. When slider is released, the vehicle continues to cruise at that speed. Reducing set speed is accomplished by depressing and holding the Set/Coast

button until the desired speed is obtained.

The system can be disengaged at any time by depressing the brake or clutch pedal, or by moving the slide switch to off. If the system is disengaged by depressing the brake or clutch pedal, the last set speed will be retained in the module memory until the slide switch or ignition switch is moved to off.

SYSTEM COMPONENTS
ELECTRONIC MODULE

The electronic module interprets the po-

```
TROUBLE SHOOTING WITHOUT CIRCUIT ANALYZER
SYMPTOM                  CAUSE                    SOLUTION/TEST

Unit fails to engage     A. Blown fuse in         A. Replace 3 amp fuse. Check
(vehicle must be moving     power source             wiring and electrical connections
at least 30 mph)            circuit.                 for "shorting" to ground.

Prior to following       B. Insufficient ground   B. Inspect ground ring terminal
diagnostic procedures                                 attachment. Check pin 13 to
check overall integrity                               ground with ohmmeter. Should
of wiring and all                                     be less than 1/2 ohm. Insure
electrical connections                                proper connection.

                         C. Control mode "ON/OFF" C. Replace control arm if there
                            switch inoperative       is more than 100 ohms resistance
                                                      between pins 8 & 9 on main
                                                      wiring harness when switch is
                                                      actuated. (electronics module
                                                      disconnected).

                         D. Control mode "SET/     D. Replace control arm if there is
                            COAST switch             more than 100 ohms resistance
                            inoperative              between pins 7 & 9 on main
                                                      wiring harness when switch is
                                                      actuated (electronics module
                                                      disconnected).

                         E. Defective or           E. Verify proper electrical and
                            improperly adjusted       mechanical operation of brake
                            brake and/or clutch       and/or clutch switch. Switches
                            switch                    should interrupt 12 volts to
                                                      pin 20 on main wiring harness
                                                      when pedal(s) are depressed.
                                                      Repair or replace components if
                                                      necessary (refer to service
                                                      manual for correct switch
                                                      adjustment).

                         F. Defective speed        F. Replace sensor if continuity
                            sensor                    is not indicated with ohmmeter
                                                      4 times when speedometer cable
                                                      is turned one full rotation.
                                                      (Continuity should be less than
                                                      1 ohm.)
                                                      CAUTION Test the speed sensor
                                                      only with as ohmmeter to prevent
                                                      damage to the sensor contacts.
```

Fig. 1   Cruise control diagnostic procedure (Part 1 of 4). 1988 Sprint & Spectrum

sition of the servo unit, the position of the mode control switches, and the output of the speed sensor. In response to these inputs, the module electrically signals the servo motor to drive the actuating rack in or out. The electronic module is located under the dash on the driver's side.

SPEED SENSOR

The sensor utilizes a magnetic reel switch which opens and closes 4 times per revolution of the speedometer cable. The speed sensor is located near the transmission at the speedometer cable attachment point.

BRAKE DISENGAGEMENT SWITCH

When the brake pedal is depressed, the brake disengagement switch illuminates the stop lights and disengages the cruise function. One set of electrical contacts operates the stop lights, the other set operates the cruise disengage function. The stop light section of the switch also sends a disengage signal to the control module.

CLUTCH DISENGAGEMENT SWITCH

Used on vehicles with manual transmissions, the clutch disengagement switch disengages the cruise function whenever the clutch is depressed. The cruise function remains disengaged after the clutch pedal is released.

SERVO UNIT

The servo consists of an electric motor with reduction gearing, an electro magnetic clutch, an actuating rack, and a variable voltage position sensor. The servo operates the throttle in response to signals from the electronics module.

DIAGNOSIS

For cruise control system diagnosis, refer to **Fig. 1** for diagnostic procedures and to cruise control electrical circuits and connector pin locations, **Fig. 2**.

SPEED CONTROLS
ADJUST
CENTERING ADJUSTMENT

Operate vehicle at steady 55 mph, then depress set button. The speed control system should hold the vehicle at 55 mph. If speed control does not hold the vehicle speed, locate hole in electronic module cover and rotate adjusting up or down as required to adjust speed, **Fig. 3**.

SERVO CABLE ADJUSTMENT

Loosen servo cable clamp locknut. Adjust servo cable casing to place a light tension on servo cable, **Fig. 4**. Ensure tension on servo cable is not pulling the throttle off idle setting. Tighten servo cable clamp locknut.

DISENGAGEMENT SWITCH ADJUSTMENT

1. Measure brake pedal height, ensuring pedal return spring has completely returned pedal.
2. If measured value deviates from specifications, adjust as follows:
   a. Loosen stop light switch.
   b. Loosen push rod lock nut.
   c. Adjust push rod so brake pedal extends 6.07 inches from floorboard.
   d. Position tip of stop light switch against rubber stopper on pedal arm.
   e. Rotate stop light switch until free-play between pedal arm and push rod (about .1–.5 mm) is gone from brake pedal.
   f. Tighten lock nut.

CLUTCH SWITCH ADJUSTMENT

Loosen clutch switch locknut. Rotate clutch switch until threaded portion bottoms on switch bracket, then tighten locknut, **Fig. 5**.

SYMPTOM	CAUSE	SOLUTION/TEST
	G. Servo or servo cable malfunction	G. Replace servo or servo cable. Servo can be tested as follows: **ENGINE MUST NOT BE RUNNING** -Motor and Gear Drive Test 1. Disconnect the servo harness in the engine compartment. 2. Supply a ground to the orange and green wires. 3. Apply 12v to the blue and yellow wires. 4. With 12v applied to the blue and yellow wires (for less than 3 seconds) and ground supplied to the orange and green wires, the servo should pull the cable in. CAUTION DO NOT pull the servo full throttle when testing; a half inch is adequate. During this test the servo clutch is locked and will not disengage. By continuing to apply voltage, damage to the servo or the throttle linkage will occur. -Voltage Position Sensor Test 1. Disconnect the servo harness in the engine compartment. 2. The resistance between the red and green wire should be between 5000 and 7000 ohms. 3. At idle position the resistance between the white and green wires should be less than 500 ohms.
	H. Defective electronics module	H. Replace electronics module.
Unit engages, however unit does not operate properly.		
Surge or hunt during control operation	A. Damaged or improperly adjusted servo cable	A. Make any required repairs or adjustments (refer to service manual for correct cable adjustments)
	B. Speedometer flutter	B. Inspect speedometer cable for binding. Repair or replace if necessary.

Fig. 1 Cruise control diagnostic procedure (Part 2 of 4). 1988 Sprint & Spectrum

SYMPTOM	CAUSE	SOLUTION
	C. Defective electronics module	C. Replace electronics module.
	D. Defective servo	D. Replace servo.
	E. Vehicle engine or electrical malfunction	E. Tune engine as required. Inspect vehicles electrical system.
Servo motor runs with throttle at the idle position	A. Excess slack in servo cable	A. Adjust servo cable (refer to service manual for correct cable adjustment)
Unit does not "ACCELERATE" when "RESUME/ACCEL" switch is held in the R/A position (cruise control operates properly using "SET/COAST" mode)	A. Control mode "RESUME/ACCEL" switch inoperative	A. Replace control arm if there is more than 100 ohms resistance between pins 4 and 9 on main wiring harness when switch is activated. (electronics module disconnected)
	B. Damaged servo cable	B. Repair or replace if necessary.
	C. Defective electronics module	C. Replace electronics module.
Unit does not "RESUME" when "RESUME/ACCEL" switch is momentarily placed in the R/A position. (cruise control operates properly using "SET/COAST" mode)	A. Control mode "RESUME/ACCEL" switch inoperative	A. Replace control arm if there is more than 100 ohms resistance between pins 4 and 9 on the main wiring harness when switch is activated (electronics module disconnected)
	B. Control mode "RESUME/ACCEL" switch improperly operated.	B. Momentarily actuate switch for less than 1/2 second (Refer to mode control operation section)
	C. Damaged servo cable	C. Repair or replace if necessary.
	D. Defective electronics module	D. Replace electronics module.
Unit does not "TAP-UP" or "TAP-DOWN". (cruise control operates properly using "SET/COAST" and "RESUME/ACCEL" modes)	A. Defective electronics module	A. Replace electronics module.
Unit has poor response (speed loss on hills)	A. Restricted throttle linkage	A. Repair or replace servo cable.
	B. Vehicle engine or electrical malfunction	B. Tune engine as required. Inspect vehicles electrical system. (voltage to unit should be at least 12 1/2 volts when engine is running)

Fig. 1 Cruise control diagnostic procedure (Part 3 of 4). 1988 Sprint & Spectrum

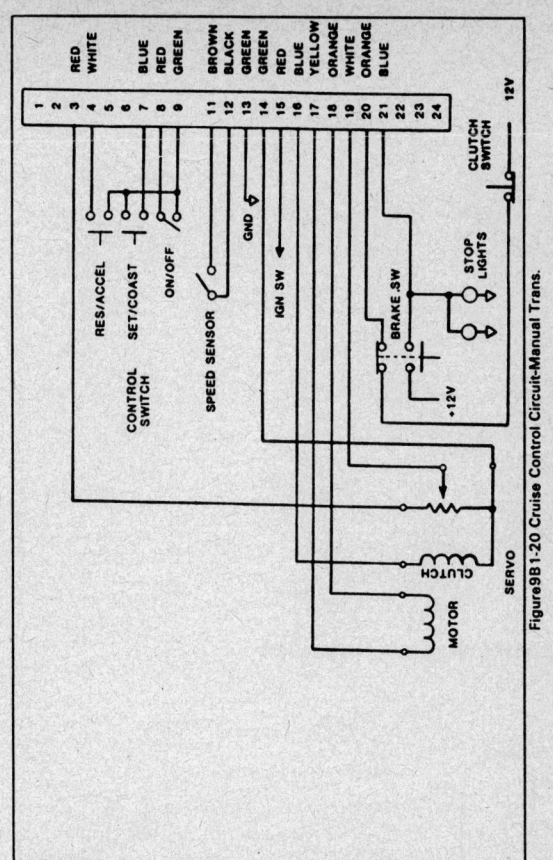

Figure 9B1-20 Cruise Control Circuit-Manual Trans.

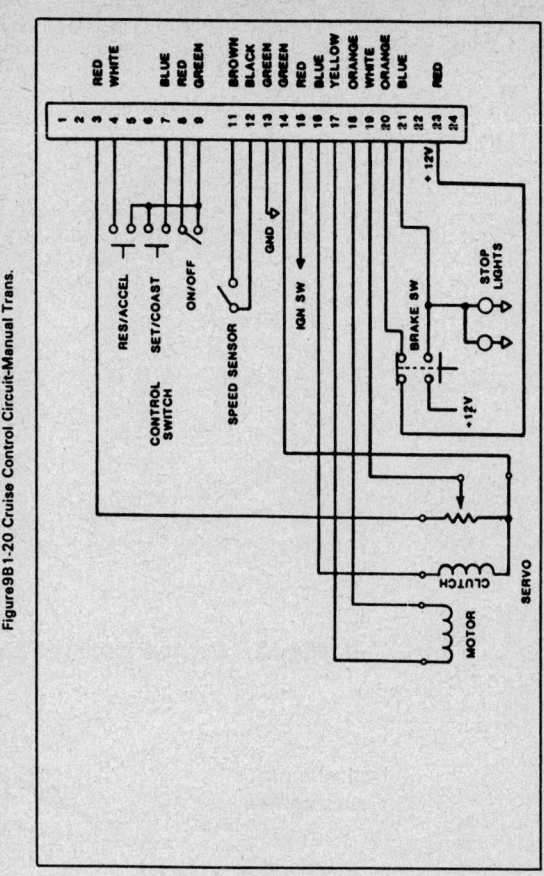

Fig. 2 Cruise control electrical circuit. 1988 Sprint & Spectrum

SYMPTOM	CAUSE	SOLUTION
Vehicle will not set to the desired speed within 2 mph.	C. Defective electronics module	C. Replace electronics module.
	A. Excess slack in servo cable	A. Adjust servo cable (refer to service manual for correct cable adjustments.
	B. Improper "centering" calibration	B. See centering adjustment procedure.
Cruise control disengages	A. Loose wiring connections	A. Check integrity of wiring and all electrical connectors.
	B. Improperly adjusted brake and/or clutch switch	B. Make needed adjustments (refer to service manual for correct switch adjustments)

Fig. 1 Cruise control diagnostic procedure (Part 4 of 4). 1988 Sprint & Spectrum

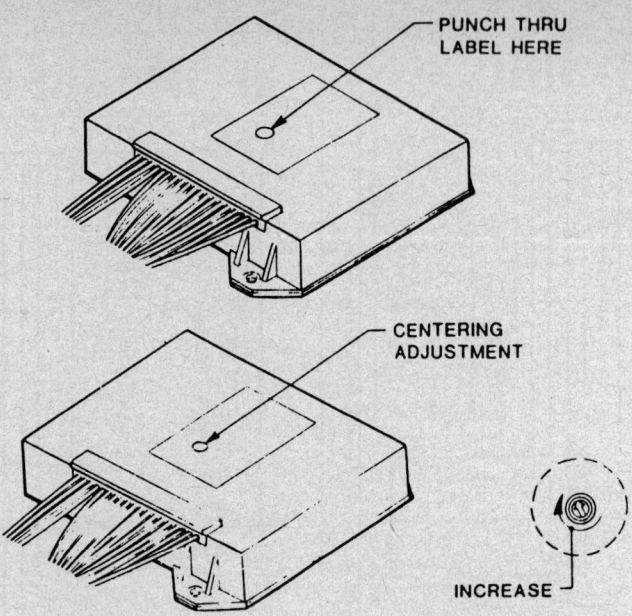

Fig. 3   Cruise control centering adjustment

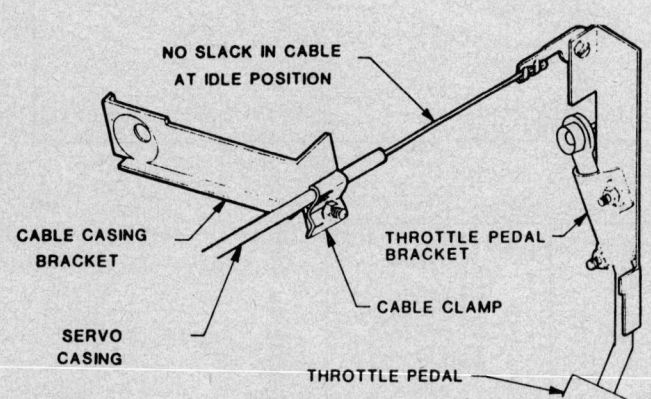

Fig. 4   Servo cable adjustment

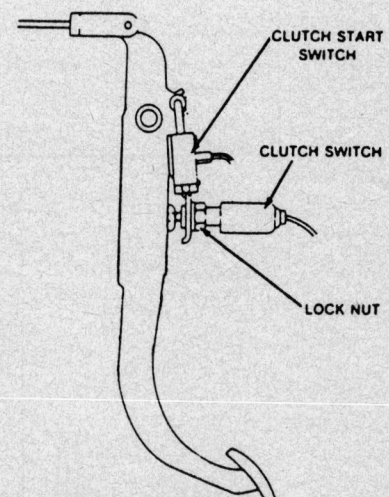

Fig. 5   Clutch switch adjustment

TROUBLESHOOTING SUPPLEMENT

TABLE OF CONTENTS

COOLING SYSTEM TROUBLESHOOTING

Refer to **Figs. 1 through 3,** for diagnostic procedures.

ELECTRICAL SYSTEM TROUBLESHOOTING

Refer to **Figs. 4 through 19,** for diagnostic procedures.

1988 Broughams models equipped with theft deterrent may experience a an inoperative or intermittent condition in theft deterrent system. This may be caused by an improperly installed door lock cylinder tamper switch. Refer to **Fig. 20,** for proper installation of tamper switch.

ENGINE TROUBLESHOOTING

For diagnostic procedures, refer to **Fig. 21** for all models except Metro, Spectrum and Sprint; **Fig. 22** for Metro and Sprint models and **Figs. 23 through 34** for Spectrum models.

SUSPENSION SYSTEM TROUBLESHOOTING

Refer to **Figs. 35 through 38** for diagnostic procedures.

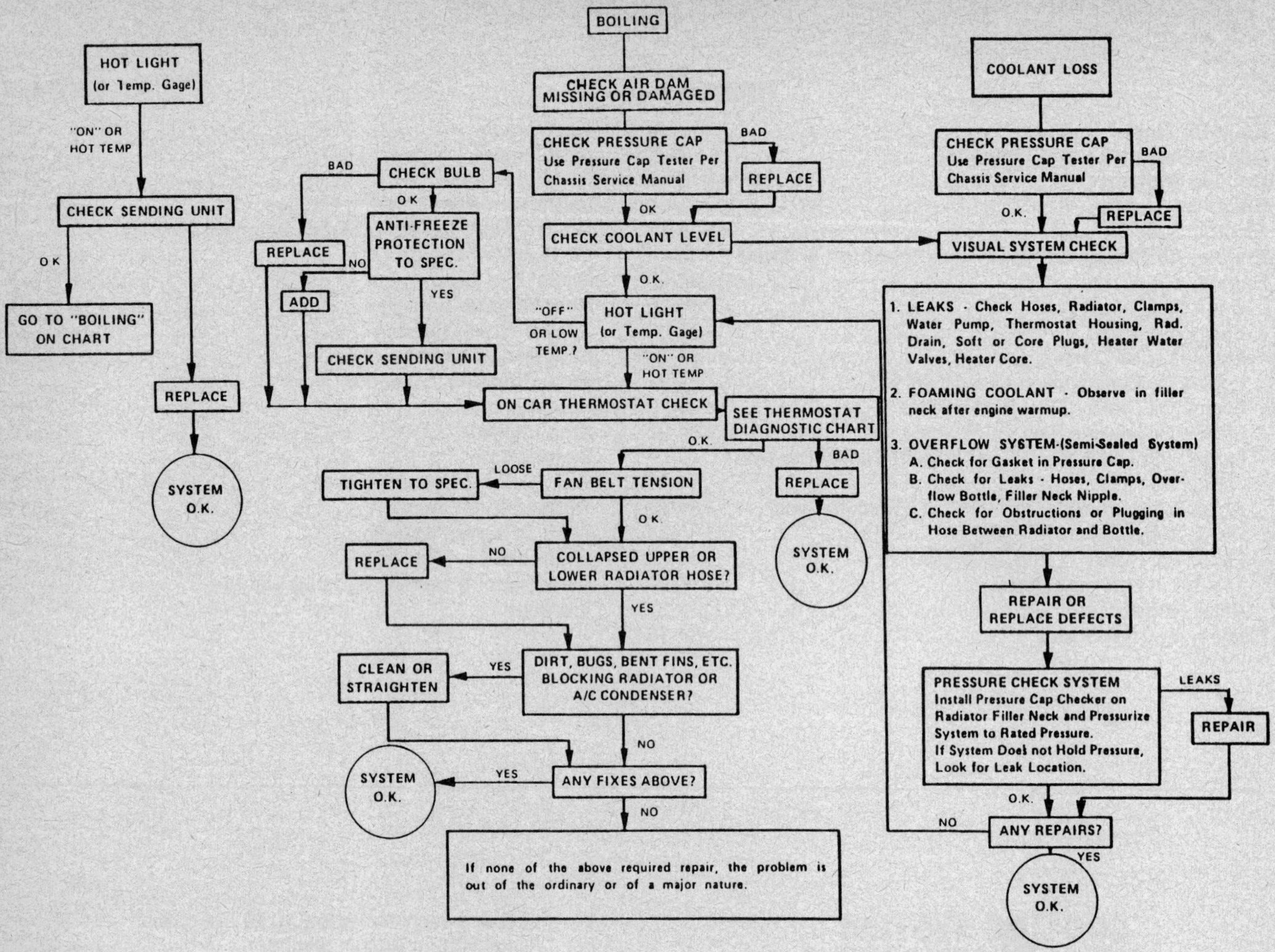

BOILING
CHECK AIR DAM MISSING OR DAMAGED
CHECK PRESSURE CAP Use Pressure Cap Tester Per Chassis Service Manual
BAD
REPLACE
OK
CHECK COOLANT LEVEL
O.K.
HOT LIGHT (or Temp. Gage)
"OFF" OR LOW TEMP ?
"ON" OR HOT TEMP
CHECK BULB
BAD
REPLACE
OK
ANTI-FREEZE PROTECTION TO SPEC.
NO
ADD
YES
CHECK SENDING UNIT
ON CAR THERMOSTAT CHECK
SEE THERMOSTAT DIAGNOSTIC CHART
O.K.
BAD
REPLACE
SYSTEM O.K.
FAN BELT TENSION
LOOSE
TIGHTEN TO SPEC.
O.K.
COLLAPSED UPPER OR LOWER RADIATOR HOSE?
NO
REPLACE
YES
DIRT, BUGS, BENT FINS, ETC. BLOCKING RADIATOR OR A/C CONDENSER?
YES
CLEAN OR STRAIGHTEN
NO
ANY FIXES ABOVE?
YES
SYSTEM O.K.
NO
If none of the above required repair, the problem is out of the ordinary or of a major nature.
HOT LIGHT (or Temp. Gage)
"ON" OR HOT TEMP
CHECK SENDING UNIT
OK
GO TO "BOILING" ON CHART
REPLACE
SYSTEM O.K.
COOLANT LOSS
CHECK PRESSURE CAP Use Pressure Cap Tester Per Chassis Service Manual
BAD
REPLACE
O.K.
VISUAL SYSTEM CHECK
1. LEAKS - Check Hoses, Radiator, Clamps, Water Pump, Thermostat Housing, Rad. Drain, Soft or Core Plugs, Heater Water Valves, Heater Core.
2. FOAMING COOLANT - Observe in filler neck after engine warmup.
3. OVERFLOW SYSTEM-(Semi-Sealed System)
A. Check for Gasket in Pressure Cap.
B. Check for Leaks - Hoses, Clamps, Overflow Bottle, Filler Neck Nipple.
C. Check for Obstructions or Plugging in Hose Between Radiator and Bottle.
REPAIR OR REPLACE DEFECTS
PRESSURE CHECK SYSTEM Install Pressure Cap Checker on Radiator Filler Neck and Pressurize System to Rated Pressure. If System Does not Hold Pressure, Look for Leak Location.
LEAKS
REPAIR
O.K.
ANY REPAIRS?
NO
YES
SYSTEM O.K.

Fig. 1 Cooling system

ENGINE OVERHEAT – BOILING – POOR ENGINE COOLING
1. RELIEVE PRESSURE AND CAREFULLY REMOVE RADIATOR CAP.
2. RUB 206°F. TEMPERATURE STICK* ONTO THERMOSTAT HOUSING.
3. WARM UP ENGINE AT FAST IDLE.
WATCH FOR COOLANT FLOW BEFORE MARK BEGINS TO MELT.
NO COOLANT FLOW
INSTALL NEW THERMOSTAT.
RE-CHECK TO BE SURE SYSTEM OK
COOLANT FLOW
PROBLEM IS CAUSED BY OTHER THAN BAD THERMOSTAT.
COLD ENGINE – SLOW WARMUP – NOT ENOUGH HEAT
1. RELIEVE PRESSURE AND CAREFULLY REMOVE RADIATOR CAP.
2. RUB 188°F. TEMPERATURE STICK* ONTO THERMOSTAT HOUSING.
3. WARM UP ENGINE AT FAST IDLE.
WATCH FOR COOLANT FLOW BEFORE MARK BEGINS TO MELT.
COOLANT FLOW
INSTALL NEW THERMOSTAT.
RE-CHECK TO BE SURE SYSTEM OK
NO COOLANT FLOW
PROBLEM IS CAUSED BY OTHER THAN BAD THERMOSTAT.

*NOTE: THE TEMPERATURE STICK IS A PENCIL LIKE DEVICE WHICH HAS A WAX MATERIAL CONTAINING CERTAIN CHEMICALS WHICH MELT AT A GIVEN TEMPERATURE. THEMPERATURE STICKS CAN BE USED TO DETERMINE A THERMOSTAT'S OPERATING TEMPERATURE BY RUBBING 188°F. AND 206°F. STICKS ON THE THERMOSTAT HOUSING. THE MARKS MADE BY THE STICKS SHOULD MELT WHEN COOLANT TEMPERATURES OF 188°F. AND 206°F. ARE REACHED, RESPECTIVELY. THESE TEMPERATURES ARE THE NORMAL OPERATING RANGE OF THE THERMOSTAT, THEREFORE, IF THE COOLANT FLOWS AS INDICATED ON THE DIAGNOSIS CHART, THE THERMOSTAT MAY BE DEFECTIVE.

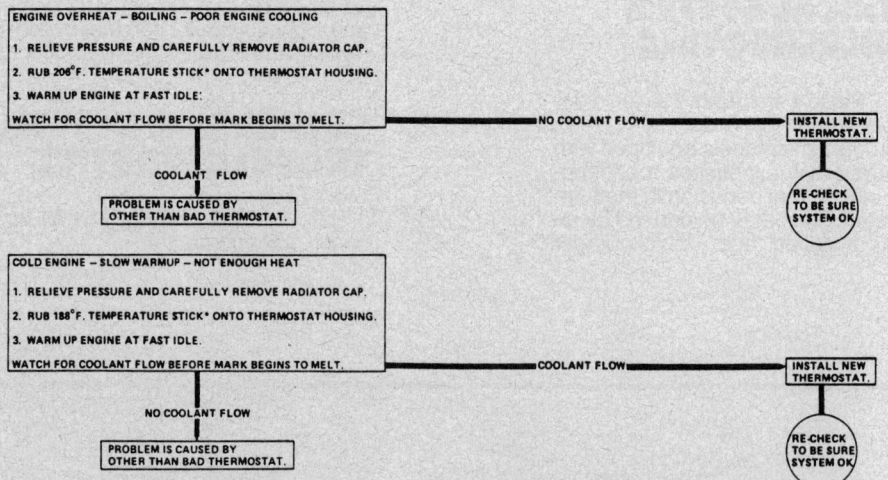

Fig. 2 Thermostat

HEATER TROUBLE DIAGNOSIS

INSUFFICIENT HEATING

Cause	Correction
Slow warming in car.	Incorrect operation of controls. Advise operator of proper operation of heater controls. Explain operation of vents and controls. Low coolant level. Check control cable and blower operation.
Objectionable engine or exhaust fumes in car.	Check for seal between engine compartment and plenum. Check for proper sealing between air inlet duct assembly and cowl. Locate and seal any other air leaks.
Cold drafts on floor.	Check operation and adjustment of vent cables. Advise operator of proper operation of heater system. Advise operator to use blower to force air to rear seat area. Check to be sure front floor mat is under floor mat retainer at cowl.
Insufficient heat to rear seat.	Obstruction on floor, possibly wrinkled or torn insulator material between front seat and floor. Advise operator to use HI blower speed.
Low engine coolant level - drop in heater air temperature at all blower speeds.	Check radiator and cooling system for leaks, correct and fill to proper level. Run engine to clear any air lock.
Failure of engine cooling system to warm up.	Check engine thermostat; replace if required. Check coolant level.
Kinked heater hoses.	Remove kink or replace hose.
Foreign material obstructing water flow through heater core.	Remove foreign material if possible, otherwise, replace core - can usually be heard as squishing noise in core.
Temperature door (valve) may be improperly adjusted. Air doors do not operate.	Adjust cable. Check installation and/or adjustment of air control or air-defrost cable.

INADEQUATE REMOVAL OF FOG OR ICE

Cause	Correction
Air door does not open. Defroster door does not open fully.	Check cable operation.
Air door does not open.	Check installation and/or adjustment of air control or air-defrost cable.
Temperature door does not open.	Check and adjust temperature control cable if necessary.
Obstructions in defroster outlets at windshield.	Remove obstruction. Look for and fix loose instrument panel pad cover at defroster outlet.
Damaged defroster outlets.	Reshape outlet flange with pliers. The outlet should have a uniform opening.
Blower motor not connected.	Connect wire. Check ground.
Inoperative blower motor.	Check heater fuse and wiring. Replace motor if necessary.
Inoperative blower motor switch.	Replace switch if necessary.

TOO WARM IN CAR

Cause	Correction
Temperature door improperly adjusted.	Adjust temperature cable.
Incorrect operation of controls.	Advise operator of proper operation of heater system.

BLOWER INOPERATIVE

Cause	Correction
Blown fuse.	Replace fuse.
Open circuit.	Repair circuit between ignition switch, blower switch and blower motor.
Inoperative blower motor switch.	Replace faulty switch.
Shorted or open blower resistor.	Check blower motor resistor.
Inoperative motor.	Replace motor.

MISCELLANEOUS

Cause	Correction
Blown fuses caused by short in electrical system.	Locate and correct short.
Front floor mat wet under heater caused by improperly sealed windshield or leaking heater core.	Reseal windshield, or lead-in from radio antenna. Repair (if possible) or replace heater core. Check for proper seal to cowl and for leak at hose connection on heater core. Hose leaking into the heater case is often misdiagnosed as leaking core.
Heater "gurgle," whine or "swish."	Check engine coolant level in radiator. Check for obstruction in core and/or hoses.

Fig. 3 Heater

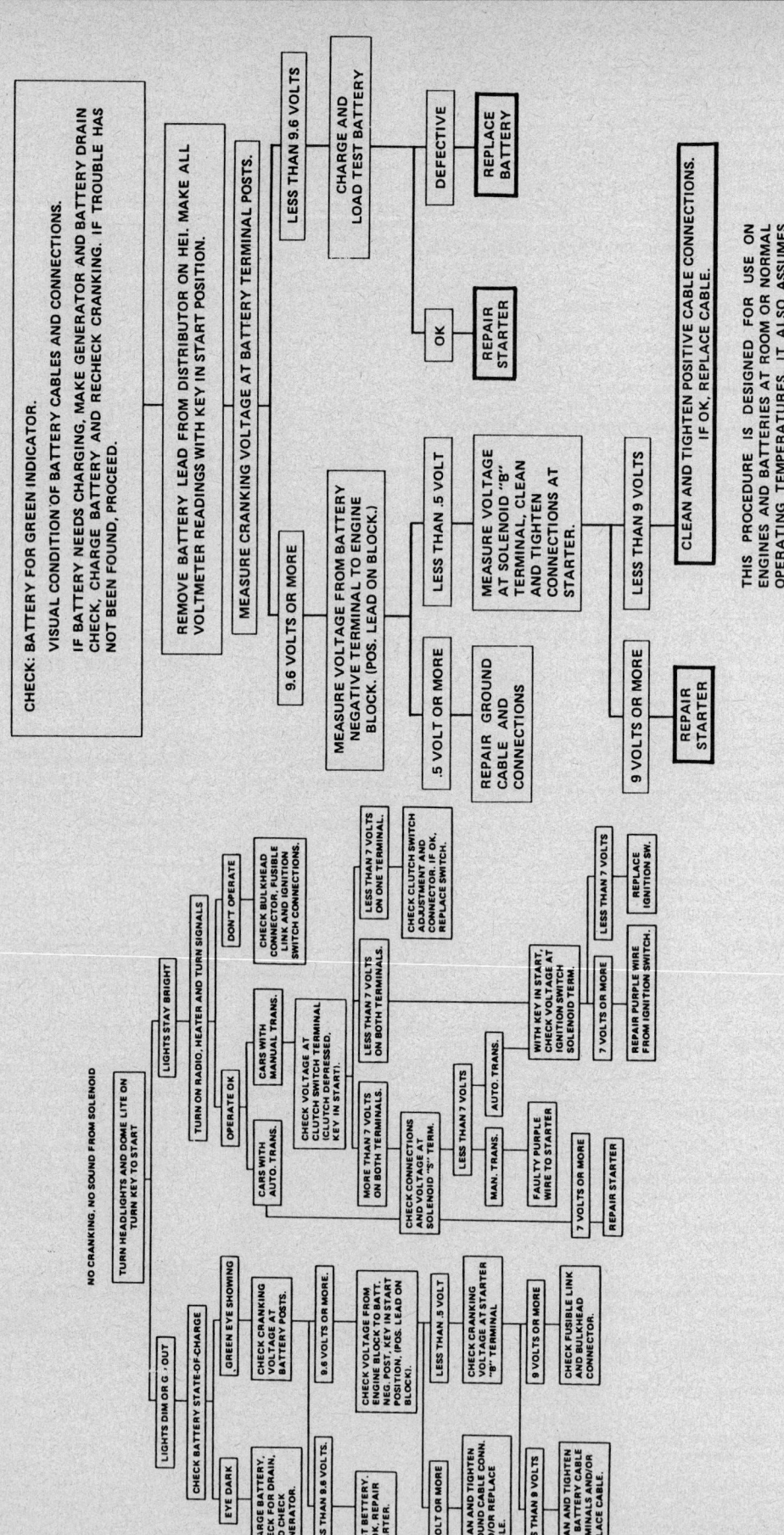

Fig. 4 Electrical system

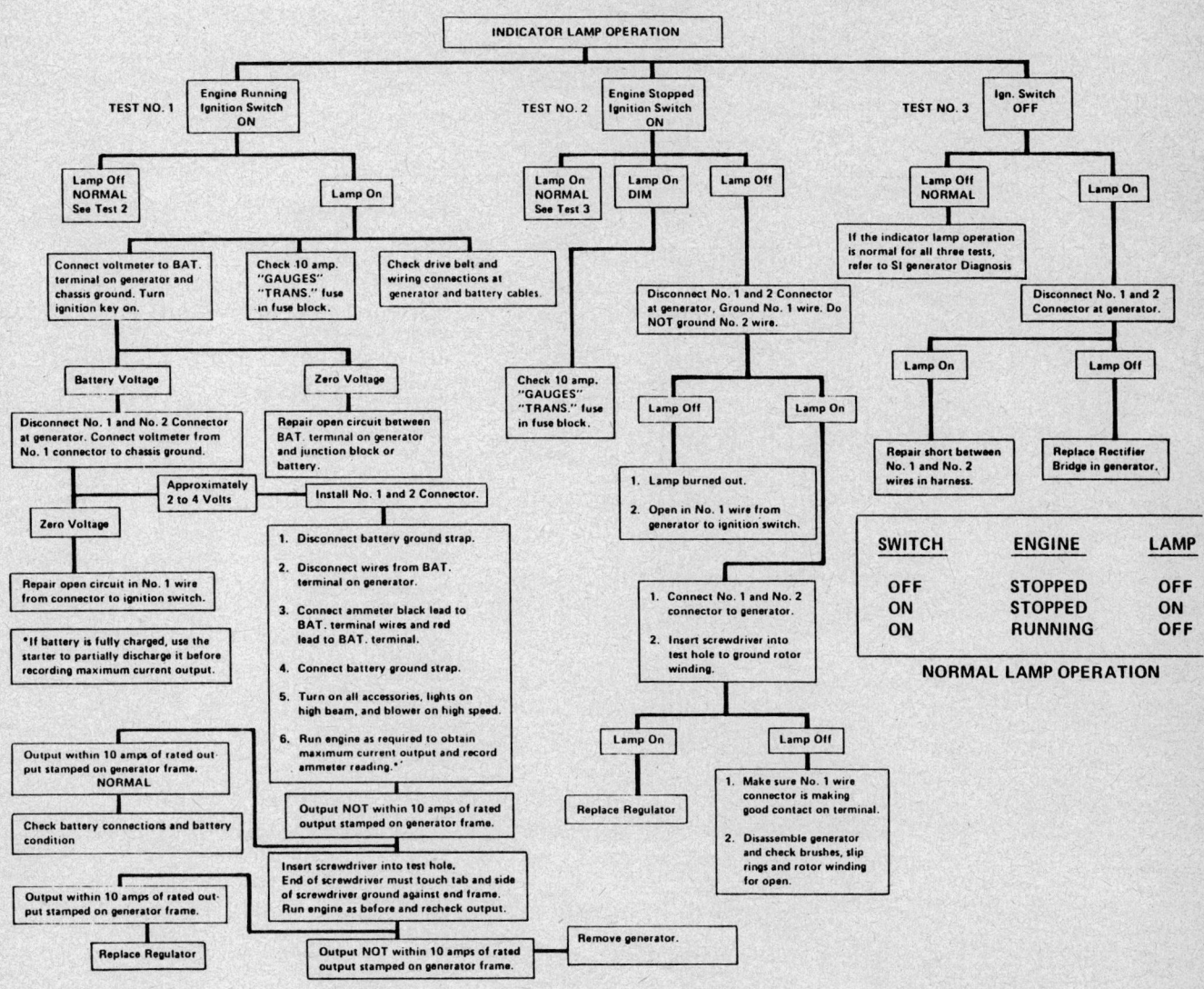

Fig. 5   Charge Indicator lamp system. 10Si, 12Si, 15Si, 17Si & 27Si models only

Condition	Possible Cause	correction
One headlight inoperative or intermittent	1. Loose connection	1. Secure connections to sealed beam including ground (black wire)
	2. Defective sealed beam unit.	2. Replace sealed beam.
One or more headlights are dim.	1. Open ground connection at headlight.	1. Repair black wire connection between sealed beam and body ground.
	2. Black ground wire mislocated in headlight connector (three-wire, hi-lo, connector only)	2. Relocate black wire in connector.
One or more headlights short life	1. Charge circuit problem.	charging system diagnosis.
All headlights inoperative or intermittent	1. Loose connection.	1. Check and secure connections at dimmer switch and light switch.
	2. Defective dimmer switch.	2. Check voltage at dimmer switch with test light.
	3. Open wiring - light switch to dimmer switch.	3. Check yellow wire with test light. If bulb lights at light switch yellow wire terminal but not at dimmer switch, repair open wire.
	4. Open wiring - light switch to battery.	4. Check red wire terminal at light switch with test light. If bulb does not light, repair open red wire circuit to battery (possible open fusible link).
	5. Shorted ground circuit.	5. If, after a few minutes operation, headlights flicker "ON" and "OFF" and or a thumping noise can be heard from the light switch (circuit breaker opening and closing), repair short to ground in circuit between light switch and headlights. After repairing short, check for headlight flickering after one minute operation. If flickering occurs, the circuit breaker has been damaged and light switch must be replaced.
	6. Defective light switch.	6. Check red and yellow wire terminals at light switch with test light. If bulb lights at red wire terminal but not at yellow terminal, replace light switch.
Upper or lower beam will not light or intermittent.	1. Open connection or defective dimmer switch.	1. Check dimmer switch terminals with test light. If bulb lights at light green or tan wire terminals, repair open wiring between dimmer switch and headlights. If bulb will not light at either of these terminals, depending upon switch position, replace dimmer switch.
	2. Short circuit to ground.	2. Follow diagnosis above (all headlights inoperative or intermittent)

Fig. 6   Headlights

Fig. 8 Tail, park and license light

Condition	Possible Cause	Correction
One side inoperative	1. Bulb burnt out	1. Replace bulb.
	2. Open connection at at bulb socket or ground wire terminal	2. Jumper bulb base socket connection to ground. If bulb lights, repair open ground circuit.
Both sides inoperative	1. Tail light fuse blown	1. Replace fuse. If new fuse blows, repair short to ground in **ground** wire circuit between fuse panel through light switch to lights.
	2. Loose connection	2. Secure connector at light switch.
	3. Open wiring	3. Using test light, check circuit on both sides of fuse. If test bulb does not light on either side, repair open circuit between fuse panel and battery (possible open fusible link). If test bulb lights at light switch **ground** wire terminal, repair open wiring between light switch and lamps.
	4. Multiple bulb burnout	4. If test bulb lights at lamp socket **ground** wire terminal, replace bulb(s).
	5. Defective light switch	5. If test bulb lights at light switch **power** wire but not at **ground** wire, replace defective light switch.

Fig. 7 Side marker light

Condition	Possible Cause	Correction
One light inoperative	1. Turn signal bulb burnt out (front light)	1. Switch turn signals on. If signal bulb does not light, replace bulb. (Bulb filament provides ground path for marker lamp bulb through the dark blue or brown wires.)
	2. Side marker bulb burnt out.	2. Replace bulb.
	3. Loose connection or open in wiring.	3. Using test light, check **ground** wire terminal at bulb socket. If test bulb lights, repair open ground circuit. If bulb does not light, repair open in **ground** wire circuit.
Front or rear lights inoperative.	1. Loose connection or open ground circuit.	1. If associated tail or park lights do not operate, check all connectors in **ground** wire circuit. If park and turn lights inoperative, repair open ground connections.
	2. Multiple bulbs burnt out.	2. Replace burnt out bulbs.
All lights inoperative	1. Blown fuse	1. If park and taillights do not operate, replace blown fuse. If new fuse blows, check for short to ground between fuse panel and lights.
	2. Loose connection	2. Secure connector to light switch.
	3. Open in wiring	3. Check taillight fuse with test light. If test bulb lights, repair open wiring between fuse and light switch. If not, repair open wiring between fuse and battery. (Possible open fusible link.)
	4. Defective light switch	4. Check light switch with test light. If test bulb lights at **power** wire but not at **ground** wire, replace light switch.

TURN SIGNAL AND HAZARD WARNING LIGHT(S)

Condition	Possible Cause	Correction
Turn signals inoperative one side	1. Bulb(s) burnt out (flasher cannot be heard)	1. Turn hazard warning system "ON." If one or more bulbs are inoperative, replace bulbs as necessary.
	2. Open wiring or ground connector	2. Turn hazard warning system on. If one or more bulbs are inoperative, use test light and check circuit at bulb socket. If test bulb lights, repair open ground connection. If not, repair open wiring between bulb socket and turn signal switch.
	3. Improper bulb or defective turn signal switch.	3. Turn hazard warning system on. If all front and rear lights operate, check for improper bulb. If bulbs are OK, replace defective turn signal switch.
	4. Short to ground. (Flasher can be heard, no bulbs operate)	4. Locate and repair short to ground by disconnecting front and rear circuits separately.
Turn signals inoperative	1. Blown turn signal fuse	1. Turn hazard warning system on. If all lights operate, replace blown fuse. If new fuse blows, repair short to ground between fuse and lamps.
	2. Defective flasher (located in convenience center near steering column)	2. If turn signal fuse is OK and hazard warning system will operate lights, replace defective turn signal flasher.
	3. Loose connection	3. Secure steering column connector.
Hazard Warning Inoperative	1. Blown stop-hazard fuse	1. Switch turn signals "ON." If lights operate, replace stop-hazard fuse if blown. If new fuse blows, repair short to ground. (Could be in stop light circuit.)
	2. Defective hazard warning flasher. (Located in convenience center).	2. If stop-hazard fuse is OK, switch turn signals on. If lights operate, replace defective hazard flasher.
	3. Open in wiring or defective turn signal switch.	3. Using test light, check input wire in turn signal steering column connector. If test bulb does not light, repair open circuit between flasher and connector. If test light indicates power on input wire and connection is good, use test light to check output terminals

Fig. 9 Turn signal & hazard warning lights

BACKUP LIGHT

Condition	Possible Cause	Correction
One light inoperative or intermittent	1. Loose or burnt out bulb. 2. Loose connection 3. Open ground connections.	1. Secure or replace bulb. 2. Tighten connectors. 3. Repair bulb ground circuit.
Both lights inoperative or intermittent.	1. Gear selector switch misadjusted (open when shifter lever is in reverse position) 2. Loose connection or open circuit 3. Blown fuse 4. Defective gear selector or backup light switch 5. Defective ignition switch	1. Readjust gear selector switch. 2. Check all connectors. If OK, check continuity of circuit from fuse to light on either side of fuse, correct open circuit from battery to fuse. 3. Replace fuse. If new fuse blows, repair short to ground in circuit from fuse through gear selector or from fuse through gear selector or backup light switch to backup lights. 4. With ignition "ON," check switch terminals in backup position with test light. If test bulb lights at the fuse block side, but not the other, replace light switch. 5. If test bulb lights at ignition switch battery terminal but not as output terminal, replace ignition switch.
Light will not turn off	1. Gear selector switch misadjusted (closed when shift lever is not in reverse position)	1. Readjust gear selector switch.

Fig. 10 Back-Up light

STOP LIGHTS

Condition	Possible Cause	Correction
One bulb inoperative	1. Bulb burnt out.	1. Replace bulb.
One side inoperative (multi-bulb design)	1. Loose connection, open wiring or defective bulbs. 2. Defective directional signal switch or cancelling cam	1. Turn on directional signal. If light does not operate, check bulbs. If bulbs are OK, check all connections. If light still does not operate, use test light and check for open wiring. 2. If light will operate by turning directional signal on, the switch is not centering properly during cancelling operation. Replace defective cancelling cam or directional signal switch.
All stop lights inoperative	1. Stop-hazard fuse blown 2. Open in wire from fuse to stop-switch 3. Stop-switch misadjusted or defective	1. Replace fuse. If new fuse blows, repair short to ground in circuit between fuse and lights. 2. Check for power at input wire at stop-switch and at fuse. If there is power at fuse but not at switch, check for open in brown wire. 3. With brake pedal depressed, check I/P side wire terminal in steering column connector with test light. If bulb does not light, check stop switch for proper adjustment. If adjustment is OK, jumper stop switch. If stop lights operate, replace stop switch.
Will not turn off	1. Stop switch misadjusted or defective	1. Readjust switch. If switch still malfunctions, replace.

Fig. 11 Stop light

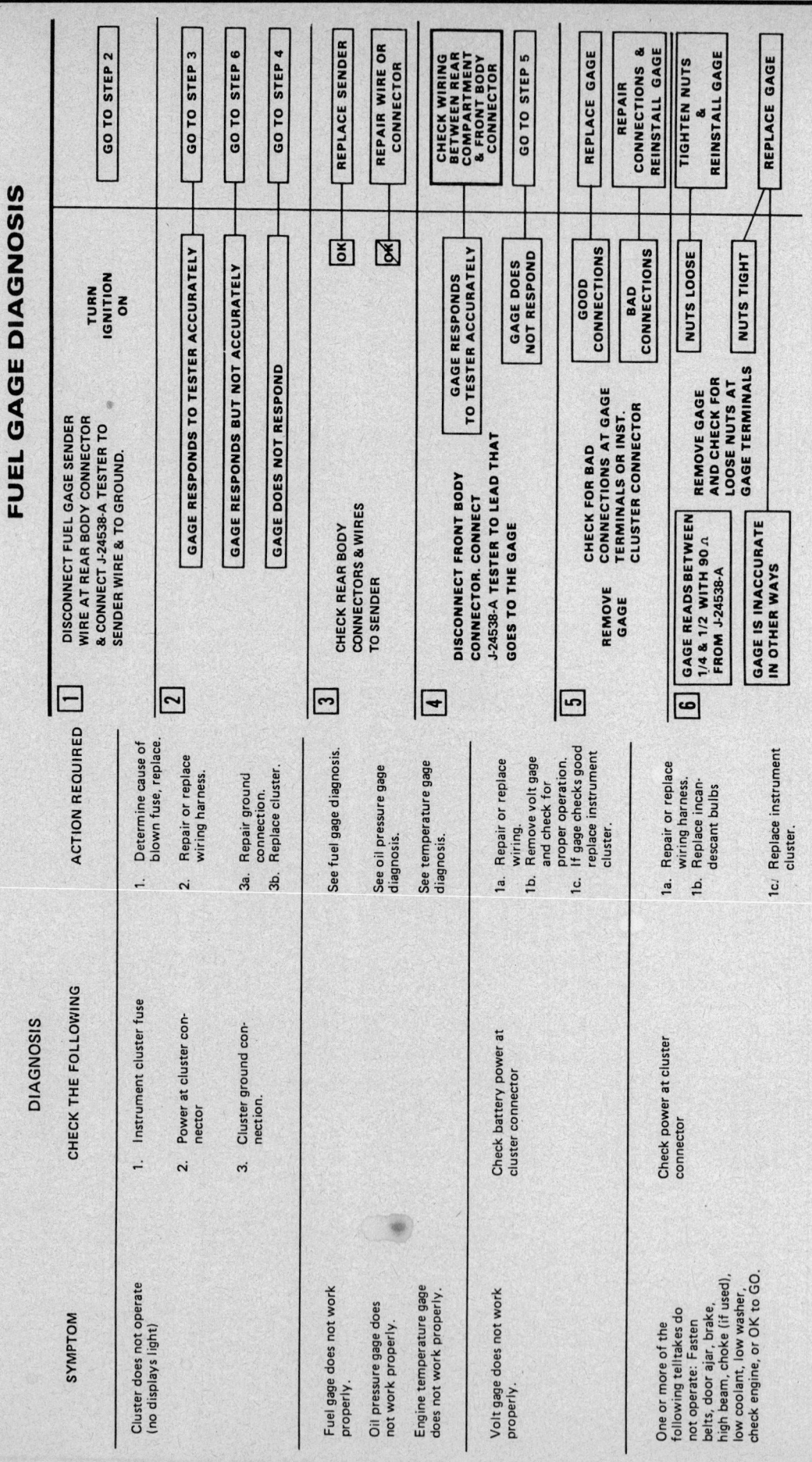

FUEL GAGE DIAGNOSIS

Fig. 13 Fuel gauge

Fig. 12 Gauges

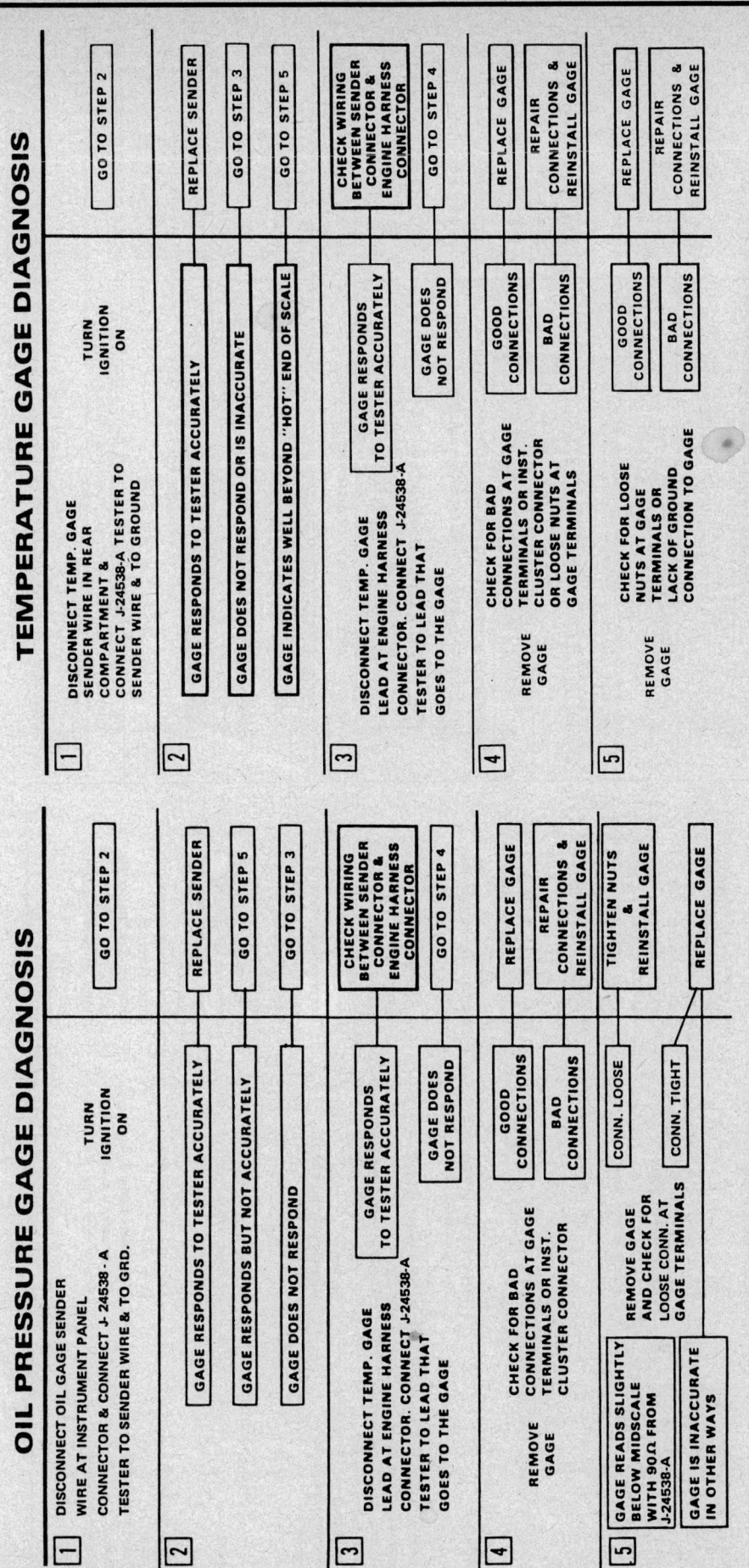

TEMPERATURE GAGE DIAGNOSIS

1. DISCONNECT TEMP. GAGE SENDER WIRE IN REAR COMPARTMENT & CONNECT J-24538-A TESTER TO SENDER WIRE & TO GROUND — TURN IGNITION ON — GO TO STEP 2

2. GAGE RESPONDS TO TESTER ACCURATELY — REPLACE SENDER
   GAGE DOES NOT RESPOND OR IS INACCURATE — GO TO STEP 3
   GAGE INDICATES WELL BEYOND "HOT" END OF SCALE — GO TO STEP 5

3. DISCONNECT TEMP. GAGE LEAD AT ENGINE HARNESS CONNECTOR. CONNECT J-24538-A TESTER TO LEAD THAT GOES TO THE GAGE — GAGE RESPONDS TO TESTER ACCURATELY — CHECK WIRING BETWEEN SENDER CONNECTOR & ENGINE HARNESS CONNECTOR
   GAGE DOES NOT RESPOND — GO TO STEP 4

4. REMOVE GAGE — CHECK FOR BAD CONNECTIONS AT GAGE TERMINALS OR INST. CLUSTER CONNECTOR OR LOOSE NUTS AT GAGE TERMINALS — GOOD CONNECTIONS — REPLACE GAGE
   BAD CONNECTIONS — REPAIR CONNECTIONS & REINSTALL GAGE

5. REMOVE GAGE — CHECK FOR LOOSE NUTS AT GAGE TERMINALS OR LACK OF GROUND CONNECTION TO GAGE — GOOD CONNECTIONS — REPLACE GAGE
   BAD CONNECTIONS — REPAIR CONNECTIONS & REINSTALL GAGE

Fig. 15 Temperature gauge

OIL PRESSURE GAGE DIAGNOSIS

1. DISCONNECT OIL GAGE SENDER WIRE AT INSTRUMENT PANEL CONNECTOR & CONNECT J-24538-A TESTER TO SENDER WIRE & TO GRD. — TURN IGNITION ON — GO TO STEP 2

2. GAGE RESPONDS TO TESTER ACCURATELY — REPLACE SENDER
   GAGE RESPONDS BUT NOT ACCURATELY — GO TO STEP 5
   GAGE DOES NOT RESPOND — GO TO STEP 3

3. DISCONNECT TEMP. GAGE LEAD AT ENGINE HARNESS CONNECTOR. CONNECT J-24538-A TESTER TO LEAD THAT GOES TO THE GAGE — GAGE RESPONDS TO TESTER ACCURATELY — CHECK WIRING BETWEEN SENDER CONNECTOR & ENGINE HARNESS CONNECTOR
   GAGE DOES NOT RESPOND — GO TO STEP 4

4. REMOVE GAGE — CHECK FOR BAD CONNECTIONS AT GAGE TERMINALS OR INST. CLUSTER CONNECTOR — GOOD CONNECTIONS — REPLACE GAGE
   BAD CONNECTIONS — REPAIR CONNECTIONS & REINSTALL GAGE

5. GAGE READS SLIGHTLY BELOW MIDSCALE WITH 90Ω FROM J-24538-A — REMOVE GAGE AND CHECK FOR LOOSE CONN. AT GAGE TERMINALS — CONN. LOOSE — TIGHTEN NUTS & REINSTALL GAGE
   CONN. TIGHT — REPLACE GAGE
   GAGE IS INACCURATE IN OTHER WAYS — REPLACE GAGE

Fig. 14 Oil pressure gauge

DIAGNOSIS - SPEEDOMETER SYSTEM

COMPLAINT	POSSIBLE CAUSE	PROCEDURE
Noisy	Kinked, pinched or burned casings.	Replace both the cable and casing. Recheck for noise.
Noisy	Bent or improper length cable tips.	Replace both the cable and casing. Recheck for noise. If cable is too long, carefully clip a short length, then check for noise.
Noisy	Improper or insufficient lubrication of cable.	Lubricate cable with P/N 6478535 lubricant or equivalent. Pack ferrule with lubricant.
Noisy	Faulty driven gear or rough drive gear.	Remove driven gear assembly from transmission. Check for free rotation of gear in sleeve. Check for burrs, flash or unusual worn spots. If gears appear faulty, replace and recheck for noise.
Whine	Oversize driven gear stem in transmission binds with adapter.	Replace driven gear and stem.
Buzzing sound with manual transmission.	Shift linkage vibration.	Adjust transmission shift linkage.
Ticking or ringing sound with jumpy pointer between 0 and 30 MPH.	Faulty speedometer head, or kinked cable (see above).	Remove speedometer head for repair.
Sticky speedometer pointer.	Speedometer pointer is bent and rubs.	Remove speedometer cluster or lens and straighten pointer. Recheck speedometer operation.
Incorrect calibration.	Wrong transmission adapter, driven gear, drive gear, or sleeve.	Check speedometer gear reference for correct application and replace if necessary.
Incorrect calibration.	Oversize or undersize tires.	Check calibration using correct tire size.
Incorrect calibration.	Faulty speedometer head (if odometer is correct).	Remove speedometer for repair.
Incorrect calibration.	Wrong axle ratio.	Check for proper axle ratio and repair as necessary.

Fig. 16 Speedometer system

ELECTRIC SPEEDOMETER DIAGNOSIS
WITH TOOL: (SPEEDOMETER SIGNAL GENERATOR)

Step	Procedure	Result	Action
1.	VISUALLY EXAMINE THE TRANSMISSION SENSOR (PM GENERATOR) CONNECTOR TO INSURE THAT IT IS NOT LOOSE, CORRODED, BROKEN, OR OTHERWISE DEFECTIVE.	OK	GO TO STEP 3.
		X	GO TO STEP 2.
2.	REPLACE, CLEAN, OR TIGHTEN CONNECTOR AS REQUIRED.		RECHECK FOR OPERATIVE SPEEDOMETER AND ODOMETER MODULES.
3.	DISCONNECT THE SPEEDOMETER SENSOR HARNESS AT THE PM GENERATOR. CONNECT THE SPEEDOMETER HARNESS TO THE SIGNAL GENERATOR SENSOR CONNECTOR AND TURN TESTER ON. CHECK THAT THE SPEEDOMETER READS 54 ± 2 MPH.	OK	GO TO STEP 4.
		X	GO TO STEP 5.
4.	REPLACE PM GENERATOR.	OK	RECHECK FOR OPERATIVE SPEEDOMETER AND ODOMETER MODULES.
5.	REMOVE CLUSTER FROM VEHICLE AND VISUALLY CHECK HARNESS AND CLUSTER PRINTED CIRCUIT FOR DISCONTINUITY IN WIRING.	OK	GO TO STEP 7.
		X	GO TO STEP 6.
6.	REPLACE WIRING OR PRINTED CIRCUIT AS REQUIRED.		RECHECK FOR OPERATIVE SPEEDOMETER AND ODOMETER MODULES.
7.	CONNECT SIGNAL GENERATOR TO SPEEDOMETER EDGE-BOARD CONNECTOR AND TURN TESTER ON.		GO TO STEP 8.
8.	SPEEDOMETER READS 54 ± 2 MPH AND ODOMETER TURNS.		GO TO STEP 9.
	SPEEDOMETER DOES NOT READ 54 ± 2 MPH AND ODOMETER DOES NOT TURN.		GO TO STEP 10.
	SPEEDOMETER DOES NOT READ 54 ± 2 MPH BUT ODOMETER TURNS.		GO TO STEP 10.
	SPEEDOMETER READS 54 ± 2 MPH ODOMETER DOES NOT TURN.		GO TO STEP 12.
9.	CHECK CONNECTION BETWEEN CLUSTER AND WIRING HARNESS.		REPLACE WIRING HARNESS AS REQUIRED.
10.	DISASSEMBLE CLUSTER AND CHECK GAGE		GO TO STEP 11.
11.	GAGE FUNCTIONS		GO TO STEP 12 FOR ODOMETER DIAGNOSIS.
	GAGE DOES NOT FUNCTION		OBTAIN REPLACEMENT SPEEDOMETER ASSEMBLY.
12.	CHECK FOR LOOSE WIRING CONNECTION BETWEEN ODOMETER MOTOR TERMINALS AND CIRCUIT BOARD.		IF CONNECTION IS NOT LOOSE OR BROKEN, GO TO STEP 13 OTHERWISE REPLACE ODOMETER MOTOR TO OBTAIN EXCHANGE CIRCUIT BOARD ASSEMBLY AS REQUIRED.
13.	CONNECT SIGNAL GENERATOR ODOMETER CONNECTOR TO ODOMETER MOTOR LEAD AND TURN TESTER ON.		
	ODOMETER MOTOR WORKS.		GO TO STEP 14.
	ODOMETER MOTOR DOES NOT WORK.		OBTAIN EXCHANGE CIRCUIT BOARD ASSEMBLY.
14.			REPLACE ODOMETER MOTOR AND RECONNECT MOTOR TO CIRCUIT BOARD ASSEMBLY.

Fig. 17 Electrical speedometer

Complaint	Probable Cause	Correction
System totally inoperative.	Open in one of the following wires: 1. Ground wire (black) in controller cavity. (A) 2. Battery feed. (N) 3. Electric door lock wire. 4. Blown fuses. 5. Malfunctioning Controller.	Repair or replace as needed. / Same as above.
	Check for loose connectors at controller to instrument panel harness or instrument panel harness to body harness.	Repair or replace as needed.
Inoperative horn in alarm mode.	Malfunctioning Controller. Horn Fuse.	Replace after investigating previously listed causes.
Unable to reverse arming process with "UNLOCK" switch.	Open in door "UNLOCK" wire circuit.	Inspect circuit from door lock to controller.
	Malfunctioning controller.	Replace after investigating previously listed causes.
System operates normally except does not disarm.	Check for: 1. Open door jamb wire to driver's door. 2. Malfunctioning door key lock switch. 3. Open ground wire inside door. B. If system cannot be disarmed: 1. Check for open at door jamb wire at controller with door lock cylinder in unlock position. 2. Malfunctioning controller.	Repair or replace as needed. / Replace after investigating previously listed causes.

Complaint	Probable Cause	Correction
Upon closing doors, system will not arm.	LOCK CYLINDER VIOLATED or unwanted ground at door jamb switches, door tamper roof panels, switch or pinched wires leading to these components. Door lock tamper switch out of adjustment.	Check for unwanted ground in light blue wire (cavity D) in body to dash harness connector. Repair as necessary.
Alarm activates by itself.	Check for too close adjustment of door jamb switches.	Readjust or replace as necessary.
System cannot be armed.	1. Check for ground at body to dash harness connector (cavity C). 2. Courtesy lights do not shut off, also 3. Check for ground at gm-lgt wire at controller.	Readjust or replace as necessary. / Repair or replace as needed. / Repair grounding condition. / Repair or replace as needed.

Fig. 19 Theft deterrent system

CONDITION	CAUSE	CORRECTION
System is inoperative (monitor lamp will not light)	Circuit breaker open from an electrical short in the power feed circuit	Check for electrical short in power feed circuit of body harness. Circuit breaker will reset itself when short circuit is corrected.
	Burned fusible link	Check for short circuit between starter solenoid and circuit breaker.
	Burned out or missing monitor lamp	Check lamp mounted in switch.
	Open circuit in either of the wiring harnesses	Check affected wiring for open circuit and check wiring connectors.
	Inoperative or disconnected control timer assembly	Check harness connection to timer assembly.
		Check for proper ground.
	Defective control switch	Check for relay "pull in" (click) when 12 volts is applied to the light blue wire terminal of timer assembly. If no pull in, replace timer assembly.
		With switch held in "ON" position and connector installed on switch, connect a test light to the light blue wire terminal with connector on rear of switch to ground. Test light should glow brightly; if not, replace switch.
System operates but will not turn off automatically in 10-15 minutes	Defective control switch	With test light connected to center terminal as described in step above, test light should glow brightly in "ON" position and dim when switch is released. If not, switch is defective.
	Defective control timer assembly	Replace timer assembly.
System operates but won't stay on for full time cycle	Defective control timer assembly	Replace timer assembly.

Fig. 18 Rear window defogger

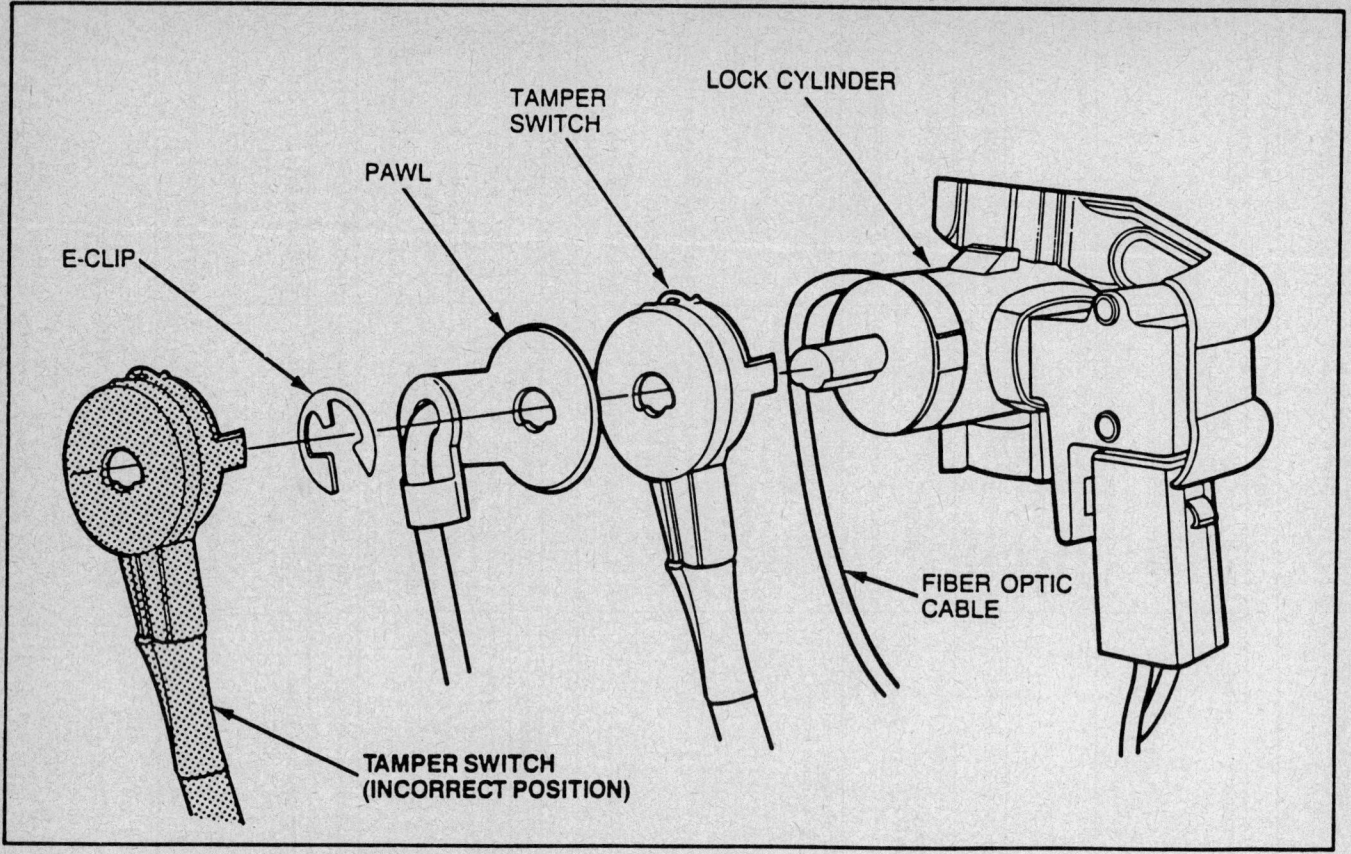

Fig. 20 Theft deterrent system door lock cylinder tamper switch installation

EXCESSIVE OIL LOSS

- External oil leaks. Tighten bolts and/or replace gaskets and seals as necessary.

- Improper reading of dipstick. Check oil with car on a level surface and allow adequate drain-down time.

- Improper oil viscosity. Use recommended S.A.E. viscosity for prevailing temperatures. See Owner's Manual for proper specifications.

- Continuous high speed driving, and/or severe usage such as trailer hauling, will normally cause decreased oil mileage.
- PCV system malfunctioning.
- Valve guides and/or valve stem seals worn, or seals omitted. Ream guides and install oversize service valves and/or new valve stem seals.
- Piston rings broken, worn, or not seated. Allow adequate time for rings to seat. Replace broken or worn rings as necessary.
- Piston improperly installed or misfitted.

LOW OIL PRESSURE

- Slow idle speed. Set idle speed to correct specification, if not ECM controlled.
- Incorrect or malfunctioning oil pressure switch.
- Incorrect or malfunctioning oil pressure gage. Replace with proper gage.
- Improper oil viscosity or diluted oil. Install oil of proper viscosity for expected temperature, or install new oil if diluted with moisture or unburned fuel mixtures.

- Oil pump worn or dirty.
- Plugged oil filter.
- Oil pickup screen loose or plugged.
- Hole in oil pickup tube.
- Excessive bearing clearance. Replace if necessary.
- Cracked, porous or plugged oil galleys. Repair or replace block.
- Galley plugs missing or misinstalled. Install plugs or repair as necessary.
- Poor seal at timing cover gasket (VINS A, E, 3, 4, and 9 engine only). Replace gasket.

VALVE TRAIN NOISE

- Low oil pressure. Repair as necessary. (See diagnosis above for low oil pressure.)
- Loose rocker arm attachments. Inspect and repair as necessary.
- Worn rocker arm and/or pushrod.

- Broken valve spring.
- Sticking valves.
- Lifters worn, dirty, or defective. Clean, inspect, test and replace as necessary.
- Camshaft worn, or poor machining. Replace camshaft.
- Worn valve guides.

**Fig. 21 Engine, mechanical (Part 1 of 2). Except Metro,
Spectrum & Sprint**

KNOCKS COLD AND CONTINUES FOR TWO TO THREE MINUTES.

INCREASES WITH TORQUE.

- Vacuum operated EFE engines may have valve knock. Replace EFE valve.
- Flywheel contacting splash shield. Reposition splash shield.
- Loose or broken balancer or drive pulleys. Tighten or replace as necessary.

- Excessive piston to bore clearance. Replace piston.
  Cold engine piston knock usually disappears when the cylinder is grounded out. Cold engine piston knock which disappears in 1.5 minutes should be considered acceptable.
- Bent connecting rod.

HEAVY KNOCK HOT WITH TORQUE APPLIED

- Broken balancer or pulley hub. Replace parts as necessary.
- Loose torque converter bolts.
- Accessory belts too tight or nicked. Replace and/or tension to specs as necessary.

- Exhaust system grounded. Reposition as necessary.
- Flywheel cracked.
- Excessive main bearing clearance. Replace as necessary.
- Excessive rod bearing clearance. Replace as necessary.

LIGHT KNOCK HOT

- Detonation or spark knock. Check operation of EST or ESC   Check engine timing and fuel quality.

- Loose torque converter bolts.
- Exhaust leak at manifold. Tighten bolts and/or replace gasket.
- Excessive rod bearing clearance. Replace bearings as necessary.

KNOCKS ON INITIAL START-UP BUT ONLY LASTS A FEW SECONDS

- Noisy mechanical fuel pump. Replace pump.
- Improper oil viscosity. Install proper oil viscosity for expected temperatures.
- Hydraulic lifter bleed down. Clean, test and replace as necessary.

When the engine is stopped, some valves will be open. Spring pressure against lifters will tend to bleed lifter down. Attempts to repair should be made only if the problem is consistent.
- Excessive crankshaft end clearance. Replace crankshaft thrust bearing.
- Excessive front main bearing clearance. Replace worn parts.

KNOCKS AT IDLE HOT

- Loose or worn drive belts. Tension and/or replace as necessary.
- A/C Compressor or generator bearing. Replace as necessary.
- Noisy mechanical fuel pump. Replace pump.
- Valve train. Replace parts as necessary.
- Improper oil viscosity. Install proper viscosity oil for expected temperature.

- Excessive piston pin clearance. Ream and install oversize pins. (VIN R and 2) or replace piston and pin.
- Connecting rod alignment. Check and replace rods as necessary.
- Insufficient piston to bore clearance. Hone bore and fit new piston.
- Loose crankshaft balancer. Torque and/or replace worn parts.
- Piston pin offset to wrong side. Install correct piston.

ENGINE OVERHEATS

1. Coolant system leak, oil cooler system leak or coolant recovery system not operating. Check for leaks and correct as required. Check coolant recovery tank, hose and radiator cap.

2. Belt slipping or damaged. Replace tensioner or belt as required.

3. Thermostat stuck closed. Check and replace if required.
4. Electrical cooling fan operation.

5. Head gasket leaking. Check and repair as required.

INSTRUMENT PANEL OIL WARNING LAMP "ON" AT IDLE

1. Oil cooler or oil or cooler line restricted. Remove restrictions in cooler or cooler line.

2. Oil pump pressure low.

Fig. 21   Engine, Mechanical (Part 2 of 2). Except Metro, Spectrum & Sprint

ENGINE DIAGNOSIS

Condition	Possible Causes	Correction
Hard Starting	IGNITION SYSTEM OUT OF ORDER.	
(Engine cranks OK)	• Faulty spark plug	Clean and adjust plug gap or replace.
	• Loose or disconnected spark plug wires or coil wire.	Repair or replace.
	• Improper ignition timing	Adjust.
	• Faulty ignition coil	Replace.
	Fuel system out of order	
	• Dirty fuel filter	Replace.
	• Dirty or clogged fuel pipe	Clean.
	• Dirty or clogged carburetor	Disassemble and clean.
	• Fuel pump will not work properly	Replace.
	• Carburetor choke will not work properly	Check and adjust.
	• Improper adjustment	Adjust.
	• Malfunctioning fuel cut solenoid valve	Check solenoid valve for proper opertion. Replace if necessary.
	• Lack of fuel in fuel tank	Refill
	LOW COMPRESSION	
	• Incorrect spark plug tightening or faulty gasket	Tighten to specified torque or replace gasket.
	• Improper grade engine oil or low viscosity	Replace with proper grade oil.
	• Incorrect valve lash	Adjust.
	• Compression leak from valve seat	Remove cylinder head and lap valves.
	• Sticky valve stem	Correct or replace valve and valve guide.
	• Weak or damaged valve springs	Replace valve springs.
	• Compression leak at cylinder head gasket	Replace gasket.
	• Sticking or damaged piston ring	Replace piston rings.
	• Worn piston, ring or cylinder	Replace ring and piston. Rebore or replace cylinder.
	EMISSION CONTROL	
	• Malfunctioning PCV	Replace
	• Loose or disconnected vacuum hoses	Connect securely.
	• Malfunctioning fuel cut solenoid valve	Check and replace as necessary.
	• ECM is poorly grounded	Ground ECM securely.
Engine has no power.	Low compression.	Previously outlined.
	IGNITION SYSTEM OUT OF ORDER.	
	• Incorrect ignition timing.	Adjust.
	• Defective spark plugs	Replace.
	• Worn distributor terminals	Clean or replace. Also check rotor.
	• Loose or disconnected spark plug wires or coil wire.	Connect or replace as necessary.
	FUEL SYSTEM OUT OF ORDER.	
	• Malfunction of choke system	Adjust or replace.
	• Clogged fuel pipe	Clean.
	• Dirty or clogged fuel filter	Replace.
	• Fuel pump will not work properly	Replace.
	• Clogged carburetor jets.	Disassemble and clean.
	AIR INTAKE SYSTEM OUT OF ORDER.	
	• Clogged air cleaner	Clean or replace.
	• Malfunction of thermostatically controlled air cleaner	Check and correct.

Fig. 22 Engine, (Part 1 of 7). Metro & Sprint

Part 2 of 7

Symptom	Probable Cause	Remedy
Improper engine idling.	• Air leaking from intake manifold gasket or carburetor gasket	Replace gasket.
	EMISSION CONTROL.	
	• Malfunctioning EGR valve	Check and replace as necessary.
	• Malfunctioning bowl vent solenoid valve	Check and replace as necessary.
	• Malfunctioning high altitude switch	Check and replace as necessary.
	• Malfunctioning throttle position switch (wide open switch)	Check and replace as necessary.
	Others	
	• Dragging brakes	Adjust or replace.
	• Slipping clutch	Adjust or replace.
	FUEL SYSTEM OUT OF ORDER.	
	• Clogged carburetor jets	Clean.
	• Incorrect idle adjustment	Adjust.
	• Clogged air cleaner element	Clean or replace.
	• Leaky manifold, carburetor or cylinder head gaskets	Replace.
	• Improper float level	Adjust.
	• Malfunctioning carburetor choke	Check and adjust.
	IGNITION SYSTEM OUT OF ORDER.	
	• Defective spark plug	Check and replace as necessary.
	• Worn or disconnected coil wire	Connect or replace as necessary.
	• Worn distributor terminals	Replace.
	• Improper ignition timing	Adjust.
	EMISSION CONTROL	
	• Loose connection or disconnected vacuum hoses	Connect.
	• Malfunctioning PCV valve	Check and replace as necessary.
	• Malfunctioning EGR valve	Check and replace as necessary.
	• Malfunctioning fuel cut solenoid valve	Check and replace as necessary.
	Others	
	• Low compression	Previously outlined.
	• Loose carburetor and intake manifold bolts and nuts	Tighten bolts and nuts.
	• Leaky carburetor and intake manifold gaskets	Replace.

Fig. 22 Engine, (Part 2 of 7). Metro & Sprint

Part 3 of 7

Symptom	Probable Cause	Remedy
Engine hesitates (Momentary lack of response as the accelerator is depressed. Can occur at all car speeds. Usually most severe when first trying to make the car move, as from a stop sign.)	**IGNITION SYSTEM OUT OF ORDER**	
	• Improper ignition timing	Adjust.
	• Defective spark plug or plug gap out of adjustment	Replace or adjust gap.
	• Defective coil wire	Replace.
	FUEL SYSTEM OUT OF ORDER.	
	• Improper adjustment of float level	Adjust.
	• Clogged carburetor jets	Clean.
	• Clogged air cleaner element	Clean or replace.
	• Loose manifold and carburetor bolts and nuts	Retighten.
	• Leaky manifold and carburetor gaskets	Replace.
	• Malfunctioning accelerator pump	Check and replace as necessary.
	EMISSION CONTROL	
	• Malfunctioning bowl vent solenoid valve	Check and replace as necessary.
	• Malfunctioning throttle position switch (wide open switch)	Check and replace as necessary.
	• Malfunctioning high altitude switch	Check and replace as necessary.
	• Malfunctioning EGR valve	Check and replace as necessary.
	• Malfunctioning thermostatically controlled air cleaner	Check and replace as necessary.
	OTHERS	
	• Low compression	Previously outlined.
	• Poorly seating valve	Repair or replace.
	• Improper valve lash	Adjust.
Surges (Engine power variation understeady throttle or cruise. Feels like the car speeds up and down with no change in the accelerator pedal.)	**FUEL SYSTEM OUT OF ORDER.**	
	• Clogged fuel filter	Replace.
	• Kinked, leaky or damaged fuel hoses and lines	Check and replace as necessary.
	• Malfunctioning fuel pump	Check and replace as necessary.
	• Leaky manifold and carburetor gaskets	Replace.
	IGNITION SYSTEM OUT OF ORDER.	
	• Improper ignition timing	Adjust.
	• Incorrect ignition timing	Check and repair or replace.

Fig. 22 Engine, (Part 3 of 7). Metro & Sprint

Overheating

Probable Cause	Remedy
• Insufficient coolant	Replenish.
• Loose water pump belt	Adjust.
• Inoperative thermostat	Replace.
• Poor water pump performance	Replace.
• Improper ignition timing	Adjust.
• Clogged or leaky radiator	Flush, repair or replace.
• Clogged carburetor jets	Clean.
• Improper engine oil grade	Replace with proper grade oil.
• Clogged oil filter or oil strainer	Replace or clean (oil strainer).
• Poor oil pump	Repair or replace.
• Dragging brakes	Adjust or repair.
• Slipping clutch	Adjust or repair.

Poor gasoline mileage

FUEL AND AIR INTAKE SYSTEM OUT OF ORDER.

Probable Cause	Remedy
• Malfunctioning carburetor choke.	Check and repair or replace.
• Improper float level	Adjust.
• Dirty or clogged carburetor jets.	Clean.
• Fuel leakage from fuel tank, lines, and carburetor	Repair or replace.
• Clogged air cleaner element	Clean or replace.
• Restricted air intake system	Repair.
• Air leaks at carburetor or intake manifold	Tighten bolts and nuts. Replace gasket.

IGNITION SYSTEM OUT OF ORDER

Probable Cause	Remedy
• Improper ignition timing	Adjust.
• Worn or loose coil wire	Repair or replace.
• Defective spark plug (improper gap, heavy deposits, and burned electrodes, etc.)	Clean, adjust or replace.

EMISSION CONTROL

Probable Cause	Remedy
• Malfunctioning mechanical and vacuum advance in distributor	Check and repair or replace.
• Malfunctioning pulse air control valve	Check and replace as necessary.
• Air leaks at exhaust manifold	Tighten manifold bolts and nuts. Replace gasket.

Fig. 22 Engine, (Part 5 of 7). Metro & Sprint

Probable Cause	Remedy
• Worn or loosely connected coil wire	Check and repair or replace.
• Defective spark plug (excess carbon deposits, improper gap, and burned electrodes, etc.)	Check and clean, adjust or replace.

Emission control

Probable Cause	Remedy
• Malfunctioning bowl vent solenoid valve	Check and replace as necessary.
• Malfunctioning throttle position switch (wide open switch)	Check and replace as necessary.
• Malfunctioning high altitude switch	Check and replace as necessary.
• Malfunctioning EGR valve	Check and replace as necessary.
• Malfunctioning thermostatically controlled air cleaner	Check and replace as necessary.

Excessive detonation (The engine makes sharp metallic knocks that change with throttle opening.)

ENGINE OVERHEATING — Refer to the section "Overheating".

IGNITION SYSTEM OUT OF ORDER.

Probable Cause	Remedy
• Improper ignition	Adjust timing

FUEL SYSTEM OUT OF ORDER

Probable Cause	Remedy
• Clogged fuel filter and fuel lines	Replace or clean.
• Clogged carburetor jets	Clean.
• Improper adjustment of float level	Adjust.
• Malfunctioning fuel pump	Replace.
• Air leaking from intake manifold and carburetor gaskets	Replace.

OTHERS

Probable Cause	Remedy
• Malfunctioning EGR valve	Replace.
• Excessive combustion changer deposits	Remove carbon.

Dieseling (Engine continues to run after ignition switch is turned off It runs unevenly and may make knocking noise.)

Probable Cause	Remedy
• Malfunctioning fuel cut solenoid valve in carburetor	Check the valve for proper operation, and replace as necessary.

Fig. 22 Engine, (Part 4 of 7). Metro & Sprint

Condition	Possible Cause	Correction
	• Oxygen sensor out of order	Replace.
	• Water temperature switch out of order	Replace.
	• Malfunctioning throttle position switch	Replace.
	• Malfunctioning MCS (mixture control solenoid) valve in carburetor	Replace.
	• Malfunctioning EGR valve	Replace.
	• Abnormal idle-up actuator operation (Actuator is operated although heater, cooling fan, rear defogger, and air conditioner are "OFF")	Check and adjust or replace
	OTHERS	
	• Low compression	Previously outlined.
	• Poor valve seating	Repair or replace.
	• Improper valve lash	Adjust.
	• Dragging brakes	Adjust.
	• Slipping clutch	Adjust or replace.
	• Thermostat	Replace.
	• Improper tire pressure	Adjust.
Excessive engine oil consumption	**OIL LEAKAGE**	
	• Loose oil drain plug	Tighten.
	• Loose oil drain plug	Tighten.
	• Loose oil pan bolts	Tighten.
	• Deteriorated or broken oil pan seal	Replace sealant.
	• Leaky crankshaft oil seals	Replace.
	• Leaky cylinder head cover gasket	Replace.
	• Improper tightening of oil filter	Tighten.
	• Loose oil pressure switch	Tighten.
	• Leaky camshaft oil seals and fuel pump gasket	Replace.
	OIL ENTERING COMBUSTION CHAMBER THROUGH HEAD AREA.	
	• Worn piston and cylinder	Replace or rebore cylinder and replace piston.
	• Worn piston ring groove and ring	Replace piston and ring.
	• Improper location of piston ring gap	Reposition ring gap
	• Worn or damaged valve stem seal	Replace.
	• Worn valve stem	Replace stem and guide.

Fig. 22 Engine, (Part 6 of 7). Metro & Sprint

Condition	Possible Cause	Correction
	• Improper oil viscosity	Use oil of proper viscosity.
	• Malfunctioning oil pressure switch	Replace.
	• Clogged oil filter	Replace.
	• Clogged oil strainer	Clean.
	FUNCTIONAL DETERIORATION OR OIL PUMP	Replace.
Low oil pressure	• Worn oil pump relief valve	Replace.
	VALVE NOISE	
	• Improper valve lash	Adjust.
	• Worn valve stem and guide	Replace.
	• Worn camshaft lobe	Replace camshaft.
	• Worn rocker arm	Replace.
	• Weak or broken valve spring	Replace.
	• Warped or bent valve	Replace.
	PISTON, RING AND CYLINDER NOISE	
	• Worn piston, ring and cylinder bore	Rebore or replace cylinder. Replace piston and ring.
	CONNECTING ROD BEARING NOISE	
	• Worn rod bearing	Replace.
	• Worn crankpin	Repair by grinding or Replace crankshaft.
	• Loose connecting rod nuts	Tighten nuts to specification.
	• Low oil pressure	Previously outlined.
	CRANKSHAFT JOURNAL BEARING NOISE	
	• Low oil pressure	Previously outlined.
	• Worn bearing	Replace.
	• Worn crankshaft journal	Repair by grinding, or replace crankshaft.
	• Loose bearing cap bolts	Tighten bolts to specification.
	• Excessive crankshaft end play	Replace thrust bearing.

Engine noise
Note: Before checking the mechanical noise, make sure that:
- Ignition timing is properly adjusted.
- Specified spark plug is used.
- Specified fuel is used.

Fig. 22 Engine, (Part 7 of 7). Metro & Sprint

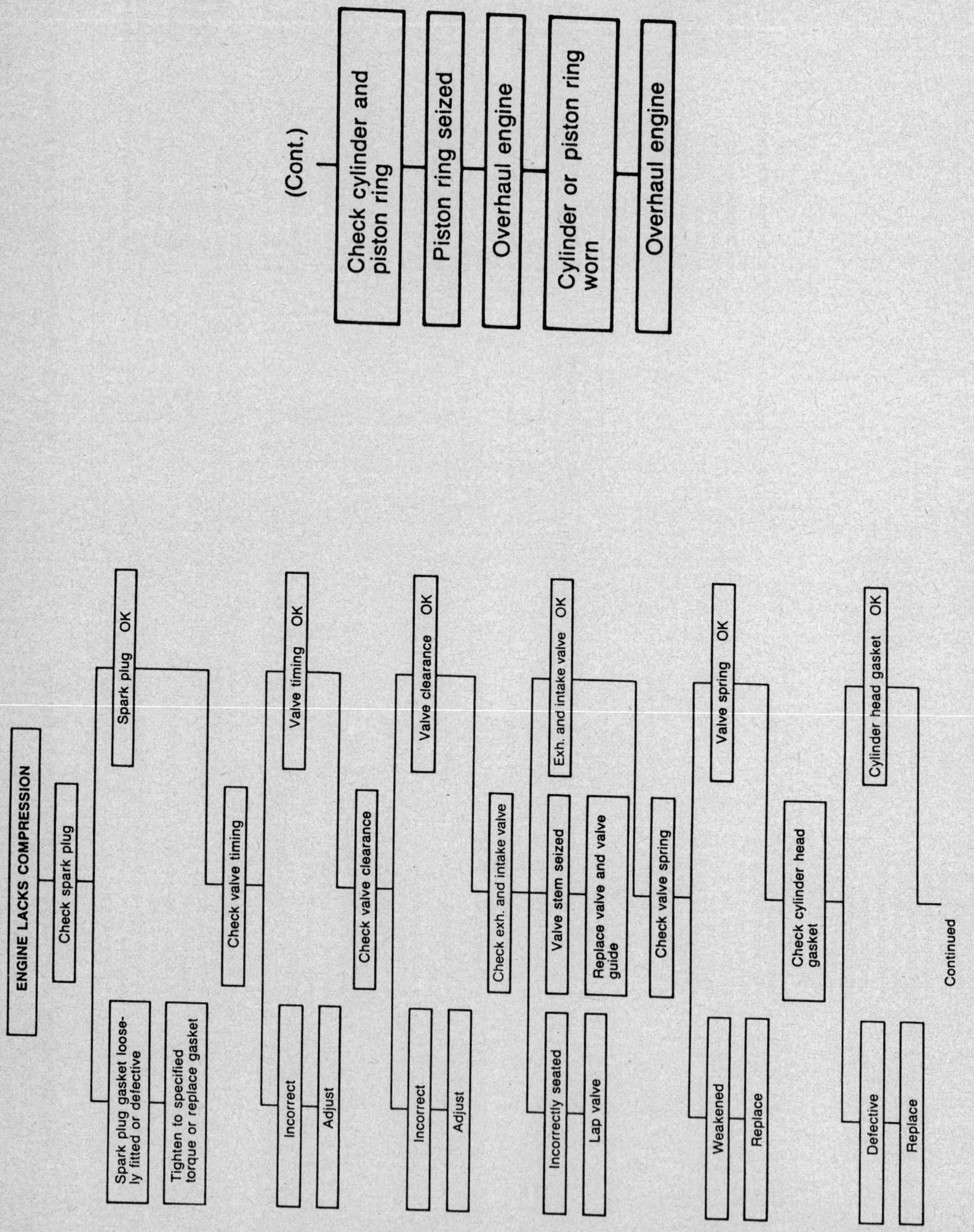

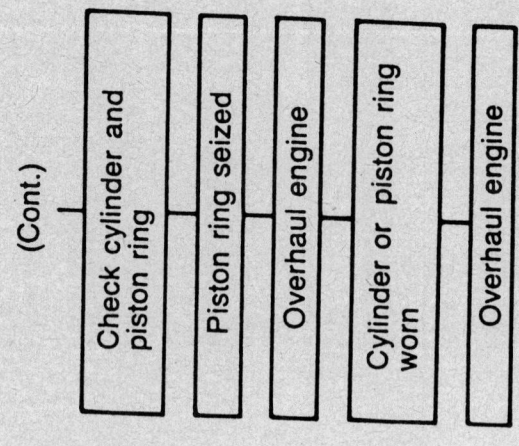

Fig. 23 Engine lacks compression. Spectrum

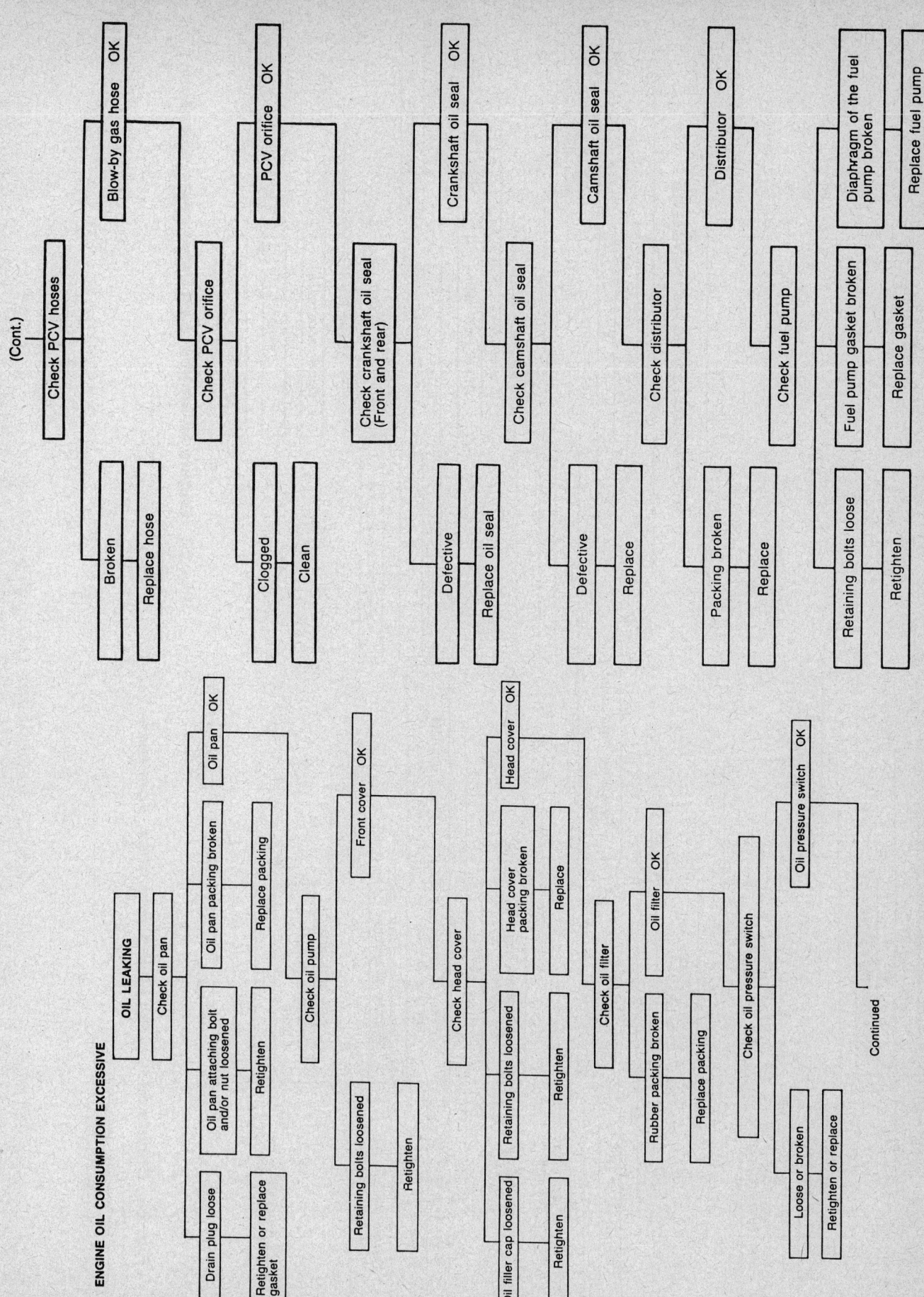

Fig. 24 Engine oil consumption excessive. Spectrum

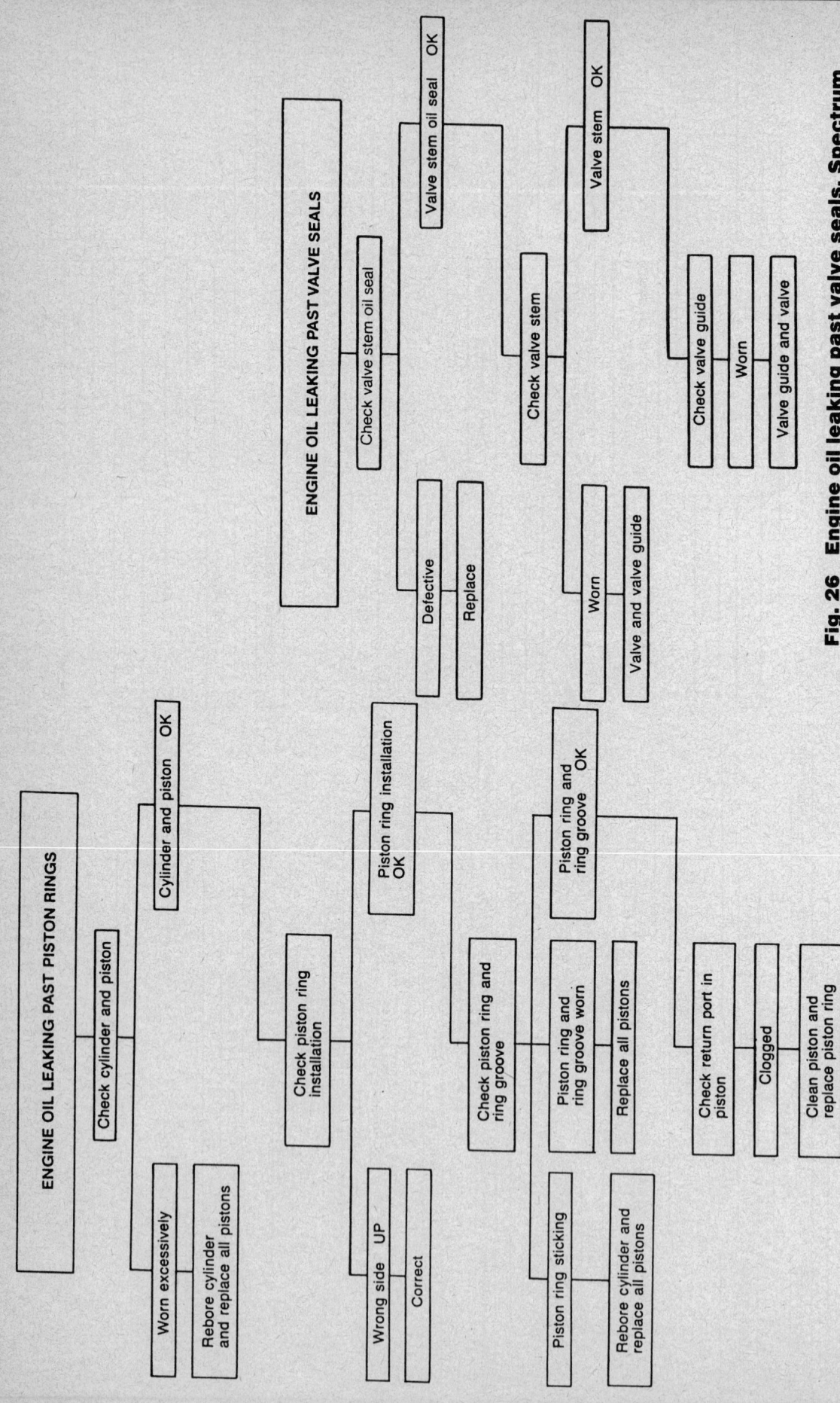

Fig. 26   Engine oil leaking past valve seals. Spectrum

Fig. 25   Engine oil leaking past piston rings. Spectrum

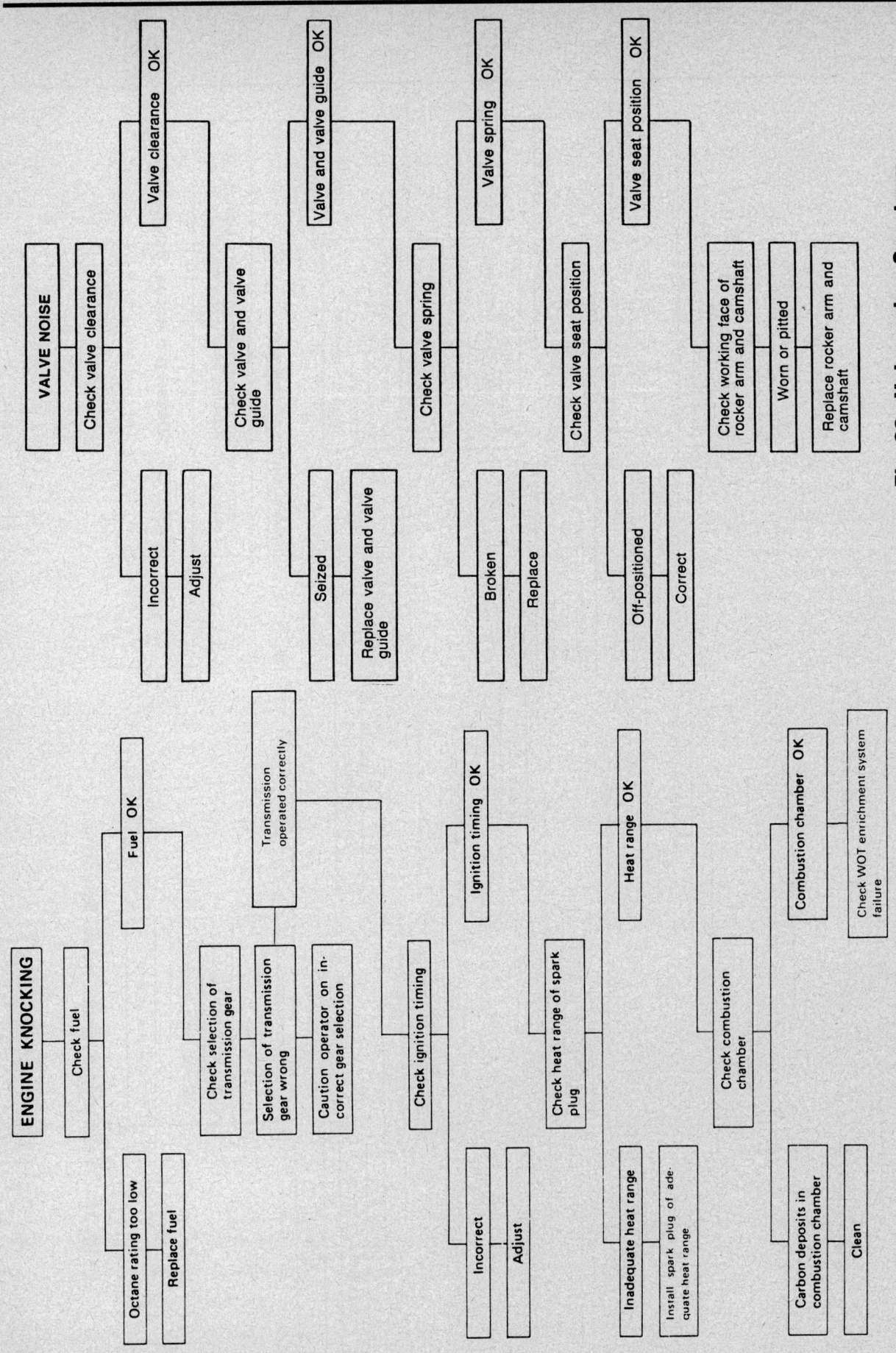

Fig. 28 Valve noise. Spectrum

Fig. 27 Engine knocking. Spectrum

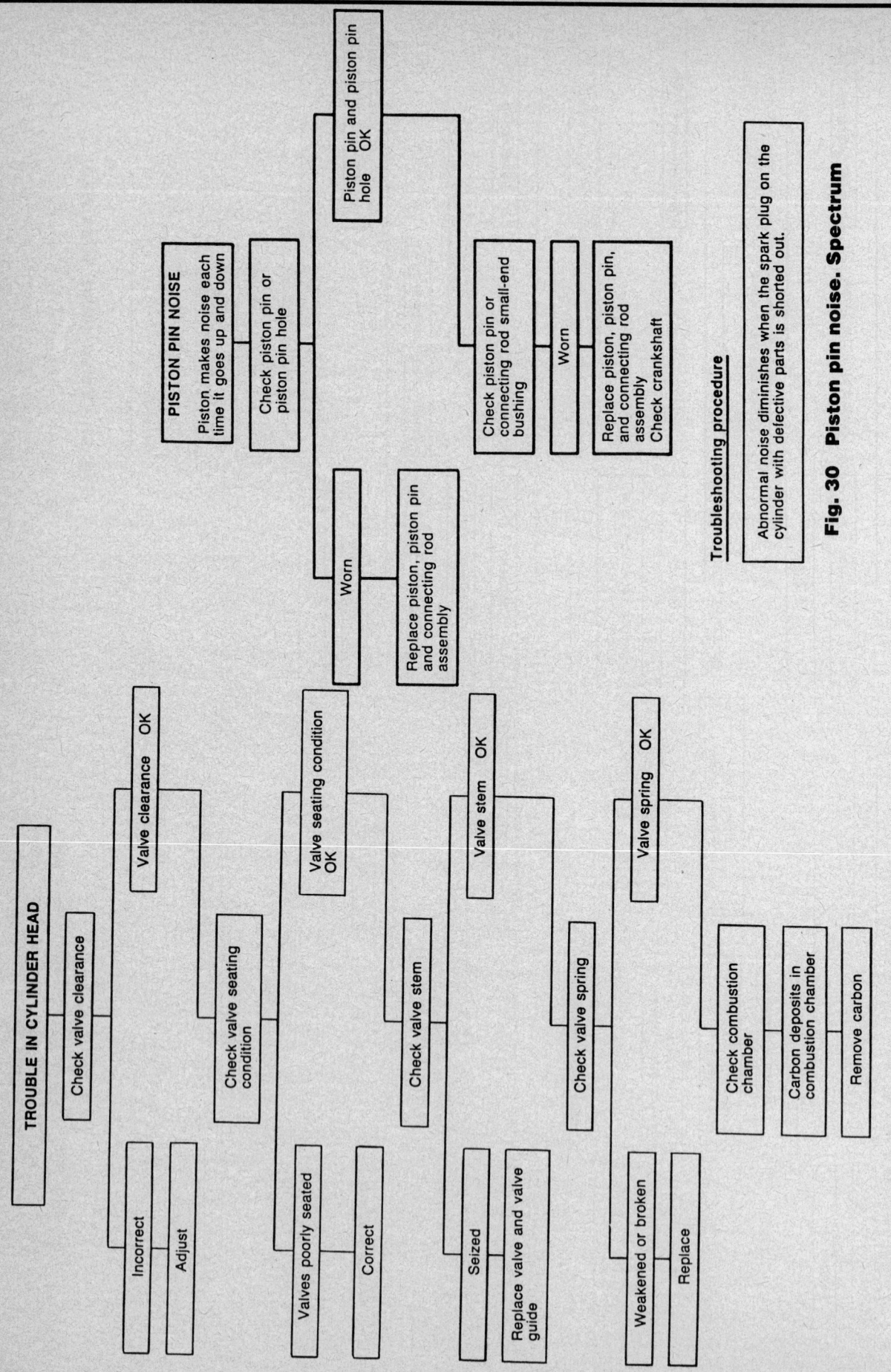

PISTON PIN NOISE

Piston makes noise each time it goes up and down

Check piston pin or piston pin hole

Piston pin and piston pin hole   OK

Worn

Replace piston, piston pin and connecting rod assembly

Check piston pin or connecting rod small-end bushing

Worn

Replace piston, piston pin, and connecting rod assembly
Check crankshaft

Troubleshooting procedure

Abnormal noise diminishes when the spark plug on the cylinder with defective parts is shorted out.

Fig. 30   Piston pin noise. Spectrum

TROUBLE IN CYLINDER HEAD

Check valve clearance

Valve clearance   OK

Incorrect

Adjust

Check valve seating condition

Valve seating condition OK

Valves poorly seated

Correct

Check valve stem

Valve stem   OK

Seized

Replace valve and valve guide

Check valve spring

Valve spring   OK

Weakened or broken

Replace

Check combustion chamber

Carbon deposits in combustion chamber

Remove carbon

Fig. 29   Trouble in cylinder head. Spectrum

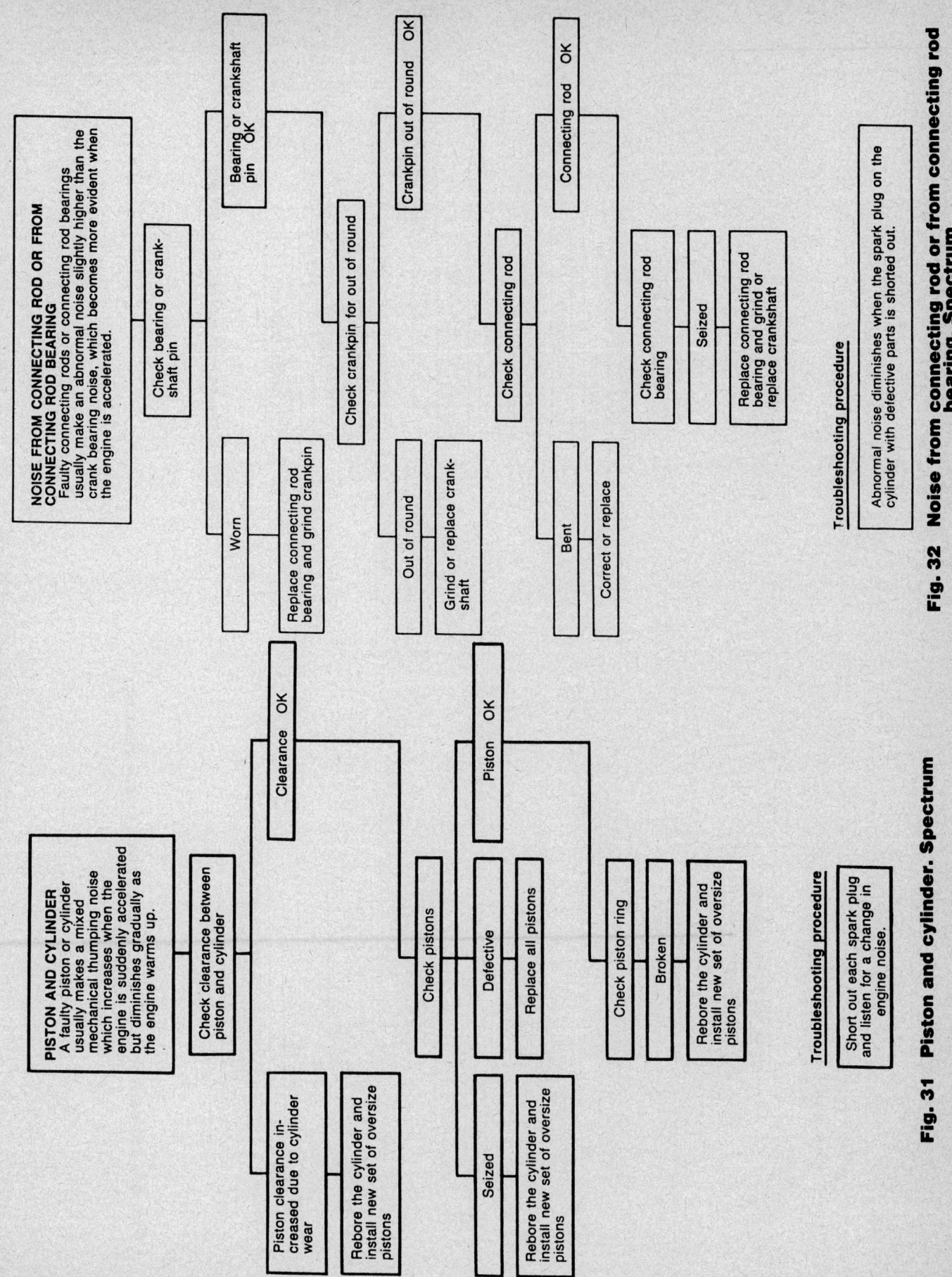

NOISE FROM CONNECTING ROD OR FROM CONNECTING ROD BEARING
Faulty connecting rods or connecting rod bearings usually make an abnormal noise slightly higher than the crank bearing noise, which becomes more evident when the engine is accelerated.

Check bearing or crankshaft pin

Bearing or crankshaft pin   OK

Worn → Replace connecting rod bearing and grind crankpin

Check crankpin for out of round

Crankpin out of round   OK

Out of round → Grind or replace crankshaft

Check connecting rod

Connecting rod   OK

Bent → Correct or replace

Check connecting rod bearing

Seized → Replace connecting rod bearing and grind or replace crankshaft

Troubleshooting procedure

Abnormal noise diminishes when the spark plug on the cylinder with defective parts is shorted out.

Fig. 32   Noise from connecting rod or from connecting rod bearing. Spectrum

PISTON AND CYLINDER
A faulty piston or cylinder usually makes a mixed mechanical thumping noise which increases when the engine is suddenly accelerated but diminishes gradually as the engine warms up.

Check clearance between piston and cylinder

Clearance   OK

Piston clearance increased due to cylinder wear → Rebore the cylinder and install new set of oversize pistons

Check pistons

Piston   OK

Defective → Replace all pistons

Seized → Rebore the cylinder and install new set of oversize pistons

Check piston ring

Broken → Rebore the cylinder and install new set of oversize pistons

Troubleshooting procedure

Short out each spark plug and listen for a change in engine noise.

Fig. 31   Piston and cylinder. Spectrum

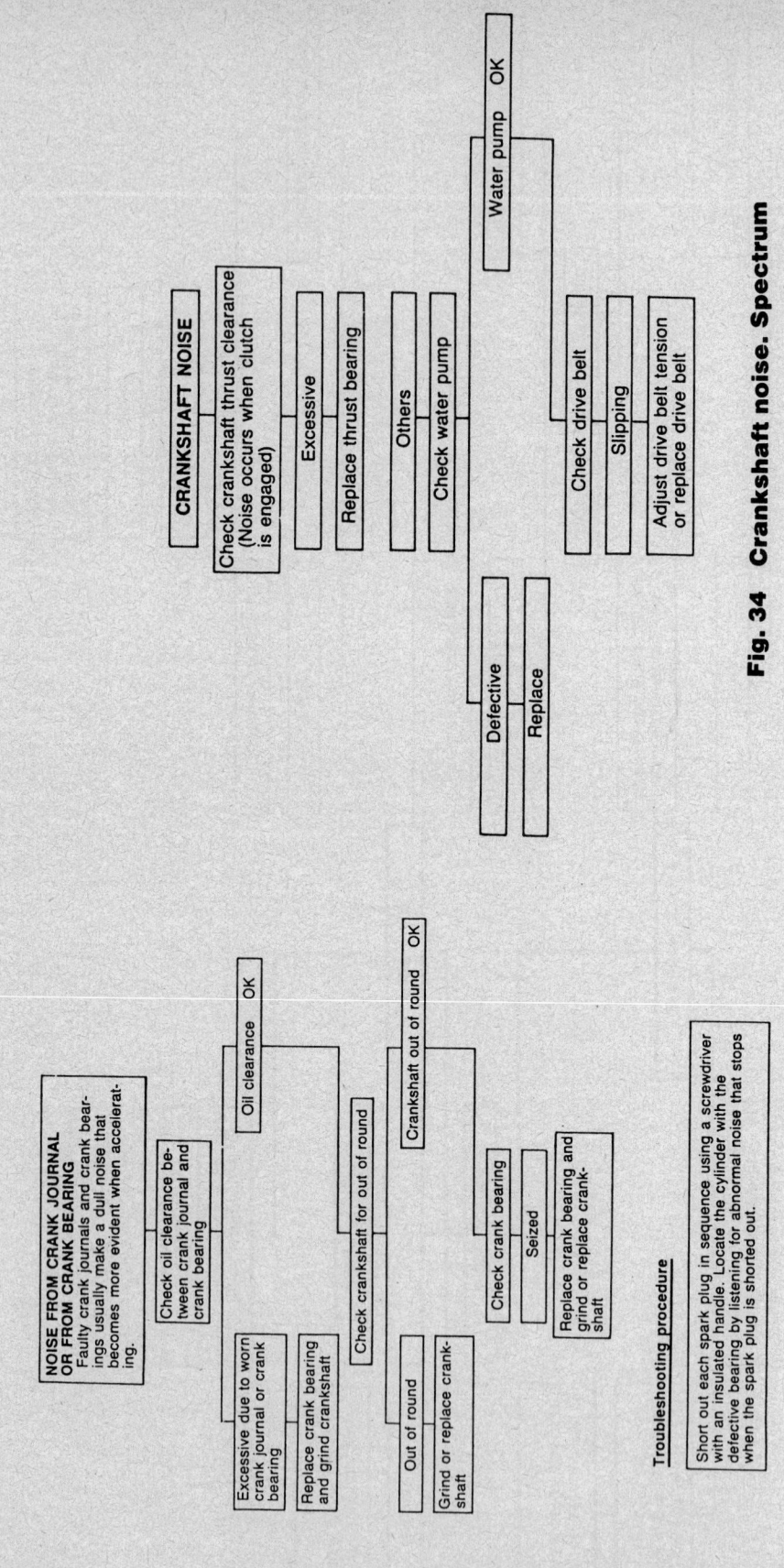

Fig. 34   Crankshaft noise. Spectrum

Fig. 33   Noise from crank journal or from crank bearing. Spectrum

GENERAL DIAGNOSIS

Since the problems in steering, suspension, wheels and tires involve several systems, they must all be considered when diagnosing a complaint. To avoid using the wrong symptom, always road test the car first. Proceed with the following preliminary checks and correct any defects which are found.

1. Check tires for proper pressure and uneven wear.
2. Raise car on a hoist and check front and rear suspension and rack and pinion for loose or damaged parts.
3. Spin front wheels. Check for out-of-round tires, out-of-balance tires, bent rims, loose and/or rough wheel bearings.
4. Check for oil leaks on power steering, power steering fluid level and pump drive belt tension.

Car Pulls (Leads)
1. Mismatched or uneven tires.
2. Broken or sagging springs.
3. Radial tire lateral force.
4. Front end alignment.
5. Rear axle alignment.
6. Rack and pinion valve off center (unbalanced).
7. Front brakes dragging.

Abnormal or Excessive Tire Wear
1. Sagging or broken springs.
2. Tire out of balance.
3. Front end alignment.
4. Faulty shock absorber.
5. Hard driving.
6. Overloaded car.
7. Not rotating tires.

Scuffed Tires
1. Toe-in incorrect.
2. Excessive speed on turns.
3. Suspension arm bent or twisted.

Wheel Tramp
1. Blister or bump on tire.
2. Improper shock absorber action.

Shimmy, Shake or Vibration
1. Tire or wheel out of balance.
2. Loose wheel bearings.
3. Worn tie rod ends.
4. Worn lower ball joints.
5. Excessive wheel runout.
6. Blister or bump on tire.
7. Excessive loaded radial runout of tire/wheel assembly.

Hard Steering (Manual)
1. Lack of lubrication, ball joints and rack and/or pinion.
2. Front end alignment.
3. Rack and pinion adjustment.

Hard Steering (Power)
1. Hydraulic system - Make test with gage J-5176-1 or J-25323.
2. Rack and pinion adjustment.
3. Bind or catch in rack and pinion.

Too Much Play In Steering
1. Wheel bearings incorrectly adjusted or worn.
2. Rack and pinion attachments loose.
3. Rack and pinion adjustment.

Poor Returnability (Manual)
1. Lack of lubrication - ball joints and tie rod ends.
2. Bind in ball joints.
3. Bind in steering column.
4. Lack of lubricant rack and pinion.
5. Front end alignment.
6. Rack and pinion adjustment.

Poor Returnability (Power)
1. Lack of lubrication - ball joints and tie rod ends.
2. Bind in ball joints.
3. Bind in steering column.
4. Front end alignment.
5. Rack and pinion adjustment.
6. Sticking valve.

Abnormal Noise Power Rack and Pinion

Pump Noise
1. Groan
   a. Low oil level.
   b. Air in oil.
   c. Pump mounting loose.
2. Rattle
   a. Vane improperly installed.
   b. Vane sticking in rotor.
3. Growl
   a. Back pressure caused by restriction.
   b. Scored pressure plates, thrust plate, or rotor.
   c. Badly worn cam ring.
4. Whine
   a. Pump shaft bearing scored.
5. Squeal or Chirp
   a. Loose belt.

Rack and Pinion Noise
1. Rattle or Chuckle
   a. Rack and pinion attachments loose.
   b. Pressure hose touching.
   c. Rack and pinion adjustment.

Abnormal Noise, Front End
1. Lubrication - ball joints and tie rod ends.
2. Damaged shock absorbers or mountings.
3. Worn control arm bushings or tie rod ends.
4. Loose stabilizer bar.
5. Loose wheel nuts.
6. Loose suspension bolts.
7. Wheel covers.

Wander Or Poor Steering Stability
1. Mismatched or uneven tires.
2. Lubrication - ball joints and tie rod ends.
3. Faulty shock absorbers or mounting.
4. Loose stabilizer bar.
5. Broken or sagging springs.
6. Rack and pinion adjustment.
7. Front end alignment.

Erratic Steering When Braking
1. Wheel bearings incorrectly adjusted or worn.
2. Broken or sagging springs.
3. Leaking wheel cylinder or caliper.
4. Rack and pinion off high point.
5. Warped rotors.

Low Or Uneven Trim Height
1. Broken or sagging springs.
2. Overloaded.
3. Incorrect springs.

Ride Too Soft
1. Faulty Shock Absorbers.

Ride Too Harsh
1. Incorrect shock absorbers.
2. Incorrect springs.

Body Leans Or Sways In Corners
1. Loose stabilizer bar.
2. Faulty shock absorbers or mounting.
3. Broken or sagging springs.
4. Overloaded.

Suspension Bottoms
1. Overloaded.
2. Faulty shocks.
3. Incorrect broken or sagging springs.

"Dog" Tracking
1. Damaged rear suspension arm or worn bushings.
2. Bent rear axle.
3. Frame or underbody alignment.

Steering Wheel Kick-Back (Power)
1. Air in system.
2. Rack pinion attachment loose.
3. Tie rod ends loose.
4. Wheel bearings incorrectly adjusted or worn.

Steering Wheel Surges Or Jerks (Power)
1. Hydraulic system - Make pressure test with gage J-5176-1 or J-25323.
2. Sluggish flow control valve.

Cupped Tires
1. Front shock absorbers defective.
2. Wheel bearing incorrectly adjusted or worn.
3. Excessive tire or wheel run-out.
4. Worn ball joint.

Fig. 35 Suspension

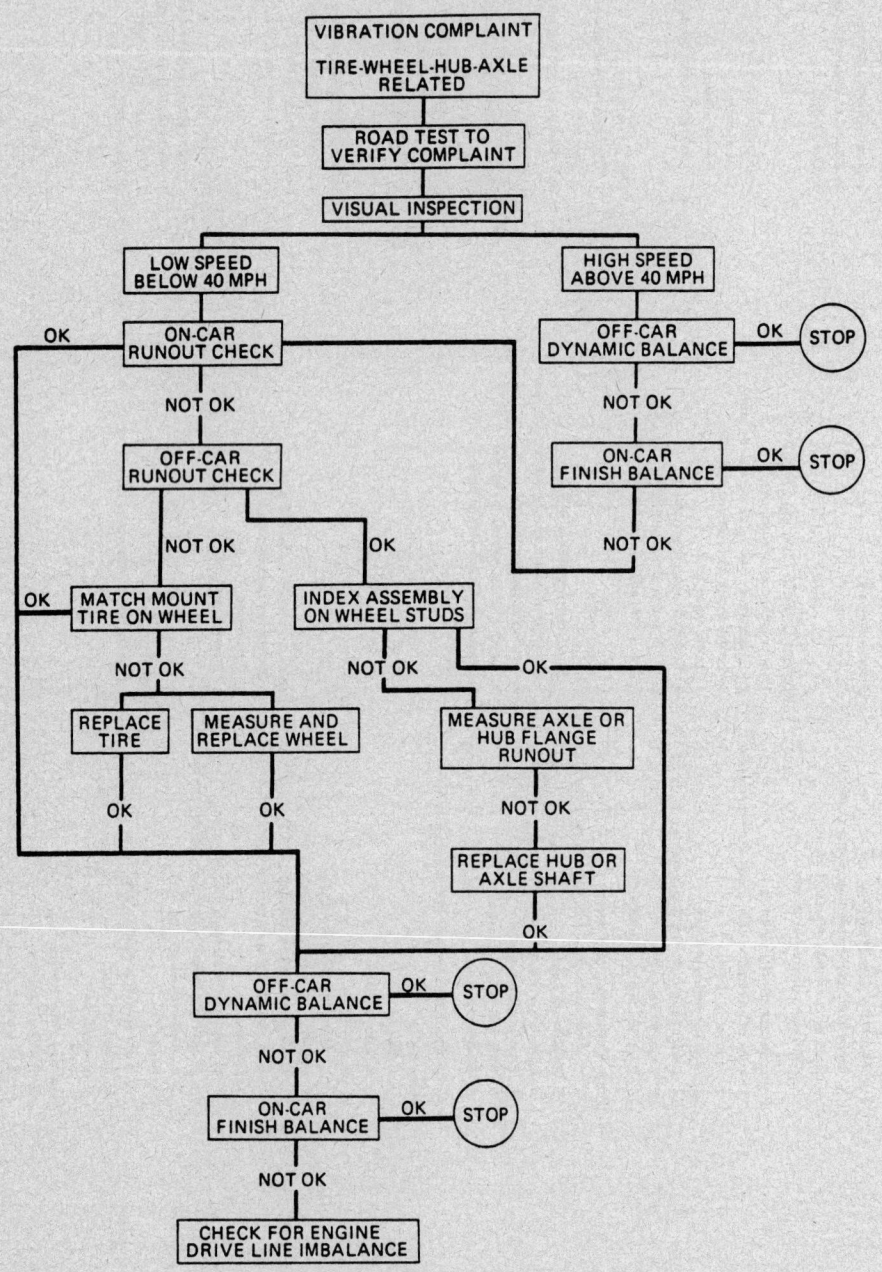

Fig. 36   Vibration

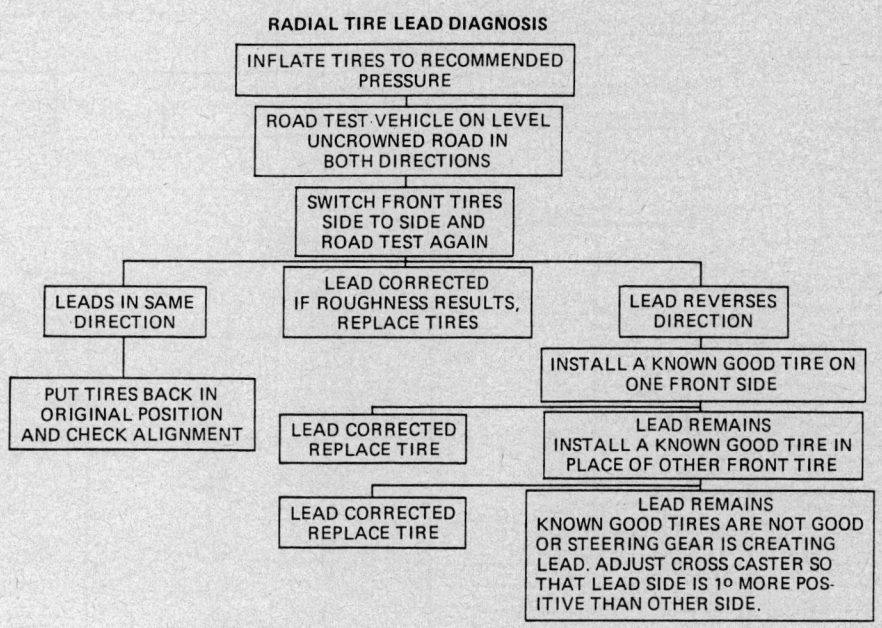

RADIAL TIRE LEAD DIAGNOSIS

INFLATE TIRES TO RECOMMENDED PRESSURE

ROAD TEST VEHICLE ON LEVEL UNCROWNED ROAD IN BOTH DIRECTIONS

SWITCH FRONT TIRES SIDE TO SIDE AND ROAD TEST AGAIN

LEADS IN SAME DIRECTION

LEAD CORRECTED IF ROUGHNESS RESULTS, REPLACE TIRES

LEAD REVERSES DIRECTION

PUT TIRES BACK IN ORIGINAL POSITION AND CHECK ALIGNMENT

LEAD CORRECTED REPLACE TIRE

INSTALL A KNOWN GOOD TIRE ON ONE FRONT SIDE

LEAD REMAINS INSTALL A KNOWN GOOD TIRE IN PLACE OF OTHER FRONT TIRE

LEAD CORRECTED REPLACE TIRE

LEAD REMAINS KNOWN GOOD TIRES ARE NOT GOOD OR STEERING GEAR IS CREATING LEAD. ADJUST CROSS CASTER SO THAT LEAD SIDE IS 1º MORE POSITIVE THAN OTHER SIDE.

Fig. 37 Radial tire lead

SEALED WHEEL BEARING DIAGNOSIS

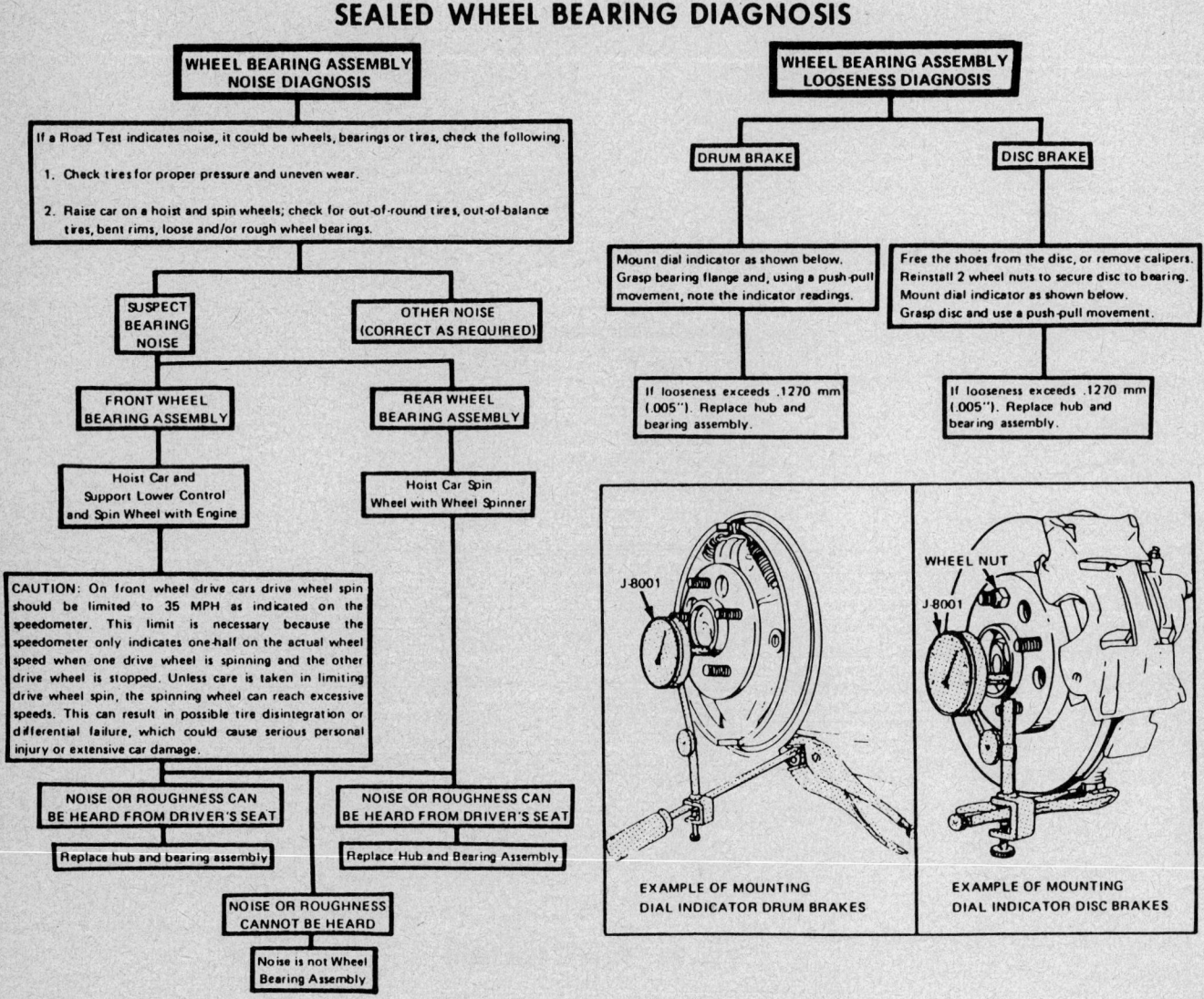

WHEEL BEARING ASSEMBLY NOISE DIAGNOSIS

If a Road Test indicates noise, it could be wheels, bearings or tires, check the following.

1. Check tires for proper pressure and uneven wear.

2. Raise car on a hoist and spin wheels; check for out-of-round tires, out-of-balance tires, bent rims, loose and/or rough wheel bearings.

SUSPECT BEARING NOISE

OTHER NOISE (CORRECT AS REQUIRED)

FRONT WHEEL BEARING ASSEMBLY

REAR WHEEL BEARING ASSEMBLY

Hoist Car and Support Lower Control and Spin Wheel with Engine

Hoist Car Spin Wheel with Wheel Spinner

CAUTION: On front wheel drive cars drive wheel spin should be limited to 35 MPH as indicated on the speedometer. This limit is necessary because the speedometer only indicates one-half on the actual wheel speed when one drive wheel is spinning and the other drive wheel is stopped. Unless care is taken in limiting drive wheel spin, the spinning wheel can reach excessive speeds. This can result in possible tire disintegration or differential failure, which could cause serious personal injury or extensive car damage.

NOISE OR ROUGHNESS CAN BE HEARD FROM DRIVER'S SEAT

Replace hub and bearing assembly

NOISE OR ROUGHNESS CAN BE HEARD FROM DRIVER'S SEAT

Replace Hub and Bearing Assembly

NOISE OR ROUGHNESS CANNOT BE HEARD

Noise is not Wheel Bearing Assembly

WHEEL BEARING ASSEMBLY LOOSENESS DIAGNOSIS

DRUM BRAKE

DISC BRAKE

Mount dial indicator as shown below. Grasp bearing flange and, using a push-pull movement, note the indicator readings.

Free the shoes from the disc, or remove calipers. Reinstall 2 wheel nuts to secure disc to bearing. Mount dial indicator as shown below. Grasp disc and use a push-pull movement.

If looseness exceeds .1270 mm (.005"). Replace hub and bearing assembly.

If looseness exceeds .1270 mm (.005"). Replace hub and bearing assembly.

J-8001

WHEEL NUT

J-8001

EXAMPLE OF MOUNTING DIAL INDICATOR DRUM BRAKES

EXAMPLE OF MOUNTING DIAL INDICATOR DISC BRAKES

Fig. 38   Sealed wheel bearing

ENGINE REBUILDING SPECIFICATIONS

NOTE: All Specifications Given In Inches Unless Otherwise Noted.

CYLINDER HEAD, VALVE GUIDES & VALVE SEATS

Engine Liter/CID/ VIN	Year	Cylinder Head Warpage Limit	Cylinder Head Overall Thickness	Valve Guides				Valve Seats			Run Out
				Standard Inside Diameter	Stem To Guide Clearance		Seat Angle	Seat Width			
					Intake	Exhaust		Intake	Exhaust		
1.0L/3-61/5	1988-90	.002	—	.2165-.2170	.0008-.0021	.0014-.0024	45°	.0512-.0590	.0512-.0590	—
1.5L/4-90/7	1988-89	.008	3.3858	—	.0009-.0022	.0012-.0025	45°	.0470-.0630	.0470-.0630	—
1.6L/4-97/4 ①	1988	.002	—	—	.0010-.0024	.0012-.0026	45°	.0470-.0630	.0470-.0630	—
1.6L/4-97/5 ②	1988	.002	—	.2366-.2374	.0010-.0024	.0012-.0026	45°	.0390-.0550	.0390-.0550	—
1.6L/4-97/6 ③	1988-90	—	—	.2770-.2780	.0008-.0020	.0016-.0028	46°	.0500-.0701	.0500-.0701	.002
1.6L/4-97/6 ④	1990	.002	—	—	.0031	.0039	45°	.0390-.0551	.0390-.0551	—
1.6L/4-97/5 ⑤	1990	.002	—	.2366-.2374	.0010-.0024	.0012-.0026	45°	.0390-.0551	.039-.0551	—
1.6L/4-97/5,6 ⑥ ⑦	1990	—	—	—	.0009	.0012	—	.0870	.0790	—
2.0L/4-121/K,M	1988-90	⑧	—	.2766-.2772	.0006-.0017	.0012-.0024	45°	.0500-.0701	.0500-.0701	—
2.2L/4-133/G	1990	⑧	—	—	.0011-.0026	.0014-.0030	46°	.0490-.0590	.0630-.0750	.002
2.3L/4-138/A,D	1988-90	.008	—	.2762-.2772	.0010-.0027	.0015-.0032	45°	.0370-.0748	.0370-.0748	—
2.5L/4-151/R,U	1988-90	.007	—	—	.0011-.0027	.0013-.0040	46°	.0350-.0750	.0580-.1050	.002
2.8L/V6-173/S	1988-89	—	—	—	.0010-.0026	.0010-.0026	46°	.0492-.0590	.0629-.0748	.002
2.8L/V6-173/W	1988-89	—	—	—	.0010-.0026	.0010-.0026	46°	.0610-.0728	.0669-.0787	.001
3.0L/V6-181/L	1988	—	—	—	.0015-.0035	.0015-.0032	46°	.0620	.0750-.1050	.002
3.1L/V6-192/T,V	1989-90	⑧	—	—	.0010-.0027	.0010-.0027	46°	.0610-.0730	.0670-.0790	.001
3.3L/V6-204/N	1989-90	.002	—	—	.0015-.0035	.0015-.0032	45°	.0600-.0800	.0900-.1100	.002
3.8L/V6-231/C	1988	①	—	—	.0015-.0035	.0015-.0032	45°	.0600-.0800	.0900-.1100	.002
3.8L/V6-231/3	1988	①	—	—	.0015-.0035	.0015-.0032	46°	.0620	.0750-.1050	.002
3.8L/V6-231/C	1989-90	—	—	—	.0015-.0035	.0015-.0032	45°	.0600-.0800	.0900-.1100	.002
4.3L/V6-262/Z	1988-90	—	—	—	.0011-.0027	.0011-.0027	46°	.0310-.0620	.0620-.0930	.002
4.5L/V8-273/5	1988-90	—	—	.343	.0010-.0030	.0020-.0040	45°	.0620	.0930	.004
5.0L/V8-305/E,F	1988-90	—	—	—	.0011-.0027	.0011-.0027	46°	.0310-.0620	.0620-.0930	.002
5.0L/V8-307/Y	1988	.006	—	—	.0010-.0027	.0015-.0032	⑨	.0370-.0750	.0500-.1000	⑩
5.7L/V8-350/7,8	1988-90	—	—	—	.0011-.0027	.0011-.0027	46°	.0310-.0620	.0620-.0930	.002
5.7L/V8-350/J	1989-90	—	—	—	.0012-.0026	.0014-.0030	44°	.0569-.0734	.0569-.0734	.004

①—Nova 4A-LC engine.
②—Nova 4A-GE 16 valve engine.
③—LeMans.
④—Prizm 4A-FE 16 valve engine.
⑤—Prizm GSI 4A-GE 16 valve engine.
⑥—Storm 12 valve engine, VIN 6.
⑦—Storm 16 valve engine, VIN 5.
⑧—Maximum surface refinish, .010 inch.
⑨—Intake, 45°; exhaust, 31°.
⑩—Intake, .002 inch; exhaust, .004 inch.

VALVES & VALVE SPRINGS

| Engine Liter/CID/VIN | Year | Valves | | | | | Face Angle | Margin ① | Valve Springs | | | | Out Of Square Limit |
| | | Stem Diameter | | Clearance | | | | | | | Seated Press. Pounds @ Inches | Comp. Press. Pounds @ Inches | |
		Intake	Exhaust	Intake	Exhaust				Free Length	Installed Height			
1.0L/3-61/5	1988-90	.2148-.2157	.2146-.2151	—	—	45°	②	1.6035	1.28	41-47.2 @ 1.28	—	.079
1.5L/4-90/7	1988-89	.2740-.2750	.2740-.2744 ⑤	.006 ③	.010 ③	45°	.0315	1.9095	1.57	47.4 @ 1.57	—	.039
1.6L/4-97/4 ④	1988	—	—	.008 ⑤	.012 ⑤	44.5°	⑥	1.756	1.520	46.3 @ 1.52	—	.079
1.6L/4-97/5 ⑦	1988	.2350-.2356	.2348-.2354	.006-.010 ③	.008-.012 ③	44.5°	.031-.047	1.618	1.366	32.2 @ 1.366	—	.071
1.6L/4-97/6 ⑧	1988-90	.2755-.2760	.2747-.2758	—	—	46°	—	—	1.24	62 @ 1.24	140 @ .85	—
1.6L/4-97/6 ⑨	1990	.2350-.2356	.2348-.2354	.006-.010 ③	.008-.012 ③	45.5°	.020	1.724	—	—	—	.098
1.6L/4-97/5 ⑩	1990	.2350-.2356	.2348-.2354	.006-.010 ③	.008-.012 ③	45.5°	.0315	1.6177	—	—	—	.098
1.6L/4-97/6 ⑪	1990	.2335	.2335	.006 ③	.010 ③	—	.0315	⑫	—	—	—	—
1.6L/4-97/5 ⑬	1990	.2335	.2335	.004-.008 ③	.008-.012 ③	—	.0315	—	—	—	—	—
2.0L/4-121/K,M	1988-90	.2755-.2760	.2747-.2753	—	—	46°	.031	—	1.476	⑭	165-179 @ 1.043	—
2.2L/4-133/G	1990	—	—	—	—	45°	.031	2.06	1.61	100-110 @ 1.61	208-222 @ 1.22	—
2.3L/4-138/A,D	1988-90	.2745-.2752	.2740-.2747	—	—	⑮	—	—	1.437	⑯	⑰	—
2.5L/4-151/R,U	1988	.3133-.3141	.3118-.3133	—	—	45°	—	1.779	1.4401	71-78 @ 1.4401	158-170 @ 1.0401	—
	1989-90	—	—	—	—	45°	—	2.20	1.68	75 @ 1.68	173 @ 1.24	—
2.8L/V6-173/S	1988-89	—	—	—	—	45°	—	1.909 ⑱	1.574	87.9 @ 1.574	194.9 @ 1.181	—
2.8L/V6-173/W	1988-89	—	—	—	—	45°	—	1.909	1.574	90 @ 1.291	215 @ 1.291	—
3.0L/V6-181/L	1988	—	—	—	—	45°	.025	2.03	1.69-1.75	85-95 @ 1.727	175-195 @ 1.34	—
3.1L/V6-192/T,V	1989-90	—	—	—	—	45°	—	1.91	1.5748	90 @ 1.701	215 @ 1.291	—
3.3L/V6-204/N	1989-90	—	—	—	—	45°	.025	1.981	1.69-1.75	76-84 @ 1.750	200-220 @ 1.315	—
3.8L/V6-231/C	1988	—	—	—	—	45°	.025	2.03	1.69-1.75	100-110 @ 1.730	214-236 @ 1.255	—
3.8L/V6-231/3	1988	—	—	—	—	45°	.025	2.03	1.69-1.75	85-95 @ 1.727	175-195 @ 1.340	—
3.8L/V6-231/C	1989-90	—	—	—	—	45°	.025	1.981	1.69-1.75	76-84 @ 1.75	200-220 @ 1.315	—

Continued

VALVES & VALVE SPRINGS—Continued

Engine Liter/CID/ VIN	Year	Valves Stem Diameter Intake	Stem Diameter Exhaust	Clearance Intake	Clearance Exhaust	Face Angle	Margin ①	Valve Springs Free Length	Installed Height	Seated Press. Pounds @ Inches	Comp. Press. Pounds @ Inches	Out Of Square Limit
4.3L/V6-262/Z	1988-90	—	—	—	—	45°	—	2.03	1.7	76-84 @ 1.70	194-206 @ 1.25	—
4.5L/V8-273/5	1988-90	.3413-.3420	.3401-.3408	—	—	44°	⑲	2.125	1.73	68-76 @ 1.73	214-232 @ 1.35	—
5.0L/V8-305/E,F	1988-90	—	—	—	—	45°	.031	2.03⑯	⑳	㉑	㉒	—
5.0L/V8-307/Y	1988-90	.3425-.3432	.3420-.3427	—	—	44°	.025	1.96	1.67	76-84 @ 1.67	180-194 @ 1.27	—
5.7L/V8-350/7,8	1988-90	—	—	—	—	45°	—	2.03⑯	⑳	㉑	㉒	—
5.7L/V8-350/J	1989-90	—	—	—	—	45°	—	㉓	㉔	㉕	㉖	—

①—Minimum.
②—Intake, .039 inch; exhaust, .047 inch.
③—Cold.
④—Nova 4A-LC engine.
⑤—Hot.
⑥—Intake, .020 inch; exhaust, .039 inch.
⑦—Nova 4A-GE 16 valve engine.
⑧—LeMans.
⑨—Prizm 4A-FE 16 valve engine.
⑩—Prizm GSI 4A-GE 16 valve engine.
⑪—Storm 12 valve engine.
⑫—Intake, 1.73 inch; exhaust, 1.67 inch.
⑬—Storm 16 valve engine.
⑭—VIN K, 63-71 lbs. @ 1.476 inch; VIN M, 74-82 lbs. @ 1.476 inch.
⑮—Intake, 44°; exhaust, 44.5°.

⑯—1988 VIN D, 64-70 lbs. @ 1.4370 inch; 1989 VIN A, 71-79 lbs. @ 1.4370 inch; 1989 VIN D, 64-70 lbs. @ 1.4370 inch; 1990 VIN A & D, 71-79 lbs. @ 1.4370 inch.
⑰—1988 VIN D, 159-173 lbs. @ 1.0433 inch; 1989 VIN A, 188-202 lbs. @ 1.0433 inch; 1989 VIN D, 159-173 lbs. @ 1.0433 inch; 1990 VIN A & D, 188-202 lbs. @ 1.0433 inch.
⑱—Damper spring, 1.86 inch.
⑲—Intake, .005 inch; exhaust, .030 inch.
⑳—Intake, 1.7187 inch; exhaust, 1.5937 inch.
㉑—1988 models: intake, 76-84 lbs. @ 1.7 inch; exhaust, 76-84 lbs. @ 1.61 inch.

1989-90 models: intake & exhaust, 76-84 lbs. @ 1.7 inch.
㉒—1988 models: intake, 194-206 lbs. @ 1.25 inch; exhaust, 194-206 lbs. @ 1.16 inch. 1989-90 models: intake & exhaust, 194-206 lbs. @ 1.25 inch.
㉓—Inner spring, 1.54 inch; outer spring, 1.71 inch.
㉔—Inner spring, 1.18 inch; outer spring, 1.34 inch.
㉕—Inner spring, 34.2-37.8 lbs. @ 1.18 inch; outer spring, 64.1-76.4 lbs. @ 1.34 inch.
㉖—Inner spring, 75.5-81.8 lbs. @ .79 inch; outer spring, 146.8-166.4 lbs. @ .95 inch.

CYLINDER BLOCK

Engine Liter/CID/VIN	Year	Cylinder Bore Diameter (Std.)	Cylinder Bore Taper Max.	Cylinder Bore Out of Round Max.
1.0L/3-61/5	1988-90	①	.0039	.0039
1.5L/4-90/7	1988-89	②	—	—
1.6L/4-97/4 ③	1988	3.1890-3.1902	.008	.008
1.6L/4-97/5 ④	1988	3.1890-3.1902	.008	.008
1.6L/4-97/6 ⑤	1988-90	3.110	.0005	.0005
1.6L/4-97/5,6 ⑥ ⑦	1990	—	.005	.005
1.6L/4-97/5,6 ⑧ ⑨	1990	3.1496-3.1512	.005	.005
2.0L/4-121/K,M	1988-90	3.3852-3.3868	.0005	.0005
2.2L/4-133/G	1990	3.5036-3.5043	.0005	.0005
2.3L/4-138/A,D	1988-90	3.6217-3.6223	.0003	.0004
2.5L/4-151/R,U	1988-90	4.0000	.005	.001
2.8L/V6-173/S	1988-89	3.5036-3.5066	.0008	.0008
2.8L/V6-173/W	1988	3.5036-3.5066	.0005	.0005
	1989	3.5045-3.5052	.0005	.0005
3.0L/V6-181/L	1988	3.800	.0051	.0039
3.1L/V6-192/T,V	1989-90	3.5045-3.5052	.0005	.0005
3.3L/V6-204/N	1989-90	3.700	.0005	.0004
3.8L/V6-231/C,3	1988-90	3.800	.0005	.0004
4.3L/V6-262/Z	1988-90	3.9995-4.0025	⑩	.001
4.5L/V8-273/5	1988-90	⑪	.0005	.0008
5.0L/V8-305/E,F	1988-90	3.7350-3.7385	⑩	.001
5.0L/V8-307/Y	1988-90	3.800	.0015	.0015
5.7L/V8-350/7,8	1988-90	3.9995-4.0025	⑩	.001
5.7L/V8-350/J	1989-90	3.8971-3.8981	—	—

① —Cylinder bore diameter Nos. are stamped on the top of the block in sequence. No. 1, 2.9138-2.9142 inch and No. 2, 2.9134-2.9138 inch.

② —Cylinder bore diameter grade letter is stamped on the block at the back of each cylinder. A, 3.0315-3.0318 inch; B, 3.0319-3.0322 inch; C, 3.0323-3.0326 inch and D, 3.0327-3.0330 inch.

③ —Nova 4A-LC engine.

④ —Nova 4A-GE 16 valve engine.

⑤ —LeMans.

⑥ —Prizm 4A-FE 16 valve engine, VIN 6.

⑦ —Prizm GSI 4A-GE 16 valve engine, VIN 5.

⑧ —Storm 12 valve engine, VIN 6.

⑨ —Storm 16 valve engine, VIN 5.

⑩ —Thrust side, .0005 inch; relief side, .0010 inch.

⑪ —Nominal cylinder bore diameter, 3.622 inches. Liner protrusion, flush to .0032 inch above block deck. Maximum variation between liners, .0039 inch. Piston & liner are matched set and must be replaced as an assembly if liner protrusion, taper, out of round or piston to liner clearance are not within specifications.

PISTONS, PINS & RINGS

Engine Liter/CID/VIN	Year	Piston Diameter (Std.)	Piston Clearance	Piston Pin Diameter[1]	Piston Pin To Piston Clearance	Piston Ring End Gap[2]		Piston Ring Side Clearance	
						Comp.	Oil	Comp.	Oil
1.0L/3-60/5	1988-90	[3]	.0008-.0015	—	—	.0079	.0079	[4]	—
1.5L/4-90/7	1988-89	[5]	.0011-.0019	.7085-.7088	.0002-.0004	.0098	.0039	.0010-.0025	—
1.6L/4-97/4[6]	1988	3.8164-3.1858	.0035-.0043	—	—	[7]	.0118	[8]	—
1.6L/4-97/5[9]	1988	3.8460-3.8580	.0039-.0047	.7876-.7880	.0002-.0003	[10]	.0059	[8]	—
1.6L/4-97/6[11]	1988-90	3.110	.0008	.7200	.0003-.0004	.0118	—	[12]	—
1.6L/4-97/6[13]	1990	[14]	.0024-.0031	—	—	[7]	.0039	[8]	—
1.6L/4-97/5[15]	1990	[16]	.0039-.0047	.7876-.7880	.0002-.0003	[17]	.0059	.0012-.0028	.0039-.0236
1.6L/4-97/5,6[18][19]	1990	[20]	.0024-.0031	.7094-.7095	—	[21]	.0039	[22]	.0039-.0236
2.0L/4-121/K,M	1988-90	[23]	[24]	.8264-.8267	.0004-.0005	[25]	—	[26]	—
2.2L/4-133/G	1990	—	.0007-.0017	.8000-.8002	.0004-.0009	.010	.010	.0019	.0019
2.3L/4-138/A,D	1988-90	3.6203-3.6210	.0007-.0020	.8660-.8661	[27]	[28]	.0157	[29]	—
2.5L/4-151/R,U	1988-90	—	.0014-.0022	[30]	[31]	.0118	.0196	[32]	.0149-.0551
2.8L/V6-173/S	1988-89	—	.0006-.0016	.9052-.9055	.0002-.0003	.0098	.0200	[33]	.0007
2.8L/V6-173/W	1988-89	—	[34]	.9052-.9055	.0002-.0003	.0098	.0200	.0011-.0031	.0078
3.0L/V6-181/L	1988	—	.0010-.0045	.9391-.9394	.0003-.0009	.010	.015	.001-.003	.0005-.0065
3.1L/V6-192/T	1989	—	.0009-.0022	.9052-.9056	.0002-.0003	.001	.020	.001-.003	.008
3.1L/V6-192/T,V	1990	—	.0009-.0022	.9052-.9054	.0004-.0008	[35]	.010	.0020-.0035	.008
3.3L/V6-204/N	1989-90	—	.0004-.0022	.9053-.9055	.0004-.0008	.010	.010	.0013-.0031	.0011-.0081
3.8L/V6-231/C	1988	—	[36]	.9053-.9055	.0004-.0008	.010	.015	.0013-.0031	.0011-.0081
3.8L/V6-231/3	1988	—	.0004-.0022	.9391-.9394	.0003-.0009	.010	.015	.001-.003	.0005-.0065
3.8L/V6-231/C	1989-90	—	.0004-.0022	.9053-.9055	.0004-.0008	.010	.015	.0013-.0031	.0011-.0081
4.3L/V6-262/Z	1988-90	—	.0007-.0017	.9270-.9273	.0002-.0003	.010	.015	.0012-.0032	.002-.007
4.5L/V8-273/5	1988-90	—	.0010-.0018	.8656-.8661	.0002-.0004	.015	.010	.016-.0037	[37]
5.0L/V8-305/E,F	1988-90	—	.0007-.0017	.9270-.9273	.0002-.0003	.010	.015	.0012-.0032	.002-.007
5.0L/V8-307/Y	1988-90	3.800	.0007-.0017	.9803-.9805	.0003-.0005	.009	.015	.0018-.0038	.001-.005
5.7L/V8-350/7,8	1988-90	—	.0007-.0021	.9270-.9273	.0002-.0003	.010	.015	.0012-.0032	.002-.007
5.7L/V8-350/J	1989-90	—		.9841-.9843	.0002-.0007	[38]	.012	.002-.003	.001-.002

[1]—Pistons & pins are matched set and should be replaced as an assembly.

[2]—Minimum.

[3]—Pistons are stamped with a No. on top for correct assembly of piston to cylinder. No. 1 stamped piston with No. 1 stamped cylinder, No. 2 stamped piston with No. 2 stamped cylinder. No. 1, 2.9126-2.9130 inch and No. 2, 2.9122-2.9126 inch.

[4]—Top ring, .0012-.0027 inch; 2nd ring, .0008-.0023 inch.

[5]—Pistons are stamped with a letter on top for correct assembly of piston to cylinder. A stamped piston with A stamped cylinder, B stamped piston with B stamped cylinder, etc. A, 3.02992-3.03031 inch; B, 3.03035-3.03070 inch; C, 3.03074-3.03110 inch and D, 3.03114-3.03149 inch.

[6]—Nova 4A-LC engine.

[7]—Top ring, .0098 inch; 2nd ring, .0059 inch.

[8]—Top ring, .0016-.0031 inch; 2nd ring, .0012-.0028 inch.

[9]—Nova 4A-GE 16 valve engine.

[10]—Top ring, .0098-.0138 inch; 2nd ring, .0078-.0118 inch.

[11]—LeMans.

[12]—Top ring, .0024-.0036 inch; 2nd ring, .0019-.0032 inch.

[13]—Prizm 4A-FE 16 valve engine.

[14]—There are three standard sizes of pistons marked with a No. on top. No. 1, 3.1862-3.1866 inch; No. 2, 3.1866-3.1870 inch; No. 3, 3.1870-3.1874 inch.

[15]—Prizm GSI 4A-GE 16 valve engine.

[16]—There are three standard sizes of pistons marked with a No. on top. No. 1, 3.1846-3.1850 inch; No. 2, 3.1850-3.1854 inch; No. 3, 3.1854-3.1858 inch.

[17]—Top ring, .0098 inch; 2nd ring, .0079 inch.

[18]—Storm 12 valve engine, VIN 6.

[19]—Storm 16 valve engine, VIN 5.

[20]—There are three standard sizes of pistons marked with a No. on top. No. 1, 3.1473-3.1477 inch; No. 2, 3.1477-3.1481 inch; No. 3, 3.1481-3.1485 inch.

[21]—Top ring, .0011 inch; 2nd ring, .0018 inch.

[22]—Top ring, .0018-.0031 inch; 2nd ring, .0008-.0024 inch.

[23]—VIN K, 3.3844-3.3860 inch; VIN M, 3.3837-3.3852 inch.

[24]—VIN K, .0004-.0012 inch; VIN M, .0012-.0020 inch.

[25]—Top ring, .0098 inch; 2nd ring, .0118 inch.

[26]—Top ring, .0024-.0036 inch; 2nd ring, .0019-.0032 inch.

[27]—1988-89 VIN D, .00004-.00035 inch. 1989-90 VIN A, .0003-.0006 inch. 1990 VIN D, .00008-.00040 inch.

[28]—1988 both, .0157 inch. 1989-90 top ring, .0138 inch; 2nd ring, .0157 inch.

[29]—1988-89 VIN D: top ring, .0019-.0035 inch; 2nd ring, .0157-.0031 inch. 1989 VIN A: top ring, .0023-.0039 inch; 2nd ring, .0157-.0031 inch. 1990 VIN A: top ring, .0027-.0047 inch; 2nd ring, .0157-.0031 inch. 1990 VIN D: top ring, .0019-.0039 inch; 2nd ring, .0157-.0031 inch.

[30]—1988, .9380-.9420 inch; 1989-90, .9270-.9276 inch.

[31]—1988, .0020-.0040 inch; 1989-90, .0040-.0060 inch.

[32]—Top ring, .0020-.0031 inch; 2nd ring, .0011-.0031 inch.

[33]—Top ring, .0011-.0027 inch; 2nd ring, .0015-.0037 inch.

[34]—1988, .0020-.0028 inch; 1989, .0009-.0022 inch.

[35]—Top ring, .010 inch; 2nd ring, .020 inch.

[36]—Skirt top, .0007-.0027 inch; skirt bottom, .0010-.0045 inch.

[37]—Zero clearance; side sealing ring.

[38]—Top ring, .016 inch; 2nd ring, .031 inch.

CAMSHAFT & LIFTERS

Engine Liter/ CID/VIN	Year	Camshaft Journal Diameter	Maximum Journal Run-out	Camshaft Bearing Clearance	Camshaft End Play	Rocker Arm Oil Clearance	Lifter Bore Diameter	Lifter Diameter	Lifter To Bore Clearance
1.0L/3-60/5	1988-90	①	.0039	.0008-.0024	—	—	1.2205-1.2214	1.2188-1.2194	.0010-.0025
1.5L/4-98/7	1988-89	1.021-1.022	.0039	.0023-.0043	.0040-.0071	.0002-.0018	—	—	—
1.6L/4-97/4 ③	1988	1.1015-1.1022	.0024	.0015-.0029	.0031-.0071	.0024	—	—	—
1.6L/4-97/5 ③	1988	1.0610-1.0616	.0016	.0014-.0028	.0031-.0075	—	—	—	—
1.6L/4-97/6 ④	1988-90	⑤	—	.0018-.0035	.0035-.0083	—	—	—	—
1.6L/4-97/6 ⑥	1990	⑦	.0016	.0014-.0028	.0043	—	—	—	.0006-.0018
1.6L/4-97/5 ③	1990	1.0610-1.0616	.0016	.0014-.0028	.0031-.0075	—	—	1.1014-1.1018	.0006-.0018
1.6L/4-97/6 ⑨	1990	1.0157	.0040	.0059	.008	.0002-.0018	—	—	—
1.6L/4-97/5 ⑩	1990	1.0157	.0040	.0059	.008	—	—	1.218	—
2.0L/4-121/K,M	1988-90	⑪	—	.0011-.0035	.0016-.0063	—	—	—	—
2.2L/4-133/G	1990	1.867-1.869	—	.0010-.0039	—	—	—	—	—
2.3L/4-138/A,D	1988-90	⑫	—	.0019-.0043	⑬	—	—	—	⑭
2.5L/4-151/R,U	1988-90	1.869	—	.0007-.0027	⑮	—	.8435-.8444	.8412-.8427	.0006-.0023
2.8L/V6-173/S,W	1988-89	1.8677-1.8696	—	.0010-.0039	—	—	—	—	—
3.0L/V6-181/L	1988	1.785-1.786	—	.0005-.0035	—	—	—	—	—
3.1L/V6-192/T,V	1989-90	1.8678-1.8815	—	.0001-.0004	—	—	—	—	—
3.3L/V6-204/N	1989-90	1.785-1.786	—	.0005-.0035	—	—	—	—	—
3.8L/V6-231/C,3	1988-90	1.785-1.786	—	.0005-.0035	—	—	—	—	—
4.3L/V6-262/Z	1988-90	1.8682-1.8692	—	—	.004-.012	—	—	—	—
4.5L/V8-273/5	1988-90	—	.002	.0018-.0037	—	—	—	—	.0007-.0027
5.0L/V8-305/E,F	1988-90	1.8682-1.8692	—	—	.004-.012	—	—	—	—
5.0L/V8-307/Y	1988-90	⑯	.002	.0020-.0058	.006-.022	—	—	.920-.922	.0005-.0022
5.7L/V8-350/7,8	1988-90	1.8682-1.8692	—	—	.004-.012	—	—	—	—
5.7L/V8-350/J	1989-90	1.140-1.141	—	—	.0055-.0138	—	—	—	—

①—Journal No. 1, 1.0220-1.0228; journal No. 2 & 3, 1.1795-1.1803.
②—Nova 4A-LC engine.
③—Nova 4A-GE 16 valve engine.
④—LeMans.
⑤—Journal No. 1, 1.5520-1.5530 inch; journal No. 2, 1.5624-1.5630 inch; journal No. 3, 1.5722-1.5730 inch; journal No. 4, 1.5820-1.5828 inch; journal No. 5, 1.5919-1.5927 inch.
⑥—Prizm 4A-FE 16 valve engine.
⑦—Journal No. 1, .9822 inch; journal No. 2, 3, 4 & 5, .9035 inch.

⑧—Prizm GSI 4A-GE 16 valve engine.
⑨—Storm 12 valve engine.
⑩—Storm 16 valve engine.
⑪—Journal No. 1, 1.6706-1.6712; No. 2, 1.6812-1.6818; No. 3, 1.6911-1.6917; No. 4, 1.7009-1.7015; No. 5, 1.7100-1.7106.
⑫—1988-89 VIN D, 1.3751-1.3759 inch. 1989 VIN A & 1990 VIN A & D: journal No. 1, 1.5720-1.5728 inch; journal No. 2, 3, 4 & 5, 1.3751 1.3759 inch.

⑬—1988-89, .0059-.0137 inch; 1990, .0010-.0088 inch.
⑭—1988-89, .0005-.0021 inch; 1990, .0005-.0023 inch.
⑮—1988-89, .0015-.0050 inch; 1990, .0009-.0020 inch.
⑯—Journal No. 1, 2.0352-2.0365; journal No. 2, 2.0152-2.0166; journal No. 3, 1.9952-1.9965; journal No. 4, 1.9752-1.9765; journal No. 5, 1.9552-1.9565.

OIL PUMP

Engine Liter/CID/VIN	Year	Gear Backlash	Gear To Body Clearance	Gear End Play ①	Gear Pocket		Pump Gear Thickness	Pump Gear Diameter	Relief Valve To Body Clearance
					Depth	Diameter			
1.0L/3-60/5	1988-90	—	.0122	.0059	—	—	—	—	—
1.5L/4-90/7	1988-89	—	.004-.007	.0039	—	—	—	—	—
1.6L/4-97/4 ②	1988	—	.008	.004	—	—	—	—	—
1.6L/4-97/5 ③	1988	—	—	—	—	—	—	—	—
1.6L/4-97/6 ④	1988-90	.004-.008	.0043-.0074	.001-.004	.3948-.3968	⑤	—	⑥	—
1.6L/4-97/6 ⑦	1990	.0138	.0039	.0079	—	—	—	—	—
1.6L/4-97/5 ⑧	1990	.0012	.004	.0078	—	—	—	—	—
1.6L/4-97/5,6 ⑨ ⑩	1990	.0012	.004	.0078	—	—	—	—	—
2.0L/4-121/K,M	1988-90	.004-.008	.0043-.0074	.001-.004	.395-.397	⑤	—	⑥	—
2.2L/4-133/G	1990	.004-.008	.0015-.0040	.002-.006	1.195-1.198	1.503-1.506	1.199-1.200	1.498-1.500	.0015-.0035
2.3L/4-138/D	1988	.010-.014	.010-.014	—	.689-.691	2.010-2.012	.686-.687	1.998-2.00	.002-.005
	1989-90	.0091-.0201	—	.0059	.6736-.6756	2.1273-2.1292	.6727-.6731	2.124-2.126	—
2.5L/4-151/R,U	1988-90	—	—	—	.514-.516	—	.511-.512	—	—
2.8L/V6-173/S,W	1988-89	—	—	—	—	—	—	—	—
3.0L/V6-181/L	1988	.006	.008-.015	.001-.0035	.4610-.4625	3.508-3.512	—	—	.0015-.0030
3.1L/V6-192/T	1989	—	—	—	—	—	—	—	—
3.1L/V6-192/T ⑪	1990	.0037-.0077	.003-.004	.0016-.0067	1.195-1.198	1.503-1.506	1.199-1.200	1.498-1.500	.0015-.0035
3.1L/V6-192/T ⑫	1990	.0037-.0077	.003-.004	.002-.006	1.202-1.205	1.504-1.506	1.199-1.200	1.498-1.500	.0015-.0035
3.1L/V6-192/V ⑫	1990	.004-.008	.0025-.0040	.003-.007	1.434-1.436	1.504-1.506	1.438-1.439	1.498-1.499	—
3.3L/V6-204/N	1989-90	—	.008-.015	.001-.0035	.4610-.4625	3.508-3.512	—	—	.0015-.0030
3.8L/V6-231/C,3	1988-90	.006	.008-.015	.0010-.0035	.4610-.4625	3.508-3.512	—	—	.0015-.0030
4.3L/V6-262/Z	1988	⑬	⑬	⑬	⑬	⑬	⑬	⑬	⑬
4.5L/V8-273/5	1988-90	.0010-.0013	.0018-.0031	—	—	—	—	—	—
5.0L/V8-305/E,F	1988-90	⑬	⑬	⑬	⑬	⑬	⑬	⑬	⑬
5.0L/V8-307/Y	1988-90	.0004-.0065	.0015-.0045	.0025-.0065	1.500-1.509	1.534-1.539	1.5075-1.5095	1.529-1.531	.0025-.0050
5.7L/V8-350/7,8	1988-90	⑬	⑬	⑬	⑬	⑬	⑬	⑬	⑬
5.7L/V8-350/J	1989-90	⑬	⑬	⑬	⑬	⑬	⑬	⑬	⑬

①—Measured between pump cover and end of gears using straightedge & feeler gauge.
②—Nova 4A-LC engine.
③—Nova 4A-GE 16 valve engine.
④—LeMans.
⑤—Inner gear, 1.614-1.615 inch; outer gear, 3.231-3.234 inch.
⑥—Inner gear, 1.612-1.613 inch; outer gear, 3.2248-3.2269 inch.
⑦—Prizm 4A-FE 16 valve engine.
⑧—Prizm GSI 4A-GE 16 valve engine.
⑨—Storm 12 valve engine, VIN 6.
⑩—Storm 16 valve engine, VIN 5.
⑪—Aluminum body pump.
⑫—Cast iron body pump.
⑬—Pump components are not serviced separately. If any component is damaged or worn, pump should be replaced.

CRANKSHAFT, BEARINGS & CONNECTING RODS

Engine Liter/ CID/VIN	Year	Crankshaft		Out of Round All ①	Taper All ①	Bearing Clearance			Connecting Rods	
		Standard Journal Diameter				Main Bearings	Connecting Rod Bearings	Thrust Bearing Clearance	Pin Bore Diameter	Side Clearance
		Main Bearing	Crank Pin							
1.0L/3-61/5	1988-90	②	1.6529-1.6535	.0004	.0004	.0008-.0015	.0012-.0019	.0044-.0122	—	.0039-.0078
1.5L/4-90/7	1988-89	1.8865-1.8873	1.5720-1.5726	.002	.002	.0008—.0020	.0010-0023	.0024-.0095	—	.0079-.0138
1.6L/4-97/4③	1988	1.8892-1.8898	1.5742-1.5748	.0008	.0008	.0006-.0013	.0008-.0020	.0008-.0073	—	.012
1.6L/4-97/5④	1988	⑤	1.6529-1.6535	.0008	.0008	.0006-.0013	.0008-.0020	.0008-.0087	.7879-.7883	.0059-.0098
1.6L/4-97/6⑥	1988-90	2.1653	1.6918-1.6920	.0002	.0002	.0006-.0020	.0007-.0025	.0047-.0138	—	.0028-.0095
1.6L/4-97/6⑦	1990	1.8891-1.8898	1.5742-1.5748	.008	.008	.0006-.0013	.0008-.0020	.0118	—	.0059-.0098
1.6L/4-97/5⑧	1990	1.8891-1.8898	1.6529-1.6535	.0004	.0004	.0006-.0013	.0008-.0020	.0008-.0087	—	.0059-.0098
1.6L/4-97/6⑨	1990	2.0440-2.0448	1.5722-1.5728	.0020	.0020	.0008-.0020	.0008-.0018	.0024-.0095	—	.0079-.0138
1.6L/4-97/5⑩	1990	2.0440-2.0448	1.5722-1.5728	.0020	.0020	.0008-.0020	.0010-.0023	.0024-.0095	—	.0079-.0138
2.0L/4-121/K,M	1988-90	2.2828-2.2833	1.9279-1.9287	.0002	.0002	.0006-.0016	.0007-.0025	.0028-.0118	—	.0028-.0095
2.2L/4-133/G	1990	2.4945-2.4954	1.9983-1.9994	.0002	.0002	.0006-.0019	.0010-.0031	.002-.007	—	.0039-.0149
2.3L/4-138/A,D	1988-90	2.0470-2.0480	1.8887-1.8890	.0005	.0005	.0005-.0023	.0005-.0020	.0034-.0095	—	.0059-.0177
2.5L/4-151	1988-89	2.300	2.00	.0005	.0005	.0005-.0220	.0005-.0027	⑪	—	.0059-.0236
2.8L/V6-173/S	1988-89	2.6472-2.6482	1.9983-1.9993	.0002	.0002	.0016-.0031	.0013-.0037	.0021-.0033	—	.0062-.0173
2.8L/V6-173/W	1988	2.6472-2.6482	1.9983-1.9993	.0002	.0002	.0016-.0031	.0011-.0025	.0021-.0033	—	.0062-.0173
	1989	2.6472-2.6482	1.9983-1.9993	.0002	.0002	.0012-.0027	.0014-.0036	.0016-.0027	—	.0059-.0170
3.0L/V6-181/L	1988	2.4988-2.4998	2.2487-2.2499	.0003	.0003	.0003-.0018	.0003-.0028	.003-.011	—	.003-.015
3.1L/V6-192/T	1989	2.6473-2.6483	1.9983-1.9994	.0002	.0002	.0012-.0027	.0014-.0036	.0016-.0027	—	.014-.027
3.1L/V6-192/T,V	1990	2.6473-2.6483	1.9983-1.9994	.0002	.0002	.0012-.0030	.0011-.0034	.0012-.0030	—	.014-.027
3.3L/V6-204/N	1989-90	2.4988-2.4998	2.2487-2.2499	.0003	.0003	.0003-.0018	.0003-.0026	.003-.011	—	.003-.015
3.8L/V6-231/C,3	1988-90	2.4988-2.4998	2.2487-2.2499	.0003	.0003	.0003-.0018	.0003-.0028	.003-.011	—	.003-.015
4.3L/V6-262/Z	1988-90	⑫	2.2487-2.2498	.0002	.0002	⑬	.0013-.0035	.001-.007	—	.006-.014
4.5L/V8-273/5	1988-90	2.6354-2.6364	1.927	.0003	—	⑭	—	.0010-.007	—	.008-.020
5.0L/V8-305/E,F	1988-90	⑫	2.0893-2.0998	.0002	.0002	⑬	.0013-.0035	.001-.007	—	.006-.014
5.0L/V8-307/Y	1988-90	⑮	2.1238-2.1248	.0002	.0002	⑯	.0004-.0033	.0035-.0135	—	.006-.020
5.7L/V8-350/7,8	1988-90	⑫	2.0893-2.0998	.0002	.0002	⑬	.0013-.0035	.001-.007	—	.006-.014
5.7L/V8-350/J	1989-90	2.755-2.756	2.0993-2.1000	.0003	.0002	.0007-.0023	.0007-.0027	.0006-.0010	—	.008-.028

① —Maximum.
② —The counter weights of No. 1 cylinder have four stamped numbers, they indicate the journal diameters at bearing caps reseptively. No. 1, 1.7714-1.7716 inch; No. 2, 1.7712-1.7714 inch and No. 3, 1.7710-1.7712 inch.
③ —Nova 4A-LC engine.
④ —Nova 4A-GE 16 valve engine.
⑤ —Crankshaft journal diameter codes are stamped on the crankshaft counterweights. No. 0, 1.8895-1.8898 inch; No. 1, 1.8893-1.8895 inch; No. 2, 1.8891-1.8893 inch.
⑥ —LeMans.
⑦ —Prizm 4A-FE engine.
⑧ —Prizm 4A-GE 16 valve engine.
⑨ —Storm 12 valve engine.
⑩ —Storm 16 valve engine.
⑪ —1988, .0035-.0085 inch; 1989-90, .0005-.0220 inch.
⑫ —Journal No. 1, 2.4488-2.4493 inch; journal No. 2, 3 & 4, 2.4481-2.4490 inches; journal No. 5, 2.4481-2.4488 inches.
⑬ —Journal No. 1, .0008-.0020 inch; journal No. 2, 3 & 4, .0011-.0020 inch; journal No. 5, .0017-.0032 inch.
⑭ —Journal No. 1, .0008-.0031 inch; journal No. 2, 3, 4 & 5, .0016-.0039 inch.
⑮ —No. 1, 2.4988-2.4998 inches; Nos. 2, 3, 4 & 5, 2.4985-2.4995 inches.
⑯ —Nos. 1, 2, 3 & 4, .0005-.0021 inch; No. 5, .0015-.0031 inch.